Stanley Gibbons
SIMPLIFIED CATALOGUE

Stamps of the World

2005 Edition

IN COLOUR

An illustrated and priced four-volume guide to the postage stamps of the whole world, excluding changes of paper, perforation, shade and watermark

VOLUME 2

COUNTRIES E–J

STANLEY GIBBONS LTD
London and Ringwood

By Appointment to
Her Majesty the Queen
Stanley Gibbons Limited
London
Philatelists

70th Edition

Published in Great Britain by
Stanley Gibbons Ltd
Publications Editorial, Sales Offices and Distribution Centre
Parkside, Christchurch Road,
Ringwood, Hampshire BH24 3SH
Telephone 01425 472363

ISBN: 085259-569-7

Published as Stanley Gibbons Simplified Stamp Catalogue from 1934 to 1970, renamed Stamps of the World in 1971, and produced in two (1982-88), three (1989-2001) or four (from 2002) volumes as Stanley Gibbons Simplified Catalogue of Stamps of the World.
This volume published October 2004

S.G. Item No. 2882 (05)

Printed in Great Britain by CPI Bath Press, Somerset

Stanley Gibbons
SIMPLIFIED CATALOGUE
Stamps of the **World**

This popular catalogue is a straightforward listing of the stamps that have been issued everywhere in the world since the very first–Great Britain's famous Penny Black in 1840.

This edition, in which both the text and the illustrations have been captured electronically, is arranged completely alphabetically in a four-volume format. Volume 1 (Countries A–D), Volume 2 (Countries E–J), Volume 3 (Countries K–R) and Volume 4 (Countries S–Z).

Readers are reminded that the Catalogue Supplements, published in each issue of **Gibbons Stamp Monthly**, can be used to update the listings in **Stamps of the World** as well as our 22-part standard catalogue. To make the supplement even more useful the Type numbers given to the illustrations are the same in the Stamps of the World as in the standard catalogues. The first Catalogue Supplement to this Volume appeared in the September 2004 issue of **Gibbons Stamp Monthly**.

Gibbons Stamp Monthly can be obtained through newsagents or on postal subscription from Stanley Gibbons Publications, Parkside, Christchurch Road, Ringwood, Hants BH24 3SH.

The catalogue has many important features:

- The vast majority of illustrations are now in full colour to aid stamp identification.
- All Commonwealth and all Western Europe miniature sheets are now included.
- As an indication of current values virtually every stamp is priced. Thousands of alterations have been made since the last edition.
- By being set out on a simplified basis that excludes changes of paper, perforation, shade, watermark, gum or printer's and date imprints it is particularly easy to use. (For its exact scope see "Information for users" pages following.)
- The thousands of colour illustrations and helpful descriptions of stamp designs make it of maximum appeal to collectors with thematic interests.
- Its catalogue numbers are the world-recognised Stanley Gibbons numbers throughout.
- Helpful introductory notes for the collector are included, backed by much historical, geographical and currency information.
- A very detailed index gives instant location of countries in this volume, and a cross-reference to those included in the other volumes.

Over 2,635 stamps and miniature sheets and 907 new illustrations have been added to the listings in this volume. This year's four-volumes now contain over 417,545 stamps and 100,767 illustrations.

The listings in this edition are based on the standard catalogues: Part 1, Commonwealth & British Empire Stamps 1840–1952, Part 2 (Austria & Hungary) (6th edition), Part 3 (Balkans) (4th edition), Part 4 (Benelux) (5th edition), Part 5 (Czechoslovakia & Poland) (6th edition), Part 6 (France) (5th edition), Part 7 (Germany) (6th edition), Part 8 (Italy & Switzerland) (6th edition), Part 9 (Portugal & Spain) (4th edition), Part 10 (Russia) (5th edition), Part 11 (Scandinavia) (5th edition), Part 12 (Africa since Independence A-E) (2nd edition), Part 13 (Africa since Independence F-M) (1st edition), Part 14 (Africa since Independence N-Z) (1st edition), Part 15 (Central America) (2nd edition), Part 16 (Central Asia) (3rd edition), Part 17 (China) (6th edition), Part 18 (Japan & Korea) (4th edition), Part 19 (Middle East) (5th edition), Part 20 (South America) (3rd edition), Part 21 (South-East Asia) (4th edition) and Part 22 (United States) (5th edition).

This edition includes major repricing for some Western Europe countries in addition to the changes for South-East Asia Part 21.

Acknowledgements

A wide-ranging revision of prices for Western European countries has been undertaken for this edition with the intention that the catalogue should be more accurate to reflect the market for foreign issues.

Many dealers in both Great Britain and overseas have participated in this scheme by supplying copies of their retail price lists on which the research has been based.
We would like to acknowledge the assistance of the following for this edition:

ALMAZ CO
of Brooklyn, U.S.A.

AMATEUR COLLECTOR LTD, THE
of London, England

E. ANGELOPOULOS
of Thessaloniki, Greece

AVION THEMATICS
of Nottingham, England

J BAREFOOT LTD
of York, England

BELGIAN PHILATELIC SPECIALISTS INC
of Larchmont, U.S.A.

Sir CHARLES BLOMEFIELD
of Chipping Camden, England

T. BRAY
of Shipley, West Yorks, England

CENTRAL PHILATELIQUE
of Brussels, Belgium

JEAN-PIERRE DELMONTE
of Paris, France

EUROPEAN & FOREIGN STAMPS
of Pontypridd, Wales

FILATELIA LLACH SL
of Barcelona, Spain

FILATELIA RIVA RENO
of Bologna, Italy

FILATELIA TORI
of Barcelona, Spain

FORMOSA STAMP COMPANY, THE
of Koahsiung, Taiwan

FORSTAMPS
of Battle, England

ANTHONY GRAINGER
of Leeds, England

HOLMGREN STAMPS
of Bollnas, Sweden

INDIGO
of Orewa, New Zealand

ALEC JACQUES
of Selby, England

M. JANKOWSKI
of Warsaw, Poland

D.J.M. KERR
of Earlston, England

H. M. NIELSEN
of Vejle, Denmark

LEO BARESCH LTD
of Hassocks, England

LORIEN STAMPS
of Chesterfield, England

MANDARIN TRADING CO
of Alhambra, U.S.A.

MICHAEL ROGERS INC
of Winter Park, U.S.A.

PHILATELIC SUPPLIES
of Letchworth, England

PHIL-INDEX
of Eastbourne, England

PHILTRADE A/S
of Copenhagen, Denmark

PITTERI SA
of Chiasso, Switzerland

KEVIN RIGLER
of Shifnal, England

ROLF GUMMESSON AB
of Stockholm, Sweden

R. D. TOLSON
of Undercliffe, England

JAY SMITH
of Snow Camp, U.S.A.

R. SCHNEIDER
of Belleville, U.S.A.

ROBSTINE STAMPS
of Hampshire, England

SOUTHERN MAIL
of Eastbourne, England

STAMP CENTER
of Reykjavik, Iceland

REX WHITE
of Winchester, England

Some Western European countries have been repriced this year in Stamps of the World and where there is no up-to-date specialised foreign volume in a country these will be the new Stanley Gibbons prices.

It is hoped that this improved pricing scheme will be extended to other foreign countries and thematic issues as information is consolidated.

Information for users

Aim

The aim of this catalogue is to provide a straightforward illustrated and priced guide to the postage stamps of the whole world to help you to enjoy the greatest hobby of the present day.

Arrangement

The catalogue lists countries in alphabetical order and there is a complete index at the end of each volume. For ease of reference country names are also printed at the head of each page.

Within each country, postage stamps are listed first. They are followed by separate sections for such other categories as postage due stamps, parcel post stamps, express stamps, official stamps, etc.

All catalogue lists are set out according to dates of issue of the stamps, starting from the earliest and working through to the most recent.

Scope of the Catalogue

The *Simplified Catalogue of Stamps of the World* contains listings of postage stamps only. Apart from the ordinary definitive, commemorative and air-mail stamps of each country – which appear first in each list – there are sections for the following where appropriate:

postage due stamps
parcel post stamps
official stamps
express and special delivery stamps
charity and compulsory tax stamps
newspaper and journal stamps
printed matter stamps
registration stamps
acknowledgement of receipt stamps
late fee and too late stamps
military post stamps
recorded message stamps
personal delivery stamps

We receive numerous enquiries from collectors about other items which do not fall within the categories set out above and which consequently do not appear in the catalogue lists. It may be helpful, therefore, to summarise the other kinds of stamp that exist but which we deliberately exclude from this postage stamp catalogue.

We do *not* list the following:

Fiscal or revenue stamps: stamps used solely in collecting taxes or fees for non-postal purposes. Examples would be stamps which pay a tax on a receipt, represent the stamp duty on a contract or frank a customs document. Common inscriptions found include: Documentary, Proprietary, Inter. Revenue, Contract Note.

Local stamps: postage stamps whose validity and use are limited in area, say to a single town or city, though in some cases they provided, with official sanction, services in parts of countries not covered by the respective government.

Local carriage labels and Private local issues: many labels exist ostensibly to cover the cost of ferrying mail from one of Great Britain's offshore islands to the nearest mainland post office. They are not recognised as valid for national or international mail. Examples: Calf of Man, Davaar, Herm, Lundy, Pabay, Stroma. Items from some other places have only the status of tourist souvenir labels.

Telegraph stamps: stamps intended solely for the prepayment of telegraphic communication.

Bogus or "phantom" stamps: labels from mythical places or non-existent administrations. Examples in the classical period were Sedang, Counani, Clipperton Island and in modern times Thomond and Monte Bello Islands. Numerous labels have also appeared since the War from dissident groups as propaganda for their claims and without authority from the home governments. Common examples are labels for "Free Albania", "Free Rumania" and "Free Croatia" and numerous issues for Nagaland, Indonesia and the South Moluccas ("Republik Maluku Selatan").

Railway letter fee stamps: special stamps issued by railway companies for the conveyance of letters by rail. Example: Talyllyn Railway. Similar services are now offered by some bus companies and the labels they issue likewise do not qualify for inclusion in the catalogue.

Perfins ("perforated initials"): numerous postage stamps may be found with initial letters or designs punctured through them by tiny holes. These are applied by private and public concerns as a precaution against theft and do not qualify for separate mention.

Information for users

Labels: innumerable items exist resembling stamps but – as they do not prepay postage – they are classified as labels. The commonest categories are:

- propaganda and publicity labels: designed to further a cause or campaign;
- exhibition labels: particularly souvenirs from philatelic events;
- testing labels: stamp-size labels used in testing stamp-vending machines;
- Post Office training school stamps: British stamps overprinted with two thick vertical bars or SCHOOL SPECIMEN are produced by the Post Office for training purposes;
- seals and stickers: numerous charities produce stamp-like labels, particularly at Christmas and Easter, as a means of raising funds and these have no postal validity.

Cut-outs: items of postal stationery, such as envelopes, cards and wrappers, often have stamps impressed or imprinted on them. They may usually be cut out and affixed to envelopes, etc., for postal use if desired, but such items are not listed in this catalogue.

Collectors wanting further information about exact definitions are referred to *Philatelic Terms Illustrated*, published by Stanley Gibbons and containing many illustrations in colour.

There is also a priced listing of the postal fiscals of Great Britain in our *Commonwealth & British Empire Stamps 1840–1952* Catalogue and in Volume 1 of the *Great Britain Specialised* Catalogue (5th and later editions).

Catalogue Numbers

Stanley Gibbons catalogue numbers are recognised universally and any individual stamp can be identified by quoting the catalogue number (the one at the left of the column) prefixed by the name of the country and the letters "S.G.". Do not confuse the catalogue number with the type numbers which refer to illustrations.

Prices

Prices in the left-hand column are for unused stamps and those in the right-hand column for used. Prices are given in pence and pounds:

100 pence (p) 1 pound (£1).

Prices are shown as follows:

10 means 10p (10 pence);
1.50 means £1.50 (1 pound and 50 pence);
For £100 and above, prices are in whole pounds.

Our prices are for stamps in fine condition, and in issues where condition varies we may ask more for the superb and less for the sub-standard.

The minimum catalogue price quoted is 10p. For individual stamps prices between 10p and 45p are provided as a guide for catalogue users. The lowest price charged for individual stamps purchased from Stanley Gibbons is 50p.

The prices quoted are generally for the cheapest variety of stamps but it is worth noting that differences of watermark, perforation, or other details, outside the scope of this catalogue, may often increase the value of the stamp.

Prices quoted for mint issues are for single examples. Those in se-tenant pairs, strips, blocks or sheets may be worth more.

Where prices are not given in either column it is either because the stamps are not known to exist in that particular condition, or, more usually, because there is no reliable information as to value.

All prices are subject to change without prior notice and we give no guarantee to supply all stamps priced. Prices quoted for albums, publications, etc. advertised in this catalogue are also subject to change without prior notice.

Due to different production methods it is sometimes possible for new editions of Parts 2 to 22 to appear showing revised prices which are not included in that year's *Stamps of the World*.

Unused Stamps

In the case of stamps from *Great Britain* and the *Commonwealth*, prices for unused stamps of Queen Victoria to King George V are for lightly hinged examples; unused prices of King Edward VIII to Queen Elizabeth II issues are for unmounted mint. The prices of unused Foreign stamps are for lightly hinged examples for those issued before 1946, thereafter for examples unmounted mint.

Used Stamps

Prices for used stamps generally refer to fine postally used examples, though for certain issues they are for cancelled-to-order.

Information for users

Guarantee

All stamps supplied by us are guaranteed originals in the following terms:

If not as described, and returned by the purchaser, we undertake to refund the price paid to us in the original transaction. If any stamp is certified as genuine by the Expert Committee of the Royal Philatelic Society, London, or by B.P.A. Expertising Ltd., the purchaser shall not be entitled to make any claim against us for any error, omission or mistake in such certificate.

Consumers' statutory rights are not affected by the above guarantee.

Currency

At the beginning of each country brief details give the currencies in which the values of the stamps are expressed. The dates, where given, are those of the earliest stamp issues in the particular currency. Where the currency is obvious, e.g. where the colony has the same currency as the mother country, no details are given.

Illustrations

Illustrations of any surcharges and overprints which are shown and not described are actual size; stamp illustrations are reduced to $\frac{3}{4}$ linear, *unless otherwise stated.*

"Key-Types"

A number of standard designs occur so frequently in the stamps of the French, German, Portuguese and Spanish colonies that it would be a waste of space to repeat them. Instead these are all illustrated on page xiv together with the descriptive names and letters by which they are referred to in the lists.

Type Numbers

These are the bold figures found below each illustration. References to "Type **6**", for example, in the lists of a country should therefore be understood to refer to the illustration below which the number **"6"** appears. These type numbers are also given in the second column of figures alongside each list of stamps, thus indicating clearly the design of each stamp. In the case of Key-Types – see above – letters take the place of the type numbers.

Where an issue comprises stamps of similar design, represented in this catalogue by one illustration, the corresponding type numbers should be taken as indicating this general design.

Where there are blanks in the type number column it means that the type of the corresponding stamps is that shown by the last number above in the type column of the same issue.

A dash (–) in the type column means that no illustration of the stamp is shown.

Where type numbers refer to stamps of another country, e.g. where stamps of one country are overprinted for use in another, this is always made clear in the text.

Stamp Designs

Brief descriptions of the subjects of the stamp designs are given either below or beside the illustrations, at the foot of the list of the issue concerned, or in the actual lists. Where a particular subject, e.g. the portrait of a well-known monarch, recurs frequently the description is not repeated, nor are obvious designs described.

Generally, the unillustrated designs are in the same shape and size as the one illustrated, except where otherwise indicated.

Surcharges and Overprints

Surcharges and overprints are usually described in the headings to the issues concerned. Where the actual wording of a surcharge or overprint is given it is shown in bold type.

Some stamps are described as being "Surcharged in words", e.g. **TWO CENTS**, and others "Surcharged in figures and words", e.g. **20 CENTS**, although of course many surcharges are in foreign languages and combinations of words and figures are numerous. There are often bars, etc., obliterating old values or inscriptions but in general these are only mentioned where it is necessary to avoid confusion.

No attention is paid in this catalogue to colours of overprints and surcharges so that stamps with the same overprints in different colours are not listed separately.

Numbers in brackets after the descriptions of overprinted or surcharged stamps are the catalogue numbers of the unoverprinted stamps.

Note – the words "inscribed" or "inscription" always refer to wording incorporated in the design of a stamp and not surcharges or overprints.

Coloured Papers

Where stamps are printed on coloured paper the description is given as e.g. "4 c. black on blue" – a stamp printed in black on blue paper. No attention is paid in this catalogue to difference in the texture of paper, e.g. laid, wove.

Information for users

Watermarks

Stamps having different watermarks, but otherwise the same, are not listed separately. No reference is therefore made to watermarks in this volume.

Stamp Colours

Colour names are only required for the identification of stamps, therefore they have been made as simple as possible. Thus "scarlet", "vermilion", "carmine" are all usually called red. Qualifying colour names have been introduced only where necessary for the sake of clearness.

Where stamps are printed in two or more colours the central portion of the design is in the first colour given, unless otherwise stated.

Perforations

All stamps are perforated unless otherwise stated. No distinction is made between the various gauges of perforation but early stamp issues which exist both imperforate and perforated are usually listed separately.

Where a heading states "Imperf. or perf". or "Perf. or rouletted" this does not necessarily mean that all values of the issue are found in both conditions.

Dates of Issue

The date given at the head of each issue is that of the appearance of the earliest stamp in the series. As stamps of the same design or issue are usually grouped together a list of King George VI stamps, for example, headed "1938" may include stamps issued from 1938 to the end of the reign.

Se-tenant Pairs

Many modern issues are printed in sheets containing different designs or face values. Such pairs, blocks, strips or sheets are described as being "se-tenant" and they are outside the scope of this catalogue, although reference to them may occur in instances where they form a composite design.

Miniature Sheets

As an increasing number of stamps are now only found in miniature sheets, Stamps of the World will, in future, list these items. This edition lists all Commonwealth countries' miniature sheets, plus those of all non-Commonwealth countries which have appeared in the catalogue supplement during the past year. Earlier miniature sheets of non-Commonwealth countries will be listed in future editions.

"Appendix" Countries

We regret that, since 1968, it has been necessary to establish an Appendix (at the end of each country as appropriate) to which numerous stamps have had to be consigned. Several countries imagine that by issuing huge quantities of unnecessary stamps they will have a ready source of income from stamp collectors – and particularly from the less-experienced ones. Stanley Gibbons refuse to encourage this exploitation of the hobby and we do not stock the stamps concerned.

Two kinds of stamp are therefore given the briefest of mentions in the Appendix, purely for the sake of record. Administrations issuing stamps greatly in excess of true postal needs have the offending issues placed there. Likewise it contains stamps which have not fulfilled all the normal conditions for full catalogue listing.

These conditions are that the stamps must be issued by a legitimate postal authority, recognised by the government concerned, and are adhesives, valid for proper postal use in the class of service for which they are inscribed. Stamps, with the exception of such categories as postage dues and officials, must be available to the general public at face value with no artificial restrictions being imposed on their distribution.

The publishers of this catalogue have observed, with concern, the proliferation of 'artificial' stamp-issuing territories. On several occasions this has resulted in separately inscribed issues for various component parts of otherwise united states or territories.

Stanley Gibbons Publications have decided that where such circumstances occur, they will not, in the future, list these items in the SG catalogue without first satisfying themselves that the stamps represent a genuine political, historical or postal division within the country concerned. Any such issues which do not fulfil this stipulation will be recorded in the Catalogue Appendix only.

Stamps in the Appendix are kept under review in the light of any newly acquired information about them. If we are satisfied that a stamp qualifies for proper listing in the body of the catalogue it is moved there.

Information for users

"Undesirable Issues"

The rules governing many competitive exhibitions are set by the Federation Internationale de Philatelie and stipulate a downgrading of marks for stamps classed as "undesirable issues".

This catalogue can be taken as a guide to status. All stamps in the main listings and Addenda are acceptable. Stamps in the Appendix should not be entered for competition as these are the "undesirable issues".

Particular care is advised with Aden Protectorate States, Ajman, Bhutan, Chad, Fujeira, Khor Fakkan, Manama, Ras al Khaima, Sharjah, Umm al Qiwain and Yemen. Totally bogus stamps exist (as explained in Appendix notes) and these are to be avoided also for competition. As distinct from "undesirable stamps" certain categories are not covered in this catalogue purely by reason of its scope (see page viii). Consult the particular competition rules to see if such are admissable even though not listed by us.

Where to Look for More Detailed Listings

The present work deliberately omits details of paper, perforation, shade and watermark. But as you become more absorbed in stamp collecting and wish to get greater enjoyment from the hobby you may well want to study these matters.

All the information you require about any particular postage stamp will be found in the main Stanley Gibbons Catalogues.

Commonwealth countries before 1952 are covered by the Commonwealth & British Empire Stamps 1840–1952 published annually.

For foreign countries you can easily find which catalogue to consult by looking at the country headings in the present book.

To the right of each country name are code letters specifying which volume of our main catalogues contains that country's listing.

The code letters are as follows:

Pt. 2 Part 2
Pt. 3 Part 3 etc.

(See page xiii for complete list of Parts.)

So, for example, if you want to know more about Chinese stamps than is contained in the *Simplified Catalogue of Stamps of the World* the reference to

CHINA Pt. 17

guides you to the Gibbons Part 17 *(China)* Catalogue listing for the details you require.

New editions of Parts 2 to 22 appear at irregular intervals.

Correspondence

Whilst we welcome information and suggestions we must ask correspondents to include the cost of postage for the return of any stamps submitted plus registration where appropriate. Letters should be addressed to The Catalogue Editor at Ringwood.

Where information is solicited purely for the benefit of the enquirer we regret we cannot undertake to reply.

Identification of Stamps

We regret we do not give opinions as to the genuineness of stamps, nor do we identify stamps or number them by our Catalogue.

Users of this catalogue are referred to our companion booklet entitled *Stamp Collecting – How to Identify Stamps.* It explains how to look up stamps in this catalogue, contains a full checklist of stamp inscriptions and gives help in dealing with unfamiliar scripts.

Stanley Gibbons would like to complement your collection

At Stanley Gibbons we offer a range of services which are designed to complement your collection.

Our modern stamp shop, the largest in Europe, together with our rare stamp department has one of the most comprehensive stocks of Great Britain in the world, so whether you are a beginner or an experienced philatelist you are certain to find something to suit your special requirements.

Alternatively, through our Mail Order services you can control the growth of your collection from the comfort of your own home. Our Postal Sales Department regularly sends out mailings of Special Offers. We can also help with your wants list—so why not ask us for those elusive items?

Why not take advantage of the many services we have to offer? Visit our premises in the Strand or, for more information, write to the appropriate address on page x.

The Stanley Gibbons Group Addresses

Stanley Gibbons Limited,
Stanley Gibbons Auctions
339 Strand, London WC2R 0LX
Telephone 020 7836 8444, Fax 020 7836 7342,
E-mail: enquiries@stanleygibbons.co.uk
Internet: www.stanleygibbons.com for all departments.

Auction Room and Specialist Stamp Departments.
Open Monday–Friday 9.30 a.m. to 5 p.m.

Shop. Open Monday–Friday 9 a.m. to 5.30 p.m. and Saturday 9.30 a.m. to 5.30 p.m.

Fraser's
(a division of Stanley Gibbons Ltd)
399 Strand, London WC2R 0LX
Autographs, photographs, letters and documents
Telephone 020 7836 8444, Fax 020 7836 7342,
E-mail: info@frasersautographs.co.uk
Internet: www.frasersautographs.com
Monday–Friday 9 a.m. to 5.30 p.m. and Saturday 10 a.m. to 4 p.m.

Stanley Gibbons Publications
Parkside, Christchurch Road, Ringwood, Hants BH24 3SH.
Telephone 01425 472363 (24 hour answer phone service), Fax 01425 470247,
E-mail: info@stanleygibbons.co.uk

Publications Mail Order. FREEPHONE 0800 611622
Monday–Friday 8.30 a.m. to 5 p.m.

Stanley Gibbons Publications Overseas Representation

Stanley Gibbons Publications are represented overseas by the following sole distributors (*), distributors (**) or licensees (***).

Australia
Lighthouse Philatelic (Aust.) Pty. Ltd.*
Locked Bag 5900 Botany DC, New South Wales, 2019 Australia.

Stanley Gibbons (Australia) Pty. Ltd.***
Level 6, 36 Clarence Street, Sydney, New South Wales 2000, Australia.

Belgium and Luxembourg**
Davo c/o Philac, Rue du Midi 48, Bruxelles, 1000 Belgium.

Canada*
Lighthouse Publications (Canada) Ltd., 255 Duke Street, Montreal Quebec, Canada H3C 2M2.

Denmark**
Samlerforum/Davo, Ostergade 3, DK 7470 Karup, Denmark.

Finland**
Davo c/o Kapylan Merkkiky Pohjolankatu 1 00610 Helsinki, Finland.

France*
Davo France (Casteilla), 10, Rue Leon Foucault, 78184 St. Quentin Yvelines Cesex, France.

Hong Kong**
Po-on Stamp Service, GPO Box 2498, Hong Kong.

Israel**
Capital Stamps, P.O. Box 3769, Jerusalem 91036, Israel.

Italy*
Ernesto Marini Srl, Via Struppa 300, I-16165, Genova GE, Italy.

Japan**
Japan Philatelic Co. Ltd., P.O. Box 2, Suginami-Minami, Tokyo, Japan.

Netherlands*
Davo Publications, P.O. Box 411, 7400 AK Deventer, Netherlands.

New Zealand***
Mowbray Collectables.
P.O. Box 80, Wellington, New Zealand.

Norway**
Davo Norge A/S, P.O. Box 738 Sentrum, N-0105, Oslo, Norway.

Singapore**
Stamp Inc Collectibles Pte Ltd., 10 Ubi Cresent, #01-43 Ubi Tech Park, Singapore 408564.

Sweden*
Chr Winther Soerensen AB, Box 43, S-310 Knaered, Sweden.

Switzerland**
Phila Service, Burgstrasse 160, CH 4125, Riehen, Switzerland.

Abbreviations

Anniv.	denotes	Anniversary
Assn.	,,	Association
Bis.	,,	Bistre
Bl.	,,	Blue
Bldg.	,,	Building
Blk.	,,	Black
Br.	,,	British or Bridge
Brn.	,,	Brown
B.W.I.	,,	British West Indies
C.A.R.I.F.T.A.	,,	Caribbean Free Trade Area
Cent.	,,	Centenary
Chest.	,,	Chestnut
Choc.	,,	Chocolate
Clar.	,,	Claret
Coll.	,,	College
Commem.	,,	Commemoration
Conf.	,,	Conference
Diag.	,,	Diagonally
E.C.A.F.E.	,,	Economic Commission for Asia and Far East
Emer.	,,	Emerald
E.P.T. Conference	,,	European Postal and Telecommunications Conference
Exn.		Exhibition
F.A.O.	,,	Food and Agriculture Organization
Fig.	,,	Figure
G.A.T.T.	,,	General Agreement on Tariffs and Trade
G.B.	,,	Great Britain
Gen.	,,	General
Govt.	,,	Government
Grn.	,,	Green
Horiz.	,,	Horizontal
H.Q.	,,	Headquarters
Imperf.	,,	Imperforate
Inaug.	,,	Inauguration
Ind.	,,	Indigo
Inscr.	,,	Inscribed or inscription
Int.	,,	International
I.A.T.A.	,,	International Air Transport Association
I.C.A.O.	,,	International Civil Aviation Organization
I.C.Y.	,,	International Co-operation Year
I.G.Y.	,,	International Geophysical Year
I.L.O.	,,	International Labour Office (or later, Organization)
I.M.C.O.	,,	Inter-Governmental Maritime Consultative Organization
I.T.U.	,,	International Telecommunication Union
Is.	,,	Islands
Lav.	,,	Lavender
Mar.	,,	Maroon
mm.	,,	Millimetres
Mult.	,,	Multicoloured
Mve.	denotes	Mauve
Nat.	,,	National
N.A.T.O.	,,	North Atlantic Treaty Organization
O.D.E.C.A.	,,	Organization of Central American States
Ol.	,,	Olive
Optd.	,,	Overprinted
Orge. or oran.	,,	Orange
P.A.T.A.	,,	Pacific Area Travel Association
Perf.	,,	Perforated
Post.	,,	Postage
Pres.	,,	President
P.U.	,,	Postal Union
Pur.	,,	Purple
R.	,,	River
R.S.A.	,,	Republic of South Africa
Roul.	,,	Rouletted
Sep.	,,	Sepia
S.E.A.T.O.	,,	South East Asia Treaty Organization
Surch.	,,	Surcharged
T.	,,	Type
T.U.C.	,,	Trades Union Congress
Turq.	,,	Turquoise
Ultram.	,,	Ultramarine
U.N.E.S.C.O.	,,	United Nations Educational, Scientific Cultural Organization
U.N.I.C.E.F.	,,	United Nations Children's Fund
U.N.O.	,,	United Nations Organization
U.N.R.W.A.	,,	United Nations Relief and Works Agency for Palestine Refugees in the Near East
U.N.T.E.A.	,,	United Nations Temporary Executive Authority
U.N.R.R.A.	,,	United Nations Relief and Rehabilitation Administration
U.P.U.	,,	Universal Postal Union
Verm.	,,	Vermilion
Vert.	,,	Vertical
Vio.	,,	Violet
W.F.T.U.	,,	World Federation of Trade Unions
W.H.O.	,,	World Health Organization
Yell.	,,	Yellow

Arabic Numerals

As in the case of European figures, the details of the Arabic numerals vary in different stamp designs, but they should be readily recognised with the aid of this illustration:

٠	١	٢	٣	٤
0	1	2	3	4
٥	٦	٧	٨	٩
5	6	7	8	9

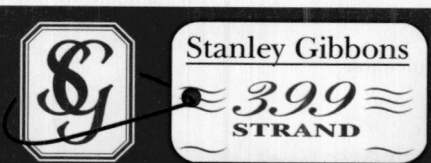

Stanley Gibbons Stamp Catalogue
Complete List of Parts

1 Commonwealth & British Empire Stamps 1840–1952 (Annual)

Foreign Countries

2 Austria & Hungary (6th edition, 2002)
Austria · U.N. (Vienna) · Hungary

3 Balkans (4th edition, 1998)
Albania · Bosnia & Herzegovina · Bulgaria · Croatia · Greece & Islands · Macedonia · Rumania · Slovenia · Yugoslavia

4 Benelux (5th edition, 2003)
Belgium & Colonies · Luxembourg · Netherlands & Colonies

5 Czechoslovakia & Poland (6th edition, 2002)
Czechoslovakia · Czech Republic · Slovakia · Poland

6 France (5th edition, 2001)
France · Colonies · Post Offices · Andorra · Monaco

7 Germany (6th edition, 2002)
Germany · States · Colonies · Post Offices

8 Italy & Switzerland (6th edition, 2003)
Italy & Colonies · Liechtenstein · San Marino · Switzerland · U.N. (Geneva) · Vatican City

9 Portugal & Spain (4th edition, 1996)
Andorra · Portugal & Colonies · Spain & Colonies

10 Russia (5th edition, 1999)
Russia · Armenia · Azerbaijan · Belarus · Estonia · Georgia · Kazakhstan · Kyrgyzstan · Latvia · Lithuania · Moldova · Tajikistan · Turkmenistan · Ukraine · Uzbekistan · Mongolia

11 Scandinavia (5th edition, 2001)
Aland Islands · Denmark · Faroe Islands · Finland · Greenland · Iceland · Norway · Sweden

12 Africa since Independence A-E (2nd edition, 1983)
Algeria · Angola · Benin · Burundi · Cameroun · Cape Verdi · Central African Republic · Chad · Comoro Islands · Congo · Djibouti · Equatorial Guinea · Ethiopia

13 Africa since Independence F-M (1st edition, 1981)
Gabon · Guinea · Guinea-Bissau · Ivory Coast · Liberia · Libya · Malagasy Republic · Mali · Mauritania · Morocco · Mozambique

14 Africa since Independence N-Z (1st edition, 1981)
Niger Republic · Rwanda · St. Thomas & Prince · Senegal · Somalia · Sudan · Togo · Tunisia · Upper Volta · Zaire

15 Central America (2nd edition, 1984)
Costa Rica · Cuba · Dominican Republic · El Salvador · Guatemala · Haiti · Honduras · Mexico · Nicaragua · Panama

16 Central Asia (3rd edition, 1992)
Afghanistan · Iran · Turkey

17 China (6th edition,1998)
China · Taiwan · Tibet · Foreign P.O.s · Hong Kong · Macao

18 Japan & Korea (4th edition, 1997)
Japan · Korean Empire · South Korea · North Korea

19 Middle East (5th edition, 1996)
Bahrain · Egypt · Iraq · Israel · Jordan · Kuwait · Lebanon · Oman · Qatar · Saudi Arabia · Syria · U.A.E. · Yemen

20 South America (3rd edition, 1989)
Argentina · Bolivia · Brazil · Chile · Colombia · Ecuador · Paraguay · Peru · Surinam · Uruguay · Venezuela

21 South-East Asia (4th edition, 2004)
Bhutan · Burma · Indonesia · Kampuchea · Laos · Nepal · Philippines · Thailand · Vietnam

22 United States (5th edition, 2000)
U.S. & Possessions · Marshall Islands · Micronesia · Palau · U.N. (New York, Geneva, Vienna)

Thematic Catalogues

Stanley Gibbons Catalogues for use with **Stamps of the World.**
Collect Aircraft on Stamps (out of print)
Collect Birds on Stamps (5th edition, 2003)
Collect Chess on Stamps (2nd edition, 1999)
Collect Fish on Stamps (1st edition, 1999)
Collect Fungi on Stamps (2nd edition, 1997)
Collect Motor Vehicles on Stamps (1st edition, 2004)
Collect Railways on Stamps (3rd edition, 1999)
Collect Shells on Stamps (1st edition, 1995)
Collect Ships on Stamps (3rd edition, 2001)

Key-Types

(see note on page vii)

French Group

A. "Blanc."

B. "Mouchon."

C "Merson."

D. "Tablet."

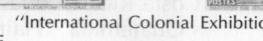

"International Colonial Exhibition."

E. F. G. H.

I. "Faidherbe."

J. "Palms."

K. "Balay."

L. "Natives."

M. "Figure."

German Group

N. "Yacht."

O. "Yacht."

Spanish Group

X. "Alfonso XII."

Y. "Baby."

Z. "Curly Head"

Portuguese Group

P. "Crown."

Q. "Embossed."

R. "Figures."

S. "Carlos."

T. "Manoel."

U. "Ceres."

V. "Newspaper."

W. "Due."

STANLEY GIBBONS SIMPLIFIED CATALOGUE OF STAMPS OF THE WORLD—VOLUME 2 COUNTRIES E–J

EAST SILESIA Pt. 5

Special overprints were applied to Czechoslovakian and Polish stamps prior to a plebiscite. The plebiscite was never held, due to disorders, and the area was divided between Czechoslovakia and Poland in 1920.

100 haleru = 1 krone.
100 fenni = 1 korona.

1920. Stamps of Czechoslovakia optd **SO 1920.** Imperf or perf.

23	3	1h. brown	20	10
2	2	3h. mauve	15	10
24	3	5h. green	25	30
25		10h. green	25	30
26		15h. red	40	15
6	2	20h. green	20	10
27	3	20h. red	40	30
28		25h. purple	40	30
9	2	30h. olive	20	30
35	3	30h. mauve	40	30
10	2	40h. orange	25	30
11	3	50h. purple	55	45
12		50h. blue	1·50	1·25
36		60h. orange	45	45
14		75h. green	45	45
15		80h. olive	45	45
16	2	100h. brown	80	60
17	3	120h. black	1·40	1·25
18	2	200h. blue	1·40	1·25
19	3	300h. green	6·50	1·90
20	2	400h. violet	1·90	1·50
21	3	500h. brown	4·25	3·75
22		1000h. purple	13·00	7·50

1920. Stamps of Poland of 1919 optd **S. O. 1920.** Perf.

57	15	5f. green	10	10
58		10f. brown	10	10
59		15f. red	10	10
60	16	25f. olive	10	10
61		50f. green	10	10
62	17	1k. green	10	10
63		1k.50 brown	10	10
64		2k. blue	10	10
65	18	2k.50 purple	10	10
66	19	5k. blue	10	10

EXPRESS STAMPS FOR PRINTED MATTER

1920. Express stamps of Czechoslovakia optd **S O 1920.**

E39	E 4	2h. purple on yellow	15	10
E40		5h. green on yellow	15	10

NEWSPAPER STAMPS

1920. Newspaper stamps of Czechoslovakia optd **SO 1920.** Imperf.

N41	N 4	2h. green	20	30
N42		6h. red	20	10
N43		10h. lilac	35	30
N44		20h. blue	50	30
N45		30h. brown	50	30

POSTAGE DUE STAMPS

1920. Postage Due stamps of Czechoslovakia optd **SO 1920.** Imperf.

D46	D 4	5h. olive	20	15
D47		10h. olive	20	10
D48		15h. olive	20	15
D49		20h. olive	30	30
D50		25h. olive	30	30
D51		30h. olive	30	30
D52		40h. olive	45	45
D53		50h. olive	2·10	45
D54		100h. brown	2·25	90
D55		500h. green	5·75	3·75
D56		1000h. violet	9·00	6·75

EASTERN ROUMELIA AND SOUTH BULGARIA Pt. 3

This area, part of the Turkish Empire, situated south of the Balkan Mts., became semi-autonomous after 1878. In 1885 the population revolted against the Turks, changing the district's name to South Bulgaria. Incorporation into Bulgaria followed in 1886.

40 paras = 1 piastre.

A. EASTERN ROUMELIA

1880. Stamps of Turkey optd **R.O.**

1	2	½pre. on 20pa. green (No. 78)	35·00	35·00
2	9	20pa. purple & green (No. 83)	38·00	38·00
3		2pi. black & orange (No. 85)	60·00	60·00
4		5pi. red and blue (No. 86)	£200	£200

1881. Stamp of Turkey optd **R.O** and **ROUMELIE ORIENTALE.**

5	9	10pa. black and mauve	45·00	45·00

1881. As T **9** of Turkey but inscr "ROUMELIE ORIENTALE" at left.

6	9	5pa. black and olive	1·50	50
11		5pa. lilac	25	25
7		10pa. black and green	4·00	50
12		10pa. green	10	25
8		20pa. black and red	40	50
9		1pi. black and blue	2·50	3·00
10		5pi. red and blue	25·00	45·00

B. SOUTH BULGARIA

1885. As T **9** of Turkey, but inscr "RO" at left and optd with lion.

13	9	5pa. black and olive	£225	£225
29		5pa. lilac	7·50	24·00
14		10pa. black and green	£550	£550
30		10pa. green	15·00	30·00
15		20pa. black and red	£225	
34		20pa. red	14·00	48·00
18		1pi. black and blue	45·00	90·00
26		5pi. red and blue	£375	

1885. As T **9** of Turkey, but inscr "ROUMELIE ORIENTALE" and optd with lion and inscription in frame.

43	9	5pa. black and olive	£250	£250
48a		5pa. lilac	9·00	15·00
44		10pa. black and green	£250	£250
49		10pa. green	12·00	18·00
45		20pa. black and red	60·00	75·00
50		20pa. red	12·00	18·00
46		1pi. black and blue	60·00	75·00
47		5pi. red and blue	20·00	25·00

ECUADOR Pt. 20

A Republic on the W. Coast of S. America. Independent since 1830.

1865. 8 reales = 1 peso.
1881. 100 centavos = 1 sucre.
2002. 100c. = 1 dollar (U.S.)

1

2

1865. Imperf.

1b	1	½r. blue	13·00	6·75
2d		1r. yellow	10·00	7·25
3		1r. green	£150	17·50
4	2	4r. red	£160	80·00

3

4

5

1872.

10	3	½r. blue	10·00	2·10
11	4	1r. orange	11·50	3·50
12a	3	1p. red	2·10	7·00

1881. Various frames.

13	5	1c. brown	10	10
14		2c. lake	10	10
15		5c. blue	1·90	25
16		10c. orange	10	10
17		20c. violet	30	25
18		50c. green	40	1·50

1883. Surch **DIEZ CENTAVOS.**

19	5	10c. on 50c. green	15·00	11·50

13

19 Pres. Juan Flores

20 Pres. Rocafuerte

1887. Various frames.

26	13	1c. green	10	10
27		2c. red	15	10
28		5c. blue	85	15
29		80c. olive	1·50	4·25

1892.

34	19	1c. orange	10	10
35		2c. brown	10	10
36		5c. red	10	10
37		10c. green	10	10
38		20c. brown	10	10
39		50c. red	10	20
40		1s. blue	10	75
41		5s. violet	25	75

1893. Surch **5 CENTAVOS.**

53	19	5c. on 50c. red	40	35
49		5c. on 1s. blue	65	55
50		5c. on 5s. violet	3·00	2·75

1894. Dated "1894".

57	20	1c. blue	10	10
58		2c. brown	10	10
59		5c. green	15	15
60		10c. red	30	15
61		20c. black	30	15
62		50c. orange	2·00	75
63		1s. red	3·75	1·50
64		5s. blue	4·75	2·25

1895. Dated "1895".

74	20	1c. blue	25	25
75		2c. brown	25	25
76		5c. green	20	20
77		10c. red	20	10
78		20c. black	30	30
79		50c. orange	1·40	75
80		1s. red	7·00	3·00
81		5s. blue	3·00	1·50

These two series were re-issued in 1897 optd "1897–1898".

22

F 1

1896. Arms designs, inscr "U.P.U. 1896".

89	22	1c. green	30	10
90		2c. red	30	10
91		5c. blue	30	10
92		10c. brown	25	25
93		20c. orange	40	70
94		50c. blue	25	1·25
95		1s. brown	1·25	1·50
96		5s. lilac	5·50	2·10

This series was re-issued in 1897 optd "1897–1898".

1896. Dated "1887 1888". Surch.

112	F 1	5c. on 10c. orange	75	15
113		10c. on 4c. brown	75	30

1896. As Type F 1, but dated "1891 1892".

114	F 1	10c. on 4c. brown	6·50	5·25

1896. As Type F 1, but dated "1893 1894". Surch.

115	F 1	1c. on 1c. red	40	15
116		2c. on 2c. blue	75	50
117		5c. on 10c. orange	2·10	1·90

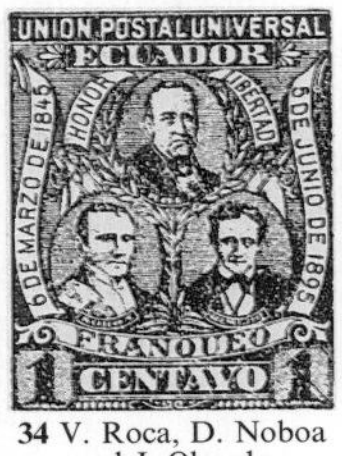
34 V. Roca, D. Noboa and J. Olmedo

(40)

1896. Triumph of Liberal Party. Dated "1845–1895".

118	34	1c. red	40	40
119	–	2c. blue	40	40
120	34	5c. green	30	50
121	–	10c. yellow	30	50
122	34	20c. red	35	75
123	–	50c. lilac	50	1·25
124	34	1s. orange	95	1·50

DESIGN: 2c., 10c., 50c. Gen. Elizalde.
This series was re-issued in 1897 optd "1897–1898".

1896. Surch.

125	22	5c. on 20c. orange	13·50	13·50
126		10c. on 50c. blue	13·50	13·50

1897. 1896 Jubilee issue optd with T **40.**

167	34	1c. red	1·75	1·50
168	–	2c. blue (No. 119)	1·75	1·50
169	34	5c. green	1·75	1·50
170	–	10c. yellow (No. 121)	1·75	1·50

41

45 Louis Varags Torres

1897.

173	41	1c. green	10	10
174		2c. red	10	10
175		5c. lake	10	10
176		10c. brown	10	10
177		20c. yellow	15	25
178		50c. blue	15	40
179		1s. grey	20	50
180		5s. purple	60	75

1899. Surch.

191	41	1c. on 2c. red	1·25	50
192		5c. on 10c. brown	1·00	25

1899.

193	45	1c. black and grey	10	10
205		1c. black and red	10	10
194	–	2c. black and brown	10	10
206	–	2c. black and green	10	10
195	–	5c. black and red	10	10
207	–	5c. black and lilac	10	10
196	–	10c. black and lilac	10	10
208	–	10c. black and blue	10	10
197	–	20c. black and green	10	10
209	–	20c. black and grey	10	10
198	–	50c. black and red	60	30
210	–	50c. black and blue	35	30
199	–	1s. black and yellow	3·25	1·00
211	–	1s. black and brown	2·75	1·40
200	–	5s. black and lilac	6·25	3·00
212	–	5s. black and grey	4·50	2·25

PORTRAITS: 2c. A. Calderon. 5c. J. Montalvo. 10c. Mejia. 20c. Espejo. 50c. Carbo. 1s. J. J. Olmendo. 5s. Moncayo.

73 Capt. Abdon Calderon

76 President Roca

1904. Birth Centenary of Captain Calderon.

310	73	1c. black and red	25	20
311		2c. black and blue	25	20
312		5c. black and yellow	1·00	70
313		10c. black and red	1·75	70
314		20c. black and blue	4·50	1·60
315		50c. black and yellow	42·00	23·00

The 5c. and 50c. are larger (25 × 30 mm).

1907. Portraits in black.

323	76	1c. red (Roca)	20	10
324	–	2c. blue (Noboa)	40	10
325	–	3c. orange (Robles)	50	10
326	–	5c. purple (Urvina)	75	10
327	–	10c. blue (Garcia Moreno)	1·50	15
328	–	20c. green (Carrion)	2·25	20
329	–	50c. lilac (Espinoza)	4·50	50
330	–	1s. green (Borrero)	6·25	1·10

84 Baldwin Steam Locomotive

86 Mount Chimborazo

85 Garcia Moreno

1908. Opening of Guayaquil to Quito Railway.

331	**84**	1c. brown	65	50
332	**85**	2c. black and blue	90	70
333	–	5c. black and red	2·00	1·40
334	–	10c. black and yellow	1·50	85
335	–	20c. black and green	1·50	1·00
336	–	50c. black and grey	1·50	1·00
337	**86**	1s. black	3·00	2·00

PORTRAITS—As Type **85**: 5c. Gen E. Alfaro. 10c. A. Moncayo. 20c. A. Harman (engineer). 50c. Sivewright.

87 Jose Mejia Vallejo

88 Exhibition Buildings

1909. National Exhibition. Portraits as T **87**.

340	**87**	1c. green	15	25
341	–	2c. blue (Espejo)	15	25
342	–	3c. orange (Ascasubi)	15	35
343	–	5c. lake (Salinas)	15	35
344	–	10c. brown (Alegre)	20	35
345	–	20c. grey (Montufar)	20	50
346	–	50c. red (Morales)	20	50
347	–	1s. olive (Quiroga)	20	70
348	**88**	5s. violet	70	1·40

1909. Surch **CINCO CENTAVOS**.

349	5c. on 50c. red (No. 346)	60	50

90 Pres. Roca

91 Pres. Dr. Noboa

92 Robles

98 Valdez

93 Pres. Gen. Urvina

94 Pres. Dr. Garcia Moreno

99 Espinoza

95 Dr. Borrero

1911.

354	**90**	1c. black and red	25	10
366		1c. orange	25	10
355	**91**	2c. black and blue	25	10
367		2c. green	10	10
356	**92**	3c. black and orange	85	25
368		3c. black	40	10
369	**98**	4c. black and red	10	10
357	**93**	5c. black and red	40	10
370		5c. violet	60	10
358	**94**	10c. black and blue	70	10
371		10c. blue	70	10
373	**99**	50c. black and violet	1·75	35
359	**95**	1s. black and green	4·00	75

See also Nos. 413/6b.

1912. Large Fiscal stamps inscr "TIMBRE CONSULAR" at top. Surch **POSTAL** and new value.

362	1c. on 1s. green	25	25
363	2c. on 2s. red	75	35
364	2c. on 5s. blue	35	35
365	2c. on 10s. yellow	1·50	1·50

1920. Optd **CASA de CORREOS**.

374	**90**	1c. orange	25	10

103

108 Olmedo

109 Monument to "Fathers of the Country"

1920. Obligatory Tax. Optd **CASA de CORREOS** or surch also. Dated as shown.

375	**103**	1c. bl & red (no date)	40	10
376		1c. bl ("1919–20")	45	10
379		1c. on 2c. green ("1917–18")	20	10
380		1c. on 5c. green ("1911–12")	30	10
380a		1c. on 5c. green ("1913–14")	2·75	35
377		20c. bl ("1913–14")	85	35
378		20c. ol ("1917–18")	2·25	40

1920. Centenary of Liberation of Guayaquil. Portraits as T **108**.

381	**108**	1c. green	15	10
382	–	2c. red (Ximena)	10	10
383	–	3c. bistre (Roca)	10	10
384	–	4c. green (Vivero)	15	10
385	–	5c. blue (Cordero)	15	10
386	–	6c. orange (Lavayen)	30	30
387	–	7c. brown (Elizalde)	85	60
388	–	8c. green (Garcia)	45	25
389	–	9c. red (Antepara)	1·75	75
390	**109**	10c. blue	60	10
391	–	15c. black (Urdaneta)	85	45
392	–	20c. purple (Villamil)	85	15
393	–	30c. violet (Letamendi)	1·75	65
394	–	40c. sepia (Escobedo)	3·00	1·10
395	–	50c. green (Sucre)	1·90	45
396	–	60c. blue (Illingworth)	3·75	1·10
397	–	70c. grey (Roca)	6·25	2·50
398	–	80c. yellow (Rocafuerte)	6·50	2·50
399	–	90c. green (Star and wreath)	7·00	2·50
400	–	1s. blue (Bolivar)	9·75	4·25

112 Post Office, Quito

123 Post Office, Quito

1920. Obligatory Tax. G.P.O. Rebuilding Fund.

401	**112**	1c. olive	10	10
402		2c. green	15	10
403		20c. brown	50	10
404		2s. violet	3·00	2·25
405		5s. blue	5·50	3·75

1921. Obligatory Tax. Surch **Casa de Correos VEINTE CTS. 1921–1922.**

405a	**103**	20c. on 1c. blue	19·00	2·25
405b		20c. on 2c. green	19·00	2·25

1924. Obligatory Tax. Surch **DOS CENTAVOS – 2 –**.

406	**112**	2c. on 20c. brown	10	10

1924. Oblong Tobacco Tax stamps optd **CASA–CORREOS**.

407	1c. red (Loco.)	4·50	75
408	2c. blue (Arms)	20	15

1924. Telegraph stamps as T **103**, but inscr "TELEGRAFOS DEL ECUADOR" optd **CASA-CORREOS**. (a) Inscr "TIMBRE FISCAL".

409	1c. yellow	1·50	50
410	2c. blue	25	10

(b) Inscr "REGION ORIENTAL".

411	1c. yellow	25	20
412	2c. blue	50	20

1925.

413	**90**	1c. blue	10	10
414	**91**	2c. violet	10	10
415	**93**	5c. red	15	10
415a		5c. brown	20	10
416	**94**	10c. green	15	10
416a		10c. black	50	10
416b	**95**	1s. black and orange	2·75	20

1925. Optd **POSTAL** over ornament.

417	**112**	20c. brown	1·00	35

1926. Opening of Quito–Esmeraldas Railway. Optd **QUITO**, railway train and **ESMERALDAS 1926**.

418	**90**	1c. blue	11·00	5·00
419	**91**	2c. violet	11·00	5·00
420	**92**	3c. black	8·75	5·00
421	–	4c. green (No. 384)	8·75	5·00
422	**93**	5c. red	16·00	5·00
423	**94**	10c. green	16·00	5·00

1927. Optd **POSTAL**.

424	**112**	1c. olive	10	10
425		2c. green	10	10
426		20c. brown	70	10

1927. Opening of New Post Office, Quito.

427	**123**	5c. orange	20	10
428		10c. green	15	10
429		20c. purple	35	10

1928. Opening of Quito-Cayambe Railway. Stamps of 1920 issue surch **Frril. Norte Julio 8 de 1928 Est. Cayambe** and value.

431	10c. on 30c. (No. 393)	12·00	10·50
432	50c. on 70c. (No. 397)	19·00	18·00
433	1s. on 80c. (No. 398)	22·00	21·00

1928. National Assembly. Stamps of 1920 surch **ASAMBLEA NCNAL. 1928** and value.

434	**108**	1c. on 1c. green (381)	6·25	5·25
435	–	1c. on 2c. red (382)	15	15
436	–	2c. on 3c. bistre (383)	95	95
437	–	2c. on 4c. green (384)	50	50
438	–	2c. on 5c. (No. 385)	25	25
440	–	5c. on 6c. (No. 386)	15	10
441	–	10c. on 2c. on 7c. (387)	15	10
442	–	10c. on 7c. (No. 387)	40	40
443	–	20c. on 8c. (No. 388)	15	10
444	**109**	40c. on 10c. (No. 390)	1·75	1·50
445	–	40c. on 15c. (No. 391)	35	35
446	–	50c. on 20c. (No. 392)	5·75	4·50
447	–	1s. on 40c. (No. 394)	1·40	1·40
448	–	5s. on 50c. (No. 395)	1·90	1·90
449	–	10s. on 60c. (No. 396)	7·00	4·50

1928. Opening of Railway at Otavalo. Consular Service stamps inscr "TIMBRE-CONSULAR" surch **Postal–Frril Norte Est. OTAVALO** and value.

450	5c. on 20c. lilac	3·50	1·60
451	10c. on 20c. lilac	3·75	1·60
452	20c. on 1s. green	3·75	1·60
453	50c. on 1s. green	4·25	1·25
454	1s. on 1s. green	5·50	1·60
455	5s. on 2s. red	13·00	7·25
456	10s. on 2s. red	16·00	11·50

130 Ryan B-5 Brougham over the River Guayas

133 Ploughing

1929. Air.

458	**130**	2c. black	10	10
459		5c. red	10	10
460		10c. brown	15	10
461		20c. purple	25	10
462		50c. green	60	25
463		1s. blue	1·75	95
467		1s. red	1·75	35
709		1s. green	40	10
464		5s. yellow	5·00	3·75
468		5s. olive	2·50	1·90
710		5s. violet	60	10
465		10s. red	25·00	20·00
469		10s. black	7·75	2·75
711		10s. blue	1·10	10

1929. As T **103**, but inscr "MOVILES" and optd **POSTAL**.

466	**103**	1c. blue	10	10

1930. Air. Official Air stamps of 1929 optd **MENDEZ BOGOTA–QUITO Junio 4 de 1930.**

470	**130**	1s. red	13·50	13·50
471		5s. olive	13·50	13·50
472		10s. black	13·50	13·50

1930. Independence Cent. Dated "1830 1930".

473	**133**	1c. red and yellow	10	10
474	–	2c. green and yellow	10	10
475	–	5c. purple and green	10	10
476	–	6c. red and yellow	20	10
477	–	10c. olive and orange	90	15
478	–	16c. green and red	2·50	40
479	–	20c. yellow and blue	35	10
480	–	40c. sepia and yellow	40	10
481	–	50c. sepia and yellow	50	10
482	–	1s. black and green	1·40	10
483	–	2s. black and deep blue	2·50	35
484	–	5s. black and purple	4·50	50
485	–	10s. black and red	12·50	3·00

DESIGNS—As Type **133**: 1c. Labourer and oxen, ploughing; 2c. Cocoa cultivation; 6c. Tobacco plantation; 10c. Exportation of fruit; 10s. Bolivar's monument (41 × 37½ mm). LARGER (27 × 42½ mm): 5c. Cocoa pod; 20c. Sugar plantation; 1s. Olmedo; 2s. Sucre; 5s. Bolivar. (41½ × 28 mm): 16c. Mountaineer, steam train and airplane; 40, 50c. Views of Quito.

1933. Optd **CORREOS**.

486	**103**	10c. brown	40	10

1933. Optd **CORREOS Emision Junio 1933 Dcto. No 200.**

487	**103**	10c. brown	15	10

1933. Nos. 476 and 478 surch.

488	5c. on 6c. red and yellow	20	10
489	10c. on 16c. green and red	90	20

1934. Obligatory Tax. Optd **CASA de Correos y Telegrafos de Guayaquil**. (a) Fiscal stamp as T **103**, but inscr "MOVILES" (instead of dates at top).

490	**103**	2c. green	10	10

(b) Centenary stamp of 1930 (No. 479).

491	20c. yellow and blue	15	10

(c) Telegraph stamp as T **103**, but inscr "TELEGRAFOS DEL ECUADOR" surch **2 ctvos.** also.

492	**103**	2c. on 10c. brown	25	10

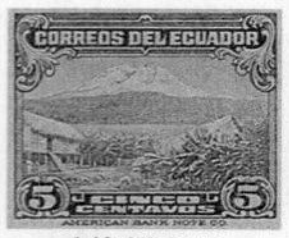
143 Mount Chimborazo

144 Mount Chimborazo

1934.

493	**143**	5c. mauve	10	10
494		5c. blue	15	10
495		5c. brown	15	10
495a		5c. grey	15	10
496		10c. red	15	10
497		10c. green	15	10
498		10c. orange	15	10
499		10c. brown	15	10
500		10c. olive	15	10
500a		10c. black	10	10
500b		10c. lilac	10	10

1934.

501	**144**	1s. red	75	40

1934. Optd **CASA de Correos y Teleg. de Guayaquil**.

502	**112**	2c. green (No. 425)	10	10

146 Symbol of Telegraphy

150 Map of Galapagos Islands

1934. G.P.O. Rebuilding Fund.

503	**146**	2c. green	10	10
504	–	20c. red	10	10

The symbolic design of the 20c. is 38 × 18½ mm.

1935. Unveiling of Bolivar Monument, Quito. Optd **INAUGURACION MONUMENTO A BOLIVAR QUITO, 24 DE JULIO DE 1935** or surch also. (a) Postage. On 1930 Independence Issue.

505	5c. on 6c. red and yellow	20	10
506	10c. on 6c. red and yellow	25	10
507	20c. yellow and blue	25	10
508	40c. sepia and yellow	35	20
509	50c. sepia and yellow	45	35
510	$1 on 5s. black and purple	1·10	60
511	$2 on 5s. black and purple	1·50	1·10
512	$5 on 10s. black and red	2·50	2·50

(b) Air. On Official stamps of 1929.

513	**130**	50c. green	3·25	3·25
514		50c. brown	3·25	3·25
515		$1 on 5s. olive	3·25	3·25
516		$2 on 10s. black	3·25	3·25

1935. Fiscal stamp, but without dates and inscr "TELEGRAFOS DEL ECUADOR", optd **POSTAL**.

517	**103**	10c. brown	15	10

1935. Rural Workers Social Insurance Fund. No. 503 surch **Seguro Social del Campesino Quito, 16 de Otbre.-1935** and value.

518	**146**	3c. on 2c. green	10	10

1936. Centenary of Darwin's Visit to the Galapagos Islands.

519	**150**	2c. black	10	10
520	–	5c. olive	25	10
521	–	10c. brown	40	10
522	–	20c. purple	2·50	40
523	–	1s. red	85	35
524	–	2s. blue	1·10	70

DESIGNS—HORIZ: 10c. Galapagos tortoise. VERT: 5c. Giant lizard; 20c. Charles Darwin and H.M.S. "Beagle"; 1s. Columbus; 2s. View of Galapagos Islands.

1936. Oblong Tobacco Tax Stamps. (a) Charity. Surch **Seguro Social del Campesino 3 ctvs.**
525 – 3c. on 1c. red . . . . 1·90 55

(b) Charity. Surch **SEGURO SOCIAL DEL CAMPESINO 3 ctvs.**
526 – 3c. on 1c. red . . . . 1·90 55

(c) Optd **POSTAL**.
527 – 1c. red . . . . 1·90 55

1936. No. 479 optd **Casa de Correos y Telegrafos de Guayaquil**.
528 – 20c. yellow and blue 20 10

160 Ulloa, La Condamine and Juan

162 Woodman

1936. Bicentenary of La Condamine Scientific Expedition. (a) Postage.
529 – 2c. blue 10 10
530 **160** 5c. green 10 10
531 – 10c. orange 10 10
532 **160** 20c. violet 20 10
533 – 50c. red 40 25

(b) Air. Nos. 531/3 optd **AEREO**.
534 – 10c. orange 20 10
535 **160** 20c. violet 20 10
536 – 50c. red 35 10

(c) Air. Inscr "CORREO AEREO".
537 – 70c. grey 55 25
DESIGNS: 2c., 10c., 50c. Godin. La Condamine and Bouguer; 70c. La Condamine, Arms and Maldonado.

1936. Building and National Defence Funds. Surch **5 Centavos Dect. Junio 13 de 1936**.
539 **162** 5c. on 3c. blue 10 10

1936. Social Insurance.
540 **162** 3c. blue 10 10

1936. Oblong Tobacco Tax stamp surch **TIMBRE PATRIOTICO DIEZ CENTAVOS**.
541 – 10c. on 1c. red . . . . . . 2·25 40

165 Independence Monument, Quito

166 Condor and Martin M-130 Flying Boat

1936. 1st International Philatelic Exn, Quito.
541a **165** 2c. green (postage) . . . 85 20
542 5c. purple 85 20
543 10c. red 85 25
543a 20c. black 85 60
544 50c. blue . . . . 1·50 1·00
545 1s. red . . . . 1·75 1·50
546 **166** 70c. brown (air) 90 50
547 1s. violet 90 70

1936. Air. Optd **AEREA**.
547a **165** 2c. red . . . . 3·25 3·25
547b 5c. orange . . . . 3·25 3·25
547c 10c. brown . . . . 3·25 3·25
547d 20c. blue . . . . 3·25 3·25
547e 50c. purple . . . . . . 3·25 3·25
547f 1s. green . . . . 3·25 3·25

167 Symbolical of Defence

169

1937. Obligatory Tax. National Defence Fund. (a) Surch **POSTAL ADICIONAL** and value in figures.
548 **167** 5c. on 10c. blue 40 10

(b) Without surch.
549 **167** 10c. blue 10 10

1937. Fiscal stamps inscr "MOVILES" at top optd **POSTAL** or surch also.
550 **169** 5c. olive (I) 40 10
955a 5c. olive (II) 20 10
551 10c. blue 40 10
819 10c. orange 50 10
952 20c. on 30c. blue 20 10
953 30c. blue 20 10
954 40c. on 50c. purple . . . 10 10
955 50c. purple 30 10
Nos. 952/3 are smaller (19¼ × 25½ mm). Nos. 550 (I) with imprint. 955a (II) without imprint.
See also No. 685.

171 Andean Landscape

172 Andean Condor over El Altar

1937. (a) Postage.
552 **171** 2c. green 10 10
553 – 5c. red 10 10
554 – 10c. blue 15 10
555 – 20c. red 40 10
556 – 1s. olive 55 25
DESIGNS—VERT: 5c. Atahualpa; 1s. Gold washer. HORIZ: 10c. Straw-hat makers; 20c. Salinas Beach.

(b) Air.
557 **172** 10c. brown 30 10
558 20c. olive 40 10
558a 40c. red 40 10
559 70c. brown 55 10
560 1s. slate 65 15
561 2s. violet 80 25

173

1937. Optd **TIMBRE PATRIOTICO**.
562 **173** 5c. brown 75 20

174 "Liberty" supporting Ecuadorian Flag between American Bald Eagle and Andean Condor

1938. 150th Anniv of U.S. Constitution. Flags in yellow, blue and red.
563 **174** 2c. blue (postage) 20 10
564 5c. violet 30 10
565 10c. black 30 10
566 20c. purple 45 15
567 50c. black 65 15
568 1s. olive . . . . 1·10 30
569 2s. brown . . . . 2·00 45
570 – 2c. olive (air) 15 10
571 – 5c. black 15 10
572 – 10c. brown 20 10
573 – 20c. blue 45 10
574 – 50c. purple 70 15
575 – 1s. black . . . . 1·25 15
576 – 2s. violet . . . . 2·50 65
DESIGN (air): Washington portrait, American bald eagle and flags.

176 Ecuador

178 "Road Transport"

1938. Obligatory Tax. Social Insurance Fund for Rural Workers and Guayaquil G.P.O. Rebuilding Funds.
577 **176** 5c. red 25 10

1938. Obligatory Tax. No. 537 surch **CASA DE CORREOS Y TELEGRAFOS DE GUAYAQUIL** and **20** in each corner.
578 – 20c. on 70c. grey 20 10

1938. National Progress Exn. Inscr "1830 – 1937".
579 **178** 10c. blue 10 10
580 – 50c. purple . . . . 1·00 15
581 – 1s. red . . . . 1·40 25
582 – 2s. green 50 10

DESIGNS—VERT: 50c. "Railways"; 1s. "Communication". HORIZ: 2s. "Building" (inscr "CONSTRUCCION").

1938. Air. Surch **AEREO SEDTA** and value.
582a **162** 65c. on 3c. blue 10 10

1938. Obligatory Tax. International Anti-cancer Fund. No. 476 surch **CAMPANA CONTRA EL CANCER 5 5**.
583 5c. on 6c. red and yellow . . 10 10

181 Running

182 Ryan B-5 Brougham over Mt. Chimborazo

1939. Ecuadorean Victories at South American Olympic Games, La Paz. Inscr "EN CONMEMORACION DE LA PRIMERA OLIMPIADA BOLIVARIANA DE 1938".
584 – 5c. red (postage) . . . . 1·60 35
585 **181** 10c. blue . . . . 2·25 40
586 – 50c. olive . . . . 3·75 50
587 – 1s. violet . . . . 6·50 50
588 – 2s. green . . . . 11·00 70
DESIGNS—HORIZ: 5c. Parade of athletes; 50c. Basketball. VERT: 1s. Wrestling; 2s. Diving.
589 – 5c. green (air) 40 10
590 – 10c. orange 55 15
591 – 50c. brown . . . . 3·50 15
592 – 1s. sepia . . . . 8·00 35
593 – 2s. red . . . . 12·00 70
DESIGNS—HORIZ: 5c. Riding; 1s. Boxing. VERT: 10c. Running; 50c. Tennis; 2s. Olympic flame.

1939. Air.
594 **182** 1s. brown 40 15
595 2s. purple 85 15
596 5s. black . . . . 1·25 15

183 Dolores Mission, San Francisco

184 Golden Gate Bridge and Mountain

1939. San Francisco International Exhibition.
597 **183** 2c. green (postage) . . . 10 10
598 5c. red 10 10
599 10c. blue 10 10
600 50c. brown 25 10
601 1s. slate 45 10
602 2s. violet 80 15
603 **184** 2c. black (air) 10 10
604 5c. red 10 10
605 10c. blue 10 10
606 50c. purple 10 10
607 1s. brown 25 10
608 2s. brown 25 10
609 5s. green 55 10

185 Symbol of N.Y. World's Fair

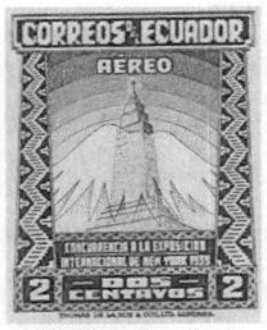
186 Empire State Building and Mountain

1939. New York World's Fair.
610 **185** 2c. olive (postage) 10 10
611 5c. orange 10 10
612 10c. blue 10 10
613 50c. grey 40 10
614 1s. red 60 15
615 2s. brown 75 20
616 **186** 2c. brown (air) 10 10
617 5c. red 10 10
618 10c. blue 10 10
619 50c. olive 10 10
620 1s. orange 20 10
621 2s. mauve 35 15
622 5s. black 70 10

1939. Obligatory Tax. Social Insurance Fund for Rural Workers. Oblong Tobacco Tax stamps surch **POSTAL ADICIONAL CINCO CENTAVOS**.
623 5c. on 1c. pink . . . . 1·50 25

1940. Obligatory Tax. G.P.O. Rebuilding Fund. Oblong Tobacco Tax stamp surch **CASAS DE CORREOS Y TELEGRAFOS CINCO CENTAVOS**.
624 5c. on 1c. pink . . . . 1·25 20

1940. Obligatory Tax. Guyaquil G.P.O. Rebuilding Fund. No. 567 surch **CASA DE CORREOS y TELEGRAFOS DE GUAYAQUIL 20 20**.
625 **174** 20c. on 50c. multicoloured 40 15

1940. Obligatory Tax. National Defence Fund. Oblong Tobacco Tax stamps surch **TIMBRE PATRIOTICO VEINTE CENTAVOS**.
625b 20c. on 1c. pink . . . . . 16·00 3·50

191 Pan-American Union Flags

192 Allegory of Union

1940. 50th Anniv of Pan-American Union.
626 **191** 5c. black & red (postage) 10 10
627 10c. black and blue . . . 10 10
628 50c. black and green . . . 35 10
629 1s. black and violet . . . 50 20
630 **192** 10c. blue & orange (air) 15 10
631 70c. blue and purple . . . 25 10
632 1s. blue and brown . . . 35 10
633 10s. blue and black . . . 85 50

193 Ploughing

194 Symbolic of Communications

1940. Obligatory Tax. Social Insurance Fund for Rural Workers and Guayaquil G.P.O. Rebuilding Funds.
634 **193** 5c. red 15 10

1940. Obligatory Tax. G.P.O. Rebuilding Fund.
635 **194** 5c. brown 10 10
636 5c. green 10 10

195 Fighter Aircraft

196 Dr. de Santa Cruz y Espejo

1941. Obligatory Tax. National Defence Fund.
637 **195** 20c. blue 40 10

1941. 1st National Periodical Exhibition.
638 **196** 30c. blue (postage) . . . 25 10
639 1s. orange . . . . 1·10 10
640 3s. red (air) 70 10
641 10s. orange . . . . 1·40 25

197 Francisco de Orellana

198 Early Map of S. America

1942. 400th Anniv of Discovery of R. Amazon.
642 **197** 10c. brown (postage) . . 25 10
643 – 40c. red 25 10
644 – 1s. violet 70 10
645 – 2s. blue 95 25
646 **198** 40c. bistre & black (air) 35 10
647 – 70c. olive 60 10
648 – 2s. green 70 25
649 – 5s. red 75 35
DESIGNS—VERT: 40c. (No. 643); 70c. Portraits of G. Pizarro and G. Diaz de Pineda; 2s. (No. 645) Quito; 5s. Expedition leaving Quito. HORIZ: 1s. Guayaquil; 2s. (No. 648) Relief map of R. Amazon.

199 R. Crespo Toral

201 Mt. Chimborazo

1942.

650 **199** 10c. green (postage) 10 10
651 50c. brown 20 10
652 10c. violet (air) 25 10

1942. As T **199** but portrait of Pres. A. B. Moreno.
653 10c. green 10 10

1942.

654 **201** 30c. brown 20 10
654a 30c. blue 20 10
654b 30c. orange 20 10
654c 30c. green 20 10

202 "Defence"

203 Guayaquil Riverside

1942. Obligatory Tax. National Defence Fund.
655 **202** 20c. blue 40 10
655a 40c. brown 40 10

1942. Obligatory Tax. National Defence Fund. As T **173** surch.
655b **173** 20c. on 5c. pink — 5·00
655c 20c. on 1s. brown — 5·00
655d 20c. on 2s. green — 5·00

1942. Obligatory Tax. Guayaquil G.P.O. Rebuilding Fund. No. 567 surch **CASA DE CORREOS Y TELEGRAFOS DE GUAYAQUIL VEINTE CENTAVOS.**
655e – 20c. on 50c. mult 60 25

1943.

656 **203** 20c. red 2·40 10
656a 20c. blue 2·40 10

1943. Guayaquil G.P.O. Rebuilding Fund. Surch **ADICIONAL CINCO CENTAVOS 5 Centavos CASA DE CORREOS DE GQUIL. y.**
657 **162** 5c.+5c. on 3c. blue 20 10

1943. Surch **ADICIONAL CINCO CENTAVOS.**
658 **162** 5c. on 3c. blue 20 10

206 Gen. Alfaro

207 Alfaro's Birthplace

1943. Birth Centenary of Alfaro.
659 **206** 10c. black & red (postage) 10 10
660 – 20c. brown and olive 1·50 75
661 – 30c. green and olive 45 45
662 **207** 1s. red and grey 75 75
663 **206** 70c. black and red (air) 40 20
664 – 1s. brown and olive 2·50 90
665 – 3s. green and olive 60 60
666 **207** 5s. red and grey 95 70
DESIGNS—HORIZ: 20c., 1s. Devil's Nose Zigzag, Guayaquil-Quito Rly; 30c., 3s. Alfaro Military College.

208 Labourers

213 Arms of Ecuador

1943. Obligatory Tax. Social Insurance Fund for Rural Workers and Guayaquil G.P.O. Rebuilding Funds.
667 **208** 5c. blue 30 10

1943. Welcome to Henry A. Wallace, Vice-President of U.S.A. Optd **BIENVENIDO – WALLACE Abril 15 – 1943.**
668 **174** 50c. mult (postage) 75 60
669 1s. multicoloured 1·60 1·25
670 2s. multicoloured 2·50 1·90
671 – 50c. multicoloured (No. 574) (air) 2·00 70
672 – 1s. multicoloured (No. 575) 2·50 85
673 – 2s. multicoloured (No. 576) 3·00 1·25

1943. Obligatory Tax. National Defence Fund. Fiscal stamp optd **TIMBRE PATRIOTICO.**
674 20c. orange 23·00 1·10

1943. Air. Visits of Presidents of Bolivia, Paraguay and Venezuela to Ecuador. (a) Optd **AEREO LOOR A BOLIVIA JUNIO 11 – 1943.**
675 – 50c. purple (No. 580) 1·75 1·10
676 – 1s. red (No. 581) 2·50 1·50
677 – 2s. green (No. 582) 50 35

(b) Optd **AEREO LOOR AL PARAGUAY JULIO 5 – 1943.**
678 – 50c. purple (No. 580) 1·75 1·10
679 – 1s. red (No. 581) 2·50 1·50
680 – 2s. green (No. 582) 50 35

(c) Optd **AEREO LOOR A VENEZUELA JULIO 23 – 1943.**
681 – 50c. purple (No. 580) 1·75 1·10
682 – 1s. red (No. 581) 2·50 1·50
683 – 2s. green (No. 582) 50 35

1943. Obligatory Tax National Defence Fund. Fiscal stamp surch **TIMBRE PATRIOTICO VEINTE CENTAVOS.**
684 – 20c. on 10c. orange 75 20

1943. Fiscal stamp as T **169** surch **POSTAL 30 Centavos** with or without bars.
685 **169** 30c. on 50c. brown 25 10
As No. 685 but surch **POSTAL 30 Ctvs.**
780 **169** 30c. on 50c. brown 10 10

1943. Obligatory Tax. National Defence Fund.
686 **213** 20c. red 20 10

214 Arms of Ecuador and Map of Central America

215 Pres. Arroyo del Rio at Washington

1943. President's Visit to Washington.
687 **214** 10c. violet (postage) 20 10
698 10c. green 10 10
688 20c. brown 20 10
699 20c. pink 15 10
689 30c. orange 15 15
700 30c. brown 20 15
690 50c. olive 35 20
701 50c. purple 35 25
691 1s. violet 40 20
702 1s. grey 40 35
692 10s. brown 2·50 2·40
703 10s. orange 2·50 2·50
693 **215** 50c. brown (air) 40 35
704 50c. purple 40 20
694 70c. red 50 50
705 70c. brown 40 35
695 3s. blue 40 50
706 3s. green 40 35
696 5s. green 85 60
707 5s. blue 70 55
697 10s. olive 3·50 3·00
708 10s. red 95 95

1944. Nos. 698/708 surch **Hospital Mendez** and new value.
711a **214** 10c.+10c. grn (postage) 35 25
711b 20c.+20c. pink 35 25
711c 30c.+20c. brown 35 35
711d 50c.+20c. purple 45 50
711e 1s.+50c. grey 75 85
711f 10s.+2s. orange 2·75 2·75
711g **215** 50c.+50c. pur (air) 2·25 2·25
711h 70c.+30c. brown 2·25 2·25
711i 3s.+50c. green 2·25 2·25
711j 5s.+1s. blue 2·25 2·25
711k 10s.+2s. red 2·25 2·25

1944. No. 600. Surch **30 Centavos.**
712 **183** 30c. on 50c. brown 15 10

1944. Obligatory Tax. National Defence Fund. No. 686 surch **POSTAL 30 Centavos.**
713 **213** 30c. on 20c. red 25 10

1944. 606 and 619 Surch **POSTAL 30 Centavos.**
714 **184** 30c. on 50c. purple 15 10
715 **186** 30c. on 50c. olive 15 10

218 F. Gonzales Suarez

219 Cathedral, Quito

1944. Birth Cent of F. G. Suarez (Archbishop).
716 **218** 10c. blue (postage) 10 10
717 20c. green 10 10
718 30c. purple 20 15
719 1s. violet 40 10
720 **219** 70c. green (air) 50 25
721 1s. olive 50 25
722 3s. red 60 30
723 5s. red 75 35

1944. Surch **CINCO Centavos.**
724 **183** 5c. on 2c. green 10 10
725 **185** 5c. on 2c. green 10 10

221 Government Palace, Quito

222 Red Cross Symbol

1944.

726 **221** 10c. green (postage) 10 10
727 30c. blue 10 10
728 3s. orange (air) 25 10
729 5s. brown 40 10
730 10s. red 85 10
730a 10s. violet 85 10

1945. 80th Anniv of Int Red Cross. Cross in red.
731 **222** 30c. brown (postage) 50 10
732 1s. brown 35 20
733 5s. green 75 70
734 10s. red 2·10 1·25
735 2s. blue (air) 40 40
736 3s. green 70 40
737 5s. violet 1·10 70
738 10s. red 2·75 2·10

1945. Air. Surch **AEREO 40 Ctvs.**
739 **208** 40c. on 5c. blue 15 10

1945. Obligatory Tax. Air. No. 726 surch **FOMENTO-AERO-COMUNICACIONES 20 Ctvs.**
740 **221** 20c. on 10c. green 25 10

1945. Air. Victory. Optd **V SETIEMBRE 5 1945.**
742 **221** 3s. orange 50 50
743 5s. brown 40 40
744 10s. red 1·40 1·40

1945. Visit of Pres. Juan Antonio Rios of Chile. Optd **LOOR A CHILE OCTUBRE 2 1945** and five-pointed star. Flags in yellow, blue and red.
745 **174** 50c. black (postage) 50 25
746 1s. olive 80 40
747 2s. brown 1·50 75
748 – 50c. pur (No. 574) (air) 1·10 75
749 – 1s. black (No. 575) 1·25 85
750 – 2s. violet (No. 576) 1·25 85

227 Marshal Sucre

230 Pan-American Highway

1945. 150th Birth Anniv of Marshal Sucre.
751 **227** 10c. green (postage) 20 10
752 20c. brown 20 10
753 40c. grey 20 10
754 1s. green 20 20
755 2s. brown 45 25
756 – 30c. blue (air) 15 10
757 – 40c. red 25 10
758 – 1s. violet 50 25
759 – 3s. black 60 40
760 – 5s. purple 85 55
DESIGN—Air stamps: Liberty Monument.

1945. Surch **c VEINTE CENTAVOS.**
761 **221** 20c. on 10c. green 10 10

1946. Completion of Pan-American Highway.
762 **230** 20c. brown (postage) 10 10
763 30c. green 10 10
764 1s. blue 10 10
765 5s. purple 60 60
766 10s. red 1·10 85
767 1s. red (air) 35 20
768 2s. violet 45 30
769 3s. green 45 35
770 5s. orange 60 50
771 10s. blue 85 45

231 Torch of Democracy

232 Popular Suffrage

1946. 2nd Anniv of Revolution.
772 **231** 5c. blue (postage) 10 10
773 **232** 10c. green 10 10
774 – 20c. red 20 10
775 – 30c. brown 35 10
776 **231** 40c. red (air) 10 10
777 **232** 1s. brown 10 10
778 – 2s. blue 40 10
779 – 3s. green 55 30
DESIGNS—VERT: 20c., 2s. National flag; 30c., 3s. Pres. J.M. Velasco Ibarra.

1946. Nos. O567/8 optd **POSTAL.**
781 **172** 10c. brown 15 15
782 20c. olive 25 25

237 Teacher and Scholar

238 Seal of National Periodicals Union

1946. Adult Instruction.
783 **237** 10c. blue (postage) 10 10
784 20c. brown 10 10
785 30c. green 15 10
786 50c. black 35 20
787 1s. red 50 15
788 10s. purple 2·10 50
789 **238** 50c. violet (air) 35 25
790 70c. green 40 25
791 3s. red 45 35
792 5s. blue 60 25
793 10s. brown 1·75 40

239 "Liberty", "Mercury" and Aeroplanes

240 "Mariana de Jesus Paredes y Flores"

1946. Obligatory Tax. Air. National Defence Fund.
794 **239** 20c. brown 15 10

1946. 300th Death Anniv of Blessed Mariana de Jesus Paredes y Flores.
795 **240** 10c. brown (postage) 15 10
796 20c. green 10 10
797 30c. violet 20 10
798 – 1s. brown 40 30
799 – 40c. brown (air) 25 10
800 – 60c. blue 30 30
801 – 3s. yellow 45 60
802 – 5s. green 85 75
DESIGNS: 40c., 60c. Mariana teaching children; 1s. Urn; 3s., 5s. Cross and lilies.

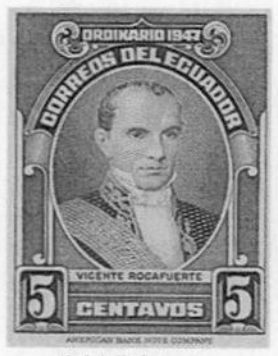
244 Vicente Rocafuerte

245 Jesuit Church, Quito

1947.

803 **244** 5c. brown (postage) 10 10
804 10c. purple 10 10
805 15c. black 10 10
806 **245** 20c. lake 15 10
807 30c. mauve 15 10
808 40c. blue 25 10
809 – 45c. green 25 10
810 – 50c. grey 35 15
811 – 80c. red 40 10
PORTRAIT: 45c. to 80c. F. J. E. de Santa Cruz y Espejo.
812 – 60c. green (air) 10 10
813 – 70c. violet 10 10
814 – 1s. brown 10 10
815 – 1s.10 red 10 10
816 – 1s.30 blue 10 10

817	–	1s.90 brown	35	10
818	–	2s. olive	35	10

DESIGNS: 60c. to 1s.10, Father J. de Velasco; 1s.30 to 2s. Riobamba Irrigation Canal.

250 Andres Bello

1948. 83rd Death Anniv of Andres Bello (educationalist).

820	**250**	20c. blue (postage)	15	10
821		30c. pink	25	10
822		40c. green	25	10
823		1s. black	50	15
824		60c. mauve (air)	20	10
825		1s.30 green	40	25
826		1s.90 red	35	25

1948. Economic Conference Optd **CONFERENCIA ECONOMICA GRANCOLOMBIANA MAYO 24 DE 1.948.**

827	**245**	40c. blue (postage)	20	10
828	–	70c. vio (No. 813) (air)	40	25

252 The "Santa Maria"

253 Christopher Columbus

1948. Completion of Columbus Memorial Lighthouse.

829	**252**	10c. green (postage)	60	20
830		20c. brown	1·00	20
831		30c. violet	1·40	30
832		50c. red	1·75	30
833		1s. blue	2·50	30
834		5s. red	6·50	85
835	**253**	50c. green (air)	20	10
836		70c. red	20	10
837		3s. blue	40	30
838		5s. brown	70	25
839		10s. violet	95	35

1948. National Fair. Nos. 811 and 816 optd **Feria Nacional 1948 ECUADOR de hoy y del MANANA.**

840		80c. red (postage)	25	25
841		1s.30c. blue (air)	40	30

255 "Telegrafo I" on First Postal Flight

256 Elia Liut and "Telegrafo I"

1948. 25th Anniv of First Ecuadorian Postal Flight.

842	**255**	30c. orange (postage)	20	10
843		40c. mauve	20	10
844		60c. blue	25	10
845		1s. brown	35	10
846		3s. brown	1·00	20
847		5s. black	80	30
848	**256**	60c. red (air)	35	25
849		1s. green	45	25
850		1s.30 red	45	30
851		1s.90 violet	50	30
852		2s. brown	60	35
853		5s. blue	90	55

257 "Reading and Writing"

258 "Education For All"

1948. National Education Campaign.

854	**257**	10c. claret (postage)	10	10
855		20c. brown	20	20
856		30c. green	10	30
857		50c. red	40	20
858		1s. violet	55	40
859		10s. blue	1·50	60
860	**258**	50c. violet (air)	35	20
861		70c. blue	35	20
862		3s. green	55	30
863		5s. red	70	25
864		10s. brown	1·40	45

259 "Freedom from Fear"

260 "Freedom of Religion"

261 "Freedom of Speech and Expression"

262 "Freedom from Want"

1948. Homage to Franklin D. Roosevelt.

865	**259**	10c. red & grey (postage)	15	10
866		20c. olive and blue	15	15
867	**260**	30c. olive and red	25	10
868		40c. purple and sepia	35	10
869		1s. brown and red	40	25
870	**261**	60c. green & brn (air)	10	10
871		1s. red and black	10	10
872	**262**	1s.50 green & brown	25	15
873		2s. red and black	50	15
874		5s. blue and black	75	20

263 Maldonado at Academy of Sciences, Paris

264 Riobamba Aqueduct

1948. Death Bicentenary of Maldonado (geographer and scientist).

875	**263**	5c. red & black (postage)	15	10
876	**264**	10c. black and red	20	10
877	–	30c. blue and brown	25	10
878	**264**	40c. violet and green	60	10
879	**263**	50c. red and green	40	10
880	–	1s. blue and brown	75	10
881	–	60c. red & orange (air)	25	10
882	–	90c. black and red	25	10
883	–	1s.30 orange & mauve	40	20
884	–	2s. green and blue	40	20

DESIGN—VERT: 30c., 60c., 1s.30, Maldonado making road to Esmeraldas; 90c., 1s., 2s. P. Vicente Maldonado.

266 Cervantes, Don Quixote and Windmill

267 Don Quixote and Sheep

1949. 400th Birth Anniv of Cervantes.

885	–	30c. blue & pur (postage)	10	10
886	**266**	60c. brown & purple	25	10
887	–	1s. red and green	75	15
888	**266**	2s. black and red	1·50	25
889	–	5s. green and brown	2·75	75
890	–	1s.30 brown & blue (air)	1·50	1·50
891	**267**	1s.90 red and green	40	25
892	–	3s. violet and red	40	25
893	**267**	5s. black and red	95	10
894	–	10s. purple and green	1·60	10

DESIGNS—HORIZ: 30c., 1s., 5s. (No. 889) Cervantes, Don Quixote and Sancho Panza; 1s.30, 3s., 10s. Don Juan Montalvo and Cervantes.

1949. 2nd Eucharistic Congress. Stamps of 1947 surch **II CONGRESO Junio 1949 Eucaristico Ncl.** and values. (a) Postage. No. 808 surch.

895	**245**	10c. on 40c. blue	15	10
896		20c. on 40c. blue	25	10
897		30c. on 40c. blue	25	15

(b) Air. No. 815 surch.

898	–	50c. on 1s.10 red	10	10
899	–	60c. on 1s.10 red	10	10
900	–	90c. on 1s.10 red	20	20

269 Equatorial Line Monument

274 Lake San Pablo

1949.

901	**269**	10c. purple	20	10

1949. 75th Anniv of U.P.U. Surch **75 ANIVERSARIO** (or **Aniversario** on air stamps) **U.P.U.** and value.

902	**274**	10c. on 50c. grn (postage)	10	10
903		20c. on 50c. green	15	10
904		30c. on 50c. green	25	10
905	**221**	60c. on 3s. orge (air)	40	35
906		90c. on 3s. orange	35	25
907		1s. on 3s. orange	40	35
908		2s. on 3s. orange	90	45

For unoverprinted stamp Type **274**, see No. 926.

272

272a

1949. Consular Service stamps optd or surch for postal use. I. On T **272**. A. Postage. (a) Vert surch **POSTAL** and value before **ct vs**.

908a	**272**	5c. on 10c. red	10	10
909		20c. on 25c. brown	10	10
910		30c. on 50c. black	10	10

(b) Optd **CORREOS** diag.

927	**272**	10c. red	10	10

(c) Optd **POSTAL** diag.

929	**272**	10c. red	10	10

(d) Vert surch with figs. before and after **Ctvs.** (i) **CORREOS** upwards.

928	**272**	30c. on 50c. black	10	10

(ii) **POSTAL** upwards.

930	**272**	20c. on 25c. brown	10	10
931		30c. on 50c. black	20	10

(e) Surch **POSTAL centavos** with figs between.

969	**272**	10c. on 20s. blue	15	10
970		20c. on 10s. grey	15	10
971		20c. on 20s. blue	15	10
972		30c. on 10s. grey	15	10
973		30c. on 20s. blue	10	10

B. Air. Surch **AEREO** and value.

913	**272**	60c. on 50c. black	20	10
913a		60c. on 2s. brown	20	10
913b		1s. on 2s. brown (D.)	30	10
913c		1s. on 2s. brown (U.)	30	10
913d		2s. on 2s. brown	30	10
913e		3s. on 5s. violet	55	15

In No. 913b the surch reads down and in No. 913c it reads up.

II. On T **272a**. A. Postage. Surch **POSTAL** and value.

935	**272a**	30c. on 50c. red	15	10
934		40c. on 25c. blue	15	10
936		50c. on 25c. blue	15	10

B. Air. Surch **AEREO** and value.

913f	**272a**	60c. on 1s. green	10	10
913g		60c. on 5s. sepia	15	10
913h		70c. on 5s. sepia	20	10
913i		90c. on 50c. red	30	10
913j		1s. on 1s. green	20	10

1950. Optd **POSTAL**.

911	**194**	5c. green	10	10
912	**208**	5c. blue	10	10

1950. Air. (a) Nos. 816/7 surch **90 ctvs. 90.**

914		90c. on 1s.30 blue	15	10
914a		90c. on 1s.90 brown	35	10

(b) No. 816 surch **90 CENTAVOS**.

914b		90c. on 1s.30 blue	10	10

1950. Literary Campaign. Optd **ALFABETIZACIÓN**. Four values also surch with new values and No. 920 also optd **POSTAL**.

915	**269**	10c. purple (postage)	20	20
916	**264**	20c. on 40c. (878)	30	30
917		30c. on 40c. (878)	40	40
918	**263**	50c. red and green	60	60
919	–	1s. blue & brown (880)	70	70
920	**221**	10s. violet	1·90	95
921	–	50c. on 1s.10 (815) (air)	25	10
922	–	70c. on 1s.10 (815)	20	25
923	**221**	3s. orange	45	30
924		5s. brown	80	40
925		10s. violet	85	30

1950.

926	**274**	50c. green	20	10

1951. Air. Panagra Airlines' 20,000th Flight across Equator. Optd **20.000 Cruce Linea Ecuatorial PANAGRA 26-Julio-1951**.

932	**221**	3s. orange	50	50
933		5s. brown	90	70

1951. Adult Education. Surch **CAMPANA Alfabetizacion** and values. (a) Postage.

937	**272a**	20c. on 25c. blue	10	10
938		30c. on 25c. blue	15	10

(b) Air.

939	–	60c. on 1s.30 (890)	20	10
940	**267**	1s. on 1s.90 (891)	20	10

278 Reliquary and St. Peter's, Vatican City

279 St. Mariana de Jesus

1952. Canonization of St. Mariana de Jesus.

941	**278**	10c. green & lake (postage)	20	10
942		20c. blue and violet	10	10
943		30c. red and green	25	10
944	**279**	60c. red & turquoise (air)	35	10
945		90c. green and blue	40	10
946		1s. red and green	45	10
947		2s. blue and mauve	45	10

280 Presidents Plaza and Truman

1952. Visit of President of Ecuador to U.S.A.

948	**280**	1s. black & red (postage)	25	15
949	–	2s. sepia and blue	50	20
950	**280**	3s. green and lilac (air)	40	30
951	–	5s. olive and brown	80	65

DESIGN: 2s., 5s. Pres. Plaza addressing U.S. Congress.

1952. Consular Service stamps surch **TIMBRE ESCOLAR 20 ctvs. 20.**

957	**272**	20c. on 1s. red	10	10
958		20c. on 2s. brown	10	10
959		20c. on 5s. violet	10	10

282 Pres. Urvina, Slave and "Liberty"

284 Teacher and Scholars

1952. Centenary of Abolition of Slavery in Ecuador. Roul.

960	**282**	20c. green & red (postage)	10	10
961		30c. red and blue	20	10
962		50c. blue and red	35	20
963	–	60c. red and blue (air)	85	25
964	–	90c. lilac and red	85	30
965	–	1s. orange and green	85	10
966	–	2s. brown and blue	85	20

DESIGN—VERT: Nos. 963/6, Pres. Urvina, condor and freed slave.

1952. Obligatory Tax. Literacy Campaign.

967	**284**	20c. green	20	10

1952. Obligatory Tax. Public Health Fund. Fiscal stamp optd **PATRIOTICO y SANITARIO**.

968	**103**	40c. olive	40	10

286 Learning Alphabet

287 Flag-bearer and Health Emblem

1953. Literacy Campaign. Inscr "UNP LAE".
974 – 5c. blue (postage) 25 10
975 – 10c. red 15 10
976 – 20c. orange 25 10
977 – 30c. purple 30 10
978 – 1s. blue (air) 35 10
979 **286** 2s. red 60 10
DESIGNS—VERT: 5c. Teacher and pupils; 10c. Instructor and student; 1s. Hand and torch. HORIZ: 20c. Men and ballot-box; 30c. Teaching the alphabet.

1953. Obligatory Tax. Public Health Fund.
980 **287** 40c. blue 45 10

288

289 Equatorial Line Monument

1953. Air. Crossing of Equator by Pan-American Highway.
981 **288** 60c. yellow 25 20
982 90c. blue 35 20
983 3s. red 40 35

1953.
984 – 5c. blue and black 10 10
985 **289** 10c. green and black . . . 10 10
986 – 20c. lilac and black 10 10
987 – 30c. brown and black . . . 10 10
988 – 40c. orange and black . . . 10 10
989 – 50c. red and black 25 10
DESIGNS: 5c. Cuicocha Lagoon; 20c. Quininde landscape; 30c. River Tomebamba; 40c. La Chilintosa rock; 50c. Iliniza Mountains.

290 Cardinal de la Torre

291 Cardinal de la Torre

1954. 1st Anniv of Elevation of De la Torre to Cardinal.
990 **290** 30c. blk & red (postage) 20 10
991 50c. black and purple . . 15 10
992 **291** 60c. black & pur (air) . . 15 10
993 90c. black and green . . . 20 10
994 3s. black and orange . . . 35 20

292 Isabella the Catholic

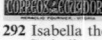

293 Isabella the Catholic

1954. 500th Birth Anniv of Isabella the Catholic.
995 **292** 30c. blk & bl (postage) 15 25
996 50c. black and yellow . . 15 10
997 **293** 60c. green (air) 10 20
998 90c. purple 10 10
999 1s. black and pink . . . 25 20
1000 2s. black and blue . . . 15 10
1001 5s. black and flesh . . . 35 25

294 Guayaquil Post Office

1954. Air. Silver Jubilee of Panagra Air Lines. Unissued stamp surch as in T **294**.
1002 **294** 80c. on 20c. red 15 10
1003 1s. on 20c. red 20 10

1954. Obligatory Tax. Literacy Campaign. Telegraph stamp (18½ × 22½ mm) surch **ESCOLAR 20 Centavos**.
1004 20c. on 30c. brown 45 10

1954. Obligatory Tax. Literacy Campaign. Fiscal stamp as T **103** (19¾ × 25½ mm) optd **ESCOLAR**.
1004a **103** 20c. olive 60 10

1954. Obligatory Tax. Tourist Promotion Fund.
(a) Telegraph stamp as No. 1004 but surch **Pro-Turismo 1954 10 ctvs. 10**.
1005 10c. on 30c. brown 60 10
(b) Judicial stamp as T **103** (19¾ × 25½ mm) optd **PRO TURISMO 1954**.
1006 10c. red 25 10
(c) Fiscal stamp as T **103** (19¾ × 25½ mm) surch **PRO TURISMO 1954 10 ctvs. Diez Centavos**.
1006a **103** 10c. on 50c. red 45 10
(d) Consular Service stamp surch **PRO TURISMO 1954 10 ctvs.**
1007 **272a** 10c. on 25c. blue 45 10

1954. Consular Service stamp surch **0.20 0.20 ESCOLAR Veinte centavos.**
1007a **272** 20c. on 10s. grey . . . 60 10

299 "Chasqui" (Inca Message Carrier)

300 Airliner over Building

1954. Postal Employees' Day.
1008 **299** 30c. sepia (postage) . . . 20 10
1009 **300** 80c. blue (air) 20 10

301 Bananas

302 Douglas DC-4 over San Pablo Lake

1954.
1010 **301** 10c. orange (postage) . . 10 10
1011 20c. red 10 10
1012 30c. mauve 10 10
1013 40c. myrtle 20 10
1014 50c. brown 25 10
1015 **302** 60c. orange (air) 20 10
1016 70c. mauve 10 10
1017 90c. green 10 10
1018 1s. myrtle 25 10
1019 2s. blue 50 10
1020 3s. brown 50 10

302a

303 Death on Battlefield

1954. Obligatory Tax. Literacy Fund.
1020a **302a** 20c. red 25 10

1954. Air. 150th Death Anniv of Captain Calderon Garaicoa.
1021 **303** 80c. mauve 20 10
1022 – 90c. blue 20 10
PORTRAIT—VERT: 90c. Capt. Calderon.

304 El Cebollar College

305 "Transport"

1954. Air. Birth Centenary of F. F. Cordero.
1023 **304** 70c. myrtle 10 10
1024 – 80c. sepia 10 10
1025 – 90c. blue 10 10
1026 – 2s.50 slate 20 15
1027 – 3s. lilac 30 25
DESIGNS—VERT: 80c. Febres Cordero and boys; 90c. Febres Cordero; 2s.50, Tomb. HORIZ: 3s. Monument.

1954. Obligatory Tax. Tourist Promotion Fund.
1028 **305** 10c. mauve 25 10

306 Kissing the Flag

308 La Rotonda, Guayaquil

1955. Obligatory Tax. National Defence Fund.
1029 **306** 40c. blue 60 10

1955. Air. World Press Exhibition. No. 730a surch **E. M. P. 1955** and value.
1030 **221** 1s. on 10s. violet 20 10
1031 1s.70 on 10s. violet . . . 30 10
1032 4s.20 on 10s. violet . . . 50 35

1955. Air. 50th Anniv of Rotary International.
1033 **308** 80c. brown 30 20
1034 – 90c. green 30 25
DESIGN: 90c. Eugenio Espejo Hospital, Quito.

310 Castillo and "Telegrafo 1"

1955. Birth Centenary of Jose Abel Castillo (pioneer aviator).
1035 – 30c. bistre (postage) . . 10 10
1036 – 50c. black 10 10
1037 **310** 60c. brown (air) 45 10
1038 90c. green 45 10
1039 1s. mauve 45 10
1040 – 2s. red 45 15
1041 – 5s. blue 90 45
DESIGNS—VERT: 30c., 50c. Bust of Castillo. HORIZ: 2s., 5s. Castillo and map of Ecuador.

1955. Air. Surch **1 X SUCRE X** over ornamental bar.
1042 **130** 1s. on 5s. violet 20 15

312 Palm Trees

313 Vazquez in 1883

1955. Pictorial designs as T **312**.
1043 **312** 5c. green (postage) . . 10 10
1043a 5c. blue 10 10
1043b B 5c. green 10 10
1044 C 10c. blue 20 10
1044a 10c. brown 35 10
1044b B 10c. brown 35 10
1045 A 20c. brown 30 10
1045a 20c. pink 30 10
1045b 20c. green 35 10
1045c B 20c. plum 10 10
1046 D 30c. black 10 10
1046a 30c. red 10 10
1046b B 30c. blue 10 10
1046c E 40c. blue . . . . . . 1·25 25
1047 F 50c. green 30 10
1047a 50c. violet 35 10
1048 E 70c. olive . . . . . . 1·75 25
1049 G 80c. violet 60 10
1049a B 80c. red 10 10
1049b G 90c. blue 20 20
1050 H 1s. orange 20 10
1050a 1s. sepia 15 10
1050b I 1s. black 50 10
1051 J 2s. red 60 15
1051a 2s. brown 25 10
1052 K 50c. slate (air) 25 10
1052a 50c. green 20 10
1053 L 1s. blue 50 10
1053a 1s. orange 40 10
1054 M 1s.30 red 30 15
1055 N 1s.50 green 20 10
1056 O 1s.70 brown 20 10
1057 P 1s.90 olive 25 25
1058 Q 2s.40 red 30 15
1059 R 2s.50 violet 30 15
1060 S 4s.20 black 40 25
1061 T 4s.80 yellow 50 35
DESIGNS—POSTAGE: A, River Babahoyo; B, "The Virgin of Quito" (after L. y del Arco); C, Manta fisherman; D, Guayaquil; E, Cactus; F, River Pital; G, Orchids; H, Agucate Mission; I, San Pablo; J, Jibaro Indian. AIR: K, Rumichaca Grotto; L, San Pablo; M, "The Virgin of Quito"; N, Cotopaxi Volcano; O, Tungurahua Volcano; P, Guanaco; Q, Selling mats; R, Ingapirca ruins; S, El Carmen, Cuenca; T, Santo Domingo Church.

1956. Air. Birth Centenary of Vazquez.
1062 **313** 1s. green 10 10
1063 – 1s.50 red 20 10
1064 – 1s.70 blue 15 10
1065 – 1s.90 slate 20 10
PORTRAITS OF VAZQUEZ: 1s.50, 1905. 1s.70, 1910. 1s.90, 1931.

314 J. A. Schwarz

315 Title Page of First Book printed in Ecuador

1956. Bicentenary of Printing in Ecuador.
1066 **314** 5c. green (postage) . . . 10 10
1067 10c. red 10 10
1068 20c. violet 10 10
1069 30c. green 10 10
1070 40c. blue 10 10
1071 50c. blue 10 10
1072 70c. orange 15 10
1073 **315** 1s. black (air) 10 10
1074 1s.70 slate 15 10
1075 2s. sepia 25 20
1076 3s. brown 30 25

316 Hands reaching for U.N. Emblem

1956. Air. 10th Anniv of U.N.O.
1077 **316** 1s.70 red 40 20
For stamp as Type **316** see No. 1095.

317 Emblem and Girl with Ball

1956. Air. 6th S. American Women's Basketball Championships.
1078 **317** 1s. mauve 50 25
1079 – 1s.70 green 30 15
DESIGN: 1s.70, Map, flags and players.

318 Marquis of Canete

319 Cuenca Cathedral

1957. 400th Anniv of Cuenca.
1082 **318** 5c. blue on flesh (post) 10 10
1083 – 10c. bronze on green . . 10 10
1084 – 20c. brown on buff . . 10 10
1085 – 50c. sep on cream (air) 10 10
1086 **319** 80c. red on blue 10 10
1087 – 1s. violet on yellow . . 20 10
DESIGNS— HORIZ: 10c. Gil Ramirez Davalos and Cuenca landscape; 50c. Early plan of Cuenca; 1s. Municipal Palace. VERT: 20c. Father Vicente Solano.

320 Delegates to the 1838 Postal Congress

321 Gabriela Mistral (Chilean poet)

1957. 7th U.P.A.E. Postal Congress, 1955.
1088 **320** 40c. yellow 10 10
1089 50c. blue 10 10
1090 2s. red 40 10

1957. Air. Gabriela Mistral Commem.
1091 **321** 2s. grey, black & red . . 20 10

322 Arms of Espejo

323 Blue and Yellow Macaw

1957. Air. Carchi Cantonal Arms. Inscr "PROVINCIA DEL CARCHI". Arms mult.
1092 **322** 1s. red 15 10
1093 – 2s. black (Montufar) . . 20 10
1094 – 4s.20 blue (Tulcan) . . . 45 30
For other Arms as Type **322** see Nos 1124/7, 1147/51, 1155/9, 1197 and 1220/3.

1957. Air. United Nations Day. As T **316** but without dates.
1095 2s. blue 35 25

1958. Tropical Birds. Birds in natural colours.
(a) As T **323**.
1096 **323** 10c. brown 60 20
1097 – 20c. grey and buff . . . 60 25
1098 – 30c. green . . . . 1·60 30
1099 – 40c. orange . . . . . . 1·60 35
BIRDS: 20c. Red-breasted Toucan. 30c. Andean Condor. 40c. Sword-billed Hummingbird and Black-tailed Trainbearer.
(b) As T **323** but "ECUADOR" at top in black.
1120 – 20c. turquoise and red . . 1·00 20
1121 – 30c. blue and yellow . . . 1·10 30
1122 – 50c. orange and green . . 1·60 45
1123 – 60c. pink & turquoise . . . 1·90 45
BIRDS: 20c. Masked Crimson Tanager. 30c. Andean Cock of the Rock. 50c. Solitary Cacique. 60c. Red-fronted Conures.

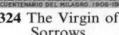

324 The Virgin of Sorrows

325 Vice-Pres. Nixon and Flags of Ecuador and the U.S.A.

1958. Air. 50th Anniv of The Miracle of the Virgin of Sorrows of St. Gabriel College, Quito.
1100 **324** 30c. purple on purple . . 10 10
1101 – 30c. purple on purple . . 10 10
1102 – 1s. blue on blue 15 10
1103 **324** 1s.70 blue on blue . . . 15 15
DESIGN: Nos. 1101/2, Gateway of St. Gabriel College, Quito.

1958. Visit of Vice-Pres. of the United States. Flags in red, blue and yellow.
1104 **325** 2s. salmon and green . . 40 10

1958. Visit of Pres. Morales of Honduras. As T **325** but with portrait of Pres. Morales, flags of Ecuador and Honduras, and inscriptions changed. Flags in red, blue and yellow.
1105 2s. brown 40 10

326 Dr. C. Sanz de Santamaria

1958. Visit of Chancellor of Colombia.
1106 **326** 1s.80 multicoloured . . . 40 10

327 Dr. R. M. Arizaga

328 Gonzalo Icaza Cornejo Bridge

1958. Air. Birth Cent of Arizaga (diplomat).
1107 **327** 1s. multicoloured 10 10
See also Nos. 1135, 1142 and 1241.

1958. Air. Inauguration of Gonzalo Icaza Cornejo Bridge.
1108 **328** 1s.30 green 20 10

329 Steam Locomotive

330 Basketball Player

1958. 50th Anniv of Opening of Guayaquil–Quito Railway.
1109 **329** 30c. black . . . . 1·75 20
1110 – 50c. red . . . . 2·75 20
1111 – 5s. brown 95 25
DESIGNS—HORIZ: 50c. Diesel-electric train; DIAMOND, 5s. State presidents.

1958. Air. South American Basketball Champions' Tournament, Quito.
1112 **330** 1s.30 green & brown . . 40 30

331 J. C. de Macedo Soares

332 Monstrance and Doves

1958. Visit of Brazilian Chancellor.
1113 **331** 2s.20 multicoloured . . . 40 10

1958. Air. 3rd National Eucharistic Congress, Guayaquil. Inscr as in T **332**.
1114 **332** 10c. violet and yellow . . 10 10
1115 – 60c. violet and salmon 10 10
1116 **332** 1s. sepia and turquoise 15 10
DESIGN: 60c. Guayaquil Cathedral.

333 Stamps of 1865 and 1920

1958. Air. National Stamp Exn, Guayaquil.
1117 **333** 1s.30 red and green . . . 20 15
1118 – 2s. violet and blue . . . 35 20
1119 – 4s.20 sepia 45 45
DESIGNS: 2s. Stamps of 1920 and 1948; 4s.20, Guayaquil Municipal Library and Museum.

1958. Air. Imbabura Cantonal Arms. As T **322**. Inscr "PROVINCIA DE IMBABURA". Arms multicoloured.
1124 50c. red and black 10 10
1125 60c. blue, red and black . . 10 10
1126 80c. yellow and black . . . 10 10
1127 1s.10 red and black 15 10
ARMS: 50c. Cotacachi. 60c. Antonio Ante. 80c. Otavalo. 1s.10, Ibarra.

335 U.N.E.S.C.O. Headquarters, Paris

336 Emperor Charles V (after Titian)

1958. Inauguration of U.N.E.S.C.O. Headquarters Building, Paris.
1128 **335** 80c. brown 20 10

1958. Air. 400th Death Anniv of Emperor Charles V.
1129 **336** 2s. sepia and red 20 10
1130 4s.20 brown & black . . 40 35

337 Globe and Satellites

338 Paul Rivet (anthropologist)

1958. International Geophysical Year.
1131 **337** 1s.80 blue 60 35

1958. Air. Rivet Commemoration.
1132 **338** 1s. sepia 10 10
See also No. 1134.

339 Front page of "El Telegrafo"

1959. Air. 75th Anniv of "El Telegrafo" (newspaper).
1133 **339** 1s.30 black and green . . 15 10

1959. Air. Death Centenary of Alexander von Humboldt (naturalist). Portrait in design as T **338**.
1134 2s. grey 20 10

1959. Air. Birth Centenary of Dr. Jose L. Tamayo (statesman). Portrait in design as T **327**.
1135 1s.30 multicoloured 15 10

340 House of M. Canizares

341 Pope Pius XII

1959. Air. 150th Anniv of Independence.
1136 **340** 20c. brown and blue . . 10 10
1137 – 80c. brown and blue . . 10 10
1138 – 1s. myrtle and brown . . 10 10
1139 – 1s.30 orange and blue . . 25 10
1140 – 2s. brown and blue . . . 25 10
1141 – 4s.20 blue and red . . . 35 30
DESIGNS—HORIZ: 80c. St. Augustine's chapter-house; 1s. The Constitution. VERT: 1s.30, Condor with broken chains; 2s. Royal Palace; 4s.20, "Liberty" (statue).

1959. Air. Birth Centenary of Dr. A. B. Moreno (statesman). Portrait in design as T **327**.
1142 1s. multicoloured 10 10

1959. Air. Pope Pius XII Commem.
1143 **341** 1s.30 multicoloured . . . 25 20

342 Flags of Argentina, Bolivia, Brazil, Guatemala, Haiti, Mexico and Peru

1959. Air. Organization of American States Commemoration. Flag design inscr "OEA".
1144 **342** 50c. multicoloured . . . 10 10
1145 – 80c. red, blue & yellow 15 10
1146 – 1s.30 multicoloured . . . 25 15
FLAGS: 80c. Chile, Costa Rica, Cuba, Dominican Republic, Panama, Paraguay and U.S.A. 1s.30. Colombia, Ecuador, Honduras, Nicaragua, El Salvador, Uruguay and Venezuela.

1959. Air. Pichincha Cantonal Arms. As T **322**. Inscr "PROVINCIA DE PICHINCHA". Arms multicoloured.
1147 10c. red and black 10 10
1148 40c. yellow and black . . . 10 10
1149 1s. brown and black 10 10
1150 1s.30 green and black . . . 10 10
1151 4s.20 yellow and black . . . 40 25
ARMS: 10c. Ruminahui. 40c. Pedro Moncayo. 1s. Mejia. 1s.30, Cayambe. 4s.20, Quito.

343 Arms of Quito and Flags

1960. Air. 11th Inter-American Conference, Quito (1st issue). Centres multicoloured within red circle.
1152 **343** 1s.30 turquoise 10 10
1153 2s. sepia 20 15

344 "Uprooted Tree"

1960. World Refugee Year.
1154 **344** 80c. green and lake . . . 10 10

1960. Air. Cotopaxi Cantonal Arms. As T **322**. Inscr "PROVINCIA DE COTOPAXI". Arms multicoloured.
1155 40c. red and black 10 10
1156 60c. blue and black 15 10
1157 70c. turquoise and black . . 20 10
1158 1s. red and black 25 10
1159 1s.30 orange and black . . . 15 30
ARMS: 40c. Pangua. 60c. Pujili. 70c. Saquisili. 1s. Salcedo. 1s.30. Latacunga.

345 Giant Ant-eater

1960. 4th Cent of Baeza. Inscr as in T **345**.
1160 **345** 20c. black, orge & grn 10 10
1161 – 40c. brown, grn & turq 15 10
1162 – 80c. black, blue & brown 30 10
1163 – 1s. orange, blue & purple 50 20
DESIGNS: 40c. Mountain tapir; 80c. Spectacled bear; 1s. Puma.

346 Quito Airport

1960. 11th Inter-American Conference, Quito. (2nd issue). Views of Quito. Inscr as in T **346**.
1164 **346** 1s. blue and deep blue 20 10
1165 – 1s. violet and black . . . 15 10
1166 – 1s. red and violet 15 10
1167 – 1s. green and blue . . . 15 10
1168 – 1s. blue and violet . . . 15 10
1169 – 1s. brown and blue . . . 15 10
1170 – 1s. brown and violet . . 15 10
1171 – 1s. red and black . . . 15 10
1172 – 1s. brown and black . . 15 10
VIEWS: No. 1165, Legislative Palace. No. 1166, Southern approach motorway and flyover. No. 1167, Government Palace. No. 1168, Foreign Ministry. No. 1169, Students' Quarters, Catholic University. No. 1170, Hotel Quito. No. 1171, Students' Quarters, Central University. No. 1172, Social Security Bank.

347 Ambato Railway Bridge

348 "Liberty of Expression"

1960. Air. New Bridges.
1173 – 1s.30 brown 20 10
1174 – 1s.30 green 20 10
1175 **347** 2s. brown . . . . 1·10 30
DESIGNS—No. 1173, Bridge of the Juntas; No. 1174, Saracay Bridge.

1960. Five Year Development Plan (1st issue).
(a) Postage.
1176 **348** 5c. blue 10 10
1177 – 10c. violet 10 10
1178 – 20c. orange 10 10
1179 – 30c. turquoise 10 10
1180 – 40c. brown and blue . . 15 15
DESIGNS—VERT: 10c. Mother voting; 20c. People at bus-stop; 30c. Coins. HORIZ: (37 × 22 mm): 40c. Irrigation project Manabi.

349 Road at Chone Bay

(b) Air.
1181 **349** 1s. 30 black and ochre 15 10
1182 – 4s. 20 lake and green . . 35 35
1183 – 5s. brown and lemon . . 70 40
1184 – 10s. indigo and blue . . 70 50
DESIGNS—As Type **349**: 4s.20, Ministry of Works and Communications, Cuenca; 5s. El Coca Airport; 10s. New port of Guayaquil under construction.
See also Nos. 1214/17.

350 Pres. Camilo Ponce Enriquez and Constitution

1960. Air. 5th Anniv of Constitution.
1185 **350** 2s. black and brown . . 1·10 30

351 H. Dunant and Red Cross Buildings, Quito

1960. Air. Red Cross Commem.
1186 **351** 2s. purple and red . . . 30 15

352 "El Belen" Church, Quito

1961. Air. 1st Int Philatelic Congress, Barcelona.
1187 **352** 3s. multicoloured 40 15

353 Map of River Amazon

1961. Air. "Amazon Week". Map in green.
1188 **353** 80c. purple and brown 20 10
1189 1s.30 blue and grey . . . 25 15
1190 2s. red and grey 30 20

354 J. Montalvo, J. L. Mera and J. B. Vela

1961. Air. Cent of Tungurahua Province.
1191 **354** 1s.30 black & salmon . . 20 10

355 1936 Philatelic Exhibition Air Stamp

1961. Air. 3rd International Philatelic Exn, Quito.
1192 **355** 80c. violet and orange 25 15
1193 – 1s.30 multicoloured . . . 35 20
1194 – 2s. black and red 40 25
DESIGNS: 1s.30, San Lorenzo–Belem route map of S. America and 1r. stamp of 1865. (41 × 33½ mm); 2s., 10s. Independence stamp of 1930 postmarked "QUITO" (41 × 36 mm).

356 Statue of H. Ortiz Garces

357 Arms of Los Rios and Great Egret

1961. Air. H. Ortiz Garces (national hero). Commemoration. Multicoloured.
1195 1s.30 Type **356** 15 10
1196 1s.30 Portrait 15 10

1961. Air. Centenary of Los Rios Province.
1197 **357** 2s. multicoloured 60 30

358 "Graphium pausianus"

359 Collared Peccary

1961. Butterflies.
1198 **358** 20c. yellow, green, black and salmon . . 25 10
1198a 20c. yell, grey, blk & grn 15 10
1199 – 30c. yell, black & blue 35 10
1200 – 50c. black, grn & yell 45 10
1200a – 50c. blk, grn & salmon 25 10
1201 – 80c. pur, yell, blk & grn 70 20
1201a – 80c. turq, yell, blk & brn 40 15
BUTTERFLIES: 30c. "Papilio torquatus leptalea". 50c. "Graphium molops molops". 80c. "Battus lycidas".

1961. 4th Centenary of Tena.
1202 **359** 10c. blue, green & red 10 10
1203 – 20c. brown, violet & blue 10 10
1204 – 80c. orange, blk & bistre 30 10
1205 – 1s. brown, orge & green 20 15
ANIMALS: 20c. Kinkajou. 80c. Jaguar. 1s. Little coatimundi.

360 G. G. Moreno

362 R. Crespo Toral

1961. Air. Centenary of Re-establishment of "National Integrity".
1206 **360** 1s. brown, buff & blue 15 10

1961. Opening of Marine Biology Station on Galapagos Is. and 15th Anniv of U.N.E.S.C.O. Nos. 1/6 of Galapagos Is. optd with UNESCO emblem, obliterating crosses and **1961 Estacion de Biologia Maritima de Galapagos**.
1207 **1** 20c. brown (postage) . . . 15 10
1208 – 50c. violet 15 15
1209 – 1s. green 35 25
1210 – 1s. blue (air) 25 20
1211 – 1s.80 purple 35 20
1212 – 4s.20 black 55 30

1961. Air. Birth Centenary of Remigio Crespo Toral (writer).
1213 **362** 50c. multicoloured . . . 10 10

362a Soldier and Flag

363 Daniel Enrique Proana School, Quito

1961. Obligatory Tax. National Defence Fund.
1213a **362a** 40c. blue 10 10

1961. Five Year Development Plan.
1214 **363** 50c. black and blue . . . 10 10
1215 – 60c. black and green . . 10 10
1216 – 80c. black and red . . . 15 10
1217 – 1s. black and purple . . 20 10
DESIGNS—VERT: 60c. Loja-Zamora Highway. HORIZ: 80c. Aguirre Abad College, Guayaquil; 1s. Epiclachima Barracks, Quito.

364 Pres. C. Arosemena and Duke of Edinburgh

1962. Air. Visit of Duke of Edinburgh.
1218 **364** 1s.30 multicoloured . . . 20 10
1219 2s. multicoloured 20 10

1962. Air. Tungurahua Cantonal Arms. As T **322**. Inscr "PROVINCIA DE TUNGURAHUA". Arms multicoloured.
1220 50c. black (Pillaro) 10 10
1221 1s. black (Pelileo) 15 10
1222 1s.30 black (Banos) 20 10
1223 2s. black (Ambato) 25 15

365 Mountain and Spade in Field

366 Mosquito

1963. Air. Freedom from Hunger.
1224 **365** 30c. black, grn & yell . . 10 10
1225 3s. black, red & orange 40 20
1226 4s.20 black, blue & yell 50 35

1963. Air. Malaria Eradication.
1227 **366** 50c. black, yellow & red 10 10
1228 80c. black, green & red 10 10
1229 2s. black, pink & purple 20 20

367 Mail Coach and Boeing 707

370 Pres. Arosemena and Flags of Ecuador

1963. Air. Centenary of Paris Postal Conf.
1230 **367** 2s. red and orange . . . 40 15
1231 4s.20 blue and purple . . 60 30

1963. Air. Unissued Galapagos Is. stamps in designs as Ecuador T **321** surch **ECUADOR** and value.
1232 **321** 5s. on 2s. mult 40 30
1233 10s. on 2s. mult 80 60

1963. Air. Red Cross Cent. Optd **1863–1963 Centenario de la Fundacion de la Cruz Roja Internacional**.
1234 **351** 2s. purple and red . . . 25 15

1963. Presidential Goodwill Tour. Mult.
1235 10c. Type **370** (postage) . . 10 10
1236 20c. Ecuador & Panama flags 10 10
1237 60c. Ecuador & U.S.A. flags 10 10
1238 70c. Type **370** (air) . . . 10 10
1239 2s. Ecuador and Panama flags 25 10
1240 4s. Ecuador & U.S.A. flags 40 30

1963. 150th Birth Anniv of Dr. M. Cueva (statesman). Portrait in design as T **327**.
1241 2s. multicoloured 20 10

371 "Shield of Security"

372 Terminal Building

1963. 25th Anniv of Social Insurance Scheme. Multicoloured.
1242 10c. Type **371** (postage) . . 10 10
1243 10s. "Statue of Security" (air) . . . . 5·25 1·25

1963. Air. Inauguration of Simon Bolivar Airport, Guayaquil.
1244 **372** 60c. black 15 10
1245 70c. black and blue . . . 20 10
1246 5s. purple and black . . 75 25

373 Nurse and Child

380 "Commerce"

1963. Air. 7th Pan-American Pediatrics Congress, Quito.
1247 **373** 1s.30 blue, black and orange 20 15
1248 5s. lake, red and grey . . 45 30

1963. Postal Employees' Day. No. 1049a optd **1961 DIA DEL EMPLEADO POSTAL** and posthorn or surch also.
1249 B 10c. on 80c. red 10 10
1250 20c. on 80c. red 10 10
1251 50c. on 80c. red 10 10
1252 60c. on 80c. red 10 10
1253 80c. red 20 10

1964. Nos. 1164, etc, surch.
1254 10c. on 1s. blue and violet 10 10
1255 10c. on 1s. brown & violet 10 10
1256 20c. on 1s. green and blue 10 10
1257 20c. on 1s. brown and blue 10 10
1258 30c. on 1s. red and violet . . 10 10
1259 40c. on 1s. brown & black 10 10
1260 60c. on 1s. red and black . . 10 10
1261 80c. on 1s. blue & dp blue 30 10
1262 80c. on 1s. violet & black 20 10

1964. Optd **1961** and ornaments.
1263 **344** 80c. green and lake . . . 1·10 75

1964. Air. Optd **AEREO**. Honduras flag in red, blue and yellow.
1264 **326** 1s.80 violet 40 25
1265 – 2s. brown (No. 1105) . . 40 25
1266 **331** 2s.20 sepia and green . . 40 25

1964. "Columbus Lighthouse". (a) Optd **FARO DE COLON**.
1267 **337** 1s.80 blue (postage) . . 1·50 1·50

(b) Optd **FARO DE COLON AEREO**.
1268 **337** 1s.80 blue (air) . . . . . 1·90 1·25

1964. Air. Nos. 1144/6 optd **1961**.
1269 **342** 50c. multicoloured . . . 50 20
1270 – 80c. red, blue & yellow 50 20
1271 – 1s.30 multicoloured . . . 50 20

1964. O.E.A. Commemoration. Optd **OEA** with decorative frame across a block of four stamps.
1272 **344** 80c. green and lake . . . 1·50 25
The unused price is for the block of four.

1964. "Alliance for Progress".
1273 – 40c. bistre and violet . . 10 10
1274 – 50c. red and black . . . 15 10
1275 **380** 80c. blue and brown . . 10 10
DESIGNS: 40c. "Agriculture"; 50c. "Industry".

1964. Air. 15th Anniv of Declaration of Human Rights. Optd **DECLARATION DERECHOS HUMANOS 1964 XV-ANIV**.
1276 **316** 1s.70 red 30 15

382 Banana Tree and Map

1964. Banana Conference, Quito.
1277 **382** 50c. olive, brown and grey (postage) . . . 10 10
1278 80c. olive, blk & orge . . . 10 10
1279 4s.20 olive, black & ochre (air) 30 20
1280 10s. olive, blk & red . . . 55 40

383 Pres. Kennedy and his Son

1964. Air. Pres. Kennedy Commem.
1281 **383** 4s.20 brn, red, bl & grn 70 55
1282 5s. brown, blue & violet 85 70
1283 10s. brown, blue & mve 85 75

384 Old Map of Ecuador and Philip II of Spain

1964. 400th Anniv of Royal High Court, Quito.
1284 **384** 10c. black, buff & red 10 10
1285 – 20c. black, buff & green 10 10
1286 – 30c. black, buff & blue 10 10
DESIGNS: As Type **384** but portrait of Juan de Salinas Loyola (20c.), Hernando de Santillan (30c.).

385 Pole vaulting

1964. Olympic Games, Tokyo. Mult.

1287		80c. Type **385** (postage)	10	10
1288		1s.30 Gymnastics (vert) (air)	20	10
1289		1s.80 Hurdling	20	15
1290		2s. Basketball	25	15

386 Two-toed Sloth and P. Fleming (missionary)

1965. Death of Missionaries in Ecuador's Eastern Forests. Multicoloured.

1291		20c. Nine-banded armadillo and J. Elliot	10	10
1292		30c. Eurasian red squirrel and E. McCully	10	10
1293		40c. Peruvian guemal and R. Youderian	10	10
1294		60c. Piper Vagabond airplane over Napo River, and N. Saint	30	10
1295		80c. Type **386**	40	20

387 Dr. J. B. Vazquez (founder) and College Buildings

1965. Centenary of Benigno Malo College.

1296	**387**	20c. multicoloured	10	10
1297		60c. multicoloured	10	10
1298		80c. multicoloured	10	10

388 J. L. Mera (wrongly inscr "MERAN"), A. Neumane and Part of Anthem

1965. Centenary of National Anthem.

1299	**388**	50c. black and red	10	10
1300		80c. black and green	20	10
1301		5s. black and ochre	40	30
1302		10s. black and blue	80	60

389 "Olympic" Flame and Athletic Events

1965. 5th Bolivar Games, Quito. Flame in gold and black; athletes in black.

1303	**389**	40c. orange (postage)	15	10
1304	–	50c. red	15	10
1305	–	60c. blue	15	10
1306	**389**	80c. green	10	10
1307	–	1s. violet	25	10
1308	–	1s.50 mauve	40	25
1309	–	2s. blue (air)	15	10
1310	–	2s.50 orange	20	10
1311	–	3s. mauve	25	15
1312	–	3s.50 violet	25	20
1313	–	4s. green	30	20
1314	–	5s. red	35	25

DESIGNS: 50c., 1s. Running; 60c., 1s.50, Football; 2s., 3s. Diving, gymnastics, etc; 2s.50, 4s. Cycling; 3s.50, 5s. Pole-vaulting, long-jumping, etc.

390 ½r. and Two 1r. Stamps of 1865 391 Golden-headed Trogon

1965. Stamp Centenary.

1315	**390**	80c. multicoloured	15	10
1316		1s.30 multicoloured	20	10
1317		2s. multicoloured	25	10
1318		4s. multicoloured	75	20

1966. Birds. Multicoloured.

1320		40c. Type **391** (postage)	1·40	15
1321		50c. Blue-crowned mot-mot	1·40	15
1322		60c. Paradise tanager	1·40	15
1323		80c. Wire-tailed manakin	1·40	20
1324		1s. Yellow bellied grosbeak (air)	1·40	20
1325		1s.30 Black-headed caique	2·00	20
1326		1s.50 Scarlet tanager	2·00	20
1327		2s. Sapphire quail dove	2·10	20
1328		2s.50 Violet-tailed sylph	2·50	25
1329		3s. Lemon-throated barbet	3·00	30
1330		4s. Yellow-tailed oriole	3·25	40
1331		10s. Collared puffbird	6·25	1·00

1967. Various stamps surch. (a) Postage.

1332		30c. on 1s.10 (No. 1127)	15	15
1332a		40c. on 1s.70 (No. 1056)	15	15
1333		40c. on 3s.50 (No. 1312)	15	10
1334		80c. on 1s.50 (No. 1308)	10	10
1335		80c. on 2s.50 (No. 1328)	40	25
1336		1s. on 4s. (No. 1330)	50	25
		(b) Air.		
1337		80c. on 1s.50 (No. 1326)	40	25
1338		80c. on 2s.50 (No. 1310)	15	10

396 Law Books 399 Pres. Arosemena Gomez

1967. Birth Centenary (1964) of Dr. V. M. Penaherrera (law reformer).

1339	**396**	50c. blk & grn (postage)	10	10
1340	–	60c. black and red	10	10
1341	–	80c. black and purple	10	10
1342	–	1s.30 blk & orge (air)	10	10
1343	–	2s. black and blue	10	10

DESIGNS—VERT: 60c. Penaherrera's bust, Central University, Quito; 1s.30, Penaherrera's monument, Avenida Patria, Quito; 2s. Penaherrera's statue, Ibarra. HORIZ: 80c. Open book and laurel.

1967. Nos. 1301/2 surch.

1344	**388**	50c. on 5s. blk & ochre	10	15
1345		2s. on 10s. black & blue	30	10

1968. No. 1057 surch.

1346	P	1s.30 on 1s.90 olive	15	10

1968. 1st Anniv of Dr. Otto Arosemena Gomez as Interim President. Multicoloured.

1347		80c. Type **399** (postage)	10	10
1348		1s. Page from 1967 Constitution	10	10
1349		1s.30 President's inauguration (air)	10	10
1350		2s. Pres. Arosemena Gomez at Punta del Este Conference	15	10

400 Lions Emblem 404 I.L. Arcaya, Foreign Minister of Venezuela

1968. 50th Anniv (1967) of Lions Int.

1351	**400**	80c. multicoloured	15	15
1352		1s.30 multicoloured	20	10
1353		2s. multicoloured	15	10

1969. Various stamps surch. (a) "AEREO" obliterated.

1355	**333**	40c. on 1s.30	20	20
1356	**330**	50c. on 1s.30	20	20
		(b) Air. Inscr "AEREO".		
1357	–	80c. on 10s. (No. 1331)	60	25
1358	–	1s. on 10s. (No. 1331)	60	25
1359	–	2s. on 10s. (No. 1331)	60	25

1969. Unissued stamp surch or optd only (No. 1363) **RESELLO**.

1360	**404**	50c. on 2s. mult	15	15
1361		80c. on 2s. mult	15	15
1362		1s. on 2s. mult	15	15
1363		2s. multicoloured	10	15

405 Map of Ecuador

1969. Revenue stamp surch.

1364	**405**	20c. on 30c. mult	10	10
1365		40c. on 30c. mult	10	10
1366		50c. on 30c. mult	10	10
1367a		60c. on 30c. mult	10	10
1368		80c. on 30c. mult	10	10
1369		1s. on 30c. mult	10	10
1370		1s.30 on 30c. mult	25	10
1371		1s.50 on 30c. mult	15	25
1372		2s. on 30c. mult	25	15
1373		3s. on 30c. mult	35	25
1374		4s. on 30c. mult	25	15
1375		5s. on 30c. mult	25	20

406 John F. Kennedy, Robert Kennedy and Martin Luther King 407 Handshake Emblem

1969. "Apostles for Peace".

1376	**406**	4s. multicoloured	30	10
1377		4s. blk, green & blue	30	10

1969. Air. "Operation Friendship". Multicoloured. Emblem's background colour given.

1378	**407**	2s. blue	15	10
1379		2s. yellow	15	10

408 "Papilio zabreus" (inscr "zagreus" on stamp) 411 Arms of Zamora Chinchipe

1970. Butterflies. Multicoloured. (a) Coloured backgrounds.

1380		10c. "Thecla coronata" (postage)	10	25
1381		20c. Type **408**	10	25
1382		30c. "Heliconius erato"	15	25
1383		40c. "Eurytides pausanias"	15	10
1384		50c. "Pereute leucodrosime"	15	10
1385		60c. "Philaethria dido"	15	10
1386		80c. "Morpho cypris"	15	10
1387		1s. "Catagramma astarte"	35	10
1388		1s.30 "Morpho peleides" (air)	35	10
1389		1s.50 "Anartia amathea"	40	10
		(b) White backgrounds. As Nos. 1380/9.		
1390	–	10c. mult (postage)	25	10
1391	**408**	20c. multicoloured	10	25
1392	–	30c. multicoloured	15	25
1393	–	40c. multicoloured	15	10
1394	–	50c. multicoloured	15	10
1395	–	60c. multicoloured	15	10
1396	–	80c. multicoloured	15	10
1397	–	1s. multicoloured	25	10
1398	–	1s.30 mult (air)	35	10
1399	–	1s.50 multicoloured	40	10

1970. Air. No. 1104 surch **S/. 5 AEREO**.

1400	**325**	5s. on 2s. mult	1·10	45

1970. Public Works Fiscal Stamps surch **POSTAL** and value.

1401		1s. on 1s. blue	10	10
1402		1s.30 on 1s. blue	15	10
1403		1s.50 on 1s. blue	15	20
1404		2s. on 1s. blue	20	15
1405		5s. on 1s. blue	40	15
1406		10s. on 1s. blue	85	35

The basic stamps are inscr "TIMBRE DE LA RECONSTRUCCION".

1970. Provincial Arms and Flags. Mult.

1407		50c. Type **411** (postage)	15	10
1408		1s. Esmeraldas	15	10
1409		1s.30 El Oro (air)	15	10
1410		2s. Loja	25	10
1411		3s. Manabi	15	10
1412		5s. Pichincha	30	20
1413		10s. Guayas	60	40

412 413 "Presentation of the Virgin"

1971. Revenue stamps surch for postal use.

1414	**412**	60c. on 1s. violet	10	10
1415		80c. on 1s. violet	10	10
1416		1s. on 1s. violet	10	10
1417		1s.10 on 1s. violet	10	15
1418		1s.10 on 2s. green	10	10
1419		1s.30 on 1s. violet	10	10
1420		1s.30 on 2s. green	15	10
1421		1s.50 on 1s. violet	20	10
1422		1s.50 on 2s. green	20	10
1423		2s. on 1s. violet	15	10
1424		2s. on 2s. green	15	10
1425		2s.20 on 1s. violet	25	10
1426		3s. on 1s. violet	35	10
1427		3s. on 5s. blue	25	10
1428		3s.40 on 2s. green	35	10
1429		5s. on 2s. green	50	15
1430		5s. on 5s. blue	50	20
1431		10s. on 2s. green	85	20
1432		10s. on 40s. orange	70	40
1433		20s. on 2s. green	1·40	35
1434		50s. on 2s. green	3·00	1·50

1971. Air. Quito Religious Art. Mult.

1435		1s.30 Type **413**	10	10
1436		1s.50 "St. Anne"	15	10
1437		2s. "St. Teresa of Jesus"	25	10
1438		2s.50 Retable, Carmen altar (horiz)	25	10
1439		3s. "Descent from the Cross"	35	10
1440		4s. "Christ of St. Mariana"	50	20
1441		5s. St. Anthony Shrine	50	25
1442		10s. Cross of San Diego	75	50

414 Flags of Chile and Ecuador 415 Emblem on Globe

1971. Visit of Pres. Allende of Chile. Mult.

1443		1s.30 Type **414** (postage)	10	10
1444		2s. Pres. Allende (horiz) (air)	10	10
1445		2s.10 Pres. Ibarra of Ecuador and Pres. Allende (horiz)	10	10

1971. Air. Opening of Postal Museum, Quito.

1446	**415**	5s. blue and black	50	25
1447		5s.50 purple & black	50	30

416 Ismael Paz Pazmino (founder) 417 Punch-card and Map

1971. 50th Anniv of "El Universo" (newspaper).

1448	**416**	1s. mult (postage)	10	10
1449		1s.50 multicoloured (air)	10	10
1450		2s.50 multicoloured	10	10

1971. Air. Pan-American Road Conference.

1451	**417**	5s. multicoloured	50	30
1452	–	10s. black and orange	90	60
1453	–	20s. black, red & blue	1·25	65
1454	–	50s. black, lilac & blue	1·90	95

DESIGNS: 10s. Converging roads; 20s. Globe and equator; 50s. Mountain road.

418 C.A.R.E. Parcel 419 Flags of Ecuador and Argentine Republic

1972. 25th Anniv of C.A.R.E. Organization.

1455	**418**	30c. purple	10	10
1456		40c. green	10	10
1457		50c. blue	10	10
1458		60c. red	10	10
1459		80c. brown	10	10

1972. State Visit of President Lanusse of Argentine Republic. Multicoloured.

1460	1s. Type **419** (postage)	10	10
1461	3s. Arms of Ecuador and Argentine Republic (horiz) (air)	20	15
1462	5s. Presidents Velasco Ibarra and Lanusse (horiz)	35	20

420 "Jesus giving Keys to St. Peter" (M. de Santiago)

421 Map in Flame, and Scales of Justice

1972. Religious Paintings of 18th-century Quito School. Multicoloured.

1463	50c. Type **420** (postage)	10	10
1464	1s.10 "Virgin of Mercy" (Quito School)	20	20
1465	2s. "The Immaculate Conception" (M. Samaniego)	15	30
1466	3s. "Virgin of the Flowers" (M. de Santiago) (air)	20	20
1467	10s. "Virgin of the Rosary" (Quito School)	70	50

1972. Air. Inter-American Lawyers' Federation Congress, Quito.

1469	**421**	1s.30 blue and red	10	10

422 "Our Lady of Sorrow" (Caspicara)

1972. 18th-century Ecuador Statues. Mult.

1470	50c. Type **422** (postage)	10	10
1471	1s.10 "Nativity" (Quito School) (horiz)	10	20
1472	2s. "Virgin of Quito" (anon.)	15	10
1473	3s. "St. Dominic" (Quito School) (air)	20	20
1474	10s. "St. Rosa of Lima" (B. de Legarda)	70	40

423 Juan Ignacio Pareja

424 Woman in Poncho

1972. 150th Anniv of Battle of Pichincha (1st issue). Multicoloured.

1476	30c. Type **423** (postage)	10	10
1477	40c. Juan Jose Flores	10	10
1478	50c. Leon de Febres Cordero	10	10
1479	60c. Ignacio Torres	10	10
1480	70c. F. de Paula Santander	10	10
1481	1s. Jos M. Cordova	10	10
1482	1s.30 Jose M. Saenz (air)	10	15
1483	3s. Tomas Wright	20	15
1484	4s. Antonio Farfan	25	20
1485	5s. A. Jose de Sucre	35	25
1486	10s. Simon Bolivar	35	25
1487	20s. Arms of Ecuador	2·00	2·10

See also Nos. 1508/19.

1972. Ecuador Handicrafts and Costumes. Mult.

1488	2s. Type **424** (postage)	15	15
1489	3s. Girl in striped poncho	25	25
1490	5s. Girl in embroidered poncho	40	40
1491	10s. Copper urn	85	75
1492	2s. Woman in floral poncho (air)	15	10
1493	3s. Girl in banded poncho	20	15
1494	5s. Woman in rose poncho	35	25
1495	10s. "Sun" sculpture	70	75

425 Epidendrum orchid

1972. Air. Ecuador Flowers. Multicoloured.

1497	4s. Type **425**	75	45
1498	6s. Canna	1·00	60
1499	10s. Jimson weed	1·75	1·00

426 Oil Rigs

427 Arms

1972. Air. Oil Industry.

1501	**426**	1s.30 multicoloured	10	10

1972. Air. Civic and Armed Forces Day.

1502	**427**	2s. multicoloured	15	15
1503		3s. multicoloured	25	15
1504		4s. multicoloured	35	20
1505		4s.50 multicoloured	35	25
1506		6s.30 multicoloured	40	35
1507		6s.90 multicoloured	40	40

428 Statue of Sucre, Santo Domingo

429 Dish Aerial

1972. 150th Anniv of Battle of Pichincha (2nd issue). Multicoloured.

1508	1s.20 Type **428** (postage)	10	10
1509	1s.80 San Augustin Monastery	15	10
1510	2s.30 Independence Square	20	10
1511	2s.50 Bolivar's statue, La Alameda	25	15
1512	4s.75 Carved chapel doors	40	20
1513	2s.40 Cloister, San Augustin Monastery (air)	15	10
1514	4s.50 La Merced Monastery	30	25
1515	5s.50 Chapel column	40	30
1516	6s.30 Altar, San Augustin Monastery	45	35
1517	6s.90 Ceiling, San Augustin Monastery	45	35
1518	7s.40 Crucifixion, Cantuna Chapel	50	40
1519	7s.90 Ceiling detail, San Augustin Monastery	55	45

1973. Inauguration (1972) of Satellite Earth Station, Chillotal.

1520	**429**	1s. multicoloured	20	10

431 U.N. Emblem

432 O.E.A. Emblem

1973. Air. 25th Anniv of U.N. Economic Committee for Latin America (C.E.P.A.L.).

1521	**431**	1s.30 black and blue	15	10

1973. Air. "Day of the Americas".

1522	**432**	1s.50 multicoloured	15	10

433 Presidents Rodriguez Lara and Caldera

1973. Air. Visit of Pres. Caldera of Venezuela.

1523	**433**	3s. multicoloured	30	15

434 Blue-footed Boobies

1973. Formation of Galapagos Islands Province. Multicoloured.

1524	30c. Type **434** (postage)	40	15
1525	40c. Blue-faced boobies	40	15
1526	50c. Oystercatcher	40	15
1527	60c. Basking Galapagos fur seals	50	10
1528	70c. Giant tortoise	50	10
1529	1s. Californian sealion	50	10
1530	1s.30 Blue-footed boobies (different) (air)	2·00	25
1531	3s. Brown pelican	2·00	25

435 Silver Coin, 1934

436 Black-chinned Mountain Tanager

1973. Air. Coins. Multicoloured.

1532	5s. Type **435**	35	15
1533	10s. Reverse of silver coin, showing arms	70	30
1534	50s. Gold Coin, 1928	3·00	1·50

1973. Birds. Multicoloured.

1536	1s. Type **436**	55	25
1537	2s. Maniche oriole	90	40
1538	3s. Toucan barbet (vert)	90	50
1539	5s. Masked crimson tanager (vert)	2·25	90
1540	10s. Blue-necked tanager (vert)	4·75	1·60

437 OPEC Emblem

438 Dr. Marco Tulio Varea Quevedo (botanist)

1974. Air. OPEC (Oil exporters) Meeting, Quito.

1542	**437**	2s. multicoloured	15	10

1974. Ecuadorian Personalities (1st series).

1543	**438**	1s. blue	10	10
1544	–	1s. orange	10	10
1545	–	1s. green	10	10
1546	–	1s. brown	10	10

PERSONALITIES: No. 1544, Dr. J. M. Carbo Noboa (medical scientist). No. 1545, Dr. A. J. Valenzuela (physician). No. 1546, Capt. E. Chiriboga (national hero).

See also Nos. 1551/6 and 1565/9.

439 Flag of Ecuador and U.P.U. Emblem

440 Postman with Letter

1974. Air. Centenary of U.P.U.

1548	**439**	1s.30 multicoloured	10	10

1974. Personalities (2nd series). As T **438**.

1551	60c. red (postage)	10	10
1552	70c. lilac	10	10
1553	1s.20 green	10	10
1554	1s.80 blue	20	10
1555	1s.30 blue and black (air)	10	10
1556	1s.50 grey on pale grey	10	10

PERSONALITIES: 60c. Dr. Pio Jaramillo Alvarado (sociologist). 70c. Prof. Luciano Andrade Marin (naturalist). 1s.20, Dr. Francisco Campos Ruiadaneira (entomologist). 1s.30, Teodore Wolf (geographer). 1s.50, Capt. Edmundo Chiriboga G. (national hero). 1s.80, Luis Vernaza Lazarte (philanthropist).

1974. Air. 8th Inter-American Postmasters' Congress, Auibo.

1557	**440**	5s. multicoloured	30	15

441 Map of the Americas and F.I.A.F. Emblem

442 Colonnade

1974. Air. "Exfigua" Stamp Exhibition and Inter-American Philatelic Federation 5th General Assembly, Guayaquil (1973).

1558	**441**	3s. multicoloured	20	10

1974. Colonial Monastery, Tilipulo, Cotopaxi Province. Multicoloured.

1559	20c. Type **442**	10	10
1560	30c. Entrance	10	10
1561	40c. Church	10	10
1562	50c. Archway (vert)	10	10
1563	60c. Chapel (vert)	10	10
1564	70c. Cemetery (vert)	15	10

1975. Personalities (3rd series). As T **438**.

1565	80c. blue (postage)	10	10
1566	80c. red and pink	10	10
1567	5s. red (air)	40	20
1568	5s. grey	40	20
1569	5s. violet	40	20

PORTRAITS: No. 1565, Dr. Angel Polibio Chaves (statesman). No. 1566, Emilio Estrada Ycaza (archaeologist). No. 1567, Manuel J. Calle (journalist). No. 1568, Leopoldo Benites Vinueza (statesman). No. 1569, Adolfo H. Simmonds G. (journalist).

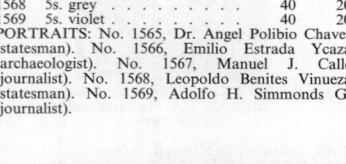

443 President Rodriguez Lara

1975. Air. State Visits of President Rodriguez Lara to Algeria, Rumania and Venezuela.

1570	**443**	5s. black and red	40	20

444 Ministerial Greetings

445 "The Sacred Heart"

1975. Meeting of Public Works' Ministers of Ecuador and Colombia, Quito. Multicoloured.

1571	1s. Type **444** (postage)	10	10
1572	1s.50 Ministers at opening ceremony (air)	15	10
1573	2s. Ministers signing treaty	15	10

1975. Air. 3rd Eucharistic Congress, Quito. Multicoloured.

1574	1s.30 Type **445**	10	10
1575	2s. Golden monstrance	15	10
1576	3s. Quito Cathedral	20	10

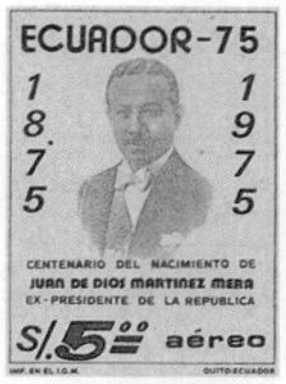

446 President Martinez Mera

447 Jorge Delgado Panchana (swimming champion)

1975. Air. Birth Centenary of Juan de Dios Martinez Mera (President, 1932–33).
1577 **446** 5s. red and black 40 20

1975. Air. Jorge Delgado Panchana Commemoration. Multicoloured.
1578 1s.30 Type **447** 15 10
1579 3s. Delgado Panchana in water (horiz) 30 10

448 "Women of Peace"

449 "Armed Forces"

1975. International Women's Year. Mult.
1580 1s. Type **448** 10 10
1581 1s. "Women of Action" . . 10 10

1975. 3rd Anniv of 15th February Revolution.
1582 **449** 2s. multicoloured 80 20

450 Hurdling

451 "Phragmipedum candatum"

1975. 3rd Ecuadorian Games, Quito.
1583 **450** 20c. black and orange (postage) 10 10
1584 – 20c. black and yellow . . 10 10
1585 – 30c. black and mauve . . 10 10
1586 – 30c. black and buff . . . 10 10
1587 – 40c. black and yellow . . 10 10
1588 – 40c. black and mauve . . 10 10
1589 – 50c. black and green . . 10 10
1590 – 50c. black and red . . . 10 10
1591 – 60c. black and green . . 10 10
1592 – 60c. black and pink . . 10 10
1593 – 70c. black and drab . . 10 10
1594 – 70c. black and grey . . . 10 10
1595 – 80c. black and blue . . . 10 10
1596 – 80c. black and orange . . 10 10
1597 – 1s. black and olive . . . 10 10
1598 – 1s. black and brown . . 10 10
1599 1s.30 black & orge (air) . . 10 10
1600 – 2s. black and yellow . . 15 10
1601 – 2s.80 black and red . . . 20 10
1602 – 3s. black and blue . . . 25 10
1603 – 5s. black and purple . . 40 20

DESIGNS: No. 1584, Chess; No. 1585, Boxing; No. 1586, Basketball; No. 1587, Showjumping; No. 1588, Cycling; No. 1589, Football; No. 1590, Fencing; No. 1591, Golf; No. 1592, Gymnastics; No. 1593, Wrestling; No. 1594, Judo; No. 1595, Swimming; No. 1596, Weightlifting; No. 1597, Handball; No. 1598, Table tennis; No. 1599, Squash; No. 1600, Rifle shooting; No. 1601, Volleyball; No. 1602, Rafting; No. 1603, Inca mask.

1975. Flowers. Multicoloured.
1604 20c. Type **451** (postage) . . 10 10
1605 30c. "Genciana" (horiz) . . 10 10
1606 40c. "Bromeliaeae cactaceae" 10 10
1607 50c. "Cachlioda volcanica" (horiz) 10 10
1608 60c. "Odontoglossum hallii (horiz) 10 10
1609 80c. "Cactaceae sp." (horiz) 10 10
1610 1s. "Odontoglossum sp." (horiz) 10 10
1611 1s.30 "Pitcairnia pungens" (horiz) (air) 15 10
1612 2s. "Salvia sp." (horiz) . . . 25 10
1613 3s. "Bomarea" (horiz) . . . 30 10
1614 4s. "Opuntia quitense" (horiz) 25 15
1615 5s. "Bomarea" (different) (horiz) 30 20

452 Aircraft Tail-fins

453 Statue of Benalcazar

1976. Air. 23rd Anniv of TAME Airline. Mult.
1616 1s.30 Type **452** 10 10
1617 3s. Douglas DC-3 and Lockheed L.188 Electra encircling map 40 10

1976. Air. Sebastian de Benalcazar Commem.
1618 **453** 2s. multicoloured 20 10
1619 3s. multicoloured 30 10

454 "Venus" (Chorrera Culture)

455 Strawberries

1976. Archaeological Discoveries. Mult.
1620 20c. Type **454** (postage) . . 10 10
1621 30c. "Venus" (Valdivia) . . 10 10
1622 40c. Seated monkey (Chorrera) 10 10
1623 50c. Man wearing poncho (Panzaleo Tardio) 10 10
1624 60c. Mythical figure (Cashaloma) 10 10
1625 80c. Musician (Tolita) . . . 10 10
1626 1s. Chief priest (censer-Mantema) 10 10
1627 1s. Female mask (Tolita) . . 10 10
1628 1s. Gold and platinum brooch (Tolita) 10 10
1629 1s. "Angry person" mask (Tolita) 10 10
1630 1s.30 Coconut-dealer (Carchi) (air) 15 15
1631 2s. Funerary urn (Tuncahuan) 15 10
1632 3s. Priest (Bahia de Caraquez) 25 10
1633 4s. Seashell (Cuasmal) . . . 35 10
1634 5s. Bowl supported by figurines (Guangala) . . . 40 20

1976. Flowers and Fruits Festival, Ambato. Multicoloured.
1635 1s. Type **455** (postage) . . . 10 10
1636 2s. Apples (air) 10 10
1637 5s. Rose 40 15

456 S. Cueva Celi

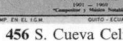

457 Douglas DC-10 crossing "50" and Dornier Wal Flying Boat

1976. Musical Celebrities. Multicoloured.
1638 1s. Type **456** 10 10
1639 1s. C. Ojeda Davila 10 10
1640 1s. S. Maria Duran 10 10
1641 1s. C. Amable Ortiz 10 10
1642 1s. L. Alberto Valencia . . 10 10

1976. Air. 50th Anniv of Lufthansa Airline.
1643 **457** 10s. multicoloured . . . 1·25 50

458 Cerros del Carmen y Santa Ana

1976. Air. 441st Anniv of Guayaquil. Mult.
1644 1s.30 Type **458** 10 10
1645 1s.30 "Pregonero" (vert) . . 10 10
1646 1s.30 "Estibador" (vert) . . 10 10
1647 2s. Sebastian de Benalcazar (vert) 15 10
1648 2s. Francisco de Orellana (vert) 15 10
1649 2s. Guayas and Quil (vert) 15 10

459 New Post Office Building

461 The Americas on Globe

460 Emblem and Wreath

1976. Air. Post Office Building Project.
1650 **459** 5s. multicoloured 30 15

1976. Air. 50th Anniv of Bolivarian Society.
1651 **460** 1s.30 multicoloured . . . 10 10

1976. Air. 3rd Pan-American Ministers' Conference on Transport Infrastructure, Quito.
1652 **461** 2s. multicoloured 10 10

462 Congress Emblem

463 George Washington

1976. Air. 10th Inter-American Construction Industry Congress, Quito.
1654 **462** 1s.30 multicoloured . . . 10 10
1655 3s. multicoloured 20 25

1976. Air. Bicentenary of American Revolution. Multicoloured.
1657 3s. Type **463** 45 25
1658 5s. Battle of Flamborough Head, 1779 (horiz) . . . 2·50 50

464 Dr. H. Noguchi

465 Bolivar Memorial

1976. Air. Birth Centenary of Dr. Hideyo Noguchi (bacteriologist).
1659 **464** 3c. multicoloured 25 10

1976. Air. Meeting of Agricultural Ministers of Andean Countries, Quito.
1661 **465** 3s. multicoloured 20 10

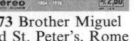

466 M. Febres Cordero

467 Dr. Luis Cordero

1976. Air. Mariuxi Febres Cordero, South American Swimming Champion.
1663 **466** 3s. multicoloured 25 10

1976. Air. Pres. Cordero Commemoration.
1664 **467** 2s. multicoloured 10 10

468 Sister Catalina de Jesus Herrera

469 General Assembly Emblem

1977. Air. 260th Birth Anniv of Sister Catalina de Jesus Herrera (religious author).
1665 **468** 1s.30 pink and black . . 10 10

1977. 11th General Assembly of Technical Committees of the Pan-American Historical and Geographical Institute. Multicoloured.
1666 2s. Type **469** (postage) . . . 10 10
1667 5s. Congress Building, Quito (air) 30 15

470 Mythological Figure ("La Tolita" ceramic)

1977. Air. 50th Anniv of Foundation of Central Bank of Ecuador. Multicoloured.
1669 7s. Type **470** 45 20
1670 9s. "The Holy Shepherdess Spinning" (B. de Legarda) 60 30
1671 11s. "The Fruitseller" (B. de Legarda) 75 60

471 Hands holding Rotary Emblem

1977. 50th Anniv of Guayaquil Rotary Club.
1673 **471** 1s. multicoloured 15 10
1674 2s. multicoloured 25 10

472 President Michelsen of Colombia

1977. Air. Meeting of the Presidents of Colombia and Ecuador. Multicoloured.
1676 2s.60 Type **472** 25 10
1677 5s. Ecuador junta 45 15
1678 7s. Ecuador junta (vert) . . 45 20
1679 9s. President Michelsen with Ecuador junta 75 40

473 Brother Miguel and St. Peter's, Rome

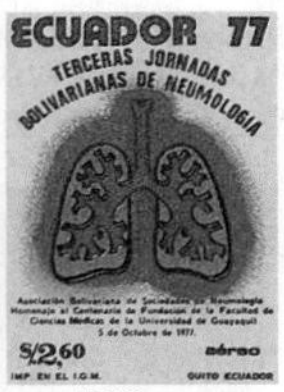

474 Lungs

1977. Air. Beatification of Brother Hermano Miguel.
1681 **473** 2s.60 multicoloured . . . 20 10

1977. Air. 3rd Bolivarian Pneumological Seminar.
1682 **474** 2s.60 multicoloured . . . 25 10

475 Jose Peralta

476 Blue-faced Booby

1977. 40th Death Anniv of Jose Peralta (writer).
1683 **475** 1s.80 mult (postage) . . 10 10
1684 – 2s.40 multicoloured . . . 15 15
1685 – 2s.60 blk, red & yell (air) 15 10
DESIGNS: 2s.40, Statue of Peralta; 2s.60, Titles of Peralta's works, and his "ex libris".

1977. Birds of the Galapagos Islands. Mult.
1686 1s.20 Type **476** 60 10
1687 1s.80 Red-footed booby . . 80 10
1688 2s.40 Blue-footed boobies 90 15
1689 3s.40 Dusky gull . . . . . 1·40 15
1690 4s.40 Galapagos hawk . . . 1·75 30
1691 5s.40 Map of the islands and finches (vert) . . . . 2·25 35

477 Broadcast Tower

478 Dr. Remigio Romero y Cordero

1977. Air. World Telecommunications Day.
1692 **477** 5s. multicoloured 30 15

1978. Air. 10th Death Anniv of Dr. Remigio Romero y Cordero (poet).
1693 **478** 3s. multicoloured 15 10
1694 10s.60 multicoloured . . . 60 30

479 Children

480 General San Martin

1978. Air. 50th Anniv of Social Insurance Institute. Multicoloured.
1696 7s. Type **479** 45 20
1697 9s. Insurance emblem . . . 40 30
1698 11s. Hands reaching for sun 70 35

1978. Air. Birth Bicent of General San Martin.
1700 **480** 10s.60 multicoloured . . 50 40

481 Air Survey of Ecuador

482 Dr. Vicente Corral Moscoso Hospital

1978. 50th Anniv of Military Geographical Institute. Multicoloured.
1702 6s. Type **481** (postage) . . . 60 25
1703 7s.60 Air survey of mountains (air) 80 30

1978. Inauguration of Dr. Vicente Corral Moscoso Regional Hospital. Multicoloured.
1705 3s. Type **482** (postage) . . . 25 10
1706 7s.60 Dr. Moscoso (air) . . 60 30

483 Map of the Americas and Lions Emblem

484 Anniversary Emblem

1978. 7th Meeting of Latin American Lions. Multicoloured.
1708 3s. Type **483** (postage) . . . 25 10
1709 4s.20 Type **483** 35 10
1710 5s. As Type **483** but smaller emblem (air) 40 20
1711 6s.20 As No. 1710 . . . . . 25 25

1978. 70th Anniv of Filanbanco (Philanthropic Bank). Multicoloured.
1713 4s.20 Type **484** (postage) . . 30 10
1714 5s. Bank emblem (air) . . . 35 15

485 Goal

1978. World Cup Football Championship, Argentina. Multicoloured.
1715 1s.20 Type **485** (postage) . . 10 10
1716 1s.80 Gauchito and emblem (vert) 15 10
1717 4s.40 Gauchito (vert) . . . 35 15
1718 2s.60 Gauchito, "78" and emblem (air) 20 10
1719 7s. Football 30 20
1720 9s. Emblem (vert) 40 35

486 Old Men of Vilcabamba

487 Bernardo O'Higgins

1978. Air. Vilcabamba (valley of longevity).
1722 **486** 5s. multicoloured 35 15

1978. Air. Birth Bicentenary of General Bernardo O'Higgins (national hero of Chile).
1723 **487** 10s.60 multicoloured . . 50 30

488 Hubert Humphrey (former U.S. Vice-President)

489 "Virgin and Child"

1978. Air. Hubert Humphrey Commem.
1725 **488** 5s. multicoloured 35 15

1978. Air. Christmas. Children's Paintings. Mult.
1726 2s.20 Type **489** 15 10
1727 4s.60 "Holy Family" . . . 25 15
1728 6s.20 "Candle and Children" 40 20

490 "Village" (Anibal Villacis)

491 Male and Female Symbols

1978. Air. Ecuadorian Painters. Mult.
1729 5s. Type **490** 35 20
1730 5s. "Mountain Village" (Gilberto Almeida) 35 20
1731 5s. "Bay" (Roura Oxandaberro) 35 20
1732 5s. "Abstract" (Luis Molinari) 35 20
1733 5s. "Statue" (Oswaldo Viteri) 35 20
1734 5s. "Tools" (Enrique Tabara) 35 20

1979. 50th Anniv of Inter-American Women's Commission.
1735 **491** 3s.40 multicoloured . . . 20 10

492 House and Monument

1979. Air. 150th Anniv of Battle of Portete and Tarqui. Multicoloured.
1736 2s.40 Type **492** 15 10
1737 3s.40 Monument (vert) . . . 20 10

493 Bank Emblem

494 Deep Sea Trawler and Fish

1979. 16th Anniv of Ecuadorian Mortgage Bank.
1739 **493** 4s.40 multicoloured . . . 30 15
1740 5s.40 multicoloured . . . 35 15

1979. Air. 25th Anniv of Extension to 200-mile Offshore Limit. Multicoloured.
1741 5s. Type **494** 90 25
1742 7s. Map of Ecuador and territorial waters (horiz) 55 25
1743 9s. Map of South America 70 35

495 Street Scene

496 Coat of Arms

1979. Galapagos Islands. Multicoloured.
1744 3s.40 Type **495** (postage) . . 25 15
1745 10s.60 Church bells in tower (horiz) (air) 50 20
1746 13s.60 Aerial view of coast 55 20

1979. Air. 5th Anniv of Ecuador-American Chamber of Commerce.
1748 **496** 7s.60 multicoloured . . . 45 25
1749 10s.60 multicoloured . . 65 35

497 Young Girl

498 Games Emblem

1979. Air. International Year of the Child.
1751 **497** 10s. multicoloured . . . 50 40

1979. Air. 5th National Games.
1752 **498** 28s. multicoloured . . . 1·10 80

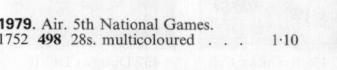

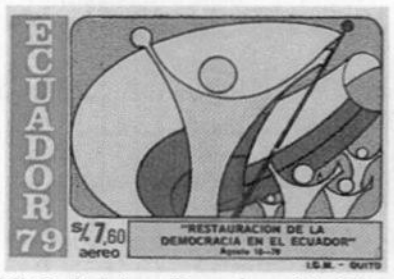
499 Rejoicing People with Flags

1979. Air. Restoration of Democracy. Mult.
1753 7s.60 Type **499** 55 30
1754 10s.60 President Jamie Roldos Aguilera 70 35

500 CIESPAL Building, Quito

1980. Air. Inauguration of CIESPAL (Ecuadorian Institute of Engineers) Building.
1755 **500** 10s.60 multicoloured . . 50 35

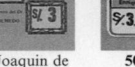

501 Jose Joaquin de Olmedo

502 Enriquillo (Dominican Republic)

1980. Birth Bicentenary of Jose Joaquin de Olmedo (physician).
1756 **501** 3s. multicoloured (postage) 25 10
1757 5s. multicoloured . . . 40 20
1758 10s. multicoloured (air) 50 40

1980. Chiefs of the Indo-American Indian Tribes. Multicoloured.
1759 3s. Type **502** (postage) . . . 25 10
1760 3s.40 Guaycaypuro (Venezuela) 30 15
1761 5s. Abayuba (Uruguay) . . 40 20
1762 5s. Atlacati (El Salvador) . . 40 20
1763 7s.60 Cuantemoc (Mexico) (air) 60 30
1764 7s.60 Lempira (Honduras) 60 30
1765 7s.60 Nicaragua (Nicaragua) 60 30
1766 10s. Lambare (Paraguay) . . 50 40
1767 10s. Urraca (Panama) . . . 50 40
1768 10s.60 Anacaona (Haiti) . . 50 45
1769 10s.60 Caupolican (Chile) 50 45
1770 10s.60 Tecun-Uman (Guatemala) 50 45
1771 12s.80 Calarca (Colombia) 65 30
1772 12s.80 Garabito (Costa Rica) 65 30
1773 12s.80 Hatuey (Cuba) . . . 65 30
1774 13s.60 Camarao (Brazil) . . 65 30
1775 13s.60 Tehuelche (Argentina) 65 30
1776 13s.60 Tupaj Katari (Bolivia) 65 30
1777 17s.80 Sequoyah (U.S.A.) 75 40
1778 22s.80 Ruminahui (Ecuador) 1·10 55

503 King Juan Carlos and Queen Sophia of Spain

504 Provincial Administration Council Building, Pichincha

1980. Visit of King and Queen of Spain.
1779 **503** 3s.40 mult (postage) . . 30 15
1780 10s.60 mult (air) 50 40

1980. Air. Pichincha Provincial Council.
1781 **504** 10s.60 multicoloured . . 80 40

505 Cofan Indian (Napo Province)

506 U.P.U. Monument

1980. Equatorial Indians. Multicoloured.
1782 3s. Type **505** (postage) . . . 25 10
1783 3s.40 Zuleta woman (Imbabura) 30 15
1784 5s. Chota negro woman (Imbabura) 40 20
1785 7s.60 Salasaca boy (Tungurahua) (air) . . . 60 30
1786 10s. Girl from Amula (Chimborazo) 50 40
1787 10s.60 Girl from Canar (Canar) 50 45
1788 13s.60 Colorado Indian (Pichincha) 65 30

1980. Air. Cent of U.P.U. Membership. Mult.
1789 10s.60 Type **506** 70 35
1790 17s.80 Mail box, 1880 . . . 95 65

507 Our Lady of Mercy Basilica, Quito

508 Olympic Torch

1980. Virgin of Mercy, Patron Saint of Ecuadorian Armed Forces. Multicoloured.

1792	3s.40 Type **507** (postage) . .	30	15
1793	3s.40 Balcony	30	15
1794	3s.40 Tower and cupola . .	30	15
1795	7s.60 Cupola and cloisters (air)	60	30
1796	7s.60 Tower and view of Quito	60	30
1797	7s.60 Gold screen	60	30
1798	10s.60 Retable	60	45
1799	10s.60 Pulpit	60	45
1800	13s.60 Cupola	75	30
1801	13s.60 Statue of Virgin . . .	75	30

1980. Olympic Games, Moscow. Multicoloured.

1803	5s. Type **508** (postage) . . .	40	20
1804	7s.60 Type **508**	35	30
1805	10s.60 Moscow games emblem (air)	50	45
1806	13s.60 As No. 1805	65	55

509 Rotary Anniversary Emblem

510 "Marshal Sucre" (after Marco Salas)

1980. Air. 75th Anniv of Rotary International.

1808 **509**	10s. multicoloured . . .	75	40

1980. Air. 150th Death Anniv of Marshal Antonio Jose de Sucre.

1809 **510**	10s.60 multicoloured . .	50	45

511 J. J. Olmeda, Father de Velasco, Government Building and Constitution

512 The Virgin of the Swans

1980. 150th Anniv of Constitutional Assembly of Riobamba. Multicoloured.

1810	3s.40 Type **511** (postage) . .	25	10
1811	5s. Type **511**	40	15
1812	7s.60 Monstrance, Riobamba Cathedral (vert) (air)	55	25
1813	10s.60 As No. 1812	50	35

1980. 50th Anniv of Coronation of the Virgin of the Swans. Multicoloured.

1815	1s.20 Type **512**	10	10
1816	3s.40 The Virgin (different)	20	10

513 Young Indian

514 O.P.E.C. Emblem and Globe

1980. 1st Anniv of Return to Democracy. Multicoloured.

1817	1s.20 Type **513** (postage) . .	10	10
1818	3s.40 Type **513**	20	10
1819	7s.60 President Roldos with Indian (air)	55	25
1820	10s.60 As No. 1819	50	35

1980. 20th Anniv of Organization of Petroleum Exporting Countries. Multicoloured.

1822	3s.40 Type **514** (postage) . .	30	10
1823	7s.60 Figures supporting O.P.E.C. emblem (air) . .	60	30

515 Dr. Isidro Ayora Cueva

516 Ornamental Hedge, Capitol Gardens

1980. Air. Birth Centenary of Dr. Isidro Ayora Cueva (President, 1926–31).

1824 **515**	18s.20 multicoloured . .	1·10	75

1980. Centenary of Carchi Province. Mult.

1825	3s. Type **516** (postage) . . .	20	10
1826	10s.60 Governor's palace (air)	70	35
1827	17s.80 Freedom statue, Zulcan	95	65

517 "Cattleya maxima"

1980. Orchids. Multicoloured.

1828	1s.20 Type **517** (postage) . .	10	10
1829	3s. "Comparettia speciosa"	25	10
1830	3s.40 "Cattleya iricolor" . .	30	15
1831	7s.60 "Anguloa uniflora" (air)	60	20
1832	10s.60 "Scuticaria salesiana"	80	35
1833	50s. "Helcia sanguinolenta" (vert)	1·10	85
1834	100s. "Anguloa virginalis"	1·50	1·50

518 Emblem and Radio Waves

519 Simon Bolivar (after Marco Salas)

1980. 50th Anniv of Radio Station HCJB.

1836	2s. Type **518** (postage) . . .	15	10
1837	7s.60 Emblem and radio waves (horiz) (air)	50	25
1838	10s.60 Anniversary emblem	65	35

1980. Air. 150th Death Anniv of Simon Bolivar.

1839 **519**	13s.60 multicoloured . .	1·10	55

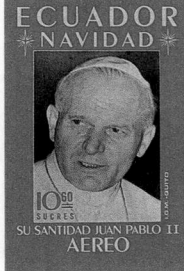

520 Pope John Paul II

1980. Christmas. Multicoloured.

1840	3s.40 Pope John Paul II with children (horiz) (postage)	30	15
1841	7s.60 Pope blessing crowd (air)	60	25
1842	10s.60 Type **520**	50	35

521 Carlos and Jorge Mantilla Ortega (editors)

1981. 75th Anniv of "El Comercio" (newspaper). Multicoloured.

1843	2s. Type **521**	15	10
1844	3s.40 Cesar and Carlos Mantilla Jacome	25	15

522 Oldest letter-box, Galapagos, 1793

1981. Air. Galapagos Islands.

1845	– 50s. yellow and black . .	3·00	2·25
1846 **522**	100s. multicoloured . . .	4·50	3·00

DESIGN—HORIZ: 50s. Turtle.

523 Flag, Map and Soldier

1981. National Defence. Multicoloured.

1847	3s.40 Type **523**	25	15
1848	3s.40 Flag, map and Pres. Roldos Aguilera	25	15

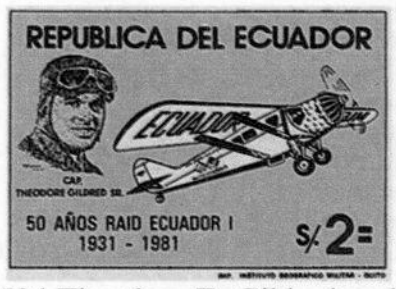

524 Theodore E. Gildred and "Ecuador 1"

525 Dr. Octavio Cordero Palacios

1981. 50th Anniv of Flight of "Ecuador 1" from San Diego to Quito.

1849 **524**	2s. black and blue . . .	30	15

1981. 50th Death Anniv (1980) of Dr. Octavio Cordero Palacios.

1850 **525**	2s. multicoloured	15	10

526 Miraculous Painting of the Virgin of Sorrows

527 Football Emblem

1981. 75th Anniv of Miracle of the Virgin blinking at San Gabriel College. Multicoloured.

1851	2s. Type **526**	15	10
1852	2s. San Gabriel College Church	15	10

1981. Air. World Cup Football Championship, Spain (1982). Multicoloured.

1853	7s.60 Type **527**	60	30
1854	10s.60 Footballer	90	45
1855	13s.60 World Cup trophy	1·10	55

528 Mendoza Aviles and Bridge

1981. Inauguration of Dr. Rafael Mendoza Aviles Bridge.

1857 **528**	2s. multicoloured	15	10

529 "Still-life"

1981. Air. Birth Centenary of Pablo Picasso (artist). Multicoloured.

1858	7s.60 Type **529**	35	30
1859	10s.60 "First Communion" (vert)	50	45
1860	13s.60 "Las Meninas" (vert)	60	55

530 Ear of Wheat on World Map

1981. World Food Day. Multicoloured.

1862	5s. Type **530** (postage) . . .	40	20
1863	10s.60 Agricultural products and farmer sowing seed (air)	50	35

531 "Isla Salango" (freighter)

532 Person in Wheelchair

1982. 10th Anniv of Transnave Shipping Company.

1864 **531**	3s.50 multicoloured . . .	1·50	30

1982. International Year of Disabled Persons (1981).

1865 **532**	3s.40 brown, red and black (postage) . . .	30	15
1866	– 7s.60 silver, green and blue (air)	60	30
1867	– 10s.60 brn, blk and red	50	45

DESIGNS: 7s.60, I.Y.D.P. emblem; 10s.60, Man breaking crutch.

533 Gateway, Quito

534 Flags of Member Countries and Emblem

1982. "Quitex '82" National Stamp Exn.

1868 **533**	2s. yellow, brown & blk	15	10
1869	– 3s. yellow, brown & blk	20	10

DESIGN. 3s. Old houses, Quito.

1982. 22nd American Air Forces' Commanders Conference.

1871 **534**	5s. multicoloured	40	20

535 Juan Montalvo (after C. A. Villacres)

536 Swimming Pool

1982. 150th Birth Anniv of Juan Montalvo (writer).

1872 **535**	2s. pink, brown and black (postage) . . .	15	10
1873	– 3s. multicoloured	20	10
1874	– 5s. multicoloured (air)	35	20

DESIGNS—VERT: 3s. Mausoleum. HORIZ: 5s. Montalvo's villa.

1982. World Swimming Championships, Guayaquil. Multicoloured.

1875	1s.80 Type **536** (postage) . .	20	10
1876	3s.40 Water polo	30	10
1877	10s.20 Games emblem (vert) (air)	60	50
1878	14s.20 Diving (vert)	85	70

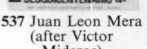

537 Juan Leon Mera (after Victor Mideros)

538 "The Ecstasy of St. Theresa" (detail of sculpture by Bernini)

1982. 150th Birth Anniv of Juan Leon Mera (author).
1879 **537** 5s.40 brn, blk & lt brn . . . 30 15
1880 – 6s. multicoloured 40 15
DESIGN: 6s. Statue of Mera, Ambato.

1983. 400th Death Anniv of St. Theresa of Avila.
1881 **538** 2s. multicoloured 15 10

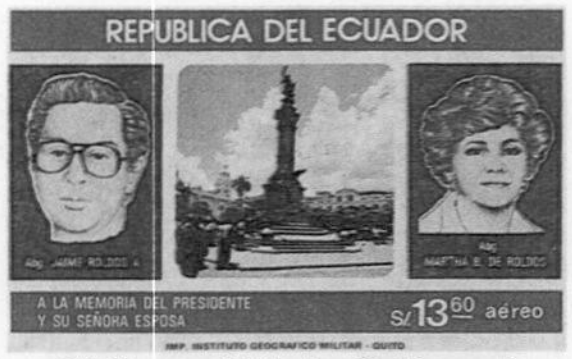

539 Pres. and Martha Roldos and Independence Monument

1983. Air. 2nd Death Anniv of President and Martha Roldos.
1882 **539** 13s.60 multicoloured . . 35 35

540 Californian Sealions

541 Statue of Rocafuerte in Guayaquil

1983. 150th Anniv of Ecuadorian Rule over Galapagos Islands and Death Centenary of Charles Darwin (evolutionary biologist). Multicoloured.
1883 3s. Type **540** 10 10
1884 5s. James's flamingoes and inset portrait of Darwin 1·50 30

1983. Birth Bicentenary of Vicente Rocafuerte Bejarano (President, 1835–39). Multicoloured.
1885 5s. Type **541** 20 10
1886 20s. Painting of Rocafuerte 45 35

542 Bolivar (after Antonio Salguero)

543 Long-distance View of Daniel Palacios Dam

1983. Birth Bicentenary of Simon Bolivar.
1887 **542** 20s. multicoloured . . . 45 35

1983. Inauguration of First Stage of Paute Hydro-electric Project. Multicoloured.
1888 5s. Type **543** 20 10
1889 10s. Close-up of dam . . . 40 15

544 W.C.Y. Emblem

545 Bolivar and Bananas

1983. World Communications Year.
1891 **544** 2s. multicoloured 10 10

1983. Centenaries of Provinces of Bolivar and El Oro.
1892 **545** 3s. multicoloured 10 10

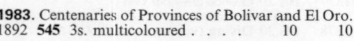

546 Atahualpa

547 "Holy Family"

1984. 450th Death Anniv (1983) of Atahualpa (last Inca emperor).
1893 **546** 15s. multicoloured . . . 20 10

1984. Christmas. Multicoloured.
1894 5s. Type **547** 10 10
1895 5s. Jesus and the lawyers . . 10 10
1896 5s. Marzipan kings 10 10
1897 6s. Marzipan preacher (vert) 10 10

548 Visit to Brazil

1984. President Hurtado's International Policies. Multicoloured.
1898 8s. Type **548** 10 10
1899 9s. Visit to China 15 10
1900 24s. Addressing U.N. General Assembly . . . 15 10
1901 28s. Meeting President Reagan of U.S.A. 20 15
1902 29s. Visit to Caracas, Venezuela, for Bolivar's birth bicentenary 45 15
1903 37s. Opening Latin-American Economic Conference, Quito 60 20

549 Diaz and Scales

1984. Birth Centenary of Miguel Diaz Cueva (lawyer).
1904 **549** 10s. multicoloured . . . 25 10

550 Games Emblem

551 Montgolfier Balloon

1984. Winter Olympic Games, Sarajevo. Mult.
1905 2s. Type **550** 10 10
1906 4s. Ice skating 10 10
1907 6s. Ice skating (different) . . 15 10
1908 10s. Skiing 15 10

1984. Bicent of Manned Fight (1983). Mult.
1910 3s. Type **551** 10 10
1911 6s. Charles's hydrogen balloon 20 10

552 La Marimba (dance)

1984. "San Mateo '83" Provincial Stamp Exhibition, Esmeraldas.
1913 **552** 8s. multicoloured 10 10

553 Language Academy

554 Yerovi

1984. Canonization of Brother Miguel. Mult.
1915 9s. Type **553** 10 10
1916 24s. Pope, St. Miguel and St. Peter's, Rome (vert) 35 25

1984. 165th Birth Anniv of Jose Maria de Jesus Yerovi, Archbishop of Quito.
1918 **554** 5s. multicoloured 15 10

555 Pope's Arms

556 Mercedes de Jesus Molina

1985. Visit of Pope John Paul II. Mult.
1919 1s.60 Type **555** 10 10
1920 5s. Pope holding crucifix . . 10 10
1921 9s. Map of papal route . . 15 10
1922 28s. Pope waving 35 20
1923 29s. Pope 40 20

1985. Beatification of Mercedes de Jesus Molina. Multicoloured.
1925 1s.60 Type **556** 10 10
1926 5s. "Madonna of Czestochowa" (icon) . . . 10 10
1927 9s. "Our Lady of La Alborada" (statue) . . . 10 10

557 Hummingbird

558 Exhibition Emblem

1985. Samuel Valarezo Delgado (ornithologist and former Director of Posts).
1929 **557** 2s. red, green & brown 30 15
1930 – 3s. green, yellow and bl 10 10
1931 – 6s. black and brown . . 10 10
DESIGNS: 3s. Sailfish and tuna; 6s. Valarezo Delgado.

1985. "Espana 84" International Stamp Exhibition, Madrid.
1932 **558** 6s. brn & cinnamon . . 10 10
1933 – 10s. brn & cinnamon . . 15 10
DESIGN: 10s. Spanish royal family.

559 Dr. Pio Jaramallo Alvarado

560 Sugar Cane and Water Tower

1985. Death Centenary (1984) of Dr. Pio Jaramallo Alvarado (historian).
1935 **559** 6s. multicoloured 15 10

1985. Centenary of Valdez Sugar Refinery. Mult.
1936 50s. Type **560** 60 25
1937 100s. Rafael Valdez Cervantes (founder) . . . 1·25 50

561 Emblem

1985. 10th Anniv of Chamber of Commerce.
1939 **561** 24s. multicoloured . . . 30 20
1940 28s. multicoloured . . . 35 25

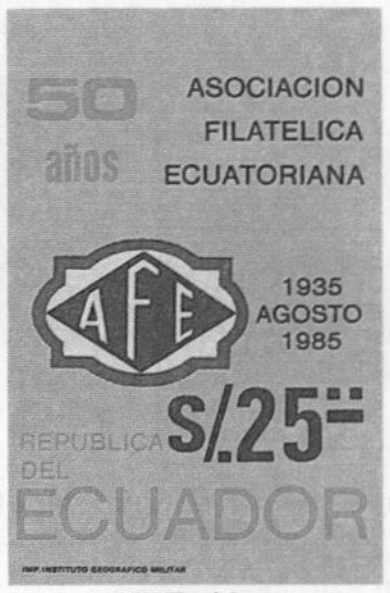

562 Emblem

1985. 50th Anniv of Ecuador Philatelic Association. Multicoloured.
1942 25s. Type **562** 30 15
1943 30s. Philatelic Exhibition 1s. stamp, 1936 (horiz) . . . 35 20

563 Fire Engine, 1882

564 Children and Tree

1985. 150th Anniv of Guayaquil Fire Station. Multicoloured.
1944 6s. Type **563** 10 10
1945 10s. Fire-engine, 1899 . . . 10 10
1946 20s. Fire service anniversary emblem 20 10

1985. Infant Survival Campaign.
1947 **564** 10s. multicoloured . . . 10 10

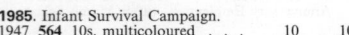

565 Israeli Aircraft Industry Kfir-C2

566 Boxer

1985. Armed Forces. Multicoloured.
1948 10s. Type **565** (65th anniv of Air Force) 30 10
1949 10s. Seaman and gunboat "Calderon" (centenary of Navy) . . . . 1·25 30
1950 10s. Insignia (30th anniv of Parachute Regiment) . . 40 25

1985. Bolivar Games, Cuenca. Each silver, blue and red.
1951 10s. Type **566** 15 10
1952 25s. Gymnast 30 20
1953 30s. Discus thrower 35 25

567 "Royal Audience Quarter, Quito" (J. M. Roura)

568 U.N. Emblem

1985. First National Philatelic Congress and "50th Anniv of Ecuador Philatelic Association" Stamp Exhibition, Quito.
1954 **567** 5s. black, yellow & orge 10 10
1955 – 10s. black, green & red 20 10
1956 – 15s. black, blue and red 20 10
1957 – 20s. black, red and lilac 30 15
DESIGNS—VERT: 10s. "Riobamba Cathedral" (O. Munoz). HORIZ: 15s. "House of a Hundred Windows, Guayaquil" (J.M. Roura); 20s. "Rural House, near Cuenca" (J.M. Roura).

1985. 40th Anniv of U.N.O. Multicoloured.
1959 10s. Type **568** 15 10
1960 20s. State flag 30 15

569 Child on Donkey

570 "Embotrium grandiforum"

1985. Christmas. Multicoloured.

1962	5s. Type **569**	10	10
1963	10s. Food display	15	10
1964	15s. Child seated upon display	20	10

1986. Flowers. Multicoloured.

1966	24s. Type **570**	35	15
1967	28s. Orchid ("Topobea" sp.)	35	15
1968	29s. "Befaria resinosa mutis"	35	15

571 Land Iguana

1986. Galapagos Islands. Multicoloured.

1970	10s. Type **571**	15	10
1971	20s. Californian sealion	25	15
1972	30s. Magnificent frigate birds	1·50	80
1973	40s. Galapagos penguins	1·75	1·10
1974	50s. Tortoise (25th anniv (1984) of Charles Darwin Foundation)	60	30
1975	100s. Charles Darwin (150th anniv (1985) of visit)	3·00	1·40
1976	200s. Bishop Tomas de Berlanga and map (450th anniv (1985) of Islands' discovery)	2·10	1·40

572 Antonio Ortiz Mena (President)

573 Andres Gomez Santos

1986. 25th Anniv (1985) of Inter-American Development Bank. Multicoloured.

1978	5s. Type **572**	10	10
1979	10s. Felipe Herrera (President, 1960–71)	15	10
1980	50s. Emblem	75	30

1986. 75th Anniv (1985) of Guayaquil Tennis Club. Multicoloured.

1981	10s. Type **573**	15	10
1982	10s. Francisco Segura Cano	15	10
1983	10s. Emblem (horiz)	15	10

574 Prawn

1986. Exports. Seafoods.

1984	**574** 35s. red and blue	35	20
1985	– 40s. green and red	60	20
1986	– 45s. yellow & mauve	65	25

DESIGNS: 40s. Yellow-finned tuna; 45s. Pacific sardines in tin.

575 Goalkeeper diving for Ball

1986. World Cup Football Championship, Mexico. Multicoloured.

1988	5s. Type **575**	10	10
1989	10s. Player tackling	15	10

576 Betancourt and Cordero

1986. Rumichaca Meeting of Pres. Belisario Betancourt of Colombia and Pres. Leon Febres Cordero of Ecuador. Multicoloured.

1991	20s. Type **576**	20	15
1992	20s. Presidents embracing	20	15

577 Charles-Marie de La Condamine

1986. 250th Anniv of First Geodetic Expedition (to measure Arcs of Meridian).

1993	**577** 10s. green and light green	15	10
1994	– 15s. violet and lilac	15	10
1995	– 20s. green and brown	20	10

DESIGNS: No. 1994, Maldonado; 1995, Centre of World Monument, Quito.

578 Emblem of Pichincha Chamber of Trade

579 National Railways Emblem

1986. 50th Anniversaries of Chambers of Trade.

1997	**578** 10s. black and brown	10	10
1998	– 10s. black and blue	10	10
1999	– 10s. black and green	10	10

DESIGNS: No. 1998, Cuenca; 1999, Guayaquil.

1986. 57th Anniv of Ministry of Public Works and Communications. Multicoloured.

2000	5s. Type **579**	2·75	75
2001	10s. Post Office emblem	10	10
2002	15s. IETEL (telecommunications) emblem	15	10
2003	20s. Ministry of Public Works emblem	20	15

580 Emblem

581 Vargas

1987. 50th Anniv of First Zone Chamber of Agriculture.

2004	**580** 5s. multicoloured	10	10

1988. Death Centenary of Luis Vargas Torres (revolutionary).

2005	**581** 50s. black, gold & grn	40	20
2006	– 100s. blue, gold and red	1·00	35

DESIGN: No. 2006, Group of soldiers.

582 Las Penas Quarter

1988. 450th Anniv of Guayaquil City. Mult.

2008	15s. Type **582**	10	10
2009	30s. Rafael Mendoza Aviles Bridge of National Unity (horiz)	20	10
2010	40s. Federico de Orellana (founder) (horiz)	15	15

583 Family within Hands

1988. 60th Anniv of Social Security Work. Multicoloured.

2011	50s. Type **583**	30	20
2012	100s. Anniversary emblem	55	35

584 Yaguarcocha Lake

1988. Death Centenary of Dr. Pedro Moncayo y Esparza (politician). Multicoloured.

2013	10s. Type **584**	10	10
2014	15s. Dr. Moncayo	10	10
2015	20s. Dr. Moncayo's house	10	10

585 Junkers F-13 Seaplane

1988. 60th Anniv of Avianca National Airline. Multicoloured.

2017	10s. Type **585**	10	10
2018	20s. Dornier Wal flying boat	10	10
2019	30s. Ford "Tin Goose"	15	10
2020	40s. Boeing 247D	20	10
2021	50s. Boeing 720-059D	25	15
2022	100s. Douglas DC-3	45	25
2023	200s. Boeing 727-200	1·40	50
2024	300s. Sikorsky S-38 flying boat	2·00	1·00
2025	500s. Anniversary emblem (vert)	3·25	1·60

586 New Building

1988. 125th Anniv of San Gabriel College. Multicoloured.

2026	15s. Type **586**	10	10
2027	35s. Door of old building	25	10

587 Institute

588 St. John Bosco

1988. 60th Anniv of Military Geographical Institute, Quito. Multicoloured.

2028	25s. Type **587**	25	10
2029	50s. Inside planetarium	35	20
2030	60s. Anniversary emblem	40	20
2031	500s. Mural by E. Kingman	3·25	1·60

No. 2028 was issued surcharged 800s. on 25 June 1996. Only a few sets were made available to the public at face value, the remainder sold by postal employees at considerably inflated prices.

1988. Centenary of Salesian Brothers in Ecuador and Death Centenary of St. John Bosco (founder). Multicoloured.

2033	10s. Type **588**	10	10
2034	50s. Group of Brothers	25	20

589 Dr. Francisco Campos Coello (founder)

590 Bank

1988. Cent of Guayaquil Welfare Society.

2036	**589** 15s. multicoloured	10	10
2037	– 20s. multicoloured	10	10
2038	– 45s. black, silver & blue	10	10

DESIGNS: 20s. Eduardo M. Arosemena (first Director); 45s. Emblem.

No. 2038 was issued surcharged 2600s. on 25 June 1996. Only a few sets were made available to the public at face value, the remainder sold by postal employees at considerably inflated prices.

1989. 75th Anniv (1988) of Azuay Bank, Cuenca. Multicoloured.

2040	20s. Type **590**	10	10
2041	40s. Bank (vert)	10	10

591 Athletics

592 "Bird" (sculpture, Joaquin Tinta)

1989. Olympic Games, Seoul (1988). Designs showing Hodori the Tiger (mascot).

2043	10s. Type **591**	10	10
2044	20s. Boxing	10	10
2045	30s. Cycling	10	10
2046	40s. Shooting	10	10
2047	100s. Swimming	20	10
2048	200s. Weightlifting	75	20
2049	300s. Taekwondo	1·10	60

1989. 50th Anniv of Ruminahui State. Mult.

2051	50s. Type **592**	10	10
2052	70s. Sangolqui church (horiz)	15	15

593 Dr. Carrion Mora

594 "The Gilt Mirror" (Myrna Baez)

1989. Birth Centenary of Dr. Benjamin Carrion Mora (writer). Multicoloured.

2054	50s. Type **593**	10	10
2055	70s. Loja (horiz)	15	15
2056	1000s. Loja university (horiz)	3·75	1·90

1989. 2nd Art Biennale, Cuenca. Mult.

2058	40s. Type **594**	10	10
2059	70s. "Paraguay III" (Carlos Colombino) (vert)	15	15
2060	180s. "Modulation 892" (Julio Le Parc) (vert)	75	20

595 Ignacio C. Roca Molestina (founding President)

596 Emblems

1989. Centenary of Guayaquil Chamber of Commerce. Multicoloured.

2062	50s. Type **595**	10	10
2063	300s. Chamber building (horiz)	1·10	60
2064	500s. Trade and progress symbol (horiz)	1·90	95

1989. 60th Anniv of Ministry of Public Works and Communications. Multicoloured.

2066	50s. Type **596**	90	40
2067	100s. IETEL emblem (telecommunications)	20	10
2068	200s. Ministry of Public Works emblem	75	20

597 Birds

598 Red Cross Worker

1989. Bicent of French Revolution. Mult.

2070	20s. Type **597**	10	10
2071	50s. Cathedral fresco (horiz)	10	10
2072	100s. French cock	20	10

1989. 125th Anniv of Red Cross in Ecuador. Multicoloured.

2074	10s. Type **598**	10	10
2075	30s. Emblem (horiz)	10	10
2076	200s. Masked Red Cross workers (horiz)	75	20

599 Montalvo's Tomb

1989. Death Cent of Juan Montalvo (writer).

2077	50s. Type **599**	10	10
2078	100s. Photograph of Montalvo	45	10
2079	200s. Statue of Montalvo	90	45

600 Dr. Jaramillo Leon (founder)

601 Tolita Head-shaped Censer

1990. 70th Anniv of Cuenca Chamber of Commerce. Multicoloured.

2081	100s. Type **600**	30	15
2082	100s. Federico Malo Andrade (first Honorary President)	30	15
2083	130s. Roberto Crespo Toral (first President)	40	20
2084	200s. Alfonso Jaramillo Leon (founder of savings and credit departments)	60	25

1990. America. Pre-Columbian Artefacts. Mult.

2086	200s. Type **601**	25	25
2087	300s. Carchi plate with warrior design (horiz)	65	20

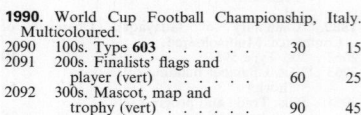

602 Mercedes de Jesus Molina

603 Mascot, Quarter Finalists and Ball

1990. Anniversaries. Multicoloured.

2088	100s. Type **602** (centenary of Marianitas)	30	15
2089	200s. Clock tower and roses on open book (centenary of Santa Mariana de Jesus College)	60	25

1990. World Cup Football Championship, Italy. Multicoloured.

2090	100s. Type **603**	30	15
2091	200s. Finalists' flags and player (vert)	60	25
2092	300s. Mascot, map and trophy (vert)	90	45

604 Emblem

1990. 5th Population Census and 4th Housing Census. Multicoloured.

2094	100s. Type **604**	25	10
2095	200s. Logo of National Statistics and Census Institute (horiz)	50	25
2096	300s. Pencil and population statistics	75	20

605 Iguana (Galapagos)

606 Members' Flags

1990. Tourism. Multicoloured.

2098	100s. Type **605**	25	10
2099	200s. Church of Companionship (Quito) (vert)	50	25
2100	300s. Old man of Vilcabamba	75	20

1990. 30th Anniv of Organization of Petroleum Exporting Countries. Multicoloured.

2102	200s. Type **606**	50	25
2103	300s. Emblem	75	20

607 Anniversary Emblem

608 "Blakea sp."

1990. 25th Anniv of Organization for Preservation of Traditional Handicrafts. Multicoloured.

2104	200s. Type **607**	50	25
2105	300s. Carved and painted parrots	75	20

1990. Flowers. Multicoloured.

2107	100s. Type **608**	10	10
2108	100s. "Loasa sp."	10	10
2109	100s. "Cattleya sp."	10	10
2110	100s. "Sobralia sp." (horiz)	10	10

609 Ingapirca

1991. America. World found by the Discoverers. Multicoloured.

2111	100s. Type **609**	10	10
2112	200s. Forest pool	50	25

610 Globe and Means of Information

611 Broadcaster

1991. 50th Anniv of National Journalists' Federation. Multicoloured.

2113	200s. Type **610**	50	25
2114	300s. Eugenio Espejo	75	20
2115	400s. Emblem	1·00	50

1991. 50th Anniv of Radio Quito. Mult.

2116	200s. Type **611**	20	20
2117	500s. Family listening to radio (horiz)	90	35

612 Suarez

613 Columbus's Ships

1991. Birth Cent of Dr. Pablo Arturo Suarez.

2118	**612**	70s. multicoloured	15	10

1991. America. Multicoloured.

2119	200s. Type **613**	45	30
2120	500s. Columbus and landing party	1·25	55

614 Cat-shaped Censer

615 Hand and Woman's Face

1991. Archaeology. La Tolita Culture (1st series). Multicoloured.

2121	100s. Type **614**	10	10
2122	200s. Head of old man	20	10
2123	300s. Human/animal statuette	60	20

See also No. 2144.

1991. No Violence to Women Day. Mult.

2124	300s. Type **615**	60	20
2125	500s. Woman's profile and hand	95	30

616 Presidents Borja and Paz Zamora

1991. Visit of President Jaime Paz Zamora of Bolivia.

2126	**616**	500s. multicoloured	95	30

617 Jijon y Caamano

1991. Birth Centenary of Jacinto Jijon y Caamano (historian and geographer).

2127	**617**	200s. multicoloured	20	10
2128	–	300s. blue, blk & mve	60	20

DESIGN—HORIZ: 300s. Books and Jijon y Caamano.

618 Pres. Borja

1992. President Rodrigo Borja's Speech to United Nations. Multicoloured.

2129	100s. Type **618**	10	10
2130	1000s. Map and flags of U.N. Security Council members	1·60	65

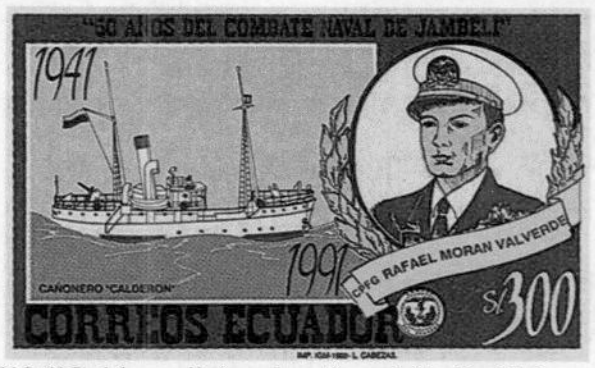

619 "Calderon" (gunboat) and Rafael Moran Valverde

1992. 50th Anniv (1991) of Battle of Jambeli. Multicoloured.

2131	300s. Type **619**	60	15
2132	500s. "Atahualpa" (despatch vessel) and Victor Naranjo Fiallo	95	30

620 Land Iguana

1992. Galapagos Islands Animals.

2134	100s. Type **620**	15	10
2135	100s. Giant tortoise	15	10
2136	100s. Swallow-tailed gull	55	30
2137	100s. Great frigate bird ("Fregata minor")	55	30
2138	100s. Galapagos penguin (vert)	55	30
2139	100s. Californian sea-lion (vert)	15	10

621 College

1992. 150th Anniv (1991) of Vicente Rocafuerte National College, Guayaquil. Multicoloured.

2140	200s. Type **621**	15	10
2141	400s. Vicente Rocafuerte (Ecuador President 1835–39 and College founder)	65	15

622 Alfaro

623 Ceremonial Mask

1992. 150th Birth Anniv of General Eloy Alfaro. Multicoloured.

2142	300s. Type **622**	20	10
2143	700s. Alfaro's house (horiz)	1·00	30

1992. Archaeology. La Tolita Culture (2nd series).

2144	**623**	400s. multicoloured	60	15

624 "Santa Maria"

1992. America. 500th Anniv of Discovery of America by Columbus. Multicoloured.

2145	200s. Type **624**	60	20
2146	400s. Columbus and map of Americas (vert)	70	15

625 Cordova

626 Narcisa de Jesus

1992. Birth Centenary of Andres Cordova (President, 1940).

2147	**625**	300s. multicoloured	45	10

1992. Beatification of Narcisa de Jesus.

2148	**626**	100s. multicoloured	10	10

627 Infant Jesus

628 Velasco (statue)

1992. Christmas. Multicoloured.

2149	300s. Type **627**	45	10
2150	600s. Children, lamb and baby Jesus	1·00	25

1992. Death Bicentenary of Juan de Velasco.

2151	**628**	200s. multicoloured	15	10

629 "Atelopus bomolochos"

630 Paez

1993. Frogs. Multicoloured.
2152 300s. Type **629** 20 10
2153 300s. Spurrell's tree frog ("Agalychnis spurrelli") 20 10
2154 600s. "Hyla picturata" . . . 40 20
2155 600s. "Gastrotheca plumbea" 40 20
2156 900s. Splendid poison-arrow frog ("Dendrobates" sp.) 60 25
2157 900s. "Sphaenorhynchus lacteus" 60 25

1993. Birth Centenary of J. Roberto Paez (co-founder of social security system and writer).
2158 **630** 300s. blue 20 10

631 1907 3c. Robles Stamp

632 Arms

1993. Death Centenary of Francisco Robles Garcia (President 1856–59).
2159 **631** 500s. multicoloured . . . 60 15

1993. National Police.
2160 **632** 300s. multicoloured . . . 45 10

633 Velasco

1993. Birth Centenary of Jose Maria Velasco Ibarra (President, 1934–35, 1944–47, 1952–56, 1960–61 and 1968–72).
2161 **633** 500s. multicoloured . . . 60 15

634 Lantern Fly

1993. Insects. Multicoloured.
2162 150s. Type **634** 10 10
2163 200s. "Semiotus ligneus" . . 15 10
2164 300s. "Taeniotes pulverulenta" 45 10
2165 400s. Orange tiger caterpillar 55 15
2166 600s. "Erotylus onagga" . . 85 20
2167 700s. Carpenter bee . . . . 1·00 20

635 Cevallos Villacreces

636 Boy releasing Doves

1993. Death Centenary of Pedro Fermin Cevallos Villacreces (historian and founder of Language Academy).
2168 **635** 1000s. multicoloured . . 1·25 55

1993. 1st Latin-American Children's Peace Assembly, Quito.
2169 **636** 300s. multicoloured . . . 45 10

637 Vela Hervas

638 "Cinchonia cordifolia"

1993. 150th Birth Anniv of Juan Benigno Vela Hervas (politician).
2170 **637** 2000s. multicoloured . . 2·50 1·00

1993. 250th Anniv of Maldonado and La Condamine's Amazon Expedition. Multicoloured.
2171 150s. Type **638** 10 10
2172 250s. Pedro Maldonado . . 15 10
2173 1500s. Charles de la Condamine . . . . 1·75 65

639 Anniversary Emblem

1993. 300th Anniv of Faculty of Medical Sciences, Ecuador Central University.
2174 **639** 300s. multicoloured . . . 45 10

640 Bustamante

642 Arroyo del Rio

641 Pacarana

1993. Birth Centenary of Guillermo Bustamante (writer).
2175 **640** 1500s. multicoloured . . 2·10 75

1993. America. Endangered Animals. Mult.
2176 400s. Type **641** 30 15
2177 800s. Chestnut-fronted macaw (vert) . . . . . . 1·90 75

1993. Birth Centenary of Dr. Carlos Arroyo del Rio (President, 1939–44).
2178 **642** 500s. multicoloured . . . 60 15

643 "Nativity" (ivory nut carvings)

644 Scouts Emblem and Map on Wall

1993. Christmas. Multicoloured.
2179 600s. Type **643** 70 15
2180 900s. Madonna and Child in landscape (vert) . . . . . 1·10 45

1994. Scouting Movement.
2181 **644** 400s. multicoloured . . . 50 10

645 Emblem

646 Donoso

1994. International Year of the Family.
2182 **645** 300s. red, green & black 15 10

1994. Birth Cent of Dr. Julio Tobar Donoso.
2183 **646** 500s. multicoloured . . . 80 40

647 "Sobralia dichotoma"

648 Cabezas

1994. 1st Andean Orchid Conservation Convention. Multicoloured.
2184 150s. Type **647** 10 10
2185 150s. "Dracula hirtzii" . . . 10 10
2186 300s. "Encyclia pulcherrima" 40 10
2187 300s. "Lepanthes delhierroi" 40 10
2188 600s. "Masdevallia rosea" 70 40
2189 600s. "Telipogon andicola" 70 40

1994. Death Cent of Dr. Miguel Egas Cabezas.
2190 **648** 100s. multicoloured . . . 10 10

649 Gonzalez Suarez

650 Earth as Football

1994. 150th Birth Anniv of Federico Gonzalez Suarez, Archbishop of Quito.
2191 **649** 200s. multicoloured . . . 10 10

1994. World Cup Football Championship, U.S.A. Multicoloured.
2192 300s. Type **650** 50 10
2193 600s. Striker (mascot) . . . 1·10 45
2194 900s. Footballer . . . . . . 1·75 70

651 Cyclists on "Road" of National Colours to Equator Monument

652 Espinosa Polit

1994. International Junior Cycling Championship, Quito. Multicoloured.
2196 300s. Type **651** 15 10
2197 400s. Stylized cyclist and monument (vert) 20 10

1994. Birth Centenary of Father Aurelio Espinosa Polit (writer).
2198 **652** 200s. multicoloured . . . 35 10

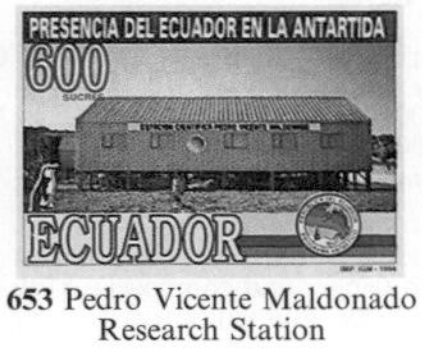

653 Pedro Vicente Maldonado Research Station

1994. Ecuador's Presence in Antarctica. Mult.
2199 600s. Type **653** . . . . . . 1·10 45
2200 900s. "Orion" (survey ship) 1·75 70

654 Anniversary Emblem

1994. Centenary of National Lottery.
2201 **654** 1000s. multicoloured . . 2·00 80

655 Benjamon Carrion (founder)

1994. 50th Anniv of House of Ecuadorean Culture. Multicoloured.
2202 700s. Type **655** . . . . . . 1·25 60
2203 900s. House of Culture (horiz) . . . . 1·75 70

656 Worker and "75"

1994. 75th Anniv of I.L.O.
2204 **656** 100s. multicoloured . . . 10 10

657 Globe and Postal Emblem

1994. Christmas. Multicoloured.
2205 600s. Type **657** 25 10
2206 900s. Nativity (vert) 40 20

658 Airplane and Sack of Mail

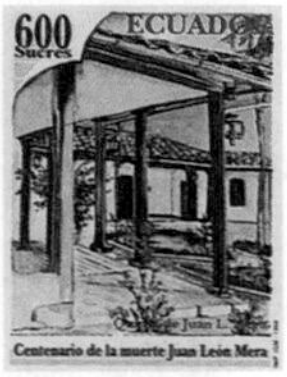

659 Mera's Country Villa

1994. America. Postal Transport. Mult.
2207 600s. Type **658** 25 10
2208 600s. Airplane, ship and van (horiz) 40 10

1994. Death Centenary of Juan Leon Mera (author). Multicoloured.
2209 600s. Type **659** 50 10
2210 900s. Mera (after Victor Mideros) . . . . 1·25 60

660 Sucre

1995. Birth Bicent of Marshal Antonio Jose de Sucre (first Bolivian President). Multicoloured.
2211 1500s. Type **660** . . . . . 1·25 55
2212 2000s. Sucre (looking to left) 1·75 70

661 Escriva

663 Girl

662 Eloy Alfaro (President 1897–1901 and 1907–11)

1995. 3rd Anniv of Beatification of Josemaria Escriva de Balaguer (founder of Opus Dei).
2214 **661** 900s. multicoloured . . . 75 20

1995. Centenary of Alfarist Revolution.
2215 **662** 800s. multicoloured . . . 70 15

1995. 50th Anniv of CARE (Co-operative for Assistance and Remittances Overseas).
2216 **663** 400s. black, grn & gold 20 10
2217 – 800s. multicoloured . . . 70 15
DESIGN—HORIZ: 800s. People working land.

664 Soldier thinking of Children

1995. "Peace with Dignity". Multicoloured.
2218 200s. Type **664** 10 10
2219 400s. Hand holding Ecuador flag (25 × 34 mm) 20 10
2220 800s. Soldier amongst bamboo 70 15

No. 2118 was issued surcharged 200s. on 25 June 1996. Only a few sets were made available to the public at face value, the remainder sold by postal employees at considerably inflated prices.

665 Anniversary Emblem

666 "Our Lady of Cisne" (statue, Diego de Robles)

1995. 25th Anniv of Andean Development Corporation.
2221 **665** 1000s. multicoloured . . 1·10 45

1995.
2222 **666** 500s. multicoloured . . . 45 10

667 Anniversary Emblem

668 Anniversary Emblem

1995. 35th Anniv of INNFA (child welfare organization).
2223 **667** 400s. multicoloured . . . 20 10

1995. 50th Anniv of U.N.O.
2224 **668** 1000s. blue, gold & blk 95 45

669 Man with Book (preparation for natural disasters)

1995. International Decade for the Reduction of Natural Disasters. Ecuador Civil Defence Organization. Multicoloured.
2225 1000s. Type **669** 90 45
2226 1000s. Family hiding beneath table (protection) 95 45
2227 1000s. Couple escaping from flooded house (maintenance of elevated refugee centres) 95 45
2228 1000s. Children planting sapling (reforestation) . . 95 45
2229 1000s. Family escaping erupting volcano (awareness of warning signs) 95 45

670 Emblem

1995. 50th Anniv of F.A.O.
2230 **670** 1300s. multicoloured . . 1·25 55

671 Woman, Piano and Book

1995. 50th Anniv of Women's Cultural Club.
2231 **671** 1500s. multicoloured . . 1·40 60

672 Emblem

1995. 39th Annual Assembly of Inter-American Philately Federation.
2232 **672** 1000s. blue and red . . . 95 40

673 Combat Planes flying over Mountains

674 Long-tailed Sylphs ("Aglaiocercus kingi")

1995. 75th Anniv of Ecuadorean Air Force.
2233 **673** 1000s. multicoloured . . 95 40

1995. Hummingbirds. Multicoloured.
2234 1000s. Type **674** . . . . . 1·00 40
2235 1000s. Collared incas ("Coeligena torquata") . . 1·00 40
2236 1000s. Long-tailed hermits ("Phaethornis superciliosus") . . . . . . 1·00 40
2237 1000s. Booted racquet-tails ("Ocreatus underwoodii") 1·00 40
2238 1000s. Chimbarazo hillstars ("Oreotrochilus chimborazo") . . . . . . 1·00 40
2239 1000s. Violet-tailed sylphs ("Aglaiocercus coelestis") 1·00 40

675 "World Post" (Gishella Alejandro Reyes)

676 Jaramillo

1995. Christmas. Children's Painting Competition Winners. Multicoloured.
2240 2000s. Type **675** . . . . . 2·00 80
2241 2600s. "Procession" (Juan Jaramillo Leon) . . . . . 2·50 1·00

1996. National Music Year. 60th Birth Anniv of Julio Jaramillo (singer and composer). Multicoloured.
2242 **676** 2000s. multicoloured . . 2·00 80

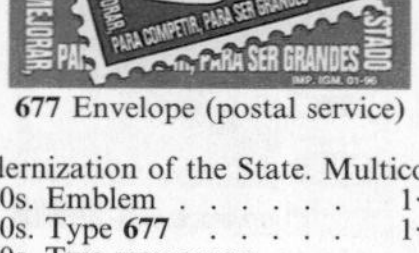

677 Envelope (postal service)

1996. Modernization of the State. Multicoloured.
2244 1000s. Emblem . . . . . . 1·10 40
2245 1500s. Type **677** . . . . . . 1·50 70
2246 2000s. Two-way arrow (customs clearance) . . . 2·10 90
2247 2600s. Telecommunications 2·50 1·00
2248 3000s. Ports . . . . 3·25 1·40

678 Table Tennis and Boxing

1996. 8th National Games, Esmeraldas. Multicoloured.
2249 400s. Type **678** 40 20
2250 400s. Basketball and football 40 20
2251 600s. Tennis and swimming 55 30
2252 800s. Weight-lifting and karate 75 35
2253 1000s. Volleyball and gymnastics 95 45
2254 1200s. Athletics and judo . . 1·10 55
2255 2000s. Chess and wrestling 2·00 90

679 Airplane and Emblem

1996. 50th Anniv of Civil Aviation Organization.
2257 **679** 2000s. multicoloured . . 2·00 90

680 Mascot

1996. Olympic Games, Atlanta. Multicoloured.
2258 1000s. Type **680** . . . . . 1·00 45
2259 2000s. Ecuador Olympic emblem . . . . 1·75 90
2260 3000s. Jefferson Perez (gold medal, 20km walk) (vert) 2·75 1·40

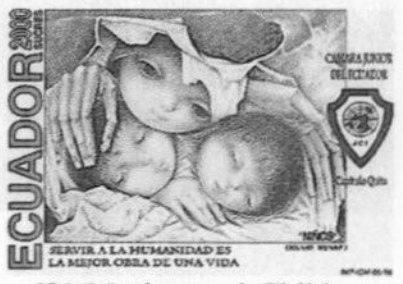

681 Mother and Children

1996. 40th Anniv of International Junior Chambers. Multicoloured.
2262 2000s. Type **681** . . . . . 1·25 1·25
2263 2600s. "Tree of Life" (relief, Eduardo Vega) (vert) . . 1·60 1·60

682 University Building (Munoz Marino)

1996. 50th Anniv of Catholic University of Ecuador. Multicoloured.
2264 400s. Type **682** 25 25
2265 800s. Window (Munoz Marino) (vert) 50 50
2266 2000s. University emblem 1·25 1·25

683 Gomez

684 Syringe and Outline Map of Ecuador

1996. Birth Centenary (1995) of Eduardo Salzar Gomez (lawyer and politician).
2267 **683** 1000s. multicoloured . . 60 60

1996. Anti-drugs Campaign.
2268 **684** 2000s. multicoloured . . 1·25 1·25

685 Emblem

1996. 25th Anniv of Private Technical University, Loja.
2269 **685** 4700s. multicoloured . . 2·75 2·75

686 Lorito (mascot)

1996. 50th Anniv of United Nations International Children's Emergency Fund.
2270 **686** 2000s. multicoloured . . 1·25 1·25

687 Headquarters

1996. 75th Anniv of *El Universo* (newspaper).
2271 **687** 2000s. multicoloured . . 1·25 1·25

688 Globe and Letters (Maria Belen Canas)

1996. Christmas. Designs showing winning entries in children's painting competition. Multicoloured.
2272 600s. Type **688** 35 35
2273 800s. Globe and dove (Beatriz Santana) 50 50
2274 2000s. Child in bed and bird (Oscar Perugachi) (54 × 34 mm) . . . . . . 1·25 1·25

689 Andean Condor *(Vultur grypus)*

1996. America (1995). Endangered Species. Multicoloured.
2275 1000s. Type **689** 65 65
2276 1500s. Harpy eagle and chick (*Harpia harpyja*) (vert) 95 95

690 Child in Traditional Dress

1996. America. National Costume. Multicoloured.
2277 2600s. Type **690** 95 95
2278 2600s. Child wearing hat . . 3·25 3·25

691 Jose Mejia Lequerica and Institute Facade

1997. Centenary of Mejia National Institute.
2279 **691** 1000s. multicoloured . . 85 55

692 Emblem

1997. 75th Anniv of Escula Politecnica del Ejercito (military school).
2280 **692** 400s. multicoloured . . . 40 25

693 College

1997. 50th Anniv of National Experimental College, Ambato.
2281 **693** 600s. multicoloured . . . 55 35

694 Rocafuerte **696** *Actinote equatoria*

695 Emblem

1997. 150th Death Anniv of Vicente Rocafuerte (President 1835–39).
2282 **694** 400s. multicoloured . . . 40 25

1997. 49th International Congress of Americanists, Quito.
2283 **695** 2000s. multicoloured . . 1·75 1·10

1997. Butterflies. Multicoloured.
2284 400s. Type **696** 40 25
2285 600s. Tiger pierid (*Dismorphia amphione*) . . 50 30
2286 800s. *Marpesia corinna* . . . 65 40
2287 2000s. *Marpesia berania* . . 1·75 1·00
2288 2600s. *Morpho helenor* . . . 2·40 1·40

697 Emblem

1997. 66th Anniv of Ecuador Flying Club.
2289 **697** 2600s. multicoloured . . 2·40 1·40

698 *Epidendrum secundum*

1997. Orchids of Mazan Forest. Multicoloured.
2290 400s. Type **698** 40 25
2291 600s. *Epidendrum sp.* 55 35
2292 800s. *Oncidium cultratrum* 70 40
2293 2000s. *Oncidium sp. mariposa* . . . . 1·75 1·10
2294 2600s. *Pleurothalis corrulensis* . . . . 2·40 1·40

699 Quartz **700** Santa Claus carrying Envelopes (Maria Daniela Delgado)

1997. International Mining Congress, Cuenca. Minerals. Multicoloured.
2295 400s. Type **699** 40 25
2296 600s. Chalcopyrite 55 35
2297 800s. Gold 70 40
2298 2000s. Petrified wood . . . 1·75 1·10
2299 2600s. Iron pyrites . . . . 2·40 1·40

1997. Christmas. "Design a Stamp" Competition Winners. Multicoloured.
2300 400s. Type **700** 40 25
2301 2600s. Star on Christmas tree holding envelopes (Dora Pinargote Tejena) 2·40 1·40
2302 3000s. Child dreaming of Christmas tree of envelopes (Christina Pazmino Montano) . . . 2·75 1·75

701 Postman with Wings on Heels **702** Matilde Hidalgo de Procel (first female politician)

1997. America. The Postman. Multicoloured.
2303 800s. Type **701** 70 45
2304 2000s. Postman on bicycle 1·75 1·10

1998. International Women's Day.
2305 **702** 2000s. multicoloured . . 1·60 95

703 Acosta Solis

1998. Misael Acosta Solis (botanist) Commemoration.
2306 **703** 2000s. multicoloured . . 2·75 1·75

704 Emblem

1998. 50th Anniv of Organization of American States.
2307 **704** 2600s. multicoloured . . 2·00 1·25

705 Emblem and Trophy

1998. World Cup Football Championship, France. Multicoloured.
2308 2000s. Type **705** . . . . . 1·60 95
2309 2600s. Mascot and trophy (vert) . . . . 2·00 1·25
2310 3000s. Players and trophy 2·40 1·50

706 Red Roses and Gypsophila **707** Cactus (*Jasminocereus thouarsii var. delicatus*)

1998. Flowers. Multicoloured.
2311 600s. Type **706** 50 30
2312 800s. *Musa sp.* 65 40
2313 2000s. Yellow roses . . . . 1·60 95
2314 2600s. Asters and astilbes 2·00 1·25

1998. Galapagos Flora. Multicoloured.
2315 600s. Type **707** 50 30
2316 1000s. *Cordia lutea lamarck* 80 50
2317 2600s. *Montondica charantica* . . . . 2·00 1·25

708 San Agustin Church, Quito

1998. Tourism. Multicoloured.
2318 600s. Type **708** 50 30
2319 800s. Independence Monument, Guayaquil . . 65 40
2320 2000s. Mitad del Mundo Monument, Quito (horiz) 1·60 1·00
2321 2600s. Mojanda Lagoon (horiz) . . . . 2·00 1·25

709 Beatriz Cueva de Ayora Institute and Ortega Espinosa (founder)

1998. Birth Centenary of Emiliano Ortega Espinosa (teacher). Multicoloured.
2322 400s. Type **709** 40 25
2323 4700s. Ortega . . . . 4·25 2·75

710 Mascot **711** Cueva Tamariz

1998. 6th South American Games, Cuenca. Mult.
2324 400s. Type **710** 40 25
2325 1000s. Games emblems and sports pictograms 80 50
2326 2600s. Mascot and sports pictograms (different) . . 2·00 1·25

1998. Birth Centenary of Carlos Cueva Tamariz (United Nations ambassador).
2327 **711** 2600s. multicoloured . . 2·00 1·25

712 Emblem **713** "Ecuadorian Woman"

1998. 75th Anniv of Guayaquil Radio Club.
2328 **712** 600s. multicoloured . . . 50 30

1998. 85th Birth Anniv of Eduardo Kigman (artist). Multicoloured.
2329 600s. Type **713** 50 30
2330 800s. "World without Answer" (horiz) 65 40

714 Father Christmas reading Letters

1998. Christmas. Multicoloured.
2331 1000s. Type **714** 70 45
2332 2600s. Children holding letter (vert) . . . . 1·75 1·10
2333 3000s. Father Christmas and letters falling from sack (vert) . . . . 2·00 1·25

715 Manuelita Saenz **716** Caves

1999. Manuelita Saenz Commemoration.
2334 **715** 1000s. multicoloured . . 70 45

1999. Los Tayos Caves. Multicoloured.
2335 1000s. Type **716** 65 40
2336 2600s. Caves (horiz) . . . . 1·75 1·10

717 Man's Face

1999. 80th Birth Anniv of Oswaldo Guayasamin (artist).
2337 **717** 2000s. multicoloured . . 1·40 85

718 Women

1999. International Campaign to Prevent Violence Against Women.
2338 **718** 4000s. multicoloured . . 2·75 1·75

719 Building Facade

1999. Centenary of Eloy Alfaro Military College. Multicoloured.
2339 5200s. Type **719** . . . . . 3·50 2·10
2340 9400s. Soldier and college building . . . . 6·00 3·75

720 *Bromelia sp.*

1999. Centenary of Del Puyo Foundation. Mult.
2341 4000s. Type **720** . . . . . 2·75 2·00
2342 4000s. Scarlet macaws . . . 2·75 2·00

721 Barahona

1999. Death Centenary of Dr. Rafael Barahona.
2343 **721** 5200s. multicoloured . . 3·50 2·10

722 De Luzarraga **723** Wright

1999. 140th Death Anniv of Gen. Manuel Antonio de Luzarraga.
2344 **722** 2000s. multicoloured . . 1·40 85

No. 2344 is inscribed for the bicentenary of the birth of Gen. Manuel de Luzarraga, who was born in 1776.

1999. Birth Bicentenary of Gen. Tomas Carlos Wright.
2345 **723** 4000s. multicoloured . . 2·75 1·75

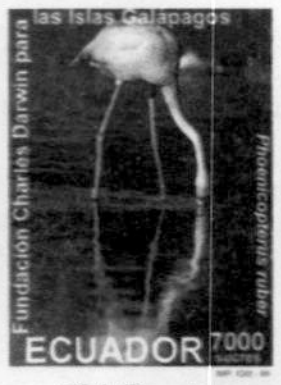

724 Greater Flamingo (*Phoenicopterus ruber*)

725 Emblem

1999. Charles Darwin Galapagos Islands Protection Foundation. Multicoloured.
2346 7000s. Type **724** . . . . . 3·00 1·90
2347 7000s. Galapagos hawk (*Buteo galapagoensis*) . . 3·00 1·90
2348 7000s. Marine iguana (*Amblyrhynchus cristatus*) 3·00 1·90
2349 7000s. Galapagos land iguana (*Conolophus subcristaus*) . . . . 3·00 1·90
2350 7000s. *Opuntia galapagela* (plant) . . . . 3·00 1·90
2351 7000s. Vermilion flycatcher (*Pyrocephalus rubinus*) . . 3·00 1·90
2352 7000s. Blue-footed booby (*Sula nebouxii*) . . . . 3·00 1·90
2353 7000s. Blue-faced booby (*Sula dactylatra*) . . . . 3·00 1·90
2354 7000s. *Scalesia villosa* (plant) 3·00 1·90
2355 7000s. Galapagos giant tortoise (*G. elephantopus abingdoni*) . . . . . . 3·00 1·90
2356 15000s. *Brachycereus nesioticus* (coral) (horiz) 6·25 4·00
2357 15000s. Yellow warbler (*Dendroica petechia*) (horiz) . . . . 6·25 4·00
2358 15000s. Flightless cormorants (*Nannopterum harrisi*) (horiz) . . . 6·25 4·00
2359 15000s. Bottle-nosed dolphin (*Tursiops truncatus*) (horiz) . . . . 6·25 4·00
2360 15000s. *Pentaceraster cumingi* (starfish) (horiz) 6·25 4·00
2361 15000s. Galapagos giant tortoise (*G. elephantopus porteri*) (horiz) . . . . 6·25 4·00
2362 15000s. Galapagos lava lizards (*Microlophus albemarlensis*) (horiz) . . 6·25 4·00
2363 15000s. Galapagos fur seal (*Arctocephalus galapagoensis*) (horiz) . . 6·25 4·00
2364 15000s. Galapagos penguins (*Spheniscus mendiculus*) (horiz) . . . . 6·25 4·00
2365 15000s. Cactus ground finch (*Geospiza scandens*) (horiz) 6·25 4·00

1999. International Year of the Older Person. Multicoloured.
2366 1000s. Type **725** 60 40
2367 1000s. Child and older person holding hands . . 60 40

726 Young Boys

1999. 50th Anniv of S.O.S. Children's Villages. Multicoloured.
2368 2000s. Type **726** 90 55
2369 2000s. Young girl 90 55

727 Postman

1999. 125th Anniv of Universal Postal Union. Multicoloured.
2370 1000s. Type **727** 35 20
2371 4000s. Dove carrying letter 1·40 80
2372 8000s. Emblem (horiz) . . . 2·75 1·75

728 World Map

1999. America. Millennium without Arms. Mult.
2373 4000s. Type **728** . . . . 2·00 1·25
2374 4000s. Tree, Globe and bird 2·00 1·25

729 Cliff Face

730 Statue

1999. 5th Anniv of South Pacific Commission.
2375 **729** 7000s. multicoloured . . 3·00 1·90

1999. "Machala, City of Tourism and the Banana". Multicoloured.
2376 3000s. Type **730** . . . . . 1·25 75
2377 3000s. Building facade . . . 1·25 75
2378 3000s. View over city (horiz) 1·25 75

731 Jorge Bolanos

732 Society Headquarters

2000. 70th Anniv of Emelec Football Club (1999). Multicoloured.
2379 1000s. Type **731** 15 10
2380 1000s. Carlos Raffo 15 10
2381 2000s. Ivan Kavedes 30 20
2382 2000s. Team photograph (national championship winners, 1957 (horiz)) . . 30 20

2000. 150th Anniv (1999) of Guayas Philanthropic Society. Multicoloured.
2383 1000s. Type **732** 15 10
2384 2000s. Juan Maria Martinez Coello (founder) 30 20
2385 4000s. Emblem 55 35

733 Statue of Liberty, New York, Equatorial Monument, Quito, Eiffel Tower, Paris and Coliseum, Rome

735 Lapenti

734 Buildings

2000. Ecuadorians living Abroad.
2386 **733** 7000s. multicoloured . . 1·00 60

2000. World Heritage Sites. Cuenca. Multicoloured.
2387 4000s. Type **734** 55 30
2388 4000s. Buildings and church tower (Puente Roto y Barranco del Rio Tomebamba) 55 30
2389 4000s. Monastery of the Conception Church . . . 55 30
2390 4000s. City view 55 30
2391 4000s. San Jose Church . . 55 30

2000. Nicolas Lapenti (tennis player).
2392 **735** 8000s. multicoloured . . 1·25 75

736 Masked Flowerpiercer (*Diglossa cyanea*)

737 Riobamba Cathedral

2000. Birds of Mazan. Multicoloured.
2393 8000s. Type **736** . . . . . 1·25 75
2394 8000s. Chimborazo hillstar (*Oreotrochilus chimborazo*) 1·25 75
2395 8000s. Masked trogon (*Trogon personatus*) . . . 1·25 75
2396 8000s. Sparkling violetear (*Colibri coruscans*) . . . . 1·25 75
2397 8000s. Rufus-naped brush finch (*Atlapetes rufinucha*) 1·25 75

2000. Bicentenary of the Rebuilding of Riobamba. Multicoloured.
2398 8000s. Type **737** . . . . . 1·25 75
2399 8000s. Pedro Vicente Maldonado (statue) . . . 1·25 75
2400 8000s. El Chimborazo mountain (horiz) . . . . 1·25 75

738 General Eloy Alfaro (founder)

739 *Guayas* (sail training ship) and Armed Forces Emblem

2000. Centenary of National Music Conservatory.
2401 **738** 10000s. multicoloured . . 1·20 75

2000. Ships. Multicoloured.
2402 68c. Type **739** 75 45
MS2403 91 × 111 mm. $1 As No. 2402 but with country name and emblem in gold. Imperf . . 1·10 70

740 Ivan Ricaurte

741 Dolores Sucre Lavayen

2000. 1st Anniv of Ivan Vallejo Ricaurte's Ascent of Everest without Oxygen.
2404 **740** 8000s. multicoloured . . 90 55

2000. 50th Anniv of Dolores Sucre Lavayen College.
2405 **741** 32c. multicoloured . . . 35 25

742 Commander Rafael Valverde and *Calderon* (battle ship)

743 Malecon 2000 and Emblem

2000. 59th Anniv of Jambeli Naval Battle. Day of the Armed Forces.
2406 **742** 16c. multicoloured . . . 20 15

2000. Opening of Malecon 2000 (waterside development), Guayaquil.
2407 **743** 84c. multicoloured . . . 95 60

744 Humpback Whale (*Megaptera novaeangliae*)

2000. Yaqu pacha (organization for the conservation of South American marine animals). Multicoloured.
2408 84c. Type **744** 95 60
MS2409 91 × 111 mm. $1 Humpback whales. Imperf . . . . 1·10 70

745 Flags encircling Map of Americas and Emblem

2000. Americas and Caribbean Dog Show.
2410 **745** 68c. multicoloured . . . 75 45

746 Club Emblem

747 Games Emblem

2000. 90th Anniv of Guayaquil Tennis Club.
2411 **746** 84c. multicoloured . . 85 55

2000. Olympic Games, Sydney. Multicoloured.
2412 32c. Type **747** 35 25
2413 68c. Jefferson Perez (race walker) (1996 gold medallist) 75 45
2414 84c. Boris Burov (weightlifter) (gold medallist) (horiz) 85 55

748 Alberto Spencer

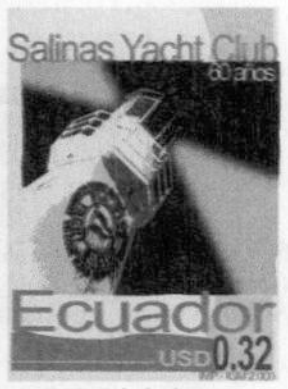

749 Lighthouse

2000. Alberto Spencer (footballer). Multicoloured.
2415 68c. Type **748** 75 45
MS2416 69 × 100 mm. $1 As No. 2415 but with design enlarged and reversed . . . . 1·10 70

2000. 60th Anniv of Salinas Yacht Club. Multicoloured.
2417 32c. Type **749** 35 25
2418 32c. Yacht with "60" on sail 35 25
2419 68c. Photo montage of yacht, water-skier and coast 75 45
MS2420 69 × 100 mm. $1 As. No. 2418 but with design enlarged 1·10 70

750 Felipe Herrera (1st President) and Salsipuedes Bridge

751 Dancer wearing Black Makeup and carrying Doll

2000. 40th Anniv of Inter-American Development Bank. Multicoloured.
2421 68c. Type **750** 75 45
2422 68c. Antonio Ortiz Mena Duale-Peripa dam 75 45
2423 84c. Enrique Inglesias and Ucubamba water treatment works 95 60
2424 84c. Bank emblem and Quito History Musuem 95 60
MS2425 151 × 91 mm. 25c. × 4, As Nos. 2422/4 but with designs enlarged . . . . 1·10 70

2000. La Mama Negra Festival, Latacunga. Multicoloured.
2426 32c. Type **751** 35 25
2427 32c. Bearded man (Rey Moro (moorish king)) . . 35 25
MS2428 100 × 68 mm. $1 Dancer wearing black makeup and doll (different). Imperf . . . . . . 1·10 70

EXPRESS LETTER STAMPS

1928. Oblong Tobacco Tax stamp surch **"CORREOS EXPRESO"** and new value.
E457 2c. on 2c. blue . . . . . . 3·00 3·50
E458 5c. on 2c. blue . . . . . . 2·75 3·50

E459 10c. on 2c. blue . . . . . 2·75 2·25
E460 20c. on 2c. blue . . . . . 3·75 3·50
E461 50c. on 2c. blue . . . . . 4·50 3·50

1945. Surch **EXPRESO 20 Ctvs.**
E742 **194** 20c. on 5c. green 15 10

LATE FEE STAMP

1945. Surch **U. H. 10 Ctvs.**
L742 **194** 10c. on 5c. green 10 10

OFFICIAL STAMPS

1886. Stamps of 1881 optd **OFICIAL**.
O20 **5** 1c. brown 60 60
O21 2c. red 75 75
O22 5c. blue . . . . 1·50 1·90
O23 10c. orange . . . . . . 1·10 70
O24 20c. violet . . . . 1·10 1·10
O25 50c. green . . . . 3·25 2·75

1887. Stamps of 1887 optd **OFICIAL**.
O30 **13** 1c. green 75 10
O31 2c. red 75 10
O32 5c. blue . . . . 1·10 50
O33 80c. green . . . . 3·75 2·25

1892. Stamps of 1892 optd **FRANQUEO OFICIAL**.
O42 **15** 1c. blue 10 15
O43 2c. blue 10 15
O44 5c. blue 10 15
O45 10c. blue 10 10
O46 20c. blue 10 10
O47 50c. blue 10 25
O48 1s. blue 20 25

1894. Stamps of 1894 (dated "1894") optd **FRANQUEO OFICIAL**.
O65 **20** 1c. grey 25 25
O66 2c. grey 25 25
O67 5c. grey 25 25
O68 10c. grey 10 20
O69 20c. grey 30 35
O70 50c. grey 75 75
O71 1s. grey . . . . 1·10 1·10
This series was re-issued in 1897 optd "1897–1898".

1895. Postal Fiscals as Type F **1** but dated "1891–1892", optd **OFICIAL 1894 y 1895**.
O72 F **1** 1c. grey . . . . 6·25 4·00
O73 2c. red . . . . 6·25 4·00

1895. Stamps of 1895 (dated "1895") optd **FRANQUEO OFICIAL**.
O82 **20** 1c. grey . . . . 1·10 1·10
O83 2c. grey . . . . 1·60 1·60
O84 5c. grey 25 25
O85 10c. grey . . . . 1·60 1·60
O86 20c. grey . . . . 2·75 2·75
O87 50c. grey . . . . 6·75 6·75
O88 1s. grey 75 75
This series was re-issued in 1897 optd "1897–1898".

1896. Stamps of 1896 optd **FRANQUEO OFICIAL** in oval.
O 97 **22** 1c. bistre 20 15
O 98 2c. bistre 20 15
O 99 5c. bistre 25 15
O100 10c. bistre 25 15
O101 20c. bistre 25 15
O102 50c. bistre 25 15
O103 1s. bistre 50 35
O104 5s. bistre 85 80

F 10

O **245** Government Building, Quito

1898. Fiscal stamps as Type F **10**, surch **CORREOS OFICIAL** and value in frame.
O181 F **10** 5c. on 50c. purple . . 15 15
O184 10c. on 20s. orange . . 40 40
O185 20c. on 50c. purple . . 1·25 1·25
O187 20c. on 50s. green . . 1·25 1·25

1899. Stamps as 1899 optd **OFICIAL**.
O201 2c. black and orange . . . 25 55
O202 10c. black and orange . . . 25 55
O203 20c. black and orange . . . 25 85
O204 50c. black and orange . . . 25 1·10

1913. Stamps of 1911 (except No. O396) optd **OFICIAL**.
O374 **90** 1c. black and red 50 50
O387 1c. orange 10 15
O388 **91** 2c. black and blue . . . 55 55
O424 2c. green 15 15
O368 **92** 3c. black and orange . . 25 25
O390 3c. black 20 15
O437 **98** 4c. black and red . . . 15 15
O369 **93** 5c. black and red . . . 70 50
O393 5c. violet 25 10
O370 **94** 10c. black and blue . . . 70 55
O395 10c. blue 10 10
O396 – 20c. blk & grn (No. 328) 1·50 60
O429 **95** 1s. black and green . . . 1·90 1·90

1920. Stamps of 1920 (Nos. 381/400) optd **OFICIAL**.
O401 **108** 1c. green 40 40
O402 – 2c. red 30 30
O403 – 3c. bistre 30 30
O404 – 4c. green 10 10
O405 – 5c. blue 10 10
O406 – 6c. orange 40 40
O407 – 7c. brown 60 60
O408 – 8c. green 75 75
O409 – 9c. red 95 95
O410 **109** 10c. blue 60 60
O411 – 15c. black . . . . . . 3·00 3·00
O412 – 20c. purple . . . . . . 3·75 3·75
O413 – 30c. violet . . . . . . 4·50 4·50
O414 – 40c. sepia . . . . . . 6·25 6·25
O415 – 50c. green . . . . . . 3·75 3·75
O416 – 60c. blue . . . . . . 4·50 4·50
O417 – 70c. grey . . . . . . 4·50 4·50
O418 – 80c. yellow . . . . . . 5·75 5·75
O419 – 90c. green . . . . . . 6·25 6·25
O420 – 1s. blue . . . . 12·50 12·50

1924. Fiscal stamps of 1919 optd **OFICIAL**.
O421 **103** 1c. blue 60 60
O422 2c. green . . . . 3·25 3·25

1924. No. O204 optd **Acuerdo No 4.228**.
O430 50c. black and orange . . . 70 70

1925. Stamps of 1925 optd **OFICIAL**.
O457 **90** 1c. blue 30 30
O439 **93** 5c. red 15 15
O440 **94** 10c. green 10 10

1928. Stamp of 1927 optd **OFICIAL**.
O463 **123** 20c. purple . . . . . . 1·10 75

1929. Official Air stamps. Air stamps of 1929 optd **OFICIAL**.
O466 **130** 2c. black 40 40
O467 5c. red 40 40
O468 10c. brown 40 40
O469 20c. purple 40 40
O470 50c. green 95 95
O474 50c. brown 75 85
O471 1s. blue 95 95
O475 1s. red . . . . 1·10 1·10
O472 5s. yellow . . . . . . 5·00 4·25
O476 5s. olive . . . . 2·25 2·25
O473 10s. red . . . . 55·00 42·00
O477 10s. black . . . . . . 5·75 5·75

1936. Stamps of 1936 (Nos. 520/4) optd **OFICIAL**.
O525 5c. olive 15 10
O526 10c. brown 15 10
O527 20c. purple . . . . 2·50 30
O528 1s. red 25 20
O529 2s. blue 40 60

1937. Stamps of 1937 optd **OFICIAL**.
O562 **171** 2c. green (postage) . . . 10 10
O563 – 5c. red 10 10
O564 – 10c. blue 10 10
O565 – 20c. red 10 10
O566 – 1s. olive 10 10
O567 **172** 10c. brown (air) 25 25
O568 20c. olive 25 25
O569 70c. brown 35 25
O570 1s. slate 40 25
O571 2s. violet . . . . . . 1·40 40

1941. Air stamp of 1939 optd **OFICIAL**.
O638 **184** 5s. green 60 60

1946. Oblong Tobacco Tax stamp optd **CORRESPONDENCIA OFICIAL**. Roul.
O803 1c. red . . . . 12·00 3·50

1947.
O804 O **245** 30c. blue 20 10
O805 30c. brown 20 10
O806 30c. violet 20 10

1964. Air. Nos. 1269/71 optd **Oficial**.
O1272 **342** 50c. multicoloured . . 70 70
O1273 – 80c. red, blue & yellow 70 70
O1274 – 1s.30 multicoloured . . 70 70

1964. No. 1272 optd **oficial** on each stamp.
O1275 **344** 80c. green and lake . . 1·50 30
The "OEA" overprint is across four stamps; the "oficial" overprint is on each stamp. The unused price is for a block of four.

POSTAGE DUE STAMPS

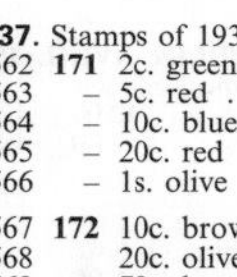
D 32

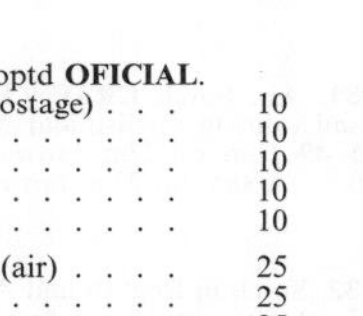
D 131

1896.
D105 D **32** 1c. green . . . . . . 1·50 1·50
D106 2c. green . . . . . . 1·50 1·50
D107 5c. green . . . . . . 1·50 1·50
D108 10c. green . . . . . . 1·90 2·25
D109 20c. green . . . . . . 1·90 3·00
D110 50c. green . . . . . . 1·50 3·75
D111 100c. green . . . . . 1·50 3·00

1929.
D466 D **131** 5c. blue 10 10
D467 10c. yellow 10 10
D468 20c. red 20 15

D 335

1958.
D1128 D **335** 10c. violet 10 10
D1129 50c. green 10 10
D1130 1s. brown 15 10
D1131 2s. red 25 15

APPENDIX

The following stamps have either been issued in excess of postal needs or have not been available to the public in reasonable quantities at face value. Such stamps may later be given full listing if there is evidence of regular postal use.

1966.

Cent of I.T.U. Postage 10, 10, 80c.; Air 1s.50, 3, 4s.

Space Achievements. Postage 10c., 1s.; Air 1s.30, 2s., 2s.50, 3s.50.

Dante and Galileo. Postage 10, 80c.; Air 2, 3s.

Pope Paul VI. Postage 10c.; Air 1s.30, 3s.50.

Famous Persons. Postage 10c., 1s.; Air 1s.50, 2s.50, 4s.

Olympic Games. Postage 10, 10, 80c.; Air 1s.30, 3s., 3s.50.

Winter Olympics. Postage 10c., 1s.; Air 1s.50, 2s., 2s.50, 4s.

Franco-American Space Research. Postage 10c.; Air 1s.50, 4s.

Italian Space Research. Postage 10c.; Air 1s.30, 3s.50.

Exploration of the Moon's Surface. Postage 10, 80c., 1s.; Air 2s., 2s.50, 3s.

1967.

Olympic Games, Mexico. Postage 10c., 1s.; Air 1s.30, 2s., 2s.50, 3s.50.

Olympic Games, Mexico. Postage 10, 10, 80c.; Air 1s.50, 3, 4s.

Eucharistic Conference. Postage 10, 60, 80c., 1s.; Air 1s.50, 2s.

Paintings of the Madonna. Postage 10, 40, 50c.; Air 1s.30, 2s.50, 3s.

Famous Paintings. Postage 10c., 1s.; Air 1s.50, 2s., 2s.50, 4s.

50th Birth Anniv of J. F. Kennedy. Postage 10, 10, 80c.; Air 1s.30, 3s., 3s.50.

Christmas Postage 10, 10, 40, 50, 60c.; Air 2s.50.

1968.

Religious Paintings and Sculptures. Postage 10, 80c., 1s.; Air 1s.30, 1s.50, 2s.

COTAL Tourist Organization Congress. Postage 20, 30, 40, 50, 60, 80c., 1s.; Air 1s.30, 1s.50, 2s.

1969.

Visit of Pope Paul VI to Latin America. Postage 40, 40c.; Air 1s.30.

39th Int Eucharistic Congress, Bogota. Postage 1s.; Air 2s.

Paintings of the Virgin Mary. Postage 40, 60c., 1s.; Air 1s.30, 2s.

EGYPT Pt. 1, Pt. 19

Formerly a kingdom of N.E. Africa. Turkish till 1914, when it became a British Protectorate. Independent from 1922. A republic from 1953.

In 1958 the United Arab Republic was formed, comprising Egypt and Syria, but separate stamps continued to be issued for each territory as they have different currencies. In 1961 Syria became an independent Arab republic and left the U.A.R. but the title was retained by Egypt until a new federation was formed with Libya and Syria in 1971, when the country's name was changed to Arab Republic of Egypt.

1866. 40 paras = 1 piastre.
1888. 1000 milliemes = 1 piastre.
100 piastres = £1 Egyptian.

1

4

1866. Designs as T **1**. Imperf or perf.
1 **1** 5pa. grey . . . . 42·00 27·00
2 10pa. brown . . . . 55·00 29·00
3 20pa. blue . . . . 70·00 30·00
4 1pi. purple . . . . 60·00 4·75
5 2pi. yellow . . . . 90·00 42·00
6 5pi. pink £250 £170
7 10pi. grey £275 £250

1867.
11 **4** 5pa. yellow . . . . 27·00 8·00
12b 10pa. violet . . . . 55·00 9·00
13 20pa. green . . . . £100 13·00
14 1pi. red . . . . 14·00 1·00
15 2pi. blue . . . . £110 16·00
16 5pi. brown £300 £180
On the piastre values the letters "P" and "E" appear on the upper corners.

7

10

1872.
28 **7** 5pa. brown . . . . 7·00 4·50
29 10pa. mauve . . . . 6·00 3·00
37d 20pa. blue . . . . 9·00 2·50
38 1pi. red . . . . 7·50 65
39c 2pi. yellow . . . . 5·50 6·00
40 2½pi. violet . . . . 8·50 5·00
41 5pi. green . . . . 55·00 19·00

1875. As T **7**, but "PARA" inscr at left-hand side and figure "5"s inverted.
35 – 5pa. brown . . . . 8·50 3·75

1879. Surch in English and Arabic.
42 **7** 5pa on 2½pi. violet . . . . . 6·00 6·00
43 10pa. on 2½pi. violet . . . . 11·00 10·00

1879. Various frames.
44 **10** 5pa. brown . . . . 2·00 30
45 10pa. lilac . . . . 50·00 3·00
50 10pa. purple . . . . . . 50·00 7·00
51 10pa. grey . . . . 9·00 1·75
52 10pa. green . . . . 1·75 90
46 20pa. blue . . . . 60·00 1·75
53a 20pa. red . . . . 14·00 50
47 1pi. pink . . . . 26·00 20
54b 1pi. blue . . . . 4·50 20
55b 2pi. brown . . . . 12·00 10
55ba 2pi. orange . . . . 22·00 1·00
49a 5pi. green . . . . 55·00 10·00
56a 5pi. grey . . . . 11·00 50

1884. Surch **20 PARAS** in English and Arabic.
57 **10** 20pa. on 5pi. green . . . . 7·00 1·25

18

1888. Various frames.
58 **18** 1m. brown . . . . 2·00 10
59 2m. green . . . . 1·25 10
60 3m. purple . . . . 3·00 1·00
61c 3m. yellow . . . . 2·25 10
62 4m. red . . . . 3·00 10
63 5m. red . . . . 3·25 10
64 10pi. mauve . . . . 15·00 80

29 Nile Feluccas

35 Archway of Ptolemy III, Karnak

41 Statue of Rameses II

42 Statue of Rameses II (different inscription)

1914.
73 **29** 1m. brown . . . . 1·00 40
74 – 2m. green . . . . 2·00 20
86 – 2m. red . . . . 3·50 65
75 – 3m. orange . . . . . . 1·50 35
76 – 4m. red . . . . 2·75 65
88 – 4m. green . . . . 5·00 6·00
77 – 5m. red . . . . 3·00 10
90 – 5m. pink . . . . 4·00 10
91 – 10m. blue . . . . 4·00 20
92 – 10m. red . . . . 1·75 30
93 **41** 15m. blue . . . . 4·00 15
94 **42** 15m. blue . . . . 22·00 3·00
79 **35** 20m. green . . . . 6·50 30
96 – 50m. purple . . . . . . 10·00 1·25
81 – 100m. grey . . . . 13·00 60
82 – 200m. purple . . . . . . 26·00 3·50

DESIGNS—AS Type **29**: 2m. Cleopatra; 3m. Ras-el-Tin Palace, Alexandria; 4m. Pyramids, Giza; 5m. Sphinx; 10m. Colossi of Amenophis III at Thebes. As Type **35**: 50m. Citadel, Cairo; 100m. Rock Temple, Abu Simbel; 200m. Aswan Dam.

1915. Surch **2 Milliemes** in English and Arabic.

83	**29**	2m. on 3m. orge (No. 75)	55	2·00

(**43** "The Kingdom of Egypt, 15 March, 1922")

44 King Fuad I

1922. Stamps of 1914 optd with T **43**.

98	**29**	1m. brown	75	60
99	–	2m. red	65	35
100	–	3m. orange	50	60
101	–	4m. green	25	55
102	–	5m. pink	1·50	10
103	–	10m. red	1·50	10
104	**41**	15m. blue	3·00	60
105	**42**	15m. blue	2·50	60
106	**35**	20m. green	3·25	40
107	–	50m. purple	4·00	60
108	–	100m. grey	14·50	75
110	–	200m. purple	13·50	90

1923.

111	**44**	1m. orange	15	10
112		2m. black	60	10
113		3m. brown	55	40
114		4m. green	35	15
115		5m. brown	25	10
116		10m. pink	1·10	10
117		15m. blue	1·60	10
118		20m. green	3·25	10
119		50m. green	5·75	10
120		100m. purple	13·50	40
121		200m. mauve	25·00	1·10
122	–	£E1 violet and blue	£150	15·00

The 20m. to £E1 values are larger ($22\frac{1}{2} \times 28$ mm). The £E1 shows the King in military uniform.

46 Thoth writing name of King Fuad

1925. Int Geographical Congress, Cairo.

123	**46**	5m. brown	3·75	3·75
124		10m. red	7·00	7·75
125		15m. blue	7·50	8·75

47 Ploughing with Oxen

1926. 12th Agricultural Exhibition, Cairo.

126	**47**	5m. brown	1·25	1·25
127		10m. red	1·00	1·25
128		15m. blue	85	1·75
129		50m. green	8·00	5·50
130		100m. purple	9·50	12·50
131		200m. violet	20·00	24·00

49 De Havilland D.H.34 Biplane over Nile

1926. Air.

132	**49**	27m. violet	11·50	14·50
133		27m. brown	3·75	1·25

50 King Fuad

1926. King's 58th Birthday.

134	**50**	50p. purple	75·00	16·00

1926. Surch.

135	**47**	5m. on 50m. green	1·90	2·25
136		10m. on 100m. purple	1·10	1·90
137		15m. on 200m. violet	1·50	2·25

52 Ancient Egyptian Ship, Temple of Deir-el-Bahari

1926. International Navigation Congress.

138	**52**	5m. black and brown	1·50	1·25
139		10m. black and red	1·75	2·00
140		15m. black and blue	1·75	2·00

1926. Inauguration of Port Fuad. Optd **PORT FOUAD**.

141	**52**	5m. black and brown	£180	£120
142		10m. black and red	£180	£120
143		15m. black and blue	£180	£120
144	**50**	50p. purple	£1000	£750

55

1927. Int Cotton Congress, Cairo.

145	**55**	5m. green and brown	80	80
146		10m. green and red	1·50	2·25
147		15m. green and blue	1·50	1·75

56

57

58

1927.

148	**56**	1m. orange	10	10
149		2m. black	10	10
150		3m. brown	10	45
151		3m. green	35	10
153		4m. green	70	60
154		4m. brown	65	50
156		5m. brown	25	10
157		10m. red	75	10
158		10m. violet	2·00	10
159		13m. red	75	15
160a		15m. blue	85	10
161		15m. purple	2·50	10
162		20m. blue	4·25	10
163a	**57**	20m. olive	1·75	10
164		20m. blue	5·25	10
165		40m. brown	2·25	10
166a		50m. blue	1·75	10
167a		100m. purple	7·00	25
168a		200m. mauve	6·50	70
171	**58**	500m. blue and brown	45·00	5·00
172	–	£E1 brown and green	50·00	5·00

DESIGN—VERT: As Type **58**: £E1, King Fuad I.

See also Nos. 233/9.

60 Amenhotep

61 Imhotep

1927. Statistical Congress, Cairo.

173	**60**	5m. brown	55	1·10
174		10m. red	65	1·25
175		15m. blue	65	1·10

1928. Medical Congress, Cairo.

176	**61**	5m. brown	45	55
177	–	10m. red	50	55

DESIGN: 10m. Mohammed Ali Pasha.

63 King Farouk when Crown Prince

64 Ancient Agriculture

1929. Prince's 9th Birthday.

178	**63**	5m. grey and purple	1·25	1·40
179		10m. grey and red	90	1·40
180		15m. grey and blue	90	1·75
181		20m. grey and turquoise	90	1·75

1931. Agricultural and Industrial Exhibition, Cairo.

182	**64**	5m. brown	55	60
183		10m. red	60	1·10
184		15m. blue	80	1·10

1931. Air. Surch **GRAF ZEPPELIN AVRIL 1931** and value in English and Arabic.

185	**49**	50m. on 27m. brown	42·00	42·00
186		100m. on 27m. brown	42·00	48·00

1932. Surch in English and Arabic.

187	**50**	50m. on 50p. purple	5·00	90
188	–	100m. on £E1 violet and blue (No. 122)	£140	£150

67 Locomotive No. 1, 1852

1933. International Railway Congress, Cairo.

189	**67**	5m. black and brown	5·50	5·50
190	–	13m. black and red	10·00	10·00
191	–	15m. black and violet	10·00	12·00
192	–	20m. black and blue	10·00	10·00

DESIGNS: 13m. Locomotive No. 41, 1859; 15m. Locomotive No. 68, 1862; 20m. Locomotive No. 787, 1932.

68 Handley Page H.P.42 over Pyramids

1933. Air.

193	**68**	1m. black and orange	15	50
194		2m. black and grey	65	1·40
195		2m. black and orange	2·25	2·50
196		3m. black and brown	70	35
197		4m. black and green	95	1·00
198		5m. black and brown	1·00	10
199		6m. black and green	1·25	1·40
200		7m. black and blue	1·25	1·00
201		8m. black and violet	70	25
202		9m. black and red	1·40	1·40
203		10m. brown and violet	45	80
204		20m. brown and green	60	20
205		30m. brown and blue	1·75	20
206		40m. brown and red	11·00	60
207		50m. brown and orange	11·00	15
208		60m. brown and grey	6·00	1·10
209		70m. green and blue	2·50	1·00
210		80m. green and sepia	2·50	1·10
211		90m. green and orange	3·50	1·10
212		100m. green and violet	7·50	65
213		200m. green and red	9·50	1·25

See also Nos. 285/8.

69 Armstrong-Whitworth Atalanta of Imperial Airways

1933. Int Aviation Congress. Inscr as in T **69**.

214	**69**	5m. brown	3·50	2·50
215		10m. violet	13·00	9·25
216	–	13m. red	12·50	16·00
217	–	15m. purple	10·00	14·00
218	–	20m. blue	13·00	17·00

DESIGNS: 13, 15m. Dornier Do-X flying boat; 20m. Airship "Graf Zeppelin".

72 Khedive Ismail Pasha

73

1934. 10th U.P.U. Congress, Cairo.

219	**72**	1m. orange	30	65
220		2m. black	30	65
221		3m. brown	35	70
222		4m. green	65	20
223		5m. brown	75	15
224		10m. violet	1·40	15
225		13m. red	2·25	1·25
226		15m. purple	2·25	1·00
227		20m. blue	1·60	20
228		50m. blue	5·00	35
229		100m. green	11·00	75
230		200m. violet	42·00	4·00
231	**73**	50p. brown	£150	60·00
232		£E1 blue	£225	£100

1936. As T **56** but inscribed "POSTES".

233	**56**	1m. orange	10	50
234		2m. black	60	10
235		4m. green	80	10
236		5m. brown	40	30
237		10m. violet	1·25	20
238		15m. purple	2·00	15
239		20m. blue	2·00	15

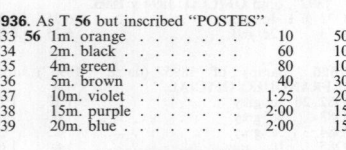

75 Exhibition Entrance

1936. 15th Agricultural and Industrial Exn, Cairo.

240	**75**	5m. brown	1·10	1·00
241	–	10m. violet	1·25	1·40
242	–	13m. red	1·00	2·25
243	–	15m. purple	75	1·00
244	–	20m. blue	2·00	2·50

DESIGN—HORIZ: 10m., 13m. Palace of Agriculture; 15m., 20m. Palace of Industry.

77 Nahas Pasha and Treaty Delegates

1936. Anglo-Egyptian Treaty.

245	**77**	5m. brown	40	85
246		15m. purple	25	95
247		20m. blue	65	1·10

78 King Farouk

79 Medal commemorating Abolition of Capitulations

1937. Investiture of King Farouk.

248	**78**	1m. orange	10	10
249		2m. red	10	10
250		3m. brown	10	10

No.	Type	Description	Mint	Used
251		4m. green	10	10
252		5m. brown	10	10
253		6m. green	55	20
254		10m. violet	20	10
255		13m. red	20	20
256		15m. purple	20	10
257		20m. blue	30	10
258		20m. violet	55	15

1937. Abolition of Capitulations at the Montreux Conference.

No.	Type	Description	Mint	Used
259	**79**	5m. brown	25	20
260		15m. purple	35	80
261		20m. blue	65	1·25

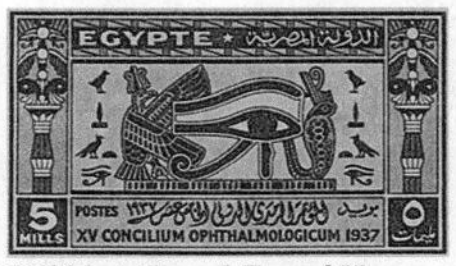

80 Nekhbet, Sacred Eye of Horus and Buto

1937. 15th Ophthalmological Congress, Cairo.

No.	Type	Description	Mint	Used
262	**80**	5m. brown	25	70
263		15m. purple	30	1·10
264		20m. blue	30	1·10

81 King Farouk and Queen Farida

1938. Royal Wedding.

No.	Type	Description	Mint	Used
265	**81**	5m. brown	1·75	3·75

82 Gathering Cotton

83 Pyramids of Giza and Colossus of Thebes

1938. 18th International Cotton Congress, Cairo.

No.	Type	Description	Mint	Used
266	**82**	5m. brown	20	90
267		15m. purple	40	1·50
268		20m. blue	35	1·40

1938. Int Telecommunications Conf, Cairo.

No.	Type	Description	Mint	Used
269	**83**	5m. brown	55	1·40
270		15m. purple	90	2·00
271		20m. blue	95	2·00

1938. King Farouk's 18th Birthday. Portrait similar to T **81** with inscr "11 FEVRIER 1938" at foot.

No.	Type	Description	Mint	Used
272	–	£E1 brown and green	£100	£120

84 Hydnocarpus

1938. Leprosy Research Congress.

No.	Type	Description	Mint	Used
273	**84**	5m. brown	75	80
274		15m. purple	75	80
275		20m. blue	75	80

85 King Farouk and Pyramids

86 King Farouk

87

1939.

No.	Type	Description	Mint	Used
276a	**85**	30m. grey	20	10
277		30m. green	20	10
278	–	40m. brown	25	10
279	–	50m. blue	85	10
280	–	100m. purple	1·25	10
281	–	200m. violet	4·50	15
282	**86**	50p. brown and green	5·00	65
283	**87**	£E1 brown and blue	11·50	1·50

DESIGNS (As Type **85**): 40m. Mosque; 50m. Cairo Citadel; 100m. Aswan Dam; 200m. Fuad I University, Giza.

For similar issue with portrait looking to left, see 1947 issue.

88 Princess Ferial (18 months old)

90 King Fuad I

1940. Child Welfare.

No.	Type	Description	Mint	Used
284	**88**	5m.+5m. red	35	30

1941. Air.

No.	Type	Description	Mint	Used
285	**68**	5m. red	25	20
286		10m. violet	45	50
287a		25m. purple	35	20
288		30m. green	50	15

1943. 5th Birthday of Princess Ferial. Optd **1943** in English and Arabic.

No.	Type	Description	Mint	Used
289	**88**	5m.+5m. red	3·25	9·00

1944. 8th Death Anniv of King Fuad.

No.	Type	Description	Mint	Used
290	**90**	10m. purple	50	10

91 King Farouk

92 King Farouk

1944.

No.	Type	Description	Mint	Used
291	**91**	1m. brown	10	10
292		2m. red	10	10
293		3m. brown	25	35
294		4m. green	20	10
295		5m. brown	20	10
296		10m. violet	45	10
297		13m. red	8·00	3·00
298		15m. purple	85	10
299		17m. olive	75	10
300		20m. violet	85	10
301		22m. blue	85	10

1945. 25th Birthday of King Farouk.

No.	Type	Description	Mint	Used
302	**92**	10m. violet	15	10

93 Khedive Ismail Pasha

94 Flags of the Arab Union

1945. 50th Death Anniv of Ismail Pasha.

No.	Type	Description	Mint	Used
303	**93**	10m. green	15	10

1945. Arab Union.

No.	Type	Description	Mint	Used
304	**94**	10m. violet	10	10
305		22m. green	15	15

95 Flags of Egypt and Saudi Arabia

1946. Visit of King of Saudi Arabia.

No.	Type	Description	Mint	Used
306	**95**	10m. green	15	10

96 Reproduction of First Egyptian Stamp

1946. 80th Anniv of First Egyptian Postage Stamp.

No.	Type	Description	Mint	Used
307	**96**	1m.+1m. grey	10	10
308	–	10m.+10m. purple	15	10
309	–	17m.+17m. brown	15	15
310	–	22m.+22m. green	20	15

DESIGNS: 10m. Khedive Ismail Pasha; 17m. King Fuad; 22m. King Farouk.

98 King Farouk, Egyptian Flag and Citadel

1946. Evacuation of Cairo Citadel.

No.	Type	Description	Mint	Used
313	**98**	10m. brown and green	20	15

1946. Air. Cairo Aviation Congress. Optd **Le Caire 1946** and Arabic characters.

No.	Type	Description	Mint	Used
314	**68**	30m. green (No. 288)	20	15

100 King Farouk and Inshas Palace

1946. Arab League Congress. Portraits.

No.	Type	Description	Mint	Used
315	**100**	1m. green	35	10
316	–	2m. brown	35	10
317	–	3m. blue	35	10
318	–	4m. brown	35	15
319	–	5m. red	35	10
320	–	10m. grey	40	15
321	–	15m. violet	50	20

DESIGNS: 2m. Prince Abdullah of Yemen; 3m. President of Lebanon, Beshara al-Khoury; 4m. King Ibn Saud of Saudi Arabia; 5m. King Faisal II of Iraq; 10m. King Abdullah of Jordan; 15m. Pres of Syria, Shukri Bey al-Quwatli.

101 King Farouk, Delta Barrage and Douglas Dakota Transport

102 Triad of Mycerinus

1947. Air.

No.	Type	Description	Mint	Used
322	**101**	2m. red	10	40
323		3m. brown	10	45
324		5m. red	10	10
325		7m. orange	25	15
326		8m. green	25	40
327		10m. violet	25	10
328		20m. blue	35	15
329		30m. purple	45	15
330		40m. red	65	20
331		50m. blue	85	25
332		100m. olive	1·50	35
333		200m. grey	2·75	1·50

1947. International Exhibition of Fine Arts. Inscr "EXPOSITION INTERNATIONALE D'ART CONTEMPORIAN".

No.	Type	Description	Mint	Used
334	**102**	5m.+5m. grey	20	65
335	–	15m.+15m. blue	30	1·10
336	–	30m.+30m. red	45	1·40
337	–	50m.+50m. brown	55	1·60

DESIGNS—HORIZ: 15m. Temple of Rameses. VERT: 30m. Queen Nefertiti; 50m. Tutankhamun.

104 Egyptian Parliament Buildings

105 King Farouk hoisting Flag

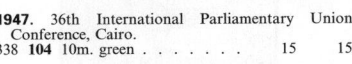

1947. 36th International Parliamentary Union Conference, Cairo.

No.	Type	Description	Mint	Used
338	**104**	10m. green	15	15

1947. Withdrawal of British Troops from Nile Delta.

No.	Type	Description	Mint	Used
339	**105**	10m. purple and green	15	15

106 King Farouk and Sultan Hussein Mosque, Cairo

107 King Farouk

1947. Designs as 1939 issue but with portrait altered as T **106** and **107**.

No.	Type	Description	Mint	Used
340	–	30m. olive	35	10
341	**106**	40m. brown	25	10
342	–	50m. blue	35	10
343	–	100m. purple	2·75	60
344	–	200m. violet	7·75	1·00
345	**107**	50p. brown and green	21·00	9·25
346	–	£El brown and blue	23·00	2·25

DESIGNS—AS Type **106**: 30m. Pyramids; 50m. Cairo Citadel; 100m. Aswan Dam; 200m. Fuad I University, Cairo. As T **107**: £El, King Farouk (different).

109 Cotton Plant

110 Egyptian Soldiers Entering Palestine

1948. International Cotton Congress.

No.	Type	Description	Mint	Used
347	**109**	10m. green	15	60

1948. Arrival of Egyptian Troops in Gaza.

No.	Type	Description	Mint	Used
348	**110**	10m. green	45	95

1948. Air. Air Mail Service to Athens and Rome. Surch **S.A.I.D.E. 23-8-1948** and value in English and Arabic.

No.	Type	Description	Mint	Used
349	**101**	13m. on 100m. olive	35	1·50
350		22m. on 200m. grey	65	2·00

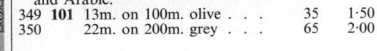

112 Ibrahim Pasha and Battle of Navarino, 1827

1948. Death Centenary of Ibrahim Pasha (statesman and General).

No.	Type	Description	Mint	Used
351	**112**	10m. green and red	30	25

113 Reclining Male Figure symbolising River Nile

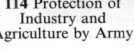

114 Protection of Industry and Agriculture by Army

115 Mohammed Ali and Map

1949. 16th Agricultural and Industrial Exn, Cairo.

No.	Type	Description	Mint	Used
352	**113**	1m. green	10	60
353		10m. violet	15	60
354		17m. red	15	1·00

355 22m. blue 15 25
356 **114** 30m. sepia 20 40

1949. Death Centenary of Mohammed Ali (statesman and General).
358 **115** 10m. green and brown . . 15 55

116 Globe

1949. 75th Anniv of U.P.U.
359 **116** 10m. red 65 40
360 22m. violet 75 80
361 30m. blue 85 90

117 Scales of Justice

1949. Abolition of Mixed Courts.
362 **117** 10m. green & dp green . . 15 15

118 Camels by Water-hole

1950. Inaug of Fuad I Desert Institute.
363 **118** 10m. brown and violet . . 65 1·10

119 King Fuad University

1950. 25th Anniv of Fuad I University.
364 **119** 22m. purple and green . . 65 1·25

120 Khedive Ismail and Globe — 121 Girl and Cotton

1950. 75th Anniv of Royal Egyptian Geographical Society.
365 **120** 30m. green and purple . . 70 2·00

1951. International Cotton Congress, Cairo.
366 **121** 10m. green 25 80

122 King Farouk and Queen Narriman

1951. Royal Wedding.
367 **122** 10m. brown and green . . 1·25 2·25

123 Triumphal Arch

1951. 1st Mediterranean Games, Alexandria.
369 **123** 10m. brown . . . . . . 85 1·25
370 – 22m. green . . . . 85 1·75
371 – 30m. blue and green . . . 85 2·00

DESIGNS—VERT: 22m. Badge of Alexandria and map of Mediterranean. HORIZ: 30m. King Farouk and waves.

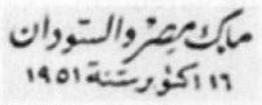

(**124** "King of Egypt and the Sudan 16th October 1951")

1952. Optd as T **124** (different sizes).
373 **91** 1m. brown (postage) . . . 60 70
374 2m. red 20 20
375 **78** 3m. brown . . . . 20 1·25
376 **91** 4m. green 20 20
377 **78** 6m. green . . . . 90 1·25
378 **91** 10m. violet 30 10
379 13m. red . . . . 1·00 1·25
380 15m. purple . . . . 1·75 1·25
381 17m. green . . . . 1·25 20
382 20m. violet . . . . 1·00 20
383 22m. blue . . . . 2·00 2·25
384 – 30m. green (No. 340) . . 1·50 70
386 **106** 40m. brown 50 15
387 – 50m. blue (No. 342) . . . 1·10 20
388 – 100m. purple (No. 343) . . 2·00 35
389 – 200m. violet (No. 344) . . 9·75 1·60
390 **107** 50p. brown and green . . 10·00 5·50
391 – £El brn & bl (No. 346) . . 25·00 6·00

392 **101** 2m. red (air) 20 20
393 3m. brown . . . . 80 1·00
394 5m. red 30 30
395 7m. brown 35 25
396 8m. green . . . . 1·10 1·25
397 10m. violet . . . . 80 1·00
398 20m. blue . . . . 1·25 2·25
399 30m. purple . . . . 90 1·50
400 40m. red . . . . 1·25 1·75
401 50m. blue . . . . 1·60 2·25
402 100m. green . . . . . . 2·75 3·25
403 200m. grey . . . . 6·50 5·50

125 "Egypt" — 126 Egyptian Flag

1952. Abrogation of Anglo-Egyptian Treaty of 1936. Inscr "16 Oct. 1951".
404 **125** 10m. green . . . . 15 1·00
405 – 22m. green and purple . . 35 1·10
406 – 30m. green and brown . . 35 1·25
DESIGNS: 22m. King Farouk and map of Nile Valley; 30m. King Farouk and flag.

1952. Birth of Crown Prince Ahmed Fuad.
408 **126** 10m. green, yellow & blue 25 1·25

127 "Freedom, Hope and Peace"

1952. Revolution of 23 July 1952. Inscr "23 JUILLET 1952".
410 **127** 4m. orange and green . . 20 25
411 – 10m. brown and green . . 20 80
412 – 17m. brown and green . . 75 90
413 – 22m. green and brown . . 1·00 60
DESIGNS—HORIZ: 10m. Allegory of Egyptian freedom. VERT: 17m. Map of Nile Valley, and Egyptian citizens; 22m. Rejoicing crowd and Egyptian flag.

129 "Agriculture" — 130 "Defence"

131 Sultan Hussein Mosque, Cairo — 132 Queen Nefertiti

133 Douglas Dakota Transport over Delta Barrage

1953. Inscr "DEFENCE" (A) or "DEFENSE" (B).
414 **129** 1m. brown (postage) . . . 40 20
415 2m. purple 25 20
416 3m. blue 40 35
417 4m. green 25 25
418 **130** 10m. brown (A) 25 35
419 10m. brown (B) 50 20
420 15m. grey (B) 40 25
421 17m. blue (B) 50 25
422 20m. violet (B) 25 25
423 **131** 30m. green 25 20
424 32m. blue 60 25
425 35m. violet 50 25
426 37m. brown . . . . 85 1·00
427 40m. brown 50 25
428 50m. purple . . . . 1·50 10
429 **132** 100m. brown . . . . . . 1·25 20
430 200m. blue . . . . 3·50 45
431 500m. violet . . . . 6·50 1·00
432 £El red and green . . . . 10·00 1·75

433 **133** 5m. brown (air) 25 50
434 15m. green 65 70
See also No. 619.

1953. Various issues of King Farouk with portrait obliterated by three horiz bars. (i) Stamps of 1937.
435 **78** 1m. orange . . . . 13·50 21·00
436 3m. brown 45 60
437 6m. green 25 25

(ii) Stamps of 1944.
438 **91** 1m. brown 25 25
439 2m. red 25 10
440 3m. brown 50 60
441 4m. green 25 20
442 10m. violet 25 20
443 13m. red 80 90
444 15m. purple 50 20
445 17m. green 45 25
446 20m. violet 50 10
447 22m. blue 70 20

(iii) Stamps of 1947.
448 – 30m. green (No. 340) . . 50 25
449 **106** 40m. brown . . . . 32·00 45·00
450 – 50m. blue (No. 342) . . . 80 20
451 – 100m. pur (No. 343) . . . 1·10 50
452 – 200m. violet (No. 344) . . 4·50 1·10
453 **107** 50p. brown and green . . 5·00 4·00
454 – £El brn & bl (No. 346) . . 9·50 2·75

(iv) Air stamps of 1947.
455 **101** 2m. red . . . . 1·70 2·00
456 3m. brown . . . . 1·25 2·75
457 5m. red . . . . 80 1·25
458 7m. brown 20 25
459 8m. green . . . . 1·10 1·75
460 10m. violet . . . . 30·00 32·00
461 20m. blue . . . . 1·25 25
462 30m. purple . . . . 1·75 85
463 40m. red . . . . 1·75 95
464 50m. blue . . . . 3·00 1·00
465 100m. green . . . . . . 4·75 2·50
466 200m. grey . . . . 48·00 50·00

(v) Stamps of 1952 with "Egypt-Sudan" opt T **124**.
467 **91** 1m. brown (postage) . . 5·25 7·75
468 2m. red . . . . 70 1·90
469 **78** 3m. brown . . . . 6·00 8·25
470 **91** 4m. green . . . . 6·50 8·25
471 **78** 6m. green . . . . 8·75 8·75
472 **91** 10m. violet . . . . 3·00 4·25
473 13m. red . . . . 70 1·50
474 15m. purple . . . . 13·00 16·00
475 17m. green . . . . 13·00 16·00
476 20m. violet . . . . 14·00 16·00
477 22m. blue . . . . 38·00 42·00
477a – 30m. green (No. 384) . . 17·00 17·00
478 **106** 40m. brown . . . . 80 1·60
479 – 200m. violet (No. 389) . . 3·75 3·25

480 **101** 2m. red (air) 50 30
481 3m. brown . . . . 1·00 90
482 5m. red 25 25
483 7m. brown . . . . 11·00 12·00
484 8m. green . . . . 60 1·60
485 10m. violet . . . . 50 1·25
486 20m. blue . . . . 45·00 48·00
487 30m. purple . . . . 1·10 1·10
488 40m. red . . . . 45·00 48·00
489 50m. blue . . . . 1·40 60
490 100m. green . . . . . . 2·50 2·50
491 200m. grey . . . . 5·00 7·00

135

1953. Electronics Exhibition, Cairo.
492 **135** 10m. blue 40 60

136 "Young Egypt" — 137 "Agriculture"

1954. 1st Anniv of Republic.
493 **136** 10m. brown 50 25
494 – 30m. blue 80 70

DESIGN: 30m. Marching crowd, Egyptian flag and eagle.

1954.
495 **137** 1m. brown 25 20
496 2m. purple 25 20
497 3m. blue 20 25
498 4m. green 90 80
499 5m. red 25 25

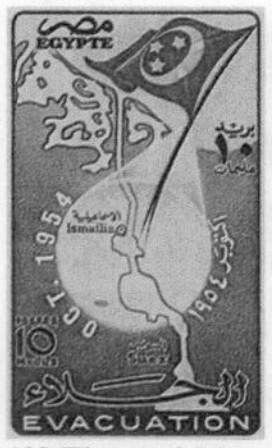

138 Flag and Map showing Area watered by Canal — 139

1954. Evacuation of British Troops from Suez Canal. Inscr "EVACUATION".
500 **138** 10m. purple and green . . 35 25
501 – 35m. green and red . . . 55 60
DESIGN: 35m. Egyptian army bugler, machine-gunner and map.

1955. Arab Postal Union.
502 **139** 5m. brown 35 25
503 10m. green 35 50
504 37m. violet . . . . 60 1·75

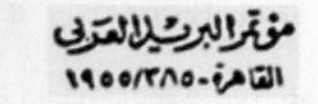

140 P. P. Harris and Rotary Emblem — (141)

1955. 50th Anniv of Rotary International.
505 **140** 10m. purple . . . . . . 1·00 25
506 – 35m. blue . . . . 1·25 60
DESIGN: 35m. Globe and Rotary emblem.

1955. 2nd Arab Postal Union Conference, Cairo. Optd with T **141**.
507 **139** 5m. brown . . . . 80 1·25
508 10m. green . . . . 1·00 1·10
509 37m. violet . . . . 1·25 1·60

142 Scout Badge

1956. 2nd Arab Scout Jamboree, Aboukir (Alexandria). Inscr "2EME JAMBOREE ARABE", etc.
510 **142** 10m.+10m. green . . . . 60 1·60
511 – 20m.+10m. ultramarine 70 1·90
512 – 35m.+15m. blue . . . . . 60 2·00
DESIGNS: 20m. Sea Scout badge; 35m. Air Scout badge.

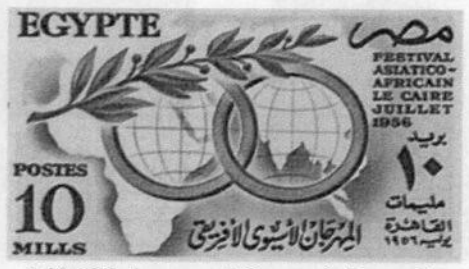

143 Globes and Laurel Branch

1956. Afro-Asian Festival, Cairo. Inscr "FESTIVAL ASIATICO-AFRICAIN".
515 **143** 10m. green and brown . 40 25
516 – 35m. purple and yellow 70 1·50
DESIGN—VERT: 35m. Globe, lamp, dove and ear of corn.

144 Freighter and Map of Suez Canal — **145** Queen Nefertiti

1956. Nationalisation of Suez Canal.
517 **144** 10m. blue and buff . . . 40 40

1956. International Museum Week.
518 **145** 10m. green . . . . 70 1·40

146 Defence of Port Said

1956. "Port Said, Nov. 1956".
519 **146** 10m. purple . . . . . . 1·00 1·25

1957. Evacuation of British and French Troops from Port Said. Optd **EVACUATION 22-12-56** in English and Arabic.
520 **146** 10m. purple . . . . . . 55 1·25

148 Locomotive No. 1, 1852, and Diesel Train

1957. Centenary of Egyptian Railways.
521 **148** 10m. purple and brown 75 1·25

149 Mother and Children

1957. Mothers' Day.
522 **149** 10m. red . . . . 50 1·10

150 Battle Scene

1957. 150th Anniv of Victory over British at Rosetta.
523 **150** 10m. blue . . . . 25 1·10

1957. Re-opening of Suez Canal. As T **144** but inscr "REOPENING 1957" in English and Arabic.
524 100m. blue and green . . . . 1·10 1·40

151 Al-Azhar University — **152** Map of Gaza

1957. Millenary of Al-Azhar University, Cairo. Unissued stamps of 1942 as T **151** optd with the present Arabic year (1376).
525 **151** 10m. violet . . . . . . 40 1·25
526 15m. purple 60 50
527 20m. grey 90 80

1957. Re-occupation of Gaza Strip.
528 **152** 10m. blue . . . . 90 1·75

153 Motor Ambulance

1957. 50th Anniv of Public Aid Society.
529 **153** 10m.+5m. red . . . . . 30 1·40

154 Shepheard's Hotel — **156** Egyptian Parliament Buildings

1957. Re-opening of Shepheard's Hotel, Cairo.
530 **154** 10m. violet 30 30

1957. Opening of National Assembly.
531 **156** 10m. brown & yellow . . 25 1·25

157 Avaris, 1580 B.C.

1957. 5th Anniv of 1952 Revolution.
532 **157** 10m. red . . . . 70 1·00
533 – 10m. green . . . . 70 1·00
534 – 10m. purple . . . . . . 70 1·00
535 – 10m. blue . . . . 70 1·00
536 – 10m. brown . . . . . . 70 1·00
DESIGNS—HORIZ: No. 533, Saladin at Hattin, A.D. 1187; 534, Ein Galout, A.D. 1260 (Middle East map); 536, Evacuation of Port Said, 1956. VERT: No. 534, Louis IX in chains at Mansourah, A.D. 1250.

159 Ahmed Arabi addressing Revolutionaries

1957. 75th Anniv of Arabi Revolution.
537 **159** 10m. violet 30 40

160 Rameses II — **162** Ahmed Shawqi

1957.
540 – 1m. turquoise 25 50
541 – 5m. sepia 25 35
539 **160** 10m. violet 40 25
DESIGNS: 1m. Country woman and cotton plant; 5m. Factory skyline.
See also Nos. 553/9, 603/19 and 669/72.

1957. 25th Death Anniv of Ahmed Shawqi and Hafez Ibrahim (poets).
543 **162** 10m. olive . . . . 25 1·10
544 – 10m. brown (Hafez Ibrahim) . . . . 25 1·10

163 Vickers Viscount Airliner and Airline Badge

1957. 25th Anniv of Egyptian Civil Airlines "MISRAIR", and Air Force.
545 **163** 10m. green 70 65
546 – 10m. blue . . . . 30 1·10
DESIGN: No. 546, Ilyushin Il-28 bomber, two Mikoyan Gurevich MiG-17 jet fighters and Air Force emblem.

164 Pyramids, Dove of Peace and Globe

1957. Afro-Asian People's Conference, Cairo.
547 **164** 5m. brown . . . . 50 1·00
548 10m. green . . . . 30 1·00
549 15m. violet . . . . 30 1·00

165 Racing Cyclists — **166** Mustapha Kamil

1958. 5th Egyptian International Cycle Race.
550 **165** 10m. brown . . . . . . 30 1·00

1958. 50th Death Anniv of Mustapha Kamil (patriot).
551 **166** 10m. slate 50 25

UNITED ARAB REPUBLIC

> For stamps inscribed "UAR" but with value in piastres, see under Syria.

167 Congress Emblem — **168** Princess Nofret

1958. 1st Afro-Asian Ophthalmology Congress.
552 **167** 10m.+5m. orange 65 65

1958. Inscr "U A R EGYPT".
553 – 1m. red (as No. 538) . . 20 20
554 – 2m. blue 15 15
555 **168** 3m. brown 15 15
556 – 4m. green 20 15
557 – 5m. sepia (as No. 541) . . 20 10
558 **160** 10m. violet 50 10
559 – 35m. blue . . . . 2·75 25
DESIGNS—VERT: 2m. Ahmed Ibn Toulon Mosque; 4m. Glass lamp and mosque; 35m. Ship and crate on hoist.
See also Nos. 603/19, 669/72 and 739.

169 Union of Egypt and Syria — **170** Cotton Plant

1958. Birth of United Arab Republic.
560 **169** 10m. grn & yell (postage) 35 25
561 15m. brn & blue (air) . . 35 25

1958. International Cotton Fair, Cairo.
562 **170** 10m. turquoise 25 15

171 Qasim Amin — **172** Dove of Peace

1958. 50th Death Anniv of Qasim Amin (reformer).
563 **171** 10m. blue 40 20

1958. 5th Anniv of Republic.
564 **172** 10m. violet 40 20

173 "Iron and Steel" — **174** Sayed Darwich

1958. 6th Anniv of 1952 Revolution. Egyptian Industries.
565 – 10m. brown 35 20
566 – 10m. green 35 20
567 **173** 10m. red 50 30
568 – 10m. myrtle 35 20
569 – 10m. blue 35 20
DESIGNS: Industrial views representing: No. 565, "Cement"; No. 566, "Textiles"; No. 568, "Petroleum"; No. 569, "Electricity and Fertilizers".

1958. 35th Death Anniv of Sayed Darwich.
580 **174** 10m. purple 40 20

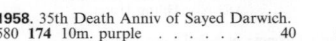

175 Torch and Broken Chains

1958. Republic of Iraq Commem.
581 **175** 10m. red 25 15

176 Cogwheels, Maps and Emblems of Productivity

1958. Afro-Asian Economic Conf, Cairo.
582 **176** 10m. blue 40 20

1958. Industrial and Agricultural Fair, Cairo. As No. 582 but colour changed, optd **INDUSTRIAL & AGRICULTURAL PRODUCTION FAIR** in Arabic and English.
583 **176** 10m. brown 40 25

178 Dr. Mahmoud Azmy (Egyptian U.N.O. representative)

1958. 10th Anniv of Declaration of Human Rights.
584 **178** 10m. violet 35 25
585 35m. green 75 65

179 "Learning"

1958. 50th Anniv of Cairo University.
586 **179** 10m. green 25 15

180 Egyptian Postal Emblem

1959. Post Day and Postal Employees Social Fund.
587 **180** 10m.+5m. red, black and turquoise 25 20

1959. Surch **UAR 55** and equivalent in Arabic.
588 **132** 55m. on 100m. red 45 40

182

1959. Afro-Asian Youth Conf, Cairo.
589 **182** 10m. green 25 15

183 Nile Hilton Hotel

1959. Opening of Nile Hilton Hotel.
590 **183** 10m. brown 25 15

184 State Emblem

1959. 1st Anniv of United Arab Republic.
591 **184** 10m. red, black & green 25 15

185 "Telecommunications"

1959. Arab Telecommunications Union Commemoration.
592 **185** 10m. violet 25 15

186 U.A.R. and Yemeni Flags

1959. 1st Anniv of Proclamation of United Arab States (U.A.R. and Yemen).
593 **186** 10m. red and green 25 15

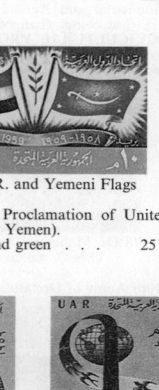

187 Oil Derrick and Pipe-lines

189 "Migration"

188 "Railways" (Diesel-electric Train)

1959. 1st Arab Petroleum Congress.
594 **187** 10m. blue & turquoise 25 20

1959. 7th Anniv of Revolution and Transport and Communications Commemoration. Frames in slate. Centre colours given.
595 **188** 10m. lake 1·10 30
596 – 10m. green 70 30
597 – 10m. blue 90 30
598 – 10m. violet 90 30
599 – 10m. plum 70 30
600 – 10m. red 70 30
DESIGNS: No. 596, "Highways" (bus passing bridge); 597, "Seaways" ("Al Mokattam" (freighter)); 598, "Nile Transport" (motorised river barge); 599, "Telecommunications" (telephone and radio mast); 600, "Postal Services" (Post Office H.Q., Cairo).

1959. 3rd Arab Emigrants' Association Convention, Middle East.
602 **189** 10m. lake 25 15

1959. As Types **132**, **160** and **168**, but inscr "UAR" only.
603 – 1m. red (as No. 553) 10 30
604 – 2m. blue (as No. 554) 10 30
605 **168** 3m. brown 10 20
606 – 4m. green (as No. 556) 10 10
607 – 5m. black (as No. 557) 10 10
608 **160** 10m. green 20 10
609 – 15m. brown 30 10
610 – 20m. red 70 10
611 – 30m. purple 45 10
612 – 35m. blue (as No. 559) 55 10
613 – 40m. brown 75 15
614 – 45m. blue 1·60 20
615 – 55m. green 1·25 15
616 – 60m. violet 2·00 15
617 – 100m. green & orange 1·50 20
618 – 200m. brown and blue 3·00 35
619 **132** 500m. red and blue 9·00 1·10
DESIGNS—VERT: 15m. Omayad Mosque, Damascus; 20m. Tutankhamun's Lamp; 40m. Statue; 55m. Cotton and ears of corn; 60m. Barrage and plant; 100m. Egyptian eagle and hand holding agricultural products. HORIZ: 30m. Stone archway; 45m. Citadel Gate, Aleppo; 200m. Temple ruins.
See also Nos. 669/72 and No. 739.

191 Airplane over Pyramids

1959. Air.
620 **191** 5m. red 20 20
621 – 15m. purple 25 25
622 – 60m. green 60 50
623 – 90m. purple 1·25 1·00
DESIGNS: 15m. Boeing Flying Fortress bomber over Colossi of Thebes; 60m. Douglas DC-6B airliner over Al-Azhar University; 90m. Airplane over St. Catherine's Monastery, Sinai.
See also Nos. 758/62.

192 "Shield against Aggression"

193 Children and U.N. Emblem

1959. Army Day.
624 **192** 10m. red 25 15

1959. U.N. Day. UNICEF.
625 **193** 10m.+5m. purple 25 25
626 35m.+10m. blue 50 35

194 Cairo Museum

1959. Centenary of Cairo Museum.
627 **194** 10m. brown 25 15

195 Rock Temples of Abu Simbel

1959. U.N.E.S.C.O. Campaign for Preservation of Nubian Monuments (1st issue).
628 **195** 10m. brown 40 30
See also Nos. 650, 676, 728, 754/6, 825/7, 864/6 and 878/9.

196 Mounted Postman

1960. Post Day.
629 **196** 10m. blue 25 20

197

198 View of projected Aswan High Dam

1960. Laying of Foundation Stone of Aswan High Dam.
630 **197** 10m. lake 45 50
631 **198** 35m. lake 75 55

199 Aswan Dam Hydro-electric Power Station

1960. Projected Aswan Dam Hydro-electric Power Station.
632 **199** 10m. black 25 15

200

1960. Industrial and Agricultural Fair.
633 **200** 10m. green 30 20

1960. No. 432 optd **UAR** and Arabic equivalent.
634 **132** £E1 red and green 12·00 3·00

202 State Emblem with U.A.R. Flag

203 Sculpture and Palette

1960. 2nd Anniv of U.A.R.
635 **202** 10m. red, black & green 25 20

1960. 3rd Fine Arts Biennale. Alexandria.
636 **203** 10m. sepia 25 20

204 Arab League Centre, Cairo

1960. Inaug of Arab League Centre, Cairo.
637 **204** 10m. green and black 25 20

205 Mother and Child pointing to Map of Palestine

1960. World Refugee Year.
638 **205** 10m. red 20 20
639 35m. turquoise 55 55

206 Weightlifting

1960. Sports Campaign and Olympic Games.
640 **206** 5m. grey 20 20
641 – 5m. brown 20 20
642 – 5m. purple 20 20
643 – 10m. red 20 20
644 – 10m. green 20 20
645 – 30m. violet 45 45
646 – 35m. blue 55 50
DESIGNS—VERT: No. 641, Basketball; 642, Football; 643, Fencing; 644, Rowing. HORIZ: No. 645, Horse-jumping; 646, Swimming.

207 U.N. Emblem within 15 candles

1960. 15th Anniv of U.N.O.
648 – 10m. violet 20 15
649 **207** 35m. red 50 40
DESIGN—VERT: 10m. Dove and U.N. Emblem.

208 Rock Temples of Abu Simbel

1960. U.N.E.S.C.O. Campaign for Preservation of Nubian Monuments (2nd issue).
650 **208** 10m. brown 50 35

209 Modern Post Office

1961. Post Day.
651 **209** 10m. red 25 20

210 State Emblem and Wreath

211 Globe, Flags and Wheat

1961. 3rd Anniv of U.A.R.
652 **210** 10m. purple 25 20

1961. International Agricultural Exn, Cairo.
653 **211** 10m. red 25 20

212 Patrice Lumumba and Map of Africa
213 Hands "reading" Braille

1961. 3rd All African Peoples' Conf, Cairo.
654 **212** 10m. black 25 20

1961. World Health Organization Day.
655 **213** 10m. brown 30 20
656 35m.+15m. yellow & brn 65 70

214 Tower of Cairo
215 Refugee Mother and Child, and Map

1961. Inauguration of Tower of Cairo.
657 **214** 10m. blue 25 20

1961. Air. As No. 657, but with aircraft replacing inscr in upper corners and inscr "AIR MAIL" in English and Arabic.
658 **214** 50m. blue 65 60

1961. Palestine Day.
659 **215** 10m. green 25 20

216 "Transport and Communications"

1961. 9th Anniv of Revolution and Five Year Plan. Inscr "1961".
660 **216** 10m. purple 40 20
661 – 10m. red 20 15
662 – 10m. blue 20 15
663 – 35m. myrtle 55 35
664 35m. violet 55 35
DESIGNS: No. 661, Worker turning cogwheel and pylons; No. 662, Apartment houses; No. 663, Cotton plant and dam; No. 664, Family moving towards lighted candle.

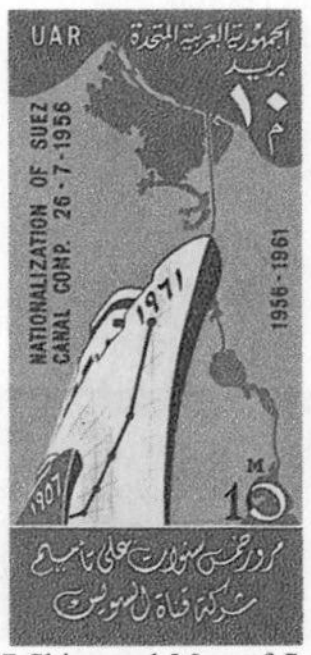

217 Ships and Map of Suez Canal

1961. 5th Anniv of Nationalization of Suez Canal.
666 **217** 10m. olive 40 25

218 Mehalla El Kobra Textile Factories

1961. Misr Bank Organization and 20th Death Anniv of Talaat Harb (founder).
667 **218** 10m. brown 25 20

219 Ship's Wheel and "Al Nasser" (destroyer)
220 "Industrial Worlds"

1961. Navy Day.
668 **219** 10m. blue 30 20

1961. As Nos. 553, etc. Inscr "UAR" only (in English). New colours.
669 1m. turquoise (as No. 603) 15 15
670 4m. olive (as No. 606) . . . 15 15
671 10m. violet 25 15
672 35m. slate (as No. 612) . . . 45 15
NEW DESIGN: 10m. Eagle of Saladin.
See also No. 739.

1961. U.N. Technical Co-operation. Programme and 16th Anniv of U.N.O.
674 – 10m. black and brown . . 20 15
675 **220** 35m. brown and green . . 50 35
DESIGN—VERT: 10m. Corncob, wheel and book ("Agriculture, Industry and Education").

221 Philae Temple

1961. 15th Anniv of U.N.E.S.C.O. and Preservation of Nubian Monuments Campaign (3rd issue).
676 **221** 10m. blue 60 30

222 "Fine Arts"
223 "Arts and Sciences"

1961. 4th Fine Arts Biennale, Alexandria.
677 **222** 10m. brown 25 20

1961. Education Day.
678 **223** 10m. purple 25 20

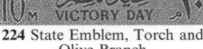

224 State Emblem, Torch and Olive Branch
225 Sphinx and Pyramid

1961. Victory Day.
679 **224** 10m. green and red . . . 25 20

1961. "Son et Lumiere" Display.
680 **225** 10m. black 35 20

226 Postal Authority Press Building, El Nasr

1962. Post Day.
681 **226** 10m. brown 25 20

227 King of Morocco and Map
229 Gaza Family with Egyptian Flag

228 Guide and Badge

1962. 1st Anniv of African Charter of Casablanca.
682 **227** 10m. blue 25 20

1962. Silver Jubilee of Egyptian Girl Guides Association.
683 **228** 10m. blue 30 20

1962. 5th Anniv of Egyptian Occupation of Gaza.
684 **229** 10m. myrtle 25 20

230 Mother and Child
231 League Centre, Cairo, and Emblem

1962. Mothers' Day.
694 **230** 10m. purple 25 15

1962. Arab League Week.
695 **231** 10m.+5m. black 40 35

232 W.M.O. Emblem and Weather-vane

1962. World Meteorological Day.
696 **232** 60m. blue and yellow . . 65 65

233 Posthorn on North Africa
235 Campaign Emblem

234 Cadets on Parade

1962. African Postal Union Commemoration.
697 **233** 10m. brown and red . . . 20 15
698 50m. brown and blue . . 60 50

1962. 150th Anniv of Military Academy.
699 **234** 10m. green 25 15

1962. Malaria Eradication.
700 **235** 10m. red and sepia . . . 20 15
701 – 35m. blue and myrtle . . 50 40
DESIGN: 35m. As Type **235** but with laurel and inscription around emblem.

237 Bilharz and Microscope
238 Lumumba

1962. Death Centenary of Dr. Theodore Bilharz (discoverer of parasitic disease: bilharzia).
702 **237** 10m. brown 35 20

1962. Lumumba Commemoration.
703 **238** 10m. red (postage) . . . 25 20
704 – 35m. multicoloured (air) 65 45
DESIGN: 35m. Lumumba with laurel sprays and flaming torch.

239 "The Charter"
240 "Birth of the Revolution"

1962. Proclamation of National Charter.
705 **239** 10m. brown and blue . . 25 15

1962. 10th Anniv of 1952 Revolution.
706 **240** 10m. brown and pink . . 30 25
707 A 10m. sepia and blue . . . 30 25
708 B 10m. blue and sepia . . . 30 25
709 C 10m. blue and olive . . . 30 25
710 D 10m. red, black & green 30 25
711 E 10m. slate and brown . . 30 25
712 F 10m. purple and brown 30 25
713 G 10m. sepia and orange . . 30 25
DESIGNS: A, Scroll and book; B, Agricultural Scene; C, Globe and dove; D, Flag and eagle emblem; E, Industrial scene and cogwheel; F, Dam construction; G, Eagle, building, cogwheel and ear of corn.

241 M. Moukhtar (sculptor) and "La Vestale des Secrets"

1962. Moukhtar Museum Inaug.
716 **241** 10m. olive and blue . . . 25 15

242 Algerian Flag and map
243 Rocket

1962. Independence of Algeria.
717 **242** 10m. red, green & pink 25 15

1962. Launching of U.A.R. Rocket.
718 **243** 10m. red, black & green 30 20

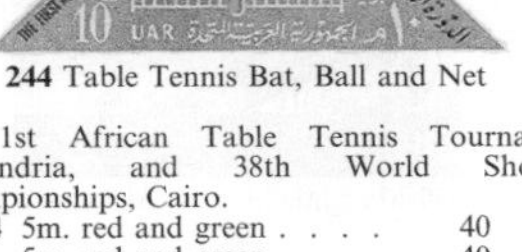

244 Table Tennis Bat, Ball and Net

1962. 1st African Table Tennis Tournament, Alexandria, and 38th World Shooting Championships, Cairo.
719 **244** 5m. red and green 40 40
720 – 5m. red and green 40 40
721 **244** 10m. blue and ochre . . . 60 50
722 – 10m. blue and ochre . . . 60 50
723 **244** 35m. red and blue . . . . 1·25 1·00
724 – 35m. red and blue . . . . 1·25 1·00
DESIGN: Nos. 720, 722, 724, Rifle and target.

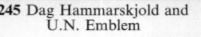

245 Dag Hammarskjold and U.N. Emblem

246 Coronation of Queen Nefertari (from small temple of Abu Simbel)

1962. 17th Anniv of U.N.O. and Dag Hammarskjold (Secretary-General, 1953–61) Commemoration.
725 **245** 5m. blue and violet . . . 20 15
726 10m. blue and green . . 35 20
727 35m. blue & ultramarine 60 45

1962. U.N.E.S.C.O. Campaign for Preservation of Nubian Monuments (4th issue).
728 **246** 10m. brown and blue . . 45 25

247 Al Kahira Jet Trainer, College Emblem and De Havilland Tiger Moth Biplane

1962. Silver Jubilee of U.A.R. Air Force College.
729 **247** 10m. red and blue 30 20

248 Postal Authority Emblem

1963. Post Day and 1966 International Stamp Exhbition. Inscr "1866 1966".
736 **248** 20m.+10m. red & green 75 75
737 – 40m.+20m. sepia & brn 1·25 1·50
738 – 40m.+20m. brn & sepia 1·25 1·50
DESIGNS—TRIANGULAR: Egyptian stamps of 1866 – No. 737, 5 paras; No. 738, 10 paras.

1963. As No. 670 but inscr "1963" in English and Arabic and new colours.
739 4m. red, green and sepia . . 20 15

249 Yemeni Republican Flag and Torch

1963. Proclamation of Yemeni Arab Republic.
740 **249** 10m. red and olive . . . 20 15

250 Maritime Station, Alexandria

1963. Air.
741 **250** 20m. sepia 45 20
742 – 30m. mauve 60 35
743 – 40m. black 90 75
DESIGNS: 30m. International Airport, Cairo; 40m. Railway Station, Luxor.

251 Tennis-player

1963. 51st Int Lawn Tennis Championships held in U.A.R.
744 **251** 10m. brown and black . . 50 25

252 Cow and Emblems

1963. Freedom from Hunger.
745 **252** 5m. brown and violet . . 25 20
746 – 10m. yellow and blue . . 30 20
747 – 35m. yellow and blue . . 45 45
DESIGNS—VERT: 10m. Corncob and ear of wheat. HORIZ: 35m. Corncob, ear of wheat, U.N. and F.A.O. emblems.

253 Centenary Emblem within Red Crescent

254 "Arab Socialist Union"

1963. Centenary of Red Cross.
748 **253** 10m. red, purple & blue 30 20
749 – 35m. red and blue 65 65
DESIGN: 35m. Emblem, Red Crescent, olive branches and Globe.

1963. 11th Anniv of Revolution.
750 **254** 10m. mauve and blue . . 20 15

255 T.V. Building, Cairo, and Television Receiver

1963. 2nd Int Television Festival, Alexandria.
753 **255** 10m. yellow and blue . . 20 15

256 Queen Nefertari

257 Swimmer and Map

1963. U.N.E.S.C.O. Campaign for preservation of Nubian Monuments (5th issue).
754 **256** 5m. yellow and blue . . . 35 20
755 – 10m. orange and black . . 45 35
756 – 35m. yellow and black . . 80 60
DESIGNS—(28 × 61 mm): 10m. Great Hall of Pillars, Abu Simbel. As Type **256**: 35m. Heads of Colossi, Abu Simbel.

1963. Suez Canal Int Long-distance Swimming Race.
757 **257** 10m. red and blue 30 20

1963. Air.
758 50m. brown and blue . . . . 2·00 80
759 80m. purple and blue . . . . 2·50 1·25
761 115m. yellow and brown . . 2·75 1·10
762 140m. red and violet . . . . 2·75 1·50
DESIGNS—VERT: 50m. Cairo Tower and Arch. HORIZ: 80m. As No. 622; 115m. Colossi of Rameses II and Queen Nefertari, Abu Simbel; 140m. Seated colossi of Rameses II (Great Temple, Abu Simbel).

258 Ministry Building

1963. 50th Anniv of Egyptian Ministry of Agriculture.
763 **258** 10m. blue and brown . . 20 15

259 Map and Blocks of Flats

1963. Afro-Asian Housing Congress.
764 **259** 10m. blue and brown . . 20 15

259a Globe and Scales of Justice

1963. 15th Anniv of Declaration of Human Rights.
765 **259a** 5m. yellow and green . . 20 15
766 – 10m. black, brown & bl 25 15
767 – 35m. blk, pink & red . . 60 40
DESIGNS: 10, 35m. As Type **259a** but arranged differently.

259b Statuette, Palette and Arms of Alexandria

1963. 5th Fine Arts Biennale, Alexandria.
768 **259b** 10m. brown and blue . . 20 15

260 El Mitwalli Gate, Cairo

261 Glass and Enamel Urn

263 King Osircaf

1964.
769 – 1m. blue and green . . . 10 10
770 – 2m. bistre and purple . . 10 10
771 – 3m. blue, orge & salmon 10 10
772 – 4m. brown, black & blue 10 10
773 – 5m. brown, lt brn & blue 10 10
774 – 10m. lt brn, brn & grn . . 20 10
775 – 15m. yell, ultram & bl . . 20 10
776 – 20m. brown and blue . . 50 10
777 **260** 20m. green . . . . . . 1·10 15
778 **261** 30m. brown & yellow . . 45 10
779 – 35m. brown, bl & orge . . 55 10
780 – 40m. blue and yellow . . 1·10 20
781 – 55m. violet . . . . . . 1·60 20
782 – 60m. brown and blue . . 75 30
783 **263** 100m. blue and purple . . 2·00 45
784 – 200m. brown and blue . . 4·50 65
785 – 500m. orange and blue . . 9·75 1·90
DESIGNS—As Type **260**. 55m. Kiosk, Sultan Hussein Mosque. As Type **261**—VERT: 1m. 14th-century glass vase; 4m. Minaret and archway; 10m. Eagle emblem and pyramids; 35m. Queen Nefertari; 40m. Nile near Agouza; 60m. Al-Azhar Mosque. HORIZ: 2m. Ancient Egyptian headrest; 3m. Alabaster funerary barge; 5m. Aswan High Dam; 15m. Window, Ahmed ibn Toulon Mosque; 20m. (No. 776), Nile Hilton Hotel and Kasr el Nile Bridge. As Type **263**: 200m. Rameses; 500m. Tutankhamun.
For the 4m. in different colours, and with date "1964" added to design see No. 791.
For stamps as Nos. 777 and 781 but larger and in different colours, see Nos. 1042, 1044, 1134/5 and 1137.

264 Eagle and Pyramids

265 Emblems on Map of Africa

1964. Post Day.
786 **264** 10m.+5m. green & yell . . 1·50 1·00
787 80m.+40m. blk & bl . . . 2·50 1·90
788 115m.+55m. blk & brn . . 3·25 2·50

1964. 1st Health, Sanitation and Nutrition Commission Conference, Cairo.
789 **265** 10m. yellow and blue . . 20 15

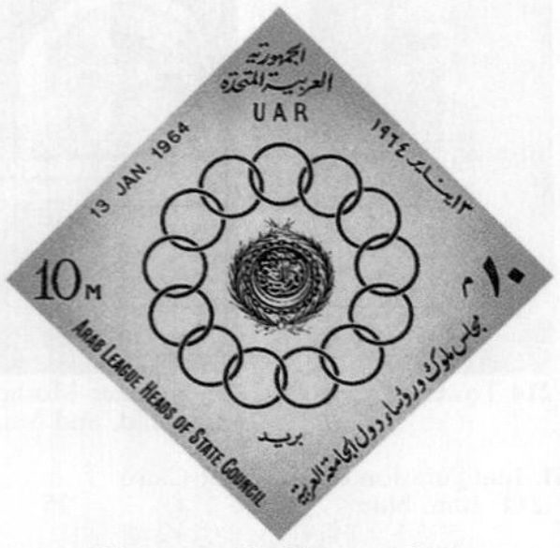

266 League Emblem and Links

1964. Arab League Heads of State Council, Cairo.
790 **266** 10m. black and green . . 20 15

267 Arch and Minaret

269 King Akhnaton and Family (Tutankhamun's tomb)

268 Map and Old and New Houses

1964. Ramadan Festival.
791 **267** 4m. green, red & black . . 20 10

1964. Nubians' Resettlement.
792 **268** 10m. yellow & purple . . 20 15

1964. Mothers' Day.
793 **269** 10m. brown and blue . . 20 15

270 Diesel Train and Afro-Asian Map

1964. Asian Railways Conference.
794 **270** 10m. yellow and blue . . 40 20

271 Office Emblem

272 W.H.O. Emblem

1964. 10th Anniv of Arab Postal Union's Permanent Office.
795 **271** 10m. blue and brown . . 20 10

1964. World Health Day.
796 **272** 10m. blue and red 20 10

273 Statue of Liberty, U.A.R. Pavilion and Pyramids

1964. New York World's Fair.
797 **273** 10m. green, brn & olive 20 10

274 Site of Diversion

1964. Nile High Dam (Diversion of Flow).
798 **274** 10m. black and blue . . . 25 20

275 Map of Africa and Flags

1964. O.A.U. Assembly, Cairo.
799 **275** 10m. black, blue & brn 35 20

276 "Electricity"

1964. Aswan Dam Projects.
800 **276** 10m. blue and green . . . 35 20
801 – 10m. green and yellow . . 35 20
DESIGN: No. 801, "Land Reclamation" (tractor and symbols of land cultivation).

277 Jamboree Badge

1964. 6th Pan Arab Scout Jamboree, Alexandria.
803 **277** 10m. green and red . . . 35 25
804 – 10m. red and green . . . 35 25
DESIGN: No. 804, Air Scout badge.

278 Algerian Flag

1964. 2nd Arab League Heads of State Council. Flags in national colours; inscr in green (except Sudan, in blue). Each with country name at foot.
805 10m. Type **278** 60 30
806 10m. Iraq 60 30
807 10m. Jordan 60 30
808 10m. Kuwait 60 30
809 10m. Lebanon 60 30
810 10m. Libya 60 30
811 10m. Morocco 60 30
812 10m. Saudi Arabia 60 30
813 10m. Sudan 60 30
814 10m. Syria 60 30
815 10m. Tunisia 60 30
816 10m. U.A.R. 60 30
817 10m. Yemen 60 30

279 Globe, Dove and Pyramids

1964. Non-aligned Countries Conf, Cairo.
818 **279** 10m. yellow and blue . . 20 15

280 Emblem and Map

281 Gymnastics

1964. 1st Afro-Asian Medical Congress.
819 **280** 10m. violet and yellow . . 20 15

1964. Olympic Games, Tokyo.
820 – 5m. orange and green . . 20 20
821 **281** 10m. ochre and blue . . . 20 20
822 – 35m. ochre and purple . . 65 65
823 – 50m. brown and blue . . 90 90
DESIGNS—As Type **281**. HORIZ: 5m. Gymnastics. VERT: 35m. Wrestling. LARGER (61 × 28 mm): 50m. Charioteer hunting lions.

282 Emblems of Posts and Telecommunications and Map

283 Rameses II

1964. Pan-African and Malagasy Posts and Telecommunications Congress, Cairo.
824 **282** 10m. sepia and green . . 20 15

1964. U.N.E.S.C.O. Campaign for Preservation of Nubian Monuments (6th issue).
825 – 5m. brown and blue . . . 20 15
826 **283** 10m. yellow and sepia . . 45 20
827 – 35m. blue and brown . . 1·40 95
DESIGNS—SQUARE (40 × 40 mm): 5m. Horus and facade of Abu Simbel; 35m. Wall sculpture, Abu Simbel.

284 Handicrafts and Weaving

285 U.N. and U.N.E.S.C.O. Emblems

1964. 25th Anniv of Ministry of Social Affairs.
829 **284** 10m. blue and yellow . . 20 15

1964. U.N.E.S.C.O. Day.
830 **285** 10m. blue and yellow . . 20 15

286 Emblem and Posthorn

1965. Post Day and 1966 Int Stamp Exn.
831 **286** 10m.+5m. red, purple and green 65 65
832 – 10m.+5m. red, black and blue 65 65
833 – 80m.+40m. black, green and red . . . . . . 2·00 2·00
DESIGNS—As Type **286**: No. 832, Posthorn over emblem. As Type **248**: 80m. Bird carrying letter, inscr "STAMP CENTENARY EXHIBITION".

286a Al-Maridani Mosque Minaaret

287 Police Emblem

1965. Ramadan Festival.
834 **286a** 4m. brown and blue . . 35 20

1965. Police Day.
835 **287** 10m. yellow and sepia . . 65 20

288 Oil Derrick

289 Emblem and Flags

1965. 5th Arab Petroleum Congress and 2nd Petroleum Exhibition.
836 **288** 10m. sepia and yellow . . 50 25

1965. 20th Anniv of Arab League.
837 **289** 10m. green and red . . . 65 30
838 – 20m. brown and blue . . 85 50
DESIGN—HORIZ: 20m. Arab League emblem.

290 W.M.O. Emblem and Weather-vane

1965. Air. World Meteorological Day.
839 **290** 80m. purple and blue . . 2·50 1·25

291 W.H.O. Emblem within Red Crescent

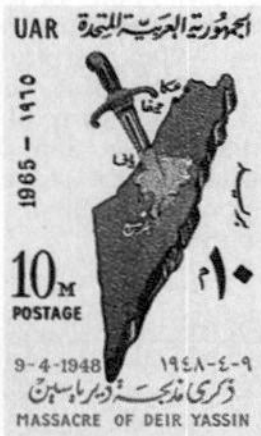

292 Dagger on Deir Yassin, Palestine

1965. World Health Day.
840 **291** 10m. red and blue 45 25

1965. Deir Yassin Massacre.
841 **292** 10m. red and sepia . . . 1·10 25

293 I.T.U. Emblem and Symbols

1965. Centenary of I.T.U.
842 **293** 5m. purple, yell & blk . . 30 25
843 10m. pink, yellow & red 45 25
844 35m. blue, yell & dp bl 1·40 1·10

294 Lamp and Burning Library

1965. Reconstitution of Algiers University Library.
845 **294** 10m. green, red & black 40 20

295 Senet Table of 1350 B.C.

296 Shaikh Mohamed Abdo

1965. Air. Re-establishment of Egyptian Civil Airlines, "MISRAIR".
846 **295** 10m. blue and yellow . . 1·25 25

1965. 60th Death Anniv of Shaikh Abdo (mufti).
847 **296** 10m. brown and blue . . 25 20

297 "Housing"

1965. 13th Anniv of Revolution.
848 **297** 10m. black and brown . . 50 30
849 – 10m. brown & yellow . . 50 30
850 – 10m. indigo and blue . . 85 30
851 – 100m. black and green . . 3·75 3·25
DESIGNS—SQUARE: No. 849, "Heavy Industry" (ladle and furnace); 850, "Petroleum and Mining" (refinery and oil rig "Discoverer"). 80 × 80 mm: No. 851, President Nasser.

298 Stadium, Flag and Torch

1965. 4th Pan-Arab Games, Cairo.
857 **298** 5m. blue & red on blue 30 30
858 – 10m. brown and blue . . 60 30
859 – 35m. brown and green . . 1·00 95
DESIGNS—As Type **298**: 35m. Horse "Saadoon". DIAMOND (56 × 56 mm): 10m. Map and emblems of Arab countries.

299 Swimmers Zeitun and Abd el Gelil

1965. Long-distance Swimming Championships, Alexandria.
860 **299** 10m. sepia and blue . . . 50 25

300 Map and Arab League Emblem

301 Land Forces Emblem

1965. 3rd Arab Summit Conf, Casablanca.
861 **300** 10m. sepia and yellow . . 30 20

1965. Land Forces Day.
862 **301** 10m. black and brown . . 45 25

302 Flaming Torch on Africa

1965. O.A.U. Assembly, Accra.
863 **302** 10m. purple and red . . . 30 15

303 Rameses II, Abu Simbel

1965. U.N.E.S.C.O. Campaign for Preservation of Nubian Monuments (7th issue).
864 **303** 5m. blue and yellow . . . 55 30
865 – 10m. black and blue . . . 1·00 35
866 – 35m. violet and yellow . . 1·90 1·25
DESIGNS—As Type **303**: 35m. Colossi, Abu Simbel. VERT: (28 × 61½ mm): 10m. Hall of Pillars, Abu Simbel.

304 Al-Maqrizi, Scrolls and Books

305 Bust and Flag

1965. 600th Birth Anniv of Al-Maqrizi (historian).
868 **304** 10m. blue and olive . . . 30 15

1965. 6th Fine Arts Biennale, Alexandria.
869 **305** 10m. multicoloured . . . 30 15

306 Pigeon, Parchment and Horseman

307 Glass Lamp

1966. Post Day.
870 **306** 10m. orange, yellow and blue (postage) 65 20
871 – 80m.+40m. purple, yellow and blue (air) . . . . 2·50 2·50
872 – 115m.+55m. blue, yellow and purple . . . . . 3·25 3·50
DESIGNS: 80m. Pharaonic messengers; 115m. De Havilland D.H.34 airplane and 1926 27m. air stamp.

1966. Ramadan Festival.
874 **307** 4m. orange and violet . . 30 15

308 Exhibition Emblem

309 Arab League Emblem

1966. Industrial Exhibition, Cairo.
875 **308** 10m. black, blue & lt bl 30 15

1966. Arab Publicity Week.
876 **309** 10m. violet and yellow . . 30 15

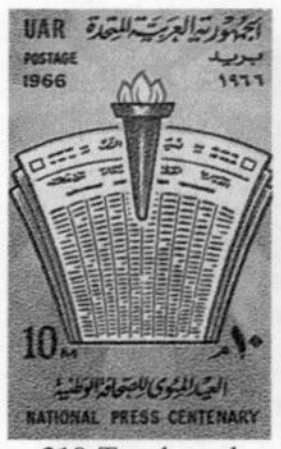

310 Torch and Newspapers

312 Traffic Signals

311 Rock Temples of Abu Simbel

1966. Centenary of Egyptian National Press.
877 **310** 10m. slate and orange . . 30 15

1966. Air. U.N.E.S.C.O. Campaign for Preservation of Nubian Monuments (8th issue).
878 **311** 20m. multicoloured . . . 65 40
879 80m. multicoloured . . . 1·60 1·25

1966. Traffic Day.
880 **312** 10m. red, emerald & grn 65 25

313 Torch

314 "Labourers"

1966. U.A.R.–Iraq Union Agreement.
881 **313** 10m. red, grn & pur . . . 30 15

1966. 50th Session of I.L.O. Conference.
882 **314** 5m. black & turquoise . . 25 20
883 10m. green and purple . . 25 20
884 35m. black and orange . . 1·00 75

315 Emblem, People and City

316 Building "Salah-el-Deen"

1966. 1st Population Census.
885 **315** 10m. purple and brown 25 15

1966. 14th Anniv of Revolution.
886 **316** 10m. black, blue & orge 50 25
887 – 10m. purple, yell & grn 50 25
888 – 10m. blue, yellow & blk 50 25
889 – 10m. turq, bl & red . . . 50 25
DESIGNS: No. 886, Type **316** (shipbuilding); 887, Transfer of first stones at Abu Simbel; 888, Map (development of Sinai); 889, El Mahdi hospital, nurse and patient.

318 Suez Canal H.Q., "Southern Cross" (liner), Freighter and Map

1966. 10th Anniv of Suez Canal Nationalization.
891 **318** 10m. red and blue 85 30

319 Jamboree Emblem and Camp

1966. Air. 7th Pan-Arab Scout Jamboree, Libya.
892 **319** 20m. red and olive . . . 95 45

320 Cotton

1966. Peasants' Day.
893 **320** 5m. violet, yell & blue . . 25 20
894 – 10m. brn & grn (Rice) . . 25 20
895 – 35m. orge & bl (Onions) 1·00 75

321 W.H.O. Building

1966. U.N. Day.
896 **321** 5m. violet and olive . . . 25 20
897 – 10m. violet and orange . . 25 20
898 – 35m. violet and blue . . . 75 50
DESIGNS: 10m. U.N.R.W.A. (Refugees) emblem; 35m. U.N.I.C.E.F. emblem.

322 Globe and Festival Emblem

1966. 5th Int Television Festival.
899 **322** 10m. violet and yellow . . 30 15

323 St. Catherine's Monastery

1966. Air. 1400th Anniv of St. Catherine's Monastery, Mt. Sinai.
900 **323** 80m. red. yellow & blue 2·25 1·60

324 Eagle and Torch

1966. Victory Day.
901 **324** 10m. red and green . . . 35 15

325 Anubis (God)

1967. Post Day. Designs showing items from Tutankhamun's Tomb.
902 **325** 10m. multicoloured . . . 50 20
903 – 35m. brown. pur & bl . . 75 45
904 – 80m.+20m. brown, yellow and blue . . . . 2·25 2·25
905 – 115m.+40m. brown, black and blue . . . . 3·75 3·50
DESIGNS—As T **325**: 35m. Alabaster head (stopper from canopic urn); 27 × 60 mm: 80m. Ushabti figure; 115m. Statue of Tutankhamun.

326 Carnations

327 Tree-planting

1967. Ramadan Festival.
906 **326** 4m. violet and olive . . . 30 15

1967. Tree Festival.
907 **327** 10m. lilac and green . . . 30 15

328 Gamal el-Dine el-Afghani and Arab League Emblem

329 Workers, Factories and Census Symbol

1967. Arab Publicity Week.
908 **328** 10m. brown and green . . 30 15

1967. 1st Industrial Census.
909 **329** 10m. green & orange . . 30 15

330 Hawker Siddeley Comet 4 Aircraft at Cairo Airport

1967. Air.
910 **330** 20m. blue and brown . . 95 30

331 "Workers" (rock-carving)

1967. Labour Day.
911 **331** 10m. orange and olive . . 35 20

332 Nefertari and Rameses II

1967. International Tourist Year.
912 **332** 10m. red, yellow and green (postage) 65 35
913 – 35m. orange, yell & bl . . 2·25 55
914 – 20m. lilac, black and orange (air) 65 20
915 – 80m. brown, yell & bl . . 1·60 1·10
916 – 115m. orange, bl & brn 3·50 1·60
DESIGNS—As T **332**: 35m. Shooting red-breasted geese; 40 × 40 mm: 20m. Hotel, El Alamein; 80m. Virgin's Tree; 115m. Hotel and fishes, Red Sea.

333 Pres. Nasser and Map

1967. Arab Solidarity for Palestine Defence.
917 **333** 10m. olive, yell & orge . . 1·90 1·25

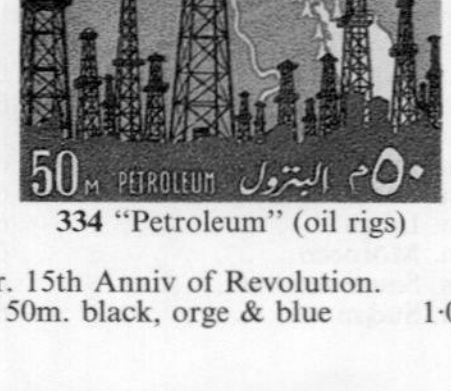

334 "Petroleum" (oil rigs)

1967. Air. 15th Anniv of Revolution.
930 **334** 50m. black, orge & blue 1·00 65

336 Salama Higazi **337** Porcelain Dish

1967. 50th Death Anniv of Higazi (lyric stage impresario).
932 **336** 20m. brown and blue . . 65 20

1967. U.N. Day. Egyptian Art.
933 20m. blue & red (postage) . . 55 30
934 55m. multicoloured . . . . . 1·00 65
935 80m. red, yellow & blue (air) 1·10 85
DESIGNS: 20m. Type **337**. 55m. "Christ in Glory" (painting); 80m. Tutankhamun and Ankhesenamun (back of throne).

338 Savings Bank "Coffer"

1967. World Savings Day.
936 **338** 20m. blue and pink . . . 45 25

339 Ca d'Oro Palace (Venice) and Santa Maria Cathedral (Florence)

1967. "Save the Monuments of Florence and Venice".
937 **339** 80m.+20m. brown, yellow and green . . . . . . 1·25 1·60
938 – 115m.+30m. bl, yell & ol 2·25 2·40
DESIGN: 115m. Palace of the Doges and Campanile (Venice) and Vecchio Palace (Florence).

340 Rose **341** Isis

1967. Ramadan Festival.
939 **340** 5m. purple and green . . 40 20

1968. Post Day. Pharaonic Dress.
940 **341** 20m. sepia, green & yell 65 20
941 – 55m. brown, yellow & grn 1·25 75
942 – 80m. red, blue & blk . . 1·75 95
DESIGNS: 55m. Nefertari; 80m. Isis (different).
See also Nos. 970/3.

342 High Dam and Power Station

1968. Electrification of High Dam.
943 **342** 20m. purple, yellow & bl 40 20

343 Alabaster Vessel (Tutankhamun) **344** Head of Woman

1968. International Museums Festival.
944 **343** 20m. brown, yellow & bl 45 15
945 – 80m. grn, vio & emer . . 1·10 85
DESIGN—39 × 39 mm: 80m. Capital of Coptic limestone pillar.

1968. 7th Fine Arts Biennale, Alexandria.
946 **344** 20m. black and blue . . . 25 15

345 "The Glorious Koran" (½-size illustration)

1968. Air. 1400th Anniv of The Holy Koran.
947 **345** 30m. violet, blue & yell 95 95
948 80m. violet, blue & yell 1·25 1·25

346 Tending Cattle

1968. Arab Veterinary Congress.
949 **346** 20m. brown, grn & yell 40 20

347 St. Mark and St. Mark's Cathedral

1968. Air. 1900th Anniv of Martyrdom of St. Mark.
950 **347** 80m. sepia, mauve & grn 1·25 95

348 Human Rights Emblem **349** Open Book and Symbols

1968. Human Rights Year.
951 **348** 20m. red, green & olive 30 15
952 60m. red, green & blue . . 65 65

1968. 16th Anniv of Revolution.
953 **349** 20m. green and pink . . . 25 15

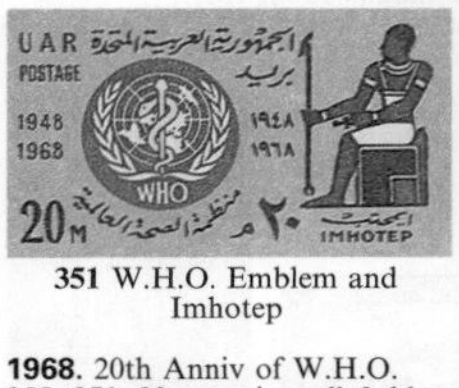

351 W.H.O. Emblem and Imhotep **352** Table Tennis Bats, Net and Ball

1968. 20th Anniv of W.H.O.
955 **351** 20m. sepia, yell & blue . . 50 40
956 – 20m. turq, sep & yell . . 50 40
DESIGN: No. 956, W.H.O. emblem and Avicenna.

1968. 1st Mediterranean Table Tennis Tournament.
957 **352** 20m. brown and green . . 65 25

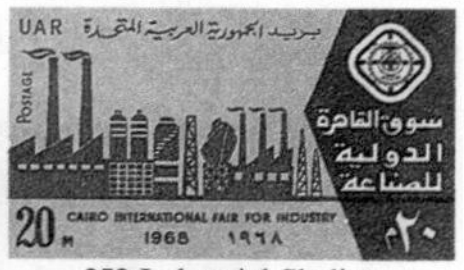

353 Industrial Skyline

1968. International Industrial Fair, Cairo.
958 **353** 20m. red, indigo and blue 35 20

354 Philae Temple **355** Scout Badge

1968. United Nations Day.
959 – 20m. salmon, vio & blue 45 20
960 – 30m. blue, orge & yell . . 65 50
961 **354** 55m. purple, yell & blue 1·10 75
DESIGNS (62 × 29 mm): 20m. Philae Temples (aerial view); (As Type **354**): 30m. Refugee women and children.

1968. 50th Anniv of Egyptian Scout Movement.
962 **355** 10m. blue and orange . . 50 20

356 Ancient Games

1968. Olympic Games Mexico.
963 **356** 20m. violet, olive & orge 45 20
964 – 30m. violet, blue & buff 65 50
DESIGN: 30m. Ancient Games (different).

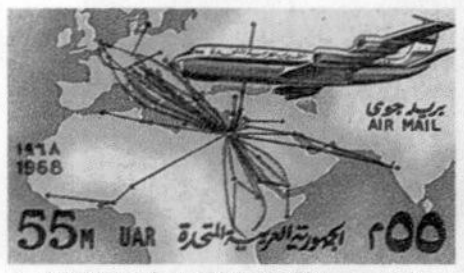

357 Boeing 707 Jetliner and Route Map **358** Ali Moubarek (educator)

1968. Air. 1st United Arab Airlines Boeing Flight, Cairo–London.
965 **357** 55m. red, blue & orange 95 65

1968. 75th Death Anniv of Ali Moubarek.
966 **358** 20m. lilac, orange & grn 40 20

359 Boy and Girl **360** Lotus

1968. World Children's Day.
967 **359** 20m.+10m. red, bl & brn 65 65
968 – 20m.+10m. bl, brn & grn 65 65
DESIGN: No. 968, Group of Children.

1968. Ramadan Festival.
969 **360** 5m. yellow, bl & grn . . . 35 15

1968. Post Day. Pharaonic Dress. As T **341**.
970 5m. brown, yellow and blue 40 20
971 20m. yellow, red and blue . . 65 40
972 20m. brown, cinnamon & bl 75 45
973 55m. orange, yellow & blue 1·75 1·10
DESIGNS: No. 970, Son of Ramess III; 971, Rameses III; 972, Maiden carrying offerings; 973, Queen Nefertari.

361 H. Nassef (poet and writer) **363** Teacher at Blackboard

362 Ilyushin Il-18 and Route Map

1969. 50th Death Anniv of Hefni Nassef and Mohamed Farid.
974 **361** 20m. brown and violet . . 40 40
975 – 20m. brown and green . . 40 40
DESIGN: No. 975, M. Farid (politician).

1969. Air. Inauguration of Ilyushin Il-18 Aircraft by United Arab Airlines.
976 **362** 55m. purple, yellow & bl 95 65

1969. Arab Teachers' Day.
977 **363** 20m. multicoloured . . . 35 15

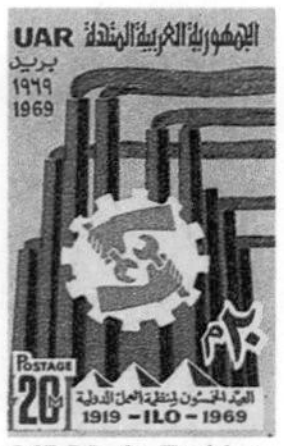

364 Flags of Arab Nations **365** I.L.O. Emblem and Factory Stacks

1969. Arab Publicity Week.
978 **364** 20m.+10m. red, bl & grn 45 45

1969. 50th Anniv of I.L.O.
979 **365** 20m. multicoloured . . . 40 20

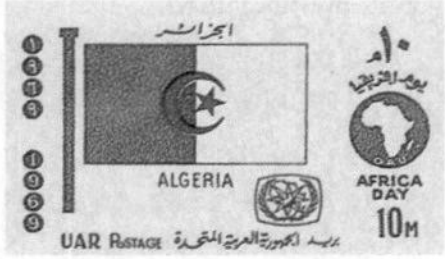

366 Algerian Flag

1969. African Tourist Year. Flags of African Nations.
980 **366** 10m. red and green . . . 60 30
981 – 10m. black, blue & grn 60 30
982 – 10m. red and green . . . 60 30
983 – 10m. red, yellow & grn 60 30
984 – 10m. multicoloured . . . 60 30
985 – 10m. yellow, red & blue 60 30
986 – 10m. brown, red & grn 60 30
987 – 10m. red, yellow & blue 60 30
988 – 10m. brown, red & grn 60 30
989 – 10m. green, red & black 60 30
990 – 10m. multicoloured . . . 60 30
991 – 10m. multicoloured . . . 60 30
992 – 10m. yellow, grn & bl . . 60 30
993 – 10m. blue, red & green 60 30
994 – 10m. multicoloured . . . 60 30
995 – 10m. brown, red & grn 60 30
996 – 10m. orange & green . . 60 30
997 – 10m. black, red & green 60 30
998 – 10m. blue, red & green 60 30
999 – 10m. red and blue . . . 60 30
1000 – 10m. black, red & green 60 30
1001 – 10m. red and green . . . 60 30
1002 – 10m. red, black & green 60 30
1003 – 10m. brown, red & grn 60 30
1004 – 10m. yellow & green . . 60 30
1005 – 10m. multicoloured . . . 60 30
1006 – 10m. green and red . . . 60 30
1007 – 10m. orange & green . . 60 30
1008 – 10m. green 60 30
1009 – 10m. multicoloured . . . 60 30
1010 – 10m. green, brown & red 60 30
1011 – 10m. blue and green . . 60 30
1012 – 10m. blue and green . . 60 30
1013 – 10m. yellow, green & bl 60 30
1014 – 10m. multicoloured . . . 60 30
1015 – 10m. multicoloured . . . 60 30
1016 – 10m. yellow, grn & red 60 30
1017 – 10m. red and green . . . 60 30
1018 – 10m. black, yellow & red 60 30
1019 – 10m. black, red & green 60 30
1020 – 10m. multicoloured . . . 60 30

FLAGS: No. 981, Botswana. 982, Burundi. 983, Cameroun. 984, Central African Republic. 985, Chad. 986, Congo-Brazzaville. 987, Congo-Kinshasa. 988, Dahomey. 989, Egypt-U.A.R. 990, Equatorial Guinea. 991, Ethiopia. 992, Gabon. 993, Gambia. 994, Ghana. 995, Guinea. 996, Ivory Coast. 997, Kenya. 998, Lesotho. 999, Liberia. 1000, Libya. 1001, Malagasy Republic. 1002, Malawi. 1003, Mali. 1004, Mauritania. 1005, Mauritius. 1006, Morocco. 1007, Niger. 1008, Nigeria. 1009, Rwanda. 1010, Senegal. 1011, Sierra Leone. 1012, Somalia. 1013, Sudan. 1014, Swaziland. 1015, Tanzania. 1016, Togo. 1017, Tunisia. 1018, Uganda. 1019, Upper Volta. 1020, Zambia.

367 El Fetouh Gate

368 Development Bank Emblem

1969. Cairo Millenary.
1021 **367** 10m. brown, yellow & bl 35 15
1022 – 10m. multicoloured . . . 35 15
1023 – 10m. pink and blue . . . 35 15
1024 – 20m. multicoloured . . . 65 30
1025 – 20m. purple, yellow & bl 65 30
1026 – 20m. blue, yellow & brn 65 30
DESIGNS—As Type **367**. No. 1022, Al-Azhar University; 1023, Citadel. (57½ × 24½ mm); No. 1024, Two sculptures from Pharaonic period; 1025, Carved decorations, Coptic era; 1026. Glassware, Fatimid dynasty.

1969. 5th Anniv of African Development Bank.
1028 **368** 20m. green, vio & yell 30 15

369 Mahatma Gandhi

370 "King and Queen" Abu Simbel (U.N.E.S.C.O.)

1969. Air. Birth Cent of Mahatma Gandhi.
1029 **369** 80m. orange, brn & bl 2·50 1·25

1969. United Nations Day.
1030 **370** 5m. yellow, blue & brn 20 20
1031 – 20m. blue and yellow . . 40 20
1032 – 30m.+10m. mult 75 75
1033 – 55m. multicoloured . . . 95 50
DESIGNS—As T **370**: 20m. Ancient Egyptian Ship (I.M.C.O.); 36 × 36mm: 30m.+10m. Arab refugees (U.N.R.W.A.); 55m. Partly submerged temple, Philae (U.N.E.S.C.O.).

371 Demonstrators

1969. Anniversaries.
1034 **371** 20m. purple, red & grn 75 35
1035 – 20m. brown, yellow & bl 1·00 40
1036 – 20m. multicoloured . . . 75 35
DESIGNS AND EVENTS: No. 1034, (50th anniv of 1919 Revolution). LARGER (58 × 25 mm); No. 1035, Labourers, merchant ships of 1869 and 1969 and map (Suez Canal Centenary); 1036, Performance of "Aida" (Cairo Opera-house Centenary).

372 "Ancient Egyptian Accountants"

1969. International Scientific Accounts Congress, Cairo.
1037 **372** 20m. purple, grn & yell 45 20

373 Poinsettia

1969. Ramadan Festival.
1038 **373** 5m. red, green & yellow 40 20

374 Step Pyramid, Sakkara

375 President Nasser

1969.
1039 **374** 1m. brown, ochre & bl 20 30
1040 – 5m. brown, yellow & bl 30 10
1041 – 10m. purple, ochre & bl 30 10
1042 **260** 20m. brown (22 × 27½ mm) . . . . 1·60 25
1043 – 50m. brn, ochre & bl . . 1·60 35
1044 – 55m. green . . . . . . 2·25 25
1045 **375** 200m. blue & purple . . 5·00 95
1046 500m. black and blue . . 9·50 3·50
1047 – £El green and orange . . 19·00 5·50
DESIGNS—As Type **374**: 5m. Al-Azhar Mosque, Cairo; 10m. Temple, Luxor; 50m. Qaitbay Fort, Alexandria. 22 × 27½ mm: 55m. As No. 781. As T **375**: £El, Khafre.
See also Nos. 1131/41.

376a Imam Mohamed El Boukhary

377 Azzahir Beybars Mosque

1969. Air. 1100th Death Anniv of Imam El Boukhary (philosopher and writer).
1048 **376a** 30m. brown and olive 45 20

1969. Air. 700th Anniv of Azzahir Beybars Mosque.
1049 **377** 30m. purple 45 20

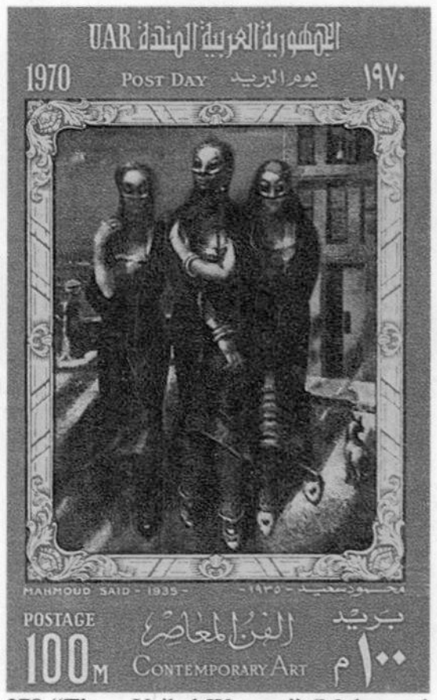
378 "Three Veiled Women" (Mahmoud Said)

1970. Post Day.
1050 **378** 100m. multicoloured . . 2·75 2·25

379 Parliament Building and Emblems

1970. Int Conf on Middle East Crisis, Cairo.
1051 **379** 20m. ultram, brn & bl 45 20

380 Human Rights Emblem and "Three Races"

1970. Racial Equality Day.
1052 **380** 20m.+10m. yellow, brown and green . . . 65 65

381 Arab League Flag, Arms and Map

1970. 25th Anniv of Arab League.
1053 **381** 20m.+10m. green, brown and blue 50 55
1054 30m. grn, plum & orge 55 25

382 Mina House Hotel, Giza, and Sheraton Hotel, Cairo

1970. Centenary of Mina House Hotel and Opening of Sheraton Hotel.
1055 **382** 20m. green, orange & bl 50 25

383 Pharmacists

1970. 30th Anniv of Egyptian Pharmaceutical Industry.
1056 **383** 20m. blue, brown & yell 85 25

384 Mermaid

385 Lenin

1970. 8th Fine Arts Biennale, Alexandria.
1057 **384** 20m. blk, bl & orge . . 45 20

1970. Air. Birth Centenary of Lenin.
1058 **385** 80m. brown and green 1·25 95

386 Emblem and Bombed Factory

1970. Air. Attack on Abu Zaabal Factory.
1059 **386** 80m. purple, bl & yell 1·25 95

387 Talaat Harb (founder) and Bank

388 I.T.U. Emblem

1970. 50th Anniv of Misr Bank.
1060 **387** 20m. brn, ochre & bl . . 45 20

1970. World Telecommunications Day.
1061 **388** 20m. blue, yell & brn . . 50 20

389 New Headquarters Building

390 Basketball Player, Cup and Map

1970. New U.P.U. Headquarters Building, Berne.
1062 **389** 20m. purple, green and yellow (postage) . . . 50 20
1063 80m. black, green and yellow (air) 95 80

1970. 5th Africa Men's Basketball Championships.
1064 **390** 20m. blue, brn & yell . . 75 30

391 Emblems of U.P.U., U.N. and African Postal Union

1970. African Postal Union Seminar.
1065 **391** 20m. green, vio & orge 50 20

392 Footballer and Cup

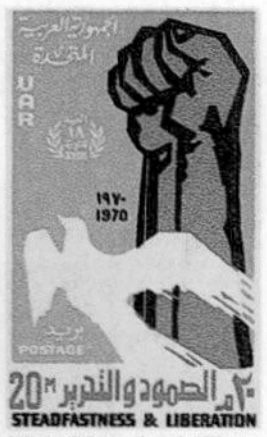
393 Clenched Fists and Dove

1970. Africa Cup Football Championships.
1066 **392** 20m. brown, yellow & bl 65 30

1970. 18th Anniv of Revolution.
1067 **393** 20m. orge, blk & grn . . 60 25

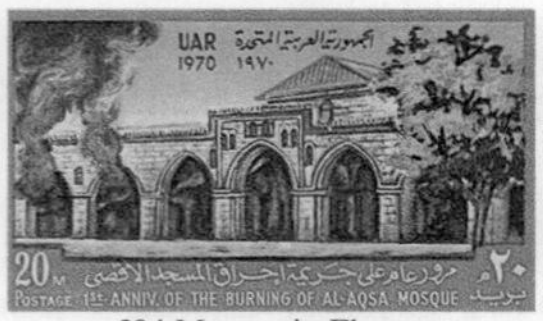
394 Mosque in Flames

1970. 1st Anniv of Burning of Al Aqsa Mosque, Jerusalem.
1069 **394** 20m. brn, orge & grn . . 65 30
1070 60m. brown, red & blue 1·75 1·25

395 Globe, Wheat and Cogwheel

1970. World Standards Day.
1071 **395** 20m. brn, blue & grn . . 50 20

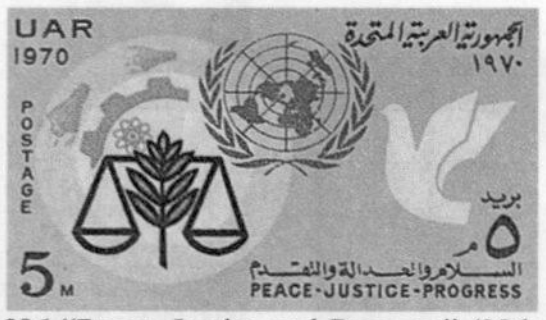
396 "Peace, Justice and Progress" (25th Anniv of U.N.)

1970. United Nations Day.
1072 **396** 5m. blue, lt bl & mve . . 20 10
1073 – 10m. bl, ochre & brn . . 20 15
1074 – 20m. multicoloured . . . 40 20
1075 – 20m.+10m. mult 60 60
1076 – 55m. brn, bl & ochre . . 90 80
1077 – 55m. brn, bl & ochre . . 90 80
DESIGNS AND EVENTS—37 × 37 mm: 10m. U.N. emblem; 55m. (2) Philae Temple (composite design) (U.N.E.S.C.O. Campaign for Preservation of Nubian Monuments); 36 × 36 mm: 20m. Frightened child and bombed school (Int Education Year); 41 × 25 mm: 20m.+10m. Palestinian guerrillas and refugees ("Int support for Palestinians").

397 President Nasser

398 Medical Association Building

1970. Pres. Gamal Nasser Memorial Issue.
1078 **397** 5m. black and bl (postage) 20 15
1079 – 20m. black and green . . 45 20
1080 – 30m. black & grn (air) 65 30
1081 – 80m. black & brown . . 1·90 95

DESIGN—46 × 27 mm: 30, 80m. Pres. Nasser and mosque.

1970. Egyptian Anniversaries.
1082 **398** 20m. brown, yellow and blue 60 40
1083 – 20m. brown, yellow and blue 60 40
1084 – 20m. brown and blue . . 60 40
1085 – 20m. brown, yellow and blue 60 40
1086 – 20m. brown, yellow and blue 60 40
DESIGNS AND EVENTS: No. 1082, Type **398** (50th anniv of Egyptian Medical Assn); 1083, Old and new library buildings (centenary of National Library); 1084, "The most significant victory…" Pres. Nasser text ("Egyptian Credo"); 1085, Old and new printing works (150th anniv of Govt. Printing Office); 1086, Old and new headquarters (50th anniv of Egyptian Engineering Society).

399 Map of Egypt, Libya and Sudan

1970. Signing of Tripoli Charter.
1087 **399** 20m. green, black & red 50 20

400 Minaret, Qalawun Mosque

402 Fair Emblem

1970. Post Day. Mosque Minarets. Each brown, blue and yellow.
1088 5m. Type **400** 30 25
1089 10m. As-Salem Mosque . . 40 30
1090 20m. Isna Mosque 60 50
1091 55m. Al-Hakim Mosque . . 1·25 1·00
See also Nos. 1142/5 and 1189/92.

1971. Cairo International Fair.
1093 **402** 20m. yellow, blk & pur 45 20

403 Map of Arab States and A.P.U. Emblem

1971. 9th Arab Postal Union Congress, Cairo.
1094 **403** 20m. blue, orange and green (postage) . . . 50 20
1095 30m. brown, orange and green (air) 70 35

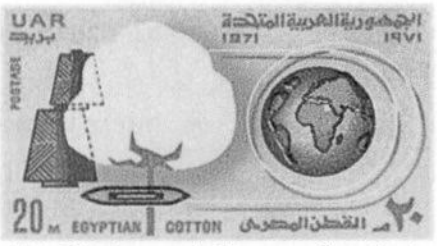
404 Globe and Cotton Symbols

1971. Egyptian Cotton Production.
1096 **404** 20m. brown, blue & grn 50 20

405 Army Emblem

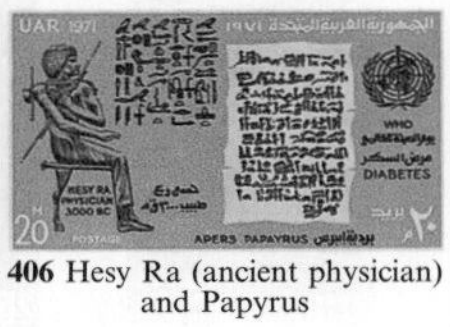
406 Hesy Ra (ancient physician) and Papyrus

1971. Forces' Mail.
1097 **405** 10m. violet . . . . . . 1·00 40

The above stamp was issued for civilian use on letters addressed to servicemen and was not valid for any other purpose.

1971. World Health Day.
1098 **406** 20m. purple & yellow . . 65 20

407 Pres. Gamal Nasser

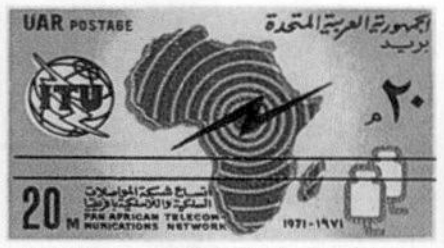
408 Map and I.T.U. Emblem

1971.
1099 **407** 20m. blue and purple . . 65 20
1100 55m. plum and blue . . 2·25 75

1971. African Telecommunications Year.
1101 **408** 20m. multicoloured . . . 65 20

409 El Rifaei and Sultan Hussein Mosques

1971. Air. Multicoloured.
1102 30m. Type **409** 95 45
1103 85m. Rameses Square, Cairo 2·25 85
1104 110m. Sphinx and Pyramids 2·25 1·90

410 "Industrial Progress"

411 A.P.U. Emblem

1971. 19th Anniv of Revolution. Mult.
1105 20m. Type **410** 45 30
1106 20m. Ear of Wheat and Laurel ("Land Reclamation") 45 30

1971. 25th Anniv of Founding of Arab Postal Union at Sofar Conference.
1108 **411** 20m. emerald, yellow and green (postage) . . 50 20
1109 30m. mult (air) 85 50

412 Federal Links

413 Pres. Gamal Nasser

1971. Inaug of Confederation of Arab Republics.
1110 **412** 20m. brown, black and purple (postage) . . . 50 25
1111 30m. green, black and purple (air) 80 40

1971. 1st Death Anniv of President Nasser.
1112 **413** 5m. blue and purple . . 25 15
1113 20m. purple and blue . . 40 15
1114 30m. blue and brown . . 75 45
1115 55m. brown and green 1·25 75

414 "Princess and Child"

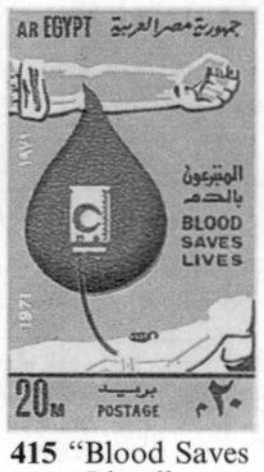
415 "Blood Saves Lives"

1971. United Nations Day.
1116 **414** 5m. black, brown and cinnamon (postage) . . 20 15
1117 – 20m. multicoloured . . . 45 20
1118 – 55m. multicoloured . . . 1·10 85
1119 – 30m. mult (air) 85 45
DESIGNS—As Type **414**. VERT: 5m. (U.N.I.C.E.F.). HORIZ: 20m. Emblem and four heads (Racial Equality Year); 36 × 36 mm: 30m. Refugee and Al-Aqsa Mosque (U.N.R.W.A.); 24 × 58 mm: 55m. Partly submerged pillar, Philae (25th anniv of U.N.E.S.C.O.).

1971. Blood Donors.
1120 **415** 20m. red and green . . . 85 20

416 New Post Office

417 Sunflower

1971. Opening of New Head Post Office, Alexandria.
1121 **416** 20m. brown and blue . . 75 20

1971. Ramadan Festival.
1122 **417** 5m. multicoloured . . . 30 15

418 Abdallah El Nadim

419 Globe and Earth's Strata

1971. 75th Death Anniv of Abdallah El Nadim (poet and journalist).
1123 **418** 20m. brown & green . . 50 20

1971. 75th Anniv of Egyptian Geological Survey.
1124 **419** 20m. multicoloured . . . 95 25

420 A.P.U. Emblem and Dove with Letter

1971. 10th Anniv of African Postal Union.
1125 **420** 5m. mult (postage) . . . 25 10
1126 20m. green, orge & blk 50 15
1127 – 55m. black, bl & red . . 1·25 80
1128 – 30m. mult (air) 65 40
DESIGN: 30m., 55m. A.P.U. emblem and airmail envelope.

421 "Savings Bank"

1971. 70th Anniv of Post Office Savings Bank.
1129 **421** 20m. multicoloured . . . 75 25

421a Victory Parade (scene from "Aida")

423 Cairo Citadel

1971. Air. Centenary of First Performance of Verdi's Opera "Aida", in Cairo.
1130 **421a** 110m. yell, grn & brn 4·50 2·50

1972. Inscr "A. R. EGYPT".
1131 **374** 1m. blue and brown . . 10 20
1131a 1m. brown 10 20
1132 – 5m. blue, yellow & brn (as No. 1040) 25 15
1132a – 5m. green 30 15
1132b – 5m. bistre 30 15
1133 – 10m. purple, brown & bl (as No. 1041) . . 40 15
1133a – 10m. brown 40 10
1134 **260** 20m. green (22 × 27½ mm) . . . 65 20
1135 20m. mauve (22 × 27½ mm) . . . 95 25
1136 – 50m. brown, ochre & blue (as No. 1043) 1·50 25
1136a – 50m. blue . . . . . . 1·75 25
1137 – 55m. mauve (as No. 1044) . . . . . 2·25 55
1137a – 55m. green . . . . . . 1·40 20
1138a **423** 100m. blk, red & bl . . 1·10 45
1139 – 200m. brown & grn . . 4·50 95
1140 – 500m. brown and blue (as No. 1046) . . . . 9·50 2·25
1141 – £El green & orange (as No. 1047) . . . . . 19·00 5·50
DESIGNS—As Type **423**: Nos. 1132a/b, Rameses II; 1133a, Head of Seti I; 1136a, Goddess Hathar; 1137a, Sphinx and pyramid. As Type **375**: No. 1139, Head of Userkaf.

1972. Post Day. Mosque Minarets. As T **400**. Multicoloured.
1142 5m. Western minaret, An-Nasir Mosque 35 25
1143 20m. Eastern minaret, An-Nasir Mosque 50 45
1144 30m. Al-Gawli Mosque . . 80 65
1145 55m. Ahmed Ibn Toulon Mosque . . . . 1·25 95

424a Police Emblem and Activities

1972. Police Day.
1146 **424a** 20m. yellow, bl & brn 1·25 25

425 Book Year Emblem

426 Globe, Glider, Rocket and Emblem

1972. International Book Year.
1147 **425** 20m. violet, yellow & grn 75 20

1972. Air. International Aerospace Education Conference, Cairo.
1148 **426** 30m. brown, blue & yell 1·25 45

427 Monastery Aflame

1972. Air. Burning of St. Catherine's Monastery, Sinai.
1149 **427** 110m. black, brn & red 3·75 3·25

428 "Palette" (Seif Wanli)

1972. 9th Fine Arts Biennale, Alexandria.
1150 **428** 20m. red, yellow & blk 75 20

429 Fair Emblem

430 Brig. Abdel Moniem Riad and Battle Scene

1972. Int Fair, Cairo.
1151 **429** 20m. multicoloured . . . 75 20

1972. 2nd Death Anniv of Brig. Abdel Moniem Riad.
1152 **430** 20m. brown, turq & bl 95 25

431 Birds in Tree

1972. Mother's Day.
1153 **431** 20m. multicoloured . . . 75 20

432 Head of Tutankhamun (wooden statuette)

1972. 50th Anniv of Discovery of Tutankhamun's Tomb.
1154 **432** 20m. mult (postage) . . 85 30
1155 – 55m. multicoloured . . . 1·75 80
1156 – 110m. grn brn & bl (air) 3·75 2·75
1157 – 110m. grn, brn & bl . . 3·75 2·75
DESIGNS—As Type **432**: No. 1155, Decorated chair back. 28 × 62 mm: No. 1156, Tutankhamun; 1157, Ankhesenamun.
Nos. 1156/7 were issued together, se-tenant, forming a composite design.

433 Nefertiti **434** Map of Africa

1972. 50th Anniv of Society of Friends of Art.
1159 **433** 20m. blk, gold & red . . 75 20

1972. Africa Day.
1160 **434** 20m. brown, bl & vio . . 75 20

436 Eagle Emblem

1972. 20th Anniv of Revolution.
1167 **436** 20m. gold, blk & grn . . 75 20
1168 20m. red, blk & blue . . 75 20

437 Al-Azhar Mosque and St. George's Church, Cairo

1972. Air.
1170 **437** 30m. brn, ochre & bl . . 1·60 30
1171 – 85m. brn, ochre & bl . . 2·75 1·25
1172 – 110m. brn, ochre & bl 3·25 1·25
DESIGNS: 85m. Temple, Abu Simbel; 110m. Pyramids, Giza.

438 Boxing

1972. Olympic Games, Munich.
1173 **438** 5m. mult (postage) . . . 20 10
1174 – 10m. yellow, blk & red 25 10
1175 – 20m. grn, red & orge . . 40 20
1176 – 30m. green, buff and red (air) 75 30
1177 – 30m. violet, red & turq 75 30
1178 – 50m. black, blue & grn 1·25 80
1179 – 55m. red, green & blue 1·50 95
DESIGNS—HORIZ: 10m. Wrestling; 20m. Basketball, VERT: 30m. (No. 1176), Weightlifting; 30m. (No. 1177), Handball; 50m. Swimming; 55m. Gymnastics.

439 Confederation Flag

1972. 1st Anniv of Confederation of Arab Republics.
1180 **439** 20m. brown, red & blk 75 25

440 J. -F. Champollion and Rosetta Stone

1972. Air. 150th Anniv of Champollion's Translation of Egyptian Heiroglyphics.
1181 **440** 110m. grn, blk & brn . . 5·00 2·00

441 Heart (World Health Day)

1972. United Nations Day.
1182 – 10m. red, blue & brown 25 15
1183 **441** 20m. black, yell & grn 45 15
1184 – 30m. brown, vio & bl . . 85 30
1185 – 55m. gold, brown & bl 1·90 95
DESIGNS—22 × 40 mm: 10m. Emblem of 14th Regional Tuberculosis Conference, Cairo. 47 × 28 mm: 30m. Refugees (U.N.R.W.A.). 37 × 37 mm: 55m. Flooded temple, Philae (UNESCO Campaign for Preservation of Nubian Monuments).

442 Hibiscus **443** Work Day Emblem

1972. Ramadan Festival.
1186 **442** 10m. purple, grn & brn 50 20

1972. Social Work Day.
1187 **443** 20m. blue, brown & grn 75 20

444 "Rowing Fours" on Nile

1972. 3rd Nile Rowing Festival, Luxor.
1188 **444** 20m. brown and blue . . 95 25

1973. Post Day. Mosque Minarets. As T **400**. Each brown, yellow and green.
1189 10m. Al-Maridani Mosque 40 30
1190 20m. Bashtak Mosque . . . 60 45
1191 30m. Qusun Mosque . . . 95 65
1192 55m. Al-Gashankir Mosque 1·25 90

445 Ears of Corn and Globe within Cogwheel

1973. International Fair, Cairo.
1193 **445** 20m. blue, black & grn 55 25

446 Symbolic Family

1973. Family Planning Week.
1194 **446** 20m. black, orge & grn 75 25

447 Telecommunications Map

1973. Air. 5th Int Telecommunications Day.
1195 **447** 30m. blue, black & brn 1·00 25

448 Temple Column, Karnak **449** Bloody Hand and Boeing 727 Jetliner

1973. Air. "Son et Lumiere", Karnak Temples, Luxor.
1196 **448** 110m. black, mve & bl 3·00 1·90

1973. Air. Attack on Libyan Airliner over Sinai.
1197 **449** 110m. red, black & bis 4·25 1·90

451 Rifaa el Tahtawi **452** Mrs. Hoda Sharawi and Sania Girls Secondary School

1973. Death Centenary of Rifaa el Tahtawi (educationist).
1200 **451** 20m. brn, grn & dp grn 65 25

1973. Centenary of Egyptian Female Education and 50th Anniv of Women's Union.
1201 **452** 20m. green, brn & bl . . 65 25

453 Mohamed Korayem **454** Refugees and Map of Palestine

1973. 21st Anniv of Revolution. Leaders of the 1798 Resistance Movement.
1202 **453** 20m. brown, blue & grn 65 25
1203 – 20m. brown, blue & grn 65 25
1204 – 20m. choc, pk & brn . . 65 25
DESIGNS: No. 1203, Omar Makram; 1204, Abdel Rahman el Gaberti.

1973. Air. Palestinian Refugees.
1206 **454** 30m. purple, brn & bl 1·90 50

455 Rose **456** "Light and Hope"

1973. Ramadan Festival.
1207 **455** 10m. red, yellow & blue 40 15

1973. 25th Anniv of W.H.O.
1208 **456** 20m.+10m. bl & gold . . 60 60

457 Bank Building **458** Emblem and Weather-vane

1973. 75th Anniv of National Bank of Egypt.
1209 **457** 20m. blk, grn & orge . . 65 25

1973. Air. Centenary of World Meteorological Organization.
1210 **458** 110m. gold, vio & bl . . 2·50 1·50

459 Global Emblem

1973. 10th Anniv of World Food Programme.
1211 **459** 10m. blue, grn & brn . . 45 25

460 Philae Temples

1973. U.N.E.S.C.O. Campaign for the Preservation of Nubian Monuments.
1212 **460** 55m. orge, blue & violet 2·50 95

461 Interpol Emblem **462** Flame Emblem

1973. Air. 50th Anniv of International Criminal Police Organization (Interpol).
1213 **461** 110m. multicoloured . . 3·75 1·90

1973. 25th Anniv of Declaration of Human Rights.
1214 **462** 20m. red, green & blue 55 20

463 Laurel and Map of Africa **464** "Donation"

1973. 10th Anniv of Organization of African Unity.
1215 **463** 55m.+20m. mult . . . . 2·25 2·50

1973. Social Work Day.
1216 **464** 20m.+10m. blue, lilac and red 65 75

465 Dr. Taha Hussein (scholar)

467 Egyptian Postal Services Emblem

466 Pres. Sadat and Flag

1973. Hussein Commemoration.
1217 **465** 20m. brown, blue & grn 55 20

1973. Crossing of the Suez Canal, 6 October 1973.
1218 **466** 20m. black, red & brn 1·00 35
See also No. 1233.

1973. Air. Post Day.
1219 **467** 20m. blk, red & grey . . 25 15
1220 – 30m. vio, orge & blk . . 30 15
1221 – 55m. mve, grn & blk . . 90 85
1222 – 110m. gold, bl & blk . . 1·75 1·60
DESIGNS—As T **467**: 30m. Arab Postal Union emblem; 55m. African Postal Union emblem; 37 × 37 mm: 110m. U.P.U. emblem.

468 Cogwheel, Ear of Corn and Fair Emblem

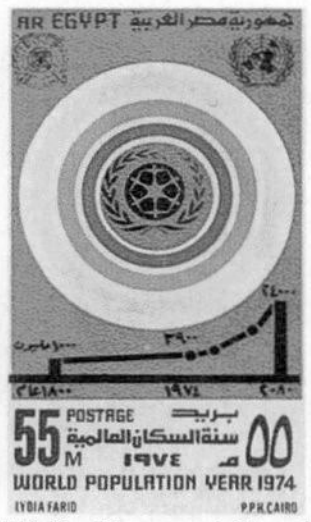

470 Emblem and Graph

469 Madame Sadat with Patient

1974. International Fair, Cairo.
1223 **468** 20m. multicoloured . . . 50 20

1974. Society of Faith and Hope (for rehabilitation of the disabled).
1224 **469** 20m.+10m. purple, gold and green 85 85

1974. World Population Year.
1225 **470** 55m. black, orge & grn 1·10 60

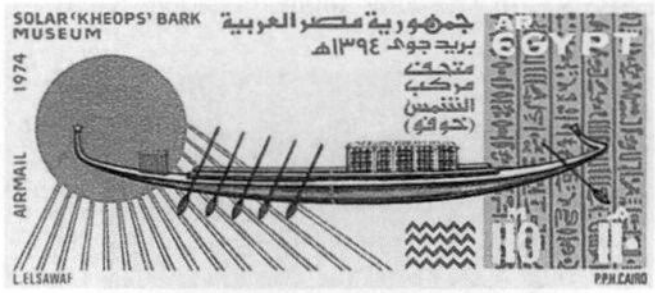

471 Solar Boat of Cheops

1974. Air. Inauguration of Solar Boat Museum.
1226 **471** 110m. brown, gold & bl 2·25 1·60

472 "Ancient Egyptian Workers" (carving from Queen Tee's tomb, Sakara)

1974. Labour Day (1 May).
1227 **472** 20m. black, yellow & bl 55 20

473 Nurse with Syringe

474 Troops crossing Barlev Line during October War

1974. Nurses' Day.
1228 **473** 55m. gold, red & green 1·25 40

1974. 22nd Anniv of Revolution.
1229 – 20m. gold, black & blue 65 35
1230 – 20m. silver, blk & pur 65 35
1231 **474** 20m. black, orge & bl . . 65 35
DESIGNS—As T **474**: No. 1229, Map of Suez Canal and "Reconstruction". 36 × 36 mm: No. 1230, Sheet of aluminium.

476 Pres. Sadat and Flag

1974. 1st Anniv of Suez Crossing.
1233 **476** 20m. black, red & yell 1·00 40
See also No. 1218.

477 Teachers' Badge

478 Artists' Palette

1974. Teachers' Day.
1234 **477** 20m. brown, blk & bl . . 55 20

1974. 6th Plastic Arts Exhibition.
1235 **478** 30m. black, yellow & vio 95 35

479 Meridian Hotel

1974. Air. Opening of Meridian Hotel, Cairo.
1236 **479** 110m. multicoloured . . 1·60 95

481 Child and Emblems

1974. Social Work Day.
1238 **481** 30m. green, brown & bl 85 30

482 Emblems of Standardization

1974. World Standards Day.
1239 **482** 10m. orange, bl & blk 40 20

483 "Aggression Registers"

484 Philae Temples

1974. Refugees Propaganda.
1240 **483** 20m. blue and red . . . 60 20

1974. U.N.E.S.C.O. Campaign for Preservation of Nubian Monuments.
1241 **484** 55m. brn, stone & bl . . 1·90 55

485 Arum Lily

486 Pile of Coins

1974. Ramadan Festival.
1242 **485** 10m. multicoloured . . . 45 20

1974. International Savings Day.
1243 **486** 20m. grey, blue & grn 55 20

487 Organization Emblems and Cameos

487a Abbas Mahmoud El Akkad (writer)

1974. Health Insurance Organization.
1244 **487** 30m. violet, red & brn 80 30

1974. Famous Egyptians.
1245 **487a** 20m. blue and brown 50 25
1246 – 20m. brown and blue 50 25
DESIGNS: No. 1245, (10th death anniv); No. 1246, Mustafa Lutfy El Manfalouty (journalist).

488 Sacred Ibis

1975. Post Day. Ancient Treasures.
1247 **488** 20m. brown, bl & sil . . 55 20
1248 – 30m. bl, orge & mve . . 75 20
1249 – 55m. brn, gold & grn . . 1·10 65
1250 – 110m. yellow, brn & bl 1·90 1·40
DESIGNS—HORIZ: 30m. Glass "fish" vase. VERT: 55m. Pharaonic gold vase; 110m. Ankh-shaped mirror.

489 Om Kolthoum (Arab singer)

490 Crescent and Globe

1975. Om Kolthoum Commemoration.
1251 **489** 20m. brown 75 25

1975. Mohammed's Birthday.
1252 **490** 20m. violet, silver & bl 75 25

491 Fair Emblem

492 Kasr El Ainy Hospital

1975. Cairo International Fair.
1253 **491** 20m. green, blue & red 45 20

1975. World Health Day.
1254 **492** 20m. brown and blue . . 75 25

493 Children Reading Book

495 Belmabgoknis Flower

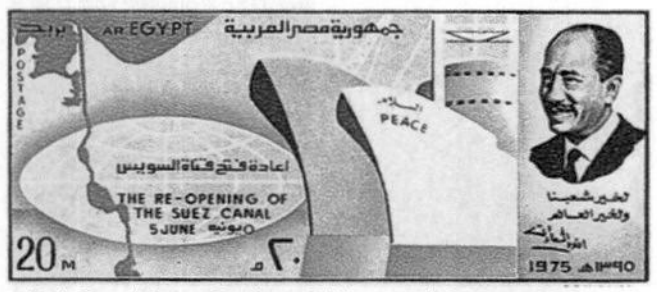

494 President Sadat, Ships and Map of Canal

1975. Science Day.
1255 **493** 20m. blue, red & yell . . 60 25
1256 – 20m. black & brown . . 60 25
DESIGN: No. 1256, Pupils and graph.

1975. Re-opening of Suez Canal.
1257 **494** 20m. brown, blue and black (postage) . . . 60 25
1258 30m. turquoise, green and blue (air) . . . . 1·25 45
1259 110m. bl blk & turq . . 1·90 1·60

1975. Festivals.
1260 **495** 10m. blue, grn & lt grn 45 20

496 I.C.I.D. Emblem

497 Spotlight on Village

1975. Air. 25th Anniv of International Commission on Irrigation and Drainage.
1261 **496** 110m. green, bl & orge 2·25 1·25

1975. 23rd Anniv of Revolution.
1262 **497** 20m. blue and brown . . 50 25
1263 – 20m. orge, blk & grn . . 50 25
1264 – 110m. multicoloured . . 2·50 2·50
DESIGNS—38 × 22 mm: No. 1263, "Tourism" (pyramids and sphinx). 70 × 79 mm: No. 1264, Tourist map of Egypt.

498 Volleyball

499 Flag and Tanks

1975. 6th Arab School Sports Tournament. Each blue, orange and green.
1265 20m. Type **498** 65 40
1266 20m. Running 65 40
1267 20m. Tournament emblem 65 40

1268 20m. Basketball 65 40
1269 20m. Football 65 40

1975. 2nd Anniv of Battle of 6 October.
1270 **499** 20m. multicoloured . . . 75 25

1975. International Symposium on October War, Cairo University. As T **499** but with additional commemorative inscription at foot and "M" above figures of value.
1271 20m. multicoloured 65 25

500 Schistosomiasis Conference Emblem

501 University Emblem

1975. United Nations Day.
1272 **500** 20m. blue, mauve and brown (postage) . . . 65 25
1273 – 55m. purple, yell & bl 1·50 80
1274 – 30m. brn, grn & pur (air) 85 40
1275 – 110m. blk, orge & grn 2·25 1·60
DESIGNS—27 × 47 mm: 55m. Wall relief (UNESCO Campaign for Preservation of Nubian Monuments). 48 × 40 mm: 30m. Refugees and barbed wire (U.N.R.W.A.). 22 × 40 mm: 110m. Women (International Women's Year).

1975. 25th Anniv of Ein Shams University.
1276 **501** 20m. blue, yell & grey 40 20

501a Al-Kanady

502 Ibex

1975. Arab Philosophers.
1277 **501a** 20m. brown, grn & bl 50 35
1278 – 20m. brown, grn & bl 50 35
1279 – 20m. brown, grn & bl 50 35
DESIGNS: No. 1278, Al-Farabi, and lute; No. 1279, Al-Biruni, and open book.

1976. Post Day. Treasures from Tutankhamun's Tomb. Multicoloured.
1280 20m. Type **502** 50 20
1281 30m. Lioness 85 25
1282 55m. Sacred Cow . . . . . 1·40 75
1283 110m. Hippopotamus . . . 2·00 1·50

503 High Dam and Industrial Potential

504 Fair Emblem

1976. Filling of High Dam Lake.
1284 **503** 20m. multicoloured . . . 75 25

1976. Cairo International Fair.
1285 **504** 20m. violet & orange . . 30 15

505 Biennale Commemorative Emblem

506 Protective Hands

1976. 11th Fine Arts Biennale, Alexandria.
1286 **505** 20m. yellow, blk & grn 35 15

1976. Society of Faith and Hope.
1287 **506** 20m. yell, grn & dp grn 35 15

507 "Pharaonic Eye" and Emblem

508 Scales of Justice

1976. World Health Day.
1288 **507** 20m. brn, yell & grn . . 60 15

1976. 5th Anniv of Rectification Movement.
1289 **508** 20m. black, grn & red 50 15

509 Pres. Sadat and Emblem

1976. Centenary of Arbitration Service.
1290 **509** 20m. yellow, grn & ol . . 50 15

510 Front Page of First Issue

1976. Cent of Newspaper "Al-Ahram".
1291 **510** 20m. brown, blk & red 50 15

511 Pres. Sadat and World Map

1976. 24th Anniv of Revolution.
1292 **511** 20m. yellow, blue & black 60 20

512 Amaryllis

513 Map of Red Sea, Pres. Sadat and Abu Redice Oil Refinery

1976. Festivals.
1294 **512** 10m. multicoloured . . . 45 10

1976. 3rd Anniv of Suez Canal Crossing. Mult.
1295 20m. Type **513** 50 25
1296 20m. Irrigation and reconstruction—map of Suez Canal (48 × 40 mm) 50 25
1297 110m. Monument to Soldiers of October 6th, 1973 (65 × 80 mm) . . . . 2·50 2·50

514 Animals on Papyrus Leaf ("Literature for Children")

1976. United Nations Day.
1298 **514** 20m. brown, stone & bl 40 20
1299 – 30m. brown, grn & blk 50 25
1300 – 55m. brown and blue . . 95 40
1301 – 110m. red, grn & vio . . 1·50 1·10
DESIGNS—39 × 22 mm: 30m. Dome of the Rock (Palestinian Refugees); 110m. UNESCO emblem on figure "30" (30th anniv of UNESCO). 25 × 59 mm: 55m. Relief showing goddess Isis, Philae Temple (UNESCO Campaign for Preservation of Nubian Monuments).

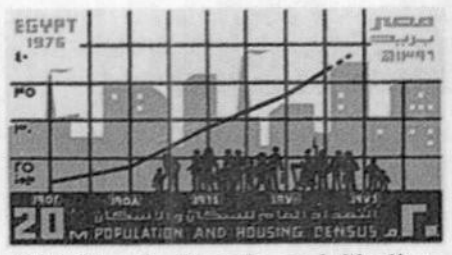

515 Graph, People and Skyline

516 Society Medal and Map of the Nile

1976. Population and Housing Census.
1302 **515** 20m. sepia, blue & brn 50 10

1976. Cent of Egyptian Geographical Society.
1303 **516** 20m. brown, green & bl 50 10

517 King Akhnaton

518 Patrolman, Police Car and Map

1977. Post Day.
1304 **517** 20m. brown & black . . 30 15
1305 – 30m. brown & black . . 45 20
1306 – 55m. brown & purple . . 60 30
1307 – 110m. brown & purple 1·25 95
DESIGNS: 30m. Head of Akhnaton's daughter; 55m. Head of Nefertiti, wife of Akhnaton; 110m. Bust of Akhnaton.

1977. Police Day.
1308 **518** 20m. red, blue & black 95 25

519 Pharaonic Ship

520 O.A.U. and Arab League Emblems on Map

1977. Cairo International Fair.
1309 **519** 20m. green, blk & red 45 10

1977. 1st Afro-Arab Summit Conference.
1310 **520** 55m. blue, blk & orge 75 40

521 King Faisal

522 Healthy Children and Paralysed Child

1977. King Faisal of Saudi Arabia Commemoration.
1311 **521** 20m. brown and blue . 50 10

1977. National Campaign for Prevention of Poliomyelitis.
1312 **522** 20m. dp brn, brn & red 75 20

523 A.P.U. Emblem and National Flags

1977. Silver Jubilee of Arab Postal Union.
1313 **523** 20m. multicoloured . . . 35 20
1314 30m. multicoloured . . . 45 25

524 Children's Village

525 Earth and Satellite

1977. Inaug of S.O.S. Children's Village, Cairo.
1315 **524** 20m. brown, blue & grn 35 20
1316 55m. red, blue & green 95 60

1977. World Telecommunications Day.
1317 **525** 110m. blue, yell & blk 1·60 1·00

526 Loom, Spindle and Factories

1977. 50th Anniv of Egyptian Spinning and Weaving Company, El Mehalla El Kobra.
1318 **526** 20m. green, brn & bis . . 40 10

527 Egyptian Flag and Symbol of the Revolution

528 Saad Zaghoul

1977. 25th Anniv of Revolution.
1319 **527** 20m. black, red & silver 35 10

1977. 50th Death Anniv of Saad Zaghoul (revolutionary).
1321 **528** 20m. brown & green . . 25 10

529 Archbishop Capucci and Map of Palestine

530 Bird of Paradise Flowers

1977. 3rd Anniv of Arrest of Archbishop Capucci.
1322 **529** 45m. blk, grey & grn . . 95 40

1977. Festivals.
1323 **530** 10m. multicoloured . . . 35 10

531 Title Deeds overshadowing Map of Egypt

532 Soldier, Tanks and 6th October Medal

1977. 25th Anniv of Agrarian Reform Law.
1324 **531** 20m. black, bl & grn . . 25 10

1977. 4th Anniv of Suez Canal Crossing.
1325 **532** 20m. brn, red & orge . . 35 20
1326 – 140m. brn, red & gold 3·50 3·50
DESIGN—46 × 55 mm: 140m. President Sadat.

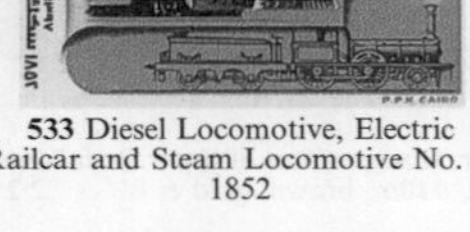

533 Diesel Locomotive, Electric Railcar and Steam Locomotive No. 1, 1852

1977. 125th Anniv of Egyptian Railways.
1327 **533** 20m. green, blue & vio 85 30

534 Refugees and the Al-Aqsa Mosque (U.N.R.W.A.)

1977. United Nations Day.
1328 **534** 45m. green, red & blk 50 30
1329 – 55m. yellow and blue . . 75 40
1330 – 140m. ochre & brown . . 1·60 1·25
DESIGNS—36 × 36 mm: 55m. Relief from Philae showing Horus and goddess Taueret. As T **534** but vert: 140m. Relief from Philae in frame of pharaonic column (UNESCO Campaign for Preservation of Nubian Monuments).

535 Ancient Egyptian Symbol for "Vision" and Film

536 Natural Gas Rig and Factories

1977. 50th Anniv of Egyptian Cinema.
1331 **535** 20m. blk, gold & grey 65 20

1977. National Petroleum Festival.
1332 **536** 20m. blue, blk & grn . . 85 20

537 President Sadat, Olive Branches and Dome of the Rock, Jerusalem

1977. President Sadat's Peace Mission to Israel.
1333 **537** 20m. brown, grn & blk 35 20
1334 140m. blk, grn & brn . . 1·60 1·25

538 The Three Pyramids at Giza

1978. Air.
1335 **538** 45m. yellow & brown 45 20
1335b 60m. brown . . . . . 1·10 60
1336 – 115m. brown & blue . . 80 40
1337 – 140m. lilac and blue . . 1·25 70
1337a – 185m. brown & blue . . 2·75 1·40
DESIGNS: 115, 185m. Step Pyramid and temple entrance, Sakkara. 140m. Nile feluccas.

539 Statue of Rameses II

1978. Post Day. Multicoloured.
1338 20m. Type **539** 30 20
1339 45m. Relief showing coronation of Queen Nefertari, Abu Simbel . . 85 60

540 Irrigation Wheels, Fayoum

541 Fair Emblem

1978.
1340 **540** 1m. blue 10 10
1341 – 5m. brown 10 10
1342 – 10m. green 10 10
1343 – 20m. brown 20 10
1343b – 30m. brown 20 10
1344 – 50m. blue 30 15
1345 – 55m. brown 40 25
1346 – 70m. brown 50 25
1346a – 80m. brown 45 10
1347 – 85m. purple 60 30
1348 – 100m. brown 85 25
1349 – 200m. indigo & blue . . 1·60 50
1350 – 500m. brn, bl & yell . . 4·50 1·60
1351 – £E1 blue, yell & brn . . 6·50 3·00
DESIGNS—As T **540**: 5m. Pigeon-loft; 10m. Statue of Horus; 20, 30m. El Rifaei Mosque, Cairo; 50m. Syrian monastery, Wady el Netroon; 55m. Edfu temple; 70, 80m. October Bridge over Suez Canal; 85m. Medom pyramid; 100m. Facade of Abu el Abbas el Morsy Mosque, Alexandria; 200m. El Sawary column and sphinx, Alexandria; 37 × 45 mm: 500m. Arab horse; £E1, Bird (floor decoration from Akhnaton's palace).

1978. 11th Cairo International Fair.
1352 **541** 20m. grn, blk & orge . . 30 10

542 Old Kasr el Ainy Medical School and New Tower

543 Youssef el Sebai

1978. 150th Anniv of Kasr el Ainy Medical School.
1353 **542** 20m. brown, blue & gold 40 20

1978. Youssef el Sebai (assassination victim) and Commando Heroes Commemoration.
1354 – 20m. brown 35 25
1355 **543** 20m. black, brn & yell 35 25
DESIGN: No. 1354, Group of Commandos and emblems.

544 Bienniale Medal and Statue, Port Said

1978. 12th Fine Arts Biennale, Alexandria.
1356 **544** 20m. black, green & bl 40 20

545 Child with Smallpox

1978. World Health Day.
1357 **545** 20m. orge, blk & grn . . 50 25
1358 – 20m. red, orge & blk . . 50 25
DESIGN AND EVENT: No. 1357, Type **545** (World Year for the Eradication of Smallpox); 21 × 38 mm: No. 1358, Heart and downwards pointing arrow (World Hypertension Month).

546 President Sadat

1978. 7th Anniv of Rectification Movement.
1359 **546** 20m. brn, grn & gold . . 20 10

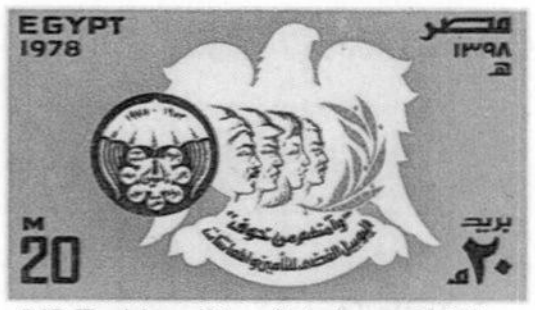
547 Emblem, Beneficiaries and Olive-branch

1978. 25th Anniv of General Organization of Insurance and Pensions.
1360 **547** 20m. brown and green 20 10

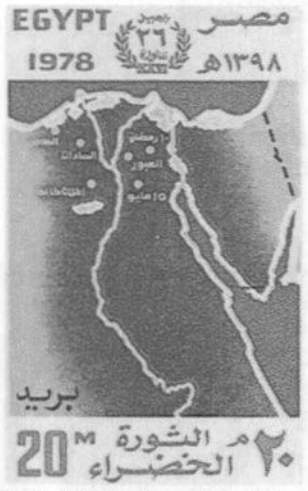
548 Map showing New Cities and Regions suitable for Cultivation (The Green Revolution)

549 Wall of Ministerial Emblems

1978. 26th Anniv of Revolution.
1361 **548** 20m. green, yellow & bl 30 20
1362 – 45m. orange, grn & brn 60 30
DESIGN: 45m. Map of Egypt and Sudan with ear of wheat (Economic integration of Egypt and Sudan).

1978. Cent of Egyptian Ministerial System.
1363 **549** 20m. violet, grn & yell 25 10

550 President Sadat, Statue of the Crossing and Factories

1978. 5th Anniv of Suez Canal Crossing.
1364 **550** 20m. yellow, brn & grn 40 10

551 Anti-Apartheid Emblem

552 Tahtib Folk-dance on Horseback

1978. United Nations Day.
1365 **551** 20m. orge, blk & grn . . 25 10
1366 – 45m. yell, brn & grn . . 55 35
1367 – 55m. orange, brn & bl 70 55
1368 – 140m. orge, blk & grn 1·40 95
DESIGNS—As T **551**. HORIZ: 55m. Philae temples (UNESCO Campaign for Preservation of Nubian Monuments). VERT: 140m. Dove, flame and olive branch (30th anniv of Declaration of Human Rights); 37 × 37 mm: 45m. Kobet al-Sakhra Mosque, refugee camp and U.N. emblem (U.N.R.W.A.).

1978. Festivals.
1369 **552** 10m. orange, brn & bl 20 10
1370 20m. bistre, brn & bl . . 35 10

553 Pilgrims at Mount Arafat and Script of Islamic Prayer

1978. Islamic Pilgrimage.
1371 **553** 45m. brown, yell & bl 65 35

554 U.N. and Conference Emblems

1978. U.N. Conference on Technical Co-operation amongst Developing Countries.
1372 **554** 20m. black, grn & yell 25 10

555 Oil Pipeline "Sumed", Badge and Map

1978. 1st Anniv of Inauguration of "Sumed" Oil Pipeline.
1373 **555** 20m. brown, orge & bl 50 10

556 Mastheads and Editors

557 Ibn Roshd

1978. 150th Anniv of "El Wakaea el Massreya" Newspaper.
1374 **556** 20m. black & brown . . 30 10

1978. 800th Death Anniv of Ibn Roshd (philosopher).
1375 **557** 45m. blue, emer & grn 40 20

558 Old and Modern Observatories and Chart of Planet Movements

1978. 75th Anniv of Helwan Observatory.
1376 **558** 20m. blue, brn & yell . . 70 25

559 Wright Brothers' Type A Biplane and I.C.A.O. Emblem

560 Daughter of Rameses II

1978. Air. 75th Anniv of First Powered Flight.
1377 **559** 140m. brown, bl & blk 1·90 1·25

1979. Post Day.
1378 **560** 20m. yellow & brown . . 30 20
1379 – 140m. yellow, brn & bl 95 65
DESIGN:-(37½ × 43 mm). 140m. Small temple and statues of Rameses II, Abu Simbel.

561 Open Book, Globe and Reader

1979. 11th Cairo International Book Fair.
1380 **561** 20m. brown and green 35 10

562 Fair Emblem and Symbols of Industry and Agriculture

1979. Cairo International Fair.
1381 **562** 20m. brown, orge & bl 35 10

563 Poppy and Skull

1979. 50th Anniv of Anti-narcotics General Administration.
1382 **563** 70m. green, red & yell 1·40 50

564 Isis and Horus **566** Doves, President Sadat's Signature and "Peace"

565 World Map, Koran and Symbols of Arab Accomplishments

1979. Mother's Day.
1383 **564** 140m. yell, brn & blue 1·10 75

1979. The Arabs.
1384 **565** 45m. sep, yell & turq . . 40 20

1979. Signing of Egyptian-Israeli Peace Treaty.
1385 **566** 20m. violet & yellow . . 25 10
1386 70m. red and green . . . 75 35
1387 140m. red and green . . 1·25 95

567 Honeycomb of Food Projects

1979. Food Security.
1388 **567** 20m. yellow, grn & blk 25 10

568 Examining 1979 Peace Stamp

1979. 50th Anniv of Egyptian Philatelic Society.
1389 **568** 20m. emer, blk & brn . . 40 20

569 Coins of 1954 and 1979

1979. 25th Anniv of Egyptian Mint.
1390 **569** 20m. grey and yellow . . 30 10

570 "Sun of Freedom" and Open Book

1979. 27th Anniv of Revolution.
1391 **570** 20m. brown, orge & bl 25 10

571 Musicians playing Rabab and Arghoul **572** Dove and Map of Sinai

1979. Festivals.
1393 **571** 10m. blk, brn & orge . . 10 10

1979. 6th Anniv of Suez Canal Crossing.
1394 **572** 20m. brown and blue . . 35 10

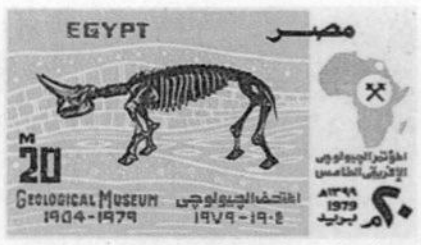

573 Skeleton of "Arsinotherium zittelli"

1979. 75th Anniv of Egyptian Geological Museum.
1395 **573** 20m. brown, yell & bl 50 20

574 Symbols of Engineering

1979. Engineers' Day.
1396 **574** 20m. pur, yell & emer 40 10

575 Human Rights Flame over Globe

1979. United Nations Day.
1397 **575** 45m. orange, bl & grn 45 20
1398 – 140m. brn, yell & red . . 1·10 95
DESIGN: 140m. Child with flower (International Year of the Child).

576 Buildings and Hand placing Coin in Box

1979. International Savings Day.
1399 **576** 70m. multicoloured . . . 60 35

577 Championship Emblem **578** Figure clothed in Palestinian Flag

1979. 20th International Military Sports Council Shooting Championship.
1400 **577** 20m. red, blue & yellow 35 10

1979. International Day of Solidarity with Palestinian People.
1401 **578** 45m. multicoloured . . . 55 15

579 Dove, Globe and Rotary Club Emblem

1979. 50th Anniv of Cairo Rotary Club and 75th Anniv (1980) of Rotary International.
1402 **579** 140m. green, blue and yellow . . . . . . 1·10 75

580 Cogs and Factories **581** Ali el Garem (educational writer, 1881–1949)

1979. 25th Anniv of Military Factories.
1403 **580** 20m. green and brown 25 10

1979. Writers.
1404 **581** 20m. brown & dp brn 20 15
1405 – 20m. dp brown & brn 20 15
DESIGN: No. 1405, Mahmoud el Baroudy (poet, 1839–1904).

582 Capital of Pharaonic Column **583** Goddess of Writing and Fair Emblem

1980. Post Day. Pharaonic Capitals.
1406 **582** 20m. brown and violet 25 25
1407 – 45m. brown and violet 40 40
1408 – 70m. brown and violet 50 50
1409 – 140m. brown and violet 1·10 1·10
DESIGNS: 45m. Head capital; 70m. Leaf capital; 140m. Capital with cartouche.

1980. 12th Cairo International Book Fair.
1410 **583** 20m. brown, blue & yell 25 10

584 Exhibition Catalogue and Medal **585** Fair Emblem and Branch

1980. 13th Fine Arts Biennale, Alexandria.
1411 **584** 20m. multicoloured . . . 25 10

1980. 13th Cairo International Fair.
1412 **585** 20m. blk, grn & orge . . 35 10

586 Trajan Monument

1980. 20th Anniv of Nubian Monuments Preservation Campaign.
1413 **586** 70m. orange, brn & bl 80 55
1414 – 70m. orange, brn & bl 80 55
1415 – 70m. orange, brn & bl 80 55
1416 – 70m. orange, brn & bl 80 55
DESIGNS: No. 1414, Qortasi monument; 1415, Kalabasha monument; 1416, Philae temple.

587 Doctors' Day Medal **588** President Sadat

1980. Doctors' Day.
1417 **587** 20m. green, blk & brn 30 10

1980. 9th Anniv of Rectification Movement.
1418 **588** 20m. green, blk & red 30 10

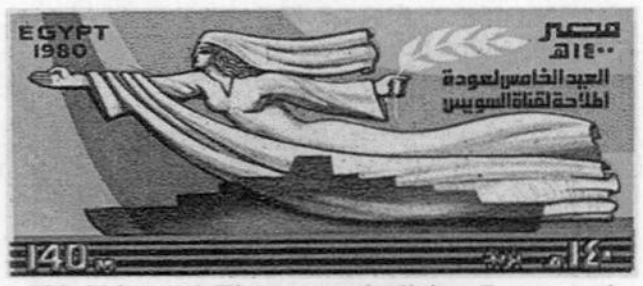

589 Ship and Figure symbolizing Peace and Freedom

1980. 5th Anniv of Re-opening of Suez Canal.
1419 **589** 140m. black, orge & bl 1·10 75

590 Pharaonic Cat

1980. Centenary of Society for the Prevention of Cruelty to Animals.
1420 **590** 20m. grey and green . . 35 15

591 Worker pushing Cogwheel

1980. Industry Day.
1421 **591** 20m. orange, brn & bl 25 10

592 Symbolic Tree

593 Erksous Seller and Nakrazan Player

1980. 28th Anniv of Revolution. Social Security Year.
1422 **592** 20m. purple, grn & brn 25 10

1980. Festivals 1980.
1424 **593** 10m. multicoloured . . . 25 10

594 "6 October", Building Construction and Doves

1980. 7th Anniv of Suez Crossing.
1425 **594** 20m. multicoloured . . . 30 10

595 Islamic and Coptic Capitals

1980. United Nations Day.
1426 **595** 70m. yellow and blue . . 60 40
1427 – 140m. red, grn & brn . . 1·10 90
DESIGN: 140m. I.T.U. emblem (International Telecommunications Day).

596 Spider's Web, Dove and Olive Branch

1980. 1400th Anniv of Hegira.
1428 **596** 45m. yellow, brn & grn 50 25

597 Tankers

1980. Opening of Third Channel of Suez Canal.
1429 **597** 70m. blue, turq & grn 65 40

598 Mustafa Sadek el Rafai (writer)

599 Scarab from Tutankhamun Collection

1980. Arab Personalities. Brown and green.
1430 20m. Type **598** (birth cent) 25 20
1431 20m. Dr. Ali Mustafa Mousharafa (scientist, 30th death anniv) 25 20
1432 20m. Dr. Ali Ibrahim (surgeon, birth centenary) 25 20

1981. Post Day.
1433 **599** 70m. multicoloured . . . 65 35
1434 – 70m. yell, brn & grn . . 65 35
DESIGN: No. 1434, Other side of scarab.

600 Heinrich von Stephan

602 Symbols of Agriculture and Industry

601 Fair Emblem, Globe and Books

1981. 150th Birth Anniv of Heinrich von Stephen (founder of U.P.U.).
1435 **600** 140m. brown & blue . . 1·60 95

1981. 13th Cairo International Book Fair.
1436 **601** 20m. green, yell & brn 35 10

1981. 14th Cairo International Fair.
1437 **602** 20m. pink, brown & grn 35 10

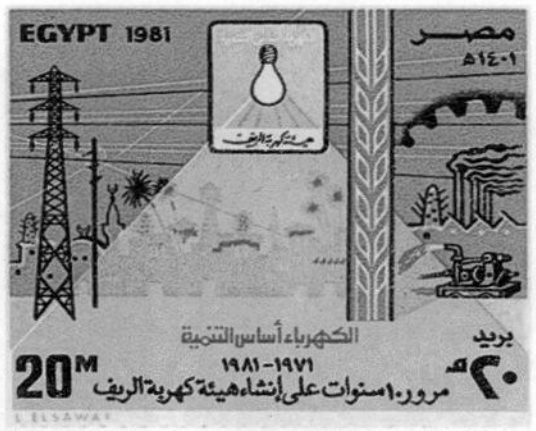

603 R.E.A. Emblem, Pylon and Village

1981. 10th Anniv of Rural Electrification Authority.
1438 **603** 20m. yellow, grn & blk 35 10

604 Soldier, Olive Branch and Veteran's Association Emblem

605 Conference Emblem

1981. Veteran's Day.
1439 **604** 20m. green, red & brn 35 10

1981. International Dentistry Conference, Cairo.
1440 **605** 20m. brown and red . . 35 10

606 Confederation Emblem

607 Nurse

1981. 25th Anniv of International Confederation of Arab Trade Unions.
1441 **606** 20m. brown and blue . . 35 10

1981. Nurses' Day.
1442 **607** 20m. orange, grn & red 35 10

608 Irrigation Spray

609 Rocket and Military Equipment

1981. 10th Anniv of Rectification Movement.
1443 **608** 20m. green, brn & yell 35 10

1981. Air Defence Day.
1444 **609** 20m. green, blue & red 40 20

610 Map of Afghanistan

1981. Solidarity with Afghan People.
1445 **610** 20m.+10m. brn, red & black (37 × 36 mm) . . 40 20
1446 20m.+10m. brn, red & black (27 × 22 mm) . . 40 20

611 "29" and Social Defence Badge

612 Water Lilies

1981. 29th Anniv of Revolution.
1447 **611** 20m. yellow, grn & brn 30 10
1448 – 20m. blue, black & red 30 10
DESIGN: No. 1448, Map of Suez Canal and ships on graph surrounded by Egyptian flag (25th anniv of Suez Canal nationalization).

1981. Festivals 1981.
1449 **612** 10m. multicoloured . . . 20 10

613 Kemal Ataturk

614 Ahmed Arabi

1981. Birth Centenary of Kemal Ataturk (Turkish statesman).
1450 **613** 140m. brown & green . . 1·60 95

1981. Centenary of Arabi Revolution.
1451 **614** 20m. brown and green 25 10

615 Muscular Athlete, Sphinx and Pyramids

616 Factory on Graph and Atomic Symbol

1981. World Muscular Athletics Championship, Cairo.
1452 **615** 45m. yell, blk & brn . . 45 25

1981. 25th Anniv of Ministry of Industry.
1453 **616** 45m. yellow, bl & red . . 35 20

617 Congress Emblem and Imhotep (god of Medicine)

1981. 20th International Medical Industries Congress, Cairo.
1454 **617** 20m. green, blk & orge 35 15

618 Eye

1981. Air.
1455 **618** 230m. bl, orge & brn . . 1·90 95

619 Olive, Dove, Canal and Wheat

1981. 8th Anniv of Suez Crossing.
1456 **619** 20m. green, stone & bl 30 10

620 I.T.U. and W.H.O. Emblems

1981. United Nations Day.
1457 – 10m. yellow, bl & brn 20 10
1458 **620** 20m. blue, orge & blk 25 15
1459 – 45m. purple, grn & blk 55 35
1460 – 230m. orange, grn & blk 2·50 1·60
DESIGNS—HORIZ: 10m. Food and Agriculture Organization Emblem (World Food Day); 230m. Olive branches (Racial Discrimination Day). VERT: 20m. Type **620** (World Telecommunications Day); 45m. International Year of Disabled Persons emblem.

621 President Sadat and Memorial

1981. President Sadat Commemoration.
1461 **621** 30m. brown, grn & red 30 20
1462 230m. brn, grn & red . . 1·90 1·60

622 Dome of Shura Council, Hands and Candle

623 Bank Emblem

1981. 1st Anniv of Shura Council.
1463 **622** 45m. yellow & lilac . . . 35 20

1981. 50th Anniv of Bank for Development and Agricultural Credit.
1464 **623** 20m. buff, grn & blk . . 25 10

624 Ali el Gayati **625** Dove and Globe forming Figure "20"

1981. Celebrities.
1465 **624** 30m. brown & green . . 25 25
1466 – 60m. brown & green . . 40 40
DESIGNS: Type **624** (journalist, 25th death anniv). 60m. Omar Ebn el Fared (poet, 1181–1234).

1981. 20th Anniv of African Postal Union.
1467 **625** 60m. yellow, bl & red . . 65 30

626 Book and Writing Materials **627** Federation Emblem

1982. 14th Cairo International Book Fair.
1468 **626** 3p. brown and yellow . . 25 10

1982. 25th Anniv of Egyptian Trade Unions Federation.
1469 **627** 3p. blue and green . . . 25 10

628 Map, "25" and Dome of University

1982. 25th Anniv of Cairo University, Khartoum Branch.
1470 **628** 6p. green and blue . . . 50 35

629 Fair Emblem **630** Hilton Ramses Hotel

1982. 15th Cairo International Fair
1471 **629** 3p. black, green & orge 25 10

1982. Air. Opening of Hilton Ramses Hotel.
1472 **630** 18½p. brown, yell & bl 1·25 85

631 Long-finned Batfish

1982. International Conference on Marine Science and 50th Anniv of Marine Biological Station, El Ghardaka. Multicoloured.
1473 10m. Type **631** 60 40
1474 30m. Blue-lined snapper . . 90 45
1475 60m. Yellow boxfish . . . . 1·00 70
1476 230m. Lined butterflyfish . . 2·50 1·50

632 Map of Sinai, Olive Branch and Dove

1982. Sinai Restoration.
1477 **632** 3p. brown, stone & grn 35 15

633 De Havilland D.H.86B Dragon Express Biplane and Boeing 737 Jetliner

1982. 50th Anniv of Egyptair (state airline).
1478 **633** 23p. blue, mauve & yell 2·50 1·60

634 Minaret **635** Dove

1982. Millenary of El Azhar Mosque.
1479 **634** 6p. yellow, brn & grn . . 65 45
1480 – 6p. yellow, brn & grn . . 65 45
1481 – 6p. yellow, brn & grn . . 65 45
1482 – 6p. yellow, brn & grn . . 65 45
DESIGNS: No. 1480, Dome and minaret (different); 1481, Minaret with three stages and one ball on top; 1482, Minaret with two balls on top.

1982. 30th Anniv of Revolution.
1484 **635** 3p. grn, dp grn & orge 25 15

636 Hotel, Citadel, Sphinx, Pyramid and St. Catherine's

1982. International Tourism Day.
1486 **636** 23p. blue, orge & brn . . 2·50 1·60

637 Martyrs' Monument, Egyptian Flag and Map

1982. 9th Anniv of Suez Crossing.
1487 **637** 3p. black, pink & blue 35 15

638 Biennale Emblem and Sailboat **639** Trees and Factory Pollution (World Environment Day)

1982. 14th Fine Arts Biennale, Alexandria.
1488 **638** 3p. orange, blue & lilac 35 15

1982. United Nations Day.
1489 **639** 3p. brown, yell & grn . . 25 15
1490 – 6p. blue and green . . . 50 40
1491 – 6p. blue and brown . . . 50 40
1492 – 8p. brown, blue & red 75 65
DESIGNS—HORIZ: No. 1490, Olive branch and dove encircling globe (2nd Conference on the Exploration and Peaceful Uses of Outer Space, Vienna); 1492, Dr. Robert Koch and bacillus (centenary of discovery of tubercle bacillus); 36 × 36 mm: No. 1491, Lord Baden-Powell and scout emblems (125th birth anniv of Lord Baden-Powell (founder) and 75th anniv of boy scout movement).

640 Avro Type 618 Ten and General Dynamics Fighting Falcon

1982. 50th Anniv of Egyptian Air Force.
1493 **640** 3p. blue and black . . . 40 20

641 Ahmed Shawqi and Hafez Ibrahim

1982. 50th Death Annivs of Ahmed Shawqi and Hafez Ibrahim (poets).
1494 **641** 6p. blue and brown . . . 50 35

642 Jubilee Emblem **643** Hands holding Flower

1982. 25th Anniv of National Research Centre.
1495 **642** 3p. blue and red 25 15

1982. Aged People Year.
1496 **643** 23p. green, red & blue 2·50 1·60

644 "Academy" on Open Books

1982. 50th Anniv of Arab League Academy.
1497 **644** 3p. brown, stone & blue 45 35

645 Postal Emblem and Postcoded Letter **647** Emblem, Globe and Open Book

646 Police Emblem

1983. Post Day.
1498 **645** 3p. blue, red and blk . . 25 20

1983. Police Day.
1499 **646** 3p. blue, black & grn . . 45 20

1983. 15th Cairo International Book Fair.
1500 **647** 3p. blue and red 25 20

648 Satellite and Map of Africa **649** Conference Emblem

1983. 5th U.N. Regional Conference for African Maps, Cairo.
1501 **648** 3p. green and blue . . . 25 20

1983. 3rd African Ministers of Transport, Communication and Planning Conference, Cairo.
1502 **649** 23p. blue and green . . 1·10 75

650 Emblem, Olive Branch and Cogwheel **651** Footballer heading Ball

1983. 16th Cairo International Fair.
1503 **650** 3p. green, black & red 25 20

1983. Egyptian Football Victories in Africa Cup and African Cup-winners Cup.
1504 **651** 3p. stone, brown & red 30 25
1505 – 3p. stone, brown & red 30 25
DESIGNS: No. 1504, Type **651** (African Cup-winners Cup, Arab Contractors Club); No. 1505, Footballer kicking ball (Africa Cup, National Club).

652 Emblem within Heart

1983. World Health Day. Blood Donation.
1506 **652** 3p. black, red & green 30 20

653 Organization Emblem

1983. 10th Anniv of Trade Union Unity Organization.
1507 **653** 3p. blue and green . . . 25 20

654 Map Dove and Flag **655** Scarab and Microscope

1983. 1st Anniv of Restoration of Sinai.
1508 **654** 3p. green, black & red 35 20

1983. 75th Anniv of Egyptian Entomological Society.
1509 **655** 3p. black and blue . . . 35 20

656 Chrysanthemums

1983. Festivals.
1510 **656** 20m. red and green . . . 25 15

657 Stadium, Player and Championship Emblem

1983. 5th African Handball Championship, Cairo.
1511 **657** 6p. brown and green . . 45 25

658 Ears of Wheat and "23" **659** Simon Bolivar (statue)

1983. 31st Anniv of Revolution.
1512 **658** 3p. green, yell & brn . . 25 15

1983. Birth Bicentenary of Simon Bolivar (South American revolutionary leader).
1513 **659** 23p. brown and blue . . 1·25 75

660 Arabi Pasha, Maps of Egypt and Ceylon and House

1983. Centenary of Exile to Ceylon of Arabi Pasha.
1514 **660** 3p. brown, grn & orge 35 20

661 Jar and Museum

1983. Reopening of Islamic Museum.
1515 **661** 3p. lt brown & brown 35 20

662 Monument, Martyrs, Cogwheel, Wheat and Oil Well **663** Rally Cars

1983. 10th Anniv of Suez Crossing.
1516 **662** 3p. green, red & blk . . 40 20

1983. 2nd International Pharaonic Motor Rally.
1517 **663** 23p. brown, bl & stone 1·60 75

664 Radar, Modern Freighter and Pharaonic Ship

1983. United Nations Day.
1518 **664** 3p. blue and black . . . 50 15
1519 – 6p. green and blue . . . 50 40
1520 – 6p. green, orge & blk . . 50 40
1521 – 23p. blue and brown . . 1·75 1·25
DESIGNS: No. 1518, Type **664** (25th anniv of International Maritime Organization); 1519, Emblems and concentric circles (World Communications Year); 1520, Ear of wheat and emblems (20th anniv of World Food Programme); 1521, Fishing boat and fish (Fishery Resources).

665 Karate, Pyramids and Sphinx

1983. 4th World Karate Championship, Cairo.
1522 **665** 3p. multicoloured . . . 45 25

666 Dome of the Rock, Jerusalem

1983. International Day of Solidarity with Palestinian People.
1523 **666** 6p. brown, ochre & grn 75 25

667 Artist's Palette **668** Statue and Cairo University

1983. 75th Anniv of Faculty of Fine Arts, Helwan University.
1524 **667** 3p. yellow, red & blue 25 20

1983. 75th Anniv of Cairo University.
1525 **668** 3p. lt brn, brn & bl . . . 25 20

669 "Mother and Child" and Emblem

1983. International Egyptian Maternity and Child Care Society.
1526 **669** 2p. blue, black & orge 30 20

670 Emblem and Maps **671** Rameses II, Thebes

1983. 20th Anniv of Organization of African Unity.
1527 **670** 3p. green and red . . . 30 20

1983. 10th Anniv (1982) of World Heritage Convention. Each stone, brown and green.
1528 3p. Type **671** 40 30
1529 3p. Coptic weaving (detail) 40 30
1530 3p. Islamic carved wooden panel 40 30

672 Qaitbay Fort

1984. Post Day. Multicoloured.
1531 6p. Type **672** 50 35
1532 23p. Mohammed Ali Mosque, Saladin's Citadel 1·50 95

673 Emblem, Family and Insurance Document **674** Open Book and Emblem

1984. 50th Anniv of Misr Insurance Company.
1533 **673** 3p. ochre, grn & brn . . 25 20

1984. 16th Cairo International Book Fair.
1534 **674** 3p. pink, green & brn . . 25 20

675 Fair Emblem within Pyramids **676** University Emblem and Map

1984. 17th Cairo International Fair.
1535 **675** 3p. orange, brn & grn 25 20

1984. 25th Anniv of Assiout University.
1536 **676** 3p. orange, blue and lilac 25 20

677 Emblem **678** Curtains, Masks and Globe

1984. 75th Anniv of Egyptian Co-operatives.
1537 **677** 3p. orange, blue & grn 25 20

1984. World Theatre Day.
1538 **678** 3p. brown, blue and red 25 20

679 Mahmoud Moukhtar and Sculptures

1984. 50th Death Anniv of Mahmoud Moukhtar (sculptor).
1539 **679** 3p. brown and green . . 25 20

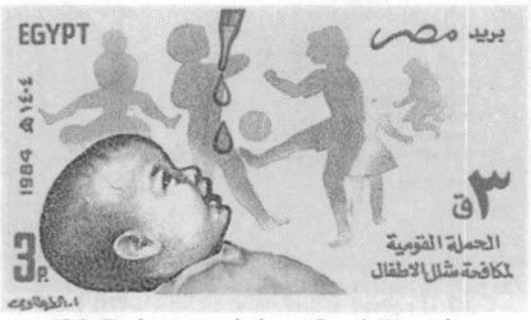

680 Baby receiving Oral Vaccine

1984. World Health Day. Anti-poliomyelitis Campaign.
1540 **680** 3p. yellow, brn & grn . . 40 20

681 Doves over Sinai **682** Map of Africa showing Namibia

1984. 2nd Anniv of Restoration of Sinai.
1541 **681** 3p. stone, green & blue 30 20

1984. Africa Day.
1542 **682** 3p. blue and brown . . . 25 20

683 Globe and Transmitter **684** Carnation

1984. 50th Anniv of Egyptian Broadcasting.
1543 **683** 3p. blue, black and red 30 20

1984. Festivals.
1544 **684** 2p. red and green . . . 25 10

685 Decorated Mask **686** Atomic Power

1984. 1st Cairo International Biennale.
1545 **685** 3p. multicoloured . . . 30 20

1984. 32nd Anniv of Revolution.
1546 **686** 3p. blue, yellow and red 25 20

687 Boxing **688** Conference Emblem

1984. Olympic Games, Los Angeles.
1547 **687** 3p. green, blue and red 30 20
1548 – 3p. green, blue and red 30 20
1549 – 3p. green, blue and red 30 20
1550 – 3p. green, blue and red 30 20
DESIGNS: No. 1548, Basketball; 1549, Volleyball; 1550, Football.

1984. 2nd Egyptians Abroad Conference, Cairo.
1552 **688** 3p. brn, bl & blk 30 20
1553 23p. brn, grn & blk . . 1·60 95

689 Couple and Emblem **690** Emblem and Sphinx

1984. 30th Anniv of Egyptian Youth Hostels Association.
1554 **689** 3p. green, blk & orge . . 25 20

1984. 50th Anniv of Misr Travel Company.
1555 **690** 3p. brown, yellow & bl 25 20

691 Eagle's Head and Map of Sinai **692** Map of Nile Valley and Integration Badge

1984. 11th Anniv of Suez Crossing.
1556 **691** 3p. green, red and black 25 20

1984. 2nd Anniv of Signing of Egypt–Sudan Co-operation Treaty.
1557 **692** 3p. red, black and green 25 20

693 Child's Face within Blossom

694 Tank, Anti-aircraft Gun and Emblem

1984. United Nations Children's Fund.
1558 **693** 3p. multicoloured . . . 25 20

1984. Defence Equipment Exhibition, Cairo.
1559 **694** 3p. yellow, black and red 25 20

695 Kamel Kilany and Books

696 Ahmed ibn Toulon Mosque

1984. 25th Death Anniv of Kamel Kilany (children's author and poet).
1560 **695** 3p. brown, yell & bl . . 25 20

1984. 1100th Death Anniv of Ahmed ibn Toulon (governor of Egypt).
1561 **696** 3p. lt brn, bl & brn . . . 30 20

697 Congress Emblem

698 Emblem and Spotlights

1984. 29th International History of Medicine Congress, Cairo.
1562 **697** 3p. blue, black & red . . 25 20

1984. 25th Anniv of Academy of Art.
1563 **698** 3p. multicoloured . . . 25 20

699 Pharaoh receiving Letter (monument) and Postal Museum

1985. Post Day.
1564 **699** 3p. blue, brown & red 25 20

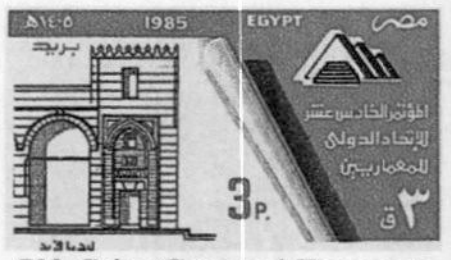
700 Cairo Gate and Tower on Scroll and Emblem

701 Scribe (statue) and Emblem

1985. 15th International Union of Architects Conference.
1565 **700** 3p. lilac and blue 25 20

1985. 17th Cairo International Book Fair.
1566 **701** 3p. blue and orange . . 25 20

702 Edfu Temple

703 Ear of Wheat, Cogwheels and Emblem

1985. Air.
1567 **702** 6p. green and blue . . . 50 25
1568 15p. brown and blue . . 75 35
1569 – 18p.50 grn, yell & brn 95 95
1570 – 23p. brown, yell & bl . . 1·25 1·25
1571 – 25p. blue, yell & brn . . 1·25 65
1572 – 30p. brown, orge & bl 1·60 85
DESIGNS—HORIZ: 23, 30p. Giza Pyramids. VERT: 18p. 50, 25p. Akhnaton.

1985. 18th Cairo International Fair.
1573 **703** 3p. multicoloured . . . 25 20

704 Woman holding Heart

705 Priest of god Mout

1985. 3rd Anniv of Restoration of Sinai.
1574 **704** 5p. multicoloured . . . 30 20

1985. (a) Size 22 × 27 mm.
1575 **705** 1p. brown 10 10
1576 – 2p. blue 10 10
1577 – 3p. brown 15 10
1578 – 5p. purple 25 15
1579 – 8p. brown and green . . 35 25
1580 – 10p. blue and purple . . 15 15
1581 – 11p. purple 45 40
1582 – 15p. brown and ochre 70 45
1583 – 20p. green . . . . 1·00 45
1584 – 20p. green and yellow . . 30 20
1585 – 30p. brn & cinnamon . . 35 10
1586 – 35p. yellow & brown . . 1·60 1·00
1587 – 50p. lilac and brown . . 55 25
(b) Mosques. Size 22 × 39 mm.
1588 – £E1 brown and orange . . 1·10 45
1589 – £E2 brown and yellow . . 2·25 60
DESIGNS: 2, 20p. (1583) Wading birds (relief sculpture); 3, 5p. Statue of Rameses II, Luxor; 8, 15p. Slave kneeling with tray and fruit (wall painting); 10p. Vase; 11p. Carved head; 20p. (1584) Jug; 30p. Flagon; 35p. Capitals of pharaonic columns; 50p. Flask; £E1, Al-Maridani Mosque; £E2, Al-Azhar Mosque, Cairo.
For designs size 18 × 22 mm, see Nos. 1772/5.

707 Treble Clef

708 El Moulid Bride (doll)

1985. 50th Anniv of Helwan University Musical Faculty.
1595 **707** 5p. blue and yellow . . . 30 20

1985. Festivals 1985.
1596 **708** 2p. violet, orge & yell . . 20 10
1597 5p. red, blue & green . . 30 20

709 Player and Cup

710 Television Headquarters and Radio Waves

1985. Egyptian Football Victories. Mult.
1598 5p. Cairo Stadium (left-hand) 50 40
1599 5p. Cairo Stadium (right-hand) 50 40
1600 5p. El Zamalek Club player and Africa Cup (winners, 1984) 50 40
1601 5p. National Club player (red shirt) and African Cup-winners Cup (winners 1984) 50 40
1602 5p. Type **709** (Arab Contractors Club, African Cup-winners Cup winners, 1983) 50 40
Nos. 1598/9 were printed together, se-tenant, forming a composite design.

1985. Anniversaries. Multicoloured.
1603 5p. Type **710** (25th anniv of Egyptian television) . . . 35 20
1604 5p. Flag and olive branch entwined, ships and maps of world and Suez Canal (10th anniv of re-opening) (horiz) 35 20
1605 5p. Cars in Ahmed Hamdi Tunnel under Suez Canal (33rd anniv of revolution) 35 20

711 Map within Heart and Emblem

1985. 3rd Egyptians Abroad Conference, Cairo.
1607 **711** 15p. multicoloured . . . 75 45

712 Akhnaton worshipping Aton and Emblem

1985. 50th Anniv of Tourism Organization.
1608 **712** 5p. multicoloured . . . 30 20

713 Flag and Olive Branch on Map of Sinai

1985. 12th Anniv of Suez Crossing.
1609 **713** 5p. multicoloured . . . 30 20

714 Air Scouts Emblem

1985. 30th Anniv of Air Scouts.
1610 **714** 5p. blue, red & yellow 50 25

715 International Youth Year Emblem

716 Conference and Association Emblems

1985. United Nations Day.
1611 **715** 5p. lilac, yellow & grn 35 20
1612 – 5p. multicoloured . . . 35 20
1613 – 15p. blue, yellow and red 90 60
1614 – 15p. blue & light blue . . 90 60
DESIGNS: No. 1612, Meteorological map of Egypt (World Meteorology Day); 1613, Dove and U.N. emblem (40th Anniv of United Nations Organization); 1614, International communications development programme emblem.

1985. 2nd International Conference of Egyptian Association of Dental Surgeons, Cairo.
1615 **716** 5p. blue and brown . . . 40 20

717 Conference Banner and Koran

718 Squash Player

1985. 4th International Conference of Biography and Sunna (sayings) of Prophet Mohammed.
1616 **717** 5p. blue, yellow & brn 30 20

1985. World Squash Championships, Cairo.
1617 **718** 5p. green, yellow & brn 45 20

719 Emblem, Flag and Hand holding Tools

720 Emblem and Tomb Paintings

1985. 1st Technical Industrial Education Conference.
1618 **719** 5p. blue, red & black . . 30 20

1985. 75th Anniv of Egyptian Olympic Committee.
1619 **720** 5p. multicoloured . . . 30 20

721 Narmer Board

722 Emblem and Relief of Scribe

1986. Air. Post Day. Multicoloured.
1620 15p. Type **721** 95 95
1621 15p. Narmer Board (opposite side) 95 95

1986. 18th Cairo International Book Fair.
1622 **722** 5p. brown, yellow & bl 30 20

723 Conference Emblem

1986. 3rd International Conference for Transport in Developing Countries, Cairo.
1623 **723** 5p. blue, green & red . . 30 20

724 Emblem on Islamic Ornament

1986. 25th Anniv of Central Bank.
1624 **724** 5p. multicoloured . . . 30 20

725 Globe, Sorting Office and Map

1986. Inauguration of Cairo Postal Sorting Centre.
1625 **725** 5p. blue and brown . . . 30 20

726 Tomb Painting, Sakkara

1986. 75th Anniv of Cairo University Commerce Faculty.
1626 **726** 5p. yellow, brown & pur 30 20

727 Wheat, Cogwheel, Flags and Emblem

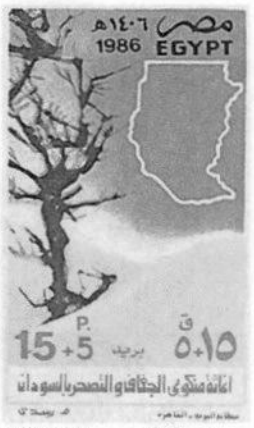

728 Map of Sudan and dead Tree

1986. 19th Cairo International Fair.
1627 **727** 5p. multicoloured . . . 30 20

1986. Relief of Drought Victims in Sudan.
1628 **728** 15p.+5p. bl, brn & yell 1·25 95

729 Map of Africa, Boeing 707 and Emblem

1986. 18th Annual General Assembly of African Airlines Association.
1629 **729** 15p. blue, yell & blk . . 85 40

730 Ankh, Red Crescent and Hands

1986. 50th Anniv of Ministry of Health.
1630 **730** 5p. multicoloured . . . 30 20

731 Queen Nefertari and Map of Sinai

1986. 4th Anniv of Restoration of Sinai.
1631 **731** 5p. blue, red & green . . 45 20

732 Profiles and Map

1986. Census.
1632 **732** 15p. brown, yell & bl . . 80 30

733 Map, Cup and Emblem

734 Roses

1986. Victory in African Nations Cup Football Championship. Multicoloured.
1633 5p. Type **733** 40 25
1634 5p. As No. 1633 but emblem inscr in Arabic 40 25

1986. Festivals 1986.
1635 **734** 5p. purple, green & lilac 30 20

735 Smoke issuing from Factory

736 Eagle and "23 July"

1986. World Environment Day.
1636 **735** 15p. black, green & blue 85 35

1986. 34th Anniv of Revolution.
1637 **736** 5p. yellow, green & red 25 20

737 Road on Map of Africa

1986. 6th African Road Conference, Cairo.
1638 **737** 15p. multicoloured . . . 75 30

738 Map, Eagle, Olive Branch and Flag

739 Workers holding Books and Tools

1986. 13th Anniv of Suez Crossing.
1639 **738** 5p. multicoloured . . . 35 20

1986. 25th Anniv of Workers' Cultural Association.
1640 **739** 5p. orange and lilac . . 25 15

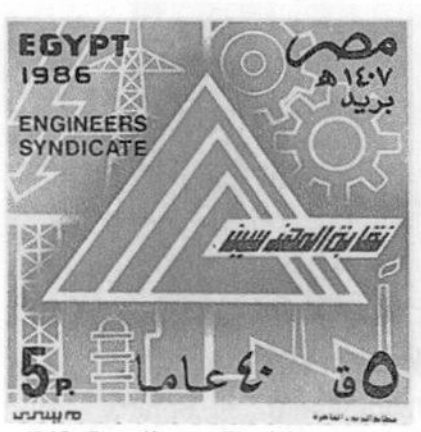

740 Syndicate Emblem and Engineering Symbols

741 Dove and Emblem (International Peace Year)

1986. Engineers' Day. 40th Anniv of Engineers' Syndicate.
1641 **740** 5p. green, brown & blue 25 15

1986. United Nations Day.
1642 **741** 5p. green, blue & red . . 25 15
1643 – 15p. yellow, grn & brn 75 40
1644 – 15p. multicoloured . . . 75 40
DESIGNS—HORIZ: As T **741**: No. 1643, Harvester and ears of wheat (40th anniv of Food and Agriculture Organization). 46 × 27 mm: 1644, Emblem, globe and "U.N.E.S.C.O." in Arabic (40th anniv of U.N.E.S.C.O.).

742 Map and Old and New Drilling Towers

1986. Centenary of First Egyptian Oilwell, Gemsa.
1645 **742** 5p. green, yellow & blk 35 20

743 Children holding Flower

1986. Children's Day.
1646 **743** 5p. multicoloured . . . 35 20

744 Ahmed Amin

745 Mask and Eye in Spotlight

1986. Birth Centenary of Ahmed Amin (literary researcher).
1647 **744** 5p. yellow, brn & grn . . 25 20

1986. 50th Anniv of National Theatre.
1648 **745** 5p. multicoloured . . . 25 20

746 Statue of King Zoser and Step Pyramid, Sakkara

1987. Post Day.
1649 **746** 5p. multicoloured . . . 30 20

747 Book and Pencil as "19"

1986. 19th Cairo International Book Fair.
1650 **747** 5p. multicoloured . . . 25 20

748 Emblem

749 Medal

1987. 5th International Conference on Islamic Education.
1651 **748** 5p. multicoloured . . . 25 20

1987. 20th Cairo International Fair.
1652 **749** 5p. black, gold & red . . 25 20

750 Olive Branch, Profile and National Colours

1987. Veterans' Day.
1653 **750** 5p. red, green & gold . . 25 20

751 Plants and Emblem

1987. Air. International Garden Festival, Cairo.
1654 **751** 15p. multicoloured . . . 75 40

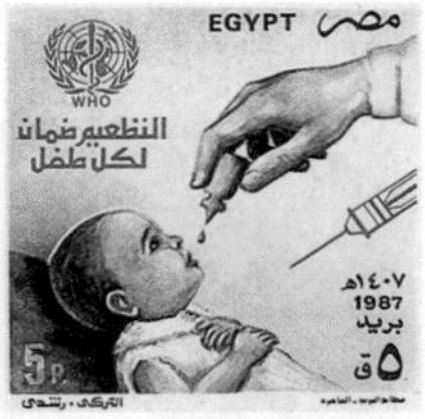

752 Oral Vaccination

1987. International Health Day.
1655 **752** 5p. multicoloured . . . 30 20
1656 – 5p. yellow, grn & blk . . 30 20
DESIGN: No. 1656, Woman giving baby oral rehydration therapy.

753 Africa Cup

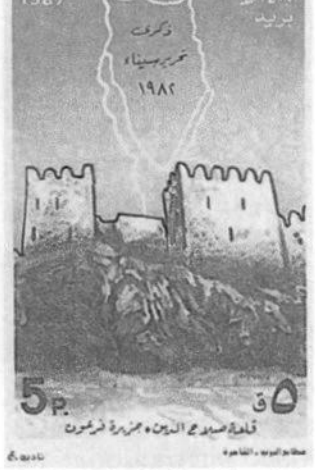

754 Saladin's Citadel and Map

1987. Egyptian Victories in Football Championships. Multicoloured.
1657 5p. Type **753** (El Zamalek team) 30 25
1658 5p. African Nations Cup (national team) 30 25
1659 5p. African Cup Winners Cup (El Ahly team) . . . 30 25

1987. 5th Anniv of Restoration of Sinai.
1661 **754** 5p. blue and brown . . . 25 20

755 Dahlia

1987. Festivals 1987.
1662 **755** 5p. blue, yellow & mauve 25 15

756 Pyramid and Camel Train

1987. "Saudi Arabia—Yesterday and Today" Exhibition, Cairo.
1663 **756** 15p. multicoloured . . . 75 35

757 El Sawary Column and Sphinx and Qaitbay Fort, Alexandria

1987. Tourism. Multicoloured.
1664 15p. Type **757** 75 65
1665 15p. St. Catherine's Monastery, Sinai 75 65
1666 15p. Colossi of Thebes . . . 75 65
1667 15p. Temple, Luxor 75 65
Nos. 1664/7 were printed together, se-tenant, forming a composite design of a map with each illustrated subject pinpointed.

758 Pharaonic Eye on Map

1987. Loyalty Day. 32nd Anniv of General Intelligence Service.
1669 **758** 5p. multicoloured . . . 25 15

759 Ears of Wheat and Emblem

1987. Industrial and Agricultural Exhibition, Alexandria.
1670 **759** 5p. black, grn & orge . . 25 20

760 Emblems

1987. International Year of Shelter for the Homeless. World Architects' Day.
1671 **760** 5p. yellow, brn & grn . . 25 20

761 Scene from Opera and Sphinx

1987. Performance of Verdi's "Aida" (opera) at the Pyramids, Giza.
1672 **761** 15p. multicoloured . . . 95 40

762 Train in Station

1987. Inauguration of Cairo Underground Railway.
1674 **762** 5p. multicoloured . . . 65 25

763 Head composed of Industrial Symbols

764 Horseman and Map

1987. Production Day.
1675 **763** 5p. multicoloured . . . 25 15

1987. 800th Anniv of Battle of Hattin.
1676 **764** 5p. multicoloured . . . 30 20

765 U.P.U. Emblem

1987. 40th Anniv of Executive Council and 30th Anniv of Consultative Council of U.P.U.
1677 **765** 5p. black, orange & bl 25 15

766 Eye and Art Materials

1987. 16th Fine Arts Biennale. Alexandria.
1678 **766** 5p. multicoloured . . . 25 15

767 Emblem and Ancient Egyptians making Weapons

1987. 2nd International Defence Equipment Exhibition, Cairo.
1679 **767** 5p. multicoloured . . . 25 15

768 Profile and Emblem

1987. 2nd Pan-Arab Anaesthesia and Intensive Care Congress.
1680 **768** 5p. multicoloured . . . 30 20

769 Globe and Emblem on Skeleton

770 Selim Hassan (archaeologist) and Hieroglyphics

1987. International Orthopaedic and Traumatology Conference, Luxor.
1681 **769** 5p. grey, brown & blue 30 20

1987. Birth Centenaries. Multicoloured.
1682 5p. Type **770** 25 15
1683 5p. Abdel Hamid Badawi (politician and International Court of Justice judge) 25 15

771 Mycerinus and Left-hand Pyramid, Giza

773 Emblem, Hieroglyphics and Scribe

772 Map

1988. Post Day. Multicoloured.
1684 15p. Type **771** 75 65
1685 15p. Chefren (with beard) and middle pyramid . . . 75 65
1686 15p. Cheops and righthand pyramid 75 65

1988. 30th Anniv of Asia–Africa Organization.
1687 **772** 15p. multicoloured . . . 75 35

1988. 20th Cairo International Book Fair.
1688 **773** 5p. multicoloured . . . 25 15

774 Container Ship

1988. 25th Anniv of Martrans Shipping Line.
1689 **774** 5p. multicoloured . . . 50 15

775 Fair Facade, Globe and Emblem

1988. 21st Cairo International Fair.
1690 **775** 5p. multicoloured . . . 25 15

776 Bowl of Sugar and Emblem

777 Prince Ossrite and Fig Tree

1988. World Health Day. Diabetic Care.
1691 **776** 5p. multicoloured . . . 30 15

1988. Festivals 1988.
1692 **777** 5p. orange, grn & brn 25 15

778 Letters and Emblem

1988. 25th Anniv of African Postal Union.
1693 **778** 15p. blue 65 30

779 Hands of Different Races reaching for Torch

1988. Anti-racism Campaign.
1694 **779** 5p. multicoloured . . . 25 20

780 Maps of Africa around Emblem

1988. 25th Anniv of Organization of African Unity.
1695 **780** 15p.+10p. mult 65 50

781 Tawfek el Hakem

1988. 1st Death Anniv of Tawfek el Hakem (dramatist).
1696 **781** 5p. brown and blue . . . 25 20

782 Cubic Art (M. el Razaz)

1988. 50th Anniv of Faculty of Art Education.
1697 **782** 5p. multicoloured . . . 20 15

783 Games Emblem

1988. Air. Olympic Games, Seoul.
1698 **783** 15p. multicoloured . . . 75 35

784 Torch, Flag and Palestinians

1988. Air. Palestinian "Intifida" Movement.
1700 **784** 25p. multicoloured . . . 65 35

785 Soldier and Flag

1988. 15th Anniv of Suez Crossing.
1701 **785** 5p. multicoloured . . . 20 15

786 Model of Opera House

1988. Inauguration of Opera House.
1702 **786** 5p. multicoloured . . . 25 20

787 Red Crescent and Red Cross (125th Anniv of Red Cross)

1988. U.N. Day.
1704 **787** 5p. black, red and green (postage) 25 20
1705 – 20p. yellow, blue and orange 60 30
1706 – 25p. mult (air) 65 35
DESIGNS—22 × 39 mm. 20p. Anniversary emblem (40th anniv of W.H.O.); 47 × 28 mm. 25p. Globes on scales (40th anniv of Human Rights Declaration).

788 Naguib Mahfouz

1988. Award of Nobel Prize for Literature to Naguib Mahfouz.
1707 **788** 5p. mult (postage) . . . 25 20
1708 25p. mult (air) 60 30

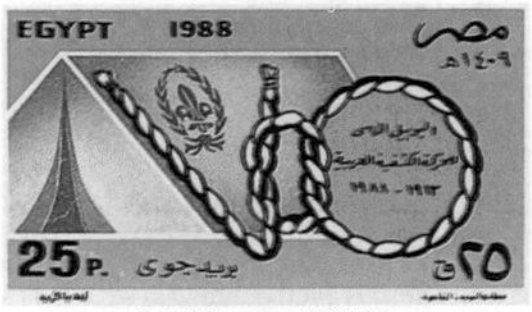

789 Tent and "75"

1988. 75th Anniv of Arab Scout Movement.
1709 **789** 25p. multicoloured . . . 60 30

790 Ein Shams University and Association Emblems

1988. Egyptian Orthopaedic Association International Conference, Cairo.
1710 **790** 5p. yellow, brn & grn . . 20 10

791 Pharaonic Eye and Map

1988. Restoration of Taba.
1711 **791** 5p. multicoloured . . . 20 10

792 "75" in Sun above Plant

793 Mohamed Hussein Hekal (writer and politician)

1988. 75th Anniv of Ministry of Agriculture.
1712 **792** 5p. blue, yell & orge . . 20 10

1988. Anniversaries. Each brown and green.
1713 5p. Type **793** (birth cent) . . 20 10
1714 5p. Ahmed Lofty el Sayed (philosopher and politician) (25th death anniv) 20 10

794 Priest (5th dynasty)

795 Nehru

1989. Post Day. Statues. Multicoloured.
1715 5p. Type **794** 20 15
1716 25p. Princess Nefert (4th dynasty) 60 35
1717 25p. Prince Ra-Hoteb (4th dynasty) 60 35

1989. Birth Centenary of Jawaharlal Nehru (Indian statesman).
1718 **795** 5p. green 20 10

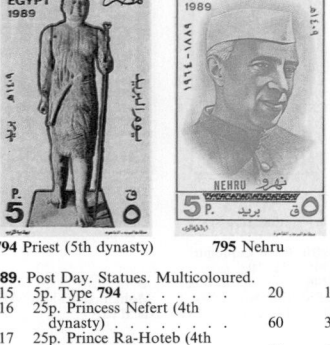

796 Nile Hilton

1989. 30th Anniv of Nile Hilton Hotel.
1719 **796** 5p. multicoloured . . . 20 10

797 Route Map and Train leaving Tunnel

1989. Inauguration of Second Stage of Cairo Underground Railway.
1720 **797** 5p. multicoloured . . . 25 15

798 Arms and Map

799 Balcony

1989. Restoration of Taba.
1721 **798** 5p. multicoloured . . . 20 10

1989. Air.
1722 **799** 20p. purple, brn & bl 40 20
1723 – 25p. brn, yell & grn . . 50 25
1724 – 35p. pur, orge & bl . . 60 35
1725 – 45p. yell, blk & red . . 70 40
1725a – 45p. pur, orge & grn 45 15
1726 – 50p. bl, stone & pur . . 80 50
1726a – 55p. brn, buff & bl . . 80 30
1727 – 60p. pur, stone & bl . . 1·10 50
1727a – 65p. pur, brn & grn . . 75 30
1728 **799** 70p. pur, brn & orge 80 30
1729 – 85p. yellow, light yellow and brown 95 45
DESIGNS: 25, 35, 45p. (1725a) Lantern; 45p. (1725) Carpet; 50, 60, 65p. Dish with gazelle motif; 55, 85p. Dish with fluted edge.

800 Lamp

801 Members' Flags

1989. Festivals 1989.
1730 **800** 5p. multicoloured . . . 10 10

1989. Air. Formation of Arab Co-operation Council.
1731 **801** 25p. multicoloured . . . 55 25

802 Olympic Rings, Map and Sports

1989. 1st Arab Olympic Day.
1733 **802** 5p. green, brown & blk 15 10

803 Pyramids and Parliament Building

1989. Cent of Interparliamentary Union.
1734 **803** 25p. multicoloured . . . 55 25

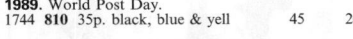

804 Egyptian and French Flags

1989. Air. Bicentenary of French Revolution.
1736 **804** 25p. multicoloured . . . 60 25

805 Bank Emblem

1989. 25th Anniv of African Development Bank.
1737 **805** 10p. blue, yellow & pur 15 10

806 Conference Centre

1989. Cairo International Conference Centre.
1738 **806** 5p. brown, green & blue 15 10

807 October Panorama

808 Mohammed Ali Mosque, Saladin's Citadel

1989. 16th Anniv of Suez Crossing. Mult.
1739 10p. Egyptians in El Qantara (47 × 28 mm) . . 20 10
1740 10p. Type **807** 20 10
1741 10p. Crossing the Suez (47 × 28 mm) 20 10
See also No. 1766.

1989. Aga Khan Architecture Prize.
1742 **808** 35p. brown, grn & pur 70 25

809 Emblem sheltering Family

810 Envelopes forming World Map

1989. 25th Anniv of Health Insurance Scheme.
1743 **809** 10p. red, grey & black 15 10

1989. World Post Day.
1744 **810** 35p. black, blue & yell 45 20

811 Colossi of Thebes

1989. International Congress and Convention Association Meeting, Cairo.
1745 **811** 10p. lilac, green & blk 20 10

812 Faculty Emblem

814 University Emblem

813 Children at Crossings

1989. Centenary of Faculty of Agriculture, Cairo University.
1746 **812** 10p. purple, grn & yell 20 10

1989. 20th Anniv of Egyptian Road Safety Society.
1747 **813** 10p. multicoloured . . . 20 10

1989. 50th Anniv of Alexandria University.
1748 **814** 10p. brown and blue . . 20 10

815 Abdel Kader el Mazni (writer)

816 Statue of Priest Renofr

1989. Birth Anniversaries.
1749 **815** 10p. ochre and brown 20 10
1750 – 10p. olive and green . . 20 10
1751 – 10p. multicoloured . . . 20 10
DESIGNS—VERT: No. 1750, Abdel Rahman el Rafei (historian and politician). HORIZ: No. 1751, Ibrahim Pasha and statue in Opera Square, Cairo (son of Mohammed Ali and Viceroy of Egypt, July-November 1848).

1990. Post Day. Multicoloured.
1752 30p. Type **816** 50 25
1753 30p. Relief of Betah Hoteb from Sakkara 50 25

817 Emblem

1990. 1st Anniv of Arab Co-operation Council.
1754 **817** 10p. multicoloured . . . 20 10
1755 35p. multicoloured . . . 60 30

818 Emblem

819 Road Sign and Steering Wheel

1990. African Parliamentary Union Conf.
1756 **818** 10p. black, red & green 20 10

1990. International Conference. Road Safety and Accidents in Developing Countries.
1758 **819** 10p. multicoloured . . . 20 10

820 Daisies

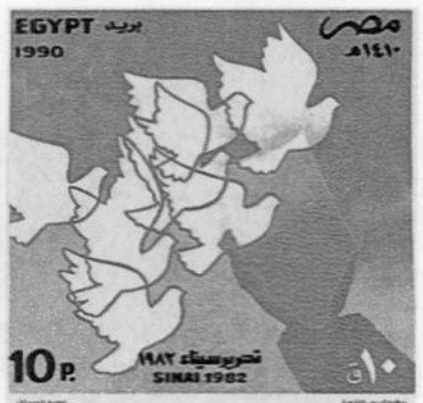

821 Doves and Map

1990. Festivals 1990.
1759 **820** 10p. multicoloured . . . 20 10

1990. 8th Anniv of Restoration of Sinai.
1760 **821** 10p. blue, yellow & blk 20 10

822 Trophy and Ball

824 Figures forming Pyramid

823 Pyramid, Sphinx, Mascot and Ball in Basket

1990. World Cup Football Championship, Italy.
1761 **822** 10p. multicoloured . . . 20 10

1990. World Basketball Championship, Argentina.
1763 **823** 10p. black, blue & orge 20 10

1990. 5th Anniv of National Population Council.
1764 **824** 10p. brn, lt grn & grn 20 10

825 Battlefield

1990. 17th Anniv of Suez Crossing. Mult.
1765 10p. Type **825** 20 10
1766 10p. As Type **807** but dated "1990" 20 10
1767 10p. Egyptian soldiers with flamethrower 20 10

826 Anniversary Emblem

1990. 125th Anniv of Egyptian Post.
1768 **826** 10p. black, red & blue 20 10

827 Faculty Emblem and Al-Azhar Mosque, Cairo

1990. Centenary of Dar el Eloum Faculty.
1769 **827** 10p. multicoloured . . . 20 10

828 Emblem and Map (40th anniv of U.N. Development Programme)

1990. United Nations Day.
1770 **828** 30p. blue, grn & yell . . 45 20
1771 – 30p. multicoloured . . . 45 20
DESIGN—VERT: No. 1771, Cables and emblem forming Arabic "125" (125th anniv of I.T.U.).

1990. As previous designs and new design as T **705** but size 18 × 22 mm.
1772 5p. buff and brown 10 10
1773 10p. blue and lilac 10 10
1774 30p. brown and ochre . . . 15 10
1775 50p. brown and yellow . . . 20 10
DESIGNS: 5p. Jar; 10p. Vase (as No. 1580); 30p. Flagon (as No. 1585); 50p. Flask (as No. 1587).

829 Pictogram, Hand and Disabled Person

1990. Disabled Persons' Day.
1790 **829** 10p. multicoloured . . . 20 10

830 Crown Butterflyfish and Coral

1990. Ras Mohamed National Park. Mult.
1791 10p. Type **830** 40 20
1792 10p. Zebra lionfish 40 20
1793 20p. Two-banded anemonefish and emperor angelfish 40 20
1794 20p. Coral hind 40 20

831 Nabaweya Moussa (educationist)

832 1866 5pa. Stamp

1990. Birth Centenaries.
1795 **831** 10p. orge, grey & grn . . 20 10
1796 – 10p. orange, brn & bl . . 20 10
DESIGN: No. 1796, Dr. Mohamed Fahmy Abdel Meguid (pioneer of free medical care).

1991. Post Day. 125th Anniv of First Egyptian Stamps (1st issue).
1797 **832** 5p. grey and black . . . 10 10
1798 – 10p. brown and black . . 20 10
1799 – 20p. blue and black . . . 20 10
DESIGNS: 10p. 1866 10pa. stamp; 20p. 1866 20pa. stamp.
See also Nos. 1815/17 and 1831.

833 Birth of Calf

1991. 50th Anniv (1990) of Veterinary Surgeons' Syndicate.
1800 **833** 10p. multicoloured . . . 20 10

834 Newspaper, Quill, Ink and Lens

835 Narcissi

1991. 50th Anniv of Journalists' Syndicate.
1801 **834** 10p. multicoloured . . . 20 10

1991. Festivals 1991.
1802 **835** 10p. multicoloured . . . 20 10

836 "Procession" and Mohamed Nagi

839 Score and Mohamed Abdel el Wahab

838 Saladin's Citadel and Faculty Building

1991. Artists' Anniversaries. Multicoloured.
1803 10p. Type **836** (35th death) 20 10
1804 10p. Mahmoud Mokhtar and sculptures (birth centenary) (horiz) 20 10

1991. Centenary of Technical Faculty, University of Cairo.
1814 **838** 10p. multicoloured . . . 20 10

1991. 125th Anniv of First Egyptian Stamps (2nd issue) and "Cairo 1991" Stamp Exhibition (1st issue). As T **832**.
1815 10p. orange and black . . . 20 10
1816 10p. yellow and black . . . 20 10
1817 10p. purple and black . . . 20 10
DESIGNS: No. 1815, 1866 5pi. stamp; 1816, 1866 2pi. stamp; 1817, 1866 1pi. stamp.

1991. Mohamed Abdel el Wahab (composer) Commemoration.
1819 **839** 10p. multicoloured . . . 20 10

840 Session Emblem

1991. 48th Session of International Statistics Institute, Nasr.
1820 **840** 10p. multicoloured . . . 20 10

841 Horus (mascot)

842 New Building

1991. 5th African Games, Cairo. Mult.
1821 10p. Type **841** 20 10
1822 10p. Running, gymnastics and swimming pictograms (horiz) 20 10
1823 10p. Football, basketball and shooting pictograms (horiz) 20 10
1824 10p. Taekwondo, karate and judo pictograms (horiz) 20 10
1825 10p. Table tennis, hockey and tennis pictograms (horiz) 20 10

1826 10p. Boxing, wrestling and weightlifting pictograms (horiz) 20 10
1827 10p. Handball, cycling and volleyball pictrograms (horiz) 20 10

1991. Opening of Dar El Eftaa's New Building.
1829 **842** 10p. multicoloured . . . 20 10

843 Troops in Inflatable Dinghy

1991. 18th Anniv of Suez Crossing.
1830 **843** 10p. multicoloured . . . 30 10

1991. 125th Anniv of First Egyptian Stamps (3rd issue). As T **832**.
1831 10p. black and blue 20 10
DESIGN: 10p. 1866 10pi. stamp.

844 Woman writing **845** Dr. Zaki Mubarak (poet, birth centenary)

1991. United Nations Day. Multicoloured.
1833 10p. Type **844** (Int Literacy Year) 20 10
1834 10p. Brick "hands" sheltering people (World Shelter for the Homeless Day) (horiz) 20 10
1835 10p. Egyptian and International Standards Organizations emblems (World Standardization Day) (horiz) 20 10

1991. Writers' Anniversaries.
1836 **845** 10p. brown 20 10
1837 – 10p. grey 20 10
DESIGN: No. 1837, Abd el Kader Hamza (journalist and historian, 50th death anniv).

846 Scarab Pectoral (from Tutankhamun's tomb)

1992. Post Day. Multicoloured.
1838 10p. Type **846** (postage) . . 15 10
1839 45p. Eagle pectoral (from Tutankhamun's tomb) (air) 30 15
1840 70p. Golden saker falcon head (27 × 47 mm) . . . 55 25

847 Arabic "40" and Emblem **849** Darwish and Opening Bars of "Stand up O Egyptian"

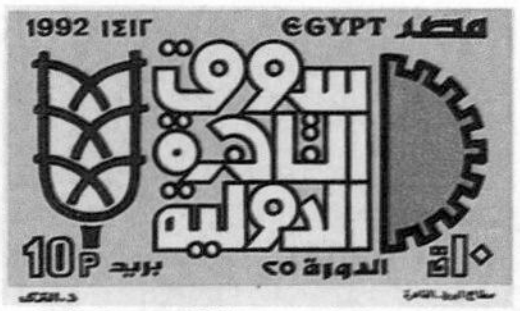

848 Ear of Wheat and Cogwheel

1992. Police Day.
1841 **847** 10p. multicoloured . . . 15 10

1992. 25th Cairo International Fair.
1842 **848** 10p. multicoloured . . . 15 10

1992. Birth Centenary of Sayed Darwish (composer).
1843 **849** 10p. green and yellow . . 15 10

850 Hoopoe

1992. Festivals 1992.
1844 **850** 10p. orange, blk & grn 25 15

851 Heart and Cardiograph

1992. World Health Day.
1845 **851** 10p. multicoloured . . . 15 10

852 Tent, Emblem and Map

1992. 20th Arab Scout Jamboree.
1846 **852** 10p. multicoloured . . . 15 10

853 Games Emblem, Mascot and Pictograms **854** U.A.R. 1960 60m. Dam Stamp

1992. Olympic Games, Barcelona. Mult.
1847 **853** 10p. multicoloured . . . 15 10

1992. 90th Anniv of Aswan Dam.
1849 **854** 10p. mauve, yell & blk 15 10

855 "Dar El Helal"

1992. Centenary of "El Helal" (periodical).
1850 **855** 10p. brown, gold & blk 15 10

856 Sphinx and Pyramids

1992. Federation of Travel Companies International Congress, Cairo.
1851 **856** 70p. multicoloured . . . 45 20

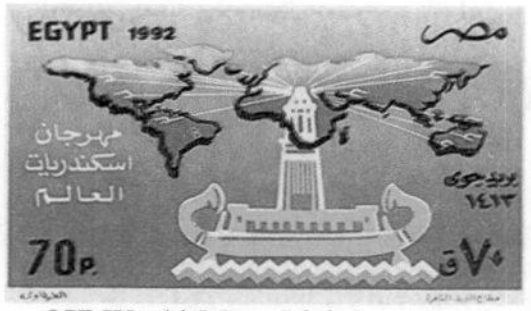

857 World Map, Lighthouse and Pharaonic Ship

1992. Alexandria World Festival.
1852 **857** 70p. multicoloured . . . 60 20

858 U.P.U. Emblem

1992. World Post Day.
1853 **858** 10p. bl, blk & ultram . . 15 10

859 Girl **860** Emblem

1992. United Nations Day. Multicoloured.
1854 10p. Type **859** (Children's Day) 15 10
1855 70p. Wall paintings of agriculture and medicine (International Food, Agriculture and World Health Conference) (36 × 37 mm) 45 20

1992. 20th Arab Scout Conference, Cairo.
1856 **860** 10p. multicoloured . . . 15 10

861 Mohamed Taymour **862** Sesostris I

1992. Birth Anniversaries.
1857 **861** 10p. blue, dp blue & bis 15 10
1858 – 10p. blue, dp blue & bis 15 10
1859 – 10p. brown, orge & bl 15 10
DESIGNS: No. 1857, Type **861** (dramatist and theatre critic, centenary); 1851, Ahmed Zaki Abu Shadi (physician and poet, centenary); 1859, Talaat Harb (economist, 125th anniv).

1993. Post Day. Statues of Pharaohs. Mult.
1860 10p. Type **862** 15 10
1861 45p. Amenemhet III 25 10
1862 70p. Hur I 40 20

863 Book and Statue of Scribe **864** Bust

1993. 25th Cairo International Book Fair.
1863 **863** 15p. multicoloured . . . 15 10

1993. Size 18 × 22 mm.
1864 **864** 5p. orange and black . . 10 10
1865 – 15p. brown and ochre 10 10
1866 – 15p. brown and ochre 15 10
1867 – 25p. lt brown & brown 20 10
1868 – 55p. blue and black . . 30 15
DESIGNS—15p. Sphinx*; 25p. Bust of woman; 55p. Bust of Pharaoh.
*On No. 1865 the illustration of the sphinx countinues behind the face value; on No. 1866 the sphinx is cropped so that the value appears on a white background.
For same designs but larger, 21 × 26 mm, see Nos. 1916/19.

865 Plan and Set Square on Drawing Board

1993. 75th Anniv (1992) of Architects' Association.
1869 **865** 15p. black, orange & bl 15 10

866 Gold Mask of Tutankhamun

1993.
1870 – £E1 brown and blue (postage) 40 20
1871 – £E2 green and brown . . 75 35
1872 – £E5 gold and brown . . 1·90 95
1873 **866** 55p. gold and brown (air) 20 10
1874 – 80p. gold and brown . . 30 15
DESIGNS: 80p. Side view of Tutankhamun's mask; £E1, Bust of woman; £E2, Head of Queen Tiye; £E5, Carved head capital.

867 Old and New Foreign Ministry Buildings and Globe **868** Cactus

1993. (a) Egyptian Diplomacy Day.
1875 **867** 15p. multicoloured . . . 15 10
(b) Air. Inauguration of New Foreign Ministry Building. As T **867** but inscr "AIR MAIL MINISTRY OF FOREIGN AFFAIRS".
1876 **867** 80p. multicoloured . . . 40 20

1993. Festivals 1993.
1877 **868** 15p. multicoloured . . . 15 10

869 First Issue and Emblem

1993. Centenary of "Le Progres Egyptien" (newspaper).
1878 **869** 15p. multicoloured . . . 15 10

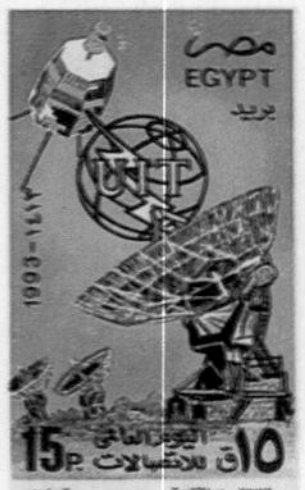

870 Dish Aerial, I.T.U. Emblem and Satellite

871 Globe

1993. World Telecommunications Day.
1879 **870** 15p. multicoloured . . . 15 10

1993. U.N. World Conference on Human Rights, Vienna.
1880 **871** 15p. ultram, bl & orge 15 10

872 Emblem, Map of Africa and Stars

1993. 30th Anniv of Organization of African Unity.
1881 **872** 15p. black, silver and green (postage) . . . 15 10
1882 80p. black, gold and mauve (air) 40 20

873 Conference Emblem

1993. International Post, Telegraph and Telecommunications Union Conference, Cairo.
1883 **873** 15p. multicoloured . . . 15 10

874 Saladin and Dome of the Rock, Jerusalem

1993. 800th Death Anniv of Saladin.
1884 **874** 55p. multicoloured . . . 35 15

875 Soldiers

876 Pres. Mubarak

1993. 20th Anniv of Suez Crossing.
1885 **875** 15p. blk, mve & orge 15 10

1993. Mohammed Hosni Mubarak's 3rd Consecutive Term as President.
1886 **876** 15p. multicoloured . . . 15 10
1887 55p. multicoloured . . . 35 15
1888 80p. multicoloured . . . 40 20

877 Map of Egypt and Electricity Symbol

878 Emblem and Caring Hands

1993. Centenary of Electricity in Egypt.
1890 **877** 15p. multicoloured . . . 15 10

1993. Air. International Decade for Natural Disaster Reduction.
1891 **878** 80p. violet, blue & red 40 20

879 Pyramids, Sphinx and Dam (congress emblem)

1993. 2nd International Large Dams Congress, Cairo.
1892 **879** 15p. yellow, mve & blk 15 10

880 Trophy and Emblem

1993. Egyptian Victories in International Sports Competitions. Multicoloured.
1893 15p. Type **880** (Junior Men's World Handball Championship) 15 10
1894 15p. Trophy and emblem (World Military Football Championship) 15 10

881 Abdel Aziz al Bishry (50th death)

882 Amenhotep III

1993. Writers' Anniversaries.
1895 **881** 15p. blue 15 10
1896 – 15p. turquoise 15 10
1897 – 15p. green 15 10
1898 – 15p. mauve 15 10
DESIGNS: No. 1896, Mohamed Fareed Abu Hadeed (birth centenary); 1897, Ali Moubarak (death centenary); 1898, M. Beram al Tunisy (birth centenary).

1994. Post Day. Statues of Pharaohs. Multicoloured.
1899 15p. Type **882** 10 10
1900 55p. Queen Hatshepsut . . 25 10
1901 85p. Thutmose III 40 20

883 Pyramids

1994. Egyptian Sedimentary Society Congress.
1902 **883** 15p. multicoloured . . . 10 10

884 Firecrests

885 Scout Salute and Emblem

1994. Festivals 1994. Multicoloured.
1903 15p. Type **884** 15 15
1904 15p. Barn swallows (one perching, one flying) . . . 15 15
1905 15p. Alexandrine parakeets (on tree trunk and branch) 15 15
1906 15p. Eurasian goldfinches (on blossoming branch) 15 15
Nos. 1903/6 were issued together, se-tenant, forming a composite design.

1994. 40th Anniv of Arab Scout Movement.
1907 **885** 15p. black, yell & grn . . 10 10

886 Emblem

887 Radio Waves over Map of Africa

1994. 27th Cairo International Fair.
1908 **886** 15p. multicoloured . . . 10 10

1994. "Africa Telecom 94" Exhibition, Cairo.
1909 **887** 15p. green and brown . . 10 10

888 Map, Palestine Flag and Olive Branch

1994. Signing in Cairo of Israel-Palestine Agreement on Self-rule for Gaza and Jericho.
1910 **888** 15p. multicoloured . . . 10 10

889 Conference Emblem and Oil Well

1994. 5th Arab Energy Conference, Cairo.
1911 **889** 15p. multicoloured . . . 10 10

890 Emblem

1994. 18th Mediterranean Countries' Biennial Art Exhibition, Alexandria.
1912 **890** 15p. lilac, yellow & blk 10 10

891 Map of Africa and Dove

892 Campaign Emblem Magnfied

1994. Africa Day
1913 **891** 15p. multicoloured . . . 10 10

1994. Tree Planting Campaign.
1914 **892** 15p. blue, green & black 10 10

893 Library, Family and Open Book

1994. "Reading for All" Summer Festival.
1915 **893** 15p. multicoloured . . . 10 10

1994. As previous designs but size 21 × 26 mm.
1916 **864** 5p. red and purple . . . 10 10
1917 – 15p. brown and cinnamon (as No. 1866) 10 10
1918 – 25p. orange and brown (as No. 1867) 10 10
1919 – 55p. blue and black (as No. 1868) 20 10

894 Emblem

1994. 75th Anniv of I.L.O.
1925 **894** 15p. grey, blue & black 10 10

895 Conference and United Nations Emblems

1994. U.N. International Conference on Population and Development, Cairo. Multicoloured.
1926 15p. Type **895** (postage) . . 10 10
1927 80p. Emblems and pharaonic murals (vert) (air) 30 15

896 Player and Trophy

1994. Egyptian Victories in Junior World Squash Championship.
1928 **896** 15p. multicoloured . . . 10 10

897 Anniversary Emblem

1994. Air. 50th Anniv of Signing of Int Civil Aviation Agreement, Chicago.
1929 **897** 80p. blue, yellow & blk 30 15

898 Map on Envelopes

1994. World Post Day.
1930 **898** 15p. multicoloured . . . 10 10

899 Akhenaten and Nefertiti (International Year of the Family)

1994. United Nations Day.
1931 **899** 80p. lilac, red and black (postage) 30 15
1932 – 80p. mult (air) 30 15
DESIGN—VERT: No. 1931, Nurses (75th anniv of International Red Crescent/Red Cross Union).

900 Arabic Script over Globes

1994. 50th Anniv of "Akhbar El Yom" (newspaper).
1933 **900** 15p. multicoloured . . . 10 10

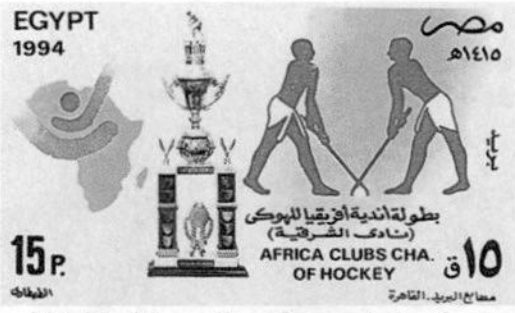

901 Emblem, Trophy and Ancient Egyptian Players

1994. African Clubs Hockey Championship.
1934 **901** 15p. multicoloured . . . 10 10

902 Pharaoh and Radames

903 Centenary Emblem

1994. Performance of Verdi's "Aida" (opera) at Deir al-Bahari Temple, Luxor.
1935 **902** 15p. Type **902** 10 10

1994. Cent of Int Olympic Committee.
1937 **903** 15p. multicoloured . . . 10 10

904 Map showing Hostels and Association Emblem

906 Emblem as Flower

905 Player and Globe

1994. 40th Anniv of Egyptian Youth Hostels Association.
1938 **904** 15p. multicoloured . . . 10 10

1994. 10th Anniv of International Speedball Federation.
1939 **905** 15p. multicoloured . . . 10 10

1994. 30th Anniv of African Development Bank.
1940 **906** 15p. multicoloured . . . 10 10

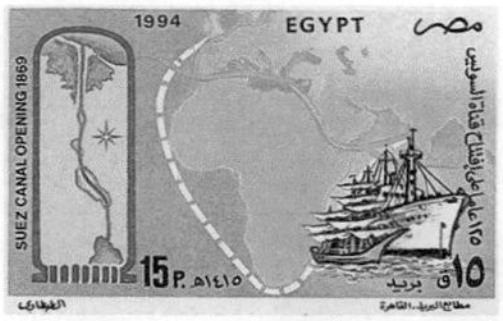

907 Route Maps through Canal and around Africa

1994. 125th Anniv of Suez Canal. Mult.
1941 15p. Type **907** 30 10
1942 80p. Inauguration ceremony, 1869 . . . . 30 15

908 Hassan Fathy (5th death anniv)

910 Akhenaten (statuette)

909 Anniversary Emblem

1994. Anniversaries.
1943 **908** 15p. brown and flesh . . 10 10
1944 – 15p. red and pink . . . 10 10
DESIGN: No. 1944, Mahmoud Taimour (birth centenary).

1995. 20th Anniv of World Tourism Organization.
1945 **909** 15p. multicoloured . . . 10 10

1995. Post Day. Multicoloured.
1946 15p. Type **910** 10 10
1947 55p. Gold mask of Tutankhamun 20 10
1948 80p. Nefertiti (bust) 30 15

911 Flowers

1995. Festivals 1995.
1949 **911** 15p. multicoloured . . . 10 10

912 Demonstration, 1919

1995. National Women's Day.
1950 **912** 15p. multicoloured . . . 10 10

913 Emblem and Map

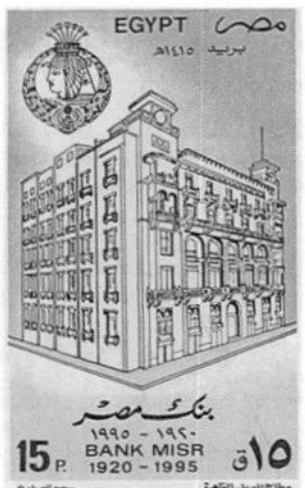

915 Misr Bank

914 Hotel

1995. 50th Anniv of Arab League.
1951 **913** 15p. green, bl & gold . . 10 10
1952 55p. multicoloured . . . 20 10

1995. 25th Anniv of Cairo Sheraton Hotel.
1953 **914** 15p. multicoloured . . . 10 10

1995. 75th Anniv of Misr Bank.
1954 **915** 15p. multicoloured . . . 10 10

916 Dish Aerial and Globe

1995. International Telecommunications Day.
1955 **916** 80p. orange, blk & bl . . 30 15

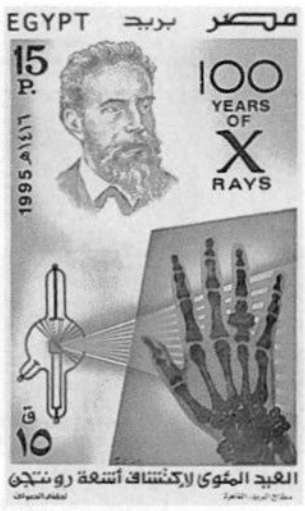

917 Rontgen and X-ray of Hand

918 Goddess Hathor

1995. Centenary of Discovery of X-rays by Wilhelm Rontgen.
1956 **917** 100p. multicoloured . . 10 10

1995. 20th Anniv of Membership of World Heritage Committee. Luxor Statues. Multicoloured.
1957 15p. Type **918** (postage) . . 10 10
1958 15p. God Atoum 10 10
1959 80p. God Amon with Horemheb (air) 30 15
Nos. 1957/8 were issued together, se-tenant, forming a composite design.

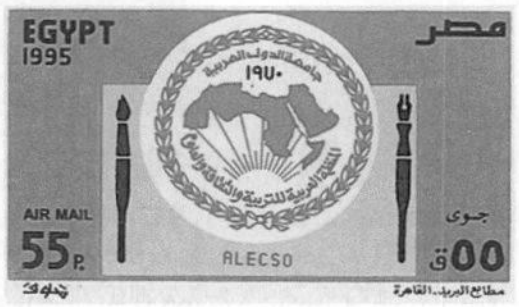

919 Emblem

1995. Air. 25th Anniv of Arab Educational, Scientific and Cultural Organization.
1960 **919** 55p. multicoloured . . . 20 10

920 Children as Flowers

921 Ozone Bands over Globe

1995. 21st Int Pediatrics Conf, Cairo.
1961 **920** 15p. multicoloured . . . 10 10

1995. International Ozone Day.
1962 **921** 15p. multicoloured . . . 10 10
1963 55p. multicoloured . . . 20 10
1964 – 80p. multicoloured . . . 30 15
DESIGNS: 80p. As Type **921** but inscribed "The Ozonaction Protection Programme".
See also Nos. 1994/5.

922 Pharaonic Ship and Globe

1995. World Tourism Day.
1965 **922** 15p. multicoloured . . . 30 10

923 Emblem and Works, Imbaba

1995. 175th Anniv of Government Printing Offices.
1966 **923** 15p. multicoloured . . . 10 10

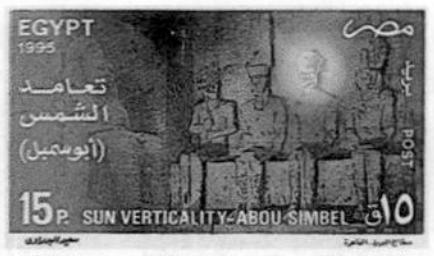

924 Sun illuminating Statue

1995. Overhead Sun Festival, Abu Simbel.
1967 **924** 15p. multicoloured . . . 10 10

925 Gold Mask of Tutankhamun

926 Dam and Ship

1995. Air. United Nations Day. 50th Anniversaries.
1968 **925** 80p. multicoloured . . . 30 15
1969 – 80p. lilac, blue & violet 30 15
1970 – 80p. multicoloured . . . 30 15
DESIGNS—VERT: No. 1968, Type **925** (U.N.E.S.C.O.). HORIZ: No. 1969, Globe, dove, emblem and "50" (U.N.O.); 1970, Farmer and wife working in field (ancient Egyptian mural) (F.A.O.).

1995. Inauguration of Esna Dam.
1971 **926** 15p. black, blue & grn 30 10

927 Emblem and Pharaonic Mural

928 Youssef Wahby

1995. 75th Anniv of Egyptian Engineers Society.
1972 **927** 15p. multicoloured . . . 10 10

1995. Artists.
1973 **928** 15p. blue and black . . 10 10
1974 – 15p. green 10 10
1975 – 15p. red and yellow . . 10 10
DESIGNS: No. 1974, Nagib el Rihany; 1975, Abdel Hallim Hafez.

929 "100"

930 Pharaonic Mural (left detail)

1995. Centenary of Motion Pictures.
1976 **929** 15p. multicoloured . . . 10 10

1996. Post Day. Multicoloured.
1977 55p. Type **930** 20 10
1978 80p. Right detail of Pharaonic mural 30 15
Nos. 1977/8 were issued together, se-tenant, forming a composite design.

931 Convolvulus

932 Summit Emblem

1996. Festivals 1996. Multicoloured.
1980 15p. Type **931** 10 10
1981 15p. Poppies 10 10

1996. Middle East Peace Process Summit, Sharm el Shaikh.
1982 **932** 15p. multicoloured . . . 10 10
1983 80p. multicoloured . . . 30 15

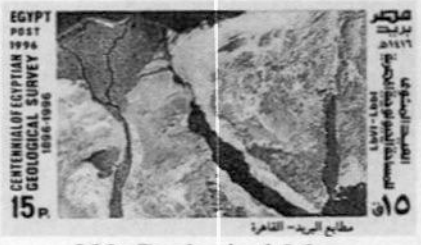

933 Geological Map

934 Fair Emblem

1996. Centenary of Egyptian Geological Survey Authority.
1984 **933** 15p. multicoloured . . . 10 10

1996. 29th Cairo International Fair.
1985 **934** 15p. multicoloured . . . 10 10

935 Emblem

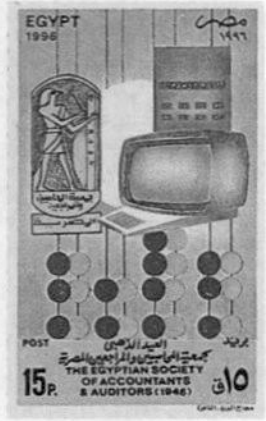

936 Emblem, Calculator, Computer and Abacus

1996. Signing of Pelindaba Treaty declaring Africa a Nuclear Weapon-free Zone, Cairo.
1986 **935** 15p. multicoloured . . . 10 10
1987 80p. multicoloured . . . 30 15

1996. 50th Anniv of Egyptian Society of Accountants and Auditors.
1988 **936** 15p. multicoloured . . . 10 10

937 "People" forming Graph

938 Emblem

1996. General Population and Housing Census.
1989 **937** 15p. multicoloured . . . 10 10

1996. Arab Summit, Cairo.
1990 **938** 55p. multicoloured . . . 20 10

939 Games Emblem

940 Emblems

1996. Olympic Games, Atlanta.
1991 **939** 15p. multicoloured . . . 10 10

1996. Air. 16th International Congress on Irrigation and Drainage, Cairo.
1993 **940** 80p. multicoloured . . . 30 15

1996. International Ozone Day. As T **921** but inscr "2nd ANNUAL OZONE INTERNATIONAL DAY".
1994 **921** 15p. mult (postage) . . . 10 10
1995 80p. multicoloured (air) . . . 30 15

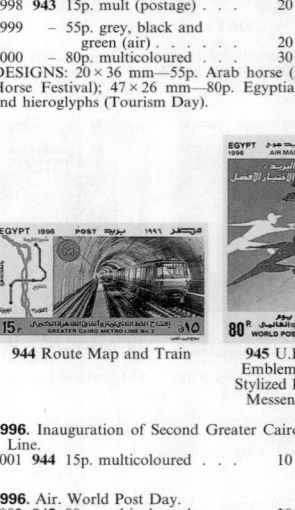

941 Fireworks over City

942 Test Tube, Microscope and Atomic Symbol

1996. 2nd Alexandria World Festival.
1996 **941** 80p. multicoloured . . . 30 15

1996. 25th Anniv of Academy of Scientific Research and Technology.
1997 **942** 15p. multicoloured . . . 10 10

943 Pharaonic Boat (Rowing Festival)

1996. International Tourism Day.
1998 **943** 15p. mult (postage) . . . 20 10
1999 – 55p. grey, black and green (air) 20 10
2000 – 80p. multicoloured . . . 30 15
DESIGNS: 20 × 36 mm—55p. Arab horse (Arabian Horse Festival); 47 × 26 mm—80p. Egyptian figure and hieroglyphs (Tourism Day).

944 Route Map and Train

945 U.P.U. Emblem and Stylized Postal Messengers

1996. Inauguration of Second Greater Cairo Metro Line.
2001 **944** 15p. multicoloured . . . 10 10

1996. Air. World Post Day.
2002 **945** 80p. multicoloured . . . 30 15

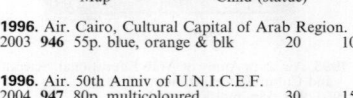

946 Emblems and Map

947 Mother and Child (statue)

1996. Air. Cairo, Cultural Capital of Arab Region.
2003 **946** 55p. blue, orange & blk 20 10

1996. Air. 50th Anniv of U.N.I.C.E.F.
2004 **947** 80p. multicoloured . . . 30 15

948 Council of State Courts

949 Emblem

1996. 50th Anniv of Council of State.
2005 **948** 15p. lilac, ultram & bl 10 10

1996. 25th Conference of International Federation of Training Development Organizations.
2006 **949** 15p. black, blue & yell 10 10

950 Emblem

951 Emblem and Ear of Wheat

1996. Economic Summit, Cairo.
2007 **950** 15p. multicoloured . . . 10 10

1996. International Nutrition Conf, Rome.
2009 **951** 15p. green, yell & red . . 10 10

952 Al-Said Ahmed el Badawi Mosque, Tanta

953 George Abyad

1996. National Day. El Gharbia Governate.
2010 **952** 15p. multicoloured . . . 10 10

1996. Artists.
2011 **953** 20p. rose and pink . . . 10 10
2012 – 20p. black and grey . . 10 10
2013 – 20p. deep brown and brown 10 10
2014 – 20p. black and grey . . 10 10
DESIGNS: No. 2012, Ali el Kassar; 2013, Mohamed Kareem; 2014, Fatma Roshdi.

954 Tutankhamun and Ankhesenamun (painted ivory plaque)

1996. Post Day. 75th Anniv of Discovery of Tutankhamun's Tomb (1st issue).
2015 **954** 20p. multicoloured . . . 10 10
See also No. 2056.

955 Computer, Officers, Emblem and Vehicle

1997. Police Day.
2017 **955** 20p. multicoloured . . . 10 10

956 Pink Asters

957 Queen Tiye

1997. Festivals 1997. Multicoloured.
2018 20p. Type **956** 10 10
2019 20p. White asters 10 10

1997.
2020 **957** 5p. brown and sepia (postage) 10 10
2020a – 10p. yellow and mauve 10 10
2021 – 20p. brown, ochre and grey 35 20
2022 – 20p. black and grey . . 10 10
2023 – 25p. yellow and green 10 10
2023a – 30p. yellow, brown and blue 15 10
2024 – 75p. black and orange 25 15
2025 – £E1 multicoloured . . . 35 20
2026 – £E2 multicoloured . . . 70 35
2027 – £E5 green, lilac and black . . . . . . 1·75 90
2029 – 25p. blue, buff and brown (air) 10 10
2030 – 75p. black, grey and blue 25 15
2031 – 125p. brown, yellow and green 45 25
2032 – £E1 brown, yellow and black 35 20
DESIGNS—POSTAGE—21 × 26 mm: No. 2020a, 2023, 2023a, Goddess Silakht. 23 × 27 mm: No. 2021, Queen Nofret. 21 × 26 mm: No. 2022, Horemheb; 75p. Amenhotep III. 21 × 38 mm: £E1 Queen Nefertari; £E5 Thutmose V ("Thotmes IV"). 22 × 38 mm: £E2 Mummiform coffin of Tutankhamun. AIR—22 × 40 mm: 25p. Akhnaton. 21 × 39 mm: 75p. Thutmose III ("Thotmes III"); 125p. Wooden statue of Tutankhamun; £E1 Gilded wooden statue of Tutankhamun.

958 Globe and Emblem

959 Emblem and Colours

1997. World Civil Defence Day.
2035 **958** 20p. multicoloured . . . 10 10

1997. 30th Cairo International Fair.
2036 **959** 20p. multicoloured . . . 10 10

960 Compass Rose and Wind Vane

961 Said

1997. Air. World Meteorological Day.
2037 **960** £E1 multicoloured . . . 35 20

1997. Birth Centenary of Mahmoud Said (artist).
2038 **961** 20p. multicoloured . . . 10 10

962 Stephan and U.P.U. Monument, Berne

1997. Death Cent of Heinrich von Stephan (founder of Universal Postal Union).
2040 **962** £E1 multicoloured . . . 35 20

963 Emblem

1997. 50th Anniv of Institute of African Research and Studies.
2041 **963** 75p. multicoloured . . . 25 15

964 Emblem, Building and Satellite

1997. Inauguration of State Information Service's New Headquarters.
2042 **964** 20p. multicoloured . . . 10 10

965 Emblem, Mascot and Trophy
966 Mascot with Torch and Gold Medal

1997. Under-17 Football World Championship, Egypt.
2043 **965** 20p. mult (postage) . . . 10 10
2044 75p. mult (air) 25 15

1997. Air. Egypt's Winning Medal Tally at Eighth Pan-Arab Games, Beirut.
2046 **966** 75p. multicoloured (wrongly inscr "Ban Arab Games") 25 15

967 Emblem
968 Emblem

1997. Air. 98th Interparliamentary Union Conference, Cairo.
2047 **967** £E1 multicoloured . . . 35 20

1997. 10th Anniv of Montreal Protocol (on reduction of use of chlorofluorocarbons).
2048 **968** 20p. mult (postage) . . . 10 10
2049 £E1 mult (air) 35 20

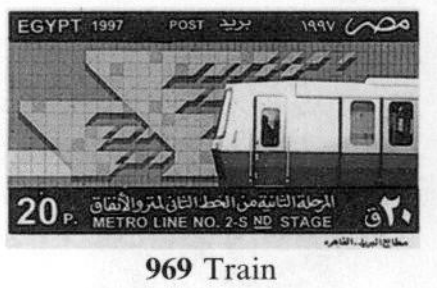

969 Train
970 Sarabas

1997. Inauguration of Second Stage of Underground Railway.
2050 **969** 20p. multicoloured . . . 25 10

1997. Air. "Fayoum's Portraits" Exhibition.
2051 **970** £E1 multicoloured . . . 35 20

971 Pharaonic Musician and Queen Hatshepsut's Temple

1997. 125th Anniv of First Performance of "Aida" (opera by Verdi), at Old Opera House, Cairo.
2052 **971** 20p. multicoloured . . . 10 10

972 Open Book showing Emblem

1997. Air. World Book and Copyright Day.
2054 **972** £E1 green, black & blue 35 20

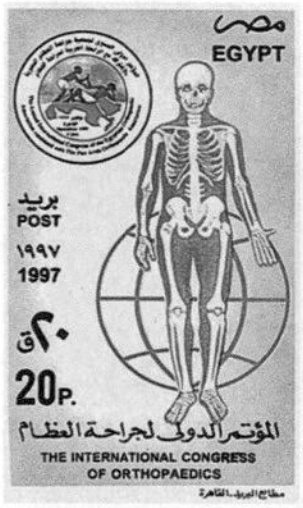

973 Skeleton and Globe
974 Goddess Serket (statuette protecting canopic chest)

1997. Int Orthopaedics Congress, Cairo.
2055 **973** 20p. multicoloured . . . 10 10

1997. 75th Anniv of Discovery of Tutankhamun's Tomb (2nd issue).
2056 **974** 20p. multicoloured . . . 10 10

975 Conference Emblem
977 Emblem and Scout Bugler

976 Museum

1997. Air. 11th African Transport and Communications Ministers' Conference, Cairo.
2058 **975** 75p. multicoloured . . . 25 15

1997. Inaug of Nubia Monuments Museum.
2059 **976** 20p. multicoloured . . . 10 10

1997. Air. 85th Anniv of Arab Scout Movement.
2060 **977** 75p. multicoloured . . . 25 15

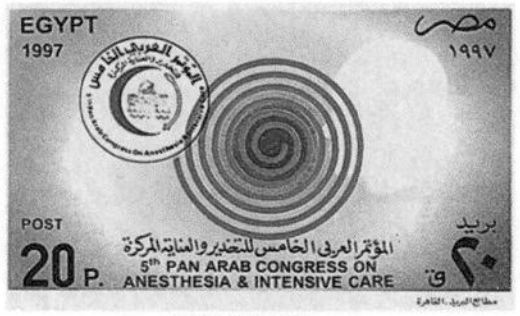
978 Emblem

1997. 5th Pan-Arab Anaesthesia and Intensive Care Congress.
2061 **978** 20p. multicoloured . . . 10 10

979 Emblem
980 "Egypt is the Cradle of Arts throughout the Ages"

1997. 50th Anniv of Arab Land Bank.
2062 **979** 20p. multicoloured . . . 10 10

1997. Dramatic Arts.
2063 **980** 20p. blue 10 10
2064 – 20p. black 10 10
2065 – 20p. black 10 10
2066 – 20p. black 10 10
2067 – 20p. black 10 10
DESIGNS: No. 2064, Zaky Tolaimat (founder and director of Institute of Drama); 2065, Ismael Yassen (actor); 2066, Zaky Roustom (actor); 2067, Soliman Naguib (actor and director of Opera House).

981 Map showing Canal

1997. 15th Anniv of Restoration of Sinai. Inaug of El Salaam ("Peace") Canal.
2068 **981** 20p. multicoloured . . . 10 10

982 Guard to Tutankhamun (statue)
983 Flowers

1998. Post Day. Multicoloured.
2069 20p. Type **982** 10 10
2070 75p. "Coronation of Rameses III" (sculpture) 25 15
2071 £E1 Mummiform coffin of Tutankhamun (29 × 49 mm) 35 20

1998. Festivals 1998. Multicoloured.
2072 20p. Type **983** 10 10
2073 20p. Pale pink flowers . . . 10 10

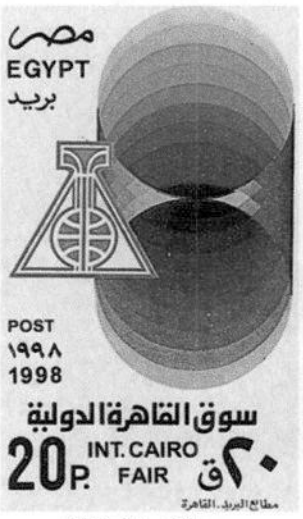

984 Emblem
985 New and Old Headquarters

1998. Cairo International Fair.
2074 **984** 20p. multicoloured . . . 10 10

1998. Centenary of National Bank of Egypt.
2075 **985** 20p. multicoloured . . . 10 10

986 Ancient Egyptians supporting Trophy

1998. Victory of Egypt in 21st African Nations Cup Football Championship.
2076 **986** 20p. mult (postage) . . . 10 10
2077 75p. mult (air) 25 15

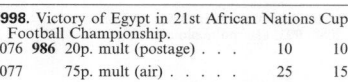

987 Emblem
988 Lighthouse of Alexandria and Bust of Alexander the Great

1998. Air. 8th Summit Meeting of G-15 Countries, Cairo.
2079 **987** £El multicoloured . . . 35 20

1998. Air.
2080 **988** £El multicoloured . . . 35 20

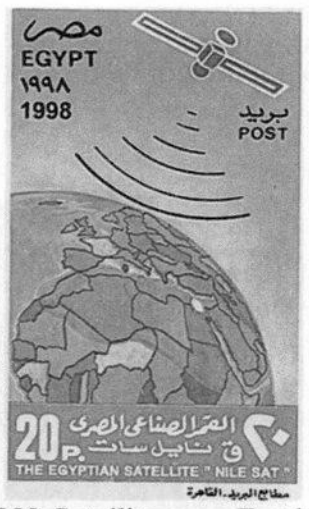
989 Satellite over Earth

1998. Egyptian "Nile Sat" Satellite.
2081 **989** 20p. multicoloured . . . 10 10

990 Emblem of Environment Agency within Pharaonic Eye

1998. World Environment Day.
2082 **990** 20p. multicoloured . . . 10 10

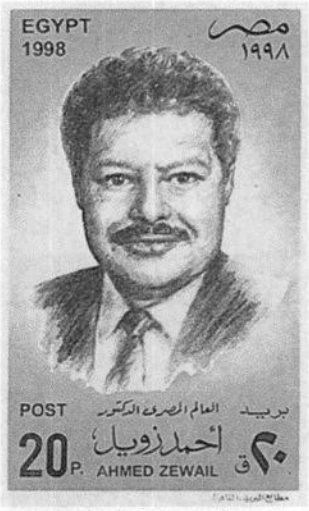

991 Zewail
992 Mohamed el Shaarawi

1998. Receipt of Franklin Institute Award by Dr. Ahmed Zewail.
2084 **991** 20p. black and blue (postage) 10 10
2085 £El black & yell (air) . . 35 20

1998. Imam Sheikh Mohamed Metwalli el-Shaarawi (preacher) Commemoration.
2086 **992** 20p. brown, ochre and black (postage) . . . 10 10
2087 £El brown, green and black (air) 35 20

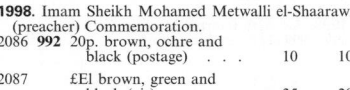

993 Ornament
994 Pharaonic Mermaid

1998. Air. Arab Post Day.
2088 **993** £El multicoloured . . . 35 20

1998. Nile Flood Day.
2089 **994** 20p. multicoloured . . . 10 10

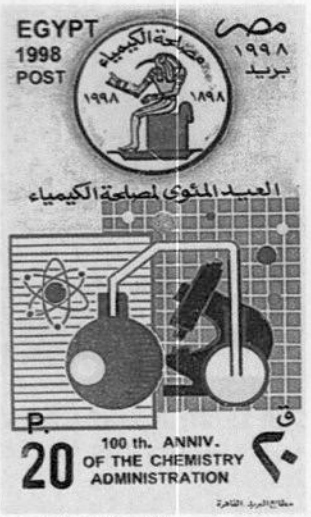

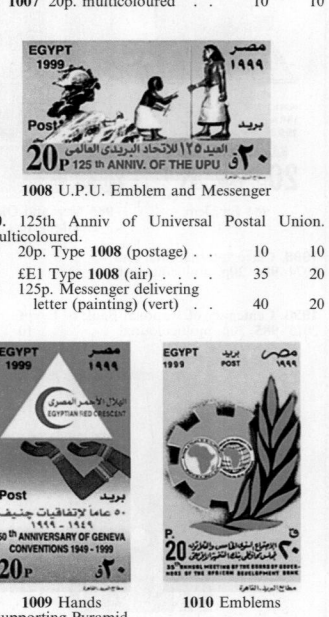

995 Emblem and Scientific Equipment

996 Anniversary Emblem

1998. Cent of Chemistry Administration.
2090 **995** 20p. multicoloured . . . 10 10

1998. 25th Anniv of Suez Crossing.
2091 **996** 20p. multicoloured . . . 10 10

997 Globe in Envelope

1998. Air. World Post Day.
2093 **997** 125p. multicoloured . . 45 25

998 Pharaonic Survey

1998. Centenary of Egyptian Survey Authority.
2094 **998** 20p. multicoloured . . . 10 10

999 Emblems in Handcuffs

1000 Anniversary Emblem

1998. Air. 67th Interpol Meeting, Cairo.
2095 **999** 125p. multicoloured . . 40 20

1998. Air. 50th Anniv of Universal Declaration of Human Rights.
2096 **1000** 125p. multicoloured . . 40 20

1001 Woman and University

1998. 90th Anniv of Cairo University.
2097 **1001** 20p. multicoloured . . 10 10

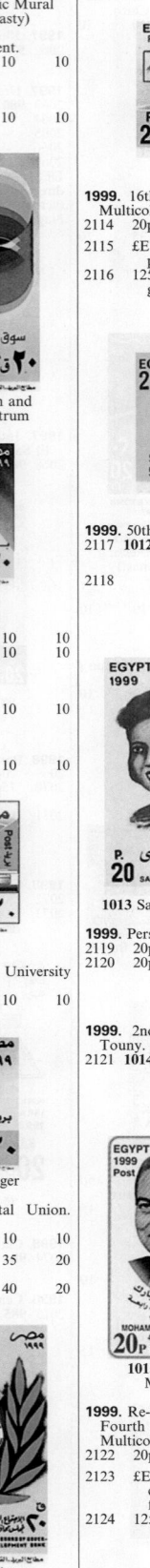

1002 Emblem and Pharaonic Workers

1003 Pharaonic Mural (19th Dynasty)

1998. Centenary of Trade Union Movement.
2098 **1002** 20p. multicoloured . . 10 10

1999. Post Day.
2099 **1003** 20p. multicoloured . . 10 10

1004 Flowers

1006 Emblem and Colour Spectrum

1005 Emblem and Globe

1999. Festivals 1999. Multicoloured.
2101 20p. Type **1004** 10 10
2102 20p. Gladioli 10 10

1999. International Women's Day.
2103 **1005** 20p. multicoloured . . 10 10

1999. Cairo International Fair.
2104 **1006** 20p. multicoloured . . 10 10

1007 Train passing under Nile

1999. Inauguration of El Tahrir–Cairo University Section of Underground Railway.
2105 **1007** 20p. multicoloured . . 10 10

1008 U.P.U. Emblem and Messenger

1999. 125th Anniv of Universal Postal Union. Multicoloured.
2106 20p. Type **1008** (postage) . . 10 10
2107 £E1 Type **1008** (air) 35 20
2108 125p. Messenger delivering letter (painting) (vert) . . 40 20

1009 Hands supporting Pyramid and Egyptian Red Crescent Emblem

1010 Emblems

1999. 50th Anniv of Geneva Conventions.
2110 **1009** 20p. multicoloured (postage) 10 10
2111 125p. multicoloured (air) 40 20

1999. 35th Annual Board of Governors Meeting of African Development Bank.
2112 **1010** 20p. multicoloured (postage) 10 10
2113 £E1 multicoloured (air) 35 20

1011 Player and Pyramids

1999. 16th World Men's Handball Championship. Multicoloured.
2114 20p. Type **1011** (postage) . . 10 10
2115 £E1 Games mascot and pyramids (air) 35 20
2116 125p. Mascot and goalkeeper 40 20

1012 Emblem

1999. 50th Anniv of S.O.S. Children's Villages.
2117 **1012** 20p. blue, green and black (postage) . . . 10 10
2118 125p. blue, stone and black (air) 40 20

1013 Sameera Moussa

1014 Touny

1999. Personalities. Multicoloured.
2119 20p. Type **1013** 10 10
2120 20p. Aisha Abdel Rahman 10 10

1999. 2nd Death Anniv of Ahmed Eldemerdash Touny.
2121 **1014** 20p. multicoloured . . 10 10

1015 President Mubarak

1016 Harpist and Sphinx

1999. Re-election of Mohammed Hosni Mubarak to Fourth Consecutive Term as President. Multicoloured.
2122 20p. Type **1015** (postage) . . 10 10
2123 £E1 As T **1015** but with coloured border instead of frame line (air) 35 20
2124 125p. As No. 2123 . . . . 40 20

1999. Air. Performance of Verdi's Opera "Aida" at the Pyramids.
2126 **1016** 125p. multicoloured . . 40 20

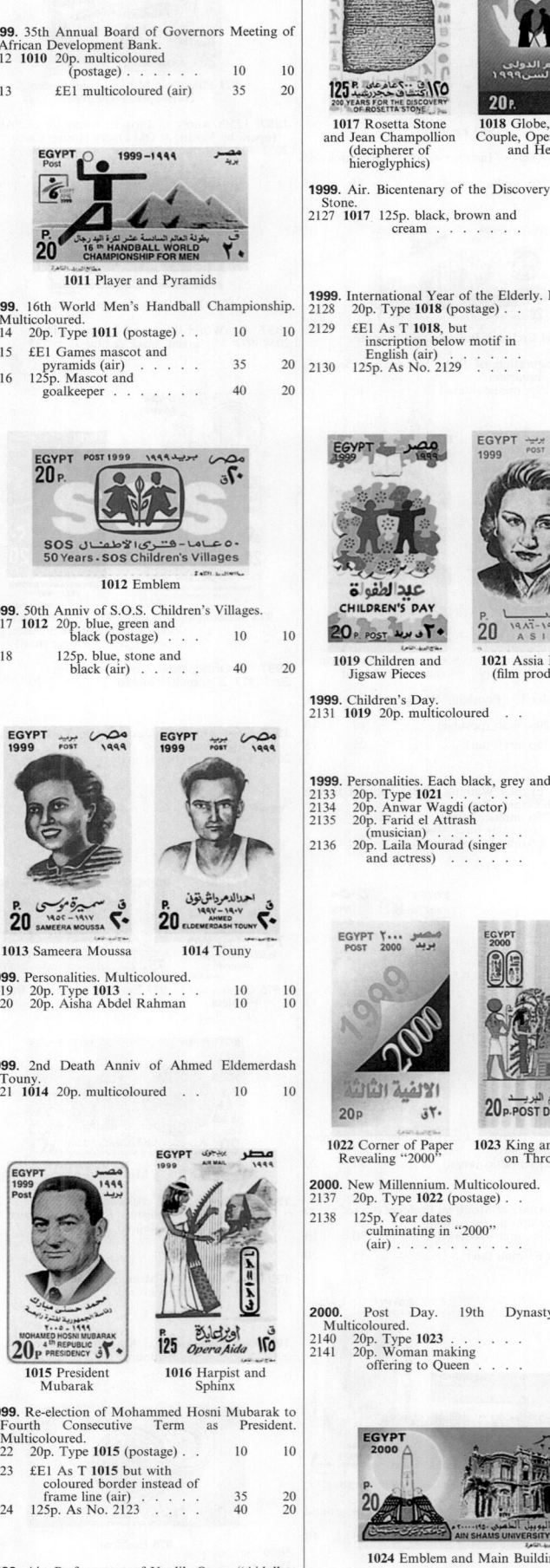

1017 Rosetta Stone and Jean Champollion (decipherer of hieroglyphics)

1018 Globe, Elderly Couple, Open Hands and Heart

1999. Air. Bicentenary of the Discovery of Rosetta Stone.
2127 **1017** 125p. black, brown and cream 40 20

1999. International Year of the Elderly. Mult.
2128 20p. Type **1018** (postage) . . 10 10
2129 £E1 As T **1018**, but inscription below motif in English (air) 35 20
2130 125p. As No. 2129 . . . . 45 25

1019 Children and Jigsaw Pieces

1021 Assia Dagher (film producer)

1999. Children's Day.
2131 **1019** 20p. multicoloured . . 10 10

1999. Personalities. Each black, grey and blue.
2133 20p. Type **1021** 10 10
2134 20p. Anwar Wagdi (actor) 10 10
2135 20p. Farid el Attrash (musician) 10 10
2136 20p. Laila Mourad (singer and actress) 10 10

1022 Corner of Paper Revealing "2000"

1023 King and Prince on Thrones

2000. New Millennium. Multicoloured.
2137 20p. Type **1022** (postage) . . 10 10
2138 125p. Year dates culminating in "2000" (air) 45 25

2000. Post Day. 19th Dynasty Murals. Multicoloured.
2140 20p. Type **1023** 10 10
2141 20p. Woman making offering to Queen 10 10

1024 Emblem and Main Building

2000. 50th Anniv of Ain Shams University, Cairo.
2143 **1024** 20p. multicoloured . . 10 10

1025 Flower **1026** Emblem

2000. Festivals 2000. Multicoloured.
2144 20p. Type **1025** 10 10
2145 20p. Roses 10 10
Nos. 2144/5 were issued together, se-tenant, forming a composite design.

2000. 25th Anniv of Islamic Development Bank.
2146 **1026** 20p. multicoloured . . 10 10

1027 Emblem and Pyramids **1028** Thoum

2000. 1st Common Market for Eastern and Southern Africa Regional Economic Conference.
2147 **1027** 125p. multicoloured . . 45 25

2000. 25th Death Anniv of Omkol Thoum.
2148 **1028** 20p. black and green 10 10

1029 Congress Emblem and Pyramids

2000. 8th International Congress of Egyptologists, Cairo.
2149 **1029** 20p. multicoloured . . 10 10

1030 Emblem

2000. Europe—Africa Summit, Cairo.
2150 **1030** 125p. multicoloured . . 45 25

1031 Emblem and Pyramids

2000. 10th Group 15 Summit, Cairo.
2151 **1031** 125p. multicoloured . . 45 25

1032 Skull and Syringe

2000. International Day Against Drug Abuse.
2152 **1032** 20p. multicoloured . . 10 10
See also No. 2202.

1033 Emblem and Arabic Inscription

2000. Centenary of National Insurance Company.
2153 **1033** 20p. multicoloured . . 10 10

1034 Emblem **1036** Emblem

1035 Pottery

2000. Olympic Games, Sydney. Multicoloured.
2155 20p. Type **1034** (postage) . . 10 10
2156 15p. As No. 2155 (air) . . . 45 25
There are some minor differences in the designs of Nos. 2155/6.

2000. 25th Anniv of Co-operative Production Union.
2157 **1035** 20p. multicoloured . . 10 10

2000. Air. World Tourism Day.
2158 **1036** 125p. multicoloured . . 45 25

1037 Train and Pyramids

2000. Inaug of Fourth Stage of Second Metro Line.
2159 **1037** 20p. multicoloured . . 10 10

1038 Emblem and Olive Branch

2000. World Post Day.
2160 **1038** 125p. green, mauve and black 45 25

1039 Flag and Dome of the Rock

2000. Solidarity.
2161 **1039** 20p. mult (postage) . . 10 10
2162 125p. mult (horiz) . . . 40 20
2163 125p. mult (air) 40 20

1040 Map and Train on Bridge

2000. Inauguration of El Ferdan Bridge.
2164 **1040** 20p. multicoloured . . 10 10

1041 Disabled Sign and Olympic Medal **1042** Emblem

2000. Disabled Persons' Day.
2165 **1041** 20p. multicoloured . . 10 10

2000. Air. 50th Anniv of United Nations High Commission for Refugees.
2166 **1042** 125p. multicoloured . . 40 20

1043 Building

2000. Inauguration of New Al Azhar Professoriate Building.
2167 **1043** 20p. multicoloured . . 10 10

1044 Red and Yellow Flowers **1045** Karem Mahmoud

2000. Festivals 2001. Multicoloured.
2168 20p. Type **1044** 10 10
2169 20p. Mauve flowers 10 10

2000. Artists.
2170 **1045** 20p. black and ochre 10 10
2171 – 20p. black and green 10 10
2172 – 20p. black and pink . . 10 10
2173 – 20p. black and lilac . . 10 10
2174 – 20p. black and blue . . 10 10
DESIGNS: No. 2171, Mahmoud el Miligi; 2172, Mohamed Fawzi; 2173, Hussein Riyad; 2174, Abdel Wares Asser.

1047 Mural

2001. Post Day. Multicoloured.
2176 20p. Type **1047** (postage) . . 10 10
2178 125p. Mural including pair of scales (air) 40 20

1048 Emblem **1049** Pass Book

2001. Arab Labour Organization.
2179 **1048** 20p. multicoloured . . 10 10

2001. Centenary of Postal Savings Bank.
2180 **1049** 20p. multicoloured . . 10 10

1050 Emblem

2001. 1st Anniv of National Council of Women.
2181 **1050** 30p. mult (postage) . . 10 10
2182 **1050** 125p. mult (air) 40 20

1051 Emblem

2001. Cairo International Fair.
2183 **1051** 30p. multicoloured . . 10 10

1052 Emblem

2001. 25th Anniv of Helwan University.
2195 **1052** 30p. multicoloured . . 10 10

1053 New Library Building

2001. Ancient Library of Alexandria Project.
2196 **1053** 12p. multicoloured . . 10 10

1054 Emblem **1055** Globe on Sunflower

2001. Pan-African Conference on Future of Children, Cairo. Multicoloured.
2197 30p. Type **1054** (postage) . . 10 10
2198 125p. As Type **1054** but with English inscr (air) . . 40 20

2001. World Environment Day.
2199 **1055** 125p. multicoloured . . 40 20

1056 Mascot

2001. World Military Football Championship, Cairo. Multicoloured.
2200 30p. Type **1056** 10 10
2201 125p. Mascot and emblem 40 20

2001. International Day against Drug Abuse.
2202 **1032** 30p. multicoloured . . 10 10

1057 Trophy and Emblem (⅔-size illustration)

2001. Egyptian Victory in 39th World Military Football Championship, Cairo.
MS2203 **1057** 125p. multicoloured 25 15

1058 Steam Locomotive

2001. 150th Anniv of Egyptian Railways.
2204 **1058** 30p. multicoloured . . 10 10

1059 Aziz Abaza Pasha (28th anniv)

1060 Emblem

2001. Poets' Death Anniversaries.
2205 **1059** 30p. black and blue . . 10 10
2206 – 30p. black and pink . . 10 10
DESIGN: No. 2206, Ahmed Rami (20th anniv).

2001. International Year of Volunteers.
2207 **1060** 125p. yellow and blue 25 15

1061 Couple dancing

2001. Ismaelia Folklore Festival.
2208 **1061** 30p. multicoloured . . 10 10

1062 Building and Satellite Dish

2001. 25th Anniv of First Telecommunications Ground Station.
2209 **1062** 30p. multicoloured . . 10 10

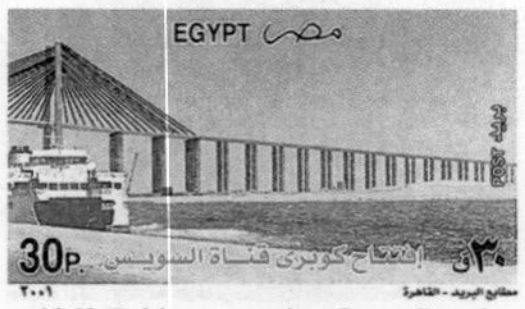

1063 Bridge spanning Suez Canal

2001. Inauguration of Suez Canal Road Bridge. Multicoloured.
2210 30p. Type **1063** 10 10
2211 125p. Bridge spanning road 25 15
MS2212 81 × 60 mm. 125p. Bridge spanning Suez Canal. Imperf 25 15
Nos. 2110/11 were issued together, se-tenant, forming a composite design.

1064 Children encircling Globe

2001. United Nations Year of Dialogue Among Civilizations. Multicoloured.
2213 125p. Type **1064** 25 15
2214 125p. Globe and symbols of Egypt (horiz) 25 15

1065 Mask of San Xing Dui

2001. Egypt–China Joint Issue. Golden Masks. Multicoloured.
2215 30p. Type **1065** 10 10
2216 30p. Mask of Tutankhamun 10 10

1066 Cars leaving Tunnel

1067 Emblem

2001. Inauguration of Al Azhar Road Tunnel, Cairo.
2217 **1066** 30p. multicoloured . . 10 10

2001. 25th Anniv of El Menoufia University.
2218 **1067** 30p. multicoloured . . 10 10

1068 Zakareya Ahmed

2001. Composers' Death Anniversaries. Each black and lilac.
2219 30p. Type **1068** (40th anniv) 10 10
2220 30p. Riyadh el Sonbati (20th anniv) 10 10
2221 30p. Mahmoud el Sherif (11th anniv) 10 10
2222 30p. Mohamed el Kasabgi (35th anniv) 10 10

1069 Bird

2001. Festivals 2002. Birds. Multicoloured.
2223 30p. Type **1069** 10 10
2224 30p. Gulls 10 10
2225 30p. Parrot 10 10
2226 30p. Blue bird 10 10

1070 Tomb of Anhur Khawi (mural, 20th dynasty)

2002. Post Day. Multicoloured.
2227 30p. Type **1070** 10 10
MS2228 80 × 59 mm. 125p. Tomb of Irinefer (mural). Imperf 25 10

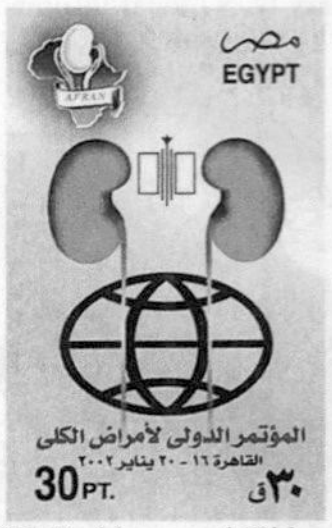

1071 Emblems and Kidneys

2002. International Nephrology Congress.
2229 **1071** 30p. multicoloured . . 10 10

1072 Emblem

2002. 50th Anniv of Police Day.
2230 **1072** 30p. multicoloured . . 10 10
MS2231 79 × 50 mm. **1072** 30p. multicoloured. Imperf 10 10

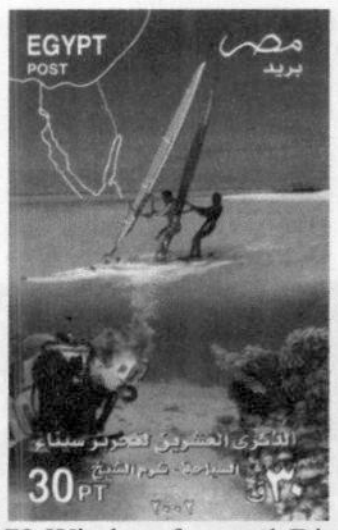

1073 Wind-surfers and Diver

2002. 20th Anniv of Return of Sinai to Egypt.
2232 **1073** 30p. multicoloured . . 10 10

1074 Facade

1075 Man wearing Animal Skin and Couple Enthroned (20th Dynasty wall painting)

2002. 50th Anniv of Cairo Bank.
2233 **1074** 30p. multicoloured . . 10 10

2002. Multicoloured.
2234 **1075** 10p. multicoloured . . 10 10
2235 – 25p. yellow, mauve and black 10 10
2236 – 30p. yellow, mauve and blue 10 10
2237 – 50p. multicoloured . . 10 10
2238 – 110p. yellow, brown and violet 25 15
2239 – 125p. multicoloured . . 30 15
2240 – 150p. multicoloured . . 35 20
2241 – 225p. multicoloured . . 50 25
2242 – £E1 orchre, blue and brown 25 15
2243 – £E5 multicoloured . . . 1·10 55

DESIGNS: As Type **1075**—25p. Sesostris (statue); 30p. Merit Aton (bust); HORIZ:50p. Royal couple, children and musicians (20th Dynasty wall painting); £E1 Snefru's pyramid, Dahshur. 24 × 41 mm:110p. Wife of Ka-Aper ("Sheikh el Balad") (bust); 125p. Psusennes I (bust); 150p. Tutankhamun holding spear (statue); 225p. Ramses II obelisk, Luxor; £E5 Karnak Temple ruins.

1076 Ibrahim Shams (1948)

2002. Olympic Gold Medal Weightlifters. Multicoloured.
2244 30p. Type **1076** 10 10
2245 30p. Khidre El Tourney (1936) 10 10

1077 Building and World Map

2002. 50th Anniv of *Al Akhba* (newspaper).
2246 **1077** 30p. multicoloured . . 10 10

1078 Stamps of 1952 (⅓-size illustration)

2002. 50th Anniv of Revolution of 23 July 1952. Sheet 80 × 95 mm. Imperf.
MS2247 **1078** 125p. multicoloured 25 10

1079 Aswan Dam

2002. Centenary of Aswan Dam. Multicoloured.
2248 30p. Type **1079** 10 10
2249 30p. Part of dam and shoreline 10 10
Nos. 2248/9 were issued together, se-tenant, forming a composite design.

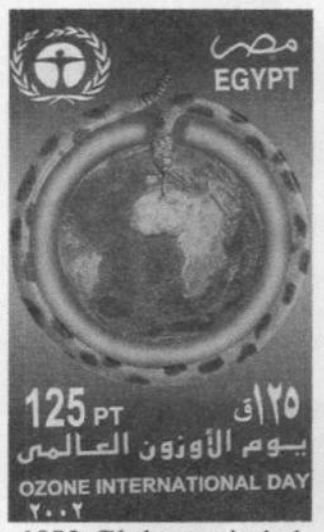

1080 Globe encircled by Snake

1081 Man with Bandaged Head and Traffic Lights

2002. International Ozone Day.
2250 **1080** 125p. multicoloured . . 25 10

2002. International Road Safety Conference.
2251 **1081** 30p. multicoloured . . 10 10

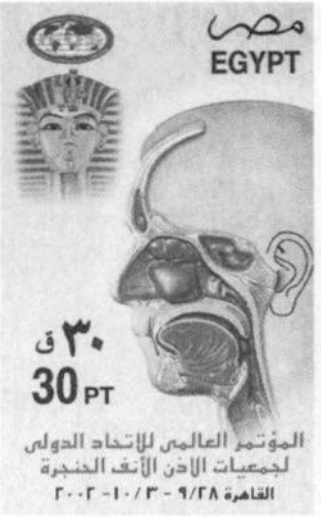

1082 Cross Section of Head showing Cavities   **1083** UPU Emblem

2002. 17th Oto-Rhino Laryngological Societies (IFOS) Congress, Cairo.
2252 **1082** 30p. multicoloured . . 10 10

2002. World Post Day. 125th Anniv of Universal Postal Union.
2253 **1083** 125p. multicoloured . . 25 10

1084 Library Building

2002. Inauguration of Bibliotheca Alexandrina (library), Alexandria. Multicoloured.
2254 30p. Type **1084** 10 10
2255 125p. Inscribed column and sunset (vert) 25 10
MS2256 60 × 81 mm. 125p. Interior of ancient Alexandria library. Imperf 25 25

1085 Hassan Faek   **1086** Bee-eater

2002. Actors. Each pink and grey.
2257 30p. Type **1085** 10 10
2258 30p. Aziza Amir 10 10
2259 30p. Farid Shawki 10 10
2260 30p. Mary Mounib 10 10

2002. Festivals 2003. Multicoloured.
2261 30p. Type **1086** 10 10
2262 30p. Swallow 10 10
2263 30p. Red-throated bee-eater 10 10
2264 30p. Roller 10 10
Nos. 2261/4 were issued together, se-tenant, forming a composite design.

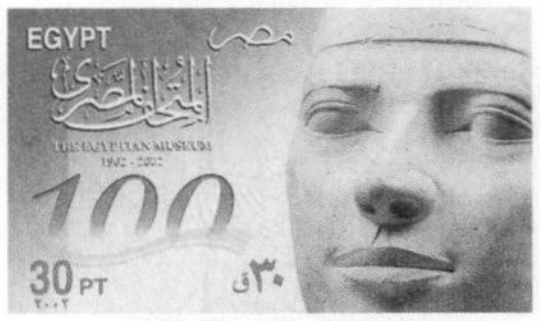

1087 Face (sculpture)

2002. Centenary of Egyptian Museum, Cairo. Multicoloured.
2265 30p. Type **1087** 10 10
MS2266 80 × 60 mm. 125p. Building facade and statue. Imperf . . . 25 25

1088 Bridge

2002. Inauguration of Aswan Suspension Bridge. Multicoloured.
2267 30p. Type **1088** 10 10
2268 30p. Bridge right 10 10
Nos. 2267/8 were issued together, se-tenant, forming a composite design of the bridge.

1089 University Emblem

2002. 25th Anniv of Suez Canal University, Ismailia.
2269 **1089** 30p. multicoloured . . 10 10

1090 Pumping Station

2002. Inauguration of Toshka Irrigation Project.
2270 **1090** 30p. multicoloured . . 10 10

1091 Pharaonic Tomb Mural

2003. Post Day. Multicoloured.
2271 30p. Type **1091** 10 10
2272 30p. Mural showing wings 10 10
2273 125p. Mural showing pharaoh and goddess . . 25 10

1092 Emblem

2003. International Communications and Information Technology Fair, Cairo.
2274 **1092** 30p. multicoloured . . 10 10

1093 Festival Emblem

2003. 4th International Nile Children's Song Festival.
2275 **1093** 30p. multicoloured . . 10 10
2276 125p. multicoloured . . 25 10

1094 Association Emblem, Bat and Ball

2003. Egypt International Open Table Tennis Championship, Cairo.
2277 **1094** 30p. multicoloured . . 10 10
2278 125p. multicoloured . . 25 10

1095 Exhibition Emblem and Construction Workers

2003. 10th International Building and Construction Conference.
2279 **1095** 30p. multicoloured . . 10 10
2280 125p. multicoloured . . 25 10

1096 Emblem

2003. 80th Anniv of Arab Lawyers Union.
2281 **1096** 30p. multicoloured . . 10 10
2282 125p. multicoloured . . 25 10

1097 Smart Village Emblem and Building

2003. Smart Village (technology business park), Cairo. Multicoloured.
2283 30p. Type **1097** 10 10
2284 125p. No. 2283 . . . . . . 25 10
MS2285 80 × 59 mm. 100p. Smart Village and environs. Imperf 20 10

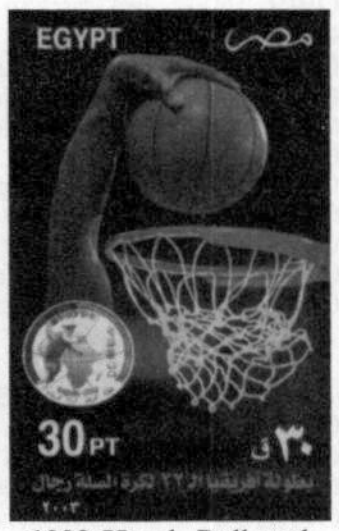

1098 Ihsan Abdul Qudous   **1099** Hand, Ball and Net

2003. Writers. Multicoloured.
2286 30p. Type **1098** 10 10
2287 30p. Youssef Idris 10 10

2003. Men's African Nations Basketball Championship.
2288 **1099** 30p. multicoloured . . 10 10
2289 125p. multicoloured . . 25 10

1100 Planets and Emblem

2003. Centenary of National Institute for Astrological and Geophysical Research.
2290 **1100** 30p. multicoloured . . 10 10

1101 Emblem

2003. Egypt's Bid to Host 2010 World Cup Football Championship. Multicoloured.
2291 30p. Type **1101** 10 10
2292 125p. Emblem and Tutankhamen (vert) . . . 25 10

1102 Tent Maker and Market

2003. World Tourism Day.
2293 **1102** 30p. multicoloured . . 10 10
2294 125p. multicoloured . . 25 10

1103 Soldier   **1104** UPU Emblem and Computer

2003. 30th Anniv of October War.
2295 **1103** 30p. multicoloured . . 10 10

2003. World Post Day.
2296 **1104** 125p. multicoloured . . 25 10

1105 Emblem   **1106** Alstromeria

2003. 91st Anniv of Bar Association.
2297 **1105** 30p. multicoloured . . 10 10

2003. Festivals 2004. Multicoloured.
2298 30p. Type **1106** 10 10
2299 30p. White rose 10 10
2300 30p. Red rose 10 10
2301 30p. Sunflower 10 10
Nos. 2298/2301 were issued together, se-tenant, forming a composite design.

1107 Salah Abou Seif   **1109** Emblem and Building

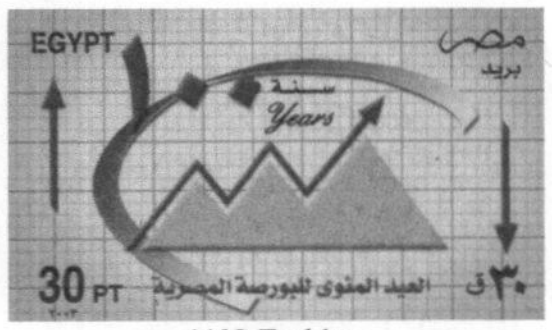

1108 Emblem

2003. Cinema Directors. Each black and azure.
2302 30p. Type **1107** 10 10
2303 30p. Kamal Selim 10 10
2304 30p. Henri Bakarat 10 10
2305 30p. Hassan el Emam . . . 10 10

2003. Centenary of Cairo Bourse (stock exchange).
2306 **1108** 30p. multicoloured . . 10 10

2003. 50th Anniv of El Gomhoreya Newspaper.
2307 **1109** 30p. multicoloured . . 10 10

1110 Mrs. Suzanne Mubarak

2003. 5th E-9 Ministerial Meeting.

2308	**1110**	30p. multicoloured	10	10
2309		125p. multicoloured	25	10
MS2310		80×60 mm. **1110** £E2 multicoloured. Imperf	45	30

EXPRESS LETTER STAMPS

E 52 Postman on Motor-cycle

1926.

E138	E **52**	20m. green	10·00	5·00
E139		20m. black and red	3·25	1·25

1943. As Type E **52**, but inscr "POSTES".

E289	E **52**	26m. black and red	3·25	4·50
E290		40m. black and brown	1·60	1·60

1952. No. E290 optd as T **124**.

E404	E **52**	40m. black & brown	1·40	1·25

OFFICIAL STAMPS

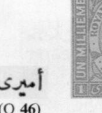

O 25

أميري

(O 46)

O 52

1893.

O64	O **25**	(–) brown	2·50	10

1907. Stamps of 1879 and 1888 optd **O.H.H.S.**and Arabic equivalent.

O73	**18**	1m. brown	1·75	30
O74		2m. green	4·00	10
O75		3m. yellow	2·75	1·25
O86		4m. red	4·00	1·75
O76		5m. red	5·00	10
O77	**10**	1p. blue	2·00	20
O78		5p. grey	16·00	3·00

1913. No. 63 optd in English only. (a) Optd **"O.H.H.S."** (with inverted commas).

O79	**18**	5m. pink	–	£300

(b) Optd **O.H.H.S.** (without inverted commas).

O80	**18**	5m. pink	7·00	60

1915. Stamps of 1914 optd **O.H.H.S.** and Arabic equivalent.

O 83	**29**	1m. sepia	1·50	3·75
O 99	–	2m. red	7·50	16·00
O 85	–	3m. orange	2·00	3·75
O 87	–	5m. lake	4·00	1·00
O101	–	5m. pink	17·00	4·25

1922. Stamps of 1914 optd **O.H.E.M.S.** and Arabic equivalent.

O111	**29**	1m. brown	1·60	2·75
O112		2m. red	1·50	3·50
O113		3m. orange	2·00	4·25
O114		4m. green	4·25	10·00
O115		5m. pink	2·75	60
O116		10m. blue	4·75	5·75
O117		10m. red	6·50	2·00
O118	**41**	15m. blue	6·50	5·50
O119	**42**	15m. blue	£120	£120
O120	–	50m. purple	16·00	16·00

1923. Stamps of 1923 optd with Type O **46**.

O123	**44**	1m. orange	90	2·00
O124		2m. black	1·25	3·25
O125		3m. brown	3·25	4·75
O126		4m. green	3·75	5·50
O127		5m. brown	1·40	70
O128		10m. red	2·00	2·25
O129		15m. blue	4·00	6·00
O130	–	50m. green	6·00	7·50

1926.

O138	O **52**	1m. orange	50	25
O139		2m. black	30	20
O140		3m. brown	90	70
O141		4m. green	85	80
O142		5m. brown	95	25
O143		10m. lake	2·50	25
O144		10m. violet	1·50	30
O145		15m. blue	2·50	60
O146		15m. purple	2·50	55
O147		20m. blue	2·50	75
O148		20m. olive	4·25	1·25
O149		50m. green	5·50	1·10

Nos. O148/9 are larger, 22½×27½ mm.

O 85

O 174

1938.

O276	O **85**	1m. orange	20	1·00
O277		2m. red	20	25
O278		3m. brown	85	1·25
O279		4m. green	55	1·25
O280		5m. brown	25	35
O281		10m. mauve	35	60
O282		15m. purple	85	85
O283		20m. blue	80	80
O284		50m. green	2·00	1·75

1952. Optd as T **124**.

O404	O **85**	1m. orange	1·00	1·10
O405		2m. red	85	1·10
O406		3m. brown	1·10	1·10
O407		4m. green	1·10	1·10
O408		5m. brown	1·10	1·10
O409		10m. mauve	1·65	1·10
O410		15m. purple	1·50	1·10
O411		20m. blue	1·75	1·25
O412		50m. green	4·00	2·75

1958.

O685	O **174**	1m. orange	20	30
O686		4m. green	40	45
O687		5m. brown	40	15
O571		10m. purple	45	15
O688		10m. brown	40	15
O572		35m. blue	1·10	20
O689		35m. violet	1·50	35
O690		50m. green	2·40	40
O691		100m. lilac	4·75	1·25
O692		200m. red	10·50	5·75
O693		500m. black	15·00	11·00

O 334 Eagle

O 435 Eagle

1967.

O918	O **334**	1m. blue	10	20
O919		4m. brown	15	20
O920		5m. olive	20	10
O921		10m. brown	75	45
O922		10m. purple	65	25
O923		20m. purple	40	20
O924		35m. violet	60	25
O925		50m. orange	75	30
O926		55m. violet	75	30
O927		100m. red and green	1·60	70
O928		200m. red and blue	3·25	1·25
O929		500m. red and olive	6·50	4·50

1972.

O1161a	O **435**	1m. blue & black	10	10
O1162a		10m. red & black	10	10
O1163		20m. green & blk	60	25
O1165		20m. brown & vio	10	10
O1166		30m. brown & lilac	20	20
O1294		50m. orange & blk	20	10
O1295		55m. lilac & black	25	10
O1169		60m. orange & blk	40	20
O1170		70m. green & blk	50	30
O1171		80m. green & blk	45	25

O 706 Eagle

1985. Size 20×25 mm.

O1589	O **706**	1p. red	10	10
O1590		2p. brown	10	10
O1591		3p. brown	10	10
O1592a		5p. orange	20	20
O1593		8p. green	35	25
O1594		10p. brown	10	10
O1595		15p. lilac	70	45
O1596		20p. blue	50	50
O1597		25p. red	55	55
O1598		30p. purple	40	40
O1599		50p. green	1·25	1·25
O1600		60p. green	75	75

1991. As Nos. O1589/1600 but smaller, 17×22 mm.

O1806	O **706**	5p. orange	10	10
O1807		10p. brown	10	10
O1808		15p. brown	10	10
O1808a		20p. blue	10	10
O1808b		20p. violet	10	10
O1809		25p. lilac	15	15
O1810		30p. lilac	15	15
O1811		50p. green	20	20
O1812		55p. red	20	20
O1812a		75p. brown	25	25
O1813		£E1 blue	40	40
O1814		£E2 green	75	75

POSTAGE DUE STAMPS

D 16

D 24

1884.

D57	D **16**	10pa. red	45·00	9·00
D58		20pa. red	£110	28·00
D64		1pi. red	30·00	8·00
D65		2pi. red	30·00	3·75
D61		5pi. red	14·00	42·00

1888. As Type D **16**, but values in "Milliemes" and "Piastres".

D66	D **16**	2m. green	13·00	20·00
D67		5m. red	32·00	20·00
D68		1p. blue	£130	35·00
D69		2p. orange	£150	12·00
D70		5p. grey	£200	£180

1889. Inscr "A PERCEVOIR POSTES EGYPTIENNES".

D71	D **24**	2m. green	7·00	50
D72		4m. purple	2·25	50
D73		1p. blue	5·50	50
D74bw		2p. orange	5·00	70

1898. Surch **3 Milliemes** in English and Arabic.

D75	D **24**	3m. on 2p. orange	1·25	4·00

1921. As Type D **24**, but inscr "POSTAGE DUE EGYPT POSTAGE".

D 98	D **23**	2m. green	2·75	4·00
D 99		2m. red	1·00	1·50
D100		4m. red	5·00	14·00
D101		4m. green	4·00	1·00
D102	–	10m. blue	6·50	18·00
D103	–	10m. red	5·50	70

The 10m. values have "MILLIEMES" in a bar across the figure of value.

1922. Optd with T **43** inverted.

D111	D **24**	2m. red (No. D99)	90	4·00
D112		4m. green (No. D101)	1·25	4·25
D113		10m. red (No. D103)	1·90	1·40
D114		2p. orge (No. D74)	4·00	11·00

D 59

D 298

1927.

D173	D **59**	2m. black	50	30
D730		2m. orange	45	70
D175a		4m. green	50	30
D176		4m. sepia	4·25	2·75
D177		5m. brown	2·50	75
D575		6m. green	1·60	1·25
D179		8m. purple	90	40
D180a		10m. lake	65	20
D732		10m. brown	1·50	90
D181		12m. red	1·10	3·00
D182		20m. brown	1·25	1·75
D183		30m. violet	2·50	2·50

The 30m. is larger, 22×27½ mm.

1952. Optd as T **124**.

D404	D **59**	2m. orange	1·10	1·25
D405		4m. green	1·10	1·40
D406		6m. green	1·25	2·00
D407		8m. purple	1·50	1·60
D408		10m. lake	2·50	2·25
D410		12m. red	1·50	1·75
D411		30m. violet	2·25	2·50

1965.

D852	D **298**	2m. violet on orange	85	85
D853		8m. blue on lt blue	1·10	1·10
D854		10m. green on yell.	1·60	1·50
D855		20m. violet on lt bl	1·90	1·75
D856		40m. green on orge	3·50	3·25

ELOBEY, ANNOBON AND CORISCO Pt. 9

A group of Spanish islands off the west coast of Africa in the Gulf of Guinea. In 1909 became part of Spanish Guinea. In 1959 Annobon became part of Fernando Poo, and Elobey and Corisco part of Rio Muni.

100 centimos = 1 peseta.

1903. "Curly Head" key-type inscr "ELOBEY, ANNOBON Y CORISCO". Dated "1903".

1	Z	¼c. red	55	35
2		½c. purple	55	35
3		1c. black	55	35
4		2c. red	55	35
5		3c. green	55	35
6		4c. green	55	35
7		5c. lilac	55	35
8		10c. red	1·10	1·10
9		15c. orange	3·25	1·10
10		25c. blue	5·25	4·25
11		50c. brown	7·00	7·75
12		75c. brown	7·00	9·75
13		1p. red	11·00	14·00
14		2p. brown	30·00	41·00
15		3p. green	45·00	50·00
16		4p. purple	£100	70·00
17		5p. green	£120	70·00
18		10p. blue	£225	£120

1905. "Curly Head" key-type inscr "ELOBEY, ANNOBON Y CORISCO" and dated "1905".

19	Z	1c. pink	95	55
20		2c. purple	4·00	55
21		3c. black	95	55
22		4c. red	95	55
23		5c. green	95	55
24		10c. green	3·25	70
25		15c. lilac	4·00	3·50
26		25c. red	4·00	3·50
27		50c. orange	7·00	5·50
28		75c. blue	7·00	5·50
29		1p. brown	14·00	12·00
30		2p. brown	16·00	17·00
31		3p. red	16·00	17·00
32		4p. brown	£120	60·00
33		5p. green	£120	60·00
34		10p. red	£300	£200

1906. Preceding issue surch **1906** and value, with or without ornamental frame.

35d	Z	10c. on 1c. pink	10·50	5·25
36		15c. on 2c. purple	10·50	8·50
38		25c. on 3c. black	10·50	8·50
40		50c. on 4c. red	10·50	8·50

3 King Alfonso XIII

1907.

41	**3**	1c. purple	35	35
42		2c. black	35	35
43		3c. red	35	35
44		4c. green	35	35
45		5c. green	35	35
46		10c. lilac	3·50	4·00
47		15c. pink	1·30	1·30
48		25c. buff	1·30	1·30
49		50c. blue	1·30	1·30
50		75c. brown	4·00	1·90
51		1p. brown	6·25	3·25
52		2p. red	8·75	5·75
53		3p. brown	8·75	5·75
54		4p. green	8·75	5·75
55		5p. red	12·50	5·75
56		10p. pink	31·00	18·00

1908. Surch **HABILITADO PARA 05 CTMS.**

57	**3**	05c. on 1c. purple	2·75	1·50
58		05c. on 2c. black	3·00	1·50
59		05c. on 3c. red	3·00	1·50
60		05c. on 4c. green	3·00	1·50
61		05c. on 10c. lilac	5·75	5·25
62		25c. on 10c. lilac	26·00	14·50

1909. Fiscal stamps inscr "POSESIONES ESPANOLES DE AFRICA OCCIDENTAL", surch **1909 CORREOS 10 cen de peseta.**

63		10c. on 50c. green	22·00	14·50
64		10c. on 1p.25 lilac	33·00	18·00
65		10c. on 2p. brown	£130	£100
66		10c. on 2p.50 blue	£130	£100
67		10c. on 10p. brown	£140	£100
68		10c. on 15p. grey	£130	£100
69		10c. on 25p. brown	£130	£100

For later issues see **SPANISH GUINEA.**

EL SALVADOR Pt. 15

A republic of C. America, independent since 1838.

1867. 8 reales = 100 centavos = 1 peso.
1912. 100 centavos = 1 colón.

1 San Miguel Volcano

4

1867.

1	1	½r. blue	90	90
2		1r. red	90	90
3		2r. green	1·75	2·50
4		4r. brown	4·25	4·00

1874. Optd **CONTRA SELLO 1874** and arms in circle.

5	1	½r. blue	4·00	4·00
6		1r. red	4·00	4·00
7		2r. green	4·00	4·00
8		4r. brown	11·00	10·50

1879.

9	4	1c. green	1·25	75
15		2c. red	1·75	1·75
16		5c. blue	3·00	1·50
12		10c. black	6·00	4·00
13		20c. purple	15·00	12·00

8

9

10

14

1887.

18	8	3c. brown (perf)	40	40
19	9	5c. blue (roul)	40	30
20	10	10c. orange (perf)	4·00	1·10

1889. Surch **1 centavo.**

21	8	1c. on 3c. brown	1·00	60

A number of postage stamps listed above are found overprinted **1889**.

1889. As T **8**, but with bar at top. Perf.

22	8	1c. green	50	50

1890.

30	14	1c. green	15	20
31		2c. brown	15	25
32		3c. yellow	15	25
33		5c. blue	15	25
34		10c. violet	15	25
35		20c. orange	15	30
36		25c. red	15	40
37		50c. purple	15	80
38		1p. red	15	2·00

15

19 Landing of Columbus

1891.

39	15	1c. red	40	20
40		2c. green	40	20
41		3c. violet	40	30
42		5c. red	40	30
43		10c. blue	40	30
44		11c. violet	40	85
45		20c. green	40	1·10
46		25c. brown	40	1·25
47		50c. blue	40	2·50
48		1p. brown	45	5·00

1891. Surch **1 centavo.**

49	15	1c. on 2c. green	8·50	6·00

1891. Surch **UN CENTAVO.**

50	15	1c. on 2c. green	3·50	4·50

1891. Surch **5 CENTAVOS.**

51	15	5c. on 3c. violet	7·50	6·00

1892.

52	19	1c. green	15	15
53		2c. brown	15	15
54		3c. blue	15	15
55		5c. grey	15	15
56		10c. red	15	20
57		11c. brown	15	1·00
58		20c. orange	15	1·00
59		25c. purple	15	1·50
60		50c. yellow	15	2·00
61		1p. red	15	3·00

1892. Surch.

62a	19	1c. on 5c. grey	75	80
64		1c. on 20c. orange	1·00	1·10
66		1c. on 25c. purple	1·50	90

23 Gen. Ezeta

24 Founding the City of Isabella

1893. Dated "1893".

67	23	1c. blue	15	20
68		2c. red	15	20
69		3c. violet	15	20
70		5c. brown	15	25
71		10c. brown	15	25
72		11c. red	15	30
73		20c. green	15	40
74		25c. black	15	50
75		50c. orange	15	60
76		1p. black	15	90
77	24	2p. green	50	
78	–	5p. violet	50	
79	–	10p. red	50	

DESIGNS—VERT: 5p. Columbus Statue, Genoa; 10p. Departure from Palos.

1893. Surch **UN CENTAVO.**

80	23	1c. on 2c. red	60	60

28 Liberty

29 Columbus before the Council

1894. Dated "1894".

81	28	1c. brown	15	20
82		2c. blue	15	20
83		3c. purple	15	20
84		5c. brown	15	30
85		10c. violet	15	30
86		11c. red	15	30
87		20c. blue	15	40
88		25c. orange	15	50
89		50c. black	15	80
90		1p. blue	15	1·10
91	29	2p. blue	40	
92	–	5p. red	50	
93	–	10p. brown	50	

DESIGNS—HORIZ: 5p. Columbus protecting hostages; 10p. Columbus received by King and Queen.

1894. Surch **1 Centavo.**

94	28	1c. on 11c. red	90	60

31

34

1895. Optd with Arms obliterating portrait. Various frames.

95	31	1c. olive	15	
96		2c. green	15	
97		3c. brown	15	
98		5c. blue	15	
99		10c. orange	15	
100		12c. red	15	
101		15c. red	15	
102		20c. yellow	15	
103		24c. violet	15	
104		30c. blue	15	
105		50c. red	15	
106		1p. black	15	

1895. Various frames.

115	34	1c. olive	90	60
116		2c. green	20	20
117		3c. brown	20	20
118		5c. blue	20	20
119		10c. orange	80	40
120		12c. red	80	40
121		15c. red	25	40
122		20c. green	30	60
123		24c. lilac	40	60
124		30c. blue	25	60
125		50c. red	1·25	1·50
126		1p. brown	1·50	2·25

1895. Surch.

132	34	1c. on 12c. red	1·25	1·10
133		1c. on 24c. lilac	1·25	1·10
134		1c. on 30c. blue	1·25	1·10
135		2c. on 20c. green	1·25	1·10
136		3c. on 30c. blue	1·50	1·40

37 Peace

38 Arms

39 Government Building

1896.

137	37	1c. brown	15	15
138		2c. brown	15	30
139		3c. green	15	20
140		5c. olive	15	30
141		10c. yellow	15	30
142		12c. blue	90	1·10
143		15c. violet	15	30
144		20c. red	70	60
145		24c. red	15	30
146		30c. orange	15	50
147		50c. black	15	60
148		1p. red	15	1·10

1896. Dated "1896".

158	38	1c. green	15	15
159	39	2c. lake	15	15
160	–	3c. orange	25	35
161	–	5c. blue	15	15
162	–	10c. brown	30	25
163	–	12c. grey	30	30
164	–	15c. green	15	30
165	–	20c. red	20	40
166	–	24c. violet	15	50
167	–	30c. green	15	50
168	–	50c. orange	15	50
169	–	100c. blue	15	1·00

DESIGNS: 3c. Locomotive; 5c. Mt. San Miguel; 10, 12c. Steamship; 15c. Post Office; 20c. Lake Ilopango; 24c. Magra Falls; 30, 50c. Arms; 100c. Columbus.

1896. No. 166 surch **Quince centavos.**

218		15c. on 24c. violet	5·00	5·00

1897. As Nos. 158/69. New colours.

220		1c. red	15	15
221		2c. green	15	15
222		3c. brown	25	30
223		5c. orange	15	15
224		10c. green	15	20
225		12c. blue	50	40
226		15c. black	2·50	2·50
227		20c. slate	15	40
228		24c. yellow	15	50
229		30c. red	15	40
230		50c. violet	25	80
231		100c. lake	3·50	3·50

55

57 Union of Central America

1897. Federation of Central America.

270	55	1c. multicoloured	75	3·00
271		5c. multicoloured	75	3·50

1897. Nos. 228/31 surch **TRECE centavos.**

272		13c. on 24c. yellow	3·00	3·00
273		13c. on 30c. red	3·00	3·00
274		13c. on 50c. violet	3·00	3·00
275		13c. on 100c. lake	3·00	3·00

1898.

276	57	1c. red	10	15
277		2c. red	10	15
278		3c. green	15	20
279		5c. green	15	15
280		10c. blue	15	20
281		12c. violet	25	30
282		13c. lake	15	20
283		20c. blue	15	40
284		24c. blue	15	50
285		26c. brown	15	50
286		50c. orange	15	90
287		1p. yellow	25	1·25

Some values of the above set exist optd with a wheel as Type **58**.

(58)

59 Ceres

1899. Optd with T **58**.

318	59	1c. brown	30	15
319		2c. green	40	10
320		3c. blue	50	25
321		5c. orange	35	15
322		10c. brown	35	15
323		12c. green	85	60
324		13c. red	75	70
325		24c. blue	10·00	10·00
326		26c. red	2·00	1·75
327		50c. red	2·00	1·75
328		100c. violet	2·50	1·25

1899. Optd **1900**.

398	57	1c. red	1·40	1·00

1900. Stamps of 1898 surch **1900** and new value, with or without wheel opt. T **58**.

400	57	1c. on 10c. blue	4·00	3·50
401		1c. on 13c. lake	£225	
414		2c. on 12c. violet	2·00	2·00
403		2c. on 13c. lake	1·25	1·10
404		2c. on 20c. blue	1·00	1·25
406b		3c. on 12c. violet	42·00	42·00
407		3c. on 50c. orange	15·00	15·00
419		5c. on 12c. violet	25·00	25·00
409		5c. on 24c. blue	13·00	13·00
410a		5c. on 26c. brown	42·00	42·00
411		5c. on 1p. yellow	15·00	15·00

On Nos. 406b and 410a the surcharge is inverted.

1900. Stamps of 1899 surch **1900** and new value, with or without wheel optd as T **58**.

424	59	1c. on 2c. green	25	15
420		1c. on 13c. red	40	40
426		2c. on 12c. green	85	60
422		2c. on 13c. red	85	70
423		3c. on 12c. green	85	70
429		5c. on 24c. blue	2·00	90
430		5c. on 26c. red	80	60

(66)

70 Columbus Monument

1900. T **59** with date altered to "1900" and optd as T **66**.

438	59	1c. green	15	15
468		2c. red	15	15
469		3c. black	15	15
470		5c. blue	15	10
471		10c. blue	35	20
472		12c. green	35	25
473		13c. brown	15	15
474		24c. black	40	35
475		26c. brown	50	40
447		50c. red	1·60	1·50

1902. Nos. 468, 469 and 472 surch **1 centavo.**

483	59	1c. on 2c. red	2·00	1·60
484		1c. on 3c. black	1·40	1·00
485		1c. on 5c. blue	90	70

1903.

486	70	1c. green	25	20
487		2c. red	25	20
488		3c. orange	60	50
489		5c. blue	25	20
490		10c. purple	25	20
491		12c. grey	35	20
492		13c. brown	35	25
493		24c. red	1·75	90
494		26c. brown	1·75	90
495		50c. yellow	90	55
496		100c. blue	3·50	1·75

1905. Surch in words or figures and words.

514	70	1c. on 2c. red	40	35
517		5c. on 12c. grey	55	45

1905. Surch in figures only and two black circles.

515	70	1c. on 13c. brown	1·40	1·40
516		3c. on 13c. brown	50	50

1905. Surch in figures twice.

527	70	5c. on 12c. grey	2·00	1·25

1905. Surcharged in figures repeated four times.

529	70	5c. on 12c. grey	2·75	2·40

1905. Surch **1 1** at top of stamp and **1 CENTAVO 1** at foot.

523	70	1c. on 2c. red	25	20
524		1c. on 10c. purple	25	20
525		1c. on 12c. grey	70	55
526		1c. on 13c. brown	3·00	2·50
530		6c. on 12c. grey	50	40
531		6c. on 13c. brown	85	35

1905. Stamps dated "1900", with or without opt T **66**, and optd **1905** or **01905**.

552	59	1c. green	3·25	2·25
546		2c. red	30	25
543		3c. black	3·50	2·10
547		5c. blue	90	50
548		10c. blue	50	40

1906. Stamps dated "1900", with or without opt T **66**, and optd **1906** or surch also.

560	59	2c. on 26c. brown	40	35
562		3c. on 26c. brown	2·40	2·00
564		10c. blue	90	90

89 President Pedro Jose Escalon

91 President's Palace

1906.

570 89 1c. black and green 15 10
571 2c. black and red 15 10
572 3c. black and yellow 15 10
573 5c. black and blue 15 10
574 6c. black and red 15 10
575 10c. black and violet 15 10
576 12c. black and violet 15 10
577 13c. black and brown 15 10
578 24c. black and red 35 35
579 26c. black and brown 35 35
580 50c. black and yellow 35 50
581 100c. black and blue 1·90 1·90

1907. Nos. 570/2 optd as T **66**.
592 89 1c. black and green 25 20
593 2c. black and red 25 20
594 3c. black and yellow 25 20

1907. Surch with new value and black circles and optd with shield, T **66**.
595 89 1c. on 5c. black & blue 10 10
596 1c. on 6c. black and red 20 15
597 2c. on 6c. black and red 1·40 70
598 10c. on 6c. black & red 50 35

1907. Optd with shield, T **66**.
599 91 1c. black and green 15 10
600 2c. black and red 15 10
601 3c. black and yellow 15 10
602 5c. black and blue 15 10
603b 6c. black and red 15 10
604 10c. black and violet 15 10
605 12c. black and violet 15 10
606 13c. black and sepia 15 10
607 24c. black and red 15 10
608 26c. black and brown 35 15
609 50c. black and yellow 50 25
610 100c. black and blue 70 50

1908. Surch **UN CENTAVO** and one black circle.
621 91 1c. on 2c. black and red 35 25

1909. Optd **1821 15 septiembre 1909**.
633 91 1c. black and green 1·40 1·00

1909. Surch with new value and **1909**.
634 91 2c. on 13c. black & brown 1·00 90
635 3c. on 26c. black & brown 1·25 1·00

99 Gen. Figueroa

100 M. J. Arce

1910.

642 99 1c. black and brown 15 10
643 2c. black and green 15 10
644 3c. black and orange 15 15
645 4c. black and red 15 15
646 5c. black and violet 15 15
647 6c. black and red 15 15
648 10c. black and violet 20 15
649 12c. black and blue 20 15
650 17c. black and green 20 15
651 19c. black and brown 20 15
652 29c. black and brown 20 15
653 50c. black and yellow 15 15
654 100c. black and blue 20 15

1911. Centenary of Insurrection of 1811.
655 – 5c. brown and blue 10 10
656 100 6c. brown and orange 10 10
657 – 12c. black and mauve 10 10
DESIGNS: 5c. Portrait of J. M. Delgado; 12c. Centenary Monument.

1911. T **91** without shield optd as T **66**.
658 91 1c. red 10 10
659 2c. brown 35 35
660 13c. green 15 15
661 24c. yellow 20 20
662 50c. brown 20 20

101 Jose Matias Delgado

107 Independence Monument

108 National Palace

110 National Arms

1912.

663 101 1c. black and blue 15 10
664 – 2c. black and brown 20 15
665 – 5c. black and red 20 15
666 – 6c. black and green 15 15
667 – 12c. black and olive 60 25
668 – 17c. grey and purple 50 20
669 107 19c. grey and red 75 20
670 108 29c. grey and orange 90 25
671 – 50c. grey and blue 1·10 50
672 110 1col. grey and black 1·50 70
DESIGNS—As Type **101**: 2c. M. J. Arce; 5c. F. Morazan; 6c. R. Campo; 12c. T. Cabanas; 17c. Barrios Monument. As Type **108**: 50c. Rosales Hospital.

111 J. M. Rodriguez

1914.

673 111 10c. brown and orange 1·50 70
674 – 25c. brown and violet 1·50 70
PORTRAIT: 25c. Dr. M. E. Araujo.

1915. Re-issue of T **91**. No shield. Optd **1915**.
675 91 1c. grey 15 10
676 2c. red 15 10
677 5c. blue 15 10
678 6c. blue 15 10
679 10c. yellow 55 40
680 12c. brown 40 20
681 50c. purple 20 15
682 100c. brown 85 85

113 National Theatre

114 Pres. Carlos Melendez

1916. Various frames.
683 113 1c. green 1·50 30
684 2c. red 1·50 30
685 5c. blue 1·50 20
686 6c. violet 2·00 20
687 10c. brown 3·00 25
688 12c. purple 5·25 1·50
689 17c. orange 1·50 45
690 25c. brown 3·75 1·25
691 29c. black 7·50 2·00
692 50c. grey 4·50 2·00
693 114 1col. black and blue 1·50 90

1917. Official stamps of 1915, with word "OFICIAL" cancelled with five bars.
694 91 2c. red (No. O686) 40 25
695 5c. blue (No. O687) 50 35

1918. Official stamps of 1915 optd **CORRIENTE** and bar.
696 91 1c. grey (No. O685) 1·10 90
697 2c. red 1·10 90
698 5c. blue 7·00 4·50
699 6c. blue 70 50
700 10c. yellow 75 40
701 12c. brown 60 50
702 50c. purple 50 50

1918. Official stamps of 1916 optd **CORRIENTE** and bar or surch also.
704 113 1c. on 6c. violet (No. O696) 6·50 4·75
705 5c. blue 8·50 6·50
706 6c. violet 11·00 8·00

1919. Surch with new value and square or circles or bars.
710 113 1c. on 6c. violet 6·50 4·75
711 1c. on 12c. purple 4·25 2·75
712 1c. on 17c. orange 5·50 4·00
713 2c. on 10c. brown 4·25 3·25
714 5c. on 50c. grey 6·50 4·00
715 6c. on 25c. brown 5·50 4·50
716 15c. on 29c. black 2·75 2·25
717 26c. on 29c. black 7·00 8·00
719 35c. on 50c. grey 8·00 10·00
720 60c. on 1col. blk & bl 95 90

1919. No. O699 surch **1 CENTAVO 1**.
721 113 1c. on 12c. purple 4·25 3·45

1920. Municipal stamps (Arms) surch **Correos Un centavo 1919**.
722 1c. olive 10 10
723 1c. on 5c. yellow 10 10
724 1c. on 10c. blue 15 10
725 1c. on 25c. green 10 10
726 1c. on 50c. olive 15 15
727 1c. on 1p. black 25 25

130 F. Menendez

131 Confederation Coin

132 Delgado Speaking

133 Arms of the Confederation

135 Independence Monument

139 J. S. Canas

1921. Portraits are as T **130**.
728 130 1c. green 25 10
729 – 2c. black (M. J. Arce) 25 10
730 131 5c. orange 60 15
731 132 6c. red 50 10
732 133 10c. blue 50 10
733 – 25c. grn (F. Morazan) 1·50 15
734 135 60c. violet 3·75 50
735 – 1col. sepia (Columbus) 6·00 50

1921. Centenary of Independence. Nos. 728/31 optd **CENTENARIO**.
735a 130 1c. green 4·50 2·40
735b – 2c. black 4·50 2·40
735c 131 5c. orange 4·50 2·40
735d 132 6c. red 4·50 2·40

1923. As last, surch.
745 131 1c. on 5c. orange 35 25
741 – 1c. on 25c. green 15 15
746 131 2c. on 5c. orange 35 35
737 132 5c. on 6c. red 35 20
747 133 6c. on 10c. blue 35 25
742 – 6c. on 25c. green 20 15
738 – 10c. on 2c. black 50 20
739 132 20c. on 6c. red 35 35
743 – 20c. on 25c. green 45 35
744 – 20c. on 1col. sepia 55 25

1923. Centenary of Abolition of Slavery.
740 139 5c. blue 50 35

1924. U.P.U. Commemoration. Surch **15 Sept. 1874 – 1924 5 5 U.P.U. CINCO CENTAVOS**.
749 135 5c. on 60c. violet 3·25 3·00

141 Daniel Hernandez

146 Central America

150

1924.

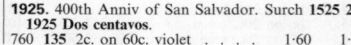

750 141 1c. purple 10 10
751 – 2c. red 25 10
752 – 3c. brown 20 10
753 – 5c. black 20 10
754 – 6c. blue 3·25 25
755 146 10c. orange 55 20
756 – 20c. green 70 35
757 – 35c. green and red 1·75 30
758 – 50c. brown 1·50 40
759 150 1col. blue and green 2·25 40
DESIGNS—VERT: 2c. National Gymnasium; 3c. Atlacatl; 20c. Balsam tree; 35c. Senora T. S. Morazan. HORIZ: 5c. Conspiracy of 1811; 6c. Bridge over R. Lempa; 50c. Columbus at La Rabida.

1925. 400th Anniv of San Salvador. Surch **1525 2 2 1925 Dos centavos**.
760 135 2c. on 60c. violet 1·60 1·50

152 View of San Salvador

1925. 400th Anniv of San Salvador.
761 152 1c. blue 50 50
762 2c. green 50 50
763 3c. red 50 50

1928. Santa Ana Industrial Exn. Surch **Exposicion Santaneca Julio de 1928** and value in figures.
764 3c. on 10c. orange 50 40

1928. No. 753 surch.
765 1c. on 5c. black 35 25

155 Dr. P. R. Bosque and Gen. L. Chacon

1930. Inauguration of Railway Link between Salvador and Guatemala.
766 155 1c. purple and mauve 2·25 1·40
767 3c. purple and brown 2·25 1·40
768 5c. purple and green 2·75 1·60
769 10c. purple and orange 2·75 1·60

1930. Air. Nos. 755/759 optd **Servicio Aereo** or surch also.
770 146 15c. on 10c. orange 45 45
771 – 20c. green 45 45
772 – 25c. on 35c. grn & red 40 40
773 – 40c. on 50c. brown 55 40
774 150 50c. on 1col. bl & grn 1·00 1·00

158 Curtiss "Jenny" over San Salvador

1930. Air.
775 158 15c. red 30 10
776 20c. green 35 10
777 25c. purple 35 10
778 40c. blue 70 10

158a Tomb of F. Menendez

158b Simon Bolivar

1930. Birth Centenary of Menendez.
779 158a 1c. violet 3·00 2·75
780 3c. brown 3·00 2·75
781 5c. green 3·00 2·75
782 10c. orange 3·00 2·75

1930. Air. Death Centenary of Bolivar.
783 158b 15c. red 5·25 4·00
784 20c. green 5·25 4·00
785 25c. purple 5·25 4·00
786 40c. blue 5·25 4·00

1931. Air. Optd with Curtiss "Jenny" Biplane.
787 150 1col. blue and green 3·00 2·50

1931. New G.P.O. Building Fund. Nos. 756 and 758 surch **EDIFICIOS POSTALES** and value.
790 1c. on 20c. green 15 15
788 1c. on 50c. brown 15 15
789 2c. on 20c. green 15 15
791 2c. on 50c. brown 15 15

162 Church of Mercy, San Salvador

164 Jose Matias Delgado

1931. Air. 120th Anniv of Independence.
792 162 15c. red 3·50 3·00
793 20c. green 3·50 3·00

794 25c. purple . . . . 3·50 3·00
795 40c. blue . . . . 3·50 3·00

1932. Issues of 1924–26 optd **1932**.
796 **141** 1c. purple 15 10
797 – 2c. red 20 15
798 – 3c. brown 25 10
799 – 5c. black 25 10
800 – 6c. blue . . . . 3·75 1·50
801 **146** 10c. orange 85 20
802 – 20c. green . . . . . . 1·10 45
803 – 35c. green and red . . . . 1·60 55
804 – 50c. brown . . . . . . 2·25 70
805 **150** 1col. blue and green . . . 4·00 1·60

1932. Air. Death Centenary of J. M. Delgado.
806 **164** 15c. red and violet . . . 1·00 1·00
807 20c. green and blue . . . 1·50 1·50
808 25c. violet and red . . . 1·50 1·50
809 40c. blue and green . . . 1·75 1·75

166 Ford "Tin Goose" over Columbus's Fleet

169 Police Headquarters

1933. Air. 441st Anniv of Departure of Columbus from Palos.
810 **166** 15c. orange . . . . 6·00 1·75
811 20c. green . . . . 8·00 3·75
812 25c. mauve . . . . 8·00 3·75
813 40c. blue . . . . 8·00 3·75
814 1col. bronze . . . . . . 8·00 3·75

1934. Issues of 1924 and 1926 surch.
815 – 2 on 5c. blk (No. 753) . . 15 10
816 – 2 on 50c. brn (No. 758) 25 15
817 **146** 3 on 10c. orange 15 10
818 **150** 8 on 1col. blue & green 15 15
819 – 15 on 35c. green and red (No. 757) 25 25

1934.
820 **169** 2c. brown 20 10
821 5c. red 20 10
822 8c. blue 20 10

1934. Air. Inscr "SERVICIO AEREO".
823 **169** 25c. violet 45 20
824 30c. brown 65 30
825 1col. black . . . . 1·75 55

171 Discus Thrower

172 Runner breasting the Tape

1935. 3rd Central American Athletic Games.
826 **171** 5c. red (postage) . . . . 3·00 2·40
827 8c. blue . . . . 3·25 2·75
828 10c. yellow . . . . 4·00 3·00
829 15c. brown . . . . 4·75 3·25
830 37c. green . . . . 6·00 4·75
831 **172** 15c. red (air) . . . . . . 4·00 4·00
832 25c. violet . . . . 4·00 4·00
833 30c. brown . . . . 3·50 3·00
834 55c. blue . . . . 17·00 15·00
835 1col. black . . . . 13·00 12·00

1935. Nos. 826/35 optd **HABILITADO**.
836 **171** 5c. red (postage) . . . . 4·00 3·00
837 8c. blue . . . . 6·00 3·00
838 10c. yellow . . . . 6·00 3·50
839 15c. brown . . . . 6·00 3·50
840 37c. green . . . . 9·50 6·00
841 **172** 15c. red (air) . . . . . . 4·00 1·75
842 25c. violet . . . . 4·00 1·75
843 30c. brown . . . . 4·00 1·75
844 55c. blue . . . . 26·00 22·00
845 1col. black . . . . 13·00 12·00

174 National Flag

175 The Settlers' Oak

1935.
846 **174** 1c. blue (postage) 15 10
847 2c. grey 15 10
848 3c. purple 15 10
849 5c. red 25 10
850 8c. blue 35 15
851 15c. brown 40 15
852 30c. black (air) 60 25

1935. Tercentenary of San Vicente. Value in black.
853 **175** 2c. grn & brn (postage) 35 25
854 3c. green 40 25
855 5c. green and red 55 35
856 8c. green and blue 55 40
857 15c. green and brown . . 55 50
858 10c. green & yell (air) . . 1·25 90
859 15c. green and brown . . 1·25 90
860 20c. green . . . . 1·25 90
861 25c. green and violet . . . 1·25 90
862 30c. green and brown . . 1·25 90

178 Cutuco Harbour

179 D. Vasconcelos

181 Sugar Refinery

182 Coffee Cargo

1935.
863 – 1c. violet 15 10
864 **178** 2c. brown 90 35
865 **179** 3c. green 15 10
866 – 5c. red 40 10
867 – 8c. blue 15 10
868 **181** 10c. yellow 25 10
869 **182** 15c. bistre 40 20
870 – 50c. blue . . . . 1·25 75
871 – 1col. black . . . . 3·50 2·25
DESIGNS—As Type **178**: 1c. Mt. Izalco; 5c. Campo de Marte playing-fields. As Type **179**: 8c. T. G. Palomo. As Type **181**: 1col. Dr. M. Araujo; 50c. Balsam tree.

1937. Air. Optd **AEREO** in frame.
872 **182** 15c. bistre 40 25

1937. Air. No. 844 surch **30** in frame.
873 **172** 30 on 55c. blue . . . . . 1·25 55

186 Panchimalco Church

1937. Air.
874 **186** 15c. orange 30 15
875 20c. green 30 15
876 25c. violet 30 15
877 30c. brown 25 10
878 40c. blue 45 35
879 1col. black 85 35
880 5col. red . . . . 3·75 2·50

1938. Surch.
881 **178** 1c. on 2c. brown . . . . 1·60 90
882 – 1c. on 5c. red (No. 866) 15 10
883 **181** 3c. on 10c. yellow 15 10
884 **182** 8c. on 15c. bistre 20 15

1938. Death Cent of J. Simeon Canas. Surch **3**.
885 **139** 3 on 5c. blue 25 30

190 Flags and Book of Constitution

1938. 150th Anniv of U.S. Constitution. (a) Postage (without airliner).
886 **190** 8c. red, yellow and blue 60 50
(b) Air.
887 **190** 30c. multicoloured . . . . 1·50 1·00

191 J. S. Canas

192 Native Women at Washing Pool

1938. Air. Death Centenary of J. S. Canas.
888 **191** 15c. orange . . . . 1·00 1·00
889 20c. green . . . . 1·25 1·00
890 30c. brown . . . . 1·25 1·00
891 1col. black . . . . 4·00 3·50

1938.
892 – 1c. violet 15 10
893 **192** 2c. green 15 10
894 – 3c. brown 25 10
895 – 5c. red 25 10
896 – 8c. blue 90 20
897 – 10c. orange . . . . . . 1·50 20
898 – 20c. brown . . . . 1·25 25
899 – 50c. violet . . . . 1·60 35
900 – 1col. black . . . . 1·50 60
DESIGNS: 1c. Native sugar-mill; 3c. Girl at spring; 5c. Native ploughing; 8c. Yucca plant; 10c. Champion cow; 20c. Extraction of Peruvian balsam; 50c. Maquilishuat tree in flower; 1col. G.P.O., San Salvador.

195 Golden Gate Bridge

1939. Air. Golden Gate Int Exn, San Francisco.
901 **195** 15c. black and yellow . . 30 15
902 30c. black and brown . . 45 15
903 40c. black and blue . . . 65 35

1939. Centenary of Battle of San Pedro Perulapan. Surch **25 Sept 1839 1939 BATALLA SAN PEDRO PERULAPAN** and value.
904 – 8c. on 50c. bl (No. 870) 35 20
905 – 10c. on 1col. black (No. 871) 50 20
906 **150** 50c. on 1col. bl & grn . . 2·75 2·75

197 Sir Rowland Hill

199 Coffee Tree in Bloom

198 Western Hemisphere and "Peace"

1940. Cent of 1st Adhesive Postage Stamps.
907 **197** 8c. black & blue (postage) 3·00 60
908 30c. black & brown (air) 4·75 1·75
909 80c. black and red . . . . 12·00 9·00

1940. Air. 50th Anniv of Pan-American Union.
910 **198** 30c. blue and brown . . . 50 35
911 80c. black and red 75 50

1940. Air.
912 **199** 15c. orange 75 25
913 20c. green 90 15
914 25c. violet . . . . 1·10 30
915 – 30c. brown . . . . 1·25 25
916 – 1col. black . . . . 4·75 35
DESIGN: 30c., 1col. Coffee tree in fruit.

200 Dr. Lindo, Gen. Mallespin and New National University of El Salvador

1941. Air. Cent of El Salvador University.
917 **200** 20c. red and green 75 50
918 – 40c. orange and blue . . 75 50
919 – 60c. brown and violet . . 75 50
920 – 80c. green and red . . . . 2·75 2·00
921 – 1col. orange and black . . 2·75 2·00
922 **200** 2col. purple and orange 2·75 2·00
PORTRAITS: 40c., 80c. Dr. N. Monterey and A. J. Canas; 60c., 1col. Dr. I. Menendez and Dr. C. Salazar.

201 Map of El Salvador

1942. 1st National Eucharistic Congress. Inscr "NOVIEMBRE 1942".
923 – 8c. blue (postage) 40 25
924 **201** 30c. orange (air) 40 30
DESIGN 8c. Patron Saint and Cathedral of San Salvador, in medallions.

1943. Air. Surch in large figures.
925 **195** 15 on 15c. black & yellow 35 30
926 20 on 30c. black & brown 40 30
927 25 on 40c. black & blue 50 35

1944. Air. Surch in small figures.
928 **195** 15 on 15c. black & yell 25 20
929 20 on 30c. black & brn 40 30
930 25 on 40c. black & blue 50 30

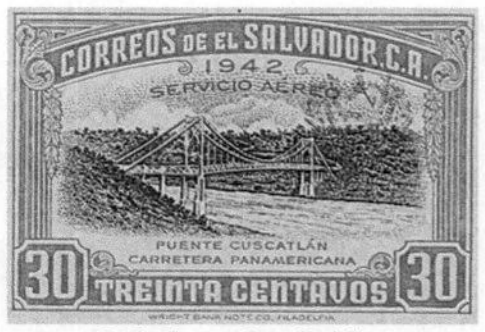

205 Cuscatlan Bridge

1944. Optd with small shield.
931 **205** 8c. black & blue (postage) 20 15
932 30c. black & red (air) . . 45 25

206 Presidential Palace

207 Gen. J. J. Canas

1944. Air.
933 **206** 15c. mauve 15 10
934 – 20c. green 25 10
935 – 25c. purple 25 10
936 – 30c. red 25 10
937 – 40c. blue 35 25
938 – 1col. black 75 35
DESIGNS: 20c. National Theatre; 25c. National Palace; 30c. Mayan Pyramid; 40c. Public Gardens; 1col. Aeronautics School.

1945. Gen. J. J. Canas (author of National Anthem).
939 **207** 8c. blue 15 10

1945. No. 893 surch **1**.
940 1c. on 2c. green 15 10

1945. Air. Optd **Aereo**.
942 1col. black (No. 900) 65 25

210 Juan Ramon Uriarte

211 Alberto Masferrer

1945. Air. J. R. Uriarte, former Director General of Posts.
943 **210** 12c. blue 25 15
944 14c. orange 25 10

1945. Air. Alberto Masferrer (writer).
945 **211** 12c. red 25 15
946 14c. green 25 10

212 Lake Ilopango

215 Isidro Menendez

1946.
947 **212** 1c. blue 10 10
948 – 2c. green 25 10
949 – 5c. red 15 10
DESIGNS: 2c. Ceiba tree; 5c. Water carriers (larger).

1947.
950 **215** 1c. red 10 10
951 – 2c. yellow (Salazar) . . . 10 10
952 – 3c. violet (Bertis) . . . 10 10
953 – 5c. grey (Duenas) 10 10
954 – 8c. blue (Belloso) 10 10
955 – 10c. bistre (Trigueros) . . 15 10
956 – 20c. green (Gonzalez) . . 25 15
957 – 50c. black (Castaneda) . . 45 25
958 – 1col. red (Castro) . . . . 1·00 35

217 Alfredo Espino

218 M. J. Arce

1947. Air.
959 – 12c. brown (F. Soto) . . . 25 15
960 **217** 14c. blue 20 10

1948. Death Centenary of M. J. Arce.
961 **218** 8c. blue (postage) 20 15
962 12c. green (air) 20 15
963 14c. red 25 15
964 1col. purple . . . . . . 2·00 1·60

219 Mackenzie King, Roosevelt and Churchill

220 Franklin D. Roosevelt

1948. 3rd Death Anniv of Franklin D. Roosevelt.
965 – 5c. black & bl (postage) 15 10
966 – 8c. black and green . . 15 10
967 **220** 12c. black and violet . . 25 15
968 **219** 15c. black and red . . . 25 15
969 – 20c. black and lake . . 35 30
970 – 50c. black and grey . . 55 45
971 **220** 12c. black & grn (air) 40 25
972 – 14c. black and olive . . 40 25
973 – 20c. black and brown . . 40 35
974 – 25c. black and red . . . 40 40
975 **219** 1col. black and purple . . 1·00 60
976 – 2col. black and lilac . . 2·00 1·25

DESIGNS—HORIZ: 5c., 14c. Pres. Roosevelt bestowing decorations; 8c., 25c. Pres. and Mrs. Roosevelt; 20c. (2) Pres. Roosevelt and Secretary Hull; 50c., 2col. Pres. Roosevelt's funeral.

1948. Air. Optd **Aereo**.
977 5c. grey (No. 953) 10 10
978 10c. bistre (No. 955) 15 10
979 1col. red (No. 958) . . . . . 1·40 80

1949. Air. No. 936 surch **10**.
980 10c. on 30c. red 20 10

222 Torch and Wings

1949. 75th Anniv of U.P.U.
981 **222** 8c. blue (postage) 50 25
982 5c. brown (air) 15 10
983 10c. black 25 10
984 1col. violet . . . . 8·50 8·50

223 Civilian and Soldier

224 Flag and Arms

1949. 1st Anniv of Revolution. (a) Postage.
985 **223** 8c. blue 30 10

(b) Air. Centres in blue and yellow.
986 **224** 5c. brown 15 10
987 10c. green 25 10
988 15c. violet 30 10
989 1col. red 40 25
990 5col. purple . . . . . . 3·75 2·75

225 Isabella the Catholic

1951. Air. 500th Birth Anniv of Isabella the Catholic. Backgrounds in blue, red and yellow.
991 **225** 10c. green 40 10
992 20c. violet 40 20
993 40c. red 40 20
994 1col. brown 90 40

226

227

1952. 1948 Revolution and 1950 Constitution. (a) Postage. Wreath in green.
995 **226** 1c. green 10 10
996 2c. purple 10 10
997 5c. brown 10 10
998 10c. yellow 10 10
999 20c. green 20 15
1000 1col. red 70 55

(b) Air. Flag in blue.
1001 **227** 10c. blue 10 10
1002 15c. brown 20 10
1003 20c. blue 20 10
1004 25c. grey 20 10
1005 40c. violet 40 30
1006 1col. orange 50 30
1007 2col. brown . . . . . . 1·75 1·25
1008 5col. blue . . . . 1·75 65

1952. Surch in figures and words (No. 1009) or in figures only (remainder). (a) Postage.
1009 – 2c. on 3c. violet (952) . . 10 10
1010 – 2c. on 8c. blue (954) . . 15 10
1011 – 2c. on 12c. brn (959) . . 15 10
1012 **217** 2c. on 14c. blue 15 10
1013 – 3c. on 8c. blue (954) . . 15 10
1014 – 5c. on 8c. blue (954) . . 15 10
1015 – 5c. on 12c. brn (959) . . 15 10
1016 – 7c. on 8c. blue (954) . . 15 10
1017 **217** 10c. on 14c. blue 15 15
1018 – 10c. on 50c. blk (957) . . 20 15

(b) Air.
1019 – 20c. on 25c. pur (935) . . 25 20

230 Jose Marti

232 Signing Act of Independence

233 Campanile of Our Saviour

234 General Barrios

1953. Birth Centenary of Marti.
1020 **230** 1c. red (postage) 10 10
1021 2c. green 15 10
1022 10c. blue 15 10
1023 10c. violet (air) 20 15
1024 20c. brown 20 15
1025 1col. orange 50 30

1953. 4th Pan-American Social Medicine Congress. Nos. 952 and 953 optd **"IV Congreso Medico Social Panamericano 16/19 Abril, 1953"**.
1026 3c. violet (postage) 15 10
1027 25c. purple (air) 40 25

1953. Independence.
1028 **232** 1c. red (postage) 10 10
1029 2c. turquoise 10 10
1030 3c. violet 10 10
1031 5c. blue 10 10
1032 7c. brown 10 10
1033 10c. ochre 20 10
1034 20c. orange 25 20
1035 50c. green 60 25
1036 1col. grey 90 65
1037 **233** 5c. red (air) 10 10
1038 10c. turquoise 10 10
1039 20c. blue 20 15
1040 1col. violet 50 35

1953. Optd **C de C**.
1041 **234** 1c. green 10 10
1042 2c. blue 10 10
1043 – 3c. green 10 10
1044 **234** 5c. red 10 10
1045 – 7c. blue 15 10
1046 – 10c. red 15 10
1047 **234** 20c. violet 20 15
1048 – 22c. violet 25 20
PORTRAIT: 3c., 7c., 10c., 22c. Gen. Morazan.

235

236

237 General Barrios Square

238 Balboa Park

1954.
1049 A 1c. red & olive (postage) 10 10
1050 **237** 1c. violet 10 10
1051 B 1c. olive and green . . . 10 10
1052 **235** 2c. red 15 10
1053 **236** 2c. red 15 10
1054 **237** 2c. green and blue . . . 15 10
1055 F 3c. slate and blue . . . 15 10
1056 C 3c. green and blue . . . 15 10
1057 I 3c. lake 15 10
1058 F 5c. violet and blue . . . 15 10
1059 I 5c. green 15 10
1060 C 7c. brown and buff . . . 15 10
1061 B 7c. green and blue . . . 20 10
1062 **238** 7c. red and brown . . . 15 10
1063 G 10c. blue, brown & red 15 10
1064 **236** 10c. turquoise 15 10
1065 D 10c. lake and pink . . . 15 10
1066 H 20c. orange and buff . . 35 15
1067 E 22c. blue . . . . 1·00 35
1068 J 50c. black and drab . . 45 35
1069 G 1col. blue, brn & chest 90 55
1070 E 1col. blue . . . . 1·25 35
1071 **235** 5c. red (air) 20 10
1072 B 5c. brown and buff . . . 30 10
1073 G 10c. blue, green & emer 25 10
1074 **237** 10c. olive and grey . . . 25 10
1075 E 10c. red 55 10
1076 **238** 10c. violet and brown . . 25 10
1077 I 10c. blue 30 10
1078 D 15c. slate and blue . . . 40 15
1079 A 20c. violet and slate . . 45 15
1080 E 25c. green and blue . . 90 15
1081 H 30c. red and pink . . . 45 15
1082 J 40c. chestnut & brown 50 35
1083 **236** 80c. lake . . . . 1·00 65
1084 C 1col. red and pink . . . 1·25 65
1085 **236** 2col. orange . . . . . . 2·25 65
DESIGNS—$32\frac{1}{2} \times 22\frac{1}{2}$ mm: A, Litoral Bridge; B, Fishing boats; C, Izalco Volcano and Atecosol Baths; D, Lake Ilopango and Apulo Baths; E, "Fle-Ja-Lis" (coastguard cutter). $37\frac{1}{2} \times 22\frac{1}{2}$ mm: F, Guayabo Dam; G, Six Prime Ministers and flag of O.D.E.C.A.; H, Workers' houses. $22\frac{1}{2} \times 32\frac{1}{2}$ mm: I, Gen. Arce. $21 \times 35\frac{1}{2}$ mm: J, Sonsonate–Puerto Acajutla Highway.

239 Captain General Barrios

240 Gathering Coffee Beans

1956.
1086 **239** 1c. red (postage) 10 10
1087 2c. green 15 10
1088 3c. blue 15 10
1089 20c. violet 20 15
1090 20c. brown (air) 20 15
1091 30c. lake 25 25

1956. Centenary of Santa Ana.
1092 **240** 3c. brown (postage) . . . 10 10
1093 5c. orange 15 10
1094 10c. blue 20 15
1095 2col. red . . . . 1·25 75
1096 5c. brown (air) 10 10
1097 10c. green 10 10
1098 40c. purple 25 20
1099 80c. green 45 30
1100 5col. slate . . . . 2·50 1·50

241

1956. Centenary of Chalatenango Province.
1101 **241** 2c. blue (postage) . . . 15 10
1102 7c. red 35 25
1103 50c. brown 55 40
1104 10c. red (air) 10 10
1105 15c. orange 15 10
1106 20c. olive 15 10
1107 25c. lilac 35 25
1108 50c. brown 55 35
1109 1col. blue 60 50

242 Arms of Nueva San Salvador

1957. Centenary of Nueva San Salvador City.
1110 **242** 1c. red (postage) 10 10
1111 2c. green 10 10
1112 3c. violet 10 10
1113 7c. orange 35 35
1114 10c. blue 15 10
1115 50c. brown 40 40
1116 1col. red 60 50
1117 10c. salmon (air) 15 10
1118 20c. red 20 10
1119 50c. red 35 30
1120 1col. green 60 35
1121 2col. red . . . . 1·50 90

1957. Surch.
1121a **242** 1c. on 2c. green 10 10
1121b 5c. on 7c. orange . . . 20 15
1122 C 6c. on 7c. brown and buff (No. 1060) . . . 25 15
1123 B 6c. on 7c. green and blue (No. 1061) . . . 30 15
1124 **241** 6c. on 7c. red 20 10
1125 **242** 6c. on 7c. orange . . . 25 15

244 Salvador Hotel

1958. Salvador Hotel Commem. Centre mult, frame colour below.

1126	**244**	3c. brown	10	10
1127		6c. red	10	10
1128		10c. blue	10	10
1129		15c. green	15	10
1130		20c. violet	25	15
1131		30c. green	35	25

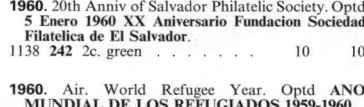

245 Presidents Eisenhower and Lemus

1959. Visit of Pres. Lemus to U.S. Flags in red and blue. Portraits in brown.

1132	**245**	3c. pink & blue (postage)	15	10
1133		6c. green and blue	15	10
1134		10c. red and blue	20	10
1135		15c. orge & blue (air)	20	15
1136		20c. green and blue	25	15
1137		30c. red and blue	30	25

1960. 20th Anniv of Salvador Philatelic Society. Optd **5 Enero 1960 XX Aniversario Fundacion Sociedad Filatelica de El Salvador**.

1138	**242**	2c. green	10	10

1960. Air. World Refugee Year. Optd **ANO MUNDIAL DE LOS REFUGIADOS 1959-1960**.

1139	**240**	10c. green	25	20

248 Block of Flats

249 Poinsettias

1960. "I.V.U." Building Project. Centres multicoloured.

1140	**248**	10c. red	10	10
1141		15c. purple	15	10
1142		25c. green	20	15
1143		30c. turquoise	25	15
1144		40c. olive	35	25
1145		80c. blue	55	45

1960. Christmas. Flowers in yellow, red and green. Background colours given.

1146	**249**	3c. yellow (postage)	10	10
1147		6c. orange	15	10
1148		10c. blue	20	10
1149		15c. blue	25	15
1150		20c. mauve (air)	35	15
1151		30c. grey	40	25
1152		40c. grey	40	35
1153		50c. salmon	65	35

250 Fathers Nicolas, Vincent and Manuel Aguilar

1961. 150th Anniv of Revolution against Spain.

1154	**250**	1c. sepia and grey	10	10
1155		2c. brown and pink	10	10
1156	–	5c. green and brown	15	10
1157	–	6c. sepia and mauve	15	10
1158	–	10c. sepia and blue	15	10
1159	–	20c. sepia and violet	25	10
1160	–	30c. mauve and blue	35	15
1161	–	40c. sepia and brown	50	20
1162	–	50c. sepia & turquoise	70	40
1163	–	80c. blue and grey	1·00	60

DESIGNS: 5c., 6c. Manuel Arce, Jose Delgado and Juan Rodriguez; 10c., 20c. Pedro Castillo, Domingo de Lara and Santiago Celis; 30c., 40c. Parochial Church of San Salvador, 1808; 50c., 80c. Monument, Plaza Libertad.

1962. 3rd Central American Industrial Exn. Nos. 1048, 1069, 1116 and 1121 optd **"III Exposicion Industrial Centroamericana Diciembre de 1962"**. Nos. 1166/7 additionally optd **AEREO**.

1165	–	22c. violet (postage)	20	15
1166	G	1col. blue, brown and chestnut (air)	50	45
1167	**242**	1col. red	50	45
1168		2col. red	1·00	85

1962. Nos. 1161/2, 1141 and 1070 surch.

1169	–	6c. on 40c. sep & brn	25	10
1170	–	6c. on 50c. sep & turq	25	10
1164	**248**	10c. on 15c. purple	25	10
1171	E	10c. on 1col. blue	40	10

1963. Surch in figures.

1172	**248**	6c. on 15c. purple (postage)	25	10
1173	–	10c. on 50c. sepia and turquoise (No. 1162)	25	10
1174	–	10c. on 80c. blue and grey (No. 1163) (air)	25	10
1175	**242**	10c. on 1col. green	1·10	15
1176	**249**	10c. on 30c. grey	15	10
1177	**242**	10c. on 1col. red (No. 1167)	15	15
1178		10c. on 2col. red (No. 1168)	1·10	10

1963. Freedom from Hunger. No. 1161 optd **CAMPANA MUNDIAL CONTRA EL HAMBRE** and Campaign emblem.

1179		40c. sepia and brown	60	40

259 Coyote

260 Statue of Christ on Globe

1963. Fauna. Multicoloured.

1180		1c. Type **259** (postage)	25	10
1181		2c. Black spider monkey (vert)	25	10
1182		3c. Common racoon	25	10
1183		5c. King vulture (vert)	1·10	25
1184		6c. Northern coati	25	10
1185		10c. Kinkajou	25	10
1186		5c. As No. 1183 (vert) (air)	1·10	25
1187		6c. Yellow-headed amazon (vert)	1·10	25
1188		10c. Spotted-breasted oriole	1·10	25
1189		20c. Turquoise-browed motmot	1·60	35
1190		30c. Great-tailed grackle	2·10	50
1191		40c. Great curassow (vert)	3·75	60
1192		50c. White-throated magpie-jay	4·00	70
1193		80c. Golden-fronted woodpecker (vert)	6·50	1·75

1964. 2nd National Eucharistic Congress, San Salvador.

1194	**260**	6c. bl & brn (postage)	10	10
1195		10c. blue and bistre	10	10
1196		10c. slate & blue (air)	10	10
1197		25c. blue and red	20	15

261 President Kennedy

262 Water-lily

1964. Pres. Kennedy Commem.

1198	**261**	6c. blk & stone (postage)	10	10
1199		10c. black and drab	15	10
1200		50c. black and pink	50	30
1201		15c. black & grey (air)	20	15
1202		20c. black and green	25	15
1203		40c. black and yellow	40	30

1965. Flora. Multicoloured.

1204		3c. Type **262** (postage)	10	10
1205		5c. "Maquilishuat"	10	10
1206		6c. "Cinco Negritos"	10	10
1207		30c. Hydrangea	20	15
1208		50c. "Maguey"	60	25
1209		60c. Geranium	70	25
1210		10c. Rose (air)	10	10
1211		15c. "Platanillo"	15	10
1212		25c. "San Jose"	20	15
1213		40c. Hibiscus	25	25
1214		45c. Bougainvillea	40	25
1215		70c. "Flor de Fuego"	55	45

263 I.C.Y. Emblem

1965. International Co-operation Year. Laurel in gold.

1216	**263**	5c. brn & yell (postage)	10	10
1217		6c. brown and red	10	10
1218		10c. brown and grey	15	10
1219		15c. brn & blue (air)	10	10
1220		30c. brown and violet	25	15
1221		50c. brown and orange	35	30

1965. Death Centenary of Captain General Barrios. No. 1163 optd **1er. Centenario Muerte Cap. Gral. Gerardo Barrios 1865 29 de Agosto 1965**.

1222		80c. blue and grey	70	40

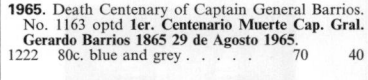

265 F. A. Gavidia (philosopher)

1965. Gavidia Commemoration.

1223	**265**	2c. mult (postage)	15	10
1224		3c. multicoloured	15	10
1225		6c. multicoloured	15	10
1226		10c. multicoloured (air)	15	10
1227		20c. multicoloured	25	15
1228		1col. multicoloured	90	40

1965. Birth Centenary of Dr. M. E. Araujo. Optd **1865 12 de Octubre 1965 Dr. Manuel Enrique Araujo**. Laurel in gold.

1229	**263**	10c. brn & grey (postage)	10	10
1230		50c. brown & orge (air)	45	30

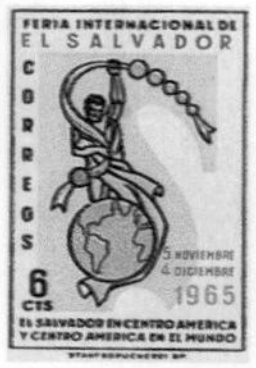

267 Fair Emblem

268 W.H.O. Building

1965. International Fair, El Salvador.

1231	**267**	6c. mult (postage)	10	10
1232		10c. multicoloured	10	10
1233		20c. multicoloured	20	15
1234		20c. multicoloured (air)	15	10
1235		80c. multicoloured	50	30
1236		5col. multicoloured	2·50	1·75

1966. Inaug of W.H.O. Headquarters, Geneva.

1237	**268**	15c. mult (postage)	15	10
1238		50c. multicoloured (air)	45	30

1966. Air. 150th Birth Anniv of St. Juan Bosco. No. 1197 optd **1816 1966 150 anos Nacimiento San Juan Bosco**.

1239	**260**	25c. blue and red	35	25

1966. Civic Commem of Independence Month. No. 1163 optd **Mes de Conmemoracion Civica de la Independencia Centroamericana 15 Sept. 1821 1966**.

1240		80c. ultramarine and grey	55	45

271 U.N.E.S.C.O. Emblem

1966. 20th Anniv of U.N.E.S.C.O.

1241	**271**	20c. blue, grey and black (postage)	15	15
1242		1col. blue, green & blk	60	30
1243		30c. blue, brown and black (air)	35	15
1244		2col. blue, green & blk	1·25	75

272 Map, Cogwheels and Flags

1966. 2nd International Fair, El Salvador.

1245	**272**	6c. mult (postage)	10	10
1246		10c. multicoloured	10	10
1247		15c. multicoloured (air)	15	10
1248		20c. multicoloured	20	15
1249		60c. multicoloured	50	35

1967. Air. 9th International Catholic Education Congress. No. 1197 optd **IX-Congreso Interamericano de Educacion Catolica 4 Enero 1967**.

1250	**260**	25c. blue and red	35	20

274 Father Canas pleading for Slaves

1967. Birth Centenary of Father J. S. Canas y Villacorta (slavery emancipator).

1251	**274**	6c. mult (postage)	10	10
1252		10c. multicoloured	10	10
1253		5c. mult (air)	10	10
1254		45c. multicoloured	55	35

1967. 15th Lions Convention, El Salvador. No. 1161 optd **"XV Convencion de Clubes de Leones**, etc.

1255		40c. sepia and brown	45	20

276 Central Design of First El Salvador Stamp

1967. Stamp Centenary.

1256	**276**	70c. brn & mve (postage)	75	60
1257		50c. brn & olive (air)	50	30

1967. 8th Central-American Pharmaceutical and Biochemical Congress. Nos. 1237/8 optd **VIII CONGRESO CENTROAMERICANO**, etc.

1258	**268**	15c. mult (postage)	15	10
1259		50c. mult (air)	45	30

1967. 1st Central American and Caribbean Basket-ball Games, San Salvador. Nos. 1204 and 1212 optd **1 Juegos Centroamericanos**, etc.

1260	**262**	3c. mult (postage)	10	10
1261	–	25c. mult (air)	25	15

1968. Human Rights Year. Nos. 1216 and 1220 optd **1968 ANO INTERNACIONAL DE LOS DERECHOS HUMANOS**.

1262	**263**	5c. mult (postage)	10	10
1263		30c. mult (air)	40	25

280 Weather Map, Satellite and W.M.O. Emblem

1968. World Meteorological Day.

1264	**280**	1c. multicoloured	10	10
1265		30c. multicoloured	30	15

1968. 20th Anniv of W.H.O. Nos. 1237/8 optd **1968 XX ANIVERSARIO DE LA ORGANIZACION MUNDIAL DE LA SALUD**.

1266	**268**	15c. mult (postage)	20	10
1267		50c. mult (air)	50	25

1968. Rural Credit Year. Nos. 1231 and 1235 optd **1968 Ano del Sistema de Credito Rural**.

1268	**267**	6c. mult (postage)	10	10
1269		80c. mult (air)	50	40

283 A. Masferrer (philosopher)

284 Building Construction ("Service to the Community")

1968. Birth Centenary of Alberto Masferrer.

1270	**283**	2c. mult (postage)	10	10
1271		6c. multicoloured	10	10
1272		25c. multicoloured	35	15
1273		5c. multicoloured (air)	10	10
1274		15c. multicoloured	15	10

1968. 7th Inter-American Scout Conference, San Salvador.

1275	**284**	25c. mult (postage)	25	15
1276	–	10c. multicoloured (air)	10	10

DESIGN—HORIZ: 10c. Scouts and Conference emblem.

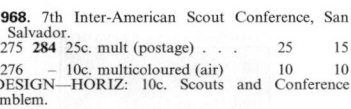

285 Map, Presidents and Flags

1968. Meeting of Pres. Lyndon B. Johnson (U.S.A.) with Central American Presidents, San Salvador.

1277	**285**	10c. mult (postage)	10	10
1278		15c. multicoloured	15	10
1279		20c. mult (air)	15	10
1280		1col. multicoloured	55	50

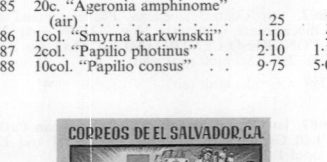

286 "Heliconius charithonius"

1969. Butterflies. Multicoloured.

1281		5c. Type **286** (postage)	10	10
1282		10c. "Diaethria astala"	15	10
1283		30c. "Heliconius hortense"	40	20
1284		50c. "Pyrrhogyra arge"	55	35
1285		20c. "Ageronia amphinome" (air)	25	10
1286		1col. "Smyrna karkwinskii"	1·10	50
1287		2col. "Papilio photinus"	2·10	1·10
1288		10col. "Papilio consus"	9·75	5·00

287 Red Cross Activities

1969. 50th Anniv of League of Red Cross Societies. Multicoloured.

1289		10c. Type **287** (postage)	10	10
1290		20c. Type **287**	15	10
1291		40c. Type **287**	25	15
1292		30c. Red Cross emblems (air)	25	15
1293		1col. As No. 1292	60	45
1294		4col. As No. 1292	2·40	1·75

Nos. 1292/4 are smaller, size 34 × 25 mm.

1969. 1st Man on the Moon. Nos. 1200 and 1203 (Kennedy) optd **Alunizaje Apolo - 11 21 Julio 1969**.

1295	**261**	50c. blk & pink (postage)	40	25
1297		40c. blk & yellow (air)	30	20

289 Social Security Hospital

1969. Salvador Hospitals. Multicoloured.

1299		6c. Type **289** (postage)	10	10
1300		10c. Type **289**	10	10
1301		30c. Type **289**	25	15
1302		1col. Benjamin Bloom Children's Hospital, San Salvador (air)	60	45
1303		2col. As No. 1302	1·25	70
1304		5col. As No. 1302	3·00	1·75

290 I.L.O. Emblem

1969. 50th Anniv of I.L.O.

1305	**290**	10c. mult (postage)	10	10
1306		50c. multicoloured (air)	40	25

291 Los Chorros Baths

1969. Tourism. Multicoloured.

1307		10c. Type **291** (postage)	10	10
1308		40c. Jaltepeque estuary	60	25
1309		80c. Fountains, Ampalupa	70	45
1310		20c. Devil's Gate (air)	15	10
1311		35c. Gardens, Ichanmichen	25	15
1312		60c. Port of Acajutla	50	25

292 "Euchroma gigantea"

1970. Insects. Multicoloured.

1313		5c. Type **292** (postage)	10	10
1314		25c. "Pterophylla" sp.	15	15
1315		30c. "Chlorion cyaneum"	30	20
1316		2col. "Eulema dimidiata" (air)	2·00	95
1317		3col. "Elaterida"	2·75	1·50
1318		4col. "Tenodora sinensis"	3·50	2·00

293 Map, Emblem and Arms

1970. "Human Rights".

1319	**293**	10c. mult (postage)	10	10
1320		40c. multicoloured	45	20
1321	–	20c. multicoloured (air)	15	10
1322	–	80c. multicoloured	50	40

DESIGN—VERT: Nos. 1321/2 are similar to Type **293**.

294 Infantry with National Flag

1970. Army Day. Multicoloured.

1323		10c. Type **294** (postage)	10	10
1324		30c. Anti-aircraft gun position	30	15
1325		20c. Fighter aircraft (air)	15	10
1326		40c. Artillery gun and crew	35	15
1327		50c. "Nohaba" (coastguard patrol boat)	2·00	35

295 Brazilian Team

1970. Air. World Cup Football Championship, Mexico. National Teams. Multicoloured.

1328		1col. Belgium	70	50
1329		1col. Type **295**	70	50
1330		1col. Bulgaria	70	50
1331		1col. Czechoslovakia	70	50
1332		1col. El Salvador	70	50
1333		1col. England	70	50
1334		1col. West Germany	70	50
1335		1col. Israel	70	50
1336		1col. Italy	70	50
1337		1col. Mexico	70	50
1338		1col. Morocco	70	50
1339		1col. Peru	70	50
1340		1col. Rumania	70	50
1341		1col. Russia	70	50
1342		1col. Sweden	70	50
1343		1col. Uruguay	70	50

296 Lottery Building

297 Education Year and U.N. Emblems

1970. Centenary of National Lottery.

1344	**296**	20c. mult (postage)	20	10
1345		80c. multicoloured (air)	50	35

1970. International Education Year.

1346	**297**	50c. mult (postage)	40	15
1347		1col. multicoloured	60	40
1348		20c. multicoloured (air)	15	10
1349		2col. multicoloured	1·25	70

298 Globe and Fair Symbols

1970. 4th International Fair, El Salvador.

1350	**298**	5c. mult (postage)	10	10
1351		10c. multicoloured	10	10
1352		20c. multicoloured (air)	25	10
1353		30c. multicoloured	35	15

1970. Cent of National Library. Nos. 1212/3 optd **Ano del Centenario de la Biblioteca Nacional 1970**.

1354	**283**	25c. mult (postage)	20	15
1355		5c. mult (air)	10	10

300 Beethoven and Music

1971. 2nd Int Music Festival, San Salvador.

1356	**300**	50c. brown, yellow and green (postage)	45	25
1357	–	40c. multicoloured (air)	45	25

DESIGN: 40c. Bach, manuscript and harp.

301 Maria Elena Sol

302 Michelangelo's "Pieta"

1971. Maria Elena Sol's Election as "World Tourism Queen", Punta del Este, Uruguay.

1358	**301**	10c. mult (postage)	10	10
1359		30c. multicoloured	25	15
1360		20c. mult (air)	15	10
1361		60c. multicoloured	40	30

1971. Mothers' Day.

1362	**302**	10c. pur & pink (post)	10	10
1363		40c. pur & grn (air)	45	20

1971. 104th Anniv of National Police Force. Nos. 1320/1 optd **1867 CIV Aniversario Fundacion de la Policia Nacional 6-Julio 1971**.

1364	**293**	40c. mult (postage)	45	25
1365	–	20c. mult (air)	25	10

304 Tiger Shark

1971. Fishes. Multicoloured.

1366		10c. Type **304** (postage)	15	10
1367		40c. Swordfish	35	15
1368		30c. Small-toothed sawfish (air)	35	15
1369		1col. Sailfish	70	50

305 Izalco Church

1971. Churches. Multicoloured.

1370		20c. Type **305** (postage)	25	10
1371		30c. Sonsonate Church	40	15
1372		15c. Metapan Church (air)	15	10
1373		70c. Panchimalco Church	45	25

1971. Air. 20th Anniv of El Salvador Navy. No. 1327 optd **1951-12 Octubre-1971 XX Aniversario MARINA NACIONAL**.

1374		50c. multicoloured	85	30

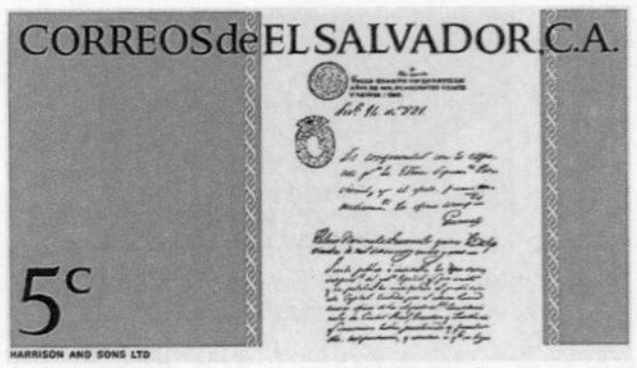

307 Declaration of Independence

1971. 150th Anniv of Central American Independence.

1375	**307**	5c. blk & grn (postage)	10	10
1376	–	10c. black and purple	10	10
1377	–	15c. black and red	10	10
1378	–	20c. black and mauve	15	10
1379	–	30c. black & blue (air)	25	15
1380	–	40c. black and brown	40	20
1381	–	50c. black and yellow	30	25
1382	–	60c. black and grey	40	35

DESIGNS: Nos. 1376/82 as Type **307**, but showing different manuscripts.

1972. Air. 5th Int Fair, El Salvador. No. 1235 optd **V Feria Internacional 3-20 Noviembre de 1972**.

1384	**267**	80c. multicoloured	1·25	40

1972. American Tourist Year. No. 1359 optd **1972 Ano del Turismo de las Americas**.

1385	**301**	30c. multicoloured	25	10

1972. Air. 30th Anniv of Inter-American Agricultural Science Institute. No. 1221 optd **1972 - XXX Aniversario Creacion Instituto Interamericano de Ciencias Agricolas**.

1386	**263**	50c. multicoloured	30	25

1973. 3rd Int Music Festival. Nos. 1356/7 optd **III Festival Internacional de Musica 9 - 25 Febrero - 1973**.

1387	**300**	50c. brown, yellow and green (postage)	35	20
1388	–	40c. multicoloured (air)	40	20

312 Lions Emblem

318 Institute Emblem

314 Hurdling

1973. 31st Convention of Lions International District D.

1389	**312**	10c. mult (postage)	10	10
1390		25c. multicoloured	15	10
1391	–	20c. mult (air)	20	10
1392	–	40c. multicoloured	40	15

DESIGN: 20c., 40c. Map of Central America.

1973. 50th Anniv of El Salvador Air Force. No. 1324 optd **1923 1973 50 ANOS FUNDACION FUERZA AEREA**.

1393		30c. multicoloured	25	15

1973. Olympic Games, Munich (1972). Mult.

1394		5c. Type **314** (postage)	10	10
1395		10c. High-jumping	10	10
1396		25c. Running	15	10
1397		60c. Pole-vaulting	35	20
1398		20c. Throwing the javelin (air)	15	10
1399		80c. Throwing the discus	45	35
1400		1col. Throwing the hammer	55	40
1401		2col. Putting the shot	1·10	65

1973. Nos. 1256/7 surch.

1402	**276**	10c. on 70c. brown and mauve (postage)	10	10
1403		25c. on 50c. brown and olive (air)	15	10

1973. 150th Anniv of Slaves' Liberation in Central America. Nos. 1251 and 1253 surch **1823 – 1973 150 Aniversario Liberacion Esclavos en Centroamerica** and value.

1404	**274**	5c. on 6c. multicoloured	10	10
1405		10c. on 45c. mult	10	10

No. 1405 has the word "AEREO" obliterated.

1974. Nos. 1198 and 1238 surch.
1407 **261** 5c. on 6c. black and stone (postage) 10 10
1408 **268** 25c. on 50c. mult (air) 15 10

1974. 10th Anniv of Institute for the Rehabilitation of Invalids.
1409 **318** 10c. mult (postage) . . . 10 10
1410 25c. multicoloured (air) 15 10

1974. Air. No. 1235 surch.
1411 **267** 10c. on 80c. mult 10 10

1974. Air. West Germany's Victory in World Cup Football Championship. Nos. 1328/43 optd **ALEMANIA 1974.**
1412 1col. Belgium 60 50
1413 1col. Type **158** 60 50
1414 1col. Bulgaria 60 50
1415 1col. Czechoslovakia 60 50
1416 1col. El Salvador 60 50
1417 1col. England 60 50
1418 1col. West Germany 60 50
1419 1col. Israel 60 50
1420 1col. Italy 60 50
1421 1col. Mexico 60 50
1422 1col. Morocco 60 50
1423 1col. Peru 60 50
1424 1col. Rumania 60 50
1425 1col. Russia 60 50
1426 1col. Sweden 60 50
1427 1col. Uruguay 60 50

1974. No. 1271 surch.
1428 **283** 5c. on 6c. multicoloured 10 10

322 Interpol Headquarters, Paris

323 F.A.O. and W.F.P. Emblems

1974. 50th Anniv of International Criminal Police Organization (Interpol).
1429 **322** 10c. mult (postage) . . . 10 10
1430 25c. multicoloured (air) 15 10

1974. 10th Anniv of World Food Programme.
1431 **323** 10c. gold, turquoise and blue (postage) 10 10
1432 25c. gold, turquoise and blue (air) 15 10

1974. Surch.
1432a **271** 25c. on 1col. blue, green & black (postage) 15 10
1433 **276** 10c. on 50c. brown and olive (air) 10 10
1434 **271** 25c. on 2col. blue, green and black . . . 45 25

1974. 12th Central American and Caribbean Chess Tournament. Surch **XII Serie Ajedrez de Centro America y del Caribe Oct. 1974.**
1435 **265** 5c. on 6c. mult 10 10

1974. Surch.
1436 **289** 5c. on 6c. mult (postage) 10 10
1437 **265** 10c. on 3c. mult 10 10
1438 – 10c. on 45c. mult (No. 1214) (air) . . . 10 10
1439 – 10c. on 70c. mult (No. 1215) 10 10
1440 – 25c. on 2col. mult (No. 1287) 20 10
1441 – 25c. on 1col. mult (No. 1293) 20 15
1442 – 25c. on 4col. mult (No. 1294) 20 15
1443 – 25c. on 5col. mult (No. 1304) 20 15

327 25-cent Silver Coin, 1914

1974. El Salvador Coins. Multicoloured.
1445 10c. Type **327** (postage) . . 10 10
1446 15c. 50-cent silver coin, 1953 10 10
1447 25c. 25-cent silver coin, 1943 15 10
1448 30c. 1-centavo copper coin, 1892 . . . . 15 10
1449 20c. 1-peso silver coin, 1892 (air) 10 10
1450 40c. 20-cent silver coin, 1828 20 15
1451 50c. 20-peso gold coin, 1892 25 20
1452 60c. 20-col. gold coin, 1925 35 25

328 U.P.U. Emblem

1975. Centenary of U.P.U.
1453 **328** 10c. mult (postage) . . . 10 10
1454 60c. multicoloured . . . 35 20
1455 25c. mult (air) 15 10
1456 30c. multicoloured . . . 15 15

329 Acajutla Harbour

1975. Opening of Acajutla Port.
1457 **329** 10c. mult (postage) . . . 10 10
1458 15c. mult (air) 10 10

331 Central Post Office, San Salvador

1975.
1459 **331** 10c. mult (postage) . . . 10 10
1460 25c. mult (air) 15 10

332 Map of El Salvador and the Americas

1975. "Miss Universe" Contest.
1461 **332** 10c. mult (postage) . . . 10 10
1462 40c. multicoloured . . . 35 25
1463 25c. mult (air) 25 15
1464 60c. multicoloured . . . 50 35

333 Claudia Lars (poet)

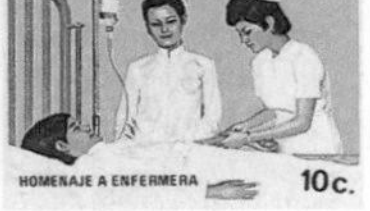

334 Nurses with Patient

1975. International Women's Year.
1465 **333** 10c. blue & yellow (post) 10 10
1466 15c. blue & lt blue (air) 10 10
1467 – 25c. blue & green . . . 15 10
DESIGN: 25c. I.W.Y. emblem.

1975. Honouring Nursing Profession.
1468 **334** 10c. mult (postage) . . . 10 10
1469 25c. mult (air) 25 15

335 Conference Emblem

337 Congress Emblem and Flags

1975. 15th Conference of Inter-American Security Printers Federation, San Salvador.
1470 **335** 10c. mult (postage) . . . 10 10
1471 30c. mult (air) 15 15

1975. 16th Central American Medical Congress, San Salvador. Optd **XVI CONGRESO MEDICO CENTROAMERICANO SAN SALVADOR, EL SALVADOR DIC. 10-13, 1975.**
1472 **268** 15c. multicoloured . . . 15 10

1975. 8th Iberian and Latin-American Dermatological Congress, El Salvador.
1473 **337** 15c. mult (postage) . . . 10 10
1474 50c. multicoloured . . . 25 20
1475 20c. mult (air) 15 10
1476 30c. multicoloured . . . 15 15

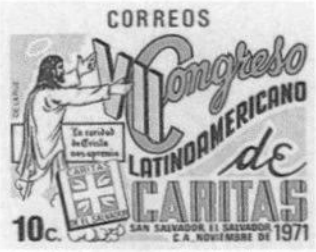

338 Congress Emblem

339 U.N.I.C.E.F. Emblem

1975. 7th Latin-American Charity Congress, San Salvador.
1477 **338** 10c. brn & red (postage) 10 10
1478 20c. lt blue & blue (air) 15 10

1975. Air. 25th Anniv (1971) of U.N.I.C.E.F.
1479 **339** 15c. silver and green . . 10 10
1480 20c. silver and red . . . 15 10

1976. Air. Nos. 1316/18 surch.
1481 25c. on 2col. multicoloured 20 15
1482 25c. on 3col. multicoloured 20 15
1483 25c. on 4col. multicoloured 20 15

341 "Caularthron bilamellatum"

343 Map of El Salvador

1976. Air. Orchids. Multicoloured.
1484 25c. Type **341** 20 10
1485 25c. "Oncidium oliganthum" 20 10
1486 25c. "Epidendrum radicans" 20 10
1487 25c. "Cyrtopodium punctatum" 20 10
1488 25c. "Epidendrum vitellinum" 20 10
1489 25c. "Pleurothallis schiedei" 20 10
1490 25c. "Lycaste cruenta" . . . 20 10
1491 25c. "Spiranthes speciosa" 20 10

1976. "Cencamex '76" 3rd Nurses' Congress. Surch **III CONGRESO ENFERMERIA CENCAMEX 76.**
1492 **334** 10c. multicoloured . . . 10 10

1976. 10th Anniv of Central Inter-American Tax-collectors Association.
1493 **343** 10c. mult (postage) . . . 10 10
1494 50c. multicoloured (air) 25 20

344 Torch and Flags of El Salvador and U.S.A.

1976. Bicent of American Revolution. Mult.
1495 10c. Type **344** (postage) . . 10 10
1496 40c. "Spirit of '76" (A. M. Willard) (vert) 20 15
1497 25c. Type **344** (air) 15 10
1498 5col. As 40c. . . . . 2·25 1·50

345 "Crocodylus acutus"

1976. Reptiles. Multicoloured.
1499 10c. Type **345** (postage) . . 10 10
1500 20c. "Iguana iguana rhinolopha" 10 10
1501 30c. "Ctenosaura similis" . . 20 15
1502 15c. "Sceloporus malachiticus" (air) 10 10
1503 25c. "Basiliscus vittatus" . . 15 10
1504 60c. "Anolis sp." 35 25

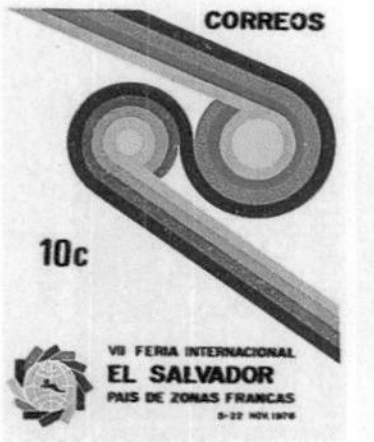

346 Fair Emblem

347 Post-classical Lead Vase (San Salvador)

1976. 7th International Fair.
1505 **346** 10c. mult (postage) . . . 10 10
1506 30c. multicoloured . . . 15 10
1507 25c. multicoloured (air) 15 10
1508 70c. multicoloured . . . 35 25

1976. Pre-Columbian Art. Multicoloured.
1509 10c. Type **347** (postage) . . 10 10
1510 15c. Brazier with classical effigy (Tazumal) 10 10
1511 40c. Vase with classical effigy (Tazumal) 20 15
1512 25c. Brazier with pre-classical effigy (El Trapiche) (air) 15 10
1513 50c. Kettle with pre-classical effigy (Atiquizaya) 25 20
1514 70c. Classical whistling vase (Tazumal) 35 30

348 Child beside Christmas Tree

349 Rotary Emblem on Map of El Salvador

1976. Christmas.
1515 **348** 10c. mult (post) 10 10
1516 15c. multicoloured . . . 10 10
1517 30c. multicoloured . . . 15 10
1518 40c. multicoloured . . . 20 15
1519 25c. multicoloured (air) 15 10
1520 50c. multicoloured . . . 25 20
1521 60c. multicoloured . . . 35 25
1522 75c. multicoloured . . . 40 30

1977. 50th Anniv of San Salvador Rotary Club.
1523 **349** 10c. gold, bl & blk (post) 10 10
1524 15c. multicoloured . . . 15 10
1525 25c. mult (air) 25 15
1526 1col. multicoloured . . . 60 50

350 Hydro-electric Station, Cerron Grande

1977. Industrial Development. Multicoloured.
1527 10c. Type **350** (postage) . . 10 10
1528 10c. Sugar refinery, Jiboa 10 10
1529 15c. As No. 1528 . . . . . 10 10
1530 30c. Radar station, Izalco (vert) 15 10
1531 25c. As No. 1530 (air) . . . 15 10
1532 50c. As No. 1528 . . . . . 25 20
1533 75c. Type **192** 40 30

1977. Surch.
1534 **283** 15c. on 2c. mult (postage) 10 10
1535 **274** 25c. on 6c. mult 15 10
1536 – 25c. on 80c. mult (No. 1322) (air) . . . 30 15
1537 **274** 30c. on 5c. mult 20 15
1538 40c. on 5c. mult 25 15
1539 50c. on 5c. mult 25 20

352 Microphone and A.S.D.E.R. Emblem

1977. 50th Anniv of Broadcasting in El Salvador.
1540 **352** 10c. mult (postage) . . . 10 10
1541 15c. multicoloured . . . 10 10
1542 20c. multicoloured (air) 20 10
1543 25c. multicoloured . . . 25 15

353 King, Pawn and Championship Emblem

354 Basketball

1977. Air. El Salvador's Victory in Arab Chess Olympiad, Tripoli.
1544 **353** 25c. multicoloured . . . 15 10
1545 50c. multicoloured . . . 25 25

1977. Air. 2nd Central American Games, San Salvador. Multicoloured.
1546 10c. Type **354** 10 10
1547 10c. Football 10 10
1548 15c. Javelin throwing . . . 10 10
1549 15c. Weightlifting 10 10
1550 20c. Boxing (horiz) 10 10
1551 20c. Volleyball 10 10
1552 25c. Baseball 15 10
1553 25c. Softball (horiz) 15 10
1554 30c. Swimming (horiz) . . . 15 10
1555 30c. Fencing (horiz) 15 10
1556 40c. Cycle-racing (horiz) . . 20 15
1557 50c. Rifle-shooting (horiz) 25 20
1558 50c. Tennis (horiz) 25 20
1559 60c. Judo 35 25
1560 75c. Wrestling (horiz) . . . 40 30
1561 1col. Gymnastics (horiz) . . 55 40
1562 1col. Horse-jumping (horiz) 55 40
1563 2col. Table-tennis (horiz) . . 1·10 80

1978. Air. Centenary of Chalchuapa City. No. 1514 optd **CENTENARIO CIUDAD DE CHALCHUAPA 1878-1978**.
1565 70c. Classical whistling vase (Tazumal) 35 30

356 Map of South America and Emblem

1978. Air. World Cup Football Championship, Argentina.
1566 **356** 25c. multicoloured . . . 15 10
1567 60c. multicoloured . . . 35 20
1568 5col. multicoloured . . . 2·40 2·00

357 Wooden Drum

1978. Musical Instruments. Multicoloured.
1569 5c. Type **357** (postage) . . . 10 10
1570 10c. Flutes 10 10
1571 25c. Drum (vert) (air) . . . 15 10
1572 50c. Rattles 25 20
1573 80c. Xylophone 45 30

358 "Man and Engineering"

1978. 4th Nat Engineers' Congress, San Salvador.
1574 **358** 10c. mult (postage) . . . 10 10
1575 25c. multicoloured (air) 15 10

359 Dish Aerials

1978. Inauguration of Izalco Satellite Earth Station.
1576 **359** 10c. mult (postage) . . . 10 10
1577 75c. multicoloured (air) 40 30

360 Softball, Bat and Hemispheres

1978. Air. 4th Women's Softball Championships, San Salvador.
1578 **360** 25c. multicoloured . . . 15 10
1579 1col. multicoloured . . . 55 40

361 Henri Dunant

1978. 150th Birth Anniv of Henri Dunant (founder of Red Cross).
1580 **361** 10c. yellow, black and red (postage) 10 10
1581 25c. turquiose, black and red (air) 15 10

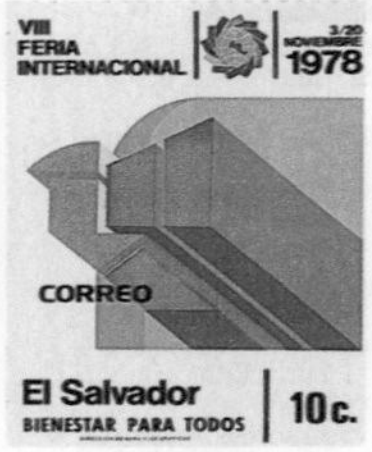

362 Fair Poster

1978. 8th International Fair.
1582 **362** 10c. mult (postage) . . . 10 10
1583 20c. multicoloured . . . 10 10
1584 15c. multicoloured (air) 10 10
1585 25c. multicoloured . . . 15 10

363 Globe as Cotton Boll

1978. 37th Plenary Session of Cotton Growers' Association, San Salvador.
1586 **363** 15c. mult (postage) . . . 10 10
1587 40c. multicoloured (air) 25 15

364 "Nativity with Angel" (stained glass window)

1978. Christmas.
1588 **364** 10c. mult (postage) . . . 10 10
1589 15c. multicoloured . . . 10 10
1590 25c. multicoloured (air) 15 10
1591 1col. multicoloured . . . 55 40

365 Arms of Salvador Athenium

1978. Millenary of Castilian Language.
1592 **365** 5c. mult (postage) . . . 10 10
1593 25c. mult (air) 15 10

366 Four Candles

1979. Four Year Plan "Welfare for All".
1594 **366** 10c. mult (postage) . . . 10 10
1595 15c. multicoloured . . . 10 10
1596 25c. multiclured (air) 15 10
1597 1col. multicoloured . . . 55 40

367 Torch and Letter beside U.P.U. Statue

1979. Centenary of U.P.U. Membership.
1598 **367** 10c. mult (postage) . . . 10 10
1599 75c. multicoloured (air) 40 30

368 Emblem and "75"

1979. 75th Anniv of Pan-American Health Organization.
1600 **368** 10c. turq & yell (postage) 10 10
1601 25c. turq & rose (air) . . 15 10

369 I.S.S.S. Emblem

370 Pope John Paul II and Map of Americas

1979. Air. 25th Anniv of Social Insurance Institute (I.S.S.S.).
1602 **369** 25c. blue and black . . 15 10
1603 60c. mauve and black . . 35 25

1979. Pope John Paul II. Multicoloured.
1604 10c. Type **370** (postage) . . 10 10
1605 20c. Type **370** 15 10
1606 60c. Pope John Paul II and Aztec pyramid (air) . . . 35 25
1607 5col. As 60c. . . . . 2·75 2·10

371 Games Emblem

1979. Air. 8th Pan-American Games, Puerto Rico.
1608 **371** 25c. multicoloured . . . 15 10
1609 40c. multicoloured . . . 25 20
1610 70c. multicoloured . . . 40 30

372 Mastodon

373 J. Cauas (lyric writer) and Chorus of Anthem

1979. Prehistoric Animals. Multicoloured.
1611 10c. Type **372** (postage) . . 10 10
1612 20c. Sabre-toothed tiger . . 15 10
1613 30c. Toxodon 15 15
1614 15c. Mammoth (air) 10 10
1615 25c. Giant sloth (vert) . . . 15 15
1616 2col. Hyenas . . . . 1·10 70

1979. Centenary of National Anthem.
1617 10c. Type **373** (postage) . . 10 10
1618 40c. J. Aberle (composer) and score (air) 25 15

374 Cogwheel encircling Central America

376 Map of Central and South America

375 Children of Different Races

1979. 8th Mechanical, Electrical and Allied Trade Engineers' Congress, San Salvador.
1619 **374** 10c. mult (postage) . . . 10 10
1620 50c. multicoloured (air) 30 20

1979. International Year of the Child.
1621 **375** 10c. mult (postage) . . . 10 10
1622 – 15c. multicoloured . . . 10 10
1623 – 25c. yell, red & blk (air) 15 15
1624 – 30c. blue and black . . . 15 15
DESIGNS—HORIZ: 30c. S.O.S. Children's Village emblem. VERT: 15c. Children with nurses; 25c. Children dancing in circle.

1979. 5th Latin-American Clinical Biochemistry Congress, San Salvador.
1625 **376** 10c. orange, red and black (postage) . . . 10 10
1626 25c. yellow, red and black (air) 15 10

377 Coffee Bushes in Bloom

1979. 50th Anniv of Salvador Coffee Association. Multicoloured.
1627 10c. Type **377** (postage) . . 10 10
1628 30c. Planting coffee bushes (vert) 15 15
1629 40c. Coffee beans 25 15
1630 50c. Picking coffee beans (air) 30 20
1631 75c. Drying coffee beans (vert) 45 30
1632 1col. Coffee exports . . . . 1·00 45

378 Dove, Star and Children holding Candles

1979. Christmas.
1633 **378** 10c. multicoloured . . . 10 10

379 Diseased Animal

1980. Campaign against Foot and Mouth Disease.
1634 **379** 10c. mult (postage) . . . 10 10
1635 60c. multicoloured (air) 35 25

380 Grand Ark

1980. Shells. Multicoloured.
1636 10c. Type **380** (postage) . . 15 10
1637 30c. "Ostrea iridescens" . . 30 15
1638 40c. White-mouthed turritella 50 20
1639 15c. Regal murex (air) . . . 20 10
1640 25c. Spiral moon 30 15
1641 75c. Jenner's cowrie 85 45
1642 1col. Prostitute venus . . . 1·00 65

381 Resplendent Quetzal

1980. Birds. Multicoloured.
1643 10c. Type **381** (postage) . . 1·10 15
1644 20c. Highland guan . . . . 1·75 30
1645 25c. Emerald toucanet (air) 2·10 50
1646 50c. Fulvous owl . . . . . 3·00 75
1647 75c. Slate-coloured solitaire 3·75 1·10

382 "Porthidium godmani" **383** Corporation Emblem

1980. Snakes. Multicoloured.
1648 10c. Type **382** (postage) . . 10 10
1649 20c. "Agkistrodon bilineatus" 15 10
1650 25c. "Crotalus durissus" (air) 15 10
1651 50c. "Micrurus nigrocinctus" 30 20

1980. 50th Anniv of Corporation of Auditors.
1652 **383** 15c. mult (postage) . . . 10 10
1653 20c. multicoloured . . . 15 10
1654 50c. multicoloured (air) 30 20
1655 75c. multicoloured . . . 45 30

384 Hands releasing Dove (cartoon by "Nando")

1980. "Man and Peace" Caricature Contest Winner.
1656 **384** 5c. bl, blk & brn (post) 10 10
1657 10c. blue, black & yellow 10 10
1658 25c. bl, blk & grn (air) 15 10
1659 60c. blue, black & orge 35 25

385 Decade Emblem **386** Black-handed Spider Monkey

1981. Air. International Decade for Women.
1660 **385** 25c. black and green . . 15 10
1661 1col. black & orange . . 55 45

1981. Air. Protected Animals. Multicoloured.
1662 25c. Type **386** 15 10
1663 40c. Tropical gar 35 20
1664 50c. Common iguana . . . 30 20
1665 60c. Hawksbill turtle 35 25
1666 75c. Ornate hawk eagle . . 3·25 60

387 Heinrich von Stephan **389** Dental Association Emblems

1981. Air. 150th Birth Anniv of Heinrich von Stephan (founder of U.P.U.).
1667 **387** 15c. pink and black . . 10 10
1668 2col. blue and black . . 1·10 70

1981. Air. Nos. 1573 and 1610 surch.
1669 – 50c. on 80c. mult 30 20
1670 **371** 1col. on 70c. mult . . . 55 45

1981. 50th Anniv of El Salvador Dental Society, and 25th Anniv of Odontological Federation of South America and Panama.
1671 **389** 15c. grn & blk (postage) 10 10
1672 5col. blue & blk (air) . . 2·40 2·10

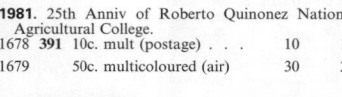

390 Eye, Hands and Braille Book **391** Los Proceres Auditorium

1981. International Year of Disabled People.
1673 **390** 10c. mult (postage) . . . 10 10
1674 25c. multicoloured (air) 15 10
1675 – 50c. green and blue . . . 30 20
1676 **390** 75c. multicoloured . . . 45 30
1677 – 1col. black and blue . . 55 40
DESIGN: 50c., 1col. I.Y.D.P. emblem.

1981. 25th Anniv of Roberto Quinonez National Agricultural College.
1678 **391** 10c. mult (postage) . . . 10 10
1679 50c. multicoloured (air) 30 20

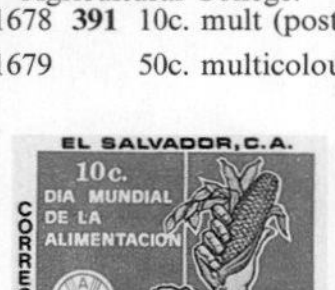

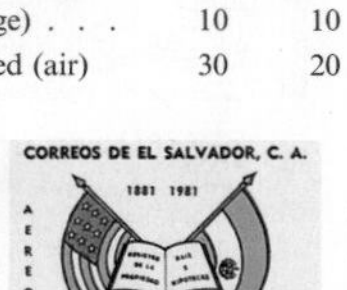

392 Map of El Salvador and Hand holding Maize **393** Open Book and El Salvador Flags of 1881 and 1981

1981. World Food Day.
1680 **392** 10c. mult (postage) . . . 10 10
1681 25c. multicoloured (air) 15 10

1981. Air. Centenary of Land Registry Office.
1682 **393** 1col. black, bl & red . . 55 40

394 Boeing 737

1981. Air. 50th Anniv of "TACA" National Airline.
1683 **394** 15c. multicoloured . . . 15 10
1684 25c. multicoloured . . . 30 15
1685 75c. multicoloured . . . 90 50

395 Goalkeeper

1981. World Cup Football Preliminary Round, Honduras. Multicoloured.
1686 10c. Type **395** (postage) . . 10 10
1687 40c. World Cup, football and flags of competing countries 25 20
1688 25c. Type **395** (air) 15 10
1689 75c. As No. 1687 . . . . . 45 30

396 Salvador Lyceum

1981. Centenary of Salvador Lyceum.
1690 **396** 10c. mult (postage) . . . 10 10
1691 25c. multicoloured (air) 15 10

397 Ceremonial Axe

1982. Pre-Columbian Stone Sculptures. Mult.
1692 10c. Type **397** (postage) . . 10 10
1693 20c. Sun disc 15 10
1694 40c. Stela of Tazumal . . . 25 20
1695 25c. Ehecatl (god of the winds) (air) 15 10
1696 30c. Rock mask of jaguar 15 15
1697 80c. Flint sculpture 50 35

398 Scout Salute, Flag and Globe **399** Dr. Robert Koch

1982. Boy Scout and Girl Guide Movements. Multicoloured.
1698 10c. Type **398** (Scout Movement, 75th anniv) (postage) 10 10
1699 30c. Girl guide helping old lady 15 10
1700 25c. Scout and Lord Baden-Powell (125th birth anniv) (air) 15 10
1701 50c. Girl Guide with emblem and national flag 30 20

1982. Air. Cent of Discovery of Tubercle Bacillus.
1702 **399** 50c. multicoloured . . . 30 20

400 Emblem and Soldier

1982. Armed Forces.
1703 **400** 10c. black, green and brown (postage) . . . 10 10
1704 25c. multicoloured (air) 15 10

401 Converging Lines **402** Hexagonal Pattern

1982. Air. 25th Anniv of Confederation of Latin American Tourist Organizations.
1705 **401** 75c. yellow, grn & blk 45 30

1982. Air. World Telecommunications Day.
1706 **402** 15c. multicoloured . . . 10 10
1707 2col. multicoloured . . . 1·10 60

403 Salvador Football Team

1982. World Cup Football Championship, Spain (1st issue). Multicoloured.
1708 10c. Type **403** (postage) . . 10 10
1709 25c. As 10c. but different logo (air) 15 10
1710 60c. Trophy and map of El Salvador 35 25
1711 2col. National team and results of qualifying rounds (66 × 45 mm) . . . 1·10 60

404 Flag of Italy **405** Fair Poster

1982. Air. World Cup Football Championship, Spain (2nd issue). Multicoloured. (a) Flags.
1712 15c. Type **404** 10 10
1713 15c. West Germany 10 10
1714 15c. Argentine Republic . . 10 10
1715 15c. England 10 10
1716 15c. Spain 10 10
1717 15c. Brazil 10 10
1718 15c. Poland 10 10
1719 15c. Algeria 10 10
1720 15c. Belgium 10 10
1721 15c. France 10 10
1722 15c. Honduras 10 10
1723 15c. Russia 10 10
1724 15c. Peru 10 10
1725 15c. Chile 10 10
1726 15c. Hungary 10 10
1727 15c. Czechoslovakia 10 10
1728 15c. Yugoslavia 10 10
1729 15c. Scotland 10 10
1730 15c. Cameroun 10 10
1731 15c. Austria 10 10
1732 15c. El Salvador 10 10
1733 15c. Kuwait 10 10
1734 15c. Northern Ireland . . . 10 10
1735 15c. New Zealand 10 10

(b) Coat of Arms.
1736 25c. Italy 15 10
1737 25c. Poland 15 10
1738 25c. West Germany 15 10
1739 25c. Algeria 15 10
1740 25c. Argentine Republic . . 15 10
1741 25c. Belgium 15 10
1742 25c. Peru 15 10
1743 25c. Cameroun 15 10
1744 25c. Chile 15 10
1745 25c. Austria 15 10
1746 25c. Hungary 15 10
1747 25c. El Salvador 15 10
1748 25c. England 15 10
1749 25c. France 15 10
1750 25c. Spain 15 10
1751 25c. Honduras 15 10
1752 25c. Brazil 15 10

1753 25c. Russia 15 10
1754 25c. Czechoslovakia . . . 15 10
1755 25c. Kuwait 15 10
1756 25c. Yugoslavia 15 10
1757 25c. Northern Ireland . . . 15 10
1758 25c. Scotland 15 10
1759 25c. New Zealand 15 10

(c) 89 × 67 mm.

1760 5col. El Salvador team, World Cup and flags of competing countries . . . 2·40 1·50

1982. 10th International Fair. Multicoloured.
1761 10c. Type **405** (postage) . . 10 10
1762 15c. Fair emblem (air) . . . 10 10

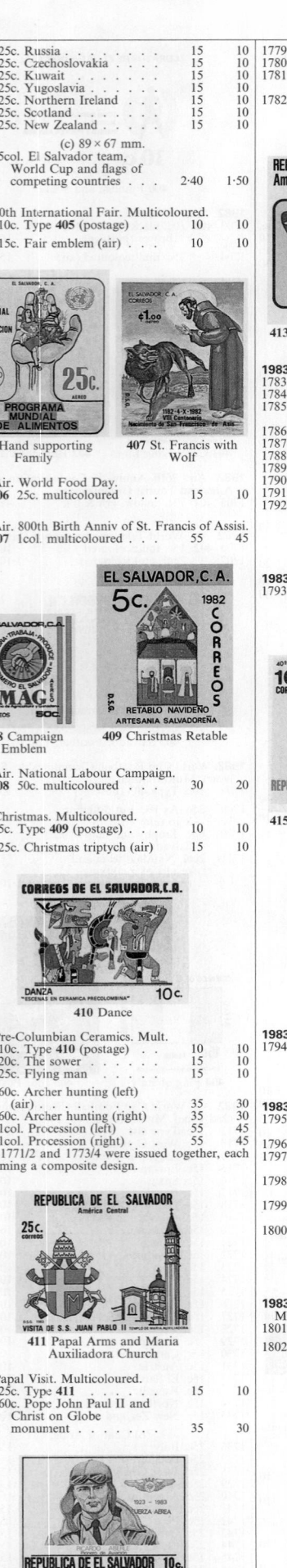

406 Hand supporting Family

407 St. Francis with Wolf

1983. Air. World Food Day.
1763 **406** 25c. multicoloured . . . 15 10

1982. Air. 800th Birth Anniv of St. Francis of Assisi.
1764 **407** 1col. multicoloured . . . 55 45

408 Campaign Emblem

409 Christmas Retable

1982. Air. National Labour Campaign.
1765 **408** 50c. multicoloured . . . 30 20

1982. Christmas. Multicoloured.
1766 5c. Type **409** (postage) . . . 10 10
1767 25c. Christmas triptych (air) 15 10

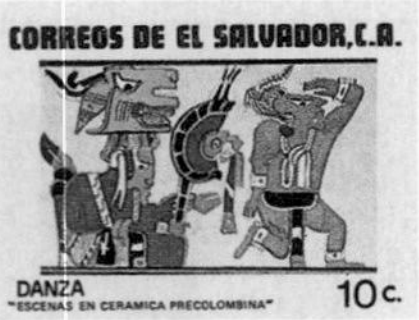
410 Dance

1983. Pre-Columbian Ceramics. Mult.
1768 10c. Type **410** (postage) . . 10 10
1769 20c. The sower 15 10
1770 25c. Flying man 15 10
1771 60c. Archer hunting (left) (air) 35 30
1772 60c. Archer hunting (right) 35 30
1773 1col. Procession (left) . . . 55 45
1774 1col. Procession (right) . . . 55 45

Nos. 1771/2 and 1773/4 were issued together, each pair forming a composite design.

411 Papal Arms and Maria Auxiliadora Church

1983. Papal Visit. Multicoloured.
1775 25c. Type **411** 15 10
1776 60c. Pope John Paul II and Christ on Globe monument 35 30

412 Ricardo Aberle

1983. 50th Anniv of Air Force. Mult.
1777 10c. Type **412** 10 10
1778 10c. Air Force emblem . . . 10 10
1779 10c. Enrico Massi 10 10
1780 10c. Juan Ramon Munes . . 20 10
1781 10c. American Airforces Co-operation emblem 10 10
1782 10c. Belisario Salazar . . . 20 10

413 "Papilio torquatus" (male)

414 Simon Bolivar

1983. Butterflies. Multicoloured.
1783 5c. Type **413** 10 10
1784 5c. "Metamorpha steneles" 10 10
1785 10c. "Papilio torquatus" (female) 10 10
1786 10c. "Anaea marthesia" . . 10 10
1787 15c. "Prepona brooksiana" 15 10
1788 15c. "Caligo atreus" 15 10
1789 25c. Emperor 30 15
1790 25c. "Dismorphia praxinoe" 30 15
1791 50c. "Morpho polyphemus" 70 25
1792 50c. "Metamorpha epaphus" 70 25

1983. Birth Bicentenary of Simon Bolivar.
1793 **414** 75c. multicoloured . . . 45 30

415 Dr. Jose Mendoza (founder)

417 David J. Guzman (founder)

416 "Rural School" (L. A. Caceres Madrid)

1983. 40th Anniv of Medical College.
1794 **415** 10c. pink, black & grn 10 10

1983. Air. Paintings. Multicoloured.
1795 25c. "Potters of Paleca" (M. Ortiz Villacorta) . . . 15 10
1796 25c. Type **416** 15 10
1797 75c. "To the Wash" (Julia Diaz) (vert) 45 30
1798 75c. "La Pancha" (Mejia Vides) (vert) 45 30
1799 1col. "Meanguera del Golfo" (Elas Reyes) (vert) 1·40 60
1800 1col. "The Muleteers" (Noe Canjura) (vert) 55 45

1983. Centenary of David J. Guzman National Museum. Multicoloured.
1801 10c. Type **417** (postage) . . 10 10
1802 50c. Guzman and Museum (air) 30 20

418 Gen. Juan Jose Canas and Dr. Francisco Duenas

1983. World Communications Year. Mult.
1803 10c. Type **418** (postage) . . 10 10
1804 25c. Postman delivering letter (vert) (air) 15 10
1805 50c. Central sorting office 30 20

419 Dove and Globe

420 Bus emitting Exhaust Fumes

1983. Christmas. Multicoloured.
1806 10c. Type **419** (postage) . . 10 10
1807 25c. Christmas crib (air) . . 15 10

1983. Environmental Protection. Mult.
1808 10c. Type **420** (postage) . . 10 10
1809 15c. Fig tree (air) 10 10
1810 25c. Paca 20 15

421 Fisherman with Catch

1983. Air. Fishery Resources. Multicoloured.
1811 25c. Type **421** 70 30
1812 75c. Fish farming 70 30

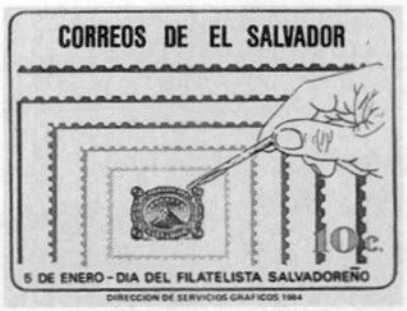
422 Tweezers holding First Stamp of El Salvador

1984. Philatelists' Day.
1813 **422** 10c. blue, blk & orge . . 10 10

423 Maize

424 Caluco Church

1984. Agricultural Products. Multicoloured.
1814 10c. Type **423** 10 10
1815 15c. Cotton 10 10
1816 25c. Coffee 20 15
1817 50c. Sugar 35 25
1817a 55c. Cotton 20 20
1817b 70c. Type **423** 25 20
1818 75c. Kidney bean 25 20
1818a 90c. Sugar cane 25 20
1819 1col. Agave 30 25
1819a 2col. Beans 60 50
1820 5col. Balsam . . . . 2·40 1·75
1820c 10col. Agave . . . . 4·75 3·50

1984. Colonial Churches. Multicoloured.
1821 5c. Type **424** (postage) . . . 10 10
1822 10c. Salcoatitan 10 10
1823 15c. Huizucar (air) 10 10
1824 25c. Santo Domingo 20 15
1825 50c. Pilar 35 25
1826 75c. Nahuizalco 40 30

425 Banknote

426 Running

1984. 50th Anniv of General Reserve Bank. Multicoloured.
1827 10c. Type **425** (postage) . . 10 10
1828 25c. Bank Building (air) . . 20 15

1984. Olympic Games, Los Angeles. Multicoloured.
1829 10c. Boxing (horiz) (postage) 10 10
1830 25c. Type **426** (air) 20 15
1831 40c. Cycling (horiz) 30 20
1832 50c. Swimming (horiz) . . . 35 25
1833 75c. Judo 40 30
1834 1col. Pierre de Coubertin (horiz) 50 40

427 New Building

1984. New Servicios Graficos (Government printer) Building.
1835 **427** 10c. multicoloured . . . 10 10

428 "5th November" Hydro-electric Plant

1984. National Energy Resources. Mult.
1836 20c. Type **428** (postage) . . 10 10
1837 55c. "Cerron Grande" hydro-electric plant . . . 30 20
1838 70c. Ahuachapan geothermal plant (air) . . 40 30
1839 90c. Mural, Guajoyo hydro-electric plant 45 35
1840 2col. "15th September" hydro-electric plant . . . 60 50

429 Playing Marbles

1984. Children's Games. Multicoloured.
1841 55c. Type **429** 30 20
1842 70c. Spinning a top 40 30
1843 90c. Flying a kite 45 35
1844 2col. "Capirucho" 60 50

430 Fair Emblem

1984. 11th International Fair, El Salvador. Mult.
1845 25c. Type **430** (postage) . . 15 10
1846 70c. Fair building and flags (air) 40 30

431 Los Chorros Tourist Centre

1984. Tourism. Multicoloured.
1847 15c. Type **431** 10 10
1848 25c. The Americas Square 15 10
1849 70c. El Salvador International Airport . . . 70 30
1850 90c. El Tunco beach . . . 45 35
1851 2col. Sihuatehucan Tourist Centre 60 50

432 "The White Nun" (Salarrue)

1984. Paintings. Multicoloured.
1852 20c. Type **432** (postage) . . 10 10
1853 55c. "The Paper of Papers" (Roberto Antonio Galicia) (horiz) (air) . . 30 20

1854 70c. "Supreme Elegy to Masferrer" (Antonio Garcia Ponce) (wrongly inscr "Figuras en Palco") 40 30
1854a 70c. "Supreme Elegy to Masferrer" (correct inscription) 40 30
1855 90c. "Transmutation" (Armando Solis) (horiz) 45 35
1856 2col. "Figures in Theatre Box" (Carlos Canas) (wrongly inscr "Suprema Elegia a Masferrer") 1·10 90
1856a 2col. "Figures in Theatre Box" (correct inscription) 1·10 90

Nos. 1854a and 1856a are overprinted with the correct inscription.

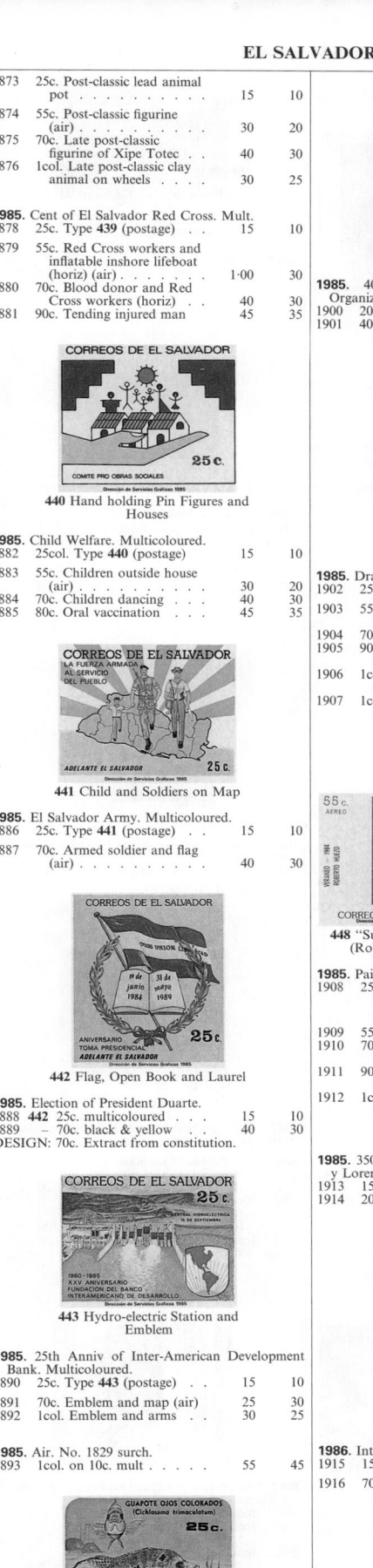

433 Christmas Tree Decoration

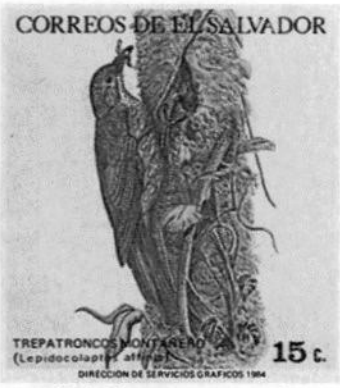

434 Spot-crowned Woodcreeper

1984. Christmas. Multicoloured.
1857 25c. Type **433** (postage) 15 10
1858 70c. Christmas tree decorations and dove (air) 40 30

1984. Birds. Multicoloured.
1859 15c. Type **434** (postage) 50 20
1860 25c. Slaty finch 80 45
1861 55c. Purple-breasted ground dove (air) 2·00 85
1862 70c. Tody-motmot 2·40 1·50
1863 90c. Belted flycatcher 2·00 1·00
1864 1col. Red-faced warbler 3·00 1·75

435 Emblem and Share Certificate

1985. Centenary of El Salvador Bank.
1865 **435** 25c. multicoloured 15 10

436 Share Certificate and Emblem

1985. 50th Anniv of El Salvador Mortgage Bank.
1866 **436** 25c. multicoloured 15 10

437 I.Y.Y. Emblem

1985. International Youth Year.
1867 **437** 25c. blk & grn (postage) 15 10
1868 – 55c. mult (air) 30 20
1869 – 70c. multicoloured 40 30
1870 – 1col.50 multicoloured 50 40

DESIGNS: 55c. Woodwork class; 70c. Boys raising tray of equipment by pulley; 1col.50, Parade.

438 Pre-classic seated Figurine

439 Red Cross and Hand holding "100"

1985. Archaeological Finds. Multicoloured.
1871 15c. Type **438** (postage) 10 10
1872 20c. Late classic engraved vase 10 10
1873 25c. Post-classic lead animal pot 15 10
1874 55c. Post-classic figurine (air) 30 20
1875 70c. Late post-classic figurine of Xipe Totec 40 30
1876 1col. Late post-classic clay animal on wheels 30 25

1985. Cent of El Salvador Red Cross. Mult.
1878 25c. Type **439** (postage) 15 10
1879 55c. Red Cross workers and inflatable inshore lifeboat (horiz) (air) 1·00 30
1880 70c. Blood donor and Red Cross workers (horiz) 40 30
1881 90c. Tending injured man 45 35

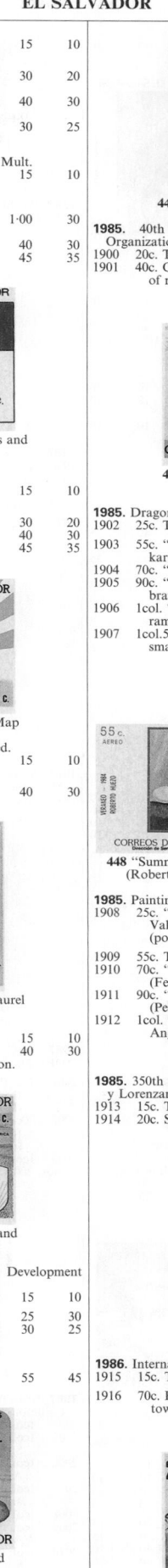

440 Hand holding Pin Figures and Houses

1985. Child Welfare. Multicoloured.
1882 25col. Type **440** (postage) 15 10
1883 55c. Children outside house (air) 30 20
1884 70c. Children dancing 40 30
1885 80c. Oral vaccination 45 35

441 Child and Soldiers on Map

1985. El Salvador Army. Multicoloured.
1886 25c. Type **441** (postage) 15 10
1887 70c. Armed soldier and flag (air) 40 30

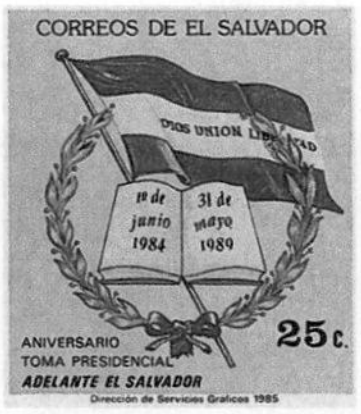

442 Flag, Open Book and Laurel

1985. Election of President Duarte.
1888 **442** 25c. multicoloured 15 10
1889 – 70c. black & yellow 40 30

DESIGN: 70c. Extract from constitution.

443 Hydro-electric Station and Emblem

1985. 25th Anniv of Inter-American Development Bank. Multicoloured.
1890 25c. Type **443** (postage) 15 10
1891 70c. Emblem and map (air) 25 30
1892 1col. Emblem and arms 30 25

1985. Air. No. 1829 surch.
1893 1col. on 10c. mult 55 45

445 Three-spotted Cichlid

1985. Fresh Water Fishes. Multicoloured.
1894 25c. Type **445** (postage) 25 15
1895 55c. Guatemalan long-whiskered catfish (air) 60 30
1896 70c. Black molly 80 40
1897 90c. Convict cichlid 90 50
1898 1col. Banded astyanax 1·10 60
1899 1col.50 Pacific fat sleeper 1·90 1·10

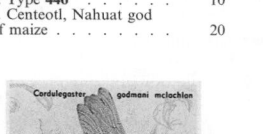

446 Food spilling from Basket

1985. 40th Anniv of Food and Agriculture Organization. Multicoloured.
1900 20c. Type **446** 10 10
1901 40c. Centeotl, Nahuat god of maize 20 15

447 "Cordulegaster godmani mclachlan"

1985. Dragonflies. Multicoloured.
1902 25c. Type **447** (postage) 20 15
1903 55c. "Libellula herculea karsch" (air) 45 30
1904 70c. "Cora marina selys" 65 45
1905 90c. "Aeshna cornigera braver" 70 50
1906 1col. "Mecistogaster ornata rambur" 90 60
1907 1col.50 "Hetaerina smaragdalis de marmels" 1·50 1·00

448 "Summer Holiday" (Roberto Huezo)

449 St. Vicente Tower

1985. Paintings. Multicoloured.
1908 25c. "Profiles" (Rosa Mena Valenzuela) (vert) (postage) 15 10
1909 55c. Type **448** (air) 30 20
1910 70c. "La Entrega" (Fernando Llort) 35 25
1911 90c. "For Decorating Pots" (Pedro Acosta Garcia) 45 35
1912 1col. "Still Life" (Miguel Angel Orellana) (vert) 55 45

1985. 350th Anniv of City of St. Vicente de Austria y Lorenzana. Multicoloured.
1913 15c. Type **449** 10 10
1914 20c. St. Vicente Cathedral 10 10

450

1986. International Peace Year. Mult.
1915 15c. Type **450** (postage) 10 10
1916 70c. People reaching towards peace dove (air) 20 15

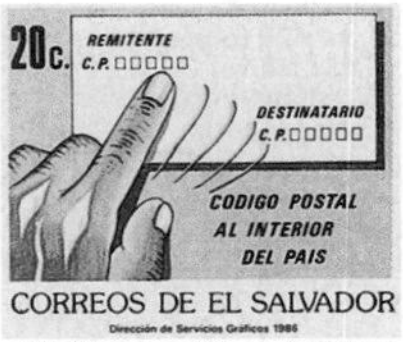

451 Hand and Interior Mail Envelope

1986. Introduction of Post Codes. Mult.
1917 20c. Type **451** 10 10
1918 25c. Hand and airmail envelope 10 10

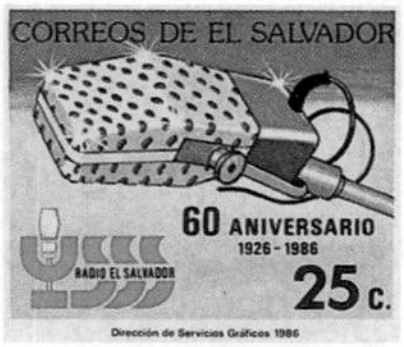

452 Microphone

1986. 60th Anniv of Radio El Salvador. Multicoloured.
1919 25c. Type **452** (postage) 10 10
1920 70c. "60", map and radio waves (air) 20 15

453 Margay

1986. Mammals. Multicoloured.
1921 15c. Type **453** (postage) 10 10
1922 20c. Tamandua 10 10
1923 1col. Nine-banded armadillo (air) 30 25
1924 2col. Collared peccary 95 75

454 Flags and Mascot

1986. World Cup Football Championship, Mexico. Multicoloured.
1925 70c. Type **454** 20 15
1926 1col. Footballers and Trophy (vert) 30 25
1927 2col. Footballer (vert) 95 75
1928 5col. Goal and emblem 2·40 1·90

455 Dr. Dario Gonzalez (medicine)

456 Tlaloc Seal

1986. Teachers (1st series). Multicoloured.
1929 20c. Type **455** (postage) 10 10
1930 20c. Valero Lecha (art) 10 10
1931 40c. Prof. Marcelino Garcia Flamenco 10 10
1932 40c. Camilo Campos 10 10
1933 70c. Prof. Saul Flores (educationist) (air) 20 15
1934 70c. Prof. Jorge Larde (law) 20 15
1935 1col. Prof. Francisco Moran 30 25
1936 1col. Mercedes Maiti de Luarca 30 25

See also Nos. 1973/80.

1986.
1937 **456** 25c. mult (postage) 10 10
1938 55c. mult (air) 15 15
1939 70c. multicoloured 20 15
1940 90c. multicoloured 25 20
1941 1col. multicoloured 30 25
1942 1col.50 multicoloured 45 40

457 Open Book on "100" as Stand

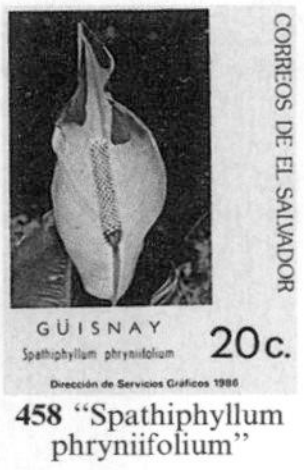

458 "Spathiphyllum phryniifolium"

1986. Air. Centenary of Constitution.
1943 **457** 1col. multicoloured 30 25

1986. Flowers. Multicoloured.
1944 20c. Type **458** (postage) 10 10
1945 25c. "Asclepias curassavica" (horiz) 10 10

1946 70c. "Tagetes tenuifolia" (horiz) (air) 20 15
1947 1col. "Ipomoea lilacea" . . 30 25

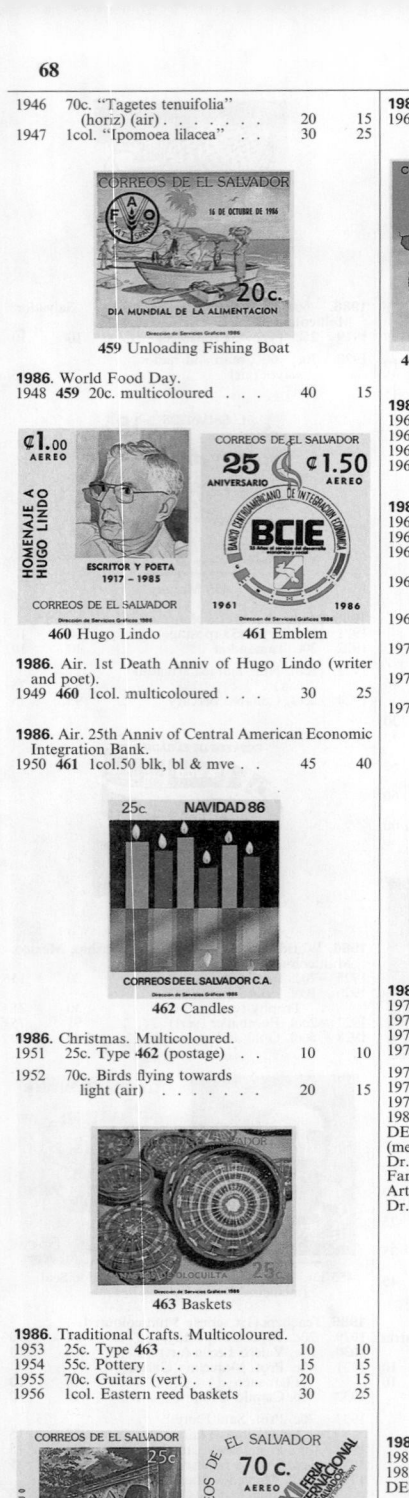

459 Unloading Fishing Boat

1986. World Food Day.
1948 **459** 20c. multicoloured . . . 40 15

460 Hugo Lindo

461 Emblem

1986. Air. 1st Death Anniv of Hugo Lindo (writer and poet).
1949 **460** 1col. multicoloured . . . 30 25

1986. Air. 25th Anniv of Central American Economic Integration Bank.
1950 **461** 1col.50 blk, bl & mve . . 45 40

462 Candles

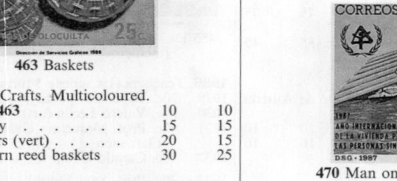

1986. Christmas. Multicoloured.
1951 25c. Type **462** (postage) . . 10 10
1952 70c. Birds flying towards light (air) 20 15

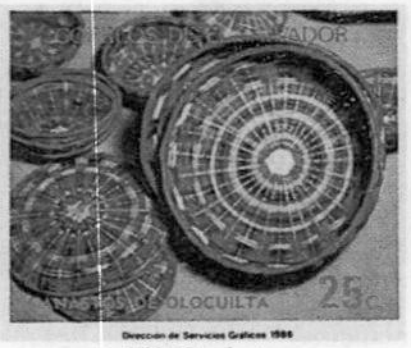

463 Baskets

1986. Traditional Crafts. Multicoloured.
1953 25c. Type **463** 10 10
1954 55c. Pottery 15 15
1955 70c. Guitars (vert) 20 15
1956 1col. Eastern reed baskets . . 30 25

464 "Church" (Mario Araujo Rajo)

465 Emblem

1986. Paintings. Multicoloured.
1957 25c. Type **464** (postage) . . 10 10
1958 70c. "Landscape" (Francisco Reyes) (air) 20 15

1987. Air. 12th International Fair, El Salvador.
1959 **465** 70c. multicoloured . . . 20 15

466 Stamps

1987. Philately.
1960 **466** 25c. multicoloured . . . 15 10

467 Maps, Globe and Foodstuffs

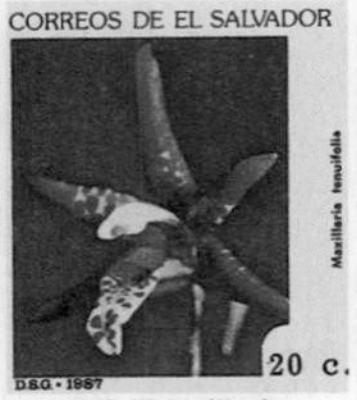

468 "Maxillaria tenuifolia"

1987. International Solidarity.
1961 **467** 15c. multicoloured . . . 10 10
1962 70c. multicoloured . . . 20 15
1963 1col.50 mult 40 35
1964 5col. multicoloured . . . 1·50 1·00

1987. Orchids. Multicoloured.
1965 20c. Type **468** (postage) . . 10 10
1966 20c. "Ponthieva maculata" 10 10
1967 25c. "Meiracyllium trinasutum" (horiz) . . . 10 10
1968 25c. "Encyclia vagans" (horiz) 10 10
1969 70c. "Encyclia cochleata" (horiz) (air) 20 15
1970 70c. "Maxillaria atrata" (horiz) 20 15
1971 1col.50 "Sobrialia xantholeuca" (horiz) . . . 40 35
1972 1col.50 "Encyclia microcharis" (horiz) . . . 40 35

469 C. de Jesus Alas (music)

1987. Teachers (2nd series).
1973 **469** 15c. black & bl (postage) 10 10
1974 – 15c. black and blue . . 10 10
1975 – 20c. black and brown . . 10 10
1976 – 20c. black and brown . . 10 10
1977 – 70c. black & orange (air) 20 15
1978 – 70c. black and orange 20 15
1979 – 1col.50 black & green . . 40 35
1980 – 1col.50 black & green . . 40 35

DESIGNS: No. 1974, Dr. Luis Edmundo Vasquez (medicine); 1975, Dr. David Rosales (law); 1976, Dr. Guillermo Trigueros (medicine); 1977, Manuel Farfan Castro; 1978, Iri Sol (singing); 1979, Carlos Arturo Imendia (primary education); 1980, Dr. Benjamin Orozco (chemistry).

470 Man on Roof above Houses

1987. Air. Int Year of Shelter for the Homeless.
1981 **470** 70col. multicoloured . . 20 15
1982 – 1col. blue 25 20
DESIGN: 1p. Emblem.

471 Emblem

472 Nicolas Aguilar

1987. 10th Pan-American Games, Indianapolis, U.S.A. Multicoloured.
1983 20c. Type **471** (postage) . . 10 10
1984 20c. Table tennis 10 10
1985 25c. Wrestling (horiz) . . . 10 10
1986 25c. Fencing (horiz) 10 10
1987 70c. Softball (horiz) (air) . . 20 15
1988 70c. Showjumping (horiz) 20 15
1989 5col. Weightlifting . . . . . 1·40 1·10
1990 5col. Hurdling . . . . . . 1·40 1·10

1987. Independence Leaders. Multicoloured.
1991 15c. Type **472** (postage) . . 10 10
1992 20c. Domingo Antonio de Lara 10 10
1993 70c. Juan Manuel Rodriguez (air) 20 15
1994 1col.50 Pedro Pablo Castillo 40 35

473 Man tending Crops

1987. World Food Day.
1995 **473** 50c. multicoloured . . . 15 10

474 The Three Kings (crochet)

1987. Christmas. Multicoloured.
1996 25c. Stained glass window from Church of Virgin of the Everlasting Succour (postage) 10 10
1997 70c. Type **474** (air) 20 15

475 "Self-portrait"

1987. Salvador Salazar Arrue (writer and painter). Multicoloured.
1998 25c. Type **475** (postage) . . 10 10
1999 70c. "Lake" (air) 20 15

476 Man with Ceramic Drum

1987. Pre-Columbian Musical Instruments. Mult.
2000 20c. Type **476** (postage) . . 10 10
2001 70c. Parade of musicians from Saluan ceramic vase (left) (air) 20 15
2002 70c. Parade of musicians from Saluan ceramic vase (right) 20 15
2003 1col.50 Conch shell trumpet 65 45
Nos. 2001/2 are each 31 × 30 mm.

477 King Ferdinand of Spain

1987. 500th Anniv (1992) of Discovery of America by Columbus (1st issue). Multicoloured.
2004 1col. Type **477** 25 20
2005 1col. Queen Isabella of Spain 25 20
2006 1col. Banner and North America 25 20
2007 1col. Islands, coat of arms and ships 25 20
2008 1col. Caribbean 25 20
2009 1col. Ships and South America 25 20
2010 1col. Native figure and South America 25 20
2011 1col. South America and compass rose 25 20
2012 1col. Anniversary logo . . . 25 20
2013 1col. Columbus 25 20

Nos. 2004/13 were printed together in se-tenant sheetlets, Nos. 2006/11 forming a composite design of a contemporary map.

See also Nos. 2040/9, 2065/70, 2116/21, 2166/71 and 2206/9.

478 Words and Stamps

1988. Philately.
2014 **478** 25c. multicoloured . . . 10 10

479 Crowd and Emblem

1988. Empesarios Juveniles (youth education programme).
2015 **479** 25c. multicoloured . . . 10 10

480 Bosco (after N. Musio)

1988. Death Centenary of St. John Bosco (founder of Salesian Brothers).
2016 **480** 20c. multicoloured . . . 10 10

481 Felling of Trees and Children Planting Saplings

1983. Environmental Protection. Mult.
2017 20c. Type **481** (postage) . . 10 10
2018 70c. Rubbish in river and monkey in forest (air) . . 20 15

482 High Jumping

1988. Olympic Games, Seoul (1988) and Barcelona (1992). Multicoloured.
2019 1col. Type **482** 25 20
2020 1col. Throwing the javelin 25 20
2021 1col. Pistol shooting 25 20
2022 1col. Wrestling 25 20
2023 1col. Basketball 25 20

483 Rural Youth

1988. World Food Day.
2025 **483** 20c. multicoloured . . . 10 10

484 Fair Emblem

486 Father and Son flying Heart-shaped Kite

1988. 13th International Fair, El Salvador.
2026 **484** 70c. multicoloured . . . 20 15

1988. "Prenfil '88" International Philatelic Literature and Press Exhibition, Buenos Aires. No. 1905 surch **C5.00 PRENFIL '88 EXPOSICION MUNDIAL DE LITERATURA Y PRENSA FILATELICA BUENOS AIRES ARGENTINA DEL 25 DE NOVIEMBRE AL 2 DE DICEMBRE** and emblem.
2027 5col. on 90c. multicoloured 1·40 1·25

1988. Infant Protection Campaign. Mult.
2028 15c. Type **486** 10 10
2029 20c. Happy child hugging adult's leg 10 10

487 "Virgin and Child with St. John and St. Anthony"

1988. Christmas. 500th Birth Anniv of Titian (painter). Multicoloured.
2030 25c. Type **487** (postage) . . 10 10
2031 70c. "Virgin and Child in Glory with St. Francis and St. Alvise" (vert) (air) 20 15

488 Emblems

1988. Air. 18th Organization of American States General Assembly.
2032 **488** 70c. multicoloured . . . 20 15

489 Hands holding Scroll

1988. "Return to Moral Values".
2033 **489** 25c. multicoloured . . . 10 10

490 "Esperanza de los Soles" (Victor Rodriguez Preza)

491 Emblem within Laurel Wreath, People and Map

1988. Paintings. Multicoloured.
2034 40c. Type **490** (postage) . . 10 10
2035 1col. "Pastoral" (Luis Angel Salinas) (horiz) (air) . . . 25 20
2036 2col. "Children" (Julio Hernandez Aleman) (horiz) 60 45
2037 5col. "El Nino de las Alcancias" (Camilo Minero) . . . . 1·50 1·25

1988. 40th Anniv of Declaration of Human Rights. Multicoloured.
2038 25c. Type **491** (postage) . . 10 10
2039 70c. U.N. and Human Rights emblems and map (air) (horiz) 20 15

492 El Tazumal

1988. 500th Anniv (1992) of Discovery of America by Columbus (2nd issue). Multicoloured.
2040 1col. Type **492** 25 20
2041 1col. Earthenware bowl . . 25 20
2042 1col. San Andres 25 20
2043 1col. Dish for burning aromatic substances . . . 25 20
2044 1col. Sihuatan 25 20
2045 1col. Effigy of rain god . . 25 20
2046 1col. Cara Sucia 25 20
2047 1col. Monkey-shaped pot . . 25 20
2048 1col. San Lorenzo 25 20
2049 1col. Round pot with monkey-head spout . . . 25 20

493 Margay

1989. Endangered Animals. Multicoloured.
2051 25c. Type **493** 10 10
2052 25c. Margay (different) . . . 10 10
2053 55c. Ocelot in tree 15 10
2054 55c. Ocelot resting 15 10

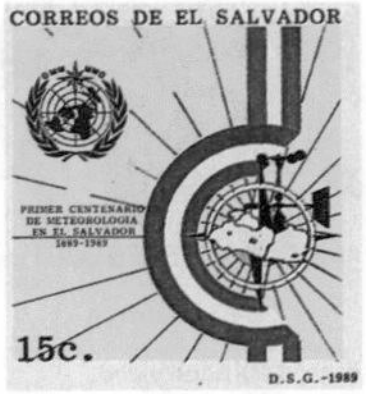

494 Flag, Map and Compass Rose

1989. Centenary of El Salvador Meteorological Services. Multicoloured.
2055 15c. Type **494** 10 10
2056 20c. Sea, land and measuring equipment . . 20 10

495 El Salvador Philatelic Society Emblem

496 Basketball

1989. Philately.
2057 **495** 25c. grey, black & bl . . 10 10

1989. Olympic Games, Barcelona (1992). Mult.
2058 20c. Type **496** (postage) . . 10 10
2059 25c. Boxing 10 10
2060 25c. Athletics 10 10
2061 40c. Showjumping 10 10
2063 55c. Badminton (horiz) (air) 15 10
2064 55c. Handball (horiz) . . . 15 10

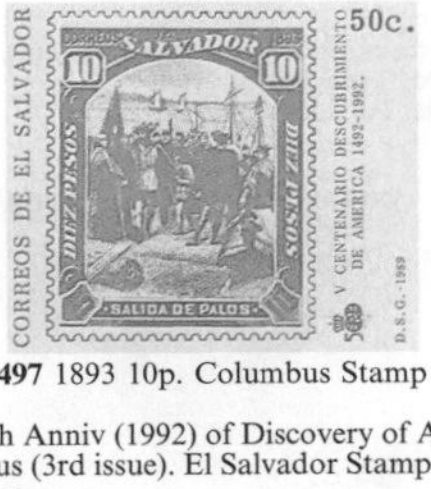

497 1893 10p. Columbus Stamp

1989. 500th Anniv (1992) of Discovery of America by Columbus (3rd issue). El Salvador Stamps featuring Columbus.
2065 **497** 50c. orange 15 10
2066 – 50c. blue 15 10
2067 – 50c. green 15 10
2068 – 50c. red 15 10
2069 – 50c. violet 15 10
2070 – 50c. brown 15 10

DESIGNS: No. 2066, 1894 2p. stamp; 2067, 1893 2p. stamp; 2068, 1894 5p. stamp; 2069, 1893 5p. stamp; 2070, 1894 10p. stamp.

498 Fire Engine

1989. 106th Anniv of Fire Service. Mult.
2072 25c. Type **498** 10 10
2073 70c. Firemen fighting fire . . 15 10

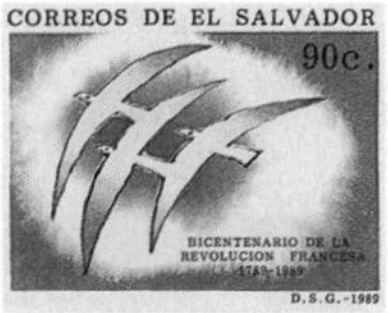

499 Birds

1989. Bicent of French Revolution. Mult.
2074 90c. Type **499** 25 20
2075 1col. Storming the Bastille 25 20

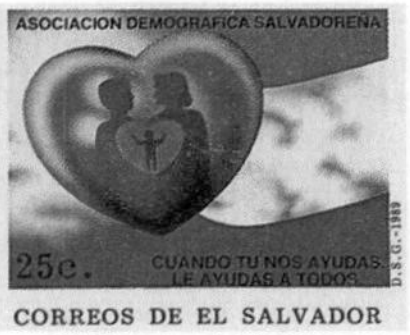

500 People within Heart

1989. 27th Anniv of El Salvador Demographic Association.
2076 **500** 25c. multicoloured . . . 10 10

501 "Signing the Act of Independence" (Luis Vergara Ahumada)

1989. 168th Anniv of Independence. Mult.
2077 25c. Type **501** (postage) . . 10 10
2078 70c. Flag, independence leaders and arms (air) . . 15 10

502 Flags of El Salvador and United States

1989. World Cup Football Championship, Italy (1990) (1st issue). Preliminary Rounds. Multicoloured.
2079 20c. Type **502** 10 10
2080 20c. Flags of El Salvador and Guatemala 10 10
2081 25c. Flags of El Salvador and Costa Rica 10 10
2082 25c. Flags of El Salvador and Trinidad and Tobago 10 10
2083 55c. Flags and ball 15 10
2084 1col. Ball and Cuscatlan Stadium 25 20

See also Nos. 2109/15.

503 Marcelino Champagnat and Arms of Order

1989. Birth Bicent of Jose Benito Marcelino Champagnat (founder of Maristas Brothers).
2085 **503** 20c. multicoloured . . . 10 10

504 "The Farmer" (bowl decoration)

1989. America. Multicoloured.
2086 25c. Type **504** 10 10
2087 70c. Pre-Columbian pottery production 15 10

505 Man tending Crops

1989. World Food Day. "One Land, One Community, One Future". Multicoloured.
2088 15c. Type **505** 10 10
2089 55c. Food production activities in chain links . . 15 10

506 Children under Umbrella

507 Holy Family in Stable

1989. Children's Rights.
2090 **506** 25c. multicoloured . . . 10 10

1989. Christmas. Multicoloured.
2091 25c. Type **507** 10 10
2092 70c. Holy Family 15 10

508 King Vulture

1989. Birds. Multicoloured.
2093 70c. Type **508** 35 25
2094 1col. Common caracara (horiz) 65 50
2095 2col. Sharp-shinned hawk 1·40 90
2096 10col. Ferruginous pygmy owl (horiz) . . . . 7·00 5·25

509 Treasury, Map and "50"

1990. 50th Anniv of Treasury.
2097 **509** 50c. blue, gold & black 15 10

510 Baden-Powell

1990. 133rd Birth Anniv of Lord Baden-Powell (founder of Boy Scouts Movement).
2098 **510** 25c. multicoloured . . . 10 10

511 Young Girl

1990. International Women's Day.
2099 **511** 25c. multicoloured . . . 10 10

512 Hourglass

1990. 50th Anniv of El Salvador Philatelic Society.
2100 **512** 25c. mult (postage) . . . 10 10
2101 55c. mult (air) 10 10

513 "No to Alcoholic Drinks"

1990. Problems of Addiction. Multicoloured.
2103 20c. Type **513** (postage) . . 10 10
2104 25c. "No to Tobacco" . . . 10 10
2105 1col.50 "No to Drugs" (air) 25 20

514 Player

515 First Page and Map

1990. Air. Victory by El Salvador at Fourth International Football Championship for Amputees (1989).
2106 **514** 70c. multicoloured . . . 15 10

1990. 75th Anniv of "La Prensa Grafica" (newspaper). Multicoloured.
2107 15c. Type **515** 10 10
2108 25c. Newspaper as diamond and "75" 10 10

516 Group A

1990. World Cup Football Championship, Italy (2nd issue). Multicoloured.
2109 55c. Type **516** 10 10
2110 55c. Group B 10 10
2111 70c. Group C 15 10
2112 70c. Group D 15 10
2113 1col. Group E 15 10
2114 1col. Group F 15 10
2115 1col.50 Winner's medal (vert) 25 20

517 Ferdinand the Catholic

1990. 500th Anniv (1992) of Discovery of America by Columbus (4th issue). Multicoloured.
2116 1col. Type **517** 15 10
2117 1col. Isabella the Catholic 15 10
2118 1col. Arms and topsail . . 15 10
2119 1col. Anniversary emblem 15 10
2120 1col. "Santa Maria" 50 15
2121 1col. "Pinta" and "Nina" 50 15

1990. Germany, World Cup Football Championship Winner. No. 2112 surch **90c. ALEMANIA CAMPEON.**
2123 90c. on 70c. multicoloured 15 10

519 Globe and Figures

1990. World Summit on Children, New York.
2124 **519** 5col. blue, bis & blk . . 85 80

520 Sir Rowland Hill (instigator of first postage stamps)

1990. 150th Anniv of the Penny Black.
2125 **520** 2col. multicoloured . . . 30 25
2126 – 2col. multicoloured . . . 30 25
2127 – 2col. multicoloured . . . 30 25
2128 – 2col. multicoloured . . . 30 25
2129 – 2col. multicoloured . . . 30 25
2130 – 2col. multicoloured . . . 30 25
DESIGNS: No. 2126, 1d. Black; 2127, El Salvador 1889 1c. stamp; 2128, Post Headquarters; 2129, United Kingdom and El Salvador flags; 2130, El Salvador 1949 1col. U.P.U. stamp.

521 Chichontepec Volcano

1990. America. Natural World. Multicoloured.
2131 25c. Type **521** 40 25
2132 70c. Coatepeque Lake . . . 90 25

522 "Food for the Future"

1990. World Food Day.
2133 **522** 5col. multicoloured . . . 85 80

523 Light Bulb

1990. Centenary of San Salvador Electric Light Company. Multicoloured.
2134 20c. Type **523** 10 10
2135 90c. Maintenance of overhead power lines . . 15 10

524 Road Signs

1990. 8th Anniv of National Commission for Education and Road Safety. Multicoloured.
2136 25c. Type **524** 10 10
2137 40c. Family at road junction (horiz) 10 10

525 Anniversary Emblem

1990. 75th Anniv of Chamber of Trade and Commerce.
2138 **525** 1col. blue, gold & black 15 10

526 "Papilio garamas amerias"

1990. Butterflies. Multicoloured.
2139 15c. "Eurytides calliste" . . 10 10
2140 20c. Type **526** 10 10
2141 25c. "Papilio garamas" . . 10 10
2142 55c. "Hypanartia godmani" (vert) 10 10
2143 70c. "Anaea (Consul) excellens" (vert) 10 10
2144 1col. "Papilio pilumnus" (vert) 15 10

527 Children

1990. Christmas. Multicoloured.
2146 25c. Type **527** 10 10
2147 70c. Nativity (vert) 10 10

528 Elderly Couple

529 University Emblem

1991. Month of the Third Age.
2148 **528** 15c. black and violet . . 10 10

1991. 150th Anniv of El Salvador University.
2149 **529** 25c. black and silver . . 10 10
2150 – 70c. multicoloured . . 10 10
2151 – 1col.50 multicoloured . . 20 15
DESIGNS: 70c. Footsteps leading to light; 1col.50, Pencil, pen and dove on globe.

530 Auditorium

1991. Restoration of Santa Ana Theatre. Mult.
2152 20c. Type **530** 10 10
2153 70c. Facade 10 10

531 Mexican Tree Frog

1991. Frogs. Multicoloured.
2154 25c. Type **531** 10 10
2155 70c. Robber frog 10 10
2156 1col. "Plectrohyla guatemalensis" 15 10
2157 1col.50 Morelet's frog . . . 20 15

532 National Colours, Map and Child

1991. S.O.S. Children's Villages. Mult.
2158 20c. Type **532** 10 10
2159 90c. Children playing in village 15 10

533 Family building Map

534 Blue and White Mockingbird

1991. Family Unity Month.
2160 **533** 50c. multicoloured . . . 10 10

1991. Birds. Multicoloured.
2161 20c. Type **534** 30 35
2162 25c. Red-winged blackbird 30 40
2163 70c. Rufous-naped wren . . 30 40
2164 1col. Bushy-crested jay . . . 55 40
2165 5col. Long-tailed manakin 3·00 1·75

535 Hourglass and Atlas

1991. 500th Anniv (1992) of Discovery of America by Columbus (5th issue). Multicoloured.
2166 1col. Type **535** 15 10
2167 1col. "Santa Maria's" sails and atlas 50 15
2168 1col. Map and caravel . . . 50 15
2169 1col. Caravels and edge of atlas 50 15
2170 1col. Compass rose and map 15 10
2171 1col. Map and anniversary emblem 15 10
Nos. 2166/71 were issued together, se-tenant, forming a composite design.

536 Battle of Acaxual

537 Tree-globe and Plant and Animal Life

1991. America. Voyages of Discovery. Mult.
2173 25c. Type **536** 10 10
2174 70c. First Mass in Cuzcatlan 10 10

1991. World Food Day. "The Tree, Fountain of Life for the World".
2175 **537** 50c. multicoloured . . . 35 20

538 Manuscript and Mozart

1991. Death Bicentenary of Wolfgang Amadeus Mozart (composer).
2176 **538** 1col. multicoloured . . . 15 10

539 Nativity

1991. Christmas. Multicoloured.
2177 25c. Type **539** 10 10
2178 70c. Carol singers (horiz) . . 10 10

540 Moon and Left Half of Eclipse

1991. Total Eclipse of the Sun. Mult.
2179 70c. Type **540** 10 10
2180 70c. Right half of eclipse and Moon 10 10
Nos. 2179/80 were issued together, se-tenant, forming a composite design.

541 Lifeguards with rescued Swimmer

1992. Red Cross Lifeguards. Multicoloured.
2181 3col. Type **541** 45 30
2182 4col.50 Lifeguards in sea . . 1·00 45

542 St. Vincent de Paul and Sick Man **543** Anniversary Emblem

1992. Centenary of St. Vincent de Paul Society of Sisters of Charity.
2183 **542** 80c. multicoloured . . . 10 10

1992. 50th Anniv of Lions International in El Salvador.
2184 **543** 90c. multicoloured . . . 15 10

544 Cyclist ("Non-polluting Transport") **545** Roberto Orellana Valdes (gynaecologist)

1992. Ecology. Multicoloured.
2185 60c. Type **544** 10 10
2186 80c. Children and butterfly ("Fauna, ecology and education") 10 10
2187 1col.60 Man working on allotment ("Harmony with nature") 15 10
2188 2col.20 Animals beside clean river ("Do not pollute rivers") 30 20
2189 3col. Fruits ("Eat natural foods") 45 30
2190 5col. Recycling bins ("Energy without contamination") 75 50
2191 10col. Landscape ("Conserve nature") . . . 1·50 1·00
2192 25col. Wild animals ("Do not destroy fauna") . . . 3·50 2·40

1992. Doctors. Multicoloured.
2193 80c. Type **545** 10 10
2194 1col. Carlos Gonzalez Bonilla (surgeon) 15 10
2195 1col.60 Andres Gonzalez Funes (paediatrician) . . 25 20
2196 2col.20 Joaquin Coto (anaesthetist) 30 20

546 Mascot and Census Document **548** Simon Bolivar

1992. 5th Population and Fourth Housing Census. Multicoloured.
2197 60c. Type **546** 10 10
2198 80c. Graph and globe . . . 10 10

1992.
2205 **548** 2col.20 multicoloured . . 30 20

549 Carvings

1992. 500th Anniv of Discovery of America by Columbus (6th series). Multicoloured.
2206 1col. Type **549** 15 10
2207 1col. Caravel reflected in human eye 40 15
2208 1col. Caravel and Mexican pyramids 40 15
2209 1col. "500", caravel and satellite 40 15

550 Footprints on Globe

1992. Emigration. Multicoloured.
2211 2col.20 Type **550** 30 20
2212 2col.20 Happy cloud and footprints 30 20

551 Morazan **552** Radio Waves on Map

1992. Birth Bicent of General Francisco Morazan.
2213 **551** 1col. multicoloured . . . 15 10

1992. Salvadoran and Int Broadcasting Day.
2214 **552** 2col.20 multicoloured . . 30 20

553 Cross, Pyramid, Church and Carving

1992. America. 500th Anniv of Discovery of America by Columbus. Multicoloured.
2215 80c. Type **553** 10 10
2216 2col.20 Map and stern of caravel 70 25

554 Map and Sails

1992. "Exfilna '92" National Stamp Exn.
2217 **554** 5col. multicoloured . . . 75 50

555 Sun and Stylized Dove

1992. Peace.
2218 **555** 50c. blue, yellow & blk 10 10

556 Christmas Tree and Children

1992. Christmas. Multicoloured.
2219 80c. Type **556** 10 10
2220 2col.20 Holy Family (vert) 30 20

557 Baird's Tapir

1993. Mammals. Multicoloured.
2221 50c. Type **557** 10 10
2222 70c. Water opossum 10 10
2223 1col. Tayra 15 10
2224 3col. Jaguarundi 45 30
2225 4col.50 White-tailed deer . . 65 45

558 Head

1993. "Third Age" Month.
2226 **558** 80c. black 10 10
2227 – 2col.20 multicoloured . . 30 20
DESIGN: 2col.20, Young boy beside elderly man holding tree.

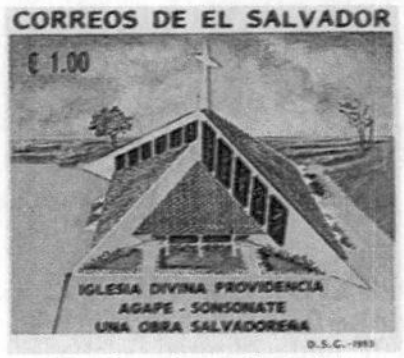

559 Church of the Divine Providence

1993. AGAPE (social organization). Mult.
2228 1col. Type **559** 15 10
2229 1col. Family and AGAPE emblem 15 10

560 Secretary

1993. Secretary's Day. 25th Anniv of Salvadoran Association of Executive Secretaries.
2230 **560** 1col. multicoloured . . . 15 10

561 Hospital

1993. Inauguration of Reconstructed Benjamin Bloom Children's Hospital.
2231 **561** 5col. multicoloured . . . 80 55

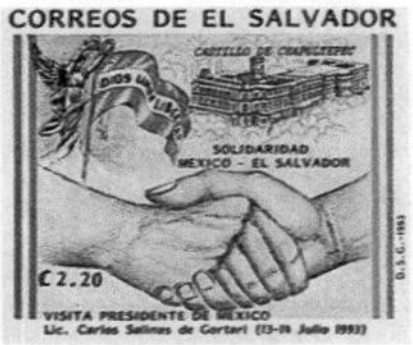

562 Flags, Clasped Hands and Chapultepec Castle

1993. State Visit of Pres. Carlos Salinas de Gortari of Mexico.
2232 **562** 2col.20 multicoloured . . 35 25

563 White Ibis

1993. Birds. Multicoloured.
2233 80c. Type **563** 30 25
2234 1col. American wood ibis 45 25
2235 2col.20 Great blue heron . . 1·10 60
2236 5col. Roseate spoonbill . . 2·50 1·25

564 Anniversary Emblem

1993. Centenary of Pharmaceutical Industry Standards Council.
2237 **564** 80c. mauve, blk & yell 10 10

565 Agouti

1993. America. Endangered Animals. Mult.
2238 80c. Type **565** 10 10
2239 2col.20 Common racoon . . 30 20

566 Pulgarcito (mascot) **568** Masferrer

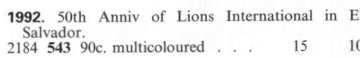

567 Holy Family

1993. 5th Central American Games, El Salvador (1994). Multicoloured.
2240 50c. Type **566** 10 10
2241 1col.60 Games emblem, flags and Olympic rings 25 20

2242 2col.20 Mascot and map of Central America (horiz) . . . 30 20
2243 4col.50 Mascot and map of El Salvador (horiz) . . . 65 45

1993. Christmas. Multicoloured.
2244 80c. Type **567** 10 10
2245 2col.20 Nativity scene and Christmas tree 30 20

1993. 125th Birth Anniv of Alberto Masferrer (sociologist).
2246 **568** 2col.20 multicoloured . . 30 20

569 "Solanum mammosum"

1993. Medicinal Plants. Multicoloured.
2247 1col. Type **569** 15 10
2248 1col. "Hamelia patens" . . 15 10
2249 1col. "Tridax procumbens" 15 10
2250 1col. "Calea urticifolia" . . 15 10
2251 1col. "Ageratum conyzoides" 15 10
2252 1col. "Pluchea odorata" . . 15 10

570 I.Y.F. and United Nations Emblems

1994. International Year of the Family.
2253 **570** 2col.20 multicoloured . . 30 20

571 Hospital

1994. Centenary of Military Hospital. Mult.
2254 1col. Type **571** 15 10
2255 1col. Medical corps soldier treating wounded 15 10

572 Santa Ana Arms

1994. Centenary of Uprising of the 44 at Santa Ana. Multicoloured.
2256 60c. Type **572** 10 10
2257 80c. Commemorative inscription, laurel wreath and ribbon 10 10

573 Goalkeeper and Flags of U.S.A., Switzerland, Colombia and Rumania

1994. World Cup Football Championship, U.S.A. Various footballing scenes and flags of participating countries. Multicoloured.
2258 60c. Type **573** 10 10
2259 80c. Brazil, Russia, Cameroun and Sweden 10 10
2260 1col. Germany, Bolivia, South Korea and Spain 15 10
2261 2col.20 Argentina, Greece, Nigeria and Bulgaria . . 30 20
2262 4col.50 Italy, Ireland, Norway and Mexico . . . 65 45
2263 5col. Belgium, Morocco, Holland and Saudi Arabia 75 50

574 Order of Malta Square, Santa Elena, Cuscatlan

1994. Work of Sovereign Military Order of Malta in El Salvador.
2264 **574** 2col.20 multicoloured . . 30 20

575 Tiger and the Stag (San Juan Nonualco)

1994. Traditional Dances. Multicoloured.
2265 1col. Type **575** 15 10
2266 2col.20 The Speckled Bull (Santa Cruz Analquito and Estanzuelas) 30 20

576 Sweet Pepper

1994. Edible Plants. Multicoloured.
2267 70c. Type **576** 10 10
2268 80c. Cacao 10 10
2269 1col. Sweet potato 15 10
2270 5col. Pacaya 75 50

577 Mail Van

1994. America. Postal Vehicles. Mult.
2271 80c. Type **577** 10 10
2272 2col.20 Steam mail train . . 2·75 1·50

578 Cyclists

579 National Colours and Globe as Crate

1994. 22nd Tour of El Salvador Cycling Championship.
2273 **578** 80c. multicoloured . . . 10 10

1994. 16th International Fair.
2274 **579** 5col. multicoloured . . . 75 50

580 Holy Family and Donkey

1994. Christmas. Multicoloured.
2275 80c. Type **580** 10 10
2276 2col.20 Wise men and baby Jesus 30 20

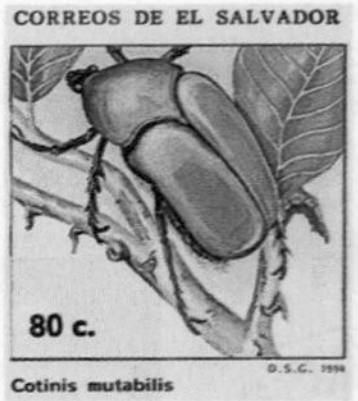

581 "Cotinis mutabilis"

1994. Beetles. Multicoloured.
2277 80c. Type **581** 10 10
2278 1col. "Phyllophaga sp." . . 15 10
2279 2col.20 "Galofa sp." . . . 30 20
2280 5col. Longhorn beetle . . . 75 50

582 Books

1995. 40th Anniv of Cultural Centre. Anniversary emblems. Multicoloured.
2281 70c. Type **582** 10 10
2282 1col. "40" and arrows . . . 15 10

583 Vase

584 Menendez

1995. World Heritage Site. Joya de Ceren. Multicoloured.
2283 60c. Type **583** 10 10
2284 70c. Three-footed dish . . . 10 10
2285 80c. Two-handled pot . . . 10 10
2286 2col.20 Jug 35 25
2287 4col.50 Building No. 3 . . . 65 45
2288 5col. Building No. 4 . . . . 75 50

1995. Birth Bicent of Isidro Menendez (politician).
2289 **584** 80c. multicoloured . . . 10 10

585 Anniversary Emblem

1995. 80th Anniv of La Centro Americana, S.A. (welfare organization). Multicoloured.
2290 80c. Type **585** (safeguarding the future of the child) . . 10 10
2291 2col.20 "Child in Fancy Dress" (Jorge Driottez) (first "Expresiones" painting competition) . . 35 25

586 College and Map of Founding Sisters' Voyage

1995. Cent of College of the Sacred Heart.
2292 **586** 80c. multicoloured . . . 30 10

587 Emblem

1995. 50th Anniv of F.A.O.
2293 **587** 2col.20 multicoloured . . 35 25

588 Los Almendros Beach, Sonsonate

1995. 20th Anniv of World Tourism Organization. Multicoloured.
2294 50c. Type **588** 10 10
2295 60c. Apaneca Lake 10 10
2296 2col.20 Guerrero Beach, La Union 35 25
2297 5col. Usulutan Volcano . . 3·25 1·25

589 National Arms and Symbols of Development

1995. 174th Anniv of Central American Independence. Multicoloured.
2298 80c. Type **589** 30 10
2299 25col. El Salvador exports (sustained economic development) . . . . . . 3·75 2·50

590 "Lemboglossum stellatum"

1995. Orchids. Multicoloured.
2300 60c. "Pleurothallis glandulosa" 10 10
2301 60c. "Pleurothallis grobyi" 10 10
2302 70c. Type **590** 10 10
2303 70c. "Pleurothallis fuegii" 10 10
2304 1col. "Pleurothallis hirsuta" 15 10
2305 1col. "Lepanthes inaequalis" 15 10
2306 3col. "Hexadesmia micrantha" 45 30
2307 3col. "Pleurothallis segoviense" 45 30
2308 4col.50 "Stelis aprica" . . . 65 45
2309 4col.50 "Platystele stenostachya" 65 45
2310 5col. "Stelis barbata" . . . 75 50
2311 5col. "Pleurothallis schiedeii" 75 50

591 Pygmy Kingfisher

1995. America. Conservation. Multicoloured.
2312 80c. Type **591** 60 45
2313 2col. Green kingfisher . . . 1·75 90

592 Anniversary Emblem

1995. 50th Anniv of U.N.O. Multicoloured.
2314 80c. Type **592** 10 10
2315 2col.20 Hands supporting emblem 35 25

593 Children with Sparklers

1995. Christmas. Multicoloured.
2316 80c. Type **593** 10 10
2317 2col.20 Family celebrating at midnight 35 25

594 Great Horned Owl ("Bubo virginianus")

1995. Wildlife of Montecristo. Multicoloured.
2318 80c. Type **594** 10 10
2319 80c. Kinkajou ("Potos flavus") 10 10
2320 80c. "Porthidium godmani" (snake) 10 10
2321 80c. Ocelot ("Felis pardalis") 10 10
2322 80c. "Deliathis bifurcata" (longhorn beetle) 10 10
2323 80c. Puma ("Felis concolor") 10 10
2324 80c. Red brocket ("Mazama americana") 10 10
2325 80c. "Leptophobia aripa" (butterfly) 10 10
2326 80c. Salamander ("Bolitoglossa salvinii") 10 10
2327 80c. Rivoli's hummingbird ("Eugenes fulgens") . . . 10 10
Nos. 2318/27 were issued together, se-tenant, forming a composite design of a forest.

595 Pope John Paul II in Mitre

1996. 2nd Papal Visit. Multicoloured.
2328 1col.50 Type **595** 20 15
2329 5col.40 Pope and Metropolitan Cathedral 75 50

596 Arrival of Spaniards

1996. 450th Anniv of Grant of City Status to San Salvador. Multicoloured.
2330 2col.50 Type **596** 35 25
2331 2col.70 Diego de Holguin (first governor) and chapel 40 30
2332 3col.30 Former National Palace, 1889 . . . . . . 45 30
2333 4col. Boulevard de los Heroes 55 40

597 ANTEL Emblem incorporating Globes

1996. Telecommunications Workers' Day. Mult.
2334 1col.50 Dish aerial and hand holding optic fibres (horiz) 20 15
2335 5col. Type **597** 70 50

598 Rey Avila (El Chele) (singer)

1996. Entertainers' Death Anniversaries. Mult.
2336 1col. Type **598** (1st death) 15 10
2337 1col.50 Maria Moreira (Dona Teresfora) (singer, 1st death) 20 15
2338 2col.70 Francisco Lara (Pancho Lara) (musician and composer, 7th death) 40 30
2339 4col. Carlos Pineda (Aniceto Porsisoca) (singer, 3rd death) 55 40

599 Anniversary Emblem

1996. 40th Anniv of YSKL Radio Station.
2340 **599** 1col.40 multicoloured . . 20 15

600 Throwing the Discus

1996. Centenary of Modern Olympic Games and Olympic Games, Atlanta. Ancient Greek athletes. Multicoloured.
2341 1col.50 Type **600** 20 15
2342 3col. Hurdling 45 30
2343 4col. Wrestling 55 40
2344 5col. Throwing the javelin 70 50

601 Northern Oriole ("Icterus galbula")

1996. Migratory Birds. Multicoloured.
2345 1col.50 Type **601** 20 15
2346 1col.50 American kestrel ("Falco sparverius") . . . 20 10
2347 1col.50 Yellow warbler ("Dendroica petechia") 20 15
2348 1col.50 Kingbird ("Tyrannus forficatus") 20 15
2349 1col.50 Rose-breasted grosbeak ("Pheucticus ludovicianus") 20 15

602 Printed Hand releasing Letters

1996. 60th Anniv of "El Diario de Hoy" (newspaper).
2350 **602** 5col.20 multicoloured . . 70 50

603 Station Emblem

1996. 30th Anniv of Channel 2 (television station).
2351 **603** 10col. multicoloured . . 1·40 95

604 Child and Anniversary Emblem

1996. 50th Anniv of U.N.I.C.E.F.
2352 **604** 1col. multicoloured . . . 15 10

605 Nahuizalco Woman

1996. America. Costumes. Multicoloured.
2353 1col.50 Type **605** 20 15
2354 4col. Panchimalco woman 55 40

606 Christmas Eve Mass (Doris Landaverde)

1996. Christmas. Children's Paintings. Mult.
2355 2col.50 Type **606** 35 25
2356 4col. Christmas morning (Isabel Perez) 55 40

607 Jerusalem

1996. 3000th Anniv of Jerusalem.
2357 **607** 1col. multicoloured . . . 15 10

608 White-nosed Sharks ("Nasolamia velox")

1996. Marine Life. Multicoloured.
2358 1col. Type **608** 15 10
2359 1col. Pacific sierra ("Scomberomorus sierra") 15 10
2360 1col. Common dolphins ("Delphinus delphis") . . 15 10
2361 1col. Hawksbill turtle ("Eretmochelys imbricata") 15 10
2362 1col. Starry grouper ("Epinephelus labriformis") 15 10
2363 1col. Cortez angelfish ("Pomacanthus zonipectus") 15 10
2364 1col. Mexican parrotfish ("Scarus perrico") 15 10
2365 1col. Pacific seahorse ("Hippocampus ingens") 15 10
Nos. 2358/65 were issued together, se-tenant, forming a composite design.

609 Gong and 1983 Constitution

1996. Constitution Day.
2366 **609** 1col. multicoloured . . . 15 10

610 Newspapers and Computer

1997. 30th Anniv of "El Mundo" (newspaper).
2367 **610** 10col. multicoloured . . 1·40 95

611 Steam Locomotive No. 58441, 1925

1997. "Exfilna 97" National Stamp Exhibition, San Salvador.
2368 **611** 4col. multicoloured . . . 1·40 90

612 Church and Mother Clara

1997. 80th Anniv of Foundation of Carmelite Order of St. Joseph.
2369 **612** 1col. multicoloured . . . 15 10

613 Anniversary Emblem

1997. 50th Anniv of American School.
2370 **613** 25col. multicoloured . . 3·50 2·40

614 Custard Apple ("Annona diversifolia")

1997. Tropical Fruits. Multicoloured.
2371 1col.50 Type **614** 20 15
2372 1col.50 Cashew ("Anacardium occidentale") 20 15
2373 1col.50 Melon ("Cucumis melo") 20 15
2374 1col.50 Sapodilla ("Pouteria mammosa") 20 15

615 Anniversary Emblem

1997. 55th Anniv of Lions International in El Salvador.
2376 **615** 4col. multicoloured . . . 55 40

616 Hand protecting Ecosystem

1997. Int Ozone Layer Day (2377) and Int-American Water Day (2378). Multicoloured.
2377 1col.50 Type **616** 20 15
2378 4col. Boy drinking clean water 55 40

617 Flag, Duck, Face and Wreath

1997. 176th Anniv of Independence. Mult.
2379 2col.50 Type **617** 35 25
2380 5col.20 National flag, celebrating crowd and peace dove 70 50

618 Cervantes, Book and Don Quixote and Sancho

1997. 450th Birth Anniv of Miguel de Cervantes (writer).
2381 **618** 4col. multicoloured . . . 55 40

619 Emblem **620** Postman handing Letter to Woman

1997. 75th Anniv of Scout Movement in El Salvador.
2382 **619** 1col.50 multicoloured . . 20 15

1997. America. The Postman. Multicoloured.
2383 1col. Type **620** 15 10
2384 4col. Dog chasing postman on scooter 55 40

621 Motor Car

1997. 26th Anniv of El Salvador Automobile Club.
2385 **621** 10col. multicoloured . . 1·40 95

622 Open-air Feast

1997. Christmas. Children's paintings. Mult.
2386 1col.50 Type **622** 20 15
2387 1col.50 Family gathering . . 20 15

623 Map and St. John Bosco (founder)

1997. Centenary of Salesian Brothers in El Salvador. Multicoloured.
2388 1col.50 Type **623** 20 15
2389 1col.50 St. Cecilia College, Santa Tecla 20 15
2390 1col.50 St. Joseph College, Santa Ana 20 15
2391 1col.50 Ricaldone Technical College 20 15
2392 1col.50 Maria Auxiliadora Church and statue 20 15
2393 1col.50 Don Bosco Citadel, Soyapango, and electronics class 20 15

624 Standard, 1946

1997. Motor Cars. Multicoloured.
2394 2col.50 Type **624** 35 25
2395 2col.50 Chrysler, 1936 . . . 35 25
2396 2col.50 Jaguar, 1954 . . . . 35 25
2397 2col.50 Ford, 1930 . . . . 35 25
2398 2col.50 Mercedes Benz, 1953 35 25
2399 2col.50 Porsche, 1956 . . . 35 25

625 St. Joseph's Church, Ahuachapan

1998. 125th Anniv of St. Joseph's Order. Mult.
2400 1col. Type **625** 15 10
2401 4col. Jose Vilaseca and Cesarea Esparza (founders) 55 40

626 Air Traffic Control Tower

1998. Modernisation of El Salvador International Airport.
2402 **626** 10col. multicoloured . . 1·40 95

627 Player with Ball and Sacre Coeur, Paris

1998. World Cup Football Championship, France. Multicoloured.
2403 1col.50 Type **627** 20 15
2404 1col.50 Player and Eiffel Tower, Paris 20 15
2405 1col.50 Player and the Louvre, Paris 20 15
2406 1col.50 Goalkeeper and Notre Dame Cathedral, Paris 20 15

628 Sun around Map of Americas

1998. 50th Anniv of Organization of American States.
2408 **628** 4col. multicoloured . . . 55 40

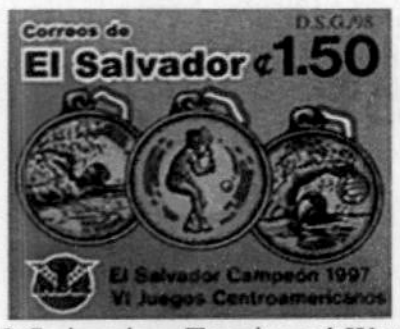

629 Swimming, Tennis and Water Polo Medals

1999. El Salvador, Champion of Sixth Central American Games. Multicoloured.
2409 1col.50 Type **629** 20 15
2410 1col.50 Body-building, judo and shooting medals . . . 20 15
2411 1col.50 Gymnastics, weightlifting and karate medals 20 15
2412 1col.50 Discus, volleyball and netball medals . . . 20 15

630 Guerrero

1998. 40th Death Anniv of Dr. Jose Gustano Guerrero (former President of Tribunal of Justice, The Hague).
2413 **630** 1col. multicoloured . . . 15 10

631 Maps on Cubes

1998. 18th International Fair.
2414 **631** 4col. multicoloured . . . 55 40

632 Arce's Deathbed

1998. 150th Death Anniv of Manuel Jose Arce (President of United Provinces of Central America, 1825–29).
2415 **632** 4col. multicoloured . . . 55 40

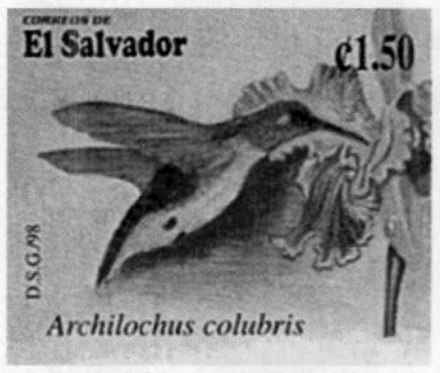

633 Ruby-throated Hummingbird

1998. Hummingbirds. Multicoloured.
2416 1col.50 Type **633** 20 15
2417 1col.50 Cinnamon hummingbird ("Amazilia rutila") 20 15
2418 1col.50 Blue-throated hummingbird ("Hylocharis eliciae") . . 20 15
2419 1col.50 Green violetear ("Colibri thalassinus") . . 20 15
2420 1col.50 Violet sabrewing ("Campylopterus hemileucurus") 20 15
2421 1col.50 Amethyst-throated hummingbird ("Lampornis amethystinus") 20 15

634 House and Figure **635** Scroll

1998. 25th Anniv of Housing Social Fund.
2422 **634** 10col. multicoloured . . 1·40 95

1998. 50th Anniv of National Archives.
2423 **635** 1col.50 multicoloured . . 20 15

636 Alice Larde de Venturino (writer)

1998. America. Famous Women. Multicoloured.
2424 1col. Type **636** 15 10
2425 4col. Maria de Baratta (composer) 55 40

637 Nativity

1998. Christmas. Children's Paintings. Mult.
2426 1col. Type **637** 15 10
2427 4col. Angels and shepherds going to church 55 40

638 Planets and Philatelic Emblems on Pyramid

1998. World Post Day.
2428 **638** 1col. multicoloured . . . 15 10

639 C47T Transport and Badge

1998. 75th Anniv of El Salvador Air Force. Mult.
2429 1col.50 Type **639** 20 15
2430 1col.50 TH-300 training helicopter and badge . . 20 15
2431 1col.50 UH-1H utility helicopter and badge . . 20 15
2432 1col.50 Cessna A-37B Dragonfly bomber and badge 20 15

640 Papaw and Palm Leaf Salad

1998. Traditional Dishes. Multicoloured.
2433 1col.50 Type **640** 20 15
2434 1col.50 Black pudding soup ("Sopa de Mondongo") 20 15
2435 1col.50 Alhuaiste prawns . . 20 15
2436 1col.50 Panela honey fritters 20 15
2437 1col.50 Chilled salad ("Refresco de Ensalada") 20 15
2438 1col.50 Avocado salad ("Ensalada de Aguacate") 20 15
2439 1col.50 Water rice and cabbage soup ("Sopa de Arroz ...") 20 15
2440 1col.50 Typical El Salvador dish 20 15
2441 1col.50 Banana rissoles ("Empanadas de Platano") 20 15
2442 1col.50 Barley water ("Horchata") 20 15

641 Roberto d'Aubuisson signing Constitution

1998. 15th Anniv of Constitution.
2443 **641** 25col. black and blue . . 3·50 2·40

642 "Salvador" (steamship)

1999. 1st National Thematic Stamps Exhibition, San Salvador.
2444 **642** 2col.50 multicoloured . . 35 25

643 Anniversary Emblem

1999. 40th Anniv of National Television.
2445 **643** 4col. multicoloured . . . 55 40

644 Moorhen

1999. Water Birds. Multicoloured.
2446 1col. Type **644** 15 10
2447 1col. American purple gallinule ("Porphyrula martinica") 15 10
2448 1col. Spotted rail ("Pardirallus maculatus") 15 10
2449 1col. Blue-winged teal ("Anas discors") 15 10
2450 1col. Red-billed whistling duck ("Dendrocygna autumnalis") 15 10
2451 1col. American coot ("Fulica americana") . . 15 10
2452 1col. Northern jacana ("Jacana spinosa") . . . 15 10
2453 1col. Sora crake ("Porzana carolina") 15 10
2454 1col. Limpkin ("Aramus guarauna") 15 10
2455 1col. Masked duck ("Oxyura dominica") . . 15 10

645 E.U. and El Salvador Flags

1999. Co-operation between European Union and El Salvador. Multicoloured.
2457 5col.20 Type **645** 70 50
2458 10col. Handshake, El Salvador arms and E.U. emblem . . . . 1·40 95

646 Flags and Arms of El Salvador and U.S.A.

1999. Visit of U.S. President William Clinton to El Salvador. Multicoloured.
2459 5col. Type **646** 70 50
2460 5col. Presidents Armando Calderon Sol and Clinton 70 50

Nos. 2459/60 were issued together, se-tenant, forming a composite design.

647 Stylized People and Globe

1999. 5th Anniv of Salvadoran Institute for Professional Development.
2461 **647** 5col.40 multicoloured . . 75 50

648 Common Long-tongued Bat

1999. Bats. Multicoloured.
2462 1col.50 Type **648** 20 15
2463 1col.50 Common vampire bat ("Desmodus rotundus") 20 15
2464 1col.50 Mexican bulldog bat (Noctilio leporinus) . . . 20 15
2465 1col.50 False vampire bat ("Vampyrum spectrum") 20 15
2466 1col.50 Honduran white bat ("Ectophylla alba") . . . 20 15
2467 1col.50 Black-whiskered bat ("Myotis nigricans") . . . 20 15

649 Drilling Tower, Ahuachapan

1999. Energy in the 21st Century. Geothermal Technology. Multicoloured.
2468 1col. Type **649** 15 10
2469 4col. Geothermal power station, Berlin, Usulutan 55 40

650 Globe and Items for Export

1999. 24th Anniv of Corporation of Exporters.
2470 **650** 4col. multicoloured . . . 55 40

651 Dove, Typewriter and Map

1999. National Journalists' Day.
2471 **651** 1col.50 multicoloured . . 20 15

652 "Cattleya skinneri var. alba"

1999. Orchids. Multicoloured.
2472 1col.50 Type **652** 20 15
2473 1col.50 "Cattleya skinneri var. coerulea" 20 15
2474 1col.50 "Cattleya skinneri" 20 15
2475 1col.50 "Cattleya guatemalensis" 20 15
2476 1col.50 "Cattleya aurantiaca var. flava" 20 15
2477 1col.50 "Cattleya aurantiaca" 20 15

653 Self-portrait

1999. 120th Birth Anniv of Tono Salazar (caricaturist). Each blue and black.
2478 1col.50 Type **653** 20 15
2479 1col.50 Salarrue 20 15
2480 1col.50 Claudia Lars 20 15
2481 1col.50 Francisco Gavidia 20 15
2482 1col.50 Miguel Angel Asturias 20 15

654 Flask, Computer and Children eating

1999. Central American Institute of Nutrition, Panama. Multicoloured.
2483 5col.20 Type **654** 80 50
2484 5col.40 Foodstuffs 85 55

655 Gen. Manuel Jose Arce and Capt. Gen. Gerardo Barrios

1999. 175th Anniv of the Army. Multicoloured.
2485 1col. Type **655** 15 10
2486 1col.50 Soldier and flag . . 25 15

656 Emblem

1999. International Year of the Elderly.
2487 **656** 10col. multicoloured . . 1·60 1·10

657 Dove, Globe and Children

1999. America. A New Millennium without Arms. Multicoloured
2488 1col. Type **657** 15 10
2489 4col. Globe and sign crossing out gun 65 40

658 Emblem

1999. 125th Anniv of Universal Postal Union. Mult.
2490 4col. Type **658** 65 40
2491 4col. Mail and modes of transport 65 40

Nos. 2490/1 were issued together, se-tenant, forming a composite design.

659 Star and Temples (Delmy Guandique)

1999. Christmas. Paintings. Multicoloured.
2492 1col.50 Type **659** 25 15
2493 1col.50 Woman holding poinsettias (Margarita Orellana) 25 15
2494 4col. The Holy Family (Lolly Sandoval) 65 40
2495 4col. The Nativity (Jose Francisco Guadron) . . . 65 40

660 Emblem

1999. 40th Anniv of International Development Bank.
2496 **660** 25col. multicoloured . . 3·25 2·10

661 Golden-fronted Woodpecker

1999. Woodpeckers. Multicoloured.
2497 1col.50 Type **661** 25 15
2498 1col.50 Golden-olive woodpecker (*Piculus rubiginosus*) 25 15
2499 1col.50 Yellow-bellied sapsucker (*Sphyrapicus varius*) 25 15
2500 1col.50 Lineated woodpecker (*Dryocopus lineatus*) 25 15
2501 1col.50 Acorn woodpecker (*Melanerpes formicivorus*) 25 15

662 Emblem

1999. 70th Anniv of Coffee Farmers' Association.
2502 **662** 10col. multicoloured . . 1·60 1·10

663 Emblem

2000. New Year.
2503 **663** 1col.50 multicoloured . . 25 15

664 Fireman rescuing Child

2000. 25th Anniv of National Fire Service. Mult.
2504 2col.50 Type **664** 40 25
2505 25col. Fire service emblem 3·25 2·10

665 Children, Books and Map of El Salvador

2000. 30th Anniv of Educational Work.
2506 **665** 1col. multicoloured . . . 15 10

666 Temple and Dancer

2000. New Millennium (1st series). Multicoloured.
2507 1col.50 Type **666** 25 15
2508 1col.50 *Santa Maria* and Columbus (discovery of America by Columbus) 25 15
2509 1col.50 Soldier and native 25 15
2510 1col.50 Court room (Declaration of Independence, 1841) . . . 25 15
See also Nos. 2533/6.

667 Acceso Gate

2000. El Imposible National Park, Ahuachapan. Multicoloured.
2511 1col. Type **667** 15 10
2512 1col. Ocelot cub 15 10
2513 1col. Paca 15 10
2514 1col. Venado River falls . . . 15 10
2515 1col. Great curassow . . . 15 10
2516 1col. Tree with yellow leaves 15 10
2517 1col. Orchid 15 10
2518 1col. Blue-crowned motmot 15 10
2519 1col. Painted bunting . . . 15 10
2520 1col. Plant 15 10
2521 1col. Information centre . . 15 10
2522 1col. White-eared ground sparrow 15 10
2523 1col. Green frog 15 10
2524 1col. Fungi growing on branch 15 10
2525 1col. Flower (Guaco de Tierra) 15 10
2526 1col. Emerald toucanet . . . 15 10
2527 1col. View over park . . . 15 10
2528 1col. Brazilian agouti . . . 15 10
2529 1col. Tamandua 15 10
2530 1col. El Imposible River falls 15 10

668 Ink Pen, Text and Emblem

2000. 85th Anniv of *La Prensa Grafica* (bilingual newspaper).
2531 **668** 5col. multicoloured . . . 80 50

669 Champagnat

2000. Canonization (1999) of Marcelino Champagnat (Catholic priest).
2532 **669** 10col. multicoloured . . 1·60 1·00

670 Casa Blanca, San Salvador, 1890

2000. New Millennium (2nd series). Each black and brown.
2533 1col.50 Type **670** 25 15
2534 1col.50 Market, 1920 . . . . 25 15
2535 1col.50 Tram outside Nuevo Mundo Hotel, 1924 . . . 25 15
2536 1col.50 Motor cars, 2a South Avenue, 1924 . . . 25 15

671 Athletics

2000. Olympic Games, Sydney. Multicoloured.
2537 1col. Type **671** 15 10
2538 1col. Gymnastics 15 10
2539 1col. High-jumping 15 10
2540 1col. Weightlifting 15 10
2541 1col. Fencing 15 10
2542 1col. Cycling 15 10
2543 1col. Swimming 15 10
2544 1col. Shooting 15 10
2545 1col. Archery 15 10
2546 1col. Judo 15 10

672 Baldwin Steam Locomotive

2000. Trains. Multicoloured.
2547 1col.50 Type **672** 25 15
2548 1col.50 General Electric Corporation locomotive 25 15
2549 1col.50 Open-sided carriage 25 15
2550 1col.50 Presidential carriage 25 15

673 Globe, Envelope and Computer

2000. World Post Day.
2551 **673** 5col. multicoloured . . . 80 50

674 Snowman

2000. Christmas. Multicoloured.
2552 1col. Type **674** 15 10
2553 1col. Bells 15 10
2554 1col. Baubles 15 10
2555 1col. Candy stick 15 10
2556 1col. Candles 15 10
2557 1col. Sleigh 15 10
2558 1col. Presents 15 10
2559 1col. Father Christmas . . . 15 10
2560 1col. Christmas hat 15 10
2561 1col. Boot 15 10

675 "The Traveller" (Roberto Mejia Ruiz)

2000. Paintings. Multicoloured.
2562 4col. Type **675** 65 40
2563 4col. Man kneeling (Alex Cuchilla) 65 40
2564 4col. Woman wearing hat (Nicolas Fredy Shi Quan) 65 40
2565 4col. Swallows (Jose Bernardo Pacheco) . . . 65 40
2566 4col. Man on Globe (Oscar Soles) 65 40

676 West Highland White Terriers

2001. Pets. Multicoloured.
2567 1col.50 Type **676** 20 15
2568 1col.50 West highland white terrier and cat 20 15
2569 2col.50 Budgerigars 35 20
2570 2col.50 Rough-coated terrier and English toy terrier . . 35 20

677 Children's Playground

2001. 25th Anniv of Saburo Hirao Park, San Salvador. Multicoloured.
2571 5col. Type **677** 75 45
2572 25col. Japanese garden . . . 3·75 1·50

678 Claudia Lars and Federico Proano

2001. Latin American Writers.
2573 **678** 10col. multicoloured . . 1·40 85

679 Building, Nun and Children

2001. 125th Anniv of Hogar del Nino San Vicente de Paul (children's home), Quito, Ecuador.
2574 **679** 4col. multicoloured . . . 60 35

680 Indigo Milky (*Lactarius indigo*)

2001. Fungi. Multicoloured.
2575 1col.50 Type **680** (inscr Lactaius) 20 15
2576 1col.50 Oyster mushroom (*Pleurotus ostreatus*) . . . 20 15
2577 1col.50 *Ramaria sp.* 20 15
2578 1col.50 White worm coral fungus (*Clavaria vermicularis*) 20 10
2579 4col. Fly agaric (*Amanita muscaria*) 60 35
2580 4col. *Phillipsia sp.* 60 35
2581 4col. Emetic russula (*Russula*) 60 35
2582 4col. Collared earthstar (*Geastrum triplex*) 60 35

ACKNOWLEDGEMENT OF RECEIPT STAMP

AR 53

1897.
AR264 **AR 53** 5c. green 15

EXPRESS STAMPS

E **547** Throwing the Hammer

1992. Olympic Games, Barcelona. Mult.
E2199 60c. Type E **547** 10 10
E2200 80c. Volleyball 10 10
E2201 90c. Putting the shot (decathlon) 15 10
E2202 2col.20 Long jumping . . . 30 20
E2203 3col. Gymnastics (vaulting) 45 30
E2204 5col. Gymnastics (floor exercise) 75 50

OFFICIAL STAMPS

1896. Stamps of 1896 (first issue) optd **FRANQUEO OFICIAL** in oval.
O170 **37** 1c. blue 10
O171 2c. brown 10
O172 3c. green 40
O173 5c. olive 10
O174 10c. yellow 10
O175 12c. blue 20
O176 15c. violet 10
O177 20c. red 40
O178 24c. red 10
O179 30c. orange 40
O180 50c. black 30
O181 1p. red 20

1896. Stamps of 1896 (second issue) optd **FRANQUEO OFICIAL** in oval.
O182 **38** 1c. green 10
O183 **39** 2c. lake 10
O184 3c. orange 50
O185 5c. blue 20
O186 10c. brown 10
O187 12c. grey 25
O188 15c. green 25
O189 20c. red 25
O190 24c. violet 25
O191 30c. green 15
O192 50c. orange 25
O193 100c. blue 30

1896. Stamps of 1895 (first issue) optd **CORREOS DE EL SALVADOR DE OFICIO** in circle and band.
O194 **37** 1c. blue . . . . 8·50
O195 2c. brown . . . . 8·50
O196 3c. green . . . . 8·50
O197 5c. olive . . . . 8·50
O198 10c. yellow . . . . 10·00
O199 12c. blue . . . . 13·00
O200 15c. violet . . . . 13·00
O201 20c. red . . . . 13·00
O202 24c. red . . . . 13·00
O203 30c. orange . . . . . . 13·00
O204 50c. black . . . . 17·00
O205 1p. red . . . . 17·00

1896. Stamps of 1896 (second issue) optd **CORREOS DE EL SALVADOR DE OFICIO** in circle and band.
O206 **38** 1c. green . . . . 7·00
O207 **39** 2c. lake . . . . 7·00
O208 3c. orange . . . . 30·00
O209 5c. blue . . . . 7·00
O210 10c. brown . . . . 7·00
O211 12c. grey . . . . 12·00
O212 15c. green . . . . 12·00
O219 15c. on 24c. violet (No. 218) . . . . . . 12·00
O213 20c. red . . . . 12·00
O214 24c. violet . . . . 12·00
O215 30c. green . . . . 12·00

O216 50c. orange . . . . . . 12·00
O217 100c. blue . . . . 12·00

1897. Stamps of 1897 optd **FRANQUEO OFICIAL** in oval.
O232 1c. red 10 10
O233 2c. green 70
O234 3c. brown 60
O235 5c. orange 20 25
O236 10c. green 25
O237 12c. blue 30
O238 15c. black 35 45
O239 20c. grey 15
O240 24c. yellow 25 35
O241 30c. red 25 65
O242 50c. violet 90
O243 100c. lake . . . . 80 1·75

1897. Stamps of 1897 optd **CORREOS DE EL SALVADOR DE OFICIO** in circle and band.
O244 1c. red . . . . 9·00 9·00
O245 2c. green . . . . 9·00 9·00
O246 3c. brown . . . . 30·00 32·00
O247 5c. orange . . . . 9·00 9·00
O248 10c. green . . . . 10·00 10·00
O249 12c. blue . . . . 13·00
O250 15c. black . . . . 13·00
O251 20c. grey . . . . 15·00
O252 24c. yellow . . . . 20·00
O253 30c. red . . . . 17·00
O254 50c. violet . . . . 22·00
O255 100c. lake . . . . 20·00

1898. Stamps of 1898 optd **FRANQUEO OFICIAL** in oval.
O288 **57** 1c. red 10
O289 2c. red 15
O290 3c. green . . . . 1·75
O291 5c. green 15
O292 10c. blue 10
O293 12c. violet . . . . 1·75
O294 13c. lake 15
O295 20c. blue 15
O296 24c. blue 10
O297 26c. brown 15
O298 50c. orange 15
O299 1p. yellow 15

1899. Stamps of 1899, with wheel opt as T **58** optd **FRANQUEO OFICIAL** in curved type.
O329 **59** 1c. brown 40 40
O330 2c. green 70 70
O331 3c. blue 40 40
O332 5c. orange 40 40
O333 10c. brown 50 50
O334 12c. green . . . .
O335 13c. red 95 95
O336 24c. blue . . . . 18·00 18·00
O337 26c. red 50 50
O338 50c. red . . . . 1·00 1·00
O339 100c. violet . . . . 1·00 1·00

1900. Federation issue of 1897 optd **CORREOS DE EL SALVADOR DE OFICIO** in circle and band.
O355 **55** 1c. multicoloured . . . . 20·00 20·00
O356 5c. multicoloured . . . . 20·00 20·00

1900. Stamps of 1900, dated "1900", optd **FRANQUEO OFICIAL** in oval, and with or without shield opt T **66**.
O448 **59** 1c. green (No. 438) . . . 35 35
O449 2c. red 40 35
O450 3c. black 25 25
O451 5c. blue 25 25
O452 10c. blue 50 50
O453 12c. green 50 50
O454 13c. brown 50 50
O455 24c. black 30 50
O461 26c. brown 35 35
O462 50c. red 55 40

1903. As T **70**, but inscr "FRANQUEO OFICIAL" across statue.
O497 1c. green 35 25
O498 2c. red 35 15
O499 3c. orange 70 60
O500 5c. blue 35 15
O501 10c. purple 50 35
O502 13c. brown 50 35
O503 15c. brown . . . . 2·50 1·25
O504 24c. red 35 35
O505 50c. brown 50 25
O506 100c. blue 50 55

1905. Nos. O500/502 surch with new value and two black circles.
O518 2c. on 5c. blue . . . . . . 2·40 2·00
O519 3c. on 5c. blue . . . . . .
O520 3c. on 10c. purple . . . . 6·50 4·50
O521 3c. on 13c. brown 60 50

1905. No. O450 optd **1905**.
O558 **59** 3c. black . . . . 1·25 1·10

1906. Nos. O449/50 optd **1906**.
O567 **59** 2c. red . . . .
O568 3c. black 90 70

1906. As T **89**, but inscr "FRANQUEO OFICIAL" at foot of portrait.
O582 1c. black and green 15 10
O583 2c. black and red 15 10
O584 3c. black and yellow . . . 15 10
O585 5c. black and blue 15 35
O586 10c. black and violet . . . 15 10
O587 13c. black and brown . . . 15 10
O588 15c. black and red 20 10
O589 24c. black and red 25 25
O590 50c. black and orange . . . 25 50
O591 100c. black and blue . . . 25 1·50

1908. As T **91**, but inscr "FRANQUEO OFICIAL" below building.
O611 1c. black and green 10 10
O612 2c. black and red 10 10
O613 3c. black and yellow . . . 10 10
O614 5c. black and blue 10 10
O615 10c. black and violet . . . 10 10
O616 13c. black and violet . . . 15 15
O617 15c. black and sepia . . . 15 15
O618 24c. black and red 15 15
O619 50c. black and yellow . . . 25 15
O620 100c. black and blue . . . 25 15
These stamps also exist optd with shield, Type **66**.

1910. As T **99**, but inscr "OFICIAL" below portrait.
O655 2c. black and green 15 15
O656 3c. black and orange . . . 15 15
O657 4c. black and red 15 15
O658 5c. black and violet 15 15
O659 6c. black and red 15 15
O660 10c. black and violet . . . 15 15
O661 12c. black and blue 15 15
O662 17c. black and green . . . 15 15
O663 19c. black and brown . . . 15 15
O664 29c. black and brown . . . 15 15
O665 50c. black and yellow . . . 15 15
O666 100c. black and blue . . . 15 15

1911. Stamps of 1900, dated "1900", optd **OFICIAL** and black circles or surch also.
O667 **59** 1c. green 10 10
O668 3c. on 13c. brown . . . 10 10
O669 5c. on 10c. green 10 10
O670 10c. green 10 10
O671 12c. green 10 10
O672 13c. brown 10 10
O673 50c. on 10c. green . . . 10 10
O674 1col. on 13c. brown . . . 15 15

O 112

O 113

1914. Words of background in green, shield and word "PROVISIONAL" in black.
O675 **O 112** 2c. brown 10 10
O676 3c. yellow 10 10
O677 5c. blue 10 10
O678 10c. red 10 10
O679 12c. green 10 10
O680 17c. violet 10 10
O681 50c. brown 10 10
O682 100c. brown 10 10

1915.
O683 **O 113** 2c. green 10 10
O684 3c. orange 10 10

1915. Stamps of 1915, with opt **1915** optd **OFICIAL**.
O685 **91** 1c. grey (No. 675) . . . 25 20
O686 2c. red 25 20
O687 5c. blue 25 20
O688 6c. blue 50 40
O689 10c. yellow 25 25
O690 12c. brown 60 60
O691 50c. purple 60 50
O692 100c. brown 90 70

1916. Stamps of 1916 optd **OFICIAL**.
O694 **113** 1c. green . . . . 1·10 1·10
O695 2c. red . . . . 6·00 3·00
O696 5c. blue . . . . 5·50 3·00
O697 6c. violet . . . . 1·10 1·10
O698 10c. brown . . . . . . 1·10 1·10
O699 12c. purple . . . . . . 7·25 5·50
O700 17c. orange . . . . . . 1·10 1·10
O701 25c. brown . . . . . . 1·10 1·10
O702 29c. black . . . . . . 1·10 1·10
O703 50c. grey . . . . 1·10 1·10

1922. Stamps of 1921 optd **OFICIAL**.
O736 **130** 1c. green 15 10
O737 – 2c. black 15 10
O738 **131** 5c. orange 20 15
O739 **132** 6c. red 15 10
O740 **133** 10c. blue 25 20
O741 – 25c. green 40 35
O742 **135** 60c. sepia 50 50
O743 – 1col. sepia 50 60

1925. Stamps of 1924 optd **OFICIAL**.
O768 **141** 1c. purple 15 10
O769 – 2c. red 35 10
O770 – 5c. black 15 10
O765 – 6c. blue . . . . 35·00 18·00
O766 **146** 10c. orange 35 15
O767 **150** 1col. blue and green . . 1·10 70

1947. Stamps of 1947 optd **OFICIAL**.
O959 **155** 1c. red . . . . 30·00 14·00
O960 – 2c. yellow . . . . . . 30·00 14·00
O961 – 5c. grey . . . . 30·00 14·00
O962 – 10c. yellow . . . . . . 30·00 14·00
O963 – 20c. green . . . . . . 30·00 14·00
O964 – 50c. black . . . . . . 30·00 14·00

1964. No. O963 further surch **1 CTS. X X**.
O1198 1c. on 20c. green . . . .

OFFICIAL REGISTRATION STAMP

1897. Registration stamp optd **FRANQUEO OFICIAL** in oval.
OR268 R **54** 10c. blue 20

PARCEL POST STAMPS

P **35** Hermes

1895.
P127 **P 35** 5c. orange 30 50
P128 10c. blue 30 50
P129 15c. red 30 75
P130 20c. orange 30 75
P131 50c. green 30 75

POSTAGE DUE STAMPS

D **33**

D **72** Columbus Monument

1895.
D107 **D 33** 1c. green 10 15
D108 2c. green 10 15
D109 3c. green 10 15
D110 5c. green 10 20
D111 10c. green 10 20
D112 15c. green 10 25
D113 25c. green 10 50
D114 50c. green 30 50

1896.
D150 **D 33** 1c. red 10 15
D151 2c. red 10 15
D152 3c. red 10 15
D153 5c. red 10 15
D154 10c. red 10 20
D155 15c. red 15 30
D156 25c. red 15 30
D157 50c. red 15 40

1897.
D256 **D 33** 1c. blue 10 15
D257 2c. blue 10 15
D258 3c. blue 10 15
D259 5c. blue 10 15
D260 10c. blue 15 20
D261 15c. blue 15 25
D262 25c. blue 15 30
D263 50c. blue 10 40

1898.
D302 **D 33** 1c. violet 15 15
D303 2c. violet 15 15
D304 3c. violet 15 15
D305 5c. violet 15 15
D306 10c. violet 30 50
D307 15c. violet 15 20
D308 25c. violet 15 25
D309 50c. violet 20 50

1899. Optd with T **35**.
D347 **D 33** 1c. orange 35 35
D348 2c. orange 35 35
D349 3c. orange 35 35
D350 5c. orange 55 55
D351 10c. orange 70 70
D352 15c. orange 70 70
D353 25c. orange 90 90
D354 50c. orange . . . . . 1·00 1·00

1903.
D507 **D 72** 1c. green 90 70
D508 2c. red . . . . 1·50 1·10
D509 3c. orange . . . . . . 1·50 1·10
D510 5c. blue . . . . 1·50 1·10
D511 10c. purple . . . . . 1·50 1·10
D512 25c. green . . . . . . 1·50 1·10

1908. Stamps of 1907 optd **Deficiencia de franqueo**.
D623 **91** 1c. black and green . . . 20 20
D624 2c. black and red . . . 20 20
D625 3c. black & yellow . . . 25 25
D626 5c. black & blue . . . 40 40
D627 10c. black & violet . . . 70 70

1908. Stamps of 1907 optd **DEFICIENCIA DE FRANQUEO**.
D628 **91** 1c. black and green . . . 30 30
D629 2c. black and red . . . 20 20
D630 5c. black and blue . . . 55 40
D631 10c. black & mauve . . . 80 70
D632 – 3c. blk & yell (No. O613) 55 50

1910. As T **99**, but inscr "FRANQUEO DEFICIENTE" below portrait.
D655 1c. black and brown . . . 15 15
D656 2c. black and green . . . 15 15
D657 3c. black and yellow . . . 15 15
D658 4c. black and red 15 15
D659 5c. black and violet 15 15
D660 12c. black and blue 15 15
D661 24c. black and red 15 15

REGISTRATION STAMP

R **54** Gen. R. A. Gutierrez

1897.
R266 R **54** 10c. lake 20 30

EQUATORIAL GUINEA Pt. 12

The former Spanish Overseas Provinces of Fernando Poo and Rio Muni united on 12 October 1968, to become the Republic of Equatorial Guinea.

1968. 100 centimos = 1 peseta.
1973. 100 centimos = 1 ekuele (plural: bipkwele).
1985. 100 centimos = 1 franc (CFA).

1 Clasped Hands

2 President Macias Nguema

1968. Independence.
1 **1** 1p. sepia, gold and blue . . . 10 10
2 1p.50 sepia, gold & green . . 10 10
3 6p. sepia, gold and red 15 10

1970. 1st Anniv (12.10.69) of Independence.
4 **2** 50c. red, purple & orange . . 10 10
5 1p. purple, green & mauve 10 10
6 1p.50 green and purple . . . 10 10
7 2p. green and buff 10 10
8 2p.50 blue and green 10 10
9 10p. purple, blue & brown 60 10
10 25p. brown, black & grey . . 1·10 15

3 Pres. Macias Nguema and Cockerel

1971. 2nd Anniv of Independence.
11 **3** 3p. multicoloured 10 10
12 5p. multicoloured 15 10
13 10p. multicoloured 25 10
14 25p. multicoloured 40 20

5 Flaming Torch

1972. 3rd Year of Independence.
17 **5** 50p. multicoloured . . . . . 1·00 35

Issues of 1972–79. These are listed at the end of Equatorial Guinea in the Appendix.

6 Pres. Macias Nguema, Hands and Fruit

1979. 4th Anniv of Independence (1972). Mult.
18 1p.50 Type **6** 10 10
19 2p. Classroom 10 10
20 3p. Soldiers and sailors on parade 10 10
21 4p. As No. 19 . . . . 10 10
22 5p. As No. 20 . . . . 15 10

7 Party Emblem

1979. United National Workers' Party.
23 7 1p. multicoloured 10 10
24 1p.50 multicoloured 10 10
25 2p. multicoloured 10 10
26 4p. multicoloured 10 10
27 5p. multicoloured 15 10

8 Ekuele Coin

1979. 5th Anniv of Independence (1973) (1st issue).
28 8 1e. multicoloured 10 10

9 State Palace

10 Pres. Macias Nguema

1979. Independence (1973) (2nd issue). National Enterprises. Multicoloured.
29 1e. Bata harbour 30 10
30 1e.50 Type 9 . . . . 10 10
31 2e. Bata Central Bank 10 10
32 2e.50 Nguema Biyogo bridge . . 10 10
33 3e. Pres. Nguema and scenes as on Nos. 29/32 . . . . . 15 10

1979. 3rd Congress of United National Workers' Party.
34 10 1e.50 multicoloured 10 10

11 Salvador Ndongo Ekang

12 Hands cupping Seedling

1979. Martyrs of Independence. Mult.
35 1e. Enrique Nvo 10 10
36 1e.50 Type 11 . . . . . . 10 10
37 2e. Acacio Mane 10 10

1979. Experimental Agriculture Year.
38 12 1e. multicoloured 10 10
39 1e.50 multicoloured 10 10

12a Boy and Bells

1980. Christmas.
39b 12a 25b. multicoloured . . . 70 50

13 Obiang Esono Nguema

14 King Juan Carlos and Pres. Obiang Nguema

1981. National Heroes.
40 13 5b. blue, yellow & black . . 10 10
41 – 15b. purple, brown & blk . 10 10
42 – 25b. red, grey and black . . 20 10
43 – 35b. green, pink & black . . 30 15
44 – 50b. blue, green & black . . 40 20
45 – 100b. multicoloured . . . 75 40
DESIGNS: 15b. Fernando Nvara Engonga; 25b. Ela Edjodjomo Mangue; 35b. Lt.-Col. Obiang Nguema Mbasogo; 50b. Hipolito Micha Eworo; 100b. National coat of arms.

1981. Visit of King and Queen of Spain. Mult.
46 50b. Royal couple and President at reception . . . 40 20
47 100b. Official welcoming ceremony at airport . . . . 1·00 50
48 150b. Type 14 . . . . 1·00 60

15 Choristers

16 Pope John Paul II

1981. Christmas.
49 15 100b. multicoloured 75 90
50 – 150b. brown, blue & yellow 1·00 60
DESIGN: 150b. Three Kings on camels and head of African.

1982. Papal Visit. Multicoloured.
51 100b. Arms of Pope and Equatorial Guinea 75 40
52 200b. President Obiang Nguema greeting Pope . . 1·25 75
53 300b. Type 16 . . . . 1·75 1·25

17 Footballer and Emblem

1982. World Cup Football Championship, Spain. Multicoloured.
54 40b. Type 17 . . . . 35 15
55 60b. Footballer and championship mascot . . . 45 25
56 100b. World Cup and footballer 75 40
57 200b. Footballers . . . . . . 1·25 75

18 Stars

1982. Christmas. Multicoloured.
58 100b. Type 18 . . . . 75 40
59 200b. King offering gift . . . 1·25 75

19 Gorilla

1982. Protected Animals. Multicoloured.
60 40b. Type 19 . . . . 40 15
61 60b. Hippopotamus 55 30
62 80b. African brush-tailed porcupine 65 35
63 120b. Leopard 90 60

20 Postal Runner

1983. World Communications Year. Mult.
64 150b. Type 20 . . . . 1·00 60
65 200b. Drummer and microwave station . . . . . 1·25 75

21 Tropical Flowers

1983. Multicoloured.
66 300b. Type 21 . . . . 1·25 80
67 400b. Forest . . . . 1·60 1·25

22 Great Egret, Dancer and Musical Instruments

1983. Christmas. Multicoloured.
68 80b. Type 22 . . . . 80 40
69 100b. Holy Family 40 25

23 Annobon and Bioko

1984. Constitution of State Powers. Multicoloured.
70 50b. Type 23 . . . . 20 10
71 100b. Mainland regions . . . 40 25

24 Hunting Sperm Whales

1984. Marine Resources. Multicoloured.
72 125b. Type 24 . . . . 1·40 75
73 150b. Capturing a turtle . . . 1·40 75

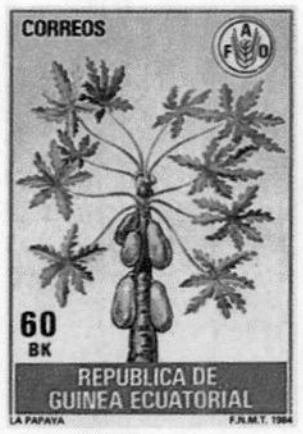

25 Pawpaw

26 Mother and Child

1984. World Food Day. Multicoloured.
74 60b. Type 25 . . . . 30 20
75 80b. Malanga 40 25

1984. Christmas. Multicoloured.
76 60b. Type 26 . . . . 30 20
77 100b. Musical instruments . . 50 30

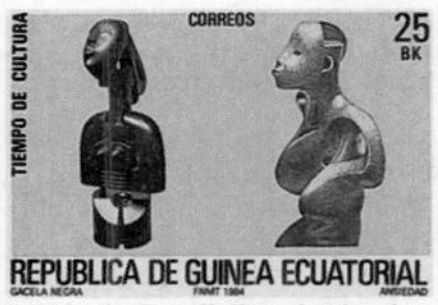

27 "Black Gazelle" and "Anxiety" (wood carvings)

1985. Art.
78 27 25b. multicoloured 15 10
79 – 30b. multicoloured 15 10
80 – 60b. multicoloured 30 20
81 – 75b. black, red & yellow . . 40 25
82 – 100b. multicoloured 50 30
83 – 150b. multicoloured 75 45
DESIGNS—HORIZ: 30b. "Black Gazelle" (different) and "Woman" (wood carvings); 150b. "Man and Woman" and "Bust of Woman" (wood carvings). VERT: 60b. "Man and Woman" (different); 75b. Poster; 100b. "Mother and Child" (wood carving).

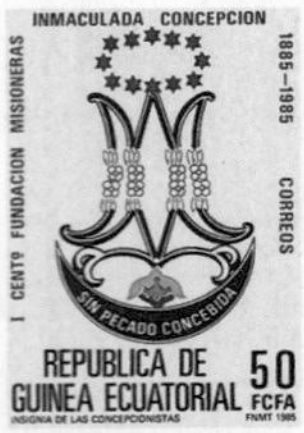

28 Mission Emblem

29 Postal Emblem

1985. Immaculate Conception Mission. Centenary. Multicoloured.
84 50f. Type 28 . . . . 20 15
85 60f. Nun teaching children in African village 20 15
86 80f. First Guinean nuns . . . 30 20
87 125f. Nuns landing on Bata beach 45 25

1985. Postal Service. Multicoloured.
88 50f. Type 29 . . . . 20 15
89 80f. Jose Mavule Ndjong, first Guinean postman 30 20

30 Nativity

1985. Christmas. Multicoloured.
90 40f. Type 30 . . . . 15 10
91 70f. Musicians, dancer and woman with baby 30 20

31 Crab and Snail

1986. Nature Protection. Multicoloured.
92 15f. Type 31 . . . . 20 10
93 35f. Butterflies, bees, chaffinch and grey-headed kingfisher 1·25 55
94 45f. Plants 20 15
95 65f. Men working on cacao crop 30 20

32 Mekuyo Dancers

1986. Folk Customs. Multicoloured.
96 10f. Type 32 . . . . 10 10
97 50f. Kokom dancers 20 15
98 65f. Bisila girl 30 20
99 80f. Ndong-Mba man 35 20

33 Footballers and Emblem

1986. World Cup Football Championship, Mexico. Designs showing various footballing scenes.
100 33 50f. multicoloured 20 15
101 – 100f. multicoloured 45 25
102 – 150f. mult (vert) 65 40
103 – 200f. mult (vert) 85 50

34 Musical Instruments

1986. Christmas. Multicoloured.
104 100f. Type **34** 40 25
105 150f. Mother breast-feeding baby 60 35

35 Map and Member Countries' Flag

1986. Union of Central African States Conference. Multicoloured.
106 80f. Type **35** 35 20
107 100f. Maps 40 25

36 Coins and Hen with Chick

1987. Campaign against Hunger.
108 **36** 60f. purple, orange & blk 25 15
109 – 80f. blue, orange & black 35 20
110 – 100f. brown, orange & blk 40 25
DESIGNS: 80f. Coins and fish in net; 100f. Coins and ear of wheat.

37 Dove and Open Door

1987. International Peace Year. Mult.
111 100f. Type **37** 40 25
112 200f. Hands holding dove . . 80 50

38 Night Sky and Envelope

1987. World Stamp Day. Multicoloured.
113 150f. Type **38** 60 35
114 300f. Banner of national colours and envelope . . . 1·10 75

39 Mother and Child **40** Man climbing Palm Tree

1987. Christmas. Wood Sculptures. Mult.
115 80f. Type **39** 30 15
116 100f. Mother and child (different) 40 20

1988. International Labour Day. Mult.
117 50f. Type **40** 20 15
118 75f. Woman with catch of fish 40 20
119 150f. Chopping down tree . . 60 35

41 Ribbons

1988. Cultural Revolution Day. Mult.
120 35f. Type **41** 15 10
121 50f. Cubes and sphere . . . 20 15
122 100f. Stylized dove 40 25

42 Party Badge **43** Musician

1988. 1st Anniv of Democratic Party of Equatorial Guinea. Multicoloured.
123 40f. Type **42** 15 10
124 75f. Torch and concentric circles (horiz) 30 20
125 100f. Torch (horiz) 40 25

1988. Christmas. Multicoloured.
126 50f. Type **43** 20 15
127 100f. Mother, child and stars 40 25

44 Lorry loaded with Logs

1989. 20th Anniv of Independence. Mult.
128 10f. Type **44** 10 10
129 35f. Traditional folk gathering 15 10
130 45f. President at official function 20 15

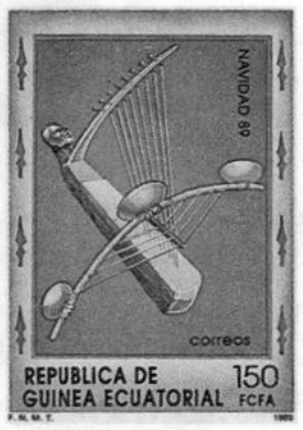

45 Bathers at Ilachi Waterfall **47** Stringed Instrument

46 Palace of Congresses

1989. Water. Multicoloured.
131 15f. Type **45** 10 10
132 25f. La Selva waterfall . . . 10 10
133 60f. Boy drinking from green coconut and youths in water 25 15

1989. 1st Democratic Party Congress. Mult.
134 25f. Type **46** 10 10
135 35f. Torch (party emblem) (vert) 15 10
136 40f. Pres. Obiang Nguema Mbasogo (vert) 15 10

1989. Christmas. Multicoloured.
137 150f. Type **47** 60 35
138 300f. Mother with child and drummer (horiz) . . . . . 1·25 80

48 Sir Robert Baden-Powell (founder)

1990. Boy Scout Movement. Multicoloured.
139 100f. Type **48** 40 25
140 250f. Scout saluting . . . . 1·00 70
141 350f. Scout with bugle . . . 1·40 90

49 Player and Map of Italy

1990. World Cup Football Championship, Italy. Multicoloured.
142 100f. Type **49** 40 25
143 250f. Goalkeeper and ball in net . . . . 1·00 70
144 350f. Trophy and globe . . . 1·40 90

50 Drums and Horn (Ndowe tribe)

1990. Musical Instruments. Multicoloured.
145 100f. Type **50** 40 25
146 250f. Drums, horn, pipes and stringed instruments (Fang) 1·00 70
147 350f. Flute and cup, bell and horn (Bubi) . . . . 1·40 90

51 Arrival in America of Columbus

1990. 500th Anniv (1992) of Discovery of America by Columbus (1st issue). Multicoloured.
148 170f. Type **51** . . . . 1·10 55
149 300f. "Santa Maria", "Pinta" and "Nina" . . . . 1·90 1·10
See also Nos. 165/7.

52 Mother and Child

1990. Christmas. Multicoloured.
150 170f. Type **52** 70 40
151 300f. Bubi man ringing handbell . . . . 1·25 80

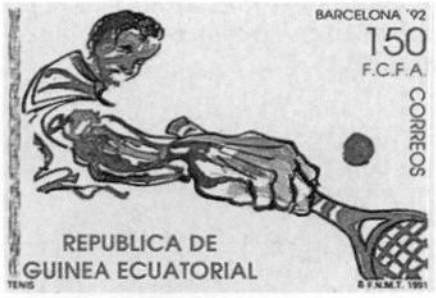

53 Tennis

1991. Olympic Games, Barcelona (1992) (1st issue). Multicoloured.
152 150f. Type **53** 70 45
153 250f. Cycling . . . . 1·10 70
See also Nos. 168/9.

54 "The Naked Maja" (Francisco de Goya)

1991. Paintings. Multicoloured.
155 100f. Type **54** 45 25
156 250f. "Eve" (Albrecht Durer) (vert) . . . . 1·10 70
157 350f. "The Three Graces" (Peter Paul Rubens) (vert) 1·60 1·00

55 Mandrill

1991. The Mandrill. Multicoloured.
158 25f. Type **55** 10 10
159 25f. Close-up of face 10 10
160 25f. On all fours (horiz) . . . 10 10
161 25f. With foreleg raised . . . 10 10

56 Class EF53 Electric Locomotive, 1932, Japan

1991. Railway Locomotives. Multicoloured.
162 150f. Type **56** . . . . 1·50 25
163 250f. Steam locomotive, 1873, U.S.A. . . . . 3·25 35

57 Vicente Pinzon and "Nina"

1991. 500th Anniv (1992) of Discovery of America by Columbus (2nd issue). Multicoloured.
165 150f. Type **57** . . . . 1·00 45
166 250f. Martin Pinzon and "Pinta" . . . . 1·10 70
167 350f. Christopher Columbus and "Santa Maria" . . . . 1·90 1·00

58 Basketball

1992. Olympic Games, Barcelona (2nd issue). Multicoloured.
168 200f. Type **58** 90 60
169 300f. Swimming . . . . . . 1·40 90

60 Blue-breasted Kingfisher and Black-winged Stilt **62** "Termitomyces globulus"

61 Scene from "Casablanca"

1992. Nature Protection. Multicoloured.
172 150f. Type **60** 40 25
173 250f. Great blue turaco and grey parrot 65 40

1992. Centenary of Motion Pictures.
175 **61** 100f. blue and black . . . 25 15
176 – 250f. green and black . . . 65 40
177 – 350f. brown and black . . 90 60
DESIGNS: 250f. Scene from "Viridiana"; 350f. Scene from "A Couple of Gypsies".

1992. Fungi. Multicoloured.
178 75f. Type **62** 35 15
179 125f. "Termitomyces letestui" 55 30
180 150f. "Termitomyces robustus" 65 35

63 "Virgin and Child amongst the Saints" (Claudio Coello)

1993. Painters' Anniversaries. Multicoloured.
181 200f. Type **63** (300th death anniv) 50 30
182 300f. "Apollo, Conqueror of Marsyas" (Jacob Jordaens) (400th birth anniv) 80 50

64 Scene from "Romeo and Juliet" and Pyotr Ilyich Tchaikovsky

1993. Composers' Death Centenaries. Mult.
184 100f. Type **64** 25 15
185 200f. Scene from "Faust" (opera) and Charles Gounod 50 30

65 Quincy Watts (400 m)

1993. Gold Medal Winners at Olympic Games, Barcelona, and Winter Olympic Games, Albertville. Multicoloured.
186 100f. Type **65** 25 15
187 250f. Martin Lopez Zubero (200 m backstroke) 65 40
188 350f. Petra Kronbreger (slalom and combined) . . 90 60
189 400f. "Flying Dutchman" class yacht (Luis Doreste and Domingo Manrique) 1·50 65

66 Ford's First Motor Car

1993. 130th Birth Anniv of Henry Ford (motor car manufacturer).
190 **66** 200f. multicoloured 50 30
191 – 300f. multicoloured 80 50
192 – 400f. black and red . . . . 1·00 65
DESIGNS—HORIZ: 300f. Model "T" motor car. VERT: 400f. Henry Ford.

67 Pres. Obiang Nguema Mbasogo

1993. 25th Anniv of Independence. Mult.
193 150f. Type **67** 40 25
194 250f. Oil refinery, ship, map and radio mast (horiz) . . 90 40
195 300f. Hydro-electric station, Riaba, and waterfall (horiz) 80 50
196 350f. Woman, bridge and man (horiz) 90 60

68 Lunar Module "Eagle"

1994. 25th Anniv of First Manned Moon Landing. Multicoloured.
197 500f. Type **68** . . . . 1·25 80
198 700f. Buzz Aldrin, Michael Collins and Neil Armstrong (astronauts) . . 1·75 1·10
199 900f. Footprint on Moon and module reflected in astronaut's visor . . . . . 2·25 1·50

69 German Team (1990 champions)

1994. World Cup Football Championship, U.S.A. Multicoloured.
200 200f. Type **69** 50 30
201 300f. Rose Bowl Stadium, Los Angeles 75 45
202 500f. Player dribbling ball (vert) . . . . 1·25 80

70 "Chasmosauraus belli"

1994. Prehistoric Animals. Multicoloured.
203 300f. Type **70** 75 45
204 500f. "Tyrannosaurus rex" 1·25 80
205 700f. "Triceratops horridus" 1·75 1·10

71 Gold Calcite

1994. Minerals. Multicoloured.
207 300f. Type **71** 75 45
208 400f. Pyromorphite 95 60
209 600f. Fluorite . . . . 1·40 90
210 700f. Halite . . . . 1·75 1·10

72 Poster for "Elena y los Hombres" and Jean Renoir (film director)

1994. Anniversaries. Multicoloured.
211 300f. Type **72** (birth cent) . . 75 45
212 500f. Map and Ferdinand Marie de Lesseps (director of Suez Canal development, death centenary) . . . . 1·25 80
213 600f. Illustration from "The Little Prince" and Antoine de Saint-Exupery (pilot and writer, 50th death anniv) 1·40 90
214 700f. Bauhaus (75th anniv) and Walter Gropius (architect) . . . . 1·75 1·10

73 Kitten

1995. Domestic Animals. Multicoloured.
215 500f. Type **73** . . . . 1·25 80
216 500f. Pekingese . . . . . . 1·25 80
217 500f. Pig . . . . 1·25 80

74 Blue Diadem ("Hypolimnas salmacis")

1995. Butterflies. Multicoloured.
218 400f. Type **74** . . . . 1·00 65
219 400f. Fig-tree blue ("Myrina silenus") . . . . 1·00 65
220 400f. "Palla ussheri" . . . . 1·00 65
221 400f. Boisduval's false acraea ("Pseudacraea boisduvali") 1·00 65

75 Steam Locomotive, Great Britain

1995. Railways. Multicoloured.
222 500f. Type **75** . . . . 1·25 80
223 500f. Diesel locomotive, Germany . . . . 1·25 80
224 500f. "Hikari" express train, Japan . . . . 1·25 80

76 Signing of Japanese Surrender Document

1995. Anniversaries. Multicoloured.
226 350f. Type **76** (50th anniv of end of Second World War) 90 60
227 450f. Palais des Nations, Geneva (50th anniv of U.N.O.) . . . . 1·10 70
228 600f. Basel 1845 2½r. stamp and Sir Rowland Hill (birth bicentenary) . . . . 1·50 1·00

77 J. Manuel Fangio (1951 and 1954–7)

1996. Formula 1 Racing Champions. Mult.
229 400f. Type **77** . . . . 1·00 65
230 400f. Ayrton Senna (1988, 1990, 1991) . . . . 1·00 65
231 400f. Jim Clark (1963, 1965) 1·00 65
232 400f. Jochen Rindt (1970) . . 1·00 65

78 Alfred Nobel (chemist)

1996. Anniversaries. Multicoloured.
233 500f. Type **78** (death centenary) 90 60
234 500f. Anton Bruckner (composer, death centenary) 90 60
235 500f. "Abraham and the Three Angels" (Giovanni Tiepolo), (painter, birth tercentenary) 90 60

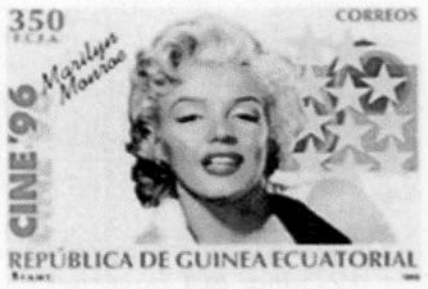

79 Marilyn Monroe (actress)

1996. Personalities. Multicoloured.
237 350f. Type **79** 60 40
238 350f. Elvis Presley (entertainer) 60 40
239 350f. James Dean (actor) . . 60 40
240 350f. Vittorio de Sica (actor and film director) 60 40

80 Illustration from *Book of Chess, Dice and Tablings* by King Alfonso X of Castile and Leon

1996. Chess Competitions. Multicoloured.
241 400f. Type **80** (32nd Chess Olympiad, Yerevan, Armenia) 70 45
242 400f. Girl playing chess (World Junior Chess Championship, Minorca, Spain) 70 45
243 400f. Chess pieces (Women's World Chess Championship, Jaen, Spain) 70 45
244 400f. Anatoly Yevgenievich Karpov (World Chess Championship title match, Elisa, Russian Federation) 70 45

81 19th-century Sail/Steam Warship

1996. Ships. Multicoloured.
245 500f. Type **81** 90 60
246 500f. *Galatea* (cadet ship) . . 90 60
247 500f. Modern ferry 90 60

82 Olympic Stadium, Athens, 1896

1996. Olympic Games, Atlanta. Centenary of Modern Olympic Games. Multicoloured.
248 400f. Type **82** 70 45
249 400f. Cycling 70 45
250 400f. Tennis 70 45
251 400f. Show jumping 70 45

83 False Blusher

1997. Fungi. Multicoloured.
252 400f. Type **83** 70 45
253 400f. Common morel (*Morchella esculenta*) . . . 70 45
254 400f. Orange peel fungus (*Aleuria aurantia*) 70 45
255 400f. *Sparassis laminosa* . . . 70 45

84 Franz Schubert and Score

85 Players

1997. Anniversaries and Events. Multicoloured.
256 500f. Type **84** (composer, birth bicentenary) 90 60
257 500f. Head of ox (Chinese New Year—Year of the Ox) 90 60
258 500f. Johannes Brahms and score (composer, death centenary) 90 60

1997. World Cup Football Championship, France
260 300f. Type **85** 55 35
261 300f. Stadium 55 35
262 300f. Players wearing yellow and blue shirts 55 35

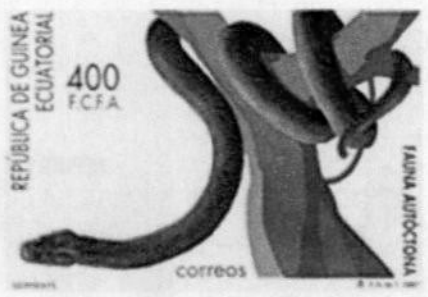

86 Snake

1998. Fauna. Multicoloured.
263 400f. Type **86** 70 45
264 400f. Snail 70 45
265 400f. Turtle 70 45
266 400f. Lizard 70 45

87 French Infantry, Alsace Regiment, 1767

88 "The Crucifixion" (Velazquez)

1998. Military Uniforms. Multicoloured.
267 400f. Type **87** 70 45
268 400f. 18th-century British Admiral 70 45
269 400f. 18th-century Georgian Hussars, Russia 70 45
270 400f. 19th-century Prussian field artillery 70 45

1999. Birth Bimillenary (2000) of Jesus Christ.
271 500f. Type **88** 90 60
272 500f. "Adoration of the Magi" (Peter Paul Rubens) 90 60
273 500f. "The Holy Family" (Miguel Angel Buonarroti) 90 60

89 *Cattleya leopoldii*

1999. Orchids. Multicoloured.

274	400f. Type **89**	70	45
275	400f. *Angraecum eburneum*	70	45
276	400f. *Paphiopedilum insigne*	70	45
277	400f. *Ansellia africana*	70	45

90 "The Coronation of Thorns" (Anthony van Dyck)

91 Golden Conure

1999. Anniversaries. Multicoloured.

278	100f. Type **90** (artist, 400th birth anniv)	15	10
279	250f. Johann Wolfgang Goethe (writer, 250th birth anniv)	45	30
280	500f. Bust of Jacques-Etienne Montgolfier (balloonist, death bicentenary)	90	60
281	750f. Frederic Chopin (composer, 150th death anniv)	1·40	90

1999. Birds. Multicoloured.

282	500f. Type **91**	90	60
283	500f. Buffon's macaw (*Ara ambigua*)	90	60
284	500f. Hyacinth macaw (*Anodorhynchus hyacinthinus*)	90	60

92 Purple Emperor (*Apatura iris*)

1999. Butterflies. Multicoloured.

286	400f. Type **92**	85	40
287	400f. Peacock (*Inachis io*)	85	40
288	400f. Purple-edged copper (*Palaeochrysophanus hippothoe*)	85	40
289	400f. Niobe fritillary (*Fabriciana niobe*)	85	40

93 Swiss Electric Locomotive, Linares–Almeria Line, Spain

1999. Railway Locomotives. Multicoloured.

290	500f. Type **93**	1·10	55
291	500f. German diesel locomotive	1·10	55
292	500f. Japanese series 269 electric locomotive	1·10	55
MS293	82 × 106 mm. 800f. A.V.E. (Spanish high-speed train)	1·75	85

94 Anniversary Emblem

2000. 125th Anniv of UPU.

294 **94**	40f. multicoloured	10	10

95 Carnotaurus

2001. Prehistoric Fauna. Multicoloured.

295	500f. Type **95**	1·00	60
296	500f. Iberomesornis	1·00	60
297	500f. Troodon	1·00	60
MS298	107 × 78 mm. 800f. Diplodocus	1·60	1·00

96 Indigo Boletus (*Gyroporus cyanescens*)

2001. Fungi. Multicoloured.

299	400f. Type **96**	80	50
300	400f. *Terfezia arenaria*	80	50
301	400f. *Battarrea stevenii*	80	50
302	400f. Fly agaric (*Amanita muscaria*)	80	50

97 Merryweather Fire Appliance (1915)

2001. Fire Engines. Multicoloured.

303	400f. Type **97**	80	50
304	400f. De Dion Bouton appliance TE-450 (1943)	80	50
305	400f. Magirus appliance E-2 (1966)	80	50
306	400f. Merryweather appliance (1888)	80	50

98 Infantry Officer, 1700

2001. Military Uniforms. Multicoloured.

307	400f. Type **98**	80	50
308	400f. Arquebusier, 1534	80	50
309	400f. 17th-century musketeer	80	50
310	400f. Fusilier, 1815	80	50

EXPRESS LETTER STAMPS

E 4 Guinea Archer

1971. 3rd Anniv of Independence.

E15	E **4**	4p. multicoloured	10	10
E16		8p. multicoloured	10	10

APPENDIX

The following stamps have either been issued in excess of postal needs or have not been available to the public in reasonable quantities at face value. Such stamps may later be given full listing if there is evidence of regular postal use.

1972.

Space Flight of "Apollo 15". Postage 1, 3, 5, 8, 10p.; Air 15, 25p.

Winter Olympic Games, Sapporo, Japan. Postage 1, 2, 3, 5, 8p.; Air 15, 50p.

Christmas 1971. Paintings. Postage 1, 3, 5, 8, 10p.; Air 15, 25p.

Easter. Postage 1, 3, 5, 8, 10p.; Air 15, 25p.

Olympic Games, Munich 1972. Augsburg Events. Postage 1, 2, 3, 5, 8p.; Air 15, 50p.

Winter Olympic Games, Sapporo, Japan. Gold medal winners. Postage 1, 2, 3, 5, 8p.; Air 15, 50p.

Olympic Games, Munich 1972. Buildings and previous medal winners. Postage 1, 2, 3, 5, 8p.; Air 15, 50p.

Olympic Games. Sailing and rowing, Kiel. Postage 1, 2, 3, 5, 8p.; Air 15, 50p.

Olympic Games Munich. Modern sports. Postage 1, 2, 3, 5, 8p.; Air 15, 50p.

Olympic Games, Munich. Equestrian events. Postage 1, 2, 3, 5, 8p.; Air 15, 50p.

Centenary of Japanese Railway. Various steam locomotives. Postage 1, 3, 5, 8, 10p.; Air 15, 25p.

Olympic Games, Munich. Gold medal winners. Postage 1, 2, 3, 5, 8p.; Air 15, 50p.

Christmas 1972. Paintings by Cranach. Postage 1, 3, 5, 8, 10p.; Air 15, 25p.

Cosmonauts Memorial. Designs with black borders. Postage 1, 3, 5, 8, 10p.; Air 15, 25p.

1973.

Transatlantic Yacht Race 1972. Postage 1, 2, 3, 5, 8p.; Air 15, 50p.

Renoir Paintings. Postage 1, 2, 3, 5, 8p.; Air 15, 50p.

Conquest of Venus. Postage 1, 3, 5, 8, 10p.; Air 15, 25p.

Easter. Religious Paintings by Old Masters. Postage 1, 3, 5, 8, 10p.; Air 15, 25p.

"Tour de France" Cycle Race. Postage 1, 2, 3, 5, 8p.; Air 15, 50p.

Paintings by European Old Masters. Postage 1, 2, 3, 5, 8p.; Air 15, 50p.

World Football Cup Championship, West Germany (1974) (1st issue). Previous Finals. Postage 5, 10, 15, 20, 25, 60c.; Air 5, 70p.

Paintings by Rubens. Postage 1, 2, 3, 5, 8p.; Air 15, 50p.

Christmas. Religious Paintings. Postage 1, 3, 5, 8, 10p.; Air 15, 25p.

World Cup Football Championship, West Germany (1974) (2nd issue). Famous players. Postage 30, 35, 40, 45, 50, 65, 70c.; Air 8, 60p.

Paintings by Picasso. Postage 30, 35, 40, 45, 50c.; Air 8, 60e.

1974.

500th Birth Anniv of Nicolas Copernicus (astronomer). Postage 5, 10, 15, 20c.; Air 4, 10, 70e.

World Cup Football Championship, West Germany (3rd issue). Venues of Qualifying Matches. Postage 75, 80, 85, 90, 95c., 1e., 1e.25; Air 10, 50e.

Easter. Postage 1, 3, 5, 8, 10p.; Air 15, 25p.

Holy Year. Postage 5, 10, 15, 20c., 3e.50; Air 10, 70e.

World Cup Football Championship, West Germany (4th issue). Famous Players. Postage 1e.50, 1e.75, 2e., 2e.25, 2e.50, 3e., 3e.50; Air 10, 60e.

Centenary of U.P.U. (1st issue). Postage 60, 70, 80c., 1e.50; Air 30, 50e.

First Death Anniv of Picasso. Postage 55, 60, 65, 70, 75c.; Air 10, 50e.

"The Wild West". Postage 30, 35, 40, 45, 50c.; Air 8, 60p.

Protected Flowers. Postage 5, 10, 15, 20, 25c., 1, 3, 5, 8, 10p.; Air 5, 15, 25, 70p.

Christmas. Postage 60, 70, 80c., 1e., 1e.50; Air 30, 50e.

75th Anniv of FC Barcelona. Postage 1, 3, 5, 8, 10e.; Air 15, 60e.

Centenary of U.P.U. (2nd issue) and "Espana '75" International Stamp Exhibition, Madrid. Postage 1e.25, 1e.50, 1e.75, 2e., 2e.25; Air 35, 60e.

Nature Protection (1st series). Australian Animals. Postage 80, 85, 90, 95c., 1e.; Air 15, 40e.

Nature Protection (2nd series). African Animals. Postage 50, 60, 65, 70, 75c.; Air 10, 70e.

Nature Protection (3rd series). South American and Australian Birds. Postage 1p.25, 1p.50, 1p.75, 2p., 2p.25, 2p.50, 2p.75, 3p., 3p.50, 4p.; Air 20, 25, 30, 35p.

Nature Protection (4th series). Endangered Species. Postage 10, 15, 20, 25, 30, 35, 40, 45, 50, 55, 60c., 1e.; Air 2, 10, 70e.

1975.

Paintings by Picasso. Postage 5, 10, 15, 20, 25c.; Air 5, 70e.

Easter. Postage 60, 70, 80c., 1e., 1e.50; Air 30, 50e.

Winter Olympic Games, Innsbruck (1976). 5, 10, 15, 20, 25, 30, 35, 40, 45c., 25, 70e.

Paintings of Don Quixote. Postage 30, 35, 40, 45, 50c.; Air 25, 60e.

Bicent of American Revolution (1st issue). Postage 5, 20, 40, 75c., 2, 5, 8e.; Air 25, 30e.

Bullfighting. Postage 80, 85, 90c., 8e.; Air 35, 40e.

"Apollo–Soyuz" Space Test Project. Postage 1, 2, 3, 5e., 5e.50, 7e., 7e.50, 9, 15e.; Air 20, 30e.

Bicent of American Revolution (2nd issue). Postage 10, 30, 50c., 1, 3, 6, 10e.; Air 12, 40e.

Nude Paintings. Postage 5, 10, 15, 20, 25, 30, 35, 40, 45, 50, 55, 60c., 1, 2e.; Air 10, 70e.

Ships. Postage 30, 35, 40, 45, 50, 55, 60, 65, 70, 75c.; Air 8, 10, 50, 60e.

Christmas. Postage 60, 70, 80c., 1e., 1e.50; Air 30, 50e.

Olympic Games, Montreal (1st issue). Postage 50, 60, 70, 80, 90, c.; Air 35, 60e.

Bicent of American Revolution (3rd issue). Presidents. Postage 5, 10, 20, 30, 40, 50, 75c., 1, 2, 3, 5, 6, 8, 10e.; Air 12, 25, 30, 40e.

Monkeys. Postage 5, 10, 15, 20, 25, 30, 35, 40, 45, 50, 55, 60c., 1, 2e.; Air 10, 70e.

Butterflies (1st series). Postage 5, 10, 15, 20, 25, 30, 35, 40, 45, 50, 55, 60c., 1, 2e.; Air 10, 70e.

Fishes (1st series). Postage 5, 10, 15, 20, 25, 30, 35, 40, 45, 50, 55, 60c., 1, 2e.; Air 10, 70e.

Cats (1st series). Postage 5, 10, 15, 20, 25, 30, 35, 40, 45, 50, 55, 60c., 1, 2e.; Air 10, 70e.

Pres. Francisco Macias Nguema. Postage 1e.50, 3e.50, 7e.; Air 300e.

Arms. Postage 3e.; Air 100e.

Government House. 5e.

International Women's Year. 10e.

1976.

Winter Olympic Games, Innsbruck (1st issue). Postage 50, 55, 60, 65, 70, 75, 80, 85, 90c.; Air 35, 60e.

Winter Olympic Games, Innsbruck (2nd issue). Postage 3, 5, 50e.; Air 200e.

Bicent of American Revolution (4th issue). Flora and Fauna. Postage 1e.50, 3, 5, 7, 25, 100e.; Air 200e.

Apollo–Soyuz Project. Optd on Arms issue. Air 100e.

Concorde's First Commercial Flight. Optd on Arms issue. Air 100e.

Nude Paintings. 7, 10, 25e.

Easter. Air 200e.

Olympic Games, Montreal (2nd issue). Postage 7, 10, 25e.; Air 200e.

Apollo–Soyuz Project, Concorde, and Telephone Centenary. Postage 3, 5, 50e.; Air 200e.

Bicent of American Revolution (5th issue). Fauna. Postage 1e.50, 3, 5, 7, 25, 100e.; Air 200e.

Cavalry Officers. Postage 5, 10, 15, 20, 25c.; Air 5, 70p.

Paintings by El Greco. Postage 1, 3, 5, 8, 10p.; Air 15, 25p.

Olympic Games, Montreal (3rd issue). Rowing and Sailing events. Postage 50, 60, 70, 80, 90c.; Air 30, 60e.

Olympic Games, Montreal (4th issue). Postage 50, 55, 60, 65, 70, 75, 80, 85, 90c.; Air 35, 60e.

Veteran Cars. Postage 1, 3, 5, 8, 10p.; Air 15, 25p.

Nature Protection (5th series). European animals. Postage 5, 10, 15, 20, 25c.; Air 5, 70p.

Racing Motorcyclists. 1, 2, 3, 4, 5, 10, 30, 40e.

Nature Protection (6th series). Flowers of South America and Oceania. Postage 30, 35, 40, 45, 50, 80, 85, 90, 95c., 1p.; Air 8, 15, 40, 60p.

Nature Protection (7th series). Asian animals and birds. Postage 30, 35, 40, 45, 55, 60, 65, 70, 75c., 8p.; Air 50c., 10, 50, 60p.

Chess Pieces. 1, 3, 5, 8, 15, 30, 60, 100e.

Nature Protection (8th series). African birds and flowers. Postage 30, 35, 40, 45, 50, 55, 60, 65, 70, 75c.; Air 8, 10, 50, 60p.

Steamships. Postage 80, 85, 90, 95c., 1p.; Air 15, 40p.

Nature Protection (9th series). European birds. Postage 5, 10, 15, 20, 25c.; Air 5, 70p.

Paintings of Ships. Postage 5, 10, 15, 20, 25, 30e.; Air 50, 60, 65, 70e.

1977.

Nature Protection (10th series). Birds of North America. Postage 80, 85, 90, 95c., 1p.; Air 15, 40p.

Cats (2nd series). Postage 5, 10, 15, 20, 25c.; Air 15, 70e.

Silver Jubilee of Queen Elizabeth II. Postage 2, 4, 5, 8, 10, 15e.; Air 20, 35e.

Nude Drawings. Postage 5, 10, 50, 50e.; Air 15, 200e.

Dogs (1st series). Postage 5, 10, 15, 20, 25, 30, 35, 40, 45, 50, 55, 60c., 1, 2e.; Air 10, 70e.

World War Air Aces. Postage 5, 10, 15, 20, 25, 30, 35, 40, 45, 50, 55, 60c.; Air 10, 70e.

Football. Postage 2, 4, 5, 8, 10, 15e.; Air 20, 35e.

Butterflies (2nd series). Postage 80, 85, 90, 95c., 8e.; Air 35, 40e.

Cars. Postage 5, 10, 15, 20, 25, 30, 35, 40, 45, 50, 55, 60c., 1, 2e.; Air 10, 70e.

Chinese Art. Postage 60, 70, 80c., 1e., 1e.50; Air 30, 50e.

African Masks. Postage 5, 10, 15, 20, 25c.; Air 5, 70e.

Nature Protection (11th series). Animals of North America. Postage 1e.25, 1e.50, 1e.75, 2e., 2e.25; Air 20, 50e.

Napoleon. Scenes from his life. Postage 5, 10, 15, 20, 25, 30, 35, 40, 45, 50, 55, 60c., 1, 2e.; Air 10, 70e.

Napoleon. Military uniforms. Postage 5, 10, 15, 20, 25, 30, 35, 40, 45, 50, 55, 60c., 1, 2e.; Air 10, 70e.

Nature Protection (12th series). Animals of South America. Postage 2e.50, 2e.75, 3e., 3e.50, 4e.; Air 25, 35e.

Nature Protection (13th series). European flowers. Postage 2e.50, 2e.75, 3e.50, 4e.; Air 25, 30e.

1978.

25th Anniv of Queen Elizabeth II's Coronation. Members of Royal Family. Postage 2, 5, 8, 10, 12, 15e.; Air 30, 50, 150e.

Knights. Postage 5, 10, 15, 20, 25c.; Air 15, 70e.

Cats (3rd series). 1, 3, 5, 8, 15, 30, 60, 100e.

American Astronauts. 1, 3, 5, 8, 15, 30, 60, 100e.

25th Anniv of Queen Elizabeth II's Coronation. Medals. 1, 3, 5, 8, 25, 50, 75, 200e.

Queen Elizabeth II's Coronation. 25th Anniv Scenes from previous coronations. Air 1, 3, 5, 8, 15, 30, 60, 100e.

Dogs (2nd series). 1, 3, 5, 8, 15, 30, 60, 100e.

World Famous Paintings. 1, 3, 5, 8, 25, 50, 75, 200e.

Butterflies (3rd series). 1, 3, 5, 8, 15, 30, 60, 100e.

Nature Protection (14th series). Asian flowers. Postage 1e.25, 1e.50, 1e.75, 2e., 2e.25; Air 20, 50e.

Flowers. 1, 3, 5, 8, 15, 30, 60, 100e.

Water Birds. 1, 3, 5, 8, 15, 30, 60, 100e.

World Cup Football Championship. Air 150e.

Belgrade Conference. Air 250e.

"Eurphila 78" Exhibition. Air 250e.

Winter Olympic Games, Lake Placid (1980). Postage 5, 10, 20, 25e.; Air 70e.

150th Death Anniv of Goya. Air 150e.

Christmas. Painting by Titian. Air 150e.

Prehistoric Animals. Postage 30, 35, 40, 45, 50c.; Air 25, 60e.

Cats (4th series). Postage 2e.50, 2e.75, 3e., 3e.50, 4e.; Air 25, 40e.

1979.

Death Centenary of Sir Rowland Hill (1st series). 3, 5, 8, 15, 30, 75, 220e.

Wright Brothers. 1, 3, 5, 8, 15, 30, 60, 100e.

Death Bicentenary of Capt. James Cook. Air 100e.

Fishes (2nd series). Postage 5, 10, 20, 25c., 1e.50; Air 15, 70e.

Death Centenary of Sir Rowland Hill (2nd series). Stamps. Postage 8, 15, 20, 20, 30e.; Air 50e.

International Year of the Child (1st series). Postage 5, 7, 11, 24e.; Air 75e.

Death Anniversaries of Schubert, Voltaire, Rousseau and Cranach. Air 100, 100, 100, 100e.

10th Anniv (1972) of "Apollo XI" Space Flight. "Apollo 15" stamps each surch 50e. and inscription. Postage 50e. on 1, 3, 5, 8, 10p.; Air 50e. on 15, 25p.

European Space Agency Satellite. 200e.

Fairy Tales. Postage 2, 3, 5, 10, 15, 18e.; Air 24, 35e.

Automobiles. Air 35, 50e.

Fishes (3rd series). 5, 10, 15, 20, 25, 30, 35, 40, 45, 50, 55, 60, 70c., 1, 2, 10e.

International Year of the Child (2nd series). Various 1978 stamps optd with I.Y.C. emblem. On Cats (3rd series). 1, 3, 5, 8, 15, 30, 60, 100e. On Dogs. 1, 3, 5, 8, 15, 30, 60, 100e. On Butterflies. 1, 3, 5, 8, 15, 30, 60, 100e. On Water Birds. 1, 3, 5, 8, 15, 30, 60, 100e.

"London 1980" Stamp Exhibition. Rowland Hill (1st series) stamps optd 1, 3, 5, 8, 15, 30, 75, 200e.

Olympic Games, Moscow (1st series). Postage 2, 3, 5, 8, 10, 15c.; Air 30, 50e.

Olympic Games, Moscow (2nd series). Water sports. Postage 5, 10, 20, 25e.; Air 70e.

ERITREA Pt. 8

A former Italian colony on the Red Sea, north-east Africa. Under British Administration from 1942 to September 1952, when Eritrea was federated with Ethiopia.

Eritrea was declared an independent state in May 1993.

1893. 100 centesimi = 1 lira.
1991. 100 cents = 1 birr.
1997. Nakfa.

ITALIAN COLONY

1893. Stamps of Italy optd **Colonia Eritrea** (1 to 5c.) or **COLONIA ERITREA** (others).

1 **4** 1c. green 4·00 2·00
2 **5** 2c. brown 1·40 85
3 **23** 5c. green 45·00 2·75
4 **12** 10c. red 55·00 2·75
5 20c. orange £120 2·00
6 25c. blue £400 14·50
7 **14** 40c. brown 4·50 6·50
8 45c. green 4·50 9·75
9 60c. mauve 4·50 20·00
10 1l. brown and orange 13·00 20·00
11 **29** 5l. red and blue £225 £160

1895. Stamps of Italy optd **Colonia Eritrea** (1 to 5c.) or **COLONIA ERITREA** (others).

12 **21** 1c. brown 8·00 4·75
13 **22** 2c. brown 85 85
14 **24** 5c. green 85 85
15 **25** 10c. lake 85 85
16 **26** 20c. orange 1·25 1·00
17 **27** 25c. blue 1·40 1·60
18 45c. olive 11·50 11·50

1903. Stamps of Italy optd **Colonia Eritrea**.

19 **30** 1c. brown 30 75
20 **31** 2c. brown 30 45
21 5c. green 26·00 45
22 **33** 10c. red 32·00 45
30 15c. on 20c. orange 24·00 5·25
23 20c. orange 2·00 75
24 25c. blue £200 9·00
25 40c. brown £275 13·00
26 45c. olive 2·75 5·50
27 50c. violet 80·00 15·00
28 **34** 1l. brown and green 2·75 60
29 5l. blue and red 16·00 21·00

1908. Stamps of Italy optd **ERITREA** (20c.) or **Colonia Eritrea** (others).

31 **37** 5c. green 80 75
32 10c. red 80 75
41 15c. grey 13·00 5·75
42 **41** 20c. orange 3·00 7·25
33 **39** 25c. blue 3·75 1·50
43 40c. brown 24·00 21·00
44 50c. violet 8·00 1·60
45 60c. red 16·00 14·00
46 **34** 10l. green and red £225 £325

3 Ploughing

1910.

34 **3** 5c. green 65 1·60
35 10c. red 3·00 2·40
40 – 15c. grey 32·00 29·00
37 – 25c. blue 4·00 6·50
DESIGN: 15, 25c. Government Palace, Massawa.

1916. Red Cross Society stamps of Italy optd **ERITREA**.

47 **53** 10c.+5c. red 2·00 8·00
48 **54** 15c.+5c. grey 10·50 18·00
49 20c. on 15c.+5c. grey 10·50 18·00
50 20c.+5c. orange 3·25 18·00

1916. No. 40 surch with new value and bars or crosses.

51 – 5c. on 15c. grey 5·00 8·50
52 – 20c. on 15c. grey 2·40 2·10

1922. Victory stamps of Italy optd **ERITREA**.

53 **62** 5c. green 1·25 5·00
54 10c. red 1·25 5·00
55 15c. grey 1·25 6·50
56 25c. blue 1·25 6·50

1922. Stamps of Somalia optd **ERITREA** and bars.

57 **1** 2c. on 1b. brown 3·75 9·75
58 5c. on 2b. green 3·75 6·50
59 **2** 10c. on 1a. red 3·75 1·60
60 15c. on 2a. brown 3·75 1·60
61 25c. on 2½a. blue 3·75 1·60
62 50c. on 5a. orange 11·50 6·50
63 1l. on 10a. lilac 13·00 11·50

1923. Propagation of the Faith stamps of Italy optd **ERITREA**.

64 **66** 20c. orange and green 4·00 18·00
65 30c. orange and red 4·00 18·00
66 50c. orange and violet 2·75 20·00
67 1l. orange and blue 2·75 26·00

1923. Fascist March on Rome stamps of Italy optd **ERITREA**.

68 **73** 10c. green 4·25 7·25
69 30c. violet 4·25 7·25
70 50c. red 4·25 8·25
71 **74** 1l. blue 4·25 21·00
72 2l. brown 4·25 24·00
73 **75** 5l. black and blue 4·25 35·00

1924. Manzoni stamps of Italy optd **ERITREA**.

74 **77** 10c. black and purple 5·00 20·00
75 – 15c. black and green 5·00 20·00
76 – 30c. black 5·00 20·00
77 – 50c. black and brown 5·00 20·00
78 – 1l. black and blue 40·00 £150
79 – 5l. black and purple £400 £1300

1924. Stamps of Italy optd **ERITREA**.

80 **30** 1c. brown 5·75 6·50
81 **31** 2c. orange 3·25 5·50
82 **37** 5c. green 5·75 6·00

1925. Holy Year stamps of Italy optd **ERITREA**.

90 – 20c.+10c. brown & green 2·50 11·50
91 **81** 30c.+15c. brown & dp brn 2·50 13·00
92 – 50c.+25c. brown & violet 2·50 11·50
93 – 60c.+30c. brown & red 2·50 14·50
94 – 1l.+50c. purple and blue 2·50 20·00
95 – 5l.+2l.50 purple & red 2·50 29·00

1925. Stamps of Italy optd **Colonia Eritrea**.

123 **92** 7½c. brown 11·50 38·00
124 **39** 20c. purple 3·25 2·75
96 20c. green 9·75 7·25
97 30c. grey 9·75 9·00
125 **92** 50c. mauve 38·00 23·00
126 **39** 60c. orange 65·00 75·00
127 **34** 75c. red and carmine 48·00 4·50
128 1l.25 blue & ultramarine 23·00 2·75
98 2l. green and orange 45·00 42·00
129 2l.50 green and orange £100 32·00

1925. Royal Jubilee stamps of Italy optd **ERITREA**.

99 **82** 60c. red 65 3·00
100 1l. blue 65 5·00
101 1l.25 blue 4·00 16·00

1926. St. Francis of Assisi stamps of Italy optd **ERITREA** (20 to 60c.) or **Eritrea** (others).

102 **83** 20c. green 1·50 6·50
103 – 40c. violet 1·50 6·50
104 – 60c. red 1·50 11·50
105 – 1l.25 blue 1·50 18·00
106 – 5l.+2l.50 brown 4·00 38·00

1926. Colonial Propaganda stamps Nos. 30/5 of Cyrenaica, but inscr "ERITREA".

107 5c.+5c. brown 60 4·00
108 10c.+5c. olive 60 4·00
109 20c.+5c. green 60 4·00
110 40c.+5c. red 60 4·00
111 60c.+5c. orange 60 4·00
112 1l.+5c. blue 60 4·00

1926. Portrait stamps of Italy optd **ERITREA**.

113 **34** 75c. red and carmine 38·00 7·25
114 1l.25 blue & ultramarine 23·00 7·25
115 2l.50 green and orange 75·00 21·00

1927. 1st National Defence issue of Italy optd **ERITREA**.

116 **89** 40c.+20c. black & brn 1·90 14·50
117 60c.+30c. brown & red 1·90 14·50
118 1l.25+60c. black and blue 1·90 29·00
119 5l.+2l.50 blk & grn 2·75 40·00

1927. Centenary of Volta issue of Italy optd **Eritrea**.

120 **90** 20c. violet 5·00 18·00
121 50c. orange 6·50 11·50
122 1l.25 blue 9·75 26·00

1928. Portrait stamps of Italy optd Eritrea (130) or **ERITREA** (others).

130 **91** 50c. grey and brown 10·50 3·25
131 **92** 50c. mauve 29·00 23·00
132 **91** 1l.75 brown 48·00 16·00

1928. 45th Anniv of the Italian-African Society. As Nos. 43/6 of Cyrenaica but inscr "ERITREA".

133 20c.+5c. green 1·60 5·25
134 30c.+5c. red 1·60 5·25
135 50c.+10c. violet 1·60 9·00
136 1l.25+20c. blue 1·75 10·50

1929. 2nd National Defence issue of Italy (colours changed) optd **ERITREA**.

137 **89** 30c.+10c. black & red 3·00 10·50
138 50c.+20c. grey & lilac 3·00 12·00
139 1l.25+50c. blue & brn 3·75 20·00
140 5l.+2l. black and green 3·75 38·00

1929. Montecassino stamps of Italy (colours changed) optd Eritrea (10l.) or **ERITREA** (others).

141 **104** 20c. green 3·75 8·00
142 – 25c. red 3·75 8·00
143 – 50c.+10c. red 3·75 9·75
144 – 75c.+15c. brown 3·75 9·75
145 **104** 1l.25+25c. purple 7·25 16·00
146 – 5l.+1l. blue 7·25 23·00
147 – 10l.+2l. brown 7·25 26·00

1930. Royal Wedding stamps of Italy (colours changed) optd **ERITREA**.

148 **109** 20c. green 1·00 3·00
149 50c.+10c. red 85 4·00
150 1l.25+25c. red 85 9·25

21 Telegraph Linesman

22

24 King Victor Emmanuel III

1930.

151 – 2c. black and blue 1·00 4·75
152 – 5c. black and violet 1·40 65
153 – 10c. black and brown 1·40 35
154 **21** 15c. black and green 1·40 50
155 – 25c. black and green 1·40 35
156 – 35c. black and red 4·50 8·75
157 – 1l. black and blue 1·40 35
158 – 2l. black and brown 4·50 8·75
159 – 5l. black and green 8·00 14·50
160 – 10l. black and blue 11·50 26·00
DESIGNS—VERT: 2, 35c. Lancer; 5, 10c. Postman; 25c. Rifleman. HORIZ: 1l. Massawa; 2l. Railway Bridge; 5l. Asmara Deghe Selam; 10l. Camel transport.

1930. Ferrucci issue of Italy (colours changed) optd **ERITREA**.

161 **114** 20c. violet 1·60 1·60
162 – 25c. green (283) 1·60 1·60
163 – 50c. black (284) 1·60 3·25
164 – 1l.25 blue (285) 1·60 6·50
165 – 5l.+2l. red (286) 5·00 13·00

1930. 3rd National Defence issue of Italy (colours changed) optd **ERITREA**.

166 **89** 30c.+10c. grn & dp grn 13·00 16·00
167 50c.+10c. purple & grn 13·00 20·00
168 1l.25+30c. lt brn & brn 13·00 29·00
169 5l.+1l.50 green & blue 42·00 65·00

1930. 25th Anniv of Italian Colonial Agricultural Institute.

170 **22** 50c.+20c. brown 2·25 9·75
171 1l.25+20c. blue 2·25 9·75
172 1l.75+20c. green 2·25 12·00
173 2l.55+50c. violet 3·25 20·00
174 5l.+1l. red 3·25 28·00

1930. Bimillenary of Virgil issue of Italy (colours changed) optd **ERITREA**.

175 15c. grey 85 4·00
176 20c. brown 85 2·00
177 25c. green 85 1·60
178 30c. brown 85 2·00
179 50c. purple 85 1·60
180 75c. red 85 3·00
181 1l.25 blue 85 4·00
182 5l.+1l.50 purple 3·00 21·00
183 10l.+2l.50 brown 3·00 32·00

1931. St. Antony of Padua issue of Italy (colours changed) optd **ERITREA**.

184 **121** 20c. brown 1·40 8·00
185 – 25c. green 1·40 3·25
186 – 30c. brown 1·40 3·25
187 – 50c. purple 1·40 3·25
188 – 75c. grey 1·40 8·00
189 – 1l.25 blue 1·40 16·00
190 – 5l.+2l.50 brown 3·75 38·00

1931.

191 **24** 7½c. brown 45 1·50
192 20c. red and blue 35 10
193 30c. purple and olive 45 10
194 40c. green and blue 50 10
195 50c. olive and brown 10 10
196 75c. red 1·50 10
197 1l.25 blue and purple 2·40 1·00
198 2l.50 green 2·40 3·25

25 Dromedary

1933.

199 **25** 2c. blue 50 2·25
200 – 5c. black 65 25
201 **25** 10c. brown 1·00 10
202 – 15c. brown 1·25 1·25
203 – 25c. green 80 10
204 – 35c. violet 3·00 4·25
205 – 1l. blue 10 10
206 – 2l. olive 11·50 2·00
207 – 5l. red 5·75 3·25
208 – 10l. orange 8·00 13·00
DESIGNS—HORIZ: 5c., 15c. Fish wharf; 25c. Baobab tree; 35c. Native village; 2l. African Elephant. VERT: 1l. Ruins at Cholloe; 5l. Eritrean man; 10l. Eritrean woman.

1934. Honouring the Duke of the Abruzzi. Designs as Nos. 201/2 and 204/8 optd **ONORANZE AL DUCA DEGLI ABRUZZI**.

209 **25** 10c. blue 7·75 11·50
210 – 15c. blue 5·75 11·50
211 – 35c. green 3·75 11·50
212 – 1l. red 3·75 11·50
213 – 2l. red 10·50 11·50
214 – 5l. violet 6·00 16·00
215 – 10l. green 6·00 20·00

30 Grant's Gazelle

1934. 2nd International Colonial Exn, Naples.

216 **30** 5c. brown & grn (postage) 2·75 9·00
217 10c. black and brown 2·75 9·00
218 20c. slate and red 2·75 7·25
219 50c. brown and violet 2·75 7·25
220 60c. blue and brown 2·75 9·75
221 1l.25 green and blue 2·75 16·00
222 – 25c. orange & blue (air) 2·75 9·00
223 – 50c. blue and green 2·75 7·25
224 – 75c. orange and brown 2·75 7·25
225 – 80c. green and brown 2·75 9·00
226 – 1l. green and red 2·75 9·75
227 – 2l. brown and blue 2·75 16·00
DESIGNS—36 × 43 mm: Nos. 222/4, Caproni Ca 101 airplane over landscape; 225/7, Savoia Marchetti S-66 flying boat over globe.

31 King Victor Emmanuel III and Caproni Ca 101 Airplane

1934. Air. Rome–Mogadiscio Flight.

228 **31** 25c.+10c. green 3·25 5·00
229 50c.+10c. brown 3·25 5·00
230 75c.+15c. red 3·25 5·00
231 80c.+15c. black 3·25 5·00
232 1l.+20c. brown 3·25 5·00
233 2l.+20c. blue 3·25 5·00
234 3l.+25c. violet 16·00 40·00
235 5l.+25c. red 16·00 40·00
236 10l.+30c. purple 16·00 40·00
237 25l.+2l. green 16·00 40·00

33 Macchi Castoldi MC-94 Flying Boat over Zebu-drawn Plough

1936. Air.
238 **33** 25c. green . . . . 85 2·25
239 – 50c. brown 50 10
240 – 60c. orange . . . . 1·40 5·25
241 – 75c. brown . . . . 1·25 1·00
242 – 1l. blue 10 10
243 **33** 1l.50 violet 80 35
244 – 2l. blue . . . . 1·00 2·00
245 – 3l. lake . . . . 18·00 8·75
246 – 5l. green . . . . 6·50 4·00
247 – 10l. red . . . . 16·00 8·75
DESIGNS: 50c., 2l. Caproni Ca 101 airplane over Massawa–Asmara Railway; 60c., 5l. Savoia Marchetti S-74 airplane over Dom palm trees; 75c., 10l. Savoia Marchetti S-73 airplane over roadway through cactus trees; 1, 3l. Caproni Ca 101 airplane over bridge.

INDEPENDENT STATE

35 Soldier with Flag and Scales of Justice **36** Map on Ballot Box

1991. 30th Anniv of Liberation Struggle. (a) As T **35**. Size 26 × 36 mm.
250 5c. black, orange and blue . .
251 15c. black, orange & green
252 20c. black, orange & yellow

(b) As T **35**, but redrawn with dates added either side of "30". Size 24 × 33 mm.
253 3b. black, orange & silver . .
254 5b. black, orange and gold

1993. Independence Referendum.
255 **36** 15c. multicoloured 10 10
256 – 60c. red, violet & green . . 15 10
257 – 75c. black, red and blue . . 15 10
258 – 1b. multicoloured 20 15
259 – 2b. blue, black & green . . 45 30
DESIGNS: 60c. Arrows; 75c. "YES" and "NO" signpost; 1b. Candle; 2b. Dove, posthorn and map.

38 Eritrean Flag

1993. Multicoloured, colour of frame given.
260 **38** 5c. brown 10 10
261 5c. blue 10 10
262 15c. red 10 10
263 20c. gold 10 10
264 20c. blue 10 10
265 25c. blue 10 10
266 35c. blue 10 10
267 40c. blue 10 10
268 50c. blue 10 10
269 60c. yellow 15 10
270 70c. mauve 15 10
271 70c. blue 15 10
272 80c. blue 20 15
273 3b. green 65 45
274 5b. silver . . . . 1·10 80

39 National Flag and Map

1994. Multicoloured, colour of frame given.
275 **39** 5c. yellow 10 10
276 10c. green 10 10
277 20c. orange 10 10
278 25c. red 10 10
279 40c. mauve 10 10
280 60c. turquoise 15 10
281 70c. green 15 10
282 1b. orange 20 15
283 2b. orange 45 30
284 3b. blue 65 45
285 5b. mauve . . . . 1·10 80
286 10b. lilac . . . . 2·25 1·60

40 Fishermen

1995. 20th Anniv of World Tourism Organization. Multicoloured.
287 10c. Type **40** 10 10
288 35c. Monument (vert) 10 10
289 85c. Mountain road . . . . 1·00 65
290 2b. Archaeological site (vert) 45 30

41 Red Sea Bannerfish

1995. Marine Life. Multicoloured.
291 30c. Type **41** 15 10
292 55c. Hooded butterflyfish . . 15 10
293 70c. Shrimp and lobster . . . 15 10
294 1b. Blue-lined snapper . . . 35 15

42 Mountain and broken Manacles

1995. Independence Day. Multicoloured.
295 25c. Type **42** 10 10
296 40c. Planting national flag on mountain top (vert) . . . 10 10
297 70c. Men with national flag and scimitar (vert) 15 10
298 3b. National flag and fireworks (vert) 65 45

43 Construction Works **44** Dove flying around Map

1995. "Towards the Bright Future".
299 **43** 60c. black, orange & red 15 10
300 – 80c. multicoloured 20 15
301 – 90c. black, orange & red 20 15
302 – 1b. brown, orange & red 20 15
DESIGNS: 80c. Tree; 90c. Village; 1b. Camels.

1995. Council for Mutual Economic Assistance in Africa. Multicoloured.
303 40c. Type **44** 10 10
304 50c. Tree with member countries' names on leaves 10 10
305 60c. Emblem and handshake 15 10
306 3b. Emblem and flags of member countries (horiz) 65 45

45 Headquarters, New York, and Anniversary Emblem **46** Bowl and Spoon

1995. 50th Anniv of U.N.O. Multicoloured.
307 40c. Type **45** 10 10
308 60c. U.N. Emblem forming tree 15 10
309 70c. Anniversary emblem and peace dove 15 10
310 2b. Type **45** 45 30

1995. 50th Anniv of F.A.O. Multicoloured.
311 5c. Type **46** 10 10
312 25c. Agriculture 10 10
313 80c. Bird feeding young . . 20 15
314 3b. Cornucopia of crops . . 65 45

47 Eritreans raising Flag

1996. Martyrs' Day. Multicoloured.
315 40c. Type **47** 10 10
316 60c. Man laying wreath on grave 10 10
317 70c. Breast-feeding 15 10
318 80c. Planting seedlings . . . 15 10

48 Adult and Young

1996. Endangered Animals. Multicoloured.
(a) Gemsbok.
319 3b. Type **48** 60 45
320 3b. Adult eating 60 45
321 3b. Encounter between two males 60 45
322 3b. Gemsbok 60 45

(b) Mammals.
323 3b. Savanna (inscr "Green") monkey 60 45
324 3b. Aardwolf 60 45
325 3b. Dugong 60 45
326 3b. Maned rat 60 45

(c) White-eyed Gull.
327 3b. Preening 60 45
328 3b. Flying 60 45
329 3b. Pair of gulls on rock . . 60 45
330 3b. Gull on rock 60 45

49 Emblem and Mother and Child

1996. 50th Anniv of U.N.I.C.E.F. Designs showing Fund emblem. Multicoloured.
331 40c. Type **49** 10 10
332 55c. Nurse and child 10 10
333 60c. Weighing baby 10 10
334 95c. Amputee beside bed . . 15 10

50 Taking Oath of Allegiance **52** Volleyball

51 Track-laying

1996. National Service. Multicoloured.
335 40c. Type **50** 10 10
336 55c. National rebuilding programmes 10 10
337 60c. Road-building (horiz) . . 10 10
338 95c. Man with club (horiz) 15 10

1997. Revival of Eritrean Railways. Mult.
339 40c. Type **51** 35 20
340 55c. Steam locomotive on seafront line 45 30
341 60c. Seafront tourist diesel locomotive 50 35
342 95c. Railway tunnel through mountain 80 55

1997. Olympic Games, Atlanta (1996). Mult.
343 2b. Type **52** 35 25
344 2b. Laurel wreath and stars 35 25
345 2b. Basketball (three players reaching for ball) 35 25
346 2b. Torch (with flame to right) 35 25
347 2b. Cycling (facing forward) 35 25
348 2b. Torch (with flame to left) 35 25
349 2b. Cycling (facing right) . . 35 25
350 2b. Gold medal 35 25
351 2b. Football 35 25
352 3b. Football match (horiz) . . 55 40
353 3b. Cycling road race (horiz) 55 40
354 3b. Volleyball match 55 40
355 3b. Basketball match 55 40

53 "Heliconius melpomerie cytherea"

1997. Butterflies and Moths. Multicoloured.
357 1b. Mustard white 20 15
358 2b. Type **53** 35 25
359 3b. "Papilio polymnestor" . . 55 40
360 3b. Paradise birdwing ("Ornithoptera paradisea") 55 40
361 3b. "Graphium marcellus" 55 40
362 3b. Jersey tiger moth ("Panaxia quadripunctaria") 55 40
363 3b. "Cardui japonica" . . . 55 40
364 3b. "Papilio childrence" . . . 55 40
365 3b. "Philosamea cynthis" . . 55 40
366 3b. Luna moth ("Actias luna") 55 40
367 3b. "Heticopis acit" 55 40
368 3b. "Psaphis eusehemoides" (vert) 55 40
369 3b. "Papilio brookiana" (vert) 55 40
370 3b. "Parnassius charitonius" (vert) 55 40
371 3b. Blue morpho ("Morpho cypris") (vert) 55 40
372 3b. Monarch ("Danaus plexippus") (vert) 55 40
373 3b. Gaudy commodore ("Precis octavia") (vert) . . 55 40
374 3b. Kaiser-i-hind ("Teinopalpus imperialis") (vert) 55 40
375 3b. "Samia gloreri" (moth) (vert) 55 40
376 3b. "Automeris nyctimene" (vert) 55 40
377 4b. "Ornithoptera goliath" 75 55
378 8b. "Heliconius astraea rondonia" . . . . 1·40 1·00
Nos. 359/67 and 368/76 respectively were issued together, se-tenant, the backgrounds forming composite designs.
There are some errors in the Latin inscriptions.

54 Agricultural Land

1997. Environmental Conservation. Mult.
380 60c. Type **54** 10 10
381 90c. Hillside tree plantation 15 10
382 95c. Terraced hillside 15 10

55 Local Meeting **57** Village Weaver

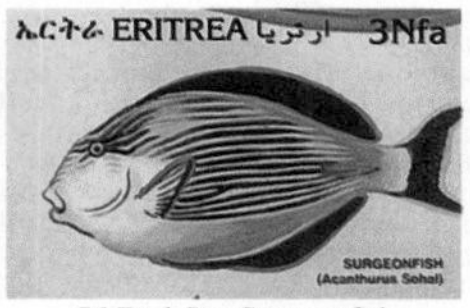

56 Red Sea Surgeonfish

1997. Adoption of National Constitution. Mult.
383 10c. Type **55** 10 10
384 40c. Dove holding open book 10 10
385 85c. Open book in hands . . 15 10

1997. Marine Life. Multicoloured.
386 3n. Sergeant major and white-tipped reef shark . . 50 35
387 3n. Hawksbill turtle and manta ("Devil") ray . . 50 35
388 3n. Type **56** 50 35
389 3n. Needlefish ("Red Sea Houndfish") and humpback whale 50 35
390 3n. Manta ("Devil") ray . . 50 35
391 3n. Manta ("Devil") ray and two-banded anemonefishes ("Clownfishes") 50 35

392		3n. Forceps ("Long-nosed") butterflyfish	50	35
393		3n. Needlefish ("Red Sea Houndfish") and yellow sweetlips	50	35
394		3n. White moray eel	50	35
395		3n. Blue-cheeked ("Masked") butterflyfishes	50	35
396		3n. Shark sucker ("Suckerfish") and whale shark	50	35
397		3n. Sunrise dottyback and bluefin trevally	50	35
398		3n. Moon wrasse, purple moon angel and yellow-tailed ("Two-banded") anemonefish	50	35
399		3n. Lionfish	50	35
400		3n. White-tipped reef shark and Niki's sanddiver	50	35
401		3n. Golden trevallys ("Golden Jacks") and yellow-edged lyretail ("Lunar tailed grouper")	50	35
402		3n. Narrow-banded batfishes	50	35
403		3n. Red-toothed ("Black") triggerfish	50	35

Nos. 386/94 and 395/403 respectively were issued together, se-tenant, forming a composite design.

1998. Birds. Multicoloured.

405		3n. Type **57** (inscr "Black Headed Weaver")	50	35
406		3n. Abyssinian roller	50	35
407		3n. Abyssinian ground hornbills	50	35
408		3n. Lichtenstein's sandgrouse	50	35
409		3n. Erckel's francolin	50	35
410		3n. Arabian bustard	50	35
411		3n. Chestnut-backed sparrow-lark ("Chestnut-backed Finchlark")	50	35
412		3n. Desert lark	50	35
413		3n. Hoopoe lark ("Bifasciated Lark")	50	35
414		3n. African darter	50	35
415		3n. White-headed vulture	50	35
416		3n. Egyptian vultures	50	35
417		3n. Yellow-billed hornbill	50	35
418		3n. Helmet guineafowl	50	35
419		3n. Secretary bird	50	35
420		3n. Martial eagle	50	35
421		3n. Bateleur	50	35
422		3n. Red-billed quelea	50	35

Nos. 405/13 and 414/22 were respectively issued together, se-tenant, forming a composite design.

58 Highland Dwelling **59** Cunama Hair Style

1998. Traditional Houses. Multicoloured.

424		50c. Type **58**	10	10
425		60c. Lowland dwelling	10	10
426		85c. Danakil dwelling	15	10

1998. Traditional Hair Styles. Multicoloured.

427		10c. Type **59**	10	10
428		50c. Tigrinya	10	10
429		85c. Bilen	15	10
430		95c. Tigre	15	10

60 Chirawata

1998. Traditional Musical Instruments. Mult.

431		15c. Type **60**	10	10
432		60c. Imbilta, malaket and shambeko (wind instruments)	10	10
433		75c. Kobero (drum)	10	10
434		85c. K'rar (stringed instrument)	15	10

61 Planting Flag

1999. 8th Anniv of Independence.

435	**61**	60c. multicoloured	10	10
436		1n. multicoloured	15	10
437		3n. multicoloured	45	35

62 1 Nafka Banknote

1999. 2nd Anniv of Currency Reform. Multicoloured.

438		10c. Type **62**	10	10
439		60c. 5 nafka banknote	10	10
440		80c. 10 nafka banknote	15	10
441		1n. 20 nafka banknote	20	15
442		2n. 50 nafka banknote	40	30
443		3n. 100 nafka banknote	50	40

63 Girl carrying Baby **64** Flag and Man

1999. 20th Anniv of National Union of Eritrean Women. Multicoloured.

444		5c. Type **63**	10	10
445		10c. Women reading (horiz)	10	10
446		25c. Crowd (horiz)	10	10
447		1n. Soldier using binoculars (horiz)	1·75	1·25

2000. Millennium. Designs showing the Eritrean Flag and a local scene. Multicoloured.

448		5c. Type **64**	10	10
449		10c. *Denden Assab* (freighter)	10	10
450		25c. Procession in stadium	10	10
451		60c. Soldiers and camp	10	10
452		1n. Raised hand and names of indigenous language groups	20	15
453		2n. Crowd sitting beneath tree	35	25
454		3n. Hand posting ballot paper	55	40
455		5n. Military equipment	90	65
456		7n. State emblem	1·25	90
457		10n. Eritrean 10n. banknote	1·75	1·25

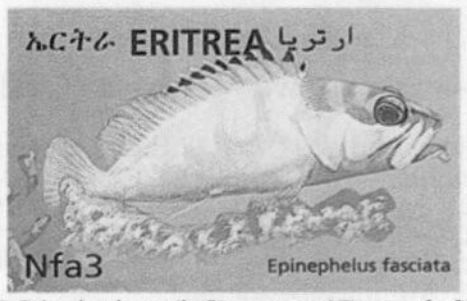

65 Black-tipped Grouper (*Epinephelus fasciata*)

2000. Marine Life. Multicoloured.

458		3n. Type **65**	55	40
459		3n. Regal angelfish (*Pygoplites diacanthus*)	55	40
460		3n. Coral hind (*Cephalopholis miniata*)	55	40
461		3n. Eibl's angelfish (*Centropyge eibli*)	55	40
462		3n. Yellow boxfish (*Ostracion cubicus*)	55	40
463		3n. Pennant coralfish (*Heniochus acuminatus*)	55	40
464		3n. *Chilomycterus spilostylus*	55	40
465		3n. Gray humbug (*Dascyllus marginatus*)	55	40
466		3n. Undulate triggerfish (*Balistapus undulatus*)	55	40
467		3n. Semicircle angelfish (*Pomacanthus semicirculatus*)	55	40
468		3n. Picasso triggerfish (*Rhinecanthus assasi*)	55	40
469		3n. Millepora (coral)	55	40
470		3n. Coachwhip ray	55	40
471		3n. Sulfur damselfish	55	40
472		3n. Grey moray	55	40
473		3n. Sabre squirrelfish	55	40
474		3n. Rusty parrotfish	55	40
475		3n. Striped eel catfish	55	40
476		3n. Spangled emperor	55	40
477		3n. Devil scorpionfish	55	40
478		3n. Crown squirrelfish	55	40
479		3n. Vanikoro sweeper	55	40
480		3n. Sergeant major	55	40
481		3n. Giant manta	55	40

66 Women talking

2001. 10th Anniv of Independence. Multicoloured.

483		20c. Type **66**	10	10
484		60c. Flag and doves (vert)	10	10
485		1n. Emblem (vert)	15	15
486		3n. Celebrating (vert)	45	35
MS487		200 × 115 mm. Nos. 483/6	80	80

67 Adult lying down

2001. Aardwolf (*Proteles cristatus*). Multicoloured.

488		3n. Type **67**	45	35
489		3n. Cubs	45	35
490		3n. Adult walking	45	35
491		3n. Adult head	45	35

68 Aardvark

2001. Wild Animals. Two sheets, each 149 × 83 mm, containing T **68** and similar horiz designs. Multicoloured.

MS492 (a) 3n. Type **68**; 3n. Black-backed jackal; 3n. Striped hyaena; 3n. Spotted hyaena; 3n. Leopard; 3n. African elephant; (b) 3n. Salts dik-dik (inscr "Dick Dick"); 3n. Klipspringer; 3n. Greater kudu (inscr "Tragelophus"); 3n. Soemmerring's gazelle (inscr "soemmering"); 3n. Dorcas gazelle; 3n. African ass (inscr "Equu") Set of 2 sheets . . . 5·50 4·75

CONCESSIONAL LETTER POST

1939. No. CL267 of Italy optd **ERITREA.**

CL248	CL **109**	10c. brown	13·00	16·00

EXPRESS LETTER STAMPS

1907. Express Letter stamps of Italy optd **Colonia Eritrea.**

E31	E **35**	25c. red	14·50	11·50
E34	E **41**	30c. blue and red	75·00	90·00
E53	E **35**	50c. red	2·00	13·00

E 13

1924.

E83	E **13**	60c. brown and red	5·00	14·50
E84		2l. pink and blue	11·50	18·00

1926. Surch.

E113	E **13**	70 on 60c. brn & red	5·00	9·00
E116		1l.25 on 60c. brown and red	9·00	2·25
E114		2l.50 on 2l. pink and blue	11·50	17·00

OFFICIAL AIR STAMP

1934. Optd **SERVIZIO DI STATO** and Crown.

O238	**31**	25l.+2l. red	£1600	

PARCEL POST STAMPS

PRICES: Unused prices are for complete stamps, used prices for a half stamp.

1916. Parcel Post stamps of Italy optd **ERITREA** on each half of stamp.

P61	P **53**	5c. brown	1·60	1·60
P62		10c. blue	1·60	1·60
P63		20c. black	1·60	1·60
P64		25c. red	1·60	1·60
P65		50c. orange	3·25	1·10
P66		1l. violet	3·25	1·10
P67		2l. green	3·25	1·40
P68		3l. yellow	3·25	1·40
P69		4l. grey	3·25	1·60
P70		10l. purple	45·00	4·50
P71		12l. brown	£110	6·00
P72		15l. green	£110	9·00
P73		20l. purple	£110	18·00

1927. Parcel Post stamps of Italy optd **ERITREA** on each half of stamp.

P123	P **92**	10c. blue	£3500	4·25
P124		25c. red	£180	80
P125		30c. blue	85	60
P126		50c. orange	£180	1·00
P127		60c. red	80	30
P128		1l. violet	£160	30
P129		2l. green	£130	30
P130		3l. yellow	3·25	30
P131		4l. grey	3·25	30
P132		10l. mauve	£275	6·00
P133		20l. purple	£275	9·50

POSTAGE DUE STAMPS

1903. Postage Due stamps of Italy optd **Colonia Eritrea.**

D 53	D **12**	5c. mauve & orange	1·00	5·00
D 54		10c. mauve & orge	2·00	5·00
D 32		20c. mauve & orge	7·25	11·50
D 33		30c. mauve & orge	9·75	14·50
D 57		40c. mauve & orge	26·00	18·00
D 58		50c. mauve & orge	11·50	14·50
D 59		60c. mauve & orge	14·50	18·00
D116		60c. brown & orge	65·00	70·00
D 37		1l. mauve and blue	8·00	16·00
D 38		2l. mauve and blue	80·00	65·00
D 39		5l. mauve and blue	£160	£120
D 63		10l. mauve and blue	25·00	29·00
D 41	D **13**	50l. yellow	£375	£120
D 42		100l. blue	£225	60·00

1934. Postage Due stamps of Italy optd **ERITREA.**

D216	D **141**	5c. brown	25	3·25
D217		10c. blue	25	85
D218		20c. red	2·00	1·60
D219		25c. green	2·00	2·00
D220		30c. orange	2·00	3·75
D221		40c. brown	2·00	3·75
D222		50c. violet	2·00	65
D223		60c. blue	4·00	6·50
D224	D **142**	1l. orange	2·00	80
D225		2l. green	9·75	18·00
D226		5l. violet	21·00	21·00
D227		10l. blue	23·00	25·00
D228		20l. red	28·00	28·00

For British Administration see **BRITISH OCCUPATION OF ITALIAN COLONIES.**

ESTONIA Pt. 10

A former province of the Russian Empire on the S. Coast of the Gulf of Finland. Under Russian rule until 1918 when it became an independent republic. The area was incorporated into the Soviet Union from 1940; for issues made during 1941 see GERMAN OCCUPATION OF ESTONIA.

Estonia once again became independent in 1991.

1918. 100 kopeks = 1 rouble.
1919. 100 penni = 1 Estonian mark.
1928. 100 senti = 1 kroon.
1991. 100 kopeks = 1 rouble.
1992. 100 senti = 1 kroon.

Note. An asterisk * after the date indicates that the stamps have a network background in colour.

2 **4** Seagulls

1918. Imperf.

1	**2**	5k. pink	65	50
2		15k. blue	65	50
3		35p. brown	90	75
4		70p. olive	2·00	2·00

1919. Imperf.

5	**4**	5p. yellow	2·00	2·00

5 **6**

7 **9** Viking Longship

1919. Imperf (10p., 15m. and 25m. also perf).

6	**5**	5p. orange	10	10
7		10p. green	20	10
8	**6**	15p. red	15	10
9	**7**	35p. blue	25	10
10		70p. lilac	30	20
11a	**9**	1m. blue and brown	40	25
12a		5m. yellow and black	1·25	20
33		15m. green and violet	2·75	50
34		25m. blue and brown	4·00	2·00

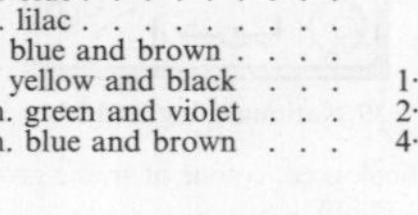

10 L.V.G. Schneider Biplane

1920. Air. Imperf.

15	**10**	5m. black, blue & yellow	4·00	4·00

11 Tallinn

12 Wounded Soldier

13

1920. Imperf.
16 **11** 25p. green 30 15
17 25p. yellow 25 40
18 35p. red 40 15
19 50p. green 30 15
20 1m. red 90 20
21 2m. blue 70 40
23 2m.50 blue . . . . 1·00 30

1920. War Victims' Fund. Imperf.
24 **12** 35+10p. grey and red . . . 60 1·50
25 **13** 70+15p. bistre and blue . . 60 1·50

1920. Surch.
26 **6** 1m. on 15p. red 40 40
27 **11** 1m. on 35p. red 50 50
29 **12** 1m. on 35+10p. grey and red 50 35
28 **7** 2m. on 70p. lilac 75 40
30 **13** 2m. on 70+15p. bistre and blue 50 35

17

18 Weaver

19 Blacksmith

1921. Red Cross. Imperf or perf.
31 **17** 2½–3½m. brn, red & orge . . 1·00 5·00
32 5–7m. brn, red & blue . . . 1·00 5·00

1922. Imperf or perf.
35 **18** ½m. orange 75 30
36 1m. brown . . . . 1·25 30
37 2m. green . . . . 1·40 15
38 2½m. red . . . . 3·00 30
39 3m. green . . . . 1·50 20
40 **19** 5m. red . . . . 1·75 10
41 9m. red . . . . 2·50 1·50
42 10m. blue . . . . 3·50 10
72 10m. grey . . . . 3·00 5·50
42a 12m. red . . . . 4·00 1·50
42b 15m. purple . . . . 3·00 60
42c 20m. blue . . . . 10·00 30

20 Map of Estonia

1923.*
43 **20** 100m. blue and olive . . . 16·00 2·00
43a 300m. blue and brown . . 35·00 10·00

1923. Air. No. 15 optd **1923** or surch **15 Marka 1923**.
44 **10** 5m. black, blue & yellow . . 7·00 20·00
45 15m. on 5m. blk, bl & yell 13·00 30·00

1923. Air. Pairs of No. 15 surch **1923** and new value.
46 **10** 10m. on 5m. . . . . 8·50 25·00
47 20m. on 5m. . . . . 18·00 35·00
48 45m. on 5m. . . . . 60·00 £170

1923. Red Cross stamps optd **Aita hadalist**. Imperf or perf.
49 **17** 2½–3½m. brn, red & orge . . 25·00 75·00
50 5–7m. brown, red & blue . . 25·00 75·00

24 Junkers F-13 with Floats

1924.* Air. Various aircraft. Imperf or perf.
51 – 5m. black and yellow . . . 1·25 4·00
52 – 10m. black and blue . . . . 1·25 4·00
53 **24** 15m. black and red . . . . 1·25 6·00
54 – 20m. black and green . . . 1·25 4·00
55 – 45m. black and violet . . . 1·25 8·00
DESIGNS: 5m. Sabaltnig PIII; 10m. Sabaltnig PIII with floats; 20m. Junkers F-13 with wheels; 45m. Junkers F-13 with skis.

25 National Theatre

1924.* Perf.
57 **25** 30m. black and violet . . . 10·00 3·00
58 – 40m. sepia and blue . . . . 8·00 2·00
59 **25** 70m. black and red . . . . 12·00 5·00
DESIGN: 40m. Vanemuine Theatre, Tartu.

1926. Red Cross stamps surch in figures only. Perf.
60 **17** 5–6 on 2½–3½ brown, red and orange . . . . . . 3·00 5·00
61 10–12 on 5–7m. brown, red and blue . . . . 3·00 5·00

28 Kuressaare Castle

30 Tallinn

1927. Liberation War Commemoration Fund.
62 **28** 5m.+5m. brown & green . . 75 3·00
63 – 10m.+10m. brown & blue 75 3·00
64 – 12m.+12m. green & red . . 75 3·00
65 – 20m.+20m. purple & blue 85 5·00
66 **30** 40m.+40m. grey & brown 90 5·00
DESIGNS—As Type **28**: 10m. Tartu Cathedral; 12m. Parliament House, Tallinn. As Type **30**: 20m. Narva Fortress.

1928. 10th Anniv of Independence. Surch **1918 24/11 1928 S. S.** Perf.
67 **18** 2s. on 2m. green . . . . . 1·00 75
68 **19** 5s. on 5m. red . . . . . 1·00 75
69 10s. on 10m. blue . . . . . 1·75 75
70 15s. on 15m. purple . . . . 2·50 1·00
71 20s. on 20m. blue . . . . . 2·25 75

32 Arms of Estonia

35 "Succour"

1928.*
73 **32** 1s. grey 40 10
74 2s. green 40 10
75 4s. green . . . . 1·25 15
76 5s. red 90 10
77 8s. purple . . . . 3·00 20
78 10s. blue . . . . 1·00 10
79 12s. red . . . . 2·00 10
80 15s. yellow . . . . 2·50 10
80a 15s. red . . . . 15·00 1·00
81 20s. blue . . . . 2·75 10
82 25s. mauve . . . . 10·00 15
83 25s. blue . . . . 18·00 1·00
84 40s. orange . . . . 6·50 60
86 60s. grey . . . . 8·50 50
87 80s. sepia . . . . 11·00 1·10

1930.* Surch in **KROON**.
88 **25** 1k. on 70m. black & red . . 8·00 5·00
89 **20** 2k. on 300m. blue & brown 18·00 10·00
90 3k. on 300m. blue & brown 35·00 25·00

1931. Red Cross Fund.
91 **35** 2s.+3s. green and red . . . 4·50 7·50
92 – 5s.+3s. rose and red . . . 4·50 7·50
93 – 10s.+3s. blue and red . . . 4·50 7·50
94 **35** 20s.+3s. blue and red . . . 8·50 14·00
DESIGN: 5s., 10s. "The Light of Hope".

37 Tartu Observatory

39 Narva Falls

1932.* 300th Anniv of Tartu University.
95 **37** 5s. red . . . . 4·50 40
96 – 10s. blue . . . . 1·25 30
97 **37** 12s. red . . . . 10·00 4·00
98 – 20s. blue . . . . 3·50 1·00
DESIGN: 10s., 20s. Tartu University.

1933.
99 **39** 1k. black . . . . 5·00 2·00
99a 1k. green . . . . 1·00 7·50

40 Ancient Bard
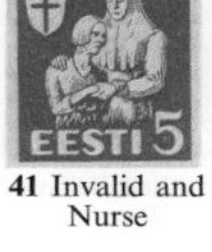
41 Invalid and Nurse

1933.* 10th All-Estonian Choral Festival.
100 **40** 2s. green . . . . 2·00 30
101 5s. red . . . . 3·00 30
102 10s. blue . . . . 4·00 20

1933.* Anti-tuberculosis Fund.
103 **41** 5s.+3s. red . . . . 6·00 7·50
104 – 10s.+3s. blue . . . . . . 6·00 7·50
105 – 12s.+3s. red . . . . . . 7·50 10·00
106 – 20s.+3s. blue . . . . . . 9·00 12·00
DESIGNS—HORIZ: 10s., 20s. Taagepera Sanatorium. VERT: 12s. Cross of Lorraine.

43 Harvesting

44 Arms of Narva

1935.
107 **43** 3k. brown . . . . 1·25 3·00

1936.* Charity. Social Relief Fund.
108 **44** 10s.+10s. blue & green . . 3·75 7·50
109 – 15s.+15s. blue and red . . 4·00 9·00
110 – 25s.+25s. orange & blue . . 6·00 12·50
111 – 50s.+50s. yellow & blk . . 16·00 38·00
DESIGNS—Arms of Parnu (15s.), Tartu (25s.) and Tallinn (50s.).

45 Pres. Konstantin Pats

46 Restored Portal

1936.
112 **45** 1s. brown 50 20
113 2s. green 50 20
113a 3s. orange . . . . 7·50 8·00
114 4s. purple . . . . 1·75 50
115 5s. green . . . . 1·00 20
116 6s. red . . . . 1·25 20
117 6s. green . . . . 30·00 38·00
118 10s. blue . . . . 1·50 20
119 15s. red . . . . 2·50 40
119a 15s. blue . . . . 4·00 45
120 18s. red . . . . 18·00 7·50
121 20s. mauve . . . . 2·25 20
122 25s. blue . . . . 10·00 1·00
123 30s. yellow . . . . 14·00 1·25
123a 30s. blue . . . . 20·00 6·00
124 50s. brown . . . . 7·00 1·50
125 60s. mauve . . . . 15·00 5·00

1936.* 500th Anniv of St. Brigitte Abbey.
126 **46** 5s. green 60 40
127 – 10s. blue 60 50
128 – 15s. red . . . . 1·75 4·00
129 – 25s. blue . . . . 2·00 5·50
DESIGNS: 10s. Ruins of the Abbey; 15s. Ruined facade; 25s. Old seal.

47 Paide

48 Paldiski (Port Baltic)

1937.* Social Relief Fund. Inscr "CARITAS 1937".
130 **47** 10s.+10s. green . . . . . 3·00 5·00
131 – 15s.+15s. red . . . . . . 3·00 6·00
132 – 25s.+25s. blue . . . . . . 5·50 10·00
133 – 50s.+50s. purple . . . . . 10·00 22·00
DESIGNS—Arms of: Rakvere (15s.); Valga (25s.); Viljandi (50s.).

1938.* Social Relief Fund. Inscr "CARITAS 1938".
134 **48** 10s.+10s. brown . . . . . 3·00 5·00
135 – 15s.+15s. grn & red . . . 3·00 6·00
136 – 25s.+25s. red & blue . . . 4·25 12·00
137 – 50s.+50s. yell & blue . . . 14·00 30·00
MS138 106 × 150 mm. Nos. 134/7 32·00 60·00
DESIGNS: Arms of: Voru (15s.); Haapsalu (25s.); Kuresaare (50s.).

49 Cargo Liner "Aegna" in Tallinn Harbour

1938.
139 **49** 2k. blue . . . . 1·25 5·00

50 Dr. F. R. Faehlmann

51 Arms of Viljandi

1938. Centenary of Estonian Literary Society. Designs showing Society founders.
140 **50** 5s. green 30 40
141 – 10s. brown 55 50
142 – 15s. red . . . . 1·00 5·00
143 **50** 25s. blue . . . . 1·75 7·50
MS143a 90 × 40 mm. Nos. 140/3 12·00 55·00
DESIGN: 10s., 15s. Dr. F. R. Kreutzwald.

1939.* Social Relief Fund. Inscr "CARITAS 1939".
144 **51** 10s.+10s. green . . . . . 3·25 4·50
145 – 15s.+15s. red (Parnu) . . . 3·25 5·00
146 – 25s.+25s. blue (Tartu) . . 7·50 12·00
147 – 50s.+50s. pur (Harju) . . . 12·50 30·00
MS147a 90 × 137 mm. Nos. 144/7 45·00 90·00

52 Sanatorium, Parnu

53 Laanemaa

1939. Centenary of Parnu.
148 **52** 5s. green . . . . 1·00 50
149 – 10s. violet 75 50
150 **52** 18s. red . . . . 2·00 5·00
151 – 30s. blue . . . . 2·75 6·00
MS151a 137 × 90 mm. Nos. 148/51 20·00 65·00
DESIGN—10s., 30s. Beach Hotel, Parnu.

1940. Social Relief Fund. Arms. Inscr "CARITAS 1940".
152 – 10s.+10s. green and blue (Vorumaa) . . . . . . 3·00 5·00
153 – 15s.+15s. red and blue (Jarvemaa) . . . . . . 3·00 7·50
154 **53** 25s.+25s. blue and red . . 3·50 14·00
155 – 50s.+50s. orange and blue (Saaremaa) . . . . . . 7·50 20·00

54 Carrier Pigeon and Airplane

55 State Arms

1940. Cent of 1st Adhesive Postage Stamps.
156 **54** 3s. orange 30 45
157 10s. violet 30 15
158 15s. brown 30 15
159 30s. blue . . . . 1·90 1·25

1991.
161 **55** 5k. red and orange 10 10
162 10k. green & emerald . . . 10 10
163 15k. blue and light blue . . 10 10
164 30k. black and grey . . . 20 15
165 50k. brown and orange . . 30 20
166 70k. purple and mauve . . 40 20
167 90k. magenta & mauve . . 50 30
168 1r. brown (21 × 27 mm) . . 60 40
169 2r. blue (21 × 27 mm) . . . 1·25 60
See also Nos. 194/205.

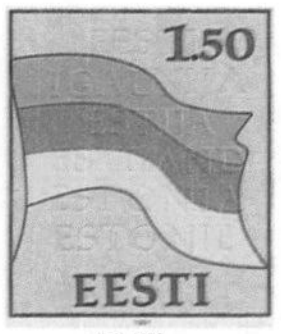
56 Flag

57 State Arms

1991.
170 **56** 1r.50 multicoloured 75 75
171 – 2r.50 black, grey & green 1·40 1·40
DESIGN—HORIZ: 2r.50, Map of Europe showing Estonia.

1992. Value expressed by letter.
172 **57** E (1r.) green and yellow . . 10 10
173 R (10r.) red and pink . . . 25 15
174 I (20r.) green & blue . . . 50 30
175 A (40r.) blue & lt blue . . 1·10 70
See also Nos. 179/81 and 182/4.

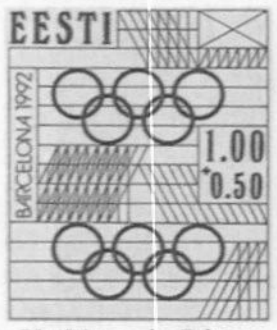

58 Olympic Rings and Pattern

59 Osprey ("Pandion haliaetus")

1992. Olympic Games, Barcelona.
176 **58** 1k.+50s. red 20 20
177 – 3k.+1k.50 green 60 60
178 – 5k.+2k.50 black & blue . . 1·25 1·25
DESIGNS: 3k. Olympic rings and pattern (different); 5k. Estonian flag, rings and pattern.

1992. As Nos. 172 and 174/5 but colours changed.
179 **57** E (10s.) orange & yellow 10 10
180 I (1k.) green 20 20
181 A (2k.) blue 30 30

1992. Value expressed by letter. Size 21 × 27 mm.
182 **57** X (10s.) brown 20 10
183 X (10s.) green 20 10
184 X (10s.) black 20 10

1992. Birds of the Baltic.
185 **59** 1k. black and red 65 65
186 – 1k. brown, black & red . . 65 65
187 – 1k. sepia, brown & red . . 65 65
188 – 1k. brown, black & red . . 65 65
DESIGNS: No. 186, Black-tailed godwit ("Limosa limosa"); 187, Goosander ("Mergus merganser"); 188, Common shelducks ("Tadorna tadorna").

1992. Value expressed by letter. Size 21 × 27 mm.
189 **57** Z (30s.) mauve 20 10
190 Z (30s.) red 20 10
191 Z (30s.) black 20 10

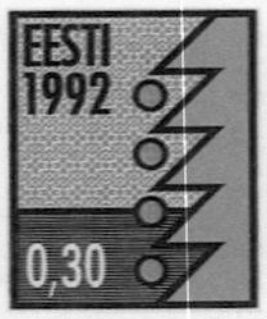

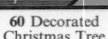

60 Decorated Christmas Tree

61 Birds, Flowers and Envelope within Heart

1992. Christmas.
192 **60** 30s. multicoloured 10 10
193 2k. multicoloured 15 15

1993. As Nos. 161/9 but face values in senti.
194 **55** 10s. grey and blue (18 × 21 mm) 10 10
194a 10s. brown and blue (18 × 21 mm) 10 10
195 20s. black and green (21 × 27 mm) 10 10
196 30s. purple and grey (21 × 27 mm) 10 10
197 50s. blue and brown (18 × 21 mm) 10 10
198 60s. green and purple (18 × 21 mm) 10 10
209 60s. brn (21 × 27 mm) . . . 10 10
199 80s. blue and mauve (21 × 27 mm) 15 10
200 2k.50 turquoise and green (18 × 21 mm) 20 10
201 3k.10 red and violet . . . 25 10
202 3k.30 lilac and violet (18 × 21 mm) 30 15
203 3k.60 blue & cobalt . . . 35 15
203a 3k.60 violet and blue (18 × 21 mm) 30 15
204 4k.50 brown & lt brn . . . 40 20
205 5k. mauve and brown (23 × 28 mm) 40 20
205a 5k. mauve and yellow (23 × 28 mm) 40 20
206 10k. green and blue (23 × 28 mm) 85 45
207 20k. green and lilac (23 × 28 mm) . . . . . 1·75 1·00

1993. Friendship.
210 **61** 1k. multicoloured 15 10

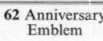

62 Anniversary Emblem

64 Wrestling

1993. 75th Anniv of Republic.
211 **62** 60s. multicoloured 10 10
212 1k. multicoloured 15 10
213 2k. multicoloured 30 15

1993. No. 163 surch **0.60.**
214 **55** 60s. on 15k. blue & lt blue 10 10

1993. Baltic Sea Games. Multicoloured.
215 60s. Type **64** 10 10
216 1k.+25s. Ship with map of Baltic on sail and colours of participating countries as shields 25 10
217 2k. Athlete putting the rock and sports pictograms . . 30 20

65 Toompea Castle, Tallinn

66 1918 5k. Stamp and Anniversary Emblem

1993.
218 – 1k. black and brown . . 10 10
219 **65** 2k. brown & lt brown . . 15 10
219a – 2k.50 deep lilac and lilac 25 15
219b – 2k.50 grey 20 15
220 – 2k.70 blue and cobalt . . 25 15
221 – 2k.90 dp green & green . . 25 15
222 – 3k. brown and pink . . . 25 15
222a – 3k.20 dp green & green . . 25 15
223 – 4k. violet and lilac . . . 35 20
224 – 4k.80 brown and pink . . 40 20
DESIGNS—HORIZ: 1k. Toolse Castle; 2k.70, Hermann's Castle, Narva; 2k.90, Haapsalu Castle; 3k.20, Rakvere Castle; 4k. Kuressaare Castle; 4k.80, Viljandi Castle. VERT: 2k.50 (219a), Paide Castle; 2k.50 (219b), Purtse Castle; 3k. Kiiu Castle.

1993. 75th Anniv of First Estonian Stamps.
225 **66** 1k. multicoloured 15 10
MS226 74 × 91 mm. 4k. Type **66** against enlarged background of posthorn blower (sold at 5k.) 1·75 1·75

1993. "Mare Balticum" Stamp Exhibition. No. **MS**226 optd **FILATEELIANAITUS MARE BALTICUM '93 24. – 28. NOVEMBER 1993.**
MS227 **66** 4k. multicoloured . . 3·25 3·25

68 Haapsalu Church

69 Lydia Koidula

1993. Christmas.
228 **68** 80s. red 10 10
229 – 2k. blue 25 15
DESIGN—VERT: 2k. Tallinn church.

1993. 150th Birth Anniv of Lydia Koidula (writer).
230 **69** 1k. multicoloured 10 10

70 Ski Jumping

71 Tartu 1869 Emblem

1994. Winter Olympic Games, Lillehammer, Norway. Multicoloured.
231 1k.+25s. Type **70** 20 15
232 2k. Speed skating 30 20

1994. 125th Song Festival. Multicoloured.
233 **71** 1k.+25s. yell, brn & grn . . 20 15
234 – 2k. brown and blue 30 20
235 – 3k. bistre, brown and stone 45 30
MS236 120 × 95 mm. 15k. multicoloured . . . . 2·50 2·50
DESIGNS: 2k. Tallinn 1923 emblem; 3k. Tallinn 1969 emblem; 15k. 1994 emblem.

72 Squirrel

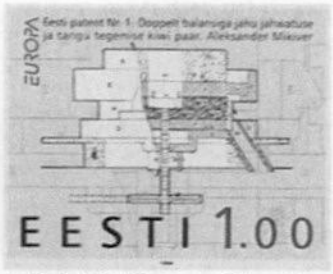

73 Mill (Patent No. 1. Aleksander Mikiver)

1994. The Siberian Flying Squirrel. Mult.
237 1k. Type **72** 15 10
238 2k. Squirrel on broad-leafed branch 30 20
239 3k. Squirrel on pine branch 45 30
240 4k. Squirrel with young . . . 65 40

1994. Europa. Inventions. Multicoloured.
241 1k. Type **73** 15 10
242 2k.70 "Minox" mini camera (Patent No. 2628, Walter Zapp) 35 20

74 Mustjala Woman

75 Kadriorg Palace

1994. Costumes (1st series). Multicoloured.
243 1k. Type **74** 15 10
244 1k. Jamaja couple 15 10
See also Nos. 254/5, 274/5, 298/9, 316/17, 340/1, 377/8 and 411/12.

1994. 75th Anniv of Estonian Art Museum, Tallinn.
245 **75** 1k.70 multicoloured . . . 30 15

76 "The Holy Family" (Lichtenstein Master)

77 Ruhnu Church

1994. International Year of the Family.
246 **76** 1k.70 multicoloured . . . 30 15

1994. Christmas.
247 **77** 1k.20 brown 20 10
248 – 2k.50 green 40 25
DESIGN—HORIZ: 2k.50, Urvaste Church.

1994. Victims of the "Estonia" Ferry Disaster Fund. No. 248 surch **+20 kr 28. 09. 1994 59°23' POHJALAIUST 21°42' IDAPIKKUST "ESTONIA" laevahuku ohvrite fondi.**
249 2k.50+20k. green . . . . . . 3·00 2·50

79 Gustav II Adolphus

80 Barnacle Geese

1994. 400th Birth Anniv of King Gustav II Adolphus of Sweden.
250 **79** 2k.50 purple 35 20

1995. Matsalu Wetland Reserve. Mult.
251 1k.70 Type **80** 25 25
252 3k.20 Greylag geese 50 50

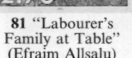

81 "Labourer's Family at Table" (Efraim Allsalu)

82 Beach Hotel, Parnu (Estonia)

1995. 50th Anniv of F.A.O.
253 **81** 2k.70 multicoloured . . . 35 20

1995. Costumes (2nd series). As T **74**. Mult.
254 1k.70 Muhu couple 25 15
255 1k.70 Muhu women 25 15

1995. Via Baltica Motorway Project. Multicoloured.
256 1k.70 Type **82** 20 15
MS257 99 × 109 mm. 3k.20 Type **82**; 3k.20 Bauska Castle (Latvia); 3k.20 Kaunas (Lithuania) . . . 1·50 1·50

83 Broken Barbed Wire

84 U.N. Emblem and Landscape

1995. Europa. Peace and Freedom.
258 **83** 2k.70 brown and mauve . . 35 30

1995. 50th Anniv of U.N.O.
259 **84** 4k. multicoloured 55 45

85 Lighthouse and Chart

86 Vanemuine Theatre

1995. Pakri Lighthouse.
260 **85** 1k.70 multicoloured . . . 25 15

1995. 125th Anniv of Vanemuine Theatre.
261 **86** 1k.70 orange, black & grn 25 15

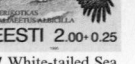

87 White-tailed Sea Eagle

88 Pasteur and Bacteria

1995. "Keep the Estonian Sea Clean".
262 **87** 2k.+25s. black and blue . . 30 30

1995. Death Cent of Louis Pasteur (chemist).
263 **88** 2k.70 multicoloured . . . 30 30

89 Bronze Bear Amulet (Samoyedic group)

90 Kunileid and Music

1995. Finno-Ugric Peoples. Multicoloured.
264 2k.50 Shaman's drum (Saami group) 30 15
265 2k.50 Karelian writing (Baltic-Finnic group) . . . 30 15
266 3k.50 Duck brooch of Kama area (Volga group) 40 20
267 3k.50 Type **89** 40 20
268 4k.50 Duck-feet pendant (Permic group) 55 25
269 4k.50 Khanty band ornament (Ugric group) 55 25

1995. 150th Birth Anniv of Aleksandr Kunileid (composer).
270 **90** 2k. blue 20 15

91 St. Martin's Church, Turi

92 "Lembit" (submarine)

1995. Christmas.
271 **91** 2k. yellow 20 15
272 – 3k.50 red 40 20
DESIGN: 3k.50, Charles's Church, Tallinn.

1996. 60th Anniv of "Lembit".
273 **92** 2k.50 multicoloured . . . 25 15

1996. Costumes (3rd series). As T **74**. Mult.
274 2k.50 Emmaste mother and bride 25 15
275 2k.50 Reigi women 25 15

93 1896 Gold Medal

1996. Centenary of Modern Olympic Games and Olympic Games, Atlanta. Sheet 110 × 66 mm containing T **93** and similar vert designs. Mult.
MS276 2k.50 Type **93**; 3k.50 Alfred Neuland (weightlifter and first Estonian gold medal winner, 1920); 4k. Cycling . . . . . . 1·00 1·00

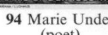

94 Marie Under (poet)

95 Marconi and Wireless Telegraph

1996. Europa. Famous Women.
277 **94** 2k.50 multicoloured . . . 25 15

1996. Centenary of Guglielmo Marconi's Patented Wireless Telegraph.
278 **95** 3k.50 multicoloured . . . 50 25

96 "Suur Toll"

97 Lighthouse and Chart

1996. 82nd Anniv of "Suur Toll" (ice-breaker).
279 **96** 2k.50 multicoloured . . . 30 15

1996. 125th Anniv of Vaindloo Lighthouse.
280 **97** 2k.50 multicoloured . . . 25 15

98 Class Gk Steam Locomotive

99 Elf and Mother and Child

1996. Cent of Narrow-gauge Railway. Mult.
281 3k.20 Type **98** 60 20
282 3k.50 Class DeM diesel railcar 65 25
283 4k.50 Class Sk steam locomotive 75 30

1996. Christmas (1st issue).
284 **99** 2k.50 multicoloured . . . 25 15

100 Harju-Madise Church

101 Map and Lighthouse

1996. Christmas (2nd issue).
285 **100** 3k.30 blue 30 20
286 – 4k.50 purple 50 30
DESIGNS: 4k.50, Church of the Holy Spirit, Tallinn.

1997. 120th Anniv of Ruhnu Lighthouse.
287 **101** 3k.30 multicoloured . . . 30 15

102 Steller's Sea Eagle

103 Von Stephan (after Anton Weber)

1997. Captive Breeding Programmes at Tallinn Zoo. Multicoloured.
288 3k.30 Type **102** 50 20
289 3k.30 European mink 30 20
290 3k.30 Cinereous vulture . . . 50 20
291 3k.30 Amur leopard 30 20
292 3k.30 Black rhinoceros . . . 30 20
293 3k.30 East Caucasian tur . . 30 20

1997. Death Cent of Heinrich von Stephan (founder of Universal Postal Union).
294 **103** 7k. gold and black . . . 60 30

104 Goldspinner

105 Maasilinn Ship

1997. Europa. Tales and Legends. "The Goldspinners".
295 **104** 4k.80 multicoloured . . . 40 20

1997. Baltic Sailing Ships.
296 **105** 3k.30 multicoloured . . . 50 20

1997. Costumes (4th series). Folk Costumes of Swedish Communities in Estonia. As T **74**. Multicoloured.
298 3k.30 Couple, Ruhnu Island 25 15
299 3k.30 Family, Vormsi Island 25 15

106 1 Kroon Coin

107 "Tormilind"

1997.
299a **106** 10k. silver, black & red 80 40
300 25k. silver, black & grn 2·10 1·10
301 50k. silver, black & grn 4·50 2·50
302 100k. gold, black & blue 8·50 4·25

1997. 75th Anniv of Completion of "Tormilind" (barquentine).
305 **107** 5k.50 multicoloured . . . 60 30

108 "Stone Bridge, Tartu" (Tiina Tarve)

1997.
306 **108** 3k.30 multicoloured . . . 30 15

109 Title Page

110 St. Anne's Church, Halliste

1997. 311th Anniv of Publication of "Wastne Testament" (first translation, by Andreas Verginius, into South Estonian dialect of New Testament).
307 **109** 3k.50 black, ochre & bl 30 15

1997.
308 **110** 3k.30 brown 30 15

111 Dwarves

112 Cross-country Skier

1997. Christmas.
309 **111** 2k.90 multicoloured . . . 30 15

1998. Winter Olympic Games, Nagano, Japan.
310 **112** 3k.60 multicoloured . . . 30 15

113 Arms

114 "Porgu", 1932

1998. 80th Anniv of 1918 Declaration of Independence. Sheet 68 × 58 mm. Imperf.
MS311 **113** 7k. multicoloured . . 60 60

1998. Birth Centenary of Eduard Wiiralt (artist). Sheet 79 × 94 mm containing T **114** and similar vert designs. Each black.
MS312 3k.60 Type **114**; 3k.60 "Porgu", 1930; 5k.50 "Enfer", 1932 . . . . 1·50 1·50

115 Chart and Lighthouse

116 Players

1998. 99th Anniv of Kunda Lighthouse.
313 **115** 3k.60 multicoloured . . . 30 15

1998. World Cup Football Championship, France.
314 **116** 7k. black, red and violet 65 30

117 St. John's Eve Bonfire

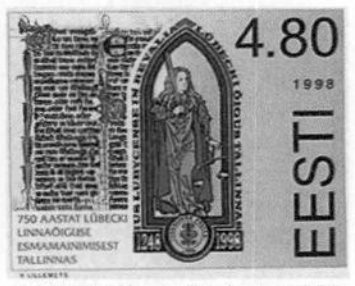

118 Tallinn Codex, 1282

1998. Europa. National Festivals.
315 **117** 5k.20 multicoloured . . . 45 25

1998. 750th Anniv of Adoption by Tallinn of Lubeck Law in Charter by King Erik IV of Denmark.
316 **118** 4k.80 multicoloured . . . 40 40

119 Barn Swallow over House

120 Yacht

1998. Beautiful Homes Year.
317 **119** 3k.60 multicoloured . . . 30 15

1998. World 470 Class Junior Yachting Championships, Tallinn Bay.
318 **120** 5k.50 dp blue, bl & red 45 25

1998. Costumes (5th series). As T **74**. Mult.
319 3k.60 Couple, Kihnu Island 30 15
320 3k.60 Family, Kihnu Island 30 15

121 "The Bottle Genie" (illustrated by Eduard Jarv)

122 Siberian Tiger

1998. 50th Death Anniv of Juhan Jaik (children's writer).
321 **121** 3k.60 yellow, blue & blk 30 15

1998. Tallinn Zoo.
322 **122** 3k.60 multicoloured . . . 30 15

123 1923 9m. Stamp

124 Freedom Cross

1998. 80th Anniv of Estonian Post.
323 **123** 3k.60 red, orange & blk 30 15

1998. Estonian–Finnish Friendship.
324 **124** 4k.50 multicoloured . . . 40 20

125 Father Christmas and Boy

126 Faehlmann

1998. Christmas. Multicoloured.
325 3k.10 Type **125** 25 15
326 5k. Angels and Christmas tree 40 20

1998. Birth Bicentenary of Friedrich Robert Faehlmann (writer and founder of Learned Estonian Society).
327 **126** 3k.60 multicoloured . . . 30 15

127 Chart and Lighthouse

128 Snow Leopards

1999. 190th Anniv of Vilsandi Lighthouse.
328 **127** 3k.60 multicoloured . . . 30 15

1999. Tallinn Zoo.
329 **128** 3k.60 multicoloured . . . 30 15

129 Emblem and Palais de l'Europe, Strasbourg

130 Meri

1999. 50th Anniv of Council of Europe.
330 **129** 5k.50 multicoloured . . . 45 25

1999. 70th Birth Anniv of President Lennart Meri.
331 **130** 3k.60 multicoloured . . . 30 15

131 Tolkuse Bog, Parnu

1999. Europa. Parks and Gardens.
332 **131** 5k.50 multicoloured . . . 45 25

132 Emblem and Bank Headquarters, Tallinn

1999. 80th Anniv of Bank of Estonia.
333 **132** 5k. multicoloured 40 20

133 Olustvere Hall

1999.
334 **133** 3k.60 multicoloured . . . 30 15

134 Band and Score

1999. 130th Anniv of National Anthem.
335 **134** 3k.60 multicoloured . . . 30 15

135 Observation Tower

136 Family and State Flag

1999. 60th Anniv of Observation Tower on Suur Munamagi (highest point in Baltics).
336 **135** 5k.20 multicoloured . . . 45 25

1999. 10th Anniv of Baltic Chain (human chain uniting the Capitals of Estonia, Latvia and Lithuania). Multicoloured.
337 3k.60 Type **136** 30 15
MS338 110 × 72 mm. 5k.50 Type **136** (28 × 38 mm); 5k.50 Family and Latvian flag (28 × 38 mm); 5k.50 Family and Lithuanian flag (28 × 38 mm) . . . . 1·40 1·40

137 U.P.U. Emblem

138 State Arms

1999. 125th Anniv of Universal Postal Union.
339 **137** 7k. multicoloured 80 40

1999. Costumes (6th series). Setu Costumes of South-east Estonia. As T **74**. Multicoloured.
340 3k.60 Bride and bridegroom 30 15
341 5k. Two young men 40 20

1999.

342	**138**	10s. red and pink	10	10
343		20s. brown and grey . .	10	10
344		30s. light blue and blue	10	10
346		1k. brown and pink . .	10	10
348		2k. black	15	10
352		3k.60 blue and turquoise	30	15
354		4k.40 deep green and green	35	20
355		5k. green and light green	40	20
355a		5k. deep green and green	45	20
356		6k. brown and yellow . .	45	25
357		6k.50 brown and yellow	50	25
359		8k. brown and pink . .	60	30

139 Santa's Helpers

1999. Christmas. Multicoloured.
360 3k.10 Type **139** 25 15
361 7k. Christmas tree (558th anniv of first public Christmas tree in Tallinn) (vert) 80 40

1999. New Year Lottery. As No. 360 but with additional premium and lottery numbers.
362 **139** 3k.10+1k.90 mult 40 20

140 Hands of Clock

141 Faces

1999. Year 2000.
363 **140** 5k.50 multicoloured . . . 45 20

2000. Population and Housing Census.
364 **141** 3k.60 multicoloured . . . 30 15

142 Signatures on Treaty

2000. 80th Anniv of Tartu Peace Treaty (between Estonia and Russia).
365 **142** 3k.60 multicoloured . . . 30 15

143 Ristna Lighthouse and Chart

2000. Lighthouses on Kopu Peninsula. Mult.
366 3k.60 Type **143** 30 15
367 3k.60 Kopu lighthouse and chart 30 15
Nos. 366/7 were issued together, se-tenant, forming a composite design.

144 State Arms and Emblem

145 Cornflower

2000. 10th Anniv of Estonian Congress.
368 **144** 3k.60 multicoloured . . . 25 15

2000. National Flower.
369 **145** 4k.80 multicoloured . . . 35 20

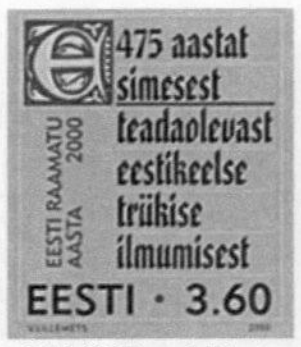
146 "E" and Text

147 Building Europe

2000. National Book Year. 475th Anniv of Publication of Lutheran Catechism (oldest known publication in Estonian).
370 **146** 3k.60 multicoloured . . . 25 15

2000. Europa.
371 **147** 4k.80 multicoloured . . . 35 20

148 Palmse Hall

2000.
372 **148** 3k.60 multicoloured . . . 25 15

149 Amur Long-tailed Goral

2000. Tallinn Zoo (1st series).
373 **149** 3k.60 multicoloured . . . 25 15
See also No. 409.

150 Locomotive

2000. Centenary of Viljandi–Tallinn Narrow Gauge Railway.
374 **150** 4k.50 multicoloured . . . 35 20

151 Hand-woven Girdle

152 Discus thrower

2000. 9th Finno–Ugric Congress, Tartu.
375 **151** 5k. multicoloured 35 20

2000. Olympic Games, Sydney.
376 **152** 8k. multicoloured 60 30

2000. Costumes (7th series). As T **74**. Mult.
377 4k.40 Family, Hargla 30 15
378 8k. Women, Polva 60 30

153 Malk

2000. Birth Centenary of August Malk (author).
379 **153** 4k.40 multicoloured . . . 60 30

154 European Smelt (*Osmerus eperlanus spirinchus*) and Vendace (*Coregonus albula*)

2000. Fish from Lake Peipsi. Multicoloured.
380 6k.50 Type **154** 50 25
381 6k.50 Zander (*Stizostedion lucioperca*) and whitefish (*Coregonus lavaretus manaenoides*) 50 25

155 Illustration and Emblem

2000. Centenary of National Bookplate. Sheet 80 × 58 mm containing T **155** and similar vert design. Multicoloured.
MS382 6k. Type **155**; 6k. Man ploughing and emblem 50 25

156 Horn with Ribbon

2000. Christmas. Multicoloured.
383 3k.60 Type **156** 30 15
384 6k. Tree decorations 50 25

157 Nool celebrating

2001. Olympic Games, Sydney. Erki Nool (decathlete, gold medallist).
385 **157** 4k.40 multicoloured . . . 35 20

158 Mohni Lighthouse, Lahemaa National Park, Cape Purekkari

159 Couple kissing

2001.
386 **158** 4k.40 multicoloured . . . 35 20

2001. St. Valentines Day.
387 **159** 4k.40 yellow, blue & red 35 20

160 Facade

2001. Inauguration (2000) of Stenbock House as Seat of Government and State Chancellery.
388 **160** 6k.50 multicoloured . . . 50 25

161 "Girl at the Spring" (detail)

2001. 175th Birth Anniv of Johann Koler (artist). Sheet 58 × 83 mm containing T **161** and similar horiz design. Multicoloured.
MS389 4k.40 Type **161**; 4k.40 "Eve of the Pomegranate" (detail) 70 35

162 Text and Emblem

2001. European Year of Languages.
390 **162** 4k.40 multicoloured . . . 35 20

163 Northern Lapwing

2001. Northern Lapwing (*Vanellus vanellus*).
391 **163** 4k.40 multicoloured . . . 35 20

164 Laupa Hall

2001.
392 **164** 4k.40 multicoloured . . . 35 20

165 Sluice, Lake Soodla

166 Emblem

2001. Europa. Water Resources.
393 **165** 6k.50 multicoloured . . . 50 25

2001. Cent of Kalev (Estonian Sports Association).
394 **166** 6k.50 multicoloured . . . 50 25

167 Mud Baths Main Building

2001. 750th Anniv of Parnu.
395 **167** 4k.40 multicoloured . . . 35 20

168 Pockus beside Lake

169 Barn Swallow

2001. *Pokuland* (children's book by Edgar Valter). Multicoloured.
396 3k.60 Type **168** 30 15
397 3k.60 Pocku and owl 30 15
398 3k.60 Pocku and stork . . . 30 15
399 3k.60 Pocku on branch and bird in nest 30 15
400 4k.40 Two Pockus on fence 35 20
401 4k.40 Pocku smelling flower 35 20
402 4k.40 Pocku hugging dog . . 35 20
403 4k.40 Pocku watching moon 35 20

2001. 10th Anniv of Independence.
404 **169** 4k.40 multicoloured . . . 35 20

170 Virgin and Child (wooden altarpiece)

171 1991 5k. State Arms Stamp

2001. 800th Anniv of St. Mary's Land (conversion to Christianity of Estonia, Livonia and Courland).
405 **170** 6k.50 multicoloured . . . 50 25

2001. 10th Anniv of Re-adoption of Estonian Stamps.
406 **171** 4k.40 multicoloured . . . 35 20

172 Rocky Coastline, Lahemaa, Estonia

2001. Baltic Sea Coast. Multicoloured.
407 4k.40 Type **172** 40 20
MS408 125 × 60 mm. 6k. As Type **172** (36 × 30 mm); 6k. Beach, Vidzeme, Latvia (36 × 30 mm); 6k. Sand dunes, Palanga, Lithuania (36 × 30 mm) . . . . 1·60 80
Stamps in similar designs were issued by Latvia and Lithuania.

173 Chinese Alligator (*Alligator sinenesis*)

2001. Tallinn Zoo (2nd series).
409 **173** 4k.40 multicoloured . . . 40 20

174 Estonia 26-9 Racing Car

175 Snowflake

2001.
410 **174** 6k. multicoloured 55 30

2001. Costumes (8th series). As T **74**. Multicoloured.
411 4k.40 Woman, Paistu 40 20
412 7k.50 Man, Tarvastu 70 35

2001. Christmas. Multicoloured.
413 3k.60 Type **175** 30 15
414 6k.50 Dove (horiz) 60 30

176 First Radio Station Building and Felix Moor (presenter)

2001. 75th Anniv of National Radio Broadcasting.
415 **176** 4k.40 multicoloured . . . 40 20

177 Skier

2002. Winter Olympic Games, Salt Lake City.
416 **177** 8k. multicoloured 70 35

178 Sangaste Hall

179 Laidunina Lighthouse, Saaremaa Island, Gulf of Riga

2002.
417 **178** 4k.40 multicoloured . . . 40 20

2002.
418 **179** 4k.40 multicoloured . . . 40 20

180 Eurasian Tree Sparrow (*Passer montanus*) and House Sparrow(*Passer domesticus*)

2002.
419 **180** 4k.40 multicoloured . . . 40 20

181 Apple Blossom

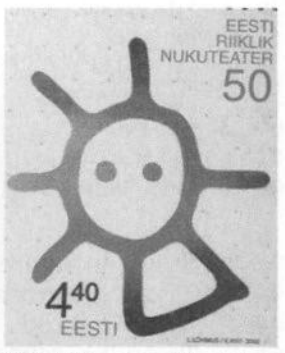

182 Theatre Emblem (E. Kivi)

2002.
420 **181** 4k.40 multicoloured . . . 40 20

2002. 50th Anniv Estonian Puppet Theatre, Tallinn.
421 **182** 4k.40 multicoloured . . . 40 20

183 PTO-4 Training Aircraft

2002.
422 **183** 6k. multicoloured 50 25

184 Andrus Veerpalu

2002. Andrus Veerpalu Nordic Skiing Olympic Gold Medallist.
423 **184** 4k.40 multicoloured . . . 40 20

185 University Building

2002. 370th Anniv of Tartu University. Bicentenary of Re-opening. Multicoloured.
424 4k.40 Type **185** 40 20
425 4k.40 Library building . . . 40 20

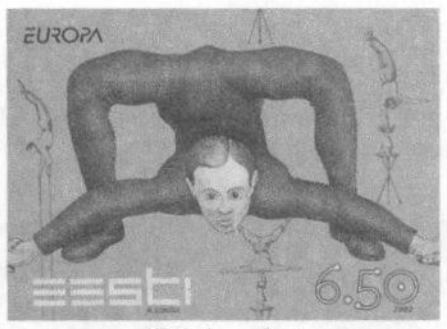

186 Acrobat

2002. Europa. Circus.
426 **186** 6k.50 multicoloured . . . 55 25

187 Emblem

188 Ancient Coin and Modern Arms

2002. 10th Anniv of New Constitution.
427 **187** 4k.40 ultramarine and blue 40 20

2002. 700th Anniv of Granting of Lubek Charter to Rakvere.
428 **188** 4k.40 multicoloured . . . 40 20

189 Lydia Koidula (poet)

2002. 10th Anniv of Re-introduction of the Kroon (currency). Sheet 53 × 76 mm containing T **189** and similar horiz design. Multicoloured.
MS429 4k.40 Type **189**; 4k.40 Carl Robert Jackson (writer) . . . 75 75

190 Top Left Quarter of Decorated Plate

2002. Birth Centenary of Adamson-Eric (artist). Sheet 86 × 75 mm containing T **190** and similar horiz designs. Multicoloured.
MS430 4k.40 Type **190**; 4k.40 Top right; 4k.40 Bottom left; 4k.40 Bottom right . . . . 1·50 1·50
The stamps in No. **MS**430 form a composite design of a decorated plate.

191 Wild Boar (*Sus scofa*)

2002.
431 **191** 4k.40 multicoloured . . . 40 20

192 Limestone Cliff, Cape Pakri

2002. Limestone (National Stone).
432 **192** 4k.40 multicoloured . . . 40 20

193 Women, Kolga-Jaani Region

194 Lamb wearing Ribbon

2002. Folk Costumes. Multicoloured.
433 4k.40 Type **193** 40 20
434 5k.50 Couple dancing, Suure-Janni region 45 20

2002. Christmas. Multicoloured.
435 3k.60 Type **194** 30 15
436 6k.50 Tree covered in snow (vert) 55 25

195 Keri Lighthouse, Prangli Island, Gulf of Riga

2003.
437 **195** 4k.40 multicoloured . . . 40 20

196 Anton Tammsaare (sculpture, Jaak Soans and Rein Luup)

2003. 125th Birth Anniv of Anton Hansen Tammsaare (writer).
438 **196** 4k.40 multicoloured . . . 40 20

197 Magpie (*Pica pica*)

2003.
439 **197** 4k.40 multicoloured . . . 40 20

198 Tulips (*Tulipa*)

199 Alatskivi Hall

2003. Flowers. Sheet 130 × 67 mm containing T **198** and similar vert designs. Multicoloured.
MS440 4k.40 × 4, Type **198**; Hellebore (*Helleborus purpurascens*); Pheasant's eye daffodil (*Narcissus poeticus*) (inscr "Nartcissus"); Crocus (*Crocus vernus*) . . . . 1·60 1·60

2003.
441 **199** 4k.40 multicoloured . . . 40 20

200 President Ruutel

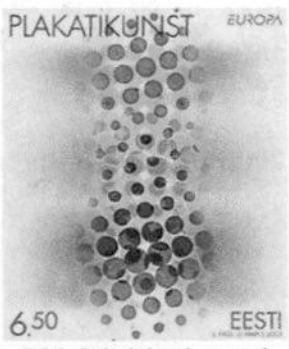

201 Multicoloured Printing Raster

2003. 75th Birth Anniv of Arnold Ruutel, President of Estonia.
442 **200** 4k.40 multicoloured . . . 40 20

2003. Europa. Poster Art.
443 **201** 6k.50 multicoloured . . . 55 25

202 Globe Flower (*Trollius ledebourii*)

2003. Bicentenary of Tartu University Botanic Garden.
444 **202** 4k.40 multicoloured . . . 40 20

203 Championship Emblem

2003. 14th World Under 21 Orienteering Championship, Polva.
445 **203** 7k.50 multicoloured . . . 65 30

204 Adam von Krusenstern and *Neva* and *Nadezhda*

2003. Bicentenary of Adam Johann von Krusenstern's Circumnavigation of the World.
446 **204** 8k. multicoloured 70 35

205 Ringed Seal (*Phoca hispida*)

2003.
447 **205** 4k.40 multicoloured . . . 40 20

206 *Vostok* and Fabian von Bellingshausen

2003. 225th Birth Anniv of Fabian Gottlieb von Bellingshausen (explorer).
448 **206** 8k. blue, sepia and ochre 70 35

207 Danish Coin and "Arrival of Scandinavian Seamen" (detail)

2003. Ancient Trade Route along Gulf of Finland and Dnieper River, Ukraine. Multicoloured.
449 6k.50 Type **207** 55 25
450 6k.50 11th-century silver coin and Viking ship 55 25

2003. Folk Costumes. As T **193**. Multicoloured.
451 4k.40 Aksi women, Tartu . . 40 20
452 5k.50 Family, Otepää region 45 20

208 Great Tit holding Rose

209 "Voyage to the End of the World" (book illustration, Kristjan Raud)

2003. Christmas. Multicoloured.
453 3k.60 Type **208** 30 15
454 6k. Mary and Jesus (stained glass) 50 25

2003. Birth Bicentenary of Friedrich Reinhold Kreutzwald (writer). Sheet 100 × 73 mm containing T **209** and similar vert design.
MS455 4k.40 blue and black; 6k.50 multicoloured 95 95
DESIGNS: Type **209**; 6k.50 Friedrich Reinhold Kreutzwald.

210 Lighthouse, Sorgu Island, Gulf of Riga

2004. Centenary of Sorgu Lighthouse.
456 **210** 4k.40 multicoloured . . . 40 20

211 Wolf (*Canis lupus*)

2004.
457 **211** 4k.40 multicoloured . . . 40 20

212 Map and Wheel

213 Violet (*Viola riviniana*)

2004. 150th Anniv of *Hioma* (Estonian barque) Voyage around Cape Horn.
458 **212** 8k. multicoloured 70 35

2004. Flowers. Sheet 130 × 66 mm containing T **213** and similar vert designs. Multicoloured.
MS459 4k.40 × 4, Type **213**; Wood anemone (*Anemone nemorosa*); Hepatica nobilis; Globeflower (*Trollius europaeus*) . . . . . 1·50 1·50

214 Adult and Chicks

2004. Endangered Species. White Stork (*Ciconia ciconia*).
460 **214** 4k.40 multicoloured . . . 40 20

ETHIOPIA Pt. 12

Formerly called Abyssinia. An ancient empire on the E. coast of Africa. From 1936 to 1941, part of Italian East Africa. Federated with Ethiopia from 1952 to 1993. In 1974 Emperor Haile Selassie was deposed and a republic proclaimed.

1894. and 1907. 16 guerche = 1 Maria Theresa-Thaler.
1905. 100 centimes = 1 franc.
1908. 16 piastres = 1 thaler.
1928. 16 mehaleks = 1 thaler.
1936. 100 centimes = 1 thaler.
1936. 100 centesimi = 1 lira.
1946. 100 cents = 1 Ethiopian dollar.
1976. 100 cents = 1 birr.

INDEPENDENT EMPIRE

1 Menelik II

2 Lion of the Tribe of Judah

1894.
1 **1** ¼g. green . . . . 3·25 5·00
2 ½g. red . . . . 1·90 3·75
3 1g. blue . . . . 1·90 3·75
4 2g. brown . . . . 1·90 5·00
5 **2** 4g. red . . . . 1·90 5·00
6 8g. mauve . . . . 1·90 5·00
7 16g. black . . . . 2·75 5·00

1901. Optd **Ethiopie**.
15 **1** ¼g. green . . . . 9·25 9·25
16 ½g. red . . . . 9·25 9·25
17 1g. blue . . . . 10·00 10·00
18 2g. brown . . . . 10·00 10·00
19 **2** 4g. red . . . . 10·00 10·00
20 8g. mauve . . . . 13·50 13·50
21 16g. black . . . . 18·00 18·00

ቡስጣ። (4)   መልክት። (5)

1902. Optd with T **4**.
22 **1** ¼g. green . . . . 5·25 5·25
23 ½g. red . . . . 5·25 5·25
24 1g. blue . . . . 7·25 7·25
25 2g. brown . . . . 7·25 7·25
26 **2** 4g. red . . . . 11·50 11·50
27 8g. mauve . . . . 15·00 15·00
28 16g. black . . . . 30·00 30·00

1903. Optd with T **5**.
29 **1** ¼g. green . . . . 4·50 4·50
30 ½g. red . . . . 4·50 4·50
31 1g. blue . . . . 7·00 7·00
32 2g. brown . . . . 8·25 8·25
33 **2** 4g. red . . . . 8·25 8·25
34 8g. mauve . . . . 20·00 20·00
35 16g. black . . . . 28·00 28·00

ምልክት (6)   ምኒልክ (10)

1904. Optd with T **6**.
36 **1** ¼g. green . . . . 8·25 8·25
37 ½g. red . . . . 10·00 10·00
38 1g. blue . . . . 13·50 13·50
39 2g. brown . . . . 15·00 15·00
40 **2** 4g. red . . . . 17·00 17·00
41 8g. mauve . . . . 32·00 32·00
42 16g. black . . . . 50·00 50·00

1905. Surch in figures.
43 **1** 05 on ¼g. green . . . . . . 6·00 6·00
44 10 on ½g. red . . . . 6·00 6·00
45 20 on 1g. blue . . . . 6·00 6·00
46 40 on 2g. brown . . . . . . 7·75 8·00
47 **2** 80 on 4g. red . . . . 13·50 13·50
48 1.60 on 8g. mauve . . . . . 12·00 17·00
49 3.20 on 16g. black . . . . . 24·00 24·00
The above surcharge was also applied to some stamps optd with **Ethiopie** and Types **4**, **5** and **6**.

1905. Surch in figures and words.
90 **2** 5c. on 16g. blk (No. 28) . . . 85·00 £100

1905. No. 2 divided diagonally and surch **5c/m**.
86 **1** 5c. on half of ½g. red . . . . 4·25 4·25

1905. Surch **5c/m.**
71 **1** 5c. on ½g. grn (No. 22) . . . 10·00 11·50

1906. Optd with T **10** and surch in figures.
94 **1** 05 on ¼g. green . . . . . . 5·25 5·25
95 10 on ½g. red . . . . 7·00 7·00
96 20 on 1g. blue . . . . 7·00 7·00
97 40 on 2g. brown . . . . . . 7·00 7·00
98 **2** 80 on 4g. red . . . . 8·75 8·75
99 1.60 on 8g. mauve . . . . . 12·00 12·00
100 3.20 on 16g. black . . . . . 32·00 32·00

1906. Surch with figures and Amharic characters.
101 **1** 05 on ¼g. green . . . . . . 5·75 5·75
102 10 on ½g. red . . . . 7·00 7·00
103 20 on 1g. blue . . . . 9·75 9·75
104 40 on 2g. brown . . . . . . 9·75 9·75
105 **2** 80 on 4g. red . . . . 13·50 13·50
106 1.60 on 8g. mauve . . . . . 13·50 13·50
107 3.20 on 16g. black . . . . . 32·00 32·00

ዳግማዊ። (13)

1907. Optd with T **13** and surch in figures between stars.
115 **1** ¼ on ¼g. green . . . . . . 6·00 6·00
116 ½ on ½g. red . . . . 6·00 6·00
117 1 on 1g. blue . . . . 7·25 7·25
118 2 on 2g. brown . . . . . . 8·75 8·75
119 **2** 4 on 4g. red . . . . 8·75 8·75
120 8 on 8g. mauve . . . . . . 18·00 18·00
121 16 on 16g. black . . . . . . 25·00 25·00

1908. Entry into U.P.U. Nos. 1/7 surch in figures and words.
133 **1** ¼pi. on ¼g. green . . . . . 2·10 2·10
134 ½pi. on ½g. red . . . . . . 2·10 2·10
129 1pi. on ½g. red . . . . . . 7·75 7·75
135 1pi. on 1g. blue . . . . . . 2·75 2·75
136 2pi. on 2g. brown . . . . . 4·75 4·75
137 **2** 4pi. on 4g. red . . . . . . 6·75 6·75
138 8pi on 8g. mauve . . . . . 13·50 13·50
139 16pi. on 16g. black . . . . 18·00 18·00

19 Throne of Solomon

20 Emperor Menelik

1909.
147 **19** ¼g. green 85 85
148 ½g. red 85 65
149 1g. orange and green . . . 2·75 2·75
150 **20** 2g. blue . . . . 3·25 2·75
151 4g. red and green . . . . . 5·00 4·25
152 – 8g. grey and red . . . . . 8·25 5·75
153 – 16g. red . . . . 12·50 9·25
DESIGN: 8g., 16g. Another portrait.

1911. T 1 and 2 optd **AFF EXCEP FAUTE TIMB** and surch in manuscript.
154 **1** ¼g. on ¼g. green . . . . . £110 60·00
155 ½g. on ½g. red . . . . . . £110 60·00
156 1g. on 1g. blue . . . . . . £110 60·00
157 2g. on 2g. brown . . . . . £110 60·00
158 **2** 4g. on 4g. red . . . . . . £110 60·00
159 8g. on 8g. mauve . . . . . £110 60·00
160 16g. on 16g. black . . . . . £110 60·00

(22)

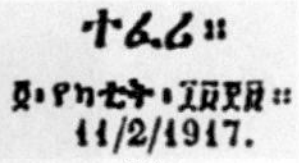

(24)

1917. Coronation. Optd with T **22** (and similar type).
161 **19** ¼g. green . . . . 4·25 5·00
162 ½g. red . . . . 4·25 5·00
163 **20** 2g. blue . . . . 5·00 6·00
164 4g. red and green . . . . . 8·25 8·25
165 – 8g. grey and red (No. 152) 15·00 15·00
166 – 16g. red (No. 153) . . . . . 23·00 25·00

1917. Optd with **T 24** (and similar type).
168 **19** ¼g. green 25 25
169 ½g. red 25 25
170 1g. orange and green . . . 2·10 2·10
171 **20** 2g. blue 70 70
174 4g. red and green . . . . . 1·40 1·40
175 – 8g. grey & red (No. 152) . 1·10 1·10
176 – 16g. red (No. 153) . . . . . 2·10 2·10

1917. Nos. 175/6 surch with large figure.
177 ¼ on 8g. grey and red . . . . 3·00 3·00
178 ½ on 8g. grey and red . . . . 3·00 3·00
179 1 on 16g. red . . . . 7·00 7·00
180 2 on 16g. red . . . . 7·00 7·00

28 Gerenuk

29 Ras Tafari, later Emperor Haile Selassie

30 African Buffalo

1919.
181 **28** ⅛g. brown and violet . . . 15 10
182 – ¼g. grey and green 15 10
183 – ½g. green and red 15 10
184 – 1g. black and purple . . . 10 10
185 **29** 2g. brown and blue 10 10
186 – 4g. orange and blue . . . 20 20
187 – 6g. orange and blue . . . 25 25
188 – 8g. black and olive 40 40
189 – 12g. grey and purple . . . 90 90
190 – $1 black and red . . . . . 1·40 1·10
191 **30** $2 brown and black . . . 3·25 3·00
192 – $3 red and green . . . . . 5·00 5·00
193 – $4 pink and brown . . . . 5·00 5·00
194 – $5 grey and red . . . . . 6·75 6·75
195 – $10 yellow and olive . . . 10·00 10·00
DESIGNS—VERT: As Type **28**: ¼g. Giraffes; ½g. Leopard. As Type **29**: 1g., 4g. Ras Tafari (different portraits); $4, $5, $10, Empress Zauditu (different portraits). HORIZ: As Type **30**: 6g. St. George's Cathedral, Addis Ababa; 8g. Black rhinoceros; 12g. Ostriches; $1, African elephant; $3, Lions.

1919. Stamps of 1919 variously surch.
197 **28** ½g. on ⅛g. brn & violet . . 50 50
207 – ½g. on 8g. blk & olive . . 1·00 80
202 – ½g. on $1 black and red 50 50
203 – ½g. on $5 grey and red . . 1·00 1·00
198 – 1g. on ¼g. grey & green 1·40 1·40
204 – 1g. on 6g. orge & blue . . 85 85
208 – 1g. on 12g. grey & pur . . 1·60 1·50
205 – 1g. on $3 red and green 90 90
206 – 1g. on $10 yell & olive . . 1·40 1·40
198c – 2g. on 1g. black & pur . . 50 50
199 – 2g. on $4 pink & brown 18·00 18·00
200 – 2½g. on ½g. grn & red . . 90 90
201 **29** 4g. on 2g. brn & blue . . 90 90
196 – 4g. on $4 pink & brown 1·40 1·40

39 Ras Tafari, later Emperor Haile Selassie

40 Empress Zauditu

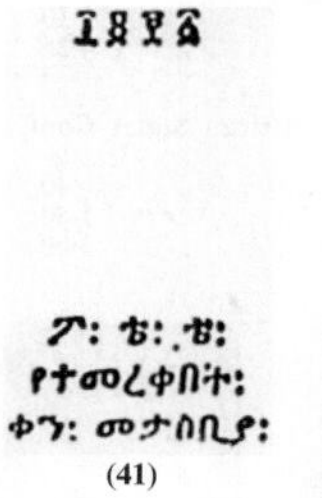

(41)

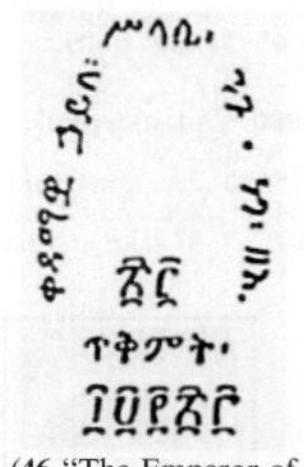

(46 "The Emperor of the Kings of Ethiopia, 2 Nov., 1930, Haile Selassie")

1928. Opening of P.O. at Addis Ababa. Optd with T **41**.
213 **39** ⅛m. blue and orange . . . 1·60 2·50
214 **40** ¼m. red and blue . . . . . 1·60 2·50
215 **39** ½m. black and green . . . 1·60 2·50
216 **40** 1m. black and red . . . . 1·60 2·50
217 **39** 2m. black and blue . . . . 1·60 2·50
218 **40** 4m. olive and yellow . . . 1·60 2·50
219 **39** 8m. olive and mauve . . . 1·60 2·40
220 **40** 1t. mauve and brown . . . 2·00 3·00
221 **39** 2t. brown and green . . . 2·75 4·25
222 **40** 3t. green and purple . . . 2·75 4·25

1928.
223 **39** ⅛m. blue and orange . . . 85 95
224 **40** ¼m. red and blue 50 85
225 **39** ½m. black and green . . . 95 1·10
226 **40** 1m. black and red 45 50
227 **39** 2m. black and blue 45 50
228 **40** 4m. olive and yellow . . . 45 50
229 **39** 8m. olive and mauve . . . 1·40 1·75
230 **40** 1t. mauve and brown . . . 1·75 2·10
231 **39** 2t. brown and green . . . 2·50 2·75
232 **40** 3t. green and purple . . . 3·25 4·25

1928. Elevation of Ras Tafari to Negus. Optd with crown, Amharic characters and **NEGOUS TEFERI**.
233 **39** ⅛m. blue and orange . . . 2·75 5·00
234 ½m. black and green . . . 2·75 5·00
235 2m. black and blue . . . . 2·75 6·75
236 8m. olive and mauve . . . 2·75 6·75
237 2t. brown and green . . . 2·75 6·75

1929. Air. Arrival of First Airplane of the Ethiopian Government. Optd with airplane and Amharic text (= "16 Aug 1929. Ethiopian Government Air Mail").
238 **39** ⅛m. blue and orange . . . 1·40 1·90
239 **40** ¼m. red and blue . . . . . 1·40 1·90
240 **39** ½m. black and green . . . 1·50 2·00
241 **40** 1m. black and red . . . . 1·50 2·00
242 **39** 2m. black and blue . . . . 1·50 2·00
243 **40** 4m. olive and yellow . . . 1·50 2·00
244 **39** 8m. olive and mauve . . . 1·50 2·00
245 **40** 1t. mauve and brown . . . 2·00 3·25
246 **39** 2t. brown and green . . . 3·25 4·25
247 **40** 3t. green and purple . . . 3·25 4·25

1930. Accession of Ras Taffari as Emperor Haile Selassie. Optd **HAYLE** (or **HAILE**) **SELASSIE 1er 3 Avril 1930** and Amharic text.
248 **39** ⅛m. blue and orange . . . 65 65
249 **40** ¼m. red and blue 65 65
250 **39** ½m. black and green . . . 65 65
261 **40** 1m. black and red 50 50
262 **39** 2m. black and blue 50 50
263 **40** 4m. olive and yellow . . . 1·00 1·00
264 **39** 8m. olive and mauve . . . 1·40 1·40
265 **40** 1t. mauve and brown . . . 2·40 2·40
266 **39** 2t. brown and green . . . 2·75 2·75
267 **40** 3t. green and purple . . . 4·25 4·25

1930. Coronation of Emperor Haile Selassie (1st issue). Optd with T **46**.
268 **39** ⅛m. blue and orange . . . 50 70
269 **40** ¼m. red and blue 50 70
270 **39** ½m. black and green . . . 50 70
271 **40** 1m. black and red 50 70
272 **39** 2m. black and blue 50 70
273 **40** 4m. olive and yellow . . . 50 70
274 **39** 8m. olive and mauve . . . 85 85
275 **40** 1t. mauve and brown . . . 1·40 1·40
276 **39** 2t. brown and green . . . 2·10 2·10
277 **40** 3t. green and purple . . . 3·25 3·25

47 The Ethiopian Lion and Symbols

1930. Coronation of Emperor Haile Selassie (2nd issue).
278 **47** 1g. orange 25 25
279 2g. blue 25 25
280 4g. purple 40 50
281 8g. green 40 55
282 1t. brown 50 65
283 3t. green . . . . 1·10 1·10
284 5t. brown . . . . 1·50 1·50

1931. Issue of 1928 surch in mehaleks.
285 **40** ⅛m. on 1m. black & red . . 45 85
286 **39** ⅛m. on 2m. black & blue 45 85
287 **40** ⅛m. on 4m. green & yell . . 45 85
288 ¼m. on 1m. black & red . . 45 85
289 **39** ¼m. on 2m. black & blue 1·00 1·40
290 **40** ¼m. on 4m. green & yell 1·00 1·40
291 ½m. on 1m. black & red . . 1·00 1·40
292 **39** ½m. on 2m. black & blue 1·00 1·40
293 **40** ½m. on 4m. green & yell 1·00 1·40
294 ½m. on 3t. green & purple 6·75 8·25
295 **39** 1m. on 2m. black & blue 1·40 1·60

49 Potez 25A2 over Map of Ethiopia

50 Ras Makonnen

1931. Air.
296 **49** 1g. red 30 50
297 2g. blue 30 50
298 4g. mauve 45 65
299 8g. green . . . . 1·00 1·10
300 1t. brown . . . . 1·60 1·60
301 2t. red . . . . 4·00 5·25
302 3t. green . . . . 6·00 7·25

1931.
303 **50** ⅛g. red 15 40
304 – ¼g. olive 65 55
305 **50** ½g. purple 45 45
306 – 1g. orange 45 45
307 – 2g. blue 45 45
308 – 4g. lilac . . . . 95 1·00
309 – 8g. green . . . . 2·00 2·00
310 – 1t. brown . . . . 5·25 5·25
311 – 3t. green . . . . 5·75 6·00
312 – 5t. brown . . . . 8·25 8·25
DESIGNS—HORIZ: ¼g. Railway Bridge over R. Awash. VERT: 1g. Empress Menen (profile); 2g., 8g. Haile Selassie (profile); 4g., 1t. Statue of Menelik II; 3t. Empress Menen (full face); 5t. Haile Selassie (full face).

1936. Red Cross. As T **50** optd with red cross.
313 1g. green 90 90
314 2g. pink 90 90
315 4g. blue 90 90
316 8g. brown . . . . 1·10 1·10
317 1t. violet . . . . 1·10 1·10

1936. As T **50** surch with value and Amharic text.
318 **50** 1c. on ⅛g. red . . . . . 1·40 1·40
319 – 2c. on ¼g. green . . . . 1·40 1·00
320 **50** 3c. on ½g. purple . . . . 1·40 1·40
321 – 5c. on 1g. orange . . . . 1·10 1·10
322 – 10c. on 2g. blue . . . . 1·10 1·00

54 King Victor Emmanuel III

56 Haile Selassie I in Coronation Robes

ITALIAN COLONY

1936. Annexation of Ethiopia.
322a **54** 10c. brown . . . . . . 8·00 4·75
322b – 20c. violet . . . . . . 7·25 1·90
322c – 25c. green . . . . . . 3·50 45
322d – 30c. brown . . . . . . 3·50 90
322e – 50c. red . . . . 2·00 20
322f – 75c. orange . . . . . . 16·00 4·00
322g – 1l.25 blue . . . . . . 16·00 5·75
DESIGNS—VERT: 25c., 30c., 50c. Victor Emmanuel III. HORIZ: Victor Emmanuel III and: 20c. Mountain scenery; 75c. Gonder Castle; 1l.25, Tomb of Scec Hussen and Dordola Hills.

INDEPENDENCE RESTORED

1942. 1st issue. "Centimes" with capital initial and small letters.
323 **56** 4c. black and green . . . . 1·40 75
324 10c. black and red . . . . 2·75 1·10
325 20c. black and blue . . . . 4·00 2·00

1942. 2nd issue. "CENTIMES" in block capital letters.
326 **56** 4c. black and green . . . 85 25
327 8c. black and orange . . . 90 25
328 10c. black and red . . . 1·25 30
329 12c. black and violet . . . 1·25 60
330 20c. black and blue . . . 1·60 85
331 25c. black and green . . . 2·40 1·40
332 50c. black and brown . . . 4·00 1·60
333 60c. black and mauve . . . 5·25 2·40

1943. Restoration of Obelisk and 13th Anniv of Coronation of Haile Selassie. Stamps of 1942 inscr "CENTIMES" surch **OBELISK 3 NOV. 1943** and value.
334 **56** 5c. on 4c. black & grn . . 50·00 50·00
335 10c. on 8c. black & orge 50·00 50·00
336 15c. on 10c. black & red 50·00 50·00
337 20c. on 12c. black & vio 50·00 50·00
338 30c. on 20c. black & bl . . 50·00 50·00
In No. 338 the figure "3" is surcharged on the "2" of "20" to make "30" and this value is confirmed by the Amharic characters.

58 Royal Palace, Addis Ababa

59 Menelik II

1944. Birth Cent of Emperor Menelik II.
339 **58** 5c. green . . . . 1·60 85
340 **59** 10c. red . . . . 2·50 1·25
341 – 20c. blue . . . . 4·75 3·00
342 – 50c. violet . . . . 5·25 3·25
343 – 65c. orange . . . . 9·25 4·25
DESIGNS—VERT: 20c. Equestrian statue of Menelik II; 65c. Menelik in royal robes. HORIZ: 50c. Menelik's mausoleum.

60 Patient and Nurse (Amharic characters = "Victory")

63 Lion of the Tribe of Judah

64 Postal Transport by Mule and by Bus

1945. Victory. Optd **V** in red.
344 – 5c. green . . . . 3·25 2·00
345 – 10c. red . . . . 4·00 3·25
346 **60** 25c. blue . . . . 5·00 4·75
347 – 50c. brown . . . . 6·75 5·00
348 – 1t. violet . . . . 8·25 8·25
DESIGNS: 5c. Nurse and baby; 10c. Native soldier; 50c. Nurse and child; 1t. "Supplication".
The above stamps without the "V" were not issued for postal purposes.

1946. Air. Resumption of National Air Mail Services. (a) Surch at sides and top in Amharic, with **20-4-39** and value below.
349 **56** 12c. on 4c. blk & grn . . . 55·00 55·00

(b) Surch **REPRISE POSTE AERIENNE ETHIOPIENNE** at sides and top, with **29.12.46** and values below.
350 **56** 0.50 on 25c. black & green 55·00 55·00
351 $2 on 60c. black & mauve 75·00 75·00

1947. 50th Anniv of Postal Service.
352 **63** 10c. yellow . . . . 2·50 2·00
353 – 20c. blue . . . . 3·25 2·40
354 **64** 30c. brown . . . . 4·75 3·25
355 – 50c. green . . . . 12·50 6·75
356 – 70c. mauve . . . . 19·00 10·50
DESIGNS—VERT: 20c. Menelik II (as in Type **1**). HORIZ: 50c. G.P.O., Addis Ababa; 70c. Menelik and Haile Selassie.

65 Negus Sahle Selassie

1947. 150th Anniv of Selassie Dynasty.
357 **65** 20c. blue . . . . 2·50 1·60
358 – 30c. purple . . . . 3·25 2·75
359 – $1 green . . . . 9·25 4·00
DESIGNS—HORIZ: 30c. View of Ancober. VERT: $1, Negus Sahle Selassie.

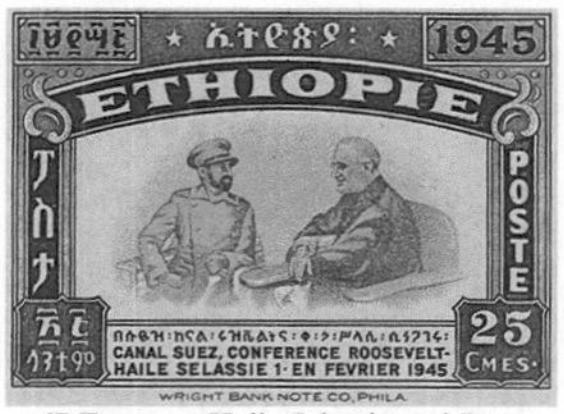

67 Emperor Haile Selassie and Pres. Roosevelt

1947. 2nd Death Anniv of Pres. Roosevelt.
360 **67** 12c. green & red (postage) 1·40 1·60
361 25c. red and blue . . . . 2·75 3·25
362 – 65c. blue, red and black . . 5·00 6·25
363 – $1 brown & purple (air) . . 10·00 12·00
364 – $2 blue and red . . . . . 20·00 23·00
DESIGNS—HORIZ: 65c. Pres. Roosevelt and U.S. flags. VERT: $1, Pres. Roosevelt; $2, Haile Selassie.

1947. Surch **12 centimes** in French and Amharic with six bars.
365 **56** 12c. on 25c. black & grn 50·00 50·00

69 Lake Tana

70 Douglas DC-3 over Zoquala Volcano

1947. Views with medallion portrait of Haile Selassie inset. (a) Postage.
366 – 1c. purple 15 10
367 – 2c. violet 15 15
368 – 4c. green 20 15
369 – 5c. green 15 10
370 **69** 8c. orange 50 15
371 – 12c. red 40 15
371a – 15c. olive 50 25
372 – 20c. blue 65 30
373 – 30c. brown . . . . 1·10 50
373a – 60c. red . . . . 1·90 60
374 – 70c. mauve . . . . 2·40 65
375 – $1 red . . . . 4·75 55
376 – $3 blue . . . . 12·00 3·25
377 – $5 olive . . . . 18·00 5·75
DESIGNS: 1c. Amba Alagi; 2c. Trinity Church, Addis Ababa; 4c. Debra Sina; 5c. Mecan mountain pathway, near Ashangi; 12c., 15c. Parliament Building, Addis Ababa; 20c. Aiba mountain scenery, near Mai Chio; 30c. Nile Bridge; 60c., 70c. Canoe on Lake Tana; $1, Omo Falls; $3, Mt. Alamata; $5, Ras Dashan Mountains.

(b) Air.
378 – 8c. purple 15 10
379 **70** 10c. green 25 10
379a – 25c. purple 50 20
380 – 30c. orange 75 25
380a – 35c. blue . . . . 1·00 40
380b – 65c. purple 75 35
381 – 70c. red . . . . 1·75 40
382 – $1 blue . . . . 2·75 65
383 – $3 mauve . . . . 8·25 4·00
384 – $5 brown . . . . 13·00 6·50
385 – $10 violet . . . . 24·00 16·00
DESIGNS: 8c. Ploughing with oxen; 30c., 35c. Tehis Isat Falls, Blue Nile; 65c., 70c. Amba Alagi; $1, Sacala source of River Nile; $3, Gorgora and Dembia on Lake Tana; $5, Magdala Fort; $10, Ras Dasnan Mountains and Lake.

72 Emperor, Empress, Lion and Map

1949. 8th Anniv of Liberation.
386 – 20c. blue . . . . 1·40 30
387 **72** 30c. orange . . . . 1·40 65
388 – 50c. violet . . . . 3·00 1·60
389 – 80c. green . . . . 4·25 2·10
390 – $1 red . . . . 7·00 3·25
DESIGNS: 20c. Emperor and Empress with sceptres and orb; 50c. Coat of arms; 80c. Shield and spears; $1, Star of Solomon.

1949. Industrial and Agricultural Exn. Nos. 370/1 and 373/5 surch **EXPOSITION 1949**, and new value and two lines of Amharic characters.
391 8c.+8c. orange . . . . . . 3·25 3·25
392 12c.+5c. red . . . . 3·25 3·25
393 30c.+15c. brown . . . . . 6·75 6·75
394 70c.+70c. mauve . . . . . 17·00 17·00
395 $1+80c. red . . . . 20·00 20·00

74 Emperor and U.P.U. Monument, Berne

1950. Air. 75th Anniv of U.P.U.

396	74	5c. red and green	90	70
397		15c. red and blue	1·10	70
398		25c. green and yellow	1·75	90
399		50c. blue and red	3·00	2·10

1950. Red Cross Fund. As Nos. 344/8 but without **V** opt and surch **+ 10 ct.** below a cross.

399a	5c.+10c. green	1·40	1·40
399b	10c.+10c. red	1·60	1·60
399c	25c.+10c. blue	3·25	3·25
399d	50c.+10c. brown	5·25	5·25
399e	$1+10c. violet	12·50	12·50

75 Lion of the Tribe of Judah **76** Emperor and Abbaye Bridge

1950. 20th Anniv of Coronation.

400	–	5c. violet	1·40	45
401	–	10c. mauve	2·75	1·00
402	–	20c. red	3·25	1·50
403	75	30c. green	4·00	2·00
404	–	50c. blue	5·00	3·25

DESIGNS—HORIZ: 5c. Dejach Balcha Hospital; 50c. Emperor, Empress and palace. VERT: 10c. Abuna Petros; 20c. Emperor hoisting flag.

1951. Opening of Abbaye Bridge.

405	76	5c. brown and green	3·25	1·00
406		10c. black and orange	5·00	1·60
407		15c. brown and blue	6·75	2·50
408		30c. mauve and olive	10·00	3·25
409		60c. blue and brown	13·50	5·00
410		80c. green and violet	20·00	6·75

1951. 55th Anniv of Battle of Adwa. As T **76**, but Emperor and Tomb of Ras Makonnen.

411	5c. black and green	1·60	1·00
412	10c. black and blue	2·00	1·40
413	15c. black and blue	3·00	2·00
414	30c. black and red	4·00	2·40
415	80c. black and red	6·00	3·25
416	$1 black and brown	10·00	4·00

1951. Industrial and Agricultural Exhibition. Nos. 391/5 further optd **1951** with Amharic characters above.

417	8c.+8c. orange	1·00	1·00
418	12c.+5c. red	1·00	1·00
419	30c.+15c. brown	1·40	1·40
420	70c.+70c. mauve	11·50	11·50
421	$1+80c. red	18·00	18·00

79 "Tree of Health" **80** Haile Selassie I

1951. Anti-tuberculosis Fund. Cross and inscr in red.

422	79	5c.+2c. green	55	55
423		10c.+3c. orange	55	55
424		15c.+3c. blue	1·00	1·00
425		30c.+5c. red	1·60	1·60
426		50c.+7c. brown	2·50	2·50
427		$1+10c. purple	4·00	4·00

1952. Emperor Haile Selassie's 60th Birthday.

428	80	5c. green	25	25
429		10c. orange	45	30
430		15c. black	1·00	40
431		25c. blue	1·40	45
432		30c. violet	2·00	1·00
433		50c. red	2·75	65
434		65c. sepia	5·25	2·00

81 Ethiopian Flag over the Sea

1952. Celebration of Federation of Eritrea with Ethiopia.

435	–	15c. lake	1·00	85
436	–	25c. brown	1·60	1·10
437	–	30c. brown	2·40	1·50
438	–	50c. purple	2·75	1·60
439	–	65c. black	7·50	2·00
440	–	80c. green	5·00	3·00
441	–	$1 red	8·25	4·00
442	81	$2 blue	15·00	6·75
443	–	$3 mauve	27·00	10·00

DESIGNS: 15c., 30c. Port Assab; 25c., 50c. Port Massawa; 65c. Map; 80c. Allegory of Federation; $1, Emperor raising flag; $3, Emperor in 1936.

82 Emperor and Massawa Harbour

1953. 1st Anniv of Federation of Ethiopia and Eritrea.

444	82	10c. brown and red	4·75	2·00
445	–	15c. green and blue	3·25	2·50
446	82	25c. brown and orange	13·00	7·50
447	–	30c. green and brown	6·75	4·25
448	82	50c. brown and purple	13·00	7·50

DESIGN—HORIZ: 15c., 30c. Emperor aboard freighter at sea.

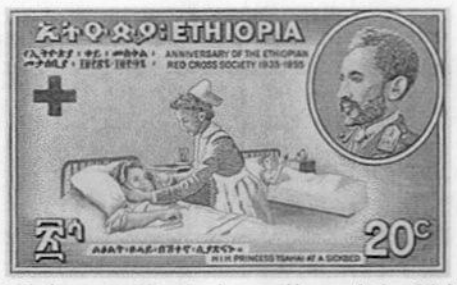

83 Princess Tsahai tending sick Child

1953. 20th Anniv of Ethiopian Red Cross Society. Cross in red.

449	83	15c. blue and brown	1·60	50
450		20c. orange and green	2·50	1·00
451		30c. green and blue	4·25	1·60

84 Promulgating the Constitution **85** Emperor Haile Selassie

1955. Silver Jubilee of Emperor. Inscr "1930–1955".

452	84	5c. brown and green	50	20
453	–	20c. green and red	1·60	40
454	–	25c. black and mauve	2·00	50
455	–	35c. red and brown	2·50	1·00
456	–	50c. blue and brown	7·75	2·25
457	–	65c. red and lilac	5·25	3·00

DESIGNS—HORIZ: 20c. Bishop's consecration; 25c. Emperor presenting standard to troops; 50c. Emperor, Empress and symbols of progress; 65c. Emperor and Empress in coronation robes. VERT: 35c. Allegory of re-union of Ethiopia and Eritrea.

1955. Silver Jubilee Fair, Addis Ababa.

458	85	5c. olive and green	65	15
459		10c. blue and red	1·00	25
460		15c. green and black	1·40	40
461		50c. lake and mauve	2·10	1·60

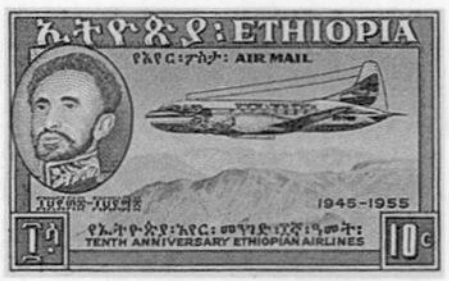

86 Convair CV 240 Airliner

1955. Air. 10th Anniv of Ethiopian Airlines.

462	86	10c. multicoloured	75	25
463		15c. multicoloured	1·10	85
464		20c. multicoloured	1·50	90

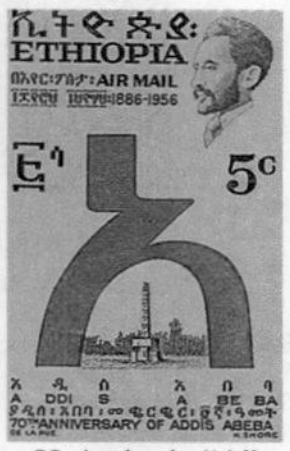

87 Promulgating the Constitution **89** Amharic "A"

88 Aksum

1956. Air. 25th Anniv of Constitution.

465	87	10c. blue and brown	65	35
466		15c. green and red	90	45
467		20c. orange and blue	1·25	60
468		25c. green and lilac	1·60	75
469		30c. brown and green	2·10	85

1957. Air. Ancient Capitals of Ethiopia. Centres in green.

470	88	5c. brown	50	15
471	–	10c. red (Lalibela)	60	50
472	–	15c. orange (Gondar)	80	65
473	–	20c. blue (Makalle)	1·40	1·00
474	–	25c. mauve (Ankober)	2·10	1·40

1957. Air. 70th Anniv of Addis Ababa. Amharic characters in red and miniature views of buildings as in T **89**.

475	89	5c. blue on salmon	50	15
476	–	10c. green on flesh	30	25
477	–	15c. purple on buff	45	35
478	–	20c. green on buff	1·10	50
479	–	25c. mauve on lavender	1·40	65
480	–	30c. brown on green	1·60	1·10

AMHARIC CHARACTERS: 10c. "DD1"; 15c. "S"; 20c. "A"; 25c. "BE"; 30c. "BA".
The set spells out "Addis Ababa" in Amharic.

90 Emperor Haile Selassie, Map of Africa, Building and Monument

1958. Air. Conference of Independent African States, Accra.

481	90	10c. green	30	20
482		20c. red	85	85
483		30c. blue	1·40	1·00

1958. Anti-tuberculosis Fund. As Nos. 422/7 but new values.

483a	79	20c.+3c. purple & red	50	65
483b		25c.+4c. green & red	65	85
483c		35c.+5c. purple & red	1·25	1·25
483d		60c.+7c. blue and red	2·00	2·00
483e		65c.+7c. violet & red	2·75	2·75
483f		80c.+9c. carmine & red	4·50	4·50

91 Emperor Haile Selassie, Map of Africa and U.N. Emblem **96** Woman with Torch

1958. Air. 1st Session of U.N. Economic Conference for Africa, Addis Ababa.

484	91	5c. green	20	15
485		20c. red	35	25
486		25c. blue	50	35
487		50c. purple	1·00	50

1959. Red Cross Commem. Surch **RED CROSS CENTENARY 1859-1959** in English and Amharic and premium. Colours changed. Cross in red.

488	83	15c.+2c. red & brown	70	70
489		20c.+3c. green & violet	1·50	1·50
490		30c.+5c. blue and red	2·00	2·00

1959. Air. 30th Anniv of Air Mail Service in Ethiopia. Nos. 378/81 optd **30th Airmail Ann. 1929-1959**.

491	8c. purple	40	25
492	10c. green	50	40
493	25c. purple	65	50
494	30c. orange	1·10	65
495	35c. blue	1·50	1·00
496	65c. violet	2·00	1·10
497	70c. red	2·25	1·25

1960. World Refugee Year. Optd **World Refugee Year 1959-1960** in English and Amharic.

498	20c. blue (No. 372)	1·00	1·00
499	60c. red (No. 373a)	1·60	1·60

1960. Ethiopian Red Cross Society's Silver Jubilee. As Nos. 344/8 but without **V** opt surch **Silver Jubilee 1960** in English and Amharic and premium.

500	5c.+1c. green	20	15
501	10c.+2c. red	55	55
502	25c.+3c. blue	1·00	1·00
503	50c.+4c. brown	2·10	2·10
504	$1+5c. violet	4·25	4·25

1960. 2nd Independent African States Conf, Addis Ababa.

505	96	20c. green and red	40	50
506		80c. violet and red	1·50	65
507		$1 lake and red	3·00	2·10

97 Emperor Haile Selassie **98** Africa Hall, Addis Ababa

1960. 30th Anniv of Emperor's Coronation.

508	97	10c. brown and blue	65	65
509		25c. violet and green	1·10	1·10
510		50c. blue and buff	2·00	2·00
511		65c. green and salmon	2·75	2·75
512		$1 blue and purple	4·25	4·25

1961. Africa Day.

513	98	80c. blue	2·00	1·10

99 Emperor Haile Selassie and Map of Ethiopia

1961. 20th Anniv of Liberation.

514	99	20c. green	40	30
515		30c. blue	55	45
516		$1 brown	1·40	85

100 African Ass

1961. Ethiopian Fauna.

517	100	5c. black and green	50	15
518	–	15c. brown and green	50	20
519	–	25c. sepia and green	65	30
520	–	35c. brown and green	1·50	40
521	–	50c. red and green	1·40	50
522	–	$1 brown and green	3·00	1·50

DESIGNS: 15c. Eland; 25c. African elephant; 35c. Giraffe; 50c. Gemsbok; $1, Lion and lioness.
See also Nos. 641/5.

101 Emperor Haile Selassie I and Empress Menen

1961. Golden Wedding of Emperor and Empress.

523	101	10c. green	45	20
524		50c. blue	1·10	45
525		$1 red	1·60	1·40

102 Guks (jousting)

1962. Sports.

526	102	10c. red and green	40	30
527	–	15c. brown and red	50	45
528	–	20c. black and red	70	50
529	–	30c. purple and blue	80	65
530	–	50c. green and buff	1·50	75

DESIGNS: 15c. Ganna (Ethiopian hockey); 20c. Cycling; 30c. Football (3rd Africa Cup game); 50c. Abbebe Bikila (Marathon winner, Olympic Games Rome, 1960).

103 Mosquito on World Map

1962. Malaria Eradication.
531 **103** 15c. black 25 15
532 30c. purple 40 30
533 60c. brown 1·40 60

104 Abyssinian Ground Hornbill

105 "Collective Security"

1962. Ethiopian Birds (1st series). Mult.
534 5c. Type **104** (postage) 85 20
535 15c. Abyssinian roller 1·40 45
536 30c. Bateleur (vert) 1·75 1·00
537 50c. Double-toothed barbet (vert) 3·00 1·25
538 $1 Didric cuckoo 7·25 2·10
539 10c. Dark-headed oriole (air) 85 15
540 15c. Broad-tailed paradise whydah (vert) 1·25 45
541 20c. Lammergeier (vert) 1·50 55
542 50c. White-cheeked turaco 3·00 1·25
543 80c. Village indigobird 3·50 1·40
See also Nos 633/7 and 673/7.

1962. Air. 2nd Anniv of Ethiopian U.N. Forces in Congo and 70th Birthday of Emperor.
544 **105** 15c. multicoloured 25 20
545 50c. multicoloured 60 35
546 60c. multicoloured 1·10 45

106 Assab Hospital

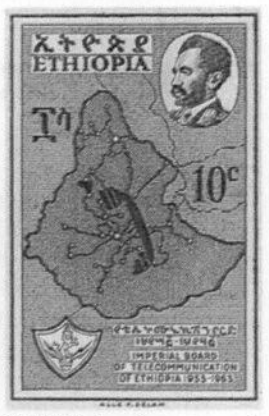

108 Telephone and Communications Map

107 Bazan, "The Nativity" and Bethlehem

1962. 10th Anniv of Federation of Ethiopia and Eritrea.
547 **106** 3c. purple 10 10
548 – 15c. blue 15 15
549 – 20c. green 25 15
550 – 50c. brown 25 25
551 – 60c. red 1·00 40
DESIGNS: 15c. Assab school; 20c. Massawa church; 50c. Massawa mosque; 60c. Assab port.

1962. Ethiopian Rulers (1st issue). Mult.
552 10c. Type **107** 15 10
553 15c. Ezana and monuments, Aksum 25 15
554 20c. Kaleb and fleet in Adulis port 90 20
555 50c. Lalibela, Christian figures from Lalibela churches (vert) 90 40
556 60c. Yekuno Amlak and Abuna Tekle Haimanot preaching in Ankober 1·10 50
557 75c. Zara Yacob and ceremonial pyre 1·40 90
558 $1 Lebna Bengel and battle against Mohammed Gragn 2·10 1·10

1963. 10th Anniv of Ethiopian Imperial Telecommunications Board.
559 **108** 10c. red 50 25
560 – 50c. blue 1·40 65
561 – 60c. brown 1·60 1·00
DESIGNS: 50c. Radio aerial; 60c. Telegraph pole.

109 Campaign Emblem

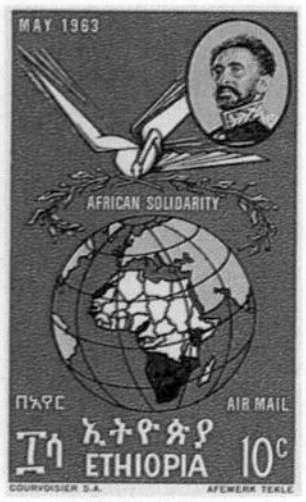

110 "African Solidarity"

1963. Freedom from Hunger.
562 **109** 5c. red 10 10
563 10c. mauve 15 10
564 15c. violet 25 15
565 30c. green 40 20

1963. Air. Conference of African Heads of States, Addis Ababa.
566 **110** 10c. black and purple 40 10
567 40c. black and green 90 40
568 60c. black and blue 1·40 45

111 Disabled Boy

112 Bishop Abuna Salama

1963. "Aid for the Disabled" Fund.
569 **111** 10c.+2c. blue 25 25
570 15c.+3c. red 45 45
571 50c.+5c. green 1·10 1·10
572 60c.+5c. purple 2·40 2·40

1964. Ethiopian Spiritual Leaders.
573 **112** 10c. blue 25 20
574 – 15c. green (Abuna Aregawi) 40 30
575 – 30c. lake (Abuna Tekle Haimanot) 1·10 50
576 – 40c. blue (Yared) 1·40 1·10
577 – 60c. brn (Zara Yacob) 2·10 1·60

113 Queen Sheba

114 Priest teaching Alphabet

1964. Ethiopian Empresses. Multicoloured.
578 10c. Type **113** 30 35
579 15c. Helen 65 50
580 50c. Seble Wongel 1·10 85
581 60c. Mentiwab 2·50 1·50
582 80c. Taitu 3·25 2·00

1964. "Education".
583 **114** 5c. brown 15 10
584 – 10c. green 15 10
585 – 15c. purple 20 15
586 – 40c. blue 50 35
587 – 60c. purple 1·10 50
DESIGNS—HORIZ: 10c. Pupils in classroom. VERT: 15c. Teacher with pupil; 40c. Students in laboratory; 60c. Graduates in procession.

115 Swimming

116 Eleanor Roosevelt

1964. Air. Olympic Games, Tokyo. Mult.
588 5c. Type **115** 15 10
589 10c. Basketball (vert) 25 20
590 15c. Throwing the javelin 30 25
591 80c. Football at Addis Ababa stadium 1·60 1·10

1964. Eleanor Roosevelt Commem.
592 **116** 10c. blue and bistre 15 15
593 60c. blue and brown 1·00 75
594 80c. blue, gold and green 1·40 1·00

1964. Ethiopian Rulers (2nd issue). As T **107**. Multicoloured.
595 5c. Serse Dengel and view of Gondar, 1563 10 10
596 10c. Fasiladas and Gondar, 1632 20 15
597 20c. Yassu the Great and Gondar, 1682 40 20
598 25c. Theodore II and map of Ethiopia 45 25
599 60c. John IV and Battle of Gura, 1876 1·25 95
600 80c. Menelik II and Battle of Adwa, 1896 1·40 1·00

118 Queen Elizabeth II and Emperor Haile Selassie

1965. Air. Visit of Queen Elizabeth II.
601 **118** 5c. multicoloured 10 10
602 35c. multicoloured 50 50
603 60c. multicoloured 1·00 75

119 Abyssinian Rose

120 I.T.U. Emblem and Symbols

1965. Ethiopian Flowers. Multicoloured.
604 5c. Type **119** 15 10
605 10c. Kosso tree 20 15
606 25c. St. John's wort 75 50
607 35c. Parrot tree 1·10 90
608 60c. Maskal daisy 2·00 1·50

1965. Centenary of I.T.U.
609 **120** 5c. yellow, indigo & blue 15 10
610 10c. orange, dp blue & bl 20 10
611 60c. mauve, dp blue & bl 1·25 85

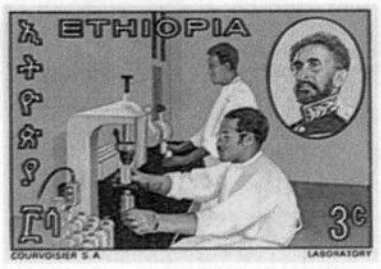

121 Laboratory Technicians

1965. Multicoloured.
612 3c. Type **121** (postage) 10 30
613 5c. Textile mill 15 10
614 10c. Sugar factory 10 10
615 20c. Mountain highway 40 15
616 25c. Motor coach 45 10
617 30c. Diesel locomotive 1·75 35
618 35c. Railway Station, Addis Ababa 1·75 35
619 15c. Sisal (inscr "SUGAR CANES") (air) 25 15
620 40c. Koka Dam 45 25
621 50c. Blue Nile Bridge 70 40
622 60c. Gondar castles 75 35
623 80c. Coffee tree 1·00 40
624 $1 Cattle 1·50 45
625 $3 Camels 4·75 2·10
626 $5 Boeing 720B airliner 9·00 4·25

122 I.C.Y. Emblem

1965. I.C.Y.
627 **122** 10c. red and turquoise 25 15
628 50c. red and blue 90 65
629 80c. red and blue 1·40 75

123 Commercial Bank's Seal

1965. Ethiopian National and Commercial Banks.
630 **123** 10c. black, blue and red 25 25
631 – 30c. black, blue & ultram 85 60
632 – 60c. yellow, blue & black 1·10 85
DESIGNS: 30c. National Bank's Seal; 60c. Banking halls and main building.

1966. Air. Ethiopian Birds (2nd series). As T **104**. Multicoloured.
633 10c. White-collared kingfisher 80 35
634 15c. Blue-breasted bee eater 1·10 50
635 25c. African paradise fly-catcher 1·40 65
636 40c. Village weaver 2·50 90
637 60c. White-collared pigeon 3·25 1·25

124 Press Building

1966. Inauguration of "Light and Peace" Printing Press, Addis Ababa.
638 **124** 5c. black and red 10 10
639 15c. black and green 25 25
640 30c. black and yellow 45 45

125 Black Rhinoceros

126 Kebero Drum

1966. Air. Animals.
641 **125** 5c. black, grey & green 15 10
642 – 10c. brown, black & grn 50 15
643 – 20c. black, green & ol 80 20
644 – 30c. ochre, black & green 1·40 60
645 – 60c. brown, black & grn 2·40 1·25
ANIMALS: 10c. Leopard; 20c. Eastern black and white colobus; 30c. Mountain nyala; 60c. Ibex.

1966. Musical Instruments.
646 **126** 5c. black and green 15 10
647 – 10c. black and blue 25 10
648 – 35c. black and orange 75 60
649 – 50c. black and yellow 1·50 90
650 – 60c. black and red 2·00 1·25
INSTRUMENTS: 10c. Begena harp; 35c. Mesenko stringed instrument; 50c. Krar lyre; 60c. Washent flutes.

127 Emperor Haile Selassie

1966. "Fifty Years of Leadership".
651 **127** 10c. multicoloured 15 10
652 15c. multicoloured 20 20
653 40c. black, grey & gold 1·00 75

128 U.N.E.S.C.O. Emblem and Map of Africa

1966. 20th Anniv of U.N.E.S.C.O.
654 **128** 15c. red, black and blue 25 25
655 60c. blue, brown & green 1·10 70

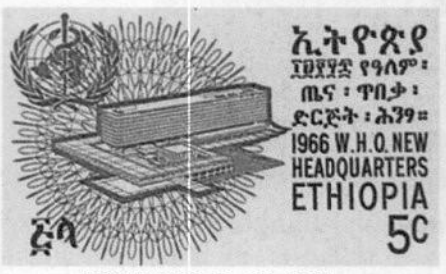

129 W.H.O. Building

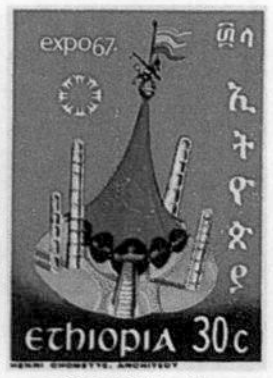

130 Ethiopian Pavilion

1966. Inaug of W.H.O. Headquarters, Geneva.

656	129	5c. green, sepia & blue . .	25	15
657		40c. sepia, green & violet	95	65

1967. World Fair, Montreal.

658	130	30c. multicoloured	80	50
659		45c. multicoloured	90	65
660		80c. multicoloured	1·60	1·10

131 Diesel Train and Route-Map

1967. 50th Anniv of Completion of Djibouti–Addis Ababa Railway.

661	131	15c. multicoloured	75	30
662		30c. multicoloured	1·75	1·00
663		50c. multicoloured	3·00	1·75

132 "Papilio aethiops" (inscr "Papilionidae")

1967. Butterflies (1st series). Multicoloured.

664	5c. Type **132**	10	10
665	10c. "Charaxes epijasius" . .	20	25
666	20c. "Charaxes varans" . . .	45	45
667	35c. "Euphaedra neophron"	1·10	90
668	40c. "Salamis aethiops" . . .	1·40	1·10

See also Nos. 915/19.

133 Haile Selassie I

1967. Emperor Haile Selassie's 75th Birthday.

669	133	10c. multicoloured	25	25
670		15c. multicoloured	40	35
671		$1 multicoloured	2·00	1·50

1967. Air. Birds (3rd series). As T **104**. Mult.

673	10c. Blue-winged goose (vert)	80	75
674	15c. African yellow-bill . . .	1·00	30
675	20c. Wattled ibis	1·40	55
676	25c. Lesser striped swallow	2·10	65
677	40c. Black-winged lovebird (vert)	3·50	1·00

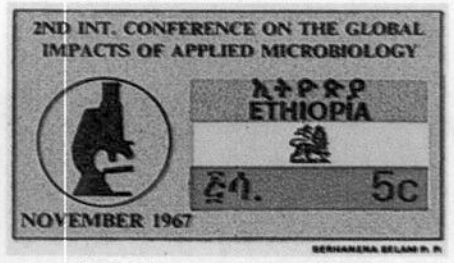

134 Microscope and Flag

1967. 2nd International Conference on Global Impacts of Applied Microbiology, Addis Ababa.

678	134	5c. multicoloured	10	10
679		30c. multicoloured	35	20
680		$1 multicoloured	1·90	1·50

135 Wall Painting, Gondar

1967. International Tourist Year. Multicoloured.

681	15c. Type **135**	60	45
682	25c. Ancient votive stone and statuary, Atsbe Dera (vert)	1·25	65
683	35c. Cave paintings of animals, Harrar Province	90	75
684	50c. Prehistoric stone tools, Melke Kontoure (vert) . .	1·60	1·00

136 Cross of Biet-Maryam (bronze)

137 Emperor Theodore II with Lions

1967. Crosses of Lalibela (1st series). Crosses in black and silver.

685	136	5c. black and lemon . . .	15	10
686	–	10c. black and orange . .	15	15
687	–	15c. black and violet . . .	20	10
688	–	20c. black and red	50	40
689	–	50c. black and yellow . .	1·50	1·10

CROSSES: 10c. "Zagwe King's" cross; 15c. Copper, Biet-Maryam; 20c. Typical cross of Lalibela region; 50c. Copper, Medhani Alem.

See also Nos. 737/40.

1968. Death Cent of Emperor Theodore II.

690	–	10c. brown, lilac & yellow	20	10
691	137	20c. lilac, brown & mauve	35	20
692	–	50c. red, orange & green	1·10	85

DESIGNS—VERT: 10c. Emperor Theodore; 50c. Imperial crown.

138 Human Rights Emblem

1968. Human Rights Year.

693	138	15c. black and red	55	15
694		$1 black and blue	2·40	1·60

139 Shah of Iran and Haile Selassie I

1968. State Visit of Shah of Iran.

695	139	5c. multicoloured	20	10
696		15c. multicoloured	35	20
697		30c. multicoloured	1·00	75

140 Haile Selassie I and Addressing League of Nations, 1936

1968. "Ethiopia's Struggle for Peace".

698	140	15c. multicoloured	20	20
699	–	35c. multicoloured	40	45
700	–	$1 multicoloured	2·40	1·40

HAILE SELASSIE and: 35c. Africa Hall; $1, World map ("International Relations").

141 W.H.O. Emblem

1968. 20th Anniv of W.H.O.

701	141	15c. black and green	20	15
702		60c. black and purple . .	1·00	65

142 Running

1968. Olympic Games, Mexico. Multicoloured.

703	10c. Type **142**	15	10
704	15c. Football	20	15
705	20c. Boxing	25	20
706	40c. Basketball	85	55
707	50c. Cycling	1·10	85

143 Arrussi Costume

1968. Ethiopian Costumes (1st series). Mult.

708	5c. Type **143**	10	10
709	15c. Gemu Gofa	20	10
710	20c. Godjam	25	10
711	30c. Kaffa	30	20
712	35c. Harar	45	25
713	50c. Illubabor	95	35
714	60c. Eritrea	1·10	85

See also Nos. 768/74.

144 Postal Service Emblem and Initials

1969. 75th Anniv of Ethiopian Postal Service.

715	144	10c. black, brown & green	15	10
716		15c. black, brown & yell	50	50
717		35c. black, brown & red	90	90

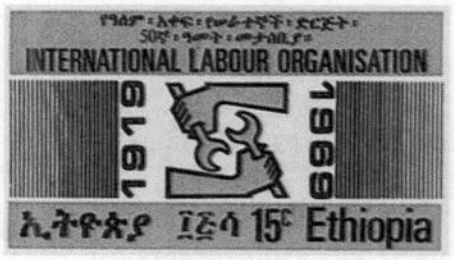

145 I.L.O. Emblem

1969. 50th Anniv of I.L.O.

718	145	15c. orange and black . .	25	15
719		60c. green and black . . .	1·40	1·40

146 Red Cross Emblems

147 Silver Coin of Endybis (3rd cent)

1969. 50th Anniv of League of Red Cross Societies.

720	146	5c. red, black and blue . .	20	15
721		15c. red, green & blue . .	65	50
722		30c. red, ultram & blue	1·10	1·00

1969. Ancient Ethiopian Coins.

723	147	5c. silver, black & blue . .	15	15
724	–	10c. gold, black & red . .	30	25
725	–	15c. gold, black & brown	25	35
726	–	30c. bronze, black & red	85	65
727	–	40c. bronze, black & grn	95	85
728	–	50c. silver, black & violet	1·25	1·10

COINS: 10c. Gold coin of Ezana (4th century); 15c. Gold coin of Kalob (6th century); 30c. Bronze coin of Armah (7th century); 40c. Bronze coin of Wazena (7th century); 50c. Silver coin of Gersem (8th century);

148 "Hunting"

1969. African Tourist Year. Multicoloured.

729	5c. Type **148**	10	10
730	10c. "Camping"	10	10
731	15c. "Fishing"	55	10
732	20c. "Watersports"	65	65
733	25c. "Mountaineering" (vert)	1·10	1·00

149 Dove of Peace

1969. 25th Anniv of U.N. Multicoloured.

734	10c. Type **149**	10	10
735	30c. Stylized flowers (vert) . .	50	65
736	60c. Peace dove and emblem	1·25	1·25

150 Ancient Cross and "Holy Family"

1969. Ancient Ethiopian Crosses (2nd series).

737	150	5c. black, yellow & green	10	10
738	–	10c. black and yellow . .	10	10
739	–	25c. black, green & yell	75	60
740	–	60c. black and yellow . .	1·90	1·40

DESIGNS—VERT: 10c., 25c. and 60c. show different crosses and drawings similar to Type **150**.

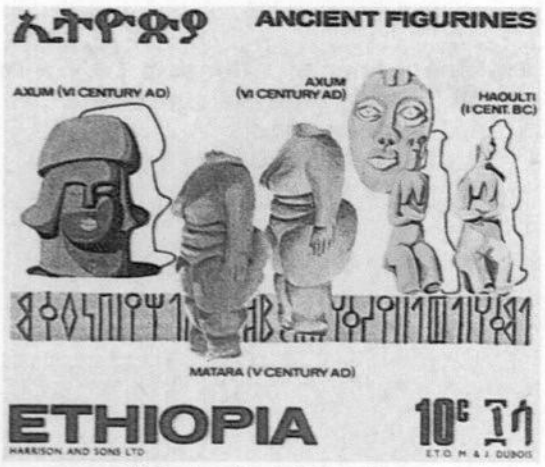

151 Ancient Figurines

1970. Ancient Ethiopian Pottery. Mult.

741	10c. Type **151**	10	10
742	20c. Decorated jar, Yeha . .	45	45
743	25c. Axum Pottery	60	60
744	35c. "Bird" jug, Matara . . .	75	75
745	60c. Christian pottery, Adulis	1·40	1·40

152 Medhane Alem Church

1970. Rock Churches of Lalibela. Mult.

746	5c. Type **152**	10	10
747	10c. Bieta Amanuel	10	10
748	15c. Four churches	20	35
749	20c. Bieta Mariam	55	55
750	50c. Bieta Giorgis	1·40	1·40

153 Sail-finned Tang

1970. Fishes. Multicoloured.

751	5c. Type **153**	15	15
752	10c. Undulate triggerfish . .	35	35
753	15c. Blue-cheeked butterflyfish	65	65
754	25c. Hooded butterflyfish . .	1·10	1·10
755	50c. Emperor angelfish . . .	1·60	1·60

154 I.E.Y. Emblem

156 Haile Selassie I

155 O.A.U. Emblem

1970. International Education Year.
756 **154** 10c. multicoloured 15 10
757 20c. multicoloured 25 15
758 50c. multicoloured 65 85

1970. Organization of African Unity. Mult.
759 20c. Type **155** 20 15
760 30c. O.A.U. flag 50 50
761 40c. O.A.U. Headquarters, Addis Ababa 85 85

1970. 40th Anniv of Haile Selassie's Coronation.
762 **156** 15c. multicoloured 15 10
763 50c. multicoloured 70 70
764 60c. multicoloured . . . . 1·25 1·25

157 Ministry Buildings

1970. Inauguration of New Posts and Telecommunications Buildings, Addis Ababa.
765 **157** 10c. multicoloured 15 10
766 50c. multicoloured 95 95
767 80c. multicoloured . . . . 1·25 1·25

1971. Ethiopian Costumes (2nd series). As T **143**. Multicoloured.
768 5c. Begemedir and Semain Costume 10 10
769 10c. Bale 15 10
770 15c. Wolega 20 10
771 20c. Showa 40 40
772 25c. Sidamo 50 50
773 40c. Tigre 75 75
774 50c. Wello 95 95

159 Tail of Boeing 707 160 "Fountain of Life" (15th-cent Gospel)

1971. Air. 25th Anniv of Ethiopian Airlines. Multicoloured.
775 5c. Type **159** 10 10
776 10c. "Ethiopian Life" 10 10
777 20c. Nose of Boeing 707 and control tower 40 40
778 60c. Airliner's flight deck and jet engine . . . . 1·10 1·10
779 80c. Route map . . . . . . 1·60 1·60

1971. Ethiopian Paintings. Multicoloured.
780 5c. Type **160** 10 10
781 10c. "King David" (15th-cent manuscript) 10 10
782 25c. "St. George" (17th-cent canvas) 45 45
783 50c. "King Kaleb" (18th-cent triptych, Lalibela) 95 95
784 60c. "Yared singing to King Kaleb" (18th-cent mural, Axum) . . . . 1·60 1·60

161 Black and White Heads

1971. Racial Equality Year.
785 **161** 10c. black, red & orange 15 10
786 – 60c. multicoloured 75 75
787 – 80c. multicoloured . . . . 1·25 1·25
DESIGN: 60c. Black and white hands holding Globe; 80c. Heads of four races.

162 Emperor Menelik II and Proclamation

1971. 75th Anniv of Victory of Adwa. Mult.
788 10c. Type **162** 15 10
789 30c. Ethiopian army on the march 55 55
790 50c. Battle of Adwa 85 85
791 60c. Ethiopian soldiers . . . 90 1·00

163 Emperor Menelik II, Ras Makonnen and Early Telephones

1971. 75th Anniv of Ethiopian Telecommunications. Multicoloured.
792 5c. Type **163** 10 10
793 10c. Emperor Haile Selassie and radio masts 10 10
794 30c. T.V. set and Ethiopians 55 55
795 40c. Microwave equipment 65 65
796 60c. Telephone dial and part of Globe . . . . 1·00 1·00

164 Mother and Child

1971. 25th Anniv of U.N.I.C.E.F. Mult.
797 5c. Type **164** 10 10
798 10c. Refugee children 10 10
799 15c. Man embracing child . . 35 35
800 30c. Children with toys . . . 60 60
801 50c. Students 90 90

165 Lion's Head

1971. Tourism. Embossed on gold foil.
802 **165** $15 gold . . . . 20·00
803 – $15 gold . . . . 20·00
DESIGN: No. 803, Visit of Queen of Sheba to King Solomon.

1972. 1st U.N. Security Council Meeting in Africa (1st issue). Nos. 615/8 Optd **U.N. SECURITY COUNCIL FIRST MEETING IN AFRICA 1972** in English and Amharic.
804 20c. multicoloured 25 15
805 25c. multicoloured 40 25
806 30c. multicoloured . . . . . 3·25 2·00
807 35c. multicoloured . . . . . 3·25 1·75
See also Nos. 832/4.

167 Reed Raft, Lake Haik

1972. Ethiopian River Craft. Multicoloured.
808 10c. Type **167** 10 10
809 20c. Canoes, Lake Abaya . . 45 45
810 30c. Punts, Lake Tana . . . 75 75
811 60c. Dugout canoes, Baro River . . . . 1·75 1·75

168 Cuneiform Proclamation of Cyrus the Great

1972. 2500th Anniv of Persian Empire.
812 **168** 10c. multicoloured 20 20
813 60c. multicoloured . . . . 1·00 1·00
814 80c. multicoloured . . . . 1·50 1·50

169 "Beehive" Hut, Sidamo Province

1972. Architecture of Ethiopian Provinces.
815 **169** 5c. multicoloured 10 10
816 – 10c. black, grey & brown 10 10
817 – 20c. multicoloured 55 55
818 – 40c. multicoloured 90 90
819 – 80c. multicoloured . . . . 1·60 1·60
DESIGNS: 10c. Two-storey houses, Tigre Province; 20c. House with veranda, Eritrea Province; 40c. Town house, Addis Ababa; 80c. Thatched huts, Shoa Province.

170 "Development" within Cupped Hands 171 Running

1972. Emperor Haile Selassie's 80th Birthday. Multicoloured.
820 5c. Type **170** 10 10
821 10c. Ethiopians within cupped hands 10 10
822 25c. Map, hands and O.A.U. emblem 45 45
823 50c. Handclasp and U.N. emblem 90 90
824 60c. Peace dove within hands 1·25 1·25

1972. Olympic Games, Munich. Mult.
825 10c. Type **171** 20 20
826 30c. Football 60 60
827 50c. Cycling 95 95
828 60c. Boxing . . . . 1·40 1·40

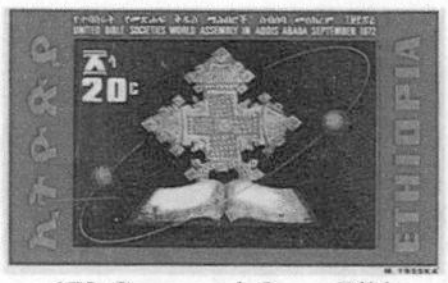

172 Cross and Open Bible

1972. World Assembly of United Bible Societies, Addis Ababa. Multicoloured.
829 20c. Type **172** 35 35
830 50c. First office of B.F.B.S., and new H.Q. (vert) . . . 75 75
831 80c. Amharic Bible . . . . . 1·40 1·40

173 Council in Session

1972. 1st U.N. Security Council Meeting in Africa (2nd issue). Multicoloured.
832 10c. Type **173** 10 10
833 60c. Africa Hall, Addis Ababa . . . . 1·00 1·00
834 80c. Map of Africa and flags 1·50 1·50

174 "Polluted Waters"

1973. World Campaign against Sea Pollution. Multicoloured.
835 20c. Type **174** 25 10
836 30c. Fishing in polluted sea 40 25
837 80c. Beach pollution . . . . 1·10 1·10

175 Interpol and Ethiopian Police Badges

1973. 50th Anniv of International Criminal Police Organization (Interpol).
838 **175** 40c. black and orange . . 65 65
839 – 50c. black, brown & bl . . 85 85
840 – 60c. black and red . . . . 1·00 1·00
DESIGNS: 50c. Interpol badge and Headquarters, Paris; 60c. Interpol badge.

176 "The Virgin and Child" (Fere Seyoum Zana Yacob period)

1973. Ethiopian Fine Arts. Multicoloured.
841 5c. Type **176** 10 10
842 15c. "The Crucifixion" (Zara Yacob period) 15 15
843 30c. "St. Mary" (Entoto Mariam church painting) 65 65
844 40c. "Saint" mosaic (Addis Ababa Art School) 75 75
845 80c. Sculptured relief (Addis Ababa Art School) . . . . 1·60 1·60

177 African Colonial Maps, 1963 and 1973 178 Ethiopian Scout Flags

1973. 10th Anniv of Organization of African Unity. Multicoloured.
846 5c. Type **177** 15 15
847 10c. Map, Headquarters and flags 10 10
848 20c. Map and emblems . . . 40 40
849 40c. Map and "population" ranks 85 85
850 80c. Map on globe, O.A.U. and U.N. emblems . . . . 1·60 1·60

1973. 40th Anniv of Scouting in Ethiopia. Mult.
851 5c. Type **178** 10 10
852 15c. "Scout" sign on highway 15 15
853 30c. Guide teaching old man to read 65 65
854 40c. "First Aid" 90 90
855 60c. Ethiopian scout . . . . 1·90 1·90

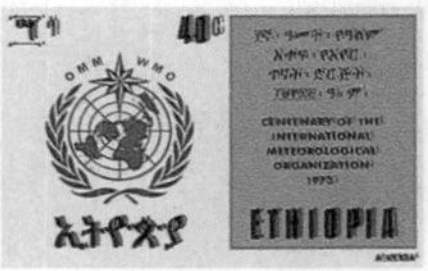

179 W.M.O. Emblem 180 Old Wall, Harar

1973. Cent of World Meteorological Organization.
856 **179** 40c. black, blue & lt blue 75 75
857 – 50c. black and blue 95 95
858 – 60c. multicoloured . . . . 1·10 1·10
DESIGNS: 50c. Wind gauge and emblem; 60c. Weather satellite.

1973. Inauguration of Prince Makonnen Memorial Hospital. Multicoloured.
859 5c. Type **180** 10 10
860 10c. Prince Makonnen, equipment and patients . . 10 10
861 20c. Operating theatre . . . 40 40
862 40c. Scouts giving first-aid . . 70 70
863 80c. Prince Makonnen . . . 1·40 1·40

181 Haile Selassie I

182 Flame Emblem

1973.

864	**181**	5c. multicoloured	10	10
865		10c. multicoloured	10	10
866		15c. multicoloured	10	10
867		20c. multicoloured	15	10
868		25c. multicoloured	20	10
869		30c. multicoloured	25	15
870		35c. multicoloured	30	15
871		40c. multicoloured	35	15
872		45c. multicoloured	35	20
873		50c. multicoloured	40	20
874		55c. multicoloured	50	35
875		60c. multicoloured	65	45
876		70c. multicoloured	70	45
877		90c. multicoloured	1·10	60
878		$1 multicoloured	1·40	1·00
879		$2 multicoloured	3·25	1·90
880		$3 multicoloured	4·75	2·40
881		$5 multicoloured	8·00	4·25

1973. 25th Anniv of Declaration of Human Rights.

882	**182**	40c. gold, green & yell	65	65
883		50c. gold, grn & emerald	85	85
884		60c. gold, grn & orge	1·00	1·00

183 Wicker Furniture

184 Cow, Calf and Syringe

1974. Ethiopian Wickerwork. Various Wicker handicrafts.

885	**183**	5c. multicoloured	10	10
886	–	10c. multicoloured	10	10
887	–	30c. multicoloured	45	45
888	–	50c. multicoloured	80	80
889	–	60c. multicoloured	1·00	1·00

1974. Campaign Against Rinderpest. Mult.

890	5c. Type **184**	10	10
891	15c. Inoculation	10	10
892	20c. Bullock and syringe	40	40
893	50c. Laboratory technician	95	95
894	60c. Symbolic map	1·40	1·40

185 Umbrella Manufacture

1974. 20th Anniv of Haile Selassie I Foundation. Multicoloured.

895	10c. Type **185**	10	10
896	30c. Weaving	50	50
897	50c. Children with books and toys	95	95
898	60c. Foundation building	1·10	1·10

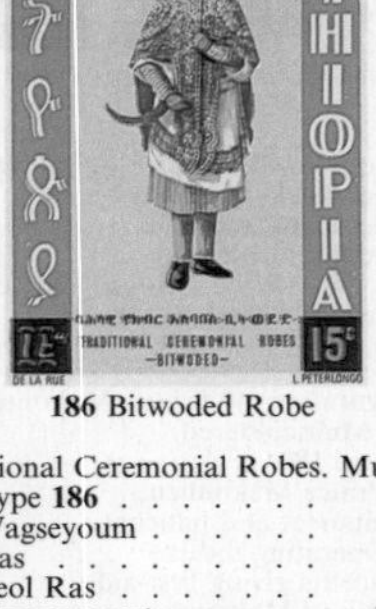

186 Bitwoded Robe

1974. Traditional Ceremonial Robes. Mult.

899	15c. Type **186**	10	10
900	25c. Wagseyoum	25	20
901	35c. Ras	35	35
902	40c. Leol Ras	45	45
903	60c. Negusenegest	1·00	1·00

187 "Population Growth"

1974. World Population Year. Multicoloured.

904	40c. Type **187**	35	35
905	50c. Diagram with large family	45	45
906	60c. "Rising Population"	1·00	1·00

188 U.P.U. and Ethiopian P.T.T. Emblems

1974. Centenary of Universal Postal Union. Multicoloured.

907	15c. Type **188**	10	10
908	50c. Emblem and letters	75	75
909	60c. U.P.U. emblem	90	90
910	70c. U.P.U. emblem and H.Q., Berne	1·00	1·00

189 Landscape

190 "Nymphalidae precis clelia CR"

1974. Meskel Festival.

911	**189**	5c. multicoloured	10	10
912	–	10c. multicoloured	10	10
913	–	20c. multicoloured	20	20
914	–	80c. multicoloured	1·10	1·10

DESIGNS: Nos. 912/4, Various festive scenes similar to Type **189**.

1975. Butterflies (2nd series). Multicoloured.

915	10c. Type **190**	15	15
916	25c. "Nymphalidae charaxes achaemenes F."	30	30
917	45c. "Papilionidae P. dardanus"	80	80
918	50c. "Nymphalidae charaxes druceanus B."	1·10	1·10
919	60c. "Papilionidae P. demodocus"	1·25	1·25

191 "The Magi"

192 Warthog

1975. Religious Paintings in Ethiopian Churches. Multicoloured.

920	5c. Type **191**	10	10
921	10c. "The Entombment"	10	10
922	15c. "Christ with the Apostles"	10	10
923	30c. "The Miracle of the Blind"	25	20
924	40c. "The Crucifixion"	55	55
925	80c. "Christ in Majesty"	1·10	1·10

1975. Animals. Multicoloured.

926	5c. Type **192**	10	10
927	10c. Aardvark	10	10
928	20c. Simien jackal	20	15
929	40c. Gelada	85	85
930	80c. African civet	1·60	1·60

193 Dove crossing Globe

194 Reception Desk

1975. International Women's Year. Mult.

931	40c. Type **193**	50	50
932	50c. I.W.Y. emblem and symbols	65	65
933	90c. "Equality"	1·10	1·10

1975. Opening of National Postal Museum.

934	**194**	10c. multicoloured	10	10
935	–	30c. multicoloured	25	15
936	–	60c. multicoloured	85	85
937	–	70c. multicoloured	1·00	1·00

DESIGNS: 30c. to 70c. Views of museum display area.

195 Map Emblem

196 U.N. Emblem

1975. 1st Anniv of Socialist Government.

938	**195**	5c. multicoloured	10	10
939		10c. multicoloured	10	10
940		25c. multicoloured	15	15
941		50c. multicoloured	65	65
942		90c. multicoloured	1·10	1·10

1975. 30th Anniv of United Nations.

943	**196**	40c. multicoloured	55	55
944		50c. multicoloured	65	65
945		90c. multicoloured	1·10	1·10

197 Illubabor

198 "Delphinium wellbyi"

1975. Regional Hairstyles (1st series). Mult.

946	5. c. Type **197**	10	10
947	15c. Arussi	10	10
948	20c. Eritrea	20	15
949	30c. Bale	25	20
950	35c. Kaffa	45	45
951	50c. Begemder	55	65
952	60c. Shoa	85	85

See also Nos. 1027/33.

1975. Ethiopian Flowers. Multicoloured.

953	5c. Type **198**	10	10
954	10c. "Plectocephalus varians"	10	10
955	20c. "Brachystelma asmarensis" (horiz)	35	35
956	40c. "Ceropegia inflata"	80	80
957	80c. "Erythrina brucei"	1·25	1·25

199 Goalkeeper diving

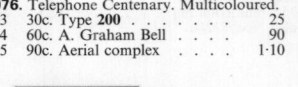

200 Early and Modern Telephones

1976. 10th African Football "Cup of Nations" Championship. Multicoloured.

958	5c. Type **199**	10	10
959	10c. Footballers in tackle	10	10
960	25c. Player shooting at goal	15	15
961	50c. Defender clearing ball	85	85
962	90c. Ball and Ethiopian flag	1·40	1·40

1976. Telephone Centenary. Multicoloured.

963	30c. Type **200**	25	15
964	60c. A. Graham Bell	90	90
965	90c. Aerial complex	1·10	1·10

201 Amulets

202 Boxing

1976. Ethiopian Jewellery.

966	**201**	5c. multicoloured	10	10
967	–	10c. multicoloured	10	10
968	–	20c. multicoloured	35	35
969	–	40c. multicoloured	65	65
970	–	80c. multicoloured	1·10	1·10

Nos. 967/70 are similar to Type **201** showing models with jewellery.

1976. Olympic Games, Montreal. Mult.

971	10c. Type **202**	10	10
972	80c. Shot-putting	1·10	1·10
973	90c. Cycling	1·10	1·10

203 Campaign Emblem

204 Map Emblem

1976. "Development Through Co-operation" Campaign.

974	**203**	5c. multicoloured	10	10
975		10c. multicoloured	10	10
976		25c. multicoloured	15	15
977		50c. multicoloured	65	65
978		90c. multicoloured	1·00	1·00

1976. 2nd Anniv of Republic.

979	**204**	5c. multicoloured	10	10
980		10c. multicoloured	10	10
981		25c. multicoloured	30	30
982		50c. multicoloured	65	65
983		90c. multicoloured	1·00	1·00

205 Crest with Sunburst

206 Donkey Boy and Aircraft

1976.

984	**205**	5c. gold, green & black	10	10
985		10c. gold, orange & blk	10	10
986		15c. gold, blue & black	10	10
987		20c. gold, lilac & black	15	10
988		25c. gold, green & blk	15	10
989		30c. gold, red & black	20	15
990		35c. gold, yellow & blk	25	15
991		40c. gold, green & blk	55	20
992		45c. gold, green & blk	65	50
993		50c. gold, mauve & blk	75	55
994		55c. gold, blue & black	85	65
995		60c. gold, brown & blk	90	65
996		70c. gold, pink & black	1·00	75
997		90c. gold, blue & black	1·10	85
998		$1 gold, green & black	1·40	1·00
999		$2 gold, grey & black	2·50	2·00
1000		$3 gold, purple & black	3·75	2·75
1001		$5 gold, blue & black	6·75	4·75

See also Nos. 1263a/c.

1976. 30th Anniv of Ethiopian Airlines. Multicoloured.

1002	5c. Type **206**	10	10
1003	10c. Crescent on globe	15	15
1004	25c. "Star" of crew and passengers	35	35
1005	50c. Propeller and jet engines	65	65
1006	90c. Aircraft converging on map	1·10	1·10

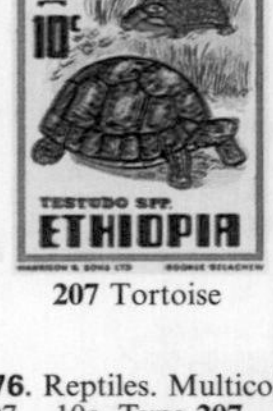

207 Tortoise

208 Cessna 170A dropping Supplies

1976. Reptiles. Multicoloured.

1007	10c. Type **207**	10	10
1008	20c. Chameleon	15	10
1009	30c. Python	25	45
1010	40c. Monitor (lizard)	75	75
1011	80c. Crocodile	1·25	1·25

1976. Relief and Rehabilitation. Mult.

1012	5c. Type **208**	10	10
1013	10c. Carved hand with hammer	10	10
1014	45c. Child supported by banknote	65	65
1015	60c. Map of Ogaden region and desert tracks	85	85
1016	80c. Waif within broken eggshell, camera & film	1·10	1·10

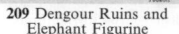

209 Dengour Ruins and Elephant Figurine

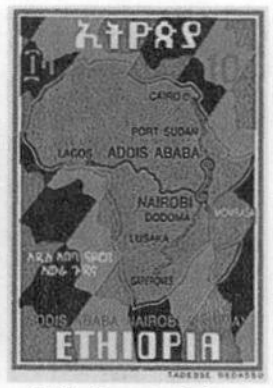

210 Route Map

1977. Ethiopian Archaeology. Multicoloured.
1017 5c. Type **209** 10 10
1018 10c. Yeha temple and bronze ibex 10 10
1019 25c. Sourre Kabanawa dolmen and ancient pot 20 10
1020 50c. Melka Kontoure site and stone axe 75 75
1021 80c. Omo Valley, skull and jawbone . . . . 1·10 1·10

1977. Inauguration of Trans-East African Highway.
1022 **210** 10c. multicoloured . . . 10 10
1023 20c. multicoloured . . . 20 15
1024 40c. multicoloured . . . 50 50
1025 50c. multicoloured . . . 65 65
1026 60c. multicoloured . . . 85 85

1977. Regional Hairstyles (2nd series). As T **197**. Multicoloured.
1027 5c. Wollega 10 10
1028 10c. Godjam 10 10
1029 15c. Tigre 10 10
1030 20c. Harrar 40 40
1031 25c. Gemu Gofa 40 40
1032 40c. Sidamo 80 80
1033 50c. Wollo 90 90

211 Addis Ababa

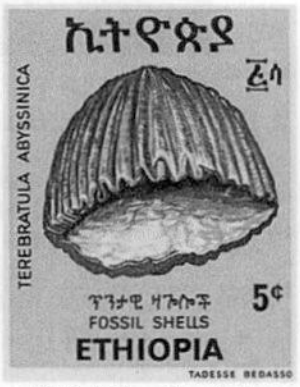

212 "Terebratula abyssinica"

1977. Ethiopian Towns. Multicoloured.
1034 5c. Type **211** 10 10
1035 10c. Asmara 10 10
1036 25c. Harrar 20 15
1037 50c. Jimma 75 75
1038 90c. Dessie . . . . 1·25 1·25

1977. Fossil Shells. Multicoloured.
1039 5c. Type **212** 10 10
1040 10c. "Terebratula subalata" 10 10
1041 25c. "Cuculloea lefeburiaua" 40 40
1042 50c. "Ostrea (gryphea) plicatissima" 75 75
1043 90c. "Trigonia cousobrina" 1·40 1·40

213 Shattered Imperial Crown

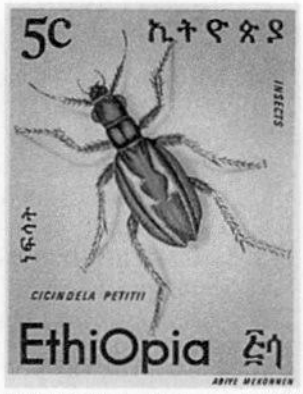

214 "Cicindela petitii"

1977. 3rd Anniv of Republic. Mult.
1044 5c. Type **213** 10 10
1045 10c. Emblem of revolutionary regime . . . 10 10
1046 25c. Warriors with hammer and sickle 20 15
1047 60c. Soldiers and map . . . 50 40
1048 80c. Crest of revolutionary regime . . . . 1·10 1·10

1977. Insects. Multicoloured.
1049 5c. Type **214** 10 10
1050 10c. "Heliocopris dillonii" 10 10
1051 25c. "Poekilocerus vignaudii" 30 20
1052 50c. "Pepsis heros" 80 80
1053 90c. "Pepsis dedjaz" . . . . 1·40 1·40

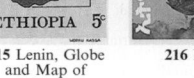

215 Lenin, Globe and Map of Ethiopia

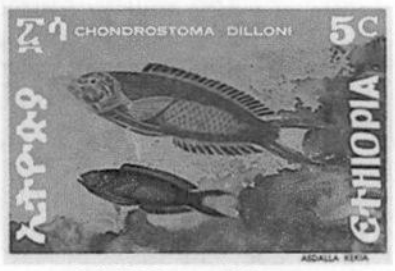

216 Moon Wrasse

1977. 60th Anniv of Russian Revolution.
1054 **215** 5c. multicoloured 10 10
1055 10c. multicoloured . . . 10 10
1056 25c. multicoloured . . . 20 15
1057 50c. multicoloured . . . 65 65
1058 90c. multicoloured . . . 1·10 1·10

1978. Fishes. Multicoloured.
1059 5c. Type **216** 10 10
1060 10c. Yellow boxfish 10 10
1061 25c. Summan grouper . . . 50 50
1062 50c. Sea perch . . . . . . 1·00 1·00
1063 90c. Northern pufferfish . . 1·90 1·90

217 Cattle

218 Emblem and Weapons

1978. Domestic Animals. Multicoloured.
1064 5c. Type **217** 10 10
1065 10c. Donkeys 10 10
1066 25c. Sheep 20 15
1067 50c. Camels 85 85
1068 90c. Horses . . . . 1·40 1·40

1978. "Call of the Motherland". Mult.
1069 5c. Type **218** 10 10
1070 10c. Armed workers 10 10
1071 25c. Map of Africa 20 15
1072 60c. Soldiers 50 65
1073 80c. Nurse and blood donor 70 90

219 Ibex

220 Globe and Emblem

1978. Ancient Bronzes. Multicoloured.
1074 5c. Type **219** 10 10
1075 10c. Lion (horiz) 10 10
1076 25c. Lamp 40 40
1077 50c. Goat (horiz) 90 90
1078 90c. Axe, chisel and sickle 1·50 1·50

1978. World Cup Football Championship, Argentina. Multicoloured.
1079 5c. Type **220** 10 10
1080 20c. Player kicking ball . . 20 15
1081 30c. Ball in net 25 20
1082 55c. F.I.F.A. emblem and ball 80 80
1083 70c. World Cup emblem and pitch (vert) 90 90

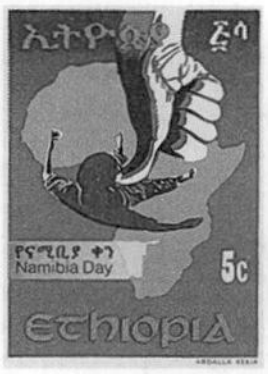

221 Man under Thumb

222 Armed Forces

1978. Namibia Day. Multicoloured.
1084 5c. Type **221** 10 10
1085 10c. Man with pistol 10 10
1086 25c. Soldier 20 20
1087 60c. Bound figure 65 65
1088 80c. Head of African . . . 90 90

1978. 4th Anniv of Revolution. Mult.
1089 80c. Type **222** 90 90
1090 1b. Revolutionaries . . . . 1·10 1·10

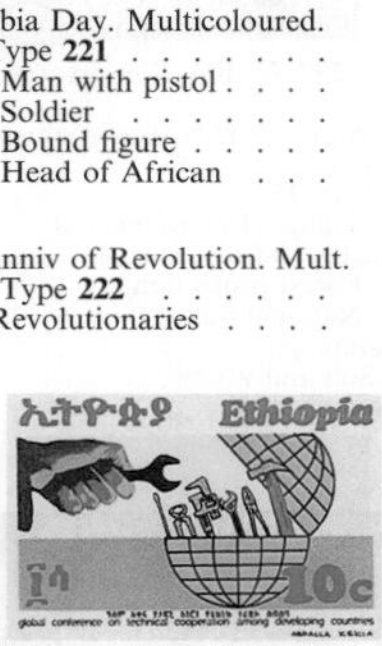

223 Open Globe filled with Tools

1978. U.N. Conference on Technical Co-operation among Developing Countries. Multicoloured.
1091 10c. Type **223** 10 10
1092 15c. Symbols 10 10
1093 25c. World map and gear wheels 20 20
1094 60c. Hands passing spanner over globe 65 65
1095 70c. Geese and tortoise over world map 85 85

224 Human Rights Emblem

225 Manacled Hands and Anti-Apartheid Emblem

1978. 30th Anniv of Human Rights Declaration.
1096 **224** 5c. multicoloured 10 10
1097 15c. multicoloured . . . 10 10
1098 25c. multicoloured . . . 20 20
1099 35c. multicoloured . . . 40 40
1100 1b. multicoloured . . . 1·25 1·25

1978. International Anti-Apartheid Year.
1101 **225** 5c. multicoloured 10 10
1102 20c. multicoloured . . . 15 10
1103 30c. multicoloured . . . 20 20
1104 55c. multicoloured . . . 65 65
1105 70c. multicoloured . . . 75 75

226 Stone Monument at Osole

1979. Ancient Carved Stones from Soddo. Mult.
1106 5c. Type **226** 10 10
1107 10c. Garashino 10 10
1108 25c. Wado 20 20
1109 60c. Ambeut 90 90
1110 80c. Detail of decoration, Tiya . . . . 1·00 1·00

227 Cotton Plant

228 Grar

1979. Cotton Industry. Multicoloured.
1111 5c. Type **227** 10 10
1112 10c. Women spinning cotton 10 10
1113 20c. Reeling cotton onto poles 45 45
1114 65c. Weaving 90 90
1115 80c. Shemma work . . . . 1·10 1·10

1979. Trees. Multicoloured.
1116 5c. Type **228** 10 10
1117 10c. Weira 10 10
1118 25c. Tidh 20 20
1119 50c. Shola 75 75
1120 90c. Zigba . . . . 1·10 1·10

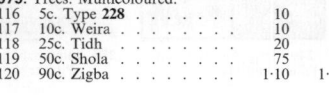

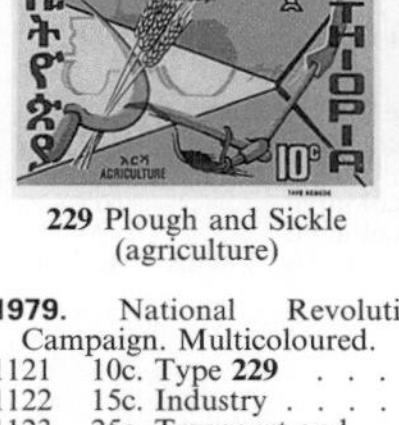

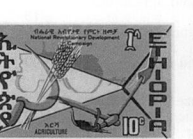

229 Plough and Sickle (agriculture)

230 Family holding Hands

1979. National Revolutionary Development Campaign. Multicoloured.
1121 10c. Type **229** 10 10
1122 15c. Industry 10 10
1123 25c. Transport and communications . . . . . 2·25 75
1124 60c. Education and Health 85 85
1125 70c. Commerce 90 90

1979. International Year of the Child. Mult.
1126 10c. I.Y.C. Emblem 10 10
1127 15c. Type **230** 10 10
1128 25c. Helping a crippled child 40 40
1129 60c. Circle of children . . . 90 90
1130 70c. Black and white children embracing . . . 1·00 1·00

231 Revolutionaries and Emblem

1979. 5th Anniv of Revolution. Mult.
1131 10c. Type **231** 10 10
1132 15c. Soldiers and agriculture 10 10
1133 25c. Emblem of revolution 20 20
1134 60c. Students with torch . . 65 65
1135 70c. Citizens and emblems 75 75

232 "Communications"

233 Incense Container

1979. 3rd World Telecommunications Exhibition, Geneva.
1136 **232** 5c. blue, mauve & blk 10 10
1137 – 30c. multicoloured . . . 50 50
1138 – 35c. multicoloured . . . 50 50
1139 – 45c. multicoloured . . . 70 70
1140 – 65c. multicoloured . . . 90 90
DESIGN: 30c. Telephone handset; 35c. Communications satellite; 45c. Ground receiving aerial; 65c. Television camera.

1979. Wickerwork. Multicoloured.
1141 5c. Type **233** 10 10
1142 10c. Flower vase 10 10
1143 25c. Earthenware cover . . 40 40
1144 60c. Milk container 90 90
1145 80c. Storage container . . . 1·10 1·10

234 Dish

235 Lappet-faced Vulture

1980. Woodwork. Multicoloured.
1146 5c. Type **234** 10 10
1147 30c. Table and chair 50 50
1148 35c. Pestles and mortars . . 50 50
1149 45c. Stools 70 70
1150 65c. Pots 90 90

1980. Birds of Prey. Multicoloured.
1151 10c. Type **235** 70 70
1152 15c. Long-crested eagle . . 80 80
1153 25c. Secretary bird . . . . 1·00 1·00
1154 60c. Abyssinian long-eared owl . . . . 2·75 2·75
1155 70c. Lanner falcon . . . . 3·25 3·25

236 W.H.D. Emblem and Cigarette

237 Lenin in Hiding at Rasliv

1980. Anti-smoking Campaign. Multicoloured.
1156 20c. Skull superimposed on cigarette packet 40 40
1157 60c. Type **236** 85 85
1158 1b. Pipe, cigarette and infected lungs . . . . . . 1·25 1·25

1980. 110th Birth Anniv of Lenin. Mult.
1159 5c. Lenin's House, Pskov . . 10 10
1160 15c. Type **237** 10 10
1161 20c. Lenin as student . . . 20 15
1162 40c. Lenin returns to Russia 50 50
1163 1b. Lenin speaking on the Goerlo plan . . . . . . 1·10 1·10

238 Grevy's Zebra **239** Running

1980. Endangered Animals. Multicoloured.
1164 10c. Type **238** 10 10
1165 15c. Dibatag 15 10
1166 25c. Hunting dog 40 40
1167 60c. Hartebeest 1·00 1·00
1168 70c. Cheetahs 1·10 1·10

1980. Olympic Games, Moscow. Multicoloured.
1169 30c. Type **239** 45 45
1170 70c. Cycling 95 95
1171 80c. Boxing 1·10 1·10

240 Man cutting Blindfold **241** Meal Basket

1980. 6th Anniv of Revolution. Mult.
1172 30c. Type **240** 35 35
1173 40c. Crowd 50 50
1174 50c. Woman cutting chain 65 65
1175 70c. Crowd and flags 1·00 1·00

1980. Bamboo Folk Craft. Multicoloured.
1176 5c. Type **241** 10 10
1177 15c. Hand basket 10 10
1178 25c. Stool 40 40
1179 35c. Fruit compote 65 65
1180 1b. Lamp shade 1·40 1·40

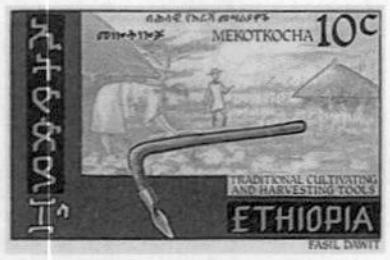

242 Mekotkocha (weeding tool)

1980. Traditional Cultivating and Harvesting Tools. Multicoloured.
1181 10c. Type **242** 10 10
1182 15c. Layda 10 10
1183 40c. Mensh 50 50
1184 45c. Medekdekia 60 60
1185 70c. Mofer and kenber 1·00 1·00

243 Baro River

1981. Baro River Bridge. Multicoloured.
1186 15c. Type **243** 20 10
1187 65c. Bridge under construction 90 90
1188 1b. Bridge 1·40 1·40

244 Wawel Castle, Poland

1981. World Heritage (1st series). Mult.
1189 5c. Type **244** 10 10
1190 15c. Quito Cathedral, Ecuador 10 10
1191 20c. Island of Goree, Senegal 10 10
1192 30c. Messa Verde, U.S.A. 35 35
1193 80c. Simien National Park, Ethiopia 1·00 1·00
1194 1b. L'Anse aux Meadows, Canada 1·10 1·10
See also Nos. 1200/1205.

245 Drinking Vessel

1981. Ancient Pottery. Multicoloured.
1195 20c. Type **245** 15 10
1196 25c. Spice container 15 10
1197 35c. Jug 45 45
1198 40c. Cooking apparatus 55 55
1199 60c. Animal figurine 90 90

246 Biet Medhani Alem Church, Ethiopia

1981. World Heritage (2nd series). Mult.
1200 10c. Type **246** 10 10
1201 15c. Nehanni National Park, Canada 10 10
1202 20c. Lower Falls of the Yellowstone River, U.S.A. 15 10
1203 30c. Aachen Cathedral, West Germany 45 45
1204 80c. Kicker Rock, San Cristobel Island, Ecuador 1·00 1·00
1205 1b. Holy Cross Chapel, Poland (vert) 1·40 1·40

247 Disabled Child learning to write **248** Children at Work and Play

1981. International Year of Disabled Persons. Multicoloured.
1206 5c. Disabled, artificial limbs and crutch 10 10
1207 15c. Type **247** 10 10
1208 20c. Artificial limbs 15 15
1209 40c. Disabled hands learning to knit 50 50
1210 1b. Disabled people learning to weave 1·25 1·25

1981. 7th Anniv of Revolution. Mult.
1211 20c. Type **248** 15 15
1212 60c. Disabled revolutionaries 75 75
1213 1b. Printing and distributing "Serto Ader Gazette" 1·10 1·10

249 Ploughing by Oxen, Tilling and Harvesting by hand **250** Animal-shaped Pitcher

1981. World Food Day. Multicoloured.
1214 5c. Air-drop of food and starving Ethiopians 10 10
1215 15c. Type **249** 10 10
1216 20c. Desert and agricultural scenes 15 15
1217 40c. Agricultural lecture and farmlands 55 55
1218 1b. Cattle and corn 1·40 1·40

1981. Ancient Bronze Implements.
1219 **250** 15c. multicoloured 10 10
1220 – 45c. silver, black & brn 60 60
1221 – 50c. multicoloured 65 65
1222 – 70c. multicoloured 90 90
DESIGNS: 45c. Tsenatsil; 50c. Pitcher; 70c. Pot.

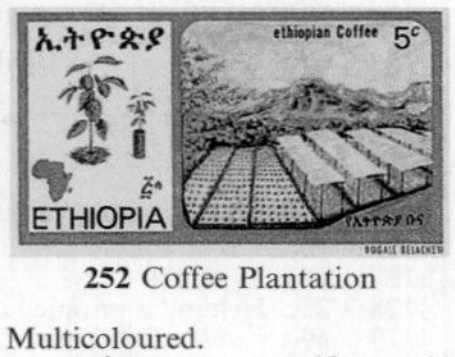

251 Cup **252** Coffee Plantation

1981. Horn Work. Multicoloured.
1223 10c. Tobacco container 10 10
1224 15c. Type **251** 10 10
1225 40c. Tej container 50 50
1226 45c. Goblet 60 60
1227 70c. Spoon 1·00 1·00

1982. Ethiopian Coffee. Multicoloured.
1228 5c. Type **252** 10 10
1229 15c. Coffee bush 10 10
1230 25c. Mature plantation 15 10
1231 35c. Picking coffee 45 45
1232 1b. Pouring and drinking coffee 1·40 1·40

253 Players and Football

1982. World Cup Football Championship, Spain. Multicoloured.
1233 5c. Type **253** 10 10
1234 15c. Player with ball 10 10
1235 20c. Goalkeeper saving ball 15 15
1236 40c. Player kicking ball 60 60
1237 1b. Ball, clasped hands and shirts 1·40 1·40

254 Cattle **255** Preventing Theft

1982. Centenary of Discovery of Tubercle Bacillus. Multicoloured.
1238 15c. Type **254** 10 10
1239 20c. Magnifying glass and bacillus 15 15
1240 30c. Koch with microscope 20 15
1241 35c. Dr. Robert Koch 45 45
1242 80c. T.B. patient and Dr. Koch 1·10 1·10

1982. 8th Anniv of Revolution. Mult.
1243 80c. Type **255** 1·00 1·00
1244 1b. Voting 1·25 1·25

256 Primitive Measurements of Length

1982. World Standards Day. Multicoloured.
1245 5c. Type **256** 10 10
1246 15c. Primitive balance 10 10
1247 20c. Metric measurement 15 10
1248 40c. Weights and scales 50 50
1249 1b. Ethiopian standards emblem 1·40 1·40

257 Wildlife Conservation

1982. 10th Anniv of U.N. Environment Programme. Multicoloured.
1250 5c. Type **257** 10 10
1251 15c. Village (Environmental health and settlement) 10 10
1252 20c. Forest protection 15 10
1253 40c. National literacy campaign 50 50
1254 1b. Soil and water conservation 1·40 1·40

258 Grand Gallery

1983. Sof Omar Caves. Multicoloured.
1255 5c. Type **258** 10 10
1256 10c. Chamber of Columns 10 10
1257 15c. Route through cave 10 10
1258 70c. Map of caves 90 90
1259 80c. Entrance to cave 1·00 1·00

259 "25" on Emblem **260** I.M.O. Emblem and Waves

1983. 25th Anniv of Economic Commission for Africa.
1260 **259** 80c. multicoloured 1·10 1·10
1261 1b. multicoloured 1·40 1·40

1983. 25th Anniv of International Maritime Organization. Multicoloured.
1262 85c. Type **260** 1·10 1·10
1263 1b. Lighthouse and liner 3·75 1·60

1983. As Nos. 998/1000 but with value expressed in "BIRR".
1263a **205** 1b. grn, gold & blk
1263b 2b. grey, gold & blk
1263c 3b. pur, gold & blk

261 U.P.U. Monument, Berne **262** Peace Dove on Globe

1983. World Communications Year. Mult.
1264 25c. Type **261** 15 10
1265 55c. Antenna, satellite and drum 65 65
1266 1b. River bridge and railway tunnel 12·00 13·00

1983. 9th Anniv of Revolution. Mult.
1267 25c. Type **262** 15 10
1268 55c. Red star 75 75
1269 1b. Crest 1·10 1·10

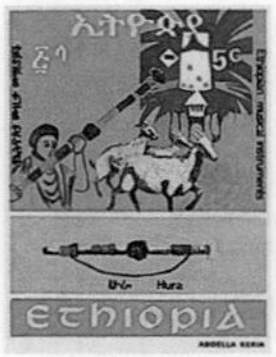

263 Hura and Shepherd **264** "Charaxes galawadiwosi"

1983. Musical Instruments. Multicoloured.
1270 5c. Type **263** 10 10
1271 15c. Dinke and funeral 10 10
1272 20c. Meleket and announcing royal proclamation 35 35
1273 40c. Embilta and royal procession 65 65
1274 1b. Tom and dancers 1·50 1·50

1983. Butterflies. Multicoloured.
1275 10c. Type **264** 15 10
1276 15c. "Epiphora elianae" 30 10
1277 55c. "Batiama rougeoti" 1·00 1·00
1278 1b. "Achaea saboeaereginae" 1·90 1·90

265 I.A.A.Y. Emblem **266** "Protea gaguedi"

1984. International Anti-Apartheid Year.
1279 **265** 5c. multicoloured 10 10
1280 15c. multicoloured 10 10
1281 20c. multicoloured 15 10
1282 40c. multicoloured 55 55
1283 1b. multicoloured 1·40 1·40

1984. Flowers. Multicoloured.
1284 5c. Type **266** 10 10
1285 25c. "Sedum epidendrum" 55 55
1286 50c. "Echinops amplexicaulis" 95 95
1287 1b. "Canarina eminii" 1·90 1·90

267 Konso House

268 Torch on Map and Crowd of Workers

1984. Ethiopian House Architecture. Mult.
1288 15c. Type **267** 15 15
1289 65c. Dorze house 95 95
1290 1b. Harer houses . . . . . 1·50 1·50

1984. 10th Anniv of Revolution. Mult.
1291 5c. Type **268** 10 10
1292 10c. Countrywoman and ploughing with oxen . . . 10 10
1293 15c. Crowd with flag . . . 15 10
1294 20c. Pres. Mengistu, flag, map and crowd 20 15
1295 25c. Soldiers ploughing with oxen 25 20
1296 40c. Workers writing . . . 60 60
1297 45c. Pres. Mengistu addressing Party conference 65 65
1298 50c. Schoolchildren 75 75
1299 70c. Pres. Mengistu and statue . . . . 1·00 1·00
1300 1b. Pres. Mengistu addressing Organization of African Unity meeting 1·40 1·40

269 "Gugs"

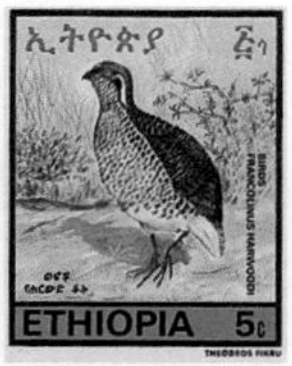
270 Harwood's Francolin

1984. Traditional Games. Multicoloured.
1301 5c. Type **269** 10 10
1302 25c. Tigil (wrestling) 35 35
1303 50c. Gerna (hockey) 75 75
1304 1b. Gebeta (board game) . . 1·40 1·40

1985. Birds. Multicoloured.
1305 5c. Type **270** 35 35
1306 15c. Rouget's rail 50 50
1307 80c. Little bee eater . . . . 2·75 2·25
1308 85c. Red-headed weaver . . 3·25 3·25

271 Hippopotamuses

1985. Mammals. Multicoloured.
1309 20c. Type **271** 20 15
1310 25c. Gerenuk 20 15
1311 40c. Common duiker . . . 65 65
1312 1b. Gunther's dik-dik . . . 1·90 1·90

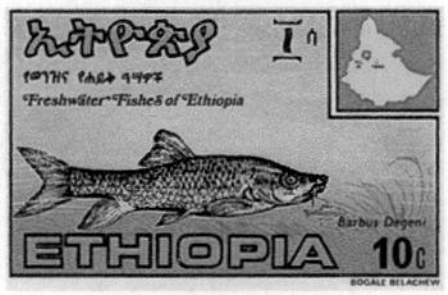
272 Degen's Barb

1985. Fishes. Multicoloured.
1313 10c. Type **272** 20 15
1314 20c. Cylinder labeo 35 15
1315 55c. Toothed tetra . . . . 1·75 1·40
1316 1b. African lungfish . . . . 3·25 2·75

273 "Securidaca longepedunculata"

274 "50" and First Aid

1985. Medicinal Plants. Multicoloured.
1317 10c. Type **273** 10 10
1318 20c. "Plumbago zeylanicum" 15 10
1319 55c. "Brucea antidysenteric" 85 85
1320 1b. "Dorstenia barminiana" 1·60 1·60

1985. 50th Anniv of Ethiopian Red Cross. Multicoloured.
1321 35c. Type **274** 50 50
1322 55c. Community aid scenes 85 85
1323 1b. Nursing scenes . . . . 1·60 1·60

275 Kombolcha Textile Mills

276 U.N. Emblem

1985. 11th Anniv of Revolution. Mult.
1324 10c. Type **275** 10 10
1325 80c. Mugher cement factory 1·10 1·10
1326 1b. Views of famine and drought and resettlement of victims . . . . 1·60 1·60

1985. 40th Anniv of U.N.O.
1327 **276** 25c. multicoloured . . . 15 10
1328 55c. multicoloured . . . 85 85
1329 1b. multicoloured . . . 1·60 1·60

277 Man with Caliper, Boy, Microscope and Crutch

1986. Anti-polio Campaign. Multicoloured.
1330 5c. Type **277** 10 10
1331 10c. Child on crutches . . . 10 10
1332 20c. Doctor fitting child with caliper 15 10
1333 55c. Man with caliper working sewing machine 85 85
1334 1b. Doctor vaccinating baby 1·60 1·60

278 "Millettia ferruginea"

279 Ginger

1986. Trees. Multicoloured.
1335 10c. Type **278** 10 10
1336 30c. "Syzygium guineense" 45 45
1337 50c. "Cordia africana" . . . 80 80
1338 1b. "Hagenia abyssinica" . . 1·60 1·60

1986. Spices and Herbs. Multicoloured.
1339 10c. Type **279** 10 10
1340 15c. Basil 10 10
1341 55c. Mustard 85 85
1342 1b. Cumin . . . . 1·60 1·60

280 One Cent Coin

1986. Coins. Multicoloured.
1343 5c. Type **280** 10 10
1344 10c. 25 cents 10 10
1345 35c. 5 cents 50 50
1346 50c. 50 cents 75 75
1347 1b. 10 cents . . . . 1·60 1·60

281 Globe, Map and Skeleton

1986. 12th Anniv of Discovery of Oldest Known Hominid Skeleton.
1348 **281** 2b. multicoloured . . . 3·75 3·75

282 Military Training

1986. 12th Anniv of Revolution. Mult.
1349 20c. Type **282** 15 10
1350 30c. Tiglachin Monument, Addis Ababa 40 40
1351 55c. Emblem of Delachin Historical Exhibition . . 85 85
1352 85c. Merti food-processing plant . . . . 1·10 1·10

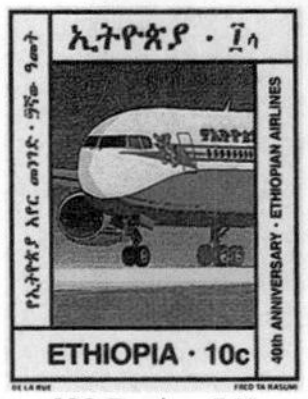
283 Boeing 767

284 Emblem

1986. 40th Anniv of Ethiopian Airlines. Mult.
1353 10c. Type **283** 15 10
1354 20c. Douglas DC-3 . . . . 20 10
1355 30c. Emblem on tail-fin of airplane and crew 20 40
1356 40c. Mechanic working on engine 60 60
1357 1b. Map and Boeing 727 airliner . . . . 1·60 1·60

1986. International Peace Year.
1358 **284** 10c. multicoloured . . . 15 15
1359 80c. multicoloured . . . 1·10 1·10
1360 1b. multicoloured . . . 1·60 1·60

285 Mother breastfeeding Baby

1986. U.N.I.C.E.F. Child Survival Campaign. Multicoloured.
1361 10c. Type **285** 10 10
1362 35c. Doctor vaccinating child and vaccination chart 50 50
1363 50c. Fly on feeding bottle and oral rehydration therapy formula 75 75
1364 1b. Baby on scales and growth chart . . . . . . 1·60 1·60

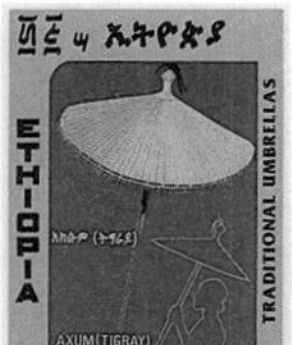
286 Auxum, Tigray

287 "Affar"

1987. Traditional Umbrellas. Multicoloured.
1365 35c. Type **286** 50 50
1366 55c. Negele-Borena, Sidamo 85 85
1367 1b. Jimma, Kafa . . . . . 1·50 1·50

1987. "Defender of his Country". Paintings by Afewerk Tekle. Multicoloured.
1368 50c. Type **287** 75 75
1369 2b. "Adwa" . . . . 2·75 2·75

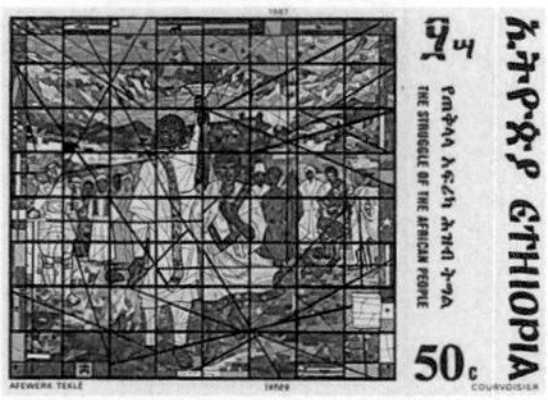
288 People behind Man holding Torch

1987. "The Struggle of the African People" (stained glass windows) by Afewerk Tekle. Multicoloured.
1370 50c. Type **288** 75 75
1371 80c. Robed skeleton, dragon and men covering their faces (23 × 36 mm) . . . 1·10 1·10
1372 1b. Robed skeleton, man killing dragon and people on map of Africa (23 × 36 mm) . . . . . . 1·50 1·50

289 Simien Fox

1987.
1373 **289** 5c. multicoloured 10 10
1374 10c. multicoloured . . . 10 10
1375 15c. multicoloured . . . 10 10
1376 20c. multicoloured . . . 25 20
1377 25c. multicoloured . . . 15 10
1378 45c. multicoloured . . . 60 45
1379 55c. multicoloured . . . 75 55

290 Finfine, Empress Taitu and Emperor Menelik II in "100"

1987. Centenary of Addis Ababa. Mult.
1380 5c. Type **290** 10 10
1381 10c. Traditional housing . . 10 10
1382 80c. Central Addis Ababa 1·10 1·10
1383 1b. Aerial view of city . . . 1·50 1·50

291 Newspaper and People on Map

1987. 13th Anniv of Revolution. Mult.
1384 5c. Type **291** 10 10
1385 10c. People queuing by ballot box and open book 10 10
1386 80c. Ballot paper and map 1·10 1·10
1387 1b. Boeing 727 airliner on runway at Bahir Dar airport . . . . 1·50 1·50

292 Spoon fron Hurso, Harerge

1987. Wooden Spoons. Multicoloured.
1388 85c. Type **292** 95 95
1389 1b. Spoon from Borena, Sidamo . . . . 1·10 1·10

293 Village Programme

1988. International Year of Shelter for the Homeless (1987). Multicoloured.
1390 10c. Type **293** 10 10
1391 35c. Resettlement programme 20 15
1392 50c. Urban improvement programme 50 50
1393 1b. Co-operative and Government housing . . 1·00 1·00

294 Lenin and Delegates

1988. 70th Anniv of Russian Revolution.
1394 **294** 1b. multicoloured . . . 1·10 1·10

295 Bow and Arrows

296 Anniversary Emblem

1988. Traditional Hunting Weapons. Mult.

1395	85c. Type **295**	90	90
1396	1b. Double-pronged spear	1·10	1·10

1988. 125th Anniv of Red Cross.

1397 **296**	85c. multicoloured	85	85
1398	1b. multicoloured	1·10	1·10

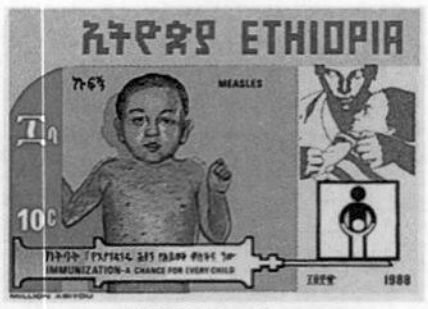

297 Measles

1988. U.N.I.C.E.F. Child Vaccination Campaign. Multicoloured.

1399	10c. Type **297**	10	10
1400	35c. Tetanus	20	15
1401	50c. Whooping cough	45	45
1402	1b. Diphtheria	85	85

298 "Let there be Peace in Africa and the World" (detail, Afewerk Tekle)

299 Mikoyan Gurevich MiG-23 above Simien Mountains and Farmland

1988. 25th Anniv of Organization of African Unity.

1403 **298**	2b. multicoloured	1·90	1·90

1988. "The Victory of Ethiopia" (triptych) by Afewerk Tekle. Details of the mural in Heroes' Centre, Debre Zeit. Multicoloured.

1404	10c. Type **299**	20	10
1405	20c. Coffee plantation, rural homelife and farmers going to work	15	10
1406	35c. New Ethiopia rising above flags and people	20	15
1407	55c. Mikoyan Gurevich MiG-21 over port of Assab (horiz)	40	45
1408	80c. Worker in foundry (horiz)	50	65
1409	1b. Villagers engaged in cottage industries (horiz)	85	85

300 Sidamo Bracelet

1988. Bracelets. Multicoloured.

1410	15c. Type **300**	10	10
1411	85c. Arsi bracelet	85	85
1412	1b. Harerge bracelet	1·00	1·00

301 Dollars on Map

1988. International Agricultural Development Fund. Multicoloured.

1413	15c. Type **301**	10	10
1414	85c. Agricultural activities	85	85
1415	1b. Farmer and produce	1·00	1·00

302 First Session of National Shengo (assembly)

1988. 1st Anniv of People's Democratic Republic of Ethiopia. Multicoloured.

1416	5c. Type **302**	10	10
1417	10c. President Lt.-Col. Mengistu Haile Mariam	10	10
1418	80c. State emblem and flag	85	85
1419	1b. State Council building	1·00	1·00

303 One Birr Note

1988. Banknotes. Multicoloured.

1420	5c. Type **303**	10	10
1421	10c. Five birr note	10	10
1422	20c. Ten birr note	15	10
1423	75c. 50 birr note	75	75
1424	85c. 100 birr note	85	85

1988. World Aids Day. Nos. 1376/9 optd **WORLD AIDS DAY.**

1425 **289**	20c. multicoloured	15	10
1426	25c. multicoloured	15	10
1427	45c. multicoloured	60	60
1428	55c. multicoloured	75	75

305 Emblem within "40"

1988. 40th Anniv of W.H.O.

1429 **305**	50c. multicoloured	50	50
1430	65c. multicoloured	65	65
1431	85c. multicoloured	85	85

306 Gambella Gere (leg rattle)

1989. Musical Instruments. Multicoloured.

1432	30c. Type **306**	35	35
1433	40c. Konos fanfa (pipes)	40	40
1434	50c. Konso chancha (waist rattle)	50	50
1435	85c. Gendeberet negareet (drum)	85	85

307 "Abyot" (container ship)

1989. 25th Anniv of Ethiopian Shipping Lines. Multicoloured.

1436	15c. Type **307**	80	20
1437	30c. "Wolwol" (container ship)	95	25
1438	55c. "Queen of Sheba" (freighter)	1·10	40
1439	1b. "Abbay Wonz" under construction	1·75	90

308 Yellow-faced Parrot

1989. Birds. Multicoloured.

1440	10c. Type **308**	15	15
1441	35c. White-winged chiffchat	75	75
1442	50c. Yellow-rumped seedeater	95	95
1443	1b. Dark-headed oriole	2·10	2·10

309 Making Vellum

310 Greater Kudu

1989. Ethiopian Manuscripts. Multicoloured.

1444	5c. Type **309**	10	10
1445	10c. Making inks, ink horns and pens	10	10
1446	20c. Preparing writing materials and scribe	10	10
1447	75c. Binding books	75	75
1448	85c. Finished books	85	85

1989. Wildlife. Multicoloured.

1449	30c. Type **310**	40	40
1450	40c. Lesser kudu	50	50
1451	50c. Roan antelope	50	50
1452	85c. Nile lechwe	85	85

311 Melka Wakana Hydro-electric Power Station

312 Bank Emblem

1989. 2nd Anniv of People's Democratic Republic of Ethiopia. Multicoloured.

1453	15c. Type **311**	10	10
1454	75c. Adea Berga Dairy Farm	75	75
1455	1b. Pawe Hospital	1·00	1·00

1989. 25th Anniv of African Development Bank.

1456 **312**	20c. multicoloured	15	10
1457	80c. multicoloured	85	85
1458	1b. multicoloured	1·00	1·00

313 Emblem

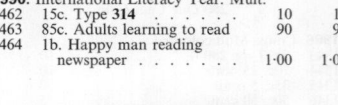

314 Unhappy Man with Newspaper Upside Down

1990. 10th Anniv of Pan-African Postal Union.

1459 **313**	50c. multicoloured	50	50
1460	70c. multicoloured	70	70
1461	80c. multicoloured	80	80

1990. International Literacy Year. Mult.

1462	15c. Type **314**	10	10
1463	85c. Adults learning to read	90	90
1464	1b. Happy man reading newspaper	1·00	1·00

315 Marathon Race

1990. Abebe Bikila (marathon runner). Mult.

1465	5c. Type **315**	10	10
1466	10c. Bikila carrying national flag during Olympic opening ceremony	10	10
1467	20c. Bikila running in number 11 vest	10	10
1468	75c. Bikila running in number 69 vest	80	80
1469	85c. Bikila with medals and cups (vert)	90	90

316 Revolutionary Flag

1990.

1470 **316**	5c. multicoloured	10	10
1471	10c. multicoloured	10	10
1472	15c. multicoloured	10	10
1473	20c. multicoloured	10	10
1474	25c. multicoloured	15	10
1475	30c. multicoloured	15	10
1476	35c. multicoloured	15	15
1477	40c. multicoloured	20	15
1478	45c. multicoloured	40	40
1479	50c. multicoloured	40	40
1480	55c. multicoloured	45	45
1481	60c. multicoloured	50	50
1482	70c. multicoloured	60	60
1483	80c. multicoloured	65	65
1484	85c. multicoloured	70	70
1485	90c. multicoloured	75	75
1486	1b. multicoloured	85	85
1487	2b. multicoloured	1·60	1·60
1488	3b. multicoloured	2·50	2·50

317 Ploughing and Sowing

1990. Teff. Multicoloured.

1489	5c. Type **317**	10	10
1490	10c. Harvesting	10	10
1491	20c. Oxen threshing grain underfoot	10	10
1492	75c. Grinding teff flour and making starter batter	75	75
1493	85c. Family eating baked injera	85	85

318 Male and Female Ibexes

319 Deterioration in Victim's Health

1990. Walia Ibex. Multicoloured.

1494	5c. Type **318**	10	10
1495	15c. Male ibex	10	10
1496	20c. Male ibex (different)	10	10
1497	1b. Male ibexes fighting (horiz)	1·00	1·00

1991. World Aids Day. Multicoloured.

1498	15c. Type **319**	10	10
1499	85c. Aids education	80	80
1500	1b. Preventive measures and family sheltered by umbrella	95	95

320 Volcano

1991. International Decade for Natural Disaster Reduction. Multicoloured.

1501	5c. Type **320**	10	10
1502	10c. Earthquake	10	10
1503	15c. Drought	10	10
1504	30c. Flood	15	10
1505	50c. W.H.O. hygiene instruction	30	45
1506	1b. Red Cross workers helping disaster victims	95	95

321 Constructing Cannon

1991. Emperor Theodor's Cannon "Sevastopol". Multicoloured.

1507	15c. Type **321**	10	10
1508	85c. Completed cannon on carriage	80	80
1509	1b. Hauling cannon uphill	95	95

322 Diadem Squirrelfish

323 Balambaras

1991. Fishes. Multicoloured.

1510		5c. Type **322**	20	20
1511		15c. Blue-cheeked butterflyfish	20	20
1512		80c. Regal angelfish	1·50	1·50
1513		1b. Grey reef shark	2·00	2·00

1992. Traditional Ceremonial Robes (military group). Multicoloured.

1514		5c. Type **323**	10	10
1515		15c. Kegnazmatch	10	10
1516		80c. Fitawurari (Army Commander)	75	75
1517		1b. Dedjazmatch	90	90

324 Devil's Mortar

326 Plate

325 Afar House

1992. Flowers. Multicoloured.

1518		5c. Type **324**	10	10
1519		15c. "Delphinium dasycaulon"	10	10
1520		80c. Cow's salt	65	65
1521		1b. Red hot poker	85	85

1992. Ethiopian Houses. Multicoloured.

1522		15c. Type **325**	10	10
1523		35c. Anuak house	20	15
1524		50c. Gimira house	30	20
1525		1b. Oromo house	85	85

1992. Pottery from Sixth Tomb, Yeha. Mult.

1526		15c. Type **326**	10	10
1527		85c. Milk jar	50	35
1528		1b. Wine vessel	55	40

327 Campaign Emblem

328 Catchel (hand rattle)

1992. Pan-African Rinderpest Campaign.

1529	**327**	20c. gold, green & black	10	10
1530		80c. multicoloured	45	30
1531		1b. multicoloured	55	40

1993. Traditional Musical Instruments. Mult.

1532		15c. Type **328**	10	10
1533		35c. Huldudwa (wind instrument)	10	10
1534		50c. Dita (stringed instrument)	15	10
1535		1b. Atamo (drum)	30	20

329 Banded Barbets

331 Caraway Seed

330 Honey Badger

1993. Birds. Multicoloured.

1536		15c. Type **329**	45	45
1537		35c. Ruppell's chats	45	45
1538		50c. Abyssinian catbirds	65	65
1539		1b. White-billed starling	1·40	1·40

1993. Mammals. Multicoloured.

1540		15c. Type **330**	10	10
1541		35c. Spotted-necked otter	10	10
1542		50c. Rock hyrax	15	10
1543		1b. White-tailed mongoose	30	20

1993. Spicy Herbs. Multicoloured.

1544		5c. Type **331**	10	10
1545		15c. Garlic	10	10
1546		80c. Turmeric	20	15
1547		1b. Capsicum peppers	30	20

332 Southern White-banded Papilio

333 "C. variabilis"

1993. Butterflies. Multicoloured.

1548		20c. Type **332**	10	10
1549		30c. King swallowtail	10	10
1550		50c. Small striped swallowtail	15	10
1551		1b. Veined swallowtail	30	20

1993. Beetles. Multicoloured.

1552		15c. Type **333**	10	10
1553		35c. "Lycus trabeatus"	10	10
1554		50c. "Malachius bifasciatus"	15	10
1555		1b. "Homoeogryllus xanthographus"	30	20

334 "Euphorbia amliphylla"

335 Lake Wonchi

1993. Trees. Multicoloured.

1556		15c. Type **334**	10	10
1557		35c. "Erythrina brucei"	10	10
1558		50c. "Draceana steudneri"	15	10
1559		1b. "Allophylus abbyssinicus"	30	20

1993. Lakes. Multicoloured.

1560		15c. Type **335**	10	10
1561		35c. Lake Zuquala	10	10
1562		50c. Lake Ashengi	10	10
1563		1b. Lake Tana	25	15

336 Simien Fox

1994. Dated "1991". Mult, frame colours given.

1564	**336**	5c. lilac		
1565		10c. brown		
1566		15c. yellow		
1567		20c. pink		
1568		40c. pink		
1569		55c. green		
1570		60c. blue		
1571		80c. blue		
1572		85c. green		
1573		1b. green		

For similar stamps dated "1993" see Nos. 1596/1615.

337 Flag and Fighter

338 Emblem

1994. 3rd Anniv of Ethiopian People's Revolutionary Democratic Front Transitional Government. Multicoloured.

1574		15c. Type **337** (control of Addis Ababa, May 1991)	10	10
1575		35c. Peaceful and Democratic Transition Conference, Addis Ababa, July 1991	10	10
1576		50c. Elections, June 1994	10	10
1577		1b. Flag and Government arms	25	15

1994. International Year of the Family.

1578	**338**	15c. multicoloured	10	10
1579		85c. multicoloured	20	15
1580		1b. multicoloured	25	15

339 Postal Messengers

1994. Centenary of Postal Services in Ethiopia. Multicoloured.

1581		60c. Postal workers, magnifying glass over 1st Ethiopian stamp and early postal messenger	15	10
1582		75c. Type **339**	20	15
1583		80c. Old post office and early mechanized post transport	2·00	40
1584		85c. Rural service	20	15
1585		1b. Express Mail Service	2·00	40

340 Plant

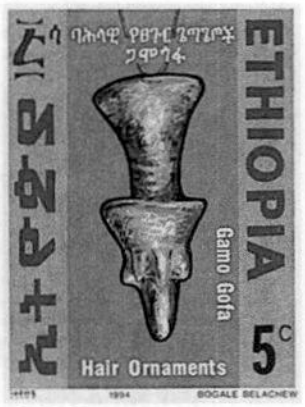

341 Iron Ornament, Gamo Gofa

1994. The Enset Plant. Multicoloured.

1587		10c. Type **340**	10	10
1588		15c. Enset growing beside house	10	10
1589		25c. Gathering and preparation	10	10
1590		50c. Plantation	10	10
1591		1b. Prepared food	20	15

1994. Hair Ornaments. Multicoloured.

1592		5c. Type **341**	10	10
1593		15c. Aluminium beads, Sidamo	10	10
1594		80c. Metal ornament, Gamo Gofa (different)	20	15
1595		1b. Silver hairpin, Wello	20	15

342 Simien Fox

1994. Dated "1993". Mult, frame colours given.

1596	**342**	5c. lilac	10	10
1597		10c. brown	10	10
1598		15c. yellow	10	10
1599		20c. pink	10	10
1600		25c. yellow	15	10
1601		30c. yellow	15	10
1602		35c. orange	20	15
1603		40c. pink	25	20
1604		45c. orange	25	20
1605		50c. mauve	30	25
1606		55c. green	30	25
1607		60c. blue	35	30
1608		65c. lilac	35	30
1609		70c. green	40	35
1610		75c. green	45	40
1611		80c. blue	45	40
1612		85c. green	50	45
1614		1b. green	55	50
1615		2b. brown	1·10	95

344 Anniversary Emblem

1994. 50th Anniv of I.C.A.O.

1620	**344**	20c. blue, yell & mve	10	10
1621		80c. blue and yellow	20	15
1622		1b. bl, yell & ultram	20	15

1994. 30th Anniv of African Development Bank. Nos. 1608/10 and 1612 optd with map of Africa and **30TH ANNIVERSARY OF BANQUE AFRICAINE DE DEVELOPPEMENT AFRICAN DEVELOPMENT BANK.**

1623	**342**	65c. multicoloured	35	30
1624		70c. multicoloured	40	35
1625		75c. multicoloured	45	40
1626		85c. multicoloured	55	50

346 Erbo (dish)

1995. Traditional Food Serving Utensils. Multicoloured.

1627		30c. Type **346**	10	10
1628		70c. Sedieka (round table)	15	10
1629		1b. Tirar (rectangular table)	20	15

347 Kuncho (young boys and girls)

1995. Traditional Hairstyles. Multicoloured.

1630		25c. Type **347**	10	10
1631		75c. Gamme (unmarried women)	15	10
1632		1b. Sadulla (married women until birth of first child)	20	15

348 Anniversary Emblem

1995. 50th Anniv of F.A.O.

1633	**348**	20c. multicoloured	10	10
1634		80c. multicoloured	15	10
1635		1b. multicoloured	20	15

349 Dangora (digging tool)

1995. Traditional Agricultural Tools. Mult.

1636		15c. Type **349**	10	10
1637		35c. Gheso (hoe)	10	10
1638		50c. Akafa (hoe)	10	10
1639		1b. Ankasse (digging tool)	20	15

350 Anniversary Emblem

1995. 50th Anniv of U.N.O.

1640	**350**	20c. multicoloured	10	10
1641		80c. multicoloured	15	10
1642		1b. multicoloured	20	15

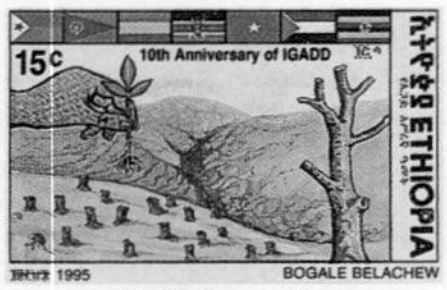
351 Reforestation

1995. 10th Anniv of Intergovernmental Authority on Drought and Development. Multicoloured.
1643 15c. Type **351** 10 10
1644 35c. People moving from drought area 10 10
1645 50c. Boy picking fruit . . . 10 10
1646 1b. Member countries' flags and map of East Africa 20 15

352 Map of Battle Site

1996. Cent of Victory at Battle of Adwa. Mult.
1647 40c. Type **352** 10 10
1648 50c. Map of Africa and emblem 10 10
1649 60c. Ship and Italian soldiers 30 10
1650 70c. Battle scenes 15 10
1651 80c. Soldiers surrendering and frontline 15 10
1652 1b. Emperor Menelik II and Empress Zauditu 20 10

353 Village

1996. 25th Anniv of United Nations Volunteers' Service. Multicoloured.
1654 20c. Type **353** 10 10
1655 30c. Planting 10 10
1656 50c. Teacher and pupils . . . 10 10
1657 1b. Parents and child . . . 20 10

354 Boxing

355 Child Vaccination

1996. Olympic Games, Atlanta. Unissued stamps (for 1984 Olympics) optd with Atlanta Olympics emblem as in T **354**. Multicoloured.
1658 15c. Type **354** 10 10
1659 20c. Swimming 10 10
1660 40c. Cycling 10 10
1661 85c. Running 20 10
1662 1b. Football 20 10

1996. 50th Anniv of U.N.I.C.E.F. Mult.
1663 10c. Anniversary emblem . . 10 10
1664 15c. Type **355** 10 10
1665 25c. Girl carrying water bottle and boy drinking from tap 10 10
1666 50c. School children writing 10 10
1667 1b. Mother breastfeeding . . 20 15

356 Discussion of Constitution

1996. Establishment of Federal Democratic Republic (August 1995). Multicoloured.
1668 10c. Type **356** 10 10
1669 20c. Ballot papers and boxes 10 10
1670 30c. Voting methods and Parliament building . . . 10 10
1671 40c. Parliament building, ballot paper and meeting of legislature 10 10
1672 1b. New national flag, President and Prime Minister, Parliament Building and legislature 20 10

357 Baskets from Jimma

1997. Basketwork (1st series). Multicoloured.
1673 5c. Type **357** 10 10
1674 15c. Containers from Wello 10 10
1675 80c. Baskets from Welega 15 10
1676 1b. Bags from Shewa . . . 20 10
See also Nos. 1677/9 and 1718/20.

1997. Basketwork (2nd series). As T **357**. Mult.
1677 35c. Baskets from Arssi (vert) 10 10
1678 65c. Baskets from Gojam (vert) 10 10
1679 1b. Baskets from Harer (vert) 20 10

358 Emblem

1997. United Nations Decade against Drug Abuse and Trafficking.
1680 **358** 20c. multicoloured . . . 10 10
1681 80c. multicoloured . . . 15 10
1682 1b. multicoloured . . . 15 10

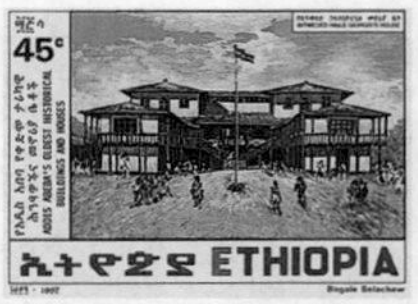
359 Bitweded Haile Giorgis's House

1997. Historic Buildings of Addis Ababa (1st series). Multicoloured.
1683 45c. Type **359** 10 10
1684 55c. Alfred Elg's house (vert) 10 10
1685 3b. Menelik's elfign 50 35

360 Ras Biru W/Gabriel's House

1997. Historic Buildings of Addis Ababa (2nd series). Multicoloured.
1686 60c. Type **360** 10 10
1687 75c. Sheh Hojele Alhassen's house 10 10
1688 80c. Fitawrari H/Giorgis Dinegde's house 10 10
1689 85c. Etege Taitu Hotel . . . 15 10
1690 1b. Dejazmach Wube Atnafseged's house . . . 15 10

361 Golden-mantled Woodpecker ("Golden-backed Woodpecker")

363 Map of Italy and Removal of Obelisk

362 Emblem and Bushbuck

1998. Multicoloured, colour of panel at right given.
1691 **361** 5c. blue 10 10
1692 10c. yellow 10 10
1693 15c. blue 10 10
1694 20c. orange 10 10
1695 25c. violet 10 10
1696 30c. blue 10 10
1697 35c. red 10 10
1698 40c. mauve 10 10
1699 45c. green 10 10
1700 50c. pink 10 10
1701 55c. blue 10 10
1702 60c. red 10 10
1703 65c. violet 10 10
1704 70c. yellow 10 10
1705 75c. lilac 10 10
1706 80c. green 10 10
1707 85c. grey 15 10
1708 90c. orange 15 10
1709 1b. green 15 10
1710 2b. pink 30 20
1711 3b. mauve 45 30
1712 5b. yellow 75 55
1713 10b. yellow . . . . . . 1·50 1·10

1998. 18th Anniv of Pan-African Postal Union. Multicoloured.
1714 45c. Type **362** (inscr "Deculla Bushback") . . 10 10
1715 55c. Soemmerring's gazelle 10 10
1716 1b. Defassa waterbuck . . . 15 10
1717 2b. African ("Black") buffalo 30 20

1998. Basketwork (3rd series). As T **357**. Mult.
1718 45c. Baskets from Gonder 10 10
1719 55c. Baskets from Harere 10 10
1720 3b. Baskets from Tigray . . 45 30

1998. Project to Return the Axum Obelisk from Rome to Ethiopia. Multicoloured.
1721 45c. Type **363** 10 10
1722 55c. Axum obelisk in Rome 10 10
1723 3b. Map of Ethiopia, obelisk and Axum 45 30

364 Workers carrying Rail

1998. Centenary (1997) of Addis Ababa–Djibouti Railway. Multicoloured.
1724 45c. Type **364** 10 10
1725 55c. Steam locomotive No. 404 . . . . 10 10
1726 1b. Railway station, Addis Ababa 15 10
1727 2b. Diesel locomotive . . . 30 20

365 Anniversary Emblem and Globe of People

1998. 50th Anniv of Universal Declaration of Human Rights.
1728 **365** 45c. multicoloured . . . 10 10
1729 55c. multicoloured . . . 10 10
1730 1b. multicoloured . . . 15 10
1731 2b. multicoloured . . . 30 20

366 Mother Teresa

1999. Mother Teresa (founder of Missionaries of Charity) Commemoration. Multicoloured.
1732 45c. Type **366** 10 10
1733 55c. Praying 10 10
1734 1b. Carrying child 15 10
1735 2b. Smiling 30 20

367 Head of Fish

1999. International Year of the Ocean.
1736 **367** 45c. multicoloured . . . 10 10
1737 55c. multicoloured . . . 10 10
1738 1b. multicoloured . . . 15 10
1739 2b. multicoloured . . . 30 20

368 Emblem and Globe

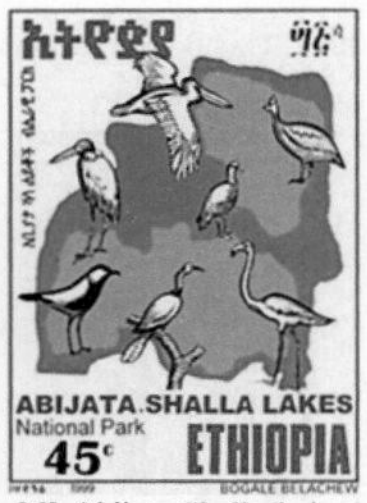
369 Abijata-Shalla Lakes National Park

1999. World Environment Day.
1740 **368** 45c. multicoloured . . . 10 10
1741 55c. multicoloured . . . 10 10
1742 1b. multicoloured . . . 15 10
1743 2b. multicoloured . . . 30 20

1999. National Parks (1st series). Multicoloured.
1744 45c. Type **369** 10 10
1745 70c. Nechisar National Park 10 10
1746 85c. Bale Mountains National Park 15 10
1747 2b. Awash National Park (horiz) 30 20
See also Nos 1752/5.

370 "125" and Emblem

371 Omo National Park

1999. 125th Anniv of Universal Postal Union.
1748 **370** 20c. multicoloured . . . 10 10
1749 80c. multicoloured . . . 10 10
1750 1b. multicoloured . . . 15 10
1751 2b. multicoloured . . . 30 20

1999. National Parks (2nd series). Multicoloured.
1752 50c. Type **371** 15 10
1753 70c. Mago National Park 15 10
1754 80c. Yangudi-Rassa National Park 20 15
1755 2b. Gambella National Park (horiz) 25 15

372 Woman nursing Elderly Man

1999. International Year of the Elderly. Mult.
1756 45c. Type **372** 15 10
1757 70c. Elderly couple gardening 15 10
1758 85c. Elderly man with three youths 20 15
1759 2b. Elderly man with two youths 25 15

EXPRESS LETTER STAMPS

E 65 Motor-cycle Messenger

1947. Inscr "EXPRESS".

E357	E 65	30c. brown	2·75	75
E358	–	50c. blue	3·25	90

DESIGN: 50c. G.P.O., Addis Ababa.

POSTAGE DUE STAMPS

(D 3)

D 77

1896. Optd with Type D **3**.

D 8	1	¼g. green	1·25	
D 9		½g. red	1·25	
D10		1g. blue	1·25	
D11		2g. brown	1·25	
D12		4g. red	90	
D13		8g. mauve	90	
D14		16g. black	90	

1905. Optd **TAXE a PERCEVOIR T**.

D108	1	¼g. green	10·00	10·00
D109		½g. red	10·00	10·00
D110		1g. blue	10·00	10·00
D111		2g. brown	10·00	10·00
D112	2	4g. red	10·00	10·00
D113		8g. mauve	15·00	15·00
D114		16g. black	17·00	17·00

1907. As above further optd with value in figures between stars.

D122	1	¼g. green	17·00	17·00
D123		½g. red	17·00	17·00
D124		1g. blue	17·00	17·00
D125		2g. brown	17·00	17·00
D126	2	4g. red	17·00	17·00
D127		8g. mauve	17·00	17·00
D128		16g. black	25·00	25·00

1908. Optd with Amharic inscription and large **T** in triangle.

D140	1	¼g. green	1·60	1·60
D141		½g. red	1·60	1·60
D142		1g. blue	1·60	1·60
D143		2g. brown	2·00	2·00
D144	2	4g. red	3·00	3·00
D145		8g. mauve	7·50	7·50
D146		16g. black	13·50	13·50

1913. Stamps of 1909 and the 1g. of 1919 optd with Amharic inscription and large **T** in triangle.

D161	19	¼g. green	75	75
D162		½g. red	1·10	1·10
D163		1g. orange and green	2·50	2·50
D210	–	1g. black & pur (No. 184)	3·75	3·75
D164	20	2g. blue	3·00	3·00
D165		4g. red and green	4·75	4·75
D166	–	8g. grey & red (No. 152)	6·00	6·00
D167	–	16g. red (No. 153)	16·00	16·00

1951.

D417	D 77	1c. green	10	15
D418		5c. red	20	20
D419		10c. violet	55	55
D420		20c. brown	80	85
D421		50c. blue	2·00	2·25
D422		$1 purple	4·00	4·00

FALKLAND ISLANDS Pt. 1

A British colony in the South Atlantic.

1878. 12 pence = 1 shilling;
20 shillings = 1 pound.
1971. 100 (new) pence = 1 pound.

3

6

1878.

17b	3	½d. green	2·00	3·00
23		1d. red to brown	5·50	2·00
26		2d. purple	5·00	11·00
30		2½d. blue	26·00	11·00
32		4d. black	10·00	21·00
3		6d. green	70·00	65·00
34		6d. yellow	30·00	42·00
35		9d. red	35·00	55·00
38		1s. brown	48·00	48·00
41	–	2s.6d. blue	£225	£250
42	6	5s. red	£190	£225

DESIGN: 2s.6d. As Type **6**, but different frame.

1891. No. 23 bisected diagonally and each half surch **½d.**

13	3	½d. on half of 1d. brown	£550	£300

7

8

1904.

43	7	½d. green	4·25	1·50
44b		1d. red	1·00	2·50
45		2d. purple	16·00	26·00
46		2½d. blue	29·00	7·50
47		6d. orange	38·00	48·00
48		1s. brown	40·00	32·00
49b	8	3s. green	£130	£120
50		5s. red	£190	£150

1912. As T **7/8** but portrait of King George V.

60		½d. green	2·75	3·50
74		1d. red	5·00	1·25
75		2d. purple	15·00	7·00
76b		2½d. blue	6·50	16·00
77		2½d. purple on yellow	4·50	35·00
64		6d. orange	14·00	20·00
65		1s. brown	32·00	30·00
66		3s. green	85·00	80·00
67		5s. red	95·00	£100
67b		5s. purple	80·00	£110
68		10s. red on green	£160	£250
69		£1 black on red	£425	£500

1918. As 1912, optd **WAR STAMP**.

70b		½d. green	50	6·50
71c		1d. red	50	3·75
72a		1s. brown	4·00	45·00

1928. No. 75 surch **2½D**.

115		2½d. on 2d. purple	£850	£850

13 Fin Whale and Gentoo Penguins

15 Romney Marsh Ram

1929.

116	13	½d. green	1·25	3·00
117		1d. red	3·75	80
118		2d. grey	2·75	2·75
119		2½d. blue	2·75	2·25
120		4d. orange	16·00	13·00
121		6d. purple	16·00	13·00
122		1s. black on green	20·00	35·00
123		2s.6d. red on blue	48·00	48·00
124		5s. green on yellow	75·00	90·00
125		10s. red on green	£140	£180
126		£1 black on red	£300	£375

1933. Centenary of British Administration. Inscr "1833–1933".

127	15	½d. black and green	1·75	6·50
128	–	1d. black and red	3·50	2·25
129	–	1½d. black and blue	14·00	17·00
130	–	2d. black and brown	10·00	22·00
131	–	3d. black and violet	15·00	18·00
132	–	4d. black and orange	16·00	16·00
133	–	6d. black and grey	50·00	60·00
134	–	1s. black and olive	45·00	70·00
135	–	2s.6d. black and violet	£170	£190
136	–	5s. black and yellow	£550	£750
137	–	10s. black and brown	£600	£850
138	–	£1 black and red	£1600	£2000

DESIGNS—HORIZ: 1d. Iceberg; 1½d. Whale-catcher; 2d. Port Louis; 3d. Map of Falkland Islands; 4d. South Georgia; 6d. Fin whale; 1s. Government House, Stanley. VERT: 2s.6d. Battle Memorial; 5s. King penguin; 10s. Arms; £1 King George V.

1935. Silver Jubilee. As T **10a** of Gambia.

139		1d. blue and red	3·25	40
140		2½d. brown and blue	10·00	1·75
141		4d. green and blue	11·00	4·50
142		1s. grey and purple	8·00	3·50

1937. Coronation. As T **10b** of Gambia.

143		½d. green	30	10
144		1d. red	50	45
145		2½d. blue	1·00	1·00

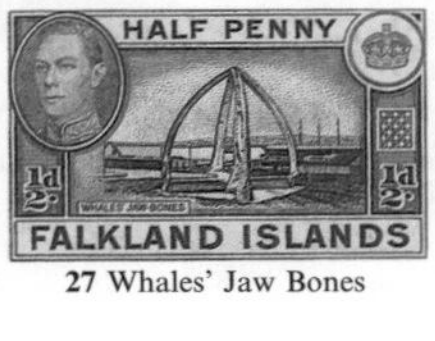

27 Whales' Jaw Bones

1938.

146	27	½d. black and green	30	75
147a	A	1d. black and red	3·75	85
148	B	1d. black and violet	2·50	1·75
149		2d. black and violet	1·25	50
150	A	2d. black and red	1·00	2·25
151	C	2½d. black and blue	1·25	30
152	D	2½d. black and blue	6·50	7·00
153	C	3d. black and blue	6·50	2·50
154	D	4d. black and purple	3·00	65
155	E	6d. black and brown	2·50	1·50
156		6d. black	6·00	4·25
157	F	9d. black and blue	20·00	1·40
158a	G	1s. blue	19·00	3·00
159	H	1s.3d. black and red	2·50	1·40
160	I	2s.6d. black	55·00	12·00
161	J	5s. blue and orange	£120	70·00
162	K	10s. black and orange	£100	35·00
163	L	£1 black and violet	£130	50·00

DESIGNS—HORIZ: A, Black-necked swan; B, Battle memorial; C, Flock of sheep; D, Magellan goose; E, "Discovery II" (polar supply vessel); F, "William Scoresby" (research ship); G, Mount Sugar Top; H, Turkey vultures; I, Gentoo penguins; J, Southern sealion; K, Deception Is.; L, Arms of Falkland Islands.

1946. Victory. As T **11a** of Gambia.

164		1d. mauve	30	35
165		3d. blue	45	35

1948. Silver Wedding. As T **11b/c** of Gambia.

166		2½d. blue	2·00	1·00
167		£1 mauve	90·00	55·00

1949. U.P.U. As T **11d/g** of Gambia.

168		1d. violet	1·50	75
169		3d. blue	5·00	2·00
170		1s.3d. green	3·00	2·25
171		2s. blue	3·00	7·50

39 Sheep

1952.

172	39	½d. green	1·00	70
173	–	1d. red	2·25	40
174	–	2d. violet	4·25	2·50
175	–	2½d. black and blue	1·00	50
176	–	3d. blue	1·75	1·00
177	–	4d. purple	8·00	1·50
178	–	6d. brown	12·00	1·00
179	–	9d. yellow	9·00	2·00
180	–	1s. black	24·00	80
181	–	1s.3d. orange	15·00	5·00
182	–	2s.6d. olive	20·00	11·00
183	–	5s. purple	13·00	9·00
184	–	10s. grey	26·00	13·00
185	–	£1 black	26·00	17·00

DESIGNS—HORIZ: 1d. "Fitzroy" (supply ship); 2d. Magellan goose; 2½d. Map; 4d. Auster Autocrat aircraft; 6d. "John Biscoe I" (research ship); 9d. View of the Two Sisters; 1s.3d. Kelp goose and gander; 10s. Southern sealion and South American fur seal; £1 Hulk of "Great Britain". VERT: 3d. Arms; 1s. Gentoo penguins; 2s.6d. Sheep shearing; 5s. Battle Memorial.

1953. Coronation. As T **11h** of Gambia.

186		1d. black and red	80	1·50

1955. As 1952 issue but with portrait of Queen Elizabeth II.

187		½d. green	70	1·25
188		1d. red	1·25	1·25
189		2d. violet	3·25	4·50
190		6d. brown	7·00	60
191		9d. yellow	10·00	17·00
192		1s. black	6·00	1·25

54 Austral Thrush

1960. Birds.

227	54	½d. black and green	30	40
194	–	1d. black and red	2·25	1·25
195	–	2d. black and blue	4·25	1·25
196	–	2½d. black and bistre	2·00	75
197	–	3d. black and olive	80	50
198	–	4d. black and red	1·25	1·25
199	–	5½d. black and violet	2·75	2·50
200	–	6d. black and sepia	3·00	30
201	–	9d. black and red	2·25	1·25
202	–	1s. black and purple	80	40
203	–	1s.3d. black and blue	10·00	13·00
204	–	2s. black and brown	28·00	2·50
205	–	5s. black and turquoise	27·00	11·00
206	–	10s. black and purple	48·00	16·00
207	–	£1 black and yellow	48·00	27·00

BIRDS: 1d. Southern black-backed gull; 2d. Gentoo penguins; 2½d. Long-tailed meadow lark; 3d. Magellan goose; 4d. Falkland Island flightless steamer ducks; 5½d. Rock-hopper penguins; 6d. Black-browed albatross; 9d. Silver grebe; 1s. Magellanic oystercatcher; 1s.3d. Chilean teal; 2s. Kelp geese; 5s. King cormorants; 10s. Common caracara; £1 Black-necked swan.

69 Morse Key

72 H.M.S. "Glasgow"

1962. 50th Anniv of Establishment of Radio Communications.

208	69	6d. red and orange	75	40
209	–	1s. green and olive	80	40
210	–	2s. violet and blue	90	1·75

DESIGNS: 1s. One-valve receiver; 2s. Rotary spark transmitter.

1963. Freedom from Hunger. As T **20a** of Gambia.

211		1s. blue	10·00	1·50

1963. Centenary of Red Cross. As T **20b** of Gambia.

212		1d. red and black	3·00	50
213		1s. red and blue	13·00	4·50

1964. 400th Birth Anniv of Shakespeare. As **22a** of Gambia.

214		6d. black	1·50	50

1964. 50th Anniv of Battle of the Falkland Islands.

215	72	2½d. black and red	11·00	3·25
216	–	6d. black and blue	50	25
217	–	1s. black and red	50	1·00
218	–	2s. black and blue	35	75

DESIGNS—HORIZ: 6d. H.M.S. "Kent"; 1s. H.M.S. "Invincible". VERT: 2s. Battle Memorial.

1965. Centenary of I.T.U. As T **44** of Gibraltar.

219		1d. light blue and deep blue	50	30
220		2s. lilac and yellow	4·50	1·75

1965. I.C.Y. As T **45** of Gibraltar.

221		1d. purple and turquoise	1·50	20
222		1s. green and lavender	4·00	1·10

1966. Churchill Commemoration. As T **46** of Gibraltar.

223		½d. blue	65	1·25
224		1d. green	1·75	15
225		1s. brown	6·00	2·50
226		2s. violet	4·00	2·50

76 Globe and Human Rights Emblem

77 Dusty Miller

1968. Human Rights Year.

228	76	2d. multicoloured	40	20
229		6d. multicoloured	40	20
230		1s. multicoloured	50	20
231		2s. multicoloured	50	30

1968. Flowers. Multicoloured.

232		½d. Type **77**	15	1·75
233		1½d. Pig vine	40	15
234		2d. Pale maiden	50	15
235		3d. Dog orchid	6·00	1·00
236		3½d. Sea cabbage	30	75
237		4½d. Vanilla daisy	1·50	2·00
238		5½d. yellow, brown and green (Arrowleaf marigold)	1·50	2·00
239		6d. red, black and green (Diddle dee)	75	20
240		1s. Scurvy grass	75	1·50
241		1s.6d. Prickly burr	4·50	12·00
242		2s. Fachine	5·50	6·50
243		3s. Lavender	8·00	8·00
244		5s. Felton's flower	29·00	13·00
245		£1 Yellow orchid	13·00	2·00

Nos. 233, 236, 238/40 and 244 are horiz.

91 De Havilland Beaver Seaplane

1969. 21st Anniv of Government Air Services. Multicoloured.

246		2d. Type **91**	50	30
247		6d. Noorduyn Norseman V	50	35
248		1s. Auster Autocrat	50	35
249		2s. Arms of the Falkland Islands	1·50	2·00

92 Holy Trinity Church, 1869

1969. Centenary of Bishop Stirling's Consecration.
250 92 2d. black, grey and green . . 40 60
251 – 6d. black, grey and red . . 40 60
252 – 1s. black, grey and lilac . . 40 60
253 – 2s. multicoloured 50 75
DESIGNS: 6d. Christ Church Cathedral, 1969; 1s. Bishop Stirling; 2s. Bishop's Mitre.

96 Mounted Volunteer

1970. Golden Jubilee of Defence Force. Mult.
254 2d. Type **96** . . . . 1·75 70
255 6d. Defence Post (horiz) . . . 1·75 70
256 1s. Corporal in No. 1 Dress uniform . . . . 1·75 70
257 2s. Badge (horiz) . . . . . . 2·00 75

97 S.S. "Great Britain" (1843)

1970. S.S. "Great Britain" Restoration. Stamps show S.S. "Great Britain" in year given. Multicoloured.
258 2d. Type **97** 80 40
259 4d. 1845 . . . . 80 75
260 9d. 1876 . . . . 80 75
261 1s. 1886 . . . . 80 75
262 2s. 1970 . . . . 1·10 75

1971. Decimal Currency. Nos. 232/44 surch.
263 ½p. on ½d. multicoloured . . 25 20
264 1p. on 1½d. multicoloured . . 30 15
265 1½p. on 2d. multicoloured . . 30 15
266 2p. on 3d. multicoloured . . 50 20
267 2½p. on 3½d. multicoloured 30 20
268 3p. on 4½d. multicoloured . . 30 20
269 4p. on 5½d. yellow, brn & grn 30 20
270 5p. on 6d. red, black and green 30 20
271 6p. on 1s. multicoloured . . 7·50 6·50
272 7½p. on 1s.6d. multicoloured 7·00 7·00
273 10p. on 2s. multicoloured . . 7·50 3·00
274 15p. on 3s. multicoloured . . 4·50 2·75
275 25p. on 5s. multicoloured . . 5·00 3·25

1972. Decimal Currency. Nos. 232/44 inscr in decimal currency.
276 ½p. multicoloured . . . . . 35 4·50
277 1p. multicoloured 30 40
278 1½p. multicoloured . . . . . 30 4·00
279 2p. multicoloured . . . . . 13·00 1·25
280 2½p. multicoloured . . . . . 35 4·00
281 3p. multicoloured . . . . . 35 1·25
282 4p. yellow, brown and green 40 1·00
283 5p. red, black and green . . 40 55
295 6p. multicoloured . . . . . 1·50 2·25
285 7½p. multicoloured . . . . . 1·50 4·00
286 10p. multicoloured . . . . . 9·00 4·50
287 15p. multicoloured . . . . . 3·25 5·00
288 25p. multicoloured . . . . . 3·25 6·00

1972. Royal Silver Wedding. As T **98** of Gibraltar but with Romney Marsh Sheep and Giant Sea Lions in background.
289 1p. green 40 40
290 10p. blue 85 85

1973. Royal Wedding. As T **101a** of Gibraltar. Background colour given. Multicoloured.
291 5p. mauve 25 10
292 15p. brown 35 20

101 South American Fur Seal

1974. Tourism. Multicoloured.
296 2p. Type **101** . . . . 2·25 1·25
297 4p. Trout-fishing . . . . . . 3·00 1·25
298 5p. Rockhopper penguins . . 9·50 2·50
299 15p. Long-tailed meadow lark ("Military Starling") . . . 12·00 4·50

102 19th-century Mail-coach

1974. U.P.U. Multicoloured.
300 2p. Type **102** 20 25
301 5p. Packet ship, 1841 . . . . 25 45
302 8p. First U.K. aerial post, 1911 . . . . 30 55
303 16p. Ship's catapult mail, 1920s 35 75

103 Churchill and Houses of Parliament

1974. Birth Centenary of Sir Winston Churchill. Multicoloured.
304 16p. Type **103** . . . . 80 1·25
305 20p. Churchill with H.M.S. "Inflexible" and H.M.S. "Invincible", 1914 . . . . 80 1·25
MS306 108 × 83 mm. Nos. 304/5 9·00 8·00

104 H.M.S. "Exeter"

1974. 35th Anniv of Battle of the River Plate. Multicoloured.
307 2p. Type **104** . . . . 3·00 1·60
308 6p. H.M.N.Z. "Achilles" . . 4·50 3·50
309 8p. "Admiral Graf Spee" . . 5·00 4·50
310 16p. H.M.S. "Ajax" . . . . 8·50 15·00

105 Seal and Flag Badge

1975. 50th Anniv of Heraldic Arms. Multicoloured.
311 2p. Type **105** 80 35
312 7½p. Coat of arms, 1925 . . 1·60 1·40
313 10p. Coat of arms, 1948 . . 1·75 1·60
314 16p. Arms of the Dependencies, 1952 . . . . 2·50 3·25

106 ½p. Coin and Brown Trout

1975. New Coinage. Multicoloured.
316 2p. Type **106** . . . . 1·00 50
317 5½p. 1p. coin and Gentoo penguin . . . . 1·50 1·50
318 8p. 2p. coin and Magellan goose . . . . 1·90 1·75
319 10p. 5p. coin and Black-browed albatross . . . . . 2·00 2·00
320 16p. 10p. coin and Southern sealion . . . . 2·50 2·50

107 Gathering Sheep

1976. Sheep Farming Industry. Multicoloured.
321 2p. Type **107** 50 40
322 7½p. Shearing . . . . 75 1·50
323 10p. Dipping . . . . 1·00 1·60
324 20p. Shipping . . . . 1·50 3·00

108 The Queen awaiting Anointment

1977. Silver Jubilee. Multicoloured.
325 6p. Visit of Prince Philip, 1957 . . . . 1·50 1·00
326 11p. The Queen, ampulla and anointing spoon 20 60
327 33p. Type **108** 30 75

109 Map of Falkland Islands

1977. Telecommunications. Multicoloured.
328 3p. Type **109** 75 15
329 11p. Ship to shore communications . . . . . 1·00 40
330 40p. Telex and telephone service . . . . 1·75 1·75

110 "A.E.S.", 1957–74

1978. Mail Ships. Multicoloured.
331A 1p. Type **110** 20 30
332A 2p. "Darwin", 1957–73 . . 30 30
333A 3p. "Merak-N", 1951–52 25 1·25
334A 4p. "Fitzroy", 1936–57 . . 30 1·00
335A 5p. "Lafonia", 1936–41 . . 30 30
336A 6p. "Fleurus", 1924–33 . . 30 40
337A 7p. "Falkland", 1914–34 . . 30 2·25
338A 8p. "Oravia", 1900–12 . . 35 1·00
339A 9p. "Memphis", 1890–97 35 50
340A 10p. "Black Hawk", 1873–80 . . . . 35 50
341B 20p. "Foam", 1863–72 . . 1·25 3·00
342B 25p. "Fairy", 1857–61 . . 1·25 3·00
343B 50p. "Amelia", 1852–54 . . 1·75 3·75
344B £1 "Nautilus", 1846–48 . . 1·75 4·50
345B £3 "Hebe", 1842–46 . . . 4·00 9·50
Nos. 331/45 come with and without date imprint.

111 Short Hythe at Stanley

112 Red Dragon of Wales

1978. 26th Anniv of First Direct Flight, Southampton–Port Stanley. Multicoloured.
346 11p. Type **111** . . . . 3·25 2·50
347 33p. Route map and Short Hythe flying boat . . . . 3·75 3·00

1978. 25th Anniv of Coronation. Multicoloured.
348 **112** 25p. brown, blue and silver . . . . 60 1·00
349 – 25p. multicoloured . . . 60 1·00
350 – 25p. brown, blue and silver . . . . 60 1·00
DESIGNS: No. 349, Queen Elizabeth II; 350, Hornless ram.

113 First Fox Bay P.O. and 1d. Stamp of 1878

114 "Macrocystis pyrifera"

1978. Centenary of First Falkland Islands Postage Stamp. Multicoloured.
351 3p. Type **113** 25 20
352 11p. Second Stanley P.O. and 4d. stamp of 1878 . . . . 30 50
353 15p. New Island P.O. and 6d. stamp of 1878 . . . . . . 40 60
354 22p. First Stanley P.O. and 1s. stamp of 1878 . . . . 60 1·00

1979. Kelp and Seaweed. Multicoloured.
355 3p. Type **114** 30 25
356 7p. "Durvillea sp." 40 45
357 11p. "Lessonia sp." (horiz) 50 60
358 15p. "Callophyllis sp." (horiz) 60 80
359 25p. "Iradaea sp." . . . . . 75 1·40

115 Britten Norman Islander over Falkland Islands

1979. Opening of Stanley Airport. Multicoloured.
360 3p. Type **115** 40 20
361 11p. Fokker F.27 Friendship over South Atlantic . . . 80 60
362 15p. Fokker F.28 Fellowship over Airport 90 60
363 25p. Cessna 172 Skyhawk, Britten Norman Islander, Fokker F.27 Friendship and Fokker F.28 Fellowship over runway . . 1·50 80

116 Sir Rowland Hill and 1953 Coronation 1d. Commemorative

1979. Death Centenary of Sir Rowland Hill.
364 3p. Type **116** 25 25
365 11p. 1878 1d. stamp (vert) . . 40 70
366 25p. Penny Black 60 85
MS367 137 × 98 mm. 33p. 1916 5s. stamp (vert) . . . . 85 1·50

117 Mail Drop by De Havilland Beaver Aircraft

1979. Centenary of U.P.U. Membership. Multicoloured.
368 3p. Type **117** 20 20
369 11p. Mail by horseback . . . 40 55
370 25p. Mail by schooner "Gwendolin" . . . . . . 50 1·00

118 Peale's Porpoise

1980. Dolphins and Porpoises. Multicoloured.
371 3p. Type **118** 30 45
372 6p. Commerson's dolphin (horiz) 35 55
373 7p. Hour-glass dolphin (horiz) 35 55
374 11p. Spectacled porpoise . . 40 70
375 15p. Dusky dolphin (horiz) 40 80
376 25p. Killer whale (horiz) . . 55 1·40

119 1878 Falkland Islands Postmark

1980. "London 1980" International Stamp Exhibition.
377 **119** 11p. black, gold and blue 20 30
378 – 11p. black, gold and yellow 20 30
379 – 11p. black, gold and green 20 30
380 – 11p. black, gold and purple 20 30
381 – 11p. black, gold and red 20 30
382 – 11p. black, gold and flesh 20 30
POSTMARKS: No. 378, 1915 New Island; 379, 1901 Falkland Islands; 380, 1935 Port Stanley; 381, 1952 Port Stanley first overseas airmail; 382, 1934 Fox Bay.

120 Queen Elizabeth the Queen Mother at Ascot, 1971

1980. 80th Birthday of Queen Mother.
383 **120** 11p. multicoloured . . . 40 30

121 Forster's Caracara

1980. Birds of Prey. Multicoloured.
384 3p. Type **121** 60 25
385 11p. Red-backed buzzard . . 75 60
386 15p. Common caracara . . . 80 75
387 25p. Peregrine falcon . . . . 90 1·00

122 Stanley

1981. Early Settlements. Multicoloured.
388 3p. Type **122** 15 15
389 11p. Port Egmont 20 35
390 25p. Port Louis 45 65
391 33p. Mission House, Keppel Island 50 80

123 Sheep

1981. Farm Animals. Multicoloured.
392 3p. Type **123** 15 30
393 11p. Cattle 20 55
394 25p. Horse . . . . 40 1·00
395 33p. Dogs . . . . 50 1·25

124 Bowles and Carver, 1779

1981. Early Maps.
396 **124** 3p. multicoloured 25 30
397 – 10p. multicoloured . . . 35 50
398 – 13p. multicoloured . . . 35 60
399 – 15p. multicoloured . . . 35 60
400 – 25p. multicoloured . . . 40 80
401 – 26p. black, pink and stone 40 80
MAPS: 10p. J. Hawkesworth, 1773; 13p. Eman Bowen, 1747; 15p. T. Boutflower, 1768; 25p. Philippe de Pretot, 1771; 26p. Bellin "Petite Atlas Maritime", Paris, 1764.

125 Wedding Bouquet from Falkland Islands

126 "Handicrafts"

1981. Royal Wedding. Multicoloured.
402 10p. Type **125** 30 40
403 13p. Prince Charles riding . . 40 50
404 25p. Prince Charles and Lady Diana Spencer . . . . . . 70 1·00

1981. 25th Anniv of Duke of Edinburgh Award Scheme. Multicoloured.
405 10p. Type **126** 15 20
406 13p. "Camping" 20 30
407 15p. "Canoeing" 30 40
408 26p. Duke of Edinburgh . . 35 60

127 "The Adoration of the Holy Child" (16th-century Dutch Artist)

1981. Christmas. Paintings. Multicoloured.
409 3p. Type **127** 20 20
410 13p. "The Holy Family in an Italian Landscape" (17th-century Genoan artist) 35 45
411 26p. "The Holy Virgin" (Reni) 55 75

128 Patagonian Sprat

1981. Shelf Fishes. Multicoloured.
412 5p. Type **128** 15 20
413 13p. Gunther's rockcod (vert) 20 35
414 15p. Argentine hake 20 40
415 25p. Southern blue whiting 35 75
416 26p. Grey-tailed skate (vert) 35 75

129 "Lady Elizabeth", 1913

1982. Shipwrecks. Multicoloured.
417 5p. Type **129** 20 50
418 13p. "Capricorn", 1882 . . . 25 70
419 15p. "Jhelum", 1870 . . . . 30 85
420 25p. "Snowsquall", 1864 . . 40 1·10
421 26p. "St. Mary", 1890 . . . 40 1·10

130 Charles Darwin

1982. 150th Anniv of Charles Darwin's Voyage. Multicoloured.
422 5p. Type **130** 30 25
423 17p. Darwin's microscope . . 35 60
424 25p. Falkland Islands wolf 55 80
425 34p. H.M.S. "Beagle" . . . 75 1·10

131 Falkland Islands Coat of Arms

134 Blackish Cinclodes ("Tussock Bird")

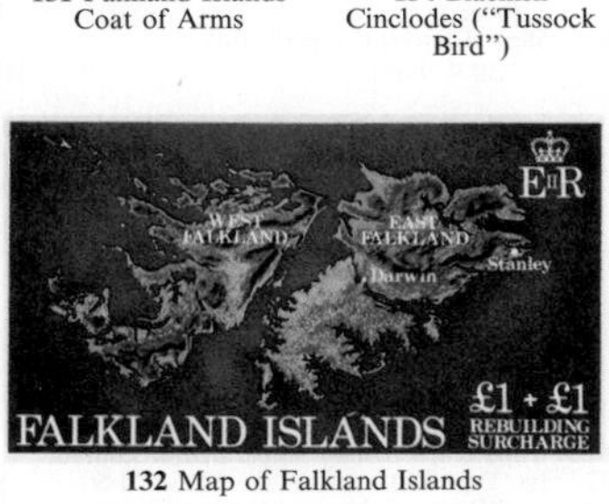

132 Map of Falkland Islands

1982. 21st Birthday of Princess of Wales. Multicoloured.
426 5p. Type **131** 15 20
427 17p. Princess at Royal Opera House, Covent Garden, November, 1981 . . . . . 30 40
428 37p. Bride and groom in doorway of St. Paul's . . . 50 70
429 50p. Formal portrait 65 90

1982. Rebuilding Fund.
430 **132** £1+£1 multicoloured . . . 1·50 4·00

1982. Commonwealth Games, Brisbane. Nos. 335 and 342 optd **1st PARTICIPATION COMMONWEALTH GAMES 1982**.
431 5p. "Lafonia", 1936–41 . . . 15 30
432 25p. "Fairy", 1857–61 . . . 35 1·10

1982. Birds of the Passerine Family. Multicoloured.
433 5p. Type **134** 25 35
434 10p. Black-chinned siskin . . 30 45
435 13p. Sedge wren ("Grass Wren") 30 55
436 17p. Black-throated finch . . 30 65
437 25p. Correndera pipit ("Falkland-Correndera Pipit") 35 85
438 34p. Dark-faced ground-tyrant . . . . 40 1·10

135 Raising Flag, Port Louis, 1833

1983. 150th Anniv of British Administration. Multicoloured.
439 1p. Type **135** 20 30
440 2p. Chelsea pensioners and barracks, 1849 (horiz) . . . 25 40
441 5p. Development of wool trade, 1874 . . . . 25 40
442 10p. Ship-repairing trade, 1850–1890 (horiz) 35 70
443 15p. Government House, early 20th century (horiz) 35 80
444 20p. Battle of Falkland Islands, 1914 . . . . . . 45 1·25
445 25p. Whalebone Arch (horiz) 45 1·25
446 40p. Contribution to War effort, 1939–45 . . . . . . 50 1·25
447 50p. Duke of Edinburgh's visit, 1957 (horiz) . . . . 60 1·25
448 £1 Royal Marine uniforms 75 1·75
449 £2 Queen Elizabeth II . . . 1·50 2·25

136 1933 British Administration Centenary 3d. Commemorative

1983. Commonwealth Day. Multicoloured.
450 5p. Type **136** 15 15
451 17p. 1933 British Administration Centenary ½d. commemorative 20 35
452 34p. 1933 British Administration Centenary 10s. commemorative (vert) 40 80
453 50p. 1983 British Administration 150th anniv £2 commemorative (vert) 60 1·00

137 British Army advancing across East Falkland

1983. 1st Anniv of Liberation. Multicoloured.
454 5p. Type **137** 25 30
455 13p. S.S. "Canberra" and M.V. "Norland" at San Carlos 40 60
456 17p. R.A.F. Hawker Siddeley Harrier fighter 45 70
457 50p. H.M.S. "Hermes" (aircraft carrier) . . . . 1·00 1·40
MS458 169 × 130 mm. Nos. 454/7 1·60 2·75

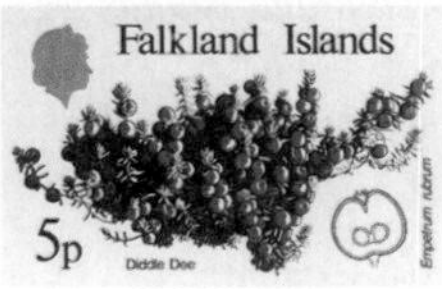

138 Diddle Dee

1983. Native Fruits. Multicoloured.
459 5p. Type **138** 15 20
460 17p. Tea berry 25 35
461 25p. Mountain berry 35 50
462 34p. Native strawberry . . . 45 70

139 Britten Norman Islander

1983. Bicentenary of Manned Flight. Mult.
463 5p. Type **139** 15 20
464 13p. De Havilland Beaver . . 25 35
465 17p. Noorduyn Norseman V 30 40
466 50p. Auster Autocrat . . . . 70 1·00

1984. Nos. 443 and 445 surch.
467 17p. on 15p. Government House, early 20th century 60 45
468 22p. on 25p. Whalebone Arch, 1933 . . . . 65 55

141 "Araneus cinnabarinus" (juvenile spider) **142** "Wavertree" (sail merchantman)

1984. Insects and Spiders. Multicoloured.
469A 1p. Type **141** 20 80
470A 2p. "Alopophion occidentalis" (fly) . . . . 2·00 2·00
471A 3p. "Pareuxoina falklandica (moth) 40 80
472A 4p. "Lissopterus quadrinotatus" (beetle) 30 80
473A 5p. "Issoria cytheris" (butterfly) 30 80
474A 6p. "Araneus cinnabarinus" (adult spider) 30 80
475A 7p. "Trachysphyrus penai" (fly) 30 65
476A 8p. "Caphornia ochricraspia" (moth) . . 30 65
477A 9p. "Caneorhinus biangulatus" (weevil) . . 30 65
478A 10p. "Syrphus octomaculatus" (fly) . . 30 65
479A 20p. "Malvinius compressiventris" (weevil) . . . . 2·00 75
480A 25p. "Metius blandus" (beetle) 50 90
481A 50p. "Parudenus falklandicus" (cricket) . . 80 1·50
482A £1 "Emmenomma beauchenieus" (spider) . . 1·00 2·25
483A £3 "Cynthia carye" (butterfly) . . . . 2·75 6·00
No. 470 comes with or without imprint date.

1984. 250th Anniv of "Lloyd's List" (newspaper). Multicoloured.
484 6p. Type **142** 55 40
485 17p. "Bjerk" (whale catcher) at Port Stanley . . . . . 1·10 60
486 22p. "Oravia" (liner) stranded . . . . 1·10 65
487 52p. "Cunard Countess" (liner) . . . . 1·60 2·00

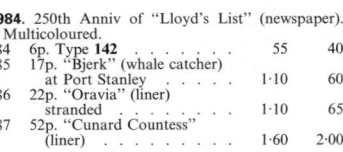

143 Ship, Lockheed Hecules Aircraft and U.P.U. Logo

1984. Universal Postal Union Congress, Hamburg.
488 **143** 22p. multicoloured . . . 55 75

144 Great Grebe **145** Black-browed Albatross, Wilson's Storm Petrel and South American Tern

1984. Grebes. Multicoloured.
489 17p. Type **144** . . . . 1·40 1·25
490 22p. Silvery grebe ("Silver Grebe") . . . . 1·50 1·40
491 52p. White-tufted grebe ("Rolland's Grebe") . . . 2·00 3·50

1984. Nature Conservation. Multicoloured.
492 6p. Type **145** . . . . 1·25 70
493 17p. Tussock grass . . . . . 1·00 80
494 22p. Dusky dolphin and Southern sea lion . . . . . 1·10 1·00
495 52p. Rockcod (fish) and krill 1·50 2·50
MS496 130 × 90 mm. Nos. 492/5 4·75 7·00

146 Technical Drawing of Class "Wren" Locomotive

1985. 70th Anniv of Camber Railway. Each black, brown and light brown.
497 7p. Type **146** 35 30
498 22p. Sail-propelled trolley . . 60 90
499 27p. Class "Wren" locomotive at work . . . . 65 1·25
500 54p. "Falkland Islands Express" passenger train (76 × 25 mm) . . . . . . 1·10 2·00

147 Construction Workers' Camp

1985. Opening of Mount Pleasant Airport. Multicoloured.
501 7p. Type **147** 75 40
502 22p. Building construction . . 1·00 75
503 27p. Completed airport . . . 1·25 80
504 54p. Lockheed TriStar 500 airliner over runway . . . 1·50 1·75

148 The Queen Mother on 84th Birthday

149 Captain J. McBride and H.M.S. "Jason", 1765

1985. Life and Times of Queen Elizabeth the Queen Mother. Multicoloured.
505 7p. Attending reception at Lancaster House 25 20
506 22p. With Prince Charles, Mark Phillips and Princess Anne at Falklands Memorial Service 60 50
507 27p. Type **148** 70 60
508 54p. With Prince Henry at his christening (from photo by Lord Snowdon) . . . . . 1·25 1·25
MS509 91 × 73 mm. £1 With Princess Diana at Trooping the Colour 3·25 2·25

1985. Early Cartographers. Multicoloured.
510 7p. Type **149** 80 40
511 22p. Commodore J. Byron and H.M.S. "Dolphin" and "Tamar", 1765 . . . . . 1·25 80
512 27p. Vice-Admiral R. FitzRoy and H.M.S. "Beagle", 1831 . . . . . . 1·40 85
513 54p. Admiral Sir B. J. Sullivan and H.M.S. "Philomel", 1842 . . . . . 2·00 1·75

149a Philibert Commerson and Commerson's Dolphin

1985. Early Naturalists. Multicoloured.
514 7p. Type **149a** 75 40
515 22p. Rene Primevere Lesson and "Lessonia sp." (kelp) 1·00 1·10
516 27p. Joseph Paul Gaimard and Common diving petrel ("Diving Petrel") . . . . . 1·75 1·90
517 54p. Charles Darwin and "Calceolaria darwinii" . . 2·00 2·75

150 Painted Keyhole Limpet

1986. Seashells. Multicoloured.
518 7p. Type **150** 75 60
519 22p. "Provocator palliata" 1·25 1·10
520 27p. Patagonian or Falkland scallop . . . . 1·40 1·60
521 54p. Rough thorn drupe . . 2·25 3·00

1986. 60th Birthday of Queen Elizabeth II. As T **120a** of Hong Kong. Multicoloured.
522 10p. With Princess Margaret at St. Paul's, Walden Bury, Welwyn, 1932 . . . . . . 15 25
523 24p. Queen making Christmas television broadcast, 1958 . . . . . 25 50
524 29p. In robes of Order of the Thistle, St. Giles Cathedral, Edinburgh, 1962 . . . . . 25 60
525 45p. Aboard Royal Yacht "Britannia", U.S.A., 1976 1·00 1·25
526 58p. At Crown Agents Head Office, London, 1983 . . . 60 1·50

151 S.S. "Great Britain" crossing Atlantic, 1845

1986. "Ameripex '86" International Stamp Exhibition, Chicago. Centenary of Arrival of S.S. "Great Britain" in Falkland Islands. Multicoloured.
527 10p. Type **151** 25 60
528 24p. Beached at Sparrow Cove, 1937 . . . . 30 80
529 29p. Refloated on pontoon, 1970 . . . . 35 90
530 58p. Undergoing restoration, Bristol, 1986 . . . . . . 50 2·25
MS531 109 × 100 mm. Nos. 527/30 1·10 2·75

152 Head of Rockhopper Penguin

153 Prince Andrew and Miss Sarah Ferguson presenting Polo Trophy, Windsor

1986. Rockhopper Penguins. Multicoloured.
532 10p. Type **152** . . . . . . 1·00 70
533 24p. Rockhopper penguins at sea . . . . 1·75 1·75
534 29p. Courtship display . . . 2·00 2·00
535 58p. Adult with chick . . . . 2·50 4·50

1986. Royal Wedding. Multicoloured.
536 17p. Type **153** . . . . . . 1·00 50
537 22p. Prince Andrew and Duchess of York on wedding day . . . . . . 1·10 65
538 29p. Prince Andrew in battledress at opening of Fox Bay Mill . . . . . . 1·40 90

154 Survey Party, Sapper Hill

1987. Bicentenary of Royal Engineers' Royal Warrant. Multicoloured.
539 10p. Type **154** . . . . 1·25 80
540 24p. Mine clearance by robot 1·75 1·50
541 29p. Boxer Bridge, Stanley 2·00 2·50
542 58p. Unloading mail, Mount Pleasant Airport . . . . . 2·75 4·00

155 Southern Sea Lion

1987. Seals. Multicoloured.
543 10p. Type **155** 85 55
544 24p. Falkland fur seal . . . 1·50 90
545 29p. Southern elephant seal 1·60 1·50
546 58p. Leopard seal . . . . . 2·25 3·00

156 "Suillus luteus"

1987. Fungi. Multicoloured.
547 10p. Type **156** . . . . 1·75 85
548 24p. "Mycena sp." . . . . . 2·75 2·00
549 29p. "Hygrophorus adonis" ("Camarophyllus adonis") 3·00 3·00
550 58p. "Gerronema schusteri" 4·50 5·00

157 Victoria Cottage Home, c. 1912

1987. Local Hospitals. Multicoloured.
551 10p. Type **157** 50 25
552 24p. King Edward VII Memorial Hospital, c. 1914 85 55
553 29p. Churchill Wing, King Edward VII Memorial Hospital, c. 1953 . . . . . 95 60
554 58p. Prince Andrew Wing, New Hospital, 1987 . . . 1·50 1·25

158 Morris Truck, Fitzroy, 1940

159a Silver from Lloyd's Nelson Collection

159 Kelp Goose

1988. Early Vehicles. Multicoloured.
555 10p. Type **158** 50 25
556 24p. Citroen "Kegresse" half-track, San Carlos, 1929 . . 85 55
575 29p. Ford one ton truck, Port Stanley, 1933 . . . . . . 95 60
558 58p. Ford "Model T" car, Darwin, 1935 . . . . . . 1·50 1·25

1988. Falkland Islands Geese. Multicoloured.
559 10p. Type **159** . . . . 2·00 55
560 24p. Magellan ("Upland") goose . . . . 2·75 70
561 29p. Ruddy-headed goose . . 3·00 90
562 58p. Ashy-headed goose . . . 4·50 2·00

1988. 300th Anniv of Lloyd's of London. Mult.
563 10p. Type **159a** 40 30
564 24p. Falkland Islands hydroponic market garden (horiz) 75 65
565 29p. "A.E.S." (mail ship) (horiz) . . . . 1·25 75
566 58p. "Charles Cooper" (full-rigged ship), 1866 . . . . 1·50 1·25

160 "Padua" (barque)

1989. Cape Horn Sailing Ships. Multicoloured.
567 1p. Type **160** . . . . 1·50 80
613 2p. "Priwall" (barque) (vert) 60 1·00
614 3p. "Passat" (barque) . . . . 60 1·00
570 4p. "Archibald Russell" (barque) (vert) . . . . . . 2·00 80
571 5p. "Pamir" (barque) (vert) 2·00 80
617 6p. "Mozart" (barquentine) 70 1·25
573 7p. "Pommern" (barque) . . 2·25 1·00
574 8p. "Preussen" (full-rigged ship) . . . . 2·25 1·00
620 9p. "Fennia" (barque) . . . 80 1·40
576 10p. "Cassard" (barque) . . 2·25 1·00
577 20p. "Lawhill" (barque) . . . 3·50 2·00
578 25p. "Garthpool" (barque) 3·50 2·00
579 50p. "Grace Harwar" (full-rigged ship) . . . . 4·50 3·00
625 £1 "Criccieth Castle" (full-rigged ship) . . . . 2·75 3·75
581 £3 "Cutty Sark" (full-rigged ship) (vert) . . . . . . 13·00 8·50
582 £5 "Flying Cloud" (full-rigged ship) . . . . 14·00 9·00

161 Southern Right Whale

1989. Baleen Whales. Multicoloured.
583 10p. Type **161** . . . . 1·25 40
584 24p. Minke whale . . . . . 2·00 85
585 29p. Humpback whale . . . 2·25 1·25
586 58p. Blue whale . . . . . . 3·50 2·50

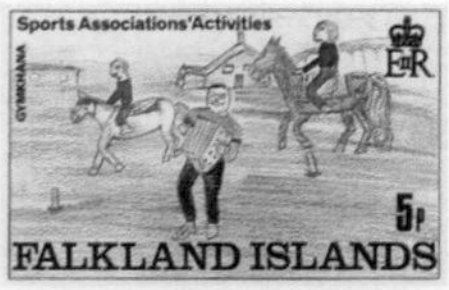

162 "Gymkhana" (Sarah Gilding)

1989. Sports Associations' Activities. Children's Drawings. Multicoloured.
587 5p. Type **162** 20 20
588 10p. "Steer Riding" (Karen Steen) 30 30
589 17p. "Sheep Shearing" (Colin Shepherd) 45 45
590 24p. "Sheepdog Trials" (Rebecca Edwards) 60 70
591 29p. "Horse Racing" (Dilys Blackley) 70 80
592 45p. "Sack Race" (Donna Newell) . . . . 1·00 1·10

163 Vice-Admiral Sturdee and H.M.S. "Invincible" (battle cruiser)

164 Southern Sea Lions on Kidney Island

1989. 75th Anniv of the Battle of the Falkland Islands and 50th Anniv of Battle of the River Plate. Mult.
593 10p. Type **163** 80 30
594 24p. Vice-Admiral Graf von Spee and "Scharnhorst" (German cruiser) . . . . . 1·50 75
595 29p. Commodore Harwood and H.M.S. "Ajax" (cruiser) . . . . 1·60 85
596 58p. Captain Langsdorff and "Admiral Graf Spee" (German pocket battleship) 2·25 2·00

1990. Nature Reserves and Sanctuaries. Mult.
597 12p. Type **164** 60 35
598 26p. Black-browed albatrosses on Beauchene Island . . . . 1·40 70
599 31p. Penguin colony on Bird Island . . . . 1·40 90
600 62p. Tussock grass on Elephant Jason Island . . 1·50 1·75

165 Supermarine Spitfire Mk. I "Falkland Islands I"

1990. "Stamp World London 90" International Stamp Exhibition, London. Presentation Spitfires. Multicoloured.
601 12p. Type **165** 65 45
602 26p. Supermarine Spitfire Mk. I "Falkland Islands VII" . . . . 1·25 80
603 31p. Cockpit and wing of "Falkland Islands I" . . . 1·25 1·10
604 62p. Squadron scramble, 1940 . . . . 1·75 2·50
MS605 114 × 100 mm. £1 Supermarine Spitfire Mk I in action, 1940 . . . . 4·00 2·50

For No. **MS**605 with additional inscription see No. **MS**628.

165a Queen Mother in Dover

166 Black-browed Albatrosses

1990. 90th Birthday of Queen Elizabeth the Queen Mother.

606	**165a**	26p. multicoloured	1·00	65
607	–	£1 black and red	2·75	2·75

DESIGN: £1 On bridge of liner "Queen Elizabeth", 1946 (29 × 33 mm).

1990. Black-browed Albatrosses. Multicoloured.

608	12p. Type **166**	75	50
609	26p. Female with egg	1·40	1·00
610	31p. Adult and chick	1·60	1·25
611	62p. Black-browed albatrosses in flight	2·75	3·00

1991. 2nd Visit of H.R.H. The Duke of Edinburgh. As No. **MS**605, but with Exhibition emblem replaced by "SECOND VISIT OF HRH THE DUKE OF EDINBURGH".

MS628	144 × 100 mm. £1 Spitfire Mk. I in action	6·50	8·50

The margin of No. **MS**628 also shows the exhibition emblem omitted and has the same commemorative inscription added.

167 "Gavilea australis"

168 Heads of Two King Penguins

1991. Orchids. Multicoloured.

629	12p. Type **167**	75	70
630	26p. Dog orchid	1·25	1·00
631	31p. "Chlorea gaudichaudii"	1·40	1·50
632	62p. Yellow orchid	2·50	3·75

1991. Endangered Species. King Penguin. Mult.

633	2p. Type **168**	70	70
634	6p. Female incubating egg	90	90
635	12p. Female with two chicks	1·25	1·00
636	20p. Penguin underwater	1·50	1·25
637	31p. Parents feeding their chick	1·60	1·90
638	62p. Courtship dance	2·25	2·75

Nos. 637/8 do not include the W.W.F. panda emblem.

169 ½d. and 2½d. Stamps of September, 1891

1991. Cent of Bisected Surcharges. Mult.

639	12p. Type **169**	60	50
640	26p. Cover of March, 1891 franked with strip of five ½d. bisects	1·00	1·00
641	31p. Unsevered pair of ½d. surcharge	1·25	1·50
642	62p. "Isis" (mail ship)	2·00	3·25

169a Map of Re-enactment Voyages and "Eye of the Wind" (cadet brig)

1991. 500th Anniv of Discovery of America by Columbus. Re-enactment Voyages. Multicoloured.

643	14p. Type **169a**	60	60
644	29p. Compass rose and "Soren Larsen" (cadet brigantine)	1·25	1·40
645	34p. "Santa Maria", "Pinta" and "Nina"	1·50	1·75
646	68p. Columbus and "Santa Maria"	2·50	4·00

1992. 40th Anniv of Queen Elizabeth II's Accession. As T **179a** of Gibraltar. Multicoloured.

647	7p. "Stanley through the Narrows" (A. Asprey)	45	35
648	14p. "Hill Cove" (A. Asprey)	70	60
649	29p. "San Carlos Water" (A. Asprey)	1·10	95
650	34p. Three portraits of Queen Elizabeth	1·25	1·25
651	68p. Queen Elizabeth II	1·75	2·00

170 Laying Foundation Stone, 1890

170a San Carlos Cemetery

1992. Centenary of Christ Church Cathedral, Stanley. Multicoloured.

652	14p. Type **170**	75	55
653	29p. Interior of Cathedral, 1920	1·40	1·00
654	34p. Bishop's chair	1·60	1·25
655	68p. Cathedral in 1900 (horiz)	2·00	1·90

1992. 10th Anniv of Liberation. Multicoloured.

656	14p.+6p. Type **170a**	75	1·50
657	29p.+11p. War Memorial, Port Stanley	1·40	2·00
658	34p.+16p. South Atlantic medal	1·60	2·00
659	68p.+32p. Government House, Port Stanley	2·75	3·00
MS660	115 × 115 mm. Nos. 656/9	6·00	7·00

The premiums on Nos. 656/9 were for the S.S.A.F.A.

171 Captain John Davis and Backstaff

1992. 400th Anniv of First Sighting of the Falkland Islands. Multicoloured.

661	22p. Type **171**	1·25	80
662	29p. Captain John Davis	1·50	1·10
663	34p. Queen Elizabeth I and Queen Elizabeth II	1·75	1·50
664	68p. "Desire" sighting Falkland Islands	2·75	3·00

172 Private, Falkland Islands Volunteers, 1892

173 South American Tern

1992. Centenary of Falkland Islands Defence Force and 50th Anniv of Affiliation to West Yorkshire Regiment. Multicoloured.

665	7p. Type **172**	45	30
666	14p. Officer, Falkland Islands Defence Corps, 1914	70	50
667	22p. Officer, Falkland Islands Defence Force, 1920	90	70
668	29p. Private, Falkland Islands Defence Force, 1939–45	1·10	90
669	34p. Officer, West Yorkshire Regiment, 1942	1·40	1·25
670	68p. Private, West Yorkshire Regiment, 1942	2·40	2·10

1993. Gulls and Terns. Multicoloured.

671	15p. Type **173**	1·00	75
672	31p. Brown-hooded gull ("Pink-breasted Gull")	1·25	1·25
673	36p. Magellan gull ("Dolphin Gull")	1·75	1·75
674	72p. Southern black-backed gull ("Dominican Gull")	2·75	5·00

174a Avro Vulcan B.1A

1993. 75th Anniv of Royal Air Force. Multicoloured.

676	15p. Type **174a**	75	85
677	15p. Lockhead Hercules	75	85
678	15p. Boeing-Vertol Chinook	75	85
679	15p. Lockhead TriStar 500	75	85
MS680	110 × 77 mm. 36p. Hawker Siddeley Andover CC.2; 36p. Westland Wessex HC-2 helicopter; 36p. Panavia Tornado F Mk 3; 36p. McDonnell Douglas F-4M Phantom II	3·75	4·75

175 Short-finned Squid

1993. Fisheries. Multicoloured.

681	15p. Type **175**	60	60
682	31p. Catch of whip-tailed hake	1·25	1·40
683	36p. "Falklands Protector" (fisheries patrol vessel)	1·50	1·75
684	72p. Britten Norman Islander patrol aircraft and "Pomorze" (fish factory ship)	2·25	4·50

176 "Great Britain" in Dry Dock, Bristol

178 Pony

177 "Explorer" (liner)

1993. 150th Anniv of Launch of "Great Britain" (liner). Multicoloured.

685	8p. Type **176**	75	50
686	£1 "Great Britain" at sea	2·75	4·50

1993. Tourism. Multicoloured.

687	16p. Type **177**	1·25	70
688	34p. Rockhopper penguins	2·00	1·50
689	39p. "World Discoverer" (liner)	2·25	2·00
690	78p. "Columbus Caravelle" (liner)	2·75	4·50

1993. Pets. Multicoloured.

691	8p. Type **178**	60	60
692	16p. Lamb	75	75
693	34p. Puppy and cat	1·75	1·75
694	39p. Kitten (vert)	2·00	2·00
695	78p. Collie dog (vert)	2·75	4·00

1994. "Hong Kong '94" International Stamp Exhibition. Nos. 691/5 optd **HONG KONG '94** and emblem.

696	8p. Type **178**	70	80
697	16p. Lamb	85	95
698	34p. Puppy and cat	2·00	2·25
699	39p. Kitten (vert)	2·25	2·50
700	78p. Collie dog (vert)	3·00	4·75

179 Goose Barnacles

1994. Inshore Marine Life. Multicoloured.

701	1p. Type **179**	50	50
702	2p. Painted shrimp (horiz)	1·00	50
703	8p. Patagonian copper limpet (horiz)	1·25	75
704	9p. Elegimops ("Mullet") (horiz)	1·25	75
705	10p. Sea anemones (horiz)	1·25	60
706	20p. Flathead eelpout (horiz)	1·75	90
707	25p. Spider crab (horiz)	1·75	90
708	50p. Lobster krill	2·50	2·00
709	80p. Falkland skate (horiz)	2·50	2·50
710	£1 Centollon crab (horiz)	2·50	2·50
711	£3 Wilton's notothen ("Rock Cod") (horiz)	7·50	6·25
712	£5 Octopus	11·00	10·50

180 Dockyard Blacksmith's Shop and Sir James Clark Ross (explorer)

1994. 150th Anniv of Founding of Stanley. Multicoloured.

713	9p. Type **180**	60	50
714	17p. 21 Fitzroy Road (home of Chaplain James Moody)	85	60
715	30p. Stanley Cottage (built by Dr. Henry Hamblin)	1·40	1·25
716	35p. Pioneer Row and Sgt.-Maj. Henry Felton	1·60	1·75
717	40p. Government House (designed by Governor R. Moody)	1·75	1·90
718	65p. View of Stanley and Edward Stanley, Earl of Derby (Secretary of State for Colonies)	2·50	3·00

181 Lockheed L-1011 TriStar over Gypsy Cove

1994. Falkland Beaches. Multicoloured.

719	17p. Type **181**	85	70
720	35p. "Explorer" (liner) off Sea Lion Island	1·60	1·40
721	40p. Britten Norman Islander aircraft at Pebble Island	2·00	2·00
722	65p. Landrover at Volunteer Beach	2·25	3·50

182 Mission House, Keppel Island

1994. 150th Anniv of South American Missionary Society. Multicoloured.

723	5p. Type **182**	35	40
724	17p. Thomas Bridges (compiler of Yahgan dictionary)	65	65
725	40p. Fuegian Indians	1·40	1·75
726	65p. Capt. Allen Gardiner and "Allen Gardiner" (schooner)	1·75	2·50

183 "Lupinus arboreus"

1995. Flowering Shrubs. Multicoloured.

727	9p. Type **183**	50	50
728	17p. "Hebe elliptica"	70	70
729	30p. "Fuschia magellanica"	95	95
730	35p. "Berberis ilicifolia"	1·10	1·10
731	40p. "Ulex europaeus"	1·25	1·25
732	65p. "Hebe x franciscana"	2·00	2·75

184 Magellanic Oystercatcher

1995. Shore Birds. Multicoloured.

733	17p. Type **184**	1·00	80
734	35p. Rufous-chested dotterel	1·60	1·40
735	40p. Blackish oystercatcher	1·75	1·75
736	65p. Two-banded plover	3·00	5·00

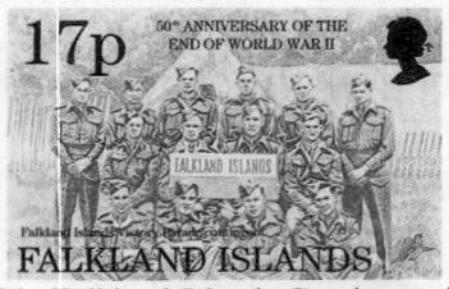

184a Falkland Islands Contingent in Victory Parade

1995. 50th Anniv of End of Second World War. Multicoloured.
737 17p. Type **184a** 75 75
738 35p. Governor Sir Alan Cardinall on Bren gun-carrier . . . . 1·40 1·40
739 40p. H.M.A.S. "Esperance Bay" (troopship) . . . . . 1·50 1·75
740 65p. H.M.S. "Exeter" (cruiser) . . . . 2·75 3·75
MS741 75 × 85 mm. £1 Reverse of 1939–45 War Medal (vert) . . 3·50 3·75

185 Ox and Cart

1995. Transporting Peat. Multicoloured.
742 17p. Type **185** 60 60
743 35p. Horse and cart . . . . 1·10 1·10
744 40p. Caterpillar tractor pulling sleigh . . . . . . 1·25 1·25
745 65p. Lorry . . . . 2·25 3·50

186 Kelp Geese

1995. Wildlife. Multicoloured.
746 35p. Type **186** . . . . 1·40 1·25
747 35p. Black-browed albatross 1·40 1·25
748 35p. Blue-eyed cormorants 1·40 1·25
749 35p. Magellanic penguins . . 1·40 1·25
750 35p. Fur seals . . . . 1·40 1·25
751 35p. Rockhopper penguins 1·40 1·25
Nos. 746/51 were printed together, se-tenant, forming a composite design.

187 Cottontail Rabbit

1995. Introduced Wild Animals. Multicoloured.
752 9p. Type **187** 65 65
753 17p. Brown hare 90 75
754 35p. Guanacos . . . . 1·40 1·40
755 40p. Fox . . . . 1·60 1·60
756 65p. Otter . . . . 2·50 3·00

188 Princess Anne and Government House

1996. Royal Visit. Multicoloured.
757 9p. Type **188** 70 45
758 19p. Falklands War Memorial, San Carlos Cemetery 80 65
759 30p. Christ Church Cathedral 1·10 1·10
760 73p. Helicopter over Goose Green . . . . 4·00 3·00

188a Steeple Jason

1996. 70th Birthday of Queen Elizabeth II. Each incorporating a different photograph of the Queen. Multicoloured.
761 17p. Type **188a** 60 50
762 40p. "Tamar" (container ship) . . . . 1·50 1·25
763 45p. New Island . . . . . . 1·50 1·40
764 65p. Falkland Islands Community School . . . . 1·60 1·60
MS765 64 × 66 mm. £1 Queen Elizabeth II . . . . 2·75 3·25

189 Mounted Postman, c. 1890

1996. "CAPEX '96" International Stamp Exhibition. Mail Transport. Multicoloured.
766 9p. Type **189** 75 60
767 40p. Noorduyn Norseman V seaplane . . . . 1·75 1·50
768 45p. "Forrest" (freighter) at San Carlos . . . . 1·75 1·60
769 76p. De Havilland D.H.C.2 Beaver seaplane . . . . . 2·75 2·75
MS770 110 × 80 mm. £1 L.M.S. Class "Jubilee" steam locomotive No. 5606 "Falkland Islands" (47 × 31 mm) . . . . 2·40 3·50

190 Southern Bottlenose Whale

1996. Beaked Whales. Multicoloured.
771 9p. Type **190** 55 45
772 30p. Cuvier's beaked whale 1·10 1·10
773 35p. Straptoothed beaked whale . . . . 1·25 1·25
774 75p. Gray's beaked whale . . 2·40 2·40

191 Magellanic Penguins performing Courtship Dance

1997. Magellanic Penguins. Multicoloured.
775 17p. Type **191** . . . . . . 1·00 55
776 35p. Penguins in burrow . . 1·75 1·00
777 40p. Adult and chick . . . . 1·75 1·25
778 65p. Group of Penguins swimming . . . . 2·50 1·75

192 Black Pejerry

1997. "HONG KONG '97" International Stamp Exhibition. Sheet 130 × 90 mm.
MS779 **192** £1 multicoloured . . 2·50 2·50

193 Coral Fern

193a Queen Elizabeth II

1997. Ferns. Multicoloured.
780 17p. Type **193** 80 45
781 35p. Adder's tongue fern . . 1·40 1·00
782 40p. Fuegian tall fern . . . 1·60 1·10
783 65p. Small fern . . . . 2·00 1·75

1997. Return of Hong Kong to China. Sheet 130 × 90 mm, containing design as No. 710.
MS784 £1 Centollón crab . . . . 2·50 2·50

1997. Golden Wedding of Queen Elizabeth II and Prince Philip. Multicoloured.
785 9p. Type **193a** 70 40
786 9p. Prince Philip and horse, 1995 . . . . 70 40
787 17p. Queen Elizabeth in phaeton at Trooping the Colour, 1996 . . . . . . 1·00 65
788 17p. Prince Philip in R.A.F. uniform . . . . 1·00 65
789 40p. Queen Elizabeth wearing red coat, 1986 . . . . . . 1·25 1·00
790 40p. Prince William and Princess Beatrice on horseback . . . . 1·25 1·00
MS791 110 × 71 mm. £1.50, Queen Elizabeth and Prince Philip in landau (horiz) . . . . 6·00 3·75
Nos. 785/6, 787/8 and 789/90 respectively were printed together, se-tenant, with the backgrounds forming composite designs.

194 Bull Point Lighthouse

1997. Lighthouses. Multicoloured.
792 9p. Type **194** 75 40
793 30p. Cape Pembroke Lighthouse . . . . 1·50 1·25
794 £1 Cape Meredith Lighthouse 3·00 3·00

195 Forster's Caracara ("Johnny Rock")

1997. Endangered Species. Multicoloured.
795 17p. Type **195** . . . . 1·25 60
796 19p. Southern sealion . . . . 1·00 75
797 40p. Felton's flower . . . . 1·75 1·50
798 73p. Trout . . . . 2·50 2·50

196 Merryweather and Son Greenwich Gem Fire Engine

196a Wearing Black Jacket, 1990

1998. Centenary of Falkland Islands Fire Service. Multicoloured.
799 9p. Type **196** . . . . 1·00 45
800 17p. Merryweather's Hatfield trailer pump . . . . 1·50 60
801 40p. Coventry Climax Godiva trailer pump . . . 2·50 1·50
802 65p. Carmichael Bedford "Type B" water tender . . 2·75 2·50

1998. Diana, Princess of Wales Commemoration.
MS803 145 × 70 mm. 30p. Type **196a**, 30p. Wearing red dress, 1988; 30p. Resting head on hand, 1991; 30p. Wearing landmine protection clothing, Angola (sold at £1.20 + 20p. charity premium) . . . . . . 3·25 3·25

197 Tawny-throated Dotterel

1998. Rare Visiting Birds. Multicoloured. (a) Designs $39\frac{1}{2} \times 23\frac{1}{2}$ mm.
804 1p. Type **197** 50 70
805 2p. Hudsonian godwit . . . 50 70
806 5p. Eared dove 60 70
807 9p. Great grebe 80 80
808 10p. Southern lapwing 80 80
809 16p. Buff-necked ibis . . . . 1·25 1·00
810 30p. Ashy-headed goose . . . 1·75 1·25
811 65p. Red-legged cormorant ("Red-legged Shag") . . . 2·50 2·00
812 88p. Argentine shoveler ("Red Shoveler") . . . . . 3·00 3·00
813 £1 Red-fronted coot . . . . 3·50 3·75
814 £3 Chilian flamingo . . . . 7·00 7·50
815 £5 Fork-tailed flycatcher . . 11·00 12·00

(b) Designs 35 × 22 mm.
816 9p. Roseate spoonbill 60 70
817 17p. Austral conure ("Austral Parakeet") . . . . 1·00 1·10
818 35p. American kestrel . . . . 1·60 2·00

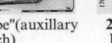

198 "Penelope"(auxillary ketch)

200 Marine at Port Egmont, Saunders Island, 1766

199 First Medivac Air Ambulance Service, 1948

1998. Local Vessels. Multicoloured.
819 17p. Type **198** 75 55
820 35p. "Ilen" (auxillary ketch) 1·40 1·25
821 40p. "Weddell" (schooner) 1·60 1·40
822 65p. "Lively" (tug) (31 × 22 mm) . . . . . . 2·25 2·00

1998. 50th Anniv of Falkland Islands Government Air Service. Multicoloured.
823 17p. Type **199** . . . . 2·00 50
824 £1 F.I.G.A.S. Beaver and Islander aircraft over map 4·00 3·00

1998. Royal Marine Uniforms. Multicoloured.
825 17p. Type **200** . . . . 1·25 70
826 30p. Officer at Port Louis, East Falklands, 1833 . . . 1·75 1·50
827 35p. Corporal and H.M.S. "Kent" (cruiser), 1914 . . 1·75 1·60
828 65p. Bugler at Government House, 1976 . . . . 3·00 3·50

201 Altar, St. Mary's Church

1999. Centenary of St. Mary's Roman Catholic Church, Stanley. Multicoloured.
829 17p. Type **201** . . . . 1·25 70
830 40p. St. Mary's Church . . . 1·90 1·75
831 75p. Laying of foundation stone, 1899 . . . . 3·25 4·25

202 H.M.S. "Beagle" (Darwin)

1999. "Australia '99" World Stamp Exhibition, Melbourne. Maritime History. Multicoloured.
832 25p. Type **202** . . . . 1·50 1·25
833 35p. H.M.A.S. "Australia" (battle cruiser) . . . . . . 1·75 1·25
834 40p. "Canberra" (liner) . . . 1·90 1·60
835 50p. "Great Britain" (steam/sail) . . . . 2·25 2·75
836 50p. All-England Cricket Team, 1861–62 . . . . . 2·25 2·75

203 Prince of Wales (from photo by Clive Arrowsmith)

203a Prince Edward and Miss Sophie Rhys-Jones

1999. Royal Visit.
837 **203** £2 multicoloured . . . . 6·00 5·50

1999. Royal Wedding. Multicoloured.
838 80p. Type **203a** . . . . 3·25 2·00
839 £1.20 Engagement photograph . . . . 4·25 3·50

204 "Jeanne d'Arc" (French cruiser)

1999. "PHILEXFRANCE '99", International Stamp Exhibition, Paris. First Flight over Falkland Islands, 1931. Multicoloured.
840 35p. Type **204** . . . . 1·40 1·25
841 40p. CAMS 37 (flying boat) taking off . . . . 1·40 1·25
MS842 115 × 63 mm. £1 CAMS 37 over Port Stanley (47 × 31 mm) 4·50 3·00

204a On Board Ship, Port of London, 1939

1999. "Queen Elizabeth the Queen Mother's Century". Multicoloured.
843 9p. Type **204a** 80 60
844 20p. With Queen Elizabeth II, 1996 . . . . 1·40 90
845 30p. With Prince Charles and his sons, 1995 . . . . . . 1·50 1·10
846 67p. Presenting colours to Queen's Royal Hussars . . 3·00 4·00
MS847 145 × 70 mm. £1.40, Duchess of York, 1936, and Shackleton, Scott and Wilson in the Antarctic, 1902 . . . . 7·00 7·00

205 Chiloe Wigeon

1999. Waterfowl. Multicoloured.
848 9p. Type **205** 85 70
849 17p. Crested duck . . . . . . 1·25 90
850 30p. Georgian teal ("Brown Pintail") . . . . 1·90 1·50
851 35p. Versicolor teal ("Silver Teal") . . . . 1·90 1·50
852 40p. Chilean teal ("Yellow-billed Teal") . . . . 2·00 1·60
853 65p. Falkland Islands flightless steamer duck . . 2·75 3·75

206 Hulk of "Vicar of Bray", 1999

1999. 150th Anniv of California Goldrush. Mult.
854 9p. Type **206** . . . . 1·25 75
855 35p. Panning for gold, 1849 1·90 1·50
856 40p. Gold rocking cradle, 1849 . . . . 1·90 1·50
857 80p. "Vicar of Bray" (barque) at sea, 1849 . . . 3·25 4·00
MS858 105 × 63 mm. £1 "Vicar of Bray" in San Francisco (47 × 31 mm) . . . . 4·75 5·50

207 Magellan Goose ("Upland Goose") on Nest

1999. New Millennium. Multicoloured.
859 9p. Type **207** 75 80
860 9p. Southern black-backed gull ("Kelp Gull") at sunrise 75 80
861 9p. Christ Church Cathedral, Stanley 75 80
862 30p. Black-crowned night heron ("Night Heron") at sunset . . . . 1·40 1·60
863 30p. Family and Christmas tree . . . . 1·40 1·60
864 30p. King penguins . . . . . 1·40 1·60

208 Princess Alexandra and Meadow

2000. Visit of Princess Alexandra. Multicoloured.
865 9p. Type **208** 75 50
866 £1 Princess Alexandra and plantation of saplings . . . 3·75 4·00

208a "Endurance" off Caird Coast

2000. Shackleton's Trans-Antarctic Expedition, 1914–1917, Commemoration.
867 **208a** 17p. multicoloured . . . 1·25 75
868 – 45p. blue and black . . 2·25 2·00
869 – 75p. multicoloured . . . 3·25 3·50
DESIGNS: 45p. "Endurance" beset in the Weddell Sea pack-ice; 75p. Sir Ernest Shackleton and "Yelcho" (Chilean resone tug).

208b Queen Elizabeth I **208c** Wearing Fireman's helmet, 1988

2000. "Stamp Show 2000" International Stamp Exhibition, London. Kings and Queens of England. Multicoloured.
870 40p. Type **208b** . . . . . . 1·50 1·50
871 40p. King James II . . . . . 1·50 1·50
872 40p. King George I . . . . . 1·50 1·50
873 40p. King William IV . . . . 1·50 1·50
874 40p. King Edward VIII . . . 1·50 1·50
875 40p. Queen Elizabeth II . . . 1·50 1·50

2000. 18th Birthday of Prince William. Mult.
876 10p. Type **208c** 70 60
877 20p. At Eton, 1995 . . . . . 85 75
878 37p. Prince William in Cardiff, 2000 (horiz) . . . 1·40 1·40
879 43p. Prince William in 1998 (horiz) . . . . 1·40 1·60
MS880 175 × 95 mm. 50p. With golden retriever, 1997 (horiz) and Nos. 876/9 . . . . 5·50 6·00

2000. Queen Elizabeth the Queen Mother's 100th Birthday. No. **MS**847 optd **100 birthday.**
MS881 145 × 70 mm. £1.40, Duchess of York, 1936, and Shackleton, Scott and Wilson in the Antarctic, 1902 . . . . 5·00 5·50

210 Malo River Bridge

2000. Bridges. Multicoloured.
882 20p. Type **210** . . . . 1·25 75
883 37p. Bodie Creek Bridge . . 1·75 1·50
884 43p. Fitzroy River Bridge . . 1·90 2·00

211 Shepherd with Lamb

2000. Christmas. Multicoloured.
885 10p. Type **211** 60 45
886 20p. Angel with Shepherds 90 60
887 33p. The Nativity . . . . . 1·25 90
888 43p. Angel with Wise Men 1·50 1·10
889 78p. Camel . . . . 2·50 3·50
MS890 160 × 75 mm. Nos. 885/9 6·50 6·50

212 Sunset over Islands

2001. Sunrise and Sunsets. Multicoloured.
891 10p. Type **212** 55 50
892 20p. Sunset over Stanley . . 85 70
893 37p. Sunset over Stanley Harbour . . . . 1·40 1·25
894 43p. Sunrise over islands . . 1·60 1·60

213 Forster's Caracara ("Striated caracara")

2001. "HONG KONG 2001" Stamp Exhibition. Sheet 150 × 90 mm, containing T **213** and similar horiz design showing bird of prey. Multicoloured.
MS895 37p. Type **213**; 37p. Hodgsons hawk eagle ("Mountain hawk") . . . . 3·00 3·50

214 1878 1d. Claret Stamp

2001. Death Centenary of Queen Victoria. Multicoloured.
896 3p. Type **214** 40 40
897 10p. *Great Britain* (steam/sail) (horiz) 70 60
898 20p. Stanley Harbour, 1888 (horiz) 90 70
899 43p. Cape Pembroke Lighthouse and first telephone line, 1897 . . . 1·75 1·00
900 93p. Royal Marines, 1900 . . 3·00 3·25
901 £1.50 "Queen Victoria, 1859" (Franz Winterhalter) . . . 4·00 4·50
MS902 105 × 80 mm. £1 Queen Victoria's funeral cortege in the streets of Windsor . . . . . . 3·50 3·75

215 *Welfare* (first British landing on Falkland Islands, 1690)

2001. Royal Navy Connections with the Falkland Islands. Multicoloured.
903 10p. Type **215** 70 60
904 17p. H.M.S. *Invincible* (battle cruiser), 1914 . . . . . . 1·00 65
905 20p. H.M.S. *Exeter* (cruiser), 1939 . . . . 1·10 75
906 37p. SR N6 hovercraft, 1967 1·50 1·25
907 43p. H.M.S. *Protector* (ice patrol ship) . . . . 1·60 1·40
908 68p. *Desire* (Cavendish and Davis), 1592 . . . . 2·50 3·00

216 Blackish Cinclodes ("Tussac Bird") **217** Young Gentoo Penguins

2001. Off-shore Islands (1st series). Carcass Island. Multicoloured.
909 37p. Type **216** . . . . . . 1·25 1·40
910 37p. Yellow violet . . . . . 1·25 1·40
911 43p. Black-crowned night heron . . . . 1·40 1·50
912 43p. Carcass Island settlement . . . . 1·40 1·50
See also Nos. 941/4 and 972/5.

2001. Gentoo Penguins. Multicoloured.
913 10p. Type **217** 65 60
914 33p. Adult feeding chick . . 1·25 1·10
915 37p. Adult on eggs . . . . . 1·40 1·40
916 43p. Group of penguins . . . 1·50 1·60

218 Rounding-up Wild Cattle

2002. 150th Anniv of Falkland Islands Company. Multicoloured.
917 10p. Type **218** 65 60
918 20p. *Amelia*, (postal schooner), 1852 . . . . . 1·25 75
919 43p. F. E. Cobb (Colonial Manager), 1867 . . . . . 1·50 1·00
920 £1 W. W. Bertrand, (sheep farmer) and sheep dipping 3·00 3·50

219 Princess Elizabeth reading, 1945

2002. Golden Jubilee.
921 **219** 20p. agate, violet and gold 90 70
922 – 37p. multicoloured . . . 1·40 1·00
923 – 43p. brown, violet and gold . . . . 1·50 1·10
924 – 50p. multicoloured . . . 1·75 2·00
MS925 162 × 95 mm. Nos. 921/4 and 50p. multicoloured . . . . . . 6·50 7·50
DESIGNS—HORIZ: 37p. Queen Elizabeth, New Zealand, 1977; 43p. Princess Elizabeth with Prince Charles at his christening, 1949; 50p. Queen Elizabeth in Garter robes, Windsor, 1994. VERT (38 × 51 mm)—50p. Queen Elizabeth after Annigoni.
Designs as Nos. 921/4 in No. **MS**925 omit the gold frame around each stamp and the "Golden Jubilee 1952–2002" inscription.

220 H.M.S. *Hermes* (aircraft carrier), 1982

2002. 20th Anniv of Liberation. Multicoloured.
926 22p. Type **220** 70 80
927 22p. *Dorada* (fishery patrol vessel), 2002 . . . . . . 70 80
928 40p. Troops landing, 1982 . . 1·25 1·40
929 40p. Mine clearing, 2002 . . 1·25 1·40
930 45p. Harrier jet on H.M.S. *Hermes*, 1982 . . . . . 1·40 1·50
931 45p. R.A.F. Tristar, 2002 . . 1·40 1·50

221 Queen Elizabeth visiting Royal Farms, Windsor, 1946

2002. Queen Elizabeth the Queen Mother Commemoration.
932 **221** 22p. brown, gold and purple 70 60
933 – 25p. multicoloured . . . 75 60
934 – 95p. black, gold and purple . . . . 2·50 2·75
935 – £1.20 multicoloured . . . 3·00 3·50
MS936 145 × 70 mm. Nos. 934/5 7·00 7·50
DESIGNS: 25p. Queen Mother at Guildhall lunch for Queen's Golden Wedding, 1997; 95p. Queen Elizabeth at a garden party, 1947; £1.20, Queen Mother at Scrabster, 1986.
Designs as Nos. 934/5 in No. **MS**936 omit the "1900–2002" inscription and the coloured frame.

222 Rockhopper Penguin

2002. Endangered Species. Penguins. Multicoloured.
937 36p. Type **222** . . . . 1·10 85
938 40p. Magellanic penguin . . 1·25 95

939 45p. Gentoo penguin . . . . 1·40 1·10
940 70p. Macaroni penguin . . . 2·00 2·50

2002. Off-shore Islands (2nd series). West Point Island. As T **216**, but horiz. Multicoloured.
941 40p. *Calandrinia feltonii* (plant) . . . . 1·25 1·40
942 40p. Black-browed albatross 1·25 1·40
943 45p. Rockhopper penguin . . 1·40 1·50
944 45p. West Point Island settlement . . . . 1·40 1·50

223 Prince Andrew as Naval Helicopter Pilot, 1982

2002. Visit of Duke of York to Falkland Islands.
945 **223** 22p. black and blue . . . 1·00 50
946 – £1.52 multicoloured . . . 4·50 5·00
DESIGN: £1.52, Duke of York and San Carlos Cemetery.

224 Gun Hill Shanty, Little Chartres

2003. Shepherds' Houses. Multicoloured.
947 10p. Type **224** 40 40
948 22p. Paragon House, Lafonia 65 55
949 45p. Dos Lomas, Lafonia . . 1·25 1·00
950 £1 The Old House, Shallow Bay Farm . . . . 2·40 2·75

225 Queen Elizabeth II

226 Prince William at Queen Mother's 101st Birthday and at Eton College

2003.
951 **225** £2 black, orange and brown . . . . 4·00 4·25

2003. 21st Birthday of Prince William of Wales. Multicoloured.
952 95p. Type **226** . . . . . . 2·75 2·75
953 95p. With Prince Harry at polo match and at Sighthill Community Education Centre . . . . 2·75 2·75

227 Chiloe Wigeon

2003. Birds. Multicoloured.
954 1p. Type **227** 10 10
955 2p. Dolphin gull (vert) . . . 10 10
956 5p. Falkland Islands flightless steamer duck 10 10
957 10p. Black-throated finch (vert) 20 25
958 22p. White-tufted grebe . . . 45 50
959 25p. Rufous-chested dotterel (vert) 50 55
960 45p. Magellan goose ("Upland Goose") 90 95
961 50p. Dark-faced ground tyrant (vert) . . . . . . 1·00 1·10
962 95p. Black-crowned night heron . . . . 2·00 2·25
963 £1 Red-backed buzzard ("Red-backed Hawk") (vert) . . . . 2·00 2·25
964 £3 Black-necked swan . . . 6·00 6·25
965 £5 Short-eared owl (vert) . . 10·00 10·50

(b) Self-adhesive.
966 (–) Rockhopper penguins . . . 80 80
No. 966 was inscribed "Airmail Postcard".

228 Albatross on Nest

2003. Bird Life International. Black-browed Albatross. Multicoloured.
967 22p. Type **228** 60 60
968 22p. Nestling 60 60
969 40p. Adults displaying (vert) 1·25 1·40
970 £1 Immature bird (grey beak) on nest (vert) . . . . . . 2·50 2·75
MS971 175 × 80 mm. 16p. Albatrosses in flight and Nos. 967/70 . . . . 5·00 5·25

2003. Off-shore Islands (3rd series). New Island. Multicoloured. As T **216**, but horiz.
972 40p. Forster's caracara ("Striated Caracara") . . . 1·25 1·40
973 40p. Lady's slipper orchids 1·25 1·40
974 45p. The Stone Cottage . . . 1·40 1·50
975 45p. King penguin . . . . . 1·40 1·50

229 Pale Maiden Flowers

2003. Christmas. National Flower. Pale Maiden (*Olysnium filifolium*). Multicoloured.
976 16p. Type **229** 55 40
977 30p. Bouquet of Pale Maiden flowers . . . . 1·00 80
978 40p. Pale Maiden plant . . . 1·25 1·00
979 95p. Pale Maiden plant growing on moorland . . . 2·75 3·00

POSTAGE DUE STAMPS

D 1 King Penguin

1991.
D1 **D 1** 1p. red and mauve 15 30
D2 2p. orange and light orange 15 30
D3 3p. ochre and yellow 15 30
D4 4p. green and light green . . 15 30
D5 5p. blue and light blue . . . 15 30
D6 10p. deep blue and blue . . . 20 30
D7 20p. violet and lilac 40 60
D8 50p. green and light green . . 1·00 1·40

FALKLAND ISLANDS DEPENDENCIES Pt. 1

Four groups of Islands situated between the Falkland Is. and the South Pole. In 1946 the four groups ceased issuing separate issues which were replaced by a single general issue. From 1963 the stamps of British Antarctic Territory were used in all these islands except South Georgia and South Sandwich for which separate stamps were issued inscribed "SOUTH GEORGIA" from 1963 until 1980.

Under the new constitution effective on 3 October 1985, South Georgia and South Sandwich Islands ceased to be dependencies of the Falkland Islands.

1944. 12 pence = 1 shilling;
20 shillings = 1 pound.
1971. 100 (new) pence = 1 pound.

GRAHAM LAND

1944. Stamps of Falkland Islands of 1938 optd **GRAHAM LAND DEPENDENCY OF.**
A1 **27** ½d. black and green . . . . 30 1·75
A2 – 1d. black and violet . . . . 30 1·00
A3 – 2d. black and red . . . . . 50 1·00
A4 – 3d. black and blue . . . . 50 1·00
A5 – 4d. black and purple . . . 2·00 1·75
A6 – 6d. black and brown . . . 16·00 2·25
A7 – 9d. black and blue . . . . 1·00 1·25
A8 – 1s. blue . . . . 1·00 1·25

SOUTH GEORGIA

1944. Stamps of Falkland Islands of 1938 optd **SOUTH GEORGIA DEPENDENCY OF.**
B1 **27** ½d. black and green . . . . 30 1·75
B2 – 1d. black and violet . . . . 30 1·00
B3 – 2d. black and red . . . . . 50 1·00
B4 – 3d. black and blue . . . . 50 1·00
B5 – 4d. black and purple . . . 2·00 1·75
B6 – 6d. black and brown . . . 16·00 2·25
B7 – 9d. black and blue . . . . 1·00 1·25
B8 – 1s. blue . . . . 1·00 1·25

SOUTH ORKNEYS

1944. Stamps of Falkland Islands of 1938 optd **SOUTH ORKNEYS DEPENDENCY OF.**
C1 **27** ½d. black and green . . . . 30 1·75
C2 – 1d. black and violet . . . . 30 1·00
C3 – 2d. black and red . . . . . 50 1·00
C4 – 3d. black and blue . . . . 50 1·00
C5 – 4d. black and purple . . . 2·00 1·75
C6 – 6d. black and brown . . . 16·00 2·25
C7 – 9d. black and blue . . . . 1·00 1·25
C8 – 1s. blue . . . . 1·00 1·25

SOUTH SHETLANDS

1944. Stamps of Falkland Islands of 1938 optd **SOUTH SHETLAND DEPENDENCY OF.**
D1 **27** ½d. black and green . . . . 30 1·75
D2 – 1d. black and violet . . . . 30 1·00
D3 – 2d. black and red . . . . . 50 1·00
D4 – 3d. black and blue . . . . 50 1·00
D5 – 4d. black and purple . . . 2·00 1·75
D6 – 6d. black and brown . . . 16·00 2·25
D7 – 9d. black and blue . . . . 1·00 1·25
D8 – 1s. blue . . . . 1·00 1·25

GENERAL ISSUES

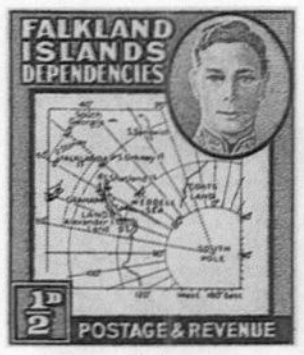

G 1

G 3 "Trepassey", 1945–47

1946.
G 1 **G 1** ½d. black and green . . 1·00 3·00
G 2 1d. black and violet . . 1·25 1·75
G 3 2d. black and red . . . 1·25 2·50
G11a 2½d. black and blue . . 6·50 6·00
G 4 3d. black and blue . . 1·25 4·75
G 5 4d. black and red . . . 2·25 4·75
G 6 6d. black and orange . . 3·25 4·75
G 7 9d. black and brown . . 2·00 3·75
G 8 1s. black and purple . . 2·00 4·25

1946. Victory. As T **11a** of Gambia.
G17 1d. violet 50 30
G18 3d. blue 75 30

1949. Silver Wedding. As T **11b/c** of Gambia.
G19 2½d. blue . . . . 1·75 2·00
G20 1s. blue . . . . 1·75 2·25

1949. U.P.U. As T **11d/g** of Gambia.
G21 1d. violet . . . . 1·00 2·00
G22 2d. red . . . . 5·00 3·25
G23 3d. blue . . . . 3·25 1·25
G24 6d. orange . . . . 4·00 3·00

1953. Coronation. As T **11h** of Gambia.
G25 1d. black and violet . . . . 1·10 1·25

1954. Ships.
G26 – ½d. black and green . . 30 2·50
G27 **G 3** 1d. black and sepia . . . 1·75 1·50
G28 – 1½d. black and olive . . 2·00 2·50
G29 – 2d. black and red . . . 1·75 60
G30 – 2½d. black and yellow . . 1·25 25
G31 – 3d. black and blue . . . 1·25 25
G32 – 4d. black and purple . . 4·25 1·25
G33 – 6d. black and lilac . . . 4·25 1·25
G34 – 9d. black . . . . 4·25 2·00
G35 – 1s. black and brown . . 4·25 1·50
G36 – 2s. black and red . . . 19·00 10·00
G37 – 2s.6d. black and turquoise . . . . . . 20·00 8·00
G38 – 5s. black and violet . . . 42·00 9·00
G39 – 10s. black and blue . . . 55·00 19·00
G40 – £1 black . . . . 90·00 48·00
SHIPS—VERT: 1½d. "John Biscoe"; 6d. "Discovery"; 9d. "Endurance"; 2s.6d. "Francais"; 5s. "Scotia"; £1 "Belgica". HORIZ: 1½d. "Wyatt Earp"; 2d. "Eagle"; 2½d. "Penola"; 3d. "Discovery II"; 4d. "William Scoresby"; 1s. "Deutschland"; 2s. "Pourquoi pas?"; 10s. "Antarctic".

1956. Trans-Antarctic Expedition. Nos. G27, G30/1 and G33 optd **TRANS-ANTARCTIC EXPEDITION 1955-1958.**
G41 **G 3** 1d. black and sepia . . . 10 30
G42 – 2½d. black and yellow . . 50 50
G43 – 3d. black and blue . . . 50 30
G44 – 6d. black and lilac . . . 50 30

For later issues see **BRITISH ANTARCTIC TERRITORIES** and **SOUTH GEORGIA**.

ISSUES FOR SOUTH GEORGIA AND SOUTH SANDWICH ISLANDS

In 1980 stamps were again inscribed "FALKLAND ISLANDS DEPENDENCIES" for use in the above area.

14 Map of Falkland Islands Dependencies

1980. Multicoloured.
74A 1p. Type **14** 30 30
75A 2p. Shag Rocks 30 30
76A 3p. Bird and Willis Islands 30 30
77A 4p. Gulbrandsen Lake . . . 30 30
78A 5p. King Edward Point . . . 30 30
79A 6p. Sir Ernest Shackleton's memorial cross, Hope Point 40 30
80A 7p. Sir Ernest Shackleton's grave, Grytviken 40 40
81A 8p. Grytviken Church . . . 30 40
82A 9p. Coaling Hulk "Louise" at Grytviken 30 45
83A 10p. Clerke Rocks 30 45
84B 20p. Candlemas Island . . . 1·50 1·50
85B 25p. Twitcher Rock and Cook Island, Southern Thule . . . . 1·50 2·50
86A 50p. R.R.S. "John Biscoe II" in Cumberland Bay . . . 70 1·50
87A £1 R.R.S. "Bransfield" in Cumberland Bay . . . . 75 2·25
88A £3 H.M.S. "Endurance" in Cumberland Bay . . . . 2·00 4·50
These stamps come with or without date imprint.

15 Magellanic Clubmoss

16 Wedding Bouquet from Falkland Islands Dependencies

1981. Plants. Multicoloured.
89 3p. Type **15** 10 25
90 6p. Alphine cat's-tail 10 30
91 7p. Greater burnet 10 30
92 11p. Antarctic bedstraw . . . 15 30
93 15p. Brown rush 15 35
94 25p. Antarctic hair grass . . . 25 50

1981. Royal Wedding. Multicoloured.
95 10p. Type **16** 15 30
96 13p. Prince Charles dressed for skiing 20 35
97 52p. Prince Charles and Lady Diana Spencer 65 85

17 Introduced Reindeer during Calving, Spring

1982. Reindeer. Multicoloured.
98 5p. Type **17** 20 65
99 13p. Bull at rut, Autumn . . 20 85
100 25p. Reindeer and mountains, Winter . . . . 30 1·10
101 26p. Reindeer feeding on tussock, late Winter . . . 30 1·10

18 "Gamasellus racovitzai" (tick)

19 Lady Diana Spencer at Tidworth, Hampshire, July 1981

1982. Insects. Multicoloured.
102 5p. Type **18** 10 25
103 10p. "Alaskozetes antarcticus" (mite) 15 35
104 13p. "Cryptopygus antarcticus" (spring-tail) . . 15 40
105 15p. "Notiomaso australis" (spider) 15 40

106 25p. "Hydromedion sparsutum" (beetle) 25 50
107 26p. "Parochlus steinenii" (midge) 25 50

1982. 21st Birthday of Princess of Wales. Multicoloured.
108 5p. Falkland Islands Dependencies coat of arms 10 15
109 17p. Type **19** 40 35
110 37p. Bride and groom on steps of St. Paul's 45 80
111 50p. Formal portrait . . . . 1·00 1·10

20 Map of South Georgia

1982. Rebuilding Fund.
112 **20** £1+£1 multicoloured . . . 1·50 3·25

21 Westland Whirlwind

1983. Bicentenary of Manned Flight. Multicoloured.
113 5p. Type **21** 25 35
114 13p. Westland Wasp helicopter 35 60
115 17p. Vickers Supermarine Walrus II 35 60
116 50p. Auster Autocrat . . . . 70 1·25

22 "Euphausia superba"

1983. Crustacea. Multicoloured.
117 5p. Type **22** 40 20
118 17p. "Glyptonotus antarcticus" 50 50
119 25p. "Epimeria monodon" 60 60
120 34p. "Serolis pagenstecheri" 70 80

23 Zavodovski Island

1984. Volcanoes of South Sandwich Islands. Mult.
121 6p. Type **23** 80 80
122 17p. Mt. Michael, Saunders Island . . . . 2·00 1·60
123 22p. Bellingshausen Island . . 2·00 1·75
124 52p. Bristol Island . . . . . 2·50 3·25

24 Grey-headed Albatross

1985. Albatrosses. Multicoloured.
125 7p. Type **24** . . . . 1·50 85
126 22p. Black-browed albatross 2·00 1·40
127 27p. Wandering albatross . . 2·25 1·60
128 54p. Light-mantled sooty albatross . . . . 2·50 2·50

25 The Queen Mother

1985. Life and Times of Queen Elizabeth the Queen Mother. Multicoloured.
129 7p. At Windsor Castle on Princess Elizabeth's 14th Birthday, 1940 . . . . . . 30 30
130 22p. With Princess Anne, Lady Sarah Armstrong-Jones and Prince Edward at Trooping the Colour . . 60 70
131 27p. Type **25** 70 80
132 54p. With Prince Henry at his christening (from photo by Lord Snowdon) . . . . . 1·25 1·40
MS133 91 × 73 mm. £1 Disembarking from Royal Yacht *Britannia* . . . . 2·75 2·75

1985. Early Naturalists. As T **149a** of Falkland Islands. Multicoloured.
134 7p. Dumont d'Urville and "Durvillea antarctica" (kelp) . . . . 1·00 1·00
135 22p. Johann Reinhold Forster and king penguin . . . . 1·75 2·00
136 27p. Johann Georg Adam Forster and tussock grass 1·75 2·25
137 54p. Sir Joseph Banks and dove prion . . . . 2·25 3·50

For later issues see **SOUTH GEORGIA AND THE SOUTH SANDWICH ISLANDS**.

FARIDKOT Pt. 1

A state of the Punjab, India. Now uses Indian stamps.

1879. 1 folus = 1 paisa = ¼ anna.
1886. 12 pies = 1 anna; 16 annas = 1 rupee.

N 1 (1 folus)

N 2 (1 paisa)

1879. Imperf.
N5 N **1** 1f. blue . . . . 2·00 3·50
N6 N **2** 1p. blue . . . . 3·25 8·00

1887. Stamps of India (Queen Victoria) optd **FARIDKOT STATE**.
17 **40** 3p. red . . . . 90 38·00
1 **23** ½a. turquoise . . . . 1·25 1·10
3 – 1a. purple . . . . 1·50 1·25
4 – 2a. blue . . . . 2·75 4·50
7 – 3a. orange . . . . 2·50 3·50
8 – 4a. green (No. 96) . . . . 6·50 13·00
11 – 6a. brown (No. 80) . . . . 2·00 13·00
12 – 8a. mauve . . . . 10·00 32·00
14 – 12a. purple on red . . . . 35·00 £375
15 – 1r. grey . . . . 40·00 £350
16 **37** 1r. green and red . . . . . 32·00 85·00

OFFICIAL STAMPS

1886. Stamps of India (Queen Victoria) optd **SERVICE FARIDKOT STATE**.
O 1 **23** ½a. turquoise 30 60
O 2 – 1a. purple . . . . 75 1·40
O 4 – 2a. blue . . . . 1·75 8·50
O 6 – 3a. orange . . . . 5·50 7·50
O 8 – 4a. green (No. 96) . . . . 4·25 20·00
O11 – 6a. brown (No. 80) . . . 18·00 24·00
O12 – 8a. mauve . . . . 5·50 25·00
O14 – 1r. grey . . . . 45·00 £170
O15 **37** 1r. green and red . . . . 80·00 £475

FAROE ISLANDS Pt. 11

A Danish possession in the North Atlantic Ocean. Under British Administration during the German Occupation of Denmark, 1940/5.

100 ore = 1 krone.

1940. Stamps of Denmark surch with new value (twice on Type **43**).
2 **43** 20ore on 1ore green . . . . 36·00 55·00
3 20ore on 5ore purple . . . . 36·00 23·00
1 **40** 20ore on 15ore red . . . . 55·00 12·50
4 **43** 50ore on 5ore purple . . . . £275 55·00
5 60ore on 6ore orange £110 £170

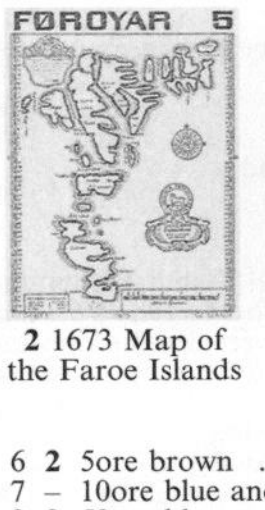

2 1673 Map of the Faroe Islands

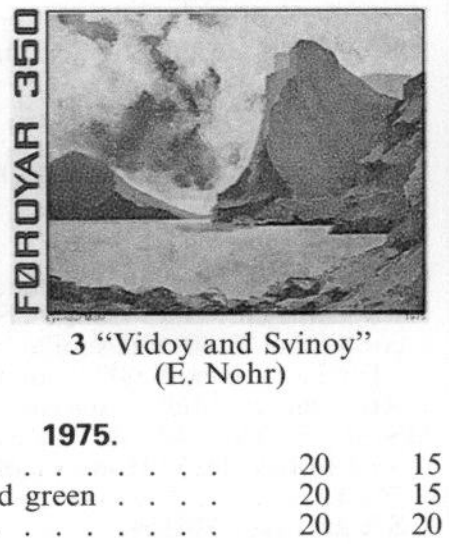

3 "Vidoy and Svinoy" (E. Nohr)

1975.
6 **2** 5ore brown 20 15
7 – 10ore blue and green 20 15
8 **2** 50ore blue 20 20
9 – 60ore brown and blue . . . 90 75
10 – 70ore black and blue 90 75
11 – 80ore brown and blue . . . 45 45
12 **2** 90ore red 85 75
13 – 120ore blue and deep blue . . 45 30
14 – 200ore black and blue . . . 70 70
15 – 250ore green, brown & blue 75 60
16 – 300ore green, brown & blue 3·75 1·90
17 **3** 350ore multicoloured 90 85
18 – 450ore multicoloured . . . . 1·00 95
19 – 500ore multicoloured . . . . 1·10 1·00
DESIGNS—As Type **2** but HORIZ: 10, 60, 80, 120ore Northern map (A. Ortelius); 70, 200ore West Sandoy; 250, 300ore Streymoy and Vagar. As Type **3**: 450ore "Nes" (R. Smith); 500ore "Hvitanes and Skalafjordur" (S. Joensen-Mikines).

4 Rowing Boat

5 Motor Fishing Boat

1976. Inauguration of Faroese Post Office.
20 **4** 125ore red . . . . 2·00 1·30
21 – 160ore multicoloured 40 35
22 – 800ore green . . . . 1·40 95
DESIGNS—24 × 34 mm: 160ore Faroese flag. 24 × 31 mm: 800ore Faroese postman.

1977. Faroese Fishing Vessels.
23 **5** 100ore black, lt green & green . . . . 5·00 4·25
24 – 125ore black, rose and red 65 70
25 – 160ore black, lt blue & blue 1·00 90
26 – 600ore black, ochre & brown 1·40 90
DESIGNS: 125ore "Niels Pauli" (inshore fishing cutter); 160ore "Krunborg" (seine fishing boat); 600ore "Polarfisk" (deep-sea trawler).

6 Common Snipe

7 Atlantic Puffins over North Coast

1977. Birds. Multicoloured.
27 70ore Type **6** 35 20
28 180ore Oystercatcher 45 45
29 250ore Whimbrel 50 55

1978. Views of Mykines Island. Multicoloured.
30 100ore Type **7** 25 25
31 130ore Mykines village (horiz) 35 25
32 140ore Cultivated fields (horiz) 45 40
33 150ore Aerial view of Mykines 45 35
34 180ore Map of Mykines (37 × 26 mm) 45 40

8 Northern Gannet

9 Old Library Building

1978. Sea Birds. Multicoloured.
35 140ore Type **8** 60 50
36 180ore Atlantic puffin 80 65
37 400ore Common guillemot . . 85 70

1978. 150th Anniv of National Library.
38 **9** 140ore olive and blue 50 45
39 – 180ore brown and flesh . . . 50 50
DESIGN: 180ore New National Library building.

10 Guide, Tent and Campfire

11 Ram

1978. 50th Anniv of Girl Guides.
40 **10** 140ore multicoloured . . . 50 60

1979. Sheep-rearing.
41 **11** 25k. multicoloured . . . . 5·00 3·75

12 Bisect of Denmark 4ore Blue, 1919

13 Girl in Festive Costume

1979. Europa. Multicoloured.
42 **12** 140ore bl & yell on stone . . 50 50
43 – 180ore ol & mve on stone 50 50
DESIGN: 180ore Denmark 1919 2ore surcharge on 5ore.

1979. International Year of the Child. Multicoloured designs showing childrens' drawings.
44 110ore Type **13** 35 25
45 150ore Man fishing from boat 35 35
46 200ore Two friends 50 45

14 Sea Plantain

15 Jakob Jakobsen (linguist and folklorist)

1980. Flowers. Multicoloured.
47 90ore Type **14** 20 25
48 110ore Glacier buttercup . . . 20 25
49 150ore Purple saxifrage . . . 35 25
50 200ore Starry saxifrage 60 35
51 400ore Faroese lady's mantle 1·00 70

1980. Europa.
52 **15** 150ore green 35 35
53 – 200ore brown 45 35
DESIGN: 200ore Vensel Ulrich Hammershaimb (theologian and linguist).

16 Virgin and Child

17 Timber Houses, Torshavn

1980. Pews of Kirkjubour Church (1st series).
54 **16** 110ore multicoloured . . . 45 30
55 – 140ore multicoloured . . . 45 25
56 – 150ore multicoloured . . . 45 30
57 – 200ore black and buff . . . 50 35
DESIGNS: 140ore St. John the Baptist; 150ore St. Peter; 200ore St. Paul.
See also Nos. 90/3.

1981. Old Torshavn. Designs show different views.
58 **17** 110ore green 45 25
59 – 140ore black 45 30
60 – 150ore brown 45 30
61 – 200ore blue 45 40

18 Garter Dance

1981. Europa.
62 **18** 150ore green and brown . . 30 30
63 – 200ore brown and green . . 40 45
DESIGN: 200ore Ring dance.

19 Rune Stone

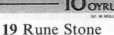

20 Map of Viking Voyages in North Atlantic

1981. Historic Writings of the Faroes.
64 **19** 10ore blue, black and grey 15 15
65 – 1k. lt brown, black & brn 35 25
66 – 3k. grey, black and red . . 1·00 55
67 – 6k. red, black and grey . . 1·40 1·10
68 – 10k. stone, brown and black 2·50 2·40

DESIGNS: 1k. Score of folksong, 1846; 3k. Manuscript of Sheep Farming Law, 1298; 6k. Seal showing heraldic ram, 1533; 10k. Title page of "Faeroae et Faeroa Reserata" and library.

1982. Europa.
69 **20** 1k.50 blue 30 40
70 – 2k. black 55 45
DESIGN: 2k. Archaeological excavations at Kvivik village.

21 Gjogv

22 Elinborg's Promise to remain Faithful

1982. Villages.
71 **21** 180ore black and blue . . . 50 40
72 – 220ore black and brown . . 1·00 50
73 – 250ore black and brown . . 80 50
DESIGNS: 220ore Hvalvik; 250ore Kvivik.

1982. The Ballad of Harra Paetur and Elinborg. Multicoloured.
74 220ore Type **22** 70 40
75 250ore Elinborg longing for Paetur 70 45
76 350ore Paetur in disguise greets Elinborg . . . . . . 1·00 65
77 450ore Elinborg and Paetur sail away . . . . 1·30 95

23 "Arcturus"

24 King

1983. Old Cargo Liners on the Faroes Run. Multicoloured.
78 220ore Type **23** 65 55
79 250ore "Laura" 85 60
80 700ore "Thyra" . . . . 2·30 1·90

1983. 19th-century Chess Pieces by Pol i Bud from Nolsoy.
81 **24** 250ore brown and black . . 1·50 1·40
82 – 250ore blue and black . . . 1·50 1·40
DESIGN: No. 82, Queen.

25 Niels R. Finsen (founder of phototherapy)

1983. Europa.
83 **25** 250ore blue 70 65
84 – 400ore purple . . . . 1·30 1·00
DESIGN: 400ore Sir Alexander Fleming (discoverer of penicillin).

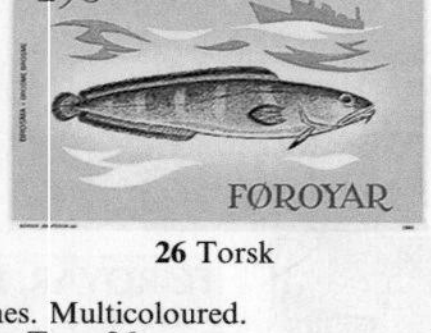

26 Torsk

1983. Fishes. Multicoloured.
85 250ore Type **26** 60 45
86 280ore Haddock 80 65
87 500ore Atlantic halibut . . . 1·40 1·20
88 900ore Atlantic wolffish . . . 2·50 2·20

27 Greenland, Halsingland (Sweden) and Iceland Costumes

1983. Inauguration of Nordic House (cultural centre), Torshavn. Sheet 120 × 67 mm containing T **27** and similar horiz designs.
MS89 250ore Type **27**; 250ore Finnmark (Norway), Funen (Denmark) and Aland costumes; 250ore Telemark (Norway), Faroes and Ostra Nyland (Finland) costumes . . . . . 7·00 8·00

1984. Pews of Kirkjubour Church (2nd series). As T **16**.
90 250ore multicoloured 80 65
91 300ore lt brown, black & brn 1·30 1·00
92 350ore brown, grey & black 90 85
93 400ore multicoloured . . . . 1·50 1·30
DESIGNS: 250ore St. John; 300ore St. Jacob; 350ore St. Thomas; 400ore Judas Taddeus.

28 Bridge

1984. Europa. 25th Anniv of European Post and Telecommunications Conference.
94 **28** 250ore red 70 70
95 500ore blue . . . . 1·40 1·30

29 Sverri Patursson

30 Fisherman

1984. Writers.
96 **29** 200ore green 60 50
97 – 250ore red 80 70
98 – 300ore blue 90 75
99 – 450ore violet . . . . . . 1·30 1·10
DESIGNS: 250ore Joannes Patursson; 300ore Janus Djurhuus; 450ore Hans Andrias Djurhuus.

1984. Fishing Industry.
100 – 280ore blue 70 75
101 – 300ore brown 85 85
102 **30** 12k. green . . . . 3·00 3·24
DESIGNS—HORIZ: 280ore Fishing ketch "Westward Ho". VERT: 300ore Fishermen on deck.

31 "Beauty of the Veils"

32 Torshavn

1984. Fairy Tales. Designs showing woodcuts by Elinborg Lutzen.
103 **31** 140ore blue, green & brn 4·00 4·25
104 – 280ore green and brown 4·00 4·25
105 – 280ore dp green, grn & brn 4·00 4·25
106 – 280ore brown and green 4·00 4·25
107 – 280ore dp green, grn & brn 4·00 4·25
108 – 280ore brn, grn & dp brn 4·00 4·25
DESIGNS: No. 104, "Beauty of the Veils" (different); 105, "The Shy Prince"; 106, "The Glass Sword"; 107, "Little Elin"; 108, "The Boy and the Ox".

1985. J. T. Stanley's Expedition to the Faroes, 1789. Paintings by Edward Dayes.
109 **32** 250ore brown and blue . . 80 70
110 – 280ore brown, green & bl 75 85
111 – 550ore green, brown & bl 1·50 1·70
112 – 800ore brown, green & bl 2·50 2·40
DESIGNS: 280ore Mount Skaeling; 550ore Hoyvik; 800ore The Rocking Stones, Eysturoy.

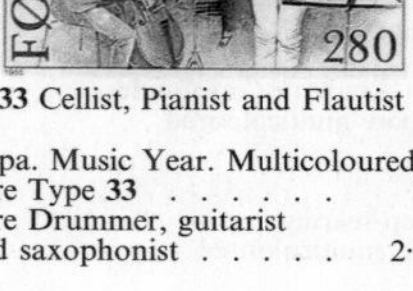

33 Cellist, Pianist and Flautist

1985. Europa. Music Year. Multicoloured.
113 280ore Type **33** 75 80
114 550ore Drummer, guitarist and saxophonist . . . . . 2·10 2·10

34 "Self-portrait" (Ruth Smith)

1985. Paintings. Multicoloured.
115 280ore "The Garden, Hoyvik" (Tummas Arge) (horiz) . . . . 1·00 80
116 450ore Type **34** . . . . . . 1·60 1·50
117 550ore "Winter's Day in Nolsoy" (Steffan Danielsen) (horiz) . . . . 2·50 2·00

35 Nolsoy Lighthouse

1985. Lighthouses. Multicoloured.
118 270ore Type **35** . . . . . . 1·20 1·30
119 320ore Torshavn . . . . . . 1·30 1·50
120 350ore Mykines . . . . . . 1·40 1·60
121 470ore Map of the Faroes showing lighthouse sites . . 2·00 2·00

36 Douglas DC-3, Faroe Airways

1985. Aircraft. Multicoloured.
122 300ore Type **36** . . . . . . 2·40 2·20
123 300ore Fokker F.27 Friendship, Flugfelag Islands . . . . 2·40 2·20
124 300ore Boeing 737 Special, Maersk Air . . . . . . 2·40 2·20
125 300ore Beech 50 Twin Bonanza, Bjorum Fly . . . 2·40 2·20
126 300ore Bell 212 helicopter, Snipan . . . . 2·40 2·20

37 Peasant in Forest

38 Ship dumping Dangerous Canisters at Sea

1986. Skrimsla (dancing ballad). Mult.
127 300ore Type **37** . . . . . . 1·00 85
128 420ore Giant challenges peasant to chess game . . 1·30 1·40
129 550ore Peasant beats giant 2·00 1·90
130 650ore Peasant and castle . . 2·30 2·10

1986. Europa. Multicoloured.
131 3k. Type **38** . . . . 1·30 1·50
132 5k.50 Contents of damaged canister escaping into sea 2·20 2·50

39 Birds escaping from Cage

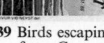

40 Ship at Anchor in Bay

1986. 25th Anniv of Amnesty International. Multicoloured.
133 3k. Type **39** . . . . 1·20 1·00
134 4k.70 Faces (horiz) . . . . . 1·40 1·40
135 5k.50 Man behind bars and woman with children . . . 2·00 1·90

1986. "Hafnia 87" International Stamp Exhibition, Copenhagen (1st issue). Sheet 108 × 76 mm containing T **40** and similar vert designs showing "Torshavn East Bay" (watercolour) by Christian Rosenmeyer. Multicoloured.
MS136 3k. Type **40**; 4k.70 Rowing boat in bay; 6k.50 Houses (sold at 20k.) . . . . 8·75 8·50
See also No. **MS**154.

41 Glyvrar Bridge, Eysturoy

1986. Bridges.
137 **41** 2k.70 brown . . . . 2·00 1·90
138 – 3k. blue . . . . 2·10 1·80
139 – 13k. green . . . . 5·00 4·25
DESIGNS—VERT: 3k. Leypanagjogv, Vagar. HORIZ: 13k. Skaelingur, Streymoy.

42 Farmhouse, Depli

43 Windows

1987. Farm Buildings.
140 **42** 300ore dp blue & blue . . 1·00 90
141 – 420ore brown & lt brown 2·30 1·90
142 – 470ore green & lt green . . 2·50 1·70
143 – 650ore black & grey . . 2·75 2·30
DESIGNS: 420ore Barn, Depli; 470ore Cowshed and blacksmith's, Frammi vid Gjonna; 650ore Farmhouse, Frammi vid Gjonna.

1987. Europa. Architecture. Details of Nordic House, Torshavn (by O. Steen and K. Ragnarsdottir).
144 **43** 300ore blue . . . . 1·30 1·20
145 – 550ore brown . . . . . . 2·30 2·20
DESIGN: 550ore Entrance.

44 "Joannes Patursson"

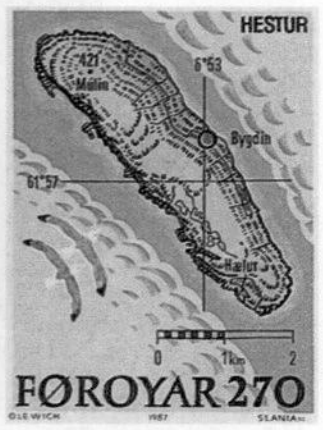

45 Map

1987. Trawlers. Multicoloured.
146 300ore Type **44** . . . . . . 1·20 85
147 550ore "Magnus Heinason" (side trawler) . . . . . . 2·50 2·20
148 800ore "Sjurdarberg" (stern trawler) . . . . 4·50 3·00

1987. Hestur Island. Multicoloured.
149 270ore Type **45** . . . . . . 1·00 1·00
150 300ore Harbour (horiz) . . . 90 90
151 420ore Alvastakkur needle . . 1·40 1·50
152 470ore Fagradalsvatn Lake (horiz) . . . . 1·60 1·50
153 550ore Bygdin village . . . . 2·00 1·80

46 Ships in Bay

1987. "Hafnia 87" International Stamp Exhibition, Copenhagen (2nd issue). Sheet 75 × 54 mm showing "Torshavn West Bay" (watercolour) by Christian Rosenmeyer.
MS154 **46** 3k. multicoloured (sold at 4k.) . . . . 2·75 3·25

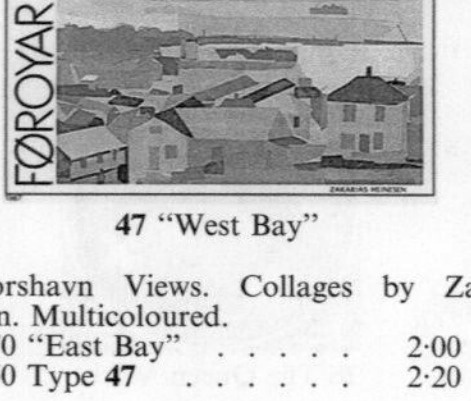

47 "West Bay"

1987. Torshavn Views. Collages by Zacharias Heinesen. Multicoloured.
155 4k.70 "East Bay" . . . . . 2·00 1·80
156 6k.50 Type **47** . . . . . . 2·20 2·40

48 Daisy

49 Container Ship and Dockside Scene

1988. Flowers. Multicoloured.
157 2k.70 Type **48** . . . . . . 1·20 90
158 3k. Heath spotted orchid . . 1·00 90
159 4k.70 Tormentil . . . . . . 1·60 1·60
160 9k. Common butterwort . . 3·25 2·75

1988. Europa. Transport and Communications. Multicoloured.
161 3k. Dish aerial and satellite 1·10 1·40
162 5k.50 Type **49** . . . . . . 2·40 2·30

50 Jorgen-Frantz Jacobsen

51 Notice of Christmas Meeting and Conveners

1988. Writers.
163 **50** 270ore green . . . . . . 1·30 1·40
164 – 300ore red 90 85
165 – 470ore blue . . . . . . 2·20 1·80
166 – 650ore brown . . . . . 3·00 2·40
DESIGNS: 300ore Christian Matras; 470ore William Heinesen; 650ore Hedin Bru.

1988. Centenary of Christmas Meeting to Establish National Movement. Multicoloured.
167 3k. Type **51** . . . . 1·00 90
168 3k.20 Drawing by William Heinesen of a People's Meeting, 1908, and conveners . . . . 1·30 1·30
169 12k. Opening words of Joannes Patursson's poem "Now the Hour has Come", conveners and oystercatcher . . . . . . 5·00 4·25

52 Exterior View of Cathedral

1988. Kirkjubour Cathedral Ruins.
170 **52** 270ore green . . . . . . 1·40 1·70
171 – 300ore blue . . . . . . 1·20 1·10
172 – 470ore brown . . . . . 2·30 1·30
173 – 550ore purple . . . . . 2·50 2·10
DESIGNS—VERT: 300ore Window; 470ore Crucifixion (relief). HORIZ: 550ore Nave.

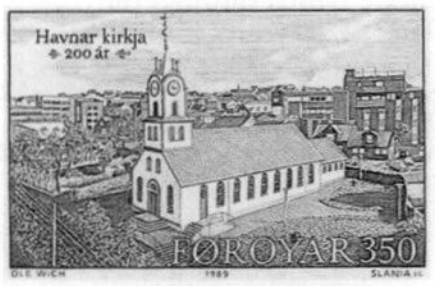

53 Church

1989. Bicentenary of Torshavn Church.
174 **53** 350ore green . . . . . . 1·30 1·10
175 – 500ore brown . . . . . . 1·80 1·80
176 – 15k. blue . . . . 5·75 5·00
DESIGNS—VERT: 500ore "The Last Supper" (altarpiece); 15k. Bell from "Norske Love" (shipwreck).

54 Wooden Toy Boat

55 Sjostuka Man

1989. Europa. Children's Toys. Multicoloured.
177 3k.50 Type **54** . . . . . 1·30 1·40
178 6k. Wooden horse . . . . . 2·30 2·30

1989. Nordic Countries' Postal Co-operation. Traditional Costumes. Multicoloured.
179 350ore Type **55** . . . . . . 1·10 1·30
180 600ore Stakkur woman . . . 2·10 2·10

56 Rowing

57 Tvoran

1989. Sports. Multicoloured.
181 200ore Type **56** 90 95
182 350ore Handball . . . . . . 1·30 1·20
183 600ore Football . . . . . . 2·30 2·00
184 700ore Swimming . . . . . 2·50 2·30

1989. Bird Cliffs of Suduroy. Each brown, green and blue.
185 320ore Type **57** . . . . . . 1·00 95
186 350ore Skuvanes . . . . . . 1·40 1·20
187 500ore Beinisvord . . . . . 1·70 1·60
188 600ore Asmundarstakkur . . 2·50 2·00

58 Unloading Boxes of Fish from Trawler

59 Old Post Office, Gjogv

1990. Fish Processing Industry. Mult.
189 3k.50 Type **58** . . . . . . 1·00 90
190 3k.70 Cleaning Atlantic cod 1·40 1·20
191 5k. Filleting fish . . . . . . 2·20 1·60
192 7k. Packed processed fish . . 2·50 2·20

1990. Europa. Post Office Buildings. Mult.
193 3k.50 Type **59** . . . . . . 1·40 1·60
194 6k. Klaksvik post office . . . 2·50 2·20

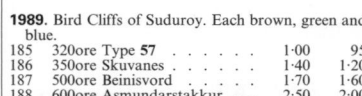

60 Faroese Flag

1990. 50th Anniv of Official Recognition of Faroese Flag. Sheet 116 × 75 mm containing T **60** and similar vert designs. Multicoloured.
MS195 3k.50 Type **60**; 3k.50 "Nyggjaberg" (trawler); 3k.50 "Sanna" (schooner) . . . . . 4·75 3·75

61 Sowerby's Beaked Whale

1990. Whales. Multicoloured.
196 320ore Type **61** . . . . . . 1·20 1·10
197 350ore Bowhead whale . . . 1·30 1·50
198 600ore Black right whale . . 2·50 2·10
199 700ore Northern bottle-nosed whale . . . . 3·50 2·20

62 Nolsoy from Hilltop

63 Ribwort Plantain

1990. Nolsoy. Paintings by Steffan Danielsen. Multicoloured.
200 50ore Type **62** 15 25
201 350ore Church . . . . 1·20 90
202 500ore Village . . . . 2·00 1·80
203 1000ore Cliffs by moonlight 4·25 3·00

1991. Anthropochora. Multicoloured.
204 3k.70 Type **63** . . . . . . 1·80 1·20
205 4k. Northern dock . . . . . 2·10 1·20
206 4k.50 Black beetle . . . . . 2·50 2·00
207 6k.50 Earthworm . . . . . 3·50 2·50

64 Town Hall

1991. 125th Anniv of Torshavn as Capital. Multicoloured.
208 3k.70 Type **64** . . . . . . 1·50 1·70
209 3k.70 Eastern Tinganes (old part of Torshavn) . . . . 1·40 1·40

65 Satellite, Earth and Weather Map

66 Arctic Terns

1991. Europa. Europe in Space. Mult.
210 3k.70 Type **65** . . . . . . 1·60 1·40
211 5k.50 Chart of Plough constellation and Pole Star, and sailors navigating by stars . . . . 2·50 2·50

1991. Birds. Multicoloured.
212 3k.70 Type **66** . . . . . . 1·60 1·30
213 3k.70 Black-legged kittiwakes 1·60 1·30

67 Saksun

1991. Nordic Countries' Postal Co-operation. Tourism. Multicoloured.
214 370ore Type **67** . . . . . . 1·30 1·20
215 650ore Vestmanna cliffs . . . 2·50 2·30

68 "Handanagardur"

1991. 85th Birth Anniv of Samal Joensen-Mikines (painter). Multicoloured.
216 340ore "Funeral Procession" 1·70 1·30
217 370ore "The Farewell" . . . 1·60 1·20
218 550ore Type **68** . . . . . . 2·00 1·70
219 1300ore "Winter Morning" 5·75 4·25

69 "Ruth"

1991. Mail Ships. Multicoloured.
220 200ore Type **69** . . . . . . 1·00 1·00
221 370ore "Ritan" . . . . . . 1·60 1·10
222 550ore "Sigmundur" . . . . 2·30 1·20
223 800ore "Masin" . . . . . . 3·25 2·30

70 Map and Viking Ship (Leif Eriksson)

1992. Europa. 500th Anniv of Discovery of America by Columbus. Multicoloured.
224 3k.70 Type **70** . . . . . . 1·40 1·40
225 6k.50 Map and "Santa Maria" . . . . 2·20 2·10
MS226 85 × 67 mm. Nos. 224/5 5·75 4·75

71 Grey Seal ("Halichoerus grypus")

1992. Seals. Multicoloured.
227 3k.70 Type **71** . . . . . . 1·50 1·20
228 3k.70 Common seal ("Phoca vitulina") . . . . 1·50 1·20

72 Desmine

73 Glyvra Hanus's House

1992. Minerals. Multicoloured.
229 370ore Type **72** . . . . . . 1·20 2·00
230 650ore Mesolite . . . . . . 2·30 2·20

1992. Old Houses in Nordragota, Eysturoy. Multicoloured.
231 3k.40 Type **73** . . . . . . 1·30 1·20
232 3k.70 Village and church . . 1·60 1·40
233 6k.50 Blasastova . . . . . . 2·75 2·10
234 8k. Jakupsstova . . . . . . 3·25 2·50

74 Musicians at Jazz, Folk and Blues Festival

1993. 10th Anniv of Nordic House, Torshavn. Multicoloured.
235 400ore "The Lost Musicians" (William Heinesen) . . . . 1·60 1·30
236 400ore Joannes Andreassen (pianist) . . . . 1·60 1·30
237 400ore Type **74** . . . . . . 1·60 1·30
MS238 140 × 80 mm. Nos. 235/7 3·75 4·00

75 Landscape

76 "Reflection"

1993. Nordic Countries' Postal Co-operation. Gjogv. Multicoloured.
239 4k. Type **75** . . . . 1·50 1·30
240 4k. Village . . . . 1·50 1·30

1993. Europa. Contemporary Art. Bronzes by Hans Pauli Olsen. Multicoloured.
241 4k. Type **76** . . . . 1·50 1·30
242 7k. "Movement" . . . . . . 2·30 2·20

77 Horse's Head

1993. Horses.
243 **77** 400ore brown . . . . . . 1·40 1·00
244 – 20k. lilac . . . . 7·00 6·00
DESIGN—HORIZ: 20k. Mare and foal.

78 "Apamea zeta"

1993. Butterflies and Moths. Multicoloured.
245 350ore Type **78** . . . . . . 1·30 1·00
246 400ore "Hepialus humuli" . . 1·40 1·00
247 700ore Red admiral . . . . 2·75 2·20
248 900ore "Perizoma albulata" 3·75 2·75

79 Three-spined Stickleback

1994. Fishes. Multicoloured.
249 10ore Type **79** 20 15
250 4k. False boarfish . . . . . 2·20 1·40
251 7k. Brown trout . . . . . 2·50 2·00
252 10k. Orange roughy . . . . 5·00 3·00

80 St. Brendan discovering Faroe Islands

1994. Europa. St. Brendan's Voyages. Mult.
253 4k. Type **80** . . . . 1·60 1·30
254 7k. St. Brendan visiting Iceland . . . . 2·40 2·00
MS255 81 × 76 mm. Nos. 253/4 4·25 3·00

81 Sailing Ship and Sailor using Sextant

1994. Centenary (1993) of Faroese Nautical School, Torshavn. Multicoloured.
256 3k.50 Type **81** . . . . . . 5·00 1·40
257 7k. Modern ship and sailor using modern equipment 2·20 1·90

82 Dog and Sheep **83** Viking Ship

1994. Sheepdogs. Multicoloured.
258 4k. Type **82** . . . . 1·50 1·30
259 4k. Dog's head (18 × 25 mm) 1·50 1·40

1994. "Brusajokil's Lay" (traditional song). Multicoloured.
260 1k. Type **83** 40 40
261 4k. Asbjorn at entrance to Brusajokil's cave . . . . . 1·50 1·30
262 6k. Trolls appearing after Ormar had killed cat . . . 1·00 1·80
263 7k. Ormar pulling off Brusajokil's beard . . . . 2·50 2·10

84 First to Tenth Days **85** "Ulopa reticulata"

1994. Christmas. Designs illustrating "On the First Day of Christmas St. Martin gave to Me". Multicoloured.
264 400ore Type **84** . . . . . . 1·50 1·50
265 400ore 11th to 15th days . . 1·40 1·40

1995. Leafhoppers. Multicoloured.
266 50ore Type **85** 20 20
267 4k. "Streptanus sordidus" . . 1·40 1·30
268 5k. "Anoscopus flavostriatus" 1·60 1·50
269 13k. "Macrosteles alpinus" 5·25 4·00

86 Vatnsdalur

1995. Nordic Countries' Postal Co-operation. Tourism. Multicoloured.
270 400ore Type **86** . . . . . . 1·50 1·10
271 400ore Fomjin . . . . 1·50 1·10

87 Vidar, Vali and Baldur

1995. Europa. Peace and Freedom. Mult.
272 4k. Type **87** . . . . 1·40 1·30
273 7k. Liv and Livtrasir . . . . 2·20 2·00

88 Museum of Art, Torshavn

1995. 50th Anniv of Nordic Artists Association. Multicoloured.
274 2k. Type **88** 80 65
275 4k. "Woman" (Frimod Joensen) (vert) . . . . . . 1·40 1·30
276 5k.50 Self-portrait (Joensen) (vert) . . . . 2·10 1·80

89 Common Raven

1995. The Raven. Multicoloured.
277 400ore Type **89** . . . . . . 1·20 1·30
278 400ore White speckled raven 1·20 1·30

90 St. Olaf

1995. Birth Millenary of St. Olaf
279 **90** 4k. multicoloured . . . . 1·20 1·20

91 Dairy Maids **92** St. Mary's Catholic Church

1995. Rural Life.
280 **91** 4k. green . . . . 1·30 1·20
281 – 6k. brown . . . . 2·50 1·80
282 – 15k. blue . . . . 5·00 4·75
DESIGNS—VERT: 6k. Sheep shearing; 15k. Fishermen.

1995. Christmas. Multicoloured.
283 400ore Type **92** . . . . . . 1·30 1·20
284 400ore Stained glass window, St. Mary's Church . . . . 1·30 1·20

93 Risin and Kellingin (rocks) **94** "Ptilota plumosa"

1996.
285 **93** 450ore multicoloured . . . 1·30 1·20

1996. Seaweed. Multicoloured.
286 4k. Type **94** . . . . 1·40 1·10
287 5k.50 Flat wrack . . . . . 2·10 1·60
288 6k. Knotted wrack . . . . . 2·50 2·00
289 9k. Forest kelp . . . . . . 3·00 2·40

95 "Young Girl" **96** Bohemian Waxwing

1996. Europa. Famous Women. Paintings by Samal Joensen-Mikines. Multicoloured.
290 4k.50 Type **95** . . . . . . 1·60 1·30
291 7k.50 "Old Woman" (vert) 2·00 2·00

1996. Birds (1st series). Multicoloured.
292 4k.50 Type **96** . . . . . . 1·30 1·40
293 4k.50 Red crossbill ("Loxia curvirostra") . . . . . . 1·30 1·40
See also Nos. 321/2, 336/7 and 355/6.

97 Faroe Islands and Compass Rose **98** Boy Playing with Hoop (Bugvi)

1996. Maps.
301 **97** 10k. multicoloured . . . . 2·30 2·40
302 11k. multicoloured . . . . 2·75 2·50
303 14k. multicoloured . . . . 3·50 3·50
304 15k. multicoloured . . . . 3·75 3·50
305 16k. multicoloured . . . . 4·25 4·25
306 18k. multicoloured . . . . 4·25 4·50
309 22k. multicoloured . . . . 4·50 4·50

1996. "Nordatlantex 96" Stamp Exhibition, Torshavn. Children's Drawings. Sheet 98 × 61 mm containing T **98** and similar vert designs. Mult.
MS314 4k.50 Type **98**; 4k.50 Girls and traffic lights (Gudrid); 4k.50 Street and child on bicycle (Herborg) . . . . 3·75 4·00

99 "Flock of Sheep" **100** Klaksvik Church

1996. Paintings by Janus Kamban. Mult.
315 4k.50 Type **99** . . . . . . 1·40 1·20
316 6k.50 "Fishermen on way Home" . . . . 2·00 1·70
317 7k.50 "View from Torshavn's Old Quarter" . . . . . . 2·30 2·20

1996. Christmas. Multicoloured.
318 4k.50 Type **100** . . . . . . 1·20 1·20
319 4k.50 Altarpiece depicting biblical scenes (21 × 38 mm) 1·20 1·20

101 Queen Margrethe in Faroese National Costume **102** "Hygrocybe helobia"

1997. Silver Jubilee of Queen Margrethe. Sheet 81 × 61 mm.
MS320 **101** 450ore multicoloured 1·80 1·50

1997. Birds (2nd series). As T **96**. Mult.
321 4k.50 Redpolls ("Carduelis flammea") . . . . 1·10 1·10
322 4k.50 Northern bullfinches ("Pyrrhula pyrrhula") . . . 1·10 1·10

1997. Fungi. Multicoloured.
323 4k.50 Type **102** . . . . . . 1·40 1·30
324 6k. "Hygrocybe chlorophana" . . . . . . 2·10 1·60
325 6k.50 Snowy wax cap . . . . 2·30 1·90
326 7k.50 Parrot wax cap . . . . 2·50 2·10

103 Seal **104** "Temptations of Saint Anthony"

1997. 600th Anniv of Kalmar Union (of Denmark, Norway and Sweden).
327 **103** 4k.50 violet . . . . . . 1·30 1·10

1997. Europa. Tales and Legends. Illustrations by William Heinesen. Multicoloured.
328 4k.50 Type **104** . . . . . . 1·20 1·20
329 7k.50 "The Merman" (eating fish bait) . . . . 1·90 1·90

105 Hvalvik Church **106** Arrival of Poul Aggerso

1997. Christmas. Multicoloured.
330 4k.50 Type **105** . . . . . . 1·30 1·20
331 4k.50 Church interior . . . . 1·30 1·30

1997. "Barbara" (film from novel by Jorgen-Frantz Jacobsen). Scenes from the film. Multicoloured.
332 4k.50 Type **106** . . . . . . 1·20 1·20
333 6k.50 Annike van der Lippe and Lars Simonsen as Barbara and Aggerso . . . 1·75 1·60
334 7k.50 Barbara and men in boat . . . . 2·30 1·80
335 9k. Barbara in rowing boat 2·50 2·20

107 Blackbird **108** Wall of Fire around King Budle and Brynhild

1998. Birds (3rd series). Multicoloured.
336 4k.50 Type **107** . . . . . . 1·20 1·00
337 4k.50 Common starling ("Sturnus vulgaris") . . . 1·20 1·00

1998. "Brynhild's Ballad" (traditional poem). Multicoloured.
338 450ore Type **108** . . . . . 1·20 1·00
339 650ore Sigurd on his horse Grane jumps through the flames . . . . 1·80 1·50
340 750ore Golden rings around Sigurd and Brynhild . . . 2·10 1·80
341 1000ore Gudrun (Sigurd's widow) leading Grane . . 2·50 2·40

109 Atlantic White-sided Dolphin

1998. International Year of the Ocean. Whales and Dolphins. Multicoloured.
342 4k. Type **109** . . . . 1·20 1·00
343 4k.50 Killer whale . . . . . 1·20 1·10
344 7k. Bottle-nosed dolphin . . 2·20 1·80
345 9k. White whale . . . . . . 2·50 2·40

110 Procession with Flags **111** Hands cradling Family

1998. Europa. National Festivals. St. Olav's Day. Multicoloured.
346 4k.50 Type **110** . . . . . . 1·10 1·00
347 7k.50 Members of Parliament and clergy processing through the streets . . . . 1·90 1·90

1998. 50th Anniv of Universal Declaration of Human Rights.
348 **111** 750ore multicoloured . . 1·90 1·90

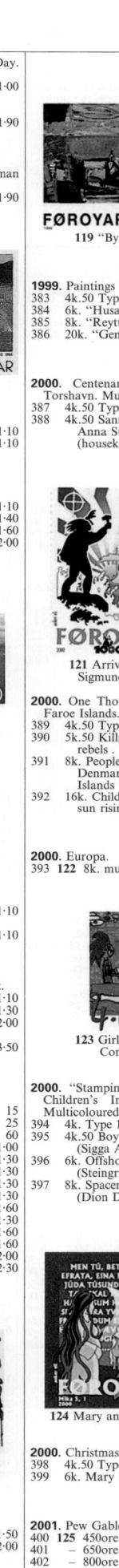

112 Interior of Frederik's Church, Nes

113 "Hagamynd"

1998. Christmas. Multicoloured.
349 4k.50 Type **112** . . . . . . 1·20 1·10
350 4k.50 Exterior of church . . 1·20 1·10

1998. Paintings by Hans Hansen. Mult.
351 4k.50 Type **113** . . . . . . 1·20 1·10
352 5k.50 "Bygdarmynd" . . . . 1·70 1·40
353 6k.50 "Portrait of a Man" 2·00 1·60
354 8k. "Self-portrait" . . . . . 2·50 2·00

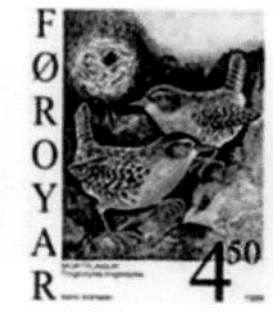

114 Winter Wren

116 Kalsoy

115 "Smiril" (ferry), 1896

1999. Birds (4th series). Multicoloured.
355 4k.50 Type **114** . . . . . . 1·10 1·10
356 4k.50 House sparrow ("Passer domesticus") . . . 1·10 1·10

1999. Suduroy–Torshavn Passenger Ferries. Mult.
357 4k.50 Type **115** . . . . . . 1·00 1·10
358 5k. "Smiril", 1932 . . . . . 1·20 1·30
359 8k. "Smyril", 1967 . . . . . 2·10 2·00
360 13k. "Smyril" (car ferry), 1975 . . . . 3·00 3·50

1999. Islands of the Faroes. Multicoloured.
361 50ore Type **116** 20 15
362 100ore Vidoy 25 25
363 200ore Skuvoy 50 60
365 400ore Svinoy . . . . . . 1·30 1·00
366 450ore 50 Fugloy . . . . . 1·60 1·30
367 500ore Bour . . . . 1·60 1·30
368 500ore Gasadalur . . . . . 1·60 1·30
368a 550ore Stora Dimun . . . . 1·70 1·30
369 600ore Kunoy . . . . . . 1·60 1·60
370 650ore Hestoy . . . . . . 2·00 1·30
370a 700ore Litla Dimun . . . . 1·90 1·60
371 750ore Koltur . . . . . . 2·30 1·60
372 800ore Bardoy . . . . . . 2·30 2·00
375 1000ore Nolsoy . . . . . . 3·25 2·30

117 Svartifossur, Hoydalar

118 Adam and Eve

1999. Europa. Waterfalls. Multicoloured.
379 6k. Type **117** . . . . 1·60 1·50
380 8k. Foldarafossur, Hov . . . 2·00 2·00

1999. Christmas. Multicoloured.
381 450ore Type **118** . . . . . 1·10 1·10
382 600ore The Annunciation . . 1·20 1·40

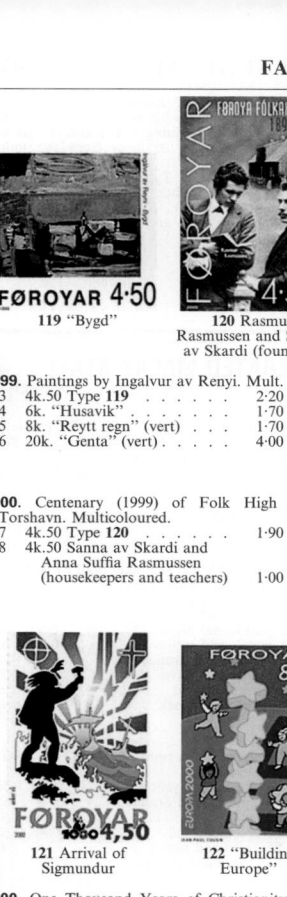

119 "Bygd"

120 Rasmus Rasmussen and Simun av Skardi (founders)

1999. Paintings by Ingalvur av Renyi. Mult.
383 4k.50 Type **119** . . . . . . 2·20 1·10
384 6k. "Husavik" . . . . 1·70 1·30
385 8k. "Reytt regn" (vert) . . . 1·70 2·00
386 20k. "Genta" (vert) . . . . . 4·00 4·50

2000. Centenary (1999) of Folk High School, Torshavn. Multicoloured.
387 4k.50 Type **120** . . . . . . 1·90 1·10
388 4k.50 Sanna av Skardi and Anna Suffia Rasmussen (housekeepers and teachers) 1·00 1·10

121 Arrival of Sigmundur

122 "Building Europe"

2000. One Thousand Years of Christianity on the Faroe Islands. Multicoloured.
389 4k.50 Type **121** . . . . . . 1·20 1·00
390 5k.50 Killing of bishop by rebels . . . . 1·20 1·30
391 8k. People with flags of Denmark and Faroe Islands . . . . 1·80 1·80
392 16k. Children on shore and sun rising . . . . 4·25 3·75

2000. Europa.
393 **122** 8k. multicoloured . . . . 1·90 1·80

123 Girl unlocking Door by Remote Control and House (Katrin Mortensen)

2000. "Stampin' the Future". Winning Entries in Children's International Painting Competition Multicoloured.
394 4k. Type **123** . . . . 1·00 95
395 4k.50 Boy dreaming of future (Sigga Andreassen) . . . . 1·20 1·10
396 6k. Offshore oil rig (Steingrimur Joensen) . . . 1·40 1·20
397 8k. Spaceman and television (Dion Dam Frandsen) . . 2·10 1·60

124 Mary and Joseph

125 Apostle holding Cross

2000. Christmas. Multicoloured.
398 4k.50 Type **124** . . . . . . 95 1·00
399 6k. Mary holding Jesus . . . 1·20 1·30

2001. Pew Gables, St. Olav's Church, Kirkjubour.
400 **125** 450ore buff, black & grey 95 1·40
401 – 650ore buff, black & cinn 1·50 1·50
402 – 800ore buff, black & grn 1·60 2·00
403 – 18k. buff, black and brown . . . . 3·75 4·25
DESIGNS: 650ore Apostle holding knife; 800ore Apostle holding book in right hand; 18k. Apostle holding book in left hand.

126 Elderly Woman

2001. 75th Anniv of Faroese Red Cross. Multicoloured.
404 4k.50 Type **126** . . . . . . 95 1·00
405 6k. Red Cross volunteers carrying patient on stretcher . . . . 1·20 1·20

127 Skjuts (early postal service) Boat

2001. 25th Anniv of Faroese Postal Administration. Sheet 138 × 101 mm containing T **127** and similar vert designs. Each buff, black and silver.
MS406 4k.50 Type **127**; 4k.50 First Post Office, Torshavn; 4k50 Postman . . . . 4·25 4·00

128 Hognis and Tidrik Tattneson ("Hognis Ballad")

2001. Nordic Myths and Legends. Multicoloured.
407 6k. Type **128** . . . . 1·40 1·40
408 6k. Tree and birds nests ("The Tree of the Year") 1·40 1·40
409 6k. Woman beside river ("The Harp") . . . . . . 1·40 1·40
410 6k. Sigurd the Dragonslayer's horse Grane and sword Gram . . . . 1·40 1·40
411 6k. Sigurd fighting dragon ("Ballad of Nornagest") . . 1·40 1·40
412 6k. Hogni Jukeson and brothers on ship ("Hognis Ballad") . . . . 1·40 1·40

129 Hydro-electric Power Station, Fossaverkio, Vestmanna

2001. Europa. Water Resources. Multicoloured.
413 6k. Type **129** . . . . 1·20 1·20
414 8k. Hydro-electric power station, Eidisverkio, Eysturoy . . . . 1·60 1·50

130 "The Artist's Mother"

2001. Paintings by Zacharias Heinesen. Multicoloured.
415 4k. Type **130** 70 90
416 4k.50 "Uti a Reyni" . . . . 75 1·00
417 10k. "Ur Vagunum" . . . . 1·90 1·70
418 15k. "Sunrise" . . . . 2·75 2·75

131 Sperm Whale (*Physeter macrocephalusi*)

132 Simeon and Mary

2001. Whales. Multicoloured.
419 4k.50 Type **131** . . . . . . 80 1·00
420 6k.50 Fin whales (*Balaenoptera physalus*) . . 1·60 1·60
421 9k. Blue whales (*Balaenoptera musculus*) . . . . 2·00 2·10
422 20k. Sei whales (*Balaenoptera borealis*) . . . . 4·25 4·75

2001. Christmas. Multicoloured.
423 5k. Type **132** . . . . 1·00 1·10
424 6k.50 Flight into Egypt . . . 1·40 1·30

133 Atlantic Bob-tailed Squid (*Sepiola atlantica*)

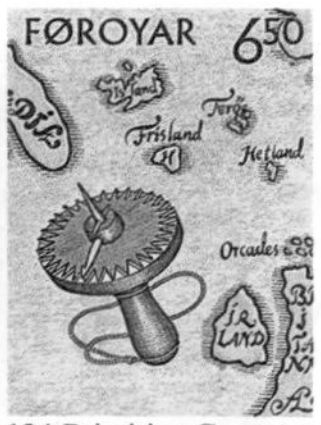

134 Primitive Compass

2002. Molluscs. Multicoloured.
425 5k. Type **133** . . . . 1·30 1·10
426 7k. Horse mussel (*Modiolus modiolus*) . . . . 1·30 1·40
427 7k.50 Sea slug (*Polycera faeroensis*) . . . . 1·30 1·50
428 18k. Common northern whelk (*Buccinum undatum*) 3·00 3·50

2002. Viking Voyages. Sheet 160 × 70 mm containing T **134** and similar vert designs. Multicoloured.
MS429 6k.50 Type **134**; 6k.50 Viking sailor using compass; 6k.50 Viking ship . . . . 4·75 4·75

135 "Depths of the Ocean"

2002. Nordic Countries' Postal Co-operation. Art by Trondur Patursson. Multicoloured.
430 5k. Type **135** . . . . 1·00 1·10
431 6k.50 "Cosmic Space" . . . 1·10 1·20

136 Clowns (Anna Katrina Olsen)

2002. Europa. Circus. Showing winning designs in children's painting competition. Multicoloured.
432 6k.50 Type **136** . . . . . . 1·20 1·20
433 8k. Animals in Circus Tent (Sara Zachariasardottir) . . 1·50 1·60

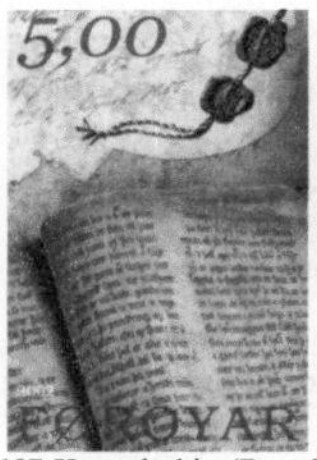

137 Kongsbokin (Royal Book)

138 Whimbrel (*Numenius phaeopus*)

2002. 150th Anniv of Foroya Logting (Faroese Representative Council). Sheet 100 × 70 mm containing T **137** and similar vert design. Multicoloured.
MS434 5k. Type **137**; 6k.50, Introduction of the 1852 Logting protocol . . . . 2·20 2·30

2002. Birds. Showing chicks and eggs. Multicoloured.
435 5k. Type **138** . . . . 95 1·00
436 7k.50 Common snipe (*Gallinago gallinago*) . . . 1·40 1·40
437 12k. Oystercatcher (*Haematopus ostralegus*) . . 2·30 2·40
438 20k. Golden plover (*Pluvialis apricaria*) . . . . 3·75 3·75

139 Church

140 Cliffs and Blue Whiting (*Micromesistius poutassou*)

2002. Gøta Church. Multicoloured.
439 5k. Type **139** . . . . 90 1·00
440 6k.50 Church interior . . . . 1·20 1·30

2002. Centenary of International Council for the Exploration of the Sea. Sheet 186 × 61 mm, containing T **140** and similar vert design. Multicoloured.
MS441 8k. Type **140**; 8k. *Magnus Heinason* (trawler) and blue whiting . . . . 3·00 3·25
Stamps of a similar design were issued by Denmark and Greenland.

141 Male Merlin (*Falco columbarius subaesalon*)

2002.
442 **141** 30k. multicoloured . . . 5·75 5·75

142 Engine Drilling

2003. Completion of Vagatunnilin (tunnel under Vestmannasund). Multicoloured..
443 5k. Type **142** 90 90
444 5k. Miners and equipment . . 90 90

143 Heid

144 "Omma Ludvik"

2003. Norse Myths and Legends. Voluspa. Multicoloured.
445 6k.50 Type **143** . . . . . . 1·20 1·20
446 6k.50 Creation of the universe . . . . 1·20 1·20
447 6k.50 Creation of humans . . 1·20 1·20
448 6k.50 Norns (deities of fate) and Yggdrasil (world tree) 1·20 1·20
449 6k.50 Thor with raised hammer . . . . 1·20 1·20
450 6k.50 Odin hurling spear . . 1·20 1·20
451 6k.50 Baldur dying and his infant brother Hodlyn . . 1·20 1·20
452 6k.50 Ship and Nidhog (giant serpent) . . . . 1·20 1·20
453 6k.50 Hodlyn killing serpent 1·20 1·20
454 6k.50 Hodur and Baldur . . 1·20 1·20

2003. Children's Songs. Sheet 166 × 80 mm containing T **144** and similar vert designs. Multicoloured.
MS455 5k. × 10, Type **144** and nine different designs depicting children's songs . . . . 9·00 9·00

145 "Fish Tree" (tapestry) (Astrid Andreasen)

147 Jesper Rasmussen Brochmand

146 Fuglafjordur

2003. Europa. Poster Art. Multicoloured.
456 6k.50 Type **145** . . . . . . 1·20 1·20
457 8k. "Chrysalis", "Reclining Form" and "Jazz III" (ceramics) (Gudrid Poulsen) . . . . 1·40 1·40

2003. Island Post Office Centenaries. Sheet 170 × 120 mm containing T **146** and similar horiz designs. Each black and grey.
MS458 5k. Type **146**; 5k. Strendur; 5k. Sandur; 5k. Eidi; 5k. Vestmanna; 5k. Vagur; 5k. Midvagur; 5k. Hvalba . . . . 7·25 7·25

2003. Theologians. Multicoloured.
459 5k. Type **147** 90 90
460 6k.50 Thomas Kingo . . . . 1·20 1·20

148 "Dance in Main Room" (Emil Krause)

2003. Czeslaw Slania's 100th Stamp for Faroese Posts. Sheet 88 × 72 mm.
MS461 **148** 25k. multicoloured 4·50 4·50

149 Sandvok

2004. Settlements on Suduroy Island. Sheet 135 × 204 mm containing T **149** and similar horiz designs. Multicoloured.
MS462 5k. × 10, Type **149**; Hvalba; Frodba; Oravok; Fámjin; Hov; Porkeri; Akrar; Sumba; Akraberg 9·00 9·00

150 Thor (god) and the Midgard Serpent

2004. Nordic Mythology. Sheet 105 × 70 mm containing T **150** and similar vert design. Multicoloured.
MS463 6k.50 × 2, Type **150**; Ran (sea goddess) . . . . 2·25 2·25
Stamps of a similar theme were issued by Aland Islands, Denmark, Finland, Greenland, Iceland, Norway and Sweden.

151 Gasholmur and Tindholmur

2004. 150th Anniv of *Journal of Cruise of Maria* (yacht) by Samuel Rathbone and E. H. Greig. Sheet 176 × 140 mm containing T **151** and similar horiz designs showing illustrations from the journal. Multicoloured.
MS464 6k.50 × 8, Type **151**; *Diamantunum* (yacht); Houses; Mylingur; Mylingur (different); Kalsoyggin; Yacht and rowing boats; Kunoynni . . . . . . 10·00 10·00

FEDERATED MALAY STATES Pt. 1

A British protectorate in South East Asia, comprising the States of Negri Sembilan (with Sungei Ujong), Pahang, Perak and Selangor.
Separate issues for each of these states appeared in 1936.

100 cents = $1 (Straits).

1900. Stamps of Negri Sembilan optd **FEDERATED MALAY STATES** and bar.
1 **3** 1c. purple and green . . . . . 3·00 7·00
2 2c. purple and brown . . . . 29·00 65·00
3 3c. purple and black . . . . 2·50 4·00
4 5c. purple and yellow . . . . 70·00 £170
5 10c. purple and orange . . . 7·00 26·00
6 20c. green and olive . . . . 85·00 £100
7 25c. green and red £225 £350
8 50c. green and black . . . . 90·00 £130

1900. Stamps of Perak optd **FEDERATED MALAY STATES** and bar.
9 **31** 5c. purple and yellow . . . 15·00 55·00
10 10c. purple and orange . . . 70·00 65·00
11 **32** $1 green £170 £225
12 $2 green and red £140 £225
13 $5 green and blue £350 £500
14 $25 green and orange . . . £7500

3

4

1900.
15 a **3** 1c. black and green . . . 3·25 1·00
29 1c. green . . . . 4·75 20
30 1c. brown . . . . 2·25 90
53 1c. black 75 20
31 2c. green . . . . 2·50 30
54 2c. brown . . . . 6·50 6·00
16 b 3c. black and brown . . . 4·25 20
58 3c. brown . . . . 1·75 50
34 3c. red . . . . 3·00 10
35 3c. grey . . . . 2·00 20
57 3c. green . . . . 1·25 1·50
36 d 4c. black and red . . . . 5·00 80
38 4c. red . . . . 1·75 15
60 4c. orange . . . . 1·50 10
18 5c. green and red on yellow . . . . 2·25 3·00
61 5c. mauve on yellow . . . 1·00 20
62 5c. brown . . . . 3·50 10
63 6c. orange . . . . 1·00 45
64 6c. red . . . . 1·50 10
41bb 8c. black and blue . . . . 8·00 4·75
42 8c. blue . . . . 13·00 1·00
43 b 10c. black and mauve . . 24·00 65
44 a 10c. blue . . . . 6·50 1·00
66 10c. black and blue . . . 2·00 75
67 10c. purple and yellow . . 3·75 40
68 12c. blue . . . . 1·25 10
69 20c. mauve and black . . 4·00 1·00
70 25c. purple and mauve . . 2·75 1·50
71 30c. purple and orange . . 3·25 3·50
46 35c. red on yellow . . . . 5·50 12·00
73 35c. red and purple . . . 13·00 14·00
74 50c. black and orange . . 13·00 9·00
75 50c. black on green . . . 4·00 2·50
76 a **4** $1 green . . . . 17·00 45·00
77 **3** $1 black and red on blue 12·00 3·50
78 **4** $2 green and red . . . . . 19·00 70·00
79 **3** $2 green and red on yellow 38·00 35·00
80 **4** $5 green and blue . . . . 95·00 £160
81 **3** $5 green and red on green £140 £150
82 **4** $25 green and orange . . . £800 £600

POSTAGE DUE STAMPS

D 1

1924.
D1 **D 1** 1c. violet . . . . 4·75 28·00
D2 2c. black . . . . 1·75 4·25
D3 4c. green . . . . 2·25 5·00
D4 8c. red . . . . 5·50 28·00
D5 10c. orange . . . . 9·00 17·00
D6 12c. blue . . . . 9·00 26·00

FERNANDO POO Pt. 9

A Spanish island off the west coast of Africa, in the Gulf of Guinea. Became part of Spanish Guinea in 1909. In 1959 Fernando Poo became an overseas province of Spain, comprising the island and Annobon. On 12 October 1968 became independent and joined Rio Muni to form Equatorial Guinea.

1868. Currencies stated below issue.
1894. 1000 milesimas = 100 centavos = 1 peso.
1901. 100 centimos = 1 peseta.

1 Isabella II

(**3**)

1868.
1 **1** 20c. brown £450 £130
The face value of No. 1 is expressed in centimos de escudo. It was in use until Dec 1868. Stamps of Cuba were then used until 1879.

1879. "Alfonso XII" key-type inscr "FERNANDO POO".
5 X 1c. green . . . . 8·25 5·00
6 2c. red . . . . 12·00 8·75
2 5c. green . . . . 45·00 12·00
7 5c. lilac . . . . 40·00 12·00
3 10c. red . . . . 22·00 12·00
8 10c. brown . . . . 60·00 6·25
4 50c. blue . . . . 80·00 12·00
Nos. 2, 3 and 4 have face values expressed in centimos de peseta and the remainder are in centavos de peso.

1884. Nos. 5, 6 and 7 surch as T **3**.
9 X 50c. on 1c. green . . . . . 85·00 23·00
10 50c. on 2c. red . . . . . . 24·00 6·75
11 50c. on 5c. lilac . . . . . 95·00 30·00

1893. On plain paper.
12 **3** 50c. on blue . . . . 11·00 9·50

1894. "Baby" key-type inscr "FERNANDO POO".
13 Y ⅛c. grey . . . . 21·00 3·75
14 2c. red . . . . 15·00 2·75
15 5c. green . . . . 15·00 2·75
16 6c. purple . . . . 12·50 3·75
18 10c. red . . . . 46·00 10·50
19 10c. brown . . . . 9·50 2·75
20 12½c. brown . . . . 11·00 3·25
21 20c. blue . . . . 11·00 3·25
22 25c. red . . . . 21·00 3·25

1896. Nos. 13/22 surch **HABILITADO 5 C. DE PESO** in circle.
23 Y 5c. on ⅛c. grey . . . . . . 80·00 28·00
24 5c. on 2c. red . . . . . . 39·00 17·00
25 5c. on 6c. purple . . . . . £120 46·00
26a 5c. on 10c. brown . . . . 50·00 46·00
28 5c. on 12½c. brown . . . . 29·00 13·50
29 5c. on 20c. blue . . . . . £120 46·00
30 5c. on 25c. red . . . . . £120 37·00

7

1896. Fiscal stamps optd **HABILITADO PARA CORREOS** (Nos. 60/1) or surch **CORREOS 5 CENTAVOS** (59).
59 **7** 5c. on 10c. red . . . . 22·00 11·00
60 10c. red . . . . 22·00 11·00
61 15c. on 10c. green . . . . . 25·00 13·00

1897. Nos. 13 etc surch **5 Cen.** in circle.
31 Y 5c. on ⅛c. grey . . . . . . 23·00 12·50
32 5c. on 2c. red . . . . . . 23·00 12·50
33a 5c. on 5c. green . . . . . £110 40·00
34c 5c. on 6c. purple . . . . . 17·00 24·00
35 5c. on 10c. brown . . . . £130 48·00
36 5c. on 10c. red £300 £120
38 5c. on 12½c. brown . . . . 49·00 20·00
39a 5c. on 20c. blue . . . . . 29·00 18·00
40 5c. on 25c. red . . . . . . 29·00 20·00

1898. Nos. 13 etc surch as T **3**.
41 Y 50c. on ⅛c. grey . . . . . £225 85·00
42 50c. on 2c. red . . . . . . 60·00 21·00
43 50c. on 5c. green . . . . . £160 60·00
44 50c. on 10c. brown . . . . £140 60·00
45a 50c. on 10c. red . . . . . £160 60·00
47 50c. on 12½c. brown . . . £120 37·00
48 50c. on 25c. red . . . . . £140 50·00

10

1899. Fiscal stamps variously optd. (a) Surch **Fernando Poo 1899 Habilitado para Correos** and new value.
62 **10** 10c. on 25c. green . . . . . 65·00 44·00
63 15c. on 25c. green . . . . . 95·00 60·00

(b) Optd or surch **CORREOS**.
65 **10** 15c. on 25c. green £1800 £1400
64 25c. green £350 £170

1899. "Curly Head" key-type inscr "FERNANDO POO 1899".
66 Z 1m. brown . . . . 1·80 65
67 2m. brown . . . . 1·80 65
68 3m. brown . . . . 1·80 65
69 4m. brown . . . . 1·80 65
70 5m. brown . . . . 1·80 65
71 1c. purple . . . . 1·80 65
72 2c. green . . . . 1·80 65
73 3c. brown . . . . 1·80 65
74 4c. orange . . . . 10·50 1·60
75 5c. red . . . . 1·80 65
76 6c. blue . . . . 1·80 65
77 8c. brown . . . . 6·50 65
78 10c. red . . . . 4·25 65
79 15c. grey . . . . 4·25 65
80 20c. purple . . . . 11·50 1·60
81 40c. lilac . . . . 80·00 28·00
82 60c. black . . . . 80·00 28·00
83 80c. brown . . . . 80·00 28·00
84 1p. green £275 £140
85 2p. blue £275 £140

1900. No. 80 surch **HABILITADO 5 C. DE PESO**.
86 Z 5c. on 20c. purple . . . . . £250 17·00

1900. No. 80 surch **5 Cen.** in circle.
87 Z 5c. on 20c. purple . . . . . 8·25 4·50

1900. No. 80 surch with T **3**.
88 Z 50c. on 20c. purple . . . . . 10·50 4·50

1900. "Curly Head" key-type inscr "FERNANDO POO 1900".
91 Z 1m. black . . . . 2·75 65
92 2m. black . . . . 2·75 65
93 3m. black . . . . 2·75 65
94 4m. black . . . . 2·75 65
95 5m. black . . . . 2·75 65
96 1c. green . . . . 2·75 65
97 2c. lilac . . . . 2·75 65
98 3c. pink . . . . 2·75 65
99 4c. brown . . . . 2·75 65
100 5c. blue . . . . 2·75 65
101 6c. orange . . . . 2·75 2·75
102 8c. green . . . . 2·75 2·75
103 10c. red . . . . 2·75 65
104 15c. purple . . . . 2·75 65
105 20c. brown . . . . 2·75 65
106 40c. brown . . . . 6·75 3·00
107 60c. green . . . . 15·00 3·00
108 80c. blue . . . . 15·00 5·00
109 1p. brown . . . . 85·00 37·00
110 2p. orange . . . . £140 80·00

1900. Fiscal stamps as T **7** but dated 1900 optd or surch. (a) **CORREOS** and **5 Cen.** in circle.
111 **7** 5c. on 10c. blue . . . . . . 55·00 28·00

(b) **CORREOS CORREOS** and **5 Cen.** in circle.
113 **7** 5c. on 10c. blue . . . . . . £140 85·00

(c) **CORREOS**.
114a **7** 10c. blue . . . . 32·00 8·25

1900. Fiscal stamp as T **7** but dated 1900 surch **CORREOS 5 CENTAVOS**.
115 **7** 5c. on 10c. blue £550 £400

1900. Nos. 74 and 105 surch with T **3**.
116a Z 50c. on 4c. orange . . . . 12·00 6·50
117 50c. on 20c. brown . . . . 9·50 4·00

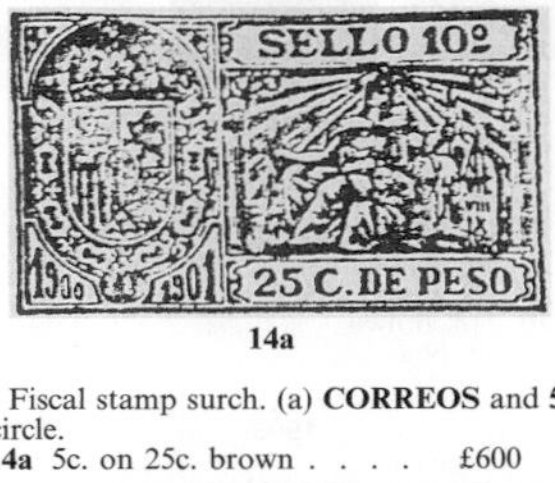

14a

1900. Fiscal stamp surch. (a) **CORREOS** and **5 Cen.** in circle.
118 **14a** 5c. on 25c. brown £600 £350

(b) **CORREOS HABILITADO 5 C. DE PESO**.
119 **14a** 5c. on 25c. brown £650 £350

1901. "Curly Head" key-type inscr "FERNANDO POO 1901".
124 Z 1c. black . . . . 1·90 1·10
125 2c. brown . . . . 1·90 1·10
126 3c. purple . . . . 1·90 1·10
127 4c. lilac . . . . 1·90 1·10
128 5c. red . . . . 1·20 1·10
129 10c. brown . . . . 1·20 1·10
130 25c. blue . . . . 1·20 1·10
131 50c. purple . . . . 1·90 1·10
132 75c. brown . . . . 1·40 1·10
133 1p. green . . . . 41·00 8·75
134 2p. brown . . . . 25·00 13·50
135 3p. green . . . . 25·00 19·00
136 4p. red . . . . 25·00 19·00
137 5p. green . . . . 32·00 19·00
138 10p. orange . . . . 70·00 55·00

1902. "Curly Head" key-type inscr "FERNANDO POO 1902". With control figures on back.
140 Z 5c. green . . . . 1·70 30
141 10c. grey . . . . 1·70 30
142 25c. red . . . . 4·00 85
143 50c. brown . . . . 9·25 3·25
144 75c. lilac . . . . 9·25 3·25
145 1p. red . . . . 12·00 4·75
146 2p. green . . . . 24·00 12·00
147 5p. red . . . . 37·00 28·00

1903. "Curly Head" key-type inscr "FERNANDO POO PARA 1903". With control figures on back.
154 Z ¼c. purple 25 25
155 ½c. black 25 25
156 1c. red 25 25
157 2c. green 25 25
158 3c. green 25 25
159 4c. lilac 25 25
160 5c. red 35 25
161 10c. orange 45 35
162 15c. green . . . . 1·80 1·20
163 25c. brown . . . . 1·90 1·80
164 50c. brown . . . . 3·25 3·25
165 75c. red . . . . 11·50 6·00
166 1p. brown . . . . 17·00 8·75
167 2p. green . . . . 22·00 13·50
168 3p. purple . . . . 22·00 13·50
169 4p. blue . . . . 27·00 24·00
170 5p. blue . . . . 40·00 28·00
171 10p. orange . . . . 85·00 44·00

1905. "Curly Head" key-type inscr "FERNANDO POO PARA 1905". With control figures on back.
172 Z 1c. purple 30 30
173 2c. black 30 30
174 3c. red 30 30
175 4c. green 30 30
176 5c. green 35 30
177 10c. lilac . . . . 1·20 60
178 15c. red . . . . 1·20 60
179 25c. orange . . . . 10·00 2·00
180 50c. green . . . . 6·75 3·25
181 75c. brown . . . . 8·75 8·75
182 1p. brown . . . . 10·00 8·75
183 2p. red . . . . 18·00 13·00
184 3p. brown . . . . 27·00 15·00
185 4p. green . . . . 32·00 20·00
186 5p. red . . . . 50·00 30·00
187 10p. blue . . . . 80·00 44·00

17 King Alfonso XIII

24 Woman at Prayer

1907. With control figures on back.
188 **17** 1c. black 15 15
189 2c. pink 15 15
190 3c. purple 15 15
191 4c. black 15 15
192 5c. buff 15 15
193 10c. purple . . . . 1·00 55
194 15c. black 25 25
195 25c. brown . . . . 16·00 12·50
196 50c. green 15 15
197 75c. red 20 15
198 1p. blue . . . . 1·70 60
199 2p. brown . . . . 6·00 5·00
200 3p. pink . . . . 6·00 5·00
201 4p. lilac . . . . 6·00 5·00
202 5p. brown . . . . 6·00 5·00
203 10p. brown . . . . 6·00 5·00

1908. Surch **HABILITADO PARA 05 CTMS.**
204 **17** 05c. on 10c. purple . . . . 3·25 2·10

1929. Seville and Barcelona Exhibition stamps of Spain (Nos. 504, etc) optd **FERNANDO POO**.
209 5c. red 20 20
210 10c. green 20 20
211 15c. blue 20 20
212 20c. violet 20 20
213 25c. red 20 20
214 30c. brown 20 20
215 40c. blue 60 60
216 50c. orange . . . . 1·30 1·30
217 1p. grey . . . . 4·75 4·75
218 4p. red . . . . 24·00 24·00
219 10p. brown . . . . 31·00 31·00

1960.
220 **24** 25c. grey 15 15
221 50c. drab 15 15
222 75c. brown 15 15
223 1p. red 15 15
224 1p.50 turquoise 15 15
225 2p. purple 15 15
226 3p. blue . . . . 1·80 55
227 5p. brown 20 15
228 10p. olive 25 20

25 De Falla (composer)

1960. Child Welfare.
229 **25** 10c.+5c. purple 20 20
230 – 15c.+5c. brown 20 20
231 – 35c. green 20 20
232 **25** 80c. green 20 20
DESIGNS—VERT: (De Falla's ballets): 15c. Spanish dancer ("Love, the Magician"); 35c. Tricorne, stick and windmill ("Three-cornered Hat").

26 Sperm Whale

27 "The Blessing"

1960. Stamp Day.
233 **26** 10c.+5c. red 20 20
234 – 20c.+5c. green 20 20
235 **26** 30c.+10c. brown 20 20
236 – 50c.+20c. brown 20 20
DESIGN: 20, 50c. Natives harpooning humpback whale.

1961. Child Welfare. Inscr "PRO-INFANCIA 1961".
237 **27** 10c.+5c. lake 20 20
238 – 25c.+10c. violet 20 20
239 **27** 80c.+20c. green 20 20
DESIGN: 25c. African kneeling before Cross.

28

1961. 25th Anniv of Gen. Franco as Head of State.
240 – 25c. grey 20 20
241 **28** 50c. brown 20 20
242 – 70c. green 20 20
243 **28** 1p. orange 20 20
DESIGNS—VERT: 25c. Map; 70c. St. Isabel Cathedral.

29 Great Turtle

1961. Stamp Day. Inscr "DIA DEL SELLO 1961".
244 **29** 10c.+5c. red 20 20
245 – 25c.+10c. plum 20 20
246 **29** 30c.+10c. purple 20 20
247 – 1p.+10c. orange 20 20
DESIGN: 25c., 1p. Native porters, palm trees and shore.

30 Spanish Freighter "Okume"

1962. Child Welfare. Inscr "PRO-INFANCIA 1962".
248 **30** 25c. violet 20 20
249 – 50c. olive 20 20
250 **30** 1p. brown 20 20
DESIGN: 50c. Spanish freighter "San Francisco".

31 Postman

32 Native Shrine

1962. Stamp Day. Inscr "DIA DEL SELLO 1962".
251 **31** 15c. green 20 20
252 – 35c. mauve 65 90
253 **31** 1p. brown 20 20
DESIGN—HORIZ: 35c. Mail transport.

1963. Seville Flood Relief.
254 **32** 50c. brown 20 20
255 1p. purple 20 20

33 Sister and Child

1963. Child Welfare.
256 – 25c. purple 20 20
257 **33** 50c. green 20 20
258 – 1p. red 20 20
DESIGN—HORIZ: 25c., 1p. Two sisters.

34 Child and Arms

1963. "For Barcelona".
259 **34** 50c. brown 20 20
260 1p. red 20 20

35 Governor Chacon

36 Canoe

1964. Stamp Day.
261 **35** 25c. violet 20 20
262 – 50c. brown 20 20
263 **35** 1p. red 20 20
DESIGN—VERT: 50c. Orange blossom.

1964. Child Welfare. Inscr "PRO INFANCIA 1964".
264 **36** 25c. violet 20 20
265 – 50c. olive (Pineapple) . . . 20 20
266 **36** 1p. purple 20 20

37 Ring-necked Francolin

38 "The Three Kings"

1964. Birds.
267 **37** 15c. brown 15 15
268 – 25c. violet 15 15
269 – 50c. green 15 15
270 **37** 70c. green 15 15
271 – 1p. brown 15 15
272 – 1p.50 blue 15 15
273 **37** 3p. blue 35 15
274 – 5p. purple 95 15
275 – 10p. green . . . . 1·50 45
DESIGNS: 25c., 1, 5p. Mallard; 50c., 1p.50, 10p. Great blue turaco.

1964. Stamp Day.
276 – 50c. green 20 20
277 **38** 1p. red 20 20
278 – 1p.50 green 20 20
279 **38** 3p. blue 90 90
DESIGN—VERT: 50c., 1p.50, King presenting gift to Infant Jesus.

39 Native

40 "Metopodontus savagei" (stag beetle)

1965. 25th Anniv of End of Spanish Civil War.
280 **39** 50c. blue 20 20
281 – 1p. red 20 20
282 – 1p.50 turquoise 20 20
DESIGNS: 1p. "Agriculture" (fruit farming); 1p.50, "Education" (child writing).

1965. Child Welfare. Insects.
283 – 50c. green 20 20
284 **40** 1p. red 20 20
285 – 1p.50 blue 20 20
DESIGN—VERT: 50c., 1p.50, "Plectrocnemia cruciata" (squashbug).

41 Pole Vaulting

1965. Stamp Day.
286 **41** 50c. green 20 20
287 – 1p. brown 20 20
288 **41** 1p.50 blue 20 20
DESIGN—VERT: 1p. Arms of Fernando Poo.

42 European and African Women

1966. Child Welfare.
289 **42** 50c. green 20 20
290 1p. red 20 20
291 – 1p.50 blue 20 20
DESIGN—VERT: 1p.50, St. Isabel of Hungary.

43 Greater White-nosed Monkey

44 Flowers

1966. Stamp Day.
292 **43** 10c. blue and yellow . . . 20 20
293 – 40c. blue and brown . . . 20 20
294 **43** 1p.50 olive and brown . . 20 20
295 – 4p. brown and green . . . 20 20
DESIGN—VERT: 40c., 4. p. Moustached monkey.

1967. Child Welfare and similar floral design.
296 **44** 10c. red and green 20 20
297 – 40c. brown and orange . . 20 20
298 **44** 1p.50 purple & brown . . . 20 20
299 – 4p. blue and green 20 20

45 African Linsang

47 Libra (scales)

46 Arms of San Carlos and Stamp of 1868

1967. Stamp Day.
300 **45** 1p. black and bistre . . . 20 20
301 – 1p.50 brown and olive . . 20 20
302 – 3p.50 purple and green . . 30 30
DESIGNS—VERT: 1p.50, Western needle-clawed bush-baby. HORIZ: 3p.50, Lord Derby's flying squirrel.

1968. Stamp Centenary.
303 **46** 1p. brown and purple . . . 20 20
304 – 1p.50 brown and blue . . . 20 20
305 – 2p.50 chestnut & brown . . 30 30
DESIGNS—Each with stamp of 1868: 1p.50, Arms of Santa Isabel; 2p.50, Arms of Fernando Poo.

1968. Child Welfare. Signs of the Zodiac.
306 **47** 1p. mauve on yellow . . . 20 20
307 – 1p.50 brown on pink . . . 20 20
308 – 2p.50 violet on yellow . . 30 30
DESIGNS: 1p.50, Lion (Leo); 2p.50, Water carrier (Aquarius).

For later issues see **EQUATORIAL GUINEA**.

FEZZAN Pt. 6

A desert territory in N. Africa taken from Turkey by Italy and captured by French forces in 1943. Algerian stamps used from April 1944, until 1946, and then under French control until the end of 1951 when it was incorporated in the independent kingdom of Libya.

100 centimes = 1 franc.

(a) Issues For Fezzan And Ghadames

1943. Optd **FEZZAN Occupation Francaise** or surch in addition. (a) Postage. No. 247 of Italy optd.
1 **103** 50c. violet . . . . 48·00 48·00

Stamps of Libya surch.
2 **4** 0f.50 on 5c. green & black . . £100 95·00
3 **5** 1f. on 10c. pink and black . . £140 £140
4 **6** 2f. on 30c. brown & black . . £275 £275
5 **9** 3f. on 20c. green . . . . . 65·00 55·00
6 **5** 3f.50 on 25c. blue & dp blue 80·00 70·00
7 **6** 5f. on 50c. green & black . . 19·00 19·00
8 10f. on 1l.25 blue and indigo £900 £800
9 **9** 20f. on 1l.75 orange £2750 £2750
10 **7** 50f. on 75c. red & purple . . £3250 £3250

(b) Air. No. 271 of Italy optd.
11 **10** 50c. brown . . . . 70·00 70·00

(c) Air. No. 72 of Libya surch.
12 **18** 7f.50 on 50c. red . . . . . 75·00 75·00

1943. Handstamped locally. (a) Postage. No. 247 of Italy handstamped **R.F. 0,50 FEZZAN** around circle and within dotted circle.
13 **103** 0f.50 on 50c. violet £2750 £275

(b) Postage. No. 27 of Libya handstamped **R.F. 1 Fr FEZZAN** in two lines.
14 **5** 1f. on 25c. blue & dp blue . . £3000 £250

(c) Air. No. 271 of Italy handstamped as No. 13.
15 **110** 0f.50 on 50c. brown . . . – £750

1943. Parcel Post stamps of Libya handstamped across each half as No. 14.
16 **P 53** 1f. on 5c. brown £500 £200
17 **P 92** 1f. on 10c. blue £500 £200
18 1f. on 50c. orange £500 £200
19 1f. on 1l. violet £500 £200
20 1f. on 2l. green . . . . . – £1000
21 1f. on 3l. bistre . . . . . – £1400
22 1f. on 4l. black . . . . . – £1000
The prices are for each half of the parcel post stamps.

4 Fort of Sebha

6 Map and Fort of Sebha

1946.
23 **4** 10c. black . . . . 15 2·75
24 50c. red . . . . 50 3·00
25 1f. brown . . . . 35 3·00
26 1f.50 green . . . . 55 3·00
27 2f. blue . . . . 40 3·25
28 – 2f.50 violet . . . . 65 3·50
29 – 3f. red . . . . 60 3·50
30 – 5f. brown . . . . 60 3·75
31 – 6f. green . . . . 80 3·50
32 – 10f. blue . . . . 55 3·50
33 **6** 15f. violet . . . . 1·50 3·75
34 20f. red . . . . 1·25 4·50
35 25f. brown . . . . 1·75 4·50
36 40f. green . . . . 2·25 4·75
37 50f. blue . . . . 1·75 4·75
DESIGN—36 × 21½ mm: 2f.50 to 10f. Turkish fort and mosque at Murzuk.

(b) Issues For Fezzan Only

7 Douglas C-47B Skytrain at Fezzan Airfield

1948. Air.
38 **7** 100f. red . . . . 2·50 11·00
39 – 200f. blue . . . . 5·00 16·00
DESIGN—VERT: 200f. Airplane over Fezzan.

9 Djerma

10 Well at Gorda

1949.
40 **9** 1f. black . . . . 1·25 3·50
41 2f. pink . . . . 1·40 3·50
42 – 4f. brown . . . . 1·60 4·50
43 – 5f. green . . . . 1·75 4·50
44 **10** 8f. blue . . . . 1·75 4·25
45 10f. brown . . . . 1·90 5·50
46 12f. green . . . . 1·75 10·00
47 – 15f. red . . . . 2·75 11·00
48 – 20f. black . . . . 2·25 6·25
49 – 25f. blue . . . . 1·75 7·75
50 – 50f. red . . . . 3·00 11·00
DESIGNS—HORIZ: 4f., 5f. Beni Khettab tombs; 15f., 20f. Col. Colonna d'Ornano and fort; 25f., 50f. Gen. Leclerc and map of Europe and N. Africa.

11 "Charity"

12 Mother and Child

1950. Charity.
51 **11** 15f.+5f. lake . . . . 1·75 4·75
52 **12** 25f.+5f. blue . . . . 2·25 4·75

14 Camel Breeding

15 Ahmed Bey

1951.
59 **14** 30c. brown (postage) . . . 3·00 3·75
60 1f. blue . . . . 2·50 3·75
61 2f. red . . . . 2·75 3·75
62 – 4f. red . . . . 3·00 3·75
63 – 5f. green . . . . 3·00 4·00
64 – 8f. blue . . . . 2·50 4·00
65 – 10f. brown . . . . 5·50 8·25
66 – 12f. green . . . . 5·75 8·75
67 – 15f. red . . . . 6·75 10·50
68 **15** 20f. brown . . . . 2·00 10·50
69 25f. blue and deep blue . . 2·75 14·00
70 50f. brown and blue . . . . 2·50 14·00

71 – 100f. blue (air) . . . . . 12·50 21·00
72 – 200f. red . . . . 12·00 24·00
DESIGNS—HORIZ: 4f. to 8f. Arab hoeing; 100f. Brak Oasis; 200f. Sebha Fort. VERT: 10f. to 15f. Artesian well.

POSTAGE DUE STAMPS

1943. Postage Due stamps of Libya optd **FEZZAN Occupation Francaise** or surch in addition with bars obliterating old inscr and values.
D13 **D 141** 0f.50 on 5c. brown . . £850 £750
D14 1f. on 10c. blue . . . £850 £750
D15 2f. on 25c. green . . . £850 £750
D16 3f. on 50c. violet . . . £900 £850
D17 **D 142** 5f. on 1l. orange . . . £7500 £7500

D 13 Brak Oasis

1950.
D53 **D 13** 1f. black . . . . 2·50 3·75
D54 2f. green . . . . 1·90 3·75
D55 3f. lake . . . . 2·25 4·00
D56 5f. violet . . . . 2·75 4·25
D57 10f. red . . . . 3·00 6·50
D58 20f. blue . . . . 3·25 10·00

FIJI Pt. 1

A British colony in the South Pacific, which became independent within the Commonwealth during October 1970. Following a military coup on 25 September 1987 Fiji was declared a republic on 7 October. The Governor-General resigned on 15 October 1987 and Fiji's Commonwealth membership lapsed until 1 October 1997 when the country was readmitted following further constitutional changes.

1870. 12 pence = 1 shilling;
20 shillings = 1 pound.
1969. 100 cents = 1 dollar.

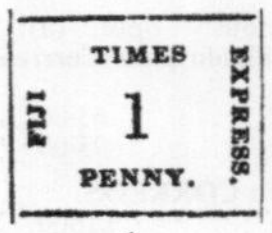

1

2

1870.
5 **1** 1d. black on pink £900 £1800
6 3d. black on pink £1500 £2750
7 6d. black on pink £1100 £1800
8 9d. black on pink £1900 £3000
9 1s. black on pink £1200 £1400

1871.
10 **2** 1d. blue . . . . 50·00 £120
11 3d. green £110 £350
12 6d. red £140 £300

1872. Surch in words.
13a **2** 2c. on 1d. blue . . . . . . 35·00 50·00
14 6c. on 3d. green . . . . . 70·00 70·00
15 12c. on 6d. red . . . . . . 95·00 80·00

V.R.
(5)

(8)

1874. Optd as T **5**.
16 **2** 2c. on 1d. blue £900 £250
17 6c. on 3d. green £1500 £650
18 12c. on 6d. red £650 £200

1875. Nos. 17 and 18 surch **2d.**
22 **2** 2d. on 6c. on 3d. green . . . £550 £180
26 2d. on 12c. on 6d. red . . . £1900 £800

1876. Optd with T **8**, and the 3d. surch in words also.
31 **2** 1d. blue . . . . 18·00 29·00
29a 2d. on 3d. green . . . . . 45·00 55·00
34 4d. on 3d. mauve . . . . . 85·00 25·00
33 6d. red . . . . 50·00 28·00

10

12

1878. Surch on Nos. 36 and 41/2 in words.
35 **10** 1d. blue . . . . 9·00 9·00
40 2d. green . . . . 15·00 1·00
36 2d. on 3d. green . . . . . 6·00 20·00
54 4d. mauve . . . . 10·00 11·00
41 4d. on 1d. mauve . . . . . 42·00 30·00
42 4d. on 2d. mauve . . . . . 75·00 12·00
59a 6d. red . . . . 8·00 3·75
67 **12** 1s. brown . . . . 35·00 9·00
69 5s. red and black . . . . . 55·00 28·00

1891. Surch in figures or words.
72a **10** ½d. on 1d. blue . . . . . . 42·00 70·00
70 2½d. on 2d. green . . . . . 45·00 48·00
73 5d. on 4d. mauve . . . . . 50·00 70·00
74a 5d. on 6d. red . . . . . . 55·00 60·00

20

21 Native Canoe

23

1891.
99 **20** ½d. grey . . . . 1·00 3·25
87 **21** 1d. black . . . . 4·75 4·75
101 1d. mauve . . . . 5·50 80
89 2d. green . . . . 6·00 80
103a **10** 2½d. brown . . . . 5·00 5·00
85 **21** 5d. blue . . . . 13·00 7·50

1903.
104 **23** ½d. green . . . . 2·25 2·00
105 1d. purple and black on red . . . . 13·00 55
119 1d. red . . . . 8·50 10
106 2d. purple and orange . . 3·75 1·25
107 2½d. purple and blue on blue . . . . 14·00 3·50
120 2½d. blue . . . . 6·50 7·50
108 3d. purple . . . . 1·50 4·00
109 4d. purple and black . . . 1·50 2·50
110 5d. purple and green . . . 1·50 2·75

111		6d. purple and red	1·50	1·75
121		6d. purple	13·00	28·00
112		1s. green and red	11·00	65·00
122		1s. black on green	4·25	10·00
113		5s. green and black	55·00	£140
123		5s. green and red on yellow	55·00	60·00
114		£1 black and blue	£300	£375
124		£1 purple and black on red	£300	£275

1912. As T **23**, but portrait of King George V.

125a		¼d. brown	1·50	40
126b		½d. green	1·25	50
127		1d. red	2·00	10
231		1d. violet	1·25	10
232		1½d. red	4·00	1·75
233		2d. grey	1·25	10
129		2½d. blue	3·00	3·50
130		3d. purple on yellow	4·25	5·50
234		3d. blue	2·75	1·00
235		4d. black and red on yellow	5·00	7·00
236		5d. purple and olive	1·50	2·00
237		6d. purple	2·00	1·25
134a		1s. black on green	1·00	11·00
239		2s. purple and blue on blue	25·00	60·00
240		2s.6d. black and red on blue	11·00	32·00
136		5s. green and red on yellow	32·00	40·00
137		£1 purple and black on red	£250	£275

1916. Nos. 126/7 optd **WAR STAMP**.

138b		½d. green	75	2·75
139a		1d. red	1·75	75

1935. Silver Jubilee. As T **10a** of Gambia.

242		1½d. blue and red	80	7·00
243		2d. blue and grey	1·50	35
244		3d. brown and blue	2·50	3·00
245		1s. grey and purple	4·50	6·00

1937. Coronation. As T **10b** of Gambia.

246		1d. violet	60	1·00
247		2d. grey	60	1·75
248		3d. blue	60	1·75

28 Native Sailing Canoe

29 Native Village

32 Government Offices

1938.

249	**28**	½d. green	20	75
250	**29**	1d. brown and blue	50	20
252c	–	1½d. red	1·00	1·25
254	–	2d. brown and green	16·00	16·00
255	**32**	2d. green and mauve	40	60
256b	–	2½d. brown and green	1·00	50
257	–	3d. blue	1·00	30
258	–	5d. blue and red	42·00	10·00
259	–	5d. green and red	20	30
261b	–	6d. black	1·50	1·50
261c	–	8d. red	1·00	2·25
262	–	1s. black and yellow	75	70
263	–	1s.5d. black and red	20	10
263a	–	1s.6d. blue	3·50	2·75
264	–	2s. violet and orange	2·50	40
265	–	2s.6d. green and brown	2·75	1·50
266	–	5s. green and purple	2·75	1·75
266a	–	10s. orange and green	35·00	40·00
266b	–	£1 blue and red	48·00	50·00

DESIGNS—HORIZ (As Type **32**): 1½d. Camakua (canoe); 2d. (No. 254), 2½d., 6d. Map of Fiji Is. HORIZ (As Type **29**): 3d. Canoe and arms; 8d., 1s.5d., 1s.6d. Arms; 2s. Suva Harbour; 2s.6d. River scene; 5s. Chief's hut. VERT (As Type **29**): 5d. (Nos. 258/9), Sugar cane; 1s. Spearing fish; 10s. Pawpaw tree; £1 Police bugler.

1941. No. 254 surch **2½d.**

267		2½d. on 2d. brown and green	2·00	20

1946. Victory. As T **11a** of Gambia.

268		2½d. green	10	1·00
269		3d. blue	10	10

1948. Silver Wedding. As T **11b/c** of Gambia.

270		2½d. green	40	1·25
271		5s. blue	14·00	7·00

1949. U.P.U. As T **11d/g** of Gambia.

272		2d. purple	30	40
273		3d. blue	2·00	2·50
274		8d. red	30	2·50
275		1s.6d. blue	35	1·00

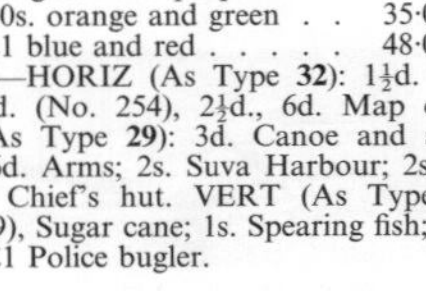

43 Children Bathing

1951. Health stamps. Inscr "HEALTH".

276	**43**	1d.+1d. brown	10	70
277	–	2d.+1d. green	30	70

DESIGNS—VERT: 2d. Rugby footballer.

1953. Coronation. As T **11h** of Gambia.

278		2½d. black and green	1·00	40

1953. Royal Visit. As No. 261c, but with portrait of Queen Elizabeth II and inscr "ROYAL VISIT 1953".

279		8d. red	30	15

46 Queen Elizabeth II (after Annigoni)

48 Loading Copra

1954. Queen Elizabeth II. (I) inscr "FIJI". (II) Inscribed "Fiji".

280	**28**	½d. green	15	1·25
298	**46**	½d. green	15	1·75
281		1d. turquoise (I)	1·75	10
299		1d. blue (II)	2·25	1·75
282		1½d. sepia (I)	1·00	65
300		1½d. sepia (II)	1·75	1·25
283	**32**	2d. green and mauve	1·25	40
312	**46**	2d. red (I)	50	10
284		2½d. violet (I)	2·50	10
302		2½d. brown (I)	1·50	2·75
285	**48**	3d. brown and purple	2·75	20
287	–	6d. black (As No. 261)	2·50	85
303	A	6d. red and black	1·25	10
288	–	8d. red (As No. 261d)	3·75	1·25
316	B	10d. brown and red	60	50
289	–	1s. black and yellow (As No. 262)	2·50	10
306	C	1s. blue	1·50	10
290	D	1s.6d. blue and green	19·00	1·00
291	E	2s. black and red	5·50	50
292a	–	2s.6d. green and brown (As No. 265)	1·25	10
320	F	2s.6d. black and purple	2·50	90
293	G	5s. ochre and blue	15·00	1·25
294	–	10s. orange and green (As No. 266a)	7·00	20·00
309	H	10s. green and sepia	3·50	1·50
295	–	£1 bl & red (As No. 266b)	38·00	19·00
310	I	£1 black and orange	13·00	4·00

DESIGNS—HORIZ (As Type **48**): A, Fijian beating lali; B, Yaqona ceremony; C, Location map; D, Sugar cane train; E, Preparing bananas for export; F, Nadi Airport; G, Gold industry; H, Cutting sugar-cane; I, Arms of Fiji.

52 River Scene

56 Hibiscus

1954. Health stamps.

296	**52**	1½d.+½d. brown and green	10	50
297	–	2½d.+½d. orange and black	10	10

DESIGN: 2½d. Queen's portrait and Cross of Lorraine inscribed "FIJI WAR MEMORIAL" and "ANTI-TUBERCULOSIS CAMPAIGN".

1959.

313	–	3d. multicoloured	25	10
304	**56**	8d. multicoloured	50	25
315		9d. multicoloured	90	65
318	–	1s.6d. multicoloured	2·00	90
319	–	2s. yellow, green and copper	13·00	3·50
308	–	4s. multicoloured	1·75	1·50
323	–	5s. red, yellow and grey	12·00	35

DESIGNS—HORIZ: 1s.6d. International date line; 4s. Kandavu shining parrot ("Kandavu Parrot"); 5s. Orange dove. VERT: 2s. White orchid. 23 × 28 mm: 3d. Queen Elizabeth II.

1963. Royal Visit. Optd **ROYAL VISIT 1963**.

326	–	3d. mult (No. 313)	30	20
327	C	1s. blue (No. 306)	30	20

1963. Freedom from Hunger. As T **20a** of Gambia.

328	–	2s. blue	1·00	1·00

69 Running

1963. 1st South Pacific Games, Suva. Inscr as in T **69**.

329	**69**	3d. brown, yellow and black	25	10
330	–	9d. brown, violet and black	25	1·50
331	–	1s. brown, green and black	25	10
332	–	2s.6d. brown, blue and black	60	60

DESIGNS—VERT: 9d. Throwing the discus; 1s. Hockey. HORIZ: 2s.6d. High-jumping.

1963. Centenary of Red Cross. As T **20b** of Gambia.

333		2d. red and black	35	10
334		2s. red and blue	75	2·50

1963. Opening of COMPAC (Trans-Pacific Telephone Cable). No. 306 optd **COMPAC CABLE IN SERVICE DECEMBER 1963** and ship.

335	C	1s. blue	55	10

74 Jamborette Emblem

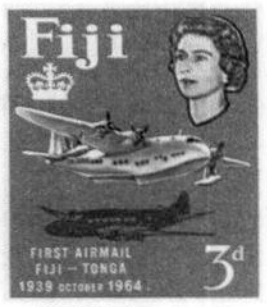

76 Flying-boat "Aotearoa"

1964. 50th Anniv of Fijian Scout Movement.

336	**74**	3d. multicoloured	15	25
337	–	1s. violet and brown	15	30

DESIGN: 1s. Scouts of three races.

1964. 25th Anniv of 1st Fiji–Tonga Airmail Service.

338	**76**	3d. black and red	40	10
339	–	6d. red and blue	70	1·00
340	–	1s. black and turquoise	70	1·00

DESIGNS—VERT: 6d. De Havilland Heron 2. HORIZ (37½ × 25 mm): 1s. "Aotearoa" and map.

1965. Centenary of I.T.U. As T **44** of Gibraltar.

341		3d. blue and red	20	10
342		2s. yellow and bistre	50	25

1965. I.C.Y. As T **45** of Gibraltar.

343		2d. purple and turquoise	20	10
344		2s.6d. green and lavender	80	25

1966. Churchill Commemoration. As T **46** of Gibraltar.

345		3d. blue	70	10
346		9d. green	90	85
347		1s. brown	90	10
348		2s.6d. violet	1·00	85

1966. World Cup Football Championships. As T **47** of Gibraltar.

349		2d. multicoloured	25	10
350		2s. multicoloured	75	20

79 H.M.S. "Pandora" approaching Split Island, Rotuma

1966. 175th Anniv of Discovery of Rotuma. Mult.

351		3d. Type **79**	30	10
352		10d. Rotuma chiefs	30	10
353		1s.6d. Rotumans welcoming H.M.S. "Pandora"	50	30

1966. Inauguration of W.H.O. Headquarters, Geneva. As T **54** of Gibraltar.

354		6d. black, green and blue	1·25	25
355		2s.6d. black, purple and ochre	2·75	2·50

82 Running

1966. 2nd South Pacific Games.

356	**82**	3d. black, brown and green	10	10
357	–	9d. black, brown and blue	15	15
358	–	1s. multicoloured	15	15

DESIGNS—VERT: 9d. Putting the shot. HORIZ: 1s. Diving.

85 Military Forces Band

1967. International Tourist Year. Multicoloured.

360		3d. Type **85**	40	10
361		9d. Reef diving	15	10
362		1s. Beqa fire walkers	15	10
363		2s. "Oriana" (cruise liner) at Suva	40	15

89 Bligh (bust), H.M.S. "Providence" and Chart

1967. 150th Death Anniv of Admiral Bligh.

364	**89**	4d. multicoloured	10	10
365	–	1s. multicoloured	10	10
366	–	2s.6d. multicoloured	15	15

DESIGNS (As Type **89**): 2s.6d. Bligh's tomb. (54 × 20 mm): 1s. "Bounty's longboat being chased in Fiji waters".

92 Simmonds Spartan Seaplane

1968. 40th Anniv of Kingsford Smith's Pacific Flight via Fiji.

367	**92**	2d. black and green	15	10
368	–	6d. blue, black and lake	15	10
369	–	1s. violet and green	20	10
370	–	2s. brown and blue	30	15

DESIGNS: 6d. Hawker Siddeley H.S.748 and airline insignias; 1s. "Southern Cross" and crew; 2s. "Lady Southern Cross".

96 Bure Huts

1968.

371	**96**	½d. multicoloured	10	10
372	–	1d. blue, red and yellow	10	10
373	–	2d. blue, brown and ochre	10	10
374	–	3d. green, blue and ochre	35	10
375	–	4d. multicoloured	80	1·75
376	–	6d. multicoloured	25	10
377	–	9d. multicoloured	15	1·75
378	–	10d. blue, orange and brown	1·25	20
379	–	1s. blue and red	20	10
380	–	1s.6d. multicoloured	4·00	4·25
381	–	2s. turquoise, black and red	75	2·00
382	–	2s.6d. multicoloured	75	50
383	–	3s. multicoloured	2·75	6·00
384	–	4s. ochre, black and olive	6·00	2·75
385	–	5s. multicoloured	3·00	2·00
386	–	10s. brown, black and ochre	1·00	2·25
387	–	£1 multicoloured	1·25	3·00

DESIGNS—As T **96**: 1d. Passion flowers; 2d. Chambered or pearly nautilus; 4d. "Psilogramma jordana" (moth); 6d. Pennant coralfish; 9d. Bamboo raft; 10d. "Asota woodfordi" (moth); 3s. Golden cowrie shell. 33 × 22 mm: 2s. Sea snake; 2s.6d. Outrigger canoes; 5s. Bamboo orchids; £1 Queen Elizabeth and Arms of Fiji. 23 × 33 mm: 3d. Reef heron; 1s. Black marlin; 1s.6d. Orange-breasted honeyeaters ("Sun Birds"); 4s. Mining industry; 10s. Ceremonial whale's tooth.

113 Map of Fiji, W.H.O. Emblem and Nurses

1968. 20th Anniv of W.H.O. Multicoloured.

388		3d. Type **113**	15	10
389		9d. Transferring patient to medical ship "Vuniwai"	20	15
390		3s. Recreation	25	30

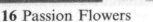

116 Passion Flowers

120 Javelin Throwing

117 Fijian Soldiers overlooking the Solomon Islands

1969. Decimal Currency. Designs as T **96** etc, but with values inscr in decimal currency as in T **116**.
391 **116** 1c. blue, red and yellow . . . 10 10
392 – 2c. blue, brown and ochre (As 373) 10 10
393 – 3c. green, blue and ochre (As 374) . . . . 1·25 1·00
394 – 4c. multicoloured (As 375) 1·50 1·00
395 – 5c. multicoloured (As 376) 20 10
396 **96** 6c. multicoloured 10 10
397 – 8c. multicoloured (As 377) 10 10
398 – 9c. blue, orange and brown (As 378) . . . . . 1·50 2·50
399 – 10c. blue and red (As 379) 20 10
400 – 15c. multicoloured (As 380) . . . . 9·00 4·50
401 – 20c. turquoise, black and red (As 381) . . . . . 1·25 80
402 – 25c. multicoloured (As 382) . . . . 1·00 30
403 – 30c. multicoloured (As 383) . . . . 6·50 1·50
404 – 40c. ochre, black and olive (As 384) . . . . 7·50 4·00
405 – 50c. multicoloured (As 385) . . . . 4·50 30
406 – $1 brown, black and ochre (As 386) . . . . 1·50 60
407 – $2 multicoloured (As 387) 1·50 1·50

1969. 25th Anniv of Fijian Military Forces' Solomons Campaign.
408 **117** 3c. multicoloured 20 10
409 – 10c. multicoloured 25 10
410 – 25c. multicoloured 35 20
DESIGNS: 10c. Regimental flags and soldiers in full dress and battledress; 25c. Sefanaia Sukanai-valu and Victoria Cross.

1969. 3rd South Pacific Games, Port Moresby.
411 **120** 4c. black, brown and red 10 10
412 – 8c. black, grey and blue 10 10
413 – 20c. multicoloured . . . 20 20
DESIGNS: 8c. Sailing dinghy; 20c. Games medal and winner's rostrum.

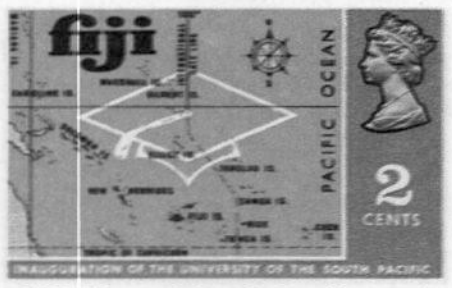

123 Map of South Pacific and "Mortar-board"

1969. Inauguration of University of the South Pacific. Multicoloured.
414 2c. Type **123** 10 15
415 8c. R.N.Z.A.F. Badge and Short S25 Sunderland flying boat over Laucala Bay (site of University) . . 15 10
416 25c. Science students at work 25 15

1970. Royal Visit. Nos. 392, 399 and 402 optd **ROYAL VISIT 1970.**
417 2c. blue, brown and ochre . . 10 20
418 10c. blue and red 10 10
419 25c. multicoloured 20 10

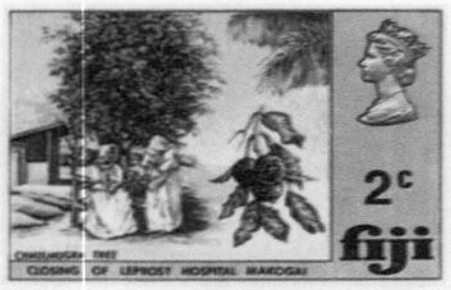

127 Chaulmugra Tree, Makogai

1970. Closing of Leprosy Hospital, Makogai.
420 **127** 2c. multicoloured 10 30
421 – 10c. green and black (vert) 15 30
422 – 10c. blue, black and mauve (vert) 15 30
423 – 30c. multicoloured 20 50
DESIGNS: 10c. (No. 421) "Cascade" (Semisi Maya); 10c. (No. 422) "Sea Urchins" (Semisi Maya); 30c. Makogai Hospital.

131 Abel Tasman and Log, 1643

1970. Explorers and Discoverers.
424 **131** 2c. black, brown & turq 30 25
425 – 3c. multicoloured 60 25
426 – 8c. multicoloured 60 15
427 – 25c. multicoloured 30 15
DESIGNS: 3c. Captain Cook and H.M.S. "Endeavour", 1774; 8c. Captain Bligh and long-boat, 1789; 25c. Fijian and ocean-going Canoe.

135 King Cakobau and Cession Stone

1970. Independence. Multicoloured.
428 2c. Type **135** 10 10
429 3c. Children of the world . . 10 10
430 10c. Prime Minister and Fijian flag 10 10
431 25c. Dancers in costume . . 20 20

139 1d. and 6d. Stamps of 1870

1970. Stamp Centenary. Multicoloured.
432 4c. Type **139** 15 10
433 15c. Fijian stamps of all reigns (61 × 21 mm) . . . 40 15
434 20c. "Fiji Times" office and modern G.P.O. 40 15

140 Grey-backed White-eye **142** Women's Basketball

1971. Birds and Flowers. Multicoloured.
435 1c. "Cirrhopetalum umbellatum" 15 30
436 2c. Cardinal honeyeater . . . 30 10
437 3c. "Calanthe furcata" . . . 85 20
438 4c. "Bulbophyllum sp. nov." 75 1·50
439 5c. Type **140** 35 10
510 6c. "Phaius tancarvilliae" . . 2·75 20
441 8c. Blue-headed flycatcher ("Blue-crested Broadbill") 35 10
442 10c. "Acanthephippium vitiense" 40 10
513 15c. "Dendrobium tokai" . . 2·50 40
444 20c. Slaty flycatcher . . . . 1·50 30
468 25c. Yellow-faced honeyeater ("Kandavu Honeyeater") 1·75 90
516 30c. "Dendrobium gordonii" 5·00 1·00
517 40c. Masked shining parrot ("Yellow-breasted Musk Parrot") . . . . 4·50 60
448 50c. White-throated pigeon 3·50 50
449 $1 Collared lory . . . . . 4·00 1·00
520 $2 "Dendrobium platygastrium" . . . . . 1·50 1·50
The 25c. to $2 are larger, $22\frac{1}{2} \times 35\frac{1}{2}$ mm.

1971. 4th South Pacific Games, Tahiti.
451 **142** 8c. multicoloured 10 10
452 – 10c. blue, black and brown 10 10
453 – 25c. green, black and brown 30 25
DESIGNS: 10c. Running; 25c. Weightlifting.

143 Community Education **144** "Native Canoe"

1972. 25th Anniv of South Pacific Commission. Multicoloured.
454 2c. Type **143** 10 25
455 4c. Public health 10 10
456 50c. Economic growth . . . 70 80

1972. South Pacific Festival of Arts, Suva.
457 **144** 10c. black, orange and blue 10 10

145 Flowers, Conch and Ceremonial Whale's Tooth

1972. Royal Silver Wedding. Multicoloured. Background colour given.
474 **145** 10c. green 20 15
475 25c. purple 30 15

1972. Hurricane Relief. Nos. 400 and 403 surch **HURRICANE RELIEF +** and premium.
476 15c.+5c. multicoloured . . . 15 15
477 30c.+10c. multicoloured . . . 15 15

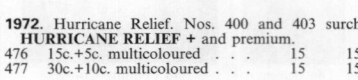

147 Line Out **149** Christmas

148 Forestry Development

1973. Diamond Jubilee of Rugby Union. Mult.
478 2c. Type **147** . . . . . . 45 2·50
479 8c. Body tackle 85 10
480 25c. Conversion . . . . . . 1·50 40

1973. Development Projects. Multicoloured.
481 5c. Type **148** 10 35
482 8c. Rice irrigation scheme . . 10 10
483 10c. Low income housing . . 10 10
484 25c. Highway construction 20 30

1973. Festivals of Joy. Multicoloured.
485 3c. Type **149** 10 10
486 10c. Diwali 10 10
487 20c. Id-Ul-Fitar 15 25
488 25c. Chinese New Year . . . 15 25

150 Athletics **151** Bowler

1974. Commonwealth Games, Christchurch, New Zealand. Multicoloured.
489 3c. Type **150** 15 10
490 8c. Boxing 15 10
491 50c. Bowling 50 75

1974. Centenary of Cricket. Multicoloured.
492 3c. Type **151** 40 15
493 25c. Batsman and wicket-keeper 60 15
494 40c. Fielder (horiz) . . . . . 70 1·10

152 Fiji Postman

1974. Centenary of U.P.U. Multicoloured.
495 3c. Type **152** 10 10
496 8c. Loading mail onto "Fijian Princess" 10 10
497 30c. Fijian post office and mailbus 20 40
498 50c. B.A.C. One Eleven 200/400 modern aircraft . . 35 2·50

153 Cubs lighting Fire

1974. 1st National Scout Jamboree, Lautoka. Multicoloured.
499 3c. Type **153** 15 10
500 10c. Scouts reading map . . 20 10
501 40c. Scouts and Fijian flag (vert) . . . . 65 3·00

154 Cakobau Club and Flag **155** "Diwali" (Hindu Festival)

1974. Centenary of Deed of Cession and 4th Anniv of Independence. Multicoloured.
502 3c. Type **154** 10 10
503 8c. King Cakobau and Queen Victoria 10 10
504 50c. Raising the Royal Standard at Nasova Ovalau . . . . 30 1·75

1975. "Festivals of Joy". Multicoloured.
521 3c. Type **155** 10 10
522 15c. "Id-Ul-Fitar" (Muslim Festival) 10 10
523 25c. Chinese New Year . . . 15 15
524 30c. Christmas . . . . 20 1·75
MS525 121 × 101 mm. Nos. 521/4 1·00 6·00

156 Steam Locomotive No. 21

1976. Sugar Trains. Multicoloured.
526 4c. Type **156** 25 20
527 15c. Diesel loco No. 8 . . . 45 40
528 20c. Diesel loco No. 1 . . . 50 1·00
529 30c. Free passenger train . . 60 2·75

157 Fiji Blind Society and Rotary Symbols

1976. 40th Anniv of Rotary in Fiji.
530 **157** 10c. blue, green and black 15 25
531 – 25c. multicoloured 40 75
DESIGN: 25c. Ambulance and Rotary Symbol.

158 De Havilland Drover 1

1976. 25th Anniv of Air Services. Multicoloured.
532 4c. Type **158** 40 20
533 15c. B.A.C. One Eleven 200/400 . . . . 75 1·50
534 25c. Hawker Siddeley H.S.748 . . . . 80 1·50
535 30c. Britten Norman "long nose" Trislander . . . . . 90 3·50

159 The Queen's Visit to Fiji, 1970

1977. Silver Jubilee. Multicoloured.

536	10c. Type **159**	10	10
537	25c. King Edward's Chair	15	10
538	30c. The Queen wearing cloth of gold supertunica	25	15

160 Map of the World

1977. E.E.C./A.C.P.* Council of Ministers Conference. Multicoloured.

539	4c. Type **160**	10	10
540	30c. Map of Fiji group	30	1·75

*A.C.P. = African, Caribbean, Pacific Group.

161 "Hibiscus rosa-sinensis"

1977. 21st Anniv of Fiji Hibiscus Festival.

541 **161**	4c. multicoloured	10	10
542 –	15c. multicoloured	15	15
543 –	30c. multicoloured	25	30
544 –	35c. multicoloured	40	1·25

Nos. 542/44 show different varieties of "Hibiscus rosa-sinensis".

162 Drua

1977. Canoes. Multicoloured.

545	4c. Type **162**	15	10
546	15c. Tabilai	25	20
547	25c. Takai	30	25
548	40c. Camakua	40	80

163 White Hart of Richard II

165 Shallow Wooden Oil Dish in Shape of Human Figure

164 Defence Force surrounding "Southern Cross", Suva

1978. 25th Anniv of Coronation. Multicoloured.

549 **163**	25c. brown, green and silver	15	20
550 –	25c. multicoloured	15	20
551 –	25c. brown, green and silver	15	20

DESIGNS: No. 550, Queen Elizabeth II; No. 551, Banded iguana.

1978. Aviation Anniversaries. Multicoloured.

552	4c. Type **164**	30	10
553	15c. "Southern Cross" prior to leaving Naselai Beach	50	30
554	25c. Wright Flyer I	60	60
555	30c. Bristol F2B Brisfit	60	1·25

The 25c. value commemorates the 75th anniv of Powered Flight, the 30c. the 60th anniv of R.A.F. and the other values the 50th anniv of First Trans-Pacific Flight by Kingsford-Smith.

1978. Fijian Artifacts. Multicoloured.

556	4c. Type **165**	10	10
557	15c. Necklace of cachalot teeth (horiz)	10	10
558	25c. Double water bottle (horiz)	15	10
559	30c. Finely carved Ula or throwing club	15	15

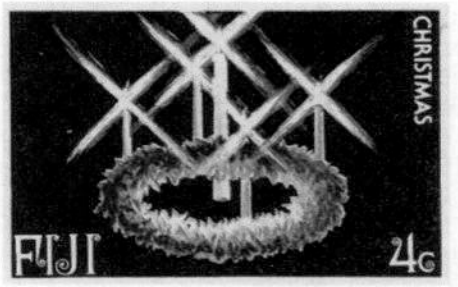

166 Advent Crown with Candles (Christmas)

1978. Festivals. Multicoloured.

560	4c. Type **166**	10	10
561	15c. Lamps (Diwali)	15	10
562	25c. Coffee pot, cups and fruit (Id-Ul-Fitr)	20	10
563	40c. Lion (Chinese New Year)	35	40

167 Banded Iguana

1979. Endangered Wildlife. Multicoloured.

564	4c. Type **167**	60	10
565	15c. Tree frog	1·10	15
566	25c. Long-legged warbler	4·25	40
567	30c. Pink-billed parrot finch	4·25	2·40

168 Women with Dholak

1979. Centenary of Arrival of Indians. Multicoloured.

568	4c. Type **168**	10	10
569	15c. Men sitting around tanoa	10	10
570	30c. Farmer and sugar cane plantation	15	10
571	40c. Sailing ship "Leonidas"	40	25

169 Soccer

1979. 6th South Pacific Games. Multicoloured.

572	4c. Type **169**	30	10
573	15c. Rugby Union	70	20
574	30c. Lawn tennis	80	80
575	40c. Weightlifting	80	1·40

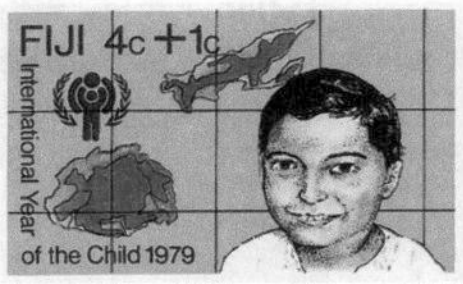

170 Indian Child and Map of Fiji

1979. International Year of the Child. Multicoloured.

576	4c.+1c. Type **170**	10	10
577	15c.+2c. European child	15	15
578	30c.+3c. Chinese child	15	15
579	40c.+4c. Fijian child	15	20

171 Old Town Hall, Suva

1979. Architecture. Multicoloured.

580A	1c. Type **171**	15	60
581Bc	2c. Dudley Church, Suva	30	20
582A	3c. Fiji International Telecommunications Building, Suva	35	80
722	4c. Lautoka Mosque	30	30
583A	5c. As 4c.	15	10
584B	6c. General Post Office, Suva	15	10
724	8c. Public School, Levuka	1·75	2·25
585A	10c. Fiji Visitors Bureau, Suva	20	10
586A	12c. As 8c.	20	2·25
726	15c. Colonial War Memorial Hospital, Suva	30	20
588A	18c. Labasa sugar mill	20	30
589A	20c. Rewa Bridge, Nausori	55	30
590A	30c. Sacred Heart Cathedral, Suva (vert)	65	50
591A	35c. Grand Pacific Hotel, Suva	30	1·00
592A	45c. Shiva Temple, Suva	30	45
593A	50c. Serua Island Village	30	40
594A	$1 Solo Rock Lighthouse (30 × 46 mm)	75	2·25
595A	$2 Baker Memorial Hall, Nausori (46 × 30 mm)	75	1·60
595cA	$5 Government House (46 × 30 mm)	1·00	2·75

Most values come with or without date imprint.

172 "Southern Cross", 1873

1980. "London 1980" Int Stamp Exhibition. Mult.

596	6c. Type **172**	25	10
597	20c. "Levuka", 1910	35	10
598	45c. "Matua", 1936	40	50
599	50c. "Oronsay", 1951	40	70

173 Sovi Bay

1980. Tourism. Multicoloured.

600	6c. Type **173**	10	10
601	20c. Evening scene, Yanuca Island	15	15
602	45c. Dravuni Beach	20	40
603	50c. Wakaya Island	20	45

174 Official Opening of Parliament, 1979

1980. 10th Anniv of Independence. Multicoloured.

604	6c. Type **174**	10	10
605	20c. Fiji coat of arms (vert)	15	10
606	45c. Fiji flag	20	20
607	50c. Queen Elizabeth II (vert)	25	35

175 "Coastal Scene" (painting, Semisi Maya)

1981. Int Year for Disabled Persons. Mult.

608	6c. Type **175**	10	10
609	35c. "Underwater Scene" (Semisi Maya)	35	30
610	50c. Semisi Maya (disabled artist) at work (vert)	40	40
611	60c. "Peacock" (Semisi Maya) (vert)	45	45

176 Prince Charles Sailing

1981. Royal Wedding. Multicoloured.

612	6c. Wedding bouquet from Fiji	10	10
613	45c. Type **176**	30	15
614	$1 Prince Charles and Lady Diana Spencer	50	60

177 Operator Assistance Centre

1981. Telecommunications. Multicoloured.

615	6c. Type **177**	10	10
616	35c. Microwave station	35	50
617	50c. Satellite earth station	40	75
618	60c. Cable ship "Retriever"	55	90

178 "Eat Fiji Foods"

1981. World Food Day.

619 **178**	20c. multicoloured	30	10

179 Ratu Sir Lala Sukuna (first Speaker, Legislative Council)

1981. Commonwealth Parliamentary Association Conference, Suva.

620 **179**	6c. black, buff and brown	10	10
621 –	35c. multicoloured	20	30
622 –	50c. multicoloured	30	45
MS623	73 × 53 mm. 60c. mult	70	1·00

DESIGNS: 35c. Mace of the House of Representatives; 50c. Suva Civic Centre; 60c. Flags of C.P.A. countries.

180 Bell P-39 Airacobra

1981. World War II Aircraft. Multicoloured.

624	6c. Type **180**	1·00	10
625	18c. Consolidated PBY-5 Catalina	1·75	40
626	35c. Curtiss P-40E Warhawk	2·25	95
627	60c. Short Singapore III	2·75	6·00

181 Scouts constructing Shelter

1982. 75th Anniv of Boy Scout Movement. Mult.

628	6c. Type **181**	15	10
629	20c. Scouts sailing (vert)	35	30
630	45c. Scouts by campfire	40	50
631	60c. Lord Baden-Powell (vert)	50	1·00

182 Fiji Soldiers at U.N. Checkpoint

1982. Disciplined Forces. Multicoloured.

632	12c. Type **182**	50	10
633	30c. Soldiers engaged on rural development	60	45
634	40c. Police patrol	1·75	1·25
635	70c. "Kiro" (minesweeper)	1·75	5·50

183 Footballers and Fiji Football Association Logo

1982. World Cup Football Championship, Spain.

636 **183**	6c. red, black and yellow	10	10
637 –	18c. multicoloured	25	20
638 –	50c. multicoloured	70	70
639 –	90c. multicoloured	1·10	2·00

DESIGNS: 18c. Footballers and World Cup emblem; 50c. Football and Bernabeu Stadium; 90c. Footballers and Naranjito (mascot).

184 Bride and Groom leaving St. Paul's

185 Prince Philip

1982. 21st Birthday of Princess of Wales. Mult.
640 20c. Fiji coat of arms 20 15
641 35c. Lady Diana Spencer at Broadlands, May 1981 . . 35 25
642 45c. Type **184** 40 40
643 $1 Formal portrait . . . . . 1·25 2·25

1982. Royal Visit. Muticoloured.
644 6c. Type **185** 60 25
645 45c. Queen Elizabeth II . . . 1·00 2·75
MS646 128 × 88 mm. Nos. 644/5 and $1 Royal Yacht "Britannia" (horiz) . . . . 2·00 3·00

186 Baby Jesus with Mary and Joseph

187 Red-throated Lorikeet ("Red-throated Lory")

1982. Christmas. Multicoloured.
647 6c. Type **186** 10 10
648 20c. Three Wise Men presenting gifts 30 20
649 35c. Carol-singing 45 35
MS650 94 × 42 mm. $1 "Faith" (from the "Three Virtues" by Raphael) . . . . 1·25 1·50

1983. Parrots. Multicoloured.
651 20c. Type **187** . . . . 1·25 20
652 40c. Blue-crowned lory . . . 1·50 50
653 55c. Masked shining parrot ("Sulphur-breasted Musk Parrot") . . . . 1·75 1·50
654 70c. Kandavu shining parrot ("Red-breasted Musk Parrot") . . . . 2·25 4·75

188 Bure in Traditional Village

1983. Commonwealth Day. Multicoloured.
655 8c. Type **188** 10 10
656 25c. Barefoot firewalkers . . 20 15
657 50c. Sugar industry 30 35
658 80c. Kava "Yagona" ceremony 55 70

189 First Manned Balloon Flight, 1783

1983. Bicentenary of Manned Flight. Multicoloured.
659 8c. Type **189** 25 10
660 20c. Wright brothers' Flyer I 35 30
661 25c. Douglas Super DC-3 . . 40 40
662 40c. De Havilland Comet 1 60 60
663 50c. Boeing 747 . . . . . . 70 70
664 58c. Space shuttle 80 80

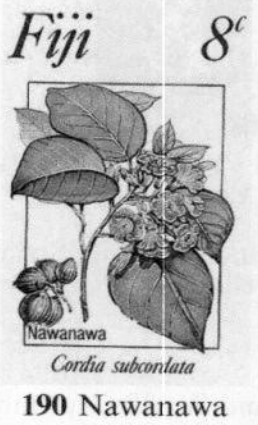

190 Nawanawa

191 Fijian beating Lali and Earth Satellite Station

1983. Flowers (1st series). Multicoloured.
665 8c. Type **190** 10 10
666 25c. Rosawa 25 30
667 40c. Warerega 30 50
668 $1 Saburo . . . . 50 1·40
See also Nos. 680/3.

1983. World Communications Year.
669 **191** 50c. multicoloured . . . . 50 1·25

192 "Dacryopinax spathularia"

193 "Tui Lau" (freighter) on Reef

1984. Fungi. Multicoloured.
670 8c. Type **192** 85 15
671 15c. "Podoscypha involuta" 1·25 25
672 40c. "Lentinus squarrosulus" 2·25 1·00
673 50c. "Scleroderma cepa" ("Scleroderma flavidum") (horiz) . . . . 2·25 1·25
674 $1 "Phillipsia domingensis" (horiz) . . . . 2·75 3·50

1984. 250th Anniv of "Lloyd's List" (newspaper). Multicoloured.
675 8c. Type **193** 70 10
676 40c. "Tofua" (cargo liner) . . 1·50 80
677 55c. "Canberra" (liner) . . . 1·50 1·50
678 60c. "Nedlloyd Madras" (freighter) at Suva wharf 1·50 1·75

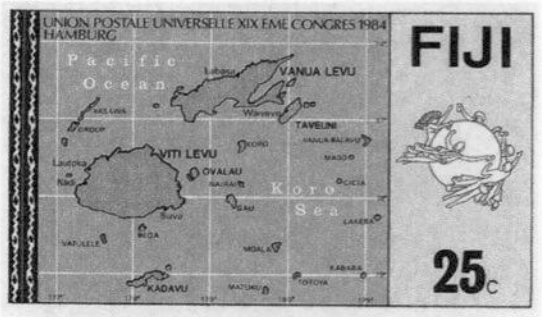

194 Map of Fijian Islands

1984. Universal Postal Union Congress, Hamburg. Sheet 77 × 65 mm.
MS679 **194** 25c. multicoloured 2·50 2·25

1984. Flowers (2nd series). As T **190**. Multicoloured.
680 15c. Drividrivi 25 25
681 20c. Vesida 30 40
682 50c. Vuga 40 90
683 70c. Qaiqi . . . . 45 1·40

195 Prize Bull, Yalavou Cattle Scheme

1984. "Ausipex" International Stamp Exhibition, Melbourne. Multicoloured.
684 8c. Type **195** 15 10
685 25c. Wailoa Power Station (vert) 30 40
686 40c. Air Pacific Boeing 737 airliner . . . . 1·50 1·25
687 $1 Container ship "Fua Kavenga" . . . . 1·10 3·50

196 The Stable at Bethlehem

1984. Christmas. Children's Paintings. Mult.
688 8c. Type **196** 10 10
689 20c. Outrigger canoe 30 20
690 25c. Father Christmas and Christmas tree 30 25
691 40c. Going to church 30 70
692 $1 Decorating Christmas tree (vert) . . . . 45 1·75

197 "Danaus plexippus"

1985. Butterflies. Multicoloured.
693 8c. Type **197** . . . . 1·50 15
694 25c. "Hypolimnas bolina" . . 2·50 60
695 40c. "Lampides boeticus" (vert) . . . . 3·25 2·25
696 $1 "Precis villida" (vert) . . 4·50 7·00

198 Outrigger Canoe off Toberua Island

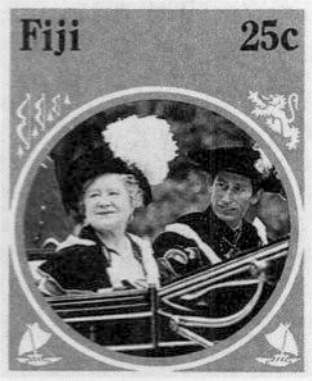

199 With Prince Charles at Garter Ceremony

1985. "Expo '85" World Fair, Japan. Multicoloured.
697 20c. Type **198** 55 30
698 25c. Wainivula Falls . . . . 1·00 40
699 50c. Mana Island . . . . . 1·10 1·10
700 $1 Sawa-I-Lau Caves . . . . 1·40 2·50

1985. Life and Times of Queen Elizabeth the Queen Mother. Multicoloured.
701 8c. With Prince Andrew on her 60th Birthday 20 10
702 25c. Type **199** 50 40
703 40c. The Queen Mother at Epsom Races . . . . . . 1·25 80
704 50c. With Prince Henry at his christening (from photo by Lord Snowdon) . . . . . 1·25 1·25
MS705 91 × 73 mm. $1 With Prince Andrew at Royal Wedding, 1981 3·25 2·00

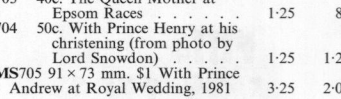

200 Horned Squirrelfish

1985. Shallow Water Marine Fishes. Multicoloured.
706 40c. Type **200** . . . . 1·25 55
707 50c. Yellow-banded goatfish 1·50 1·10
708 55c. Yellow-edged lyretail ("Fairy cod") . . . . . . 1·50 1·75
709 $1 Peacock hind . . . . . . 2·00 5·00

201 Collared Petrel

202 Children and "Peace for Fiji and the World" Slogan

1985. Seabirds. Multicoloured.
710 15c. Type **201** . . . . 2·00 50
711 20c. Lesser frigate bird . . . 2·00 55
712 50c. Brown booby . . . . . 3·75 3·75
713 $1 Crested tern . . . . . . 5·50 8·00

1986. 60th Birthday of Queen Elizabeth II. As T **120a** of Hong Kong. Multicoloured.
714 20c. With Duke of York at Royal Tournament, 1936 20 25
715 25c. Royal Family on Palace balcony after Princess Margaret's wedding, 1960 20 25
716 40c. Queen inspecting guard of honour, Suva, 1982 . . 25 45
717 50c. In Luxembourg, 1976 . . 30 60
718 $1 At Crown Agents Head Office, London, 1983 . . . 45 1·60

1986. International Peace Year. Multicoloured.
736 8c. Type **202** 40 25
737 40c. Peace dove and houses 1·00 1·00

203 Halley's Comet in Centaurus Constellation and Newton's Reflector

1986. Appearance of Halley's Comet. Multicoloured.
738 25c. Type **203** . . . . 2·00 40
739 40c. Halley's Comet over Lomaiviti . . . . 2·25 85
740 $1 "Giotto" spacecraft photographing comet nucleus . . . . 3·25 7·00

204 Ground Frog

1986. Reptiles and Amphibians. Multicoloured.
741 8c. Type **204** 55 10
742 20c. Burrowing snake . . . . 1·00 30
743 25c. Spotted gecko . . . . . 1·10 35
744 40c. Crested iguana . . . . . 1·25 90
745 50c. Blotched skink . . . . . 1·40 3·25
746 $1 Speckled skink . . . . . . 1·75 6·00

205 Gatawaka

206 Weasel Cone

1986. Ancient War Clubs. Multicoloured.
747 25c. Type **205** 90 35
748 40c. Siriti . . . . 1·25 60
749 50c. Bulibuli . . . . 1·40 1·60
750 $1 Culacula . . . . 2·50 3·00

1987. Cone Shells of Fiji. Multicoloured.
751 15c. Type **206** 75 30
752 20c. Pertusus cone 80 40
753 25c. Admiral cone 85 40
754 40c. Leaden cone . . . . . . 1·00 1·40
755 50c. Imperial cone . . . . . 1·00 2·75
756 $1 Geography cone . . . . . 1·25 5·00

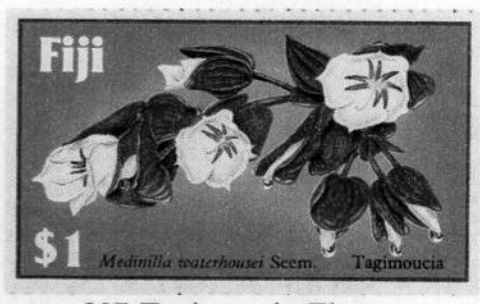

207 Tagimoucia Flower

1987. Tagimoucia Flower. Sheet 72 × 55 mm.
MS757 **207** $1 multicoloured . . 2·75 2·00

1987. "Capex '87" International Stamp Exhibition, Toronto. No. **MS**757 optd **CAPEX '87**.
MS758 72 × 55 mm. $1 Type **207** 8·00 8·00
Stamps from Nos. **MS**757 and **MS**758 are identical as the overprint on **MS**758 appears on the margin of the sheet.

209 Traditional Fijian House

1987. Int Year of Shelter for the Homeless. Mult.
759 55c. Type **209** 45 50
760 70c. Modern bungalows . . . 55 60

210 "Bulbogaster ctenostomoides" (stick insect)

1987. Fijian Insects. Multicoloured.
761 20c. Type **210** . . . . 2·25 50
762 25c. "Paracupta flaviventris" (beetle) . . . . 2·25 50
763 40c. "Cerambyrhynchus schoenherri" (beetle) . . . 3·00 1·75
764 50c. "Rhinoscapha lagopyga" (weevil) . . . . 3·00 3·50
765 $1 "Xixuthrus heros" (beetle) 4·00 9·00

211 The Nativity

1987. Christmas. Multicoloured.

766	8c. Type **211**	85	10
767	40c. The Shepherds (horiz)	2·25	40
768	50c. The Three Kings (horiz)	2·75	1·50
769	$1 The Three Kings presenting gifts	3·50	4·50

212 Windsurfer and Beach

1988. "Expo '88" World Fair, Brisbane.

770 **212**	30c. multicoloured	1·50	1·10

213 Woman using Fiji "Nouna" (stove)

1988. Centenary of International Council of Women.

771 **213**	45c. multicoloured	1·00	1·00

214 Pottery Bowl

1988. Ancient Fijian Pottery. Multicoloured.

772	9c. Type **214**	15	10
773	23c. Cooking pot	25	25
774	58c. Priest's drinking vessel	50	1·10
775	63c. Drinking vessel	55	1·40
776	69c. Earthenware oil lamp	60	1·50
777	75c. Cooking pot with relief pattern (vert)	70	1·60

215 Fiji Tree Frog **216** "Dendrobium mohlianum"

1988. Fiji Tree Frog. Multicoloured.

778	18c. Type **215**	2·50	1·25
779	23c. Frog climbing grass stalks	2·75	1·25
780	30c. On leaf	3·25	3·25
781	45c. Moving from one leaf to another	3·75	4·00

1988. Native Flowers. Multicoloured.

782	9c. Type **216**	65	15
783	30c. "Dendrobium cattilare"	90	45
784	45c. "Degeneria vitiensis"	90	70
785	$1 "Degeneria roseiflora"	1·60	2·75

217 Battle of Solferino, 1859

1989. 125th Anniv of International Red Cross.

786 **217**	58c. multicoloured	1·10	80
787 –	63c. multicoloured	1·10	1·00
788 –	69c. multicoloured	1·40	1·25
789 –	$1 black and red	1·50	1·50

DESIGNS—VERT: 63c. Henri Dunant (founder); $1 Anniversary logo. HORIZ: 69c. Fijian Red Cross worker with blood donor.

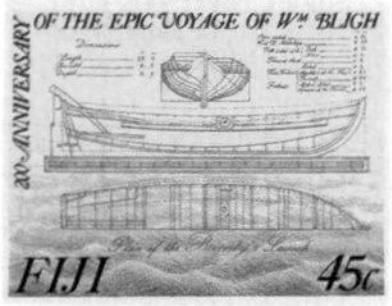

218 Plan of "Bounty's" Launch

1989. Bicent of Capt. Bligh's Boat Voyage. Mult.

790	45c. Type **218**	1·75	50
791	58c. Cup, bowl and Bligh's journal	1·90	1·25
792	80c. Bligh and extract from journal	3·00	2·75
793	$1 "Bounty's" launch and map of Fiji	4·00	3·00

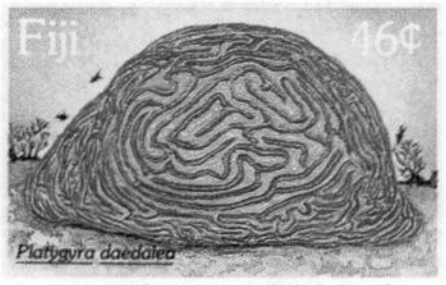

219 "Platygyra daedalea"

1989. Corals. Multicoloured.

794	46c. Type **219**	2·00	75
795	60c. "Caulastrea furcata"	2·25	1·75
796	75c. "Acropora echinata" (vert)	2·50	2·25
797	90c. "Acropora humilis" (vert)	2·75	2·75

220 Goalkeeper

1989. World Cup Football Championship, Italy (1990). Multicoloured.

798	35c. Type **220**	1·25	40
799	63c. Goalkeeper catching ball	2·00	2·25
800	70c. Player with ball	2·25	2·50
801	85c. Tackling	2·25	3·00

221 Congregation in Church

1989. Christmas. Multicoloured.

802	9c. Type **221**	25	10
803	45c. "Delonix regia" (Christmas tree)	75	35
804	$1 The Nativity	1·50	2·00
805	$1.40 Fijian children under tree	1·75	4·00

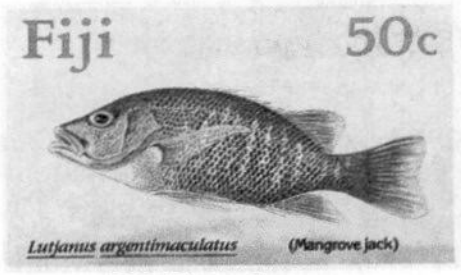

222 River Snapper

1990. Freshwater Fishes. Multicoloured.

806	50c. Type **222**	2·25	70
807	70c. Kner's grunter ("Orange-spotted Therapon")	2·75	3·00
808	85c. Spotted scat	3·25	3·50
809	$1 Rock flagtail	3·50	4·00

223 1968 3d. Reef Heron Definitive

1990. "Stamp World London 90" International Stamp Exhibition, London. Sheet 120×70 mm, containing T **223** and similar vert design. Multicoloured.

MS810	$1 Type **223**; $2 1968 1s.6d. Orange-breasted honeyeaters definitive	6·50	8·00

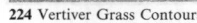

224 Vertiver Grass Contours **225** "Dacrydium nidulum"

1990. Soil Conservation. Multicoloured.

811	50c. Type **224**	1·50	50
812	70c. Mulching	1·75	1·75
813	90c. Hillside contour cultivation	1·90	2·25
814	$1 Land use rotation (vert)	2·00	2·50

1990. Timber Trees. Multicoloured.

815	25c. Type **225**	75	20
816	35c. "Decussocarpus vitiensis"	85	30
817	$1 "Agathis vitiensis"	2·50	3·00
818	$1.55 "Santalum yasy"	3·50	5·00

226 "Hark the Herald Angels sing"

1990. Christmas. Carols. Multicoloured.

819	10c. Type **226**	30	10
820	35c. "Still the Night, Holy the Night"	75	30
821	65c. "Joy to the World!"	1·25	1·75
822	$1 "The Race that long in Darkness pined"	2·00	2·75

227 Sigatoka Sand Dunes

1991. Environmental Protection. Multicoloured.

823	35c. Type **227**	1·00	30
824	50c. Monu and Monuriki Islands	1·75	1·00
825	65c. Ravilevu Nature Reserve, Taveuni	2·00	2·75
826	$1 Colo-I-Suva Forest Park	3·00	4·25

228 H.M.S. "Pandora" (frigate)

1991. Bicentenary of Discovery of Rotuma Island. Multicoloured

827	54c. Type **228**	2·00	90
828	70c. Map of Rotuma	2·25	2·50
829	75c. Natives welcoming H.M.S. "Pandora"	2·25	2·50
830	$1 Mount Solorua and Uea Island	3·50	4·00

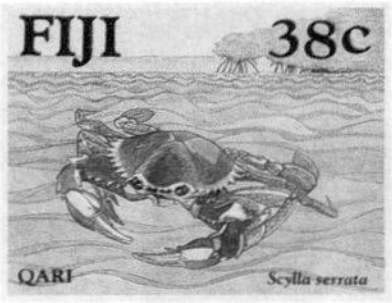

229 "Scylla serrata"

1991. Mangrove Crabs. Multicoloured.

831	38c. Type **229**	90	35
832	54c. "Metopograpsus messor"	1·25	85
833	96c. "Parasesarma erythrodactyla"	2·25	3·00
834	$1.65 "Cardisoma carnifex"	3·25	5·00

230 Mary and Joseph travelling to Bethlehem

1991. Christmas. Multicoloured.

835	11c. Type **230**	40	10
836	75c. Manger scene	1·50	1·25
837	96c. Presentation in the Temple	1·75	3·00
838	$1 Infant Jesus with symbols	1·75	3·00

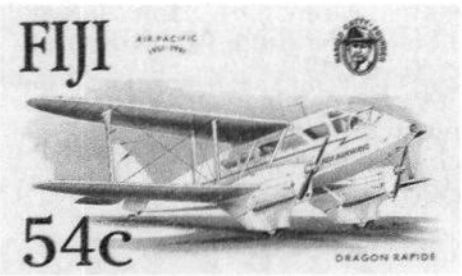

231 De Havilland D.H.89 Dragon Rapide of Fiji Airways

1991. 40th Anniv of Air Pacific. Multicoloured.

839	54c. Type **231**	1·75	1·00
840	75c. Douglas DC-3	2·25	2·25
841	96c. Aerospatial/Aeritalia ATR42	2·50	3·25
842	$1.40 Boeing 767	3·50	4·50

232 Ethnic Dancers

1992. "Expo 92" World's Fair, Seville, Spain. Multicoloured.

843	27c. Type **232**	65	45
844	75c. Peoples of Fiji	1·40	1·75
845	96c. Gold bars and sugar cane train	6·50	5·50
846	$1.40 "Queen Elizabeth 2" (cruise liner) at Suva	7·00	7·00

233 "Tabusoro"

1992. Inter-Islands Shipping. Multicoloured.

847	38c. Type **233**	2·25	55
848	54c. "Degei II"	2·75	1·40
849	$1.40 "Dausoko"	4·75	4·25
850	$1.65 "Nivanga"	4·75	4·25

234 Running **235** European War Memorial, Levuka

1992. Olympic Games, Barcelona. Multicoloured.

851	20c. Type **234**	1·00	20
852	86c. Dinghy sailing	3·00	2·50
853	$1.34 Swimming	3·50	3·75
854	$1.50 Judo	3·50	3·75

1992. Historic Levuka (former capital). Mult.

855	30c. Type **235**	30	30
856	42c. Map of Fiji	45	55
857	59c. Beach Street	65	1·00
858	77c. Sacred Heart Church (vert)	80	1·50
859	$2 Deed of Cession site (vert)	1·75	3·50

236 The Nativity

1992. Christmas. Multicoloured.

860	12c. Type **236**	75	10
861	77c. Shepherds and family giving presents	2·25	1·60

862 83c. Shepherds at manger and giving presents to pensioners . . . . 2·25 1·75
863 $2 Wise Men and collecting Fiji produce . . . . 3·75 5·50

237 International Planned Parenthood Federation Logo

1992. 40th Anniv of International Planned Parenthood Federation. Multicoloured.
864 77c. Type **237** . . . . 1·00 85
865 $2 Man weeping and pregnant mother with children . . . . 2·75 3·50

238 Dove and Peace Corps Emblem

1993. 25th Anniv of Peace Corps in Fiji. Mult.
866 59c. Type **238** . . . . 1·10 75
867 77c. Handshake . . . . 1·40 1·40
868 $1 Educational symbols . . . 1·75 1·75
869 $2 Symbols of home businesses scheme . . . . 3·00 4·50

239 Fijian Players performing Cibi (traditional dance)

1993. Hong Kong Rugby Sevens Competition. Multicoloured.
870 77c. Type **239** . . . . 1·75 1·40
871 $1.06 Players and map of Pacific . . . . 2·50 2·75
872 $2 Scrum and stadium . . . . 4·25 5·50

1993. 75th Anniv of Royal Air Force. As T **173** of Falkland Islands. Multicoloured.
873 59c. Gloster Gauntlet II . . . 1·00 75
874 77c. Armstrong Whitworth Whitley Mk V . . . . . . 1·25 1·40
875 83c. Bristol F2B "Brisfit" . . 1·40 1·60
876 $2 Hawker Tempest Mk V . . 2·25 3·50
MS877 110 × 77 mm. $1 Vickers Vildebeest III; $1 Handley Page Hampden; $1 Vickers FB-27 Vimy; $1 British Aerospace Hawk T.1 . . . . 6·50 6·50

240 "Chromodoris fidelis"

1993. Nudibranchs. Multicoloured.
878 12c. Type **240** 50 10
879 42c. "Halgerda carlsoni" . . 1·10 55
880 53c. "Chromodoris lochi" . . 1·40 1·25
881 83c. Blue sea lizard . . . . 2·00 2·25
882 $1 "Phyllidia bourguini" . . 2·25 2·50
883 $2 Spanish dancer . . . . 3·50 5·00

241 Mango **242** "Anaphaesis java"

1993. Tropical Fruits. Multicoloured.
884 30c. Type **241** . . . . 1·50 45
885 42c. Guava . . . . 1·60 80
886 $1 Lemon . . . . 3·00 2·50
887 $2 Soursop . . . . 5·00 6·50

1994. "Hong Kong '94" International Stamp Exhibition. (a) No. **MS**877 optd **HONG KONG '94** and emblem on each stamp.
MS888 110 × 77 mm. $1 Vickers Vildebeest III; $1 Handley Page Hampden; $1 Vickers FB-27 Vimy; $1 British Aerospace Hawk T.1 . . . . 4·50 6·00

(b) Sheet 122 × 85 mm containing T **242** and similar vert designs showing butterflies. Multicoloured.
MS889 $1 Type **242**; $1 *Euploea leucostictos*; $1 *Vagrans egista*; $1 *Acraea andromache* . . . . . 4·50 6·00

243 The Last Supper

1994. Easter. Multicoloured.
890 59c. Type **243** . . . . 1·25 60
891 77c. The Crucifixion (vert) . . 1·50 1·25
892 $1 The Resurrection . . . . 2·00 2·25
893 $2 Examining Christ's wounds (vert) . . . . . . 3·50 6·00

244 Sagati **245** White-collared Kingfisher on Branch

1994. Edible Seaweeds. Multicoloured.
894 42c. Type **244** 90 45
895 83c. Nama . . . . 1·75 2·00
896 $1 Lumicevata . . . . 2·00 2·50
897 $2 Lumiwawa . . . . 3·50 6·00

1994. White-collared Kingfisher. Sheet 98 × 84 mm, containing T **245** and similar vert design. Multicoloured.
MS898 $1.50, Type **245**; $1.50, Kingfisher with crab in beak . . . . 7·50 8·00

246 "Neoveitchia storckii" **247** Father Ioane Batita

1994. "Singpex '94" International Stamp Exhibition. Endemic Palm. Sheet 97 × 69 mm, containing T **246** and similar vert design. Multicoloured.
MS899 $1.50, Type **246**; $1.50, Palm flowers . . . . 6·50 7·50

1994. 150th Anniv of Arrival of Catholic Missionaries in Fiji. Multicoloured.
900 23c. Type **247** 35 25
901 31c. Local catechist 45 30
902 44c. Sacred Heart Cathedral, Suva 60 70
903 63c. Lomary Church . . . . 80 1·10
904 81c. Pope Gregory XVI . . . 1·50 1·75
905 $2 Pope John Paul II . . . 3·00 4·25

248 Waterfall and Banded Iguana **249** Red-headed Parrot Finch

1995. Eco-Tourism in Fiji. Sheet 140 × 80 mm, containing T **248** and similar square designs. Multicoloured.
MS906 81c. Type **248**; 81c. Mountain trekkers and Fiji Tree Frog; 81c. Bilibili River trip and White-collared kingfisher ("Kingfisher"); 81c. Historic sites and Flying Fox . . . . 4·50 5·50

1995. 50th Anniv of End of Second World War. As T **184a** of Falkland Islands. Multicoloured.
907 13c. Fijian soldiers guarding crashed Japanese Mitsubishi A6M Zero-Sen aircraft 60 20
908 63c. American spotter plane landing on Kameli Airstrip, Solomon Islands . . . . . 1·75 1·50
909 87c. Corporal Sukanaivalu and Victoria Cross . . . . 2·00 2·50
910 $1.12 H.M.S. "Fiji" (cruiser) 2·50 2·75
MS911 75 × 85 mm. $2 Reverse of 1939–45 War Medal (vert) . . 2·25 2·75

1995. Birds. Multicoloured.
912 1c. Type **249** 10 10
913 2c. Golden whistler 10 10
914 3c. Ogea flycatcher 10 10
915 4c. Peale's pigeon 10 10
916 6c. Blue-headed flycatcher ("Blue-crested Broadbill") 10 10
917 13c. Island thrush 10 10
918 23c. Many-coloured fruit dove 15 20
919 31c. Green-backed heron ("Mangrove heron") . . . 20 25
920 44c. Purple swamphen . . . 30 35
921 63c. Fiji goshawk 40 45
922 81c. Kandavu fantail ("Kadavu Fantail") . . . 50 55
923 87c. Collard lory 55 60
924 $1 Scarlet robin 65 70
925 $2 Peregrine falcon . . . . 1·30 1·40
926 $3 Barn owl . . . . 1·90 2·00
927 $5 Masked shining parrot ("Yellow-breasted musk parrot") . . . . 3·25 3·50

1995. "JAKARTA '95" Stamp Exhibition, Indonesia. No. **MS**898 optd "JAKARTA '95" and emblem on sheet margin.
MS928 $1.50, Type **245**; $1.50, White-collared kingfisher with crab in beak . . . . 7·50 9·00

250 "Arundina graminifolia"

1995. Orchids. Sheet 100 × 80 mm, containing T **250** and similar vert design.
MS929 $1 Type **250**; $1 "Phaius tankervilliae" . . . . 4·50 6·00
No. **MS**929 also includes "Singapore '95" and emblem on the sheet margin.

251 Pres. Ratu Sir Kamisese Mara, Parliament Building and National Flag

1995. 25th Anniv of Independence. Multicoloured.
930 81c. Type **251** . . . . 1·25 1·00
931 87c. Young citizens of Fiji . . 1·00 1·10
932 $1.06 Rugby players . . . . 1·75 2·25
933 $2 Boeing 747 "Island of Viti Levu" . . . . 3·25 5·00

252 "Praying Madonna with the Crown of Stars" (workshop of Correggio) **253** Trolling Lure

1995. Christmas. Multicoloured.
934 10c. Type **252** 25 10
935 63c. "Madonna and Child with Crowns" (on porcelain) 90 80
936 87c. "The Holy Virgin with Holy Child and St. John" (after Titian) . . . . . 1·25 1·25
937 $2 "The Holy Family and St. John" (workshop of Rubens) . . . . 2·75 4·50

1996. 50th Anniv of Resettlement of Banabans (inhabitans of Ocean Island) in Fiji. Multicoloured.
938 81c. Type **253** . . . . 1·00 1·10
939 87c. Banaban fishing canoes 1·25 1·25
940 $1.12 Banaban warrior (vert) 1·40 2·00
941 $2 Great frigate bird (vert) 5·00 6·00

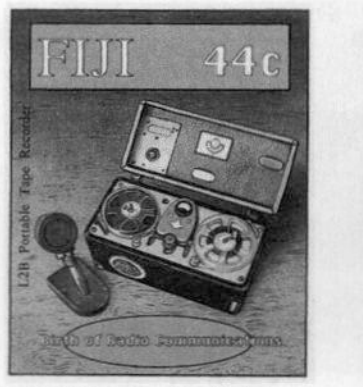

254 L2B Portable Tape Recorder **255** Winged Monster and Ring (bronze), c. 450 B.C.

1996. Centenary of Radio. Multicoloured.
942 44c. Type **254** 70 45
943 63c. Broadcasting House, Fiji 90 70
944 81c. Communications satellite 1·40 1·25
945 $3 Guglielmo Marconi . . . 4·00 6·50

1996. "CHINA '96" 9th Asian International Stamp Exhibition, Peking. Multicoloured.
946 63c. Type **255** 85 65
947 81c. Archer (terracotta sculpture), 210 B.C . . . . 1·10 1·10
948 $1 Dragon plate, 1426–35 . . 1·40 1·50
949 $2 Central Asian horseman (sculpture), 706 . . . . . 2·75 5·00
MS950 81 × 127 mm. 30c. "Yan Deng Mountains" (painting) (48½ × 76 mm) . . . . 1·75 2·00

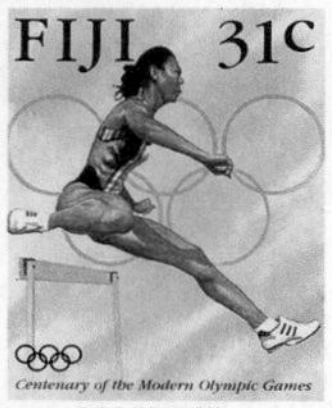

256 Hurdling

1996. Cent of Modern Olympic Games. Mult.
951 31c. Type **256** 65 30
952 63c. Judo . . . . 1·25 80
953 87c. Sailboarding . . . . . . 1·40 1·75
954 $1.12 Swimming . . . . . . 1·60 2·50
MS955 59 × 99 mm. $2 Winning athlete, 1896 . . . . 2·50 3·25

257 Computerized Telephone Exchange

1996. Inauguration of Independent Postal and Telecommunications Companies. Multicoloured.
956 31c. Type **257** 40 30
957 44c. Unloading mail from aircraft 80 65
958 81c. Manual telephone exchange (vert) . . . . . 1·00 1·50
959 $1 Postman on motorbike (vert) . . . . 1·75 2·00
MS960 120 × 77 mm. $1.50, Fiji 1938 ½d. Sailing canoe stamp (vert); $1.50, Fiji 1985 20c. "Expo '85" stamp (vert) . . . . 8·00 8·50

258 "Our Children Our Future"

1996. 50th Anniv of U.N.I.C.E.F. Children's Paintings. Multicoloured.
961 81c. Type **258** . . . . 1·50 1·25
962 87c. "Village Scene" . . . . 1·50 1·25
963 $1 "Living in Harmony the World over" . . . . 1·60 1·60
964 $2 "Their Future" . . . . . 2·50 4·75

259 First Seaplane in Fiji, 1921

1996. 50th Anniv of Nadi International Airport. Multicoloured.

965	31c. Type **259**	65	30
966	44c. Nadi Airport in 1946	80	50
967	63c. Arrival of first jet airliner, 1959	1·25	1·00
968	87c. Airport entrance	1·40	1·50
969	$1 Control tower	1·60	1·75
970	$2 Diagram of Global Positioning System	2·75	5·00

260 The Annunciation and Fijian beating Lali (drum)

1996. Christmas. Multicoloured.

971	13c. Type **260**	40	15
972	81c. Shepherds with sheep, and canoe	1·40	85
973	$1 Wise men on camels, and people on cross	1·60	1·40
974	$3 The Nativity, and Fijian blowing conch	4·75	6·50

261 Brahman

1997. "HONG KONG '97" International Stamp Exhibition. Cattle. Sheet 130 × 92 mm, containing T **261** and similar horiz designs. Multicoloured.

MS975 $1 Type **261**; $1 Friesian (Holstein); $1 Hereford; $1 Fiji draught bullock . . . 5·00 6·50

No. **MS**975 is inscribed "FREISIAN" in error.

262 Black-throated Shrikebill

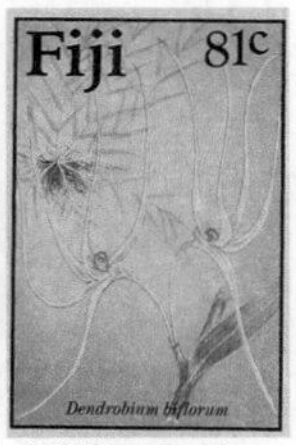

263 "Dendrobium biflorum"

1997. "SINGPEX '97" Stamp Exhibition, Singapore. Sheet 92 × 78 mm.

MS976 **262** $2 multicoloured . . . 2·40 3·00

1997. Orchids. Multicoloured.

977	81c. Type **263**	1·50	1·25
978	87c. "Dendrobium dactylodes"	1·50	1·25
979	$1.06 "Spathoglottis pacifica"	1·75	2·00
980	$2 "Dendrobium macropus"	3·00	4·00

264 Hawksbill Turtle laying Eggs

1997. Life Cycle of Hawksbill Turtle. Sheet 140 × 85 mm, containing T **264** and similar horiz designs. Multicoloured.

MS981 63c. Type **264**; 81c. Turtles hatching; $1.06, Young turtles swimming; $2 Adult turtle . . . 7·00 7·50

265 Branching Hard Coral

1997. Year of the Coral Reef. Multicoloured.

982	63c. Type **265**	1·00	55
983	87c. Massive hard coral	1·40	1·25
984	$1 White soft coral	1·60	1·60
985	$3 Pink soft coral	4·25	6·50

266 Fijian Monkey-faced Bat

267 Waisale Serevi (Captain)

1997. Endangered Species. Fijian Monkey-faced Bat.

986	**266**	44c. multicoloured	70	40
987	–	63c. multicoloured	90	60
988	–	81c. multicoloured	1·25	1·10
989	–	$2 multicoloured	2·50	4·50

MS990 157 × 106 mm. Nos. 986/9 × 2 . . . 8·00 10·00

DESIGNS: 63c. to $2 Showing different bats.

1997. Fiji Rugby Club's Victory in Hong Kong Rugby Sevens Competition. Multicoloured.

991	50c. Type **267**	65	80
992	50c. Taniela Qauqau	65	80
993	50c. Jope Tuikabe	65	80
994	50c. Leveni Duvuduvukula	65	80
995	50c. Inoke Maraiwai	65	80
996	50c. Aminiasi Naituyaga	65	80
997	50c. Lemki Koroi	65	80
998	50c. Marika Vunibaka	65	80
999	50c. Luke Erenavula	65	80
1000	50c. Manasa Bari	65	80
1001	$1 Fijian rugby team (56 × 42 mm)	80	1·00

268 Shepherd and Angel

1997. Christmas. Multicoloured.

1002	13c. Type **268**	25	10
1003	31c. Mary, Joseph and baby Jesus	50	30
1004	87c. The Three Kings	1·25	90
1005	$3 Mary and baby Jesus	3·50	6·00

269 Chief in War Dress

270a Diana, Princess of Wales, 1990

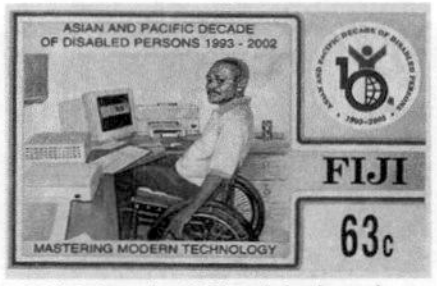

270 Man in Wheelchair using Computer

1998. Traditional Chiefs' Costumes. Multicoloured.

1006	81c. Type **269**	85	75
1007	87c. Formal dress	95	90
1008	$1.12 Presentation dress	1·40	1·75
1009	$2 War dress of Highland chief	2·00	3·25

1998. Asian and Pacific Decade of Disabled People. Multicoloured.

1010	63c. Type **270**	1·00	60
1011	87c. Woman with child	1·10	80
1012	$1 Man at desk	1·40	1·25
1013	$2 Wheelchair race	2·25	3·25

1998. Diana, Princess of Wales Commemoration.

1014	**270a**	81c. multicoloured	1·00	1·00

MS1015 145 × 70 mm. 81c. As No. 1014; 81c. Wearing blue jacket, 1991; 81c. Wearing high-necked blouse, 1990; 81c. Carrying bouquet. Sold at $3.24 + 50c. charity premium . . . 2·75 3·25

270b R34 Airship

1998. 80th Anniv of Royal Air Force. Multicoloured

1016	44c. Type **270b**	70	30
1017	63c. Handley Page Heyford	1·00	60
1018	87c. Supermarine Swift FR.5	1·40	1·00
1019	$2 Westland Whirlwind	2·25	3·00

MS1020 110 × 77 mm. $1 Sopwith Dolphin; $1 Avro 504K; $1 Vickers Warwick V; $1 Shorts Belfast . . . 3·75 4·50

271 Pod of Sperm Whales Underwater

1998. Sperm Whales. Multicoloured.

1021	63c. Type **271**	1·00	55
1022	81c. Female and calf	1·25	90
1023	87c. Pod on surface	1·40	1·00
1024	$2 Ceremonial whale tooth	2·00	3·00

MS1025 90 × 68 mm. No. 1024 . . . 3·00 3·25

272 Athletics

1998. 16th Commonwealth Games, Kuala Lumpur. Multicoloured.

1026	44c. Type **272**	60	30
1027	63c. Lawn bowls	85	45
1028	81c. Throwing the javelin	1·10	90
1029	$1.12 Weightlifting	1·40	2·00

MS1030 63 × 77 mm. $2 Waisale Serevi (Fiji rugby captain) . . . 2·50 2·75

273 Takia (traditional raft)

1998. Maritime Past and Present (1st series). Multicoloured.

1031	13c. Type **273**	25	10
1032	44c. Camakau (outrigger canoe)	50	30
1033	87c. Drua (outrigger canoe)	1·00	90
1034	$3 "Pioneer" (inter-island ship)	3·75	5·50

MS1035 105 × 75 mm. $1.50, Camakau (outrigger canoe) . . . 2·25 2·50

See also Nos. 1044/48.

274 "Jesus in a Manger" (Grace Lee)

1998. Christmas. Children's Paintings. Multicoloured.

1036	13c. Type **274**	40	10
1037	50c. "A Time with Family and Friends" (Brian Guevara)	90	35
1038	$1 "What Christmas Means to Me" (Naomi Tupou) (vert)	1·50	1·00
1039	$2 "The Joy of Christmas" (Lauretta Ah Sam) (vert)	2·00	3·50

275 Women's Sitting Dance

1999. Traditional Fijian Dances. Multicoloured.

1040	13c. Type **275**	40	10
1041	81c. Club dance	1·50	1·00
1042	87c. Women's fan dance	1·50	1·00
1043	$3 Kava-serving dance	4·00	5·00

1999. Maritime Past and Present (2nd series). As T **273**. Multicoloured.

1044	63c. "Tofua I" (cargo liner)	1·00	45
1045	81c. "Adi Beti" (government launch)	1·25	65
1046	$1 "Niagara" (liner)	1·50	1·25
1047	$2 "Royal Viking Sun" (liner)	2·25	3·00

MS1048 105 × 75 mm. $1.50, "Makatea" (inter-island freighter) . . . 2·50 2·75

276 Wandering Whistling Duck

1999. "iBRA '99" International Stamp Exhibition, Nuremberg. Sheet 100 × 95 mm, containing T **276** and similar vert design. Multicoloured.

MS1049 $2 Type **276**; $2 Pacific black duck . . . 3·50 4·00

277 "Calanthe ventilabrum"

277a Astronaut preparing to enter Module

1999. Orchids. Multicoloured.

1050	44c. Type **277**	75	35
1051	63c. "Dendrobium prasinum"	95	45
1052	81c. "Dendrobium macrophyllum"	1·10	70
1053	$3 "Dendrobium tokai"	2·75	4·00

1999. 30th Anniv of First Manned Landing on Moon. Multicoloured.

1054	13c. Type **277a**	35	10
1055	87c. Third stage rockets firing near Moon	1·00	70
1056	$1 Buzz Aldrin on Moon's surface	1·10	1·00
1057	$2 Command module returning to Earth	1·75	2·50

MS1058 90 × 80 mm. $2 Earth as seen from Moon (circular, 40 mm diam) . . . 2·00 2·50

1999. "Queen Elizabeth the Queen Mother's Century." As T **204a** of Falkland Islands. Mult.

1059	13c. Inspecting bomb damage, Hull, 1940	50	10
1060	63c. With Prince Charles, 1950	1·00	55
1061	81c. Meeting soldiers from the Light Infantry	1·50	85
1062	$3 Saying goodbye to Prince Charles, 1986	2·75	3·75

MS1063 145 × 70 mm. $2 Lady Elizabeth Bowes-Lyon, 1923 and Armistice Day celebrations, 1918 . . . 2·50 2·75

278 Sugar Mills Diesel Locomotive

1999. 125th Anniv of U.P.U. Sugar Mill Locomotives. Multicoloured.

1064	50c. Type **278**	65	35
1065	87c. Steam locomotive	1·00	75

1066 $1 Diesel locomotive "Hunsley" . . . . . . 1·10 90
1067 $2 Free passenger service . . 2·00 3·00

279 Exchanging Gifts

1999. Christmas. Multicoloured.
1068 13c. Type **279** 20 15
1069 31c. Two angels over Earth 40 30
1070 63c. Open Bible 70 45
1071 87c. Joseph and Mary on donkey (vert) 85 70
1072 $1 The Nativity (vert) . . . 95 80
1073 $2 Children and Father Christmas (vert) . . . . . 1·60 2·75

280 Sun rising over Islands and Hands holding Ceremonial Objects

2000. New Millennium. Multicoloured.
1074 $5 Type **280** . . . . . . 3·25 4·00
1075 $5 Traditional sailing canoe and globe (vert) . . . . . 3·25 4·00
1076 $5 Fijian warrior beating drum, palm trees and hut 3·25 4·00
1077 $5 Fijian flag and map of islands (vert) . . . . . . 3·25 4·00
MS1078 133 × 93 mm. $10 Macgillivary's petrel; $10 Crested iguana; $10 Prawns; $10 Indigenous flowers . . . . . . 24·00 27·00

281 *Paracupta sulcata* (beetle)

2000. Beetles. Multicoloured.
1079 15c. Type **281** 35 10
1080 87c. *Agrilus* sp. . . . . . . 1·00 65
1081 $1.06 *Cyphogastra abdominalis* . . . . . . 1·25 1·25
1082 $2 *Paracupta* sp. . . . . . 2·00 2·75

282 Big Bird

2000. *Sesame Street* (children's T.V. programme). Multicoloured.
1083 50c. Type **282** 55 65
1084 50c. Oscar the Grouch in dustbin 55 65
1085 50c. Cookie Monster eating cookie 55 65
1086 50c. Grover (turquoise background) 55 65
1087 50c. Elmo (blue background) 55 65
1088 50c. Ernie (yellow background) 55 65
1089 50c. Zoe (pink background) 55 65
1090 50c. The Count (blue background) 55 65
1091 50c. Bert (green background) 55 65
MS1092 Two sheets, each 139 × 86 mm. (a) $2 Bert and birthday cake (horiz). (b) $2 Big Bird, Elmo and Ernie in tree house (horiz) Set of 2 sheets . . . . 3·00 3·50

283 President Ratu Sir Kamisese Mara and Forestry Plantation

284 Swimming

2000. 80th Birthday of President Ratu Sir Kamisese Mara. Multicoloured.
1093 15c. Type **283** 25 15
1094 81c. Pres. Mara and Fijians 70 55
1095 $1 Pres. Mara and harvesting sugar 80 65
1096 $3 Wearing naval uniform and patrol boats . . . . 3·25 4·00

2000. 18th Birthday of Prince William. As T **208c** of Falkland Islands. Multicoloured.
1097 $1 Prince William wearing fireman's helmet . . . . 1·10 1·10
1098 $1 At Clarence House, 1995 1·10 1·10
1099 $1 Prince William waving (horiz) . . . . 1·10 1·10
1100 $1 At Christmas service, 1998 (horiz) . . . . . . 1·10 1·10
MS1101 175 × 95 mm. $1 Wearing Parachute Regiment uniform and Nos. 1097/1100 . . . . . . 5·50 5·50

2000. Olympic Games, Sydney. Multicoloured.
1102 44c. Type **284** 60 35
1103 87c. Judo 95 60
1104 $1 Running (horiz) . . . . 1·10 85
1105 $2 Windsurfing (horiz) . . . 2·00 2·75

285 Top Left Leaf Fronds of *Alsmithia longpipes*

2000. *Alsmithia longpipes* (Endemic Palm of Fiji). Sheet 121 × 85 mm, containing T **285** and similar horiz designs forming a complete palm.
MS1106 $1 Type **285**; $1 Top right leaf fronds; $1 Flower and stem of palm; $1 Stem of palm and berries 3·50 4·25

286 Pottery Fragment and Site on Yanuca Island, Nadroga

2000. Lapita Pottery. Showing excavation sites and pottery fragments. Multicoloured.
1107 44c. Type **286** 55 35
1108 63c. Vutua, Mago Island . . 75 55
1109 $1 Ugaga Island, Beqa . . . 1·10 1·10
1110 $2 Sigatoka Sand Dunes . . 1·75 2·50

287 Three Kings in Jungle

288 Orange Dove

2000. Christmas. Journey of the Three Kings in Fijian Setting. Multicoloured.
1111 15c. Type **287** 30 10
1112 81c. Three Kings on precipice 95 55
1113 87c. Three Kings by lagoon 1·00 60
1114 $3 Three Kings on canoe . . 2·75 3·50

2001. Taveuni Rainforest. Sheet 122 × 86 mm, containing T **288** and similar vert design. Multicoloured.
MS1115 $2 Type **288**; $2 *Xisuthrus heyrovskyi* (beetle) . . . . . . 3·25 4·00

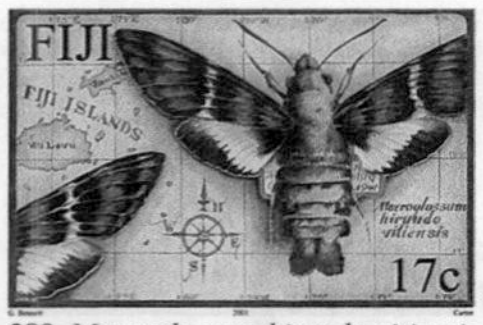

289 *Macroglossum hirundo vitiensis* (moth)

2001. Hawk Moths of Fiji. Multicoloured.
1116 17c. Type **289** 30 10
1117 48c. *Hippotion celerio* . . . 55 40
1118 69c. *Gnatholhlibus erotus eras* 75 65
1119 89c. *Theretra pinastrina intersecta* 85 85
1120 $1.17 *Deilephila placida torenia* . . . . 95 1·10
1121 $2 *Psilogramma jordana* . . 1·50 2·25

290 Red Junglefowl Hen

2001. Jungle Fowl of Fiji. Sheet 122 × 86 mm, containing T **290** and similar horiz dseign. Multicoloured.
MS1122 $2 Type **290**; $2 Red junglefowl cock . . . . 3·50 3·50

291 Girl with "Mile-a-Minute" (cat)

2001. Fijian Society for the Prevention of Cruelty to Animals. Multicoloured.
1123 34c. Type **291** 40 30
1124 96c. Boy with two puppies 90 90
1125 $1.23 Girl with "Twistie" (cat) . . . . 1·00 1·10
1126 $2 Boy with "Rani" (dog) 1·50 2·25

292 White-throated Pigeon

2001. Pigeons. Multicoloured.
1127 69c. Type **292** 70 70
1128 89c. Pacific pigeon (vert) . . 85 85
1129 $1.23 Peale's pigeon (vert) 1·00 1·10
1130 $2 Rock pigeon . . . . . . 1·50 2·25
No. 1129 is inscribed "PEAL'S PIGEON" in error.

293 Bank of New South Wales (1901)

2001. Centenary of the Westpac Bank. Multicoloured.
1131 48c. Type **293** 45 40
1132 96c. Bank of New South Wales (1916) 80 75
1133 $1 Bank of New South Wales (1934) 80 75
1134 $2 Westpac Bank (2001) . . 1·50 2·25

294 Yellow-finned Tuna

2001. Game Fish. Multicoloured.
1135 50c. Type **294** 65 55
1136 96c. Wahoo 90 75
1137 $1.17 Dolphin fish . . . . 1·00 1·10
1138 $2 Blue marlin . . . . . . 1·75 2·50

295 Angel appearing to Mary on Beach

2001. Christmas. The Nativity Story in a Fijian setting. Multicoloured.
1139 17c. Type **295** 30 10
1140 34c. Birth of Jesus in stable 45 15
1141 48c. Local shepherds visiting the baby 60 45
1142 69c. Fijian wise men bringing gifts 85 70
1143 89c. Holy family boarding canoe . . . . 1·00 75
1144 $2 Jesus with purple-capped fruit dove . . . . 1·75 2·50

296 Colonial Building

2001. 125th Anniv of Colonial Mutual Life Assurance Ltd in Fiji. Multicoloured.
1145 17c. Type **296** 20 10
1146 48c. Women at Colonial cash point 50 35
1147 $1 Private hospital, Suva . . 90 75
1148 $3 Deed of Cession ceremony, 1874 . . . . . 2·40 2·75

297 Fiji Airways De Havilland Drover Aircraft (1950s)

298 Pepper

2001. 50th Anniv of Air Pacific. Multicoloured.
1149 89c. Type **297** . . . . . . 90 1·00
1150 96c. Hawker Siddeley 748 (1967) . . . . 1·00 1·10
1151 $1 Douglas DC-10 (1980s) 1·00 1·10
1152 $2 Boeing 747-200 (1985) . . 1·40 1·50
Nos. 1149/52 were printed together, se-tenant, with the backgrounds forming a composite design.

2002. Spices. Multicoloured.
1153 69c. Type **298** 70 55
1154 89c. Nutmeg 90 70
1155 $1 Vanilla . . . . 1·00 1·00
1156 $2 Cinnamon . . . . 1·50 2·00

299 Balaka Palm Tree with Bird and Butterfly

2002. Seemann's Balaka Palm. Sheet 97 × 107 mm, containing T **299** and similar vert design. Multicoloured.
MS1157 $2 Type **299**; $2 Balaka palm in fruit with lizard on trunk . . . . . . 3·00 3·25

300 *Redigobius sp.*

2002. Freshwater Fish. Multicoloured.

1158	48c. Type **300**	50	35
1159	96c. Spotted flagtail	90	75
1160	$1.23 Silver-stripe mudskipper	1·10	1·10
1161	$2 Snakehead gudgeon	1·50	2·00

301 Breadfruit 302 Saul's Murex Shell

2002. Tropical Fruit. Multicoloured.

1162	25c. Type **301**	30	20
1163	34c. Wi fruit	40	25
1164	$1 Jakfruit	1·00	75
1165	$3 Avocado	2·50	3·00

2002. Murex Shells. Multicoloured.

1166	69c. Type **302**	45	50
1167	96c. Caltrop murex	60	65
1168	$1 Purple Pacific drupe	65	70
1169	$2 Ramose murex	1·30	1·40

303 Adult Fiji Goshawk and Eggs 304 Drs. Nicholson and Menzie operating on Patient

2002. Fiji Goshawk. Multicoloured.

1170	48c. Type **303**	30	35
1171	89c. Chicks in nest	55	60
1172	$1 Juvenile Fiji goshawk on branch	65	70
1173	$3 Adult Fiji goshawk	1·90	2·00

2002. "Operation Open Heart" (Work of Australian cardiac team in Fiji). Multicoloured.

1174	34c. Type **304**	20	25
1175	69c. Dr. Gale listening to boy's heart (horiz)	45	50
1176	$1.17 Beverly Jacobsen (ultrasound technician) using echocardiograph (horiz)	75	80
1177	$2 Dr. Baines (anaesthetist) and Nurse Scarfe preparing patient	1·30	1·40

305 Bottle of Fiji Natura Artesian Water 306 Methodist Church, Wakaya Island

2002. Fiji Natural Water Industry. Multicoloured.

1178	25c. Type **305**	15	20
1179	48c. Bottling plant, Viti Levu (horiz)	30	35
1180	$1 Local delivery van (horiz)	65	70
1181	$3 Fijian children with bottled water	1·90	2·00

2002. Christmas. Religious Buildings. Mult.

1182	17c. Type **306**	10	15
1183	89c. Mosque, Yaqara	55	60
1184	$1 Hindu temple, Suva	65	70
1185	$3 Methodist church, Suva	1·90	2·00

307 General Post Office, Suva

2003. Opening of New Mail Centre. Multicoloured.

1186	48c. Type **307**	30	35
1187	96c. Mail Centre	60	65
1188	$1 Postal Logistics Centre	65	70
1189	$2 Smart Mail installation	1·30	1·40

308 Orchids and Waterfall

2003. International Year of Fresh Water. Sheet 86 × 104 mm containing T **308** and similar horiz design. Multicoloured.

MS1190	$2 Type **308**; $2 Butterfly on vegetation and waterfall plunging into pool	2·60	2·75

309 Athlete

2003. South Pacific Games, Fiji (1st issue). Multicoloured.

1191	10c. Type **309**	10	10
1192	14c. Baseball	10	10
1193	20c. Netball	15	20
1194	$5 Shot put	3·25	3·50

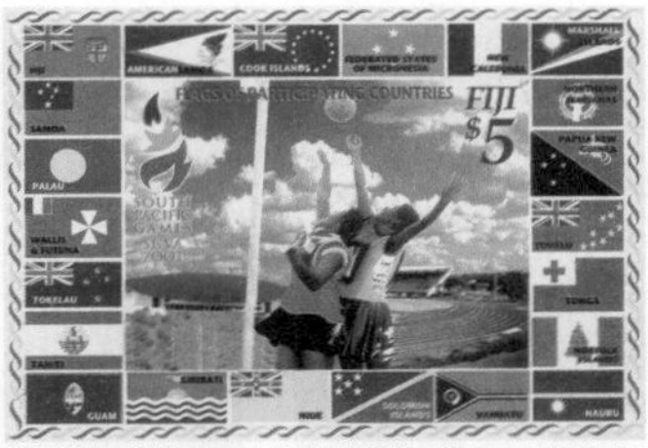

310 Netball Players, National Stadium and Multi-Purpose Sports Complex

2003. South Pacific Games, Fiji (2nd issue). Sheet 120 × 85 mm. Imperf.

MS1195	**310** $5 multicoloured	3·25	3·50

311 Uspi Rabbitfish

2003. Uspi Rabbitfish. Multicoloured.

1196	58c. Type **311**	30	35
1197	83c. Two rabbitfish	55	60
1198	$1.15 Rabbitfish, coral and moorish idols	65	70
1199	$3 Rabbitfish feeding on algae	1·90	2·00

312 Long-legged Warbler

2003. Bird Life International. Fiji's Rarest Land Birds. Multicoloured.

1200	41c. Type **312**	30	35
1201	60c. Silktail	40	45
1202	$1.07 Red-throated lorikeet	60	65
1203	$3 Pink-billed parrot finch	1·90	2·00

313 Pacific Slender-toed Gecko

2003. Geckos. Multicoloured.

1204	83c. Type **313**	55	60
1205	$1.07 Indopacific tree gecko	65	70
1206	$1.15 Mann's gecko	65	70
1207	$2 Voracious gecko	1·00	1·10

314 Christmas Tree and Children (Shalini Amrita Nand)

2003. Christmas. Showing winning entries from Christmas "United Fiji for all" stamp design competition. Multicoloured.

1208	18c. Type **314**	15	20
1209	41c. Children with Fiji flag (Kelerayani Gavidi)	40	35
1210	58c. Santa and children in reindeer-drawn sleighs (Ronald Patrick) (vert)	35	40
1211	83c. Christmas presents and Santa on chimney (Cadillac Graphics) (vert)	55	60
1212	$1.07 Children with candles and Christmas tree (Shuetal Shamlee) (vert)	65	70
1213	$1.15 Santa with children (Roselyn Roshika) (vert)	65	70
MS1214	100 × 75 mm. $1.41 Handshake and cross (Viliame Vosabeci)	85	90

POSTAGE DUE STAMPS

D 1 D 3

1917.

D5a	D 1	½d. black	£475	£275
D2		1d. black	£350	85·00
D3		2d. black	£300	70·00
D4		3d. black	£350	80·00
D5		4d. black	£800	£400

1918.

D 6	D 3	½d. black	3·00	20·00
D 7		1d. black	3·50	5·00
D 8		2d. black	3·25	7·50
D 9		3d. black	3·25	48·00
D10		4d. black	6·00	27·00

D 4

1940.

D11	D 4	1d. green	7·00	60·00
D12		2d. green	9·00	60·00
D13		3d. green	13·00	65·00
D14		4d. green	15·00	70·00
D15		5d. green	17·00	70·00
D16		6d. green	19·00	75·00
D17		1s. red	22·00	£100
D18		1s.6d. red	23·00	£150

FINLAND Pt. 11

A country to the east of Scandinavia. A Russian Grand-Duchy until 1917, then a Republic.

1856. 100 kopeks = 1 rouble.
1865. 100 pennia = 1 markka.
2002. 100 cents = 1 euro.

1 2

1856. Imperf.

1	1	5k. blue	£4750	£800
2		10k. pink	£6000	£275

Used prices are for stamps with penmark cancellation only. Stamps with postmark as well are worth more.

1860. Values in "KOP". Roul.

10	2	5k. blue on blue	£475	£120
13		10k. pink on pink	£450	50·00

1866. As T **2**, but values in "PEN" and "MARK". Roul.

19	2	5p. brown on grey	£250	£140
46		8p. black on green	£180	£120
31		10p. black on buff	£550	£250
36		20p. blue on blue	£425	50·00
40		40p. pink on lilac	£375	50·00
49		1m. brown	£1500	£600

5 6

1875. Perf.

81	5	2p. grey	12·00	9·50
82		5p. yellow	50·00	4·50
83		5p. red	50·00	9·50
97		5p. green	13·00	40
71		8p. green	£150	47·00
85		10p. brown	75·00	15·00
99		10p. pink	21·00	2·00
87		20p. blue	55·00	1·30
102		20p. orange	28·00	30
89		25p. red	£250	17·00
103		25p. blue	41·00	1·60
79		32p. red	£225	26·00
90		1m. mauve	£250	31·00
105		1m. grey and pink	28·00	14·00
106		5m. green and pink	£350	£275
107		10m. brown and pink	£450	£450

1889.

108	6	2p. grey	65	50
148		5p. green	75	20
149		10p. red	90	25
150		20p. yellow	90	25
151		25p. blue	90	30
119		1m. grey and pink	3·00	2·50
120a		5m. green and red	26·00	36·00
122		10m. brown and red	36·00	65·00

7 8 9

10 11

1891. Similar to Russian types, but with circles added in designs.

133	7	1k. yellow	4·25	7·25
134		2k. green	5·50	6·75
135		3k. pink	9·75	11·00
136	8	4k. pink	13·50	10·50
137	7	7k. blue	7·25	1·30
138	8	10k. blue	14·00	9·50
139	9	14k. red and blue	20·00	18·00
140	8	20k. red and blue	17·00	12·50
141	9	35k. green and purple	22·00	31·00
142	8	50k. green and purple	30·00	24·00
143	10	1r. orange and brown	90·00	65·00
144	11	3½r. grey and black	£300	£300
145		7r. yellow and black	£250	£160

12 13

14 15

1901. Similar to Russian types, but value in Finnish currency.

161	12	2p. orange	55	75
162b		5p. green	1·50	30

169a 13 10p. red 35 25
170 12 20p. blue 35 25
165a 14 1m. green and purple . . 75 25
166 15 10m. grey and black . . . £130 38·00

16 17 18

1911.

176 16 2p. orange 30 30
177 5p. green 35 15
180 17 10p. red 45 20
181 16 20p. blue 30 15
182 18 40p. blue and purple . . 25 20

19 20 23

1917.

187a 19 5p. green 20 20
188 5p. grey 20 20
189 10p. red 25 20
190 10p. green . . . . 1·60 35
191a 10p. blue 30 20
192 20p. orange 25 20
193 20p. red 45 20
194 20p. brown 80 40
195 25p. blue 30 20
196 25p. brown 20 20
234 30p. green 35 30
198a 40p. purple 25 20
246 40p. green 25 90
200 50p. brown 45 30
201 50p. blue . . . . 4·00 25
247 50p. green 25 45
237 60p. purple 45 30
204 75p. yellow 25 35
205 1m. black and pink . . . 12·00 20
248 1m. orange 25 35
207 1½m. purple and green . . 20 30
208a 2m. black and green . . . 3·50 45
250 2m. blue 25 35
251 3m. black and blue . . . 25 30
242 5m. black and purple . . 40 20
212 10m. black and bistre . . 95 80
213 25m. orange and red . . . 55 15·00

1918. With white circle round figure of value.
214 20 5p. green 30 55
215 10p. pink 30 55
216 30p. grey . . . . 75 1·50
217 40p. lilac 35 50
218 50p. brown . . . . 50 1·70
219 70p. brown . . . . 2·00 10·50
220 1m. black and red 40 80
221 5m. black and lilac . . . . 47·00 55·00

1919. Surch with new figure of value three times.
222 19 10 on 5p. green 25 30
223 20 on 10p. red 30 25
224 50 on 25p. blue 90 30
225 75 on 20p. orange 25 25

1921. Surch with value, **P** and bars.
226 19 30p. on 10p. green 75 25
227 60p. on 40p. purple . . . . 2·75 40
228 90p. on 20p. red 25 25
229 1½m. on 50p. blue . . . . . 1·60 20

1922. Red Cross.
230 23 1m.+50p. red and grey . . 80 6·75

26 28 Freighter "Bore" leaving Turku (Abo)

1927. 10th Anniv of Independence.
255 26 1½m. mauve 15 30
256 2m. blue . . . . 20 1·10

1928. Philatelic Exhibition. Optd **Postim. naytt. 1928 Frim. utstalln.**
258 19 1m. orange . . . . 6·50 10·50
259 1½m. purple and green . . 7·25 10·50

1929. 700th Anniv of Abo.
260 28 1m. olive . . . . 1·80 3·25
261 – 1½m. brown . . . . 2·00 2·20
262 – 2m. grey . . . . 55 3·50
DESIGNS—VERT: 1½m. Cathedral. HORIZ: 2m. Castle.

31 32 Olavinlinna

1930.

263 31 5p. brown 20 20
264 10p. lilac 20 20
265 20p. green 55 30
266 25p. brown 20 15
267 40p. green . . . . 2·75 15
268 50p. yellow 70 30
268a 50p. green 20 15
269 60p. grey 55 35
371 75p. orange 35 35
270 1m. orange 75 25
372 1m. green 25 20
271 1m.20 red 45 55
271a 1m.25 yellow 30 25
272 1½m. mauve . . . . 3·25 15
272a 1½m. red 30 25
272b 1½m. grey 25 15
272c 1m.75 yellow 50 30
273 2m. blue 35 20
273a 2m. mauve . . . . 6·50 15
273b 2m. red 30 15
373 2m. orange 25 20
373a 2m. green 35 20
273c 2½m. blue . . . . 2·50 20
374 2½m. red 20 15
425 2½m. green 35 20
273d 2m.75 purple 15 15
427 3m. green . . . . 1·60 20
375 3m. red 40 20
375a 3m. yellow 45 50
426 3m. grey 45 40
274a 3½m. blue . . . . 8·00 20
376 3½m. green 20 15
377 4m. green 50 15
378 4½m. blue 25 20
275 32 5m. blue 35 20
379 31 5m. blue 75 15
379a 5m. violet 75 25
379b 5m. yellow 80 15
379c 6m. red 60 20
429 6m. green 75 40
430 7m. red 45 20
379d 8m. violet 30 15
431 8m. green . . . . 85 1·30
432 9m. red 85 25
433 9m. orange . . . . 1·10 25
276b – 10m. lilac 85 25
379e 31 10m. blue . . . . 1·10 20
434 10m. violet . . . . 1·40 20
435 10m. brown . . . . 3·25 20
436 10m. green . . . . 1·70 20
437 12m. blue . . . . 1·70 20
438 12m. red 65 20
410 32 15m. purple . . . . 1·00 20
439 31 15m. blue . . . . 3·00 20
440 15m. purple . . . . 8·50 20
441 15m. red . . . . 2·40 20
442 20m. blue . . . . 3·50 20
443 24m. purple 95 30
277 – 25m. brown . . . . 2·30 30
444 31 25m. blue . . . . 2·75 20
445 32 35m. violet . . . . 4·25 25
445a – 40m. brown . . . . 3·25 25
DESIGNS—As Type **32**: 10m. Lake Saimaa; 25, 40m. Wood-cutter.

35

1930. Red Cross Fund.
278 35 1m.+10p. red & orange . . 1·10 7·25
279 – 1½m.+15p. red & green . . 75 5·50
280 – 2m.+20p. red and blue . . 1·70 27·00
DESIGNS: 1½m. Drapery; 2m. Viking longship.

1930. Air. No. 276b optd **ZEPPELIN 1930.**
281 10m. lilac . . . . 90·00 £110

39 Church at Hattula 40 Elias Lonnrot

1931. Red Cross Fund.
282 39 1m.+10p. green & red . . 1·50 5·75
283 – 1½m.+15p. brown & red . . 4·75 9·50
284 – 2m.+20p. blue & red . . . 95 12·50
DESIGNS: 1½m. Hameen Castle; 2m. Viipuri Castle.

1931. Finnish Literary Society's Centenary.
285 40 1m. brown . . . . 4·00 3·00
286 – 1½m. blue . . . . 10·50 3·75
DESIGN—HORIZ: 1½m. Society's seal with inscr as T **40**.

42

1931. 75th Anniv of First Finnish Postage Stamps.
287 42 1½m. red . . . . 2·50 4·25
288 2m. blue . . . . 2·50 4·25

43 45

1931. Granberg Collection Fund.
289 43 1m.+4m. black . . . . . . 14·50 30·00

1931. Surch.
290 31 50PEN. on 40p. green . . 1·00 30
291 1,25 MK. on 50p. yellow . . 3·50 1·00

1931. President Svinhufvud's 70th Birthday.
292 45 2m. black and blue . . . . 1·80 1·80

47 St. Nicholas Cathedral 48 Magnus Tawast

1932. Red Cross Fund.
293 – 1½m.+10p. bistre & red . . 1·20 11·00
294 47 2m.+20p. purple & red . . 65 5·50
295 – 2½m.+25p. blue & red . . 80 18·00
DESIGNS—HORIZ: 1½m. University Library, Helsinki; 2½m. Houses of Parliament.

1933. Red Cross Fund.
296 48 1½m.+10p. brown & red . . 4·00 7·50
297 – 2m.+20p. purple & red . . 70 2·00
298 – 2½m.+25p. blue & red . . 90 3·50
DESIGNS: 2m. Michael Agricola; 2½m. Isacus Rothovius.

51 Evert Horn 52 Aleksis Kivi, after medallion by V. Aaltonen

1934. Red Cross Fund.
299 51 1½m.+10p. brown & red . . 50 1·90
300 – 2m.+20p. mauve & red . . 1·90 4·25
301 – 2½m.+25p. blue & red . . 65 2·75
DESIGNS: 2m. Torsten Stalhandske; 2½m. Jacob de la Gardie ("Lazy Jack").

1934. Birth Centenary of Kivi (poet).
302 52 2m. purple . . . . 2·20 2·50

53 Calonius 54 Finnish Bards

1935. Red Cross Fund. Cross in red.
303 53 1½m.+15p. brown . . . . 50 1·50
304 – 2m.+20p. mauve . . . . . 1·20 4·25
305 – 2½m.+25p. blue . . . . . 70 1·30
PORTRAITS: 2m. H. G. Porthan. 2½m. A. Chydenius.

1935. Centenary of Publication of "Kalevala" (Finnish National Poems).
306 54 1½m. red . . . . 1·20 1·30
307 – 2m. brown . . . . 3·00 85
308 – 2½m. blue . . . . 3·00 1·20
DESIGNS: 2m. Louhi's failure to recover the "Sampo"; 2½m. Kullervo's departure to war.

57 R. H. Rehbinder 58 "Lodbrok", 1771 60 Marshal Mannerheim

1936. Red Cross Fund. Cross in red.
309 57 1½m.+15p. brown . . . . 50 2·10
310 – 2m.+20p. purple . . . . . 2·00 4·75
311 – 2½m.+25p. blue . . . . . 50 2·10
PORTRAITS: 2m. G. M. Armfeldt. 2½m. Arvid Horn.

1937. Red Cross Fund. Warships. Cross in red.
312 – 1½m.+15p. brown . . . . 90 1·60
313 58 2m.+20p. red . . . . . . 12·00 3·25
314 – 3½m.+35p. blue . . . . . 1·20 2·10
DESIGNS—HORIZ: 1½m. "Thorborg" (inscr "Uusiman"); 3½m. "Styrbjorn" (inscr "Hameenmaa").

1937. Surch **2 MARKKAA.**
315 31 2m. on 1½m. red . . . . . 4·50 50

1937. Marshal Mannerheim's 70th Birthday.
316 60 2m. blue 55 70

61 A. Makipeska 62 Cross-country Skiing 63 War Veteran

1938. Red Cross Fund. Cross in red.
317 61 50p.+5p. green . . . . . . 25 1·20
318 – 1½m.+15p. brown . . . . 50 1·70
319 – 2m.+20p. red . . . . . . 5·00 5·50
320 – 3½m.+35p. blue . . . . . 40 2·40
PORTRAITS: 1½m. R. I. Orn. 2m. E. Bergenheim, 3½m. J. M. Nordenstam.

1938. International Skiing Contest, Lahti.
321 62 1m.25+75p. black . . . . 2·30 7·25
322 – 2m.+1m. red . . . . 2·50 6·75
323 – 3m.50+1m.50 blue and light blue . . . . . . 2·50 6·75
DESIGNS: 2m. Ski jumping; 3m.50, Downhill skiing contest.

1938. Disabled Soldiers' Relief Fund. 20th Anniv of Independence.
324 63 2m.+½m. blue . . . . . . 1·80 2·75

64 Colonizers felling Trees 65 Ahvenkoski P.O., 1787

1938. Tercentenary of Scandinavian Settlement in America.
325 64 3½m. brown . . . . 1·10 1·70

1938. Tercentenary of Finnish Postal Service.
326 65 50p. green 25 60
327 – 1½m. blue . . . . 1·10 2·10
328 – 2m. red . . . . 1·10 65
329 – 3½m. grey . . . . 3·50 5·00
DESIGNS: 1½m. Sledge-boat; 2m. Junkers Ju 52/3m mail plane; 3½m. G.P.O., Helsinki.

66 Battlefield of Solferino 67 G.P.O., Helsinki

1939. Red Cross Fund and 75th Anniv of International Red Cross. Cross in red.
330 66 50p.+5p. green . . . . . 60 1·50
331 1½m.+15p. brown . . . . 90 2·20
332 2m.+20p. red . . . . . . 8·25 9·50
333 3½m.+35p. blue . . . . . 60 2·30

1939.
334 67 4m. brown 30 25
See also Nos. 382/4.

68 Crossbowman

69 Lion of Finland

1940. Red Cross Fund. Cross in red.
335 **68** 50p.+5p. green . . . . . . 50 1·50
336 – 1½m.+15p. brown . . . . 50 2·20
337 – 2m.+20p. red . . . . . 85 2·20
338 – 3½m.+35p. blue . . . . . 80 3·25
DESIGNS: 1½m. Mounted cavalrymen; 2m. Unmounted cavalrymen; 3½m. Officer and infantryman.

1940. National Defence Fund.
339 **69** 2m.+2m. blue . . . . . . 25 1·00

70 Helsinki University

72 Builder

1940. 300th Anniv of Founding of Helsinki University.
340 **70** 2m. deep blue and blue . . 35 80

1940. Surch.
341 **31** 1m.75 on 1m.25 yellow . . 1·10 1·40
342 2m.75 on 2m. red . . . . 3·00 35

1941. Red Cross Fund. Cross in red.
343 **72** 50p.+5p. green 25 60
344 – 1m.75+15p. sepia . . . . 65 1·30
345 – 2m.75+25p. brown . . . . 3·00 7·25
346 – 3m.50+35p. blue . . . . . 70 2·10
DESIGNS: 1m.75, Farmer; 2m.75, Mother and child; 3m.50, Flag.
See also Nos. 405/8.

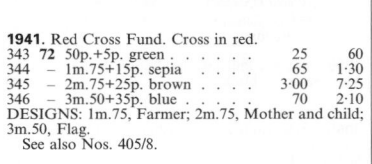

73 Farewell Review

74 Knight

1941. President Kallio Memorial.
347 **73** 2m.75 black 35 65

1941. "Brothers-in-Arms" Welfare Fund.
348 **74** 2m.75+25p. blue 35 85

75 Viipuri Castle

1941. Reconquest of Viipuri.
349 **75** 1m.75 orange 30 85
350 2m.75 purple 25 60
351 3m.50 blue . . . . . . 65 1·30

76 Pres. Risto Ryti

77 Marshal Mannerheim

1941. (a) President Ryti.
352 **76** 50p. green 40 90
353 1m.75 brown . . . . . . 50 1·10
354 2m. red . . . . 40 1·10
355 2m.75 violet . . . . . . 55 1·10
356 3m.50 blue . . . . . . 45 1·10
357 5m. grey . . . . 45 1·10
(b) Marshal Mannerheim.
358 **77** 50p. green 40 80
359 1m.75 brown . . . . . . 40 1·20
360 2m. red . . . . 40 1·20
361 2m.75 violet . . . . . . 60 1·20
362 3m.50 blue . . . . . . 60 1·20
363 5m. grey . . . . 60 1·20

79 Aland

80 Tampere

1942. Red Cross Fund. Cross in red.
364 **79** 50p.+5p. green . . . . . . 25 1·20
365 – 1m.75+15p. brown . . . . 65 2·30
366 – 2m.75+25p. red . . . . . 95 2·30
367 – 3m.50+35p. blue . . . . . 65 2·30
368 – 4m.75+45p. grey . . . . . 45 2·30
ARMS: 1m.75, Uusimaa (Nyland); 2m.75, Finland Proper; 3m.50, Karelia; 4m.75, Satakunta.

1942.
369 **80** 50m. violet . . . . 1·20 20
370 – 100m. blue . . . . 1·70 20
DESIGN: 100m. Helsinki Harbour.
For 100m. in green without "mk" see No. 557b.

81 New Testament

82 Mediaeval Press

83 Lapland

1942. Tercentenary of Introduction of Printing into Finland.
380 **81** 2m.75 brown 25 75
381 **82** 3m.50 blue . . . . 40 1·30

1942.
382 **67** 7m. brown 40 20
383 9m. mauve 45 20
384 20m. brown 80 15

1943. Red Cross Fund. Cross in red.
385 **83** 50p.+5p. green 20 70
386 – 2m.+20p. brown . . . . . 40 1·90
387 – 3m.50+35p. red . . . . . 40 1·90
388 – 4m.50+45p. blue . . . . . 1·40 4·25
ARMS: 2m. Hame (Tavastland); 3m.50, Pohjanmaa (Osterbotten); 4m.50, Savo (Savolaks).

1943. Surch **3½mk.**
389 **31** 3½m. on 2m.75 purple . . 20 20

85 Military Tokens

1943. National Relief Fund.
390 **85** 2m.+50p. brown 25 60
391 – 3m.50+1m. purple 25 80
DESIGN—VERT: 3m.50, Widow and Orphans.

87 Red Cross Train

1944. Red Cross Fund. Inscr "1944". Cross in red.
392 **87** 50p.+25p. green 25 35
393 – 2m.+50p. violet 20 70
394 – 3m.50+75p. red 20 70
395 – 4m.50+1m. blue . . . . . 50 2·50
DESIGNS: 2m. Ambulance; 3m.50, Hospital, Helsinki; 4m.50, Airplane.

88 Minna Canth

89 Douglas DC-2 Mail Plane

1944. Birth Cent of Minna Canth (authoress).
396 **88** 3m.50 green 30 65

1944. Air. 20th Anniv of Air Mail Service.
397 **89** 3m.50 brown 30 70

90 Pres. Svinhufvud

91

92 Wrestling

1944. Mourning for Pres. P. E. Svinhufvud.
398 **90** 3½m. black 30 65

1944. National Relief Fund.
399 **91** 3m.50+1m.50 brown . . . 30 70

1945. Sports Fund.
400 **92** 1m.+50p. green 15 55
401 – 2m.+1m. red 15 55
402 – 3m.50+1m.75 violet . . . 15 65
403 – 4m.50+2m.25 blue 15 55
404 – 7m.+3m.50 brown . . . . 45 1·60
DESIGNS: 2m. Vaulting; 3m.50, Running; 4m.50, Skiing; 7m. Throwing the javelin.

1945. Red Cross Fund. As Nos. 343/6, but dated "1945". Cross in red.
405 1m.+25p. green 15 40
406 2m.+50p. brown 15 50
407 3m.50+75p. brown 15 50
408 4m.50+1m. blue . . . . . . 45 1·00
DESIGNS: 1m. Builder; 2m. Farmer; 3m.50, Mother and child; 4m.50, Flag.

93 Pres. Stahlberg

94 Sibelius

95 Fishermen

1945. 80th Birth Anniv of Pres. K. J. Stahlberg.
409 **93** 3m.50 violet 35 45

1945. 80th Birthday of Sibelius (composer).
411 **94** 5m. green 25 25

1946. Red Cross Fund. Cross in red.
412 **95** 1m.+25p. green 20 35
413 – 3m.+75p. purple 20 35
414 – 5m.+1m.25 red 20 35
415 – 10m.+2m.50 blue 20 50
DESIGNS: 3m. Butter-making; 5m. Harvesting; 10m. Logging.

1946. Surch with bold figures and bars.
416 **31** 8m. on 5m. violet 30 25
416a 12m. on 10m. violet . . . 75 25

97 Athletes

98 Nurse and Children

99 Uto Lighthouse, and Sailing Ship

1946. National Games.
417 **97** 8m. purple 35 50

1946. Anti-tuberculosis Fund.
418 **98** 5m.+1m. green 25 45
419 – 8m.+2m. purple 25 45
DESIGN: 8m. Lady doctor examining child.

1946. 250th Anniv of Foundation of Pilotage Institution.
420 **99** 8m. violet 35 45

100 Postal Motor Coach

101 Town Hall

1946.
421 **100** 16m. black 45 70
421a 30m. black . . . . . . 1·50 25

1946. 600th Anniv of Founding of Porvoo (Borga).
422 **101** 5m. black 25 35
423 – 8m. purple 25 35
DESIGN—VERT: 8m. Bridge and church.

103 Tammisaari

104 Pres. Paasikivi

1946. 400th Anniv of Tammisaari (Ekenas).
424 **103** 8m. green 35 40

1947.
446 **104** 10m. black 35 35

1947. Anti-tuberculosis Fund. Nos. 418/19 surch.
447 **98** 6+1 on 5m.+1m. grn . . . 30 65
448 – 10+2 on 8m.+2m. pur . . 30 65

106 Bank Emblem

107 Athletes

1947. 60th Anniv of Finnish Postal Savings Bank.
449 **106** 10m. purple 35 40

1947. National Sports Festival.
450 **107** 10m. blue 35 40

108 Ilmarinen Ploughing

109 Emblem of Savings Bank Association

1947. Conclusion of Peace Treaty.
451 **108** 10m. black 35 40

1947. 125th Anniv of Savings Bank Assn.
452 **109** 10m. brown 35 50

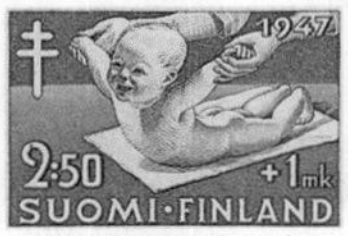
110 Physical Exercise

111 Sower

1947. Anti-tuberculosis Fund.
453 **110** 2m.50+1m. green 35 95
454 – 6m.+1m.50 red . . . . . 35 1·00
455 – 10m.+2m.50 brown . . . 35 1·00
456 – 12m.+3m. blue . . . . . 50 1·50
457 – 20m.+5m. mauve . . . . 50 1·90
DESIGNS—VERT: 6, 10, 20m. Various infant exercises. HORIZ: 12m. Mme. Paasikivi and child.

1947. 150th Anniv of Central League of Agricultural Societies.
458 **111** 10m. grey 35 40

112 Heights of Koli

113 Z. Topelius

1947. 60th Anniv of Tourist Society.
459 **112** 10m. blue 35 40

1948. Red Cross Fund. Dated "1948". Cross in red.
460 **113** 3m.+1m. green 25 50
461 – 7m.+2m. red 35 95
462 – 12m.+3m. blue . . . . . 35 1·00
463 – 20m.+5m. violet . . . . 40 1·30
PORTRAITS: 7m. Fr. Pacius; 12m. J. L. Runeberg; 20m. F. R. Cygnaeus.

1948. Anti-tuberculosis Fund. Nos. 454/5 and 457 surch.
464 7m.+2m. on 6m.+1m.50 red 65 1·70
465 15m.+3m. on 10m.+2m.50 brown . . . . 85 1·70
466 24m.+6m. on 20m.+5m. mauve . . . . 1·20 3·00

115 Michael Agricola (after sculpture by C. Sjostrand)

116 King's Gate, Suomenlinna

1948. 400th Anniv of Translation of New Testament into Finnish by Michael Agricola.
467 **115** 7m. purple . . . . 75 1·20
468 – 12m. blue . . . . 75 1·30
DESIGN: 12m. Agricola translating New Testament (after painting by A. Edelfelt).

1948. Bicentenary of Suomenlinna (Sveaborg).
469 **116** 12m. green . . . . 1·00 1·60

117 Finnish Mail-carrier's Badge

118 Girl Bundling Twigs

119 Anemone

1948. Helsinki Philatelic Exhibition.
470 **117** 12m. green . . . . 4·50 9·50
Sold only at the Exhibition, at 62m. (including 50m. entrance fee).

1949. Red Cross Fund. Inscr "SAUNA BASTU 1949". Cross in red.
471 **118** 5m.+2m. green 40 55
472 – 9m.+3m. red 40 85
473 – 15m.+5m. blue 55 75
474 – 30m.+10m. brown . . . . 40 2·30
DESIGNS: 9m. Bathing scene; 15m. Heating sauna in winter; 30m. Bathers leaving sauna for plunge in lake.

1949. Tuberculosis Relief Fund.
475 **119** 5m.+2m. green 45 55
476 – 9m.+3m. red 45 80
477 – 15m.+5m. brown 65 80
DESIGNS: 9m. Rose; 15m. Coltsfoot.

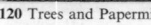

120 Trees and Papermill

121 Girl with Torch

1949. 3rd World Forestry Congress. Inscr "IIIE CONGRES FORESTIER MONDIAL 1949".
478 **120** 9m. brown . . . . 1·40 2·40
479 – 15m. green (Tree and Globe) . . . . 1·40 2·30

1949. 50th Anniv of Labour Movement.
480 **121** 5m. green . . . . 3·00 8·25
481 – 15m. red (Man with mallet) . . . . 3·00 8·25

122 Kristiinankaupunki

123 "Salmetar" (lake steamer), Lappeenranta

1949. Tercent of Kristiinankaupunki (Kristinestad).
482 **122** 15m. blue . . . . 1·10 2·10

1949. Tercent of Lappeenranta (Villmanstrand).
483 **123** 5m. green 75 65

124 Church, Raahe

125 Seal of Technical High School

126 Hannes Gebhard (founder)

1949. Tercentenary of Raahe (Brahestad).
484 **124** 9m. purple 80 95

1949. Cent of Technical High School, Helsinki.
485 **125** 15m. blue 90 90

1949. 50th Anniv of Finnish Co-operative Movement.
486 **126** 15m. green 85 70

127

128 Douglas DC-6

129 White Water-lily

1949. 75th Anniv of U.P.U.
487 **127** 15m. blue . . . . 85 1·10

1950. Air.
488 **128** 300m. blue . . . . 7·25 4·75
For 300m. stamp without "mk" see No. 585 and for 3m. stamp see No. 679.

1950. Tuberculosis Relief Fund.
489 **129** 5m.+2m. green . . . . . 1·20 1·50
490 – 9m.+3m. mauve . . . . . 95 1·40
491 – 15m.+5m. blue . . . . . 95 1·40
DESIGNS: 9m. Pasque flower; 15m. Clustered bellflower.

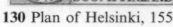

130 Plan of Helsinki, 1550

131 President Paasikivi

1950. 400th Anniv of Helsinki.
492 **130** 5m. green 25 50
493 – 9m. brown . . . . 40 1·00
494 – 15m. blue 40 65
DESIGNS: 9m. J. A. Ehrenstrom and C. L. Engel; 15m. Town Hall and Cathedral.

1950. President's 80th Birthday.
495 **131** 20m. blue 45 35

132 Hospital, Helsinki

133 Town Hall

134 Western Capercaillie

1951. Red Cross Fund. Cross in red.
496 **132** 7m.+2m. brown 55 80
497 – 12m.+3m. violet 55 85
498 – 20m.+5m. red . . . . . 75 1·50
DESIGNS: 12m. Blood donor and nurse; 20m. Blood donor's badge.

1951. 300th Anniv of Kajaani (Kajana).
499 **133** 20m. brown 45 55

1951. Tuberculosis Relief Fund.
500 **134** 7m.+2m. green . . . . . 1·40 2·20
501 – 12m.+3m. lake . . . . . 1·40 2·20
502 – 20m.+5m. blue . . . . . 1·40 2·20
DESIGNS: 12m. Common Cranes; 20m. Caspian Terns.

135 Diving

138 Marshal Mannerheim

139 Arms of Pietarsaari

1951. 15th Olympic Games, Helsinki.
503 **135** 12m.+2m. red . . . . . . 45 1·00
504 – 15m.+2m. green . . . . . 45 1·00
505 – 20m.+3m. blue . . . . . 1·10 1·10
506 – 25m.+4m. brown . . . . 1·40 1·50
DESIGNS—HORIZ: 15m. Football; 25m. Running. VERT: 20m. Olympic stadium.

1952. Red Cross Fund. Cross in red.
507 **138** 10m.+2m. black . . . . . 75 1·40
508 15m.+3m. purple . . . . 75 1·60
509 25m.+5m. blue . . . . . 75 1·40

1952. 300th Anniv of Founding of Pietarsaari (Jakobstad).
510 **139** 25m. blue 55 70

140 Vaasa

141 Knight, Rook and Chessboard

142 Great Tit

1952. Centenary of Fire of Vaasa (Vasa).
511 **140** 25m. brown 55 75

1952. 10th Chess Olympiad, Helsinki.
512 **141** 25m. black . . . . 1·20 1·80

1952. Tuberculosis Relief Fund. Birds.
513 **142** 10m.+2m. green . . . . . 1·60 1·90
514 – 15m.+3m. red . . . . . 1·60 1·90
515 – 25m.+5m. blue . . . . . 1·60 1·90
BIRDS: 15m. Spotted Flycatchers; 25m. Eurasian Swifts.

143 "Flame of Temperance"

144 Aerial view of Hamina

1953. Cent of Finnish Temperance Movement.
516 **143** 25m. blue 65 80

1953. 300th Anniv of Hamina (Fredrikshamn).
517 **144** 25m. slate 55 75

145 Eurasian Red Squirrel

1953. Tuberculosis Relief Fund.
518 **145** 10m.+2m. brown . . . . 1·80 2·20
519 – 15m.+3m. violet . . . . 1·80 2·20
520 – 25m.+5m. green . . . . 1·80 2·20
DESIGNS: 15m. Brown bear; 25m. Elk.

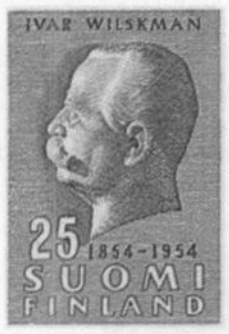

146 Wilskman

147 Mother and Children

1954. Birth Centenary of Ivar Wilskman (gymnast).
521 **146** 25m. blue 55 75

1954. Red Cross Fund. Cross in red.
522 **147** 10m.+2m. green . . . . . 55 1·10
523 – 15m.+3m. blue . . . . . 75 1·00
524 – 25m.+5m. brown . . . . 75 1·00
DESIGNS: 15m. Old lady knitting; 25m. Blind man and dog.

148

149 "In the Outer Archipelago" (after Edelfelt)

1954.
525 **148** 1m. brown 30 30
526 2m. green 30 20
527 3m. orange 25 20
527a 4m. grey 35 30
528 5m. blue 45 20
529 10m. green 55 25
530 15m. red . . . . 2·40 20
530a 15m. orange . . . . . . 4·00 20
531 20m. purple . . . . . . 6·00 25
531a 20m. red . . . . 1·10 20
532 25m. blue . . . . 2·20 20
532a 25m. purple . . . . . . 6·25 20
532b 30m. blue . . . . 1·30 20
See also Nos. 647, etc.

1954. Birth Centenary of A. Edelfelt (painter).
533 **149** 25m. black 55 65

150 White-tailed Bumble Bees collecting Pollen

151 J. J. Nervander

1954. Tuberculosis Relief Fund. Cross in red.
534 **150** 10m.+2m. brown . . . . 1·20 1·10
535 – 15m.+3m. red . . . . . 1·40 1·40
536 – 25m.+5m. blue . . . . . 1·50 1·40
DESIGNS: 15m. Apollo (butterfly) and wild rose; 25m. "Aeshna juncea" (dragonfly).

1955. 150th Birth Anniv of Nervander (astronomer and poet).
537 **151** 25m. blue 65 80

152 Parliament Building

153 St. Henry

1955. National Philatelic Exhibition, Helsinki.
538 **152** 25m. black . . . . 5·75 10·00

1955. 800th Anniv of Establishment of Christianity in Finland.
539 **153** 15m. purple 55 60
540 – 25m. green 55 65
DESIGN: 25m. Arrival of Christian preachers in 1155.

154 Conference in Session

155 Barque "Ilma" and Cargo

1955. Interparliamentary Conference, Helsinki.
541 **154** 25m. green . . . . 75 1·10

1955. 350th Anniv of Oulu (Uleaborg).
542 **155** 25m. brown . . . . . . 1·00 1·10

156 Eurasian Perch

157 Town Hall, Lahti

1955. Tuberculosis Relief Fund. Cross in red.
543 **156** 10m.+2m. green . . . . . 1·00 1·10
544 – 15m.+3m. brown (Northern pike) . . . . 1·30 1·20
545 – 25m.+5m. blue (Atlantic salmon) . . . . 1·30 1·20

1955. 50th Anniv of Lahti.
546 **157** 25m. blue . . . . 75 1·30

158 J. Z. Duncker

159 "Telegraphs"

1955. Red Cross. Cross in red.
547 – 10m.+2m. blue 45 90
548 **158** 15m.+3m. brown . . . . 65 1·10
549 – 25m.+5m. green . . . . . 65 1·10

DESIGNS: 10m. Von Dobeln on horseback; 25m. Young soldier.

1955. Centenary of Telegraphs in Finland. Inscr "1855–1955 Telegrafen".
550 **159** 10m. green 90 95
551 – 15m. violet 75 80
552 – 25m. blue . . . . 75 1·20
DESIGNS: 15m. Otto Nyberg; 25m. Telegraph pole.

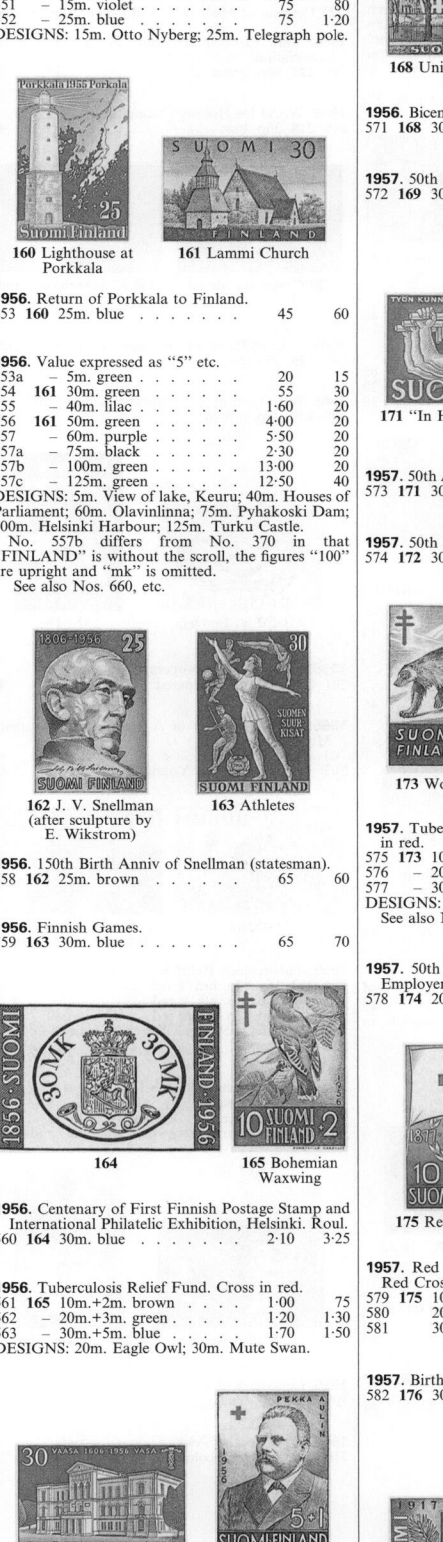

160 Lighthouse at Porkkala **161** Lammi Church

1956. Return of Porkkala to Finland.
553 **160** 25m. blue 45 60

1956. Value expressed as "5" etc.
553a – 5m. green 20 15
554 **161** 30m. green 55 30
555 – 40m. lilac . . . . 1·60 20
556 **161** 50m. green . . . . . . 4·00 20
557 – 60m. purple . . . . . . 5·50 20
557a – 75m. black . . . . . . 2·30 20
557b – 100m. green . . . . . . 13·00 20
557c – 125m. green . . . . . . 12·50 40
DESIGNS: 5m. View of lake, Keuru; 40m. Houses of Parliament; 60m. Olavinlinna; 75m. Pyhakoski Dam; 100m. Helsinki Harbour; 125m. Turku Castle.
No. 557b differs from No. 370 in that "FINLAND" is without the scroll, the figures "100" are upright and "mk" is omitted.
See also Nos. 660, etc.

162 J. V. Snellman (after sculpture by E. Wikstrom) **163** Athletes

1956. 150th Birth Anniv of Snellman (statesman).
558 **162** 25m. brown 65 60

1956. Finnish Games.
559 **163** 30m. blue 65 70

164 **165** Bohemian Waxwing

1956. Centenary of First Finnish Postage Stamp and International Philatelic Exhibition, Helsinki. Roul.
560 **164** 30m. blue . . . . 2·10 3·25

1956. Tuberculosis Relief Fund. Cross in red.
561 **165** 10m.+2m. brown . . . . 1·00 75
562 – 20m.+3m. green . . . . . 1·20 1·30
563 – 30m.+5m. blue . . . . . 1·70 1·50
DESIGNS: 20m. Eagle Owl; 30m. Mute Swan.

166 Vaasa Town Hall **167** P. Aulin

1956. 350th Anniv of Vaasa.
564 **166** 30m. blue 65 75

1956. Northern Countries' Day. As T **100** of Denmark.
565 20m. red . . . . 2·10 1·00
566 30m. blue . . . . 5·75 1·00

1956. Red Cross. Inscr "1956". Cross in red.
567 **167** 5m.+1m. green . . . . . 2·50 60
568 – 10m.+2m. brown . . . . 1·00 1·10
569 – 20m.+3m. red . . . . . 1·00 1·70
570 – 30m.+5m. blue . . . . . 1·00 1·30
PORTRAITS: 10m. L. von Pfaler; 20m. G. Johansson; 30m. V. M. von Born.

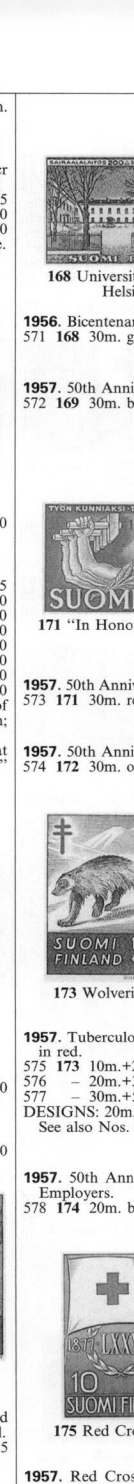

168 University Hospital, Helsinki **169** Scout Badge and Saluting Hand

1956. Bicentenary of National Health Service.
571 **168** 30m. green . . . . 1·00 70

1957. 50th Anniv of Boy Scout Movement.
572 **169** 30m. blue . . . . 1·20 95

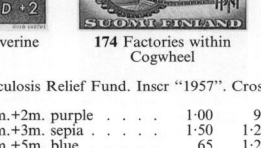

171 "In Honour of Work" **172** "Lex" (sculpture by W. Runeberg)

1957. 50th Anniv of Finnish Trade Union Movement.
573 **171** 30m. red 65 75

1957. 50th Anniv of Finnish Parliament.
574 **172** 30m. olive 95 80

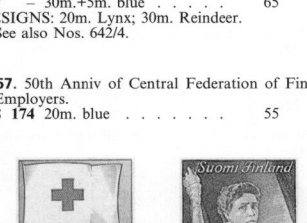

173 Wolverine **174** Factories within Cogwheel

1957. Tuberculosis Relief Fund. Inscr "1957". Cross in red.
575 **173** 10m.+2m. purple . . . . 1·00 90
576 – 20m.+3m. sepia . . . . . 1·50 1·20
577 – 30m.+5m. blue . . . . . 65 1·20
DESIGNS: 20m. Lynx; 30m. Reindeer.
See also Nos. 642/4.

1957. 50th Anniv of Central Federation of Finnish Employers.
578 **174** 20m. blue 55 60

175 Red Cross Flag **176** Ida Aalberg (after Edelfelt)

1957. Red Cross Fund and 80th Anniv of Finnish Red Cross. Cross in red.
579 **175** 10m.+2m. green . . . . . 1·00 1·70
580 20m.+3m. lake . . . . . 1·00 1·60
581 30m.+5m. blue . . . . . 1·00 1·60

1957. Birth Cent of Ida Aalberg (actress).
582 **176** 30m. maroon & purple . . 65 70

177 Arms of Finland **178** Bust of Sibelius (Waino Aaltonen)

1957. 40th Anniv of Independence.
583 **177** 30m. blue 65 75

1957. Death of Sibelius (composer).
584 **178** 30m. black . . . . 1·00 90

1958. Air. As No. 488 but with "mk" omitted.
585 **128** 300m. blue . . . . 19·00 70
See also No. 679.

179 Ski Jumping **180** "March of the Bjorneborgienses" (after Edelfelt)

1958. World Ski Championships.
586 **179** 20m. green . . . . 75 1·00
587 – 30m. blue 60 65
DESIGN—VERT: 30m. Cross-country skiing.

1958. 400th Anniv of Founding of Pori (Bjorneborg).
588 **180** 30m. purple . . . . . . 1·00 65

181 Lily of the Valley **182** Lyceum Seal

1958. Tuberculosis Relief Fund. Cross in red.
589 **181** 10m.+2m. green . . . . . 95 1·00
590 – 20m.+3m. red . . . . . 1·40 1·50
591 – 30m.+5m. blue . . . . . 1·40 1·50
DESIGNS: 20m. Red clover; 30m. Anemone.

1958. Centenary of Jyvaskyla Lyceum (secondary school).
592 **182** 30m. red 85 90

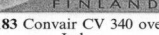

183 Convair CV 340 over Lakes **184** Cloudberry

1958. Air.
593 **183** 34m. blue 60 65
594 45m. blue . . . . 1·40 1·10
See also Nos. 678/a.

1958. Red Cross Fund. Cross in red
595 **184** 10m.+2m. orange 75 95
596 – 20m.+3m. red . . . . . 1·10 1·30
597 – 30m.+5m. blue . . . . . 1·10 1·40
DESIGNS: 20m. Cowberry; 30m. Blueberry.

185 Missionary Emblem and Globe **186** Opening of Diet, 1809

1959. Centenary of Finnish Missionary Society.
598 **185** 30m. purple 55 50

1959. 150th Anniv of Re-convening of Finnish Diet at Porvoo.
599 **186** 30m. blue 55 50

1959. Air. No. 593 surch **45**.
600 45m. on 34m. blue . . . . . 1·30 2·75

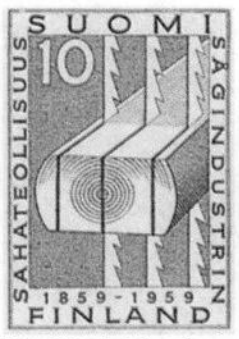

188 Multiple Saws **189** Gymnast

1959. Centenaries of Kestila Sawmill (10m.) and Finnish Forestry Department (30m.).
601 **188** 10m. brown 35 45
602 – 30m. grn (Forest firs) . . 35 50

1959. Tuberculosis Relief Fund. As T **181** but inscr "1959". Cross in red.
603 10m.+2m. green . . . . . . 1·40 1·10
604 20m.+3m. brown . . . . . . 1·80 1·80
605 30m.+5m. blue . . . . . . 1·80 1·80

DESIGNS: 10m. Marguerite; 20m. Cowslip; 30m. Cornflower.

1959. Birth Centenary of Elin Oihonna Kallio (Women's Gymnastics pioneer).
606 **189** 30m. purple 65 60

190 Oil Lamp **191** Arms of the Towns

1959. Cent of Trade Freedom in Finland.
607 **190** 30m. blue 55 60

1960. Extra Privileges for Finnish Towns–Hyvinkaa, Kouvola, Riihimaki, Rovaniemi, Salo and Seinajoki.
608 **191** 30m. violet 55 70

192 5k. "Serpentine Roulette" Stamp of 1860

1960. Stamp Exhibition, Helsinki, and Centenary of "Serpentine Roulette" stamps. Roul.
609 **192** 30m. blue and grey . . . 3·50 6·50

193 Refugees and Symbol **194** J. Gadolin

1960. World Refugee Year.
610 **193** 30m. red 30 45
611 40m. blue 30 45

1960. Birth Bicent of Johan Gadolin (chemist).
612 **194** 30m. brown 45 60

195 H. Nortamo **196** European Cuckoo

1960. Birth Cent of H. Nortamo (writer).
613 **195** 30m. green 45 60

1960. Karelian National Festival, Helsinki.
614 **196** 30m. red 55 60

197 "Geodesy" (Geodetic instrument) **198** Pres. Kekkonen

1960. 12th International Geodesy and Geophysics Union Assembly, Helsinki.
615 **197** 10m. sepia and blue . . . 35 45
616 – 30m. brn, red & verm . . 35 55
DESIGN: 30m. "Geophysics" (representation of Northern Lights).

1960. President Kekkonen's 60th Birthday.
617 **198** 30m. blue 55 35

1960. Europa. As T **373** of Belgium but size 31 × 20½ mm.
618 30m. blue and ultramarine . . 40 50
619 40m. purple and sepia . . . 40 50

199 Pastor Cygnaeus

200 Reindeer

1960. 150th Birth Anniv of Pastor Uno Cygnaeus (founder of elementary schools).

620 **199**	30m. purple	55	55

1960. Red Cross Fund. Cross in red.

621 **200**	10m.+2m. purple	75	1·10
622 –	20m.+3m. violet	95	1·40
623 –	30m.+5m. purple	95	1·40

DESIGNS: 20m. Hunter with lasso; 30m. Mountain and lake.

201 "Pommern" (barque)

202 Savings Bank's New Emblem

1961. Cent of Marianhamina (Mariehamn).

624 **201**	30m. blue	1·60	1·60

1961. 75th Anniv of Finnish Postal Savings Bank.

625 **202**	30m. blue	60	35

203 Symbol of Standardization

204 J. Aho

1961. General Assembly of Int. Organization for Standardization, Helsinki.

626 **203**	30m. green & orange	45	50

1961. Tuberculosis Relief Fund. As T **173**. Cross in red.

627	10m.+2m. purple	95	1·10
628	20m.+3m. blue	95	1·30
629	30m.+5m. green	95	1·50

ANIMALS: 10m. Muskrat; 20m. European otter; 30m. Ringed seal.

1961. Birth Centenary of Aho (writer).

630 **204**	30m. brown	45	50

205 Helsinki Cathedral

206 A. Jarnefelt

1961. 150th Anniv of Finnish Central Building Board.

631 **205**	30m. black	45	50

1961. Birth Centenary of Arvid Jarnefelt (writer).

632 **206**	30m. purple	45	50

207 Bank Facade

208 First locomotive, "Ilmarinen"

1961. 150th Anniv of Bank of Finland.

633 **207**	30m. purple	45	50

1962. Centenary of Finnish Railways.

634 **208**	10m. green	95	40
635 –	30m. blue	1·30	50
636 –	40m. purple	2·75	45

LOCOMOTIVES: 30m. Class Hr-1 steam locomotive and Type Hk wagon; 40m. Class Hr-12 diesel locomotive and passenger carriages.

209 Mora Stone

210 Senate Place, Helsinki

1962. 600th Anniv of Finnish People's Political Rights.

637 **209**	30m. purple	45	60

1962. 150th Anniv of Proclamation of Helsinki as Finnish Capital.

638 **210**	30m. brown	45	55

211 Customs Board Crest

212 Emblem of Commerce

1962. 150th Anniv of Finnish Customs Board.

639 **211**	30m. red	45	55

1962. Cent of 1st Finnish Commercial Bank.

640 **212**	30m. green	45	50

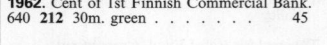

213 S. Alkio

214 Finnish Labour Emblem on Conveyor Belt

1962. Birth Cent of Santeri Alkio (writer and founder of Young People's Societies' Movement).

641 **213**	30m. purple	45	55

1962. Tuberculosis Relief Fund. As T **173**. Cross in red.

642	10m.+2m. black	1·10	1·10
643	20m.+3m. purple	1·30	1·40
644	30m.+5m. blue	1·30	1·40

DESIGNS: 10m. Brown hare; 20m. Pine marten; 30m. Stoat.

1962. Home Production.

645 **214**	30m. purple	45	30

215 Hunting Pembroke making Aerial Survey

216

1962. 150th Anniv of Finnish Land Survey Board.

646 **215**	30m. green	55	60

Currency reform. 100 (old) markkaa = 1 (new) markka.

1963. (a) Lion Type.

647 **216**	1p. brown	20	25
648	2p. green	20	15
649	4p. grey	55	30
650c	5p. blue	35	15
651c	10p. green	35	30
652	15p. orange	95	25
653	20p. red	95	30
654a	25p. purple	55	30
656a	30p. blue	90	30
657	35p. blue	1·00	15
657a	35p. yellow	55	25
658	40p. blue	95	30
658b	40p. orange	80	30
659	50p. blue	1·60	15
659a	50p. purple	65	25
659b	60p. blue	55	25

(b) Views. Values expressed as "0,05" (pennia values) or "1,00" (mark values).

660 –	5p. green (As No. 553a) (postage)	35	15
661 –	25p. multicoloured	20	25
662 –	30p. multicoloured	95	25
663 –	40p. lilac (As No. 555)	2·40	15
664 **161**	50p. green	3·75	15
665 –	60p. purple (As No. 557)	4·25	15
666 –	65p. purple (As No. 557)	55	25
667 –	75p. black (As No. 557a)	1·40	15
668 –	80p. multicoloured	3·00	25
669 –	90p. multicoloured	95	40
670 –	1m. green (As No. 557b)	70	20
671 –	1m.25 green (As No. 557c)	1·30	25
672 –	1m.30 multicoloured	60	30
673 –	1m.50 green	95	15
674 –	1m.75 blue	95	15
675 –	2m. green	6·00	20
676 –	2m.50 blue & yellow	3·25	35
677 –	5m. green	9·25	25
678 **183**	45p. blue (air)	95	25
678a	57p. blue	1·10	85
679 –	3m. blue (585)	1·90	25

NEW DESIGNS: As Type **161**—VERT: 30p. Nasinneula Tower, Tampere; 80p. Keuruu church; 1m.30, Helsinki Railway Station. HORIZ: 25p. Country mail bus; 90p. Hameen Bridge, Tampere; 1m.50, Loggers afloat; 1m.75, Parainen Bridge; 2m. Country house by lake; 2m.50, Aerial view of Punkaharju; 5m. Ristikallio Gorge.

No. 679 is as No. 585, but with a comma after "3".

217 Mother and Child

218 Hands reaching for Red Cross

1963. Freedom from Hunger.

680 **217**	40p. brown	25	40

1963. Centenary of Red Cross.

681 **218**	10p.+2p. brn & red	35	65
682	20p.+3p. violet & red	45	1·20
683	30p.+5p. green & red	45	1·30

219 Crown of Thorns

220 "Co-operation"

1963. Lutheran World Federation Assembly, Helsinki.

684 **219**	10p. lake	25	25
685 –	30p. green	35	50

DESIGN: 30p. Head of Christ.

1963. Europa.

686 **220**	40p. purple	90	45

221 House of Estates, Helsinki

222 Convair CV 440 Metropolitan Airliner

1963. Cent of Finnish Representative Assembly.

687 **221**	30p. purple	35	45

1963. 40 Years of Finnish Civil Aviation.

688 **222**	35p. green	45	50
689 –	40p. blue	45	40

DESIGN: 40p. Sud-Aviation SE 210 Caravelle in flight.

223 M. A. Castren (after E. J. Lofgren)

224 Soapstone Elk's Head

1963. 150th Birth Anniv of M. A. Castren (explorer and scholar).

690 **223**	35p. blue	35	40

1964. "For Art" (centenary of Finnish Artists' Society).

691 **224**	35p. green and buff	35	30

225 E. N. Setala

226 Doctor tending Patient on Sledge

1964. Birth Centenary of Emil Setala (philologist and statesman).

692 **225**	35p. brown	35	45

1964. Red Cross Fund. Cross in red.

693 **226**	15p.+3p. blue	35	65
694 –	25p.+4p. green	65	90
695 –	35p.+5p. purple	50	90
696 –	40p.+7p. green	50	90

DESIGNS: 25p. Red Cross hospital ship; 35p. Military sick parade; 40p. Distribution of Red Cross parcels.

227 Emblem of Medicine

228 Ice Hockey Players

1964. 18th General Assembly of World Medical Association.

697 **227**	40p. green	35	45

1965. World Ice Hockey Championships.

698 **228**	35p. blue	35	45

229 Centenary Medal

230 K. J. Stahlberg and Runeberg's sculpture, "Lex"

1965. Cent of Finnish Communal Self-Government.

699 **229**	35p. green	35	45

1965. Birth Cent of K. J. Stahlberg (statesman).

700 **230**	35p. brown	35	45

231 I.C.Y. Emblem

232 "The Fratricide"

1965. International Co-operation Year.

701 **231**	40p. multicoloured	35	45

1965. Birth Centenary of A. Gallen-Kallela (artist). Multicoloured.

702	25p. Type **232**	80	60
703	35p. "Head of a Young Girl"	80	60

233 Spitz

234 Piano, Profile and Score of "Finlandia"

1965. Tuberculosis Relief Fund. Dogs.

704 **233**	15p.+3p. brn & red	80	1·00
705 –	25p.+4p. blk & red	1·00	1·50
706 –	35p.+5p. sep & red	1·00	1·50

FINNISH DOGS: 25p. Karelian bear dog. 35p. Finnish stovare.

1965. Birth Centenary of Sibelius (composer).

707 **234**	25p. violet	55	45
708 –	35p. green	55	60

DESIGN: 35p. Part of score of "Finlandia" and dove.

235 Dish Aerial

236 "Winter Day" (after P. Halonen)

1965. Centenary of I.T.U.

709 **235**	35p. blue	35	50

1965. Birth Cent of Pekka Halonen (painter).

710 **236**	35p. multicoloured	35	35

237 Europa "Sprig"

238 "Kiss of Life"

1965. Europa.

711 **237**	40p. multicoloured	90	35

1966. Red Cross Fund. Multicoloured.

712	15p.+3p. Type **238**	45	80
713	25p.+4p. Diver and submerged car	45	95
714	35p.+5p. Sud-Aviation SE 3130 Alouette II Red Cross helicopter	45	95

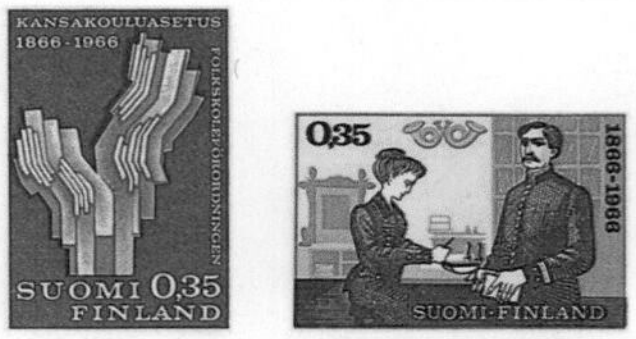

239 "Growing Up" **240** Old Post Office

1966. Cent of Finnish Elementary School Decree.
715 **239** 35p. bl & ultramarine . . 35 35

1966. "Nordia 1966" Stamp Exn., Helsinki, and Centenary of 1st Postage Stamps in Finnish Currency.
716 **240** 35p. blue, brown & yell 2·40 4·25

241 Globe and U.N.E.S.C.O. Emblem **242** Police Emblem

1966. 20th Anniv of U.N.E.S.C.O.
717 **241** 40p. multicoloured . . . 35 45

1966. 150th Anniv of Finnish Police Force.
718 **242** 35p. silver, black & blue 35 45

243 Anniversary Medal (after K. Kallio) **244** U.N.I.C.E.F Emblem

1966. 150th Anniv of Finnish Insurance.
719 **243** 35p. olive and lake . . . 35 45

1966. 20th Anniv of U.N.I.C.E.F.
720 **244** 15p. violet, green & blue 25 25

245 FINEFTA Symbol **246** Windmill

1967. Abolition of Industrial Customs Tariffs by European Free Trade Association.
721 **245** 40p. blue 35 30

1967. 350th Anniv of Uusikaupunki (Nystad).
722 **246** 40p. multicoloured . . . 35 30

247 Birch Tree and Foliage **248** Mannerheim Statue (A. Tukiainen)

1967. Tuberculosis Relief Fund. Mult.
723 20p.+3p. Type **247** 35 70
724 25p.+4p. Pine and foliage . . 35 80
725 40p.+7p. Spruce and foliage 35 80
See also Nos. 753/5.

1967. Birth Cent of Marshal Mannerheim.
726 **248** 40p. multicoloured . . . 35 35

249 "Solidarity" **250** Watermark of Thomasbole Factory

1967. Finnish Settlers in Sweden.
727 **249** 40p. multicoloured . . . 35 30

1967. 300th Anniv of Finnish Paper Industry.
728 **250** 40p. blue and bistre . . . 35 35

251 Martin Luther (from painting by Lucas Cranach the Elder) **252** Horse-drawn Ambulance

1967. 450th Anniv of the Reformation.
729 **251** 40p. multicoloured . . . 35 30

1967. Red Cross Fund. Multicoloured.
730 20p.+3p. Type **252** 40 90
731 25p.+4p. Modern ambulance 60 85
732 40p.+7p. Red Cross emblem 60 85

253 Northern Lights **254** Z. Topelius and "Bluebird"

1967. 50th Anniv of Independence.
733 **253** 20p. green and blue 30 30
734 – 25p. blue & light blue . . 30 25
735 – 40p. mauve and blue . . 30 25
DESIGNS: 25p. Flying swan; 40p. Ear of wheat.

1968. 150th Anniv of Zacharias Topelius (writer).
736 **254** 25p. multicoloured . . . 35 45

255 Skiing

1968. Winter Tourism.
737 **255** 25p. multicoloured . . . 35 65

256 "Paper-making" (from wood relief by H. Autere) **257** W.H.O. Emblem

1968. 150th Anniv of Tervakoski Paper Factory.
738 **256** 45p. brown, buff & red 25 35

1968. 20th Anniv of W.H.O.
739 **257** 40p. multicoloured . . . 35 30

258 "Infantryman" (statue by L. Leppanen, Vaasa) **259** Holiday Camp

1968. 50th Anniv of Finnish Army. Mult.
740 20p. Type **258** 30 40
741 25p. Memorial (V. Aaltonen), Hietaniemi cemetery . . . 30 40
742 40p. Modern soldier 30 40

1968. Tourism.
743 **259** 25p. multicoloured . . . 35 75

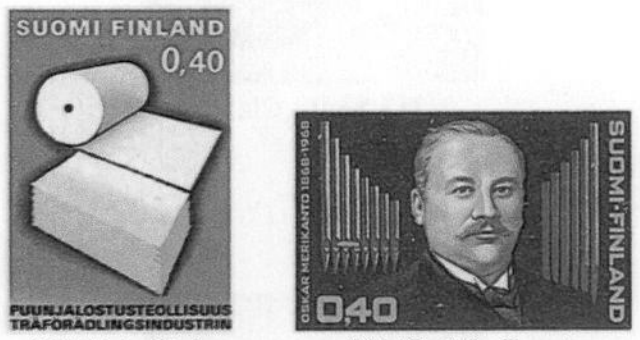

260 Pulp Bale (with outline of tree in centre) and Paper Reel **261** O. Merikanto

1968. Finnish Wood-processing Industry.
744 **260** 40p. multicoloured . . . 35 40

1968. Birth Cent of Oskar Merikanto (composer).
745 **261** 40p. multicoloured . . . 35 35

262 Mustola Lock **263** Dock Cranes, "Ivalo" (container ship) and Chamber of Commerce Emblem

1968. Opening of Saima Canal.
746 **262** 40p. multicoloured . . . 35 35

1968. "Finnish Economic Life". 50th Anniv of Finnish Central Chamber of Commerce.
747 **263** 40p. multicoloured . . . 35 30

264 Welding **265** Lyre Emblem

1968. Finnish Metal Industry.
748 **264** 40p. multicoloured . . . 35 25

1968. Finnish Student Unions.
749 **265** 40p. brn, bl & ultram . . 35 30

1969. 50th Anniv of Northern Countries' Union. As T **159** of Denmark.
750 40p. blue 65 40

266 City Hall and Arms, Kemi **267** Colonnade

1969. Centenary of Kemi (Kemin).
751 **266** 40p. multicoloured . . . 35 30

1969. Europa.
752 **267** 40p. multicoloured . . . 2·50 55

1969. Tuberculosis Relief Fund. As T **247**, but inscr "1969". Multicoloured.
753 20p.+3p. Juniper and berries 35 75
754 25p.+4p. Aspen and catkins 40 85
755 40p.+7p. Wild cherry and flowers 40 85

268 I.L.O. Emblem

1969. 50th Anniv of I.L.O.
756 **268** 40p. blue, lt blue & red 35 30

269 A. Jarnefelt (after V. Sjostrom) **270** Fairs Symbol

1969. Birth Cent of Armas Jarnefelt (composer).
757 **269** 40p. multicoloured . . . 35 25

1969. Finnish National and Int. Fairs.
758 **270** 40p. multicoloured . . . 35 25

271 J. Linnankoski **272** Board Emblems

1969. Birth Centenary of Johannes Linnankoski (writer).
759 **271** 40p. multicoloured . . . 35 30

1969. Centenary of Central Schools Board.
760 **272** 40p. violet, green & grey 35 30

273 Douglas DC-8-62F over Helsinki Airport **274** Golden Eagle and Eyrie

1969. Aviation.
761 **273** 25p. multicoloured . . . 35 70

1970. Nature Conservation Year.
762 **274** 30p. multicoloured . . . 70 80

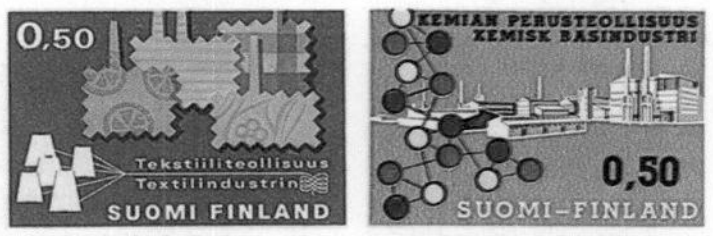

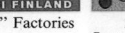

275 "Fabric" Factories **276** "Molecular Structure" and Factories, Nysta

1970. Finnish Textile Industry.
763 **275** 50p. multicoloured . . . 35 35

1970. Finnish Chemical Industry.
764 **276** 50p. multicoloured . . . 35 35

277 U.N.E.S.C.O. Emblem and Lenin **278** "The Seven Brothers"

1970. Finnish Co-operation with United Nations.
765 **277** 30p. multicoloured . . . 35 35
766 – 30p. multicoloured . . . 45 30
767 – 50p. gold, ultram & bl . . 35 30
DESIGNS—VERT: 30p. (No. 765), Type **277** (Lenin Symposium of U.N.E.S.C.O., Tampere); 30p. (No. 766), "Nuclear data" (Int. Atomic Energy Agency Conference, Otaniemi). HORIZ: 50p. U. N. emblem and globe (United Nations 25th Anniv).

1970. Red Cross Fund. Multicoloured.
768 25p.+5p. Type **278** 30 75
769 30p.+6p. "Juhani on top of Impivaara" (vert) 30 80
770 50p.+10p. "The Pale Maiden" 30 80

279 Invalid playing Handball **280** "Aurora Society Meeting" (E. Jarnefelt)

1970. 30th Anniv of Finnish Invalids League.
771 **279** 50p. black, red & orange 35 35

1970. Bicentenary of Aurora Society.
772 **280** 50p. multicoloured . . . 35 30

281 City Hall and Old Schoolhouse, Uusikaarlepyy **282** Pres. Kekkonen (from medal by A. Tukiainen)

1970. 350th Anniv of Uusikaarlepyy (Nykarleby) and Kokkola (Gamlakarleby) (towns). Mult.
773 50p. Type **281** 35 35
774 50p. Kokkola and arms . . . 35 35

1970. President Urho Kekkonen's 70th Birthday.
775 **282** 50p. silver and blue . . . 35 30

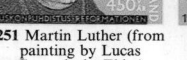

283 "S.A.L.T." and Globe
284 Pres. Paasikivi (after sculpture by E. Renvall)

1970. Strategic Arms Limitation Talks, Helsinki.
776 **283** 50p. multicoloured . . . 35 30

1970. Birth Centenary of President Paasikivi.
777 **284** 50p. black, blue & gold 35 25

285 Cogwheels
286 Felling Trees

1971. Finnish Industry.
778 **285** 50p. multicoloured . . . 35 35

1971. Tuberculosis Relief Fund. Timber Industry. Multicoloured.
779 25p.+5p. Type **286** 25 70
780 30p.+6p. Tug and log raft . . 35 75
781 50p.+10p. Sorting logs . . . 35 85

287 Europa Chain
288 Tornio Church

1971. Europa.
782 **287** 50p. yellow, pink & blk 3·00 55

1971. 350th Anniv of Tornio (Torneaa).
783 **288** 50p. multicoloured . . . 35 35

289 "Front-page News" (in Swedish, Finnish and French)
290 Hurdling, High-jumping and Discus-throwing

1971. Bicentenary of Finnish Press.
784 **289** 50p. multicoloured . . . 35 35

1971. European Athletic Championships, Helsinki. Multicoloured.
785 30p. Type **290** 55 55
786 50p. Throwing the javelin and running 65 55
These two designs form a composite picture when placed side by side.

291 "Lightning" Dinghies
292 Silver Pot, Seal and Tools

1971. Int "Lightning" Class Sailing Championships, Helsinki.
787 **291** 50p. multicoloured . . . 45 50

1971. 60th Anniv of Jewellery and Precious-metal Crafts.
788 **292** 50p. multicoloured . . . 35 30

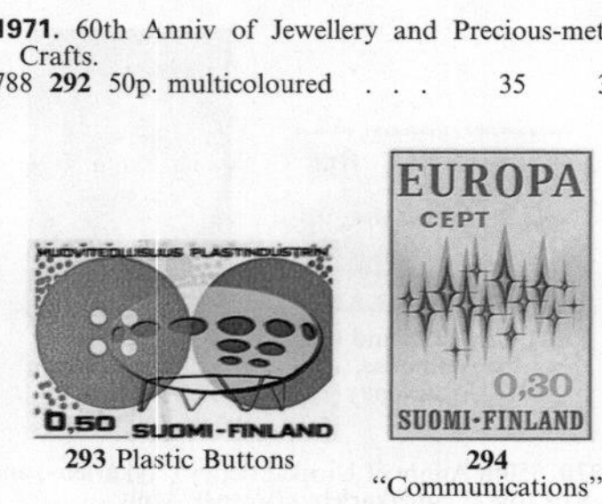

293 Plastic Buttons
294 "Communications"

1971. Finnish Plastics Industry.
789 **293** 50p. multicoloured . . . 35 35

1972. Europa.
790 **294** 30p. multicoloured . . . 2·20 50
791 50p. multicoloured . . . 2·40 50

295 National Theatre Building
296 Globe

1972. Centenary of Finnish National Theatre.
792 **295** 50p. multicoloured . . . 35 45

1972. Conclusion of the Strategic Arms Limitation Talks, Helsinki.
793 **296** 50p. multicoloured . . . 35 30

297 Map and Arms
298 Cadet Ship "Suomen Joutsen"

1972. 50th Anniv of Local Self-government for the Aland Islands.
794 **297** 50p. multicoloured . . . 1·10 65

1972. Start of the Tall Ships' Race, Helsinki.
795 **298** 50p. multicoloured . . . 1·10 35

299 Post Office, Tampere
301 Blood Donation

1972. Multicoloured.
797 40p. Type **299** 25 20
798 60p. National Museum (28 × 40 mm) 35 35
799 70p. Market Place, Helsinki (39 × 27 mm) 30 20
800 80p. As 70p. 35 25

1972. Red Cross Fund. Blood Service. Mult.
820 25p.+5p. Type **301** 45 85
821 30p.+6p. Laboratory research (vert) 50 85
822 50p.+10p. Blood transfusion 50 1·00

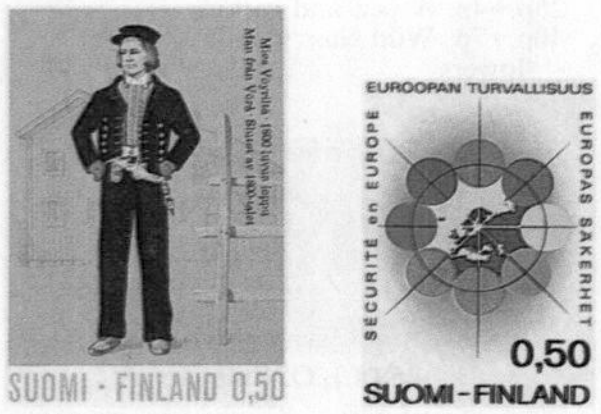

302 Voyri Man
303 "European Co-operation"

1972. Ancient and National Costumes. Multicoloured.
823 50p. Pernio woman . . . . . 1·10 30
824 50p. Married couple, Tenala 1·10 30
825 50p. Nastola girl . . . . . . 1·10 30
826 50p. Type **302** . . . . . . 1·10 30
827 50p. Lapp winter costumes 1·10 30
828 60p. Kaukola girl . . . . . 2·75 25
829 60p. Jaaski woman . . . . . 2·75 25
830 60p. Koivisto couple . . . . 2·75 25
831 60p. Mother and son, Sakyla 2·75 25
832 60p. Heinavesi girl . . . . . 2·75 25

1972. European Security and Co-operation Conf, Helsinki (1st issue).
833 **303** 50p. multicoloured . . . 75 45
See also No. 839.

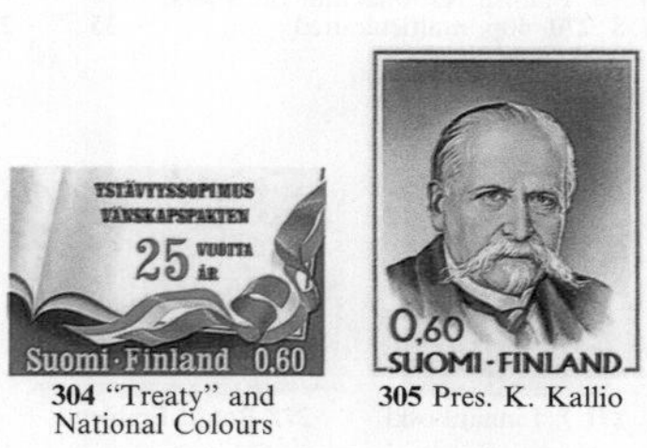

304 "Treaty" and National Colours
305 Pres. K. Kallio

1973. 25th Anniv of Friendship Treaty with Russia.
834 **304** 60p. multicoloured . . . 25 40

1973. Birth Cent of Pres. Kyosti Kallio.
835 **305** 60p. multicoloured . . . 25 25

306 Europa "Posthorn"
307 "EUROPA" on Map

1973. Europa.
836 **306** 60p. green, turq & blue 1·10 45

1973. Nordic Countries' Postal Co-operation. As T **201** of Denmark.
837 60p. multicoloured 30 25
838 70p. multicoloured 30 25

1973. European Security and Co-operation Conf, Helsinki (2nd issue).
839 **307** 70p. multicoloured . . . 40 40

308 Canoe Paddle
309 Radiosonde Balloon

1973. World Canoeing Championships, Tampere.
840 **308** 60p. multicoloured . . . 35 35

1973. Cent of World Meteorological Organization.
841 **309** 60p. multicoloured . . . 25 35

310 E. Saarinen

1973. Birth Cent of Eliel Saarinen (architect).
842 **310** 60p. multicoloured . . . 25 45

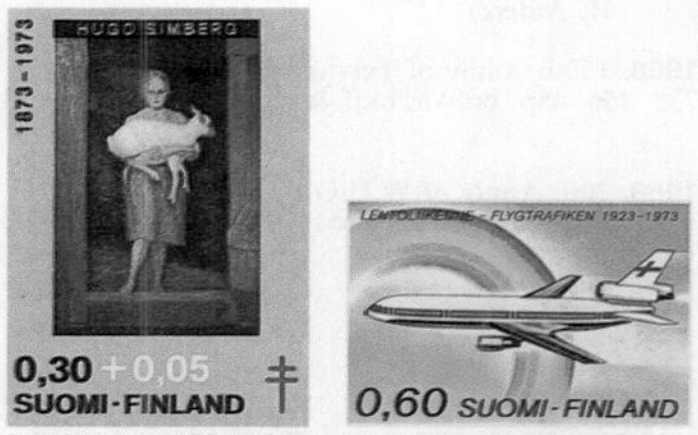

311 "Young Girl with Lamb" (H. Simberg)
312 Douglas DC-10-30

1973. Tuberculosis Relief Fund. Artists' Birth Centenaries. Multicoloured.
843 30p.+5p. Type **311** 65 85
844 40p.+10p. "Summer Evening" (W. Sjostrom) . . 85 1·10
845 60p.+15p. "At a Mountain Spring" (J. Rissanen) . . . 85 1·10

1973. 50th Annivs. of Finnair (airline) and Regular Air Services in Finland.
846 **312** 60p. multicoloured . . . 35 35

313 Santa Claus

1973. Christmas.
847 **313** 30p. multicoloured . . . 40 25

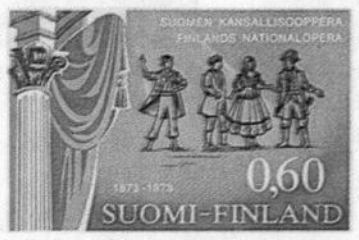

314 Scene from "The Barber of Seville"

1973. Centenary of Finnish State Opera Company.
848 **314** 60p. multicoloured . . . 25 35

315 Porcelain Products
316 "Paavo Nurmi" (Statue by W. Aaltonen)

1973. Finnish Porcelain Industry.
849 **315** 60p. green, blk & bl . . . 25 35

1973. Paavo Nurmi (Olympic athlete) Commem.
850 **316** 60p. multicoloured . . . 35 35

317 Hanko Casino, Harbour and Map
318 Arms of Finland, 1581

1974. Centenary of Hanko (Hango).
851 **317** 60p. multicoloured . . . 35 35

1974.
852 **318** 10m. multicoloured . . . 1·90 30
852a – 20m. multicoloured . . . 4·75 50
DESIGN: 20m. Arms as in T **318** but different border.

319 Ice Hockey Players

1974. World and European Ice Hockey Championships.
853 **319** 60p. multicoloured . . . 35 25

320 Herring Gulls

1974. Baltic Area Marine Environmental Conference, Helsinki.
854 **320** 60p. multicoloured . . . 35 30

321 "Goddess of Victory bestowing Wreath on Youth" (W. Aaltonen)
322 Ilmari Kianto

1974. Europa.
855 **321** 70p. multicoloured . . . 2·50 45

1974. Birth Centenary of Ilmari Kianto ("Iki Kianto") (writer).
856 **322** 60p. multicoloured . . . 30 35

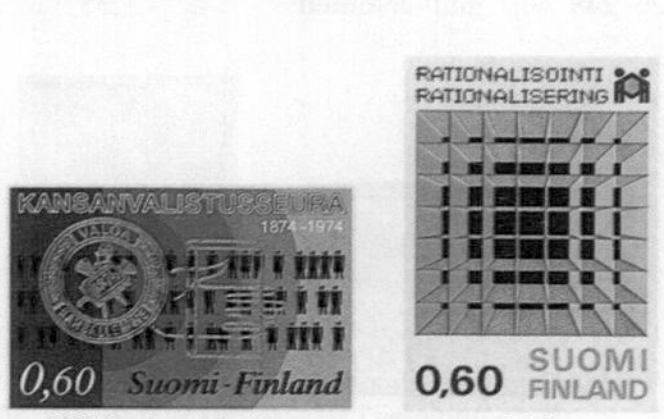

323 Society Emblem
324 "Rationalization"

1974. Finnish Society for Popular Education.
857 **323** 60p. multicoloured . . . 30 35

1974. Finnish Rationalization in Social Development.
858 **324** 60p. multicoloured . . . 30 35

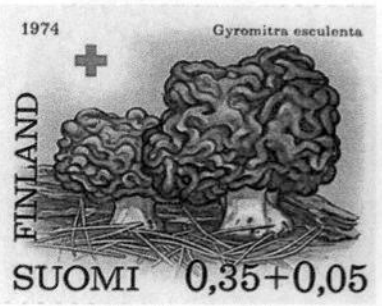

325 Beefsteak Morel **326** U.P.U. Emblem

1974. Red Cross Fund. Mushrooms (1st series). Multicoloured.

859 35p.+5p. Type **325** . . . . . 1·10 80
860 50p.+10p. Chanterelle . . . . 95 1·00
861 60p.+15p. Cep . . . . 95 1·00

See also Nos. 937/9 and 967/9.

1974. Centenary of Universal Postal Union.

862 **326** 60p. multicoloured . . . 25 25
863 70p. multicoloured . . . 25 25

327 Christmas Gnomes **328** Aunessilta Granite Bridge and Modern Reinforced Concrete Bridge

1974. Christmas.

864 **327** 35p. multicoloured . . . 1·10 45

1974. 175th Anniv of Finnish Road and Waterways Board.

865 **328** 60p. multicoloured . . . 35 30

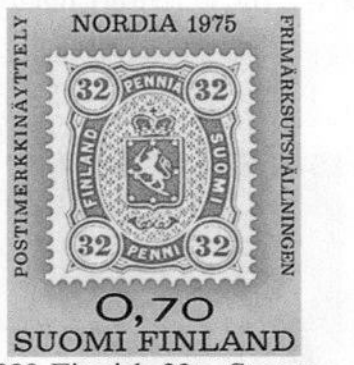

329 National Arms **330** Finnish 32p. Stamp of 1875

1975.

865a	**329**	10p. purple	25	20
865c		20p. yellow	25	20
865d		30p. red	25	25
866		40p. orange	25	20
867		50p. green	25	20
868		60p. blue	25	20
869		70p. brown	25	20
870		80p. red and green . .	25	20
871		90p. violet	25	20
872		1m. brown	30	20
873		1m.10 yellow	35	20
874		1m.20 blue	35	30
875		1m.30 green	35	30
875a		1m.40 violet	45	20
875b		1m.50 blue	45	25
875c		1m.60 red	45	20
875d		1m.70 grey	45	20
875e		1m.80 green	55	25
875f		1m.90 orange	50	20
1161		2m. green	55	45

1975. "Nordia 1975" Stamp Exhibition.

876 **330** 70p. brown, black & buff 1·40 2·20

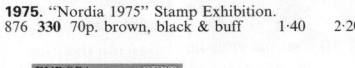

331 "A Girl Combing Her Hair" (M. Enckell) **332** Office Seal

1975. Europa. Multicoloured.

877 70p. Type **331** . . . . . . 1·10 25
878 90p. "Washerwomen" (T. Sallinen) . . . . 1·40 25

1975. 150th Anniv of State Economy Controllers' Office.

879 **332** 70p. multicoloured . . . 30 25

333 "Niilo Saarinen" (lifeboat) and Sinking Ship

1975. 12th International Salvage Conference, Helsinki.

880 **333** 70p. multicoloured . . . 30 25

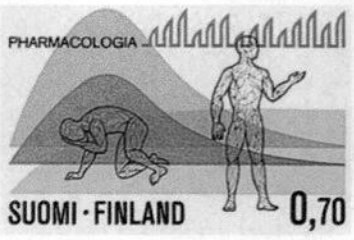

334 "Pharmacology" **335** Olavinlinna Castle

1975. 6th International Pharmacological Congress, Helsinki.

881 **334** 70p. multicoloured . . . 30 25

1975. 500th Anniv of Olavinlinna Castle.

882 **335** 70p. multicoloured . . . 30 25

336 Finlandia Hall (Conference Headquarters) and Barn Swallow **337** "Echo" (E. Thesleff)

1975. European Security and Co-operation Conference, Helsinki.

883 **336** 90p. multicoloured . . . 35 25

1975. Tuberculosis Relief Fund. Paintings by female artists. Multicoloured.

884 40p.+10p. Type **337** 35 70
885 60p.+15p. "Portrait of Hilda Wiik" (Maria Wiik) . . . 65 95
886 70p.+20p. "At Home" (Helene Schjerfbeck) . . . 65 80

338 Men and Women supporting Globe **339** Graphic Quarter-circle

1975. International Women's Year.

887 **338** 70p. multicoloured . . . 30 30

1975. Centenary of Finnish Society of Industrial Art.

888 **339** 70p. multicoloured . . . 30 30

340 Nativity Play **341** State Debenture

1975. Christmas.

889 **340** 40p. multicoloured . . . 30 25

1975. Cent. of Finnish State Treasury.

890 **341** 80p. multicoloured . . . 30 25

342 Finnish Glider **343** Disabled Ex-servicemen's Association Emblem

1976. 15th World Gliding Championships, Rayskala.

891 **342** 80p. multicoloured . . . 35 30

1976. Finnish War Invalids Fund.

892 **343** 70p.+30p. mult 35 50

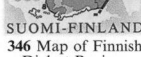

344 Cheese Frames **345** Heikki Klemetti

1976. Traditional Finnish Arts.

893	– 1m.50 multicoloured . .	35	25
893a	– 2m. multicoloured . .	45	25
893b	– 2m.20 multicoloured . .	65	30
894	**344** 2m.50 multicoloured . .	65	35
895	– 3m. multicoloured . . .	95	35
896	– 4m.50 multicoloured . .	1·00	35
896b	– 4m.80 multicoloured . .	1·40	45
897	– 5m. multicoloured . . .	1·60	30
898	– 6m. multicoloured . . .	1·30	25
899	– 7m. multicoloured . . .	1·90	35
899a	– 8m. brown and black . .	1·90	30
899b	– 9m. black and blue . . .	2·50	55
899c	– 12m. ochre, drab & brn	2·75	60

DESIGNS—VERT: 1m.50, Rusko drinking bowl, 1542; 4m.50, Spinning distaffs; 5m. Weathercock, Kirvu (metalwork); 6m. Kaspaikka (Karelian towel); 7m. Bridal rug, 1815; 8m. Arsenal door, Hollola church (iron forging). HORIZ: 2m., 4m.80, Old-style sauna; 2m.20, Kerimaki Church and belfry (peasant architecture); 3m. Shuttle and raanu (patterned cover); 9m. Four-pronged fish spear, c. 1000; 12m. Damask with tulip pattern.

1976. Birth Centenary of Professor Heikki Klemetti (composer).

900 **345** 80p. multicoloured . . . 30 25

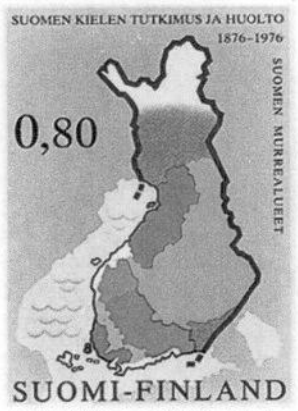

346 Map of Finnish Dialect Regions **347** "Aino Ackte in Paris" (A. Edelfelt)

1976. Centenary of Finnish Language Society.

901 **346** 80p. multicoloured . . . 30 25

1976. Birth Cent of Aino Ackte (opera singer).

902 **347** 70p. multicoloured . . . 35 30

348 Ancient Knives and Belts

1976. Europa.

903 **348** 80p. multicoloured . . . 2·10 35

349 "Radio Broadcasting"

1976. 50th Anniv of Radio Broadcasting in Finland.

904 **349** 80p. multicoloured . . . 30 25

350 Wedding Dance

1976. Tuberculosis Relief Fund. Traditional Wedding Customs. Multicoloured.

905 50p.+10p. Wedding procession (horiz) 35 55
906 70p.+15p. Type **350** 45 85
907 80p.+20p. Wedding breakfast (horiz) 45 85

351 Sleigh arriving at Church

1976. Christmas.

908 **351** 50p. multicoloured . . . 30 25

352 Medieval Seal and Text

1976. 700th Anniv of Cathedral Chapter, Turku.

909 **352** 80p. multicoloured . . . 30 25

353 Hugo Alvar Aalto and Finlandia Hall, Helsinki

1976. Hugo Alvar Aalto (architect) Commem.

910 **353** 80p. multicoloured . . . 30 30

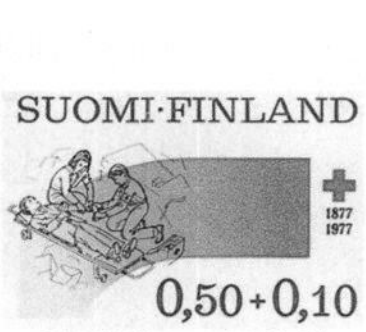

354 "Disaster Relief" **355** Figure Skating

1977. Red Cross Fund. Centenary of Finnish Red Cross. Multicoloured.

911 50p.+10p. Type **354** 30 75
912 80p.+15p. "Community Work" 35 75
913 90p.+20p. "Blood Transfusion Service" . . . 35 75

1977. European Figure Skating Championships, Helsinki.

914 **355** 90p. multicoloured . . . 35 25

1977. Northern Countries' Co-operation in Nature Conservation and Environment Protection. As T **229** of Denmark.

915 90p. multicoloured 35 30
916 1m. multicoloured 35 30

356 "Urho" (ice-breaker) and Freighter

1977. Centenary of Winter Navigation between Finland and Sweden.

917 **356** 90p. multicoloured . . . 50 25

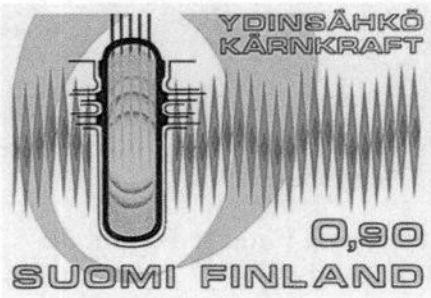

357 "Nuclear Reactor"

1977. Inauguration of Hastholm Island Nuclear Power Station.

918 **357** 90p. multicoloured . . . 30 25

358 Autumn Landscape

1977. Europa.

919 **358** 90p. multicoloured . . . 1·60 35

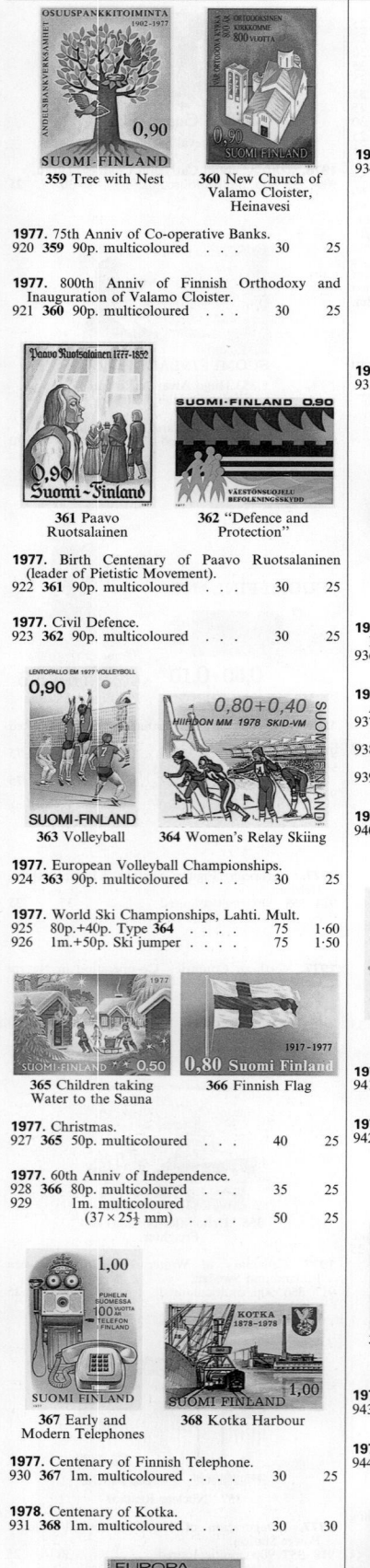

359 Tree with Nest **360** New Church of Valamo Cloister, Heinavesi

1977. 75th Anniv of Co-operative Banks.
920 **359** 90p. multicoloured . . . 30 25

1977. 800th Anniv of Finnish Orthodoxy and Inauguration of Valamo Cloister.
921 **360** 90p. multicoloured . . . 30 25

361 Paavo Ruotsalainen **362** "Defence and Protection"

1977. Birth Centenary of Paavo Ruotsalaninen (leader of Pietistic Movement).
922 **361** 90p. multicoloured . . . 30 25

1977. Civil Defence.
923 **362** 90p. multicoloured . . . 30 25

363 Volleyball **364** Women's Relay Skiing

1977. European Volleyball Championships.
924 **363** 90p. multicoloured . . . 30 25

1977. World Ski Championships, Lahti. Mult.
925 80p.+40p. Type **364** . . . . 75 1·60
926 1m.+50p. Ski jumper . . . . 75 1·50

365 Children taking Water to the Sauna **366** Finnish Flag

1977. Christmas.
927 **365** 50p. multicoloured . . . 40 25

1977. 60th Anniv of Independence.
928 **366** 80p. multicoloured . . . 35 25
929 1m. multicoloured (37 × 25½ mm) 50 25

367 Early and Modern Telephones **368** Kotka Harbour

1977. Centenary of Finnish Telephone.
930 **367** 1m. multicoloured 30 25

1978. Centenary of Kotka.
931 **368** 1m. multicoloured 30 30

369 Sanatorium, Paimio

1978. Europa. Multicoloured.
932 1m. Type **369** . . . . . . 2·10 80
933 1m.20 Studio House, Hvittrask (37 × 25½ mm) 5·75 6·50

370 Buses

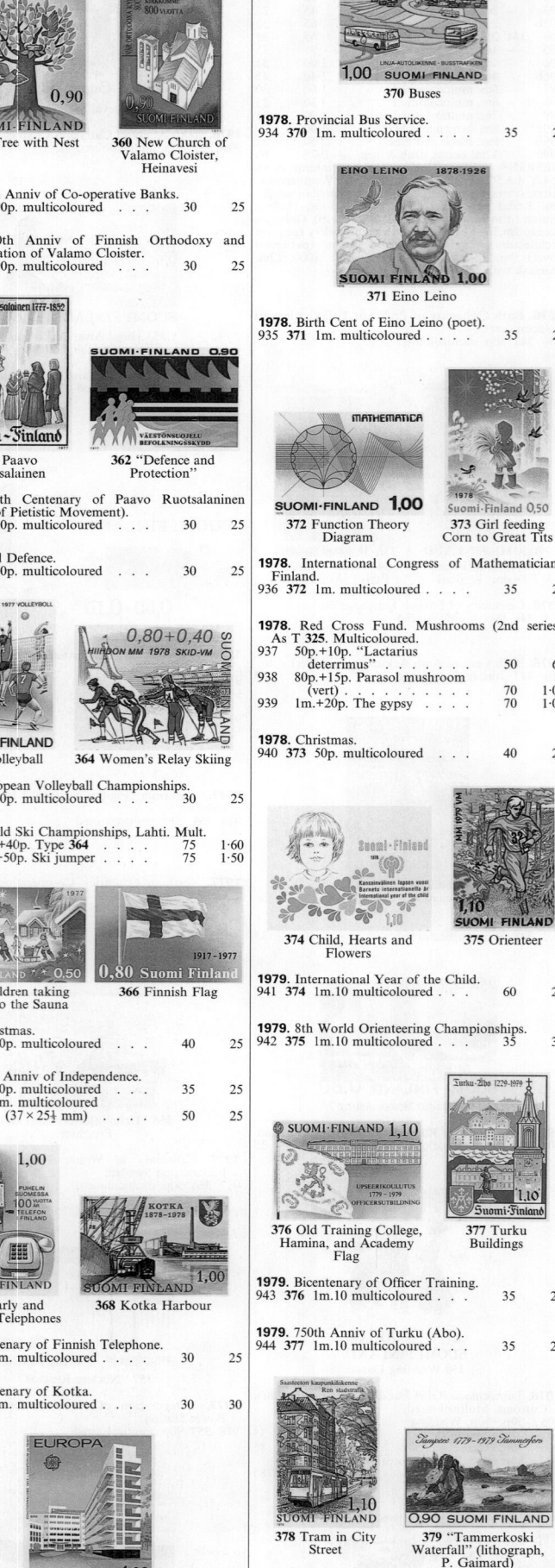

1978. Provincial Bus Service.
934 **370** 1m. multicoloured 35 25

371 Eino Leino

1978. Birth Cent of Eino Leino (poet).
935 **371** 1m. multicoloured 35 25

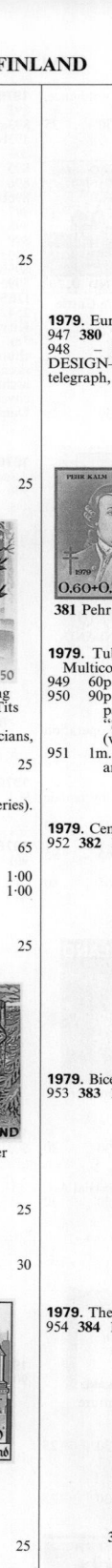

372 Function Theory Diagram **373** Girl feeding Corn to Great Tits

1978. International Congress of Mathematicians, Finland.
936 **372** 1m. multicoloured 35 25

1978. Red Cross Fund. Mushrooms (2nd series). As T **325**. Multicoloured.
937 50p.+10p. "Lactarius deterrimus" 50 65
938 80p.+15p. Parasol mushroom (vert) . . . . 70 1·00
939 1m.+20p. The gypsy . . . . 70 1·00

1978. Christmas.
940 **373** 50p. multicoloured . . . 40 25

374 Child, Hearts and Flowers **375** Orienteer

1979. International Year of the Child.
941 **374** 1m.10 multicoloured . . . 60 25

1979. 8th World Orienteering Championships.
942 **375** 1m.10 multicoloured . . . 35 30

376 Old Training College, Hamina, and Academy Flag **377** Turku Buildings

1979. Bicentenary of Officer Training.
943 **376** 1m.10 multicoloured . . . 35 25

1979. 750th Anniv of Turku (Abo).
944 **377** 1m.10 multicoloured . . . 35 25

378 Tram in City Street **379** "Tammerkoski Waterfall" (lithograph, P. Gaimard)

1979. Helsinki Tram Service.
945 **378** 1m.10 multicoloured . . . 35 25

1979. Bicent of Tampere (Tammerfors) (1st issue).
946 **379** 90p. brown, buff & black 35 30
See also No. 953.

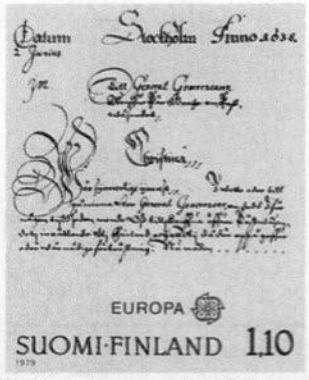

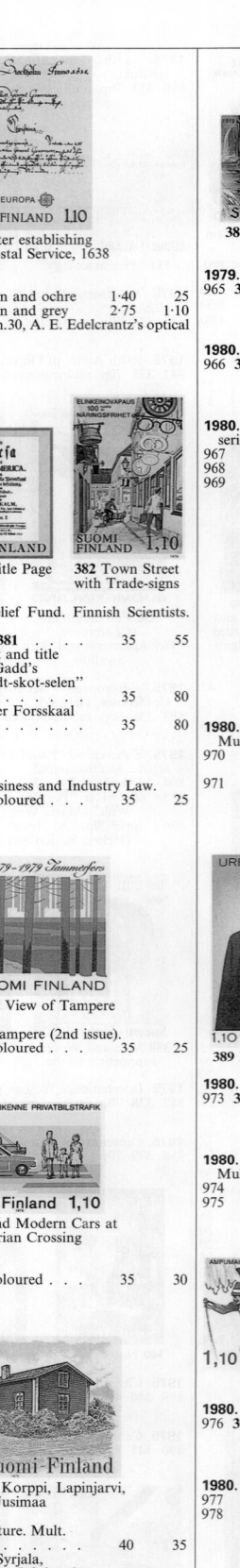

380 Letter establishing Finnish Postal Service, 1638

1979. Europa.
947 **380** 1m.10 blk, brn and ochre 1·40 25
948 – 1m.30 blk, brn and grey 2·75 1·10
DESIGN—HORIZ: 1m.30, A. E. Edelcrantz's optical telegraph, 1796.

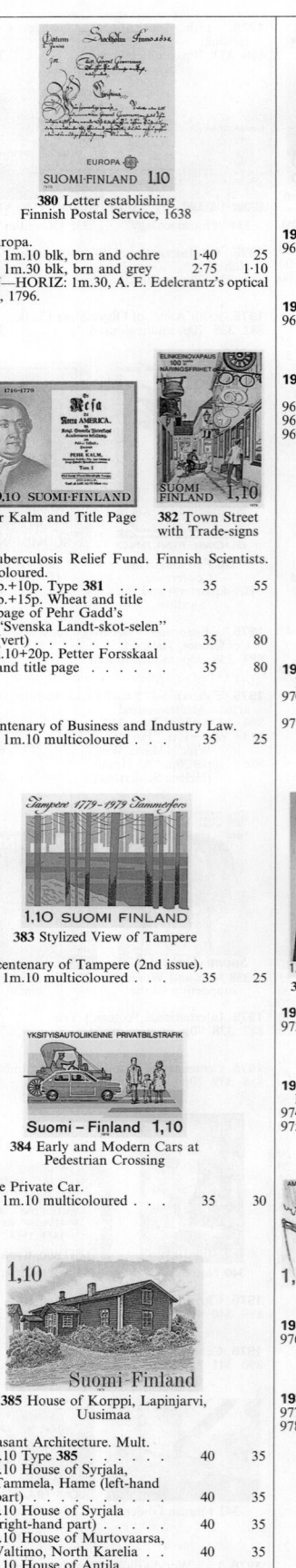

381 Pehr Kalm and Title Page **382** Town Street with Trade-signs

1979. Tuberculosis Relief Fund. Finnish Scientists. Multicoloured.
949 60p.+10p. Type **381** 35 55
950 90p.+15p. Wheat and title page of Pehr Gadd's "Svenska Landt-skot-selen" (vert) 35 80
951 1m.10+20p. Petter Forsskaal and title page 35 80

1979. Centenary of Business and Industry Law.
952 **382** 1m.10 multicoloured . . . 35 25

383 Stylized View of Tampere

1979. Bicentenary of Tampere (2nd issue).
953 **383** 1m.10 multicoloured . . . 35 25

384 Early and Modern Cars at Pedestrian Crossing

1979. The Private Car.
954 **384** 1m.10 multicoloured . . . 35 30

385 House of Korppi, Lapinjarvi, Uusimaa

1979. Peasant Architecture. Mult.
955 1m.10 Type **385** 40 35
956 1m.10 House of Syrjala, Tammela, Hame (left-hand part) 40 35
957 1m.10 House of Syrjala (right-hand part) 40 35
958 1m.10 House of Murtovaarsa, Valtimo, North Karelia . . 40 35
959 1m.10 House of Antila, Lapua, Pohjanmaa 40 35
960 1m.10 Gable loft of Luukila, Haukipudas and loft of Keskikangas, Yliharma, Pohjanmaa 40 35
961 1m.10 Gate, house of Kanajarvi, Kalvola, Hame 40 35
962 1m.10 Porch, house of Havuselka, Kauhajoki, Pohjanmaa 40 35
963 1m.10 Dinner bell and House of Maki-Rasinpera, Kuortane, Pohjanmaa . . 40 35
964 1m.10 Gable and eaves of granary of Rasula, Kuortane, Pohjanmaa . . 40 35
See also Nos. 1024/33.

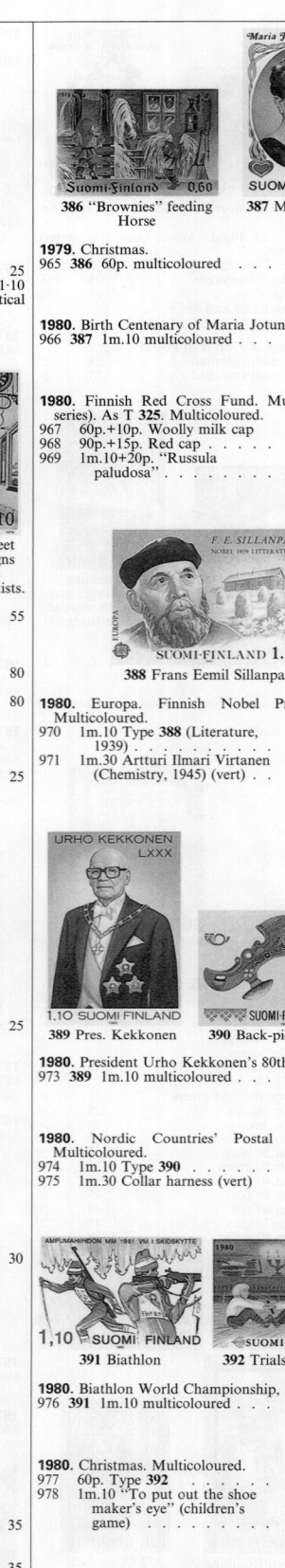

386 "Brownies" feeding Horse **387** Maria Jotuni

1979. Christmas.
965 **386** 60p. multicoloured . . . 30 25

1980. Birth Centenary of Maria Jotuni (writer).
966 **387** 1m.10 multicoloured . . . 35 25

1980. Finnish Red Cross Fund. Mushrooms (3rd series). As T **325**. Multicoloured.
967 60p.+10p. Woolly milk cap 45 70
968 90p.+15p. Red cap . . . . . 70 1·00
969 1m.10+20p. "Russula paludosa" . . . . 60 1·00

388 Frans Eemil Sillanpaa

1980. Europa. Finnish Nobel Prize Winners. Multicoloured.
970 1m.10 Type **388** (Literature, 1939) 85 30
971 1m.30 Artturi Ilmari Virtanen (Chemistry, 1945) (vert) . . 1·60 95

389 Pres. Kekkonen **390** Back-piece Harness

1980. President Urho Kekkonen's 80th Birthday.
973 **389** 1m.10 multicoloured . . . 35 25

1980. Nordic Countries' Postal Co-operation. Multicoloured.
974 1m.10 Type **390** 35 30
975 1m.30 Collar harness (vert) 35 30

391 Biathlon **392** Trials of Strength

1980. Biathlon World Championship, Lahti.
976 **391** 1m.10 multicoloured . . . 35 30

1980. Christmas. Multicoloured.
977 60p. Type **392** 40 25
978 1m.10 "To put out the shoe maker's eye" (children's game) 35 25

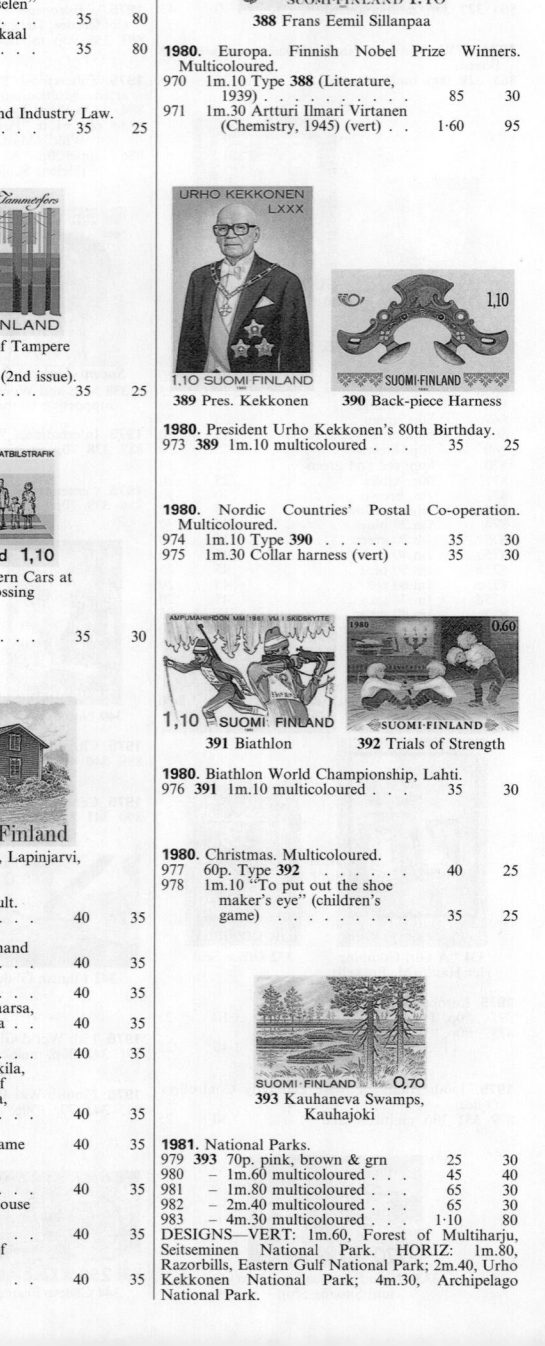

393 Kauhaneva Swamps, Kauhajoki

1981. National Parks.
979 **393** 70p. pink, brown & grn 25 30
980 – 1m.60 multicoloured . . . 45 40
981 – 1m.80 multicoloured . . . 65 30
982 – 2m.40 multicoloured . . . 65 30
983 – 4m.30 multicoloured . . . 1·10 80
DESIGNS—VERT: 1m.60, Forest of Multiharju, Seitseminen National Park. HORIZ: 1m.80, Razorbills, Eastern Gulf National Park; 2m.40, Urho Kekkonen National Park; 4m.30, Archipelago National Park.

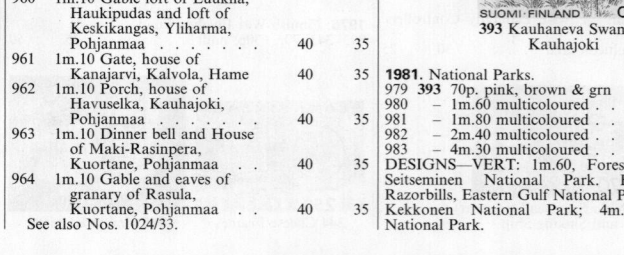

394 Boxing

395 Glass-blowing and 19th-century Bottle

1981. European Boxing Championships, Tampere.
990 **394** 1m.10 multicoloured . . . 35 35

1981. 300th Anniv of Finnish Glass Industry.
991 **395** 1m.10 multicoloured . . . 35 30

396 "Furst Menschikoff" (paddle-steamer)

1981. "Nordia 1981" Stamp Exhibition, Helsinki.
992 **396** 1m.10 brown & stone . . 1·50 2·50

397 Rowing to Church

1981. Europa. Multicoloured.
993 1m.10 Type **397** 90 30
994 1m.50 Midsummer Eve celebrations . . . . 1·10 60

398 "International Traffic Movement"

399 Children on Winged Horse

1981. Council Session of European Conference of Ministers of Transport, Finland.
995 **398** 1m.10 multicoloured . . . 35 25

1981. Centenary of Finnish Youth Associations.
996 **399** 1m. multicoloured 30 30

400 Fuchsia

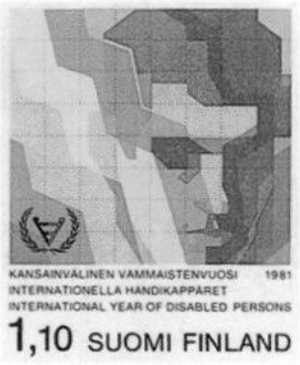

401 Face on Graph

1981. Tuberculosis Relief Fund. Potted Plants. Multicoloured.
997 70p.+10p. Type **400** 35 65
998 1m.+15p. African violet ("Saintpaulia ionantha") 35 70
999 1m.10+20p. Pelargonium . . 35 70

1981. International Year of Disabled Persons.
1000 **401** 1m.10 multicoloured . . 35 30

402 Children bringing Home Christmas Tree

404 Hame Castle

1981. Christmas. Multicoloured.
1001 70p. Type **402** 30 25
1002 1m.10 Decorating the Christmas tree (vert) . . . 30 25

1982.
1007 **404** 90p. brown 30 30
1008 – 1m. brown and blue . . 35 35
DESIGN—VERT: 1m. Windmill, Harrstrom.

405 First Issue of "Om konsten att ratt Behaga" and Modern Periodical

406 Kuopio Cathedral and Puijo Tower

1982. Bicentenary of Finnish Periodicals.
1015 **405** 1m.20 multicoloured . . 35 25

1982. Bicentenary of Kuopio.
1016 **406** 1m.20 multicoloured . . 35 25

407 Neck of Stringed Instrument and Staves of Music

408 Flats, Factories and Houses

1982. Music Jubilee.
1017 **407** 1m.20 multicoloured . . 35 30

1982. Centenary of Electricity in Finland.
1018 **408** 1m.20 multicoloured . . 35 30

409 Vegetable and Fruit Garden

410 Cover of "Abckiria" and sculpture of M. Agricola by O. Jauhiainen

1982. Cent of First Finnish Horticultural Society.
1019 **409** 1m.10 multicoloured . . 35 30

1982. Europa. Multicoloured.
1020 1m.20 Type **410** . . . . . 1·10 25
1021 1m.50 "Turku Academy Inaugural Procession in 1640" (fresco copied by Johannes Gebhard from painting by Albert Edelfelt) (47 × 31 mm) . . 1·60 55

411 Emblems and Symbolic Design

1982. International Monetary Fund and World Bank Committees' Meetings, Helsinki.
1022 **411** 1m.60 multicoloured . . 45 35

412 Interior of Parliament and "Future" (sculpture by W. Aaltonen)

1982. 75th Anniv of Single Chamber Parliament.
1023 **412** 2m.40 blue, dp bl & blk 65 65

1982. Manor Houses. As T **385**. Mult.
1024 1m.20 Kuitia, 1490s 45 40
1025 1m.20 Louhisaari, 1655 . . 45 40
1026 1m.20 Frugard, 1780 . . . 45 40
1027 1m.20 Jokioinen, 1798 . . 45 40
1028 1m.20 Moisio, 1820 . . . . 45 40
1029 1m.20 Sjundby, 1560s . . . 45 40
1030 1m.20 Fagervik, 1773 . . . 45 40
1031 1m.20 Mustio, 1792 . . . . 45 40
1032 1m.20 Fiskars, 1818 . . . . 45 40
1033 1m.20 Kotkaniemi, 1836 . . 45 40

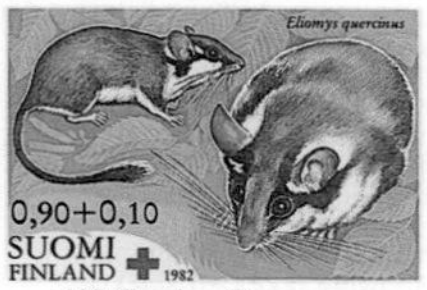

413 Garden Dormouse

1982. Red Cross Fund. Endangered Mammals. Multicoloured.
1034 90p.+10p. Type **413** 50 60
1035 1m.10+15p. Siberian flying squirrel (vert) 65 90
1036 1m.20+20p. European mink 65 90

414 Brownie Children feeding Forest Animals

1982. Christmas. Multicoloured.
1037 90p. Type **414** 40 25
1038 1m.20 Brownie children eating porridge 40 25

415 Gold Prospector

1983. Nordic Countries' Postal Co-operation. "Visit the North". Multicoloured.
1039 1m.20 Type **415** 30 25
1040 1m.30 Descending the Kitajoki river rapids . . . 45 25

416 Postman, Letters and Computer

1983. World Communications Year. Mult.
1041 1m.30 Type **416** 40 25
1042 1m.70 Modulated wave, pulse stream and optical cables 40 40

418 Flash Smelting

1983. Europa. Multicoloured.
1044 1m.30 Type **418** . . . . . 2·75 25
1045 1m.70 Interior of Temppeliaukio Church (Timo and Tuomo Suomalainen) . . . . . . 3·75 95

419 President Relander

420 Throwing the Javelin

1983. Birth Centenary of Lauri Kristian Relander (President, 1925–1931).
1046 **419** 1m.30 multicoloured . . 35 25

1983. World Athletics Championships, Helsinki. Multicoloured.
1047 1m.20 Type **420** 35 25
1048 1m.30 Running (vert) 35 25

421 Kuula and Ostrobothnia

422 Chickweed Wintergreen

1983. Birth Cent of Toivo Kuula (composer).
1049 **421** 1m.30 multicoloured . . 35 25

1983. Tuberculosis Relief Fund. Wild Flowers. Multicoloured.
1050 1m.+20p. Type **422** 35 65
1051 1m.20+25p. Marsh Violet 40 65
1052 1m.30+30p. Marsh Marigold 40 65

423 "Santa Claus" (Eija Myllyviita)

424 Koivisto

1983. Christmas. Children's Drawings.
1053 **423** 1m. blue & deep blue . . 35 25
1054 – 1m.30 multicoloured . . 35 25
DESIGN—VERT: 1m.30, "Two Candles" (Camilla Lindberg).

1983. President Mauno Henrik Koivisto's 60th Birthday.
1055 **424** 1m.30 bl, blk & dp bl . . 35 25

425 Second Class Letters

426 Hydraulic Turbine Manufacture

1984. Re-classification of Postal Items.
1056 **425** 1m.10 green 35 20
1057 – 1m.40 orange & red . . 35 20
DESIGN—VERT: 1m.40, First class letter.

1984. "Work and Skill" Centenary of Workers' Associations.
1058 **426** 1m.40 multicoloured . . 45 25

427 Crossbow, Pot and Chalice

428 Bridge

1984. Museum Activities.
1059 **427** 1m.40 multicoloured . . 45 25

1984. Europa. 25th Anniv of European Post and Telecommunications Conference.
1060 **428** 1m.40 orange, deep orange and black . . . 1·50 25
1061 2m. blue, violet and black . . . . 3·25 1·00

429 Globe as Jigsaw Puzzle

430 Teeth and Dentist treating Patient

1984. Finnish Red Cross Fund. Multicoloured.
1062 1m.40+35p. Type **429** . . . 45 70
1063 2m.+40p. Spheres around globe 45 75

1984. International Dental Federation Congress, Helsinki.
1064 **430** 1m.40 multicoloured . . 35 25

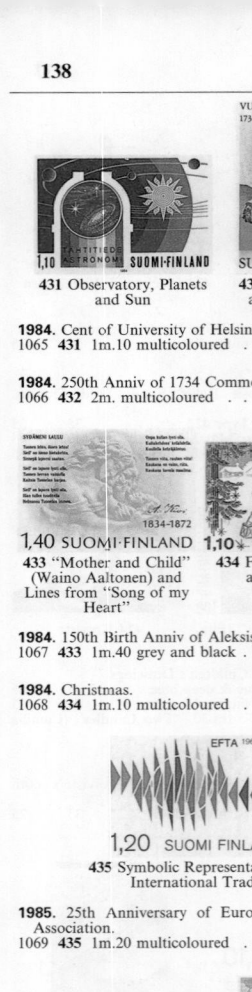

431 Observatory, Planets and Sun
432 Statute Book and Title Page

1984. Cent of University of Helsinki Observatory.
1065 **431** 1m.10 multicoloured . . 35 30

1984. 250th Anniv of 1734 Common Law.
1066 **432** 2m. multicoloured . . . 55 50

433 "Mother and Child" (Waino Aaltonen) and Lines from "Song of my Heart"
434 Father Christmas and Brownie

1984. 150th Birth Anniv of Aleksis Kivi (writer).
1067 **433** 1m.40 grey and black . . 45 25

1984. Christmas.
1068 **434** 1m.10 multicoloured . . 35 25

435 Symbolic Representation of International Trade

1985. 25th Anniversary of European Free Trade Association.
1069 **435** 1m.20 multicoloured . . 35 35

436 Medal of Johan Ludwig Runeberg (by Walter Runeberg) and Emblem
437 "Saints Sergei and Herman" (icon, Petros Sasaki)

1985. Centenary of Society of Swedish Literature in Finland.
1070 **436** 1m.50 multicoloured . . 45 25

1985. Centenary of Saint Sergei and Saint Herman Order (home missionary organization of Finnish Orthodox Church).
1071 **437** 1m.50 multicoloured . . 45 25

438 Pedri Semeikka (rune singer)
439 "Mermaid" (Ville Vallgren)

1985. 150th Anniv of "Kalevala" (Karelian poems collected by Elias Lonnrot). Multicoloured.
1072 1m.50 Type **438** 35 35
1073 2m.10 Larin Paraske (legend teller) (after Albert Edelfelt) 55 50

1985. "Nordia 1985" International Stamp Exhibition, Helsinki.
1074 **439** 1m.50 black, grey and blue . . . . 2·20 3·25

440 1886 5m. Banknote
441 Children playing Recorders

1985. Centenary of Finnish Banknote Printing. Multicoloured.
1075 1m.50 Type **440** 55 50
1076 1m.50 1909 50m. banknote showing sailing ship (horiz) 55 50
1077 1m.50 50m. banknote showing waterfall 55 50
1078 1m.50 1000m. banknote showing lake (left side) . . 55 50
1079 1m.50 1000m. banknote showing lake (right side) 55 50
1080 1m.50 500m. banknote showing harvesters . . . 55 50
1081 1m.50 1000m. banknote showing arms and tree, and part of 50m. banknote (horiz) 55 50
1082 1m.50 1955 5000m. banknote showing J. V. Snellman 55 50

1985. Europa. Music Year. Multicoloured.
1083 1m.50 Type **441** . . . . . 3·25 25
1084 2m.10 Cathedral columns and score of "Ramus Virens Olivarum" . . . . 3·10 1·10

442 Finlandia Hall and Barn Swallow
443 Provincial Arms and Seal of Per Brahe

1985. 10th Anniv of European Security and Co-operation Conference, Helsinki.
1085 **442** 2m.10 multicoloured . . 55 55

1985. 350th Anniv of Provincial Administration.
1086 **443** 1m.50 multicoloured . . 45 25

444 Foot Messenger

1985. "Finlandia 88" International Stamp Exhibition, Helsinki (1st issue). Sheet 135×90 mm containing T **444** and similar multicoloured designs forming a composite design of 1698 postal map of Sweden and Finland.
MS1087 1m.50 Type **444**; 1m.50 Raft; 1m.50 Mounted messanger (vert); 1m.50 Iceboat (sold at 8m.) 5·50 7·25
See also Nos. **MS**1107, **MS**1122, 1149 and **MS**1152.

445 I.Y.Y. Emblem
446 Bird Decoration and Tulips

1985. International Youth Year.
1088 **445** 1m.50 multicoloured . . 45 25

1985. Christmas. Multicoloured.
1089 1m.20 Type **446** 35 25
1090 1m.20 St. Thomas's cross and hyacinths 35 25

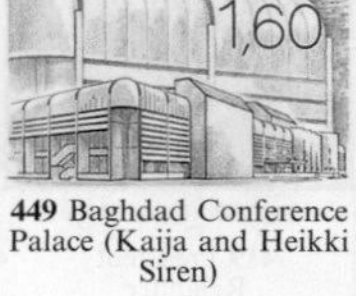

447 Orbicular Granite
449 Baghdad Conference Palace (Kaija and Heikki Siren)

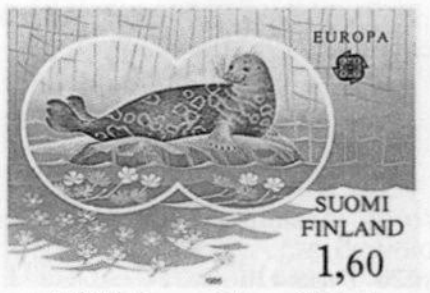

448 Saimaa Ringed Seal

1986. Centenary of Geological Society. Mult.
1091 1m.30 Type **447** 40 35
1092 1m.60 Rapakivi (granite) . . 40 25
1093 2m.10 Veined gneiss 40 35

1986. Europa. Multicoloured.
1094 1m.60 Type **448** . . . . . 2·50 25
1095 2m.20 Landscape seen through window . . . . 3·25 80

1986. Modern Architecture. Multicoloured.
1096 1m.60 Type **449** 45 45
1097 1m.60 Lahti Theatre (Pekka Salminen and Esko Koivisto) (value in blue) 45 45
1098 1m.60 Kuusamo Municipal Offices (Marja and Keijo Petaja) (value in red) . 45 45
1099 1m.60 Hamina police and court building (Timo and Tuomo Suomalainen) and Greek church (value in green) 45 45
1100 1m.60 Finnish Embassy, New Delhi (Raili and Reima Pietila) (value in green) 45 45
1101 1m.60 Day care centre, Western Sakyla (Kari Jarvinen and Timo Airas) (value in red) 45 45

450 Orange-tip
451 Auditorium, Joensuu

1986. Finnish Red Cross Fund. Butterflies. Multicoloured.
1102 1m.60+40p. Type **450** . . . 75 75
1103 2m.10+45p. Camberwell beauty . . . . 1·20 1·50
1104 5m.+50p. Apollo . . . . . 2·00 2·30

1986. Nordic Countries' Postal Co-operation. Twinned Towns. Multicoloured.
1105 1m.60 Type **451** 45 25
1106 2m.20 Emblem of University of Jyvaskyla 55 70

452 Paddle-steamer "Aura"

1986. "Finlandia 88" International Stamp Exhibition, Helsinki (2nd issue). Sheet 135×90 mm containing T **452** and similar designs, each deep brown and buff.
MS1107 1m.60 Type **452**; 1m.60 Steamship "Alexander"; 2m.20 Steamship "Nicolai"; 2m.20 Ice-breaker "Express II" (vert) (sold at 10m.) . . . . 5·50 7·25

453 Maupertuis, Globe, Quadrant and Sledge

1986. 250th Anniv of Measurement of Arcs of Meridian.
1108 **453** 1m.60 bl, ultram & blk 45 25

454 Kekkonen
455 Cloud, Rainbow and Emblem

1986. Urho Kekkonen (President, 1956–81). Commemoration.
1109 **454** 5m. black . . . . 1·20 65

1986. International Peace Year.
1110 **455** 1m.60 multicoloured . . . 45 25

456 Angels and Garland

1986. Christmas. Multicoloured.
1111 1m.30 Type **456** 55 25
1112 1m.30 Angels and garland (different) 55 25
1113 1m.60 Brownies and garland 45 25

457 Microchip
458 Prototype Metre Measuring Bar as Parcel

1987. Centenary of Postal Savings Bank.
1114 **457** 1m.70 multicoloured . . 45 30

1987. Centenary of Metric System in Finland.
1115 **458** 1m.40 multicoloured . . 35 45

459 "Borea" (liner), Diesel Train, Snow Scene and Skier
460 Wrestlers

1987. Tourism. Multicoloured.
1116 1m.70 Type **459** 45 25
1117 2m.30 Douglas DC-10 airplane, bus, yachts on lake and hiker 55 70

1987. European Wrestling Championships, Helsinki.
1118 **460** 1m.70 multicoloured . . 60 30

461 Madetoja and Score of Cradlesong
462 Balls and Pins

1987. Birth Centenary of Leevi Madetoja (composer).
1119 **461** 2m.10 multicoloured . . 55 30

1987. 11th World Ten Pin Bowling Championships.
1120 **462** 1m.70 multicoloured . . 45 30

463 Profiles
465 "Strawberry Girl" (Nils Schillmark)

464 Locomotive "Lemminkainen", 1862

1987. 90th Anniv of Finnish Association for Mental Health.
1121 **463** 1m.70 multicoloured . . 45 25

1987. "Finlandia 88" International Stamp Exhibition, Helsinki (3rd issue). Sheet 135 × 90 mm containing T **464** and similar horiz designs, depicting trains on the Helsinki–Hameenlinna and Riihimaki–St. Petersburg routes.
MS1122 1m.70 green, orange and blue (Type **464**); 1m.70 multicoloured (Mail van No. 9935, 1871); 1m.70 multicoloured (Mail van No. 9991, 1899); 2m.30 green and blue (Locomotive No. 57, 1874) (sold at 10m.) . . . . . 5·50 7·25

1987. Centenary of Ateneum Art Museum. Paintings. Multicoloured.
1123 1m.70 Type **465** . . . . . 1·00 55
1124 1m.70 "Still Life on a Lady's Work-table" (Ferdinand von Wright) 1·00 55
1125 1m.70 "Old Woman with Basket" (Albert Edelfelt) 1·00 55
1126 1m.70 "Boy and Crow" (Akseli Gallen-Kallela) . . 1·00 55
1127 1m.70 "Late Winter" (Tyko Sallinen) . . . . 1·00 55

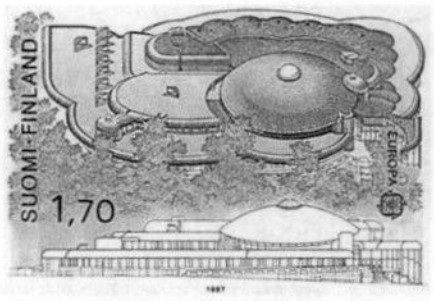

466 Tampere Main Library (Railia and Reima Pietila)

467 Arrows

1987. Europa. Art and Architecture. Mult.
1128 1m.70 Type **466** . . . . . 2·75 30
1129 2m.30 "Stoa" (Hannu Siren) 3·75 1·00

1987. 7th European Physics Society General Conference.
1130 **467** 1m.70 multicoloured . . 45 25

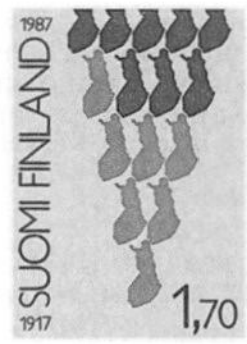

468 Outline Maps of Finland

469 Baby with Ball and Prof. Ylppo

1987. 70th Anniv of Independence.
1131 **468** 1m.70 silver, grey & bl 45 25
1132 10m. silver, blue and azure (26 × 37 mm) . . 2·30 1·30

1987. 100th Birthday of Arvo Ylppo (paediatrician).
1133 **469** 1m.70 multicoloured . . 55 25

470 Father Christmas and Brownies

471 Birds flying from Globe to Finland

1987. Christmas. Multicoloured.
1134 1m.40 Type **470** 45 25
1135 1m.70 Mother Christmas and brownie (vert) . . . 40 25

1987. Centenary of Finnish News Agency.
1136 **471** 2m.30 multicoloured . . 55 75

472 Pihkala

473 Telephone and Mail Boxes

1988. Birth Centenary of Lauri Pihkala ("Tahko") (writer and sport organizer).
1137 **472** 1m.80 deep blue, blue and black 45 25

1988. 350th Anniv of Posts and Telecommunications Services (1st issue). Multicoloured.
1138 1m.80 Type **473** 90 25
1139 1m.80 Airplane and lorry 90 25
1140 1m.80 Fork-lift truck carrying parcels 90 25
1141 1m.80 Postman 90 25
1142 1m.80 Woman receiving letter 90 25

Nos. 1138/42 were printed together, se-tenant, Nos. 1141/2 forming a composite design.
See also Nos. 1165/70.

474 Conifer Branches (Christmas)

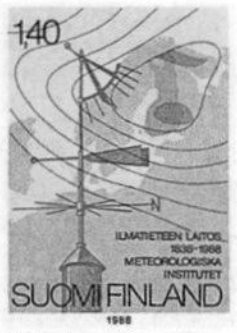

475 Weather Chart and Measuring Equipment

1988. Finnish Red Cross Fund. Festivals. Multicoloured.
1143 1m.40+40p. Type **474** . . . 45 55
1144 1m.80+45p. Narcissi (Easter) 45 65
1145 2m.40+50p. Rose (Midsummer) . . . . . . 80 1·00

1988. 150th Anniv of Meteorological Institute.
1146 **475** 1m.40 multicoloured . . 45 25

476 Map, Settlers, Indians, "Calmare Nyckel" and "Fagel Grip"

1988. 350th Anniv of Founding of New Sweden (Finnish and Swedish settlement in North America).
1147 **476** 3m. multicoloured . . . 90 55

477 Matti Nykanen (triple gold medal winner)

478 Agathon Faberge (philatelist)

1988. Finnish Success at Winter Olympic Games, Calgary.
1148 **477** 1m.80 multicoloured . . 45 30

1988. "Finlandia 88" International Stamp Exhibition, Helsinki.
1149 **478** 5m. multicoloured . . . 11·00 12·00

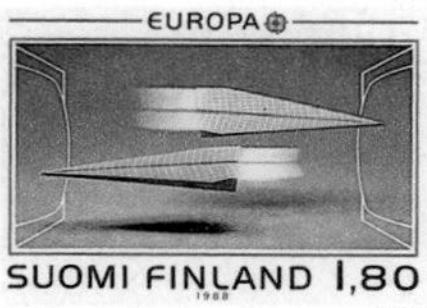

479 Paper Airplanes between VDUs

1988. Europa. Transport and Communications. Multicoloured.
1150 1m.80 Type **479** . . . . . 3·25 25
1151 2m.40 Horse tram, 1890 . . 3·75 95

480 Breguet 14 Biplane with Skis

1988. "Finlandia 88" International Stamp Exhibition, Helsinki (5th issue). Sheet 135 × 90 mm containing T **480** and similar horiz designs.
MS1152 1m.80 blue and red (Type **480**); 1m.80 blue and mauve (Junkers F-13); 1m.80 blue and orange (Douglas DC-3); 2m.40 ultramarine and blue (Douglas DC-10-30) (sold at 11m.) . . . 6·50 8·50

481 Steam-driven Fire Pump, Turku Fire Brigade

482 "Missale Aboense" and Illuminated Page

1988. 150th Anniv of Fire Brigades in Finland.
1163 **481** 2m.20 multicoloured . . 55 45

1988. 500th Anniv of Publishing of "Missale Aboense" (first printed book for Finland).
1164 **482** 1m.80 multicoloured . . 45 25

483 1638 Postal Tariffs

484 Teacher with Children

1988. 350th Anniv of Posts and Telecommunications Services (2nd issue). Multicoloured.
1165 1m.80 Type **483** 55 35
1166 1m.80 Rural postman, 1860s 55 35
1167 1m.80 Postman delivering from mail van 55 35
1168 1m.80 Malmi Post Office . . 55 35
1169 1m.80 Skiers using mobile telephone 55 35
1170 1m.80 Communications satellite 55 35

1988. Church Playgroups.
1171 **484** 1m.80 multicoloured . . 45 25

485 Decorations

486 Market Place, Town Plan and Arms

1988. Christmas.
1172 **485** 1m.40 multicoloured . . 45 25
1173 1m.80 multicoloured . . 45 25

1989. 350th Anniv of Hameenlinna Town Charter.
1174 **486** 1m.90 multicoloured . . 55 25

487 Skier

488 Photographer with Box Camera on Tripod

1989. World Skiing Championships, Lahti.
1175 **487** 1m.90 multicoloured . . 45 25

1989. 150th Anniv of Photography.
1176 **488** 1m.50 multicoloured . . 45 35

489 Christmas Collection

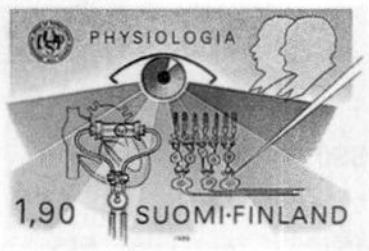

490 Professors Tigerstedt and Granit and Research Fields

1989. Cent of Salvation Army in Finland.
1177 **489** 1m.90 multicoloured . . 55 25

1989. 31st International Physiological Sciences Congress, Helsinki.
1178 **490** 1m.90 multicoloured . . 45 25

491 Skiing

1989. Sport. Multicoloured.
1179 1m.90 Type **491** 55 40
1180 1m.90 Jogging 55 40
1181 1m.90 Cycling 55 40
1182 1m.90 Canoeing 55 40

492 Lapponian Herder

1989. Centenary of Finnish Kennel Club. Sheet 114 × 90 mm containing T **492** and similar horiz designs. Multicoloured.
MS1183 1m.90 Type **492**; 1m.90 Finnish spitz; 1m.90 Karelian bear dog; 1m.90 Finnish hound . . 3·25 3·25

493 Hopscotch

1989. Europa. Children's Activities. Mult.
1184 1m.90 Type **493** . . . . . 1·40 25
1185 2m.50 Sledging . . . . . . 2·30 65

494 Man from Sakyla

495 Foxglove and Pharmaceutical Equipment

1989. Nordic Countries' Postal Co-operation. Traditional Costumes. Multicoloured.
1186 1m.90 Type **494** 55 25
1187 2m.50 Woman from Veteli 65 65

1989. 300th Anniv of Pharmacies in Finland.
1188 **495** 1m.90 multicoloured . . 55 25

496 Snow Leopard

497 Savonlinna

1989. Cent of Helsinki Zoo. Multicoloured.
1189 1m.90 Type **496** 55 25
1190 2m.50 Markhor goat . . . 65 60

1989. 350th Anniv of Savonlinna.
1191 **497** 1m.90 multicoloured . . 45 25

498 Brown Bear

499 Open Book and Mercury's Staff

1989.
1192 **498** 50m. multicoloured . . . 11·00 8·00

1989. 150th Anniv of Commercial Studies in Finland.
1193 **499** 1m.50 multicoloured . . 45 35

500 Emblem and Columns in Finland's Parliament

1989. Cent of Interparliamentary Union.
1194 **500** 1m.90 multicoloured . . 55 30

501 Bridges

1989. Accession of Finland to, and 40th Anniv of Council of Europe.
1195 **501** 2m.50 multicoloured . . 65 55

502 Kolehmainen winning 5000 m, Olympic Games, 1912

503 Students, Open Book and Keyboard

1989. Birth Cent of Hannes Kolehmainen (runner).
1196 **502** 1m.90 multicoloured . . 55 25

1989. Centenary of Folk High Schools.
1197 **503** 1m.90 multicoloured . . 45 30

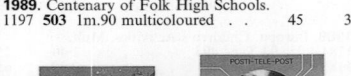

504 Decorated Street

505 Emblem and Lake Paijanne

1989. Christmas. Multicoloured.
1198 1m.50 Type **504** 40 25
1199 1m.90 Sodankyla Church, Lapland 70 25

1990. Formation of Posts and Telecommunications into State Commercial Company.
1200 **505** 1m.90 multicoloured . . 60 75
1201 2m.50 multicoloured . . 65 1·10

506 Wood Anemone (Uusimaa province)

507 Erik Ferling (first orchestra leader) conducting

1990. Provincial Plants. Multicoloured.
1205 2m. Type **506** 55 25
1206 2m.10 Rowan (Northern Savo) 55 25
1207 2m.70 Heather (Kainuu) . . 70 25
1208 2m.90 Shrub sea buck-thorn (Satakunta) 75 25
1209 3m.50 Oak (Varsinais Suomi) 95 35
No. 1206 also comes self-adhesive and imperforate.
See also Nos. 1273/4, 1303, 1309, 1327 and 1354.

1990. Bicentenary of Foundation of Turku Musical Society (first Finnish orchestra).
1220 **507** 1m.90 multicoloured . . 55 30

508 Snowflake

509 Disabled Ex-serviceman

1990. 50th Anniv of End of Russo–Finnish Winter War.
1221 **508** 2m. blue & ultramarine 45 25

1990. 50th Anniv of Disabled Ex-servicemen's Association.
1222 **509** 2m. multicoloured . . . 55 25

510 Nuvvus Postal Agency

1990. Europa. Post Office Buildings. Mult.
1223 2m. Type **510** . . . . . 1·60 25
1224 2m.70 Turku Postal Centre 2·50 40

511 Queen Christina

1990. 350th Anniv of Grant of Charter to Turku Academy (later Helsinki University). Mult.
1225 2m. Type **511** 55 30
1226 3m.20 Main building of Helsinki University . . . 80 70

512 Scarce Copper on Goldrod

1990. Finnish Red Cross Fund. Butterflies. Multicoloured.
1227 1m.50+40p. Type **512** . . . 45 70
1228 2m.+50p. Amanda's blue on meadow vetchling 65 95
1229 2m.70+60p. Peacock on tufted vetch . . . . . . 95 1·10
See also Nos. 1279/81.

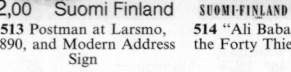

513 Postman at Larsmo, 1890, and Modern Address Sign

514 "Ali Baba and the Forty Thieves"

1990. Compilation of Address Register and Centenary of Rural Postal Service.
1230 **513** 2m. multicoloured . . . 55 25

1990. Birth Centenary of Rudolf Koivu (artist). Designs showing Koivu's illustrations of fairy tales. Multicoloured.
1231 2m. Type **514** 45 35
1232 2m. "The Great Musician" (Raul Roine) 45 35
1233 2m. "The Giants, the Witches and the Daughter of the Sun" (Koivu) . . . 45 35
1234 2m. "The Golden Bird, the Golden Horse and the Princess" (Grimm Brothers) 45 35
1235 2m. "Lamb Brother" (Koivu) 45 35
1236 2m. "The Snow Queen" (Hans Christian Andersen) 45 35

515 Youth feeding Horse

1990. Youth Hobbies. Horse Riding. Sheet 118 × 63 mm containing T **515** and similar vert designs. Multicoloured.
MS1237 2m. Type **515**; 2m. Two riders; 2m. Girl saddling pony; 2m. Girl grooming horse . . . . . 4·25 4·50

516 Brownies dealing with Father Christmas's Mail

517 Player and Turku Castle

1990. Christmas. Multicoloured.
1238 1m.70 Type **516** 55 25
1239 2m. Father Christmas and reindeer 60 25

1991. World Ice Hockey Championship, Turku, Tampere and Helsinki.
1246 **517** 2m.10 multicoloured . . 55 30

518 Teacher and Pupils preparing Meal

519 "Green Still Life"

1991. Cent of Domestic Science Teacher Training.
1247 **518** 2m.10 multicoloured . . 55 25

1991. Pro Filatelia. Paintings by Helene Schjerfbeck. Multicoloured.
1248 2m.10+50p. Type **519** . . . 90 1·50
1249 2m.10+50p. "The Little Convalescent" . . . . . 90 1·70

520 Great Tit

521 Fly-fishing for RainbowTrout

1991. Birds (1st series). Multicoloured.
1250 10p. Type **520** 20 25
1251 60p. Pair of chaffinches . . 75 30
1252 2m.10 Northern bullfinch . . 45 25
See also Nos. 1282/4 and 1322/4.

1991. Centenary of Central Fishery Organization. Multicoloured.
1253 2m.10 Type **521** 50 35
1254 2m.10 Stylized Eurasian perch and float 50 35
1255 2m.10 Stylized fish and crayfish 50 35
1256 2m.10 Trawling for Baltic herring 50 35
1257 2m.10 Restocking with whitefish from lorry . . . 50 35

522 Seurasaari Island

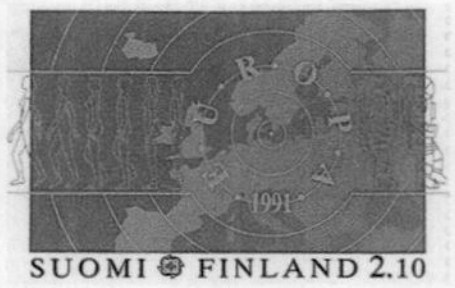

523 Map of Europe and Human Figures

1991. Nordic Countries' Postal Co-operation. Multicoloured.
1258 2m.10 Type **522** 55 25
1259 2m.90 Saimaa ferry 75 50

1991. Europa. Europe in Space. Mult.
1260 2m.10 Type **523** . . . . . 2·30 30
1261 2m.90 Map of Europe, satellites and dish aerials 3·25 55

524 Iris Vase

525 Kittens and "Kiss-Kiss" Sweet

1991. 61st Death Anniv of Alfred Finch (painter and ceramic artist). Multicoloured.
1262 2m.10 Type **524** 65 25
1263 2m.90 "The English Coast at Dover" 90 55

1991. Centenary of Opening of Karl Fazer's Confectionery (beginning of Finnish Sweet Industry).
1264 **525** 2m.10 multicoloured . . 55 25

526 "Sun" (Kaisa Niemi)

527 Leisure Skiing

1991. Children's Stamp Design Competition Winners. Sheet 100 × 60 mm containing T **526** and similar horiz design. Multicoloured.
MS1265 2m.10 Type **526**; 2m.10 "Rainbow" (Elina Aro); 2m.10 "Cows grazing" (Noora Kaunisto) 2·75 2·75

1991. Youth Hobbies. Skiing. Sheet 118 × 64 mm containing T **527** and similar vert designs. Mult.
MS1266 2m.10 Type **527**; 2m.10 Ski-boarding; 2m.10 Freestyle skiing; 2m.10 Speed skating . . . . . 3·25 3·25

528 Iisalmi

529 Forest Animals and Elf

1991. Centenary of Granting of Town Rights to Iisalmi.
1267 **528** 2m.10 multicoloured . . 55 30

1991. Christmas. Multicoloured.
1268 1m.80 Type **529** 45 25
1269 2m.10 Father Christmas in sleigh over new Arctic Circle post office (vert) . . 70 25

530 Camphor Molecule and Erlenmeyer Flask

531 Skiing

1991. Cent of Organized Chemistry in Finland.
1270 **530** 2m.10 multicoloured . . 75 25
No. 1270 covers either of two stamps which were issued together as a horizontal gutter pair, the stamps differing very slightly in the diagram of the molecule. The gutter pair is stated to produce a three-dimensional image without use of a special viewer.

1992. Winter Olympic Games, Albertville (1271) and Summer Games, Barcelona (1272). Multicoloured.
1271 2m.10 Type **531** 70 25
1272 2m.90 Swimming 80 40

532 Globe Flower (Lapland)

533 Finnish Exhibition Emblem

1992. Provincial Plants. With service indicator. Multicoloured.
1273 2KLASS (1m.60) Type **532** 75 25
1274 1KLASS (2m.10) Hepatica (Hame) 95 25
See also Nos. 1303, 1309, 1327 and 1354.

1992. "Expo '92" World's Fair, Seville.
1275 **533** 3m.40 multicoloured . . 85 75

534 Map of Europe

1992. 3rd Meeting of Council of Foreign Ministers of European Security and Co-operation Conference, Helsinki.
1276 **534** 16m. multicoloured . . . 4·50 3·25

535 Church of the Holy Cross, Town Hall and Brigantine

536 Thoughts within Head

1992. 550th Anniv of Rauma Town Charter.
1277 **535** 2m.10 multicoloured . . 60 25

1992. Healthy Brains Campaign.
1278 **536** 3m.50 multicoloured . . 90 1·00

1992. Finnish Red Cross Fund. Centenary of Training of Visually Handicapped. Moths. As T **512**. Multicoloured.
1279 1m.60+40p. Taiga dart . . . 80 90
1280 2m.10+50p. Fjeld tiger . . . 90 1·10
1281 5m.+60p. Baneberry looper moth . . . . 1·80 2·30

537 Pied Wagtail

538 "Santa Maria" and Route Map

1992. Birds (2nd series). Multicoloured.
1282 10p. Type **537** 20 35
1283 60p. European robin . . . . 1·00 85
1284 2m.10 Three Bohemian waxwings 55 40

1992. Europa. 500th Anniv of Discovery of America by Columbus. Multicoloured.
1285 2m.10 Type **538** . . . . . 1·20 25
1286 2m.10 Route map and Columbus . . . . 1·20 25
Nos. 1285/6 were issued together, se-tenant, forming a composite design.

539 Blowing Machine (first Finnish patent, 150th anniv)

540 Currant Harvesting

1992. Technology. Multicoloured.
1287 2m.10 Type **539** (50th anniv of National Board of Patents and Registration of Trademarks) 55 65
1288 2m.90 Triangles and circuits (Finnish chairmanship of EUREKA (European technology development scheme)) 75 75
1289 3m.40 Inverted triangles (50th anniv of Government Technology Research Centre) 95 80

1992. Cent of National Board of Agriculture.
1290 **540** 2m.10 multicoloured . . 60 25

541 Aurora Karamzin

542 Flag in Garden (Niina Pennanen)

1992. Notable Finnish Women. Mult.
1291 2m.10 Type **541** (founder of Helsinki Deaconesses' Institution) 75 50
1292 2m.10 Sophie Mannerheim (nursing pioneer) 75 50
1293 2m.10 Laimi Leidenius (Professor of Obstetrics and Gynaecology, Helsinki University) . . . 75 50
1294 2m.10 Miina Sillanpaa (first woman Cabinet Minister) 75 50
1295 2m.10 Edith Sodergran (poet) 75 50
1296 2m.10 Kreetta Haapasalo (folk singer) 75 50

1992. 75th Anniv of Independence.
1297 **542** 2m.10 multicoloured . . 60 25
MS1298 116 × 53 mm. 2m.10 Birds and birch grove (29 × 36 mm) 95 85

543 Moomin looking into River ("Moominland Midwinter")

544 Rosebay Willowherb (Etela-Pohjanmaa)

1992. "Nordia 1993" International Stamp Exhibition. Stamp Day. Designs showing illustrations from her stories by Tove Jansson. Multicoloured.
1299 2m.10 Type **543** . . . . . 1·90 50
1300 2m.10 Moomin and trolls ("Moominland Midwinter") . . . . . . 1·90 50
1301 2m.10 Theatre performance on water ("Moomin Summer Madness") . . . 1·90 50
1302 2m.10 Moomin and inhabitants ("Tales from Moomin Valley") . . . . 1·90 50

1992. Provincial Plants. With service indicator. Self-adhesive. Imperf.
1303 **544** 1KLASS (2m.10) mult 95 25

545 Computerized and Hot Metal Typesetting

546 St. Lawrence's Church, Vantaa

1992. 350th Anniv of Printing in Finland.
1304 **545** 2m.10 multicoloured . . 55 25

1992. Christmas. Multicoloured.
1305 1m.80 Type **546** 60 25
1306 2m.10 Stained glass window, Karkkila Church (vert) . . 60 25

547 Couple

548 Birds, Flowers and Envelope within Heart

1993. 75th Anniv of Central Chamber of Commerce.
1307 **547** 1m.60 multicoloured . . 45 45

1993. Friendship.
1308 **548** 1KLASS (2m.10) mult 95 25

549 Iris (Kymenlaakso)

550 Fox in Winter Coat

1993. Provincial Plants. With service indicator. Self-adhesive. Imperf.
1309 **549** 2KLASS (1m.90) mult 80 30

1993. Endangered Species. The Arctic Fox. Multicoloured.
1310 2m.30 Type **550** 95 60
1311 2m.30 Two foxes in winter coat 95 60
1312 2m.30 Mother with young in summer coat 95 60
1313 2m.30 Two foxes in summer coat 95 60

551 "Autumn Landscape of Lake Pielisjarvi" (left half)

1993. Pro Filatelia. 130th Birth Anniv of Eero Jarnefelt (painter). Multicoloured.
1314 2m.30+70p. Type **551** . . . 85 1·20
1315 2m.30+70p. "Autumn Landscape of Lake Pielisjarvi" (right half) . . 85 1·20
Nos. 1314/15 were issued together, se-tenant, forming a composite design of the entire painting.

552 "Rumba" (Martti Aiha)

553 Burnet Rose

1993. Europa Contemporary Art. Sculptures. Multicoloured.
1316 2m. Type **552** 95 25
1317 2m.90 "Complete Works" (Kari Caven) . . . . . . 1·40 55

1993. Centenary of Helsinki Philatelic Association.
1318 **553** 2m.30 multicoloured . . 75 55

554 Castle and Courier Route Map

1993. 700th Anniv of Vyborg Castle.
1319 **554** 2m.30 multicoloured . . 55 25

555 Naantali

556 Tengmalm's Owl

1993. Nordic Countries' Postal Co-operation. Tourism. Multicoloured.
1320 2m.30 Type **555** 65 25
1321 2m.90 Imatra 80 50

1993. Birds (3rd series). Multicoloured.
1322 10p. Type **556** 20 50
1323 20p. Common redstart . . . 2·20 1·50
1324 2m.30 White-backed woodpecker 55 50

557 Finnish Landscape in Soldier's Silhouette

558 Labrador Tea (Northern Ostrobothnia)

1993. 75th Anniv of Military Forces. Mult.
1325 2m.30 Type **557** 55 25
1326 3m.40 Checkpoint of Finnish soldiers serving with U.N. peacekeeping force . . . . 1·00 75

1993. Provincial Plants. With service indicator. Self-adhesive. Imperf.
1327 **558** 1KLASS (2m.30) mult 1·00 25

559 Child skiing (cover illustration from "Kotiliesi")

561 Gymnastics and Football

560 Flock of Black-throated Divers

1993. Birth Centenary of Martta Wendelin (artist). Multicoloured.
1328 2m.30 Type **559** 80 40
1329 2m.30 Mother and daughter knitting (illustration from "First Book of the Home and School") 80 40
1330 2m.30 Children making snowman (illustration from "First Book of the Home and School") . . . 80 40
1331 2m.30 Rural scene (postcard) 80 40
1332 2m.30 Young girl and lamb (cover illustration from "Kotiliesi") 80 40

1993. Water Birds. Multicoloured.
1333 2m.30 Type **560** 95 80
1334 2m.30 Pair of black-throated divers ("Gavia arctica") (53 × 28 mm) 95 80
1335 2m.30 Goosander ("Mergus merganser") (26 × 39 mm) 95 80
1336 2m.30 Mallards ("Anas platy rhynchos") (26 × 39 mm) 95 80
1337 2m.30 Red-breasted merganser ("Mergus serrator") (26 × 39 mm) 95 80

1993. 150th Anniv of Compulsory Physical Education in Schools.
1338 **561** 2m.30 multicoloured . . 55 25

562 "Ostobothnians" (Leevi Madetoja)

1993. Inauguration of New National Opera House. Sheet 120 × 80 mm containing T **562** and similar horiz designs showing scenes from operas and ballets. Multicoloured.
MS1339 2m.30 Type **562**; 2m.30 "The Faun" (Claude Debussy, choreographed by Jorma Uotinen); 2m.90 "The Magic Flute" (Mozart); 3m.40 "Giselle" (Adolphe Adam) . . . . . . 4·25 4·00

563 Brownies and Christmas Tree (Anna Kymalainen)

564 Koivisto

1993. Christmas. Children's Drawings. Mult.
1340 1m.80 Type **563** 55 25
1341 2m.30 Three angels and star (Taina Tuomola) 55 25

1993. 70th Birthday of President Mauno Koivisto.
1342 **564** 2m.30 multicoloured . . 55 30

565 "Moominland Winter"

566 Marja-Liisa Kirvesniemi and Marjo Matikainen

1994. Moomin. With service indicator. Illustrations from her stories by Tove Jansson. Multicoloured.
1343 1klass (2m.30) Type **565** . . 95 25
1344 1klass (2m.30) "Moominland Storm" . . 95 25

1994. "Finlandia 95" International Stamp Exhibition, Helsinki (1st issue) and Centenary of International Olympic Committee. Sheet 120 × 80 mm containing T **566** and similar vert designs showing Finnish Winter Olympic Games Competitors. Multicoloured.
MS1345 4m.20 Type **566**; 4m.20 Clas Thunberg; 4m.20 Veikko Kankkonen; 4m.20 Veikko Hakulinen . . . . 5·50 6·25

567 "Peace"

1994. Birth Centenary of Waino Aaltonen (sculptor). Multicoloured.

1346	2m. Type **567**	60	25
1347	2m. "Muse"	60	25

568 Postal Clerk and Customer

1994. Centenary of Postal Service Civil Servants Federation.

1348	**568** 2m.30 multicoloured	55	25

569 Ploughing

1994. Finnish Red Cross Fund. Horses. Multicoloured.

1349	2m. Type **569**	50	85
1350	2m.30 Marinka (trotting horse)	60	95
1351	4m.20 Cavalry horses (vert)	1·40	1·80

570 Paper Roll, Nitrogen-fixing Technique, Padlock and "Fennica" (ice-breaker)

571 Rose (North Karelia)

1994. Europa. Discoveries and Inventions. Multicoloured.

1352	2m.30 Type **570**	65	40
1353	4m.20 Balloon, radiosonde, mobile telephone, fishing lure and lake oxygenation equipment	1·60	1·30

1994. Provincial Plants. With service indicator. Self-adhesive. Imperf.

1354	**571** 1KLASS (2m.30) mult	95	30

572 Riitta Salin and Pirjo Haggman (runners)

1994. "Finlandia 95" International Stamp Exhibition (2nd issue) and European Athletics Championships, Helsinki. Sheet 120 × 80 mm containing T **572** and similar vert designs showing Finnish athletes. Multicoloured.

MS1355	4m.20 Type **572**; 4m.20 Lasse Viren (runner); 4m.20 Tiina Lillak (javelin thrower); 4m.20 Pentti Nikula (pole vaulter)	5·50	6·25

573 Seven-spotted Ladybirds

1994. "Finlandia 95" International Stamp Exhibition, Helsinki.

1356	**573** 16m. multicoloured	5·25	5·00

See also No. 1393.

574 Perforate St. John's Wort ("Hypericum perforatum")

575 Patrik Sjoberg (high jump)

1994. Flowers. With service indicator. Mult.

1357	1klass (2m.30) Type **574**	95	35
1358	1klass (2m.30) Sticky catchfly ("Lychnis viscaria")	95	35
1359	1klass (2m.30) Harebell ("Campanula rotundifolia")	95	35
1360	1klass (2m.30) Clustered bellflower ("Campanula glomerata")	95	35
1361	1klass (2m.30) Bloody cranesbill ("Geranium sanguineum")	95	35
1362	1klass (2m.30) Wild strawberry ("Fragaria vesca")	95	35
1363	1klass (2m.30) Germander speedwell ("Veronica chamaedrys")	95	35
1364	1klass (2m.30) Meadow saxifrage ("Saxifraga granulata")	95	35
1365	1klass (2m.30) Wild pansy ("Viola tricolor")	95	35
1366	1klass (2m.30) Silver-weed ("Potentilla anserina")	95	35

1994. Sweden–Finland Athletics Meeting, Stockholm. Multicoloured.

1367	2m.40 Sepo Raty (javelin)	55	30
1368	2m.40 Type **575**	55	30

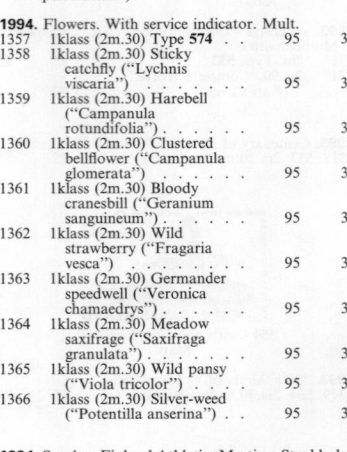

576 Crowd on Registration List

577 Emblem

1994. 450th Anniv of Population Registers.

1369	**576** 2m.40 multicoloured	65	25

1994. International Year of the Family.

1370	**577** 3m.40 multicoloured	95	65

578 Postman greeting Woman

1994. Stamp Day. Dog Hill Kids (cartoon characters) at the Post Office. Sheet 112 × 88 mm containing T **578** and similar horiz designs. Mult.

MS1371	2m.80 Type **578**; 2m.80 Postmaster handing letter to postman; 2m.80 Messenger playing bugle; 2m.80 Couple posting letters	3·75	5·25

579 Northern Bullfinches on Reindeer's Antlers

580 Postman delivering Letter to Alien

1994. Christmas. Multicoloured.

1372	2m.10 Type **579**	60	25
1373	2m.80 Father and son selecting Christmas tree (vert)	70	30

1995. Greetings stamps. Multicoloured.

1374	2m.80 Type **580**	95	40
1375	2m.80 Cat writing letter	95	40
1376	2m.80 Postman delivering letter to elderly dog	95	40
1377	2m.80 Teenage dog writing letter	95	40
1378	2m.80 Dog receiving postcard	95	40
1379	2m.80 Dog on train reading letter	95	40
1380	2m.80 Guitarist dog with Valentine greeting	95	40
1381	2m.80 Baby dog	95	40

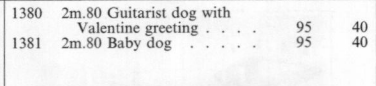

581 Paivi Ikola (Pesapallo)

1995. "Finlandia 95" International Stamp Exhibition, Helsinki (4th issue). Team Sports. Sheet containing T **581** and similar vert designs. Multicoloured.

MS1382	3m.40 Type **581**; 3m.40 Jari Kurri (ice hockey); 3m.40 Jari Litmanen (football); 3m.40 Lea Hakala (basketball)	4·75	5·25

582 Shooting Star and Stars

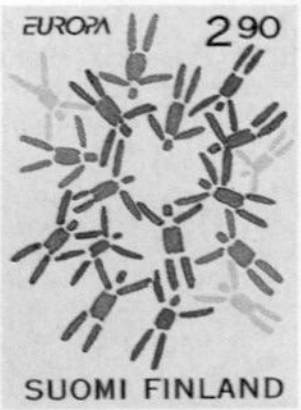

584 Figures forming Parachute

583 "Boys playing on the Shore"

1995. Admission of Finland to European Union.

1383	**582** 3m.50 blue, yell & blk	95	60

1995. Pro Filatelia. Paintings by Albert Edelfelt. Multicoloured.

1384	2m.40+60p. Type **583**	95	1·10
1385	2m.40+60p. "Queen Blanche" (21 × 30½ mm)	95	1·10

1995. Europa. Peace and Freedom.

1386	**584** 2m.90 multicoloured	1·10	80

585 Lynx

586 Daisy (Keski-Suomi)

1995. Endangered Animals. Multicoloured.

1387	2m.90 Type **585**	80	95
1388	2m.90 Landscape	80	95
1389	2m.90 Shoreline	80	95
1390	2m.90 Ringed seal	80	95

1995. Provincial Plants. With service indicator. Self-adhesive. Imperf.

1391	**586** 1KLASS (2m.80) mult	95	25

587 Mini

1995. "Finlandia 95" International Stamp Exhibition, Helsinki (5th issue). Motor Sports. Sheet 120 × 80 mm containing T **587** and similar vert designs. Multicoloured.

MS1392	3m.50 Type **587** (Timo Makinen, rally driver); 3m.50 Rally car (Juha Kankkunen, rally driver); 3m.50 Tommi Ahvala on motor cycle (trials); 3m.50 Heikki Mikkola on motor cycle (motocross)	4·75	5·25

588 Dung Beetle

1995. "Finlandia 95" International Stamp Exhibition, Helsinki.

1393	**588** 19m. multicoloured	6·00	6·50

589 Linnanmaki Amusement Park, Helsinki

590 Loviisa Market and Church

1995. Nordic Countries' Postal Co-operation. Tourism. Multicoloured.

1394	2m.80 Type **589**	80	25
1395	2m.90 Mantyharju church (400th anniv of parish)	85	75

1995. 250th Anniv of Loviisa.

1396	**590** 3m.20 multicoloured	75	70

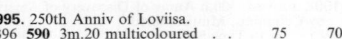

591 Silver Birch (incorrectly inscr "Betula pendula")

592 Rontgen Tube and X-Ray Theory

1995. 20th International Union of Forestry Research Organizations World Congress, Tampere. Leaves and flowers of trees. Multicoloured.

1397	2m.80 Type **591**	80	40
1398	2m.80 Scots pine ("Pinus sylvestris")	80	40
1399	2m.80 Norway spruce ("Picea abies")	80	40
1400	2m.80 Propagating tree from needle	80	40

1995. Centenary of Discovery of X-Rays by Wilhelm Rontgen.

1401	**592** 4m.30 multicoloured	1·20	85

593 Somali

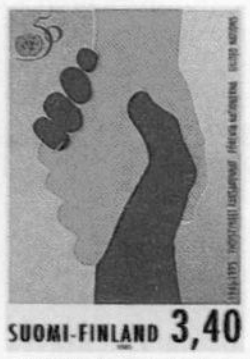

594 Handshake

1995. Cats. Multicoloured.

1402	2m.80 Type **593**	1·20	45
1403	2m.80 Siamese	1·20	45
1404	2m.80 Domestic cat in grass (58 × 35 mm)	1·20	45
1405	2m.80 Norwegian forest cat	1·20	45
1406	2m.80 Colourpoint Persian	1·20	45
1407	2m.80 Kittens playing in grass (58 × 35 mm)	1·20	45

Nos. 1404 and 1407 form a composite design.

1995. 50th Anniv of U.N.O.

1408	**594** 3m.40 multicoloured	85	70

595 Father Christmas on Skates

596 "O"

1995. Christmas. Multicoloured.
1409 2m. Type **595** 55 25
1410 2m.80 Poinsettias in snow (horiz) 45 35

1996. Greeting Stamps. Letters of the Alphabet.
1411 **596** 1m. vio, grn & blk ("M") 35 40
1412 1m. bl, mauve and black (Type **596**) 35 40
1413 1m. red, yell & blk ("i") 35 40
1414 1m. bl, red & blk ("H") 35 40
1415 1m. red, grn & blk ("E") 35 40
1416 1m. yell, bl & blk ("J") 35 40
1417 1m. grn, red & blk ("A") 35 40
1418 1m. yellow, mauve and black ("N") 35 40
1419 1m. yell, grn & blk ("T") 35 40
1420 1m. red, bl & blk ("P") 35 40
1421 1m. lt bl, bl & blk ("U") 35 40
1422 1m. yell, mve & blk ("S") 35 40
Nos. 1411/22 were intended to be arranged on envelopes to spell out a desired message.

597 "Smile" (Mauno Paavola)

598 Hoop Exercise

1996. 50th Anniv of U.N.I.C.E.F.
1423 **597** 2m.80 multicoloured . . 65 30

1996. Centenary of Women's Gymnastics Associations in Finland.
1424 **598** 2m.80 multicoloured . . 75 30

599 Mother and Children at Polling Station

1996. Europa. 90th Anniv of Women's Suffrage in Finland.
1425 **599** 3m.20 multicoloured . . 1·00 80

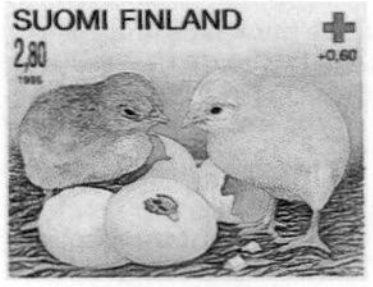

600 Chicks

1996. Finnish Red Cross Fund. Chickens. Multicoloured.
1426 2m.80+60p. Type **600** . . . 1·00 1·40
1427 3m.20+70p. Hens . . . . 1·20 1·40
1428 3m.40+70p. Cock (vert) . . 1·50 1·70

601 J. Gronroos (circus director) at Film Projector

1996. Centenary of Motion Pictures. Mult.
1429 2m.80 Valle Saikko and Irma Seikkula in "Juha" 75 45
1430 2m.80 Alli Riks and Theodor Tugai in "Wide Road" ("Den Breda Vagen") 75 45
1431 2m.80 Ake Lindman in "The Unknown Soldier" ("Okana Soldat") 75 45
1432 2m.80 Type **601** 75 45
1433 2m.80 Antti Litja in "Year of the Hare" ("Harens Ar") 75 45
1434 2m.80 Mirjami Kuosmanen in "The White Forest" ("Den Vita Renen") . . . 75 45
1435 2m.80 Ansa Ikonen and Tauno Palo in "Complete Love" ("Alla Alskar") . . 75 45
1436 2m.80 Matti Pellonpaa in "Shadow in Paradise" ("Skuggor i Paradiset") 75 45

602 Radio Waves

1996. Centenary (1995) of First Radio Transmission
1437 **602** 4m.30 multicoloured . . 1·00 1·20

603 Canoeing

604 White Water Lily (Southern Savonia)

1996. Centenary of Modern Olympic Games. Watersports. Multicoloured.
1438 3m.40 Type **603** . . . . . 95 1·10
1439 3m.40 Sailing . . . . . . 95 1·10
1440 3m.40 Rowing . . . . . . 95 1·10
1441 3m.40 Swimming . . . . . 95 1·10

1996. Provincial Plants. With service indicator. Self-adhesive. Imperf.
1442 **604** 1KLASS (2m.80) mult 95 25

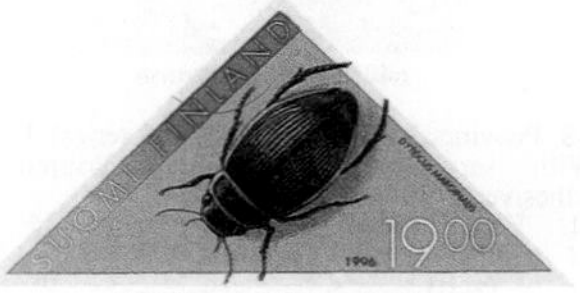

605 Great Diving Beetle

1996.
1443 **605** 19m. multicoloured . . . 6·00 6·25

606 Common Snipe ("Gallinago gallinago")

607 Professor Itikaisen (Ilmari Vainio)

1996. Stamp Day. Wading Birds. Sheet 121 × 72 mm containing T **606** and similar vert designs. Multicoloured.
MS1444 2m.80 Curlew ("Numenius arquata") (29 × 53 mm); 2m.80 Type **606**; 2m.80 Oystercatcher ("Haematopus ostralegus"); 2m.80 Woodcock ("Scolopax rusticola"); 2m.80 Lapwing ("Vanellus vanellus") . . . . 4·75 5·00

1996. Centenary of Comic Strips. Each red and black.
1445 2m.80 Type **607** 75 50
1446 2m.80 Pekka Puupaa (Peter Blockhead) receiving letter from booth (Ola Fogelberg) 75 50
1447 2m.80 Joonas resting chin on hand (Veikko Savolainen) 75 50
1448 2m.80 Posti-Aune from "Mammila" in motor cycle helmet (Tarmo Koivisto) 75 50
1449 2m.80 Rymy-Eetu smoking pipe (Erkki Tanttu) . . . 75 50
1450 2m.80 Kieku (duck) writing letter (Asmo Alho) . . . 75 50
1451 2m.80 Pikku Risunen from "Hyvissa naimisissa" (Well-married) in headdress with big ears (Riitta Uusitalo) 75 50
1452 2m.80 Kiti from "Vihrea Rapsodia" (Green Rhapsody) holding pencil (Kati Kovacs) 75 50

608 Father Christmas and Musicians

609 Player

1996. Christmas. Multicoloured.
1453 2m. Type **608** 55 25
1454 2m.80 Reindeer and hare . . 65 30
1455 3m.20 Father Christmas reading letters (vert) . . . 85 50

1997. World Ice Hockey Championship, Helsinki, Turku and Tampere.
1456 **609** 2m.80 multicoloured . . 75 25

610 Parcel

1997. Cent of Mail Order Sales in Finland.
1457 **610** 2m.80 multicoloured . . 65 60

611 Angels

1997. Greetings Stamps. With service indicator. Old Scrapbook Illustrations. Multicoloured.
1458 1klass (2m.80) Type **611** . . 1·00 35
1459 1klass (2m.80) Basket of mixed flowers . . . . . . 1·00 40
1460 1klass (2m.80) Barn swallow on hand extended through wreath of roses . . . . . 1·00 40
1461 1klass (2m.80) Children playing . . . . 1·00 40
1462 1klass (2m.80) Child and four-leaf clovers in envelope . . . . 1·00 40
1463 1klass (2m.80) Man's and woman's hands extended through heart-shaped wreaths of roses . . . . . 1·00 40
1464 1klass (2m.80) Roses . . . 1·00 40
1465 1klass (2m.80) Angel . . . 1·00 40

612 Arctic Hares

1997. Easter.
1466 **612** 2m.80 multicoloured . . 70 30

613 Golden Merganser casting Reflection of Girl

614 Bird Cherry (Birkaland)

1997. Europa. Tales and Legends. "The Girl who turned into a Golden Merganser" (folktale). Illustrations by Mika Launis. Multicoloured.
1467 3m.20 Type **613** . . . . . 1·00 30
1468 3m.40 Girl falling into water 1·40 85

1997. Provincial Plants. With service indicator. Self-adhesive. Imperf.
1469 **614** 1KLASS (2m.80) mult 95 50

615 Nurmi running 3000 m (Olympic Games, Paris, 1924)

616 Couple dancing in Meadow

1997. Birth Cent of Paavo Nurmi (runner).
1470 **615** 3m.40 multicoloured . . 95 55

1997. The Tango. With service indicator.
1471 **616** 1klass (2m.80) black and pink 95 50

617 "Astrid" (galeasse)

618 Globe and Ahtisaari

1997. Centenary of Finnish Lifeboat Society. Sailing Ships. Multicoloured.
1472 2m.80 Type **617** 80 40
1473 2m.80 "Jacobstads Wapen" (replica of schooner) . . . 80 55
1474 2m.80 "Suomen Joutsen" (cadet ship) (48 × 25 mm) 80 55
1475 2m.80 "Tradewind" (brigantine) 80 55
1476 2m.80 "Merikokko" (lifeboat) 80 55
1477 2m.80 "Sigyn" (barque) (48 × 25 mm) 80 55

1997. 60th Birthday of President Martii Ahtisaari.
1478 **618** 2m.80 multicoloured . . 65 25

619 Clouds (Summer)

620 Crane with Chick

1997. 80th Anniv of Independence. The Four Seasons. Multicoloured.
1479 2m.80 Lily of the valley (Spring) 85 50
1480 2m.80 Type **619** 85 50
1481 2m.80 Leaves (Autumn) . . 85 50
1482 2m.80 Snowflakes (Winter) 85 50

1997. The Common Crane (Grus grus). Sheet 120 × 80 mm containing T **620** and similar multicoloured designs.
MS1483 2m.80 Type **620**; 2m.80 Adults, one with frog in beak; 2m.80 Courting dance; 2m.80 Adults in flight (31 × 34 mm) 3·75 3·75

621 Vainamoinen proposing to Aino

622 "Seven Brothers" (Aleksis Kivi)

1997. Pro Filatelia. "Aino" (triptych) by Akseli Gallen-Kallela. Multicoloured.
1484 2m.80+60p. Type **621** . . . 1·30 1·10
1485 2m.80+60p. Aino in water escaping from Vainamoinen (33 × 47 mm) . . . . . . 1·30 1·10
1486 2m.80+60p. Mermaids luring Aino into water . . 1·30 1·10

1997. Centenary of Finnish Writers' Association. Book Covers. Multicoloured.
1487 2m.80 Type **622** 75 50
1488 2m.80 "Sinuhe the Eyptian" (Mika Waltari) 75 50
1489 2m.80 "Under the North Star" (Vaino Linna) . . . 75 50
1490 2m.80 "Farewell River Iijoki" (Kalle Paatalo) . . 75 50
1491 2m.80 "Eagle, My Beloved" (Kaari Utrio) 75 50
1492 2m.80 "Midsummer Dance" (Hannu Salama) 75 50
1493 2m.80 "Manilla Rope" (Veijo Meri) 75 50
1494 2m.80 "Uppo-Nalle ja Kumma" (Elina Karjalainen) 75 50

623 Church and Houses

1997. Christmas. Multicoloured.
1495 2m. Type **623** 55 25
1496 2m.80 Candelabra, Petajavesi Church (vert) 75 35
1497 3m.20 St. John's Church, Eira, Helsinki (35 × 24 mm) 85 50

624 Zander

1998. Provincial Birds and Fish (1st series). Uusimaa. With service indicator. Mult. Self-adhesive.
1498 2klass (2m.40) Type **624** . . 75 70
1499 1KLASS (2m.80) Blackbird 95 25

625 Moominpappa writing Play

626 Nurses of 1898 and 1998

1998. Moomin. Illustrations from her stories by Tove Jansson. With service indicator. Multicoloured.
1500 1klass (2m.80) Type **625** . . 1·30 40
1501 1klass (2m.80) Moomin-mamma making jam . . . 1·30 40
1502 1klass (2m.80) Too-ticky playing barrel organ and Littly My dancing . . . . 1·30 40
1503 1klass (2m.80) Moomintroll dancing with the Snork Maiden . . . . 1·30 40

1998. Cent of Finnish Federation of Nurses.
1504 **626** 2m.80 multicoloured . . 70 25

627 Gold Heart and Musical Notes

628 Harebell (Central Ostrobothnia)

1998. St. Valentine's Day. With service indicator. Multicoloured.
1505 1klass (2m.80) Type **627** . . 1·00 50
1506 1klass (2m.80) Gold heart and elephant . . . . . . 1·00 50
1507 1klass (2m.80) Gold heart and puppy on blanket . . 1·00 50
1508 1klass (2m.80) Gold heart and kittens . . . . 1·00 50
1509 1klass (2m.80) Gold heart and dog . . . . 1·00 50
1510 1klass (2m.80) Gold heart and flowers . . . . . . 1·00 50
The gold hearts could be scratched off to reveal a complete design.

1998. Provincial Plants. With service indicator. Self-adhesive. Imperf.
1511 **628** 1KLASS (2m.80) mult 95 25

629 Sow and Litter

630 Coltsfoot

1998. Finnish Red Cross Fund. Pigs. Mult.
1512 2m.80+60p. Type **629** . . . 1·00 1·30
1513 3m.20+70p. Three piglets . . 1·30 1·50
1514 3m.40+70p. Boar . . . . . 1·30 1·50

1998. Spring.
1515 **630** 2m.80 multicoloured . . 70 25

631 Students with Balloons (Labour Day)

1998. Europa. National Festivals. Mult.
1516 3m.20 Type **631** 95 40
1517 3m.40 Couple by lake (Midsummer) . . . . . . 1·30 1·20

632 "Aranda" (research vessel)

1998. Nordic Countries' Postal Co-operation. Shipping. Multicoloured.
1518 2m.80 Type **632** (80th anniv of Finnish Marine Research Institute) . . . 75 30
1519 3m.20 "Vega" (120th anniv of Nils Nordenskjold's navigation of the North-east Passage) 95 70

633 Flag and Score

1998. 150th Anniv of First Performance of "Our Country" (national anthem).
1520 **633** 5m. multicoloured . . . 1·40 90

634 Bernese Mountain Dog

635 Downhill Competitor and 19th-century Cyclist

1998. World Dog Show, Helsinki. With service indicator. Multicoloured.
1521 1klass (2m.80) Type **634** . . 1·00 50
1522 1klass (2m.80) Pumis . . . 1·00 50
1523 1klass (2m.80) Boxers . . . 1·00 50
1524 1klass (2m.80) Bichon frises 1·00 50
1525 1klass (2m.80) Finnish lapphounds . . . . 1·00 50
1526 1klass (2m.80) Dachshunds 1·00 50
1527 1klass (2m.80) Cairn terriers 1·00 50
1528 1klass (2m.80) Labrador retrievers . . . . 1·00 50

1998. Centenary of Cycling Union of Finland.
1529 **635** 3m. multicoloured . . . 85 65

636 Eagle Owl "Bubo bubo"

638 Children and Christmas Tree

637 Kilta Tableware (Kaj Franck)

1998. Stamp Day. Owls. Sheet 120 × 80 mm containing T **636** and similar multicoloured designs.
MS1530 3m. Type **636**; 3m. Wing-tip of eagle owl (25 × 49 mm); 3m. Tengmalm's owl ("Aegolius funereus") (23 × 42 mm); 3m. Great grey owl ("Stris nebulosa") (24 × 42 mm); 3m. Snowy owl ("Nyctea scandiaca") (29 × 42 mm) . . . . 4·75 4·75

1998. Finnish Industrial Design. Mult.
1531 3m. Savoy Vase (Alvar Aalto) 95 70
1532 3m. Karuselli 412 chair (Yrjo Kukkapuro) (29 × 34 mm) 95 70
1533 3m. Tasaraita T-shirts (Annika Rimala) (29 × 34 mm) 95 70
1534 3m. Type **637** 95 70
1535 3m. Cast-iron cooking pot (Timo Sarpaneva) (29 × 34 mm) 95 70
1536 3m. Carelia cutlery (Bertel Gardberg) (29 × 34 mm) 95 70

1998. Christmas. Multicoloured.
1537 2m. Type **638** 55 25
1538 3m. Children tobogganing (horiz) 75 35
1539 3m.20 Snow-bound cottage on island (horiz) 95 50

639 Hakkinen and Racing Car

1999. Mika Hakkinen, Formula 1 World Champion 1998. Sheet 115 × 70 mm.
MS1540 **639** 3m. multicoloured 1·40 1·20

640 Atlantic Salmon

1999. Provincial Birds and Fish (2nd series). Lapland. With service indicator. Multicoloured. Self-adhesive.
1541 2klass (2m.40) Type **640** . . 75 55
1542 1KLASS (3m.) Bluethroat (vert) 95 35

641 Zebra and Lion Tails

1999. Friendship. Multicoloured. Self-adhesive.
1543 3m. Type **641** 95 70
1544 3m. Cat and dog tails . . . 95 70

642 Monument to Eetu Salin (founder) (Aimo Tukiainen)

1999. Centenary of Founding of Finnish Labour Party (predecessor of Social Democrat Party).
1545 **642** 4m.50 multicoloured . . 1·20 1·30

643 Horse Brooch

1999. 150th Anniv of New Kalevala (Karelian poems collected by Elias Lonnrot). Sheet 120 × 74 mm containing T **643** and similar vert designs. Multicoloured.
MS1546 3m. Type **643**; 3m. Kuhmoinen Cocks brooch; 3m. Virusmaki brooch . . . . . . 2·75 3·00

644 Road by River Tenojoki, Utsjoki

1999. Bicentenary of National Road Administration. Multicoloured.
1547 3m. Type **644** 95 55
1548 3m. Motorway intersection, Jyvaskyla 95 55
1549 3m. Raippaluoto bridge, Vaasa 95 55
1550 3m. North Karelian forest road, Kitee 95 55

645 Esplanade, Helsinki

1999. Europa. Parks and Gardens. Multicoloured.
1551 2m.70 Type **645** 95 80
1552 3m.20 Ruissalo island, Turku . . . . 1·10 65

646 Martha Circle

647 Crocuses

1999. Centenary of Martha Organization (for education and development of women).
1553 **646** 3m. multicoloured . . . 75 70

1999. Easter.
1554 **647** 3m. multicoloured . . . 75 35

648 Cowslip (Aland Islands)

649 Nightingale ("Luscinia luscinia")

1999. Provincial Plants. With service indicator. Self-adhesive. Imperf.
1555 **648** 1KLASS (3m.) mult . . 95 25

1999. Nocturnal Summer Birds. Sheet 120 × 80 mm containing T **649** and similar multicoloured designs.
MS1556 3m. Type **649**; 3m. European cuckoo ("Cuculus canorus) (24 × 39½ mm); 3m. Eurasian bittern ("Botaurus stellaris") (44 × 29 mm); 3m. European nightjar ("Caprimulgus europaeus") (24½ × 36 mm); 3m. Corncrake ("Crex crex") (24½ × 37 mm) . . . . 4·75 4·75

650 Figure reaching for E.U. Stars

1999. Finland's Presidency of European Union.
1557 **650** 3m.50 multicoloured . . 95 45

651 Harmony Sisters

1999. Entertainers. Multicoloured.
1558 3m.50 Type **651** . . . . . 1·00 70
1559 3m.50 Olavi Virta (tango and jazz singer) (29 × 34 mm) . . . . . . 1·00 70
1560 3m.50 Georg Malmsten (composer and band leader) (29 × 34 mm) . . . 1·00 70
1561 3m.50 Topi Karki (composer) and Reino Helismaa (lyricist) . . . . 1·00 70
1562 3m.50 Tapio Rautavaara (composer and folk singer) (29 × 34 mm) . . . 1·00 70
1563 3m.50 Esa Pakarinen (folk artist and actor) (29 × 34 mm) . . . . . . 1·00 70

652 "Garden of Death"

654 Santa Claus

653 Fiskars Secateurs and Pruning Shears Designed by Olavi Linden

1999. Pro Filatelia. Paintings by Hugo Simberg. Multicoloured.
1564 3m.50+50p. Type **652** . . . 1·00 1·30
1565 3m.50+50p. "Wounded Angel" . . . . 1·00 1·30

1999. Finnish Industrial Design. Multicoloured.
1566 3m.50 Type **653** . . . . . 1·00 70
1567 3m.50 Zoel Versoul guitar (Kari Nieminen) (29 × 34½mm) . . . . . . 1·00 70
1568 3m.50 Ergo II Silenta hearing protectors (Jyrki Jarvinen) (29 × 34½ mm) 1·00 70
1569 3m.50 Ponsse Cobra HS10 harvester (Pentti Hukkanen, Jorma Hyvonen, Jouko Kelppe and Heikki Koivurova) 1·00 70
1570 3m.50 Suunto sailing compass (Heikki Metsa-Ketela and Erikki Vainio) (29 × 34½ mm) . . . . . 1·00 70
1571 3m.50 Exel Avanti QLS ski stick (Pasi Jarvinen, Matti Lyly and Mika Vesalainen) (29 × 34½ mm) 1·00 70

1999. Christmas. Multicoloured.
1572 2m.50 Type **654** 75 30
1573 3m. "Nativity" (Giorgio de Chirico) (horiz) 75 55
1574 3m.50 Two hares (horiz) . . 95 45

655 Earth, Sun and Moon

2000. Friendship. Multicoloured.
1575 3m.50 Type **655** . . . . . 1·10 65
1576 3m.50 Painting a smile on Jupiter . . . . 1·10 65
1577 3m.50 Birds using Neptune as balloon . . . . 1·10 65
1578 3m.50 Martian using magnet to rescue traveller from Mars . . . . 1·10 65
1579 3m.50 People on Saturn's rings . . . . 1·10 65
1580 3m.50 Pluto as igloo and polar bear . . . . 1·10 65

656 Herring Market

2000. 450th Anniv of Helsinki (European City of Culture, 2000). Multicoloured.
1581 3m.50 Type **656** . . . . . 1·00 95
1582 3m.50 Museum of Contemporary Art, Kiasma (24 × 48 mm) . . 1·00 1·00
1583 3m.50 Statue and Cathedral, Senate Square (42 × 24 mm) . . . . . . 1·00 1·00
1584 3m.50 Finlandia Hall (42 × 24 mm) . . . . . . 1·00 1·00
1585 3m.50 Glass Palace Film and Media Centre (24 × 48 mm) . . . . . . 1·00 1·00
1586 3m.50 "Looking for the Lost Crown" (children's tour), Suomenlin Sea Fortress (24 × 48 mm) . . 1·00 1·00
1587 3m.50 Type **656** . . . . . 1·00 1·00
1588 3m.50 "Forces of Light" celebration (42 × 24 mm) 1·00 1·00
1589 3m.50 Open-air concert, Kaivopuisto Park (24 × 48 mm) 85 80

657 Fortifications at Sveaborg

659 Marsh Marigold

658 Makinen at Wheel of Rally Car

2000. Sveaborg Fortress.
1590 **657** 7m.20 multicoloured . . 1·80 1·40

2000. Tommi Makinen, Rally World Champion (1999). Sheet 109 × 80 mm containing T **658** and similar horiz design. Multicoloured.
MS1591 3m.50 Type **658**; 3m.50 Mitsubishi Lancer rally car . . 2·20 2·20

2000. Spring.
1592 **659** 3m.50 multicoloured . . 95 45

660 Interior of Turku Cathedral

2000. Holy Year 2000. 700th Anniv of Turku Cathedral. Multicoloured.
1593 3m.50 Type **660** . . . . . 1·00 90
1594 3m.50 Woman lighting candle . . . . 1·00 1·00
1595 3m.50 "Transfiguration of Christ" (altarpiece) . . . 1·00 1·00
1596 3m.50 Christening . . . . . 1·00 90

661 Emma the Theatre Rat and Moomins at Table

662 Bull

2000. Moomin. Illustrations from her stories by Tove Jansson. With service indicator. Multicoloured.
1597 1klass (3m.50) Type **661** . . 1·00 55
1598 1klass (3m.50) Park keeper and Hattifatteners growing from the grass 1·00 55
1599 1klass (3m.50) Snufkin walking through forest . . 1·00 55
1600 1klass (3m.50) Snufkin surrounded by forest children . . . . 1·00 55

2000. Finnish Red Cross Fund. Cattle. Multicoloured.
1601 3m.50+70p. Type **662** . . . 1·30 1·10
1602 4m.80+80p. Cow and calf (horiz) . . . . 1·50 1·50

663 "Building Europe"

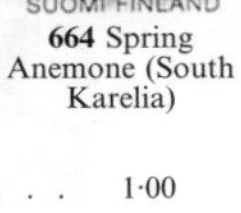

664 Spring Anemone (South Karelia)

2000. Europa.
1603 **663** 3m.50 multicoloured . . 1·00 55

2000. Provincial Plants. With service indicator. Self-adhesive. Imperf.
1604 **664** 1KLASS (3m.50) mult 95 25

665 Girls in Laboratory

2000. Heureka Science Centre. Sheet 120 × 80 mm containing T **665** and similar multicoloured designs.
MS1605 3m.50 Type **665**; 3m.50 DNA double helix and man's face (parallelogram, 20 × 20 mm); 3m.50 Man's face and Sierinski Triangle aerial (27 × 27 mm) . . 3·25 3·25

666 Common Whitefish

2000. Provincial Birds and Fish (3rd series). Southern Lapland. With service indicator. Multicoloured. Self-adhesive.
1606 2klass (2m.70) Type **666** . . 75 60
1607 1KLASS (3m.30) Willow grouse 95 65

667 "Flame" Rug (Akseli Gallen-Kallela)

2000. Finnish Industrial Design. Multicoloured.
1608 3m.50 Type **667** 90 65
1609 3m.50 Pearl Bird (Birger Kaipiainen) (29 × 34 mm) 90 65
1610 3m.50 Pot (Kyllikki Salmenhaara) (29 × 34 mm) 90 65
1611 3m.50 "Leaf" platter (Tapio Wirkkala) 90 65
1612 3m.50 "Lichen" (furnishing fabric pattern, Dora Jung) (29 × 34 mm) 90 65
1613 3m.50 Glass vase (Valter Jung) (29 × 34 mm) . . . 90 65

668 Three Wise Men and Star

2000. Christmas. Multicoloured. Self-adhesive.
1614 2m.50 Type **668** 70 30
1615 3m.50 Northern bullfinch sitting on wreath (vert) . . 95 45

669 Woman's Head

2001. European Year of Languages. With service indicator.
1616 **669** 1KLASS (3m.50) mult 95 35

670 Janne Ahonen (ski jumper)

2001. Nordic World Skiing Championships, Lahti. Multicoloured.
1617 3m.50 Type **670** 65 40
1618 3m.50 Mika Myllyla 65 40

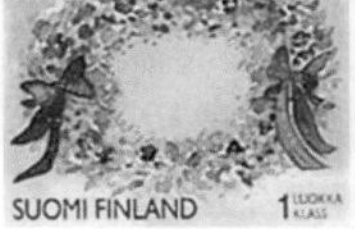

671 Garland of Flowers

672 Cover of First Magazine published in Finland, 1951

2001. Greetings Stamps. Flowers. Multicoloured. Self-adhesive.
1619 1KLASS (3m.50) Type **671** 90 55
1620 1KLASS (3m.50) Basket of flowers 90 55
1621 1KLASS (3m.50) Heart-shaped garland 90 55
1622 1KLASS (3m.50) Bouquet 90 55
1623 1KLASS (3m.50) Flowers, cake and cups 90 55
1624 1KLASS (3m.50) Flowers and heart-shaped cake . . 90 55

2001. 50th Anniv of The Donald Duck Magazine in Finland. Sheet 130 × 80 mm containing T **672** and similar vert designs. Multicoloured.
MS1625 1klass Type **672**; 1klass Silhouette of boy and page from magazine; 1klass Toy carrying flag and Chip and Dale (24 × 30 mm); 1klass Silhouette of Donald Duck and Vainamoinen; 1klass Donald Duck and Helsinki Cathedral 5·50 3·75

673 Father Christmas in Sleigh

2001. Santa Claus. With service indicator. Self-adhesive.
1630 **673** 1klass (3m.50) multicoloured . . . . 1·00 75

674 Haapavitja Rapids, Ruunaa

2001. Europa. Water Resources.
1631 **674** 5m.40 multicoloured . . 1·60 1·40

675 Face of Chick

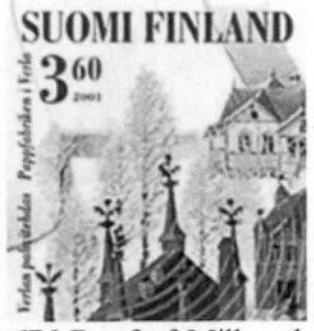

676 Roof of Mill and Trees

2001. Easter. Multicoloured.
1632 3m.60 Type **675** 90 45
1633 3m.60 Easter egg 90 45

2001. Verla Groundwood and Board Mill Museum, Jaala. Sheet 80 × 120 mm containing T **676** and similar vert designs. Multicoloured.
MS1634 3m.60 Type **676**; 3m.60 Mill manager's house, mill building and river; 3m.60 Main mill building and trees; 3m.60 Mill building and river . . . . 4·75 3·00

677 Lesser Spotted Woodpecker (*Dendrocopos minor*)

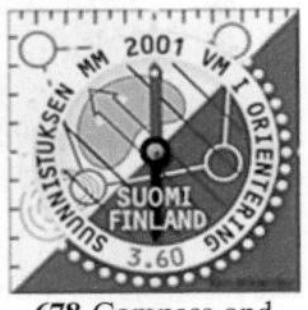

678 Compass and Emblem

2001. Woodpeckers. Sheet 79 × 119 mm containing T **677** and similar vert designs. Mult.
MS1635 3m.60 Type **677**; 3m.60 Three-toed woodpecker (*Picoides tridactylus*) (28 × 35 mm); 3m.60 White-backed woodpecker (*Dendrocopos leucotos*) (32 × 41 mm); 3m.60 Great spotted woodpecker (*Dendrocopos major*) (28 × 41 mm); 3m.60 Grey-headed green woodpecker (*Picus canus*) (32 × 41 mm); 3m.60 Black woodpecker (*Dryocopus martius*) (28 × 41 mm) . . . . 6·50 6·50

2001. Orienteering World Championship, Tampere.
1636 **678** 3m.60 multicoloured . . 1·10 45

679 Cornflower (Pajat-Hame)

680 Lampern (*Lampetra fluviatilis*)(Satakunta)

2001. Provincial Flowers. With service indicator. Self-adhesive.

1637 1KLASS (3m.50) Type **679** 80 45
1638 1KLASS (3m.50) Pasque flower (Kanta-Hame) . . 80 45

2001. Provincial Fish. With service indicator. Multicoloured. Self-adhesive.

1639 2klass (2m.70) Type **680** . . 65 65
1640 2klass (2m.70) Asp (*Aspius aspius*) (Pirkanmaa) . . . 65 65
1641 2klass (2m.70) Vendace (*Coregonus albula*) (Savonia) 65 65

681 Golden Oriole (*Oriolus oriolus*) (Satakunta)

2001. Provincial Birds. With service indicator. Multicoloured. Self-adhesive.

1642 1KLASS (3m.60) Type **681** 85 50
1643 1KLASS (3m.60) Blue tit (*Parus caeruleus*) (Pirkanmaa) 85 50
1644 1KLASS (3m.60) Pied wagtail (*Motacilla alba*) (South Savonia) 85 55

682 18th-century Captain's Quarters, Merchant Ship

2001. Gulf of Finland (1st series). Multicoloured.

1645 1KLASS (3m.60) Type **682** 90 60
1646 1KLASS (3m.60) Uto Lighthouse (32 × 27 mm) 90 60
1647 1KLASS (3m.60) *Sankt Mikael* (Dutch sailing ship) (33 × 27 mm) . . . 90 60
1648 1KLASS (3m.60) Diver on *Sankt Mikael* and treasure (33 × 27 mm) 90 60
1649 1KLASS (3m.60) Opossum shrimp, isopod and bladder wrack (33 × 27 mm) 90 60

See also Nos. 1675/9.

683 Elf Girl reading

684 Water Forget-me-not (*Myosotis scorpoides*)

2001. Christmas. Multicoloured. Self-adhesive.

1650 2m.50 Type **683** 85 30
1651 3m.60 Elf boy sledding (horiz) . . . . 1·00 45

New currency. 100cents = 1 euro

2002. Flowers. Showing water forget-me-nots (5c.) or lily-of-the-valley (10c.). Multicoloured. Self-adhesive.

1652 5c. Type **684** 15 20
1653 5c. Four flowers 15 20
1654 5c. One open flower and four buds 15 20
1655 5c. Spray of flowers 15 20
1656 5c. Five flower heads 15 20
1657 10c. Spray of five lily-of-the-valley flowers (*Convallaria majallis*) 25 20
1658 10c. Spray of eight flowers between two leaves . . . 25 20
1659 10c. Two flowers 25 20
1660 10c. Spray of six flowers against leaf 25 20
1661 10c. Lily-of-the-valley growing through grass . . 25 20

685 Whooper Swan (*Cygnus cygnus*)

686 Birch (*Betula pendula*)

2002. Self-adhesive.

1662 **685** 50c. multicoloured . . . 75 55

2002. Trees. Self-adhesive.

1663 60c. Type **686** 85 30
1664 €2.50 Norway spruce (*Picea abies*) . . . . . . 3·75 2·20
1665 €3.50 Scots pine (*Pinus sylvestris*) . . . . 5·00 3·50

687 National Flag .

2002. With service indicator. Self-adhesive.

1666 **687** 1klass (60c.) multicoloured 95 70

No. 1666 was for use on domestic first class mail.

688 "Kymintehtaalta" (Victor Westerholm)

689 Heraldic Lion

2002. Finnish Landscapes. Self-adhesive. Multicoloured.

1667 90c. Type **688** . . . . . . 1·30 1·20
1668 €1.30 Granite substrata . . 1·90 1·40

2002. Winning entry in Stamp Design Competition. Multicoloured. Self- adhesive.

1669 €1 Type **689** . . . . . . 1·40 1·10
1670 €5 No. 1668 . . . . 7·00 4·75

690 Witch riding Broomstick

2002. Easter. Self-adhesive.

1671 **690** 60c. multicoloured . . . 95 65

691 Plantain

693 Circus Performers

692 Houses

2002. Birth Bicentenary of Elias Lonnrot (linguist, botanist and physician). Sheet 120 × 80 mm, containing T **691** and similar vert designs. Multicoloured.

MS1672 60c. Type **691**; 60c. Tip of feather and text; 60c. Base of feather and text; 60c. Elias Lonnrot . . . . 3·50 3·75

2002. U.N.E.S.C.O. World Heritage Site. 560th Anniv of Rauma. Sheet 82 × 122 mm, containing T **692** and similar vert designs. Multicoloured.

MS1673 60c. Type **692**; 60c. Church of the Holy Cross; 60c. Left side of Rauma museum (face value at left); 60c. Right side of museum (face value at right) . . . . . 3·50 3·75

2002. Europa. Circus.

1674 **693** 60c. multicoloured . . . 95 65

694 Fishing Boat and Net

2002. Gulf of Finland (2nd series). Multicoloured.

1675 1KLASS (60c.) Type **694** . . 85 80
1676 1KLASS (60c.) Arctic terns, island and perch (fish) (32 × 27 mm) 85 80
1677 1KLASS (60c.) Island, dinghy and buoy (32 × 27 mm) 85 80
1678 1KLASS (60c.) Flounder (32 × 27 mm) 85 80
1679 1KLASS (60c.) Zooplankton, herring and cod (32 × 27 mm) 85 80

Nos. 1675/9 were issued together, se-tenant, forming a composite design.

695 "Passio Muscicae" (Sibelius Monument) (sculpture, Eila Hiltunen)

2002. Nordic Countries' Postal Co-operation. Modern Art.

1680 **695** 60c. multicoloured . . . 95 40

696 Juniper (*Juniperus communis*)

2002. Self-adhesive.

1681 **696** 60c. multicoloured . . . 95 50

697 Reindeer, Lapland

2002. Self-adhesive.

1682 **697** 60c. multicoloured . . . 95 65

698 Horse-drawn Sleigh

2002. Christmas. Multicoloured. Self-adhesive.

1683 45c. Type **698** 65 60
1684 60c. Angel (vert) 95 70

699 Northern Pike (*Esox lucius*)

2003. Provincial Fish. With service indicator. Multicoloured. Self-adhesive.

1685 2KLASS (50c.) Type **699** . . 95 95
1686 2KLASS (50c.) Bream (*Abramis brama*) 95 95
1687 2KLASS (50c.) Lake trout (*Salmo trutta lacustris*) . . 95 95

700 European Cuckoo (*Cuculus canorus*)

2003. Provincial Birds. With service indicator. Multicoloured. Self-adhesive.

1688 1KLASS (60c.) Type **700** . . 1·10 1·10
1689 1KLASS (60c.) Eurasian sky lark (*Alauda arvensis*) . . 1·10 1·10
1690 1KLASS (60c.) Siberian jay (*Perisoreus infaustus*) . . . 1·10 1·10

701 Viivi and Wagner

2003. Friendship. With service indicator. Showing Viivi and Wagner (cartoon characters). Multicoloured. Self-adhesive.

1691 1KLASS (60c.) Type **701** . . 1·10 1·10
1692 1KLASS (60c.) Dancing . . 1·10 1·10
1693 1KLASS (60c.) Viivi writing letter . . . . 1·10 1·10
1694 1KLASS (60c.) In bed . . . 1·10 1·10
1695 1KLASS (60c.) Kissing . . 1·10 1·10
1696 1KLASS (60c.) Wagner receiving letter . . . . . 1·10 1·10

702 Games Mascot

703 Pansy (*Viola wittrockiana*)

2003. World Ice Hockey Championships, Helsinki, Tampere and Turku.

1697 **702** 65c. multicoloured . . . 1·20 1·20

2003. Self-adhesive.

1698 **703** 65c. multicoloured . . . 1·20 1·20

704 St. Birgitta (Bridget) (detail, altar screen, Naantali Convent Church)

705 Super Caravelle

2003. 700th Birth Anniv of St. Birgitta.

1699 **704** 65c. multicoloured . . . 1·20 1·20

2003. Centenary of First Powered Flight. 80th Anniv of Finnair. Multicoloured.

1700 65c. Type **705** . . . . . . 1·20 1·20
1701 65c. Airbus 320 . . . . . . 1·20 1·20
1702 65c. Junkers Ju 52/3m . . . 1·20 1·20
1703 65c. Douglas DC-3 . . . . . 1·20 1·20

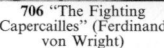

706 "The Fighting Capercailles" (Ferdinand von Wright)

707 Heart (Lasse Hietala)

2003. Self-adhesive.
1704 **706** 90c. multicoloured . . . 1·70 1·70

2003. Europa. Poster Art. Design showing "Someone is waiting for your letter" posters by Lasse Hietala. Multicoloured.
1705 65c. Type **707** . . . . . . 1·20 1·20
1706 65c. Mother . . . . 1·20 1·20

708 Butterfly

709 Moomin Family

2003. Summer. T **708** and similar multicoloured designs.
MS1707 65c. Type **708**; 65c. Dragonfly (45 × 35 mm); 65c. Flowers and caterpillar; 65c. Frog (45 × 36 mm); 65c. Magpie (36 × 46 mm) (vert); 65c. Hedgehogs (45 × 29 mm) . . . 7·50 7·50

2003. Moomins. With service indicator. Illustrations from Moominland Midwinter by Tove Jansson. Multicoloured. Self-adhesive.
1708 1klass (65c.) Type **709** . . . 1·20 1·20
1709 1klass (65c.) Tooticky, Little My and Moomintroll sitting by stove . . . . . 1·20 1·20
1710 1klass (65c.) Moomintroll performing handstand and Little My . . . . 1·20 1·20
1711 1klass (65c.) Moonmintroll and squirrel . . . . . . 1·20 1·20
1712 1klass (65c.) Tooticky, Moominmamma and Little My in snow . . . . 1·20 1·20
1713 1klass (65c.) Snufkin walking through forest . . 1·20 1·20

710 Ligonberry (*Vaccinium vitis-idaea*)

711 Russaro Lighthouse

2003. Self-adhesive.
1714 **710** 65c. multicoloured . . . 95 35

2003. Lighthouses. With service indicator. Sheet 120 × 80 mm containing T **711** and similar vert designs. Multicoloured.
MS1715 1klass (65c.) Bengtskar (29 × 40 mm); 1klass (65c.) Type **711**; 1klass (65c.) Ronnskar; 1klass (65c.) Harmaja Grahara; 1klass (65c.) Soderskar . . . . 6·75 6·75

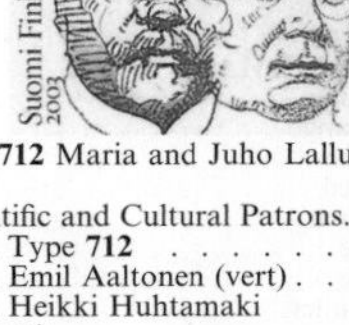

712 Maria and Juho Lallukka

2003. Scientific and Cultural Patrons. Multicoloured.
1716 65c. Type **712** . . . . . . 1·20 1·20
1717 65c. Emil Aaltonen (vert) . . 1·20 1·20
1718 65c. Heikki Huhtamaki (vert) . . . . 1·20 1·20
1719 65c. Jenny and Antti Wihuri 1·20 1·20
1720 65c. Alfred Kordelin (vert) 1·20 1·20
1721 65c. Amos Andersson (vert) 1·20 1·20

713 Elf Boy posting Letters

714 President Halonen

2003. Christmas. Multicoloured. Self-adhesive.
1722 45c. Type **713** 60 60
1723 65c. Elf girl holding ginger bread on tray (vert) . . . 85 85

2003. 60th Birth Anniv of Tarja Halonen, President of Finland.
1724 **714** 65c. multicoloured . . . 85 85

715 *Linnaea borealis*

716 Jean Sibelius' Hands playing Piano

2004. Self-adhesive.
1725 **715** 30c. multicoloured . . . 40 40

2004. Ainola Museum (Jean Sibelius (composer)'s house). Multicoloured. Self-adhesive.
1726 2klass (55c.) Type **716** . . . 75 75
1727 2klass (55c.) Swans and score 75 75
1728 2klass (55c.) *En Saga Jean Sibelius* (painting, Akseli Gallen-Kalhla) 75 75
1729 1klass (65c.) *Voices Intimae* score (detail) . . . . . . 1·20 1·20
1730 1klass (65c.) Drawing of Ainola . . . . 1·20 1·20
1731 1klass (65c.) *Aino Sibelius* (Eero Järnfelt) and *Jean Sibelius* (Albert Edelfelt) 1·20 1·20

717 Silhouette of Johan Runeberg

718 Rose

2004. Birth Bicentenary of Johan Ludvig Runeberg (writer). Sheet 118 × 80 mm containing T **717** and similar vert designs. Each stone, black and red.
MS1732 65c. × 4, Type **717**; Sven Dufa at the Battle of Koljonvirta (Albert Edelfelt) Landscape (Albert Edelfelt) and Värt Land (national anthem); Johan Runeberg (statue, Walter Runeberg) . . . . 1·70 1·70

2004. Greetings Stamps. Each black and red. Self-adhesive.
1733 1klass (65c.) Type **718** . . . 1·20 1·20
1734 1klass (65c.) Pursed lips . . 1·20 1·20
1735 1klass (65c.) Eye . . . . . 1·20 1·20
1736 1klass (65c.) Man and woman . . . . 1·20 1·20
1737 1klass (65c.) Elderly woman 1·20 1·20
1738 1klass (65c.) Hand and flower . . . . 1·20 1·20

719 Bear Cub

720 Rose

2004. Self-adhesive.
1739 **719** 2klass (55c.) multicoloured 75 75

2004. Self-adhesive.
1740 **720** 1klass (65c.). multicoloured 90 90

721 Daffodils, Narcissi and Grape Hyacinths

2004. Easter. Self-adhesive.
1741 **721** 65c. multicoloured . . . 90 90

2004. As T **689**. Self-adhesive.
1742 **689** €3 multicoloured . . . 4·00 4·00

MILITARY FIELD POST

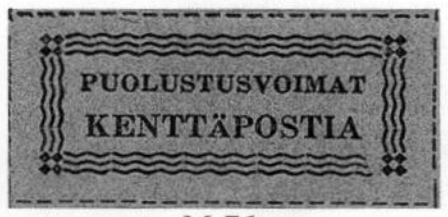

M 76

1941. No value indicated. Imperf.
M352 M **76** (–) black on red . . . 30 60

M 86

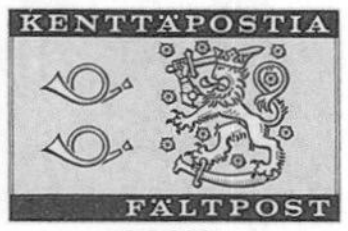

M 222

1943. No value indicated.
M392 M **86** (–) green 30 30
M393 (–) purple 30 30

1943. Optd **KENTTA-POSTI FALTPOST**.
M394 **31** 2m. orange 25 40
M395 3½m. blue 25 40

1944. As Type M **86**, but smaller (20 × 16 mm) and inscr "1944".
M396 (–) violet 20 25
M397 (–) green 20 30

1963. No value indicated.
M688 M **222** (–) violet . . . . . 90·00 £100

1983. No. M688 optd **1983**.
M1043 M **222** (–) violet £130 £100

PARCEL POST STAMPS

P 118

1949. Printed in black on coloured backgrounds. Roul.
P471 P **118** 1m. green . . . . . . 1·80 2·25
P472 5m. red . . . . 13·00 11·00
P473 20m. orange . . . . . 24·00 19·00
P474 50m. blue . . . . . . 11·50 11·00
P475 100m. brown . . . . 11·00 11·00

P 137

P 216

1952.
P507 P **137** 5m. red . . . . 2·20 2·50
P508 20m. orange . . . . . 7·00 4·00
P509 50m. blue . . . . . . 12·50 9·00
P510 100m. brown . . . . 18·00 16·00

1963. Figures of value in black.
P647 P **216** 5p. mauve . . . . . 2·40 2·00
P648 20p. orange . . . . . 2·75 3·25
P649 50p. blue . . . . . . 2·75 3·00
P650 1m. brown . . . . . 1·80 5·50

P 403 "SISU" Bus

1981. Figures of values in black.
P1003 P **403** 50p. blue . . . . . 90 3·75
P1004 1m. brown . . . . . 1·10 4·00
P1005 5m. green . . . . . 3·50 8·00
P1006 10m. purple . . . . 4·25 18·00

FINNISH OCCUPATION OF AUNUS Pt. 10

The Russian town of Olonets was occupied by Finnish troops from April 1919 to May 1919.

1919. Arms of Finland optd **Aunus**.
1 **19** 5p. green . . . . 5·50 8·75
2 10p. pink . . . . 5·50 8·75
3 20p. orange . . . . 5·50 8·75
4 40p. violet . . . . 5·50 8·75
5 50p. brown . . . . 75·00 £110
6 1m. black and pink . . . . . 85·00 £120
7 5m. black and lilac £325 £450
8 10m. black and brown . . . £800 £1100

FINNISH OCCUPATION OF EASTERN KARELIA Pt. 10

Part of Russia, extending East to Lake Onega, occupied by Finland from 1941 to 1944.

100 penni = 1 markka.

1941. Types of Finland in unissued colours optd **ITA-KARJALA Sot.hallinto**. (a) Arms and pictorial issue.
1 **31** 50p. green 50 75
2 1m.75 grey . . . . 1·00 1·10
10 2m. orange . . . . 2·00 2·25
11 2m.75 orange . . . . 85 1·10
12 3½m. blue . . . . 2·10 6·25
13 **32** 5m. purple . . . . 5·25 8·25
14 – 10m. brown (as No. 276b) 5·25 7·25
15 – 25m. green (as No. 277) . . 4·25 7·25

(b) President Ryti.
16 **76** 50p. green . . . . 50 1·25
17 1m.75 slate . . . . 50 1·25
18 2m. red . . . . 75 1·25
19 2m.75 brown . . . . 75 1·10
20 3m.50 blue . . . . 75 1·10
21 5m. purple . . . . 75 1·10

(c) Marshal Mannerheim.
22 **77** 50p. green . . . . 75 1·25
23 1m.75 slate . . . . 75 1·25
24 2m. red . . . . 75 1·25
25 2m.75 brown . . . . 55 1·25
26 3m.50 blue . . . . 55 1·25
27 5m. purple . . . . 55 1·25

4 Arms of E. Karelia

1943. National Relief Fund.
28 **4** 3m.50+1m.50 olive . . . . . 60 1·75

FIUME Pt. 8

A seaport and territory on the Adriatic Sea formerly belonging to Hungary and occupied by the Allies in 1918/19. Between 1919 and 1924 the territory was a Free State, controlled by D'Annunzio and his legionaries, until annexation to Italy in 1924. For later issues see Fiume and Kupa Zone; Venezia Giulia. Ceded to Yugoslavia in 1947 and now known as Rijeka.

1918. 100 filler = 1 krone.
1919. 100 centesimi = 1 corona.
1920. 100 centesimi = 1 lira.

1918. Various issues of Hungary optd **FIUME**. On "Harvesters" and "Parliament" issue of 1916.
1 **18** 2f. brown . . . . 2·50 1·25
2 3f. red . . . . 2·50 1·25
3 5f. green . . . . 2·50 1·25
4 6f. green . . . . 2·50 1·25
5 10f. red (No. 250) . . . . . 35·00 16·00
6 10f. red (No. 243) . . . . . 50·00 24·00
7 15f. violet (No. 251) . . . . 2·50 1·25
8 15f. violet (No. 244) . . . . 22·00 16·00
9 20f. brown . . . . 2·50 1·25
10 25f. blue . . . . 1·60 1·50
11 35f. brown . . . . 4·50 2·50
12 40f. olive . . . . 23·00 13·00
13 **19** 50f. purple . . . . 3·25 1·90
14 75f. blue . . . . 7·25 2·50
15 80f. green . . . . 7·25 1·90
16 1k. lake . . . . 19·00 5·75
17 2k. brown . . . . 3·25 1·90
18 3k. grey and violet . . . . 22·00 9·50

19		5k. brown	50·00	13·00
20		10k. lilac and brown	£190	£140

On "Charles" and "Zita" issue of 1918.

21	27	10f. red	1·90	1·60
22		20f. brown	1·75	1·25
23	28	40f. olive	14·50	5·00

On War charity issue of 1916.

24	20	10+2f. red	3·25	2·25
25	–	15+2f. violet	3·25	2·25
26	22	40+2f. lake	5·00	2·25

On Newspaper issue of 1900.

27	N 9	(2f.) orange	2·40	95

On Express Letter stamp of 1916.

28	E 18	2f. olive and red	2·40	95

On Saving Bank stamp and surch **FRANCO** and value.

29	B 17	15 on 10f. purple	9·50	6·50

On Postage Due stamps of 1915 with figures in red and surch **FRANCO** and value.

30	D 9	45 on 6f. green	6·50	6·50
31		45 on 20f. green	16·00	6·50

2 Liberty

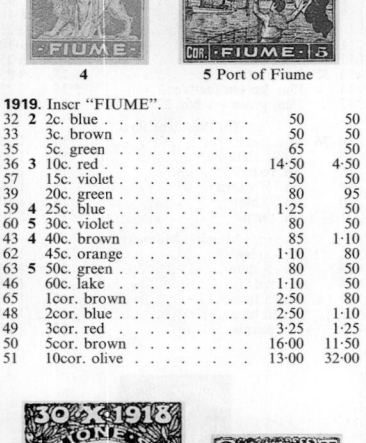

3 Clock Tower over Market in Fiume

4

5 Port of Fiume

1919. Inscr "FIUME".

32	2	2c. blue	50	50
33		3c. brown	50	50
35		5c. green	65	50
36	3	10c. red	14·50	4·50
57		15c. violet	50	50
39		20c. green	80	95
59	4	25c. blue	1·25	50
60	5	30c. violet	80	50
43	4	40c. brown	85	1·10
62		45c. orange	1·10	80
63	5	50c. green	80	50
46		60c. lake	1·10	50
65		1cor. brown	2·50	80
48		2cor. blue	2·50	1·10
49		3cor. red	3·25	1·25
50		5cor. brown	16·00	11·50
51		10cor. olive	13·00	32·00

6 Statue of Romulus, Remus and Wolf

9 Dr. Grossich

1919. Students' Education Fund. 200th Day of Peace.

71	6	5c.+5l. green	8·75	5·00
72		10c.+5l. red	8·75	5·00
73		15c.+5l. grey	8·75	5·00
74		20c.+5l. orange	8·75	5·00
75	–	45c.+5l. olive	8·75	5·00
76	–	60c.+5l. red	8·75	5·00
77	–	80c.+5l. violet	8·75	5·00
78	–	1cor.+5l. grey	8·75	5·00
79	–	2cor.+5l. red	8·75	5·00
80	–	3cor.+5l. brown	8·75	5·00
81	–	5cor.+5l. brown	8·75	5·00
82	–	10cor.+5l. violet	8·75	5·00

DESIGNS—HORIZ: 45, 60, 80c., 1cor. 13th-century Venetian war galley; 2, 3, 5, 10cor. Piazza of St. Mark, Venice.

1919. As T **2** to **5**, but inscr "POSTA FIUME".

83	2	5c. green	65	50
84	3	10c. red	65	50
85	5	30c. violet	3·75	1·40
86	4	40c. brown	95	1·10
87		45c. orange	3·75	1·90
88	5	50c. green	3·75	2·25
89		60c. lake	3·75	2·25
90		10cor. olive	3·50	6·50

1919. Dr. Grossich Foundation.

91	9	25c. (+2cor.) blue	1·60	1·60

1919. Stamps of 1919 surch **FRANCO** and value.

(a) Inscr "FIUME".

92	3	5 on 20c. green	30	30
93	4	10 on 45c. orange	1·90	30
94	5	25 on 50c. green	9·50	14·50
95		55 on 1cor. brown	19·00	14·50
96		55 on 2cor. blue	3·25	4·75
97		55 on 3cor. red	3·25	3·75
98		55 on 5cor. brown	3·25	3·75

(b) Inscr "POSTA FIUME".

99	4	5 on 25c. blue	3·25	35
100	5	15 on 30c. violet	3·25	35
101	4	15 on 45c. orange	3·25	35
102	5	15 on 60c. lake	50	50
103		25 on 50c. green	50	50
104		55 on 10cor. olive	14·50	13·00

1919. Nos. 71/82 and 91 surch **Valore globale** and value.

105	6	5c. on 5c. green	60	60
106		10c. on 10c. red	60	60
107		15c. on 15c. grey	60	60
108		20c. on 20c. orange	60	60
122	9	25c. on 25c. blue	30	30
109	–	45c. on 45c. green	80	80
110	–	60c. on 60c. red	80	80
111	–	80c. on 80c. violet	1·10	1·10
112	–	1cor. on 1cor. grey	1·10	1·10
113	–	2cor. on 2cor. brown	1·10	1·10
114	–	3cor. on 3cor. brown	2·50	2·50
115	–	5cor. on 5cor. brown	3·25	3·25
130	–	10cor. on 10cor. violet	1·10	1·10

16 Gabriele d'Annunzio

21 Medieval Ship

1920. Background in ochre.

131	16	5c. green	50	50
132		10c. red	50	50
133		15c. grey	50	50
134		20c. orange	60	60
135		25c. blue	80	80
136		30c. brown	90	90
137		45c. olive	1·40	1·40
138		50c. lilac	1·40	1·40
139		55c. yellow	1·40	1·40
140		1l. black	8·00	11·00
141		2l. red	8·00	11·00
142		3l. green	8·00	11·00
143		5l. brown	40·00	20·00
144		10l. lilac	8·00	11·50

1920. Nos. M145/8 optd **Reggenza Italiana del Carnaro** or surch also.

146	M 17	1 on 5c. green	95	40
147	–	2 on 25c. blue	40	40
148	M 17	5c. green	13·00	1·10
149	–	10c. red	13·00	1·10
150	–	15 on 10c. red	95	50
151	–	15 on 20c. brown	40	50
152	–	15 on 25c. blue	50	65
153	–	20c. brown	65	65
154	–	25c. blue	65	65
155	–	25 on 10c. red	1·60	1·90
156	–	55 on 20c. brown	3·50	1·25
157	M 17	55 on 5c. green	13·00	2·25
158	–	1l. on 10c. red	21·00	13·00
159	–	1l. on 25c. blue	50·00	50·00
160	M 17	2l. on 5c. green	21·00	13·00
161	–	5l. on 10c. red	85·00	90·00
162	–	10l. on 20c. brown	£375	£275

1921. Issue of d'Annunzio optd **Governo Provvisorio** or also surch **LIRE UNA** (No. 173).

163	16	5c. green	30	30
164		10c. red	30	30
165		15c. grey	30	40
166		20c. orange	1·10	80
167		25c. blue	1·10	80
168		30c. brown	1·10	80
169		45c. olive	65	65
170		50c. lilac	1·25	95
171		55c. yellow	1·10	75
172		1l. black	70·00	65·00
173		1l. on 30c. brown	65	65
174		2l. red	16·00	14·50
175		3l. green	16·00	14·50
176		5l. brown	16·00	14·50
177		10l. lilac	16·00	14·50

1921. Charity Stamps of 1919 optd **24 - IV - 1921 Costituente Fiumana** (and **L** over "Cor." in high values).

178		5c. green	1·60	1·60
179		10c. red	1·60	1·60
180		15c. grey	1·60	1·60
181		20c. orange	1·60	1·60
182		45c. green	4·50	3·50
183		60c. red	4·50	3·50
184		80c. violet	5·75	4·75
185		1l. on 1cor. grey	7·75	6·50
186		1l. on 2cor. brown	35·00	95
187		3l. on 3cor. brown	35·00	35·00
188		5l. on 5cor. brown	35·00	1·60
189		10l. on 10cor. violet	42·00	40·00

1922. Charity Stamps of 1919 optd **24 - IV - 1921 Costituente Fiumano 1922** (and **L** over "Cor." in high values).

190		5c. green	3·00	1·25
191		10c. red	30	30
192		15c. grey	10·00	4·50
193		20c. orange	95	95
194		45c. green	7·75	4·75
195		60c. red	65	1·40
196		80c. violet	65	1·40
197		1l. on 1cor. grey	95	95
198		2l. on 2cor. brown	10·00	6·50
199		3l. on 3cor. brown	95	1·25
200		5l. on 5cor. brown	65	1·25

1923.

201	21	5c. green	30	30
202		10c. mauve	30	30
203		15c. brown	30	30
204	–	20c. red	30	30
205	–	25c. grey	30	30
206	–	30c. green	30	30
207	–	50c. blue	30	30
208	–	60c. red	50	1·10
209	–	1l. blue	50	1·40
210	–	2l. brown	32·00	8·00
211	–	3l. olive	22·00	16·00
212	–	5l. brown	22·00	19·00

DESIGNS: 20, 25, 30c. Roman Arch; 50, 60c., 1l. St. Vitus; 2, 3, 5l. Tarsatic Column.

1924. Issue of 1923 optd **REGNO D'ITALIA** in frame.

213	21	5c. green	65	3·00
214		10c. mauve	65	3·00
215		15c. brown	80	3·00
216	–	20c. red	80	3·00
217	–	25c. grey	80	3·00
218	–	30c. green	80	3·00
219	–	50c. blue	80	3·00
220	–	60c. red	80	3·00
221	–	1l. blue	80	3·00
222	–	2l. brown	2·10	7·00
223	–	3l. olive	3·25	8·25
224	–	5l. brown	3·25	8·25

1924. Issue of 1923 optd **ANNESSIONE ALL'ITALIA** in frame with **22 Febb 1924** below.

225	21	5c. green	30	1·25
226		10c. mauve	30	1·25
227		15c. brown	30	1·25
228	–	20c. red	30	1·25
229	–	25c. grey	30	1·25
230	–	30c. green	30	1·25
231	–	50c. blue	30	1·25
232	–	60c. red	30	1·25
233	–	1l. blue	30	1·25
234	–	2l. brown	65	2·50
235	–	3l. olive	65	2·50
236	–	5l. brown	65	2·50

EXPRESS LETTER STAMPS

E 17

1920.

E145	E 17	30c. green	16·00	12·00
E146		50c. red	16·00	12·00

1920. Nos. M147 and M145 surch **Reggenza Italiana del Carnaro ESPRESSO** and new value.

E163		30c. on 20c. bistre	60·00	60·00
E164		50c. on 5c. green	85·00	48·00

1921. Optd **Governo Provvisorio**.

E178	E 17	30c. blue	6·50	8·00
E179		50c. red	9·50	8·00

E 25 Fiume in 16th Century

1923.

E213	E 25	60c. red	12·00	7·25
E214		2l. blue	12·00	8·75

1924. Optd **REGNO D'ITALIA** in frame with arms between the two words.

E225	E 25	60c. red	80	4·00
E226		2l. blue	80	4·00

1924. Optd **ANNESSIONE ALL'ITALIA** in frame with **22 Febbraio 1924** below.

E237	E 25	60c. red	80	3·25
E238		2l. blue	80	3·25

MILITARY POST STAMPS

M 17 Severing the Gordian Knot

1920. 1st Anniv of Capture of Fiume by D'Annunzio's "Legionaries".

M145	M 17	5c. green	35·00	16·00
M146	–	10c. red	21·00	13·00
M147	–	20c. bistre	35·00	13·00
M148	–	25c. blue	65·00	65·00

DESIGNS: 10c. Arms of Fiume; 20c. "Crown of Thorns"; 25c. Daggers raised in clenched fists.

NEWSPAPER STAMPS

N 9

1919.

N91	N 9	2c. brown	4·75	6·50

N 17 Mail Steamer

1920.

N145	N 17	1c. green	1·60	95

POSTAGE DUE STAMPS

1918. Postage Due stamps of Hungary of 1903 (figures in black), optd **FIUME**.

D29	D 9	6f. green (D21)	£225	85·00
D30		12f. green (D31)	£350	£140
D31		50f. green (D33)	70·00	55·00

1918. Postage Due stamps of Hungary of 1915 (figures in red), optd **FIUME**.

D32	D 9	1f. green	80·00	70·00
D33		2f. green	50	40
D34		5f. green	3·25	3·25
D35		6f. green	50	40
D36		10f. green	6·40	1·90
D37		12f. green	65	50
D38		15f. green	14·50	13·00
D39		20f. green	65	50
D40		30f. green	14·50	11·00

D 9

1919.

D91	D 9	2c. brown	1·10	95
D92		5c. brown	1·40	95

1921. Nos. 105/30 surch **Segnatasse**, new value and device obliterating old surch.

D191	6	2c. on 15c. grey	80	80
D192		4c. on 10c. red	65	55
D193	9	5c. on 25c. blue	65	55
D194	6	6c. on 20c. orange	65	55
D195		10c. on 20c. orange	95	95
D188	–	20c. on 45c. green	1·10	1·60
D183	–	30c. on 1cor. grey	1·25	1·60
D184	–	40c. on 80c. violet	65	80
D185	–	50c. on 60c. red	65	80
D189	–	60c. on 45c. green	1·10	1·60
D190	–	80c. on 45c. green	1·10	1·60
D187	–	1l. on 2cor. brown	1·60	1·90

For stamps of Italy surch **3-V-1945 FIUME RIJEKE** and new value, see Venezia Giulia and Istria, Nos 18/24.

FIUME AND KUPA ZONE Pt. 3

The zone comprised Fiume (Rijeka), Susak and the Kupa River area.

100 pares = 1 dinar.

1941. Nos 414, etc. of Yugoslavia optd **ZONA OCCUPATA FIUMANO KUPA**.

1	99	25p. black	2·40	2·50
2		50p. orange	1·25	1·40
3		1d. green	1·25	1·40
4		1d.50 red	1·25	1·40
5		3d. brown	1·60	1·75
6		4d. blue	2·75	3·50
7		5d. blue	5·50	6·00
8		5d.50 violet	5·50	6·00
9		6d. blue	20·00	20·00
10		8d. brown	14·00	16·00
11		12d. violet	£300	£325
12		16d. purple	95·00	£100

13 20d. blue £1100 £1100
14 30d. pink £6000 £6000

1941. Maternity and Child Welfare Fund. Nos 2/4 further optd **O.N.M.I.**
15 **99** 50p. orange 2·25 5·00
16 1d. green 2·25 5·00
17 1d.50 red 2·25 5·00

1941. Italian Naval Exploit at Buccari (Bakar), 1918. No. 415 of Yugoslavia surch **MEMENTO AVDERE SEMPER L1 BVCCARI.**
18 **99** 1l. on 50p. orange 14·00 32·00

1942. Maternity and Child Welfare. Nos 15/17 further optd **Pro Maternita e Infanzia.**
19 **99** 50p. orange 5·25 12·00
20 1d. green 5·25 12·00
21 1d.50 red 5·25 12·00

Nos. 1/21 were valid until 26.5.42 after which unoverprinted Italian stamps were used until the Italian Occupation ended.

FRANCE Pt. 6

A republic in the W. of Europe.

1849. 100 centimes = 1 franc.
2002. 100 cents = 1 euro.

NOTE. Stamps in types of France up to the 1877 issue were also issued for the French Colonies and where the values and colours are the same they can only be distinguished by their shade or postmark or other minor differences which are outside the scope of this Catalogue. They are priced here by whichever is the lower of the quotations under France or French Colonies in the Stanley Gibbons Catalogue, Part 6 (France). Numbers with asterisks are French Colonies numbers.

1 Ceres **2** Louis Napoleon, President **3** Napoleon III, Emperor of the French

1849. Imperf.
157 **1** 5c. green £180 £110
15* 10c. bistre £325 £120
4 15c. green £13000 £650
6 20c. black £225 27·00
17* 20c. blue £400 95·00
18* 25c. blue £140 11·00
22* 30c. brown 90·00 18·00
19* 40c. orange £210 10·00
23* 80c. red £500 £130
17 1f. orange £32000 £9500
19 1f. red £5000 £500
For 10c. brown on pink and 15c. bistre, imperf, see French Colonies Nos. 16 and 20.

1852. Imperf.
37a **2** 10c. yellow £27000 £450
39 25c. blue £2000 30·00

1853. Imperf.
42 **3** 1c. olive £140 46·00
45 5c. green £400 45·00
50a 10c. yellow £375 11·00
51 20c. blue £120 2·00
63 25c. blue £2000 £180
64 40c. orange £2000 10·50
70 80c. red £1700 33·00
72 1f. red £4250 £2500

1862. Perf.
87 **3** 1c. green £110 26·00
89 5c. green £130 7·25
91 10c. bistre £825 3·00
95 20c. blue £200 60
97 40c. orange £1000 4·00
98 80c. pink £850 21·00

4 Head with Laurel Wreath **5** Head with Laurel Wreath

1863. Perf.
102 **4** 1c. green 17·00 8·50
104 2c. brown 50·00 18·00
109 4c. grey £140 43·00
113a **5** 10c. bistre £375 4·50
115a 20c. blue £160 1·30
116 30c. brown £600 11·00
120 40c. orange £700 6·50
122 80c. pink £800 13·00
For imperforate stamps in these designs see French Colonies.

6 **7** Ceres

1869.
131 **6** 5f. lilac £4000 £1000

1870. Imperf.
148 **7** 1c. green 80·00 80·00
152 2c. brown £180 18·00
156 4c. grey £180 18·00
For 1c. green on blue, 2c. brown on yellow and 5c. green as Type **7** and imperf, see French Colonies.

1870. Perf.
185 **7** 1c. green 29·00 8·75
187 2c. brown 60·00 8·75
189 4c. grey £200 25·00
192 5c. green £130 5·00
136 **1** 10c. bistre £450 00
194 10c. bistre on pink £225 7·50
204 15c. bistre £250 2·50
137 20c. blue £200 5·00
198 25c. blue £100 85
205 30c. brown £400 5·00
140 40c. orange £350 3·50
142 40c. red £425 5·00
208 80c. red £500 10·50

10 Peace and Commerce **11** "Blanc" type **12** "Mouchon" type

13 "Olivier Merson" type

1876.
212 **10** 1c. green £120 50·00
245 1c. black on blue 2·75 1·40
225 2c. green 85·00 9·25
248 2c. brown on buff 5·00 1·40
249 3c. brown on yellow £190 29·00
251 3c. grey 2·00 1·10
214 4c. green £110 36·00
252 4c. brown on grey 2·75 1·50
254 4c. purple on blue 5·00 2·30
282 5c. green 9·00 90
216 10c. green £500 14·00
284 10c. black on lilac 13·50 2·00
232 15c. lilac £550 1·70
279 15c. blue 9·00 1·40
219 20c. brown on yellow £350 11·50
260 20c. red on green 40·00 2·50
234 25c. blue £325 1·20
262 25c. black on red £650 15·00
263 25c. bistre on yellow £225 3·25
267 25c. black on pink 50·00 70
237 30c. brown 85·00 95
268 35c. brown on yellow £325 23·00
269 40c. red on yellow 85·00 1·50
273 50c. red £190 1·60
223 75c. red £550 7·75
274 75c. brown on orange £200 27·00
240 1f. green £120 4·50
287 2f. brown on blue 60·00 26·00
277 5f. mauve on lilac £350 48·00
For imperforate stamps in this design see French Colonies.
For 5f. red, perf, see No. 412.

1900.
288 **11** 1c. grey 70 20
289 2c. purple 90 20
290 3c. red 80 30
292a 4c. brown 3·25 1·00
295 5c. green 1·20 20
300 **12** 10c. red 20·00 1·00
301 15c. orange 8·00 25
297 20c. brown 50·00 5·50
302 25c. blue 90·00 1·00
299 30c. mauve 50·00 4·50
303 **13** 40c. red and blue 11·00 35
304 45c. green and blue 16·00 1·30
305 50c. brown and lilac 50·00 55
306 1f. red and green 25·00 40
369 1f. red and yellow 55·00 90
307 2f. lilac and buff £850 60·00
308 5f. blue and buff 85·00 2·75
For further values in these designs, see 1920 issues (following No. 379).

14 "Mouchon" type redrawn **15** Sower

1902.
309 **14** 10c. red 30·00 85
310 15c. red 12·00 30
311 20c. brown 90·00 11·50
312 25c. blue £100 1·40
313 30c. mauve £225 11·00

1903.
314 **15** 10c. red 9·50 25
316 15c. green 3·50 20
317 20c. purple 75·00 2·10
320 25c. blue 90·00 1·10
321 30c. lilac £150 5·50

16 Ground below Feet **18** No Ground **20**

1906.
325 **16** 10c. red 2·75 2·50

1906.
331 **18** 5c. green 1·70 15
335 10c. red 2·00 15
337 20c. brown 4·00 40
341 25c. blue 3·50 20
343 30c. orange 18·00 1·20
346 35c. violet 7·50 1·10
See also Nos. 497 etc. and 454/a.

1914. Red Cross Fund. Surch with red cross and **5c.**
351 **18** 10c.+5c. red 5·00 5·25

1914. Red Cross Fund.
352 **20** 10c.+5c. red 26·00 3·00

21 War Widow **26** Spirit of War

23 Woman replaces Man **27** Sinking of "Charles Roux" Hospital Ship, and Bombed Hospital

1917. War Orphans' Fund.
370 **21** 2c.+3c. red 4·25 4·25
371 – 5c.+5c. green 15·00 9·25
372 **23** 15c.+10c. green 24·00 21·00
373 25c.+15c. blue 80·00 48·00
374 – 35c.+25c. violet and grey £130 £100
375 – 50c.+50c. brown £200 £150
376 **26** 1f.+1f. red £325 £325
377 5f.+5f. blue and black £1200 £1100
DESIGNS—As Type **21**: 5c. Orphans. As Type **26**: 35c. Front line trench; 50c. Lion of Belfort.
See also Nos. 450/3.

1918. Red Cross Fund.
378 **27** 15c.+5c. red & green £110 50·00

1919. Surch ½ **centime.**
379 **11** ½c. on 1c. grey 25 35

1920.
497 **18** 1c. bistre 15 20
497a 1c. brown 15 35
498 2c. green 15 20
499 3c. red 15 25
380 5c. orange 1·70 25
500 5c. mauve 15 20
413 **11** 7½c. mauve* 80 85
381 **18** 10c. green 50 20
501 10c. blue 1·70 20
413a **11** 10c. lilac 4·75 35
414 **18** 15c. brown 25 20
415 20c. mauve 25 20
415b 25c. brown 10 15
503 30c. red 50 30
382a 30c. mauve 1·00 75
416 30c. blue 3·50 25
505 35c. green 75 45
417 40c. green 1·20 40
418 40c. red 2·00 35
418a 40c. violet 1·90 70
418b 40c. blue 1·20 20
419 **15** 45c. violet 6·25 1·30
592 50c. blue 1·20 35
420 50c. green 6·25 1·00
421 50c. red 1·20 35
384 **13** 60c. violet and blue 90 60
385 **15** 60c. violet 6·25 1·40
385a 65c. red 2·75 1·30
422 65c. green 6·00 1·50
423 75c. mauve 5·25 30
424 80c. red 25·00 7·50
386 85c. red 12·00 2·10
425 1f. blue 6·00 40
426 **18** 1f.05 red 14·00 5·00
427 1f.10 mauve 10·50 2·20
428 1f.40 mauve 20·00 21·00
387 **13** 2f. orange and green 48·00 40
428a **18** 2f. green 12·50 1·20
429 **13** 3f. violet and blue 25·00 6·00
430 3f. mauve and red 48·00 3·00
431 10f. green and red £100 14·00
432 20f. mauve and green £160 29·00
***PRECANCEL.** No. 413 was issued only precancelled. The "unused" price is for stamp with full gum and the used price for stamp without gum.

1922. War Orphans' Fund. Nos. 370/7 surch with new value, cross and bars.
388 **21** 1c. on 2c.+3c. red 40 65
389 – 2½c. on 5c.+5c. green 65 85
390 **23** 5c. on 15c.+10c. green 1·10 1·30
391 5c. on 25c.+15c. blue 2·00 2·30
392 – 5c. on 35c.+25c. violet and grey 12·00 14·00
393 – 10c. on 50c.+50c. brn 18·00 17·00
394 **26** 25c. on 1f.+1f. red 29·00 29·00
395 1f. on 5f.+5f. blue and black £140 £140

30 Pasteur **31** Stadium and Arc de Triomphe

1923.
396 **30** 10c. green 65 20
396a 15c. green 1·30 25
396b 20c. green 2·50 80
397 30c. red 80 1·40
397a 30c. green 70 35
398 45c. red 2·00 2·00
399 50c. blue 3·75 25
400 75c. blue 4·00 85
400a 90c. red 11·00 3·25
400b 1f. blue 20·00 20
400c 1f.25 blue 23·00 8·00
400d 1f.50 blue 5·25 20

1923. Optd **CONGRES PHILATELIQUE DE BORDEAUX 1923.**
400e **13** 1f. red and green £325 £425

1924. Olympic Games.
401 **31** 10c. green & light green 2·00 1·00
402 – 25c. deep red and red 2·75 70
403 – 30c. red and black 8·50 10·50
404 – 50c. ultramarine & blue 24·00 4·00
DESIGNS—HORIZ: 25c. Notre Dame and Pont Neuf. VERT: 30c. Milan de Crotone (statue); 50c. The victor.

35 Ronsard **36**

1924. 400th Birth Anniv of Ronsard.
405 **35** 75c. blue 1·80 1·50

1924. International Exhibition of Modern Decorative Arts. Dated "1925".
406 **36** 10c. yellow and green 65 70
407 – 15c. green & deep green 65 80
408 – 25c. red and purple 65 40
409 – 25c. mauve and blue 1·30 70
410 – 75c. blue and grey 3·00 1·90
411 **36** 75c. blue and deep blue 16·00 6·00
DESIGNS—HORIZ: 25c. (No. 408); 75c. (No. 410) Potter and vase; 25c. (No. 409), Chateau and steps. VERT: 15c. Stylized vase.

1925. Paris Int Philatelic Exhibition.
412 **10** 5f. red 95·00 95·00
MS412a 140×220 mm. No. 412 in block of four £800 £800

1926. Surch with new value and bars.
433 **18** 25c. on 30c. blue 25 40
434 25c. on 35c. violet 25 40
436 **15** 50c. on 60c. violet 1·20 1·00
437 50c. on 65c. red 70 60
438 **30** 50c. on 75c. blue 3·00 1·50
439 **15** 50c. on 80c. red 1·20 1·00
440 50c. on 85c. red 2·00 90
441 **18** 50c. on 1f.05 red 1·20 60
442 **30** 50c. on 1f.25 blue 2·50 2·00
443 **15** 55c. on 60c. violet* £130 49·00
444 **18** 90c. on 1f.05 red 2·50 2·75
445 1f.10 on 1f.40 red 90 90
***PRECANCEL.** No. 443 was issued only precancelled. The "unused" price is for stamp with full gum and the used price for stamp without gum.

1926. War Orphans' Fund.
450 **21** 2c.+1c. purple 1·60 1·50
451 – 50c.+10c. brn (as No. 375) 22·00 11·50
452 **26** 1f.+25c. red 49·00 37·00
453 5f.+1f. blue and black 95·00 85·00

1927. Strasbourg Philatelic Exhibition.
454 **18** 5f. blue £250 £275
454a 10f. red £250 £275
MS454b 110×140 mm. 5f.+10f. and label inscr "STRASBOURG 1927" £750 £750

1927. Air. 1st International Display of Aviation and Navigation, Marseilles. Optd with Bleriot XI airplane and **Poste Aerienne.**
455 **13** 2f. red and green £180 £200
456 5f. blue and yellow £150 £200

44 Marcelin Berthelot

45 Lafayette, Washington, "Paris" (liner) and Lindbergh's Airplane "Spirit of St. Louis"

1927. Birth Centenary of Berthelot.
457 **44** 90c. red . . . . 1·90 45

1927. Visit of American Legion.
458 **45** 90c. red . . . . 1·30 1·50
459 1f.50 blue . . . . 4·00 1·70

1927. Sinking Fund. Surch **Caisse d'Amortissement** or **C A** and premium.
460 **18** 40c.+10c. blue . . . . . . 5·25 5·75
461 **15** 50c.+25c. green . . . . . 8·25 8·50
462 **30** 1f.50+50c. orange . . . . 13·00 13·50
See also Nos. 466/8, 476/8, 485/7 and 494/6.

48

50 Joan of Arc

1928. Sinking Fund.
463 **48** 1f.50+8f.50 blue £100 £120

1928. Air ("Ile de France"). Surch **10 FR.** and bars.
464 **44** 10f. on 90c. red £1600 £1600
465 **30** 10f. on 1f.50 blue £11000 £11000

1928. Sinking Fund. Surch as Nos. 460/2.
466 **18** 40c.+10c. violet . . . . . 9·25 10·00
467 **15** 50c.+25c. red . . . . . . 29·00 29·00
468 **30** 1f.50+50c. mauve . . . . 45·00 39·00

1929. 500th Anniv of Relief of Orleans.
469 **50** 50c. blue . . . . 2·00 25

1929. Optd **EXPOSITION LE HAVRE 1929 PHILATELIQUE.**
470 **13** 2f. red and green £500 £500

52 Reims Cathedral

53 Mont St. Michel

1929. Views.
470a – 90c. mauve . . . . 3·25 85
471 – 2f. red . . . . 36·00 55
472 **52** 3f. blue . . . . 80·00 2·30
473a **53** 5f. brown . . . . 22·00 45
474b – 10f. blue . . . . 75·00 9·50
475 – 20f. brown . . . . £250 34·00
DESIGNS—HORIZ: 90c. Le Puy-en-Velay; 2f. Arc de Triomphe; 10f. Port de la Rochelle; 20f. Pont du Gard.

1929. Sinking Fund. Surch as Nos. 460/2.
476 **18** 40c.+10c. green . . . . . 17·00 16·00
477 **15** 50c.+25c. mauve . . . . . 31·00 28·00
478 **30** 1f.50+50c. brown . . . . 60·00 55·00

54 Bay of Algiers

1930. Centenary of French Conquest of Algeria.
479 **54** 50c. red and blue . . . . 2·75 40

55 "Le Sourire de Reims"

1930. Sinking Fund.
480 **55** 1f.50+3f.50 purple . . . . 70·00 75·00

1930. I.L.O. Session, Paris. Optd **CONGRES DU B.I.T. 1930.**
481 **15** 50c. red . . . . 2·40 2·00
482 **30** 1f.50 blue . . . . 20·00 14·50

57 Notre Dame de la Garde, Marseilles

1930. Air.
483 **57** 1f.50 red . . . . 21·00 2·75
484 1f.50 blue . . . . 19·00 1·60

1930. Sinking Fund. Surch as Nos. 460/2.
485 **18** 40c.+10c. red . . . . . . 20·00 17·00
486 **15** 50c.+25c. brown . . . . 38·00 35·00
487 **18** 1f.50+50c. violet . . . . 65·00 60·00

58 Woman of the Fachi tribe

59 "French Colonies"

1930. International Colonial Exhibition.
488 **58** 15c. black . . . . 1·00 30
489 40c. brown . . . . 2·50 30
490 50c. red 75 10
491 1f.50 blue . . . . 9·50 40
492 **59** 1f.50 blue . . . . 42·00 1·70

60 "French Provinces"

1931. Sinking Fund.
493 **60** 1f.50+3f.50 green £120 £120

1931. Sinking Fund. Surch as Nos. 460/2.
494 **18** 40c.+10c. green . . . . . 37·00 35·00
495 **15** 50c.+25c. violet . . . . 90·00 90·00
496 **18** 1f.50+50c. red . . . . . 90·00 90·00

61 Peace

62 Briand

65 Dove of Peace

1932.
502 **61** 30c. green 85 45
506 40c. mauve 25 25
507 45c. brown . . . . 1·80 1·00
508 50c. red 15 10
508d 55c. violet 70 25
508e 60c. bistre 30 35
509 65c. purple 45 40
509a 65c. blue 35 15
510 75c. green 15 15
510a 80c. orange 55 25
511 90c. red . . . . 30·00 1·80
511a 90c. green 55 45
511b 90c. blue 70 35
512 1f. orange . . . . 2·75 20
512a 1f. pink . . . . 3·25 20
513 1f.25 olive . . . . 65·00 4·50
513a 1f.25 red . . . . 1·70 1·80
513b 1f.40 mauve . . . . . . 6·25 6·25
514 1f.50 blue 25 20
515 1f.75 mauve . . . . . . 4·00 30

1933. Surch ½ **centime.**
515a **18** ½c. on 1c. bistre 20 55
515b ½c. on 1c. brown . . . . . 90 1·40

1933. Portraits.
516 **62** 30c. green . . . . 17·00 8·00
517 – 75c. mauve (Doumer) . . . 25·00 1·20
518 – 1f.25 red (Victor Hugo) . . 7·00 1·90

1934.
519 **65** 1f.50 blue . . . . 45·00 13·00

66 J. M. Jacquard

67 Jacques Cartier, "Grande Hermine" and "Petite Hermine"

1934. Death Centenary of Jacquard.
520 **66** 40c. blue . . . . 3·25 85

1934. 4th Cent of Cartier's Discovery of Canada.
521 **67** 75c. mauve . . . . 23·00 1·70
522 1f.50 blue . . . . 40·00 3·00

68 Bleriot XI

1934. Air. 25th Anniv of Channel Flight.
523 **68** 2f.25 violet . . . . 19·00 6·25

1934. Surch in figures and bars.
524 **61** 50c. on 1f.25 olive . . . . 3·50 50
524a 80c. on 1f. orange 45 55

69 Breton River Scene

1935.
525 **69** 2f. green . . . . 33·00 65

70 "Normandie"

71 St. Trophime, Arles

1935. Maiden Trip of Liner "Normandie".
526 **70** 1f.50 blue . . . . 13·00 1·50

1935.
527 **71** 3f.50 brown . . . . 27·00 3·50

72 B. Delessert

73 Victor Hugo

1935. Opening of Int Savings Bank Congress.
528 **72** 75c. green . . . . 18·00 1·10

1935. 50th Death Anniv of Victor Hugo.
529 **73** 1f.25 purple . . . . 4·25 1·70

74 Cardinal Richelieu

1935. Tercentenary of French Academy by Richelieu.
530 **74** 1f.50 red . . . . 20·00 1·20

75 Jacques Callot

77 Symbolic of Art

1935. Death Tercentenary of Callot (engraver).
531 **75** 75c. red . . . . 10·50 45

1935. Unemployed Intellectuals' Relief Fund. Inscr "POUR L'ART ET LA PENSEE".
532 – 50c.+10c. blue . . . . . . 2·75 2·75
533 **77** 50c.+2f. red . . . . . . 45·00 47·00
DESIGN—HORIZ: No. 532, Help for intellectuals (inscr "POUR LES CHOMEURS INTELLECTUELS").

78 Caudron C-635 Simoun over Paris

1936. Air.
534 **78** 85c. green . . . . 2·75 2·40
535 1f.50 blue . . . . 9·25 4·75
536 2f.25 violet . . . . 20·00 6·50
537 2f.50 red . . . . 30·00 10·50
538 3f. blue . . . . 24·00 1·70
539 3f.50 brown . . . . 60·00 23·00
540 50f. green £650 £375

79 Caudron C-635 Simoun over Paris

1936. Air.
541 **79** 50f. blue and pink £650 £300

80 Statue of Liberty

81 Andre-Marie Ampere

1936. Nansen (Refugee) Fund.
541a **80** 50c.+25c. blue . . . . . 3·50 4·00
542 75c.+50c. violet . . . . . 8·50 9·25

1936. Death Centenary of Ampere.
543 **81** 75c. brown . . . . 16·00 1·70

82 Daudet's Mill, Fontvieille

1936.
544 **82** 2f. blue . . . . 3·50 35

83 Children of the Unemployed

84 Pilatre de Rozier

1936. Children of the Unemployed Fund.
545 **83** 50c.+10c. red . . . . . . 4·25 4·75

1936. 150th Death Anniv of Pilatre de Rozier.
546 **84** 75c. blue . . . . 16·00 2·50

85 Rouget de Lisle

87 Canadian War Memorial, Vimy

1936. Death Centenary of Rouget de Lisle, Composer of the "Marseillaise".
547 **85** 20c. green . . . . 3·25 1·70
548 – 40c. brown . . . . 5·00 2·50
DESIGN—HORIZ: 40c. Female figure inscr "LA MARSEILLAISE".

1936. Unveiling of Canadian War Memorial, Vimy Ridge.
549 **87** 75c. red . . . . 13·00 3·50
550 1f.50 blue . . . . 12·50 7·50

88 Jean Jaures as an Orator

1936. Jaures Commemoration.
551 **88** 40c. brown . . . . 3·25 1·20
552 – 1f.50 blue . . . . 11·50 2·40
The 1f.50 has a head and shoulders portrait of Jaures.

91 Latecoere 300 Flying Boat

1936. 100th Flight between France and S. America.
553 – 1f.50 blue . . . . 15·00 3·00
554 **91** 10f. green £275 £110
DESIGN—VERT: 1f.50, Airplane and old-time sailing ship.

92 Herald

93 "World Exhibition"

1936. Paris International Exhibition.
555 **92** 20c. mauve 40 50
556 30c. green . . . . 2·50 1·60
557 40c. blue . . . . 1·10 60
558 50c. orange . . . . 1·30 25
559 **93** 90c. red . . . . 11·00 7·50
560 1f.50 blue . . . . 30·00 3·25

94 "Vision of Peace"

1936. Universal Peace Propaganda.
561 **94** 1f.50 blue . . . . 14·50 2·75

1936. Unemployed Intellectuals' Fund. No. 533 surch **+ 20c.**
562 **77** 20c. on 50c.+2f. red . . . 3·00 3·25

96 Jacques Callot

1936. Unemployed Intellectuals' Fund. Inscr as in T **96**.
563 **96** 20c.+10c. lake . . . . . . 2·50 2·75
564 – 40c.+10c. green . . . . . 2·75 3·25
565 – 50c.+10c. red . . . . . . 3·00 3·25
566 – 1f.50+50c. blue . . . . . 19·00 18·00
DESIGNS: 40c. Hector Berlioz; 50c. Victor Hugo; 1f.50, Louis Pasteur.
See also Nos. 603/5 and 607.

97 Ski Jumper

1937. Chamonix-Mont Blanc Skiing Week.
567 **97** 1f.50 blue . . . . 5·75 1·40

98 Pierre Corneille (author)

99 France and Minerva

1937. 300th Anniv of First Performance of "Le Cid" (play).
568 **98** 75c. red . . . . 1·90 1·10

1937. Paris International Exhibition.
569 **99** 1f.50 blue . . . . 2·10 85

100 Mermoz

101 Jean Mermoz Memorial

1937. Mermoz Commemoration.
570 **100** 30c. green 45 60
571 **101** 3f. violet . . . . 5·50 3·25

102 Paris–Orleans Midi Electric Train

1937. 13th International Railway Congress, Paris.
572 **102** 30c. green . . . . 95 1·20
573 – 1f.50 blue . . . . 6·25 6·25
DESIGN: 1f.50, Nord streamlined steam locomotive.

103 Rene Descartes

1937. 300th Anniv of Publication of "Discours".
(a) Wrongly inscr "DISCOURS SUR LA METHODE".
574 **103** 90c. red . . . . 1·90 1·30
(b) Corrected to "DISCOURS DE LA METHODE".
575 **103** 90c. red . . . . 5·75 1·60

104 Anatole France

107 Ramblers

1937. Unemployed Intellectuals' Relief Fund.
576 **104** 30c.+10c. green . . . . 2·20 2·50
577 – 90c.+10c. red . . . . . 5·25 5·75
DESIGN—HORIZ: 90c. Auguste Rodin.
See also Nos. 602 and 606.

1937. Postal Workers' Sports Fund.
578 – 20c.+10c. brown . . . . 1·70 2·00
579 – 40c.+10c. lake . . . . . 1·70 2·00
580 **107** 50c.+10c. purple . . . . 1·70 2·00
DESIGNS—HORIZ: 20c. Tug-of-War; 40c. Runners and discus thrower.

1937. International Philatelic Exhibition, Paris. As T **1**, printed in miniature sheets of four (5⅞ × 8⅜ ins.) inscr "PEXIP PARIS 1937" between stamps.
MS581 5c. brown and blue; 15c. carmine and red; 30c. red and blue; 50c. brown and red . . . £275 £275

108 Pierre Loti and Constantinople

109 "Victory" of Samothrace

1937. Pierre Loti Memorial Fund.
585 **108** 50c.+20c. red . . . . . . 3·50 4·00

1937. National Museums.
586 **109** 30c. green . . . . 65·00 39·00
587 55c. red . . . . 65·00 39·00

110 "France" and Child

1937. Public Health Fund.
588 **110** 65c.+25c. purple . . . . 2·75 2·50
588a 90c.+30c. blue . . . . . 2·50 2·50

111 France congratulating U.S.A.

1937. 150th Anniv of U.S. Constitution.
589 **111** 1f.75 blue . . . . 2·10 1·30

112 Iseran Pass

113 Ceres

1937. Opening of Col de l'Iseran Road.
590 **112** 90c. green . . . . 1·90 35

1938.
591 **113** 1f.75 blue 65 45
591a 2f. red 20 20
591b 2f.25 blue . . . . 8·50 65
591c 2f.50 green . . . . . . 1·30 50
591d 2f.50 blue 65 60
591e 3f. mauve 60 30

1938. Shipwrecked Mariners Society. As T **104** but portrait of Jean Charcot.
593 65c.+35c. green . . . . . . 1·80 2·50
593a 90c.+35c. purple . . . . . 10·50 11·50

113a Gambetta

113b Champagne Girl

1938. Birth Centenary of Leon Gambetta (politician).
594 **113a** 55c. lilac 45 50

1938.
594a – 90c. red on blue . . . . 1·00 1·10
595 **113b** 1f.75 blue . . . . . . 3·25 3·00
596 – 2f. brown 70 85
597 – 2f.15 purple . . . . . 4·00 70
598 – 3f. red . . . . 11·00 3·50
599 – 5f. blue 50 40
600 – 10f. purple on blue . . 1·20 1·30
601 – 20f. green . . . . . . 41·00 16·00
DESIGNS—VERT: 2f.15, Coal miners; 10f. Vincennes. HORIZ: 90c. Chateau de Pau; 2f. Arc de Triomphe at Orange; 3f. Papal Palace, Avignon; 5f. Carcassonne; 20f. St. Malo.

1938. Unemployed Intellectuals' Relief Fund. As Nos. 563/6 and 576/7, inscr "POUR LES CHOMEURS INTELLECTUELS".
602 30c.+10c. red . . . . 2·10 2·20
603 35c.+10c. green . . . . . . 2·50 2·50
604 55c.+10c. violet . . . . . . 5·75 4·50
605 65c.+10c. blue . . . . 5·75 4·75
606 1f.+10c. red . . . . 5·25 5·00
607 1f.75+25c. blue . . . . . . 16·00 17·00
PORTRAITS—As Type **96**: 35c. Callot; 55c. Berlioz; 65c. Victor Hugo; 1f.75, Louis Pasteur. As No. 577: 1f. Auguste Rodin. As Type **104**: 30c. Anatole France.

114 Palais de Versailles

115 Soldier in Trench

1938. French National Music Festivals.
608 **114** 1f.75+75c. blue . . . . . 18·00 18·00

1938. Infantry Monument Fund.
609 **115** 55c.+70c. purple . . . . 4·50 4·75
610 65c.+1f.10 blue . . . . . 4·50 4·75

116 Medical Corps Monument at Lyons

117 Saving a Goal

1938. Military Medical Corps' Monument Fund.
611 **116** 55c.+45c. red . . . . . . 9·75 10·50

1938. World Football Cup.
612 **117** 1f.75 blue . . . . 11·50 9·50

117a Clement Ader

118 Jean de La Fontaine

1938. Clement Ader (air pioneer).
612a **117a** 50f. blue . . . . 85·00 65·00

1938. La Fontaine (writer of fables).
613 **118** 55c. green . . . . 1·20 95

1938. Reims Cathedral Restoration Fund. As T **52**, but inscr "REIMS 10.VII.1938".
614 65c.+35c. blue . . . . 7·75 10·50

119 Houses of Parliament, "Friendship" and Arc de Triomphe

120 "France" welcoming Frenchmen repatriated from Spain

1938. Visit of King George VI and Queen Elizabeth to France.
615 **119** 1f.75 blue 60 90

1938. French Refugees' Fund.
616 **120** 65c.+60c. red . . . . . . 3·75 5·25

121 Pierre and Marie Curie

1938. International Anti-cancer Fund. 40th Anniv of Discovery of Radium.
617 **121** 1f.75+50c. blue . . . . . 8·50 10·50

122 Arc de Triomphe and Allied Soldiers

123 Mercury

1938. 20th Anniv of 1918 Armistice.
618 **122** 65c.+35c. red . . . . . . 3·25 4·25

1938. Inscr "REPUBLIQUE FRANCAISE".
618a **123** 1c. brown 25 25
619 2c. green 25 25
620 5c. red 10 15
621 10c. blue 10 15
622 15c. orange 15 30
622a 15c. brown 60 70
623 20c. mauve 10 15
624 25c. green 10 15
625 30c. red 10 15
626 40c. violet 10 15
627 45c. green 65 70
627b 50c. green 40 45
627c 50c. blue 10 15
628 60c. orange 15 25
629 70c. mauve 15 20
629a 75c. brown . . . . . . 4·25 3·25
For similar stamps inscr "POSTES FRANCAISES", see Nos. 750/3.

124 Nurse and Patient

125 Blind Radio Listener

1938. Students' Fund.
630 **124** 65c.+60c. blue . . . . . 6·75 7·75

1938. "Radio for the Blind" Fund.
631 **125** 90c.+25c. purple . . . . 6·75 8·00

126 Monument to Civilian War Victims, Lille

127 Paul Cezanne

1939. War Victims' Monument Fund.
632 **126** 90c.+35c. brown . . . . 7·50 8·75

1939. Birth Cent of Paul Cezanne (painter).
633 **127** 2f.25 blue . . . . 3·25 2·75

128 Red Cross Nurse

129 Military Engineer

1939. 75th Anniv of Red Cross Society. Cross in red.
634 **128** 90c.+35c. blue & black . . 5·50 6·75

1939. To the Glory of French Military Engineers.
635 **129** 70c.+50c. red . . . . . . 5·75 6·75

130 Ministry of Posts, Telegraphs and Telephones

1939. P.T.T. Orphans' Fund.
636 **130** 90c.+35c. blue . . . . . 18·00 18·00

131 "Dunkerque" Class Battleship

1939. Laying down Keel of Battleship "Clemenceau".
637 **131** 90c. blue 60 75

132 French Pavilion, New York Exhibition

1939. New York World's Fair.
638 **132** 2f.25 blue . . . . 7·25 5·75
638a 2f.50 blue . . . . 7·25 7·75

133 Mother and Child

134 Niepce and Daguerre

1939. Children of the Unemployed Fund.
639 **133** 90c.+35c. red . . . . . . 2·50 2·50

1939. Photographic Centenary.
640 **134** 2f.25 blue . . . . 5·75 5·00

135 Eiffel Tower

136 Iris

1939. 50th Anniv of Erection of Eiffel Tower.
641 **135** 90c.+50c. purple . . . . 7·25 7·75

1939.
642 **136** 80c. brown 25 35
643 1f. green 65 20
643a 1f. red 25 20
643b 1f.30 blue 15 35
643c 1f.50 orange 15 30
See also Nos. 861/8.

137 Marly Water Works

1939. International Water Exhibition, Liege.
644 **137** 2f.25 blue . . . . 9·50 4·00

138 Balzac

1939. Unemployed Intellectuals' Fund.
645 – 40c.+10c. red . . . . . 80 1·20
646 – 70c.+10c. purple . . . 3·75 2·75
647 **138** 90c.+10c. mauve . . . . 3·25 2·75
648 – 2f.25+25c. blue . . . . 15·00 12·50
PORTRAITS—VERT: 40c. Puvis de Chavannes. HORIZ: 70c. Claude Debussy; 2f.25, Claude Bernard.
See also Nos 667b/d.

139 St. Gregory of Tours

140 Mother and Children

1939. 1400th Birth Anniv of St. Gregory of Tours.
649 **139** 90c. red 45 65

1939. Birth-rate Development Fund.
650 – 70c.+80c. vio, bl & grn 3·75 4·25
651 **140** 90c.+60c. brn, pur & sep 4·75 5·75
DESIGN: 70c. Mother and children admiring infant in cot.

141 Oath of the Tennis Court

142 Strasbourg Cathedral

1939. 150th Anniv of French Revolution.
652 **141** 90c. green . . . . 1·80 1·70

1939. 5th Centenary of Completion of Strasbourg Cathedral Spire.
653 **142** 70c. red . . . . 90 1·20

143 Porte Chaussee, Verdun

144 "The Letter"

1939. 23rd Anniv of Battle of Verdun.
654 **143** 90c. grey 60 95

1939. Postal Museum Fund.
655 **144** 40c.+60c. brown & pur 2·75 3·50

145 Statue to Sailors lost at Sea

146 Languedoc

1939. Boulogne Monument Fund.
656 **145** 70c.+30c. plum . . . . . 11·00 11·50

1939.
657 **146** 70c. black on blue 45 50

147 Lyons

1939.
658 **147** 90c. purple 60 80

148 French Soldier and Strasbourg Cathedral

1940. Soldiers' Comforts Fund.
659 **148** 40c.+60c. purple . . . . 2·10 2·50
660 – 1f.+50c. blue . . . . . . 2·30 2·50
DESIGN: 1f. Veteran French colonial soldier and African village.

149 French Colonial Empire

1940. Overseas Propaganda Fund.
661 **149** 1f.+25c. red . . . . . . 1·90 2·40
See also Nos. 708 and 953.

150 Marshal Joffre

1940. War Charities. Inscr as in T **150**.
662 **150** 80c.+45c. brown . . . . 4·75 6·00
663 – 1f.+50c. violet . . . . 4·00 6·00
664 – 1f.50+50c. red . . . . 4·00 4·75
665 – 2f.50+50c. blue . . . . 8·50 10·50
DESIGNS—HORIZ: 1f.50, General Gallieni; 2f.50, Ploughing. VERT: 1f. Marshal Foch.

151 Nurse and Wounded Soldier

1940. Red Cross. Cross in red.
666 – 80c.+1f. green . . . . . 4·75 6·25
667 **151** 1f.+2f. brown . . . . . . 5·75 6·25
DESIGN: 80c. Doctor, nurse, soldier and family.

152 G. Guynemer (pilot)

153 Nurse, wounded Soldier and Family

1940.
667a **152** 50f. blue . . . . 9·00 8·75

1940. Unemployed Intellectuals' Fund. As T **138**. Inscr "POUR LES CHOMEURS INTELLECTUELS".
667b 80c.+10c. brown . . . . . 4·50 7·25
667c 1f.+10c. purple . . . . . 4·50 7·25
667d 2f.50+25c. blue . . . . . 4·50 7·00
PORTRAITS: 80c. Debussy; 1f. Balzac.; 2f.50, Bernard.

1940. War Victim's Fund.
667e **153** 1f.+2f. violet . . . . . . 85 1·10

154 Harvesting

1940. National Relief Fund. Inscr "SECOURS NATIONAL".
668 **154** 80c.+2f. sepia . . . . . 1·90 2·20
669 – 1f.+2f. brown . . . . . 1·90 2·20
670 – 1f.50+2f. violet . . . . 1·90 2·20
671 – 2f.50+2f. green . . . . 2·50 2·20
DESIGNS: 1f. Sowing; 1f.50, Gathering grapes; 2f.50, Cattle.

1940. Surch with new value and with bars on all except T **113**.
672 **18** 30c. on 35c. green . . . 15 30
673 **61** 50c. on 55c. violet . . . 15 30
674 50c. on 65c. blue 15 15
675 50c. on 75c. green . . . 25 30
676 **123** 50c. on 75c. brown . . . 25 30
677 **61** 50c. on 80c. orange . . . 20 35
678 50c. on 90c. blue 15 15
679 1f. on 1f.25 red 25 35
680 1f. on 1f.40 mauve . . . 20 35
681 1f. on 1f.50 blue . . . . 75 1·20
682 **113** 1f. on 1f.75 blue 15 25
683 – 1f. on 2f.15 purple (No. 597) 25 40
684 **113** 1f. on 2f.25 blue 15 25
685 1f. on 2f.50 green . . . 90 1·10
686 – 2f.50 on 5f. blue (No. 599) 25 40
687 – 5f. on 10f. purple on blue (No. 600) . . . 1·50 2·10
688 – 10f. on 20f. green (No. 601) . . . . . . 1·30 1·90
689 **117a** 20f. on 50f. blue . . . . 35·00 39·00

155 Marshal Petain

156 Prisoners of War

1940.
690 **155** 40c. brown 35 50
691 80c. green 40 55
692 1f. red 20 30
693 2f.50 blue . . . . 95 1·30
See also Nos. 774/5.

1941. Prisoners of War Fund.
696 **156** 80c.+5f. green . . . . . 1·20 1·70
697 – 1f.+5f. red . . . . . . 1·20 1·70
DESIGN: 1f. Group of soldiers.

157 Frederic Mistral **158** Science against Cancer

1941. Frederic Mistral (poet).

698	**157**	1f. red	20	30

1941. Anti-cancer Fund.

699	**158**	2f.50+50c. blk and brn	1·10	1·60

159 Beaune Hospital, 1443

1941. Views.

700	**159**	5f. brown	25	30
701	–	10f. violet	35	55
702	**159**	15f. red	50	75
703	–	20f. brown	80	1·20

DESIGNS: 10f. Angers; 20f. Ramparts of St. Louis, Aigues-Mortes.

1941. National Relief Fund. Surch **+ 10c.**

704	**155**	1f.+10c. red	15	20

160

1941. Winter Relief Fund. Inscr as in T **160**.

705	**160**	1f.+2f. purple	1·60	1·80
706	–	2f.50+7f.50 blue	5·50	4·25

DESIGN: 2f.50, "Charity" helping a pauper.

162 Liner "Pasteur"

1941. Seamen's Dependants Relief Fund. Surch.

707	**162**	1f.+1f. on 70c. green	30	40

1941. As No. 661, but without "R.F." and dated "1941".

708	**149**	1f.+1f. multicoloured	40	60

163 **164** Marshal Petain **165**

1941. Frame in T **164** is 17 × 20½ mm.

709	**163**	20c. purple	20	40
710		30c. red	15	30
711		40c. blue	20	30
712	**164**	50c. green	15	20
713		60c. violet	15	20
714		70c. blue	15	20
715		70c. orange	15	20
716		80c. brown	20	20
717		80c. green	15	20
718		1f. red	15	20
719		1f.20 brown	15	20
720	**165**	1f.50 pink	20	20
721		1f.50 brown	15	20
722		2f. green	15	20
723		2f.40 red	15	45
724		2f.50 blue	65	1·10
725		3f. orange	20	20
725a	**164**	4f. blue	20	35
725b		4f.50 green	65	70

See also Nos. 740/1.

166 Fisherman **167** Arms of Nancy

1941. National Seamen's Relief Fund.

726	**166**	1f.+9f. green	80	1·00

1942. National Relief Fund.

727	**167**	20c.+30c. black	1·80	2·75
728	–	40c.+60c. brown	1·80	2·75
729	–	50c.+70c. blue	1·90	3·00
730	–	70c.+80c. red	2·50	3·00
731	–	80c.+1f. red	2·50	3·00
732	–	1f.+1f. black	2·50	3·00
733	–	1f.50+2f. blue	2·50	3·00
734	–	2f.+2f. violet	2·50	3·00
735	–	2f.50+3f. green	2·50	3·00
736	–	3f.+5f. brown	2·50	3·00
737	–	5f.+6f. blue	2·50	3·00
738	–	10f.+10f. red	2·75	3·00

DESIGNS—As Type **167**. Nos. 728/38 show respectively the Arms of Lille, Rouen, Bordeaux, Toulouse, Clermont-Ferrand, Marseilles, Lyons, Rennes, Reims, Montpellier and Paris.

See also Nos. 757/68.

168 Jean-Francois de La Perouse, "L'Astrolabe" and "La Boussole"

1942. Birth Bicentenary of La Perouse (navigator and explorer) and National Relief Fund.

739	**168**	2f.50+7f.50 blue	1·20	1·80

1942. Frame 18 × 21½ mm.

740	**164**	4f. blue	25	35
741		4f.50 green	25	35

169 Potez 63-11 Bombers

1942. Air Force Dependants Relief Fund.

742	**169**	1f.50+3f.50 violet	1·60	2·75

170 Alexis Emmanuel Chabrier

1942. Birth Centenary of Chabrier (composer) and Musicians' Mutual Assistance Fund.

743	**170**	2f.+3f. brown	85	1·40

171 Symbolical of French Colonial Empire

1942. Empire Fortnight and National Relief Fund.

744	**171**	1f.50+8f.50 black	75	1·30

172 Marshal Petain **173** Marshal Petain

1942.

745	**172**	5f. green	25	30
746	**173**	50f. black	3·75	4·50

See also Nos. 772/3.

174 Jean de Vienne **175** Jules Massenet

1942. 600th Birth Anniv of Jean de Vienne (admiral) and Seamen's Relief Fund.

748	**174**	1f.50+8f.50 brown	70	1·20

1942. Birth Centenary of Massenet (composer).

749	**175**	4f. green	20	30

1942. As T **123**, but inscr "POSTES FRANCAISES".

750		10c. blue	15	20
751		30c. red	15	20
752		40c. violet	15	25
753		50c. blue	15	20

1942. National Relief Fund. Surch **+ 50 S N.**

754	**165**	1f.50+50c. blue	10	15

177 Stendhal (Marie Henri Beyle) **178** Andre Blondel

1942. Death Centenary of Stendhal (novelist).

755	**177**	4f. brown and red	45	65

1942. Andre Blondel (physicist).

756	**178**	4f. blue	50	60

1942. National Relief Fund. Arms of French towns as T **167**.

757		50c.+60c. black	2·50	4·50
758		60c.+70c. green	2·50	3·25
759		80c.+1f. red	2·50	3·50
760		1f.+1f.30 green	2·75	3·50
761		1f.20+1f.50 red	3·00	3·75
762		1f.50+1f.80 blue	3·00	3·75
763		2f.+2f.30 red	3·00	4·00
764		2f.40+2f.80 green	3·00	4·00
765		3f.+3f.50 violet	3·00	4·00
766		4f.+5f. blue	3·00	4·25
767		4f.50+6f. red	3·00	4·25
768		5f.+7f. lilac	3·50	4·50

DESIGNS: Nos. 757/68 respectively show the Arms of Chambery, La Rochelle, Poitiers, Orleans, Grenoble, Angers, Dijon, Limoges, Le Havre, Nantes, Nice and St. Etienne.

179 Legionary and Grenadiers **180** Belfry, Arras Town Hall

1942. Tricolor Legion.

769	**179**	1f.20+8f.80 blue	8·00	11·00
770		1f.20+8f.80 red	8·00	11·00

1942.

771	**180**	10f. green	25	30

1943. National Relief Fund.

772	**173**	1f.+10f. blue	2·30	3·25
773		1f.+10f. red	2·30	3·25
774	**155**	2f.+12f. blue	2·30	3·25
775		2f.+12f. red	2·30	3·25

182 Arms of Lyonnais

1943. Provincial Coats of Arms.

776	**182**	5f. red, blue & yellow	30	40
777	–	10f. black and brown	45	55
778	–	15f. yellow, blue & red	1·40	1·60
779	–	20f. yellow, blue & brn	1·10	1·60

ARMS: 10f. "Bretagne"; 15f. "Provence"; 20f. "Ile-de-France".

For other provinces in this series, see Nos. 814/7, 971/4, 1049/53, 1121/5, 1178/83, 1225/31, 1270/3.

For arms of French towns, see Nos. 1403/10, etc.

183 "Work" **184** Marshal Petain

1943. National Relief Fund.

780	–	1f.20+1f.40 purple	13·00	18·00
781	**183**	1f.50+2f.50 red	13·00	18·00
782	–	2f.40+7f. brown	13·00	18·00
783	–	4f.+10f. violet	13·00	18·00
784	**184**	5f.+15f. brown	13·00	18·00

DESIGNS: 1f.20, Marshal Petain bareheaded; 2f.40, "Family"; 4f. "Country".

185 Lavoisier **186** Lake Lerie and the Meije Peak

1943. Birth Bicentenary of Lavoisier (chemist).

785	**185**	4f. blue	45	35

1943.

786	**186**	20f. green	70	85

187 Nicholas Rolin and Guisone de Salins **188** Victims of Bombed Towns

1943. 500th Anniv of Beaune Hospital.

787	**187**	4f. blue	15	30

1943. National Relief Fund.

788	**188**	1f.50+3f.50 black	45	70

189 Prisoners' Families' Relief Work **190** Chevalier de Bayard

1943. Prisoners' Families Relief Fund. Inscr as in T **189**.

789	–	1f.50+8f.50 brown	85	1·20
790	**189**	2f.40+7f.60 green	85	1·40

DESIGN—VERT: 1f.50, Prisoner's family.

1943. National Relief Fund.

791	–	60c.+80c. green	1·50	2·10
792	–	1f.20+1f.50 black	1·50	2·10
793	–	1f.50+3f. blue	1·50	2·10
794	**190**	2f.40+4f. red	1·70	2·10
795	–	4f.+6f. brown	1·70	2·30
796	–	5f.+10f. green	1·70	2·40

PORTRAITS: 60c. Michel de Montaigne (essayist); 1f.20, Francois Clouet (painter); 1f.50, Ambroise Pare (surgeon); 4f. Due de Sully (King Henri IV's finance minister); 5f. King Henri IV.

191 Picardy **196** Admiral de Tourville

1943. National Relief Fund. Provincial costumes.

797	**191**	60c.+1f.30 brown	1·70	2·20
798	–	1f.20+2f. violet	1·70	2·20
799	–	1f.50+4f. blue	1·70	2·20
800	–	2f.40+5f. red	1·70	2·20
801	–	4f.+6f. blue	2·00	3·25
802	–	5f.+7f. red	2·00	3·25

DESIGNS: 1f.20, "Bretagne"; 1f.50, "Ile de France"; 2f.40, "Bourgogne"; 4f. "Auvergne"; 5f. "Provence".

1944. 300th Birth Anniv of Admiral de Tourville.

810	**196**	4f.+6f. red	70	90

197 Branly **198** Gounod

1944. Birth Centenary of Branly (physicist).

811	**197**	4f. blue	25	40

1944. 50th Death Anniv of Gounod (composer).

812	**198**	1f.50+3f.50 brown	75	1·00

200 Flanders

202 Petain gives France Workers' Charter

201 Marshal Petain

1944. Provincial Coats of Arms.

814	**200**	5f. black, orange & red	25	40
815	–	10f. yellow, red & brown	25	40
816	–	15f. yellow, blue & brown	55	1·10
817	–	20f. yellow, red & blue	95	1·30

ARMS: 10f. "Languedoc"; 15f. "Orleanais"; 20f. "Normandie".

1944. Petain's 88th Birthday.

818	**201**	1f.50+3f.50 brown	2·40	4·25
819	–	2f.+3f. blue	60	70
820	**202**	4f.+6f. red	60	70

DESIGN—As Type **202**: 2f. inscr "Le Marechal institua la Corporation Paysanne" (Trans. "The Marshal set up the Peasant Corporation").

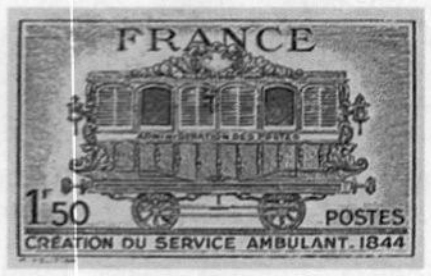
203 Paris–Rouen Travelling Post Office Van, 1844

1944. Centenary of Mobile Post Office.

821	**203**	1f.50 green	45	75

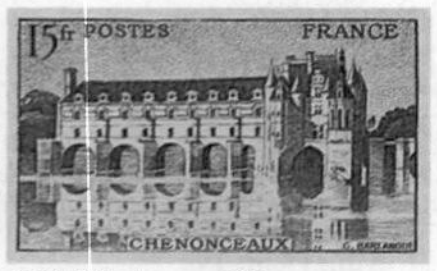
204 Chateau of Chenonceaux

1944.

822	**204**	15f. brown	45	60
823		25f. black	45	70

The 15f. is inscr "FRANCE".

205 Louis XIV

206 Old and Modern Locomotives

1944. National Relief Fund.

824	–	50c.+1f.50 red	1·30	1·90
825	–	80c.+2f.20 green	1·10	1·80
826	–	1f.20+2f.80 black	1·10	1·70
827	–	1f.50+3f.50 blue	1·10	1·80
828	–	2f.+4f. brown	1·10	1·80
829	**205**	4f.+6f. orange	1·10	2·10

DESIGNS: 50c. Moliere (dramatist); 80c. Jean Hardouin-Manzart (scholar); 1f.20, Blaise Pascal (mathematician); 1f.50, Louis, Prince de Conde; 2f. Jean-Baptiste Colbert (King Louis XIV's chief minister).

1944. National Relief Fund. Centenary of Paris–Orleans and Paris–Rouen Railways.

830	**206**	4f.+6f. black	1·40	2·40

207 Claude Chappe

208 Gallic Cock

209 "Marianne"

1944. 150th Anniv of Invention of Semaphore Telegraph.

831	**207**	4f. blue	15	30

1944.

832	**208**	10c. green	10	15
833		30c. lilac	20	50
834		40c. blue	10	25
835		50c. red	10	15
836	**209**	60c. brown	10	25
837		70c. mauve	10	15
838		80c. green	95	1·30
839		1f. violet	10	25
840		1f.20 red	10	25
841		1f.50 blue	10	15
842	**208**	2f. blue	10	25
843	**209**	2f.40 red	1·30	1·70
844		3f. green	20	30
845		4f. blue	20	30
846		4f.50 black	20	20
847		5f. blue	4·00	4·25
848	**208**	10f. violet	4·25	5·25
849		15f. brown	4·25	5·25
850		20f. green	4·25	4·25

210 Arc de Triomphe, Paris

211 "Marianne"

1944.

851	**210**	5c. purple	15	15
852		10c. grey	15	15
853		25c. brown	15	15
854		50c. green	15	15
855		1f. green	15	15
856		1f.50 pink	15	15
857		2f.50 violet	15	35
858		4f. blue	15	35
859		5f. black	15	35
860		10f. orange	25·00	27·00

See also Nos. 936/45.

1944. New colours and values.

861	**136**	80c. green	15	45
862		1f. blue	15	15
863		1f.20 violet	15	15
864		1f.50 brown	15	15
865		2f. brown	15	15
866		2f.40 red	20	30
867		3f. orange	20	20
868		4f. blue	20	35

1944.

869	**211**	10c. blue	10	10
870		30c. brown	10	10
871		40c. blue	10	10
872		50c. orange	10	10
873		60c. blue	10	10
874		70c. brown	10	10
875		80c. green	10	10
876		1f. lilac	10	10
877		1f.20 green	10	10
878		1f.50 red	10	10
879		2f. brown	10	15
880		2f.40 red	15	15
881		3f. olive	15	20
882		4f. blue	15	30
883		4f.50 grey	15	30
884		5f. orange	15	30
885		10f. green	20	35
886		15f. red	25	35
887		20f. orange	1·30	1·80
888		50f. violet	2·75	3·00

212 St. Denis Basilica

1944. 8th Centenary of St. Denis Basilica.

889	**212**	2f.40 brown	30	45

213 Marshal Bugeaud

214 Angouleme Cathedral

1944. Centenary of Battle of Isly.

890	**213**	4f. green	15	30

1944. Cathedrals of France (1st issue).

891	**214**	50c.+1f.50 black	45	85
892	–	80c.+2f.20 purple	45	85
893	–	1f.20+2f.80 red	60	85
894	–	1f.50+3f.50 blue	60	85
895	–	4f.+6f. red	60	85

DESIGNS: 80c. Chartres; 1f.20, Amiens; 1f.50, Beauvais; 4f. Albi.

1944. Nos. 750/3 optd **RF**.

896	10c. blue	10	15
897	30c. red	10	15
898	40c. violet	10	15
899	50c. blue	10	15

215 Arms of De Villayer

216 "France" exhorting Resistance Forces

1944. Stamp Day.

900	**215**	1f.50+3f.50 brown	15	25

1945. Liberation.

901	**216**	4f. blue	35	45

217 Shield and Broken Chains

218 Ceres

219 Marianne

220 Marianne

221 Arms of Strasbourg

1945.

902	**217**	10c. brown	15	15
903		30c. green	15	20
904		40c. mauve	25	30
905		50c. blue	15	15
906	**218**	60c. blue	15	15
907		80c. green	15	15
908		90c. green*	85	85
909		1f. red	15	15
910		1f.20 black	25	35
997		1f.30 blue	25	25
911		1f.50 purple	15	15
912	**219**	1f.50 red	15	25
913		2f. green	20	15
914	**218**	2f. green	15	15
915	**219**	2f.40 red	50	50
916	**218**	2f.50 brown	15	15
997a	**219**	2f.50 brown*	2·10	1·70
917		3f. brown	15	15
918		3f. red	15	10
998		3f. green	1·90	40
999		3f. mauve	25	20
1000		3f.50 red	75	60
919		4f. blue	25	20
920		4f. violet	15	20
1001		4f. green	30	30
1001a		4f. orange	3·25	95
1002		4f.50 blue	15	10
921		5f. green	20	10
1003		5f. red	15	10
1004		5f. blue	25	20
1004b		5f. violet	40	10
922		6f. blue	35	40
1005		6f. red	25	10
1005a		6f. green	6·75	45
1006		8f. blue	40	20
924		10f. orange	75	65
928		10f. blue	1·40	50
1007		10f. violet	50	10
1007a		12f. blue	3·00	35
1007b		12f. orange	70	80
926		15f. purple	4·25	2·30
1007c		15f. red	95	20
1007d		15f. blue	35	10
1007e		18f. red	17·00	1·20
930		20f. green	1·00	70
932	**220**	20f. green	1·40	1·40
931	**219**	25f. red	9·00	1·90
933	**220**	25f. violet	1·80	1·60
934		50f. brown	2·20	2·50
935		100f. red	14·50	9·50

***PRECANCELS.** See note below No. 432.

1945.

936	**210**	30c. black and orange	20	10
937		40c. black and grey	20	10
938		50c. black and green	20	10
939		60c. black and violet	20	10
940		80c. black and green	15	10
941		1f.20 black and brown	15	10
942		1f.50 black and red	15	10
943		2f. black and yellow	15	25
944		2f.40 black and red	15	30
945		3f. black and purple	15	30

1945. Liberation of Metz and Strasbourg.

946	–	2f.40 blue	30	30
947	**221**	4f. brown	30	30

DESIGN: 2f.40, Arms of Metz.

222 Patient in Deck Chair

223 Refugee Employee and Family

1945. Anti-tuberculosis Fund.

948	**222**	2f.+1f. orange	25	30

1945. Postal Employees War Victims' Fund.

949	**223**	4f.+6f. brown	25	30

224 Sarah Bernhardt

225 Alsatian and Lorrainer in Native Dress

1945. Birth Cent of Sarah Bernhardt (actress).

950	**224**	4f.+1f. brown	40	45

1945. Liberation of Alsace-Lorraine.

951	**225**	4f. brown	25	30

226 Children in Country

227 Destruction of Oradour

1945. Fresh Air Crusade.

952	**226**	4f.+2f. green	30	30

1945. As No. 661 but incorporating Cross of Lorraine and inscr "1945".

953	**149**	2f. blue	30	30

1945. Destruction of Oradour-sur-Glane.

954	**227**	4f.+2f. brown	30	30

228 Louis XI

1945. Stamp Day.

955	**228**	2f.+3f. blue	60	60

229 Dunkirk

230 Alfred Fournier

1945. Devastated Towns.

956	**229**	1f.50+1f.50 red	65	60
957	–	2f.+2f. violet	65	55
958	–	2f.40+2f.60 blue	80	75
959	–	4f.+4f. black	80	75

DESIGNS: 2f. Rouen; 2f.40c. Caen; 4f. St. Malo.

1946. Prophylaxis Fund.

960	**230**	2f.+3f. red	40	45
961		2f.+3f. blue	45	40

231 Henri Becquerel **233** "Les Invalides"

1946.

962	**231**	2f.+3f. violet	40	35

1946. Surcharged **3F.**

963	**222**	3f. on 2f.+1f. orange	25	30

1946. War Invalids' Relief Fund.

964	**233**	4f.+6f. brown	40	45

234 "Emile Bertin" (cruiser) and "Lorraine" (battleship) **235** "The Letter"

1946. Naval Charities.

965	**234**	2f.+3f. black	80	80

1946. Postal Museum Fund.

966	**235**	2f.+3f. red	70	60

236 Iris **237** Jupiter carrying off Egine

1946. Air.

967	–	40f. green	60	40
968	**236**	50f. pink	60	25
969	**237**	100f. blue	8·50	90
970	–	200f. red	6·25	1·40

DESIGNS—VERT: 40f. Centaur. HORIZ: 200f. Apollo and chariot.

239 Arms of Corsica **241** Fouquet de la Varane

1946. Provincial Coats of arms.

971	**239**	10c. black and blue	15	15
972	–	30c. black, red and yellow	15	15
973	–	50c. brown, yellow & red	15	15
974	–	60c. red, blue & black	15	15

DESIGNS: 30c. Alsace; 50c. Lorraine; 60c. Nice.

1946. Stamp Day.

975	**241**	3f.+2f. brown	75	75

244 Luxembourg Palace **245** Roc-Amadour

1946. Views.

976	–	5f. mauve	25	15
977	–	6f. red	1·50	65
978	**244**	10f. blue	30	15
979		12f. red	3·00	60
980	**245**	15f. purple	5·00	45
980a	**244**	15f. red	75	80
981	–	20f. blue	1·40	20
982	–	25f. brown	5·00	25
982a	–	25f. blue	12·50	80

DESIGNS—HORIZ: 5f. Vezelay; 6f. Cannes; 20f. Pointe du Raz; 25f. (both) Stanislas Place, Nancy.

248 "Peace"

1946. Peace Conference.

983	**248**	3f. green	30	30
984	–	10f. blue	30	30

DESIGN: 10f. Woman releasing dove.

250 Francois Villon **251**

1946. National Relief Fund. 15th-century Figures.

985	**250**	2f.+1f. blue	1·70	1·70
986	–	3f.+1f. blue	1·70	1·70
987	–	4f.+3f. red	1·70	1·70
988	–	5f.+4f. blue	1·90	1·90
989	–	6f.+5f. brown	1·90	2·00
990	–	10f.+6f. orange	1·90	2·00

DESIGNS: 3f. Jean Fouquet; 4f. Philippe de Commynes; 5f. Joan of Arc; 6f. Jean Gerson; 10f. Charles VII.

1946. U.N.E.S.C.O. Conference, Paris.

991	**251**	10f. blue	30	30

252 St. Julien Cathedral, Le Mans **253** Louvois

1947. National Relief Fund. Cathedrals of France (2nd issue). As T **214** and **252**.

992	–	1f.+1f. red	1·10	1·30
993	–	3f.+2f. black	3·25	3·75
994	–	4f.+3f. red	1·70	1·80
995	**252**	6f.+4f. blue	1·70	1·80
996	–	10f.+6f. green	3·25	3·75

DESIGNS—VERT: 1f. St. Sernin, Toulouse; 3f. Notre-Dame du Port, Clermont-Ferrand; 10f. Notre-Dame, Paris. HORIZ: 4f. St. Front, Perigueux.

1947. Stamp Day.

1008	**253**	4f.50+5f.50 red	1·50	1·60

254 The Louvre Colonnade

255 Herring Gull over Ile de la Cite

1947. 12th U.P.U. Congress.

1009	**254**	3f.50 purple (postage)	50	45
1010	–	4f.50 grey	60	60
1011	–	6f. red	1·20	1·00
1012	–	10f. blue	1·30	1·10
1013	**255**	500f. green (air)	60·00	55·00

DESIGNS—As Type **254**: 4f.50, La Conciergerie; 6f. La Cite; 10f. Place de la Concorde.

256 Auguste Pavie **257** Fenelon

1947. Birth Cent of Auguste Pavie (explorer).

1014	**256**	4f.50 purple	45	50

1947. Fenelon, Archbishop of Cambrai.

1015	**257**	4f.50 brown	45	45

258 St. Nazaire Monument **259**

1947. 5th Anniv of British Commando Raid on St. Nazaire.

1016	**258**	6f.+4f. blue	75	60

1947. Boy Scouts' Jamboree.

1017	**259**	5f. brown	60	50

260 Milestone on Road of Liberty **261** "Resistance"

1947. Road Maintenance Fund.

1018	**260**	6f.+4f. green	1·20	1·20

1947. Resistance Movement.

1019	**261**	5f. purple	75	70

1947. No. 997 surch **1F.**

1020	**218**	1f. on 1f.30 blue	30	30

263 Conques Abbey **264** Louis Braille

1947.

1021	**263**	15f. red	5·25	65
1022		18f. blue	3·50	25

No. 1022 is inscribed "FRANCE".

1948. Louis Braille (inventor of system of writing and printing for the blind).

1023	**264**	6f.+4f. violet	45	50

265 A. de Saint-Exupery (pilot and writer) **267** Etienne Arago

1948. Air. Famous Airmen.

1026	–	40f.+10f. blue	1·60	1·70
1024	**265**	50f.+30f. purple	3·50	3·75
1025	–	100f.+70f. blue	4·25	4·50

DESIGNS: 40f. "Avion III" and Douglas DB-7 (Clement Ader); 100f. Jean Dagnaux.

1948. Stamp Day and Centenary of First French Adhesive Postage Stamps.

1027	**267**	6f.+4f. violet	65	65

268 Lamartine **269** Dr. Calmette

1948. National Relief Fund and Cent of 1848 Revolution. Dated "1848 1948".

1028	**268**	1f.+1f. green	1·50	1·60
1029	–	3f.+2f. red	1·50	1·60
1030	–	4f.+3f. purple	1·60	1·60
1031	–	5f.+4f. blue	3·75	3·50
1032	–	6f.+5f. blue	2·75	2·75
1033	–	10f.+6f. red	2·75	2·75
1034	–	15f.+7f. blue	3·50	3·75
1035	–	20f.+8f. violet	3·75	3·75

PORTRAITS: 3f. Alexandre-Auguste Ledru-Rollin; 4f. Louis Blanc; 5f. A. M. Albert; 6f. Pierre Joseph Proudhon; 10f. Louis-Auguste Blanqui; 15f. Armand Barbes; 20f. Denis-Auguste Affre.

1948. 1st International B.C.G. (Vaccine) Congress.

1036	**269**	6f.+4f. slate	65	65

270 Gen. Leclerc

1948. Gen. Leclerc Memorial.

1037	**270**	6f. black	45	45

See also Nos. 1171/a.

271 Chateaubriand

1948. Death Centenary of Chateaubriand.

1038	**271**	18f. blue	45	45

272 Genissiat Barrage

1948. Inauguration of Genissiat Barrage.

1039	**272**	12f. red	75	80

273 Aerial View of Chaillot Palace **274** Paul Langevin

1948. U.N. Assembly, Paris.

1040	–	12f. red	55	55
1041	**273**	18f. blue	60	60

DESIGN: 12f. Ground level view of Chaillot Palace.

1948. Transfer of Ashes of Paul Langevin and Jean Perrin to the Pantheon.

1042	**274**	5f. brown	40	35
1043	–	8f. green (Perrin)	35	30

1949. Surch **5F.**

1044	**219**	5f. on 6f. red	30	30

276 Ploughing **277** Arms of Burgundy

1949. Workers.

1045	**276**	3f.+1f. purple	1·10	90
1046	–	5f.+3f. blue	1·10	1·00
1047	–	8f.+4f. blue	1·10	1·10
1048	–	10f.+6f. red	1·40	1·30

DESIGNS: 5f. Fisherman; 8f. Miner; 10f. Industrial worker.

1949. Provincial Coats of Arms.
1049 **277** 10c. red, yellow & blue 15 15
1050 – 50c. yellow, red & blue 15 15
1051 – 1f. red and brown 70 35
1052 – 2f. red, yellow & green 70 20
1053 – 4f. blue, yellow & red 50 45
ARMS: 50c. "Guyenne"; 1f. "Savoie"; 2f. "Auvergne"; 4f. "Anjou".
See also Nos. 1121/5, 1178/83, 1225/31 and 1270/3.

278 Due de Choiseul

279 Lille

279a Paris

1949. Stamp Day.
1054 **278** 15f.+5f. green 1·30 1·30

1949. Air. Views.
1055 **279** 100f. purple 1·40 20
1056 – 200f. green 16·00 90
1057 – 300f. violet 20·00 11·50
1058 – 500f. red 70·00 5·75
1059 **279a** 1000f. purple & black £120 23·00
DESIGNS—As Type **279**: 200f. Bordeaux; 300f. Lyons; 500f. Marseilles.

280 Polar Scene

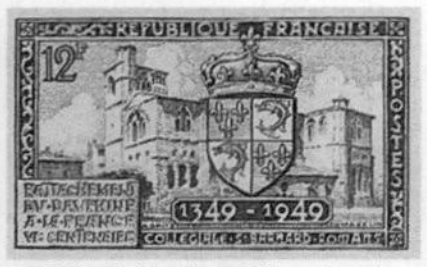
281 Collegiate Church of St. Bernard, Romans

1949. Polar Expeditions.
1060 **280** 15f. blue 45 45

1949. French Stamp Centenary. (a) Imperf.
1061 **1** 15f. red 7·25 5·75
1062 25f. blue 7·25 5·75

(b) Perf.
1063 **219** 15f. red 7·25 5·75
1064 25f. blue 7·25 5·75

1949. 600th Anniv of Cession of Dauphiny to King of France.
1065 **281** 12f. brown 45 45

282 Emblems of U.S.A. and France

1949. Franco-American Amity.
1066 **282** 25f. blue and red 95 75

284 St. Wandrille Abbey

285 Jean Racine

1949. Views.
1067 – 20f. red 30 20
1068 **284** 25f. blue 40 20
1068a 30f. blue 5·75 4·50
1068b – 30f. blue 1·10 25
1069 – 40f. green 16·00 45
1070 – 50f. purple 2·50 20

DESIGNS: 20f. St. Bertrand de Comminges; 30f. (1068b) Arbois (Jura); 40f. Valley of the Meuse (Ardennes); 50f. Mt. Gerbier-de-Jone, Vivarais.

1949. 250th Death Anniv of Racine (dramatist).
1071 **285** 12f. purple 55 50

1949. French Stamp Centenary ("CITEX"). T **1** with dates "1849 1949" below, repeated ten times (2 × 5) with "1849–1949" centred above.
MS1071a 280 × 155 mm. 10f. (+100f.) red. Complete sheet of ten £400 £400

286 Claude Chappe

288 Allegory of Commerce

287 Alexander III Bridge and "Petit Palais"

1949. International Telephone and Telegraph Congress, Paris.
1072 **286** 10f. red (postage) 1·10 1·00
1073 – 15f. violet 1·20 1·10
1074 – 25f. red 2·75 2·50
1075 – 50f. blue 7·00 5·00

1076 **287** 100f. red (air) 8·25 7·50
PORTRAITS—As Type **286**: 15f. Arago and Ampere; 25f. Emile Baudot; 50f. Gen. Ferrie.

1949. French Chambers of Commerce.
1077 **288** 15f. red 30 30

289 Allegory

290 Montesquieu

1949. 75th Anniv of U.P.U.
1078 **289** 5f. green 40 35
1079 15f. red 40 35
1080 25f. blue 1·50 1·00

1949. National Relief Fund.
1081 **290** 5f.+1f. green 3·50 3·50
1082 – 8f.+2f. blue 3·50 3·50
1083 – 10f.+3f. brown 4·50 4·50
1084 – 12f.+4f. violet 4·50 4·50
1085 – 15f.+5f. red 6·00 5·50
1086 – 25f.+10f. blue 7·25 7·25
PORTRAITS: 8f. Voltaire; 10f. Watteau; 12f. Buffon; 15f. Dupleix; 25f. Turgot.

291 "Spring"

1949. National Relief Fund. Seasons.
1087 **291** 5f.+1f. green 1·90 1·90
1088 – 8f.+2f. yellow 2·75 2·75
1089 – 12f.+3f. violet 2·75 2·75
1090 – 15f.+4f. blue 4·25 4·50
DESIGNS: 8f. "Summer"; 12f. "Autumn"; 15f. "Winter".

292 Postman

293 Raymond Poincare

1950. Stamp Day.
1091 **292** 12f.+3f. blue 4·25 3·25

1950. Honouring Poincare.
1092 **293** 15f. blue 45 50

294 Charles Peguy

295 Francois Rabelais

1950. Honouring Charles Peguy (writer).
1093 **294** 12f. purple 45 50

1950. Honouring Francois Rabelais (writer).
1094 **295** 12f. lake 80 70

296 Andre Chenier

297 Chateaudun

1950. National Relief Fund (revolutionaary celebrities). Frames in blue.
1095 **296** 5f.+2f. purple 10·50 10·50
1096 – 8f.+3f. sepia 10·50 10·50
1097 – 10f.+4f. red 11·50 12·00
1098 – 12f.+5f. brown 13·00 13·50
1099 – 15f.+6f. green 14·00 14·00
1100 – 20f.+10f. blue 14·00 14·00
PORTRAITS: 8f. Louis David; 10f. Lazare Carnot; 12f. Danton; 15f. Robespierre; 20f. Hoche.

1950.
1101 **297** 8f. brown & lt brown 75 70
1102 – 12f. brown 1·00 85
DESIGN: 12f. Palace of Fontainebleau.

298 Madame Recamier

299 "L'Amour" (after Falconet)

1950.
1103 **298** 12f. green 55 55
1104 – 15f. blue 55 55
PORTRAIT: 15f. Madame de Sevigne.

1950. Red Cross. Cross in red.
1105 – 8f.+2f. blue 2·75 2·50
1106 **299** 15f.+3f. purple 3·25 3·00
DESIGN: 8f. Bust of Alexandre Brongniart (after Houdon).

300 T.P.O. Sorting Van

301 J. Ferry (statesman)

1951. Stamp Day.
1107 **300** 12f.+3f. violet 3·75 4·50

1951.
1108 **301** 15f. red 60 60

302 Shuttle

303 De La Salle

1951. Textile Industry.
1109 **302** 25f. blue 95 75

1951. Birth Tercentenary of Jean Baptiste de la Salle (educational reformer).
1110 **303** 15f. brown 65 55

304 Anchor and Map

1951. 50th Anniv of Formation of Colonial Troops.
1111 **304** 15f. blue 70 60

305 Vincent D'Indy

1951. Birth Centenary of Vincent D'Indy (composer).
1112 **305** 25f. green 2·20 2·10

306 A. de Musset

307 Nocard, Bouley and Chauveau

1951. National Relief Fund. Frames in sepia.
1113 **306** 5f.+1f. green 7·25 7·25
1114 – 8f.+2f. purple 8·75 8·75
1115 – 10f.+3f. green 7·25 7·25
1116 – 12f.+4f. brown 8·75 8·50
1117 – 15f.+5f. red 8·75 8·50
1118 – 30f.+10f. blue 14·00 16·00
PORTRAITS: 8f. Delacroix; 10f. Gay-Lussac; 12f. Surcouf; 15f. Talleyrand; 30f. Napoleon.

1951. French Veterinary Research.
1119 **307** 12f. mauve 65 65

308 Picque, Roussin and Villemin

309 St. Nicholas

1951. Military Health Service.
1120 **308** 15f. purple 75 60

1951. Provincial Coats of Arms as T **277**.
1121 10c. yellow, blue and red 15 20
1122 50c. black, red and green 15 20
1123 1f. red, yellow and blue 30 25
1124 2f. yellow, blue and red 1·00 35
1125 3f. yellow, blue and red 90 45
ARMS: 10c. "Artois"; 50c. "Limousin"; 1f. "Bearn"; 2f. "Touraine"; 3f. "Franche-Comte".

1951. Popular Pictorial Art Exhibition, Epinal. Multicoloured centre.
1126 **309** 15f. blue 1·30 90

310 Seal of Mercantile Guild

311 M. Nogues

1951. Bimillenary of Paris.
1127 **310** 15f. brown, blue & red 65 50

1951. M. Nogues (aviator).
1128 **311** 12f. indigo and blue 1·00 80

312 C. Baudelaire

1951. Famous French Poets.

1129	**312**	8f. violet	65	65
1130	–	12f. grey	65	65
1131	–	15f. green	65	65

DESIGNS: 12f. Paul Verlaine; 15f. Arthur Rimbaud.

313 Eiffel Tower and Chaillot Palace

314 L. G. Clemenceau (statesman)

1951. U.N.O. General Assembly.

1132	**313**	18f. red	1·40	80
1133		30f. blue	2·40	1·10

1951. 110th Birth Anniv of Clemenceau and 33rd Anniv of Armistice.

1134	**314**	15f. sepia	55	50

315 Chateau Clos-Vougeot

316 15th-century Child

1951. 400th Anniv of Chateau Clos-Vougeot.

1135	**315**	30f. dp brown & brown	5·75	2·50

1951. Red Cross. Cross in red.

1136	**316**	12f.+3f. brown	3·50	3·25
1137	–	15f.+5f. blue	4·50	4·25

DESIGN: 15f. 18th-century child (De La Tour).

317 Observatory, Pic du Midi de Bigorre

1951.

1138	**317**	40f. violet	6·25	15
1139	–	50f. brown	5·25	15

VIEW—VERT: 50f. Church of St. Etienne, Caen.

319 19th-cent Mail Coach

1952. Stamp Day.

1140	**319**	12f.+3f. green	5·00	4·50

320 Marshal de Lattre de Tassigny

321 Gate of France, Vaucouleurs

1952.

1140a	**320**	12f. indigo and blue	2·40	1·50
1141		15f. brown	1·00	70

1952.

1142	**321**	12f. brown	1·50	1·30

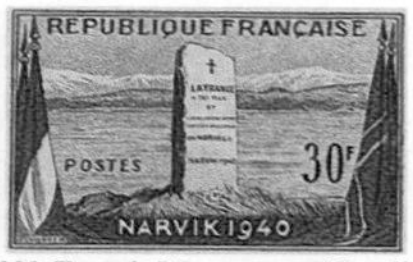
322 French Monument, Narvik

1952. Battle of Narvik.

1143	**322**	30f. blue	3·25	2·20

323 Chambord Chateau

1952.

1144	**323**	20f. violet	60	15

324 Council of Europe Building, Strasbourg

1952. Council of Europe Assembly.

1145	**324**	30f. green	8·25	6·25

325 Bir Hakeim Monument

326 Abbey of the Holy Cross, Poitiers

1952. 10th Anniv of Battle of Bir Hakeim.

1146	**325**	30f. lake	3·75	2·40

1952. 1400th Anniv of Abbey of the Holy Cross, Poitiers.

1147	**326**	15f. red	55	50

327 Medaille Militaire, in 1852 and 1952

328 Garabit Railway Viaduct

1952. Centenary of Medaille Militaire.

1148	**327**	15f. brown, yell & grn	55	50

1952.

1149	**328**	15f. blue	80	65

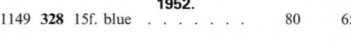

329 Leonardo, Amboise Chateau and Town of Vinci

330 Flaubert (after E. Giraud)

1952. 500th Birth Anniv of Leonardo da Vinci.

1150	**329**	30f. blue	8·50	7·50

1952. National Relief Fund. Frames in sepia.

1151	**330**	8f.+2f. blue	6·25	7·25
1152	–	12f.+3f. blue	7·75	7·75
1153	–	15f.+4f. green	7·75	7·75
1154	–	18f.+5f. sepia	10·50	10·00
1155	–	20f.+6f. red	10·50	10·00
1156	–	30f.+7f. violet	10·50	10·00

PORTRAITS: 12f. Manet; 15f. Saint-Saens; 18f. H. Poincare; 20f. Haussmann (after Yvon); 20f. Thiers.

331 R. Laennec (physician)

332 "Cherub" (bas-relief)

1952.

1157	**331**	12f. green	70	55

1952. Red Cross Fund. Sculptures from Basin of Diana, Versailles. Cross in red.

1158	**332**	12f.+3f. green	5·50	5·25
1159	–	15f.+5f. blue	5·50	5·25

DESIGN: 15f. "Cherub" (facing left).

333 Versailles Gateway

334 Count D'Argenson

1952.

1160	**333**	18f. purple	2·75	2·10
1160a		18f. indigo, blue & brn	11·50	7·00

1953. Stamp Day.

1161	**334**	12f.+3f. blue	3·25	3·25

335 "Gargantua" (Rabelais)

337 Mannequin and Place Vendome, Paris

1953. Literary Figures and National Industries.

1162	**335**	6f. lake and red	45	20
1163	–	8f. blue and indigo	25	15
1164	–	12f. green and brown	25	15
1165	–	18f. sepia and purple	70	30
1166	–	25f. sepia, red & brown	15·00	40
1166a	–	25f. blue and black	85	20
1167	**337**	30f. violet and blue	1·00	20
1167a	–	30f. blue & turquoise	1·90	15
1168	–	40f. brown & chocolate	5·00	15
1169	–	50f. brn, turq & blue	1·60	15
1170	–	75f. lake and red	16·00	1·00

DESIGNS—As Types **335/337**: 8f. "Celimene" (Moliere); 12f. "Figaro" (Beaumarchais); 18f. "Hernani" (Victor Hugo); 25f. (No. 1166) Tapestry; 25f. (No. 1166a) Mannequin modelling gloves; 30f. (No. 1167a) Rare books and book-binding; 40f. Porcelain and cut-glass; 50f. Gold plate and jewellery; 75f. Flowers and perfumes.

1953. General Leclerc. As T **270** but inscr "GENERAL LECLERC MARECHAL DE FRANCE".

1171	**270**	8f. brown	1·10	80
1171a		12f. turquoise & green	3·50	1·90

338 Olivier de Serres

339 Cyclists and Map

1953. National Relief Fund.

1172	–	8f.+2f. blue	6·25	6·50
1173	**338**	12f.+3f. green	6·25	6·50
1174	–	15f.+4f. lake	10·50	10·00
1175	–	18f.+5f. blue	11·50	11·00
1176	–	20f.+6f. violet	11·50	11·00
1177	–	30f.+7f. brown	13·00	12·50

PORTRAITS: 8f. St. Bernard; 15f. Rameau; 18f. Monge; 20f. Michelet; 30f. Marshal Lyautey.

1953. Provincial Coats of Arms as T **277**.

1178	50c. yellow, red and blue	25	30
1179	70c. yellow, blue and red	30	30
1180	80c. yellow, red and blue	30	30
1181	1f. yellow, red and black	30	25
1182	2f. yellow, blue and brown	50	30
1183	3f. yellow, blue and red	75	40

ARMS: 50c. "Picardie"; 70c. "Gascogne"; 80c. "Berri"; 1f. "Poitou"; 2f. "Champagne"; 3f. "Dauphine".

1953. 50th Anniv of "Tour de France" Cycle Race.

1184	**339**	12f. black, blue & red	2·30	1·40

340 Swimming

341 Mme. Vigee-Lebrun and Daughter (self-portrait)

1953. Sports.

1185	**340**	20f. brown and red	2·75	20
1186	–	25f. brown and green	14·50	60
1187	–	30f. brown and blue	2·75	40
1188	–	40f. indigo and brown	13·00	55
1189	–	50f. brown and green	7·75	30
1190	–	75f. lake and orange	39·00	14·50

SPORTS: 25f. Running; 30f. Fencing; 40f. Canoeing; 50f. Rowing; 75f. Horse-jumping.

See also Nos. 1297/1300.

1953. Red Cross Fund. Cross in red.

1191	**341**	12f.+3f. brown	7·50	7·25
1192	–	15f.+5f. blue	11·00	9·75

DESIGN: 15f. "The Return from the Baptism" (L. Le Nain).

1953. Surch **15F**.

1193	**219**	15f. on 18f. red	70	55

343 Air Fouga Magister

1954. Air.

1194	–	100f. brown and blue	3·25	20
1195	–	200f. purple and blue	12·00	35
1196	**343**	500f. red and orange	£160	13·50
1197	–	1000f. blue, pur & turq	£130	19·00

AIRCRAFT: 100f. Dassault Mystere IVA; 200f. Nord 2501 Noratlas; 1000f. Breguet Provence.

See also No. 1457.

344 Harvester

345 Gallic Cock

346 Lavallette

1954. (a) Precancelled*.

1198	**344**	4f. blue	30	20
1198a	**345**	5f. brown	40	35
1199	**344**	8f. red	5·25	1·60
1199a	**345**	8f. violet	65	50
1199b		10f. blue	2·30	60
1200		12f. mauve	4·50	1·10
1200b		15f. purple	2·50	1·10
1200c		20f. green	2·10	1·50
1201		24f. green	23·00	7·50
1201a		30f. red	8·75	4·50
1201b		40f. red	5·25	4·00
1201c		45f. green	35·00	30·00
1201d		55f. green	30·00	25·00
		(b) Without precancel.		
1201e	**344**	6f. brown	15	10
1201f		10f. green	65	10
1201g		12f. purple	25	15

***PRECANCELS.** See note below No. 432. See also Nos. 1470/3.

1954. Stamp Day.

1202	**346**	12f.+3f. green & brown	5·00	4·00

347 Exhibition Buildings

348 "D-Day"

1954. 50th Anniv of Paris Fair.
1203 **347** 15f. lake and blue . . . 45 45

1954. 10th Anniv of Liberation.
1204 **348** 15f. red and blue . . . . 2·10 1·40

349 Lourdes

350 Jumieges Abbey

1954. Views.
1205 **349** 6f. indigo, blue & grn 40 20
1206 – 8f. green and blue . . . 30 15
1207 – 10f. brown and blue . . 35 10
1208 – 12f. lilac and violet . . 40 10
1209 – 12f. brown & chocolate 1·70 1·60
1210 – 18f. indigo, blue & grn 3·25 85
1211 – 20f. brn, chestnut & bl 3·25 15
1211a **349** 20f. brown and blue . . 40 25
VIEWS—HORIZ: 8f. Seine Valley at Andelys; 10f. Royan; 12f. (No. 1209), Limoges; 18f. Cheverny Chateau; 20f. (No. 1211), Ajaccio Bay. VERT: 12f. (No. 1208), Quimper.

1954. 13th Centenary of Jumieges Abbey.
1212 **350** 12f. indigo, blue & grn 1·70 1·40

351 Abbey Church of St. Philibert, Tournus

352 Stenay

1954. 1st Conference of Romanesque Studies, Tournus.
1213 **351** 30f. blue and indigo . . 6·00 4·50

1954. Tercent of Return of Stenay to France.
1214 **352** 15f. brown and sepia . . 90 80

353 St. Louis

354 Villandry Chateau

1954. National Relief Fund.
1215 **353** 12f.+4f. blue . . . . . 21·00 19·00
1216 – 15f.+5f. violet . . . . . 21·00 21·00
1217 – 18f.+6f. sepia . . . . . 21·00 19·00
1218 – 20f.+7f. red . . . . . 28·00 29·00
1219 – 25f.+8f. blue . . . . . 28·00 27·00
1220 – 30f.+10f. purple . . . . 28·00 25·00
PORTRAITS: 15f. Bossuet; 18f. Sadi Carnot; 20f. A. Bourdelle; 25f. Dr. E. Roux; 30f. Paul Valery.

1954. Four Centuries of Renaissance Gardens.
1221 **354** 18f. green and blue . . . 4·75 4·00

355 Cadet and Flag

1954. 150th Anniv of St. Cyr Military Academy.
1222 **355** 15f. indigo, blue & red 1·40 1·40

356 Napoleon Conferring Decorations

357 "Basis of Metric System"

1954. 150th Anniv of First Legion of Honour Presentation.
1223 **356** 12f. red . . . . 1·50 1·20

1954. 150th Anniv of Metric System.
1224 **357** 30f. sepia and blue . . . 6·50 4·75

1954. Provincial Coats of Arms as T **277**.
1225 50c. yellow, blue and black 30 35
1226 70c. yellow, red and green 30 35
1227 80c. yellow, blue and red . . 30 35
1228 1f. yellow, blue and red . . 20 15
1229 2f. yellow, red and black . . 15 15
1230 3f. yellow, red and brown 15 15
1231 5f. yellow and blue 15 10
ARMS: 50c. "Maine"; 70c. "Navarre"; 80c. "Nivernais"; 1f. "Bourbonnais"; 2f. "Angoumois"; 3f. "Aunis"; 5f. "Saintonge".

359 "Young Girl with Doves" (J.-B. Greuze)

360 Saint-Simon

1954. Red Cross Fund. Cross in red.
1232 – 12f.+3f. indigo & blue 12·00 10·50
1233 **359** 15f.+5f. brn & dp brn 13·00 12·00
DESIGN: 12f. "The Sick Child" (E. Carriere).

1955. Death Bicentenary of Saint-Simon (writer).
1234 **360** 12f. purple & brown . . 85 65

361 "Industry", "Agriculture" and Rotary Emblem

362 "France"

1955. 50th Anniv of Rotary International.
1235 **361** 30f. orange, blue and deep blue . . . . . . 2·50 1·60

1955.
1236 **362** 6f. brown . . . . . . 3·25 2·40
1237 12f. green . . . . . . 3·50 1·70
1238 15f. red 35 10
1238a 18f. green 15 25
1238b 20f. blue 30 10
1238c 25f. red . . . . 1·40 10

363 Thimonnier and Sewing-machines

1955. French Inventors (1st series).
1239 – 5f. blue & light blue . . 85 70
1240 **363** 10f. brown & chestnut 1·10 1·10
1241 – 12f. green . . . . . . 1·80 1·20
1242 – 18f. blue and grey . . . 3·00 2·50
1243 – 25f. violet and plum . . 3·25 2·75
1244 – 30f. vermilion & red . . 3·25 2·75
DESIGNS: 5f. Le Bon (gaslight); 12f. Appert (food canning); 18f. Sainte-Claire Deville (aluminium); 25f. Martin (steel); 30f. Chardonnet (artificial silk).
See also Nos. 1324/7.

364 Mail Balloon "Armand Barbes", 1870

1955. Stamp Day.
1245 **364** 12f.+3f. brown, green and blue . . . . . . 5·25 4·75

365 Florian and Pastoral scene

1955. Birth Bicent of Florian (fabulist).
1246 **365** 12f. turquoise 80 75

366 Eiffel Tower and Television Aerials

1955. Television Development.
1247 **366** 15f. blue & deep blue . . 1·10 1·00

367 Observation Tower and Fence

1955. 10th Anniv of Liberation of Concentration Camps.
1248 **367** 12f. black and grey . . . 1·10 1·10

368 Electric Locomotive

369 The "Jacquemart" (campanile), Moulins

1955. Electrification of Valenciennes–Thionville Railway Line.
1249 **368** 12f. brown and grey . . 2·40 1·40

1955.
1250 **369** 12f. brown . . . . . . 1·70 1·30

370 Jules Verne and Capt. Nemo on the "Nautilus"

1955. 50th Death Anniv of Jules Verne (author).
1251 **370** 30f. blue . . . . 7·75 5·75

371 Maryse Bastie (airwoman)

372 Vauban

1955. Air. Maryse Bastie Commemoration.
1252 **371** 50f. claret and red . . . 7·75 5·25

1955. National Relief Fund.
1253 – 12f.+5f. violet . . . . . 15·00 14·00
1254 – 15f.+6f. blue . . . . . 15·00 14·00
1255 **372** 18f.+7f. green . . . . . 17·00 17·00
1256 – 25f.+8f. slate . . . . . 22·00 22·00
1257 – 30f.+9f. lake . . . . . . 25·00 24·00
1258 – 50f.+15f. turquoise . . . 29·00 29·00
PORTRAITS: 12f. King Philippe-Auguste; 15f. Malherbe; 25f. Vergennes; 30f. Laplace; 50f. Renoir.

373 A. and L. Lumiere

1955. 60th Anniv of French Cinema Industry.
1259 **373** 30f. brown . . . . . . 6·50 4·75

374 Jacques Coeur (merchant prince)

1955.
1260 **374** 12f. violet . . . . 2·40 1·60

375 "La Capricieuse"

1955. Centenary of Voyage of "La Capricieuse" (sail warship).
1261 **375** 30f. blue & turquoise . . 5·75 4·75

376 Marseilles

377 Gerard de Nerval

1955. Views.
1262 – 6f. red . . . . 8·25 15
1263 **376** 8f. blue 55 15
1264 – 10f. blue 30 10
1265 – 12f. brown and grey . . . 30 10
1265a – 15f. indigo and blue . . 65 65
1266 – 18f. blue and green . . 80 20
1267 – 20f. violet & dp violet 3·75 15
1268 – 25f. brown & chestnut 1·20 15
1268a – 35f. turquoise & green 4·75 70
1268b – 70f. black and green . . 20·00 2·30
DESIGNS—HORIZ: 6f., 35f. Bordeaux; 10f. Nice; 12f., 70f. Valentre Bridge, Cahors; 18f. Uzerche; 20f. Mount Pele, Martinique; 25f. Ramparts of Brouage. VERT: 15f. Douai Belfry.

1955. Death Centenary of De Nerval (writer).
1269 **377** 12f. sepia and red . . . 60 50

1955. Provincial Coats of Arms as T **277**.
1270 50c. multicoloured 20 20
1271 70c. yellow, blue and red . . 20 20
1272 80c. yellow, red & brown . . 20 20
1273 1f. yellow, red and blue . . 20 10
ARMS: 50c. "Comte de Foix"; 70c. "Marche"; 80c. "Roussillon"; 1f. "Comtat Venaissin".

379 "Child and Cage" (after Pigalle)

380

1955. Red Cross Fund. Cross in red.
1274 **379** 12f.+3f. lake . . . . . . 7·75 7·00
1275 – 15f.+5f. blue . . . . . 4·75 5·00
DESIGN: 15f. "Child and goose" (Greek sculpture).

1956. National Deportation Memorial.
1276 **380** 15f. sepia and brown . . 65 55

381 Colonel Driant

382 Trench Warfare

1956. Birth Centenary of Col. Driant.
1277 **381** 15f. blue 45 40

1956. 40th Anniv of Battle of Verdun.
1278 **382** 30f. blue and brown . . 2·10 1·60

383 Francis of Taxis

1956. Stamp Day.
1279 **383** 12f.+3f. brn, grn & bl 2·75 3·25

384 J. H. Fabre (entomologist)

1956. French Scientists.
1280 **384** 12f. dp brown & brn . . 90 75
1281 – 15f. black and grey . . . 1·20 65
1282 – 18f. blue . . . . 1·70 1·90
1283 – 30f. green & dp green . . 4·50 3·50
DESIGNS: 15f. C. Tellier (refrigeration engineer); 18f. C. Flammarion (astronomer); 30f. P. Sabatier (chemist).

385 Grand Trianon, Versailles

1956.
1284 **385** 12f. brown, green & blk 1·60 1·30

386 "Latin America" and "France"

1956. Franco-Latin American Friendship.
1285 **386** 30f. brown and sepia . . 2·20 1·60

387 "Reims" and "Florence"

388 Order of Malta and Leper Colony

1956. Reims-Florence Friendship.
1286 **387** 12f. green and black . . 90 80

1956. Order of Malta Leprosy Relief.
1287 **388** 12f. red, brown & sepia 60 55

389 St. Yves de Treguier

390 Marshal Franchet d'Esperey

1956. St. Yves de Treguier Commemoration.
1288 **389** 15f. black and grey . . . 45 50

1956. Birth Centenary of Marshal d'Esperey.
1289 **390** 30f. purple . . . . . . 2·50 1·90

391 Monument

392 Bude

1956. Centenary of Montceau-les-Mines.
1290 **391** 12f. sepia 60 55

1956. National Relief Fund.
1291 **392** 12f.+3f. blue . . . . . 7·75 5·25
1292 – 12f.+3f. grey . . . . . 7·75 5·25
1293 – 12f.+3f. red . . . . . 7·75 5·25
1294 – 15f.+5f. green . . . . . 8·75 8·75
1295 – 15f.+5f. brown . . . . . 8·75 8·75
1296 – 15f.+5f. violet . . . . . 8·75 8·75
PORTRAITS: No. 1292, Goujon; No. 1293, Champlain; No. 1294, Chardin; No. 1295, Barres; No. 1296, Ravel.

393 Pelota

395 Donzere-Mondragon Barrage

1956. Sports.
1297 – 30f. black and grey . . . 1·60 15
1298 **393** 40f. purple and brown 6·00 35
1299 – 50f. violet and purple . . 2·10 15
1300 – 75f. grn, black & blue 12·50 2·20
DESIGNS: 30f. Basketball; 50f. Rugby; 75f. Alpine climbing.

1956. Europa. As T **320** of Belgium.
1301 15f. red and pink . . . . . 1·00 20
1302 30f. ultramarine and blue 5·00 1·00

1956. Technical Achievements.
1303 **395** 12f. grey and brown . . 1·70 1·20
1304 – 18f. blue . . . . 2·75 2·40
1305 – 30f. blue and indigo . . 14·00 7·00
DESIGNS—VERT: 18f. Aiguille du Midi cable railway. HORIZ: 30f. Port of Strasbourg.

396 A. A. Parmentier (agronomist)

397 Petrarch

1956. Parmentier Commemoration.
1306 **396** 12f. brown and sepia . . 70 70

1956. Famous Men.
1307 **397** 8f. green 75 70
1308 – 12f. purple (Lully) . . . 75 65
1309 – 15f. red (Rousseau) . . . 1·00 90
1310 – 18f. blue (Franklin) . . . 2·75 2·30
1311 – 20f. violet (Chopin) . . . 4·00 1·90
1312 – 30f. turq (Van Gogh) . . 6·00 3·50

398 Pierre de Coubertin (reviver of Olympic Games)

399 "Jeune Paysan" (after Le Nain)

1956. Coubertin Commemoration.
1313 **398** 30f. purple and grey . . 1·90 1·20

1956. Red Cross Fund. Cross in red.
1314 **399** 12f.+3f. olive . . . . . 3·00 3·25
1315 15f.+5f. lake . . . . . 3·00 3·25
DESIGN: 15f. "Gilles" (after Watteau).

400 Pigeon and Loft

1957. Pigeon-fanciers' Commemoration.
1316 **400** 15f. blue, indigo & pur 40 40

401 Sud Aviation Caravelle

402 Victor Schoelcher (slavery abolitionist)

1957. Air.
1318 – 300f. olive & turquoise 16·00 3·25
1319 **401** 500f. black and blue . . 33·00 3·50
1320 – 1000f. black, vio & sep 55·00 21·00
AIRCRAFT: 300f. Morane Saulnier Paris I airplane; 1000f. Sud Aviation Alouette II helicopter.
See also Nos. 1458/60.

1957. Schoelcher Commem.
1321 **402** 18f. mauve 70 70

403 18th-century Felucca

1957. Stamp Day.
1322 **403** 12f.+3f. black & grey . . 1·90 1·50

404 "La Baigneuse" (after Falconet) and Sevres Porcelain

1957. Bicentenary of National Porcelain Industry at Sevres.
1323 **404** 30f. blue and light blue 85 70

405 Plante and Accumulators

1957. French Inventors (2nd series).
1324 **405** 8f. purple and sepia . . 45 45
1325 – 12f. black, blue & green 60 55
1326 – 18f. lake and red . . . . 1·40 1·40
1327 – 30f. myrtle and green . . 2·50 2·50
DESIGNS: 12f. Beclere (radiology); 18f. Terrillon (antiseptics); 30f. Oehmichen (helicopter).

406 Uzes Chateau

407 Jean Moulin

1957.
1334 – 8f. green 20 15
1328 **406** 12f. black, brown & bl 50 45
1335 – 15f. black and green . . 20 10
DESIGNS—VERT: 8f., 15f. Le Quesnoy.

1957. Heroes of the Resistance (1st issue). Inscr as in T **407**.
1329 **407** 8f. chocolate & brown 1·20 60
1330 – 10f. blue and black . . . 1·20 60
1331 – 12f. green and brown . . 1·20 1·10
1332 – 18f. black and violet . . 2·00 1·70
1333 – 20f. blue & turquoise . . 1·80 1·10
PORTRAITS: 10f. H. d'Estienne d'Orves; 12f. R. Keller; 18f. P. Brossolette; 20f. J.-B. Lebas.
See also Nos. 1381/4, 1418/22, 1478/82 and 1519/22.

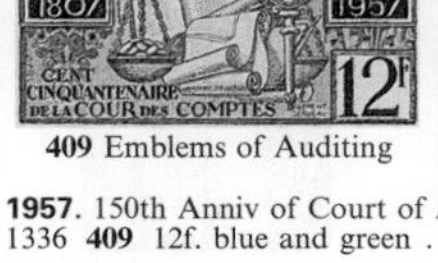
409 Emblems of Auditing

410 Joinville

1957. 150th Anniv of Court of Accounts.
1336 **409** 12f. blue and green . . . 35 25

1957. National Relief Fund.
1337 **410** 12f.+3f. olive & sage . . 2·50 2·50
1338 – 12f.+3f. black & turq . . 2·75 2·75
1339 – 15f.+5f. red & verm . . 3·25 3·25
1340 – 15f.+5f. bl & ultram . . 3·50 3·50
1341 – 18f.+7f. black & grn . . 4·25 4·25
1342 – 18f.+7f. choc & brn . . 4·25 4·50
PORTRAITS: No. 1338, Bernard Palissy; No. 1339, Quentin de la Tour; No. 1340, Lamennais; No. 1341, George Sand; No. 1342, Jules Guesde.
See also Nos. 1390/5.

411 "Public Works"

1957. French Public Works.
1343 **411** 30f. brn, dp brn & grn 2·00 1·30

412 Port of Brest

1957.
1344 **412** 12f. green and brown . . 1·00 1·20

413 Leo Lagrange (founder) and Stadium

414 Auguste Comte

1957. Universities World Games.
1345 **413** 18f. black and grey . . . 60 55

1957. Death Centenary of Auguste Comte (philosopher).
1346 **414** 35f. sepia and brown . . 50 50

415 "Agriculture and Industry"

416 Roman Theatre, Lyons

1957. Europa.
1347 **415** 20f. green and brown . . 55 30
1348 35f. blue and sepia . . . 1·30 75

1957. Bimillenary of Lyons.
1349 **416** 20f. purple & brown . . 45 55

417 Sens River, Guadeloupe

418 Copernicus

1957. Tourist Publicity Series.
1350 **417** 8f. brown and green . . 15 10
1351 – 10f. chocolate & brown 15 10
1351a – 15f. multicoloured . . . 55 50
1352 – 18f. brown and blue . . 25 15
1353 – 25f. brown and grey . . 70 15
1353a – 30f. green . . . . . . 2·50 15
1354 – 35f. mauve and red . . 25 10
1355 – 50f. brown & green . . 60 15
1356 – 65f. blue and indigo . . 75 30
1356a – 85f. purple . . . . . . 4·00 25
1356b **417** 100f. violet . . . . . . 31·00 40
DESIGNS—HORIZ: 10f., 30f., Palais de l'Elysee, Paris; 15f. Chateau de Foix; 25f. Chateau de Valencay; 50f. Les Antiques, Saint Remy; 65f., 85f. Evian-les-Bains. VERT: 18f. Beynac-Cazenac (Dordogne); 35f. Rouen Cathedral.

1957. Famous Men.
1357 **418** 8f. brown 80 70
1358 – 10f. green 80 70
1359 – 12f. violet 85 90
1360 – 15f. brown & dp brown 90 95
1361 – 18f. blue . . . . 1·60 1·30
1362 – 25f. purple and lilac . . 1·60 1·20
1363 – 35f. blue . . . . 1·90 1·60
PORTRAITS: 10f. Michelangelo; 12f. Cervantes; 15f. Rembrandt; 18f. Newton; 25f. Mozart; 35f. Goethe.
See also Nos. 1367/74.

419 L.-J. Thenard

420 "The Blind Man and the Beggar" (after J. Callot)

1957. Death Centenary of Thenard (chemist).
1364 **419** 15f. green and bistre . . 45 45

1957. Red Cross Fund. Cross in red.
1365 **420** 15f.+7f. blue . . . . . 3·75 4·25
1366 – 20f.+8f. brown . . . . . 4·75 5·25
DESIGN: 20f. "The Beggar and the One-eyed Woman" (after J. Callot).

1958. French Doctors. As T **418**.
1367 8f. brown 85 80
1368 12f. violet 75 80
1369 15f. blue . . . . 1·50 1·00
1370 35f. black . . . . 1·90 1·40
PORTRAITS: 8f. Dr. Pinel; 12f. Dr. Widal; 15f. Dr. C. Nicolle; 35f. Dr. R. Leriche.

1958. French Scientists. As T **418**.
1371 8f. violet and blue 85 75
1372 12f. grey and brown . . . . 1·10 90
1373 15f. green and deep green 2·00 90
1374 35f. red and lake . . . . . 2·50 1·50
PORTRAITS: 8f. Lagrange (mathematician); 12f. Le Verrier (astronomer); 15f. Foucault (physicist); 35f. Berthollet (chemist).

421 Rural Postal Services

1958. Stamp Day.
1375 **421** 15f.+5f. deep green, green and brown . . . 1·80 1·50

422 Le Havre

1958. Municipal Reconstruction.
1376 **422** 12f. red and olive . . . 75 65
1377 – 15f. brown and violet . . 75 60
1378 – 18f. indigo and blue . . 1·20 1·00
1379 – 25f. brown, turq & blue 1·50 1·00
DESIGNS—VERT: 15f. Maubeuge; 18f. Saint-Die. HORIZ: 25f. Sete.

423 French Pavilion

1958. Brussels International Exhibition.
1380 **423** 35f. green, blue & brn 25 30

1958. Heroes of the Resistance (2nd issue). Portraits inscr as in T **407**.
1381 8f. black and violet 65 80
1382 12f. green and blue 65 80
1383 15f. grey and sepia . . . . 2·10 1·40
1384 20f. blue and brown . . . . 1·60 1·40
PORTRAITS: 8f. Jean Cavailles; 12f. Fred Scamaroni; 15f. Simone Michel-Levy; 20f. Jacques Bingen.

424 Boules

425 Senlis Cathedral

1958. French Traditional Games.
1385 **424** 12f. brown and red . . . 1·30 1·00
1386 – 15f. dp grn, grn & bl . . 1·60 1·00
1387 – 18f. brown and green . . 2·30 1·40
1388 – 25f. blue and brown . . 3·50 2·30
DESIGNS—HORIZ: 15f. Nautical jousting. VERT: 18f. Archery; 25f. Breton wrestling.

1958. Senlis Cathedral Commemoration.
1389 **425** 15f. blue and indigo . . 45 50

1958. Red Cross Fund. French Celebrities as T **410**.
1390 12f.+4f. green . . . . . . 1·90 2·00
1391 12f.+4f. blue . . . . . . 1·90 2·00
1392 15f.+5f. purple . . . . . . 2·20 2·30
1393 15f.+5f. blue . . . . . . 2·50 2·50
1394 20f.+8f. red . . . . . . 2·50 2·50
1395 35f.+15f. green . . . . . 2·75 2·75
PORTRAITS: No. 1390, J. du Bellay; No. 1391, Jean Bart; No. 1392, D. Diderot; No. 1393, G. Courbet; No. 1394, J. B. Carpeaux; No. 1395, Toulouse-Lautrec.

426 Fragment of the Bayeux Tapestry

1958.
1396 **426** 15f. red and blue 40 45

1958. Europa. As T **345** of Belgium. Size 22 × 36 mm.
1397 20f. red 25 20
1398 35f. blue 70 70

427 Town Halls of Paris and Rome

1958. Paris–Rome Friendship.
1399 **427** 35f. grey, blue & red . . 40 45

428 U.N.E.S.C.O. Headquarters, Paris

429 Flanders Grave

1958. Inauguration of U.N.E.S.C.O. Building.
1400 **428** 20f. bistre and turq . . . 15 15
1401 – 35f. red and myrtle . . . 30 30
DESIGN: 35f. Different view of building.

1958. 40th Anniv of First World War Armistice.
1402 **429** 15f. blue and green . . . 50 40

430 Arms of Marseilles

431 St. Vincent de Paul

1958. Arms of French Towns.
1403 **430** 50c. blue & deep blue . . 15 25
1404 – 70c. multicoloured . . . 15 25
1405 – 80c. red, yellow & bl . . 15 25
1406 – 1f. red, yellow & blue . . 15 15
1407 – 2f. red, green & blue . . 15 15
1408 – 3f. multicoloured . . . 15 15
1409 – 5f. red and brown . . . 15 15
1410 – 15f. multicoloured . . . 30 15
ARMS: 70c. "Lyon"; 80c. "Toulouse"; 1f. "Bordeaux"; 2f. "Nice"; 3f. "Nantes"; 5f. "Lille"; 15f. "Alger".
See also Nos. 1452, 1454, 1498a/99f, 1700/1 and 1735.

1958. Red Cross Fund. Cross in red.
1411 **431** 15f.+7f. green . . . . . 1·40 1·50
1412 – 20f.+8f. violet . . . . . 1·40 1·50
PORTRAIT: 20f. J. H. Dunant (founder).

432 Arc du Carrousel and Flowers

433 Symbols of Learning and "Academic Palms"

1959. Paris Flower Festival.
1413 **432** 15f. multicoloured . . . 50 40

1959. 150th Anniv of "Academic Palms".
1414 **433** 20f. black, vio & lake . . 30 30

434 Father Charles de Foucauld (missionary)

1959. Charles de Foucauld Commem.
1415 **434** 50f. multicoloured . . . 60 55

435 Douglas DC-3 Mail Plane making Night-landing

1959. Stamp Day.
1416 **435** 20f.+5f. mult 60 60
See also No. 1644.

436 Miner's Lamp, Picks and School Building

437 "Five Martyrs"

1959. 175th Anniv of School of Mines.
1417 **436** 20f. turq, blk & red . . 30 30

1959. Heroes of the Resistance (3rd series).
1418 **437** 15f. black and violet . . 50 35
1419 – 15f. violet and purple . . 50 35
1420 – 20f. brown & chestnut 55 55
1421 – 20f. turquoise & green 50 50
1422 – 30f. violet and purple . . 75 65
PORTRAITS—As T **407**: No. 1419, Yvonne Le Roux; No. 1420, Martin Bret; No. 1421, Mederic-Vedy; No. 1422, Moutardier.

438 Foum el Gherza Dam

1959. French Technical Achievements.
1423 **438** 15f. turq and brown . . 40 35
1424 – 20f. purple, red & brn 55 60
1425 – 30f. brn, turq & blue . . 55 60
1426 – 50f. blue and green . . . 1·10 75
DESIGNS—VERT: 20f. Marcoule Atomic Power Station; 30f. Oil derrick and pipe-line at Hassi-Messaoud, Sahara. HORIZ: 50f. National Centre of Industry and Technology, Paris.

439 C. Goujon and C. Rozanoff (test pilots)

1959. Goujon and Rozanoff Commem.
1427 **439** 20f. brown, red & blue 50 50

440 Villehardouin (chronicler)

1959. Red Cross Fund.
1428 **440** 15f.+5f. blue . . . . . 1·70 1·40
1429 – 15f.+5f. myrtle . . . . . 1·40 1·40
1430 – 20f.+10f. bistre . . . . 1·40 1·60
1431 – 20f.+10f. grey . . . . . 1·70 1·60
1432 – 30f.+10f. lake . . . . . 1·70 1·50
1433 – 30f.+10f. brown . . . . 2·00 1·70
PORTRAITS: No. 1429, Le Notre (Royal gardener); No. 1430, D'Alembert (philosopher); No. 1431, D'Angers (sculptor); No. 1432, Bichat (physiologist); No. 1433, Bartholdi (sculptor).

441 M. Desbordes-Valmore

442 "Marianne" in Ship of State

1959. Death Centenary of Marceline Desbordes-Valmore (poetess).
1434 **441** 30f. brown, blue & grn 25 25

1959.
1437 **442** 25f. red and black . . . 40 10
See also No. 1456.

443 Tancarville Bridge

1959. Inauguration of Tancarville Bridge.
1438 **443** 30f. green, brown & blue 40 40

444 Jean Jaures

445 "Giving Blood"

1959. Birth Centenary of Jean Jaures (socialist leader).
1439 **444** 50f. brown 40 30

1959. Europa. As T **360** of Belgium but size 22 × 36 mm.
1440 25f. green 30 15
1441 50f. violet . . . . 1·00 65

1959. Blood Donors.
1442 **445** 20f. grey and red 30 25

446 Clasped Hands of Friendship

447 Youth throwing away Crutches

1959. Tercent of Treaty of the Pyrenees.
1443 **446** 50f. red, blue & mauve 45 45

1959. Infantile Paralysis Relief Campaign.
1444 **447** 20f. blue 35 30

448 Henri Bergson

449 Avesnes-sur-Helpe

1959. Birth Centenary of Bergson (philosopher).
1445 **448** 50f. brown 40 40

1959.
1446 **449** 20f. blue, brown & blk 40 30
1447 – 30f. brown, purple & bl 40 40
DESIGN: 30f. Perpignan Castle.

450 Abbe C. M. de l'Epee (teacher of deaf mutes)

451 N.A.T.O. Headquarters, Paris

1959. Red Cross Fund. Cross in red.
1448 **450** 20f.+10f. purple & blk 2·20 2·30
1449 – 25f.+10f. black & blue 2·50 2·50
PORTRAIT: 25f. V. Hauy (teacher of the blind).

1959. 10th Anniv of N.A.T.O.
1450 **451** 50f. brown, green & bl 65 55

1959. Frejus Disaster Fund. Surch **FREJUS + 5f.**
1451 **442** 25f.+5f. red & black . . 30 35

(New currency. 100 (old) francs = 1 (new) franc.)

453 Sower

454 Laon Cathedral

1960. T **453** and previous designs but new currency.
1452 – 5c. red & brn (as 1409) 7·25 20
1453 **344** 10c. green 55 10
1454 – 15c. mult (as 1410) . . 85 20
1455 **453** 20c. red & turquoise . . 25 10
1456 **442** 25c. blue and red . . . 2·50 10
1456a **453** 30c. blue and indigo . . 1·70 35

1960. Air. As previous designs but new currency and new design (No. 1457b).
1457 – 2f. pur & blk (as 1195) 1·50 20
1457b – 2f. indigo and blue . . 90 20
1458 – 3f. brn & bl (as 1318) 1·60 15
1459 **401** 5f. black and blue . . . 2·75 60
1460 – 10f. black, violet and brown (as 1320) . . 13·00 2·20
DESIGN: No. 1457b, Mystere "20" jetliner.

1960. Tourist Publicity.
1461 **454** 15c. indigo and blue . . 40 35
1462 – 30c. pur, grn & blue . . 3·00 35
1463 – 45c. vio, pur & sepia . . 65 20
1464 – 50c. purple and green . . 2·00 10
1465 – 65c. brn, grn & blue . . 1·50 40
1466 – 85c. sepia, grn & blue . . 2·75 45
1467 – 1f. violet, grn & turq . . 2·75 20
DESIGNS—HORIZ: 30c. Fougeres Chateau; 65c. Valley of the Sioule; 85c. Chaumont Railway Viaduct. VERT: 45c. Kerrata Gorges, Algeria; 50c. Tlemcen Mosque, Algeria; 1 f. Cilaos Church and Great Bernard Mountains, Reunion.
See also Nos. 1485/7.

455 Pierre de Nolhac

1960. Birth Centenary (1959) of Pierre de Nolhac (historian).
1468 **455** 20c. black 65 55

456 St. Etienne Museum

1960. Museum of Art and Industry, St. Etienne.
1469 **456** 30c. brown, red & blue 70 65

1960. As T **345** but with values in new currency.
1470 **345** 8c. violet 60 15
1471 20c. green . . . . 2·00 75
1472 40c. red . . . . 8·50 3·25
1473 55c. green . . . . 30·00 25·00
Nos. 1470/3 were only issued precancelled (see note below No. 432).

457 Assembly Emblem and View of Cannes

1960. 5th Meeting of European Mayors Assembly.
1474 **457** 50c. brown and green . . 85 90

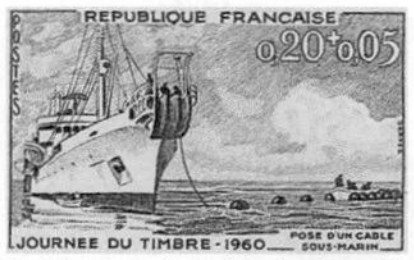
458 "Ampere" (cable-laying ship)

1960. Stamp Day.
1475 **458** 20c.+5c. blue & turq . . 1·50 1·60

459 Girl of Savoy

460 Child Refugee

1960. Centenary of Attachment of Savoy and Nice to France.
1476 **459** 30c. green 65 75
1477 – 50c. brown, red and yellow (Girl of Nice) 55 55

1960. Heroes of the Resistance (4th series). Portraits as T **407**.
1478 20c. black and brown . . . 2·50 1·80
1479 20c. lake and red . . . . . 2·00 1·80
1480 30c. violet & deep violet . . 2·00 1·80
1481 30c. blue and indigo . . . . 3·00 2·50
1482 50c. brown and green . . . 3·50 3·50
PORTRAITS: No. 1478, E. Debeaumarche; No. 1479, P. Masse; No. 1480, M. Ripoche; No. 1481, L. Vieljeux; No. 1482, Abbe Rene Bonpain.

1960. World Refugee Year.
1483 **460** 25c.+10c. bl, brn & grn 40 45

461 "The Road to Learning"

1960. 150th Anniv of Strasbourg Teachers' Training College.
1484 **461** 20c. violet, pur & blk . . 35 30

1960. Views as T **454**.
1485 15c. sepia, grey and blue 45 40
1485a 20c. blue, green and buff 35 35
1486 30c. sepia, green and blue 85 75
1487 50c. brown, green & red 75 75
DESIGNS: 15c. Lisieux Basilica; 20c. Bagnoles de l'Orne; 30c. Chateau de Blois; 50c. La Bourboule.

462 L'Hospital (statesman)

463 "Marianne"

1960. Red Cross Fund.
1488 **462** 10c.+5c. violet & red . . 2·50 2·75
1489 – 20c.+10c. turq & grn . . 3·25 3·50
1490 – 20c.+10c. green & brn 3·25 3·50
1491 – 30c.+10c. blue & vio . . 5·50 6·00
1492 – 30c.+10c. crim & red . . 5·00 5·25
1493 – 50c.+15c. blue and slate 6·50 6·25
DESIGNS: No. 1489, Boileau (poet); No. 1490, Turenne (military leader); No. 1491, Bizet (composer); No. 1492, Charcot (neurologist); No. 1493, Degas (painter).

1960.
1494 **463** 25c. grey and red . . . 25 10

464 Cross of Lorraine

465 Jean Bouin and Olympic Stadium

1960. 20th Anniv of De Gaulle's Appeal.
1495 **464** 20c. brown, grn & sep 70 40

1960. Olympic Games.
1496 **465** 20c. brown, red & blue 40 45

1960. Europa. As T **373** of Belgium, but size 36 × 22½ mm.
1497 25c. turquoise and green . . 15 10
1498 50c. purple and red 35 35

1960. Arms. As T **430**.
1498a 1c. blue and yellow 10 10
1498b 2c. yellow, green and blue 10 10
1499 5c. multicoloured 20 15
1499a 5c. red, yellow and blue . . 10 10
1499b 10c. blue, yellow and red 10 10
1499c 12c. red, yellow and black 10 10
1499d 15c. yellow, blue and red 10 10
1499e 18c. multicoloured 40 40
1499f 30c. red and blue 50 10
ARMS: 1c. "Niort"; 2c. "Gueret"; 5c. (No. 1499) "Oran"; 5c. (No. 1499a) "Amiens"; 10c. "Troyes"; 12c. "Agen"; 15c. "Nevers"; 18c. "Saint-Denis (Reunion)"; 30c. "Paris".

466 Madame de Stael (after Gerard)

467 Gen. Estienne, Morane Saulnier Type L Airplane and Tank

1960. Madame de Stael (writer).
1500 **466** 30c. olive and purple . . 35 35

1960. Birth Centenary of Gen. Estienne.
1501 **467** 15c. sepia and lilac . . . 40 45

468 Sangnier

469 Order of the Liberation

1960. 10th Death Anniv of Marc Sangnier (patriot).
1502 **468** 20c. black, violet & blue 25 30

1960. 20th Anniv of Order of the Liberation.
1503 **469** 20c. green and black . . 40 45

470 Atlantic Puffins at Les Sept Iles

1960. Nature Protection.
1504 **470** 30c. multicoloured . . . 30 30
1505 – 50c. multicoloured . . . 85 45
DESIGN: 50c. European bee eaters, Camargue.

471 A. Honnorat

472 Mace of St. Martin's Brotherhood

1960. 10th Death Anniv of Andre Honnorat (philanthropist).
1506 **471** 30c. black, green & blue 30 30

1960. Red Cross Fund. Cross in red.
1507 **472** 20c.+10c. lake . . . . . 3·00 3·25
1508 – 25c.+10c. blue . . . . . 3·00 3·25
DESIGN: 25c. St. Martin (after 16th-cent. wood-carving).

473 St. Barbe and College

1960. 500th Anniv of St. Barbe College.
1509 **473** 30c. multicoloured . . . 40 40

474 Northern Lapwings

1960. Study of Bird Migration. Inscr "ETUDE DES MIGRATIONS".
1510 **474** 20c. multicoloured . . . 35 35
1511 – 45c. multicoloured . . . 95 1·00
DESIGN: 45c. Green-winged teal.

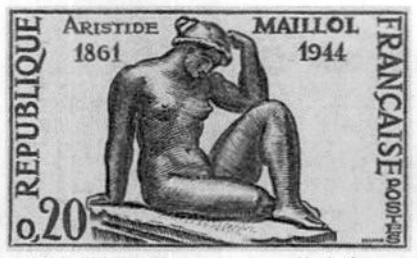
475 "Mediterranean" (after Maillol)

476 "Marianne"

1961. Birth Cent of Aristide Maillol (sculptor).
1512 **475** 20c. blue and red 25 30

1961.
1513 **476** 20c. red and blue 25 10

477 Orly Airport

1961. Opening of New Installations at Orly Airport.
1514 **477** 50c. turq, blue & blk . . 45 45

478 Georges Melies

479 Postman of Paris "Little Post" 1760

1961. Birth Centenary of Georges Melies (cinematograph pioneer).
1515 **478** 50c. blue, brown & vio 80 70

1961. Stamp Day and Red Cross Fund.
1516 **479** 20c.+5c. grn, red & brn 90 95

480 Jan Nicquet and Tobacco Flowers and Leaves

481 Father Lacordaire (after Chasseriau)

1961. 400th Anniv of Introduction of Tobacco into France.
1517 **480** 30c. red, brown & grn 25 30

The portrait on No. 1517 is of Jan Nicquet, a Flemish merchant, and not Jean Nicot as inscribed.

1961. Death Centenary of Father Lacordaire (theologian).
1518 **481** 30c. black and brown . . 40 40

1961. Heroes of the Resistance (5th issue). Portrait inscr as in T **407**.
1519 20c. violet and blue 80 80
1520 20c. blue and green . . . . 1·00 85
1521 30c. black and brown . . . 1·40 1·00
1522 30c. black and blue . . . . 1·30 1·10
PORTRAITS: No. 1519, J. Renouvin; No. 1520, L. Dubray; No. 1521, P. Gateaud; No. 1522, Mother Elisabeth.

482 Dove, Globe and Olive Branch

483 Deauville, 1861

1961. World Federation of Old Soldiers Meeting, Paris.
1523 **482** 50c. red, blue & green 40 40

1961. Centenary of Deauville.
1524 **483** 50c. lake . . . . 1·90 1·60

484 Du Guesclin (Constable of France)

485 Champmesle ("Roxane")

1961. Red Cross Fund.
1525 **484** 15c.+5c. black & pur . . 2·40 2·50
1526 – 20c.+10c. green & blue 2·40 2·50
1527 – 20c.+10c. crimson & red 2·40 2·50
1528 – 30c.+10c. black & brn 3·75 3·25
1529 – 45c.+10c. brown & grn 4·00 4·00
1530 – 50c.+15c. violet & red 4·25 4·00
PORTRAITS: No. 1526, Puget (sculptor); No. 1527, Coulomb (physicist); No. 1528, General Drouot; No. 1529, Daumier (caricaturist); No. 1530, Apollinaire (writer).

1961. French Actors and Actresses. Frames in red.
1531 **485** 20c. brown and green . . 75 45
1532 – 30c. brown and red . . . 95 65
1533 – 30c. myrtle and green . . 95 65
1534 – 50c. brown & turquoise 1·40 75
1535 – 50c. brown and olive . . 1·20 65
PORTRAITS: No. 1532, Talma ("Oreste"); No. 1533, Rachel ("Phedre"); No. 1534, Raimu ("Cesar"); No. 1535, Gerard Philipe ("Le Cid").

486 Mont Dore, Snow Crystal and Cable Rly

487 Thann

1961. Mont Dore.
1536 **486** 20c. purple and orange 25 30

1961. 800th Anniv of Thann.
1537 **487** 20c. violet, brn & grn . . 65 60

488 Pierre Fauchard

489 Doves

1961. Birth Bicentenary of Pierre Fauchard (dentist).
1538 **488** 50c. black and green . . 55 55

1961. Europa.
1539 **489** 25c. red 20 15
1540 50c. blue 40 40

490 Sully-sur-Loire

1961. Tourist Publicity.
1541 – 15c. slate, pur & turq . . 10 10
1542 – 20c. brown and green . . 30 30
1543 – 30c. blue, grn & sepia . . 25 25
1544 – 30c. black, grey & grn 1·80 1·40
1545 **490** 45c. brown, green & blue 25 10
1546 – 50c. myrt, turq & grn . . 1·10 15
1547 – 65c. blue, brown & myrt 40 15
1548 – 85c. blue, brown & myrt 65 25
1549 – 1f. brown, blue & myrt 4·50 15
1550 – 1f. brown, green & blue 40 10
VIEWS—HORIZ: 15c. Saint-Paul; 30c. (No. 1543), Arcachon; 30c. (No. 1544), Law Courts, Rennes; 50c. Cognac; 65c. Dinan; 85c. Calais; 1f. (No. 1549), Medea, Algeria; 1f. (No. 1550), Le Touquet-Paris-Plage, golf-bag and Handley Page Dart Herald airplane. VERT: 20c. Laval, Mayenne.
See also Nos. 1619/23, 1654/7, 1684/8, 1755/61, 1794, 1814/18, 1883/5, 1929/33, 1958/61, 2005/8, 2042/4, 2062/4, 2115/20, 2187/97, 2258/64, 2310/15, 2360/5, 2403/10, 2503/8, 2566/70, 2630/4, 2652/6, 2710/14, 2762/6, 2834/6, 2883/6, 2973/6, 3024/6, 3077/80, 3124/9, 3180/3, 3240/3, 3330/3, 3375/9, 3487/91, 3580/3, 3642/5, 3720/3, 3800/1, 3908/11 and 3946.

491 "14th July" (R. de la Fresnaye)

1961. Modern French Art.
1551 – 50c. multicoloured . . . 2·75 1·90
1552 – 65c. blue, green & violet 4·25 2·75
1553 – 85c. red, bistre and blue 2·00 2·20
1554 **491** 1f. multicoloured . . . . 4·25 3·25
PAINTINGS: 50c. "The Messenger" (Braque); 65c. "Blue Nudes" (Matisse); 85c. "The Cardplayers" (Cezanne).
See also Nos. 1590/2, 1603/6, 1637/9, 1671/4, 1710/4, 1742/5, 1786/9, 1819/22, 1877/80, 1908/10, 1944/7, 1985/8, 2033/6, 2108/13, 2159/60, 2243, 2290/2, 2338/41, 2398/9, 2531/4, 2580/2, 2608/12, 2672/6, 2721/5, 2773/6, 2850/3, 2858/60, 2966/8, 3008/9, 3085, 3245/7, 3306/7, 3368/9, 3483/6, 3561/3, 3638/4, 3702/5, 3899, 3990, 3902 and 3951.

493 "It is so sweet to love" (Wood-carving from Rouault's "Miserere")

494 Liner "France"

1961. Red Cross Fund. Cross in red.
1555 **493** 20c.+10c. black & pur 2·40 2·75
1556 – 25c.+10c. black & pur 3·25 2·75
DESIGN: 25c. "The blind leading the blind" (from Rouault's "Miserere").

1962. Maiden Voyage of Liner "France".
1557 **494** 30c. black, red & blue 70 55

495 Skier at Speed

496 M. Bourdet

1962. World Ski Championships, Chamonix.
1558 **495** 30c. violet and blue . . . 25 25
1559 – 50c. green, blue & vio 45 35
DESIGN: 50c. Slalom-racer.

1962. 60th Birth Anniv of Maurice Bourdet (journalist and radio commentator).
1560 **496** 30c. grey 25 30

497 Dr. P.-F. Bretonneau

498 Gallic Cock

1962. Death Centenary of Dr. Pierre-Fidele Bretonneau (medical scientist).
1561 **497** 50c. violet and blue . . . 40 40

1962.
1562 **498** 25c. red, blue & brown 45 10
1562a 30c. red, green & brn 75 10

499 Royal Messenger of late Middle Ages

500 Vannes

1962. Stamp Day.
1563 **499** 20c.+5c. brn, bl & red 85 90

1962.
1564 **500** 30c. blue 80 90

501 Globe and Stage Set

502 Harbour Installations

1962. World Theatre Day.
1565 **501** 50c. lake, grn & ochre 65 40

1962. 300th Anniv of Cession of Dunkirk to France.
1566 **502** 95c. purple, brown & green . . . . 1·00 55

503 Mount Valerien Memorial

504 Emblem and Swamp

1962. Resistance Fighters' Memorials (1st issue).
1567 **503** 20c. myrtle and drab . . 85 65
1568 – 30c. blue 80 65
1569 – 50c. indigo and blue . . 1·00 75
MEMORIALS—VERT: 30c. Vercors; 50c. Ile de Sein.
See also Nos. 1609/10.

1962. Malaria Eradication.
1570 **504** 50c. red, blue & green 40 40

505 Nurses and Child

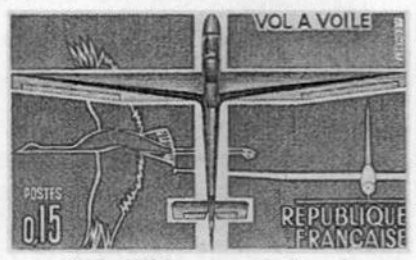

506 Gliders and Stork

1962. National Hospitals Week.
1571 **505** 30c. brown, grey & grn 25 30

1962. Civil and Sports Aviation.
1572 **506** 15c. brown and chest . . 45 50
1573 – 20c. red and purple . . . 45 50
DESIGN: 20c. Jodel Ambassadeur and early aircraft.

507 Emblem and School of Horology

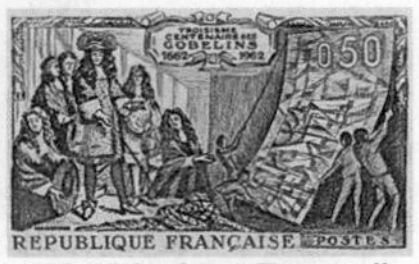

508 "Selecting a Tapestry"

1962. Cent of School of Horology, Besancon.
1574 **507** 50c. vio, brown & red 45 50

1962. Tercentenary of Manufacture of Gobelin Tapestries.
1575 **508** 50c. turq, red & grn . . 50 50

509 Pascal

510 Denis Papin (inventor)

1962. Death Tercent of Pascal (philosopher).
1576 **509** 50c. red and green . . . 50 50

1962. Red Cross Fund.
1577 15c.+5c. sepia & turquoise 2·30 2·50
1578 20c.+10c. brown and red . . 2·75 3·00
1579 20c.+10c. blue and grey . . 2·75 2·50
1580 30c.+10c. indigo and blue 3·75 4·00
1581 45c.+15c. pur and brown . . 4·50 4·00
1582 50c.+20c. black and blue . . 3·75 4·00
DESIGNS: No. 1577, Type **510**; 1578, Edme Bouchardon (sculptor); 1579, Joseph Lakanal (politician); 1580, Gustave Charpentier (composer); 1581, Edouard Estauni (writer); 1582, Hyacinthe Vincent (scientist).

511 "Modern" Rose

512 Europa "Tree"

1962. Rose Culture.
1583 **511** 20c. red, green & olive 55 40
1584 – 30c. red, myrt & olive 60 55
DESIGN: 30c. "Old fashioned" rose.

1962. Europa.
1585 **512** 25c. violet 20 15
1586 50c. brown 40 45

513 Telecommunications Centre, Pleumeur-Bodou

1962. 1st Trans-Atlantic Telecommunications Satellite Link.
1587 **513** 25c. buff, green & grey 25 30
1588 – 50c. bl, grn & indigo . . 50 40
1589 – 50c. brown and blue . . 50 45
DESIGNS: 50c. (No. 1588), "Telstar" satellite, globe and television receiver; 50c. (No. 1589), Radio telescope, Nancay (Cher).

1962. French Art. As T **491**.
1590 50c. multicoloured . . . . . 3·25 2·50
1591 65c. multicoloured . . . . . 2·50 2·10
1592 1f. multicoloured . . . . . 5·50 4·00
PAINTINGS—HORIZ: 50c. "Bonjour, Monsieur Courbet" (Courbet); 65c. "Madame Manet on a Blue Sofa" (Manet). VERT: 1f. "Officer of the Imperial Horse Guards" (Gericault).

514 "Rosalie Fragonard" (after Fragonard)

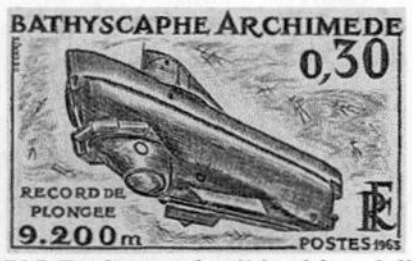

515 Bathyscaphe "Archimede"

1962. Red Cross Fund. Cross in red.
1593 **514** 20c.+10c. brown . . . . 1·60 1·60
1594 – 25c.+10c. green . . . . 2·20 2·30
PORTRAIT: 25c. "Child as Pierrot" (after Fragonard).

1963. Record Undersea Dive.
1595 **515** 30c. black and blue . . . 25 30

516 Flowers and Nantes Chateau

1963. Nantes Flower Show.
1596 **516** 30c. blue, red & green 25 30

517 Jacques Amyot (Bishop of Auxerre)

1963. Red Cross Fund.
1597 **517** 20c.+10c. purple, violet and grey . . . . . . 1·00 1·30
1598 – 20c.+10c. deep brown, brown and blue . . . . 1·70 1·60
1599 – 30c.+10c. grn & pur . . 1·00 1·20
1600 – 30c.+10c. black, green and brown . . . . . 1·30 1·30
1601 – 50c.+20c. grn, brn & bl 1·20 1·30
1602 – 50c.+20c. blk, bl & brn 2·20 2·20
DESIGNS: No. 1598, Etienne Mehul (composer); No. 1599 Pierre de Marivaux (dramatist); No. 1600, N.-L. Vauquelin (chemist); No. 1601, Jacques Daviel (oculist); No. 1602, Alfred de Vigny (poet).

1963. French Art. As T **491**.
1603 50c. multicoloured . . . . . . 3·50 2·75
1604 85c. multicoloured . . . . . 2·10 1·50
1605 95c. multicoloured 65 80
1606 1f. multicoloured . . . . . 5·00 4·25
DESIGNS—VERT: 50c. "Jacob's Struggle with the Angel" (Delacroix); 85c. "The Married Couple of the Eiffel Tower" (Chagall); 95c. "The Fur Merchants" (stained glass window, Chartres Cathedral); 1f. "St. Peter and the Miracle of the Fishes" (stained glass window, Church of St. Foy de Conches).

518 Roman Post Chariot

1963. Stamp Day.
1607 **518** 20c.+5c. purple & brn 35 40

519 Woman reaching for Campaign Emblem

520 Glieres Memorial

1963. Freedom from Hunger.
1608 **519** 50c. brown & myrtle . . 40 40

1963. Resistance Fighters' Memorials (2nd issue).
1609 **520** 30c. olive and brown . . 55 55
1610 – 50c. black 55 55
DESIGN: 50c. Deportees Memorial, Ile de la Cite (Paris).

521 Beethoven (West Germany)

1963. Celebrities of European Economic Community Countries.
1611 **521** 20c. blue, brown & grn 40 45
1612 – 20c. black, violet & red 40 45
1613 – 20c. blue, pur & olive . . 40 45
1614 – 20c. brown, pur & brn 40 45
1615 – 30c. sepia, violet & brn 40 45
PORTRAITS AND VIEWS: No. 1611, Birthplace and modern Bonn; No. 1612, Emile Verhaeren (Belgium: Family grave and residence, Roisin); No. 1613, Giuseppe Mazzini (Italy: Marcus Aurelius statue and Appian Way, Rome); No. 1614, Emile Mayrisch (Luxembourg: Colpach Chateau and Steel Plant, Esch); No. 1615, Hugo de Groot (Netherlands: Palace of Peace, The Hague, and St. Agatha's Church, Delft).

522 Hotel des Postes, Paris

523 College Building

1963. Centenary of Paris Postal Conference.
1616 **522** 50c. sepia 40 40

1963. 400th Anniv of Louis the Great College, Paris.
1617 **523** 30c. myrtle 25 25

524 St. Peter's Church and Castle Keep, Caen

1963. 36th French Philatelic Societies Federation Congress, Caen.
1618 **524** 30c. brown and blue . . 35 35

1963. Tourist Publicity. As T **490**. Inscr "1963".
1619 30c. ochre, blue & green . . 35 15
1620 50c. red, blue & turquoise 35 10
1621 60c. red, turquoise & blue 65 30
1622 85c. purple, turquoise & grn 1·50 30
1623 95c. black 65 30
DESIGNS—HORIZ: 30c. Amboise Chateau; 50c. Cote d'Azur, Var; 85c. Vittel. VERT: 60c. Saint-Flour; 95c. Church and cloisters, Moissac.

525 Water-skiing

1963. World Water-skiing Championships, Vichy.
1624 **525** 30c. black, red & turq 25 30

526 "Co-operation"

527 "Child with Grapes" (Angers)

1963. Europa.
1625 **526** 25c. brown 25 20
1626 50c. green 35 35

1963. Red Cross Fund. Cross in red.
1627 **527** 20c.+10c. black 85 95
1628 – 25c.+10c. green 85 95
DESIGN: 25c. "The Piper" (Manet).

528 "Philately"

1963. "PHILATEC 1964" International Stamp Exhibition, Paris (1st issue).
1629 **528** 25c. red, green & grey 25 15
See also Nos. 1640/3 and 1651.

529 Radio-T.V. Centre

1963. Opening of Radio-T.V. Centre, Paris.
1630 **529** 20c. slate, ol & brn . . . 25 15

530 Emblems of C.P. Services

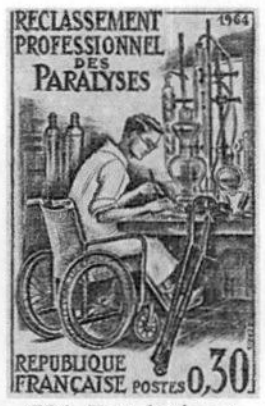

531 Paralytic at Work in Invalid Chair

1964. Civil Protection.
1631 **530** 30c. blue, red & orange 40 45

1964. Professional Rehabilitation of Paralytics.
1632 **531** 30c. brn, chestnut & grn 25 30

532 18th-century Courier

533 "Deportation"

1964. Stamp Day.
1633 **532** 20c.+5c. myrtle 25 30

1964. 20th Anniv of Liberation (1st issue).
1634 **533** 20c.+5c. slate 75 75
1635 – 50c.+5c. green 95 95
DESIGN: 50c. "Resistance" (memorial).
See also Nos. 1652/3 and 1658.

534 Pres. Rene Coty

535 "Blanc" 2c. Stamp of 1900

1964. Pres. Coty Commemoration.
1636 **534** 30c.+10c. brown & red 40 45

1964. French Art. As T **491**.
1637 1f. multicoloured . . . . . 2·10 1·70
1638 1f. multicoloured . . . . . 1·50 1·40
1639 1f. multicoloured 95 80
DESIGNS—VERT: No. 1637, Jean le Bon (attributed to Girard of Orleans); No. 1638, Tomb plaque of Geoffrey IV (12th-century "champleve" (grooved) enamel from Limousin); No. 1639, "The Lady with the Unicorn" (15th-century tapestry).

1964. "PHILATEC 1964" International Stamp Exhibition, Paris (2nd issue).
1640 – 30c. blue, black & brn 45 45
1641 **535** 25c. purple and bistre . . 45 45
1642 – 25c. blue and bistre . . . 45 45
1643 – 30c. red, black & blue 45 45
DESIGNS: No. 1640, "Postal Mechanization" (letter-sorting equipment and parcel conveyor); No. 1642, "Mouchon" 25c. stamp of 1900; No. 1643, "Telecommunications" (telephone dial, teleprinter and T.V. tower).

1964. 25th Anniv of Night Airmail Service. As T **435** but additionally inscr "25E ANNIVERSAIRE" and colours changed.
1644 **435** 25c. multicoloured . . . 25 20

536 Stained Glass Window

537 Calvin

1964. 800th Anniv of Notre Dame, Paris.
1645 **536** 60c. multicoloured . . . 60 60

1964. 400th Death Anniv of Calvin (reformer).
1646 **537** 30c.+10c. brown, sepia and turquoise 35 45

538 Gallic Coin

539 Pope Sylvester II

1964. Pre-cancels.
1647 **538** 10c. brown and green 55 30
1647a 15c. brown & orange 30 30
1647b 22c. violet and green 70 60
1647c 25c. brown and violet 65 65
1647d 26c. brown & purple 65 55
1647e 30c. brn & lt brown . . 75 75
1647f 35c. blue and red . . . 1·60 1·30
1648 45c. brown and green 1·70 1·50
1648a 50c. brown and blue . . 1·20 1·20
1648b 70c. brown and blue . . 7·50 7·50
1649 90c. brown and red . . 2·30 3·00
See note below No. 432 (1920).
For stamps as Type **538** but inscribed "FRANCE", see Nos. 2065a/1.

1964. Pope Sylvester II Commemoration.
1650 **539** 30c.+10c. pur & grey . . 35 45

540 Rocket and Horseman

1964. "PHILATEC 1964" International Stamp Exhibition, Paris (3rd issue).
1651 **540** 1f. blue, red & brown . . 23·00 24·00
MS1651a 145×285 mm. No. 1651 ×8 plus labels bearing "PHILATEC" emblem £180 £140
Sold at 4f. incl. entrance fee to Exhibition.

541 Landings in Normandy and Provence

1964. 20th Anniv of Liberation (2nd issue).
1652 **541** 30c.+5c. sep, brn & bl 85 90
1653 – 30c.+5c. red, sep & brn 90 95
DESIGN: No. 1653, Taking prisoners in Paris, and tank in Strasbourg.

1964. Tourist Publicity. As T **490**. Inscr "1964".
1654 40c. brown, green & chest 25 15
1655 70c. purple, turquoise & blue 35 10
1656 1f.25 green, blue & bistre . . 70 50
1657 1f.30 chestnut, choc & brn 1·20 50
DESIGNS—HORIZ: 40c., 1f.25, Notre-Dame Chapel, Haut-Ronchamp (Haute-Saone). VERT: 70c. Caesar's Tower, Provins; 1f.30, Joux Chateau (Doubs).

542 De Gaulle's Appeal of 18th June, 1940 **543** Judo

1964. 20th Anniv of Liberation (3rd issue).
1658 **542** 25c.+5c. blk, red & bl . . 90 1·00

1964. Olympic Games, Tokyo.
1659 **543** 50c. purple and blue . . 40 40

544 G. Mandel **545** Soldiers departing for the Marne by Taxi-cab

1964. 20th Death Anniv of Georges Mandel (statesman).
1660 **544** 30c. purple 25 15

1964. 50th Anniv of Victory of the Marne.
1661 **545** 30c. black, red & blue . . 35 25

546 Europa "Flower" **547** Co-operation

1964. Europa.
1662 **546** 25c. red, brown & grn . . 15 10
1663 50c. red, green & vio . . 35 25

1964. French, Africa and Malagasy Co-operation.
1664 **547** 25c. choc, blue & brn . . 25 20

548 J. N. Corvisart (physician) **549** La Rochefoucauld

1964. Red Cross Fund.
1665 **548** 20c.+10c. black and red 45 45
1666 – 25c.+10c. black and red 45 45
DESIGN: 25c. D. Larrey (military surgeon).

1965. Red Cross Fund. Inscr "1965".
1667 **549** 30c.+10c. blue & brn . . 50 50
1668 – 30c.+10c. brown & red 65 65
1669 – 40c.+10c. slate and brown 65 70
1670 – 40c.+10c. brown, blue and chestnut 65 65
PORTRAITS: No. 1668, Nicolas Poussin (painter); No. 1669, Paul Dukas (composer); No. 1670, Charles d'Orleans.

1965. French Art. As T **491**.
1671 1f. multicoloured 80 75
1672 1f. multicoloured 40 45
1673 1f. multicoloured 40 45
1674 1f. black, rose and red 40 45
DESIGNS—VERT: No. 1671, "L'Anglaise du 'Star' au Havre" (Toulouse-Lautrec); No. 1673, "The Apocalypse" (14th-century tapestry). HORIZ: No. 1672, "Hunting with Falcons" (miniature from manuscript "Les Tres Riches Heures du Duc de Berry", by the Limbourg brothers); No. 1674, "The Red Violin" (R. Dufy).

550 "La Guienne" (steam packet) **551** Deportees

1965. Stamp Day.
1675 **550** 25c.+10c. blk, grn & bl 80 80

1965. 20th Anniv of Return of Deportees.
1676 **551** 40c. green 60 50

552 Youth Club **553** Girl with Bouquet

1965. 20th Anniv of Youth Clubs ("Maisons des Jeunes et de la Culture").
1677 **552** 25c. blue, brn & grn . . 25 30

1965. "Welcome and Friendship" Campaign.
1678 **553** 60c. red, orge & grn . . 35 35

554 Allied Flags and Broken Swastika **555** I.T.U. Emblem, "Syncom", Morse Key and Pleumeur-Bodou Centre

1965. 20th Anniv of Victory in World War II.
1679 **554** 40c. red, blue & black 40 30

1965. Centenary of I.T.U.
1680 **555** 60c. brown, black & bl 50 55

556 Croix de Guerre **557** Bourges Cathedral

1965. 50th Anniv of Croix de Guerre.
1681 **556** 40c. brown, red & green 50 55

1965. National Congress of Philatelic Societies, Bourges.
1682 **557** 40c. brown and blue . . 35 30

558 Stained Glass Window

1965. 800th Anniv of Sens Cathedral.
1683 **558** 1f. multicoloured 65 55

1965. Tourist Publicity. As T **490**. Inscr "1965".
1684 50c. blue, green and bistre 35 15
1685 60c. brown and blue 70 15
1686 75c. brown, green & blue . . 1·00 95
1687 95c. brown, green & blue . . 5·50 1·00
1688 1f. grey, green and brown 1·10 15
DESIGNS—HORIZ: 50c. Moustiers Ste. Marie (Basses-Alpes); 95c. Landscape, Vendee; 1f. Monoliths, Carnac. VERT: 60c. Yachting, Aix-les-Bains; 75c. Tarn gorges.

559 Mont Blanc from Chamonix **560** Europa "Sprig"

1965. Opening of Mont Blanc Road Tunnel.
1689 **559** 30c. violet, blue & plum 30 25

1965. Europa.
1690 **560** 30c. red 35 25
1691 60c. grey 80 80

561 Etienne Regnault and "Le Taureau" **562** "One Million Hectares"

1965. Tercent of Colonisation of Reunion.
1692 **561** 30c. blue and red 25 30

1965. Reafforestation.
1693 **562** 25c. brown, yellow & grn 25 25

563 Atomic Reactor and Emblems **564** Aviation School, Salon-de-Provence

1965. 20th Anniv of Atomic Energy Commission.
1694 **563** 60c. black and blue . . 60 45

1965. 30th Anniv of Aviation School.
1695 **564** 25c. green, indigo & blue 30 25

565 Rocket "Diamant"

1965. Launching of 1st French Satellite.
1696 **565** 30c. blue, turq & ind . . 25 30
1697 – 60c. blue, turq & ind . . 30 40
DESIGN: 60c. Satellite "A1".

566 "Le Bebe a la Cuiller" **568** St. Pierre Fourier and Basilica, Mattaincourt (Vosges)

1965. Red Cross Fund. Paintings by Renoir.
1698 **566** 25c.+10c. blue and red 35 30
1699 – 30c.+10c. brown & red 45 35
DESIGN: 30c. "Coco ecrivant" (portrait of Renoir's small son writing).

1966. Arms. As T **430**.
1700 5c. red and blue 20 10
1701 25c. blue and brown 80 15
DESIGNS: 5c. "Auch"; 25c. "Mont-de-Marsan".

1966. Red Cross Fund.
1702 **568** 30c.+10c. brown & grn 50 55
1703 – 30c.+10c. purple & grn 50 55
1704 – 30c.+10c. bl, brn & grn 50 55
1705 – 30c.+10c. blue & brn . . 45 50
1706 – 30c.+10c. brown & grn 50 50
1707 – 30c.+10c. black & brn 45 50

DESIGNS: No. 1703, F. Mansart (architect) and Carnavalet House, Paris; No. 1704, M. Proust (writer) and St. Hilaire Bridge, Illiers (Eure-et-Loir); No. 1705, G. Faure (composer), statuary and music; No. 1706, Hippolyte Taine (philosopher) and birthplace; No. 1707, Elie Metchnikoff (scientist), microscope and Pasteur Institute.

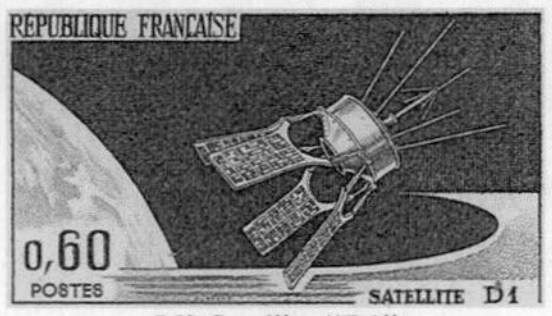

569 Satellite "D1"

1966. Launching of Satellite "D1".
1708 **569** 60c. red, blue & green 25 30

570 Engraving a die **571** Knight and Chessboard

1966. Stamp Day.
1709 **570** 25c.+10c. deep brown, grey and brown . . . 35 35

1966. French Art. As T **491**.
1710 1f. bronze, green & purple 40 45
1711 1f. multicoloured 45 45
1712 1f. multicoloured 45 50
1713 1f. multicoloured 45 50
1714 1f. multicoloured 45 50
DESIGNS—HORIZ: No. 1710, Detail of Vix Crater (wine-bowl); No. 1711, "The New-born Child" (G. de la Tour); No. 1712, "Baptism of Judas" (stained glass window, Sainte Chapelle, Paris); No. 1714, "Crispin and Scapin" (after H. Daumier). VERT: No. 1713, "The Moon and the Bull" (Lurcat tapestry).

1966. International Chess Festival, Le Havre.
1715 **571** 60c. grey, brown & vio 60 50

572 Pont St. Esprit Bridge **573** St. Michel

1966. 700th Anniv of Pont St. Esprit.
1716 **572** 25c. black and blue . . . 25 15

1966. Millenary of Mont St. Michel.
1717 **573** 25c. multicoloured . . . 25 25

574 King Stanislas, Arms and Palace

1966. Bicentenary of Reunion of Lorraine and Barrois with France.
1718 **574** 25c. brown, grn & blue 25 15

575 Niort **576** "Angel of Verdun"

1966. National Congress of Philatelic Societies, Niort.
1719 **575** 40c. slate, green & blue 25 25

1966. 50th Anniv of Verdun Victory.
1720 **576** 30c.+5c. slate, bl & grn 30 35

577 Fontenelle

1966. Tercentenary of Academy of Sciences.
1721 **577** 60c. brown and lake . . 40 40

578 William the Conqueror, Castle and Landings

1966. 900th Anniv of Battle of Hastings.
1722 **578** 60c. brown and blue . . 40 45

579 Globe and Railway Track

1966. 19th International Railway Congress, Paris.
1723 **579** 60c. brown, blue & lake 1·00 65

580 Oleron Bridge

581 Europa "Ship"

1966. Opening of Oleron Bridge.
1724 **580** 25c. brown, green & bl 25 30

1966. Europa.
1725 **581** 30c. blue 25 20
1726 60c. red 60 50

582 Vercingetorix

1966. History of France (1st series). Inscr "1966".
1727 **582** 40c. brown, blue & grn 35 35
1728 – 40c. brown and black . . 35 35
1729 – 60c. red, brown & violet 45 40
DESIGNS—VERT: 40c. (No. 1728), Clovis. 60c. Charlemagne.
See also Nos. 1769/71, 1809/11, 1850/2, 1896/8, 1922/4, 1975/7 and 2017/19.

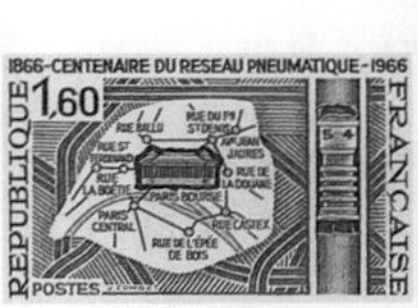
583 Route Map

584 Chateau de Val

1966. Centenary of Paris Pneumatic Post.
1730 **583** 1f.60 blue, lake & brn 80 65

1966. Chateau de Val.
1731 **584** 2f.30 brown, grn & bl 1·40 30

585 Rance Barrage

586 Nurse tending wounded soldier (1859)

1966. Inauguration of Rance River Tidal Power Station.
1732 **585** 60c. slate, grn & brn . . 50 50

1966. Red Cross Fund. Cross in red.
1733 **586** 25c.+10c. green 45 45
1734 – 30c.+10c. blue 45 45
DESIGN: 30c. Nurse tending young girl (1966).

1966. Arms. As T **430**. Multicoloured.
1735 20c. "Saint-Lo" 10 10

588 Beaumarchais (playwright)

589 Congress Emblem

1967. Red Cross Fund.
1736 **588** 30c.+10c. violet & red 40 40
1737 – 30c.+10c. blue & indigo 40 45
1738 – 30c.+10c. purple & brn 40 40
1739 – 30c.+10c. violet & bl . . 45 45
PORTRAITS: No. 1737, Emile Zola (writer); No. 1738, A. Camus (writer); No. 1739, St. Francois de Sales (reformer).

1967. 3rd International Congress of European Broadcasting Union (U.E.R.).
1740 **589** 40c. red and blue 25 30

590 Postman of the Second Empire

591 Winter Olympics Emblem

1967. Stamp Day.
1741 **590** 25c.+10c. grn, red & bl 25 30

1967. French Art. As T **491**.
1742 1f. multicoloured 50 50
1743 1f. multicoloured 50 50
1744 1f. brown, blue and black 50 50
1745 1f. multicoloured 50 50
DESIGNS—HORIZ: No. 1742, "Old Juniet's Trap" (after H. Rousseau); No. 1745, "The Window-makers" (stained glass window, St. Madeleine's Church, Troyes). VERT: No. 1743, "Francois I" (after Jean Clouet); No. 1744, "The Bather" (Ingres).

1967. Publicity for Winter Olympic Games, Grenoble (1968).
1746 **591** 60c. red, lt blue & bl . . 35 45

592 French Pavilion

593 Cogwheels

1967. World Fair, Montreal.
1747 **592** 60c. green and blue . . . 35 35

1967. Europa.
1748 **593** 30c. blue and grey . . . 25 25
1749 60c. brown and blue . . 85 50

594 Nungesser, Coli and "L'Oiseau Blanc"

1967. 40th Anniv of Trans-Atlantic Flight Attempt by Nungesser and Coli.
1750 **594** 40c. blue, brown & pur 50 35

595 Great Bridge, Bordeaux

596 Gouin Mansion, Tours

1967. Inauguration of Great Bridge, Bordeaux.
1751 **595** 25c. black, olive & brn 25 25

1967. National Congress of Philatelic Societies, Tours.
1752 **596** 40c. brown, blue & red 60 55

597 Gaston Ramon (vaccine pioneer) and College Gates

1967. Bicentenary of Alfort Veterinary School.
1753 **597** 25c. brown, green & bl 25 20

598 Esnault-Pelterie, Rocket and Satellite

1967. 10th Death Anniv of Robert Esnault-Pelterie (rocket pioneer).
1754 **598** 60c. indigo and blue . . 50 50

1967. Tourist Publicity. As T **490**. Inscr "1967".
1755 50c. brown, dp blue & blue 35 15
1756 60c. brown, dp blue & blue 60 40
1757 70c. brown, blue and red . . 35 15
1758 75c. blue, red and brown . . 2·40 1·40
1759 95c. violet, green & blue . . 1·60 1·40
1760 1f. blue 65 10
1761 1f.50 red, blue and green . . 1·10 35
DESIGNS—VERT: 50c. Town Hall, St. Quentin (Aisne); 60c. Clock-tower and gateway, Vire (Calvados); 1f. Rodez Cathedral; 1f.50, Morlaix-views and carved buttress. HORIZ: 70c. St. Germain-en-Laye Chateau; 75c. La Baule; 95c. Boulogne-sur-Mer.

599 Orchids

600 Scales of Justice

1967. Orleans Flower Show.
1762 **599** 40c. red, purple & violet 85 70

1967. 9th Int Accountancy Congress, Paris.
1763 **600** 60c. brown, blue & pur 85 70

601 Servicemen and Cross of Lorraine

602 Marie Curie and Pitchblende

1967. 25th Anniv of Battle of Bir-Hakeim.
1764 **601** 25c. ultramarine, bl & brn 25 25

1967. Birth Centenary of Marie Curie.
1765 **602** 60c. ultramarine & blue 40 45

603 Lions Emblem

604 "Republique"

1967. 50th Anniv of Lions International.
1766 **603** 40c. violet and lake . . . 1·10 55

1967.
1767 **604** 25c. blue 50 40
1768 30c. purple 45 10
1843 30c. green 45 10
1768b 40c. red 45 10
See also No. 1882.

1967. History of France (2nd series). As T **582**, but inscr "1967".
1769 40c. ultramarine, grey & bl 40 40
1770 40c. black and slate 40 35
1771 60c. green and brown . . . 45 45
DESIGNS—HORIZ: No. 1769, Hugues Capet elected King of France. VERT: No. 1770, Philippe-Auguste at Bouvines; 1771, Saint-Louis receiving poor.

605 "Flautist"

606 Anniversary Medal

1967. Red Cross Fund. Ivories in Dieppe Museum. Cross in red.
1772 **605** 25c.+10c. brown & vio 50 60
1773 – 30c.+10c. brown & grn 50 60
DESIGNS: 30c. "Violinist".

1968. 50th Anniv of Postal Cheques Service.
1774 **606** 40c. bistre and green . . 25 25

607 Cross-country Skiing and Ski Jumping

608 Road Signs

1968. Winter Olympic Games, Grenoble.
1775 30c.+10c. brown, grey & red 40 40
1776 40c.+10c. pur, bis & dp pur 40 45
1777 60c.+20c. red, purple & grn 50 50
1778 75c.+25c. brown, grn & pur 65 75
1779 95c.+35c. brown, mve & bl 65 75
DESIGNS: 30c. Type **607**; 40c. Ice hockey; 60c. Olympic flame; 75c. Figure skating; 95c. Slalom.

1968. Road Safety.
1780 **608** 25c. red, blue and purple 25 30

609 Rural Postman of 1830

610 F. Couperin (composer) and Concert Instruments

1968. Stamp Day.
1781 **609** 25c.+10c. indigo, blue and red 25 30

1968. Red Cross Fund. Inscr "1968".
1782 **610** 30c.+10c. lilac & vio . . 25 30
1783 – 30c.+10c. brown & grn 25 30
1784 – 30c.+10c. red & brown 25 30
1785 – 30c.+10c. purple & lil . . 25 30
DESIGNS: No. 1783, General Desaix, and death scene at Marengo; No. 1784, Saint Pol-Roux (poet) and "Evocation of Golgotha"; No. 1785, Paul Claudel (poet) and "Joan of Arc".

1968. French Art. As T **491**.
1786 1f. multicoloured 50 55
1787 1f. multicoloured 65 55
1788 1f. olive and red 65 50
1789 1f. multicoloured 85 60
DESIGNS—HORIZ: No. 1786, Wall painting, Lascaux; No. 1787, "Arearea" (Gauguin). VERT: No. 1788, "La Danse" (relief by Bourdelle in Champs-Elysees Theatre, Paris); No. 1789, "Portrait of a Model" (Renoir).

611 Congress Palace, Royan

1968. World Co-operation Languages Conf, Royan.
1790 **611** 40c. blue, brown & grn . . . 45 30

612 Europa "Key"

613 Alain R. Le Sage

1968. Europa.
1791 **612** 30c. brown and purple . . 20 15
1792 60c. red and brown . . . 95 60

1968. 300th Birth Anniv of Le Sage (writer).
1793 **613** 40c. purple and blue . . 25 30

1968. Tourist Publicity. As T **490**, but inscr "1968".
1794 60c. blue, purple & green . . 65 60
DESIGN—HORIZ: 60c. Langeais Chateau.

614 Pierre Larousse (encyclopedist)

615 Forest Trees

1968. Larousse Commem.
1795 **614** 40c. brown & violet . . 35 40

1968. Link of Black and Rambouillet Forests.
1796 **615** 25c. brown, green & blue 40 40

616 Presentation of the Keys, and Map

1968. 650th Anniv of Papal Enclave, Valreas.
1797 **616** 60c. violet, bistre & brn 50 55

617 Louis XIV, and Arms of Flanders and France

1968. 300th Anniv of (First) Treaty of Aix-la-Chapelle.
1798 **617** 40c. lake, bistre & grey 25 25

618 Martrou Bridge, Rochefort

1968. Inauguration of Martrou Bridge.
1799 **618** 25c. black, brown & blue 25 30

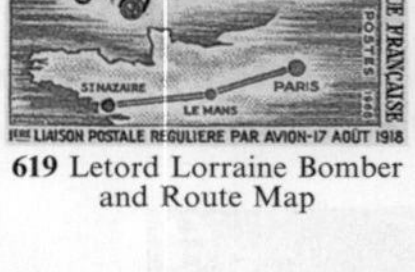

619 Letord Lorraine Bomber and Route Map

620 Tower of Constance, Aigues-Mortes

1968. 50th Anniv of 1st Regular Internal Airmail Service.
1800 **619** 25c. indigo, blue & red 50 45

1968. Bicent. of Release of Huguenot Prisoners.
1801 **620** 25c. purple, brown & bl 25 30

621 Cathedral and Old Bridge, Beziers

1968. National Congress of Philatelic Societies, Beziers.
1802 **621** 40c. ochre, green & blue 90 60

622 "Victory" and White Tower, Salonika

623 Louis XV and Arms of Corsica and France

1968. 50th Anniv of Armistice on Salonika Front.
1803 **622** 40c. purple & lt purple 25 25

1968. Bicent of Union of Corsica and France.
1804 **623** 25c. blue, green & blk 25 25

624 Relay-racing

626 "Ball of the Little White Beds" (opera) and Bailby

625 Polar Landscape

1968. Olympic Games, Mexico.
1805 **624** 40c. blue, green & brn 50 50

1968. French Polar Exploration.
1806 **625** 40c. turq, red & blue . . 40 45

1968. 50th Anniv of "Little White Beds" Children's Hospital Charity.
1807 **626** 40c. red, orge & brn . . 25 30

627 "Angel of Victory" over Arc de Triomphe

628 "Spring"

1968. 50th Anniv of Armistice on Western Front.
1808 **627** 25c. blue and red 25 30

1968. History of France (3rd series). Designs as T **582**, but inscr "1968".
1809 40c. green, grey and red . . 40 45
1810 40c. blue, green & brown . . 40 45
1811 60c. brown, blue & ultram 60 55
DESIGNS—HORIZ: No. 1809, Philip the Good presiding over States-General. VERT: No. 1810, Death of Du Guesclin; No. 1811, Joan of Arc.

1968. Red Cross Fund. Cross in red.
1812 **628** 25c.+10c. blue & vio . . 35 45
1813 – 30c.+10c. red & brown 35 45
DESIGN: 30c. "Autumn".
See also Nos. 1853/4.

1969. Tourist Publicity. Similar to T **490** but inscr "1969".
1814 45c. green, brown and blue 35 20
1815 70c. brown, indigo and blue 40 40
1816 80c. brown, purple & bistre 40 15
1817 85c. grey, blue and green . . 1·00 1·10
1818 1f.15 lt brown, brown & blue 95 75
DESIGNS—HORIZ: 45c. Brou Church, Bourg-en-Bresse (Ain); 70c. Hautefort Chateau; 80f. Vouglans Dam, Jura; 85f. Chantilly Chateau; 1f.15, La Trinite-sur-Mer, Morbihan.

1969. French Art. As T **491**.
1819 1f. brown and black 55 55
1820 1f. multicoloured 55 55
1821 1f. multicoloured 55 55
1822 1f. multicoloured . . . . . 1·00 75
DESIGNS—VERT: No. 1819, "February" (bas-relief, Amiens Cathedral); No. 1820, "Philippe le Bon" (Rogier de la Pasture, called Van der Weyden); No. 1822, "The Circus" (Georges Seurat). HORIZ: No. 1821, "Savin and Cyprien appearing before Ladicius" (Romanesque painting, Church of St. Savin, Vienne).

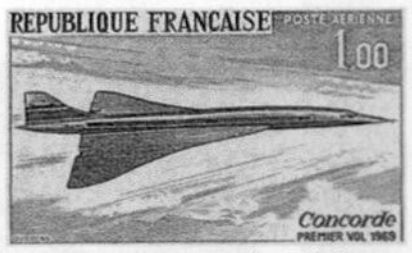

629 Concorde in Flight

1969. Air. 1st Flight of Concorde.
1823 **629** 1f. indigo and blue . . . 90 75

630 Postal Horse-bus of 1890

1969. Stamp Day.
1824 **630** 30c.+10c. green, brown and black 25 30

631 A. Roussel (composer)

632 Irises

1969. Red Cross Fund. Celebrities.
1825 **631** 50c.+10c. blue 50 60
1826 – 50c.+10c. red 50 60
1827 – 50c.+10c. grey 50 60
1828 – 50c.+10c. brown 60 65
1829 – 50c.+10c. purple 60 65
1830 – 50c.+10c. green 60 65
PORTRAITS: No. 1826, General Marceau; No. 1827, C. A. Sainte-Beuve (writer); No. 1828, Marshal Lannes; No. 1829, G. Cuvier (anatomist and naturalist); No. 1830, A. Gide (writer).

1969. International Flower Show, Paris.
1831 **632** 45c. multicoloured . . . 40 45

633 Colonnade

1969. Europa.
1832 **633** 40c. mauve 25 15
1833 70c. blue 40 35

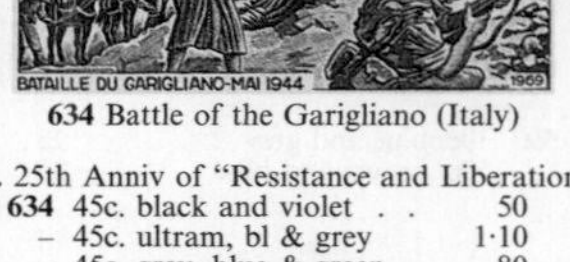

634 Battle of the Garigliano (Italy)

1969. 25th Anniv of "Resistance and Liberation".
1834 **634** 45c. black and violet . . 50 55
1835 – 45c. ultram, bl & grey 1·10 55
1836 – 45c. grey, blue & green 80 70
1837 – 45c. brown and grey . . 1·10 60
1838 – 45c. indigo, blue & red 1·10 75
1839 – 45c.+10c. green & grey 1·10 1·30
1840 – 70c.+10c. grn, pur & brn 3·00 3·25
DESIGNS—VERT: No. 1835, Parachutists and Commandos ("D-Day Landings"); 1836, Memorial and Resistance fighters (Battle of Mont Mouchet). HORIZ: No. 1837, Troops storming beach (Provence Landings); 1838, French pilot, Soviet mechanic and Yakovlev Yak-9 fighter aircraft (Normandy-Niemen Squadron); 1839, General Leclerc, troops and Les Invalides (Liberation of Paris); 1840, As No. 1839 but showing Strasbourg Cathedral (Liberation of Strasbourg).

635 "Miners" (I.L.O. Monument, Geneva) and Albert Thomas (founder)

636 Chalons-sur-Marne

1969. 50th Anniv of I.L.O.
1841 **635** 70c. brn, bl & dp brn . . 40 45

1969. National Congress of Philatelic Societies, Chalons-sur-Marne.
1842 **636** 45c. ochre, blue & grn 45 45

637 Canoeing

639 "Diamond Crystal" in Rain Drop

638 Napoleon as Young Officer, and Birthplace

1969. World Kayak-Canoeing Championships, Bourg-St. Maurice.
1844 **637** 70c. brown, green & blue 45 45

1969. Birth Bicent of Napoleon Bonaparte.
1845 **638** 70c. grn, violet & blue 45 50

1969. European Water Charter.
1846 **639** 70c. black, green & bl 55 45

640 Mouflon

641 Aerial View of College

1969. Nature Conservation.
1847 **640** 45c. black, brn & grn . . 90 90

1969. College of Arts and Manufactures, Chatenay-Malabry.
1848 **641** 70c. grn, orge & dp grn 50 50

642 "Le Redoutable"

1969. 1st French Nuclear Submarine "Le Redoutable".
1849 **642** 70c. green, emer & bl . . 40 45

1969. History of France (4th series). As T **582** but inscr "1969".
1850 80c. bistre, brown & green 50 50
1851 80c. brown, blk & lt brn . . 50 50
1852 80c. blue, black and violet 55 55
DESIGNS—HORIZ: No. 1850, Louis XI and Charles the Bold; 1852, Henry IV and Edict of Nantes, VERT: No. 1851, Bayard at the Battle of Brescia.

1969. Red Cross Fund. Paintings by N. Mignard. As T **628**. Cross in red.
1853 40c.+15c. brown & choc . . 50 60
1854 40c.+15c. blue & violet . . 50 60
DESIGNS: No. 1853, "Summer"; 1854, "Winter".

643 Gerbault aboard "Firecrest"

1970. Alain Gerbault's World Voyage, 1923–29.
1855 **643** 70c. indigo, grey & blue 70 70

644 Gendarmerie Badge and Activities

1970. National Gendarmerie.
1856 **644** 45c. blue, green & brown 1·30 55

645 L. Le Vau (architect)

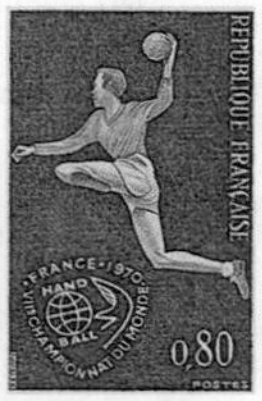

646 Handball Player

1970. Red Cross Fund.
1857 **645** 40c.+10c. lake 50 65
1858 – 40c.+10c. blue 50 65
1859 – 40c.+10c. green 50 65
1860 – 40c.+10c. brown 50 65
1861 – 40c.+10c. slate 50 65
1862 – 40c.+10c. blue 50 65
DESIGNS: No. 1858, Prosper Merimee (writer); 1859, Philbert de l'Orme (architect); 1860, Edouard Branly (scientist); 1861, Maurice de Broglie (physicist); 1862, Alexandre Dumas (pere) (writer).

1970. 7th World Handball Championship.
1863 **646** 80c. green 45 50

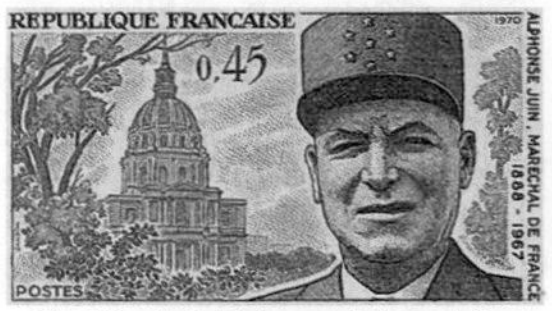

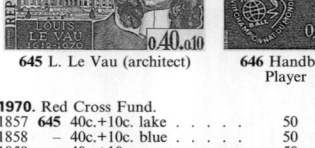

647 Marshal Alphonse Juin and Les Invalides, Paris

1970. Marshal Juin Commem.
1864 **647** 45c. brown and blue . . 35 35

648 Gas-turbine Monorail Aerotrain "Orleans 1-80"

649 Postman of 1830 and Paris Scene

1970. 1st Aerotrain in Service.
1865 **648** 80c. drab and violet . . 65 55

1970. Stamp Day.
1866 **649** 40c.+10c. black, blue and red 45 50

650 P.-J. Pelletier and J. B. Caventou with Formula

1970. 150th Anniv of Discovery of Quinine.
1870 **650** 50c. green, mauve & bl 40 45

651 Greater Flamingo

652 Rocket and Dish Aerial

1970. Nature Conservation Year.
1871 **651** 45c. mauve, grey & grn 35 30

1970. Launching of "Diamant B" Rocket from Guyana.
1872 **652** 45c. green 60 55

653 "Health and Sickness"

654 "Flaming Sun"

1970. W.H.O. "Fight Cancer" Day (7th April).
1873 **653** 40c.+10c. mauve, brown and blue 35 45

1970. Europa.
1874 **654** 40c. red 30 30
1875 80c. blue 50 50

655 Marshal de Lattre de Tassigny and Armistice Meeting

1970. 25th Anniv of Berlin Armistice.
1876 **655** 40c.+10c. blue & turq . . 85 85

1970. French Art. As T **491**.
1877 1f. multicoloured 50 55
1878 1f. chestnut 60 55
1879 1f. multicoloured . . . . . 1·20 80
1880 1f. multicoloured . . . . . 1·10 80
DESIGNS—VERT: No. 1877, 15-cent. Savoy Primitive painting on wood; No. 1880, "The Ballet-dancer" (Degas). HORIZ: No. 1878, "The Triumph of Flora" (sculpture by J. B. Carpeaux); No. 1879, "Diana's Return from the Hunt" (F. Boucher).

656 Arms of Lens, Miner's Lamp and Pithead

1970. 43rd French Federation of Philatelic Societies Congress, Lens.
1881 **656** 40c. red 25 30

657 "Republique" and Perigueux

658 Javelin-thrower in Wheel-chair

1970. Transfer of French Govt Printing Works to Perigueux.
1882 **657** 40c. red 40 40
The above stamp and label which together comprise No. 1882 were issued together se-tenant in sheets for which special printing plates were laid down. The stamp is virtually indistinguishable from the normal 40c. definitive, No. 1768b.

1970. Tourist Publicity. As T **490**, but inscr "1970".
1883 50c. purple, blue & green . . 35 20
1884 95c. brown, red and olive 1·70 1·20
1885 1f. green, blue and red . . . 45 15

DESIGNS: 50c. Diamond Rock, Martinique; 95c. Chancelade Abbey (Dordogne); 1f. Gosier Island, Guadeloupe.

1970. World Games for the Physically Handicapped, St.-Etienne.
1886 **658** 45c. red, green & blue 45 45

659 Hand and Broken Chain

660 Observatory and Nebula

1970. 25th Anniv of Liberation from Concentration Camps.
1887 **659** 45c. brown, ultram & bl 45 40

1970. Haute-Provence Observatory.
1888 **660** 1f.30 violet, blue & grn 2·20 1·40

661 Pole Vaulting

663 Bath-House, Arc-et-Senans (Doubs)

662 Didier Daurat, Raymond Vanier and Douglas DC-4

1970. 1st European Junior Athletic Championships, Paris.
1889 **661** 45c. indigo, blue & purple 50 45

1970. Air. Pioneer Aviators.
1890 **662** 5f. brown, green & blue 1·90 25
1891 – 10f. grey, violet & red 4·00 45
1892 – 15f. grey, mauve & brn 6·00 95
1893 – 20f. indigo and blue . . 8·00 95
DESIGNS: 10f. Helene Boucher, Maryse Hilsz and De Havilland Gipsy Moth and Caudron aircraft; 15f. Henri Guillaumet, Paul Codos, "Lieutenant de Vaisseau Paris" (flying boat) and wreck of Potez 25A2 airplane; 20f. Jean Mermoz, Antoine de Saint-Exupery and Concorde airplane.

1970. Royal Salt Springs, Chaux (founded by N. Ledoux).
1895 **663** 80c. brown, grn & bl . . 1·50 85

1970. History of France (5th series). As T **582**, but inscr "1970".
1896 45c. mauve, grey & black 85 60
1897 45c. brown, green & yellow 70 60
1898 45c. grey, brown & orange 70 70
DESIGNS: No. 1896, Richelieu and siege of La Rochelle, 1628; 1897, King Louis XIV; 1898, King Louis XV at Battle of Fontenoy (after painting by H. Vernet).

664 U.N. Emblem, New York Headquarters and Palais des Nations, Geneva

1970. 25th Anniv of United Nations.
1899 **664** 80c. violet, green & blue 50 50

665 Bordeaux and "Ceres" Stamp

1970. Centenary of Bordeaux "Ceres" Stamp Issue.
1900 **665** 80c. violet and blue . . . 50 50

666 Col. Denfert-Rochereau and "Lion of Belfort" (after Bartholdi)

1970. Centenary of Belfort Siege.
1901 **666** 45c. blue, brown & grn 40 45

667 "Lord and Lady" (c. 1500)

668 "Marianne"

1970. Red Cross Fund. Frescoes from Dissay Chapel, Vienne. Cross in red.
1902 **667** 40c.+15c. green 70 75
1903 – 40c.+15c. red 70 75
DESIGN: No. 1903, "Angel with instruments of mortification".

1971.
1904 **668** 45c. blue 50 10
1905 50c. red 20 10
1904ap 60c. green . . . . . . 1·90 25
1905bp 80c. red 50 20
1904b 80c. green 40 20
1905d 1f. red 45 40

669 Balloon "Ville d'Orleans" leaving Paris

670 Ice Skaters

1971. Air. Centenary of Paris Balloon Post.
1907 **669** 95c. multicoloured . . . 95 90

1971. French Art. As T **491**.
1908 1f. brown . . . . 1·00 75
1909 1f. multicoloured 80 70
1910 1f. multicoloured 65 65
DESIGNS: No. 1908, "St. Matthew" (sculpture, Strasbourg Cathedral); No. 1909, "The Winnower" (Millet); No. 1910, "Songe Creux" (G. Rouault).

1971. World Ice Skating Championships, Lyon.
1911 **670** 80c. ultramarine, blue and indigo 50 55

671 Diver and Bathysphere

672 General D. Brosset and Fourviere Basilica, Lyon

1971. "Oceanexpo" Exhibition, Bordeaux.
1912 **671** 80c. turquoise & blue . . 45 45

1971. Red Cross Fund. Celebrities.
1913 **672** 50c.+10c. brown & grn 65 65
1914 – 50c.+10c. brn & choc . . 75 65
1915 – 50c.+10c. brown & red 75 60
1916 – 50c.+10c. lilac & blue . . 75 60
1917 – 50c.+10c. pur & plum 85 75
1918 – 50c.+10c. bl & indigo . . 85 75
DESIGNS: No. 1914, Esprit Auber (composer) and manuscript of "Fra Diavolo"; 1915, Victor Grignard (chemist) and Nobel Prize for Chemistry; 1916, Henri Farman (aviation pioneer) and Farman Voisin No. 1 bis (airplane); 1917, General C. Delestraint (Resistance leader) and "Secret Army" proclamation; 1918, J. Robert-Houdin (magician) and levitation act.

673 Field Post Office, World War I

1971. Stamp Day.
1919 **673** 50c.+10c. blue, brown and bistre 55 55

674 Barque "Antoinette"

1971. French Sailing Ships.
1920 **674** 80c. violet, indigo & bl 1·20 1·00
See also Nos. 1967, 2011 and 2100.

675 Chamois

676 Basilica of Santa Maria, Venice

1971. Inaug of Western Pyrenees National Park.
1921 **675** 65c. brown, bl & choc 60 60

1971. History of France (6th series). As T **582** but inscr "1971".
1922 45c. purple, blue & red . . 55 60
1923 45c. red, brown & blue . . 60 60
1924 65c. brown, purple & blue 90 95
DESIGNS: No. 1922, Cardinal, noble and commoner (Opening of the States-General, 1789); No. 1923, Battle of Valmy, 1792; No. 1924, Fall of the Bastille, 1789.

1971. Europa.
1925 **676** 50c. brown and blue . . 45 40
1926 – 80c. purple 55 55
DESIGN: 80c. Europa chain.

677 View of Grenoble

678 A.F.R. Emblem and Town

1971. 44th French Federation of Philatelic Societies Congress, Grenoble.
1927 **677** 50c. red, pink & brown 1·00 30

1971. 25th Anniv (1970) of Rural Family Aid.
1928 **678** 40c. blue, violet & green 30 30

1971. Tourist Publicity. As T **490**, but inscr "1971".
1929 60c. black, blue and green 35 20
1930 65c. black, violet & brown 55 30
1931 90c. brown, green & ochre 45 20
1932 1f.10 brown, blue & green 70 70
1933 1f.40 purple, blue & green 65 30
DESIGNS—VERT: 60c. Sainte Chapelle, Riom; 65c. Church and fountain, Dole; 90c. Gate-tower and houses, Riquewihr; 1f.40, Ardeche gorges. HORIZ: 1f.10, Fortress, Sedan.

679 Bourbon Palace, Paris

1971. 59th Interparliamentary Union Conference, Paris.
1934 **679** 90c. blue 80 70

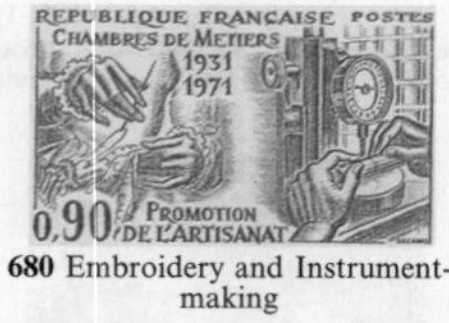

680 Embroidery and Instrument-making

1971. 40th Anniv of 1st Meeting of Crafts Guilds Association.
1935 **680** 90c. purple and red . . . 55 45

681 Reunion Chameleon

682 De Gaulle in Uniform (June 1940)

1971. Nature Conservation.
1936 **681** 60c. green, brn & yell . . 1·00 85

1971. 1st Death Anniv of General Charles de Gaulle.
1937 **682** 50c. black . . . . 1·20 95
1938 – 50c. blue . . . . 1·20 95
1939 – 50c. red . . . . 1·20 95
1940 – 50c. black . . . . 1·20 95
DESIGNS: No. 1938, De Gaulle at Brazzaville, 1944; No. 1939, Liberation of Paris, 1944; No. 1940, De Gaulle as President of the French Republic, 1970.

683 Baron Portal (1st President) and First Assembly

1971. 150th Anniv of National Academy of Medicine.
1941 **683** 45c. plum and purple . . 40 40

684 "Young Girl with Little Dog"

685 King Penguin, Map and "Le Mascarin" (Dutresne)

1971. Red Cross Fund. Paintings by J.-B. Greuze. Cross in red.
1942 **684** 30c.+10c. blue 70 80
1943 – 50c.+10c. red 70 80
DESIGN: No. 1943. "The Dead Bird".

1972. French Art. As T **491**. Multicoloured.
1944 1f. "L'Etude" (portrait of a young girl) (Fragonard) (vert) 95 95
1945 1f. "Women in a Garden" (Monet) (vert) . . . . 1·80 85
1946 2f. "St. Peter presenting Pierre de Bourbon" (Master of Moulins) (vert) 1·80 1·40
1947 2f. "The Barges" (A. Derain) . . . . 2·75 1·70

1972. Bicentenary of Discovery of Crozet Islands and Kerguelen (French Southern and Antarctic Territories).
1948 **685** 90c. black, blue & orge 65 60

686 Skier and Emblem

687 Aristide Berges (hydro-electric engineer)

1972. Winter Olympic Games, Sapporo, Japan.
1949 **686** 90c. red and green 60 45

1972. Red Cross Fund. Celebrities.
1950 **687** 50c.+10c. black, emerald and green 70 90
1951 – 50c.+10c. black, blue and ultramarine . . . 70 90
1952 – 50c.+10c. black, purple and plum 70 90
1953 – 50c.+10c. black, red and crimson 70 90
1954 – 50c.+10c. black, chestnut and brown 95 90
1955 – 50c.+10c. black, orange and red 85 90

DESIGNS: No. 1951, Paul de Chomedey, Sieur de Maisonneuve (founder of Montreal); No. 1952, Edouard Belin (communications scientist); No. 1953, Louis Bleriot (pioneer airman); No. 1954, Theophile Gautier (writer); No. 1955, Admiral Francois de Grasse.

688 Rural Postman of 1894

689 Heart and W.H.O. Emblems

1972. Stamp Day.
1956 **688** 50c.+10c. blue, drab and yellow . . . . 1·00 1·00

1972. World Heart Month.
1957 **689** 45c. red, orange & grey 40 45

1972. Tourist Publicity. As Type **490**, but inscr "1972".
1958 1f. brown and yellow . . . 60 30
1959 1f.20 blue and brown . . . 60 25
1960 2f. purple and green 80 30
1961 3f.50 brown, red and blue 1·50 55
DESIGNS—VERT: 1f. Red deer stag and forest, Sologne Nature Reserve. HORIZ: 1f.20, Charlieu Abbey; 2f. Bazoches-du-Morvand Chateau; 3f.50, St. Just Cathedral, Narbonne.

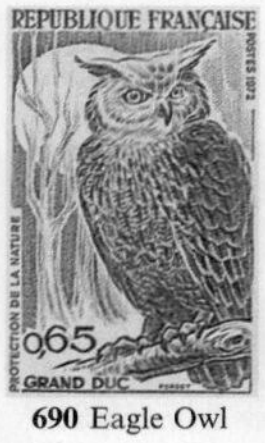

690 Eagle Owl

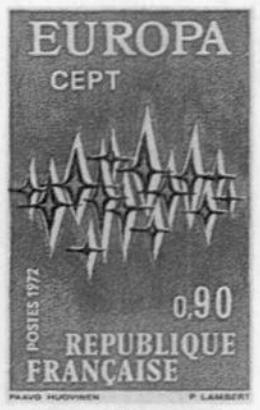

691 "Communications"

1972. Nature Conservation.
1962 – 60c. black, green & bl 2·20 1·30
1963 **690** 65c. brown, bis & grey 95 80
DESIGN—HORIZ: 60c. Atlantic salmon.

1972. Europa.
1964 – 50c. purple, yellow & brn 40 30
1965 **691** 90c. multicoloured . . . 55 55
DESIGN: 50c. Aix-la-Chapelle Cathedral.

692 "Tree of Hearts"

693 "Cote d'Emeraude" Grand Banks Fishing barquentine

1972. 20th Anniv of Post Office Employees' Blood-donors Association.
1966 **692** 40c. red 35 35

1972. French Sailing Ships.
1967 **693** 90c. blue, green & orge 1·10 90

694 St.-Brieuc Cathedral (from lithograph of 1840)

1972. 45th French Federation of Philatelic Societies Congress, St.-Brieuc.
1968 **694** 50c. red 35 35

695 Hand and Code Emblems

696 Old and New Communications

1972. Postal Code Campaign.
1969 **695** 30c. red, black & green 15 15
1970 50c. yellow, black & red 35 20

1972. 21st World Congress of Post Office Trade Union Federation (I.P.T.T.), Paris.
1971 **696** 45c. blue and grey . . . 35 30

697 Hurdling

698 Hikers on Road

1972. Olympic Games, Munich.
1972 **697** 1f. green 60 40

1972. "Walking Tourism Year".
1973 **698** 40c. multicoloured . . . 1·50 1·00

699 Cycling

701 Nicholas Desgenettes (military physician)

700 J.-F. Champollion and Hieroglyphics

1972. World Cycling Championships.
1974 **699** 1f. brown, purple & grey 1·80 1·00

1972. History of France (7th series). The Directory. As T **582** but dated "1972".
1975 45c. purple, olive & green 40 50
1976 60c. blue, red and black . . 80 65
1977 65c. purple, brown & blue 90 85
DESIGNS—VERT: 45c. "Incroyables et Merveilleuses" (fashionable Parisians), 1794; 60c. Napoleon Bonaparte at the Bridge of Arcole, 1796; 65c. Discovery of antiquities, Egyptian Expedition, 1798.

1972. 150th Anniv of Champollion's Translation of Egyptian Hieroglyphics.
1978 **700** 90c. brown, blue & blk 50 45

1972. Red Cross Fund. Doctors of the 1st Empire. Cross in red.
1979 **701** 30c.+10c. green and bronze 70 80
1980 – 50c.+10c. red & brown 70 75
DESIGN: No. 1980, Francois Broussais (pathologist).

702 St. Theresa and Porch of Notre Dame, Alencon

703 Anthurium

1973. Birth Centenary of St. Theresa of Lisieux.
1981 **702** 1f. indigo & turquoise 65 55

1973. Martinique Flower Cultivation.
1982 **703** 50c. multicoloured . . . 40 45

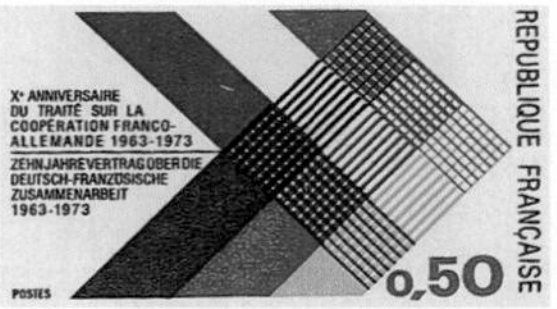

704 National Colours of France and West Germany

1973. 10th Anniv of Franco-German Co-operation Treaty.
1983 **704** 50c. multicoloured . . . 40 45

705 Polish Immigrants

1973. 50th Anniv of Polish Immigration.
1984 **705** 40c. red, green & brown 25 30

1973. French Art. As T **491**.
1985 2f. multicoloured . . . . . 1·60 1·30
1986 2f. red and yellow . . . . . 1·60 1·40
1987 2f. maroon and brown . . . 1·60 1·50
1988 2f. multicoloured . . . . . 1·90 1·30
DESIGNS: No. 1985, "The Last Supper" (carved capital, St. Austremoine Church, Issoire); No. 1986, "Study of a Kneeling Woman" (Charles le Brun); No. 1987, Wood-carving, Moutier d'Ahun; No. 1988, "La Finette" (girl with lute) (Watteau).

706 Admiral G. de Coligny (Protestant leader)
707 Mail Coach, c. 1835

1973. Red Cross Fund. Celebrities' Annivs.
1989 **706** 50c.+10c. blue, brown and purple . . . . . 85 1·10
1990 – 50c.+10c. mauve, grey and orange . . . . . 85 1·10
1991 – 50c.+10c. green, purple and yellow . . . . . 85 1·10
1992 – 50c.+10c. red, purple and bistre . . . . . 85 1·10
1993 – 50c.+10c. grey, purple and brown . . . . . 85 1·10
1994 – 50c.+10c. brown, lilac and blue . . . . . 95 1·00
1995 – 50c.+10c. blue, purple and brown . . . . . 95 1·00
DESIGNS: No. 1989, 400th death anniv (1972); 1990, Ernest Renan (philologist and writer, 150th birth anniv); 1991, Santos-Dumont (pioneer aviator, birth centenary); 1992, Colette (writer, birth centenary); 1993, Duguay-Trouin (naval hero, 300th birth anniv); 1994, Louis Pasteur (scientist, 150th birth anniv 1972); 1995, Tony Garnier (architect, 25th death anniv).

1973. Stamp Day.
1996 **707** 50c.+10c. blue 45 50

708 Tuileries Palace and New Telephone Exchange
709 Town Hall, Brussels

1973. French Technical Achievements.
1997 **708** 45c. blue, grey & green 25 30
1998 – 90c. black, blue & pur 65 50
1999 – 3f. black, blue & grn . . 1·50 1·00
DESIGNS: 90c. Francois I Lock, Le Havre; 3f. Airbus Industrie A300B2-100 airplane.

1973. Europa.
2000 **709** 50c. brown and red . . . 35 25
2001 – 90c. multicoloured . . . 1·60 85
DESIGN—HORIZ: 90c. Europa "Posthorn".

710 Guadeloupe Racoon

1973. Nature Conservation.
2002 **710** 40c. mauve, grn & pur 40 30
2003 – 60c. black, red & blue 55 55
DESIGN: 60c. White storks.

711 Masonic Emblem
712 Globe and "Heart"

1973. Bicentenary of Masonic Grand Orient Lodge of France.
2004 **711** 90c. blue and purple . . 55 45

1973. Tourist Publicity. As T **490**, but inscr "1973".
2005 60c. blue, green and light blue 35 15
2006 65c. violet and red 35 25
2007 90c. brown, dp blue & bl . . 40 15
2008 1f. green, brown and blue 40 15
DESIGNS—VERT: 60c. Waterfall, Doubs; 1f. Clos-Luce Palace, Amboise; HORIZ: 65c. Palace of the Dukes of Burgundy, Dijon; 90c. Gien Chateau.

1973. 50th Anniv of Academy of Overseas Sciences.
2009 **712** 1f. green, brown & pur 50 45

713 Racing-car at Speed
715 Bell-tower, Toulouse

714 Five-masted Barque "France II"

1973. 50th Anniv of Le Mans 24-hour Endurance Race.
2010 **713** 60c. blue and brown . . 70 55

1973. French Sailing Ships.
2011 **714** 90c. lt blue, indigo & bl 1·10 75

1973. 46th French Federation of Philatelic Societies Congress, Toulouse.
2012 **715** 50c. brown and violet . . 40 30

716 Dr. G. Hansen
717 Eugene Ducretet (radio pioneer)

1973. Centenary of Hansen's Identification of Leprosy Bacillus.
2013 **716** 45c. brown, olive & grn 35 25

1973. 75th Anniv of Eiffel Tower–Pantheon Experimental Radio Link.
2014 **717** 1f. green and red 55 55

718 Moliere as "Sganarelle"
719 Pierre Bourgoin (parachutist) and Philippe Kieffer (Marine Commando)

1973. 300th Death Anniv of Moliere (playwright).
2015 **718** 1f. brown and red . . . 60 50

1973. Heroes of World War II.
2016 **719** 1f. claret, blue & red . . 50 45

1973. History of France (8th series). As Type **582**, but inscr "1973".
2017 45c. purple, grey and blue 45 45
2018 60c. brown, bistre & green 55 65
2019 1f. red, brown and green . . 65 65
DESIGNS—HORIZ: 45c. Napoleon and Portalis (Preparation of Civil Code, 1800–1804); 60c. Paris Industrial Exhibition, Les Invalides, 1806. VERT: 1f. "The Coronation of Napoleon, 1804" (David).

720 Eternal Flame, Arc de Triomphe
721 "Mary Magdalene"

1973. 50th Anniv of Tomb of the Unknown Soldier, Arc de Triomphe.
2020 **720** 40c. red, blue and lilac 40 35

1973. Red Cross Fund. Tomb Figures, Tonnerre.
2021 **721** 30c.+10c. grn & red . . 55 65
2022 – 50c.+10c. blk & red . . 65 65
DESIGN: 50c. Female saint.

722 Weathervane
723 Figure and Human Rights Emblem

1973. 50th Anniv of French Chambers of Agriculture.
2023 **722** 65c. black, blue & green 40 50

1973. 25th Anniv of Declaration of Human Rights.
2024 **723** 45c. brown, orge & red 25 30

724 Facade of Museum
725 Exhibition Emblem

1973. Opening of New Postal Museum Building.
2025 **724** 50c. lt brown, pur & brn 25 30

1974. "ARPHILA 75" International Stamp Exhibition, Paris.
2026 **725** 50c. brown, blue & pur 25 30

726 St. Louis-Marie Grignion de Montfort
727 Automatic Letter-sorting

1974. Red Cross Fund. Celebrities.
2027 **726** 50c.+10c. brown, green and red . . . . 1·10 1·10
2028 – 50c.+10c. red, purple and blue 85 90
2029 – 80c.+15c. purple, deep purple & blue 80 90
2030 – 80c.+15c. blue, black and purple 80 90
DESIGNS: No. 2028, Francis Poulenc (composer); No. 2029, Jean Giraudoux (writer); No. 2030, Jules Barbey d'Aurevilly (writer).

1974. Stamp Day.
2031 **727** 50c.+10c. brn, red & grn 40 45

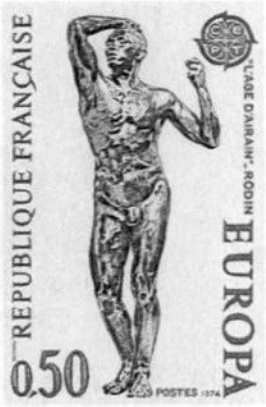

728 Concorde over Airport
730 "The Brazen Age" (Rodin)

729 French Alps and Gentian

1974. Opening of Charles de Gaulle Airport, Roissy.
2032 **728** 60c. violet and brown . . 40 45

1974. "Arphila 1975" Stamp Exhibition. French Art. As Type **491**. Multicoloured.
2033 2f. "Cardinal Richelieu" (P. de Champaigne) . . . . 1·40 1·40
2034 2f. "Abstract after Original Work" (J. Miro) . . . . 1·70 1·60
2035 2f. "Loing Canal" (A. Sisley) . . . . 1·70 1·60
2036 2f. "Homage to Nicolas Fouquet" (E. de Mathieu) 1·70 1·60

1974. Centenary of French Alpine Club.
2037 **729** 65c. vio, grn & blue . . 45 45

1974. Europa. Sculptures.
2038 **730** 50c. black and purple . . 35 30
2039 – 90c. brown and bistre . . 70 60
DESIGN—HORIZ: 90c. "The Expression" (reclining woman) (A. Maillol).

731 Shipwreck and "Pierre Loti" (lifeboat)

1974. French Lifeboat Service.
2040 **731** 90c. blue, red & brown 50 40

732 Council Headquarters, Strasbourg

1974. 25th Anniv of Council of Europe.
2041 **732** 45c. blue, lt blue & brn 40 40

733 "Cornucopia of St. Florent" (Corsica)

1974. Tourist Publicity.
2042 – 65c. brown and green . . 40 45
2043 – 1f.10 brown & green . . 55 50
2044 – 2f. purple and blue . . . 80 30
2045 **733** 3f. blue, red & green . . 1·00 50
DESIGNS—As Type **490**. HORIZ: 65c. Salers; 1f.10, Lot Valley; VERT: 2f. Basilica of St. Nicolas-de-Port.

734 European Bison

1974. Nature Conservation.
2046 **734** 40c. purple, bl & brn . . 40 30
2047 – 65c. grey, green & blk 40 45
DESIGN: 65c. Giant Armadillo of Guiana.

735 Normandy Landings

1974. 30th Anniv of Liberation.
2048 **735** 45c. blue, red & green 65 60
2049 – 1f. red, brown & violet 50 50
2050 – 1f. brown, blk & red . . 65 65
2051 – 1f.+10c. brn, grn & blk 75 85
DESIGNS—HORIZ: No. 2050, Resistance medal and torch; 2051, Order of Liberation and honoured towns. VERT: No. 2049, General Koenig and liberation monuments.

736 Colmar

737 Board and Chess Pieces

1974. 47th Congress of French Philatelic Societies.
2052 **736** 50c. red, purple & brn 25 35

1974. 21st Chess Olympiad, Nice.
2053 **737** 1f. red, brown & blue . . 65 45

738 Commemorative Medallion

1974. 300th Anniv of "Hotel des Invalides".
2054 **738** 40c. black, brn & bl . . 25 30

739 French Turbotrain TGV 001

1974. Completion of Turbotrain TGV 001 Project.
2055 **739** 60c. red, black & blue 95 75

740 "Nuclear Power"

1974. Completion of Phenix Nuclear Generator.
2056 **740** 65c. brown, mve & red 40 45

741 Peacocks with Letter

1974. Centenary of Universal Postal Union.
2057 **741** 1f.20 red, green & blue 45 50

742 Copernicus and Heliocentric System

1974. 500th Birth Anniv (1973) of Nicolas Copernicus (astronomer).
2058 **742** 1f.20 mauve, brn & blk 45 45

743 Children playing on Beach

744 Dr. Albert Schweitzer

1974. Red Cross Fund. Seasons. Cross in red.
2059 **743** 60c.+15c. red, brown and blue 55 65
2060 – 80c.+15c. red, brown and blue 65 80
DESIGN: 80c. Child in garden looking through window.
See also 2098/9.

1975. Birth Centenary of Dr. Albert Schweitzer.
2061 **744** 80c.+20c. brown, red and green 55 75

1975. Tourist Publicity. As Type **490** but inscr "1975".
2062 85c. blue and brown 45 30
2063 1f.20 brown, dp brn & bl 40 20
2064 1f.40 blue, brown & green 55 35
DESIGNS—HORIZ: 85c. Law Courts, Rouen; 1f.40, Chateau de Rochechouart. VERT: 1f.20, St. Pol-de-Leon.

745 Little Egrets

746 Edmond Michelet (politician)

1975. Nature Conservation.
2065 **745** 70c. brown and blue . . 40 50

1975. Precancels. As T **538**, but inscribed "France".
2065a 42c. red and orange . . . 2·75 2·10
2065b 48c. red and turquoise . . 2·50 2·00
2065c 50c. brown & turquoise . . 2·50 2·00
2065d 52c. brown and red . . . 1·50 1·10
2065e 60c. brown and mauve . . 3·50 3·50
2065f 62c. brown & mauve . . . 2·20 2·20
2065g 70c. red and mauve . . . 4·50 4·50
2065h 90c. brown and pink . . . 4·50 4·50
2065i 95c. brown and sepia . . . 2·75 2·10
2065j 1f.35 red and green . . . . 4·50 4·50
2065k 1f.60 brown and violet . . 7·00 7·00
2065l 1f.70 brown and blue . . . 5·00 5·00
See note below No. 432 (1920).

1975. Red Cross Fund. Celebrities.
2066 **746** 80c.+20c. ind & bl . . . 55 60
2067 – 80c.+20c. blk & bl . . . 80 90
2068 – 80c.+20c. blk & bl . . . 55 60
2069 – 80c.+20c. blk, turq & bl 55 65
DESIGNS—VERT: No. 2067, Robert Schuman (statesman); No. 2068, Eugene Thomas (former Telecommunications Minister). HORIZ: No, 2069, Andre Siegfried (geographer and humanist).

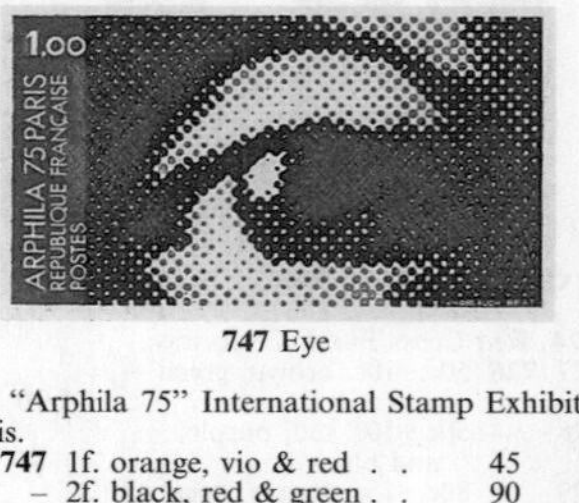
747 Eye

1975. "Arphila 75" International Stamp Exhibition, Paris.
2070 **747** 1f. orange, vio & red . . 45 50
2071 – 2f. black, red & green . . 90 75
2072 – 3f. green, grey & brown 1·10 1·00
2073 – 4f. green, red & orange 1·70 1·60
MS2074 152×143 mm. 2f. blue and red (Type **747**); 3f. deep blue, red and blue (as No. 2071); 4f. blue, deep blue and red (as No. 2072); 6f. deep blue, blue and red (as No. 2073) . . . . 8·00 8·00
DESIGNS: 2f. Capital; 3f. "Arphila 75 Paris"; 4f. Head of Ceres.

748 Postman's Badge

749 Pres. G. Pompidou

1975. Stamp Day.
2075 **748** 80c.+20c. blk, yell & bl 60 60

1975. Pres. Georges Pompidou Commem.
2076 **749** 80c. black and blue . . . 40 30

750 "Paul as Harlequin" (Picasso)

1975. Europa. Multicoloured.
2077 80c. Type **750** 45 35
2078 1f.20 "In the Square" or "Woman leaning on Balcony" (Van Dongen) (horiz) 80 75

751 Machine Tools and Emblem

1975. 1st World Machine-Tools Exhibition, Paris.
2079 **751** 1f.20 black, red & blue 50 50

752 First Assembly at Luxembourg Palace

1975. Centenary of French Senate.
2080 **752** 1f.20 bistre, brn & red 50 50

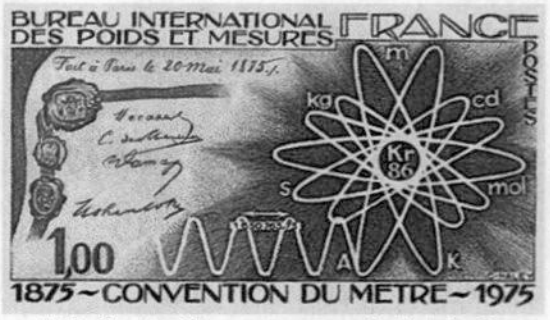
753 Seals, Signatures and Symbols

1975. Centenary of Metre Convention.
2081 **753** 1f. purple, mve & brn . . 50 45

754 Sud Aviation Gazelle Helicopter

755 Youth and Health Symbols

1975. Development of Gazelle Helicopter.
2082 **754** 1f.30 green and blue . . 65 60

1975. Students' Health Foundation.
2083 **755** 70c. black, purple & red 40 40

756 Underground Train

1975. Opening of Metro Regional Express Service.
2084 **756** 1f. deep blue and blue 75 50

757 Bussang Theatre and M. Pottecher (founder)

758 Picardy Rose

1975. 80th Anniv of People's Theatre, Bussang.
2085 **757** 85c. lilac, brown & blue 40 40

1975. Regions of France.
2086 **758** 85c. orange, turq & blue 70 45
2087 – 1f. lake, red & yellow . . 70 45
2088 – 1f.15 green, bl & ochre 70 50
2089 – 1f.30 black, red & blue 75 60
2090 – 1f.90 blue, bistre & blk 90 55
2091 – 2f.80 blue, red, & black 1·60 1·30
DESIGNS—VERT: 1f. Bourgogne agriculture emblems; 1f.15, Loire scene; 1f.30, Auvergne (bouquet of carnations); 1f.90, Allegory, Poitou-Charentes. HORIZ: 2f.80, "Nord-Pas-de-Calais".
See also Nos. 2102/6, 2150/7, 2246/8, 2329, 2508, 2555 and 2613.

759 Concentration Camp Victims

760 "Ballon d'Alsace" (Mine-clearers Monument)

1975. 30th Anniv of Liberation of Concentration Camps.
2092 **759** 1f. green, blue and red 50 55

1975. 30th Anniv of Mine Clearance Service.
2093 **760** 70c. green, bistre & blue 40 30

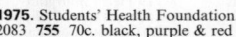

761 "Urban Development"

1975. New Towns.
2094 **761** 1f.70 blue, grn & brn . . 80 75

762 St. Nazaire Bridge

763 Rainbow over Women's Faces

1975. Opening of St. Nazaire Bridge.
2095 **762** 1f.40 black, bl & grn . . 65 45

1975. International Women's Year.
2096 **763** 1f.20 multicoloured . . . 50 55

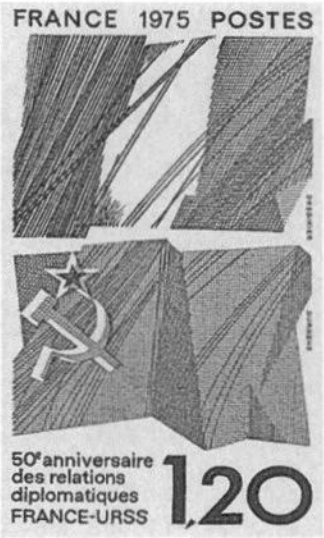

764 French and Russian Flags

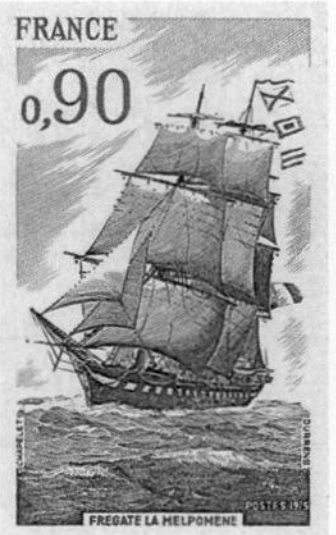

765 Cadet Ship "La Melpomene"

1975. 50th Anniv of Franco-Soviet Diplomatic Relations.
2097 **764** 1f.20 yellow, red & blue 45 45

1975. Red Cross Fund. "The Seasons". As T **743**.
2098 60c.+15c. red and green . . 60 65
2099 80c.+20c. brn, orge & red 70 70
DESIGNS: 60c. Child on swing; 80c. Rabbits under umbrella.

1975. French Sailing Ships.
2100 **765** 90c. blue, orge & red . . 1·10 70

766 Concorde

767 French Stamp Design of 1876

1976. Air. Concorde's First Commercial Flight, Paris–Rio de Janeiro.
2101 **766** 1f.70 black, blue & red 85 65

1976. Regions of France. As T **758**.
2102 25c. green and blue 25 30
2103 60c. green, blue & purple . . 25 30
2104 70c. blue, green, & black . . 50 45
2105 1f.25 blue, brown & green 80 85
2106 2f.20 multicoloured . . . . 1·30 1·20
DESIGNS—HORIZ: 25c. Industrial complex in the Central region; 60c. Aquitaine; 2f.20, Pyrenees. VERT: 70c. Limousin; 1f.25, Guiana.

1976. French Art. As T **491**.
2108 2f. grey and blue . . . . . 1·30 1·00
2109 2f. yellow and brown . . . 1·20 1·10
2110 2f. multicoloured . . . . . 1·30 1·20
2111 2f. multicoloured 85 95
2112 2f. multicoloured . . . . . 1·00 95
2113 2f. multicoloured . . . . . 1·10 95
DESIGNS—VERT: No. 2108, "The Two Saints", St.-Genis-des-Fontaines (wood-carving); No. 2109, "Venus of Brassempouy" (ivory sculpture); No. 2110, "La Joie de Vivre" (Robert Delaunay). HORIZ: No. 2111, Rameses II in war-chariot (wall-carving); No. 2112, Painting by Carzou; No. 2113, "Still Life with Fruit" Maurice de Vlaminck).

1976. International Stamp Day.
2114 **767** 80c.+20c. lilac & blk . . 50 50

1976. Tourist Publicity. As T **490**, but dated "1976".
2115 1f. brown, green and red . . 35 30
2116 1f.10 blue 50 45
2117 1f.40 blue, green & brown 55 30
2118 1f.70 purple, green & blue 60 25
2119 2f. mauve, red and brown 75 30
2120 3f. brown, blue and green 1·00 30
DESIGNS—HORIZ: 1f. Chateau Bonaguil; 1f.40, Basque coast, Biarritz. 3f. Chateau de Malmaison. VERT: 1f.10, Lodeve Cathedral; 1f.70, Thiers. 2f. Ussel.

768 Old Rouen

769 "Duguay Trouin VIII" (cruiser), "Duguay Trouin IX" (destroyer) and Naval Emblem

1976. 49th Congress of French Philatelic Societies.
2121 **768** 80c. green and brown . . 40 35

1976. 50th Anniv of Central Marine Officers' Reserve Association.
2122 **769** 1f. yellow, blue & red . . 50 45

770 Youth

771 Strasbourg Jug

1976. "Juvarouen 76" Youth Stamp Exhibition, Rouen.
2123 **770** 60c. indigo, blue & red 35 35

1976. Europa. Multicoloured.
2124 80c. Type **771** 35 30
2125 1f.20 Sevres plate 70 65

772 Vergennes and Franklin

1976. Bicentenary of American Revolution.
2126 **772** 1f.20 black, red & blue 50 45

773 Marshal Moncey

774 People talking

1976. Red Cross. Celebrities.
2127 **773** 80c.+20c. purple, black and brown 60 70
2128 – 80c.+20c. grn & brn . . 60 70
2129 – 80c.+20c. mve & grn . . 60 70
2130 – 1f.+20c. black, light blue and blue 65 75
2131 – 1f.+20c. blue, mauve and purple 65 75
2132 – 1f.+20c. grey & red . . . 65 75
DESIGNS: No. 2128, Max Jacob (poet); 2129, Mounet-Sully (tragedian); 2130, General Daumesnil; 2131, Eugene Fromentin (writer and painter); 2132, Anna de Noailles.

1976. "Communication".
2133 **774** 1f.20 black, red & yell 50 55

775 Verdun Memorial

776 Troncais Forest

1976. 60th Anniv of Verdun Offensive.
2134 **775** 1f. red, brown & green 45 45

1976. Nature Conservation.
2135 **776** 70c. brown, green & blue 45 35

777 Cross of Lorraine Emblem

778 Satellite "Symphonie"

1976. 30th Anniv of Free French Association.
2136 **777** 1f. red, dp blue & blue 65 45

1976. Launch of "Symphonie No. 1" Satellite.
2137 **778** 1f.40 brn, choc & vio . . 60 55

779 Carnival Figures

780 Yachting

1976. "La Fete" (Summer Festivals Exhibition, Tuileries, Paris).
2138 **779** 1f. red, green & blue . . 65 40

1976. Olympic Games, Montreal.
2139 **780** 1f.20 ind, ultram & bl 60 45

781 Officers in Military and Civilian Dress

1976. Centenary of Reserve Officers Corps.
2140 **781** 1f. grey, red & blue . . . 40 30

782 Early and Modern Telephones

1976. Telephone Centenary.
2141 **782** 1f. grey, brown & blue 40 30

783 Bronze Statue and Emblem

784 Police and Emblems

1976. 10th Anniv of International Tourist Film Association.
2142 **783** 1f.40 brown, red & grn 65 55

1976. 10th Anniv of National Police Force.
2143 **784** 1f.10 green, red & blue 50 50

785 Symbol of Nuclear Science

1976. European Research into Nuclear Science.
2144 **785** 1f.40 multicoloured . . . 80 70

786 Fair Emblem

787 St. Barbara

1976. 50th Anniv of French Fairs and Exhibitions Federation.
2145 **786** 1f.50 blue, green & brn 75 55

1976. Red Cross Fund. Statuettes in Brou Church.
2146 **787** 80c.+20c. vio & red . . 60 65
2147 – 1f.+25c. brn & red . . . 90 95
DESIGN: 1f. Cumaean Sybil.

788 "Douane" Symbol

1976. French Customs Service.
2148 **788** 1f.10 multicoloured . . . 55 55

789 Museum and "Duchesse Anne" (cadet ship)

1976. Atlantic Museum, Port Louis.
2149 **789** 1f.45 brown, blue & blk 65 65

1977. Regions of France. As T **758**.
2150 1f.45 mauve and green . . . 60 50
2151 1f.50 multicoloured 65 55
2152 2f.10 yellow, blue & green 1·00 90
2153 2f.40 brown, green & blue 1·00 55
2154 2f.50 multicoloured . . . . 1·10 85
2155 2f.75 green . . . . 1·60 1·00
2156 3f.20 brown, green & blue 1·60 1·20
2157 3f.90 red, brown and blue 2·10 1·30
DESIGNS—HORIZ: 1f.45, Birds and flowers (Reunion); 2f.40, Coastline (Bretagne); 2f.75, Mountains (Rhone-Alpes). VERT: 1f.50, Banana tree (Martinique); 2f.10, Arms and transport (Franche-Comte); 2f.50, Fruit and yachts (Languedoc-Roussillon); 3f.20, Champagne and scenery (Champagne-Ardenne); 3f.90, Village church (Alsace).

790 Centre Building

1977. Opening of Georges Pompidou National Centre of Arts and Culture, Paris.
2158 **790** 1f. red, blue & green . . 40 30

1977. French Art. As T **491**.
2159 2f. multicoloured . . . . . 1·00 90
2160 2f. multicoloured . . . . . 1·20 1·10
DESIGNS—HORIZ: No. 2159, "Mantes Bridge" (Corot). VERT: No. 2160, "Virgin and Child" (Rubens).

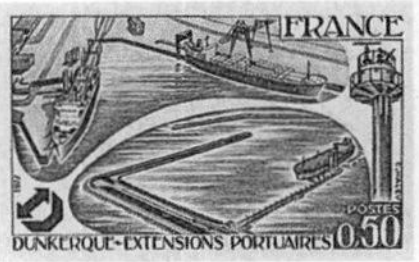

791 Dunkirk Harbour

792 Torch and Dagger Emblem

1977. Dunkirk Port Extensions.
2161 **791** 50c. blue, indigo & brn 25 30

1977. 90th Anniv of "Le Souvenir Francais" (French War Graves Organization).
2162 **792** 80c. brown, red & blue 50 45

793 Marckolsheim Post Relay Sign

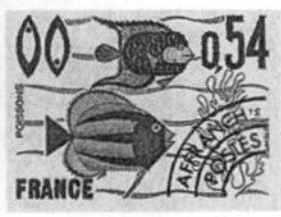

794 "Pisces"

1977. Stamp Day.
2163 **793** 1f.+20c. grey & blue . . 55 65

1977. Precancels. Signs of the Zodiac.
2164 **794** 54c. violet 65 65
2165 – 58c. green . . . . 1·60 1·60
2166 – 61c. blue 70 70
2167 – 68c. brown . . . . . . 1·10 1·10
2168 – 73c. red . . . . 2·50 2·50
2169 – 78c. orange . . . . . . 1·30 1·30
2170 – 1f.05 mauve . . . . . . 2·40 2·40
2171 – 1f.15 orange . . . . . . 4·00 4·00
2172 – 1f.25 green . . . . . . 1·80 1·80
2173 – 1f.85 green . . . . . . 5·00 5·00
2174 – 2f. turquoise . . . . . . 5·00 5·00
2175 – 2f.10 mauve . . . . . . 2·50 2·50

DESIGNS: 58c. Cancer; 61c. Sagittarius; 68c. Taurus; 73c. Aries; 78c. Libra; 1f.05, Scorpio; 1f.15, Capricorn; 1f.25, Leo; 1f.85, Aquarius; 2f. Virgo; 2f.10, Gemini.
See note below No. 432 (1920).

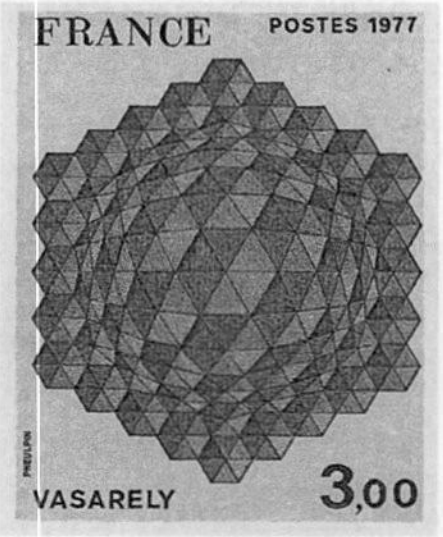

795 "Geometric Design" (Victor Vasarely)

1977. Philatelic Creations. Works of Art by Modern Artists.
2176 **795** 3f. green and lilac . . . 1·40 95
2177 – 3f. black and red . . . . 2·00 1·80
2178 – 3f. multicoloured . . . . 1·90 1·50
DESIGNS—VERT: No. 2177, Profile heads of man and hawk (Pierre-Yves Tremois). HORIZ: No. 2178, Abstract in Blue (R. Excoffon).
See also Nos. 2249, 2331/2, 2346/8, 2434/5, 2547 and 2578/9.

796 Flowers and Ornamental Garden

1977. 50th Anniv of National Horticultural Society.
2179 **796** 1f.70 red, brown & grn 80 55

797 Provencal Village

1977. Europa.
2180 **797** 1f. red, brown & blue . . 50 30
2181 – 1f.40 blk, brn & grn . . 85 35
DESIGN: 1f.40, Breton port.

798 Stylized Plant

1977. International Flower Show, Nantes.
2182 **798** 1f.40 mve, yell & bl . . 70 70

799 Battle of Cambrai

1977. 300th Anniv of Reunification of Cambrai with France.
2183 **799** 80c. mauve, brown & bl 55 45

800 Church, School and Map

801 Modern Constructions

1977. Centenary of French Catholic Institutes.
2184 **800** 1f.10 brown, bl & choc 55 65

1977. Meeting of European Civil Engineering Federation, Paris.
2185 **801** 1f.10 red, bistre & blue 60 45

802 Annecy

1977. 50th Congress of French Philatelic Societies.
2186 **802** 1f. brown, grn & olive 55 40

1977. Tourist Publicity. As T **490**.
2187 1f.25 grey, brown & red . . 50 45
2188 1f.40 blue, purple & pink . . 60 40
2189 1f.45 sepia, brown & blue 60 40
2190 1f.50 olive, red & brown . . 60 30
2191 1f.90 yellow and black . . . 70 55
2192 2f.40 bistre, green & black 90 50
DESIGNS—HORIZ: 1f.25, Premontres Abbey, Pont-a-Mousson; 1f.50, Statue and cloisters, Fontenay Abbey, Cote d'Or; 2f.40, Chateau de Vitre. VERT: 1f.40, Abbey tower of St. Amand-les-Eaux, Nord; 1f.45, Le Dorat Church, Haute-Vienne; 1f.90, Bayeux Cathedral.

803 School Building

1977. Polytechnic School, Palaiseau.
2193 **803** 1f.70 green, red & blue 70 50

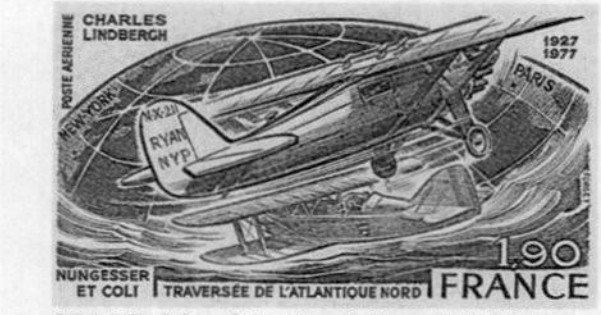

804 "Spirit of St. Louis" and "L'Oiseau Blanc"

1977. Air. 50th Anniv of North Atlantic Flights.
2194 **804** 1f.90 indigo, blue & grn 95 75

805 French Football Cup and Players

1977. 60th Anniv of French Football Cup.
2195 **805** 80c. bistre, blue & red 1·00 65

806 De Gaulle Memorial

807 "Map of France"

1977. 5th Anniv of General de Gaulle Memorial.
2196 **806** 1f. multicoloured . . . . 1·00 65

1977. 25th Anniv of Junior Chambers of Commerce.
2197 **807** 1f.10 blue and red . . . 65 50

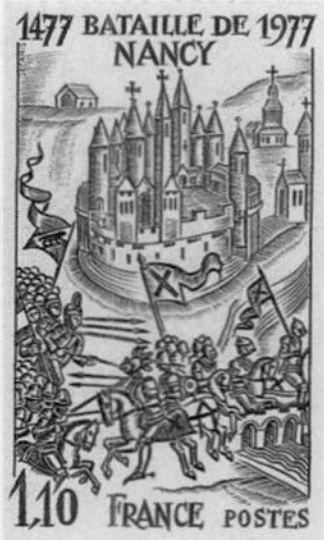

808 Battle of Nancy

809 Seal of Burgundy

1977. 500th Anniv of Battle of Nancy.
2198 **808** 1f.10 slate and blue . . . 90 70

1977. 500th Anniv of Union of Burgundy with France.
2199 **809** 1f.25 green and olive . . 50 50

810 Compass on Globe

811 Red Cicada

1977. 10th Anniv of International Association of French Language Parliaments.
2200 **810** 1f.40 red and blue . . . 60 55

1977. Nature Protection.
2201 **811** 80c. multicoloured . . . 50 50

812 Hand and Examples of Craftsmanship

813 Edouard Herriot (statesman)

1977. French Craftsmanship.
2202 **812** 1f.40 brown and olive . . 65 60

1977. Red Cross Fund. Celebrities.
2203 **813** 1f.+20c. black 70 75
2204 – 1f.+20c. brn & grn . . . 70 75
2205 – 1f.+20c. brn, bis & grn 70 75
2206 – 1f.+20c. bl, lt bl & red 70 75
DESIGNS: No. 2204, Abbe Breuil (archaeologist); 2205, Guillaume de Machault (poet); 2206, Charles Cros (poet).

814 "Agriculture and Industry"

815 "Old Man"

1977. 30th Anniv of Economic and Social Council.
2207 **814** 80c. bistre, green & brn 35 30

1977. Red Cross Fund. Carved Christmas Crib Figures from Provence.
2208 **815** 80c.+20c. black & red 55 65
2209 – 1f.+25c. green & red . . 70 75
DESIGN: 1f. "Old Woman".

816 "Sabine" (after Louis David)

817 Table Tennis

1977. Inscr "FRANCE".
2210 **816** 1c. black 15 30
2211 2c. blue 15 30
2212 5c. green 10 10
2213 10c. red 10 15
2214 15c. blue 40 45
2215 20c. green 10 20
2216 30c. orange 10 10
2216a 40c. brown 25 25
2217 50c. violet 20 15
2217a 60c. red 30 40
2218 70c. blue 25 30
2219 80c. green 75 45
2220 80c. yellow 25 35
2221 90c. mauve 35 40
2222 1f. red 60 20
2223 1f. emerald 40 15
2224 1f. olive 25 15
2225 1f.10 green 55 20
2226 1f.20 red 40 15
2226a 1f.20 green 40 20
2227 1f.30 red 55 10
2228 1f.40 blue . . . . . . 1·20 60
2228a 1f.40 red 55 15
2229 1f.60 violet 80 45
2230 1f.70 blue 75 55
2230a 1f.80 brown 80 60
2231 2f. green 55 15
2232 2f.10 purple 60 45
2233 3f. brown 80 45
2233a 3f.50 green . . . . . . 1·30 90
2234 4f. red . . . . . . 1·50 80
2234a 5f. blue . . . . . . 1·70 70
For values inscr "REPUBLIQUE FRANCAISE" see Nos. 2423/5.

1977. 50th Anniv of French Table Tennis Federation.
2240 **817** 1f.10 grn, pur & orge . . 2·30 1·90

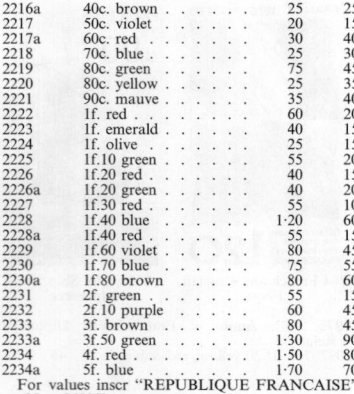

818 Percheron

1978. Nature Conservation.
2241 **818** 1f.70 multicoloured . . . 1·00 95
2242 – 1f.80 brn, olive & grn . . 85 70
DESIGN—VERT: (23 × 37 mm) 1f.80, Osprey.

1978. French Art. As T **491**.
2243 2f. black . . . . 2·40 1·80
DESIGN: 2f. Tournament under Louis XIV, Les Tuileries, 1662.

819 Flags of France and Sweden of 1878

820 College Building

1978. Centenary of Return of St. Barthelemy Island to France.
2244 **819** 1f.10 brn, red & mve . . 50 45

1978. Centenary of National Telecommunications College.
2245 **820** 80c. blue 35 30

1978. Regions of France. As T **758**.
2246 1f. red, blue and black . . . 40 35
2247 1f.40 blue, orange & green 70 55
2248 1f.70 gold, red and black . . 1·00 80
DESIGNS—VERT: 1f. Symbol of Ile de France. HORIZ: 1f.40, Flower and port (Haute-Normandie); 1f.70, Ancient Norman ship (Basse-Normandie).

1978. "Philatelic Creations". As T **795**.
2249 3f. multicoloured . . . . . 2·30 1·50
2250 3f. multicoloured . . . . . 1·80 1·20
DESIGNS—HORIZ: No. 2249 "Institut de France and Pont des Arts, Paris" (B. Buffet); 2250, "Camargue Horses" (Yves Brayer).

821 Marie Noel (poet)

822 Jigsaw Map of France

1978. Red Cross Fund. Celebrities.
2251 **821** 1f.+20c. indigo & bl . . 75 80
2252 – 1f.+20c. green, brown and blue 75 80
2253 – 1f.+20c. mve & vio . . . 75 80
2254 – 1f.+20c. green & brn . . 75 80
2255 – 1f.+20c. mve & red . . . 75 80
2256 – 1f.+20c. black, brown and red 75 80

DESIGNS: No. 2252, Georges Bernanos (writer); 2253, Leconte de Lisle (poet); 2254, Leo Tolstoy (novelist); 2255, Voltaire and J.-J. Rousseau; 2256, Claude Bernard (physician).

1978. 15th Anniv of Regional Planning Boards.
2257 **822** 1f.10 green & violet . . 45 35

1978. Tourist Publicity. As T **490**.
2258 50c. green, blue & dp green 30 25
2259 80c. dp green, blue & grn 35 35
2260 1f. black 35 35
2261 1f.10 violet, brown & grn 55 50
2262 1f.10 brown, blue & green 50 50
2263 1f.25 brown and red 70 50
2264 1f.70 black and brown . . . 85 80
DESIGNS—VERT: 50c. Verdon Gorge; 1f. Church of St. Saturnin, Puy de Dome. HORIZ: 80c. Pont-Neuf, Paris; 1f.10 (No. 2261), Notre-Dame du Bec-Hellouin Abbey; 1f.10 (No. 2262), Chateau d'Esquelbecq; 1f.25, Abbey Church of Aubazine; 1f.70, Fontevraud Abbey.

823 Head of Girl

824 Postman emptying Pillar Box, 1900

1978. "Juvexniort" Youth Philately Exhibition, Niort.
2265 **823** 80c. brn, choc & mve . . 35 35

1978. Stamp Day.
2266 **824** 1f.+20c. grn & blue . . . 50 60

825 Underwater Scene and Rainbow Wrasse

826 Floral Arch and Garden

1978. Port Cros National Park.
2267 **825** 1f.25 multicoloured . . . 1·10 1·20

1978. "Make France Bloom".
2268 **826** 1f.70 red, blue & green 1·60 65

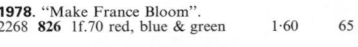

827 Hands encircling Sun

828 War Memorial, Notre Dame de Lorette

1978. Energy Conservation.
2269 **827** 1f. yellow, brn & bistre 55 40

1978. Hill of Notre Dame de Lorette (War Cemetery).
2270 **828** 2f. brown and bistre . . 90 50

829 Fontaine des Innocents, Paris

830 Hotel de Mauroy, Troyes

1978. Europa. Fountains.
2271 **829** 1f. blk, bistre & blue . . 50 30
2272 – 1f.40 brn, grn & blue . . 75 50
DESIGN: 1f.40, Fontaine du Parc Floral, Paris.

1978. 51st Congress of French Philatelic Societies.
2273 **830** 1f. black, red & blue . . 45 45

831 Tennis Player and Stadium

1978. 50th Anniv of Roland Garros Tennis Stadium.
2274 **831** 1f. grey, brown & blue 1·90 55

832 Open Hand

833 Citadel and Church

1978. Handicrafts.
2275 **832** 1f.30 brown, grn & red 55 50

1978. 300th Anniv of Reunification of Franche-Comte with France
2276 **833** 1f.20 grey, blue & grn 50 35

834 Emblem

835 Valenciennes and Maubeuge

1978. State Printing Office.
2277 **834** 1f. green, black & blue 45 35

1978. 300th Anniv of Return of Valenciennes and Maubeuge to France.
2278 **835** 1f.20 brown, vio & grey 55 45

836 Sower

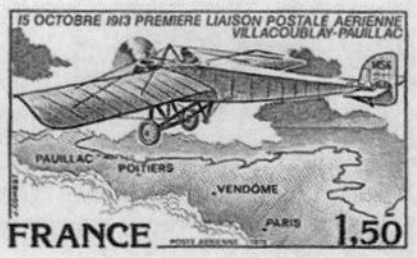

837 Morane-Saulnier Type H and Route

1978. 50th Anniv of Academie de Philatelie.
2279 **836** 1f. blue, purple & violet 45 50

1978. Air. 65th Anniv of First Airmail Flight Villacoublay–Pauillac.
2280 **837** 1f.50 brown, blue & grn 85 55

838 Gymnasts, White Stork and Strasbourg Cathedral

839 Sporting Activities

1978. 19th World Gymnastics Championships, Strasbourg.
2281 **838** 1f. red, sepia & brown 55 50

1978. Sport for All.
2282 **839** 1f. violet, mauve & blue 95 80

840 "Freedom holding Dying Warrior" (A. Greck)

841 Railway Carriage, Rethondes, and Armistice Monument

1978. Polish Fighters' War Memorial.
2283 **840** 1f.70 lake, red & green 85 80

1978. 60th Anniv of Armistice.
2284 **841** 1f.20 black 55 50

842 Symbols of Readaptation

1978. Help for Convalescents.
2285 **842** 1f. red, brown & orge . . 45 50

843 "The Hare and the Tortoise"

844 Human Figures balanced on Globe

1978. Red Cross Fund. Fables of La Fontaine.
2286 **843** 1f.+25c. brown, red and green 80 85
2287 – 1f.20+30c. green, red and brown 80 85
DESIGN: 1f.20, "The Town and the Country Mouse".

1978. 30th Anniv of Human Rights.
2288 **844** 1f.70 blue and brown . . 70 45

845 Seated Child

846 Marshal de Bercheny (Cavalry leader)

1979. International Year of the Child.
2289 **845** 1f.70 red, vio & brn . . 3·00 2·75

1979. French Art. As T **491**.
2290 2f. multicoloured . . . . . 1·40 1·20
2291 2f. brown, black & dp brn 1·40 1·10
2292 2f. multicoloured . . . . . 3·75 1·50
DESIGNS—HORIZ: No. 2290, "Music" (15th century miniature by Robinet Testart). VERT: No. 2291, "Diana in her Bath" (mantelpiece originally from Chalons-sur-Marne, now in Chateau d'Ecouen); 2292, "Auvers-sur-Oise Church" (Vincent van Gogh).

1979. Red Cross Fund. Celebrities.
2293 **846** 1f.20+30c. brown, blue and deep blue 85 90
2294 – 1f.20+30c. black and yellow 90 90
2295 – 1f.20+30c. deep brown, red & brown 85 90
2296 – 1f.20+30c. blue, mauve and red 85 90
2297 – 1f.30+30c. red and brown 90 90
2298 – 1f.30+30c. blue and ultramarine 90 90
DESIGNS: No. 2294, Leon Jouhaux (Nobel Peace Prize winner); 2295, Abelard and Heloise; 2296, Georges Courteline (playwright); 2297, Simone Weil (social philosopher); 2298, Andre Malraux (writer and politician).

847 "Amanita caesarea"

848 Segalen, Pirogue, Pagoda and "Durance"

1979. Precancelled. Mushrooms.
2299 **847** 64c. red 55 55
2300 – 83c. brown 60 60
2301 – 1f.30 yellow 95 95
2302 – 2f.25 lilac . . . . 1·50 1·50
DESIGNS: 83c. "Craterellus comucopioides"; 1f.30, "Omphalotus olearius"; 2f.20, "Ramaria botrytis".
See note below No. 432 (1920).

1979. 60th Death Anniv of Victor Segalen (writer and explorer).
2303 **848** 1f.50 turq, brn & red . . 60 40

849 Hibiscus Flower

850 Seated Buddha

1979. International Flower Show, Martinique.
2304 **849** 35c. lilac, mve & grn . . 25 30

1979. Borobudur Temple Preservation.
2305 **850** 1f.80 turquoise & green 70 50

851 Head Post Office, Paris

852 Street Urchin

1979. Stamp Day.
2306 **851** 1f.20+30c. blue, red and brown 65 60

1979. Birth Centenary of Francisque Poulbot (artist).
2307 **852** 1f.30 multicoloured . . . 50 45

853 "Apis mellifera"

1979. Nature Conservation.
2308 **853** 1f. green, brown & orge 70 50

854 St.-Germain-des-Pres Abbey

1979. St.-Germain-des-Pres Abbey Restoration.
2309 **854** 1f.40 red, grey and blue 60 50

1979. Tourist Publicity. As T **490**.
2310 45c. violet, blue & ultram 30 30
2311 1f. green, dp grn & lt grn 40 40
2312 1f. sepia, brown and lilac . . 40 35
2313 1f.20 brown, blue and green 45 40
2314 1f.50 sepia, red & brown . . 60 45
2315 1f.70 blue and brown . . . 75 80
DESIGNS—VERT: No. 2311, Interiors of Abbeys of Bernay and St. Pierre-sur-Dives, Normandy; 2312, Auray; 2313, Windmill at Steenvoorde, Dunkirk (after Pierre Spas). HORIZ: No. 2310, Chateau de Maisons-Laffitte; 2314, Niaux Grotto; 2315, Palace of Kings of Majorca, Perpignan.

855 Caudron C.635 Monoplanes

1979. Europa.
2316 **855** 1f.20 blue, grn & turq 70 35
2317 – 1f.70 green, turq & red 1·10 75
DESIGN: 1f.70, Boule de Moulins (floating container used to carry letters during the Siege of Paris).

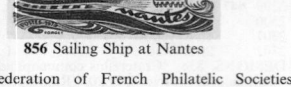

856 Sailing Ship at Nantes

1979. Federation of French Philatelic Societies Congress, Nantes.
2318 **856** 1f.20 blue, vio & grey . . 50 45

857 "Camille Desmoulins addressing Crowd" (engraving by Huyot)

1979. 190th Anniv of Palais Royal, Paris.
2319 **857** 1f. red and violet 35 35

858 Flags of Member Countries and Strasbourg Cathedral

1979. First Direct Elections to European Assembly.
2320 **858** 1f.20 multicoloured . . . 45 35

859 Joan of Arc Monument, Rouen

1979. National Monument.
2321 **859** 1f.70 mauve 75 60

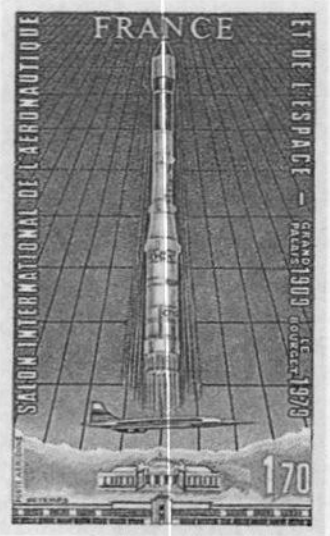

860 "Ariane" Rocket and Concorde over Grand Palais, Paris and Le Bourget Airport

862 Lantern Tower, La Rochelle

861 Felix Guyon (urologist)

1979. Air. International Aeronautics and Space Exhibition, Le Bourget.
2322 **860** 1f.70 bl, orge & brn . . 1·10 1·20

1979. 18th Congress of International Society of Urologists, Paris.
2323 **861** 1f.80 blue and brown . . 70 50

1979. Pre-cancelled. Historic Monuments (1st series).
2324 **862** 68c. lilac 50 50
2325 – 88c. blue 60 60
2326 – 1f.40 green 95 95
2327 – 2f.35 brown . . . . . . 1·30 1·30
DESIGNS: 88c. Cathedral towers, Chartres; 1f.40, Cathedral towers, Bourges; 2f.35, Cathedral towers, Amiens.
See note below No. 432 (1920).
See also Nos. 2342/5, 2383/6 and 2509/12.

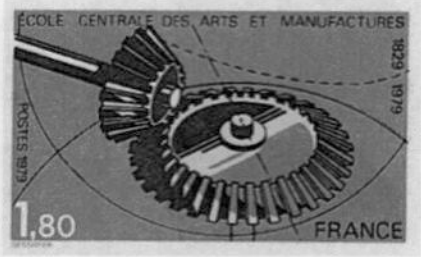

863 "Telecom 79"

864 Gear-wheels

1979. Third World Telecommunications Exhibition, Geneva.
2328 **863** 1f.10 brn, turq & grn . . 40 35

1979. Regions of France. As T **758**.
2329 2f.30 black, yellow & red . . 90 50
DESIGN: 2f.30, Thistle, Lorraine.

1979. 150th Anniv of Central Technical School, Paris.
2330 **864** 1f.80 yellow, blk & grn 85 75

1979. "Philatelic Creations". As T **795**.
2331 3f. multicoloured . . . . 1·40 1·20
2332 3f. brown and green . . . . 1·40 1·20
DESIGNS: No. 2331, "Marianne" (Salvador Dali); 2332, "Fire Dancer from 'The Magic Flute'" (Chapelain-Midy).

865 Judo

866 Women's Head

1979. World Judo Championships, Paris.
2333 **865** 1f.60 blk, lt grn & grn 65 45

1979. Red Cross Fund. Stained Glass Windows, Church of St. Joan of Arc, Rouen.
2334 **866** 1f.10+30c. brown, green and red 70 75
2335 – 1f.30+30c. brown, green and red 80 80
DESIGN: 1f.30, Simon the Magician.
The windows came originally from the Church of St. Vincent, Rouen, destroyed during the Second World War.

867 Violins

868 Eurovision Satellite

1979. Handicrafts. Violin Manufacture.
2336 **867** 1f.30 blk, red & lake . . 55 45

1980. 25th Anniv of Eurovision (European Broadcasting Union).
2337 **868** 1f.80 bl, dp bl & blk . . 95 95

1980. French Art. Design similar to T **491**.
2338 3f. brown, ochre & green . . 1·40 1·10
2339 3f. multicoloured . . . . 1·40 1·10
2340 3f. multicoloured . . . . 1·40 1·10
2341 4f. multicoloured . . . . 2·20 1·40
DESIGNS—VERT: No. 2338, "Woman with Fan" (sculpture by Ossip Zadkine); 2340, "The Peasant Family" (Louis le Nain); 2341, "Woman with Blue Eyes" (Modigliani). HORIZ: No. 2339, "Homage to J. S. Bach" (tapestry by Jean Picart Le Doux).

1980. Pre-cancelled. Historic Monuments (2nd series). Designs as T **862**.
2342 76c. turquoise 35 35
2343 99c. green 55 55
2344 1f.60 red 85 85
2345 2f.65 brown . . . . . . 1·40 1·40
DESIGNS: 76c. Chateau d'Angers; 99c. Chateau de Kerjean; 1f.60, Chateau de Pierrefonds; 2f.65, Chateau de Tarascon.
See note below No. 432 (1920).

1980. Philatelic Creations. Design similar to T **795**.
2346 3f. blue, black and brown 1·50 1·20
2347 4f. multicoloured . . . . . 2·75 1·70
2348 4f. black and blue . . . . 1·90 1·70
DESIGNS—As T **795**: HORIZ: No. 2346, Abstract (Raoul Ubac). VERT: No. 2348, Abstract (Hans Hartung). 43 × 49 mm: No. 2347, "Message of Peace" (Yaacov Agam).

869 Processional Figures and Carnival Crowd

870 Viollet-le-Duc (architect and writer)

1980. "Giants of the North" Festival.
2349 **869** 1f.60 red, grn & blue . . 60 50

1980. Red Cross Fund. Celebrities.
2350 **870** 1f.30+30c. black and grey 85 90
2351 – 1f.30+30c. brown and green . . . . 1·10 1·30
2352 – 1f.40+30c. deep blue and blue 85 90
2353 – 1f.40+30c. black 85 90
2354 – 1f.40+30c. grey and black 85 90
2355 – 1f.40+30c. turquoise and green 85 90
DESIGN—VERT: No. 2351, Jean Monnet (statesman); 2352, Jean-Marie de la Mennais (Christian educationalist) (portrait after Paulin-Guerin); 2353, Frederic Mistral (poet); 2355, Saint-John Perse (poet and diplomat). HORIZ: No. 2354, Pierre Paul de Riquet (constructor of Canal du Midi).

871 French Cuisine

873 "Woman Embroidering" (Toffoli)

872 "The Letter to Melie" (Mario Avati)

1980. French Gastronomical Exn, Paris.
2356 **871** 90c. brown and red . . . 95 75

1980. Stamp Day.
2357 **872** 1f.30+30c. mult 75 80

1980. Handicrafts. Embroidery.
2358 **873** 1f.10 blue, yell & brn . . 50 45

874 Smoker and Non-smoker (poster)

875 Aristide Briand (statesman)

1980. Anti-smoking Campaign.
2359 **874** 1f.30 blue, red & black 45 35

1980. Tourist Publicity. Designs as T **490**.
2360 1f.50 orange, brown & blue 55 35
2361 2f. black and red 75 55
2362 2f.20 brown, blue & green 75 45
2363 2f.30 green, brown & blue 90 55
2364 2f.50 blue, violet and mauve 85 35
2365 3f.20 brown and blue . . . 1·20 75
DESIGNS—VERT: 1f.50, Cordes; 2f.30, Montauban; 2f.50, Praying nun and St. Peter's Abbey, Solesmes; 3f.20, Puy Cathedral. HORIZ: 2f. Chateau de Maintenon; 2f.20, Chateau de Rambouillet.

1980. Europa.
2366 **875** 1f.30 multicoloured . . . 50 35
2367 – 1f.80 red and brown . . 80 70
DESIGN: 1f.80, St. Benedict (illuminated letter from manuscript).

876 La Rouchefoucauld-Liancourt (founder) and Map

1980. Bicentenary of National Technical High School.
2368 **876** 2f. green and violet . . . 70 55

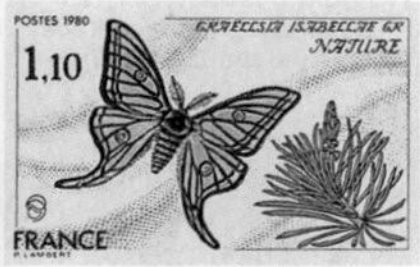

877 Town Hall and Cranes, Dunkirk

878 Isabel

1980. Federation of French Philatelic Societies Congress, Dunkirk.
2369 **877** 1f.30 bl, red & ultram 45 40

1980. Nature Conservation.
2370 **878** 1f.10 multicoloured . . . 75 50

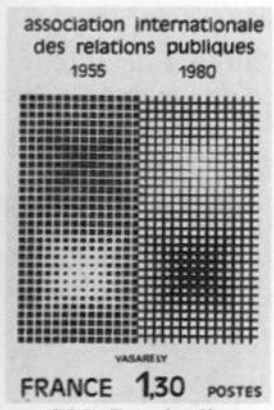

879 Albert Durer (self portrait)

880 Symbolic Design

1980. "Philexfrance 82" International Stamp Exhibition, Paris (1st issue).
2371 **879** 2f. multicoloured . . . . 1·50 1·50
See also Nos. 2415/16, 2520/1 and **MS**2539.

1980. 25th Anniv of International Public Relations Association.
2372 **880** 1f.30 blue and red . . . 55 45

881 "Marianne" and Architecture

1980. Heritage Year.
2373 **881** 1f.50 blue and black . . 60 50

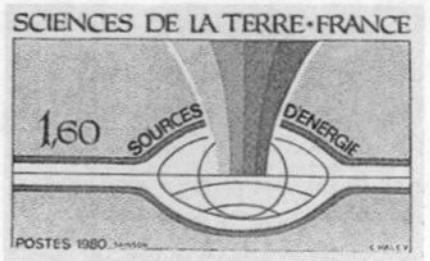

882 Sources of Energy

1980. 26th International Geological Congress, Paris.
2374 **882** 1f.60 red, brown & ol . . 80 50

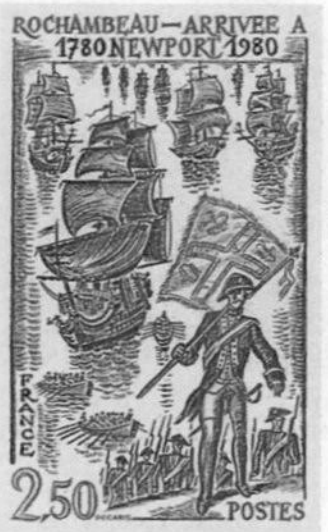

883 Rochambeau landing at Newport

1980. Bicentenary of Rochambeau's arrival at Newport, Rhode Island.
2375 **883** 2f.50 mve, red & grey . . 1·20 95

884 Breguet 19 Super TR "Point d'Interrogation"

1980. Air. 50th Anniv of First Non-stop Paris–New York Flight.
2376 **884** 2f.50 purple and blue . . 95 60

885 Golf

1980. French Golf Federation.
2377 **885** 1f.40 brown & green . . 65 50

886 Comedie-Francaise

1980. 300th Anniv of Comedie-Francaise.
2378 **886** 2f. blue, red and grey . . 80 55

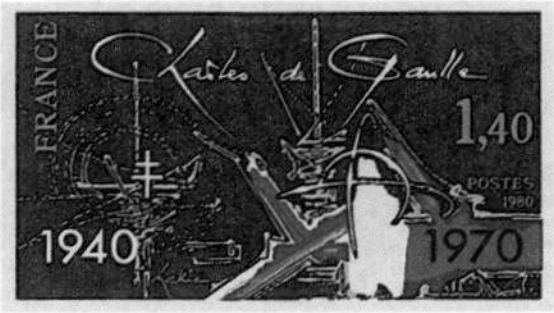

887 Abstract based on Lorraine Cross and French Flag

1980. 40th Anniv of Appeal by, and 10th Death Anniv of, General de Gaulle.
2379 **887** 1f.40 multicoloured . . . 1·00 50

888 Guardsman **889** "Filling the Granaries"

1980. Centenary of Reorganization and Naming of Republican Guard.
2380 **888** 1f.70 blue and red . . . 90 60

1980. Red Cross Fund. Stall Carvings from Amiens Cathedral.
2381 **889** 1f.20+30c. brown and red 75 85
2382 – 1f.40+30c. brown and red 75 85
DESIGN: 1f.40, "Grapes from the Promised Land".

1981. Pre-cancelled. Historic Monuments (3rd series). Horiz designs as T **862**.
2383 88c. mauve 45 45
2384 1f.14 blue 50 50
2385 1f.84 green 90 90
2386 3f.05 brown . . . . 1·40 1·40
DESIGNS: 88c. Imperial Chapel, Ajaccio; 1f.14, Astronomical Clock, Besancon; 1f.84, Castle ruins, Coucy-le-Chateau; 3f.05, Cave paintings, Font-de Gaume, Les Eyzies-de Tayac.
See note below No. 432 (1920).

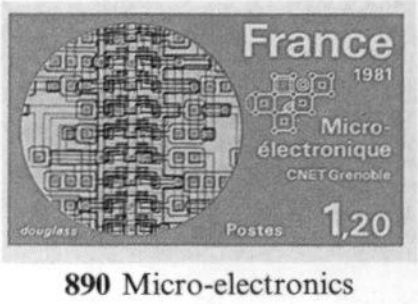

890 Micro-electronics **891** Louis Armand (engineer and Academician)

1981. Technology.
2387 **890** 1f.20 multicoloured . . . 60 45
2388 – 1f.20 multicoloured . . . 50 35
2389 – 1f.40 multicoloured . . . 60 40
2390 – 1f.80 dp bl, bl & yell . . 80 65
2391 – 2f. blue, red and black 1·00 80

DESIGNS: No. 2388, Biology; 2389, New energy sources; 2390, Sea bed exploitation; 2391, Telematics.

1981. Red Cross Fund. Celebrities.
2392 **891** 1f.20+30c. green and brown 80 85
2393 – 1f.20+30c. mult 80 85
2394 – 1f.40+30c. deep green and green 90 95
2395 – 1f.40+30c. blue and black 90 95
2396 – 1f.40+30c. blue and violet . . . . 90 1·00
2397 – 1f.40+30c. brown and bistre . . . . 1·00 1·10
DESIGNS—VERT: No. 2393, Louis Jouvet (theatre and film director and actor); 2396, R. P. Pierre Teilhard de Chardin (palaeontologist and philosopher). HORIZ: No. 2394, Anne-Marie Javouhey (missionary); 2395, Jacques Offenbach (composer); 2397, Pastor Marc Boegner.

1981. French Art. As T **491**. Multicoloured.
2398 2f. "The Footpath" (Camille Pissarro) (horiz) . . . . . 1·10 1·10
2399 4f. "Composition 1920/23" (Albert Gleizes) (vert) . . 1·80 1·20

892 "The Love Letter" (Goya)

1981. Stamp Day.
2400 **892** 1f.40+30c. mult . . . . 95 1·00

893 Angel pouring Water on France **894** Bookbinding Press

1981. Water.
2401 **893** 1f.40 red, blue & blk . . 65 40

1981. Tourist Publicity. Designs similar to T **490**.
2403 1f.40 brown and red 60 35
2404 1f.70 brown, green & blue 90 55
2405 2f. black and red 85 55
2406 2f.20 black and blue 95 60
2407 2f.20 sepia and brown . . . 85 55
2408 2f.50 brown, blue & green 90 55
2409 2f.60 red and green . . . . 1·00 60
2410 2f.90 green . . . . 1·00 45
DESIGNS—VERT: 1f.40, St. John's Cathedral, Lyon; 1f.70, Maison Carree, Nimes; 2f.20 (2406), St. Anne's Church, Auray; 2f.90, Crest. HORIZ: 2f. Interior, Notre Dame Abbey, Vaucelles; 2f.20 (2407), Notre Dame Church, Louviers; 2f.50, Chateau de Sully, Rosny-sur-Seine; 2f.60, Saint-Emilion.

1981. Handicrafts. Bookbinding.
2411 **894** 1f.50 olive and red . . . 80 55

895 Bourree Croisee dance **896** Military and Sporting Scenes

1981. Europa.
2412 **895** 1f.40 brown, blk & grn 50 35
2413 – 2f. black, brn & blue . . 1·00 55
DESIGN: 2f. Sardane (Catalan dance).

1981. Cent of Saint-Maixent Military Academy.
2414 **896** 2f.50 mauve, blue & vio 80 55

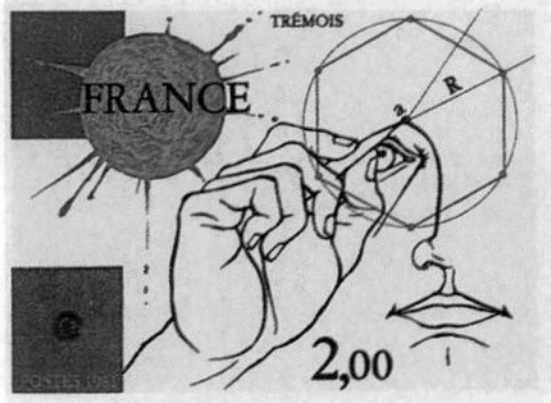

897 "France"

1981. "Philexfrance 82" International Stamp Exhibition, Paris (2nd issue). Multicoloured.
2415 2f. Type **897** . . . . 1·50 1·40
2416 2f. "Paris" . . . . 1·50 1·50

898 Theophraste Renaudot and Emile de Girardin **899** Thermal Waters of Vichy

1981. 350th Anniv of First French Newspaper "La Gazette", Death Centenary of Emile de Girardin (founder of newspaper "La Presse") and Cent of Law on Freedom of the Press.
2417 **898** 2f.20 black and red . . . 85 75

1981. Federation of French Philatelic Societies Congress, Vichy.
2418 **899** 1f.40 brown, bl & grn 65 50

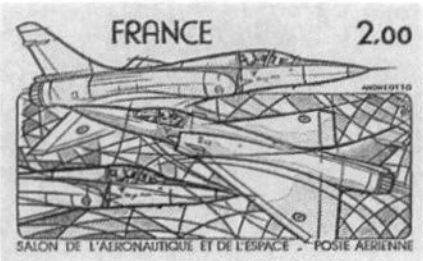

900 Dassault Mirage 2000 Aircraft

1981. Air. 34th International Aeronautics and Space Exhibition.
2419 **900** 2f. mauve, blue & violet 1·60 55

901 "HEC"

1981. Centenary of Paris Commercial College.
2420 **901** 1f.40 blue, green & red 60 50

902 Grey Heron and La Palissade, Camargue

1981. Conservation of Littoral Regions.
2421 **902** 1f.60 green, brn & red 80 65

903 Fencing

1981. World Fencing Championships, Clermont-Ferrand.
2422 **903** 1f.80 black & brown . . 85 75

1981. Vert designs as T **816** but inscr "REPUBLIQUE FRANCAISE".
2423 1f.40 green 45 25
2424 1f.60 red 55 25
2425 2f.30 blue . . . . 1·90 1·10

904 Car colliding with Glass

1981. Campaign against Drinking and Driving.
2428 **904** 1f.60 brown, red & olive 75 50

905 Costes, Le Brix and Breguet 19 "Nungesser et Coli"

1981. Air. Dieudonne Costes and Joseph Le Brix (pilots of first non-stop South Atlantic flight) Commemoration.
2429 **905** 10f. black, brn & red . . 4·00 1·10

906 Bird **907** Stylized Bird

1981. 45th International Congress of P.E.N. Club, Lyon and Paris.
2430 **906** 2f. black, violet & grn 85 55

1981. Centenary of National Savings Bank.
2431 **907** 1f.40 green, bl & red . . 55 35
2432 1f.60 carmine, blue & red 65 40

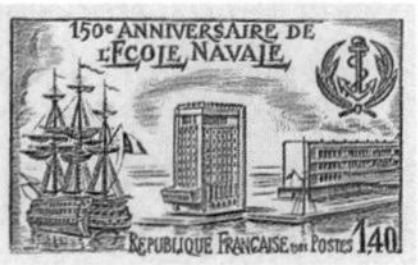

908 Jules Ferry (education reformer) **909** "Borda" (warship) and Naval School, Lanveoc-Poulmic

1981. Cent of National Education System.
2433 **908** 1f.60 vio, brn & blk . . 75 40

1981. Philatelic Creations. As T **795**. Mult.
2434 4f. "The Divers" (Edouard Pignon) (horiz) . . . . . 1·70 1·20
2435 4f. "Alleluia" (Alfred Manessier) . . . . 1·70 1·20

1981. 150th Anniv of Naval School.
2436 **909** 1f.40 brown, blue & red 70 50

910 "Vision of St. Hubert" (15th-cent sculpture) **911** J. Moulin, J. Jaures, V. Schoelcher and Pantheon

1981. Hunting and Nature Museum, Hotel de Guenegaud, Paris.
2437 **910** 1f.60 brown & stone . . 75 40

1981. Pantheon.
2438 **911** 1f.60 purple and blue . . 70 35

912 Disabled Draughtsman

1981. International Year of Disabled Persons.
2439 **912** 1f.60 black, bl & red . . 65 45

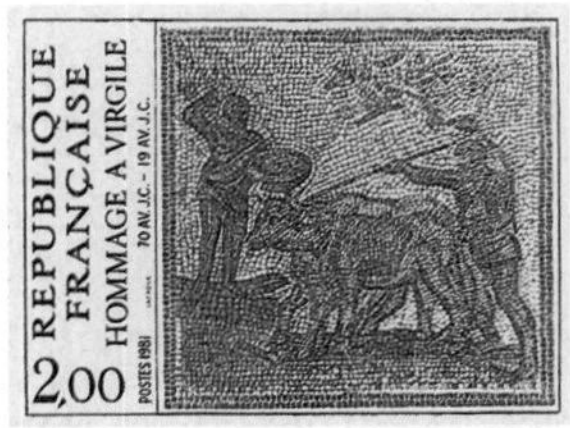

913 Pastoral Scene (2nd-century mosaic)

1981. 2000th Death Anniv of Virgil (poet).
2440 **913** 2f. multicoloured . . . . 1·20 1·00

914 "Scourges of the Passion"

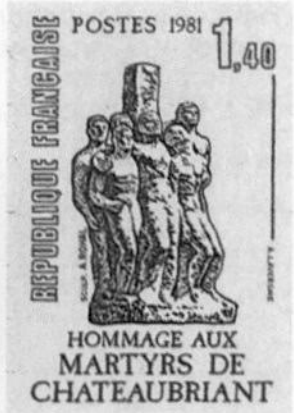

915 Memorial (Antoine Rohal)

1981. Red Cross Fund. Stained Glass Windows by Fernand Leger from the Church of the Sacred Heart, Audincort. Multicoloured.
2441 1f.40+30c. Type **914** . . . 85 95
2442 1f.60+30c. "Peace" 85 95

1981. Martyrs of Chateaubriant (Second World War victims).
2443 **915** 1f.40 black, purple & bl 55 45

916 "Liberty" (from "Liberty guiding the People" by Delacroix)

918 Guillaume Postel (scholar)

1982.
2444 **916** 5c. green 20 15
2445 10c. red 10 10
2446 15c. purple 35 40
2447 20c. green 10 10
2448 30c. orange 10 10
2449 40c. brown 20 20
2450 50c. mauve 25 10
2451 60c. brown 25 15
2452 70c. blue 30 25
2453 80c. green 35 20
2454 90c. mauve 35 30
2455 1f. green 40 15
2456 1f.40 green 65 25
2457 1f.60 red 55 20
2458 1f.60 green 65 10
2484 1f.70 green 95 65
2460 1f.80 red 65 20
2461 1f.80 green 75 35
2487 1f.90 green . . . . . . 1·10 65
2465 2f. green 00 30
2464 2f. red 65 10
2466 2f.10 red 65 10
2467 2f.20 red 65 10
2468 2f.30 blue . . . . . . 2·20 1·20
2469 2f.60 blue . . . . . . 2·00 1·20
2470 2f.80 blue . . . . . . 1·70 1·10
2471 3f. brown 95 35
2472 3f. blue . . . . . . 1·70 90
2473 3f.20 blue . . . . . . 1·90 85
2474 3f.40 blue . . . . . . 2·20 1·10
2475 3f.60 blue . . . . . . 1·30 85
2476 3f.70 purple . . . . . . 1·30 65
2477 4f. red . . . . . . 1·30 55
2478 5f. blue . . . . . . 1·70 45
2479 10f. violet . . . . . . 2·75 85

1982. Tourist Publicity. As T **490**.
2503 1f.60 blue, green and black 70 40
2504 2f. red and mauve 85 55
2505 2f.90 green, dp brn & brn 1·20 90
2506 3f. deep blue and blue . . . 1·10 70
2507 3f. red, yellow and blue . . 1·00 65
DESIGNS—VERT: No. 2503, Fishing boats and map of St. Pierre et Miquelon. HORIZ: No. 2504, Aix-en-Provence; 2505, Chateau de Ripaille, Haute-Savoie; 2506, Chateau Henri IV, Pau; 2507, Collonges-la-Rouge.

1982. Regions of France. As T **758**.
2508 1f.90 blue and red 75 45
DESIGN: 1f.90, Map of Corsica, containing sun and sea, superimposed on mountain.

1982. Pre-cancelled. Historic Monuments (4th series). As T **862**.
2509 97c. green 50 45
2510 1f.25 red 60 60
2511 2f.03 brown 95 95
2512 3f.36 blue . . . . . . 1·40 1·40
DESIGNS: 97c. Chateau de Tanlay; 1f.25, Salses Fort; 2f.03, Montlhery Tower; 3f.36, Chateau d'If. See note below No. 432 (1920).

1982. Red Cross Fund. Celebrities.
2513 **918** 1f.40+30c. black and brown 85 95
2514 – 1f.40+30c. brown and grey 85 95
2515 – 1f.60+30c. lilac, violet and purple 95 95
2516 – 1f.60+40c. blue and brown 85 90
2517 – 1f.60+40c. blue 85 90
2518 – 1f.80+40c. brown . . . 1·20 1·30
DESIGNS: No. 2514, Henri Mondor (doctor and writer); 2515, Andre Chantemesse (doctor and bacteriologist); 2516, Louis Pergaud (writer); 2517, Robert Debre (professor of medicine); 2518, Gustave Eiffel (engineer).

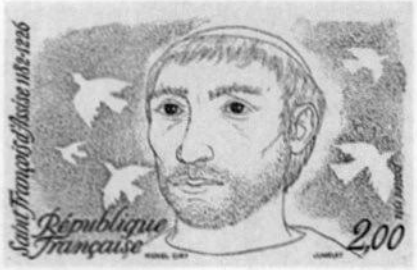

919 St. Francis of Assisi

1982. 800th Birth Anniv of St. Francis of Assisi.
2519 **919** 2f. black and blue . . . 80 60

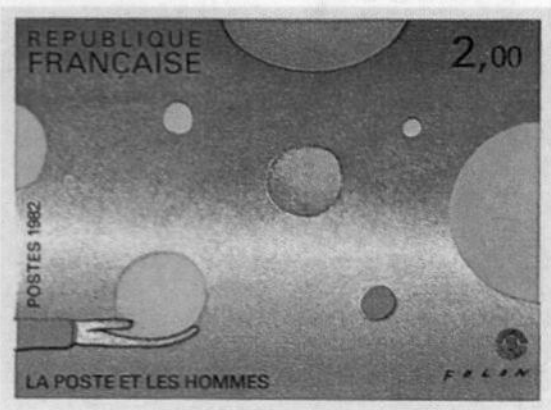

920 "The Post and Man"

1982. "Philexfrance 82" International Stamp Exhibition, Paris (3rd issue). Multicoloured.
2520 2f. Type **920** . . . . . . 3·75 3·25
2521 2f. Cogwheels ("The Post and Technology") . . . . 3·75 3·25

921 Lord Baden-Powell and Scouts

922 "Marianne" on Map of France

1982. 75th Anniv of Boy Scout Movement and 125th Birth Anniv of Lord Baden-Powell (founder).
2522 **921** 2f.30 black & green . . . 85 60

1982. Population Census.
2523 **922** 1f.60 multicoloured . . . 55 40

923 Basel-Mulhouse Airport

1982.
2524 **923** 1f.90 blue, brn & red . . 95 60

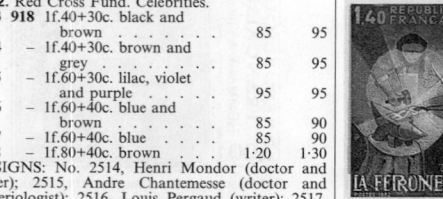

924 Clasped Wrists

1982. Anti-racism Campaign.
2525 **924** 2f.30 orange & brown 95 65

925 "Woman Reading" (Picasso)

1982. Stamp Day.
2526 **925** 1f.60+40c. mult 95 85

926 "Blacksmith" (Toffoli)

927 Map of Europe and Seal (Treaty of Rome)

1982. Handicrafts. Iron Work.
2527 **926** 1f.40 yellow, red & blk 65 55

1982. Europa.
2528 **927** 1f.60 blue 75 45
2529 – 2f.30 brn, blk & grn . . 95 65
DESIGN: 2f.30, Seal of Charles the Bald (Treaty of Verdun, 843).

928 Goalkeeper and Stadium

1982. World Cup Football Championship, Spain.
2530 **928** 1f.80 green, red & bl . . 1·20 55

1982. Art. Designs as T **491**.
2531 4f. yellow, blue and brown 1·80 1·30
2532 4f. multicoloured . . . . . 1·80 1·20
2533 4f. multicoloured . . . . . 1·90 1·30
2534 4f. pink and grey . . . . 1·80 1·30
DESIGNS—VERT: No. 2531, "Ephebus of Agde" (ancient Greek bronze sculpture); 2533, "The Lacemaker" (Vermeer); 2534, "The Family" (sculpture, Marc Boyan). HORIZ: 2532, "Embarkation of St. Paul at Ostia" (Claude Gellee (Le Lorrain)).

929 Festival Poster (Federico Fellini)

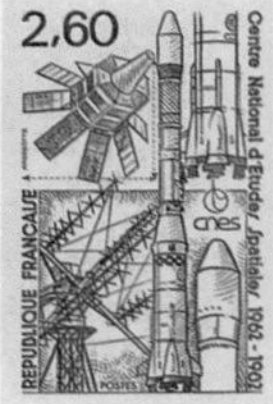

930 "Eole" Satellite, "Ariane" Rocket and Antenna

1982. 35th International Film Festival, Cannes.
2535 **929** 2f.30 multicoloured . . . 95 90

1982. 20th Anniv of National Space Studies Centre.
2536 **930** 2f.60 dp blue, bl & red 95 85

931 Interlocking Lines

932 Valles

1982. Industrialized Countries Summit, Versailles.
2537 **931** 2f.60 multicoloured . . . 1·00 90

1982. 150th Birth Anniv of Jules Valles (journalist).
2538 **932** 1f.60 dp green & green 70 40

933 "Marianne"

934 The Joliot-Curies

1982. "Philexfrance 82" International Stamp Exhibition, Paris (4th issue). Sheet 100 × 71 mm.
MS2539 **933** 4f. blue and red; 6f. red and blue . . . . 15·00 15·00

1982. Frederic and Irene Joliot-Curie (nuclear physicists) Commemoration.
2540 **934** 1f.80 pur, mve & vio . . 75 50

935 Grenoble Street Scene

936 Firemen

1982. Centenary of Electric Street Lighting.
2541 **935** 1f.80 purple, bl & vio . . 70 40

1982. Cent of National Federation of Fire Fighters.
2542 **936** 3f.30 brown and red . . 1·40 75

937 Marionnettes

1982.
2543 **937** 1f.80 red, blue & lilac . . 75 50

938 Rugby

1982.
2544 **938** 1f.60 blue, grn & red . . 1·60 55

939 Lecture Room

940 Lille

1982. Teacher Training Colleges.
2545 **939** 1f.80 grey & brown . . . 75 50

1982.
2546 **940** 1f.80 red and green . . . 75 40

1982. Philatelic Creations. As T **795**. Mult.
2547 4f. "The Turkish Room" (Balthus) . . . . 1·80 1·30

941 Dr. Robert Koch, Microscope and Bacillus

942 "Five Weeks in a Balloon"

1982. Cent of Discovery of Tubercle Bacillus.
2548 **941** 2f.60 black and red . . . 95 65

1982. Red Cross Fund. Works by Jules Verne.
2549 **942** 1f.60+30c. brown & red 85 85
2550 – 1f.80+40c. green & red 75 75
DESIGN: 1f.80, "20,000 Leagues Under the Sea".

943 St. Theresa of Avila

1982. 400th Death Anniv of St. Theresa of Avila.
2551 **943** 2f.10 brn, blk & grn . . 80 50

944 Latecoere 300 Flying Boat "Croix du Sud"

1982. Air. 46th Anniv of Disappearance of "Croix du Sud".
2552 **944** 1f.60 lilac and blue . . . 85 90

945 Cavelier de la Salle and Map of Louisiana

946 Leon Blum

1982. 300th Anniv of Discovery of Louisiana.
2553 **945** 3f.25 brn, red & grn . . 1·10 75

1982. 110th Birth Anniv of Leon Blum (politician).
2554 **946** 1f.80 brown & lt brn . . 70 35

1983. Regions of France. As T **758**.
2555 1f. multicoloured 45 25
DESIGN—HORIZ: 1f. Map and coastline, Provence, Alpes, Cote d'Azur.

947 Andre Messager (composer)

948 Budding Plant (spring)

1983. Red Cross Fund. Celebrities.
2556 **947** 1f.60+30c. blk & bl . . . 1·00 1·00
2557 – 1f.60+30c. blk & yell . . 95 95
2558 – 1f.80+40c. blk & vio . . 1·10 1·10
2559 – 1f.80+40c. blk & red . . 1·10 1·10
2560 – 2f.+40c. blk & grn . . . 1·10 1·10
2561 – 2f.+40c. black & bl . . . 1·10 1·10
DESIGNS: No. 2557, Jacques-Ange Gabriel (architect); 2558, Hector Berlioz (composer); 2559, Max-Pol Fouchet (writer); 2560, Rene Cassin (diplomat); 2561, Stendhal (writer).

1983. Pre-cancelled. The Four Seasons.
2562 **948** 1f.05 green 45 45
2563 – 1f.35 red 60 60
2564 – 2f.19 brown 90 90
2565 – 3f.63 violet . . . . . . 1·50 1·50
DESIGNS: 1f.35, Wheat (summer); 2f.19, Berries (autumn); 3f.63, Tree in snow (winter).
See note below No. 432 (1920).

949 Charleville Mezieres (½-size illustration)

1983. Tourist Publicity.
2566 – 1f.80 brown, grn & bl 65 40
2567 – 2f. brown and black . . 70 55
2568 – 3f. brown and blue . . . 1·10 80
2569 **949** 3f.10 brown and red . . 1·30 95
2570 – 3f.60 black, brn & bl . . 1·20 70
DESIGNS—As T **490**: 1f.80, Brantome, Perigord; 2f. Jarnac; 3f. Concarneau; 3f.60, Noirlac Abbey.
See also Nos. 2838 and 3642/5.

950 Martin Luther

951 Woman reading and Globe

1983. 500th Birth Anniv of Martin Luther (Protestant reformer).
2571 **950** 3f.30 brown & stone . . 1·20 75

1983. Centenary of French Alliance (language-teaching and cultural institute).
2572 **951** 1f.80 blue, red & brn . . 70 40

952 "Man dictating Letter" (Rembrandt)

1983. Stamp Day.
2573 **952** 1f.80+40c. stone and black . . . . 1·10 1·10

953 Danielle Casanova (resistance leader)

1983. International Women's Day.
2574 **953** 3f. brown and black . . 1·00 55

954 Figure within Globe releasing Dove

955 Montgolfier Brothers' Hot-air Balloon

1983. World Communications Year.
2575 **954** 2f.60 multicoloured . . . 1·00 85

1983. Bicentenary of Manned Flight. Mult.
2576 2f. Type **955** (first manned flight by Pilatre de Rozier and Marquis d'Arlandes, Nov 1783) . . . . 1·00 1·10
2577 3f. Hydrogen balloon over Tuileries, Paris (flight by J. Charles and M. N. Robert, Dec 1783) . . . . 1·30 1·40

1983. Philatelic Creations. As T **795**. Mult.
2578 4f. "Aurora-Set" (Dewasne) (horiz) . . . . 1·90 1·50
2579 4f. "Marianne" licking envelope (Jean Effel) (vert) . . . . 1·80 1·50

1983. Art. As T **491**.
2580 4f. brown and buff . . . . 1·90 1·50
2581 4f. black and red . . . . . 1·90 1·50
2582 4f. multicoloured . . . . . 1·70 1·20
DESIGNS—VERT: No. 2580, "Venus and Psyche" (preparatory sketch for fresco, Raphael); 2581, "Blue-beard giving Keys to his wife" from Perrault's "Tales" (engraving by Gustave Dore). HORIZ: 2582, "The agile Rabbit Inn" (Utrillo).

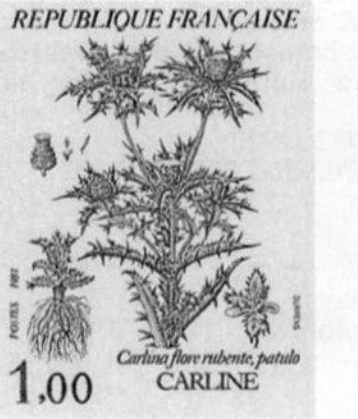

956 Thistle

957 Camera Diaphragm (photography)

1983. Flowers. Engravings from Paris Natural History Museum Library. Multicoloured.
2583 1f. Type **956** 40 30
2584 2f. Turk's cap lily (after Nicolas Robert) 75 45
2585 3f. Aster (after Nicolas Robert) . . . . 1·10 75
2586 4f. Aconite . . . . 1·60 85

1983. Europa. Each brown and deep brown.
2587 1f.80 Type **957** . . . . . . 1·80 65
2588 2f.60 Light rays entering eye and film (cinema) . . . . 2·10 1·10

958 Hands on Globe

959 Marseille

1983. Centenary of Paris Convention for the Protection of Industrial Property.
2589 **958** 2f. multicoloured 65 40

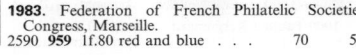

1983. Federation of French Philatelic Societies Congress, Marseille.
2590 **959** 1f.80 red and blue . . . 70 50

960 Air France Colours and Emblem

1983. 50th Anniv of Air France.
2591 **960** 3f.45 blue, red & black 1·40 1·10

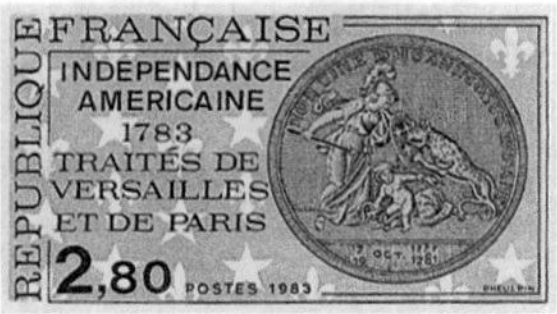

961 "France defending U.S.A. from England" (medal by Augustin Dupre)

1983. Bicentenary of Treaties of Versailles and Paris.
2592 **961** 2f.80 brown & black . . 1·00 85

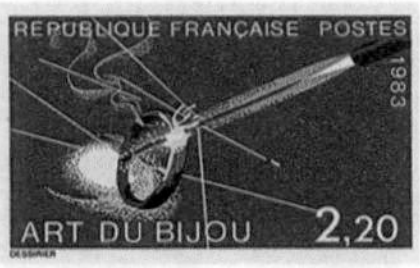

962 Forging a Ring

1983. Handicrafts. Jewellery.
2593 **962** 2f.20 multicoloured . . . 80 50

963 Customs Museum, Bordeaux

1983. 30th Anniv of Customs Co-operation Council.
2594 **963** 2f.30 blk, dp grn & grn 90 60

964 Pierre and Ernest Michaux's Bicycle

965 Globe and Weather-Satellite and Map

1983. The Bicycle.
2595 **964** 1f.60 black, blue & red 1·10 50

1983. National Meteorology.
2596 **965** 1f.50 dp blue, brn & bl 70 40

966 Renee Levy

967 Virgin and Child, Baillon

1983. Heroines of the Resistance.
2597 **966** 1f.60 brown & blue . . . 50 55
2598 – 1f.60 brown and green 65 45
DESIGN: No. 2598, Berthie Albrecht.

1983. Red Cross Fund. Wood Sculptures.
2599 **967** 1f.60+40c. brn & red . . 85 90
2600 – 2f.+40c. blue & red . . . 85 90
DESIGN: 2f. Virgin and Child, Genainville.

968 Pierre Mendes France

969 Emile Littre (lexicographer and writer)

1983. 1st Death Anniv of Pierre Mendes France (statesman).
2601 **968** 2f. black and red 65 40

1984. Red Cross Fund. Celebrities.
2602 **969** 1f.60+40c. purple and black 85 90
2603 – 1f.60+40c. green and black 85 90
2604 – 1f.70+40c. violet and black . . . . 1·00 1·10
2605 – 2f.+40c. grey and black 1·00 1·10
2606 – 2f.10+40c. brown and black . . . . 1·00 1·10
2607 – 2f.10+40c. blue and black . . . . 1·00 1·10
DESIGNS: No. 2603, Jean Zay (politician); 2604, Pierre Corneille (dramatist); 2605, Gaston Bachelard (philosopher and poet); 2606, Jean Paulhan (writer); 2607, Evariste Galois (mathematician).

1984. Art. As T **491**. Multicoloured.
2608 4f. "Cesar" film award (Cesar Baldaccini) (vert) 1·70 1·30
2609 4f. "The Four Corners of Heaven" (Jean Messagier) (horiz) . . . . 1·70 1·30
2610 4f. "Corner of Dining Room at Cannet" (Pierre Bonnard) (horiz) . . . . 1·70 1·40
2611 5f. "Pythia" (Andre Masson) (vert) . . . . . 2·10 1·40
2612 5f. "The Painter trampled by his Model" (Jean Helion) (vert) . . . . . . 2·10 1·40

1984. Regions of France. As T **758**.
2613 2f.30 violet, purple & red . . 90 50
DESIGN—HORIZ: 2f.30, Map and dancers, Guadeloupe.

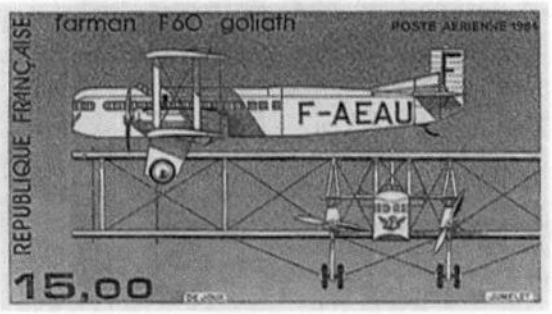

970 Farman F60 Goliath

1984. Air.
2614a **970** 15f. blue . . . . . . 2·75 90
2614ba – 20f. red . . . . 3·75 1·10
2614ca – 30f. violet . . . . . . 8·25 3·75
2614d – 50f. green . . . . . . 13·50 9·50
DESIGNS: 20f. CAMS 53 flying boat; 30f. Wibault 283 trimotor; 50f. Dewoitine D-338 trimotor.

971 Flora Tristan

1984. International Women's Day.
2615 **971** 2f.80 purple and black 1·00 65

972 "Diderot" (L. M. van Loo)

1984. Stamp Day.
2616 **972** 2f.+40c. blue & blk . . . 1·10 1·20

973 Pierre Waldeck-Rousseau (politician)

974 Emblem

1984. Centenary of Trade Union Legislation.
2617 **973** 3f.60 black and blue . . 1·10 70

1984. 2nd Direct Elections to European Parliament.
2618 **974** 2f. orange, yell & bl . . 70 40

975 Hearts

976 Jacques Cartier and "Grande Hermine"

1984. Precancels. Playing Cards.
2619 **975** 1f.14 violet and red . . . 55 55
2620 – 1f.47 blue and black . . 75 75
2621 – 2f.38 brown and red . . 1·30 1·30
2622 – 3f.95 green and black . . 1·90 1·90
DESIGNS: 1f.47, Spades; 2f.38, Diamonds; 3f.95, Clubs.
See note below No. 432 (1920).

1984. 450th Anniv of Jacques Cartier's Voyage to Canada.
2623 **976** 2f. multicoloured 70 35

977 Children and "Sower" Stamp

1984. "Philex-Jeunes 84" Stamp Exhibition, Dunkirk.
2624 **977** 1f.60 brn, red & vio . . 65 50

978 Bridge

1984. Europa. 25th Anniv of European Post and Telecommunications Conference.
2625 **978** 2f. red 95 50
2626 2f.80 blue . . . . 1·20 80

979 Legionnaires at Camerone, Mexico, 1863

1984. Foreign Legion.
2627 **979** 3f.10 red, grn & blk . . 1·10 75

980 Resistance Fighter

1984. 40th Anniv of Liberation.
2628 **980** 2f. red, brown and black 1·10 1·00
2629 – 3f. red, brown and black 1·30 1·40
DESIGN: 3f. Soldiers disembarking.

1984. Tourist Publicity. As T **490**.
2630 1f.70 blue and red 70 40
2631 2f.10 brown, green & red . . 80 40
2632 2f.50 brown, green & blue 70 60
2633 3f.50 purple and black . . . 1·50 80
2634 3f.70 purple, violet & red . . 1·20 80
DESIGNS—HORIZ: 1f.70, Monastery of Grande, Chartreuse; 2f.10, Cheval's Ideal Palace, Hauterives; 2f.50, Vauban's Citadel, Belle-Ile-en-Mer, Brittany; 3f.70, Chateau de Montsegur. VERT: 3f.50, Cordouan lighthouse, Gironde.

981 Olympic Sports (½-size illustration)

1984. Olympic Games, Los Angeles, and 90th Anniv of International Olympic Committee.
2635 **981** 4f. lilac, blue & green . . 1·50 1·20

982 Engraver

983 Bordeaux

1984. Handicrafts. Engraving.
2636 **982** 2f. brown, blk & grn . . 70 40

1984. Federation of French Philatelic Societies Congress, Bordeaux.
2637 **983** 2f. red 70 40

984 Anniversary Emblem

1984. 40th Anniv of National Centre for Telecommunications Studies.
2638 **984** 3f. blue and deep blue 1·00 55

985 Contour Map of Alps (½-size illustration)

1984. 25th International Geography Congress, Paris.
2639 **985** 3f. blue, black & orge . . 1·00 80

986 "Telecom 1"

1984. "Telecom 1" Communications Satellite.
2640 **986** 3f.20 multicoloured . . . 1·30 85

987 TGV Mail Train

988 Marx Dormoy

1984. Inauguration of TGV High-speed Paris–Lyon Mail Service.
2641 **987** 2f.10 multicoloured . . . 95 40

1984. Marx Dormoy (politician) Commemoration.
2642 **988** 2f.40 black and blue . . 85 40

989 Lammergeier

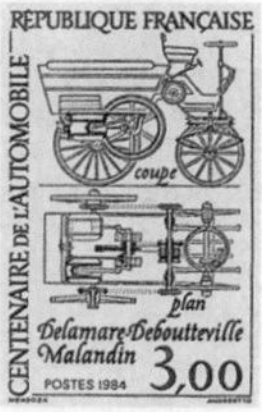

990 Delmare-Debouteville Malandin Automobile

1984. Birds of Prey. Multicoloured.
2643 1f. Type **989** 35 35
2644 2f. Short-toed eagle 90 45
2645 3f. Northern sparrowhawk 1·20 95
2646 5f. Peregrine falcon . . . . 1·60 95

1984. Centenary of Motor Car.
2647 **990** 3f. brown, blue & red . . 1·30 65

991 Vincent Auriol

992 "The Pink Basket" (Caly)

1984. Birth Centenary of Vincent Auriol (President, 1947–54).
2648 **991** 2f.10 brown & green . . 75 45

1984. Red Cross Fund.
2649 **992** 2f.10+50c. mult . . . . 1·10 1·20

993 Emblem

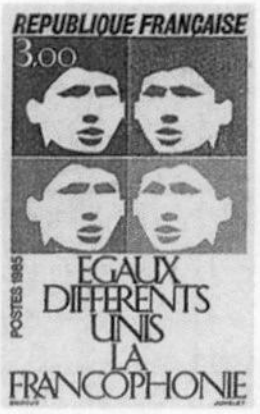

994 Four Heads

1984. 9th Five-year Plan.
2650 **993** 2f.10 blue, red and black 80 40

1985. Promotion of French Language.
2651 **994** 3f. deep blue & blue . . 1·00 65

1985. Tourist Publicity. As T **490**.
2652 1f.70 green, olive & brown 85 40
2653 2f.10 brown and orange . . 1·00 50
2654 2f.20 multicoloured . . . . 1·00 45
2655 3f. brown, red and blue . . 1·30 70
2656 3f.90 brown, red and blue 1·70 75
DESIGNS—HORIZ: 1f.70, Vienne, Isere; 2f.10, Montpellier Cathedral; 3f. Talmont Church; 3f.90, Solutre. VERT: 2f.20, St. Michael of Cuxa Abbey.

995 Coloured Dots

1985. 50th Anniv of French Television.
2657 **995** 2f.50 multicoloured . . . 1·10 60

996 Snowflake (January)

997 Couple, Heart-shaped Letter-box and Cherubs

1985. Precancels. Months of the Year (1st series).
2658 **996** 1f.22 violet and lilac . . 75 75
2659 – 1f.57 grey and blue . . . 85 1·20
2660 – 2f.55 brown & green . . 1·20 1·40
2661 – 4f.23 green & orange . . 1·90 2·40
DESIGNS: 1f.57, Bare branch and bird (February); 2f.55, Rain-drops and sun-rays (March); 4f.23, Flowers (April).
See note below No. 432 (1920).
See also Nos. 2699/2702 and 2750/3.

1985. St. Valentine's Day.
2662 **997** 2f.10 multicoloured . . . 1·00 40

998 Jean-Paul Sartre

1985. Red Cross Fund. Writers.
2663 **998** 1f.70+40c. violet and purple . . . . 2·50 2·75
2664 – 1f.70+40c. purple and violet . . . . 2·50 2·75
2665 – 1f.70+40c. violet and deep violet . . . . . 2·50 2·75
2666 – 2f.10+50c. deep violet and violet . . . . . 2·50 2·75
2667 – 2f.10+50c. violet and purple . . . . 2·50 2·75
2668 – 2f.10+50c. purple and violet . . . . 2·50 2·75
DESIGNS: No. 2664, Romain Rolland; 2665, Jules Romains; 2666, Francois Mauriac; 2667, Victor Hugo; 2668, Roland Dorgeles.

1000 Pauline Kergomard

1001 Daguin Cancelling Machine

1985. International Women's Day. 60th Death Anniv of Pauline Kergomard (reformer of infant schools).
2670 **1000** 1f.70 blue and brown 85 40

1985. Stamp Day.
2671 **1001** 2f.10+50c. brown, grey and black . . . . . 1·10 1·20

1985. Art. As T **491**.
2672 5f. multicoloured . . . . . 3·75 1·50
2673 5f. multicoloured . . . . . 3·25 1·50
2674 5f. multicoloured . . . . . 2·40 1·40
2675 5f. red, green and black . . 2·40 1·40
2676 5f. black and yellow . . . . 2·40 1·40
DESIGNS—VERT: No. 2672, "Judgement of Solomon" (stained glass window, Strasbourg Cathedral); 2675, Painting by Pierre Alechinsky. HORIZ: No. 2673, "Still Life with Candlestick" (Nicholas de Stael); 2674, Painting by Dubuffet; 2676, "The Dog" (sculpture by Alberto Giacometti).

1002 Landevennec Abbey

1985. 1500th Anniv of Landevennec Abbey.
2677 **1002** 1f.70 green & purple . . 85 40

1003 Modern Housing, Givors (Jean Renaudie)

1985. Contemporary Architecture.
2678 **1003** 2f.40 blk, grn & orge 1·10 60

1004 Adam de la Halle (composer)

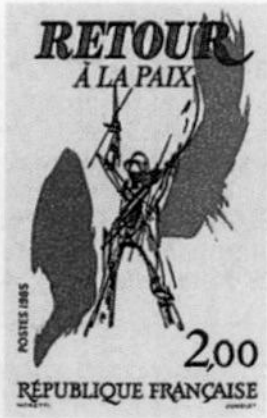

1005 Soldier with Rifle

1985. Europa. Music Year.
2679 **1004** 2f.10 dp bl, bl & blk . . 1·10 50
2680 – 3f. black, bl & dp bl . . 1·70 85
DESIGN: 3f. Darius Milhaud (composer).

1985. 40th Anniv of V.E. (Victory in Europe) Day.
2681 **1005** 2f. black, red & blue . . 90 80
2682 – 3f. black, red & blue . . 1·20 1·00
DESIGN: 3f. Prisoners of war.

1006 Tours Cathedral

1007 Vaccinating Patient (after Le Riverend)

1985. Federation of French Philatelic Societies Congress, Tours.
2683 **1006** 2f.10 indigo and blue 90 50

1985. Centenary of Anti-rabies Vaccination.
2684 **1007** 1f.50 brn, grn & red . . 75 40

1008 Dassault Breguet Mystere Falcon 900

1985. 36th International Aeronautics and Space Exhibition, Le Bourget.
2685 **1008** 10f. blue . . . . 4·75 2·75

1009 Capsized Boat and Lifeboat — **1010** U.N. Emblem

1985. Centenary of Lake Geneva International Life-Saving Society.
2686 **1009** 2f.50 black, red & bl . . 1·00 55

1985. 40th Anniv of U.N.O.
2687 **1010** 3f. blue, grey & dp bl 1·20 65

1011 Huguenot Cross — **1012** Beech

1985. French Huguenots (300th Anniv of Revocation of Edict of Nantes).
2688 **1011** 2f.50 brown, red & bl 1·10 60

1985. Trees.
2689 **1012** 1f. black, green & blue 55 30
2690 – 2f. black, green & red 1·10 45
2691 – 3f. black, green & violet 1·40 90
2692 – 5f. black, green & brn 2·30 1·00
DESIGNS: 2f. Scotch elm; 3f. Pedunculate oak; 5f. Norwegian spruce.

1013 "Marianne" — **1014** Dullin and Theatre

1985. National Memorial Day.
2693 **1013** 1f.80 pur, orge & blk 90 40

1985. Birth Centenary of Charles Dullin (actor).
2694 **1014** 3f.20 black & blue . . . 1·30 65

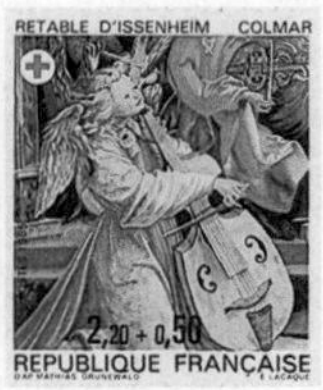

1015 World Map on Open Book and Keyboard — **1016** "Concert of Angels" (M. Grunewald) (detail, Isenheim Altarpiece)

1985. 40th Anniv of French Information Service.
2695 **1015** 2f.20 black and red . . 90 40

1985. Red Cross Fund.
2696 **1016** 2f.20+50c. mult . . . . 1·10 1·10

1017 Siamese Envoys before King Louis XIV — **1019** Masked Revellers

1018 "Leisure Activities" (Fernand Leger)

1986. 300th Anniv of Diplomatic Relations with Thailand.
2697 **1017** 3f.20 purple & black . . 1·30 95

1986. 50th Anniv of Popular Front.
2698 **1018** 2f.20 multicoloured . . 1·00 40

1986. Precancels. Months of the Year (2nd series). As T **996**.
2699 1f.28 pink and green 90 95
2700 1f.65 green & turquoise . . 1·10 1·10
2701 2f.67 blue and red . . . . . 1·40 1·50
2702 4f.44 orange and brown . . 2·30 2·50
DESIGNS: 1f.28, Butterflies (May); 1f.65, Flowers (June); 2f.67, Phrygian cap (July); 4f.44, Sun (August).
See note below No. 432 (1920).

1986. Venetian Carnival in Paris.
2703 **1019** 2f.20 multicoloured . . 1·00 40

1020 Francois Arago (physicist and politician) — **1021** Woman's Head

1986. Red Cross Fund. Celebrities.
2704 **1020** 1f.80+40c. black, blue & turquoise 85 95
2705 – 1f.80+40c. black, blue & turquoise 85 95
2706 – 1f.80+40c. black, blue & turquoise 85 95
2707 – 2f.20+50c. black, turquoise & blue . . 95 1·10
2708 – 2f.20+50c. black, turquoise & blue . . 1·10 1·20
2709 – 2f.20+50c. brown . . . 2·40 2·30
DESIGNS: No. 2705, Henri Moissan (chemist); 2706, Henri Fabre (engineer); 2707, Marc Seguin (locomotive engineer); 2708, Paul Heroult (chemist); 2709, Pierre Cot (politician).

1986. Tourist Publicity. As T **490** and **949**.
2710 1f.80 multicoloured 85 40
2711 2f. blue and black 90 60
2712 2f.20 brown, blue & green 1·00 50
2713 2f.50 dp brown & brown . . 1·20 50
2714 3f.90 orange and black . . . 2·10 1·20
DESIGNS: As T **490**—HORIZ: 1f.80, Filitosa, Corsica; 2f. Chateau de Loches; 2f.20, Manor of St. Germain de Livet, Calvados. VERT: 2f.50, Cloisters, Notre Dame en Vaux, Marne. As T **949**: 3f.90, Monpazier, Dordogne.

1986. Typography.
2715 **1021** 5f. black and red . . . 2·50 1·40

1022 Louise Michel (writer)

1986. International Women's Day.
2716 **1022** 1f.80 black and red . . 85 40

1023 La Villette

1986. Science and Industry City, La Villette.
2717 **1023** 3f.90 multicoloured . . 1·70 85

1024 Britska Mail Coach

1986. Stamp Day.
2718 **1024** 2f.20+60c. pink and brown . . . . 1·30 1·20
2719 2f.20+60c. yellow and black . . . . 1·40 1·50

1025 Map and Latitude Lines

1986. 50th Anniv of African and Asian Studies Centre.
2720 **1025** 3f.20 multicoloured . . 1·40 80

1986. Art. As T **491**.
2721 5f. multicoloured . . . . . 2·40 1·50
2722 5f. multicoloured . . . . . 2·40 1·60
2723 5f. multicoloured . . . . . 2·50 1·30
2724 5f. multicoloured . . . . . 2·50 1·40
2725 5f. grey, black & violet . . . 2·50 1·40
DESIGNS—HORIZ: No. 2721, "Skibet" (Maurice Esteve); 2722, "Virginia" (Alberto Magnelli); 2725, Abstract by Pierre Soulages. VERT: 2723, "The Dancer" (Hans Arp); 2724, "Isabelle d'Este" (Leonardo da Vinci).

1026 Genet — **1027** Victor Basch

1986. Europa.
2726 **1026** 2f.20 black and red . . 1·20 45
2727 – 3f.20 black and red . . 1·70 75
DESIGN: 3f.20, Lesser horseshoe bat.

1986. International Peace Year.
2728 **1027** 2f.50 black & green . . 1·10 55

1028 Vianney — **1029** City Gate

1986. Birth Bicentenary of Saint J. M. B. Vianney, Cure d'Ars.
2729 **1028** 1f.80 brown, deep brown and orange . . 85 40

1986. Federation of French Philatelic Societies Congress, Nancy.
2730 **1029** 2f. blue and green . . . 90 40

1030 Players — **1031** Head of Statue

1986. Men's World Volleyball Championships.
2731 **1030** 2f.20 purple, vio & red 90 50

1986. Centenary of Statue of Liberty.
2732 **1031** 2f.20 blue and red . . . 1·00 50

1032 "Liberty" (after Delacroix) — **1033** Mont Blanc, J. Balmat and M. G. Paccard

1986. No value expressed.
2733 **1032** (1f.90) green 85 40
See also Nos. 2784 and 2949/50.

1986. Bicentenary of First Ascent of Mont Blanc.
2734 **1033** 2f. blue, dp bl & brn 90 60

1034 Maupertuis and La Condamine

1986. 250th Anniv of Measurement of Arcs of Meridian.
2735 **1034** 3f. black, lt bl & bl . . 1·30 70

1035 Marcasite — **1037** Woman's Head, Printed Circuit and Drawing Instruments

1036 Musidora in "The Vampires" (dir. Louis Feuillade)

1986. Minerals.
2736 **1035** 2f. multicoloured . . . 95 45
2737 – 3f. multicoloured . . . 1·20 60
2738 – 4f. blue, brown & mve 1·80 1·20
2739 – 5f. turq, mve & bl . . . 2·20 1·20
DESIGNS: 3f. Quartz; 4f. Calcite; 5f. Fluorite.

1986. 50th Anniv of French Film Institute. Sheet 143 × 179 mm containing T **1036** and similar horiz designs, each black, deep grey and deep grey-brown.
MS2740 2f.20 Type **1036**; 2f.20 Max Linder; 2f.20 Sacha Guitry in "Story of a Cheat" (dir. Guitry); 2f.20 Pierre Fresnay and Eric von Stroheim in "The Great Illusion" (dir. Jean Renoir); 2f.20 Raimu and Ginette Leclerc in "The Baker's Wife" (dir. Marcel Pagnol); 2f.20 Rene Ferte in "The Triple Mirror" (dir. Jean Epstein); 2f.20 Gerard Philipe and Martine Carol in "Beauties in the Night" (dir. Rene Clair); 2f.20 Jean Gabin and Mireille Balin in "Face of Love" (dir. Jean Gremillon); 2f.20 Simone Signoret in "Casque d'Or" (Golden Marie) (dir. Jacques Becker); 2f.20 Francois Truffaut and Jean-Pierre Cargol in "The Wild Child" (dir. Truffaut) . . 9·50 9·50

1986. Centenary of Technical Education.
2741 **1037** 1f.90 blue & mauve . . 85 40

1038 Scene from "Le Grand Meaulnes" — **1039** Emblem

1986. Birth Centenary of Henri Alain-Fournier (writer).
2742 **1038** 2f.20 brown & red . . 90 45

1986. World Energy Conference, Cannes.
2743 **1039** 3f.40 blue, mve & red 1·40 85

1041 Detail of Window by Vieira da Silva, St. John's Church, Rheims — **1042** Car, Steam Locomotive and Carpet

1986. Red Cross Fund.
2745 **1041** 2f.20+60c. mult . . . . 1·20 1·30

1986. Mulhouse Technical Museums.
2746 **1042** 2f.20 red, black & blue 1·70 50

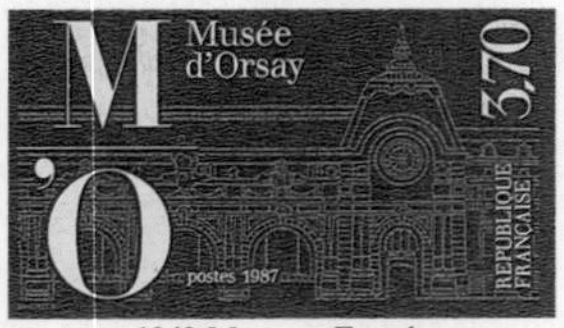

1043 Museum Facade

1986. Quai d'Orsay Museum.
2747 **1043** 3f.70 dp blue & blue . . 1·50 85

1044 Underground Train in Tunnel

1045 Raoul Follereau

1987. 50th Death Anniv (1986) of Fulgence Bienvenue (designer of Paris Metro).
2748 **1044** 2f.50 pur, grn & brn . . 1·20 60

1987. 10th Death Anniv of Raoul Follereau (leprosy pioneer).
2749 **1045** 1f.90 dp grn & grn . . 85 40

1987. Precancels. Months of the Year (3rd series). As T **996**.
2750 1f.31 brown and orange . . 95 1·00
2751 1f.69 orange and purple . . 1·20 1·40
2752 2f.74 grey and blue . . . . 1·40 1·50
2753 4f.56 green and mauve . . . 2·40 2·75
DESIGNS: 1f.31, Grapes (September); 1f.69, Posthorn (October); 2f.74, Falling leaves (November); 4f.56, Christmas tree (December).
See note below No. 432 (1920).

1046 Charles Richet (physiologist)

1047 Grinding Blades

1987. Red Cross Fund. Medical Celebrities.
2754 **1046** 1f.90+50c. blue . . . . 1·00 1·10
2755 – 1f.90+50c. lilac . . . . 1·00 1·10
2756 – 1f.90+50c. grey . . . . 1·00 1·10
2757 – 2f.20+50c. grey . . . . 1·10 1·30
2758 – 2f.20+50c. blue . . . . 1·10 1·30
2759 – 2f.20+50c. lilac . . . . 1·10 1·30
DESIGNS: No. 2755, Eugene Jamot (sleeping sickness pioneer); 2756, Bernard Halpern (immunologist); 2757, Alexandre Yersin (bacteriologist, discoverer of plague bacillus); 2758, Jean Rostand (geneticist); 2759, Jacques Monod (molecular biologist).

1987. Handicrafts. Thiers Cutlery.
2760 **1047** 1f.90 black and red . . 80 40

1048 "Liberty" and "Philexfrance 89"

1987. "Philexfrance 89" International Stamp Exhibition, Paris (1st issue).
2761 **1048** 2f.20 red . . . . 1·00 45
The stamp and label which together comprise No. 2761 were printed together se-tenant. For stamp without label, see No. 2466.
See also No. 2821.

1987. Tourist Publicity. As T **490** and **949**.
2762 2f.20 green, grey & mauve 1·10 45
2763 2f.20 multicoloured . . . . 1·10 55
2764 2f.50 green and blue . . . . 1·20 70
2765 2f.50 black, red and blue . . 1·10 65
2766 3f. brown and violet . . . . 1·30 85
2767 3f.70 blue, lilac & brown . . 3·00 1·80
DESIGNS—As T **490**: No. 2762, Redon Abbey; 2763, Etretat (after Eugene Delacroix); 2764, Azay-le-Rideau Chateau; 2765, Montbenoit le Saugeais; 2766, Les Baux-de-Provence. As T **949**: No. 2767, Cotes de Meuse.

1049 Berlin

1987. Stamp Day.
2768 **1049** 2f.20+60c. brown and yellow . . . . 1·20 1·20
2769 2f.20+60c. deep blue and blue . . . . . . 1·30 1·40

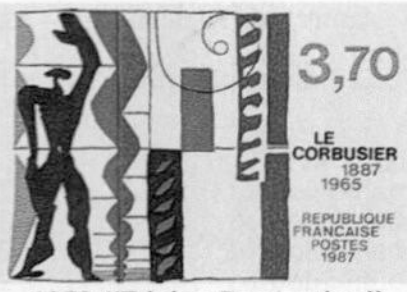

1050 "Divine Proportion"

1987. Birth Centenary of Charles-Edouard Jeanneret "Le Corbusier" (architect).
2770 **1050** 3f.70 multicoloured . . 1·60 85

1051 "57 Metal", Boulogne-Billancourt (Claude Vasconi)

1052 Gaspard of the Mountains

1987. Europa. Architecture.
2771 **1051** 2f.20 blue and green . . 1·70 55
2772 – 3f.40 brown & green . . 2·50 80
DESIGN: 3f.40, Rue Mallet-Stevens, Paris (Robert Mallet-Stevens).

1987. Art. As T **491**.
2773 5f. multicoloured . . . . . 2·40 1·50
2774 5f. multicoloured . . . . . 2·40 1·50
2775 5f. multicoloured . . . . . 2·40 1·50
2776 5f. brn, lt brn & blk . . . . 2·40 1·50
DESIGNS—HORIZ: No. 2773, "Abstract" (Bram van Velde); 2774, "Woman with Parasol" (Eugene Boudin); 2776, "World" (sculpture, Antoine Pevsner). VERT: No. 2775, "Pre-Cambrian" (Camille Bryen).

1987. Birth Centenary of Henri Pourrat (writer).
2777 **1052** 1f.90 brown and green 85 40

1053 Lens

1987. Federation of French Philatelic Societies Congress, Lens.
2778 **1053** 2f.20 red & brown . . 1·10 65

1054 Gen. Pershing, Soldiers and U.S. Flag

1055 Cable Cars

1987. 70th Anniv of Entry of U.S. Troops into First World War.
2779 **1054** 3f.40 red, blue & green 1·40 90

1987. 6th International Cable Transport Congress, Grenoble.
2780 **1055** 2f. black, bl & grn . . 85 65

1056 Noyon Cathedral and Symbol

1057 Prytanee

1987. Millenary of Election of Hugues Capet as King of France.
2781 **1056** 1f.90 black and blue . . 80 50

1987. Prytanee National Military School (for French Soldiers' Children), La Fleche.
2782 **1057** 2f.20 black, grn & red 90 50

1058 Black Footprints on Map of France

1059 Globe and Wrestlers

1987. "25 Years After" World Assembly of Repatriated French-Algerians, Nice.
2783 **1058** 1f.90 multicoloured . . 85 60

1987. No value expressed. As T **1032** but inscr "B".
2784 (2f.) green 85 55

1987. World Wrestling Championship, Clermont-Ferrand.
2785 **1059** 3f. brown, grey & vio 1·30 85

1060 "Gyroporus cyanescens"

1061 Bayeux Tapestry (detail)

1987. Fungi.
2786 **1060** 2f. multicoloured . . . 1·10 55
2787 – 3f. multicoloured . . . 1·40 80
2788 – 4f. black, bistre & brn 1·90 1·40
2789 – 5f. multicoloured . . . 2·40 1·20
DESIGNS: 3f. "Gomphus clavatus"; 4f. "Morchella conica"; 5f. "Russula virescens".

1987. 900th Death Anniv of William the Conqueror.
2790 **1061** 2f. multicoloured . . . 85 50

1062 Institute

1063 Cendrars (after Modigliani)

1987. Centenary of Pasteur Institute.
2791 **1062** 2f.20 red and blue . . . 1·00 45

1987. Birth Centenary of Blaise Cendrars (writer).
2792 **1063** 2f. buff, black and green 85 50

1064 "Flight into Egypt" (Melchior Broederlam) (detail, Champmol Charterhouse retable)

1987. Red Cross Fund.
2793 **1064** 2f.20+60c. mult . . . . 1·00 1·20

1065 Leclerc, Oasis, Tank, Pantheon and Strasbourg Cathedral

1066 Treaty Document, Brunehaut, Childebert II and King Guntram of Burgundy

1987. 40th Death Anniv of Marshal Leclerc.
2794 **1065** 2f.20 blk, brn & dp brn 1·10 45

1987. 1400th Anniv of Treaty of Andelot.
2795 **1066** 3f.70 blk, dp bl & bl . . 1·60 80

1067 Dr. Konrad Adenauer (West German Chancellor) and Charles de Gaulle (French President)

1988. 25th Anniv of Franco–German Co-operation Treaty.
2796 **1067** 2f.20 purple & black . . 1·20 50

1068 Dassault and Aircraft

1988. 2nd Death Anniv of Marcel Dassault (aircraft engineer).
2797 **1068** 3f.60 brown, red & bl 2·10 1·10

1069 People on Airplane flying around Globe (Rene Pellos)

1070 Bird flying (Air)

1988. Communications. Designs by comic strip artists. Multicoloured.
2798 2f.20 Type **1069** . . . . . 90 1·00
2799 2f.20 Monkey writing in light from table lamp (Jean-Marc Reiser) . . . 90 1·00
2800 2f.20 Sitting Bull and smoke signals (Marijac (Jacques Dumas)) . . . . 90 1·00
2801 2f.20 Couple with love letter (Fred (Othon Aristides)) 90 95
2802 2f.20 Man watching levitating letter (Moebius (Jean Giraud)) . . . . . 90 1·00
2803 2f.20 Globe and astronaut (Paul Gillon) . . . . . . 90 1·00
2804 2f.20 Man playing letter and pen "guitar" (Claire Bretecher) . . . . 90 1·00
2805 2f.20 Hand posting letter in talking letter-box (Jean-Claude Forest) . . . . . 90 1·00
2806 2f.20 Rocket behind astronaut reading letter (Jean-Claude Mezieres) . . 90 1·00
2807 2f.20 Woman with mystery letter (Jacques Tardi) . . 90 1·00
2808 2f.20 Baby reading letter in pram with attached letter-box (Jacques Lob) . . . 90 1·00
2809 2f.20 Woman pilot with letters (Enki Bilal) . . . . 90 1·00

1988. Precancels. The Elements.
2810 **1070** 1f.36 blue and black . . 1·00 95
2811 – 1f.75 blue and black . . 1·20 1·20
2812 – 2f.83 red and black . . 1·50 1·60
2813 – 4f.75 green & black . . 2·75 3·00
DESIGNS: 1f.70, Splash of water (Water); 2f.83, Flames (Fire); 4f.75, Tree (Earth).
See note below No. 432 (1920).

1071 Dove and Interior **1072** Abraham Duquesne and Map

1988. Rue Victoire Synagogue, Paris.
2814 **1071** 2f. black and gold . . . 85 60

1988. Red Cross Fund. Explorers. Each blue, brown and black.
2815 2f.+50c. Type **1072** . . . . 95 1·00
2816 2f.+50c. Pierre Andre de Suffren Saint Tropez . . 95 1·00
2817 2f.+50c. Jean Francois de Galaup, Comte de La Perouse . . . . 95 1·00
2818 2f.+50c. Bertrand Francois Mahe de La Bourdonnais 95 1·10
2819 2f.20+50c. Louis Antoine de Bougainville . . . . . . 95 1·10
2820 2f.20+50c. Jules Dumont d'Urville . . . . 95 1·10

1073 "Liberty" and Emblem

1988. "Philexfrance 89" International Stamp Exhibition, Paris (2nd issue).
2821 **1073** 2f.20 red, black & bl . . 90 45

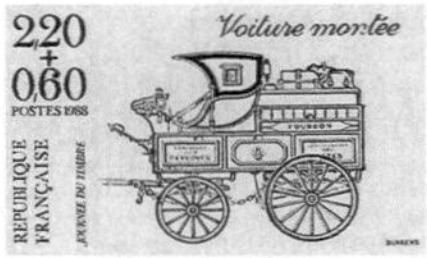

1074 Mail Coach

1988. Stamp Day.
2822 **1074** 2f.20+60c. purple and mauve . . . . 1·20 1·30
2823 2f.20+60c. brown and flesh . . . . 1·20 1·30

1075 Emblem

1988. Centenary of Post Office National College.
2824 **1075** 3f.60 bl, grn & red . . 1·40 85

1076 "Stamps"

1988. "Philex-Jeunes 88" Stamp Exhibition, Nevers.
2825 **1076** 2f. blue, violet & mve 85 40

1077 Blood Drop **1080** Monnet

1079 Cable and Satellite Communications

1988. Blood Donation Service.
2826 **1077** 2f.50 red, blk & yell . . 1·10 60

1988. No. 2467 surch **ECU 0,31..**
2827 **916** 0.31ECU on 2f.20 red 1·10 50
ECU stands for European Currency Unit.

1988. Europa. Transport and Communications.
2828 **1079** 2f.20 grey, black & bl 1·90 50
2829 – 3f.60 pur, blk & lt pur 2·50 85
DESIGN: 3f.60, Two-car electric train.

1988. Birth Centenary of Jean Monnet (statesman).
2830 **1080** 2f.20 blue and brown 1·10 45

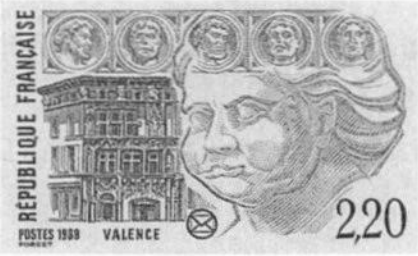

1081 Town Hall and Roman Carved Stone Heads

1988. Federation of French Philatelic Societies Congress, Valence.
2831 **1081** 2f.20 orge, dp bl & bl 90 55

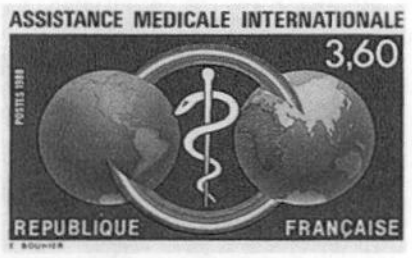

1082 Rod of Aesculapius, Globes and Rainbows

1988. International Medical Assistance.
2832 **1082** 3f.60 multicoloured . . 1·40 90

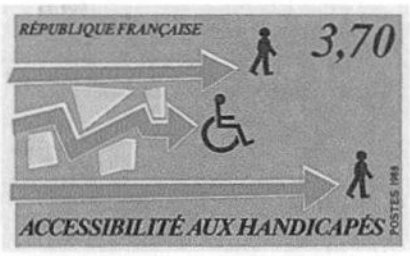

1083 Typical Access Routes

1988. Easy Access for the Handicapped.
2833 **1083** 3f.70 multicoloured . . 1·50 90

1988. Tourist Publicity.
2834 2f. multicoloured 90 40
2835 2f.20 brown, bl & turq . . . 90 50
2836 2f.20 blue, turq & grn . . . 95 45
2837 3f. violet, green and brown 1·30 65
2838 3f.70 black, blue and red . . 1·80 1·10
DESIGNS—As T **490**. HORIZ: No. 2834, Ship Museum, Douarnenez; 2836, Perouges; 2837, Cirque de Gavarnie (rock formation). VERT: No. 2835, Sedieres Chateau, Correze. As T **949**: No. 2838, "Double-headed Hermes of Frejus" (Roman sculpture).

1084 Otters **1086** Soldiers of 1888 and 1988

1085 "Assembly of the Three Estates, Vizille" (Alexandre Debelle)

1988. Animals. Illustrations from "Natural History" by Comte de Buffon.
2839 **1084** 2f. black and green . . 90 45
2840 – 3f. black and red . . . 1·30 70
2841 – 4f. black and mauve . . 1·70 1·20
2842 – 5f. black and blue . . . 2·20 1·00
DESIGNS: 3f. Stag; 4f. Fox; 5f. Badger.

1988. Bicentenary of French Revolution (1st issue). Each black, blue and red.
2843 3f. Type **1085** . . . . . . 1·30 1·40
2844 4f. "Day of the Tiles, Grenoble" (Alexandre Debelle) . . . . 1·50 1·50

See also Nos. 2857, 2863/8, 2871/3, **MS**2889, **MS**2890, **MS**3005 and **MS**3083.

1988. Centenary of Alpine Troops.
2845 **1086** 2f.50 dp bl, bl & red . . 1·20 85

1087 Bleriot XI

1988. Birth Centenary of Roland Garros (aviator).
2846 **1087** 2f. green, olive and blue 1·00 40

1088 Soldiers

1988. 70th Anniv of Armistice.
2847 **1088** 2f.20 multicoloured . . 95 45

1089 "Tribute to Leon Degand" (Robert Jacobsen) **1090** City Arms

1988. French–Danish Cultural Year.
2848 **1089** 5f. red & black on grey 2·40 1·40

1988. 2000th Anniv of Strasbourg.
2849 **1090** 2f.20 multicoloured . . 95 45

1988. Art. As T **491**.
2850 5f. brown . . . . 2·40 1·50
2851 5f. multicoloured . . . . . 2·40 1·50
2852 5f. multicoloured . . . . . 3·50 1·60
2853 5f. multicoloured . . . . . 2·50 1·60
DESIGNS—48 × 38 mm: No. 2850, St. Mihiel's Sepulchre (Ligier Richier); 2851, "Composition" (Serge Poliakoff); 2852, "Meta" (Tinguely). 48 × 43 mm: No. 2853, "Pieta de Villeneuve-les-Avignon" (Enguerrand Quarton).

1091 Activities at Spas

1988. Thermal Spas.
2854 **1091** 2f.20 red, blue & grn 95 45

1092 Cross

1988. Red Cross Fund.
2855 **1092** 2f.20+60c. red, blue and black . . . . 1·10 1·10

1093 Earth

1988. 40th Anniv of Universal Declaration of Human Rights.
2856 **1093** 2f.20 dp blue & blue . . 1·40 50

1094 Birds

1989. Bicentenary of French Revolution (2nd issue).
2857 **1094** 2f.20 blue, red & blk 95 50

1989. Art. As T **491**. Multicoloured.
2858 5f. "Anthropometry of the Blue Era" (Yves Klein) 2·30 1·50
2859 5f. "Oath of the Tennis Court" (sketch, David) . . 2·20 1·40
2860 5f. "Regetta with Wind Astern" (Lapicque) (vert) 2·40 1·60

1095 Page of Braille

1989. The Blind.
2861 **1095** 2f.20 bl, orge & mve . . 95 75

1096 "E"

1989. Centenary of Estienne School.
2862 **1096** 2f.20 blk, grey & red 95 50

1097 Comte de Sieyes

1989. Red Cross Fund. Bicentenary of French Revolution (3rd issue). Personalities. Mult.
2863 2f.20+50c. Type **1097** . . . 1·00 1·20
2864 2f.20+50c. Comte de Mirabeau . . . . 1·00 1·20
2865 2f.20+50c. Vicomte de Noailles . . . . 1·00 1·20
2866 2f.20+50c. Marquis de Lafayette . . . . 1·00 1·20
2867 2f.20+50c. Antoine Barnave 1·00 1·20
2868 2f.20+50c. Jean Baptiste Drouet . . . . 1·00 1·20

1098 Emblem on Spectrum

1989. Direct Elections to European Parliament.
2869 **1098** 2f.20 multicoloured . . 95 45

1099 Flags, Astronauts and Satellite

1989. French–Soviet Space Flight.
2870 **1099** 3f.60 multicoloured . . 1·90 95

1100 "Liberty"

1989. Bicentenary of French Revolution (4th issue) and Declaration of Rights of Man (1st issue). Paintings by Roger Druet. Multicoloured.

2871 2f.20 Type **1100** 95 45
2872 2f.20 "Equality" 95 45
2873 2f.20 "Fraternity" 95 45

1101 Paris–Lyon Stage Coach

1989. Stamp Day.

2874 **1101** 2f.20+60c. deep blue and blue . . . . . . 1·30 1·30
2875 2f.20+60c. lilac and mauve . . . . 1·30 1·30

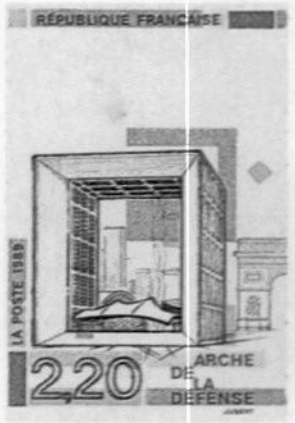

1102 Arche de la Defense

1103 Hopscotch

1989. Paris Panorama. Multicoloured.

2876 2f.20 Type **1102** . . . . . 1·10 1·10
2877 2f.20 Eiffel Tower . . . . 1·10 1·10
2878 2f.20 Pyramid, Louvre . . . 1·10 1·10
2879 2f.20 Notre Dame Cathedral 1·10 1·10
2880 2f.20 Bastille Opera House 1·10 1·10

1989. Europa. Children's Games. Mult.

2881 2f.20 Type **1103** 95 50
2882 3f.60 Ball game . . . . . . 1·70 95

1989. Tourist Publicity. As T **490** and **949**.

2883 2f.20 green, brown & orge 95 45
2884 3f.70 red, blue and black . . 1·50 90
2885 3f.70 black and brown . . . 1·50 1·00
2886 4f. blue . . . . 1·80 1·10

DESIGNS—As T **490**. HORIZ: No. 2883, Fontainebleau forest. VERT: No. 2884, Malestroit. As T **949**: No. 2885, Chateau of Vaux-le-Vicomte; 2886, La Brenne.

1104 Emblems and Buildings

1989. International Telecommunications Union Plenipotentiaries Conference, Nice.

2887 **1104** 3f.70 red, blue & orge 1·40 85

1105 Cyclists

1989. International Cycling Championships, Chambery.

2888 **1105** 2f.20 multicoloured . . 1·10 45

1106 Madame Roland

1989. Bicentenary of French Revolution (5th issue). Personalities. Sheet 78 × 105 mm containing T **1106** and similar vert designs. Multicoloured.

MS2889 2f.20 Type **1106**; 2f.20 Camille Desmoulins; 2f.20 Marquis de Condorcet; 2f.20 Major-Gen. Francois Kellerman 3·50 3·50

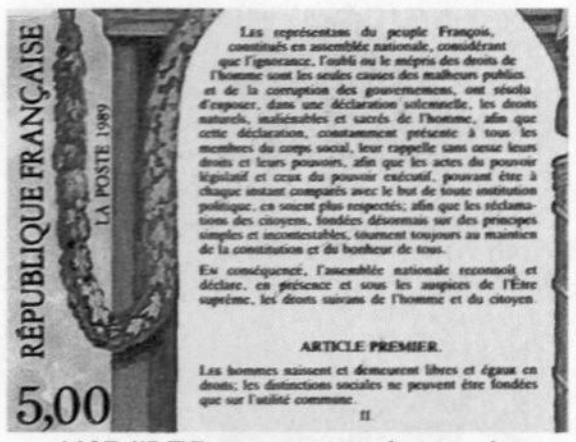

1107 "LES represantans du people Francois,..."

1989. Bicentenary of French Revolution (6th issue) and Declaration of Rights of Man (2nd issue). Sheet 130 × 143 mm containing T **1107** and similar horiz designs. Multicoloured.

MS2890 5f. Type **1107**; 5f. "NUL home ne peut etre accuse..."; 5f. "LE but de toute association politique..."; 5f. "LA garantie des droits de l'homme..." (sold at 50f.) 15·00 15·00

1108 Arche de la Defense

1989. Summit Conference of Industrialised Countries, Paris.

2891 **1108** 2f.20 multicoloured . . 95 55

1109 Preamble

1989. Bicentenary of Declaration of Rights of Man (3rd issue). Multicoloured.

2892 2f.50 Type **1109** . . . . . 1·10 1·30
2893 2f.50 Articles II to VI . . . 1·30 1·30
2894 2f.50 Articles VII to XI . . 1·30 1·30
2895 2f.50 Articles XII to XVII . 1·30 1·30

1110 Harp

1111 Train

1989. Precancels. Musical Instruments (1st series).

2896 **1110** 1f.39 lt blue & blue . . 90 95
2897 – 1f.79 brn & lt brn . . 1·00 1·00
2898 – 2f.90 orange & brn . . 2·10 2·40
2899 – 4f.84 orange & brn . . 2·75 2·75

DESIGNS: 1f.79, Piano; 2f.90, Trumpet; 4f.84, Violin.

See note below No. 432 (1920).

See also Nos. 2993/9, 3052/62, 3095/8 and 3145/8.

1989. TGV "Atlantique" Express Train.

2900 **1111** 2f.50 blue, silver & red 2·00 50

1112 Tram

1113 King Francois I

1989. Cent of Clermont-Ferrand Electric Tramway.

2901 **1112** 3f.70 black & brown . . 1·70 90

1989. 450th Anniv of Villers-Cotterets Ordinance.

2902 **1113** 2f.20 red and black . . . 95 50

1114 Cauchy, Graphs and Formula

1989. Birth Bicentenary of Augustin Louis Cauchy (mathematician).

2903 **1114** 3f.60 blue, blk & red 1·60 90

1115 Marshal Lattre de Tassigny

1989. Birth Centenary of Marshal Jean de Lattre de Tassigny.

2904 **1115** 2f.20 black, blue & red 95 50

1116 Bird feeding Chicks (18th-century silk painting)

1989. Red Cross Fund.

2905 **1116** 2f.20+60c. mult . . . . 1·10 1·20

1117 Harkis

1118 "Marianne"

1989. Harkis (French North African troops).

2906 **1117** 2f.20 multicoloured . . 1·20 45

1989. Imperf (2943), perf or imperf (2910, 2915, 2916), perf (others).

2907 **1118** 10c. brown 20 10
2908 20c. green 20 10
2909 50c. violet 25 10
2943b 70c. brown . . . . . 5·00 3·00
2910 1f. orange 40 20
2911 2f. green 85 25
2912 2f. blue 75 20
2913 2f.10 green . . . . . 1·00 40
2914 2f.20 green . . . . . 1·20 35
2916 2f.30 red . . . . . . 1·00 30
2917 2f.40 green . . . . . 1·20 65
2918 2f.50 red . . . . . . 1·30 45
2919 2f.70 green . . . . . 1·40 60
2920 3f.20 blue . . . . . 1·50 80
2921 3f.40 blue . . . . . 1·40 75
2922 3f.50 green . . . . . 1·70 65
2923 3f.80 mauve . . . . . 1·60 75
2924 3f.80 blue . . . . . 1·70 80
2925 4f. mauve . . . . . 1·90 75
2926 4f.20 mauve . . . . . 1·60 80
2927 4f.40 blue . . . . . 1·80 95
2928 4f.50 mauve . . . . . 2·75 80
2929 5f. blue . . . . . . 1·80 70
2930 10f. violet . . . . . 3·50 1·30

The imperforate stamps are self-adhesive.

For designs as T **1118** but inscr "D" for face value, see Nos. 3036/7, and with no value at all see No. 3122b.

1990. No value expressed. As T **1032** but inscr "C".

2949 (2f.10) green 95 65
2950 (2f.30) red . . . . 1·10 65

1119 Lace

1120 Games Emblem

1990.

2951 **1119** 2f.50 white and red . . 1·10 55

1990. Winter Olympic Games, Albertville (1992) (1st issue).

2952 **1120** 2f.50 multicoloured . . 1·10 45

See also Nos. 2953/62 and 3048.

1121 Emblem and Ice Skaters

1122 Cross of Lorraine and De Gaulle

1990. Winter Olympic Games, Albertville (1992) (2nd issue). Each black, blue and red.

2953 2f.30+20c. Type **1121** . . . 1·10 1·00
2954 2f.30+20c. Ski jumping . . 1·10 90
2955 2f.30+20c. Speed skiing . . 1·10 90
2956 2f.30+20c. Slalom . . . . . 1·10 95
2957 2f.30+20c. Cross-country skiing . . . . 1·10 95
2958 2f.30+20c. Ice hockey . . . 1·10 95
2959 2f.50+20c. Luge . . . . . 1·10 95
2960 2f.50+20c. Curling . . . . 1·10 95
2961 2f.50+20c. Artistic skiing . . 1·20 95
2962 2f.50+20c. Downhill skiing 1·20 95
MS2963 143 × 126 mm. 10 × 2f.50+20c. As Nos. 2953/62 13·00 13·00

1990. Birth Centenary of Charles de Gaulle (President, 1959–69).

2964 **1122** 2f.30 blue, black & vio 1·40 45

1123 Aircraft and Hymans

1124 Eyes and Keyboard

1990. 90th Birth Anniv of Max Hymans (civil aviation pioneer).

2965 **1123** 2f.30 green, violet & bl 1·00 50

1990. Art. As T **491**.

2966 5f. multicoloured . . . . . 2·30 1·60
2967 5f. blue, brown and ochre 2·30 1·60
2968 5f. multicoloured . . . . . 2·75 1·60
2969 5f. multicoloured . . . . . 2·30 1·70

DESIGNS—VERT: No. 2966, "Woman's Profile" (Odilon Redon); 2967, "Seated Cambodian Woman" (Auguste Rodin); 2968, "Head of Christ of Wissembourg"; 2969, "Yellow and Grey" (Roger Bissiere).

1990. Stamp Day.

2970 **1124** 2f.30+60c. blue, ultramarine and yellow . . . . 1·20 1·40
2971 2f.30+60c. deep green, green, blue and yellow . . . . 1·30 1·30

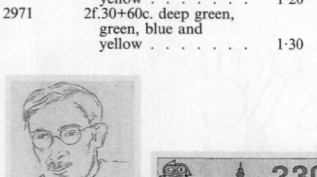

1125 Guehenno

1126 Macon Post Office

1990. Birth Cent of Jean Guehenno (writer).

2972 **1125** 3f.20 brown & lt brn 1·40 75

1990. Tourist Publicity. As T **490**.

2973 2f.30 orange, blue & black 1·00 60
2974 2f.30 black, blue & green . . 1·00 55
2975 3f.80 brown and green . . . 1·70 90
2976 3f.80 purple, brown & blue 1·50 90

DESIGNS: No. 2973, Cluny; 2974, Aqueduct, Briare Canal; 2975, Flaran-Gers Abbey; 2976, Cap Canaille Cassis.

1990. Europa. Post Office Buildings.
2978 **1126** 2f.30 black, ochre and blue . . . . 1·20 60
2979 – 3f.20 multicoloured . . 2·00 1·20
DESIGN: 3f.20, Cerizay post office.

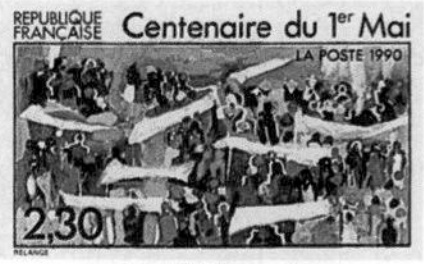

1127 Crowd

1990. Centenary of Labour Day.
2980 **1127** 2f.30 multicoloured . . 1·00 50

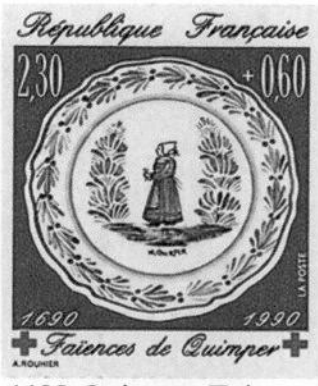

1128 Quimper Faience Plate **1129** Institute Building

1990. Red Cross Fund.
2981 **1128** 2f.30+60c. mult . . . . 1·20 1·30

1990. Arab World Institute.
2982 **1129** 3f.80 dp blue, bl & red 1·60 1·00

1130 Detail of Stonework, Notre Dame des Marais **1131** "La Poste"

1990. Federation of French Philatelic Societies Congress, Villefranche-sur-Saone.
2983 **1130** 2f.30 black, grn & red 1·00 55

1990. Round the World Yacht Race.
2984 **1131** 2f.30 multicoloured . . 1·00 50

1132 Georges Brassens **1133** Cross of Lorraine and Marianne

1990. Red Cross Fund. French Singers. Mult.
2985 2f.30+50c. Aristide Bruant 1·10 1·30
2986 2f.30+50c. Maurice Chevalier . . . . 1·10 1·30
2987 2f.30+50c. Tino Rossi . . . 1·10 1·30
2988 2f.30+50c. Edith Piaf . . . 1·10 1·30
2989 2f.30+50c. Jacques Brel . . 1·10 1·30
2990 2f.30+50c. Type **1132** . . . 1·10 1·30

1990. 50th Anniv of De Gaulle's Call to Resist.
2991 **1133** 2f.30 red, blue & blk 1·10 55

1134 Aerial View of House

1990. 5th Anniv of France–Brazil House, Rio de Janeiro.
2992 **1134** 3f.20 multicoloured . . 1·40 1·10

1990. Precancels. Musical Instruments (2nd series). As T **110**.
2993 1f.46 emerald and green . . 1·10 1·10
2994 1f.80 brown and orange . . 1·40 1·20
2995 1f.93 green & deep green . . 1·40 1·30
2996 2f.39 mauve and purple . . 1·70 1·50
2997 2f.74 violet and blue . . . . 2·30 2·10
2998 3f.06 blue and deep blue . . 2·40 2·20
2999 5f.10 violet and purple . . . 3·25 3·25

DESIGNS: 1 f 46, Accordion; 1f.89, Breton bagpipe; 1f.93, Harp; 2f.39, Piano; 2f.74, Violin; 3f.06, Provencal drum; 5f.10, Hurdy-gurdy.
See note below No. 432 (1920).

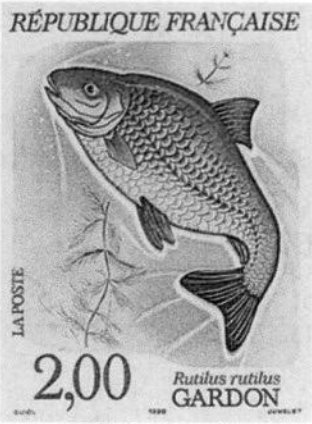

1135 Relief Map of France **1136** Roach

1990. 50th Anniv of National Geographical Institute.
3000 **1135** 2f.30 multicoloured . . 1·10 65

1990. Freshwater Fishes. Multicoloured.
3001 2f. Type **1136** 90 50
3002 3f. Eurasian perch . . . . . 1·20 95
3003 4f. Atlantic salmon . . . . 1·90 1·30
3004 5f. Northern pike . . . . . 2·00 1·30

1137 Gaspard Monge (Navy Minister)

1990. Bicentenary of French Revolution (7th issue). Sheet 79 × 106 mm containing T **1137** and similar vert designs.
MS3005 2f.50 Type **1137**; 2f.50 Abbe Henri Gregorie; 2f.50 Creation of national flag; 2f.50 Creation of departments . . . . 3·50 3·50

1138 Genevoix **1139** World Map

1990. Birth Centenary of Maurice Genevoix (writer).
3006 **1138** 2f.30 green & black . . 1·00 45

1990. 30th Anniv of Organization for Economic Co-operation and Development.
3007 **1139** 3f.20 blue & ultram . . 1·30 90

1991. Art. As T **491**.
3008 5f. multicoloured . . . . . 2·30 1·60
3009 5f. black and stone . . . . 2·30 1·60
3010 5f. black . . . . 2·30 1·70
3011 5f. multicoloured . . . . . 2·30 1·70
DESIGNS—VERT: No. 3008, "The Swing" (Auguste Renoir); 3009, "The Black Knot" (Georges Seurat); 3010, "Volta faccia" (Francois Rouan). HORIZ: No. 3011, "Oh Black Painting" (Roberto Matta).

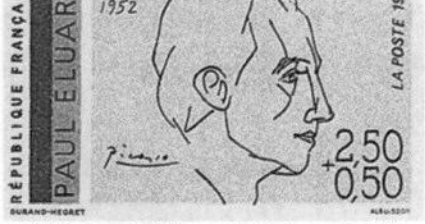

1140 Paul Eluard (after Pablo Picasso)

1991. Red Cross Fund. French Poets. Each grey, black and blue.
3013 2f.50+50c. Type **1140** . . . 1·20 1·30
3014 2f.50+50c. Andre Breton (after Man Ray) . . . . 1·20 1·30
3015 2f.50+50c. Louis Aragon (after Henri Matisse) . . 1·20 1·30
3016 2f.50+50c. Francis Ponge (after Stella Mertens) . . 1·20 1·30
3017 2f.50+50c. Jacques Prevert (after Picasso) . . . . 1·20 1·30
3018 2f.50+50c. Rene Char (after Valentine Hugo) . . . . 1·20 1·30

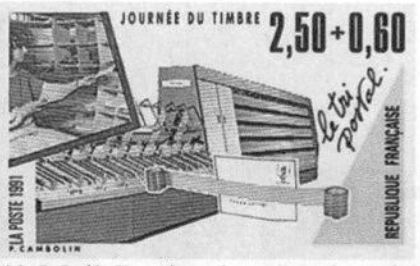

1141 Mail Sorting by Hand and by Machine

1991. Stamp Day. Multicoloured, colour of machine given.
3019 **1141** 2f.50+60c. blue . . . . 1·30 1·30
3020 2f.50+60c. violet . . . 1·40 1·50

1142 Children, Bicycle and Dove

1991. "Philexjeunes 91" Youth Stamp Exhibition, Cholet.
3021 **1142** 2f.50 multicoloured . . 1·10 70

1143 Mozart and Globe **1144** Eyes and Forms of Writing

1991. Death Bicentenary of Wolfgang Amadeus Mozart (composer).
3022 **1143** 2f.50 black, blue & red 1·10 75

1991. 350th Anniv of State Printing Office.
3023 **1144** 4f. multicoloured . . . 1·60 1·00

1991. Tourist Publicity. As T **490**.
3024 2f.50 multicoloured . . . . 1·10 50
3025 2f.50 multicoloured . . . . 1·30 65
3026 4f. lilac . . . . 1·60 95
DESIGNS—VERT: No. 3024, Chevire Bridge, Nantes. HORIZ: No. 3025, Carennac; 3026, Munster Valley.

1145 Poster **1146** "Ariane" Rocket and Map of French Guiana

1991. 90th Anniv of Concours Lepine (French Association of Small Manufacturers and Inventors).
3028 **1145** 4f. multicoloured . . . 1·60 1·10

1991. Europa. Europe in Space. Each blue, red and green.
3029 2f.50 Type **1146** . . . . . 1·50 55
3030 3f.50 "TDF-1" broadcasting satellite, eyes and globe 2·10 1·00

1147 Perpignan **1148** Painting by Joan Miro

1991. Federation of French Philatelic Societies Congress, Perpignan.
3031 **1147** 2f.50 red, grey & blue 1·10 50

1991. Centenary of French Open Tennis Championships.
3032 **1148** 3f.50 multicoloured . . 1·60 80

1149 La Tour d'Auvergne ("First Grenadier of France")

1991. Bicentenary of French Revolution (8th issue). Sheet 105 × 80 mm containing T **1149** and similar horiz designs. Multicoloured.
MS3033 2f.50 Type **1149**; 2f.50 Tree of Liberty; 2f.50 Mounted gendarme; 2f.50 Louis Saint-Just 4·00 4·00

1150 Organ Pipes **1151** Illustration from Gaston's "Book of Hunting"

1991. Organ of St. Nicholas's, Wasquehal.
3034 **1150** 4f. buff and brown . . 1·60 95

1991. 600th Death Anniv of Gaston III Phoebus, Count of Foix.
3035 **1151** 2f.50 multicoloured . . 1·10 65

1991. No value expressed. As T **1118** but inscr "D". Imperf (self-adhesive) or perf (3037), perf (3036).
3036 (2f.20) green . . . . 1·10 55
3037 (2f.50) red . . . . 1·10 50

1152 Brown Bear

1991. Nature. Multicoloured.
3039 2f. Type **1152** 95 60
3040 3f. Hermann's tortoise . . . 1·20 75
3041 4f. Eurasian beaver . . . . 1·60 1·20
3042 5f. River kingfisher . . . . 2·10 1·60

1153 Forest

1991. 10th World Forestry Congress, Paris.
3043 **1153** 2f.50 green, bl & blk . . 1·10 50

1154 Aspects of Public Works

1991. Centenary of School of Public Works.
3044 **1154** 2f.50 multicoloured . . 1·10 70

1155 "Bird Monument" (detail)

1991. Birth Centenary of Max Ernst (painter).
3045 **1155** 2f.50 multicoloured . . 1·30 90

1156 Cerdan

1991. 75th Birth Anniv of Marcel Cerdan (boxer).
3046 **1156** 2f.50 black and red . . 1·10 60

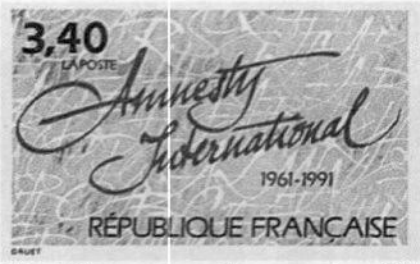

1157 "Amnesty International"

1158 Stylized Flame

1991. 30th Anniv of Amnesty International.
3047 **1157** 3f.40 bl, mve & blk . . 1·50 90

1991. Winter Olympic Games, Albertville (1992) (3rd issue).
3048 **1158** 2f.50 blue, blk & red 1·10 50

1159 "Toulon" (Francois Nardi)

1160 Bird

1991. Red Cross Fund.
3049 **1159** 2f.50+60c. mult . . . . 1·20 1·20

1991. 5th Paralympic Games, Tignes (1992).
3050 **1160** 2f.50 blue . . . . . . 1·10 60

1161 Shore

1991. 150th Anniv of Voluntary Adhesion of Mayotte to France.
3051 **1161** 2f.50 multicoloured . . 1·10 50

1992. Precancels. Musical Instruments (3rd series). As T **1110**.
3052a 1f.60 brown and orange . . 6·50 5·75
3053 1f.98 bistre and ochre . . . 3·50 4·00
3054 2f.08 orange and yellow . . 1·80 2·10
3055 2f.46 violet . . . . 1·80 2·10
3056 2f.98 lilac and mauve . . . 1·80 2·10
3057 3f.08 purple and red . . . 5·50 5·50
3058 3f.14 green and turquoise . 2·40 2·75
3059 3f.19 grey and black . . . 5·50 5·75
3060 5f.28 green and lt green . . 4·75 4·75
3061 5f.30 ultramarine & blue . 3·00 3·50
3062 5f.32 brown & dp brown 3·00 3·50
DESIGNS: 1f.60, Guitar; 1f.98, Accordion; 2f.08, Saxophone; 2f.46, Breton bagpipe; 2f.98, Banjo; 3f.08, Provencal drum; 3f.14, Hurdy-gurdy; 3f.19, Harp; 5f.28, Xylophone; 5f.30, Piano; 5f.32, Violin.
See note below No. 432 (1920).

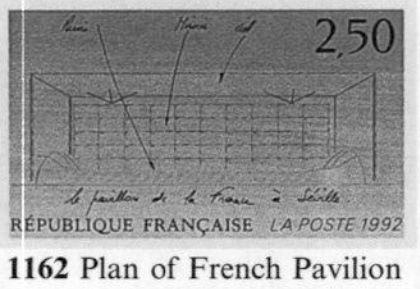

1162 Plan of French Pavilion

1992. "Expo '92" World's Fair, Seville.
3063 **1162** 2f.50 blue, blk & grn 1·10 50

1163 Post Office, Reception Area and Postal Self-service Machines

1992. Stamp Day.
3064 **1163** 2f.50+60c. black, blue and yellow . . . . . 1·20 1·20
3065 2f.50+60c. red, blue, black & yell . . . . 1·30 1·30

1164 Runner

1165 Cesar Franck

1992. Olympic Games, Barcelona.
3066 **1164** 2f.50 multicoloured . . 1·50 50

1992. Red Cross Fund. Composers. Mult.
3067 2f.50+50c. Type **1165** . . . 1·20 1·30
3068 2f.50+50c. Erik Satie . . . 1·20 1·30
3069 2f.50+50c. Florent Schmitt 1·20 1·30
3070 2f.50+50c. Arthur Honegger 1·20 1·30
3071 2f.50+50c. Georges Auric 1·20 1·30
3072 2f.50+50c. Germaine Tailleferre . . . . 1·20 1·30

1166 Marguerite d'Angouleme (after Clouet)

1167 "Madonna, Child and Angel" (Botticelli)

1992. 500th Birth Anniv of Marguerite d'Angouleme, Queen of Navarre.
3073 **1166** 3f.40 multicoloured . . 1·40 1·10

1992. 500th Anniv of Ajaccio.
3074 **1167** 4f. multicoloured . . . 1·70 1·00

1168 Navigational Instruments and Map

1169 Wheat, Poppies and Loaves

1992. Europa. 500th Anniv of Discovery of America by Columbus. Multicoloured.
3075 2f.50 Type **1168** . . . . . 1·20 50
3076 3f.40 Caravel, map and compass rose . . . . . . 2·10 90

1992. Tourist Publicity. As T **490**.
3077 2f.50 brown, blue & green 1·10 50
3078 3f.40 brown, green & blue 1·50 95
3079 4f. blue, black and green . . 1·60 85
3080 4f. green, lt green & brown 1·60 1·00
DESIGNS—VERT: No. 3077, Chateau de Biron, Dordogne; 3078, Mont Aiguille, Isere (500th anniv of first ascent). HORIZ: No. 3079, 4f. L'Ourcq Canal; 3080, Lorient.

1992. International Bread and Cereals Congress.
3081 **1169** 3f.40 multicoloured . . 1·50 1·50

1170 Couple leaping through Stamp

1992. Federation of French Philatelic Societies Congress, Niort.
3082 **1170** 2f.50 multicoloured . . 1·10 50

1171 Olympic Rings

1992. Winter Olympic Games, Albertville, and Summer Games, Barcelona.
3083 **1171** 2f.50 multicoloured . . 1·70 60

1172 Tautavel Man

1992.
3084 **1172** 3f.40 multicoloured . . 1·50 1·00

1992. Art. As T **491**.
3085 5f. black and stone . . . . 2·30 1·70
DESIGN—VERT: 5f. "Portrait of Claude Deruet" (Jacques Callot).

1173 Sand Lily

1992. Flowers. Multicoloured.
3086 2f. Type **1173** 85 50
3087 3f. Sundew . . . . 1·30 80
3088 4f. "Orchis palustris" . . . 1·60 1·10
3089 5f. Yellow water lily . . . . 2·00 1·50

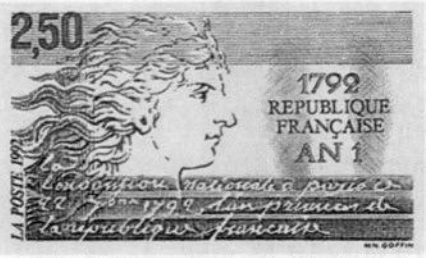

1174 Marianne and National Colours

1175 Marianne

1992. Bicentenary of Year One of First Republic.
3090 **1174** 2f.50 multicoloured . . 1·10 50

1992. Bicentenary of Declaration of First Republic. Each red.
3091 2f.50 Type **1175** . . . . . 1·00 55
3092 2f.50 Tree of Liberty . . . 1·00 55
3093 2f.50 Marianne as cockerel 1·00 55
3094 2f.50 "Republique Francaise" . . . . 1·00 55

1992. Precancels. Musical Instruments (4th series). As T **1110**.
3095 1f.73 deep green & green . . 85 80
3096 2f.25 red and orange . . . 1·10 1·10
3097 3f.51 ultramarine & blue . . 2·10 1·90
3098 5f.40 red and mauve . . . . 2·50 2·75
DESIGNS: 1f.73, Guitar; 2f.25, Saxophone; 3f.51, Banjo; 5f.40, Xylophone.
See note below No. 432 (1920).

1176 Symbol of Market

1992. European Single Market.
3099 **1176** 2f.50 multicoloured . . 1·10 60

1177 Farman HF16 and Boeing 737-500

1992. 80th Anniv of Nancy–Luneville Air Mail Service.
3100 **1177** 2f.50 multicoloured . . 1·10 65

1178 Paul and Electricity Pylon

1992. 10th Death Anniv of Marcel Paul (politician).
3101 **1178** 4f.20 blue & purple . . 1·90 80

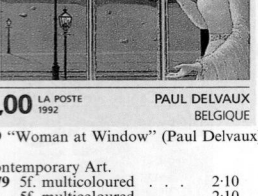

1179 "Woman at Window" (Paul Delvaux)

1992. Contemporary Art.
3102 **1179** 5f. multicoloured . . . 2·10 1·40
3103 – 5f. multicoloured . . . 2·10 1·40
3104 – 5f. black, mauve & yell 2·10 1·40
3105 – 5f. black and yellow . . 2·10 1·40
DESIGNS: No. 3103, "Portrait of Man" (Francis Bacon); 3104, Abstract (Alberto Burri); 3105, Abstract (Antoni Tapies).
See also Nos. 3154, 3176, 3285 and 3301/2.

1180 Birds holding Strings (T. Ungerer)

1181 Horse, Guitar and Dancer

1992. Red Cross Fund. Mutual Aid Meeting, Strasbourg.
3106 **1180** 2f.50+60c. mult . . . . 1·20 1·30

1992. Gypsies.
3107 **1181** 2f.50 multicoloured . . 1·10 60

1182 Smew Pair

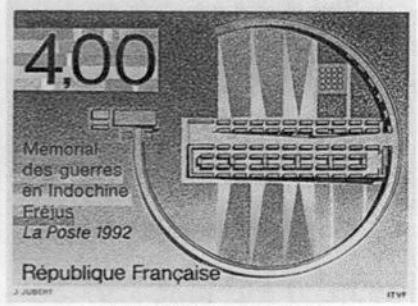

1184 Memorial

1183 "La Poste" (yacht) and Globe

1993. Ducks. Multicoloured.
3108 2f. Type **1182** 90 45
3109 3f. Ferruginous duck and drake . . . . 1·40 65
3110 4f. Common sheldrake pair 1·80 1·00
3111 5f. Red-breasted merganser pair . . . . 2·20 1·10

1993. "Postmen around the World". Post Office Team Participation in Around the World Yacht Race.
3112 **1183** 2f.50 yell, ultram & bl 1·20 65
3113 2f.80 yell, ultram & bl 1·60 80

1993. Indo–China Wars Memorial, Frejus.
3114 **1184** 4f. multicoloured . . . 1·70 85

1185 Postman with Bicycle

1186 Yacht and Runner

1993. Stamp Day.
3115 **1185** 2f.50 multicoloured . . 1·90 1·70
3116 2f.50+60c. mult . . . . 1·30 1·30

1993. Mediterranean Games, Agde and Roussillon (Languedoc).
3117 **1186** 2f.50 multicoloured . . 1·10 55

1187 Maria Deraismes and Georges Martin (founders)

1189 Guy de Maupassant

1188 "Red Rhythm Blue" (Olivier Debre)

1993. Centenary of Le Droit Humain (International Mixed Freemasons Order).
3118 **1187** 3f.40 black and blue . . 1·50 1·00

1993. Europa. Contemporary Art. Mult.
3119 2f.50 Type **1188** . . . . . 1·20 65
3120 3f.40 "Le Griffu" (bronze, Germaine Richier) (vert) 1·70 1·10

1993. As T **1118** but no value expressed. Imperf (self-adhesive) or perf.
3122b **1118** (–) red . . . . 1·10 25
No. 3122b was sold at the current inland rate (at time of issue 2f.50).

1993. Tourist Publicity. As T **490** and **949**.
3124 2f.80 green, brown and blue 1·30 65
3125 3f.40 red, green and blue . . 1·60 75
3126 4f.20 dp green, green & brn 1·60 1·00
3127 4f.20 brown and green . . . 1·80 1·00
3128 4f.40 black, green and red 2·00 1·10
3129 4f.40 multicoloured . . . . 2·00 1·10
DESIGNS—As T **490**. HORIZ: No. 3124, La Chaise-Dieu Abbey, Haute-Loire; 3128, Montbeliard-Doubs. VERT: No. 3125, Artouste train, Laruns; 3126, Minerve-Herault; 3129, Le Jacquemard, Lambesc. As T **949**: No. 3127, Chinon.

1993. Red Cross Fund. Writers. Mult.
3131 2f.50+50c. Type **1189** . . . 1·30 1·30
3132 2f.50+50c. Alain . . . . . 1·30 1·30
3133 2f.50+50c. Jean Cocteau . . 1·30 1·30
3134 2f.50+50c. Marcel Pagnol 1·30 1·30
3135 2f.50+50c. Andre Chamson 1·30 1·30
3136 2f.50+50c. Marguerite Yourcenar . . . . 1·30 1·30

1190 Map of Europe and Liberty

1993. 9th European Constitutional Court Conference on Human Rights.
3137 **1190** 2f.50 multicoloured . . 1·10 55

1191 Reinhardt

1192 Weiss

1993. 40th Death Anniv of Django Reinhardt (guitarist).
3138 **1191** 4f.20 multicoloured . . 1·80 1·00

1993. Birth Centenary of Louise Weiss (women's rights campaigner).
3139 **1192** 2f.50 blk, orge & red 1·10 60

1193 TGV and Eurostar Trains at Lille

1993. Federation of French Philatelic Societies Congress, Lille.
3140 **1193** 2f.50 lt bl, bl & mve . . 1·10 55

1194 Emblem

1993. Bicentenary of National Natural History Museum, Paris.
3141 **1194** 2f.50 multicoloured . . 1·10 50

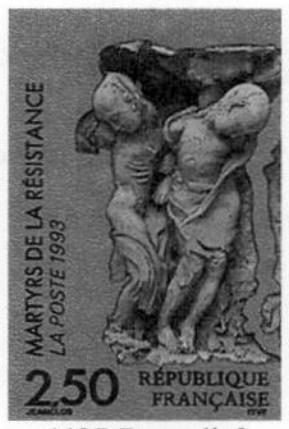

1195 Bas-relief (Georges Jeanclos) (left half)

1196 Central Telegraph Tower, Paris

1993. Martyrs and Heroes of the Resistance. Multicoloured.
3142 2f.50 Type **1195** . . . . . 1·40 1·20
3143 4f.20 Right half of bas-relief 1·80 1·70
Nos. 3142/3 were issued together, se-tenant, forming a composite design.

1993. Bicentenary of Chappe's Optical Telegraph.
3144 **1196** 2f.50 black, stone and blue . . . . 1·10 50

1993. Precancels. Musical Instruments (5th series). As T **1110**.
3145 1f.82 grey and black 85 80
3146 2f.34 brown and orange . . 1·10 1·10
3147 3f.86 red and pink . . . . 2·00 1·90
3148 5f.93 violet and mauve . . . 2·50 2·75
DESIGNS: 1f.82, Trumpet; 2f.34, Drum; 3f.86, Hurdy-gurdy; 5f.93, Xylophone.

1197 Map of Corsica and "Casabianca" (submarine)

1198 Le Val-de-Grace, Paris

1993. 50th Anniv of Liberation of Corsica.
3149 **1197** 2f.80 black, red & bl . . 1·30 60

1993. Art. As T **491**. Multicoloured.
3150 5f. "Saint Thomas" (Georges de la Tour) (vert) . . . . 2·30 1·70
3151 5f. "The Muses" (Maurice Denis) (vert) . . . . . . 2·40 1·80

1993. Bicentenary of Conversion of Monastery of Le Val-de-Grace to Military Hospital (now museum).
3152 **1198** 3f.70 black, grn & brn 1·60 75

1199 Clowns

1200 Girl studying Flower ("Happy Holiday") (C. Wendling)

1993. National Centre for Circus Arts, Chalons-sur-Marne.
3153 **1199** 2f.80 multicoloured . . 1·30 50

1993. Contemporary Art. As T **1179**.
3154 5f. red and black . . . . . 2·30 1·80
3155 5f. multicoloured . . . . . 2·30 1·80
DESIGNS: No. 3154, Abstract (Takis); 3155, "Enhanced Engraving" (Maria Elena Vieira da Silva).

1993. Greetings Stamps. "The Pleasure of Writing". Designs by comic strip artists. Multicoloured.
3156A 2f.80 Type **1200** . . . . 1·30 85
3157A 2f.80 Clowns ("Happy Holiday") (B. Olivie) . . 1·30 85
3158A 2f.80 Cat on birthday cake ("Happy Birthday") (S. Colman) . . . . . 1·30 85
3159A 2f.80 Girl with cake ("Happy Birthday") (G. Sorel) . . . . . . 1·30 85
3160A 2f.80 Man courting woman on balcony ("With Passion") (J. M. Thiriet) . . . . 1·30 85
3161A 2f.80 Man playing large fountain pen ("Pleasure of Writing") (E. Davodeau) . . . . 1·30 85
3162A 2f.80 Pig with letter ("Greetings") (J. de Moor) . . . . 1·30 85
3163A 2f.80 Jester in horseshoe ("Good Luck") (Mezzo) 1·30 85
3164A 2f.80 Clowns running ("Best Wishes") (N. de Crecy) . . . . 1·30 85
3165A 2f.80 Girl and cat watching tree fairy ("Best Wishes") (F. Magnin) . . . . . 1·30 85
3166A 2f.80 Cards tumbling from Santa Claus's sack ("Happy Christmas") (T. Robin) . . . . . . 1·30 85
3167A 2f.80 Mouse dressed as Santa Claus ("Happy Christmas") (P. Prugne) 1·30 85

1201 Rhododendron

1993. 1st European Stamp Salon, Flower Gardens, Paris (1994) (1st issue). Sheet 106 × 78 mm containing T **1201** and similar horiz design. Multicoloured.
MS3168 2f.40 Type **1201**; 2f.40 View of Gardens (sold at 15f.) . . . 12·00 12·00

1202 Louvre, 1793

1993. Bicentenary of Louvre Museum. Mult.
3169 2f.80 Type **1202** . . . . . 1·30 1·10
3170 4f.40 Louvre, 1993 . . . . . 2·10 1·60
Nos. 3169/70 were issued together, se-tenant, forming a composite design.

1203 "St. Nicholas"

1204 Cast-iron Sign at Metro Entrance, Paris (detail, Hector Guimard)

1993. Red Cross Fund. Metz Engravings.
3171 **1203** 2f.80+60c. mult . . . . 1·40 1·30

1994. Art Nouveau. Multicoloured.
3172 2f.80 Type **1204** . . . . . 1·30 55
3173 2f.80 "Roses of France Cup" (vase, Emile Galle) 1·30 55
3174 4f.40 Drawing-room table with bronze water-lily decoration (Louis Majorelle) . . . . 2·00 95
3175 4f.40 Stoneware teapot (Pierre-Adrien Dalpayrat) 2·00 95

1994. Contemporary Art. As T **1179**. Mult.
3176 6f.70 Abstract (Sean Scully) 3·00 1·90
3177 6f.70 "Couple" (Georg Baselitz) . . . . 3·00 2·10

1205 "Death of St. Stephen"

1994. 12th-century Stained Glass Window, Le Mans Cathedral.
3179 **1205** 6f.70 multicoloured . . 3·00 2·00

1994. Tourist Publicity. As T **490**.
3180 2f.80 multicoloured . . . . 1·20 50
3181 2f.80 blue . . . . 1·20 50
3182 3f.70 brown, dp green & grn 1·60 1·10
3183 4f.40 brown and blue . . . 1·80 1·10
3184 4f.40 brown and red . . . . 1·80 1·10
DESIGNS—HORIZ: No. 3180, "Mount Sainte Victoire" (Paul Cezanne); 3181, Bridge at Rupt aux Nonains, Saulx Region, Meuse; 3184, Argentat. VERT: No. 3182, La Grand Cascade, Saint-Cloud Park; 3183, Old port and St. John the Baptist Church, Bastia.

1206 European Union Flag

1994. European Parliament Elections.
3185 **1206** 2f.80 blue, yell & grey 1·20 50

1207 Mourguet and Guignol

1994. 150th Death Anniv of Laurent Mourguet (creator of Guignol (puppet)).
3186 **1207** 2f.80 multicoloured . . 1·20 60

1208 Emblem

1994. Bicent of Polytechnic Institute, Paris.
3187 **1208** 2f.80 multicoloured . . 1·20 75

1209 "Marianne"

1210 "The Vikings" (detail, Bayeux Tapestry)

1994. Stamp Day. 50th Anniv of Edmond Dulac's "Marianne" Design.
3188 **1209** 2f.80 red and blue . . . 1·60 1·60
3190 2f.80+60c. red & bl . . 1·80 2·10

1994. Franco–Swedish Cultural Relations. Mult.
3191 2f.80 Type **1210** . . . . . 2·75 2·40
3192 2f.80 Viking longships (different detail) . . . . . 2·75 2·40
3193 2f.80 Costume design for sailor by Fernand Leger in Swedish Ballet production of "Skating Rink" . . . . 2·75 2·40
3194 2f.80 Costume design for gentleman in "Skating Rink" . . . . 2·75 2·40
3195 3f.70 "Banquet for Gustav III at the Trianon, 1784" (Niclas Lafrensen the younger) . . . . 4·50 3·00
3196 3f.70 Swedish and French flags . . . . 4·50 3·00
Nos. 3195/6 are larger, 49 × 37 mm.

1211 Mountain Ambush

1212 Pompidou

1994. 50th Anniv of Liberation. The Maquis (resistance movement).
3197 **1211** 2f.80 multicoloured . . 1·20 50

1994. 20th Death Anniv of Georges Pompidou (Prime Minister 1962–68, President 1969–74).
3198 **1212** 2f.80 brown . . . . . . 1·20 60

1213 Boy netting Stamps

1994. "Philex Jeunes 94" Youth Stamp Exhibition, Grenoble.
3199 **1213** 2f.80 multicoloured . . 1·20 50

1214 AIDS Virus

1994. Europa. Discoveries. Multicoloured.
3200 2f.80 Type **1214** (11th anniv of discovery) . . . . . . 1·40 60
3201 3f.70 Wavelength formula (70th anniv of Louis de Broglie's proof of undulatory theory of matter) . . . . 1·70 1·20

1215 Bank Emblem

1994. 27th Assembly of Asian Development Bank, Nice.
3202 **1215** 2f.80 multicoloured . . 1·20 55

1216 British Lion and French Cockerel over Tunnel

1994. Opening of Channel Tunnel. Mult.
3203 2f.80 Type **1216** . . . . . . 1·10 65
3204 2f.80 Symbolic hands over Eurostar express train . . 1·20 65
3205 4f.30 Type **1216** . . . . 1·70 1·60
3206 4f.30 As No. 3204 . . . . . 1·70 1·60

1217 Martigues inside Fish

1994. Federation of French Philatelic Societies Congress, Martigues.
3207 **1217** 2f.80 violet, bl & grn 1·20 50

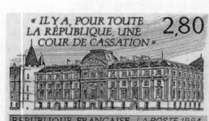

1218 Court Building, Ile de la Cite, Paris

1994. Court of Cassation.
3208 **1218** 2f.80 multicoloured . . 1·20 50

1219 Landing Forces and Beach Defences

1994. 50th Anniv of Normandy Landings.
3209 **1219** 4f.30 red, ind & bl . . 1·90 95

1220 Allied Forces

1994. 50th Anniv of Liberation.
3210 **1220** 4f.30 multicoloured . . 1·90 1·10

1221 Sorbonne University and Pierre de Coubertin (founder)

1222 Organ Pipes

1994. Centenary of International Olympic Committee.
3211 **1221** 2f.80 multicoloured . . 1·40 60

1994. Poitiers Cathedral Organ.
3212 **1222** 4f.40 multicoloured . . 1·80 1·10

1223 Flag, Map and Soldier

1224 Oak

1994. 50th Anniv of Allied Landings in Southern France.
3213 **1223** 2f.80 multicoloured . . 1·20 55

1994. Precancels. Leaves.
3321 – 1f.87 brown & green . . 1·00 95
3214 **1224** 1f.91 olive & green . . 85 85
3322 – 2f.18 red and lake . . . 1·20 1·10
3215 – 2f.46 green & lt green . . 1·10 1·00
3216 – 4f.24 red and orange . . 1·90 1·90
3323 – 4f.66 yellow & green . . 2·00 2·00
3217 – 6f.51 turquoise & blue . 3·00 3·00
3324 – 7f.11 turquoise & blue 3·00 3·25
DESIGNS: 1f.87, Ash; 2f.18, Beech; 2f.46, Plane; 4f.24, Chestnut; 4f.66, Walnut; 6f.51, Holly; 7f.11, Elm.

1225 "Moses and the Daughters of Jethro" (drawing) (½-size illustration)

1994. 400th Birth Anniv of Nicolas Poussin (artist).
3218 **1225** 4f.40 brown & black . . 1·90 1·30

1226 Yvonne Printemps (singer and actress)

1227 Map and Foucault's Pendulum

1994. Entertainers. Multicoloured.
3219 2f.80+60c. Type **1226** . . . 1·40 1·60
3220 2f.80+60c. Fernandel (Fernand Contandin) (actor) . . . . 1·40 1·60
3221 2f.80+60c. Josephine Baker (music hall performer) . . 1·40 1·60
3222 2f.80+60c. Bourvil (Andre Raimbourg) (actor) . . . 1·40 1·60
3223 2f.80+60c. Yves Montand (singer and actor) . . . 1·40 1·60
3224 2f.80+60c. Coluche (Michel Colucci) (comedian) . . . 1·40 1·60

1994. Bicentenary of National Conservatory of Arts and Craft.
3225 **1227** 2f.80 pur, bl & red. . . 1·20 55

1228 Doorway

1229 Simenon and Quai des Orfevres, Paris

1994. Bicent of Ecole Normale Superieure.
3226 **1228** 2f.80 blue and red . . . 1·20 55

1994. 5th Death Anniv of Georges Simenon (novelist).
3227 **1229** 2f.80 multicoloured . . 1·20 65

1230 Headless Drug Addict (after Vladimir Velickovic)

1231 Gardens

1994. National Drug Addiction Prevention Day.
3228 **1230** 2f.80 multicoloured . . 1·20 65

1994. 1st European Stamp Salon, Flower Gardens, Paris (2nd issue). Sheet 106 × 78 mm containing T **1231** and similar multicoloured designs.
MS3229 2f.80 Type **1231**; 2f.80 Dahlias (25 × 39 mm) (sold at 16f.) 12·00 12·00

1232 Lodge Emblem and Symbols of Freemasonry

1994. Centenary of Grand Lodge of France.
3230 **1232** 2f.80 brown, red & bl 1·20 60

1233 Stormy Sea and Colas

1994. 16th Death Anniv of Alain Colas (yachtsman).
3231 **1233** 3f.70 blk, grn & emer 1·70 1·10

1234 St. Vaast

1994. Red Cross Fund. 15th-century Arras Tapestry.
3232 **1234** 2f.80+60c. mult . . . . 1·40 1·50

1235 AIDS Virus (½-size illustration)

1994. AIDS Day.
3233 **1235** 2f.80 multicoloured . . 1·50 95
The stamp and se-tenant label, as illustrated, comprise No. 3233. For stamp without attached label, see No. 3200.

1236 Slogan

1994. 50th Anniv of National Press Federation.
3234 **1236** 2f.80 purple & yellow 1·20 55

1237 Champs Elysees (½-size illustration)

1994. New Year.
3235 **1237** 4f.40 multicoloured . . 2·10 1·40

1238 Projector and Scene from Film

1995. Centenary of Motion Pictures. Sheet 105 × 78 mm containing T **1238** and similar horiz designs. Multicoloured.
MS3236 2f.80 Type **1238**; 2f.80 Projector and head of man in cap; 2f.80 Projector and monster's head; 2f.80 Reel of films and Indian's head . . . . 4·50 4·50

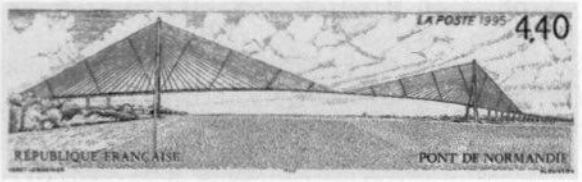

1239 Normandy Bridge (½-size illustration)

1995. Inauguration of Normandy Bridge (over Seine between Le Havre and Honfleur).
3237 **1239** 4f.40 multicoloured . . 2·40 1·20

1240 Emblem

1241 Pasteur

1995. European Public Notaries.
3238 **1240** 2f.80 multicoloured . . 1·20 55

1995. Death Centenary of Louis Pasteur (chemist).
3239 **1241** 3f.70 multicoloured . . 1·60 1·20

1995. Tourist Publicity. As T **490**.
3240 2f.80 green and olive . . . 1·20 55
3241 2f.80 green, brown & blue 1·20 55
3242 4f.40 multicoloured . . . . 2·00 1·10
3243 4f.40 black, lilac & green . . 2·00 1·10
DESIGNS—HORIZ: No. 3240, Malt works, Stenay; 3241, Remiremont, Vosges; 3242, Nyons Bridge, Drome. VERT: No. 3243, Margot gate and St. Martial's Church, Correze.

1995. Art. As T **491**.
3245 6f.70 black, yellow & red . . 3·00 2·10
3246 6f.70 black, blue & dp blue 3·00 2·10
3247 6f.70 multicoloured . . . . 3·00 2·10
3248 6f.70 multicoloured . . . . 2·75 2·00
DESIGNS—VERT: No. 3245, Reliquary of St. Taurin, Evereux; 3248, "The Cradle" (Berthe Morisot). HORIZ: No. 3246, Study for "The Dream of Happiness" (Pierre Prud'hon); 3247, Seascape (Zao Wou-Ki).

1242 Band-tailed Pigeons

1995. Bird Paintings by John James Audubon (ornithologist). Multicoloured.
3249 2f.80 Type **1242** . . . . . 1·30 65
3250 2f.80 Snowy egret . . . . . 1·30 65
3251 4f.30 Common tern . . . . 2·10 1·20
3252 4f.40 Rough-legged buzzards 2·10 1·30
MS3253 113 × 120 mm. Nos. 2149/52 4·50 4·50

1243 "Marianne"

1995. Stamp Day. 50th Anniv of Pierre Gandon's "Marianne" Design.
3255 **1243** 2f.80 green, bl & red . . 4·00 3·75
3254 2f.80+60c. green, ultramarine & red . . 1·80 1·80

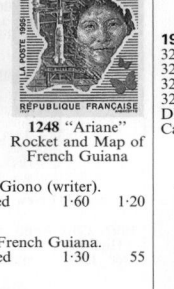

1244 Hour Glass **1245** Means of Communications

1995. 50th Anniv of Works Councils.
3257 **1244** 2f.80 brown, lt bl & bl 1·20 55

1995. Centenary (1994) of Advanced Institute of Electricity.
3258 **1245** 3f.70 lt blue, bl & red 1·60 1·20

1246 Forms of Writing

1995. Bicentenary of School of Oriental Languages.
3259 **1246** 2f.80 multicoloured . . 1·20 65

1247 Giono **1248** "Ariane" Rocket and Map of French Guiana

1995. Birth Centenary of Jean Giono (writer).
3260 **1247** 3f.70 blk, blue & red 1·60 1·20

1995. French Space Centre in French Guiana.
3261 **1248** 2f.80 blue, grn & red 1·30 55

1249 Steel and Worker

1995. Lorraine's Iron and Steel Industry.
3262 **1249** 2f.80 multicoloured . . 1·20 55

1250 "Freedom"

1995. Europa. Peace and Freedom. Mult.
3263 2f.80 Type **1250** . . . . . 1·30 55
3264 3f.70 "Peace" . . . . 1·80 1·10

1251 Lumberjack **1252** Paris Landmarks and Charles de Gaulle

1995. Forestry in the Ardennes.
3265 **1251** 4f.40 brn, blk & grn . . 2·00 1·20

1995. 50th Anniv of End of Second World War.
3266 **1252** 2f.80 multicoloured . . 1·20 65

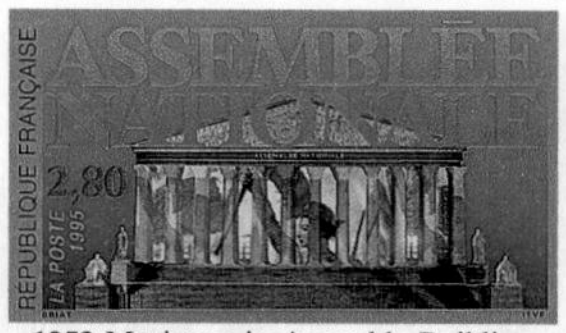

1253 Marianne in Assembly Building

1995. National Assembly.
3267 **1253** 2f.80 multicoloured . . 1·20 75

1254 "King Louis XIII on Horseback" (Saumur tapestry)

1995. Red Cross Fund.
3268 **1254** 2f.80+60c. mult . . . . 1·40 1·30

1255 Winged Hand **1256** Brittany

1995. 50th Anniv of French People's Relief Association (welfare organization).
3270 **1255** 2f.80 multicoloured . . 1·20 75

1995. Landscapes.
3271 **1256** 2f.40 green . . . . . . 1·10 50
3272 – 2f.40 green . . . . . . 1·10 50
3273 – 2f.80 red . . . . 1·30 50
3274 – 2f.80 red . . . . 1·30 50
DESIGNS: No. 3272, Vosges; 3273, Auvergne; 3274, Camargue.

1257 Orleans **1258** "The Grasshopper and The Ant"

1995. Federation of French Philatelic Societies Congress, Orleans.
3275 **1257** 2f.80 multicoloured . . 1·20 55

1995. 300th Death Anniv of Jean de la Fontaine (writer of fables). Multicoloured.
3276 2f.80 Type **1258** . . . . . 2·00 1·10
3277 2f.80 "The Fat Frog and the Ox" . . . . 2·00 1·10
3278 2f.80 "The Wolf and the Lamb" . . . . 2·00 1·10
3279 2f.80 "The Raven and the Fox" . . . . 2·00 1·10
3280 2f.80 "The Cat, the Weasel and the Little Rabbit" . . 2·00 1·10
3281 2f.80 "The Hare and the Tortoise" . . . . 2·00 1·10

1259 Flower, Star and Wire **1260** Maginot and Roof

1995. 53rd Anniv of Internment of Jews in Velodrome d'Hiver, Paris.
3282 **1259** 2f.80 multicoloured . . 1·20 70

1995. 63rd Death Anniv of Andre Maginot (politician and instigator of Maginot Line (fortifications on French–German border)).
3283 **1260** 2f.80 brown, grn & red 1·20 55

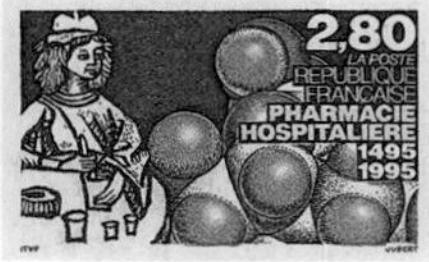

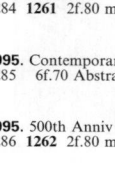

1261 Lodge Emblem **1262** Apothecary and Molecules

1995. 50th Anniv of Women's Grand Masonic Lodge of France.
3284 **1261** 2f.80 multicoloured . . 1·20 55

1995. Contemporary Art. As T **1179**. Mult.
3285 6f.70 Abstract (Kirkeby) . . 2·75 2·10

1995. 500th Anniv of Hospital Pharmacies.
3286 **1262** 2f.80 multicoloured . . 1·20 55

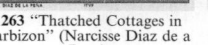

1263 "Thatched Cottages in Barbizon" (Narcisse Diaz de a Pena) **1264** Institute Emblem

1995. 170th Anniv of Barbizon School (artists' settlement).
3287 **1263** 4f.40 multicoloured . . 2·00 1·00

1995. 50th Anniv of National Civil Servants' Training Institute, Paris.
3288 **1264** 2f.80 multicoloured . . 90 40

1265 Institute Building **1266** New and Old Motor Vehicles and Headquarters

1995. Bicentenary of French Institute, Paris.
3289 **1265** 2f.80 black, red & grn 90 40

1995. Centenary of French Automobile Club.
3290 **1266** 4f.40 black, bl & red . . 1·50 85

1267 Dove, Blue Helmet and Anniversary Emblem **1268** Shepherd

1995. 50th Anniv of U.N.O.
3291 **1267** 4f.30 multicoloured . . 1·50 95

1995. Red Cross Fund. Crib Figures from Provence. Multicoloured.
3292 2f.80+60c. Type **1268** . . . 1·20 1·20
3293 2f.80+60c. Miller . . . . . 1·20 1·20
3294 2f.80+60c. Simpleton and tambourine player . . . . 1·20 1·20
3295 2f.80+60c. Fishmonger . . . 1·20 1·20
3296 2f.80+60c. Knife grinder . . 1·20 1·20
3297 2f.80+60c. Elderly couple . . 1·20 1·20

1269 Jammes

1995. 127th Birth Anniv of Francis Jammes (poet).
3298 **1269** 3f.70 black and blue . . 1·20 95

1270 Architect's Plans **1271** Pitch and Balls

1995. Completion of Evry Cathedral.
3299 **1270** 2f.80 multicoloured . . 95 40

1995. World Cup Football Championship, France (1998).
3300 **1271** 2f.80 multicoloured . . 95 45

1996. Contemporary Art. As T **1179**.
3301 6f.70 black, red and blue . . 2·20 1·60
3302 6f.70 multicoloured . . . . 2·20 1·60
DESIGNS: No. 3301, "Sculpture" (Lucien Wercollier); 3302, "Horizon" (Jan Dibbets).

1272 Pottery Dog **1273** "St. Patrick" (stained glass window, Evie Hone)

1996. Completion of Archaeological Excavations in Saint-Martin Island, Guadeloupe.
3305 **1272** 2f.80 multicoloured . . 95 50

1996. Art. As T **491**.
3306 6f.70 multicoloured . . . . 2·30 1·60
3307 6f.70 multicoloured . . . . 2·20 1·50
3308 6f.70 gold, copper & blk . . 1·90 1·20
DESIGNS—HORIZ: No. 3306, "Narni Bridge" (Camille Corot); 3308, "Cellos" (Arman). VERT: No. 3307, Bronze horse (found at Neuvy-en-Sullias).

1996. "L'imaginaire Irlandais" Festival of Contemporary Irish Arts, France.
3311 **1273** 2f.80 multicoloured . . 95 55

1274 "The Sower" **1276** Descartes (after Frans Hals)

1275 Rueff and New 1 Franc Coin of 1960

1996. Stamp Day. 93rd Anniv of Louis-Oscar Roty's "The Sower" design.
3312 **1274** 2f.80+60c. mauve and violet . . . . 1·30 1·10
3313 2f.80 mauve & violet 3·50 3·25

1996. Birth Centenary of Jacques Rueff (economist).
3315 **1275** 2f.80 black, bl & brn 85 50

1996. 400th Birth Anniv of Rene Descartes (philosopher and scientist).
3316 **1276** 4f.40 red . . . . 1·40 1·10

1277 Lightbulb and Flame

1996. 50th Anniv of Electricite de France and Gaz de France.
3317 **1277** 3f. multicoloured . . . 1·00 55

1278 Eurasian Beaver and Columbine, Cevennes

1280 Mme. de Sevigne (writer)

1996. National Parks. Multicoloured.
3318 3f. Type **1278** . . . . . . 1·00 60
3319 4f.40 Lammergeier and saxifrage, Mercantour . . 1·50 95
3320 4f.40 Ibex and gentian, Vanoise . . . . 1·50 95
See also Nos. 3380/3.

1996. Europa. Famous Women.
3325 **1280** 3f. multicoloured . . . 1·00 70

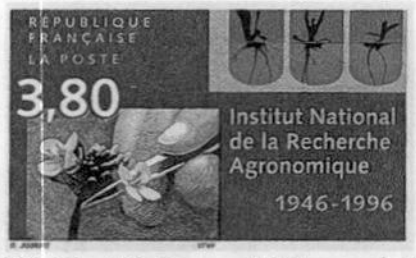

1281 Test Tubes and Flower held with Tweezers

1996. 50th Anniv of National Institute for Agronomic Research.
3326 **1281** 3f.80 multicoloured . . 1·30 90

1282 Joan of Arc's Cottage, Domremy la Pucelle, Vosges

1996. 75th Anniv (1995) of Canonization of Joan of Arc.
3327 **1282** 4f.50 multicoloured . . 1·60 85

1283 Fishes, Sea and Coastline

1996. 20th Anniv of Ramoge Agreement on Environmental Protection of the Mediterranean.
3328 **1283** 3f. multicoloured . . . 1·10 50

1284 Notre-Dame de Clermont and the Jacquemart (Cathedral clock)

1996. Federation of French Philatelic Societies Congress, Clermont-Ferrand.
3329 **1284** 3f. green, brown & red 1·00 55

1996. Tourist Publicity. As T **490**.
3330 3f. multicoloured . . . . . 1·00 55
3331 3f. multicoloured . . . . . 1·00 55
3332 3f.80 brown and mauve . . 1·20 80
3333 4f.50 multicoloured . . . . 1·50 85
DESIGN—HORIZ: 3f. (No. 3330), Bitche Castle, Moselle; 3f. (No. 3331), Sanguinaries Islands, Corsica; 3f.80, Cloisters, Thoronet Abbey, Var; 4f.50, Detail of trompe l'oeil by Casimir Vicario, Chambery Cathedral.

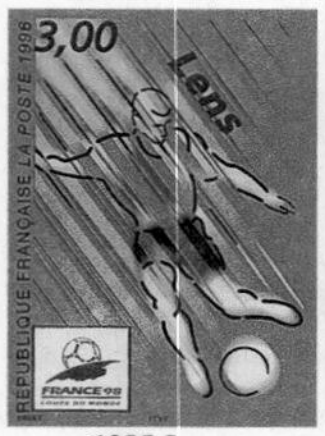

1285 Lens

1286 Throwing the Discus

1996. World Cup Football Championship, France (1998) (1st issue). Host Cities. Multicoloured.
3335 3f. Type **1285** . . . . . . 1·00 55
3336 3f. Montpellier . . . . . . 1·00 55
3337 3f. Saint-Etienne . . . . . 1·00 55
3338 3f. Toulouse . . . . 1·00 55
See also Nos. 3401/4, 3464/5 and 3472.

1996. Centenary of Modern Olympic Games.
3339 **1286** 3f. multicoloured . . . 1·00 55

1287 Marette

1288 Diesel Railcar Set

1996. 12th Death Anniv of Jacques Marette (journalist and politician).
3340 **1287** 4f.40 lilac . . . . . . 1·50 90

1996. Centenary of Ajaccio–Vizzavona Railway, Corsica.
3341 **1288** 3f. multicoloured . . . 1·00 55

1289 Basilica

1996. Centenary of Our Lady of Fourviere Basilica, Lyon.
3342 **1289** 3f. black and yellow . . 1·00 50

1290 Baptism of Clovis (illus from "Grandes Chroniques de France")

1291 Arsene Lupin (Maurice Leblanc)

1996. Inauguration of Committee for Commemoration of Origins: from Gaul to France. 1500th Anniv of Baptism of Clovis.
3343 **1290** 3f. multicoloured . . . 1·00 50

1996. Red Cross Fund. Heroes of Crime Novels. Multicoloured.
3344 3f.+60c. Rocambole (Pierre Ponson du Terrail) . . . 1·20 1·20
3345 3f.+60c. Type **1291** . . . 1·20 1·20
3346 3f.+60c. Joseph Rouletabille (Gaston Leroux) . . . . 1·20 1·20
3347 3f.+60c. Fantomas (Pierre Souvestre and Marcel Allain) . . . . 1·20 1·20
3348 3f.+60c. Commissioner Maigret (Georges Simenon) . . . . . . 1·20 1·20
3349 3f.+60c. Nestor Burma (Leo Malet) . . . . 1·30 1·10

1292 School Building

1293 Children of Different Nations

1996. Bicentenary of Henri IV School, Paris.
3350 **1292** 4f.50 blue, brn & grn 1·50 85

1996. 50th Anniv of U.N.I.C.E.F.
3351 **1293** 4f.50 multicoloured . . 1·50 85

1294 Iena Palace (headquarters)

1295 Headquarters, Paris

1996. 50th Anniv of Economic and Social Council.
3352 **1294** 3f. black, red & blue . . 1·00 50

1996. 50th Anniv of U.N.E.S.C.O.
3353 **1295** 3f.80 multicoloured . . 1·20 80

1296 Magnifying Glass over Eiffel Tower

1297 "Woman"

1996. 50th Anniv of Autumn Stamp Show, Paris.
3354 **1296** 3f. multicoloured . . . 1·00 65

1996. 50th Anniv of Creation of French Overseas Departments of Martinique, Guadeloupe, Guiana and La Reunion.
3355 **1297** 3f. multicoloured . . . 1·00 55

1298 Snowman and Polar Bear in Hot-air Balloon

1996. Red Cross Fund. Christmas.
3356 **1298** 3f.+60c. mult . . . . . 1·10 1·00

1299 Temple, Delphi

1996. 150th Anniv of French School in Athens.
3357 **1299** 3f. multicoloured . . . 1·00 55

1300 Malraux

1996. 20th Death Anniv of Andre Malraux (writer and politician).
3358 **1300** 3f. blue . . . . 1·00 50

1301 Clapperboard, Camera and Golden Palm

1996. 50th Int Film Festival, Cannes.
3359 **1301** 3f. multicoloured . . . 1·00 50

1302 New Building

1996. Inauguration of New National Library Building, Paris.
3360 **1302** 3f. yellow, blue & red 1·00 50

1303 Mitterrand

1304 Wire Figures

1997. Francois Mitterrand (President, 1981–95) Commemoration.
3361 **1303** 3f. multicoloured . . . 1·00 50

1997. "Participatory Innovation" (suggestions schemes).
3362 **1304** 3f. multicoloured . . . 1·00 50

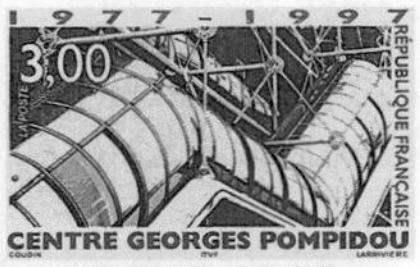

1305 Detail of Building

1997. 20th Anniv of Georges Pompidou National Centre of Art and Culture.
3363 **1305** 3f. multicoloured . . . 1·00 50

1306 "bonne fete" (Happy Holiday)

1997. Greetings stamps. Multicoloured.
3364 3f. Type **1306** . . . . . . 1·00 50
3365 3f. "joyeux anniversaire" (Happy Birthday) . . . . 1·00 50

1307 New Building, Marne-la-Vallee

1997. 250th Anniv of National School of Bridges and Highways.
3366 **1307** 3f. multicoloured . . . 1·00 50

1308 Gateway and Buildings

1997. National Historic Landmark Status of Former Penal Colony, Saint-Laurent-du-Maroni, French Guiana.
3367 **1308** 3f. multicoloured . . . 1·00 50

1997. Art. As T **491**.
3368 6f.70 Fresco (detail), St. Nicholas's Church, Tavant (Indre et Loire) (vert) . . . . 2·20 1·50
3369 6f.70 Abstract (Bernard Moninot) . . . . . . 2·20 1·50
3370 6f.70 "The Thumb" (sculpture, Cesar Baldaccini) (vert) . . . . 2·20 1·70
3371 6f.70 "Grapes and Pomegranates" (Jean Baptiste Chardin) . . . . 2·20 1·70

1309 "Mouchon" type

1310 "Puss in Boots" (engraving by Gustav Dore)

1997. Stamp Day. 97th Anniv of Louis-Eugene Mouchon's Design.
3374 **1309** 3f. blue, mauve & silver 1·60 1·70
3372 3f.+60c. blue, mauve and silver . . . . . 1·20 1·20

1997. Tourist Publicity. As T **490**.
3375 3f. emerald, dp green & grn 1·00 45
3376 3f. green, red and orange . . 1·00 45

3377 3f. brown, blue and green 1·00 50
3378 3f. brown, choc & green 1·00 50
3379 3f. green, blue and brown 1·00 50
DESIGN—VERT: No. 3375, Millau, Aveyron; 3376, Buttress of "Calvary" and church, Guimiliau. HORIZ: No. 3377, Sable-sur-Sarthe; 3378, St. Maurice's Cathedral, Epinal; 3379, Sceaux estate.

1997. National Parks. As T **1278**. Mult.
3380 3f. Golden eagle and blue thistle, Ecrins 1·10 60
3381 3f. Racoon and La Soufriere (volcano), Guadeloupe 1·20 75
3382 4f.50 Manx shearwater and coves, Port-Cros 1·30 85
3383 4f.50 Chamois and mountain, Pyrenees 1·30 85

1997. Europa. Tales and Legends.
3384 **1310** 3f. blue 1·00 60

1311 Teenager "flying" Stamp

1997. "Philexjeunes 97" Youth Stamp Exhibition, Nantes.
3385 **1311** 3f. multicoloured 1·50 1·20

1312 Envelope writing Letter

1997. The Journey of a Letter. Multicoloured. Ordinary or self-adhesive gum.
3386 3f. Type **1312** 1·80 1·30
3387 3f. Smiling letter climbing up to post box 1·30 1·20
3388 3f. Letter as van 1·80 1·20
3389 3f. Letters holding hands and postman carrying letter 1·80 1·20
3390 3f. Girl kissing letter 1·80 1·20
3391 3f. Girl reading long letter 1·30 65

1313 Soldier and Map

1997. French Army Operations in North Africa, 1952–62.
3398 **1313** 3f. multicoloured 1·00 50

1314 Palace of Versailles (½-size illustration)

1997. 70th Federation of French Philatelic Societies Congress, Versailles.
3399 **1314** 3f. multicoloured 1·20 75

1315 Chateau du Plessis-Bourre

1997.
3400 **1315** 4f.40 multicoloured 1·30 70

1997. World Cup Football Championship, France (1998) (2nd issue). Host Cities. As T **1285**. Multicoloured.
3401 3f. Lyon 1·00 50
3402 3f. Marseille 1·00 50
3403 3f. Nantes 1·00 50
3404 3f. Paris 1·20 55

1316 Detail of Fresco

1997. Restoration of Frescoes in St. Eutrope's Church, Les Salles-Lavauguyon.
3405 **1316** 4f.50 multicoloured 1·50 70

1317 St. Martin (from Tours Missal)

1997. 1600th Death Anniv of St. Martin, Bishop of Tours.
3406 **1317** 4f.50 multicoloured 1·50 75

1318 "Marianne of 14 July"

1319 Rowers

1997. No value expressed.
3407 **1318** (3f.) red 1·00 40

1997.
3415 **1318** 10c. brown 10 10
3416 20c. green 10 15
3417 50c. violet 20 20
3417a 50c. red 25 20
3418 1f. orange 35 25
3419 2f. blue 70 35
3420 2f.70 green 90 35
3423 3f.50 green 1·10 50
3425 3f.80 blue 1·20 65
3427 4f.20 red 1·40 65
3428 4f.40 blue 1·60 75
3429 4f.50 mauve 1·60 60
3430 5f. blue 1·70 65
3431 6f.70 green 2·30 80
3432 10f. violet 3·25 1·10
MS3439 (a) Nos. 3415/19, 3430 and 3432; (b) Nos. 3407, 3420/9 and 3431 12·00 12·00

1997. World Rowing Championships, Lake Aiguebelette, Savoie.
3440 **1319** 3f. mauve, bl & red 1·00 45

1320 Sailors and Privateer Ship

1997. Basque Corsairs.
3441 **1320** 3f. multicoloured 1·00 50

1321 Horse-drawn Fish Cart

1997. Fresh Fish Merchants from Boulogne.
3442 **1321** 3f. green, violet & blue 1·00 50

1322 Kudara Kannon (statue from Horyu Temple, Nara) and Japanese Cultural Centre, Paris

1997. Japan Year.
3443 **1322** 4f.90 blue, orge & blk 1·60 1·10

1323 Contest

1997. World Judo Championships, Paris.
3444 **1323** 3f. multicoloured 1·00 50

1324 Emblem

1997. Sar-Lor-Lux (Saarland–Lorraine–Luxembourg) European Region.
3445 **1324** 3f. multicoloured 1·00 50

1325 College and King Francois I (founder)

1326 Team with Coloured Ribbons

1997. Le College de France.
3446 **1325** 4f.40 green, brn & blk 1·40 85

1997. French Movement for Quality.
3447 **1326** 4f.50 multicoloured 1·40 90

1327 Lancelot (Chretien de Troyes)

1997. Red Cross Fund. Literary Heroes. Multicoloured.
3448 3f.+60c. Type **1327** 1·20 1·30
3449 3f.+60c. Pardaillan (Michel Zevaco) 1·20 1·30
3450 3f.+60c. D'Artagnan ("The Three Musketeers" by Alexandre Dumas) 1·20 1·30
3451 3f.+60c. Cyrano de Bergerac (Edmond Rostand) 1·20 1·30
3452 3f.+60c. Captain Fracasse (Theophile Gautier) 1·20 1·30
3453 3f.+60c. Lagardere as Le Bossu (Paul Feval) 1·20 1·30

1328 Teddy Bear with Gifts in Spaceship

1329 Mouse giving Gift to Cat

1997. Red Cross Fund. Christmas.
3454 **1328** 3f.+60c. mult 1·20 1·20

1997. "Best Wishes".
3455 **1329** 3f. multicoloured 1·00 50

1330 Breguet 14 Biplane

1997. Air.
3456 **1330** 20f. multicoloured 6·75 4·25

1331 Teddy Bear holding Toy Windmill

1997. Protection of Abused Children Campaign.
3457 **1331** 3f. multicoloured 1·00 50

1332 Flying Postman

1997. "Best Wishes".
3458 **1332** 3f. multicoloured 1·00 50

1333 Cross of Lorraine on Map of France and Leclerc

1997. 50th Death Anniv of Marshal Leclerc.
3459 **1333** 3f. multicoloured 1·00 50

1334 "Marianne of 14 July" and Emblem

1997. "Philexfrance 99" International Stamp Exhibition, Paris.
3460 **1334** 3f. red and blue 1·20 65

1335 Carving and Buildings

1997. Millenary of Foundation of Moutier D'Ahun Monastery, Creuse.
3461 **1335** 4f.40 multicoloured 1·60 95

1336 Debre

1998. 2nd Death Anniv of Michel Debre (Prime Minister, 1958–62).
3462 **1336** 3f. black, blue & red 1·00 50

1337 Anniversary Emblem

1338 Cherub with Letter and Flowers

1998. Bicentenary of National Assembly.
3463 **1337** 3f. red and blue 1·00 50

1998. World Cup Football Championship, France (3rd issue). Host Cities. As T **1285**. Multicoloured.
3464 3f. Bordeaux 1·00 55
3465 3f. Saint-Denis, Paris 1·00 55
MS3466 148 × 140 mm. Nos. 3335/8, 3401/4 and 3464/5 9·00 9·00

1998. St. Valentine's Day.
3467 **1338** 3f. multicoloured 1·00 50

1339 Mediator and People

1998. 25th Anniv of Mediator of the Republic (ombudsman).
3468 **1339** 3f. multicoloured 1·00 50

1340 "Blanc" Type **1341** Football

1998. Stamp Day. 98th Anniv of Joseph Blanc's Design.
3470 **1340** 3f. red, grn & silver . . 3·25 3·25
3469 3f.+60c. red, green and silver . . . . 1·20 1·10

1998. World Cup Football Championship, France (4th issue). Ordinary or self-adhesive gum.
3472 **1341** 3f. multicoloured . . . 1·00 50
MS3474 No. 3472 plus 7 labels showing the World Cup mascot demonstrating various shots . . 3·00 3·00

1342 Stock **1343** "Happy Birthday"

1998. 50th Death Anniv of Father Franz Stock (wartime prison chaplain).
3475 **1342** 4f.50 blue . . . . . . 1·40 1·00

1998. Greeting Stamp.
3476 **1343** 3f. multicoloured . . . 1·00 50

1344 Citeaux Abbey

1998. 900th Anniv of Founding of Citeaux Abbey.
3477 **1344** 3f. multicoloured . . . 1·00 50

1345 Mulhouse, 1798

1998. Bicentenary of Union of Mulhouse with France.
3478 **1345** 3f. multicoloured . . . 1·00 50

1346 Sub-prefect's Residence, Saint-Pierre

1998. Reunion's Architectural Heritage.
3479 **1346** 3f. multicoloured . . . 1·00 50

1347 "The Return"

1998. Birth Centenary of Rene-Ghislain Magritte (painter).
3480 **1347** 3f. multicoloured . . . 1·00 55

1348 King Henri IV

1998. 400th Anniv of Edict of Nantes.
3481 **1348** 4f.50 multicoloured . . 1·50 95

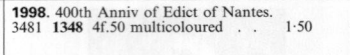

1349 Slave wearing Cap of Liberty

1998. 150th Anniv of Abolition of Slavery by France.
3482 **1349** 3f. multicoloured . . . 1·00 50

1998. Art. As T **491**. Multicoloured.
3483 6f.70 "The Crusaders' Arrival in Constantinople" (detail, Eugene Delacroix) (vert) 2·20 1·70
3484 6f.70 "Spring" (Pablo Picasso) . . . . 2·20 1·60
3485 6f.70 "Nine Idiot Bachelors" (Marcel Duchamp) . . . 2·20 1·70
3486 6f.70 "Vision after the Sermon" (Paul Gaugin) 2·20 1·70

1998. Tourist Publicity. As T **490**.
3487 3f. multicoloured . . . . . 1·00 55
3488 3f. multicoloured . . . . . 1·00 50
3489 3f. green, blue and cream 1·00 50
3490 3f. multicoloured . . . . . 1·00 50
3491 4f.40 multicoloured . . . . 1·50 1·00
DESIGNS—As Type **490**: No. 3487, Le Gois Causeway, Noirmoutiers Island; 3489, Crussol Chateau, Ardeche; 3490, Liberty Tower, Saint-Die, Vosges. 26 × 38 mm: No. 3488, Bay of Somme. 26 × 36 mm: No. 3491, Mantes-la-Jolie collegiate church, Yvelines.

1350 Dove Carrying Letter to Noah's Ark **1351** Figure with Butterfly Wings

1998. History of the Letter. Multicoloured. Ordinary or self-adhesive gum.
3492 3f. Type **1350** . . . . . . 1·80 95
3493 3f. Egyptian carving tablet 1·80 95
3494 3f. Ancient Greek carrying letter from Marathon to Athens . . . . 1·80 95
3495 3f. Knight on horseback carrying letter and pen . . 1·80 95
3496 3f. Man writing with quill 1·80 95
3497 3f. Spaceman posting letter 1·80 95

1998. Cent of League of Human Rights.
3504 **1351** 4f.40 multicoloured . . 1·50 80

1352 Collet

1998. 47th Death Anniv of Henri Collet (composer).
3505 **1352** 4f.50 black & stone . . 1·50 85

1353 Statue of Jean Bart, Cathedral and "Sandettie II" (light-ship)

1998. Federation of French Philatelic Societies Congress, Dunkirk.
3506 **1353** 3f. red, orange & blue 1·00 45

1354 Mont Saint Michel **1355** Pan playing Flute (Festival of Music)

1998.
3507 **1354** 3f. multicoloured . . . 1·00 50

1998. Europa. National Festivals.
3508 **1355** 3f. multicoloured . . . 1·00 50

1998. France, World Cup Football Champion. As No. 3472 but additionally inscribed "Champion du Monde FRANCE".
3509 3f. multicoloured . . . . . 1·00 50

1356 Potez 25 Biplane

1998. Air.
3510 **1356** 30f. multicoloured . . . 10·50 8·75

1357 Convolvulus **1358** Mallarme

1998. Precancels. Flowers. Multicoloured.
3511 1f.87 Type **1357** 65 60
3512 2f.18 Poppy 95 90
3513 4f.66 Violet . . . . . . 1·70 1·70
3514 7f.11 Buttercup . . . . . . 1·90 2·00

1998. Death Centenary of Stephane Mallarme (poet).
3515 **1358** 4f.40 multicoloured . . 1·40 1·00

1359 Balloon and Early Airplane **1360** The Little Prince

1998. Centenary of Aero Club of France.
3516 **1359** 3f. multicoloured . . . 1·00 50

1998. "Philexfrance 99" International Stamp Exhibition, Paris (1st issue). "The Little Prince" (novel) by Antoine de Saint-Exupery. Multicoloured.
3517 3f. Type **1360** . . . . . 1·20 80
3518 3f. On wall watching snake (vert) . . . . 1·00 70
3519 3f. On planet (vert) . . . . 1·00 70
3520 3f. Watering flower (vert) . 1·00 70
3521 3f. On hillside with fox . . 1·00 70
MS3522 111 × 157 mm. Nos. 3517/21 (sold at 25f.) . . . . 7·50 7·50
See also No. **MS**3576.

1361 Hall of Supreme Harmony, Forbidden City, Peking, China **1362** Violin and Ballet Dancer

1998. Cultural Heritage. Multicoloured.
3523 3f. Type **1361** . . . . . 1·00 50
3524 4f.90 Louvre Palace, Paris 1·50 1·00

1998. National Opera House, Paris.
3525 **1362** 4f.50 multicoloured . . 1·40 95

1363 Camargue

1998. Horses. Multicoloured.
3526 2f.70 Type **1363** 95 55
3527 3f. French trotter . . . . . 1·00 50
3528 3f. Pottok . . . . 1·00 50
3529 4f.50 Ardennais . . . . . . 1·50 90

1364 Dion-Bouton and Racing Cars

1998. Centenary of Paris Motor Show.
3530 **1364** 3f. multicoloured . . . 90 55

1365 Marianne and Flag **1366** Romy Schneider

1998. 40th Anniv of Constitution of Fifth Republic.
3531 **1365** 3f. multicoloured . . . 1·00 50

1998. Film Stars. Multicoloured.
3532 3f.+60c. Type **1366** . . . . 1·30 1·30
3533 3f.+60c. Simone Signoret . . 1·30 1·40
3534 3f.+60c. Jean Gabin . . . . 1·30 1·40
3535 3f.+60c. Louis de Funes . . 1·30 1·40
3536 3f.+60c. Bernard Blier . . . 1·30 1·40
3537 3f.+60c. Lino Ventura . . . 1·30 1·40

1367 State Flags

1998. 80th Anniv of Signing of First World War Armistice.
3538 **1367** 3f. multicoloured . . . 1·00 50

1368 Flora and Fauna, Child and Emblem

1998. 50th Anniv of International Union for the Conservation of Nature and Natural Resources.
3539 **1368** 3f. multicoloured . . . 1·00 50

1369 Elf on Christmas Bauble **1370** Father Christmas Snowboarding

1998. Red Cross Fund. Christmas.
3540 **1369** 3f.+60c. mult . . . . . 1·20 95

1998. Christmas and New Year. Multicoloured.
3541 3f. Type **1370** (violet background) . . . . . . 1·10 45
3542 3f. Decorated house (daytime) . . . . 1·10 45
3543 3f. Type **1370** (bright yellow background) . . . . . . 1·10 45

3544 3f. Decorated house (night-time) . . . . 1·10 45
3545 3f. Type **1370** (green background) . . . . . . 1·10 45

1371 Child expressing Ambition and People of Different Nations

1998. Medecins sans Frontieres (volunteer medical and relief organization).
3546 **1371** 3f. multicoloured . . . 1·00 55

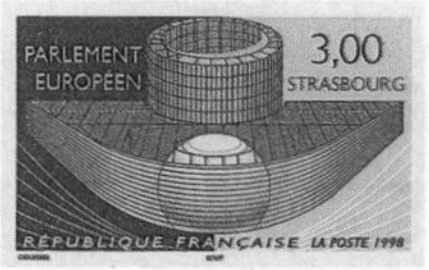

1372 Architectural Drawing

1998. Construction of New European Parliament Building, Strasbourg (designed by Architecture Studio Europe).
3547 **1372** 3f. multicoloured . . . 1·00 55

1373 Rene Cassin, Eleanor Roosevelt and Palais de Chaillot

1998. 50th Anniv of Universal Declaration of Human Rights. Multicoloured.
3548 3f. Type **1373** . . . . . . 1·00 50
3549 3f. Globe and people of different races . . . . . 1·00 50

1374 Radium

1998. Centenary of Discovery of Radium by Marie and Pierre Curie and 50th Anniv of ZOE Reactor, Chatillon.
3550 **1374** 3f. multicoloured . . . 1·00 50

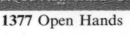

1375 1849 Ceres Design **1376** Euro Symbol

1999. 150th Anniv of First French Postage Stamp (1st issue).
3551 **1375** 3f. black and red . . . 4·00 3·00
3552 – 3f. black and red . . . 95 35
DESIGN: No. 3552, As Type **1375** but with stamp and text transposed.
See also No. 3596.

1999. Introduction of the Euro (European currency). Ordinary or self-adhesive gum.
3553 **1376** 3f. red and blue 95 40
No. 3553 is denominated both in French francs and in euros.

1377 Open Hands **1378** Flags of France and Israel

1999. 150th Anniv of Public Welfare Hospitals of Paris (administration of Paris health services).
3555 **1377** 3f. blue, mve & grn . . 1·10 50

1999. 50th Anniv of Diplomatic Relations between France and Israel.
3556 **1378** 4f.40 multicoloured . . 1·50 1·00

1379 Heart

1999. St. Valentine's Day. Multicoloured. Ordinary and self-adhesive gum.
3557 3f. Type **1379** . . . . 1·30 55
3558 3f. Heart-shaped rose . . . 1·30 55

1999. Art. As T **491**.
3561 6f.70 brown and orange . . 2·40 2·00
3562 6f.70 multicoloured . . . . 2·20 1·70
3563 6f.70 multicoloured . . . . 2·40 1·90
3564 6f.70 multicoloured . . . . 2·40 1·90
DESIGNS—VERT: No. 3561, "St. Luke the Evangelist" (sculpture, Jean Goujon); 3562, Stained glass window (Arnaud de Moles), Chapelle de la Compassion, Auch Cathedral; 3564, "Charles I, King of England" (Anton van Dyck). HORIZ: No. 3563, "Water Lilies, Effect of Evening" (Claude Monet).

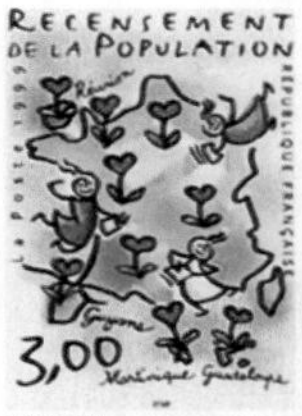

1380 Flowers on Map of France **1382** Asterix

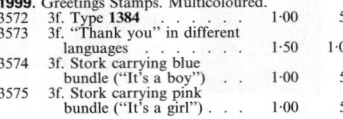

1381 "The Capture of Europa" (mosaic from Byblos)

1999. 33rd Population Census.
3565 **1380** 3f. multicoloured . . . 1·10 55

1999. Cultural Heritage of Lebanon.
3566 **1381** 4f.40 multicoloured . . 1·50 1·00

1999. Stamp Day. Asterix the Gaul (cartoon character) by Albert Uderzo and Rene Goscinny.
3567 **1382** 3f. multicoloured . . . 95 50
3569 3f.+60c. mult . . . . . 2·10 1·60
MS3570 102 × 77 mm. No. 3569 1·50 1·50

1383 Council Emblem on World Map

1999. 50th Anniv of Council of Europe.
3571 **1383** 3f. multicoloured . . . 1·00 50

1384 Two Doves and Hearts (wedding)

1999. Greetings Stamps. Multicoloured.
3572 3f. Type **1384** . . . . 1·00 50
3573 3f. "Thank you" in different languages . . . . 1·50 1·00
3574 3f. Stork carrying blue bundle ("It's a boy") . . 1·00 50
3575 3f. Stork carrying pink bundle ("It's a girl") . . . 1·00 50

1385 "Venus de Milo" (statue)

1999. "Philexfrance 99" International Stamp Exhibition, Paris (2nd issue). Art. Sheet 159 × 111 mm containing T **1385** and similar designs.
MS3576 5f. sepia (Type **1385**); 5f. multicoloured ("Mona Lisa" (Leonardo da Vinci)) (37 × 49 mm); 10f. multicoloured ("Liberty guiding the People" (Eugene Delacroix)) (36 × 37 mm) (sold at 50f.) . . . . 25·00 25·00

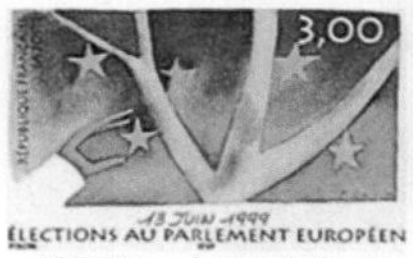

1386 Branches and Hand reaching for Star **1387** Richard the Lion Heart (from "Historia Anglorum")

1999. European Parliament Elections.
3577 **1386** 3f. multicoloured . . . 1·00 50

1999. 800th Death Anniv of King Richard I of England.
3578 **1387** 3f. multicoloured . . . 1·00 50

1388 Airbus A300-B4

1999. Air.
3579 **1388** 15f. multicoloured . . . 3·50 3·50

1389 Dieppe Castle

1999. Tourist Publicity.
3580 **1389** 3f. multicoloured . . . 1·00 50
3581 – 3f. multicoloured . . . 1·00 60
3582 – 3f. multicoloured . . . 1·00 50
3583 – 3f. multicoloured . . . 1·00 50
DESIGNS—As T **949**: No. 3581, Haut-Koenigsbourg Castle, Lower Rhine. As T **490**: No. 3582, Place des Ecritures, Figeac; 3583, Arnac-Pompadour Chateau.
No. 3583 is denominated in both francs and euros.

1390 The Camargue

1999. Europa. Parks and Gardens.
3584 **1390** 3f. multicoloured . . . 1·00 50

1391 Cake and Music Notes ("Happy Birthday")

1999. Greetings Stamps. Multicoloured.
3585 3f. Type **1391** . . . . . . 1·00 50
3586 3f. Seagull and sun wearing sunglasses ("Have a nice holiday") . . . . 1·00 50
3587 3f. Float on water ("Long live holidays") (vert) . . . 1·00 50

1392 St. Pierre and Mt. Pelee

1999. Heritage of Martinique.
3588 **1392** 3f. multicoloured . . . 1·00 50

1393 "Noctuelles" Dish (detail, Emile Galle)

1999. Nancy School (art movement).
3589 **1393** 3f. multicoloured . . . 1·00 50

1394 "Mme. Alfred Carriere"

1999. Old Roses. Sheet 111 × 160 mm containing T **1394** and similar vert designs. Multicoloured.
MS3590 3f. Type **1394**; 4f.50 "Mme. Caroline Testout"; 4f.50 "La France" . . . . 4·50 4·50

1395 Ruins, Grape Vines and Seal

1999. 800th Anniv of Granting of City Rights to Saint-Emilion and 50th Anniv of Re-institution of the Jurade (controllers of St.-Emilion wine appellation).
3591 **1395** 3f.80 multicoloured . . 1·20 1·00

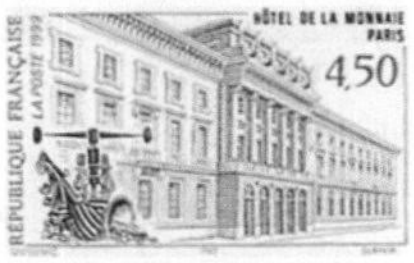

1396 The Mint, Paris

1999.
3592 **1396** 4f.50 red, blue & black 1·50 95

1397 Model Girls **1398** Sun and Doves in Mosaic

1999. Birth Bicentenary of Countess de Segur (children's writer).
3593 **1397** 3f. multicoloured . . . 1·00 50

1999. Post Office "Pleasure to Welcome" Customer Campaign.
3594 **1398** 3f. multicoloured . . . 1·00 65

1399 Caillie

1999. Birth Bicentenary of Rene Caillie (explorer).
3595 **1399** 4f.50 violet, yellow and orange . . . . 1·50 1·00

1400 1849 Ceres Design

1999. 150th Anniv of First French Postage Stamp (2nd issue).
3596 **1400** 6f.70 multicoloured . . 1·80 1·30

DENOMINATION. From No. 3597 French stamps are denominated both in francs and in euros. As no cash for the latter is in circulation, the catalogue continues to use the franc value.

1401 Spinning Globe

1999. Year 2000.
3597 **1401** 3f. multicoloured . . . 1·00 55

1402 Winning Entry by Morgane Toulouse

1999. "Design a Stamp for Year 2000" Children's Drawing Contest.
3598 **1402** 3f. multicoloured . . . 1·00 50

1403 Total Eclipse

1999. Solar Eclipse (11 August).
3599 **1403** 3f. multicoloured . . . 75 65

1404 "Simon Bolivar" (Venezuelan cadet barque)

1999. "Armada of the Century", Rouen. Sailing Ships. Multicoloured.
3600 1f. Type **1404** 35 40
3601 1f. "Iskra" (Polish cadet ship) 35 40
3602 1f. "Statsraad Lehmkuhl" (barque) 35 40
3603 1f. "Asgard II" (cadet brigantine) 35 40
3604 1f. "Belle Poule" (sail frigate) 35 40
3605 1f. "Belem" (barque) . . . 35 40
3606 1f. "Amerigo Vespucci" (cadet ship) 35 40
3607 1f. "Sagres" (cadet barque) 35 40
3608 1f. "Europa" (barque) . . . 35 40
3609 1f. "Cuauhtemoc" (barque) 35 40

1405 "School, 1956" (Robert Doisneau)

1999. French Photographers. Multicoloured.
3610 3f.+60c. Type **1405** . . . . 1·30 1·40
3611 3f.+60c. "St. James's Tower, View of Notre Dame, 1936" (Gilberte Brassai) 1·30 1·40
3612 3f.+60c. "Renee on the way to Paris, Aix-les-Bains" (Jacques Henri Lartigue) 1·30 1·40
3613 3f.+60c. "Hyeres, France, 1932" (Henri Cartier-Bresson) . . . . 1·30 1·40
3614 3f.+60c. "Travelling Salesman" (Eugene Atget) 1·30 1·40
3615 3f.+60c. "Debureau at the Camera" (Nadar) . . . . 1·30 1·40

1406 Players

1999. 4th World Cup Rugby Championship, Great Britain, Ireland and France.
3616 **1406** 3f. multicoloured . . . 1·20 70

1407 Ozanam (after Louis Janmot)

1999. 146th Death Anniv of Frederic Ozanam (historian and social campaigner).
3617 **1407** 4f.50 deep green, brown and red . . . . 1·30 70

1408 People holding Hands

1999. 50th Anniv of Emmaus Movement (welfare organization).
3618 **1408** 3f. multicoloured . . . 1·00 50

1409 Chartreuse Cat

1999. Domestic Pets. Multicoloured.
3619 2f.70 Type **1409** . . . . . 1·00 60
3620 3f. European tabby cat . . . 1·00 60
3621 3f. Pyrenean mountain dog 1·30 75
3622 4f.50 Brittany spaniel . . . 1·50 1·20

1410 Chopin (after George Sand)

1999. 150th Death Anniv of Frederic Chopin (composer).
3623 **1410** 3f.80 blue, deep violet and orange . . . . . 1·40 1·10

1411 Star playing Drum with Clock Face

1999. Red Cross Fund. New Year.
3624 **1411** 3f.+60c. mult . . . . . 1·40 1·10

1412 "2000"

1999. Year 2000. Multicoloured.
3625 3f. Type **1412** . . . . . . 1·00 55
3626 3f. Half-unwrapped parcel (vert) . . . . 1·00 55

1413 Metro Signs

1999. Centenary of Paris Metro.
3627 **1413** 3f. multicoloured . . . 1·00 55

1414 Column and Pediment

1999. Bicentenary of Council of State.
3628 **1414** 3f. blue and grey . . . 1·10 55

1415 San Juan de Salvamento and La Rochelle Lighthouses

2000. Reconstruction of San Juan de Salvamento Lighthouse, Staten Island.
3629 **1415** 3f. multicoloured . . . 1·00 60

1416 Snakes forming Heart 1417 Bank Entrance

2000. Yves St. Laurent (couturier). Multicoloured. Ordinary or self-adhesive gum.
3630 3f. Type **1416** . . . . . . 1·10 50
3631 3f. Woman's face . . . . . 1·00 50
MS3632 95 × 150 mm. Nos. 3630 × 3 and No. 3631 × 2 . . . . . . 5·25 5·25

2000. Bicentenary of Bank of France.
3635 **1417** 3f. multicoloured . . . 95 50

1418 Couzinet 70 *Arc en Ciel*

2000. Air.
3636 **1418** 50f. multicoloured . . . 15·00 15·00

1419 Emblem 1420 Tintin and Snowy

2000. Bicentenary of Prefectorial Corps.
3637 **1419** 3f. multicoloured . . . 1·00 50

2000. Art. As T **491**.
3638 6f.70 multicoloured (vert) 1·80 1·30
3639 6f.70 multicoloured (vert) 2·40 1·90
3640 6f.70 multicoloured (vert) 2·30 1·70
DESIGNS: No. 3638, Detail of "Venus and the Graces offering Gifts to a Young Girl" (Sandro Botticelli); 3639, "The Waltz" (sculpture, Camille Claudel); 3640, "Visage Rouge" (Gaston Chaissac).

2000. Tourist Publicity. As T **949**.
3642 3f. multicoloured 95 55
3643 3f. multicoloured 95 50
3644 3f. multicoloured 95 50
3645 3f. multicoloured . . . . . 1·00 50
DESIGNS: No. 3642, Carcassonne. As Type **490**: 37 × 27 mm—No. 3643, Saint Guilhem le Desert, Herault; 3644, Valley of the Lakes, Gerardmer. 36 × 23 mm—No. 3645, Ottmarsheim Abbey church.

2000. Tintin (cartoon character) by Georges Renu (Herge).
3646 **1420** 3f. multicoloured . . . 1·00 55
3648 3f.+60c. mult . . . . . 2·30 1·30
MS3649 101 × 76 mm. No. 3648 1·20 1·20

1421 Parliament Building

2000. Restoration of Breton Regional Parliament, Rennes.
3650 **1421** 3f. multicoloured . . . 95 50

1422 Periwinkle

2000.
3651 **1422** 4f.50 multicoloured . . 1·50 85

1423 "Congratulations"

2000. Greetings Stamp. Multicoloured.
3652 3f. Type **1423** . . . . . . 1·10 60
3653 3f. "bonnes vacances" . . . 95 50

1424 Football World Cup Trophy (France, World Champions, 1998)

2000. The Twentieth Century (1st series). Sporting Achievements. Sheet 185 × 245 mm containing five different 3f. designs as T **1424**, each × 2. Multicoloured.
MS3654 3f. Type **1424**; 3f. Marcel Cerdan (World Middleweight Champion, 1948); 3f. Carl Lewis (Olympic Gold medallist 100m, 200m, 100m relay and long jump, 1984) (vert); 3f. Charles Lindbergh and *Spirit of St. Louis* (first solo Atlantic crossing,1927); 3f. Jean-Claude Killy (Winter Olympic Gold medallist downhill, giant slalom and special slalom, 1968) (vert) . . . . 6·50 6·50
See also No. **MS**3687, **MS**3710, **MS**3756, **MS**3814 and **MS**3861.

1425 Bugatti 35

2000. "Philexjeunes 2000" International Youth Stamp Exhibition, Annely. Vintage Cars. Multicoloured.
3655 1f. Type **1425** 45 45
3656 1f. Citroen Traction 45 45

3657 1f. Renault 4CV 45 40
3658 1f. Simca Chamord 45 45
3659 1f. Hispano Suiza K6 . . . 45 45
3660 2f. Volkswagen Beetle . . . 70 55
3661 2f. Cadillac 62 . . . . . . 70 55
3662 2f. Peugeot 203 . . . . . . 70 55
3663 2f. Citroen DS19 . . . . . 70 55
3664 2f. Ferrari 250 GTO 70 55

1426 "Building Europe"

2000. Europa.
3665 **1426** 3f. multicoloured . . . 80 45

1427 Du Monceau

2000. 300th Birth Anniv of Henry-Louis Duhamel du Monceau (technologist and natural scientist).
3666 **1427** 4f.50 multicoloured . . 1·40 90

1428 Porte du Croux and Earthenware Jug **1429** Mountaineers

2000. 73rd French Philatelic Federation Congress, Nevers.
3667 **1428** 3f. multicoloured . . . 95 50

2000. 50th Anniv of French Ascent of Mt. Annapurna, Himalayas.
3668 **1429** 3f. multicoloured . . . 95 50

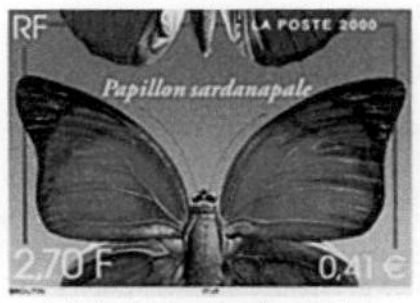

1430 *Agrias sardanapalus*

2000. National Museum of Natural History. Mult.
3669 2f.70 Type **1430** 95 50
3670 3f. Giraffe (vert) . . . . . 1·00 55
3671 3f. Allosaurus . . . . . . 1·00 55
3672 4f.50 *Tulipa lutea* (vert) . . 1·50 1·00
MS3673 110 × 160 mm. Nos. 3669/72 3·25 3·25

1431 Saint-Exupery **1432** Train

2000. Birth Centenary of Antoine de Saint-Exupery (aviator and writer).
3674 **1431** 3f. multicoloured . . . 95 50

2000. Centenary of the Yellow Train (Villefranch de Conflent–Latourde Card service), Cerdagne.
3675 **1432** 3f. multicoloured . . . 80 50

1433 "Folklores" and Characters

2000.
3676 **1433** 4f.50 multicoloured . . 1·50 75

1434 Cycling, Fencing and Relay

2000. Olympic Games, Sydney. Multicoloured.
3677 3f. Type **1434** . . . . . . 1·00 50
3678 3f. Relay, judo and diving 1·00 50
MS3679 210 × 143 mm. Nos. 3677/8, each × 5 plus label . . . . . . 7·25 7·25
Nos. 3677/8 were issued together, se-tenant, forming a composite design.

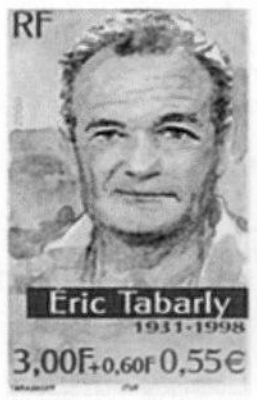

1435 Eric Tabarly (yachtsman) **1436** Stanke

2000. French Adventurers. Multicoloured.
3680 3f.+60c. Type **1435** . . . . 1·20 1·20
3681 3f.+60c. Alexandra David-Neel (explorer) . . . . . 1·20 1·20
3682 3f.+60c. Haroun Tazieff (geologist and vulcanologist) . . . . . . 1·20 1·20
3683 3f.+60c. Paul-Emile Victor (polar explorer) . . . . . 1·20 1·20
3684 3f.+60c. Jacques-Yves Cousteau (underwater explorer) . . . . 1·20 1·20
3685 3f.+60c. Norbert Casteret (archeologist and speleologist) . . . . . . 1·20 1·20

2000. 25th Death Anniv of Brother Alfred Stanke (German wartime prison hospital Chaplain who helped French prisoners).
3686 **1436** 4f.40 brown, ultramarine and blue 1·50 1·10

1437 Edwin E. Aldrin on Moon (first manned Moon landing, 1969)

2000. The Twentieth Century (2nd series). Sheet 185 × 245 mm containing five different 3f. designs as T **1437**, each × 2. Multicoloured.
MS3687 3f. Type **1437**; 3f. Family paddling in sea (entitlement to paid holiday, 1936); 3f. Modern washing machine (invention of washing machine, 1901); 3f. Women posting voting slips (women given right to vote, 1944); 3f. Graffiti (Declaration of Human Rights, 1948) . . . . 6·25 6·25

1438 Man telephoning Helpline

2000. 40th Anniv of S.O.S. Amitie (telephone support service).
3688 **1438** 3f. multicoloured . . . 1·00 50

1439 Globe and Methods of Communication

2000. New Millennium.
3689 **1439** 3f. multicoloured . . . 1·00 50

1440 Detail of Mosaic

2000. Germigny-des-Pres Mosaic, Loire Valley.
3690 **1440** 6f.70 multicoloured . . 2·30 1·70

1441 Young Couple and Bandstand (R. Peynet)

2000.
3691 **1441** 3f. multicoloured . . . 1·20 50

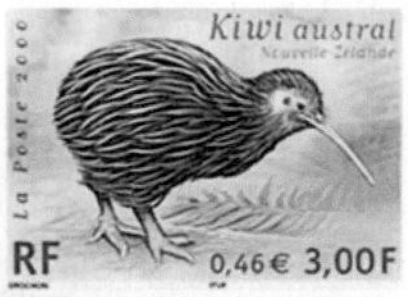

1442 Brown Kiwi (New Zealand)

2000. Endangered Species. Multicoloured.
3692 3f. Type **1442** 90 40
3693 5f.20 Lesser kestrel (France) 1·50 1·10

1443 Toy Aeroplane and Gifts

2000. Red Cross Fund. New Year.
3694 **1443** 3f.+60c. mult . . . . . 1·10 90

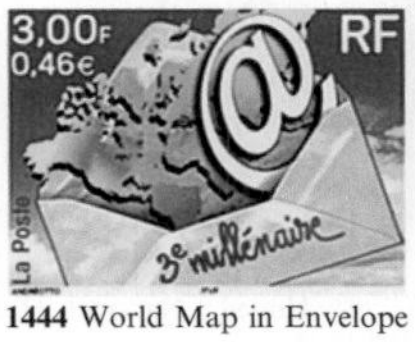

1444 World Map in Envelope **1446** Eiffel Tower and Space Rocket

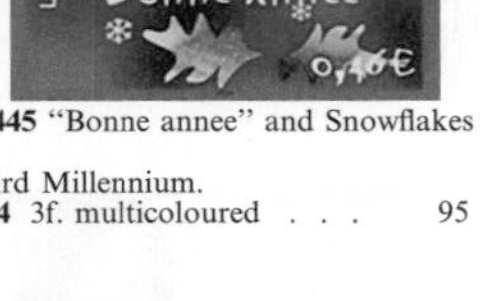

1445 "Bonne annee" and Snowflakes

2000. Third Millennium.
3695 **1444** 3f. multicoloured . . . 95 50

2000. Christmas and New Year. Multicoloured.
3696 3f. Type **1445** 95 50
3697 3f. "Meilleurs voeux", Globe and gifts 95 50

2000. Centenary of Union of Metallurgy and Mining Industries.
3698 **1446** 4f.50 multicoloured . . 1·50 1·00

1447 Emblem

2001. World Handball Championship, France.
3699 **1447** 3f. multicoloured . . . 95 45

1448 Stone covered Heart

2001. St. Valentine's Day.
3700 **1448** 3f. multicoloured . . . 95 50
MS3701 136 × 143 mm. No. 3700 × 5 . . . . 4·00 4·00

2001. Art. As T **491**.
3702 6f.70 multicoloured . . . . 2·20 1·70
3703 6f.70 multicoloured . . . . 2·20 1·70
3704 6f.70 multicoloured . . . . 2·10 1·90
3705 6f.70 multicoloured . . . . 2·10 1·90
DESIGNS—Horiz: No. 3702, "The Peasant Dance" (Pieter Brugel the Elder); 3703, St. James of Compostela and Angel (mural, hospital of Order of St. John of Jerusalem, Toulouse), 3705, "Honfleur at Low Tide" (Johan Barthold Jongkind). VERT: 3704, "Yvette Guilbert singing Linger, Longer Loo" (Henri Toulouse-Lautrec).

1449 Gaston Lagaffe

2001. Gaston Lagaffe (cartoon character) by Andre Franquin.
3706 **1449** 3f. multicoloured . . . 1·00 50
3708 3f.+60c. multicoloured 2·20 1·40
MS3709 101 × 75 mm. No. 3708 1·20 1·20

1450 Nounours, Pimprenelle and Nicolas from "Bonne Nuit les Petits" (chilren's televison programme, 1965)

2001. The Twentieth Century (3rd series). Forms of Communication. Sheet 186 × 245 mm containing five different 3f. designs as T **1450**, each × 2. Multicoloured.
MS3710 3f. Type **1450**; 3f. Hand holding compact disc (development of analogue technology); 3f. The Little Miner and road sign (cinema advertising character created by Jean Mineur, 1950); 3f. Couple dancing and early radio (*Salut les Copians* (first broadcast by popular radio programme, 1959)); 3f. Baby, mobile phone and globe (development of digital mobile phone technology, 1991) . . . 7·25 7·25

1451 Flower ("merci")

2001. Greetings Stamps. Multicoloured.
3711 3f. Type **1451** 95 45
3712 3f. Teddy bear wearing bow tie ("c'est un garcon") . . 95 50
3713 3f. Teddy bear wearing yellow ribbon ("c'est une fille") 95 50
3714 4f.50 Two hearts ("oui") . . 1·50 1·20

1452 Eurasian Red Squirrel

1453 Water Droplet and Globe

2001. Animals. Multicoloured.
3715 2f.70 Type **1452** 95 50
3716 3f. Roe deer (horiz) . . . . 1·00 55
3717 3f. West European hedgehog (horiz) . . . . 1·10 55
3718 4f.50 Stoat . . . . 1·50 95
MS3719 161 × 111 mm. Nos. 3715/18 3·00 3·00

2001. Tourist Publicity. As T **490**. Multicoloured.
3720 3f. Nogent-le-Rotrou (vert) 95 45
3721 3f. Besancon, Doubs 95 45
3722 3f. Calais 95 45
3723 3f. Chateau de Grignan, Drome 95 55

2001. Europa. Water Resources.
3724 **1453** 3f. multicoloured . . . 95 45

1454 Gardens (½-size illustration)

2001. Versailles Palace Gardens.
3725 **1454** 4f.40 multicoloured . . 1·50 1·30

1455 Lyon

1456 Claude Francois

2001.
3726 **1455** 3f. multicoloured . . . 95 45

2001. Singers. Multicoloured.
3727 3f. Type **1456** . . . . . . 1·00 60
3728 3f. Leo Ferre . . . . 1·00 60
3729 3f. Serge Gainsbourg . . . 1·00 60
3730 3f. Dalida . . . . 1·00 60
3731 3f. Michel Berger . . . . . 1·00 60
3732 3f. Barbara . . . . 1·00 60
MS3733 135 × 143 mm. Nos. 3727/32 (sold at 28f.) . . . . 7·25 7·25

1457 Craftsman, Wilson Bridge and St. Gatien Cathedral

2001. 74th French Philatelic Federation Congress, Tours.
3734 **1457** 3f. multicoloured . . . 95 45

1458 Vilar

2001. 30th Death Anniv of Jean Vilar (theatre director).
3735 **1458** 3f. multicoloured . . . 95 45

1459 Footprint in Sand

2001. Greetings Stamps. Holidays. Ordinary or self-adhesive gum.
3736 **1459** 3f. multicoloured . . . 95 50

1460 1 Euro Coin

2001. The European Currency.
3738 **1460** 3f. multicoloured . . . 95 45

1461 Caquot, Airship and Bridge

2001. 120th Birth Anniv of Albert Caquot (civil engineer).
3739 **1461** 4f.50 multicoloured . . 1·40 90

1462 Jigsaw Pieces

2001. Centenary of Freedom of Association Law.
3740 **1462** 3f. multicoloured . . . 95 45

1463 Eurostar Express Train

2001. Locomotives. Multicoloured.
3741 1f.50 Type **1463** 50 45
3742 1f.50 American 220 steam locomotive 50 45
3743 1f.50 Ae 6/8 "Crocodile" locomotive 50 45
3744 1f.50 Crampton steam locomotive 50 45
3745 1f.50 Garratt type 59 steam locomotive 50 45
3746 1f.50 Pacific Chapelon steam locomotive 50 45
3747 1f.50 LNER Class A4 steam locomotive No. 4468 *Mallard*, 1938, Great Britain 50 45
3748 1f.50 Capitole electric locomotive 50 45
3749 1f.50 Autorail 50 45
3750 1f.50 230 Class P8 type 230 steam locomotive 50 45

1464 Emblem

2001. 50th Anniv of United Nations High Commissioner for Refugees.
3751 **1464** 4f.50 green, magenta and blue . . . . . . 1·50 1·00

2001. No value expressed. As T **1318** but with "RF" in lower left corner and "LA POSTE" in upper right corner.
3752 (3.f) red 90 40

1465 Fermat and Mathematical Equations

2001. 400th Birth Anniv of Pierre de Fermat (mathematician).
3755 **1465** 4f.50 multicoloured . . 1·50 90

1466 Yuri Gagarin and Vostok 1 (first man in space, 1961)

2001. The Twentieth Century (4th issue). Science. Sheet 185 × 244 mm containing five different 3f. designs as T **1466**, each × 2. Multicoloured.
MS3756 3f. Type **1466**; 3f. Human body and DNA double helix (identification of DNA molecule, 1953); 3f. Hand holding credit card (development of chip card) (horiz); 3f. Laser treatment for correcting eye sight (development of laser technology); 3f. Bacteriologist and penicillin culture (discovery of penicillin, 1928) (horiz) . . . . 7·25 7·25

1467 Astrolabe (sculpture, Alain Le Boucher)

2001. 25th Anniv of Val-de-Reuil.
3757 **1467** 3f. multicoloured . . . 95 55

1468 Pumpkin

2001. Halloween.
3758 **1468** 3f. multcoloured . . . 95 55
MS3759 135 × 144 mm. No. 3759 × 5 . . . . 3·75 3·75

1469 Father Christmas

1470 Pierre-Bloch

2001. Red Cross Fund. Christmas.
3760 **1469** 3f.+60c. multicoloured 1·10 1·10

2001. 2nd Death Anniv of Jean Pierre-Bloch (politician).
3761 **1470** 4f.50 blue, ultramarine and deep blue . . . 1·40 1·20

1471 Eiffel Tower and Arc de Triomphe dancing

2001. Birth Centenary of Albert Decaris (artist and engraver).
3762 **1471** 3f. violet, brown and blue 85 70

1472 Children and Snowman

1473 Chaban-Delmas

2001. New Year. Multicoloured. Self-adhesive or ordinary gum.
3763 3f. Type **1472** 90 55
3764 3f. Children and wheelbarrow 90 55

2001. Jaques Chaban-Delmas (politician) Commemoration.
3767 **1473** 3f. multicoloured . . . 95 45

1474 Nejjarine Fountain, Fez, Morocco

1475 *Orchis insularis*

2001. French–Moroccan Cultural Heritage. Fountains. Multicoloured.
3768 3f. Type **1474** 95 50
3769 3f.80 Wallace Fountain, Paris . . . . 1·20 1·10

After the adoption by France of the euro currency on 1 January 2002, No. 3752 were sold at 46c.

2002. As T **1318** but with "RF" in lower left corner, "LAPOSTE" in upper right corner and values expressed in euros. (a) Sheet stamps.
3770 1c. yellow 10 10
3771 2c. brown 10 10
3772 5c. green 10 10
3773 10c. violet 20 15
3774 20c. orange 30 20
3775 41c. green 95 45
3776 50c. blue . . . . 1·80 55
3777 53c. green . . . . 1·50 60
3778 58c. blue 85 55
3778a 58c. green 90 20
3779 64c. orange 95 70
3780 67c. blue . . . . 1·30 75
3781 69c. mauve . . . . 1·00 50
3782 70c. green 95 15
3783 75c. blue . . . . 1·00 25
3784 90c. blue . . . . 1·20 30
3785 €1 turquoise . . . . . . 1·40 35
3786 €1.02 green . . . . 1·40 35
3787 €1.11 purple . . . . . . 1·50 40
3788 €1.90 purple . . . . . . 2·50 65
3789 €2 violet . . . . 2·75 70

(b) Coil stamp. (i) No Value expressed.
3790 (41c.) green . . . .
3791 (46c.) red 60 15

(ii).
3792 41c. green 55 15

(c) Miniature sheets. Two sheets, each 145 × 143 mm.
MS3794 (a) Nos. 3770/4, 3776, 3785 and 3789; (b) Nos. 3775, 3752, 3777/8, 3779/81 and 3789 . . . 13·50 13·50

2002. Orchids. Multicoloured.
3795 29c. Type **1475** . . . . . 1·50 1·10
3796 33c. *Orphrys fuciflora* . . . 1·30 1·10
Nos. 3795/6 were only issued precancelled.

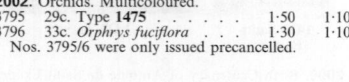

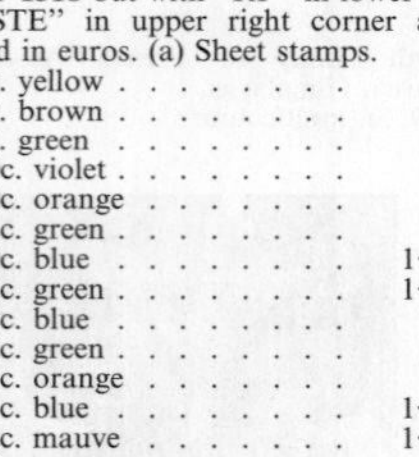

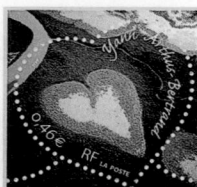

1476 Heart Shape in Landscape, New Caledonia

2002. St. Valentine's Day.
3797 **1476** 46c. multicoloured . . . 90 35
MS3798 135 × 142 mm. No. 3797 × 5 3·50 5·25

1477 Snowboarder

1478 Bosquet

2002. Winter Olympic Games, Salt Lake City, U.S.A.
3799 **1477** 46c. multicoloured . . . 1·00 35

2002. Art. Designs as T **491**. Multicoloured.
3800 €1.02 "The Kiss" (Gustav Klimt) . . . . 1·50 1·80
3801 €1.02 "The Dancers" (painting, Fernando Botero) . . . . 1·90 1·80

2002. 4th Death Anniv of Alain Bosquet (Anatole Bisk) (writer).
3804 **1478** 58c. brown, orange and blue . . . . 90 1·10

1479 Bee wearing Crown ("c'est une fille")

2002. Greetings Stamps. Multicoloured.
3805 46c. Type **1479** 90 35
3806 46c. Bee wearing cap ("c'est un garcon") 90 35
3807 69c. "Oui" in flowers . . . 1·20 1·10

1481 Elephant, Performers and Horse

1482 Boule, Bill and Birds

2002. Europa. Circus.
3808 **1481** 46c. multicoloured . . . 85 35

2002. Boule and Bill (cartoon characters) by Jean Roba. Multicoloured.
3809 46c. Type **1482** 85 40
3811 46c. + 9c. Boule, Bill and ball . . . . 1·10 1·40
MS3812 100 × 75 mm. As No. 3811 1·40 1·40

1483 Amphitheatre, Nimes

2002.
3813 **1483** 46c. multicoloured . . . 85 35

1484 Concorde (first flight, 1969)

2002. The Twentieth Century (5th series).Transport. Sheet 185 × 245 mm, containing five different 46c. designs as T **1484**, each × 2. Multicoloured.
MS3814 46c. Type **1484**; 46c. TGV train (high speed passenger train); 46c. "La Mobylette" (motorcycle) (vert); 46c. *France* (transatlantic passenger liner) (vert); 46c. 2CV (motor car) (vert) . . . . . . 13·50 11·50

1485 Matthew Flinders, Map of Australia and H.M.S. *Investigator* (ship of the line)

2002. France—Australia Joint Issue. Bicentenary of Nicolas Baudin–Matthew Flinders Meeting at Encounter Bay, Australia. Multicoloured.
3815 46c. Type **1485** 85 35
3816 79c. *Geographie* (corvette), map of Australia and Nicolas Baudin . . . . . 1·80 1·40

1486 La Charite-sur-Loire Church, Nievre

2002. U.N.E.S.C.O. World Heritage Site.
3817 **1486** 46c. multicoloured . . . 85 35

1487 Butterflies and Gift ("Anniversaire")

1488 Cyclists

2002. Greetings Stamps. Multicoloured.
3818 46c. Type **1487** 85 40
3819 46c. Bird and envelopes ("Invitation") 85 40

2002. 100th Paris–Roubaix Cycle Race.
3820 **1488** 46c. multicoloured . . . 85 70

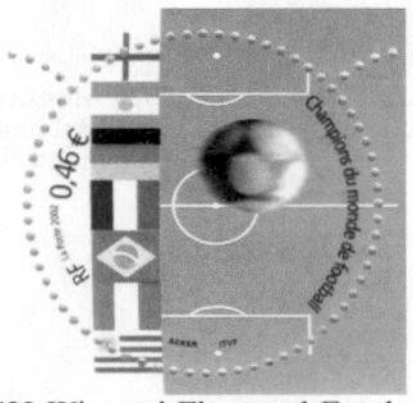
1489 Winners' Flags and Football

2002. World Cup Football Championship, Japan and South Korea. Multicoloured.
3821 46c. Type **1489** 85 40
3822 46c. Footballer 85 40
MS3823 143 × 210 mm. Nos. 3821/2, each × 5 . . . . 9·00 10·50
No. **MS**3823 was inscribed on the back, with the groups around the edge and with facilities for recording the results between the stamps, over the gum.

1490 Leatherback Turtle

2002. Animals. Multicoloured.
3824 41c. Type **1490** 70 40
3825 46c. Killer whale (horiz) . . 85 35
3826 46c. Bottle-nosed dolphin (horiz) 85 30
3827 69c. Common seal . . . . . 1·20 70
MS3828 109 × 160 mm. Nos. 3824/7 4·25 4·25

1491 Old Port, Marseille (½-size illustration)

2002. 75th French Federation of Philatelic Societies Congress, Marseille.
3829 **1491** 46c. multicoloured . . . 85 45

1492 Medal

1493 Rocamadour, Lot

2002. Bicentenary of Legion d'Honneur (medal).
3830 **1492** 46c. multicoloured . . . 85 35

2002.
3831 **1493** 46c. multicoloured . . . 85 35

1494 Delgres

2002. Death Bicentenary of Louis Delgres (soldier and anti-slavery campaigner).
3832 **1494** 46c. multicoloured . . . 85 40

1495 Woman in Hammock

2002. Holidays. Ordinary or self-adhesive gum.
3833 **1495** 46c. multicoloured . . . 85 40

1496 Wheelchair Racers

2002. World Disabled Athletics Championship, Lille-Villeneuve-d'Ascq.
3835 **1496** 46c. multicoloured . . . 85 35

1497 Collioure Lighthouse (painting, Andre Derain)

1498 Chapel

2002. Collioure, Pyrenees.
3836 **1497** 46c. multicoloured . . . 85 35

2002. Saint-Ser Chapel, Puyloubier, Bouches-du-Rhone.
3837 **1498** 46c. multicoloured . . . 85 35

1499 Stained Glass Window (Mark Chagall)

2002. Metz Cathedral.
3838 **1499** 46c. multicoloured . . . 85 50

2002. Tourist Publicity. As Type **490**. Multicoloured.
3839 46c. Lacronan, Finistere (vert) 85 25
3840 46c. Neufchateau, Vosges 85 45

1500 Louis Armstrong

1501 Building Facade

2002. Jazz. Multicoloured.
3841 46c. Type **1500** 85 40
3842 46c. Ella Fitzgerald 85 40
3843 46c. Duke Ellington 85 40
3844 46c. Stephane Grappelli . . 85 40
3845 46c. Michel Petrucciani (horiz) 85 40
3846 46c. Sidney Bechet (horiz) 85 40
MS3847 135 × 143 mm. Nos. 3841/6 (sold at €4.36) . . . . 8·50 10·50
No. **MS**3847 was sold with a premium of €1.60 for the benefit of the Red Cross.

2002. 150th Anniv of Notre-Dame de la Salette, Isere.
3848 **1501** 46c. multicoloured . . . 90 40

1502 Hands (½-size illustration)

2002. Choreography.
3849 **1502** 53c. multicoloured . . . 1·10 1·20

1503 Honda CB 750 Four

2002. Motorcycles. Multicoloured.
3850 16c. Type **1503** 30 40
3851 16c. Terrot 500 RGST . . . 30 40
3852 16c. Majestic 350 . . . . . 30 40
3853 16c. Norton Commando 750 30 40
3854 16c. Voxon 1000 Cafe Racer 30 75
3855 30c. BMW R 90 S 60 55
3856 30c. Harley Davidson FL Hydra-Glide 60 60
3857 30c. Triumph T120 Bonneville 650 . . . . . 60 60
3858 30c. Ducati 916 . . . . . . 60 60
3859 30c. Yamaha 500 XT . . . 60 60

1504 Perec

1505 Family on Motor Scooter

2002. 20th Death Anniv of Georges Perec (writer).
3860 **1504** 46c. multicoloured . . . 90 40

2002. The Twentieth Century (6th series). Everyday Life. Sheet 185 × 243 mm, containing five different 46c. designs as T **1505**, each × 2. Multicoloured.
MS3861 46c. Type **1505**; 46c. Man with horse and cart (horiz); 46c. Woman ironing (horiz); 46c. Boy at water pump; 46c. Girl at school desk . . . . 4·75 8·00

1506 Zola

2002. Death Centenary of Emile Zola (writer).
3862 **1506** 46c. multicoloured . . . 95 45

1507 Self-portrait (Uffizi museum, Florence)

2002. 160th Death Anniv of Elisabeth Vigee-Lebrun (artist).
3863 **1507** €1.02 multicoloured 1·80 2·10

1508 Airbus

2002. 30th Anniv of First Flight of Airbus A 300-B1.
3864 **1508** €3 multicoloured . . . 5·00 2·50

1509 "Sleeping Jesus" (Giovanni Battista Salvi)
1510 Trevi Fountain

2002. Red Cross Fund. Christmas.
3865 **1509** 46c.+9c. multicoloured 1·10 1·20

2002. European Capitals. Rome. Sheet 144 × 36 mm containing T **1510** and similar multicoloured designs.
MS3866 46c. Type **1510**; 46c. Coliseum (horiz); 46c. Trinita dei Monti church; 46c. St. Peter's Basilica (horiz) . . . . 3·50 4·00

1511 World embedded in Computer Circuit

2002. Enterprise.
3867 **1511** 46c. multicoloured . . . 90 45

1512 Snow-covered House

2002. New Year. Ordinary or Self-adhesive gum.
3868 **1512** 46c. multicoloured . . . 90 45

1513 "Sphere Concorde" (Jesus Rafael)

2002.
3870 **1513** 75c. multicoloured . . . 1·40 1·70

1514 Dumas

2002. Birth Bicentenary of Alexandre Dumas (writer).
3871 **1514** 46c. multicoloured . . . 90 45

1515 Senghor

2002. 1st Death Anniv of Leopold Sedar Senghor (writer and linguist).
3872 **1515** 46c. multicoloured . . . 1·10 45

1516 Baby and "naissance"

2003. Greetings Stamps. Multicoloured.
3873 46c. Type **1516** 65 20
3874 46c. "MERCI" and oak leaf 65 20

1517 Heart

2003. St. Valentine's Day. Multicoloured.
3875 46c. Type **1517** 65 20
3876 69c. Heart and roses 95 25
MS3877 136 × 144 mm. As No. 3875 × 5 . . . . 3·25 3·25

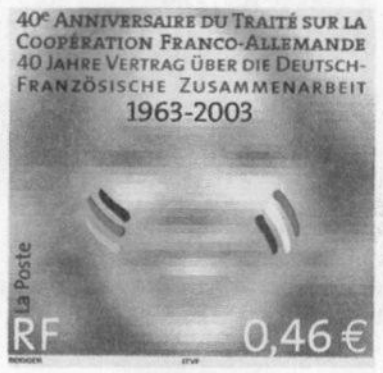

1518 Face

2003. 40th Anniv of French–German Co-operation Treaty.
3878 **1518** 46c. multicoloured . . . 65 20

1519 Map

2003. 40th Anniv of Delegation for Land Use Planning and Regional Action (DATAR).
3879 **1519** 46c. multicoloured . . . 65 20

1520 Genevieve De Gaulle Anthioniz
1521 Eiffel Tower

2003. 1st Death Anniv of Genevieve De Gaulle Anthioniz (resistance fighter and writer).
3880 **1520** 46c. multicoloured . . . 65 20

2003. Bicentenary of Chamber of Commerce and Industry.
3881 **1521** 46c. multicoloured . . . 65 20

1522 Lucky Luke

2003. Lucky Luke (cartoon character) by Morris. Multicoloured.
3882 46c. Type **1522** 65 20
3884 46c. + 9c. Lucky Luke and Rantanplan (dog) 65 20
MS3885 101 × 75 mm. 46c. As No. 3882 . . . . 65 65

1523 Blue-headed Hummingbird

2003. Birds. Multicoloured.
3886 41c. Type **1523** 55 15
3887 46c. Toucan 65 20
3888 46c. Purple-throated carib 65 20
3889 69c. Mascarene paradise fly-catcher 90 25
MS3890 110 × 160 mm. Nos. 3886/9 2·75 2·75

1524 Tram and Nantes Town Hall

2003. Nantes City.
3891 **1524** 46c. multicoloured . . . 65 20

1525 Pierre Beregovoy
1527 Monsavon Cow and Dubonnet Man (Raymond Savignac)

1526 Milan Stefanik

2003. 10th Death Anniv of Pierre Beregovoy (resistance fighter and politician).
3892 **1525** 46c. multicoloured . . . 65 20

2003. Milan Rastislav Stefanik Commemoration (founder of Czechoslovakia).
3893 **1526** 50c. multicoloured . . . 65 20

2003. Europa. Poster Art.
3894 **1527** 50c. multicoloured . . . 65 20

1528 *Charles de Gaulle* (aircraft carrier)

2003.
3895 **1528** 50c. multicoloured . . . 65 20

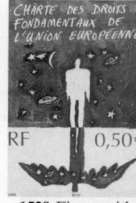

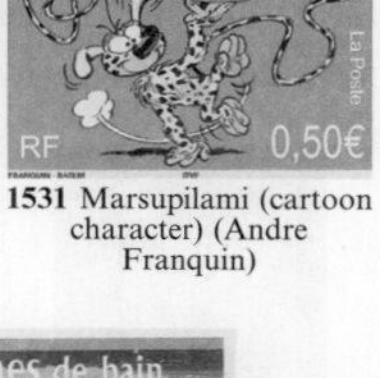

1529 Figure with Winged Shadow
1531 Marsupilami (cartoon character) (Andre Franquin)

1530 Beach Huts

2003. European Union Charter of Fundamental Rights.
3896 **1529** 50c. multicoloured . . . 65 20

2003. Regions (1st issue). Sheet 286 × 110 mm containing T **1530** and similar multicoloured designs.
MS3897 50c. Type **1530**; 50c. Fishing hut; 50c. Vinyards; 50c. Camembert cheese (vert); 50c. Foie gras; 50c. Petanque; 50c. "Guignol" (puppet) (vert); 50c. Crepes (vert); 50c. Cassoulet (casserole); 50c. Porcelain . . . 6·75 6·75
See also No. **MS**3926 and **MS**3962.

2003. Art. Design as T **491**. Multicoloured.
3898 75c. "La Boulee Rouge" (Paul Signac) . . . . . . 1·00 25
3899 75c. "The Dying Slave" and "The Rebel Slave" (sculptures, Michelangelo) 1·00 25
3900 €1.11 "Untitled" (Vassily Kandinsky) . . . . 1·50 40

2003. Greetings Stamp. Birthday.
3902 **1531** 50c. multicoloured . . . 65 20

2003. Orchids. As T **1475**. Multicoloured.
3903 30c. *Platanthera chlorantha* 40 10
3904 35c. *Dactylorhiza savogiensis* 45 15

1532 Mulhouse Museums Building and Car
1533 Woman and Children Bugatti Sunbathing

2003. 76th French Federation of Philatelic Associations Congress.
3905 **1532** 50c. multicoloured . . . 65 20

2003. Holidays. Ordinary or self-adhesive gum.
3906 **1533** 50c. multicoloured . . . 65 20

2003. Tourist Publicity. As T **490**.
3908 50c. multicoloured 65 20
3909 50c. lilac, orange and green 65 20
3910 50c. multicoloured 65 20
3911 50c. multicoloured 65 20
DESIGNS: No. 3908, Tulle (35 × 26 mm); No. 3909, Notre-Dame de l'Epine (vert). 50c. Arras (80 × 24 mm). 50c. Pontarlier (25 × 39 mm).

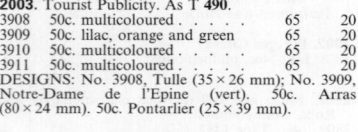

1534 Jaqueline Auriol and Dassault Mirage III Fighter

2003. Air. 3rd Death Anniv of Jaqueline Auriol (aviation pioneer).
3912 **1534** €4 multicoloured . . . 5·50 1·50

1535 Square and Compass

2003. 1275th Anniv of French Freemasonry.
3913 **1535** 50c. blue, orange and red 65 20

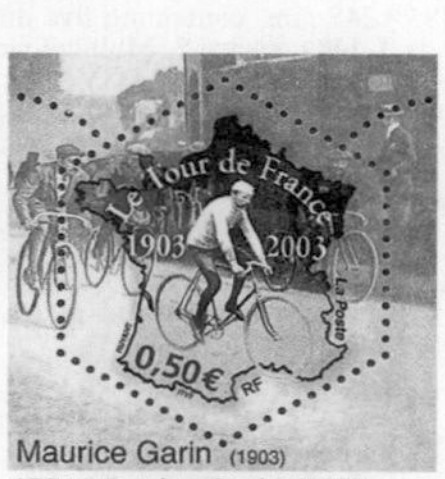

1536 Maurice Garin (1903 race winner)

2003. Centenary of Tour de France Cycle Race. Multicoloured.
3914 50c. Type **1536** 65 20
3915 50c. Modern competitor . . 65 20

1537 Saint-Pere-sous-Vezelay Church, Yonne

1539 Eugene-Francois Vidocq (undercover police officer and writer)

1538 Athletes

2003.
3916 **1537** 50c. multicoloured . . . 65 20

2003. 9th IAAF World Athletics Championships, Paris and Saint Denis.
3917 **1538** 50c. multicoloured . . . 65 20

2003. Literature. Multicoloured.
3918 50c. Type **1539** 65 20
3919 50c. Esmeralda (character from *The Hunchback of Notre Dame*, Victor Hugo) 65 20
3920 50c. Claudine (character from Claudine novels, *Colette*) 65 20
3921 50c. Nana (character from *Nana*, Emile Zola) 65 20
3922 50c. Edmond Dantes (character from *The Count of Monte-Cristo*, Alexandre Dumas) . . . 65 20
3923 50c. Gavroche (character from Les *Miserables*, Victor Hugo) 65 20
MS3924 135 × 144 mm. 50c. × 6 Nos. 3918/23 . . . . 2·00 2·00
No. **MS**3924 was sold with a premium of €1.60 for the benefit of the Red Cross.

1540 Ahmad Massoud

1541 Buttes-Chaumont Park, Paris

2003. 50th Birth Anniv of Ahmad Shah Massoud (Afghan resistance fighter).
3925 **1540** 50c. multicoloured . . . 65 20

2003. Regions (2nd issue). Sheet 286 × 110 mm containing multicoloured designs as T **1530**.
MS3926 50c. Chenonceau Chateau; 50c. Alsatian house; 50c. Dormer windows, Hospices de Beaune; 50c. Genoese tower, Cap Corse (vert); 50c. Arc de Triomphe, Paris (vert); 50c. Mas (country house), Provence; 50c. Pointe de Raz (vert); 50c. Mont Blanc (vert); 50c. Basque house; 50c. Pont du Gard (Roman bridge) . . . . 6·75 6·75

2003. French Gardens. Sheet 286 × 109 mm containing T **1541** and similar design. Multicoloured.
MS3927 €1.90 Type **1541**; €1.90 Luxembourg Gardens . . . . 2·75 2·75

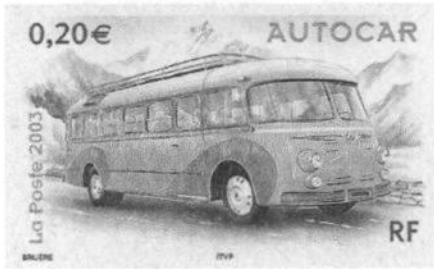

1542 Isobloc Type 648 DP 102 Coach (1954)

2003. Philexjeunes 2003 International Stamp Exhibition, Annely. Utility Vehicles. Sheet 108 × 183 mm containing T **1542** and similar horiz designs. Multicoloured.
MS3928 20c. × 5 Type 1542; SVF Type 302 tractor (1950); Delahaye Fire appliance with ladder (1938); Renault Kangoo postal van; Renault Type TN6 coach (1932); 30c. × 5 Berliet 22 HP Type M delivery truck (1910); Berliet T 100 (1957); Citroen Police van (1960); Heuliez and Citroen DS ambulance; Hotchkiss Type PL 50 rescue truck (1964) 3·50 3·50

1543 "Meilleurs Voeux"

2003. New Year.
3929 **1543** 50c. multicoloured . . . 65 20
No. 3929 was intended for use by corporate customers.

1544 Robin

2003. New Year. Ordinary or Self-adhesive gum
3930 **1544** 50c. multicoloured . . . 65 20

1545 "The Virgin of the Grapes" (Pierre Mignard)

1546 "The Sower"

2003. Red Cross Fund. Christmas.
3932 **1545** 50c. multicoloured . . . 65 20

2003. Centenary of "The Sower" (sculpture, O. Roty). Self-adhesive.
3933 **1546** 50c. red 65 20

1547 Notre-Dame Cathedral

2002. European Capitals. Luxembourg. Sheet 144 × 136 mm containing T **1547** and similar multicoloured designs.
MS3934 50c. × 4, Type **1547**; Saint Esprit plateau (vert); Grand Ducal Palace; Adolphe Bridge (vert) 2·75 2·75

1548 "Marilyn"

2003. 16th Death Anniv of Andy Warhol (artist).
3935 **1548** €1.11 multicoloured 1·50 40

1549 Cockerel amongst Foliage

2003. 15th-century Illuminations. Multicoloured.
3936 50c. Type **1549** 65 20
3937 90c. Peacock . . . . 1·20 40
Stamps of a similar design were issued by India.

1550 *Queen Mary 2*

2003. Launch of *Queen Mary 2* (ocean liner).
3938 **1550** 50c. multicoloured . . . 65 20

1551 "ceci est une invitation"

2004. Greetings Stamps. Multicoloured.
3939 50c. Type **1551** 65 20
3940 50c. "un grand merci" . . . 65 20

1552 Baby wearing Bee Costume ("c'est une fille")

2004. Greetings Stamps. Multicoloured. Self-adhesive.
3941 50c. Type **1552** 65 20
3942 50c. Baby wearing butterfly costume ("c'est un garcon") 65 20

1553 Perfume Bottle

2004. St. Valentine's Day. Multicoloured.
3943 50c. Type **1553** 65 20
3944 75c. Eiffel tower and woman
MS3945 135 × 143 mm. No. 3944 × 5

2004. Tourist Publicity. As T **490**. Multicoloured.
3946 50c. Lille (European capital of culture, 2004) 65 20

2004. Art. As T **491**.
3951 90c. green, red and gold . . 1·40 40
DESIGN: "The Statue of Liberty" (sculpture, Auguste Bartholdi) (vert).

1554 Eleanor of Aquitaine

1555 Mickey Mouse

2004. 600th Death Anniv of Eleanor of Aquitaine (wife of King Henry II of England).
3955 **1554** 50c. multicoloured . . . 65 20

2004. 75th Anniv of Mickey Mouse (cartoon character). Multicoloured.
3956 45c. Donald Duck 60 15
3957 50c. Type **1555** 65 20
3958 75c. Minnie Mouse . . . . 1·00 40

1556 Emblem

2004. Bicentenary of Civil Code.
3959 **1556** 50c. blue, black and red 65 20

1557 George Sand

2004. Birth Bicentenary of George Sand (Aurore Dupin) (writer).
3960 **1557** 50c. multicoloured . . . 65 20

1558 Vercingetorix (Gaullist leader) (statue) (Auguste Bartholdi)

2004. Clermont-Ferrand, Puy-de-Dome, Auvergne.
3961 **1558** 50c. multicoloured . . . 65 20

2004. Regions (3rd issue). Sheet 286 × 110 mm containing multicoloured designs as T **1530**.
MS3962 50c. × 10 Cutlery; Vegetables of Provence (vert); Grapes, Beaujolais (vert); Bread; Madras cotton Creole headdress (vert); Oyster (vert); Quiche Lorraine; Course Landes, Aquitaine; Clafoutis (fruit flan); Pipe band . . . . 6·50 6·50

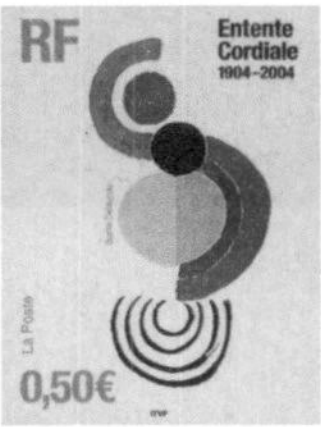

1559 "Coccinelle" (Sonia Delaunay)

1560 Heart-shaped Seat Belt Buckle and Body as Map

2004. Centenary of the Entente Cordiale. Contemporary Paintings.
3963 **1559** 50c. grey, black and rose 65 20
3964 — 75c. multicoloured . . . 1·00 25
DESIGN: 75c. "Lace 1 (trial proof) 1968" (Sir Terry Frost). Stamps of similar designs were issued by Great Britain.

2004. Road Safety. Two phosphor bands.
3965 **1560** 50c. multicoloured . . . 65 20

FRANK STAMP

1939. Optd **F.**
F652 **61** 90c. blue . . . . 1·60 2·75

MILITARY FRANK STAMPS

1901. Optd **F. M.**
M309 **12** 15c. orange . . . . . . 48·00 6·50

1903. Optd **F. M.**
M314 **14** 15c. red . . . . 50·00 5·25

1904. Optd **F. M.**
M323 **15** 10c. red . . . . 26·00 6·50
M324 15c. green . . . . 32·00 6·00

1907. Optd **F. M.**
M348 **18** 10c. red . . . . 2·00 65

1929. Optd **F. M.**
M471 **15** 50c. red . . . . 4·00 60

1933. Optd **F. M.**
M516 **61** 50c. red . . . . 3·00 65
M517 65c. blue 35 40
M518 90c. blue 70 45

M 236

M 545 Flag

1946. No value indicated.
M967 **M 236** green . . . . 1·80 1·00
M968 red 45 50

1964. No value indicated.
M1661 **M 545** multicoloured . . . 45 50

NEWSPAPER STAMPS

J 6

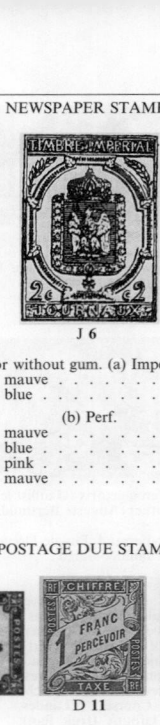

1868. With or without gum. (a) Imperf.

J131	J 6	2c. mauve	£275	65·00
J132		2c. blue	£550	£275

(b) Perf.

J133	J 6	2c. mauve	40·00	15·00
J134		2c. blue	65·00	28·00
J135		2c. pink	£170	85·00
J136		5c. mauve	£1000	£600

POSTAGE DUE STAMPS

D 4

D 11

D 19

1859.

D 87	D 4	10c. black	27·00	13·00
D 88		15c. black	30·00	13·00
D212		25c. black	90·00	40·00
D213		30c. black	£140	£100
D214		40c. blue	£180	£300
D216		60c. yellow	£350	£700
D217		60c. blue	32·00	80·00

1882.

D279	D 11	1c. black	1·30	1·30
D280		2c. black	18·00	19·00
D281		3c. black	18·00	18·00
D282		4c. black	35·00	25·00
D283		5c. black	65·00	21·00
D297		5c. blue	30	1·60
D284		10c. black	65·00	1·30
D298		10c. brown	30	30
D285		15c. black	50·00	7·00
D317		15c. green	19·00	1·00
D286		20c. black	£250	95·00
D300		20c. green	5·00	50
D301		25c. red	5·00	3·50
D287		30c. black	£160	1·60
D302		30c. red	30	25
D288		40c. black	£100	36·00
D304		40c. red	6·00	5·25
D305		45c. green	5·50	4·00
D289		50c. black	£450	£150
D306		50c. purple	70	55
D307		60c. green	1·50	80
D290		60c. black	£450	40·00
D291		1f. black	£600	£275
D310		1f. brown	1·10	75
D308		1f. pink on yellow	£400	£350
D309		1f. brown on yellow	5·50	70
D293		2f. black	£1100	£650
D294		2f. brown	£180	£120
D311		2f. red	£170	50·00
D312		2f. mauve	1·20	90
D313		3f. mauve	2·10	95
D295		5f. black	£2500	£1600
D296		5f. brown	£300	£225
D314		5f. orange	1·70	2·50

1908.

D348	D 19	1c. olive	1·90	1·70
D349		10c. violet	95	60
D350		20c. bistre	32·00	1·20
D351		30c. bistre	21·00	40
D352		50c. red	£225	55·00
D353		60c. red	4·00	4·00

1917. Surch.

D378	D 19	20c. on 30c. bistre	20·00	3·00
D379		40c. on 50c. red	9·00	2·75
D433		50c. on 10c. violet	3·25	3·75
D434		60c. on 1c. olive	5·50	4·00
D435		1f. on 60c. red	17·00	10·50
D436		2f. on 60c. red	17·00	10·50

D 43

D 187 Wheat Sheaves

D 457

1927.

D454	D 43	1c. green	1·30	2·10
D455		10c. red	1·80	1·90
D456		30c. bistre	5·50	75
D457		60c. red	4·75	95
D458		1f. purple	12·50	2·75
D459		1f. green	15·00	1·10
D460		2f. blue	48·00	32·00
D461		2f. brown	£120	24·00

1929. Surch.

D471	D 43	1f.20 on 2f. blue	34·00	8·50
D472		5f. on 1f. purple	45·00	9·00

1931. Surch **UN FRANC**.

D494	D 43	1f. on 60c. red	25·00	1·80

1943. Inscr "CHIFFRE-TAXE".

D787	D 187	10c. brown	10	55
D788		30c. purple	10	90
D789		50c. green	10	55
D790		1f. blue	10	45
D791		1f.50 red	15	75
D792		2f. blue	15	65
D793		3f. red	15	55
D794		4f. violet	4·50	3·25
D795		5f. pink	35	70
D796		10f. orange	3·25	2·10
D797		20f. bistre	9·00	2·75

1946. As Type D **187** but inscr "TIMBRE TAXE".

D985	10c. brown	1·00	1·50
D986	30c. purple	85	1·30
D987	50c. green	20·00	8·25
D988	1f. blue	35	45
D989	2f. blue	35	45
D990	3f. red	30	65
D991	4f. violet	30	75
D992	5f. pink	30	90
D993	10f. red	40	50
D994	20f. brown	1·00	55
D995	50f. green	18·00	1·60
D996	100f. green	55·00	7·50

1960. New Currency.

D1474	D 457	5c. mauve	3·00	85
D1475		10c. red	4·50	65
D1476		20c. brown	4·25	1·00
D1477		50c. green	12·00	1·50
D1478		1f. green	50·00	2·30

D 539 Poppies

D 917 "Ampedus cinnabarinus"

1964.

D1650	–	5c. red. grn & pur	15	15
D1651	–	10c. bl, grn & pur	15	40
D1652	D 539	15c. red, green & brown	35	40
D1653	–	20c. pur, grn & turq	25	30
D1654	–	30c. bl, grn & brn	15	70
D1655	–	40c. yell, red & turq	45	45
D1656	–	50c. red, grn & bl	45	35
D1657	–	1f. vio, grn & bl	80	45

DESIGNS: 5c. Knapweed; 10c. Gentian; 20c. Little periwinkle; 30c. Forget-me-not; 40 c Columbine; 50c. Clover; 1f. Soldanella.

1982. Beetles.

D2493	D 917	10c. brown & black	50	40
D2494	–	20c. black	35	30
D2495	–	30c. red, brn & blk	35	45
D2496	–	40c. bl, brn & blk	55	50
D2497	–	50c. red and black	55	50
D2498	–	1f. black	60	60
D2499	–	2f. yellow and black	80	80
D2500	–	3f. black and red	1·10	60
D2501	–	4f. brown and black	1·30	65
D2502	–	5f. bl, red & blk	1·80	75

DESIGNS: 20c. "Dorcadion fuliginator"; 30c. "Leptura cordigera"; 40c. "Paederus littoralis"; 50c. "Pyrochroa coccinea"; 1f. "Scarites laevigatus"; 2f. "Trichius gallicus"; 3f. "Adalia alpina"; 4f. "Apoderus coryli"; 5f. "Trichodes alvearius".

COUNCIL OF EUROPE STAMPS

Until March 25th, 1960, these stamps could only be used by delegates and permanent officials of the Council of Europe on official correspondence at Strasbourg. From that date they could be used on all correspondence posted within the Council of Europe building.

1950. No. 1354 optd **CONSEIL DE L'EUROPE**.

C1	35f. mauve and red	1·30	2·00

C 2 Council Flag

1958.

C2	C 2	8f. blue, orange & pur	50	50
C3		20f. blue, yellow & brn	55	55
C4		25f. blue, pur & myrtle	1·40	1·30
C5		35f. blue and red	95	90
C6		50f. blue and purple	1·90	1·90

(New currency. 100 (old) francs = 1 (new) franc).

1963.

C 7	C 2	20c. blue, yellow & brn	95	1·00
C 8		25c. blue, pur & myrt	2·20	2·10
C 9		25c. multicoloured	1·10	1·10
C10		30c. blue, yellow & red	1·20	1·10
C11		40c. multicoloured	1·40	1·40
C12		50c. blue and purple	2·10	2·00
C13		50c. multicoloured	2·50	2·00
C14		60c. multicoloured	1·30	1·50
C15		70c. multicoloured	2·50	3·25

1975. As Type C **2**, but inscr "FRANCE".

C16	60c. multicoloured	1·40	1·50
C17	80c. yellow, blue and red	1·60	1·70
C18	1f. multicoloured	3·50	4·25
C19	1f.20 multicoloured	5·00	4·50

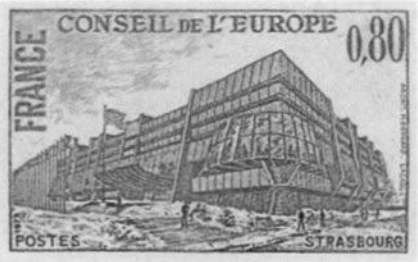
C **3** New Council of Europe Building, Strasbourg

1977.

C20	C 3	80c. red, lt brn & brn	1·10	1·10
C21		1f. brown, blue & grn	40	55
C22		1f.40 grey, grn & brn	2·75	2·30
C23		1f.40 green	60	80
C24		2f. blue	70	85

1978. 25th Anniv of European Convention on Human Rights. As Type C **3** with the addition of the Human Rights emblem.

C25	1f.20 black, purple & grn	55	65
C26	1f.70 turquoise, blue & grn	75	75

C **5** Exterior and Interior of New Council Building, Strasbourg

1981.

C27	C 5	1f.40 violet, blue & pur	65	60
C28		1f.60 green & brown	65	60
C29		1f.70 green	65	80
C30		1f.80 red, green & pur	80	90
C31		2f. red, green & blue	75	80
C32		2f.10 red	90	1·00
C33		2f.30 green, turq & bl	1·10	80
C34		2f.60 purple, bl & grey	1·00	95
C35		2f.80 brown, dp bl & bl	1·10	1·20
C36		3f. blue	1·30	1·40

C **6** Foot Breaking through Shell

1985.

C37	C 6	1f.80 green	75	95
C38		2f.20 red	85	95
C39		3f.20 blue	1·20	1·50

C **7** Council of Europe Building, Strasbourg

1986.

C40	C 7	1f.90 green	95	1·00
C41		2f. green	1·10	1·30
C42		2f.20 red	95	1·00
C43		3f.40 blue	1·70	1·90
C44		3f.60 blue	2·10	2·40

C **8** Stars, Doves and Girl

1989. 40th Anniv of Council of Europe.

C45	C 8	2f.20 multicoloured	1·40	1·60
C46		3f.60 multicoloured	2·20	2·75

C **9** Map of Europe

C **10** "36 Heads" (Friedensreich Hundertwasser)

1990.

C47	C 9	2f.30 multicoloured	1·40	1·30
C48		2f.50 multicoloured	1·10	1·30
C49		3f.20 multicoloured	2·00	1·80
C50		3f.40 multicoloured	1·50	1·70

1994.

C51	C 10	2f.80 multicoloured	1·00	1·00
C52		3f.70 multicoloured	1·90	1·90

C **11** Palace of Human Rights, Strasbourg

1996.

C53	C 11	3f. multicoloured	1·30	1·40
C54		3f.80 multicoloured	1·70	1·90

C **12** "Charioteer of Delphi" (replica of ancient Greek statue)

C **14** "Walking on Stars" (drawing, Tom Ungerer)

C **13** "I am black, I am white, I am black and white" (drawing, Tom Ungerer)

1999. Sculptures presented by Member states.

C55	3f. Type C **12**	1·10	1·30
C56	3f.80 "Nike" (Petras Mazuras)	1·40	1·50

2001.

C57	C 13	3f. multicoloured	1·10	1·10
C58		3f.80 multicoloured	1·50	1·50

2003.

C59	C 14	50c. multicoloured	65	20
C60		75c. multicoloured	1·40	40

U.N.E.S.C.O. STAMPS

For use on correspondence posted within the U.N.E.S.C.O. headquarters building.

U **1** Buddha and Hermes

1961.

U1	U 1	20c. bistre, blue & brown	45	55
U2		25c. purple, green & blk	45	55
U3		30c. brown & dp brown	1·50	1·40
U4		50c. red, violet & black	1·60	1·70
U5		60c. brown, mauve & bl	2·75	2·50

U **2** Open Book and Globe

U **3** "Human Rights"

1966.

U6	U 2	25c. brown	55	55
U7		30c. red	80	80
U8		60c. green	1·00	1·30

1969.

U 9	U 3	30c. red, green & brown	75	70
U10		40c. red, mauve & brn	90	95
U11		50c. red, blue & brown	2·10	2·10
U12		70c. red, violet & blue	3·00	3·25

1975. As Type U 3, but inscribed "France".

U13	60c. red, green and brown	80	1·20
U14	80c. red, brown and lake	1·30	1·40
U15	1f.20 red, blue and purple	4·25	4·50

U **4** "Leaf"

1976.

U16	U 4	80c. blue, brown & pur	85	95
U17		1f. orange, green & blue	35	60
U18		1f.20 blue, red & green	50	65
U19		1f.40 brn, mve & orge	2·00	2·10
U20		1f.70 red, green & brn	70	80

U **5** Old Slave Dungeons, Goree, Senegal

U **6** Gateway, Fez, Morocco

1980. Sites in Need of Protection.

U21	U 5	1f.20 blue, green & red	60	60
U22	–	1f.40 mauve, blue & grn	75	70
U23	–	2f. violet, green & red	90	80

DESIGNS: 1f.40, Moenjodaro, Pakistan; 2f. Palace of Sans-Souci, Haiti.

1981. Sites in Need of Preservation.

U24	U 6	1f.40 brown, blue & red	70	75
U25	–	1f.60 blue, red & grn	70	75
U26	–	1f.80 violet, pur & bl	80	75
U27	–	2f.30 brown, grn & bl	90	95
U28	–	2f.60 black, bl & red	80	1·20

DESIGNS—VERT: 1f.60, Seated Buddha Sukhotai, Thailand; 1f.80, Hue, Vietnam; 2f.60, Sao Miguel Cathedral, Brazil. HORIZ: 2f.30, Fort St. Elmo, Malta.

U **7** Chinguetti Mosque, Mauritania

U **8** Amphitheatre, Carthage

1983. Sites in Need of Preservation.

U29	–	1f.70 brown and green	75	80
U30	U 7	2f. brown, blue & blk	75	75
U31	–	2f.10 brown, bl & turq	65	85
U32	–	2f.80 black, bl & brn	1·10	1·10
U33	–	3f. orange, brn & grn	1·20	1·40

DESIGNS: 1f.70, Lalibela Church, Ethiopia; 2f.10, Sana'a, Yemen Arab Republic; 2f.80, City walls, Istanbul, Turkey; 3f. St. Mary's Church, Kotor, Yugoslavia.

1985. Protected Sites. Each grey, green and blue.

U34	1f.80 Type U **8**	90	1·20
U35	2f.20 Old Square, Havana, Cuba	95	1·20
U36	3f.20 Temple of Anuradhapura, Sri Lanka	1·80	2·20

U **9** Temple of Tikal, Guatemala

U **10** Acropolis, Athens

1986. Protected Sites. Each grey, brown and green.

U37	1f.90 Type U **9**	1·30	1·30
U38	3f.40 Bagerhat Mosque, Bangladesh	1·90	2·20

1987. Protected Sites. Each brown, chestnut and blue.

U39	2f. Type U **10**	1·10	1·20
U40	3f.60 Philae Temple, Egypt	2·10	2·10

U **11** St. Francis's Monastery, Lima, Peru

U **12** Temple of Bagdaon, Nepal

1990. Protected Sites.

U41	U 11	2f.30 brn, grn & blk	1·00	1·20
U42	–	3f.20 brn, orge & bl	1·40	1·60

DESIGN—HORIZ: 3f.20 Shibam, People's Democratic Republic of Yemen.

1991. Protected Sites.

U43	U 12	2f.50 brown and red	1·10	1·30
U44	–	3f.40 brown & green	1·60	1·70

DESIGN—HORIZ: 3f.40, Herat Fort, Afghanistan.

U **13** Angkor, Cambodia

U **14** Ayers Rock, Uluru, Australia

1993. Protected Sites. Multicoloured.

U45	2f.80 Type U **13**	1·30	1·40
U46	3f.70 Cave paintings, Tassili n'Ajjer National Park, Algeria (horiz)	1·70	1·80

1996. Protected Sites. National Parks. Mult.

U47	3f. Type U **14**	1·30	1·30
U48	3f.80 Glacier, Los Glaciares, Argentine Republic	1·60	1·60

U **15** Detail of Fresco from Villa of Mysteries, Pompeii

U **16** Sphinx and Pyramids, Giza, Egypt

1998. Protected Sites. Multicoloured.

U49	3f. Type U **15**	1·30	1·40
U50	3f.80 Statues, Easter Island (horiz)	1·60	1·70

2001. Protected Sites. Multicoloured.

U51	3f. Type U **16**	1·30	1·30
U52	3f.80 Komodo National Park, Indonesia	1·60	1·60

U **17** Reindeer, Lapland

2003. Protected Sites. Multicoloured.

U53	50c. Type U **17**	65	20
U54	75c. Church of the Resurrection, St. Petersburg (300th anniv) (vert)	1·40	40

FREE FRENCH FORCES IN THE LEVANT Pt. 19

After British and Free French troops had occupied Syria and Lebanon in June 1941 the following stamps were issued for the use of Free French forces in those areas.

100 centimes = 1 franc.

1942. Surch with Lorraine Crosses, **FORCES FRANCAISES LIBRES LEVANT** and value. (i) On No. 252 of Syria.

1	–	50c. on 4p. orange	6·25	9·50

(ii) On Nos. 251 and 212 of Lebanon.

2	16a	1f. on 5p. blue	3·25	9·50
3	22	2f.50 on 12½p. blue	4·00	8·75

1942. Air. Nos. 269/70 of Syria surch with Lorraine Crosses, **LIGNES AERIENNES F.A.F.L.** and value.

4		4f. on 50p. black	4·25	8·75
5		6f.50 on 50p. black	4·00	6·25
6		8f. on 50p. black	3·50	6·25
7		10f. on 100p. mauve	4·25	9·75

3 Camelry and Ruins at Palmyra

4 Wings bearing Lorraine Crosses

1942. Buff background.

8	3	1f. red (postage)	20	2·25
9		1f.50 violet	20	3·25
10		2f. orange	20	3·50
11		2f.50 brown	15	3·50
12		3f. blue	15	3·50
13		4f. green	35	5·25
14		5f. purple	30	4·00
15	4	6f.50 red (air)	30	4·25
16		10f. purple and blue	35	4·00
MS17		106 × 16 mm. Nos. 15/16. No gum	14·00	38·00

1942. Air. No. 15 surch **4** and bars.

17	4	4f. on 6f.50 red	70	4·25

1943. Surch **RESISTANCE** and premium.

18	3	1f.+9f. red (postage)	3·50	3·50
19		5f.+20f. purple	3·50	3·50
20	4	6f.50+48f.50 red (air)	3·00	45·00
21		10f.+100f. pur & bl	35·00	45·00

1943. Air. No. 12 surch **4F**, bars and airplane.

22	3	4f. on 3f. blue and buff	90	2·50

FRENCH COLONIES Pt. 6

General issues for use in French Colonies which had no special stamps.

100 centimes = 1 franc.

> **NOTE**. For other stamps issued for French Colonies see the note at the beginning of France.

A Eagle

B Laureated

D Laureated

1859. Imperf.

1	A	1c. green	16·00	14·00
2		5c. green	20·00	11·00
3		10c. brown	23·00	7·25
4a		20c. blue	25·00	10·50
5		40c. orange	19·00	5·50
6		80c. red	80·00	42·00

1871. Imperf.

7	B	1c. green	48·00	48·00
9	D	30c. brown	£110	36·00
10		80c. red	£750	85·00

E Ceres

F Ceres

1871. Imperf.

11	E	1c. green on blue	11·00	7·75
12		2c. brown on buff	£350	£600
14a		5c. green	11·00	3·75
20	F	10c. brown on pink	£170	11·00
16		15c. bistre	£250	8·75

H Peace and Commerce

J Commerce

1877. Imperf.

24	H	1c. green	22·00	34·00
25		2c. green	11·00	9·00
26		4c. green	13·00	9·75
27		5c. green	13·50	1·90
28		10c. green	65·00	8·25
29		15c. grey	£200	55·00
30		20c. brown on yellow	48·00	3·75
31a		25c. blue	30·00	3·75
32		30c. brown	30·00	30·00
33		35c. black on yellow	34·00	21·00
34		40c. red on yellow	19·00	17·00
35a		75c. red	60·00	48·00
36		1f. green	42·00	13·50

1878. Imperf.

37	H	1c. black on blue	14·00	14·00
38		2c. brown on buff	13·50	10·00
39		4c. brown on grey	18·00	18·00
40		10c. black on lilac	85·00	16·00
41		15c. blue on blue	22·00	7·00
42		20c. red on green	60·00	11·00
43		25c. black on red	£425	£225
44		25c. brown on yellow	£525	30·00

1881. Perf.

45	J	1c. black on blue	2·00	2·50
46		2c. brown on buff	4·50	2·50
47		4c. brown on grey	3·50	3·75
48a		5c. green on green	6·75	85
49		10c. black on lilac	7·75	2·50
50		15c. blue on blue	12·00	1·40
51		20c. red on green	40·00	12·00
52		25c. brown on yellow	10·00	2·25
53		25c. black on pink	10·50	90
54		30c. brown on drab	15·00	14·50
55		35c. black on orange	30·00	20·00
56		40c. red on yellow	29·00	32·00
57		75c. red on pink	75·00	42·00
58		1f. green	55·00	26·00

K Map of France

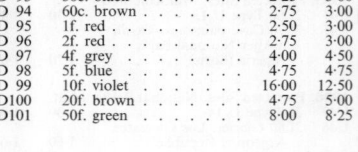

L Colonies offering France Aid

1943. Aid to Resistance Movement.

82	K	50c.+4f.50 green	2·00	3·25
83		1f.50+8f.50 red	1·40	3·25
84		3f.+12f. blue	1·10	3·25
85		5f.+15f. grey	1·50	3·50
86	L	9f.+41f. purple	2·50	4·50

M Resisters

1943. Aid to Resistance Movement. Roul.

87	M	1f.50+98f.50 bl & grey	30·00	44·00

N

O

1943. French Solidarity Fund.

88	N	10f.+40f. blue	4·25	8·75

1944. Air. Aviation Fund.

89	O	10f.+40f. green	5·25	9·50

POSTAGE DUE STAMPS

U

V

1884. Imperf.

D59	U	1c. black	1·40	3·50
D60		2c. black	1·40	3·50
D61		3c. black	1·60	2·25
D62		4c. black	2·25	2·75
D63		5c. black	2·50	1·40
D64		10c. black	6·25	2·25
D65		15c. black	6·00	3·75
D66		20c. black	7·25	4·50
D67		30c. black	10·00	3·00
D68		40c. black	14·00	8·25
D69		60c. black	22·00	14·00
D70		1f. brown	26·00	19·00
D71		2f. brown	16·00	12·50
D72		5f. brown	70·00	48·00

1893. Imperf.

D73	U	5c. blue	40	25
D74		10c. brown	30	25
D75		15c. green	1·40	1·10
D76		20c. olive	90	2·75
D77		30c. red	1·50	1·10
D78		50c. red	1·25	1·90
D79		60c. brown on yellow	3·00	2·75
D81		1f. red on yellow	4·75	6·25

1945. Perf.

D 90	V	10c. blue	15	2·75
D 91		15c. green	70	2·75
D 92		25c. orange	95	2·75
D 93		50c. black	2·25	3·00
D 94		60c. brown	2·75	3·00
D 95		1f. red	2·50	3·00
D 96		2f. red	2·75	3·00
D 97		4f. grey	4·00	4·50
D 98		5f. blue	4·75	4·75
D 99		10f. violet	16·00	12·50
D100		20f. brown	4·75	5·00
D101		50f. green	8·00	8·25

FRENCH CONGO Pt. 6

A French colony in central Africa, in 1903 divided into Gabon, Middle Congo, Ubangi-Shari and Chad.

100 centimes = 1 franc.

1891. Stamps of French Colonies, "Commerce" type, surch **Congo francais** and value in figures.

2	J	5c. on 1c. black on blue	£110	80·00
3		5c. on 15c. blue	£200	£110
4		5c. on 25c. black on red	£100	32·00
11		10c. on 25c. black on red	£150	95·00
12		15c. on 25c. black on red	£200	75·00

1892. Stamps of French Colonies. "Commerce" type, surch **COngo Francais** and value in figures.

5	J	5c. on 20c. red on green	£850	£300
6		5c. on 25c. black on red	£120	75·00
7		10c. on 25c. black on red	£130	50·00
8		10c. on 40c. red on yellow	£1600	£275
9		15c. on 25c. black on red	£130	35·00

1892. Postage Due stamps of French Colonies surch **Congo francais Timbre poste** and value in figures.

13	U	5c. on 5c. black	£120	£110
14		5c. on 20c. black	£110	£110
15		5c. on 30c. black	£160	£110
16		10c. on 1f. brown	£130	£120

1892. "Tablet" key-type inscr "CONGO FRANCAIS" in red (1, 5, 15, 25, 50 (No. 31), 75c. and 1f.) or blue (others).

17	D	1c. black on blue	85	1·25
18		2c. brown on buff	2·50	3·25
19		4c. brown on grey	1·90	3·50
20		5c. green on light green	3·50	5·25
21		10c. black on lilac	11·00	9·75
22		10c. red	1·50	1·60
23		15c. blue	48·00	8·00
24		15c. grey	6·25	10·00
25		20c. red on green	11·00	14·00
26		25c. black on pink	18·00	8·25
27		25c. blue	8·00	10·50
28		30c. brown on drab	20·00	16·00
29		40c. red on yellow	35·00	20·00
30		50c. red on pink	48·00	10·50
31		50c. brown on blue	5·75	8·75
32		75c. brown on orange	34·00	20·00
33		1f. green	50·00	25·00

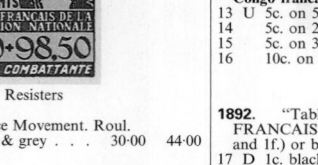

6 Leopard in Ambush

8 Woman of the Bakalois Tribe

1900.

36c	6	1c. brown and grey	95	1·60
37		2c. brown and yellow	1·25	65
38		4c. red and grey	1·90	1·40
39		5c. green and light green	1·40	80
40		10c. red and light red	5·50	2·50
41		15c. violet and green	2·00	1·10
42	8	20c. green and red	2·50	2·75
43		25c. blue and light blue	3·00	3·00
44		30c. red and yellow	3·00	2·50
45		40c. brown and green	3·75	2·75
46		50c. violet and lilac	3·50	3·00
47		75c. red and orange	9·00	9·25
48	–	1f. grey and green	16·00	13·00
49	–	2f. red and brown	27·00	21·00
50	–	5f. orange and black	75·00	80·00

DESIGN—28 × 40 mm: 1, 2, 5f. Coconut palms, Libreville.

1903. Surch in figures.

51	8	5c. on 30c. red & yellow	£225	£110
52	–	0,10 on 2f. red & brn (No. 49)	£275	£110

PARCEL POST STAMPS

P 3

1891.

P13	P 3	10c. black on blue	£180	£120

1893. Receipt stamp of France optd **Congo Francais COLIS POSTAUX**.

P34		10c. grey	£130	£120

FRENCH EQUATORIAL AFRICA Pt. 6

In 1910 Gabon, Middle Congo and Ubangi-Shari-Chad were federated to form French Equatorial Africa: each colony continued to issue its own stamps until 1936.

In 1958 the four constituent colonies became autonomous republics as Gabon, Congo Republic, Central African Republic (formerly Ubangi-Shari) and Chad.

100 centimes = 1 franc.

1936. Middle Congo stamps of 1933 optd **AFRIQUE EQUATORIALE FRANCAISE**.

1	15	1c. brown	30	2·50
2		2c. blue	15	2·75
3		4c. green	1·50	3·00
4		5c. purple	1·25	3·25
5		10c. green	2·75	3·25
6		15c. purple	2·75	3·00
7		20c. red on pink	2·50	3·50
8		25c. orange	4·00	4·25
9	–	40c. brown	3·75	4·00
10	–	50c. purple	3·25	1·25
11	–	75c. black on pink	4·25	3·25
12	–	90c. red	3·75	4·25
13	–	1f.50 blue	3·00	3·00
14	–	5f. blue	42·00	25·00
15	–	10f. black	22·00	17·00
16	–	20f. brown	24·00	20·00

1936. Gabon Stamps of 1933 optd **AFRIQUE EQUATORIALE FRANCAISE**.

17	21	1c. red	15	2·75
18		2c. black on pink	15	2·75
19		4c. green	1·40	3·25
20		5c. blue	1·75	2·75
21		10c. red on yellow	2·00	2·75
22	22	40c. purple	2·75	3·75
23		50c. brown	2·75	1·50
24		1f. green on blue	20·00	11·00
25		1f.50 blue	4·00	3·50
26		2f. red	10·00	6·00

1937. International Exhibition, Paris. As Nos. 110/16 of Cameroun.

27		20c. violet	1·60	4·00
28		30c. green	1·75	3·50
29		40c. red	65	3·25
30		50c. brown and blue	50	3·00
31		90c. red	95	2·00
32		1f.50 blue	1·25	4·75
MS33		120 × 100 mm. 3f. red. Imperf	9·00	18·00

8 Logging near Mayumba

9 Chad Family

10 Count Savorgnan de Brazza

12 Savoia Marchetti S-73 over Stanley Pool

1937.

34	8	1c. brown & yell (postage)	15	2·75
35		2c. violet and green	15	2·75
36		3c. blue and yellow	55	3·00
37		4c. mauve and blue	15	2·75
38		5c. deep green & green	20	2·25
39	9	10c. mauve and blue	15	1·90
40		15c. blue and pink	15	10
41		20c. brown and yellow	60	1·25
42		25c. red and blue	85	65
44	10	30c. deep green & green	1·60	2·75
45		30c. blue and pink	65	2·75
46	9	35c. green & light green	1·00	2·25
47	10	40c. red and blue	15	70
48		45c. blue and green	3·75	4·50
49		45c. green & light green	1·00	3·25
50		50c. brown and yellow	15	10
51		55c. violet and blue	1·25	2·25
52		60c. purple and blue	1·00	3·00
53	A	65c. blue and green	80	70
54		70c. violet and orange	1·10	3·00
55		75c. black and yellow	5·25	5·25
56		80c. brown and yellow	65	1·60
57		90c. red and orange	90	1·25
58		1f. violet and green	2·50	50
59	10	1f. red and orange	2·00	1·10
60	A	1f. green and blue	85	2·00
61	B	1f.25 red and orange	2·00	1·90
62		1f.40 brown and green	1·10	2·25
63		1f.50 blue and light blue	2·50	2·50
64		1f.60 violet and orange	90	3·00
65		1f.75 brown and yellow	1·75	2·00
66	A	1f.75 blue and light blue	1·10	2·75
67	B	2f. green and light green	1·00	20
68	C	2f.15 violet and yellow	1·50	2·75
69		2f.25 blue and light blue	2·25	3·25
70		2f.50 purple and orange	1·00	1·25
71		3f. blue and pink	35	15
72		5f. green and light green	1·10	80
73		10f. violet and blue	2·50	2·75
74		20f. black and yellow	3·00	2·50
75	D	1f.50 black & yellow (air)	65	3·00
76		2f. mauve and blue	2·25	3·25
77		2f.50 green and pink	35	80
78		3f.75 brown and green	2·00	3·00
79	12	4f.50 red and blue	2·25	1·90
80		6f.50 blue and green	2·50	3·50
81		8f.50 red and orange	2·50	3·00
82		10f.75 violet and green	2·50	3·00

DESIGNS: A, Emile Gentil; B, Paul Crampel; C, Victor Liotard; D, Latecoere 300 flying boat over Pointe Noire.

1938. Anti-cancer Fund. As T **58b** of Guadeloupe.

94	1f.75+50c. blue	5·25	27·00

1938. Social Welfare. Surch with premium in figures.

95	A	65c.+35c. (No. 53)	75	3·50
96		1f.75+50c. (No. 66)	1·00	4·00

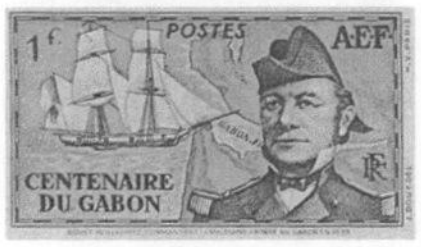

16 Bouet-Willaumez and "La Malouine"

1938. Centenary of Landing of Bouet-Willaumez in Gabon.

97	16	65c. brown	65	2·25
98		1f. red	70	2·00
99		1f.75 blue	1·00	3·50
100		2f. violet	1·40	1·10

1939. New York World's Fair. As T **58c** of Guadeloupe.

101	1f.25 red	1·75	2·75
102	2f.25 blue	2·50	3·75

1939. 150th Anniv of French Revolution. As T **58d** of Guadeloupe.

103	45c.+25c. green and black (postage)	8·50	22·00
104	70c.+30c. brown & black	6·50	22·00
105	90c.+35c. orange & black	6·50	22·00
106	1f.25+1f. red and black	6·50	22·00
107	2f.25+2f. blue and black	6·50	22·00
108	4f.50+4f. blk & orge (air)	12·50	45·00

1940. Adherence to General de Gaulle. A. Postage stamps of 1936 and 1937. (a) Optd **AFRIQUE FRANCAISE LIBRE**.

109	8	1c. brown and yellow	90	3·25
110		2c. violet and green	1·25	3·50
111		3c. blue and yellow	1·40	3·25
112		5c. green & light green	70	3·50
113	9	10c. mauve and blue	85	2·75
114		15c. blue and pink	85	2·75
115		20c. brown and yellow	80	1·50
116		25c. red and blue	2·00	8·50
117		35c. green & lt green	1·00	2·75

(b) Optd **LIBRE**.

118	–	4c. green (No. 3)	11·50	8·50
119a	10	30c. dp green & green	4·00	1·25
120a		30c. blue and pink	8·25	11·00
121		40c. red and blue	40	20
122		45c. green & lt green	40	2·25
123a		50c. brown and yellow	2·25	2·75
124		55c. violet and blue	45	70
125		60c. purple and blue	30	65
126	A	65c. blue and green	60	1·40
127		70c. violet and orange	80	2·50
128		75c. black and yellow	48·00	38·00
129		80c. brown and yellow	50	1·40
130		90c. red and orange	40	90
131	10	1f. red and orange	80	1·90
132	A	1f. green and blue	1·50	7·75
133	B	1f.40 brown and green	40	1·40
134		1f.50 blue & light blue	50	1·50
135		1f.60 violet & orange	50	1·75
136		1f.75 brown & yellow	75	2·50
137	C	2f.15 violet and yellow	75	2·50
138		2f.25 blue & light blue	60	1·75
139		2f.50 purple & orange	60	35
140		3f. blue and pink	1·10	2·75
141		5f. green & light green	1·00	70
142		10f. violet and blue	1·00	40
143		20f. black and yellow	75	60

(c) Surch **LIBRE** and value in figures.

144	10	75c. on 50c. brn & yell	75	90
145	A	1f. on 65c. blue & green	45	10

(d) Optd **Afrique Francaise Libre**.

146	8	1c. brown and yellow	2·25	45
147		2c. violet and green	2·25	1·60
148		3c. blue and yellow	2·75	2·50
149		5c. blue and green	2·50	1·75
150	9	10c. mauve and blue	2·25	45
151		15c. blue and pink	2·00	45
152		20c. brown and yellow	1·40	45
153		25c. red and blue	4·25	4·00
154		35c. green & light green	3·50	1·10

B. Air stamps of 1937 optd **Afrique Francaise Libre** or surch also.

155	D	1f.50 black and yellow	£150	£150
156		2f.50 green and pink	1·25	1·60
157		3f.75 brown and green	£160	£160
158	12	4f.50 red and blue	1·25	1·90
159		6f.50 blue and green	1·90	3·00
160		8f.50 red and orange	1·75	2·75
161	D	10f. on 2f.50 grn & pk	70·00	70·00
162	12	50f. on 10f.75 vio & grn	6·00	17·00

C. No. 71 of Middle Congo optd **AFRIQUE FRANCAISE LIBRE**.

163	15	4c. green	40·00	32·00

22 Phoenix

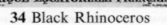

24 Count Savorgnan de Brazza and Stanley Pool

1941. Free French Issue. (a) Postage.

164	22	5c. brown	10	2·25
165		10c. blue	10	2·50
166		25c. green	10	2·75
167		30c. orange	10	2·25
168		40c. green	20	2·00
169		80c. purple	20	2·25
170		1f. mauve	90	40
171		1f.50 red	90	45
172		2f. black	90	50
173		2f.50 blue	1·25	90
174		4f. violet	55	15
175		5f. yellow	90	55
176		10f. brown	85	30
177		20f. green	1·25	65

(b) Air. As T **63a** of Guadeloupe.

178	–	1f. orange	70	1·75
179	–	1f.50 red	1·60	2·75
180	–	5f. purple	2·00	2·50
181	–	10f. black	2·00	2·25
182	–	25f. blue	1·90	2·75
183	–	50f. green	1·75	2·25
184	–	100f. red	2·00	2·75

1941. De Brazza Memorial Fund.

185	24	1f.+2f. brown and red	1·90	3·50

1942. Commemorating the Arrival of Gen. de Gaulle at Brazzaville in 1940. Optd **LIBRE 24-10-40**.

186	A	80c. brown and yellow	22·00	11·50
187	10	1f. red and orange	22·00	11·50
188	A	1f. green and blue	22·00	11·50
189	B	1f.50 blue and pale blue	22·00	11·50

1943. Free French Funds. Nos. 69, 73 and 82 surch **Afrique Francaise Combattante**, cross and value.

190	2f.25+50f. bl & lt bl (postage)	11·00	13·50
191	10f.+100f. violet and blue	35·00	42·00
192	10f.75+200f. vio & grn (air)	£120	£130

1944. French Aid Fund. Various stamps surch **RESISTANCE** and value.

195	22	5c.+10f. brn (No. 164)	8·50	9·00
196		10c.+10f. blue (No. 165)	7·50	9·00
197		25c.+10f. grn (No. 166)	7·50	9·00
198		30c.+10f. orge (No. 167)	7·50	9·00
199		40c.+10f. grn (No. 168)	7·50	9·00
193	A	80c.+10f. brown and yellow (No. 169)	27·00	32·00
200	22	1f.+10f. mve (No. 170)	28·00	32·00
194	B	1f.50+15f. blue and light blue (No. 171)	28·00	32·00
201	22	2f.+20f. black (No. 172)	7·50	8·75
202		2f.50+25f. bl (No. 173)	8·00	8·75
203		4f.+40f. violet (No. 174)	7·50	8·75
204		5f.+50f. yellow (No. 175)	7·50	5·75
205		10f.+100f. brn (No. 176)	12·00	12·50
206		20f.+200f. grn (No. 177)	12·00	12·50

1944. French Aid Fund. Nos. 164/8, 170, 172/3, 186 and 189 surch **LIBERATION** and value.

209	22	5c.+10f. brown	8·50	10·00
210		10c.+10f. blue	8·50	10·00
211		25c.+10f. green	8·50	10·00
212		30c.+10f. orange	8·50	10·00
213		40c.+10f. green	8·75	10·00
207	A	80c.+10f. brown & yell	27·00	32·00
214	22	1f.+10f. mauve	8·50	10·00
208	B	1f.50+15f. bl & lt blue	28·00	32·00
215	22	2f.+20f. black	8·75	10·00
216		2f.50+25f. blue	8·75	10·00

1944. Mutual Aid and Red Cross Funds. As T **58e** of Guadeloupe.

217	5f.+20f. blue	1·10	3·00

1945. Surch with new values and bars.

218	22	50c. on 5c. brown	1·75	3·25
219		60c. on 5c. brown	1·75	3·25
220		70c. on 5c. brown	1·90	3·25
221		1f.20 on 5c. brown	2·25	3·25
222		2f.40 on 25c. green	2·25	3·50
223		3f. on 25c. green	2·00	3·50
224		4f.50 on 25c. green	2·50	3·50
225		15f. on 2f.50 blue	2·75	3·50

1945. Eboue. As T **58f** of Guadeloupe.

226	2f. black	20	25
227	25f. green	1·25	3·75

1946. Air. Victory. As T **63b** of Guadeloupe.

228	8f. red	35	80

1946. Air. From Chad to the Rhine. As Nos. 226/31 of Cameroun.

229	5f. purple	2·75	3·50
230	10f. green	1·50	3·75
231	15f. blue	2·50	4·25
232	20f. red	3·00	4·00
233	25f. black	2·50	4·25
234	50f. red	2·75	4·00

34 Black Rhinoceros

36 Boatman

37 Caudron Goeland over Beach

1947.

235	34	10c. blue (postage)	10	2·75
236		30c. violet	10	2·75
237		40c. orange	45	2·50
238	–	50c. blue	50	2·50
239	–	60c. red	15	2·75
240	–	80c. green	25	3·00
241	–	1f. orange	1·00	10
242	–	1f.20 red	40	2·50
243	–	1f.50 green	1·60	2·50
244	–	2f. brown	1·60	35
245	–	3f. red	1·25	80
246	–	3f.60 brown	2·75	4·50
247	–	4f. blue	1·40	20
248	36	5f. purple	1·50	30
249		6f. blue	1·25	55
250		10f. black	1·40	55
251	–	15f. brown	1·60	25
252	–	20f. red	1·75	10
253	–	25f. black	1·00	10
254	–	50f. brown (air)	2·25	1·25
255	37	100f. green	4·00	2·25
256	–	200f. blue	5·75	3·50

DESIGNS—As Type **36**: 50c. to 80c. Palms and cataract; 1f. to 1f.50, River view; 2f. to 4f. Tropical forest; 15f. to 25f. Bakongo girl. As Type **37**: 50f. Savoia Marchetti S.M.75 airplane over village; 200f. Savoia Marchetti S.M.75 over column of porters.

39 People of Five Races, Aircraft and Globe

1949. Air. 75th Anniv of U.P.U.

267	39	25f. green	4·50	17·00

40 Doctor and Patient

1950. Colonial Welfare Fund.

268	40	10f.+2f. purple & green	3·50	7·50

42 De Brazza and Landscape

1951. Birth Cent of Count Savorgnan de Brazza.

269	–	10f. green & blue (postage)	80	10
270	42	15f. red, blue & brn (air)	3·25	1·90

DESIGN—22 × 31½ mm: 10f. De Brazza.

43 Monseigneur Augouard

1952. Air. Birth Centenary of Mgr. Augouard (First Bishop of the Congo).

271	43	15f. sepia, purple & olive	4·50	3·25

44

1952. Centenary of Military Medal.

272	44	15f. multicoloured	5·50	7·50

45 Sailing Canoe

1953. Air.

273	–	50f. brown, green & blue	1·60	90
274	45	100f. grn, turq & sepia	4·25	65
275	–	200f. red and lake	3·75	2·00
276	–	500f. blue, black & grn	30·00	6·00

DESIGNS: 50f. Logs in river; 200f. Native driver and docks; 500f. African darters.

46 Normandy Landings, 1944

1954. Air. 10th Anniv of Liberation.

277	**46**	15f. brown and violet	4·75	4·75

47 Lieut.-Governor Cureau

1954.

278	**47**	15f. brown and green	90	25

48 Felix Eboue

1955. Air. Governor-General Eboue Commem.

279	**48**	15f. sepia, brown & blue	2·25	1·40

49 Lizard

1955. Nature Protection.

280	**49**	8f. green and purple	1·00	1·25

50 Boali Waterfall and Power Station

1956. Economic and Social Development Fund.

281	**50**	5f. purple and sepia	70	10
282	–	10f. green and black	55	15
283	–	15f. grey and blue	25	10
284	–	20f. vermilion and red	65	20

DESIGNS: 10f. Cotton production, Chad; 15f. Brazzaville Hospital, Middle Congo; 20f. Libreville harbour, Gabon.

51 Coffee

1956. Coffee.

285	**51**	10f. violet and lilac	90	60

52 Riverside Hospital

1957. Order of Malta Leprosy Relief.

286	**52**	15f. turquoise, grn & red	1·40	95

53 Gen. Faidherbe and African Trooper

54 Lion and Lioness

1957. Air. Centenary of African Troops.

287	**53**	15f. brown & chestnut	3·25	4·75

1957.

288	–	1f. brown and green	95	2·75
289	**54**	2f. olive and green	1·00	2·50
290	–	3f. black, blue & green	1·40	2·25
291	–	4f. brown and grey	1·50	1·90

DESIGNS—HORIZ: 1f. Giant eland. VERT: 3f. African elephant; 4f. Greater kudu.

55 Regional Bureau, Brazzaville

56 "Euadania"

1958. 10th Anniv of W.H.O.

292	**55**	20f. brown and green	1·10	1·25

1958. Tropical Flora.

293	**56**	10f. yellow, grn & violet	35	55
294	–	25f. red, yellow & green	35	30

DESIGN: 25f. "Spathodea".

57 "Human Rights"

1958. 10th Anniv of Declaration of Human Rights.

295	**57**	20f. turquoise and blue	55	1·10

POSTAGE DUE STAMPS

D 13

D 38

1937.

D83	**D 13**	5c. blue and purple	10	2·75
D84		10c. pink and red	10	2·75
D85		20c. lt green & green	10	2·75
D86		25c. pink and brown	10	2·75
D87		30c. blue and red	10	2·75
D88		45c. green & mauve	35	3·00
D89		50c. pink and green	20	3·00
D90		60c. yellow & purple	80	3·25
D91		1f. yellow and brown	30	3·25
D92		2f. pink and blue	65	2·75
D93		3f. blue and brown	85	2·75

1947.

D257	**D 38**	10c. red	10	2·75
D258		30c. orange	10	2·75
D259		50c. black	25	2·75
D260		1f. red	10	2·75
D261		2f. green	1·25	2·75
D262		3f. mauve	1·75	3·00
D263		4f. blue	2·25	3·25
D264		5f. brown	2·00	2·50
D265		10f. blue	2·75	3·50
D266		20f. brown	2·50	3·75

FRENCH GUIANA Pt. 6

Formerly a French colony on the N.E. coast of S. America, now an overseas department using the stamps of France.

100 centimes = 1 franc.

Nos. 1 to 32 and 51 are all stamps of French Colonies surcharged or overprinted.

1886. "Peace and Commerce" and "Commerce" types surch **Dec. 1886. GUY. FRANC. 0f 05**.

2	H	0f.05 on 2c. green	£425	£425
4	J	0f.05 on 2c. brown on buff	£425	£375

1887. "Ceres" and "Peace and Commerce" types surch **Avril 1887. GUY. FRANC.** and value.

6	H	0f.05 on 2c. green	£110	£110
7b		0f.20 on 35c. blk on yell	50·00	42·00
8	F	0f.25 on 30c. brown	30·00	35·00

No. 7b has the "Av" of "Avril" inverted; stamps with these letters normal are worth more.

1887. "Ceres" and "Peace and Commerce" types surch **DEC. 1887. GUY. FRANC. 5c**.

9	F	5c. on 30c. brown	£120	£110
10	H	5c. on 30c. brown	£850	£850

1888. "Ceres" and "Peace and Commerce" types surch **Fevrier 1888 GUY. FRANC.** and value.

11	F	5 on 30c. brown	£110	£110
12	H	10 on 75c. red	£170	£170

1892. Optd **GUYANE**. (a) On "Ceres" type.

14	F	30c. brown	£120	£120

(b) On "Peace and Commerce" type.

15	H	2c. green	£600	£600
16		35c. black on orange	£1700	£1800
17		40c. red on yellow	£100	£100
18		75c. red	£110	£100
19		1f. green	£120	£120

(c) On "Commerce" type.

20	J	1c. black on blue	45·00	35·00
21		2c. brown on buff	25·00	35·00
22		4c. brown on grey	35·00	35·00
23		5c. green on light green	38·00	32·00
24		10c. black on lilac	60·00	40·00
25		15c. blue on light blue	60·00	35·00
26		20c. red on green	32·00	20·00
27		25c. black on pink	65·00	29·00
28		30c. brown on drab	26·00	35·00
29		35c. black on orange	£160	£160
30		40c. red on yellow	£110	£100
31		75c. red on pink	£110	£100
32		1f. green	£170	£160

1892. "Tablet" key-type inscr "GUYANE" in red (1, 5, 15, 25, 50 (No. 56), 75c., 1, 2f.) or blue (others).

38	D	1c. black on blue	35	1·75
39		2c. brown on buff	80	60
40		4c. brown on grey	1·90	2·75
52		5c. green	1·10	1·25
42		10c. black on lilac	11·50	5·75
53		10c. red	3·25	1·10
43		15c. blue	42·00	4·25
54		15c. grey	95·00	85·00
44		20c. red on green	18·00	14·00
45		25c. black on red	17·00	4·75
55		25c. blue	17·00	19·00
46		30c. brown on drab	16·00	15·00
47		40c. red on yellow	27·00	12·50
48		50c. red on pink	30·00	13·00
56		50c. brown on blue	29·00	22·00
49		75c. brown on yellow	38·00	20·00
50		1f. green	13·00	10·50
57		2f. violet on pink	£160	5·25

1892. "Commerce" type surch **DEC. 92. 0f05 GUYANE.**

51	J	0.05 on 15c. blue on blue	26·00	28·00

8 Giant Anteater

9 Gold-washer

10 Plantation of Coconut Palms, Cayenne

1904.

58	**8**	1c. black	15	15
59		2c. blue	15	40
60		4c. brown	15	1·40
61		5c. green	1·00	1·25
83		5c. orange	30	2·40
62		10c. red	1·10	15
84		10c. green	65	2·50
104		10c. red on blue	55	1·40
63		15c. violet	1·25	75
64	**9**	20c. brown	85	2·25
65		25c. blue	2·50	55
85		25c. violet	1·10	1·00
66		30c. black	1·60	1·40
86		30c. red	65	2·75
105		30c. orange	25	2·50
106		30c. green	2·00	3·25
66a		35c. black on yellow	1·60	1·25
67		40c. red	30	1·60
87		40c. black	1·75	2·75
68		45c. brown	2·00	3·00
69		50c. lilac	3·00	2·75
88		50c. blue	25	2·50
107		50c. grey	1·60	1·25
108		60c. mauve on pink	1·50	2·75
109		65c. green	2·25	3·00
70		75c. green	2·25	2·50
110		85c. purple	30	2·75
71	**10**	1f. red	1·40	1·25
111		1f. blue on light blue	2·25	3·00
112		1f. blue on green	2·75	4·25
113		1f.10 pink	2·00	3·25
72		2f. blue	2·00	2·25
114		2f. red on yellow	2·50	3·75
73		5f. black	7·00	6·00
115		10f. green on yellow	13·00	18·00
116		20f. red	19·00	23·00

1912. "Tablet" key-type surch in figures.

74	D	05 on 2c. brown on buff	1·60	3·00
75		05 on 4c. brown on grey	15	2·75
76		05 on 20c. red on green	35	3·25
77		05 on 25c. black on pink	3·50	4·75
78		05 on 30c. brown on drab	40	3·50
79		10 on 40c. red on yellow	70	3·00
80		10 on 50c. red	3·50	4·25

1915. Red Cross. Surch with red cross and **5**.

81	**8**	10c.+5c. red	17·00	19·00

1915. Red Cross. Surch **5c** and red cross.

82	**8**	10c.+5c. red	95	3·00

1922. Surch in figures with bars.

89	**8**	0,01 on 15c. violet	15	2·75
90		0,02 on 15c. violet	15	2·00
91		0,04 on 15c. violet	15	2·50
92		0,05 on 15c. violet	1·25	3·00
95		25c. on 15c. violet	1·50	3·00
96	**10**	25c. on 2f. blue	1·50	2·75
97	**9**	65 on 45c. brown	1·75	3·25
98		85 on 45c. brown	2·25	3·25
99		90 on 75c. red	2·50	3·00
100	**10**	1f.05 on 2f. brown	2·00	3·25
101		1f.25 on 1f. blue on blue	1·25	3·25
102		1f.50 on 1f. blue	2·25	3·00
103		3f. on 5f. violet	50	1·90

1924. Surch in words.

93	**10**	10f. on 1f. green on yellow	15·00	21·00
94		20f. on 5f. mauve on red	14·50	21·00

20 Carib Archer

21 Shooting the Rapids, R. Maroni

22 Government Building, Cayenne

1929.

117	**20**	1c. blue and lilac	15	2·50
118		2c. green and red	15	2·00
119		3c. green and violet	15	2·50
120		4c. mauve and brown	15	2·50
121		5c. red and blue	40	2·25
122		10c. brown and mauve	15	1·40
123		15c. red and brown	80	2·50
124		20c. green and blue	15	2·50
125		25c. brown and red	85	2·25
126	**21**	30c. lt green & green	70	2·50
127		30c. brown and green	15	2·50
128		35c. green and blue	2·00	3·00
129		40c. drab and brown	25	2·50
130		45c. brown and green	2·10	3·00
131		45c. green and olive	1·25	2·50
132		50c. brown and blue	40	30
133		55c. red and blue	2·25	3·25
134		60c. green and red	85	2·50
135		65c. green and red	85	2·75
136		70c. green and blue	1·00	3·00
137		75c. light blue and blue	2·50	3·25
138		80c. blue and black	2·10	2·50
139		90c. red and carmine	2·00	2·75
140		90c. brown and mauve	2·00	3·00
141		1f. brown and mauve	40	2·50
142		1f. red and carmine	3·00	4·00
143		1f. blue and black	85	3·00
144	**22**	1f.05 green and red	4·25	7·00
145		1f.10 mauve and brown	3·25	6·25
146		1f.25 green and brown	2·00	3·25
147		1f.25 red and carmine	1·50	2·75
148		1f.40 mauve and brown	2·00	3·00
149		1f.50 light blue & blue	1·40	2·75
150		1f.60 green and brown	1·60	2·75
151		1f.75 brown and red	2·75	3·00
152		1f.75 ultramarine & bl	2·25	3·00
153		2f. red and green	1·40	1·50
154		2f.25 ultramarine & bl	1·25	3·25
155		2f.50 brown and red	1·25	2·75
156		3f. mauve and brown	2·00	2·75
157		5f. green and violet	1·60	2·50
158		10f. blue and brown	2·00	2·50
159		20f. red and blue	3·00	4·00

1931. "Colonial Exhibition" key-types inscr "GUYANE FRANCAISE".

160	E	40c. black and green	3·50	5·75
161	F	50c. black and mauve	3·50	5·50
162	G	90c. black and red	3·75	6·00
163	H	1f.50 black and blue	4·25	6·00

25 Cayenne

1933. Air.

164	**25**	50c. brown	85	70
165		1f. green	25	70
166		1f.50 blue	25	90
167		2f. orange	75	80
168		3f. black	1·25	2·75
169		5f. violet	70	1·25
170		10f. olive	35	1·60
171		20f. red	65	1·25

26 Cayenne recaptured by D'Estrees, 1676

27 Local Products

1935. West Indies Tercentenary.
172 **26** 40c. brown . . . . 6·00 6·75
173 50c. red . . . . 13·00 10·00
174 1f.50 blue . . . . 5·75 6·25
175 **27** 1f.75 red . . . . 16·00 17·00
176 5f. brown . . . . 12·50 9·00
177 10f. green . . . . 13·50 12·00

1937. International Exhibition, Paris. As Nos. 110/16 of Cameroun.
178 20c. violet . . . . 30 3·00
179 30c. green . . . . 25 2·75
180 40c. red . . . . 25 2·75
181 50c. brown and agate . . . . 25 2·75
182 90c. red . . . . 40 3·25
183 1f.50 blue . . . . 50 3·25
MS183a 120 × 100 mm. 3f. violet. Imperf . . . . 8·25 13·00

1938. International Anti-cancer Fund. As T **58b** of Guadeloupe.
184 1f.75+50c. blue . . . . . . 7·25 16·00

1939. New York World's Fair. As T **58c** of Guadeloupe.
185 1f.25 red . . . . 1·10 3·25
186 2f.25 blue . . . . 1·40 3·00

1939. 150th Anniv of French Revolution. As T **58d** of Guadeloupe.
187 45c.+25c. grn & blk (post) . . 7·50 13·00
188 70c.+30c. brown & black . . 7·50 13·00
189 90c.+35c. orange & black . . 7·50 13·00
190 1f.25+1f. red & black . . . . 7·75 14·00
191 2f.25+2f. blue & black . . . 8·25 13·00
192 5f.+4f. black & orange (air) 11·50 23·00

28 View of Cayenne and Marshal Petain

1941. Marshal Petain Issue.
192a **28** 1f. purple . . . . 35 3·00
192b 2f.50 blue . . . . 15 3·00

1944. Mutual Aid and Red Cross Funds. As T **58e** of Guadeloupe.
193 5f.+20f. purple . . . . 80 3·00

1945. Felix Eboue. As T **58f** of Guadeloupe.
194 2f. black . . . . 20 3·00
195 25f. green . . . . 50 3·25

28a Arms of French Guiana

1945.
196 **28a** 10c. blue . . . . 1·00 2·75
197 30c. brown . . . . 15 2·75
198 40c. blue . . . . 70 2·75
199 50c. purple . . . . 70 2·75
200 60c. yellow . . . . 20 2·75
201 70c. brown . . . . 20 2·75
202 80c. green . . . . 65 2·75
203 1f. blue . . . . 60 2·75
204 1f.20 lilac . . . . 1·00 2·75
205 1f.50 orange . . . . . . 1·25 2·75
206 2f. black . . . . 1·10 3·00
207 2f.40 red . . . . 1·10 3·00
208 3f. pink . . . . 85 3·00
209 4f. blue . . . . 1·40 3·00
210 4f.50 green . . . . 60 3·00
211 5f. brown . . . . 50 3·00
212 10f. violet . . . . 55 2·75
213 15f. red . . . . 70 3·25
214 20f. olive . . . . 1·75 3·25

1945. Air. As T **63a** of Guadeloupe.
215 50f. green . . . . 1·00 3·00
216 100f. red . . . . 1·75 3·50

1946. Air. Victory. As T **63b** of Guadeloupe.
217 8f. black . . . . 30 3·75

1946. Air. From Chad to the Rhine. As T **63c** of Guadeloupe.
218 5f. blue . . . . 85 3·00
219 10f. red . . . . 55 3·00
220 15f. purple . . . . 40 3·00
221 20f. green . . . . 85 3·50
222 25f. purple . . . . 75 3·50
223 50f. mauve . . . . 1·60 4·00

29 Hammock

33 Red-billed Toucans

35 Yellow-throated Caracara

1947.
224 **29** 10c. green (postage) . . . 15 2·75
225 30c. red . . . . 15 2·75
226 50c. purple . . . . 15 2·75
227 – 60c. grey . . . . 15 2·75
228 – 1f. brown . . . . 15 2·75
229 – 1f.50 brown . . . . . . 15 2·75
230 – 2f. green . . . . 30 3·00
231 – 2f.50 blue . . . . 50 3·00
232 – 3f. brown . . . . 85 3·00
233 – 4f. brown . . . . 2·25 3·25
234 – 5f. blue . . . . 2·00 3·00
235 – 6f. brown . . . . 1·75 3·25
236 **33** 10f. blue . . . . 4·50 3·75
237 15f. brown . . . . 4·50 4·00
238 20f. brown . . . . 6·75 4·00
239 – 25f. green . . . . 8·00 6·00
240 – 40f. brown . . . . 6·75 6·00
241 **35** 50f. green (air) . . . . . 13·50 13·50
242 – 100f. lake . . . . 11·50 22·00
243 – 200f. blue . . . . 25·00 24·00
DESIGNS—As Types **29** and **33**—HORIZ: 60c. to 1f.50, Riverside village; 2f. to 3f. Pirogue; 25f., 40f. Blue and yellow macaw, military macaw and white-eyed conure. VERT: 4f. to 6f. Girl. As Type **35**—VERT: 100f. Airplane over peccary and palms. HORIZ: 200f. Sud Ouest Corse II airplane, channel-billed toucan, red-billed toucan and black-necked aracari.

POSTAGE DUE STAMPS

1925. Postage Due stamps of France optd **GUYANE FRANCAISE** or surch also **centimes a percevoir** and value in figures.
D117 **D 11** 5c. blue . . . . 15 3·00
D118 10c. brown . . . . 15 2·75
D119 15c. on 20c. olive . . . 15 3·00
D120 20c. olive . . . . 75 3·00
D121 25c. on 5c. blue . . . . 1·25 3·00
D122 30c. on 20c. olive . . . 70 3·25
D123 45c. on 10c. brown . . . 1·40 2·75
D124 50c. red . . . . 85 3·25
D125 60c. on 5c. blue . . . . 1·00 3·00
D126 1f. on 20c. olive . . . . 1·00 3·50
D127 2f. on 50c. red . . . . . 1·25 3·75
D128 3f. mauve . . . . 7·00 12·50

D 23 Palm Trees

D 36

1929.
D160 **D 23** 5c. blue & dp blue . . 15 2·50
D161 10c. blue & brown . . 15 2·50
D162 20c. red and green . . 20 2·50
D163 30c. red and brown . . 45 2·50
D164 50c. brown & mauve . . 1·60 2·50
D165 60c. brown and red . . 1·60 2·50
D166 – 1f. red and blue . . . 1·75 3·00
D167 – 2f. green and red . . . 2·50 4·00
D168 – 3f. grey and mauve . . 2·75 4·50
DESIGN: 1f. to 3f. Creole girl.

1947.
D244 **D 36** 10c. red . . . . 15 2·50
D245 30c. green . . . . 15 2·50
D246 50c. black . . . . 15 2·50
D247 1f. blue . . . . 20 3·00
D248 2f. lake . . . . 25 3·00
D249 3f. violet . . . . 30 3·00
D250 4f. red . . . . 45 3·25
D251 5f. purple . . . . 60 3·50
D252 10f. green . . . . 1·00 4·25
D253 20f. purple . . . . . . 1·75 4·75

FRENCH GUINEA Pt. 6

A French colony on the W. coast of Africa incorporated in French West Africa in 1944. Became completely independent in 1958 (see Guinea).

100 centimes = 1 franc.

1892. "Tablet" key-type inscr "GUINEE FRANCAISE" in red (1, 5, 15, 50 (No. 17), 75c., 1f.) or blue (others).
1 **D** 1c. black on blue . . . . . 1·60 2·25
2 2c. brown on buff . . . . . 1·40 2·50
3 4c. brown on grey . . . . . 2·25 2·50
4 5c. green on light green . . 3·50 4·00
5 10c. black on lilac . . . . . 5·50 5·25
14 10c. red . . . . 30·00 35·00
6 15c. blue . . . . 5·50 3·75
15 15c. grey . . . . £100 90·00
7 20c. red on green . . . . . 14·50 14·00
8 25c. black on pink . . . . . 6·75 3·75
16 25c. blue . . . . 13·00 18·00
9 30c. brown on drab . . . . 17·00 20·00
10 40c. red on yellow . . . . . 22·00 21·00
11 50c. red on pink . . . . . . 28·00 30·00
17 50c. brown on blue . . . . 24·00 24·00
12 75c. brown on yellow . . . 55·00 65·00
13 1f. green . . . . 48·00 35·00

1 Fulas Shepherd

3 Ford at Kitim

1904.
18 **1** 1c. black on green 45 35
19 2c. brown on yellow 20 20
20 4c. red on blue . . . . . . 85 1·50
21 5c. green on light green . . 1·25 35
22 10c. red . . . . 2·50 80
23 15c. lilac on pink . . . . . 4·25 3·00
24 20c. red on green . . . . . 7·50 11·00
25 25c. blue . . . . 10·00 11·00
26 30c. brown . . . . 10·00 15·00
27 40c. red on yellow . . . . . 18·00 22·00
28 50c. brown on green . . . . 17·00 15·00
29 75c. blue on yellow . . . . 21·00 28·00
30 1f. green . . . . 45·00 32·00
31 2f. red on orange . . . . . 85·00 80·00
32 5f. blue on green £110 £110

1906. "Faidherbe", "Palms" and "Balay" key-types inscr "GUINEE" in blue (10c., 5f.) or red (others).
33 **I** 1c. slate 15 25
34 2c. brown . . . . 1·75 90
35 4c. brown on blue 75 80
36 5c. green . . . . 2·50 95
37 10c. red . . . . 12·00 80
38 **J** 20c. black on blue . . . . 2·25 3·75
39 25c. blue . . . . 3·25 3·75
40 30c. brown on pink . . . . 3·75 4·25
41 35c. black on yellow . . . . 1·25 1·40
43 45c. brown on green . . . . 3·00 4·00
44 50c. violet . . . . 7·25 9·25
45 75c. green on orange . . . . 4·50 4·25
46 **K** 1f. black on blue . . . . . 13·00 11·00
47 2f. blue on pink . . . . . . 32·00 38·00
48 5f. red on yellow . . . . . 35·00 50·00

1912. Surch in figures.
49 **D** 05 on 2c. brown on buff . . 90 2·50
50 05 on 4c. brown on grey . . 1·25 2·00
51 05 on 15c. blue 50 50
52 05 on 20c. red on green . . 2·00 5·00
53 05 on 30c. brown on drab . 2·75 6·00
54 10 on 40c. red on yellow . . 75 5·25
55 10 on 75c. brown on yellow 4·00 9·50

1912. Surch in figures.
56 **1** 05 on 2c. brown on yellow 70 1·90
57 05 on 4c. red on blue . . . 25 70
58 05 on 15c. lilac on pink . . 30 1·60
59 05 on 20c. red on green . . 35 1·60
60 05 on 25c. blue . . . . . . 60 1·25
61 05 on 30c. brown . . . . . 70 2·00
62 10 on 40c. red on yellow . . 50 2·50
63 10 on 50c. brown on green 1·90 4·50

1913.
64 **3** 1c. blue and violet 10 10
65 2c. chocolate and brown . . 10 10
66 4c. black and grey 10 85
67 5c. green and light green . 50 30
83 5c. green and purple . . . 10 2·00
68 10c. pink and red 95 70
84 10c. green & light green . . 1·00 1·75
85 10c. red and lilac 10 55
69 15c. red and purple 50 95
86 15c. green & light green . . 40 1·75
87 15c. mauve and purple . . 1·10 1·40
70 20c. violet and brown . . . 10 1·75
88 20c. green . . . . 75 3·00
89 20c. brown and red . . . . 80 1·10
71 25c. blue & ultramarine . . 2·25 1·90
90 25c. violet and black . . . 45 20
72 30c. green and purple . . . 2·00 2·75
91 30c. pink and red . . . . . 1·25 2·25
92 30c. green and red . . . . 50 1·75
93 30c. green and olive . . . . 2·00 2·00
73 35c. pink and blue . . . . 1·25 2·50
74 40c. grey and green . . . . 1·75 1·25
75 45c. red and brown . . . . 2·00 2·75
76 50c. black and blue . . . . 5·50 3·75
94 50c. blue & ultramarine . . 1·10 2·25
95 50c. green and brown . . . 1·90 15
96 60c. violet on pink . . . . 95 2·50
97 65c. blue and brown . . . . 2·25 2·75
77 75c. blue and pink . . . . 1·60 3·00
98 75c. light blue and blue . . 60 2·50
99 75c. green and mauve . . . 2·00 2·00
100 85c. purple and green . . . 90 3·25
101 90c. mauve and red . . . . 3·00 6·75
78 1f. black and violet . . . . 1·60 1·10
102 1f.10 brown and violet . . 4·50 8·75
103 1f.25 brown and violet . . 2·25 3·50
104 1f.50 light blue and blue . . 4·50 3·00
105 1f.75 mauve and brown . . 1·10 1·75
79 2f. brown and orange . . . 3·25 2·50
106 3f. mauve on pink . . . . . 7·25 6·75
80 5f. violet and black . . . . 8·50 16·00
107 5f. black and blue . . . . . 1·40 3·00

1915. Surch **5c** and red cross.
81 **3** 10c.+5c. pink and red . . . . 1·75 2·75

1922. Surch in figures and bars.
108 **3** 25c. on 2f. brown & orange 95 2·75
109 25c. on 5f. black & blue . . 90 2·75
110 60 on 75c. violet on pink . . 1·50 3·00
111 65 on 75c. blue and pink . . 1·25 4·00
112 85 on 75c. blue and pink . . 1·60 4·00
113 90c. on 75c. mve & red . . 60 3·75
114 1f.25 on 1f. ultram & bl . . 1·25 3·00
115 1f.50 on 1f. lt blue & blue 75 1·75
116 3f. on 5f. grey & mauve . . 3·00 5·75
117 10f. on 5f. green & blue . . 7·00 8·25
118 20f. on 5f. brown and mauve on pink . . . . . 17·00 27·00

1931. "Colonial Exhibition" key-types inscr "GUINEE FRANCAISE".
119 **E** 40c. black and green . . . 3·25 4·50
120 **F** 50c. black and purple . . . 3·25 4·75
121 **G** 90c. black and red . . . . 4·00 5·25
122 **H** 1f.50 black and blue . . . 4·00 4·50

1937. International Exhibition, Paris. As T **58a** of Guadeloupe.
123 20c. violet . . . . 50 2·25
124 30c. green . . . . 90 2·75
125 40c. red . . . . 80 2·50
126 50c. brown and agate . . . . 25 1·75
127 90c. red . . . . 30 1·40
128 1f.50 blue . . . . 30 1·00
MS128a 120 × 100 mm. 3f. green and deep green. Imperf . . . . 6·75 13·00

4 Native Village

7 Ford at Kitim and Marshal Petain

6a Airplane over Jungle

1938.
129 **4** 2c. red 10 95
130 3c. blue . . . . 10 1·40
131 4c. green 10 95
132 5c. red 65 40
133 10c. blue 10 65
134 15c. purple . . . . 10 1·50
135 – 20c. red 15 25
136 – 25c. blue 70 85
137 – 30c. blue 15 10
138 – 35c. green . . . . 1·25 1·25
139 – 40c. brown . . . . 30 2·75
140 – 45c. green . . . . 1·90 2·75
141 – 50c. red . . . . 30 1·25
142 – 55c. blue . . . . 55 1·75
143 – 60c. blue . . . . 1·75 3·00
144 – 65c. green . . . . 55 1·00
145 – 70c. green . . . . 2·25 3·00
146 – 80c. purple . . . . 85 2·50
147 – 90c. purple . . . . 2·00 3·00
148 – 1f. red . . . . 2·50 2·50
149 – 1f. brown . . . . 60 1·60
150 – 1f.25 red . . . . 2·25 3·25
151 – 1f.40 brown . . . . . . 2·00 2·25
152 – 1f.50 brown . . . . . . 1·50 1·75
153 – 1f.60 red . . . . 2·25 1·75
154 – 1f.75 blue 50 55
155 – 2f. mauve 90 55
156 – 2f.25 blue . . . . 1·60 2·50
157 – 2f.50 brown . . . . . . 2·00 65
158 – 3f. blue 65 40
159 – 5f. purple 65 60
160 – 10f. green 45 55
161 – 20f. brown . . . . 1·75 1·75

DESIGNS—HORIZ: 20c. to 50c. Wooden pot makers; 55c. to 1f.50, Waterfall. VERT: 1f.60 to 20f. Native women.

1938. International Anti-cancer Fund. As T **58b** of Guadeloupe.
162 1f.75+50c. blue 4·25 13·50

1939. Death Centenary of R. Caillie. As T **21** of French Sudan.
163 90c. orange 25 1·60
164 2f. violet 25 90
165 2f.25 blue 40 3·25

1939. New York World's Fair. As T **58c** of Guadeloupe.
166 1f.25 red 2·25 3·25
167 2f.25 blue 2·00 3·00

1939. 150th Anniv of French Revolution. As T **58d** of Guadeloupe.
168 45c.+25c. green & black 7·00 10·00
169 70c.+30c. brown & black 5·25 10·00
170 90c.+35c. orange & black 6·00 10·00
171 1f.25+1f. red and black 6·25 10·00
172 2f.25+2f. blue and black 6·50 10·00

1940. Air.
173 **6a** 1f.90 blue 1·25 2·50
174 2f.90 red 30 2·75
175 4f.50 green 1·25 3·00
176 4f.90 olive 1·10 3·25
177 6f.90 orange 1·40 3·50

1941. National Defence Fund. Surch **SECOURS NATIONAL** and value.
178 +1f. on 50c. (No. 141) 1·25 3·50
179 +2f. on 80c. (No. 146) 6·00 6·25
180 +2f. on 1f.50 (No. 152) 5·50 7·50
181 +3f. on 2f. (No. 155) 6·00 7·25

1941.
182 **7** 1f. green 35 2·75
183 2f.50 blue 40 2·75

8 Dakar Maternity Hospital

1942. Air. Colonial Child Welfare.
184 **8** 1f.50+3f.50 green 45 3·25
185 2f.+6f. brown 65 3·25
186 3f.+9f. red 90 3·25

9a "Vocation"

1942. Air.
187 **9a** 50f. olive and green 1·75 4·00

POSTAGE DUE STAMPS

D 2 Woman of Futa Jallon

D 7 Native Idol

1905.
D33 **D 2** 5c. blue 1·00 70
D34 10c. brown 1·60 1·00
D35 15c. green 2·75 2·75
D36 30c. red 3·25 3·25
D37 50c. black 5·50 6·25
D38 60c. orange 9·75 7·50
D39 1f. lilac 32·00 34·00

1906. "Natives" key-type inscr "GUINEE".
D49 L 5c. green 7·00 6·00
D50 10c. purple 1·50 2·75
D51 15c. blue on blue 1·75 4·00
D52 20c. black on yellow 1·75 4·50
D53 30c. red on cream 13·00 30·00
D54 50c. violet 5·75 30·00
D55 60c. black on buff 5·25 28·00
D56 1f. black on pink 3·00 17·00

1914. "Figure" key-type inscr "GUINEE".
D81 M 5c. green 15 2·50
D82 10c. red 20 2·50
D83 15c. grey 1·10 2·75
D84 20c. brown 1·00 2·75
D85 30c. blue 75 2·75
D86 50c. black 85 3·00
D87 60c. orange 1·60 3·50
D88 1f. violet 1·10 3·50

1927. Surch in figures.
D119 M 2F. on 1f. mauve 4·00 10·50
D120 3F. on 1f. brown 2·50 12·00

1938.
D162 **D 7** 5c. violet 10 2·50
D163 10c. red 10 2·50
D164 15c. green 10 2·50
D165 20c. brown 10 2·75
D166 30c. purple 40 2·75
D167 50c. brown 40 3·00
D168 60c. blue 60 3·25
D169 1f. red 55 3·25
D170 2f. blue 1·25 3·50
D171 3f. black 85 3·75
For later issues see **GUINEA**.

FRENCH INDIAN SETTLEMENTS Pt. 6

A group of five small French settlements in India. The inhabitants voted to join India in 1954.

1892. 100 centimes = 1 franc.
1923. 24 caches = 1 fanon; 8 fanons = 1 rupee.

1892. "Tablet" key-type inscr "ETABLISSEMENTS DE L'INDE" in red (1, 5, 15, 25, 35, 45, 50 (No. 19), 75c., 1f.) or blue (others).
1 D 1c. black on blue 70 95
2 2c. brown on buff 1·40 1·25
3 4c. brown on grey 2·75 3·00
4 5c. green on light green 4·25 3·50
5 10c. black on lilac 9·25 3·25
14 10c. red 3·00 2·25
6 15c. blue 5·25 5·25
15 15c. grey 25·00 27·00
7 20c. red on green 6·00 6·00
8 25c. black on pink 3·50 3·75
16 25c. blue 16·00 16·00
9 30c. brown on drab 45·00 40·00
17 35c. black on yellow 12·00 9·00
10 40c. red on yellow 4·50 6·00
18 45c. black on green 5·00 5·00
11 50c. red on pink 5·25 6·00
19 50c. brown on blue 11·00 13·00
12 75c. brown on yellow 7·25 11·00
13 1f. green 4·75 10·00

1903. Surch in figures.
20 D 0,05 on 25c. blk on pink £225 £160
21 0,10 on 25c. blk on pink £250 £170
22 0,15 on 25c. blk on pink 70·00 85·00
23 0,40 on 50c. red on pink £400 £325

1903. Fiscal stamp bisected and each half surch **Inde Fcaise POSTES 0,05**.
24 0.05 black and blue 19·00 22·00

3 Brahma

4 Temple near Pondicherry

1914.
26 **3** 1c. black and grey 70 15
27 2c. black and purple 15 1·00
52 2c. purple and green 40 3·00
28 3c. black and brown 20 1·50
29 4c. black and orange 90 2·00
30 5c. black and green 40 2·25
53 5c. black and purple 1·25 2·75
31 10c. black and red 2·10 2·50
54 10c. black and green 1·40 3·00
32 15c. black and violet 2·25 2·50
33 20c. black and red 2·75 3·25
34 25c. black and blue 2·75 2·75
55 25c. red and blue 2·50 2·75
35 30c. black and blue 2·75 3·25
56 30c. black and red 1·50 3·00
36 **4** 35c. black and brown 2·75 3·25
37 40c. black and red 3·00 3·25
38 45c. black and green 3·00 3·50
39 50c. black and red 2·50 3·25
57 50c. blue and ultramarine 1·60 3·25
40 75c. black and blue 3·25 4·00
41 1f. black and yellow 3·50 4·00
42 2f. black and violet 6·00 7·00
43 5f. black and blue 3·25 4·00
58 5f. black and deep red 3·00 4·50
See also Nos. 88/107.

1915. Red Cross surch with plain cross and premium.
44 **3** 10c.+5c. black and red 85 3·25

1916. Surch **5** and Maltese cross.
48 **3** 10c.+5c. black and red 5·75 21·00

1916. Surch with Maltese cross and **5 C**.
49 **3** 10c.+5c. black and red 45 4·25

1922. Surch in figures and bars.
59 **3** 0.01 on 15c. black & violet 75 3·00
60 0.02 on 15c. black & violet 10 3·00
61 0.05 on 15c. black & violet 10 3·00

1923. Surch in new currency (caches, fanons and rupees) in figures and words.
62 **3** 1ca. on 1c. black and grey 15 2·75
63 2ca. on 5c. black & purple 20 2·00
64 3ca. on 3c. black & brown 40 2·75
65 4ca. on 4c. black & orange 40 2·40
66 6ca. on 10c. black & green 1·40 2·25
67 **4** 6ca. on 45c. black & green 40 3·00
68 **3** 10ca. on 20c. green & red 3·25 3·75
69 12ca. on 15c. black & violet 1·90 2·75
70 15ca. on 20c. black & red 65 3·00
71 **4** 16ca. on 35c. brown & blue 3·25 3·75
72 **3** 18ca. on 30c. black & red 2·25 75
73 **4** 20ca. on 45c. pink & green 2·50 2·75
74 **3** 1fa. on 25c. red and green 3·25 4·50
75 **4** 1fa.3ca. on 35c. blk & brn 80 2·50
76 1fa.6ca. on 40c. black & red 2·25 2·25
77 1fa.12ca. on 50c. blue and ultramarine 2·40 2·75
78 1fa.12ca. on 75c. black & bl 70 3·25
79 1fa.16ca. on 75c. grn & red 3·25 3·75
80 **3** 2fa.9ca. on 25c. red & blue 1·60 3·25
81 **4** 2fa.12ca. on 1f. brn & mve 3·50 4·00
82 3fa.3ca. on 1f. black & yell 1·60 3·25
83 6fa.6ca. on 2f. black & vio 5·00 5·75
84 1r. on 1f. blue and green 7·50 7·50
85 2r. on 5f. black and red 7·75 7·50
86 3r. on 2f. violet and grey 12·00 16·00
87 5r. on 5f. blk & pink on green 26·00 24·00

1929. As T **3** and **4** but with value in caches, fanons or rupees.
88 **3** 1ca. black and brown 15 2·50
89 2ca. black and purple 20 2·25
90 3ca. black and brown 15 2·50
91 4ca. black and orange 25 3·25
92 6ca. green and deep green 35 1·75
93 10ca. green and red 1·40 2·50
94 **4** 12ca. green & deep green 20 2·75
95 **3** 16ca. black and blue 1·25 3·25
96 18ca. red and carmine 1·60 3·25
97 20ca. green & bl on azure 40 30
98 **4** 1fa. red and green 55 2·25
99 1fa.6ca. black and orange 1·60 3·00
100 1fa.12ca. blue and dp blue 1·10 2·75
101 1fa.16ca. green and red 1·40 3·25
102 2fa.12ca. brown and mauve 60 1·75
103 6fa.6ca. black and violet 1·50 3·25
104 1r. blue and green 1·50 2·25
105 2r. black and red 1·40 1·90
106 3r. lilac and black 2·75 2·50
107 5r. black & red on green 2·75 2·75

1931. "Colonial Exhibition" key-types inscr "ETS FRANCAIS DANS L'INDE".
108 E 10ca. green 3·50 4·25
109 F 12ca. mauve 3·25 3·75
110 G 18ca. red 4·25 4·75
111 H 1fa.12 blue 3·50 4·00

1937. International Exhibition, Paris. As T **58a** of Guadeloupe.
112 8ca. violet 70 3·50
113 12ca. green 2·10 3·50
114 16ca. red 1·00 3·50
115 20ca. brown 90 3·50
116 1fa.12 red 65 3·50
117 2fa.12 blue 75 3·50
MS117a 120 × 100 mm. 5fa. purple. Imperf 7·50 14·00

1938. International Anti-cancer Fund. As T **58b** of Guadeloupe.
118 2fa.12ca.+20ca. blue 7·00 15·00

1939. New York World's Fair. As T **58c** of Guadeloupe.
119 1fa.12 red 2·75 3·25
120 2fa.12 blue 3·00 3·75

1939. 150th Anniv of French Revolution. As T **58d** of Guadeloupe.
121 18ca.+10ca. green & black 6·75 10·00
122 1fa.6ca.+12ca. brn & blk 6·75 10·00
123 1fa.12ca.+16ca. orge & blk 6·50 10·00
124 1fa.16ca.+1fa.16ca. red & blk 6·50 10·00
125 2fa.12ca.+3fa. blue & blk 6·75 10·00

1941. Optd **FRANCE LIBRE**. (a) Stamps of 1923.
126 **3** 15ca. on 20ca. black & red 65·00 85·00
127 18ca. on 30ca. black & red 2·75 4·25
128a **4** 1fa.3 on 35ca. black & brn 55·00 65·00
132 **3** 2fa.9 on 25ca. red & blue £700 £700

(b) Stamps of 1929.
133 **3** 2ca. black and purple 7·00 12·50
134 3ca. black and brown 1·40 4·00
135 4ca. black and orange 5·50 7·50
136 6ca. green and deep green 2·25 3·75
137 10ca. green and red 3·00 4·00
139 **4** 12ca. green & deep green 2·00 4·00
140 **3** 16ca. black and blue 2·00 4·00
141 18ca. red and carmine £450 £450
142 20ca. green & bl on azure 2·50 3·75
143 **4** 1fa. red and green 1·90 3·75
144 1fa.6 black and red 2·00 4·00
145 1fa.12 black and deep blue 3·50 5·75
146 1fa.16 green and red 2·50 3·50
147 2fa.12 brown and mauve 2·00 75
148 6fa.6 black and violet 2·50 4·00
149 1r. blue and green 3·00 3·75
150 2r. black and red 2·75 4·00
151 3r. lilac and black 3·00 4·25
152 5r. black & red on green 7·25 10·50

(c) Paris Exhibition stamps of 1937.
154 8ca. violet 4·50 9·50
157 12ca. green 3·50 6·00
158 16ca. red 2·50 6·00
159 1fa.12 red 2·50 6·00
160 2fa.12 blue 2·50 6·00
MS160a 5fa. bright purple (**MS**117a) £575 £575

(d) New York World's Fair stamps of 1939.
161 1fa.12 red 2·75 4·75
162 2fa.12 blue 2·75 4·75

1941. Various issues optd **FRANCE TOUJOURS** and Cross of Lorraine. (a) On Nos. 70, 72 and 75.
162a **3** 15ca. on 20c. black & red £600 £160
162b 18ca. on 30c. black & red £900 £425
162c **4** 1fa.3 on 35c. black & brn £600 £160

(b) On Nos. 89/90, 92 and 94/107.
162d **3** 2ca. black and purple £600 £140
162e 3ca. black and brown £600 £140
162f 6ca. green and deep green £600 £140
162g **4** 12ca. green and deep green £600 £140
162h **3** 16ca. black and blue £600 £140
162i 18ca. red and carmine £900 £550
162j 20ca. green & bl on azure £550 £130
162k **4** 1fa. red and green £550 £130
162l 1fa.6 black and orange £550 £130
162m 1fa.12 blue and deep blue £550 £130
162n 1fa.16 green and red £550 £130
162o 2fa.12 brown and mauve £550 £130
162p 6fa.6 black and violet £550 £130
162q 1r. blue and green £550 £140
162r 2r. black and red £550 £140
162s 3r. lilac and black £550 £140
162t 5r. black and red on green £550 £140

(c) On Nos. 112/14 and 116/17.
162u 8ca. violet £550 £160
162v 12ca. green £550 £160
162w 16ca. red £550 £160
162x 1fa.12 red £550 £160
162y 2fa.12 blue £550 £160

(d) On Nos. 119/20.
162z 1fa.12 red £550 £160
162za 2fa.12 blue £550 £160

1942. Optd **FRANCE LIBRE** and Cross of Lorraine. (a) Nos. 72 and 88/107.
164 **3** 2ca. black and purple 1·25 3·00
165 3ca. black and brown 30 3·25
166 6ca. green and deep green 2·00 3·00
167 **4** 12ca. green & deep green 2·75 4·50
168 **3** 16ca. black and blue 2·25 3·25
169 18ca. red and carmine 35 3·25
163 18ca. on 30ca. black and red (No. 72) £200 £160
171 20ca. green & bl on azure 35 3·25
172 **4** 1fa. red and green 35 3·25
173a 1fa.6 black and red 3·00 3·75
174 1fa.12 blue and deep blue 2·50 3·50
175 1fa.16 green and red 55 65
176 2fa.12 brown and mauve 1·75 85
177 6fa.6 black and violet 3·25 4·50
178 1r. blue and green 5·25 8·75
179 2r. black and red 4·00 7·25
180a 3r. lilac and black 4·50 8·25
181 5r. black & red on green 4·50 9·25

(b) Paris Exhibition stamps of 1937.
189 8ca. violet 6·50 9·00
190 12ca. green 6·00 9·00
191 16ca. red £850 £850
192 1fa.12 red 2·25 3·25
193 2fa.12 blue 3·00 4·75

(c) New York World's Fair stamps of 1939.
194 1fa.12 red 3·25 4·00
195 2fa.12 blue 4·25 5·25

1942. No. 103 surch with value only.
203 1ca. on 6fa.6 black and violet 27·00 21·00
204 4ca. on 6fa.6 black and violet 27·00 21·00
205 10ca. on 6fa.6 black & violet 13·50 9·50
206 15fa. on 6fa.6 black & violet 13·50 9·50
207 1fa.3 on 6fa.6 black & violet 21·00 20·00
208 2fa.9 on 6fa.6 black & violet 14·00 21·00
209 3fa.3 on 6fa.6 black & violet 18·00 20·00

1942. Stamps of 1929 surch **FRANCE LIBRE**, Cross of Lorraine and new value.
196 **3** 1ca. on 16ca. black & blue 60·00 40·00
210 **4** 1ca. on 6fa.6 black & violet 3·00 11·00
211 1ca. on 1r. blue and green 1·50 6·50
212 2ca. on 1r. blue and green 40 3·25
197 **3** 4ca. on 16ca. black & blue 60·00 40·00
213 **4** 4ca. on 6fa.6 black & violet 3·50 16·00
214 4ca. on 1r. blue and green 40 3·50
215 6ca. on 2r. black and red 35 3·25
198 **3** 10ca. on 16ca. black & blue 38·00 25·00
216 10ca. on 6fa.6 black & vio 80 4·00
217 10ca. on 2r. black and red 50 3·50
218 12ca. on 2r. black and red 35 3·25
199 15ca. on 16ca. black & blue 35·00 20·00
219 **4** 15ca. on 6f.6 black & violet 1·60 3·75
220 15ca. on 3r. lilac and black 30 3·25
221 16c. on 3r. lilac and black 30 3·25
200 **3** 1fa.3ca. on 16ca. black and blue 65·00 42·00
222 **4** 1fa.3 on 6fa.6 black & vio 2·50 5·50
223 1fa.3 on 3r. lilac and black 35 3·75
224 1fa.6 on 5r. black and red on green 50 3·75
225 1fa.12 on 5r. black and red on green 50 3·75
226 1fa.16 on 5r. black and red on green 50 3·50
201 **3** 2fa.9ca. on 16ca. black and blue 60·00 55·00

227 4 2fa.9 on 6fa.6 black & vio . . . 1·90 7·25
202 3 3fa.3ca. on 16ca. black and blue . . . . 42·00 28·00
228 3fa.3 on 6fa.6 black & vio . . . 3·00 8·25

20 Lotus Flowers

22 Apsara

1942. Free French issue. (a) Postage.
229 **20** 2ca. brown . . . . 15 2·75
230 3ca. blue . . . . 15 1·75
231 4ca. green . . . . 35 2·75
232 6ca. orange . . . . 35 1·90
233 12ca. green . . . . 1·40 1·90
234 16ca. purple . . . . 1·60 2·75
235 20ca. purple . . . . 1·50 2·25
236 1fa. red . . . . 1·60 2·00
237 1fa.18 black . . . . 1·40 1·25
238 6fa.6 blue . . . . 1·60 3·25
239 1r. violet . . . . 1·75 3·25
240 2r. bistre . . . . 1·90 3·25
241 3r. brown . . . . 1·75 3·50
242 5r. green . . . . 1·90 4·50

(b) Air. As T **63a** of Guadeloupe.
243 4fa. orange . . . . 75 3·25
244 1r. red . . . . 1·10 3·25
245 2r. purple . . . . 1·25 3·75
246 5r. black . . . . 1·25 3·75
247 8r. blue . . . . 1·90 5·00
248 10r. green . . . . 1·90 5·00

1944. Mutual Aid and Red Cross Funds. As T **58e** of Guadeloupe.
249 3fa.+1r.4fa. bistre . . . . . 1·10 3·50

1945. Eboue. As T **58f** of Guadeloupe.
250 3fa.8 black . . . . 20 3·00
251 5r.1fa.16 green . . . . 80 3·50

1946. Air. Victory. As T **63b** of Guadeloupe.
252 4fa. green . . . . 25 3·50

1946. Air. From Chad to the Rhine. As Nos. 226/31 of Cameroun.
253 2fa.12 brown . . . . 90 3·50
254 5fa. blue . . . . 90 3·50
255 7fa.12 violet . . . . 65 3·50
256 1r.2fa. green . . . . 1·00 3·75
257 1r.4fa.12 red . . . . 1·25 4·00
258 3r.1fa. purple . . . . 1·40 4·00

1948.
259 **22** 1ca. olive . . . . 15 2·75
260 2ca. brown . . . . 15 2·75
261 4ca. violet on cream . . . 15 2·50
262 A 6ca. orange . . . . 35 2·75
263 8ca. slate . . . . 55 2·50
264 10ca. green on green . . . 90 3·00
265 B 12ca. purple . . . . 90 2·25
266 15ca. blue . . . . 1·10 2·75
267 C 18ca. lake . . . . 3·00 3·50
268 B 1fa. violet on red . . . . 1·10 2·25
269 D 1fa.6 red . . . . 1·25 3·00
270 C 1fa.15 violet . . . . . . 3·25 4·00
271 D 2fa. green . . . . 1·10 65
272 2fa.2 blue on cream . . . 1·50 3·25
273 E 2fa.12 brown . . . . . . 1·75 3·00
274 3fa. red . . . . 1·75 1·10
275 C 4fa. olive . . . . 3·25 4·25
276 E 5fa. purple on red . . . . 1·40 2·25
277 F 7fa.12 brown . . . . . . 1·40 3·50
278 1r.2fa. black . . . . . . 3·00 6·00
279 1r.4fa.12c. green . . . . . 2·00 7·00
DESIGNS—As Type **22**: A, Dvarabalagar standing erect; B, Vishnu; C, Brahmin idol; D, Dvarabalagar with leg raised; E, Temple Guardian; F, One of the Tigoupalagar.

25 Douglas DC-4 and Bas-relief

1949. Air.
281 **25** 1r. red and yellow . . . . 4·75 5·25
282 – 2r. deep green & green . . 6·00 8·00
283 – 5r. purple and blue . . . . 18·00 12·50
DESIGNS—VERT: 2r. Wing and temple; 5r. Short-toed eagle and palm trees.

1949. Air. 75th Anniv of U.P.U. As T **39** of French Equatorial Africa.
284 6fa. red . . . . 3·00 11·00

1950. Colonial Welfare Fund. As T **40** of French Equatorial Africa.
285 1fa.+10ca. blue & grey . . . 1·90 3·50

1952. Centenary of Military Medal. As T **44** of French Equatorial Africa.
286 1fa. brown, yellow & green 2·75 5·50

1954. Air. 10th Anniv of Liberation. As T **46** of French Equatorial Africa.
287 1fa. purple and sepia . . . . 6·75 8·50

POSTAGE DUE STAMPS

1923. Postage Due stamps of France surch in figures and letters.
D88 **D 11** 4ca. on 20c. violet . . . 60 3·25
D89 6ca. on 10c. brown . . 95 3·25
D90 12ca. on 25c. red . . . 65 3·25
D91 15ca. on 20c. olive . . 85 3·50
D92 1fa. on 30c. orange . . 1·75 3·75
D93 1fa.6 on 30c. red . . . 5·25 15·00
D94 1fa.12 on 50c. purple 1·50 4·00
D95 1fa.15 on 5c. blue . . . 75 4·75
D96 1fa.16 on 5c. black . . 2·00 4·00
D97 3fa. on 1f. green . . . 2·50 4·50
D98 3fa.3 on 1f. brn on yell 90 4·50

D 14

D 24

1929.
D108 **D 14** 4ca. red . . . . 20 3·00
D109 6ca. blue . . . . . . 20 3·25
D110 12ca. green . . . . . 30 3·25
D111 1fa. brown . . . . . 1·10 3·50
D112 1fa.12 violet . . . . 1·40 3·50
D113 1fa.16 brown . . . . 1·90 3·50
D114 3fa. mauve . . . . . 2·50 4·25

1948.
D280 **D 24** 1ca. violet . . . . . . 15 2·75
D281 2ca. brown . . . . . 15 2·75
D282 6ca. green . . . . . 15 2·75
D283 12ca. red . . . . . . 20 2·75
D284 1fa. mauve . . . . . 70 2·75
D285 1fa.12 brown . . . . 1·25 3·25
D286 2fa. blue . . . . . . 1·25 3·50
D287 2fa.12 lake . . . . . 85 3·50
D288 5fa. green . . . . . 1·50 4·25
D289 1r. violet . . . . . . 1·60 5·00

FRENCH MOROCCO Pt. 6

Part of the Sultanate of Morocco, which was a French protectorate from 1912 until independence was granted on 2 March 1956. For issues before 1912 see French Post Offices in Morocco, and for stamps used in the International Zone see French Post Offices in Tangier.

100 centimes = 1 franc.

1914. Surcharged "Blanc", "Mouchon" and "Merson" key-types of French Post Offices in Morocco optd **PROTECTORAT FRANCAIS**.
40 A 1c. on 1c. grey 15 65
41 2c. on 2c. red 15 60
42 3c. on 3c. orange . . . . . 55 1·40
43 5c. on 5c. green 50 10
44 B 10c. on 10c. red 35 10
45 15c. on 15c. orange 45 10
46 20c. on 20c. red . . . . . 1·75 2·00
47 25c. on 25c. blue . . . . . 1·25 10
48 25c. on 25c. brown . . . . 1·50 10
49 30c. on 30c. brown . . . . 18·00 12·00
50 35c. on 35c. lilac . . . . . 2·25 1·25
51 C 40c. on 40c. red and blue . . 5·00 4·75
52 45c. on 45c. green & blue . . 40·00 50·00
53 50c. on 50c. brn & lilac . . 1·40 15
54 1p. on 1f. red and green . . 1·10 15
55 2p. on 2f. lilac and yellow 1·60 50
56 5p. on 5f. blue & yellow . . 6·50 7·75

1914. Surch **5c** and red cross. (a) No. 32 of French Post Offices in Morocco.
65 **5** 10c.+5c. on 10c. red . . . . 1·90 3·75

(b) As No. 43 but without previous surcharge.
62 **4** 5c.+5c. green . . . . 45 1·75

(c) No. 44.
59 **5** 10c.+5c. on 10c. red . . . . 2·00 5·00

1915. No. 352 of France optd **MAROC** and in Arabic.
63 **20** 10c.+5c. red . . . . 2·25 5·50

13

1915. Optd **PROTECTORAT FRANCAIS**.
64 **13** 10c.+5c. red . . . . 1·75 2·25

15 Tower of Hassan, Rabat

16 Fez

1917.
76 **15** 1c. black . . . . 50 1·60
123 1c. green 25 35
124 2c. purple 25 35
125 3c. brown 10 55
79 **16** 5c. green 20 10
126 5c. yellow 25 10
80 10c. red 20 10
127 10c. green 35 10
128 15c. grey 65 45
129 A 20c. purple 45 10
131 25c. blue 25 10
84 30c. lilac . . . . 4·25 4·50
132 30c. red 25 10
133 30c. blue 40 15
85 B 35c. orange . . . . . . 3·00 4·00
134 35c. purple . . . . 60 1·75
86 40c. blue 80 30
135 40c. orange 25 10
136 45c. green 35 70
88 C 50c. brown . . . . 6·00 2·75
137 50c. blue . . . . 1·40 90
138 B 50c. green . . . . 1·60 10
139 C 60c. mauve 30 45
140a 75c. purple 35 15
89 1f. grey . . . . 6·50 6·50
141 1f. brown 30 80
142 1f.05 brown . . . . . . 1·40 2·25
143 1f.40 pink 30 65
144 1f.50 blue 80 10
145 D 2f. brown 60 55
146 3f. red . . . . 1·75 25
147 5f. green . . . . 85 1·75
148 10f. brown . . . . 3·25 5·50
DESIGNS—VERT: A, Chella; B, Marrakesh. Horiz: C, Meknes; D, Volubilis.

22 Breguet 14T Biplane over Casablanca

1922. Air.
112 **22** 5c. orange 55 40
113 25c. blue . . . . 60 1·10
114 50c. blue 45 45
115 75c. blue . . . . 75·00 9·00
116 75c. green . . . . 1·10 65
117 80c. brown 20 75
118 1f. red . . . . 1·10 15
119 1f.40 red . . . . 60 2·25
120 1f.90 blue . . . . 2·25 4·00
121 2f. violet . . . . 2·25 1·40
122 3f. black . . . . 1·50 2·25

23 Ploughing with Camel and Donkey

1928. Air. Flood Relief.
149 – 5c. blue . . . . 4·25 7·50
150 **23** 25c. orange . . . . 4·75 7·25
151 – 50c. red . . . . 3·75 6·50
152 – 75c. brown . . . . 3·25 7·75
153 – 80c. green . . . . 4·00 7·00
154 – 1f. orange . . . . 3·75 7·75
155 – 1f.50 blue . . . . 3·50 7·75
156 – 2f. brown . . . . 3·50 7·75
157 – 3f. purple . . . . 4·00 3·75
158 – 5f. black . . . . 3·75 7·75
DESIGNS: 5c. Moorish tribesmen; 50c. Caravan nearing Safi; 75c. Walls of Marrakesh; 80c. Sheep grazing at Azrou; 1f. Gateway at Fez; 1f.50, Aerial view of Tangier; 2f. Aerial view of Casablanca; 3f. White storks at Rabat; 5f. "La Hedia", a Moorish entertainment.

1930. Stamps of 1917 surch.
163 B 15c. on 40c. orange 35 90
164 A 25c. on 30c. blue . . . . . 2·50 3·50
165 C 50c. on 60c. mauve 35 10
166 1f. on 1f.40 pink . . . . . 2·50 1·40

1931. Air. Surch.
167 **22** 1f. on 1f.40 red 65 55
168 1f.50 on 1f.90 blue . . . . 1·75 2·75

27 Sultan's Palace, Tangier

28 Saadian Tombs, Marrakesh

1933.
169 **27** 1c. black 40 10
170 2c. mauve . . . . 45 1·25
171 – 3c. brown . . . . 25 1·90
172 – 5c. lake 35 45
173 – 10c. green 25 10
174 – 15c. black 55 10
175 – 20c. purple . . . . 1·75 10
176 – 25c. blue . . . . 1·40 10
177 – 30c. green . . . . 1·40 10
178 – 40c. sepia 35 10
179 – 45c. purple . . . . 40 1·25
180 – 50c. green . . . . 1·75 10
181 – 65c. red 35 10
182 – 75c. purple 25 10
183 – 90c. red 65 25
184 – 1f. brown . . . . 1·00 10
185 – 1f.25 black 60 95
186 – 1f.50 blue . . . . 1·25 10
187 – 1f.75 green 55 10
188 – 2f. brown . . . . 2·50 10
189 – 3f. red . . . . 45·00 3·75
190 **28** 5f. lake . . . . 1·50 75
191 10f. black . . . . 4·75 4·00
192 20f. grey . . . . 4·25 11·50
DESIGNS—HORIZ: 3c., 5c. Agadir Bay; 10c. to 20c. G.P.O., Casablanca; 25c. to 40c. Moulay Idriss; 45c. to 65c. Rabat; 1f.50 to 3f. Quarzazat. VERT: 75c. to 1f.25, Attarine College, Fez.

29 Hassan Tower, Rabat

30 Marshal Lyautey

1933. Air.
193 **29** 50c. blue . . . . 2·10 2·50
194 80c. brown . . . . 2·10 50
195 1f.50 lake . . . . 1·25 40
196 – 2f.50 red . . . . 2·25 1·25
197 – 5f. violet . . . . 3·50 1·75
198 – 10f. green . . . . 2·10 3·25
DESIGN: 2f.50 to 10f. Casablanca.

1935. Lyautey Memorial Fund.
199 **30** 50c.+50c. red (postage) . . 10·00 16·00
200 1f.+1f. green . . . . . . 7·50 16·00
201 5f.+5f. brown . . . . . . 35·00 65·00

202 – 1f.50+1f.50 blue (air) . . . 60·00 £100
DESIGN—HORIZ: 1f.50, Lyautey in profile.

1938. Child Welfare Fund. Stamps of 1933 surch **O.S.E.** and premium.
203 **27** 2c.+2c. mauve (postage) . . 1·75 7·50
204 – 3c.+3c. brown . . . . . . 1·60 7·50
205 – 20c.+20c. purple . . . . . 1·75 7·50
206 – 40c.+40c. sepia . . . . . 1·60 7·50
207 – 65c.+65c. red . . . . . . 3·50 10·50
208 – 1f.25+1f.25 black . . . . . 1·75 7·50
209 – 2f.+2f. brown . . . . . . 1·75 7·50
210 **28** 5f.+5f. lake . . . . 1·75 7·50

211 **29** 50c.+50c. blue (air) . . . . 2·75 7·25
212 – 10f.+10f. green . . . . . . 2·75 7·50

1939. No. 180 surch **40c**.
213 40c. on 50c. green . . . . . 2·00 30

34 Mosque at Sale

36 Shepherd and Arganier Trees

42 Dewoitine D-338 Trimotor over Morocco

1939.
214 **34** 1c. mauve (postage) . . . 30 1·50
215 A 2c. green . . . . 30 1·75
216 3c. blue . . . . 35 1·50
217 **34** 5c. green 20 60
218 A 10c. purple 10 10
219 B 15c. green . . . . . . 30 1·50
220 20c. brown 10 15
221 **36** 30c. blue 10 10
222 40c. brown 30 20
223 45c. green . . . . . . 40 2·50
224 E 50c. red . . . . . . 1·90 2·00
293 50c. green 60 10
226 60c. blue 60 80
227 60c. brown 30 10
228 C 70c. violet 25 25
229 F 75c. green . . . . . . 25 3·00
230 80c. blue 10 45
231 80c. green . . . . . . 30 1·25
232 E 90c. blue . . . . . . 60 1·10
233 B 1f. brown 55 10
234 F 1f.20 mauve . . . . . 30 2·25
295 1f.20 brown 40 15
235 1f.25 red . . . . . . 35 2·25
296 A 1f.30 blue . . . . . . 1·25 2·50
236 F 1f.40 purple . . . . . 60 2·50
238 E 1f.50 pink 40 75
297 1f.50 red 20 25
239 D 2f. green 55 10
240 2f.25 blue 50 65
241 **34** 2f.40 red 40 50
242 2f.50 red 35 85
243 2f.50 blue 30 70
299 D 3f. brown 20 10
300 **36** 3f.50 red 85 45
245 **34** 4f. blue 50 50
246 F 4f.50 green 10 20
301 C 4f.50 mauve 65 30
302 5f. blue 40 45
303 F 6f. blue 10 10
248 C 10f. red . . . . . . 1·75 1·60
305 15f. green . . . . . . 1·10 45
306 20f. purple . . . . . . 1·75 3·50
307 25f. brown . . . . . . 1·25 1·25
DESIGNS—VERT: A, Mosque at Sefrou; B,Horseman and Cedar tree; C, Scimitar oryxes; D, Fez. HORIZ: E, Ramparts at Sale; F, Draa Valley.

251 G 80c. green (air) . . . . . 50 1·10
252 1f. brown 30 80
253 **42** 1f.90 blue . . . . . . 20 1·40
254 2f. purple 20 55
255 3f. brown 40 20
256 G 5f. violet . . . . . . 65 2·75
257 **42** 10f. blue . . . . . . 80 1·75
DESIGN—VERT: G, Storks and Mosque at Chella.

1940. No. 181 surch **35c.**
258a 35c. on 65c. red . . . . . . 2·25 3·50

1942. French Child Refugees in Morocco Fund. Types of 1939 surch **Enfants de France au Maroc** and premium.
259 **36** 45c.+2f. green . . . . . 2·40 7·50
260 E 90c.+4f. blue . . . . . 4·00 7·00
261 F 1f.25+6f. red . . . . . 2·40 7·00
262 **34** 2f.50+8f. red . . . . . 2·40 7·50

45 "La Marseillaise"

46 Tower of Hassan

1943.
263 **45** 1f.50 blue . . . . 1·90 3·25

1943.
264 **46** 10c. lilac 10 75
265 30c. blue . . . . 10 2·25
266 40c. red 10 10
267 50c. green 10 10
268 60c. brown 10 10
269 70c. lilac 15 10
270 80c. green 10 10
271 1f. red 10 15
272 1f.20 violet 10 10
273 1f.50 red 10 10
274 2f. green . . . . . . 30 1·25
275 2f.40 red 25 90
276 3f. brown 20 60
277 4f. blue 35 10
278 4f.50 black 25 95
279 5f. blue 30 10
280 10f. brown 30 75
281 15f. green 10 10
282 20f. purple 40 25

47 Sud Est Languedoc over Desert

49 Potez 56 over Minarets

1944. Air.
283 **47** 50c. green . . . . 70 1·10
284 2f. blue 35 80
285 5f. red 30 10
286 10f. violet 25 20
287 50f. black . . . . . . 35 2·75
288 100f. blue and red . . . . 5·00 15·00

1944. Air. Mutual Aid Fund. Surch **ENTR'AIDE FRANCAISE +98F 50.**
289 **47** 1f.50+98f.50 red & bl . . . 2·00 3·75

1945. Air.
290 **49** 50f. brown . . . . 1·75 3·00

1945. Anti-tuberculosis Fund. No. 239 surch **AIDEZ LES TUBERCULEUX + 1f.**
308 D 2f.+1f. green . . . . . . 40 2·75

51 Mausoleum

54 Marshal Lyautey Statue, Casablanca

1945. Solidarity Fund. Marshal Lyautey's Mausoleum.
309a **51** 2f.+3f. blue . . . . . . 95 1·25

1946. No. 308 surch **3f** and bars.
310 D 3f. on 2f.+1f. green . . . . 50 2·00

1946. Air. 6th Anniv of Gen. De Gaulle's Call to Arms. Surch **+ 5 F 18 Juin 1940 18 Juin 1946.**
311 **47** 5f.+5f. red . . . . . . 1·40 2·25

1946. Solidarity Fund.
312 **54** 2f.+10f. black (postage) . . 95 3·50
313 3f.+15f. red . . . . . . 35 3·50
314 10f.+20f. blue . . . . . . 35 4·00
315 10f.+30f. green (air) . . . . 1·00 4·00

1947. Stamp Day. No. 301 surch **JOURNEE DU TIMBRE 1947 +5F50.**
316 C 4f.50+5f.50 mauve . . . . 2·50 3·25

56 Coastline and Symbols of Prosperity

1947. 25th Anniv of Sherifian Phosphates Office.
317 **56** 3f.50+5f.50 green . . . . . 1·25 3·25

57 The Terraces

58 Coastal Fortress

59 Barracks on the Mountains

65 La Medina Barracks

1947. (a) Postage.
318 **57** 10c. brown . . . . 10 2·00
319 30c. red . . . . 10 2·75
320 30c. violet . . . . . . 10 2·75
321 50c. blue 10 15
322 60c. purple . . . . . . 10 2·25
323 **58** 1f. black 10 10
324 1f.50 blue 15 40
325 **59** 2f. green 45 30
325a **58** 2f. purple . . . . . . 2·00 30
326 **59** 3f. lake 40 10
327 – 4f. violet . . . . . . 1·10 50
328 – 4f. green . . . . . . 1·40 1·60
329 – 5f. green 25 90
329a – 5f. green 60 20
330 – 6f. red 60 10
330a – 8f. orange 50 60
331 – 10f. blue . . . . . . 1·10 15
332a – 10f. red . . . . . . 1·25 15
333 **58** 12f. red 90 20
334 – 15f. green . . . . . . 70 1·25
334a – 15f. red 50 20
335 – 18f. blue 95 30
336 – 20f. red 10 20
337 – 25f. violet . . . . . . 90 1·50
337a – 25f. blue 45 30
337b – 25f. violet . . . . . . 2·50 3·50
337c – 30f. blue 95 65
337d – 35f. brown . . . . . . 1·00 55
337e – 50f. slate . . . . . . 1·75 10
DESIGNS—HORIZ: 4f., 6f. Marrakesh; 5f. (No. 329), 8f., 10f. blue, The Gardens, Fez; 5f. (No. 329a) Fortified oasis; 15f. red, 25f. (Nos. 337a/b), Walled city; 30f., 35f., 50f. Todra Valley. VERT: 10f. red, 15f. green, 18f., 20f., 25f. (No. 337) Barracks in oasis.

(b) Air.
338 – 9f. red . . . . 1·25 10
339 – 40f. blue . . . . . . 1·25 35
340 – 50f. purple . . . . . . 1·40 20
341 **65** 100f. blue . . . . . . 1·10 1·40
342 200f. red . . . . . . 1·50 1·10
342a – 300f. violet . . . . . . 6·75 8·75
DESIGNS—VERT: 9, 40, 50f. Sud Est Languedoc airplane over Moulay Idriss. HORIZ: 300f. Oudayas Kasbah, Rabat.

67 "Energy"

68 Marshal Lyautey's Mausoleum

1947. Solidarity Fund. Inscr "SOLIDARITE 1947".
343 **67** 6f.+9f. red (postage) . . . 90 4·00
344 – 10f.+20f. blue . . . . . 50 4·25
345 – 9f.+16f. green (air) . . . . 2·50 4·50
346 – 20f.+35f. brown . . . . . 1·60 4·00
DESIGNS—VERT: 10f. Red Cross unit ("Health"). HORIZ: 9f. Freighter at quayside and Sud Est Languedoc airplane ("Supplies"); 20f. Sud Est Languedoc airplane over landscape ("Agriculture").

1948. Stamp Day. View of Meknes (as No. 88) inscr "JOURNEE DU TIMBRE 1948" below central vignette.
347 6f.+4f. brown . . . . 30 3·00

1948. Air. Lyautey Exhibition, Paris.
348 **68** 10f.+25f. green . . . . . 1·75 3·25

69 P.T.T. Clubhouse, Ifrane

1948. Air. P.T.T. Employees' Holiday Camp Fund.
349 **69** 6f.+34f. green . . . . . 1·75 4·00
350 9f.+51f. red . . . . . . 1·60 4·00

70 "Dunkerque" (battleship) and Coastline

1948. Naval Charities.
351 **70** 6f.+9f. violet . . . . . . 1·60 3·75

1948. Stamp of 1939 surch **8f.**
352 C 8f. on 20f. purple (No. 306) 15 2·25

72 Wheat and View of Meknes

1949. Solidarity Fund. Inscr "SOLIDARITE 1948".
353 **72** 1f.+2f. orange (postage) . . 25 3·25
354 – 2f.+5f. red . . . . . . 25 3·50
355 – 3f.+7f. blue . . . . . . 30 3·50
356 – 5f.+10f. purple . . . . . 30 3·50
MS356a 120 × 96 mm. Nos. 353/6 16·00 30·00

357 – 5f.+5f. green (air) . . . . 70 3·50
358 – 6f.+9f. red . . . . . . 60 3·50
359 – 9f.+16f. brown . . . . . 50 3·50
360 – 15f.+25f. slate . . . . . 70 3·50
MS360a 96 × 120 mm. Nos. 357/60 13·50 30·00
DESIGNS—HORIZ: (postage): 2f. Olive grove and Taroudant; 3f. Trawling; 5f. Plums and Aguedal Gardens, Marrakesh. VERT: (air): Airplane over—5f. Agadir; 6f. Fez; 9f. Atlas Mountains; 15f. Draa Valley.

74 Gazelle Hunter

75 Soldiers with Flag

1949. Stamp Day and 50th Anniv of Mazagan-Marrakesh Local Postage Stamp.
361 **74** 10f.+5f. red and purple . . 1·60 3·75

1949. Army Welfare Fund.
362 **75** 10f.+10f. red . . . . . . 95 3·50

76 Oudayas Gate, Rabat

77 Nejjarine Fountain, Fez

78 Gardens at Meknes

1949.
363 **76** 10c. black . . . . 10 2·50
364 50c. lake . . . . 15 2·75
365 1f. violet 20 10
366 **77** 2f. red 10 10
367 3f. blue 10 10
368 5f. green 10 10
369 **78** 8f. green 10 10
370 10f. red 10 10

79 Post Office, Meknes

80 Breguet 14T Biplane over Globe

1949. 75th Anniv of U.P.U.
371 **79** 5f. green . . . . 1·75 2·50
372 15f. red . . . . 1·60 3·75
373 25f. blue . . . . 1·60 4·00

1950. Air. Stamp Day and 25th Anniv of First Mail Flight from Casablanca to Dakar.
374 **80** 15f.+10f. blue, grn & red . . 1·25 4·50

81 Carpets

83 Ruins of Sala-Colonia (Chella)

1950. Solidarity Fund. Inscr "SOLIDARITE 1949".
375 **81** 1f.+2f. red (postage) . . . 40 4·00
376 – 2f.+5f. blue . . . . . . 40 3·75
377 – 3f.+7f. violet . . . . . . 40 3·75
378 – 5f.+10f. brown . . . . . 55 4·00
MS378a 96 × 120 mm. Nos. 375/8 13·00 32·00

379 – 5f.+5f. blue (air) . . . . . 70 3·75
380 – 6f.+9f. green . . . . . . 40 3·50
381 – 9f.+16f. brown . . . . . 35 3·75
382 – 15f.+25f. brown . . . . . 40 3·50
MS382a 120 × 96 mm. Nos. 379/82 16·00 32·00
DESIGNS—VERT: Postage: 2f. Pottery; 3f. Books; 5f. Copperware. HORIZ: Air—(Maps of Morocco): 5f. N.W.; 6f. N.E.; 9f. S.W.; 15f. S.E.

1950. Army Welfare Fund. Inscr "OUVRES SOCIALES DE L'ARMEE".
383 **83** 10f.+10f. red (postage) . . 55 3·25
384 15f.+15f. slate . . . . . . 55 3·50
385 – 10f.+10f. sepia (air) . . . . 2·00 3·75
386 – 15f.+15f. green . . . . . 2·25 3·75

DESIGN: 10f., 15f. Triumphal Arch of Caracalla, Volubilis.

1950. Stamps of 1939 and 1947 surch.

387	F	1f. on 1f.20 brn (No. 295)	10	15
388	A	1f. on 1f.30 blue (No. 296)	10	15
389	–	5f. on 6f. red (No. 330)	10	10

84 General Leclerc

85 New Hospital, Meknes

1951. Gen. Leclerc Monument, Casablanca.

390	**84**	10f. green (postage)	85	3·50
391		15f. red	65	3·75
392		25f. blue	75	4·00
393		50f. violet (air)	1·90	4·25

1951. Solidarity Fund. Inscr "SOLIDARITE 1950".

394	–	10f. violet & blue (postage)	25	3·00
395	**85**	15f. brown and green	25	3·50
396	–	25f. blue and brown	20	2·40
397	–	50f. green & violet (air)	65	2·75

DESIGNS: 10f. Loustau Hospital, Oujda; 25f. New Hospital, Rabat; 50f. Sanatorium, Ben Smine.

86 Fountain and Doves

87 Karaouine Mosque, Fez

88 Old Moroccan Courtyard

1951.

398	**86**	5f. purple (A)	10	10
434		5f. purple (B)	2·50	2·25
399	**87**	6f. green	45	1·25
400	**86**	8f. brown	15	25
401	**87**	10f. red	1·25	15
402		12f. blue	1·10	10
403	–	15f. brown (A)	70	30
404	–	15f. brown (B)	30	10
405	–	15f. violet (A)	1·25	15
435	–	15f. violet (B)	1·60	1·50
406	**86**	15f. green	1·40	15
407	–	18f. red	2·50	2·75
408	**88**	20f. blue	85	20

DESIGNS—As Type **86/7**: 15f. brown (2) Oudayas Courtyard; 15f. violet (2), 18f. Oudayas Point, Rabat.

Two types each of: 5f. (A) 18 × 22 mm, (B) 17 × 21½ mm: 15f. brown (A) "MAROC" not in tablet, (B) "MAROC" in white tablet; 15f. violet (A) 18 × 22½ mm, (B) 16½ × 21½ mm.

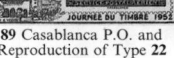

89 Casablanca P.O. and Reproduction of Type **22**

90 Saadian Capital

1952. Air. Stamp Day and 30th Anniv of First Moroccan Air Stamps.

409	**89**	15f.+5f. blue & brown	4·50	7·50

1952. Solidarity Fund. Inscr "SOLIDARITE 1951". Column capitals as T **90**.

410	–	15f. blue (Omeiyad)	80	4·50
411	–	20f. red (Almohad)	80	4·25
412	–	25f. violet (Merinid)	70	3·75
413	**90**	50f. green	70	3·00

91 Ramparts of Chella, Rabat

92 War Memorial, Casablanca

1952. Air.

414	**91**	10f. green	1·25	1·25
415	–	40f. red	1·25	20
416	–	100f. brown	1·40	30
417	–	200f. violet	2·75	3·25

DESIGN: Lockheed Constellation over—HORIZ: 40f. Marrakesh. VERT: 100f. Fort in Anti-Atlas Mts.; 200f. Fez.

1952. Centenary of Military Medal.

418	**92**	15f. brown, yellow & green	50	3·75

93 Jewellery from Fez

94 Arab Courier and Scribe

1953. Solidarity Fund. Inscr "SOLIDARITE 1952".

419	–	15f. red (postage)	85	4·25
420	**93**	20f. brown	1·10	3·50
421	–	25f. blue	80	3·50
422	–	50f. green (air)	2·00	4·25

DESIGNS: 15f. Daggers from S. Morocco; 25f. Jewellery from Anti-Atlas; 50f. Jewellery from N. Morocco.

1953. Stamp Day.

423	**94**	15f. purple	1·10	4·00

95 Bine el Ouidane Barrage

96 Mogador Battlements

1953. Inauguration of Barrage.

424	**95**	15f. blue	60	3·75
424a		15f. blue and brown	50	50

1953. Army Welfare Fund.

425	**96**	15f. green	75	3·50
426	–	30f. brown	40	3·50

DESIGN: 30f. Moorish horsemen.

1954. Nos. 324 and 335 surch.

427	**58**	1f. on 1f.50 blue	10	20
428	–	15f. on 18f. blue	20	1·75

98 Meknes

1954. Air. Solidarity Fund. Inscr "1953".

429	**98**	10f. olive	2·50	3·00
430	–	20f. violet (Rabat)	2·25	4·00
431	–	40f. brn (Casablanca)	2·25	4·00
432	–	50f. green (Fedala)	1·90	2·40

99 Mail Van and Postmen

1954. Stamp Day.

433	**99**	15f. green	1·60	3·50

100 Schooner and Destroyer

101 Marshal Lyautey at Khenifra

1954. Air. Naval Welfare Fund.

436	**100**	15f. green	2·50	2·25
437		30f. blue	1·60	1·50

1954. Birth Centenary of Marshal Lyautey.

438	–	5f. blue	2·50	4·25
439	**101**	15f. green	2·25	4·25
440	–	30f. lake	1·75	4·50
441	–	50f. brown	1·75	3·75

DESIGNS—HORIZ: 5f. Lyautey receiving Moroccan notables at Rabat. VERT: 30f. Lyautey in dockyards; 50f. Portrait of Lyautey (after Laszlo).

102 Moroccan Scholar

103 Mazagan P.O.

1955. Solidarity Fund.

442	–	5f. blue	35	1·90
443	**102**	15f. red	40	3·50
444	–	30f. brown	55	1·75
445	–	50f. green	50	2·75

DESIGNS—HORIZ: 5f. French and Moroccan schoolchildren; 30f. Muslim School, Camp-Boulhaut. VERT: 50f. Moulay Idriss College, Fez.

1955. Day of the Stamp.

446	**103**	15f. red	1·40	3·50

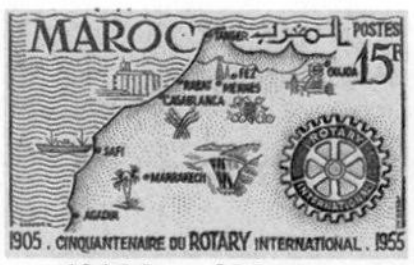

104 Map of Morocco

105 Bab el Mrissa, Sale

106 Mahakma, Casablanca

107 Bou Regreg Estuary

1955. 50th Anniv of Rotary International.

447	**104**	15f. blue and brown	60	4·25

1955.

448	**105**	50c. purple	10	1·75
449		1f. blue	10	10
450		2f. purple	10	10
451		3f. blue	30	20
452	–	5f. red	1·25	20
453	–	6f. green	55	50
454	–	8f. brown	1·60	3·00
455	–	10f. purple	45	50
456	–	12f. turquoise	55	25
457	–	15f. lake	1·50	10
458	**106**	18f. myrtle	55	60
459		20f. lake	20	10
460	–	25f. blue	1·75	65
461	–	30f. green	1·10	25
462	–	40f. red	35	15
463	–	50f. sepia	60	20
464	–	75f. turquoise	1·25	80

DESIGNS—As Type **105**: 5f., 6f., 8f. Bab Chorfa, Fez; 10f., 12f., 15f. Chella Minaret, Rabat. As Type **106**—HORIZ: 25f. Coastal castle, Safi; 30f. Menara, Marrakesh; 40f. Tafraout; 50f. Portuguese cistern, Mazagan. VERT: 75f. Oudaya gardens, Rabat.

1955. Air.

465	–	100f. violet	3·25	35
466	**107**	200f. red	4·25	75
467	–	500f. blue	4·25	2·75

DESIGNS—VERT: 100f. Village in the Anti-Atlas. HORIZ: 500f. Ksar es Souk.

PARCEL POST STAMPS

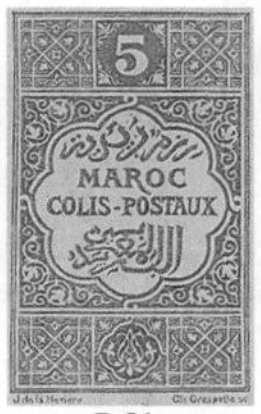

P 21

1917.

P101	P **21**	5c. green	35	1·40
P102		10c. red	40	1·25
P103		20c. brown	1·10	1·60
P104		25c. blue	1·10	80
P105		40c. brown	2·25	1·40
P106		50c. red	3·00	1·40
P107		75c. grey	2·75	2·25
P108		1f. blue	3·50	80
P109		2f. grey	3·00	35
P110		5f. violet	4·25	55
P111		10f. black	6·50	60

POSTAGE DUE STAMPS

1915. Postage Due stamps of France surch with figure and Arabic word, and further optd **PROTECTORAT FRANCAIS**.

D66	D **11**	1c. on 1c. black	95	2·40
D67		5c. on 5c. blue	1·10	2·75
D68		10c. on 10c. brown	2·75	3·50
D69		20c. on 20c. green	1·50	2·50
D70		30c. on 30c. red	1·90	6·75
D71		50c. on 50c. purple	1·75	3·75

1915. Postage Due stamps of France with surch and optd as above.

D72	D **19**	1c. on 1c. olive	70	2·75
D73		10c. on 10c. violet	2·50	3·50
D74		30c. on 30c. bistre	1·90	4·00
D75		50c. on 50c. red	2·10	3·75

D 21

1917.

D 93	D **21**	1c. black	10	75
D 94		5c. blue	10	1·75
D 95		10c. brown	10	20
D 96		20c. green	50	25
D 97		30c. red	20	15
D 98		50c. brown	10	10
D 99		1f. purple on yellow	15	20
D308		1f. red	85	3·00
D100		2f. violet	20	20
D310		3f. blue	85	2·00
D311		4f. orange	1·75	2·25
D312		5f. green	1·00	25
D313		10f. bistre	1·40	15
D314		20f. red	2·75	2·00
D315		30f. brown	3·00	4·00

1944. Surch.

D289	D **21**	50c. on 30c. red	4·25	7·50
D290		1f. on 10c. brown	4·75	7·50
D291		3f. on 10c. brown	12·00	18·00

For later issues see **MOROCCO**.

FRENCH OCCUPATION OF HUNGARY Pt. 2

ARAD

Arad later became part of Rumania.

100 filler = 1 korona.

1919. Stamps of Hungary Optd **Occupation francaise** or surch also. (a) War Charity stamps of 1916.

1	**20**	11f. (+2f.) red	22·00	22·00
2	–	15f. (+2f.) lilac	1·60	1·60
3	**22**	40f. (+2f.) red	2·25	2·25

(b) Harvesters and Parliament Types.

4	**18**	2f. brown	95	85
5		3f. red	85	85
6		5f. green	1·60	1·60
7		6f. blue	95	95
8		10f. red	1·10	1·10
9		15f. purple	95	95
10		15f. violet (No. 244)	45·00	45·00
11		20f. brown	9·00	9·00
12		35f. brown	23·00	23·00
13		40f. green	7·50	78·50
14		45 on 2f. brown	1·60	1·60
15a		45 on 3f. red	19·00	
16		50 on 3f. red	1·60	1·60
18	**19**	50f. purple	1·40	1·40
19		75f. blue	1·10	1·10
20		80f. green	1·25	1·25
21		1k. red	4·25	4·25
22		2k. brown	1·40	1·40
23		3k. grey and violet	4·00	4·00
24		5k. brown	4·00	4·00
25		10k. mauve and brown	45·00	45·00

(c) Charles and Zita stamps.

26	**27**	10f. red	12·50	12·50
27		20f. brown	85	85
28		25f. blue	1·10	1·10
29	**28**	40f. green	1·25	1·25

(d) Harvester stamps inscr "MAGYAR POSTA".

30	**18**	5f. green	10·00	10·00
31		10f. red	1·40	1·40
32		20f. brown	7·00	7·00

(e) Stamps of 1919 optd **KOZTARSASAG**. (i) Harvesters and Parliament Types.

33	**18**	2f. brown	1·10	1·10
34		3f. red	3·00	3·00
35		4f. grey	1·10	1·10
36		5f. green	85	85
37		6f. blue	2·50	2·50
38		10f. red	23·00	23·00
39		20f. brown	4·00	4·00
40		40f. green	1·10	1·10
41	**19**	1k. red	1·10	1·10
42		3k. grey and violet	4·00	4·00
43		10(k)on 1k. red	4·00	4·00

(ii) Charles and Zita stamps.

44	**27**	25f. blue	1·10	1·10
45	**28**	40f. green	21·00	21·00
46		50f. violet	1·10	1·10

EXPRESS LETTER STAMP

1919. No. E245 optd **Occupation francaise**.
E48 E **18** 2f. green and red . . . 85 85

NEWSPAPER STAMP

1919. No. N136 optd **Occupation francaise**.
N47 N **9** (2f.) orange 85 85

POSTAGE DUE STAMPS

1919. (a) No. D191 of Hungary optd **Occupation francaise**.
D49 D **9** 2f. red and green . . . . 1·25 1·25
D50 10f. red and green . . . 1·10 1·10
D51 12f. red and green . . . 10·00 10·50
D52 15f. red and green . . . 10·00 10·50
D53 20f. red and green . . . 6·00 7·00

(b) No. N47 of Arad surch **Porto** and new value.
D54 N **9** 12 on (2f.) orange . . . 2·40 2·40
D55 15 on (2f.) orange . . . 2·40 2·40
D56 30 on (2f.) orange . . . 2·40 2·40
D57 50 on (2f.) orange . . . 2·40 2·40
D58 100 on (2f.) orange . . . 2·40 2·40

FRENCH POLYNESIA Pt. 6

The French Settlements in the South Pacific, formerly called Oceanic Settlements.

100 centimes = 1 franc.

1 Girl playing Guitar

2 Polynesian

3 "The Women of Tahiti" (after Gauguin)

1958.
1 **1** 10c. brn, grn & turq (postage) . . . . 40 3·00
2 25c. purple, red and green . . 20 2·75
3 1f. sepia, red and blue . . 1·90 1·25
4 2f. violet, choc & brown . . 3·00 2·50
5 **2** 4f. myrtle, green & yellow . . 3·00 2·00
6 – 5f. brown, violet & green . . 4·00 3·25
7 **2** 7f. brown, green & orange . . 4·25 3·50
8 9f. purple, green & orange . . 5·50 3·75
9 – 10f. red, blue and brown . . 8·00 4·00
10 – 16f. multicoloured . . . . . 9·00 4·00
11 – 17f. brown, blue & turquoise 9·75 2·25
12 – 20f. brown, violet & pink . . 15·00 3·50
13 – 13f. brn, grn & drab (air) . . 9·50 5·75
14 **3** 50f. multicoloured . . . . . 9·75 8·25
15 – 100f. multicoloured . . . . . 14·50 10·50
16 – 200f. slate and lilac . . . . . 36·00 23·00
DESIGNS: As Types **1/2**—VERT: 5f. Spearfishing; 10f., 20f. Polynesian girl on beach. HORIZ: 16f. Post Office, Papeete; 17f. Tahitian dancers. As Type **3**—VERT: 13f. Mother-of-pearl engraver; 100f. "The White Horse" (after Gauguin). HORIZ: 200f. Night-fishing off Moorea.

1958. 10th Anniv of Declaration of Human Rights. As T **57** of French Equatorial Africa.
17 7f. grey and blue . . . . . . 6·25 14·00

1959. Tropical Flora. As T **56** of French Equatorial Africa. Multicoloured.
18 4f. "Artocarpus" . . . . . . 3·00 6·00

7 Douglas DC-8 over Papeete Airport

1960. Air. Inauguration of Papeete Airport.
19 **7** 13f. violet, purple & green . . 3·75 3·25

8 "Saraca indica"

1962. Flowers.
20 15f. Type **8** . . . . 12·50 17·00
21 25f. Hibiscus . . . . 14·00 23·00

9 Pacific Map and Palms

1962. 5th South Pacific Conference, Pago-Pago.
22 **9** 20f. multicoloured . . . . . 10·50 10·00

10 "Telstar" Satellite

1962. Air. 1st Trans-Atlantic T.V. Satellite Link.
23 **10** 50f. blue, brown and purple 9·50 8·75

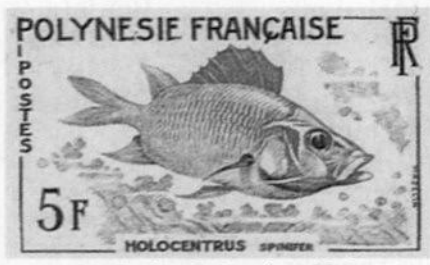

11 Spined Squirrelfish

1962. Fishes. Multicoloured.
24 5f. Type **11** . . . . 5·50 2·50
25 10f. Teardrop butterflyfish . . 5·50 3·25
26 30f. Radial lionfish . . . . . 10·00 6·25
27 40f. Long-horned cowfish . . 19·00 12·00

12 Football

1962. 1st South Pacific Games, Suva, Fiji.
28 **12** 20f. brown and blue . . . . 9·50 12·00
29 – 50f. blue and red . . . . . 12·50 12·00
DESIGN: 50f. Throwing the javelin.

13 Centenary Emblem

14 Globe and Scales of Justice

1963. Centenary of Red Cross.
30 **13** 15f. red, grey and purple . . 10·50 16·00

1963. 15th Anniv of Declaration of Human Rights.
31 **14** 7f. violet and green . . . . 11·50 8·75

1964. "PHILATEC 1964" International Stamp Exhibition, Paris. As T **528** of France.
32 25f. red, black and green . . . 13·50 17·00

16 Dancer

17 Tahitian Volunteers

1964. Tahitian Dancers.
33 **16** 1f. multicoloured (postage) 90 75
34 3f. orange, sepia & purple 1·00 1·10
35 – 15f. multicoloured (air) . . 4·00 2·50
DESIGN—VERT: (27 × 46½ mm): 15f. Dancer in full costume.

1964. Polynesia's War Effort in Second World War. Multicoloured.
36 5f. Type **17** (postage) . . . . 8·00 8·75
37 16f. Badges and map of Tahiti (48 × 27 mm) (air) . . . . . 12·50 12·50

18 Tuamotu Lagoon (after J. D. Lajoux)

1964. Landscapes. Multicoloured.
38 2f. Type **18** (postage) . . . . 1·75 95
39 4f. Bora-Bora (after Lajoux) 1·40 1·10
40 7f. Papeete (after A. Sylvain) 2·50 1·75
41 8f. Marquesas (Gauguin's grave) . . . . 2·75 1·75
42 20f. Gambier (after Mazellier) 5·50 2·25
43 23f. Moorea (after Sylvain) (48 × 27 mm) (air) . . . . . 10·00 4·25

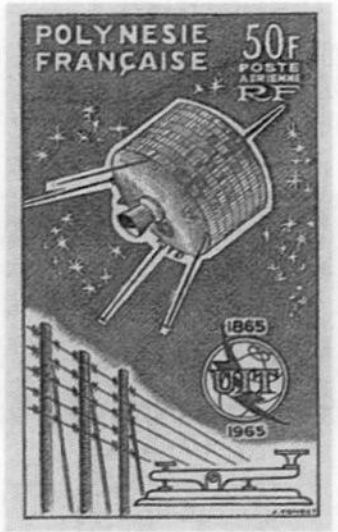

19 "Syncom" Communications Satellite, Telegraph Poles and Morse Key

1965. Air. Centenary of I.T.U.
44 **19** 50f. brown, blue & violet . . 65·00 50·00

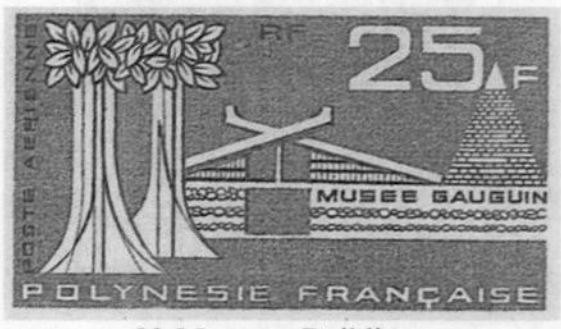

20 Museum Buildings

1965. Air. Gauguin Museum.
45 **20** 25f. green . . . . 8·50 8·00
46 – 40f. turquoise . . . . 13·50 12·00
47 – 75f. brown . . . . 25·00 19·00
DESIGNS: 40f. Statues and hut; 75f. Gauguin.

21 Skin-diver with Harpoon

1965. Air. World Under-water Swimming Championships, Tuamoto.
48 **21** 50f. blue, brown & green . . 80·00 £100

22 Tropical Foliage

23 Aerial, Globe and Palm

1965. Schools Canteen Art.
49 **22** 20f. red, green and brown (postage) . . . . 18·00 23·00
50 – 80f. red, blue and brown (27 × 48 mm) (air) . . . . 22·00 32·00
DESIGN: 80f. Totem, and garland in harbour.

1965. Air. 50th Anniv of 1st Radio Link with France.
51 **23** 60f. brown, green & orge . . 18·00 30·00

1966. Air. Launching of 1st French Satellite. As Nos. 1696/7 (plus se-tenant label) of France.
52 7f. brown, purple & green . . 9·25 12·00
53 10f. brown, purple & green . . 9·25 12·00

1966. Air. Launching of Satellite "D1". As T **569** of France.
54 20f. red, brown and green . . 6·50 8·75

26 Papeete Port

1966. Air.
55 **26** 50f. multicoloured . . . . . 14·00 22·00

27 Pirogue

1966. Polynesian Boats.
56 **27** 10f. red, green and blue . . 3·25 2·25
57 – 11f. red, green and blue . . 3·00 2·75
58 – 12f. purple, green & blue . . 4·50 3·50
59 – 14f. brown, blue & green . . 6·25 3·00
60 – 19f. green, red and blue . . 7·00 4·00
61 – 22f. green, blue & purple . . 10·00 4·75
DESIGNS—VERT: 11f. Schooner; 19f. Early schooner. HORIZ: 12f. Fishing launch; 14f. Pirogues; 22f. Coaster "Oiseau des Iles II".

28 Tahitian Dancer and Band

1966. Air. "Vive, Tahiti!" (tourist publicity).
62 **28** 13f. multicoloured . . . . . 9·25 11·00

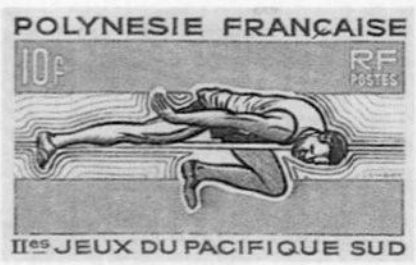

29 High-jumping

30 Stone Pestle

1966. 2nd South Pacific Games, Noumea.
63 **29** 10f. bistre and red . . . . . 3·00 4·00
64 – 20f. green and blue . . . . 6·00 3·25
65 – 40f. purple and green . . . 10·00 3·00
66 – 60f. blue and brown . . . . 12·50 16·50
DESIGNS—VERT: 20f. Pole-vaulting; 40f. Basketball. HORIZ: 60f. Hurdling.

1967. 50th Anniv of Oceanic Studies Society.
67 **30** 50f. blue and orange . . . . 14·50 11·00

31 Spring Dance

1967. July Festival.

68 **31**	5f. blue, purple and drab . .	3·25	2·75
69 –	13f. purple, violet & green	4·25	3·00
70 –	15f. brown, purple & green	5·75	3·00
71 –	16f. purple, green & blue . .	5·00	3·50
72 –	21f. brown, green & blue . .	7·25	8·00

DESIGNS—VERT: 13f. Javelin-throwing; 16f. Fruit-porters' race. HORIZ: 15f. Horse-racing; 21f. Pirogue-racing.

32 Earring **34** Bouquet, Sun and W.H.O. Emblem

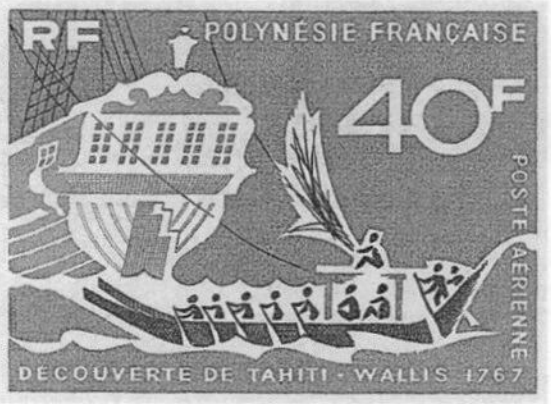

33 Ship's Stern and Canoe ("Wallis, 1767")

1967. Ancient Art of the Marquesas Islands.

73 –	10f. blue, red & purple . . .	3·75	2·75
74 –	15f. black and green	4·50	3·25
75 **32**	20f. brown, green & lake . .	4·00	3·75
76 –	23f. brown and ochre . . .	6·25	7·00
77 –	25f. brown, purple & blue	7·00	4·75
78 –	30f. brown and purple . . .	8·25	7·75
79 –	35f. blue and brown	11·00	12·50
80 –	50f. brown, blue & green . .	10·00	12·00

DESIGNS: 10f. Sculpture on mother-of-pearl; 15f. Paddle-blade; 23f. Receptacle for anointing oil; 25f. Hunting stirrups; 30f. Fan handles; 35f. Tattooed man; 50f. "Tikis".

1968. Air. Bicentenary of Discovery of Tahiti.

81 **33**	40f. brown, blue & green . .	13·00	9·50
82 –	60f. orange, black & blue	16·00	11·50
83 –	80f. salmon, lake & purple	17·00	15·00
MS84	180 × 100 mm. Nos. 81/3	£170	£180

DESIGNS—HORIZ: 60f. Ship and witch-doctor ("Cook, 1769"). VERT: 80f. "Bougainville, 1768" (portrait).

1968. 20th Anniv of World Health Organization.

85 **34**	15f. violet, red and green . .	8·00	10·00
86	16f. green, purple & orange	8·00	14·00

35 "The Meal" (Gauguin)

1968. Air.

87 **35**	200f. multicoloured	38·00	50·00

36 Human Rights Emblem **37** Putting the Shot

1968. Human Rights Year.

88 **36**	15f. red, blue and brown . .	7·25	9·75
89	16f. blue, brown & purple	8·00	9·50

1968. Air. Olympic Games, Mexico.

90 **37**	35f. green, purple & red . .	14·00	15·00

38 Tiare Apetahi

1969. Flowers. Multicoloured.

91	9f. Type **38**	3·75	3·00
92	17f. Tiare Tahiti	11·00	8·50

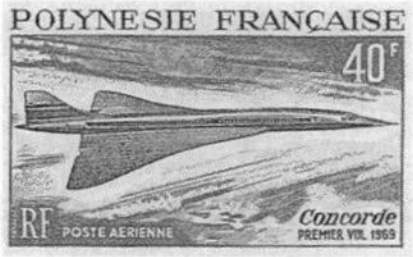

39 Concorde in Flight

1969. Air. 1st Flight of Concorde.

93 **39**	40f. brown and red	60·00	60·00

40 Polynesian with Guitar

1969. Air. Pacific Area Travel Association (P.A.T.A.) Congress, Tahiti (1970) (1st issue).

94 **40**	25f. multicoloured	26·00	13·00

See also Nos. 109/11.

41 Diver and Fish

1969. Air. World Underwater Hunting Championships.

95 **41**	48f. black, purple & turq . .	30·00	18·00
96 –	52f. black, red and blue . .	40·00	35·00

DESIGN—VERT: 52f. "Flag" Fish.

42 Boxing

1969. 3rd South Pacific Games, Port Moresby, New Guinea.

97 **42**	9f. brown and violet . . .	4·25	4·50
98 –	17f. brown and red	5·00	4·00
99 –	18f. brown and blue . . .	6·75	5·50
100 –	22f. purple and green . . .	10·00	9·25

DESIGNS—VERT: 17f. High jumping; 18f. Running; 22f. Long jumping.

43 "Bonaparte as Commander-in-Chief, Italy" (Rouillard)

1969. Air. Birth Bicentenary of Napoleon Bonaparte.

101 **43**	100f. multicoloured	80·00	£120

44 I.L.O. Building, Geneva

1969. 50th Anniv of International Labour Organization.

102 **44**	17f. drab, green & orange	9·25	10·50
103	18f. blue, brown & orange	10·00	13·00

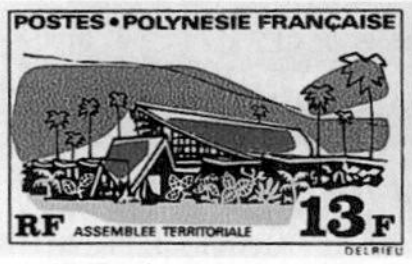

45 Territorial Assembly Building **46** Tiki holding P.A.T.A. Emblem

1969. Polynesian Buildings. Multicoloured.

104	13f. Type **45**	3·25	4·00
105	14f. Governor's residence . .	4·25	4·00
106	17f. Tourist offices	6·00	4·50
107	18f. Maeva Hotel	8·50	4·50
108	24f. Taharaa Hotel	11·00	7·00

1970. P.A.T.A. Congress (2nd issue).

109 **46**	20f. blue, brown & purple	8·00	6·00
110 –	40f. blue, purple & green	12·50	9·50
111 –	60f. dp brown, blue & brn	16·00	15·00

DESIGNS—HORIZ: 40f. Globe, airliner and "tourists". VERT: 60f. Polynesian holding globe.

47 New U.P.U. Building, Berne

1970. New U.P.U. Headquarters Building.

112 **47**	18f. lt brown, violet & brn	10·00	6·25
113	20f. blue, brown & purple	10·00	8·00

48 Tower of the Sun and Mt. Fuji

1970. Air. "EXPO 70" World Fair, Osaka, Japan. Multicoloured.

114	30f. Type **48**	12·00	12·00
115	50f. Eiffel Tower and Torii Gate (vert)	29·00	18·00

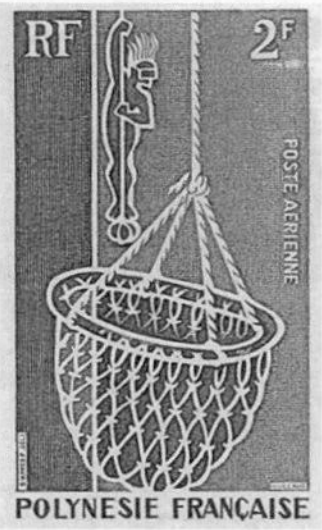

49 Diver and Basket

1970. Air. Pearl-diving.

116 **49**	2f. brown, indigo & blue	2·00	1·25
117 –	5f. ultramarine, orge & bl	4·00	2·00
118 –	18f. grey, orange & purple	5·00	4·00
119 –	27f. lilac, brown & purple	9·00	6·25
120 –	50c. orange, grey & brown	19·00	13·00

DESIGNS—VERT: 5f. Diver gathering black-lipped pearl oysters; 27f. Pearl in opened oyster; 50f. Woman with pearl jewellery. HORIZ: 18f. Opening oyster-shell.

50 I.E.Y. Emblem, Open Book and "The Thinker" (statue)

1970. Air. International Education Year.

121 **50**	50f. blue, brown & lt blue	17·00	18·00

51 "Polynesian Woman" (Y. de St. Front)

1970. Air. Paintings by Polynesian Artists (1st series). Multicoloured.

122	20f. Type **51**	10·00	7·00
123	40f. "Harbour Scene" (F. Fay)	12·00	12·00
124	60f. "Niu" (abstract, J. Guillois)	20·00	9·00
125	80f. "Beach Hut" (J. Masson)	23·00	25·00
126	100f. "Polynesian Girl" (J. C. Bouloc) (vert)	48·00	36·00

See also Nos. 147/51, 160/4, 172/6, 189/93 and 205/9.

52 Games Emblem **53** Flame of Remembrance

1971. Air. 4th South Pacific Games, Tahiti (1st issue).

127 **52**	20f. multicoloured	8·25	9·50

1971. Air. Erection of General de Gaulle Monument.

128 **53**	5f. multicoloured	9·75	6·50

54 Volunteer, Crest and Tricolour

1971. Air. 30th Anniv of Departure of Tahitian "Free French" Volunteers.

129 **54**	25f. multicoloured	12·00	12·50

55 Marara Fisherman

1971. Water Sports. Multicoloured.

130	10f. Type **55** (postage) . . .	10·50	8·25
131	15f. Surfing (vert) (air) . . .	6·75	6·50
132	16f. Skin-diving (vert)	8·25	8·25
133	20f. Paragliding	10·00	8·50

56 Red Flower **57** Yachting

1971. "Day of the 1,000 Flowers". Mult.

134	8f. Type **56**	2·50	2·00
135	12f. Hibiscus (horiz)	2·75	2·50
136	22f. Porcelain rose	6·00	3·50

1971. Air. 4th South Pacific Games, Tahiti (2nd issue). Multicoloured.

137	15f. Type **57**	9·00	6·50
138	18f. Golf	10·50	8·00
139	27f. Archery	10·50	10·50
140	53f. Tennis	45·00	40·00
MS141	138 × 170 mm. Nos. 137/40	£200	£200

58 Water-skiing

1971. 1st World Water-ski Championships, Papeete.

142	58	10f. red, green & brown	8·75	5·00
143	–	20f. red, brown & green	13·00	8·50
144	–	40f. purple, brown & grn	28·00	15·00

DESIGNS—VERT: 20f. Ski-jumping. HORIZ: 40f. Acrobatics on one ski.

1971. 1st Death Anniv of General de Gaulle. As Nos. 1937 and 1940 of France.

145	30f. black and purple	13·00	13·00
146	50f. black and purple	18·00	19·00

1971. Air. Paintings by Polynesian Artists (2nd series). As T **51**. Multicoloured.

147	20f. "Polynesian Village" (I. Wolf)	7·50	9·50
148	40f. "Lagoon" (A. Dobrowolski)	11·00	12·50
149	60f. "Polynesian Woman" (F. Seli) (vert)	18·00	18·00
150	80f. "The Holy Family" (P. Heymann) (vert)	25·00	20·00
151	100f. "Faces in a Crowd" (N. Michoutouchkine)	32·00	45·00

60 Cross Emblem

1971. 2nd French Pacific Scouts and Guides Rally, Taravao.

152	60	28f. multicoloured	12·50	14·00

61 Harbour, Papeete

1972. Air. 10th Anniv of Autonomous Port of Papeete.

153	61	28f. multicoloured	16·00	13·00

62 Figure-skating

1972. Air. Winter Olympic Games, Sapporo, Japan.

154	62	20f. red, green & violet	14·00	11·50

63 Commission H.Q., Noumea, New Caledonia

1972. Air. 25th Anniv of South Pacific Commission.

155	63	21f. multicoloured	12·50	9·75

64 Alcoholic behind Bars

65 Floral Emblem

1972. Campaign Against Alcoholism.

156	64	20f. multicoloured	11·00	7·25

1972. Air. South Pacific Arts Festival, Fiji.

157	65	36f. orange, green & blue	10·00	10·00

66 Raft "Kon-Tiki" and Route-map

1972. Air. 25th Anniv of Arrival of "Kon-Tiki" Expedition in French Polynesia.

158	66	16f. multicoloured	8·75	7·50

67 De Gaulle and Monument

1972. Air. Completion of De Gaulle Monument.

159	67	100f. grey	60·00	70·00

1972. Air. Paintings by Polynesian Artists (3rd series). As Type **51**. Multicoloured.

160	20f. "Horses" (G. Bovy)	9·00	5·50
161	40f. "Harbour" (R. Juventin) (vert)	15·00	10·50
162	60f. "Landscape" (A. Brooke)	27·00	15·00
163	80f. "Polynesians" (D. Adam) (vert)	30·00	24·00
164	100f. "Dancers" (A. Pilioko) (vert)	32·00	45·00

68 St. Theresa and Lisieux Basilica

1973. Air. Birth Centenary of St. Theresa of Lisieux.

165	68	85f. multicoloured	30·00	32·00

69 Copernicus and Planetary System

1973. Air. 500th Birth Anniv of Nicolas Copernicus (astronomer).

166	69	100f. violet, brown & pur	30·00	35·00

70 Aeroplane and Flying Fish

1973. Air. Inauguration of "Air France" Round-the-World Service via Tahiti.

167	70	80f. multicoloured	26·00	26·00

71 Douglas DC-10 over Papeete Airport

1973. Air. Inauguration of "DC-10" Service.

168	71	20f. blue, green & lt blue	24·00	12·00

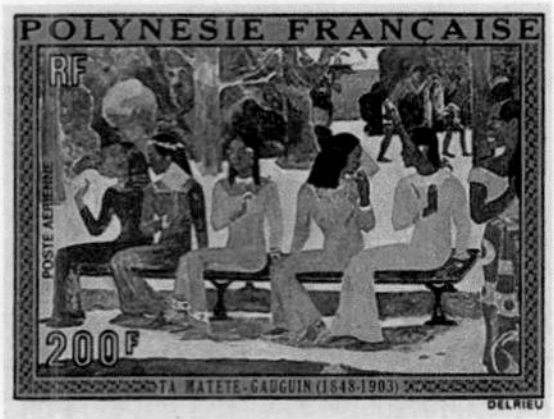

72 "Ta Matete" (Gauguin)

1973. Air. 125th Birth Anniv of Gauguin.

169	72	200f. multicoloured	32·00	35·00

73 Loti, Fishermen and Polynesian Girl

1973. Air. 50th Death Anniv of Pierre Loti (writer).

170	73	60f. multicoloured	50·00	35·00

74 Polynesian Mother and Child

75 "Teeing Off"

1973. Opening of Tahitian Women's Union Creche.

171	74	28f. multicoloured	12·00	7·50

1973. Air. Paintings by Polynesian Artists (4th series). As Type **51**. Multicoloured.

172	20f. "Sun God" (J.-F. Favre) (vert)	6·75	6·25
173	40f. "Polynesian Girl" (E. de Gennes) (vert)	13·00	10·50
174	60f. "Abstract" (A. Sidet) (vert)	17·00	15·00
175	80f. "Bus Passengers" (F. Ravello) (vert)	30·00	26·00
176	100f. "Boats" (J. Bourdin)	32·00	35·00

1974. Atimaono Golf Course, Tahiti. Mult.

177	16f. Type **75**	8·25	4·00
178	24f. View of golf course	9·50	4·75

76 "A Helping Hand"

1974. Polynesian Animal Protection Society.

179	76	21f. multicoloured	13·50	7·50

77 Mountains and Lagoon

1974. Polynesian Landscapes. Multicoloured.

180	2f. Type **77**	1·90	2·25
181	5f. Beach games	2·50	1·25
182	6f. Canoe fishing	2·25	2·75
183	10f. Mountain peak (vert)	3·25	2·50
184	15f. "Regina Maris" (schooner) in sunset scene	5·25	3·25
185	20f. Island and lagoon	5·00	2·75

78 Bird, Stylized Angelfish, Leaf and Flower

1974. Air. Protection of Nature.

186	78	12f. multicoloured	11·00	9·50

79 Catamarans

80 Polynesian Woman

1974. Air. 2nd World Catamaran Sailing Championships, Papeete.

187	79	100f. multicoloured	23·00	26·00

1974. Centenary of Universal Postal Union.

188	80	65f. multicoloured	10·00	13·00

1974. Air. Paintings by Polynesian Artists (5th series). As Type **51**. Multicoloured.

189	20f. "Flower arrangement" (R. Temarui-Masson) (vert)	13·00	13·00
190	40f. "Palms on Beach" (M. Chardon) (vert)	25·00	14·00
191	60f. "Portrait of Man" (M. F. Avril) (vert)	42·00	20·00
192	80f. "Polynesian Girl" (H. Robin) (vert)	55·00	27·00
193	100f. "Lagoon at Night" (D. Farsi)	80·00	50·00

81 "The Travelling Gods"

1975. Air. "50 Years of Tahitian Aviation".

194	81	50f. violet, red & brown	9·50	9·50
195	–	75f. blue, red & green	16·00	16·00
196	–	100f. brown, mve & grn	24·00	26·00

DESIGNS: 75f. Tourville's flying boat; 100f. Boeing 707 airliner.

82 Polynesian Girl and French "Ceres" Stamp of 1870

83 Tahiti Lions' Emblem

1975. Air. "Arphila 75" International Stamp Exhibition, Paris.

197	82	32f. red, brown & black	9·75	7·50

1975. 15th Anniv of Tahiti Lions' Club.

198	83	26f. multicoloured	20·00	11·50

84 "Protect Nature"

1975. Nature Protection.
199 **84** 19f. blue and green . . . . 7·75 8·25

85 Putting the Shot

1975. Air. 5th South Pacific Games, Guam. Mult.
200 25f. Type **85** . . . . 5·25 15·00
201 30f. Volleyball . . . . 7·25 7·25
202 40f. Swimming . . . . 9·00 9·50

86 Athlete and View of Montreal

1975. Air. Olympic Games, Montreal (1976).
203 **86** 44f. black, blue and red . . 10·00 9·50

87 Boeing 737 Airliner and Letters

1975. Air. World U.P.U. Day.
204 **87** 100f. blue, olive & brn . . 23·00 24·00

1975. Air. Paintings by Polynesian Artists (6th series). As T **51**. Multicoloured.
205 20f. "Beach Scene" (R. Marcel-Marius) . . . . 3·25 3·75
206 40f. "Rooftop Aerials" (M. Anglade) . . . . . . 6·75 5·50
207 60f. "Street Scene" (J. Day) 10·00 8·00
208 80f. "Tropical Waters" (J. Steimetz) (vert) . . . . 15·00 12·00
209 100f. "Portrait of a Woman" (A. van der Heyde) (vert) 21·00 18·00

88 Concorde

1976. Air. Concorde's First Commercial Flight.
210 **88** 100f. dp blue, blue & mve 28·00 24·00

89 President Pompidou

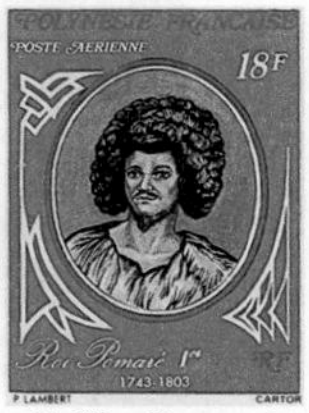

91 King Pomare I

90 Battle of the Saints

1976. 2nd Death Anniv of Georges Pompidou (President of France, 1969–74).
211 **89** 49f. grey and blue . . . . 9·50 12·00

1976. Air. Bicentenary of American Revolution.
212 **90** 24f. blue, brown & black 6·50 5·00
213 – 31f. purple, red & brown 7·50 6·00
DESIGN: 31f. Sea battle of The Chesapeake.

1976. Air. Pomare Dynasty. Multicoloured.
214 18f. Type **91** . . . . 3·00 2·25
215 21f. King Pomare II . . . . 3·50 2·50
216 26f. Queen Pomare IV . . . 3·50 2·25
217 30f. King Pomare V . . . . 3·25 4·00
See also Nos. 234/7.

92 Gerbault and "Firecrest"

1976. 50th Anniv of Alain Gerbault's Arrival at Bora-Bora.
218 **92** 90f. multicoloured . . . . 22·00 18·00

93 Turtle

1976. World Ecology Day. Multicoloured.
219 18f. Type **93** . . . . 9·50 8·25
220 42f. Doves in hand . . . . . 16·00 14·50

94 Legs of Runner

1976. Air. Olympic Games, Montreal.
221 **94** 26f. brown, purple & blue 4·00 4·00
222 – 34f. purple, brown & blue 6·00 5·00
223 – 50f. brown, blue & purple 10·00 9·50
MS224 181 × 101 mm. Nos. 222/24 85·00 £100
DESIGNS—VERT: 34f. Runners. HORIZ: 50f. Olympic Flame and flowers.

95 A. Graham Bell, early Telephone and Dish Aerial

1976. Telephone Centenary.
225 **95** 37f. red, blue & brown . . 11·50 8·25

96 "The Dream" (Gauguin)

1976. Air.
226 **96** 50f. multicoloured . . . . 22·00 13·00

97 Marquesas Pirogue

1976. Ancient Pirogues. Multicoloured.
227 25f. Type **97** . . . . 4·00 3·25
228 30f. Raiatea pirogue . . . . 4·75 4·00
229 75f. Tahiti pirogue . . . . . 10·50 6·50
230 100f. Tuamotu pirogue . . . 12·00 8·50

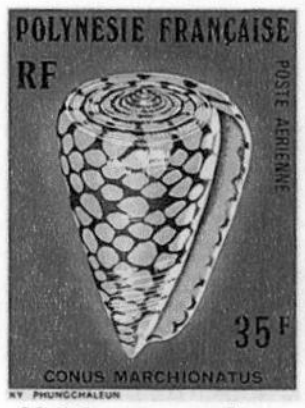

98 Marquesas Cone

101 Dancer

99 "Acropora"

1977. Air. Sea Shells (1st series). Mult.
231 25f. Maurus murex . . . . . 3·25 2·75
232 27f. Gaugin's cone . . . . . 4·25 3·00
233 35f. Type **98** . . . . 5·00 3·50
See also Nos. 268/70 and 307/9.

1977. Air. "Sovereigns of Archipelago". As T **91**. Multicoloured.
234 19f. Maputeoa (Mangareva) 2·00 2·25
235 33f. Tamatoa V (Raiatea) . . 2·25 2·50
236 39f. Vaekehu (Marquesas) . . 3·00 3·50
237 43f. Teuruarii III (Rurutu) 3·25 3·50

1977. Air. 3rd Coral Reefs Symposium, Miami.
238 25f. Type **99** . . . . 3·00 2·50
239 33f. "Pocillopora" (vert) . . 3·75 3·75

1977. Air. 5th Anniv of General de Gaulle Memorial. As T **806** of France.
255 40f. multicoloured . . . . . 5·25 5·50

1977. Air. Polynesian Dancer.
256 **101** 27f. multicoloured . . . . 5·75 3·75

102 Lindbergh and "Spirit of St. Louis"

1977. Air. 50th Anniv of Lindbergh's Transatlantic Flight.
257 **102** 28f. multicoloured . . . . 8·75 7·25

103 "Hibiscus tiliaceus"

104 Palm Tree

1977. Air. Polynesian Flowers (1st series). Multicoloured.
258 8f. Type **103** . . . . 2·00 2·75
259 12f. "Plumeria acuminata" 2·75 2·50
See also Nos. 276/7 and 288/9.

1977. Air. Forest Conservation.
260 **104** 32f. multicoloured . . . . 9·00 6·00

105 "Portrait of Rubens' Son, Albert"

1977. Air. 400th Birth Anniv of Peter Paul Rubens.
261 **105** 100f. red and blue . . . . 10·50 14·50

106 Cutter

1977. Sailing Ships. Multicoloured.
262 20f. Type **106** . . . . 3·75 3·50
263 50f. "Tiare Taporo" (schooner) . . . . 4·75 4·00
264 85f. Barque . . . . 6·75 5·50
265 120f. Full-rigged ship . . . . 9·75 7·25

107 Captain Cook and H.M.S. "Discovery"

1978. Air. Bicent of Discovery of Hawaii.
266 **107** 33f. mauve, red and blue 5·50 4·25
267 – 39f. green, blue & mauve 6·75 4·75
DESIGN: 39f. Captain Cook and H.M.S. "Resolution".

1978. Air. Sea Shells (2nd series). As T **98**. Multicoloured.
268 22f. Walled cowrie . . . . . 2·50 2·50
269 24f. Ventral cowrie . . . . . 2·50 2·50
270 31f. False scorpion conch . . 3·75 3·50

108 "Tahitian Woman and Boy" (Gauguin)

1978. Air. 75th Death Anniv of Paul Gauguin.
271 **108** 50f. multicoloured . . . . 14·00 11·00

109 Microwave Antenna

1978. Air. World Telecommunications Day.
272 **109** 80f. multicoloured . . . . 7·00 7·25

110 Match Scene

1978. Air. World Cup Football Championship, Argentina.
273 **110** 28f. multicoloured . . . . 3·25 3·75

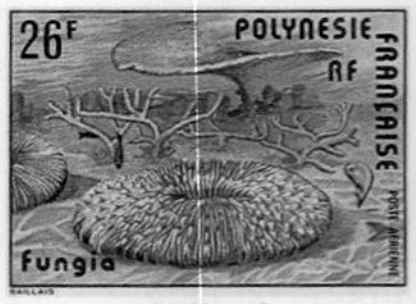

111 Fungia **112** "Hibiscus aros sinensis"

1978. Air. Coral (1st series). Multicoloured.
274 26f. Type **111** . . . . 2·75 3·25
275 34f. Millepora (vert) . . . . 3·25 3·25
See also Nos. 292/3.

1978. Flowers (2nd series). Multicoloured.
276 13f. Type **112** . . . . 2·75 3·00
277 16f. "Fagraea berteriana" . . 3·25 3·50

113 Polynesian Girl and Aerial **115** Polynesian Girl on Beach

114 Bird and Rainbow over Tropical Island

1978. Air. Papenoo Ground Receiving Station.
278 **113** 50f. black and blue . . . 5·25 3·75

1978. Air. Nature Protection.
279 **114** 23f. multicoloured . . . . 3·25 3·50

1978. 20th Anniv of First French Polynesian Stamps.
280 **115** 20f. brown, violet & red 3·75 3·50
281 – 28f. brown, green & yell 4·75 4·00
282 – 36f. brown, red and blue 5·75 4·25
MS283 130 × 100 mm. Nos. 280/82 in different colours . . . . . . 28·00 29·00
DESIGNS: 28f. Polynesian (as T **2**); 36f. Girl playing guitar (as T **1**).

116 "Tahiti" (inter-island ship)

1978. Ships. Multicoloured.
284 15f. Type **116** . . . . 2·00 3·00
285 30f. "Monowai" (liner) . . . 2·75 2·50
286 75f. "Tahitien" (inter-island ship) . . . . 4·25 3·75
287 100f. "Mariposa" (cargo liner) . . . . 6·00 5·75

1979. Flowers (3rd series). As T **112**. Mult.
288 10f. "Vanda sp." . . . . . . 2·75 2·50
289 22f. "Gardenia tahitensis" . . 3·25 2·50

1979. Air. Death Bicentenary of Captain James Cook (explorer). Nos. 266/7 optd **"1779-1979" BICENTENAIRE DE LA MORT DE.**
290 **107** 33f. mauve, red & blue . . 4·75 3·50
291 – 39f. green, blue & mauve 5·00 3·25

1979. Coral (2nd series). As T **111**. Mult.
292 32f. Porytes . . . . 2·50 3·00
293 37f. Montipora and white-tailed damselfish . . . . . 3·50 3·50

118 Raiatea

1979. Landscapes.
294 1f. Bora Bora . . . . 70 1·25
469 2f. Ua Pou . . . . 60 1·25
470 3f. Motu Tapu 75 90
470a 4f. Type **118** . . . . 1·25 1·25
471 5f. Motu . . . . 1·00 1·25
472 6f. Case au Taumotu . . . 60 1·25

119 Children and Toys

1979. Air. International Year of the Child.
300 **119** 150f. mauve, blue & turq 9·75 9·25

120 "You are waiting for a Letter?" (Gauguin)

1979. Air.
301 **120** 200f. multicoloured . . . 17·00 12·50

121 Conch and Stone Head of a Tiki

1979. Air. Tahiti and the Islands Museum.
302 **121** 44f. brown, red & lake . . 5·75 4·75

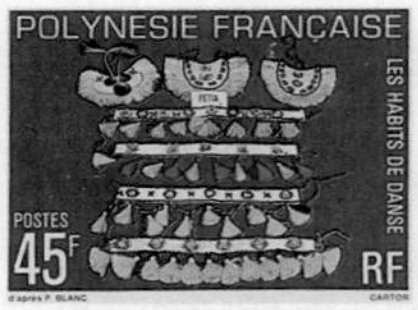

122 Fetia

1979. Traditional Dancing Costumes. Multicoloured.
303 45f. Type **122** . . . . . . 2·25 3·00
304 51f. Teanuanua . . . . . . 2·50 3·00
305 74f. Temaeva . . . . 4·75 3·75

123 Sir Rowland Hill, British and Polynesian Stamps

1979. Death Centenary of Sir Rowland Hill.
306 **123** 100f. mauve, violet & grn 5·75 5·75

1979. Sea Shells (3rd series). As T **98**. Mult.
307 20f. Strigate auger . . . . 1·75 2·50
308 28f. Snake mitre . . . . . . 2·50 2·00
309 35f. Wavy-edge spindle . . . 3·25 3·50

124 Arrows converging on Tahiti

1979. Air. 19th South Pacific Conference, Tahiti.
310 **124** 23f. multicoloured . . . . 2·75 3·50

125 Carving and Rotary Emblem

1979. 20th Anniv of Papeete Rotary Club.
311 **125** 47f. multicoloured . . . . 4·75 4·75

126 Short Sandringham 7 Bermuda Flying Boat

1979. Air. Aircraft (1st series). Multicoloured.
312 24f. Type **126** . . . . . . 2·25 1·25
313 40f. Douglas DC-4 . . . . . 3·25 2·75
314 60f. Britten Norman Islander 4·00 3·25
315 80f. Fokker/Fairchild Friendship . . . . 5·50 4·50
316 120f. Douglas DC-8 . . . . 7·00 4·50
See also Nos. 335/8.

127 Emperor Angelfish

1980. Fishes (1st series). Multicoloured.
317 7f. Big-eyed soldierfish . . . 1·75 2·75
318 8f. Hump-headed wrasse . . 1·75 2·75
319 12f. Type **127** . . . . . . 2·25 2·75
See also Nos. 339/41, 360/2 and 386/8.

128 "Window in Tahiti"

1980. Air. 50th Anniv of Henri Matisse's Visit to Tahiti.
320 **128** 150f. multicoloured . . . 8·50 7·00

1980. 75th Anniv of Rotary International. No. 311 surch **75eme ANNIVERSAIRE 1905-1980 77F.**
321 **125** 77f. on 47f. mult . . . . 6·00 5·75

130 National Centre for Exploitation of Oceans

1980. Aquaculture (1st series). Multicoloured.
322 15f. Type **130** . . . . . . 1·60 2·50
323 22f. Sea-water shrimp . . . . 1·90 2·25
See also Nos. 343/4.

131 General Post Office, Papeete

1980. Opening of New General Post Office.
324 **131** 50f. multicoloured . . . . 2·50 2·50

132 Tiki Statuette, Marquesas Islands

1980. 3rd South Pacific Arts Festival, Papua New Guinea.
325 34f. Type **132** . . . . 2·25 1·50
326 39f. Pahu (drum), Marquesas Islands . . . . 2·25 3·00
327 49f. Adze, Society Islands . . 2·50 3·50
MS328 136 × 100 mm. Nos. 325/7 18·00 18·00

133 "Tehamana's Ancestors" (Gauguin)

1980. Air.
329 **133** 500f. multicoloured . . . 24·00 22·00

134 Sydney Town Hall and 1955 Oceanic Settlements 9f. stamp

1980. Air. "Sydpex 80" Stamp Exhibition, Sydney.
330 **134** 70f. multicoloured . . . . 8·50 9·75

135 White Tern **136** Charles de Gaulle

1980. Birds (1st series). Multicoloured.
331 25f. Type **135** . . . . 2·75 1·75
332 35f. Tahitian lory (vert) . . . 3·75 2·25
333 45f. Great frigate bird . . . 4·00 2·75
See also Nos. 350/52 and 379/81.

1980. 10th Death Anniv of Charles de Gaulle (French statesman).
334 **136** 100f. multicoloured . . . 4·50 4·00

1980. Air. Aircraft (2nd series). As T **126**. Mult.
335 15f. Consolidated Catalina amphibian . . . . 1·25 2·25
336 26f. De Havilland Twin Otter 1·60 1·00
337 30f. CAMS 55 flying boat . . 1·75 1·75
338 50f. Douglas DC-6 . . . . . 3·75 2·50

1981. Fishes (2nd series). As T **127**. Mult.
339 13f. Zebra unicornfish . . . 2·00 2·25
340 16f. Black-tailed snapper . . 2·00 2·25
341 24f. Purple-spotted grouper . . 2·50 2·50

137 "And the Gold of their Bodies" (Gauguin)

1981. Air.
342 **137** 100f. multicoloured . . . 7·00 4·50

1981. Aquaculture (2nd series). As T **130**. Mult.
343 23f. Shrimp hatching room, National Centre for Exploitation of Oceans . . 1·40 2·50
344 41f. Green mussels . . . . . 1·90 2·25

138 Yuri Gagarin and Alan Shepard

1981. Air. 20th Anniv of First Men in Space.
345 **138** 300f. multicoloured . . . 10·00 9·25

139 Dancers

1981. Folklore. Multicoloured.
346 26f. Type **139** . . . . 2·50 1·50
347 28f. Drummer . . . . 1·90 2·00
348 44f. Two dancers (vert) . . . 3·50 3·00

140 Racing Pirogue

1981. Air. 1st International Pirogue Championship, Polynesia.
349 **140** 200f. multicoloured . . . 9·00 7·00

141 Common Waxbill

1981. Birds (2nd series). Multicoloured.
350 47f. Crested terns . . . . . 1·50 1·00
351 53f. Grey-green fruit dove . . 1·75 1·00
352 65f. Type **141** . . . . 2·00 1·25

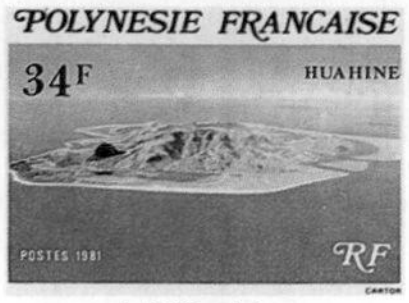

142 Huahine

1981. French Polynesian Islands (1st series). Multicoloured.
353 34f. Type **142** . . . . 2·00 2·25
354 134f. Maupiti . . . . 4·50 3·00
355 136f. Bora Bora . . . . . . 4·50 3·50
See also Nos. 376/8.

143 "Matavai Bay" (William Hodges)

1981. Air. 18th-century Paintings. Mult.
356 40f. Type **143** . . . . 2·75 2·50
357 60f. "Poedea" (John Webber) (wrongly inscr "Weber") (vert) . . . . 2·25 2·75
358 80f. "Omai" (Sir Joshua Reynolds) (vert) . . . . . 3·50 2·75
359 120f. "Point Venus" (Georges Tobin) . . . . 5·25 4·25

1982. Fishes (3rd series). As T **127**. Mult.
360 30f. Indo-Pacific hump-headed parrotfish . . . . 1·00 2·25
361 31f. Regal angelfish . . . . . 1·40 2·50
362 45f. Greasy grouper . . . . 1·50 2·50

144 Family, Bacillus and Dr Robert Koch

1982. Air. Centenary of Discovery of Tubercle Bacillus.
363 **144** 200f. blue, grey & brown 6·50 5·25

145 Oyster Farm

1982. Pearl Industry. Multicoloured.
364 7f. Type **145** . . . . 90 2·00
365 8f. Grafting oysters . . . . . 95 2·25
366 10f. Pearls . . . . 1·75 2·25

146 Girl and Tahiti 25c. stamp

1982. "Philexfrance 82" International Stamp Exhibition, Paris.
367 **146** 15f. brown, green & blue 8·00 10·00
MS368 122 × 95 mm. **146** 150f. rose, green and blue . . . . 21·00 22·00

147 Footballers **148** Priest

1982. Air. World Cup Football Championship, Spain.
369 **147** 250f. multicoloured . . . 7·25 8·75

1982. Polynesian Folklore. King's Enthroning. Multicoloured.
370 12f. Type **148** . . . . 80 1·25
371 13f. Enthroning ceremony . . 90 1·50
372 17f. Priest and King . . . . 1·10 1·60

149 "Hobie Cat 16" Class Catamaran

1982. 4th World "Hobie Cat" Championship, Tahiti.
373 **149** 90f. multicoloured . . . . 3·00 3·25

150 Island Scene **151** Sun, Man and Pacific Scene

1982. Air. Overseas Week.
374 **150** 110f. brown, blue & grn 4·00 3·50

1982. 1st South Pacific Commission Conference on New Energy Sources, Tahiti.
375 **151** 46f. multicoloured . . . . 2·00 2·75

1982. French Polynesian Islands (2nd series). As T **142**. Multicoloured.
376 20f. Motu . . . . 1·25 2·25
377 33f. Tupai Atoll . . . . . . 1·40 80
378 35f. Gambier . . . . 1·40 2·25

1982. Birds (3rd series). As T **141**. Mult.
379 37f. Reef heron (horiz) . . . 1·10 20
380 39f. Pacific golden plover . . 1·10 90
381 42f. Chestnut-breasted mannikins . . . . 2·25 1·10

152 "Tahitian Girl" (Maximilien Radiguet)

1982. Air. 19th-century Paintings. Mult.
382 50f. Type **152** . . . . 2·75 2·50
383 70f. "Tahiti Souvenir" (Charles Giraud) (horiz) . . 2·25 2·75
384 100f. "Pounding Material" (Jules Louis Le Jeune) (horiz) . . . . 3·00 3·25
385 160f. "Papeete Harbour" (Constance Gordon Cumming) (horiz) . . . . 5·00 5·50

1983. Fishes (4th series). As T **127**. Mult.
386 8f. Clown surgeonfish . . . . 1·25 2·00
387 10f. Blue-finned trevally . . . 2·00 2·00
388 12f. Black-finned reef shark 1·25 2·25

153 "The Way of the Cross" **154** "The Axeman"

1983. Religious Sculptures by Damien Haturau. Multicoloured.
389 7f. Type **153** . . . . 85 1·25
390 21f. "The Virgin and the Infant Jesus" . . . . . . 1·25 1·50
391 23f. "Christ" . . . . 1·50 2·25

1983. Air. 80th Death Anniv of Gauguin (painter).
392 **154** 600f. multicoloured . . . 17·00 16·00

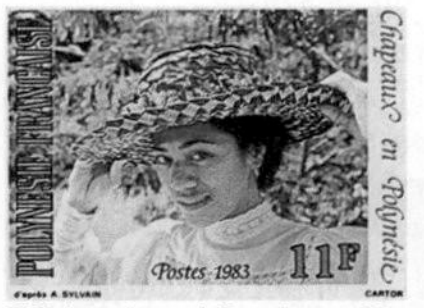

155 Acacia and Pandanus Hat

1983. Polynesian Hats (1st series). Mult.
393 11f. Type **155** . . . . 1·25 1·90
394 13f. High-crowned hat made from coconut leaves . . . 1·25 1·75
395 25f. Coffee-coloured openwork hat . . . . . . 1·40 2·00
396 35f. Bamboo hat . . . . . . 1·40 2·25
See also Nos. 423/6.

156 Bligh, Route Map and Breadfruit

1983. Air. Re-enactment of Captain William Bligh's Open-boat Voyage after the "Bounty" Mutiny.
397 **156** 200f. multicoloured . . . 8·00 6·00

157 Chief of St. Christine

1983. Costumes (1st series). Multicoloured.
398 15f. Type **157** . . . . 75 1·50
399 15f. St. Christine man . . . 80 1·60
400 28f. St. Christine woman . . 1·25 2·00
See also Nos. 427/9 and 454/6.

158 Polynesian Girls

1983. Air. "Brasiliana 83" International Stamp Exhibition, Rio de Janeiro.
401 **158** 100f. multicoloured . . . 4·00 4·25
MS402 131 × 92 mm. No. 401 . . 5·00 6·50

159 Polynesian and Thai Girls

1983. Air. "Bangkok 1983" International Stamp Exhibition.
403 **159** 110f. multicoloured . . . 4·00 4·25
MS404 92 × 131 mm. No. 403 . . 6·25 6·50

160 Fragrant Fern Headdress

1983. Floral Headdresses (1st series). Multicoloured.
405 41f. Type **160** . . . . 2·25 2·50
406 44f. Gardenias . . . . 2·50 2·50
407 45f. Mixed flowers . . . . . 2·50 2·50
See also Nos. 433/5.

161 Luther and Church **163** Me'ae of Peke, Nuku-Hiva

162 "Arrival of Escort Ship" (Nicolas Mordvinoff)

1983. 500th Birth Anniv of Martin Luther (Protestant reformer).
408 **161** 90f. black, blue & brown 3·50 3·25

1983. Air. 20th-century Paintings. Mult.
409 40f. "View of Moorea" (William MacDonald) (horiz) . . . . 2·50 2·50
410 60f. "Fei Porter" (Adrian Herman Gouwe) . . . . . 2·00 2·25
411 80f. Type **162** . . . . 3·25 3·00
412 100f. "Women on the Veranda" (Charles Lemoine) (horiz) . . . . . 3·00 2·75

1984. Marquesian Tikis. Multicoloured.
413 14f. Type **163** . . . . 80 1·50
414 16f. Me'ae of Paeke (different) . . . . 95 1·25
415 19f. Me'ae Oipona, Hiva-Oa 1·00 2·00

165 Island Canoeists

1984. Air. "Espana 84" International Stamp Exhibition, Madrid.
420 **165** 80f. red and blue . . . . 2·75 3·75
MS421 144 × 100 mm. **165** 200f. blue 10·00 12·00

166 "Woman with Mango" (Gauguin)

1984. Air.
422 **166** 400f. multicoloured . . . 17·00 12·00

1984. Polynesian Hats (2nd series). As T **155**. Multicoloured.
423 20f. Reed hat . . . . 1·40 70
424 24f. Pandanus leaves hat . . 1·60 1·60
425 26f. Fei and bamboo hat . . 1·60 1·60
426 33f. Pandanus hat decorated with toetoe flowers . . . . 2·00 1·75

1984. Costumes (2nd series). As T **157**. Mult.
427 34f. Tahitian boy playing nose flute . . . . 1·75 2·25
428 35f. Priest from Oei-Eitia . . 1·75 2·25
429 39f. Tahitian woman and her son . . . . 2·00 1·75

167 "Human Sacrifice" (detail, John Webber)

1984. Air. "Ausipex 84" International Stamp Exhibition, Melbourne. Multicoloured.
430 120f. Type **167** . . . . 7·75 5·50
431 120f. Different detail of "Human Sacrifice" . . . . 7·75 5·50
MS432 127 × 93 mm. 200f. Type **167** 17·00 21·00

1984. Floral Headdresses (2nd series). As T **160**. Multicoloured.
433 46f. Ylang ylang . . . . . . 2·25 2·25
434 47f. Garden vine . . . . . . 2·25 2·50
435 53f. Bougainvillea . . . . . 2·50 1·90

168 Tiki and Native

1984. 4th South Pacific Arts Festival, Noumea, New Caledonia.
436 **168** 150f. multicoloured . . . 4·75 4·25
See also No. 453.

169 "Tahitian Girls on the Beach" (Pierre Heyman)

1984. 20th-century Paintings. Multicoloured.
437 50f. "After Church" (Jacques Boulaire) (vert) . . . . . 2·50 2·50
438 65f. "Anaa Countryside" (Jean Masson) . . . . . 2·25 2·25
439 75f. "Festival" (Robert Tatin) 3·00 3·00
440 85f. Type **169** . . . . 3·00 3·50

170 Pair of Tikis **171** Girl wearing Lei

1985. Wooden Tikis. Multicoloured.
441 30f. Type **170** . . . . 1·25 1·60
442 36f. Joined tikis . . . . . . 1·40 45
443 40f. Tiki . . . . 1·60 1·50

1985. Polynesian Faces (1st series). Multicoloured.
444 22f. Type **171** . . . . 85 1·50
445 39f. Girl's profile . . . . . . 1·25 1·75
446 44f. Girl wearing shell necklace . . . . 1·50 1·60
See also Nos. 473/5 and 498/500.

172 "Where Have We come From? What are We? Where are We Going?" (Gauguin) (½-size illustration)

1985. Air.
447 **172** 550f. multicoloured . . . 14·50 14·00

173 East Bridge, Papeete

1985. Tahiti in Olden Days (1st series). Mult.
448 42f. Type **173** . . . . 1·60 1·75
449 45f. Inhabitants of Papeete (vert) . . . . 1·25 1·75
450 48f. Papeete market . . . . . 1·60 2·00
See also Nos. 477/9, 528/30, 703/5 and 742/4.

174 Coral Reef

1985. 5th International Coral Reefs Congress, Tahiti.
451 **174** 140f. multicoloured . . . 4·50 3·50

175 National Flag

1985.
452 **175** 9f. multicoloured . . . . 1·25 1·40

1985. 4th Pacific Arts Festival, Papeete. As T **168** but with "Sud Noumea" omitted, different emblem, inscr "29 juin au 15 juillet" and dated "1985".
453 200f. multicoloured . . . . . 5·50 4·25

The Festival was originally to be held in New Caledonia in 1984 but was cancelled and subsequently held in Tahiti in 1985.

1985. Costumes (3rd series). As T **157**. Mult.
454 38f. Tahitian dancer . . . . 1·60 1·75
455 55f. Tahitian couple . . . . 1·90 1·90
456 70f. Tahitian king . . . . . 2·75 1·10

176 Couple holding Blue-faced Booby

1985. Air. International Youth Year.
457 **176** 250f. multicoloured . . . 5·25 3·25

177 19th-century French Warship in Papeete Harbour

1985. Air. "Italia '85" International Stamp Exhibition, Rome.
458 **177** 130f. green . . . . 5·50 4·00
MS459 143 × 100 mm. **177** 240f. blue 11·00 11·50

178 Traditional Foods

1985. Tahitian Oven Pit. Multicoloured.
460 25f. Type **178** . . . . 1·40 1·60
461 35f. Man tending oven . . . 1·50 55

179 St. Michael's Cathedral, Rikitea (Gambier Island)

1985. Catholic Churches. Multicoloured.
462 90f. St Anne's Church, Otepipi (Anaa) . . . . . . 3·00 2·50
463 100f. Interior of St. Michael's Cathedral, Rikitea (Gambier Island) . . . . . 3·00 2·75
464 120f. Type **179** . . . . 4·00 3·25

180 Fiddler Crab

1986. Crabs. Multicoloured.
465 18f. Type **180** . . . . 90 1·50
466 29f. Hermit land crab . . . . 1·25 1·60
467 31f. Coconut crab . . . . . . 1·25 1·60

181 Youth with Pufferfish

1986. Polynesian Faces (2nd series). Multicoloured.
473 43f. Type **181** . . . . 1·75 1·75
474 49f. Boy holding coral . . . 1·75 1·75
475 51f. Youth and turtle (vert) 1·90 1·75

182 Marlin and Emblem **183** Tiki, Punaei Valley

1986. Air. 1st International Marlin Fishing Contest.
476 **182** 300f. multicoloured . . . 9·00 6·50

1986. Tahiti in Olden Days (2nd series). As T **173**. Multicoloured.
477 52f. Papeete . . . . 1·75 1·75
478 56f. Harpoon fishing . . . . 1·90 1·90
479 57f. King's Palace, Papeete 2·00 1·90

1986. Rock Carvings (1st series). Mult.
480 58f. Type **183** . . . . 1·90 1·90
481 59f. Human figure, Hane Valley . . . . 1·90 1·50
See also Nos. 507/8.

184 Fish in Coconut Milk

1986. Polynesian Food Dishes (1st series). Multicoloured.
482 80f. Type **184** . . . . 3·00 2·75
483 110f. Fafaru . . . . 4·00 3·25
See also Nos. 504/5 and 524/5.

185 Arrival of Sailing Ships, 1880

1986. Air.
484 **185** 400f. blue . . . . 10·00 8·50

186 "Tifaifai" (sewn collage)

1986. Polynesian Folklore. Traditional Crafts. Multicoloured.
485 8f. Type **186** . . . . 65 1·25
486 10f. Wickerwork . . . . . . 80 1·40
487 12f. Making "mores" (dance skirts) . . . . 90 1·40

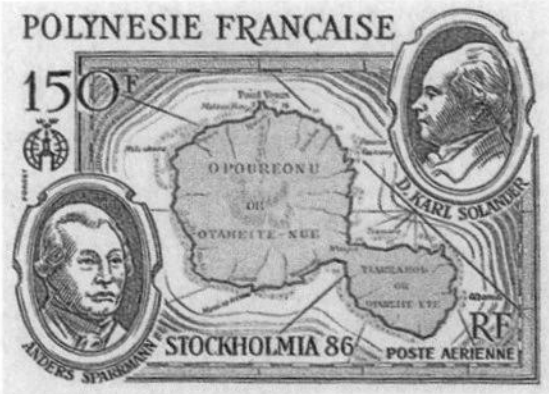

187 Map of Tahiti, Daniel Carl Solander and Anders Sparrmann

1986. Air. "Stockholmia 86" International Stamp Exhibition.
488 **187** 150f. grn, dp bl & bl . . 5·00 4·00
MS489 143 × 105 mm. **187** 210f. green, turquoise and blue . . . 8·50 8·50

188 Building a Pirogue **189** Metuapua

1986. Pirogue Construction. Multicoloured.
490 46f. Type **188** . . . . 1·25 1·75
491 50f. Constructing the hull . . 1·40 1·90

1986. Medicinal Plants (1st series). Designs showing illustrations by Gilles Cordonnier.
492 **189** 40f. green . . . . 1·75 1·75
493 – 41f. green . . . . 1·75 1·75
494 – 60f. green . . . . 2·25 2·00
DESIGNS: 41f. Hotu; 60f. Miri.
See also Nos. 514/16 and 545/7.

190 Tiva Church

1986. Air. Protestant Churches. Mult.
495 80f. Type **190** . . . . 3·00 2·50
496 200f. Avera church . . . . . 5·50 4·00
497 300f. Papetoai church . . . . 8·75 5·25

191 Old Man

1987. Polynesian Faces (3rd series). Mult.
498 28f. Type **191** . . . . 1·60 1·60
499 30f. Girl holding baby . . . 1·60 1·60
500 37f. Elderly woman . . . . . 1·75 1·60

192 Reef Crab

1987. Crustaceans. Multicoloured.
501 34f. Type **192** . . . . 1·50 1·60
502 35f. "Parribacus antarcticus" 1·50 1·75
503 39f. "Justitia longimana" . . 1·75 1·90

1987. Polynesian Food Dishes (2nd series). As T **184**. Multicoloured.
504 33f. Papaya po'e . . . . . . 1·00 1·75
505 65f. Chicken fafa . . . . . . 1·75 2·25

193 Broche Barracks

1987. Air. Centenary of Broche Army Barracks.
506 **193** 350f. multicoloured . . . 9·75 8·50

1987. Rock Carvings (2nd series). As T **183**. Multicoloured.
507 13f. Double-headed figure, Tipaerui . . . . 80 1·40
508 21f. Turtle, Raiatea . . . . . 1·10 1·50

194 George Vancouver, Map of Rapa Island and Quotation

1987. Air. "Capex '87" International Stamp Exhibition, Toronto.
509 **194** 130f. brown and red . . . 4·50 3·25
MS510 143 × 100 mm. 260f. brown, blue and deep blue. Imperf . . 8·50 8·50
DESIGN: 260f. Motifs as T **194**, Polynesian, Red Indian, and Polynesian and Canadian scenes.

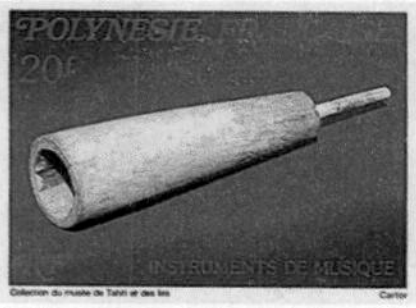

195 Marquesas Islands Miro Wood and Bamboo Horn

1987. Musical Instruments. Multicoloured.
511 20f. Type **195** . . . . 1·00 1·00
512 26f. Trumpet triton horn with coconut fibre cord . . . . 1·10 1·60
513 33f. Bamboo flutes . . . . . 1·40 1·75

1987. Medicinal Plants (2nd series). As T **189**, showing illustrations by Gilles Cordonnier.
514 46f. green . . . . 1·90 1·75
515 53f. mauve . . . . 2·00 1·90
516 54f. black . . . . 2·00 1·90
DESIGNS: 46f. Miro; 53f. Tiapito; 54f. Taataahiara.

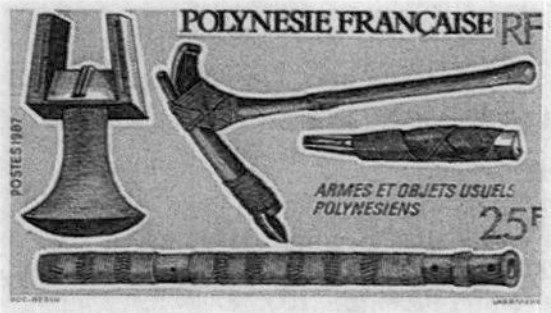

196 Penu, War Club, Adze and Nose Flute

1987. Tools and Weapons. Designs showing plates from "The Voyages of Captain Cook".
517 **196** 25f. black and green . . 1·60 1·60
518 – 27f. blue & turquoise . . 1·60 1·60
519 – 32f. dp brn & brn . . . . 2·00 1·60
DESIGNS: 27f. War club, tattooing comb, paddle and chisels; 32f. Head bands, head and chest ornaments and adze.

197 "Soyez Mysterieuses" (wood sculpture, Paul Gauguin) (½-size illustration)

1987. Air.
520 **197** 600f. multicoloured . . . 17·00 13·50

198 Mgr. Rene Dordillon, Bishop of Marquesas Islands

1987. Catholic Missionaries. Multicoloured.
521 95f. Type **198** . . . . 2·75 2·75
522 105f. Mgr. Tepano Jaussen 3·00 2·75
523 115f. Mgr. Paul Maze, Archbishop of Papeete . . 4·00 3·00

1988. Polynesian Food Dishes (3rd series). As T **184**. Multicoloured.
524 40f. Crayfish (vert) . . . . . 1·40 1·75
525 75f. Bananas in coconut milk (vert) . . . . 3·00 2·50

199 James Norman Hall

1988. Birth Centenaries (1987) of Nordhoff and Hall (writers).
526 **199** 62f. black, cream & sil . . 2·25 2·00
527 – 85f. black, grey and silver 3·25 2·50
DESIGN: 85f. Charles Bernard Nordhoff.

1988. Tahiti in Olden Days (3rd series). As T **173**. Multicoloured.
528 11f. Taranpoo house raft, Raiatea . . . . 1·25 1·25
529 15f. Small Tahitian huts . . 1·25 1·25
530 17f. Large Tahitian hut . . . 1·25 1·25

200 Lighthouse and Anchor

1988. 120th Anniv of Venus Point Lighthouse.
531 **200** 400f. multicoloured . . . 17·00 9·75

201 "River Scene"

1988. Tapa (cloth made from beaten bark) Paintings by Paul Engdahl. Multicoloured.
532 52f. Type **201** . . . . 2·25 2·00
533 54f. "River scene" (different) 2·25 2·00
534 64f. "Jungle" . . . . 2·50 2·50

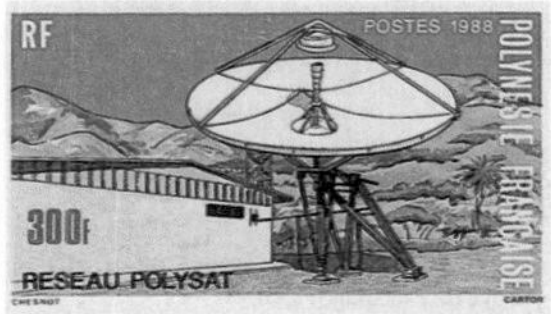

202 Dish Aerial, Papenoo, Tahiti

1988. Polysat Satellite Communications Network.
535 **202** 300f. multicoloured . . . 10·00 8·00

203 Doll in More Skirt **204** Carved Figures (detail)

1988. Polynesian Folklore. Tahitian Dolls. Mult.
536 42f. Type **203** . . . . 1·75 1·75
537 45f. Doll in city clothing . . 1·75 1·75
538 48f. Doll in city clothing (different) . . . . 1·90 2·00

1988. "Sydpex 88" International Stamp Exhibition, Australia. Engraving by J. and E. Verreaux from Atlas by Baron von Krusenstern (explorer).
539 **204** 68f. brown . . . . 3·50 2·50
MS540 142 × 100 mm. 145f. red, green and ochre. Imperf . . . 6·75 6·75
DESIGN: 145f. Russian officer in marae (cemetery) at Nuku Hiva.

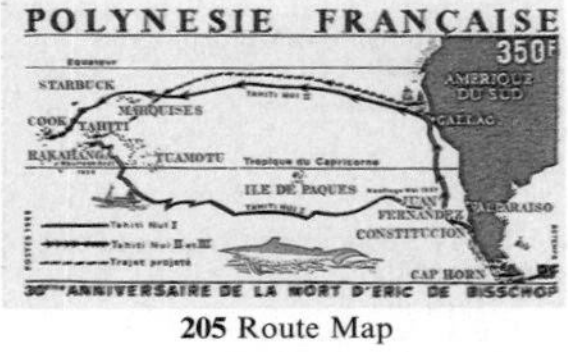

205 Route Map

1988. 30th Death Anniv of Eric de Bisschop (leader of "Tahiti Nui" expedition).
541 **205** 350f. blue, black & brown 14·50 8·00

206 "Kermia barnardi"

1988. Sea Shells (1st series). Multicoloured.
542 24f. Type **206** . . . . 1·25 1·50
543 35f. "Vexillum suavis" . . . 1·40 1·75
544 44f. "Berthelinia" sp. . . . . 1·60 1·90
See also Nos. 573/5.

1988. Medicinal Plants (3rd series). As T **189**, showing illustrations by Gilles Cordonnier.
545 23f. red . . . . 1·25 1·25
546 36f. brown . . . . 1·60 1·75
547 49f. blue . . . . 2·00 1·90
DESIGNS: 23f. Tiatiamona; 36f. Patoa purahi; 49f. Haehaa.

207 Henry Nott and "Duff"

1988. Protestant Missionaries. Multicoloured.
548 80f. Type **207** . . . . 3·50 2·50
549 90f. Papeiha . . . . 3·75 2·75
550 100f. Samuel Raapoto . . . 4·25 2·75

208 Papeete Post Office, 1875

1989. Taihitian Postal History.
551 **208** 30f. brown, green & blue 1·75 1·50
552 – 40f. brown, green & blue 1·90 1·75
DESIGN: 40f. Papeete Post Office, 1915.

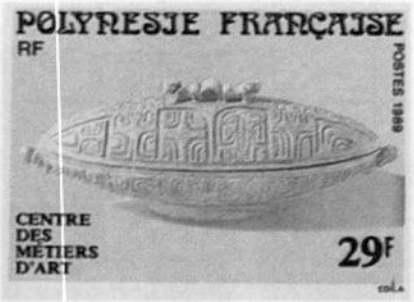
209 Bowl with Wooden Cover, Marquesas Islands

1989. 8th Anniv of Arts and Crafts Centre. Multicoloured.
553 29f. Type **209** . . . . 1·75 1·50
554 31f. Mother-of-pearl pendant, Marquesas Islands . . . . 1·75 1·50

210 Woman splitting Coconuts

211 Wooden Statue with Tapa Covering

1989. Copra Production. Multicoloured.
555 55f. Type **210** . . . . 90·00 75·00
556 70f. Drying copra (horiz) . . 3·00 2·50

1989. Tapa (bark of paper-mulberry tree) Decorations. Multicoloured.
557 43f. Type **211** . . . . 2·25 1·90
558 51f. Fern leaf decoration, Society Islands (horiz) . . 2·25 1·90
559 56f. Concentric circles decoration, Austral Islands (horiz) . . . . 2·50 2·00

212 Woman playing Ukulele

213 Lifting Stone

1989. Polynesian Environment. Mult.
560 120f. Type **212** . . . . 4·75 3·50
561 140f. Diver collecting marlin-spike auger shells . . . . 5·25 4·00

1989. Polynesian Folklore. July Festivals. Mult.
562 47f. Type **213** . . . . 2·50 1·90
563 61f. Dancer . . . . 2·75 2·00
564 67f. Group of singers (horiz) 3·25 2·25

214 "Mutineers casting Bligh adrift" (detail, Robert Dodd)

1989. Bicentenaries of French Revolution and Mutiny on the "Bounty".
565 **214** 100f. dp blue, blue & grn 4·25 3·25
MS566 140 × 100 mm. 200f. brown, green and black. Imperf . . . 8·00 8·50
DESIGN: 200f. Complete painting by Dodd and French Colonies 1939 150th Anniv of Revolution omnibus issue.

215 Fr. O'Reilly

1989. 1st Death Anniv of Father Patrick O'Reilly (founder of Gauguin Museum).
567 **215** 52f. green and brown . . 2·50 1·90

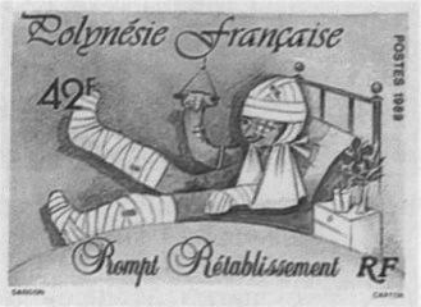
216 "Get Well Soon"

1989. Greetings Stamps. Multicoloured.
568 42f. Type **216** . . . . 2·75 2·50
569 42f. Horseshoe ("Good Luck") . . . . 2·75 2·50
570 42f. Cake ("Happy Anniversary") . . . . . . 2·75 2·50
571 42f. Letters and telephone ("In Touch") . . . . . . 2·75 2·50
572 42f. Presents ("Congratulations") . . . 2·75 2·50

1989. Sea Shells (2nd series). As T **206**. Mult.
573 60f. "Triphoridae" . . . . . 2·25 2·00
574 69f. "Favartia" . . . . . . 2·50 2·25
575 73f. Checkerboard engina and grape drupe . . . . . 2·75 2·25

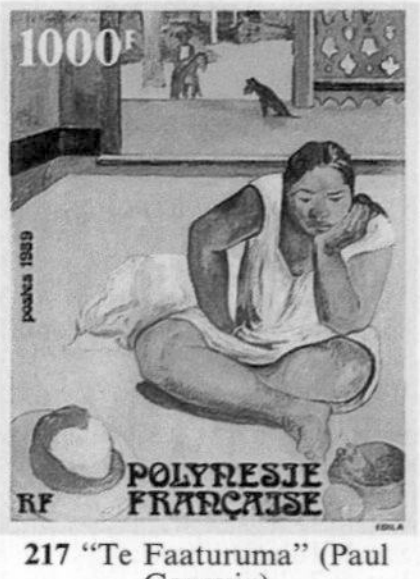
217 "Te Faaturuma" (Paul Gauguin)

1989.
576 **217** 1000f. multicoloured . . . 26·00 28·00

218 "Legend of Maui: Birth of the Islands"

1989. Polynesian Legends (1st series). Mult.
577 66f. Type **218** . . . . 2·75 2·00
578 82f. "Legend of the Pierced Mountain" (horiz) . . . . 3·50 2·50
579 88f. "Legend of Hina, the Eel from Lake Vaihiria" . . . 3·25 2·50
See also Nos. 599/601.

219 Flower

1990. Traditional Resources. Vanilla. Mult.
580 34f. Type **219** . . . . 1·75 1·50
581 35f. Pods . . . . 1·75 1·50

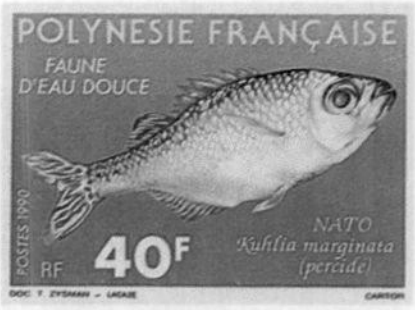
220 Spotted Flagtail

1990. Fresh Water Animals. Multicoloured.
582 40f. Type **220** . . . . 2·00 1·75
583 50f. Shrimp . . . . 2·25 1·90

221 Sandwich Islands Man and Hawaiian Islands

1990. Maori World (1st series).
584 **221** 58f. black . . . . 2·50 1·90
585 – 59f. blue . . . . 28·00 21·00
586 – 63f. green . . . . 2·50 1·90
587 – 71f. blue . . . . 2·75 2·00
DESIGNS: 59f. Easter Island man and map; 63f. New Zealand man and map; 71f. Octopus and Tahiti.
See also Nos. 610/12 and 644/6.

222 Old Town Hall

1990. Centenary of Township of Papeete. Mult.
588 150f. Type **222** . . . . . . 4·75 3·50
589 250f. New Town Hall . . . . 8·75 5·75

223 Sooty Crake

224 Young People reading

1990. Birds. Multicoloured.
590 13f. Type **223** 80 25
591 20f. Ultramarine lory 70 30

1990. 30th Anniv of Papeete Lions Club.
592 **224** 39f. multicoloured . . . . 1·60 1·75

225 New Zealand Man and Map

1990. "New Zealand 1990" International Stamp Exhibition, Auckland.
593 **225** 125f. blue, green & purple 5·50 3·50
MS594 100 × 76 mm. **225** 230f. purple, olive and green. Imperf 10·00 10·50

226 De Gaulle and Globe

1990. Birth Centenary of Charles de Gaulle (French statesman).
595 **226** 200f. blue, brown & red 7·00 5·50

227 Girls in Pareos

228 Girl wearing Tiare Headdress

1990. World Tourism Day.
596 **227** 8f. multicoloured . . . . 1·00 1·10
597 – 10f. multicoloured . . . . 1·00 1·10
598 – 12f. multicoloured . . . . 1·10 1·25
DESIGNS: 10, 12f. Girls in pareos (different).

1990. Polynesian Legends (2nd series). As T **218**. Multicoloured.
599 170f. "Legend of Uru" (horiz) . . . . 5·75 4·75
600 290f. "Legend of Pipiri-Ma" 11·00 6·00
601 375f. "Legend of Hiro, God of Thieves" . . . . 12·50 9·75

1990. Tiare Flower. Multicoloured.
602 28f. Type **228** . . . . 1·40 1·50
603 30f. Tiare bush . . . . . . 1·40 1·50
604 37f. Girl wearing flower over ear and lei . . . . 1·60 1·50

229 Pineapple Plants

230 Doridian Nudibranch

1991. Traditional Resources. The Pineapple. Multicoloured. Self-adhesive. Backing paper perf.
605 42f. Type **229** . . . . 1·60 1·75
606 44f. Plantation . . . . 1·60 1·75

1991. Undersea Wonders. Multicoloured.
607 7f. Type **230** . . . . 70 1·10
608 9f. "Galaxaura tenera" (red alga) . . . . 70 1·10
609 11f. Cuming's cowrie . . . . 75 1·25

1991. Maori World (2nd series). As T **221** showing 18th-century engravings.
610 68f. green . . . . 38·00 35·00
611 84f. black . . . . 3·75 2·50
612 94f. brown . . . . 4·25 3·25
DESIGNS—VERT: 68f. Woman, child and statues, Easter Island. HORIZ: 84f. Sandwich Islands pirogue race; 94f. Maori village, New Zealand.

231 Basketball Players

1991. Centenary of Basketball.
613 **231** 80f. multicoloured . . . . 2·75 2·25

232 Tuamotu Kingfisher **234** "Tuava"

233 "Oranges of Tahiti" (Gauguin)

1991. Protected Birds. Multicoloured.
614 17f. Type **232** 40 40
615 21f. Kuhl's lory 60 35

1991. Centenary of Paul Gauguin's Arrival in Tahiti.
616 **233** 700f. multicoloured . . . 28·00 13·50

1991. Marquesas Islands Sculptures. Mult.
617 56f. Type **234** . . . . 1·90 1·75
618 102f. "Te Hina o Motu Haka" . . . . 3·25 2·50
619 110f. "Kooka" (horiz) . . . 3·50 2·75

235 Pianist's Hands, Conductor and Orchestra

1991. Death Bicentenary of Wolfgang Amadeus Mozart (composer).
620 **235** 100f. multicoloured . . . 4·00 2·50

236 Fishing Canoes

1991. Stone Fishing. Multicoloured.
621 25f. Type **236** . . . . 1·75 1·25
622 57f. Fisherman swinging stone (used to beat the water) . . . . 2·00 1·90
623 62f. Fish in entrapment area (horiz) . . . . 2·75 2·00

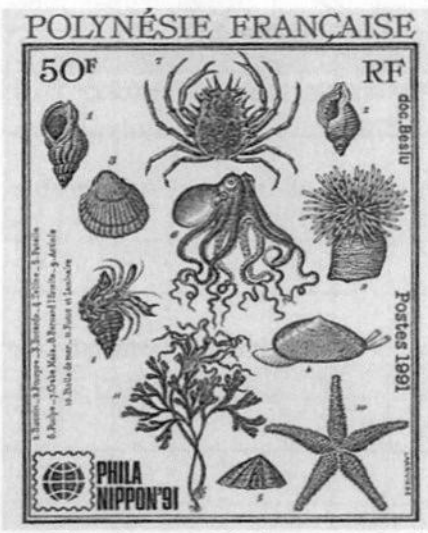

237 Sketches of Shells and Marine Life by Rene Lesson

1991. "Phila Nippon '91" International Stamp Exhibition, Tokyo.
624 **237** 50f. brown, red & violet 2·25 1·75
625 – 70f. blue, red & green . . 3·25 2·25
DESIGN—HORIZ: 70f. "View of Venus Point at Matavae, Tahiti".

238 Financed Projects

1991. 50th Anniv of Central Economic Co-operation Bank.
627 **238** 307f. multicoloured . . . 10·00 6·75

239 Father Christmas

1991. "Christmas under the Sea". Mult.
628 55f. Type **239** . . . . 2·50 1·75
629 83f. Corals decorated with baubles . . . . 3·50 2·25
630 86f. Crib among corals (vert) 3·50 2·50

240 Setting Nets along Shore

1992. Tourist Activities. Multicoloured.
631 1f. Type **240** . . . . 1·10 1·10
632 2f. Horse riding along beach 1·10 1·10
633 3f. Woman holding sailfish 1·10 1·10
634 4f. Exploring waterfall (vert) 1·10 1·10
635 5f. Yachting . . . . 1·25 1·10
636 6f. Sikorsky S-61N helicopter flight to waterfall (vert) . . 1·25 1·10

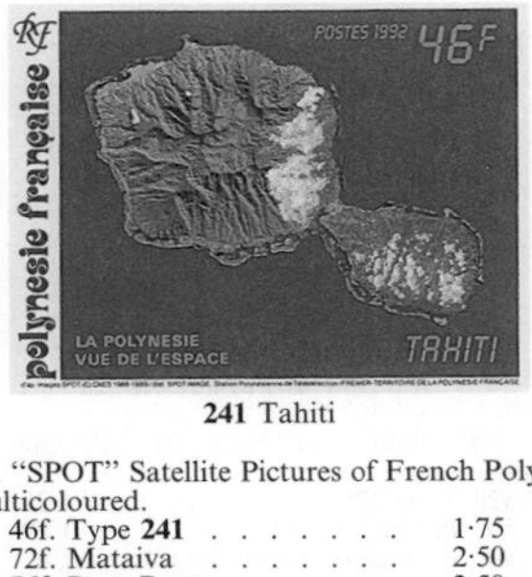

241 Tahiti

1992. "SPOT" Satellite Pictures of French Polynesia. Multicoloured.
637 46f. Type **241** . . . . 1·75 1·75
638 72f. Mataiva . . . . 2·50 2·00
639 76f. Bora-Bora . . . . 2·50 2·00
MS640 130 × 100 mm. 230f. Satellite highlighting Polynesian Islands. Imperf . . . . 7·00 7·25

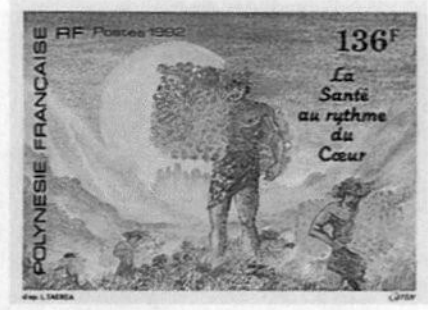

242 "Orange Carriers" (L. Taerea)

1992. World Health Day. "Health in Rhythm with the Heart".
641 **242** 136f. multicoloured . . . 4·25 3·25

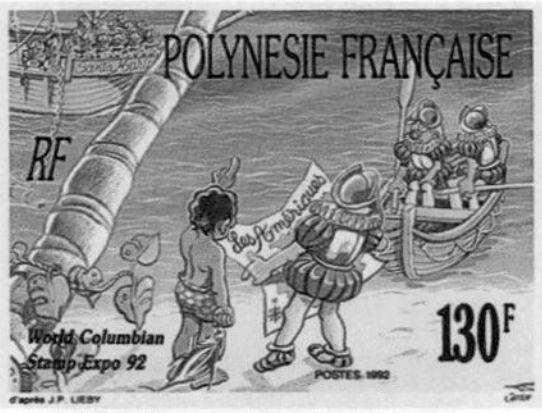

243 Sailor asking for Directions

1992. "World Columbian Stamp Expo '92" Exhibition, Chicago.
642 **243** 130f. multicoloured . . . 5·00 3·50
MS643 140 × 100 mm. 250f. Scene incorporating Type **243**. Imperf 6·75 8·00

244 Dancers, Tahiti

1992. Maori World (3rd series). Traditional Dances.
644 **244** 95f. brown . . . . 3·25 2·50
645 – 105f. brown . . . . . . 3·50 2·75
646 – 115f. green, brn & choc 3·75 2·75
DESIGNS: 105f. Hawaiian dancers; 115f. Night Dance by Tongan women.

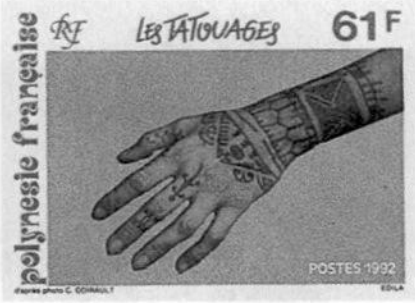

245 Tattooed Hand

1992. Tattoos. Multicoloured.
647 61f. Type **245** . . . . 2·50 1·90
648 64f. Tattooed man (vert) . . 2·50 2·00

246 Sailing Model Outrigger Canoes

1992. Children's Pastimes. Multicoloured.
649 22f. Type **246** . . . . 1·75 1·25
650 31f. String game . . . . . . 1·75 1·50
651 45f. Stilt walking (vert) . . . 2·00 1·75

247 Melville and Books

1992. Writers of the South Seas. 150th Anniv of Arrival in Polynesia of Herman Melville (novelist).
652 **247** 78f. multicoloured . . . . 3·75 2·00

248 Raft, Gambier Islands

1992. 6th Pacific Arts Festival, Rarotonga, Cook Islands.
653 **248** 40f. red . . . . 2·00 1·75
654 – 65f. blue . . . . 2·50 2·25
DESIGN: 65f. Pirogues off Taihiti.

249 Arrival of Mail at Cercle Bougainville Post Office, Papeete

1992. Centenary of First French Oceanic Settlements Stamp.
655 **249** 200f. multicoloured . . . 6·00 4·25

250 "Fare Tamarii" (Erhard Lux) **252** Cast-net Fisherman

1992. Artists in Polynesia. Multicoloured.
656 55f. Type **250** . . . . 2·25 1·75
657 60f. "Symphonie de Monettes" (Uschi) . . . . 2·25 1·75
658 75f. "Spear Fisherman" (Pierre Kienlen) . . . . . 2·75 2·00
659 85f. "Maternity" (Octave Morillot) . . . . 2·75 2·25

1993. Fishing in Couleur Lagoon. Self-adhesive. Imperf. (a) Size 26 × 36 mm.
670 **252** 46f. multicoloured . . . . 1·75 1·25

(b) Size 17 × 23 mm.
671 **252** 46f. multicoloured . . . . 1·75 1·25

253 Hanging Skipjack Tuna on Rack

1993. Bonito Fishing. Multicoloured.
672 68f. Bone hook and line . . . 2·25 1·60
673 84f. Fishing launch (horiz) . . 2·50 1·75
674 86f. Type **253** . . . . 2·75 2·00

254 U.S. Flag, Pilot and Airstrip

1993. 50th Anniv of Bora-Bora Airfield.
675 **254** 120f. multicoloured . . . 3·00 2·50

255 "Pahi Moorea"

1993. Birth Centenary of Jacques Boullaire (artist).
676 **255** 32f. brown . . . . 1·25 1·00
677 – 36f. orange . . . . 1·40 1·10
678 – 39f. violet . . . . 1·00 1·25
679 – 51f. brown . . . . 1·75 1·40
DESIGNS: 36f. "Pahi Tuamoto"; 39f. "Pahi Rurutu"; 51f. "Pahi Nuku-hiva".

256 Sportsman

1993. Sports Festival.
680 **256** 30f. multicoloured . . . . 1·25 1·00

257 Contestant

1993. 15th Anniv of Australian Mathematics Competition.
681 **257** 70f. multicoloured . . . . 2·25 1·75

258 Pele, Goddess of Volcanoes

259 Red Junglefowl crowing

1993. International Symposium on Intra-plate Volcanism, Punaauia (Tahiti).
682 **258** 140f. pink, brown & blk 3·50 2·50

1993. "Taipei 93" International Stamp Exhibition, Taipeh.
683 **259** 46f. multicoloured . . . . 1·25 60

260 Sight-seeing Canoe Trip

1993. International Tourism Day. Mult.
684 14f. Type **260** 65 40
685 20f. Tahitian women decorating tourist (vert) . . 80 50
686 29f. Beach picnic . . . . . . 1·10 70

261 Municipal Guard of 1843 and Modern Gendarme

1993. 150th Anniv of Arrival of First Gendarme in Tahiti.
687 **261** 100f. multicoloured . . . 2·75 1·90

262 Gerbault and "Firecrest"

1993. Birth Centenary of Alain Gerbault (round the world sailor).
688 **262** 150f. blue, red & green . . 4·00 3·50

263 Woman Dancing to Guitar Music (Vaea Sylvain)

1993. Artists in Polynesia. Multicoloured.
689 40f. Type **263** . . . . 1·25 75
690 70f. Portrait of Polynesian woman (Andre Marere) (vert) . . . . 1·75 1·10
691 80f. Four generations of women (Jean Shelsher) . . 2·00 1·25
692 90f. Woman in hat (Paul-Emile Victor) (vert) . . . . 2·75 1·60

264 Relief (Vahineroo Terupe)

1993. 30th Anniv of French Pacific School.
693 **264** 200f. multicoloured . . . 5·00 3·25

265 Spinner Dolphins

1994. Marine Mammals. Multicoloured.
694 25f. Spinner dolphin 75 45
695 68f. Type **265** . . . . 1·90 1·25
696 72f. Humpback whales (vert) 2·10 1·40

266 Spaniel

267 Sister Germaine Bruel and Child

1994. "Hong Kong '94" Int Stamp Exhibition.
697 **266** 51f. multicoloured . . . . 1·60 90

1994. 150th Anniv of Arrival of Sisters of St. Joseph of Cluny Congregation.
698 **267** 180f. multicoloured . . . 4·50 3·00

268 Tahiti Temple

1994. 150th Anniv of Arrival in Polynesia of Church of Jesus Christ of Latter Day Saints.
699 **268** 154f. multicoloured . . . 3·75 2·75

269 Father Gregoire (founder) and Polynesians

1994. Bicentenary of National Conservatory of Arts and Crafts, Paris, and 15th Anniv of Papeete Regional Associated Centre.
700 **269** 316f. multicoloured . . . 7·50 4·50

270 Emblem and Polynesians

1994. 10th Anniv of Internal Autonomy.
701 **270** 500f. multicoloured . . . 12·00 8·00

271 "Fare Vana'a"

1994. 20th Anniv of Tahiti Academy.
702 **271** 136f. black, red & blue . . 3·50 2·25

272 Papara

1994. Tahiti in Olden Days (4th series). Mult.
703 22f. Type **272** 75 45
704 26f. Mataiea coast 90 60
705 51f. Bamboo forest, Taravao (vert) . . . . 1·40 75

273 "Faaturuma" (Paul Gauguin)

1994.
706 **273** 1000f. multicoloured . . . 23·00 15·00

274 "Epiphyllum oxipetalum"

1994. Beauty of the Night (cactus).
707 **274** 51f. multicoloured . . . . 1·40 75

275 Bow of Pirogue No. 27

1994. "Hawaiki Nui Va'a 94" Pirogue Race. Multicoloured.
708 52f. Type **275** . . . . 1·25 75
709 76f. Pirogue (detail) . . . . 1·60 1·10
710 80f. Pirogue (different detail) 1·60 1·25
711 94f. Stern of pirogue and pirogue No. 60 . . . . . 2·00 1·40

Nos. 708/11 were issued together, se-tenant, forming a composite design.

276 Portrait by Michelle Villemin

1994. Artists in Polynesia. Paintings by artists named. Multicoloured.
712 62f. Type **276** . . . . 1·60 85
713 78f. Michele Dallet . . . . . 2·00 1·10
714 102f. Johel Blanchard . . . . 2·25 1·40
715 110f. P. Lacouture (horiz) . . 2·50 1·60

277 Don Domingo de Boenechea and Frigate

1995. 220th Anniv of Spanish Expeditions to Tautira.
716 **277** 92f. multicoloured . . . . 2·00 1·25

278 "Women on the Sea Shore" (Paul Gauguin)

280 Emblem

279 Pigs

1995. South Pacific Tourism Year.
717 **278** 92f. multicoloured . . . . 2·00 1·25

1995. Chinese New Year. Year of the Pig.
718 **279** 51f. multicoloured . . . . 1·40 75

1995. Pacific University Teachers' Training Institute.
719 **280** 59f. multicoloured . . . . 1·40 70

281 Head of Green Turtle

1995. Protected Species. Multicoloured.
720 22f. Type **281** 50 20
721 29f. Green turtle 75 40
722 91f. Black coral . . . . 2·00 1·25

282 Pasteur

1995. Death Centenary of Louis Pasteur (chemist).
723 **282** 290f. blue and lt blue . . 6·50 4·00

283 Scene from Novel

1995. 113th Anniv of Publication of "Le Mariage de Loti" by Pierre Loti.
724 **283** 66f. multicoloured . . . . 1·60 80

284 Woman with Bowl of Monoi — **285** Rapa Island Fruit Dove

1995. Tahiti Monoi (blend of coconut oil and tiare flower).
725 **284** 150f. multicoloured . . . 3·25 1·75

1995. "Unique Birds of the World". Mult.
726 22f. Type **285** 55 40
727 44f. Marquesas pigeon . . . 1·25 55

286 Black Pearls

1995. Tahitian Pearls. Multicoloured.
728 66f. Type **286** . . . . . . 1·40 75
729 84f. Coloured pearls . . . . 1·90 1·10

287 Alvaro de Mendana de Neira and "Todos los Santos" (galleon)

1995. 400th Anniv of Discovery of Marquesas Islands. Multicoloured.
730 161f. Type **287** . . . . 3·00 1·75
731 195f. Pedro Fernandez de Quiros and map of islands 3·50 2·50

288 Games Mascot — **289** Pandanus Tree

1995. 10th South Pacific Games, Tahiti.
732 **288** 83f. multicoloured . . . . 1·90 1·00

1995. "Singapore'95" International Stamp Exhibition. Multicoloured.
733 91f. Type **289** . . . . 2·00 1·25
734 91f. Pandanus (flower) . . . 2·00 1·25
735 91f. Pandanus (fruit) . . . . 2·00 1·25
736 91f. Plaiting leaves . . . . . 2·00 1·25

290 Man and Woman wearing Headdresses and Emblem

1995. 50th Anniv of U.N.O.
737 **290** 420f. multicoloured . . . 7·25 4·75

291 "Paddler with Yellow Dog" (Philippe Dubois)

1996. Artists in Polynesia. Multicoloured.
738 57f. Type **291** . . . . 1·00 70
739 76f. "Afternoon in Vaitape" (Maui Seaman) . . . . . 1·50 95
740 79f. "Woman with White Hat" (Simone Testeguide) (horiz) . . . . 1·75 1·10
741 100f. "Kellum House in Moorea" (Christian Deloffre) (horiz) . . . . . 2·10 1·40

1996. Tahiti in Olden Days (5th series). As T **272**. Multicoloured.
742 18f. La Fautaua 40 25
743 30f. Punaauia Grove 60 35
744 35f. Coconut palm forest, Tautira 70 45

292 Rats — **293** Queen Pomare

1996. Chinese New Year. Year of the Rat.
745 **292** 51f. multicoloured . . . . 1·10 55

1996. No value expressed. (a) Size 26 × 36 mm.
746 **293** (51f.) multicoloured . . . 80 50

(b) Size 17 × 23 mm. Self-adhesive.
747 **293** (51f.) multicoloured . . . 80 50

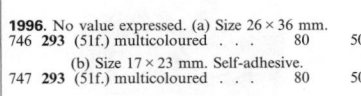

294 Victor and Hemispheres

1996. Paul-Emile Victor (polar explorer) Commemoration.
748 **294** 500f. multicoloured . . . 8·50 5·50

295 Pertusus Cone

1996. Sea Shells. Multicoloured.
749 10f. Type **295** 25 20
750 15f. "Cypraea alisonae" (cowrie) 30 20
751 25f. "Vexillum roseotinctum" (ribbed mitre) 45 30

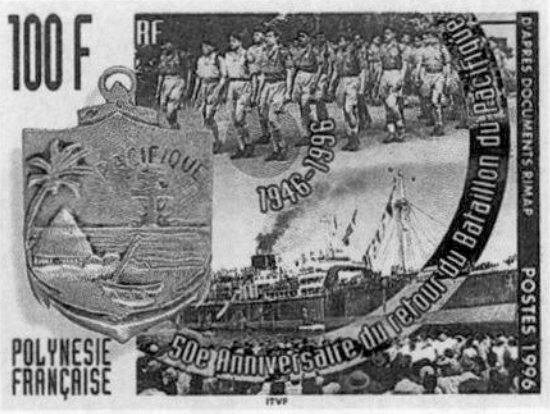

296 Badge, Soldiers and "Sagittaire" (troopship)

1996. 50th Anniv of Return of Pacific Battalion from Second World War.
752 **296** 100f. multicoloured . . . 2·00 1·40

297 Dancers

1996. "China'96" Int Stamp Exn, Peking.
753 **297** 50f. multicoloured . . . . 1·00 55
MS754 100 × 76 mm. 200f. Staff and pupils of Chinese school, Tahiti, 1940. Inmperf . . . . 4·50 4·50

298 Red-footed Booby

1996. Marine Birds. Multicoloured.
755 66f. Type **298** . . . . 1·10 70
756 79f. Great frigate bird . . . 1·60 80
757 84f. Common noddy . . . . 1·75 90

299 Pahu, Ukulele and Toere

1996. Musical Instruments. Multicoloured.
758 5f. Type **299** 10 10
759 9f. Toere 20 20
760 14f. Pu and vivo (wind instruments) 25 20

300 Polynesian Cicada

1996.
761 **300** 66f. multicoloured . . . . 1·25 75

301 Ruahatu, God of the Ocean — **302** Lemasson's 1913 Tahitian Girl Stamp Design

1996. 7th Pacific Arts Festival.
762 **301** 70f. black and blue . . . 1·40 90

1996. Stamp Day. 40th Death Anniv of Henri Lemasson (photographer and stamp designer).
763 **302** 92f. multicoloured . . . . 1·90 1·25

303 Assembly Building

1996. 50th Anniversaries of Territorial Assembly and Autumn Stamp Salon.
764 **303** 85f. multicoloured . . . . 1·60 1·10

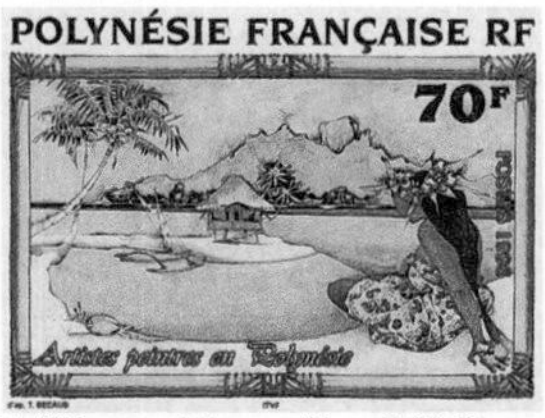

304 "Woman sitting on Shore" (T. Becaud)

1996. Artists in Polynesia. Multicoloured.
765 70f. Type **304** . . . . 1·10 70
766 85f. "Woman with leaf headdress" (M. Noguier) (vert) . . . . 1·50 80
767 92f. "Woman with yellow headdress" (C. de Dinechin) (vert) . . . . . 1·60 1·10
768 96f. "Two women" (A. Lang) (vert) . . . . 1·90 1·25

305 Hand writing — **306** Oxen

1997. 80th Anniv of Society for Oceanic Studies.
769 **305** 55f. brown 95 55

1997. Chinese New Year. Year of the Ox.
770 **306** 13f. multicoloured 25 20

307 Arrival of "Duff" (full-rigged missionary ship)

1997. Bicentenary of Evangelical Church of French Polynesia. Multicoloured.
771 43f. Type **307** 85 60
772 43f. Missionaries at Matavai 85 60

308 Uru Leaves

1997. Tifaifai. Multicoloured.
773 1f. Type **308** 10 10
774 5f. Tiare flower 15 10
775 70f. Hibiscus flowers . . . . 1·25 65

309 "Papeete-Zelee" (schooner) — **311** Male Dancer

310 Tiare Flower

1997. "Pacific '97" International Stamp Exhibition, San Francisco. Maritime Link between San Francisco and Papeete. Mult.
790 92f. Type **309** . . . . 1·75 1·10
791 92f. "Tropic Bird" (barquentine) . . . . . . 1·75 1·10
MS792 100 × 75 mm. Nos. 790/1 (sold at 400f.) . . . . 7·25 7·25

1997. Tourism. Multicoloured.
793 85f. Type **310** . . . . 1·50 70
794 85f. Canoeing . . . . 1·50 70
795 85f. Spearman . . . . 1·50 70

796 85f. Tahiti . . . . 1·50 70
797 85f. Barrier reef anemone-fish 1·50 70
798 85f. Women on shore . . . . 1·50 70
799 85f. Shell . . . . 1·50 70
800 85f. Outrigger canoe at sunset 1·50 70
801 85f. Snorkelling . . . . . . 1·50 70
802 85f. Pineapples and bananas 1·50 70
803 85f. Palm tree on beach . . . 1·50 70
804 85f. Dancers . . . . 1·50 70

1997. Dance Costumes. Multicoloured.
805 4f. Type **311** 10 10
806 9f. Female dancer 20 15
807 11f. Couple 25 20

312 "Kon Tiki" (after Christian Faugerat)

1997. 50th Anniv of Thor Heyerdahl's "Kon Tiki" (replica of balsa raft) Expedition from Peru to Tuamoto Island, South Pacific.
808 **312** 88f. multicoloured . . . . 1·75 1·10

313 Man carrying Fruits on Yoke (Monique Garnier-Bissol)

1997. Artists in Polynesia. Multicoloured.
809 85f. Type **313** . . . . 1·00 70
810 96f. Mother-of-pearl mermaid and turtles (Camelia Maraea) . . . . 1·40 95
811 110f. Pot (Peter Owen) (vert) 1·50 1·10
812 126f. Coconut halves in water (Elisabeth Stefanovitch) . . 1·90 1·40

314 "Te arii vahine" (Paul Gauguin)

1997. Autumn Salon, Paris.
813 **314** 600f. multicoloured . . . 8·25 6·00

315 Santa Claus Hat on Statue, Candy-striped Palm Tree and Dish of Gifts

1997. Christmas.
814 **315** 118f. multicoloured . . . 1·75 1·25

316 Adult and Cub

1998. Chinese New Year. Year of the Tiger.
815 **316** 96f. multicoloured . . . . 1·60 1·00

317 Grumman Widgeon

1998. Aviation. Multicoloured.
816 70f. Type **317** . . . . . . 1·10 75
817 70f. Fairchild FH-227 . . . . 1·10 75
818 85f. De Havilland D.H.C.6 Twin Otter . . . . 1·25 90
819 85f. Aerospatiale ATR 42-500 1·25 90
No. 816 is wrongly inscribed "Grumann".

318 "Dendrobium" "Royal King"

1998. Orchids. Multicoloured.
820 5f. Type **318** 15 10
821 20f. "Oncidium" "Ramsey" (vert) 35 20
822 50f. "Ascocenda" "Laksi" (vert) 75 40
823 100f. "Cattleya" hybrid . . . 1·50 90

319 "The Lovers"

1998. 150th Birth Anniv of Paul Gauguin (artist).
824 **319** 1000f. multicoloured . . . 13·00 8·00

320 Boy in Football Strip

321 Woman wearing Shell Necklaces

1998. World Cup Football Championship, France.
825 **320** 85f. multicoloured . . . . 1·25 70

1998. Necklaces and Headdresses. Mult.
826 55f. Type **321** 75 45
827 65f. Woman wearing shell necklaces and bracelet . . 95 55
828 70f. Woman in floral headdress 95 55
829 80f. Woman with floral headdress and garland . . 1·25 65

322 Painting by Stanley Haumani

1998. Undersea Life.
830 **322** 200f. multicoloured . . . 3·00 1·60

323 "Papeete Bay"

1998. Autumn Stamp Salon, Paris. Paintings by R. Gillotin. Multicoloured.
831 250f. Type **323** . . . . 3·50 2·00
832 250f. "Papeete Bay" (different) . . . . 3·50 2·00
MS833 142 × 105 mm. Nos. 831/2. Imperf . . . . 7·50 7·50

1998. French Victory in World Cup Football Championship. As No. 825 but additionally inscr "FRANCE championne du monde" on boy's shirt and with colours of French flag forming frame around design.
834 **320** 85f. multicoloured . . . . 1·25 65

324 "Return from the Market" (A. Deymonaz)

1998. Daily Life. Paintings by Andre Deymonaz. Multicoloured.
835 70f. Type **324** . . . . 1·10 55
836 100f. "Sellers of Skipjack Tuna" . . . . 1·40 90
837 102f. "Fishermen Departing" (horiz) . . . . 1·50 95
838 110f. "Women in Sunday Best" (horiz) . . . . . 1·60 95

325 Hares

1999. Chinese New Year. Year of the Hare.
839 **325** 118f. multicoloured . . . 1·75 90

326 Couple

1999. St. Valentine's Day.
840 **326** 96f. multicoloured . . . . 1·25 75

327 Thorny Seahorse

1999. Marine Life. Multicoloured.
841 70f. Lionfish . . . . 1·10 55
842 85f. Type **327** . . . . 1·25 65
843 90f. Painted angler . . . . . 1·40 70
844 120f. Three-spined scorpionfish . . . . 1·75 95

328 Tattooed Man

329 Children

1999. Tattooes. Multicoloured.
845 90f. Type **328** . . . . 1·25 80
846 120f. Tattooed man with cloak . . . . 1·90 1·10

1999. Mothers' Day. Multicoloured.
847 85f. Type **329** . . . . 1·25 60
848 120f. Two children with heart of blossoms (horiz) . . . . 1·60 90

330 Papaya

1999. Fruits of Fenua (Tahiti) (1st series). Multicoloured.
849 85f. Type **330** . . . . 1·25 75
850 85f. Guava ("La goyave") . . 1·25 75
851 85f. Red mombin . . . . . 1·25 75
852 85f. Rambutan . . . . 1·25 75
853 85f. Star-apple ("La pomme-etoile") . . . . 1·25 75
854 85f. Gooseberry tree ("La seurette") . . . . 1·25 75
855 85f. Rose apple ("La pomme-rose") . . . . 1·25 75
856 85f. Five fingers ("La carambole") . . . . 1·25 75
857 85f. Spanish lime . . . . . . 1·25 75
858 85f. Sugar-apple ("La pomme-cannelle") . . . . 1·25 75
859 85f. Cashew ("La pomme de cajou") . . . . 1·25 75
860 85f. Passion fruit . . . . . 1·25 75
See also Nos. 864/5.

331 Cancellation, 1997 9f. Stamp and Islanders

1999. 150th Anniv of First French Stamp.
861 **331** 180f. multicoloured . . . 2·75 1·60
MS862 101 × 70 mm. No. 861 . . 7·50 7·50

332 Chopin and Score

1999. 150th Death Anniv of Frederic Chopin (composer).
863 **332** 250f. multicoloured . . . 3·75 2·10

333 Breadfruit

1999. Fruit of Fenua (2nd series). Multicoloured.
864 85f. Type **333** . . . . 1·25 70
865 120f. Coconut (horiz) . . . . 1·75 1·00

334 Microscope, Disease Carriers and Atomic Model

1999. 50th Anniv of Louis Malarde Institute (for research into public health).
866 **334** 400f. multicoloured . . . 5·25 3·00

335 Nude by J. Sorgniard

1999. Painters and the Nude in Tahiti. Showing paintings by artists named. Multicoloured.

867	85f. Type **335**	1·25	70
868	120f. J. Dubrusk	1·60	1·00
869	180f. C. Deloffre	2·25	1·50
870	250f. J. Gandouin	3·25	2·10

336 Woman blowing Conch

1999. Year 2000.

871 **336**	85f. multicoloured	90	60

337 Emblem

1999. 5th Marquesas Islands' Art Festival.

872 **337**	90f. multicoloured	1·00	70

338 Adult holding Baby's Hand

2000. New Millennium. Multicoloured.

873	85f. Type **338**	90	60
874	120f. Part of child's face (horiz)	1·25	85

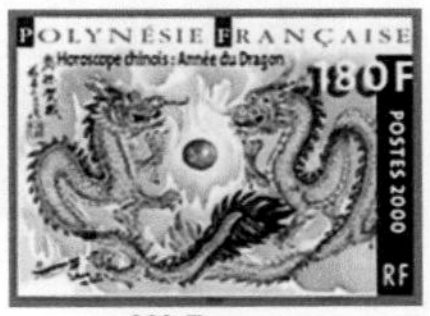
339 Dragons

2000. Chinese New Year. Year of the Dragon.

875 **339**	180f. multicoloured	2·00	1·40

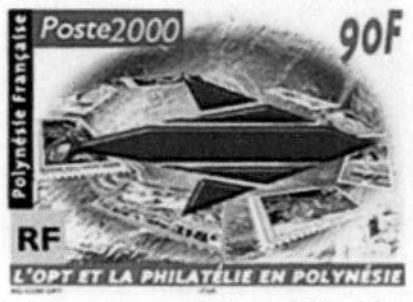
340 Stamps and Postal Emblem

2000. Philately.

876 **340**	90f. multicoloured	1·00	70

341 Tattooed Hand

2000. 1st International Tattooing Festival, Raiatea. Multicoloured.

877	85f. Type **341**	90	60
878	120f. Woman with tattooed hand and ear	1·25	85
879	130f. Man with tattooed hands	1·40	90
880	160f. Man holding tattooed hand in front of eye	1·60	1·10

342 Polynesian Women

2000. Polynesian Women.

881 **342**	300f. multicoloured	4·00	2·50
MS882	106 × 80 mm. No. 881 (sold at 500f.)	6·50	4·25

343 White Dress

2000. Traditional Costumes. Showing women wearing different traditional dresses. Multicoloured.

883	85f. Type **343**	90	60
884	120f. Green and white floral dress with hat	1·25	85
885	160f. White lace tunic and long cap skirt	1·60	1·10
886	250f. Embroidered red dress	3·25	2·10

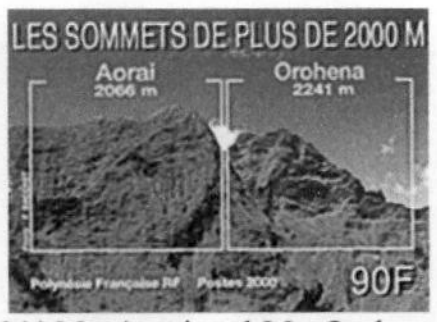
344 Mt. Aorai and Mt. Orohena

2000. Mountains over 2000 Metres on Tahiti. Mult.

887	90f. Type **344**	1·00	70
888	180f. Mt. Aorai and Mt. Orohena (different)	2·25	1·50

345 Fruit Carriers' Race

2000. Traditional Sports. Multicoloured.

889	120f. Type **345**	1·25	85
890	250f. Stone lifting (vert)	3·25	2·10

346 Woven Fans

2000. Traditional Crafts. Multicoloured.

891	85f. Type **346**	90	60
892	85f. Woven hat	90	60

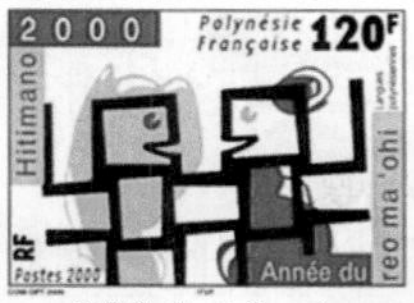
347 Stylized Couple

2000. National Tahitian Language Year.

893 **347**	120f. yellow, red & blk	1·25	85

348 Flower and Satellite

2000. New Millennium.

894 **348**	85f. multicoloured	90	60

349 Main Gateway

2001. Centenary of Ecole Centrale. Multicoloured.

895	85f. Type **349**	90	60
896	85f. Present day main building	90	60

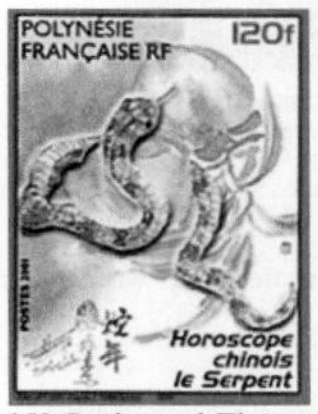
350 Snake and Flower

351 Vaiharuru Waterfall, Papenoo, Tahiti

2001. Chinese New Year. Year of the Snake.

897 **350**	120f. multicoloured	1·25	85

2001. Polynesian Nature. Multicoloured.

898	35f. Type **351**	35	30
899	50f. Lake Vaihiria, Tahiti (horiz)	55	45
900	90f. Hakaui Valley, Nuku Hiva, Marquesas Islands	95	75

352 Children

2001. Year of the Polynesian Child.

901 **352**	55f. multicoloured	60	50

353 Eddie Lund (pianist and songwriter)

2001. Entertainers. Multicoloured.

902	85f. Type **353**	85	70
903	120f. Charley Mauu (musician)	1·25	1·00
904	130f. Bimbo Moetrauri (musician)	1·40	1·10
905	180f. Marie Mariteragi (singer and dancer) and Emma Terangi (singer) (horiz)	1·90	1·50

354 *Monovai* (liner)

2001. 60th Anniv of Departure of Pacific Battalion Volunteers.

906 **354**	85f. multicoloured	85	70

355 Wave

2001. Teahupoo Wave.

907 **355**	120f. multicoloured	1·25	1·00

356 Emblem

2001. 17th Anniv of Internal Autonomy.

908 **356**	250f. multicoloured	2·50	2·00
MS909	142 × 105 mm. No. 908	2·50	2·00

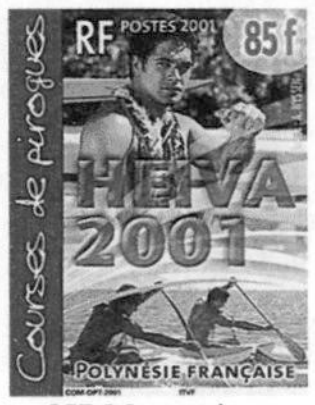
357 Men racing

2001. "Heiva 2001" Traditional Arts and Sports Festival. Canoe Racing. Multicoloured.

910	85f. Type **357**	85	70
911	120f. Women racing	1·25	1·00
MS912	140 × 105 mm. Nos. 910/11. Imperf (sold at 250f.)	2·10	1·75

358 Tou

2001. Native Hardwood Trees. Multicoloured.

913	90f. Type **358**	90	75
914	130f. Ati	1·40	1·10
915	180f. Miro	2·00	1·60

359 Couple and Emblem

2001. A.I.D.S. Awareness Campaign.

916 **359**	55f. multicoloured	60	50

360 "Building Europe"

2001. U.N. Year of Dialogue among Civilizations.

917 **360**	500f. multicoloured	5·50	4·50

361 Tiare (*Gardenia tahitensis*)

2001. Native Flowers. Multicoloured.

918	35f. Type **361**	35	30
919	50f. Pua (*Fagraea berteriana*)	55	40
920	85f. Taina (*Gardenia jasminoides*)	85	70

362 Polynesian Crib

2001.

921	**362**	120f. multicoloured	1·25	1·00

363 Parcel and Flowers ("Joyeuses fetes")

2002. Greetings Stamps. Multicoloured.

922	55c. Type **363**	65	50
923	55c. Pink hibiscus ("Felicitations")	65	50
924	85c. As No. 922 but with blue background	1·00	80
925	85c. Red hibiscus ("Felicitations")	1·00	80

364 Horses

2002. Chinese New Year. Year of the Horse.

926	**364**	130f. multicoloured	1·50	1·25

365 Canoeist and Emblem

2002. 10th World Outrigger Canoe Championship. Multicoloured.

927	120f. Type **365**	1·40	1·10
928	120f. Masked canoeist and emblem	1·40	1·10

366 Urchin (*Echinometra sp.*)

2002. Sea Urchins. Multicoloured.

929	35f. Type **366**	40	30
930	50f. *Heterocentrotus trigonarius*	60	50
931	90f. Banded urchin (*Echinothrix calamaris*)	1·10	90
932	120f. *Toxopneustes sp.*	1·40	1·10

367 Couple holding Droplet of Blood

368 Children holding Football

2002. Blood Donation.

933	**367**	130f. multicoloured	1·50	1·25

2002. World Cup Football Championship, Japan and South Korea.

934	**368**	85f. multicoloured	1·00	80

369 Coconut Pulp Peeling

2002. "Heiva 2002" Traditional Arts and Sports Festival. Multicoloured.

935	85f. Type **369**	1·00	80
936	120f. Fruit carrying races	1·40	1·10
937	250f. Javelin throwing	3·00	2·40

370 James Norman Hall and House

2002. Inauguration of James Norman Hall House (museum).

938	**370**	90f. multicoloured	1·10	90

The museum commemorates the writer James Norman Hall.

371 Market Place, Papeete (A. Deymonaz)

2002.

939	**371**	400f. multicoloured	4·75	3·75
MS940		142 × 105 mm. No. 939	4·75	3·75

No. **MS**940 is inscribed for "Amphilex 2002" International Stamp Exhibition, Amsterdam in the margin.

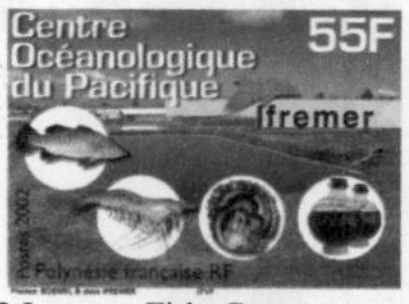

372 Lagoon, Fish, Crustaceans and Bottles

2002. French Research Institute for Marine Exploitation. Multicoloured.

941	55f. Type **372**	65	50
942	90f. Aerial view of centre	1·10	90

373 Surfer

2002. "Taapuna Master 2002" Surfing Competition, Tahiti.

943	**373**	120f. multicoloured	1·40	1·10

374 *Hibiscus tiliaceus*

2002. Seaside Flowers. Multicoloured.

944	85f. Type **374**	1·00	80
945	130f. *Scaveola sericea*	1·60	1·25
946	180f. *Guettarda speciosa*	2·25	1·75

375 Bus and Dancers

2002. Festivals. Multicoloured.

947	55f. Type **375**	70	55
948	120f. Musicians (vert)	1·50	1·25

376 Goats

377 Two Women

2003. New Year. Year of the Goat.

949	**376**	120f. multicoloured	1·40	1·10

2003. Polynesian Women.

950	**377**	55f. multicoloured	60	50

378 Waterfall, Trees and Lake

2003. Polynesian Waterfalls.

951	**378**	330f. multicoloured	3·75	3·00

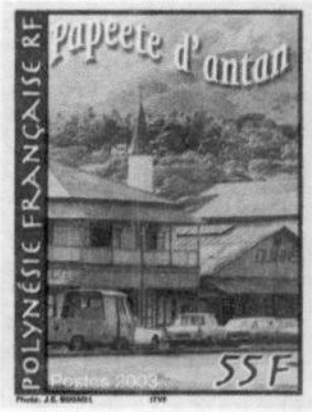

379 Building with Balcony

381 Pirogue

380 Fish

2003. Papeete in Old Photographs. Sheet 148 × 106 mm containing T **379** and similar multicoloured designs.

MS952	55f. Type **379**; 85f. Sailing ship (horiz); 90f. Men with bicycles (52 × 32 mm); 120f. Tree-lined street (52 × 32 mm)	4·00	4·00

2003. Polynesian Marine Life.

953	**380**	460f. multicoloured	5·25	4·25

2003. Pirogues (sailing canoes). Multicoloured.

954	85f. Type **381**	1·00	80
956	85f. Boy seated on sail beam	1·00	80
957	85f. Twin-sailed craft with hills behind (horiz)	1·00	80
958	85f. Craft with three crew members (horiz)	1·00	80

382 Fire Walkers

2003.

959	**382**	130f. multicoloured	1·50	1·20

383 Bi-valve

2003. Shellfish.

960	**383**	420f. multicoloured	4·75	3·75

384 "Ahaoe Feii ou Quoi?" (Are you jealous?)

2003. Death Centenary of Paul Gauguin (artist).

961	**384**	250f. multicoloured	2·75	2·20

385 Flag

2003.

962	**385**	(60f.) multicoloured	70	60

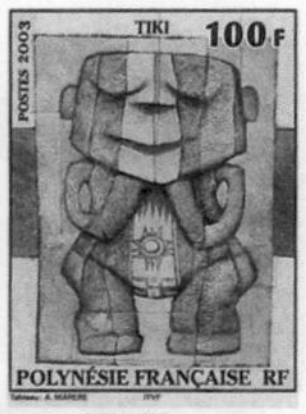

386 Figure

2003. Tiki (1st issue).

963	**386**	100f. multicoloured	1·10	90

See also No. 968.

387 Orchid

2003. Flowers. Multicoloured.

964	90f. Type **387**	1·00	80
965	130f. Rose	1·60	1·30

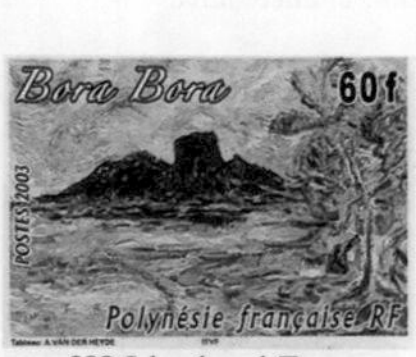

388 Island and Trees

2003. Bora Bora. Multicoloured.

966	60f. Type **388**	70	60
967	60f. Aerial view of island	70	60

389 Face

2003. Tiki (2nd issue).

968	**389**	190f. multicoloured	2·20	1·70

390 Landscape

2003.

969	**390**	90f. multicoloured	1·00	80

391 Monkeys **392** Women ironing Cloth

2004. Year of the Monkey.

970	**391**	130f. multicoloured	1·50	90

2004. Scenes from Daily Life. Multicoloured.

971	60f. Type **392**	70	45
972	90f. Street scene (vert)	1·00	80

393 Woman seated in Cane Chair

2004. Polynesian Women.

973	**393**	55f. multicoloured	60	50

OFFICIAL STAMPS

O **100** Uru O **251** 1840 French Colonies 40c. Stamps

1977. Native Fruits.

O240	O **100**	1f. multicoloured	2·25	2·25
O241		2f. multicoloured	1·90	2·25
O242		3f. multicoloured	1·90	2·25
O243		5f. multicoloured	2·50	2·00
O244	–	7f. multicoloured	2·25	2·25
O245	–	8f. multicoloured	2·25	2·25
O246	–	10f. multicoloured	2·25	2·25
O247	–	15f. multicoloured	2·75	2·75
O248	–	19f. multicoloured	2·75	2·75
O249	–	20f. multicoloured	3·00	2·75
O250	–	25f. multicoloured	3·75	3·25
O251	–	35f. multicoloured	4·25	3·75
O252	–	50f. multicoloured	4·75	4·75
O253	–	100f. multicoloured	9·00	8·25
O254	–	200f. multicoloured	16·00	12·00

DESIGNS: 7f., 8f., 10f., 15f. Vi Tahiti; 19f., 20f., 25f., 35f. Avocat; 50f., 100f., 200f. Vi Popaa.

1993.

O660	O **251**	1f. red, brown & blk	70	70
O777	–	2f. multicoloured	10	10
O662	–	3f. black, red & yell	70	70
O779	–	5f. black, red & yell	15	15
O780	–	9f. multicoloured	20	15
O781	–	10f. multicoloured	20	15
O782	–	20f. multicoloured	30	20
O666	–	46f. multicoloured	1·75	1·40
O666a	–	51f. multicoloured	1·90	1·60
O785	–	70f. multicoloured	80	60
O786	–	85f. multicoloured	1·40	1·10
O787	–	100f. multicoloured	1·10	90
O788	–	200f. multicoloured	2·25	1·75

DESIGNS—HORIZ: 2f. French Colonies 1877 Peace and Commerce 40c. and 1872 Ceres 25c. stamps; 3f. French Colonies Peace and Commerce stamp with Papeete 1884 postmark; 5f. 1884 Papeete postmark; 9f. Pair of Oceanic Settlements 1948 15f. stamps with Papeete postmark; 10f. Oceanic Settlements 1892 5c. stamp and 1894 postmark; 20f. Oceanic Settlements 1892 10 and 15c. stamps with Tahiti postmark; 46f. Oceanic Settlements 1930 90c. Kanakas stamps; 51f. Oceanic Settlements 1942 5 and 10f. Free French stamps with Vaitepaua postmark; 70f. "Visit Tahiti" postmark; 100f. Oceanic Settlements 1956 3f. Dry dock stamp; 200f. Oceanic Settlements 1953 14f. Gauguin stamps. VERT: 85f. Oceanic Settlements 1921 25 on 15c. stamp.

POSTAGE DUE STAMPS

D **4** Polynesian Mask D **164** Mother of Pearl Fish-hook

1958.

D17	D **4**	1f. green and brown	1·25	4·25
D18		3f. red and indigo	1·25	4·50
D19		5f. blue and brown	1·60	5·00

1984. Multicoloured.

D416	1f. Type D **164**	1·40	1·90
D417	3f. Tahitian bowl (horiz)	1·40	1·90
D418	5f. Marquesian fan (horiz)	1·40	1·90
D419	10f. Lamp stand	1·50	1·90
D420	20f. Wooden head-rest (horiz)	2·25	2·00
D421	50f. Scoop (horiz)	2·75	2·75

FRENCH POST OFFICES IN CHINA Pt. 6

General issues for the French post offices in China, which were closed in 1922.

1894. 100 centimes = 1 franc.
1907. 100 cents = 1 piastre.

Stamps of Indo-China optd **CHINE** are listed under Indo-Chinese Post Offices in China.

1894. Stamps of France optd **Chine**.

2	**10**	5c. green	1·60	75
4		10c. black on lilac	4·50	1·60
6		15c. blue	5·75	1·25
8		20c. red on green	4·50	2·75
9		25c. black on pink	5·50	80
10		30c. brown	4·00	4·50
11		40c. red on yellow	6·75	4·25
12		50c. red	16·00	2·75
14		75c. brown on orange	75·00	42·00
15		1f. green	9·25	2·25
16		2f. brown on blue	29·00	23·00
17		5f. mauve on lilac	80·00	48·00

1900. No. 15 surch **25**.

18	**10**	25 on 1f. green	65·00	48·00

1901. No. 9 surch.

19	**10**	2c. on 25c. black on pink	£750	£200
20		4c. on 25c. black on pink	£650	£200
21		6c. on 25c. black on pink	£750	£300
22		16c. on 25c. black on pink	£200	£160

1902. "Blanc", "Mouchon" and "Merson" key-types inscr "CHINE".

37a	A	5c. green	3·50	70
38	B	10c. red	1·75	1·60
39		15c. red	2·25	1·50
40		20c. brown	4·50	5·00
41		25c. blue	3·75	1·60
42		30c. mauve	5·25	6·50
43	C	40c. red and blue	11·00	12·00
44		50c. brown and lilac	12·50	8·75
45		1f. red and green	20·00	10·00
46		2f. lilac and buff	52·00	30·00
47		5f. blue and buff	70·00	42·00

1903. No. 39 surch **5**.

48	B	5 on 15c. red	15·00	9·25

1907. Stamps of 1902 surch with new value in French and Chinese.

92	A	1c. on 5c. orange	3·25	3·50
84		2c. on 5c. green	95	20
93	B	2c. on 10c. green	6·25	5·75
94		3c. on 15c. orange	8·75	8·25
77		4c. on 10c. red	2·25	85
95		4c. on 20c. brown	11·00	10·00
96		5c. on 25c. purple	7·50	4·50
78		6c. on 15c. red	1·75	50
97		6c. on 30c. red	15·00	12·50
87		8c. on 20c. brown	1·40	1·00
80		10c. on 25c. blue	1·25	15
98		10c. on 50c. blue	16·00	12·00
81	C	20c. on 50c. brown & lilac	2·75	1·00
89	B	20c. on 50c. blue	55·00	40·00
99	C	20c. on 1f. red and green	32·00	28·00
90		40c. on 1f. red and green	4·50	2·75
100		40c. on 2f. red and green	40·00	27·00
101		1pi. on 5f. blue and buff	£110	£110
83		2pi. on 5f. blue and buff	24·00	17·00
91		$2 on 5f. blue and buff	£120	£110

POSTAGE DUE STAMPS

1901. Postage Due stamps of France optd **Chine**.

D23	D **11**	5c. blue	3·50	1·90
D24		10c. brown	5·75	6·00
D25		15c. green	8·50	6·75
D26		20c. olive	6·00	9·25
D27		30c. red	12·50	9·00
D28		50c. red	16·00	12·00

1903. Stamps of 1894 and 1902 optd **A PERCEVOIR**.

D58	**10**	5c. green	£1300	£250
D62	A	5c. green	£900	£500
D51	**10**	10c. black on lilac	£5000	£4500
D63	B	10c. red	£325	60·00
D60	**10**	15c. blue	£700	65·00
D64	B	15c. red	£425	70·00
D61	**10**	30c. brown	£350	55·00

1911. Postage Due stamps of France surch with new value in French and Chinese.

D102	D **11**	1c. on 5c. blue	60·00	60·00
D 92		2c. on 5c. blue	1·25	2·75
D103		2c. on 10c. brown	70·00	65·00
D 93		4c. on 10c. brown	1·90	2·25
D104		4c. on 20c. olive	70·00	65·00
D 94		8c. on 20c. olive	2·25	2·00
D105		10c. on 50c. red	70·00	65·00
D 95		20c. on 50c. red	3·00	2·00

FRENCH POST OFFICES IN CRETE Pt. 6

These offices were closed in 1914.

100 centimes = 1 franc.
25 centimes = 1 piastre.

1902. "Blanc", "Mouchon" and "Merson" key-types inscr "CRETE".

1	A	1c. grey	1·50	95
2		2c. red	70	1·50
3		3c. red	1·10	2·50
4		4c. brown	1·75	3·25
5		5c. green	1·75	1·60
6	B	10c. red	2·25	2·75
7		15c. orange	2·40	4·00
8		20c. red	2·25	4·25
9		25c. blue	4·00	2·75
10		30c. mauve	6·50	8·25
11	C	40c. red and blue	12·00	13·00
12		50c. brown and lavender	9·50	14·00
13		1f. red and green	14·00	14·00
14		2f. lilac and buff	28·00	35·00
15		5f. blue and buff	35·00	45·00

1903. Surch in figures and words.

16	B	1pi. on 25c. blue	38·00	38·00
17	C	2pi. on 50c. brown & lav	60·00	55·00
18		4pi. on 1f. red and green	85·00	85·00
19		8pi. on 2f. lilac and buff	85·00	85·00
20		20pi. on 5f. blue and buff	£140	£130

FRENCH POST OFFICES IN ETHIOPIA Pt. 6

100 centimes = 1 franc.

1906. Perf or imperf.

25	A	25c. blue	40·00	40·00
26	B	50c. brown and lavender	£160	£160
27		1f. red and green	£375	£375

FRENCH POST OFFICES IN MOROCCO Pt. 6

French Post Offices were first established in Morocco in 1862, using the stamps of France. For stamps used by French Post Offices in Tangier after 1912 see under that heading.

100 centimos = 1 peseta.

1891. Stamps of France surch in Spanish currency (centimos on equivalent centime values).

1	**10**	5c. on 5c. green	7·50	1·60
5		10c. on 10c. blk on lilac	27·00	1·25
6		20c. on 20c. red on grn	27·00	19·00
7		25c. on 25c. blk on pink	14·50	60
8a		50c. on 50c. red	55·00	9·00
10		1p. on 1f. green	50·00	38·00
11		2p. on 2f. brown on blue	£150	£150

1893. Postage Due stamps of France optd **TIMBRE POSTE** and bar.

12	D **11**	5c. black	£1500	£600
13		10c. black	£1300	£400

1902. "Blanc", "Mouchon" and "Merson" key types inscr "MAROC" and surch in Spanish currency in figures and words.

14	A	1c. on 1c. grey	30	15
15		2c. on 2c. red	20	15
16		3c. on 3c. red	1·10	20
17		4c. on 4c. brown	5·50	4·50
18a		5c. on 5c. green	5·50	30
19	B	10c. on 10c. red	3·50	15
20		20c. on 20c. red	15·00	1·25
21		25c. on 25c. blue	28·00	15
22		35c. on 35c. lilac	16·00	7·00
23	C	50c. on 50c. brown & lilac	30·00	2·00
24		1p. on 1f. red and green	75·00	50·00
25		2p. on 2f. lilac and yellow	90·00	55·00

1903. Postage Due stamps of 1896 optd **P.P.** in box.

26	D **11**	5c. on 5c. blue	£850	
27		10c. on 10c. brown	£1700	

1911. Key-types surch with figure of value and Arabic word.

28	A	1c. on 1c. grey	15	20
29		2c. on 2c. red	15	20
30		3c. on 3c. orange	15	85
31		5c. on 5c. green	1·10	15
32	B	10c. on 10c. red	15	10
33		15c. on 15c. orange	1·75	2·00
34		20c. on 20c. red	1·25	2·50
35		25c. on 25c. blue	1·60	35
36		35c. on 35c. lilac	3·50	20
37	C	40c. on 40c. red and blue	6·50	7·00
38		50c. on 50c. brown & lilac	9·50	3·50
39		1p. on 1f. red and green	4·25	9·50

POSTAGE DUE STAMPS

1896. Postage Due stamps of France surch in Spanish currency in figures and words.

D14	D **11**	5c. on 5c. blue	5·50	1·90
D15		10c. on 10c. brown	9·00	1·75
D16		30c. on 30c. red	11·00	2·75
D17a		50c. on 50c. red	27·00	13·50
D18		1p. on 1f. brown	£275	£190

1909. Postage Due stamps of France surch in Spanish currency.

D28	D **19**	1c. on 1c. olive	60	2·25
D29		10c. on 10c. violet	25·00	29·00
D30		30c. on 30c. bistre	24·00	30·00
D31		50c. on 50c. red	45·00	50·00

1911. Postage Due stamps of France surch with figure and Arabic word.

D40	D **11**	5c. on 5c. blue	1·25	4·25
D41		10c. on 10c. brown	2·00	15·00
D42		50c. on 50c. purple	4·00	21·00

1911. Postage Due stamps of France surch in figures and Arabic.

D43	D **19**	1c. on 1c. olive	65	65
D44		10c. on 10c. violet	1·60	4·25
D45		30c. on 30c. bistre	2·50	6·00
D46		50c. on 50c. red	3·50	18·00

For later issues see **FRENCH MOROCCO**.

FRENCH POST OFFICES IN TANGIER Pt. 6

By Franco-Spanish Treaty of 27 November 1912, Tangier was given a special status outside the protectorates. After the Tangier Convention of 1924 the zone was administered by an international commission. Tangier was occupied by Spain in 1940 and the French P.O.s closed in 1942.

100 centimes = 1 franc.

1918. "Blanc", "Mouchon" and "Merson" key-types of French Post Offices in Morocco optd **TANGER**.

1a	A	1c. grey	20	2·25
2		2c. red	85	2·25
3		3c. orange	60	2·50
4		5c. green	1·10	1·25
5		5c. orange	2·25	2·75
6	B	10c. red	1·25	65
7		10c. green	1·75	2·75
8		15c. orange	1·25	1·10
9		20c. red	1·40	2·25
10		25c. blue	2·50	70
11		30c. red	3·50	4·50
12		35c. lilac	2·25	3·25
13	C	40c. red and blue	2·75	3·75
14		50c. brown and lilac	10·00	12·00
15	B	50c. blue	17·00	9·75
16	C	1f. red and green	4·75	7·75
17		2f. red and green	65·00	80·00
18		5f. blue and yellow	60·00	70·00

1928. Air. Nos. 149/58 of French Morocco optd **Tanger**.

30	5c. blue	1·75	7·50
31	25c. orange	2·25	7·00
32	50c. red	2·00	7·50
33	75c. brown	1·90	7·50
34	80c. green	2·25	7·50
35	1f. orange	2·00	7·50
36	1f.50 blue	1·90	7·50
37	2f. brown	2·25	7·50
38	3f. purple	4·00	4·00
39	5f. black	2·25	7·50

POSTAGE DUE STAMPS

1918. Postage Due stamps of France optd **TANGER**.

D19	D **11**	1c. black	25	2·50
D20		5c. blue	1·25	3·00
D21		10c. brown	1·75	3·00
D22		15c. green	1·75	4·75
D23		20c. olive	3·00	5·75
D24		30c. red	6·50	16·00
D25		50c. purple	6·75	20·00

1918. Postage Due stamps of France optd **TANGER**.

D26	D **19**	1c. olive	70	3·25
D27		10c. violet	2·75	3·25
D28		20c. bistre	6·50	9·50
D29		40c. red	16·00	22·00

FRENCH POST OFFICES IN TURKISH EMPIRE Pt. 6

General issues for the French Post Offices in the Turkish Empire.

1885. 25 centimes = 1 piastre.
1921. 40 paras = 1 piastre.

1885. Stamps of France surch in figures and words.
1 10 1pi. on 25c. bistre on yellow £350 3·50
4 1pi. on 25c. black on pink 3·00 15
5 2pi. on 50c. pink 18·00 70
2 3pi. on 75c. red 38·00 8·50
3 4pi. on 1f. green 35·00 3·00
7 8pi. on 2f. brown on blue 23·00 18·00
8 20pi. on 5f. mauve 80·00 45·00

1902. "Blanc", "Mouchon" and "Merson" key-types inscr "LEVANT".
9 A 1c. grey 10 25
10 2c. purple 15 60
11 3c. red 10 1·40
12 4c. brown 2·40 1·50
13a 5c. green 2·25 15
14 B 10c. red 4·75 20
15 15c. red 1·60 25
16 20c. brown 2·75 2·25
17 30c. lilac 4·25 3·50
18 C 40c. red and blue 5·50 4·25

1902. Surch in figures and words.
19 B 1pi. on 25c. blue 2·25 10
20 C 2pi. on 50c. brown & lav 3·00 65
21 4pi. on 1f. red & green 3·50 2·40
22 8pi. on 2f. lilac & yellow 23·00 12·50
23 20pi. on 5f. blue & yellow 6·00 4·75

1905. Surch **1 Piastre Beyrouth**.
24 B 1pi. on 15c. orange £1500 £225

1921. Stamps of France surch in figures and words.
28 18 30pa. on 5c. green 70 2·40
29 30pa. on 5c. orange 2·25 2·25
30 1pi.20 on 10c. red 60 1·40
31 1pi.20 on 10c. green 95 1·10
39 3pi.30 on 15c. green 25·00 26·00
32 3pi.30 on 25c. blue 60 30
33 4pi.20 on 30c. orange 50 1·10
40 7pi.20 on 35c. violet 26·00 28·00
34 15 7pi.20 on 50c. blue 35 45
35 13 15pi. on 1f. red & green 1·40 1·10
36 30pi. on 2f. red & green 7·25 9·50
37 75pi. on 5f. blue & yellow 7·75 6·00

For stamps issued by the Free French forces during 1942/3 see under **FREE FRENCH FORCES IN THE LEVANT**.

FRENCH POST OFFICES IN ZANZIBAR Pt. 6

The French post office in Zanzibar operated from 1889 to 1904.

16 annas = 1 rupee.

Stamps of France surcharged.

1894. Surch in figures and words.
1a 10 ½a. on 5c. green 7·00 5·50
3 1a. on 10c. black on lilac 13·00 9·00
4a 1½a. on 15c. blue 24·00 22·00
6 2a. on 20c. red on green 12·50 10·00
7 2½a. on 25c. black on red 11·50 6·25
8 3a. on 30c. brown 20·00 16·00
9 4a. on 40c. red on yellow 19·00 22·00
10 5a. on 50c. red 35·00 27·00
11 7½a. on 75c. brn on orge £350 £275
12a 10a. on 1f. olive 65·00 55·00
14 50a. on 5f. mve on lilac £200 £200

1894. Surch **ZANZIBAR** and value in Indian currency (in figures and words) and in corresponding French currency (in figures only on Nos. 15/18).
15 10 ½a. and 5 on 1c. black on blue £120 £120
16 1a. and 10 on 3c. grey 95·00 £100
17 2½a. and 25 on 4c. lilac on grey £140 £140
18 5a. and 50 on 20c. red on green £140 £150
19 10a. and 1f. on 40c. red on yellow £275 £275

1896. Surch **ZANZIBAR** and new value in Indian currency only.
22 10 ½a. on 5c. green 6·00 5·75
24 1a. on 10c. black on lilac 8·50 6·50
26 1½a. on 15c. blue 7·00 6·25
28 2a. on 20c. red on green 5·25 7·25
29 2½a. on 25c. black on red 10·50 6·50
30 3a. on 30c. brown 7·75 6·25
31 4a. on 40c. red on yellow 7·00 8·25
32 5a. on 50c. red 16·00 14·00
35 10a. on 1f. olive 25·00 14·00
37 20a. on 2f. brown on blue 17·00 20·00
38 50a. on 5f. mve on lilac 42·00 35·00

1897. Nos. 1/4 and 8/9 further surch with new figures of value in French and Indian currency and optd **ZANZIBAR** vert.
42 10 2½ and 25 on ½a. on 5c. £750 £100
43 2½ and 25 on 1a. on 10c. £2500 £550
44 2½ and 25 on 1½a. on 15c. £2500 £450
45 5 and 50 on 3a. on 30c. £2500 £425
46 5 and 50 on 4a. on 40c. £2500 £550

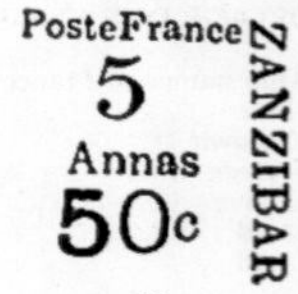

(4)

1897.
47 4 2½a. and 25c. black on green and white — £650
48 2½a. and 25c. black on lilac and white — £2250
49 2½a. and 25c. black on blue and white — £2000
50 5a. and 50c. black on buff and white — £1800
51 5a. and 50c. black on yellow and white — £2250
52 5a. and 50c. on white — £2250

1902. "Blanc", "Mouchon" and "Merson" key-types inscr "ZANZIBAR" and surch in figures and words.
53 A ½a. on 5c. green 4·50 4·75
54 B 1a. on 10c. red 6·25 7·50
55 1½a. on 15c. orange 14·00 14·00
56 2a. on 20c. red 19·00 17·00
57 2½a. on 25c. blue 19·00 16·00
58 3a. on 30c. mauve 11·00 12·00
59 C 4a. on 40c. red and blue 24·00 24·00
60 5a. on 50c. brown & lav 21·00 19·00
61 10a. on 1f. red and green 32·00 28·00
62 20a. on 2f. lilac & yellow 65·00 50·00
63 50a. on 5f. blue & yellow 90·00 85·00

1904. Nos. 30/31 further surch with both currencies in figures on either side of bars.
65 10 "25 c 2½" on 4a. on 40c. — £550
66 "50 5" on 3a. on 30c. — £650
67 "50 5" on 4a. on 40c. — £650
68 "1fr 10" on 3a. on 30c. — £1100
69 "1fr 10" on 4a. on 40c. — £1100

1904. "Blanc" key-type surch with both currencies in large figures.
70 A "2 25" on ½a. on 5c. green (No. 53) — 70·00

1904. "Mouchon" key-type surch with both currencies in figures or in figures and words.
71 B "25c 2½" on 1a. on 10c. red (No. 54) — 95·00
72 "25c 2½" on 3a. on 30c. mauve (No. 58) — £1400
73 "50 c cinq" on 3a. on 30c. mauve (No. 58) — £700
74 "1 fr dix" on 3a. on 30c. mauve (No. 58) — £900

1904. Postage Due stamps optd. (a) **Timbre**.
75 D 11 ½a. on 5c. blue — £250

(b) **Affrancht**.
76 D 11 1a. on 10c. brown — £250

(c) With red line at top and bottom obliterating words "CHIFFRE" and "TAXE".
77 D 11 1½a. on 15c. green — £600

POSTAGE DUE STAMPS

1897. Postage Due stamps of France surch **ZANZIBAR** and value in figures and words
D39 D 11 ½a. on 5c. blue 21·00 5·00
D40 1a. on 10c. brown 21·00 9·00
D41 1½a. on 15c. green 28·00 10·00
D42 3a. on 30c. red 28·00 19·00
D43 5a. on 50c. purple 35·00 18·00

FRENCH SOMALI COAST Pt. 6

A French colony on the Gulf of Aden, E. coast of Africa. Renamed French Territory of the Afars and the Issas in 1967.

100 centimes = 1 franc.

23 Mosque at Tajurah

24 Mounted Somalis

25 Somali Warriors

1902.
121 23 1c. orange and purple 95 90
137 1c. black and brown 35 1·50
122 2c. green and brown 1·00 70
138 2c. black and brown 1·25 60
123 4c. red and blue 1·25 2·75
139 4c. black and red 2·25 1·50
124 5c. green & deep green 2·25 1·60
140a 5c. black and green 5·00 1·50
125 10c. orange and red 3·50 5·75
141a 10c. black and red 8·75 55
126 15c. blue and orange 3·75 4·00
142 15c. black and brown 17·00 14·00
127 24 20c. green and lilac 7·00 10·00
143 20c. black and lilac 14·00 32·00
128 25c. blue 10·00 11·00
129 25c. blue and indigo 15·00 7·00
144 25c. black and blue 5·75 4·25
130 30c. blue and red 5·50 7·50
131 40c. blue and yellow 19·00 19·00
145 40c. black and orange 8·00 8·75
132 50c. red and green 38·00 45·00
146 50c. black and green 14·00 13·00
133 75c. mauve and orange 7·00 6·75
147 75c. black and brown 7·25 9·75
134 25 1f. purple and red 13·00 18·00
148 1f. black and red 10·00 22·00
135 2f. red and green 29·00 35·00
149 2f. black and green 6·25 9·00
136 5f. blue and orange 22·00 24·00
150 5f. black and orange 11·00 24·00

26 Mosque at Tajurah

27 Mounted Somalis

1909.
151 26 1c. brown and purple 20 20
152 2c. green and violet 20 20
153 4c. blue and brown 95 25
154 5c. olive and green 2·25 75
155 10c. orange and red 3·25 1·40
156 20c. brown and black 3·00 7·50
157 27 25c. blue and deep blue 5·25 1·75
158 30c. red and brown 5·00 9·25
159 35c. green and violet 7·00 4·50
160 40c. violet and pink 8·25 7·50
161 45c. green and brown 9·75 7·25
162 50c. brown and purple 8·50 8·50
163 75c. green and red 14·00 18·00
164 25 1f. brown and violet 17·00 28·00
165 2f. pink and brown 28·00 45·00
166 5f. green and brown 65·00 60·00

28 Drummer

29 Somali Woman

30 Railway Bridge at Holl-Holli

1915. No. 172 surch **5c** and red cross.
167 29 10c.+5c. red & carmine 4·00 8·50

1915.
168 28 1c. brown and violet 10 30
169 2c. blue and bistre 10 10
170 4c. red and brown 20 1·75
171 5c. green & light green 45 95
195 5c. red and orange 10 1·40
172 29 10c. red and carmine 1·10 2·25
196 10c. green & light green 30 3·00
214 10c. green and red 45 1·25
173 15c. pink and lilac 1·60 1·90
174 20c. brown and orange 15 1·60
215 20c. light green & green 20 2·00
216 20c. red and green 20 1·75
175 25c. blue & ultramarine 45 2·25
197 25c. green and black 15 20
176 30c. green and black 2·75 3·25
198 30c. brown and red 1·60 3·25
217 30c. green and violet 10 1·90
218 30c. olive and green 20 1·75
177 35c. pink and green 1·10 2·75
178 40c. lilac and blue 1·50 2·50
179 45c. blue and brown 2·25 3·00
180 50c. black and pink 14·50 9·75
199 50c. blue & ultramarine 1·50 3·50
219 50c. purple and brown 20 15
220 60c. purple and green 45 2·75
221 65c. green and red 35 1·75
181 75c. brown and lilac 1·00 2·25
222 75c. blue and deep blue 10 1·25
223 75c. brown and mauve 2·25 4·25
224 85c. green and purple 15 3·25
225 90c. carmine and red 4·50 5·50
182 30 1f. red and brown 1·40 30
226 1f.10 blue and brown 4·75 7·50
227 1f.25 brown and blue 12·00 12·00
228 1f.50 blue & light blue 70 55
229 1f.75 red and green 6·00 3·25
183 2f. black and violet 4·00 1·60
230 3f. mauve on pink 14·00 7·25
184 5f. black and red 9·50 3·00

1922. Surch **1922** and value in figures in frame.
193 28 10 on 5c. green & lt grn 15 1·50
194 29 50 on 25c. bl & ultram 15 2·50

1922. Surch in figures.
200 29 0.01 on 15c. pink and lilac 10 2·75
201 0.02 on 15c. pink and lilac 10 2·75
202 0.04 on 15c. pink and lilac 15 2·75
203 0.05 on 15c. pink and lilac 10 2·50
204 30 25c. on 5f. black & red 1·40 3·25
205 29 60 on 75c. violet & green 40 2·50
206 65 on 15c. pink and lilac 1·40 3·25
207 85 on 40c. lilac and blue 1·50 3·25
208 90 on 75c. red 1·25 3·75
209 30 1f.25 on 1f. ultram & bl 1·25 3·00
210 1f.50 on 1f. bl & lt bl 1·25 1·60
211 3f. on 5f. mauve & red 3·75 4·25
212 10f. on 5f. brown & red 8·75 9·75
213 20f. on 5f. pink & green 15·00 14·50

1931. "Colonial Exhibition" key-types inscr "COTE FR. DES SOMALIS".
233 E 40c. green and black 2·25 3·50
234 F 50c. mauve and black 3·75 5·75
235 G 90c. red and black 2·75 7·25
236 H 1f.50 blue and black 4·00 7·00

1937. Int Exn, Paris. As T **58a** of Guadeloupe.
237 20c. violet 55 2·75
238 30c. green 40 2·50
239 40c. red 30 2·25
240 50c. brown and blue 30 2·50
241 90c. red 80 2·50
242 1f.50 blue 35 2·00

1938. International Anti-cancer Fund. As T **58b** of Guadeloupe.
244 1f.75+50c. blue 95 10·50

34 Mosque at Djibouti

35 Somali Warriors

37 Djibouti

1938.
245 34 2c. purple 10 1·25
246 3c. green 10 1·10
247 4c. brown 10 2·75
248 5c. red 10 2·75
249 10c. blue 10 1·40
250 15c. black 10 2·75
251 20c. red 55 3·00
252 35 25c. brown 65 2·00
253 30c. blue 30 2·25
254 35c. green 35 3·00
255 34 40c. brown 75 2·75
256 45c. green 50 2·75
257 35 50c. red 55 2·50
258 55c. purple 80 3·00
259 60c. black 45 3·25
260 65c. brown 50 3·00
261 70c. violet 75 4·00
262 – 80c. black 1·00 4·00
263 35 90c. mauve 1·25 4·00
264 – 1f. red 60 2·75
265 – 1f. black 40 3·00
266 – 1f.25 red 1·40 3·75
267 – 1f.40 blue 2·25 3·75
268 – 1f.50 green 40 3·00
269 – 1f.60 red 2·75 3·75
270 – 1f.75 blue 70 3·00
271 – 2f. red 30 85
272 – 2f.25 blue 1·90 3·75
273 – 2f.50 brown 3·00 4·25
274 – 3f. purple 60 1·75
275 37 5f. brown & deep brown 1·25 3·00
276 10f. light blue and blue 85 3·75
277 20f. blue and red 1·00 3·00
DESIGN—VERT: 80c. and 1f. to 3f. Governor L. Lagarde.

1939. New York World's Fair. As T **58c** of Guadeloupe.
288 1f.25 red 1·25 3·75
289 2f.25 blue 2·50 1·60

1939. 150th Anniv of French Revolution. As T **58d** of Guadeloupe.
290 45c.+25c. green & black 5·25 12·00
291 70c.+30c. brown & black 5·25 12·00
292 90c.+35c. orange & black 6·25 12·00
293 1f.25+1f. red and black 7·50 14·00
294 2f.25+2f. blue and black 10·00 16·00

1941. Air. Free French Issue. As T **63a** of Guadeloupe, but inscr "DJIBOUTI".
295 32 1f. orange 55 65
296 1f.50 red 40 2·50
297 5f. purple 30 1·40
298 10f. black 85 2·25
299 25f. blue 80 4·00
300 50f. green 60 4·00
301 100f. red 85 3·00

1942. Optd or surch also **FRANCE LIBRE** or **France Libre**.
302 28 1c. brown and violet 2·25 3·50
303 2c. blue and bistre 2·75 3·75
304 34 2c. purple 1·25 3·50

305		3c. green	2·00	3·50
306	28	4c. red and brown	15·00	42·00
307	34	4c. brown	2·75	3·50
308	28	5c. red and orange	1·60	3·75
309	34	5c. red	1·25	4·00
310		10c. blue	50	2·50
311	29	15c. pink and lilac	4·50	11·00
312	34	15c. black	1·50	3·50
313	29	20c. red and green	1·50	4·00
314	34	20c. red	1·50	3·50
315	35	25c. brown	1·50	4·00
316	29	30c. olive and green	1·40	4·00
317	35	30c. blue	50	2·75
318		35c. green	2·50	3·75
319	34	40c. brown	50	2·75
320		45c. green	1·75	3·50
321	29	50c. purple and brown	85	4·00
322	35	50c. on 65c. brown	40	95
323		55c. purple	1·90	3·50
324		60c. black	45	2·25
325	29	65c. green and red	70	4·00
326	35	70c. violet	40	2·75
327	–	80c. black (No. 262)	40	2·75
328	35	90c. mauve	40	1·50
329	–	1f.25 red (No. 266)	95	2·75
330	–	1f.40 blue (No. 267)	50	2·75
331	30	1f.50 blue & light blue	90	3·50
332	–	1f.50 green (No. 268)	65	2·75
333	–	1f.60 red (No. 269)	1·00	2·75
334	30	1f.75 red and green	10·00	13·00
335	–	1f.75 blue (No. 270)	3·25	12·50
336	–	2f. red (No. 271)	40	2·25
337	–	2f.25 blue (No. 272)	90	3·25
338	–	2f.50 brown (No. 273)	1·10	3·50
339	–	3f. purple (No. 274)	85	4·75
340	37	5f. brown & deep brown	5·25	16·00
341		10f. light blue and blue	£140	£150
342		20f. blue and red	5·50	7·50

41 Symbolical of Djibouti

1943. Free French issue.

361	41	5c. blue	15	2·50
362		10c. red	15	2·25
363		25c. green	15	2·75
364		30c. black	15	2·50
365		40c. violet	30	2·75
366		80c. purple	20	2·75
367		1f. blue	40	35
368		1f.50 red	60	50
369		2f. bistre	60	55
370		2f.50 blue	50	60
371		4f. orange	55	1·60
372		5f. mauve	55	1·25
373		10f. blue	1·10	1·60
374		20f. green	95	95

1944. Mutual Aid and Red Cross Funds. As T **58e** of Guadeloupe.

375		5f.+20f. green	1·00	4·00

1945. Eboue. As T **58f** of Guadeloupe.

376		2f. black	65	2·75
377		25f. green	1·25	3·50

1945. Surch.

378	41	50c. on 5c. blue	20	3·00
379		60c. on 5c. blue	15	2·75
380		70c. on 5c. blue	20	2·75
381		1f.20 on 5c. blue	1·50	3·00
382		2f.40 on 25c. green	90	3·00
383		3f. on 25c. green	55	3·00
384		4f.50 on 25c. green	1·40	2·50
385		15f. on 2f.50 blue	1·50	3·50

1946. Air. Victory. As T **63b** of Guadeloupe.

386		8f. blue	25	2·75

1946. Air. From Chad to the Rhine. As T **63c** of Guadeloupe.

387		5f. black	2·25	4·25
388		10f. red	1·00	4·00
389		15f. brown	1·00	4·00
390		20f. mauve	2·25	4·00
391		25f. green	1·00	4·00
392		50f. blue	1·50	4·50

43 Danakil Tent

45 Somali

44 Outpost at Khor-Angar

46 Government Palace, Djibouti

1947.

393	43	10c. orge & vio (postage)	10	2·75
394		30c. orange and green	10	2·75
395		40c. orange and purple	10	2·75
396	44	50c. orange and green	10	2·25
397		60c. yellow and brown	10	2·75
398		80c. orange and violet	15	2·75
399	–	1f. brown and blue	15	80
400	–	1f.20 green and grey	30	3·00
401	–	1f.50 blue and orange	35	3·00
402	–	2f. mauve and grey	20	20
403	–	3f. blue and brown	65	45
404	–	3f.60 brown and red	2·00	4·00
405	–	4f. brown and grey	60	35
406	–	5f. orange and brown	45	30
407	–	6f. blue and grey	85	70
408	–	10f. purple and blue	70	25
409	–	15f. brown, blue & buff	1·75	40
410	–	20f. blue, orange & blue	1·50	40
411	–	25f. red, blue & purple	1·60	35
412	45	50f. brown & blue (air)	1·75	75
413	–	100f. yellow and green	2·00	1·75
414	46	200f. green, yell & blue	2·50	2·75

DESIGNS—HORIZ: As Type **44**: 1f. to 1f.50, Obock Tajurah road; 2f. to 4f. Woman carrying dish; 5f. to 10f. Somali village; 15f. to 25f. Mosque. Djibouti. As Type **46**: 100f. Frontier post, Loyada.

1949. Air. 75th Anniv of U.P.U. As T **39** of French Equatorial Africa.

425		30f. multicoloured	1·50	15·00

1950. Colonial Welfare Fund. As T **40** of French Equatorial Africa.

426		10f.+2f. red and brown	2·75	7·50

1952. Centenary of Medaille Militaire. As T **44** of French Equatorial Africa.

427		15f. violet, yellow and green	4·50	6·75

1954. Air. 10th Anniv of Liberation. As T **46** of French Equatorial Africa.

428		15f. violet and blue	6·00	11·00

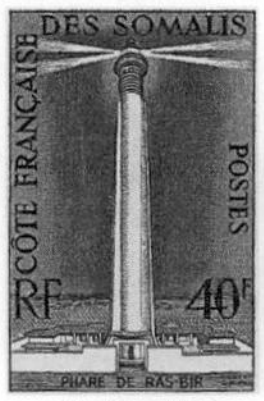

48 Ras-Bir Lighthouse

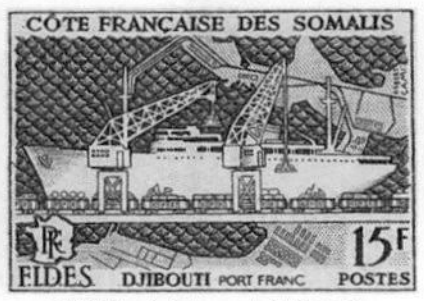

50 Freighter at Wharf, Djibouti

49 Aerial Map of Djibouti

1956.

429	48	40f. blue & dp bl (postage)	4·00	70
430	49	500f. purple & vio (air)	40·00	48·00

1956. Economic and Social Development Fund.

431	50	15f. violet	2·50	55

51 Warthog

1958. Animals, Fishes and Birds.

432	51	30c. brown & red (postage)	15	2·75
433	–	40c. brown and bistre	15	3·00
434	–	50c. purple, grey & green	15	2·75
435	–	1f. orge, blue & brown	30	30
436	–	2f. multicoloured	65	95
437	–	3f. brown and violet	1·40	70
438	–	4f. brn, orange & blue	1·25	2·25
439	–	5f. black and blue	2·25	1·10
440	–	10f. red, brown & green	2·10	1·00
441	–	15f. yellow, green & mve	3·25	1·40
442	–	20f. purple, red and blue	3·25	3·25
443	–	25f. blue, red and green	4·00	2·25
444	–	30f. black, red and blue	6·50	3·75
445	–	60f. green and blue	8·75	3·50
446	–	75f. yellow, brown & grn	11·00	7·00
447	–	100f. brown, grn & bl (air)	8·00	5·75
448	–	200f. brown, blk & orge	20·00	13·50
449	–	500f. multicoloured	23·00	21·00

DESIGNS—HORIZ: As Type **51**: 40c. Cheetah; 1f. Blue-barred orange parrotfish; 3f. Blue marlin; 4f. Blue spotted boxfish; 5f. African eagle ray; 15f. Little bee eater; 20f. Undulate triggerfish; 25f. Yellow-wedged triggerfish; 30f. Sacred ibis; 60f. Smooth hammerhead; 48 × 27 mm: 100f. Bohar reedbucks and airplane; 200f. Great bustard; 500f. Salt caravan, Lake Assal. VERT: As Type **51**: 50c. Gerenuks; 2f. Pennant coralfish; 10f. Greater flamingo; 75f. Pink-backed pelican.

1958. Tropical Flora. As T **56** of French Equatorial Africa.

450		10f. red, green and yellow	1·60	1·60

DESIGN—HORIZ: 10f. "Haemanthus".

1958. 10th Anniv of Declaration of Human Rights. As T **57** of French Equatorial Africa.

451		20f. violet and blue	60	2·25

53 Governor Bernard

1960. Air. 25th Death Anniv of Governor Bernard.

452	53	55f. brown, blue & red	1·90	2·25

54 "Forbin", Obock, 1862

1962. Air. Centenary of Obock.

453	54	100f. brown and blue	4·00	2·50

55 Dragon Tree

55a Campaign Emblem

1962. Fauna and Flora.

454	55	2f. multicoloured	1·90	2·00
455	–	4f. brown and ochre	1·90	2·00
456	–	6f. multicoloured	3·00	3·00
457	–	25f. bistre, green and red	5·00	3·50
458	–	40f. brown, black & blue	10·50	6·25
459	–	50f. brown, purple & blue	8·25	9·25

DESIGNS—HORIZ: 4f. Large-toothed rock hyrax; 6f. Giant trevally (fish); 25f. Fennec foxes; 40f. Griffon vulture. VERT: 50f. Klipspringer.

1962. Malaria Eradication.

460	55a	25f.+5f. blue	6·25	8·25

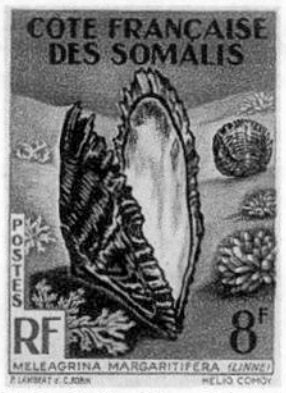

56 Black-lip Pearl Oyster

1962. Shells of the Red Sea. Multicoloured. (a) Postage. As T **56**.

461		8f. Type **56**	1·10	1·50
462		10f. Fluted giant clam (horiz)	1·10	1·40
463		25f. Three knobbed conch (horiz)	3·00	2·50
464		30f. Knobbed top	3·00	2·00

(b) Air. 50 × 28 mm.

465		60f. Arabian tibia	4·00	3·50
466		100f. Giant spider conch	5·75	4·00

1962. Air. 1st Trans-Atlantic TV Satellite Link. As T **10** of French Polynesia.

467		20f. purple and green	65	1·10

1963. Red Cross Centenary. As T **13** of French Polynesia.

468		50f. red, grey and brown	4·25	6·75

57 Large Star Coral

58 Houri

1963. Corals. Multicoloured. (a) Postage. As T **57**.

469		5f. Type **57**	1·25	1·75
470		6f. Organ-pipe coral	1·00	1·25

(b) Air. Horiz (48 × 27 mm).

471		40f. Stinging coral	2·50	1·40
472		55f. Brain coral	5·00	3·25
473		200f. Branched coral	9·00	6·25

1963. 15th Anniv of Declaration of Human Rights. As T **14** of French Polynesia.

474		70f. blue and brown	5·75	10·00

1964. "PHILATEC 1964" International Stamp Exhibition, Paris. As T **528** of France.

475		80f. brown, green & purple	6·00	10·00

1964. Local Dhows. Multicoloured. (a) Postage. As T **58**.

476		15f. Type **58**	2·00	1·90
477		25f. Sambuk	2·50	2·50

(b) Air. Size 48 × 27 mm.

478		50f. Building sambuk	3·50	2·75
479		85f. Zaruk	3·50	3·75
480		300f. Ziema	15·00	8·50

59 Rameses II and Nefertari Temple, Philae

1964. Air. Nubian Monuments Preservation.

481	59	25f.+5f. brown, green and red	5·25	11·50

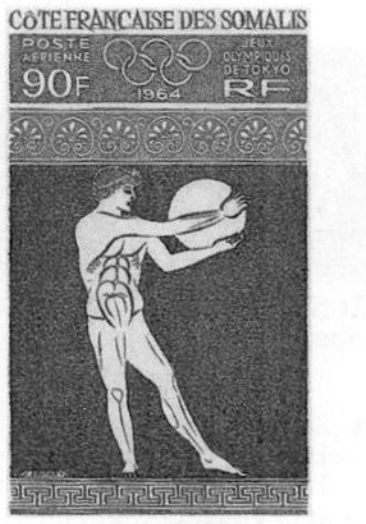

60 "The Discus Thrower" (Ancient Greece)

1964. Air. Olympic Games, Tokyo.

482	60	90f. purple, red & black	10·00	11·50

1965. Air. Centenary of I.T.U. As T **19** of French Polynesia.

483		95f. blue, brown & purple	13·00	13·50

61 Ghoubet Kharab

1965. Landscapes

484	–	6f. brn, bl & grn (postage)	1·10	1·75
485	–	20f. green, blue & brown	1·10	1·90
486	–	45f. brn, bl & dp bl (air)	2·25	3·75
487	61	65f. brown, ochre & blue	2·75	2·75

VIEWS—26 × 22 mm: 6f. Dadwayya; 20f. Tajurah. As Type **61**: 45f. Lake Abbe.

62 "Life and Death"

1965. Anti-tuberculosis Campaign.

488	62	25f.+5f. brn, grn & turq	2·75	3·00

1966. Air. Launching of 1st French Satellite. As Nos. 1696/7 of France.

489		25f. brown, bistre and red	3·75	3·75
490		30f. brown, bistre and red	4·50	4·50

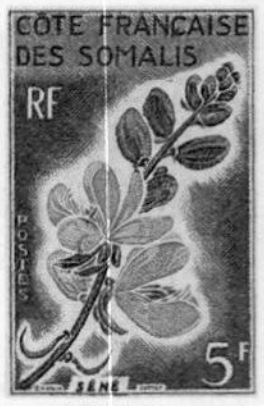

63 Senna

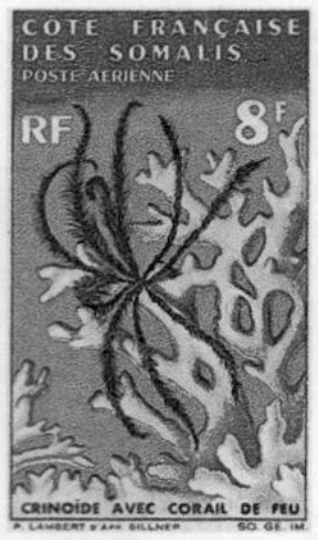

64 Feather Star and Flame Coral

1966. Flowers
491 **63** 5f. orange, green and brown (postage) . . . . 1·25 1·50
492 – 8f. orange, green & brown 1·75 1·75
493 – 25f. red, blue and green . . 1·75 2·00
494 – 55f. lake, green and myrtle (air) . . . . 4·25 3·25
FLOWERS—VERT: 8f. Poinciana; 25f. Aloes. HORIZ: (48½ × 27 mm): 55f. Stapelia.

1966. Air. Marine Life. Multicoloured.
495 8f. Type **64** . . . . 2·75 2·75
496 25f. Regal angelfish . . . . . 3·50 4·25
497 40f. Yellow-banded angelfish 5·00 6·75
498 50f. Saddle anemonefish . . . 7·25 8·75
499 70f. Spined squirrelfish . . . 12·00 15·00
500 80f. Red Sea surgeonfish . . . 13·00 16·00
501 100f. Lunulate lionfish . . . 18·00 24·00

1966. Air. Launching of Satellite "D1". As T **569** of France.
502 48f. green, brown and blue 2·75 3·50

65 Grey Monitor

1967. Somali Fauna.
503 **65** 20f. purple, chest & brn . . 3·00 3·50

POSTAGE DUE STAMPS

D 31 Somali Spears

D 47

1915.
D278 **D 31** 5c. blue . . . . 10 2·75
D279 10c. red . . . . 10 2·75
D187 15c. black . . . . . . 45 2·25
D281 20c. violet . . . . . . 15 2·75
D282 30c. yellow . . . . . 20 2·75
D190 50c. red . . . . 1·25 3·75
D283 50c. brown . . . . . . 20 3·00
D284 60c. green . . . . . . 75 3·25
D285 1f. blue . . . . 25 4·50
D286 2f. red . . . . 25 3·50
D287 3f. sepia . . . . 75 3·50

1927. Surch in figures.
D231 **D 31** 2f. on 1f. red . . . . 3·50 10·00
D232 3f. on 1f. mve . . . . 2·25 7·00

1942. (a) Optd **FRANCE LIBRE**.
D343 **D 31** 5c. blue . . . . 1·25 4·00
D344 10c. red . . . . 1·75 4·00
D345 15c. black . . . . . . 1·25 4·00
D346 20c. violet . . . . . . 1·75 4·00
D347 30c. yellow . . . . . 1·75 4·00
D348 50c. red . . . . 1·75 4·00
D349 60c. green . . . . . . 1·75 4·00
D350 1f. blue . . . . 7·75 10·50

(b) Optd **France Libre**.
D351 **D 31** 5c. blue . . . . 1·50 4·00
D352 10c. red . . . . 1·50 4·00
D353 15c. black . . . . . . 1·50 4·00
D354 20c. violet . . . . . . 60 4·00
D355 30c. yellow . . . . . 60 4·00
D356 50c. brown . . . . . . 60 4·00
D357 60c. green . . . . . . 70 4·00
D358 1f. blue . . . . 1·25 4·00
D359 2f. red . . . . 2·50 4·00
D360 3f. sepia . . . . 1·90 4·00

1947.
D415 **D 47** 10c. mauve . . . . . 10 2·25
D416 30c. brown . . . . . 10 2·75
D417 50c. green . . . . . 10 2·75
D418 1f. brown . . . . . . 10 2·75
D419 2f. red . . . . 35 2·75
D420 3f. brown . . . . . . 80 2·75
D421 4f. blue . . . . 1·10 3·00
D422 5f. red . . . . 1·25 3·00
D423 10f. green . . . . . . 1·25 3·50
D424 20f. blue . . . . . . 1·00 3·50

For later issues see **FRENCH TERRITORY OF THE AFARS AND THE ISSAS**.

FRENCH SOUTHERN AND ANTARCTIC TERRITORIES Pt. 6

Stamps issued for use in the French settlements in the southern Indian Ocean and in the Antarctic.

100 centimes = 1 franc.

1955. No. 324 of Madagascar optd **TERRES AUSTRALES ET ANTARCTIQUES FRANCAISES**.
1 **39** 15f. blue and green . . . . . 20·00 35·00

2 Rockhopper Penguins

5 Polar Camp and Meteorologist

4 Emperor Penguins, Snowy Petrel and South Pole

1956.
2 – 30c. brn, grn & bl (postage) 40 65
3 – 40c. blk, purple and blue . . 45 65
4 **2** 50c. blue, ochre & brown . . 40 65
5 1f. blue, orange and grey . . 1·40 1·60
6 – 2f. black, brown and blue . . 3·25 4·75
7 – 4f. brown, green and blue . . 15·00 20·00
8 – 5f. blue and light blue . . . 1·90 7·50
9 – 8f. brown and grey . . . . . 8·00 27·00
10 – 10f. blue . . . . 3·25 13·00
11 – 12f. black and blue . . . . 13·00 8·00
12 – 15f. purple and blue . . . . 3·75 16·00
13 – 20f. blue, yellow & lt blue . . 19·00 25·00
14 – 25f. black, brown & green . . £100 85·00
15 – 85f. orange, blue and black 21·00 14·00
16 **4** 50f. green and olive (air) . . 42·00 32·00
17 100f. indigo and blue . . . . 35·00 28·00
18 – 200f. black, blue & purple . . 42·00 50·00
DESIGNS—VERT: As Type **2**: 30c. Light-mantled sooty albatross; 2f. Black-faced sheathbills; 12f. Kerguelen cormorants; 20f. Territorial arms; 85f. King penguin. HORIZ: (36 × 22 mm). 40c. Antarctic skuas; 4f. Leopard seal; 5f., 8f. Kerguelen fur seal and settlement; 10f., 15f. Southern elephant-seal; 25f. Kerguelen fur seal. As Type **4**: 200f. Wandering albatross.
See also Nos. 26/34.

1957. International Geophysical Year.
19 **5** 5f. black and violet . . . . . 4·00 7·50
20 10f. red . . . . 5·00 10·00
21 15f. blue . . . . 6·25 10·50

1959. Tropical Flora. As T **56** of French Equatorial Africa.
22 10f. multicoloured . . . . . . 3·75 15·00
DESIGN—HORIZ: 10f. "Pringlea".

6 Yves-Joseph Kerguelen-Tremarec and "Dauphine"

1960. Kerguelen Archipelago Discovery Commem.
23 **6** 25f. brown, chestnut & blue 35·00 29·00

7 Jean Charcot, Compass and "Pourquoi Pas?"

1962. 25th Anniv of Disappearance of Jean Charcot.
24 **7** 25f. brown, red and green . . 25·00 30·00

1962. Air. 1st Trans-Atlantic T.V. Satellite Link. As T **10** of French Polynesia.
25 50f. green, olive and blue . . . 26·00 35·00

1963. Designs as T **2** and **4**.
26 5f. violet and blue (postage) 16·00 10·50
35 5f. brown, black and blue . . 65·00 35·00
27 8f. indigo, purple and blue . . 13·00 15·00
28 10f. black, blue and brown . . 30·00 25·00
29 12f. green, blue and brn . . . 16·00 20·00
30 15f. blue, black and brown . . 11·00 9·00
31 20f. grey, orange and green . . £400 £225
32 45f. green, brown and blue . . 13·50 11·50
33 25f. purple, brown & bl (air) 25·00 14·00
34 50f. black, purple and blue . . 45·00 35·00
DESIGNS—HORIZ: As Type **2**: 5f. (No. 26) Blue whale; 5f. (No. 35) Crozet Archipelago; 8f. Southern elephant-seals in combat; 12f. Phylica (tree), New Amsterdam island; 15f. Killer whale, Crozet islands. As Type **4**: 50f. Adelie penguins. VERT: As Type **2**: 10f. Pintado petrel; 20f. Black-browed albatross; 45f. Kerguelen cabbage. As Type **4**: 25f. Ionospheric research pylon, Adelie Land.

9 Observation Station

1963. "International Year of the Quiet Sun".
36 **9** 20f. slate, brown and violet (postage) . . . . 50·00 40·00
37 – 100f. red, blue & black (air) £160 £120
DESIGN—VERT: (27 × 48 mm); 100f. Pylons and Adelie penguins.

10 Landfall of Dumont d'Urville

1965. Air. Discovery of Adelie Land, 1840.
38 **10** 50f. indigo and blue £110 £120

1965. Air. Centenary of I.T.U. As T **19** of French Polynesia.
39 30f. brown, mauve and blue £140 £140

1966. Air. Launching of 1st French Satellite. As Nos. 1696/7 of France.
40 25f. blue, green and brown . . 17·00 21·00
41 30f. blue, green and brown . . 17·00 21·00

1966. Air. Launching of Satellite "D1". As T **569** of France.
42 50f. violet, purple & orange 38·00 30·00

11 Space Probe

12 Dumont D'Urville, "L'Astrolabe" and "Zelee"

1967. Launching of 1st Space Probe, Adelie Land.
43 **11** 20f. black, purple & blue . . 17·00 16·00

1968. Dumont D'Urville Commem.
44 **12** 30f. brown, dp blue & lt bl £130 £120

13 Port-aux-Francais

1968. Air.
45 – 40f. slate and blue . . . . . 38·00 40·00
46 **13** 50f. black, green & blue . . £160 £120
DESIGN: 40f. Aerial View of St. Paul Island.

14 Kerguelen and Rocket

1968. Air. Launching of "Dragon" Space Rockets.
47 **14** 25f. brown, green & blue . . 26·00 28·00
48 – 30f. blue, brown & green . . 26·00 28·00
DESIGN: 30f. Adelie Land and rocket.

1968. 20th Anniv of W.H.O. As T **34** of French Polynesia.
49 30f. blue, yellow and red . . . 55·00 26·00

1968. Human Rights Year. As T **36** of French Polynesia.
50 30f. red, blue and brown . . . 38·00 30·00

15 Eiffel Tower and Badge of Paris, and Ship in Antarctica

1969. Air. 5th Antarctic Treaty Consultative Meeting, Paris.
51 **15** 50f. blue . . . . 35·00 45·00

16 Antarctic Scene

1969. French Polar Exploration.
52 **16** 25f. blue, red & turquoise 24·00 29·00

1969. Air. 1st Flight of Concorde. As T **39** of French Polynesia.
53 85f. turquoise and blue . . . 38·00 45·00

17 Possession Island, Crozet Archipelago

1969. Air.
54 **17** 50f. green, red and blue . . 18·00 8·25
55 – 100f. black, grey and blue 55·00 75·00
56 – 200f. brown, green & blue 70·00 60·00
57 – 500f. blue . . . . 14·00 23·00
DESIGNS—HORIZ: 100f. Relief Map of Kerguelen. VERT: 200f. Cape Geology Archipelago map; 500f. Territorial arms.

1970. 50th Anniv of International Labour Organization. As T **44** of French Polynesia.
58 20f. purple, blue and red . . . 18·00 16·00

18 Relief Map of New Amsterdam Island

1970. Air. 20th Anniv of Meteorological Station, New Amsterdam Island.
59 **18** 30f. brown . . . . 16·00 10·00

1970. New U.P.U. Headquarters Building, Berne. As T **47** of French Polynesia.
60 50f. brown, purple and blue 38·00 16·00

19 Long-nosed Icefish

1971. Fishes.
61 **19** 5f. blue, yellow and green 4·00 1·90
62 – 10f. brown, violet and blue 6·00 3·00
63 – 20f. green, orange & purple 6·00 2·25
64 – 22f. red, violet and brown 8·50 9·75
65 – 25f. blue, yellow and green 5·25 2·25
66 – 30f. grey, blue and brown 7·00 4·75
67 – 35f. multicoloured . . . . . 7·25 6·00
68 – 135f. red, brown and blue 9·00 11·50
DESIGNS: 10f. Marbled rockcod; 20f. Antarctic rockcod; 22f. Hanson's rockcod; 25f. Orange-throated rockcod; 30f. Blue-gilled rockcod; 35f. Bemacchi's rockcod; 135f. Spiny pigfish.

20 Port-aux-Francais, 1950

1971. Air. 20th Anniv of Port-aux-Francais, Kerguelen.
69 **20** 40f. brown, green & blue . . 25·00 24·00
70 – 50f. green, blue & brown . . 30·00 29·00
DESIGN: 50f. Port-aux-Francais, 1970.

21 Treaty Emblem

22 "Christiansenia dreuxi"

1971. 10th Anniv of Antarctic Treaty.
71 **21** 75f. red . . . . 22·00 14·00

1972. Insects.
72 **22** 15f. brown, purple and red 11·50 8·00
73 – 22f. yellow, blue and green 11·50 9·75
74 – 25f. violet, purple & green 9·00 9·75
75 – 30f. multicoloured . . . . . 14·50 10·00
76 – 40f. black, brown & choc 9·50 8·50
77 – 140f. brown, green & blue 11·00 15·00
DESIGNS: 22f. "Phtirocoris antarcticus"; 25f. "Microzetia mirabilis" (midge); 30f. "Antarctophytosus atriceps" (rove beetle); 40f. "Paractora dreuxi"; 140f. "Pringleophaga kerguelenensis" (scavenger moth).

23 Landing on Crozet Islands

1972. Air. Bicentenary of Discovery of Crozet Islands and Kerguelen.
78 **23** 100f. black . . . . 35·00 20·00
79 – 250f. black and brown . . . 90·00 55·00
DESIGN: 250f. Hoisting the flag on Kerguelen.

1972. 1st Death Anniv of General De Gaulle. As Nos. 1937 and 1940 of France.
80 50f. black and green . . . . . 14·50 9·75
81 100f. black and green . . . . 19·00 11·00

24 "Gallieni"

1973. Air. Antarctic Voyages of the "Gallieni" (supply ship).
82 **24** 100f. black and blue . . . . 22·00 16·00

25 "Azorella selago"

1973. Plants.
83 **25** 61f. green, grey & brown . . 4·25 5·00
84 – 87f. green, blue and red . . 5·75 5·75
DESIGN: 87f. "Acaena ascendens".

26 "Mascarin", 1772

1973. Air. Antarctic Ships.
85 **26** 120f. brown . . . . 9·75 7·50
86 – 145f. blue . . . . 11·00 9·75
87 – 150f. blue . . . . 12·50 8·25
88 – 185f. brown . . . . 14·00 13·50
DESIGNS: 145f. "L'Astrolabe", 1840; 150f. "Roland", 1774; 185f. "Vitoria", 1522.
See also Nos. 93/4.

27 Part of Alfred Faure Base

1974. 10th Anniv of Alfred Faure Base, Crozet Archipelago.
89 **27** 75f. brown, blue & ultram 17·00 5·00
90 – 110f. brown, blue & ultram 17·00 6·25
91 – 150f. brown, blue & ultram 23·00 11·00
Nos. 89/91 were issued together se-tenant within the sheet, making a composite picture of the base.

28 Emperor Penguin, Globe and Letters

1974. Air. Centenary of Universal Postal Union.
92 **28** 150f. brown, black & blue 7·50 5·50

1974. Air. Charcot's Antarctic Voyages. As T **26**.
93 100f. blue . . . . 5·25 5·75
94 200f. red . . . . 6·25 7·50
DESIGN: 100f. "Francais" (1903–05 voyage); 200f. "Pourquoi Pas?" (1908–10 voyage).

29 Mail Ship "Sapmer"

1974. 25th Anniv of Postal Service.
95 **29** 75f. black, blue & mauve . . 6·50 5·00

30 Rockets over Kerguelen Islands

1975. Air. "ARAKS" Franco-Soviet Magnetosphere Research Project.
96 **30** 45f. red, blue and lilac . . . 8·00 5·25
97 – 90f. red, lilac and blue . . . 11·50 7·50
DESIGN: 90f. Map of North Coast of U.S.S.R.

31 Antarctic Tern

32 "La Curieuse" (topsail schooner)

1976.
98 **31** 40c. black, blue and orange (postage) . . . . 4·75 3·25
99 – 50c. brown, lt blue & blue 4·75 3·50
100 – 90c. brown and blue . . . 8·00 7·00
101 – 1f. brown, blue & violet . . 12·50 13·00
102 – 1f.20 green, blue & brown 13·50 10·50
103 – 1f.40 blue, green & orange 14·00 11·00
104 **32** 1f.90 bl, ultram & brn (air) 7·00 6·75
105 – 2f.70 brown, bl & ultram 8·50 8·75
106 – 4f. blue and red . . . . . 10·00 8·50
DESIGNS—As T **31**. HORIZ: 50c. Antarctic petrel; 90c. Kerguelen fur seal; 1f. Weddell seal. VERT: 1f.20, Kerguelen cormorant; 1f.40, Gentoo penguin. As T **32**: 2f.70, "Commandant Charcot" (ice patrol ship); 4f. "Marion Dufresne" (Antarctic supply ship).

33 Dumont d'Urville Base, 1956

1976. Air. 20th Anniv of Dumont d'Urville Base, Adelie Land.
107 **33** 1f.20 brown, orge & blue 14·00 10·50
108 – 4f. orange, blue & brown 18·00 18·50
DESIGNS: 4f. Dumont d'Urville Base, 1976.

34 Kerguelen Island

1976. Air. Bicent of Cook's Passage to Kerguelen.
109 **34** 3f.50 slate and blue . . . . 10·00 9·00

35 Captain Cook

36 First Ascent of Mt. Ross (5 Jan 1975)

1976. Cook Commemoration.
110 **35** 70c. blue, brown & yellow 14·50 10·00

1976. Ross Commemoration.
111 **36** 30c. red, brown and blue 4·25 4·50
112 – 3f. violet, brown and blue 5·00 4·00
DESIGN: 3f. Sir James Clark Ross.

37 Blue Whale

1977. Marine Mammals.
113 **37** 1f.10 deep blue & blue . . 6·50 7·75
114 – 1f.50 indigo, blue & brown 6·50 7·75
DESIGN: 1f.50, Commerson's dolphin.

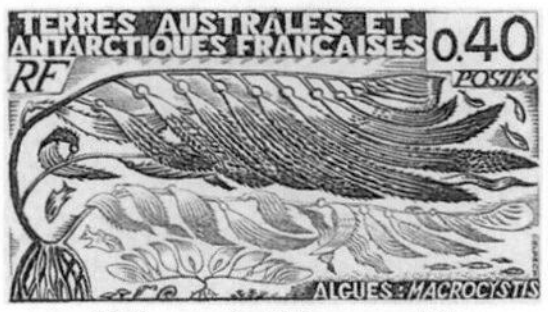
38 Seaweed, "Macrocystis"

1977.
115 **38** 40c. brown and bistre . . . 1·90 2·75
116 – 70c. green, brown & black 2·00 2·75
117 – 1f. grey . . . . 2·25 2·25
118 – 1f.20 red, green and blue 3·75 3·75
119 – 1f.40 red, blue and grey . . 4·00 5·75
DESIGNS—HORIZ: 70c. Seaweed, "Durvillea"; 1f.20, "Magga Dan" (Antarctic supply ship); 1f.40, "Thala Dan" (Antarctic supply ship). VERT: 1f. Oceanology.

39 Kerguelen Satellite

1977. Air. Satellites.
120 **39** 2f.70 multicoloured . . . . 4·25 5·00
121 – 3f. blue and light blue . . 5·50 6·75
DESIGN: 3f. Adelie Land satellite.
See also No. 143.

40 Polar Explorer with Flags

42 R. Rallier du Baty

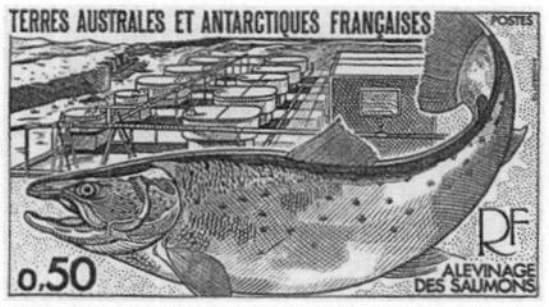
41 Atlantic Salmon and Breeding Tanks

1977. 30th Anniv of French Polar Expeditions.
122 **40** 1f.90 orange, red & blue 9·75 4·50

1977. Antarctic Fauna.
123 **41** 50c. violet & blue (postage) 2·25 3·25
124 – 90c. brown, blue & green 2·00 1·25
125 – 10f. brown, blue & red (air) . . . . 18·00 20·00
DESIGNS—As T **41**: 90c. Head of light-mantled sooty albatross. 36 × 48 mm: 10f. Kerguelen fur seal and cub.

1979. R. Rallier du Baty Commemoration.
126 **42** 1f.20 blue and bistre . . . 2·50 3·25

43 Memorial and Names of French Navigators

1979. French Navigators' Memorial, Hobart.
127 **43** 1f. brown, turq & blue . . 2·00 3·00

44 "Argos" Satellite and Geophysical Laboratory

1979. Air. Satellite Research.
128 **44** 70c. turquiose, vio & grn 2·25 3·00
129 – 1f.90 black, brown & mve 2·75 3·00
DESIGN: 1f.90, Satellite and Kerguelen Receiving Station.

45 Kerguelen Cormorant

1979. Antarctic Fauna.
130 **45** 1f.40 green, blue and sepia (postage) . . . . 1·75 1·25
131 – 4f. ultramarine, blue and green (air) . . . . 3·50 5·00
132 – 10f. brown, green & blk . . 7·25 13·00
DESIGNS—VERT: (36 × 48 mm): 4f. As No. 125, (27 × 48 mm): 10f. Southern elephant-seal.
See also Nos. 138/9.

46 Destroyer "Forbin"

1979. Ships.
133 **46** 40c. black, turquoise & grn 2·25 3·25
134 – 50c. black, turquoise & grn 2·25 2·25
DESIGN: 50c. Helicopter carrier "Jeanne d'Arc".
See also Nos. 136/7.

47 H.M.S. "Challenger" in the Antarctic (from engraving in "Illustrated London News")

1979. Air. Expedition of the "Challenger", 1872–6.
135 **47** 2f.70 black and blue . . . 3·50 3·50

1980. Frigates. As T **46**.
136 1f.10 blue, ultram & vio . . . 1·25 1·75
137 1f.50 black, blue & dp bl . . 1·25 3·00
DESIGNS—VERT: 1f.10, "Doudart de Lagree". HORIZ: 1f.50, "Commandant Bourdais".

1980. Antarctic Fauna. As T **45**.
138 70c. black, red and blue . . . 1·40 1·00
139 1f. brown and blue . . . . . 1·40 1·00
DESIGNS—VERT: 70c. Royal penguins. HORIZ: 1f. Head of soft-plumaged petrel.

50 Admiral d'Entrecasteaux
51 El Cano

1980. Admiral d'Entrecasteaux Commemoration.
140 **50** 1f.20 black, violet & blue 1·75 1·60

1980. Sebastian de El Cano (discoverer of Amsterdam Island) Commemoration.
141 **51** 1f.40 grey, orange & red 1·40 3·00
142 – 4f. multicoloured . . . . 2·50 4·00
DESIGN: 4f. El Cano's ship "Vitoria".

1980. Air. Kerguelen Satellite.
143 **39** 50c. grey, blue & brown . . 90 3·00

52 Lion Rock

1980. Air. Dumont d'Urville Base.
144 **52** 90c. multicoloured . . . . 1·25 2·75

53 "La Recherche" and "L'Esperance" (after Roux)

1980. Air. Arrival at Amsterdam Island of D'Entrecasteaux and De Kermadec Commemoration.
145 **53** 1f.90 blue . . . . 2·00 4·00

54 H.M.S. "Terror" (bomb ketch) at Arched Rock, Kerguelen (after Williams)

1980. Air.
146 **54** 2f.70 black, green & brn 1·75 3·50

55 "Phylica nitida"

1980. Air.
147 **55** 10f. black, green & brown 4·75 10·00

56 Charles de Gaulle
57 Adelie Penguins

1980. Air. 10th Death Anniv of Charles de Gaulle.
148 **56** 5f.40 purple, blue & red . . 10·00 20·00

1981. Antarctic Fauna.
149 **57** 50c. lilac . . . . 1·50 1·25
150 – 60c. blue, green & turq . . 2·75 1·00
151 **57** 1f.20 black, blue & violet 2·00 1·10
152 – 1f.30 black, brown & blue 1·50 2·75
153 – 1f.80 brown, green & bis 1·75 2·75
DESIGNS—HORIZ: 1f.30; 1f.80, Leopard seal. (48 × 28 mm) 60c. Head of Adelie penguin.

58 "HB 40 Castor"

1981. Air. Antarctic Transport.
154 **58** 2f.40 blue, orange & violet 2·50 3·00

59 "Saint Marcouf"

1981. Air. Antarctic Supply Ships.
155 **59** 3f.50 grey, blue & red . . . 1·60 3·00
156 – 7f.30 blue, turq & lilac . . 2·50 4·50
DESIGN: 7f.30, "Norsel".

60 Map of Antarctica

1981. 20th Anniv of Antarctic Treaty.
157 **60** 1f.80 blue, dp blue & brn 6·50 9·75

61 Sud Aviation Alouette II Helicopter

1981.
158 **61** 55c. blue, turq & brown . . 2·25 2·50
159 65c. turquoise, green & bl 2·25 2·50

62 Compacted Ice, Dumont d'Urville

1981. Air.
160 **62** 1f.30 dp blue, blue & grey 1·75 2·50

63 Loranchet

1981. Jean Loranchet Commemoration.
161 **63** 1f.40 dp green, green & ol 1·75 2·50

64 Black-faced Sheathbill

1981. Air.
162 **64** 1f.50 black 90 70

65 "Adele Dumont d'Urville" (Michele Garreau)

1981. Air.
163 **65** 2f. brown and black . . . 1·75 1·50

66 "Arcad III" Satellite over Antarctic

1981. Air.
164 **66** 3f.85 green, bl & dp bl . . 3·50 4·50

67 Charcot Station

1981. Air. 25th Anniv of Charcot Antarctic Station.
165 **67** 5f. red, blue and violet . . 3·25 4·25

68 "Antares" (dispatch vessel)

1981. Air.
166 **68** 8f.40 purple, grey & blue 3·25 4·50

69 Rockhopper, Gentoo and King Penguins

1982. Air. "Philexfrance 82" International Stamp Exhibition, Paris.
167 **69** 8f. brown, blue & black . . 4·25 4·50

70 "Commandant Charcot" (ice patrol ship)

1982. Air. Overseas Week.
168 **70** 5f. blue and green . . . . 3·50 4·50

71 Lighter "Le Gros Ventre"

1983.
169 **71** 55c. dp brown, green & bl 1·90 2·75

72 Apostles Islands

1983. Air.
170 **72** 65c. dp blue, brown & bl 1·75 2·75

73 Church and Statue of Virgin and Child

1983. Church of Our Lady of the Winds, Kerguelen.
171 **73** 1f.40 blue, brown & green 1·60 1·75

74 Pintails
75 Vivies

1983.
172 **74** 1f.50 dp brown, brn & bl 70 50
173 1f.80 brown and green . . 70 50

1983. Paul Martin de Vivies Commemoration.
174 **75** 1f.60 blue . . . . 1·75 3·00

76 Trawler "Austral"

1983.
175 **76** 2f.30 brown, blue & pur 2·50 3·25

77 Dog Sledge

1983. Air.
176 **77** 4f.55 blue . . . . 3·75 6·25

78 "Sputnik I" Satellite

80 "Lady Franklin" (Antarctic supply ship)

79 "Antarctica" (Georges Mathieu) (½-size illustration)

1983. Air. Anniversaries. Each black, blue and brown.
177 1f.50 Type **78** (25th anniv of International Geophysical Year) . . . . 1·10 2·00
178 3f.30 Orange Bay, Cape Horn (cent of first Polar Year) (49 × 36 mm) . . . . . . 1·50 2·50
179 5f.20 Scoresby Sound, Greenland (50th anniv of second Polar Year) (49 × 36 mm) . . . . . . 1·90 3·00

1983. Air.
180 **79** 25f. blue, black and red . . 13·00 18·00

1983.
181 **80** 5f. blue, dp blue & black 7·00 9·75

81 Drilling for Samples

1984. Glaciology.
182 **81** 15c. brown, orange & bl 1·75 1·75
183 1f.70 blue, orange & red 2·25 1·25

82 Crabeater Seal

1984. Antarctic Wildlife.
184 **82** 60c. green, grey & brown 1·75 2·75
185 – 70c. blue, dp blue & brown 60 50
186 – 2f. green, blue and brown 1·25 1·00
187 **82** 5f.90 black, blue and red 4·00 3·25
DESIGNS: 70 c, 2f. Rockhopper penguins.

83 Faure

1984. Alfred Faure Commemoration.
188 **83** 1f.80 black, brown & red 2·50 1·75

84 H.M.S. "Erebus" (bomb ketch) in Antarctic (after Davis)

1984. Air.
189 **84** 2f.60 deep blue & blue . . 1·75 3·25

85 Balloons and Airships

1984. Air. Bicentenary of Manned Flight.
190 **85** 3f.50 red, brown & blue . . 1·90 3·25
191 – 7f.80 brown, blue & violet 3·75 6·25
DESIGN: 7f.80, Montgolfier balloon, Renard and Krebs' airship "La France", balloon "Zodiac" and other balloons and airships

86 Polar Aurora

1984. Air.
192 **86** 3f.50 multicoloured . . . . 6·75 4·25

87 Port Jeanne d'Arc, Kerguelen, 1930

1984. Air.
193 **87** 4f.70 turquoise, bl & dp bl 3·00 5·25

88 "Albatros"

90 Mouflons

89 Survey Barquentine "Gauss"

1984. Air. Commissioning of Patrol Boat "Albatros".
194 **88** 11f.30 dp blue, red & bl . . 4·75 6·75

1984. Air. "Nordposta" International Stamp Exhibition, Hamburg.
195 **89** 9f. mauve and blue . . . . 5·50 4·75

1985. Antarctic Wildlife.
196 – 1f.70 black, brown and orange (postage) . . . . 1·10 90
197 – 2f.80 turquoise, blk & bl 1·40 1·25
198 **90** 70c. brown, bl & mve (air) 1·60 1·75
199 – 3f.90 brown, grey & orge 1·90 1·25
DESIGNS—HORIZ: 1f.70, Emperor penguins; 2f.80, Snow petrel. VERT: 3f.90, Amsterdam albatross.

91 Emblem, Humpback Whales, Krill and Research Vessel

1985. Biomass.
200 **91** 1f.80 dp blue, mve & bl . . 2·75 2·50
201 5f.20 blue, lt bl & red . . . 3·50 3·50

92 Liotard

93 Port Martin Base, Adelie Land

1985. Andre-Frank Liotard (explorer) Commem.
202 **92** 2f. purple and violet . . . 2·00 1·90

1985.
203 **93** 2f.20 blue, brn & dp bl . . 2·75 2·00

94 "La Novara" (frigate) at Saint Paul (after J. Noel)

1985. Air.
204 **94** 12f.80 black and orange . . 6·75 9·25

95 "Explorer and Fur Seal" (½-size illustration)

1985. Air.
205 **95** 30f. multicoloured . . . . 11·50 16·00

96 Various Motifs, Rope and Kerguelen's Ships

1985. Air. 30th Anniv of French Southern and Antarctic Territories. Each blue, green and black.
206 2f. Type **96** . . . . 1·50 2·50
207 12f.80 Motifs, rope and ships (different) . . . . 5·25 8·50

97 Southern Fulmars

1986. Birds.
208 **97** 1f. blue & black (postage) 55 70
209 – 1f.70 black, grn & brn . . 1·25 1·25
210 – 4f.60 brn, yell & red (air) 1·50 1·75
DESIGNS: 1f.70, Giant petrels; 4f.60. Southern black-backed gull.

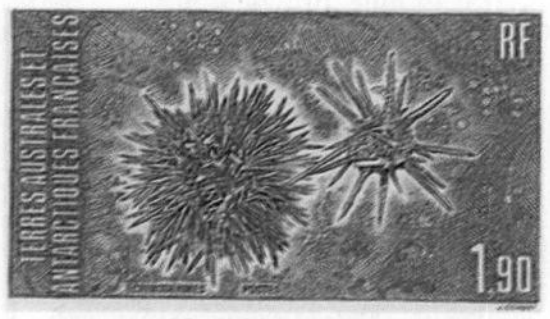

98 Echinoderms

1986.
211 **98** 1f.90 brown and blue . . . 2·50 1·75

99 "Polarbjorn" (Antarctic supply ship)

101 "Cotula plumosa"

100 Charcot and "Pourquoi Pas?" leaving Harbour

1986. Ships.
212 – 2f.10 deep blue and blue 2·25 1·75
213 **99** 3f. red, light blue and blue 3·00 2·25
DESIGN: 2f.10, B.C.A. "Var A 608" (patrol boat).

1986. Air. 50th Death Anniv of Jean Charcot (explorer). Each brown, blue and red.
214 2f.10 Type **100** . . . . 1·75 2·75
215 14f. Charcot and "Pourquoi Pas?" in heavy seas . . . . 7·25 9·25

1986. Plants.
216 **101** 2f.30 green, yell & blk . . 1·75 2·75
217 – 6f.20 green and red . . . 3·25 3·50
DESIGN: 6f.20, "Lycopodium saururus."

102 Airplane, Parachutes and Aerial

1986. Scientific Research.
218 **102** 14f. red, black & orange 5·75 10·50

103 Satellite over Antarctic

1986. Air. "SPOT" Surveillance Satellite.
219 **103** 8f. brown, green & blue 4·00 7·00

104 Starfish

1987.
220 **104** 50c. blue, orange & green 1·75 1·75

105 "Poa cookii"

1987. Plants.
221 **105** 1f.80 green and blue . . . 1·40 2·25
222 – 6f.50 green, red and blue 2·75 3·75
DESIGN: 6f.50, Lichen.

106 Marret Base, Adéelie Land

1987.
223 **106** 2f. brown, blue & purple 2·75 2·75

107 Admiral Mouchez

1987.
224 **107** 2f.20 blue, black & brown 2·75 2·75

108 Reindeer

1987. Antarctic Wildlife.
225 **108** 2f.50 black . . . . 2·75 2·50
226 – 4f.80 multicoloured . . . 2·00 1·50
DESIGN: 4f.80, Macaroni penguins.

109 Dispatch Vessel "Eure"

1987.
227 **109** 3f.20 turquoise, bl & grn 2·75 2·75

110 "J. B. Charcot" (schooner)

1987. Air.
228 **110** 14f.60 purple, bl & brn 5·75 9·00

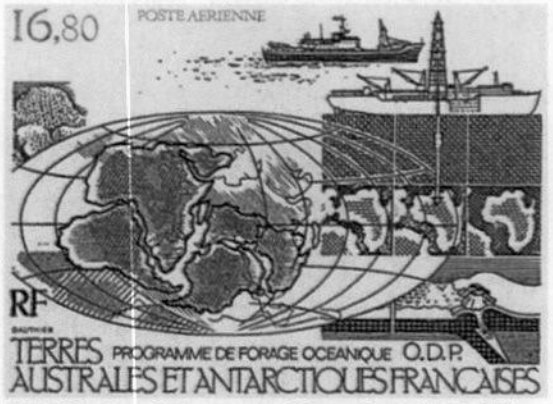

111 Globe, Research Vessel and Drilling Ship

1987. Air. Scientific Research.
229 **111** 16f.80 dp blue, bl & brn 5·25 9·00

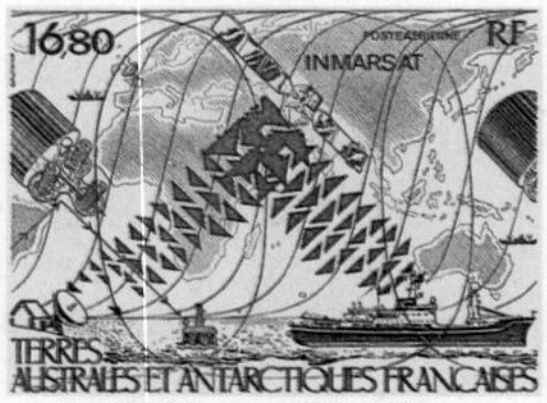

112 "Inmarsat" Satellite

1987. Air.
230 **112** 16f.80 brown and black 5·50 9·00

113 Darrieus Wind Generator

1988.
231 **113** 1f. blue, indigo & lt bl . . 1·60 1·50

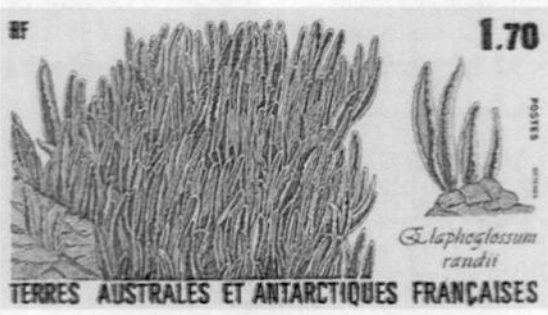

114 Elephant Grass

1988.
232 **114** 1f.70 green, bis & dp grn 1·75 1·50

115 Globe and Father Lejay

117 Gessain

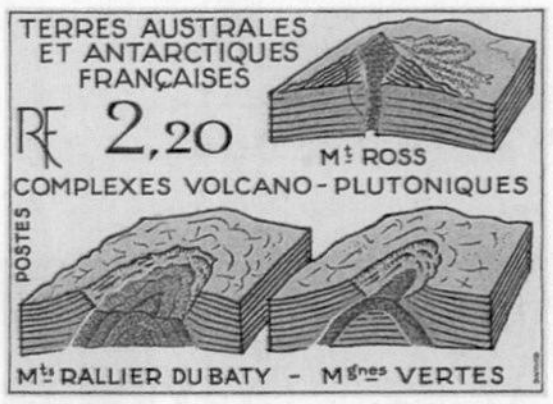

116 Geological Sections of Volcanoes

1988.
233 **115** 2f.20 black and violet . . 1·90 1·60

1988. Antarctic Geology. Multicoloured.
234 2f.20 Type **116** . . . . 1·50 1·50
235 15f.10 Geological map of Kerguelen Islands . . . . 6·75 6·00

1988. 2nd Death Anniv of Robert Gessain (explorer).
236 **117** 3f.40 red, grey and green 2·00 1·90

118 "Le Gros Ventre" (frigate)

1988. Ships.
237 **118** 3f.50 brown, grn & bl . . 1·75 1·75
238 – 4f.90 blue and black . . . 2·50 2·25
239 – 5f. blue and black . . . . 2·50 2·25
DESIGNS—HORIZ: 4f.90, Mermaid with anvil and "Jules Verne" (Antarctic supply ship). VERT: 5f. "La Fortune" (sail warship).

119 Penguin Island

1988. Air. Penguin Island.
240 **119** 3f.90 brown and blue . . 1·75 2·00
241 – 15f.10 blue, brown & grn 5·25 6·00
DESIGN: 15f.10, Views of island from sea and air.

120 Wilson's Storm Petrels

1988.
242 **120** 6f.80 blue, black & brn 2·75 2·00

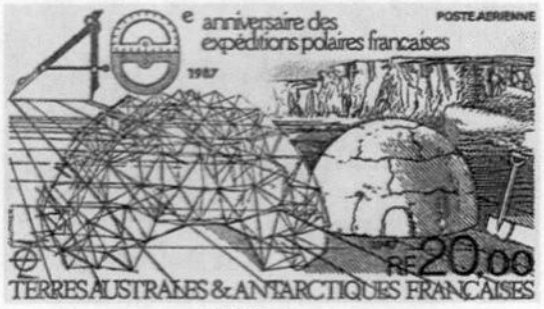

121 Igloos

1988. Air. 40th Anniv of French Polar Expeditions.
243 **121** 20f. green, purple and red 7·50 8·00

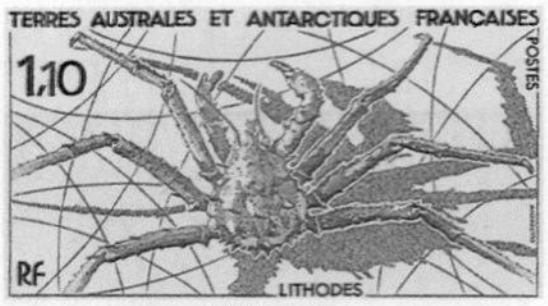

122 Crab

1989. Flora and Fauna.
244 **122** 1f.10 lt brown, bl & brn 1·00 1·10
245 – 2f. black, brn & grn . . . 1·25 1·50
246 – 2f.80 green, red & brn . . 1·60 1·50
247 – 3f.60 blue, dp bl & blk . . 1·40 80
DESIGNS: 2f. Kerguelen sheep; 2f.80, "Blechnum penna marina"; 3f.60, Blue petrel.

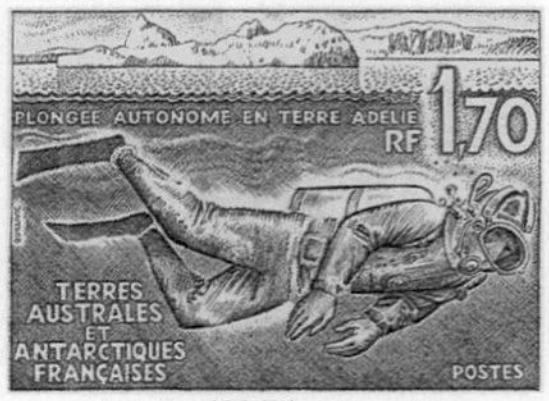

123 Diver

1989. Diving off Adelie Land.
248 **123** 1f.70 brown, green & bl 1·60 1·50

124 Henry and Rene Bossiere

1989. Kerguelen Islands Pioneers.
249 **124** 2f.20 brown, green & bl 1·60 1·50

125 "La Curieuse" (topsail schooner), 1913

1989. Air. Ships. Each blue, black and red.
250 2f.20 Type **125** . . . . 2·00 2·00
251 15f.50 "La Curieuse" (supply ship), 1989 . . . . 6·75 6·75

126 Mesotype

1989. Crystals.
252 **126** 5f.10 turquoise, blk & bl 2·25 2·50
253 – 7f.30 mauve, grn & grey 3·00 3·00
DESIGN: 7f.30, Analcime.

127 Map

1989. Air. Apostles Islands.
254 **127** 8f.40 blue, grey & green 3·75 2·75

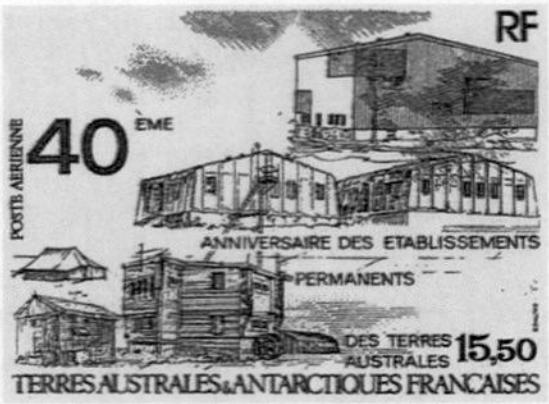

128 Buildings

1989. Air. 40th Anniv of Establishment of Permanent Antarctic Bases.
255 **128** 15f.50 brown . . . . . . 5·50 5·25

129 Allegory

1989. Air. Bicentenary of French Revolution.
256 **129** 5f. blue, green & mauve 5·75 4·25
MS257 150 × 120 mm. **129** 5f. × 4 blue, red and light blue . . . . 12·50 13·50

130 Figures around Map

1989. Air. 15th Antarctic Treaty Consultative Meeting, Paris.
258 **130** 17f.70 red, purple & blue 6·25 6·75

131 "Chonotriches", "Copepodes" and Map of Kerguelen

1990. Protistology.
259 **131** 1f.10 blue, brown & black 65 55

132 Cattle

1990. Restoration of Amsterdam Island.
260 **132** 1f.70 brown, green & blue 75 55

133 Quoy and Decollate Planaxis (shell)

135 Dumont d'Urville

134 Yellow-nosed Albatrosses

1990. Birth Bicentenary of Jean Rene C. Quoy (doctor and naturalist).
261 **133** 2f.20 blue, dp brn & brn 1·00 85

1990.
262 **134** 2f.80 multicoloured . . . 1·10 70

1990. Birth Bicentenary of Jules Dumont d'Urville (explorer).
263 **135** 3f.60 brown and blue . . 1·50 1·25

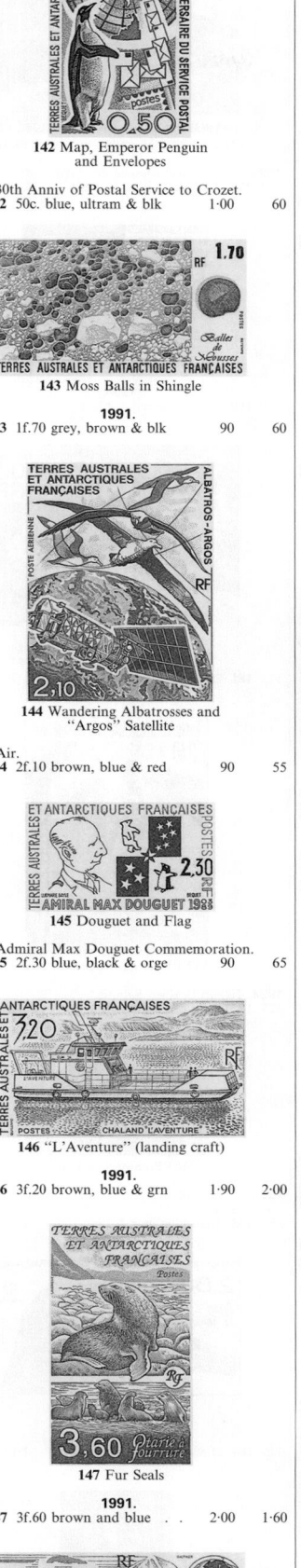

136 Aragonite

1990. Minerals.
264 **136** 5f.10 brown and blue . . 2·25 2·00

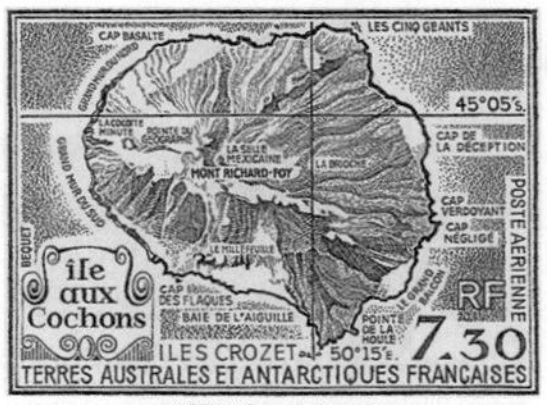

137 Pigs Island

1990. Air.
265 **137** 7f.30 green, brown & blue 3·25 2·75

138 "Ranunculus pseudo trullifolius"

1990.
266 **138** 8f.40 green, blue & orge 3·50 3·00

139 "L'Astrolabe"

1990. Air. 150th Anniv of Discovery of Adelie Land by Dumont d'Urville.
267 **139** 15f.50 brown and red . . 5·50 4·50

140 "L'Astrolabe" (fishery control vessel), 1988

1990. Air. Ships. Each blue, green and red.
268 2f.20 Type **140** . . . . 1·75 1·75
269 15f.50 "L'Astrolabe" (Dumont d'Urville's ship), 1840 . . . . 7·00 7·00

141 Bird (½-size illustration)

1990. Air.
270 **141** 30f. multicoloured . . . . 12·00 8·00

142 Map, Emperor Penguin and Envelopes

1991. 30th Anniv of Postal Service to Crozet.
271 **142** 50c. blue, ultram & blk 1·00 60

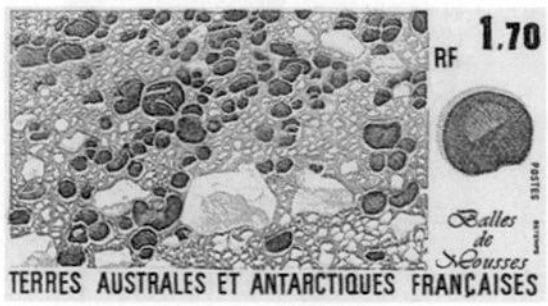

143 Moss Balls in Shingle

1991.
272 **143** 1f.70 grey, brown & blk 90 60

144 Wandering Albatrosses and "Argos" Satellite

1991. Air.
273 **144** 2f.10 brown, blue & red 90 55

145 Douguet and Flag

1991. Admiral Max Douguet Commemoration.
274 **145** 2f.30 blue, black & orge 90 65

146 "L'Aventure" (landing craft)

1991.
275 **146** 3f.20 brown, blue & grn 1·90 2·00

147 Fur Seals

1991.
276 **147** 3f.60 brown and blue . . 2·00 1·60

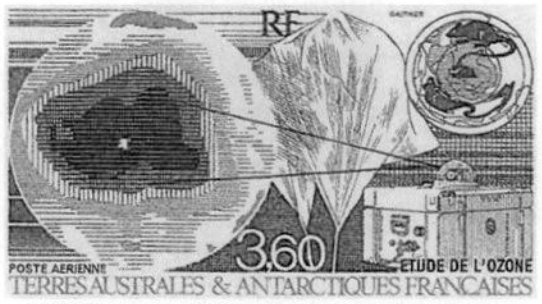

148 Infra-red Image and Measuring Equipment (study of ozone layer)

1991. Air. Climatic Research. Each green, violet and orange.
277 3f.60 Type **148** . . . . 2·00 2·00
278 20f. Research vessel and rock samples (palaeoclimatology) . . . . 8·50 8·50

149 Mordenite

1991.
279 **149** 5f.20 blue, green & black 2·00 1·50

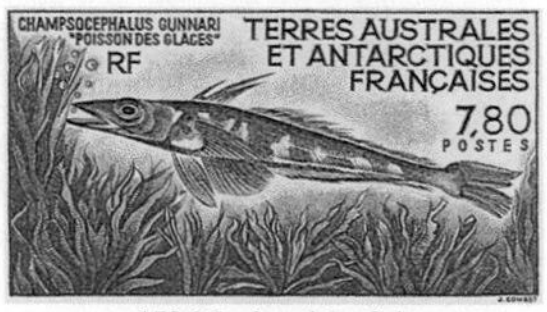

150 Mackerel Icefish

1991.
280 **150** 7f.80 green and blue . . . 3·50 2·75

151 Map **152** De Gaulle and Map

1991. 30th Anniv of Antarctic Treaty.
281 **151** 9f.30 grn, dp grn & red 3·25 3·00

1991. Air. Birth Centenary of Charles de Gaulle (French statesman).
282 **152** 18f.80 black, blue & red 8·00 4·75

153 Research Worker greeting Penguin (Antarctic)

1991. Air. French Institute for Polar Research and Technology. Multicoloured.
283 15f. Type **153** . . . . 6·25 6·25
284 15f. Research worker greeting polar bear (Arctic) . . . . 6·25 6·25

Nos. 283/4 were printed together, se-tenant, forming a composite design.

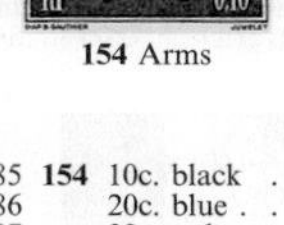

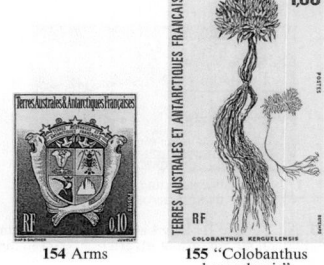

154 Arms **155** "Colobanthus kerguelensis"

1992.
285 **154** 10c. black 10 10
286 20c. blue 10 10
287 30c. red 10 10
288 40c. green 10 10
289 50c. orange 10 10

1992.
295 **155** 1f. brown, green & blue 55 40

156 "Groupe Safap-Helvim" (yacht) and Antarctic Route

1992. "Globe Challenge" Round the World Sailing Race.
296 **156** 2f.20 multicoloured . . . 1·25 1·25

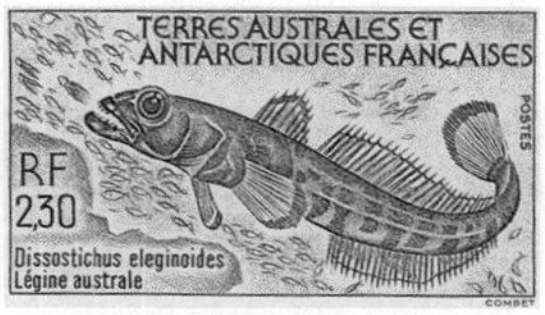

157 Blenny Rockcod

1992.
297 **157** 2f.30 green, blue & brn 1·50 1·25

158 Paul Tchernia (scientist)

1992.
298 **158** 2f.50 grn, brn & dp brn 1·40 1·25

159 Pintado Petrels **160** Marion-Dufresne (after Meryon)

1992. Air.
299 **159** 3f.40 brown, blk & grn 1·40 65

1992. 220th Death Anniv of Marion-Dufresne (explorer).
300 **160** 3f.70 black, red & blue . . 1·75 1·40

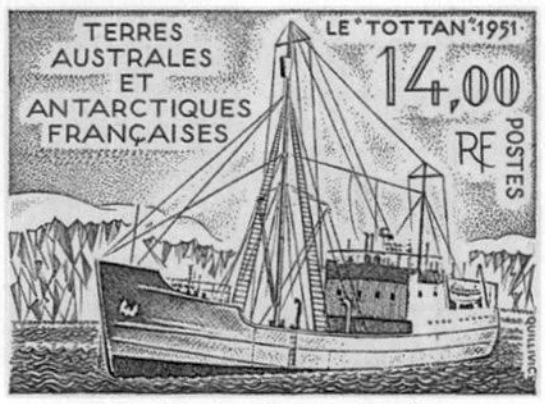

161 "Tottan" (supply ship)

1992.
301 **161** 14f. brown, turq & blue 6·00 6·00

162 Columbus's Fleet, Montgolfier Balloon and Columbus

1992. Air. 500th Anniv of Discovery of America by Columbus.
302 **162** 22f. brown, pur & dp brn 10·50 10·50

163 Satellite in Orbit

1992. Air. "Topex Poseidon" Satellite.
303 **163** 24f.50 red, black & blue 10·00 4·25

164 Ocean Currents, Research Vessel and Pipes

1992. WOCE Research Programme.
304 **164** 25f.40 brown, orge & bl 11·00 11·00

165 Adelie and Emperor Penguins on Landing Strip (½-size illustration)

1992. Air. Completion of Landing Strip at Dumont D'Urville Research Station, Adelie Land.
305 **165** 25f.70 multicoloured . . . 9·25 5·25

166 Violet-tinted Garnet

1993.
306 **166** 1f. purple, green & black 30 20

167 Radio Equipment, Handshake and Globe

1993. Air. Amateur Radio Enthusiasts.
307 **167** 2f. black, red & mauve . . 70 35

168 "Marion Dufresne" **169** "Lyallia kerguelensis"

1993. 20th Anniv of the "Marion Dufresne" (Antarctic supply ship).
308 **168** 2f.20 mauve, black & bl 1·00 60

1993.
309 **169** 2f.30 blue, green & yell 75 50

170 Killer Whale

1993.
310 **170** 2f.50 black and purple . . 85 50

171 Antarctic Skuas

1993.
311 **171** 2f.50 black . . . . 1·75 70

172 Andre Prud'homme (meteorologist)

1993. 43rd Anniv of Meteo France (weather service) in the Antarctic. Each black, blue and red.
312 2f.50 Type **172** 75 50
313 22f. Meteorologists recording wind speed on Adelie Land (35 × 37 mm) . . . . . . 6·00 4·50

173 Red-banded Snipefish

1993.
314 **173** 3f.40 red, brown & blue 1·00 75

174 "Italo Marsano"

1993. 43rd Anniv of Chartering of the "Italo Marsano" (freighter).
315 **174** 3f.70 purple, brown & bl 1·10 80

175 King Penguins on Television and Platform

1993. ECOPHY Research Programme.
316 **175** 14f. brown, blue & black 5·00 2·75

176 "L'Astrolabe" and Route Map

1993. Voyage of "L'Astrolabe" (fishery control ship) through North-East Passage.
317 **176** 22f. red and blue . . . . 6·50 4·00

177 Scientists examining Arctic Tern and using Microscope

1993. Air. Animal Biology Laboratory, Adelie Land.
318 **177** 25f.40 brn, grn & dp grn 9·00 6·00

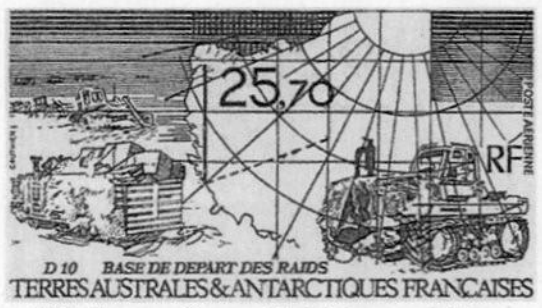

178 Camp, Snow Vehicles and Map

1993. Air. Antarctic Expedition Base D 10.
319 **178** 25f.70 brown, red & blue 7·50 5·50

179 Lockheed Hercules over Adelie Land

1993. Air. Inauguration of Air Strip, Adelie Land.
320 **179** 30f. black, blue & green 8·50 6·50

180 Cordierite

1994.
321 **180** 1f. blue, green & black . . 45 25

181 Domestic Cat

1994.
322 **181** 2f. black, green & emer 70 50

182 Lowering Probe into Sea

1994. 1000th Sea-bed Sample.
323 **182** 2f.40 black and blue . . . 1·10 60

183 Pommier and Dog

1994. 75th Birth Anniv of Robert Pommier (explorer).
324 **183** 2f.80 blue, pur & orge . . 1·25 75

184 Salvin's Prion

1994.
325 **184** 2f.80 blue . . . . 1·10 80

185 C. A. Vincendon Dumoulin (hydrographic engineer)

1994. Navy Hydrographic and Oceanographic Service. Each black and blue.
326 2f.80 Type **185** . . . . 1·00 75
327 23f. Measuring magnetic force (35 × 36 mm) . . . . 8·00 5·50

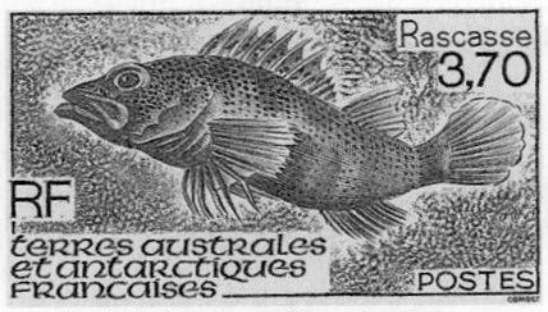

186 Rascasse Scorpionfish

1994.
328 **186** 3f.70 orange and green . . 1·40 90

187 "Kerguelen de Tremarec" (trawler)

1994.
329 **187** 4f.30 lilac, red & green . . 1·50 1·00

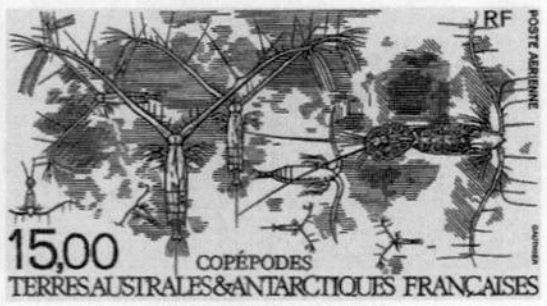

188 "Copepoda"

1994. Air.
330 **188** 15f. black . . . . 4·75 3·25

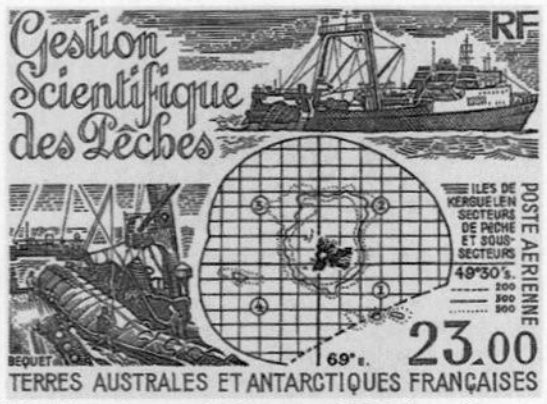

189 Trawler and Chart of Fishing Sectors around Kerguelen Islands

1994. Air. Scientific Management of Fishing Industry.
331 **189** 23f. purple, blue & red . . 7·50 5·50

190 Map of Antarctic, Satellite and Earth Station

1994. Air. National Centre for Space Study Satellite Station, Kerguelen.
332 **190** 26f.70 lilac, bl & ultram 8·50 6·00

191 Lidar Station and Map

1994. Air. Lidar Research Station, Adelie Land.
333 **191** 27f.30 blue, green & mve 9·00 6·50

192 Penguins (½-size illustration)

1994. Air. Migration of Emperor Penguins.
334 **192** 28f. black and blue . . . 10·00 6·50

193 Olivine

1995.
335 **193** 1f. olive, green and lilac 35 20

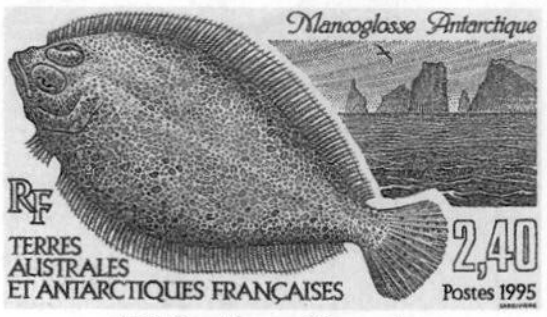

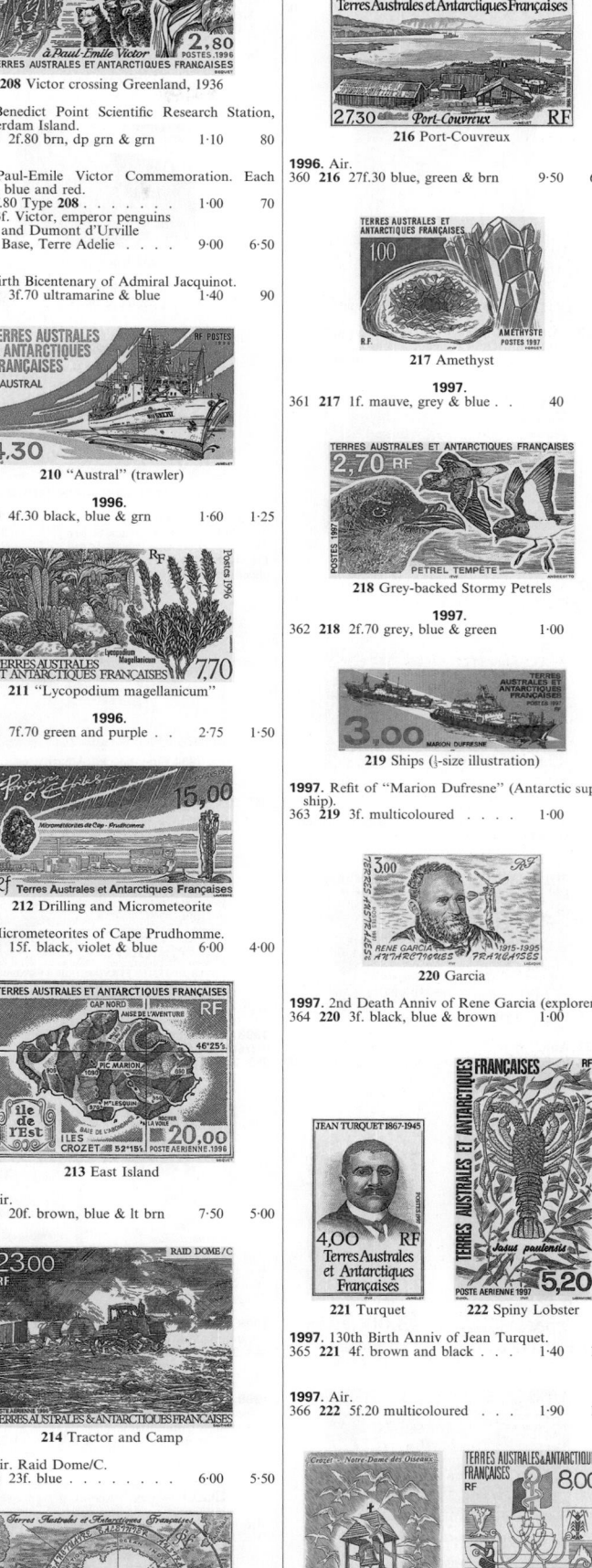

194 Southern Flounder

1995.
336 **194** 2f.40 brown, blue & mve 1·00 55

195 Andree and Edgar Aubert de la Rue (naturalists)

1995.
337 **195** 2f.80 brown, blue & mve 95 65

196 SODAR Station (wind study centre)

1995.
338 **196** 2f.80 mauve, red & violet 95 65

197 Mont d'Alsace, Kerguelen

1995.
339 **197** 3f.70 brown, violet & bl 1·40 1·10

198 "Antarctica" (research vessel)

1995. Air. Mt. Erebus Expedition.
340 **198** 4f.30 blue, green & mve 1·75 1·00

199 Waving Farewell

1995. Air. Departure of Winter Residents from Charcot Station.
341 **199** 15f. multicoloured . . . . 5·50 3·25

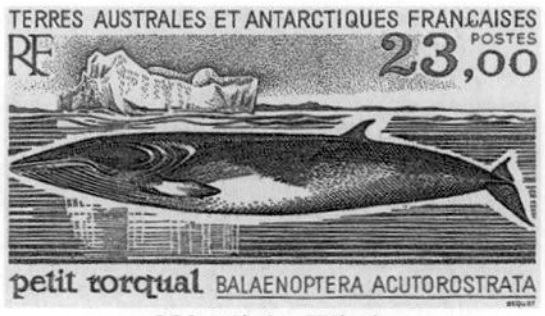

200 Minke Whale

1995.
342 **200** 23f. dp blue, blue & pur 8·50 5·00

201 "Tamaris" and Tagged Grey-headed Albatross

1995. Voyage of "Tamaris" (full-rigged ship).
343 **201** 25f.80 brn, turq & bl . . 9·25 5·50

202 "Heroine" (full-rigged ship)

1995. Expedition of "Heroine" to Crozet Islands in 1837.
344 **202** 27f.30 blue . . . . 10·00 6·25

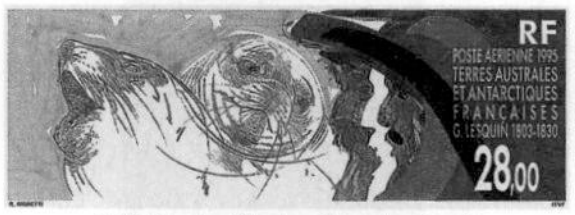

203 Seals (½-size illustration)

1995. 165th Death Anniv of G. Lesquin.
345 **203** 28f. multicoloured . . . . 10·50 6·50

204 Amazonite

1996.
347 **204** 1f. blue, green and black 40 30

205 White-chinned Petrel

1996.
348 **205** 2f.40 blue 90 75

206 "Yves de Kerguelen" (expedition ship)

1996.
349 **206** 2f.80 brown, blue & pur 1·25 80

207 Station

209 Jacquinot

208 Victor crossing Greenland, 1936

1996. Benedict Point Scientific Research Station, Amsterdam Island.
350 **207** 2f.80 brn, dp grn & grn 1·10 80

1996. Paul-Emile Victor Commemoration. Each black, blue and red.
351 2f.80 Type **208** . . . . 1·00 70
352 23f. Victor, emperor penguins and Dumont d'Urville Base, Terre Adelie . . . . 9·00 6·50

1996. Birth Bicentenary of Admiral Jacquinot.
353 **209** 3f.70 ultramarine & blue 1·40 90

210 "Austral" (trawler)

1996.
354 **210** 4f.30 black, blue & grn 1·60 1·25

211 "Lycopodium magellanicum"

1996.
355 **211** 7f.70 green and purple . . 2·75 1·50

212 Drilling and Micrometeorite

1996. Micrometeorites of Cape Prudhomme.
356 **212** 15f. black, violet & blue 6·00 4·00

213 East Island

1996. Air.
357 **213** 20f. brown, blue & lt brn 7·50 5·00

214 Tractor and Camp

1996. Air. Raid Dome/C.
358 **214** 23f. blue . . . . 6·00 5·50

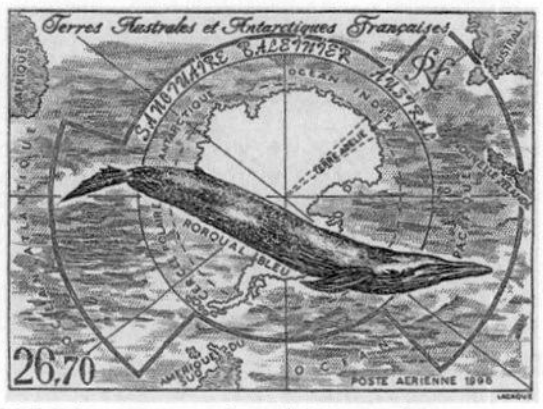

215 Blue Rorqual and Map of Sanctuary Area

1996. Air. Southern Whale Sanctuary.
359 **215** 26f.70 purple, bl & orge 9·50 6·00

216 Port-Couvreux

1996. Air.
360 **216** 27f.30 blue, green & brn 9·50 6·00

217 Amethyst

1997.
361 **217** 1f. mauve, grey & blue . . 40 20

218 Grey-backed Stormy Petrels

1997.
362 **218** 2f.70 grey, blue & green 1·00 70

219 Ships (½-size illustration)

1997. Refit of "Marion Dufresne" (Antarctic supply ship).
363 **219** 3f. multicoloured . . . . 1·00 70

220 Garcia

1997. 2nd Death Anniv of Rene Garcia (explorer).
364 **220** 3f. black, blue & brown 1·00 70

221 Turquet **222** Spiny Lobster

1997. 130th Birth Anniv of Jean Turquet.
365 **221** 4f. brown and black . . . 1·40 1·00

1997. Air.
366 **222** 5f.20 multicoloured . . . 1·90 1·25

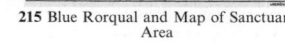

223 Antarctic Terns, Bell Tower and Church **224** Service Emblem and Operation

1997. Church of Our Lady of the Birds, Crozet.
367 **223** 5f.20 brown, blue & red 1·90 1·25

1997. Forces Health Service.
368 **224** 8f. red, brown & purple 2·75 2·00

225 Map, "Ecureuil Poitou-Charantes 2" and King Penguin

1997. Air. Unscheduled Stop at Kerguelen by Contestant in BOC Challenge Yacht Race.
369 **225** 16f. multicoloured . . . . 6·00 3·50

226 Nunn at Hope Cottage, Point Charlotte

1997. Air. John Nunn (shipwreck survivor).
370 **226** 20f. red, purple & brown 6·50 4·00

227 Lighter, Nets, Antarctic Dragonfish and Crocodile Icefish

1997. Air. Icota Programme (fish research project).
371 **227** 24f. green, blue and red 8·00 5·50

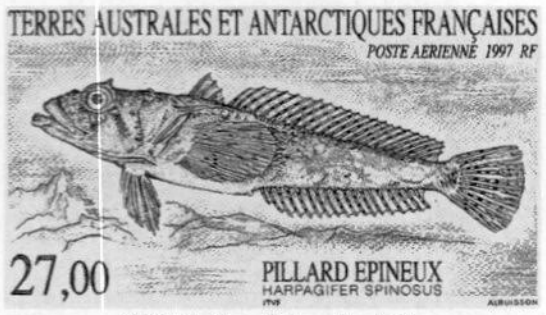

228 Spiny Plunderfish

1997. Air.
372 **228** 27f. black, purple & blue 9·00 7·00

229 "Poa kerguelensis"

231 Kerguelen-Tremarec

230 Snow Tractors, Greenland

1997.
373 **229** 29f.20 brown, grn & mve 10·00 7·50

1997. 50th Anniv of First French Polar Expedition. Multicoloured.
374 1f. Type **230** 35 35
375 1f. Port Martin and Marret Bases, Adelie Land 35 35
376 1f. Dumont d'Urville Base in 1956 and 1997 and Charcot Station 35 35

Nos. 374/6 were issued together, se-tenant, forming a composite design.

1997. Bicentenary of Disappearance of Admiral Yves Kerguelen-Tremarec (discoverer of Kerguelen Land). Each black, green and red.
377 3f. Type **231** . . . . 1·00 70
378 24f. Christmas Harbour (from "Atlas of Cook's Voyages") (37 × 38 mm) . . 8·00 5·50

232 Rock-crystal

1998.
379 **232** 1f. blue, violet & black . . 30 20

233 Launch approaching Trawlers

1998. Fisheries Control.
380 **233** 2f.60 blue, black & brn 95 60
381 – 2f.60 blue, black & red . . 95 60
DESIGN: No. 381, Inspectors measuring fish and checking records.

234 Grey-headed Albatrosses

1998.
382 **234** 2f.70 multicoloured . . . 90 70

235 Broad-billed Prion and Helicopter over Saint Paul Island

1998. Ecological Rehabilitation of Saint Paul Island (rat and rabbit eradication).
383 **235** 3f. blue, green & brown 95 70

236 Peau

237 Laclavere

1998. Etienne Peau (Antarctic researcher) Commemoration.
384 **236** 3f. blue, mauve & black 95 70

1998. 4th Death Anniv of Georges Laclavere (geographer and head of French National Antarctic Research Committee).
385 **237** 4f. brown, orange & blk 1·25 90

238 Preparation for Deep Boring and Map

1998. Air. Epica Dome C Programme.
386 **238** 5f.20 brown and mauve 1·75 1·40

239 Station Buildings

1998. Air. 1st Meteorological Radio Station, Port-aux-Francais.
387 **239** 8f. black, blue and red . . 2·75 2·75

240 "Argos" Satellite and King Penguins with Radio Transmitters

1998. Air. Penguin Research.
388 **240** 16f. multicoloured . . . . 5·50 3·75

241 "Ranunculus moseleyi"

1998.
389 **241** 24f. green, lt green & yell 7·50 5·50

242 Porbeagle Shark pursuing Fish

1998.
390 **242** 27f. grey, blue and green 8·50 6·00

243 "Le Cancalais" (schooner)

1998.
391 **243** 29f.20 sepia, blue & brn 10·00 7·00

244 Antarctic Base (½-size illustration)

1998. 40th Anniv of International Geophysical Year.
392 **244** 5f.20 blue, red and black 1·60 1·00

245 Epidote

1999.
393 **245** 1f. emerald, green & blk 30 20

246 Bearded Penguins

1999.
394 **246** 2f.70 indigo, blue & brn 80 60

247 King Penguins (½-size illustration)

1999. Crozet Penguin Colony.
395 **247** 3f. multicoloured 90 70

248 Sicaud

1999. Death Commemoration (1998) of Pierre Sicaud (scientist).
396 **248** 3f. green and black . . . 90 70

249 Martin

1999. 50th Death Anniv of Jacques-Andre Martin (scientist).
397 **249** 4f. ultramarine, blk & bl 1·25 90

250 Ray

1999.
398 **250** 5f.20 brown, blue & pur 1·60 1·25

251 "Floreal" (frigate)

1999.
399 **251** 5f.20 multicoloured . . . . 1·60 1·25

252 Cats, Scientists and Map

1999. Cat Research Programme, Kerguelen Islands.
400 **252** 8f. green, blue and red . . 2·40 1·60

253 Amsterdam Island Albatrosses and Ornithologist

1999. Artificial Nests, Amsterdam Island.
401 **253** 16f. green, black and olive 4·75 3·50

254 "Festuca contracta"

1999.
402 **254** 24f. blue, green & dp grn 7·00 5·50

255 Geologist, Fishery Control Vessel and Map

1999. Geoleta Programme, Adelie Land.
403 **255** 29f.20 blue, black and red 9·00 6·50

256 Research Base, Amsterdam Island

1999. 50th Anniv of Research Bases on Kerguelen and Amsterdam Islands. Each red, blue and green.
404 3f. Type **256** . . . . 1·00 75
405 24f. Research base, Kerguelen 6·50 5·25

257 Loading Ship at La Reunion

1999. Tourism. Booklet Stamps. No value expressed. Multicoloured.
406 (5f.20) Type **257** . . . . . . 2·75 2·25
407 (5f.20) Diners on board the "Marion Dufresne" (Antarctic supply ship) . . 2·75 2·25
408 (5f.20) King penguin colony 2·75 2·25
409 (5f.20) Handstamping letters, Crozet (vert) . . . . 2·75 2·25
410 (5f.20) Research station, Port-aux-Francais, Kerguelen 2·75 2·25
411 (5f.20) Port Couvreux, Kerguelen . . . . 2·75 2·25
412 (5f.20) Unloading ships, Port-aux-Francais, Kerguelen 2·75 2·25
413 (5f.20) Port Jeanne d'Arc, Kerguelen . . . . 2·75 2·25
414 (5f.20) St. Paul Island . . . . 2·75 2·25
415 (5f.20) Remains of crayfish canning industry, St. Paul Island . . . . 2·75 2·25
416 (5f.20) Martin de Vivies base, Amsterdam Island . . . . 2·75 2·25
417 (5f.20) Unloading ships, Amsterdam Island . . . . 2·75 2·25

258 Madagascar 1946 5f. Stamp and Kerguelen Islands Handstamp

1999. "Philexfrance 99" International Stamp Exhibition, Paris. Sheet 148 × 81 mm containing T **258** and similar multicoloured designs.
MS418 5f.20 Type **258**; 5f.20 French Southern and Antarctic Territories 1961 25f. stamp and Crozet Islands handstamp; 5f.20 Madagascar 1946 10f. stamp and Amsterdam Island handstamp (39 × 51 mm); 5f.20 Madagascar 1948 100f. overprinted stamp and Adelie Land handstamp (39 × 51 mm) (sold at 25f.) . . 7·50 7·50

259 Mica

2000.
419 **259** 1f. black, green and blue 30 20

260 Pale-footed Shearwaters

2000.
420 **260** 2f.70 multicoloured . . . 55 40

261 Beauge

2000. 3rd Death Anniv of Andre Beauge (scientist).
421 **261** 3f. black, brn & dp brn 60 45

262 Penguins (Crozet Island)

2000. "Third Millennium on French Southern and Antarctic Territories". Sheet 138 × 190 mm containing T **262** and similar vert designs.
MS422 3f. Type **262**; 3f. Walruses (Kerguelen Island); 3f. Lobster (St. Paul and Amsterdam Islands); 3f. Exploration vehicle (Adelie Land) . . . . 2·50 2·50

263 Yves Joseph Kerguelen-Tremarec

264 Abby Jane Morrell

2000. Explorers. Multicoloured.
423 3f. Type **263** 60 45
424 3f. Dumont D'Urville 60 45
425 3f. Raymond Rallier du Baty 60 45
426 3f. E. Aubert de la Rue . . . 60 45
427 3f. Paul-Emile Victor 60 45

2000.
428 **264** 4f. black, yellow & brn 80 60

265 Seal and Maps

2000. Oceanographic Survey (seal tracking).
429 **265** 4f.40 multicoloured . . . 90 65

266 Hobbs (sledge dog)

267 Yellow-nosed Albatross

2000.
430 **266** 5f.20 black, blue & orge 1·00 75

2000. Demographic Database of Birds. Mult.
431 5f.20 Type **267** . . . . 1·00 75
432 8f. Wandering albatross and graph (Crozet Island) (50 × 28 mm) . . . . . . 1·60 1·25
433 16f. Emperor penguins and graph (Adélie Land) (50 × 28 mm) . . . . . . 3·25 2·25
Nos. 431/3 were issued together, se-tenant, forming a composite design.

268 Map of Antarctica and Computer Images (½-size illustration)

2000. Sleep Research.
434 **268** 8f. multicoloured . . . . 1·60 1·10

269 *La Perouse* (supply frigate)

2000.
435 **269** 16f. deep blue, blue & grn 3·25 2·25

270 Lantern Fishes

2000.
436 **270** 24f. black, blue & purple 4·75 3·50

271 Penguins

2000. Larose Bay Penguin Colony.
437 **271** 27f. multicoloured . . . . 5·50 3·75

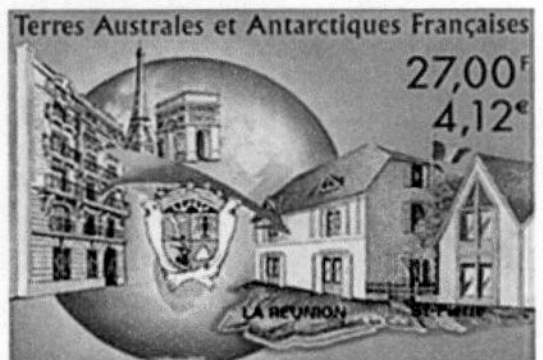

272 Old and New Headquarters

2000. Relocation of Administrative Headquarters.
438 **272** 27f. multicoloured . . . . 5·50 3·75

273 Magnetite

2001.
439 **273** 1f. grey, green & turquoise 30 20

274 Common Diving Petrels

2001.
440 **274** 2f.70 blue, violet & black 55 40

275 Richert

276 Man pulling Sledge

2001. 9th Death Anniv of Xavier-Charles Richert.
441 **275** 3f. black, blue and indigo 60 45

2001. Armee de Terre's Expedition to Adelie Land.
442 **276** 3f. multicoloured 60 45

277 L'Arche des Kerguelen, Christmas Harbour

2001.
443 **277** 3f. black 60 45

278 Albatrosses (Kerguelen Island)

2001. Wildlife on French Southern and Antarctic Territories. Sheet 138 × 190 mm containing T **278** and similar multicoloured designs.
MS444 3f. Type **278**; 3f. Emperor penguins (Adelie Land) (horiz); 3f. Eared seals (St. Paul and Amsterdam Islands) (horiz); 3f. Killer whale (Crozet Island) . . 2·50 2·50

279 Jean Coulomb

2001.
445 **279** 4f. multicoloured 80 60

280 *Carmen* (brigantine)

2001. Ships. Sheet 143 × 102 mm containing T **280** and similar horiz designs.
MS446 5f.20 azure, blue and brown (Type **280**); 5f.20 chestnut, ochre and blue (*Austral* (supply ship)); 5f.20 ochre, chestnut and blue (*Ramuntcho* (ketch)); 5f.20 azure, blue and brown (*Sapmer 1* (supply ship)) . . . . 4·00 4·00

281 Memorial Plaque

2001. 127th Anniv of French Astronomers' Visit to St. Paul Island to Observe Transit of Venus across the Sun.
447 **281** 8f. brown and black . . . 1·60 1·10

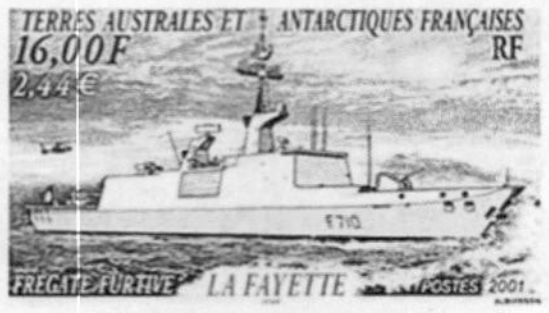

282 *La Fayette* (frigate)

2001.
448 **282** 16f. multicoloured . . . . 3·25 2·25

283 Squid

2001.
449 **283** 24f. multicoloured . . . . 4·75 3·50

284 "Mir", Earth and Computer

2001. Amateur Radio Link between "Mir" Space Station and Crozet Island.
450 **284** 27f. multicoloured . . . . 5·50 3·75

285 *Bryum laevigatum*

2001.
451 **285** 29f.20 multicoloured . . . 5·75 4·00

286 Map of Antarctica and Compass

2001. 40th Anniv of Antarctic Treaty.
452 **286** 5f.20 blue and indigo . . 1·10 90

287 Map of Antarctica and Fish

2001. 20th Anniv of Commission for the Conservation of Antarctic Marine Living Resources.
453 **287** 5f.20 multicoloured . . . 1·10 90

288 Ship in Pack Ice

2001. Adelie Land. No value expressed. Multicoloured.

454	(5f.20) Type **288**	1·10	90
455	(5f.20) Statue of Dumont d'Urville (explorer), Dumont d'Urville Base . .	1·10	90
456	(5f.20) Adelie penguin colony	1·10	90
457	(5f.20) Astrolabe glacier . . .	1·10	90
458	(5f.20) Geology Point Archipelago	1·10	90
459	(5f.20) Releasing weather balloon	1·10	90
460	(5f.20) Convoy of equipment	1·10	90
461	(5f.20) Helicopter delivering supplies	1·10	90
462	(5f.20) Emperor penguins . .	1·10	90
463	(5f.20) Radio communications centre	1·10	90
464	(5f.20) Statue of Paul Emile Victor (explorer)	1·10	90
465	(5f.20) Cap Prud'homme . .	1·10	90
466	(5f.20) *Astrolabe* (fishery control vessel) and penguins	1·10	90
467	(5f.20) Men leaving by helicopter	1·10	90

New Currency. 100 cents = 1 euro

2002. As T **154** but with face values expressed in euros.

468	1c. black	10	10
469	2c. blue	10	10
470	5c. red	10	10
471	10c. green	15	10
472	20c. orange	30	20

289 Nepheline **290** Albatross

2002.
480 **289** 15c. multicoloured 20 15

2002.
481 **290** 41c. black, yellow and blue 55 45

291 *Marion Dufresne* (Antarctic supply ship)

2002.
482 **291** 46c. blue, red and black 65 50

292 Shed and Pylon

2002. Cable Cars on Crozet Island (1963–1983).
483 **292** 46c. multicoloured 65 50

293 Albatrosses and Rock (Kerguelen Islands)

2002. "The French Southern Antarctic Olympic Games". Sheet 139 × 191 mm containing T **293** and similar multicoloured designs.
MS484 46c. Type **293**; 46c. Lobsters diving (St. Paul and Amsterdam Islands); 46c. Emperor penguins sliding (Adelie Land) (vert); 46c. Killer whales leaping (Crozet Island) (vert) 1·90 1·90

294 Geological Diagram

2002. 11th Anniv (2001) of Cartoker Geological Survey of Kerguelen Islands. Multicoloured.
485 46c. Type **294** 65 50
486 €3.66 Map of Kerguelen Islands . . . . 5·00 4·00

295 Dubois and Scientific Equipment

2002. 2nd Death Anniv of Jacques Dubois (Antarctic researcher).
487 **295** 61c. multicoloured 85 70

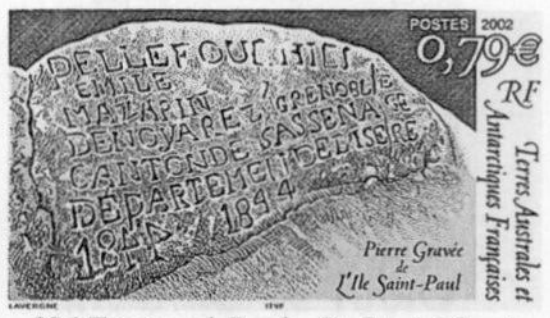

296 Engraved Rock, St. Paul Island

2002.
488 **296** 79c. sepia, blue and green 1·10 85

297 Emperor Penguin and Chicks

2002. Antarctic Animals and their Young. Sheet 104 × 143 mm, containing T **297** and similar vert designs. Multicoloured.
MS489 79c. Type **297**; 79c. Grey seal and pup; 79c. Abatross and chick; 79c. Elephant seal and pups . . . . 4·50 4·50

298 Kerguelen Cabbage

2002.
490 **298** €1.22 multicoloured . . 1·70 1·40

299 Ship

2002. Centenary of Visit of *Guass* (survey barquentine) to Kerguelen Islands.
491 **299** €2.44 multicoloured . . 3·50 3·00

300 Crab

2002.
492 **300** €3.66 multicoloured . . 5·00 4·00

301 Diatoms and Pack Ice

2002. Diatoms (microscopic algae) of the Antarctic Pack Ice.
493 **301** €4.12 multicoloured . . 5·75 5·25

302 Door and Facade

2002. 181st Anniv of French Geographical Society.
494 **302** €4.45 multicoloured . . 6·25 5·00

303 Penguins incubating "€"

2002. Introduction of the Euro.
495 **303** 46c. black and blue . . . 65 50

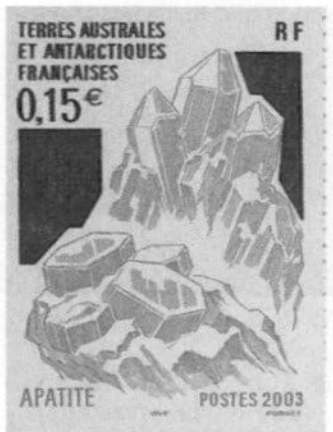

304 Apatite

2003.

496 **304** 15c. mauve, blue and black 20 15

305 Factory, St. Paul Island

2003.

497 **305** 41c. black, green and blue 55 45

306 Emperor Penguins

2003.

498 **306** 46c. multicoloured 60 50

307 Glaciers

2003. Luc Marie Bayle (artist) Commemoration.

499 **307** 46c. multicoloured 60 50

308 Louis XV and Penguins wearing Neckties on Crozet Island

2003. 18th-century French Personalities transposed to Southern Antarctic Territories. Sheet 139 × 191 mm containing T **308** and similar vert designs. Multicoloured.

MS500 Type **308**; 46c. "Triumph of Venus" on St. Paul and Amsterdam Islands; 46c. Dumont and Adele D'urville on Adelie Land; 46c. Le Chavalier Yves de Kerguelen on Kerguelen Island 2·00 2·00

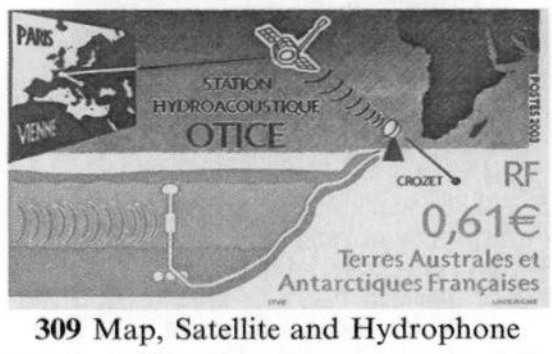

309 Map, Satellite and Hydrophone

2003. Research Station, Crozet Island.

501 **309** 61c. green and blue . . . 80 65

310 Damaged and Restored Buildings

2003. Restoration of Port Jeanne d'Arc.

502 **310** 79c. multicoloured . . . . 1·00 80

311 Man wearing Furs, 1898

313 *Bougainville* (research ship)

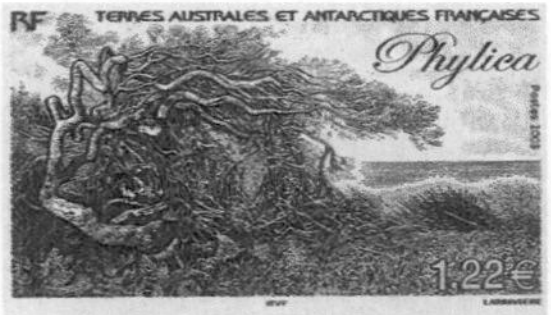

312 Phylica (tree), Amsterdam Island

2003. Polar Clothing. Multicoloured.

503 79c. Type **311** . . . . 1·00 80

504 79c. Man wearing brown hat, 1912 . . . . 1·00 80

505 79c. Penguins and man wearing yellow parka, 2002 1·00 80

506 79c. Dogs and man wearing blue jacket, 1980 . . . . . 1·00 80

507 79c. Snowmobiles and man wearing red all-in-one suit, 1996 . . . . 1·00 80

2003.

508 **312** €1.22 multicoloured . . 1·60 1·30

2003.

509 **313** €2.44 multicoloured . . 3·25 2·75

314 Penguin Island

2003.

510 **314** €3.66 black . . . . . . 4·75 3·75

315 Cabot

2003.

511 **315** €3.66 multicoloured . . 4·75 3·75

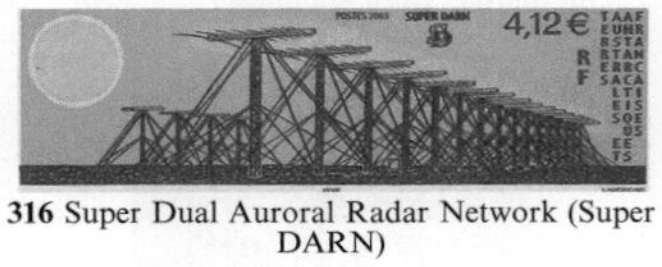

316 Super Dual Auroral Radar Network (Super DARN)

2003.

512 **316** €4.12 multicoloured . . 5·50 4·25

317 Jean-Baptiste Charcot (scientist and expedition leader)

2003. Centenary of Expedition to Antarctic Territories.

513 **317** 79c. brown, blue and violet . . . . 1·00 80

514 – €1.22 brown, blue and pink (48 × 27 mm) . . . 1·80 1·40

515 – €2.44 violet, blue and orange (48 × 27 mm) . . 3·25 2·50

DESIGNS: 79c. Type **317**; €1.22, *Le Francais* at anchor; €2.44, *Le Francais* in port.

318 Calcedone

319 Mario Marret

2004.

516 **318** 15c. purple, ochre and blue 20 15

2004. Mario Marret (Antarctic explorer and writer) Commemoration.

517 **319** 41c. blue, red and green 55 45

320 Base Camp Buildings (½-size illustration)

2004. 40th Anniv of Alfred-Faure Base, Crozet Island.

518 **320** 50c. multicoloured 65 50

321 Robert Genty

2004. Colonel Robert Genty (pilot) Commemoration.

519 **321** 50c. black, red and green 65 50

322 Whaling Museum, Jeanne d'Arc Port, Kerguelen Island

2004. Fantasy Tourist Attractions in Southern Antarctic Territories. Sheet 139 × 191 mm containing T **322** and similar horiz designs. Multicoloured.

MS520 50c. × 4, Type **322**; Showgirls and sea lions on St. Paul and Amsterdam Islands; Couple with ice creams (Ice palace on Adelie Land); Girl sunbathing amongst penguins (Hotel Marina on Crozet Island) . . . . 2·75 2·75

323 Southern Right-whale Dolphin

2004.

521 **323** 75c. multicoloured . . . . 1·00 80

324 De Havilland Twin Otter Airplane and Map of Antarctica

2004.

522 **324** 90c. multicoloured . . . . 1·20 1·00

325 Amsterdam Island Postal Buildings

2004. Antarctic Postal Buildings. Sheet 162 × 114 mm containing T **325** and similar horiz designs. Multicoloured.

MS523 90c. × 4, Type **325**; Crozet Island; Kerguelen Island; Adelie Island . . . . 4·75 3·25

326 Iceberg

2004.

524 **326** €1.30 blue and lilac . . . 1·75 1·40

327 Cairn and Cross

2004. *Volage* (British sail training ship) Sailor's Grave.

525 **327** €2.50 blue, indigo and red . . . . 3·25 2·50

328 Krill (*Euphausia superba*)

2004.

526 **328** €4 blue, orange and brown . . . . 5·25 4·25

329 *Dives*

2004.

527 **329** €4.50 multicoloured . . 6·00 4·75

330 Scientists taking Readings from Sea Bed

2004. Hydrographic Surveys in Adelie Land. Sheet 107 × 81 mm.
MS528 **330** €4.90 multicoloured 6·50 6·50

FRENCH SUDAN Pt. 6

A territory in central Africa. In 1899 parts of the colony were detached and added to neighbouring coastal colonies with the remainder becoming Senegambia and Niger (subsequently renamed Upper Senegal and Niger). In 1920 Niger became a separate colony and Upper Senegal reverted to the name of French Sudan.

From 1944 to 1959 French Sudan used the stamps of French West Africa. In 1959 French Sudan combined with Senegal to form the Mali Federation.

100 centimes = 1 franc.

1894. Stamps of French Colonies, "Commerce" type, surch **SOUDAN Fais** and value.
1 J 0.15 on 75c. red £3000 £1500
2 0.25 on 1f. olive £3250 £1100

1894. "Tablet" key-type inscr "SOUDAN FRANCAIS" in red (1, 5, 15, 25, 50 (No. 21), 75c., 1f.) or blue (others).
3 D 1c. black on blue . . . . . 2·00 3·75
4 2c. brown on buff . . . . . 2·00 1·50
5 4c. brown on grey . . . . . 3·00 6·00
6 5c. green on light green . . 3·00 4·00
7 10c. black on lilac . . . . . 13·00 6·50
18 10c. red . . . . 5·50 6·25
8 15c. blue . . . . 3·25 4·00
19 15c. grey . . . . 7·75 9·75
9 20c. red on green . . . . . 16·00 22·00
10 25c. black on pink . . . . . 20·00 21·00
20 25c. blue . . . . 7·00 8·25
11 30c. brown on drab . . . . 42·00 40·00
12 40c. red on yellow . . . . . 28·00 28·00
13 50c. red on pink . . . . . 45·00 45·00
21 50c. brown on blue . . . . 11·50 12·00
14 75c. brown on yellow . . . 20·00 20·00
15 1f. green . . . . 4·50 5·50

1921. Stamps of Upper Senegal and Niger optd **SOUDAN FRANCAIS**.
85 **7** 1c. violet and purple . . . . 10 2·75
86 2c. purple and grey . . . . 10 2·50
87 4c. blue and black . . . . . 15 2·50
88 5c. chocolate and brown . . 25 2·50
89 10c. green and light green . 1·10 2·25
121 10c. blue and mauve . . . . 50 1·10
90 15c. orange and purple . . . 1·50 2·50
122 15c. green and light green . 30 2·25
123 15c. mauve and brown . . . 1·50 3·25
91 20c. black and purple . . . 75 1·40
92 25c. green and black . . . . 2·00 75
93 30c. carmine and red . . . 2·25 2·75
124 30c. black and green . . . . 1·75 2·00
125 30c. green and olive . . . . 1·40 4·00
94 35c. violet and red . . . . . 85 2·50
95 40c. red and grey . . . . . 2·25 2·50
96 45c. brown and blue . . . . 2·50 2·75
97 50c. blue and ultramarine . 1·25 1·90
126 50c. blue and orange . . . 2·00 65
127 60c. violet on pink . . . . . 2·00 3·00
128 65c. blue and brown . . . . 3·50 3·50
98 75c. brown and yellow . . . 2·50 2·75
129 90c. carmine and red . . . 6·50 7·75
99 1f. purple and brown . . . 2·75 2·75
130 1f.10 mauve and blue . . . 3·25 3·75
131 1f.50 blue . . . . 6·25 7·50
100 2f. blue and green . . . . 3·25 3·50
132 3f. mauve on pink . . . . . 10·00 12·00
101 5f. black and violet . . . . 6·50 6·50

1922. Surch in figures and bars.
110 **7** 25c. on 45c. brown & blue 2·00 3·25
111 60 on 75c. violet on pink . . 1·75 2·25
112 65 on 75c. brown & yellow 2·25 3·50
113 85 on 2f. blue and green . . 2·25 3·75
114 85 on 5f. black and violet 2·00 4·00
115 90c. on 75c. red & carmine 2·50 4·00
116 1f.25 on 1f. lt bl & blue . . 2·25 3·50
117 1f.50 on 1f. ultram & bl . . 2·50 1·60
118 3f. on 5f. buff and pink . . 5·00 4·50
119 10f. on 5f. green and red . . 18·00 23·00
120 20f. on 5f. red and violet . . 20·00 30·00

14 Sudanese Woman marketing

15 Djenne Gateway

1931.
135 **14** 1c. black and red . . . . 20 1·75
136 2c. red and blue . . . . . 10 2·25
137 3c. black and red . . . . . 30 2·50
138 4c. red and lilac . . . . . . 1·25 2·25
139 5c. green and blue . . . . 35 1·25
140 10c. red and green . . . . 20 1·25
141 15c. violet and black . . . 55 75
142 20c. blue and brown . . . 25 1·25
143 25c. pink and mauve . . . 40 45
144 **15** 30c. light green and green 35 1·10
145 30c. red and blue . . . . . 70 3·00
146 35c. green and olive . . . 80 2·25
147 40c. red and green . . . . 15 1·75
148 45c. red and blue . . . . . 2·00 1·90
149 45c. green and olive . . . 75 2·75
150 50c. black and red 85 15
151 55c. red and blue . . . . 95 2·75
152 60c. brown and blue . . . 95 2·50
153 65c. black and violet . . . 1·00 1·75
154 70c. red and blue . . . . 1·25 3·00
155 75c. brown and blue . . . 2·25 2·50
156 80c. brown and red . . . . 50 2·00
157 90c. orange and red . . . 75 2·50
158 90c. black and violet . . . 1·40 3·25
159 1f. green and blue . . . . 8·00 2·25
160 1f. red . . . . 4·25 1·75
161 1f. brown and red . . . . 70 2·50
162 – 1f.25 mauve and violet . . 2·00 2·75
163 – 1f.25 red and scarlet . . . 1·25 2·25
164 – 1f.40 black and violet . . . 1·40 2·75
165 – 1f.50 blue and indigo . . . 2·00 2·75
166 – 1f.60 blue and brown . . . 1·50 2·75
167 – 1f.70 blue and brown . . . 2·50 1·90
168 – 1f.75 blue . . . . 1·90 3·25
169 – 2f. green and brown . . . 1·40 1·25
170 – 2f.25 ultramarine & blue 75 2·50
171 – 2f.50 brown . . . . 2·75 3·00
172 – 3f. brown and green . . . 75 35
173 – 5f. black and red . . . . . 1·10 2·00
174 – 10f. green and blue . . . . 2·00 3·75
175 – 20f. brown and mauve . . 4·00 4·50
DESIGN: 1f.25 to 20f. Niger boatman.

1931. "Colonial Exhibition" key-types inscr "SOUDAN FRANCAIS".
186 E 40c. green and black . . . 3·25 4·00
187 F 50c. mauve and black . . . 3·50 4·00
188 G 90c. red and black . . . . 3·00 3·25
189 H 1f.50 blue and black . . . 2·50 3·75

1937. International Exhibition, Paris. As T **58a** of Guadeloupe.
190 20c. violet . . . . 40 2·00
191 30c. green . . . . 1·60 3·25
192 40c. red . . . . 80 2·50
193 50c. brown and agate . . . . 40 2·75
194 90c. red . . . . 35 1·75
195 1f.50 blue . . . . 45 2·75

1938. International Anti-cancer Fund. As T **58b** of Guadeloupe.
197 1f.75+50c. blue . . . . . . 3·00 11·00

21 Rene Caillie

1939. Caillie.
198 **21** 90c. orange . . . . 50 2·50
199 2f. violet . . . . 75 1·25
200 2f.25 blue . . . . 50 2·75

1939. New York World's Fair. As T **58c** of Guadeloupe.
201 1f.25 red . . . . 1·25 2·75
202 2f.25 blue . . . . 2·25 3·25

1939. 150th Anniv of French Revolution. As T **58d** of Guadeloupe.
203 45c.+25c. green and black . . 4·50 8·25
204 70c.+30c. brown and black 8·00 12·00
205 90c.+35c. orange and black 5·00 12·00
206 1f.25+1f. red and black . . 4·25 10·50
207 2f.25+2f. blue and black . . 4·25 12·00

1940. Air. As T **6a** of French Guinea.
208 1f.90 blue . . . . 1·25 3·00
209 2f.90 red . . . . 75 3·00
210 4f.50 green . . . . 1·25 2·25
211 4f.90 olive . . . . 1·25 2·25
212 6f.90 orange . . . . 1·25 2·50

1941. National Defence Fund. Surch **SECOURS NATIONAL** and value.
213 +1f. on 50c. (No. 150) . . . 4·25 5·00
214 +2f. on 80c. (No. 156) . . . 7·00 9·50
215 +2f. on 1f.50 (No. 165) . . . 8·00 9·25
216 +3f. on 2f. (No. 169) . . . . 8·25 9·50

1941. Marshal Petain Issue. As T **16a** of Ivory Coast.
217 1f. green . . . . 40 3·00
218 2f.50 blue . . . . 55 2·50
DESIGNS—VERT: Gate at Djenne and Marshal Petain.

1942. Air. Colonial Child Welfare Fund. As T **8** of French Guinea.
219 1f.50+3f.50 green . . . . . 50 2·50
220 2f.+6f. brown . . . . 15 3·50
221 3f.+9f. red . . . . 15 3·50

1942. Air. Imperial Fortnight. As T **9a** of French Guinea.
222 1f.20+1f.80 blue and red . . 40 3·50

27 Airplane over Camel Caravan

1942. Air.
223 **27** 50f. blue and green . . . . 90 1·40

POSTAGE DUE STAMPS

1921. Postage Due stamps of Upper Senegal and Niger optd **SOUDAN FRANCAIS**.
D102 M 5c. green . . . . 20 2·75
D103 10c. red . . . . 20 1·75
D104 15c. grey . . . . 75 2·50
D105 20c. brown . . . . . . 1·10 2·25
D106 30c. blue . . . . 95 3·25
D107 50c. black . . . . . . 1·90 3·50
D108 60c. orange . . . . . . 1·75 3·50
D109 1f. violet . . . . 1·60 4·00

1927. Postage Due stamps of Upper Senegal and Niger surch **SOUDAN FRANCAIS** and value.
D133 M "2F." on 1f. mauve . . . 2·75 6·00
D134 "3F." on 1f. brown . . . 2·75 7·25

1931. "Figure" key-type inscr "SOUDAN FRANCAIS".
D176 M 5c. green . . . . 10 2·50
D177 10c. red . . . . 10 1·75
D178 15c. grey . . . . 10 2·75
D179 20c. brown . . . . . . 10 2·75
D180 30c. blue . . . . 15 2·25
D181 50c. black . . . . . . 40 3·00
D182 60c. orange . . . . . . 60 2·75
D183 1f. violet 60 90
D184 2f. mauve . . . . 1·75 2·25
D185 3f. brown . . . . 1·75 3·25

FRENCH TERRITORY OF THE AFARS AND THE ISSAS Pt. 6

Formerly French Somali Coast. Became independent in 1977 as Djibouti Republic.

100 centimes = 1 franc.

66 Grey-headed Kingfisher

1967. Fauna.
504 **66** 10f. mult (postage) . . . . 3·00 2·10
505 – 15f. multicoloured . . . . 3·75 3·00
506 – 50f. purple, brown & grn 10·00 7·50
507 – 55f. blue, violet and grey 12·50 11·50
508 – 60f. orange, emer & grn . . 22·00 19·00
509 – 200f. sepia, bistre & bl (air) 32·00 9·50
DESIGNS—HORIZ: 15f. Oystercatcher; 50f. Common greenshank; 55f. Abyssinian roller. VERT: (22 × 36 mm); 60f. Unstriped ground squirrel. (27 × 48 mm): 200f. Tawny eagles.

67 Footballers

1967. Sports.
510 **67** 25f. brn, grn & bl (postage) 2·50 2·25
511 – 30f. brown, blue & purple 4·25 3·75
512 – 48f. pur, bl & bistre (air) 4·25 2·75
513 – 85f. brown, blue & bistre 4·00 8·00
DESIGNS—HORIZ: 30f. Basketball. VERT: (27 × 48 mm) 48f. Parachute-jumping; 85f. Aquatic sports.

1968. 20th Anniv of W.H.O. As T **34** of French Polynesia.
514 15f. multicoloured . . . . . 2·25 2·25

68 Damerdjog Fort

1968. Administrative Outposts.
515 **68** 20f. blue, brown & green 1·75 1·90
516 – 25f. blue, green & brown 1·75 1·90
517 – 30f. blue, bistre & orange 2·00 2·25
518 – 40f. blue, brown & green 3·25 2·75
DESIGNS—FORTS: 25f. Ali Adde; 30f. Dorra; 40f. Assamo.

1968. Human Rights Year. As T **36** of French Polynesia.
519 10f. red, violet and yellow . . 2·25 2·25
520 70f. purple, green & orange 3·00 3·00

69 Broadcasting Station

70 Relief Map of Territory

1968. Buildings and Landmarks.
521 **69** 1f. bl, turq & red (postage) 1·25 1·10
522 – 2f. blue, green & lt blue . . 1·25 1·10
523 – 5f. brown, green & blue . . 1·50 1·25
524 – 8f. brown, blue & green . . 1·50 1·40
525 – 15f. brown, green & blue 4·00 2·50
526 – 40f. grey, brown & turq . . 3·25 2·50
527 – 60f. multicoloured . . . . 3·25 2·75
528 – 70f. brown, green & grey 4·50 3·50
529 – 85f. green, blue & brn . . 6·75 4·50
530 – 85f. grey, blue & green . . 5·50 5·00
531 – 100f. brown, grn & bl (air) 4·25 2·50
532 – 200f. blue, brown & purple 8·25 4·00
533 **70** 500f. orange, brown & bl 32·00 14·50
DESIGNS—As T **69**: HORIZ: 2f. Courts of Justice; 5f. Chamber of Deputies; 8f. Great Mosque; 40f. Post Office, Djibouti; 70f. Governor's Residence, Obock; 85f. (No. 529) Port Administration Building, Djibouti; 85f. (No. 530) Airport. VERT: 15f. Free French Forces' Monument. As T **70**: HORIZ: 60f. French High Commission, Djibouti. VERT: 100f. Djibouti Cathedral; 200f. Sayed Hassan Mosque.

1969. Air. 1st Flight of Concorde. As T **39** of French Polynesia.
534 100f. red and drab . . . . . 30·00 18·00

71 Desert Locust

1969. Anti-Locust Campaign.
535 **71** 15f. brown, slate & green 3·25 2·25
536 – 50f. brn, green & blue . . 3·50 2·00
537 – 55f. brown, blue & lake . . 3·75 2·75
DESIGNS: 50f. Sud Aviation Alouette II helicopter spraying crops; 55f. Piper Super Cub spraying crops.

1969. 50th Anniv of International Labour Organization. As T **44** of French Polynesia.
538 30f. mauve, slate and red . . 2·75 2·00

73 Afar Dagger

74 Ionospheric Station, Arta

1970.
543 **73** 10f. brown, grn & myrtle 1·75 1·25
544 15f. brown, green & blue 1·90 1·40
545 20f. brown, green & red . . 2·25 1·75
546 25f. brown, green & violet 2·50 1·60

1970. Air. Opening of Ionospheric Station, Arta.
547 **74** 70f. red, green and blue . . 5·25 4·00

1970. New U.P.U. Headquarters Building. As T **47** of French Polynesia.
548 25f. brown, green & bistre . . 2·50 2·25

75 Clay-pigeon Shooting

1970. Sports.
549 **75** 30f. brown, blue & green 3·00 2·00
550 – 48f. brown, purple & blue 3·25 2·50
551 – 50f. red, violet and blue . . 3·50 1·75
552 – 55f. brown, bistre & blue 3·25 2·75
553 – 60f. black, brown & green 5·00 3·75
DESIGNS—HORIZ: 48f. Speedboat racing; 50f. Show jumping; 60f. Pony-trekking. VERT: 55f. Yachting.

76 "Fish" Sword-guard

1970. Air "Expo 70" World Fair, Osaka, Japan.
554 **76** 100f. vio, bl & grn on gold 11·50 7·50
555 – 200f. vio, grn & red on gold 14·50 9·00
DESIGN: 200f. "Horse" sword-guard.

77 "Goubet"

1970. Inauguration of Car Ferry, Tajurah.
556 **77** 48f. brown, blue & green 3·25 2·75

78 Dolerite Basalt

1971. Geology. Multicoloured.
557 10f. Type **78** 1·75 1·60
558 15f. Olivine basalt 2·00 2·50
559 25f. Volcanic geode 3·50 2·00
560 40f. Diabase and chrysolite 4·00 2·75

79 Manta Rays

81 Mantle Clanculus

80 Aerial View of Port

1971. Marine Fauna. Multicoloured. (a) Postage. As T **79**.
561 4f. Type **79** 2·25 1·25
562 5f. Dolphin (fish) 2·25 1·75
563 9f. Small-toothed sawfish 2·75 2·00

(b) Air. Size 46 × 27 mm (30f.) or 48 × 27 mm (others).
564 30f. Queen parrotfish 4·25 3·50
565 40f. Long-armed octopus 2·50 2·50
566 60f. Dugong 5·00 3·25

1971. De Gaulle Commemoration. As Nos. 1937 and 1940 of France.
567 60f. black and blue 4·75 3·50
568 85f. black and blue 6·75 4·25

1971. Air. New Harbour, Djibouti.
569 **80** 100f. multicoloured 6·75 4·25

1972. Sea Shells. Multicoloured.
570 4f. Type **81** 1·60 1·10
571 9f. Panther cowrie 1·75 1·75
572 20f. Bull-mouth helmet 3·25 2·25
573 50f. Melon shell 4·25 2·75

82 Lichtenstein's Sandgrouse

1972. Air. Birds. Multicoloured.
574 30f. Type **82** 1·75 2·00
575 49f. Hoopoe 3·25 2·00
576 66f. Great snipe 6·00 3·50
577 500f. Pale-bellied francolin 33·00 12·00

83 Swimming

1972. Air. Olympic Games, Munich.
578 – 5f. brown, green & violet 1·50 1·40
579 – 10f. brown, green & red 1·50 1·40
580 **83** 55f. brown, blue & green 3·00 1·75
581 – 60f. violet, red and green 3·50 2·25
DESIGNS—VERT: 5f. Running; 10f. Basketball. HORIZ: 60f. Olympic flame, rings and ancient frieze.

84 Pasteur and Equipment

1972. Air. "Famous Medical Scientists".
582 **84** 20f. brown, green & red 2·50 1·75
583 – 100f. brown, green & red 5·25 4·00
DESIGN: 100f. Calmette and Guerin (B.C.G. pioneers).

85 Mosque, Map and Transport

1973. Air. Visit of President Pompidou. Mult.
584 30f. Type **85** 8·00 4·75
585 200f. Mosque and street scene, Djibouti (vert) 14·50 11·50

86 Gemsbok

1973. Air. Wild Animals. Multicoloured.
587 30f. Type **86** 3·00 2·50
588 50f. Salt's dik-dik 4·50 2·75
590 66f. Caracal 5·25 3·75
See also Nos. 603/5, 641/3, 659/60 and 662/4.

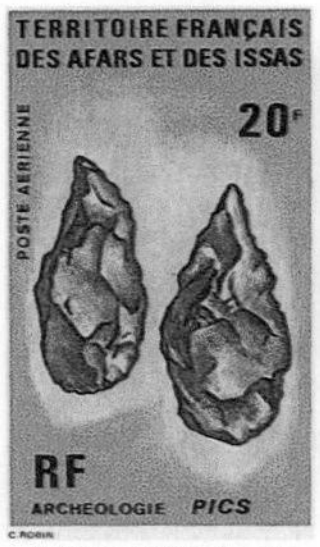

87 Flint Pick-heads

89 Nicolas Copernicus (500th birth anniv)

88 Shepherd watering Sheep

1973. Air. Archaeological Discoveries. Mult.
592 20f. Type **87** 2·75 2·25
593 40f. Arrow-heads and blade (horiz) 3·00 2·50
594 49f. Biface flint tool 5·25 3·25
595 60f. Flint axe-head and scraper (horiz) 4·00 3·25

1973. Pastoral Economy. Multicoloured.
596 9f. Type **88** 1·75 1·75
597 10f. Camel herd 1·75 1·75

1973. Air. Celebrities' Anniversaries.
598 **89** 8f. black, brown & purple 1·75 1·50
599 – 9f. purple, orange & brn 1·75 1·25
600 – 10f. purple, brown & red 1·75 1·60
615 – 10f. maroon, blue & pur 1·75 1·10
601 – 49f. purple, grn & dp grn 4·00 2·75
658 – 50f. brown, blue & green 3·25 2·00
611 – 55f. indigo, brown & blue 3·00 2·75
602 – 85f. dp blue, blue & violet 5·50 3·50
607 – 100f. purple, blue & green 5·00 2·50
657 – 150f. turq, blue & brn 5·75 2·75
656 – 250f. brn, lt brn & grn 8·75 3·75
DESIGNS: 9f. Wilhelm Rontgen (X-ray pioneer) (50th death anniv); 10f. (600) Edward Jenner (smallpox vaccination pioneer) (150th death anniv); 10f. (615) Marie Curie (physicist) (40th death anniv); 49f. Robert Koch (bacteriologist) (130th birth anniv); 50f. Clement Ader (aviation pioneer) (50th death anniv); 55f. Guglielmo Marconi (radio pioneer) (birth centenary); 85f. Moliere (playwright) (300th death anniv); 100f. Henri Farman (aviation pioneer) (birth centenary); 150f. Ampere (physicist) (birth bicentenary); 250f. Michelangelo (500th birth anniv).

1973. Air. Wild Animals (2nd series). As Type **86**. Multicoloured.
603 20f. Olive baboon (vert) 2·25 1·90
604 50f. Large-spotted genet 3·50 2·50
605 66f. Abyssinian hare (vert) 4·75 3·25

90 Afar Dagger

1974.
606 **90** 30f. purple and green 2·50 1·75

91 Greater Flamingos

1974. Lake Abbe. Multicoloured.
608 5f. Type **91** 1·60 30
609 15f. Two greater flamingos 1·50 1·00
610 50f. Greater flamingos in flight 2·50 1·75

92 Underwater Hunting

1974. Air. 3rd Underwater Hunting Trophy.
612 **92** 200f. blue, green & red 10·00 8·00
No. 612 has part of the original inscription blocked out.

93 Various Animals

1974. Air. Balho Rock Paintings.
613 **93** 200f. black and red 10·50 8·75

94 Football and Emblem

1974. World Cup Football Championship, West Germany.
614 **94** 25f. green and black 2·75 2·25

95 U.P.U. Emblem and Letters

97 "Oleo chrysophylla"

96 Sunrise over Lake

1974. Centenary of Universal Postal Union.
616 **95** 20f. violet, blue & indigo 2·50 1·40
617 100f. brown, lt brn & red 4·25 3·25

1974. Air. Lake Assal. Multicoloured.
618 49f. Type **96** 2·50 2·25
619 50f. Rocky shore 2·75 2·25
620 85f. Crystallisation on dead wood 4·75 3·75

1974. Forest Plants. Multicoloured.
621 10f. Type **97** 1·90 1·25
622 15f. "Fiscus" (tree) 2·25 1·75
623 20f. "Solanum adoense" (shrub) 3·50 2·25

1975. Surch **40F**.
624 **90** 40f. on 30f. purple & grn 2·75 2·25

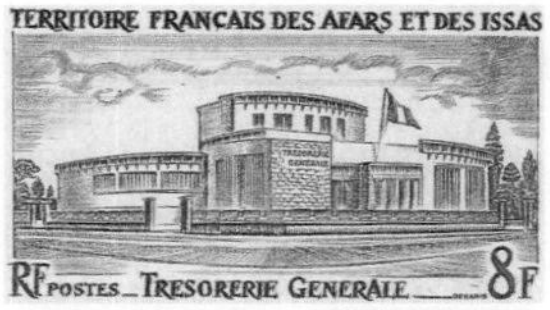

99 Treasury Building

1975. Administrative Buildings, Djibouti.
625 **99** 8f. grey, blue and red 1·75 1·60
626 – 25f. grey, blue and red 2·25 1·90
DESIGN: 25f. "Government City" complex.

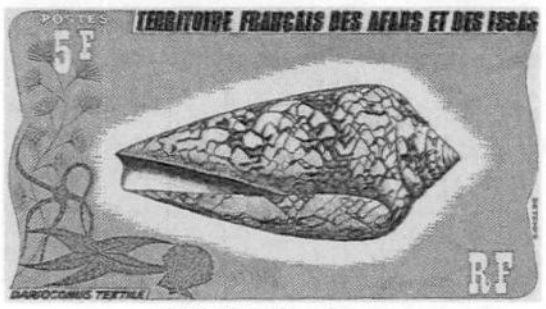

100 Textile Cone

1975. Sea Shells.
627 **100** 5f. brown and green 1·60 1·60
628 – 5f. brown and blue 1·60 1·40
629 – 5f. brown, mve & vio 1·75 1·75
630 – 10f. brown and purple 1·75 1·60
631 – 15f. brown and blue 2·25 1·75
632 – 20f. brown and violet 3·00 1·75
633 – 20f. brown and green 1·75 1·60
634 – 30f. brown, pur & grn 2·00 1·75
635 – 40f. brown and green 3·75 2·75
636 – 45f. brown, green & blue 3·00 2·50
637 – 55f. brown and blue 2·50 2·25
638 – 60f. black and brown 3·00 2·75
639 – 70f. brown, blue & black 4·00 3·00
640 – 85f. purple, blue & black 6·00 4·25
DESIGNS: 5f. (628) Rose-branch murex; 5f. (629) Tiger cowrie; 10f. Sumatran cone; 15f. Lovely cowrie; 20f. (632), 45f. Woodcock murex; 20f. (633) Burnt cowrie; 30f. Beech cowrie; 40f. Spiny frog shell; 55f. Red Sea cowrie; 60f. Ringed cone; 70f. Striate cone; 85f. Humpback cowrie.

1975. Wild Animals (3rd series). As T **86**. Mult.
641 50f. White-tailed mongoose 3·50 2·75
642 60f. North African crested porcupine (vert) 4·25 3·00
643 70f. Zorilla 5·75 3·75

101 African Monarch

1975. Butterflies and Moths (1st series). Mult.
644 25f. Type **101** 2·50 2·25
645 40f. Narrow blue-banded swallowtail 3·00 2·25
646 70f. Citrus butterfly 4·50 3·00
647 100f. Mocker swallowtail 5·50 4·25
See also Nos. 666/7 and 675/6.

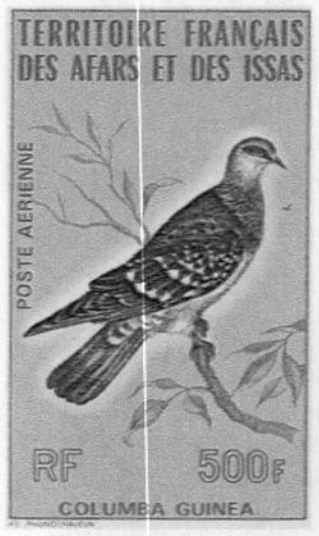

102 Speckled Pigeon

103 Palm Trees

1975. Birds. Multicoloured.
648 20f. Pin-tailed whydah (postage) 1·75 85
649 25f. Rose-ringed parakeet 2·00 1·00
650 50f. Variable sunbird 3·00 1·50
651 60f. Goliath heron 4·25 2·10
652 100f. Hammerkop 6·00 3·00
653 100f. Namaqua dove 4·00 2·00
654 300f. African spoonbill 10·00 5·00
655 500f. Type **102** (air) 25·00 13·00

1975. Wild Animals (4th series). As T **86**. Mult.
659 15f. Savanna monkeys (vert) 1·90 1·75
660 200f. Aardvarks 8·50 5·00

1975.
661 **103** 20f. multicoloured 1·90 1·60

1976. Wild Animals (5th series). As T **86**. Multicoloured.
662 10f. Striped hyena 1·75 1·50
663 15f. African ass (vert) 1·90 1·75
664 30f. Beira antelope 2·50 1·90

104 Alexander Graham Bell and Satellite

1976. Telephone Centenary.
665 **104** 200f. blue, green & orge 5·50 4·25

1976. Butterflies and Moths (2nd series). As T **101**. Multicoloured.
666 65f. Variable prince 3·50 2·75
667 100f. "Balachowsky gonimbrasia" 4·75 3·25

105 Basketball

1976. Olympic Games, Montreal. Mult.
668 10f. Type **105** 1·50 1·50
669 15f. Cycling 1·60 1·60
670 40f. Football 2·25 1·90
671 60f. Running 2·75 2·25

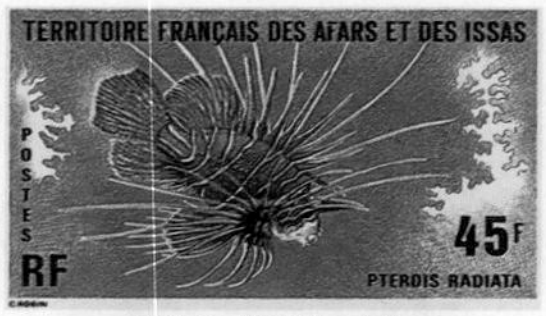

106 Radial Lionfish

1976. Marine Life.
672 **106** 45f. multicoloured 2·75 2·75

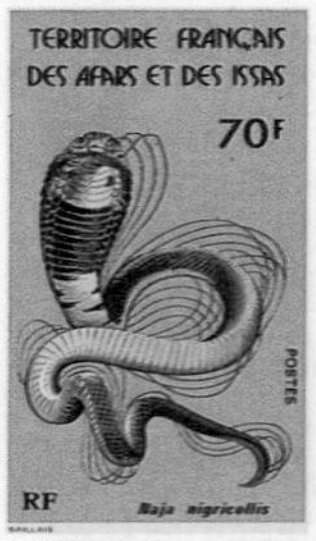

107 Black-necked Cobra

108 Motor Cyclist on Course

1976. Snakes. Multicoloured.
673 70f. Type **107** 3·50 3·00
674 80f. Elegant sand snake 4·25 3·25

1976. Butterflies and Moths (3rd series). As T **101**. Multicoloured.
675 50f. Broad bordered acraea 3·00 2·75
676 150f. Painted lady 5·00 4·25

1977. Moto-Cross.
677 **108** 200f. multicoloured 7·50 4·50

109 Air Terminal

1977. Air. Inauguration of New Djibouti Airport.
678 **109** 500f. multicoloured 16·00 12·50

110 Black-spotted Sweetlips

1977. Fishes. Multicoloured.
679 15f. Type **110** 1·90 1·90
680 65f. Great barracuda 3·00 2·25

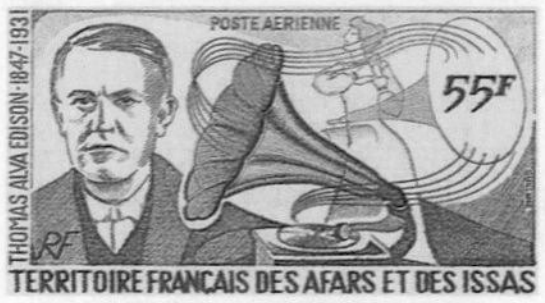

111 Edison and Phonograph

1977. Air. Celebrities.
681 **111** 55f. red, slate and green 4·00 3·00
682 – 75f. red, brown & green 7·75 5·75
DESIGN: 75f. Volta and TGV express train, France.

POSTAGE DUE STAMPS

D 72 Nomadic Milk-Jug

1969.
D539 **D 72** 1f. slate, brn & pur 1·40 1·40
D540 2f. slate, brn & grn 1·40 1·40
D541 5f. slate, brn & blue 1·75 1·75
D542 10f. slate, lake & brn 2·10 2·10

For later issues see **DJIBOUTI REPUBLIC**.

FRENCH WEST AFRICA Pt. 6

The territory in north-west Africa comprising Senegal, French Guinea, Ivory Coast, Dahomey, French Sudan, Mauritania, Niger and Upper Volta. French Sudan and Senegal became the Mali Federation and the rest independent republics.

100 centimes = 1 franc.

1944. Mutual Aid and Red Cross Funds. As T **58e** of Guadeloupe.
1 5f.+20f. purple 2·50 9·25

1945. Eboue. As T **58f** of Guadeloupe.
2 2f. black 30 1·10
3 25f. green 1·25 3·75

1 Soldiers

1945.
4 **1** 10c. blue and pink 70 1·25
5 30c. olive and cream 1·10 2·75
6 40c. blue and pink 90 2·75
7 50c. orange and grey 65 60
8 60c. olive and grey 1·00 3·00
9 70c. mauve and cream 1·40 3·00
10 80c. green and cream 80 2·25
11 1f. purple and olive 35 10
12 1f.20 brown and olive 1·40 4·00
13 1f.50 brown and red 75 15
14 2f. yellow and grey 95 25
15 2f.40 red and grey 1·10 2·25
16 3f. red and olive 60 10
17 4f. blue and red 65 20
18 4f.50 brown and olive 1·40 1·25
19 5f. violet and olive 1·00 10
20 10f. green and red 60 25
21 15f. brown and cream 90 65
22 20f. green and grey 1·25 95

1945. Stamp Day. As T **228** of France (Louis XI) but optd **A O F**.
23 2f.+3f. red 30 3·25

1945. Air. As T **63a** of Guadeloupe.
24 5f.50 blue 1·50 2·25
25 50f. green 1·25 55
26 100f. red 1·40 1·40

1946. Air. Victory. As T **63b** of Guadeloupe.
27 8f. mauve 30 35

1946. Air. From Chad to the Rhine. As T **63c** of Guadeloupe.
28 5f. red 2·75 4·25
29 10f. blue 2·75 4·00
30 15f. mauve 2·50 4·00
31 20f. green 2·50 4·25
32 25f. brown 2·50 4·25
33 50f. brown 2·50 4·75

3 War Dance

6 Sudanese Carving

9 Natives and Airplane

1947.
34 **3** 10c. blue (postage) 10 2·25
35 – 30c. brown 10 2·75
36 – 40c. green 45 2·75
37 – 50c. red 35 1·90
38 – 60c. grey 1·00 2·75
39 – 80c. lilac 60 3·25
40 – 1f. red 10 10
41 – 1f.20 green 1·40 3·50
42 – 1f.50 blue 1·75 3·25
43 **6** 2f. orange 55 10
68 – 3f. brown 1·25 90
45 – 3f.60 red 2·00 3·75
46 – 4f. blue 1·25 15
47 – 5f. green 1·10 10
48 – 6f. blue 75 15
49 – 10f. red 75 15
50 – 15f. brown 1·90 75
51 – 20f. brown 90 15
52 – 25f. black 40 25
53 – 8f. red (air) 1·75 80
54 – 50f. violet 2·75 1·25
55 – 100f. blue 8·50 3·50
56 **9** 200f. grey 3·50 2·25

DESIGNS—As Type **3**/**6**—HORIZ: 30c. Girl and bridge; 40c. Canoe; 50c. Niger landscape; 80c. Dahomey weaver; 1f. Donkey caravan; 1f.20, Crocodile and hippopotamus; 10f. Djenne Mosque; 15f. Renault model ABH railcar. VERT: 60c. Coconuts; 1f.50, Palm trees; 3f. Togo girl; 3f.60, Sudanese market; 4f. Dahomey labourer; 5f. Mauritanian woman; 6f. Guinea headdress; 20f. Ivory Coast girl; 25f. Niger washerwoman. As Type **9**—VERT: 8f. Antoine de Saint-Exupery. HORIZ: 50f. Caudron Goeland airplane over Dakar (Senegal); 100f. Flight of great egrets (Niger).

1949. 75th Anniv of U.P.U. As T **39** of French Equatorial Africa.
69 25f. multicoloured 1·75 5·00

1950. Colonial Welfare Fund. As T **40** of French Equatorial Africa.
70 10f.+2f. dp brown & brown 3·00 8·00

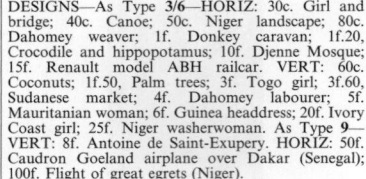

10 Medical Research

11 T. Laplene and Map of Ivory Coast

12 Logging Camp

1951.
71 – 8f. blue & brown (postage) 1·25 90
72 **10** 15f. green, brown & sepia 60 10
73 – 20f. myrtle and turquoise 1·75 4·00
74 – 25f. sepia, blue and purple 95 15
75 **11** 40f. red 1·25 20
76 **12** 50f. brown and green (air) 2·50 85
77 – 100f. brown, blue & green 4·00 90
78 – 200f. green, turq & lake 12·50 2·50
79 – 500f. green, blue & orange 20·00 5·25

DESIGNS—As Type **11**: 8f. Governor-General Ballay; 20f. Houphouet-Boigny Bridge, Abidjan; 25f. Africans, animals and sailing canoe. As Type **12**: 100f. Telephonist, Lockheed Constellation airplane and pylons; 200f. Baobab trees; 500f. Vridi Canal, Abidjan.

1952. Centenary of Military Medal. As T **44** of French Equatorial Africa.
80 15f. sepia, yellow and green 3·25 3·00

1954. Air. 10th Anniv of Liberation. As T **46** of French Equatorial Africa.
81 15f. blue and indigo 3·75 3·50

13 Chimpanzee

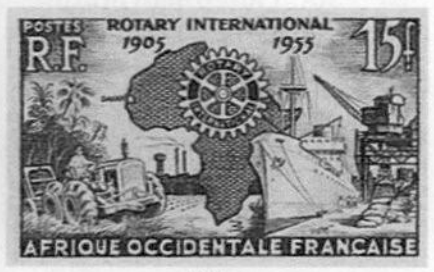

14

1955. Nature Protection. Inscr as in T **13**.
82 **13** 5f. sepia and grey 1·50 30
83 – 8f. sepia and green 75 1·25
DESIGN—HORIZ: 8f. Giant ground pangolin.

1955. 50th Anniv of Rotary International.
84 **14** 15f. blue 30 25

15 Mossi Railways

1955. Economic and Social Development Fund. Inscr "F.I.D.E.S.".
85 – 1f. green and myrtle 60 1·75
86 – 2f. myrtle and turquoise 1·25 2·75
87 **15** 3f. sepia and brown 2·00 2·50
88 – 4f. red 1·25 85
89 – 15f. blue and indigo 80 20
90 – 17f. blue and indigo 1·10 2·00

91	–	20f. purple	90	1·10
92	–	30f. purple and lilac	1·25	95

DESIGNS—HORIZ: 1f. Date palms; 2f. Milo River bridge; 4f. Herdsman and cattle; 15f. Combine harvester; 17f. Woman and aerial view; 20f. Palm oil factory; 30f. Abidjan-Abengourou road.

1956. Coffee. As T **51** of French Equatorial Africa.

93		15f. green and turquoise	35	20

16 Medical Station and Ambulance

17 Map of Africa

1957. Order of Malta Leprosy Relief.

94	16	15f. claret, purple & red	75	2·50

1957. Air. Centenary of African Troops. As T **53** of French Equatorial Africa.

95		15f. blue and indigo	1·25	2·75

1958. 6th African International Tourist Congress.

96	17	20f. red and green	30	2·50

18 "Communication"

1958. Stamp Day.

97	18	15f. brown, blue & orange	30	2·75

19 Isle of Goree and West African

1958. Air. Dakar Centenary. Inscr "CENTENAIRE DE DAKAR".

98	19	15f. multicoloured	1·25	1·60
99	–	20f. red, brown and blue	2·00	2·75
100	–	25f. multicoloured	75	75
101	–	40f. brown, green & blue	65	55
102	–	50f. violet, brown & green	95	1·25
103	–	100f. green, blue & brown	3·25	2·50
MS104		185 × 125 mm. Nos. 98/103 with view of Dakar	18·00	30·00

DESIGNS: 20f. Map of Dakar, liner, freighters and Lockheed Super Constellation and Douglas DC-6 aircraft; 25f. Town construction; 40f. Council house; 50f. Groundnuts, artisan and "L'Arachide" (freighter) at quayside; 100f. Bay of N'Gor.

20 Banana Plant and Fruit

1958. Banana Production.

105	20	20f. purple, green & olive	60	20

1958. Tropical Flora. As T **56** of French Equatorial Africa.

118		10f. multicoloured	60	15
119		25f. yellow, green and red	85	25
120		30f. brown, green and blue	1·40	45
121		40f. yellow, green & brown	1·60	2·25
122		65f. multicoloured	1·75	2·00

DESIGNS—VERT: 10f. "Gloriosa"; 25f. "Adenopus"; 30f. "Cyrtosperma"; 40f. "Cistanche"; 65f. "Crinum moorei".

22 Moro Naba Sagha and Map of Upper Volta

1958. 10th Anniv of Upper Volta Scheme.

123	22	20f. multicoloured	2·75	2·75

23 Native Chief and Musician

1958. Air. Inauguration of Nouakchott, Capital of Mauritania.

124	23	20f. sepia, brown & grey	1·75	2·75

1958. 10th Anniv of Declaration of Human Rights. As T **14** of French Polynesia.

125		20f. purple and blue	35	3·25

1959. Stamp Day. As T **18** but inscr "DAKAR-ABIDJAN" in place of "AFRIQUE OCCIDENTALE FRANÇAISE".

126		20f. green, blue and red	3·25	4·50

No. 126 was for use in Ivory Coast and Senegal.

OFFICIAL STAMPS

O 21

1958. Inscr "OFFICIEL".

O106	O 21	1f. brown	2·00	1·75
O107		3f. green	2·25	3·00
O108		5f. red	2·00	90
O109		10f. blue	2·00	2·50
O110	–	20f. red	2·25	1·60
O111	–	25f. violet	2·25	85
O112	–	30f. green	2·00	2·25
O113	–	45f. black	1·60	1·60
O114	–	50f. red	3·25	90
O115	–	65f. blue	1·60	2·25
O116	–	100f. olive	3·50	2·50
O117	–	200f. green	11·00	4·25

DESIGNS—VERT: 20f. to 45f. Head as Type O **21** but with female face; 50f. to 200f. Head as Type O **21** but with hooped headdress, portrait being diagonal on stamp.

POSTAGE DUE STAMPS.

D 10

1947.

D57	D 10	10c. red	10	2·50
D58		30c. orange	10	2·25
D59		50c. black	10	2·50
D60		1f. red	80	2·50
D61		2f. green	85	2·50
D62		3f. mauve	1·50	2·75
D63		4f. blue	1·75	3·00
D64		5f. brown	1·75	3·00
D65		10f. blue	1·10	4·00
D66		20f. brown	1·90	5·00

FUJEIRA Pt. 19

One of the Trucial States in the Persian Gulf.

With six other sheikdoms formed the State of the United Arab Emirates on 18 July 1971. Fujeira stamps were replaced by issues of United Arab Emirates on 1 January 1973.

1964. 100 naye paise = 1 rupee.
1967. 100 dirhams = 1 riyal.

1 Shaikh Mohamed bin Hamad al Sharqi and Great Crested Grebe

1964. Multicoloured. (a) Size as T **1**.

1		1n.p. Type **1**	20	10
2		2n.p. Arabian oryx	15	15
3		3n.p. Hoopoe	20	10
4		4n.p. Asiatic wild ass	15	15
5		5n.p. Great Egrets	20	10
6		10n.p. Arab horses	15	15
7		15n.p. Cheetah	15	15
8		20n.p. Dromedaries	15	15
9		30n.p. Lanner falcon	25	10

(b) Size $43\frac{1}{2} \times 28\frac{1}{2}$ mm.

10		40n.p. Type **1**	25	10
11		50n.p. Arabian oryx	30	15
12		70n.p. Hoopoe	35	20
13		1r. Asiatic wild ass	50	35
14		1r.50 Great egrets	40	25
15		2r. Arab horses	1·00	60

(c) Size $53\frac{1}{2} \times 35\frac{1}{2}$ mm.

16		3r. Leopard	2·50	1·50
17		5r. Dromedaries	3·75	2·75
18		10r. Lanner falcon	7·50	5·75

2 Shaikh Mohamed and Putting the Shot

1964. Olympic Games, Tokyo. Multicoloured. (a) Size as T **2**.

19		25n.p. Type **2**	15	15
20		50n.p. Throwing the discus	20	20
21		75n.p. Fencing	25	25
22		1r. Boxing	40	35
23		1r.50 Relay-racing	65	60
24		2r. Football	95	85

(b) Size $53 \times 35\frac{1}{2}$ mm.

25		3r. High jumping	1·90	1·60
26		5r. Hurdling	3·00	2·75
27		7r.50 Horse-riding	5·00	4·50

3 Kennedy as a Boy

1965. Pres. Kennedy Commem. Each black and gold on coloured paper as given below.

28	3	5n.p. blue	15	15
29	–	10n.p. yellow	15	15
30	–	15n.p. pink	15	15
31	–	20n.p. green	15	15
32	–	25n.p. blue	20	15
33	–	50n.p. flesh	20	20
34	–	1r. lilac	60	45
35	–	2r. yellow	1·40	90
36	–	3r. blue	1·90	1·25
37	–	5r. buff	3·75	2·75

DESIGNS (Kennedy): 10n.p. As student. 15n.p. As cadet. 20n.p. As Senator. 25n.p. Sailing. 50n.p. As President. 33 × 51 mm: 1r. With Mrs. Kennedy and guest. 2r. With Pres. Eisenhower. 3r. With family. 5r. Full face portrait.

1965. Air. Designs similar to Nos. 1/9, but with "FUJEIRA" and value transposed, and inscr "AIR MAIL". Mult. (a) Size $43\frac{1}{2} \times 28\frac{1}{2}$ mm.

39		15n.p. Type **1**	20	10
40		25n.p. Arabian oryx	15	15
41		35n.p. Hoopoe	30	10
42		50n.p. Asiatic wild ass	25	20
43		75n.p. Great egrets	40	15
44		1r. Arab horses	50	40

(b) Size $53\frac{1}{2} \times 35\frac{1}{2}$ mm.

45		2r. Leopard	1·25	95
46		3r. Dromedaries	2·75	1·60
47		5r. Lanner falcon	3·25	1·90

4 Queen Nefertiti

1966. Stamp Centenary Exn, Cairo. Mult.

57		3n.p. Type **4**	15	15
58		5n.p. Colossi, Abu Simbel	15	15
59		10n.p. Tutankhamun's mask	15	15
60		15n.p. Sphinx, Gezir	15	15
61		25n.p. Statues of Prince Rahotep and his wife Nofret	20	15
62		50n.p. Ancient Church (horiz)	25	15
63		1r. Colonnade, Great Temple of Isis, Philae (horiz)	55	25
64		2r. Nile sphinxes (horiz)	1·10	55
65		5r. Pyramids, Giza (horiz)	3·25	1·25

5 Sir Winston Churchill as Harrow Schoolboy

1966. Churchill Commem. Each design black and gold; frame in colours given.

67	5	10n.p. yellow (postage)	15	15
68	–	15n.p. blue	15	15
69	–	25n.p. buff	15	15
70	–	50n.p. blue	15	15
71	–	75n.p. mauve	25	20
72	–	1r. blue	50	25
73	–	2r. gold (air)	1·25	45
74	–	3r. gold	1·90	90

DESIGNS—Churchill: 15n.p. Wearing Hussars' uniform; 25n.p. As Boer War correspondent; 50n.p. In morning dress; 75n.p. With Eisenhower; 1r. Painting; 2r. With grandson; 3r. Giving "V" sign.

6 Lunar Satellite

1966. Space Achievements. Multicoloured.

76		5n.p. Type **6**	15	15
77		10n.p. Satellite approaching Moon	15	15
78		15n.p. Satellite and planets	15	15
79		25n.p. Satellite and Solar System	15	15
80		50n.p. Communications satellite	15	15
81		75n.p. Venus probe	40	15
82		1r. "Telstar"	60	25
83		2r. "Relay"	1·25	60

1967. Various stamps with currency names changed by overprinting. (i) Nos. 1/18 (Definitives).

85		1d. on 1n.p.	90	20
86		2d. on 2n.p.	1·00	20
87		3d. on 3n.p.	90	20
88		4d. on 4n.p.	1·00	20
89		5d. on 5n.p.	90	20
90		10d. on 10n.p.	90	20
91		15d. on 15n.p.	1·50	30
92		20d. on 20n.p.	1·00	20
93		30d. on 30n.p.	90	20
94		40d. on 40n.p.	1·10	20
95		50d. on 50n.p.	1·50	20
96		70d. on 70n.p.	1·50	20
97		1r. on 1r.	1·50	40
98		1r.50 on 1r.50	2·10	40
99		2r. on 2r.	1·00	1·00
100		3r. on 3r. on 3r.	1·50	1·25
101		5r. on 5r.	2·25	2·25
102		10r. on 10r.	5·50	3·25

(ii) Air. Nos. 39/47 (Definitives).

123		15d. on 15n.p.	90	20
124		25d. on 25n.p.	1·00	15
125		35d. on 35n.p.	1·00	20
126		50d. on 50n.p.	1·50	40
127		75d. on 75n.p.	75	75
128		1r. on 1r.	1·00	50
129		2r. on 2r.	1·25	1·00
130		3r. on 3r.	2·25	2·00
131		5r. on 5r.	2·25	2·50

Nos. 19/37 and 57/83 were also surcharged in the new currency in limited quantities, but they had little local usage.

9 "Pararge felix"

1967. Butterflies. Multicoloured. (a) Postage. (i) Size 32 × 32 mm.

167		1d. Type **9**	10	10
168		2d. African clouded yellow (male)	10	10
169		3d. African clouded yellow (female)	10	10
170		4d. "Spindasis scotti"	10	10
171		5d. "Pararge felix" (different)	10	10
172		10d. "Lepidochrysops arabicus"	10	10
173		15d. "Eumenis tewfiki"	20	10
174		20d. "Euchrysops philbyi"	30	10
175		30d. "Mylothris arabicus"	35	10

(ii) Size 40 × 40 mm.

176		40d. Type **9**	50	10
177		50d. As No. 168	55	10
178		70d. As No. 169	65	15

179	1r. As No. 170	70	20
180	1r.50 As No. 171	1·10	35
181	2r. As No. 172	1·50	60
	(iii) Size 42×42 mm.		
182	3r. As No. 173	1·75	75
183	5r. As No. 174	3·00	1·10
184	10r. As No. 175	5·25	2·25
	(b) Air. Size 45×45 mm.		
185	15d. Type **9**	15	10
186	25d. As No. 168	25	10
187	35d. As No. 169	40	10
188	50d. As No. 170	50	10
189	75d. As No. 171	65	15
190	1r. As No. 172	85	20
191	2r. As No. 173	1·25	40
192	3r. As No. 174	3·00	65
193	5r. As No. 175	5·00	1·10

10 Shaikh Mohamed bin Hamad al Sharqi and Veil-tailed Goldfish

1971. Multicoloured.

194	5d. Type **10** (postage)	45	20
195	20d. Shaikh and semicircle angelfish (air)	35	10
196	35d. Shaikh and paradise fish	40	10
197	40d. Shaikh and moorish idol	45	10
198	60d. Shaikh and daisy	40	10
199	1r. Shaikh and rose	60	15
200	2r. Shaikh and gentian	90	35
201	3r. Shaikh and wild rose	1·40	50

OFFICIAL STAMPS

1965. Designs similar to Nos. 1/9, but with "FUJEIRA" and value transposed, additionally inscr "ON STATE'S SERVICE". Multicoloured. (a) Postage. Size 43½×28½ mm.

O48	25n.p. Type **1**	15	10
O49	40n.p. Arabian oryx	40	15
O50	50n.p. Hoopoe	35	10
O51	75n.p. Asiatic wild ass	75	20
O52	1r. Great egrets	70	25
	(b) Air. (i) Size 43½×28½ mm.		
O53	75n.p. Arab horses	40	25
	(ii) Size 53½×35½ mm.		
O54	2r. Leopard	95	65
O55	3r. Dromedaries	1·90	1·00
O56	5r. Lanner falcon	3·50	1·90

1967. Nos. 48/56 with currency name changed by overprinting.

O158	25d. on 25n.p. (postage)	20	20
O159	40d. on 40n.p.	20	15
O160	50d. on 50n.p.	35	35
O161	75d. on 75n.p.	50	35
O162	1r. on 1r.	70	70
O163	75d. on 75n.p. (air)	45	30
O164	2r. on 2r.	1·40	70
O165	3r. on 3r.	2·00	1·25
O166	5r. on 5r.	3·50	3·50

APPENDIX

The following stamps have either been issued in excess of postal needs or have not been available to the public in reasonable quantities at face value. Such stamps may later be given full listing if there is evidence of regular postal use.

1967.

"One Thousand and One Nights". Postage 10, 15, 30, 75d., 1r., 1r.50; Air 25, 50, 75d., 1r., 1r.25, 2r.

Famous Paintings. Postage 25, 50, 75d., 1, 1r.50; Air 2, 3, 5r.

Cats. Postage 10, 35, 50d., 1, 1r.50; Air 1r.25, 2r.75, 3r.50.

1968.

Winter Olympic Games, Grenoble. 25, 50, 75d., 1, 1r.50, 2, 3r.

Famous Paintings (square designs). Postage 50, 75d., 1, 2, 3r.; Air 1r.50, 2r.50, 3r.50, 4, 5r.

Ships. Postage 15, 25, 50, 75d., 1r.; Air 2, 3, 4, 5r.

Olympic Games, Mexico. Optd on Nos. 22/6 and four values of 1968 Winter Olympics issue. Postage 1, 1r.50, 2, 3, 5r.; Air 1, 1r.50, 2, 3r.

Prehistoric Animals. Postage 15, 25, 50, 75d., 1r.50; Air 1, 2r.50, 3, 4, 5r.

Robert Kennedy Memorial issue. Optd on Nos. 34/7. 1, 2, 3, 5r.

Olympic Games, Mexico. Postage 15, 25, 35, 50, 75d., 1r.; Air 1r.50, 2, 3, 5r.

International Letter-writing Week. Paintings. Postage 25, 50, 75d., 1r.; Air 1r.50, 2, 3, 5r.

"EFIMEX" International Stamp Exhibition, Mexico. Optd on 1968 Letter-writing Week issue. Postage 25, 50, 75d.; 1r. Air 1r.50, 2, 3, 5r.

Gold Medal Winners, Olympic Games, Mexico. Optd on 1968 Olympic Games, Mexico issue. Postage 15, 25, 35, 50 75d., 1r.; Air 1r.50, 2, 3, 5r.

1969.

Wild Animals of the World. Postage 15, 25, 50, 75d., 1r.; Air 1r.50, 2, 3, 5r.

Scenes from Shakespeare's Plays. Postage 25, 50, 75d., 1, 2r.; Air 1r.25, 2r.50, 3, 5r.

Olympic Games, Munich (1969). Optd on 1968 Olympic Games, Mexico issue. Postage 15, 25, 35, 50, 75d., 1r.; Air 1r.50, 2r.50, 3, 5r.

Famous Railway Locomotives. Postage 15, 25, 50, 75d., 1r.; Air 2, 3, 5r.

Moon Flight of "Apollo 8". Optd or surch on Nos. 76/83. 50, 75n.p., 1, 2, 2r.50 on 25n.p., 3r. on 15n.p., 4r. on 10n.p. 5r. on 5n.p.

Winter Olympic Games, Sapporo, Japan (1972). Optd on 1968 Winter Olympic Games, Grenoble issue. 25, 50, 75d., 1, 1r.50, 2, 3r.

Birds. Postage 25, 50d., 1r., 1r.50, 2r.; Air 1r.25, 2r.50, 3, 5r.

Pres. Eisenhower Memorial issue. Postage 25, 50d., 1r., 1r.50, 2r.; Air 1r.25, 2r.50, 3, 5r.

Champions of Peace. 25, 50, 75d., 1, 2, 3, 5r.

Human Rights Year. Optd on 1969 Champions of Peace issue. 25, 50, 75d., 1, 2, 3, 5r.

Flowers. Postage 25, 50d., 1, 1r.50, 2r.; Air 1r.25, 2r.50, 3, 5r.

"Apollo" Space Flights. Postage 10, 25, 50d., 1, 2r.; Air 2r.50, 3, 4, 5r.

Space Flight of "Apollo 10". Optd on 1969 "Apollo" Space Flights issue. Postage 10, 25, 50d., 1, 2r.; Air 2r.50, 3, 4, 5r.

Moon Landing. Optd on 1969 "Apollo" Space Flights issue. Postage 10, 25, 50d., 1, 2r.; Air 2r.50, 3, 4, 5r.

First Man on the Moon. 1969 "Apollo" Space Flights issue optd with various commemoration inscriptions. Postage 10, 25, 50d., 1, 2r.; Air 2r.50, 3, 4, 5r.

1970.

Birth Bicentenary of Napoleon Bonaparte. 15, 25, 50, 75d., 1, 1r.50, 2r.

General De Gaulle Commemoration. Air 35, 60, 75d., 1r.25, 2r.50, 3, 5r.

Bible Stories. Postage 15d., 1r.; Air 35, 75d., 1r.25, 1r.50, 2r.50, 3r.

"Expo 70" World Fair, Osaka, Japan. Japanese Art. Postage 15, 25, 50, 75d., 1, 2r.; Air 75d., 1r.25, 2r.50, 4r.

Exploration of the Moon. 25, 50d., 1, 2, 3, 4, 5r.

Space Flight of "Apollo 13". Optd on 1970 Moon Exploration issue. 25, 50d., 1, 2, 3, 4, 5r.

Moon Mission of "Apollo 14". Optd on 1970 Moon Exploration issue. 25, 50d., 1, 2, 3, 4, 5r.

"Expo 70" World Fair, Osaka, Japan. Pavilions. 10, 20, 70d., 1r.×2, 2r.

World Football Cup, Mexico. 10, 20, 70d., 1r.×2, 2r.

Pres. Gamal Nasser Memorial issue. Postage 10, 20, 30, 40, 50d.; Air 5r.

Horses. Postage 10, 20d.; Air 70d., 1, 2r.

Cats. Postage 30, 70d.; Air 1, 2, 3r.

Dogs. Postage 30, 70d.; Air 1, 2, 3r.

Paintings of the Madonna. 30, 70d., 1, 2, 3r.

Stations of the Cross. 1r.×15.

Christmas. Paintings. Postage 30, 70d., 1r.; Air 2, 3r.

1971.

American and European Cars. Postage 5, 20, 30d., 4r.; Air 30, 50, 70d., 1r.50, 2r.50, 4r.

Space Exploration. Air 40, 60d., 1, 2, 5r.

History of Railways. 10, 20, 70d., 2, 3r.

General De Gaulle Memorial issue. Air 30, 70d. 1, 2, 3r.

Moon Mission of "Apollo 14" Air 70d., 1, 2, 3, 4r.

Wild Animals. Air 20, 40, 60d., 1, 2, 3r.

Olympic Games, Munich (1972) (square designs). Postage 50d., 1r.; Air 2, 3, 4r.

Winter Olympic Games, Sapporo, Japan (1972). Postage 5, 10, 15, 20, 30, 50d.; Air 70d., 4r.

500th Birth Anniv of Durer. Paintings. Air 70d., 1, 2, 3, 4r.

Birth Bicentenary of Beethoven. Portraits and instruments. Postage 30, 70d.; Air 1, 3, 4r.

Mozart Commem. Postage 30, 70d.1r.; Air 3, 4r.

Frazier v Mohammed Ali World Heavyweight Boxing Championship Fight. Air 1, 2, 3r.

World Scout Jamboree, Asagiri, Japan. Postage 20, 30, 50, 70d., 1r.×2, 2r.×2; Air 3, 4r.

Butterflies. Air. 70d., 1, 2, 3, 5r.

Cats and Dogs. 10, 20, 30d., 1, 2, 3r.

Monkeys. 30, 70d., 1, 2, 3r.

Wild Animals. 30, 70d., 1, 2, 3r.

Horses. 70d., 1, 2, 3, 4r.

Olympic Games, Munich. Sports. 1, 2, 3, 4, 5, 6, 7, 8, 9, 10, 11, 12, 13, 14, 15, 16, 17, 18, 19, 20, 21, 22, 23, 24, 25, 26, 27, 28, 29, 30d.

Olympic Games, Munich. Sports and Arenas. Postage 35, 60d., 2, 3r.; Air 4r.

Christmas. Postage 40, 60d., 2r.; Air 3, 4r.

International Labour Day. Paintings. Postage 40, 60d., 2, 3r.; Air 2, 3, 4r.

1972.

400th Birth Anniv of Kepler. Postage 35, 75d., 1, 2r.; Air 3, 5r.

Moon Mission of "Apollo 15". Postage 30, 70d.; Air 1, 2, 5r.

2500th Anniv of The Persian Empire. Postage 35, 65, 75d.; Air 1r.25, 2, 3r.

Historical Costumes. 30, 70d., 1, 2, 3r.

Winter Olympic Games, Sapporo, Japan. Postage 25, 30, 70d.; Air 1r.25, 2, 3r.

Tropical Birds 30, 70d., 1, 2, 3r.

Children's Day. Paintings. Postage 10, 30, 60d.; Air 4, 5r.

Sculptures. Postage 30, 70d.; Air 1, 2, 6r.

Paintings of the Madonna. Postage 20, 30 50d.; Air 4, 5r.

Nude Paintings. 50d., 1, 2, 3, 4r.

Gold Medal Winners, Winter Olympic Games, Sapporo. Optd on 1972 Winter Olympic Games, Sapporo issue. Postage 25, 30, 70d.; Air 1r.25, 2, 3r.

Olympic Games, Munich. Discus-thrower. Air 8r.

Space Exploration. Postage 5, 10, 15, 20, 25, 30, 35, 40, 45, 50, 55, 60d.; Air 65, 70, 75d., 1, 2, 3, 4, 5r.

Walt Disney Cartoon Characters. Postage 1, 2, 3, 4, 5, 10, 15, 20, 25, 30d.; Air 45, 55, 65, 70d., 1, 1r.50, 2, 3, 4, 5r.

History of the Olympic Games Postage 1, 2, 3, 4, 5, 10, 15, 20, 25, 30, 45, 55d.; Air 65, 70d., 1, 1r.50, 2, 3, 5r.

Summit Meeting of Pres. Nixon and Mao Tse-tung. Air 2, 3, 5r.

Pres. Nixon's Visit of Russia. Optd on 1972 Nixon–Mao Tse-tung Meeting issue. Air 2, 3, 5r.

150th Death Anniv (1971) of Napoleon Bonaparte. Air 10r.

2nd Death Anniv of General De Gaulle. Air 10r.

Olympic Games, Munich, Javelin-thrower. Air 10r.

Gold Medal Winners, Olympic Games, Munich. Optd on 1972 Discus-thrower issue. Air 8r.

Moon Mission of "Apollo 16". Air 10r.

European Birds. 30, 70d., 1, 2, 3r.

A number of issues on gold and silver foil also exist, but it is understood that these were mainly for presentation purposes, although valid for postage.

During 1970 a number of other sets came on to the market, but their official status is in doubt.

The United Arab Emirates Ministry of Communications took over the Fujeira postal service on 1 August 1972. Further stamps were released without authority and had no validity.

FUNCHAL Pt. 9

The District of Funchal (the chief town) was the administrative title of Madeira from 1892 to 1905. From 1905 the name reverted to Madeira.

1000 reis = 1 milreis.

4

1892.

85	**4**	5r. yellow	3·25	2·00
86		10r. mauve	2·75	2·00
87		15r. brown	3·75	3·25
89		20r. lilac	4·00	2·75
83		25r. green	7·00	1·80
84		50r. blue	5·25	2·75
92		75r. pink	8·25	7·00
93		80r. green	16·00	12·50
95		100r. brown on buff	10·00	5·25
107		150r. red on pink	60·00	34·00
96		200r. blue on blue	70·00	48·00
97		300r. blue on brown	70·00	60·00

1897. "King Carlos" key-type inscr "FUNCHAL". Name and value in red (Nos. 123, 130) or black (others).

110	S	2½r. grey	55	40
111		5r. red	55	40
112		10r. green	55	40
113		15r. brown	6·50	5·25
126		15r. green	3·75	3·00
114		20r. lilac	1·60	90
115		25r. green	3·00	90
127		25r. red	1·60	70
128		50r. blue	6·50	5·25
129		65r. blue	1·40	1·10
117		75r. pink	1·70	1·20
130		75r. brown on yellow	2·10	1·40
118		80r. mauve	1·70	1·50
119		100r. blue on blue	1·70	1·40
131		115r. red on pink	2·50	1·80
132		130r. brown on cream	2·50	1·80
120		150r. brown on yellow	3·25	1·60
133		180r. grey on pink	2·50	1·80
121		200r. purple on pink	3·25	2·75
122		300r. blue on pink	3·25	2·75
123		500r. black on blue	3·50	3·00

GABON Pt. 6; Pt. 13

A French colony on the W. coast of equatorial Africa. Became part of Fr. Equatorial Africa in 1937 and a republic within the French Community in 1958.

100 centimes = 1 franc.

1886. Stamps of French Colonies, "Commerce" type, surch **GAB** surrounded by dots, and value in figures.

1	J	5c. on 20c. red on green	£325	£325
2		10c. on 20c. red on green	£325	£325
3		25c. on 20c. red on green	50·00	35·00
4		50c. on 15c. blue on light blue	£1100	£1100
5		75c. on 15c. blue on light blue	£1300	£1400

1888. Stamps of French Colonies, "Commerce" type, surch in figures.

6	J	15c. on 10c. black on lilac	£4000	£800
7		15c. on 1f. olive	£1600	£650
8		25c. on 5c. green	£950	£170
9		25c. on 10c. black on lilac	£4000	£1200
10		25c. on 75c. red	£2500	£1000

1889. Postage Due stamps of French Colonies surch **GABON TIMBRE** and value in figures.

11	U	15c. on 5c. black	£190	£170
12		15c. on 30c. black	£3750	£2500
13		25c. on 20c. black	80·00	70·00

6

1889. Imperf.

14	**6**	15c. black on pink	£1100	£700
15		25c. black on green	£700	£575

1904. "Tablet" key-type inscr "GABON" in red (1, 5, 15, 25, 35, 45, 75c., 1, 2f.) or blue (others).

16	D	1c. black on blue	80	75
17		2c. brown on buff	80	65
18		4c. brown on grey	1·00	1·25
19		5c. green	1·50	80
20		10c. red	3·50	40
21		15c. grey	6·00	1·50
22		20c. red on green	8·00	6·25
23		25c. blue	5·00	2·25
24		30c. brown on drab	10·50	8·00
25		35c. black on yellow	27·00	18·00
26		40c. red on yellow	14·50	10·00
27		45c. black on green	32·00	30·00
28		50c. brown on blue	9·00	9·50
29		75c. brown on orange	18·00	19·00
30		1f. green	35·00	32·00
31		2f. violet on pink	60·00	65·00
32		5f. mauve on lilac	£100	£100

7 Gabon Warrior **9** Bantu Woman

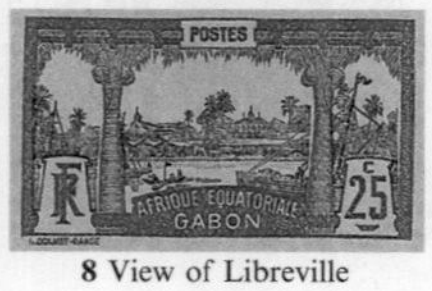

8 View of Libreville

1910.

33	**7**	1c. brown and orange	1·10	70
34		2c. black and brown	2·25	1·40
35		4c. violet and blue	65	90
36		5c. olive and green	35	80
37		10c. red and lake	2·25	1·25
38		20c. brown and violet	1·25	5·00
39	**8**	25c. brown and blue	1·90	4·75
40		30c. red and grey	19·00	30·00
41		35c. green and violet	18·00	14·00
42		40c. blue and brown	17·00	26·00
43		45c. violet and red	21·00	32·00
44		50c. grey and green	50·00	65·00
45		75c. brown and orange	80·00	85·00
46	**9**	1f. yellow and brown	80·00	85·00
47		2f. brown and red	£225	£200
48		5f. brown and blue	£200	£225

1910. As last but inscr "AFRIQUE EQUATORIALE GABON".

49	**7**	1c. brown and orange	10	10
50		2c. black and brown	10	40
51		4c. violet and blue	20	25
52		5c. grey and green	40	95
82		5c. black and yellow	90	2·75
53		10c. red and lake	1·75	75

83 10c. light green and green . . 35 3·00
54 15c. purple and pink . . . . 50 2·75
55 20c. brown and violet . . . . 7·00 9·50
56 8 25c. brown and blue . . . . 1·40 2·00
84 25c. black and green . . . . 2·25 3·50
57 30c. red and grey . . . . 1·75 2·75
85 30c. red and carmine . . . . 1·60 2·75
58 35c. green and violet . . . . 2·25 2·25
59 40c. blue and brown . . . . 2·50 2·75
60 45c. violet and red . . . . 1·75 3·75
86 45c. red and black . . . . 1·60 3·25
61 50c. grey and green . . . . 2·00 3·00
87 50c. blue and deep blue . . . 55 1·25
62 75c. brown and red . . . . 2·75 6·50
63 9 1f. bistre and brown . . . . 3·25 4·50
64 2f. brown and red . . . . 3·75 5·50
65 5f. brown and blue . . . . 7·25 10·00

1912. "Tablet" key-type surch in figures.
66 D 05 on 2c. brown on buff . . 45 1·75
67 05 on 4c. brown on grey . . 40 2·25
68 05 on 15c. grey 15 15
69 05 on 20c. red on green . . 25 1·40
70 05 on 25c. blue 20 25
71 05 on 30c. brown on drab 40 2·75
72 10 on 40c. red on yellow . . 25 75
73 10 on 45c. black on green 45 90
74 10 on 50c. brown on blue 40 1·25
75 10 on 75c. brown on orange 60 2·25
76 10 on 1f. green . . . . . 35 1·40
77 10 on 2f. violet on pink . . 20 2·25
78 10 on 5f. mauve on lilac . . 2·00 4·50

1915. Surch with red cross and **5c**.
79 7 10c.+5c. (No. 37) . . . . . 19·00 22·00
81 10c.+5c. (No. 53) . . . . . 25 2·00

1924. Inscr "AFRIQUE EQUATORIALE GABON" and optd **AFRIQUE EQUATORIALE FRANCAISE**.
88 7 1c. brown and orange . . . 10 95
89 2c. black and brown . . . . 10 2·25
90 4c. violet and blue . . . . . 10 2·75
91 5c. black and yellow . . . . 10 1·10
92 10c. light green and green 60 2·50
93 10c. blue and brown 50 15
94 15c. purple and pink . . . . 30 2·50
95 15c. pink and purple . . . . 1·25 3·00
96 20c. brown and violet . . . 70 2·75
97 8 25c. black and green 45 35
98 30c. red and carmine . . . 95 2·50
99 30c. yellow and black . . . 15 2·50
100 30c. green . . . . 2·25 2·75
101 35c. green and violet . . . . 50 2·75
102 40c. blue and brown . . . . 1·40 25
103 45c. red and black . . . . 1·25 2·75
104 50c. blue and deep blue . . 85 2·75
105 50c. green and red . . . . 1·10 15
106 65c. red and blue . . . . . 2·50 5·00
107 75c. brown and orange . . . 80 2·50
108 90c. red and scarlet . . . . 3·50 3·75
109 9 1f. bistre and brown . . . . 1·25 1·10
110 1f.10 red and green . . . . 5·25 8·75
111 1f.50 blue and light blue . . 3·25 2·00
112 2f. brown and red . . . . . 80 1·40
113 3f. mauve on pink . . . . . 5·75 10·00
114 5f. brown and blue . . . . 6·25 9·50

1925. As last, surch in figures.
115 9 65 on 1f. brown and green 85 3·00
116 85 on 1f. brown and green 60 3·00
117 8 90c. on 75c. pink and red 55 3·50
118 9 1f.25 on 1f. ultram & bl . . 25 1·40
119 1f.50 on 1f. dp blue & blue 1·25 2·75
120 3f. on 5f. brown and mauve 3·00 9·50
121 10f. on 5f. green and brown 11·50 20·00
122 20f. on 5f. red and purple 14·00 18·00

1931. "Colonial Exn" key-type inscr "GABON".
123 E 40c. green . . . . 2·75 4·50
124 F 50c. mauve . . . . 65 3·75
125 G 90c. orange . . . . 1·90 4·50
126 H 1f.50 blue . . . . 4·75 5·50

21 Log Raft on the River Ogowe

22 Count de Brazza

1932.
127 21 1c. red . . . . 15 2·25
128 2c. black on red 45 30
129 4c. green . . . . 20 2·75
130 5c. blue . . . . 35 2·25
131 10c. red on yellow . . . . 60 1·75
132 15c. red on green . . . . 2·50 3·00
133 20c. red . . . . 2·75 3·25
134 25c. brown . . . . 1·75 1·60
135 22 30c. green . . . . 3·00 3·50
136 40c. purple . . . . 2·75 3·25
137 45c. black on green . . . . 2·75 3·50
138 50c. brown . . . . 2·50 1·60
139 65c. blue . . . . 7·00 7·50
140 75c. black on orange . . . 4·00 4·75
141 90c. red . . . . 4·00 4·75
142 1f. green on blue . . . . . 11·00 24·00
143 – 1f.25 violet . . . . 3·50 3·25
144 – 1f.50 blue . . . . 4·25 3·50
145 – 1f.75 green . . . . 3·75 3·00
146 – 2f. red . . . . 23·00 23·00
147 – 3f. green on blue . . . . 5·50 6·00
148 – 5f. brown . . . . 8·75 10·00
149 – 10f. black on orange . . . 27·00 35·00
150 – 20f. purple . . . . 45·00 45·00
DESIGN—HORIZ: 1f.25 to 20f. Gabon village.

25 Prime Minister Leon Mba

26 C.C.T.A. Emblem

1959. 1st Anniv of Republic.
161 25 15f. brown 65 85
162 – 25f. green and sepia . . . 1·60 10
PORTRAIT: 25f. Prime Minister Mba (profile).

1960. 10th Anniv of African Technical Co-operation Commission.
163 26 50f. blue and purple . . . 2·25 2·75

27 Dr. Albert Schweitzer (philosopher and missionary), Organ and View of Lambarene

1960. Air.
164 27 200f. brown, green and blue . . . . 5·50 2·50

1960. Air. Olympic Games. No. 192 of French Equatorial Africa surch with Olympic rings, **XVIIe OLYMPIADE 1960 REPUBLIQUE GABONAISE 250F** and bars.
165 250f. on 500f. blue, blk & grn 6·75 6·75

29 Tree Felling

1960. Air. 5th World Forestry Congress, Seattle.
166 29 100f. brown, black & green 3·00 1·40

30 Flag, Map and U.N. Emblem

32 Combretum

31 Lyre-tailed Honeyguide in flight

1961. Admission into U.N.
167 30 15f. multicoloured 30 20
168 25f. multicoloured 35 25
169 85f. multicoloured . . . . 1·25 80

1961. Air. Birds. Multicoloured.
170 50f. Type **31** . . . . 2·50 1·10
171 100f. Madame Verreaux's sunbird . . . . 4·50 1·60
172 200f. Blue-headed bee eater (vert) . . . . 7·50 3·75
173 250f. Crowned eagle (vert) . . 9·75 5·25
174 500f. Narina's trogon (vert) 22·00 10·25

1961.
175 32 50c. red, purple and green 10 10
176 – 1f. red, turquoise and bistre 10 10
177 – 2f. yellow and green . . . 10 10
178 – 3f. yellow, green and olive 20 15
179 – 5f. multicoloured 25 20
180 32 10f. red, green & turquoise 30 25
FLOWERS—VERT: 1f., 5f. Gabonese tulip (tree). HORIZ: 2f., 3f. Yellow cassia.

33 President Mba

36 Start of Race

34 Airliners, European and African

1962.
181 33 15f. blue, red and green . . 20 10
182 20f. sepia, red and green 35 15
183 25f. brown, red and green 40 15

1962. Air. "Air Afrique" Airline.
184 34 500f. green, ochre & black 9·50 5·50

1962. Malaria Eradication. As T **55a** of French Somali Coast.
185 25f.+5f. green 80 80

1962. Sports. Multicoloured.
186 20f. Type **36** (postage) . . . 45 20
187 50f. Football 95 60
188 100f. Long jump (26 × 47 mm) (air) . . . . 2·50 1·10

37 Breguet 14 Biplane

1962. Air. Evolution of Air Transport.
189 37 10f. blue and red 50 20
190 – 20f. indigo, blue and brown 70 35
191 – 60f. blue, purple and green 1·60 85
192 – 85f. indigo, blue and orange . . . . 2·75 1·40
AIRCRAFT: 20f. De Havilland Dragon Rapide; 60f. Sud Aviation Caravelle; 85f. Rocket.

38 Union Flag

1962. 1st Anniv of Union of African and Malagasy States.
194 38 30f. green . . . . 1·10 80

39 Capt. Ntchorere and Flags

1962. Capt. Ntchorere Commemoration.
195 39 80f. multicoloured . . . . 1·10 70

41 Globe and Emblem

1963. Freedom from Hunger.
196 41 25f.+5f. green, brown and red 60 60

1963. Air. 50th Anniv of Arrival of Dr Schweitzer in Gabon. Surch **100F JUBILE GABONAIS 1913-1963**.
197 27 100f. on 200f. brown, green and blue . . . . 2·75 1·40

43 Libreville Post Office

1963. Air. Cent of Gabon Postal Services.
198 43 100f. multicoloured . . . . 1·40 85

44 "Posts and Telecommunications"

1963. Air. African and Malagasy Posts and Telecommunications Union.
199 44 85f. multicoloured . . . . 1·40 80

45 "Telecommunications"

1963. Space Telecommunications.
200 45 25f. orange, blue and green 40 35
201 100f. brown, green & blue 1·60 1·40

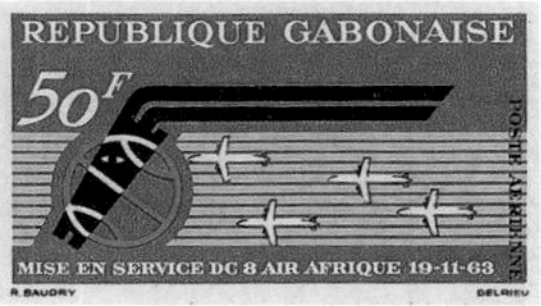

46 Airline Emblem

1963. Air. 1st Anniv of "Air Afrique" and Inauguration of "DC-8" Service.
202 46 50f. multicoloured 90 55

47 "Europafrique"

1963. Air. European–African Economic Convention.
203 47 50f. multicoloured . . . . 1·25 65

48 U.N.E.S.C.O. Emblem, Scales of Justice and Tree

1963. 15th Anniv of Declaration of Human Rights.
204 48 25f. slate, green and brown 45 30

49 Rameses and Gods, Wadi-es-Sebua

1964. Air. Nubian Monuments.

205 **49**	10f.+5f. brown and blue	85	85
206	25f.+5f. blue and red . . .	1·00	1·00
207	50f.+5f. purple & myrtle	1·50	1·50

50 Barograph

1964. World Meteorological Day.

208 **50**	25f. green, blue and bistre	55	35

51 Arms of Gabon **52** Map and African Heads of State

1964.

209 **51**	25f. multicoloured	50	30

1964. Air. 5th Anniv of Equatorial African Heads of State Conf.

210 **52**	100f. multicoloured	1·50	85

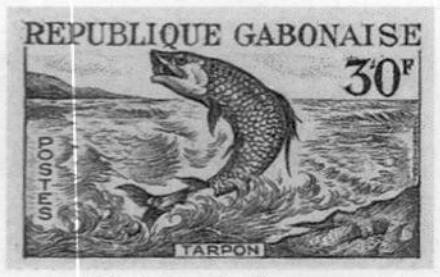

53 Atlantic Tarpon

1964. Gabon Fauna.

211 **53**	30f. black, blue and brown	90	45
212 –	60f. brown, chestnut & grn	1·50	60
213 –	80f. brown, green and blue	1·60	85

DESIGNS—VERT: 60f. Gorilla. HORIZ: 80f. African buffalo.

54 Ear of Wheat, Cogwheel and Globe

1964. Air. 1st Anniv of "Europafrique".

214 **54**	50f. blue, olive and red . .	1·25	80

55 Start of Race

1964. Air. Olympic Games, Tokyo.

215 **55**	25f. green, brown & orange	60	35
216 –	50f. brown, orange & green	1·10	45
217 –	100f. violet, purple & olive	2·25	90
218 –	200f. brown, purple and red	3·50	2·25

DESIGNS—VERT: 50f. Massaging athlete; 100f. Anointing before the Games. HORIZ: 200f. Athletes.

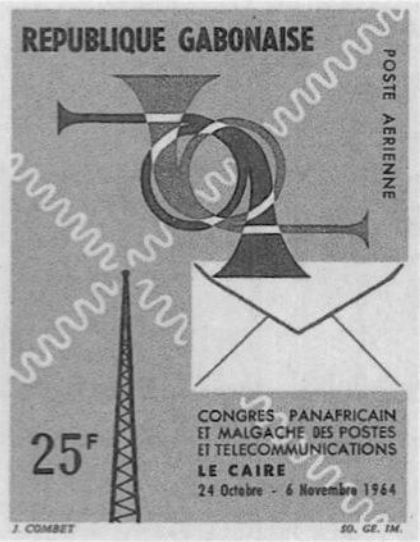

56 Posthorns, Envelope and Radio Mast

1964. Air. Pan-African and Malagasy Posts and Telecommunications Congress, Cairo.

220 **56**	25f. sepia, red and green	55	30

57 "Co-operation"

1964. French, African and Malagasy Co-operation.

221 **57**	25f. brown, blue and slate	55	40

58 "Dissotis rotundifolia" **59** Pres. Kennedy

1964. Flowers. Multicoloured.

222	3f. Type **58**	20	10
223	5f. "Gloriosa superba" . . .	30	15
224	15f. "Eulophia horsfallii" . .	55	25

1964. Air. Pres. Kennedy Commem.

225 **59**	100f. black, orange & green	1·60	1·40

60 Women in Public Service

1964. Air. Social Evolution of Gabonese Women.

227 **60**	50f. brown, blue and red	85	45

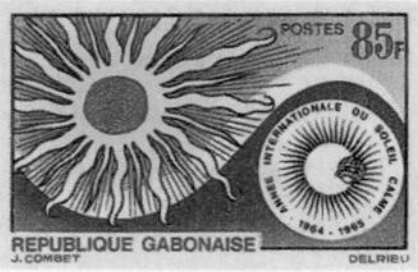

61 Sun and I.Q.S.Y. Emblem

1965. International Quiet Sun Year.

228 **61**	85f. multicoloured	1·40	85

62 Globe and I.C.Y. Emblem

1965. Air. International Co-operation Year.

229 **62**	50f. orange, turquoise & bl	85	45

63 17th-century Merchantman

1965. Air. Old Ships. Multicoloured.

230	25f. 16th-century galleon (vert)	1·25	55
231	50f. Type **63**	2·10	85
232	85f. 18th-century frigate (vert)	3·75	1·40
233	100f. 19th-century brig . . .	5·25	1·60

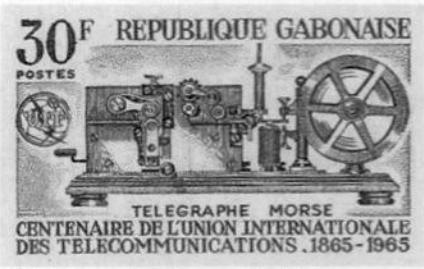

64 Morse Telegraph Apparatus

1965. Centenary of I.T.U.

234 **64**	30f. green, orange and blue	55	35

65 Manganese Mine, Moanda **67** Football

66 Nurse holding Child

1965. "Mining Riches".

235 **65**	15f. red, violet and blue . .	40	20
236 –	60f. red and blue	1·25	60

DESIGN: 60f. Uranium mine, Mounana.

1965. Air. Gabon Red Cross.

237 **66**	100f. brown, red and green	1·60	85

1965. 1st African Games, Brazzaville.

238 **67**	25f. black, red & grn (post)	55	35
239 –	100f. purple, red and brown (air)	1·90	85

DESIGN (27 × 48½ mm): 100f. Basketball.

68 "Globe", Pylon and "Sun"

1965. Air. "Europafrique".

240 **68**	50f. multicoloured	1·40	55

69 President Mba

1965. Air. 5th Anniv of Independence.

241 **69**	25f. multicoloured	50	30

70 Okoukoue Dance **71** Abraham Lincoln

1965. Gabon Dances.

242 **70**	25f. yellow, brown & green	45	20
243 –	60f. black, red and brown	1·25	60

DESIGN: 60f. Makudji dance.

1965. Death Cent of Abraham Lincoln.

244 **71**	50f. multicoloured	80	45

72 Sir Winston Churchill

1965. Air. Churchill Commem.

245 **72**	100f. multicoloured	1·60	85

73 Dr. A. Schweitzer and Map

1965. Air. Schweitzer Commem.

246 **73**	1000f. gold	48·00	48·00

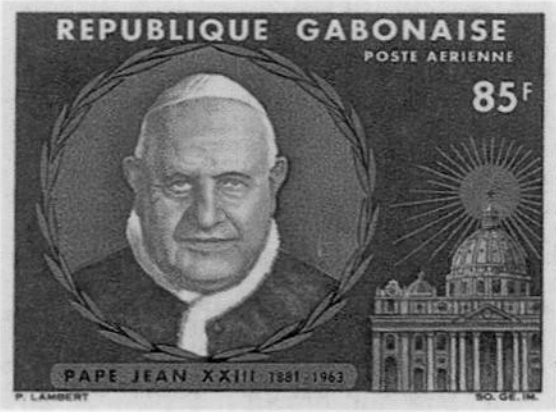

74 Pope John XXIII

1965. Air. Pope John Commem.

247 **74**	85f. multicoloured	1·10	80

75 Mail Carrier, Post Office and Van

1965. Stamp Day.

248 **75**	30f. brown, green and blue	50	40

76 Nurse and Patients

1966. Air. Red Cross. Multicoloured.

249	50f. Type **76**	95	55
250	100f. Bandaging patient . . .	1·90	85

77 Balumbu Mask **78** W.H.O. Building

1966. World Festival of Negro Arts, Dakar. Multicoloured.

253	5f. Type **77**	20	15
254	10f. Statuette—"Ancestor of the Fang (tribe), Byeri" . .	30	20
255	25f. Fang mask	70	30
256	30f. Okuyi Myene mask . . .	90	50
257	85f. Bakota copper mask . .	2·10	1·10

1966. Inaug of W.H.O. Headquarters, Geneva.

258 **78**	50f. black, yellow and blue	85	40

79 Satellite "A1" and Rocket

1966. Air. "Conquest of Space".
259 **79** 30f. lake, plum and blue 55 30
260 – 90f. plum, red and purple 1·40 60
DESIGN: 90f. Satellite "FR1" and rocket.

80 "Learning the Alphabet"

81 Footballer

1966. U.N.E.S.C.O. Literacy Campaign.
261 **80** 30f. multicoloured 55 30

1966. World Cup Football Championship, England.
262 **81** 25f. bl, grn & lake (postage) 40 20
263 – 90f. purple and blue . . . 1·60 70
264 – 100f. slate and red (air) . . 1·90 90
DESIGNS—VERT: 90f. Footballer (different). HORIZ: 100f. Footballers on world map (47½ × 27 mm).

82 Industrial Scenes within leaves of "Plant"

83 Plywood Mill

1966. Air. "Europafrique".
265 **82** 50f. multicoloured . . . . 2·75 65

1966. Economic Development.
266 **83** 20f. lake, purple and green 45 30
267 – 85f. brown, blue and green 3·50 1·40
DESIGN: 85f. "Roger Butin" (oil rig).

84 Aircraft and "Air Afrique" Emblem

1966. Air. Inauguration of Douglas DC-8F Air Services.
268 **84** 30f. grey, black and orange 40 20

85 Making Deposit

1966. Savings Bank.
269 **85** 25f. brown, green and blue 55 30

86 Scouts and Camp Fire

1966. Scouting.
270 **86** 30f. brown, red and slate 55 35
271 – 50f. brown, lake and blue 1·00 45
DESIGN—VERT: 50f. Scouts taking oath.

87 Gabonese Scholar

1966. Air. 20th Anniv of U.N.E.S.C.O.
272 **87** 100f. black, buff and blue 1·40 65

88 Libreville Airport

1966. Air.
273 **88** 200f. brown, red and blue 3·25 1·10

89 Sikorsky S-43 Amphibian, Map and Flag (Aeromaritime's First Airmail Service, 1937)

1966. Stamp Day.
274 **89** 30f. multicoloured 80 50

90 Hippopotami

1967. Gabon Fauna. Multicoloured.
275 1f. Type **90** 10 10
276 2f. Crocodiles 15 10
277 3f. Water chevrotains 15 10
278 5f. Chimpanzees 20 10
279 10f. African elephants 65 30
280 20f. Leopards . . . . 1·25 40

91 Lions Emblem and Anniversary Dates

1967. 50th Anniv of Lions Int. Mult.
281 30f. Type **91** 55 30
282 50f. Lions emblem, map and globe 90 40

92 Masked Faces

93 I.T.Y. Emblem and Transport

1967. Libreville Carnival.
283 **92** 30f. blue, brown and yellow 60 30

1967. Int Tourist Year.
284 **93** 30f. multicoloured . . . . 1·25 40

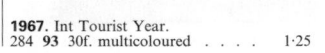

94 Diving-board (Mexico City)

96 Atomic Symbol, Dove and Globe

95 Farman F.190

1967. Publicity for 1968 Olympic Games, Mexico.
285 **94** 25f. turquoise, blue & violet 45 20
286 – 30f. purple, lake and green 65 30
287 – 50f. blue, green and purple 1·10 60
DESIGNS: 30f. Sun and snow crystal; 50f. Ice rink, Grenoble.

1967. Air. Famous Aircraft.
288 **95** 200f. plum, blue & turq . . 3·25 1·10
289 – 300f. blue, purple & brown 5·50 1·40
290 – 500f. blue, purple and green . . . . 9·50 4·25
AIRCRAFT: 300f. De Havilland Heron 2; 500f. Potez 56.

1967. International Atomic Energy Agency.
291 **96** 30f. red, blue and green . . 65 30

97 Aircraft on Flight-paths

1967. Air. I.C.A.O. Commem.
292 **97** 100f. purple, blue and green . . . . 1·50 70

98 Pope Paul VI

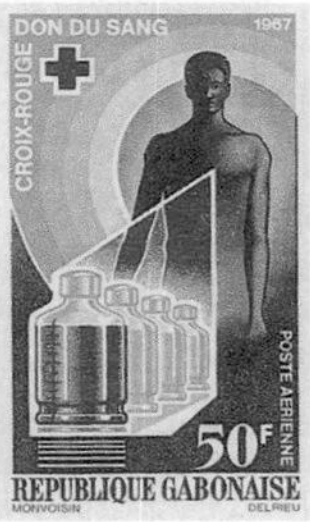

99 Blood Donor and Bank

1967. Papal Encyclical "Populorum Progressio".
293 **98** 30f. black, blue and green 65 35

1967. Air. Red Cross.
294 **99** 50f. multicoloured . . . . 1·10 45
295 – 100f. multicoloured . . . . 2·25 95
DESIGN: 100f. Heart and blood-transfusion apparatus.

100 Indigenous Emblems

101 "Europafrique"

1967. World Fair, Montreal.
297 **100** 30f. brown, green and lake 55 30

1967. Europafrique.
298 **101** 50f. multicoloured 85 35

102 Orientation Diagram and Sun

1967. Air. World Scout Jamboree, Idaho.
299 **102** 50f. green, orange and blue 80 50
300 – 100f. red, green and blue 1·40 90
DESIGN: 100f. U.S. scout greeting Gabon scout on map.

103 U.N. Emblem, Gabon Women and Child

1967. U.N. Status of Women Commission.
301 **103** 75f. blue, green and brown . . . . 1·40 55

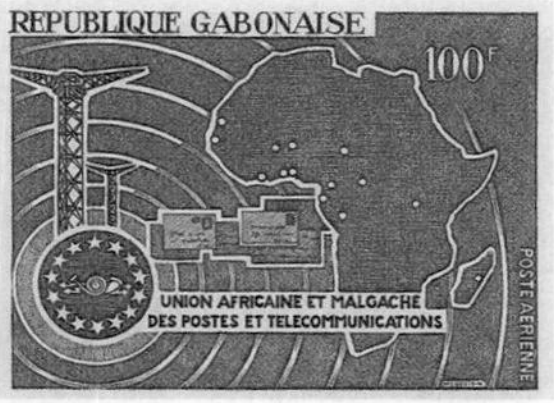

104 Map of Africa, Letters and Pylons

1967. Air. 5th Anniv of U.A.M.P.T.
302 **104** 100f. red, blue and olive 1·40 65

105 Baraka Mission, Libreville

1967. Air. 125th Anniv of American Missionaries Arrival.
303 **105** 100f. black, green and blue . . . . 1·60 85

106 U.N. Emblem and Book with Supporters

107 "Draconea fragans"

1967. Air. U.N. Int Rights Commission.
304 **106** 60f. multicoloured 90 55

1967. Gabon Trees.
305 **107** 5f. brown, green and blue (postage) 20 15
306 – 10f. green, bronze and blue 35 20
307 – 20f. red, green and brown 55 30
308 – 50f. green, bistre and blue (air) 95 40
309 – 100f. multicoloured . . . 1·90 70
DESIGNS: 10f. "Pycnanthus angolensis"; 20f. "Disthemonanthus benthamianus". (27 × 48 mm): 50f. "Baillonella toxisperma"; 100f. "Aucoumea klaineana".

108 "Belgrano" and "Jean Guiton" (19th-century steam packets)

1967. Stamp Day. Multicoloured.

311 30f. Type **108** . . . . 1·25 45
312 30f. "Ango" and "Lucie Delmas" (modern mail carriers) . . . . 1·25 45

Nos. 311/12 were issued together, se-tenant, forming a composite design.

109 Chancellor Adenauer

110 African W.H.O. Building

1968. Air. Adenauer Commem.

313 **109** 100f. sepia, red and yellow . . . . 1·90 65

1968. 20th Anniv of W.H.O.

315 **110** 20f. purple, blue and green 55 30

111 Dam and Power-station

112 President Bongo

1968. International Hydrological Decade.

316 **111** 15f. blue, orange and lake 45 20

1968.

317 **112** 25f. black, yellow & green 40 20
318 – 30f. black, turquoise & pur 45 20

DESIGN: 30f. Pres. Bongo (half-length portrait).

113 "Madonna and Child with Rosary" (Murillo)

1968. Air. Religious Paintings. Multicoloured.

319 60f. Type **113** 90 45
320 90f. "Christ in Bonds" (Luis de Morales) . . . . 1·40 65
321 100f. "St. John at Patmos" (Juan Mates) (horiz) . . . 1·60 85

114 Beribboned Rope

1968. Air. 5th Anniv of Europafrique.

322 **114** 50f. multicoloured 80 40

115 Refinery and Tanker

1968. Inauguration of Petroleum Refinery, Port Gentil, Gabon.

323 **115** 30f. multicoloured 70 30

116 Distribution to the Needy

1968. Air. Red Cross. Multicoloured.

324 50f. Type **116** 85 35
325 100f. "Support the Red Cross" . . . . 1·90 65

117 High-jumping

1968. Air. Olympic Games, Mexico.

327 **117** 25f. brown, slate and red 50 30
328 – 30f. brown, blue and red 60 35
329 – 100f. brown, yellow & blue . . . . 1·60 80
330 – 200f. brown, slate & green 3·00 1·40

DESIGNS—VERT: 30f. Cycling; 100f. Judo. HORIZ: 200f. Boxing.

118 Open Book

120 Coffee

1968. Literacy Day.

332 **118** 25f. brown, red and blue 40 20

1968. Agricultural Produce.

333 **120** 20f. red, myrtle and green 45 15
334 – 40f. orange, brown & grn 75 35

DESIGNS: 40f. Cocoa.

121 "Junon" (sail/steam warship)

123 Advocate holding "Charter"

122 President Mba and Flag

1968. Stamp Day.

335 **121** 30f. violet, green & orange . . . . 1·10 55

1968. Air. 1st Death Anniv of Pres. Mba.

336 **122** 1,000f. multicoloured . . 18·00 18·00

1968. Human Rights Year.

337 **123** 20f. black, green and red 45 30

124 President Bongo, Maps of Gabon and Owendo Port

1968. Air. "Laying of 1st Stone", Owendo Port. Multicoloured.

338 25f. Type **124** 60 25
339 30f. Harbour Project 75 20

125 "The Cloisters of Ste. Marie des Anges" (F. M. Granet)

1969. Air. "Philexafrique" Stamp Exhibition, Abidjan, Ivory Coast (1st issue).

340 **125** 100f. multicoloured . . . 2·75 2·75

See also No. 346.

126 Mahatma Gandhi

1969. Air. "Apostles of Peace".

341 **126** 25f. black and pink . . . 45 15
342 – 30f. black and green . . . 55 30
343 – 50f. black and blue . . . 85 35
344 – 100f. black and mauve . . 1·50 60

DESIGNS: 30f. J. F. Kennedy; 50f. R. F. Kennedy; 100f. Martin Luther King.

127 Oil Refinery. Port Gentil and Gabon Stamp of 1932

1969. Air. "Philexafrique" Stamp Exhibition, Abidjan, Ivory Coast (2nd issue).

346 **127** 50f. blue, red and green 1·50 1·50

128 View of Okanda Gates

1969. African Tourist Year.

347 **128** 10f. brown, green and blue 20 10
348 – 15f. blue, green and red 1·25 25
349 – 25f. purple, blue & brown 40 20
350 – 30f. brown, choc & blue 85 35

DESIGNS—HORIZ: 15f. Great barracuda. VERT: 25f. Kinguele Falls; 30f. Hunting trophies.

129 "Battle of Rivoli" (Philippoteaux)

1969. Air. Birth Bicentenary of Napoleon Bonaparte. Multicoloured.

351 50f. Type **129** . . . . 1·60 1·10
352 100f. "Oath of the Army" (J. L. David) . . . . . . 1·90 1·60
353 250f. "The Emperor Napoleon I on the Terrace at St. Cloud" (Ducis) . . . 7·50 4·50

130 Mvet

132 "Aframomum polyanthum"

131 Refugees and Red Cross Plane

1969. Traditional Musical Instruments from Folk Art Museum, Libreville.

354 **130** 25f. lake, drab and purple 40 15
355 – 30f. brown, drab and red 45 20
356 – 50f. lake, drab and purple 85 35
357 – 100f. brown, drab and red 1·60 65

DESIGNS: 30f. Ngombi harp; 50f. Ebele and Mbe drums; 100f. Medzang xylophone.

1969. Air. Red Cross. Aid for Biafra. Multicoloured.

359 15f. Type **131** 40 20
360 20f. Hospital and supplies van 45 25
361 25f. Doctor and nurse tending children 50 25
362 30f. Children and hospital . . 60 30

1969. Flowers. Multicoloured.

364 1f. Type **132** 10 10
365 2f. "Chlamydocola chlamydantha" 15 10
366 5f. "Costus dinklagei" . . . 20 10
367 10f. "Cola rostrata" 45 20
368 20f. "Dischistocalyx grandifolius" 70 45

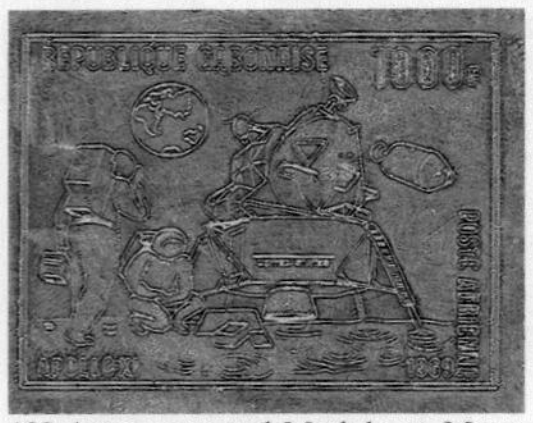
133 Astronauts and Module on Moon

1969. Air. 1st Man on the Moon. Embossed on gold foil.

369 **133** 1000f. gold . . . . 18·00 18·00

134 Tree and Insignia

135 Oil Derrick

1969. "National Renovation".

370 **134** 25f. multicoloured 40 30

1969. 20th Anniv of Elf/Spafe Petroleum Consortium.

371 25f. Type **135** 35 10
372 50f. Oil rig 90 30

136 African Workers

137 Arms of Lambarene

1969. 50th Anniv of I.L.O.
373 **136** 30f. green, blue and red 55 30

1969. Town Arms (1st series).
374 **137** 20f. multicoloured 50 15
375 – 25f. gold, black and blue 80 15
376 – 30f. multicoloured 90 45
ARMS: 25f. Port-Gentil; 30f. Libreville.
See also Nos. 405/7, 460/2, 504/6, 510/12, 539/41, 596/8, 618/20, 669/71, 684/6, 729/31, 800/2, 898/900, 953/4, 1083 and 1128.

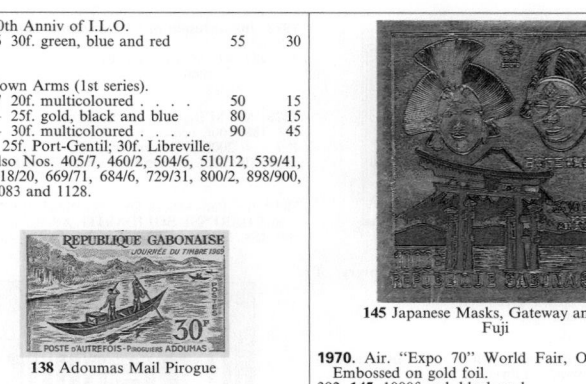

138 Adoumas Mail Pirogue

1969. Stamp Day.
377 **138** 30f. brown, emerald & grn 80 35

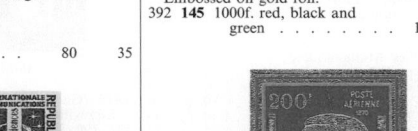

139 Satellite and Globe

1970. World Telecommunications Day.
378 **139** 25f. blue, black and lake 55 35

1970. New U.P.U. Headquarters Building, Berne. As T **81** of New Caledonia.
379 30f. green, purple and brown 50 30

140 Japanese Geisha and African

1970. "EXPO 70" World Fair, Osaka, Japan.
380 **140** 30f. multicoloured 50 30

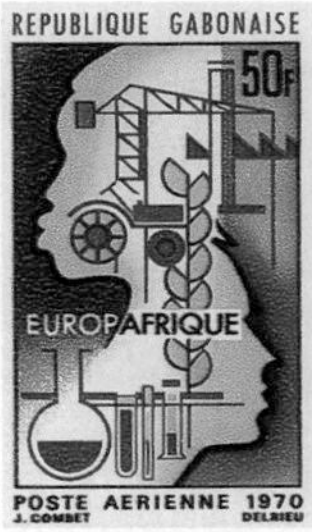

141 "Co-operation" **142** Icarus and the Sun

1970. Air. "Europafrique".
381 **141** 50f. multicoloured 85 35

1970. Air. History of Flight.
382 **142** 25f. blue, yellow and red 55 35
383 – 100f. green, brown & pur 1·40 70
384 – 200f. blue, red and slate 3·00 1·40
DESIGNS: 100f. Leonardo da Vinci's design for wings; 200f. Jules Verne's rocket approaching Moon.

143 U.A.M.P.T. Emblem

1970. Air. U.A.M.P.T. Conference, Libreville.
386 **143** 200f. gold, green and blue 2·75 1·25

144 Throwing-knives

1970. Air. Gabonaise Weapons, Folk Art Museum, Libreville. All values blue, red and green.
387 25f. Type **144** 45 30
388 30f. Assegai and crossbow (vert) 55 35
389 50f. War knives (vert) . . . 80 40
390 90f. Dagger and sheath . . . 1·60 55

145 Japanese Masks, Gateway and Mt. Fuji

1970. Air. "Expo 70" World Fair, Osaka, Japan. Embossed on gold foil.
392 **145** 1000f. red, black and green . . . . 17·00 17·00

146 President Bongo

1970. Air. 10th Anniv of Independence.
393 **146** 200f. multicoloured . . . 3·25 1·60

147 Aircraft, Map and Airport

1970. 10th Anniv (1969) of Aerial Navigation Security Agency for Africa and Madagascar.
394 **147** 100f. green and blue . . . 1·40 65

148 "Portrait of Young Man" (School of Raphael)

1970. Air. 450th Death Anniv of Raphael. Multicoloured.
395 50f. Type **148** 90 40
396 100f. "Jeanne d'Aragon" (Raphael) . . . . 1·60 70
397 200f. "The Virgin of the Blue Diadem" (Raphael) . . . . 3·25 1·60

149 U.N. Emblem, Globe, Dove and Wheat

1970. 25th Anniv of United Nations.
398 **149** 30f. multicoloured 55 35

150 Bushbucks

1970. Wild Fauna. Multicoloured.
399 5f. Type **150** 35 25
400 15f. Pel's flying squirrel . . . 55 30
401 25f. White-cheeked mangabey (vert) . . . . 1·40 55
402 40f. African golden cat . . . 2·25 1·10
403 60f. Servaline genet . . . . . 3·25 1·40

151 Presidents Bongo and Pompidou

1971. Air. Visit of Pres. Pompidou of France to Gabon.
404 **151** 50f. multicoloured . . . . 1·60 85

1971. Town Arms (2nd series). As T **137**. Multicoloured.
405 20f. multicoloured 40 15
406 25f. black, green and gold . . 40 15
407 30f. multicoloured 55 20
ARMS: 20f. Mouila; 25f. Bitam; 30f. Oyem.

152 Four Races and Emblem **154** Freesias

153 Telecommunications Map

1971. Racial Equality Year.
408 **152** 40f. black, orange & yell 55 30

1971. Pan-African Telecommunications Network.
409 **153** 30f. multicoloured 50 30

1971. Air. "Flowers by Air". Mult.
410 15f. Type **154** 35 20
411 25f. Carnations 50 20
412 40f. Roses 85 35
413 55f. Daffodils 95 35
414 75f. Orchids . . . . 1·90 60
415 120f. Tulips . . . . 2·25 80

155 Napoleon's Death Mask

1971. Air. 150th Death Anniv of Napoleon. Multicoloured.
417 100f. Type **155** . . . . 2·25 60
418 200f. "Longwood House" (after Marchand) (horiz) 3·25 1·40
419 500f. Napoleon's Tomb . . . 8·25 4·00

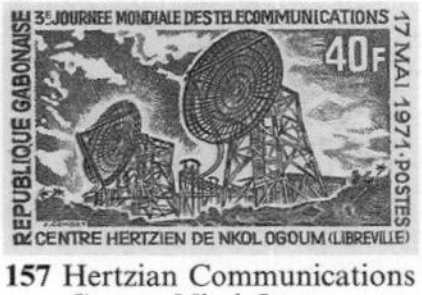

156 "Charaxes smaragdalis" **157** Hertzian Communications Centre, Nkol Ogoum

1971. Butterflies. Multicoloured.
420 5f. Type **156** 40 30
421 10f. "Euxanthe crossleyi" . . 90 40
422 15f. "Epiphora rectifascia" 1·60 45
423 25f. "Imbrasia bouvieri" . . 2·00 70

1971. World Telecommunications Day.
424 **157** 40f. red, blue and green 60 35

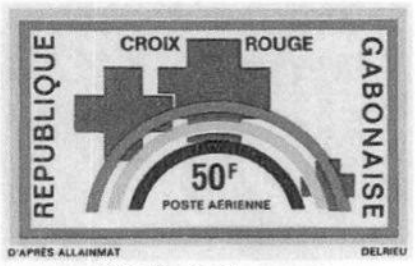

159 Red Crosses

1971. Air. Red Cross.
426 **159** 50f. multicoloured 95 40

160 Uranium

1971. Air. Minerals. Multicoloured.
427 85f. Type **160** . . . . 3·25 1·90
428 90f. Manganese . . . . . . 4·00 2·25

161 Landing Module above Moon's Surface

1971. Air. Moon Flight of "Apollo 15". Embossed on gold foil.
429 **161** 1500f. multicoloured . . . 19·00 19·00

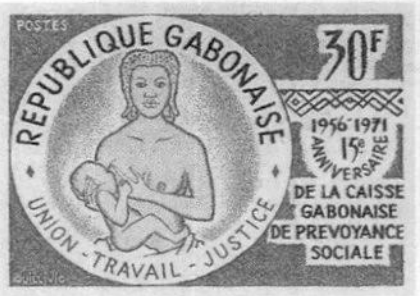

162 Mother feeding Child **163** U.N. Emblem and New York Headquarters

1971. 15th Anniv of Social Welfare Fund.
430 **162** 30f. brown, bistre & mve 50 30

1971. 10th Anniv of Gabon's Admission to United Nations.
431 **163** 30f. multicoloured 45 30

164 Great Egret

1971. Birds. Multicoloured.
432 30f. Type **164** . . . . 1·50 80
433 40f. Grey parrot . . . . . . 2·25 1·10
434 50f. Woodland kingfisher . . 2·50 1·40
435 75f. Grey-necked bald crow 3·75 1·50
436 100f. Green turaco . . . . . 5·50 2·25

166 U.A.M.P.T. Building, Brazzaville and Bakota copper mask

1971. Air. 10th Anniv of African and Malagasy Posts and Telecommunications Union.
439 **166** 100f. multicoloured . . . 1·40 65

167 Ski-jumping

1972. Air. Winter Olympic Games, Sapporo, Japan.
440 **167** 40f. violet, brown & green . . 65 35
441 – 130f. green, violet & brn . . 1·90 80
DESIGN: 130f. Speed-skating.

168 "Santa Maria della Salute" (Vanvitelli)

1972. Air. U.N.E.S.C.O. "Save Venice" Campaign. Multicoloured.
443 60f. "The Basin and Grand Canal" (Vanvitelli) (horiz) . . 1·10 55
444 70f. "Rialto Bridge" (Canaletto) . . . . 1·60 85
445 140f. Type **168** . . . . 2·75 1·10
On the stamp the design of No. 445 wrongly attributed to Caffi.

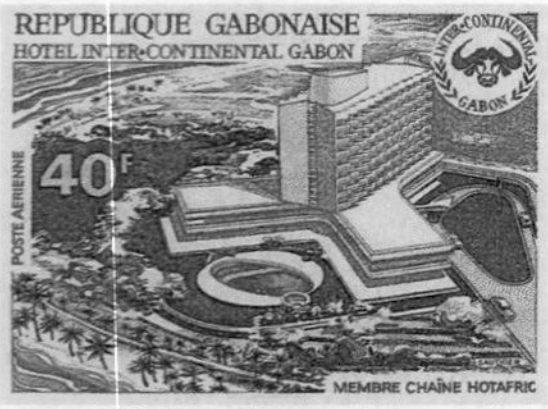

170 Hotel Intercontinental

1972. Air. Opening of Hotel Intercontinental.
447 **170** 40f. brown, green and blue 60 30

1972. Air. Visit of the Grand Master, Sovereign Order of Malta. No. 289 surch **VISITE OFFICIELLE GRAND MAITRE ORDRE SOUVERAIN DE MALTE 3 MARS 1972 50F** and emblem.
448 50f. on 300f. blue, pur & brn . . 80 40

172 "Asystasia vogeliana"

1972. Flowers. Varieties of Acanthus. Multicoloured.
449 5f. Type **172** 20 20
450 10f. "Stenandriopsis guineensis" 35 25
451 20f. "Thomandersia hensii" . . 55 35
452 30f. "Thomandersia laurifolia" 85 50
453 40f. "Physacanthus batanganus" . . . . 1·40 65
454 65f. "Physacanthus nematosiphon" . . . . . . 2·25 85

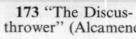

173 "The Discus-thrower" (Alcamene)

174 Pasteur with Microscope

1972. Air. Olympic Games, Munich. Ancient Sculptures.
455 **173** 30f. grey and red 60 50
456 – 100f. grey and red . . . . 1·40 70
457 – 140f. grey and red . . . . 1·90 1·00
DESIGNS: 100f. "Doryphoros" (Polyclete); 140f. "Gladiator" (Agasias).

1972. 150th Anniv of Louis Pasteur (scientist).
459 **174** 80f. purple, green & red . . 65 35

1972. Town Arms (3rd series). Vert designs as T **137**. Multicoloured.
460 30f. multicoloured 40 20
461 40f. multicoloured 55 20
462 60f. silver, black and green . . 90 30
ARMS: 30f. Franceville; 40f. Makokou; 60f. Tchibanga.

175 Global Emblem

1972. World Telecommunications Day.
463 **175** 40f. black, orange & yell . . 55 30

176 Nat King Cole

1972. Famous Negro Musicians. Mult.
464 40f. Type **176** 60 30
465 60f. Sidney Bechet 90 45
466 100f. Louis Armstrong . . . 1·60 65

177 "Boiga blandingi"

1972. Reptiles. Multicoloured.
467 1f. Type **177** 10 10
468 2f. Sand snake 15 10
469 3f. Egg-eating snake 20 15
470 15f. Pit viper 70 25
471 25f. Jameson's tree asp . . . 1·40 30
472 50f. Gabon viper . . . . . . 2·25 50

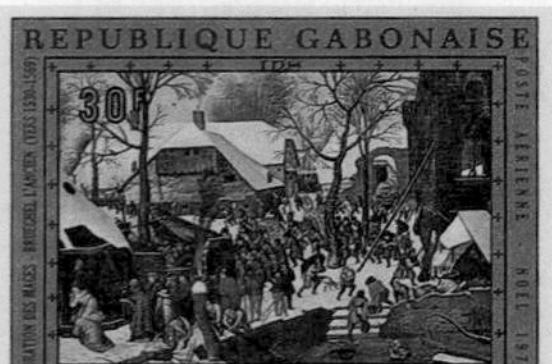

178 "The Adoration of the Magi" (Bruegel the Elder)

1972. Air. Christmas. Multicoloured.
473 30f. Type **178** 60 35
474 40f. "Madonna and Child" (Basaiti) (vert) 85 45

1972. Air. Olympic Gold Medal Winners. Nos. 455/7 surch as listed below.
475 **125** 40f. on 30f. grey and red . . 70 40
476 – 120f. on 100f. grey & red . . 1·40 65
477 – 170f. on 140f. grey & red . . 2·10 90
SURCHARGES: No. 475, **MORELON**; 476, **KEINO**; 477, **SPITZ**.

180 Dr. G. A. Hansen and Hospital, Lambarene

182 "Charaxes candiope"

181 "Thematic Collecting"

1973. Centenary of Dr. Hansen's Discovery of Leprosy Bacillus.
478 **180** 30f. brown, green and blue 65 35

1973. Air. "PHILEXGABON 73" International Stamp Exhibition, Libreville.
479 **181** 100f. multicoloured . . . 2·40 85

1973. Butterflies. Multicoloured.
481 10f. Type **182** 40 15
482 15f. "Eunica pechueli" 50 15
483 20f. "Cyrestis camillus" . . . 80 30
484 30f. "Charaxes castor" . . . 1·10 40
485 40f. "Charaxes ameliae" . . . 1·25 55
486 50f. "Pseudacrea boisduvali" . 1·40 80

183 Douglas DC-10-30 over Libreville Airport

1973. Air. Libreville-Paris Air Service by "Air Afrique" "DC 10 Libreville". No gum.
487 **183** 40f. multicoloured . . . . 1·10 55

184 Montgolfier's Balloon, 1783

186 Interpol Emblem

185 Power Station

1973. History of Flight.
488 **184** 1f. green, myrtle & brown 10 10
489 – 2f. green and blue . . . 10 10
490 – 3f. new blue, blue & orge . 10 10
491 – 4f. violet & reddish violet . 25 15
492 – 5f. green and orange . . 30 20
493 – 10f. purple and blue . . 45 20
493a – 10f. blue 45 45
DESIGNS—HORIZ: 2f. Santos-Dumont's airship "Ballon No. 6", 1901; 3f. Chanute's glider, 1896; 4f. Clement Ader's "Avion III" flying-machine, 1897; 5f. Bleriot's cross-Channel flight, 1909; 10f. (both) Fabre's seaplane "Hydravion", 1910.

1973. Air. Kinguele Hydro-electric Project.
494 **185** 30f. green and brown . . 50 25
495 – 40f. blue, green and brown 60 25
DESIGN: 40f. Dam.

1973. 50th Anniv of International Criminal Police Organization (Interpol).
496 **186** 40f. blue and red 55 35

187 Dish Aerial and Station

188 Gabon Woman

1973. Inauguration of "2 Decembre" Satellite Earth Station.
497 **187** 40f. brown, blue and green 55 30

1973. Air. M'Bigou Stone Sculptures.
498 **188** 100f. brown, blue & black . 1·50 80
499 – 200f. green and brown . . 2·75 1·40
DESIGN: 200f. Gabon man wearing head-dress.

1973. Air. Pan-African Drought Relief. No. 426 surch **SECHERESSE SOLIDARITE AFRICAINE 100F.**
500 **159** 100f. on 50f. mult . . . . 1·40 85

190 Party Headquarters

1973. Gabonaise Democratic Party Headquarters, Libreville.
501 **190** 30f. multicoloured 40 20

191 Astronauts and Lunar Rover

1973. Air. Moon Flight of "Apollo 17".
502 **191** 500f. multicoloured . . . 6·75 3·25

192 Crane with Letter and Telecommunications Emblem

1973. 12th Anniv of African and Malagasy Posts and Telecommunications Union.
503 **192** 100f. plum, purple & blue . 90 55

1973. Town Arms (4th series). As T **137** dated "1973". Multicoloured.
504 30f. Kango 55 20
505 40f. Booue 65 30
506 60f. Koula-Moutou . . . . . 1·00 35

193 St. Theresa of Lisieux

194 Flame Emblem

1973. Birth Cent of St. Theresa of Lisieux. Stained-glass windows in the Basilica at Lisieux. Multicoloured.
507 30f. Type **193** 55 25
508 40f. "St. Theresa with Saviour" 65 30

1973. 25th Anniv of Declaration of Human Rights.
509 **194** 20f. red, blue and green . . 40 20

1974. Town Arms (5th series). As T **137** dated "1974". Multicoloured.
510 5f. Gamba 15 10
511 10f. Ogooue-Lolo 15 10
512 15f. Fougamou 20 15

195 White-collared Mangabey

1974. Monkeys. Multicoloured.
513 40f. Type **195** 55 30
514 60f. Moustached monkey . . 85 35
515 80f. Mona monkey . . . . . 1·40 50

196 De Gaulle and Houphouet-Boigny

1974. Air. 30th Anniv of Brazzaville Conference.
516 **196** 40f. blue and purple . . . 1·00 55

197 "Pleasure Boats" (Monet)

1974. Air. Impressionist Paintings. Multicoloured.
517 40f. Type **197** 90 45
518 50f. "End of an Arabesque" (Degas) (vert) . . . . . . 1·40 65
519 130f. "Young Girl with Flowers" (Renoir) (vert) 2·25 1·10

198 American Bald Eagle, and Astronaut on Moon

1974. Air. 5th Anniv of First Manned Moon Landing.
520 **198** 200f. blue, brown & indigo . . . . 3·00 1·75

199 Ogooue River, Lambarene

1974. Gabon Views. Multicoloured.
521 30f. Type **199** 35 25
522 50f. Cape Esterias 50 30
523 75f. Rope bridge, Poubara 85 45

200 U.P.U. Emblem and Letters

1974. Air. Centenary of U.P.U.
524 **200** 150f. turquoise and blue 1·90 80
525 – 300f. red and orange . . 3·25 1·60
DESIGN: 300f. Similar to Type **200**, but with design reversed.

201 "Apollo" and "Soyuz" Spacecraft, Flight Badge and Maps of U.S.A. and U.S.S.R.

1974. Air. Soviet-American Co-operation in Space.
526 **201** 1000f. green, red and blue 7·75 5·50

202 Ball and Footballers

1974. Air. World Cup Football Championship, West Germany.
527 **202** 40f. red, green and brown 50 30
528 – 65f. green, brown and red 65 40
529 – 100f. brown, red and green . . . . 1·10 65
DESIGNS: 65f., 100f. Football scenes similar to Type **202**.

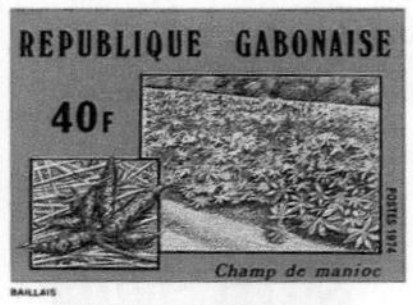

203 Manioc Plantation

1974. Agriculture. Multicoloured.
531 40f. Type **203** 50 20
532 50f. Palm-tree grove 60 20

204 African Leaders, U.D.E.A.C. Headquarters and Flags

1974. 10th Anniv of Central African Customs and Economic Union. Multicoloured.
533 40f. Type **204** (postage) . . . 50 30
534 100f. African leaders, U.D.E.A.C. Headquarters Building (air) 85 45

205 "The Visitation"

1974. Air. Christmas. Details from 15th-century tapestry of Notre Dame, Beaune. Multicoloured.
535 40f. Type **205** 80 35
536 50f. "The Annunciation" (horiz) 90 45

206 Dr. Schweitzer and Lambarene Hospital

1975. Air. Birth Centenary of Dr. Albert Schweitzer.
537 **206** 500f. green, lilac & brown 5·50 3·25

207 Dialogue Hotel

1975. Inauguration of "Hotel du Dialogue", Libreville.
538 **207** 50f. multicoloured 55 30

1975. Town Arms (6th series). As T **137** dated "1975". Multicoloured.
539 5f. Ogooue-Ivindo 10 10
540 10f. Moabi 15 10
541 15f. Moanda 25 10

208 "The Crucifixion" (Bellini)

1975. Air. Easter. Multicoloured.
542 140f. Type **208** . . . . 1·40 55
543 150f. "The Resurrection" (Burgundian School) (36 × 49 mm) . . . . . . 1·90 80

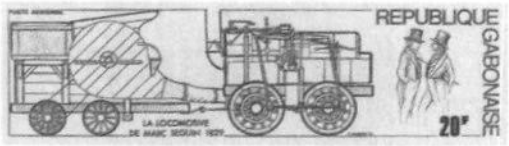

209 Marc Seguin Locomotive, 1829, France (½-size illustration)

1975. Air. Scale Drawings of Steam Locomotives.
544 **209** 20f. blue, brown & brt bl 1·10 40
545 – 25f. red, yellow and blue 1·50 50
546 – 40f. blue, purple and green . . . . 1·90 80
547 – 50f. purple, blue and green . . . . 2·75 1·10
LOCOMOTIVES: 25f. "Iron Duke", 1847, Great Britain; 40f. "Thomas Rogers", 1855, U.S.A. (inscr "1895"); 50f. Class AA steam locomotive, 1934, Russia.

210 Congress Emblem

1975. 17th Lions Club Congress, Libreville.
548 **210** 50f. multicoloured 70 30

211 Aerial and Network Map

1975. Gabonese Development of Hertzian Wave Radio Links.
549 **211** 40f. green, brown and blue 55 35

212 Man and Woman and I.W.Y. Emblem

1975. International Women's Year.
550 **212** 50f. brown, red and blue 1·75 35

213 Ange M'ba (founder of Gabonaise Scouts)

1975. "Nordjamb 75" World Scout Jamboree, Norway.
551 **213** 40f. black, purple & green 45 30
552 – 50f. purple, green and red 55 30
DESIGN: 50f. Scout camp.

214 Pink Snapper

1975. Fishes. Multicoloured.
553 30f. Type **214** 70 25
554 40f. Guinean threadfin . . . 85 40
555 50f. Round sardinella . . . . 1·50 40
556 120f. West African parrot-fish 2·50 85

215 Swimming Pool

1975. Air. Olympic Games, Montreal (1976) (1st issue). Multicoloured.
557 100f. Type **215** . . . . 1·00 45
558 150f. Boxing ring . . . . . 1·40 65
559 300f. Aerial view of Games complex . . . . 2·75 1·40
See also Nos. 591/3.

1975. Air. "Apollo–Soyuz" Space Link. No. 526 optd **JONCTION 17 Juillet 1975**.
561 **201** 1000f. green, red and blue 7·25 4·00

217 "The Annunciation" (M. Denis)

1975. Air. Christmas. Multicoloured.
562 40f. Type **217** 60 30
563 50f. "Virgin and Child with Two Saints" (Fra Filippo Lippi) 80 40

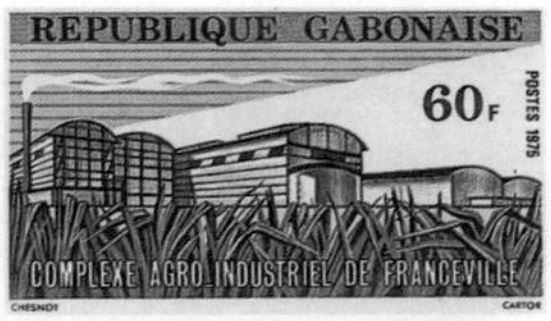

218 Franceville Complex

1975. Inauguration of Agro-Industrial Complex, Franceville.
564 **218** 60f. multicoloured 65 35

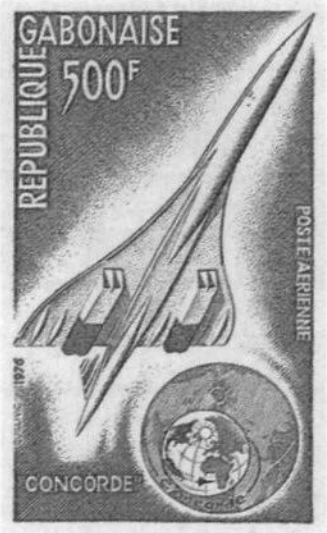

219 Concorde

1975. Air.
565 **219** 500f. ultramarine, bl & red . . . . 7·75 4·50

1975. Air. Concorde's First Commercial Flight. Surch **1000F 21 Janv. 1976 1er Vol Commercial de CONCORDE**.
566 **219** 1000f. on 500f. ultram, blue and red . . . . . 14·00 9·00

221 Tchibanga Bridge

1975. Gabon Bridges. Multicoloured.
567 5f. Type **221** 15 10
568 10f. Mouila Bridge 20 15
569 40f. Kango Bridges 45 20
570 50f. Lambarene Bridges (vert) 60 30

222 A. G. Bell and Early and Modern Telephones

1976. Telephone Centenary.
571 **222** 60f. grey, green and blue 60 30

223 Skiing (slalom)

1976. Air. Winter Olympic Games, Innsbruck.
572 **223** 100f. brown, blue & black 95 45
573 – 250f. brown, blue & black 2·10 1·25
DESIGN: 250f. Speed skating.

224 "The Crucifixion between Thieves" (wood-carving)

1976. Air. Easter. Multicoloured.
575 120f. Type **224** . . . . 1·10 60
576 130f. "Thomas placing finger in Jesus' wounds" (wood-carving) . . . . 1·40 80

225 Monseigneur Jean-Remy Bessieux

1976. Death Centenary of Bessieux.
577 **225** 50f. brown, blue & green 50 30

226 Boston Tea Party

1976. Air. Bicent of American Revolution.
578 **226** 100f. brown, orange & bl 90 50
579 – 150f. brown, orange & bl 1·40 65
580 – 200f. brown, orange & bl 2·00 1·00
DESIGNS: 150f. Battle scenes at Hudson Bay and New York; 200f. Wrecking of King George III's statue in New York.

227 Games Emblem

1976. 1st Central African Games.
581 **227** 50f. multicoloured 45 20
582 60f. multicoloured 55 30

1976. Air. U.S. Independence Day. Nos. 578/80 optd **4 JUILLET 1976.**
583 **226** 100f. brown, orange & bl 95 55
584 – 150f. brown, orange & bl 1·40 65
585 – 200f. brown, orange & bl 2·00 1·00

229 Motobecane 125-LT3 (France)

1976. Motorcycles.
586 **229** 3f. black, green and blue 15 10
587 – 5f. black, mauve & yellow 15 15
588 – 10f. black, green and blue 35 15
589 – 20f. black, green and red 65 15
590 – 100f. black, blue and red 2·00 70
MOTORCYCLES: 5f. Bultaco 125 (Spain); 10f. Suzuki 125 (Japan); 20f. Kawasaki H2R (Japan); 100f. Harley-Davidson 750-TX (USA).

230 Running

1976. Air. Olympic Games, Montreal (2nd issue). Multicoloured.
591 **230** 100f. brown, blue & violet 85 45
592 – 200f. multicoloured . . . 1·60 90
593 – 260f. brown, grn & myrtle 2·25 1·10
DESIGNS: 200f. Football; 260f. High Jumping.

231 Presidents Giscard d'Estaing and Bongo

1976. Air. Visit of Pres. Giscard d'Estaing to Gabon.
595 **231** 60f. multicoloured 90 40

1976. Town Arms (7th series). As T **137** dated "1976".
596 15f. multicoloured 15 10
597 25f. multicoloured 20 10
598 50f. black, gold and red . . . 50 15
ARMS: 15f. Nyanga; 25f. Mandji; 50f. Mekambo.

232 Ricefield and Plant

1976. Agriculture. Multicoloured.
599 50f. Type **232** 55 20
600 60f. Pepper grove and plant 65 30

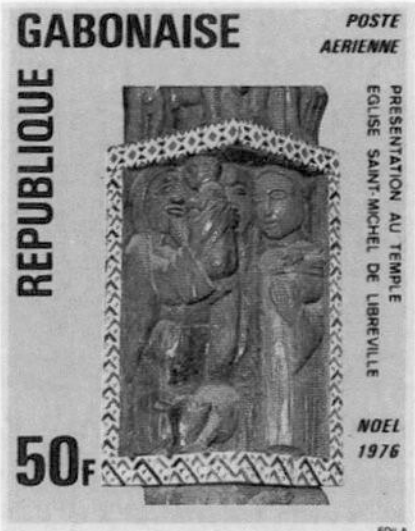

233 "Presentation at the Temple"

1976. Air. Christmas. Wood-carvings. Mult.
601 50f. Type **233** 60 30
602 60f. "The Nativity" 70 35

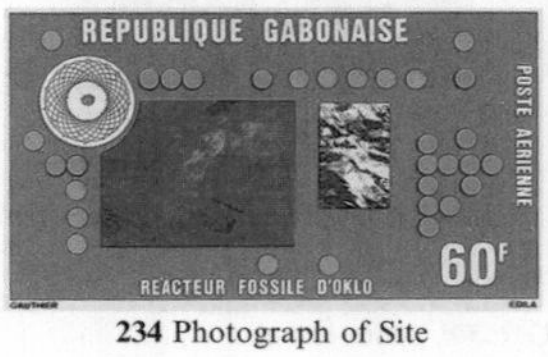

234 Photograph of Site

1976. Air. Discovery of Oklo Fossil Reactor.
603 **234** 60f. multicoloured 65 35

235 "The Last Supper" (Juste de Gand)

1977. Air. Easter. Multicoloured.
604 50f. Type **235** 80 45
605 100f. "The Deposition" (N. Poussin) . . . . . . 1·40 65

1977. Agriculture. As T **232** but dated "1977". Multicoloured.
606 50f. Banana plantation . . . 55 20
607 60f. Groundnuts and market 65 30

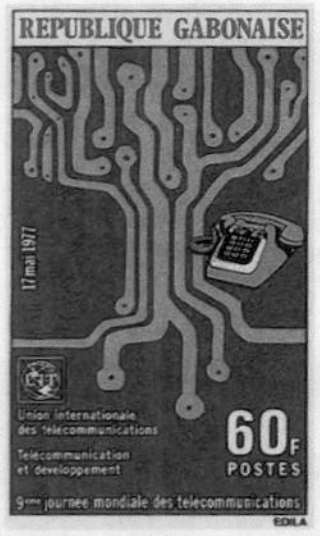

236 Printed Circuit and Telephone

1977. 9th World Telecommunications Day.
608 **236** 60f. multicoloured 55 30

237 "Air Gabon" Insignia and Boeing 747

1977. Air. 1st "Air Gabon" Intercontinental Air Service.
609 **237** 60f. blue, yellow and green 70 40

238 Cap Lopez

1977. Gabon Views and Features. Mult.
610 50f. Type **238** 45 20
611 60f. Oyem 45 20
612 70f. Lebamba grotto 60 25

239 Beethoven and Musical Score

1977. Air. 150th Death Anniv of Beethoven.
613 **239** 260f. blue . . . . 2·25 1·40

240 Palais des Congres

1977. Organization of African Unity Conference.
614 **240** 100f. multicoloured . . . 85 55

241 Gabon Coat of Arms

1977.
615 **241** 50f. blue (22 × 36 mm) . . 65 30
616 60f. orange 60 30
617 80f. red 70 35

1977. Town Arms (8th series). As T **137** but dated "1977". Multicoloured.
618 50f. Omboue 45 20
619 60f. Minvoul 50 20
620 90f. Mayumba 85 35

242 Parliament Building, Libreville

1977. National Festival.
621 **242** 50f. multicoloured 50 20

243 Renault "Voiturette" of 1902

1977. Birth Centenary of Louis Renault (motor pioneer).
622 **243** 5f. blue, red and brown 20 15
623 – 10f. brown and red . . . 20 15
624 – 30f. red, green and drab 65 30
625 – 40f. green, yellow & brown . . . . 1·10 35
626 – 100f. black, turquoise & bl . . . . 2·25 1·00
DESIGNS: 10f. Coupe of 1921; 30f. "Torpedo Scaphandrier" of 1925; 40f. "Reinastella" of 1929; 100f. "Nerva Grand Sport" of 1937.

244 Lindbergh and "Spirit of St. Louis"

1977. Air. 50th Anniv of Lindbergh's Transatlantic Flight.
628 **244** 500f. blue, brown & lt bl 5·50 3·25

245 Footballer

1977. Air. World Cup Football Championship Qualifying Rounds.
629 **245** 250f. multicoloured . . . 2·25 1·25

246 "Viking" on Mars

1977. Air. "Operation Viking".
630 **246** 1000f. multicoloured . . . 8·25 8·25

1977. Air. 1st Commercial Paris–New York Flight by "Concorde". Optd **PARIS NEW YORK PREMIER VOL 22.11.77.**
631 **219** 500f. ultramarine, bl & red . . . . 7·25 5·00

248 "Study of a Head"

1977. Air. 400th Birth Anniv of Peter Paul Rubens. Multicoloured.
632 60f. "Lion Hunt" (horiz) . . 65 25
633 80f. "Hippopotamus Hunt" (horiz) 85 40
634 200f. Type **248** . . . . 2·25 1·00

249 "Adoration of the Magi" (Rubens)

1977. Air. Christmas. Multicoloured.
636 60f. Type **249** 65 35
637 80f. "The Flight into Egypt" (Rubens) 90 45

250 "Still Life and Maori Statue"

1978. Air. 75th Death Anniv of Paul Gauguin. Multicoloured.
638 150f. Type **250** . . . . 1·90 65
639 300f. "Self-Portrait" . . . . 3·25 1·40

251 Globe

1978. World Leprosy Day.
640 **251** 80f. green, blue and red 55 30

252 Boeing 747 Airplane, Diesel Locomotive and President

1978. 10th Anniv of National Renewal.
641 **252** 500f. multicoloured . . . 10·00 5·25

253 Citroen "Cabriolet", 1922

1978. Birth Centenary of Andre Citroen (motor pioneer).
642 **253** 10f. purple, green and red 30 15
643 – 50f. green, blue & turq . . 65 20
644 – 60f. grey, brown and blue 1·00 40
645 – 80f. blue, slate and lilac 1·10 45
646 – 200f. brown, slate & orge 2·75 1·00
DESIGNS: 50f. "B14" Taxi, 1927; 60f. 8 h.p. "Berline", 1932; 80f. 7 h.p. "Berline" saloon, 1934; 200f. 2 h.p. "Berline", 1948.

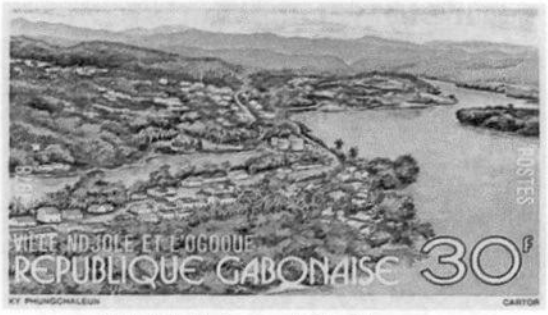

254 Ndjole and L'Ogooue

1978. Views of Gabon. Multicoloured.
648 30f. Type **254** 20 15
649 40f. Lambarene, Lake District 35 15
650 50f. Owendo Port 60 15

255 "Sternotomis mirabilis"

1978. Beetles. Multicoloured.
651 20f. Type **255** 20 15
652 60f. "Analeptes trifasciata" 65 40
653 75f. "Homoderus mellyi" . . 85 45
654 80f. "Stephanorrhina guttata" 1·00 55

257 Players heading Ball

1978. Air. World Cup Football Championship, Argentina.
660 **257** 100f. brown, red and green 70 35
661 – 120f. brown, red and green 85 45
662 – 200f. brown and red . . . 1·50 70
DESIGNS: 120f. Players tackling. VERT: 200f. F.I.F.A. World Cup.

258 Anti-Apartheid Emblem

1978. International Anti-Apartheid Year.
664 **258** 80f. orange, brown & blue 55 35

1978. Air. Argentina's Victory in World Cup Football Championship. Nos. 660/2 optd.
665 **257** 100f. brown, red and green 70 40
666 – 120f. brown, red and green 90 50
667 – 200f. brown and red . . . 1·40 80
OVERPRINTS: 100f. **ARGENTINE HOLLAND 3 - 1**; 120f. **BRESIL ITALIE 2 - 1**; 200f. **CHAMPION DU MONDE 1978 ARGENTINE**.

1978. Town Arms (9th series). As T **137**, but dated "1978".
669 5f. multicoloured 15 10
670 40f. multicoloured 30 15
671 60f. gold, black and blue . . 45 15
DESIGNS: 5f. Oyem; 40f. Okandja; 60f. Mimongo.

260 "Self-portrait at 13 years"

1978. Air. 450th Death Anniv of Albrecht Durer (artist).
672 **260** 100f. grey and red 85 40
673 – 250f. red and grey . . . . 2·50 1·00
DESIGN: 250f. "Lucas de Leyde".

261 Parthenon

1978. U.N.E.S.C.O. Campaign for the Preservation of the Acropolis.
674 **261** 80f. brown, orange & blue 55 35

262 White Stork and Saxony 1850 3f. Stamp

1978. Air. "Philexafrique" Exhibitions, Libreville, Gabon and International Stamp Fair, Essen, W. Germany. Multicoloured.
675 100f. Type **262** . . . . 1·75 1·50
676 100f. Gorilla and Gabon 1971 40f. Grey Parrot stamp . . . . 1·75 1·50

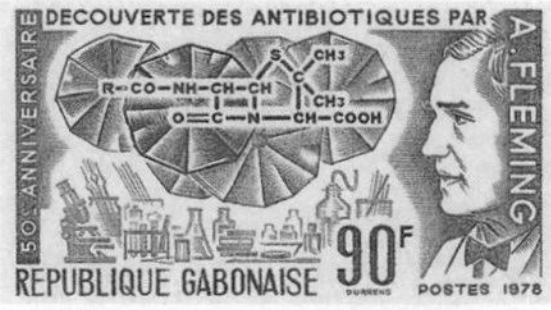

263 Sir Alexander Fleming, Chemical Formula and Laboratory Equipment

1978. 50th Anniv of Fleming's Discovery of Antibiotics.
677 **263** 90f. brown, orange & grn 80 40

264 "The Visitation"

1978. Christmas. Sculptures from the Church of St. Michel de Libreville. Multicoloured.
678 60f. Type **264** 50 20
679 80f. "Massacre of the Innocents" 60 35

265 Wright Brothers and Flyer I

1978. Air. 75th Anniv of First Powered Flight.
680 **265** 380f. brown, blue and red 3·25 1·40

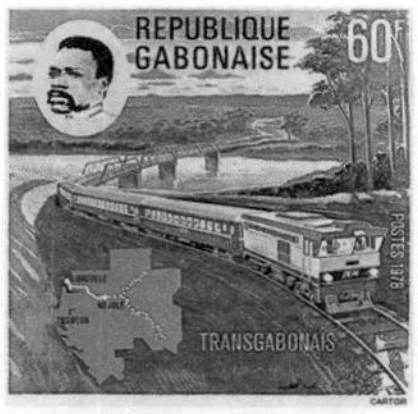

266 Diesel Train

1978. Inauguration of First Section of Trans-Gabon Railway, Libreville-Njole.
681 **266** 60f. multicoloured . . . . 1·40 45

267 Pope John Paul II

1979. Air. The Popes of 1978. Multicoloured.
682 100f. Type **267** . . . . 1·40 65
683 200f. Popes Paul VI and John Paul I with St. Peter's . . 2·50 90

1979. Town Arms (10th series). As T **137**, but dated "1979". Multicoloured.
684 5f. Ogooue-Maritime 15 10
685 10f. Lastoursville 15 10
686 15f. M'Bigou 20 10

268 "The Two Disciples"

1979. Air. Easter. Wood-carvings from St. Michel de Libreville Church. Multicoloured.
687 100f. Type **268** 75 55
688 150f. "Jesus appearing to Mary Magdalene" . . . . 1·25 65

269 Long Jumping

1979. Pre-Olympic Year.
689 – 60f. red, brown & turq . . 45 15
690 **269** 80f. brown, turq & red . . 55 30
691 – 100f. turquoise, red & brn 65 35
DESIGNS—HORIZ: 60f. Horse riding; 100f. Yachting.

270 Sir Rowland Hill, Postal Messenger and Stamp

1979. "Philexafrique 2" Exhibition, Libreville.
693 **270** 50f. multicoloured 70 55
694 – 80f. multicoloured . . . . 1·25 85
695 – 150f. green, blue & brown 1·90 1·40

DESIGNS—VERT: 80f. Bakota mask and tulip flower. HORIZ: 150f. Canoeist, mail van, U.P.U. emblem and stamps.

272 Child holding Bird

1979. International Year of the Child.
697 **272** 100f. brown, violet & blue . . . 80 40

273 Captain Cook

1979. Air. Death Bicent of Captain Cook.
698 **273** 500f. multicoloured . . . 4·50 2·25

274 Louis Bleriot and Channel Flight Route

1979. Air. Aviation History. Multicoloured.
699 250f. Type **274** (First Channel Flight, 70th anniv) . . . . 2·25 1·40
700 1000f. Astronauts and module on Moon and Gabon S.G. 369 (Moon Landing, 10th anniv) . . . 7·25 4·00

275 "Telecom 79"

276 Carved Head, Map and Rotary Emblem

1979. 3rd World Telecommunications Exhibition, Geneva.
701 **275** 80f. blue, orange & dp bl . . . 50 30

1979. Air. 75th Anniv of Rotary International.
702 **276** 80f. multicoloured 60 35

277 Harvesting Sugar Cane

278 Judo

1979. Agriculture. Multicoloured.
703 25f. Type **277** 25 10
704 30f. Igname 35 10

1979. World Judo Championships, Paris.
705 **278** 40f. olive, brown & orange . . . . 1·00 45

279 Eugene Jamot and Tsetse Fly

1979. Air. Birth Centenary of Eugene Jamot (discovery of sleeping sickness cure).
706 **279** 300f. black, brown & vio . . 2·75 1·40

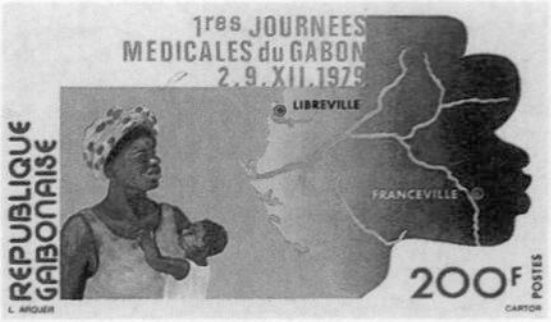

280 Mother with Child and Map of Gabon

1979. 1st Gabon Medical Days.
707 **280** 200f. multicoloured . . . 1·50 65

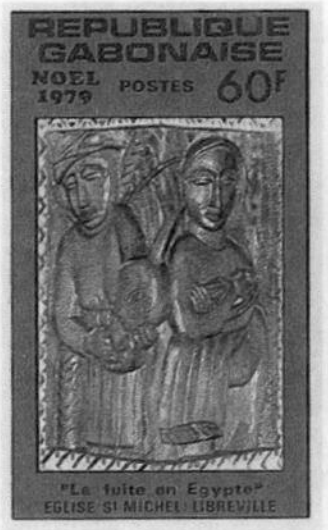

281 "The Flight into Egypt"

282 Statue of President Bongo

1979. Christmas. Carvings from St. Michael's Church, Libreville. Multicoloured.
708 60f. Type **281** 50 30
709 80f. "The Circumcision" . . 60 30

1979. 44th Anniv of President Bongo.
710 **282** 60f. multicoloured 55 20
See also No. 714.

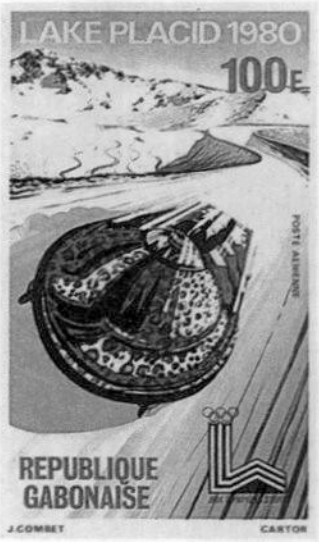

283 Bob Sleighing

284 Oil Derrick

1980. Air. Winter Olympic Games, Lake Placid. Multicoloured.
711 100f. Type **283** 70 40
712 200f. Ski jumping . . . . . 1·50 70

1980. Investiture of President. As No. 710 but inscr "INVESTITURE 27 FEVRIER 1980".
714 **282** 80f. multicoloured . . . . 1·60 1·00

1980. 20th Anniv of O.P.E.C.
715 **284** 50f. multicoloured 60 30

285 Donguila Church

1980. Easter. Multicoloured.
716 60f. Type **285** 45 15
717 80f. Bizangobibere Church 55 30

286 Dominique Ingres (artist)

1980. Air. Celebrities' Anniversaries.
718 **286** 100f. sepia, green & brown 85 40
719 – 200f. brown, pur & grey 2·25 1·00
720 – 360f. brown, green & sepia . . . . 2·50 1·40
DESIGNS: 100f. Type **286** (birth cent); 200f. Jacques Offenbach (composer, death cent); 360f. Gustave Flaubert (author, death cent).

287 Telephone

1980. Air. World Telecommunications Day.
721 **287** 80f. multicoloured 60 30

288 Savorgnan de Brazza and Map

1980. Centenary of Franceville.
722 **288** 165f. multicoloured . . . 1·40 80

289 Dieudonne Costes, Maurice Bellonte and "Point d'Interrogation"

1980. Air. Aviation Anniversaries.
723 **289** 165f. red, blue and green 1·10 55
724 – 1000f. green, red and blue 7·25 3·25
DESIGNS: 165f. Type **289** (50th anniv of first North Atlantic flight); 1000f. Jean Mermoz and seaplane "Comte de la Vaulx" (50th anniv of first South Atlantic airmail).

290 Running

1980. Air. Olympic Games, Moscow.
725 **290** 50f. multicoloured 40 15
726 – 100f. black, red and green 70 40
727 – 250f. multicoloured . . . 1·60 85
DESIGNS: 100f. Pole vaulting; 250f. Boxing.

1980. District Arms (1st series). As T **137** but dated "1980".
729 10f. silver, black and gold . . 15 10
730 20f. multicoloured 20 15
731 30f. black, silver and red . . 20 15
DESIGNS: 10f. Haut-Ogooue; 20f. L'Estuaipe; 30f. Bitam.

291 Leon Mba and El Hadj Omar Bongo

1980. 20th Anniv of Independence.
732 **291** 60f. multicoloured 60 30

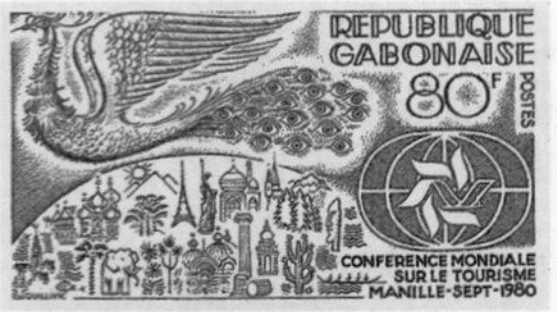

292 Peacock Emblem and Tourist Attractions

1980. World Tourism Conference, Manila.
733 **292** 80f. blue, violet and brown 60 30

293 Figures supporting O.P.E.C. Emblem

295 African River Martin

1980. 20th Anniv of Organization of Petroleum Exporting Countries. Multicoloured.
734 90f. Globe and O.P.E.C. Emblem (horiz) 85 35
735 120f. Type **293** . . . . 1·10 50

1980. Air. Olympic Medal Winners. Nos. 725/7 optd.
736 50f. **YIFTER (Eth.) NYAMBUI (Tanz.) MAANINKA (Finl.) 5000 Metres** 40 20
737 100f. **KOZIAKIEWICZ (Pol.) (record du monde) VOLKOV (Urss) et SLUSARSKI (Pol.)** 70 45
738 250f. **WELTERS ALDAMA (Cuba) MUGABI (Oug.) KRUBER (Rda) et SZCZERDA (Pol.)** . . . . 1·60 1·00

1980. Birds. Multicoloured.
740 50f. Type **295** . . . . 1·75 60
741 60f. White-fronted bee eater 2·25 90
742 80f. African pitta . . . . . 2·75 1·10
743 150f. Pel's fishing owl . . . . 4·75 2·40

296 Charles de Gaulle

1980. Air. 10th Death Anniv of Charles de Gaulle. Multicoloured.
744 100f. Type **296** 95 55
745 200f. Charles and Mme. de Gaulle . . . . 1·90 95

297 St. Matthew

1980. Christmas. Carvings from Bizangobibere Church. Multicoloured.
747 60f. St. Luke 45 20
748 80f. Type **297** 65 35

298 Heinrich von Stephan

299 Shooting at Goal

1981. 150th Birth Anniv of Heinrich von Stephan (founder of U.P.U.).
749 **298** 90f. dp brn, lt brn & brn . . . 65 35

1981. Air. World Cup Football Championship Eliminators. Multicoloured.
750 60f. Type **299** 45 30
751 190f. Players with ball . . . 1·40 85

300 Palais Renovation

1981. 13th Anniv of National Renewal.
752 **300** 60f. multicoloured 55 20

301 W. Herschel (Discovery of Uranus Bicent)

302 Lion (St. Mark)

1981. Air. Space Anniversaries. Mult.
753 150f. Type **301** . . . . 1·10 45
754 250f. Yuri Gagarin, first man in space (20th anniv) . . . 1·60 95
755 500f. Alan Shepard, first American in space (20th anniv) . . . . 3·25 1·60

1981. Easter. Wood Carvings from Bizangobibere Church. Multicoloured.
757 75f. Type **302** 55 20
758 100f. Eagle (St. John) 80 30

303 Port Gentil

304 Caduceus

1981. 23rd Congress of Lions Club District 403 Libreville. Multicoloured.
759 60f. Type **303** 45 20
760 75f. District 403 . . . . . . 55 20
761 80f. Libreville Cocotiers . . . 55 30
762 100f. Libreville Hibiscus . . . 80 35
763 165f. Ekwata . . . . 1·25 55
764 200f. Haute-Ogooue . . . . 1·40 65

1981. World Telecommunications Day.
765 **304** 125f. multicoloured . . . 80 40

305 Map of Africa and Emblems of Gabon Electricity and Water Society and U.P.D.E.A.

1981. Air. 7th Congress of African Electricity Producers and Suppliers.
766 **305** 100f. multicoloured . . . 70 40

306 Japanese D-51 Locomotive and French Turbotrain TGV 001

1981. Air. Birth Bicent of George Stephenson.
767 **306** 75f. grey, orange & brown 1·50 40
768 – 100f. green, black & blue 1·75 55
769 – 350f. green, brown & red 4·25 1·60
DESIGNS: 100f. Baltimore & Ohio Mallet 7100 and Prussian State Railway T-3 locomotives; 350f. George Stephenson, his locomotive "Rocket" (1829) and Alsthom diesel locomotive.

307 Mother Breast-feeding Child

308 R. P. Klaine (70th death anniv)

1981.
772 **307** 5f. brown and black . . 10 10
773 10f. mauve and black . . 10 10
774 15f. green and black . . 10 10
775 20f. pink and black . . . 10 10
776 25f. blue and black . . . 15 10
777 40f. pink and black . . . 25 10
778 50f. green and black . . 35 10
779 75f. brown and black . . 45 20
779a 90f. blue and black . . . 55 20
780 100f. yellow and black 60 25
780a 125f. green and black . . 85 30
780b 150f. purple and black 1·00 25

1981. Religious Personalities. Multicoloured.
781 70f. Type **308** 50 20
782 90f. Mgr. Walker (110th birth anniv) 70 30

309 Scout Badge on Map of Gabon

311 "Helping the Disabled"

1981. 4th Pan-African Scout Congress, Abidjan.
783 **309** 75f. multicoloured 60 30

1981. 28th World Scout Conference, Dakar. Optd **DAKAR 28e CONFERENCE MONDIALE DU SCOUTISME.**
784 **309** 75f. multicoloured 60 30

1981. International Year of Disabled People.
785 **311** 100f. red, dp green & grn 65 35

312 "Hypolimnas salmacis"

1981. Butterflies. Multicoloured.
786 75f. Type **312** 90 45
787 100f. "Euphaedra themis" . . 1·10 45
788 150f. "Amauris niavius" . . 1·40 90
789 250f. "Cymothoe lucasi" . . 2·50 1·25

313 "Paul as Harlequin"

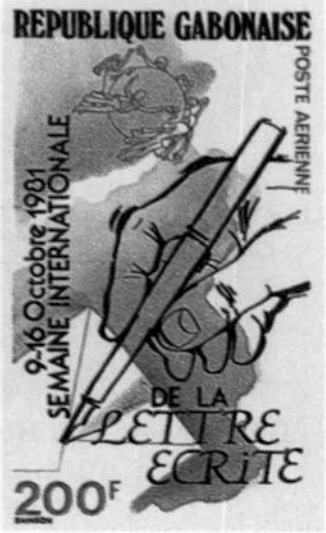

314 Hand holding Pen

1981. Birth Centenary of Pablo Picasso.
790 **313** 500f. multicoloured . . . 4·50 1·90

1981. Air. International Letter-writing Week.
791 **314** 200f. multicoloured . . . 1·40 65

315 Agricultural Scenes, Wheat and F.A.O. Emblem

1981. World Food Day.
792 **315** 350f. brown, dp brn & bl 2·75 1·40

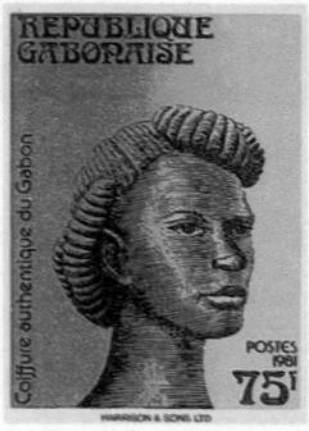

316 Traditional Hairstyle

1981. Traditional Hairstyles.
793 **316** 75f. red, yellow and black 70 35
794 – 100f. green, lilac and black 85 40
795 – 125f. lt green, green & blk 1·10 60
796 – 200f. pink, violet and black . . . . 1·75 90
DESIGNS: 100f. to 200f. Different hairstyles.
See also Nos. 964a and 1046.

317 Dancers around Fire

1981. Christmas. Multicoloured.
798 75f. Type **317** 55 20
799 100f. Christmas meal 80 35

1982. District Arms (2nd series). As T **137** but dated "1982". Multicoloured.
800 75f. Moyen-Ogooue 50 15
801 100f. Woleu-N'tem 65 15
802 150f. N'Gounie . . . . . . 1·00 30

318 Pope John Paul II

319 Alfred de Musset

1982. Papal Visit.
803 **318** 100f. multicoloured . . . 1·10 65

1982. 125th Death Anniv of Alfred de Musset (writer).
804 **319** 75f. black 55 20

320 "Leonce Veilvieux" (freighter)

1982. Merchant Ships. Multicoloured.
805 75f. Type **320** 90 55
806 100f. "Correze" (container ship) . . . . 1·10 55
807 200f. Oil tanker . . . . . . 1·90 85

321 Dr. Robert Koch, Microscope, Bacillus and Guinea Pig

1982. Centenary of Discovery of Tubercle Bacillus.
808 **321** 100f. multicoloured . . . 90 45

322 Rope Bridge, Poubara

323 Hexagonal Pattern

1982. "Philexfrance 82" International Stamp Exhibition, Paris. Multicoloured.
809 100f. Type **322** 65 35
810 100f. Bapounou sculpture . . 1·40 55

1982. World Telecommunications Day.
811 **323** 75f. multicoloured 60 35

324 Footballer (Brazil)

1982. World Cup Football Championship, Spain. Multicoloured.
812 100f. Type **324** 65 30
813 125f. Footballer (Argentina) 85 35
814 200f. Footballer (England) . . 1·25 50

325 "Caprice des Dames" (Morning)

1982. Flower "Caprice des Dames". Mult.
816 75f. Type **325** 60 35
817 100f. Midday 80 35
818 175f. Evening . . . . 1·40 65

326 Satellites

1982. Second U.N. Conference on Exploration and Peaceful Uses of Outer Space.
819 **326** 250f. blue, deep blue & red . . . . 1·90 1·10

1982. World Cup Football Championship Winners. Nos. 812/14 optd.
821 **324** 100f. multicoloured . . . 65 35
822 – 125f. multicoloured . . . 85 40
823 – 200f. multicoloured . . . 1·40 60
OPTS: 100f. **DEMIE-FINALE POLOGNE 0—ITALIE 2**; 125f. **DEMIE-FINALE R. F. ALLEMAGNE 3—FRANCE 3**; 200f. **FINALE ITALIE 3—R. F. ALLEMAGNE 1**.

329 Duplex Murex

1982. Shells. Multicoloured.
825 75f. Type **329** 80 50
826 100f. "Chama crenulata" . . 1·40 60
827 125f. "Cardium hians" . . . 2·00 1·10

330 "Still-life with Mandolin" (Braque, birth centenary)

1982. Painters' Anniversaries. Mult.
828 300f. Type **330** . . . . 2·25 70
829 350f. "Boy blowing Soap Bubbles" (Manet, death cent) (vert) . . . . 3·25 1·10

331 Okouyi Mask

332 St. Francis Xavier Church, Lambarene

1982. Artifacts. Multicoloured.
830 75f. Type **331** 45 20
831 100f. Ondoumbo reliquary . . 65 20
832 150f. Tsogho statuette . . . 1·10 40
833 250f. Forge bellows . . . . . 1·60 60

1982. Christmas.
834 **332** 100f. multicoloured . . . 65 35

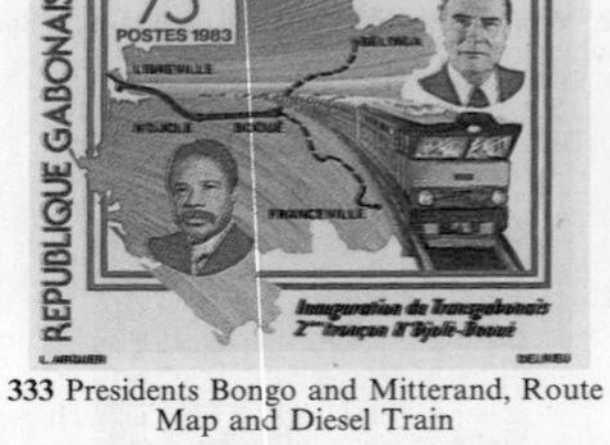

333 Presidents Bongo and Mitterand, Route Map and Diesel Train

1983. Inauguration of Second Stage of Trans-Gabon Railway.
835 **333** 75f. multicoloured . . . . 1·50 50

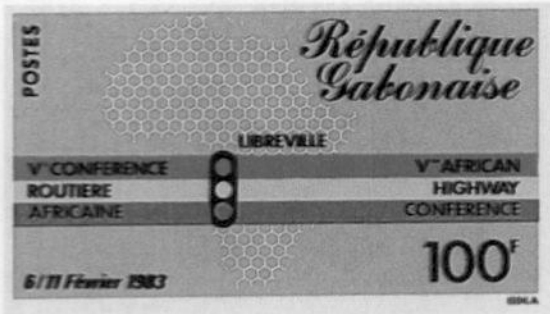

334 Stylized Highway and Map of Africa

1983. 5th African Highway Conference.
836 **334** 100f. multicoloured . . . 65 30

335 Gymnast with Hoop

336 "Epitorium trochiformis" (Estuaire)

1983. Air. Olympic Games, Los Angeles. Multicoloured.
837 90f. Type **335** 60 30
838 350f. Wind-surfing . . . . . 2·50 1·00

1983. Provinces. Multicoloured.
839 75f. Bakota mask (Ogooue Ivindo) 50 25
840 90f. African buffalo (Nyanga) 60 30
841 90f. "Charaxes druceanus" (Ogooue Lolo) 60 30
842 100f. Isogho hairstyle (Ngounie) 65 35
843 125f. Manganese (Haut Ogooue) 85 45
844 125f. Crocodiles (Moyen Ogooue) 85 45
845 125f. Atlantic tarpon (Ogooue Maritime) . . . . 1·40 60
846 135f. Type **336** . . . . 1·00 60
847 135f. Coffee flowers (Woleu Ntem) . . . . 1·00 60

337 "Ville de Rouen" (container ship) and I.M.O. Emblem

1983. 25th Anniv of International Maritime Organization.
848 **337** 125f. multicoloured . . . 1·25 45

338 Water Chevrotain

1983. Fauna. Multicoloured.
849 90f. Type **338** 60 30
850 125f. Pink-backed pelican ("Pelican") . . . . 1·50 60
851 225f. African elephant . . . 1·90 70
852 400f. Iguana . . . . 2·75 1·40

339 E.C.A. Anniversary Emblem

1983. 25th Anniv of Economic Commission for Africa.
854 **339** 125f. multicoloured . . . 85 40

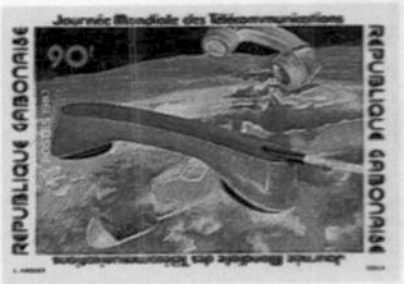

340 Telephones

341 "Double Eagle II" crossing Atlantic

1983. World Telecommunications Day. Mult.
855 90f. Type **340** 85 45
856 90f. As No. 855 but design inverted 85 45

1983. Air. Ballooning Anniversaries.
857 100f. grey, orange and blue 80 45
858 125f. green, purple and blue 90 55
859 350f. blue, green & light green . . . . 2·75 1·40
DESIGNS: 100f. Type **341** (5th anniv of first Atlantic crossing); 125f. Hot-air balloons (Bicentenary of Montgolfier Brothers' balloon); 350f. Pilatre de Rozier and Montgolfier balloon (Bicentenary of manned flight).

342 "Lady with Unicorn"

1983. Air. 150th Birth Anniv of Raphael.
860 **342** 1000f. multicoloured . . . 7·25 3·25

343 Nkoltang Satellite Receiving Station

1983. World Communications Year.
861 **343** 125f. multicoloured . . . 85 35

344 Rapids on the Ivindo River

1983. Tourism.
862 **344** 90f. blue, brown and green 55 30
863 – 125f. brown, green & grey 85 45
864 – 185f. grey, orange & green 1·25 45
865 – 350f. brown, green & blue 2·40 1·10
DESIGNS: 125f. Pirogue on the Ogooue River; 185f. Wonga Wongue Game Reserve; 350f. Coastal beach.

345 Mahongwe Drum

1983. Music and Dance. Multicoloured.
866 90f. Type **345** 55 30
867 125f. Okoukoue dance . . . 85 45
868 135f. Ngomi bateke . . . . 1·00 45
869 260f. Ndoumou dancer . . . 1·90 90

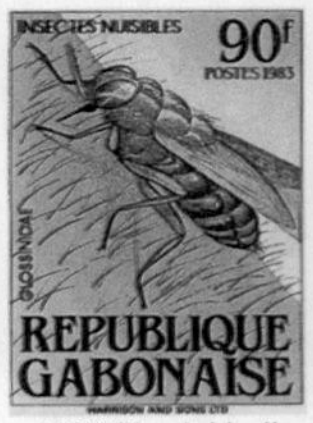

346 "Glossinidae"

347 "The Adulterous Woman"

1983. Harmful Insects. Multicoloured.
870 90f. Type **346** 90 45
871 125f. "Belonogaster junceus" 1·10 50
872 300f. "Aedes aegypti" . . . . 2·25 1·25
873 350f. "Mylabris" . . . . . . 3·25 1·40

1983. Christmas. Wood carvings from St. Michel Church, Libreville. Multicoloured.
874 90f. Type **347** 55 30
875 125f. "Parable of the Good Samaritan" 85 40

348 Boeing 747-200 Airliner and Gabon Stamp of 1966

1984. World Post Congress Stamp Exhibition, Hamburg. Multicoloured.
876 125f. Type **348** 95 45
877 225f. Douglas DC-10 and German airmail stamp of 1919 . . . . 1·90 90

349 Pylons and Buildings

1984. 3rd Anniv of "Africa 1".
878 **349** 125f. multicoloured . . . 85 35

350 Ice Hockey

1984. Air. Winter Olympic Games, Sarajevo.
879 **350** 125f. green, purple & blk 1·10 55
880 – 350f. blue, brown & black 2·50 1·10
DESIGN: 350f. Ice-dancing.

351 Coconut

1984. Fruit Trees. Multicoloured.
881 90f. Type **351** 70 35
882 100f. Pawpaw 80 35
883 125f. Mango . . . . 1·00 45
884 250f. Banana . . . . 1·90 85

352 Robin Dauphin and Piper Cherokee Six Aircraft

1984. Air. Paris–Libreville Air Rally.
885 **352** 500f. multicoloured . . . 3·25 1·90

353 "Racehorses"

1984. Air. 150th Birth Anniv of Degas.
886 **353** 500f. multicoloured . . . 4·50 2·25

354 Water Lily

1984. Flowers. Multicoloured.
887 90f. Type **354** 80 30
888 125f. Water hyacinth 80 40
889 135f. Hibiscus . . . . 1·10 45
890 350f. Bracteate orchid . . . 2·50 1·40

355 Spectrum

1984. World Telecommunications Day.
891 **355** 125f. multicoloured . . . 85 35

356 Basketball

1984. Air. Olympic Games, Los Angeles. Multicoloured.
892 90f. Type **356** 55 35
893 125f. Steeplechase 85 45

358 Lionel Hampton

1984. Jazz Musicians. Multicoloured.
895 90f. Type **358** . . . . 1·10 55
896 125f. Charlie Parker . . . . 1·40 55
897 260f. Erroll Garner . . . . . 2·75 1·40

1984. District Arms (3rd series). As T **137** but dated "1984". Multicoloured.
898 90f. Cocobeach 55 15
899 125f. Mouila 80 15
900 135f. N'Djole 90 20

359 Medouneu

1984. Tourism. Multicoloured.
901 90f. Type **359** 65 35
902 125f. Sunset over Ogooue . . 1·00 50
903 165f. Trans-Gabon train . . 3·50 1·10

360 Globe, Post and Emblem

360a Kota Reliquary

1984. Universal Postal Union Day.
905 **360** 125f. multicoloured . . . 85 35

1984. Traditional Art. Multicoloured.
905a 90f. Kouble mask . . . . .
905b 125f. Pounou fan . . . . .
905c 150f. Mahongoue reliquary
905d 250f. Type **360a** . . . . . .

361 "Icarus" (Hans Herni)

1984. 40th Anniv of International Civil Aviation Organization.
906 **361** 125f. dp blue, green & bl 85 35

362 Tympanum of Saint Michael's Church (left side)

1984. Christmas. Multicoloured.
907 90f. Type **362** 55 25
908 125f. Tympanum of Saint Michael's church (right side) 85 35
Nos. 907/8 were printed together, se-tenant, forming a composite design.

363 South African Crowned Cranes

1984. Birds. Multicoloured.
909 90f. Type **363** . . . . 1·40 75
910 125f. Snowy-breasted hummingbird . . . . . . 2·40 1·40
911 150f. Keel-billed toucan . . . 2·75 1·50

364 Leper Colony, Libreville

1985. World Lepers' Day.
912 **364** 125f. multicoloured . . . 85 40

365 I.Y.Y. Emblem

1985. International Youth Year.
913 **365** 125f. multicoloured . . . 85 35

367 Profiles and Emblem

1985. 15th Anniv of Cultural and Technical Co-operation Agency.
914 **367** 125f. blue, red & dp blue 85 35

368 Water Rat

1985. Animals. Multicoloured.
915 90f. Type **368** 90 35
916 100f. Porcupine 90 35
917 125f. Giant pangolin . . . . 1·25 55
918 350f. Antelope . . . . 3·00 1·40

369 Score and Aleka

1985. Georges Damas Aleka (composer) Commemoration.
920 **369** 90f. multicoloured 80 35

370 Emblem and Coloured Lines

371 Shield

1985. World Telecommunications Day.
921 **370** 125f. multicoloured . . . 85 35

1985. 30th Anniv of Christian Youth Workers' Movement in Gabon.
922 **371** 90f. multicoloured 60 30

372 "La Mpassa" (freighter)

1985.
923 **372** 185f. multicoloured . . . 2·25 85

373 Building and Dish Aerials

1985. 25th Anniv of Posts and Telecommunications Administration.
924 **373** 90f. multicoloured 60 30

374 President Bongo

1985. 25th Anniv of Independence.
925 **374** 250f. multicoloured . . . 2·25 1·10
926 500f. multicoloured . . . 4·50 2·75

375 Dr. Albert Schweitzer

1985. Air. 20th Death Anniv of Dr. Albert Schweitzer.
928 **375** 350f. multicoloured . . . 2·75 1·25

376 Hand holding U.N. and Gabon Flags

1985. Air. 20th Anniv of Membership of United Nations Organization.
929 **376** 225f. multicoloured . . . 1·50 70

377 O.P.E.C. Emblem

1985. 25th Anniv of Organization of Petroleum Exporting Countries.
930 **377** 350f. multicoloured . . . 2·50 1·40

378 Boy Scouts around Campfire and Elephant

1985. Air. "Philexafrique" Stamp Exhibition, Lome, Togo. Multicoloured.
931 100f. Type **378** 85 45
932 150f. Diesel train, satellite and dish aerial . . . . . . 3·75 80

379 Central Post Office, Libreville, Gabon Posts and U.P.U. Emblems

1985. Air. World Post Day.
933 **379** 300f. multicoloured . . . 2·25 1·00

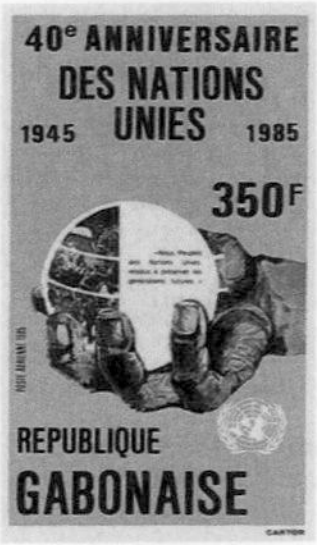

380 Hand holding Globe

1985. Air. 40th Anniv of U.N.O.
934 **380** 350f. multicoloured . . . 2·50 1·10

381 Centre

1985. International Centre of Bantu Civilisations.
935 **381** 185f. multicoloured . . . 1·40 60

381a Interior of Church

1985. Christmas. St. Andrew's Church, Libreville. Multicoloured.
935a 90f. Exterior of church . . .
935b 125f. Type **381a** . . . . . .

382 Young People within Laurel Wreath

1986. 25th Anniv of U.N.E.S.C.O. National Commission.
936 **382** 100f. multicoloured . . . 65 30

383 "Mother and Child"

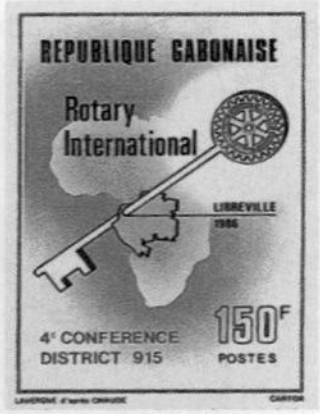

385 Key as Emblem and Map

384 Savorgnan de Brazza and Canoe

1986. Air. Gabon's Gift to United Nations Organization.
937 **383** 350f. multicoloured . . . 2·50 1·10

1986. Air. Centenary of Lastoursville.
938 **384** 100f. multicoloured . . . 85 45

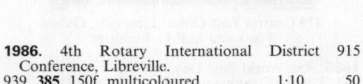

1986. 4th Rotary International District 915 Conference, Libreville.
939 **385** 150f. multicoloured . . . 1·10 50

386 Communications Equipment

1986. World Telecommunications Day.
940 **386** 300f. multicoloured . . . 2·00 1·00

387 Goalkeeper saving Ball

1986. Air. World Cup Football Championship, Mexico. Multicoloured.
941 100f. Type **387** 65 35
942 150f. Footballers and Mexican statue . . . . . 1·00 45
943 250f. World Cup trophy, footballers and map . . . 1·60 65
944 350f. Flags, ball and stadium 2·25 1·00

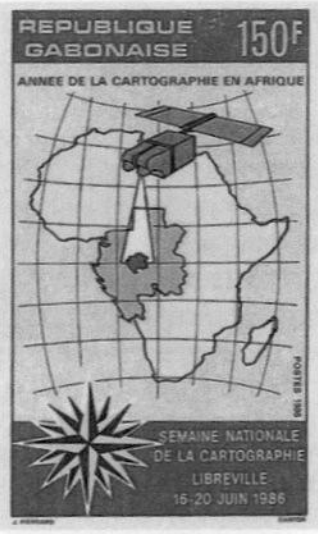

388 Map and Satellite

1986. African Cartography Year and National Cartography Week, Libreville.
946 **388** 150f. multicoloured . . . 1·10 55

389 "L'Abanga" (container ship)

1986.
947 **389** 250f. multicoloured . . . 2·25 1·10

390 River and Gabon 1886 50c. Stamp

1986. Centenary of First Gabon Stamps.
948 **390** 500f. multicoloured . . . 4·50 2·25

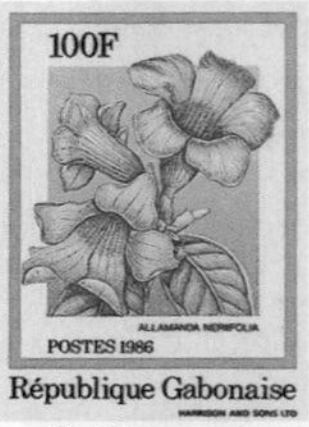

391 "Allamanda neriifolia"

392 Arms of Lambarn

1986. Flowers. Multicoloured.
949 100f. Type **391** 65 35
950 150f. "Musa cultivar" . . . . 1·00 50
951 350f. "Dissotis decumbens" . 1·10 55
952 350f. "Campylospermum laeve" . . . . 2·50 1·10

1986. District Arms (4th series). Mult.
953 100f. Type **392** 65 20
954 160f. Leconi . . . . 1·10 35

393 Coffee Berries, Flowers and Beans

1986. 25th Anniv of African and Malagasy Coffee Producers Organization.
955 **393** 125f. multicoloured . . . 95 55

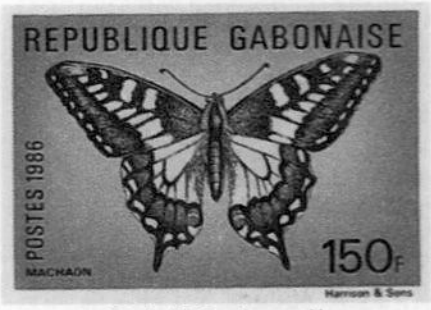

394 "Machaon"

1986. Butterflies. Multicoloured.
956 150f. Type **394** . . . . 1·90 1·25
957 290f. "Urania" . . . . 2·75 2·25

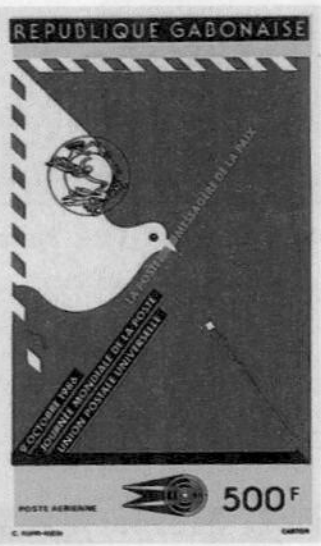

395 Dove and U.P.U. Emblem

1986. Air. World Post Day.
958 **395** 500f. multicoloured . . . 3·25 1·60

1986. Air. World Cup Football Championship Winners. Nos 941/4 optd **ARGENTINE 3-R.F.A. 2.** Multicoloured.
959 100f. Type **387** 65 45
960 150f. Footballers and Mexican statue . . . . . 1·00 55
961 250f. World Cup trophy, footballers and map . . . 1·60 1·00
962 350f. Flags, ball and stadium 2·25 1·60

397 St. Peter's Church, Libreville

1986. Christmas.
963 **397** 500f. multicoloured . . . 3·25 1·60

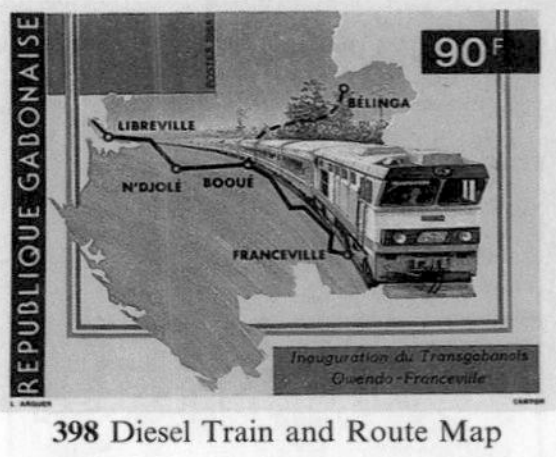

398 Diesel Train and Route Map

1986. Inauguration of Owendo–Franceville Trans-Gabon Railway.
964 **398** 90f. multicoloured . . . . 3·00 1·10

1986. Traditional Hairstyles. As T **316**.
964a 150f. black, red and grey . . 3·25 1·10

399 West African Squirrelfish

1987. Fishes. Multicoloured.
966 90f. Type **399** 85 45
967 125f. West African parrotfish 1·10 65
968 225f. Flying gurnard . . . . 2·00 1·10
969 350f. Marbled stingray . . . 3·25 2·00

400 Raoul Follereau (leprosy pioneer)

1987. World Leprosy Day.
971 **400** 125f. multicoloured . . . 1·00 65

401 Man and Child in front of Map

1987. Air. 19th Anniv of National Renewal.
972 **401** 500f. multicoloured . . . 4·00 1·60

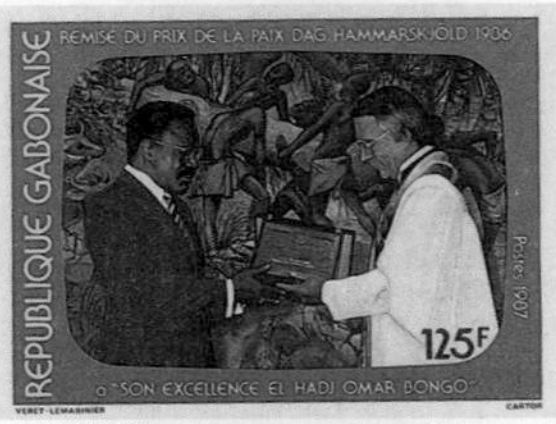

402 Pres. Bongo receiving Prize

1987. Award of Dag Hammarskjold Peace Prize to Pres. Omar Bongo.
973 **402** 125f. multicoloured . . . 85 55

403 Konrad Adenauer

404 Symbols of Communication

1987. Air. 20th Death Anniv of Konrad Adenauer (German statesman).
974 **403** 300f. multicoloured . . . 2·75 1·25

1987. World Telecommunications Day.
975 **404** 90f. multicoloured 60 35

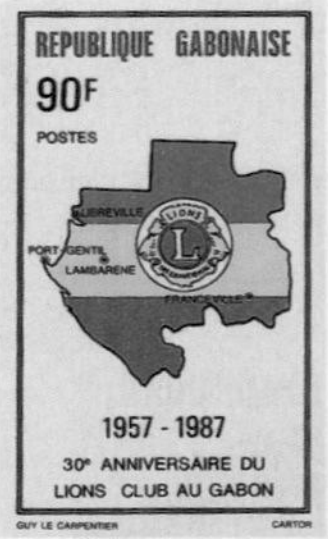

405 Emblem on Map

406 Coubertin and Runner with Torch

1987. 30th Anniv of Lions Club of Gabon.
976 **405** 90f. multicoloured 60 35

1987. 50th Death Anniv of Pierre de Coubertin (founder of modern Olympic Games).
977 **406** 200f. multicoloured . . . 1·40 65

407 Map, Emblems and People

408 Globe in Envelope

1987. 70th Anniv of Lions International.
978 **407** 165f. multicoloured . . . 1·25 65

1987. World Post Day.
979 **408** 125f. multicoloured . . . 85 35

409 Pres. Bongo and Sam Nujoma

1987. Solidarity with South-West African Peoples' Organization.
980 **409** 225f. multicoloured . . . 1·40 55

410 Fanel Moon

1987. Sea Shells. Multicoloured.
981 90f. Type **410** . . . . 1·25 70
982 125f. Lightning moon ("Natica fulminea cruentata") . . . . 1·50 70
See also Nos. 1018a/b.

411 Man, House and Machinery

1987. International Year of Shelter for the Homeless. World Shelter Day.
984 **411** 90f. multicoloured 60 35

412 Mission

1987. Centenary of St. Anne of Odimba Mission.
985 **412** 90f. multicoloured 65 35

413 Nurse vaccinating Child

1987. Universal Vaccination for Children.
986 **413** 100f. multicoloured . . . 80 40

414 President making Address

1987. 20th Anniv of Installation of President Omar Bongo.
987 **414** 1000f. multicoloured . . . 6·75 3·25

415 St. Theresa's Church, Oyem

1987. Christmas.
988 **415** 90f. multicoloured 65 35

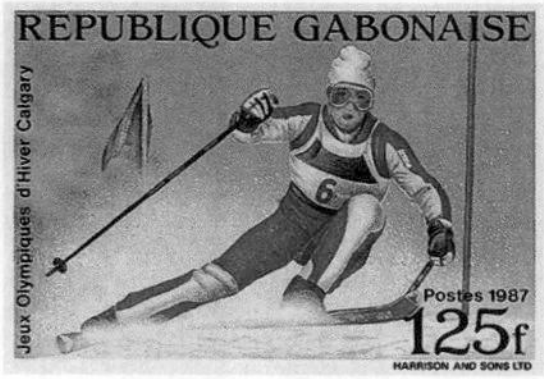

416 Skier

1987. Winter Olympic Games, Calgary (1988).
989 **416** 125f. multicoloured . . . 85 45

417 "Cassia occidentalis"

1988. Medicinal Plants. Multicoloured.
990 90f. Type **417** 65 45
991 125f. "Tabernanthe iboga" 90 45
992 225f. "Cassia alata" . . . . 1·50 80
993 350f. "Anthocleista schweinfurthii" . . . . . 2·75 1·60

418 Obamba Rattle

1988. Traditional Musical Instruments. Mult.
995 90f. Type **418** 60 35
996 100f. Fang sanza (vert) . . . 80 45
997 125f. Mitsogho harp (vert) . . 90 55
998 165f. Fang xylophone . . . . 1·40 65

419 Elephant with raised Trunk

1988. Endangered Animals. African Elephant. Multicoloured.
1000 25f. Type **419** 30 15
1001 40f. Elephant family 70 20
1002 50f. Elephant in vegetation 90 20
1003 100f. Elephant . . . . . . 1·40 55

420 Postal Delta Building

1988. Inauguration of Postal Delta.
1004 **420** 90f. multicoloured . . . 65 35

421 Village and Dr. Schweitzer

1988. Air. 75th Anniv of Arrival in Gabon of Dr. Albert Schweitzer.
1005 **421** 500f. multicoloured . . . 4·00 1·60

422 Players

1988. World Cup Rugby Championship (1987).
1006 **422** 350f. multicoloured . . . 2·75 1·60

423 Opposing Arrows

1988. World Telecommunications Day.
1007 **423** 125f. multicoloured . . . 85 40

424 Storming the Bastille, 1789

1988. "Philexfrance 89" Stamp Exhibition, Paris.
1008 **424** 125f. multicoloured . . . 1·10 55

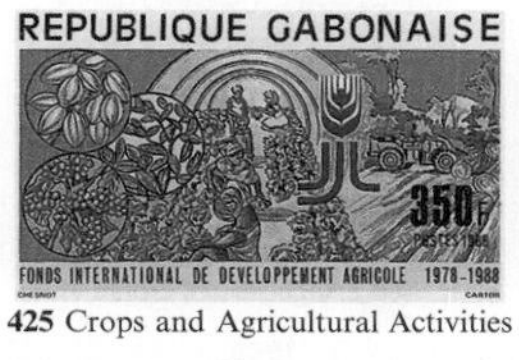

425 Crops and Agricultural Activities

1988. 10th Anniv of International Agricultural Development Fund.
1009 **425** 350f. multicoloured . . . 2·75 1·10

426 Emblem and Theatre Staff

1988. 125th Anniv of Red Cross.
1010 **426** 125f. multicoloured . . . 85 35

427 Refinery

1988. Air. 20th Anniv of Port Gentil Oil Refinery.
1011 **427** 350f. multicoloured . . . 2·50 1·10

428 Tennis

1988. Olympic Games, Seoul. Multicoloured.
1012 90f. Type **428** 65 35
1013 100f. Swimming 65 35
1014 350f. Running . . . . . . 2·50 1·00
1015 500f. Hurdling . . . . . . 4·00 1·10

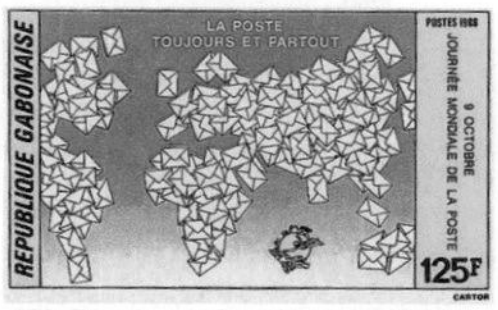

429 Envelopes forming World Map

1988. World Post Day.
1017 **429** 125f. black, blue & yell 85 35

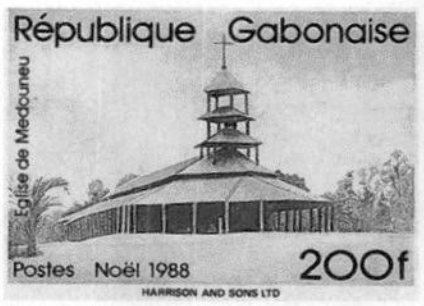

430 Medouneu Church

431 Map and Emblem

1988. Christmas.
1018 **430** 200f. multicoloured . . . 1·40 65

1988. Sea Shells. As T **410**. Multicoloured.
1018a 90f. Fanel moon ("Natica fanel var") . . . . . . 1·60 1·10
1018b 125f. "Natica variolaria" (inscr "Natica sp.") . . 2·75 1·60

1989. 10th Anniv of Chaine de Rotisseurs in Gabon.
1019 **431** 175f. multicoloured . . . 1·10 65

432 Map

434 White-crested Tiger Bittern

433 Boys playing

1989. Inauguration of Rabi Kounga Oil Field.
1020 **432** 125f. multicoloured . . . 85 50

1989. Traditional Games.
1021 **433** 90f. multicoloured . . . 60 40

1989. Birds. Multicoloured.
1022 100f. Type **434** 85 45
1023 175f. Grey parrot . . . . . 1·50 75
1024 200f. Red-billed dwarf hornbill . . . . 2·00 80
1025 500f. Blue-breasted kingfisher . . . . 4·25 2·40

435 Map and Emblem

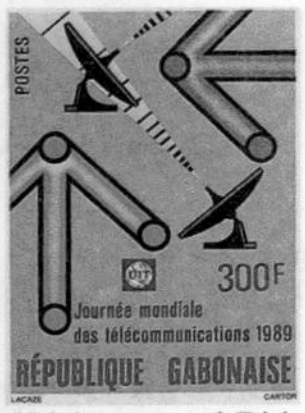

436 Arrows and Dish Aerials

1989. 8th Lions Club International Multidistrict 403 Convention, Libreville.
1027 **435** 125f. multicoloured . . . 85 45

1989. World Telecommunications Day.
1028 **436** 300f. multicoloured . . . 2·25 90

437 Palm-nuts

1989. Fruits. Multicoloured.
1029 90f. Type **437** 60 35
1030 125f. Cabosse 85 35
1031 175f. Pineapple . . . . . . 1·40 55
1032 250f. Breadfruit . . . . . . 2·00 1·00

438 "Apples and Oranges"

1989. 150th Birth Anniv of Paul Cezanne (painter).
1034 **438** 500f. multicoloured . . . 4·00 2·75

439 Phrygian Cap on Tree of Liberty and Sans-culotte

1989. "Philexfrance '89" International Stamp Exhibition, Paris.
1035 **439** 175f. multicoloured . . . 1·60 65

440 Soldier and Sans-culotte

1989. Bicentenary of French Revolution.
1036 **440** 500f. multicoloured . . . 4·50 2·75

441 Town Hall

1989. 10th Anniv of International Association of French-speaking Town Halls.
1037 **441** 100f. multicoloured . . . 90 40

442 Emblem and Map showing Development Programmes

1989. 25th Anniv of African Development Bank.
1038 **442** 100f. multicoloured . . . 65 40

443 Post Office

1989. 125th Anniv (1987) of Gabon Postal Service.
1039 **443** 90f. multicoloured . . . 65 35

444 Footballers

1989. World Cup Football Championship, Italy (1990). Multicoloured.
1040 100f. Type **444** 65 35
1041 175f. Player tackling . . . . 1·25 55
1042 300f. Goalkeeper catching ball . . . . 2·00 80
1043 500f. Goalkeeper catching ball (different) . . . . . 3·25 1·40

445 Woman and Child posting Letter

447 St. Louis' Church, Port-Gentil

1989. World Post Day.
1045 **445** 175f. multicoloured . . . 1·10 45

1989. Traditional Hairstyles. As T **316**.
1046 175f. black, lilac and grey 1·40 55

1989. Christmas.
1047 **447** 100f. multicoloured . . . 65 30

448 L'Ogooue, N'Gomo

1989.
1048 **448** 100f. multicoloured . . . 50 25

449 Axehead

1990. Prehistory. Stone Weapons. Mult.
1049 100f. Type **449** 90 45
1050 175f. Paring knife . . . . . 1·40 65
1051 300f. Flint arrowhead . . . 2·25 1·10
1052 400f. Double-edged knife . . 3·50 2·25

450 Arms of Libreville

1990. 22nd Anniv of National Renovation.
1054 **450** 100f. multicoloured . . . 65 30

451 Penny Black and Beach

1990. 150th Anniv of the Penny Black.
1055 **451** 500f. multicoloured . . . 4·50 2·75

452 Doctor and Nurse examining Patient

453 Monkey

1990. World Health Day.
1056 **452** 400f. multicoloured . . . 2·75 1·40

1990. Animals of Gabon. Multicoloured.
1057 100f. Type **453** 90 45
1058 175f. Bush pig (horiz) . . . 1·40 65
1059 200f. Antelope (horiz) . . . 1·60 1·10
1060 500f. Mandrill . . . . . . 4·50 2·75

454 De Gaulle and Map

1990. Air. 50th Anniv of De Gaulle's Call to Resist.
1062 **454** 500f. multicoloured . . . 4·50 2·25

455 Map and Arms on Flag

1990. 30th Anniv of Independence.
1063 **455** 100f. multicoloured . . . 65 45

456 "Phallus indusiatus"

1990. Fungi.
1064 100f. Type **456** . . . . . . 1·10 55
1065 175f. "Panaeolus sphinctrinus?" . . . . . 2·25 1·10
1066 300f. "Agaricus bitorquis" . . 3·25 2·25
1067 500f. "Termitomyces" sp. . . 4·50 3·25

457 Flags of Member Countries

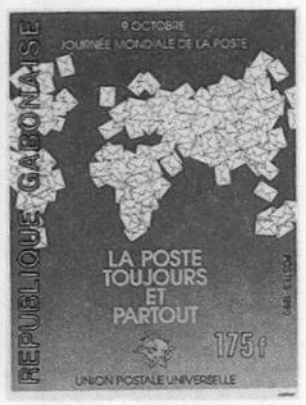

458 Envelopes as World Map

1990. 30th Anniv of Organization of Petroleum Exporting Countries.
1068 **457** 200f. multicoloured . . . 1·40 80

1990. World Post Day.
1069 **458** 175f. blue, yellow & blk 1·25 65

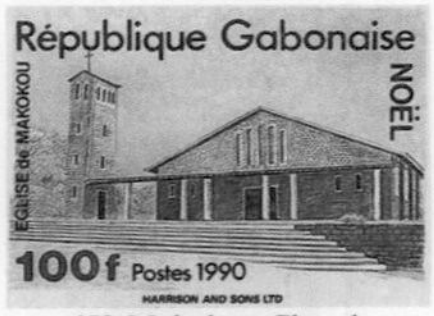

459 Makokou Church

1990. Christmas.
1070 **459** 100f. multicoloured . . . 65 45

460 Frangipani

1991. Flowers. Multicoloured.
1071 100f. Type **460** 90 45
1072 175f. Burning bush . . . . 1·40 65
1073 200f. Flame tree . . . . . 1·75 90
1074 300f. Porcelain rose . . . . 2·25 1·40

461 "Marseilles Harbour"

1991. Air. Death Centenary of Johan Barthold Jongkind (artist).
1076 **461** 500f. multicoloured . . . 4·00 1·60

462 Lizard

1991. Prehistory. Petroglyphs. Multicoloured.
1077 100f. Type **462** 70 45
1078 175f. Triangular figure . . . 1·10 65
1079 300f. Abstract pattern . . . 2·10 1·10
1080 500f. Circles and chains . . 3·50 2·25

463 Collecting Resin from Rubber Trees

465 Basket Weaving

464 Couple and Arrows

1991. Agriculture.
1082 **463** 100f. multicoloured . . . 65 45

1991. District Arms (5th series). As T **392**.
1083 100f. silver, black and green 65 20
DESIGN: 100f. Port-Gentil.

1991. World Telecommunications Day.
1084 **464** 175f. multicoloured . . . 1·10 55

1991. Arts and Crafts. Multicoloured.
1085 100f. Type **465** 65 45
1086 175f. Stone carving . . . . 1·40 80
1087 200f. Weaving . . . . . . 1·40 80
1088 500f. Straw plaiting . . . . 3·50 1·90

466 Women at Riverbank

1991. Washerwomen of the Ngounie.
1089 **466** 100f. multicoloured . . . 65 45

467 Knight **469** Post Box and Globe

468 Inspecting Fish Traps

1991. Order of the Equatorial Star. Mult.
1090 100f. Type **467** 65 45
1091 175f. Officer . . . . 1·10 65
1092 200f. Commander . . . . . 1·40 90

1991. Fishing. Multicoloured.
1093 100f. Type **468** 65 45
1094 175f. Fishing from canoe . . 1·10 65
1095 200f. Casting net . . . . . 1·40 90
1096 300f. Pulling in net . . . . 2·75 1·90

1991. World Post Day.
1098 **469** 175f. blue, black and red 1·10 45

470 "Phalloid"

1991. Termitaries. Multicoloured.
1099 100f. Type **470** 85 55
1100 175f. "Cathedral" . . . . . 1·40 85
1101 200f. "Mushroom" . . . . 1·60 1·10
1102 300f. "Treehouse" . . . . . 2·25 2·00

471 Dibwangui Church

1991. Christmas.
1103 **471** 100f. multicoloured . . . 65 45

472 Neolithic Ceramic Pot **473** Stripping Wood

1992. Prehistory. Pottery. Multicoloured.
1104 100f. Type **472** 65 45
1105 175f. Ceramic bottle (8th century) . . . . 1·10 65
1106 200f. Ceramic vase (late 8th century) . . . . 1·40 90
1107 300f. Ceramic vase (early 8th century) . . . . . . 2·25 1·40

1992. Arts and Crafts. Multicoloured.
1109 100f. Type **473** 65 45
1110 175f. Metalwork . . . . . 1·10 65
1111 200f. Boat building . . . . 1·40 80
1112 300f. Hairdressing . . . . . 2·25 1·40

474 Grand Officer of Order of Equatorial Star **475** Konrad Adenauer

1992. Gabonese Honours. Multicoloured.
1114 100f. Type **474** 65 45
1115 175f. Grand Cross of Order of Equatorial Star . . . . 1·10 65
1116 200f. Order of Merit . . . . 1·40 90

1992. 25th Death Anniv of Konrad Adenauer (German statesman).
1117 **475** 500f. black, stone & grn 4·00 2·75

476 Earth and Moon **477** Small Striped Swallowtail

1992. World Telecommunications Day.
1118 **476** 175f. multicoloured . . . 1·10 45

1992. Butterflies. Multicoloured.
1119 100f. Type **477** 65 45
1120 175f. "Acraea egina" . . . 1·10 65

478 Fang Mask **479** Cycling

1992. Gabonese Masks. Multicoloured.
1121 100f. Type **478** 65 45
1122 175f. Mpongwe mask . . . 1·10 65
1123 200f. Kwele mask . . . . . 1·40 95
1124 300f. Pounou mask . . . . 1·90 1·40

1992. Olympic Games, Barcelona. Mult.
1125 100f. Type **479** 65 45
1126 175f. Boxing . . . . 1·10 65
1127 200f. Pole vaulting . . . . 1·40 90

1992. District Arms (6th series). As T **392**.
1128 100f. silver, black and blue 65 20
DESIGN: 100f. Medouneu.

1992. World Post Day. As No. 1098 but dated "1992".
1129 **469** 175f. multicoloured . . . 1·10 55

480 Columbus and Fleet

1992. Air. 500th Anniv of Discovery of America by Columbus.
1130 **480** 500f. multicoloured . . . 3·25 1·90

481 African Owl

1992. Birds. Multicoloured.
1131 100f. Type **481** . . . . . . 1·10 50
1132 175f. Speckled mousebird 1·75 75
1133 200f. Palm-nut vulture . . . 2·50 1·10
1134 300f. Giant kingfisher . . . 4·00 2·00

482 Cattle

1992. Beef Production.
1136 **482** 100f. multicoloured . . . 65 45
1137 – 175f. multicoloured . . . 1·10 65
1138 – 200f. multicoloured . . . 1·40 85
DESIGNS: 175, 200f. Cattle (different).

483 Tchibanga Church

1992. Christmas.
1139 **483** 100f. multicoloured . . . 65 35

484 Emblems

1992. International Nutrition Conference, Rome.
1140 **484** 100f. multicoloured . . . 65 45

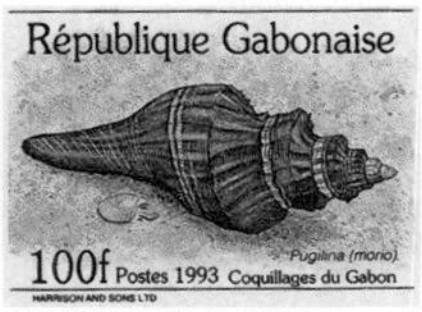

485 "Giant Hairy Melongena"

1993. Shells. Multicoloured.
1141 100f. Type **485** 50 30
1142 175f. Butterfly cone . . . . 1·10 60
1143 200f. Carpat's spindle . . . 1·25 70
1144 300f. "Cymatium linatella" 2·00 1·10

486 Crowd with Banner outside Hospital

1993. World Leprosy Day.
1146 **486** 175f. multicoloured . . . 1·10 50

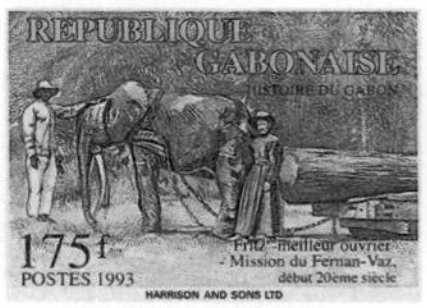

487 Fritz the Elephant

1993. Fernan-Vaz Mission.
1147 **487** 175f. multicoloured . . . 1·40 90

488 Claude Chappe **489** Schweitzer feeding Animals

1993. Bicentenary of Chappe's Optical Telegraph. Multicoloured.
1148 100f. Type **488** 45 25
1149 175f. Signals and table of signs . . . . 1·10 50
1150 200f. Emile Baudot (inventor of five-unit code telegraph printing system) 1·25 80
1151 300f. Satellite and fibre-optics . . . . 2·00 1·10

1993. 80th Anniv of First Visit of Albert Schweitzer (medical missionary) to Lambarene. Multicoloured.
1153 250f. Type **489** . . . . . . 2·00 1·10
1154 250f. Schweitzer holding babies . . . . 2·00 1·10
1155 500f. Schweitzer (36 × 49 mm) . . . . . . 3·75 2·25

490 Copernicus (astronomer) and illustration from "De Revolutionibus" **491** Emblem

1993. "Polska'93" International Stamp Exhibition, Poznan.
1156 **490** 175f. multicoloured . . . 1·10 50

1993. World Telecommunications Day.
1157 **491** 175f. multicoloured . . . 1·10 50

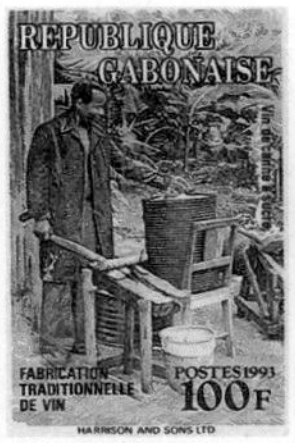

492 Making Sugar-cane Wine **493** Lobster

1993. Traditional Wine-making. Mult.
1158 100f. Type **492** 70 25
1159 175f. Filling bottle with palm wine . . . . 1·10 50
1160 200f. Gathering ingredients for palm wine . . . . . 1·40 55

1993. Crustaceans. Multicoloured.
1162 100f. Type **493** 70 25
1163 175f. Crab . . . . 1·10 50
1164 200f. Crayfish . . . . . . 1·25 80
1165 300f. Sea spider . . . . . . 2·00 1·10

494 Magnifying Glass, Flowers, Stamp and Emblem

1993. 1st European Stamp Salon, Flower Gardens, Paris.
1166 **494** 100f. multicoloured . . . 70 50

495 Squirrel Trap

1993. Trapping. Multicoloured.

1167		100f. Type **495**	70	25
1168		175f. Small game trap	1·10	50
1169		200f. Large game trap	1·25	80
1170		300f. Palm squirrel trap	2·00	1·10

496 Post Box and Globe

1993. World Post Day.

1171	**496**	175f. multicoloured	80	50

497 Making Model Airplane

499 Mandji Catholic Mission

498 Leconi Canyon

1993. Bamboo Toys.

1172	**497**	100f. multicoloured	70	50

1993. Tourism. Multicoloured.

1173		100f. Type **498**	70	25
1174		175f. La Lope tourist site	1·10	50

1993. Christmas.

1175	**499**	100f. multicoloured	70	50

OFFICIAL STAMPS

O 119 Map of Gabon River

1968.

O333	O **119**	1f. multicoloured	10	10
O334		2f. multicoloured	10	10
O335		5f. multicoloured	10	10
O336		10f. multicoloured	15	10
O337	–	25f. multicoloured	35	15
O338	–	30f. multicoloured	40	20
O339	–	50f. multicoloured	55	20
O340	–	85f. multicoloured	1·10	40
O341	–	100f. multicoloured	1·40	55
O342	–	200f. multicoloured	2·50	1·10

DESIGNS: 25f., 30f. Gabon flag; 50f. to 200f. Gabon coat of arms.

O 165 Gabon Flag

1971. Flag in actual colours; inscription in blue; background as below.

O436	O **165**	5f. blue	10	10
O437		10f. grey	15	15
O437a		20f. orange	15	10
O437b		25f. yellow	20	15
O438		30f. cobalt	30	10
O439		40f. orange	55	30
O440		50f. red	60	20
O441		60f. brown	70	30
O441a		75f. grey	55	15
O442		80f. mauve	1·10	50
O443		100f. mauve	80	30
O444		500f. green	4·50	1·40

POSTAGE DUE STAMPS

1928. Postage Due type of French Colonies optd **GABON A. E. F.**

D123	U	5c. blue	10	2·50
D124		10c. brown	10	2·50
D125		20c. olive	55	3·00
D126		25c. red	25	3·25
D127		30c. red	15	2·75
D128		45c. green	1·00	3·25
D129		50c. red	15	2·50
D130		60c. brown	25	3·25
D131		1f. purple	60	3·00
D132		2f. red	1·00	3·25
D133		3f. violet	1·10	3·75

D 19 Local Chief

D 24 Pahquin Woman

1930.

D134	D **19**	5c. drab and blue	1·00	3·00
D135		10c. brown and red	1·60	3·25
D136		20c. brown and green	1·90	3·50
D137		25c. brown and blue	2·00	3·75
D138		30c. green and brown	2·00	3·75
D139		45c. drab and green	1·40	2·75
D140		50c. brown and mauve	2·00	5·25
D141		60c. black and violet	1·50	9·00
D142	–	1f. black and brown	2·00	12·50
D143	–	2f. brown and mauve	5·00	19·00
D144	–	3f. brown and red	5·25	21·00

DESIGN—VERT: 1f. to 3f. Count Savorgnan de Brazza.

1932.

D151	D **24**	5c. blue on blue	10	2·00
D152		10c. brown	40	2·75
D153		20c. brown	2·25	3·75
D154		25c. green on blue	2·00	3·25
D155		30c. red	3·25	5·00
D156		45c. red on yellow	5·25	9·25
D157		50c. purple	3·75	6·75
D158		60c. blue	4·00	6·75
D159		1f. black on orange	2·75	6·25
D160		2f. green	13·50	16·00
D161		3f. red	10·50	16·00

D 40 Pineapple

1962. Fruits.

D196	50c. red, yellow and green	10	10
D197	50c. red, yellow and green	10	10
D198	1f. mauve, yellow and green	10	10
D199	1f. mauve, yellow and green	10	10
D200	2f. yellow, brown and green	10	10
D201	2f. yellow, brown and green	10	10
D202	5f. yellow, green and brown	30	30
D203	5f. yellow, green and brown	30	30
D204	10f. multicoloured	60	60
D205	10f. multicoloured	60	60
D206	25f. yellow, green and purple	80	80
D207	25f. yellow, green and purple	80	80

FRUITS: No. D196, Type D **40**; D197, Mangoes; D198, Mandarin oranges; D199, Avocado pears; D200, Grapefruit; D201, Coconuts; D202. Oranges; D203, Papaws; D204, Breadfruit; D205, Guavas; D206, Lemons; D207, Bananas.

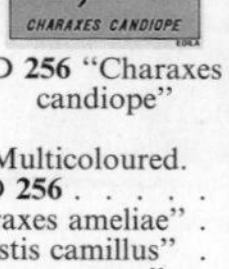

D 256 "Charaxes candiope"

1978. Butterflies. Multicoloured.

D655	5f. Type D **256**	10	10
D656	10f. "Charaxes ameliae"	10	10
D657	25f. "Cyrestis camillus"	30	15
D658	50f. "Charaxes castor"	60	35
D659	100f. "Pseudacrea boisduvali"	1·10	65

GALAPAGOS ISLANDS Pt. 20

These islands, noted for their fauna and flora, were annexed by Ecuador, and later (1973) became a province of that country.

100 centavos = 1 sucre.

1 Californian Sealions

1957. Inscr "ISLAS GALAPAGOS".

1	**1**	20c. brown (postage)	40	15
2	–	50c. violet	40	15
3	–	1s. green	1·25	45
4	–	1s. blue (air)	30	15
5	–	1s.80 purple	65	30
6	–	4s.20 black	1·75	75

DESIGNS—VERT: 50c. Map of Ecuador coastline. HORIZ: 1s. (No. 3) Iguana; 1s. (No. 4) Santa Cruz Island; 1s.80, Map of Galapagos Is; 4s.20, Giant tortoise.

1959. Air. United Nations Commem. Triangular design as T **316** of Ecuador but inscr "ISLAS GALAPAGOS".

7		2s. green	50	35

GAMBIA Pt. 1

A British colony and protectorate on the West coast of Africa. Granted full internal self-government on 4 October 1963, and achieved indepedence on 18 February 1965. Became a republic within the Commonwealth on 24 April 1970.

1869. 12 pence = 1 shilling;
20 shillings = 1 pound.
1971. 100 butut = 1 dalasi.

1

2

1869. Imperf.

5	**1**	4d. brown	£375	£190
8		6d. blue	£325	£190

1880. Perf.

11B	**1**	½d. orange	8·00	14·00
12B		1d. purple	4·50	6·00
13B		2d. pink	25·00	11·00
14cB		3d. blue	50·00	26·00
30		4d. brown	6·00	2·00
17B		6d. blue	85·00	45·00
19B		1s. green	£225	£130

1886.

21	**1**	½d. green	2·75	2·25
23		1d. red	5·50	7·50
25		2d. orange	1·60	8·00
27		2½d. blue	3·00	1·25
29		3d. grey	4·50	15·00
34		6d. green	11·00	45·00
35		1s. violet	3·25	16·00

1898.

37	**2**	½d. green	2·75	1·75
38		1d. red	1·50	75
39		2d. orange and mauve	6·00	3·50
40		2½d. blue	1·75	2·50
41		3d. purple and blue	23·00	12·00
42		4d. brown and blue	9·00	30·00
43		6d. green and red	10·00	27·00
44		1s. mauve and green	29·00	65·00

1902. As T **2**, but portrait of King Edward VII.

57	½d. green	4·50	30
46	1d. red	4·00	1·00
47	2d. orange and mauve	3·25	2·00
74	2d. grey	1·60	11·00
60	2½d. blue	6·00	4·75
61	3d. purple and blue	7·50	2·00
75	3d. purple on yellow	3·50	1·00
50	4d. brown and blue	3·25	24·00
76	4d. black and red on yellow	1·25	65
63	5d. grey and black	14·00	19·00
77	5d. orange and purple	1·50	1·25
51	6d. green and red	4·50	12·00
78	6d. purple	2·25	2·25
65	7½d. green and red	11·00	38·00
79	7½d. brown and blue	2·50	2·50
80	10d. green and red	2·50	7·00
67	1s. mauve and green	21·00	48·00
81	1s. black on green	3·25	17·00
53	1s.6d. green and red on yellow	7·00	18·00
82	1s.6d. violet and green	13·00	60·00
54	2s. grey and orange	48·00	60·00
83	2s. purple and blue on blue	14·00	20·00
55	2s.6d. purple & brown on yell	15·00	60·00
84	2s.6d. black and red on blue	21·00	20·00
56	3s. red and green on yellow	20·00	60·00
85	3s. yellow and green	23·00	48·00

1906. Surch in words.

69	½d. on 2s.6d. (No. 55)	50·00	60·00
70	1d. on 3s. (No. 56)	55·00	30·00

1912. As T **2**, but portrait of King George V.

86	½d. green	1·75	1·50
87a	1d. red	2·25	30
88	1½d. olive and green	50	30
111	2d. grey	1·00	2·25
112	2½d. blue	50	6·00
91	3d. purple on yellow	50	30
92c	4d. black and red on yellow	1·50	6·50
93	5d. orange and purple	1·00	2·00
94	6d. purple	1·00	2·50
95	7½d. brown and blue	1·25	6·50
96a	10d. green and red	2·00	15·00
97	1s. black on green	2·00	1·00
98	1s.6d. violet and green	11·00	10·00
99	2s. purple and blue on blue	3·50	6·00
100	2s.6d. black and red on blue	3·25	14·00
101	3s. yellow and green	8·50	27·00
117	4s. black and red	75·00	£130
102	5s. green and red on yellow	80·00	£130

9

10

1922.

122	**9**	½d. black and green	55	55
124		1d. black and brown	80	20
125		1½d. black and red	80	20
126		2d. black and grey	1·00	3·25
127		2½d. black and orange	1·00	11·00
128		3d. black and blue	1·00	20
118		4d. black and red on yellow	2·50	3·00
130		5d. black and olive	2·00	10·00
131		6d. black and red	1·25	30
119		7½d. black & purple on yell	3·25	6·50
133		10d. black and blue	4·50	18·00
134	**10**	1s. black & purple on yell	2·50	1·25
135		1s.6d. black and blue	11·00	14·00
136		2s. black and purple on blue	4·00	4·25
137		2s.6d. black and green	4·50	9·50
138		3s. black and purple	12·00	48·00
140		4s. black and brown	5·50	16·00
141		5s. black and green on yellow	12·00	38·00
142		10s. black and olive	70·00	£100

10a Windsor Castle

1935. Silver Jubilee.

143	**10a**	1½d. blue and red	50	60
144		3d. brown and blue	55	70
145		6d. blue and olive	1·00	3·50
146		1s. grey and purple	4·00	7·50

10b King George VI and Queen Elizabeth

1937. Coronation.

147	**10b**	1d. brown	30	70
148		1½d. red	30	35
149		3d. blue	55	1·00

11 Elephant (from Colony Badge)

1938.

150	**11**	½d. black and green	15	70
151		1d. purple and brown	20	50
152b		1½d. pink and red	30	2·00
152c		1½d. blue and black	30	1·50
153		2d. blue and black	6·00	3·25
153a		2d. pink and red	60	2·25
154		3d. blue	30	10
154a		5d. green and purple	50	50
155		6d. olive and red	1·50	35
156		1s. blue and purple	2·00	10
156a		1s.3d. purple and blue	3·00	2·50
157		2s. red and blue	4·50	3·25
158		2s.6d. brown and green	12·00	2·50
159		4s. red and purple	21·00	2·50
160		5s. blue and red	21·00	4·00
161		10s. orange and black	21·00	7·00

11a Houses of Parliament, London

1946. Victory.

162	**11a**	1½d. black	10	10
163		3d. blue	10	20

11b King George VI and Queen Elizabeth **11c** King George VI and Queen Elizabeth

1948. Silver Wedding.

164	**11b**	1½d. black	25	10
165	**11c**	£1 mauve	13·00	14·00

11d Hermes, Globe and Forms of Transport

11e Hemispheres, Jet-powered Vickers Viking Airliner and Steamer

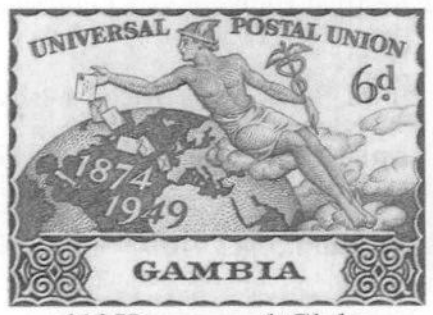

11f Hermes and Globe

11g U.P.U. Monument

1949. U.P.U.

166	**11d**	1½d. black	30	1·25
167	**11e**	3d. blue	1·25	1·75
168	**11f**	6d. mauve	50	1·00
169	**11g**	1s. violet	35	40

11h Queen Elizabeth II **12** Tapping for Palm Wine

1953. Coronation.

170	**11h**	1½d. black and blue	50	1·00

1953. Queen Elizabeth II.

171	**12**	½d. red and green	30	20
172	–	1d. blue and brown	40	50
173	–	1½d. brown and black	20	70
174	–	2½d. black and red	45	70
175	–	3d. blue and lilac	35	10
176	–	4d. black and blue	60	2·25
177	**12**	6d. brown and purple	35	15
178	–	1s. brown and green	60	60
179	–	1s.3d. ultramarine and blue	10·00	60
180	–	2s. blue and red	7·00	3·50
181	–	2s.6d. green and brown	4·00	1·50
182	–	4s. blue and brown	11·00	3·00
183	–	5s. brown and blue	2·50	1·50
184	–	10s. blue and green	21·00	8·50
185	–	£1 green and black	20·00	9·00

DESIGNS—HORIZ: 1d., 1s.3d. Cutter (sailing ship); 1½d., 5s. Wollof woman; 2½d., 2s. Barra canoe; 3d., 10s. S.S. "Lady Wright"; 4d., 4s. James Island; 1s., 2s.6d. Woman hoeing; £1 As Type **11**.

20 Queen Elizabeth II and Palm **20a** Protein Foods

1961. Royal Visit.

186	**20**	2d. green and purple	30	20
187	–	3d. turquoise and sepia	75	15
188	–	6d. blue and red	75	70
189	**20**	1s.3d. violet and green	75	2·25

DESIGN: 3d., 6d. Queen Elizabeth II and West African map.

1963. Freedom from Hunger.

190	**20a**	1s.3d. red	55	15

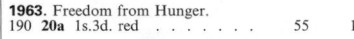

20b Red Cross Emblem

1963. Centenary of Red Cross.

191	**20b**	2d. red and black	20	10
192		1s.3d. red and blue	40	45

22 Beautiful Sunbird **36** Gambia Flag and River

22a Shakespeare and Memorial Theatre, Stratford-upon-Avon

1963. Birds. Multicoloured.

193	½d. Type **22**	50	1·00
194	1d. Yellow-mantled whydah	75	30
195	1½d. Cattle egret	2·00	70
196	2d. Senegal parrot	2·00	70
197	3d. Rose-ringed parakeet	2·00	1·00
198	4d. Violet starling	2·00	80
199	6d. Village weaver	2·00	10
200	1s. Rufous-crowned roller	2·00	10
201	1s.3d. Red-eyed dove	14·00	1·50
202	2s.6d. Double-spurred francolin	9·00	2·50
203	5s. Palm-nut vulture	9·00	3·50
204	10s. Orange-cheeked waxbill	14·00	7·00
205	£1 African emerald cuckoo	29·00	14·00

1963. New Constitution. Nos. 194, 197 and 200/1 optd **SELF GOVERNMENT 1963**.

206	1d. multicoloured	10	40
207	3d. multicoloured	25	20
208	1s. multicoloured	25	10
209	1s.3d. multicoloured	30	45

1964. 400th Birth Anniv of Shakespeare.

210	**22a**	6d. blue	20	10

1965. Independence. Multicoloured.

211	½d. Type **36**	10	40
212	2d. Arms	15	10
213	7½d. Type **36**	40	35
214	1s.6d. Arms	50	30

1965. Nos 193/205 optd **INDEPENDENCE 1965**.

215	½d. Type **22**	30	1·00
216	1d. Yellow-mantled whydah	30	20
217	1½d. Cattle egret	60	1·00
218	2d. Senegal parrot	70	30
219	3d. Rose-ringed parakeet	70	15
220	4d. Violet starling	70	1·75
221	6d. Village weaver	70	10
222	1s. Rufous-crowned roller	70	10
223	1s.3d. Red-eyed dove	70	10
224	2s.6d. Double-spurred francolin	70	60
225	5s. Palm-nut vulture	70	75
226	10s. Orange-cheeked waxbill	1·75	2·50
227	£1 African emerald cuckoo	7·50	8·50

39 I.T.U. Emblem and Symbols

1965. Centenary of I.T.U.

228	**39**	1d. silver and blue	25	10
229		1s.6d. gold and violet	1·00	40

40 Sir Winston Churchill and Houses of Parliament

1966. Churchill Commemoration.

230	**40**	1d. multicoloured	15	10
231		6d. multicoloured	35	15
232		1s.6d. multicoloured	60	75

41 Red-cheeked Cordon-bleu

1966. Birds. Multicoloured.

233	½d. Type **41**	90	40
234	1d. White-faced whistling duck	30	50
235	1½d. Red-throated bee eater	30	40
236	2d. Lesser pied kingfisher	4·25	75
237	3d. Golden bishop	30	10
238	4d. African fish eagle	50	30
239	6d. Yellow-bellied green pigeon	40	10
240	1s. Blue-bellied roller	40	10
241	1s.6d. African pygmy kingfisher	50	30
242	2s.6d. Spur-winged goose	50	70
243	5s. Cardinal woodpecker	50	75
244	10s. Violet turaco	50	2·75
245	£1 Pin-tailed whydah (25 × 39½ mm)	75	6·50

54 Arms, Early Settlement and Modern Buildings

1966. 150th Anniv of Bathurst.

246	**54**	1d. silver, brown and orange	10	10
247		2d. silver, brown and blue	10	10
248		6d. silver, brown and green	10	10
249		1s.6d. silver, brn & pur	15	15

55 I.T.Y. Emblem and Hotels

1967. International Tourist Year.

250	**55**	2d. silver, brown and green	10	10
251		1s. silver, brown and orange	10	10
252		1s.6d. silver, brn & mve	15	25

56 Handcuffs

1968. Human Rights Year. Multicoloured.

253	1d. Type **56**	10	10
254	1s. Fort Bullen	10	10
255	5s. Methodist Church	30	60

59 Queen Victoria, Queen Elizabeth II and 4d. Stamp of 1869

1969. Gambia Stamp Centenary.

256	**59**	4d. sepia and ochre	20	10
257		6d. blue and green	20	10
258	–	2s.6d. multicoloured	70	1·40

DESIGN: 2s.6d. Queen Elizabeth II with 4d. and 6d. stamps of 1869.

61 Catapult-ship "Westfalen" launching Dornier Wal

1969. 35th Anniv of Pioneer Air Service. Mult.

259	2d. Type **61**	35	20
260	1s. Dornier Wal flying boat "Boreas"	35	20
261	1s.6d. Airship "Graf Zeppelin"	40	1·40

63 Athlete and Gambian Flag

1970. 9th British Commonwealth Games, Edinburgh.

262	**63**	1d. multicoloured	10	10
263		1s. multicoloured	10	10
264		5s. multicoloured	30	90

64 President Sir Dawda Kairaba Jawara and State House

1970. Republic Day. Multicoloured.

265	2d. Type **64**	10	10
266	1s. President Sir Dawda Jawara (vert)	15	10
267	1s.6d. President and flag of Gambia (vert)	30	35

65 Methodist Church, Georgetown

1971. 150th Anniv of Establishment of Methodist Mission. Multicoloured.

268	2d. Type **65**	10	10
269	1s. Map of Africa and Gambian flag (vert)	15	15
270	1s.6d. John Wesley and scroll	15	1·00

66 Yellow-finned Tunny

1971. New Currency. Fishes. Multicoloured.

271	2b. Type **66**	10	75
272	4b. Peter's mormyrid	10	20
273	6b. Four-winged flyingfish	15	75
274	8b. African sleeper goby	15	75
275	10b. Yellow-tailed snapper	20	20
276	13b. Rock hind	20	60
277	25b. West African eel catfish	35	60
278	38b. Tiger shark	55	45
279	50b. Electric catfish	70	55
280	63b. Black swampeel	80	1·75
281	1d.25 Small-toothed sawfish	1·40	2·50
282	2d.50 Great barracuda	1·50	4·50
283	5d. Brown bullhead	1·75	7·00

67 Mungo Park in Scotland

1971. Birth Centenary of Mungo Park (explorer). Multicoloured.
284 4b. Type **67** 20 10
285 25b. Dug-out canoe 45 35
286 37b. Death of Mungo Park, Busa Rapids . . . . 75 1·50

68 Radio Gambia

1972. 10th Anniv of Radio Gambia.
287 **68** 4b. brown and black . . . 10 10
288 – 25b. blue, orange and black 10 30
289 **68** 37b. green and black . . . 20 1·25
DESIGN: 25b. Broadcast-area map.

69 High Jumping

1972. Olympic Games, Munich.
290 **69** 4b. multicoloured 10 10
291 25b. multicoloured 20 15
292 37b. multicoloured 25 20

70 Manding Woman

72 Groundnuts

71 Children carrying Fanal

1972. International Conference on Manding Studies. Multicoloured.
293 2b. Type **70** 10 10
294 25b. Musician playing the Kora 15 15
295 37b. Map of Mail Empire . . 25 25

1972. Fanals (Model Boats). Multicoloured.
296 2b. Type **71** 10 10
297 1d.25 Fanal with lanterns . . 30 45

1973. Freedom from Hunger Campaign.
298 **72** 2b. multicoloured 10 10
299 25b. multicoloured 15 10
300 37b. multicoloured 25 20

73 Planting and Drying Rice

74 Oil Palm

1973. Agriculture (1st series). Multicoloured.
301 2b. Type **73** 10 10
302 25b. Guinea corn 20 15
303 37b. Rice 25 25

1973. Agriculture (2nd series). Multicoloured.
304 2b. Type **74** 10 10
305 25b. Limes 30 30
306 37b. Oil palm (fruits) 40 40

75 Cassava

1973. Agriculture (3rd series). Multicoloured.
307 2b. Type **75** 10 10
308 50b. Cotton 40 25

76 O.A.U. Emblem

1973. 10th Anniv of O.A.U.
309 **76** 4b. multicoloured 10 10
310 25b. multicoloured 15 10
311 37b. multicoloured 15 20

77 Red Cross

1973. 25th Anniv of Gambian Red Cross.
312 **77** 4b. red and black 10 10
313 25b. red, black and blue . . 15 15
314 37b. red, black and green . . 20 20

78 Arms of Banjul

1973. Change of Bathurst's Name to Banjul.
315 **78** 4b. multicoloured 10 10
316 25b. multicoloured 15 15
317 37b. multicoloured 15 20

79 U.P.U. Emblem

1974. Centenary of U.P.U.
318 **79** 4b. multicoloured 10 10
319 37b. multicoloured 20 30

80 Churchill as Harrow Schoolboy

1974. Birth Cent of Sir Winston Churchill. Mult.
320 4b. Type **80** 10 10
321 37b. Churchill as 4th Hussars officer 20 15
322 50b. Churchill as Prime Minister 30 60

81 "Different Races"

1974. World Population Year. Multicoloured.
323 4b. Type **81** 10 10
324 37b. "Multiplication and Division of Races" . . . 15 15
325 50b. "World Population" . . 20 25

82 Dr. Schweitzer and River Scene

1975. Birth Centenary of Dr. Albert Schweitzer. Multicoloured.
326 10b. Type **82** 20 10
327 50b. Surgery scene 40 25
328 1d.25 River journey 75 55

83 Dove of Peace

1975. 10th Anniv of Independence. Multicoloured.
329 4b. Type **83** 10 10
330 10b. Gambian flag 10 10
331 50b. Gambian arms 15 10
332 1d.25 Map of The Gambia . . 35 40

84 Development Graph

85 Statue of "David" (Michelangelo)

1975. 10th Anniv of African Development Bank. Multicoloured.
333 10b. Type **84** 10 10
334 50b. Symbolic plant 20 15
335 1d.25 Bank emblem and symbols 55 60

1975. 500th Birth Anniv of Michelangelo. Mult.
336 10b. Type **85** 15 10
337 50b. "Madonna of the Steps" 30 15
338 1d.25 "Battle of the Centaurs" (horiz) . . . . 50 1·25

86 School Building

1975. Centenary of Gambia High School. Mult.
339 10b. Type **86** 10 10
340 50b. Pupil with scientific apparatus 15 10
341 1d.50 School crest 35 35

87 "Teaching"

1975. International Women's Year. Multicoloured.
342 4b. Type **87** 10 10
343 10b. "Planting rice" 10 10
344 50b. "Nursing" 35 15
345 1d.50 "Directing traffic" . . 85 35

88 Woman playing Golf

1975. 11th Anniv of Independence. Mult.
346 10b. Type **88** 55 10
347 50b. Man playing golf . . . 1·50 30
348 1d.50 President playing golf 2·25 70

89 American Militiaman

90 Mother and Child

1976. Bicentenary of American Revolution. Mult.
349 25b. Type **89** 20 10
350 50b. Soldier of the Continental Army 30 20
351 1d.25 Independence Declaration 40 60
MS352 110 × 80 mm. Nos. 349/51 1·00 4·00

1976. Christmas.
353 **90** 10b. multicoloured 10 10
354 50b. multicoloured 15 10
355 1d.25 multicoloured . . . 50 45

91 Serval Cat

1976. Abuko Nature Reserve (1st series). Mult.
356 10b. Type **91** . . . . 3·50 20
357 20b. Bushbuck . . . . 4·50 20
358 50b. Sitatunga (deer) . . . . 8·00 40
359 1d.25 Leopard . . . . . . 13·00 2·50
MS360 137 × 110 mm. Nos. 356/9 32·00 12·00
See also Nos. 400/3, 431/5 and 460/3.

92 Festival Emblem and Gambian Weaver

1977. 2nd World Black and African Festival of Arts and Culture, Nigeria.
361 **92** 25b. multicoloured 15 10
362 50b. multicoloured 20 15
363 1d.25 multicoloured . . . 50 70
MS364 118 × 114 mm. Nos. 361/3 1·75 3·75

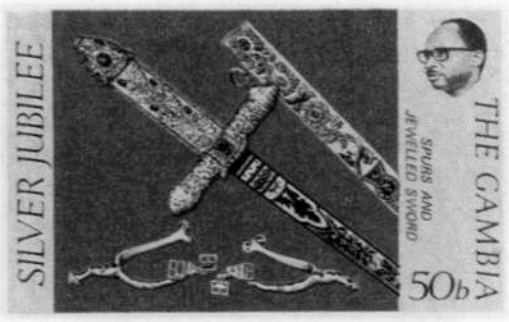

93 The Spurs and Jewelled Sword

1977. Silver Jubilee. Multicoloured.
365 25b. The Queen's visit, 1961 15 20
366 50b. Type **93** 15 20
367 1d.25 Oblation of the Sword 20 30

94 Stone Circles, Kuntaur

1977. Tourism. Multicoloured.
368 25b. Type **94** 10 10
369 50b. Ruined Fort, James Island 15 20
370 1d.25 Mungo Park Monument 40 80

95 Widow of Last Year

1977. Flowers and Shrubs. Multicoloured.
371 2b. Type **95** 10 15
372 4b. White water-lily 10 30
373 6b. Fireball lily (vert) . . . 10 30
374 8b. Cocks-comb (vert) . . . 10 15
375 10b. Broad leaved ground orchid (vert) . . . . . . 2·00 30

376 13b. Fibre plant (yellow background) (vert) . . . 15 40
376a 13b. Fibre plant (grey background) (vert) . . . 1·25 4·00
377 25b. False kapok (vert) . . 15 15
378 38b. Baobab (vert) 25 55
379 50b. Coral tree 35 35
380 63b. Gloriosa lily 40 70
381 1d.25 Bell-flowered mimosa (vert) . . . . 45 1·00
382 2d.50 Kindin dolo (vert) . . 50 1·00
383 5d. African tulip tree . . . 60 2·00

96 Endangered Animals **97** "Flight into Egypt"

1977. Banjul Declaration.
384 **96** 10b. black and blue . . . 25 10
385 – 25b. multicoloured 30 10
386 – 50b. multicoloured 45 20
387 – 1d.25 black and red . . . 1·50 75
DESIGNS: 25b. Extract from Declaration; 50b. Declaration in full; 1d.25, Endangered insects and flowers.

1977. 400th Birth of Rubens. Multicoloured.
388 10b. Type **97** 15 10
389 25b. "The Education of the Virgin" 20 10
390 50b. "Clara Serena Rubens" 30 30
391 1d. "Madonna with Saints" 45 90

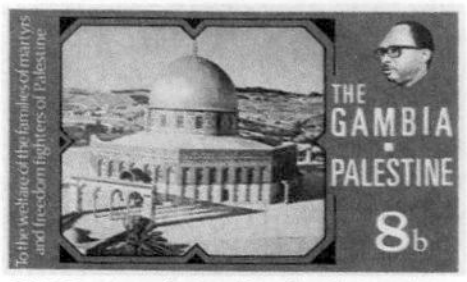

98 Dome of the Rock, Jerusalem

1978. Palestinian Welfare.
392 **98** 8b. multicoloured 50 15
393 25b. multicoloured . . . . 1·50 85

99 Walking on a Greasy Pole **100** Lion

1978. 13th Anniv of Independence. Multicoloured.
394 10b. Type **99** 10 10
395 50b. Pillow fighting 20 10
396 1d. Long boat rowing . . . 45 45

1978. 25th Anniv of Coronation.
397 – 1d. black, brown and yellow 20 45
398 – 1d. multicoloured 20 45
399 **100** 1d. black, brown and yellow 20 45
DESIGNS: No. 397, White Greyhound of Richmond; 398, Queen Elizabeth II.

101 Verreaux's Eagle Owl

1978. Abuko Nature Reserve (2nd series). Multicoloured.
400 20b. Type **101** . . . . 10·00 65
401 25b. Lizard buzzard . . . . 10·00 65
402 50b. African harrier hawk . . 13·00 2·25
403 1d.25 Long-crested eagle . . 17·00 9·00

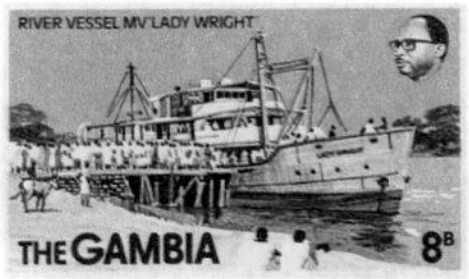

102 M.V. "Lady Wright"

1978. Launching of River Vessel "Lady Chilel Jawara". Multicoloured.
404 8b. Type **102** 15 10
405 25b. Sectional view of "Lady Chilel Jawara" 40 25
406 1d. "Lady Chilel Jawara" . . 1·25 1·40

103 Police Service

1979. 14th Anniv of Independence. Multicoloured.
407 10b. Type **103** 60 10
408 50b. Fire service . . . . . . 1·10 25
409 1d.25 Ambulance service . . 1·40 80

1979. Nos. 376 and 380/1 surch **25b**.
410 25b. on 13b. Fibre plant . . 15 35
411 25b. on 63b. Gloriosa lily . . 10 20
412 25b. on 1d.25 Bell-flowered mimosa 10 20

105 "Ramsgate Sands" (detail showing children playing on beach)

1979. International Year of the Child. "Ramsgate Sands" (William Powell Frith). Multicoloured.
413 10b. Type **105** 10 10
414 25b. Detail showing child paddling (vert) 20 10
415 1d. Complete painting (60 × 23 mm) 60 60

106 1883 2½d. Stamp

1979. Death Centenary of Sir Rowland Hill. Multicoloured.
416 10b. Type **106** 10 10
417 25b. 1869 4d. stamp 10 10
418 50b. 1965 Independence 7½d. commemorative 15 20
419 1d.25 1935 Silver Jubilee 1½d. commemorative 35 50
MS420 109 × 83 mm. No. 419 . . 65 1·00

107 Satellite Earth Station under Construction

1979. Abuko Satellite Earth Station. Multicoloured.
421 25b. Type **107** 20 10
422 50b. Satellite Earth Station (completed) 30 20
423 1d. "Intelsat" satellite 65 60

108 "Apollo 11" leaving Launch Pad

1979. 10th Anniv of Moon Landing. Multicoloured.
424 25b. Type **108** 20 10
425 38b. "Apollo 11" in Moon orbit 25 20
426 50b. Splashdown 30 40
430 2d. Lunar module on Moon 1·50 2·25
Nos. 424/6 also exist self-adhesive from booklet panes. No. 430 only exists in this form.

109 "Acraea zetes"

1980. Abuko Nature Reserve (3rd series). Butterflies. Multicoloured.
431 25b. Type **109** . . . . 5·00 20
432 50b. "Precis hierta" . . . . 6·00 50
433 1d. "Graphium leonidas" . . 8·50 1·40
434 1d.25 "Charaxes jasius" . . . 8·50 2·00
MS435 145 × 122 mm. Nos. 431/4 38·00 8·50

110 Steam Launch "Vampire"

1980. "London 1980" International Stamp Exhibition. Multicoloured.
436 10b. Type **110** 20 10
437 25b. T.S.S. "Lady Denham" 25 10
438 50b. T.S.C.M.Y. "Mansa Kila Ba" 30 20
439 1d.25 T.S.S. "Prince of Wales" 50 60
Nos. 438 and 439 are larger, 49 × 26 mm.

111 Queen Elizabeth the Queen Mother

1980. 80th Birthday of Queen Elizabeth The Queen Mother.
440 **111** 67b. multicoloured . . . 30 60

112 Phoenician Trading Vessel

1980. Early Sailing Vessels. Multicoloured.
441 8b. Type **112** 10 10
442 67b. Egyptian sea-going vessel 30 20
443 75b. Portuguese caravel . . . 35 30
444 1d. Spanish galleon 40 50

113 "Madonna and Child" (Francesco de Mura)

1980. Christmas. Multicoloured.
445 8b. Type **113** 10 10
446 67b. "Praying Madonna with Crown of Stars" (workshop of Correggio) 25 25
447 75b. "La Zingarella" (workshop replica of Correggio painting) 25 30

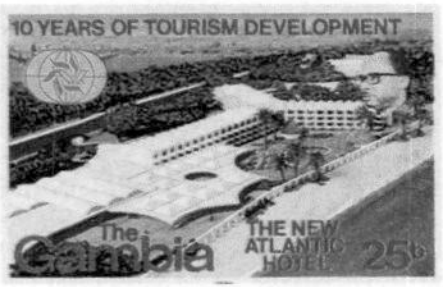

114 New Atlantic Hotel

1981. World Tourism Conference, Manila. Mult.
448 25b. Type **114** 15 10
449 75b. Ancient stone circles . . 20 40
450 85b. Conference emblem . . 30 60

115 1979 Abuko Satellite Earth Station 50b. Commemorative

1981. World Telecommunications Day.
451 **115** 50b. multicoloured . . . 45 20
452 – 50b. multicoloured . . . 45 20
453 – 85b. black and brown . . 50 45
DESIGNS: No. 452, 1975 Birth centenary of Schweitzer 50b. commemorative; 453 I.T.U. and W.H.O. emblems.

116 Prince Charles in Naval Uniform

1981. Royal Wedding. Multicoloured.
454 75b. Wedding bouquet from Gambia 20 20
455 1d. Type **116** 25 30
456 1d.25 Prince Charles and Lady Diana Spencer . . . 30 35

117 Planting-out Seedlings

1981. 10th Anniv of West African Rice Development Association. Multicoloured.
457 10b. Type **117** 10 10
458 50b. Care of the crops . . . 25 35
459 85b. Winnowing and drying 40 55

118 Bosc's Monitor

1981. Abuko Nature Reserve (4th series). Reptiles. Multicoloured.
460 40b. Type **118** . . . . 7·00 30
461 60b. Dwarf crocodile . . . . 7·50 80
462 80b. Royal python . . . . . 9·50 1·25
463 85b. Chameleon . . . . . . 9·50 1·25

119 Examination Room

1982. 30th Anniv of West African Examinations Council. Multicoloured.
464 60b. Type **119** 50 30
465 85b. First high school 65 45
466 1d.10 Council's office 85 55

1982. No. 454 surch **60B**.
467 60b. on 75b. Wedding bouquet from Gambia . . 75 1·60

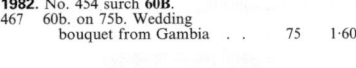

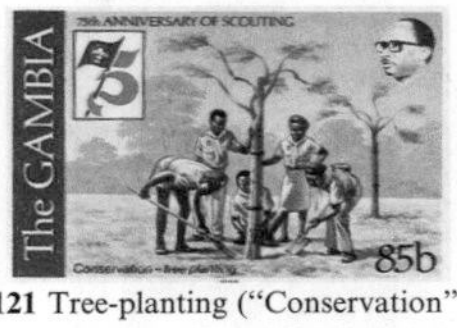

121 Tree-planting ("Conservation")

1982. 75th Anniv of Boy Scout Movement. Multicoloured.
468 85b. Type **121** . . . . 1·50 1·25
469 1d.25 Woodworking . . . . 1·75 2·50
470 1d.27 Lord Baden-Powell . . 2·00 3·25

122 Gambia Football Team

1982. World Cup Football Championship, Spain. Multicoloured.

471	10b. Type **122**	20	10
472	1d.10 Gambian team practice	1·10	70
473	1d.25 Bernabeu Stadium, Madrid	1·10	75
474	1d.55 FIFA World Cup	1·25	80
MS475	114 × 85 mm. Nos. 471/4	4·00	4·50

123 Gambia Coat of Arms

1982. 21st Birthday of Princess of Wales. Multicoloured.

476	10b. Type **123**	10	10
477	85b. Princess at City Hall, Cardiff, October 1981	30	20
478	1d.10 Bride and groom returning to Buckingham Palace	35	35
479	2d.50 Formal portrait	1·25	1·00

124 Vegetable Garden at Yundum Experimental Farm

1982. Economic Community of West African States Development. Multicoloured.

480	10b. Type **124**	30	15
481	60b. Banjul/Kaolack microwave tower	2·00	2·25
482	90b. Soap factory, Denton Bridge, Banjul	2·00	3·00
483	1d.25 Control tower, Yundum Airport	3·00	3·50

125 "Kassina cassinoides"

1982. Frogs. Multicoloured.

484	10b. Type **125**	1·75	20
485	20b. "Hylarana galamensis"	3·00	30
486	85b. "Euphlyctis occipitalis"	4·25	2·00
487	2d. "Kassina senegalensis"	6·50	11·00

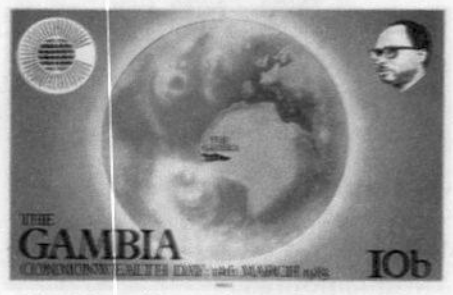

126 Satellite View of Gambia

1983. Commonwealth Day. Multicoloured.

488	10b. Type **126**	10	10
489	60b. Batik cloth	20	45
490	1d.10 Bagging groundnuts	35	65
491	2d.10 Gambia flag	55	1·25

127 Blessed Anne Marie Javouhey (foundress of Order)

1983. Centenary of Sisters of St. Joseph of Cluny's Work in Gambia. Multicoloured.

492	10b. Type **127**	10	10
493	85b. Bathurst Hospital, nun and school children (horiz)	45	50

128 Canoes

1983. River Craft. Multicoloured.

494	1b. Type **128**	15	60
495	2b. Upstream ferry	20	60
496	3b. Dredger	20	60
497	4b. "Sir Dawda" (harbour launch)	30	60
498	5b. Cargo liner	30	60
499	10b. "Lady Dale" (60ft. launch)	30	20
500	20b. "Shonga" (container ship)	45	55
501	30b. Large sailing canoe	45	55
502	40b. "Lady Wright" (river steamer)	65	75
503	50b. Container ship (different)	65	75
504	75b. Fishing boats	75	1·00
505	1d. Tug with groundnut barges	90	1·00
506	1d.25 Groundnut canoe	1·00	1·50
507	2d.50 "Banjul" (car ferry)	1·75	2·50
508	5d. "Bintang Bolong" (freighter)	2·50	4·00
509	10d. "Lady Chilel Jawara" (river vessel)	4·00	6·50

129 Osprey in Tree

1983. The Osprey. Multicoloured.

510	10b. Type **129**	1·50	50
511	60b. Osprey	2·75	2·50
512	85b. Osprey with catch	3·25	3·00
513	1d.10 In flight	3·50	5·00

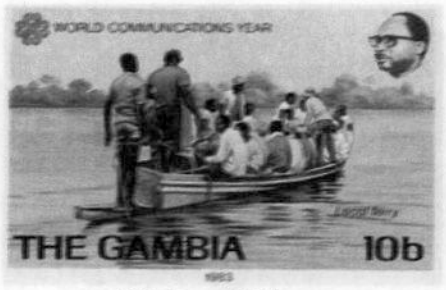

130 Local Ferry

1983. World Communications Year. Multicoloured.

514	10b. Type **130**	10	10
515	85b. Telex operator	45	50
516	90b. Radio Gambia	45	50
517	1d.10 Loading mail onto Douglas DC-9-80 aircraft	1·50	65

131 "St. Paul preaching at Athens" (detail)

1983. 500th Birth Anniv of Raphael.

518	**131** 60b. multicoloured	35	40
519	– 85b. multicoloured	45	50
520	– 1d. multicoloured	50	55
MS521	105 × 83 mm. 2d. multicoloured (vert)	1·25	1·25

Nos. 519/20 show different details of "St. Paul preaching at Athens".

132 Montgolfier Balloon and Siege of Paris Cover

1983. Bicentenary of Manned Flight. Multicoloured.

522	60b. Type **132**	35	40
523	85b. Douglas DC-10 aircraft and flown cover	45	50
524	90b. Junkers seaplane "Atlantis" and Hans Bertram cover	45	50
525	1d.25 Lunar module and H. E. Sieger's space cover	50	70
526	4d. Airship "Graf Zeppelin"	2·25	3·00

133 Shot-putting

134 Goofy

1984. Olympic Games, Los Angeles (1st issue). Multicoloured.

527	60b. Type **133**	25	30
528	85b. High jumping (horiz)	35	40
529	90b. Wrestling	35	40
530	1d. Gymnastics	40	45
531	1d.25 Swimming (horiz)	50	55
532	2d. Diving	80	85
MS533	100 × 80 mm. 5d. Yachting	2·00	2·75

See also Nos. 555/8.

1984. Easter. Multicoloured.

534	1b. Type **134**	10	10
535	2b. Mickey Mouse	10	10
536	3b. Huey, Dewey and Louie	10	10
537	4b. Goofy (different)	10	10
538	5b. Donald Duck	10	10
539	10b. Chip 'n' Dale	10	10
540	60b. Pluto	35	40
541	90b. Scrooge McDuck	50	60
542	5d. Morty and Ferdie	2·25	2·75
MS543	125 × 100 mm. 5d. Donald Duck (different)	3·50	3·50

Nos. 534/42 show Walt Disney cartoon characters painting eggs.

135 Young Crocodiles Hatching

1984. Endangered Species. The Nile Crocodile. Multicoloured.

544	4b. Type **135**	1·25	65
545	6b. Adult carrying young	1·25	65
546	90b. Adult	9·00	3·25
547	1d.50 Crocodile at riverbank	10·00	8·00
MS548	126 × 94 mm. As Nos. 544/7, but without W.W.F. logo	5·50	8·00

136 Port Banjul

1984. 250th Anniv of "Lloyd's List" (newspaper). Multicoloured.

549	60b. Type **136**	60	50
550	85b. Bulk carrier	75	80
551	90b. Sinking of the "Dagomba"	75	90
552	1d.25 19th-century frigate	1·25	1·60

1984. Universal Postal Union Congress, Hamburg. Nos. 507/8 optd **19th UPU CONGRESS HAMBURG**.

553	2d.50 "Banjul" (car ferry)	1·00	1·50
554	5d. "Bintang Bolong" (ferry)	1·75	2·50

138 Sprinting

1984. Olympic Games, Los Angeles (2nd issue). Multicoloured.

555	60b. Type **138**	25	30
556	85b. Long jumping	35	40
557	90b. Long-distance running	35	40
558	1d.25 Triple jumping	50	55

139 Airship "Graf Zeppelin"

1984. 50th Anniv of Gambia–South America Trans-Atlantic Flights. Multicoloured.

559	60b. Type **139**	1·10	1·00
560	85b. Dornier Wal on S.S. "Westfalen"	1·60	1·75
561	90b. Dornier Do-18	1·75	2·50
562	1d.25 Dornier Wal	1·75	2·75

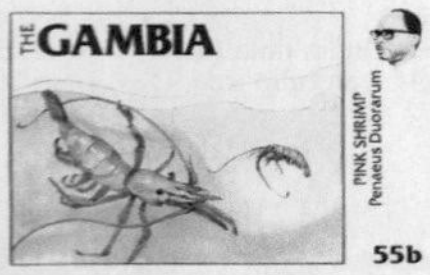

140 Pink Shrimp

1984. Marine Life. Multicoloured.

563	55b. Type **140**	35	30
564	75b. Atlantic loggerhead turtle	55	40
565	1d.50 Portuguese man-of-war	90	1·00
566	2d.35 Fiddler crab	1·40	1·60
MS567	105 × 70 mm. 5d. Cowrie snail	2·75	4·00

141 "Antanartia hippomene"

1984. Butterflies. Multicoloured.

568	10b. Type **141**	30	20
569	85b. "Pseudacraea eurytus"	80	90
570	90b. "Charaxes lactitinctus"	80	90
571	3d. "Graphium pylades"	2·00	3·75
MS572	105 × 75 mm. 5d. "Eurema hapale"	10·00	9·50

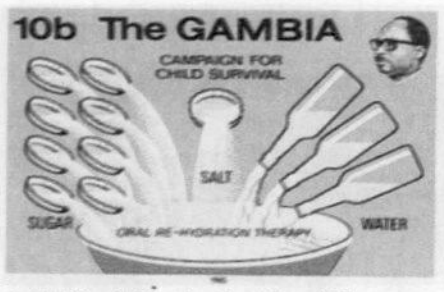

142 Oral Re-hydration Therapy

1985. Campaign for Child Survival.

573	**142** 10b. black, blue and brown	10	10
574	– 85b. multicoloured	35	45
575	– 1d.10 multicoloured	45	65
576	– 1d.50 multicoloured	60	80

DESIGNS: 85b. Growth monitoring; 1d.10, Health care worker with women and babies ("Promotion of breast feeding"); 1d.50, Universal immunization.

143 Women at Market

1985. Women and Development. Multicoloured.

577	60b. Type **143**	25	35
578	85b. Type **143**	35	50
579	1d. Woman office worker	40	60
580	1d.25 As 1d.	50	90

144 Turkey Vulture

145 The Queen Mother

1985. Birth Bicentenary of John J. Audubon (ornithologist). Designs showing original paintings. Multicoloured.

581	60b. Type **144**	1·40	75
582	85b. American darter ("American Anhinga")	1·60	1·50
583	1d.50 Green-backed heron ("Green Heron")	2·00	3·25
584	5d. Wood duck	3·25	5·50
MS585	100 × 70 mm. 10d. Great northern diver ("Common Loon")	6·50	4·00

1985. Life and Times of Queen Elizabeth the Queen Mother. Multicoloured.

586	85b. The Queen Mother and King George VI reviewing Home Guard	1·25	30
587	3d. Type **145**	1·75	1·50
588	5d. The Queen Mother with posy	2·50	2·25
MS589	56 × 85 mm. 10d. The Queen Mother in Garter robes	4·25	3·25

145a Mickey Mouse steering the "Calamity Jane"

1985. 150th Birth Anniv of Mark Twain (author). Designs showing Walt Disney cartoon characters in scenes from "Life on the Mississippi". Multicoloured.
590 1d.50 Type **145a** . . . . . . 2·00 2·00
591 2d. Mickey and Minnie Mouse at antebellum mansion . . . . 2·25 2·25
592 2d.50 Donald Duck and Goofy heaving the lead . . 2·50 2·50
593 3d. Poker game aboard the "Gold Dust" . . . . . . 2·75 2·75
MS594 126 × 101 mm. 10d. Mickey Mouse and riverboat . . . . . 7·50 4·75

145b The King (Mickey Mouse) and Portrait of the Princess (Minnie Mouse)

1985. Birth Bicentenaries of Grimm Brothers (folklorists). Designs showing Walt Disney cartoon characters in scenes from "Faithful John". Multicoloured.
595 60b. Type **145b** 75 40
596 85b. The King showing the Princess his treasures . . . 95 50
597 2d.35 Faithful John (Goofy) playing trumpet . . . . . 2·25 1·40
598 5d. Faithful John turned to stone . . . . 3·25 2·50
MS599 126 × 101 mm. 10d. Faithful John after recovery . . . . . 7·50 5·00

1985. Olympic Gold Medal Winners, Los Angeles. Nos. 527/32 optd.
600 60b. Type 133 (optd **GOLD MEDALLIST CLAUDIA LOCH WEST GERMANY**) 40 40
601 85b. High jumping (optd **GOLD MEDALLIST ULRIKE MEYFARTH WEST GERMANY**) . . . 50 50
602 90b. Wrestling (optd **GOLD MEDALLIST PASQUALE PASSARELLI WEST GERMANY**) 50 50
603 1d. Gymnastics (optd **GOLD MEDALLIST LI NING CHINA**) 55 55
604 1d.25 Swimming (optd **GOLD MEDALLIST MICHAEL GROSS WEST GERMANY**) 70 70
605 2d. Diving (optd **GOLD MEDALLIST SYLVIE BERNIER CANADA**) . . 1·00 1·00
MS606 100 × 80 mm. 5d. Yachting (optd **GOLD MEDAL STAR CLASS U.S.A.**) . . . . 2·00 2·00

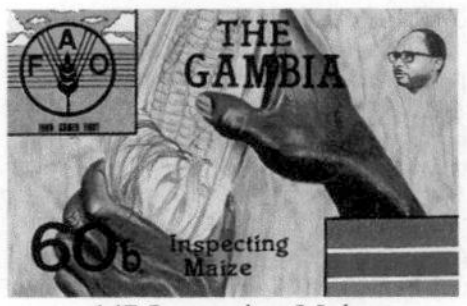

147 Inspecting Maize

1985. United Nations Anniversaries. Multicoloured.
607 60b. Type **147** 40 35
608 85b. Football match, Independence Stadium, Banjul 50 40
609 1d.10 Rice fields 60 60
610 2d. Central Bank of The Gambia . . . . 85 1·00
611 3d. Cow and calf . . . . . 1·50 1·75
612 4d. Banjul harbour . . . . . 2·00 2·25
613 5d. Gambian fruits . . . . . 2·25 2·50
614 6d. Oyster Creek Bridge . . . 2·50 3·00
Nos. 607, 609, 611 and 613 commemorate the 40th anniv of the Food and Agriculture Organization and Nos. 608, 610, 612 and 614 the 40th anniv of the United Nations Organization.

148 Fishermen in Fotoba, Guinea

1985. 50th Anniv of Diocese of The Gambia and Guinea. Multicoloured.
615 60b. Type **148** 40 30
616 85b. St. Mary's Primary School, Banjul 40 40
617 1d.10 St. Mary's Cathedral, Banjul 40 65
618 1d.50 Mobile dispensary at Christy Kunda . . . . . . 1·10 85

149 "Virgin and Child" (Dieric Bouts)

1985. Christmas. Religious Paintings. Multicoloured.
619 60b. Type **149** 20 25
620 85b. "The Annunciation" (Robert Campin) 25 30
621 1d.50 "Adoration of the Shepherds" (Gerard David) 45 50
622 5d. "The Nativity" (Gerard David) . . . . 1·60 1·75
MS623 106 × 84 mm. 10d. "Adoration of the Magi" (Hieronymus Bosch) . . . . . 3·50 4·00

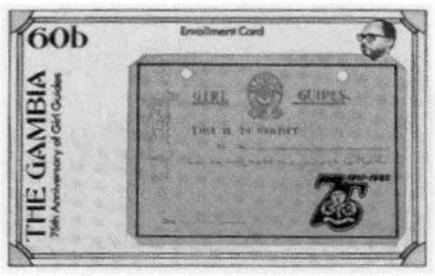

150 Enrolment Card

1985. 75th Anniv of Girl Guide Movement. Multicoloured.
624 60b. Type **150** 40 30
625 85b. 2nd Bathurst Company centre 50 35
626 1d.50 Lady Baden-Powell (vert) . . . . 70 1·00
627 5d. Miss Rosamond Fowlis (Gambian Guide Association leader) (vert) 2·00 3·75
MS628 97 × 67 mm. 10d. Gambian girl guides (vert) . . . . 4·50 6·00

151 Girl and Village Scene

1985. International Youth Year. Multicoloured.
629 60b. Type **151** 30 30
630 85b. Youth and wrestling bout 35 35
631 1d.10 Girl and Griot storyteller . . . . 45 1·00
632 1d.50 Youth and crocodile pool . . . . 70 1·40
MS633 106 × 76 mm. 5d. Herdsman with cattle . . . . 2·00 3·00

151a Maria Mitchell (astronomer) and Kitt Peak National Observatory, Arizona

1986. Appearance of Halley's Comet (1st issue). Multicoloured.
634 10b. Type **151a** 40 20
635 20b. Neil Armstrong, first man on Moon, 1969 . . . 55 25
636 75b. "Skylab 4" and Comet Kohoutek, 1973 . . . . . 85 65
637 1d. N.A.S.A.'s infra-red astronomical satellite and Halley's Comet . . . . . 1·00 80
638 2d. Comet of 1577 from Turkish painting . . . . . 1·50 1·50
639 10d. N.A.S.A.'s International Cometary Explorer . . . . 4·00 5·50
MS640 102 × 70 mm. 10d. Halley's Comet . . . . 5·00 6·00
See also Nos. 679/84.

151b Duke of York and Family, Royal Tournament, 1936

1986. 60th Birthday of Queen Elizabeth II.
641 **151b** 1d. black and yellow . . 25 30
642 – 2d.50 multicoloured . . 65 70
643 – 10d. multicoloured . . . 2·50 3·50
MS644 120 × 85 mm. 10d. black and brown . . . . 3·00 3·00
DESIGNS: Nos. 642, Queen attending christening, 1983; 643, In West Germany, 1978; **MS**644, Duchess of York with her daughters, Balmoral, 1935.

152 Two Players competing for Ball

1986. World Cup Football Championship, Mexico. Multicoloured.
645 75b. Type **152** 75 60
646 1d. Player kicking ball . . . 1·00 85
647 2d.50 Player kicking ball (different) . . . . 2·00 2·25
648 10d. Player heading ball . . . 5·00 6·00
MS649 100 × 70 mm. 10d. Goalkeeper saving goal . . . . 7·50 7·00

153 Mercedes "500" (1986)

1986. "Ameripex" International Stamp Exhibition, Chicago. Centenary (1985) of First Benz Motor Car. Multicoloured.
650 25b. Type **153** 20 10
651 75b. Cord "810" (1935) . . . 35 40
652 1d. Borgward "Isabella Coupe" (1957) 40 60
653 1d.25 Lamborghini "Countach" (1985/6) . . . 50 70
654 2d. Ford "Thunderbird" (1955) . . . . 50 1·25
655 2d.25 Citroen "DS19" (1956) 50 1·60
656 5d. Bugatti "Atlante" (1936) 70 3·00
657 10d. Horch "853" (1936) . . 80 5·00
MS658 Two sheets, each 100 × 70 mm. (a) 12d. Benz "8/20" (1913). (b) 12d. Steiger "10/50" (1924) Set of 2 sheets . . . . 4·75 12·00
The 25b. value is inscribed "MECEDES" and the 10d. "LARL BENZ".

153a John Jacob Astor (financier)

1986. Centenary of Statue of Liberty (1st issue). Multicoloured. Designs showing Statue of Liberty and immigrants to the U.S.A.
659 20b. Type **153a** 10 10
660 1d. Jacob Riis (journalist) . . 40 50
661 1d.25 Igor Sikorsky (aeronautics engineer) . . . 60 60
662 5d. Charles Boyer (actor) . . 2·50 2·50
MS663 114 × 80 mm. 10d. Statue of Liberty (vert) . . . . 4·00 4·50
See also Nos. 705/14.

153b Prince Andrew and Miss Sarah Ferguson

1986. Royal Wedding. Multicoloured.
664 1d. Type **153b** 40 45
665 2d.50 Prince Andrew . . . . 1·00 1·40
666 4d. Prince Andrew as helicopter pilot . . . . . . 2·50 2·00
MS667 88 × 88 mm. 7d. Prince Andrew and Miss Sarah Ferguson (different) . . . . 4·75 3·50

1986. World Cup Football Championship Winners, Mexico. Nos. 645/8 optd **WINNERS Argentina 3 W.Germany 2**.
668 75b. Type **152** 30 40
669 1d. Player kicking ball . . . 40 55
670 2d.50 Player kicking ball (different) . . . . 1·00 1·25
671 10d. Player heading ball . . . 4·25 4·75
MS672 100 × 70 mm. Goalkeeper saving goal . . . . 4·50 4·50

154 Minnie Mouse (Great Britain)

1986. Christmas. Designs showing Walt Disney cartoon characters posting letters in various countries. Multicoloured.
673 1d. Type **154** 75 60
674 1d.25 Huey (U.S.A.) 80 80
675 2d. Huey, Dewey and Louie (France) . . . . 1·25 1·40
676 2d.35 Kanga and Roo (Australia) . . . . 1·40 1·75
677 5d. Goofy (Germany) . . . . 2·25 3·00
MS678 127 × 101 mm. 10d. Goofy (Sweden) . . . . 7·50 6·00
Nos. 673/7 also show the "Stockholmia '86" International Stamp Exhibition emblem.

1986. Appearance of Halley's Comet (2nd issue). Nos. 634/9 optd **HALLEYS COMET 1985-OFFICIAL-1986**.
679 10b. Maria Mitchell (astronomer) and Kitt Peak National Observatory, Arizona 30 15
680 20b. Neil Armstrong, first man on Moon, 1969 . . . 50 20
681 75b. "Skylab 4" and Comet Kohoutek, 1973 . . . . . 75 50
682 1d. N.A.S.A.'s infra-red astronomical satellite and Halley's Comet 85 60
683 2d. Comet of 1577 from Turkish painting . . . . . 1·40 1·75
684 10d. N.A.S.A.'s International Cometary Explorer . . . . 3·75 6·00
MS685 102 × 70 mm. 10d. Halley's Comet . . . . 3·00 4·25

155 Bugarab and Tabala

1987. Manding Musical Instruments. Multicoloured.
686 75b. Type **155** 15 20
687 1d. Balaphong and fiddle . . 15 25
688 1d.25 Bolongbato and konting (vert) 20 35
689 10d. Antique and modern koras (vert) . . . . 1·60 3·00
MS690 100 × 70 mm. 12d. Sabarr 1·90 2·50

156 "Snowing"

1987. Birth Centenary of Marc Chagall (artist). Multicoloured.

691 75b. Type **156** 40 40
692 85b. "The Boat" 50 50
693 1d. "Maternity" 65 65
694 1d.25 "The Flute Player" 75 75
695 2d.35 "Lovers and the Beast" 1·00 1·25
696 4d. "Fishes at Saint Jean" 1·25 2·00
697 5d. "Entering the Ring" 1·50 2·50
698 10d. "Three Acrobats" 2·25 3·75
MS699 Two sheets. (a) 110 × 68 mm. 12d. "The Cattle Driver" (104 × 61 mm). (b) 109 × 95 mm. 12d. "The Sabbath" (104 × 89 mm). Imperf Set of 2 sheets 7·50 8·50

157 "America", 1851

1987. America's Cup Yachting Championship. Multicoloured.

700 20b. Type **157** 20 15
701 1d. "Courageous", 1974 35 35
702 2d.50 "Volunteer", 1887 75 1·10
703 10d. "Intrepid", 1967 2·25 3·25
MS704 114 × 89 mm. 12d. "Australia II", 1983 4·00 3·00

158 Arm of Statue of Liberty

159 "Lantana camara"

1987. Centenary of Statue of Liberty (1986) (2nd issue). Multicoloured.

705 1b. Type **158** 10 10
706 2b. Launch passing Statue (horiz) 10 10
707 3b. Schooner passing Statue (horiz) 10 10
708 5b. U.S.S. "John F. Kennedy" (aircraft carrier) and "Queen Elizabeth 2" (liner) (horiz) 10 10
709 50b. Checking Statue for damage 40 40
710 75b. Cleaning in progress 55 55
711 1d. Working on Statue 70 70
712 1d.25 Statue and fireworks 80 80
713 10d. Statue illuminated 4·25 4·75
714 12d. Statue and fireworks (different) 4·50 5·00

1987. Flowers of Abuko Nature Reserve. Multicoloured.

715 75b. Type **159** 20 15
716 1d. "Clerodendrum thomsoniae" 20 20
717 1d.50 "Haemanthus multiflorus" 30 30
718 1d.70 "Gloriosa simplex" 30 35
719 1d.75 "Combretum microphyllum" 35 40
720 2d.25 "Eulophia quineensis" 50 60
721 5d. "Erythrina senegalensis" 1·10 1·25
722 15d. "Dichrostachys glomerata" 2·75 3·50
MS723 Two sheets, each 100 × 70 mm. (a) 15d. "Costus spectabilis". (b) 15d. "Strophanthus preussii" Set of 2 sheets 5·50 7·50

160 Front of Mail Bus

161 Basketball

1987. "Capex '87" International Stamp Exhibition, Toronto and 10th Anniv of Gambia Public Transport Corporation. Mail Buses. Mult.

724 20b. Type **160** 60 20
725 75b. Bus in Banjul (horiz) 90 45
726 1d. Passengers queueing for bus (horiz) 90 45
727 10d. Two buses on rural road 3·50 6·50
MS728 77 × 70 mm. 12d. Parked bus fleet (horiz) 4·50 4·50

1987. Olympic Games, Seoul (1988) (1st issue). Multicoloured.

729 50b. Type **161** 35 20
730 1d. Volleyball 50 35
731 3d. Hockey (horiz) 1·10 85
732 10d. Handball (horiz) 2·50 2·25
MS733 100 × 85 mm. 15d. Football (horiz) 3·00 2·75
See also Nos. 779/83.

162 "A Partridge in a Pear Tree"

163 Campfire Singsong

1987. Christmas. Designs showing a Victorian couple in scenes from carol "The Twelve Days of Christmas". Multicoloured.

734 20b. Type **162** 60 50
735 40b. "Two turtle doves" 65 55
736 60b. "Three French hens" 70 60
737 75b. "Four calling birds" 70 60
738 1d. "Five golden rings" 70 60
739 1d.25 "Six geese a-laying" 80 65
740 1d.50 "Seven swans a-swimming" 80 65
741 2d. "Eight maids a-milking" 90 75
742 3d. "Nine ladies dancing" 95 85
743 5d. "Ten lords a-leaping" 1·25 1·25
744 10d. "Eleven pipers piping" 1·90 2·00
745 12d. "Twelve drummers drumming" 2·25 2·25
MS746 100 × 70 mm. 15d. Exchanging presents (horiz) 2·40 3·25

1987. World Scout Jamboree, Australia. Multicoloured.

747 75b. Type **163** 50 30
748 1d. Scouts examining African katydid 70 40
749 1d.25 Scouts watching Red-tailed tropic bird 1·50 85
750 12d. Scouts helping bus passenger 3·75 4·50
MS751 72 × 98 mm. 15d. Scouts on field trip 6·50 7·50

163a Morty and Ferdie examining Trevithick's Locomotive, 1804

1987. 60th Anniv of Mickey Mouse (Walt Disney cartoon character) (1st issue). Multicoloured.

752 60b. Type **163a** 25 25
753 75b. Clarabelle Cow in "Empire State Express", 1893 30 30
754 1d. Donald Duck inspecting Stephenson's "Rocket", 1829 40 40
755 1d.25 Piglet and Winnie the Pooh with Santa Fe Railroad locomotive, 1920 45 45
756 2d. Donald and Daisy Duck with Pennsylvania Railroad Class GG1 electric locomotive, 1933 70 70
757 5d. Mickey Mouse in "Stourbridge Lion", 1829 1·60 1·75
758 10d. Goofy in "Best Friend of Charleston", 1830 2·75 3·25
759 12d. Brer Bear and Brer Rabbit with Union Pacific diesel locomotive No. M10001, 1934 3·00 3·50
MS760 Two sheets, each 127 × 101 mm. (a) 15d. Chip n'Dale in "The General", 1855. (b) 15d. Donald Duck and Mickey Mouse in modern French "TGV" train Set of 2 sheets 7·50 8·00
See also Nos. 849/58.

164 Common Duiker and Acacia

165 Wedding Portrait, 1947

1988. Flora and Fauna. Multicoloured.

761 50b. Type **164** 20 10
762 75b. Red-billed hornbill and casuarina (vert) 65 30
763 90b. West African dwarf crocodile and rice 30 20
764 1d. Leopard and papyrus (vert) 30 20
765 1d.25 Crowned crane ("Crested Crane") and millet 65 45
766 2d. Waterbuck and baobab tree (vert) 40 60
767 3d. Oribi and Senegal palm 50 1·25
768 5d. Hippopotamus and papaya (vert) 90 1·75
MS769 98 × 69 mm. (a) 12d. Red-throated bee eater and acacia (vert). (b) 12d. Eastern white pelican ("Great White Pelican") Set of 2 sheets 2·75 4·50

1988. Royal Ruby Wedding.

770 **165** 75b. brown, black orange 30 15
771 – 1d. brown, black and blue 40 20
772 – 3d. multicoloured 90 1·00
773 – 10d. multicoloured 2·25 3·25
MS774 100 × 75 mm. 15d. multicoloured 3·00 3·25
DESIGNS: 1d. Engagement photograph; 3d. Wedding portrait, 1947 (different); 10d. Queen Elizabeth II and Prince Philip (photo by Karsh), 1986; 15d. Wedding portrait with page, 1947.

1988. Stamp Exhibitions. Nos. 689, 703, 722 and 726 optd.

775 1d. Passengers queueing for bus (optd **Independence 40**, Israel) 25 25
776 10d. Antique and modern koras (optd **FINLANDIA 88**, Helsinki) 2·00 2·50
777 10d. "Intrepid" (yacht), 1967 (optd **Praga '88**, Prague) 2·00 2·50
778 15d. "Dichrostachys glomerata" (optd **OLYMPHILEX '88**, Seoul) 2·75 3·00

1988. Olympic Games, Seoul (2nd issue). As T **161**. Multicoloured.

779 1d. Archery 50 20
780 1d.25 Boxing 50 25
781 5d. Gymnastics 1·25 1·10
782 10d. Start of 100 metre race (horiz) 2·00 2·25
MS783 74 × 102 mm. 15d. Medal winners on rostrum 2·40 3·25

166 Red Cross Flag

1988. Anniversaries and Events. Multicoloured.

784 50b. Type **166** (125th anniv) 75 55
785 75b. "Friendship 7" spacecraft (25th anniv of first American manned Earth orbit) 85 60
786 1d. British Airways Concorde (10th anniv of Concorde London–New York service) 2·00 1·00
787 1d.25 "Spirit of St. Louis" (60th anniv of first solo transatlantic flight) 1·25 1·00
788 2d. North American X-15 (20th anniv of fastest aircraft flight) 1·60 1·40
789 3d. Bell "XS-1" rocket plane (40th anniv of first supersonic flight) 1·75 1·50
790 10d. English and Spanish galleons (400th anniv of Spanish Armada) 3·75 3·75
791 12d. "Titanic" (75th anniv of sinking) 5·50 4·25
MS792 Two sheets. (a) 113 × 85 mm. 15d. Kaiser Wilhelm Memorial Church, Berlin (vert) (750th anniv of Berlin). (b) 121 × 90 mm. 15d. Kangaroo (Bicentenary of Australian Settlement) Set of 2 sheets 4·75 7·00

166a "Emperor Charles V"

1988. 500th Birth Anniv of Titian (artist). Mult.

793 25b. Type **166a** 20 20
794 50b. "St. Margaret and the Dragon" 35 35
795 60b. "Ranuccio Farnese" 40 40
796 75b. "Tarquin and Lucretia" 55 55
797 1d. "The Knight of Malta" 70 70
798 5d. "Spain succouring Faith" 2·25 2·50
799 10d. "Doge Francesco Venier" 3·50 3·50
800 12d. "Doge Grimani before the Faith" (detail) 3·75 3·75
MS801 110 × 95 mm. (a) 15d. "Jealous Husband" (detail). (b) 15d. "Venus blindfolding Cupid" Set of 2 sheets 4·75 7·00

167 John Kennedy sailing

1988. 25th Death Anniv of President John F. Kennedy. Multicoloured.

802 75b. Type **167** 15 15
803 1d. Kennedy signing Peace Corps legislation, 1962 15 20
804 1d.25 Speaking at U.N., New York (vert) 20 25
805 12d. Grave and eternal flame, Arlington National Cemetery (vert) 1·90 2·75
MS806 99 × 72 mm. 15d. John F. Kennedy (vert) 2·40 3·50

168 Airship "Graf Zeppelin" (first regular air passenger service), 1910

1988. Milestones of Transportation. Multicoloured.

807 25b. Type **168** 80 35
808 50b. Stephenson's "Locomotion" (first permanent public railway), 1825 1·50 50
809 75b. G.M. "Sun Racer" (first world solar challenge), 1987 1·25 65
810 1d. Sprague's "Premiere" (first operational electric tramway), 1888 1·50 80
811 1d.25 "Gold Rush" Bicycle (holder of man-powered land speed record), 1986 2·25 85
812 2d.50 Robert Goddard and rocket launcher (first liquid fuel rocket), 1925 2·00 1·25
813 10d. "Orukter Amphibolos" (first steam traction engine), 1805 4·00 3·25
814 12d. "Sovereign of the Seas" (largest cruise liner), 1988 4·00 3·50
MS815 Two sheets, each 71 × 92 mm. (a) 15d. U.S.S. "Nautilus" (first nuclear-powered submarine), 1954 (vert). (b) 15d. Fulton's "Nautilus" (first fish-shaped submarine), 1800's (vert) Set of 2 sheets 8·00 8·50

169 Emmett Kelley

170 Prince Henry the Navigator and Caravel

1988. Entertainers. Multicoloured.

816	20b. Type **169**	10	10
817	1d. Gambia National Ensemble	25	25
818	1d.25 Jackie Gleason	30	30
819	1d.50 Laurel and Hardy	40	40
820	2d.50 Yul Brynner	75	75
821	3d. Cary Grant	95	95
822	10d. Danny Kaye	3·00	3·00
823	20d. Charlie Chaplin	5·50	5·50
MS824	Two sheets. (a) 110 × 77 mm. 15d. Marx Brothers (horiz). (b) 70 × 99 mm. 15d. Fred Astaire and Rita Hayworth (horiz) Set of 2 sheets	9·50	9·50

1988. Exploration of West Africa. Multicoloured.

825	50b. Type **170**	80	60
826	75b. Jesse Ramsden's sextant, 1785	85	70
827	1d. 15th-century hourglass	90	80
828	1d.25 Prince Henry the Navigator and Vasco da Gama	1·40	95
829	2d.50 Vasco da Gama and ship	2·25	1·60
830	5d. Mungo Park and map of Gambia River (horiz)	3·50	2·50
831	10d. Map of West Africa, 1563 (horiz)	4·50	3·75
832	12d. Portuguese caravel (horiz)	4·50	4·00
MS833	Two sheets, each 65 × 100 mm. (a) 15d. Ship from Columbus's fleet off Gambia. (b) 15d. 15th-century ship moored off Gambia Set of 2 sheets	7·00	6·50

171 Projected Space Plane and Ernst Mach (physicist)

1988. 350th Anniv of Publications of Galileo's "Discourses". Space Achievements. Mult.

834	50b. Type **171**	70	30
835	75b. OAO III astronomical satellite and Niels Bohr (physicist)	80	40
836	1d. Space shuttle, projected space station and Robert Goddard (physicist) (horiz)	90	45
837	1d.25 Jupiter probe, 1979, and Edward Barnard (astronomer) (horiz)	1·25	60
838	2d. Hubble Space Telescope and George Hale (astronomer)	1·75	75
839	3d. Earth-to-Moon laser measurement and Albert Michaelson (physicist) (horiz)	1·75	85
840	10d. HEAO-2 "Einstein" orbital satellite and Albert Einstein "physicist"	3·25	2·75
841	20d. "Voyager" (first non-stop round-the-world flight), 1987, and Wright Brothers (aviation pioneers) (horiz)	5·50	5·00
MS842	Two sheets. (a) 99 × 75 mm. 15d. Great Red Spot on Jupiter (horiz). (b) 88 × 71 mm. 15d. Neil Armstrong (first man on Moon), 1969 Set of 2 sheets	6·00	8·00

172 Passing Out Parade

1989. Army Day. Multicoloured.

843	75b. Type **172**	25	25
844	1d. Standards of The Gambia Regiment	25	25
845	1d.25 Side drummer in ceremonial uniform (vert)	30	30
846	10d. Marksman with Atlantic Shooting Cup (vert)	2·00	2·00
847	15d. Soldiers on assault course (vert)	2·75	2·75
848	20d. Gunner with 105 mm field gun	3·00	3·00

173 Mickey Mouse, 1928

1989. 60th Birthday of Mickey Mouse (2nd issue). Multicoloured.

849	2d. Type **173**	1·00	90
850	2d. Mickey Mouse, 1931	1·00	90
851	2d. Mickey Mouse, 1936	1·00	90
852	2d. Mickey Mouse, 1955	1·00	90
853	2d. Mickey Mouse, 1947	1·00	90
854	2d. Mickey Mouse as magician, 1940	1·00	90
855	2d. Mickey Mouse with palette, 1960	1·00	90
856	2d. Mickey Mouse as Uncle Sam, 1976	1·00	90
857	2d. Mickey Mouse, 1988	1·00	90
MS858	138 × 109 mm. 15d. Mickey Mouse at 60th birthday party (132 × 103 mm) Imperf	4·25	4·00

Nos. 849/57 were printed together, se-tenant, forming a composite design.

174 "Le Coup de Lance" (detail)

176 "Druryia antimachus"

175 African Emerald Cuckoo

1989. Easter. Religious Paintings by Rubens. Multicoloured.

859	50b. Type **174**	45	25
860	75b. "Flagellation of Christ"	55	35
861	1d. "Lamentation for Christ"	55	35
862	1d.25 "Descent from the Cross"	60	40
863	2d. "Holy Trinity"	90	70
864	5d. "Doubting Thomas"	1·75	1·75
865	10d. "Lamentation over Christ"	2·50	2·75
866	12d. "Lamentation with Virgin and St. John"	2·50	3·00
MS867	Two sheets, each 96 × 110 mm. (a) 15d. "The Last Supper". (b) 15d. "Raising of the Cross" Set of 2 sheets	4·50	5·50

1989. West African Birds. Multicoloured.

868	20b. Type **175**	90	30
869	60b. Grey-headed bush shrike	1·40	50
870	75b. South African crowned crane ("Crowned Crane")	1·40	55
871	1d. Secretary bird	1·60	60
872	2d. Red-billed hornbill	2·25	1·00
873	5d. Superb sunbird	3·00	3·00
874	10d. Pearl-spotted owlet ("Little owl")	4·00	4·25
875	12d. Bateleur ("Bateleur Eagle")	4·00	4·25
MS876	Two sheets, each 115 × 86 mm. (a) 15d. Ostrich. (b) 15d. Red-billed fire finch Set of 2 sheets	7·50	8·00

1989. Butterflies of Gambia. Multicoloured.

877	50b. Type **176**	65	30
878	75b. "Euphaedra neophron"	75	45
879	1d. "Aterica rabena"	75	45
880	1d.25 "Salamis parhassus"	85	55
881	5d. "Precis rhadama"	2·25	2·25
882	10d. "Papilio demodocus"	3·00	3·00
883	12d. "Charaxes etesipe"	3·25	3·50
884	15d. "Danaus formosa"	3·25	3·75
MS885	Two sheets, each 99 × 68 mm. (a) 15d. "Euptera pluto". (b) 15d. "Euphaedra ceres" Set of 2 sheets	11·00	12·00

177 Class "River" Steam Locomotive No. 021, 1959, Nigeria

1989. African Steam Locomotive. Multicoloured.

886	50b. Type **177**	70	35
887	75b. Class 14A steam locomotive, Rhodesia	80	45
888	1d. British-built steam locomotive No. 120, Sudan	85	55
889	1d.25 Steam locomotive, 1925, U.S.A.	95	65
890	5d. North British steam locomotive, 1955	2·50	1·75
891	7d. Scottish-built steam locomotive No. 120, 1926	2·75	2·75
892	10d. East African Railways Class 1T steam tank locomotive	3·00	3·00
893	12d. American-built steam locomotive, Ghana	3·25	3·75
MS894	Two sheets, each 82 × 58 mm. (a) 15d. East African Railways Class 25 steam locomotive No. 2904 (vert). (b) 15d. East African Railways Class 25 steam locomotive No. 3700A (vert) Set of 2 sheets	9·50	10·00

1989. "Philexfrance '89" Int Stamp Exhibition, Paris. Nos. 686/9 optd **PHILEXFRANCE '89**.

895	75b. Type **155**	15	15
896	1d. Balaphong and fiddle	20	20
897	1d.25 Bolongbato and konting (vert)	25	25
898	10d. Antique and modern koras (vert)	1·75	2·50
MS899	100 × 70 mm. 12d. Sabarr	1·75	2·25

177a "Sparrow and Bamboo" (Hiroshige)

1989. Japanese Art. Multicoloured.

900	50b. Type **177a**	50	30
901	75b. "Peonies and a Canary" (Hokusai)	65	40
902	1d. "Crane and Marsh Grasses" (Hiroshige)	75	45
903	1d.25 "Crossbill and Thistle" (Hokusai)	85	60
904	2d. "Cuckoo and Azalea" (Hokusai)	1·25	80
905	5d. "Parrot on a Pine Branch" (Hiroshige)	2·00	2·00
906	10d. "Mandarin Ducks in a Stream" (Hiroshige)	2·75	3·00
907	12d. "Bullfinch and Drooping Cherry" (Hokusai)	2·75	3·25
MS908	Two sheets, each 102 × 77 mm. (a) 15d. "Tit and Peony" (Hiroshige). (b) 15d. "Peony and Butterfly" (Shigenobou) Set of 2 sheets	9·00	9·50

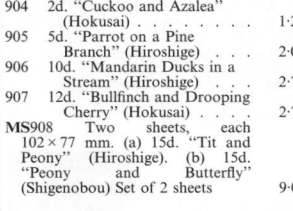

179 Rialto Bridge, Venice

1989. World Cup Football Championship, Italy (1990) (1st issue). Designs showing landmarks and players. Multicoloured.

909	75b. Type **179**	45	45
910	1d.25 The Baptistery, Pisa	60	60
911	7d. Casino, San Remo	2·25	2·75
912	12d. Colosseum, Rome	3·00	3·50
MS913	Two sheets, each 104 × 78 mm. (a) 15d. St. Mark's Cathedral, Venice. (b) 15d. Piazza Colonna, Rome Set of 2 sheets	9·50	10·00

See also Nos. 1064/8.

180 "Vitex doniana"

1989. Medicinal Plants. Multicoloured.

914	20b. Type **180**	20	20
915	50b. "Ricinus communis"	30	30
916	75b. "Palisota hirsuta"	45	45
917	1d. "Smilax kraussiana"	55	55
918	1d.25 "Aspilia africana"	65	65
919	5d. "Newbouldia laevis"	1·75	2·00
920	8d. "Monodora tenuifolia"	1·90	2·50
921	10d. "Gossypium arboreum"	2·00	2·50
MS922	Two sheets, each 87 × 72 mm. (a) 15d. "Kigelia africana". (b) 15d. "Spathodea campanulata" Set of 2 sheets	11·00	11·00

181 Lookdown Fish

1989. Fishes. Multicoloured.

923	20b. Type **181**	25	25
924	75b. Boarfish	55	55
925	1d. Grey triggerfish	65	65
926	1d.25 Skipjack tuna	75	75
927	2d. Striped rudderfish	95	95
928	4d. Atlantic manta	1·60	1·75
929	5d. Flat-headed grey mullet	1·75	1·90
930	10d. Ladyfish	2·75	3·25
MS931	Two sheets, each 104 × 72 mm. (a) 15d. Porcupinefish. (b) 15d. Shortfin mako Set of 2 sheets	12·00	12·00

181a Little Hiawatha on Daniel Muller Indian Pony

1989. "World Stamp Expo '89" International Stamp Exhibition, Washington. Designs showing Walt Disney cartoon characters and American carousel horses. Multicoloured.

932	20b. Type **181a**	70	30
933	50b. Morty on Herschell-Spillman stander	90	50
934	75b. Goofy on Gustav Dentzel stander	1·10	65
935	1d. Mickey Mouse on Daniel Muller armoured stander	1·25	70
936	1d.25 Minnie Mouse on jumper from Smithsonian Collection	1·40	80
937	2d. Webby on Illion "American Beauty"	2·00	1·25
938	8d. Donald Duck on Zalar jumper	4·25	4·50
939	10d. Mickey Mouse on Parker bucking horse	4·25	4·50
MS940	Two sheets, each 127 × 102 mm. (a) 12d. Donald, Mickey and Goofy in carousel car. (b) 12d. Donald's nephews on Roman chariot horses Set of 2 sheets	9·50	10·00

182 White House

1989. "World Stamp Expo '89" International Stamp Exhibition, Washington (2nd issue). Landmarks of Washington. Sheet 78 × 61 mm.

MS941	10d. multicoloured	1·40	2·00

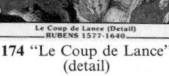

183 Mickey and Minnie Mouse in Pierce-Arrow, 1922

1989. Christmas. Designs showing Walt Disney cartoon characters with cars. Multicoloured.
942 20b. Type **183** 80 25
943 50b. Goofy in Spyker, 1919 1·00 45
944 75b. Donald and Grandma Duck with Packard, 1929 1·10 55
945 1d. Mickey Mouse driving Daimler, 1920 . . . . . . 1·25 65
946 1d.25 Mickey Mouse in Hispano "Suiza", 1924 . . 1·40 90
947 2d. Mickey and Minnie Mouse in Opel "Laubfrosch", 1924 . . . 1·90 1·25
948 10d. Donald Duck driving Vauxhall "30/98", 1927 . . 4·00 4·50
949 12d. Goofy with Peerless, 1923 . . . . 4·00 4·50
MS950 Two sheets, each 127 × 102 mm. (a) 15d. Mickey and Minnie Mouse picnicking by Stutz "Blackhawk Speedster", 1928. (b) 15d. Donald Duck, Mickey and Minnie Mouse in Bentley "Supercharged", 1930 Set of 2 sheets . . . . 11·00 13·00

184 Charles Nicolle (typhus transmission) and Vaccination

1989. Great Medical Discoveries. Multicoloured.
951 20b. Type **184** 85 20
952 50b. Paul Ehrlich (immunization pioneer) and medical examination . . . 1·25 30
953 75b. Selman Waksman (discoverer of streptomycin) and T.B. clinic . . . . . . 1·40 40
954 1d. Edward Jenner (smallpox vaccination), and Jenner conducting experiment, 1796 . . . . 1·60 50
955 1d.25 Robert Koch (developer of tuberculin test) and Gambian using vaccination gun . . . . . 1·90 75
956 5d. Sir Alexander Fleming (discoverer of penicillin) and doctor giving injection 2·50 2·75
957 8d. Max Theiler (developer of yellow fever vaccine) and child clinic . . . . . . 3·25 4·00
958 10d. Louis Pasteur (bacteriologist) and health survey . . . . 3·25 4·00
MS959 Two sheets, each 121 × 86 mm. (a) 15d. Hughes 369 Viking medical helicopter. (b) 15d. B.A.C. One Eleven Nightingale C.9 medical relief plane Set of 2 sheets . . . . 8·00 8·50
No. **MS**959a is incorrectly inscribed "Vicking".

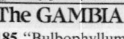

185 "Bulbophyllum lepidum"
186 John Newcombe

1989. Orchids. Multicoloured.
960 20b. Type **185** 30 30
961 75b. "Tridactyle tridactylites" 55 55
962 1d. "Vanilla imperialis" . . 70 70
963 1d.25 "Oeceoclades maculata" 80 90
964 2d. "Polystachya affinis" . . 1·10 1·25
965 4d. "Ancistrochilus rothschildianus" . . . . . 1·90 2·25
966 5d. "Angraecum distichum" 2·00 2·25
967 10d. "Liparis guineensis" . . 3·50 4·00
MS968 Two sheets, each 99 × 67 mm. (a) 15d. "Plectrelminthus caudatus". (b) 15d. "Eulophia guineensis" Set of 2 sheets . . . . 8·50 8·50

1990. Wimbledon Tennis Champions. Multicoloured.
969 20b. Type **186** 10 10
970 20b. Mrs. G. W. Hillyard . . 10 10
971 50b. Roy Emerson 20 20
972 50b. Dorothy Cummings . . . 20 20
973 75b. Donald Budge 30 30
974 75b. Suzanne Lenglen 30 30
975 1d. Laurence Doherty . . . 35 35
976 1d. Helen Wills Moody . . . 35 35
977 1d.25 Bjorn Borg 40 40
978 1d.25 Maureen Connolly . . 40 40
979 4d. Jean Borotra . . . . . 1·00 1·00
980 4d. Maria Bueno . . . . . 1·00 1·00
981 5d. Anthony Wilding . . . . 1·00 1·00
982 5d. Louise Brough . . . . 1·00 1·00
983 7d. Fred Perry . . . . . . 1·40 1·40
984 7d. Margaret Court . . . . 1·40 1·40
985 10d. Bill Tilden . . . . . . 2·00 2·00
986 10d. Billie Jean King . . . . 2·00 2·00
987 12d. Rod Laver . . . . . . 2·25 2·25
988 12d. Martina Navratilova . . 2·25 2·25
MS989 Two sheets, each 101 × 76 mm. (a) 15d. Rod Laver (different). (b) 15d. Martina Navratilova (different) Set of 2 sheets . . . . 8·50 9·50

187 Lunar Module "Eagle"

1990. 20th Anniv (1989) of First Manned Landing on Moon. Multicoloured.
990 20b. Type **187** 85 20
991 50b. Lift-off of "Apollo 11" (vert) . . . . 1·10 30
992 75b. Neil Armstrong stepping on to Moon . . . . 1·25 45
993 1d. Buzz Aldrin and American flag . . . . . . 1·40 55
994 1d.25 "Apollo 11" emblem (vert) . . . . 1·60 60
995 1d.75 Crew of "Apollo 11" 1·90 1·40
996 8d. Lunar Module "Eagle" on Moon . . . . 3·50 4·00
997 12d. Recovery of "Apollo 11" after splashdown . . . . . . 3·75 4·50
MS998 Two sheets, each 110 × 89 mm. (a) 15d. Neil Armstrong (vert). (b) 15d. View of Earth from Moon (vert) Set of 2 sheets . . . . 7·00 7·50

188 Bristol Type 142 Blenheim Mk I

1990. R.A.F. Aircraft of Second World War. Multicoloured.
999 10b. Type **188** 85 50
1000 20b. Fairey Battle . . . . . 1·10 50
1001 50b. Bristol Type 142 Blenheim Mk IV . . . . 1·40 50
1002 60b. Vickers-Armstrong Wellington Mk 1c . . . . 1·50 50
1003 75b. Armstrong Whitworth Whitley Mk V . . . . . 1·50 50
1004 1d. Handley Page Hampden Mk 1 . . . . 1·50 50
1005 1d.25 Supermarine Spitfire Mk 1A and Hawker Hurricane Mk I . . . . . 1·50 55
1006 2d. Avro Manchester . . . . 1·90 90
1007 3d. Short Stirling Mk I . . 1·90 1·60
1008 5d. Handley Page Halifax Mk I . . . . 2·25 2·25
1009 10d. Avro Lancaster Mk III 3·25 3·75
1010 12d. De Havilland Mosquito Mk IV . . . . 3·25 3·75
MS1011 Two sheets, each 107 × 77 mm. (a) 15d. Supermarine Spitfire Mk 1A. (b) 15d. Avro Type 683 Lancaster Mk III (different) Set of 2 sheets . . . 8·50 9·00

189 White-faced Scops Owl
191 Flag and National Assembly Building

190 Penny Black

1990. African Birds. Multicoloured.
1012 1d.25 Type **189** 70 70
1013 1d.25 Village weaver 70 70
1014 1d.25 Red-throated bee eater 70 70
1015 1d.25 Brown snake eagle ("Brown Harrier Eagle") 70 70
1016 1d.25 Red bishop 70 70
1017 1d.25 Scarlet-chested sunbird 70 70
1018 1d.25 Red-billed hornbill . . 70 70
1019 1d.25 Mosque swallow . . . 70 70
1020 1d.25 White-faced whistling duck 70 70
1021 1d.25 African fish eagle . . 70 70
1022 1d.25 Eastern white pelican 70 70
1023 1d.25 Carmine bee eater . . 70 70
1024 1d.25 Hadada ibis 70 70
1025 1d.25 Egyptian plover . . . 70 70
1026 1d.25 Variable sunbird . . . 70 70
1027 1d.25 African skimmer . . . 70 70
1028 1d.25 Woodland kingfisher 70 70
1029 1d.25 African jacana 70 70
1030 1d.25 African pygmy goose 70 70
1031 1d.25 Hammerkop 70 70
Nos. 1012/31 were printed together, se-tenant, forming a composite design of birds at a lake.

1990. 150th Anniv of the Penny Black.
1032 **190** 1d.25 black and blue . . 1·50 50
1033 12d. black and red . . 4·50 4·50
MS1034 79 × 73 mm. **190** 15d. black, silver and orange . . . . 6·00 7·00
The design of No. **MS**1034 is without the additional stamps behind the Penny Black as shown on Type **190**.

1990. 25th Anniv of Independence. Multicoloured.
1035 1d. Type **191** 50 25
1036 3d. President Sir Dawda Jawara 50 50
1037 12d. Map of Yundum airport and Boeing 707 airliner . . . . 6·50 6·50
MS1038 100 × 69 mm. 18d. State arms . . . . 5·00 6·50

192 Baobab Tree

1990. Gambian Life. Multicoloured.
1039 5b. Type **192** 65 65
1040 10b. Woodcarving, Albert Market, Banjul 10 30
1041 20b. President Jawara planting seedling (vert) . . 10 10
1042 50b. Sailing canoe and map 1·50 25
1043 75b. Batik fabric 20 10
1044 1d. Hibiscus and Bakau beach 30 20
1045 1d.25 Bougainvillea and Tendaba Camp 30 20
1046 2d. Shrimp fishing and sorting 45 35
1047 5d. Groundnut oil mill, Denton Bridge . . . . . 80 1·25
1048 10d. Handicraft pot and kora (musical instrument) 1·50 2·50
1049 15d. "Ansellia africana" (orchid) (vert) . . . . . 7·00 8·00
1050 30d. "Euriphene gambiae" (butterfly) and ancient stone ring near Georgetown . . . . . . 9·00 12·00

193 Daisy Duck at 10 Downing Street

1990. "Stamp World London 90" International Stamp Exhibition. Walt Disney cartoon characters in England. Multicoloured.
1051 20b. Type **193** 70 30
1052 50b. Goofy in Trafalgar Square 90 35
1053 75b. Mickey Mouse on White Cliffs of Dover (horiz) . . . . 1·00 50
1054 1d. Mickey Mouse at Tower of London . . . . . . 1·00 50
1055 5d. Mickey Mouse and Goofy at Hampton Court Palace (horiz) . . . . . . 2·75 2·50
1056 8d. Mickey Mouse by Magdalen Tower, Oxford 3·25 3·50
1057 10d. Mickey Mouse on Old London Bridge (horiz) . . 3·25 3·50
1058 12d. Scrooge McDuck and Rosetta Stone, British Museum (horiz) . . . . . 3·50 4·00
MS1059 Two sheets, each 125 × 100 mm. (a) 18d. Mickey Mouse and Donald Duck at Piccadilly Circus (horiz). (b) 18d. Mickey Mouse steering tug on River Thames (horiz) Set of 2 sheets . . . . 13·00 14·00

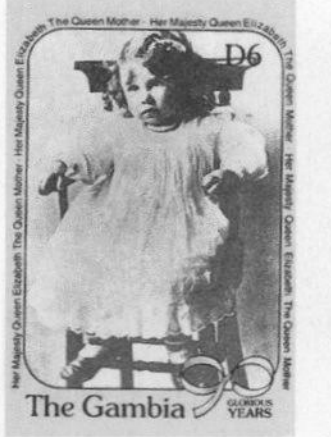

194 Lady Elizabeth Bowes-Lyon in High Chair
195 Vialli, Italy

1990. 90th Birthday of Queen Elizabeth the Queen Mother.
1060 **194** 6d. black, mve & yell . . 1·40 1·75
1061 – 6d. black, mve & yell . . 1·40 1·75
1062 – 6d. black, mve & yell . . 1·40 1·75
MS1063 90 × 75 mm. 18d. mult 4·50 5·00
DESIGNS: No. 1061, **MS**1063, Lady Elizabeth Bowes-Lyon as a young girl; 1062, Lady Elizabeth Bowes-Lyon with wild flowers.

1990. World Cup Football Championship, Italy (2nd issue). Multicoloured.
1064 1d. Type **195** 35 30
1065 1d.25 Cannegia, Argentina 40 35
1066 3d. Marchena, Costa Rica 90 1·00
1067 5d. Shaiba, United Arab Emirates . . . . 1·25 1·75
MS1068 Two sheets, each 75 × 92 mm. (a) 18d. Hagi, Rumania. (b) 18d. Van Basten, Netherlands Set of 2 sheets . . 13·00 13·00

195a Men's Discus

1990. Olympic Games, Barcelona (1992) (1st issue). Multicoloured.
1069 20b. Type **195a** 45 15
1070 50b. Men's 100 m 55 20
1071 75b. Women's 400 m . . . 65 30
1072 1d. Men's 200 m 70 40
1073 1d.25 Women's rhythmic gymnastics 75 50
1074 3d. Football . . . . 1·25 1·50
1075 10d. Men's marathon . . . 2·50 3·50
1076 12d. "Tornado" class yachting . . . . 2·50 3·50
MS1077 Two sheets, each 101 × 71 mm. (a) 15d. Parade of national flags (horiz). (b) 15d. Opening ceremony (horiz) Set of 2 sheets . . . . 12·00 13·00
See also Nos. 1289/97 and 1351/63.

195b "The Annunciation with St. Emidius" (detail) (Crivelli)

1990. Christmas. Paintings by Renaissance Masters. Multicoloured.
1078 20b. Type **195b** 45 10
1079 50b. "The Annunciation" (detail) (Campin) 65 10
1080 75b. "The Solly Madonna" (detail) (Raphael) 80 25
1081 1d.25 "The Tempi Madonna" (Raphael) . . 1·00 30
1082 2d. "Madonna of the Linen Window" (detail) (Raphael) . . . . 1·25 50
1083 7d. "The Annunciation, with St. Emidius" (different detail) (Crivelli) . . . . 2·75 3·50
1084 10d. "The Orleans Madonna" (Raphael) . . 3·00 3·50
1085 15d. "Madonna and Child" (detail) (Crivelli) . . . . 3·50 5·00
MS1086 72 × 101 mm. 15d. "Niccolini-Cowper Madonna" (Raphael) . . . . 6·00 7·00

195c "The Lion Hunt" (detail)

1990. 350th Death Anniv of Rubens. Multicoloured.

1087 20b. Type **195c** 20 15
1088 75b. "The Lion Hunt" (detail) 35 25
1089 1d. "The Tiger Hunt" (detail) 40 30
1090 1d.25 "The Tiger Hunt" (different detail) 40 35
1091 3d. "The Tiger Hunt" (different detail) . . . . . 90 1·00
1092 5d. "The Boar Hunt" (detail) . . . . 1·40 1·75
1093 10d. "The Lion Hunt" (different detail) . . . . . 2·00 2·50
1094 15d. "The Tiger Hunt" (different detail) . . . . . 2·75 3·75
MS1095 Four sheets. (a) 100 × 71 mm. 15d. "The Boar Hunt". (b) 100 × 71 mm. 15d. "The Lion Hunt". (c) 100 × 71 mm. 15d. "The Crocodile and Hippopotomus Hunt". (d) 71 × 100 mm. 15d. "St. George slays the Dragon" (vert) Set of 4 sheets . . . . 12·00 13·00

196 Summit Logo

1991. World Summit for Children, New York.

1096 **196** 1d. multicoloured . . . 80 55

196a Sir Kay and Wart searching for Lost Arrow

1991. International Literacy Year (1990). Designs showing scenes from Disney cartoon film "The Sword in the Stone". Multicoloured.

1097 3d. Type **196a** . . . . . . 1·75 1·50
1098 3d. Merlin the Magician . . . 1·75 1·50
1099 3d. Merlin teaching Wart . . 1·75 1·50
1100 3d. Wart writing on blackboard . . . . 1·75 1·50
1101 3d. Wart transformed into bird and Madame Mim 1·75 1·50
1102 3d. Merlin and Madame Mim . . . . 1·75 1·50
1103 3d. Madame Mim transformed into dragon 1·75 1·50
1104 3d. Wart pulling sword from stone . . . . 1·75 1·50
1105 3d. King Arthur on throne 1·75 1·50
MS1106 Two sheets, each 131 × 106 mm. (a) 20d. Sword in stone. (b) 20d. Merlin Set of 2 sheets . . . . 16·00 15·00

197 "Bebearia senegalensis"

1991. Wildlife. Multicoloured.

1107 1d. Type **197** 60 65
1108 1d. "Graphium ridleyanus" (butterfly) 60 65
1109 1d. "Precis antilope" (butterfly) 60 65
1110 1d. "Charaxes ameliae" (butterfly) 60 65
1111 1d. Addax 60 65
1112 1d. Sassaby 60 65
1113 1d. Civet 60 65
1114 1d. Green monkey 60 65
1115 1d. Spur-winged goose . . . 60 65
1116 1d. Red-billed hornbill . . . 60 65
1117 1d. Osprey 60 65
1118 1d. Glossy ibis 60 65
1119 1d. Egyptian plover 60 65
1120 1d. Golden-tailed woodpecker 60 65
1121 1d. Green wood hoopoe . . 60 65
1122 1d. Gaboon viper 60 65
1123 1d.50 Red-billed fire finch 60 65
1124 1d.50 Leaf-love 60 65
1125 1d.50 Piapiac 60 65
1126 1d.50 African emerald cuckoo 60 65
1127 1d.50 Red colobus monkey 60 65
1128 1d.50 African elephant . . . 60 65
1129 1d.50 Duiker 60 65
1130 1d.50 Giant eland 60 65
1131 1d.50 Oribi 60 65
1132 1d.50 Western African dwarf crocodile 60 65
1133 1d.50 Crowned crane . . . 60 65
1134 1d.50 Jackal 60 65
1135 1d.50 Yellow-throated longclaw 60 65
1136 1d.50 Abyssinian ground hornbill 60 65
1137 1d.50 "Papilio hesperus" . . 60 65
1138 1d.50 "Papilio antimachus" 60 65
1139 5d. Martial eagle . . . . . 1·00 1·10
1140 5d. Red-cheeked cordon-bleu . . . . 1·00 1·10
1141 5d. Red bishop . . . . . . 1·00 1·10
1142 5d. Eastern white pelican . . 1·00 1·10
1143 5d. Patas monkey . . . . . 1·00 1·10
1144 5d. Vervet monkey . . . . 1·00 1·10
1145 5d. Roan antelope . . . . . 1·00 1·10
1146 5d. Western hartebeest . . . 1·00 1·10
1147 5d. Waterbuck . . . . . . 1·00 1·10
1148 5d. Warthog . . . . 1·00 1·10
1149 5d. Spotted hyena . . . . . 1·00 1·10
1150 5d. Olive baboon . . . . . 1·00 1·10
1151 5d. "Palla decius" . . . . . 1·00 1·10
1152 5d. "Acraea pharsalus" . . 1·00 1·10
1153 5d. "Neptidopsis ophione" . 1·00 1·10
1154 5d. "Acraea caecilia" . . . 1·00 1·10
MS1155 Three sheets, each 101 × 69 mm. (a) 18d. African spoonbill (vert). (b) 18d. White-billed buffalo weaver ("Buffalo Weaver") (vert). (c) 18d. Lion (vert) Set of 3 sheets . . . . 16·00 15·00

Nos. 1107/22, 1123/38 and 1139/54 respectively were issued together, se-tenant, forming composite designs.

198 "Papilio dardanus"

1991. Butterflies. Multicoloured.

1156 20b. Type **198** 60 30
1157 50b. "Bematistes poggei" . . 80 40
1158 1d. "Vanessa cardui" . . . 90 55
1159 1d.50 "Amphicallia tigris" 1·00 85
1160 3d. "Hypolimnas dexithea" 1·75 1·25
1161 8d. "Acraea egina" . . . . 2·25 3·00
1162 10d. "Salamis temora" . . 2·25 3·00
1163 15d. "Precis octavia" . . . 2·75 4·00
MS1164 Four sheets, each 100 × 70 mm. (a) 18d. "Danaus chrysippus". (b) 18d. "Charaxes jasius" (male). (c) 18d. "Papilio demodocus". (d) 18d. "Papilio nireus" Set of 4 sheets . . . . 16·00 15·00

198a The Queen and Prince Charles at Windsor Polo Match

1991. 65th Birthday of Queen Elizabeth II. Mult.

1165 50b. Type **198a** 65 20
1166 1d. The Queen and Princess Anne at the Derby, 1988 80 35
1167 1d.25 The Queen at the Royal London Hospital, 1970 . . . . 90 50
1168 12d. The Queen and Prince Philip at Balmoral, 1976 3·50 4·00
MS1169 68 × 90 mm. 18d. Separate photographs of The Queen and Prince Philip . . . . 4·25 5·00

198b Prince and Princess with Sons in June, 1989

1991. 10th Wedding Anniv of Prince and Princess of Wales. Multicoloured.

1170 20b. Type **198b** 70 25
1171 75b. Separate photographs of Prince, Princess and sons . . . . 1·25 50
1172 1d.50 Prince Henry on first day of school, 1987, and Prince William at polo match . . . . 1·50 85
1173 15d. Separate photographs of Prince and Princess of Wales . . . . 5·50 6·00
MS1174 68 × 90 mm. 18d. The family in Italy, 1985 . . . . . 6·00 6·50

198c Donald Duck and Mickey Mouse playing "Go"

1991. "Phila Nippon '91" International Stamp Exhibition, Tokyo. Designs showing Walt Disney cartoon characters playing Japanese sports and games. Multicoloured.

1175 50b. Type **198c** 80 30
1176 75b. Morty, Ferdie and Pete as Sumo wrestlers 90 40
1177 1d. Minnie Mouse, Clarabelle Cow and Daisy Duck playing battledore and shuttlecock . . . . 1·00 45
1178 1d.25 Goofy and Mickey at Okinawa bullfight (vert) 1·10 55
1179 5d. Mickey flying hawk (vert) . . . . 2·75 2·50
1180 7d. Mickey, Minnie and Donald playing "jan-ken-pon" (vert) . . . . 2·75 3·25
1181 10d. Goofy as archer . . . 3·00 3·25
1182 15d. Morty and Ferdie flying kites (vert) . . . . 4·00 4·50
MS1183 Four sheets, each 127 × 102 mm. (a) 20d. Mickey climbing Mt. Fuji. (b) 20d. Mickey fishing. (c) 20d. Scrooge McDuck and Mickey playing football. (d) 20d. Goofy playing baseball Set of 4 sheets . . . . 14·00 15·00

198d "How the Whale got his Throat"

1991. International Literacy Year (1990). Designs showing Walt Disney cartoon characters in Kipling's "Just So" stories. Multicoloured.

1184 50b. Type **198d** 85 30
1185 75b. "How the Camel got his Hump" 95 40
1186 1d. "How the Leopard got his Spots" . . . . 1·10 45
1187 1d.25 "The Elephant's Child" . . . . 1·40 55
1188 1d.50 "The Singsong of Old Man Kangaroo" . . . . 1·50 1·00
1189 7d. "The Crab that played with the Sea" . . . . . . 3·00 3·25
1190 10d. "The Cat that walked by Himself" . . . . . . 3·25 3·25
1191 15d. "The Butterfly that Stamped" . . . . 4·00 4·50
MS1192 Four sheets, each 127 × 102 mm. (a) 20d. Mickey Mouse reading story to Morte and Ferdie (horiz). (b) 20d. "How the Rhinoceros got his Skin" (horiz). (c) 20d. "How the Alphabet was made". (d) 20d. "How the first Letter was written" Set of 4 sheets 14·00 15·00

199 Canadian Pacific Steel Cupola Caboose

1991. Railway Brake-vans. Multicoloured.

1193 1d. Type **199** 65 65
1194 1d. Cumberland and Pennsylvania four-wheeled caboose, U.S.A. 65 65
1195 1d. Ferrocarril Interoceanico caboose, Mexico 65 65
1196 1d. Northern Pacific Railroad steel cupola caboose, U.S.A. 65 65
1197 1d. Morristown and Erie Railroad four-wheeled caboose, U.S.A. 65 65
1198 1d. Burlington Northern Railroad streamlined cupola caboose, U.S.A. 65 65
1199 1d. McCloud River Railroad caboose-coach, U.S.A. . . 65 65
1200 1d. Santa Fe Railroad wide-vision caboose, U.S.A. . . 65 65
1201 1d. Frisco Railroad wide-vision caboose, U.S.A. . . 65 65
1202 1d.50 Colorado and Southern Railroad four-wheeled caboose, U.S.A. 65 65
1203 1d.50 Santa Fe Railroad transfer caboose, U.S.A. 65 65
1204 1d.50 Canadian National wooden cupola caboose 65 65
1205 1d.50 Union Pacific steel transfer caboose, U.S.A. 65 65
1206 1d.50 Virginia and Truckee Railroad caboose-coach, U.S.A. 65 65
1207 1d.50 British Railways standard brake van . . . 65 65
1208 1d.50 International Railways of Central America caboose 65 65
1209 1d.50 Northern Pacific Railroad steel cupola caboose, U.S.A. 65 65
1210 1d.50 Burlington Northern Railroad wooden caboose, U.S.A. 65 65
1211 2d. Oahu Railway caboose, Hawaii 65 65
1212 2d. British Railways standard brake van . . . 65 65
1213 2d. Union Pacific steel wide-view caboose, U.S.A. . . 65 65
1214 2d. Belt Railway of Chicago four-wheeled caboose, U.S.A. 65 65
1215 2d. McCloud River Railroad four-wheeled caboose, U.S.A. 65 65
1216 2d. Angelina County Lumber Co caboose, U.S.A. 65 65
1217 2d. Coahuila Zacateca caboose, Mexico 65 65
1218 2d. United Railways of Yucatan caboose, Mexico 65 65
1219 2d. Rio Grande Railroad steel cupola caboose, U.S.A. 65 65
MS1220 Three sheets, each 79 × 56 mm. (a) 20d. Wooden caboose on steam goods train. (b) 20d. Pennsylvania Railroad steel caboose on electric goods train (vert). (c) 20d. Wooden caboose on passenger train and railwayman with flag (vert) Set of 3 sheets . . . . 13·00 14·00

200 Tiger Shark

1991. Fishes. Multicoloured.

1221 20b. Type **200** 25 15
1222 25b. Common jewelfish . . 25 15
1223 50b. Five-spotted cichlid . . 35 25
1224 75b. Small-toothed sawfish 35 25
1225 1d. Spotted tilapia 40 30
1226 1d.25 Dwarf jewelfish . . . 40 35
1227 1d.50 Five-spotted jewelfish 45 40
1228 3d. Lion-headed cichlid . . 65 65
1229 10d. Egyptian mouthbrooder 2·00 2·50
1230 15d. Burton's mouthbrooder 2·75 3·50
MS1231 Two sheets, each 118 × 83 mm. (a) 18d. Great barracuda. (b) 18d. Yellow-tailed snapper Set of 2 sheets . . . . 12·00 13·00

200a Children waving

1991. Hummel Figurines. Multicoloured.

1232 20b. Type **200a** 10 10
1233 75b. Children under umbrella 15 15
1234 1d. Girl kissing friend . . . 20 20
1235 1d.50 Children at window 30 30
1236 2d.50 Two girls in aprons 45 45
1237 5d. Two boys in bow ties 85 85
1238 10d. Two girls sitting on fence with birds . . . . . 1·75 2·00
1239 15d. Boy and girl in Swiss costume . . . . 2·50 3·00
MS1240 Two sheets, each 98 × 128 mm. (a) 4d. × 4 As Nos. 1233/5 and 1239. (b) 5d. × 4 As Nos. 1232 and 1236/8 Set of 2 sheets . . . . 7·00 8·00

200b "The Old Cemetery Tower at Nuenen in the Snow"

1991. Death Centenary of Vincent van Gogh (artist). Multicoloured.
1241 20b. Type **200b** 40 25
1242 25b. "Head of Peasant Woman with White Cap" (vert) 40 25
1243 50b. "The Green Parrot" (vert) 50 25
1244 75b. "Vase with Carnations" (vert) 55 30
1245 1d. "Vase with Red Gladioli" (vert) 65 30
1246 1d.25 "Beach at Scheveningen in Calm Weather" 75 35
1247 1d.50 "Boy cutting Grass with Sickle" 85 40
1248 2d. "Coleus Plant in a Flowerpot" (detail) (vert) 90 40
1249 3d. "Self-portrait 1887" (vert) . . . . 1·10 60
1250 4d. "Self-portrait" (different) (vert) . . . . 1·40 90
1251 5d. "Self-portrait" (different) (vert) . . . . 1·60 1·25
1252 6d. "Self-portrait 1887" (different) (vert) . . . . . 1·90 1·90
1253 8d. "Still Life with Bottle, Two Glasses, Cheese and Bread" (detail) (vert) . . 2·50 2·50
1254 10d. "Still Life with Cabbage, Clogs and Potatoes" . . . . 2·75 2·75
1255 12d. "Montmartre: The Street Lamps" (vert) . . . 3·00 3·50
1256 15d. "Head of Peasant Woman with Brownish Cap" (vert) . . . . . 3·25 4·00
MS1257 Four sheets, each 127 × 102 mm. (a) 20d. "The Potato Eaters" (horiz). (b) 20d. "Montmartre: Quarry and Mills" (horiz). (c) 20d. "Autumn Landscape" (horiz). (d) 20d. "Arles: View from the Wheat Fields" (detail) (horiz). Imperf Set of 4 sheets . . . . 19·00 20·00

200c "The Madonna of Humility"

1991. Christmas. Religious Paintings by Fra Angelico. Multicoloured.
1258 20b. Type **200c** 15 10
1259 50b. "Madonna and Child with Angels" 25 20
1260 75b. "Virgin and Child with Angels" 30 25
1261 1d. "The Annunciation" . . 35 30
1262 1d.25 "Presentation in the Temple" 40 35
1263 5d. "The Annunciation" (different) . . . . 1·50 1·50
1264 10d. "Madonna della Stella" 2·25 3·00
1265 15d. "Naming of St. John the Baptist" . . . . . . 2·75 4·00
MS1266 Two sheets, each 102 × 128 mm. (a) 20d. "Coronation of the Virgin". (b) 20d. "Annunciation and Adoration of the Magi" Set of 2 sheets . . . . 7·50 8·50

201 Son House

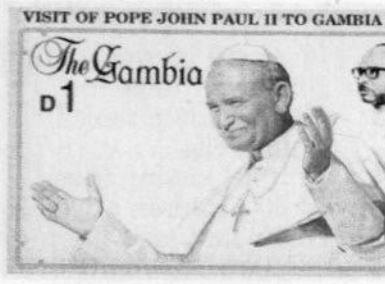

202 Pope John Paul II

1992. Famous Blues Singers. Multicoloured.
1267 20b. Type **201** 15 15
1268 25b. W. C. Handy 15 15
1269 50b. Muddy Waters 30 30
1270 75b. Lightnin Hopkins . . . 40 40
1271 1d. Ma Rainey 45 45
1272 1d.25 Mance Lipscomb . . . 50 50
1273 1d.50 Mahalia Jackson . . . 60 60
1274 2d. Ella Fizgerald 70 70
1275 3d. Howlin Wolf 85 85
1276 5d. Bessie Smith . . . . . 1·25 1·25
1277 7d. Leadbelly . . . . . . 1·50 1·75
1278 10d. Joe Willie Wilkins . . 2·00 2·25
MS1279 Three sheets, each 110 × 78 mm. (a) 20d. String drum. (b) 20d. Elvis Presley. (c) 20d. Billie Holiday Set of 3 sheets 13·00 14·00

1992. Papal Visit. Multicoloured.
1280 1d. Type **202** 40 40
1281 1d.25 Pope John Paul II and Pres. Sir Dawda Jawara 50 50
1282 20d. Gambian and Papal flags . . . . 4·75 6·00
MS1283 104 × 70 mm. 25d. Pope giving blessing . . . . 6·00 8·00

202a Pottery Market

1992. 40th Anniv of Queen Elizabeth II's Accession. Multicoloured.
1284 20b. Type **202a** 25 10
1285 50b. Ruins of early fort . . 35 20
1286 1d. Fishing boat 50 30
1287 15d. Canoes on beach . . . 4·50 5·50
MS1288 Two sheets, each 75 × 97 mm. (a) 20d. "Lady Chilel Jawara" (river vessel). (b) 20d. River ferry being loaded Set of 2 sheets . . . . 9·50 10·00

203 Nadia Comaneci (Rumania) (combined gymnastic events) and Map of Barcelona

1992. Olympic Games, Barcelona (2nd issue). Past Medal Winners. Multicoloured.
1289 20b. Type **203** 35 20
1290 50b. D. Moorcroft (G.B.) (5000 m) and map 45 20
1291 75b. M. Nemeth (Hungary) (javelin) and decorative tiles 45 25
1292 1d. J. Pedraza (Mexico) (20 km walk) and decorative plate 45 30
1293 1d.25 "Soling" class yachting (Brazil), state arms and flag 90 40
1294 1d.50 Women's hockey (G.D.R.) and Barcelona building . . . . 1·00 60
1295 12d. M. Jordan (U.S.A.) (basketball) and map . . 4·00 4·00
1296 15d. V. Borzov (U.S.S.R.) (100 m) and galleon . . . 4·00 4·25
MS1297 Two sheets. (a) 82 × 112 mm. 20d. Silhouette of flamenco dancer on map (vert). (b) 112 × 82 mm. 20d. Silhouette of bull on map Set of 2 sheets . . 8·50 9·00

204 Mickey Mouse as Christopher Columbus

1992. International Stamp Exhibitions. Walt Disney cartoon characters. Multicoloured. (a) "Granada '92", Spain. Voyage of Columbus.
1298 20b. Type **204** 50 15
1299 75b. Mickey's plans derided 65 25
1300 1d.50 Mickey lands in America 85 60
1301 15d. Mickey presents treasure to Minnie . . . . 3·75 4·75
MS1302 127 × 102 mm. 18d. Mickey embarks for America . . . . . . 5·00 5·50

(b) World Columbian Stamp "Expo '92". Chicago Landmarks.
1303 50b. Navy Pier 60 10
1304 1d. Wrigley Building 75 25
1305 1d.25 University of Chicago 85 30
1306 12d. Alder Planetarium . . 4·00 4·75
MS1307 127 × 102 mm. 18d. Goofy hanging over Chicago (horiz) 5·00 5·50

204a "Christ presented to the People" (Rembrandt)

1992. Easter. Religious Paintings. Multicoloured.
1308 20b. Type **204a** 10 10
1309 50b. "Christ carrying the Cross" (Grunewald) . . . 20 20
1310 75b. "The Crucifixion" (Grunewald) 25 25
1311 1d. "The Crucifixion" (Rubens) 30 30
1312 1d.25 "The Road to Calvary" (detail) (Tintoretto) 35 35
1313 1d.50 "The Road to Calvary" (Tintoretto) (different) 40 40
1314 15d. "The Crucifixion" (Masaccio) . . . . 2·75 3·75
1315 20d. "The Descent from the Cross" (Rembrandt) . . . 3·50 4·50
MS1316 Two sheets, each 72 × 101 mm. (a) 25d. "The Crowning with Thorns" (detail) (Van Dyck). (b) 25d. "The Crowning with Thorns" (detail) (Titian) Set of 2 sheets . . . . 8·50 9·50

205 "Hibiscus rosa-sinensis"

1992. Flowers. Multicoloured.
1317 20b. Type **205** 10 10
1318 50b. "Monodora myristica" 20 20
1319 75b. "Bombax costatum" . . 25 25
1320 1d. "Oncoba spinosa" . . . 30 30
1321 1d.25 "Combretum grandiflorum" 35 35
1322 1d.50 "Rothmannia longiflora" 40 40
1323 2d. "Clerodendrum splendens" 55 55
1324 5d. "Mussaenda erythrophylla" . . . . . 1·10 1·25
1325 10d. "Nauclea latifolia" . . 1·75 2·00
1326 12d. "Clerodendrum capitatum" . . . . 1·90 2·50
1327 15d. "Costus spectabilis" . . 2·50 3·25
1328 18d. "Strophanthus preussii" 2·75 3·50
MS1329 Four sheeets, each 102 × 71 mm. (a) 20d. "Bougainvillea glabra". (b) 20d. "Nymphaea". (c) 20d. "Adansonia digitata". (d) 20d. "Clitoria ternatea" Set of 4 sheets . . . 12·00 13·00

206 "Joven Antonia" (River Gambia)

1992. River Boats of the World. Multicoloured.
1330 20b. Type **206** 15 10
1331 50b. "Dresden" (River Elbe) 25 20
1332 75b. "Medway Queen" (River Medway) 30 25
1333 1d. "Lady Wright" (River Gambia) 35 30
1334 1d.25 "Devin" (River Vltava) 40 35
1335 1d.50 "Lady Chilel Jawara" (River Gambia) 45 50
1336 5d. "Robert Fulton" (River Hudson) . . . . 1·25 1·25
1337 10d. "Coonawarra" (River Murray) . . . . 2·00 2·25
1338 12d. "Nakusp" (River Columbia) . . . . 2·25 3·00
1339 15d. "Lucy Ashton" (Firth of Clyde) . . . . 2·75 3·50
MS1340 Two sheets, each 107 × 69 mm. (a) 20d. "City of Cairo" (Mississippi). (b) 20d. "Rüdesheim" (Rhine) Set of 2 sheets . . . . 9·00 10·00

206a U.S.S. "Pennsylvania" (battleship)

1992. 50th Anniv of Japanese Attack on Pearl Harbor. Multicoloured.
1341 2d. Type **206a** . . . . . . 1·50 1·10
1342 2d. Japanese Mitsubishi A6M Zero-Sen aircraft over Pearl Harbor . . . . 1·50 1·10
1343 2d. U.S.S. "Ward" (destroyer) sinking midget submarine . . . . 1·50 1·10
1344 2d. Ford Naval Station under attack . . . . . . 1·50 1·10
1345 2d. Agency report of Japanese attack . . . . . 1·50 1·10
1346 2d. Newspaper headline . . 1·50 1·10
1347 2d. Japanese troops on Guam . . . . 1·50 1·10
1348 2d. U.S. forces regaining Wake Island . . . . . . 1·50 1·10
1349 2d. North American B-25B Mitchell bomber raid on Japan . . . . 1·50 1·10
1350 2d. American Douglas Dauntless dive bomber attacking Japanese carrier, Midway . . . . 1·50 1·10

207 Women's Double Sculls

1992. Winter Olympic Games, Albertville, and Olympic Games, Barcelona (3rd issue). Multicoloured.
1351 20b. Type **207** 25 15
1352 50b. Men's kayak (vert) . . 35 20
1353 75b. Women's rapid precision pistol shooting 50 30
1354 1d. Judo (vert) 55 30
1355 1d.25 Men's javelin (vert) . . 65 35
1356 1d.50 Men's vaulting horse (vert) 80 40
1357 2d. Men's downhill skiing (vert) . . . . 1·00 55
1358 3d. Windsurfing (vert) . . . 1·10 90
1359 5d. Men's high jump . . . 1·50 1·50
1360 10d. Four-man bobsled (vert) . . . . 2·50 2·75
1361 12d. 90 m ski-jump (vert) . 2·75 3·00
1362 15d. Men's slalom skiing . . 3·00 4·00
MS1363 Four sheets, each 100 × 70 mm. (a) 18d. Table tennis (vert). (b) 18d. Men's 500 metre speed skating. (c) 18d. Women's 200 metre backstroke. (d) 18d. Pairs figure skating (vert) Set of 4 sheets . . . . 13·00 14·00

207a Immigration Centre, Ellis Island

1992. Postage Stamp Mega Event, New York. Sheet 100 × 70 mm.
MS1363 18d. multicoloured . . . 3·75 4·25

207b Dryosaurus

1992. "Genova '92" International Thematic Stamp Exhibition. Dinosaurs. Multicoloured.
1364 20b. Type **207b** 30 10
1365 25b. Saurolophus 30 10
1366 50b. Allosaurus 35 20
1367 75b. Fabrosaurus 40 25
1368 1d. Deinonychus 40 30
1369 1d.25 Cetiosaurus 50 35
1370 1d.50 Camptosaurus 50 35
1371 2d. Ornithosuchus 55 45
1372 3d. Spinosaurus 60 60
1373 5d. Ornithomimus . . . . . 1·00 1·25
1374 10d. Kentrosaurus . . . . . 1·75 2·25
1375 12d. Schlermochus . . . . 1·90 2·50
MS1376 Three sheets, each 104 × 75 mm. (a) 25d. As No. 1366. (b) 25d. As No. 1369. (c) 25d. As No. 1371 Set of 3 sheets 14·00 15·00

207c "The Holy Family" (Raphael)

1992. Christmas. Religious Paintings. Multicoloured.

1378 50b. Type **207c** 25 20
1379 75b. "The Little Holy Family" (Raphael) . . . 30 25
1380 1d. "The Little Holy Family" (detail) (Raphael) 35 30
1381 1d.25 "Escape to Egypt" (Melchior Broederlam) . . 40 35
1382 1d.50 "Flight into Egypt" (Adriaen Isenbrant) . . . 40 35
1383 2d. "The Holy Family" (El Greco) 55 55
1384 2d. "Flight into Egypt" (detail) (Cosimo Tura) . . 55 55
1385 2d. "Flight into Egypt" (detail) (Master of Hoogstraelen) 55 55
1386 4d. "The Holy Family" (Bernard van Orley) . . . 90 1·00
1387 5d. "Holy Family with Infant Jesus Sleeping" (detail) (Charles Le Brun) 1·10 1·25
1388 10d. "Rest on The Flight to Egypt" (Orazio Gentileschi) . . . . . . 1·90 2·50
1389 12d. "Rest on The Flight to Egypt" (detail) (Orazio Gentileschi) . . . . . . 2·25 2·75
MS1390 Three sheets, each 102 × 77 mm. (a) 25d. "The Holy Family" (detail) (Giorgione). (b) 25d. "Flight into Egypt" (detail) (Vittore Carpaccio). (c) 25d. "Rest on The Flight to Egypt" (detail) (Simone Cantarino) Set of 3 sheets 11·00 12·00

207d Goofy in "Orphan's Benefit", 1934

1992. 60th Anniv of Goofy (Disney cartoon character). Multicoloured.

1391 50b. Type **207d** 30 20
1392 75b. Goofy and Donald Duck in "Moose Hunters", 1937 . . . . . 40 30
1393 1d. Goofy in "Mickey's Amateurs", 1937 . . . . 50 40
1394 1d.25 Goofy, Donald and Mickey Mouse in "Lonesome Ghosts", 1937 55 55
1395 5d. Goofy, Donald and Mickey in "Boat Builders", 1938 . . . . . 1·40 1·40
1396 7d. Goofy, Donald and Mickey in "The Whalers", 1938 . . . . 1·75 2·00
1397 10d. Goofy and Wilbur the grasshopper in "Goofy and Wilbur", 1939 . . . 2·00 2·25
1398 15d. Goofy in "Saludos Amigos", 1941 . . . . . 2·50 2·75
MS1399 Two sheets, each 127 × 102 mm. (a) 20d. Goofy in "The Band Concert", 1935 (vert). (b) 20d. Goofy today (vert) Set of 2 sheets . . . . 10·00 11·00

208 Pres. Jawara playing Golf and Map of Australia

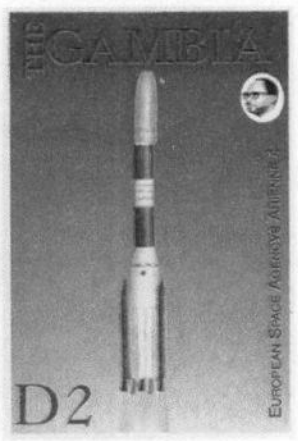

209 Launch of European "Ariane 4"

1992. Open Golf Championships. Multicoloured.

1400 20b. Type **208** 55 20
1401 1d. Pres. Jawara and Gambia Open trophy . . 85 45
1402 1d.50 Pres. Jawara (winner of Gambia Open, 1985) 1·00 55
1403 2d. Pres. Jawara and map of Japan . . . . 1·50 70
1404 3d. Pres. Jawara and map of U.S.A. . . . . 1·75 1·00
1405 5d. Gambia Open trophy . . 2·00 1·75
1406 10d. Pres. Jawara and map of Scotland . . . . 3·25 3·75
1407 12d. Pres. Jawara and map of Italy . . . . 3·25 3·75
MS1408 Two sheets. (a) 106 × 71 mm. 10d. Pres. Jawara playing shot. (b) 67 × 99 mm. 18d. Flag of Gambia (horiz) Set of 2 sheets . . . . 11·00 12·00

1993. Anniversaries and Events. Multicoloured.

1409 2d. Type **209** 70 70
1410 2d. Konrad Adenauer and Berlin Airlift (horiz) . . . 70 70
1411 2d. Airship "Hindenburg", 1928 (horiz) 70 70
1412 5d. "Santa Maria" (horiz) 1·75 1·25
1413 6d. Jentink's duiker (horiz) 1·40 1·40
1414 7d. World map and emblem (horiz) . . . . 2·25 1·60
1415 9d. Wolfgang Amadeus Mozart . . . . 3·00 2·50
1416 10d. Lions Club emblem . . 1·75 2·50
1417 10d. "Enterprise" (yacht), 1930 . . . . 1·75 2·50
1418 10d. Imperial amazon (Imperial "Sisserou Parrot") . . . . 3·00 2·50
1419 12d. American space shuttle 3·00 3·25
1420 12d. Fleet of Columbus (horiz) . . . . 3·00 3·25
1421 15d. Adenauer and returning prisoners of war (horiz) . . . . 3·00 3·25
1422 18d. Airship LZ-1, 1900 (horiz) . . . . 3·50 3·75
MS1423 Six sheets. (a) 104 × 76 mm. 18d. Nose of projected European space station "Hermes". (b) 113 × 87 mm. 18d. Konrad Adenauer. (c) 85 × 65 mm. 18d. Count von Zeppelin. (d) 103 × 75 mm. 18d. Green-winged Macaw and bow of ship. (e) 85 × 65 mm. 18d. Globe. (f) 99 × 69 mm. 18d. Dancers from "The Marriage of Figaro". Set of 6 sheets . . . . 20·00 22·00

ANNIVERSARIES AND EVENTS: Nos. 1409, 1419, **MS**1423a, International Space Year; 1410, 1421, **MS**1423b, 25th death anniv of Konrad Adenauer (German statesman); 1411, 1422, **MS**1423c, 75th death anniv of Count Ferdinand von Zeppelin; 1412, 1420, **MS**1423d, 500th anniv of discovery of America by Columbus; 1413, 1418, **MS**1423e, Earth Summit '92, Rio; 1414, International Nutrition Conference, Rome; 1415, **MS**1423f, Death bicentenary of Mozart; 1416, 75th anniv of International Association of Lions Clubs; 1417, Americas Cup Yachting Championship.

209a Elvis Presley

1993. 15th Death Anniv (1992) of Elvis Presley (singer). Multicoloured.

1424 3d. Type **209a** 70 70
1425 3d. Elvis with guitar 70 70
1426 3d. Elvis with microphone 70 70

209b "St. John the Baptist" (Da Vinci)

1993. Bicentenary of the Louvre, Paris. Paintings. Multicoloured.

1427 3d. Type **209b** 65 70
1428 3d. "Virgin of the Rocks" (Da Vinci) 65 70
1429 3d. "Bacchus" (Da Vinci) 65 70
1430 3d. "Lady of the Court, Milan" (Da Vinci) 65 70
1431 3d. "Virgin of the Rocks" (detail) (Da Vinci) 65 70
1432 3d. "Mona Lisa" (Da Vinci) 65 70
1433 3d. "Mona Lisa" (detail) (Da Vinci) 65 70
1434 3d. Sketches for "Two Horsemen" (Da Vinci) . . 65 70
1435 3d. "The Oath of Horatii" (left detail) (David) . . . 65 70
1436 3d. "The Oath of Horatii" (right detail) (David) . . . 65 70
1437 3d. "The Love of Paris and Helen" (detail) (David) . . 65 70
1438 3d. "The Sabine Women" (detail) (David) 65 70
1439 3d. "Leonidas at Thermopylae" (detail) (David) 65 70
1440 3d. "The Coronation of Napoleon" (left detail) (David) 65 70
1441 3d. "The Coronation of Napoleon" (centre detail) (David) 65 70
1442 3d. "The Coronation of Napoleon" (right detail) (David) 65 70
1443 3d. "Peasant Family at Home" (detail) (L. le Nain) 65 70
1444 3d. "Smoking Room" (left detail) (L. le Nain) . . . 65 70
1445 3d. "Smoking Room (right detail) (L. le Nain) . . . 65 70
1446 3d. "The Cart" (detail) (L. le Nain) 65 70
1447 3d. "Peasants' Repast" (detail) (L. le Nain) . . . 65 70
1448 3d. "Portrait in an Interior" (detail) (L. le Nain) . . . 65 70
1449 3d. "Portrait in an Interior" (different detail) (L. le Nain) 65 70
1450 3d. "The Forge" (L. le Nain) 65 70
MS1451 Two sheets, each 70 × 100 mm. (a) 20d. "Allegory of Victory" (M. le Nain) (52 × 86 mm). (b) 20d. "Madame Vigee-Le Brun and Daughter" (Le Brun) (52 × 86 mm) Set of 2 sheets 10·00 11·00

Nos. 1432/3 are incorrectly inscr "Monna Lisa".

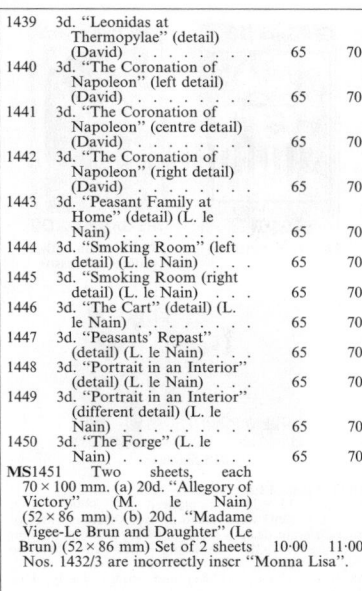

210 Peace Corps and Gambian Flags

1993. 25th Anniv of U.S. Peace Corps.

1452 **210** 2d. multicoloured . . . 1·00 1·00

211 Jackie Robinson and Ruby Dee ("The Jackie Robinson Story")

1993. Baseball Films. Multicoloured.

1453 3d. Type **211** 75 80
1454 3d. Robert De Niro ("Bang the Drum Slowly") . . . 75 80
1455 3d. James Earl Jones and Billy Dee Williams ("The Bingo Long Travelling All-Stars and Motor Kings") 75 80
1456 3d. Kevin Costner and Susan Sarandon ("Bull Durham") 75 80
1457 3d. Cast photograph ("Eight Men Out") 75 80
1458 3d. Ray Liotta ("Field of Dreams") 75 80
1459 3d. Charlie Sheen ("Major League") 75 80
1460 3d. Tom Selleck ("Mr. Baseball") 75 80
1461 3d. Wallace Beery, 1927, and Elliott Gould, 1986 ("Casey at the Bat") . . . 75 80
1462 3d. Anna Nilsson and Babe Ruth ("Babe comes Home") 75 80
1463 3d. Joe Brown ("Elmer the Great") 75 80
1464 3d. Bud Abbott and Lou Costello ("The Naughty Nineties") 75 80
1465 3d. Frank Sinatra, Gene Kelly and Esther Williams ("Take Me Out to the Ball Game") 75 80
1466 3d. Tab Hunter and Gwen Verdon ("Damn Yankees") 75 80
1467 3d. Dan Dailey ("The Pride of St. Louis") 75 80
1468 3d. John Candy and Richard Pryor ("Brewster's Millions") . . 75 80
MS1469 Four sheets, each 132 × 107 mm. (a) 20d. John Goodman ("The Babe"). (b) 20d. Ronald Reagan ("The Winning Team"). (c) 20d. Tom Hanks and Madonna ("A League of Their Own") (vert). (d) 20d. Robert Redford ("The Natural") (vert) Set of 4 sheets . . . . 15·00 17·00

212 Giraffe

213 Long-tailed Pangolin hanging by Tail

1993. Animals of West Africa. Multicoloured.

1470 2d. Type **212** 55 60
1471 2d. Baboon 55 60
1472 2d. Caracal 55 60
1473 2d. Large-spotted genet . . 55 60
1474 2d. Bushbuck 55 60
1475 2d. Red-fronted gazelle . . 55 60
1476 2d. Red-flanked duiker . . . 55 60
1477 2d. Cape buffalo 55 60
1478 2d. African civet 55 60
1479 2d. Side-striped jackal . . . 55 60
1480 2d. Ratel 55 60
1481 2d. Striped polecat 55 60
1482 5d. Vervet 85 90
1483 5d. Blackish-green guenon 85 90
1484 5d. Long-tailed pangolin . . 85 90
1485 5d. Leopard 85 90
1486 5d. Elephant 85 90
1487 5d. Hunting dog 85 90
1488 5d. Spotted hyena 85 90
1489 5d. Lion 85 90
1490 5d. Hippopotamus 85 90
1491 5d. Nile crocodile 85 90
1492 5d. Aardvark 85 90
1493 5d. Warthog 85 90
MS1494 101 × 72 mm. 20d. As No. 1483 . . . . 3·75 4·50

Nos. 1470/81 and 1482/93 were each printed together, se-tenant, with the backgrounds forming composite designs.

1993. Endangered Species. Long-tailed Pangolin. Multicoloured.

1495 1d.25 Type **213** 45 25
1496 1d.50 Sitting on branch . . 55 40
1497 2d. Climbing up branch . . 65 60
1498 5d. Climbing down branch 1·60 2·00

214 Osprey

215 Rose-ringed Parakeet

1993. Birds of Prey. Multicoloured.

1500 1d.25 Type **214** . . . . . . 1·40 50
1501 1d.50 Egyptian vulture (horiz) . . . . 1·60 50
1502 2d. Martial eagle . . . . . 1·75 55
1503 3d. Ruppell's griffon ("Ruppell's Griffon Vulture") (horiz) . . . . 2·25 75
1504 5d. Augur buzzard ("Auger Buzzard") . . . . 2·50 1·25
1505 8d. Greater kestrel . . . . 2·75 3·00
1506 10d. Secretary bird . . . . 2·75 3·00
1507 15d. Bateleur ("Bateleur Eagle") (horiz) . . . . . 3·25 4·00
MS1508 Two sheets, each 108 × 80 mm. (a) 20d. Owl sp. ("Tawny Owl") (57 × 42½ mm). (b) 20d. Verreaux's eagle (57 × 42½ mm) Set of 2 sheets 13·00 13·00

1993. African Birds. Multicoloured.

1509 2d. Type **215** . . . . 1·25 1·25
1510 2d. Variable sunbird . . . . 1·25 1·25
1511 2d. Red-billed hornbill . . . 1·25 1·25
1512 2d. Red-billed fire finch . . 1·25 1·25
1513 2d. Go-away bird ("Common Go-away Bird") . . . . 1·25 1·25
1514 2d. Burchell's gonolek ("Crimson-breasted shrike") . . . . 1·25 1·25
1515 2d. Grey-headed bush shrike ("Gray-headed Bush shrike") . . . . 1·25 1·25
1516 2d. Western nicator ("Nicator") . . . . 1·25 1·25
1517 2d. Egyptian plover . . . . 1·25 1·25
1518 2d. Congo peafowl ("Congo Peacock") . . . . 1·25 1·25
1519 2d. Painted snipe ("Greater Painted Snipe") . . . . . 1·25 1·25
1520 2d. South African crowned crane ("Crowned Crane") 1·25 1·25

215a Queen Elizabeth II (photograph by Cecil Beaton)

1993. 40th Anniv of Coronation.
1521 **215a** 2d. multicoloured . . . 95 1·00
1522 – 5d. multicoloured . . . 1·60 1·75
1523 – 8d. brown and black . . 1·75 1·90
1524 – 10d. multicoloured . . 1·90 2·00
MS1525 70 × 100 mm. 20d. mult 6·00 6·50
DESIGNS—(38 × 47 mm): 5d. Orb and sceptre; 8d. Sir Winston Churchill; 10d. Queen Elizabeth II at Trooping the Colour (28½ × 42½ mm); 20d. "Elizabeth II, 1972" (detail) (Joe King).

216 Hugo Eckener and "Graf Zeppelin"

1993. Aviation Anniversaries. Multicoloured.
1526 2d. Type **216** 55 50
1527 2d. Guyot's balloon, 1785 (vert) 55 50
1528 5d. Airship "Luftschiffe 3" and crowd . . . . . . 1·00 1·00
1529 5d. Sopwith Snipe (fighter) 1·00 1·00
1530 8d. Eckener and "Graf Zeppelin" . . . . . . 1·60 1·75
1531 10d. "Comte d'Artois" (hot air balloon), 1785 (vert) 1·90 2·00
1532 15d. Royal Aircraft Factory S.E.5 (fighter) . . . . 2·40 3·00
MS1533 Three sheets. (a) 105 × 84 mm. 20d. Eckener and LZ-127 "Graf Zeppelin" (airship). (b) 84 × 105 mm. 20d. Blanchard's balloon, 1785 (vert). (c) 84 × 105 mm. 20d. Avro 504k (biplane) Set of 3 sheets . . . 16·00 16·00
ANNIVERSARIES: Nos. 1526, 1528, 1530, **MS**1533a, Birth anniv of Hugo Eckener (airship pioneer); 1527, 1531, **MS**1533b, Bicentenary of first airmail flight; 1529, 1532, **MS**1533c, 75th anniv of Royal Air Force.

217 Henry Ford and "Model T", 1910

1993. Centenaries of Henry Ford's First Petrol Engine (Nos. 1534/45) and Karl Benz's First Four-wheeled Car (Nos. 1546/57). Multicoloured.
1534 2d. Type **217** 45 50
1535 2d. Car of 1896 . . . . . 45 50
1536 2d. Henry Ford with Barney Oldfield and "999", 1902 45 50
1537 2d. Henry Ford, 1893, and car of 1896 . . . . . . 45 50
1538 2d. "Model A", 1903 . . . 45 50
1539 2d. "Model T" with roof lowered, 1908 . . . . . 45 50
1540 2d. "Model T" with roof raised, 1908 . . . . . . 45 50
1541 2d. "Model K", 1906 . . . 45 50
1542 2d. "Model A", 1931 . . . 45 50
1543 2d. "Model A", 1906 . . . 45 50
1544 2d. "Model N", 1906 . . . 45 50
1545 2d. "Model F", 1905 . . . 45 50
1546 2d. Benz "Velo", 1894 . . . 45 50
1547 2d. Car of 1894 . . . . . 45 50
1548 2d. Three-wheeled car of 1885 from side 45 50
1549 2d. "Mannheim", 1905 . . . 45 50
1550 2d. Car of 1892 . . . . . 45 50
1551 2d. Car of 1900 from front 45 50
1552 2d. Racing car of 1911 from side 45 50
1553 2d. "Velo", 1893 . . . . . 45 50
1554 2d. Black car of 1900 from side 45 50
1555 2d. Red car of 1900 from side 45 50
1556 2d. Racing car of 1911 from front 45 50
1557 2d. Three-wheeled car of 1885 from back 45 50
MS1558 Two sheets, each 132 × 115 mm. (a) 20d. Ford car of 1896. (b) 20d. Benz car of 1900 Set of 2 sheets . . . . . . 8·50 9·00
Nos. 1534/45 and 1546/57 were each printed together, se-tenant, with the backgrounds forming composite designs.

218 Marilyn Monroe

220 "Woman with a Comb" (Picasso)

219 Siamese

1993. Musical Entertainers.
1559/93 3d. × 35 multicoloured . . . 38·00 32·00
Nos. 1559/93 were issued as four sheetlets, three of nine different designs (Nos. 1559/85) and one of eight (Nos. 1586/93), depicting Marilyn Monroe (Nos. 1559/67), Elvis Presley (Nos. 1568/76), Madonna (Nos. 1577/85) and Buddy Holly, Otis Redding, Bill Haley, Dinah Washington, musical instruments, Ritchie Valens, Clyde McPhatter, Elvis Presley (Nos. 1586/93).

1993. Oriental Cats. Multicoloured.
1594 2d. Type **219** . . . . 1·25 1·00
1595 2d. Colourpoint longhair sitting . . . . 1·25 1·00
1596 2d. Burmese . . . . 1·25 1·00
1597 2d. Birman . . . . 1·25 1·00
1598 2d. Snowshoe . . . . 1·25 1·00
1599 2d. Tonkinese . . . . . . 1·25 1·00
1600 2d. Foreign shorthair stretching . . . . 1·25 1·00
1601 2d. Balinese . . . . 1·25 1·00
1602 2d. Oriental shorthair . . . 1·25 1·00
1603 2d. Foreign shorthair lying 1·25 1·00
1604 2d. Colourpoint longhair with black face standing 1·25 1·00
1605 2d. Colourpoint longhair with white face standing 1·25 1·00
MS1606 Two sheets, each 121 × 90 mm. (a) 20d. Colourpoint shorthair (vert). (b) 20d. Burmese (vert) Set of 2 sheets . . . . 9·00 9·50
Nos. 1594/1605 were printed together, se-tenant, with the background forming a composite design.

1993. Royal Dogs. As T **219**. Multicoloured.
1607 2d. Shih tzu (Emperor of China) . . . . 1·25 1·00
1608 2d. Skye terrier (Queen Victoria) . . . . 1·25 1·00
1609 2d. Berner laufhund (King Louis XVI, France) . . . 1·25 1·00
1610 2d. Boxer (King Francis I, France) . . . . 1·25 1·00
1611 2d. Welsh corgi (Queen Elizabeth II) . . . . . . 1·25 1·00
1612 2d. Dumfriesshire (Princess Anne) . . . . 1·25 1·00
1613 2d. Lurcher (King George VI) . . . . 1·25 1·00
1614 2d. Welsh corgi (Princess Anne) . . . . 1·25 1·00
1615 2d. Pekinese (Empress Ts'Eu-Hi, China) . . . . 1·25 1·00
1616 2d. Papillon (King Louis XIII, France) . . . 1·25 1·00
1617 2d. Otterhound (King John) 1·25 1·00
1618 2d. Pug (Napoleon I, France) . . . . 1·25 1·00
MS1619 Two sheets, each 120 × 90 mm. (a) 20d. Cairn terrier (Mary, Queen of Scots). (b) 20d. Long-haired dachshund (Queen Victoria) Set of 2 sheets . . . 9·00 9·50
Nos. 1607/18 were printed together, se-tenant, with the backgrounds forming a composite design.

219a National Monument and Statue, Jakarta

1993. Asian International Stamp Exhibitions. Multicoloured. (a) "Indopex '93", Surabaya, Indonesia.
1620 20b. Type **219a** 20 20
1621 20b. Pura Taman Ayun Temple, Bali 20 20
1622 2d. Guardian statue, Singosari Palace, Java . . 60 60
1623 2d. Candi Jawi, Java 60 60
1624 5d. Telek Luh mask . . . . 1·40 1·40
1625 5d. Jero Gde mask . . . . 1·40 1·40
1626 5d. Barong Macan mask . . . 1·40 1·40
1627 5d. Monkey mask . . . . . 1·40 1·40
1628 5d. Mata Gde mask . . . . 1·40 1·40
1629 5d. Jauk Kras mask . . . . 1·40 1·40
1630 5d. "Tree Mask" (Soedibio) 1·40 1·40
1631 5d. "Dry Lizard" (Hendra Gunawan) . . . . 1·40 1·40
1632 5d. "The Corn Eater" (Sudjana Kerton) . . . . 1·40 1·40
1633 5d. "Night Watchman" (Djoko Pekik) . . . . . 1·40 1·40
1634 5d. "Hunger" (Kerton) . . . 1·40 1·40
1635 5d. "Arje Player" (Soedjojono) . . . . . . 1·40 1·40
1636 5d. Central Temple, Lara Djonggrang . . . . . . 1·40 1·40
1637 5d. Irian Jaya Monument, Jakarta . . . . 1·40 1·40
1638 15d. Brahma and Siva Temples, Java . . . . . 2·75 3·25
1639 15d. Date of the Year Temple, Java . . . . . . 2·75 3·25
MS1640 Two sheets, each 135 × 105 mm. (a) 18d. Tomb effigies, Torajaland (horiz). (b) 18d. Relief from Borobudur, Java (horiz) Set of 2 sheets . . . . 7·50 8·00

(b) "Taipei '93", Taiwan.
1641 20b. Fawang Si Pagoda, Henan 20 20
1642 20b. Wanshoubao Pagoda, Shashi 20 20
1643 2d. Red Pavilion, Shibaozhai 60 60
1644 2d. Songyue Si Pagoda, Henan 60 60
1645 5d. Pottery camel (walking) 1·40 1·40
1646 5d. Pottery horse and rider 1·40 1·40
1647 5d. Pottery camel (standing with mouth closed) . . . 1·40 1·40
1648 5d. Yellow-glazed pottery horse . . . . 1·40 1·40
1649 5d. Pottery camel (standing with mouth open) . . . 1·40 1·40
1650 5d. Pottery saddled horse . . 1·40 1·40
1651 5d. Qianlong vase . . . . . 1·40 1·40
1652 5d. Small wine cup . . . . 1·40 1·40
1653 5d. Mei-ping vase . . . . . 1·40 1·40
1654 5d. Urn vase . . . . 1·40 1·40
1655 5d. Tureen . . . . 1·40 1·40
1656 5d. Lidded potiche . . . . 1·40 1·40
1657 5d. Tianning Si Pagoda, Beijing . . . . 1·40 1·40
1658 5d. Bond Centre, Hong Kong . . . . 1·40 1·40
1659 15d. Forbidden City pavilion, Beijing . . . . 2·75 3·25
1660 15d. Xuanzhuang Pagoda, Shenxi . . . . 2·75 3·25
MS1661 Two sheets, each 135 × 105 mm. (a) 18d. Seated Buddha, Shanhua Temple, Shanxi. (b) 18d. Statues, Upper Huayan Si Temple, Datong (horiz) Set of 2 sheets . . . . 7·50 8·00

(c) "Bangkok '93", Thailand.
1662 20b. Sanctuary of Prasat Phanom Wan 20 20
1663 20b. Lai Kham Vihan, Chiang Mai 20 20
1664 2d. Upmarket spirit shrine, Bangkok 60 60
1665 2d. Walking Buddha statue, Wat Phra Si Ratana Mahathat 60 60
1666 5d. "Early Fruit Stand" . . 1·40 1·40
1667 5d. "Scene Rendered in Chinese Style" . . . . . 1·40 1·40
1668 5d. "Buddha descends from Tauatimsa" . . . . . . 1·40 1·40
1669 5d. "Sang Thong Tales" (detail) . . . . 1·40 1·40
1670 5d. "The Damned in Hell" 1·40 1·40
1671 5d. "King Sanjaya travels on Elephant" . . . . . . 1·40 1·40
1672 5d. U Thong C Buddha (bronze) . . . . 1·40 1·40
1673 5d. Seated Buddha (bronze) 1·40 1·40
1674 5d. Phra Chai Buddha (ivory and gold) . . . . . 1·40 1·40
1675 5d. Buddha (bronze) . . . . 1·40 1·40
1676 5d. U Thong A Buddha (bronze) . . . . 1·40 1·40
1677 5d. Crowned Buddha (bronze) . . . . 1·40 1·40
1678 5d. Statue of Buddha, Wat Mahathat . . . . 1·40 1·40
1679 5d. The Gopura of Prasat Phanom Rung . . . . . 1·40 1·40
1680 15d. Slender Chedis, Mongkon . . . . 2·75 3·25
1681 15d. The Prang of Prasat Hin Phimai . . . . . . 2·75 3·25
MS1682 Two sheets, each 135 × 105 mm. (a) 18d. Khon (Thai dance drama). (b) 18d. Ceramics (horiz) Set of 2 sheets 7·50 8·00

1993. Anniversaries and Events. Mult.
1683 2d. Type **220** 75 75
1684 2d. "Niedzica Castle" (horiz) 75 75
1685 5d. "The Mirror" (Picasso) 1·40 1·40
1686 5d. Early astronomical instrument . . . . 1·40 1·40
1687 7d. "Woman on a Pillow" (Picasso) . . . . 1·60 2·00
1688 10d. "Pont-Neuf in Paris" (Hanna Rudza-Cybisowa) (horiz) . . . . 2·50 3·00
1689 10d. "Honegger's Liturgical Symphony" (Marian Bogusz) (horiz) . . . . . 2·50 3·00
1690 10d. Modern telescope . . . 2·50 3·00
MS1691 Three sheets. (a) 75 × 105 mm. 18d. "The Three Dancers" (detail) (Picasso). P 14. (b) 105 × 75 mm. 18d. "When You enter here, Whisper my Name soundlessly" (detail) (Henryk Waniek) (horiz). P 14. (c) 102 × 74 mm. 18d. Copernicus Set of 3 sheets . . . . . . 14·00 14·00
ANNIVERSARIES AND EVENTS: Nos. 1683, 1685, 1687, **MS**1691a, 20th death anniv of Picasso (artist); 1684, 1688/9, **MS**1691b, "Polska '93" International Stamp Exhibition, Poznan; 1686, 1690, **MS**1691c, 450th death anniv of Copernicus (astronomer).
The captions on Nos. 1684 and 1689 are transposed in error.
No. **MS**1691b is inscribed "WHISPERT" in error.

221 Mudville Player at the Plate

1993. "Casey at the Bat". Scenes from Walt Disney's cartoon film. Multicoloured.
1692 2d. Type **221** 95 90
1693 2d. Mudville player out . . . 95 90
1694 2d. Umpire and player arguing 95 90
1695 2d. Fans applauding 95 90
1696 2d. Casey reading newspaper at plate . . . 95 90
1697 2d. Casey letting second pitch go by 95 90
1698 2d. Over-confident Casey . . 95 90
1699 2d. Casey striking out . . . 95 90
1700 2d. Casey striking out at night 95 90
MS1701 Two sheets, each 129 × 103 mm. (a) 20d. Mudville manager. (b) 20d. Pitcher (vert) Set of 2 sheets . . . . 10·00 11·00

221a Hannich (Hungary) and Stopyra (France)

1993. World Cup Football Championship, 1994, U.S.A. (1st issue). Multicoloured.
1702 1d.25 Type **221a** . . . . . 1·00 40
1703 1d.50 Labd (Morocco) and Gary Lineker (England) 1·25 50
1704 2d. Segota (Canada) and Morozov (Russia) . . . . 1·40 65
1705 3d. Roger Milla (Cameroun) 1·60 1·25
1706 5d. Rodax (Austria) and Weiss (Czechoslovakia) . 2·00 1·75
1707 10d. Claesen (Belgium), Bossis and Amoros (France) . . . . 2·75 2·75
1708 12d. Candida (Brazil) and Ramirez (Costa Rica) . . 2·75 3·00
1709 15d. Silva (Brazil) and Michel Platini (France) 3·00 3·50
MS1710 Two sheets, each 100 × 70 mm. (a) 25d. Muller (Brazil) and McDonald (Ireland) (horiz). (b) 25d. Diego Maradona (Argentina) and Matthaeus (Germany) (horiz) Set of 2 sheets 12·00 13·00
See also Nos. 1882/90.

221b "The Adoration of the Magi" (detail) (Rubens)

1993. Christmas. Religious Paintings. Black, yellow and red (Nos. 1712/13 and 1715/17) or multicoloured (others).
1711 25b. Type **221b** 30 20
1712 1d. "The Holy Family with Joachim and Anna" (Durer) 70 20

1713 1d.50 "The Annunciation" (Durer) 90 30
1714 2d. "The Adoration of the Magi" (different detail) (Rubens) . . . . 1·00 60
1715 2d. "The Virgin Mary worshipped by Albrecht Bonstetten" (Durer) . . . 1·00 60
1716 7d. "The Holy Family with Two Angels in a Portico" (detail) (Durer) . . . . . 2·50 3·25
1717 10d. "Virgin on a Throne, crowned by an Angel" (Durer) . . . . 2·75 3·25
1718 15d. "The Adoration of the Magi" (different detail) (Rubens) . . . . 3·00 4·25
MS1719 Two sheets, each 102 × 127 mm. (a) 20d. "The Adoration of the Magi" (different detail) (Rubens). (b) 20d. "The Holy Family with Two Angels in a Portico" (different detail) (Durer) (horiz) Set of 2 sheets 9·00 10·00

221c "A Man in a Cap" (Rembrandt)

1993. Famous Paintings by Rembrandt and Matisse. Multicoloured.
1720 50b. Type **221c** 65 20
1721 1d.50 "Pierre Matisse" (Matisse) . . . . 1·00 40
1722 2d. "Man with a Gold Helmet" (Rembrandt) . . 1·25 85
1723 2d. "Auguste Pellerin" (Matisse) . . . . 1·25 85
1724 5d. "Andre Derain" (Matisse) . . . . 2·25 2·25
1725 7d. "A Franciscan Monk" (Rembrandt) . . . . . . 2·75 3·25
1726 12d. "The Young Sailor (II)" (Matisse) . . . . . 3·25 4·00
1727 15d. "The Apostle Paul" (Rembrandt) . . . . . . 3·25 4·50
MS1728 Two sheets, each 127 × 102 mm. (a) 20d. "Dr. Tulp demonstrating the Anatomy of the Arm" (detail) (Rembrandt) (horiz). (b) 20d. "Pianist and Draughts Players" (detail) (Matisse) Set of 2 sheets . . . 10·00 11·00

222 Mickey Mouse performing Ski Ballet

1993. Winter Sports. Walt Disney cartoon characters. Multicoloured.
1729 50b. Type **222** 40 15
1730 75b. Clarabelle and Horace ice dancing 50 15
1731 1d. Donald Duck and Dale speed skating 55 20
1732 1d.25 Donald in biathlon . . 60 20
1733 4d. Donald and nephews in bob-sled . . . . 1·60 1·60
1734 5d. Goofy on luge . . . . . 1·75 1·75
1735 7d. Minnie Mouse figure skating . . . . 2·25 2·75
1736 10d. Goofy downhill skiing 2·50 2·75
1737 15d. Goofy playing ice hockey . . . . 2·75 3·25
MS1738 Two sheets, each 128 × 102 mm. (a) 20d. Minnie mogul skiing. (b) 20d. Goofy cross-country skiing Set of 2 sheets 8·50 9·50

222a Hong Kong 1979 $2 Butterflies Stamp and "Spring Garden" (M. Bruce)

1994. "Hong Kong '94" International Stamp Exhibition (1st issue). Multicoloured.
1739 1d.50 Type **222a** 65 75
1740 1d.50 Gambia 1990 50d. Gambian Life stamp and "Spring Garden" (M. Bruce) 65 75
MS1741 82 × 117 mm. 20d. Hong Kong 1970 Chinese New Year 10c. stamp . . . . 3·50 4·00
Nos. 1739/40 were printed together, se-tenant, forming the complete painting.
See also Nos. 1742/7.

222b Warriors and Horses

1994. "Hong Kong '94" International Stamp Exhibition (2nd issue). Qin Dynasty Terracotta Figures. Multicoloured.
1742 1d.50 Type **222b** 60 55
1743 1d.50 Head of warrior . . . 60 55
1744 1d.50 Kneeling warrior . . 60 55
1745 1d.50 Chariot driver 60 55
1746 1d.50 Dog 60 55
1747 1d.50 Warriors as excavated 60 55

223 Pluto the Racer, 1934–35

1994. Chinese New Year ("Year of the Dog"). Walt Disney cartoon dogs. Multicoloured.
1748 25b. Type **223** 55 20
1749 50b. Fifi, 1933 . . . . . . 70 30
1750 75b. Pluto Jnr, 1942 . . . . 90 30
1751 1d.25 Goofy and Bowser . . 1·25 30
1752 1d.50 Butch, 1940 . . . . . 1·25 45
1753 2d. Toliver, 1936 . . . . . 1·50 60
1754 3d. Ronnie, 1946 . . . . . 1·75 1·00
1755 5d. Primo, 1950 . . . . . . 2·00 1·40
1756 8d. Pluto's kid brother, 1946 2·25 2·25
1757 10d. The army mascot, 1942 2·25 2·50
1758 12d. Pluto and Fifi's puppies, 1937 . . . . . . 2·25 3·00
1759 18d. Bent Tail Jnr, 1949 . . 2·75 4·00
MS1760 Three sheets, each 127 × 102 mm. (a) 20d. Pluto and Fifi's puppies, 1937 (different). (b) 20d. Pluto and Dinah, 1950. (c) 20d. Pflip (horiz) Set of 3 sheets 12·00 13·00
Nos. 1758 and MS1760a are inscribed "DINAH'S PUPPIES" in error.

224 Ludwig von Drake and Easter Bunny

1994. Easter. Walt Disney cartoon characters. Multicoloured.
1761 25b. Type **224** 40 10
1762 50b. Minnie Mouse and Daisy Duck carrying banner 55 10
1763 3d. Mickey Mouse wearing top hat . . . . 1·50 85
1764 4d. Von Drake holding hatching egg . . . . . . 1·75 1·25
1765 5d. Donald Duck pushing trolley full of eggs . . . . 2·00 1·75
1766 8d. Bunny taking photograph of Von Drake 2·25 2·50
1767 10d. Goofy dressed as Easter Bunny . . . . . . 2·25 2·75
1768 12d. Von Drake holding dinosaur egg . . . . . . 2·50 3·25
MS1769 Two sheets. (a) 102 × 123 mm. 20d. Mickey and Minnie. (b) 123 × 102 mm. 20d. Ludwig von Drake Set of 2 sheets 8·50 9·50

224a Briksdal Fjord

1994. Centenary (1992) of Sierra Club (environmental protection society). Endangered Environments. Multicoloured.
1770 5d. Type **224a** . . . . . . 1·00 1·10
1771 5d. Glacier, Briksdal Fjord 1·00 1·10
1772 5d. Waterfall, Briksdal Fjord . . . . 1·00 1·10
1773 5d. Frozen lake, Yosemite 1·00 1·10
1774 5d. Cliffs and river, Yosemite . . . . 1·00 1·10
1775 5d. Forest, Yosemite 80 90
1776 5d. Mother and child, Tibetan Plateau 80 90
1777 5d. Yellowstone in winter 80 90
1778 5d. Ross Island 80 90
1779 5d. Mount Erebus 80 90
1780 5d. Tibetan Plateau 80 90
1781 5d. Waterfall, Yellowstone 80 90
1782 5d. Sunset on the Serengeti 80 90
1783 5d. Dead trees, Ansel Adams Wilderness 80 90
1784 5d. Ansel Adams Wilderness in winter (horiz) 80 90
1785 5d. Ansel Adams Wilderness in summer (horiz) 80 90
1786 5d. Ridge on Mount Erebus (horiz) 80 90
1787 5d. Mount Erebus from a distance (horiz) 80 90
1788 5d. Prince William Sound (horiz) 80 90
1789 5d. Geysers, Yellowstone (horiz) 80 90
1790 5d. Local dwelling, Tibetan Plateau (horiz) 80 90
1791 5d. Sierra Club Centennial emblem (horiz) 80 90
1792 5d. Frozen lake, Prince William Sound (horiz) . . 1·00 1·10
1793 5d. Forest, Prince William Sound (horiz) . . . . . 1·00 1·10
1794 5d. Baobab Tree, Serengeti (horiz) . . . . 1·00 1·10
1795 5d. Plains, Serengeti (horiz) 1·00 1·10
1796 5d. Volcano, Ross Island (horiz) . . . . 1·00 1·10
1797 5d. Mountains, Ross Island (horiz) . . . . 1·00 1·10

225 "Oeceoclades maculata"

226 "Girl with a Kitten" (Perronneau)

1994. Orchids. Multicoloured.
1798 1d. Type **225** 35 20
1799 1d.25 "Angraecum distichum" (horiz) 45 30
1800 2d. "Plectrelminthus caudatus" 60 35
1801 5d. "Tridactyle tridactylites" (horiz) . . . . 1·25 1·25
1802 8d. "Bulbophyllum lepidum" (horiz) . . . . 1·40 1·50
1803 10d. "Angraecum eburneum" . . . . 1·60 1·90
1804 12d. "Eulophia guineensis" 1·75 2·00
1805 15d. "Angraecum eichleranum" (horiz) . . . 2·00 2·50
MS1806 Two sheets, each 100 × 70 mm. (a) 25d. "Vanilla imperialis". (b) 25d. "Ancistrochilus rothschildianus" (horiz) Set of 2 sheets . . . . 9·00 10·00

1994. Cats. Paintings of Cats. Multicoloured.
1807 5d. Type **226** . . . . 1·40 1·40
1808 5d. "Still Life with Cat and Fish" (Chardin) . . . . . 1·40 1·40
1809 5d. "Tinkle a Cat" . . . . 1·40 1·40
1810 5d. "Naughty Puss!" (advertisement) . . . . . 1·40 1·40
1811 5d. "Cats" (T.-A. Steinlen) 1·40 1·40
1812 5d. "Girl in Red with Cat and Dog" (Phillips) . . . 1·40 1·40
1813 5d. "Cat, Butterfly and Begonia" (Harunobu) . . 1·40 1·40
1814 5d. "Cat and Kitten" (Pamela Higgins) . . . . 1·40 1·40
1815 5d. "Woman with a Cat" (Renoir) . . . . 1·40 1·40
1816 5d. "Minnie from Outskirts of the Village" (Thrall) . . 1·40 1·40
1817 5d. "The Fisher" (Raphael Tuck postcard) . . . . . 1·40 1·40
1818 5d. "Artist and His Family" (detail) (Vaenius) . . . . 1·40 1·40
1819 5d. "The Arena" (Harold Weston) (horiz) . . . . . 1·40 1·40
1820 5d. "Cat killing a Bird" (Picasso) (horiz) . . . . . 1·40 1·40
1821 5d. "Cat and Butterfly" (Hokusai) (horiz) . . . . 1·40 1·40
1822 5d. "Winter: Cat on a Cushion" (Steinlen) (horiz) . . . . 1·40 1·40
1823 5d. "Rattown Tigers" (Prang) (horiz) . . . . . 1·40 1·40
1824 5d. "Cat on the Floor" (Steinlen) (horiz) . . . . 1·40 1·40
1825 5d. "Cat and Kittens" (horiz) . . . . 1·40 1·40
1826 5d. "Cats looking over Fence" (Prang) (horiz) . . 1·40 1·40
1827 5d. "Little White Kittens into Mischief" (Ives) (horiz) . . . . 1·40 1·40
1828 5d. "Cat Bathing" (Hiroshige) (horiz) . . . . 1·40 1·40
1829 5d. "Playtime" (Tuck postcard) (horiz) . . . . 1·40 1·40
1830 5d. "Summer: Cat on a Balustrade" (Steinlen) (horiz) . . . . 1·40 1·40
MS1831 Two sheets, each 100 × 70 mm. (a) 20d. "The Graham Children" (detail) (William Hogarth). (b) 20d. "The Morning Rising" (detail) (Michel Lepicie) (horiz) Set of 2 sheets 9·00 10·00

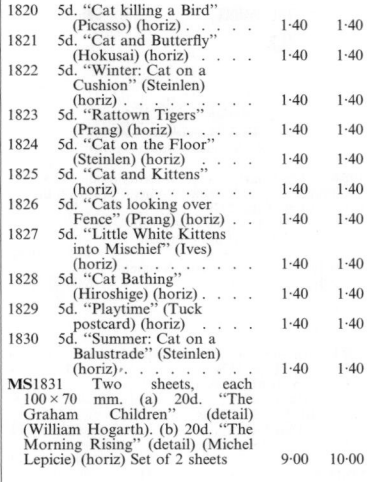

227 Patas Monkey

1994. Monkeys. Multicoloured.
1832 1d. Type **227** 45 20
1833 1d.50 Collared mangabey . . 65 30
1834 2d. Black and white colobus 75 35
1835 5d. Mona monkey . . . . . 1·25 1·10
1836 8d. Kirk's colobus . . . . . 1·50 2·00
1837 10d. Vervet . . . . 1·75 2·25
1838 12d. Red colobus . . . . . 2·00 2·50
1839 15d. Guinea baboon . . . . 2·25 2·75
MS1840 Two sheets, each 106 × 77 mm. (a) 25d. Head of Guinea baboon. (b) 25d. Head of Collared mangabey Set of 2 sheets 12·00 13·00

227a Yuri Gagarin (first cosmonaut)

1994. 25th Anniv of First Manned Moon Landing. Multicoloured.
1841 2d. Type **227a** 75 75
1842 2d. Valentina Tereshkova (first woman in Space) . . 75 75
1843 2d. Ham (first chimpanzee in Space) 75 75
1844 2d. Aleksei Leonov (first man to walk in Space) . . 75 75
1845 2d. Neil Armstrong (first man on Moon) 75 75
1846 2d. Svetlana Savitskaya (first woman to walk in Space) 75 75
1847 2d. Marc Garneau (first Canadian in Space) . . . 75 75
1848 2d. Vladimir Komarov (first Soviet Space casualty) . . 75 75
1849 2d. Ulf Merbold (first German in Space) 75 75
MS1850 81 × 81 mm. 30d. "Apollo 11" crew at news conference . . . . 7·00 7·50

227b Daley Thompson (Great Britain) (decathlon), 1980 and 1984

227d Soldiers on Horses

227c "Soema" (Dutch Sloop)

1994. Centenary of International Olympic Committee. Gold Medal Winners. Multicoloured.
1851 1d.50 Type **227b** 50 40
1852 5d. Heide Marie Rosendohl (Germany) (long jump), 1972 1·25 1·50
MS1853 106×76 mm. 20d. Sweden (ice hockey), 1994 6·00 6·50

1994. 50th Anniv of D-Day. Multicoloured.
1854 50b. Type **227c** 70 50
1855 75b. H.M.S. "Belfast" (cruiser) 80 60
1856 1d. U.S.S. "Texas" (battleship) 90 70
1857 2d. "Georges Leygues" (French cruiser) 1·40 1·40
MS1858 105×76 mm. 20d. H.M.S. "Ramillies" (battleship) firing broadside 4·25 4·50

1994. "Philakorea '94" International Stamp Exhibition, Seoul. Screen paintings of the "Sanguozhi". Multicoloured.
1859 50b. Kungnakchon Hall (38×25 mm) 45 30
1860 1d. Type **227d** 55 60
1861 1d. Soldiers defending fort 55 60
1862 1d. Archers 55 60
1863 1d. General on horse 55 60
1864 1d. Three soldiers in battle 55 60
1865 1d. Army in retreat 55 60
1866 1d. Archers using fire arrows 55 60
1867 1d. Horsemen attacking fort 55 60
1868 1d. Women in summer house 55 60
1869 1d. Old man, child and house 55 60
1870 2d. Kettle of Popchusa (38×25 mm) 80 85
1871 3d. Pomun tourist resort (38×25 mm) 90 1·10
MS1872 98×68 mm. 20d. Tomb guardian, Taenung (38×25 mm) 4·50 5·50

228 "Mylothris rhodope"

1994. Butterflies. Multicoloured.
1873 1d. Type **228** 50 25
1874 1d.25 "Iolaphilus menas" 65 35
1875 2d. "Neptis nemetes" 75 40
1876 5d. "Antanartia delius" 1·25 1·10
1877 8d. "Acraea caecilia" 1·50 2·00
1878 10d. "Papilio nireus" 1·50 2·00
1879 12d. "Papilio menestheus" 1·75 2·50
1880 15d. "Iolaphilus julus" 2·00 2·75
MS1881 Two sheets, each 97×68 mm. (a) 25d. "Bematistes epaea". (b) 25d. "Colotis evippe" Set of 2 sheets 11·00 12·00

229 Bobby Charlton (England)

1994. World Cup Football Championship, U.S.A. (2nd issue). Multicoloured.
1882 50b. Type **229** 50 30
1883 75b. Ferenc Puskas (Hungary) 60 30
1884 1d. Paolo Rossi (Italy) 75 30
1885 2d. Biri Biri (Spain) 1·00 40
1886 3d. Diego Maradona (Argentina) 1·25 80
1887 8d. Johann Cruyff (Netherlands) 2·00 2·25
1888 10d. Franz Beckenbauer (Germany) 2·00 2·25
1889 15d. Thomas Dooley (U.S.A.) 2·25 3·25
MS1890 Two sheets, each 70×100 mm. (a) 25d. Pelé (Brazil). (b) 25d. Gordon Banks (England) Set of 2 sheets 11·00 11·00

230 "Suillus luteus" **231** Marilyn Monroe

230a "Expectant Madonna with St. Joseph" (French 15th-century)

1994. Fungi. Multicoloured.
1891 5d. Type **230** 90 90
1892 5d. "Bolbitius vitellinus" 90 90
1893 5d. "Clitocybe nebularis" 90 90
1894 5d. "Omphalotus olearius" 90 90
1895 5d. "Auricularia auricula" 90 90
1896 5d. "Macrolepiota rhacodes" 90 90
1897 5d. "Volvariella volvacea" 90 90
1898 5d. "Psilocybe coprophila" 90 90
1899 5d. "Suillus granulatus" 90 90
1900 5d. "Agaricus campestris" 90 90
1901 5d. "Lepista nuda" 90 90
1902 5d. "Podaxis pistillaris" 90 90
1903 5d. "Oudemansiella radicata" 90 90
1904 5d. "Schizophyllum commune" 90 90
1905 5d. "Chlorophyllum molybdites" 90 90
1906 5d. "Hypholoma fasciculare" 90 90
1907 5d. "Mycena pura" 90 90
1908 5d. "Ganoderma lucidum" 90 90
MS1909 Two sheets, each 100×70 mm. (a) 20d. "Leucoagaricus naucinus". (b) 20d. "Cyathus striatus" Set of 2 sheets 11·00 11·00

1994. Christmas. Religious Paintings. Multicoloured.
1910 50b. Type **230a** 30 10
1911 75b. "Rest of the Holy Family" (Louis le Nain) 40 20
1912 1d. "Rest on the Flight into Egypt" (Antoine Watteau) 55 20
1913 2d. "Rest on the Flight into Egypt" (Jean-Honore Fragonard) 70 70
1914 2d. "Rest on the Flight into Egypt" (Francois Boucher) 70 70
1915 2d. "Noon" (Claude Lorrain) 70 70
1916 10d. "The Holy Family" (Nicolas Poussin) 2·50 3·25
1917 12d. "Mystical Marriage of St. Catherine" (Pierre-Francois Mignard) 2·50 3·50
MS1918 Two sheets, each 122×87 mm. (a) 25d. "Adoration of the Shepherds" (detail) (Mathieu le Nain). (b) 25d. "The Nativity by Torchlight" (detail) (Louis le Nain) Set of 2 sheets 10·00 11·00

1995. Marilyn Monroe (American entertainer) Commemoration. Multicoloured.
1919 4d. Type **231** 90 90
1920 4d. Wearing pendant necklace 90 90
1921 4d. In blue jacket 90 90
1922 4d. With sun-glasses on head 90 90
1923 4d. Looking over right arm 90 90
1924 4d. Wearing gold beret and jacket 90 90
1925 4d. Wearing hooped earrings 90 90
1926 4d. Smiling 90 90
1927 4d. Laughing 90 90
MS1928 Two sheets, each 70×100mm. (a) 25d. Marilyn Monroe in red dress. (b) 25d. With pendant earrings Set of 2 sheets 8·50 9·00

232 Elvis as a Child

1995. 60th Birth Anniv of Elvis Presley (singer). Multicoloured.
1929 4d. Type **232** 1·00 90
1930 4d. Wearing white shirt 1·00 90
1931 4d. With his mother Gladys 1·00 90
1932 4d. With his wife Priscilla 1·00 90
1933 4d. With large gold medallion 1·00 90
1934 4d. In army uniform 1·00 90
1935 4d. In purple shirt 1·00 90
1936 4d. Wearing stetson 1·00 90
1937 4d. With his daughter Lisa-Marie 1·00 90

233 Pteranodon

1995. Prehistoric Animals. Multicoloured.
1938 2d. Type **233** 65 65
1939 2d. Archaeopteryx 65 65
1940 2d. Rhamphorhynchus 65 65
1941 2d. Ornithomimus 65 65
1942 2d. Stegosaurus 65 65
1943 2d. Heterodontosaurus 65 65
1944 2d. Lystrosaurus 65 65
1945 2d. Euoplocephalus 65 65
1946 2d. Coelophysis 65 65
1947 2d. Staurikosaurus 65 65
1948 2d. Giantoperis 65 65
1949 2d. Diarthrognathus 65 65
1950 3d. Archaeopteryx 65 65
1951 3d. Vangheuanosaurus 65 65
1952 3d. Celophysis 65 65
1953 3d. Plateosaurus 65 65
1954 3d. Baryonyx 65 65
1955 3d. Ornitholestes 65 65
1956 3d. Dryosaurus 65 65
1957 3d. Estemmenosuchus 65 65
1958 3d. Macroplata 65 65
1959 3d. Shonisaurus 65 65
1960 3d. Muraeonosaurus 65 65
1961 3d. Archelon 65 65
MS1962 Four sheets, each 100×70 mm. (a) 20d. Bactrosaurus. (b) 22d. Tyrannosaurus rex (vert). (c) 25d. Triceratops (vert). (d) 25d. Spinosaurus Set of 4 sheets 20·00 20·00
Nos. 1938/49 and 1950/61 respectively were printed together, se-tenant, forming composite designs.

234 Pig (Chinese characters in green) **236** Rural Road

235 Great Egret ("Great White Egret")

1995. Chinese New Year ("Year of the Pig").
1963 **234** 3d. red, black and green 65 65
1964 – 3d. multicoloured (characters in blue) 65 65
1965 – 3d. orange, red and black (characters in white) 65 65
1966 – 3d. pink, red and black (characters in black) 65 65
MS1967 76×100 mm. 10d. mauve and red (three pigs) 2·25 2·50
DESIGNS: Nos. 1964/6, Different symbolic pigs.

1995. Water Birds. Multicoloured.
1968 2d. Type **235** 80 60
1969 3d. Pintails 80 80
1970 3d. Fulvous whistling duck ("Fulvous Tree Duck") 80 80
1971 3d. Garganey 80 80
1972 3d. White-faced whistling duck ("White-faced Tree Duck") 80 80
1973 3d. White-backed duck 80 80
1974 3d. Egyptian goose 80 80
1975 3d. African pygmy geese ("Pygmy Goose") 80 80
1976 3d. Little bitterns 80 80
1977 3d. Common redshanks ("Redshank") 80 80
1978 3d. Ringed plovers 80 80
1979 3d. Black-winged stilt 80 80
1980 3d. Squacco herons 80 80
1981 8d. Hammerkop 2·00 2·50
1982 10d. Common shovelers ("Shoveler") 2·00 2·50
1983 12d. Crowned crane 2·25 2·75
MS1984 Two sheets, each 106×76 mm. (a) 25d. Ferruginous ducks. (b) 25d. Moorhen Set of 2 sheets 11·00 12·00
Nos. 1969/80 were printed together, se-tenant, forming a composite design.

1995. 20th Anniv of Economic Community of West African States (E.C.O.W.A.S.). Multicoloured.
1985 2d. Type **236** 50 25
1986 5d. Pres. Yayah Jammeh 1·25 1·50

237 Leather Back Turtle

1995. Marine Life. Multicoloured.
1987 3d. Type **237** 70 75
1988 3d. Tiger shark 70 75
1989 3d. Powder-blue surgeonfish 70 75
1990 3d. Emperor angelfish 70 75
1991 3d. Blue parrotfish 70 75
1992 3d. Clown triggerfish 70 75
1993 3d. Sea horses 70 75
1994 3d. Lionfish 70 75
1995 3d. Moray eel 70 75
1996 3d. Melon butterflyfish 70 75
1997 3d. Octopus 70 75
1998 3d. Common stingray 70 75
1999 8d. Stoplight parrotfish ("Multicoloured Parrot Fish") (vert) 1·75 2·00
2000 8d. Stoplight parrotfish ("Sparisoma Viride") (vert) 1·75 2·00
2001 8d. Queen parrotfish (vert) 1·75 2·00
2002 8d. Bicoloured parrotfish (vert) 1·75 2·00
MS2003 Two sheets, each 98×68 mm. (a) 25d. Queen angelfish ("Angelicthys isabelita"). (b) 25d. Rock beauty ("Holacanthus ciliaris") Set of 2 sheets 13·00 13·00
Nos. 1987/98 and 1999/2002 respectively were printed together, se-tenant, forming composite designs.
No. 1991 is inscribed "BLUE PARRO FISH" in error.

238 First stage of Lariat Knot

1995. 18th World Scout Jamboree, Netherlands. T **238** amd similar vert designs. Multicoloured.
MS2004 Two sheets, each 101×65 mm. (a) 2d. Type **238**; 2d. Second stage of knot with ropes end at right; 2d. Completed Lariat knot. (b) 5d. Completed Bowline knot; 10d. Second stage of knot; 12d. First stage of knot Set of 2 sheets 7·00 8·00
MS2005 Two sheets, each 72×102 mm. (a) 25d. Scout in rope using Hitch knot. (b) 25d. Injured scout supported by Bowline knot Set of 2 sheets 8·50 9·50

238a Peter Lawford

1995. 50th Anniv of End of Second World War in Europe. Film Stars. Black and red (Nos. 2008 and 2010) or multicoloured (others).
2006 3d. Type **238a** 1·00 1·00
2007 3d. Gene Tierney and Dana Andrews 1·00 1·00

2008 3d. Groucho and Harpo Marx . . . . 1·00 1·00
2009 3d. James Stewart . . . . . 1·00 1·00
2010 3d. Chico and Zeppo Marx 1·00 1·00
2011 3d. Tyrone Power . . . . . 1·00 1·00
2012 3d. Cary Grant and Ingrid Bergman . . . . 1·00 1·00
2013 3d. Veronica Lake . . . . . 1·00 1·00
MS2014 105 × 75 mm. 25d. "A Lady Fights Back" film poster (vert) 7·50 8·50
No. 2012 is inscribed "BERMAN" in error.

238b Children in Class

1995. 50th Anniv of United Nations. Multicoloured.
2015 3d. Type **238b** . . . . . . 95 1·10
2016 3d. Teacher helping child . . 95 1·10
2017 3d. Child writing on blackboard . . . . 95 1·10
MS2018 104 × 74 mm. 25d. Nurse weighing baby . . . . 3·75 4·50
Nos. 2015/17 were printed together, se-tenant, forming a composite design.

238c Woman carrying Sack

1995. 50th Anniv of F.A.O. Multicoloured.
2019 3d. Type **238c** . . . . . . 95 1·10
2020 3d. Two men carrying sacks 95 1·10
2021 3d. Man carrying sack . . . 95 1·10
MS2022 104 × 74 mm. 25d. Fisherman with net . . . . . 3·75 4·50
Nos. 2019/21 were printed together, se-tenant, forming a composite design.

239 Paul Harris (founder) and Rotary Emblem

1995. 90th Anniv of Rotary International.
2023 **239** 15d. multicoloured . . . 2·00 2·50
MS2024 75 × 105 mm. 20d. National flag and Rotary emblem . . . 3·00 3·50

239a Queen Elizabeth the Queen Mother (pastel drawing)

1995. 95th Birthday of Queen Elizabeth the Queen Mother.
2025 **239a** 5d. brown, lt brn & blk 1·60 1·60
2026 – 5d. multicoloured . . . 1·60 1·60
2027 – 5d. multicoloured . . . 1·60 1·60
2028 – 5d. multicoloured . . . 1·60 1·60
MS2029 102 × 126 mm. 25d. multicoloured . . . . 6·50 5·50
DESIGNS: Nos. 2026, Wearing blue hat and dress; 2027, At desk (oil painting); 2028, Wearing green hat and dress; **MS**2029 Wearing lavender hat and dress.

239b Fairey Firefly

1995. 50th Anniv of End of Second World War in the Pacific. Multicoloured.
2030 5d. Type **239b** . . . . . . 1·25 1·25
2031 5d. Fairey Barracuda Mk III . . . . 1·25 1·25
2032 5d. Supermarine Seafire II 1·25 1·25
2033 5d. H.M.S. "Repulse" (battle cruiser) . . . . . 1·25 1·25
2034 5d. H.M.S. "Illustrious" (aircraft carrier) . . . . . 1·25 1·25
2035 5d. H.M.S. "Exeter" (cruiser) . . . . 1·25 1·25
MS2036 108 × 76 mm. 25d. Kamikaze aircraft heading for British "County" class cruiser 4·75 4·75

240 Kenichi Fukui (1981 Chemistry)

1995. Centenary of Nobel Prize Trust Fund. Past Prize Winners. Multicoloured.
2037 2d. Type **240** 55 40
2038 3d. Gustav Stresemann (1929 Peace) 65 50
2039 5d. Thomas Mann (1929 Literature) . . . . . . 1·00 1·10
2040 5d. Marie Curie (1911 Chemistry) . . . . 1·00 1·10
2041 5d. Adolf Butenandt (1939 Chemistry) . . . . . . 1·00 1·10
2042 5d. Susumu Tonegwa (1987 Medicine) . . . . . . 1·00 1·10
2043 5d. Nelly Sachs (1966 Literature) . . . . . . 1·00 1·10
2044 5d. Yasunari Kawabata (1968 Literature) . . . . 1·00 1·10
2045 5d. Hideki Yukawa (1949 Physics) . . . . 1·00 1·10
2046 5d. Paul Ehrlich (1908 Medicine) . . . . 1·00 1·10
2047 5d. Bisaku Sato (1974 Peace) . . . . 1·00 1·10
2048 5d. Carl von Ossietsky (1935 Peace) . . . . 1·00 1·10
2049 8d. Albert Schweitzer (1952 Peace) . . . . 2·00 2·00
2050 12d. Leo Esaki (1973 Physics) . . . . 2·00 2·50
2051 15d. Lech Walesa (1983 Peace) . . . . 2·25 3·00
MS2052 75 × 105 mm. 25d. Willy Brandt (1971 Peace) . . . . . 4·25 5·00
Nos. 2040/8 were printed together, se-tenant, forming a composite design.
No. 2048 is dated "1974" and No. 2051 inscribed "Lech Walsea", both in error.

241 Bruce Jenner (U.S.A.) (decathlon)

1995. Olympic Games, Atlanta (1996) (1st issue). Multicoloured.
2053 1d. Type **241** 50 30
2054 1d.25 Greg Louganis (U.S.A.) (diving) 55 30
2055 1d.50 Michael Gross (Germany) (50 m butterfly) 55 30
2056 2d. Vasily Alexeev (Russia) (weightlifting) 60 30
2057 3d. Ewing (U.S.A.) and Corbalan (Spain) (basketball) . . . . 1·25 80
2058 3d. Stefano Cerioni (Italy) (fencing) (vert) . . . . . 1·25 1·25
2059 3d. Alberto Cova (Italy) (10,000 m) (vert) . . . . 1·25 1·25
2060 3d. Mary Lou Retton (U.S.A.) (gymnastics) (vert) . . . . 1·25 1·25
2061 3d. Vladimir Artemov (Russia) (gymnastics) (vert) . . . . 1·25 1·25
2062 3d. Florence Griffith-Joyner (U.S.A.) (400 m relay) (vert) . . . . 1·25 1·25
2063 3d. Brazil (football) (vert) 1·25 1·25
2064 3d. Nelson Vails (U.S.A.) (sprint cycling) (vert) . . 1·25 1·25
2065 3d. Cheryl Miller (U.S.A.) (basketball) (vert) . . . . 1·25 1·25
2066 5d. U.S.A. v Brazil (men's volleyball) . . . . 1·50 1·75
2067 10d. Svenden (West Germany) and Fernandez (U.S.A.) (water polo) . . 2·00 2·25
2068 15d. Pertii Karppinen (Finland) (single sculls) 2·75 3·50
MS2069 Two sheets, each 71 × 101 mm. (a) 25d. Karen Stives (U.S.A.) (equestrian) (vert). (b) 25d. Edwin Moses (U.S.A.) (400 metre hurdles) (vert) Set of 2 sheets . . . . 10·00 11·00

No. 2059 is inscribed "Alberto Covo" and No. 2064 "Nelson Valis", both in error.
See also Nos. 2281/2303.

242 Rotary Emblem and Rotarians supporting School for the Deaf

1995. Local Rotary and Boy Scout Projects. Multicoloured.
2070 2d. Type **242** 55 30
2071 5d. Scout wood badge course, 1980 . . . . . . 1·25 1·40
2072 5d. Scout Commissioner M. J. E. Sambou (vert) 1·25 1·40

243 "Zantedeschia rehmannii"

1995. African Flowers. Multicoloured.
2073 2d. Type **243** 55 45
2074 3d. "Kigelia africana" . . . 60 65
2075 3d. "Hibiscus schizopelatus" 60 65
2076 3d. "Dombeya mastersii" . . 60 65
2077 3d. "Agapanthus orientalis" 60 65
2078 3d. "Strelitzia reginae" . . . 60 65
2079 3d. "Spathodea campanulata" 60 65
2080 3d. "Rhodolaena bakeriana" 60 65
2081 3d. "Gazania rigens" . . . 60 65
2082 3d. "Ixianthes retzioides" . . 60 65
2083 3d. "Canarina abyssinica" 60 65
2084 3d. "Nerine bowdenii" . . . 60 65
2085 3d. "Zantedeschia aethiopica" 60 65
2086 3d. "Aframomum sceptrum" 60 65
2087 3d. "Schotia brachypetala" 60 65
2088 3d. "Catharanthus roseus" 60 65
2089 3d. "Protea grandiceps" . . 60 65
2090 3d. "Plumbago capensis" . . 60 65
2091 3d. "Uncarina grandidieri" . 60 65
2092 5d. "Euadenia eminens" . . 1·10 1·25
2093 10d. "Passiflora vitifolia" . . 1·75 2·00
2094 15d. "Dietes grandiflora" . . 2·50 3·00
MS2095 Two sheets, each 106 × 75 mm. (a) 25d. "Eulophia quartiniana". (b) 25d. "Gloriosa simplex" Set of 2 sheets . . . 9·50 10·00
Nos. 2074/82 and 2083/91 respectively were printed together, se-tenant, forming composite background designs.

244 Children outside Huts

1995. Kinderdorf International S.O.S. Children's Villages. Multicoloured.
2096 2d. Type **244** 50 50
2097 2d. Charity worker with children (vert) 50 50
2098 5d. Children at party . . . 1·25 1·50

245 Roy Orbison

1995. History of Rock 'n' Roll Music. Multicoloured.
2099 3d. Type **245** 75 75
2100 3d. Mick Jagger 75 75
2101 3d. Bruce Springsteen . . . 75 75
2102 3d. Jimi Hendrix 75 75
2103 3d. Bill Haley 75 75
2104 3d. Gene Vincent 75 75
2105 3d. Buddy Holly 75 75
2106 3d. Jerry Lee Lewis 75 75
2107 3d. Chuck Berry 75 75
MS2108 116 × 86 mm. 25d. Elvis Presley . . . . 7·00 6·00

Nos. 2099/2107 were printed together, se-tenant, forming a composite design.

1995. Centenary of Cinema. As T **245** but depicting James Dean. Multicoloured.
2109 3d. As a boy 75 75
2110 3d. On motorbike 75 75
2111 3d. With sports car and trophy 75 75
2112 3d. Close-up portrait . . . 75 75
2113 3d. Facing left 75 75
2114 3d. Holding girl 75 75
2115 3d. "Rebel without a Cause" (film) 75 75
2116 3d. "Giant" (film) 75 75
2117 3d. "East of Eden" (film) 75 75
MS2118 116 × 86 mm. 25d. James Dean in "Rebel without a Cause" 4·50 4·50
Nos. 2109/17 were printed together, se-tenant, forming a composite design.

245a "Madonna and Child" (Maria della Vallicella)

1995. Christmas. Religious Paintings. Multicoloured.
2119 75b. Type **245a** 45 15
2120 1d. "Madonna" (Giotto) . . 45 15
2121 2d. "The Flight into Egypt" (Luca Giordano) 65 25
2122 5d. "The Epiphany" (Bordone) . . . . 1·50 1·00
2123 8d. "Virgin and Child" (Burgkmair) . . . . . . 2·25 2·50
2124 12d. "Madonna" (Bellini) 2·50 3·25
MS2125 Two sheets, each 101 × 127 mm. (a) 25d. "Christ" (Carpaccio). (b) 25d. "Madonna and Child" (Rubens) Set of 2 sheets . . . . 10·00 11·00

246 Terminal Building

1995. Opening of New Terminal Building, Banjul International Airport.
2126 **246** 1d. multicoloured . . . 40 10
2127 2d. multicoloured . . . 55 25
2128 3d. multicoloured . . . 70 55
2129 5d. multicoloured . . . 1·10 1·25

247 U.P.U. Emblem

1995. 121st Anniv of Universal Postal Union.
2130 **247** 1d. black and violet . . 30 10
2131 2d. black and blue . . . 50 25
2132 3d. black and red . . . 70 45
2133 7d. black and green . . 1·50 2·25

248 Commerson's Dolphin

1995. Whales and Dolphins. Multicoloured.
2134 2d. Type **248** 40 25
2135 3d. Bryde's whale 50 55
2136 3d. Sperm whale 50 55
2137 3d. Humpback whale . . . 50 55
2138 3d. Sei whale 50 55
2139 3d. Blue whale 50 55
2140 3d. Grey whale 50 55
2141 3d. Fin whale 50 55

2142 3d. Killer whale 50 55
2143 3d. Right whale 50 55
2144 3d. Northern right whale dolphin 75 75
2145 3d. Spotted dolphin 75 75
2146 3d. Common dolphin 75 75
2147 3d. Pacific white-sided dolphin 75 75
2148 3d. Atlantic humpbacked dolphin 75 75
2149 3d. Atlantic white-sided dolphin 75 75
2150 3d. White-beaked dolphin 75 75
2151 3d. Striped dolphin 75 75
2152 3d. Risso's dolphin 75 75
2153 5d. Narwhal 80 80
2154 8d. True's beaked whale 1·25 1·50
2155 10d. Rough-toothed dolphin 1·40 1·60
MS2156 Two sheets, each 110 × 80 mm. (a) 25d. Beluga and clymene dolphin. (b) 25d. Bowhead whale and blue shark (vert) Set of 2 sheets 10·00 11·00

Nos. 2135/43 and 2144/52 respectively were printed together, se-tenant, forming composite designs.

249 Big Pete as Seminole with Alligator

1995. Disney Cowboys and Indians. Walt Disney cartoon characters. Multicoloured.

2157 15b. Type **249** 20 20
2158 20b. Donald Duck as Chinook fisherman 20 20
2159 25b. Huey, Dewey and Louie as Blackfoot braves 20 20
2160 30b. Minnie Mouse shooting bottles 20 20
2161 40b. Donald riding bull 20 20
2162 50b. Mickey Mouse branding steer 20 20
2163 2d. Donald in Tlingit mask 70 25
2164 3d. Mickey bronco-busting 80 40
2165 12d. Grandma Duck with lasso 2·75 2·75
2166 15d. Mickey in Pomo canoe 3·00 3·25
2167 15d. Goofy as ranch hand 3·00 3·25
2168 20d. Goofy and Minnie with Navaho weaving 3·25 3·50
MS2169 Four sheets, each 127 × 102 mm. (a) 25d. Minnie as Massachusetts squaw. (b) 25d. Minnie as Shoshoni squaw (vert). (c) 25d. Pluto singing to the Moon (vert). (d) 25d. Donald and steer (vert) Set of 4 sheets 19·00 20·00

250 Rat

1996. Chinese New Year ("Year of the Rat").

2170 **250** 63b. multicoloured 35 25
2171 – 75b. multicoloured 40 30
2172 – 1d.50 multicoloured 70 60
2173 – 4d. multicoloured 1·50 1·50
MS2174 84 × 88 mm. 3d. × 4 As Nos. 2170/3 2·50 2·75
MS2175 76 × 106 mm. 10d. red, violet and brown 1·60 1·90

DESIGNS: 75b. to 10d. Different stylized rats.

251 "Don Tiburcio Perez y Cuervo" (detail) (Goya)

1996. 125th Anniv of Metropolitan Museum of Art, New York. Multicoloured.

2176/83 4d. × 8 (Type **251**; "Jean Antoine Moltedo" (Ingres); "The Letter" (Corot); "General Etienne Gerard" (David); "Portrait of the Artist" (Van Gogh); "Joseph Henri Altes" (Degas); "Princess de Broglie" (Ingres); "Lady at the Table" (Cassatt))
2184/91 4d. × 8 ("Broken Eggs" (Greuze); "Johann Joachim Winckleman" (Mengs); "Col. George Coussmaker" (Reynolds); "Self Portrait with Pupils" (Labille-Guiard); "Courtesan holding a Fan" (Utamaro); "The Woodgatherers" (Gainsborough); "Mrs Grace Elliott" (Gainsborough); "The Drummond Children" (Raeburn))
2192/9 4d. × 8 ("Sunflowers" (Monet); "Still Life with Pansies" (Fantin-Latour); "Parisians enjoying the Parc" (Monet); "La Mere Larcheveque" (Pissarro); "Rue de L'Epicerie, Rouen" (Pissarro); "The Abduction of Rebecca" (Delacroix); "Daughter, Abraham- Ben-Chimol" (Delacroix); "Christ on Lake of Gennesaret" (Delacroix))
2200/7 4d. × 8 ("Henry Prince of Wales" (Peake); "Saints Peter, Martha, Mary and Leonard" (Correggio); "Marriage Feast at Cana" (Juan de Flandes); "Portrait of One of Wedigh Family" (Holbein); "Guillaume Bude" (Clouet); "Portrait of a Cardinal" (El Greco); "St. Jerome as a Cardinal" (El Greco); "Portrait of a Man" (Titian))
2176/2207 Set of 32 24·00 26·00
MS2208 Four sheets, each 95 × 70 mm, containing horiz designs, 81 × 53 mm. (a) 25d. "Israelites gathering Manna in the Desert" (Rubens). (b) 25d. "Henry IV at the Battle of Ivry" (Rubens). (c) 25d. "The Creation of the World and the Expulsion from Paradise" (Giovanni di Paolo). (d) 25d. "The Harvesters" (Bruegel) Set of 4 sheets 17·00 19·00

252 Fire-eater

253 Bruce Lee

1996. Fire-eating in the Gambia.

2209 **252** 1d. multicoloured 25 15
2210 – 2d. multicoloured 40 30
2211 – 3d. multicoloured 55 50
2212 – 7d. multicoloured 1·25 1·50

DESIGNS: 2d. to 7d. Various fire-eating scenes, the 2d. and 7d. being horiz.

1996. Bruce Lee (film star) Commemoration. Different portraits. Multicoloured.

2213 3d. Wearing cap and mask 70 60
2214 3d. Type **253** 70 60
2215 3d. Facing left 70 60
2216 3d. Wearing blue jumper and with hand to face 70 60
2217 3d. Wearing buff jacket 70 60
2218 3d. Wearing brown jacket (Chinese characters in brown) 70 60
2219 3d. Wearing black shirt (Chinese characters in lilac) 70 60
2220 3d. Wearing white shirt 70 60
2221 3d. Bare-chested 70 60
MS2222 Two sheets. (a) 140 × 85 mm. 5d. Deng Xiao Ping (Chinese leader) (78 × 51 mm). (b) 70 × 100 mm. 25d. Bruce Lee Set of 2 sheets 9·50 9·50

254 Donald Duck and Big Pete giving Blood

1996. Voluntary Activities. Walt Disney cartoon characters. Multicoloured.

2223 1d. Type **254** 35 30
2224 4d. Daisy Duck and Minnie Mouse adopting pets 1·00 75
2225 5d. Goofy as one-man band raising money for the needy 1·25 85
2226 10d. Goofy teaching outdoor skills 2·00 2·25
2227 15d. Minnie teaching reading 2·50 3·00
2228 20d. Donald, Mickey and Goofy as volunteer fire fighters 2·50 3·00
MS2229 Two sheets, each 127 × 102 mm. (a) 25d. Minnie counting whales. (b) 25d. Mickey planting roadside sapling Set of 2 sheets 8·50 9·00

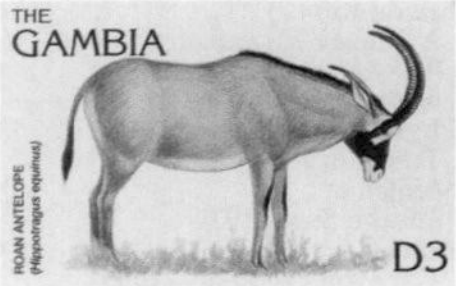

255 Roan Antelope

1996. Wildlife. Multicoloured.

2230 3d. Type **255** 50 55
2231 3d. Lesser bushbaby 50 55
2232 3d. Black leopard 50 55
2233 3d. Guinea forest red colobus 50 55
2234 3d. Kobs 50 55
2235 3d. Common eland 50 55
2236 4d. African buffalo 55 60
2237 4d. Herd of topi 55 60
2238 4d. Vervet 55 60
2239 4d. Hippopotamuses 55 60
2240 4d. Waterbuck 55 60
2241 4d. Senegal chameleon 55 60
2242 4d. Western green mamba 55 60
2243 4d. Slender-snouted crocodile 55 60
2244 4d. Adanson's mud turtle 55 60
2245 15d. African civet 2·00 2·50
MS2246 Two sheets, each 98 × 68 mm. (a) 25d. Lion (vert). (b) 25d. Chimpanzee (vert) Set of 2 sheets 7·50 8·00

Nos. 2230/5 and 2236/44 respectively were printed together, se-tenant, Nos. 2236/44 forming a composite design.

255a Queen Elizabeth II

1996. 70th Birthday of Queen Elizabeth II. Mult.

2247 8d. Type **255a** 1·60 1·60
2248 8d. Wearing tiara facing right 1·60 1·60
2249 8d. Wearing tiara facing left 1·60 1·60
MS2250 125 × 104 mm. 25d. Buckingham Palace (horiz) 5·00 5·50

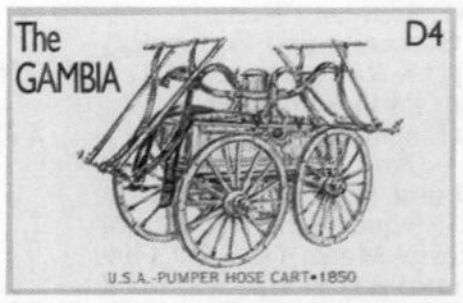

256 Pumper Hose Cart, U.S.A. (1850)

1996. Classic Road Transport. Fire Engines (Nos. 2251/6) or Cars (Nos. 2257/62). Multicoloured.

2251 4d. Type **256** 75 75
2252 4d. Steam fire engine, U.S.A. (1891) 75 75
2253 4d. Lausitzer engine, Germany (1864) 75 75
2254 4d. Chemical engine, Great Britain (1902) 75 75
2255 4d. Motor fire engine, Great Britain (1904) 75 75
2256 4d. Colonia No. 5 engine, Germany (1860) 75 75
2257 4d. Fiat Tipo 510, Italy (1912) 75 75
2258 4d. Toyota Model 4B Phaeton, Japan (1936) 75 75
2259 4d. Nag C4B, Germany (1924) 75 75
2260 4d. Cadillac, U.S.A. (1903) 75 75
2261 4d. Bentley, Great Britain (1925) 75 75
2262 4d. Renault Model AX, France (1909) 75 75
MS2263 Two sheets. (a) 76 × 58 mm. 25d. Amoskeag Steamer (fire engine), U.S.A. (1865). (b) 81 × 59 mm. 25d. Mitsubishi Model A, Japan (1917) Set of 2 sheets 8·00 8·50

257 Bulgarian Team

1996. European Football Championship, England. Multicoloured.

2264 2d. Type **257** 45 45
2265 2d. Croatian team 45 45
2266 2d. Czech Republic team 45 45
2267 2d. Danish team 45 45
2268 2d. English team 45 45
2269 2d. French team 45 45
2270 2d. German team 45 45
2271 2d. Dutch team 45 45
2272 2d. Italian team 45 45
2273 2d. Portuguese team 45 45
2274 2d. Rumanian team 45 45
2275 2d. Russian team 45 45
2276 2d. Scottish team 45 45
2277 2d. Spanish team 45 45
2278 2d. Swiss team 45 45
2279 2d. Turkish team 45 45
MS2280 Sixteen sheets. (a) 115 × 85 mm. 25d. Danish team celebrating (43 × 28 mm). (b) 85 × 115 mm. 25d. Ruud Gullit (Netherlands) (28 × 43 mm). (c) 85 × 115 mm. 25d. Gary McAllister (Scotland) (28 × 43 mm). (d) 115 × 85 mm. 25d. Oleg Salenko (Russia) (28 × 43 mm). (e) 85 × 115 mm. 25d. Hami Mandirali (Turkey) (28 × 43 mm). (f) 85 × 115 mm. 25d. Hristo Stoitchkov (Bulgaria) (28 × 43 mm). (g) 115 × 85 mm. 25d. European Championship Trophy (28 × 43 mm). (h) 85 × 115 mm. 25d. Davor Suker (Croatia) (28 × 43 mm). (i) 115 × 85 mm. 25d. Jurgen Klinsmann (Germany) (43 × 28 mm). (j) 85 × 115 mm. 25d. Juan Goikoetxea (Spain) (28 × 43 mm). (k) 85 × 115 mm. 25d. Eusebio (Portugal) (28 × 43 mm). (l) 115 × 85 mm. 25d. Bryan Robson (England) (28 × 43 mm). (m) 85 × 115 mm. 25d. Roberto Baggio (Italy) (28 × 43 mm). (n) 85 × 115 mm. 25d. Christophe Ohrel (Switzerland) (28 × 43 mm). (o) 85 × 115 mm. 25d. Pavel Hapal (Czech Republic) (43 × 28 mm). (p) 85 × 115 mm. 25d. Gheorge Hagi (Rumania) (28 × 43 mm). P 14 Set of 16 sheets 65·00 65·00

258 Ray Ewry (U.S.A.) (standing high jump), 1912

258a Boy holding Shoes

1996. Olympic Games, Atlanta (2nd issue). Previous Gold Medal Winners. Multicoloured.

2281 1d. Type **258** 25 15
2282 2d. Fanny Durack (Australia) (100 m freestyle swimming), 1912 35 20

2283	3d. Fu Mingxia (China) (platform diving), 1992	40	45
2284	3d. H. Henkel (Germany) (high jump), 1992	40	45
2285	3d. Spanish team (soccer), 1992	40	45
2286	3d. Jackie Joyner-Kersee (U.S.A.) (heptathlon), 1988 and 1992	40	45
2287	3d. T. Gutsu (Russia) (gymnastics), 1992	40	45
2288	3d. M. Johnson (U.S.A.) (400 m running), 1992	40	45
2289	3d. Lin Li (China) (200 m medley swimming), 1992	40	45
2290	3d. G. Devers (U.S.A.) (100 m running), 1992	40	45
2291	3d. Michael Powell (U.S.A.) (long jump), 1992	40	45
2292	3d. Japanese volleyball team, 1964	40	45
2293	3d. Li Neng (China) (floor exercises), 1984	40	45
2294	3d. S. Bubka (U.S.S.R.) (pole vault), 1988	40	45
2295	3d. Nadia Comaneci (Romania) (gymnastics), 1976	40	45
2296	3d. Edwin Moses (U.S.A.) (400 m hurdles), 1984	40	45
2297	3d. Victor Scherbo (Russia) (gymnastics), 1992	40	45
2298	3d. Evelyn Ashford (U.S.A.) (100 m running), 1984	40	45
2299	3d. Mohammed Ali (U.S.A.) (light heavyweight boxing), 1960	40	45
2300	3d. Carl Lewis and C. Smith (U.S.A.) (400 m relay), 1984	40	45
2301	5d. Stockholm Olympic arena, 1912	70	75
2302	10d. Jim Thorpe (U.S.A.) (decathalon and pentathlon), 1912	1·25	1·40
MS2303	Two sheets, each 100 × 70 mm. 25d. Michael Gross (Germany) (butterfly swimming), 1984 and 1988 (horiz). 25d. Ulrike Meyfarth (Germany) (high jump), 1972 and 1984 Set of 2 sheets	8·50	9·00

1996. 50th Anniv of U.N.I.C.E.F. Multicoloured.

2304	63b. Type **258a**	15	15
2305	3d. Girl being inoculated	40	35
2306	8d. Boy holding ladle	1·00	1·25
2307	10d. Child with blanket	1·25	1·40
MS2308	105 × 75 mm. 25d. Boy being inoculated (horiz)	3·25	3·75

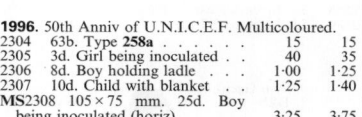

259 Roman Officer and Pillar of Absalom

1996. 3000th Anniv of Jerusalem. Multicoloured.

2309	1d.50 Type **259**	45	25
2310	2d. Turk and Gate of Mercy	50	30
2311	3d. Ancient Greek and Church of the Holy Sepulchre	60	40
2312	10d. Modern Hasidic Jew at Wailing Wall	1·75	1·75
MS2313	100 × 70 mm. 25d. City coat of arms (vert)	4·25	4·25

259a Glenn Miller

1996. Centenary of Radio. Entertainers. Mult.

2314	1d. Type **259a**	20	20
2315	4d. Louis Armstrong	60	45
2316	5d. Nat "King" Cole	70	75
2317	10d. The Andrew Sisters	1·25	1·50
MS2318	105 × 74 mm. 25d. President Truman	3·25	3·75

No. 2314 is inscribed "Glen Miller" in error.

260 Jacqueline Kennedy Onassis in Wedding Dress

1996. Famous People of the 20th Century. Multicoloured.

2319	5d. Type **260**	75	75
2320	5d. Jaqueline Kennedy and White House	75	75
2321	5d. Jaqueline Kennedy wearing pink hat	75	75
2322	5d. Jaqueline Kennedy and motor yacht	75	75
2323	5d. Jacqueline Kennedy wearing red jumper	75	75
2324	5d. Jacqueline Kennedy and horse	75	75
2325	5d. Jacqueline Kennedy on book	75	75
2326	5d. Jacqueline Kennedy in blue dress and three rows of pearls	75	75
2327	5d. Jacqueline Kennedy and corner of fountain	75	75
2328	5d. President John Kennedy	75	75
2329	5d. Jacqueline Kennedy (inscr in capitals)	75	75
2330	5d. Willy Brandt	75	75
2331	5d. Marilyn Monroe	75	75
2332	5d. Mao Tse-tung	75	75
2333	5d. Sung Ching Ling	75	75
2334	5d. Charles De Gaulle	75	75
2335	5d. Marlene Dietrich	75	75
MS2336	105 × 74 mm. 25d. Jacqueline Kennedy (different)	3·25	3·75

No. 2330 is inscr "WILLIE BRANDT", No. 2331 "MARYLYN MONROE" and No. 2332 "MAO TSE TONG", all in error.

261 Richard Petty's 1969 Ford

1996. Richard Petty (stock car driver) Commem. Multicoloured.

2337	5d. Type **261**	90	80
2338	5d. Richard Petty	90	80
2339	5d. Dodge Magnum, 1978	90	80
2340	5d. Pontiac, 1987	90	80
2341	5d. Pontiac, 1989	90	80
2342	5d. Dodge Daytona, 1975	90	80
MS2343	104 × 74 mm. 25d. Plymouth, 1972 (84 × 27 mm)	4·00	4·25

1996. Results of European Football Championship, England. As Nos. 2265/6, 2268, 2270, 2272, 2275 and **MS**2280 (d, h, i, l, m, o), but each additionally inscribed with date and match result. Multicoloured.

2344	2d. Croatian team ("23/6/96 Germany 2, Croatia 1")	45	45
2345	2d. Czech Republic team ("9/6/96 Germany 2, Czech Rep. 0")	45	45
2346	2d. English team ("26/6/96 Germany 6, England 5")	45	45
2347	2d. German team ("30/6/96 Germany 2, Czech Rep. 1")	45	45
2348	2d. Italian team ("19/6/96 Germany 0, Italy 0")	45	45
2349	2d. Russian team ("16/6/96 Germany 3, Russia 0")	45	45
MS2350	Six sheets. (a) 114 × 84 mm. 25d. Oleg Salenko (Russia) (28 × 43 mm) ("16/6/96 Germany 3, Russia 0"). (b) 84 × 114 mm. 25d. Davor Suker (Croatia) (28 × 43 mm) ("23/6/96 Germany 2, Croatia 1"). (c) 114 × 84 mm. 25d. Jurgen Klinsmann (Germany) (43 × 28 mm) ("Final 30/6/96 Germany 2, Czech Republic 1"). (d) 114 × 84 mm. 25d. Bryan Robson (England) (28 × 43 mm) ("26/6/96 Germany 6 England 5"). (e) 84 × 114 mm. 25d. Roberto Baggio (Italy) (28 × 43 mm) ("19/6/96 Germany 0 Italy 0"). (f) 84 × 114 mm. 25d. Pavel Hapal (Czech Rep) (43 × 28 mm) ("9/6/96 Germany 2 Czech Republic 0") Set of 6 sheets	24·00	26·00

262 Elvis Presley with Microphone

263 Bob Dylan

1996. Elvis Presley Commemoration. Different Portraits. Multicoloured.

2351	5d. Type **262**	90	90
2352	5d. In dinner jacket	90	90
2353	5d. In Mexican outfit	90	90
2354	5d. Wearing blue jumper	90	90
2355	5d. In leather jacket	90	90
2356	5d. Wearing lei	90	90

1996. Rock and Roll Legends. Bob Dylan.

2357	**263** 5d. multicoloured	1·25	1·00

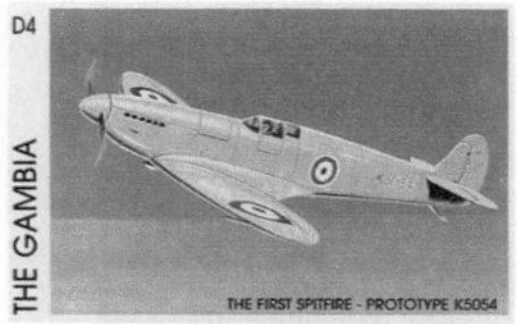

264 Supermarine Spitfire Prototype K5054

1996. 65th Anniv of Britain's Victory in Schneider Trophy Air Race. Multicoloured.

2358	4d. Type **264**	80	80
2359	4d. First production Spitfire K9787	80	80
2360	4d. Spitfire Mk 1A in Battle of Britain	80	80
2361	4d. Spitfire LF Mk IXE with D-Day markings	80	80
2362	4d. Spitfire Mk XII (first with "Griffon" engine)	80	80
2363	4d. Spitfire Mk XIVC with jungle markings	80	80
2364	4d. Spitfire XIX of Royal Swedish Air Force	80	80
2365	4d. Spitfire Mk XIX	80	80
2366	4d. Spitfire F Mk 22/24 (final variant)	80	80
2367	4d. Spitfire Mk XIX of Royal Swedish Air Force (from below)	80	80
2368	4d. Spitfire Mk VB of United States Army Air Corps	80	80
2369	4d. Spitfire Mk VC of French Air Force	80	80
2370	4d. Spitfire Mk VB of Soviet Air Force	80	80
2371	4d. Spitfire Mk IXE of Netherlands East Indies Air Force	80	80
2372	4d. Spitfire Mk IXE of Israeli Air Force	80	80
2373	4d. Spitfire Mk VIII of Royal Australian Air Force	80	80
2374	4d. Siptfire Mk VB of Turkish Air Force	80	80
2375	4d. Spitfire Mk XI of Royal Danish Air Force	80	80
MS2376	Two sheets, each 97 × 67 mm. (a) 25d. Supermarine S 6B S1595 seaplane taking off (42 × 29 mm). (b) 25d. Supermarine S 6B S1595 in flight (42 × 29 mm) Set of 2 sheets	9·00	9·00

265 Egyptian Plover

266 Sylvester Stallone as Rocky Balboa

265a "Assumption of the Madonna" (detail)

1996. Birds. Multicoloured.

2377	50b. Type **265**	30	20
2378	63b. Painted-snipe	35	20
2379	75b. Golden-breasted bunting	35	20
2380	1d. Bateleur	40	25
2381	1d.50 Didric cuckoo	50	30
2382	2d. Turtle dove ("European Turtle Dove")	55	30
2383	3d. Village weaver	65	35
2384	4d. European roller	75	50
2385	5d. Cut-throat weaver ("Cut-throat")	80	60
2386	10d. Hoopoe	1·75	1·50
2387	15d. White-faced scops owl	2·00	2·00
2388	20d. Narina's trogon	2·25	2·50
2389	25d. Lesser pied kingfisher	2·75	3·00
2390	30d. Common kestrel	3·25	3·50
2391	40d. Temminck's courser	3·75	4·25
2392	50d. European bee eater	4·50	5·00
2392a	100d. Green-winged teal	8·00	9·50

No. 2388 is inscribed "TROGAN" in error.

1996. Christmas. Religious Paintings.

2393	**265a** 1d. multicoloured	25	10
2394	– 1d.50 multicoloured	30	15
2395	– 2d. multicoloured	35	20
2396	– 3d. multicoloured	50	30
2397	– 10d. multicoloured	1·50	1·75
2398	– 15d. multicoloured	2·00	2·50
MS2399	Two sheets, each 76 × 106 mm. (a) 25d. deep brown, black and brown ("Adoration of the Magi" (Filippo Lippi)) (horiz). (b) 25d. red, black and rose ("Virgin and Child with Infant St. John" (Raphael)) Set of 2 sheets	7·50	8·50

DESIGNS: 1d.50 to 15d. Different details of "Assumption of the Madonna" (Tiziano Vecellio).

No. **MS**2399a is inscribed "Flippo Lippi" in error.

1996. 20th Anniv of *Rocky* (film). Sheet 143 × 182 mm.

MS2400	**266** 10d. × 3 multicoloured	4·25	4·50

267 Ox

268 "Arch 22" Monument

1997. Chinese New Year ("Year of the Ox").

2401	**267** 63b. multicoloured	30	25
2402	– 75b. multicoloured	30	25
2403	– 1d.50 multicoloured	50	35
2404	– 4d. multicoloured	1·00	1·10
MS2405	84 × 68 mm. 3d. × 4. As Nos. 2401/4	2·25	2·50
MS2406	76 × 106 mm. 10d. multicoloured (ox and sleeping peasant) (39½ × 24½mm)	1·60	1·75

DESIGNS: 75b. to 4d. Symbolic oxen.

1997. Economic Development. Multicoloured.

2407	63b. Type **268**	20	15
2408	1d. Tractor (horiz)	25	15
2409	1d.50 Man planting rice	30	20
2410	2d. As Type **268**, but with white panel at top	40	25
2411	3d. Model of Banjul International Airport terminal building (horiz)	75	60
2412	5d. Chamoi Bridge (horiz)	90	1·00
MS2413	Two sheets. (a) 106 × 76 mm. 20d. Workers in rice field (horiz). (b) 76 × 106 mm. 25d. As Type **268** Set of 2 sheets	7·00	8·00

269 Monkey King extinguishing Fire on Flame Mountain

1997. Mickey Mouse's Journey to the West. Disney cartoon characters. Multicoloured.

2414 2d. Type **269** 70 70
2415 2d. Demon Ox and Monkey King fighting 70 70
2416 2d. Mickey, Donald, Monkey King and Master San Tsang 70 70
2417 2d. Fighting the Spider Demon 70 70
2418 2d. Fighting the White Skeleton Demon 70 70
2419 2d. The real and the fake Monkey King 70 70
2420 3d. Monkey King trapped in furnace 70 70
2421 3d. Monkey King with magic weapon 70 70
2422 3d. Type **269** 70 70
2423 3d. At the Gate of South Heaven 70 70
2424 3d. Tasting the celestial peaches 70 70
2425 3d. Monkey King rescued from Five-Finger Mountain 70 70
MS2426 Four sheets, each 134 × 109 mm. (a) 5d. Mickey and Donald with Master San Tsang (vert). (b) 10d. Monkey King, Mickey and monkeys. (c) 10d. Monkey King, Mickey and tortoise (vert). (d) 15d. Mickey and Minnie with Buddhist scriptures Set of 4 sheets . . . 14·00 14·00

270 Jackie Chan

1997. "HONG KONG '97" International Stamp Exhibition. Jackie Chan (film star). Multicoloured.

2427 4d. Type **270** 75 75
2428 4d. Wearing red jacket . . . 75 75
2429 4d. In open-necked shirt . . 75 75
2430 4d. Bare-chested 75 75
2431 4d. Wearing black jacket . . 75 75
2432 4d. Wearing black and white spotted shirt 75 75
2433 4d. Wearing white T-shirt and red anorak 75 75
2434 4d. Wearing white sleeveless T-shirt 75 75
MS2435 76 × 106 mm. 25d. Jackie Chan in action (horiz) . . . . 4·50 4·75

271 Clouded Leopard

1997. Endangered Species. Multicoloured.

2436 1d.50 Type **271** 40 40
2437 1d.50 Audouin's gull . . . 40 40
2438 1d.50 Leatherback turtle . . 40 40
2439 1d.50 White-eared pheasant 40 40
2440 1d.50 Kakapo 40 40
2441 1d.50 Right whale 40 40
2442 1d.50 Black-footed ferret . . 40 40
2443 1d.50 Dwarf lemur 40 40
2444 1d.50 Palawan peacock-pheasant ("Peacock-Pheasant") 40 40
2445 1d.50 Brown hyena 40 40
2446 1d.50 Cougar 40 40
2447 1d.50 Gharial 40 40
2448 1d.50 Monk seal 40 40
2449 1d.50 Mountain gorilla . . . 40 40
2450 1d.50 Blyth's tragopan . . . 40 40
2451 1d.50 Malayan tapir . . . 40 40
2452 1d.50 Black rhinoceros . . . 40 40
2453 1d.50 Polar bear 40 40
2454 1d.50 Red colobus 40 40
2455 1d.50 Tiger 40 40
2456 1d.50 Arabian oryx 40 40
2457 1d.50 Baiji 40 40
2458 1d.50 Ruffed lemur 40 40
2459 1d.50 California condor . . 40 40
2460 1d.50 Blue-headed quail dove 40 40
2461 1d.50 Numbat 40 40
2462 1d.50 Congo peafowl ("Congo Peacock") . . . 40 40
2463 1d.50 White uakari 40 40
2464 1d.50 Eskimo curlew . . . 40 40
2465 1d.50 Gouldian finch . . . 40 40
2466 1d.50 Coelacanth 40 40
2467 1d.50 Toucan barbet . . . 40 40
2468 1d.50 Snow leopard 40 40
2469 1d.50 Queen Alexandra's birdwing 40 40
2470 1d.50 Dalmatian pelican . . 40 40
2471 1d.50 Chaco tortoise 40 40
2472 1d.50 Mekong catfish . . . 40 40
2473 1d.50 Helmeted hornbill . . 40 40
2474 1d.50 White-eyed river martin 40 40
2475 1d.50 Fluminense swallowtail 40 40
MS2476 Three sheets, each 103 × 72 mm. (a) 25d. Giant panda. (b) 25d. Humpback whale. (c) 25d. Manchurian crane ("Japanese Crane") Set of 3 sheets 13·00 13·00

272 Monkey

1997. "The Jungle Book" by Rudyard Kipling. Multicoloured.

2477 3d. Type **272** 60 60
2478 3d. Baloo (bear) 60 60
2479 3d. Elephant 60 60
2480 3d. Monkey and temple . . 60 60
2481 3d. Bagheera (panther) . . . 60 60
2482 3d. Buffalo 60 60
2483 3d. Mandrill 60 60
2484 3d. Shere Khan (tiger) . . . 60 60
2485 3d. Rama (wolf) 60 60
2486 3d. Kaa (cobra) 60 60
2487 3d. Mongoose 60 60
2488 3d. Mowgli 60 60

Nos. 2477/88 were printed together, se-tenant, with the backgrounds forming a composite design.

273 "Polyporus squamosus"

1997. Fungi. Multicoloured.

2489 1d. Type **273** 35 25
2490 3d. "Armillaria tabescens" 65 40
2491 4d. "Amanita caesarea" (vert) 75 80
2492 4d. "Lepiota procera" (vert) 75 80
2493 4d. "Hygrophorus psittacinus" (vert) . . . 75 80
2494 4d. "Russula xerampelina" (vert) 75 80
2495 4d. "Laccaria amethystina" (vert) 75 80
2496 4d. "Coprinus micaceus" (vert) 75 80
2497 4d. "Boletus edulis" (vert) 75 80
2498 4d. "Morchella esculenta" (vert) 75 80
2499 4d. "Otidea auricula" (vert) 75 80
2500 5d. "Collybia velutipes" . . 85 85
2501 10d. "Sarcoscypha coccinea" 1·40 1·50
MS2502 76 × 106 mm. 25d. "Volvariella bombycina" . . . 5·50 5·50

273a Cloister, Horyu-ji, Japan

1997. 50th Anniv of U.N.E.S.C.O. Multicoloured.

2503 1d. Type **273a** 30 25
2504 2d. Great Wall, China . . . 50 35
2505 3d. Statues, Ayutthaya, Thailand 55 40
2506 4d. Ascension Convent, Santa Maria, Philippines 60 65
2507 4d. Mount Nimba Nature Reserve, Guinea (vert) . . 60 65
2508 4d. Banc d'Argun National Park, Mauritania (vert) 60 65
2509 4d. Doorway, Marrakesh, Morocco (vert) 60 65
2510 4d. Ichkeul National Park, Tunisia (vert) 60 65
2511 4d. Village pottery, Mali (vert) 60 65
2512 4d. Hippopotamus, Salonga National Park, Zaire (vert) 60 65
2513 4d. Timgad Roman Ruins, Algeria (vert) 60 65
2514 4d. Wooden statue, Benin (vert) 60 65
2515 4d. Temple, Magao Caves, China (vert) 60 65
2516 4d. Statue, Magao Caves (vert) 60 65
2517 4d. Domes, Magao Caves (vert) 60 65
2518 4d. Great Wall from air, China (vert) 60 65
2519 4d. Statue, Great Wall (vert) 60 65
2520 4d. Bronze Bird, Imperial Palace, China (vert) . . . 60 65
2521 4d. Temples, Imperial Palace, China (vert) . . . 60 65
2522 4d. Dragon statue, Imperial Palace (vert) 60 65
2523 4d. Kyoto Gardens, Japan (vert) 60 65
2524 4d. Himeji Castle, Japan (vert) 60 65
2525 4d. Horyu-ji Temple, Japan (vert) 60 65
2526 4d. Buddha, Horyu-ji, Japan (vert) 60 65
2527 4d. Yakushima Forest, Japan (vert) 60 65
2528 4d. Ancient tree, Yakushima Forest, Japan (vert) . . . 60 65
2529 4d. Temple, Kyoto, Japan (vert) 60 65
2530 4d. Pavilion, Kyoto, Japan (vert) 60 65
2531 5d. Riverside houses, Inselstadt, Germany . . . 70 75
2532 5d. Rosaleda Gardens, Bamberg, Germany . . . 70 75
2533 5d. Bamberg Cathedral, Germany 70 75
2534 5d. Timbered house, Maulbronn, Germany . . 70 75
2535 5d. Maulbronn Monastry, Germany 70 75
2536 5d. Ruins at Delphi, Greece 70 75
2537 5d. Rhodes waterfront, Greece 70 75
2538 5d. Knights' Hospital, Rhodes, Greece 70 75
2539 5d. Temple, Delphi, Greece 70 75
2540 5d. Delphi from air, Greece 70 75
2541 5d. Foliage, Shirakami-Sanchi, Japan 70 75
2542 5d. Notice board, Shirakami-Sanchi, Japan 70 75
2543 5d. Tower, Himeji Castle, Japan 70 75
2544 5d. Roof tops, Himeji Castle, Japan 70 75
2545 5d. Gateway, Himeji Castle, Japan 70 75
2546 10d. Komodo Dragons, Indonesia . . . . 1·40 1·50
2547 15d. Ancient hut, Timbuktu, Mali . . . . 1·90 2·25
MS2548 Four sheets, each 127 × 102 mm. (a) 25d. Plitvice Lakes National Park, Croatia. (b) 25d. Ruins of Kilwa Kisiwani, Tanzania. (c) 25d. Santa Maria de Alcobaca cloisters, Portugal. (d) 25d. Watergarden, Kyoto, Japan Set of 4 sheets . . . . 13·00 14·00

274 Minnie Mouse, 1928

1997. Minnie Mouse Through the Years. Designs showing Disney cartoon character in years stated. Multicoloured.

2549 4d. Type **274** . . . . 1·00 1·00
2550 4d. In 1933 . . . . 1·00 1·00
2551 4d. In 1934 . . . . 1·00 1·00
2552 4d. In 1937 . . . . 1·00 1·00
2553 4d. In 1938 . . . . 1·00 1·00
2554 4d. In 1941 . . . . 1·00 1·00
2555 4d. In 1950 . . . . 1·00 1·00
2556 4d. In 1990 . . . . 1·00 1·00
2557 4d. In 1997 . . . . 1·00 1·00
MS2558 133 × 108 mm. 25d. In 1987 6·50 7·00

275 Dipstick

1997. "101 Dalmatians". Disney cartoon characters. Multicoloured.

2559 50b. Type **275** 55 55
2560 50b. Fidget 55 55
2561 50b. Jewel 55 55
2562 50b. Lucky 55 55
2563 50b. Two-Tone 55 55
2564 50b. Wizzer 55 55
2565 2d. Two puppies playing (horiz) 55 55
2566 2d. Puppy and pig (horiz) . . 55 55
2567 2d. Two puppies with butterfly (horiz) 55 55
2568 2d. Puppy lying on back (horiz) 55 55
2569 2d. Puppy with ball (horiz) 55 55
2570 2d. Puppy with bone (horiz) 55 55
2571 2d. One puppy pulling another puppy's tail (horiz) 55 55
2572 2d. Two puppies pulling third puppy's ears (horiz) 55 55
2573 2d. Puppy with teddy bear (horiz) 55 55
2574 3d. Puppy asleep on biscuit box (horiz) 55 55
2575 3d. Puppy with hose (horiz) 55 55
2576 3d. Puppy and bottle (horiz) 55 55
2577 3d. Puppy and biscuit bowl (horiz) 55 55
2578 3d. Puppy wearing hat (horiz) 55 55
2579 3d. Three puppies with lipstick (horiz) 55 55
2580 3d. Puppy tying another up with string (horiz) 55 55
2581 3d. Two puppies and lunch box (horiz) 55 55
2582 3d. Three puppies and computer (horiz) 55 55
MS2583 Six sheets, each 127 × 103 mm. (a) 25d. Sheep and puppies (horiz). (b) 25d. Cruella de Vil (horiz). (c) 25d. Puppy looking at photograph (horiz). (d) 25d. Puppies in mail sack. (e) 25d. Two puppies covered in paint (horiz). (f) 25d. Two puppies playing computer game (horiz) Set of 6 sheets . . . . 30·00 30·00

276 Juventus Team, 1897

1997. Centenary of Juventus Football Team. Multicoloured.

2584 5d. Type **276** 80 80
2585 5d. Centenary emblem and player 80 80
2586 5d. Giampiero Boniperti . . 80 80
2587 5d. Roberto Bettega 80 80
2588 5d. Juventus team, 1996 . . 80 80
2589 5d. Juventus '97 logo . . . 80 80

276a Young Girl ("I'll Tell You a Story")

1997. 300th Anniv of Mother Goose Nursery Rhymes. Sheet 72 × 102 mm.
MS2590 **276a** 25d. multicoloured 3·75 4·00

276b Child's Face and U.N.E.S.C.O. Emblem

1997. 10th Anniv of Chernobyl Nuclear Disaster. Multicoloured.

2591 15d. Type **276b** . . . . . 1·90 2·25
2592 15d. As No. 2591 but inscribed "CHABAD'S CHILDREN OF CHERNOBYL" . . . . 1·90 2·25

276c Rotary President Sydney Pascall planting Tree of Friendship

1997. 50th Death Anniv of Paul Harris (founder of Rotary International).

2593 10d. Type **276c** . . . . . 1·40 1·75
MS2594 78 × 108 mm. 25d. Paul Harris and Preserve Planet Earth emblem . . . . 3·25 3·75

276d Queen Elizabeth II

1997. Golden Wedding of Queen Elizabeth and Prince Philip. Multicoloured.
2595 4d. Type **276d** 80 80
2596 4d. Royal coat of arms . . 80 80
2597 4d. Queen Elizabeth and Prince Philip applauding 80 80
2598 4d. Queen Elizabeth and Prince Philip taking the salute 80 80
2599 4d. Royal Yacht "Britannia" 80 80
2600 4d. Prince Philip 80 80
MS2601 100 × 70 mm. 20d. Princess Elizabeth, 1948 . . . . 4·00 4·25

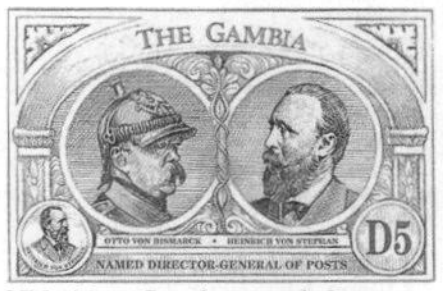

276e Von Stephan and Otto von Bismarck

1997. "Pacific '97" International Stamp Exhibition, San Francisco. Death Centenary of Henrich von Stephan (founder of U.P.U.).
2602 **276e** 5d. mauve . . . . . . 90 1·00
2603 – 5d. brown . . . . . . 90 1·00
2604 – 5d. green and black . . 90 1·00
MS2605 82 × 118 mm. 25d. green and black . . . . 4·25 4·75
DESIGNS: Nos. 2603, Von Stephan and Mercury; 2604, Mail wagon, Boston, 1900; **MS**2605, Von Stephan and Hamburg–Lubeck postilion.

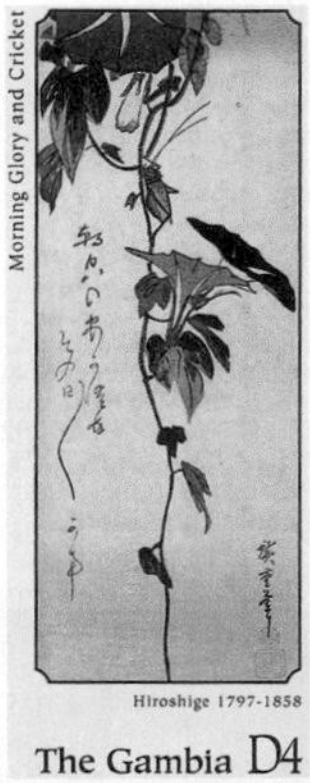

277 "Morning Glory and Cricket"

1997. Birth Bicentenary of Hiroshige (Japanese painter). Multicoloured.
2606/11 4d. × 6 (Type **277**: "Dragonfly and Begonia"; "Two Ducks swimming among Reeds"; "A Black-naped Oriole perched on a Stem of Rose Mallow"; "A Pheasant on a Snow-covered Pine"; "A Cuckoo flying through the Rain") . . . .
2612/17 4d. × 6 ("An Egret among Rushes"; "Peacock and Peonies"; "Three Wild Geese flying across the Moon"; "A Cock in the Snow"; "A Pheasant and Bracken"; "Peonies") . . . . . .
2618/23 4d. × 6 ("Sparrow and Bamboo"; "Mandarin Ducks on an Icy Pond with Brown Leaves falling"; "Blossoming Plum Tree"; "Java Sparrow and Magnolia"; "Chinese Bellflowers and Miscanthus"; "A Small Black Bird clinging to a Tendril of Ivy") . . .
2624/9 5d. × 6 ("Sparrows and Camellia in Snow"; "Parrot on a Branch of Pine"; "A Long-tailed Blue Bird on a Branch of Flowering Plum"; "Sparrow and Bamboo"; "Bird in a Tree"; "A Wild Duck swimming beneath Snow-laden reeds") . .
2630/5 5d. × 6 ("Kingfisher above a Yellow-flowered Water Plant"; "Wagtail and Roses"; "A Mandarin Duck on a Snowy Bank"; "A Japanese White-eye on a Persimmon Branch"; "Sparrows and Camellia in Snow"; "Kingfisher and Moon above a Yellow-flowered Water Plant")
2636/41 5d. × 6 ("Sparrow and Bamboo by Night"; "Birds Flying over Waves"; "Blossoming Plum Tree with Full Moon"; "Kingfisher and Iris"; "A Blue-and-White Flycatcher on a Hibiscus Flower"; "Mandarin Ducks in Snowfall") . . . . . .
2606/41 Set of 35 . . . . 26·00 27·00
MS2642 Six sheets, each 95 × 120 mm. (a) 25d. Hawk on perch. (b) 25d. Two green birds on branch. (c) 25d. Kingfisher hovering. (d) 25d. "Three Wild Geese flying across moon". (e) 25d. Red parrot on branch. (f) 25d. White bird on flowering bush Set of 6 sheets . . . . 35·00 38·00

277a Grandma's Cottage

1997. 175th Anniv of Brothers Grimm's Third Collection of Fairy Tales. Little Red Riding Hood. Multicoloured.
2643 10d. Type **277a** . . . . . 1·75 1·90
2644 10d. Little Red Riding Hood . . . . 1·75 1·90
2645 10d. The Wolf . . . . . . 1·75 1·90
MS2646 126 × 96 mm. 10d. Little Red Riding Hood (horiz) . . . 2·25 2·50

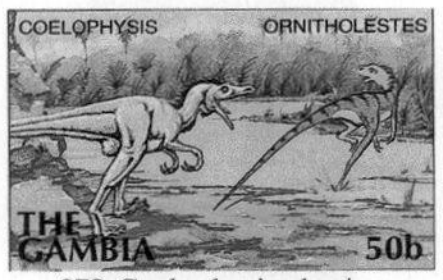

278 Coelophysis chasing Ornitholestes

1997. Dinosaurs. Multicoloured.
2647 50b. Type **278** 30 20
2648 63b. Spinosauru 35 20
2649 75b. Kentrosaurus 40 25
2650 1d. Ceratosaurus 40 25
2651 1d.50 Stygimoloch 50 35
2652 2d. Troodon 60 35
2653 3d. Velociraptor 70 45
2654 4d. Triceratops 80 80
2655 4d. Anurognathus 80 80
2656 4d. Pteranodon 80 80
2657 4d. Pterosaurus 80 80
2658 4d. Saltasaurus 80 80
2659 4d. Agathaumus 80 80
2660 4d. Stegosaurus 80 80
2661 4d. Albertosaurus libratus 80 80
2662 4d. Three Lesothosauruses running 80 80
2663 4d. Five Lesothosauruses running 80 80
2664 4d. Tarbosaurus bataar . . 80 80
2665 4d. Brachiosaurus 80 80
2666 4d. Styracosasaurus 80 80
2667 4d. Baryonyx 80 80
2668 4d. Coelophysis 80 80
2669 4d. Carnotaurus 80 80
2670 4d. Compsognathus longipes 80 80
2671 4d. Compsognathus "Elegant Jaw" 80 80
2672 4d. Stenonychosaurus . . . 80 80
2673 4d. Protoceratops 80 80
2674 10d. Ornithomimus . . . . 1·50 1·50
2675 15d. Stegosaurus . . . . . 1·90 2·25
2676 20d. Ankylosaurus saichania 2·25 2·50
MS2677 Two sheets, each 106 × 81 mm. (a) 25d. Head of Deinonychus (50 × 37 mm). (b) 25d. Seismosaurus (88 × 27 mm) Set of 2 sheets . . . . 9·00 10·00
Nos. 2655/63 and 2664/72 respectively were printed together, se-tenant, with the backgrounds forming composite designs.

279 Margaret Thatcher and Deng Xiaoping toasting Joint Declaration, 1984

1997. Return of Hong Kong to China. Multicoloured.
2678 3d. Type **279** 60 60
2679 3d. Signing Joint Declaration on Hong Kong, 1984 . . . . . 60 60
2680 3d. Signing Joint Declaration on Macao, 1987 . . . . 60 60
2681 3d. Deng Xiaoping toasting Prime Minister Anibal Silva of Portugal 60 60
2682 4d. Hong Kong in 1843 and Governor Sir Henry Pottinger 75 75
2683 4d. Kowloon in 1860 and Governor Sir Hercules Robinson 75 75
2684 4d. Reception in New Territories, 1898, and Governor Sir Henry Blake 75 75
2685 5d. Governor Sir Henry Pottinger and British warship 85 85
2686 5d. Governor Christopher Patten and Lantau Bridge 85 85
2687 5d. Chief Executive C. H. Tung and Hong Kong by night 85 85
2688 6d. Signing the Treaty of Nanking, 1842 . . . . 1·00 1·10
2689 6d. Signing the Japanese Surrender of Hong Kong, 1945 . . . . 1·00 1·10
2690 6d. Signing of the Sino-British Joint Declaration, 1984 . . . . 1·00 1·10

280 Great Mosque, Samarra, Iran

1997. Natural and Man-made Wonders of the World. Multicoloured.
2691 63b. Type **280** 40 20
2692 75b. Moai statues, Easter Island (horiz) 50 20
2693 1d. Golden Gate Bridge, San Francisco (horiz) . . 50 20
2694 1d.50 The Statue of Liberty, New York 50 25
2695 2d. The Parthenon, Athens (horiz) 50 30
2696 3d. Pyramid of the Sun, Mexico (horiz) 60 40
2697 5d. The Rock of Gibraltar (horiz) . . . . 80 1·00
2698 5d. St. Peter's Basilica, Rome (horiz) . . . . . 1·00 1·00
2699 5d. Santa Sophia, Istanbul (horiz) . . . . 80 1·00
2700 5d. "Gateway to the West" monument, St. Louis (horiz) . . . . 80 1·00
2701 5d. Great Wall of China (horiz) . . . . 80 1·00
2702 5d. City of Carcassonne, France (horiz) . . . . 80 1·00
2703 5d. Stonehenge, England (horiz) . . . . 1·00 1·00
2704 5d. Hughes HK-1 "Spruce Goose" flying boat (World's largest aircraft) (horiz) . . . . 1·00 1·00
2705 5d. Hoverspeed "Seacat" catamaran (fastest Atlantic crossing by a commercial catamaran) (horiz) . . . . 1·00 1·00
2706 5d. "Thrust 2" car (official land speed record) (horiz) 1·00 1·00
2707 5d. Stepped Pyramid, Egypt (horiz) . . . . 1·00 1·00
2708 5d. L.N.E.R. Clas A4 "Mallard" (fastest steam locomotive), 1938 (horiz) 1·00 1·00
MS2709 Three sheets, each 98 × 68 mm. (a) 5d. Mount Everest (42 × 28 mm). (b) 25d. The Grand Canyon, Colorado (42 × 28 mm). (c) 25d. Washington Monument (33 × 51 mm) Set of 3 sheets . . 12·00 13·00
No. 2702 is inscribed "CARCASSONNNE" in error.

281 Downhill Skiing

1997. Winter Olympic Games, Nagano (1998). Multicoloured.
2710 5d. Type **281** 90 90
2711 5d. Two-man bobsleigh (vert) 90 90
2712 5d. Freestyle skiing (vert) . . 90 90
2713 5d. Speed skating (vert) . . 90 90
2714 5d. Slalom skiing (No. 8 on bib) (vert) 90 90
2715 5d. Womens figure skating (vert) 90 90
2716 5d. Downhill skiing (No. 4 on bib) (vert) 90 90
2717 5d. Pairs figure skating (vert) 90 90
2718 5d. Cross-country (vert) . . 90 90
2719 5d. Ski jumping (vert) . . . 90 90
2720 5d. One-man luge 90 90
2721 5d. Ice hockey 90 90
2722 5d. Four-man bobsleigh . . 90 90
2723 5d. Ski-jumping 90 90
2724 5d. Curling 90 90
2725 5d. Figure skating 90 90
2726 5d. Speed skating 90 90
2727 5d. Biathlon 90 90
2728 5d. Downhill skiing (different) 90 90
2729 10d. One-man luge . . . . 1·60 1·75
2730 15d. Speed skating . . . . 2·25 2·50
2731 20d. Ice hockey . . . . . 3·00 3·25
MS2732 Two sheets. (a) 97 × 67 mm. 25d. Bobsleigh. (b) 67 × 97 mm. 25d. Pairs figure skating (vert) Set of 2 sheets . . . . 9·50 10·00

282 Brown Pelican

1997. Sea Birds. Multicoloured.
2733 3d. Type **282** 85 85
2734 3d. Galapagos penguin . . . 85 85
2735 3d. Red-billed tropic bird 85 85
2736 3d. Little tern 85 85
2737 3d. Dunlin 85 85
2738 3d. Black-legged kittiwake 85 85
2739 3d. Atlantic puffin 85 85
2740 3d. Wandering albatross . . 85 85
2741 3d. Blue-faced booby ("Masked Booby") . . . 85 85
2742 3d. Glaucous-winged gull . . 85 85
2743 3d. Arctic tern 85 85
2744 3d. Piping plover 85 85
2745 5d. Roseate tern . . . . . 1·00 1·00
2746 10d. Red-legged cormorant 1·50 1·60
2747 15d. Blue-footed booby . . 2·25 2·50
2748 20d. Sanderling . . . . . 2·50 2·75
MS2749 Two sheets, each 106 × 76 mm. (a) 23d. Long-tailed skua (vert). (b) 23d. Osprey (vert) Set of 2 sheets . . . . . . 7·50 8·00
No. 2743 is inscribed "ARTIC TERN" and the captions on Nos. 2745/6 are transposed, both in error.

283 Scottish Fold Cat

1997. Cats and Dogs. Multicoloured.
2750 63b. Type **283** 30 20
2751 75b. Dalmatian 35 20
2752 1d. Rottweiler 35 20
2753 1d.50 American curl cat . . 45 25
2754 2d. British bi-colour cat . . 50 25
2755 3d. Newfoundland 60 35
2756 3d. Devon Rex cat 60 35
2757 4d. Great Dane 75 50
2758 5d. Burmilla cat 85 85
2759 5d. Blue Burmese cat . . . 85 85
2760 5d. Korat cat 85 85
2761 5d. British tabby cat . . . 85 85
2762 5d. Foreign white cat . . . 85 85
2763 5d. Somali cat 85 85
2764 5d. Akita 85 85
2765 5d. Welsh corgi 85 85
2766 5d. German shepherd . . . 85 85
2767 5d. Saint Bernard 85 85
2768 5d. Bullmastiff 85 85
2769 5d. Malamute 85 85
2770 6d. Silver tabby cat . . . 95 95
2771 10d. Old English sheepdog 1·40 1·50
2772 15d. Queensland heeler . . 1·90 2·25
2773 20d. Abyssinian cat . . . . 2·25 2·50
MS2774 Four sheets, each 107 × 78 mm. (a) 25d. Cornish Rex cat. (b) 25d. Siamese cat. (c) 25d. Boxer. (d) Dobermann pinscher Set of 4 sheets . . . . 17·00 17·00

283a Uruguay Team, 1950

1997. World Cup Football Championship, France (1998).
2775 **283a** 1d. black 40 20
2776 – 1d.50 black . . . 50 25
2777 – 2d. black 55 30
2778 – 3d. black 70 40
2779/86 – 4d. × 8 mult or brown (Nos. 2782/3) 5·00
2787/94 – 4d. × 8 mult or black (No. 2788) 5·00
2795/2802 – 4d. × 8 brown (Nos. 2795/6, 2800 and 2802) or mult . . . . 5·00
2803/10 – 4d. × 8 mult . . . 5·00
2811 – 5d. black 80 80
2812 – 10d. black . . . . 1·40 1·50
MS2813 Four sheets, each 102 × 127 mm. (a) 25d. multicoloured. (b) 25d. multicoloured. (c) 25d. black. (d) 25d. brown Set of 4 sheets . . 17·00 17·00
DESIGNS—HORIZ: No. 2776, West German team, 1954; 2777, Brazilian team, 1970; 2778, Brazilian team, 1962; 2779, Brazilian team, 1994; 2780, Argentine team, 1986; 2781, Brazilian team, 1970; 2782, Italian team, 1934; 2783, Uruguay team, 1958; 2784, English team, 1966; 2785, Brazilian team, 1962; 2786, West German team, 1990; 2787, Mario Kempes, Argentina (1978); 2788, Joseph Gaetjens, U.S.A. (1950) (inscr "ADEMIR BRAZIL" in error); 2789, Muller, West Germany (1970); 2790, Lineker, England (1986); 2791, Eusebio, Portugal (1966); 2792, Schillaci, Italy (1990); 2793, Lato, Poland (1974); 2794, Rossi, Italy (1982); 2811, Italian team, 1938; 2812, Uruguay team, 1930; **MS**2813a, Philippe Albert, Belgium; **MS**2813b, Juninho, Brazil; **MS**2813c, Eusebio, Portugal; **MS**2813d, Pele, Brazil. VERT: No. 2795, Moore, England (1966); 2796, Fritzwalter, West Germany (1954); 2797, Beckenbauer, West Germany (1974); 2798, Zoff, Italy (1982); 2799, Maradona, Argentina (1986); 2800, Passarella, Argentina (1978); 2801, Matthaus, West Germany (1990); 2802, Dunga, Brazil (1994); 2803, Kinkladze, Georgia; 2804, Shearer, England; 2805, Dani, Portugal; 2806, Weah, Portugal; 2807, Ravanelli, Italy; 2808, Raducioiu, Rumania; 2809, Schmeichel, Denmark; 2810, Bergkamp, Holland.

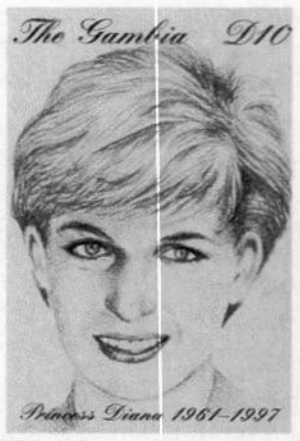

284 Diana, Princess of Wales

285 Tiger

284a "Angel" (Rembrandt)

1997. Diana, Princess of Wales Commemoration. Each brown and black.
2814 10d. Type **284** . . . . . . 1·50 1·60
2815 10d. Wearing open-necked shirt . . . . 1·50 1·60
2816 10d. Wearing polo-neck jumper . . . . 1·50 1·60
2817 10d. Wearing diamond-drop earrings . . . . 1·50 1·60
MS2818 76 × 106 mm. 25d. Diana, Princess of Wales (multicoloured) 4·25 4·50

1997. Christmas. Paintings. Multicoloured.
2819 1d. Type **284a** 40 15
2820 1d.50 "Initiation into the Rites of Dionysus" at Villa dei Misteri 50 15
2821 2d. "Pair of Erotes with Purple Cloaks" 65 20
2822 3d. "The Ecstasy of Saint Theresa" (Gianlorenzo Bernini) 80 35
2823 5d. "Virgin and Child with Angels" (Matthias Grunewald) . . . . . . 1·00 90
2824 10d. "Angel playing the Organ" (Stefan Lochner) 1·75 2·25
MS2825 Two sheets, each 105 × 95 mm. (a) 25d. "The Rest on the Flight into Egypt" (Caravaggio). (b) 25d. "The Education of Cupid" (Titian) Set of 2 sheets . . . . 8·00 9·00
No. **MS**2825a is inscribed "THE REST OF THE FLIGHT INTO EGYPT" and No. **MS**2825b "TITAN", both in error.

1998. Chinese New Year ("Year of the Tiger"). Multicoloured.
2826 3d. Type **285** ("GAMBIA" in green) 15 20
2827 3d. Tiger ("GAMBIA" in mauve) 15 20
2828 3d. Tiger ("GAMBIA" in lilac) 15 20
2829 3d. Tiger ("GAMBIA" in blue) 15 20
MS2830 73 × 100 mm. 10d. Tiger (42 × 28 mm) 55 60

286 Class 91 Electric Train, Great Britian

1998. Trains of the World. Multicoloured.
2831 5d. Type **286** 25 30
2832 5d. Class 26 steam locomotive No. 3450 "Red Devil", South Africa 25 30
2833 5d. TGV express train, France 25 30
2834 5d. People Mover railcar, Great Britain 25 30
2835 5d. ICE high speed train, Germany 25 30
2836 5d. Montmartre funicular car, France 25 30
2837 5d. Burlington Northern SD70 diesel locomotive No. 9716, U.S.A. 25 30
2838 5d. L.N.E.R. Class A4 steam locomotive "Mallard", 1938 . . . . 25 30
2839 5d. Baldwin steam locomotive, Peru 25 30
2840 5d. Amtrak Class ARM-7 electric locomotive, U.S.A. 25 30
2841 5d. Rack steam locomotive No. B2503, Amberawa, Java 25 30
2842 5d. Beyer-Peacock steam locomotive No. 3108, Pakistan 25 30
MS2843 Two sheets, each 84 × 110 mm. (a) 25d. Futuristic monorail train, Great Britain. (b) 25d. Southern Pacific GS4 stream-lined steam locomotive, U.S.A. Set of 2 sheets . . . . . . 2·75 3·00
No. 2832 is inscribed "BEACONSFIELD CHINA", No. 2836 "MOUNTMAETRE FUNICULAR" and No. 2840 "SWEDEN RAIL 125 MPH", all in error.

287 Yellow Orchid

289 Mulan

288 Wright "Flyer I", 1903

1998. African Flowers. Multicoloured.
2844 75b. Type **287** 10 10
2845 1d.50 Transvaal daisy 10 15
2846 3d. Torch lily 15 20
2847 4d. "Ancistrochilus rothschildianus" 20 25
2848 5d. "Adenium multiflorum" (horiz) 25 30
2849 5d. "Huernia namaquensis" (horiz) 25 30
2850 5d. "Gloriosa superba" (horiz) 25 30
2851 5d. "Strelitzia reginae" (horiz) 25 30
2852 5d. "Passiflora mollissima" (horiz) 25 30
2853 5d. "Bauhinia variegata" (horiz) 25 30
2854 10d. "Polystachya vulcanica" 55 60
2855 15d. Gladiolus 80 85
MS2856 Two sheets, each 106 × 76 mm. (a) 25d. "Aerangis rhodosticta". (b) 25d. "Ansella gigantea" Set of 2 sheets . . . 2·75 3·00
Nos. 2848/53 were printed together, se-tenant, forming a composite background design.

1998. History of Aviation. Multicoloured.
2857 5d. Type **288** 25 30
2858 5d. Curtiss A-1 seaplane, 1910 . . . . 25 30
2859 5d. Farman biplane, 1907 . . 25 30
2860 5d. Bristol monoplane, 1911 25 30
2861 5d. Antoinette IV, 1908 . . 25 30
2862 5d. Sopwith "Bat Boat" amphibian, 1912 . . . . 25 30
2863 5d. Short Type 38, 1913 . . 25 30
2864 5d. Fokker F.VIIb/3m, 1925 25 30
2865 5d. Junkers J.13, 1919 . . . 25 30
2866 5d. Pitcairn "Mailwing", 1927 . . . . 25 30
2867 5d. Douglas, 1920 . . . . . 25 30
2868 5d. Curtiss T-32 Condor II airliner, 1934 . . . . . 25 30
MS2869 Two sheets, each 106 × 76 mm. (a) 25d. Albatross, 1913 (84 × 28 mm). (b) 25d. Boeing 247 airliner, 1932 (84 × 28 mm) Set of 2 sheets . . . . . . 2·75 3·00
Nos. 2857/62 and 2863/8 respectively were printed together, se-tenant, forming composite background designs.
No. 2857 is dated "1902" in error.

1998. "Mulan" (film). Multicoloured.
2870 4d. Type **289** . . . . 1·10 1·10
2871 4d. Mushu . . . . 1·10 1·10
2872 4d. Little Brother . . . . . 1·10 1·10
2873 4d. Cri-kee . . . . 1·10 1·10
2874 4d. Grandmother Fa . . . . 1·10 1·10
2875 4d. Fa Li . . . . 1·10 1·10
2876 4d. Fa Zhou . . . . 1·10 1·10
2877 4d. Mulan and Khan . . . . 1·10 1·10
2878 5d. Mulan riding Khan . . . 1·10 1·10
2879 5d. Shang . . . . 1·10 1·10
2880 5d. Chi-fu . . . . 1·10 1·10
2881 5d. Chien-po . . . . 1·10 1·10
2882 5d. Yao . . . . 1·10 1·10
2883 5d. Ling . . . . 1·10 1·10
2884 5d. Shan-yu . . . . 1·10 1·10
2885 5d. Mulan, Shang and Mushu . . . . 1·10 1·10
MS2886 Four sheets. (a) 102 × 127 mm. 25d. Mulan and Khan. (b) 127 × 102 mm. 25d. Mulan and firework. (c) 127 × 102 mm. 25d. Mulan in front of house. (d) 127 × 102 mm. 25d. Mulan performing karate kick Set of 4 sheets . . . . . . 20·00 22·00

289a Sidney Bechet

1998. Millennium Series. Famous People of the Twentieth Century. Multicoloured. (a) Famous Jazz Musicians.
2887 4d. Type **289a** 20 25
2888 4d. Sidney Bechet playing saxophone (53 × 38 mm) 20 25
2889 4d. Duke Ellington conducting (53 × 38 mm) 20 25
2890 4d. Duke Ellington 20 25
2891 4d. Louis Armstrong . . . 20 25
2892 4d. Louis Armstrong playing trumpet (53 × 38 mm) 20 25
2893 4d. Charlie "Bird" Parker playing saxophone (53 × 38 mm) 20 25
2894 4d. Charlie "Bird" Parker 20 25
(b) Famous Theatrical Composers.
2895 4d. Cole Porter 20 25
2896 4d. "Born to Dance" (Cole Porter) (53 × 38 mm) . . . 20 25
2897 4d. "Porgy and Bess" (George Gershwin) (53 × 38 mm) 20 25
2898 4d. George Gershwin . . . 20 25
2899 4d. Rogers and Hammerstein 20 25
2900 4d. "The King and I" (Rogers and Hammerstein) (53 × 38 mm) 20 25
2901 4d. "West Side Story" (Leonard Bernstein) (53 × 38 mm) 20 25
2902 4d. Leonard Bernstein . . . 20 25
MS2903 Two sheets, each 76 × 106 mm. (a) 25d. Ella Fitzgerald. (b) 25d. "Oh How I Hate to Get Up in the Morning" (Irving Berlin) Set of 2 sheets 2·75 3·00

290 Chinese Junk

291 Captain Edward Smith

1998. Ships. Multicoloured.
2904 2d. Type **290** 10 15
2905 3d. H.M.S. "Victory" (ship of the line, 1765) 15 20
2906 5d. "Santa Maria" (Columbus) 25 30
2907 5d. "Mary Rose" (galleon) 25 30
2908 5d. "Mayflower" (Pilgrim Fathers) 25 30
2909 5d. "Ark Royal" (galleon, 1587) 25 30
2910 5d. H.M.S. "Beagle" (Darwin) 25 30
2911 5d. H.M.S. "Bounty" (Bligh) 25 30
2912 5d. H.M.S. "Dreadnought" (battleship) 25 30
2913 5d. American "Truxton" Class cruiser 25 30
2914 5d. "Queen Mary" (liner) 25 30
2915 5d. "Canberra" (liner) . . . 25 30
2916 5d. "Queen Elizabeth" (liner) 25 30
2917 5d. "Queen Elizabeth II" (liner) 25 30
2918 10d. British "County" Class destroyer 55 60
2919 15d. Viking longship 80 85
MS2920 Two sheets. (a) 70 × 100 mm. 25d. "Cutty Sark" (clipper) (41 × 56 mm). (b) 100 × 70 mm. 25d. "Sovereign of the Seas" (liner) (56 × 41 mm) Set of 2 sheets . . . . 2·75 3·00

1998. "Titanic" Commemoration.
2921 **291** 5d. brown, black and blue 25 30
2922 – 5d. brown, black and blue 25 30
2923 – 5d. brown and black . . 25 30
2924 – 5d. blue and black . . 25 30
2925 – 5d. mauve and black . . 25 30
2926 – 5d. mauve and black . . 25 30
MS2927 Three sheets, each 110 × 85 mm. (a) 25d. multicoloured. (b) 25d. sepia and black. (c) 25d. multicoloured Set of 3 sheets . . . . 4·00 4·25
DESIGNS—VERT: No. 2922, Mrs. J. J. "Molly" Brown (passenger); 2923, Newspaper boy with placard; 2924, Benjamin Guggenheim (passenger); 2925, Isidor Strauss (passenger); 2926, Ida Strauss (passenger). HORIZ: No. **MS**2927a, "Titanic" on postcard; **MS**2927b, "Titanic sinking"; **MS**2927c, Wreckage of "Titanic" on seabed.

291a "Death of Casagemas"

1998. 25th Death Anniv of Pablo Picasso (painter). Multicoloured.
2928 3d. Type **291a** 15 20
2929 5d. "Seated Woman" (vert) 25 30
2930 10d. "Mother and Child" (vert) 55 60
MS2931 102 × 126 mm. 25d. "Child playing with Toy Truck" (vert) 1·40 1·50

291b Scout Handshake

292 Mahatma Gandhi

1998. 19th World Scout Jamboree, Chile. Mult.
2932 10d. Type **291b** 55 60
2933 10d. Dinghy sailing 55 60
2934 10d. Scout salute 55 60
MS2935 47 × 61 mm. 25d. Lord Baden-Powell (brown and black) 1·40 1·50

1998. 50th Death Anniv of Mahatma Gandhi. Multicoloured.
2936 10d. Type **292** 55 60
2937 10d. Gandhi on Salt March with Mrs. Sarojini Naidu (53 × 38 mm) 55 60

2938 10d. Gandhi spinning yarn (53 × 38 mm) 55 60
2939 10d. Gandhi in 1916 . . . . 55 60
MS2940 53 × 71 mm. 25d. Gandhi writing . . . . 1·40 1·50

292a Sepecat Jaguar GR1A

1998. 80th Anniv of Royal Air Force. Multicoloured.
2941 5d. Type **292a** 25 30
2942 5d. Panavia Tornado GR1A 25 30
2943 5d. Sepecat Jaguar GR1A (side view) 25 30
2944 5d. BAe Hawk 200 . . . . 25 30
2945 5d. Sepecat Jaguar GR1A firing Sparrow missile . . 25 30
2946 5d. BAe Harrier GR7 firing SNEB rockets 25 30
2947 5d. Panavia Tornado GR1 firing AIM-9L missile . . 25 30
2948 5d. Panavia Tornado GR1 in low level flight 25 30
2949 7d. Panavia Tornado GR1 (facing left) 35 40
2950 7d. BAe Hawk T1A 35 40
2951 7d. Sepecat Jaguar GR1A 35 40
2952 7d. Panavia Tornado GR1 (facing right) 35 40
MS2953 Six sheets, each 90 × 68 mm. (a) 20d. EF-2000 Eurofighter. (b) 25d. Bristol F2B Fighter and bird of prey in flight. (c) 25d. Falcon's head and Bristol F2B Fighter. (d) 25d. Bristol F2B Fighter and Golden Eagle (bird). (e) 25d. Lancaster and EF-2000 Eurofighter. (f) 25d. Lightning and EF-2000 Eurofighter Set of 6 sheets . . . . 8·00 8·25

293 "Mule-drivers from Tetuan"

1998. Birth Bicentenary of Eugene Delacroix (painter). Multicoloured.
2954 4d. Type **293** 20 25
2955 4d. "Encampment of Arab Mule-drivers" 20 25
2956 4d. "An Orange Seller" . . 20 25
2957 4d. "The Banks of the River" 20 25
2958 4d. "View of Tangier from the Seashore" 20 25
2959 4d. "Arab Horses fighting in a Stable" 20 25
2960 4d. "Horses at the Trough" 20 25
2961 4d. "The Combat of Giaour and Hassan" 20 25
2962 4d. "Turk on a Sofa, Smoking" 20 25
2963 4d. "View of Tangier" . . . 20 25
2964 4d. "The Spanish Coast at Salobrena" 20 25
2965 4d. "The Aissaouas" . . . 20 25
2966 4d. "The Sea from the Cliffs of Dieppe" 20 25
2967 4d. "The Fanatics of Tangier" 20 25
2968 4d. "Arab Musicians" . . . 20 25
2969 4d. "An Arab Camp at Night" 20 25
2970 4d. "Moroccan from Tangier, standing" (vert) 20 25
2971 4d. "A Man of Tangier" (vert) 20 25
2972 4d. "Young Arab standing with a Rifle" (vert) . . . 20 25
2973 4d. "Moroccan Chieftain" (vert) 20 25
2974 4d. "Jewish Bride, Tangier" (vert) 20 25
2975 4d. "Seated Jewess from Morocco" (vert) 20 25
2976 4d. "Young Arab seated by a Wall" (vert) 20 25
2977 4d. "Arab Dancer" (vert) 20 25
MS2978 Three sheets. (a) 100 × 85 mm. 25d. "Massacre at Chios". (b) 100 × 85 mm. 25d. "Women of Algiers in their Apartment". (c) 85 × 100 mm. 25d. "Self-portrait" (vert) Set of 3 sheets . . . . 4·00 4·25

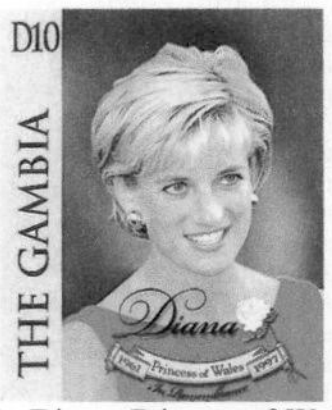

293a Diana, Princess of Wales

1998. 1st Death Anniv of Diana, Princess of Wales.
2979 **293a** 10d. multicoloured . . 55 60

294 Puppy in Stocking

295 Rabbit

1998. Christmas. Multicoloured.
2980 1d. Type **294** 10 10
2981 2d. Giraffe in Christmas wreath 10 15
2982 3d. Australian bee eater ("Rainbow Bee Eater") (bird) with bauble 15 20
2983 4d. Deer 20 25
2984 5d. Fawn 25 30
2985 10d. Puppy in gift box . . . 55 60
MS2986 Two sheets, each 105 × 76 mm. (a) 25d. Brown classic tabby. (b) 25d. Basset hound and Rough collie Set of 2 sheets . . . . 2·75 3·00

1999. Chinese New Year ("Year of the Rabbit"). Multicoloured.
2987 3d. Type **295** 15 20
2988 3d. Rabbit looking over shoulder 15 20
2989 3d. Rabbit facing left . . . 15 20
2990 3d. Rabbit running 15 20
MS2991 73 × 103 mm. 10d. Rabbit (42 × 28 mm) 55 60

296 Mowgli and Baloo (bear)

1999. "The Jungle Book" (film). Walt Disney cartoon characters. Multicoloured.
2992 5d. Type **296** . . . . 1·25 1·25
2993 5d. Kaa (snake) and Mowgli 1·25 1·25
2994 5d. King Louie at ruined temple . . . . 1·25 1·25
2995 5d. Monkey playing leaf "guitar" . . . . 1·25 1·25
2996 5d. Village girl collecting water . . . . 1·25 1·25
2997 5d. King Louie on throne with Mowgli . . . . . . 1·25 1·25
2998 5d. Mowgli and vultures . . 1·25 1·25
2999 5d. Shere Khan (tiger) . . . 1·25 1·25
MS3000 Two sheets, each 127 × 102 mm. (a) 25d. Baloo (bear) (50 × 37 mm). (b) 25d. Baby elephant (50 × 37 mm) Set of 2 sheets . . . . 8·00 9·00

297 "Danaus chrysippus"

1999. "Australia '99" World Stamp Exhibition, Melbourne. African Butterflies. Multicoloured.
3001 6d. Type **297** 30 35
3002 6d. "Papilio zalmoxis" . . . 30 35
3003 6d. "Papilio menestheus" . . 30 35
3004 6d. "Poecilmitis thysbe" . . 30 35
3005 6d. "Euxanthe wakefieldii" 30 35
3006 6d. "Pseudacraea boisduvali" 30 35
3007 6d. "Eurytela dryope" . . . 30 35
3008 6d. "Papilio demodocus" . . 30 35
3009 6d. "Hemiolaus coeculus" 30 35
3010 6d. "Charaxes jasius" . . . 30 35
3011 6d. "Junonia orithya" . . . 30 35
3012 6d. "Kallimoides rumia" . . 30 35
MS3013 Two sheets, each 106 × 76 mm. (a) 25d. "Charaxes jasius" (vert). (b) 25d. "Catacroptera cloanthe" (vert) Set of 2 sheets . . . . 2·75 3·00
No. 3003 is inscribed "Papilio mnestheus" in error.

298 Prince Edward and Miss Sophie Rhys-Jones

1999. Royal Wedding. Multicoloured.
3014 10d. Type **298** 55 60
3015 10d. Prince Edward and Miss Sophie Rhys-Jones (with long hair) 55 60
3016 10d. Prince Edward and Miss Sophie Rhys-Jones (wearing a red jacket) . . 55 60
MS3017 78 × 78 mm. 25d. Prince Edward and Miss Sophie Rhys-Jones (39 × 29 mm) . . . . . 1·40 1·50

299 Cannon and Freedom Post, Jaffureh

1999. *Roots* Homecoming Festival. Multicoloured.
3018 1d. Type **299** 10 10
3019 2d. Fort Bullen 10 15
3020 3d. James Island 15 20

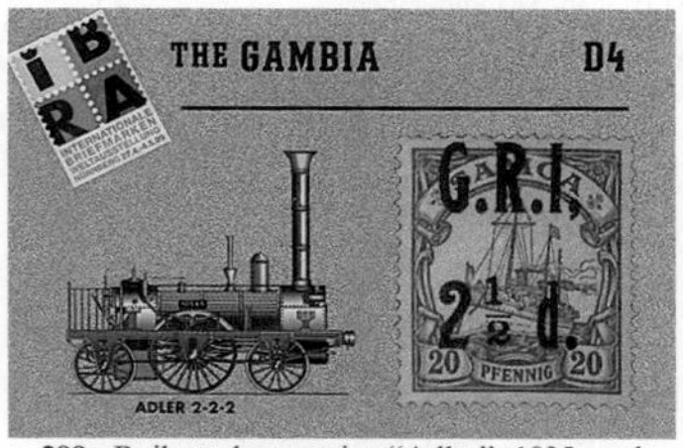

299a Railway locomotive "Adler", 1835, and Samoa 1914 G.R.I. 2½d. on 20pf. variety

1999. "iBRA '99" International Stamp Exhibition, Nuremberg. Multicoloured.
3021 4d. Type **299a** 20 25
3022 5d. Railway locomotive "Adler", 1835, and Samoa 1900 25pf. optd on Germany 25 30
3023 10d. "Friedrech August" (full-rigged ship) and Samoa 1900 Yacht type 50pf. and 80pf. stamps . . 55 60
3024 15d. "Friedrech August" (full-rigged ship) and Samoa 1900 Yacht type 2m. stamp 80 85
MS3025 162 × 107 mm. 25d. Samoa 1900 Yacht type 3m. stamp postmarked Palauli (60 × 40 mm) 1·40 1·50

299b "Exotic Beauty"

1999. 150th Death Anniv of Katsushika Hokusai (Japanese artist). Multicoloured.
3026 5d. Type **299b** 25 30
3027 5d. "Wind" (two people) . . 25 30
3028 5d. "Dancing Monkey" . . 25 30
3029 5d. "Lady and Maiden on an Outing" 25 30
3030 5d. "Wind" (three people) 25 30
3031 5d. "Courtesan with Fan" 25 30
3032 5d. "Bunshosei" 25 30
3033 5d. "Overthrower of Castles, Overthrower of Nations" 25 30
3034 5d. "Bee on Wild Rose" . . 25 30
3035 5d. "Sei Shonagon" 25 30
3036 5d. "Kuan-yu" 25 30
3037 5d. "The Fifth Month" . . 25 30
MS3038 Two sheets, each 72 × 103 mm. (a) 25d. "People on the Balcony of the Sazaido". (b) 25d. "Caocao before the Battle of Chibi" Set of 2 sheets . . . . 2·75 3·00

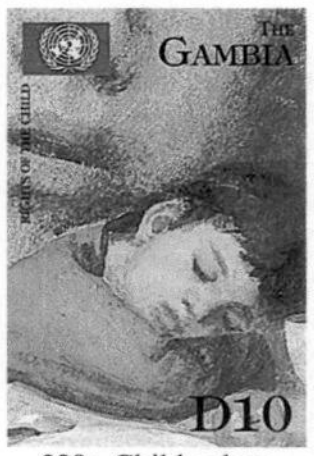

299c Child asleep

1999. 10th Anniv of United Nations Rights of the Child Convention. Multicoloured.
3039 10d. Type **299c** 55 60
3040 10d. Child drinking 55 60
3041 10d. Child drawing 55 60
MS3042 112 × 85 mm. 25d. Child laughing . . . . 1·40 1·50
Nos. 3039/41 were printed together, se-tenant, forming a composite design.

299d Road Carriage on Wagon

1999. "PhilexFrance 99" International Stamp Exhibition, Paris. Railway Transport. Two sheets, each 106 × 81 mm, containing T **299d** and similar designs. Multicoloured.
MS3043 (a) 25d. Type **299d**. (b) 25d. Passenger locomotive, 1846 Set of 2 sheets . . . . 2·75 3·00

299e Faust quaffs the Spirit's Nectar

1999. 250th Birth Anniv of Johann von Goethe (German writer).
3044 **299e** 15d. violet, black & pur 80 85
3045 – 15d. blue and black . . 80 85
3046 – 15d. brown, blk & grn 80 85
MS3047 76 × 106 mm. 25d. blue, black and brown . . . . . . 1·40 1·50
DESIGNS—HORIZ: No. 3045, Goethe and Schiller; 3046, Faust contemplates mortality. VERT: No. MS3047, Johann von Goethe.

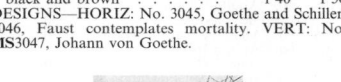

299f Bell X-14A VTOL Aircraft

1999. 30th Anniv of First Manned Landing on Moon. Multicoloured.
3048 6d. Type **299f** 30 35
3049 6d. Lunar landing practice rig 30 35
3050 6d. Early prototype lander 30 35
3051 6d. Astronaut during zero gravity training 30 35
3052 6d. Jet pack training 30 35
3053 6d. Lunar lander pilot training 30 35
MS3054 Two sheets. (a) 76 × 105 mm. 25d. "Apollo 11" splashdown. (b) 85 × 110 mm. 25d. Lunar module "Eagle" Set of 2 sheets . . . . 2·75 3·00
Nos. 3048/53 were printed together, se-tenant, forming a composite design.

300 Swallow-tailed Gull

1999. Marine Life of the Galapagos Islands. Multicoloured.
3055 1d.50 Type **300** 10 15
3056 1d.50 Magnificent frigate birds ("Frigate Bird") . . 10 15
3057 1d.50 Red-footed booby . . 10 15
3058 1d.50 Galapagos hawk . . . 10 15
3059 1d.50 Great blue heron . . 10 15

3060 1d.50 Blue-faced booby ("Masked Booby") . . . 10 15
3061 1d.50 Bottlenose dolphins 10 15
3062 1d.50 Black grunts 10 15
3063 1d.50 Surgeonfish 10 15
3064 1d.50 Stingray 10 15
3065 1d.50 Short-finned pilot whales 10 15
3066 1d.50 Pacific green sea turtle 10 15
3067 1d.50 Great white shark . . 10 15
3068 1d.50 Sealion 10 15
3069 1d.50 Marine iguana 10 15
3070 1d.50 Pacific manta ray . . 10 15
3071 1d.50 Moorish idol 10 15
3072 1d.50 Galapagos penguins 10 15
3073 1d.50 Silver grunts 10 15
3074 1d.50 Sea urchin 10 15
3075 1d.50 Wrasse 10 15
3076 1d.50 Almaco amber jack 10 15
3077 1d.50 Blue parrotfish . . . 10 15
3078 1d.50 Yellow sea urchin . . 10 15
3079 1d.50 Lobster 10 15
3080 1d.50 Grouper 10 15
3081 1d.50 Scorpionfish 10 15
3082 1d.50 Squirrelfish 10 15
3083 1d.50 Octopus 10 15
3084 1d.50 King angelfish 10 15
3085 1d.50 Horned shark 10 15
3086 1d.50 Galapagos hogfish . . 10 15
3087 1d.50 Pufferfish 10 15
3088 1d.50 Moray eel 10 15
3089 1d.50 Orange tube coral . . 10 15
3090 1d.50 Whitestripe chromis 10 15
3091 1d.50 Long-nosed hawkfish 10 15
3092 1d.50 Sea cucumbers . . . 10 15
3093 1d.50 Spotted hawkfish . . 10 15
3094 1d.50 Zebra moray eel . . . 10 15
MS3095 106 × 77 mm. 25d. Emperor penguins . . . . 1·40 1·50

Nos. 3055/94 respectively were printed together, se-tenant, forming a composite design.

301 "Telstar 1" Satellite, 1962

1999. History of Space Exploration. Multicoloured.
3096 1d. Type **301** 10 10
3097 1d.50 "Skylab", 1973 (vert) 10 15
3098 2d. "Mars 3" spacecraft, 1971 (vert) 10 15
3099 3d. "Cobe", 1989 (vert) . . . 15 20
3100 6d. "Mariner 4", 1964 . . . 30 35
3101 6d. "Viking" Mars Orbiter, 1975 . . . . 30 35
3102 6d. Giotto, 1985 . . . . . 30 35
3103 6d. "Luna 9", 1966 . . . . 30 35
3104 6d. "Voyager 1", 1977 . . . 30 35
3105 6d. Galileo, 1989 . . . . . 30 35
3106 6d. Soviet "Vostok 1", 1961 30 35
3107 6d. "Apollo" command and service module, 1968 . . . 30 35
3108 6d. "Mercury" capsule, 1961 30 35
3109 6d. "Apollo 16" lunar module, 1972 . . . . . . 30 35
3110 6d. "Gemini 8", 1966 . . . 30 35
3111 6d. Soviet "Soyuz", 1975 . . 30 35
3112 6d. German "V 2" rocket, 1942 (vert) 30 35
3113 6d. "Delta Straight 8", 1972 (vert) 30 35
3114 6d. "Ariane 4", 1988 (vert) 30 35
3115 6d. "Mercury MA-A Atlas", 1962 (vert) 30 35
3116 6d. "Saturn 1B", 1975 (vert) 30 35
3117 6d. "Cassini", 1997 (vert) 30 35
3118 10d. Bruce McCandless outside shuttle, 1984 (vert) 55 60
3119 15d. "Apollo 13" after splashdown, 1970 (vert) 80 85
MS3120 Two sheets. (a) 85 × 110 mm. 25d. "Mars Pathfinder", 1997 (56 × 41 mm). (b) 110 × 85 mm. 25d. "Apollo" and "Soyuz" joint mission, 1975 (56 × 41 mm) Set of 2 sheets . . 2·75 3·00

302 Carnotaurus

1999. Prehistoric Animals. Multicoloured.
3121 3d. Type **302** 15 20
3122 3d. Quetzalcoatlus 15 20
3123 3d. Peteinosaurus 15 20
3124 3d. Prenocephale 15 20
3125 3d. Hesperornis 15 20
3126 3d. Coelophysis 15 20
3127 3d. Camptosaurus 15 20
3128 3d. Panderichthys 15 20
3129 3d. Garudimimus 15 20
3130 3d. Cacops 15 20
3131 3d. Ichthyostega 15 20
3132 3d. Scutellosaurus 15 20
3133 3d. Diatryma 15 20
3134 3d. Pteranodon 15 20
3135 3d. Stegodon 15 20
3136 3d. Icaronycthris 15 20
3137 3d. Archaeopteryx 15 20
3138 3d. Chasmatosaurus . . . 15 20
3139 3d. Tytthostonyx 15 20
3140 3d. Hyaenodon 15 20
3141 3d. Uintatherium 15 20
3142 3d. Hesperocyon 15 20
3143 3d. Ambelodon 15 20
3144 3d. Indricotherium 15 20
MS3145 Four sheets, each 110 × 85 mm. (a) 25d. Deinonychus. (b) 25d. Sabre-tooth Tiger. (c) 25d. Lepisosteus. (d) 25d. Microceratops Set of 4 sheets 5·50 5·75

Nos. 3121/32 and 3133/44 were printed together, se-tenant, forming composite designs.

303 Seagull

1999. Marine Life. Multicoloured.
3146 1d. Type **303** 10 10
3147 1d.50 Portuguese man-o-war 10 15
3148 3d. Whale shark 15 20
3149 3d. Grey reef shark 15 20
3150 3d. New England octopus 15 20
3151 3d. Pufferfish 15 20
3152 3d. Lionfish 15 20
3153 3d. Squid 15 20
3154 3d. Chambered nautilus . 15 20
3155 3d. Clownfish 15 20
3156 3d. Moray eel 15 20
3157 3d. Spiny lobster 15 20
3158 3d. Spotted ray 15 20
3159 3d. Clown anemone . . . 15 20
3160 3d. Angelfish 15 20
3161 3d. Leafy seadragon . . . 15 20
3162 3d. Hawksbill turtle . . . 15 20
3163 3d. Mandarinfish 15 20
3164 3d. Candy cane sea star . 15 20
3165 3d. Plate coral 15 20
3166 3d. Butterflyfish 15 20
3167 3d. Coral polyp 15 20
3168 3d. Hermit crab 15 20
3169 3d. Strawberry shrimp . . 15 20
3170 3d. Giant blue clam . . . 15 20
3171 3d. Sea cucumber 15 20
3172 5d. Walrus 25 30
3173 10d. Manatee 55 60
MS3174 110 × 85 mm. 25d. Common dolphin . . . . 1·40 1·50

Nos. 3148/59 and 3160/71 were printed together, se-tenant, forming composite designs.

304 "Sophrocattleya"

1999. Orchids of the World. Multicoloured.
3175 2d. Type **304** 10 15
3176 3d. "Cattleya" and butterfly 15 20
3177 4d. "Brassolaeliocattleya" (pink) 20 25
3178 5d. "Brassoepidendrum" . . 25 30
3179 6d. "Brassolaeliocattleya" (yellow) 30 35
3180 6d. "Cattleytonia" 30 35
3181 6d. "Lacliocattleya" 30 35
3182 6d. "Miltonia" 30 35
3183 6d. "Cattleya forbesii" . . . 30 35
3184 6d. "Odontoglossum cervantesii" 30 35
3185 6d. "Lycaste macrobulbon" 30 35
3186 6d. "Laeliocattleya" 30 35
3187 6d. "Brassocattleya" (pink) 30 35
3188 6d. "Cattleya" 30 35
3189 6d. "Brassolaeliocattleya" (red spotted) 30 35
3190 6d. "Brassolaeliocattleya" (yellow and red) 30 35
3191 10d. "Sophrolaeliocattleya" and butterfly 55 60
3192 15d. "Iwanagaara" and butterfly 80 85
MS3193 Two sheets. (a) 81 × 106 mm. 25d. "Lycaste". (b) 85 × 110 mm. 25d. "Brassolaeliocattleya" (pink and white) Set of 2 sheets . . . . . 2·75 3·00

305 American Black Oystercatcher

1999. Sea Birds. Multicoloured.
3194 2d. Type **305** 10 15
3195 3d. Blue-footed booby . . . 15 20
3196 4d. Atlantic puffin 20 25
3197 4d. Red-billed tropic birds ("Red-tailed Tropic Bird") 20 25
3198 4d. Reddish egret 20 25
3199 4d. Laughing gull 20 25
3200 4d. Great egret 20 25
3201 4d. Northern gannet 20 25
3202 4d. Forster's tern 20 25
3203 4d. Common cormorant . . 20 25
3204 4d. Razorbill (perched on rocks) 20 25
3205 4d. Adelie penguin 20 25
3206 4d. Black skimmer 20 25
3207 4d. Big crested penguin ("Erect-crested Penguin") 20 25
3208 4d. Heermann's gull 20 25
3209 4d. Glaucous-winged gull . . 20 25
3210 4d. Laysan albatross 20 25
3211 4d. American white pelican 20 25
3212 4d. Tufted puffin 20 25
3213 4d. Black guillemot 20 25
3214 5d. Razorbill (in flight) . . . 25 30
3215 5d. Common shelduck ("Shelduck") 25 30
3216 5d. Sandwich tern 25 30
3217 5d. Arctic skua 25 30
3218 5d. Northern gannet ("Gannet") 25 30
3219 5d. Mew gull ("Common Gull") 25 30
3220 10d. Western gull 55 60
3221 15d. Brown pelican 80 85
MS3222 Three sheets. (a) 110 × 85 mm. 25d. American white pelican ("Pelican"). (b) 105 × 76 mm. 25d. Gentoo penguin. (c) 106 × 76 mm. 25d. California gull Set of 3 sheets 4·00 4·25

Nos. 3196/3204, 3205/13 and 3214/19 were printed together, se-tenant, forming a composite design.

Nos. 3205 and 3210 are inscribed "ADELIES PENGUIN" or "LAYSON ALBATROSS", both in error.

305a Duchess of York and Princess Elizabeth, 1928

1999. "Queen Elizabeth the Queen Mother's Century".
3223 **305a** 10d. multicoloured . . 55 60
3224 – 10d. black and gold . . 55 60
3225 – 10d. black and gold . . 55 60
3226 – 10d. multicoloured . . 55 60
MS3227 153 × 155 mm. 25d. mult 1·40 1·50

DESIGNS: No. 3224, Lady Elizabeth Bowes-Lyon, 1923; 3225, Queen Elizabeth, 1946; 3226, Queen Mother and Prince Harry. (37 × 50 mm)—**MS**3227, Queen Mother on 89th Birthday, 1989.

306 Temple of A-Ma

1999. "China '99" International Stamp Exhibition, Beijing. Return of Macao to China. Multicoloured.
3228 7d. Type **306** 35 40
3229 7d. Border Gate 35 40
3230 7d. Ruins of St. Paul's . . . 35 40

307 John F. Kennedy Jr. as Baby, 1961

1999. John F. Kennedy Jr. Commemoration. Each brown, blue and black.
3231 15d. Type **307** 80 85
3232 15d. John F. Kennedy Jr. as teenager 80 85
3233 15d. John F. Kennedy Jr. in 1997 . . . . 80 85

307a Flowers forming Top of Head

1999. Faces of the Millennium: Diana, Princess of Wales. Designs showing collage of miniature flower photographs. Multicoloured.
3234 3d. Type **307a** (face value at left) 15 20
3235 3d. Top of head (face value at right) 15 20
3236 3d. Ear (face value at left) 15 20
3237 3d. Eye and temple (face value at right) 15 20
3238 3d. Cheek (face value at left) 15 20
3239 3d. Cheek (face value at right) 15 20
3240 3d. Blue background (face value at left) 15 20
3241 3d. Chin (face value at right) 15 20

Nos. 3234/41 were printed together, se-tenant, so that the sheetlet forms a portrait of Diana, Princess of Wales.

308 Betty Boop

2000. Betty Boop (cartoon character). Mult.
3242 5d. Type **308** 25 30
3243 5d. In full-length gown . . . 25 30
3244 5d. In T-shirt and dungarees 25 30
3245 5d. In cropped trousers, sleeveless shirt and tie . . 25 30
3246 5d. Sitting in wicker chair 25 30
3247 5d. In ripped purple trousers, orange T-shirt and gilet 25 30
3248 5d. In fur coat 25 30
3249 5d. In pink crinoline 25 30
3250 5d. In the gym 25 30
MS3251 Two sheets, each 140 × 89 mm. (a) 25d. In the bath. (b) 25d. With chin on hand Set of 2 sheets . . . . 2·75 3·00

309 Lucille Ball on Sofa

2000. Scenes from *I Love Lucy* (American T.V. comedy series). Multicoloured.
3252 5d. Type **309** 25 30
3253 5d. Lucy and Desi Arnaz talking 25 30
3254 5d. Lucy holding ball of string 25 30
3255 5d. Lucy in blue coat standing in front of lamp 25 30
3256 5d. Lucy and Desi kissing 25 30
3257 5d. Lucy in front of mirror 25 30
3258 5d. Lucy excited with hands clenched 25 30
3259 5d. Lucy sitting on Desi's knee 25 30
3260 5d. Lucy looking in purse 25 30
3261 5d. Lucy clutching shelf . . 25 30
3262 5d. Lucy leaning against wall with arms raised . . 25 30
3263 5d. Lucy with right fist in the air 25 30
3264 5d. Lucy sitting on shelf (front view) 25 30
3265 5d. Lucy smoothing hair with right hand 25 30
3266 5d. Lucy sitting on shelf (side view) 25 30
3267 5d. Desi Arnaz with Lucy bound 25 30
3268 5d. Lucy lying on sofa . . . 25 30
3269 5d. Lucy being held by masked man 25 30
3270 5d. Lucy singing in Austrian costume 25 30
3271 5d. Lucy playing tambourine 25 30

3272 5d. Lucy and Desi in uniform singing 25 30
3273 5d. Lucy with stage trees 25 30
3274 5d. Lucy seated at organ with Desi 25 30
3275 5d. Desi with blonde girl sitting on bench 25 30
3276 5d. Lucy typing 25 30
3277 5d. Blonde girl with chorus 25 30
3278 5d. Lucy being carried off on bench 25 30
MS3279 Six sheets. (a) 100 × 140 mm. 25d. As No. 3256 (vert). (b) 100 × 140 mm. 25d. As No. 3257 (vert). (c) 103 × 130 mm. 25d. As No. 3269 (vert). (d) 130 × 98 mm. 25d. As No. 3270 (vert). (e) 130 × 100 mm. 25d. As No. 3273 (vert). (f) 130 × 100 mm. 25d. Lucy bound and gagged (vert) Set of 6 sheets 8·00 8·25

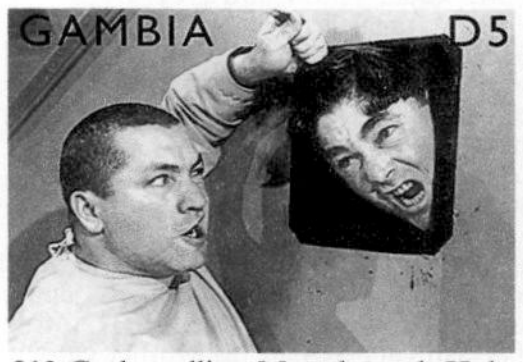

310 Curly pulling Moe through Hole

2000. Scenes from *The Three Stooges* (American T.V. comedy series). Multicoloured.
3280 5d. Type **310** 25 30
3281 5d. Curly with hands in mangle 25 30
3282 5d. Moe giving Curly a bottle 25 30
3283 5d. Larry having hair tugged 25 30
3284 5d. Moe with arms outstretched 25 30
3285 5d. Curly with finger up nose 25 30
3286 5d. Larry, Moe and Curly pointing 25 30
3287 5d. Moe biting Curly's nose with skull 25 30
3288 5d. Moe in yellow shirt and brown jacket 25 30
3289 5d. Moe in Heaven 25 30
3290 5d. Larry, Moe and Curly in Elizabethan costume 25 30
3291 5d. Larry, Moe and Curly in chemist shop 25 30
3292 5d. Moe with shotgun 25 30
3293 5d. With belly dancer 25 30
3294 5d. Larry and Moe in Scottish costume 25 30
3295 5d. Larry and Moe behind wheel 25 30
3296 5d. As postmen 25 30
3297 5d. Curly attacking Larry and Moe with stick 25 30
MS3298 Four sheets. (a) 89 × 140 mm. 25d. Larry wearing crown and leopard skin. (b) 140 × 89 mm. 25d. Curly using phone (inscr "GAMBIA") (vert). (c) 124 × 96 mm. 25d. Curly using phone (inscr "The Gambia") (vert). (d) 124 × 96 mm. 25d. Moe and Curly as postmen (vert) Set of 4 sheets 5·50 5·75
Nos. 3280/8 were printed together, se-tenant, forming a composite design.

310a Leonardo da Vinci's First Design for Flying Machine, 1480

310b Max Planck (Quantum Theory of Energy, 1900)

2000. New Millennium. People and Events of Fifteenth Century (1450–1500). Multicoloured.
3299 2d. Type **310a** 10 15
3300 2d. Johannes Gutenberg (first printed Bible, 1455) 10 15
3301 2d. Capital "B" (first colour printing, 1457) 10 15
3302 2d. Ivan III ("the Great") becomes Grand Prince of Moscow, 1462 10 15
3303 2d. Walls under attack (Fall of Constantinople, 1453) 10 15
3304 2d. Great Wall of China rebuilt, 1488 10 15
3305 2d. Lorenzo de Medici (ruler of Florence) and "Pieta" (sculpture), 1479 10 15
3306 2d. King Henry VII of England (Foundation of Tudor dynasty, 1485) 10 15
3307 2d. Sailing ship and meeting with Indians (Vasco da Gama's voyage to India, 1497) 10 15
3308 2d. King Ferdinand V and Queen Isabella I (Union of Aragon and Castile, 1479) 10 15
3309 2d. Foetus (birth of Erasmus (Dutch scholar), 1466) 10 15
3310 2d. Sailing ship and Cross of St. George (John Cabot's voyage to North America, 1497) 10 15
3311 2d. King Henry VI and Richard, Duke of Gloucester (Wars of the Roses, 1455) 10 15
3312 2d. Bartolomeu Dias and map (Discovery of Cape of Good Hope, 1487) 10 15
3313 2d. Matthias Hunyadi (crowned King of Hungary, 1458) 10 15
3314 2d. Christopher Columbus (Discovery of the Americas, 1492) (59 × 39 mm) 10 15
3315 2d. Girolamo Savonarola (religious reformer) (executed 1498) 10 15

2000. New Millennium. People and Events of Twentieth Century (1900–09). Multicoloured.
3316 3d. Type **310b** 15 20
3317 3d. Zeppelin in hangar (invention of rigid airship, 1900) 15 20
3318 3d. Guglielmo Marconi (first transatlantic radio message, 1901) 15 20
3319 3d. Funeral of Queen Victoria, 1901 15 20
3320 3d. Alfred Nobel (first Nobel Prizes awarded, 1901) 15 20
3321 3d. British infantry advancing (end of Boer War, 1902) 15 20
3322 3d. Wright Brothers and aircraft (first flight, 1903) 15 20
3323 3d. Early teddy bear, 1903 15 20
3324 3d. Panama Canal locks under construction, 1904 15 20
3325 3d. Albert Einstein (Theory of Relativity, 1905) 15 20
3326 3d. Crowd with flags (unrest in Russia, 1905) 15 20
3327 3d. Rescue squad and collapsed building, San Francisco earthquake, 1906 15 20
3328 3d. Louis Lumiere (development of colour photography, 1907) 15 20
3329 3d. "Les Demoiselles d'Avignon" (Pablo Picasso), 1907 15 20
3330 3d. Robert Peary (conquest of North Pole, 1909) 15 20
3331 3d. Henry Ford and first Model T, 1908 (59 × 39 mm) 15 20
3332 3d. Planting sapling (foundation of first Jewish kibbutz in Palestine, 1909) 15 20

311 Dragon

2000. Chinese New Year ("Year of the Dragon"). Multicoloured.
3333 5d. Type **311** 25 30
3334 5d. Multicoloured dragon 25 30
3335 5d. Purple dragon 25 30
3336 5d. Brown dragon 25 30
MS3337 106 × 76 mm. 15d. Coiled dragon (39 × 24 mm) 80 85

312 Indris (lemur)

2000. Wildlife of Africa. Multicoloured.
3338 50b. Type **312** 10 10
3339 75b. Nubian ibex 10 10
3340 1d. Grevy's zebra (vert) 10 10
3341 2d. Bongo (vert) 10 15
3342 3d. White rhinoceros 15 20
3343 4d. Lesser galago 20 25
3344 5d. Okapi 25 30
3345 5d. Sable antelope 25 30
3346 5d. Greater kudu 25 30
3347 5d. African wild ass 25 30
3348 5d. Dorcas gazelle 25 30
3349 5d. Addax 25 30
3350 5d. Pelzeln's gazelle 25 30
3351 6d. Cheetah 30 35
3352 6d. Chimpanzee 30 35
3353 6d. Angwantibo 30 35
3354 6d. Black rhinoceros 30 35
3355 6d. Bontebok 30 35
3356 6d. Giant eland 30 35
3357 7d. Sacred ibis 35 40
3358 7d. Mauritius kestrel 35 40
3359 7d. Leopard 35 40
3360 7d. Radiated tortoise 35 40
3361 7d. Pygmy hippopotamus 35 40
3362 7d. Bald ibis 35 40
3363 7d. Mountain gorilla 35 40
3364 7d. Black-faced impala 35 40
3365 7d. Crowned lemur 35 40
3366 7d. Long-tailed ground roller 35 40
3367 7d. Brown hyena 35 40
3368 7d. Mountain zebra 35 40
3369 10d. Mhorr gazelle (vert) 55 60
MS3370 Four sheets, each 106 × 76 mm. (a) 25d. African elephant. (b) 25d. Aye-Aye. (c) 25d. Nile crocodile. (d) 25d. Black lechwe (vert) Set of 4 sheets 5·50 5·75
Nos. 3345/50, 3351/6, 3357/62 and 3363/8 were each printed together, se-tenant, with the backgrounds forming composite designs.

312a "A Genoese Senator"

312b Prince William as Young Boy with Hands Clasped

2000. 400th Birth Anniv of Sir Anthony Van Dyck (Flemish painter). Multicoloured.
3371 5d. Type **312a** 25 30
3372 5d. "A Seated Gentlewoman" 25 30
3373 5d. "The Senator's Wife" 25 30
3374 5d. "Marchesa Balbi" 25 30
3375 5d. "Polyxena Spinola, Marchesa de Legones" 25 30
3376 5d. "Agostino Pallavicini" 25 30
3377 5d. "Anton Giulo Brignole-Sale" 25 30
3378 5d. "Paolina Adorno Brignole-Sale" 25 30
3379 5d. "Battina Balbi Durazzo" 25 30
3380 5d. "Man of the Cattaneo Family" 25 30
3381 5d. "Portrait of a Woman" 25 30
3382 5d. "Elena Grimaldi Cattaneo" 25 30
3383 5d. "Prince Rupert of the Palatinate" (1631–32) 25 30
3384 5d. "Prince William II of Orange-Nassau" 25 30
3385 5d. "Prince Charles Louis of the Palatinate" (1632) 25 30
3386 5d. "Prince Rupert, Count Palatinate" (1637) 25 30
3387 5d. "Princess Mary" 25 30
3388 5d. "Prince Charles Louis, Count Palatinate" (1637) 25 30
3389 5d. "Adoration of the Shepherds" (horiz) 25 30
3390 5d. "Rest on the Flight into Egypt" (Virgin of the Partridges) (horiz) 25 30
3391 5d. "Suffer the Little Children" (horiz) 25 30
3392 5d. "Christ and the Moneychangers" (horiz) 25 30
3393 5d. "At the House of Simon the Pharisee" (horiz) 25 30
3394 5d. "Lamentation over the Dead Christ" (horiz) 25 30
3395 5d. "Samson and Delilah" (1619–20) (horiz) 25 30
3396 5d. Composition study for "Samson and Delilah" (horiz) 25 30
3397 5d. "Samson and Delilah" (1628–30) (horiz) 25 30
3398 5d. "Sir George Villiers and Lady Katherine Manners as Adonis and Venus" 25 30
3399 5d. "Lady Mary Villiers with Lord Arran as Cupid" 25 30
3400 5d. "Rachel de Ruvigney, Countess Southampton, as Fortune" 25 30
3401 5d. "Venus at Forge of Vulcan" 25 30
3402 5d. "Daedalus and Icarus" 25 30
3403 5d. "The Clipping of Cupid's Wings" 25 30
MS3404 Eight sheets. (a) 101 × 127 mm. 25d. "Portrait of Genoese Lady". (b) 101 × 127 mm. 25d. "Venetia, Lady Digby, as Prudence". (c) 101 × 127 mm. 25d. "Prince William II of Orange and his Bride". (d) 101 × 127 mm. 25d. "Prince Charles". (e) 127 × 101 mm. 25d. "Princes Charles Louis and Rupert of the Palatinate". (f) 127 × 101 mm. 25d. "The Three Eldest Children of Charles I". (g) 102 × 127 mm. 25d. "A Man with His Son" (horiz). (h) 102 × 127 mm. 25d. "Drunken Silenus" Set of 8 sheets 11·00 11·50
No. 3372 is inscribed "Getlewomen" and No. 3390 "Patridges", both in error.

2000. 18th Birthday of Prince William. Multicoloured.
3405 7d. Type **321b** 35 40
3406 7d. In blue checked shirt and blue jumper 35 40
3407 7d. With bouquet 35 40
3408 7d. Wearing suit 35 40
MS3409 100 × 80 mm. 25d. With Prince Harry in countryside 1·40 1·50

2000. "EXPO 2000" World Stamp Exhibition, Anaheim. Space Satellites. As T **582a** of Ghana. Mult.
3410 7d. "Helios" (vert) 35 40
3411 7d. "Solar Max" (vert) 35 40
3412 7d. "SOHO" (vert) 35 40
3413 7d. "O.S.O." (vert) 35 40
3414 7d. Satellite rocket launch (vert) 35 40
3415 7d. "I.M.P." (vert) 35 40
3416 7d. "Uhuru" 35 40
3417 7d. "Rosat" 35 40
3418 7d. "I.U.E." 35 40
3419 7d. "Astro E" 35 40
3420 7d. "Exosat" 35 40
3421 7d. "Chandra" 35 40
MS3422 Two sheets, each 105 × 77 mm. (a) 25d. "Cassini Huygens". (b) 25d. "XMM" space telescope Set of 2 sheets 2·75 3·00
Nos. 3410/15 and 3416/21 were each printed together, se-tenant, with the backgrounds forming composite designs.

2000. 25th Anniv of "Apollo–Soyuz" Joint Project. As T **582b** of Ghana. Multicoloured.
3423 15d. Donald Slayton ("Apollo 18" docking module pilot) 80 85
3424 15d. Thomas Stafford ("Apollo 18" Commander) 80 85
3425 15d. Vance Brand ("Apollo 18" command module pilot) 80 85
MS3426 70 × 87 mm. 25d. Diagram of docking tunnel (horiz) 1·40 1·50

2000. 50th Anniv of Berlin Film Festival. As T **582c** of Ghana. Multicoloured.
3427 7d. Pane, *Amore e Fantasia*, 1954 35 40
3428 7d. Lord Olivier in *Richard III*, 1956 35 40
3429 7d. *Smultronstallet*, 1958 35 40
3430 7d. Sidney Poitier in *The Defiant Ones*, 1958 35 40
3431 7d. *The Living Desert*, 1954 35 40
3432 7d. *A Bout de Souffle*, 1960 35 40
MS3433 90 × 103 mm. 25d. Henry Fonda in "Twelve Angry Men", 1957 1·40 1·50

2000. 175th Anniv of Stockton and Darlington Line (first public railway). As T **582d** of Ghana. Multicoloured.
3434 15d. As Type **582d** of Ghana 80 85
3435 15d. Septimus Norris' locomotive *Chesapeake*, 1846 80 85

312c Bach

2000. 250th Death Anniv of Johann Sebastian Bach (German composer). Sheet 105 × 100 mm.
MS3436 **312c** 25d. multicoloured 1·40 1·50

312d Albert Einstein

2000. Election of Albert Einstein (mathematical physicist) as *Time* Magazine "Man of The Century". Sheet 117 × 90 mm.
MS3437 **321d** 25d. multicoloured 1·40 1·50

2000. Centenary of First Zeppelin Flight. As T **582e** of Ghana. Multicoloured.
3438 15d. LZ-10 *Schwaben*, 1911 80 85
3439 15d. LZ-127 *Graf Zeppelin*, 1928 80 85
3440 15d. LZ-129 *Hindenburg*, 1936 80 85
MS3441 92 × 66 mm. 25d. LZ-130 *Graf Zeppelin II* (50 × 36 mm) 1·40 1·50

Nos. 3438/40 were printed together, se-tenant, with the backgrounds forming a composite design.

2000. Olympic Games, Sydney. As T **582f** of Ghana. Multicoloured.

3442 6d. P. Nurmi (cross-country runner), 1924 . . . . . . 30 35
3443 6d. Basketball 30 35
3444 6d. Panathenian Stadium, Greece (1890) and Greek flag 30 35
3445 6d. Ancient Greek chariot racing 30 35

313 Pope John Paul II in Portugal, 1991

314 Morchella esculenta

2000. Travels of Pope John Paul II.

3446/55 6d. × 10 (Type **313**: Poland, 1991; Hungary, 1991; Brazil, 1991; Senegal, 1992; Gambia, 1992; Guinea, 1992; Angola, 1992; St. Thomas and Prince Islands, 1992; Dominican Republic, 1992) . . . .
3456/65 6d. × 10 (Benin, 1993; Uganda, 1993; Sudan, 1993; Albania, 1993; Spain, 1993; Jamaica, 1993; Mexico, 1993; U.S.A., 1993; Lithuania, 1993; Latvia, 1993) . . . .
3466/75 6d. × 10 (Estonia, 1993; Croatia, 1994; Philippines, 1994; Papua New Guinea, 1995; Australia, 1995; Sri Lanka, 1995; Czech Republic, 1995; Belgium, 1995; Slovakia, 1995; Cameroon, 1995) . . .
3476/85 6d. × 10 (South Africa, 1995; Kenya, 1995; U.S.A., 1995; United Nations, 1995; Guatemala, 1996; Nicaragua, 1996; El Salvador, 1996; Venezuela, 1996; Tunisia, 1996; Slovenia, 1996) . . .
3486/95 6d. × 10 (Germany, 1996; Hungary, 1996; France, 1996; Bosnia, 1996; Czech Republic, 1997; Lebanon, 1997; Poland, 1997; France, 1997; Brazil, 1997; Cuba, 1998) . . . . .
3496/505 6d. × 10 (Nigeria, 1998; Austria, 1998; Croatia, 1998; Mexico, 1999; U.S.A., 1999; Romania, 1999; Poland, 1999; Slovenia, 1999; India, 1999; Georgia, 1999)
3446/505 Set of 60 . . . . 19·00 20·00
MS3506 Eight sheets. (a) 80 × 75 mm. 25d. With Israeli children, 2000 (26 × 34 mm). (b) 75 × 80 mm. 25d. Rekindling "The Eternal Flame" at Yad Vashem Holocaust Museum, 2000 (26 × 34 mm). (c) 80 × 75 mm. 25d. Giving blessing from Mount Nebo, Jordan, 2000 (26 × 34 mm). (d) 80 × 75 mm. 25d. Looking down, Israel, 2000 (26 × 34 mm). (e) 80 × 75 mm. 25d. Praying at Western Wall, Jerusalem, 2000 (26 × 34 mm). (f) 80 × 75 mm. 25d. With Jewish bible, 2000 (26 × 34 mm). (g) 80 × 75 mm. 25d. Placing prayer in Western Wall, 2000 (26 × 34 mm). (h) 75 × 80 mm. 25d. Speaking at Yad Vashem Holocaust Memorial, 2000 (34 × 26 mm) Set of 8 sheets 11·00 11·50

2000. African Mushrooms. Multicoloured.

3507 4d. Type **314** 20 25
3508 5d. *Cantharellus cibarius* . . 25 30
3509 7d. *Leucocoprinus luteus* . . 35 40
3510 7d. *Panaeolus sphinctrinus* 35 40
3511 7d. *Agrocybe cylindracea* . . 35 40
3512 7d. *Amanita caesarea* . . . 35 40
3513 7d. *Pluteus aurantiorugosus* 35 40
3514 7d. *Mycena pura* 35 40
3515 7d. *Lycoperdon perlatum* . . 35 40
3516 7d. *Astraeus hygrometricus* 35 40
3517 7d. *Volvariella bombycina* . . 35 40
3518 7d. *Lycoperdon pyriforme* . . 35 40
3519 7d. *Boletus appendiculatus* 35 40
3520 7d. *Cortinarius rubellus* . . . 35 40
3521 15d. *Tricholoma ustale* . . . 80 85
3522 20d. *Clavulinopsis helvola* . . 1·10 1·25
MS3523 Two sheets, each 106 × 76 mm. (a) 25d. "Collybia erythropus". (b) 25d. "Calocybe gambosa" Set of 2 sheets . . 2·75 3·00

No. 3516 is inscribed "Astracus" and No. 3519 "apendiculatus", both in error.

314a King James IV of Scotland

2000. Monarchs of the Millennium.

3524 **314a** 7d. multicoloured . . . 35 40
3525 – 7d. multicoloured . . . 35 40
3526 – 7d. multicoloured . . . 35 40
3527 – 7d. multicoloured . . . 35 40
3528 – 7d. multicoloured . . . 35 40
3529 – 7d. multicoloured . . . 35 40
3530 – 7d. black, stone and brown 35 40
3531 – 7d. multicoloured . . . 35 40
3532 – 7d. multicoloured . . . 35 40
3533 – 7d. black, stone and brown 35 40
3534 – 7d. multicoloured . . . 35 40
3535 – 7d. black, stone and brown 35 40
3536 – 7d. multicoloured . . . 35 40
3537 – 7d. multicoloured . . . 35 40
MS3538 Three sheets, each 117 × 137 mm. (a) 25d. multicoloured. (b) 25d. multicoloured. (c) 25d. multicoloured Set of 3 sheets 4·00 4·25

DESIGNS: No. 3525, King James V of Scotland; 3526, King James VI of Scotland (I of England); 3527, Mary, Queen of Scots; 3528, Queen Mary II of England; 3529, Queen Elizabeth II of Great Britain (I of Scotland); 3530, King Charles II of France; 3531, Queen Catherine de Medici of France; 3532, Tsar Boris Godunov of Muscovy; 3533, Vasily III, Grand Prince of Moscow; 3534, Queen Anne of Great Britain; 3535, King Charles IX of France; 3536, King Charles I of England; 3537, Clovis IV, King of the Franks; **MS**3538a, King James IV of Scotland (*different*); **MS**3538b, Bahadur Shah II, King of Delhi; **MS**3538c, "King Robert I of Scotland".

No. 3537 is inscr "CLOVIS III", and No. **MS**3538a "JAMES IV OF ENGLAND"; both in error. No. **MS**3538c actually shows a portrait of Robert Walpole, first Prime Minister of Great Britain.

314b Felix IV

315 *Amphicallia tigris*

2000. Popes of the Millennium. Each black, yellow and olive.

3539 7d. Type **314b** 35 40
3540 7d. Gelasius I 35 40
3541 7d. Gregory I 35 40
3542 7d. Gregory IX 35 40
3543 7d. Gregory XII 35 40
3544 7d. Honorius III 35 40
3545 7d. Gregory XIII 35 40
3546 7d. Urban II 35 40
3547 7d. Sixtus I 35 40
3548 7d. Pius IX 35 40
3549 7d. Pius IV 35 40
3550 7d. Pascal I 35 40
3551 7d. Alexander VII 35 40
3552 7d. Benedict XI 35 40
3553 7d. Callistus III 35 40
3554 7d. Celestine V 35 40
3555 7d. Clement IX 35 40
3556 7d. Fabian 35 40
MS3557 Three sheets, each 115 × 135 mm. (a) 25d. Peter. (b) 25d. Damasus I. (c) 25d. John I. Each black, stone and brown Set of 3 sheets . . . . 4·00 4·25

2000. Butterflies. Multicoloured.

3558 1d.50 Type **315** 10 15
3559 2d. *Myrina silenus* 10 15
3560 3d. *Chrysiridia madagascariensis* 15 20
3561 5d. *Papilionidae* 25 30
3562 7d. *Salamis temora* 35 40
3563 8d. *Cryestis camillus* . . . 45 50
3564 10d. *Dasiothia medea* . . . 55 60
3565 20d. *Papilio demodocus* . . 1·10 1·25
3566 25d. *Danaus chrysippus* . . 1·40 1·50
3567 50d. *Coeliades forestan* . . 2·75 3·00
3568 75d. *Ornithoptera alexandrae* . . . . . . 4·00 4·25
3568a 100d. *Morpho cypris* . . . 5·00 5·75

No. 3558 is inscribed "Amphicalia", 3560 "madagascarensis" and 3563 "Cyrestis", all in error.

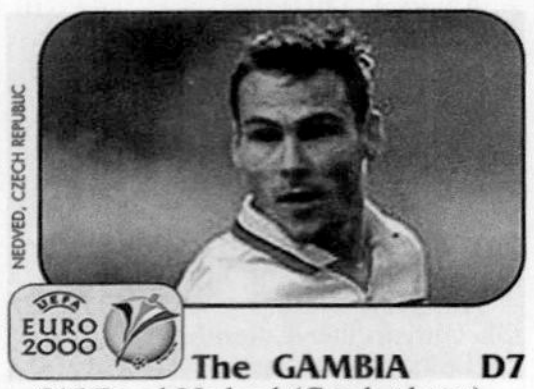

316 Pavel Nedved (Czech player)

2000. "Euro 2000" Football Championship. Multicoloured.

3569 7d. Type **316** 35 40
3570 7d. Czech Republic team . . 35 40
3571 7d. Ladislav Maier (Czech player) 35 40
3572 7d. Antonin Panenka (Czech player) 35 40
3573 7d. Selessin Stadium, Liege 35 40
3574 7d. Patrik Berger (Czech player) 35 40
3575 7d. Alan Shearer (English player) 35 40
3576 7d. English team 35 40
3577 7d. David Seaman (English player) 35 40
3578 7d. Sol Campbell (English player) 35 40
3579 7d. Philips Stadium, Eindhoven 35 40
3580 7d. Gareth Southgate (English player) 35 40
3581 7d. Oyvind Leonhardsen (Norwegian player) . . . 35 40
3582 7d. Norwegian team 35 40
3583 7d. Erik Mykland (Norwegian player) . . . 35 40
3584 7d. Stale Solbakken (Norwegian player) . . . 35 40
3585 7d. Kjetil Rekdal (Norwegian player) . . . 35 40
3586 7d. Sergen Yalcin (Turkish player) 35 40
3587 7d. Turkish team 35 40
3588 7d. Okan Buruk (Turkish player) 35 40
3589 7d. Arif Erdem (Turkish player) 35 40
3590 7d. Koning Boudewijn Stadium 35 40
3591 7d. Tayfun Korkut (Turkish player) 35 40
3592 7d. Fredrik Ljungberg (Swedish player) 35 40
3593 7d. Swedish team 35 40
3594 7d. Andersson (Swedish player) 35 40
3595 7d. Roland Nilsson (Swedish player) 35 40
3596 7d. Stefan Schwarz (Swedish player) 35 40
3597 7d. Aleksander Knavs (Slovene player) 35 40
3598 7d. Slovenian team 35 40
3599 7d. Alatko Zahovic (Slovene player) 35 40
3600 7d. Ales Ceh (Slovene player) 35 40
3601 7d. Stade Communal, Charleroi 35 40
3602 7d. Miran Pavlin (Slovene player) 35 40
MS3603 Six sheets, each 145 × 95 mm. (a) 25d. Jozef Chovanec (Czech trainer) (vert). (b) 25d. Kevin Keegan (English trainer) (vert). (c) 25d. Nils-Johan Semb (Norwegian trainer) (vert). (d) 25d. Mustafa Denizli (Turkish trainer) (vert). (e) 25d. Tommy Soderberg and Lars Lagerback (Swedish trainers) (vert). (f) 25d. Srecko Katanec (Slovene trainer) (vert) Set of 6 sheets . . . . . 8·00 8·25

No. 3581 is inscribed "LEONARDSEN" in error.

317 West Highland White Terrier Puppy

318 Queen Elizabeth the Queen Mother

2000. "The Stamp Show 2000" International Stamp Exhibition, London. Cats and Dogs of the World. (a) Dogs. Multicoloured.

3604 1d. Type **317** 10 10
3605 1d.50 Bernese mountain dog puppy 10 15
3606 3d. Yorkshire terrier puppy 15 20
3607 4d. Labrador (inscr "West Highland White Terrier Puppy") 20 25
3608 7d. Border collie puppy (brown) 35 40
3609 7d. Border collie puppy (black) 35 40
3610 7d. Yorkshire terrier puppies 35 40
3611 7d. German shepherd puppy 35 40
3612 7d. Beagle puppy 35 40
3613 7d. Spaniel puppy 35 40
3614 10d. Chow Chow puppy . . 55 60
3615 15d. Poodle puppy 80 85
MS3616 106 × 75 mm. 25d. Boxer puppy . . . . 1·40 1·50

(b) Cats. Designs as T **317**, but horiz.

3617 4d. black, green and grey . . 20 25
3618 4d. black, green and grey . . 20 25
3619 4d. black, brown and grey . 20 25
3620 4d. black, yellow and grey . 20 25
3621 4d. black, blue and grey . . 20 25
3622 4d. black, orange and grey . 20 25
3623 4d. black, blue and grey . . 20 25
3624 4d. black, yellow and grey . 20 25
3625 5d. black, blue and grey . . 25 30
3626 5d. black, yellow and grey . 25 30
3627 5d. black, green and grey . . 25 30
3628 5d. black, yellow and grey . 25 30
3629 5d. black, yellow and grey . 25 30
3630 5d. black, green and grey . . 25 30
3631 5d. black, yellow and grey . 25 30
3632 5d. black, yellow and grey . 25 30
MS3633 Two sheets, each 106 × 77 mm. (a) 25d. multicoloured. (b) 25d. multicoloured Set of 2 sheets . . 2·75 3·00

DESIGNS: No. 3617, Egyptian mau; 3618, Singapura; 3619, American shorthair; 3620, Cornish rex; 3621, Birman; 3622, Scottish fold; 3623, Turkish angora; 3624, Turkish van; 3625, Ragdoll; 3626, Bombay; 3627, Koral; 3628, Somali; 3629, British shorthair; 3630, American curl; 3631, Maine coon; 3632, Turkish van; **MS**3633a, Mother cat with kitten; **MS**3633b, Egyptian mau.

2000. Queen Elizabeth the Queen Mother's 100th Birthday.

3634 **318** 7d. multicoloured . . . 35 40

2000. Faces of the Millennium: Queen Elizabeth the Queen Mother's 100th Birthday. As T **307a** showing collage of miniature flower photographs. Multicoloured.

3635 5d. Top of head (face value at left) 25 30
3636 5d. Top of head (face value at right) 25 30
3637 5d. Eye and temple (face value at left) 25 30
3638 5d. Temple (face value at right) 25 30
3639 5d. Cheek (face value at left) 25 30
3640 5d. Cheek (face value at right) 25 30
3641 5d. Chin (face value at left) 25 30
3642 5d. Neck (face value at right) 25 30

Nos. 3635/42 were printed together, se-tenant, in sheetlets of 8 with the stamps arranged in two vertical columns separated by a gutter also containing miniature photographs. When viewed as a whole, the sheetlet forms a portrait of the Queen Mother.

2000. Faces of the Millennium: 80th Birthday of Pope John Paul II. As T **307a** showing collage of miniature religious photographs. Multicoloured.

3643 6d. Top of head (face value at left) 30 35
3644 6d. Top of head (face value at right) 30 35
3645 6d. Ear (face value at left) . 30 35
3646 6d. Forehead (face value at right) 30 35
3647 6d. Neck (face value at left) 30 35
3648 6d. Cheek (face value at right) 30 35
3649 6d. Shoulder (face value at left) 30 35
3650 6d. Hands (face value at right) 30 35

Nos. 3643/50 were printed together, se-tenant, in sheetlets of 8 with the stamps arranged in two vertical columns separated by a gutter also containing miniature photographs. When viewed as a whole, the sheetlet forms a portrait of Pope John Paul II.

319 "A White Pheasant and other Fowl in a Classical Landscape" (Abraham Bisschop)

321 Antonio Vivaldi

320 Allard on Peking–Paris Rally

2000. Bird Paintings. Multicoloured.

3651 1d.50 Type **319** 10 15
3652 3d. "Salmon-crested Cockatoo" (Bartolomeo Bimbi) 15 20

3653 4d. "Great Bustard Cock and Other Birds" (Ludger Tom Ring) 20 25
3654 5d. "Still Life of Birds" (Caravaggio) (horiz) . . . 25 30
3655 5d. "Turkeys with Young and Rock Doves" (Johan Wenzel Peter) (horiz) . . 25 30
3656 5d. "The Threatened Swan" (Jan Asselyn) (horiz) . . . 25 30
3657 5d. "Still Life of Fruit and Birds in a Landscape" (Jokob Bogdani) (horiz) 25 30
3658 5d. "Mobbing the Owl" (Tobias Stranover) (horiz) 25 30
3659 5d. "Concert of Birds" (Melchior de Hondecoeter) (horiz) . . . 25 30
3660 5d. "Owls and Young Ones" (William Tomkins) (horiz) 25 30
3661 5d. "Birds by a Stream" (Jean Baptiste Oudry) (horiz) 25 30
3662 5d. "Peacocks Hens and Mouse" (Tobias Stranover) 25 30
3663 5d. "Lady in a Red Jacket feeding a Parrot" (Frans van Mieris) 25 30
3664 5d. "Birds by a Pool" (Melchior de Hondecoeter) 25 30
3665 5d. "Ganymede and the Eagle" (Rubens) 25 30
3666 5d. "Leda and the Swan" (Cesare da Sesto) 25 30
3667 5d. "Ducks and Ducklings at the Foot of a Tree in a Mediterranean Landscape" (Adriaen van Oolen) 25 30
3668 5d. "Portrait of the Falconer Robert Cheseman carrying a Hooded Falcon" (Holbein) 25 30
3669 5d. "Golden Pheasant on a Stone Plinth, with other Birds" (Jacobus Vonck) 25 30
3670 15d. "Great Black-backed Gull and other Birds" (Jokob Bogdani) 80 85
MS3671 Two sheets, each 76 × 63 mm. (a) 25d. "Still Life of Birds" (Georg Flegel) (horiz). (b) 25d. "King Eagle pursued to the Sun" (Philip Reinagle) Set of 2 sheets . . . . 2·75 3·00

2000. 12th Classic Car Marathon. Showing cars from Himalayan Rally (No. **MS**3688a) or Peking–Paris Rally (others). Multicoloured.

3672 5d. Type **320** 25 30
3673 5d. Ford Coupe 25 30
3674 5d. Citroen Pilot 25 30
3675 5d. Packard (white) 25 30
3676 5d. Austin A90 . . . . . . 25 30
3677 5d. Bentley 25 30
3678 5d. Packard (red) 25 30
3679 5d. Aston Martin 25 30
3680 5d. Morgan 25 30
3681 5d. Rover 25 30
3682 5d. Marmon 25 30
3683 5d. Rolls Royce Silver Cloud 25 30
3684 5d. Rolls Royce Phantom 25 30
3685 5d. Mercedes 680S 25 30
3686 5d. Mercedes saloon 25 30
3687 5d. Invicta 25 30
MS3688 Two sheets, each 86 × 59 mm. (a) 25d. Morris Minor. (b) 25d. Cadillac Set of 2 sheets . . . . 2·75 3·00

2000. Classical Opera and Oratorio Composers. Multicoloured.

3689 7d. Type **321** 35 40
3690 7d. Giacomo Puccini . . . 35 40
3691 7d. Franz Joseph Haydn . . 35 40
3692 7d. Leopold Stokowski . . . 35 40
3693 7d. Felix Mendelssohn . . . 35 40
3694 7d. Gaetano Donizetti . . . 35 40
3695 7d. Witold Lutoslawski . . 35 40
3696 7d. Sir William Sterndale Bennett 35 40
3697 7d. Wolfgang Amadeus Mozart 35 40
3698 7d. Ludwig van Beethoven 35 40
3699 7d. Sergei Rachmaninov . . 35 40
3700 7d. Pyotr Tchaikovsky . . . 35 40
MS3701 Two sheets. (a) 95 × 72 mm. 25d. Frederic Chopin. (b) 67 × 95 mm. 25d. Manuel de Falla Set of 2 sheets . . . . 2·75 3·00

322 Mazda RX-Evolv

2000. Transport in the Next Millennium. Mult.

3702 7d. Type **322** 35 40
3703 7d. Isuzu Kai 35 40
3704 7d. Ford 021C 35 40
3705 7d. Pontiac GTO 35 40
3706 7d. Chevrolet Cerv III . . . 35 40
3707 7d. Toyota Will VI 35 40
3708 7d. Blended-wing body BWB-1 aircraft 35 40
3709 7d. Boeing's 767-400ERX 35 40
3710 7d. New Lockheed concept fighter 35 40
3711 7d. Boeing "X" bomber . . 35 40
3712 7d. American National Aerospaceplane X30 concept 35 40
3713 7d. Hotol space plane separating from Antonov AN-225 . . . . 35 40
3714 8d. Pendolare concept speedboat 45 50
3715 8d. Plansail catamaran . . . 45 50
3716 8d. New Airfoil concept . . 45 50
3717 8d. Ferry Sea Coaster hydrofoil concept 45 50
3718 8d. *Shinaitoku Matu*(tanker) showing new sail technology 45 50
3719 8d. Supersport luxury yacht concept 45 50
3720 8d. Maglev MLU-002 train 45 50
3721 8d. Airport magnetic rail car system 45 50
3722 8d. Modern monorail train 45 50
3723 8d. Two-car monorail, Seattle 45 50
3724 8d. New "above cabin" monorail concept 45 50
3725 8d. Streamlined monorail concept 45 50
MS3726 Four sheets, each 110 × 85 mm. (a) 25d. Honda Sproket concept. (b) 25d. Nautic Air 400 flying boat concept. (c) 25d. Triton U.S. Coast Guard patrol vessel concept (58 × 43 mm). (d) 25d. Maglev train (58 × 43 mm) Set of 4 sheets . . . . 5·50 5·75
No. 3722 is inscribed "MONRAIL" in error.

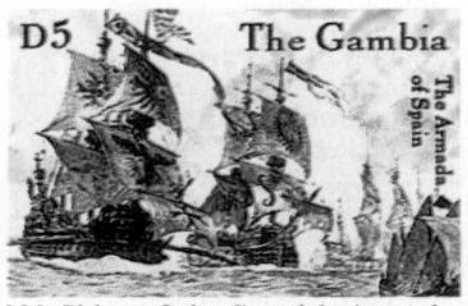

323 Ships of the Spanish Armada, 1588

2000. Historic Ships of the World. Multicoloured.

3727 5d. Type **323** 25 30
3728 7d. 18th-century Chinese junks 35 40
3729 7d. 15th-century cog 35 40
3730 7d. *Henri Grace a Dieu* (galleon) at anchor . . . 35 40
3731 7d. Tapestry of St. Brendan at sea 35 40
3732 7d. Figurehead by Grinling Gibbons 35 40
3733 7d. 16th-century British carrack 35 40
3734 7d. 18th-century British first-rate ship of the line . . . 35 40
3735 7d. 16th-century Spanish galleon 35 40
3736 7d. Russian four-masted barque 35 40
3737 7d. *Henri Grace a Dieu* (galleon) at sea 35 40
3738 7d. Frontispiece from John Dee's *Arte of Navigation* 35 40
3739 7d. 19th-century British ironclad 35 40
3740 10d. *Colombo* (Brazilian river gunboat) 55 60
3741 15d. *Jenissel* (Russian minelayer) 80 85
3742 20d. *Yamato* (Japanese ironclad) . . . . 1·10 1·25
MS3743 Two sheets, each 102 × 115 mm. (a) 25d. H.M.S. *Challenger* (survey ship). (b) 25d. *Golden Hind* (Drake) Set of 2 sheets . . . . 2·75 3·00
Nos. 3728/33 and 3734/9 were each printed together, se-tenant, with the backgrounds forming composite designs.

324 Yellow-rumped Tinkerbird

326 Head of Akhal-Teke Horse

325 "At Full Stretch" (John Skeaping)

2000. Tropical Birds. Multicoloured.

3744 7d. Type **324** 35 40
3745 7d. Black-throated honeyguide ("Greater Honeyguide") 35 40
3746 7d. Hoopoe 35 40
3747 7d. European roller 35 40
3748 7d. Carmine bee eater . . . 35 40
3749 7d. White-throated bee eater 35 40
3750 7d. Grey parrot 35 40
3751 7d. Great spotted cuckoo . . 35 40
3752 7d. Bar-tailed trogon . . . 35 40
3753 7d. African hobby 35 40
3754 7d. Green turaco 35 40
3755 7d. Trumpeter hornbill . . . 35 40
3756 7d. Pied flycatcher 35 40
3757 7d. Blackcap 35 40
3758 7d. Common stonechat . . 35 40
3759 7d. Nightingale 35 40
3760 7d. Black-headed tchagra . . 35 40
3761 7d. Yellow wagtail 35 40
MS3762 Three sheets, each 85 × 110 mm. (a) 25d. European bee eater (horiz). (b) 25d. Bateleur (horiz). (c) 25d. Secretary bird (horiz) Set of 3 sheets . . . . 4·00 4·25
Nos. 3744/9, 3750/5 and 3756/61 were each printed together, se-tenant, with the backgrounds forming composite designs.

2000. Horse Paintings. Multicoloured.

3763 4d. Type **325** 20 25
3764 5d. "The Burton" (Lionel Edwards) 25 30
3765 7d. "Horses emerging from the Sea" (Delacroix) . . . 35 40
3766 7d. "The 9th Duke of Marlborough on a Grey Hunter" (Sir Alfred Munnings) 35 40
3767 7d. "Ovid in Exile amongst the Scythians" (Delacroix) 35 40
3768 7d. "Early Morning Gallop" (John Skeaping) 35 40
3769 7d. "Mare and Foal" (Sir Alfred Munnings) 35 40
3770 7d. "Three-a-side Polo at Simla" (Lionel Edwards) 35 40
3771 7d. "A Lady hawking" (E. Vernet) (vert) 35 40
3772 7d. "Captain Robert Orme" (Reynolds) (vert) 35 40
3773 7d. "Napoleon crossing the Alps" (David) (vert) . . . 35 40
3774 7d. "Nobby Grey" (Sir Alfred Munnings) (vert) 35 40
3775 7d. "Amateur Jockeys near a Carriage" (Degas) (vert) 35 40
3776 7d. "Three-a-side Polo at Simla" (Lionel Edwards) (vert) 35 40
3777 10d. "Game of Polo" (Li-Lin) 55 60
3778 15d. "St. George and the Dragon" (Raphael) . . . 80 85
MS3779 Two sheets, each 90 × 70 mm. (a) 25d. "The Reckoning" (George Morland). (b) 25d. "One of the Family" (Frederick Cotman) Set of 2 sheets 2·75 3·00

2000. Horses of the World. Multicoloured.

3780 7d. Type **326** 35 40
3781 7d. Palomino 35 40
3782 7d. Kladuber 35 40
3783 7d. Paint horse 35 40
3784 7d. Pinto 35 40
3785 7d. Kabaroin 35 40
3786 7d. Akhal-Teke (horiz) . . . 35 40
3787 7d. Kladruber (horiz) . . . 35 40
3788 7d. Palomino (horiz) 35 40
3789 7d. Pinto (horiz) 35 40
3790 7d. Paint horse (horiz) . . . 35 40
3791 7d. Kabaroin (horiz) 35 40
MS3792 87 × 70 mm. 25d. Palomino 1·40 1·50

326a "The Madonna of the Fish" (Raphael)

2000. "Espana 2000". International Stamp Exhibition, Madrid. Paintings from the Prado Museum. Multicoloured.

3793 6d. Type **326a** 30 35
3794 6d. "The Holy Family with a Lamb" (Raphael) . . . 30 35
3795 6d. "The Madonna of the Stair" (Andrea del Sarto) 30 35
3796 6d. Moneychanger from "The Moneychanger and his Wife" (Marinus van Reymerswaele) 30 35
3797 6d. "Madonna and Child" (Jan Gossaert) 30 35
3798 6d. Wife from "The Moneychanger and his Wife" (Van Reymerswaele) 30 35
3799 6d. "St. Andrew" (Francisco Rizi) 30 35
3800 6d. "Christ Crucified" (Velazquez) 30 35
3801 6d. "St. Onuphrius" (Francisco Collantes) . . 30 35
3802 6d. "Charles II of Spain" (Juan de Miranda) . . . 30 35
3803 6d. "St. Sebastian" (De Miranda) 30 35
3804 6d. "Peter Ivanovich Potemkin" (De Miranda) 30 35
3805 6d. St. Benedict from "St. Benedict's Supper" (Juan Ricci) 30 35
3806 6d. "Our Lady of the Immaculate Conception" (Zurbaran) 30 35
3807 6d. Monk with candle from "St. Benedict's Supper" (Ricci) 30 35
3808 6d. "The Penitent Magdalen" (Jose de Ribera) 30 35
3809 6d. "Christ as Man of Sorrows" (Antonio de Pereda) 30 35
3810 6d. "St. Jerome" (De Pereda) 30 35
3811 6d. "Children with a Shell" (Murillo) 30 35
3812 6d. "Our Lady of the Immaculate Conception" (Murillo) 30 35
3813 6d. "The Good Shepherd" (Murillo) 30 35
3814 6d. Young woman from "The Parasol" (Goya) . . 30 35
3815 6d. "A Rural Gift" (Ramon Bayeu) 30 35
3816 6d. Young man from "The Parasol" (Goya) 30 35
3817 6d. "Portrait of a Young Woman" (Velazquez) . . 30 35
3818 6d. "The Painter Francisco Goya" (Vicente Portana) 30 35
3819 6d. "Portrait of a Girl" (Raphael Diaz) 30 35
3820 6d. Virgin Mary from "The Nativity" (Frederico Barocci) 30 35
3821 6d. "Madonna and Child with St. John" (Correggio) 30 35
3822 6d. Holy Child from "The Nativity" (Barocci) . . . 30 35
3823 6d. "Queen Isabelle Farnese" (Jean Ranc) . . 30 35
3824 6d. "Young Woman from Back" (Jean-Baptiste Greuze) 30 35
3825 6d. "Charles III of Spain as a Child" (Ranc) 30 35
3826 6d. "James Bordieu" (Reynolds) 30 35
3827 6d. "Dr. Isaac Henrique Sequeria" (Reynolds) . . 30 35
3828 6d. "Portrait of a Clergyman" (Reynolds) 30 35
MS3829 Six sheets, each 110 × 90 mm. (a) 25d. "The Defence of Cádiz against the English" (Zubarán). (b) 25d. "The Surrender of Juliers" (Jusepe Leonardo). (c) 25d. "The Holy Family with a Little Bird" (Murillo). (d) 25d. "Jacob's Dream" (De Ribera) (horiz). (e) 25d. "Venus and Adonis" (Veronese) (horiz). (f) 25d. "Danäe" (Titian) (horiz) Set of 6 sheets . . . . 8·00 8·25

327 Bristol Blenheim of 29 Squadron

2000. 60th Anniv of Battle of Britain. Mult.

3830 5d. Type **327** 25 30
3831 5d. Helmut Wick shooting down Hurricane 25 30
3832 5d. Spitfire of 65 Squadron attacking Dornier 217 . . 25 30
3833 5d. Bristol Beaufighter IIF of 604 Squadron 25 30
3834 5d. Boulton Paul Defiants of 264 Squadron 25 30
3835 5d. Spitfire in dogfight with Stuka JU-87 . . . . . . 25 30
3836 5d. British fighters over Tower Bridge 25 30
3837 5d. Gloster Gladiator of 615 Squadron 25 30
3838 5d. Hurricane attacking Messerschmitt Bf 109 . . 25 30
3839 5d. Spitfire attacking two Messerschmitt Bf 109s . . 25 30
3840 5d. Flt.-Lt. Gilliam attacking Dornier 217s . . 25 30
3841 5d. Two Hurricanes of 610 Squadron 25 30
3842 5d. Hurricanes of 85 Squadron 25 30
3843 5d. G. A. Langley attacking Messerschmitt 109 . . . . 25 30
3844 5d. Bristol Blenheim IV of 23 Squadron 25 30
3845 5d. Spitfires of 227 Squadron taking off . . . 25 30
MS3846 Two sheets, each 110 × 85 mm. (a) 25d. Adolf Galland (commander of Group III of JG26). (b) 25d. Group Captain Frank Carey Set of 2 sheets . . 2·75 3·00
No. 3834 is inscribed "Bolton-Paul" in error.

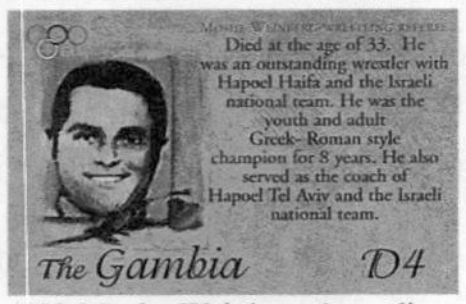

328 Moshe Weinberg (wrestling referee)

2000. Victims of Munich Olympics Massacre (1972) Commemoration. Showing Israeli athletes and officials. Multicoloured.

3847 4d. Type **328** 20 25
3848 4d. Eliezer Halffin (wrestler) 20 25
3849 4d. Mark Slavin (wrestler) 20 25
3850 4d. Ze'ev Friedman (weightlifter) 20 25
3851 4d. Joseph Romano (weightlifter) 20 25
3852 4d. Kahat Shor (shooting coach) 20 25
3853 4d. David Berger (weightlifter) 20 25
3854 4d. Joseph Gottfreund (wrestling referee) 20 25
3855 4d. Andrei Schpitzer (fencing referee) 20 25
3856 4d. Amitsur Shapira (athletics coach) 20 25
3857 4d. Yaakov Springer (weightlifting referee) . . 20 25
3858 4d. Munich Olympics emblem 20 25
MS3859 96 × 130 mm. 25d. Israeli athlete with Olympic torch (vert) 1·40 1·50

329 Ferrari 333SP Racing Car

2000. Ferrari Racing Cars. Multicoloured.

3860 4d. Type **329** 20 25
3861 5d. Ferrari 512S 25 30
3862 10d. Ferrari 312P 55 60
3863 25d. Ferrari 330P4 . . . . 1·40 1·50

330 Symbolic Snake and Chinese Characters

2001. Chinese New Year ("Year of the Snake"). Showing different snakes. Multicoloured.

3864 4d. Type **330** 20 25
3865 4d. Orange and mauve snake 20 25
3866 4d. Blue and violet snake . . 20 25
3867 4d. Green and yellow snake 20 25
MS3868 71 × 100 mm. 15d. Snake in grass 80 85

330a "Vessels in a Strong Wind" (Jan Porcellis)

2001. Bicentenary of Rijksmuseum, Amsterdam. Dutch Paintings. Multicoloured.

3869 7d. Type **330a** 35 40
3870 7d. "Seascape in the Morning" (Simon de Vlieger) 35 40
3871 7d. "Travellers at a Country Inn" (Issack van Ostade) 35 40
3872 7d. "Orpheus with Animals in a Landscape" (Aelbert Cuyp) 35 40
3873 7d. "Italian with a Mountain Plateau" (Cornelis van Poelenburch) 35 40
3874 7d. Loading boat from "Boatman Moored on a Lake Shore" (Adam Pynacker) 35 40
3875 7d. Woman playing viol from "Gallant Company" (Pieter Codde) 35 40
3876 7d. Returning hunters from "Gallant Company" (Codde) 35 40
3877 7d. Kneeling man from "The Marriage of Willem van Loon and Margaretha Bas" (Jan Molenaer) 35 40
3878 7d. Bride's party from "The Marriage of Willem van Loon and Margaretha Bas" (Molenaer) 35 40
3879 7d. Man and two women from "The Marriage of Willem van Loon and Margaretha Bas" (Molenaer) 35 40
3880 7d. "Johanna Le Maire" (Nicolaes Pickenoy) . . . 35 40
3881 7d. "The Meagre Company" (Hals and Codde) 35 40
3882 7d. "The Twins Clara and Aelbert de Bray" (Salomon de Bray) . . . 35 40
3883 7d. "Self-portrait" (Ferdinand Bol) 35 40
3884 7d. "Ambulatory of the New Church in Delft" (Gerard Houckgeest) . . 35 40
3885 7d. "Tomb of Willem the Silent in New Church of Delft" (Emanuel de Witte) 35 40
3886 7d. "Mountainous Landscape" (Hercules Segers) 35 40
3887 7d. Pie and glass of wine from "Still Life with Turkey Pie" (Pieter Claesz) 35 40
3888 7d. "Still Life with Gilt Goblet" (Willem Heda) 35 40
3889 7d. "Still Life with Lobster and Nautilus Cup" (Jan de Heem) 35 40
3890 7d. "Bacchanal" (detail) (Moses van Uyttenbroeck) 35 40
3891 7d. "The Anatomy Lesson of Dr. Nicolaes Tulp" (Rembrandt) 35 40
3892 7d. "Johannes Lutma" (Jacob Backer) 35 40
3893 7d. Decanter from "Still Life with Turkey Pie" (Claesz) 35 40
3894 7d. "Bouquet of Flowers in a Vase" (Ambrosius Bosschaert) 35 40
3895 7d. Vase of flowers from "Still Life with Flowers, Fruit and Shells" (Balthasar van der Ast) 35 40
3896 7d. Basket of flowers and building from "Still Life with Flowers, Fruit and Shells" (Van der Ast) . . 35 40
3897 7d. "Tulips in a Vase" (Hans Boulenger) 35 40
3898 7d. "Laid Table with Cheese and Fruit" (Floris van Dijck) 35 40
3899 7d. Cows from "Boatman Moored on a Lake Shore" (Pynacker) 35 40
3900 7d. "The Ford in the River" (Jan Weenix) 35 40
3901 7d. "Two Horses near a Gate in a Meadow" (Paulus Potter) 35 40
3902 7d. "Cows and Sheep at a Stream" (Karel Dujardin) 35 40
3903 7d. Fiddler from "The Duet" (Cornelis Saftleven) 35 40
3904 7d. Viol player from "The Duet" (Saftleven) 35 40
MS3905 Six sheets. (a) 118 × 69 mm. 25d. "Meadow Landscape with Cattle" (Willem Roelofs) (horiz). (b) 118 × 69 mm. 25d. "Morning Ride on the Beach" (Anton Mauve) (horiz). (c) 118 × 96 mm. 25d. "The Spendthrift" (Cornelis Troost) (horiz). (d) 118 × 92 mm. 25d "View of New Church and Town Hall in Amsterdam" (Issak Outwater) (horiz). (e) 118 × 88 mm. 25d. "The Art Gallery of Jan Gildemeester Jansz" (Jan Ekels) (horiz). (f) 88 × 118 mm. 25d. "The Fall of Man" (Cornelis van Haarlem) (horiz) Set of 6 sheets . . . . 8·00 8·25

No. 3881 is inscribed "Frans Hal" and No. **MS**3905c "The Spendthrif", both in error.

331 Cowardly Lion

2001. Centenary of Publication of *The Wizard of Oz* (children's story by L. Frank Baum). Mult.

3906 7d. Type **331** 35 40
3907 7d. Land of Oz 35 40
3908 7d. Tin Man 35 40
3909 7d. Scarecrow 35 40
3910 7d. Toto 35 40
3911 7d. Munchkins 35 40
3912 7d. Witch of the North . . 35 40
3913 7d. Poppies of Oz 35 40
3914 7d. Dorothy's house 35 40
3915 7d. Witch of the East . . . 35 40
3916 7d. Dorothy 35 40
3917 7d. Wizard of Oz 35 40
3918 7d. Witch's wolf 35 40
3919 7d. Witch's forest 35 40
3920 7d. Witch's monkey 35 40
3921 7d. Dorothy asleep in poppies 35 40
3922 7d. Queen Mouse 35 40
3923 7d. Witch and evil bees . . 35 40
MS3924 Three sheets. (a) 77 × 106 mm. 27d. Gatekeeper. (b) 106 × 77 mm. 27d. Dorothy at crossroads (horiz). (c) 77 × 106 mm. 27d. Green Maiden Set of 3 sheets 4·25 4·50

332 Head of Melpomene (Muse of Tragedy)

2001. The History of Drama. Multicoloured.

3925 6d. Type **332** 30 35
3926 6d. Ancient Greek masks . . 30 35
3927 6d. Bust of Euripides (Greek tragedian) 30 35
3928 6d. Figures of two actors playing drunks 30 35
3929 6d. Scene from a play by Tang Hsien-Tsu (Chinese dramatist) 30 35
3930 6d. Uday and Amala Shankar (Indian actors) 30 35
3931 6d. Scene from a Japanese Noh play 30 35
3932 6d. Scene from *Clytemnestra* (Alexandros Mastas) . . 30 35
3933 6d. William Shakespeare (English dramatist) . . 30 35
3934 6d. Johann von Goethe (German philosopher and author) 30 35
3935 6d. Moliere (French dramatist) 30 35
3936 6d. Henrik Ibsen (Norwegian playwright) 30 35
3937 6d. George Bernard Shaw (Irish playwright) . . . 30 35
3938 6d. Anton Chekhov (Russian dramatist) . . 30 35
3939 6d. Sholom Aleichem (Jewish writer) 30 35
3940 6d. Tennessee Williams (American playwright) . . 30 35
MS3941 Two sheets, each 67 × 109 mm. (a) 25d. Sarah Bernhardt (French actress) as Phadera (vert). (b) 25d. John Barrymore (American actor) as Hamlet (vert) Set of 2 sheets 2·75 3·00

332a "Beedrill No. 15"

2001. Characters from "Pokemon" (children's cartoon series). Multicoloured.

3942 7d. Type **332a** 35 40
3943 7d. "Arbok No. 24" 35 40
3944 7d. "Machop No. 66" . . . 35 40
3945 7d. "Vileplume No. 45" . . 35 40
3946 7d. "Clefairy No. 35" . . . 35 40
3947 7d. "Poliwirl No. 61" . . . 35 40
MS3948 74 × 115 mm. 25d. "Articuno No. 144" . . . . . 1·40 1·50

333 Succory

334 *Encyclia alata*

2001. Medicinal Plants. Multicoloured.

3949 3d. Pokeweed (horiz) 15 20
3950 5d. Bay laurel (horiz) . . . 25 30
3951 8d. Type **333** 45 50
3952 8d. Dandelion 45 50
3953 8d. Garlic 45 50
3954 8d. Hemp agrimony 45 50
3955 8d. Star thistle 45 50
3956 8d. Cypress 45 50
3957 8d. Restharrow 45 50
3958 8d. White willow 45 50
3959 8d. Sweet serge 45 50
3960 8d. Passion flower 45 50
3961 8d. Rosemary 45 50
3962 8d. Pepper 45 50
3963 10d. Coltsfoot (horiz) . . . 55 60
3964 15d. Marsh mallow (horiz) 80 85
MS3965 Two sheets, each 83 × 108 mm. (a) 25d. Arbutus. (b) 25d. Olive Set of 2 sheets . . . 2·75 3·00

2001. "Hong Kong 2001" Stamp Exhibition. Orchids. Multicoloured.

3966 1d.50 Type **334** 10 15
3967 2d. *Dendrobium lasianthera* 10 15
3968 3d. *Cymbidiella pardalina* . . 15 20
3969 4d. *Cymbidium lowianum* . . 20 25
3970 4d. *Epidendrum pseudepidendrum* 20 25
3971 4d. *Eriopsis biloba* 20 25
3972 4d. *Masdevallia coccinea* . . 20 25
3973 4d. *Odontoglossum lindleyanum* 20 25
3974 4d. *Oerstedella wallisii* . . . 20 25
3975 4d. *Paphiopedilum acmodontum* 20 25
3976 4d. *Laelia rubescens* 20 25
3977 4d. *Huntleya wallisii* 20 25
3978 4d. *Lycaste longiscapia* . . . 20 25
3979 4d. *Maxillaria variabilis* . . 20 25
3980 4d. *Mexicoa ghiesbrechtiana* 20 25
3981 4d. *Miltoniopsis phalaenopsis* 20 25
3982 5d. *Cypripedium irapeanum* 25 30
3983 7d. *Sobralia candida* 35 40
3984 7d. *Phragmipedium besseae* 35 40
3985 7d. *Phaius tankervilleae* . . 35 40
3986 7d. *Vanda rothchildiana* . . . 35 40
3987 7d. *Telipogon pulcher* . . . 35 40
3988 7d. *Rossioglossum insleayi* 35 40
3989 15d. *Doritis pulcherrima* . . 80 85
MS3990 Three sheets, each 72 × 98 mm. (a) 25d. *Cycnoches loddigesii*. (b) 25d. *Cattleya dowiana*. (c) 25d. *Chaubardia heteroclita* Set of 3 sheets 4·00 4·25

No. 3984 is inscribed "BASSEAE" and No. 3389 "DORITAS", both in error.

335 *Disa uniflora*

336 "Mount Fuji and Tea Fields" (Matsuoka Eikyu)

2001. African Flowers. Multicoloured.

3991 1d. Type **335** 10 10
3992 4d. *Monodora myristica* . . 20 25
3993 6d. *Clappertonia ficifolia* . . 30 35
3994 7d. *Canarina abyssinica* and european roller 35 40
3995 7d. *Amorphophallus abyssinicus* 35 40
3996 7d. *Calanthe rosea* and hoopoe 35 40
3997 7d. *Gloriosa simplex* 35 40
3998 7d. *Clappertonia ficifolia* (different) 35 40
3999 7d. *Ansellia gigantea* 35 40
4000 7d. *Vanilla planifolia* and antelope 35 40
4001 7d. *Strelitzia reginae* and antelope 35 40
4002 7d. *Spathiphyllum* ("Gladiolus cardinalis") 35 40
4003 7d. *Arctotis venusta* and antelope 35 40
4004 7d. *Protea obtusifolia* and antelope 35 40
4005 7d. *Geissorhiza rochensis* . . 35 40
4006 20d. *Calanthe rosea* (different) . . . . . . 1·10 1·25
MS4007 Two sheets. (a) 77 × 106 mm. 25d. *Arctotis venusta* (different). (b) 106 × 77 mm. 25d. *Geissorhiza rochensis* (horiz) Set of 2 sheets . . . . . 2·75 3·00

Nos. 3994/9 and 4000/5 were each printed together, se-tenant, with the backgrounds forming composite designs.

Nos. 3991 and 3997 are inscribed "unifloria" or "Glorosa", both in error.

2001. "Philanippon '01" Internationl Stamp Exhibition, Tokyo. Japanese Art. Multicoloured.
4008 1d. Type **336** 10 10
4009 2d. "Herons and Flowers" (one heron) (Okamo Shuki) 10 15
4010 3d. "Herons and Flowers" (two herons) (Shuki) . . . 15 20
4011 3d. "The Realm of the Gods in Yinzhou" (Timioka Tessai) 15 20
4012 4d. "Egret" (Takeuchi Seiho) 20 25
4013 4d. "Peach Blossom Spring in Wuling" (Tessai) . . . 20 25
4014 5d. "Sparrows" (Seiho) . . 25 30
4015 5d. "Spring Colours of the Lake and Mountains" (Shoda Gyokan) 25 30
4016 5d. Peonies 25 30
4017 5d. Iris 25 30
4018 5d. Hollyhocks and hydrangea 25 30
4019 5d. Fruit and Japanese white-eye on branch . . . 25 30
4020 5d. Little egret 25 30
4021 5d. Woodpecker in tree . . 25 30
4022 5d. Blossom and japonica flowers 25 30
4023 5d. Yellow flowers 25 30
4024 5d. Blossom and green pheasant in tree 25 30
4025 5d. Morning Glory 25 30
4026 5d. Blue and white flowers 25 30
4027 5d. White and red flowers 25 30
4028 7d. Workshop and man carrying pole (27 × 33 mm) 35 40
4029 7d. Two women and tree (27 × 33 mm) 35 40
4030 7d. Rocks and river (27 × 33 mm) 35 40
4031 7d. Two women on riverbank (27 × 33 mm) 35 40
4032 7d. Rocky landscape (27 × 33 mm) 35 40
4033 7d. Man by rocks (27 × 33 mm) 35 40
4034 7d. Couple by rocks (27 × 33 mm) 35 40
4035 7d. Women with scroll (27 × 33 mm) 35 40
4036 7d. White flowers and tree (27 × 33 mm) 35 40
4037 7d. Speckled cockerel by tree (27 × 33 mm) 35 40
4038 7d. Brown cockerel and red flowers (27 × 33 mm) . . . 35 40
4039 7d. Cockerel and white flowers (27 × 33 mm) . . . 35 40
4040 7d. Trees in stream (27 × 33 mm) 35 40
4041 7d. White cockerel and flowers (27 × 33 mm) . . . 35 40
4042 7d. Cockerel and chicken (27 × 33 mm) 35 40
4043 7d. Black and white cockerel by tree (27 × 33 mm) . . . 35 40
4044 10d. Branch with flower (27 × 33 mm) 55 60
4045 10d. European tree sparrows (27 × 33 mm) 55 60
4046 10d. Butterfly on blossom (27 × 33 mm) 55 60
4047 10d. Crayfish (27x33 mm) 55 60
4048 10d. "Ushiwakamaru" (Kano Osanobu) 55 60
4049 10d. "Red Lotus and White Goose" (Goun Saku) . . 55 60
4050 15d. "Woman selling Flowers" (Ito Shoha) . . 80 85
4051 20d. "The Sound of the Ocean" (Matsumoto Ichiyo) . . . . 1·10 1·25
MS4052 Five sheets, each 119 × 89 mm. (a) 30d. "Puppies and Morning Glories" (Yamaguchi Soken). (b) 30d. "Deep Pool" (Nishimura Goun). (c) 30d. "Poppies" (Tsuchida Bakusen). (d) 30d. "Spring Farming near a Riverside Village" (Mori Getsuj). (e) 30d. "Untitled" (couple and dogs by lake) (Utagawa Kuniyoshi). Imperf Set of 5 sheets . . . . 8·00 8·25

Nos. 4016/21 and 4022/27 ("Birds and Flowers of the Twelve Months" (Sakai Hoitsu)), 4028/35 (composite designs from "The Four Accomplishments" (Kaiho Yusho)), 4036/43 (composite designs from "Birds and Flowers" (Soga Chokuan)) and 4044/7 ("Book of Lacquer Paintings" (Shiban Zeshin)) were each printed together, se-tenant, in sheetlets of 4, 6 or 8.

337 Queen Victoria reading Speech from the Throne

2001. Death Centenary of Queen Victoria. Multicoloured.
4053 15d. Type **337** 80 85
4054 15d. Prime Minister Benjamin Disraeli 80 85
4055 15d. Procession for State Opening of Parliament . . 80 85
MS4056 90 × 68 mm. 25d. Queen Victoria (vert) . . . . 1·40 1·50

338 Mao Tse-tung in 1935

340 Queen Elizabeth in Guards Uniform

339 "Madame Monet on the Sofa", 1871

2001. 25th Death Anniv of Mao Tse-tung (Chinese leader).
4057 **338** 15d. black, blue and light blue 80 85
4058 – 15d. multicoloured . . . 80 85
4059 – 15d. black, deep blue and blue 80 85
MS4060 132 × 108 mm. 25d. multicoloured . . . . 1·40 1·50

DESIGNS: No. 4057, Type **338**; 4058, Mao in 1949; 4059, Mao in 1951; **MS**4060, Mao addressing meeting in 1928.

2001. 75th Death Anniv of Claude-Oscar Monet (French painter). Multicoloured .
4061 10d. Type **339** 55 60
4062 10d. "The Picnic", 1865 . . 55 60
4063 10d. "The Luncheon", 1868 55 60
4064 10d. "Jean Monet on his Mechanical Horse", 1879 55 60
MS4065 137 × 110 mm. 25d. "La Japonaise", 1875 (vert) . . . . 1·40 1·50

2001. 75th Birthday of Queen Elizabeth II. Multicoloured.
4066 15d. Type **340** 80 85
4067 15d. Queen Elizabeth in pink suit and hat 80 85
4068 15d. Queen Elizabeth wearing ruby tiara 80 85
4069 15d. Queen Elizabeth wearing sapphire necklace 80 85
MS4070 80 × 110 mm. 25d. Princess Elizabeth on her wedding day (38 × 50 mm) . . . . 1·40 1·50

341 Queen Elizabeth II **342** Verdi as an Old Man

2001. Golden Jubilee (1st issue).
4071 **341** 8d. multicoloured . . . 45 50

No. 4071 was printed in sheetlets of 8, containing two vertical rows of four, separated by a large illustrated central gutter. Both the stamp and the illustration on the central gutter are made up of a collage of miniature flower photographs.

2001. Death Centenary of Giuseppe Verdi (Italian composer). Multicoloured.
4072 10d. Type **342** 55 60
4073 10d. Singers and score for *La Traviata* (opera) . . . 55 60
4074 10d. Singer and score for *Aida* (opera) 55 60
4075 10d. Verdi as a young man 55 60
MS4076 76 × 106 mm. 25d. Verdi as an old man . . . . 1·40 1·50

Nos. 4072/5 were printed together, se-tenant, with the backgrounds forming a composite design.

343 "At Le Rat Mort"

2001. Death Centenary of Henri de Toulouse-Lautrec (French painter). Multicoloured.
4077 7d. Type **343** 35 40
4078 7d. "The Milliner" 35 40
4079 7d. "Messaline" 35 40
MS4080 66 × 85 mm. 25d. "Napoleon" . . . . 1·40 1·50

344 Marlene Dietrich in Evening Dress

2001. Birth Centenary of Marlene Dietrich (actress and singer).
4081 **344** 10d. black, purple and claret 55 60
4082 – 10d. multicoloured . . . 55 60
4083 – 10d. multicoloured . . . 55 60
4084 – 10d. black, purple and claret 55 60

DESIGNS: No. 4082, Marlene Dietrich with roses; 4083, Marlene Dietrich with arms crossed; 4084, Marlene Dietrich wearing feathered hat.

345 *Orchis morio*

2001. "Belgica 2001" International Stamp Exhibition, Brussels. African Orchids. Multicoloured.
4085 3d. Type **345** 15 20
4086 4d. *Fulophia speciosa* . . . 20 25
4087 5d. *Angraecum leonis* . . . 25 30
4088 8d. *Ceratostylis retisquama* 45 50
4089 8d. *Rangaeris rhipsalisocia* 45 50
4090 8d. *Phaius hybrid* and baby chimpanzee 45 50
4091 8d. *Disa hybrid* 45 50
4092 8d. *Disa uniflora* 45 50
4093 8d. *Angraecum leonis* and chimpanzee 45 50
4094 8d. *Satyrium erectum* (horiz) 45 50
4095 8d. *Aeranthes grandiose* (horiz) 45 50
4096 8d. *Aerangis somasticta* (horiz) 45 50
4097 8d. *Polystachya bella* (horiz) 45 50
4098 8d. *Eulophia guineensis* (horiz) 45 50
4099 8d. *Disa blacki* (horiz) . . . 45 50
4100 15d. *Oeceoclades maculata* 80 85
MS4101 78 × 97 mm. 25d. *Disa kirstenbosch Pride* . . . . . . 1·40 1·50

Nos. 4088/93 and 4094/9 were each printed together, se-tenant, with the backgrounds forming composite designs.

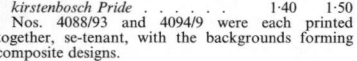

346 Children with Balloons

2001. S.O.S. Children's Villages (Kinderdorf International).
4102 **346** 10d. multicoloured . . . 55 60

GAZA Pt. 19

EGYPTIAN OCCUPATION

A strip of territory along the coast from Gaza to the Egyptian frontier, seized by Egypt when the British Mandate for Palestine ended in May 1948.

In 1967 Israeli troops seized the Gaza Strip and from that date Israeli stamps were used.

In May 1994 the area became autonomous under the Palestinian National Authority.

1000 milliemes = £1 (Egyptian).

1948. Various stamps of Egypt optd **PALESTINE** in English and Arabic.
1 **91** 1m. brown (postage) . . . 40 55
2 2m. red 40 55
3 **78** 3m. brown 40 55
4 **91** 4m. green 40 55
5 5m. brown 40 60
6 **78** 6m. green 55 60
7 **91** 10m. violet 40 60
8 **78** 13m. red . . . . 80 1·00
9 **91** 15m. purple 50 60
10 17m. green 60 65
11 20m. violet . . . . 75 1·10
12 22m. blue . . . . 80 1·10
13 – 30m. green (No. 340) . . . 80 1·10
14 **106** 40m. brown . . . . 1·25 1·40
15 – 50m. blue (No. 342) . . . 1·75 1·75
16 – 100m. purple (No. 280) . . 6·00 6·50
17 – 200m. violet (No. 281) . . 12·00 14·00
18 **86** 50p. brown and green . . . 17·00 18·00
19 **87** £E1 brown and blue . . . 30·00 32·00

20 **101** 2m. red (air) 40 55
21 3m. brown 40 55
22 5m. red 40 45
23 7m. brown 40 45
24 8m. green 40 45
25 10m. violet 40 45
26 20m. blue 60 65
27 30m. purple 80 85
28 40m. red . . . . 1·40 1·50
29 50m. blue . . . . 1·60 1·75
30 100m. green . . . . 2·25 2·75
31 200m. grey . . . . 18·00 22·00

1953. As above but with portrait obliterated by three horiz bars. (a) Postage.
32 **91** 1m. brown 40 50
33 2m. red 40 50
34 **78** 3m. brown 40 50
35 **91** 4m. green 40 50
36 5m. brown 40 50
37 **78** 6m. green 40 50
38 **91** 10m. violet 40 60
39 **78** 13m. red 80 95
40 **91** 15m. purple 80 95
41 17m. green 80 95
42 20m. violet 80 95
43 22m. blue . . . . 1·25 1·40
44 – 30m. green . . . . 2·00 2·25
45 **106** 40m. brown . . . . 2·75 3·00
46 – 50m. blue . . . . 4·00 4·25
47 – 100m. purple . . . . . . 8·00 10·00
48 – 200m. violet . . . . . . 16·00 22·00
49 **86** 50p. brown and green . . . 32·00 38·00
50 **87** £E1 brown and blue . . . 90·00 95·00

(b) Air.
51 **101** 2m. red . . . . 1·75 2·10
52 3m. brown 45 75
53 5m. red . . . . 10·00 11·00
54 7m. brown 65 90
55 8m. green . . . . 1·75 1·90
56 10m. violet . . . . 1·75 1·90
57 20m. blue . . . . 1·75 1·90
58 30m. purple . . . . 1·75 1·90
59 40m. red . . . . 1·40 1·50
60 50m. blue . . . . 14·00 15·00
61 100m. green . . . . 55·00 60·00
62 200m. grey . . . . 14·00 19·00

1953. Air. Nos. 480/2, 485 and 489/90 of Egypt optd **PALESTINE** in English and Arabic.
63 **101** 2m. red 40 55
64 3m. brown . . . . 8·75 10·00
65 5m. red 60 65
66 10m. violet . . . . 20·00 21·00
67 50m. blue . . . . 4·00 4·50
68 100m. olive . . . . 33·00 38·00

1955. Stamps of Egypt, 1953/4, optd **PALESTINE** in English and Arabic.
69 **137** 1m. brown 40 45
70 2m. purple 40 45
71 3m. blue 40 45
72 4m. green 40 45
73 5m. red 40 45
74 **130** 10m. sepia (B) 40 45
75 15m. grey 60 70
76 17m. turquoise 60 70
77 20m. violet 60 70
78 **131** 30m. green . . . . 1·00 1·10
79 32m. blue . . . . 1·00 1·10
80 35m. violet . . . . 1·00 1·10
81 40m. brown . . . . 1·75 1·90
82 50m. purple . . . . 2·00 2·10
83 **132** 100m. brown . . . . . . 5·00 5·25
84 200m. turquoise . . . . . 11·00 11·50
85 500m. violet . . . . . . 40·00 40·00
86 £E1 red and green . . . . 70·00 70·00

1955. Air. Nos. 433/4 of Egypt optd **PALESTINE** in English and Arabic.
86a **133** 5m. brown . . . . 4·00 5·25
86b 15m. green . . . . 5·00 6·00

Types of Egypt (sometimes with colours changed) overprinted **PALESTINE** in English and Arabic.

1957. Re-occupation of Gaza Strip.
87 **152** 10m. green . . . . 4·00 4·75

1957. Stamps of 1957.
88 – 1m. turquoise (No. 538) . . 10 20
89 – 5m. sepia (No. 541) . . . 40 40
90 **160** 10m. violet 40 40

UNITED ARAB REPUBLIC

1958. Stamps of 1958 (inscr "U A R EGYPT").
91 – 1m. red (No. 553) 10 10
92 – 2m. blue (No. 554) . . . 10 10
93 **168** 3m. brown 15 15
94 – 4m. green (No. 556) . . . 15 15
95 – 5m. sepia (No. 557) . . . 20 20

96 **160** 10m. violet (No. 558) . . 20 20
96a – 35m. blue (No. 559) . . . 2·75 1·75

1958. 5th Anniv of Republic.
97 **172** 10m. brown . . . . 1·75 1·75

1958. 10th Anniv of Declaration of Human Rights.
98 **178** 10m. purple . . . . 2·00 3·25
99 35m. brown . . . . 5·00 5·50

1959. No. 588.
100 **132** 55m. on 100m. red . . . 3·00 4·50

Types of Egypt with some colours changed and additionally inscribed "PALESTINE" in English and Arabic.

1960. As Nos. 603, etc.
101 **160** 1m. orange 10 10
104 – 4m. brown 10 10
105 – 5m. violet 15 15
106 – 10m. green 20 20

1960. World Refugee Year.
109 **205** 10m. brown 30 30
110 35m. black . . . . 1·50 1·25

1961. World Health Day.
111 **213** 10m. blue . . . . 1·00 1·00

1961. Palestine Day.
112 **215** 10m. violet 25 20

1961. U.N. Technical Co-operation Programme and 16th Anniv of U.N.O.
113 – 10m. blue and orange . . 50 30
114 **220** 35m. purple and red . . . 80 50

1961. Education Day.
115 **223** 10m. brown 80 50

1961. Victory Day.
116 **224** 10m. brown and chestnut 30 25

1962. 5th Anniv of Egyptian Occupation of Gaza.
117 **229** 10m. brown 30 25

1962. Arab League Week.
118 **231** 10m. purple 30 25

1962. Malaria Eradication.
119 **235** 10m. red and brown . . 25 25
120 – 35m. yellow and black . . 1·00 75

1962. 17th Anniv of U.N.O. and Hammarskjold Commemoration.
121 **245** 5m. blue and pink 20 20
122 10m. blue and brown . . 35 30
123 35m. indigo and blue . . 1·00 80

1963. As No. 739.
124 4m. blue, orange and black 20 20

1963. Freedom from Hunger.
125 **252** 5m. brown and green . . 15 10
126 – 10m. yellow and green . . 30 20
127 – 35m. yellow and purple 1·25 80

1963. Centenary of Red Cross.
128 **253** 10m. red, purple and blue 50 30
129 – 35m. ultram, blue & red 1·00 80

1963. U.N.E.S.C.O. Campaign for Preservation of Nubian Monuments (4th issue).
130 **256** 5m. yellow and purple . . 15 10
131 – 10m. yellow and black . . 20 15
132 – 35m. yellow and violet . . 1·00 80

1963. Air. As Nos. 758, 760 and 761/2.
133 50m. purple and blue 80 75
134 80m. indigo and blue . . . . 1·25 1·10
135 115m. yellow and black . . 2·00 1·75
136 140m. red and blue . . . . . 2·50 2·25

1963. 15th Anniv of Declaration of Human Rights.
137 **259a** 5m. yellow and sepia . . 15 15
138 – 10m. black, grey & pur 20 20
139 – 35m. black, green & turq 80 80

1964. As No. 769, etc.
140 – 1m. violet and green . . . 10 10
141 – 2m. blue and orange . . . 10 10
142 – 3m. blue, brown & lt blue 10 10
143 – 4m. green, brown & pink 15 10
144 – 5m. red, blue and pink . . 15 10
145 – 10m. red, brown and green 20 15
146 – 15m. yellow, violet & lilac 20 15
147 – 20m. green and violet . . 40 15
148 **261** 30m. blue and orange . . 80 15
149 – 35m. brown, green & orge 60 30
150 – 40m. blue and green . . . 80 30
151 – 60m. brown and blue . . . 1·25 70
152 **263** 100m. brown and blue . . 1·75 1·40

1964. Arab League Heads of State Congress, Cairo.
153 **266** 10m. black and olive . . 15 15

1964. Ramadan Festival.
154 **267** 4m. olive, red and lake . . 15 15

1964. 10th Anniv of Arab Postal Union's Permanent Office.
155 **271** 10m. blue and green . . . 15 10

1964. World Health Day.
156 **272** 10m. purple and red . . . 15 10

1965. Ramadan Festival. As No. 834.
157 – 4m. brown and green . . . 30 15

1965. 20th Anniv of Arab League.
158 **289** 10m. green and red . . . 15 15
159 – 20m. brown and green . . 20 20

1965. Air. World Meteorological Day.
160 **290** 80m. orange and blue . . 2·00 1·50

1965. World Health Day.
161 **291** 10m. red and green . . . 30 20

1965. Deir Yassin Massacre.
162 **292** 10m. red and blue 50 20

1965. Centenary of I.T.U.
163 **293** 5m. blue, yellow and green 30 15
164 10m. rose, blue and red 40 20
165 35m. blue, yell & ultram 1·00 60

1965. Air. Re-establishment of Egyptian Civil Airlines "MISRAIR".
166 **295** 10m. green and orange . . 40 30

1966. U.N. Day.
167 **321** 5m. violet and red 10 10
168 – 10m. violet and brown . . 20 15
169 – 35m. violet and green . . 60 30

1966. Victory Day.
170 **324** 10m. red and olive . . . 15 10

1967. Arab Publicity Week.
171 **328** 10m. brown and blue . . 15 10

1967. Labour Day.
172 **331** 10m. sepia and olive . . . 15 10

EXPRESS LETTER STAMP

1948. Express Letter stamp of Egypt optd **PALESTINE** in English and Arabic.
E32 E **52** 40m. black and brown 7·00 7·50

POSTAGE DUE STAMPS

1948. Postage Due stamps of Egypt optd **PALESTINE** in English and Arabic.
D32 D **59** 2m. orange . . . . . . 1·25 1·40
D33 4m. green . . . . . . 1·00 1·10
D34 6m. green . . . . . . 1·00 1·10
D35 8m. purple . . . . . . 1·00 1·10
D36 10m. lake . . . . . . 1·00 1·10
D37 12m. red . . . . 1·00 1·10
D38 30m. violet . . . . . . 3·00 5·50

This area was occupied by Israel on 6 June 1967. Post Offices were opened in July 1967 and Israeli stamps are now used.

GEORGIA Pt. 10

Formerly part of Russia, Georgia declared its independence after the Russian Revolution. In 1921 it became a Soviet Republic and in 1922 joined with Armenia and Azerbaijan to form the Transcaucasian Federation, whose stamps were used from September 1923. After absorption into the U.S.S.R. Russian stamps were used from 1924.

With the dissolution of the Soviet Union in 1991 Georgia again became an independent state.

1919. 100 kopeks = 1 rouble.
1993. kupon.
1995. 100 tetri = 1 lari.

1 St. George

3 Queen Tamara (A.D. 1184–1212)

1919. Imperf or perf.
10 **1** 10k. blue . . . . 20 1·00
1 40k. red . . . . 20 1·00
12 50k. green . . . . 20 1·00
2 60k. red . . . . 20 1·00
3 70k. mauve . . . . 20 1·00
15 – 1r. brown (20 × 25 mm) . . 20 1·00
16 **3** 2r. brown 30 75
17a 3r. blue . . . . 20 1·00
18 5r. yellow . . . . 50 1·00

4 Soldier

6 Industry and agriculture

1922. Perf.
28a **4** 500r. red . . . . 2·00 4·00
29 – 1000r. brown (Sower) . . . 2·75 3·50
30 **6** 2000r. grey . . . . 3·25 3·50
31 3000r. brown . . . . . . 3·00 3·50
32 5000r. green . . . . . . 3·00 3·50

7

1922. Famine Relief. Designs as T **7**. Surch.
33 – 100r. on 50r. violet . . . . 50 2·00
34 – 3000r. on 100r. red . . . . 50 2·00
35 – 5000r. on 250r. green . . . 50 2·00
36 **7** 10,000r. on 25r. blue . . . . 50 3·00

1923. Surch.
37 – 10,000r. on 1000r. (No. 29) 2·75 1·00
38 **6** 15,000r. on 2000r. grey . . 3·00 1·25
44 **4** 20,000r. on 500r. red . . . 75 1·25
40a **6** 40,000r. on 5000r. green . . 1·25 1·00
46 80,000r. on 3000r. brown . . 1·75 2·00

1923. Surch. (a) On Arms types of Russia.
47 **22** 10,000r. on 7k. blue . . . . 32·00 32·00
48 **10** 15,000r. on 15k. blue & brn 3·00 3·50

(b) On No. 75B of Armenia.
49 **10** 1,5000r. on 5r. on 15k. blue and brown . . . . 22·00 20·00

1923. Arms types of Russia surch with hammer and sickle and value. Imperf or perf.
50 **22** 75,000r. on 1k. orange . . . 4·00 4·50
52 20,000r. on 5k. red . . . . 3·00 4·00
53 **14** 30,000r. on 20k. red & blue 2·75 3·00
54 **22** 35,000r. on 3k. red . . . . 3·50 4·25
57 700,000r. on 2k. green . . . 5·00 5·00

12 Map, National Flag and U.N. Emblem

13 Arms and Flag

1993. 1st Anniv of Admission to U.N.O.
58 **12** 25r. multicoloured 20 20
59 50r. multicoloured 30 30
60 100r. multicoloured 50 50
MS61 122 × 101 mm. Nos. 58/60 1·25 1·25

1993.
62 **13** 0.50k. multicoloured 15 15

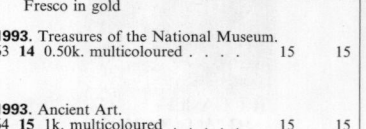

14 18th-century Fresco in gold

15 "Apostle Simon" (icon)

1993. Treasures of the National Museum.
63 **14** 0.50k. multicoloured 15 15

1993. Ancient Art.
64 **15** 1k. multicoloured 15 15

16 "Three Women" (Lado Gudiashvili)

17 Juari Monastery, Mtskheta

1993. National Paintings.
65 **16** 1k. multicoloured 15 15

1993. Places of Worship.
66 **17** 30k. blue 10 10
67 – 40k. brown 15 15
68 – 50k. brown 20 20
69 – 60k. red 20 20
70 – 70k. lilac 25 25
71 – 80k. green 30 30
72 – 90k. black 35 35
DESIGNS: 40k. Gelati Church; 50k. Nikortsminda Church; 60k. Ikorta Church; 70k. Samtavisi Church; 80k. Bolnisi Zion Synagogue; 90k. Gremi Citadel Church.

18 Emblem

1994. 2nd Anniv of International Olympic Committee Recognition of Georgian National Olympic Committee.
73 **18** 100k.+50k. multicoloured 25 25

19 Emblem

1994. Admission (1993) of Georgia to U.P.U.
74 **19** 200k. multicoloured 40 40

20 Window and Nikoladze

1994. 150th Birth Anniv (1993) of Niko Nikoladze (journalist).
75 **20** 150k. multicoloured 30 30

1994. Nos. 62/5 surch.
76 **13** 5000k. on 0.50k. mult . . . 10 10
77 **14** 5000k. on 0.50k. mult . . . 10 10
78 **15** 10000k. on 1k. mult 20 20
79 **16** 10000k. on 1k. mult 30 30

22 "Barba and the Lion"

24 Olympic Rings and Colours

1994. All-Georgian Congress.
80 **22** 100k. brown and pink . . . 70 70
81 – 200k. deep blue and blue . . 70 70
DESIGN: 200k. Equestrian statue

1994. Nos. 63/5 surch **Georgia** and new value.
82 **14** 200k. on 0.50k. mult 25 25
83 **15** 300k. on 1k. multicoloured 45 45
84 **16** 500k. on 1k. multicoloured 70 70

1995. Centenary of International Olympic Committee. Multicoloured.
85 10k. Type **24** (International Year of Sport) 20 20
86 15k. Emblem symbolizing founding congress 30 30
87 20k. Anniversary emblem . . 40 40
88 25k. Olympic rings and peace dove ("Olympic Truce") . . 50 50

25 "Giraffe"

1995. 77th Death Anniv of Niko Pirosmanashvili (painter). Multicoloured.
89 20k. Type **25** 50 50
90 20k. "Three Princes Carousing on the Grass" (horiz) . . . 50 50
91 20k. "Brooder with Chicks" (horiz) 50 50
92 20k. "Boy on a Donkey" . . . 50 50
93 20k. "Fisherman" 50 50
94 20k. "Woman with a Tankard of Beer" 50 50
95 20k. "Bear on a Moonlit Night" 50 50
96 20k. "Georgian woman with a Tambourine" 50 50
97 20k. "Still Life" (horiz) . . . 50 50
98 20k. "Deer" 50 50
MS99 113×86 mm. 100k. "Family Picnicking" (horiz) . . . . . . 2·00 2·00

26 Alaverdi

27 Sveti-Zchoveli Cathedral, Mtskheta

28 Bitschvinta

1995. Monasteries. Value expressed by letter.
100 **26** A blue and black 60 60
101 – A green and black 60 60
102 **27** I lilac and black 60 60
103 – I brown and black 60 60
104 – I green and black 60 60
105 **28** U brown and black 60 60
106 – U brown and black 60 60
DESIGNS: No. 101, Ananuri; 103, Kumurdo; 104, Dranda; 106, Metechi.
The stamps are inscribed with letters of the Georgian alphabet.

1995. Monasteries. As Nos. 106, 100 and 104 but with value expressed by figure.
107 1 purple and black 60 60
108 2 brown and black 60 60
109 3 brown and black 60 60
DESIGNS: No. 107, Metechi; 108, Alaverdi; 109, Dranda.
The numbers on Nos. 107/9 represent classes of postage rather than the face value of the stamps.

29 Iashvili and Family

1995. Birth Centenary (1994) of Paolo Iashvili (writer).
110 **29** 300k. brown and black . . 60 60

30 Brontosaurus

1995. Prehistoric Animals. Multicoloured.
111 15k. Type **30** 30 30
112 15k. Ceratosaurus 30 30
113 15k. Deinonichus 30 30
114 15k. Parasaurolophus 30 30
115 15k. Saurolophus 30 30
116 15k. Scolosaurus 30 30
117 15k. Stegosaurus 30 30
118 15k. Triceratops 30 30
119 15k. Tyrannosaurus 30 30
MS120 106×76 mm. 100k. Deinonychus . . . . 3·00 3·00

31 White-headed Stork, Bar-tailed Godwit, Mandarin Duck, Hyacinth Macaw and Deer

1995. Wildlife. Multicoloured.
121 15k. Heads of horse, monkey, eagle, deer, bird, lynx and elephant 20 20
122 15k. Dragonfly and butterfly at left, mosquitoes and fishes among heads of woolly-necked stork and greater flamingo 20 20
123 15k. Fishes and butterfly with heads of lioness, cow, parrot, monkey and owl with egret at right 20 20
124 15k. Fox's face at left, northern lapwing, skunk and fish 20 20
125 15k. Butterfly, scorpion, bluethroat, fishes and elephant's trunk at right 20 20
126 15k. Type **31** 20 20
127 15k. Fishes, shells, antelope, dogs, dolphin and silver pheasant 20 20
128 15k. Body of pipefish, Indian peacock and king eider, fox and fly 20 20
129 15k. Rhinoceros, seahorse and dolphin 20 20
130 15k. Zebra, hippopotamus, deer, fishes, spur-winged goose, northern bullfinch, common pheasant and moth 20 20
131 15k. Dog's head, Abyssinian ground hornbill, lobster, fishes and other mammals 20 20
132 15k. Seal, warthog, rabbits, fishes, beetle and red-breasted goose 20 20
133 15k. Ostrich, other birds, fish and lion's face 20 20
134 15k. Snake's head, fishes, slavonian grebe, beetle, giraffe's head and frog . . 20 20
135 15k. Sheep, antelope, fishes, ant and birds, including dove 20 20
136 15k. Whale, stoat, great crested grebe, killdeer plover, parrot, butterfly and lizard 20 20
Nos. 121/36 were issued together, se-tenant, forming a composite design.

32 Bagrati Cathedral

1995. U.N.E.S.C.O. World Heritage Sites.
137 **32** 100k. multicoloured . . . 60 60
MS138 75×105 mm. 500k. Jvari Monastery, Mtskhetha (28×42 mm) . . . . 3·00 3·00

33 Pterodactylus

1995. Prehistoric Animals. Multicoloured.
139 15t. Type **33** 35 35
140 15t. Rhamphorhynchus (inscr "Rhamphorhynghus") . . 35 35
141 15t. Pteranodon 35 35
142 15t. Spinosaurus 35 35
143 15t. Tyrannosaurus 35 35
144 15t. Velociraptor 35 35
145 15t. Monoklonius 35 35
146 15t. Ornithomimus 35 35
147 15t. Mastodon 35 35
Nos. 139/47 were issued together, se-tenant, forming a composite design.

34 Barn Swallows

1996. Birds. Multicoloured.
148 15t. Type **34** 20 20
149 15t. Redwing (spotted breast) 20 20
150 15t. Common starling (black with greenish wing) 20 20
151 15t. Hawfinch (brown with black patch on neck) . . . 20 20
152 15t. Barred warbler (black and white bird on twig) . . 20 20
153 15t. Golden oriole (yellow with black wing) 20 20
154 15t. Collared flycatcher (black and white bird on trunk of tree) 20 20
155 15t. Chaffinch (chestnut front and back and small crest) 20 20
156 15t. Crested tit (brown body, black and white head and crest) 20 20
157 15t. Yellowhammer (speckled black and yellow) 20 20
158 15t. White wagtail (white with black chest, nape and wings) 20 20
159 15t. Blackbird (black with yellow beak) 20 20
160 15t. Common redstart (grey and black head, chestnut patch on front) 20 20
161 15t. European robin (red face and chest) 20 20
162 15t. Eurasian nuthatch (bird with black stripe across eye, on tree trunk) 20 20
163 15t. Blue tit (blue head, wings and tail and green back) 20 20
164 15t. White-tailed sea eagle (white tail) 20 20
165 15t. Osprey (black and white bird in flight) 20 20
166 15t. Short-toed eagle (speckled brown and white on tip of branch) 20 20
167 15t. Long-legged buzzard (chestnut) 20 20
168 15t. Red kite (red tail, in flight) 20 20
169 15t. Western marsh harrier (white tail and white wings tipped with brown, in flight) 20 20
170 15t. Northern goshawk (grey bird with black eye stripe, on branch) 20 20
171 15t. Tawny owl (on branch, tips of fir trees) 20 20
172 15t. Northern hobby (black and white bird on branch overhanging water) 20 20
173 15t. Common kestrel (black head and tail and brown body, valley in background) 20 20
174 15t. Long-eared owl (with large ears, sitting upright) 20 20
175 15t. Great grey owl (on top of tree stump, fir trees behind) 20 20
176 15t. Imperial eagle (both wings raised above body and flying over water) . . 20 20
177 15t. Imperial eagle (brown bird with white wing-tips, on branch overhanging water) 20 20
178 15t. Little owl (white owl on thick branch at water's edge) 20 20
179 15t. Northern eagle owl (brown bird with ears, spreading wings) 20 20
MS180 Two sheets, each 100×70 mm. (a) 100t. Screech Owl; (b) 100t. Barn Swallow at nest . . . . 5·00 5·00

Nos. 148/63 and 164/79 were issued respectively together, se-tenant, forming composite designs.

35 Head of Common Crane

1996. Animals. Multicoloured.
181 10t. Type **35** 20 20
182 10t. Body of common crane 20 20
183 10t. Head of snake 20 20
184 10t. Body of snake and moth 20 20
185 10t. Lizard 20 20
186 10t. Common crane and bearded reedling 20 20
187 10t. Dragonfly 20 20
188 10t. Bees on clover and body of snake 20 20
189 10t. Butterfly 20 20
190 10t. Frog 20 20
191 10t. Snail 20 20
192 10t. Turtle 20 20
193 10t. Crayfish 20 20
194 10t. Water plant and head of salamander 20 20
195 10t. Crested salamander and body of salamander . . . 20 20
196 10t. Speckled salamander on trunk 20 20
Nos. 181/96 were issued together, se-tenant, forming a composite design of a pond.

36 Apatosaurus

1996. Prehistoric Animals. Multicoloured.
197 10t. Type **36** 25 25
198 10t. Archaeopteryx (bird) . . 25 25
199 10t. Leptoceratops (on rocks at entrance to cave) . . . 25 25
200 10t. Parasaurolophus (pair) and body of apatosaurus 25 25
201 10t. Pentaceratops (with horns and neck flap) . . . 25 25
202 10t. Hererasaurus (with mouth gaping, fronds in background) 25 25
203 10t. Hadrosaurus and nest with eggs 25 25
204 10t. Montanoceratops (green dinosaur with different dinosaur in background) 25 25
205 10t. Fulgoloterium (red dinosaur) 25 25
Nos. 197/205 were issued together, se-tenant, forming a composite design.

37 "Citizens of Paris" (Lado Gudiashvili)

1996. Paintings. Multicoloured.
206 10t. Type **37** 15 15
207 20t. "Abstract" (Wassily Kandinsky) 30 30
208 30t. "Still-life" (David Kakabadze) 45 45
209 50t. "Three Painters" (Shalva Kikodze) 80 80
MS210 83×100 mm. 80t. "Portrait of Niko Pirosmani" (Pablo Picasso) (black and gold). Imperf 1·25 1·25

38 Helsinki, 1952

1996. Cent of Modern Olympic Games. Mult.
211 1t. Type **38** 10 10
212 2t. Melbourne, 1956 . . . . 10 10
213 3t. Rome, 1960 . . . . . . 10 10
214 4t. Tokyo, 1964 . . . . . . 15 15
215 5t. Mexico, 1968 . . . . . . 20 20
216 6t. Munich, 1972 . . . . . . 25 25
217 7t. Montreal, 1976 . . . . . 30 30
218 8t. Moscow, 1980 . . . . . . 35 35
219 9t. Seoul, 1988 . . . . 35 35
220 10t. Barcelona, 1992 . . . . 40 40
MS221 Two sheets, each 99×70 mm. Each black and scarlet. (a) 50t. Wrestling; (b) 70t. Athletics . . . . 4·75 4·75

Each stamp is also inscribed with the names of Georgian gold medal winners at the relevant games.

39 Anniversary Emblem

1997. 50th Anniv of U.N.O.
222 **39** 30t. blue and purple . . . 40 40
223 125t. blue and red . . . . 1·60 1·60

40 Javakhishvili and University

1997. 120th Birth Anniv (1996) of Ivane Javakhishvili (first director of Tbilisi University).
224 **40** 50t. multicoloured . . . . 1·00 1·00

41 Anton I **42** Railway Track and Tunnel

1997. 210th Death Anniv (1998) of Anton I (head of Georgian Orthodox Church).
225 **41** 30t. brown 75 75

1997. 50th Anniv (1996) of U.N.I.C.E.F. Children's Paintings. Multicoloured.
226 20t.+5r. Type **42** 50 50
227 30t.+10r. Creature (horiz) . . 75 75

43 Rottweiler

1997. Dogs. Multicoloured.
228 10t. Type **43** 15 15
229 30t. Gordon setter 45 45
230 50t. St. Bernard 75 75
231 60t. English bulldog 90 90
232 70t. Caucasian sheepdog . . 1·00 1·00
233 125t. Caucasian sheepdog (different) . . . . 1·75 1·75
MS234 99 × 75 mm. No. 233 . . 1·75 1·75

44 Two Mice

1997. Animated Cartoon Characters. Mult.
235 20t. Type **44** 30 30
236 30t. Man in bed 45 45
237 40t. Girl and rabbit on cloud with balloons 60 60
238 50t. Dancing animals 75 75
239 60t. Duck wearing dress . . . 90 90

45 Nana Ioseliani (World Vice-Champion, 1988, 1993)

1997. Georgian Women Chess Players. Two sheets, each 90 × 90 mm, containing square design as T **45**.
MS240 Two sheets (a) 20t. ochre, brown and silver (T **45**); 20t. ochre, brown and silver (Nana Alexandria (world vice-champion, 1975, 1981)); 40t. ochre, brown and gold (Maia Chiburdanidze (world champion, 1978, 1981, 1984, 1986, 1988)); 50t. ochre, brown and gold (Nona Gaprindashvili (world champion, 1962, 1965, 1969, 1972, 1975)). (b) Each ochre, brown and gold. Winning teams at chess Olympiads; 30t. Manila, 1992; 30t. Moscow, 1994; 30t. Yerevan, 1996 4·75 4·75

The dates for Maia Chiburdanidze are inaccurate.

46 Map of Caucasus, 1745

1997. 300th Birth Anniv (1996) of Prince Vakhushti Bagration. Multicoloured.
241 40t. Type **46** 60 60
242 80t. Prince Vakhushti Bagration (vert) . . . . . 1·25 1·25

47 Tiflis Town Post **48** Congress and Cultural Emblems

1997. "Moscow '97" Int Stamp Exn.
243 **47** 80t. multicoloured . . . . 1·25 1·25
MS244 115 × 88 mm. 1l. As Type **47** but additionally dated "1857 1997". Imperf . . . . 1·50 1·50

1997. 1st World Junior (40t.) and Second World (80t.) Delphic Congresses, Tbilisi. Multicoloured.
245 40t. Type **48** 60 60
246 80t. Emblem and church, Mzcheta . . . . 1·25 1·25

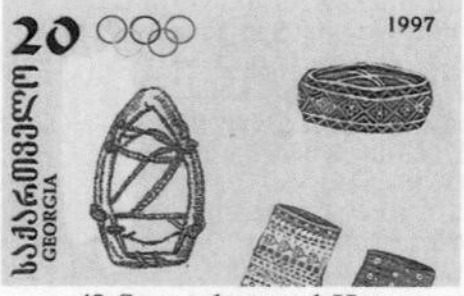

49 Snow-shoe and Hat

1998. Winter Olympic Games, Nagano, Japan. Mult.
(a) Clothes and accessories.
247 20t. Type **49** 35 35
248 30t. Glove and snow-shoe . . 50 50
249 40t. Sledge and gloves . . . 70 70
250 50t. Scarf and skates . . . . 1·50 1·50

(b) Ski Jumping.
251 20t. Ski jumper 35 35
252 30t. As No. 251 . . . . . . 50 50
253 40t. As No. 251 . . . . . . 70 70
254 50t. As No. 251 . . . . . . 1·50 1·50
MS255 Two sheets (a) 76 × 106 mm. 70t. Georgian wearing snow-shoes; (b) 99 × 70 mm. 70t. Upper body of ski jumper . . . . 2·50 2·50

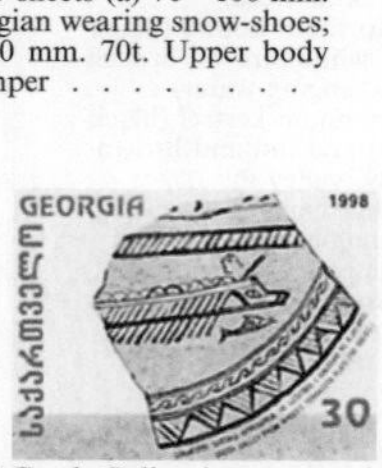

50 Greek Galley (terracotta plate)

1998. Voyage of the Argonauts (ancient Greek legend). Multicoloured.
256 30t. Type **50** 45 45
257 40t. Preparation for battle . . 60 60
258 50t. Boreads, Phineus (blind seer) and Harpy 75 75
259 60t. Punishment of King Amicus 90 90
260 70t. Argonauts in Colchis . . 1·00 1·00
261 80t. The dragon vomiting Jason . . . . 1·25 1·25

Nos. 257/61 show vase paintings.

51 Brown Horse

1998. Horses. Multicoloured.
262 10t. Type **51** 15 15
263 40t. Black horse 75 75
264 70t. Chestnut . . . . 1·00 1·00
265 80t. White horse . . . . . . 2·75 2·75
MS266 110 × 90 mm. 100t. Grey. Imperf . . . . 1·75 1·75

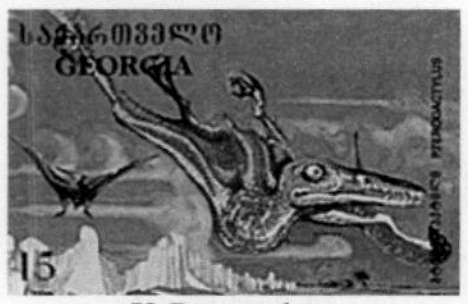

52 Pteranodon

1998. Prehistoric Animals. Multicoloured.
267 15t. Type **52** (inscr "Pterodactylus") 30 30
268 15t. Rhamphorhynchus facing right 30 30
269 15t. Pterodactyl (inscr "Pteranodon") 30 30
270 15t. Velociraptor (inscr "Spinosaurus") 30 30
271 15t. Tyrannosaurus facing right 30 30
272 15t. Spinosaurus (inscr "Velociraptor") 30 30
273 15t. Mastodon (inscr "Monoklonius") 30 30
274 15t. Ornithomimus facing left 30 30
275 15t. Monoklonius (inscr "Mastodon") 30 30

Nos. 267/75 were issued together, se-tenant, forming a composite design.

53 Class VL8 No. 888

1998. Electric Railway Locomotives built at Tbilisi. Multicoloured.
276 10t. Type **53** 15 15
277 30t. Class VL10 No. 580 . . 45 45
278 40t. Class VL11 No. 500A . . 60 60
279 50t. Class VL11 No. 001B . . 75 75
280 80t. Class VL10u No. 591 . . 1·25 1·25
MS281 107 × 73 mm. 100t. Class E13 No. 008. Imperf . . . . 1·75 1·75

54 Flag and "26 May"

1998. 80th Anniv of Declaration of National Republic.
282 **54** 80t. multicoloured . . . . 1·25 1·25

55 Berikaoba

1998. Europa. National Festivals. Value expressed by letter of Georgian alphabet.
283 A(80t.) Type **55** . . . . . . 1·25 1·25
284 B(100t.) Chiakokononba . . 1·75 1·75

56 Marbled Polecat

1999. Mammals. Multicoloured.
285 10t. Type **56** 15 15
286 40t. Striped hyena 60 60
287 80t. Brown bear . . . . . . 1·25 1·25
MS287 90 × 110 mm. 100t. Wild goat (*Capra aegagrus*). Imperf . . . 1·75 1·75

57 Michael Bridge

1999. Bridges in Tbilisi. Multicoloured.
289 10t. Type **57** 15 15
290 40t. Saarbruken 60 60
291 50t. N. Baratashvili Bridge 75 75
292 60t. Mukhrani railway bridge 90 90
293 70t. Avlabari Bridge . . . . 1·00 1·00
294 80t. Metekhi Bridge . . . . 1·25 1·25

58 Mink

1999. The European Mink. Values expressed by letter of Georgian alphabet. Multicoloured.
295 A(10t.) Type **58** 25 25
296 B(20t.) Mink with fish . . . 45 45
297 G(30t.) Two mink 65 65
298 D(60t.) Mink emerging from burrow . . . . 1·40 1·40

59 Batsara-Babaneury Reserve **61** Writing Letter

60 Emblem and Athletes

1999. Europa. Parks and Gardens. Value indicated by letter of Georgian alphabet. Multicoloured.
299 A(80t.) Type **59** . . . . . . 1·25 1·25
300 B(100t.) Lagodekhy Reserve 1·75 1·75

1999. 10th Anniv of Georgian National Olympic Committee.
301 **60** 20t. red, black and gold . . 35 35
302 50t. red, black and gold . . 1·00 1·00

1999. 125th Anniv of Universal Postal Union. Illustrations by Sergo Kobuladze from *The Knight in the Tiger's Skin* (poem). Multicoloured.
303 20t. Type **61** 35 35
304 80t. Woman writing letter . . 1·50 1·50

62 Georgian Script and Emblem

1999. Admission of Georgia to European Council. Multicoloured.
305 50t. Type **62** . . . . 1·00 1·00
306 80t. "EUROPA" and emblem 1·00 1·50

63 KAZ-585 Tipper Truck

1999. Kutaisi Automobile Factory. Trucks. Multicoloured.
307 20t. Type **63** 35 35
308 40t. KAZ-608-717 . . . . . 80 80
309 50t. KAZ-608-3 . . . . . . 1·00 1·00
310 80t. KAZ-4530 . . . . 1·50 1·50

64 Scarce Swallowtail (*Iphiclides podalirius*)

1999. Butterflies. Multicoloured.
312 10t. Type **64** 20 20
313 20t. Apollo (*Parnassius apollo*) 35 35
314 50t. Dawn clouded yellow (*Colias aurorina* Herrich-Schaffer) . . . . 1·00 1·00
315 80t. *Tomares romanovi* . . . 1·50 1·50

65 Svanetia

1999. World Heritage Sites. Sheet 110 × 69 mm.
MS316 **65** 100t. multicoloured . . 1·75 1·75

66 "Building Europe"   67 Man kneeling (Mamuka Tavakarashvili)

2000. Europa.
317 **66** 80t. multicoloured . . . . 1·50 1·50
318 100t. multicoloured . . . . 1·60 1·60

2000. 800th Anniv of *The Knight in a Tiger's Skin* (poem by Shota Rustaveli). Showing illustrations by named artists of scenes from the poem. Multicoloured.
319 10t. Type **67** 20 20
320 20t. Horsemen (Sergio Kobuladze and Jacob Nikoladze) 35 35
321 30t. Man fighting tiger (Irakli Toidze and Ucha Japaridze) 60 60
322 50t. Man and horse (Levan Tsutskiridze and Teimuraz Gotsadze) . . . . 1·00 1·00
323 60t. Woman's head (Natela Iankoshvili and Temo Natsvlishvili) . . . . . . 1·50 1·50
MS324 85 × 110 mm. 80t. Man wearing headdress (Rusudan Petviashvili) . . . . 1·50 1·50

68 St. Nino, Shio Mghvime

2000. 2000th Birth Anniv of Jesus Christ. Icons. Multicoloured.
325 20t. Type **68** 35 35
326 50t. The Saviour, Alaverdi 1·00 1·00
327 80t. The Virgin Hodigitria, Tsilkani . . . . 1·50 1·50

69 Coins

2000. 3000th Anniv of Georgia. Sheet 123 × 95 mm.
MS328 **69** 100t. multicoloured . . 1·75 1·75

70 Fish

2000. Fishes.
329 **70** 10t. multicoloured 20 20
330 – 20t. multicoloured 35 35
331 – 30t. multicoloured 60 60
332 – 50t. multicoloured . . . . 1·00 1·00
333 – 80t. multicoloured . . . . 1·50 1·50
DESIGNS: 20t. to 80t. Depicting fishes.

71 "1999"

2000. New Millennium. Each red and yellow.
334 20t. Type **71** 35 35
335 50t. "2000" . . . . 1·00 1·00
336 80t. "2001" . . . . 1·50 1·50

72 Athlete

2000. Olympic Games, Sydney. Multicoloured.
337 20t. Type **72** 35 35
338 50t. Athlete . . . . 1·00 1·00
339 80t. Athlete . . . . 1·50 1·50

73 Saradjishvili

2000. 89th Death Anniv of David Saradjishvili (first producer of brandy in Georgia).
340 **73** 80t. multicoloured . . . . 1·50 1·50

74 Cosmonauts working on Reflector

2000. Georgia–Russia Space Project. Multicoloured.
341 20t. Type **74** 35 35
342 80t. Antenna reflector in space . . . . 1·50 1·50

75 "hUMAN RighTS"

2000. Human Rights. Multicoloured.
343 50t. Type **75** . . . . 1·00 1·00
344 80t. "HuMAn RiGHtS" . . 1·50 1·50

76 Refugees

2000. 50th Anniv of United Nations High Commission for Refugees.
345 **76** 50t. multicoloured . . . . 1·00 1·00

77 Yellow Chanterelle (*Cantharellus cibarius*)   78 Church

2000. Fungi. Multicoloured.
346 10t. Type **77** 20 20
347 20t. Field mushroom (*Agaricus campestris*) . . . 35 35
348 30t. Boot-lace fungus (*Armillariella mella*) . . . 60 60
349 50t. *Russula adusta* . . . . . 1·00 1·00
350 80t. Violet cort (*Cortinarius violaceus*) . . . . 1·50 1·50

2000. Churches.
351 **78** 10t. brown 20 20
352 – 50t. blue . . . . 1·00 1·00
DESIGN: 50t. Church.

79 Alexander Kazbegi

2000. Writers.
353 **79** 30t. black, red and pink . . 60 60
354 – 40t. black, brown and yellow 80 80
355 – 50t. black, deep green and green . . . . 1·00 1·00
356 – 70t. black, lavender and blue . . . . 1·40 1·40
357 – 80t. black, brown and chestnut . . . . 1·50 1·50
DESIGNS: 40t. Jakob Gogebashvili; 50t. Vadja Pshavela; 70t. Akaki Tsereteli; 80t. Ilia Chavchavadze.

80 Republic P-47 Thunderbolt

2000. 23rd Death Anniv of Alexander Kartveli (aircraft designer). Multicoloured.
358 10t. Type **80** 20 20
359 20t. Republic F-84 . . . . . 35 35
360 80t. Republic F-105D Thunderchief . . . . . 1·50 1·50
MS361 75 × 115 mm. 100t. Kartveli (vert) . . . . 1·75 1·75

81 Emblem and Horse-drawn Vehicle

2000. 175th Anniv of Fire Service.
362 **81** 50t. multicoloured . . . . 1·00 1·00

82 Ritsa Lake   83 Synagogue, Kutaisi

2001. Europa. Water Resources. Multicoloured.
363 40t. Type **82** 80 80
364 80t. Borjomi Spa . . . . . . 1·60 1·60

2001.
365 **83** 140t. multicoloured . . . . 1·90 1·90

84 Chess Pieces and Competition Emblem

2001. 1st Europe–Asia Intercontinental Chess Match, Batumi.
366 **84** 1l. multicoloured . . . . . 1·90 1·90

85 "TRACEA" (transport corridor Europe–Caucasus–Asia) and Route

2001. The Great Silk Route. Multicoloured.
367 20t. Type **85** 60 60
MS368 74 × 76 mm. 80t. Map and route . . . . 1·50 1·50

86 Georgian and American Flags

2001. Support for America after Attacks on World Trade Buildings, New York. Multicoloured.
369 30t.+10t. Type **86** . . . . . 1·00 1·00
MS370 135 × 77 mm. 120t.+10t. As No. 369 . . . . 3·60 3·60

87 Taras Chevtchenko

2002. Poets. Multicoloured.
371 50t. Type **87** . . . . 1·75 1·75
372 50t. Akakii Tsereteli . . . . 1·75 1·75
Stamps of the same design were issued by Ukraine.

88 Passenger Ship

2002. 140th Anniv of Poti Port. Sheet 104 × 57 mm containing T **88** and similar horiz designs. Multicoloured.
MS373 30t. Type **88**; 30t. Container suspended from hoist; 30t. Tug guiding ship; 30t. Crane and rowboat; 30t. Steam tug; 30t. Tanker ship . . . . 4·50 4·50

89 Scenes from *Mtiuluri*   90 Woman and Childrenn (statue)

2002. National Ballet. Scenes from ballets by Soliko Virsaladze. Multicoloured.
374 30t. Type **89** 85 85
375 50t. *Samaya* . . . . 1·00 1·00
376 80t. *Jeirani* . . . . 1·90 1·90

2002.
377 **90** 100t. blue . . . . 1·75 1·75

91 Man holding House (bas-relief)

92 Acrobat

2002.

378	**91**	5l. brown	7·50	7·50

2002. Europa. Circus. Multicoloured.

379	40t. Type **92**	1·50	1·50
380	80t. Tbilisi circus	2·75	2·75

93 Refugees

2002. 50th Anniv of United Nations' Convention on the Status of Refugees.

381	**93**	50t. multicoloured	1·50	1·50

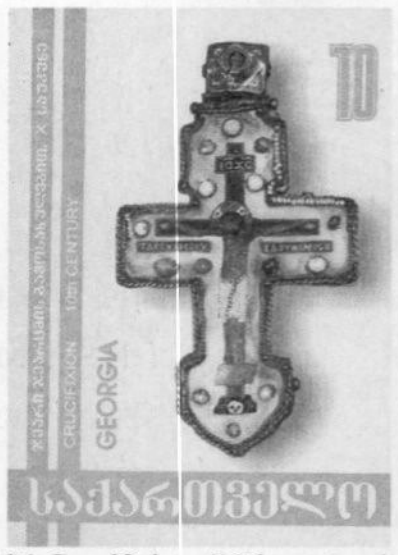

94 Crucifixion (10th-century)

95 The Annunciation

2002. Pectoral Crosses. Multicoloured.

382	10t. Type **94**	30	30
383	20t. Virgin and Child (Martvili, 7–9th century)	60	60
384	50t. Saints surrounding central stone (Martvili, 10th-century)	1·50	1·50
385	80t. Stone encrusted (King Tamari, 12th-century)	2·40	2·40

2002. Frescoes. Multicoloured.

386	10t. Type **95**	30	30
387	30t. Angel, Mary and Saints (horiz)	90	90
388	80t. Angel with upraised wings	2·40	2·40

96 Winning Football Team

2002. Dinamo Tbilisi. Winners of European Cup Winners Cup, 1981.

389	**96**	20t. multicoloured	65	65

97 Woman, House and Man holding Rifle

2002. Traditional Costumes. Multicoloured.

390	20t. Type **97**	65	65
391	30t. Woman, round tower and man holding dagger	95	95
392	50t. Woman, fortress and man holding sword and shield	1·50	1·50

98 Bell Flower

2002. Flowers. Multicoloured.

393	20t. Type **98**	70	70
394	30t. Caucasia rhododendron	95	95
395	50t. Anemone	1·50	1·50
396	80t. Marsh marigold	2·40	2·40

99 SU 25 Scorpio

2002. Aircraft. Multicoloured.

397	30t. Type **99**	95	95
398	80t. MIG 21U	2·40	2·40

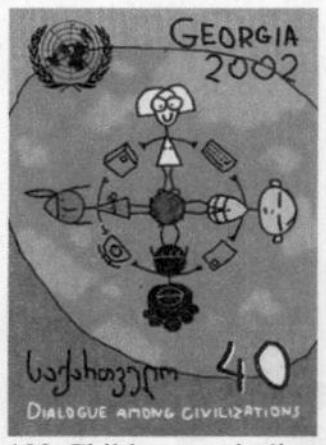

100 Children encircling Globe

101 First Georgian Stamp and Ifsda Emblem

2002. United Nations Year of Dialogue among Civilizations.

399	**100**	40t. multicoloured	1·20	1·20

2002. 50th Anniv of Ifsda (international federation of stamp dealers' association).

400	**101**	100t. multicoloured	2·50	2·50

102 Alexandre Dumas

103 Three men, Donkey and Dog

2002. Birth Bicentenary of Alexandre Dumas (writer). Sheet 124 × 104 mm.

MS401 **102**	120t. multicoloured	3·75	3·75

2003. Europa. Poster Art. Multicoloured.

402	40t. Type **103**	1·50	1·50
403	80t. Boy and men	2·75	2·75

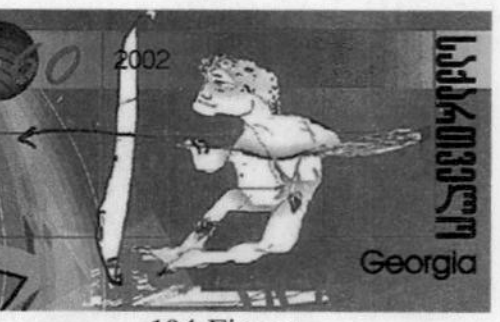

104 Figure

2003. Pre-historic Man. Sheet 130 × 76 mm containing T **104** and similar horiz design. Multicoloured.

MS404	60t. Type **104**; 60t. Skull	4·25	4·25

105 Players

106 Rainbow, Boy and Girl on Horseback

2003. World Cup Football Championship, Japan and South Korea. Sheet 82 × 105 mm.

MS405 **105**	1l. black, red and salmon	2·75	2·75

2003. Youth.

406	**106**	50t. multicoloured	1·20	1·20

107 Women holding Globe and Doves

2003. United Nations Development Fund for Women.

407	**107**	50t. multicoloured	1·20	1·20

108 Sloe (*Prunus spinosa*)

109 Elephant

2003. Fruits. Multicoloured.

408	10t. Type **108**	25	25
409	20t. Cherry laurel (*Laurocerasus officinalis*)	45	45
410	30t. Quince (*Cydonia oblonga*)	70	70
411	50t. Pomegranate (*Punica granatum*)	1·20	1·20
412	80t. Pear (*Pyrus caucasica*)	1·90	1·90

2003. Tbilisi Zoological Park. Multicoloured.

413	20t. Type **109**	45	45
414	30t. Wolf	70	70
415	40t. Ostrich	95	95
416	50t. Bear	1·20	1·20

110 Rock Crystal

2003. Minerals. Multicoloured.

417	10t. Type **110**	45	45
418	20t. Agate with amethyst	70	70
419	30t. Orpiment rose (*Arsenic Sulfide*)	95	95
420	50t. Realgar (*Arsenic Sulfide*)	1·20	1·20

111 "Old Tbilisi" and Elene Akhvlediani

2003. Birth Centenary (2001) of Elene Akhvlediani (artist). Sheet 170 × 75 mm.

MS421 **111**	80t. multicoloured	2·00	2·00

112 Self-portrait with Grey Felt Hat

2003. 150th Birth Anniv of Vincent Van Gogh (artist). Sheet 132 × 65 mm.

MS422 **112**	100t. multicoloured	2·75	2·75

(113)

2003. 10th Anniv of Georgia. No. 58 and **MS**61 optd with T **113**.

423	25t. multicoloured		
MS424	122 × 101 mm. 25, 50, 100t. multicoloured	3·00	3·00

114 Snow Slopes, Bakuriani

2003. Tourism. Multicoloured.

425	10t. Type **114**	45	45
426	20t. Caves, Vardzia	70	70
427	30t. Coastline and ship, Batumi	95	95
428	50t. Mountains and Lake Ritsa	1·20	1·20

115 Aladasturi

2003. Grapes. Multicoloured.

429	10t. Type **115**	45	45
430	20t. Rkhatsiteli	70	70
431	30t. Ojaleshi	95	95
432	50t. Goruli Mtsvane	1·20	1·20
433	80t. Aleksandrouli (Khvanchkhara)	1·90	1·90

116 Association Emblem

2003. 10th Anniv of International Association of Academies of Sciences.

434	**116**	30t. multicoloured	95	95

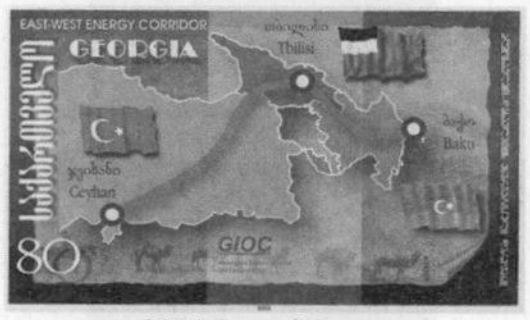

117 Map of Route

2003. Baku—Tbilisi—Ceyhan Oil Pipeline.

435	**117**	80t. multicoloured	95	95

GERMAN COMMANDS Pt. 7

EASTERN COMMAND

German occupation of Estonia, Latvia and Lithuania during the war of 1914–18.

100 pfennig = 1 mark.

1916. Stamps of Germany inscr "DEUTSCHES REICH" optd **Postgebiet Ob. Ost.**

1	**24**	2½pf. grey	60	1·50
2	**10**	3pf. brown	30	40
3		5pf. green	60	1·50
4	**24**	7½pf. orange	60	1·50
5	**10**	10pf. red	60	1·50
6	**24**	15pf. brown	3·00	3·00
7		15pf. violet	60	1·50
8	**10**	20pf. blue	95	1·50

9 25pf. black & red on yellow 40 75
10 40pf. black and red . . . . 1·25 5·50
11 50pf. black & pur on buff 1·25 2·25
12a **12** 1m. red . . . . 7·50 3·50

WESTERN COMMAND

For Forces in Belgium and Northern France.

100 centimes = 1 franc.

1916. Stamps of Germany surch with new values as **2 Cent., 1F.** or **1F.25 Cent.**
1 **10** 3c. on 3pf. brown 30 60
2 5c. on 5pf. green . . . . . 60 1·40
3 **24** 8c. on 7½pf. orange . . . . 60 1·40
4 **10** 10c. on 10pf. red . . . . . 1·40 2·75
5 **24** 15c. on 15pf. brown . . . 35 60
6 **10** 25c. on 20pf. blue . . . . 75 2·25
7 40c. on 30pf. black and orange on buff . . . . . 60 1·50
8 50c. on 40pf. black and red 75 1·50
9 75c. on 60pf. purple . . . 4·00 8·50
10 1f. on 80pf. black and red on red . . . . 3·75 7·00
11a **12** 1f.25 on 1m. red . . . . . 18·00 18·00
12 **13** 2f.50 on 2m. blue . . . . 20·00 25·00

GERMAN EAST AFRICA Pt. 7

A German colony on the east coast of Africa. Placed under British mandate after the First World War.

1893. 64 pesa = 1 rupee.
1905. 100 heller = 1 rupee.

1893. Stamps of Germany surch with value in "PESA".
1 **8** 2p. on 3pf. brown . . . . . . 38·00 42·00
2 3p. on 5pf. green . . . . . . 48·00 42·00
4 **9** 5p. on 10pf. red . . . . 30·00 18·00
5 10p. on 20pf. blue . . . . . . 22·00 10·00
6 25p. on 50pf. brown . . . . . 38·00 22·00

1896. Stamps of Germany surch **Deutsch-Ostafrika** and value in "Pesa".
7 **8** 2p. on 3pf. brown . . . . . 8·50 7·50
10 3p. on 5pf. green . . . . . . 2·00 3·50
11 **9** 5p. on 10pf. red . . . . . . 2·10 3·25
13 10p. on 20pf. blue . . . . . 4·50 4·25
14 25p. on 50pf. brown . . . . 22·00 24·00

1901. "Yacht", key-type inscr "DEUTSCH-OSTAFRIKA". Currency in pesa and rupees.
15 N 2p. brown . . . . 2·75 1·10
16 3p. green . . . . 2·75 1·50
17 5p. red . . . . 1·50 1·50
18 10p. blue . . . . 5·00 3·50
19 15p. black and orange on buff . . . . 5·50 4·50
20 20p. black and red . . . . . 7·25 11·00
21 25p. black and purple on buff . . . . 7·00 13·00
22 40p. black and red on rose 8·75 17·00
23 O 1r. red . . . . 20·00 48·00
24 2r. green . . . . 10·00 75·00
44 3r. black and red . . . . . 32·00 £180

1905. "Yacht" key-types inscr "DEUTSCH-OSTAFRIKA". Currency in heller.
34 N 2½h. brown 75 55
35 4h. green 65 50
36 7½h. red . . . . 1·00 35
37 15h. blue . . . . 1·75 65
38 20h. black and red on yellow 2·40 9·00
39 30h. black and red . . . . . 2·75 6·00
40 45h. black and mauve . . . 4·25 32·00
33 60h. black and red on rose 19·00 75·00

For stamps issued for this territory under British auspices since 1915 see under Tanganyika in Volume 4.

GERMAN NEW GUINEA Pt. 7

A German colony, part of the island of New Guinea.

100 pfennig = 1 mark.

1897. Stamps of Germany optd **Deutsch-Neu-Guinea**.
1a **8** 3pf. brown . . . . 7·00 7·00
2 5pf. green . . . . 3·25 4·00
3 **9** 10pf. red . . . . 5·75 6·75
4 20pf. blue . . . . 5·75 10·50
5 25pf. orange . . . . 24·00 48·00
6 50pf. brown . . . . 29·00 35·00

1901. "Yacht" key-types inscr "DEUTSCH-NEU-GUINEA".
7 N 3pf. brown 85 95
8 5pf. green . . . . 6·50 95
9 10pf. red . . . . 24·00 1·50
10 20pf. blue . . . . 1·40 1·50
11 25pf. black and red on yellow . . . . 1·40 10·50
12 30pf. black & orange on buff 1·40 15·00
13 40pf. black and red . . . . 1·40 16·00
14 50pf. black & purple on buff 1·90 15·00
15 80pf. black and red on rose 3·50 21·00
16 O 1m. red . . . . 4·25 35·00
17 2m. blue . . . . 4·75 60·00
18 3m. black . . . . 7·25 £120
19 5m. red and black £120 £400

Australian forces occupied German New Guinea in 1914 and it was administered as a League of Nations mandate from 1920. For stamps issued since 1914 see under New Guinea.

GERMAN OCCUPATION OF ALSACE Pt. 7

100 pfennig = 1 mark.

1940. Stamps of Germany optd **Elsa**.
1 **94** 3pf. brown 40 40
2 4pf. slate 75 75
3 5pf. green 40 40
4 6pf. green 40 40
5 8pf. orange 40 40
6 10pf. brown 40 60
7 12pf. red 40 40
8 15pf. red 75 75
9 20pf. blue 75 75
10 25pf. blue . . . . 95 1·25
11 30pf. olive . . . . 1·10 1·25
12 40pf. mauve . . . . 1·10 1·25
13 50pf. black and green . . . 1·75 1·75
14 60pf. black and red . . . . 2·00 2·00
15 80pf. black and blue . . . . 3·50 3·50
16 100pf. black and yellow . . 5·50 4·00

GERMAN OCCUPATION OF BELGIUM Pt. 4

German occupation of E. Belgium during the war of 1914–18.

100 centimes = 1 franc.

Stamps of Germany inscr "DEUTSCHES REICH" surcharged.

1914. Surch **Belgien** and value thus: **3 Centimes, 1Franc** or **1Fr.25C.**
1 **10** 3c. on 3pf. brown 40 35
2 5c. on 5pf. green 40 30
3 10c. on 10pf. red 45 30
4 25c. on 20pf. blue . . . . . 75 1·10
5 50c. on 40pf. black and red 2·75 1·40
6 75c. on 60pf. purple . . . . 1·00 1·40
7 1f. on 80pf. black and red on rose . . . . 2·10 1·60
8 **12** 1f.25 on 1m. red . . . . . 21·00 11·50
9 **13** 2f.50 on 2m. blue . . . . . 18·00 14·50

1916. Surch **Belgien** and value, thus: **2 Cent.,1F.**, or **1F.25Cent.**
10 **24** 2c. on 2pf. grey 30 80
11 **10** 3c. on 3pf. brown . . . . 40 1·40
12 5c. on 5pf. green . . . . . 40 1·40
13 **24** 8c. on 7½pf. orange . . . . 50 1·40
14 **10** 10c. on 10pf. red . . . . . 30 1·00
15 **24** 15c. on 15pf. brown 50 95
16 15c. on 15pf. violet . . . . 30 1·40
17 **10** 20c. on 25pf. black and red on yellow . . . . 35 1·40
18 25c. on 20pf. blue . . . . . 35 1·40
19 40c. on 30pf. black and orange on buff 30 40
20 50c. on 40pf. black and red 30 1·40
21 75c. on 60pf. mauve . . . . 1·50 19·00
22 1f. on 80f. black and red on rose . . . . 1·40 1·25
23a **12** 1f.25 on 1m. red . . . . . 2·50 2·50
24 **13** 2f.50 on 2m. blue . . . . . 21·00 22·00
25 **15** 6f.25 on 5m. red and black 25·00 28·00

GERMAN OCCUPATION OF DALMATIA Pt. 3

Areas formerly under Italian control which were occupied by the Germans in 1943.

A. ZARA (Zadar)

100 centesimi = 1 lira.

1943. Imperial series of Italy, 1929, optd **Deutsche Besetzung Zara**.
1 **98** 5c. brown . . . . 60·00 £120
2 – 10c. brown . . . . 5·25 9·00
3 – 15c. green . . . . 8·25 17·00
4 **99** 20c. red . . . . 5·25 10·50
5 – 25c. green . . . . 5·25 10·50
6 **103** 30c. brown . . . . 5·25 10·50
7 – 35c. blue £200 £375
8 – 75c. red . . . . 17·00 26·00
9 **99** 1l. violet . . . . 5·25 10·50
10 1l.25 blue . . . . 9·00 17·00
11 1l.75 red . . . . 25·00 48·00
12 – 2l. red . . . . 48·00 75·00
13 **98** 2l.55 green £300 £500
14 3l.70 violet £1800 £3000
15 5l. red . . . . 50·00 75·00
16 – 10l. violet £900 £1300
17 **99** 20l. green £13000 £13000
18 – 25l. black £24000 £24000
19 – 50l. violet £21000 £14000

1943. War Propaganda stamps of Italy (Nos. 571/4) optd **Deutsche Besetzung Zara** on stamp and label.
20 **103** 50c. violet (Navy) . . . . 10·50 21·00
21 50c. violet (Army) . . . . 10·50 21·00
22 50c. violet (Air Force) . . 10·50 21·00
23 50c. violet (Militia) . . . . 10·50 21·00

1943. Air. Nos. 270/7 of Italy optd **Deutsche Besetzung Zara**.
26 – 25c. green . . . . 9·00 17·00
27 **110** 50c. brown . . . . 8·25 17·00
28 – 75c. brown £325 £450
29 – 80c. red . . . . 38·00 65·00
30 – 1l. violet . . . . 10·50 17·00
31 **113** 2l. blue . . . . 24·00 38·00
32 **110** 5l. green £6500 £6500
33 10l. red £14000 £14000

1943. Imperial series of Italy, 1929, optd **ZARA** within pattern of bars.
46 **103** 50c. violet . . . . 5·75 15·00
47 – 75c. red . . . . 7·00 17·00
48 – 1l.25 blue . . . . 60·00 £110

1943. War Propaganda stamps of Italy (Nos. 563/70) optd **ZARA** within pattern of bars on stamp and label.
49 – 25c. green (Navy) . . . . 13·00 22·00
50 – 25c. green (Army) . . . . 13·00 22·00
51 – 25c. green (Air Force) . . 13·00 22·00
52 – 25c. green (Militia) . . . 13·00 22·00
53 **103** 30c. brown (Navy) . . . . 11·00 18·00
54 30c. brown (Army) . . . . 11·00 18·00
55 30c. brown (Air Force) . . 11·00 18·00
56 30c. brown (Militia) . . . 11·00 18·00

EXPRESS LETTER STAMPS

1943. Nos. E350/1 of Italy optd **Deutsche Besetzung Zara**.
E24 **E 132** 1l.25 green . . . . . . 13·00 25·00
E25 2l.50 orange . . . . . 70·00 £100

1943. Air. No. E370 of Italy optd **Deutsche Besetzung Zara**.
E34 **E 133** 2l. black . . . . 25·00 38·00

1943. Nos. E350/1 of Italy optd **ZARA** within pattern of bars, twice.
E57 **E 132** 1l.25 green . . . . . . 20·00 27·00
E58 2l.50 orange £130 £180

POSTAGE DUE STAMPS

1943. Italian Postage Due stamps optd **Deutsche Besetzung Zara**.
D35 **D 141** 5c. brown . . . . . . 28·00 75·00
D36 10c. blue . . . . . . 28·00 75·00
D37 20c. red . . . . 25·00 75·00
D38 25c. green £700 £750
D39 30c. red . . . . 25·00 75·00
D40 40c. brown . . . . . 25·00 75·00
D41 50c. violet . . . . . . 25·00 75·00
D42 60c. blue £700 £800
D43 **D 142** 1l. orange £650 £800
D44 2l. green £750 £1000
D45 5l. violet £650 £800

B. GULF OF KOTOR

Italian and German currency.

1944. Imperial series of Italy, 1929, surch **Deutsche Militar-verwaltung Kotor** and new value in lire.
1 – 0.50LIT. on 10c. brown . . 50·00 70·00
2 – 1LIT. on 25c. green . . . 50·00 70·00
3 **103** 1.50LIT. on 50c. violet . . 50·00 70·00
4 3LIT. on 30c. brown . . . 50·00 70·00
5 **99** 4LIT. on 20c. red . . . . 50·00 70·00
6 10LIT. on 20c. red . . . . 50·00 70·00

1944. Nos. 419/20 of Yugoslavia (King Petar II) surch **Boka Kotorska** and new value in Reichsmarks.
7 **99** 0,10R.M. on 3d. brown . . 4·50 4·50
8 0,15R.M. on 3d. brown . . 4·50 4·50
9 0,25R.M. on 4d. blue . . . 7·00 8·50
10 0,50R.M. on 4d. blue . . . 11·00 13·00

GERMAN OCCUPATION OF ESTONIA Pt. 10

100 kopeks = 1 rouble.

2

3 "Long Hermann" Tower, Reval (Tallinn)

1941. Tartu issue.
3A **2** 15(k.) brown . . . . 13·00 14·00
4A 20(k.) green . . . . 10·50 12·00
5A 30(k.) blue . . . . 10·50 12·00

Originally issued for local use, the above were made available for use throughout Estonia from 29.9.41 to 30.4.42. However, not many were used since the German **OSTLAND** stamps were used from 1 December 1941.

1941. Reconstruction Fund.
6 **3** 15+15(k.) sepia and brown 35 3·50
7 – 20+20(k.) purple and brown 35 3·50
8 – 30+30(k.) blue and brown . . 35 3·50
9 – 50+50(k.) green and brown 40 7·00
10 – 60+60(k.) red and brown . . 55 5·50
11 – 100+100(k.) slate and brown 95 8·75
DESIGNS—HORIZ: 20k. Stone Bridge, Tartu; 30k. Two Narva Castles; 50k. Reval of Tallinn. VERT: 60k. Tartu University; 100k. Hermann Castle, Narva.

German stamps optd **OSTLAND** (see German Occupation of Russia, Nos. 1/20) were used from 1 December 1941 until the Russian re-occupation of Estonia in 1944. Since then Russian stamps have been in use.

GERMAN OCCUPATION OF LATVIA Pt. 10

100 kopeks = 1 rouble.

1941. Russian stamps of 1936–39 optd **LATVIJA 1941. 1. VII.**
1 5k. red (No. 847a) . . . . . . 90 4·00
2 10k. blue (No. 727f) . . . . . 90 4·00
3 15k. green (No. 847c) . . . . . 25·00 70·00
4 20k. green (No. 727h) . . . . . 90 4·00
5 30k. blue (No. 847d) . . . . . 90 4·00
6 50k. brown on buff (No. 727m) 1·90 8·50

German stamps optd **OSTLAND** (see German Occupation of Russia, Nos. 1/20) were used from 4th November, 1941, until the Russian re-occupation of Latvia in 1944–45. Since then Russian stamps have been in use.

GERMAN OCCUPATION OF LITHUANIA Pt. 10

100 kopeks = 1 rouble.

1941. Russian stamps of 1936–40 optd **NEPRIKLAUSOMA LIETUVA 1941-VI-23.**
1 2k. green (No. 542) . . . . . . 32·00 £120
2 5k. red (No. 847a) . . . . . . 1·60 7·50
3 10k. blue (No. 727f) . . . . . 1·60 7·50
4 15k. green (No. 847c) . . . . . 1·60 7·50
5 20k. green (No. 727h) . . . . . 1·60 7·50
6 30k. blue (No. 847d) . . . . . 1·60 7·50
7 50k. brown on buff (No. 727m) 5·50 18·00
8 60k. red (No. 847f) . . . . . . 7·00 28·00
9 80k. blue (No. 905) . . . . . . 14·00 40·00

1941. Issue for Vilnius and South Lithuania. Russian stamps of 1936–39 optd **VILNIUS**.
10 5k. red (No. 847a) . . . . . 1·90 3·00
11 10k. blue (No. 727f) . . . . . 2·25 3·00
12 15k. green (No. 847c) . . . . 2·25 3·00
13 20k. green (No. 727h) . . . . 5·75 10·50
14 30k. blue (No. 847d) . . . . . 5·00 7·50
15 50k. brown on buff (No. 727m) . . . . 5·75 7·50
16 60k. red (No. 847f) . . . . . 5·75 8·25
17 80k. red and deep red (No. 772) £250 £225
18 1r. black and red (No. 779) . . £700 £600

German stamps optd **OSTLAND** (see German Occupation of Russia, Nos. 1/20) were used from 4th November, 1941, till the Russian re-occupation of Lithuania in 1944. Since then Russian stamps have been in use.

GERMAN OCCUPATION OF LORRAINE Pt. 7

100 pfennig = 1 mark.

1940. Stamps of Germany optd **Lothringen**.
1 **94** 3pf. brown 45 70
2 4pf. slate 45 70
3 5pf. green 45 70
4 6pf. green 45 55
5 8pf. orange 45 70
6 10pf. brown 45 65
7 12pf. red 45 65
8 15pf. lake 45 80
9 20pf. blue 45 80
10 25pf. blue . . . . 60 1·10
11 30pf. olive . . . . 70 1·25
12 40pf. mauve . . . . 80 1·25
13 50pf. black and green . . . 1·10 2·00
14 60pf. black and red . . . . 1·10 2·50
15 80pf. black and blue . . . . 2·25 2·75
16 100pf. black and yellow . . 3·00 5·00

GERMAN OCCUPATION OF POLAND Pt. 5

German occupation of Poland, 1915–18.

100 pfennig = 1 mark.

1915. Stamps of Germany inscr "DEUTSCHES REICH" optd **Russisch-Polen**.

1	10	3pf. brown	40	40
2		5pf. green	75	35
3		10pf. red	80	35
4		20pf. blue	1·50	50
5		40pf. black and red	4·25	2·40

1916. Stamps of Germany inscr "DEUTSCHES REICH" optd **Gen.-Gouv. Warschau**.

6	24	2½pf. grey	60	1·25
7	10	3pf. brown	70	1·40
8		5pf. green	70	1·10
9	24	7½pf. orange	70	95
10	10	10pf. red	70	1·25
11	24	15pf. brown	2·25	1·90
12		15pf. violet	55	1·10
13	10	20pf. blue	90	1·40
14		30pf. black & orange on buff	3·50	8·00
15		40pf. black and red	1·40	1·25
16		60pf. purple	1·25	1·60

GERMAN OCCUPATION OF RUMANIA Pt. 3

German occupation of Rumania, 1917–18.

100 bani = 1 leu.

Stamps of Germany inscr "DEUTSCHES REICH".

1917. Surch **M.V.i.R.** in frame and value in "Bani".

1	24	15b. on 15pf. violet	1·10	1·25
2	10	25b. on 20pf. blue	1·00	1·25
3		40b. on 30pf. black and orange on buff	23·00	29·00

1917. Surch **M.V.i.R.** (not in frame) and value in "Bani".

4	10	10b. on 10pf. red	60	1·25
5	24	15b. on 15pf. violet	4·25	5·00
6	10	25b. on 20pf. blue	60	2·25
7		40b. on 30pf. black and orange on buff	1·00	1·25

1918. Surch **Rumanien** and value in "Bani".

8	10	5b. on 5pf. green	20	50
9		10b. on 10pf. red	50	90
10	24	15b. on 15pf. violet	35	25
11	10	25b. on 20pf. blue	1·25	1·25
12		40b. on 30pf. black and orange on buff	40	40

1918. Stamps of Germany inscr "DEUTSCHES REICH" optd **Gultig 9. Armee** in frame.

13	10	10pf. red	12·00	48·00
14	24	15pf. violet	18·00	40·00
15	10	20pf. blue	3·25	2·25
16		30pf. black & orange on buff	15·00	24·00

POSTAGE DUE STAMPS

1918. Postage Due stamps of Rumania optd **M.V.i.R.** in frame.

D1B	D 38	5b. blue on green	6·00	14·50
D2B		10b. blue on green	6·00	12·50
D3B		20b. blue on green	6·00	5·00
D4B		30b. blue on green	6·00	5·00
D5B		50b. blue on green	6·00	5·00

GERMAN OCCUPATION OF RUSSIA Pt. 10

100 pfennig = 1 reichsmark.

1941. Issue for Ostland. Stamps of Germany of 1941 optd **OSTLAND**.

1	173	1pf. grey	15	20
2		3pf. brown	15	20
3		4pf. slate	15	20
4		5pf. green	15	20
5		6pf. violet	15	20
6		8pf. red	15	20
7		10pf. brown	1·40	1·25
10		12pf. red	55	2·50
11		15pf. lake	10	20
12		16pf. green	40	40
13		20pf. blue	10	10
14		24pf. brown	40	35
15		25pf. blue	25	20
16		30pf. olive	25	20
17		40pf. mauve	25	35
18		50pf. green	25	35
19		60pf. brown	25	35
20		80pf. blue	25	80

1941. Issue for Ukraine. Stamps of Germany of 1941 optd **UKRAINE**.

21	173	1pf. grey	10	10
22		3pf. brown	10	10
23		4pf. slate	10	10
24		5pf. green	10	10
25		6pf. violet	10	10
26		8pf. red	10	10
27		10pf. brown	1·00	1·50
29		12pf. red	1·00	1·50
31		15pf. lake	20	20
32		16pf. green	25	35
33		20pf. blue	20	11
34		24pf. brown	25	35
35		25pf. blue	25	20
36		30pf. olive	25	10
37		40pf. mauve	20	35
38		50pf. green	25	20
39		60pf. brown	25	30
40		80pf. blue	25	35

GERMAN OCCUPATION OF ZANTE Pt. 3

German occupation of Ionian Islands, 1943–44.

100 centesimi = 1 lira = 8 drachma.

(1)

1943. Stamps of Italian Occupation of Ionian Islands further optd with T **1**.

1	–	25c. green (postage)	22·00	60·00
2	103	50c. violet	22·00	60·00
3	110	50c. brown (air)	£110	£190

GERMAN POST OFFICES IN CHINA Pt. 7

German post offices in China, now closed.

1898. 100 pfennig = 1 mark.
1905. 100 cents = 1 dollar.

1898. Stamps of Germany optd **China**.

7	8	3pf. brown	5·50	4·50
8		5pf. green	2·25	1·75
9	9	10pf. red	4·75	4·50
4		20pf. blue	13·00	7·00
11		25pf. orange	27·00	25·00
12		50pf. brown	13·00	9·50

1901. Stamps of Germany inscr "REICHSPOST" optd **China**.

22	10	3pf. brown	1·10	1·40
23		5pf. green	1·10	80
24		10pf. red	1·25	55
25		20pf. blue	3·00	95
26		25pf. black & red on yellow	9·50	13·00
27		30pf. black & orge on pink	9·00	9·50
28		40pf. black and red	10·50	7·00
29		50pf. black & pur on pink	10·50	7·00
30		80pf. black and red on pink	11·00	9·00
31	12	1m. red	30·00	29·00
32	13	2m. blue	26·00	30·00
33	14	3m. black	42·00	40·00
35b	15	5m. red and black	£170	£250

1905. Stamps of Germany inscr "DEUTSCHES REICH" surch **China** and new value.

46	10	1c. on 3pf. brown	35	75
47		2c. on 5pf. green	35	40
48		4c. on 10pf. red	35	40
39		10c. on 20pf. blue	3·00	85
50		20c. on 40pf. black and red	1·40	1·75
51		40c. on 80pf. black and red on rose	1·50	30·00
42	12	½d. on 1m. red	12·00	17·00
43	13	1d. on 2m. blue	13·00	16·00
44a	14	1½d. on 3m. black	14·00	40·00
55	15	2½d. on 5m. red and black	85·00	£120

GERMAN POST OFFICES IN MOROCCO Pt. 7

German Post Offices in Morocco, now closed.

100 centimos = 1 peseta.

Stamps of Germany surcharged **Marocco** (or **Marokko**) and new value.

1889. Spelt **Marocco**.

1	8	3c. on 3pf. brown	2·75	2·00
2		5c. on 5pf. green	2·75	2·00
3	9	10c. on 10pf. red	5·00	5·00
4		25c. on 20pf. blue	12·00	12·50
5		30c. on 25pf. orange	23·00	24·00
6		60c. on 50pf. brown	18·00	27·00

1900. Inscr "REICHSPOST" surch **Marocco** (3c. to 1p.) or **Marocco Marocco** (others).

7	10	3c. on 3pf. brown	1·25	1·40
8		5c. on 5pf. green	1·40	1·00
9		10c. on 10pf. red	1·25	85
10		25c. on 20pf. blue	2·25	1·50
11		30c. on 25pf. black and red on yellow	9·00	11·00
12		35c. on 30pf. black and orange on rose	3·75	4·50
13		50c. on 40pf. black and red	6·00	4·50
14		60c. on 50pf. black and purple on rose	15·00	26·00
15		1p. on 80pf. black and red on rose	24·00	32·00
16	12	1p.25 on 1m. red	29·00	40·00
17	13	2p.50 on 2m. blue	28·00	55·00
18	14	3p.75 on 3m. black	40·00	60·00
19b	15	6p.25 on 5m. red and black	£210	£275

1905. Inscr "DEUTSCHES REICH" surch **Marocco** (3c. to 1p.) or **Marocco Marocco** (others).

26	10	3c. on 3pf. brown	2·75	2·00
27		5c. on 5pf. green	3·75	75
28		10c. on 10pf. red	4·00	65
42		25c. on 20pf. blue	16·00	4·25
30		30c. on 25pf. black and red on yellow	6·75	3·75
31		35c. on 30pf. black and orange on buff	8·00	5·25
32		50c. on 40pf. black and red	8·00	6·00
33		60c. on 50pf. black and purple on buff	26·00	17·00
34		1p. on 80pf. black and red on rose	26·00	14·00
35a	12	1p.25 on 1m. red	45·00	35·00
36	13	2p.50 on 2m. blue	80·00	85·00
37a	14	3p.75 on 3m. black	48·00	45·00
38	15	6p.25 on 5m. red & black	£120	£140

1911. Inscr "DEUTSCHES REICH". Spelt **Marokko**.

51	10	3c. on 3pf. brown	45	45
52		5c. on 5pf. green	40	70
53		10c. on 10pf. red	40	70
54		25c. on 20pf. blue	60	90
55		30c. on 25pf. black and red on yellow	1·25	13·00
56		35c. on 30pf. black and orange on buff	1·10	4·00
57		50c. on 40pf. black and red	1·25	3·75
58		60c. on 50pf. black and purple on buff	1·90	27·00
59		1p. on 80pf. black and red on rose	1·75	18·00
60	12	1p.25 on 1m. red	2·75	48·00
61	13	2p.50 on 2m. blue	5·50	30·00
62	14	3p.75 on 3m. black	7·00	£160
63	15	6p.25 on 5m. red & black	17·00	£250

GERMAN POST OFFICES IN THE TURKISH EMPIRE Pt. 7

German Post Offices in the Turkish Empire, now closed.

1884. 40 para = 1 piastre.
1908. 100 centimes = 1 franc.

1884. Stamps of Germany inscr "DEUTSCHE REICHS-POST" and "PFENNIG" without final "E" surch with new value.

1	5	10pa. on 5pf. mauve	28·00	27·00
2	6	20pa. on 10pf. red	60·00	75·00
3		1pi. on 20pf. blue	60·00	4·50
4		1¼pi. on 25pf. brown	£120	£225
6		2½pi. on 50pf. green	90·00	70·00

1889. Stamps of Germany inscr "REICHSPOST" surch.

10	8	10pa. on 5pf. green	3·00	3·25
11	9	20pa. on 10pf. red	7·00	2·00
12		1pi. on 20pf. blue	4·50	1·75
14		1¼pi. on 25pf. orange	23·00	16·00
16		2½pi. on 50pf. brown	35·00	23·00

1900. Stamps of Germany inscr "REICHSPOST" surch in **PARA** or **PIASTER**.

17	10	10pa. on 5pf. green	1·60	1·60
18		20pa. on 10pf. red	1·90	1·90
19		1pi. on 20pf. blue	4·25	1·50
20		1¼pi. on 25pf. black and red on yellow	5·75	3·50
21		1½pi. on 30pf. black and orange on buff	6·50	4·00
22		2pi. on 40pf. black and red	7·50	4·00
23		2½pi. on 50pf. black and purple on buff	11·50	11·50
24		4pi. on 80pf. black and red on rose	14·00	11·50
25	12	5pi. on 1m. red	28·00	35·00
26	13	10pi. on 2m. blue	28·00	38·00
27	14	15pi. on 3m. black	40·00	90·00
28a	15	25pi. on 5m. red and black	£140	£250

1905. Stamps of Germany inscr "DEUTSCHES REICH" surch in **Para** or **Piaster**.

47	10	10pa. on 5pf. green	1·90	50
48		20pa. on 10pf. red	2·25	50
49		1pi. on 20pf. blue	3·75	60
38		1¼pi. on 25pf. black and red on yellow	11·00	11·00
51		1½pi. on 30pf. black and orange on buff	11·50	8·75
52		2pi. on 40pf. black and red	4·50	1·75
53		2½pi. on 50pf. black and purple on buff	9·00	7·00
54		4pi. on 80pf. black and red on pink	10·50	32·00
55	12	5pi. on 1m. red	18·00	32·00
56	13	10pi. on 2m. blue	18·00	45·00
45	14	15pi. on 3m. black	25·00	48·00
58	15	25pi. on 5m. red and black	26·00	70·00

1908. Stamps of Germany inscr "DEUTSCHES REICH", surch in **Centimes**.

60	10	5c. on 5pf. green	1·40	1·90
61		10c. on 10pf. red	2·00	4·25
62		25c. on 20pf. blue	7·50	25·00
63		50c. on 40pf. black and red	27·00	60·00
64		100c. on 80pf. black and red on rose	60·00	70·00

GERMAN SOUTH WEST AFRICA Pt. 7

A German colony in S.W. Africa.

100 pfennig = 1 mark.

1897. Stamps of Germany optd. (a) **Deutsch-Sudwest-Afrika**.

1	8	3pf. brown	6·00	8·00
2		5pf. green	3·00	2·75
3	9	10pf. red	12·00	16·00
4		20pf. blue	2·10	2·10

(b) **Deutsch-Sudwestafrika**.

5	8	3pf. brown	3·50	9·00
6		5pf. green	2·75	2·00
7	9	10pf. red	2·75	2·75
8		20pf. blue	14·00	10·50
9		25pf. orange	£275	£350
10		50pf. brown	18·00	10·50

1901. "Yacht" key-types inscr "DEUTSCH-SUDWESTAFRIKA".

24	N	3pf. brown	70	75
25		5pf. green	70	60
26		10pf. red	1·00	85
27		20pf. blue	90	2·40
15		25pf. black and red on yellow	1·40	3·75
16		30pf. black & orange on buff	22·00	2·10
17		40pf. black and red	1·90	3·00
18		50pf. black & purple on buff	1·90	2·25
19		80pf. black and red on rose	2·00	6·75
29	O	1m. red	13·00	55·00
30		2m. blue	12·00	18·00
22		3m. black	28·00	38·00
32		5m. red and black	19·00	£200

South Africa occupied the colony in 1914 and administered the territory under a League of Nations mandate from 1920. For stamps issued from 1923 see under South West Africa in Volume 4.

GERMANY Pt. 7

A country in Northern Central Europe. A federation of states forming the German Reich. An empire till November 1918 and then a republic until the collapse of Germany in 1945. Until 1949 under Allied Military Control when the German Federal Republic was set up for W. Germany and the German Democratic Republic for E. Germany. See also notes before No. 899.

I. GERMANY 1871–1945

1872. Northern areas including Alsace and Lorraine: 30 groschen = 1 thaler. Southern areas: 90 kreuzer = 1 gulden.
1875. Throughout Germany: 100 pfennig = 1 mark.
1923. 100 renten-pfennig = 1 rentenmark (gold currency).
1928. 100 pfennig = 1 reichsmark

1

A

1872. Arms embossed as Type A.

1	1	¼g. violet	£225	80·00
2		⅓g. green	£475	33·00
3		½g. red	£850	33·00
4		½g. yellow	£1400	40·00
5		1g. red	£275	14·00
6		2g. blue	£1600	10·50
7		5g. bistre	£700	85·00
8		1k. green	£700	60·00
9		2k. red	£500	£325
10		2k. yellow	39·00	£180
11		3k. red	£1600	13·50
12		7k. blue	£2500	80·00
13		18k. bistre	£500	£425

2

B

1872.

14	2	10g. grey	55·00	£150
15	–	30g. blue	£120	£550
38d	2	2m. purple	75·00	3·25

On the 30g. the figures are in a rectangular frame.

1872. Arms embossed as Type B.

16	1	¼g. purple	70·00	£110
17		⅓g. green	39·00	13·50
18		½g. orange	43·00	5·75
19		1g. red	55·00	2·00
20		2g. blue	24·00	4·75
21		2½g. brown	£2000	50·00
22		5g. olive	25·00	22·00
23		1k. green	39·00	26·00
24		2k. orange	£475	£2250
25		3k. red	21·00	3·50
26		7k. blue	36·00	55·00
27		9k. brown	£325	£200
28		18k. olive	39·00	£1800

1874. Surch with bold figures over arms.

29	1	"2½" on 2½g. brown	43·00	31·00
30		"9" on 9k. brown	75·00	£350

5

6

1875. "PFENNIGE" with final "E".

31	5	3pf. green	70·00	4·50
32		5pf. mauve	£110	2·75
33	6	10pf. red	43·00	90
34a		20pf. blue	£500	1·50
35		25pf. brown	£550	13·00
36a		50pf. grey	£1700	10·50
37		50pf. green	£1900	£170

1880. "PFENNIG" without final "E".

39a	5	3pf. green	3·50	90
40a		5pf. purple	1·70	75
41b	6	10pf. red	8·25	70
42a		20pf. blue	6·75	75
43b		25pf. brown	21·00	3·75
44a		50pf. green	8·50	1·00

8

9

1889.

45	8	2pf. grey	50	75
46		3pf. brown	2·00	70
47a		5pf. green	1·50	70
48b	9	10pf. red	1·50	55
49		20pf. blue	10·50	55
50b		25pf. yellow	30·00	1·20
51b		50pf. brown	27·00	75

10 "Germania"

12 General Post Office, Berlin

13 Allegory of Union of N. and S. Germany (after Anton von Werner)

14 Unveiling of Kaiser Wilhelm I Memorial in Berlin (after W. Pape)

15 25th Anniv of German Empire Address by Wilhelm II (after W. Pape)

1899. Types **10** to **15** inscr "REICHSPOST".

52	10	2pf. grey	85	55
53		3pf. brown	1·00	55
54		5pf. green	1·30	55
55		10pf. red	2·10	55
56		20pf. blue	10·50	55
57B		25pf. black & red on yellow	14·50	3·00
58B		30pf. black & orge on rose	21·00	60
59B		40pf. black and red	26·00	95
60B		50pf. black & pur on rose	26·00	80
61B		80pf. black and red on rose	47·00	1·70
62	12	1m. red	85·00	1·80
63	13	2m. blue	85·00	5·50
64	14	3m. black	£110	55·00
65b	15	5m. red and black	£350	£375

1902. T **10** to **15** inscr "DEUTSCHES REICH".

67	10	2pf. grey	1·60	45
83a		3pf. brown	85	65
84a		5pf. green	1·60	60
85a		10pf. red	4·50	40
86d		20pf. blue	85	85
87		25pf. black & red on yellow	70	90
88a		30pf. black & orge on buff	70	90
89a		40pf. black and red	1·10	85
90a		50pf. black & pur on buff	70	90
91a		60pf. purple	1·70	1·10
92a		80pf. black and red on rose	1·30	1·50
93B	12	1m. red	2·10	1·20
94B	13	2m. blue	5·50	4·00
95B	14	3m. black	2·40	3·50
96B	15	5m. red and black	2·10	4·00

No. 93 has three pedestrians in front of the carriage in the right foreground and has no tram in the background. See No. 113 for redrawn design.

24 Unshaded background

26

27

28

1916. Inscr "DEUTSCHES REICH".

97	24	2pf. grey	20	3·50
98		2½pf. grey	15	85
140	10	5pf. brown	15	65
99a	24	7½pf. yellow	15	95
141	10	10pf. orange	15	55
100	24	15pf. brown	3·00	1·00
101		15pf. violet	15	95
102		15pf. purple	40	1·10
142	10	20pf. green	15	1·00
143a		30pf. blue	15	1·00
103	24	35pf. brown	15	1·10
144a	10	40pf. red	15	1·00
145a		50pf. purple	70	1·40
146		60pf. olive	15	1·20
104		75pf. black and green	15	95
147a		75pf. purple	15	90
148a		80pf. blue	10	1·10
149		1m. green and violet	15	1·00
113	12	1m. red	2·10	1·40
150	10	1¼m. purple and red	15	90
114	12	1m.25 green	1·70	1·20
115		1m.50 brown	5·25	4·00
151	10	2m. blue and red	70	1·00
116a	13	2m.50 red	1·00	1·50
152	10	4m. red and black	15	1·30

No. 113 has one pedestrian behind the carriage in the right foreground and a tram in the background.

1919. War Wounded Fund. Surch **5 Pf. fur Kriegs = beschadigte**.

105	10	10pf.+5pf. (No. 85a)	50	5·25
106	24	15pf.+5pf. (No. 101)	50	5·25

1919. National Assembly, Weimar.

107	26	10pf. red	15	1·30
108	27	15pf. blue and brown	15	1·30
109	28	25pf. red and green	15	1·40
110		30pf. red and purple	20	1·40

29

30 L.V.G. Schneider Biplane

1919. Air.

111	29	10pf. orange	15	2·00
112	30	40pf. green	15	3·00

1920. Stamps of Bavaria optd **Deutsches Reich**.

117	26	5pf. green	15	1·20
118		10pf. orange	15	1·10
119		15pf. red	15	1·00
120	27	20pf. purple	15	95
121		30pf. blue	15	95
122		40pf. brown	15	95
123	28	50pf. red	15	1·40
124		60pf. green	15	95
125		75pf. purple	45	4·25
126		80pf. blue	20	1·80
127	29	1m. red and grey	45	1·90
128		1¼m. blue and bistre	45	1·90
129		1½m. green and grey	45	2·75
130		2m. violet and bistre	85	3·25
131		2½m. black and grey	15	2·10
132	30	3m. blue	3·50	10·50
133		4m. red	3·50	8·50
134		5m. yellow	3·00	8·00
135		10m. green	2·75	9·50
136		20m. black	6·00	11·00

1920. Surch with new value and stars.

137	12	1m.25 on 1m. green	35	5·75
138		1m.50 on 1m. brown	35	6·50
139	13	2m.50 on 2m. purple	8·50	£200

35

36 Blacksmiths

37 Miners

38 Reapers

40

41 Ploughman

39 Posthorn

1921.

153	35	5pf. red	10	1·50
154		10pf. olive	15	1·20
155		15pf. blue	10	95
156		25pf. brown	10	90
157		30pf. green	10	90
158		40pf. orange	10	90
182		50pf. purple	25	1·10
160	36	60pf. red	4·25	90
184	35	75pf. blue	10	2·50
161	36	80pf. red	30	25·00
186	37	100pf. green	25	1·70
163		120pf. blue	10	1·00
188	38	150pf. orange	20	1·10
165		160pf. green	10	6·50
193	40	5m. orange	25	1·10
170		10m. red	35	2·30
195	41	20m. blue and green	15	4·25

1921. 1902 stamps surch.

172	10	1m.60 on 5pf. brown	20	1·10
173		3m. on 1¼m. purple and red	15	1·30
174		5m. on 75pf. purple	20	1·30
175		10m. on 75pf. purple	40	1·60

1921.

190	39	2m. violet and pink	45	1·70
204		2m. purple	20	1·00
191		3m. red and yellow	40	5·50
205		3m. red	10	85
192		4m. green and light green	10	1·10
206		4m. green	20	1·10
207		5m. orange and yellow	15	1·20
208		5m. orange	20	1·10
209		6m. blue	20	1·10
210		8m. green	20	1·20
211		10m. red and pink	15	1·00
212		20m. violet and red	25	1·00
213		20m. violet	20	1·10
214		30m. brown and yellow	20	1·00
215		30m. brown	70	24·00
216		40m. green	15	1·50
217		50m. green and purple	20	1·10

47 Arms of Munich

48

1922. Munich Exhibition.

198	47	1¼m. red	20	1·10
199		2m. violet	20	1·10
200		3m. red	20	1·20
201		4m. blue	20	1·30
202		10m. brown on buff	70	2·20
203		20m. red on rose	3·75	7·75

1922. Air.

218	48	25pf. brown	50	16·00
219		40pf. orange	45	26·00
220		50pf. purple	30	8·50
221		60pf. red	60	20·00
222		80pf. green	35	17·00
223	–	1m. green	20	4·25
224	–	2m. red and grey	15	4·25
225	–	3m. blue and grey	25	4·50
226	–	5m. orange and yellow	15	3·75
227	–	10m. purple and red	15	9·00
228	–	25m. brown and yellow	15	8·25
229	–	100m. olive and red	15	6·25

The mark values are larger (21 × 27 mm).
See also Nos. 269/73 and 358/64.

1922. New values.

235	40	50m. black	25	1·10
230		100m. purple on buff	15	1·10
231		200m. red on buff	20	1·10
238		300m. green on buff	10	1·10
239		400m. brown on buff	10	1·10
240		500m. orange on buff	10	1·10
241		1000m. grey	10	1·10
242		2000m. blue	20	1·10
243		3000m. brown	20	1·10
244		4000m. violet	10	1·30
245		5000m. green	25	1·30
246		100000m. red	15	1·10

50 Allegory of Charity

51 Miners

54

1922. Fund for the Old and for Children.

247	50	6m.+4m. blue and bistre	25	9·50
248		12m.+8m. red and lilac	25	11·00

1923.

249	51	5m. orange	10	11·50
250	38	10m. blue	10	1·00
251		12m. red	10	1·10
252	51	20m. purple	15	1·00
253	38	25m. bistre	10	1·10
254	51	30m. olive	15	1·80
255	38	40m. green	20	1·10
256	51	50m. blue	45	85·00

1923. Relief Fund for Sufferers in the Rhine and Ruhr Occupation Districts. Surch **Rhein = Ruhr = Hilfe** and premium.

257	51	5+100m. orange	15	9·50
258	38	25+500m. bistre	15	24·00
259	41	20+1000m. blue and green	2·10	90·00

1923. T = Tausend (thousand).

261	54	100m. purple	15	1·00
262		200m. red	15	1·20
263		300m. green	10	1·10
264		400m. brown	10	4·75
265		500m. red	10	8·75
266		1000m. grey	15	1·10
312		5T. blue	10	17·00
313		50T. brown	10	95
314		75T. purple	10	11·00

55 Wartburg Castle

62

1923.

267	55	5000m. blue	20	2·10
268	–	10,000m. olive	30	3·25

DESIGN—VERT: 10,000m. Cologne Cathedral.

1923. Air. As T **48**, but larger (21 × 27 mm).

269		5m. orange	15	21·00
270		10m. purple	15	8·50
271		25m. brown	15	8·50
272		100m. green	15	9·25
273		200m. blue	15	30·00

1923. Surch with new value in **Tausend** or **Millionen** (marks). Perf or rouletted.

274	35	5T. on 40pf. orange	10	1·20
275a		8T. on 30pf. green	10	1·20
276	38	15T. on 40m. green	20	1·40
277		20T. on 12m. red	10	1·20
278		20T. on 25m. brown	10	2·00
279	54	20T. on 200m. red	15	1·60
280	38	25T. on 25m. brown	10	11·50
281		30T. on 10m. blue	10	1·20
282	54	30T. on 200m. blue	10	1·20
283		75T. on 300m. green	10	11·00
284		75T. on 400m. green	15	1·20
285		75T. on 1000m. green	15	1·40
286		100T. on 100m. purple	15	1·50
287		100T. on 400m. green	10	1·10
288		125T. on 1000m. red	15	1·50
289		250T. on 200m. red	10	4·75
290		250T. on 300m. green	10	14·00
291		250T. on 400m. brown	10	17·00
292		250T. on 500m. pink	10	1·00
293		250T. on 500m. orange	10	15·00
306	35	400T. on 15pf. brown	10	4·75
307		400T. on 25pf. brown	10	4·75
308		400T. on 30pf. green	10	4·00
309		400T. on 40pf. brown	10	4·00
294		800T. on 5pf. green	10	3·50
295		800T. on 10pf. green	10	5·00
296	54	800T. on 200m. red	15	70·00
297		800T. on 300m. green	10	4·00
298		800T. on 400m. green	10	3·25
299		800T. on 400m. brown	10	12·00

300 800T. on 500m. green . . 20 £1700
301 800T. on 1000m. green . . 15 1·10
302 2M. on 200m. red . . . . 20 1·10
303 2M. on 300m. green . . . 10 1·40
304 2M. on 500m. red . . . . 10 6·00
305 2M. on 5T. red . . . . . 20 1·10

1923. Perf or rouletted.
315 **62** 500T. brown . . . . . . 10 2·20
316 1M. blue . . . . 15 1·00
317 2M. purple . . . . . . 15 19·00
318 4M. green . . . . 15 1·30
319 5M. red 15 90
320 10M. red 10 90
321 20M. blue . . . . 15 1·10
322 30M. purple . . . . . . 10 9·25
323 50M. green . . . . . . 15 1·30
324 100M. grey . . . . . . 10 1·00
325 200M. brown . . . . . . 15 1·00
326 500M. olive . . . . . . 15 1·00

1923. As T **62**, but value in "Milliarden". Perf or roul.
327 **62** 1Md. brown . . . . . . 20 1·00
328 2Md. green and flesh . . . 15 1·30
329 5Md. brown and yellow . . 15 1·10
330 10Md. green & light green 15 1·10
331 20Md. brown and green . . 15 1·40
332 50Md. blue . . . . 35 30·00

1923. Surch in **Milliarden**. Perf or roul.
342 **54** 1Md. on 100m. purple . . 35 29·00
343 **62** 5Md. on 2M. purple . . 25 £130
344 5Md. on 4M. green . . . . 40 20·00
345 5Md. on 10M. red . . . . 15 2·50
346 10Md. on 20M. blue . . . 25 3·25
347 10Md. on 50M. green . . . 15 2·75
348 10Md. on 100M. grey . . . 15 9·00

1923. As T **62**, but without value in words and tablet blank.
352 **62** 3pf. brown 45 25
353 5pf. green 70 20
354 10pf. red 70 20
355 20pf. blue 95 30
356 50pf. orange . . . . . . 3·50 80
357 100pf. purple . . . . . . 10·50 90
The values of this and the following issues are expressed on the basis of the gold mark.

1924. Air.
358 **48** 5pf. green . . . . 1·50 1·60
359 10pf. red . . . . 1·50 1·80
360 20pf. blue . . . . 6·50 5·50
361 50pf. orange . . . . . . 13·00 24·00
362 100pf. purple . . . . . . 34·00 50·00
363 200pf. blue . . . . 65·00 75·00
364 300pf. grey £100 £110

65

66

1924. Welfare Fund.
365 **65** 5+15pf. green . . . . . . 1·00 2·00
366 – 10+30pf. red . . . . . . 1·00 2·00
367 – 20+60pf. blue . . . . . . 6·25 7·00
368 – 50+1m.50 brown . . . . . 26·00 55·00
DESIGNS: St. Elizabeth feeding the hungry (5pf.); giving drink to the thirsty (10pf.); clothing the naked (20pf.); and caring for the sick (50pf.).

1924.
369 **66** 3pf. brown 40 15
370 5pf. green 45 15
371 10pf. red 65 15
372 20pf. blue . . . . 2·10 30
373 30pf. red . . . . 2·75 40
374 40pf. olive . . . . 17·00 75
375 50pf. orange . . . . . . 17·00 1·40

67 Rheinstein

71 Dr. von Stephan

1924.
376 **67** 1m. green . . . . 12·50 2·10
377 – 2m. blue (A) . . . . . . 19·00 1·90
458 – 2m. blue (B) . . . . . . 30·00 11·50
378 – 3m. red . . . . 22·00 4·75
379 – 5m. green . . . . 39·00 14·50
DESIGNS: 2m. Cologne. (A) inscr "Zwei Mark"; (B) inscr "ZWEI REICHSMARK"; 3m. Marienburg; 5m. Speyer Cathedral.

1924. 50th Anniv of U.P.U.
380 **71** 10pf. green 55 20
381 20pf. blue . . . . 1·20 50
382 – 60pf. brown . . . . . . 4·50 40
383 – 80pf. deep green . . . . 10·50 1·30
DESIGN: Nos. 382/3. Similar to Type **71** but with border changed.

73 German Eagle and Rhine

74

1925. Rhineland Millenary.
384 **73** 5pf. green 45 25
385 10pf. red 85 30
386 20pf. blue . . . . 5·25 1·00

1925. Munich Exhibition.
387 **74** 5pf. green . . . . 3·75 6·25
388 10pf. red . . . . 3·75 10·50

75 Arms of Prussia

76

78 Goethe

1925. Welfare Fund. Arms dated "1925".
389 **75** 5pf.+5pf. yell, blk & grn 45 1·10
390 – 10pf.+10pf. brn, bl & red 1·10 1·30
391 – 20pf.+20pf. brn, grn & bl 6·25 13·50
ARMS: 10pf. Bavaria; 20pf. Saxony.
See also Nos. 413/16a, 446/50 and 451/5.

1926. Air.
392 **76** 5pf. green 65 80
393 10pf. red 85 80
394 15pf. purple . . . . . . 1·70 1·10
395 20pf. blue . . . . 1·70 1·60
396 50pf. orange . . . . . . 20·00 4·75
397 1m. red and black . . . . 17·00 5·75
398 2m. blue and black . . . 19·00 21·00
399 3m. olive and black . . . 55·00 80·00

1926. Portraits.
400 **78** 3pf. brown 65 20
402 – 5pf. green (Schiller) . . . . 1·30 15
404 – 8pf. green (Beethoven) . . 1·30 15
405 – 10pf. red (Frederick the Great) . . . . . . 1·10 15
406 – 15pf. red (Kant) . . . . . 2·20 15
407 – 20pf. deep green (Beethoven) . . . . . . 11·00 90
408 **78** 25pf. blue . . . . 3·50 70
409 – 30pf. olive (Lessing) . . . 6·75 45
410 – 40pf. violet (Leibniz) . . . 11·00 55
411 – 50pf. brown (Bach) . . . 13·50 6·25
412 – 80pf. brown (Durer) . . . 30·00 5·00

1926. Welfare Fund. As T **75**. Arms, dated "1926".
413 5pf.+5pf. multicoloured . . 1·00 1·30
414 10pf.+10pf. red, gold and rose . . . . 1·50 1·90
415 25pf.+25pf. blue, yell & red 11·00 18·00
416a 50pf.+50pf. multicoloured 40·00 70·00
ARMS: 5pf. Wurttemberg; 10pf. Baden; 25pf. Thuringia; 50pf. Hesse.

79 Pres. von Hindenburg

81 Pres. Ebert

82 Pres. von Hindenburg

1927. Welfare Fund. President's 80th Birthday.
417 **79** 8pf.+7pf. green . . . . . 85 1·30
418 15pf.+15pf. red . . . . . 1·00 2·20
419 25pf.+25pf. blue . . . . . 6·75 22·00
420 50pf.+50pf. brown . . . . 11·50 25·00

1927. International Labour Office Session, Berlin. Optd **I.A.A. 10.–15. 10. 1927.**
421 – 8pf. green (No. 404) . . . 18·00 60·00
422 – 15pf. red (No. 406) . . . 18·00 60·00
423 **78** 25pf. blue . . . . 18·00 60·00

1928.
424 **81** 3pf. brown 25 25
425 **82** 4pf. blue 55 25
426 5pf. green 40 25
427 **81** 6pf. olive 75 20
428 8pf. green 25 25
429 10pf. red . . . . 1·30 1·10
430 10pf. purple . . . . . . 1·50 95
431 **82** 12pf. orange . . . . . . 1·30 20
432 15pf. red 65 20
433 **81** 20pf. deep green . . . . 6·75 3·00
434 20pf. grey . . . . 6·25 35
436 **82** 25pf. blue . . . . 7·00 40
435 **81** 30pf. olive . . . . 4·75 40
437 **82** 40pf. violet . . . . . . 13·00 45
438 **81** 45pf. orange . . . . . . 9·00 2·20
439 **82** 50pf. brown . . . . . . 9·25 1·30
440 **81** 60pf. brown . . . . . . 10·50 1·70
441 **82** 80pf. brown . . . . . . 28·00 4·75
442 80pf. yellow . . . . . . 10·50 1·30

83 Airship "Graf Zeppelin"

1928. Air.
443 **83** 1m. red . . . . 25·00 32·00
444 2m. blue . . . . 50·00 47·00
445 4m. brown . . . . 30·00 32·00

1928. Welfare Fund. As T **75**, dated "1928".
446 5pf.+5pf. green, red & yellow 60 3·50
447 8pf.+7pf. multicoloured . . . 60 3·50
448 15pf.+15pf. red, bl & yellow 85 4·25
449 25pf.+25pf. blue, red & yellow . . . . 10·50 37·00
450 50pf.+50pf. multicoloured . . 50·00 £100
ARMS: 5pf. Hamburg; 8pf. Mecklenburg-Schwerin; 15pf. Oldenburg; 25pf. Brunswick; 50pf. Anhalt.

1929. Welfare Fund. As T **75**, dated "1929".
451 5pf.+2pf. green, yellow & red 65 1·20
452 8pf.+4pf. yellow, red & green 65 1·20
453 15pf.+5pf. yellow, blk & red 85 1·40
454 25pf.+10pf. multicoloured . . 13·00 28·00
455 50pf.+40pf. yellow, red & brn 47·00 65·00
ARMS: 5pf. Bremen; 8pf. Lippe; 15pf. Lubeck; 25pf. Mecklenburg-Strelitz; 50pf. Schaumburg-Lippe.

1930. Air. "Graf Zeppelin" 1st S. American Flight. T **83** inscr "I. SUDAMERIKA FAHRT".
456 2m. blue £275 £300
457 4m. brown £275 £300

1930. Evacuation of Rhineland by Allied Forces. Optd **30. JUNI 1930.**
459 **81** 8pf. green . . . . 1·00 95
460 **82** 15pf. red . . . . 1·30 1·10

86 Aachen

92 Heidelberg Castle

1930. International Philatelic Exhibition, Berlin.
461 **86** 8pf.+4pf. green . . . . . 24·00 65·00
462 – 15pf.+5pf. red . . . . . 24·00 65·00
463 – 25pf.+10pf. blue . . . . 24·00 65·00
464 – 50pf.+40pf. brown . . . . 24·00 65·00
MS464a 195 × 148 mm. Nos. 461/4 (sold at 2m.70 in the exhibition) £300 £1500
DESIGNS: 15p. Berlin; 25pf. Marienwerder; 50pf. Wurzburg.

1930. Welfare Fund.
465 **86** 8pf.+4pf. green . . . . . 14·00 60
466 – 15pf.+5pf. red . . . . . 14·00 65
467 – 25pf.+10pf. blue . . . . 17·00 11·50
468 – 50pf.+40pf. brown . . . . 23·00 40·00
DESIGNS: 15pf. Berlin; 25pf. Marienwerder; 50pf. Wurzburg.

1931. Air. "Graf Zeppelin" Polar Flight. Optd **POLAR-FAHRT 1931.**
469 **83** 1m. red £650 £350
470 2m. blue . . . . 75·00 £190
471 4m. brown . . . . 75·00 £190

1931. Welfare Fund.
472 – 8pf.+4pf. green 35 75
473 – 15pf.+5pf. red 40 95
474 **92** 25pf.+10pf. blue . . . . 8·25 20·00
475 – 50pf.+40pf. brown . . . . 28·00 60·00
DESIGNS—VERT: 8pf. The Zwinger, Dresden; 15pf. Town Hall, Breslau; 50pf. The Holstentor, Lubeck.
See also Nos. 485/9.

1932. Welfare Fund. Nos. 472/3 surch.
476 6+4pf. on 8pf.+4pf. green . . 4·25 9·25
477 12+3pf. on 15pf.+5pf. red . . 5·75 12·50

94 President von Hindenburg

96 Frederick the Great (after A. von Menzel)

1932. 85th Birthday of Pres. von Hindenburg.
478 **94** 4pf. blue 60 35
496B 5pf. green 85 40
480 12pf. orange . . . . . . 5·25 35
481 15pf. red . . . . 3·50 10·00
503B 25pf. blue . . . . 1·30 40
483 40pf. violet . . . . 17·00 1·50
484 50pf. brown . . . . 6·50 10·50
See also Nos. 493/509 and 545/50.

1932. Welfare Fund. As T **92**.
485 4pf.+2pf. blue 30 55
486 6pf.+4pf. olive 30 55
487 12pf.+3pf. red 45 85
488 25pf.+10pf. blue . . . . . 7·50 16·00
489 40pf.+40pf. purple . . . . 27·00 55·00

CASTLES: 4pf. Wartburg; 6pf. Stolzenfels; 12pf. Nuremberg; 25pf. Lichtenstein; 40pf. Marburg.

1933. Opening of Reichstag in Potsdam.
490 **96** 6pf. green 55 80
491 12pf. red 55 80
492 25pf. blue . . . . 36·00 19·00

1933.
493B **94** 1pf. black 10 15
494B 3pf. brown 10 15
495B 4pf. grey 10 15
497B 6pf. green 10 15
498B 8pf. orange 10 15
499B 10pf. brown 20 15
500B 12pf. red 15 15
501B 15pf. red 40 15
502B 20pf. blue 40 15
504B 30pf. green 75 15
505B 40pf. mauve 75 20
506B 50pf. black and green . . 2·40 35
507B 60pf. black and red . . . 75 35
508B 80pf. black and blue . . 2·10 1·10
509B 100pf. black and yellow . 3·75 70

1933. Air. "Graf Zeppelin" Chicago World Exhibition Flight. Optd **Chicagofahrt Weltausstellung 1933.**
510 **83** 1m. red £600 £325
511 2m. blue . . . . 65·00 £160
512 4m. brown . . . . 65·00 £160

99 Tannhauser

1933. Welfare Fund. Wagner's Operas.
513 **99** 3pf.+2pf. brown . . . . 1·70 4·25
514 – 4pf.+2pf. blue . . . . . 1·30 1·70
515 – 5pf.+2pf. green . . . . . 3·25 5·00
516 – 6pf.+4pf. green . . . . . 1·30 1·20
517 – 8pf.+4pf. orange . . . . 2·10 3·00
518 – 12pf.+3pf. red . . . . . 2·10 1·50
519a – 20pf.+10pf. light blue . . 95·00 65·00
520 – 25pf.+15pf. blue . . . . 25·00 50·00
521 – 40pf.+35pf. mauve . . . £110 £110
OPERAS: 4pf. "The Flying Dutchman"; 5pf. "Rhinegold"; 6pf. "The Mastersingers"; 8pf. "The Valkyries"; 12pf. "Siegfried"; 20pf. "Tristan and Isolde"; 25pf. "Lohengrin"; 40pf. "Parsifal".

1933. Welfare Fund. Stamps as 1924, issued together in sheets of four, each stamp optd **1923–1933**.
522 **65** 5+15pf. green . . . . . . 70·00 £275
523 – 10+30pf. red . . . . . . 70·00 £275
524 – 20+60pf. blue . . . . . . 70·00 £275
525 – 50pf.+1.50m. brown . . . 70·00 £275
MS525a 210 × 148 mm. Nos. 522/5 £1200 £9000

100 Golden Eagle, Globe and Swastika

101 Count Zeppelin and Airship LZ-127 "Graf Zeppelin"

1934. Air.
526 **100** 5pf. green 55 40
527 10pf. red 70 55
528 15pf. blue . . . . 1·30 80
529 20pf. blue . . . . 2·30 1·30
530 25pf. brown . . . . 3·75 1·20
531 40pf. mauve . . . . 6·25 90
532 50pf. green . . . . 10·50 60
533 80pf. yellow . . . . . . 6·50 3·50
534 100pf. black . . . . 6·25 2·20
535 – 2m. grey and green . . . 18·00 16·00
536 **101** 3m. grey and blue . . . 38·00 33·00
DESIGN—As Type **101**: 2m. Otto Lilienthal and Lilienthal biplane glider.

103 Franz A. E. Luderitz

104 "Saar Ownership"

105 Nuremberg Castle

1934. German Colonizers' Jubilee.
537 **103** 3pf. brown and chocolate 3·50 4·50
538 – 6pf. brown and green . . 1·50 90
539 – 12pf. brown and red . . . 2·40 1·30
540 – 25pf. brown and blue . . 13·00 16·00
DESIGNS: 6pf. Gustav Nachtigal; 12pf. Karl Peters; 25pf. Hermann von Wissmann.

1934. Saar Plebiscite.
541 **104** 6pf. green . . . . 3·25 25
542 – 12pf. red . . . . 5·75 25

DESIGN: 12pf. Eagle inscribed "Saar" in rays from a swastika-eclipsed sun.

1934. Nuremberg Congress.

543	105	6pf. green	3·00	30
544		12pf. red	5·25	30

1934. Hindenburg Memorial. Portrait with black borders.

545	94	3pf. brown	85	35
546		5pf. green	85	50
547		6pf. green	1·40	30
548		8pf. orange	2·40	30
549		12pf. red	2·30	30
550		25pf. blue	7·25	6·25

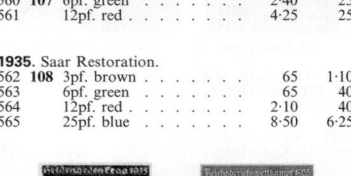

106 Blacksmith

107 Friedrich von Schiller

108 "The Saar comes home"

1934. Welfare Fund.

551	–	3pf.+2pf. brown	90	1·00
552	106	4pf.+2pf. black	75	1·00
553	–	5pf.+2pf. green	5·25	6·25
554	–	6pf.+4pf. green	50	50
555	–	8pf.+4pf. red	80	95
556	–	12pf.+3pf. red	45	45
557	–	20pf.+10pf. green	15·00	19·00
558	–	25pf.+15pf. blue	15·00	19·00
559	–	40pf.+35pf. lilac	41·00	55·00

DESIGNS: 3pf. Merchant; 5pf. Mason; 6pf. Miner; 8pf. Architect; 12pf. Farmer; 20pf. Scientist; 25pf. Sculptor; 40pf. Judge.

1934. 175th Birth Anniv of Schiller.

560	107	6pf. green	2·40	25
561		12pf. red	4·25	25

1935. Saar Restoration.

562	108	3pf. brown	65	1·10
563		6pf. green	65	40
564		12pf. red	2·10	40
565		25pf. blue	8·50	6·25

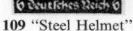

109 "Steel Helmet"

110 "Victor's Crown"

1935. War Heroes' Day.

566	109	6pf. green	1·10	1·40
567		12pf. red	1·10	1·40

1935. Apprentices Vocational Contest.

568	110	6pf. green	85	1·10
569		12pf. red	1·00	1·10

111 Heinrich Schutz

112 Allenstein Castle

1935. Musicians' Anniversaries.

570	111	6pf. green	1·00	25
571	–	12pf. red (Bach)	1·20	25
572	–	25pf. blue (Handel)	2·30	85

1935. International Philatelic Exhibition, Konigsberg. In miniature sheets.

573	112	3pf. brown	32·00	36·00
574	–	6pf. green	32·00	36·00
575	–	12pf. red	32·00	36·00
576	–	25pf. blue	32·00	36·00
MS576a		148 × 105 mm. Nos. 573/6	£750	£650

DESIGNS: 6pf. Tannenberg Memorial; 12pf. Konigsberg Castle; 25pf. Heilsberg Castle.

113 Stephenson Locomotive "Adler", 1835

114 Trumpeter

1935. German Railway Centenary. Locomotive types inscr "1835–1935".

577	113	6pf. green	1·20	50
578	–	12pf. red	1·20	50
579	–	25pf. blue	9·00	1·90
580	–	40pf. purple	12·00	2·20

DESIGNS: 12pf. Class 03 steam train, 1930s; 25pf. Diesel train "Flying Hamburger"; 40pf. Class 05 streamlined steam locomotive No. 001, 1935.

1935. World Jamboree of "Hitler Youth".

581	114	6pf. green	1·30	2·20
582		15pf. red	1·70	2·50

115 Nuremberg

116 East Prussia

1935. Nuremberg Congress.

583	115	6pf. green	75	25
584		12pf. red	1·60	25

1935. Welfare Fund. Provincial Costumes.

585	116	3pf.+2pf. brown	20	25
586	–	4pf.+3pf. blue	75	1·10
587	–	5pf.+3pf. green	20	60
588	–	6pf.+4pf. green	10	25
589	–	8pf.+4pf. brown	1·10	1·10
590	–	12pf.+6pf. red	20	25
591	–	15pf.+10pf. brown	3·00	5·00
592	–	25pf.+15pf. blue	4·75	5·00
593	–	30pf.+20pf. grey	12·50	18·00
594	–	40pf.+35pf. mauve	9·25	13·00

COSTUMES: 4pf. Silesia; 5pf. Rhineland; 6pf. Lower Saxony; 8pf. Kurmark; 12pf. Black Forest; 15pf. Hesse; 25pf. Upper Bavaria; 30pf. Friesland; 40pf. Franconia.

117 S.A. Man and Feldherrnhalle, Munich

118 Skating

1935. 12th Anniv of 1st Hitler Putsch.

595	117	3pf. brown	35	50
596		12pf. red	85	45

1935. Winter Olympic Games, Garmisch-Partenkirchen.

597	118	6pf.+4pf. green	70	55
598	–	12pf.+6pf. red	1·20	90
599	–	25pf.+15pf. blue	6·25	8·00

DESIGNS: 12pf. Ski jumping; 25pf. Bobsleighing.

119 Heinkel He 70 Blitz

120 Gottlieb Daimler

1936. 10th Anniv of Lufthansa Airways.

600	119	40pf. blue	6·50	2·20

1936. Berlin Motor Show. 50th Anniv of Invention of First Motor Car.

601	120	6pf. green	80	45
602		12pf. red (Carl Benz)	1·10	65

121 Airship LZ-129 "Hindenburg"

122 Otto von Guericke

1936. Air.

603	121	50pf. blue	21·00	60
604		75pf. green	26·00	70

1936. 250th Death Anniv of Otto von Guericke (scientist).

605	122	6pf. green	35	40

123 Gymnastics

124 Symbolical of Local Government

1936. Summer Olympic Games, Berlin.

606	123	3pf.+2pf. brown	35	30
607	–	4pf.+3pf. blue	25	60
608	–	6pf.+4pf. green	35	25
609	–	8pf.+4pf. red	3·50	1·30
610	–	12pf.+6pf. red	45	25
611	–	15pf.+10pf. red	5·25	3·00
612	–	25pf.+15pf. blue	3·00	3·75
613	–	40pf.+35pf. violet	6·75	7·50
MS613a		Two sheets, each 148 × 105 mm. (a) Nos. 606/8 and 613; (b) Nos. 609/12	49·00	85·00

DESIGNS: 4pf. Diver; 6pf. Footballer; 8pf. Javelin thrower; 12pf. Olympic torchbearer; 15pf. Fencer; 25pf. Double scullers; 40pf. Show jumper.

1936. 6th Int Local Government Congress.

614	124	3pf. brown	30	25
615		5pf. green	30	25
616		12pf. red	65	45
617		25pf. blue	1·10	1·10

125 "Brown Ribbon" Race

126 "Leisure Time"

1936. "Brown Ribbon of Germany". Single stamp in miniature sheet.

MS618	125	42pf. brown	9·00	13·50

1936. Int Recreational Congress, Hamburg.

619	126	6pf. green	40	55
620		15pf. red	65	90

127 Saluting the Swastika

128 Luitpoldhain Heroes Memorial, Nuremberg

1936. Nuremberg Congress.

621	127	6pf. green	55	30
622		12pf. red	80	40

1936. Winter Relief Fund.

623	–	3pf.+2pf. brown	10	25
624	–	4pf.+3pf. black	20	65
625	128	5pf.+3pf. green	10	25
626	–	6pf.+4pf. green	15	25
627	–	8pf.+4pf. brown	80	1·50
628	–	12pf.+6pf. red	20	25
629	–	15pf.+10pf. brown	2·00	3·75
630	–	25pf.+15pf. blue	1·80	3·50
631	–	40pf.+35pf. mauve	2·75	5·50

DESIGNS: 3pf. Munich frontier road; 4pf. Air Ministry, Berlin; 6pf. Bridge over River Saale; 8pf. Deutschlandhalle, Berlin; 12pf. Alpine road; 15pf. Fuhrerhaus, Munich; 25pf. Bridge over River Mangfall; 40pf. German Art Museum, Munich.

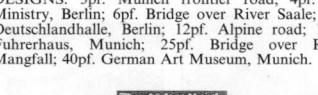

129 R(eichs) L(uftschutz) B(und) = Civil Defence Union

1937. 4th Anniv of Civil Defence Union.

632	129	3pf. brown	25	25
633		6pf. green	40	25
634		12pf. red	80	50

130 Adolf Hitler

1937. Hitler's Culture Fund and 48th birthday. Four stamps in miniature sheet (148 × 105 mm). Perf or Imperf.

MS635	130	6+19pf. green	15·00	9·50

1937. "Brown Ribbon of Germany". No. **MS**618 optd with German eagle and ornamental border surrounding, "1. AUGUST 1937 MUNCHEN-REIM" in red.

MS637a	125	42pf. (+108pf.) brown	55·00	80·00

1937. Nuremberg Congress. Four stamps in miniature sheet, as No. **MS**637, but optd **REICHSPARTEITAG NURNBERG 1937** in panels of stamps.

MS638	130	6+19pf. green	55·00	45·00

131 Fishing Smacks

132 Hitler Youth

1937. Winter Relief Fund.

639	–	3pf.+2pf. brown	15	35
640	–	4pf.+3pf. black	95	80
641	131	5pf.+3pf. green	15	35
642	–	6pf.+4pf. green	15	35
643	–	8pf.+4pf. orange	75	1·30
644	–	12pf.+6pf. red	20	35
645	–	15pf.+10pf. brown	2·10	4·00
646	–	25pf.+15pf. blue	4·25	4·00
647	–	40pf.+35pf. purple	6·00	8·00

DESIGNS: 3pf. "Bremen" (lifeboat), 1931; 4pf. "Burgemeister Oswald" (lightship); 6pf. "Wilhelm Gustloff" (liner); 8pf. "Padua" (barque); 12pf. "Tannenberg" (liner); 15pf. "Schwerin" (train ferry); 25pf. "Hamburg" (liner); 40pf. "Europa" (liner).

1938. Hitler Culture Fund. 5th Anniv of Hitler's Leadership.

648	132	6pf.+4pf. green	85	1·30
649		12pf.+8pf. red	1·40	1·70

133 "Unity"

134 Adolf Hitler

1938. Austrian Plebiscite.

650	133	6pf. green	25	35

1938. Hitler's Culture Fund and 49th Birthday.

652	134	12pf.+38pf. red	1·60	2·00

See also No. 660.

135 Breslau Cathedral

136 Airship Gondola and Airship LZ-127 "Graf Zeppelin"

1938. 16th German Sports Tournament, Breslau. Inscr as in T **135**.

653	135	3pf. brown	30	30
654	–	6pf. green	40	30
655	–	12pf. red	65	30
656	–	15pf. brown	1·10	70

DESIGNS: 6pf. Hermann Goering Stadium; 12pf. Breslau Town Hall; 15pf. Centenary Hall.

1938. Air. Birth Cent of Count Zeppelin.

657	–	25pf. blue	2·50	80
658	136	50pf. green	3·50	90

DESIGN: 25pf. Count Zeppelin in primitive airship gondola and airship LZ-5.

137 Horsewoman

138 Saarpfalz Gautheater, Saarbrucken

1938. "Brown Ribbon of Germany".

659	137	42pf.+108pf. brown	24·00	41·00

1938. Nuremberg Congress and Hitler's Culture Fund. As No. 652, but inscr "Reichsparteitag 1938".

660	134	6pf.+19pf. green	2·75	3·25

1938. Opening of Gautheater and Hitler's Culture Fund.

661	138	6pf.+4pf. green	1·20	1·50
662		12pf.+8pf. red	2·00	2·40

139 Forchtenstein Castle, Burgenland

140 Sudeten Miner and Wife

1938. Winter Relief.

663	139	3pf.+2pf. brown	20	25
664	–	4pf.+3pf. blue	1·60	1·20
665	–	5pf.+3pf. green	15	30
666	–	6pf.+4pf. green	15	20
667	–	8pf.+4pf. red	1·50	1·20
668	–	12pf.+6pf. red	25	25
669	–	15pf.+10pf. red	3·50	4·25
670	–	25pf.+15pf. blue	3·25	4·25
671	–	40pf.+35pf. mauve	6·75	7·25

DESIGNS: 4pf. Flexenstrasse; 5pf. Zell am See; 6pf. Grossglockner; 8pf. Augstein Castle, Wachau; 12pf. Wien (Prince Eugene Statue, Vienna); 15pf. Erzberg, Steiermark; 25pf. Hall-in-Tirol; 40pf. Braunau.

1938. Acquisition of Sudetenland and Hitler's Culture Fund.

672	140	6pf.+4pf. green	1·10	2·10
673		12pf.+8pf. red	2·30	3·00

141 Racing Cars

142 Eagle and Laurel Wreath

1939. Int Motor Show, Berlin, and Hitler's Culture Fund.

674	–	6pf.+4pf. green	2·50	3·25
675	141	12pf.+8pf. red	2·75	3·25
676	–	25pf.+10pf. blue	8·25	6·25

DESIGNS: 6pf. Early Benz and Daimler cars; 25pf. Volkswagen car.

1939. Apprentices' Vocational Contest.

677	142	6pf. green	1·40	2·75
678		12pf. red	1·80	2·75

143 Adolf Hitler in Braunau

144 Horticultural Exhibition Entrance and Arms of Stuttgart

1939. Hitler's 50th Birthday and Culture Fund.

679	143	12pf.+38pf. red	1·80	4·00

1939. Stuttgart Horticultural Exhibition and Hitler's Culture Fund.

680	144	6pf.+4pf. green	1·10	2·50
681		15pf.+5pf. red	1·20	2·50

145 Adolf Hitler Speaking

147 "Investment" and Jockey

1939. National Labour Day and Hitler's Culture Fund.

682	145	6pf.+19pf. brown	3·75	4·00

See also No. 689.

1939. Nurburgring Races and Hitler's Culture Fund. Nos. 674/6 optd **Nurburgring-Rennen**.

683	–	6pf.+4pf. green	32·00	26·00
684	141	12pf.+8pf. red	32·00	26·00
685	–	25pf.+10pf. blue	32·00	26·00

1939. 70th Anniv of German Derby.

686	147	25pf.+50pf. blue	13·50	13·00

148 Training Thoroughbred Horses

149 "Young Venetian Woman" after Durer

1939. "Brown Ribbon of Germany" and Hitler's Culture Fund.

687	148	42pf.+108pf. brown	13·50	23·00

1939. German Art Day.

688	149	6pf.+19pf. green	5·50	7·50

1939. Nuremberg Congress and Hitler's Culture Fund. As T **145**, but inscr "REICHS-PARTEITAG 1939".

689		6pf.+19pf. brown	3·50	8·75

150 Mechanics at Work and Play

151 St. Mary's Church, Danzig

1939. Postal Employees' and Hitler's Culture Funds. Inscr "Kameradschaftsblock der Deutschen Reichspost".

690	–	3pf.+2pf. brown	2·20	4·50
691	–	4pf.+3pf. blue	2·20	4·50
692	150	5pf.+3pf. green	70	1·30
693	–	6pf.+4pf. green	70	1·20
694	–	8pf.+4pf. orange	70	1·50
695	–	10pf.+5pf. brown	70	1·90
696	–	12pf.+6pf. red	90	1·90
697	–	15pf.+10pf. red	80	1·90
698	–	16pf.+10pf. green	95	1·90
699	–	20pf.+10pf. blue	95	1·90
700	–	24pf.+10pf. olive	2·10	3·50
701	–	25pf.+15pf. blue	2·10	3·00

DESIGNS: 3pf. Postal employees' rally; 4pf. Review in Vienna; 6pf. Youths on parade; 8pf. Flag bearers; 10pf. Distributing prizes; 12pf. Motor race; 15pf. Women athletes; 16pf. Postal police; 20pf. Glider workshop; 24pf. Mail coach; 25pf. Sanatorium, Konigstein.

See also Nos. 761/6 and 876/81.

1939. Occupation of Danzig. Inscr "DANZIG IST DEUTSCH".

702	151	6pf. green	25	55
703	–	12pf. red (Crane Gate)	35	80

1939. Stamps of Danzig surch **Deutsches Reich** and new values.

704	28	Rpf. on 3pf. brown	70	1·80
705		4Rpf. on 35pf. blue	70	1·80
706		Rpf. on 5pf. orange	70	1·90
707		Rpf. on 8pf. green	1·20	3·00
708		Rpf. on 10pf. green	2·00	3·25
709		12Rpf. on 7pf. green	1·20	1·90
710		Rpf. on 15pf. red	4·75	9·00
711		Rpf. on 20pf. grey	2·50	6·25
712		Rpf. on 25pf. red	3·50	8·50
713		Rpf. on 30pf. purple	1·70	3·50
714		Rpf. on 40pf. blue	2·30	4·50
715		Rpf. on 50pf. red and blue	2·75	6·25
716	42	1Rm on 1g. black & orge	7·25	39·00
717	–	2Rm on 2g. black and red (No. 206)	10·50	36·00

155 Elbogen Castle

156 Leipzig Library and Gutenberg

1939. Winter Relief Fund.

718	155	3pf.+2pf. brown	10	35
719	–	4pf.+3pf. black	1·30	1·60
720	–	5pf.+3pf. green	20	40
721	–	6pf.+4pf. green	20	25
722	–	8pf.+4pf. red	1·30	1·40
723	–	12pf.+6pf. red	25	25
724	–	15pf.+10pf. brown	2·00	4·00
725	–	25pf.+15pf. blue	2·40	4·00
726	–	40pf.+35pf. purple	3·50	5·50

DESIGNS: 4pf. Drachenfels; 5pf. Goslar Castle; 6pf. Clocktower, Graz; 8pf. The Romer, Frankfurt; 12pf. City Hall, Klagenfurt; 15pf. Ruins of Schreckenstein Castle; 25pf. Salzburg Fortress; 40pf. Hohentwiel Castle.

1940. Leipzig Fair.

727	156	3pf. brown	30	35
728	–	6pf. green	35	35
729	–	12pf. red	45	35
730	–	25pf. blue	80	1·00

DESIGNS: 6pf. Augustusplatz; 12pf. Old Town Hall; 25pf. View of Fair.

157 Courtyard of Chancellery, Berlin

158 Hitler and Child

1940. 2nd Berlin Philatelic Exhibition.

731	157	24pf.+76pf. green	6·50	13·00

1940. Hitler's 51st Birthday.

732	158	12pf.+38pf. red	2·20	5·25

159 Wehrmacht Symbol

160 Horseman

1940. National Fete Day and Hitler's Culture Fund.

733	159	6pf.+4pf. green	40	95

1940. Hamburg Derby and Hitler's Culture Fund.

734	160	25pf.+100pf. blue	5·00	8·75

161 Chariot

162 Malmedy

1940. Hitler's Culture Fund and "Brown Ribbon" Race.

735	161	42pf.+108pf. brown	21·00	25·00

1940. Eupen and Malmedy reincorporated in Germany, and Hitler's Culture Fund. Inscr "Eupen-Malmedy wieder Deutsch".

736	162	6pf.+4pf. green	1·10	2·30
737	–	12pf.+8pf. red	1·10	2·30

DESIGNS: 12pf. View of Eupen.

163 Heligoland

164 Artushof, Danzig

1940. 50th Anniv of Cession of Heligoland to Germany and Hitler's Culture Fund.

738	163	6pf.+94pf. red and green	6·00	7·75

1940. Winter Relief Fund.

739	164	3pf.+2pf. brown	10	25
740	–	4pf.+3pf. blue	55	80
741	–	5pf.+3pf. green	20	40
742	–	6pf.+4pf. green	20	25
743	–	8pf.+4pf. orange	80	90
744	–	12pf.+6pf. red	20	25
745	–	15pf.+10pf. brown	80	2·40
746	–	25pf.+15pf. blue	1·40	2·50
747	–	40pf.+35pf. purple	2·10	5·50

DESIGNS: 4pf. Town Hall, Thorn; 5pf. Kaub Castle; 6pf. City Theatre, Posen; 8pf. Heidelberg Castle; 12pf. Porta Nigra, Trier; 15pf. New Theatre, Prague; 25pf. Town Hall, Bremen; 40pf. Town Hall, Munster.

165 Emil von Behring (bacteriologist)

166 Postilion and Globe

1940. 50th Anniv of Development of Diphtheria Antitoxin.

748	165	6pf.+4pf. green	65	1·40
749		25pf.+10pf. blue	1·10	2·50

1941. Stamp Day.

750	166	6pf.+24pf. green	80	1·80

167 Mussolini and Hitler

168 House of Nations, Leipzig

1941. Hitler's Culture Fund.

751	167	12pf.+38pf. red	95	2·30

1941. Leipzig Fair. Buildings. Inscr "REICHSMESSE LEIPZIG 1941".

752	168	3pf. brown	25	65
753	–	6pf. green	25	65
754	–	12pf. red	35	95
755	–	25pf. blue	70	1·40

DESIGNS: 6pf. Cloth Hall; 12pf. Exhibition Building; 25pf. Railway Station.

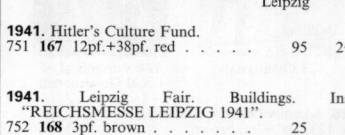

169 Dancer

170 Adolf Hitler

1941. Vienna Fair.

756	169	3pf. brown	25	50
757	–	6pf. green	25	50
758	–	12pf. red	35	60
759	–	25pf. blue	70	1·60

DESIGNS: 6pf. Arms and Exhibition Building; 12pf. Allegory and Municipal Theatre; 25pf. Prince Eugene's Equestrian Monument.

1941. Hitler's 52nd Birthday and Culture Fund.

760	170	12pf.+38pf. red	1·60	3·00

1941. Postal Employees' and Hitler's Culture Funds. Inscr "Kameradschaftsblock der Deutschen Reichspost" as Nos. 693/4, 696 and 698/700, but premium values and colours changed.

761		6pf.+9pf. green	65	1·30
762		8pf.+12pf. red	85	1·10
763		12pf.+18pf. red	85	1·10
764		16pf.+24pf. black	1·30	3·25
765		20pf.+30pf. blue	1·30	3·25
766		24pf.+36pf. violet	4·50	11·00

171 Racehorse

172 Two Amazons

1941. 72nd Anniv of Hamburg Derby.

767	171	25pf.+100pf. blue	4·00	7·00

1941. "Brown Ribbon of Germany".

768	172	42pf.+108pf. brown	2·30	4·75

173 Adolf Hitler

174 Brandenburg Gate, Berlin

1941.

769	173	1pf. grey	10	10
770		3pf. brown	10	10
771		4pf. slate	10	10
772		5pf. green	10	10
773		6pf. violet	10	10
774		8pf. red	10	10
777		10pf. brown	25	15
776		12pf. red	25	15
779		15pf. lake	10	15
780		16pf. green	10	1·10
781		20pf. blue	10	15
782		24pf. brown	10	1·10
783		25pf. blue	10	15
784		30pf. olive	10	15
785		40pf. mauve	10	15
786		50pf. green	10	15
787		60pf. brown	10	15
788		80pf. blue	10	30

Nos. 783/8 are larger (21½ × 26 mm).

1941. Berlin Grand Prix and Hitler's Culture Fund.

789	174	25pf.+50pf. blue	2·20	5·00

175 Belvedere Palace, Vienna

176 Belvedere Gardens, Vienna

1941. Vienna Fair and Hitler's Culture Fund.

790	175	12pf.+8pf. red	60	2·50
791	176	15pf.+10pf. violet	80	3·00

177 Marburg

178 Veldes

1941. Annexation of Northern Slovenia, and Hitler's Culture Fund.

792	177	3pf.+7pf. brown	65	1·80
793	178	6pf.+9pf. violet	60	2·00
794	–	12pf.+13pf. red	75	2·30
795	–	25pf.+15pf. blue	1·40	2·30

DESIGNS: 12pf. Pettau; 25pf. Triglav.

179 Mozart

180 Philatelist

1941. 150th Death Anniv of Mozart and Hitler's Culture Fund.

796	179	6pf.+4pf. purple	20	50

1942. Stamp Day and Hitler's Culture Fund.

797	180	6pf.+24pf. violet	55	2·20

181 Symbolical of Heroism

182 Adolf Hitler

1942. Heroes' Remembrance Day and Hitler's Culture Fund.

798	181	12pf.+38pf. slate	40	1·50

1942.

799a	182	1m. green	65	2·75
800		2m. violet	45	2·75
801		3m. red	45	8·75
802a		5m. blue	85	27·00

183 Adolf Hitler

184 Jockey and Three-year-old Horse

1942. Hitler's 53rd Birthday and Culture Fund.

803	183	12pf.+38pf. red	1·90	5·00

1942. Hamburg Derby and Hitler's Culture Fund.

804	184	25pf.+100pf. blue	5·50	9·75

185 Equine Trio

186 Cream Jug and Loving Cup

1942. "Brown Ribbon of Germany" and Hitler's Culture Fund.

805	185	42pf.+108pf. brown	1·80	4·75

1942. 10th Anniv of National Goldsmiths' Institution.

806	186	6pf.+4pf. red	25	85
807		12pf.+88pf. green	45	1·70

187 Badge of Armed S.A.

188 Peter Henlein

1942. S.A. Military Training Month.

808	187	6pf. violet	20	70

1942. 400th Death Anniv of Henlein (inventor of the watch).

809	188	6pf.+24pf. violet	45	1·30

189 Mounted Postilion

1942. European Postal Congress, Vienna.

810	–	3pf.+7pf. blue	15	1·20
811	–	6pf.+14pf. brown & blue	25	1·30
812	189	12pf.+38pf. brown & red	45	2·00

DESIGNS—HORIZ: 3pf. Postilion and map of Europe. VERT: 6pf. Mounted postilion and globe.

1942. Signing of European Postal Union Agreement. Nos. 810/2 optd **19.Okt.1942.**

813	–	3pf.+7pf. blue	75	2·00
814	–	6pf.+14pf. brown & blue	75	2·00
815	189	12pf.+38pf. brown & red	1·30	4·50

191 Mail Coach

192 Brandenburg Gate and Torchlight Parade

1943. Stamp Day and Hitler's Culture Fund.

816	191	6pf.+24pf. brn, yell & bl	30	90

1943. 10th Anniv of Third Reich.

817	192	54pf.+96pf. red	35	1·80

193

194 Machine Gunners

1943. Philatelic Cancellation Premium.

818	193	3pf.+2pf. bistre	20	60

1943. Armed Forces' and Heroes' Day.

819	–	3pf.+2pf. brown	35	1·10
820	194	4pf.+3pf. brown	30	1·10
821	–	5pf.+4pf. green	30	1·10
822	–	6pf.+9pf. violet	35	1·10
823	–	8pf.+7pf. red	35	1·10
824	–	12pf.+8pf. red	35	1·10
825	–	15pf.+10pf. purple	35	1·10
826	–	20pf.+14pf. blue	40	1·10
827	–	25pf.+15pf. blue	45	1·10
828	–	30pf.+30pf. green	55	1·80
829	–	40pf.+40pf. purple	55	1·90
830	–	50pf.+50pf. green	80	3·00

DESIGNS: 3pf. U-boat Type VIIA (submarine); 5pf. Armed motor cyclists; 6pf. Wireless operators; 8pf. Engineers making pontoon; 12pf. Grenade thrower; 15pf. Heavy artillery; 20pf. Anti-aircraft gunners; 25pf. Junkers Ju 87B "Stuka" dive bombers; 30pf. Parachutists; 40pf. Tank; 50pf. "S-22" (motor torpedo-boat).

195 Hitler Youth

1943. Youth Dedication Day.

831	195	6pf.+4pf. green	30	90

196 Adolf Hitler

1943. Hitler's 54th Birthday and Culture Fund.

832	196	3pf.+7pf. black	35	1·10
833		6pf.+14pf. green	35	1·10
834		8pf.+22pf. blue	35	1·10
835		12pf.+38pf. red	35	1·10
836		24pf.+76pf. purple	80	3·75
837		40pf.+160pf. olive	80	3·75

197 Attestation

198 Huntsman

1943. Labour Corps.

838	197	3pf.+7pf. brown	10	50
839	–	5pf.+10pf. green	10	40
840	–	6pf.+14pf. blue	10	40
841	–	12pf.+18pf. red	20	1·50

DESIGNS: 5pf. Harvester sharpening scythe; 6pf. Labourer wielding sledge-hammer; 12pf. "Pick and shovel fatigue".

1943. "Brown Ribbon of Germany".

842	198	42pf.+108pf. brown	20	1·00

199 Birthplace of Peter Rosegger

200 Peter Rosegger

1943. Birth Cent of Peter Rosegger (poet).

843	199	6pf.+4pf. green	40	35
844	200	12pf.+8pf. red	50	60

201 Racehorse

202 Mother and Children

1943. Grand Prix, Vienna.

845	201	6pf.+4pf. violet	20	1·00
846		12pf.+88pf. red	20	1·20

1943. 10th Anniv of Winter Relief Fund.

847	202	12pf.+38pf. red	20	95

203 St George and the Dragon

204 Lubeck

1943. 11th Anniv of National Goldsmiths' Institution.

848	203	6pf.+4pf. green	15	65
849		12pf.+88pf. purple	20	1·00

1943. 800th Anniv of Lubeck.

850	204	12pf.+8pf. red	20	85

205

1943. 20th Anniv of Munich Rising.

851	205	24pf.+26pf. red	30	90

206 Dr. Robert Koch

207 Adolf Hitler

1944. Birth Centenary of Dr. Robert Koch (bacteriologist).

852	206	12pf.+38pf. sepia	20	85

1944. 11th Anniv of Third Reich.

853	207	54pf.+96pf. brown	25	85

208 Focke Wulf Fw 200 Condor over Tempelhof Airport

209 Dornier Do-26 Flying Boat

1944. 25th Anniv of Air Mail Services.

854	208	6pf.+4pf. green	15	55
855	209	12pf.+8pf. purple	15	75
856	–	42pf.+108pf. blue	20	1·90

DESIGNS—VERT: 42pf. Junkers Ju 90B airplane seen from above.

210 Day Nursery

211 "Mothers' Help"

1944. 10th Anniv of "Mother and Child" Organization.

857	210	3pf.+2pf. brown	10	40
858	211	6pf.+4pf. green	10	40
859	–	12pf.+8pf. red	10	40
860	–	15pf.+10pf. purple	15	60

DESIGNS: 12pf. Child auscultation; 15pf. Mothers at convalescent home.

212 Landing Craft

213 Fulda Monument

1944. Armed Forces' and Heroes' Day.

861	212	3pf.+2pf. brown	25	1·00
862	–	4pf.+3pf. blue	15	55
863	–	5pf.+3pf. green	15	55
864	–	6pf.+4pf. violet	15	55
865	–	8pf.+4pf. red	15	55
866	–	10pf.+5pf. brown	15	55
867	–	12pf.+6pf. red	15	55
868	–	15pf.+10pf. purple	15	55
869	–	16pf.+10pf. green	25	1·10
870	–	20pf.+10pf. blue	25	1·10
871	–	24pf.+10pf. brown	35	1·10
872	–	25pf.+15pf. blue	65	3·00
873	–	30pf.+20pf. olive	65	3·00

DESIGNS: 4pf. Caterpillar tricar; 5pf. Parachutists; 6pf. Submarine officer; 8pf. Mortar-firing party; 10pf. Searchlight unit; 12pf. Machine gunners; 15pf. Tank; 16pf. "S-128" (motor torpedo-boat); 20pf. Arado Ar 196A seaplane; 24pf. Railway gun; 25pf. Rocket projectiles; 30pf. Alpine trooper.

1944. 1200th Anniv of Fulda.

874	213	12pf.+38pf. brown	15	85

214 Adolf Hitler

215 Postwoman

1944. Hitler's 55th Birthday.

875	214	54pf.+96pf. red	45	1·40

1944. Postal Employees' and Hitler's Culture Funds. Inscr "Kameradschaftsblock der Deutschen Reichspost".

876	215	6pf.+9pf. blue	10	40
877	–	8pf.+12pf. grey	10	40
878	–	12pf.+18pf. mauve	15	45
879	–	16pf.+24pf. green	15	50
880	–	20pf.+30pf. blue	20	1·20
881	–	24pf.+36pf. violet	30	1·30

DESIGNS—As Type **150**: 8pf. Mail coach; 16pf. Motor-car race; 20pf. Postal police march; 24pf. Glider workshop. As Type **215**: 12pf. The Field Post on Eastern Front.

216 Girl Worker

217 Labourer

1944. Labour Corps.

882	216	6pf.+4pf. green	10	45
883	217	12pf.+8pf. red	15	60

218 Riflemen

219 Duke Albrecht

1944. 7th Innsbruck Shooting Competition.

884	218	6pf.+4pf. green	10	50
885		12pf.+8pf. red	20	2·10

1944. 400th Anniv of Albert University, Konigsberg.

886	219	6pf.+4pf. green	25	85

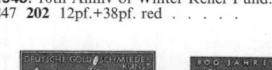

220 Racehorse and Foal

1944. "Brown Ribbon of Germany".
887 **220** 42pf.+108pf. brown . . . 30 1·10

221 Racehorse and Laurel Wreath

222 Chambered Nautilus Beaker

1944. Vienna Grand Prix.
888 **221** 6pf.+4pf. green 15 85
889 12pf.+88pf. red . . . . . 20 1·10

1944. National Goldsmiths' Institution.
890 **222** 6pf.+4pf. green 10 80
891 12pf.+88pf. red 20 90

223 Posthorn

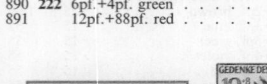

224 Eagle and Dragon

1944. Stamp Day.
892 **223** 6pf.+24pf. green 25 95

1944. 21st Anniv of Munich Rising.
893 **224** 12pf.+8pf. red 25 90

225 Adolf Hitler

226 Count Anton Gunther

1944.
894 **225** 42pf. green . . . . 10 1·20

1945. 600th Anniv of Oldenburg.
895 **226** 6pf.+14pf. purple 25 95

227 "Home Guard"

228 S.S. Troopers

1945. Mobilization of "Home Guard".
896 **227** 12pf.+8pf. red . . . . . 45 1·60

1945. 12th Anniv of Third Reich.
897 **228** 12pf.+38pf. red . . . . . 10·50 49·00
898 – 12pf.+38pf. red . . . . . 12·50 55·00
DESIGN: No. 898, S.A. man with torch.

For Nos. 899 onwards see section B of Allied Occupation.

MILITARY FIELDPOST STAMPS

M 184 Junkers Ju 52/3m

M 185

1942. Air. No value indicated. Perf. or roul.
M804 M **184** (–) blue 40 30

1942. Parcel Post. Size 28×23 mm. No value indicated. Perf or roul.
M805 M **185** (–) brown 15 40

Nos. M804/5 also exist overprinted **INSELPOST** in various types for use in Crete and the Aegean Islands and there are various other local fieldpost issues.

1944. Christmas Parcel Post. Size 22½×18 mm. No value indicated. Perf.
M895 M **185** (–) green . . . . . 2·00 1·60

1944. For 2 kilo parcels. No value indicated. No. 785 optd **FELDPOST 2kg.**
M896 **173** (–) on 40pf. mauve . . 2·75 2·10

NEWSPAPER STAMPS

N 156 Newspaper Messenger and Globe

1939.
N727 N **156** 5pf. green . . . . . 55 2·40
N728 10pf. brown . . . . 55 2·40

OFFICIAL STAMPS

O 23

O 24

1903.
O82 O **23** 2pf. grey . . . . . . 85 3·75
O83 3pf. brown . . . . . . 85 4·50
O84 5pf. green 25 40
O85 10pf. red 25 40
O86 20pf. blue 25 40
O87 25pf. black and red on yellow 25 40
O88 40pf. black and red . . 45 1·60
O89 50pf. blk & pur on buff 60 1·40

1905.
O90 O **24** 2pf. grey . . . . . . 55·00 60·00
O91 3pf. brown . . . . . . 7·75 10·00
O92 5pf. green . . . . . . 4·75 7·00
O93 10pf. red . . . . . . 75 2·20
O94 20pf. blue . . . . . . 1·90 2·75
O95 25pf. black and red on yellow . . . . . . 39·00 55·00

O 31

O 32

1920. Numeral designs as Types O **31** and O **32**.
O117 5pf. green . . . . . . 25 3·00
O118 10pf. red . . . . . . 60 1·20
O119 15pf. brown . . . . . . 20 1·10
O120 20pf. blue 15 95
O121 30pf. orange on pink . . . 10 95
O122 50pf. violet on pink . . . 35 1·10
O123 1m. red on pink . . . . 7·50 4·00

1920. Similar designs but without figures "21".
O124 5pf. green . . . . . . 55 5·50
O125 10pf. red . . . . . . 10 1·00
O126 10pf. orange 70 £475
O127 15pf. purple . . . . . . 10 1·10
O128 20pf. blue . . . . . . 15 1·00
O129 30pf. orange on pink . . . 15 1·60
O130 40pf. red . . . . . . 20 1·10
O131 50pf. violet on pink . . . 20 1·40
O132 60pf. brown . . . . . . 15 1·10
O133 1m. red on pink 10 95
O134 1m.25 blue on yellow . . 10 1·10
O135a 2m. blue . . . . . . 2·75 1·40
O136 5m. brown on yellow . . . 25 1·20

1920. Official stamps of Bavaria optd **Deutsches Reich.**
O137 O **31** 5pf. green . . . . . 10 3·00
O138 10pf. orange . . . . 10 1·70
O139 15pf. red . . . . . 10 1·70
O140 20pf. purple . . . . 10 1·40
O141 30pf. blue . . . . . 10 1·20
O142 40pf. brown . . . . 10 1·20
O143 O **32** 50pf. red . . . . . 10 1·20
O144 60pf. green . . . . 10 1·20
O145 70pf. violet . . . . 2·40 2·50
O146 75pf. red . . . . . 50 1·30
O147 80pf. blue . . . . . 10 1·10
O148 90pf. olive . . . . . 1·70 2·20
O149 O **33** 1m. brown . . . . . 10 1·20
O150 1¼m. green . . . . 10 1·20
O151 1½m. red . . . . . 10 1·20
O152 2½m. blue . . . . . 20 1·30
O153 3m. red . . . . . . 20 1·30
O154 5m. black . . . . . 11·50 24·00

1920. Municipal Service stamps of Wurttemberg optd **Deutsches Reich.**
O155 M **5** 5pf. green . . . . . 4·25 9·50
O156 10pf. red . . . . . 2·20 4·50
O157 15pf. violet . . . . 2·50 5·25
O158 20pf. blue . . . . . 4·75 8·50
O159 50pf. purple . . . . . 4·25 20·00

1920. Official stamps of Wurttemberg optd **Deutsches Reich.**
O160 O **5** 5pf. green . . . . . . 40 4·25
O161 10pf. red . . . . . . 10 2·40
O162 15pf. purple . . . . . 10 2·40
O163 20pf. blue . . . . . . 20 1·50
O164 30pf. black and orange . . 20 3·50
O165 40pf. black and red . . 30 2·40
O166 50pf. purple . . . . . 30 3·25
O167 1m. black and grey . . 30 7·00

O 48

O 50

O 81

1922. Figure designs.
O249 O **48** 75pf. blue . . . . . . 20 6·75
O247 – 3m. brown on red . . 10 1·30
O248 O **50** 10m. green on red . . 10 6·25
O251 20m. blue on red . . . 10 1·30
O252 50m. violet on red . . 10 1·30
O253 100m. red on rose . . . 10 1·30

1923. Postage stamps optd **Dienstmarke.**
O274 **51** 20m. purple . . . . . . 10 8·25
O275 30m. olive . . . . . . 10 25·00
O276 **38** 40m. green . . . . . . 20 3·25
O277 **54** 200m. red . . . . . . 10 1·10
O278 300m. green . . . . . . 10 1·10
O279 400m. brown . . . . . . 10 1·10
O280 500m. orange . . . . . . 20 1·10
O342 **62** 100M. grey 20 £170
O343 200M. brown 20 £170
O344 2Md. green and pink . . 30 £100
O345 5Md. brown and yellow 30 85·00
O346 10Md. green and light green . . . . 4·25 £150
O347 20Md. brown and green 4·75 £150
O348 50Md. blue . . . . . . 2·40 £200

1923. Official stamps of 1920 and 1922 surch **Tausend** or **Millionen** and figure.
O312 – 5T. on 5m. brown on yellow . . . . . 10 3·00
O313 – 20T. on 30pf. orange on rose (No. O129) 10 2·75
O317 O **50** 75T. on 50m. violet on rose . . . . . . 10 2·75
O314 – 100T. on 15pf. purple 10 2·75
O315 – 250T. on 10pf. red (No. O125) . . . . 10 2·75
O318 – 400T. on 15pf. purple 10 28·00
O319 – 800T. on 30pf. orge on rose (No. O129) . . 15 4·25
O320 O **48** 1M. on 75pf. blue . . 10 45·00
O321 – 2M. on 10pf. red (No. O125) . . . . . 15 3·50
O322 O **50** 5M. on 100m. red on rose . . . . . . 10 6·50

1923. Nos. 352/7 optd **Dienstmarke.**
O358 **64** 3pf. brown 40 40
O359 5pf. green 40 40
O360 10pf. red 50 40
O361 20pf. blue 95 40
O362 50pf. orange 95 80
O363 100pf. purple . . . . . . 4·25 8·25

1924. Optd **Dienstmarke.**
O376 **66** 3pf. brown . . . . . . 50 1·30
O377 5pf. green 30 40
O378 10pf. red 30 40
O379 20pf. blue 40 40
O380 30pf. red 95 50
O381 40pf. olive 95 55
O382 50pf. orange . . . . . . 6·25 2·75
O384 **72** 60pf. brown . . . . . . 2·20 4·00
O385 80pf. grey . . . . . . 9·00 36·00

1927.
O424 O **81** 3pf. brown 45 20
O425 4pf. blue 40 45
O427 5pf. green 20 20
O428 6pf. green 50 45
O429 8pf. green 40 20
O430 10pf. red . . . . . 9·50 9·50
O432 10pf. mauve 40 45
O433 10pf. brown . . . . 3·50 7·25
O434 12pf. orange 40 45
O436 15pf. red . . . . . 1·40 50
O437 20pf. green . . . . 5·75 2·40
O438 20pf. grey . . . . . 1·40 70
O439 30pf. green . . . . 1·20 40
O440 40pf. violet . . . . 1·20 40
O441 60pf. brown . . . . 1·40 1·70

O 100

1934.
O809 O **100** 3pf. brown 20 85
O810 4pf. blue 20 85
O528 5pf. green 20 65
O529 6pf. green 20 65
O812 6pf. violet 20 90
O813 8pf. red 30 85
O531 10pf. brown . . . . . 35 1·20
O815 12pf. red . . . . . . 40 1·20
O533 15pf. red . . . . . . 1·20 6·75
O534 20pf. blue . . . . . 40 1·10
O535 30pf. green . . . . . 70 1·10
O536 40pf. mauve . . . . . 70 1·10
O537 50pf. yellow . . . . . 95 1·30
O820 50pf. green . . . . . 2·20 8·50

SPECIAL STAMPS FOR USE BY OFFICIALS OF THE NATIONAL SOCIALIST GERMAN WORKERS' PARTY

P 132 Party Badge

1938.
O648 P **132** 1pf. black . . . . . . 1·20 3·25
O799 3pf. brown . . . . . . 40 1·20
O800 4pf. blue 65 85
O651 5pf. green . . . . . . 75 1·30
O652 6pf. green . . . . . . 75 1·30
O802 6pf. violet 30 60
O803 8pf. red . . . . . . 2·10 90
O804 12pf. red . . . . . . 2·75 90
O655 16pf. grey . . . . . . 2·00 13·50
O805 16pf. blue . . . . . . 4·00 17·00
O656 24pf. green . . . . . . 3·00 6·00
O806 24pf. brown 60 95
O807 30pf. green . . . . . . 1·20 3·00
O808 40pf. mauve . . . . . . 1·40 2·75

II. ALLIED OCCUPATION

The defeat of Germany in May 1945 resulted in the division of the country into four zones of occupation (British, American, French and Russian), while Berlin was placed under joint allied control. Allied Military Post Stamps came into use in the British and American zones, the French issued special stamps in their zone and in the Russian zone the first issues were made by local administrations.

The territory occupied by the Anglo-American and French Zones subsequently became the German Federal Republic (West Germany) which was set up in September 1949. By the Nine Power Agreement of 3 October 1954, the occupation of West Germany was ended and full sovereignty was granted to the German Federal Government as from 5 May 1955 (see Section III).

The territory in the Russian Zone became the German Democratic Republic (East Germany) which was set up on 7 October 1949 (see Section V).

Separate issues for the Western Sectors of Berlin came into being in 1948 (see Section IV). The Russian Zone issues inscribed "STADT BERLIN" were for use in the Russian sector of the city and Brandenburg and these were superseded first by the General Issues of the Russian Zone and then by the stamps of East Germany.

100 pfennige = 1 Reichsmark.
21.6.48. 100 pfennige = 1 Deutsche Mark (West).
24.6.48. 100 pfennige = 1 Deutsche Mark (East).

A. Allied Military Post (British and American Zones)

A 1

1945.
A16 A **1** 1pf. black 25 40
A 1 3pf. violet 25 35
A18 4pf. grey 25 35
A19a 5pf. green 90 70
A20 6pf. yellow 25 30
A 5 8pf. orange 25 35
A 6 10pf. brown 25 50
A23 12pf. purple 50 40
A24 15pf. red 25 45
A25 16pf. green . . . . . . 25 2·00
A26 20pf. blue 40 50
A27 24pf. brown . . . . . . 35 2·20
A28 25pf. blue . . . . . . 50 3·00
A29 30pf. olive . . . . . . 40 2·40
A30 40pf. mauve . . . . . . 40 1·10
A31 42pf. green . . . . . . 40 1·10
A32 50pf. slate 25 90
A33 60pf. plum . . . . . . 90 4·50
A34 80pf. blue . . . . . . 45·00 55·00
A35 1m. green . . . . . . 4·75 8·50

Values 30pf. to 80pf. are size 22×25 mm and 1m. is size 25×29½ mm.

Nos. A36 etc continue in Section C.

Used prices are for cancelled-to-order.

B. American, British and Russian Zones 1946–48

From February 1946 to June 1948 these zones used the same stamps (Nos. 899/956). It had been intended that they should be used throughout all four zones but until the creation of the German Federal Republic, in September 1949, the French Zone always had its own stamps, while after the revaluation of the currency in June 1948 separate stamps were again issued for the Russian Zone.

229 Numeral

231 1160: Leipzig obtains Charter

1946.

899	**229**	1pf. black	15	1·40
900		2pf. black	15	20
901		3pf. brown	15	2·40
902		4pf. blue	15	2·40
903		5pf. green	15	65
904		6pf. violet	15	20
905		8pf. red	15	20
906		10pf. brown	15	20
907		12pf. red	15	20
908		12pf. grey	15	20
909		15pf. red	15	3·75
910		15pf. green	15	20
911		16pf. green	15	20
912		20pf. blue	15	20
913		24pf. brown	15	20
914		25pf. blue	15	4·25
915		25pf. orange	15	95
916		30pf. green	15	20
917		40pf. purple	15	20
918		42pf. green	1·20	38·00
919		45pf. red	15	30
920		50pf. green	15	20
921		60pf. red	15	20
922		75pf. blue	15	20
923		80pf. blue	15	20
924		84pf. green	15	20
925		1m. green (24 × 30 mm)	15	20
MS925a		107 × 51 mm. Nos. 912/13 and 917 (sold at 5m.)	60·00	£225

1947. Leipzig Spring Fair. Inscr "LEIPZIGER MESSE 1947".

926	**231**	24pf.+26pf. brown	1·40	4·75
927	–	60pf.+40pf. blue	95	4·25

DESIGN: 60pf. 1268: Foreign merchants at Leipzig Fair.

See also Nos. 951/4.

233 Gardener

237 "Dove of Peace"

1947.

928	**233**	2pf. black	20	50
929		6pf. violet	20	20
930	A	8pf. red	20	20
931		10pf. green	20	50
932	B	12pf. grey	20	20
933	**233**	15pf. brown	40	1·90
934	C	16pf. green	20	50
935	A	20pf. blue	20	50
936	C	24pf. brown	20	20
937	**233**	25pf. orange	20	50
938	B	30pf. red	40	1·20
939	A	40pf. mauve	20	50
940	C	50pf. blue	40	1·20
941	B	60pf. red	20	60
942		60pf. brown	20	75
943		80pf. blue	20	75
944	C	84pf. green	50	75
945	**237**	1m. green	20	75
946		2m. violet	20	95
947		3m. lake	20	13·50
948		5m. blue	2·40	60·00

DESIGNS: A, Sower; B, Labourer; C, Bricklayer and reaper.

238 Dr. von Stephan

1947. 50th Death Anniv of Von Stephan.

949	**238**	24pf. brown	20	60
950		75pf. blue	30	1·20

1947. Leipzig Autumn Fair. As T **231**.

951		12pf. red	25	1·20
952		75pf. blue	25	1·90

DESIGNS: 12pf. 1497: Maximilian I granting Charter; 75pf. 1365: Assessment and Collection of Ground Rents.

1948. Leipzig Spring Fair. As T **231** but dated "1948".

953		50pf. blue	25	95
954		84pf. green	25	1·70

DESIGNS: 50pf. 1388: At the customs barrier; 84pf. 1433: Bringing merchandise.

For similar types, dated "1948", "1949" or "1950", but with premium values, see Nos. R31/2, R51/2, R60/1 of Russian Zone and E7/8 of East Germany.

239 Weighing Goods

1948. Hanover Trade Fair.

955	**239**	24pf. red	25	1·10
956		50pf. blue	25	1·50

C. British and American Zones 1948–49

(A **2**)

1948. Currency Reform. (a) On Pictorial issue of 1947, Nos. 928/44. (i) Optd with Type A **2**.

A36		2pf. black	10	15
A37		6pf. violet	10	15
A38		8pf. red	10	15
A39		10pf. green	15	25
A40		12pf. grey	15	10
A41		15pf. brown	7·00	16·00
A42		16pf. green	1·20	2·50
A43		20pf. blue	60	1·00
A44		24pf. brown	15	10
A45		25pf. orange	35	50
A46		30pf. red	2·50	5·75
A47		40pf. mauve	65	1·00
A48		50pf. blue	80	1·00
A49		60pf. brown	65	1·00
A50		60pf. red	49·00	£200
A51		80pf. blue	1·10	2·50
A52		84pf. green	3·25	6·50

(ii) Optd with multiple posthorns over whole stamp.

A53		2pf. black	80	1·40
A54		6pf. violet	80	1·40
A55		8pf. red	80	1·40
A56		10pf. green	15	25
A57		12pf. grey	90	1·60
A58		15pf. brown	15	65
A59		16pf. green	30	35
A60		20pf. blue	15	35
A61		24pf. brown	60	1·60
A62		25pf. orange	7·75	15
A63		30pf. red	25	65
A64		40pf. mauve	30	60
A65		50pf. blue	35	60
A66		60pf. brown	2·50	6·25
A67		60pf. red	35	65
A68		80pf. blue	40	65
A69		84pf. green	75	1·40

(b) On Numeral issue of 1946, Nos. 900 to 924. (i) Optd with Type A **2**.

A70	**229**	2pf. black	5·00	29·00
A71		8pf. red	10·50	60·00
A72		10pf. brown	1·10	4·00
A73		12pf. red	7·00	45·00
A74		12pf. grey	£130	£550
A75		15pf. red	7·00	55·00
A76		15pf. green	2·50	14·50
A77		16pf. green	41·00	£180
A78		24pf. brown	75·00	£200
A79		25pf. blue	14·50	60·00
A80		25pf. orange	1·60	7·00
A81		30pf. olive	1·60	7·00
A82		40pf. purple	60·00	£200
A83		45pf. red	2·50	7·00
A84		50pf. green	2·50	7·00
A85		75pf. blue	5·00	21·00
A86		84pf. green	5·00	21·00

(ii) Optd with multiple posthorns over whole stamp.

A 87	**229**	2pf. black	23·00	65·00
A 88		8pf. red	33·00	£120
A 89		10pf. brown	31·00	£120
A 90		12pf. red	11·00	60·00
A 91		12pf. grey	£250	£1000
A 92		15pf. red	11·00	45·00
A 93		15pf. green	1·10	7·00
A 94		16pf. green	37·00	£140
A 95		24pf. brown	41·00	£200
A 96		25pf. blue	12·50	55·00
A 97		25pf. orange	37·00	£160
A 98		30pf. olive	1·90	5·75
A 99		40pf. purple	55·00	£225
A100		45pf. red	2·50	12·00
A101		50pf. green	2·50	12·00
A102		75pf. blue	2·50	12·50
A103		84pf. green	2·50	13·50

A **4** Crowned Head

A **7** Cologne Cathedral

1948. 700th Anniv of Cologne Cathedral and Restoration Fund.

A104	A **4**	6pf.+4pf. brown	60	60
A105	–	12pf.+8pf. blue	1·40	1·90
A106	–	24pf.+16pf. red	2·30	3·00
A107	A **7**	50pf.+50pf. blue	5·75	8·25

DESIGNS—As Type A **4**: 12pf. The Three Wise Men; 24pf. Cologne Cathedral.

A **9** The Romer, Frankfurt am Main

A **10** Frauenkirche, Munich

A **13** Holstentor Lubeck

1948. Various designs.

A108	A **9**	2pf. black	15	10
A109	A **10**	4pf. brown	20	10
A110a	A	5pf. blue	25	10
A111	A **10**	6pf. brown	15	35
A112		6pf. orange	30	10
A113	A **9**	8pf. yellow	30	35
A114	A **10**	8pf. slate	25	10
A115a	A	10pf. green	30	10
A116	A **10**	15pf. orange	1·90	5·00
A117	A **9**	15pf. violet	1·10	10
A118		16pf. green	55	50
A119		20pf. blue	90	2·10
A120	B	20pf. red	60	10
A121		24pf. red	25	15
A122	A	25pf. red	90	10
A123	B	30pf. blue	1·00	15
A124	A **10**	30pf. red	2·50	5·00
A125	A	40pf. mauve	1·40	30
A126	B	50pf. blue	1·00	1·60
A127	A **10**	50pf. green	1·40	10
A128a	A	60pf. purple	70·00	10
A129	B	80pf. mauve	2·75	10
A130	A **10**	84pf. purple	1·90	5·00
A131	A	90pf. mauve	2·75	10
A132	A **13**	1Dm. green	29·00	60
A133		2Dm. violet	25·00	60
A134		3Dm. mauve	29·00	3·00
A135		5Dm. blue	33·00	23·00

DESIGNS—As Type A **9/10**: A, Cologne Cathedral; B, Brandenburg Gate.

A **15** Brandenburg Gate, Berlin

1948. Aid to Berlin.

A140	A **15**	10pf.+5pf. green	6·25	7·00
A141		20pf.+10pf. red	6·25	7·00

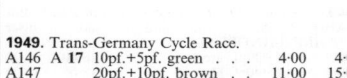

A **16** Herman Hillebrant Wedigh (after Holbein)

A **17** Racing Cyclists

1949. Hanover Trade Fair.

A142	A **16**	10pf. green	2·50	2·30
A143		20pf. red	2·50	2·30
A144		30pf. blue	3·25	3·00
MSA145		110 × 65 mm. Nos. A142/4 (sold at 1Dm.)	80·00	£200

1949. Trans-Germany Cycle Race.

A146	A **17**	10pf.+5pf. green	4·00	4·00
A147		20pf.+10pf. brown	11·00	15·00

A **18** Goethe in Italy

A **19** Goethe

1949. Birth Bicentenary of Goethe (poet).

A148	A **18**	10pf.+5pf. green	3·00	3·00
A149	A **19**	20pf.+10pf. red	5·00	5·00
A150	–	30pf.+15pf. blue	23·00	23·00

DESIGN—VERT: 30pf. Profile portrait.

OBLIGATORY TAX STAMPS

AT **14**

1948. Aid for Berlin. Perf or imperf.

AT136	AT **14**	2pf. blue	40	20

The Anglo-American Zones, together with the French Zone, became the Federal German Republic (West Germany) in September 1949.

D. French Zone.

(a) General Issues, 1945–46.

F **1** Arms of the Palatinate

F **2** Goethe

1945. (a) Arms.

F 1	F **1**	1pf. green, black & yellow	20	25
F 2	–	3pf. yellow, black and red	30	20
F 3	–	5pf. black, yellow & brn	20	20
F 4	–	8pf. red, yellow and brown	20	20
F 5	F **1**	10pf. green, brown & yell	7·75	45·00
F 6	–	12pf. yellow, black & red	20	20
F 7	–	15pf. blue, black and red	20	25
F 8	–	20pf. black, yellow & red	20	25
F 9	–	24pf. blue, black and red	20	35
F10	–	30pf. red, yellow & black	20	25

ARMS: 3, 12pf. Rhineland; 5, 20pf. Wurttemberg; 8, 30pf. Baden; 15, 24pf. Saar.

(b) Poets.

F11	**2**	1m. brown	1·80	19·00
F12	–	2m. blue (Schiller)	1·40	50·00
F13	–	5m. red (Heine)	1·50	50·00

(b) Baden, 1947–49.

FB **1** J. P. Hebel

FB **2** Rastatt Castle

FB **3** Hollental Black Forest

FB **4** Freiburg Cathedral

1947. Inscr "BADEN".

FB 1	FB **1**	2pf. grey	20	35
FB 2	–	3pf. brown	20	25
FB 3	–	10pf. blue	20	25
FB 4	FB **1**	12pf. green	20	25
FB 5	–	15pf. violet	20	40
FB 6	FB **2**	16pf. green	25	1·40
FB 7	–	20pf. blue	20	50
FB 8	FB **2**	24pf. red	20	20
FB 9	–	45pf. mauve	20	95
FB10	FB **1**	60pf. orange	20	25
FB11	–	75pf. blue	20	1·40
FB12	FB **3**	84pf. green	25	1·70
FB13	FB **4**	1m. brown	25	95

DESIGNS—18 × 23 mm: 3, 15, 45pf. Badensian girl and yachts; 10, 20, 75pf. Hans Baldung Grien.

1948. Currency Reform. As 1947 issue. (a) Value in "PF."

FB14	FB **1**	2pf. orange	25	40
FB15	–	6pf. brown	25	25
FB16	–	10pf. brown	70	1·40
FB17	FB **1**	12pf. red	40	25

FB18	–	15pf. blue	40	25
FB19	FB 2	24pf. green	50	70
FB20	–	30pf. mauve	1·20	2·40
FB21	–	50pf. blue	5·75	1·20

(b) New currency. Value in "D.PF" or "D.M." (="Deutschpfennig" or "Deutschmark").

FB22	–	8dpf. green	70	25
FB23	FB 2	16dpf. violet	1·40	1·40
FB24	–	20dpf. brown	1·40	25
FB25	FB 1	60dpf. grey	6·75	70
FB26	FB 3	84dpf. red	7·75	5·75
FB27	FB 4	1dm. blue	7·75	5·75

DESIGNS—As Types FB 1/2: 6, 15pf. Badensian girl and yachts; 10pf., 20dpf. Hans Baldung Grien; 8dpf., 30pf. Black Forest girl in festive headdress; 50pf. Grand-Duchess Stephanie of Baden.

Nos. FB14/21 were sold on the new currency basis though not inscribed "D.PF."

1948. As 1947 issue, but "PF" omitted.

FB28	FB 1	2pf. orange	40	70
FB29	–	4pf. violet	25	60
FB30	–	5pf. blue	50	85
FB31	–	6pf. brown	11·00	19·00
FB32	–	8pf. brown	50	1·40
FB33	–	10pf. green	50	1·90
FB34	–	20pf. mauve	85	50
FB35	–	40pf. brown	29·00	£100
FB36	FB 1	80pf. red	4·75	9·00
FB37	FB 3	90pf. red	31·00	£100

DESIGNS—18 × 23 mm: 4pf., 40pf. Rastatt; 5pf., 6pf. Badensian girl and yachts; 8pf. Black Forest girl in festive headdress; 10pf., 20pf. Portrait of Hans Baldung Grien.

FB 5 Cornhouse, Freiburg

FB 6 Arms of Baden

1949. Freiburg Rebuilding Fund.

FB38	FB 5	4pf.+16pf. violet	4·75	46·00
FB39	–	10pf.+20pf. green	4·75	46·00
FB40	–	20pf.+30pf. red	4·75	46·00
FB41	–	30pf.+50pf. blue	9·00	60·00
MSFB41a		65 × 78 mm. Nos. FB38/41	£120	£450
MSFB41b		Ditto but imperf	£120	£450

DESIGNS: 10pf. Freiburg Cathedral; 20pf. Trumpeting angel, Freiburg; 30pf. "Fischbrunnen", Freiburg.

1949. Red Cross Fund.

FB42	FB 6	10pf.+20pf. green	8·75	£100
FB43		20pf.+40pf. lilac	8·75	£100
FB44		30pf.+60pf. blue	8·75	£100
FB45		40pf.+80pf. grey	8·75	£100
MSFB45a		90 × 100 mm. Nos. FB42/5	95·00	£1300

FB 7 Seehof Hotel, Constance

1949. Engineers' Congress, Constance.

FB46	FB 7	30pf. blue	12·00	70·00

FB 8 Goethe

FB 9 Carl Schurz and Revolutionary Scene

FB 10 Conradin Kreutzer

1949. Birth Bicentenary of Goethe (poet).

FB47	FB 8	10pf.+5pf. green	4·75	24·00
FB48	–	20pf.+10pf. red	4·75	24·00
FB49	–	30pf.+15pf. blue	5·75	60·00

1949. Cent of Rastatt Insurrection.

FB50	FB 9	10pf.+5pf. green	4·75	36·00
FB51		20pf.+10pf. mauve	4·75	36·00
FB52		30pf.+15pf. blue	5·75	36·00

1949. Death Centenary of Conradin Kreutzer (composer).

FB53	FB 10	10pf. green	1·40	10·50

FB 11 1849 Mail Coach

FB 12 Posthorn and Globe

1949. German Stamp Centenary.

FB54	FB 11	10pf. green	2·40	13·50
FB55	–	20pf. brown	2·40	13·50

DESIGN: 20pf. Postal motor-coach with trailer and Douglas DC-4 airliner.

1949. 75th Anniv of U.P.U.

FB56	FB 12	20pf. red	3·00	15·00
FB57		30pf. blue	3·00	12·00

(c) Rhineland Palatinate, 1947–49.

FR 1 "Porta Nigra", Trier

FR 2 Karl Marx

FR 4 Statue of Charlemagne

FR 5 St. Martin

1947. Inscr "RHEINLAND-PFALZ".

FR 1	–	2pf. grey	20	25
FR 2	–	3pf. brown	20	20
FR 3	–	10pf. blue	20	20
FR 4	FR 1	12pf. green	20	20
FR 5	FR 2	15pf. violet	20	20
FR 6	–	16pf. green	20	80
FR 7	–	20pf. blue	20	30
FR 8	–	24pf. red	20	20
FR 9	–	30pf. mauve	40	2·30
FR10	–	45pf. mauve	20	55
FR11	–	50pf. blue	20	1·60
FR12	–	60pf. orange	20	25
FR13	–	75pf. blue	20	55
FR14	–	84pf. green	20	1·20
FR15	FR 4	1m. brown	20	80

DESIGNS—SMALL SIZE: 2pf., 60pf. Beethoven's death mask; 3pf. Baron von Ketteler, Bishop of Mainz; 10pf. Girl vintager; 16pf. Rocks at Arnweiler; 20pf. Palatinate village house; 24pf. Worms Cathedral; 30pf., 75pf. Gutenberg (printer); 45pf., 50pf. Mainz Cathedral. LARGE SIZE—HORIZ: 84pf. Gutenfels Castle and Rhine.

1948. Currency Reform. As 1947 issue. (a) Value in "PF."

FR16	–	2pf. orange	20	30
FR17	–	6pf. brown	20	30
FR18	–	10pf. brown	40	85
FR19	FR 1	12pf. red	45	20
FR20	FR 2	15pf. blue	95	35
FR21	–	24pf. green	95	50
FR22	–	30pf. mauve	65	1·10
FR23	–	50pf. blue	2·30	60

(b) New currency. Value in "D.PF." or "D.M." (= "Deutschpfennig" or "Deutschmark").

FR24	FR 1	8dpf. green	40	60
FR25	–	16dpf. violet	85	75
FR26	–	20dpf. brown	1·20	50
FR27	–	60dpf. grey	8·00	45
FR28	–	84dpf. red	4·25	5·75
FR29	FR 4	1dm. blue	5·00	5·75

DESIGNS—SMALL SIZE: 6pf. Baron von Ketteler; 30pf. Mainz Cathedral; 50pf. Gutenberg (printer). Others as 1947 issue.

Nos. FR16/23 were sold on the new currency basis though not inscribed "D.PF.".

1948. Ludwigshafen Explosion Relief Fund.

FR30	FR 5	20pf.+30pf. mauve	1·20	28·00
FR31	–	30pf.+50pf. blue	1·20	28·00

DESIGN: 30pf. St. Christopher.

1948. Inscr "RHEINLAND-PFALZ". As 1947 issue, but "PF" omitted.

FR32	–	2pf. orange	65	45
FR33	–	4pf. violet	65	40
FR34	FR 2	5pf. blue	80	65
FR35	–	6pf. brown	25·00	16·00
FR36	FR 1	8pf. red	70·00	£300
FR37	–	10pf. green	75	40
FR38	–	20pf. mauve	85	40
FR39	–	40pf. brown	2·75	4·00
FR40	FR 1	80pf. red	3·00	5·00
FR41	–	90pf. red	5·00	18·00

DESIGNS—SMALL SIZE: 4pf. Rocks at Arnweiler; 40pf. Worms Cathedral. LARGE SIZE—HORIZ: 90pf. Gutenfels Castle and Rhine. Others as 1947–48 issues.

1949. Red Cross Fund. As Type FB 6 of Baden, but Arms of Rhineland and inscr "RHEINLANDPFALZ".

FR42		10pf.+20pf. green	18·00	95·00
FR43		20pf.+40pf. lilac	18·00	95·00
FR44		30pf.+60pf. blue	18·00	95·00
FR45		40pf.+80pf. grey	18·00	95·00
MSFR45a		90 × 100 mm. Nos. FR42/5	85·00	£1100

1949. Birth Bicentenary of Goethe. As Nos. FB47/9 of Baden.

FR46		10pf.+5pf. green	5·50	20·00
FR47		20pf.+10pf. mauve	5·50	20·00
FR48		30pf.+15pf. blue	10·50	45·00

1949. Centenary of German Postage Stamp. As Nos. FB54/5 of Baden.

FR49		10pf. green	9·00	20·00
FR50		20pf. brown	9·00	20·00

1949. 75th Anniv of U.P.U. As Nos. FB56/7 of Baden.

FR51		20pf. red	5·25	12·00
FR52		30pf. blue	5·25	10·00

(d) Saar, 1945–47.

The Saar District, from 1945 to 1947 part of the French Zone, also had its own stamps, but as it was in a different political category, we list its stamps for convenience of reference all together under **SAAR**.

(e) Wurttemberg, 1947–49.

FW 1 Fr. von Schiller

FW 2 Bebenhausen Monastery

FW 3 Lichtenstein Castle

1947. Inscr "WURTTEMBERG".

FW 1	FW 1	2pf. grey	20	55
FW 2	–	3pf. brown	20	25
FW 3	–	10pf. blue	20	35
FW 4	FW 1	12pf. green	20	20
FW 5	–	15pf. violet	20	35
FW 6	FW 2	16pf. green	20	85
FW 7	–	20pf. blue	20	85
FW 8	FW 2	24pf. red	20	20
FW 9	–	45pf. mauve	20	85
FW10	FW 1	60pf. orange	20	65
FW11	–	75pf. blue	25	1·30
FW12	FW 3	84pf. green	25	1·40
FW13	–	1m. brown	25	1·00

DESIGNS—SMALL SIZE: 3pf., 15pf., 45pf. Holderlin (poet); 10pf., 20pf., 75pf. Wangen Gate. LARGE SIZE—VERT: 1m. Zwiefalten Monastery Church.

1948. Currency Reform. As 1947 issue. (a) Value in "PF."

FW14	FW 1	2pf. orange	30	45
FW15	–	6pf. brown	30	35
FW16	–	10pf. brown	1·20	1·30
FW17	FW 1	12pf. red	30	40
FW18	–	15pf. blue	30	40
FW19	FW 2	24pf. green	75	50
FW20	–	30pf. mauve	95	1·50
FW21	–	50pf. blue	2·40	75

(b) Value in "D.PF" (= Deutsch Pfennig) or "D.M." (= Deutsch Mark).

FW22	–	8dpf. green	95	1·20
FW23	FW 2	16dpf. violet	1·40	1·30
FW24	–	20dpf. brown	3·00	75
FW25	FW 1	60dpf. grey	14·00	65
FW26	FW 3	84dpf. red	4·75	4·75
FW27	–	1dm. blue	4·75	4·75

DESIGNS—SMALL SIZE: 6pf., 15pf. Fr. Holderlin (poet); 8 dpf., 30pf. Waldsee Castle; 50pf. Ludwig Uhland (poet). Others as 1947 issue.

Nos. FW14/21 were sold on the new currency basis though not inscribed "D.PF."

1948. Inscr "WURTTEMBERG". As 1947 issue, but "PF" omitted.

FW28	FW 1	2pf. orange	1·50	65
FW29	FW 2	4pf. violet	3·25	45
FW30	–	5pf. blue	8·25	2·50
FW31	–	6pf. brown	10·00	6·00
FW32	–	8pf. red	10·00	2·50
FW33	–	10pf. green	10·00	30
FW34	–	20pf. mauve	10·00	30
FW35	FW 2	40pf. brown	24·00	47·00
FW36	FW 1	80pf. red	55·00	47·00
FW37	FW 3	90pf. red	85·00	£120

DESIGNS—SMALL SIZE: 5pf., 6pf. Holderlin. Others as 1947 and 1948 issues.

FW 4 Isny and Coat of Arms

FW 5 Gustav Werner

1949. Ski Championships (Northern Combination) at Isny/Allgau.

FW38	FW 4	10pf.+4pf. green	8·75	23·00
FW39	–	20pf.+6pf. lake	8·75	23·00

DESIGN: 20pf. Skier and view of Isny.

1949. Red Cross Fund. As Type FB 6 of Baden, but Arms of Wurttemberg and inscr "WURTTEMBERG".

FW40		10pf.+20pf. green	37·00	£120
FW41		20pf.+40pf. lilac	37·00	£120
FW42		30pf.+60pf. blue	37·00	£120
FW43		40pf.+80pf. grey	37·00	£120
MSFW43a		90 × 100 mm. Nos. FW40/3	£130	£1400

1949. Birth Bicentenary of Goethe. As Nos. FB47/9 of Baden.

FW44		10pf.+5pf. green	9·00	21·00
FW45		20pf.+10pf. mauve	13·50	29·00
FW46		30pf.+15pf. blue	13·50	41·00

1949. Centenary of Christian Institution "Zum Bruderhaus".

FW47	FW 5	10pf.+5pf. green	6·25	14·50
FW48		20pf.+10pf. purple	6·25	14·50

1949. German Stamp Centenary. As Nos. FB54/5 of Baden.

FW49		10pf. green	7·75	30·00
FW50		20pf. brown	7·75	30·00

1949. 75th Anniv of U.P.U. As Nos. FB56/7 of Baden.

FW51		20pf. red	6·75	28·00
FW52		30pf. blue	6·75	22·00

The French Zone was incorporated in West Germany in September 1949.

E. Russian Zone.

For a list of the stamps issued by the Russian Zone Provincial Administrations of Berlin (Brandenburg), Mecklenburg-Vorpommern, Saxony (Halle, Leipzig and Dresden) and Thuringia, see Stanley Gibbons Part 7 (Germany) Catalogue.

General Issues.

In February 1946, the Provincial Issues were replaced by the General Issues, Nos. 899/956 until the revaluation of the currency in June 1948, when Nos. 928/44 were brought into use handstamped with District names and numbers as a control measure pending the introduction of the following overprinted stamps on 3rd July. There are over 1,900 different types of district handstamp.

Sowjetische Besatzungs Zone

(R 1)

R 3 Kathe Kollwitz

1948. Optd **Sowjetische Besatzungs Zone**. (a) On Pictorial issue of 1947, Nos. 928/44.

R 1	2pf. black	20	35
R 2	6pf. violet	20	20
R 3	8pf. red	20	20
R 4	10pf. green	20	20
R 5	12pf. grey	20	30
R 6	15pf. brown	20	35
R 7	16pf. green	20	40
R 8	20pf. blue	20	20
R 9	24pf. brown	20	20
R10	25pf. orange	20	45
R11	30pf. red	20	45
R12	40pf. mauve	50	45
R13	50pf. blue	75	95
R14	60pf. brown	95	95
R15	60pf. red	60·00	£100
R16	80pf. blue	1·20	1·10
R17	84pf. green	1·20	1·50

(b) On Numerical issue of 1946, Nos. 903, etc.

R18	229	5pf. green	40	1·10
R19		30pf. olive	1·10	3·25
R20		45pf. red	50	1·40
R21		75pf. blue	50	1·40
R22		84pf. green	1·40	1·90

(c) On stamps inscr "STADT BERLIN".

R23	R 1	5pf. green	40	95
R25	–	6pf. violet	40	95
R26	–	8pf. orange	40	95
R27	–	10pf. brown	40	95
R28	–	12pf. red	65	1·60
R29	–	20pf. blue	60	1·40
R30	–	30pf. olive	60	1·90

DESIGNS: 6pf. Bear with spade; 8pf. Bear on shield; 10pf. Bear holding brick; 12pf. Bear carrying plank; 20pf. Bear on small shield; 30pf. Oak sapling amid ruins.

1948. Leipzig Autumn Fair. As T **231** but dated "1948".

R31	16pf.+9pf. purple	50	65
R32	50pf.+25pf. blue	50	65

DESIGNS: 16pf. 1459: The first Spring Fair; 50pf. 1469: Foreign merchants displaying cloth.

1948. Politicians, Artists and Scientists.

R33	R 3	2pf. grey	1·20	25
R34	–	6pf. violet	1·20	25
R35	–	8pf. red	1·20	40
R36	–	10pf. green	40	40
R37	–	12pf. blue	5·25	40
R38	–	15pf. brown	95	1·70
R39	–	16pf. blue	85	55
R40	R 3	20pf. purple	85	95
R41	–	24pf. red	60	40

R42 – 25pf. olive . . . . 1·20 2·20
R43 – 30pf. red . . . . 2·75 1·90
R44 – 40pf. purple 95 95
R45 – 50pf. blue 95 65
R46 – 60pf. green . . . . . . 3·25 65
R47 – 80pf. blue . . . . 1·90 65
E95 – 80pf. red . . . . 15·00 24·00
R48 – 84pf. brown . . . . . . 3·25 3·25
PORTRAITS: 6, 40pf. Gerhart Hauptmann; 8, 50pf. Karl Marx; 10, 84pf. August Bebel; 12, 30pf. Friedrich Engels; 15, 60pf. G. F. W. Hegel; 16, 25pf. Rudolf Virchow; 24, 80pf. Ernst Thalmann.

R 4

R 5 Liebknecht and Rosa Luxemburg

1948. Stamp Day.
R49 R **4** 12pf.+3pf. red 40 60

1949. 30th Death Anniv of Karl Liebknecht and Rosa Luxemburg (revolutionaries).
R50 R **5** 24pf. red 45 85

1949. Leipzig Spring Fair. As T **231** but dated "1949".
R51 30pf.+15pf. red . . . . . . 3·75 4·50
R52 50pf.+25pf. blue . . . . . . 4·00 5·25
DESIGNS: 30pf. 1st Neubau Town Hall bazaar, 1556; 50pf. Italian merchants at Leipzig, 1536.

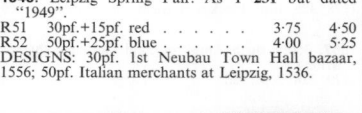

R 6 Dove

R 8 Goethe

1949. 3rd German Peoples' Congress.
R53 R **6** 24pf. red . . . . 1·30 2·20

1949. Optd **3. Deutscher Volkskongre 29.-30 Mai 1949.**
R54 R **6** 24pf. red . . . . 1·50 2·50

1949. Birth Bicent of Goethe. Portraits of Goethe.
R55 R **8** 6pf.+4pf. violet . . . . 3·00 3·50
R56 – 12pf.+8pf. brown . . . . 3·00 3·50
R57 – 24pf.+16pf. lake . . . . 2·40 2·75
R58 – 50pf.+25pf. blue . . . . 2·40 2·75
R59 – 84pf.+36pf. grey . . . . 4·25 5·50

1949. Goethe Festival Week, Weimar. Sheet 106 × 104 mm.
MSR59a R **9** 50pf. (+Dm. 4.50) blue £190 £275

1949. Leipzig Autumn Fair. As T **231** but dated "1949".
R60 12pf.+8pf. slate . . . . . . 4·50 6·25
R61 24pf.+16pf. lake . . . . . . 6·25 8·00
DESIGNS: 12pf. Russian merchants, 1650; 24pf. Goethe at Fair, 1765.

The Russian Zone was incorporated in East Germany in October 1949.

III. GERMAN FEDERAL REPUBLIC

The Federal Republic was set up on 23 May 1949. Until October 1990 it comprised the territory which formerly came under the British, American and French Zones. On 3 October 1990 the former territory of East Germany (German Democratic Republic) was absorbed into the Federal Republic.

1949. 100 pfennig = 1 Deutsche Mark (West).
2002. 100 cents = 1 euro.

257 Constructing Parliament Building

258 Reproduction of T 1 of Bavaria

1949. Opening of West German Parliament, Bonn.
1033 **257** 10pf. green . . . . . . 49·00 23·00
1034 20pf. red . . . . 60·00 27·00

1949. Centenary of 1st German Stamps.
1035 **258** 10pf.+2pf. black & grn 14·00 22·00
1036 – 20pf. blue and red . . . 42·00 42·00
1037 – 30pf. brown and blue . . 60·00 75·00
DESIGN: 20pf., 30pf. Reproductions of T **2** of Bavaria.

259 Dr. von Stephan, Old G.P.O., Berlin and Standehaus, Berne

1949. 75th Anniv of U.P.U.
1038 **259** 30pf. blue . . . . 60·00 42·00

260 St. Elisabeth of Thuringia

1949. Refugees' Relief Fund. Inscr as in T **260**.
1039 **260** 8pf.+2pf. purple . . . . 20·00 25·00
1040 – 10pf.+5pf. green . . . . 20·00 14·50
1041 – 20pf.+10pf. red . . . . 20·00 14·50
1042 – 30pf.+15pf. blue £100 £120
PORTRAITS: 10pf. Paracelsus von Hohenheim; 20pf. F. W. A. Froebel; 30pf. J. H. Wichern.

261 J. S. Bach's Seal

262 Numeral and Posthorn

1950. Death Bicent of Bach (composer).
1043 **261** 10pf.+2pf. green . . . . 65 23·00
1044 20pf.+3pf. red . . . . . 75 26·00

1951.
1045 **262** 2pf. green . . . . 5·00 95
1046 4pf. brown . . . . 3·00 20
1047 5pf. purple . . . . . . 10·00 20
1048 6pf. orange . . . . . . 22·00 3·50
1049 8pf. grey . . . . 24·00 10·00
1050 10pf. green . . . . . . 5·75 15
1051 15pf. violet . . . . . . 45·00 1·10
1052 20pf. red . . . . 4·50 15
1053 25pf. plum . . . . . . £110 5·50
1054 30pf. blue . . . . . . 60·00 35
1055 40pf. purple £170 35
1056 50pf. grey £200 35
1057 60pf. brown £140 35
1058 70pf. yellow . . . . . £450 16·00
1059 80pf. red . . . . £550 2·10
1060 90pf. green . . . . . . £600 2·40
The 30pf. to 90pf. are 20 × 24½ mm.

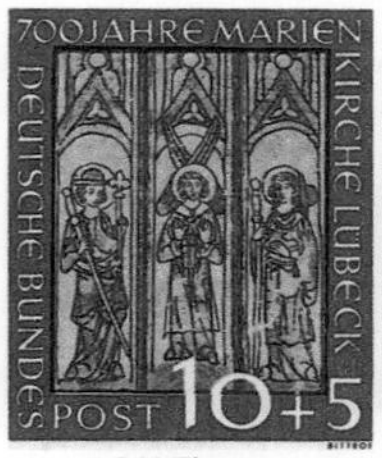
264 Figures

265 Stamps under Magnifier

1951. 700th Anniv of St. Mary's Church, Lubeck.
1065 **264** 10pf.+5pf. black & grn 95·00 33·00
1066 20pf.+5pf. black & red £110 90·00

1951. National Philatelic Exn, Wuppertal.
1067 **265** 10pf.+2pf. yellow, black and green . . . . . . 49·00 55·00
1068 20pf.+3pf. yellow, black and red . . . . 49·00 50·00

266 St. Vincent de Paul

267 W. C. Rontgen (physicist)

1951. Humanitarian Relief Fund.
1069 **266** 4pf.+2pf. brown . . . . 9·00 11·00
1070 – 10pf.+3pf. green . . . . 13·50 9·25
1071 – 20pf.+5pf. red . . . . . 13·50 9·25
1072 – 30pf.+10pf. blue . . . . 60·00 £120
PORTRAITS: 10pf. F. Von Bodelschwingh; 20pf. Elsa Brandstrom; 30pf. J. H. Pestalozzi.

1951. 50th Anniv of Award to Rontgen of 1st Nobel Prize for Physics.
1073 **267** 30pf. blue . . . . 75·00 15·00

268 Mona Lisa

269 Martin Luther

1952. 500th Birth Anniv of Leonardo da Vinci.
1074 **268** 5pf. multicoloured . . . 1·20 1·00

1952. Lutheran World Federation Assembly, Hanover.
1075 **269** 10pf. green . . . . . . 14·00 4·50

270 A. N. Otto and Diagram

271 Nuremberg Madonna

1952. 75th Anniv of Otto Gas Engine.
1076 **270** 30pf. blue . . . . 29·00 15·00

1952. Centenary of German National Museum, Nuremberg.
1077 **271** 10pf.+5pf. green . . . . 14·00 18·00

272 Trawler "Senator Schaffer" off Heligoland

273 Carl Schurz

1952. Rehabilitation of Heligoland.
1078 **272** 20pf. red . . . . 14·00 5·75

1952. Centenary of Arrival of Schurz in America.
1079 **273** 20pf. pink, black and blue . . . . 19·00 7·50

274 Boy Hikers

275 Elizabeth Fry

1952. Youth Hostels Fund. Inscr "JUGENDMARKE 1952".
1080 **274** 10pf.+2pf. green . . . . 22·00 21·00
1081 – 20pf.+3pf. red . . . . . 22·00 21·00
DESIGN: 20pf. Girl hikers.

1952. Humanitarian Relief Fund.
1082 **275** 4pf.+2pf. brown . . . . 9·00 6·75
1083 – 10pf.+5pf. green . . . . 9·00 6·50
1084 – 20pf.+10pf. lake . . . . 18·00 12·50
1085 – 30pf.+10pf. blue . . . . 90·00 95·00
PORTRAITS: 10pf. Dr. C. Sonnenschein; 20pf. T. Fliedner; 30pf. H. Dunant.

276 Postman, 1852

277 P. Reis

1952. Thurn and Taxis Stamp Centenary.
1086 **276** 10pf. multicoloured . . . 3·00 2·20

1952. 75th Anniv of German Telephone Service.
1087 **277** 30pf. blue . . . . 45·00 16·00

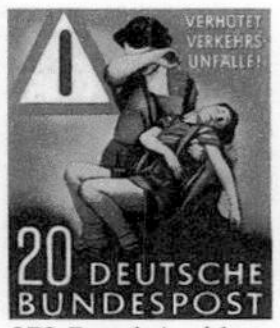
278 Road Accident Victim

279

1953. Road Safety Campaign.
1088 **278** 20pf. multicoloured . . . 16·00 4·25

1953. 50th Anniv of Science Museum, Munich.
1089 **279** 10pf.+5pf. green . . . . 27·00 27·00

280 Red Cross and Compass

281 Prisoner of War

1953. 125th Birth Anniv of Henri Dunant (founder of Red Cross).
1090 **280** 10pf. red and green . . . 21·00 6·50

1953. Commemorating Prisoners of War.
1091 **281** 10pf. black and grey . . 6·75 30

282 J. von Liebig

283 "Rail Transport"

1953. 150th Birth Anniv of Liebig (chemist).
1092 **282** 30pf. blue . . . . 45·00 20·00

1953. Transport Exn, Munich. Inscr as in T **283**.
1093 **283** 4pf. brown . . . . . . 6·75 4·50
1094 – 10pf. green . . . . . . 13·00 6·75
1095 – 20pf. red . . . . 18·00 10·00
1096 – 30pf. blue . . . . . . 55·00 23·00
DESIGNS: 10pf. "Air" (dove and aeroplanes); 20pf. "Road" (traffic lights and cars); 30pf. "Sea" (buoy and ships).

284 Gateway, Thurn and Taxis Palace

285 A. H. Francke

1953. International Philatelic Exhibition, Frankfurt am Main. Inscr "IFRABA 1953".
1097 **284** 10pf.+2pf. brown, black and green . . . . . . 27·00 28·00
1098 – 20pf.+3pf. grey, blue and red . . . . 27·00 28·00
DESIGN: 20pf. Telecommunications Buildings, Frankfurt am Main.

1953. Humanitarian Relief Fund.
1099 **285** 4pf.+2pf. brown . . . . 4·50 7·50
1100 – 10pf.+5pf. green . . . . 9·00 7·50
1101 – 20pf.+10pf. red . . . . 13·50 10·50
1102 – 30pf.+10pf. blue . . . . 60·00 70·00
PORTRAITS: 10pf. S. Kneipp; 20pf. J. C. Senckenberg; 30pf. F. Nansen.

286 Pres. Heuss

1954.

(a) Size 18¾ × 22½ mm or 18 × 22 mm.
1103 **286** 2pf. green 20 20
1104 4pf. brown 20 20
1105 5pf. mauve 20 20
1106 6pf. brown 20 75
1107 7pf. green 20 20
1108 8pf. grey 20 55
1109 10pf. green 20 20
1110 15pf. blue 65 30
1111 20pf. red 20 20
1112 25pf. purple 90 55
1122a 30pf. green 45 70
1122c 40pf. blue . . . . . . 2·75 20
1122e 50pf. olive . . . . . . 1·10 20
1122f 60pf. brown . . . . . . 4·00 60
1122g 70pf. violet . . . . . 14·00 60
1122h 80pf. orange . . . . . 7·00 2·10
1122i 90pf. green . . . . . . 22·00 1·10

(b) Size 20 × 24 mm.
1113 **286** 30pf. blue . . . . . . 17·00 4·75
1114 40pf. purple . . . . . . 6·75 20
1115 50pf. slate £225 45
1116 60pf. brown . . . . . . 45·00 55
1117 70pf. olive . . . . . . 17·00 1·80
1118 80pf. red . . . . 3·25 5·00
1119 90pf. green . . . . . . 17·00 2·75

(c) Size 25 × 30 mm.
1120 **286** 1Dm. olive . . . . . . 1·80 30
1121 2Dm. lavender . . . . . 3·25 1·20
1122 3Dm. purple . . . . . . 8·50 2·00

287 P. Ehrlich and E. von Behring

288 Gutenburg and Printing-press

1954. Birth Centenaries of Ehrlich and Von Behring (bacteriologists).
1123 **287** 10pf. green . . . . . . 10·00 3·75

1954. 500th Anniv of Gutenberg Bible.
1124 **288** 4pf. brown . . . . . . 1·20 50

289 Sword-pierced Mitre

290 Kathe Kollwitz

1954. 1,200th Anniv of Martyrdom of St. Boniface.
1125 **289** 20pf. red and brown . . 7·00 4·50

1954. Humanitarian Relief Fund.
1126 **290** 7pf.+3pf. brown . . . . 3·50 3·75
1127 – 10pf.+5pf. green . . . . 1·80 1·90
1128 – 20pf.+10pf. red . . . . 10·00 5·25
1129 – 40pf.+10pf. blue . . . . 36·00 44·00
PORTRAITS: 10pf. L. Werthmann; 20pf. J. F. Oberlin; 40pf. Bertha Pappenheim.

291 C. F. Gauss

292 "Flight"

1955. Death Cent of Gauss (mathematician).
1130 **291** 10pf. green . . . . . . 5·25 55

1955. Re-establishment of "Lufthansa" Airways.
1131 **292** 5pf. mauve and black . . 90 85
1132 10pf. green and black . . 1·30 1·20
1133 15pf. blue and black . . 8·50 6·00
1134 20pf. red and black . . . 24·00 7·75

293 O. von Miller

295 Schiller

1955. Birth Centenary of Von Miller (electrical engineer).
1135 **293** 10f. green . . . . 5·25 1·70

1955. 150th Death Anniv of Schiller (poet).
1136 **295** 40pf. blue . . . . 14·50 5·00

296 Motor-coach, 1906

297 Arms of Baden-Wurttemberg

1955. 50th Anniv of Postal Motor Transport.
1137 **296** 20pf. black and red . . . 11·50 4·50

1955. Baden-Wurttemberg Agricultural Exhibition, Stuttgart.
1138 **297** 7pf. black, brn & bistre 4·00 4·00
1139 10pf. black, grn & bistre 7·00 2·50

298 "Earth and Atom"

299 Refugees

1955. Cosmic Research.
1140 **298** 20pf. lake . . . . 8·50 1·20

1955. 10th Anniv of Expulsion of Germans from beyond the Oder–Neisse Line.
1141 **299** 20pf. red . . . . 4·25 55
See also No. 1400.

300 Orb, Arrows and Waves

301 Magnifying Glass and Carrier Pigeon

1955. Millenary of Battle of Lechfeld.
1142 **300** 20pf. purple . . . . . . 8·00 4·50

1955. West European Postage Stamp Exn.
1143 **301** 10pf.+2pf. green . . . . 5·00 6·00
1144 – 20pf.+3pf. red . . . . . 11·00 14·50
DESIGN: 20pf. Tweezers and posthorn.

302 Railway Signal

303 Stifter Monument

1955. Railway Timetable Conference.
1145 **302** 20pf. black and red . . . 9·00 2·40

1955. 150th Birth Anniv of Stifter (Austrian poet).
1146 **303** 10pf. green . . . . . . 3·50 2·10

304 U.N. Emblem

305 Amalie Sieveking

1955. U.N. Day.
1147 **304** 10pf. green and brown 3·50 4·25

1955. Humanitarian Relief Fund.
1148 **305** 7pf.+3pf. brown . . . . 3·25 3·75
1149 – 10pf.+5pf. green . . . . 2·20 1·90
1150 – 20pf.+10pf. red . . . . 2·20 1·90
1151 – 40pf.+10pf. blue . . . . 34·00 39·00
PORTRAITS: 10pf. A. Kolping; 20pf. Dr. S. Hahnemann; 40pf. Florence Nightingale.

306

307 Von Stephan's Signature

1955.
1152 **306** 1pf. grey 20 20

1955. 125th Birth Anniv of H. von Stephan.
1153 **307** 20pf. red . . . . 7·00 2·75

308 Spinet and Opening Bars of Minuet

309 Heinrich Heine

1956. Birth Bicent of Mozart (composer).
1154 **308** 10pf. black and lilac . . 90 30

1956. Death Centenary of Heine (poet).
1155 **309** 10pf. green and black . . 3·00 3·00

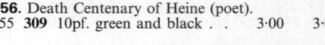

310 Old Houses and Crane

311

1956. Millenary of Luneburg.
1156 **310** 20pf. red . . . . 8·50 7·25

1956. Olympic Year.
1157 **311** 10pf. green 85 55

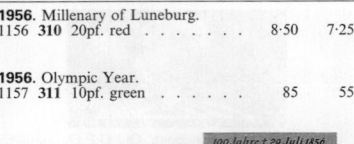

312 Boy and Dove

313 Robert Schumann

1956. Youth Hostels' Fund. Inscr "JUGEND".
1158 **312** 7pf.+3pf. grey, black and brown . . . . . . 2·40 3·75
1159 – 10pf.+5pf. grey black and green . . . . . 8·25 9·50
DESIGN: 10pf. Girl playing flute and flowers.

1956. Death Centenary of Schumann (composer).
1160 **313** 10pf. black, red & bistre 70 25

314

315 T. Mann (author)

1956. Evangelical Church Convention, Frankfurt am Main.
1161 **314** 10pf. green . . . . . . 4·50 3·75
1162 20pf. red . . . . 5·25 5·25

1956. Thomas Mann Commemoration.
1163 **315** 20pf. red . . . . 3·50 2·40

316

317 Ground Plan of Cologne Cathedral and Hand

1956. 800th Anniv of Maria Laach Abbey.
1164 **316** 20pf. grey and red . . . 2·50 2·10

1956. 77th Meeting of German Catholics, Cologne.
1165 **317** 10pf. green and brown 3·00 2·40

318

320 Nurse and Baby

1956. International Police Exhibition, Essen.
1166 **318** 20pf. green, orange & blk . . . . 3·00 2·50

1956. Europa. As Nos. 1582/3 of Belgium.
1167 10pf. green . . . . 1·60 20
1168 40pf. blue . . . . 8·50 1·30

1956. Humanitarian Relief Fund. Centres in black.
1169 **320** 7pf.+3pf. brown . . . . 1·60 2·75
1170 – 10pf.+5pf. green 90 75
1171 – 20pf.+10pf. red 90 75
1172 – 40pf.+10pf. blue . . . . 19·00 19·00
DESIGNS: 10pf. I. P. Semmelweis and cot; 20pf. Mother, and baby in cradle; 40f. Nurse maid and children.

321 Carrier Pigeon

322 "Military Graves"

1956. Stamp Day.
1173 **321** 10pf. green . . . . . . 1·60 75

1956. War Graves Commission.
1174 **322** 10pf. green . . . . . . 1·60 65

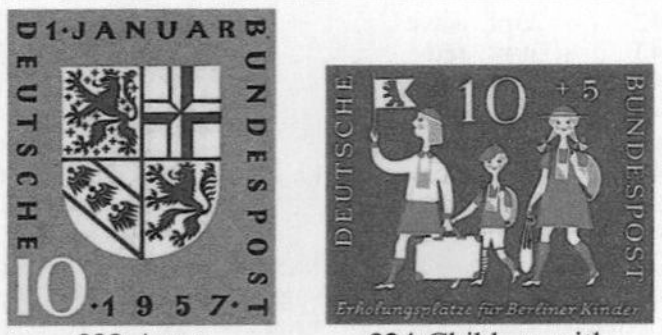
323 Arms

324 Children with Luggage

1957. Return of the Saar to West Germany.
1175 **323** 10pf. brown and green 60 50

1957. Berlin Children's Holiday Fund.
1176 **324** 10pf.+5pf. orange and green . . . . 1·60 2·40
1177 – 20pf.+10pf. blue and orange . . . . 3·50 4·50
DESIGN: 20pf. Girl returning from holiday.

325 Heinrich Hertz

326 Paul Gerhardt

1957. Birth Cent of Hertz (physicist).
1178 **325** 10pf. black and green . . 1·30 60

1957. 350th Birth Anniv of Paul Gerhardt (hymn-writer).
1179 **326** 20pf. red 60 50

327 "Flora and Philately"

328 Emblem of Aschaffenburg

1957. Exhibition and 8th Congress of Int Federation of "Constructive Philately".
1180 **327** 20pf. orange 60 50

1957. Millenary of Aschaffenburg.
1181 **328** 20pf. red and black . . . 60 55

329 University Class

1957. 500th Anniv of Freiburg University.
1182 **329** 10pf. black, red & green 35 25

330 "Bayernstein" (freighter)

1957. German Merchant Shipping Day.
1183 **330** 15pf. black, red and blue 1·20 1·10

331 Justus Liebig University

332 Albert Ballin

1957. 350th Anniv of Justus Liebig University, Giessen.
1184 **331** 10pf. green 50 30

1957. Birth Centenary of Albert Ballin (director of Hamburg-America Shipping Line).
1185 **332** 20pf. black and red . . . 1·30 40

333 Television Screen

334 "Europa" Tree

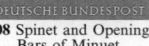

1957. Publicizing West German Television Service.
1186 **333** 10pf. green and blue . . 45 30

1957. Europa.
1187 **334** 10pf. green and blue . . 50 20
1188 40pf. blue . . . . 4·50 45

335 Young Miner

336 Water Lily

1957. Humanitarian Relief Fund.
1189 **335** 7pf.+3pf. black & brn 1·60 1·80
1190 – 10pf.+5pf. black & grn 1·10 95
1191 – 20pf.+10pf. black & red 1·60 95
1192 – 40pf.+10pf. black & bl 19·00 19·00
DESIGNS: 10pf. Miner drilling coal-face; 20pf. Miner with coal-cutting machine; 40pf. Operator at mine lift-shaft.

1957. Nature Protection Day.
1193 **336** 10pf. orange, yell & grn 50 45
1194 – 20pf. multicoloured . . . 65 45
DESIGN—VERT: 20pf. European robin.

337 Carrier Pigeons

338 Baron von Stein

1957. International Correspondence Week.
1195 **337** 20pf. black and red . . . 95 50

1957. Birth Bicentenary of Baron von Stein (statesman).
1196 **338** 20pf. red . . . . 1·60 75

339 Dr Leo Baeck (philosopher)

340 Wurttemberg Parliament House

1957. 1st Death Anniv of Dr. Leo Baeck.
1197 **339** 20pf. red . . . . 1·60 75

1957. 500th Anniv of First Wurttemberg Parliament.
1198 **340** 10pf. olive and green . . 85 55

341 Stage Coach

342 "Max and Moritz" (cartoon characters)

1957. Death Centenary of Joseph von Eichendorff (novelist).
1199 **341** 10pf. green 70 50

1958. 50th Death Anniv of Wilhelm Busch (writer and illustrator).
1200 **342** 10pf. olive and black . . 25 15
1201 – 20pf. red and black . . . 90 50
DESIGN: 20pf. Wilhelm Busch.

343 "Prevent Forest Fires"

345 "The Fox who stole the Goose"

344 Rudolf Diesel and First Oil Engine

1958. Forest Fires Prevention Campaign.
1202 **343** 20pf. black and red . . . 70 45

1958. Birth Centenary of Rudolf Diesel (engineer).
1203 **344** 10pf. myrtle 35 30

1958. Berlin Students' Fund. Inscr "Fur die Jugend".
1204 **345** 10pf.+5pf. red, black and green . . . . 2·00 2·75
1205 – 20pf.+10pf. brown, green and red . . . . 4·00 4·25
DESIGN: 20pf. "A hunter from the Palatinate" (horseman).

346 Giraffe and Lion

347 Old Munich

1958. Centenary of Frankfurt am Main Zoo.
1206 **346** 10pf. black and green . . 60 35

1958. 800th Anniv of Munich.
1207 **347** 20pf. red 60 40

348 Trier and Market Cross

349 Deutsche Mark (coin)

1958. Millenary of Trier Market.
1208 **348** 20pf. red and black . . . 60 40

1958. 10th Anniv of Currency Reform.
1209 **349** 20pf. black and orange 60 45

350 Emblem of Gymnastics

351 H. Schulze-Delitzsch

1958. 150th Anniv of German Gymnastics.
1210 **350** 10pf. black, green & grey 35 35

1958. 150th Birth Anniv of Schulze-Delitzsch (pioneer of German co-operative movement).
1211 **351** 10pf. green 45 30

1958. Europa. As No. 643 of Luxembourg, size $24\frac{1}{2} \times 30$ mm.
1212 10pf. blue and green 45 15
1213 40pf. red and blue . . . . . 3·00 40

352 Friedrich Raiffeisen (philanthropist)

353 Dairymaid

1958. Humanitarian Relief and Welfare Funds.
1214 **352** 7pf.+3pf. brown, deep brown and chestnut 50 65
1215 **353** 10pf.+5pf. red, yellow and green 50 45
1216 – 20pf.+10pf. blue, green and red 50 45
1217 – 40pf.+10pf. yellow, orange and blue . . . 7·00 7·75
DESIGNS— As Type **353**: 20pf. Vine-dresser; 40pf. Farm labourer.

354 Cardinal Nicholas of Cues (founder)

355 Jakob Fugger (merchant prince)

1958. 500th Anniv of Hospice of St. Nicholas.
1218 **354** 20pf. black and mauve 50 25

1959. As Type B **53** of West Berlin but without "BERLIN".
1219 7pf. green 30 15
1220 10pf. green 50 15
1221 20pf. red 50 15
1222 40pf. blue . . . . 16·00 95
1223 70pf. violet . . . . 5·00 70

1959. 500th Birth Anniv of Jakob Fugger.
1224 **355** 20pf. black and red . . . 35 30

356 Adam Riese (mathematician)

357 A. von Humboldt (naturalist)

1959. 400th Death Anniv of Adam Riese.
1225 **356** 10pf. black and green . . 35 30

1959. Death Cent of Alexander von Humboldt.
1226 **357** 40pf. blue . . . . 1·80 1·30

358 First Hamburg Stamp of 1859

359 Buxtehude

1959. International Stamp Exhibition, Hamburg, and Centenary of First Stamps of Hamburg and Lubeck.
1228 **358** 10pf.+5pf. brown & grn 25 45
1230 – 20pf.+10pf. brn & red 25 65
DESIGN: 20pf. First Lubeck stamp of 1859.

1959. Millenary of Buxtehude.
1231 **359** 20pf. red, black and blue 35 30

360 Holy Tunic of Trier

361 Congress Emblem

1959. Holy Tunic of Trier Exhibition.
1232 **360** 20pf. black, buff & purple 35 30

1959. German Evangelical Church Day and Congress, Munich.
1233 **361** 10pf. violet, green & blk 30 30

1959. Inauguration of Beethoven Hall, Bonn. T **361a** and similar horiz designs in sheet 148 × 104 mm with extract from Beethoven's music notebooks.
MS1233a 10pf. green (Handell); 15pf. blue (Spohr); 20pf. red (T **361a**); 25pf. brown (Haydn); 40pf. blue (Mendelssohn) . . . . . 25·00 50·00

1959. Europa. As Nos. 659/60 of Luxembourg, but size $24\frac{1}{2} \times 30$ mm.
1234 10pf. green 20 15
1235 40pf. blue . . . . 1·30 45

362 "Feeding the Poor"

363 "Uprooted Tree"

1959. Humanitarian Relief and Welfare Funds.
1236 **362** 7pf.+3pf. sepia & yellow 25 40
1237 – 10pf.+5pf. green & yell 25 35
1238 – 20pf.+10pf. red & yell 35 40
1239 – 40pf.+10pf. mult . . . . 3·50 5·00
DESIGNS: 10pf. "Clothing the Naked"; 20pf. "Bounty from Heaven" (scenes from the Brothers Grimm story "The Star Thaler"); 40pf. The Brothers Grimm.

1960. World Refugee Year.
1240 **363** 10pf. black, purple & grn 20 20
1241 40pf. black, red and blue 2·30 1·90

364 P. Melanchthon

365 Cross and Symbols of the Crucifixion

1960. 400th Death Anniv of Philip Melanchthon (Protestant reformer).
1242 **364** 20pf. black and red . . . 1·30 1·10

1960. Oberammergau Passion Play.
1243 **365** 10pf. grey, ochre and blue 25 20

366

367 Wrestling

1960. 37th World Eucharistic Congress, Munich.
1244 **366** 10pf. green 65 50
1245 20pf. red 90 70

1960. Olympic Year. Inscr as in T **367**.
1246 **367** 7pf. brown 20 20
1247 – 10pf. green 45 20
1248 – 20pf. red 45 20
1249 – 40pf. blue . . . . . . 1·30 1·30
DESIGNS: 10pf. Running; 20pf. Javelin and discus-throwing; 40pf. Chariot-racing.

368 Hildesheim Cathedral

368a Conference Emblem

1960. Birth Millenary of Bishops St. Bernward and St. Godehard.
1250 **368** 20pf. purple 80 60

1960. Europa.
1251 **368a** 10pf. green and olive 20 15
1252 20pf. vermilion and red 65 30
1253 40pf. light blue and blue . . . . 1·30 1·20

369 Little Red Riding Hood meeting Wolf

1960. Humanitarian Relief and Welfare Funds.
1254 **369** 7pf.+3pf. black, red and bistre 45 65
1255 – 10pf.+5pf. black, red and green 45 25
1256 – 20pf.+10pf. black, green and red 45 25
1257 – 40pf.+20pf. black, red and blue . . . . . 2·75 4·00
DESIGNS: 10pf. Red Riding Hood and wolf disguised as grandmother; 20pf. Woodcutter and dead wolf; 40pf. Red Riding Hood with grandmother.

1960. 1st Death Anniv of Gen. George C. Marshall. Portrait as T **364**.
1258 40pf. black and blue . . . . 2·75 1·60

371 "Adler", 1835

372 St. George and the Dragon

1960. 125th Anniv of German Railway.
1259 **371** 10pf. black and bistre . . 30 30

1961. Pathfinders (German Boy Scouts) Commemoration.
1260 **372** 10pf. green 25 20

1961. Famous Germans. As Nos. B194, etc of West Berlin but without "BERLIN".
1261 5pf. olive 20 20
1262 7pf. brown 20 20
1263 8pf. violet 20 25
1264 10pf. green 20 20
1265 15pf. blue 45 90
1266 20pf. red 45 20

1267 25pf. brown 20 20
1268 30pf. sepia 20 15
1269 40pf. blue 25 15
1270 50pf. brown 45 20
1271 60pf. red 45 30
1272 70pf. green 20 30
1273 80pf. brown 55 45
1274 90pf. bistre 45 40
1275 1Dm. violet 55 40
1276 2Dm. green . . . . 3·50 55
PORTRAIT: 90pf. Franz Oppenheimer (economist).

373 Early Daimler Motor Car

374 Nuremberg Messenger of 1700

1961. 75th Anniv of Daimler-Benz Patent.
1277 **373** 10pf. green and black . . 20 15
1278 – 20pf. red and black . . . 45 30
DESIGN: 20pf. Early Benz motor car.

1961. "The Letter during Five Centuries" Exhibition, Nuremberg.
1279 **374** 7pf. black and red . . . 15 15

375 Speyer Cathedral

376 Doves

1961. 900th Anniv of Speyer Cathedral.
1280 **375** 20pf. red 25 30

1961. Europa.
1281 **376** 10pf. green 20 15
1282 40pf. blue 35 40

377 Hansel and Gretel in the Wood

378 Telephone Apparatus

1961. Humanitarian Relief and Welfare Funds. Multicoloured.
1283 7pf.+3pf. Type **377** 15 25
1284 10pf.+5pf. Hansel, Gretel and the Witch 15 15
1285 20pf.+10pf. Hansel in the Witch's cage 15 15
1286 40pf.+20pf. Hansel and Gretel reunited with their father . . . . 1·30 2·00

1961. Centenary of Philipp Reis's Telephone.
1287 **378** 10pf. green 20 20

379 Baron W. E. von Ketteler

380 Drusus Stone

1961. 150th Birth Anniv of Baron W. E. von Ketteler (Catholic leader).
1288 **379** 10pf. black and green . . 20 20

1962. Bimillenary of Mainz.
1289 **380** 20pf. purple 20 20

381 Apollo

382 Part of "In Dulci Jubilo", from "Musae Sioniae" (M. Praetorius)

1962. Child Welfare. Butterflies. Mult.
1290 7pf.+3pf. Type **381** 45 55
1291 10pf.+5pf. Camberwell beauty 45 55
1292 20pf.+10pf. Small tortoiseshell . . . . . . 90 1·20
1293 40pf.+20pf. Scarce swallowtail . . . . 1·30 2·10

1962. "Song and Choir" (Summer Music Festivals).
1294 **382** 20pf. red and black . . . 20 30

383 "Belief, Thanksgiving and Service"

384 Open Bible

1962. Catholics' Day.
1295 **383** 20pf. mauve 20 30

1962. 150th Anniv of Wurttembergische Bibelanstalt (Bible publishers).
1296 **384** 20pf. black and red . . . 30 30

385 Europa "Tree"

386 Snow White and the Seven Dwarfs

1962. Europa.
1297 **385** 10pf. green 20 20
1298 40pf. blue 55 45

1962. Humanitarian Relief and Welfare Funds. Scenes from "Snow White and the Seven Dwarfs" (Brothers Grimm). Multicoloured.
1299 7pf.+3pf. The "Magic Mirror" 15 20
1300 10pf.+5pf. Type **386** . . . 15 15
1301 20pf.+10pf. "The Poisoned Apple" 20 15
1302 40pf.+20pf. Snow White and Prince Charming . . . . 1·10 1·50

387 "Bread for the World"

388 Relief Distribution

1963. Freedom from Hunger.
1303 **387** 20pf. brown and black . . 25 30

1963. CRALOG and CARE Relief Organizations.
1304 **388** 20pf. red 25 20

389 Ears of Wheat, Cross and Globe

390 Snake's Head Lily

1963. Freedom from Hunger.
1305 **389** 20pf. black, red and grey 25 30

1963. "Flora and Philately" Exhibition, Hamburg. Multicoloured.
1306 10pf. Type **390** 20 15
1307 15pf. Lady's slipper orchid 20 15
1308 20pf. Columbine 20 20
1309 40pf. Sea holly 45 40

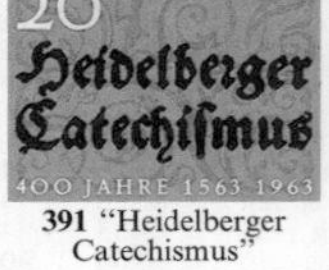

391 "Heidelberger Catechismus"

392 Cross, Sun and Moon

1963. 400th Anniv of Heidelberg Catechism.
1310 **391** 20pf. black, red and orange 30 30

1963. Consecration of Regina Martyrum Church, Berlin.
1311 **392** 10pf. multicoloured . . . 20 20

393 Emblems of Conference Participating Countries

394 Map and Flags

1963. Centenary of Paris Postal Conference.
1312 **393** 40pf. blue 45 35

1963. Opening of Denmark–Germany Railway ("Vogelfluglinie").
1313 **394** 20pf. multicoloured . . . 20 20

395 Red Cross Emblem

396 Hoopoe

1963. Red Cross Centenary.
1314 **395** 20pf. red, purple & yell 20 20

1963. Child Welfare. Bird designs inscr "FUR DIE JUGEND 1963". Multicoloured.
1315 10pf.+5pf. Type **396** . . . 55 55
1316 15pf.+5pf. Golden oriole . . 45 70
1317 20pf.+10pf. Northern bullfinch 45 70
1318 40pf.+20pf. River kingfisher 2·00 2·75

397 Congress Emblem

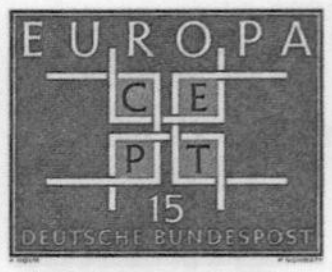

398 "Co-operation"

1963. German Evangelical Church Day and Congress, Dortmund.
1319 **397** 20pf. black and brown 35 30

1963. Europa.
1320 **398** 15pf. green 20 25
1321 20pf. red 20 15

399 Mother Goat warning kids

400 Atlantic Herring

1963. Humanitarian Relief and Welfare Funds.
1322 **399** 10pf.+5pf. mult 20 25
1323 – 15pf.+5pf. mult 20 20
1324 – 20pf.+10pf. mult 20 20
1325 – 40pf.+20pf. mult . . . . 75 1·10
DESIGNS: 15pf. Wolf entering house; 20pf. Wolf in house, threatening kids; 40pf. Mother Goat and Kids dancing round wolf in well. From Grimm's "Wolf and the Seven Kids".

1964. Child Welfare. Fish designs inscr "Fur die Jugend 1964". Multicoloured.
1326 10pf.+5pf. Type **400** . . . 20 40
1327 15pf.+5pf. Redfish 20 30
1328 20pf.+10pf. Mirror carp . . 45 40
1329 40pf.+20pf. Atlantic cod . . 1·20 1·80

401 Old Town Hall, Hanover

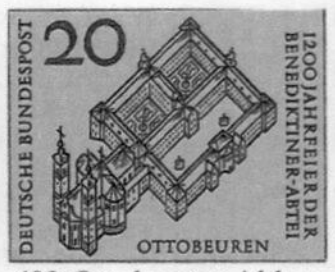

402 Ottobeuren Abbey

1964. Capitals of the Federal Lands. Mult.
1330 20pf. Type **401** 25 20
1331 20pf. Hamburg 25 20
1332 20pf. Kiel 25 20
1333 20pf. Munich 25 20
1334 20pf. Wiesbaden 25 20
1335 20pf. Berlin 25 20
1336 20pf. Mainz 25 20
1337 20pf. Dusseldorf 25 20
1338 20pf. Bonn 25 20
1339 20pf. Bremen 25 20
1340 20pf. Stuttgart 25 20
1340a 20pf. Saarbrucken 25 25

DESIGNS: No. 1331, Liner "Lichtenfels" and St. Michael's Church (775th anniv); 1332, Ferry "Kronprinz Harald"; 1333, National Theatre; 1334, Kurhaus; 1335, Reichstag; 1336, Gutenberg Museum; 1337, Jan Wellen's Monument and Town Hall; 1338, Town Hall; 1339, Market Hall; 1340, Town view; 1340a, Ludwig's Church.

1964. 1200th Anniv of Benedictine Abbey, Ottobeuren.
1341 **402** 20pf. black, red and pink 20 20

1964. Re-election of Pres. Lubke. As Type B **67** of West Berlin, inscr "DEUTSCHE BUNDESPOST" only.
1342 20pf. red 20 15
1343 40pf. blue 25 20

402b Sophie Scholl

1964. 20th Anniv of Attempt on Hitler's Life. Anti-Hitlerite Martyrs. Each black and grey.
1343a 20pf. Type **402b** . . . . . 60 1·50
1343b 20pf. Ludwig Beck . . . . 60 1·50
1343c 20pf. Dietrich Bonhoeffer 60 1·50
1343d 20pf. Alfred Delp . . . . 60 1·50
1343e 20pf. Karl Friedrich Goerdeler . . . . 60 1·50
1343f 20pf. Wilhelm Leuschner 60 1·50
1343g 20pf. Helmuth James (Von Moltke) . . . . 60 1·50
1343h 20pf. Claus Schenk (Von Stauffenberg) . . . . . 60 1·50

403 Calvin

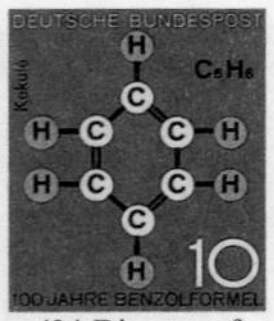

404 Diagran of Benzene Formula

1964. World Council of Reformed Churches.
1344 **403** 20pf. black and red . . . 20 20

1964. Scientific Anniversaries (1st series).
1345 10pf. green, black and brown 20 15
1346 15pf. multicoloured 20 15
1347 20pf. green, black and red 20 15
DESIGNS: 10pf. Type **404** (centenary of publication of Kekule's benzene formula); 15pf. Diagram of nuclear reaction (25th anniv of publication of Hahn-Strassman treatise on splitting the nucleus of the atom); 20pf. Gas engine (centenary of Otto-Langen internal-combustion engine).
See also Nos. 1426/7 and 1451/3.

405 F. Lassalle

406 "The Sun"

1964. Death Centenary of Ferdinand Lassalle (Socialist founder and leader).
1348 **405** 20pf. black and blue . . 25 20

1964. 80th Catholics' Day.
1349 **406** 20pf. red and blue . . . 25 20

407 Europa "Flower"

408 "The Sleeping Beauty"

1964. Europa.
1350 **407** 15pf. violet and green . . 20 25
1351 20pf. violet and red . . . 20 15

1964. Humanitarian Relief and Welfare Funds.
1352 **408** 10pf.+5pf. mult 20 25
1353 – 15pf.+5pf. mult 20 20
1354 – 20pf.+10pf. mult 20 15
1355 – 40pf.+20pf. mult . . . . 55 1·10
DESIGNS: 15pf., 20pf., 40pf. Various scenes from Grimm's "The Sleeping Beauty".

409 Judo

410 Prussian Eagle

1964. "Olympic Year".
1356 **409** 20pf. multicoloured . . . 20 20

1964. 250th Anniv of German Court of Accounts.
1357 **410** 20pf. orange and black 20 20

411 Pres. Kennedy

412 Castle Gateway, Ellwangen (Jagst)

1964. Pres. Kennedy Commemoration.
1358 **411** 40pf. blue 30 20

1964. Twelve Centuries of German Architecture.
(a) Size 18½ × 22 mm. Plain background.
1359 – 10pf. brown 20 15
1360 – 15pf. green 20 15
1361 – 20pf. brown 30 15
1362 – 40pf. blue 20 15
1363 **412** 50pf. brown 45 20
1364 – 60pf. red . . . . . . 1·10 45
1365 – 70pf. green . . . . . . 1·30 45
1366 – 80pf. brown . . . . . . 1·10 30

(b) Size 19½ × 24 mm. Coloured background.
1367 – 5pf. brown 20 15
1368 – 10pf. brown 20 15
1369 – 20pf. green 20 15
1370 – 30pf. green 25 15
1371 – 30pf. red 25 15
1372 – 40pf. brown 45 25
1373 – 50pf. blue 55 20
1374 – 60pf. orange . . . . . . 3·00 1·70
1375 – 70pf. green . . . . . . 1·30 20
1376 – 80pf. brown . . . . . . 2·40 1·40
1377 – 90pf. black . . . . . . 1·10 35
1378 – 1Dm. blue 90 20
1379 – 1Dm.10 brown . . . . . . 1·10 45
1380 – 1Dm.30 green . . . . . . 2·20 75
1381 – 2Dm. purple . . . . . . 2·20 50

BUILDINGS: 5pf. Berlin Gate, Stettin; 10pf. Zwinger pavilion, Dresden; 15pf. Tegel Castle, Berlin; 20pf. Monastery Gate, Lorsch; 30pf. North Gate, Flensburg; 40pf. Trifels Castle (Palatinate); 60pf. Treptow Portal, Neubrandenburg; 70pf. Osthofen Gate, Soest; 80pf. Ellingen Portal, Weissenburg (Bavaria); 90pf. Zschokk's Convent, Konigsberg; 1Dm. Melanchthon House, Wittenberg; 1Dm.10, Trinity Hospital, Hildesheim; 1Dm.30, Tegel Castle, Berlin (diff); 2Dm. Burghers' Hall, Lowenberg Town Hall (Silesia).

413 Owl, Hat, Walking-stick and Satchel

414 Eurasian Woodcock

1965. 150th Death Anniv of Matthias Claudius (poet).
1383 **413** 20pf. black and red on grey 20 20

1965. Child Welfare. Inscr "FUR DIE JUGEND 1965". Multicoloured.
1384 10pf.+5pf. Type **414** . . . 20 25
1385 15pf.+5pf. Common pheasant 20 25
1386 20pf.+10pf. Black grouse . . 20 30
1387 40pf.+20pf. Western capercaillie 35 95

415 Bismarck (statesman)

416 Boeing 727-100 Airliner and Space Capsule

1965. 150th Birth Anniv of Otto von Bismarck.
1388 **415** 20pf. black and red . . . 20 20

1965. Int Transport Exn, Munich. Mult.
1389 5pf. Traffic lights and road signs 20 20
1390 10pf. "Syncom" satellite and tracking station 20 20
1391 15pf. Old and modern postal buses 20 20
1392 20pf. Old semaphore station and modern signal tower 20 20
1393 40pf. Locomotive "Adler" (1835) and Class E.10.12 electric locomotive (1960s) 20 20
1394 60pf. Type **416** 35 35
1395 70pf. "Bremen" (liner) and "Hammonia" (19th-century steamship) 45 40

No. 1394 was also issued to mark the 10th anniv of Lufthansa's renewed air services.

417 Bouquet

418 I.T.U. Emblem

1965. 75th Anniv of "May 1st" (Labour Day).
1396 **417** 15pf. multicoloured . . . 20 20

1965. Centenary of I.T.U.
1397 **418** 40pf. black and blue . . 30 30

419 A. Kopling

420 Rescue Vessel "Theodor Heuss"

1965. Death Centenary of Adolf Kolping (miners' padre).
1398 **419** 20pf. black, red and grey 20 20

1965. Cent of German Sea-rescue Service.
1399 **420** 20pf. violet, black & red 20 20

1965. 20th Anniv of Influx of East German Refugees. As T **299** but inscr "ZWANZIG JAHRE VERTREIBUNG 1945 1965".
1400 20pf. purple 20 20

421 Evangelical Church Emblem

422 Radio Tower

1965. German Evangelical Church Day and Synod, Cologne.
1401 **421** 20pf. black, turq & bl . . 20 20

1965. Radio Exhibition, Stuttgart.
1402 **422** 20pf. black, blue & mve 20 20

423 Thurn and Taxis 1, 2 and 5sgr. Stamps of 1852

1965. 125th Anniv of 1st Postage Stamp.
1403 **423** 20pf. multicoloured . . . 20 20

424 Europa "Sprig"

1965. Europa.
1404 **424** 15pf. green 20 20
1405 20pf. red 20 15

425 Cinderella with Birds

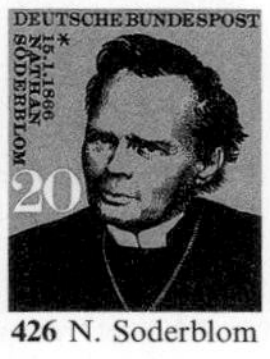

426 N. Soderblom

1965. Humanitarian Relief Funds. Mult.
1406 10pf.+5pf. Type **425** . . . 20 20
1407 15pf.+5pf. Cinderella and birds with dress 20 20
1408 20pf.+10pf. Prince offering slipper to Cinderella . . . 20 20
1409 40pf.+20pf. Cinderella and Prince on horse 60 85

1966. Birth Centenary of Nathan Soderblom (Archbishop of Uppsala).
1410 **426** 20pf. black and lilac . . 20 20

427 Cardinal von Galen

428 Brandenburg Gate, Berlin

1966. 20th Death Anniv of Cardinal Clemens von Galen.
1411 **427** 20pf. red, mauve & black 20 20

1966.
1412 **428** 10pf. brown 20 15
1413 20pf. green 45 15
1414 30pf. red 45 20
1415 50pf. blue . . . . . 1·80 25
1415a 100pf. blue . . . . . 10·00 45

429 Roe deer

430 Christ and Fishermen (Miracle of the Fishes)

1966. Child Welfare. Multicoloured.
1416 10pf.+5pf. Type **429** . . . 20 25
1417 20pf.+10pf. Chamois . . . 20 25
1418 30pf.+15pf. Fallow deer . . 20 25
1419 50pf.+25pf. Red deer . . . 70 1·00

1966. Catholics' Day.
1420 **430** 30pf. black and salmon 20 20

431 19th-cent Postman

432 G. W. Leibniz

1966. F.I.P. Meeting, Munich. Multicoloured.
1421 30pf.+15pf. Bavarian mail coach 45 75
1422 50pf.+25pf. Type **431** . . . 65 75

1966. 250th Death Anniv of Gottfried Leibniz (scientist).
1423 **432** 30pf. black and mauve 20 20

433 Europa "Ship"

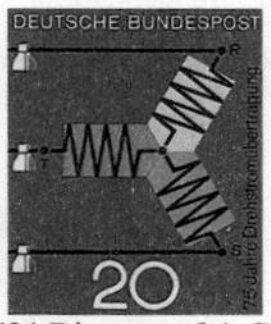

434 Diagram of A.C. Transmission (75th Anniv)

1966. Europa.
1424 **433** 20pf. multicoloured . . . 20 25
1425 30pf. multicoloured . . . 20 15

1966. Scientific Annivs (2nd series). Mult.
1426 20pf. Type **434** 20 15
1427 30pf. Diagram of electric dynamo (cent) 20 20

435 Princess and Frog

436 U.N.I.C.E.F. Emblem

1966. Humanitarian Relief Funds. Mult.
1428 10pf.+5pf. Type **435** . . . 20 25
1429 20pf.+10pf. Frog dining with Princess 20 20
1430 30pf.+15pf. Prince and Princess 20 25
1431 50pf.+25pf. In coach . . . 55 1·00

Designs from Grimm's "The Frog Prince".

1966. Award of Nobel Peace Prize to United Nations Children's Fund.
1432 **436** 30pf. sepia, black and red 20 20

437 W. von Siemens (electrical engineer)

438 Common Rabbit

1966. 150th Birth Anniv of Werner von Siemens (electrical engineer).
1433 **437** 30pf. red 20 20

1967. Child Welfare. Multicoloured.
1434 10pf.+5pf. Type **438** . . . 20 30
1435 20pf.+10pf. Stoat 30 35
1436 30pf.+15pf. Common hamster 55 60
1437 50pf.+25pf. Red fox . . . . 1·10 1·70

See also Nos. 1454/7.

439 Cogwheels

440 Francis of Taxis

1967. Europa.
1438 **439** 20pf. multicoloured . . . 20 20
1439 30pf. multicoloured . . . 20 15

1967. 450th Death Anniv of Francis of Taxis.
1440 **440** 30pf. black and orange 30 20

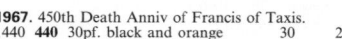

441 Evangelical Symbols

442 Friedrich von Bodelschwingh (Head of Hospital 1910–46)

1967. 13th German Evangelical Churches Day.
1441 **441** 30pf. black and mauve 20 20

1967. Cent of Bethel Hospital, Bielefeld.
1442 **442** 30pf. black and brown 20 20

443 Frau Holle at Spinning-wheel

444 Wartburg (castle), Eisenach

1967. Humanitarian Relief Funds. Mult.
1443 10pf.+5pf. Type **443** . . . 20 25
1444 20pf.+10pf. In the clouds . . 20 25
1445 30pf.+15pf. With shopping-basket and cockerel . . . 20 25
1446 50pf.+25pf. Covered with soot . . . . 60 1·30

Designs from Grimm's "Frau Holle" ("Mother Carey").

1967. Re-election of Pres. Lubke. As Type B **67** of West Berlin, but inscr "DEUTSCHE BUNDESPOST".
1447 30pf. red 20 20
1448 50pf. blue 45 30

1967. 450th Anniv of Luther's "Theses" and the Reformation.
1449 **444** 30pf. red 30 30

445 Cross on South American Map

446 Koenig's Printing Machine

1967. "Adveniat" (Aid for Catholic Church in Latin America).
1450 **445** 30pf. multicoloured . . . 20 20

1968. Scientific Anniv (3rd series). Mult.
1451 10pf. Type **446** 15 15
1452 20pf. Ore Crystals 15 15
1453 30pf. Lens Refraction . . . 20 20
ANNIVS: 10pf. 150th anniv; 20pf. Millenary of ore mining in Harz Mountains; 30pf. Centenary of Abbe-Zeiss Scientific Microscope.

1968. Child Welfare. As T **438** but inscr "1968". Multicoloured.
1454 10pf.+5pf. Wildcat 25 40
1455 20pf.+10pf. European otter 45 75
1456 30pf.+15pf. Eurasian badger 65 1·00
1457 50pf.+25pf. Eurasian beaver 2·00 3·00

447 Trade Symbols

1968. German Crafts and Trades.
1458 **447** 30pf. multicoloured . . . 20 20

448 Dr. Adenauer

1968. Adenauer Commemoration (1st issue). T **448** and similar horiz designs in sheet 149 × 106 mm.
MS1459 10pf. brown and black; 20pf. green and black; 30pf. red and black; 50pf. blue and black 2·40 2·40
DESIGNS: 10pf. Sir Winston Churchill; 20pf. Alcide de Gasperi; 30pf. Robert Schuman.
See also No. 1469.

449 Europa "Key" **450** Karl Marx

1968. Europa.
1460 **449** 20pf. yellow, brn & grn 20 20
1461 30pf. yellow, brn & red 20 15

1968. 150th Birth Anniv of Karl Marx.
1462 **450** 30pf. red, black & grey 20 20

451 F. von Langen (horseman) **453** Dr. Adenauer

452 Opening Bars of "The Mastersingers"

1968. Olympic Games (1972) Promotion Fund (1st series).
1463 **451** 10pf.+5pf. black & grn 30 30
1464 – 20pf.+10pf. black & grn 30 30
1465 – 30pf. black and lilac . . 25 20
1466 – 30pf.+15pf. black & red 65 55
1467 – 50pf.+25pf. black & bl 1·10 90
DESIGN: 20pf. R. Harbig (runner); 30pf. (No. 1465) Pierre de Coubertin (founder of Olympics); 30pf. (No. 1466) Helene Mayer (fencer); 50pf. Carl Diem (sports organiser).
See also Nos. 1493/6, 1524/7, 1589/92, 1621/4, **MS**1625 and 1629/32.

1968. Centenary of 1st Performance of Richard Wagner's Opera "The Mastersingers".
1468 **452** 30pf. multicoloured . . . 35 20

1968. Adenauer Commemoration (2nd issue).
1469 **453** 30pf. black and orange 25 20

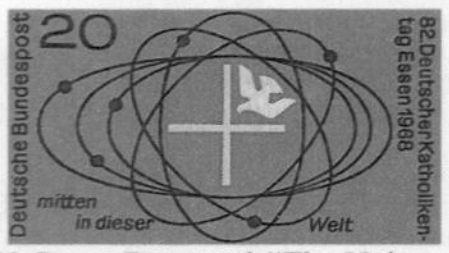

454 Cross, Dove and "The Universe"

1968. Catholics' Day.
1470 **454** 20pf. violet, yellow & grn 20 20

455 Northern District 1g. and Southern District 7k. stamps of 1868

1968. Cent of North German Postal Confederation and First Stamps.
1471 **455** 30pf. red, blue and black 20 20

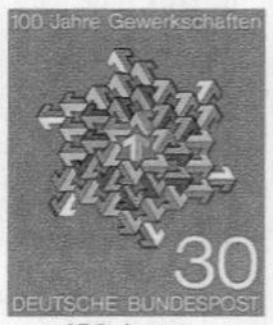

456 Arrows **457** Doll of 1878

1968. Cent of German Trade Unions.
1472 **456** 30pf. multicoloured . . . 20 20

1968. Humanitarian Relief Funds. Mult.
1473 10pf.+5pf. Type **457** . . . 20 25
1474 20pf.+10pf. Doll of 1850 . . 20 20
1475 30pf.+15pf. Doll of 1870 . . 25 25
1476 50pf.+25pf. Doll of 1885 . . 70 1·10

458 Human Rights Emblem **459** Pony

1968. Human Rights Year.
1477 **458** 30pf. multicoloured . . . 45 20

1969. Child Welfare.
1478 **459** 10pf.+5pf. brown, black and yellow 25 30
1479 – 20pf.+10pf. brown, black and buff 25 30
1480 – 30pf.+15pf. brown, black and red 65 60
1481 – 50pf.+25pf. mult . . . . 2·00 1·70
HORSES: 20pf. Draught-horse; 30pf. Saddle-horse; 50pf. Thoroughbred.

460 Junkers Ju 52/3m "Boelke"

1969. 50th Anniv of German Airmail Services. Multicoloured.
1482 20pf. Type **460** 45 20
1483 30pf. Boeing 707 airliner . . 70 20

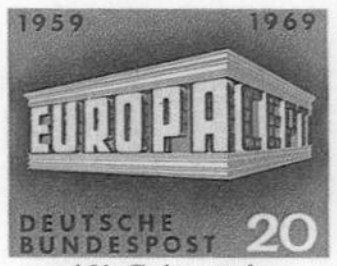

461 Colonnade **462** "The Five Continents"

1969. Europa.
1484 **461** 20pf. yellow, grn & bl 35 20
1485 30pf. yellow, red & violet 45 20

1969. 50th Anniv of I.L.O.
1486 **462** 30pf. multicoloured . . . 45 20

463 Eagle Emblems of Weimar and Federal Republics **464** "War Graves"

1969. 20th Anniv of German Federal Republic.
1487 **463** 30pf. black, gold and red 1·10 30

1969. 50th Anniv of German War Graves Commission.
1488 **464** 30pf. blue and yellow . . 35 20

465 Lakeside Landscape **466** "Running Track"

1969. Nature Protection. Multicoloured.
1489 10pf. Type **465** 20 20
1490 20pf. Highland landscape . . 45 35
1491 30pf. Alpine landscape . . 35 20
1492 50pf. River landscape . . . 1·00 45

1969. Olympic Games (1972). Promotion Fund (2nd series). Multicoloured.
1493 10pf.+5pf. Type **466** . . . 20 20
1494 20pf.+10pf. "Hockey" . . . 35 30
1495 30pf.+15pf. "Shooting target" 55 55
1496 50pf.+25pf. "Sailing" . . . 1·20 1·00

467 "Longing for Justice" **468** "Electromagnetic Field"

1969. 14th German Protestant Congress, Stuttgart.
1497 **467** 30pf. multicoloured . . . 35 20

1969. German Radio Exhibition, Stuttgart.
1498 **468** 30pf. multicoloured . . 50 20

469 Marie Juchacz

1969. "Fifty Years of German Women's Suffrage". Sheet 102 × 61 mm containing T **469** and similar vert portraits of women politicians.
MS1499 10pf. olive; 20pf. green; 30pf. red 75 65
DESIGNS: 20pf. Marie-Elizabeth Luders; 30pf. Helene Weber.

470 Maltese Cross Symbol **471** Bavaria 3k. Stamp of 1867

1969. "Malteser Hilfsdienst" (welfare organization).
1500 **470** 30pf. red and black . . . 50 25

1969. German Philatelic Federation Congress and Exn, Garmisch-Partenkirchen.
1501 **471** 30pf. red and slate . . . 50 20

472 Map of Pipeline

1969. 350th Anniv of Bad Reichenhall–Traunstein Brine Pipeline.
1502 **472** 20pf. multicoloured . . . 35 20

473 Rothenburg ob der Tauber

1969. Tourism.
1503 **473** 30pf. black and red . . . 35 20
See also Nos. 1523, 1558, 1564, 1587, 1606, 1641/2, 1655/6 and 1680/2.

474 Mahatma Gandhi **475** Pope John XXIII

1969. Birth Centenary of Mahatma Gandhi.
1504 **474** 20pf. black and green . . 35 20

1969. Pope John XXIII Commemoration.
1505 **475** 30pf. red 35 20

476 "Adler" (1835) **477** E. M. Arndt

1969. Humanitarian Relief Funds. Pewter Figurines. Mult. (a) Inscr. "WOHLFAHRTSMARKE".
1506 10pf.+5pf. Type **476** . . . 20 15
1507 20pf.+10pf. Woman watering flowers (1780) 20 25
1508 30pf.+15pf. Bird salesman (1850) 40 35
1509 50pf.+25pf. Mounted dignitary (1840) . . . . . 1·00 90
(b) Christmas. Inscr "WEIHNACHTSMARKE".
1510 10pf.+5pf. "Child Jesus in crib" (1850) 30 25

1969. Birth Bicent of Ernst Arndt (writer).
1511 **477** 30pf. lake and bistre . . 35 20

478 "H. von Rugge"

1970. Child Welfare. Minnesinger Themes. Multicoloured.
1512 10pf.+5pf. Type **478** . . . 45 35
1513 20pf.+10pf. "W. von Eschenbach" 65 40
1514 30pf.+15pf. "W. von Metz" 90 70
1515 50pf.+25pf. "W. von der Vogelweide" . . . . . . 2·00 1·00

479 Beethoven **480** Saar 1m. Stamp of 1947

1970. Birth Bicentenaries.
1516 **479** 10pf. black and blue . . 90 20
1517 – 20pf. black and olive . . 45 20
1518 – 30pf. black and pink . . 45 20
DESIGNS: 20pf. G. W. Hegel (philosopher); 30pf. F. Holderlin (poet).

1970. "Sabria 70" Stamp Exn, Saarbrucken.
1519 **480** 30pf. green, black and red 35 20

481 "Flaming Sun"

482 Von Munchhausen on Severed Horse

1970. Europa.
1520 **481** 20pf. green 35 15
1521 30pf. red 45 15

1970. 250th Birth Anniv of Baron H. von Munchhausen.
1522 **482** 20pf. multicoloured . . . 35 20

1970. Tourism. As T **473**, but with view of Oberammergau.
1523 30pf. black and orange . . . 35 20

483 Royal Palace

1970. Olympic Games (1972). Promotion Fund (3rd series).
1524 **483** 10pf.+5pf. brown . . . 20 20
1525 – 20pf.+10pf. turquoise . . 45 35
1526 – 30pf.+15pf. red 60 55
1527 – 50pf.+25pf. blue . . . . 1·40 90
DESIGNS (Munich buildings): 20pf. Propylaea; 30pf. Glyptothek; 50pf. "Bavaria" (statue and colonnade).

484 Liner "Kungsholm IV" and Road-tunnel

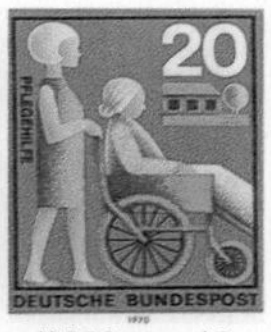

485 Nurse with Invalid

1970. 75th Anniv of Kiel Canal.
1528 **484** 20pf. multicoloured . . . 35 20

1970. Voluntary Relief Services. Mult.
1529 5pf. Oxygen-lance operator 20 15
1530 10pf. Mountain rescue . . . 20 15
1531 20pf. Type **485** 30 20
1532 30pf. Fireman with hose . . 90 20
1533 50pf. Road-accident casualty 90 45
1534 70pf. Rescue from drowning 1·10 70

486 President Heinemann

487 Illuminated Cross

1970.
1535 **486** 5pf. black 20 20
1536 10pf. brown 20 20
1537 20pf. green 20 20
1538 25pf. green 35 15
1539 30pf. brown 45 20
1540 40pf. orange 45 20
1541 50pf. blue . . . . 1·80 20
1542 60pf. blue 65 20
1543 70pf. brown 90 25
1544 80pf. green 90 30
1545 90pf. red . . . . 1·60 1·40
1546 1Dm. green . . . . . . 1·10 30
1547 110pf. grey . . . . . . 1·30 60
1548 120pf. brown . . . . . 1·60 75
1549 130pf. brown . . . . . 1·60 75
1550 140pf. green . . . . . 1·80 1·10
1551 150pf. red . . . . . . 1·80 55
1552 160pf. orange . . . . . 2·40 85
1553 170pf. orange . . . . . 2·00 55
1554 190pf. purple . . . . . 2·75 70
1555 2Dm. violet . . . . . . 2·20 35

1970. Catholic Church World Mission.
1556 **487** 20pf. yellow and green 35 20

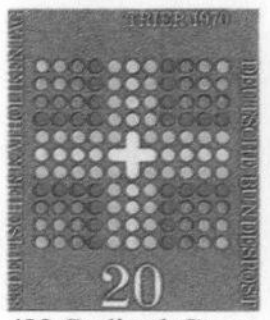

488 Stylized Cross

489 "Jester"

1970. Catholics Day and 83rd German Catholic Congress, Trier.
1557 **488** 20pf. multicoloured . . . 35 20

1970. Tourism. As T **473**.
1558 20pf. black and green . . . 35 20
DESIGN: 20pf. View of Cochem.

1970. Humanitarian Relief Funds. Puppets. Multicoloured. (a) Relief Funds
1559 10pf.+5pf. Type **489** . . . 20 25
1560 20pf.+10pf. "Buffoon" . . . 30 30
1561 30pf.+15pf. "Clown" . . . 45 40
1562 50pf.+25pf. "Harlequin" . . 1·10 90

(b) Christmas.
1563 10pf.+5pf. "Angel" 30 25

1970. Tourism. As T **473**, but with view of Freiburg im Breisgau.
1564 20pf. brown and green . . . 35 20

490 A. J. Comenius (scholar)

491 Engels as Young Man

1970. Int Education Year and 300th Death Anniv of Comenius (Jan Komensky).
1565 **490** 30pf. red and black . . . 60 20

1970. 150th Birth Anniv of Friedrich Engels.
1566 **491** 50pf. blue and red . . . 1·30 70

492 German Eagle

493 "Ebert" Stamp of 1928 and inscr "To the German People"

1971. Centenary of German Unification.
1567 **492** 30pf. black, red & orange . . . . 1·30 20

1971. Birth Centenary of Friedrich Ebert (Chancellor 1918 and President 1919–25).
1568 **493** 30pf. green, black and red . . . . 1·30 20

494 "King of Blackamoors"

495 Molecular Chain

1971. Child Welfare. Children's Drawings. Multicoloured.
1569 10pf.+5pf. Type **494** . . . 35 30
1570 20pf.+10pf. "Flea" 45 40
1571 30pf.+15pf. "Puss-in-Boots" 60 55
1572 50pf.+25pf. "Serpent" . . . 1·10 95

1971. 125 Years of Chemical Fibre Research.
1573 **495** 20pf. black, red & green 25 20

496 Road-crossing Patrol

497 Luther before Charles V

1971. New Road Traffic Regulations (1st series).
1574 **496** 10pf. black, blue and red 20 15
1575 – 20pf. black, red & green 40 20
1576 – 30pf. red, black and grey 45 20
1577 – 50pf. black, blue and red 90 55
ROAD SIGNS: 20pf. "Right-of-way across junction"; 30pf. "STOP"; 50pf. "Pedestrian Crossing".
See also Nos. 1579/82.

1971. 450th Anniv of Diet of Worms.
1578 **497** 30pf. black and red . . . 60 20

1971. New Traffic Regulations (2nd series). Horiz designs similar to T **496**.
1579 5pf. red, black and blue . . 20 15
1580 10pf. multicoloured 20 15
1581 20pf. red, black and green 45 20
1582 30pf. yellow, black and red 60 20

NEW HIGHWAY CODE: 5pf. Overtaking; 10pf. Warning of obstruction; 20pf. Lane discipline; 30pf. Pedestrian Crossing.

498 Europa Chain

499 Thomas a Kempis writing "The Imitation of Christ"

1971. Europa.
1583 **498** 20pf. gold, green & black 20 15
1584 30pf. gold, red and black 45 20

1971. 500th Death Anniv of Thomas a Kempis (devotional writer).
1585 **499** 30pf. black and red . . . 50 20

500 Durer's Monogram

501 Meeting Emblem

1971. 500th Birth Anniv of Albrecht Durer.
1586 **500** 30pf. brown & red . . . 1·20 20

1971. Tourism. As T **473**, but with view of Nuremburg.
1587 30pf. black and red 45 20

1971. Whitsun Ecumenical Meeting, Augsburg.
1588 **501** 30pf. black, orange & red 45 20

502 Ski Jumping

503 Astronomical Calculus

1971. Olympic Games (1972). Promotion Fund (4th series). Winter Games, Sapporo.
1589 **502** 10pf.+5pf. black & brn 20 20
1590 – 20pf.+10pf. black & grn 45 40
1591 – 30pf.+15pf. black & red 90 75
1592 – 50pf.+25pf. black & bl 1·60 1·30
MS1593 112 × 66 mm. Nos. 1589/92 2·75 2·40
DESIGNS: 20pf. Ice dancing; 30pf. Skiing start; 50pf. Ice hockey.

1971. 400th Birth Anniv of Johann Kepler (astronomer).
1594 **503** 30pf. gold, red and black 45 20

504 Dante

505 Alcohol and front of Car ("Don't Drink and Drive")

1971. 650th Death Anniv of Dante Alighieri.
1595 **504** 10pf. black 20 20

1971. Accident Prevention.
1596 – 5pf. orange 20 15
1597 – 10pf. brown 20 15
1598 – 20pf. violet 35 15
1599 **505** 25pf. green 45 15
1600 – 30pf. red 45 15
1601 – 40pf. mauve 45 15
1602 – 50pf. blue . . . . . . 2·20 15
1603 – 60pf. blue . . . . . . 1·60 40
1603a – 70pf. blue and green . . 1·30 30
1604 – 1Dm. green . . . . . . 2·00 20
1605 – 1Dm.50 brown . . . . 6·25 1·00
DESIGNS: 5pf. Man within flame, and spent match ("Fire Prevention"); 10pf. Fall from ladder; 20pf. Unguarded machinery ("Factory Safety"); 30pf. Falling brick and protective helmet; 40pf. Faulty electric plug; 50pf. Protruding nail in plank; 60pf., 70pf. Ball in front of car ("Child Road Safety"); 1Dm. Crate on hoist; 1Dm.50, Open manhole.

1971. Tourism. As T **473** but with view of Goslar.
1606 20pf. black and green . . . 35 25

506 Women churning Butter

507 Deaconess and Nurse

1971. Humanitarian Relief Funds. Wooden Toys. Mult. (a) Inscr. "WOHLFAHRTSMARKE".
1607 20pf.+10pf. Type **506** . . . 20 20
1608 25pf.+10pf. Horseman on wheels 20 20
1609 30pf.+15pf. Nutcracker man 45 40
1610 60pf.+30pf. Dovecote . . . 1·20 1·00

(b) Christmas. Inscr "WEIHNACHTSMARKE".
1611 20pf.+10pf. Angel with three candles 35 35

1972. Death Cent of Johann Wilhelm Lohe (founder of Deaconesses Mission, Neuendettelsau).
1612 **507** 25pf. slate, black & green 35 20

508 Ducks crossing Road

509 Senefelder's Press

1972. Child Welfare. Annimal Protection. Multicoloured.
1613 20pf.+10pf. Type **508** . . . 65 55
1614 25pf.+10pf. Hunter scaring deer 45 35
1615 30pf.+15pf. Child protecting bird from cat 90 75
1616 60pf.+30pf. Boy annoying mute swans . . . . . . 1·80 1·40

1972. "175 Years of Offset Lithography".
1617 **509** 25pf. multicoloured . . . 35 20

510 "Communications"

511 Lucas Cranach

1972. Europa.
1618 **510** 25pf. multicoloured . . . 45 20
1619 30pf. multicoloured . . . 55 20

1972. 500th Birth Anniv of Lucas Cranach the Elder (painter).
1620 **511** 25pf. black, stone & grn 55 20

512 Wrestling

514 Invalid Archer

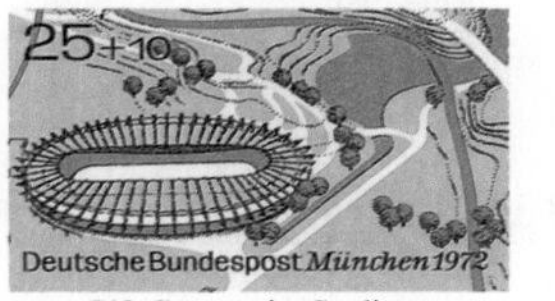

513 Gymnastics Stadium

1972. Olympic Games, Munich (5th series). Multicoloured.
1621 20pf.+10pf. Type **512** . . . 45 35
1622 25pf.+10pf. Sailing 45 35
1623 30pf.+15pf. Gymnastics . . 45 35
1624 60pf.+30pf. Swimming . . . 1·80 1·50
See also Nos. 1629/32.

1972. Olympic Games, Munich (6th series). Sheet 148 × 105 mm containing T **513** and similar multicoloured designs.
MS1625 25pf.+10pf. Type **513**; 30pf.+15pf. Athletics stadium; 40pf.+20pf. Tented area; 70pf.+35pf. TV tower . . . . 4·25 4·25

1972. 21st Int Games for the Paralysed, Heidelberg.
1626 **514** 40pf. red, black & yellow 70 20

515 Posthorn and Decree

516 K. Schumacher

1972. Cent of German Postal Museum.
1627 **515** 40pf. multicoloured . . . 70 20

1972. 20th Death Anniv of Kurt Schumacher (politician).
1628 **516** 40pf. black and red . . . 1·30 20

1972. Olympic Games, Munich (7th series). As Type **512**. Multicoloured.
1629 25pf.+5pf. Long jumping . . 90 75
1630 30pf.+10pf. Basketball . . 90 1·10
1631 40pf.+10pf. Throwing the discus . . . . 90 1·10
1632 70pf.+10pf. Canoeing . . . 90 85
MS1633 111 × 66 mm. Nos. 1629/32 4·00 4·00

517 Open Book

518 Music and Signature

1972. International Book Year.
1634 **517** 40pf. multicoloured . . . 65 20

1972. 300th Death Anniv of Heinrich Schutz (composer).
1635 **518** 40pf. multicoloured . . . 70 20

519 Knight

520 Revellers

1972. Humanitarian Relief Funds. Mult. (a) 19th-century Faience Chessmen. Inscr "WOHLFAHRTSMARKE".
1636 25pf.+10pf. Type **519** . . . 25 35
1637 30pf.+15pf. Rook 25 35
1638 40pf.+20pf. Queen 60 35
1639 70pf.+35pf. King . . . . 2·20 1·80
(b) Christmas. Inscr "WEIHNACHTSMARKE".
1640 30pf.+15pf. "The Three Wise Men" (horiz) . . . 65 55

1972. Tourism. As T **473**.
1641 30pf. black and green . . . 55 20
1642 40pf. black and orange . . . 60 20
VIEWS: 30pf. Heligoland; 40pf. Heidelberg.

1972. 150th Anniv of Cologne Carnival.
1643 **520** 40pf. multicoloured . . . 1·00 20

521 H. Heine

1972. 175th Birth Anniv of Heinrich Heine (poet).
1644 **521** 40pf. black, red and pink 1·00 20

522 "Brot fur die Welt"

523 Wurzburg Cathedral (seal)

1972. Freedom from Hunger Campaign.
1645 **522** 30pf. red and green . . . 50 40

1972. Catholic Synod '72.
1646 **523** 40pf. black, purple & red 55 20

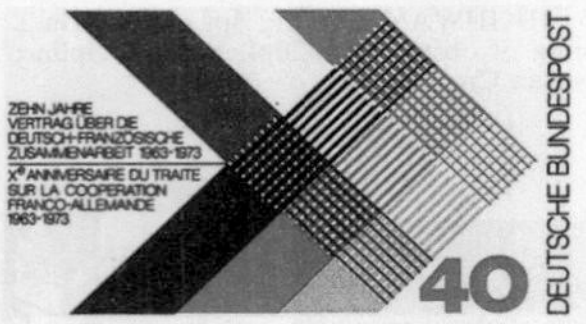

524 National Colours of France and Germany

1973. 10th Anniv of Franco-German Treaty.
1647 **524** 40pf. multicoloured . . . 1·10 30

525 Osprey

527 Radio Mast and Transmission

526 Copernicus

1973. Youth Welfare. Birds of Prey. Multicoloured.
1648 25pf.+10pf. Type **525** . . . 1·10 90
1649 30pf.+15pf. Common buzzard . . . . 1·30 1·20
1650 40pf.+20pf. Red kite . . . . 2·00 1·70
1651 70pf.+35pf. Montagu's harrier . . . . 4·50 3·75

1973. 500th Birth Anniv of Copernicus.
1652 **526** 40pf. black and red . . . 1·20 20

1973. 50th Anniv of Interpol.
1653 **527** 40pf. black, red and grey 60 20

528 Weather Chart

529 "Gymnast" (poster)

1973. Cent of Int Meteorological Organization.
1654 **528** 30pf. multicoloured . . . 45 20

1973. Tourism. As T **473**.
1655 40pf. black and red . . . 1·10 20
1656 40pf. black and orange . . 70 20
VIEWS: No. 1655, Hamburg; 1656, Rudesheim.

1973. Gymnastics Festival, Stuttgart.
1657 **529** 40pf. multicoloured . . . 45 20

530 Kassel (Hesse) Sign

532 "R" Motif

531 Europa "Posthorn"

1973. "I.B.R.A. Munchen 73" International Stamp Exhibition, Munich. F.I.P. Congress. Post-house Signs. Multicoloured.
1658 40pf.+20pf. Type **530** . . . 90 75
1659 70pf.+35pf. Prussia . . . 1·60 1·40
MS1660 74 × 105 mm. 40pf.+20pf. Wurttemberg; 70pf.+35pf. Kurpfalz (Bavaria) (sold at 2.20Dm.) . . . . 3·50 3·50

1973. Europa.
1661 **531** 30pf. yell, myrtle & grn 50 20
1662 40pf. yellow, lake & pink 65 20

1973. 1000th Death Anniv of Roswitha von Gandersheim (poetess).
1663 **532** 40pf. yellow, black & red 55 20

533 M. Kolbe

534 "Profile" (from poster)

1973. Father Maximilian Kolbe (Concentration camp victim) Commemoration.
1664 **533** 40pf. red, brown & black 55 20

1973. 15th German Protestant Church Conference.
1665 **534** 30pf. multicoloured . . . 35 6·50

535 Environmental Conference Emblem and Waste

1973. "Protection of the Environment". Multicoloured.
1666 25pf. Type **535** 45 20
1667 30pf. Emblem and "Water" 45 20
1668 40pf. Emblem and "Noise" 90 30
1669 70pf. Emblem and "Air" . . 1·50 90

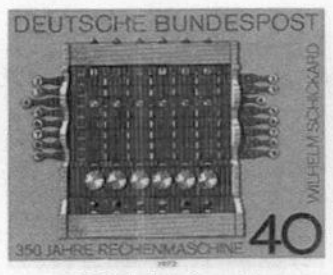

536 Schickard's Calculating Machine

537 Otto Wels

1973. 350th Anniv of Schickard's Calculating Machine.
1670 **536** 40pf. black, red and orange 50 45

1973. Birth Centenary of Otto Wels (Social Democratic Party leader).
1671 **537** 40pf. purple and lilac . . 60 20

538 Lubeck Cathedral

1973. 800th Anniv of Lubeck Cathedral
1672 **538** 40pf. multicoloured . . . 1·10 20

539 U.N. and German Eagle Emblems

1973. Admission of German Federal Republic to U.N. Organization.
1673 **539** 40pf. multicoloured . . . 1·50 20

540 French Horn

1973. Humanitarian Relief Funds. Multicoloured. (a) Musical Instruments. Inscr "WOHLFAHRTSMARKE".
1674 25pf.+10pf. Type **540** . . . 65 35
1675 30pf.+15pf. Grand piano . . 65 35
1676 40pf.+20pf. Violin 90 55
1677 70pf.+70pf. Harp . . . . . 2·20 1·50
(b) Christmas. Inscr "WEIHNACHTSMARKE".
1678 30pf.+15pf. Christmas star 65 55

541 Radio set of 1923

1973. "50 Years of German Broadcasting".
1679 **541** 30pf. multicoloured . . . 35 20

1974. Tourism. As Type **473**.
1680 30pf. black and green . . . 65 20
1681 40pf. black and red 65 20
1682 40pf. black and red 65 20
VIEWS: No. 1680, Saarbrucken; 1681, Aachen; 1682, Bremen.

542 Louise Otto-Peters

1974. Women in German Politics. Each black and orange.
1683 40pf. Type **542** 65 50
1684 40pf. Helene Lange 65 50
1685 40pf. Rosa Luxemburg . . . 65 50
1686 40pf. Gertrud Baumer . . . 65 50

543 Drop of Blood and Emergency Light

1974. Blood Donor and Accident/Rescue Services.
1687 **543** 40pf. red and blue . . . 80 20

544 "Deer in Red" (Franz Marc)

1974. German Expressionist Paintings. Mult.
1688 30pf. Type **544** 50 20
1689 30pf. "Girls under Trees" (A. Macke) 65 20
1690 40pf. "Portrait in Blue" (A. von Jawiensky) (vert) . . 65 20
1691 50pf. "Pechstein asleep" (E. Heckel) (vert) . . . . 1·20 30
1692 70pf. "Still Life with Telescope" (Max Beckmann) . . . . 1·00 75
1693 120pf. "Old Peasant" (L. Kirchner) (vert) . . . 2·00 1·50

545 St. Thomas teaching Pupils

1974. 700th Death Anniv of St. Thomas Aquinas.
1694 **545** 40pf. black and red . . . 55 20

546 Disabled Persons in Outline

1974. Rehabilitation of the Handicapped.
1695 **546** 40pf. red and black . . . 80 20

547 Construction (Bricklayer)

548 "Ascending Youth" (W. Lehmbruck)

1974. Youth Welfare. Youth Activities. Multicoloured.
1696 25pf.+10pf. Type **547** . . . 60 55
1697 30pf.+15pf. Folk dancing 1·10 90

1698 40pf.+20pf. Study . . . . . 1·80 1·60
1699 70pf.+35pf. Research . . . 3·00 2·50

1974. Europa.
1700 **548** 30pf. black, green & sil 50 15
1701 – 40pf. black, red and lilac 65 20
DESIGN: 40pf. "Kneeling Woman" (W. Lehmbruck).

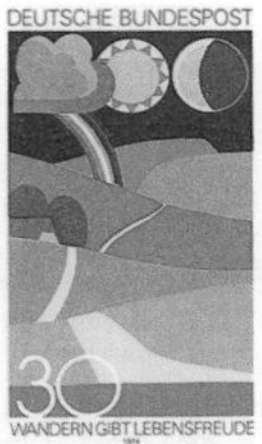

549 Immanuel Kant **551** Country Road

550 Ferderal Arms and National Colours

1974. 250th Birth Anniv of Immanuel Kant (philosopher).
1702 **549** 90pf. red . . . . 1·80 30

1974. 25th Anniv of Formation of Federal Republic. Sheet 94 × 64 mm.
MS1703 **550** 40pf. multicoloured 1·30 1·20

1974. Rambling, and Birth Centenaries of Richard Schirrman and Wilhelm Munker (founders of Youth Hostelling Assn).
1704 **551** 30pf. multicoloured . . . 30 10

552 Friedrich Klopstock **553** "Crowned Cross" Symbol

1974. 250th Birth Anniv of Friedrich Gottlieb Klopstock (poet).
1705 **552** 40pf. black and red . . . 60 20

1974. 125th Anniv of German Protestant Church Diaconal Association (charitable organization).
1706 **553** 40p. multicoloured . . . 60 20

554 Goalkeeper saving Goal

1974. World Cup Football Championship. Multicoloured.
1707 30pf. Type **554** 90 20
1708 40pf. Mid-field melee . . . 1·80 20

555 Hans Holbein (self-portrait) **556** Broken Bars of Prison Window

1974. 450th Death Anniv of Hans Holbein the Elder (painter).
1709 **555** 50pf. black and red . . . 80 25

1974. Amnesty International Commemoration.
1710 **556** 70pf. black and blue . . 1·10 35

557 "Man and Woman looking at the Moon"

1974. Birth Bicentenary of Caspar David Friedrich (artist).
1711 **557** 50pf. multicoloured . . . 1·20 30

558 Campion **559** Early German Post-boxes

1974. Humanitarian Relief Funds. Flowers. Multicoloured. (a) 25th Anniv of Welfare Stamps. Inscr "25 JAHRE WOHLFAHRTSMARKE".
1712 30pf.+15pf. Type **558** . . . 35 25
1713 40pf.+20pf. Foxglove . . . 45 35
1714 50pf.+25pf. Mallow 60 50
1715 70pf.+35pf. Campanula . . 1·60 1·30

(b) Christmas. Inscr "WEIHNACHTSMARKE".
1716 40pf.+20pf. Poinsettia . . . 70 65

1974. Cent of Universal Postal Union.
1717 **559** 50pf. multicoloured . . . 1·20 35

560 Annette Kolb **562** Mother and Child and Emblem

561 Hans Bockler (Trade Union leader)

1975. International Women's Year. Women Writers.
1718 30pf. Type **560** 60 30
1719 40pf. Ricarda Huch 60 30
1720 50pf. Else Lasker-Schuler . . 60 30
1721 70pf. Gertrud von le Fort 1·10 80

1975. Birth Centenaries.
1722 **561** 40pf. black and green . . 65 20
1723 – 50pf. black and red . . . 70 20
1724 – 70pf. black and blue . . 1·90 50
DESIGNS: 50pf. Matthias Erzberger (statesman); 70pf. Albert Schweitzer (medical missionary).

1975. 25th Anniv of Organization for the Rest and Recuperation of Mothers.
1725 **562** 50pf. multicoloured . . . 70 20

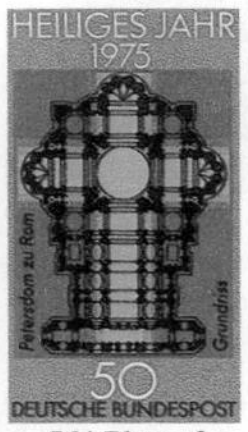

563 Detail of Ceiling Painting, Sistine Chapel **564** Plan of St. Peter's, Rome within a cross

1975. 500th Birth Anniv of Michelangelo.
1726 **563** 70pf. black and blue . . 1·60 1·20

1975. "Holy Year (Year of Reconciliation)".
1727 **564** 50pf. multicoloured . . . 65 20

565 Ice Hockey

1975. World Ice Hockey Championships, Munich and Dusseldorf.
1728 **565** 50pf. multicoloured . . . 1·10 20

566 Class 218 Diesel Locomotive

1975. Youth Welfare. Railway Locomotives. Multicoloured.
1729 30pf.+15pf. Type **566** . . . 55 55
1730 40pf.+20pf. Class 103 electric locomotive 80 75
1731 50pf.+25pf. Class 403 electric railcar . . . . . 1·10 1·00
1732 70pf.+35pf. Transrapid Maglev train (model) . . 2·00 1·70

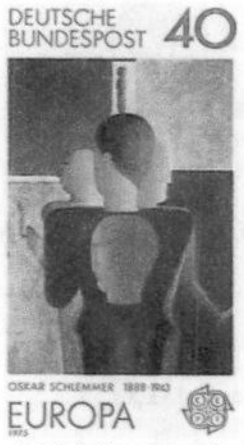

567 "Concentric Group" **569** "Nuis" (woodcarving)

568 Morike's Silhouette and Signature

1975. Europa. Paintings by Oskar Schlemmer. Multicoloured.
1733 40pf. Type **567** 55 20
1734 50pf. "Bauhaus Staircase" 70 20

1975. Death Cent of Eduard Morike (writer).
1735 **568** 40pf. multicoloured . . . 45 20

1975. 500th Anniv of Siege of Neuss.
1736 **569** 50pf. multicoloured . . . 85 20

570 Jousting Contest

1975. 500th Anniv of "Landshut Wedding" (festival).
1737 **570** 50pf. multicoloured . . . 1·10 20

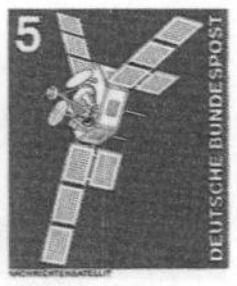

571 Mainz Cathedral **572** Telecommunication Satellite

1975. Millenary of Mainz Cathedral.
1738 **571** 40pf. multicoloured . . . 1·10 20

1975. Industry and Technology.
1739 **572** 5pf. green 15 15
1740 – 10pf. mauve 15 15
1741 – 20pf. red 20 15
1742 – 30pf. lilac 25 15
1743 – 40pf. green 35 15
1744 – 50pf. mauve 45 15
1745 – 60pf. red 60 15
1746 – 70pf. blue 20 20
1747 – 80pf. green 90 15
1748 – 100pf. brown . . . . . 1·00 20
1748a – 110pf. purple . . . . 1·60 55
1749 – 120pf. blue . . . . . 1·20 35
1749a – 130pf. red . . . . . 2·00 45
1750 – 140pf. red . . . . . . 1·30 40
1751 – 150pf. red . . . . . . 2·75 60
1752 – 160pf. green . . . . . 2·00 70
1753 – 180pf. brown . . . . 2·20 70
1753a – 190pf. brown . . . . 2·20 55
1754 – 200pf. purple . . . . 2·00 30
1754a – 230pf. purple . . . . 3·00 70
1754b – 250pf. green . . . . 4·25 1·20
1754c – 300pf. green . . . . 4·25 1·30
1755 – 500pf. black . . . . 5·25 80
DESIGNS: 10pf. Electric train; 20pf. Modern lighthouse; 30pf. MBB-Bolkow Bo 105C rescue helicopter; 40pf. Space laboratory; 50pf. Dish aerial; 60pf. X-ray apparatus; 70pf. Ship-building; 80pf. Farm tractor; 100pf. Lignite excavator; 110pf. Colour television camera; 120pf. Chemical plant; 130pf. Brewery plant; 140pf. Power station; 150, 190pf. Mechanical shovel; 160pf. Blast furnace; 180pf. Wheel loader; 200pf. Marine drilling platform; 230, 250pf. Frankfurt Airport; 300pf. Electromagnetic monorail; 500pf. Radio telescope.

573 Town Hall and Market, Alsfeld

1975. European Architectural Heritage Year. German Buildings. Multicoloured.
1756 50pf. Type **573** 85 55
1757 50pf. Plonlein corner, Siebers tower and Kobelzeller gate, Rothenburg-on-Tauber . . 85 55
1758 50pf. Town Hall ("The Steipe") Trier 85 55
1759 50pf. View of Xanten . . . 1·20 55

574 Effects of Drug-taking

1975. Campaign to Fight the Abuse of Drugs and Intoxicants.
1760 **574** 40pf. multicoloured . . . 50 20

575 Posthouse Sign, Royal Prussian Establishment for Transport 1776 **576** Edelweiss

1975. Stamp Day.
1761 **575** 10pf. multicoloured . . . 35 20

1975. Humanitarian Relief Funds. Alpine Flowers. Multicoloured. (a) Inscr "Wohlfartsmarke 1975".
1762 30pf.+15pf. Type **576** . . . 45 35
1763 40pf.+20pf. Trollflower . . 45 35
1764 50pf.+25pf. Alpine rose . . 65 60
1765 70pf.+35pf. Pasque-flower 1·80 1·70

(b) Inscr "Weihnachtsmarke 1975".
1766 40pf.+20pf. Christmas rose 1·10 80
See also Nos. 1796/9, 1839/42, 1873/6 and 1905/8.

577 Gustav Stresemann (statesman)

1975. German Nobel Peace Prize Winners. Sheet 100 × 70 mm containing T **577** and similar vert designs in black.
MS1767 50pf. Type **577**; 50pf. Ludwig Quidde (Reichstag deputy); 50pf. Carl von Ossietzky (journalist) . . . . 2·20 2·00

578 Stylized Ski-runners **579** Konrad Adenauer

1975. Winter Olympic Games, Innsbruck.
1768 **578** 50pf. multicoloured . . . 70 20

1976. Birth Centenary of Konrad Adenauer (Chancellor 1949–63).
1769 **579** 50pf. green . . . . . . 1·60 20

580 Cover Pages from Hans Sachs' Books
581 Junkers F-13 "Herta"

1976. 400th Death Anniv of Hans Sachs (poet and composer).
1770 **580** 40pf. multicoloured . . . 65 20

1976. 50th Anniv of Lufthansa (German civil airline).
1771 **581** 50pf. multicoloured . . . 1·10 20

582 Emblem and Commemorative Inscription
583 Letters "E G" representing Steel Girders

1976. 25th Anniv of Federal Constitutional Court.
1772 **582** 50pf. multicoloured . . . 90 20

1976. 25th Anniv of European Coal and Steel Community.
1773 **583** 40pf. multicoloured . . . 80 20

584 Monorail Train
585 Basketball

1976. 75th Anniv of Wuppertal Monorailway.
1774 **584** 50pf. multicoloured . . . 85 20

1976. Youth Welfare. Training for the Olympics. Multicoloured.
1775 30pf.+15pf. Type **585** . . . 45 35
1776 40pf.+20pf. Rowing 80 70
1777 50pf.+25pf. Gymnastics . . 1·10 1·00
1778 70pf.+35pf. Volleyball . . . 1·50 1·40

586 Swimming

1976. Olympic Games, Montreal. Mult.
1779 40pf.+25pf. Type **586** . . . 65 60
1780 50pf.+25pf. High jumping 1·00 90
MS1781 110 × 70 mm. 30pf.+15pf. black, orange-red and pale yellow; 70pf. + 35pf. black, new blue and pale blue . . . . 1·60 1·60
DESIGNS: 30pf. Hockey; 50pf. High jumping; 70pf. Rowing four.

587 Girl selling Trinkets and Copperplate Prints
588 Carl Sonnenschein

1976. Europa. Ludwigsburg China Figures. Multicoloured.
1782 40pf. Type **587** 55 15
1783 50pf. Boy selling copperplate prints 65 15

1976. Birthday Centenary of Dr. Carl Sonnenschein (clergyman).
1784 **588** 50pf. multicoloured . . . 65 20

589 Opening bars of Hymn "Entrust Yourself to God"

1976. 300th Birth Anniv of Paul Gerhardt (composer).
1785 **589** 40pf. multicoloured . . . 60 20

590 Carl Maria von Weber conducting

1976. 150th Death Anniv of Carl Maria von Weber (composer).
1786 **590** 50pf. black and brown 85 20

591 Carl Schurz

1976. Bicent of American Revolution.
1787 **591** 70pf. multicoloured . . . 1·10 45

592 Wagnerian Stage

1976. Centenary of Bayreuth Festival.
1788 **592** 50pf. multicoloured . . . 1·20 20

593 Bronze Ritual Chariot

1976. Archaeological Heritage. Mult.
1789 30pf. Type **593** 45 30
1790 40pf. Gold-ornamental bowl 60 30
1791 50pf. Silver necklet 90 35
1792 120pf. Roman gold goblet 2·00 1·50

594 Golden Plover
595 Mythical Creature

1976. Bird Protection.
1793 **594** 50pf. multicoloured . . . 1·20 20

1976. 300th Death Anniv of J. J. C. von Grimmelshausen (writer).
1794 **595** 40pf. multicoloured . . . 1·30 20

596 18th-century Posthouse Sign, Hochst-am-Main
597 Sophie Schroder ("Sappho")

1976. Stamp Day.
1795 **596** 10pf. multicoloured . . . 35 20

1976. Humanitarian Relief Funds. Garden Flowers. Designs similar to T **576**. Multicoloured.
1796 30pf.+15pf. Phlox 55 40
1797 40pf.+20pf. Marigolds . . . 65 55
1798 50pf.+25pf. Dahlias 75 70
1799 70pf.+35pf. Pansies . . . . 1·30 1·20

1976. Famous German Actresses. Mult.
1800 30pf. Carolin Neuber ("Medea") 45 20
1801 40pf. Type **597** 55 25
1802 50pf. Louise Dumont ("Hedda Gabler") 70 35
1803 70pf. Hermine Korner ("Macbeth") . . . . . . 1·20 95

598 "Madonna and Child" ("Marienfenster" window, Frauenkirche, Esslingen)

1976. Christmas. Sheet 71 × 101 mm.
MS1804 **598** 50pf.+25pf. multicoloured 85 80

599 Eltz Castle
600 Palais de l'Europe

1977. German Castles.
1805 – 10pf. blue 20 15
1805c – 20pf. orange 20 15
1805d – 25pf. red 45 20
1806 – 30pf. bistre 45 15
1806c – 35pf. red 60 30
1807 **599** 40pf. green 55 15
1807a – 40pf. brown 60 15
1808 – 50pf. red 65 15
1808b – 50pf. green 75 15
1809 – 60pf. brown . . . . . 1·10 15
1809a – 60pf. red 85 20
1810 – 70pf. blue . . . . . 1·10 20
1810a – 80pf. green . . . . . 1·10 20
1810c – 90pf. blue . . . . . 1·30 35
1810d – 120pf. violet . . . . 1·80 70
1811 – 190pf. red . . . . . 2·20 75
1812 – 200pf. green . . . . 2·75 70
1812a – 210pf. brown . . . . 3·50 1·00
1812b – 230pf. green . . . . 3·50 85
1812c – 280pf. blue . . . . . 4·00 75
1812d – 300pf. orange . . . . 4·75 65
DESIGNS: 10pf. Glucksburg; 20, 190pf. Pfaueninsel, Berlin; 25pf. Gemen; 30pf. Ludwigstein, Werratal; 35pf. Lichtenstein; 40pf. (1807a) Wolfsburg; 50pf. (1808) Neuschwanstein; 50pf. (1808b) Inzlingen; 60pf. (1809) Marksburg; 60pf. (1809a) Rheydt; 70pf. Mespelbrunn; 80pf. Wilhelmsthal; 90pf. Vischering; 120pf. Charlottenburg, Berlin; 200pf. Burresheim; 210pf. Schwanenburg; 230pf. Lichtenberg; 280pf. Ahrensburg; 300pf. Herrenhausen, Hanover.

1977. Inauguration of Palais de l'Europe (Council of Europe buildings), Strasbourg.
1813 **600** 140pf. green and black 2·00 60

601 Book Illustrations
603 Jean Monnet

1977. "Till Eulenspiegel" (popular fable).
1814 **601** 50pf. multicoloured . . . 60 20

1977. Award of "Citizen of Europe" honour to Jean Monnet (French statesman).
1816 **603** 50pf. black, grey & yell 70 20

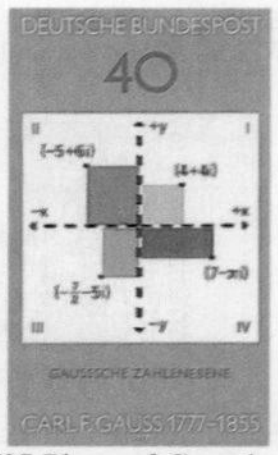

604 "Flower"
605 Plane of Complex Numbers

1977. 25th Anniv of Federal Horticultural Show.
1817 **604** 50pf. multicoloured . . . 80 20

1977. Birth Bicentenary of Carl Friedrich Gauss (mathematician).
1818 **605** 40pf. multicoloured . . . 1·20 20

606 "Wappen von Hamburg" (warship)
607 Head of Barbarossa

1977. Youth Welfare. Ships. Multicoloured.
1819 30pf.+15pf. Type **606** . . . 60 55
1820 40pf.+20pf. "Preussen" (full-rigged sailing ship) . . . 80 75
1821 50pf.+25pf. "Bremen" (liner) 1·10 95
1822 70pf.+35pf. "Sturmfels" (container ship) . . . . . 1·50 1·30

1977. Staufer Year, Baden-Wurttemberg.
1823 **607** 40pf. multicoloured . . . 1·30 20

608 Rhon Autobahn
609 "Self-Portrait" (Rubens)

1977. Europa.
1824 **608** 40pf. black and green . . 65 20
1825 – 50pf. black and red . . . 75 20
DESIGN: 50pf. Rhine landscape.

1977. 400th Birth Anniv of Peter Paul Rubens.
1826 **609** 30pf. black . . . . . . 1·00 20

610 Ulm Cathedral
611 Rector's Seal, Mainz University (500th Anniv)

1977. 600th Anniv of Ulm Cathedral.
1827 **610** 40pf. brown, green & bl 70 20

1977. University Anniversaries.
1828 **611** 50pf. black and red . . . 80 25
1829 – 50pf. black and red . . . 1·00 25
1830 – 50pf. black and red . . . 1·20 25
DESIGNS: No. 1829, Great Seal, Marburg University (450th anniv); No. 1830, Great Seal, Tubingen University (500th anniv).

612 "Morning"

1977. Birth Bicentenary of Phillipp Otto Runge (artist).
1831 **612** 60pf. multicoloured . . . 1·00 35

613 Ketteler's Coat of Arms
614 Fritz von Bodelschwingh

1977. Death Centenary of Bishop Wilhelm Emmanuel von Ketteler.
1832 **613** 50pf. multicoloured . . . 90 20

1977. Birth Centenary of Pastor Fritz von Bodelschwingh (pioneer of welfare work for the disabled).
1833 **614** 50pf. multicoloured . . . 80 20

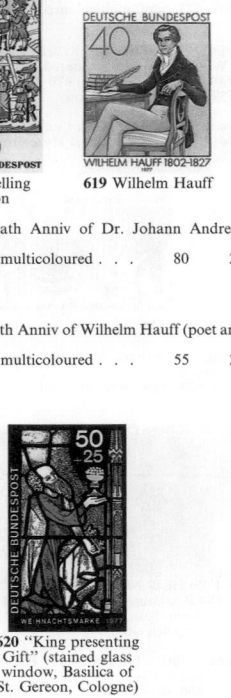

615 Golden Hat

1977. Archaeological Heritage. Multicoloured.
1834 30pf. Type **615** 45 25
1835 120pf. Gilt helmet . . . . . 2·00 1·10
1836 200pf. Bronze centaur head 2·40 2·00

616 Operator and Switchboard **617** 19th-century Posthouse Sign, Hamburg

1977. Centenary of Telephone in Germany.
1837 **616** 50pf. multicoloured . . . 1·10 20

1977. Stamp Day.
1838 **617** 10pf. multicoloured . . . 45 15

1977. Humanitarian Relief Funds. Meadow Flowers. As T **576**. Multicoloured.
1839 30pf.+15pf. Caraway . . . 45 35
1840 40pf.+20pf. Dandelion . . . 55 40
1841 50pf.+25pf. Red clover . . . 60 55
1842 70pf.+35pf. Meadow sage 1·20 1·10

618 Travelling Surgeon **619** Wilhelm Hauff

1977. 250th Death Anniv of Dr. Johann Andreas Eisenbarth.
1843 **618** 50pf. multicoloured . . . 80 20

1977. 150th Death Anniv of Wilhelm Hauff (poet and novelist).
1844 **619** 40pf. multicoloured . . . 55 20

620 "King presenting Gift" (stained glass window, Basilica of St. Gereon, Cologne)

1977. Christmas. Sheet 70 × 105 mm.
MS1845 **620** 50pf.+25pf. multicoloured 90 80

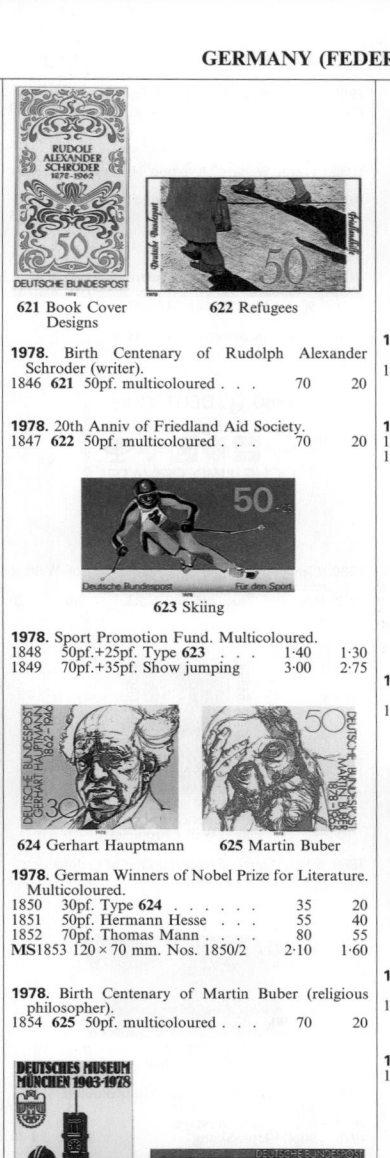

621 Book Cover Designs **622** Refugees

1978. Birth Centenary of Rudolph Alexander Schroder (writer).
1846 **621** 50pf. multicoloured . . . 70 20

1978. 20th Anniv of Friedland Aid Society.
1847 **622** 50pf. multicoloured . . . 70 20

623 Skiing

1978. Sport Promotion Fund. Multicoloured.
1848 50pf.+25pf. Type **623** . . . 1·40 1·30
1849 70pf.+35pf. Show jumping 3·00 2·75

624 Gerhart Hauptmann **625** Martin Buber

1978. German Winners of Nobel Prize for Literature. Multicoloured.
1850 30pf. Type **624** 35 20
1851 50pf. Hermann Hesse . . . 55 40
1852 70pf. Thomas Mann 80 55
MS1853 120 × 70 mm. Nos. 1850/2 2·10 1·60

1978. Birth Centenary of Martin Buber (religious philosopher).
1854 **625** 50pf. multicoloured . . . 70 20

626 Museum Tower and Cupola **627** Wilhelmine Reichart's Balloon, Munich October Festival, 1820

1978. 75th Anniv of German Scientific and Technical Museum, Munich.
1855 **626** 50pf. black, yellow & red 70 20

1978. Youth Welfare. Aviation History (1st series). Multicoloured.
1856 30pf.+15pf. Type **627** . . . 60 60
1857 40pf.+20pf. Airship LZ-1, 1900 . . . . 80 75
1858 50pf.+25pf. Bleriot XI monoplane, 1909 . . . . 1·10 90
1859 70pf.+35pf. Hans Grade's monoplane, 1909 . . . . 1·30 1·20
See also Nos. 1886/9 and 1918/21.

628 Old Town Hall, Bamberg

1978. Europa. Multicoloured.
1860 40pf. Type **628** 60 20
1861 50pf. Old Town Hall, Regensburg . . . . . . 1·10 20
1862 70pf. Old Town Hall, Esslingen am Neckar . . 1·30 75

629 Piper and Children

1978. Pied Piper of Hamelin.
1863 **629** 50pf. multicoloured . . . 1·20 20

630 Janusz Korczak **631** Fossil Bat

1978. Birth Centenary of Janusz Korczak (educational reformer).
1864 **630** 90pf. multicoloured . . . 1·20 50

1978. Archaeological Heritage, Fossils. Mult.
1865 80pf. Type **631** . . . . . . 1·80 1·40
1866 200pf. Horse ("eohippus") skeleton . . . . 2·00 1·70

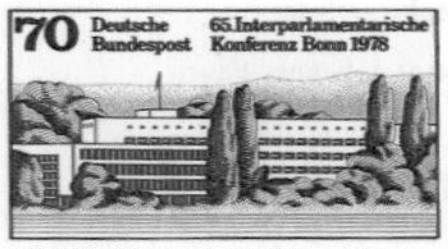

632 Parliament Building, Bonn

1978. 65th Interparliamentary Union Conference, Bonn.
1867 **632** 70pf. multicoloured . . . 1·30 35

633 Rose Window, Freiburg Minster **634** Silhouette

1978. 85th Conference of German Catholics, Freiburg.
1868 **633** 40pf. multicoloured . . . 55 20

1978. Birth Bicent of Clemens Brentano (poet).
1869 **634** 30pf. multicoloured . . . 45 20

635 Text

1978. 25th Anniv of European Convention for the Protection of Human Rights.
1870 **635** 50pf. multicoloured . . . 90 20

636 Baden Posthouse Sign **638** "Christ Child" (stained glass window, Frauenkirche, Munich)

637 "Easter at the Walchensee" (Lovis Corinth)

1978. Stamp Day and World Philatelic Movement. Multicoloured.
1871 40pf. Type **636** 50 25
1872 50pf. 1850 3pf. stamp of Saxony 50 25

1978. Humanitarian Relief Funds. Woodland Flowers. As T **576**. Multicoloured.
1873 30pf.+15pf. Arum 45 35
1874 40pf.+20pf. Weasel-snout . . 60 45
1875 50pf.+25pf. Turk's-cap lily 90 75
1876 70pf.+35pf. Liverwort . . . 1·20 1·10

1978. Impressionist Paintings. Multicoloured.
1877 50pf. Type **637** 65 40
1878 70pf. "Horseman on the Shore turning Left" (Max Liebermann) (vert) . . . 1·10 70
1879 120pf. "Lady with a Cat" (Max Slevogt) (vert) . . . 1·80 1·50

1978. Christmas. Sheet 65 × 93 mm.
MS1880 **638** 50pf.+25pf. multicoloured 85 80

639 Child

1979. International Year of the Child.
1881 **639** 60pf. multicoloured . . . 65 40

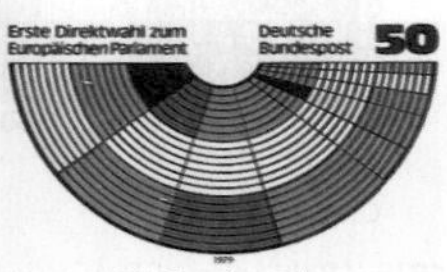

640 Agnes Miegel **641** Seating Plan

1979. Birth Cent of Agnes Miegel (poet).
1882 **640** 60pf. multicoloured . . . 90 20

1979. First Direct Elections to European Parliament.
1883 **641** 50pf. multicoloured . . . 1·00 20

642 Film **643** Rescue Services Emblems

1979. 25th West German Short Film Festival.
1884 **642** 50pf. black and turquoise 90 20

1979. Rescue Services on the Road.
1885 **643** 50pf. multicoloured . . . 90 20

1979. Youth Welfare. History of Aviation (2nd series). As T **627**. Multicoloured.
1886 40pf.+20pf. Dornier Do-J Wal flying boat, 1922 . . 60 55
1887 50pf.+25pf. Heinkel He 70 Blitz, 1932 . . . . 90 75
1888 60pf.+30pf. Junkers W.33 "Bremen", 1928 . . . . . 1·10 85
1889 90pf.+45pf. Focke Achgelis Fa 61 helicopter, 1936 . . 1·50 1·30

644 Handball

1979. Sport Promotion Fund. Multicoloured.
1890 60pf.+30pf. Type **644** . . . 1·10 95
1891 90pf.+45pf. Canoeing . . . 1·50 1·40

645 Telegraph Office, 1863 **646** Anne Frank

1979. Europa. Multicoloured.
1892 50pf. Type **645** 65 20
1893 60pf. Post Office counter, 1854 . . . . 1·00 20

1979. 50th Birth Anniv of Anne Frank (concentration camp victim and diary writer).
1894 **646** 60pf. black, grey and red 90 20

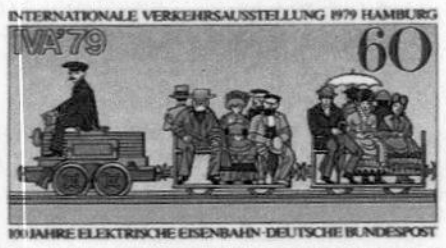

647 Werner von Siemens's Electric Railway, 1879

1979. International Transport Exhibition. Hamburg.
1895 **647** 60pf. multicoloured . . . 1·00 20

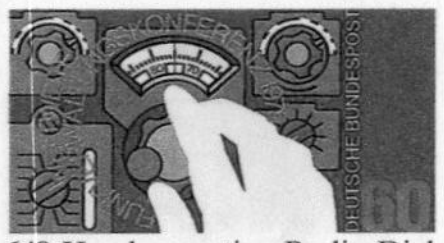

648 Hand operating Radio Dial

1979. World Administrative Radio Conference, Geneva.
1896 **648** 60f. multicoloured . . . 90 20

649 "Moses receiving the Tablets of the Law" (woodcut, Cranach the Elder)

650 Cross and Orb

1979. 450th Anniv of Publication of Martin Luther's Catechisms.
1897 **649** 50pf. black and green . . 1·20 20

1979. Pilgrimage to Aachen.
1898 **650** 50pf. multicoloured . . . 70 20

651 Hildegard von Bingen

1979. 800th Death Anniv of Hildegard von Bingen (writer and mystic).
1899 **651** 110pf. multicoloured . . 1·30 60

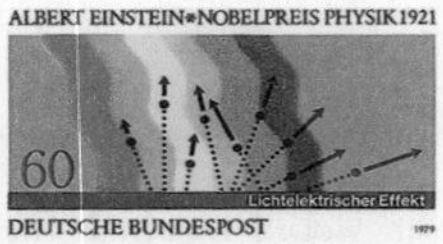

652 Photo-electric Effect

1979. Birth Centenaries of Nobel Prize Winners. Multicoloured.
1900 60pf. Type **652** (Albert Einstein, Physics, 1921) 1·00 35
1901 60pf. Splitting of uranium nucleus (Otto Hahn, Chemistry, 1944) . . . . 1·80 35
1902 60pf. Diffraction pattern of X-rays passed through crystal (Max von Laue, Physics, 1914) . . . . . 1·00 35

653 Pilot and Helmsman

654 Posthouse Sign, Altheim, Saar (German side), 1754

1979. 300th Anniv of 1st Pilotage Regulations.
1903 **653** 60pf. brown and claret 70 20

1979. Stamp Day.
1904 **654** 60pf.+30pf. mult . . . . 1·20 1·10

1979. Humanitarian Relief Funds. Woodland Flowers and Fruit. As T **576**. Multicoloured.
1905 40pf.+20pf. Red beech (horiz) 55 40
1906 50pf.+25pf. English oak (horiz) 70 60
1907 60pf.+30pf. Hawthorn (horiz) 80 70
1908 90pf.+45pf. Mountain pine (horiz) . . . . 1·30 1·30

656 "Bird Garden"

1979. Birth Cent of Paul Klee (artist).
1909 **656** 90pf. multicoloured . . . 1·20 60

657 Faust and Mephistopheles

658 Lightbulb

1979. Doctor Johannes Faust.
1910 **657** 60pf. multicoloured . . . 1·20 20

1979. "Save Energy".
1911 **658** 40pf. multicoloured . . . 60 20

659 "Nativity" (Altenberg medieval manuscript)

1979. Christmas.
1912 **659** 60pf.+30pf. mult . . . . 1·10 1·00

660 "Iphigenia"

1980. Death Centenary of Anselm Feuerbach (artist).
1913 **660** 50pf. multicoloured . . . 1·00 20

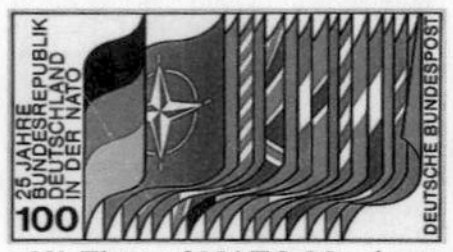

661 Flags of NATO Members

1980. 25th Anniv of NATO Membership.
1914 **661** 100pf. multicoloured . . 1·80 65

662 Town Hall, St. Mary's Church, and St Peter's Cathedral

1980. 1200th Anniv of Osnabruck Town and Bishopric.
1915 **662** 60pf. multicoloured . . . 90 20

663 "Gotz von Berlichingen" (glass picture)

1980. 500th Birth Anniv of Gotz von Berlichingen (Frankish knight).
1916 **663** 60pf. multicoloured . . . 90 20

664 Texts from 1880 and 1980 Duden Dictionaries

1980. Centenary of Konrad Duden's 1st Dictionary.
1917 **664** 60pf. multicoloured . . . 85 20

1980. Youth Welfare. Aviation History (3rd series). As T **627**. Multicoloured.
1918 40pf.+20pf. Phoenix FS 24 glider, 1957 . . . . . . 45 35
1919 50pf.+25pf. Lockheed L.1049G Super Constellation 70 60
1920 60pf.+30pf. Airbus Industrie A300B2, 1972 . . . . . 1·10 85
1921 90pf.+45pf. Boeing 747-100, 1969 . . . . 1·60 1·30
No. 1919 is incorrectly dated "1950".

665 Emblems of Association Members

1980. Centenary of German Association of Welfare Societies.
1922 **665** 60pf. blue, red and black 90 20

666 "Frederick I with his sons" (Welf Chronicle)

1980. 800th Anniv of Imperial Diet of Gelnhausen.
1923 **666** 60pf. multicoloured . . . 1·20 20

667 Football

1980. Sport Promotion Fund. Multicoloured.
1924 50pf.+25pf. Type **667** . . . 55 50
1925 60pf.+30pf. Dressage . . . 80 65
1926 90pf.+45pf. Skiing . . . . . 1·60 1·40

668 Albertus Magnus (scholar)

669 Reading the Augsburg Confession (engraving, G Kohler)

1980. Europa. Multicoloured.
1927 50pf. Type **668** . . . . . . 1·00 20
1928 60pf. Gottfried Leibniz (philosopher) . . . . . . 1·10 20

1980. 450th Anniv of Augsburg Confession.
1929 **669** 50pf. black, yellow & grn 70 20

670 Nature Reserve

1980. Nature Conservation.
1930 **670** 40pf. multicoloured . . . 1·10 20

671 Ear and Oscillogram Pulses

1980. International Congress for the Training and Education of the Hard of Hearing, Hamburg.
1931 **671** 90pf. multicoloured . . . 1·20 35

672 First Book of Daily Bible Readings, 1731

673 St. Benedict

1980. 250th Anniv of Moravian Brethren's Book of Daily Bible Readings.
1932 **672** 50pf. multicoloured . . . 85 20

1980. 1500th Birth Anniv of St. Benedict of Nursia (founder of Benedictine Order).
1933 **673** 50pf. multicoloured . . . 70 20

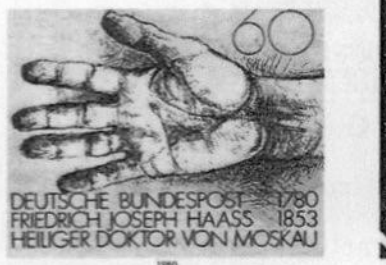

674 Helping Hand

675 Marie von Ebner-Eschenbach

1980. Birth Bicentenary of Friedrich Joseph Haass (philanthropist).
1934 **674** 60pf. multicoloured . . . 85 20

1980. 150th Birth Anniv of Marie von Ebner-Eschenbach (novelist).
1935 **675** 60pf. buff, black & orge 85 20

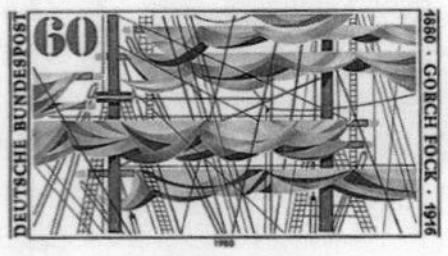

676 Rigging

1980. Birth Centenary of Johan Kinau ("Gorch Fock") (poet).
1936 **676** 60pf. multicoloured . . . 1·70 20

677 Positioning Keystone of South Tower Finial (engraving)

678 "Ceratocephalus falcatus"

1980. Centenary of Completion of Cologne Cathedral.
1937 **677** 60pf. multicoloured . . . 1·80 25

1980. Humanitarian Relief Funds. Endangered Wildflowers. Multicoloured.
1938 40pf.+20pf. Type **678** . . . 60 55
1939 50pf.+25pf. Yellow Vetchling 80 70
1940 60pf.+30pf. Corn Cockle . . 90 85
1941 90pf.+45pf. Tassel Hyacinth 1·50 1·30
See also Nos. 1972/5.

679 Wine-making (woodcuts)

1980. Bimillenary of Vine Growing in Central Europe.
1942 **679** 50pf. multicoloured . . . 85 20

680 Posthouse Sign, Altheim, Saar, 1754 (French side)

681 "Nativity" (Altomunster manuscript)

1980. 49th International Philatelic Federation Congress, Essen.
1943 **680** 60pf.+30pf. mult 80 75

1980. Christmas.
1944 **681** 60pf.+30pf. mult . . . . 1·20 1·00

682 "Landscape with Two Fir Trees" (etching)

1980. 500th Birth Anniv of Albrecht Altdorfer (painter, engraver and architect).
1945 **682** 40pf. lt brown, blk & brn 60 20

683 Elly Heuss-Knapp

1981. Birth Centenary of Elly Heuss-Knapp (social reformer).
1946 **683** 60pf. multicoloured . . . 85 20

684 Society accepting the Handicapped

1981. International Year of Disabled Persons.
1947 **684** 60pf. multicoloured . . . 90 20

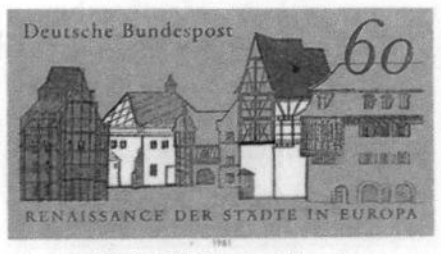

685 Old Town Houses

1981. European Campaign for Urban Renaissance.
1948 **685** 60pf. multicoloured . . . 90 20

686 Telemann and Title Page of "Singet dem Herrn"

1981. 300th Birth Anniv of Georg Philipp Telemann (composer).
1949 **686** 60pf. multicoloured . . . 90 25

687 Visiting a Foreign Family

1981. Integration of Guest Worker Families.
1950 **687** 50pf. multicoloured . . . 85 20

688 Polluted Butterfly, Fish and Plant

1981. Preservation of the Environment.
1951 **688** 60pf. multicoloured . . . 1·20 25

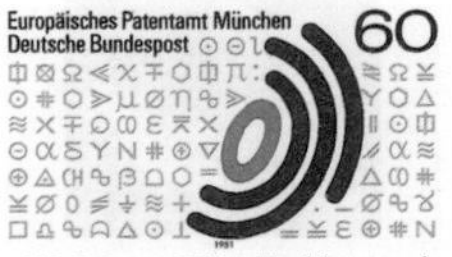

689 Patent Office Emblem and Scientific Signs

1981. Establishment of European Patent Office, Munich.
1952 **689** 60pf. grey, red and black 85 20

690 Scintigram showing Distribution of Radioactive Isotope

691 Borda Circle, 1800

1981. Cancer Prevention through Medical Check-ups.
1953 **690** 40pf. multicoloured . . . 70 20

1981. Youth Welfare. Optical Instruments. Multicoloured.
1954 40pf.+20pf. Type **691** . . . 60 50
1955 50pf.+25pf. Reflecting telescope, 1770 . . . . . 1·10 85
1956 60pf.+30pf. Binocular microscope, 1860 . . . . 1·10 85
1957 90pf.+45pf. Octant, 1775 . . 1·50 1·20

692 Rowing

1981. Sport Promotion Fund. Multicoloured.
1958 60pf.+30pf. Type **692** . . . 1·10 80
1959 90pf.+45pf. Gliding . . . . 1·60 1·40

693 South German Dancers

1981. Europa. Multicoloured.
1960 50pf. Type **693** 70 20
1961 60pf. North German dancers 90 20

694 Convention Cross

1981. 19th German Protestant Convention, Hamburg.
1962 **694** 50pf. multicoloured . . . 85 20

695 Group from Crucifixion Altar

696 Georg von Neumayer Antarctic Research Station

1981. 450th Death Anniv of Tilman Riemenschneider (woodcarver).
1963 **695** 60pf. multicoloured . . . 85 25

1981. Polar Research.
1964 **696** 110pf. multicoloured . . 1·80 50

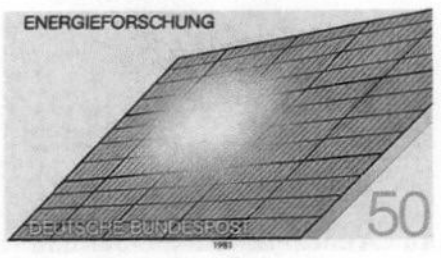

697 Solar Generator

1981. Energy Research.
1965 **697** 50pf. multicoloured . . . 1·00 20

698 Hand holding Baby Black Coot

700 Wilhelm Raabe

699 Arms of different Races forming Square

1981. Animal Protection.
1966 **698** 60pf. multicoloured . . . 1·20 20

1981. Co-operation with Developing Countries.
1967 **699** 90pf. multicoloured . . . 1·30 45

1981. 150th Birth Anniv of Wilhelm Raabe (poet).
1968 **700** 50pf. light green & green 85 20

701 Constitutional Freedom

1981. Fundamental Concepts of Democracy. Article 20 of the Basic Law. Multicoloured.
1969 40pf. Type **701** 90 20
1970 50pf. Separation of Powers 90 20
1971 60pf. Sovereignty of the People . . . . 1·30 25

1981. Humanitarian Relief Funds. Endangered Wildflowers. As T **678**. Multicoloured.
1972 40pf.+20pf. Water nut . . . 55 40
1973 50pf.+25pf. Floating Heart 70 65
1974 60pf.+30pf. Water gilly-flower 90 85
1975 90pf.+45pf. Water lobelia 1·80 1·50

702 Posthouse Scene c. 1855

703 "Nativity" (glass painting)

1981. Stamp Day.
1976 **702** 60pf. multicoloured . . . 1·20 25

1981. Christmas.
1977 **703** 60pf.+30pf. mult . . . . 1·20 95

704 St. Elisabeth

705 Clausewitz (after W. Wach)

1981. 750th Death Anniv of St. Elisabeth of Thuringia.
1978 **704** 50pf. multicoloured . . . 1·20 20

1981. 150th Death Anniv of General Carl von Clausewitz (military writer).
1979 **705** 60pf. multicoloured . . . 1·00 20

706 People forming Figure "100"

707 Map of Antarctica

1981. Cent of Social Insurance.
1980 **706** 60pf. multicoloured . . . 85 20

1981. 20th Anniv of Antarctic Treaty.
1981 **707** 100pf. blue, lt blue & blk 1·40 40

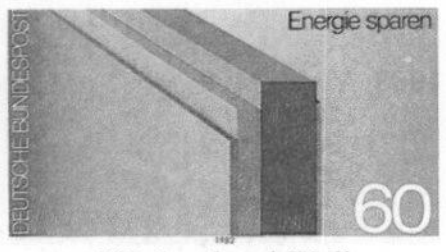

708 Pot with Lid

709 Insulated Wall

1982. 300th Birth Anniv of Johann Friedrich Bottger (founder of Meissen China Works).
1982 **708** 60pf. multicoloured . . . 85 20

1982. Energy Conservation.
1983 **709** 60pf. multicoloured . . . 85 20

710 Silhouette (Dora Brandenburg-Polster)

711 Goethe (after Georg Melchior Kraus)

1982. "The Town Band of Bremen" (German fairy tale).
1984 **710** 40pf. black and red . . . 70 20

1982. 150th Death Anniv of Johann Wolfgang von Goethe (writer).
1985 **711** 60pf. multicoloured . . . 2·40 20

712 Robert Koch

1982. Centenary of Discovery of Tubercle Bacillus.
1986 **712** 50pf. multicoloured . . . 2·75 25

713 Benz Patent "Motorwagen", 1886

1982. Youth Welfare. Motor Cars. Mult.
1987 40pf.+20pf. Type **713** . . . 60 60
1988 50pf.+25pf. Mercedes "Tourenwagen", 1913 . . 90 55
1989 60pf.+30pf. Hannomag "Kommissbrot", 1925 . . 1·10 85
1990 90pf.+45pf. Opel "Olympia", 1937 . . . . 1·80 1·50

714 Jogging

1982. Sport Promotion Fund. Multicoloured.
1991 60pf.+30pf. Type **714** . . . 1·10 90
1992 90pf.+45pf. Disabled archers 1·60 1·40

715 "Good Helene"

1982. 150th Birth Anniv of Wilhelm Busch (writer and illustrator).
1993 **715** 50pf. black, green & yell 1·10 20

716 "Procession to Hambach Castle, 1832" (wood engraving)

1982. Europa.
1994 **716** 50pf. black, yellow & red 1·20 20
1995 – 60pf. multicoloured . . . 1·80 25
DESIGN: 60pf. Excerpt from Treaty of Rome (instituting European Economic Community), 1957, and flags.

717 Racing Yachts

1982. Centenary of Kiel Regatta Week.
1996 **717** 60pf. multicoloured . . . 1·10 25

718 Young Couple

1982. Centenary of Young Men's Christian Association in Germany.
1997 **718** 50pf. multicoloured . . . 80 20

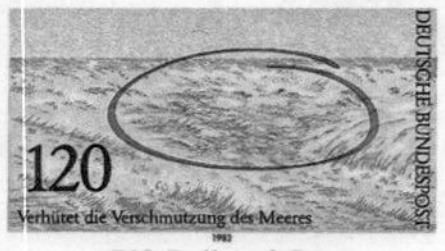

719 Polluted Sea

1982. "Prevent the Pollution of the Sea".
1998 **719** 120pf. multicoloured . . 2·40 40

720 Battered Licence Plate

1982. "Don't Drink and Drive".
1999 **720** 80pf. multicoloured . . . 1·20 25

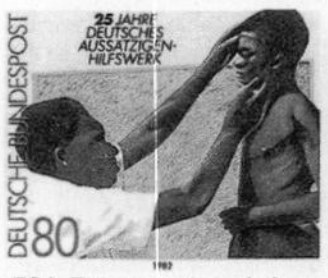

721 Doctor examining Leper **722** Franck and Born

1982. 25th Anniv of German Lepers' Welfare Organization.
2000 **721** 80pf. multicoloured . . . 1·20 25

1982. Birth Centenaries of James Franck and Max Born (physicists and Nobel Prize Winners).
2001 **722** 80pf. grey, black and red 1·30 25

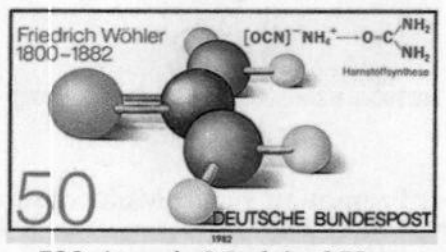

723 Atomic Model of Urea

1982. Death Centenary of Friedrich Wohler (chemist).
2002 **723** 50pf. multicoloured . . . 90 20

724 "St. Francis preaching to the Birds" (fresco by Giotto) **725** Hybrid Tea Rose

1982. 87th German Catholics' Congress, Dusseldorf and 800th Birth Anniv of St. Francis of Assisi.
2003 **724** 60pf. multicoloured . . . 80 20

1982. Humanitarian Relief Funds. Roses. Multicoloured.
2004 50pf.+20pf. Type **725** . . . 60 55
2005 60pf.+30pf. Floribunda . . . 90 70
2006 80pf.+40pf. Bourbon . . . 1·20 1·10
2007 120pf.+60pf. Polyantha hybrid . . . . 1·60 1·60

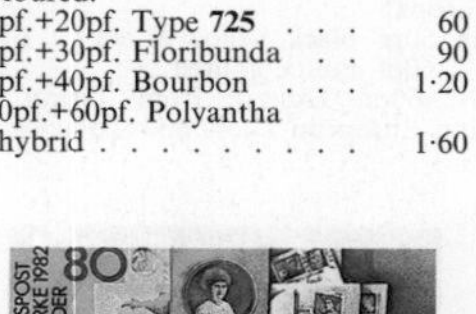

726 Letters on Desk

1982. Stamp Day.
2008 **726** 80pf. multicoloured . . . 1·60 25

727 Gregorian Calendar by Johannes Rasch, 1586 **728** Theodor Heuss

1982. 400th Anniv of Gregorian Calendar.
2009 **727** 60pf. multicoloured . . . 85 20

1982. Presidents of the Federal Republic. Sheet 130 × 100 mm containing T **728** and similar horiz designs. Multicoloured.
MS2010 80pf. Type **728**; 80pf. Heinrich Lubke; 80pf. Gustav Heinemann; 80pf. Walter Scheel; 80pf. Karl Carstens . . . . . 5·25 5·00

729 "Nativity" (detail from St. Peter Altar by Master Bertram) **730** Edith Stein

1982. Christmas.
2011 **729** 80pf.+40pf. mult . . . . 1·30 1·10

1983. 40th Death Anniv (1982) of Edith Stein (philosopher).
2012 **730** 80pf. lt grey, grey & blk 1·70 30

731 White Rose and Barbed Wire

1983. Persecution and Resistance 1933–45.
2013 **731** 80pf. multicoloured . . . 1·60 30

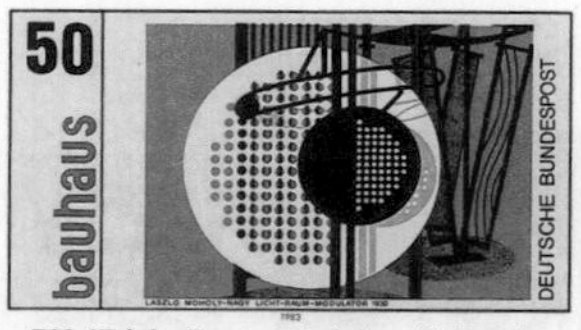

732 "Light Space Modulator" (Laszlo Moholy-Nagy)

1983. Birth Cent of Walter Gropius (founder of Bauhaus School of Art, Weimar). Bauhaus Art. Multicoloured.
2014 50pf. Type **732** 90 20
2015 60pf. "Sanctuary" (lithograph by Josef Albers) . . . . 1·10 30
2016 80pf. Skylights from Bauhaus Archives, Berlin (Walter Gropius) . . . . 1·30 30

733 Federahannes (Rottweil carnival figure)

1983. Carnival.
2017 **733** 60pf. multicoloured . . . 1·10 40

734 Daimler-Maybach, 1885

1983. Youth Welfare. Motor Cycles. Mult.
2018 50pf.+20pf. Type **734** . . . 60 60
2019 60pf.+30pf. N.S.U., 1901 . . 90 70
2020 80pf.+40pf. Megola "Sport", 1922 . . . . 1·30 1·30
2021 120pf.+60pf. B.M.W. world record holder, 1936 . . . 2·20 1·80

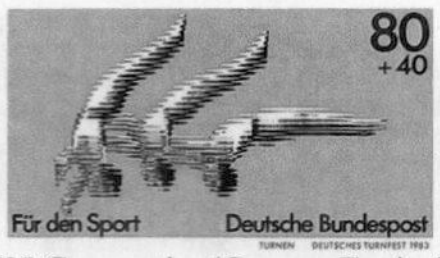

735 Gymnastics (German Festival, Frankfurt am Main)

1983. Sports Promotion Fund. Multicoloured.
2022 80pf.+40pf. Type **735** . . . 1·20 1·10
2023 120pf.+60pf. Modern pentathlon (world championships, Warendorf) . . . . 2·00 1·70

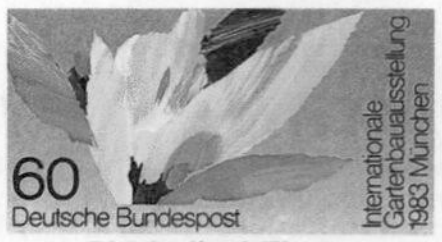

736 Stylized Flower

1983. 4th International Horticultural Show. Munich.
2024 **736** 60pf. multicoloured . . . 1·00 25

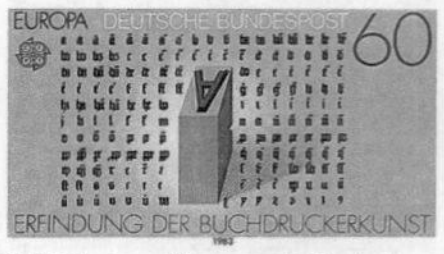

737 Modern Type and Gutenberg Letters

1983. Europa. Multicoloured.
2025 60pf. Type **737** . . . . . . 2·20 30
2026 80pf. Resonant circuit and electric flux lines . . . . 1·60 25

738 Johannes Brahms

1983. 150th Birth Anniv of Johannes Brahms (composer).
2027 **738** 80pf. multicoloured . . . 1·70 25

739 Kafka's Signature and Teyn Church, Prague

1983. Birth Cent of Franz Kafka (writer).
2028 **739** 80pf. multicoloured . . . 1·40 25

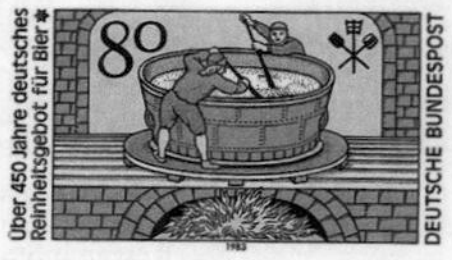

740 Brewing (frontispiece of 1677 treatise)

1983. 450th Anniv of Beer Purity Law.
2029 **740** 80pf. multicoloured . . . 1·80 25

741 "Concord"

1983. 300th Anniv of First German Settlers in America.
2030 **741** 80pf. multicoloured . . . 1·60 25

742 Children crossing Road

1983. Children and Road Traffic.
2031 **742** 80pf. multicoloured . . . 1·40 25

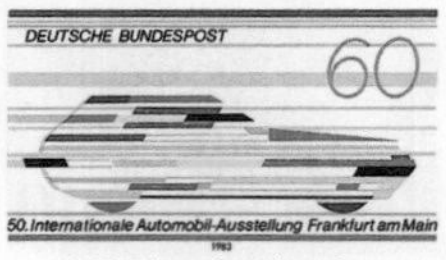

743 Flags forming Car

1983. 50th International Motor Show, Frankfurt-on-Main.
2032 **743** 60pf. multicoloured . . . 85 20

744 Warburg (after Oberland) **745** Wieland (after G. B. Bosio)

1983. Birth Centenary of Otto Warburg. (physiologist and chemist).
2033 **744** 50pf. multicoloured . . . 80 20

1983. 250th Birth Anniv of Cristoph Martin Wieland (writer).
2034 **745** 80pf. multicoloured . . . 1·30 30

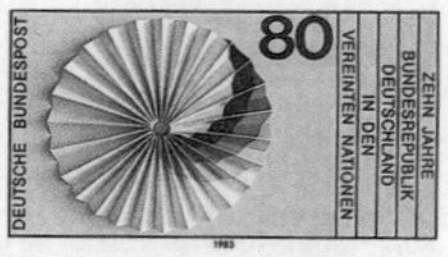

746 Rosette in National Colours

1983. 10th Anniv of U.N. Membership.
2035 **746** 80pf. multicoloured . . . 1·80 30

747 "Das Rauhe Haus" and Children

1983. 150th Anniv of "Das Rauhe Haus" (children's home, Hamburg).
2036 **747** 80pf. multicoloured . . . 1·30 25

748 Surveying Maps

1983. International Geodesy and Geophysics Union General Assembly, Hamburg.
2037 **748** 120pf. multicoloured . . 1·80 60

749 Swiss Androsace **750** Horseman with Posthorn

1983. Humanitarian Relief Funds. Endangered Alpine Flowers. Multicoloured.
2038 50pf.+20pf. Type **749** . . . 70 60
2039 60pf.+30pf. Krain groundsel 1·00 80
2040 80pf.+40pf. Fleischer's willow herb . . . . . . 1·30 1·20
2041 120pf.+60pf. Alpine sow-thistle . . . . 2·20 1·80

1983. Stamp Day.
2042 **750** 80pf. multicoloured . . . 1·60 30

751 Luther (engraving by G. Konig after Cranach)

1983. 500th Birth Anniv of Martin Luther (Protestant reformer).
2043 **751** 80pf. multicoloured . . . 2·50 25

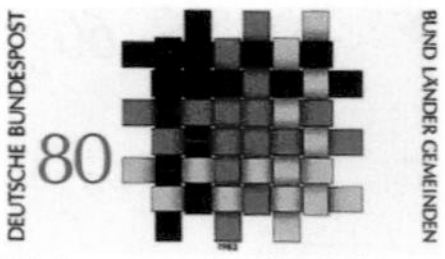

752 Interwoven National Colours

1983. Federation, Lander and Communities Co-operation.
2044 **752** 80pf. multicoloured . . . 2·00 25

753 Customs Stamps

1983. 150th Anniv of German Customs Union.
2045 **753** 60pf. multicoloured . . . 1·80 20

754 Epiphany Carol Singers

756 Reis and Telephone Apparatus

755 Black Gate, Trier

1983. Christmas.
2046 **754** 80pf.+40pf. mult . . . . 1·80 1·50

1984. 2000th Anniv of Trier.
2047 **755** 80pf. multicoloured . . . 2·00 30

1984. 150th Birth Anniv of Philipp Reis (telephone pioneer).
2048 **756** 80pf. multicoloured . . . 1·80 30

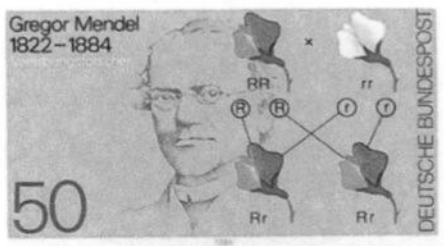

757 Mendel and Genetic Diagram

1984. Death Cent of Gregor Mendel (geneticist).
2049 **757** 50pf. multicoloured . . . 1·10 25

758 Town Hall

760 Bee-eating Beetle

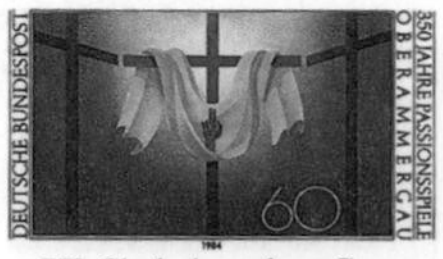

759 Cloth draped on Cross

1984. 500th Anniv of Michelstadt Town Hall.
2050 **758** 60pf. multicoloured . . . 1·00 25

1984. 350th Anniv of Oberammergau Passion Play.
2051 **759** 60pf. multicoloured . . . 1·00 25

1984. Youth Welfare. Pollinating Insects. Multicoloured.
2052 50pf.+20pf. Type **760** . . . 60 60
2053 60pf.+30pf. Red admiral . . 1·20 1·20
2054 80pf.+40pf. Honey bee . . . 1·60 1·30
2055 120pf.+60pf. "Chrysotoxum festivium" (hover fly) . . 2·30 2·10

761 Throwing the Discus

1984. Sport Promotion Fund. Multicoloured.
2056 60pf.+30pf. Type **761** . . . 1·10 90
2057 80pf.+40pf. Rhythmic gymnastics . . . . 1·40 1·30
2058 120pf.+60pf. Windsurfing 2·75 2·50

762 Parliament Emblem

763 Bridge

1984. 2nd Direct Elections to European Parliament.
2059 **762** 80pf. yellow, blue and light blue . . . . . . 1·90 30

1984. Europa. 25th Anniv of European Post and Telecommunications Conference.
2060 **763** 60pf. blue, lt blue & blk 1·20 30
2061 80pf. purple, red & black 1·30 30

764 St. Norbert (sculpture)

765 Nursery Rhyme Illustration

1984. 850th Death Anniv of St. Norbert von Xanten.
2062 **764** 80pf. green & deep green 1·30 30

1984. Death Centenary of Ludwig Richter (illustrator).
2063 **765** 60pf. black and brown 85 25

766 Cross and Shadow

1984. 50th Anniv of Protestant Churches' Barmen Theological Declaration.
2064 **766** 80pf. multicoloured . . . 1·30 30

767 Letter sorting, 1800s

1984. 19th Universal Postal Union Congress, Hamburg. Sheet 138 × 104 mm containing T **767** and similar square designs.
MS2065 60pf. brown and black; 80pf. multicoloured; 120pf. green, black and grey . . . . . 3·50 3·25
DESIGNS: 80pf. Modern automatic letter sorting machine scanning device; 120pf. Heinrich von Stephan (founder of U.P.U.).

768 Groom leading Horse (detail from tomb of Oclatius)

769 Bessel

1984. 2000th Anniv of Neuss.
2066 **768** 80pf. multicoloured . . . 1·30 30

1984. Birth Bicentenary of Friedrich Wilhelm Bessel (astronomer and mathematician).
2067 **769** 80pf. grey, black and red 1·30 30

770 Eugenio Pacelli (Pope Pius XII)

1984. 88th German Catholics' Congress, Munich.
2068 **770** 60pf. multicoloured . . . 1·10 25

771 Town Hall

772 Medieval Document and Visual Display Unit

1984. 750th Anniv of Duderstadt Town Hall.
2069 **771** 60pf. multicoloured . . . 90 25

1984. 10th International Archives Congress, Bonn.
2070 **772** 70pf. multicoloured . . . 1·30 30

773 Knoop Lock

1984. Bicent of Schleswig-Holstein Canal.
2071 **773** 80pf. multicoloured . . . 1·30 30

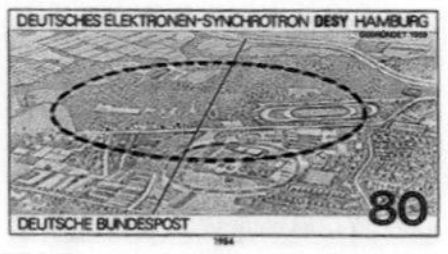

774 Research Centre and Storage Rings

1984. 25th Anniv of German Electron Synchrotron (physics research centre), Hamburg–Bahrenfeld.
2072 **774** 80pf. multicoloured . . . 1·80 30

775 "Aceras anthropophorum"

1984. Humanitarian Relief Funds. Orchids. Multicoloured.
2073 50pf.+20pf. Type **775** . . . 80 65
2074 60pf.+30pf. "Orchis ustulata" 80 65
2075 80pf.+40pf. "Limodorum abortivum" . . . . . . 1·20 1·20
2076 120pf.+60pf. "Dactylorhiza sambucina" . . . . . . 2·40 2·30

776 Taxis Posthouse, Augsburg

1984. Stamp Day.
2077 **776** 80pf. multicoloured . . . 2·00 30

777 Burning Match

1984. Anti-smoking Campaign.
2078 **777** 60pf. multicoloured . . . 1·00 25

778 Male and Female Symbols

1984. Equal Rights for Men and Women.
2079 **778** 80pf. black, mauve & bl 1·40 30

779 Ballot Slip

1984. For Peace and Understanding.
2080 **779** 80pf. grey, black & blue 1·30 30

780 St. Martin giving Cloak to Beggar

1984. Christmas.
2081 **780** 80pf.+40pf. mult . . . . 1·80 1·40

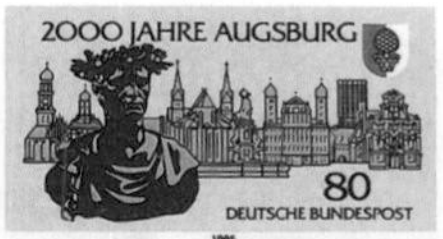

781 Emperor Augustus (bust), Buildings and Arms

1985. 2000th Anniv of Augsburg.
2082 **781** 80pf. multicoloured . . . 1·60 30

782 Spener (engraving by Bartholome Kilian after Johann Georg Wagner)

1985. 350th Birth Anniv of Philipp Jakob Spener (church reformer).
2083 **782** 80pf. black and green . . 1·30 30

783 Grimm Brothers (engraving by Lazarus Sichling)

1985. Birth Bicentenaries of Grimm Brothers (folklorists) and 7th International Union for German Linguistics and Literature Congress, Gottingen.
2084 **783** 80pf. black, grey and red 1·90 30

784 Romano Guardini

1985. Birth Centenary of Romano Guardini (theologian).
2085 **784** 80pf. multicoloured . . . 1·30 30

785 Verden

1985. Millenary of Market and Coinage Rights in Verden.
2086 **785** 60pf. multicoloured . . . 1·80 25

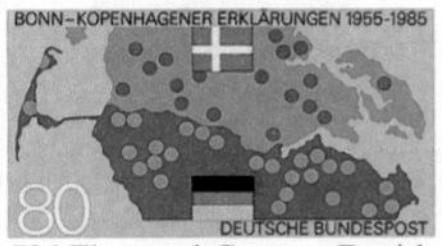

786 Flags and German–Danish Border

1985. 30th Anniv of Bonn–Copenhagen Declarations.
2087 **786** 80pf. multicoloured . . . 1·80 30

787 Bowling

1985. Sport Promotion Fund. Multicoloured.
2088 80pf.+40pf. Type **787** (cent. of German Nine-pin Bowling Association) . . 1·60 1·40
2089 120pf.+60pf. Kayak (world rapid-river and slalom canoeing championships) 2·00 2·00

788 Kisch

789 "Hebel and the Margravine"

1985. Birth Centenary of Egon Erwin Kisch (journalist).
2090 **788** 60pf. multicoloured . . . 1·10 25

1985. 225th Birth Anniv of Johann Peter Hebel (poet).
2091 **789** 80pf. multicoloured . . . 1·30 30

790 Draisienne Bicycle, 1817

791 Handel

1985. Youth Welfare International Youth Year. Cycles. Multicoloured.
2092 50pf.+20pf. Type **790** . . . 90 80
2093 60pf.+30pf. NSU Germania "ordinary", 1866 . . . 1·10 1·00
2094 80pf.+40pf. Cross-frame low bicycle, 1887 . . . . . . 1·40 1·30
2095 120pf.+60pf. Adler tricycle, 1888 . . . . 3·00 2·50

1985. Europa. Composers' 300th Birth Anniversaries. Multicoloured.
2096 60pf. Type **791** . . . . . . 2·00 35
2097 80pf. Bach . . . . 2·20 35

792 Saint George's Cathedral

793 Capital (presbytery, "Wies" Church)

1985. 750th Anniv of Limburg Cathedral.
2098 **792** 60pf. multicoloured . . . 1·20 30

1985. 300th Birth Anniv of Dominikus Zimmermann (architect).
2099 **793** 70pf. multicoloured . . . 1·30 30

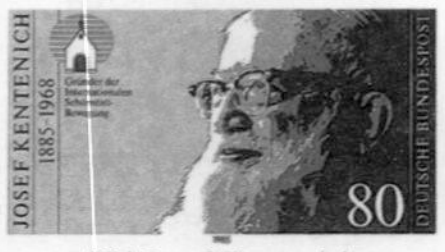

794 Josef Kentenich

1985. Birth Centenary of Father Josef Kentenich (founder of International Schonstatt (Catholic laymen's) Movement).
2100 **794** 80pf. multicoloured . . . 1·30 30

795 Clock and Forest

1985. Save the Forests.
2101 **795** 80pf. multicoloured . . . 1·80 30

796 Tug of War and Scouting Emblem

1985. 30th World Scouts Conference, Munich.
2102 **796** 60pf. multicoloured . . . 90 30

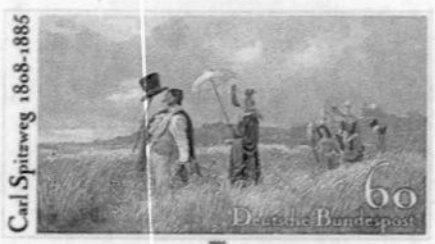

797 "Sunday Walk"

1985. Death Cent of Carl Spitzweg (artist).
2103 **797** 60pf. multicoloured . . . 1·60 30

798 Horses and Postilion

1985. "Mophila 1985" Stamp Exhibition, Hamburg. Multicoloured.
2104 60pf.+20pf. Type **798** . . . 2·20 2·00
2105 80pf.+20pf. Mail coach . . 2·20 2·00
Nos. 2104/5 were printed se-tenant, forming a composite design.

799 Stock Exchange

1985. 400th Anniv of Frankfurt Stock Exchange.
2106 **799** 80pf. black, red and grey 1·50 30

800 Flowers and Butterfly

1985. Humanitarian Relief Funds. Designs depict motifs from borders of medieval prayer book. Multicoloured.
2107 50pf.+20pf. Type **800** . . . 70 65
2108 60pf.+30pf. Flowers, bird and butterfly . . . . . . 1·00 90
2109 80pf.+40pf. Flowers, berries and snail . . . . 1·30 1·10
2110 120pf.+60pf. Flowers, snail and butterfly . . . . . . 2·20 2·00

801 Fritz Reuter

1985. 175th Death Anniv of Fritz Reuter (writer).
2111 **801** 80pf. black, grey and blue . . . . 1·90 30

802 "Inauguration of First German Railway" (Heim)

1985. 150th Anniv of German Railways and Birth Bicent. of Johannes Scharrer (joint founder).
2112 **802** 80pf. multicoloured . . . 1·90 30

803 Carpentry Joint in National Colours

805 "Nativity" (detail, High Altar, Freiburg)

804 Iron Cross and National Colours

1985. 40th Anniv of Integration of Refugees.
2113 **803** 80pf. multicoloured . . . 2·00 30

1985. 30th Anniv of Federal Armed Forces.
2114 **804** 80pf. red, black & yellow 2·40 30

1985. Christmas. 500th Birth Anniversary of Hans Baldung Grien (artist).
2115 **805** 80pf.+40pf. mult . . . . 1·60 1·30

806 Early and Modern Cars

1986. Centenary of Motor Car.
2116 **806** 80pf. multicoloured . . . 1·80 30

807 Town Buildings

1986. 1250th Anniv of Bad Hersfeld.
2117 **807** 60pf. multicoloured . . . 1·20 30

808 "Self-portrait"

1986. Birth Centenary of Oskar Kokoschka (artist and writer).
2118 **808** 80pf. black, grey and red 1·20 30

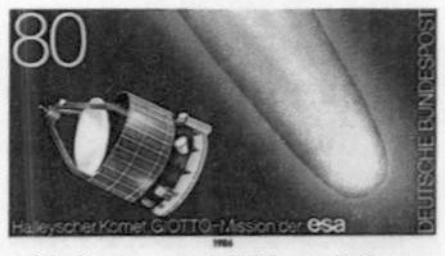

809 Comet and "Giotto" Space Probe

1986. Appearance of Halley's Comet.
2119 **809** 80pf. multicoloured . . . 1·80 30

810 Running

1986. Sport Promotion Fund. Multicoloured.
2120 80pf.+40pf. Type **810** (European Athletics Championships, Stuttgart) 1·80 1·40
2121 120pf.+55pf. Bobsleigh (World Championships, Konigsee) . . . . 2·75 2·30

811 Optician

1986. Youth Welfare. Trades (1st series). Multicoloured.
2122 50pf.+25pf. Type **811** . . . 1·10 95
2123 60pf.+30pf. Bricklayer . . . 1·20 1·10
2124 70pf.+35pf. Hairdresser . . 1·40 7·25
2125 80pf.+40pf. Baker . . . . . 2·20 1·80
See also Nos. 2179/82.

812 Walsrode Monastery

1986. Millenary of Walsrode.
2126 **812** 60pf. multicoloured . . . 1·20 30

813 Ludwig and Neuschwanstein Castle

1986. Death Centenary of King Ludwig II of Bavaria.
2127 **813** 60pf. multicoloured . . . 2·10 30

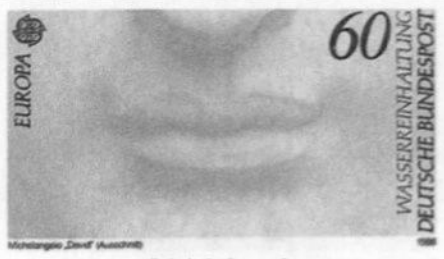

814 Mouth

1986. Europa. Details of "David" (sculpture) by Michelangelo. Multicoloured.
2128 60pf. Type **814** . . . . . . 1·40 30
2129 80pf. Nose . . . . 1·60 30

815 Karl Barth

817 Weber and Score of "Gloria"

816 Ribbons

1986. Birth Centenary of Karl Barth (theologian).
2130 **815** 80pf. black, red & purple 1·50 30

1986. Union of German Catholic Students' Societies 100th Assembly, Frankfurt am Main.
2131 **816** 80pf. multicoloured . . . 1·50 30

1986. Birth Bicentenary of Carl Maria von Weber (composer).
2132 **817** 80pf. brown, black & red 2·10 30

818 "TV-Sat" and Earth

1986. Launch of German "TV-Sat" and French "TDF-1" Broadcasting Satellites.
2133 **818** 80pf. multicoloured . . . 2·20 30

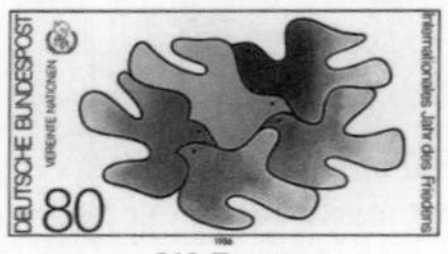

819 Doves

1986. International Peace Year.
2134 **819** 80pf. multicoloured . . . 1·80 30

820 Liszt

1986. Death Centenary of Franz Liszt (composer).
2135 **820** 80pf. blue and orange . . 1·60 30

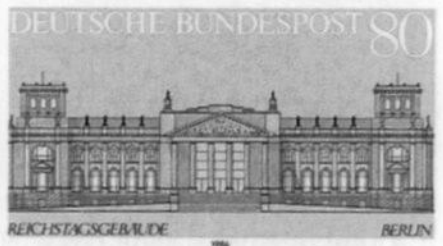

821 Reichstag, Berlin

1986. Important Buildings in West German History. Sheet 100 × 130 mm containing T **821** and similar horiz designs. Multicoloured.
MS2136 80pf. Type **821**; 80pf. Koenig Museum, Bonn (venue of 1948–49 Parliamentary Council); 80pf. Bundeshaus, Bonn (parliamentary building) . . . 3·75 3·75

822 Pollution Damage of Stained Glass Window

1986. Protection of Monuments.
2137 **822** 80pf. multicoloured . . . 1·90 30

823 Frederick the Great (after Anton Graff)

824 Congress Card

1986. Death Bicentenary of Frederick the Great.
2138 **823** 80pf. multicoloured . . . 2·40 30

1986. Centenary of First German Skat Congress and 24th Congress, Cologne.
2139 **824** 80pf. multicoloured . . . 1·40 30

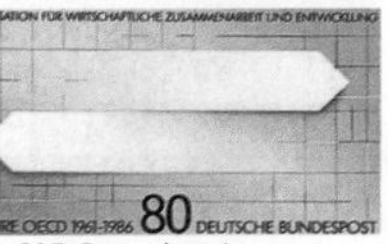

825 Opposing Arrows

1986. 25th Anniv of Organization for Economic Co-operation and Development.
2140 **825** 80pf. multicoloured . . . 1·60 30

826 Old University

1986. 600th Anniv of Heidelberg University.
2141 **826** 80pf. multicoloured . . . 1·70 30

827 Fan of Stamps behind Stagecoach

1986. 50th Anniv of Stamp Day.
2142 **827** 80pf. multicoloured . . . 1·60 30

828 Ornamental Flask, 300 A.D.

829 "Dance in Silence" from "Autumnal Dances"

1986. Humanitarian Relief Funds. Glassware. Multicoloured.
2143 50pf.+25pf. Type **828** . . . 80 75
2144 60pf.+30pf. Goblet with decorated stem, 1650 . . 1·10 95
2145 70pf.+35pf. Imperial Eagle tankard, 1662 . . . . . . 1·20 1·20
2146 80pf.+40pf. Engraved goblet, 1720 . . . . . . 1·40 1·30

1986. Birth Centenary of Mary Wigman (dancer).
2147 **829** 70pf. multicoloured . . . 1·10 30

830 Cross over Map

1986. 25th Anniv of Adveniat (Advent collection for Latin America).
2148 **830** 80pf. green, blue & blk 1·20 40

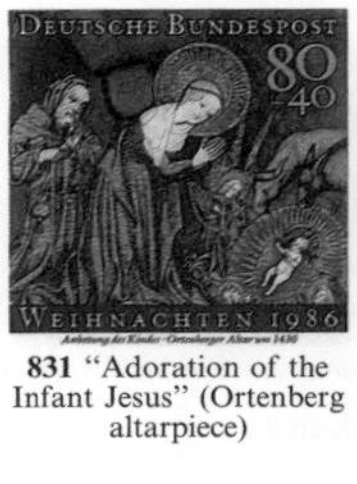

831 "Adoration of the Infant Jesus" (Ortenberg altarpiece)

832 Christine Teusch (politician)

1986. Christmas.
2149 **831** 80pf.+40pf. mult . . . . 1·60 1·40

1986. Famous German Women. Inscr "Deutsche Bundespost".
2150 – 5pf. brown and grey . . 20 15
2151 – 10pf. brown and violet 25 15
2152 – 20pf. blue and red . . . 20 15
2152a – 30pf. bistre and purple 45 25
2153 – 40pf. red and blue . . . 65 20
2154 **832** 50pf. green and brown 90 20
2155 – 60pf. lilac and green . . 90 20
2155a – 70pf. green and red . . 1·40 60
2156 – 80pf. brown and green 1·10 20
2156a – 80pf. brown and blue 70 40
2157 – 100pf. grey and red . . 1·30 20
2157a – 100pf. bistre and lilac 1·10 40
2158 – 120pf. green and brown 1·60 1·00
2159 – 130pf. violet and blue 2·50 55
2160 – 140pf. ochre and blue 3·00 1·10
2161 – 150pf. blue and red . . 3·50 1·40
2162 – 170pf. purple and green 2·20 65
2163 – 180pf. purple and blue 2·20 1·10
2164 – 200pf. red and brown 1·80 70
2165 – 240pf. brown and green 3·00 1·20
2166 – 250pf. blue and mauve 4·00 1·50
2167 – 300pf. green and purple 2·20 1·10
2168 – 350pf. brown and black 4·50 1·90
2168a – 400pf. black and red . . 5·25 1·90
2168b – 450pf. ultramarine & bl 5·25 2·10
2169 – 500pf. red and green . . 6·25 2·00

DESIGNS: 5pf. Emma Ihrer (politician and trade unionist); 10pf. Paula Modersohn-Becker (painter); 20pf. Cilly Aussem (tennis player); 30pf. Kathe Kollwitz (artist); 40pf. Maria Sibylla Merian (artist and naturalist); 60pf. Dorothea Erxleben (first German woman Doctor of Medicine); 70pf. Elisabet Boehm (founder of Agricultural Association of Housewives); 80pf. (2156), Clara Schumann (pianist and composer); 80pf. (2156a), Rahel Varnhagen von Ense (humanist) (after Wilhelm Hensel); 100pf. (2157), Therese Giehse (actress); 100pf. (2157a), Luise Henriette of Orange (mother of King Friedrich I of Prussia) (after Gerhard von Honthorst); 120pf. Elisabeth Selbert (politician); 130pf. Lise Meitner (physicist); 140pf. Cecile Vogt (medical researcher); 150pf. Sophie Scholl (resistance member); 170pf. Hannah Arendt (sociologist); 180pf. Lotte Lehmann (opera singer); 200pf. Bertha von Suttner (novelist and pacifist); 240pf. Mathilda Franziska Anneke (women's rights activist); 250pf. Queen Louise of Prussia; 300pf. Fanny Hensel (composer) (after Eduard Magnus); 350pf. Hedwig Dransfeld (politician); 400pf. Charlotte von Stein (friend of Goethe); 450pf. Hedwig Courths-Mahler (novelist); 500pf. Alice Salomon (women's rights activist).

For similar designs inscribed "Deutschland", see Nos. 2785/95.

833 Berlin Landmarks

1987. 750th Anniv of Berlin.
2170 **833** 80pf. multicoloured . . . 2·10 50

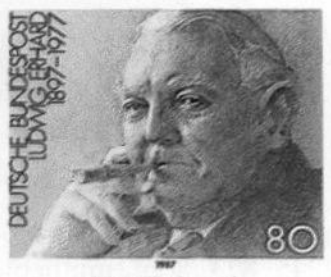

834 Staircase, Residenz Palace, Wurzburg

835 Erhard

1987. 300th Birth Anniv of Balthasar Neumann (architect).
2171 **834** 80pf. grey, black and red 1·60 30

1987. 90th Birth Anniv of Ludwig Erhard (former Chancellor).
2172 **835** 80pf. multicoloured . . . 2·00 30

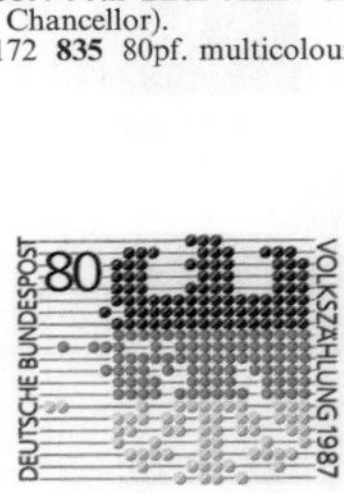

836 Abacus Beads forming Eagle

838 Chief Winnetou (from book cover)

837 Clemenswerth Castle

1987. Census.
2173 **836** 80pf. multicoloured . . . 1·80 30

1987. 250th Anniv of Clemenswerth Castle.
2174 **837** 60pf. multicoloured . . . 1·30 30

1987. 75th Death Anniv of Karl May (writer).
2175 **838** 80pf. multicoloured . . . 1·30 30

839 Solar Spectrum

1987. Birth Bicentenary of Joseph von Fraunhofer (optician and physicist).
2176 **839** 80pf. multicoloured . . . 1·30 30

840 World Sailing Championships, Kiel

1987. Sport Promotion Fund. Multicoloured.
2177 80pf.+40pf. Type **840** . . . 1·60 1·40
2178 120pf.+55pf. World Nordic Skiing Championships, Oberstdorf . . . . 2·00 2·00

1987. Youth Welfare. Trades (2nd series). As T **811**. Multicoloured.
2179 50pf.+25pf. Plumber . . . . 1·20 1·10
2180 60pf.+30pf. Dental technician . . . . 1·40 1·30
2181 70pf.+35pf. Butcher . . . . 1·60 1·50
2182 80pf.+40pf. Bookbinder . . 2·30 2·20

841 Clefs, Notes and Leaves

1987. 125th Anniv of German Choir Association.
2183 **841** 80pf. multicoloured . . . 1·40 30

842 Pope's Arms, Madonna and Child and Kevelaer

1987. Visit of Pope John Paul II to Kevelaer (venue for 17th Marian and 10th Mariological Congresses).
2184 **842** 80pf. multicoloured . . . 1·60 30

843 Dulmen's Wild Horses

1987. European Environment Year.
2185 **843** 60pf. multicoloured . . . 1·80 30

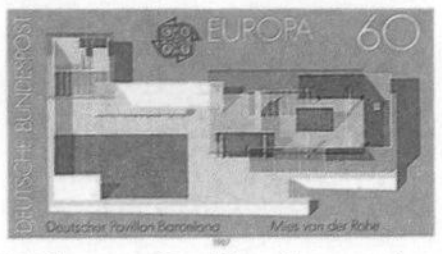

844 German Pavilion, International Exhibition, Barcelona, 1929 (Ludwig Mies van der Rohe)

1987. Europa. Architecture. Multicoloured.
2186 60pf. Type **844** . . . . . . 1·30 35
2187 80pf. Kohlbrand Bridge, Hamburg (Thyssen Engineering) . . . . . . 1·80 35

845 Emblem and Globe

1987. Rotary International Convention, Munich.
2188 **845** 70pf. ultram, yell & bl 1·40 35

846 "Without Title (With an Early Portrait)"

1987. Birth Centenary of Kurt Schwitters (artist and writer).
2189 **846** 80pf. multicoloured . . . 1·20 35

847 Organ Pipes and Signature

848 Bengal

1987. 350th Birth Anniv of Dietrich Buxtehude (composer).
2190 **847** 80pf. black, stone and red . . . . 1·20 35

1987. 300th Birth Anniv of Johann Albrecht Bengel (theologian).
2191 **848** 80pf. brown, ochre & blk 1·20 35

849 Wilhelm Kaisen

1987. Birth Centenary of Wilhelm Kaisen (Senate president and Mayor of Bremen).
2192 **849** 80pf. multicoloured . . . 1·30 35

850 Charlemagne, Bishop Willehad, Bremen Cathedral and City Arms (after mural)

1987. 1200th Anniv of Bremen Bishopric.
2193 **850** 80pf. multicoloured . . . 1·20 35

851 Target, Crossed Rifles and Wreath

1987. 7th European Riflemen's Festival, Lippstadt.
2194 **851** 80pf. multicoloured . . . 1·30 35

852 4th-century Roman Bracelet

1987. Humanitarian Relief Funds. Precious Metal Work. Multicoloured.
2195 50pf.+25pf. Type **852** . . . 1·10 90
2196 60pf.+30pf. 6th-century East Gothic buckle . . . . . 1·20 1·10
2197 70pf.+35pf. 7th-century Merovingian disc fibula 1·30 1·20
2198 80pf.+40pf. 8th-century reliquary . . . . 1·80 1·60

853 Loading and Unloading Mail Train, 1897

854 Corner Tower, Celle Castle

1987. Stamp Day.
2199 **853** 80pf. multicoloured . . . 1·30 65

1987. Tourist Sights. Inscr "DEUTSCHE BUNDESPOST".

2200	–	5pf. blue and grey . . .	65	75
2201	–	10pf. blue and indigo	25	15
2202	–	20pf. pink and blue . .	20	20
2203	**854**	30pf. brown and green	55	30
2204	–	33pf. green and red . .	45	20
2205	–	38pf. grey and blue . .	60	25
2206	–	40pf. brown, red & blue	45	25
2206a	–	41pf. grey and yellow	55	25
2207	–	45pf. pink and blue . .	55	50
2208	–	50pf. brown and blue	55	30
2209	–	60pf. green and black	90	25
2210	–	70pf. pink and blue . .	90	35
2210a	–	70pf. brown and blue	80	45
2211	–	80pf. grey and green . .	90	25
2212	–	90pf. bistre and yellow	1·60	90
2213	–	100pf. green and orange	1·10	20
2214	–	120pf. green and red . .	1·80	80
2215	–	140pf. bistre and yellow	1·90	75
2216	–	170pf. grey and yellow	2·10	90
2216a	–	200pf. blue and brown	1·90	65
2217	–	280pf. grey and blue . .	4·50	1·80
2218	–	300pf. pink and brown	3·00	45
2219	–	350pf. grey and blue . .	4·00	55
2220	–	400pf. red and brown	4·00	40
2220a	–	450pf. blue and brown	4·75	55
2220b	–	500pf. stone and purple	4·75	2·20
2220c	–	550pf. brown and blue	5·00	2·75
2220d	–	700pf. green and yellow	6·75	1·80

DESIGNS: 5pf. Brunswick Lion; 10pf. Frankfurt airport; 20, 70 (2210) pf. Head of Nefertiti, Berlin Museum; 33, 120pf. Schleswig Cathedral; 38, 280pf. Statue of Roland, Bremen; 40pf. Chile House, Hamburg; 41, 170pf. Russian Church, Wiesbaden; 45pf. Rastatt Castle; 50pf. Freiburg Cathedral; 60pf. "Bavaria" (bronze statue), Munich; 70pf. (2210a) Heligoland; 80pf. Zollern II Dortmund Mine Industrial Museum, Westphalia; 90, 140pf. Bronze flagon, Reinheim; 100pf. Pilgrimage Chapel, Altotting; 200pf. Magdeburg Cathedral; 300pf. Hambach Castle; 350pf. Externsteine (rock formation), Horn-Bad Meinberg; 400pf. Dresden Opera House; 450pf. New Gate, Neubrandenburg; 500pf. Cottbus State Theatre; 550pf. Suhl-Heinrichs Town Hall, Thuringia; 700pf. National Theatre, Berlin.

The 10, 60, 80 and 100pf. also exist imperforate and self-adhesive from booklets.

For similar designs inscribed "DEUTSCHLAND", see Nos. 2654/66.

855 Gluck and Score of "Armide"

1987. Death Bicentenary of Christoph Willibald Gluck (composer).
2221 **855** 60pf. black, grey and red 95 25

856 Poster by Emil Orlik for "The Weavers"

1987. 125th Birth Anniv of Gerhart Hauptmann (playwright).
2222 **856** 80pf. lt red, black & red 1·40 35

857 Paddy Field

1987. 25th Anniv of German Famine Aid.
2223 **857** 80pf. multicoloured . . . 1·40 35

858 "Birth of Christ" (13th-century Book of Psalms)

1987. Christmas.
2224 **858** 80pf.+40pf. mult . . . . 1·30 1·30

859 Jester

860 Kaiser

1988. 150th Anniv of Mainz Carnival.
2225 **859** 60pf. multicoloured . . . 95 35

1988. Birth Centenary of Jakob Kaiser (trade unionist and politician).
2226 **860** 80pf. black and grey . . 95 35

861 Stein and Mayer

1988. Beatification of Edith Stein and Father Rupert Mayer.
2227 **861** 80pf. multicoloured . . . 1·30 35

862 Dr Konrad Adenauer (West German Chancellor) and Charles de Gaulle (French President)

1988. 25th Anniv of Franco-German Co-operation Treaty.
2228 **862** 80pf. purple and black 1·60 55

863 "Solitude of the Green Woods" (woodcut of poem, Ludwig Richter)

865 Schopenhauer

864 Raiffeisen and Ploughed Field

1988. Birth Bicentenary of Joseph von Eichendorff (writer).
2229 **863** 60pf. multicoloured . . . 1·20 35

1988. Death Centenary of Friedrich Wilhelm Raiffeisen (philanthropist and agricultural co-operative founder).
2230 **864** 80pf. green and black . . 1·90 35

1988. Birth Bicentenary of Arthur Schopenhauer (philosopher).
2231 **865** 80pf. brown and black 1·50 35

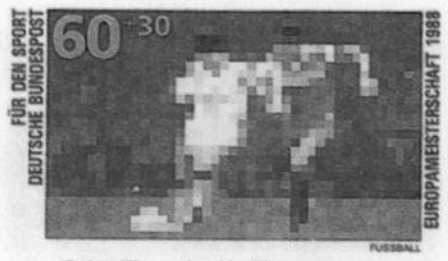

866 Football (European Championship)

1988. Sport Promotion Fund. Multicoloured.

2232	60pf.+30pf. Type **866** . . .	95	90
2233	80pf.+40pf. Tennis (Olympic Games)	1·40	1·30
2234	120pf.+55pf. Diving (Olympic Games)	2·20	2·00

867 Buddy Holly

1988. Youth Welfare. Pop Music. Mult.

2235	50pf.+25pf. Type **867** . . .	1·20	1·20
2236	60pf.+30pf. Elvis Presley . .	1·90	1·80
2237	70pf.+35pf. Jim Morrison	1·80	1·80
2238	80pf.+40pf. John Lennon	2·75	2·20

868 Hutten (wood engraving from "Conquestiones")

1988. 500th Birth Anniv of Ulrich von Hutten (writer).
2239 **868** 80pf. multicoloured . . . 1·30 55

869 City Buildings and Jan Wellem Monument

1988. 700th Anniv of Dusseldorf.
2240 **869** 60pf. multicoloured . . . 95 35

870 Airbus Industrie A320 and Manufacturing Nations' Flag

1988. Europa. Transport and Communications. Multicoloured.

2241	60pf. Type **870**	1·20	45
2242	80pf. Diagram of Integrated Services Digital Network	1·10	45

871 University Buildings and City Landmarks

872 Monnet

1988. 600th Anniv of Cologne University.
2243 **871** 80pf. multicoloured . . . 1·40 35

1988. Birth Centenary of Jean Monnet (statesman).
2244 **872** 80pf. multicoloured . . . 1·20 35

873 Storm

1988. Death Centenary of Theodor Storm (writer).
2245 **873** 80pf. multicoloured . . . 1·30 35

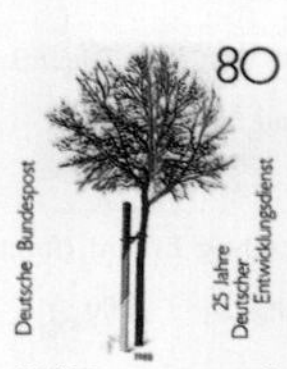

874 Tree supported by Stake in National Colours

876 Gmelin

875 Meersburg

1988. 25th Anniv of German Volunteer Service.
2246 **874** 80pf. multicoloured . . . 1·30 40

1988. Millenary of Meersburg.
2247 **875** 60pf. multicoloured . . . 90 35

1988. Birth Bicentenary of Leopold Gmelin (chemist).
2248 **876** 80pf. multicoloured . . . 1·30 35

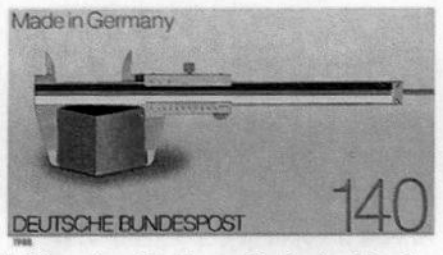

877 Vernier Caliper Rule in National Colours

1988. "Made in Germany".
2249 **877** 140pf. multicoloured . . 2·20 80

878 Bebel

1988. 75th Death Anniv of August Bebel (Social Democratic Labour Party co-founder).
2250 **878** 80pf. mauve, blue & sil 1·40 35

879 Carrier Pigeon

1988. Stamp Day.
2251 **879** 20pf. multicoloured . . . 65 20

880 13th-century Rock Crystal Reliquary

881 Red Cross

1988. Humanitarian Relief Funds. Precious Metal Work. Multicoloured.

2252	50pf.+25pf. Type **880** . . .	60	55
2253	60pf.+30pf. 14th-century bust of Charlemagne . .	1·10	95
2254	70pf.+35pf. 10th-cent. crown of Otto III	1·20	1·10
2255	80pf.+40pf. 17th-cent. jewelled flowers	1·60	1·50

1988. 125th Anniv of Red Cross.
2256 **881** 80pf. red and black . . . 1·30 35

882 Burning Synagogue, Baden-Baden

1988. 50th Anniv of "Kristallnacht" (Nazi pogrom).
2257 **882** 80pf. purple and black 1·10 35

883 Cancelled Postage Stamps

1988. Centenary of Collection of Used Stamps for the Bethel Charity.
2258 **883** 60pf. multicoloured . . . 1·30 35

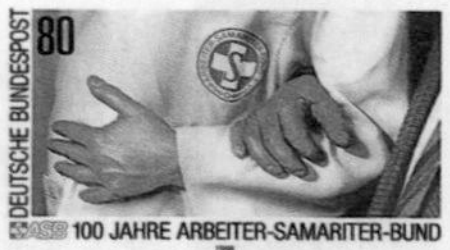

884 Linked Arms

1988. Centenary of Samaritan Workers' (first aid) Association.
2259 **884** 80pf. multicoloured . . . 1·30 35

885 "Adoration of the Magi" (illus from Henry the Lion's Gospel Book)

1988. Christmas.
2260 **885** 80pf.+40pf. mult . . . . 1·40 1·30

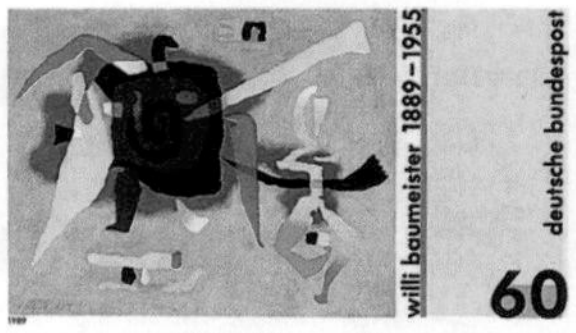

886 "Bluxao I"

1989. Birth Centenary of Willi Baumeister (painter).
2261 **886** 60pf. multicoloured . . . 1·20 35

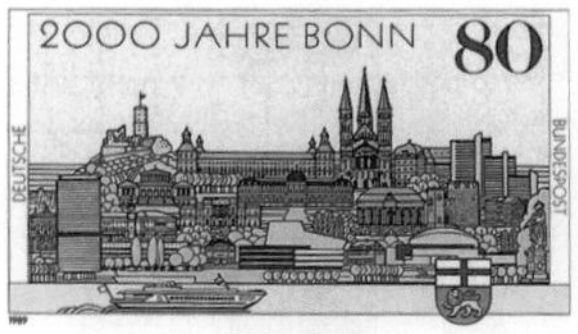

887 Bonn

1988. 2000th Anniv of Bonn.
2262 **887** 80pf. multicoloured . . . 1·80 60

888 Grass growing from Dry, Cracked Earth

1989. 30th Anniversaries of Misereor and Bread for the World (Third World relief organizations).
2263 **888** 80pf. multicoloured . . . 1·30 35

889 "Cats in the Attic" (woodcut)

1989. Birth Cent of Gerhard Marcks (artist).
2264 **889** 60pf. black, stone and red . . . . 1·10 35

890 Table Tennis (World Championships)

1989. Sport Promotion Fund. Multicoloured.
2265 100pf.+50pf. Type **890** . . 2·20 2·00
2266 140pf.+60pf. Gymnastics (World Championships) 3·00 2·00

891 Elephants

1989. Youth Welfare. Circus. Multicoloured.
2267 60pf.+30pf. Type **891** . . . 1·80 1·80
2268 70pf.+30pf. Acrobat on horseback . . . . 2·20 2·20
2269 80pf.+35pf. Clown . . . . 3·00 2·20
2270 100pf.+50pf. Caravans and Big Top . . . . 4·50 3·00

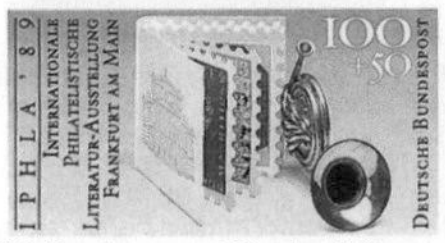

892 Posthorn and Book of Stamps

1989. "IPHLA '89" International Philatelic Literature Exhibition, Frankfurt.
2271 **892** 100pf.+50pf. mult . . . 2·75 2·20

893 European and Members' Flags

1989. 3rd Direct Elections to European Parliament.
2272 **893** 100pf. multicoloured . . 2·20 1·10

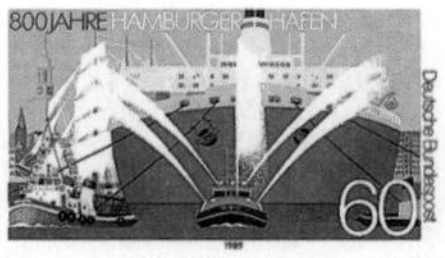

894 Shipping

1989. 800th Anniv of Hamburg Harbour.
2273 **894** 60pf. multicoloured . . . 1·30 35

895 Asam (detail of fresco, Weltenburg Abbey)

1989. 250th Death Anniv of Cosmas Damian Asam (painter and architect).
2274 **895** 60pf. multicoloured . . . 85 35

896 Kites

1989. Europa. Children's Toys. Multicoloured.
2275 60pf. Type **896** . . . . . . 1·10 45
2276 100pf. Puppet show . . . . 1·80 45

897 Emblem, National Colours and Presidents' Signatures

1989. 40th Anniv of German Federal Republic.
2277 **897** 100pf. multicoloured . . 1·80 70

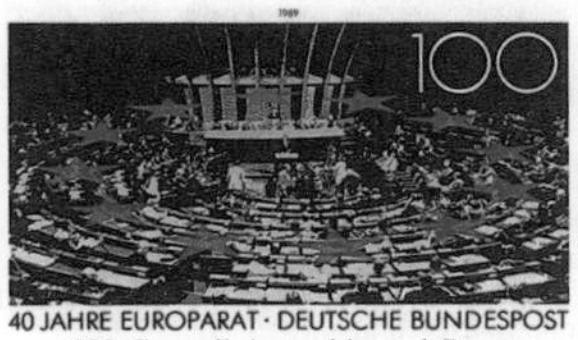

898 Council Assembly and Stars

1989. 40th Anniv of Council of Europe.
2278 **898** 100pf. blue and gold . . 1·60 70

899 Gabelsberger and Shorthand

1989. Birth Bicentenary of Franz Xaver Gabelsberger (shorthand pioneer).
2279 **899** 100pf. multicoloured . . 1·50 55

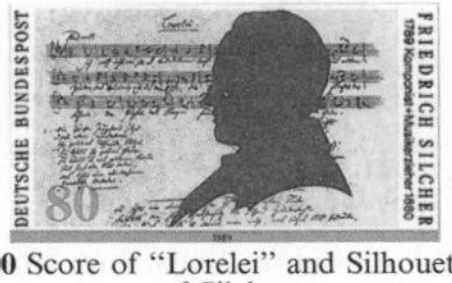

900 Score of "Lorelei" and Silhouette of Silcher

1989. Birth Bicentenary of Friedrich Silcher (composer).
2280 **900** 80pf. multicoloured . . . 1·10 35

901 Saints Kilian, Totnan and Colman (from 12th-century German manuscript)

1989. 1300th Death Anniversaries of Saints Kilian, Colman and Totnan (Irish missionaries to Franconia).
2281 **901** 100pf. multicoloured . . 1·40 55

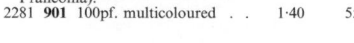

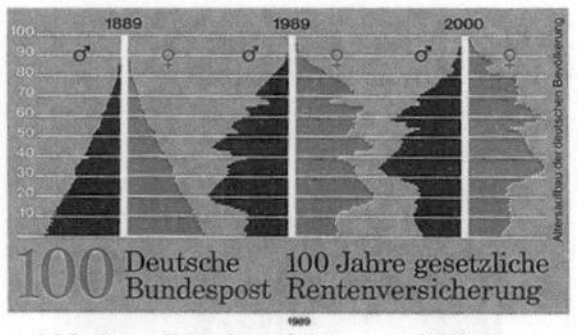

902 Age Graphs of Men and Women

1989. Centenary of National Insurance.
2282 **902** 100p. blue, red & lt blue 1·40 55

903 "Summer Evening" (Heinrich Vogler)

1989. Cent of Worpswede Artists' Village.
2283 **903** 60pf. multicoloured . . . 95 35

904 Schneider

906 Cathedral

905 List (after Kriehuber) and Train

1989. 50th Death Anniv of Reverend Paul Schneider (concentration camp victim).
2284 **904** 100pf. blk, lt grey & grey 1·30 55

1989. Birth Bicentenary of Friedrich List (economist).
2285 **905** 170pf. black and red . . 2·75 90

1989. 750th Anniv of Frankfurt Cathedral.
2286 **906** 60pf. multicoloured . . . 1·30 35

907 Children building House

1989. "Don't Forget the Children".
2287 **907** 100pf. multicoloured . . 1·80 55

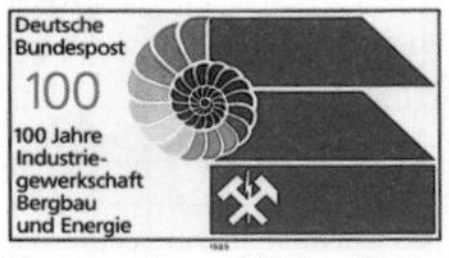

908 Ammonite and Union Emblem

1989. Centenary of Mining and Power Industries Trade Union.
2288 **908** 100pf. multicoloured . . 1·40 55

909 18th-century Mounted Courier, Thurn and Taxis

1989. Humanitarian Relief Funds. Postal Deliveries. Multicoloured.
2289 60pf.+30pf. Type **909** . . . 1·30 1·10
2290 80pf.+35pf. Hamburg postal messenger, 1808 . . . . . 1·80 1·50
2291 100pf.+50pf. Bavarian mail coach, 1900 . . . . . . 2·75 2·75

910 Maier

1989. Birth Centenary of Reinhold Maier (politician).
2292 **910** 100pf. multicoloured . . 1·50 55

911 Organ Pipes

1989. 300th Anniv of Arp Schnitger Organ, St. James's Church, Hamburg.
2293 **911** 60pf. multicoloured . . . 1·30 35

912 Angel

1989. Christmas. 16th-century Carvings by Veit Stoss, St. Lawrence's Church, Nuremberg. Multicoloured.
2294 60pf.+30pf. Type **912** . . . 1·30 1·10
2295 100pf.+50pf. "Nativity" . . 1·80 1·80

913 Speyer

1990. 2000th Anniv of Speyer.
2296 **913** 60pf. multicoloured . . . 1·30 45

914 "Courier" (Albrecht Durer) **915** Vine forming Initial "R"

1990. 500th Anniv of Regular European Postal Services.
2297 **914** 100pf. deep brown, light brown and brown . . 1·90 60

1990. 500 Years of Riesling Grape Cultivation.
2298 **915** 100pf. multicoloured . . 1·30 60

916 Old Lubeck

1990. U.N.E.S.C.O. World Heritage Site, Old Lubeck.
2299 **916** 100pf. multicoloured . . 1·30 55

917 15th-century Seal and Grand Master's Arms

1990. 800th Anniv of Teutonic Order.
2300 **917** 100pf. multicoloured . . 1·50 60

918 Frederick II's Seal and Fair Entrance Hall

1990. 750th Anniv of Granting of Fair Privileges to Frankfurt.
2301 **918** 100pf. multicoloured . . 1·80 60

919 Maze

1990. 25th Anniv of Youth Research Science Competition.
2302 **919** 100pf. multicoloured . . 1·50 60

920 Wildlife

1990. North Sea Protection.
2303 **920** 100pf. multicoloured . . 1·80 55

921 Handball

1990. Sport Promotion Fund. Multicoloured.
2304 100pf.+50pf. Type **921** . . 2·40 2·00
2305 140pf.+60pf. Keep-fit . . 3·25 2·75

922 Widow Bolte

1990. Youth Welfare. 125th Anniv of Max and Moritz (characters from books by Wilhelm Busch). Multicoloured.
2306 60pf.+30pf. Type **922** . . . 90 75
2307 70pf.+30pf. Max asleep . . 1·20 1·10
2308 80pf.+35pf. Moritz watching Max sawing through bridge . . . . 1·80 1·50
2309 100pf.+50pf. Max and Moritz . . . . 2·20 2·00

923 "1.MAI" and Factory Silhouette

1990. Centenary of Labour Day.
2310 **923** 100pf. red and black . . 1·30 60

924 Woman's Face

1990. 75th Anniv of German Association of Housewives.
2311 **924** 100pf. multicoloured . . 1·30 60

925 Collection Box

1990. 125th Anniv of German Lifeboat Institution.
2312 **925** 60pf. multicoloured . . . 1·50 35

926 Thurn and Taxis Palace, Frankfurt

1990. Europa. Post Office Buildings. Mult.
2313 60pf. Type **926** . . . . . . 1·30 60
2314 100pf. Postal Giro Office, Frankfurt . . . . 2·00 60

927 St Philip's Church, Protestant Church Flag and Candle Flames

1990. Centenary of Rummelsberg Diaconal Institution.
2315 **927** 100pf. multicoloured . . 1·30 60

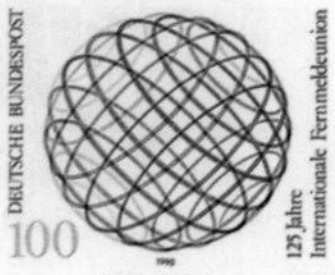

928 Leuschner **929** Globe

1990. Birth Centenary of Wilhelm Leuschner (trade unionist and member of anti-Hitler Resistance).
2316 **928** 100pf. black and lilac . . 1·80 60

1990. 125th Anniv of I.T.U.
2317 **929** 100pf. multicoloured . . 1·30 60

930 National Colours and Students

1990. 175th Anniv of German Students' Fraternity and of their Colours (now national colours).
2318 **930** 100pf. multicoloured . . 2·00 60

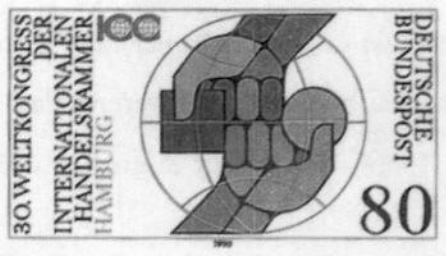

931 Hands exchanging Money and Goods

1990. 30th World Congress of International Chamber of Commerce, Hamburg.
2319 **931** 80pf. multicoloured . . . 1·20 70

932 Closing Sentence of Charter

1990. 40th Anniv of Expelled Germans Charter.
2320 **932** 100pf. multicoloured . . 1·50 60

933 Children of Different Races

1990. 10th International Youth Philatelic Exhibition, Dusseldorf. Sheet 165 × 101 mm.
MS2321 **933** 6 × 100pf.+50pf. multicoloured . . . . 15·00 15·00

934 Claudius **935** Mail Motor Wagon, 1900

1990. 250th Birth Anniv of Matthias Claudius (writer).
2322 **934** 100pf. blue, black and red . . . . 1·40 55

1990. Humanitarian Relief Funds. Posts and Telecommunications. Multicoloured.
2323 60pf.+30pf. Type **935** . . . 1·10 1·10
2324 80pf.+35pf. Telephone exchange, 1890 . . . . . 1·80 1·80
2325 100pf.+50pf. Parcel sorting office, 1900 . . . . 2·00 2·00

936 "German Unity" and National Colours

1990. Reunification of Germany.
2326 **936** 50pf. black, red & yellow 1·10 55
2327 100pf. black, red & yell 1·80 80

937 Schliemann and Lion Gate, Mycenae

1990. Death Centenary of Heinrich Schliemann (archaeologist).
2328 **937** 60pf. multicoloured . . . 1·30 45

938 Penny Black, Bavaria 1k. and West Germany 1989 100pf. Stamps

1990. Stamp Day. 150th Anniv of the Penny Black.
2329 **938** 100pf. multicoloured . . 1·50 55

939 National Colours spanning Breach in Wall **940** Angel with Candles

1990. 1st Anniv of Opening of Berlin Wall.
2330 50pf. Type **939** 90 45
2331 100pf. Brandenburg Gate and crowd . . . . 1·60 60
MS2332 146 × 100 mm. As Nos. 2330/1 . . . . 3·00 3·00

1990. Christmas. Multicoloured.
2333 50pf.+20pf. Type **940** . . . 90 90
2334 60pf.+30pf. Figure of man smoking . . . . 1·10 1·10
2335 70pf.+30pf. "Soldier" nutcrackers . . . . 1·40 1·40
2336 100pf.+50pf. Tinsel angel . . 2·20 2·20

941 Kathe Dorsch in "Mrs Warren's Profession"

1990. Birth Centenary of Kathe Dorsch (actress).
2337 **941** 100pf. violet and red . . 1·40 60

942 View of City

1991. 750th Anniv of Hanover.
2338 **942** 60pf. multicoloured . . . 1·20 55

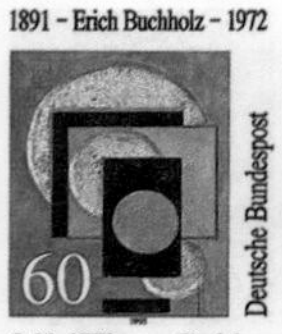

943 "Three Golden Circles with a Full Circle in Blue" (relief in wood) **944** Miniature from 13th-century French Code

1991. Birth Centenary of Erich Buchholz (artist).
2339 **943** 60pf. multicoloured . . . 1·20 55

1991. 750th Anniv of Promulgation of Pharmaceutical Ethics in Germany.
2340 **944** 100pf. multicoloured . . 1·80 75

945 Brandenburg Gate (from "Old Engravings of Berlin")

1991. Bicentenary of Brandenburg Gate.
2341 **945** 100pf. black, red and grey . . . . 1·80 55

946 Eucken **947** Globe and "25" (poster)

1991. Birth Centenary of Walter Eucken (economist).
2342 **946** 100pf. multicoloured . . 1·40 50

1991. 25th International Tourism Fair, Berlin.
2343 **947** 100pf. multicoloured . . 1·40 50

948 Two-man Bobsleigh **949** Weightlifting (World Championships)

1991. World Bobsleigh Championships, Altenberg. Sheet 55 × 80 mm.
MS2344 **948** 100pf. multicoloured 1·80 1·90

1991. Sport Promotion Fund. Multicoloured.
2345 70pf.+30pf. Type **949** . . . 1·30 1·30
2346 100pf.+50pf. Cycling (world championships) . . . . . . 1·80 1·80
2347 140pf.+60pf. Basketball (centenary) . . . . 2·20 2·20
2348 170pf.+80pf. Wrestling (European championships) 2·75 2·75

950 Title Page of "Cautio Criminalis" (tract against witch trials), Langenfeld and Score of "Trutz-Nachtigall"

1991. 400th Birth Anniv of Friedrich Spee von Langenfeld (poet and human rights pioneer).
2349 **950** 100pf. multicoloured . . 1·60 55

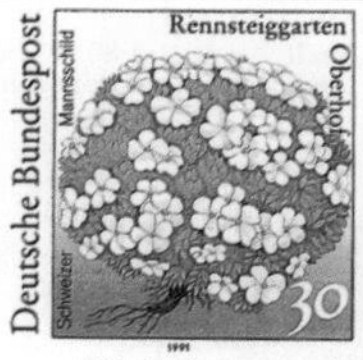

951 Androsace

952 Werth (attr Wenzel Hollar)

1991. Plants in Rennsteiggarten (botanical garden), Oberhof. Multicoloured.
2350 30pf. Type **951** 45 30
2351 50pf. Primula 65 45
2352 80pf. Gentian . . . . . . 1·10 45
2353 100pf. Cranberry . . . . . 1·50 65
2354 350pf. Edelweiss . . . . . 4·75 3·00

1991. 400th Birth Anniv of Jan von Werth (military commander).
2355 **952** 60pf. multicoloured . . . 1·10 55

953 Windthorst

955 Mountain Clouded Yellow

954 Junkers F-13, 1930

1991. Death Centenary of Ludwig Windthorst (politician).
2356 **953** 100pf. multicoloured . . 1·40 50

1991. Historic Mail Aircraft. Multicoloured.
2357 30pf. Type **954** 45 35
2358 50pf. Hans Grade's monoplane, 1909 . . . . 65 35
2359 100pf. Fokker F.III, 1922 1·80 45
2360 165pf. Airship "Graf Zeppelin", 1928 . . . . . 2·75 2·40

1991. Youth Welfare. Endangered Butterflies. Multicoloured.
2361 30pf.+15pf. Type **955** . . . 45 45
2362 50pf.+25pf. Poplar admiral 55 55
2363 60pf.+30pf. Purple emperor 1·10 1·10
2364 70pf.+30pf. Violet copper 1·20 1·20
2365 80pf.+35pf. Swallowtail . . 1·30 1·30
2366 90pf.+45pf. Small apollo . . 1·80 1·80
2367 100pf.+50pf. Moorland clouded yellow . . . . . 2·20 2·20
2368 140pf.+60pf. Large copper 2·75 2·75
See also Nos. 2449/53.

956 Academy Building, 1830

1991. Bicentenary of Choral Academy, Berlin.
2369 **956** 100pf. multicoloured . . 1·50 65

957 Typesetting School, 1875

1991. 125th Anniv of Lette Foundation (institute for professional training of women).
2370 **957** 100pf. multicoloured . . 1·40 50

958 Battle (detail of miniature, Schlackenwerth Codex, 1350)

1991. 750th Anniv of Battle of Legnica.
2371 **958** 100pf. multicoloured . . 1·40 80

959 Arms

1991. 700th Anniv of Granting of Charters to Six Towns of Trier.
2372 **959** 60pf. multicoloured . . . 1·20 55

960 Speeding Train

1991. Inauguration of Inter-City Express (ICE) Railway Service.
2373 **960** 60pf. multicoloured . . . 1·30 55

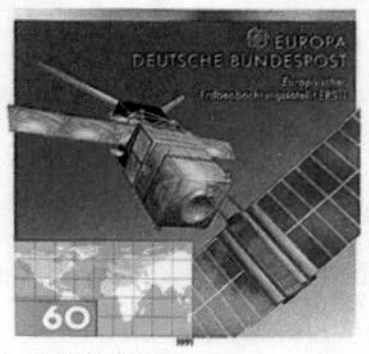

961 "ERS-1" European Remote Sensing Satellite

1991. Europa. Europe in Space. Mult.
2374 60pf. Type **961** . . . . . . 1·50 55
2375 100pf. "Kopernikus" telecommunications satellite . . . . 2·20 55

962 Reger and Organ Pipes

1991. 75th Death Anniv of Max Reger (composer).
2376 **962** 100pf. multicoloured . . 1·60 65

963 Ruffs

1991. Seabirds. Multicoloured.
2390 60pf. Type **963** 90 45
2391 80pf. Little terns . . . . . 1·30 90
2392 100pf. Brent geese . . . . . 1·30 90
2393 140pf. White-tailed sea eagles . . . . 2·20 2·00

964 Wilhelm August Lampadius (gas pioneer)

1991. 18th World Gas Congress, Berlin. Each black and blue.
2394 60pf. Type **964** 85 30
2395 100pf. Gas street lamp, Berlin . . . . 1·20 55

965 Wallot (after Franz Wurbel) and Reichstag Building, Berlin

1991. 150th Birth Anniv of Paul Wallot (architect).
2396 **965** 100pf. multicoloured . . 1·80 50

966 "Libellula depressa"

967 Hand clutching Cloak

1991. Dragonflies. Multicoloured.
2397 50pf. Type **966** 60 35
2398 60pf. Type **966** . . . . . 1·30 90
2399 60pf. "Sympetrum sanguineum" . . . . . . 1·30 90
2400 60pf. "Cordulegaster boltonii" . . . . 1·30 90
2401 60pf. "Aeshna viridis" . . . 1·30 90
2402 70pf. As No. 2399 . . . . . 1·30 90
2403 80pf. As No. 2400 . . . . . 1·30 70
2404 100pf. As No. 2401 . . . . 1·30 80

1991. 40th Anniv of Geneva Convention on Refugees.
2405 **967** 100pf. lilac and black . . 1·50 50

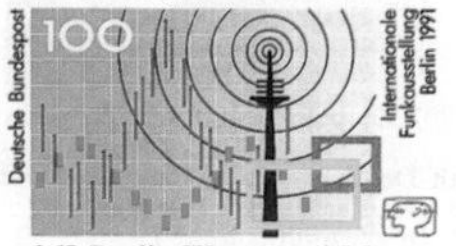

968 Radio Waves and Mast

1991. International Radio Exhibition, Berlin.
2406 **968** 100pf. multicoloured . . 1·50 50

969 Pedestrians and Traffic

1991. Road Safety Campaign.
2407 **969** 100pf. multicoloured . . 1·80 70

970 Lilienthal

1991. Centenary of First Heavier-than-Air Manned Flight by Otto Lilienthal and "Lilienthal '91" European Airmail Exhibition, Dresden. Sheet 57 × 82 mm.
MS2408 **970** 100pf.+50pf. brown, blue and red . . . . 3·50 2·40

971 August Heinrich Hoffmann von Fallersleben (lyricist) and Third Verse

1991. 150th Anniv of "Song of the Germans" (national anthem).
2409 **971** 100pf. red, black & green 1·50 50

972 Thadden-Trieglaff

1991. Birth Cent of Reinold von Thadden-Trieglaff (founder of German Protestant Convention).
2410 **972** 100pf. multicoloured . . 1·30 50

973 Transmission Test between Lauffen am Neckar and Frankfurt am Main

1991. Centenary of Three-phase Energy Transmission.
2411 **973** 170pf. multicoloured . . 2·40 1·30

974 Quill, Pen and Sword

975 Albers in "The Winner"

1991. Birth Bicentenary of Theodor Korner (poet). Sheet 55 × 80 mm containing T **974** and similar vert designs. Multicoloured.
MS2412 60pf. Type **974**; 100pf. Korner . . . . 2·40 2·40

1991. Birth Centenary of Hans Albers (actor).
2413 **975** 100pf. multicoloured . . 2·20 50

976 Harbour

1991. 275th Anniv of Rhine-Ruhr Port, Duisburg.
2414 **976** 100pf. multicoloured . . 1·50 50

977 Bethel Post Office

1991. Humanitarian Relief Funds. Postal Buildings. Multicoloured.
2415 30pf.+15pf. Type **977** . . . 55 55
2416 60pf.+30pf. Budingen post station . . . . 1·10 1·10
2417 70pf.+30pf. Stralsund post office . . . . 1·30 1·30
2418 80pf.+35pf. Lauscha post office . . . . 1·60 1·60
2419 100pf.+50pf. Bonn post office . . . . 2·10 2·10
2420 140pf.+60pf. Weilburg post office . . . . 2·75 2·75

978 Postal Delivery in Spreewald Region

1991. Stamp Day.
2421 **978** 100pf. multicoloured . . 1·40 50

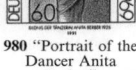

979 "Bird Monument" (detail)

980 "Portrait of the Dancer Anita Berber"

1991. Birth Centenary of Max Ernst (painter).
2422 **979** 100pf. multicoloured . . 1·40 50

1991. Birth Cent of Otto Dix (painter). Mult.
2423 60pf. Type **980** 90 55
2424 100pf. "Self-portrait in Right Profile" . . . . . 1·80 60

981 "The Violinist and the Water Sprite"

1991. Sorbian Legends. Multicoloured.
2425 60pf. Type **981** . . . . . . 1·10 55
2426 100pf. "The Midday Woman and the Woman from Nochten" . . . . . 1·60 60

982 Angel (detail of "The Annunciation")

1991. Christmas. Works by Martin Schongauer. Multicoloured.
2427 60pf.+30pf. Type **982** . . . 1·10 1·10
2428 70pf.+35pf. Virgin Mary (detail of "The Annunciation") . . . . . 1·30 1·30
2429 80pf.+35pf. Angel (detail of "Madonna in a Rose Garden") . . . . . . 2·20 2·20
2430 100pf.+50pf. "Nativity" . . 3·00 3·00

983 Leber **984** Nelly Sachs

1991. Birth Cent of Julius Leber (politician).
2431 **983** 100pf. multicoloured . . 1·40 50

1991. Birth Centenary of Nelly Sachs (writer).
2432 **984** 100pf. dp violet & violet 1·40 55

985 Mozart

1991. Death Bicentenary of Wolfgang Amadeus Mozart (composer). Sheet 82 × 56 mm.
MS2433 **985** 100pf. lilac and brown 2·40 2·40

986 Base of William I Monument and City Silhouette

1992. 2000th Anniv of Koblenz.
2434 **986** 60pf. multicoloured . . . 1·40 55

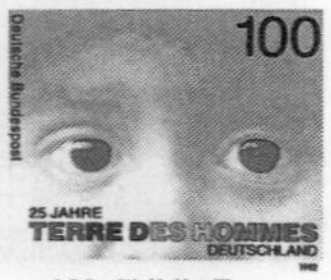

987 Niemoller **988** Child's Eyes

1992. Birth Centenary of Martin Niemoller (theologian).
2435 **987** 100pf. multicoloured . . 1·30 55

1992. 25th Anniv of Terre des Hommes (child welfare organization) in Germany.
2436 **988** 100pf. multicoloured . . 1·60 70

989 Arms of Baden-Wurttemberg

1992. Lander of the Federal Republic.
2437 **989** 100pf. multicoloured . . 1·40 80
See also Nos. 2448, 2465, 2470, 2474, 2479, 2506, 2526, 2527, 2534, 2539, 2556, 2567, 2580, 2584 and 2597.

990 Fencing **991** Honegger and Score of Ballet "Semiramis"

1992. Sport Promotion Fund. Olympic Games, Albertville and Barcelona. Multicoloured.
2438 60pf.+30pf. Type **990** . . . 90 90
2439 80pf.+40pf. Rowing eight 1·10 1·10
2440 100pf.+50pf. Dressage . . . 2·20 2·20
2441 170pf.+80pf. Skiing (slalom) 3·50 3·50

1992. Birth Centenary of Arthur Honegger (composer).
2442 **991** 100pf. black and brown 1·50 70

992 Zeppelin and "Graf Zeppelin"

1992. 75th Death Anniv of Ferdinand von Zeppelin (airship manufacturer).
2443 **992** 165pf. multicoloured . . 2·30 1·10

993 Kiel City and Harbour

1992. 750th Anniv of Kiel.
2444 **993** 60pf. multicoloured . . . 95 50

994 Andreas Marggraf, Beet, Franz Achard and Carl Scheibler

1992. 125th Anniv of Berlin Sugar Institute.
2445 **994** 100pf. multicoloured . . 1·30 60
The stamp depicts the discoverer of beet sugar, the founder of the beet sugar industry and the founder of the Institute respectively.

995 Horses and Renz **996** Adenauer

1992. Death Centenary of Ernst Jakob Renz (circus director).
2446 **995** 100pf. multicoloured . . 1·30 55

1992. 25th Death Anniv of Konrad Adenauer (Chancellor, 1949–63).
2447 **996** 100pf. brn & cinnamon 2·00 55

1992. Lander of the Federal Republic. As T **989**. Multicoloured.
2448 100pf. Bavaria . . . . . . 1·40 80

1992. Youth Welfare. Endangered Moths. As T **955**. Multicoloured.
2449 60pf.+30pf. Purple tiger moth . . . . 1·40 1·40
2450 70pf.+30pf. Hawk moth . . 1·60 1·60
2451 80pf.+40pf. "Noctuidae sp." 2·00 2·00
2452 100pf.+50pf. Tiger moth . . 2·20 2·20
2453 170pf.+80pf. "Arichanna melanaria" . . . . 2·75 2·75

997 Schall

1992. 400th Birth Anniv of Adam Schall (missionary astronomer).
2454 **997** 140pf. black, yellow & bl 2·20 90

998 Cathedral and St. Severus's Church **999** Woodcut from 1493 Edition of Columbus's Letters

1992. 1250th Anniv of Erfurt.
2455 **998** 60pf. multicoloured . . . 95 50

1992. Europa. 500th Anniv of Discovery of America by Columbus. Multicoloured.
2456 60pf. Type **999** 95 55
2457 100pf. "Rene de Laudonniere and Chief Athore" (Jacques le Moyne de Morgues, 1564) 1·70 60

1000 "Consecration of St. Ludgerus" (from "Vita Liudgeri" by Altfridus) **1001** Arithmetic Sum

1992. 1250th Birth Anniv of St. Ludgerus (first Bishop of Munster).
2458 **1000** 100pf. multicoloured . . 1·50 60

1992. 500th Birth Anniv of Adam Riese (mathematician).
2459 **1001** 100pf. multicoloured . . 1·50 50

1002 Order of Merit

1992. 150th Anniv of Civil Class of Order of Merit (for scientific or artistic achievement).
2460 **1002** 100pf. multicoloured . . 1·50 50

1003 "Landscape with Horse" (Franz Marc)

1992. 20th-century German Paintings (1st series). Multicoloured.
2461 60pf. Type **1003** 90 60
2462 100pf. "Fashion Shop" (August Macke) . . . . . 1·30 60
2463 170pf. "Murnau with Rainbow" (Wassily Kandinsky) . . . . 2·20 1·30
See also Nos. 2507/9, 2590/2, 2615/17 and 2704/6.

1004 Lichtenberg

1992. 250th Birth Anniv of Georg Christoph Lichtenberg (physicist and essayist).
2464 **1004** 100pf. multicoloured . . 1·60 70

1992. Lander of the Federal Republic. As T **989**. Multicoloured.
2465 100pf. Berlin . . . . 1·40 80

1005 Rainforest

1992. "Save the Tropical Rain Forest".
2466 **1005** 100pf.+50pf. mult . . . . 1·80 1·80
The premium was for the benefit of environmental projects.

1006 Garden

1992. Leipzig Botanical Garden.
2467 **1006** 60pf. multicoloured . . 95 50

1007 Stylized House and Globe

1992. 17th International Home Economics Congress, Hanover.
2468 **1007** 100pf. multicoloured . . 1·50 70

1008 Family **1009** "Assumption of the Virgin Mary" (Rohr Monastery Church)

1992. Family Life.
2469 **1008** 100pf. multicoloured . . 1·80 50

1992. Lander of the Federal Republic. As T **989**. Multicoloured.
2470 100pf. Brandenburg . . . . 1·40 80

1992. 300th Birth Anniv of Egid Quirin Asam (sculptor).
2471 **1009** 60pf. multicoloured . . 95 50

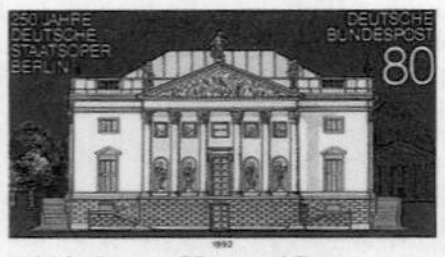

1010 Opera House (Georg von Knobelsdorff)

1992. 250th Anniv of German State Opera House, Berlin.
2472 **1010** 80pf. multicoloured . . 1·30 55

1011 Masked Actors

1992. Centenary of German Amateur Theatres Federation.
2473 **1011** 100pf. multicoloured . . 1·50 55

1992. Lander of the Federal Republic. As T **989**. Multicoloured.
2474 100pf. Bremen . . . . . . 1·40 80

1012 Globe

1992. 500th Anniv of Martin Behaim's Terrestrial Globe.
2475 **1012** 60pf. multicoloured . . 1·30 55

1013 1890 Pendant and 1990 Clock

1014 Bergengruen (after Hanni Fries)

1992. 225th Anniv of Jewellery and Watch-making in Pforzheim.
2476 **1013** 100pf. multicoloured . . 1·50 50

1992. Birth Centenary of Werner Bergengruen (writer).
2477 **1014** 100pf. grey, blue & blk 1·50 50

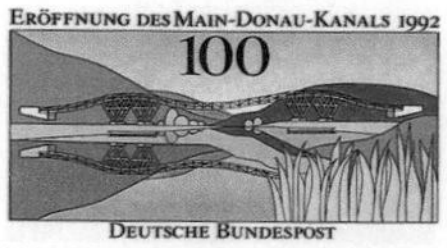

1015 Neue Holzbrucke Bridge, nr Essing

1992. Inauguration of Main–Donau Canal.
2478 **1015** 100pf. multicoloured . . 1·50 50

1992. Lander of the Federal Republic. As T **989**. Multicoloured.
2479 100pf. Hamburg . . . . . 1·40 80

1016 Turret Clock, 1400

1992. Humanitarian Relief Funds. Clocks. Multicoloured.
2480 60pf.+30pf. Type **1016** . . 1·10 1·10
2481 70pf.+30pf. Astronomical mantel clock, 1738 . . . 1·30 1·30
2482 80pf.+40pf. Flute clock, 1790 . . . . 1·50 1·50
2483 100pf.+50pf. Figurine clock, 1580 . . . . 1·90 1·90
2484 170pf.+80pf. Table clock, 1550 . . . . 2·75 2·75

1017 Distler and Score of "We Praise Our Lord Jesus Christ"

1018 Balloon Post

1992. 50th Death Anniv of Hugo Distler (composer).
2485 **1017** 100pf. black and violet 1·40 55

1992. Stamp Day.
2486 **1018** 100pf. multicoloured . . 1·40 55

1019 Otto Engine, 1892, Cogwheel and Laser Beam

1992. Centenary of German Plant and Machine Builders Association.
2487 **1019** 170pf. multicoloured . . 2·10 90

1020 "Adoration of the Magi"

1992. Christmas. Carvings by Franz Maidburg, St. Anne's Church, Annaberg-Buchholz. Mult.
2488 60pf.+30pf. Type **1020** . . 1·10 1·10
2489 100pf.+50pf. "Birth of Christ" . . . . 1·80 1·80

1021 Blucher (after Simon Meister)

1992. 250th Birth Anniv of Field Marshal Gebhard Leberecht von Blucher.
2490 **1021** 100pf. multicoloured . . 1·50 55

1022 Werner von Siemens

1023 Klepper

1992. Death Centenary of Werner von Siemens (electrical engineer).
2491 **1022** 100pf. brown & dp brn 1·30 55

1992. 50th Death Anniv of Jochen Klepper (writer).
2492 **1023** 100pf. multicoloured . . 1·30 55

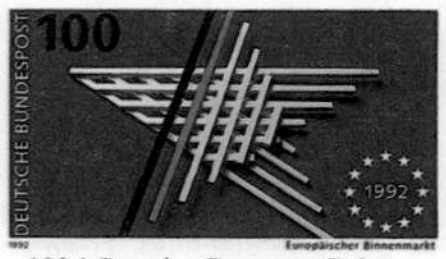

1024 Star in German Colours

1992. European Single Market.
2493 **1024** 100pf. multicoloured . . 1·40 55

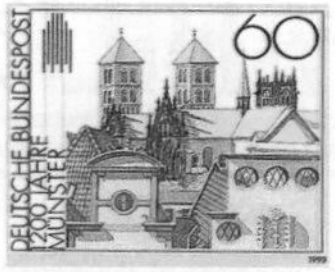

1025 Cathedral and Uberwasser Church

1993. 1200th Anniv of Munster.
2494 **1025** 60pf. multicoloured . . 1·30 55

1026 Newton, Sketch of Refraction of Light and Formula

1993. 350th Birth Anniv of Sir Isaac Newton (scientist).
2495 **1026** 100pf. multicoloured . . 1·40 55

1027 Route Map and Compass Rose

1993. 125th Anniv of North German Naval Observatory, Hamburg.
2496 **1027** 100pf. multicoloured . . 1·40 55

1028 Emblem and Safety Stripes

1993. European Year of Health, Hygiene and Safety in the Workplace.
2497 **1028** 100pf. blue, yell & blk 1·40 55

1029 Wires and Wall Socket forming House

1030 Ski-jumping Hill, Garmisch-Partenkirchen

1993. Centenary of German Association of Electrical Engineers.
2498 **1029** 170pf. multicoloured . . 2·20 1·20

1993. Sport Promotion Fund. German Olympic Venues. Multicoloured.
2499 60pf.+30pf. Type **1030** . . 1·30 1·30
2500 80pf.+40pf. Olympia-park, Munich . . . . 1·80 1·80
2501 100pf.+50pf. Olympic Stadium, Berlin . . . . . 2·20 2·20
2502 170pf.+80pf. Olympic Harbour, Kiel . . . . . 3·00 3·00

1031 Stylised Sound Vibration

1993. 250th Anniv of Leipzig Gewandhaus Orchestra.
2503 **1031** 100pf. gold and black 1·40 55

1032 Statue of St. John and Charles Bridge, Prague

1993. 600th Death Anniv of St. John of Nepomuk.
2504 **1032** 100pf. multicoloured . . 1·40 55

1033 Diagram explaining New Postcodes

1993. Introduction of Five-digit Postcode System.
2505 **1033** 100pf. multicoloured . . 1·80 55

1993. Lander of the Federal Republic. As T **989**. Multicoloured.
2506 100pf. Hesse . . . . 1·40 70

1993. 20th-century German Paintings (2nd series). As T **1003**. Multicoloured.
2507 100pf. multicoloured . . . . 1·40 85
2508 100pf. black, grey and mauve . . . . 1·40 85
2509 100pf. multicoloured . . . . 1·40 85
DESIGNS: No. 2507, "Cafe" (George Grosz); 2508, "Sea and Sun" (Otto Pankok); 2509, "Audience" (Andreas Paul Weber).

1034 Abbeys

1993. 900th Anniversaries of Maria Laach and Bursfelde Benedictine Abbeys.
2510 **1034** 80pf. multicoloured . . 1·20 50

1035 Alpine Longhorn Beetle

1993. Youth Welfare. Endangered Beetles. Multicoloured.
2511 80pf.+40f. Type **1035** . . . 1·80 1·80
2512 80pf.+40pf. Rose chafer . . 1·80 1·80
2513 100pf.+50pf. Stag beetle . . 2·20 2·20
2514 100pf.+50pf. Tiger beetle . . 2·20 2·20
2515 200pf.+50pf. Cockchafer . . 3·50 3·50

1036 Plants

1993. 5th International Horticultural Show, Stuttgart.
2516 **1036** 100pf. multicoloured . . 1·40 55

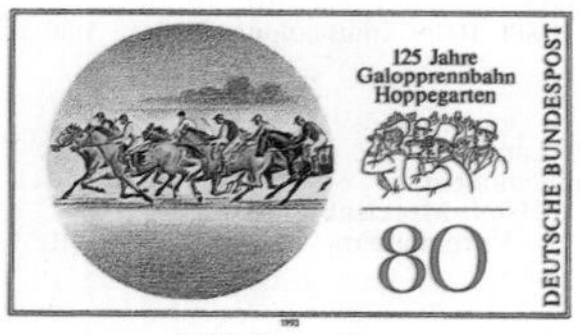

1037 Horse Race

1993. 125th Anniv of Hoppegarten Racecourse.
2517 **1037** 80pf. multicoloured . . 1·10 55

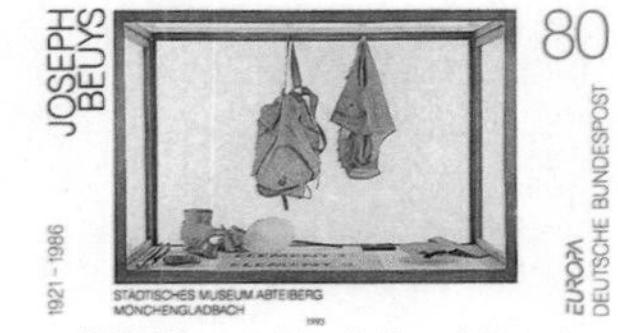

1038 "Storage Place" (Joseph Beuys)

1993. Europa. Contemporary Art. Mult.
2518 80pf. Type **1038** . . . . . 1·40 80
2519 100pf. "Homage to the Square" (Josef Albers) . . 1·40 80

1039 Church and Pupils

1993. 450th Anniv of Pforta School.
2520 **1039** 100pf. multicoloured . . 1·40 55

1040 Students, Flag, City Hall and Castle

1993. 125th Anniv of Coburg Association of University Student Unions.
2521 **1040** 100pf. black, grn & red 1·40 55

1041 "Hohentwiel" (lake steamer) and Flags

1993. Lake Constance European Region.
2522 **1041** 100pf. multicoloured . . 1·40 55

1042 "Old Market—View of St. Nicholas's Church" (detail, Ferdinand von Arnim)

1993. Millenary of Potsdam.
2523 **1042** 80pf. multicoloured . . 1·40 50

1043 Holderlin (after Franz Hiemer)

1993. 150th Death Anniv of Friedrich Holderlin (poet).
2524 **1043** 100pf. multicoloured . . 1·30 50

1044 "If People can fly to the Moon, why can't they do anything about so many Children dying?"

1993. 40th Anniv of German United Nations Children's Fund Committee.
2525 **1044** 100pf. multicoloured . . 1·30 50

1993. Lander of the Federal Republic. As T **989**. Multicoloured.
2526 100pf. Mecklenburg-Vorpommern . . . . . . 1·40 70

1993. Lander of the Federal Republic. As T **989**. Multicoloured.
2527 100pf. Lower Saxony . . . 1·40 70

1045 Fallada (after E. O. Plauen)

1993. Birth Centenary of Hans Fallada (writer).
2528 **1045** 100pf. green, brn & red 1·30 50

1046 Harz Mountain Range

1993. Landscapes (1st series). Multicoloured.
2529 100pf. Type **1046** . . . . . 1·40 70
2530 100pf. Rugen . . . . 1·40 70
2531 100pf. Hohe Rhon . . . . . 1·40 70
See also Nos. 2585/8, 2646/9, 2709/12 and 2806/8.

1047 Stages of Manufacture

1993. 250th Death Anniv of Mathias Klotz (violin maker).
2532 **1047** 80pf. multicoloured . . 1·10 50

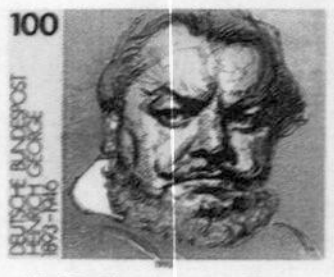

1048 George as Gotz von Berlichingen in Goethe's "Urgotz"

1050 Swedish Flag, Heart and Cross

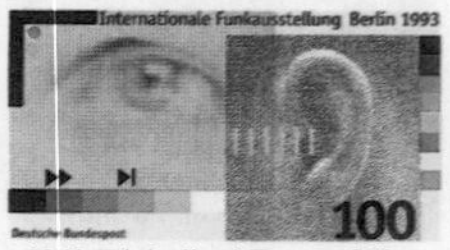

1049 Digitalised Eye and Ear

1993. Birth Centenary of Heinrich George (actor).
2533 **1048** 100pf. multicoloured . . 1·30 55

1993. Lander of the Federal Republic. As T **989**. Multicoloured.
2534 100pf. Nordrhein-Westfalen 1·40 70

1993. International Radio Exhibition, Berlin.
2535 **1049** 100pf. multicoloured . . 1·30 55

1993. Birth Centenary of Birger Forell (founder of Espelkamp (town for war refugees)).
2536 **1050** 100pf. yell, ultram & bl 1·60 55

1051 "Tuledu Bridge" (engraving)

1052 Singing Clown

1993. Birth Centenary of Hans Leip (writer and artist).
2537 **1051** 100pf. black, red & blue 1·60 55

1993. "For Us Children". Sheet 49 × 83 mm.
MS2538 **1052** 100pf. multicoloured 1·50 1·50

1993. Lander of the Federal Republic. As T **989**. Multicoloured.
2539 100pf. Rheinland-Pfalz . . . 1·40 70

1053 Postman delivering Letter

1993. Stamp Day.
2540 **1053** 100pf.+50pf. mult . . . 1·60 1·60

1054 "Swan Lake"

1993. Death Centenary of Pyotr Tchaikovsky (composer).
2541 **1054** 80pf. multicoloured . . 1·30 50

1055 Fohr, Schleswig-Holstein

1993. Humanitarian Relief Funds. Traditional Costumes (1st series). Multicoloured.
2542 80pf.+40pf. Type **1055** . . 1·30 1·30
2543 80pf.+40pf. Rugen, Mecklenburg-Vorpommern . . . . . 1·30 1·30
2544 100pf.+50pf. Oberndorf, Bavaria . . . . 1·80 1·80
2545 100pf.+50pf. Schwalm, Hesse . . . . 1·80 1·80
2546 200pf.+40pf. Ernstroda, Thuringia . . . . . . 3·25 3·25
See also Nos. 2598/2602.

1056 St. Jadwiga (miniature, Schlackenwerther Codex)

1993. 750th Death Anniv of St. Jadwiga of Silesia.
2547 **1056** 100pf. multicoloured . . 1·60 55

1057 Reinhardt on Stage

1058 Brandt

1993. 50th Death Anniv of Max Reinhardt (theatrical producer).
2548 **1057** 100pf. black, brn & red 1·60 55

1993. 80th Birth Anniv of Willy Brandt (statesman).
2549 **1058** 100pf. multicoloured . . . 1·80 60

1059 Monteverdi

1993. 350th Death Anniv of Claudio Monteverdi (composer).
2550 **1059** 100pf. multicoloured . 1·60 55

1060 Paracelsus (after Augustin Hirschvogel)

1061 "Adoration of the Magi"

1993. 500th Birth Anniv of Paracelsus (physician and philosopher).
2551 **1060** 100pf. ochre, brown and green . . . . . 1·60 55

1993. Christmas. Carvings from Altar Triptych, Blaubeuren Minster. Multicoloured.
2552 80pf.+40pf. Type **1061** . . 1·10 1·10
2553 100pf.+50pf. "Birth of Christ" . . . . 1·90 1·90

1062 Quayside Buildings, Town Hall and St. Cosmas's Church

1994. Millenary of Stade.
2554 **1062** 80pf. red, brown & blue 1·20 55

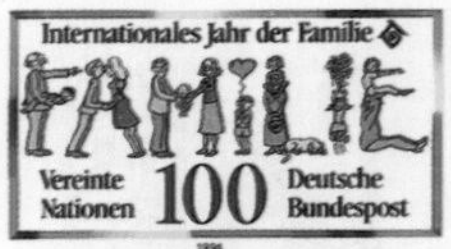

1063 "FAMILIE"

1994. International Year of the Family.
2555 **1063** 100pf. multicoloured . . 1·50 60

1994. Lander of the Federal Republic. As T **989**. Multicoloured.
2556 100pf. Saarland . . . . . . 1·40 70

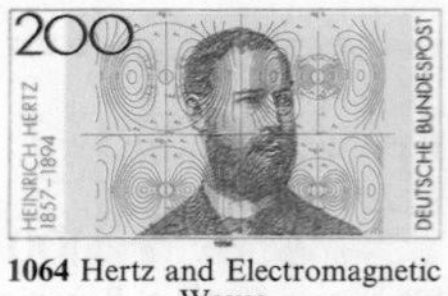

1064 Hertz and Electromagnetic Waves

1994. Death Centenary of Heinrich Hertz (physicist).
2557 **1064** 200pf. black, red and drab . . . . 2·75 1·30

1065 Frankfurt am Main

1994. 1200th Anniv of Frankfurt am Main.
2558 **1065** 80pf. multicoloured . . 1·20 55

1066 Ice Skating

1994. Sport Promotion Fund. Sporting Events and Anniversaries. Multicoloured.
2559 80pf.+40pf. Type **1066** (Winter Olympic Games, Lillehammer, Norway) . . 1·30 1·30
2560 100pf.+50pf. Football and trophy (World Cup Football Championship, U.S.A.) . . . . 1·80 1·80
2561 100pf.+50pf. Flame (cent of International Olympic Committee) . . . . . . 1·80 1·80
2562 200pf.+80pf. Skier (Winter Paralympic Games, Lillehammer) . . . . . . 3·00 3·00

1067 Cathedral, St. Michael's Church and Castle

1994. 1250th Anniv of Fulda.
2563 **1067** 80pf. multicoloured . . 1·20 50

1068 Council Emblem

1994. Cent of Federation of German Women's Associations—German Women's Council.
2564 **1068** 100pf. black, red & yell 1·50 60

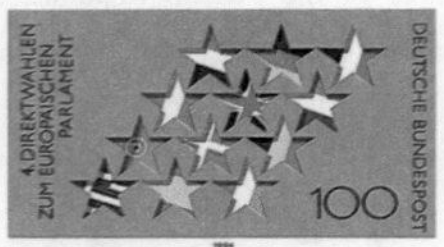

1069 Members' Flags as Stars

1994. 4th Direct Elections to European Parliament.
2565 **1069** 100pf. multicoloured . . 1·50 60

1070 People holding Banner

1994. "Living Together" (integration of foreign workers in Germany).
2566 **1070** 100pf. multicoloured . . 1·50 60

1994. Lander of the Federal Republic. As T **989**. Multicoloured.
2567 100pf. Saxony . . . . . . 1·40 70

1071 Johnny Head-in-the-Air

1994. Youth Welfare. Death Centenary of Heinrich Hoffmann (writer). Designs illustrating characters from "Slovenly Peter". Multicoloured.
2568 80pf.+40pf. Type **1071** . . 1·30 1·30
2569 80pf.+40pf. Little Pauline 1·30 1·30
2570 100pf.+50pf. Naughty Friederich . . . . 1·80 1·80
2571 100pf.+50pf. Slovenly Peter 1·80 1·80
2572 200pf.+80pf. Fidget-Philipp 3·25 3·25

1072 Frauenkirche

1994. 500th Anniv of Frauenkirche, Munich.
2573 **1072** 100pf. multicoloured . . 1·50 60

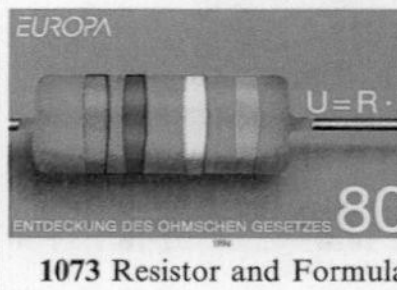

1073 Resistor and Formula

1074 Pfitzner (after Emil Orlik)

1994. Europa. Discoveries. Multicoloured.
2574 80pf. Type **1073** (Ohm's Law) . . . . 1·30 55
2575 100pf. Radiation from black body and formula (Max Planck's Quantum Theory) . . . . 1·10 60

1994. 125th Birth Anniv of Hans Pfitzner (composer).
2576 **1074** 100pf. deep blue, blue and red . . . . . . 1·50 60

1075 Hegenbeck and Animals

1994. 150th Anniversaries. Sheet 77 × 108 mm containing T **1075** and similar horiz design. Multicoloured.
MS2577 100pf. Type **1075** (birth anniv of Carl Hagenbeck (circus owner and founder of first zoo without bars)); 200pf. Animals and entrance to Berlin Zoo . . 3·75 3·75

1076 Spandau Castle

1994. 400th Anniv of Spandau Castle.
2578 **1076** 80pf. multicoloured . . 1·10 55

1077 Village Sign showing Society Emblem

1994. Centenary of Herzogsagmuhle (Society for the Domestic Missions welfare village).
2579 **1077** 100pf. multicoloured . . 1·30 60

1994. Lander of the Federal Republic. As T **989**. Multicoloured.
2580 100pf. Saxony-Anhalt . . . 1·40 70

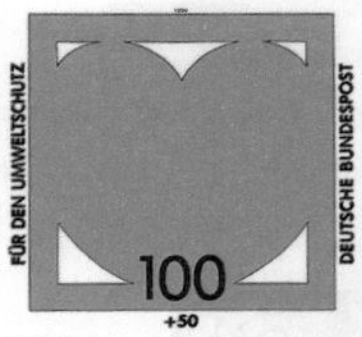

1078 Heart inside Square **1079** Friedrich II (13th-century miniature, "Book of Falcons")

1994. Environmental Protection.
2581 **1078** 100pf.+50pf. green and black . . . . 1·80 1·80

1994. 800th Birth Anniv of Emperor Friedrich II.
2582 **1079** 400pf. multicoloured . . 4·75 3·00

1080 "20 JULY 1944" behind Bars

1994. 50th Anniv of Attempt to Assassinate Hitler. Sheet 105 × 70 mm.
MS2583 **1080** 100pf. black, yellow and red . . . . 1·50 1·50

1994. Lander of the Federal Republic. As T **989**. Multicoloured.
2584 100pf. Schleswig-Holstein . . 1·40 70

1994. Landscapes (2nd series). As T **1046**. Multicoloured.
2585 100pf. The Alps . . . . . . 1·20 75
2586 100pf. Erzgebirge . . . . 1·20 75
2587 100pf. Main valley . . . . 1·20 75
2588 100pf. Mecklenburg lakes 1·20 75

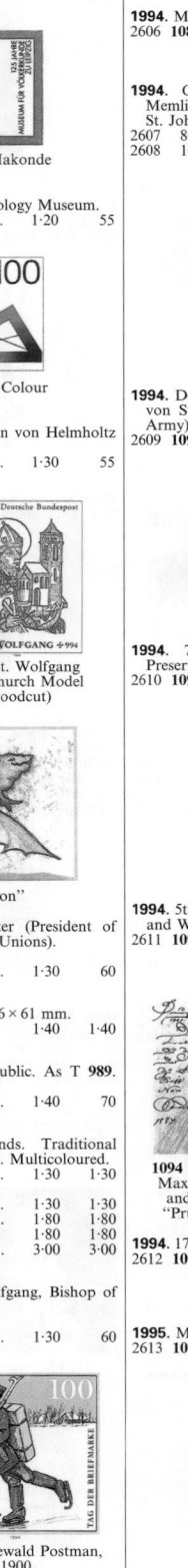

1081 Herder (after Anton Graff)

1994. 250th Birth Anniv of Johann Gottfried Herder (philosopher).
2589 **1081** 80pf. multicoloured . . 1·10 55

1994. 20th-century German Paintings (3rd series). As T **1003**. Multicoloured.
2590 100pf. "Maika" (Christian Schad) . . . . 1·10 65
2591 200pf. "Dresden Landscape" (Erich Heckel) . . . . . 2·40 2·00
2592 300pf. "Aleksei Javlensky and Marianne Werefkin" (Gabriele Munter) . . . . 3·75 2·75

1082 Early 20th-century Makonde Mask (Tanzania)

1994. 125th Anniv of Leipzig Ethnology Museum.
2593 **1082** 80pf. multicoloured . . 1·20 55

1083 Helmholtz, Eye and Colour Triangle

1994. Death Centenary of Hermann von Helmholtz (physicist).
2594 **1083** 100pf. multicoloured . . 1·30 55

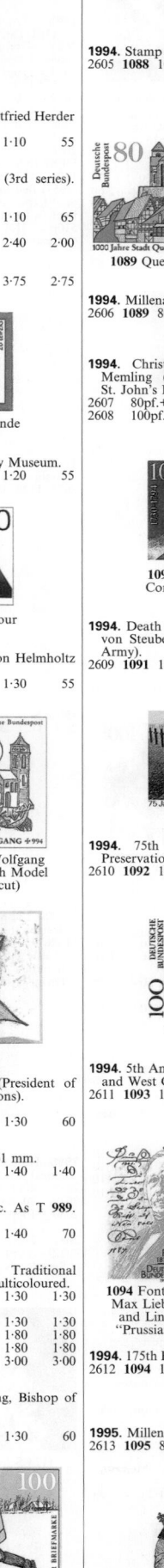

1084 Richter **1086** St. Wolfgang with Church Model (woodcut)

1085 "Flying on Dragon"

1994. Birth Cent of Willi Richter (President of Confederation of German Trade Unions).
2595 **1084** 100pf. brown, purple and black . . . . . 1·30 60

1994. "For Us Children". Sheet 106 × 61 mm.
MS2596 **1085** 100pf. multicoloured 1·40 1·40

1994. Lander of the Federal Republic. As T **989**. Multicoloured.
2597 100pf. Thuringia . . . . . 1·40 70

1994. Humanitarian Relief Funds. Traditional Costumes (2nd series). As T **1055**. Multicoloured.
2598 80pf.+40pf. Buckeburg . . . 1·30 1·30
2599 80pf.+40pf. Halle an der Saale . . . . 1·30 1·30
2600 100pf.+50pf. Minden . . . 1·80 1·80
2601 100pf.+50pf. Hoyerswerda 1·80 1·80
2602 200pf.+70pf. Betzingen . . . 3·00 3·00

1994. Death Millenary of St. Wolfgang, Bishop of Regensburg.
2603 **1086** 100pf. gold, cream and black . . . . 1·30 60

1087 Sachs **1088** Spreewald Postman, 1900

1994. 500th Birth Anniv of Hans Sachs (mastersinger and poet).
2604 **1087** 100pf. purple and green on greyish . . . . . 1·30 60

1994. Stamp Day.
2605 **1088** 100pf. multicoloured . . 1·30 60

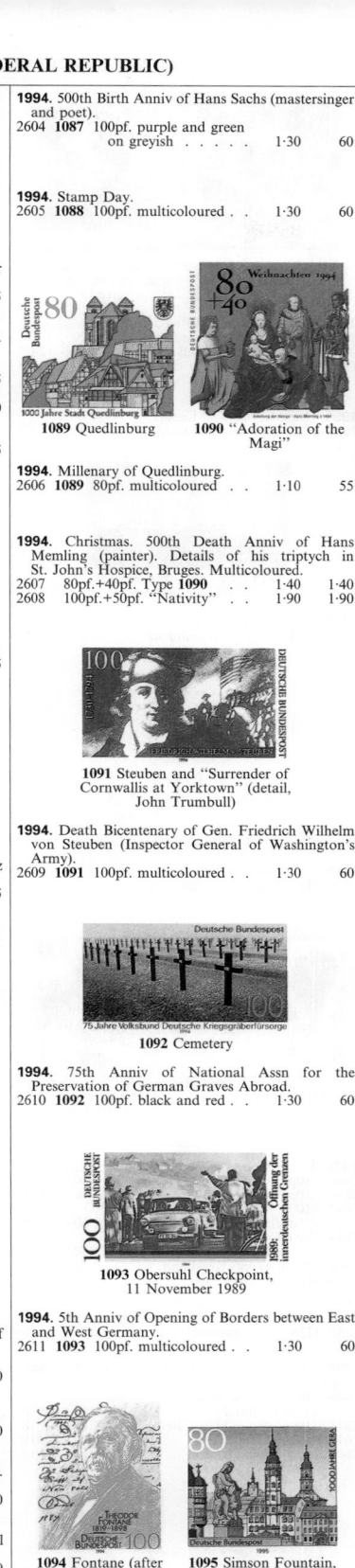

1089 Quedlinburg **1090** "Adoration of the Magi"

1994. Millenary of Quedlinburg.
2606 **1089** 80pf. multicoloured . . 1·10 55

1994. Christmas. 500th Death Anniv of Hans Memling (painter). Details of his triptych in St. John's Hospice, Bruges. Multicoloured.
2607 80pf.+40pf. Type **1090** . . 1·40 1·40
2608 100pf.+50pf. "Nativity" . . 1·90 1·90

1091 Steuben and "Surrender of Cornwallis at Yorktown" (detail, John Trumbull)

1994. Death Bicentenary of Gen. Friedrich Wilhelm von Steuben (Inspector General of Washington's Army).
2609 **1091** 100pf. multicoloured . . 1·30 60

1092 Cemetery

1994. 75th Anniv of National Assn for the Preservation of German Graves Abroad.
2610 **1092** 100pf. black and red . . 1·30 60

1093 Obersuhl Checkpoint, 11 November 1989

1994. 5th Anniv of Opening of Borders between East and West Germany.
2611 **1093** 100pf. multicoloured . . 1·30 60

1094 Fontane (after Max Liebermann) and Lines from "Prussian Song" **1095** Simson Fountain, Town Hall and St. Mary's and St Salvator's Churches

1994. 175th Birth Anniv of Theodor Fontane (writer).
2612 **1094** 100pf. green, black and mauve . . . . 1·30 60

1995. Millenary of Gera.
2613 **1095** 80pf. multicoloured . . 80 70

1096 Emperor Friedrich III, First Page of "Libellus" and Zur Munze (venue)

1995. 500th Anniv of Diet of Worms.
2614 **1096** 100pf. black and red . . 1·10 90

1995. 20th-century German Paintings (4th series). As T **1003**. Multicoloured.
2615 100pf. "The Water Tower, Bremen" (Franz Radziwill) . . . . 1·10 1·10
2616 200pf. "Still Life with Cat" (Georg Schrimpf) . . . . 2·20 2·20
2617 300pf. "Estate in Dangast" (Karl Schmidt-Rottluff) 2·75 2·75

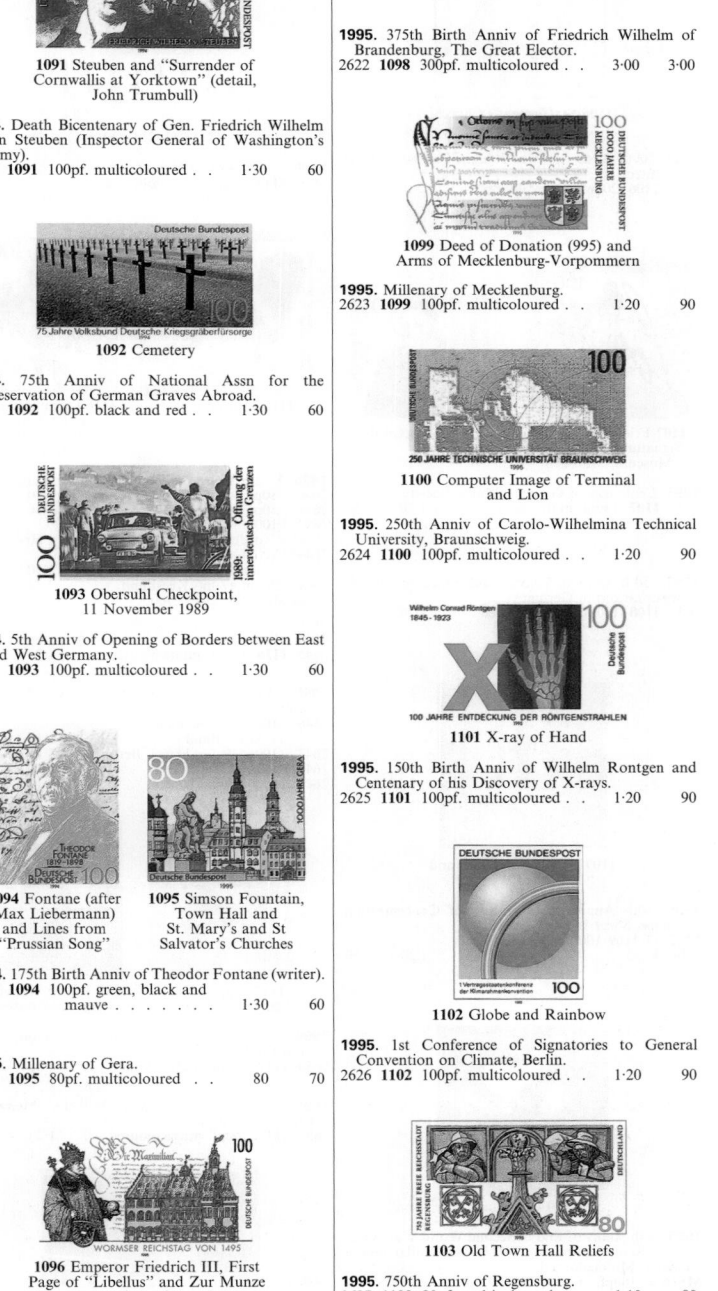

1097 Canoeing **1098** Friedrich Wilhelm (after A. Romandon)

1995. Sport Promotion Fund. Multicoloured.
2618 80pf.+40pf. Type **1097** (27th World Canoeing Championships, Duisburg) . . . . 1·20 1·20
2619 100pf.+50pf. Hoop exercises (10th Int Gymnastics Festival, Berlin) . . . . . 1·40 1·40
2620 100pf.+50pf. Boxing (8th World Amateur Boxing Championships, Berlin) 1·40 1·40
2621 200pf.+80pf. Volleyball (centenary) . . . . 3·00 3·00

1995. 375th Birth Anniv of Friedrich Wilhelm of Brandenburg, The Great Elector.
2622 **1098** 300pf. multicoloured . . 3·00 3·00

1099 Deed of Donation (995) and Arms of Mecklenburg-Vorpommern

1995. Millenary of Mecklenburg.
2623 **1099** 100pf. multicoloured . . 1·20 90

1100 Computer Image of Terminal and Lion

1995. 250th Anniv of Carolo-Wilhelmina Technical University, Braunschweig.
2624 **1100** 100pf. multicoloured . . 1·20 90

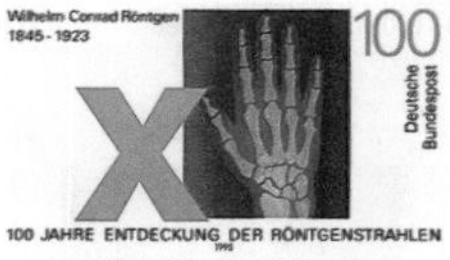

1101 X-ray of Hand

1995. 150th Birth Anniv of Wilhelm Rontgen and Centenary of his Discovery of X-rays.
2625 **1101** 100pf. multicoloured . . 1·20 90

1102 Globe and Rainbow

1995. 1st Conference of Signatories to General Convention on Climate, Berlin.
2626 **1102** 100pf. multicoloured . . 1·20 90

1103 Old Town Hall Reliefs

1995. 750th Anniv of Regensburg.
2627 **1103** 80pf. multicoloured . . 1·10 80

1104 Bonhoeffer

1995. 50th Death Anniv of Dietrich Bonhoeffer (theologian).
2628 **1104** 100pf. black, bl & grey 1·20 90

1105 Symbols of Speech, Writing and Pictures

1995. Freedom of Expression.
2629 **1105** 100pf. multicoloured . . 1·20 90

1106 St. Clement's Church, Munster

1995. 300th Birth Anniv of Johann Conrad Schlaun (architect).
2630 **1106** 200pf. multicoloured . . 2·10 1·90

1107 Friedrich Schiller, Signature and Schiller Museum, Marbach

1108 St. Vincent de Paul

1995. Centenary of German Schiller Society.
2631 **1107** 100pf. multicoloured . . 1·20 95

1995. 150th Anniv of Vincent Conferences (charitable organization) in Germany.
2632 **1108** 100pf. multicoloured . . 1·20 95

1109 Number on Cloth and Barbed Wire

1995. 50th Anniv of Liberation of Concentration Camps. Sheet 105 × 70 mm.
MS2633 **1109** 100pf. grey, blue and black . . . . 1·20 1·20

1110 City Ruins

1995. 50th Anniv of End of Second World War. Sheet 104 × 70 mm containing T **1110** and similar square design. Multicoloured.
MS2634 100pf. Type **1110**; 100pf. Refugees . . . . 2·40 2·40

1111 Returning Soldiers ("End of War")

1112 Shipping Routes before and after 1895

1995. Europa. Peace and Freedom.
2635 **1111** 100pf. black and red . . 1·20 90
2636 – 200pf. blue, yell & blk 2·10 2·00
DESIGN: 200pf. Emblem of European Community ("Moving towards Europe").

1995. Centenary of Kiel Canal.
2637 **1112** 80pf. multicoloured . . 95 80

1113 Guglielmo Marconi and Wireless Equipment

1995. 100 Years of Radio.
2638 **1113** 100pf. multicoloured . . 1·20 90

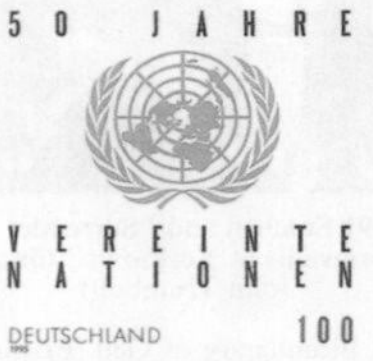

1114 U.N. Emblem

1995. 50th Anniv of U.N.O.
2639 **1114** 100pf. lilac, gold and grey . . . . 1·20 90

1115 Munsterlander

1116 Opening Bars of "Carmina Burana" and Characters

1995. Youth Welfare. Dogs (1st series). Mult.
2640 80pf.+40pf. Type **1115** . . 1·10 1·10
2641 80pf.+40pf. Giant schnauzer 1·10 1·10
2642 100pf.+50pf. Wire-haired dachshund . . . . . . 1·50 1·50
2643 100pf.+50pf. German shepherd . . . . 1·50 1·50
2644 200pf.+80pf. Keeshund . . 2·75 2·75
See also Nos. 2696/2700.

1995. Birth Centenary of Carl Orff (composer).
2645 **1116** 100pf. multicoloured . . 1·20 90

1995. Landscapes (3rd series). As T **1046**. Multicoloured.
2646 100pf. Franconian Switzerland . . . . . . 1·10 1·10
2647 100pf. River Havel, Berlin 1·10 1·10
2648 100pf. Oberlausitz . . . . 1·10 1·10
2649 100pf. Sauerland . . . . 1·10 1·10

1117 Lion (from 12th-century coin)

1118 Kaiser Wilhelm Memorial Church

1995. 800th Death Anniv of Henry the Lion, Duke of Saxony and Bavaria.
2650 **1117** 400pf. multicoloured . . 4·00 3·75

1995. Centenary of Kaiser Wilhelm Memorial Church, Berlin.
2651 **1118** 100pf. multicoloured . . 1·20 90

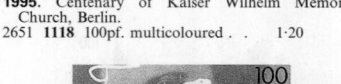

1119 Werfel and Signature

1995. 50th Death Anniv of Franz Werfel (writer).
2652 **1119** 100pf. mauve, bl & blk 1·20 90

1995. Tourist Sights. As T **854** but inscr "DEUTSCHLAND".
2654 47pf. green and black . . . 50 50
2656 100pf. blue and black . . . 90 45
2657 110pf. cinnamon and brown 1·10 45
2658 110pf. orange and blue . . . 1·10 95
2659 220pf. green and black . . . 2·00 1·10
2661 440pf. orange and blue . . . 4·50 4·50
2663 510pf. red and blue . . . . 5·25 5·25
2665 640pf. blue and brown . . . 6·00 6·00
2666 690pf. black and green . . . 6·50 6·50
DESIGNS: 47pf. Berus Monument, Uberherrn; 100pf. Goethe-Schiller Monument, Weimar; 110pf. (2657) Bellevue Castle, Berlin; 110pf. (2658) Emblem of "Expo 2000" World's Fair, Hanover; 220pf. Bruhl's Terrace, Dresden; 440pf. Town Hall, Bremen; 510pf. Holsten Gate, Lubeck; 640pf. Speyer Cathedral; 690pf. St. Michael's Church, Hamburg.

1120 Strauss

1995. 80th Birth Anniv of Franz Josef Strauss (politician).
2675 **1120** 100pf. multicoloured . . 1·20 90

1121 Postwoman

1995. Stamp Day.
2676 **1121** 200pf.+100pf. mult . . 2·75 2·75

1122 "Metropolis" (dir. Fritz Lang)

1995. Centenary of Motion Pictures. Sheet 100 × 130 mm containing T **1122** and similar horiz designs showing frames from films. Multicoloured.
MS2677 80pf. Type **1122**; 100pf. "Little Superman" (dir. Wolfgang Staudte); 200pf. "The Sky over Berlin" (dir. Wim Wenders) . . 4·75 4·75

1123 Eifel

1995. Humanitarian Relief Funds. Farmhouses (1st series). Multicoloured.
2678 80pf.+40pf. Type **1123** . . 1·20 1·20
2679 80pf.+40pf. Saxony . . . . 1·20 1·20
2680 100pf.+50pf. Lower Germany . . . . . . 1·60 1·60
2681 100pf.+50pf. Upper Bavaria 1·60 1·60
2682 200pf.+70pf. Mecklenburg 2·75 2·75
See also Nos. 2742/6.

1124 Schumacher

1126 Ranke

1125 Animals gathered on Hill

1995. Birth Centenary of Kurt Schumacher (politician).
2683 **1124** 100pf. multicoloured . . 1·20 90

1995. "For Us Children". Sheet 110 × 60 mm.
MS2684 **1125** 80pf. multicoloured 1·20 1·20

1995. Birth Bicentenary of Leopold von Ranke (historian).
2685 **1126** 80pf. multicoloured . . 90 80

1127 Hindemith

1995. Birth Centenary of Paul Hindemith (composer).
2686 **1127** 100pf. multicoloured . . 1·20 90

1128 Alfred Nobel and Will

1995. Centenary of Nobel Prize Trust Fund.
2687 **1128** 100pf. multicoloured . . 1·20 90

1129 "CARE" in American Colours

1995. 50th Anniv of CARE (Co-operative for Assistance and Remittances Overseas).
2688 **1129** 100pf. multicoloured . . 1·20 90

1130 Berlin Wall

1995. Commemorating Victims of Political Oppression, 1945–89.
2689 **1130** 100pf. multicoloured . . 1·20 90

1131 "The Annunciation"

1995. Christmas. Stained Glass Windows in Augsburg Cathedral. Multicoloured.
2690 80pf.+40pf. Type **1131** . . 1·20 1·20
2691 100pf.+50pf. "Nativity" . . 1·60 1·60

1132 Dribbling

1995. Borussia Dortmund, German Football Champions.
2692 **1132** 100pf. multicoloured . . 1·20 90

1133 Auguste von Sartorius (founder)

1996. 150th Anniv of German Institute for Children's Missionary Work.
2693 **1133** 100pf. multicoloured . . 95 90

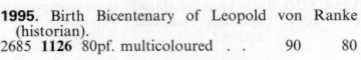

1134 Bodelschwingh

1996. 50th Death Anniv of Friedrich von Bodelschwingh (theologian).
2694 **1134** 100pf. black and red . . 95 90

1135 Luther (after Lucas Cranach)

1996. 450th Death Anniv of Martin Luther (Protestant reformer).
2695 **1135** 100pf. multicoloured . . 95 90

1996. Youth Welfare. Dogs (2nd series). As T **1115**. Multicoloured.

2696	80pf.+40pf. Borzoi	1·20	1·20
2697	80pf.+40pf. Chow chow . .	1·20	1·20
2698	100pf.+50pf. St. Bernard . .	1·60	1·60
2699	100pf.+50pf. Rough collie	1·60	1·60
2700	200pf.+80pf. Briard	2·75	2·75

1136 Siebold

1996. Birth Bicentenary of Philipp Franz von Siebold (physician and Japanologist).
2701 **1136** 100pf. multicoloured . . 95 90

1137 Cathedral Square

1996. Millenary of Cathedral Square, Halberstadt.
2702 **1137** 80pf. multicoloured . . 80 65

1138 Galen

1996. 50th Death Anniv of Cardinal Count Clemens von Galen, Bishop of Munster.
2703 **1138** 100pf. grey, blue & gold 95 95

1996. 20th-century German Paintings (5th series). As T **1003**. Multicoloured.

2704	100pf. "Seated Female Nude" (Max Pechstein)	1·10	1·10
2705	200pf. "For Wilhelm Runge" (Georg Muche)	1·90	1·90
2706	300pf. "Still Life with Guitar, Book and Vase" (Helmut Kolle)	2·00	3·00

1139 Detail of Ceiling Fresco, Prince-bishop's Residence, Wurzburg

1996. 300th Birth Anniv of Giovanni Battista Tiepolo (artist).
2707 **1139** 200pf. multicoloured . . 1·90 1·90

1140 Post Runner

1141 Paula Modersohn-Becker (self-portrait)

1996. "For Us Children". Sheet 83 × 67 mm.
MS2708 **1140** 100pf. multicoloured 95 95

1996. Landscapes (4th series). As T **1046**. Multicoloured.

2709	100pf. Eifel	95	95
2710	100pf. Holstein Switzerland	95	95
2711	100pf. Saale	95	95
2712	100pf. Spreewald	95	95

1996. Europa. Famous Women.

2713	**1141**	80pf. multicoloured . .	80	80
2714	–	100pf. black, grey and mauve	1·10	1·10

DESIGN: 100pf. Kathe Kollwitz (self-portrait).

1142 Opening Lines of Document and Town (1642 engraving, Matthaeus Merian)

1996. Millenary of Granting to Freising the Right to hold Markets.
2715 **1142** 100pf. multicoloured . . 95 90

1143 Borchert

1996. 75th Birth Anniv of Wolfgang Borchert (writer).
2716 **1143** 100pf. multicoloured . . 95 90

1144 Emblem

1996. 50th Anniv of Ruhr Festival, Recklinghausen.
2717 **1144** 100pf. multicoloured . . 95 90

1145 Ticket and Stage Curtain

1996. 150th Anniv of German Theatre Assn.
2718 **1145** 200pf. multicoloured . . 1·90 1·50

1146 Leibniz and Mathematical Diagram

1996. 350th Birth Anniv of Gottfried Leibniz.
2719 **1146** 100pf. red and black . . 95 90

1147 Kneeling Figure and Motto forming "A"

1996. 300th Anniv of Berlin Academy of Arts.
2720 **1147** 100pf. multicoloured . . 95 90

1148 Carl Schuhmann (wrestling, equestrian sports and gymnastics, 1896)

1996. Sport Promotion Fund. Centenary of Modern Olympic Games. German Olympic Champions. Multicoloured.

2721	80pf.+40pf. Type **1148** . .	1·20	1·20
2722	100pf.+50pf. Josef Neckermann (dressage, 1964 and 1968)	1·50	1·50
2723	100pf.+50pf. Annie Hubler-Horn (ice skating, 1908)	1·50	1·50
2724	200pf.+80pf. Alfred and Gustav Flatow (gymnastics, 1896)	2·75	2·75

1149 Townscape

1996. 800th Anniv of Heidelberg.
2725 **1149** 100pf. multicoloured . . 95 90

1150 Children's Handprints

1996. 50th Anniv of U.N.I.C.E.F.
2726 **1150** 100pf. multicoloured . . 95 90

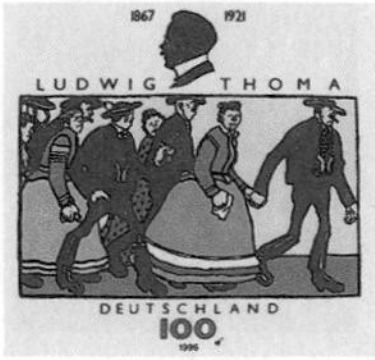

1151 "Wedding" (illustration by Bruno Paul)

1996. 75th Death Anniv of Ludwig Thoma (satirist).
2727 **1151** 100pf. multicoloured . . 95 90

1152 Beach

1996. Western Pomerania National Park. Sheet 166 × 111 mm containing T **1152** and similar horiz designs showing Park landscapes. Multicoloured.
MS2728 100pf. Type **1152**; 200pf. Mudflat; 300pf. Sea inlet . . . 5·75 5·75

1153 Map and Tropical Wildlife

1996. Environmental Protection. Preservation of Tropical Habitats.
2729 **1153** 100pf.+50pf. mult . . . 1·40 1·40

1154 Volklingen Blast Furnace

1996. U.N.E.S.C.O. World Heritage Sites.
2730 **1154** 100pf. multicoloured . . 95 90

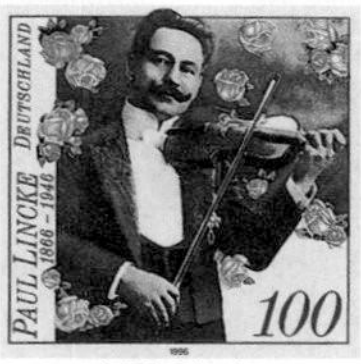

1155 Lincke

1996. 50th Death Anniv of Paul Lincke (composer and conductor).
2731 **1155** 100pf. multicoloured . . 95 90

1156 Gendarmenmarkt, Berlin

1996. Images of Germany.
2732 **1156** 100pf. multicoloured . . 95 90

1157 "50" comprising Stamp under Magnifying Glass

1996. Stamp Day. 50th Anniv of Association of German Philatelists.
2733 **1157** 100pf. multicoloured . . 95 90

1158 Book

1996. Centenary of German Civil Code.
2734 **1158** 300pf. multicoloured . . 2·75 2·75

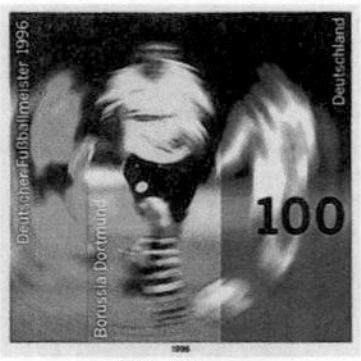

1159 Players

1996. Borussia Dortmund, German Football Champions.
2735 **1159** 100pf. multicoloured . . 95 90

1160 Bamburg Old Town

1996. U.N.E.S.C.O. World Heritage Sites.
2736 **1160** 100pf. multicoloured . . 95 90

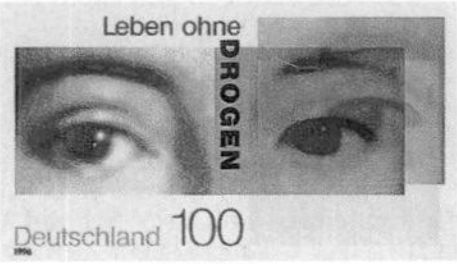

1161 Eyes

1996. "Life without Drugs".
2737 **1161** 100pf. multicoloured . . 95 90

1162 "Like will Cure Like" and Samuel Hahnemann (developer of principle)

1163 Bruckner and Symphony No. III

1996. Bicentenary of Homeopathy.
2738 **1162** 400pf. multicoloured . . 3·75 3·75

1996. Death Centenary of Anton Bruckner (composer).
2739 **1163** 100pf. multicoloured . . 95 90

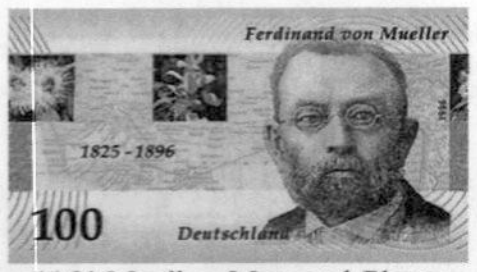

1164 Mueller, Map and Plants

1996. Death Centenary of Ferdinand von Mueller (botanist).
2740 **1164** 100pf. multicoloured . . 95 90

1165 Score by John Cage

1996. 75th Anniv of Donaueschingen Music Festival.
2741 **1165** 100pf. blue, blk & mve 95 90

1996. Humanitarian Relief Funds. Farmhouses (2nd series). As T **1123**. Multicoloured.
2742 80pf.+40pf. Spree Forest . . 1·10 1·10
2743 80pf.+40pf. Thuringia . . . 1·10 1·10
2744 100pf.+50pf. Black Forest . . 1·40 1·40
2745 100pf.+50pf. Westphalia . . 1·40 1·40
2746 200pf.+70pf. Schleswig-Holstein . . . . 3·00 3·00

1166 Titles of Plays and Zuckmayer

1996. Birth Centenary of Carl Zuckmayer (dramatist).
2747 **1166** 100pf. multicoloured . . 95 90

1167 "Adoration of the Magi"

1996. Christmas. Illustrations from Henry II's "Book of Pericopes" (illuminated manuscript of readings from the Gospels). Multicoloured.
2748 80pf.+40pf. Type **1167** . . 1·20 1·20
2749 100pf.+50pf. "Nativity" . . 1·60 1·60

1168 Schmid

1996. Birth Centenary of Carlo Schmid (politician and writer).
2750 **1168** 100pf. multicoloured . . 95 90

1169 "Friends of Schubert in Afzenbrugg" (detail, L. Kupelwieser)

1170 Pitch, Player and Herberger

1997. Birth Bicentenary of Franz Schubert (composer).
2751 **1169** 100pf. multicoloured . . 95 90

1997. Birth Centenary of Sepp Herberger (national football team coach, 1936–64).
2752 **1170** 100pf. green, red & blk 95 90

1171 Motor Cars

1997. "More Safety for Children" (road safety campaign).
2752a **1171** 10pf. multicoloured . . 15 15
2753 100pf. multicoloured 95 90

1172 Melanchthon (after Lucas Cranach the younger)

1173 Revellers "Wiggling"

1997. 500th Birth Anniv of Philipp Melanchthon (religious reformer).
2754 **1172** 100pf. multicoloured . . 95 90

1997. 175th Anniv of Cologne Carnival.
2755 **1173** 100pf. multicoloured . . 95 90

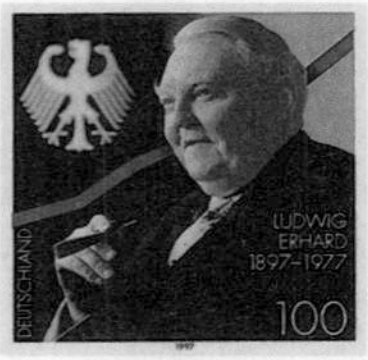

1174 Erhard

1997. Birth Centenary of Ludwig Erhard (Chancellor, 1963–66).
2756 **1174** 100pf. black and red . . 95 90

1175 Aerobics

1997. Sport Promotion Fund. Fun Sports. Multicoloured.
2757 80pf.+40pf. Type **1175** . . 1·10 1·10
2758 100pf.+50pf. Inline skating 1·50 1·50
2759 100pf.+50pf. Streetball . . . 1·50 1·50
2760 200pf.+80pf. Freeclimbing 2·75 2·75

1176 New Pavilion

1997. 500th Anniv of Granting of Imperial Fair Rights to Leipzig.
2761 **1176** 100pf. silver, red & blue 95 90

1177 Philharmonic, Berlin (Hans Scharoun)

1997. Post-1945 German Architecture. Sheet 137 × 101 mm containing T **1177** and similar square designs. Multicoloured.
MS2762 100pf. Type **1177**; 100pf. National Gallery, Berlin (Ludwig Miles van der Rohe); 100pf. St. Mary, Queen of Peace Pilgrimage Church, Neviges (Gottfried Bohm); 100pf. German Pavilion, 1967 World's Trade Fair, Montreal (Frei Otto) . . 3·75 3·75

1178 Straubing

1997. 1100th Anniv of Straubing.
2763 **1178** 100pf. multicoloured . . 95 90

1179 Stephan, Telephone and Postcards

1997. Death Centenary of Heinrich von Stephan (founder of U.P.U.).
2764 **1179** 100pf. multicoloured . . 95 90

1180 Augustusburg and Falkenlust Castles

1997. U.N.E.S.C.O. World Heritage Sites.
2765 **1180** 100pf. multicoloured . . 95 90

1181 Diamonds

1182 St. Adalbert

1997. 500th Anniv of Idar-Oberstein Region Gem Industry.
2766 **1181** 300pf. multicoloured . . 2·75 2·75

1997. Death Millenary of St. Adalbert (Bishop of Prague).
2767 **1182** 100pf. lilac 95 90

1183 "The Fisherman and His Wife" (Brothers Grimm)

1997. Europa. Tales and Legends. Mult.
2768 80pf. Type **1183** 90 90
2769 100pf. "Rubezahl" . . . . 1·10 1·10

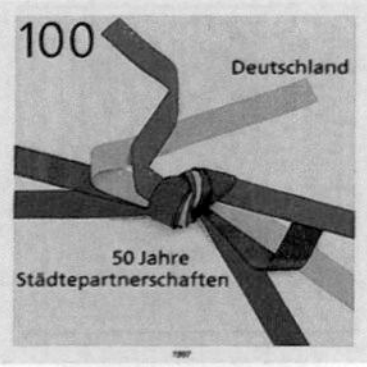

1184 Knotted Ribbons

1997. 50th Anniv of Town Twinning Movement.
2770 **1184** 100pf. multicoloured . . 95 95

1185 Deciduous Trees

1997. 50th Anniv of Society for the Protection of the German Forest. Sheet 105 × 70 mm containing T **1185** and similar square design. Multicoloured.
MS2771 100pf. Type **1185**; 200pf. Evergreen trees . . . . 2·75 2·75

1186 Kneipp

1997. Death Cent of Father Sebastian Kneipp (developer of naturopathic treatments).
2772 **1186** 100pf. multicoloured . . 95 90

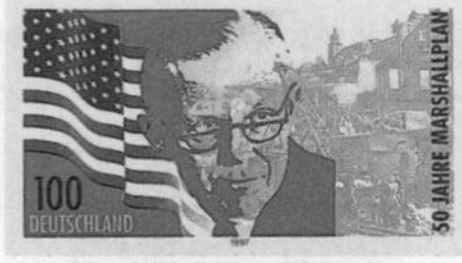

1187 United States Flag, George Marshall and Bomb Site

1997. 50th Anniv of Marshall Plan (European Recovery Program).
2773 **1187** 100pf. multicoloured . . 95 90

1188 Rheno-German Heavy Horse

1997. Youth Welfare. Horses. Multicoloured.
2774 80pf.+40pf. Type **1188** . . . 1·10 1·10
2775 80pf.+40pf. Shetland ponies 1·10 1·10
2776 100pf.+50pf. Frisian . . . . 1·50 1·50
2777 100pf.+50pf. Haflinger . . . 1·50 1·50
2778 200pf.+80pf. Hanoverian with foal . . . . 2·75 2·75

1189 Train on Bridge

1997. Centenary of Mungsten Railway Bridge.
2779 **1189** 100pf. multicoloured . . 95 95

1997. Famous Women. As T **832** but inscr "Deutschland".
2785 100pf. brown and green . . 1·10 90
2786 110pf. drab and violet . . . 95 90
2790 220pf. ultramarine and blue 2·20 2·00
2792 300pf. brown and blue . . . 3·00 2·75
2795 440pf. brown and violet . . 4·25 4·25
DESIGNS: 100pf. Elisabeth Schwarzhaupt (politician); 110pf. Marlene Dietrich (actress); 220pf. Marie-Elisabeth Luders (politician); 300pf. Maria Probst (social reformer and politician); 440pf. Gret Palucca (dancer).

1190 "Composition" (Fritz Winter)

1997. 10th "Documenta" Modern Art Exhibition, Kassel. Sheet 137 × 97 mm containing T **1190** and similar horiz designs. Multicoloured.
MS2780 100pf. Type **1190**; 100pf. "Mouth No. 15" (Tom Wesselmann); 100pf. "Quathlamba" (Frank Stella); 100pf. "Beuys/Bois" (Nam June Paik) . . . . 4·25 4·25

1191 Children holding Envelopes

1997. "For Us Children". Sheet 70 × 105 mm.
MS2781 **1191** 100pf. multicoloured 1·20 1·20

1192 Arms of Brandenburg

1997. Flood Relief Funds.
2805 **1192** 110pf.+90pf. mult . . . 1·90 1·90

1997. Landscapes (5th series). As T **1046**. Multicoloured.
2806 110pf. Bavarian Forest . . . 1·20 1·20
2807 110pf. North German Moors . . . . 1·20 1·20
2808 110pf. Luneburg Heath . . 1·20 1·20

1193 Rudolf Diesel and First Oil Engine

1997. Centenary of Diesel Engine.
2809 **1193** 300pf. black and blue 2·75 2·75

1194 Potato Plant and Cultivation

1997. 350th Anniv of Introduction of the Potato to Germany.
2810 **1194** 300pf. multicoloured . . 2·75 2·75

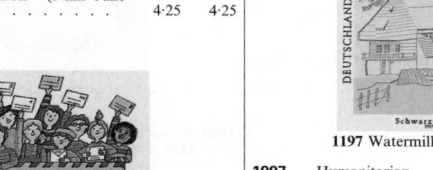

1195 Biplane and Motorized Tricycle

1997. Stamp Day. Sheet 70 × 105 mm.
MS2811 **1195** 440pf.+220pf. multicoloured . . . . 6·25 6·25

1196 Mendelssohn-Bartholdy and Music Score

1997. 150th Death Anniv of Felix Mendelssohn-Bartholdy (composer).
2813 **1196** 110pf. green, olive & yell . . . . 1·10 1·10

1197 Watermill, Black Forest

1997. Humanitarian Relief Funds. Mills. Multicoloured.
2814 100pf.+50pf. Type **1197** . . 1·80 1·80
2815 110pf.+50pf. Watermill, Hesse . . . . 2·00 2·00
2816 110pf.+50pf. Post mill, Lower Rhine . . . . . . 2·00 2·00
2817 110pf.+50pf. Scoop windmill, Schleswig-Holstein . . . . 2·00 2·00
2818 220pf.+80pf. Dutch windmill 3·00 3·00

1198 Emblem

1997. Saar–Lor–Lux European Region.
2819 **1198** 110pf. multicoloured . . 1·10 95

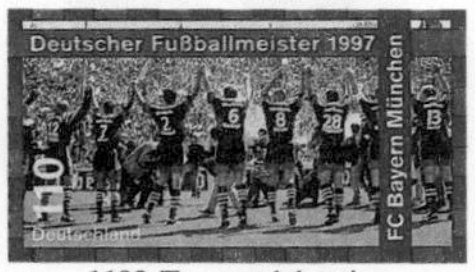

1199 Team celebrating

1997. Bayern Munchen, German Football Champions.
2820 **1199** 110pf. multicoloured . . 1·10 95

1200 Dehler

1997. Birth Centenary of Thomas Dehler (politician).
2821 **1200** 110pf. multicoloured . . 1·10 95

1201 Heine (after Wilhelm Hensel)

1997. Birth Bicentenary of Heinrich Heine (journalist and poet).
2822 **1201** 110pf. multicoloured . . 1·10 95

1202 Tree and Title of Hymn

1997. 300th Birth Anniv of Gerhard Tersteegen (religious reformer).
2823 **1202** 110pf. brown, grey and black . . . . 1·10 95

1203 Emblem

1997. Cent of Deutscher Caritas Verband (Catholic charitable association).
2824 **1203** 110pf. multicoloured . . 1·10 95

1204 Three Kings

1997. Christmas. Multicoloured.
2825 100pf.+50pf. Type **1204** . . 1·40 1·40
2826 110pf.+50pf. Nativity . . . 1·70 1·70
The premium was for the benefit of the Federal Association of Free Welfare Work, Bonn.

1205 Monastery Plan and Church

1998. U.N.E.S.C.O. World Heritage Site. Maulbronn Monastery.
2827 **1205** 100pf. multicoloured . . 95 95

1206 Walled City

1998. 1100th Anniv of Nordlingen.
2828 **1206** 110pf. multicoloured . . 1·10 95

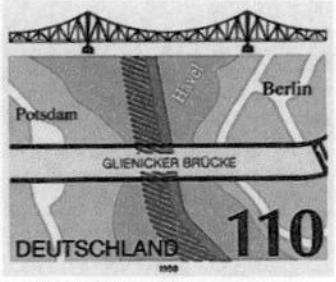

1207 Glienicke Bridge, Potsdam–Berlin

1998. Bridges. (1st series).
2829 **1207** 110pf. multicoloured . . 1·10 95
See also Nos. 2931, 2956 and 3046.

1208 Football

1998. Sport Promotion Fund. International Championships. Multicoloured.
2830 100pf.+50pf. Type **1208** (World Cup Football Championship, France) 1·40 1·40
2831 110pf.+50pf. Ski jumping (Winter Olympic Games, Nagano, Japan) . . . . . 1·60 1·60
2832 110pf.+50pf. Rowing (World Rowing Championships, Cologne) . . . . 1·60 1·60
2833 300pf.+100pf. Disabled skier (Winter Paralympic Games, Nagano) . . . . 4·00 4·00

1209 Characters in Brecht's Head

1998. Birth Centenary of Bertolt Brecht (dramatist).
2834 **1209** 110pf. multicoloured . . 1·10 95

1210 X-ray Photographs of Moon, Ionic Lattice Structure and Nerve of Goldfish and Founding Assembly

1998. 50th Anniv of Max Planck Society for the Advancement of Science.
2835 **1210** 110pf. multicoloured . . 1·10 95

1211 Bad Frankenhausen

1998. Millenary of First Documentary Mention of Bad Frankenhausen.
2836 **1211** 110pf. multicoloured . . 1·10 95

1212 Signatories

1998. 350th Anniv of Peace of Westphalia (settlements ending Thirty Years' War).
2837 **1212** 110pf. blk, grey & mve 1·10 95

1213 Baden-Wurttemberg (Kurt Viertel)

1998. Federal State Parliament Buildings (1st series). Multicoloured.
2838 110pf. Type **1213** . . . . . 1·10 1·10
2839 110pf. Bavaria (designed Friedrich Burklein) . . . 1·10 1·10
2840 110pf. Chamber of Deputies, Berlin (Friedrich Schulze) 1·10 1·10
2841 110pf. Brandenburg (Franz Schwechten) . . . . . . 1·10 1·10
See also Nos. 2885, 2893/4, 2897, 2953, 2957, 2978, 3025, 3043, 3052, 3064 and 3071.

1214 Hildegard's Vision of Life Cycle

1998. 900th Birth Anniv of Hildegard of Bingen (writer and mystic).
2842 **1214** 100pf. multicoloured . . 95 95

1215 Marine Life

1998. "For Us Children". Sheet 110 × 66 mm.
MS2843 **1215** 110pf. multicoloured 1·20 1·20

1216 St. Marienstern Abbey

1998. 750th Anniv of St. Marienstern Abbey, Panschwitz-Kuckau.
2844 **1216** 110pf. multicoloured . . 1·10 1·10

1217 Auditorium

1998. 250th Anniv of Bayreuth Opera House.
2845 **1217** 300pf. multicoloured . . 2·75 2·75

1218 Junger **1219** Doves and Tree (German Unification Day)

1998. Ernst Junger (writer) Commemoration.
2846 **1218** 110pf. multicoloured . . 1·10 95

1998. Europa. National Festivals.
2847 **1219** 110pf. multicoloured . . 1·10 95

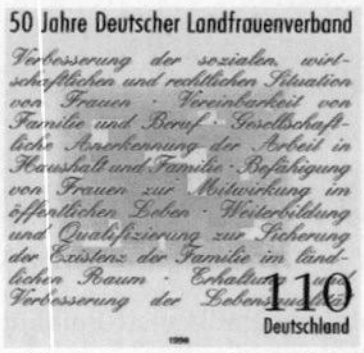

1220 Association Manifesto

1998. 50th Anniv of German Rural Women's Association.
2848 **1220** 110pf. grn, emer & blk 1·30 1·30

1221 Opening Session of Parliamentary Council, 1948

1998. Parliamentary Anniversaries. Sheet 105 × 70 mm containing T **1221** and similar square design. Multicoloured.
MS2849 110pf. Type **1221**; 220pf. First German National Assembly, St. Paul's Church, Frankfurt, 1848 3·00 3·00

1222 Coast and Ocean

1998. Environmental Protection.
2850 **1222** 110pf.+50pf. mult . . . 1·50 1·50

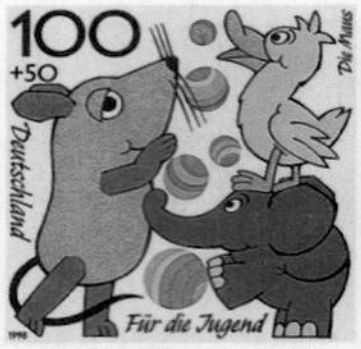

1223 "The Mouse" **1224** Crowds of People and Cross

1998. Youth Welfare. Children's Cartoons. Multicoloured.
2851 100pf.+50pf. Type **1223** . . 1·30 1·30
2852 100pf.+50pf. "The Sandman" . . . . . . 1·30 1·30
2853 110pf.+50pf. "Maja the Bee" . . . . 1·60 1·60
2854 110pf.+50pf. "Captain Bluebear" . . . . . . 1·60 1·60
2855 220pf.+80pf. "Pumuckl" . . . 3·25 3·25

1998. 150th Anniv of First Congress of German Catholics.
2856 **1224** 110pf. multicoloured . . 1·10 95

1225 One Deutschmark Coin

1998. 50th Anniv of the Deutschmark.
2857 **1225** 110pf. multicoloured . . 1·10 95

1226 Harvesting Hops

1998. 1100 Years of Hop Cultivation in Germany.
2858 **1226** 110pf. multicoloured . . 1·10 95

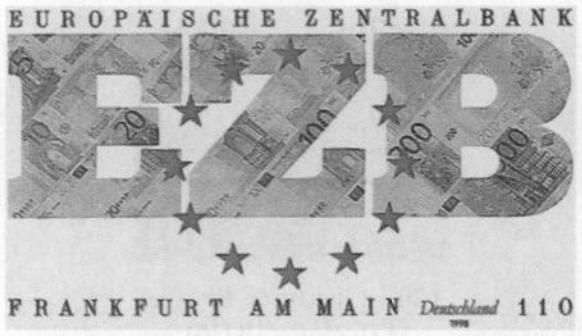

1227 Euro Banknotes forming "EZB"

1998. Inauguration of European Central Bank, Frankfurt am Main.
2859 **1227** 110pf. multicoloured . . 1·10 95

1228 Rock Face, Elbe Sandstone Mountains

1998. Saxon Switzerland National Park. Sheet 105 × 70 mm containing T **1228** and similar square design. Multicoloured.
MS2860 110pf. Type **1228**; 220pf. Elbe Sandstone Mountains . . 3·00 3·00

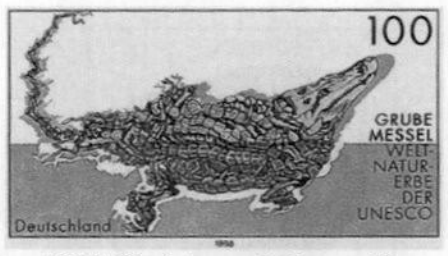

1229 Skeleton of Crocodile

1998. U.N.E.S.C.O. World Heritage Sites. Grube Messel Fossil Deposits.
2861 **1229** 100pf. multicoloured . 95 95

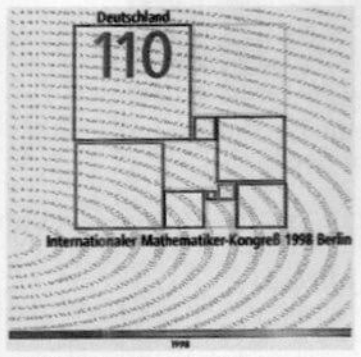

1230 Coloured Squares and Ludolphian Number **1231** Wurzburg Palace

1998. 23rd International Congress of Mathematicians, Berlin.
2862 **1230** 110pf. multicoloured . . 1·10 95

1998. U.N.E.S.C.O. World Heritage Sites. Multicoloured.
2863 110pf. Type **1231** . . . . . 1·10 1·10
2864 110pf. Puning Temple, Chengde, China . . . . . 1·10 1·10

1232 Glasses (Peter Behrens)

1998. Contemporary Design (1st series). Sheet 138 × 97 mm containing T **1232** and similar horiz designs. Multicoloured.
MS2865 110pf. Type **1232**; 110pf. Teapot (Marianne Brandt); 110pf. Table lamp (Wilhelm Wagenfeld); 110pf. "Wassily" chair (Marcel Breuer) . . . . 4·25 4·25
See also No. **MS**2922.

1233 Players, Ball and Pitch

1998. 1st FC Kaiserslautern, National Football Champions, 1998.
2866 **1233** 110pf. multicoloured . . 1·10 95

1234 Main Building **1235** Hausmann and Book Cover

1998. 300th Anniv of Francke Charitable Institutions, Halle.
2867 **1234** 110pf. multicoloured . . 1·10 95

1998. Birth Centenary of Manfred Hausmann (writer).
2868 **1235** 100pf. multicoloured . . 1·10 95

1236 Hands on T-shirt **1237** Hen Harriers and Chicks

1998. Child Protection.
2869 **1236** 110pf. red and black . . 1·10 95

1998. Humanitarian Relief Funds. Birds. Multicoloured.
2870 100pf.+50pf. Type **1237** . . 1·30 1·30
2871 110pf.+50pf. Great bustards 1·60 1·60
2872 110pf.+50pf. Ferruginous ducks . . . . 1·60 1·60
2873 110pf.+50pf. Aquatic warblers on reeds . . . . 1·60 1·60
2874 220pf.+80pf. Woodchat shrike . . . . 3·00 3·00

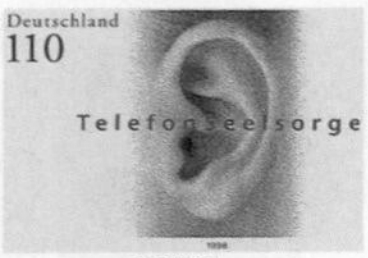

1238 Ear

1998. Telephone Help Lines.
2875 **1238** 110pf. black and orange 1·10 95

1239 "Hiorten" (sailing packet), 1692

1998. Stamp Day.
2876 **1239** 110pf. multicoloured . . 1·10 95

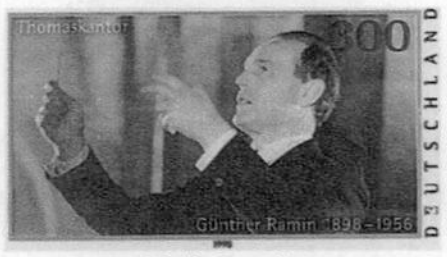

1240 Ramin

1998. Birth Centenary of Gunther Ramin (choir leader and organist).
2877 **1240** 300pf. multicoloured . . 2·75 2·75

1241 Shepherds following Star

1998. Christmas. Multicoloured.
2878 100pf.+50pf. Type **1241** . . 1·40 1·40
2879 110pf.+50pf. Baby Jesus . . 1·60 1·60

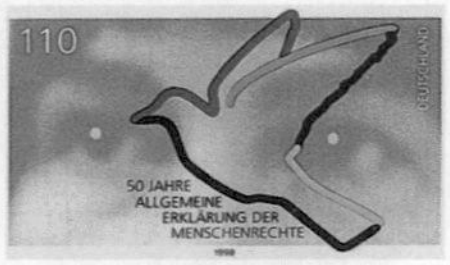

1242 Dove

1998. 50th Anniv of Declaration of Human Rights.
2880 **1242** 110pf. multicoloured . . 1·10 95
For charity stamp for Kosovo Relief Fund in similar design see No. 2899.

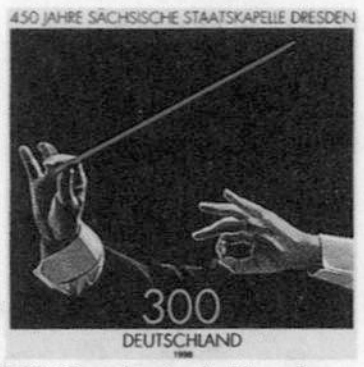

1243 Conductor's Hands and Baton

1998. 450th Anniv of Saxony State Orchestra, Dresden.
2881 **1243** 300pf. multicoloured . . 2·75 2·75

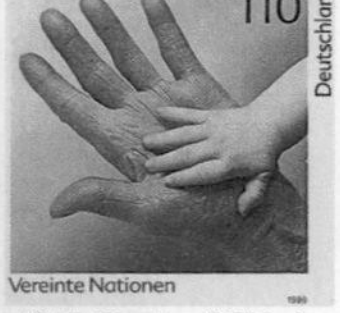

1244 National Theatre, Schiller, Goethe, Wieland and Herder **1245** Hands of Elderly Person and Child

1999. 1100th Anniv of Weimar, European City of Culture.
2882 **1244** 100pf. multicoloured . . 95 95

1999. International Year of the Elderly.
2883 **1245** 110pf. multicoloured . . 1·10 95

1246 Katharina von Bora

1999. 500th Birth Anniv of Katharina von Bora (wife of Martin Luther).
2884 **1246** 110pf. multicoloured . . 1·10 95

1999. Federal State Parliament Buildings (2nd series). As T **1213**.
2885 110pf. Hesse (Richard Goerz) (former palace of Dukes of Hesse) . . . . 1·10 95

1247 Cycle Racing

1999. Sport Promotion Fund. Multicoloured.
2886 100pf.+50pf. Type **1247** . . 1·40 1·40
2887 110pf.+50pf. Horse racing 1·60 1·60
2888 110pf.+50pf. Motor racing 1·60 1·60
2889 300pf.+100pf. Motor cycle racing . . . . 4·00 4·00

1248 Cover Illustration (by Walter Trier) of "Emil and the Detectives" (novel)

1999. Birth Centenary of Erich Kastner (writer).
2890 **1248** 300pf. multicoloured . . 2·75 2·75

1249 Coloured Diodes

1999. 50th Anniv of Fraunhofer Society (for applied research).
2891 **1249** 110pf. multicoloured . . 1·10 95

1250 Emblem and Initials

1999. 50th Anniv of North Atlantic Treaty Organization.
2892 **1250** 110pf. multicoloured . . 1·10 95

1999. Federal State Parliament Buildings (3rd series). As T **1213**. Multicoloured.
2893 110pf. City Parliament of Hamburg . . . . 1·10 1·10
2894 110pf. Mecklenburg-Western Pomerania (Schwerin Castle, rebuilt by Georg Demmler and Friedrich Stuler) . . . . 1·10 1·10

1251 Maybach Cabriolet of 1936 and Club Emblem

1999. Centenary of German Automobile Club.
2895 **1251** 110pf. multicoloured . . 1·10 95

1252 Emblem

1999. 25th Anniv of German Cancer Relief.
2896 **1252** 110pf. multicoloured . . 1·10 95

1999. Federal State Parliament Buildings (4th series). As T **1213**.
2897 110pf. Bremen (Wassili Luckhardt) . . . . 1·10 95

1253 "Man, Nature, Technology"

1999. "EXPO 2000" World's Fair, Hanover (1st issue).
2898 **1253** 110pf. multicoloured . . 1·10 95
See also Nos. 2936, 2959 and 2979.

1999. Kosovo Relief Fund. As T **1242** but with inscription changed to "KOSOVO–HILFE 1999".
2899 110pf.+100pf. multicoloured 2·00 2·00

1254 Bavaria 1849 1k. and Saxony 1850 3pf. Stamps

1999. "iBRA'99" International Stamp Exhibition, Nuremberg. Sheet 140 × 100 mm.
MS2900 **1254** 300pf.+110pf. black, red and gold/cream . . . . . 3·75 3·75

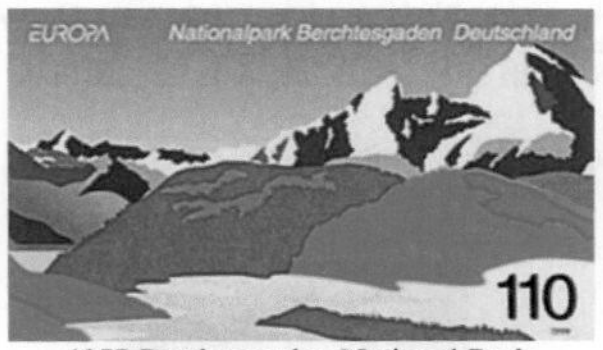

1255 Berchtesgaden National Park

1999. Europa. Parks and Gardens. Sheet 110 × 66 mm.
MS2901 **1255** 110pf. multicoloured 1·10 95

1256 Cross of St. John

1999. 900th Anniv of Order of Knights of St. John of Jerusalem.
2902 **1256** 110pf. multicoloured . . 1·10 95

1257 Flags and Children

1999. 50th Anniv of Berlin Airlift of 1948–49.
2903 **1257** 110pf. multicoloured . . 1·10 95

1258 Emblem

1999. 50th Anniv of Council of Europe.
2904 **1258** 110pf. multicoloured . . 1·10 95

1259 State Arms and Article 1

1999. 50th Anniv of German Basic Law. Sheet 110 × 66 mm.
MS2905 **1259** 110pf. multicoloured 1·10 95

1260 Politicians and New Parliament Chamber, Berlin

1999. 50th Anniv of Federal Republic of Germany. Sheet 138 × 97 mm containing T **1260** and similar horiz designs. Multicoloured.
MS2906 110pf. Type **1260**; 110pf. Child playing in rubble and child among flowers; 110pf. Berlin Wall and its fall; 110pf. Soldiers confronting civilians and debating chamber . . . . 4·25 4·25

1261 Lars, the Little Polar Bear

1999. Youth Welfare. Cartoon Characters. Mult.
2907 100pf.+50pf. Type **1261** . . 1·30 1·30
2908 100pf.+50pf. Rudi the Crow 1·30 1·30
2909 110pf.+50pf. Twipsy (mascot of "Expo 2000" World's Fair, Hanover) . . . . . 1·60 1·60
2910 110pf.+50pf. Mecki (hedgehog) . . . . 1·60 1·60
2911 220pf.+80pf. Tabaluga (dragon) . . . . 3·00 3·00

1262 Cross Clasp, Altar, Cathedral Spire and Time-line

1999. 1200th Anniv of Paderborn Diocese.
2912 **1262** 110pf. multicoloured . . 1·10 95

1263 House (child's painting) **1264** "Ball at the Viennese Hofburg" and Score

1999. 50th Anniv of S.O.S. Children's Villages.
2913 **1263** 110pf. multicoloured . . 1·10 95

1999. Death Centenary of Johann Strauss the younger (composer).
2914 **1264** 300pf. multicoloured . . 2·75 2·75

1265 Children at Desks (tapestry)

1999. 115th Anniv of Dominikus-Ringeisen Institute for Disabled People, Ursberg.
2915 **1265** 110pf. multicoloured . . 1·10 95

1266 Heinemann

1999. Birth Centenary of Gustav Heinemann (President 1969–74).
2916 **1266** 110pf. grey and red . . 1·10 95

1267 "Old Woman laughing" (Ernst Barlach)

1999. Cultural Foundation of the Federal States (1st series). Sculptures. Multicoloured.
2917 110pf. Type **1267** . . . . . 1·20 1·20
2918 220pf. "Bust of a Thinker" (Wilhelm Lehmbruck) . . 2·00 2·00
See also Nos. 2960/1.

1268 Participating Countries and Dove

1999. Centenary of First Peace Conference, The Hague.
2919 **1268** 300pf. grey, red and blue . . . . 2·75 2·75

1269 Goethe (after J. K. Stieler)

1999. 250th Birth Anniv of Johann Wolfgang von Goethe (poet and playwright).
2920 **1269** 110pf. multicoloured . . 1·10 95

1270 Mouse carrying Letter

1999. "For Us Children". Sheet 105 × 71 mm.
MS2921 **1270** 110pf. multicoloured 1·10 95

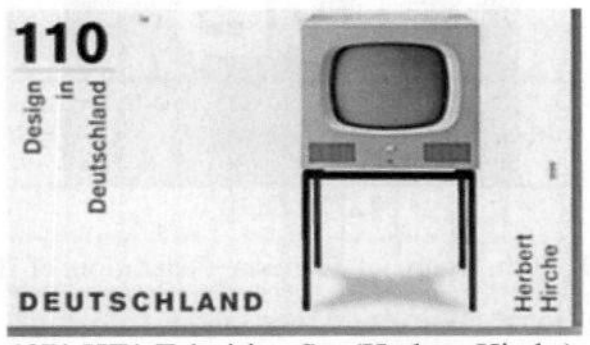

1271 HF1 Television Set (Herbert Hirche)

1999. Contemporary Design (2nd series). Sheet 138 × 97 mm containing T **1271** and similar horiz designs. Multicoloured.
MS2922 110pf. Type **1271**; 110pf. "Mono-a" cutlery (Peter Raacke); 110pf. Pearl bottles (Gunter Kupetz): 110pf. Transrapid Maglev train (Alexander Neumeister) . . . . 4·25 4·25

1272 Player

1999. FC Bayern Munich, National Football Champions.
2923 **1272** 110pf. multicoloured . . 1·10 95

1273 Book and Bookmark

1999. 50th Anniv of Federal Association of German Book Traders' Peace Prize.
2924 **1273** 110pf. multicoloured . . 1·10 95

1274 Strauss and Poster from "Salome" (opera)

1999. 50th Death Anniv of Richard Strauss (composer).
2925 **1274** 300pf. multicoloured . . 2·75 2·75

1275 Andromeda Galaxy

1999. Humanitarian Relief Funds. Outer Space. Multicoloured.
2926 100pf.+50pf. Type **1275** . . 1·40 1·40
2927 100pf.+50pf. Swan constellation . . . . . . 1·40 1·40
2928 110pf.+50pf. X-ray image of exploding star . . . . 1·60 1·60
2929 110pf.+50pf. Comet colliding with Jupiter . . 1·60 1·60
2930 300pf.+100pf. Gamma ray image of sky . . . . . . 4·00 4·00

1276 Goltzsch Valley Railway Bridge

1999. Bridges (2nd series).
2931 **1276** 110pf. multicoloured . . 1·10 95

1277 "DGB"

1999. 50th Anniv of German Federation of Trade Unions.
2932 **1277** 110pf. black and bright red . . . . 1·10 95

1278 Greater Horseshoe Bats

1999. Endangered Species.
2933 **1278** 100pf. multicoloured . . 95 95

1279 The Annunciation

1999. Christmas. Multicoloured.
2934 100pf.+50pf. Type **1279** . . 1·40 1·40
2935 110pf.+50pf. Nativity . . . 1·60 1·60

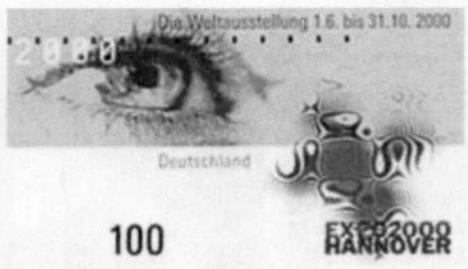

1280 Emblem and Eye

2000. "EXPO 2000" World's Fair, Hanover (2nd issue).
2936 **1280** 100pf. multicoloured . . 95 95

1281 Emblem

2000. Holy Year 2000.
2937 **1281** 110pf. multicoloured . . 1·10 95

1282 Charlemagne and Plan of Palace Chapel

2000. 1200th Anniv of Aachen Cathedral.
2938 **1282** 110pf. multicoloured . . 1·10 95

1283 Schweitzer and Signature

2000. 125th Birth Anniv of Albert Schweitzer (missionary doctor).
2939 **1283** 110pf. multicoloured . . 1·10 95

1284 Football

2000. Centenary of German Football Association.
2940 **1284** 110pf. multicoloured . . 1·10 95

1285 Wehner

2000. 10th Death Anniv of Herbert Wehner (politician).
2941 **1285** 110pf. multicoloured . . 1·10 95

1286 Woman

2000. Prevention of Violence Against Women.
2942 **1286** 110pf. red, grey and black . . . . 1·10 95

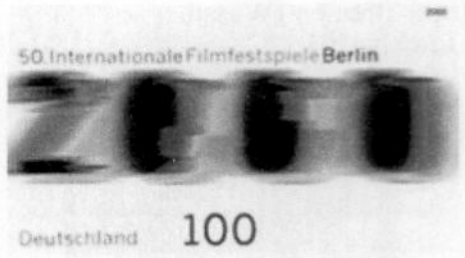

1287 "2000" in Moving Film Sequence

2000. 50th Berlin International Film Festival.
2943 **1287** 100pf. multicoloured . . 95 95

1288 Boxing

2000. Sport Promotion Fund. Multicoloured.
2944 100pf.+50pf. Type **1288** (fair play) . . . . 1·30 1·30
2945 110pf.+50pf. Rhythmic gymnastics (beauty) . . . 1·60 1·60
2946 110pf.+50pf. Running (competition) . . . . . . 1·60 1·60
2947 300pf.+100pf. Raised hands (culture of interaction) . . 4·00 4·00

1289 Gutenberg (after engraving by A. Thevet) and Letters from Gutenberg Bible

1290 Jester

2000. 600th Birth Anniv of Johannes Gutenberg (inventor of printing press).
2948 **1289** 110pf. black and red . . 1·10 95

2000. 175th Anniv of First Dusseldorf Carnival.
2949 **1290** 110pf. multicoloured . . 1·10 95

1291 Ebert

2000. 75th Death Anniv of Friedrich Ebert (President, 1919–25).
2950 **1291** 110pf. multicoloured . . 1·10 95

1292 Weill at Rehearsal of "One Touch of Venus" (musical), 1943

2000. Birth Centenary of Kurt Weill (composer).
2951 **1292** 300pf. blk, stone & red 2·75 2·75

1293 Passau

2000. Images of Germany.
2952 **1293** 110pf. multicoloured . . 1·10 95

2000. Federal State Parliament Buildings (5th series). As T **1213**. Multicoloured.
2953 110pf. Leine Palace, Lower Saxony . . . . 1·10 95

1294 Trees

2000. Hainich National Park. Sheet 105 × 70 mm.
MS2954 **1294** 110pf. multicoloured 1·10 95

1295 Toy Windmill and "Post!"

2000.
2955 **1295** 110pf. multicoloured . . 1·10 95

1296 "Blue Wonder" Bridge, Dresden

2000. Bridges (3rd series).
2956 **1296** 100pf. multicoloured . . 95 95

2000. Federal State Parliament Buildings (6th series). As T **1213**. Multicoloured.
2957 110pf. North-Rhine/ Westphalia (Fritz Eller) . . 1·10 95

1297 City Buildings

2000. 750th Anniv of Greifswald.
2958 **1297** 110pf. multicoloured . . 1·10 95

2000. "EXPO 2000" World's Fair, Hanover (3rd issue). As No. 2898 but self-adhesive.
2959 **1253** 110pf. multicoloured . . 4·00 4·00

1298 "Expulsion from Paradise" (Leonhard Kern)

2000. Cultural Foundation of the Federal States. Sculptures. Multicoloured.
2960 110pf. Type **1298** . . . . 1·10 1·10
2961 220pf. Silver table fountain (Melchior Gelb) . . . . . 2·10 2·10

1299 "Building Europe"

2000. Europa. Ordinary or self-adhesive gum.
2962 **1299** 110pf. multicoloured . . 1·10 95

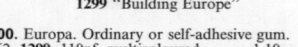

1300 Von Zinzendorf and Natives

2000. 300th Birth Anniv of Nikolaus Ludwig von Zinzendorf (leader of Moravian Brethren).
2964 **1300** 110pf. multicoloured . . 1·10 95

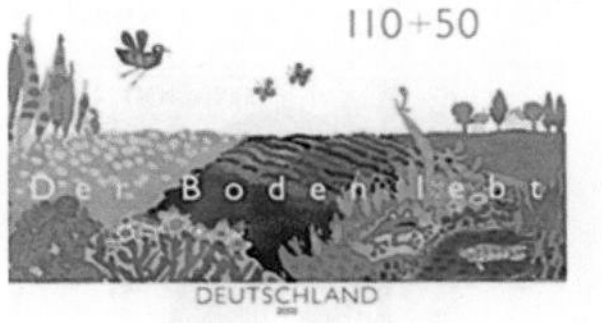

1301 Countryside

2000. Environmental Protection.
2965 **1301** 110pf.+50pf. mult . . . 1·50 1·50

1302 Crowd at Music Festival

2000. Youth Welfare. "EXPO 2000" World's Fair, Hanover (4th issue). Multicoloured.
2966 100pf.+50pf. Type **1302** . . 1·60 1·60
2967 100pf.+50pf. Back-packers 1·60 1·60
2968 110pf.+50pf. Map of Africa and text . . . . 1·80 1·80
2969 110pf.+50pf. Eye of Buddha 1·80 1·80
2970 110pf.+50pf. Chinese calligraphy . . . . 1·80 1·80
2971 300pf.+100pf. Psychedelic swirl . . . . 3·50 3·50

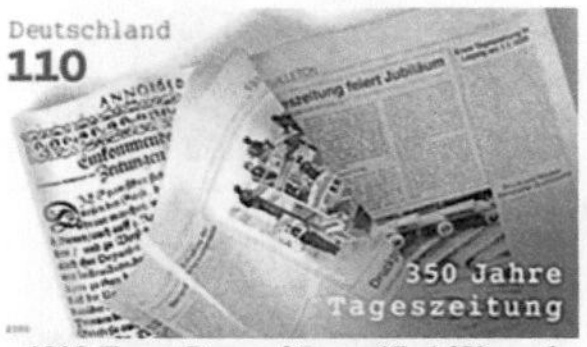

1303 Front Page of Issue 17, 1650, and Modern Pages of Newspaper

2000. 350th Anniv of Einkommende Zeitungen (first German daily newspaper).
2972 **1303** 110pf. multicoloured . . 1·10 95

1304 Emblem

2000. Centenary of Chambers of Handicrafts.
2973 **1304** 300pf. orange and black 2·75 2·75

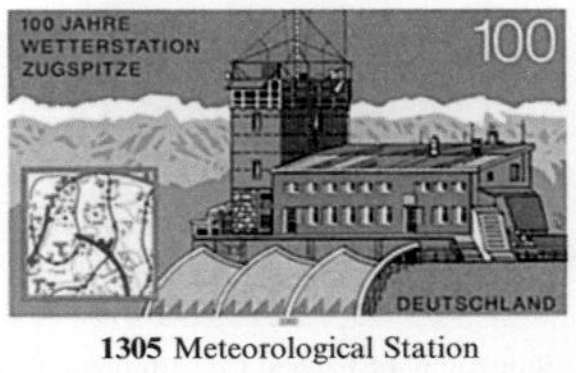

1305 Meteorological Station

2000. Centenary of the Zugspitze Meteorological Station.
2974 **1305** 100pf. multicoloured . . 95 95

1306 Road Sign and Flashing Light

2000. 50th Anniv of Technisches Hilfwerk (Federal disaster relief organization).
2975 **1306** 110pf. multicoloured . . 1·10 95

1307 Bach

2000. 250th Death Anniv of Johann Sebastian Bach (composer).
2976 **1307** 110pf. multicoloured . . 1·10 95

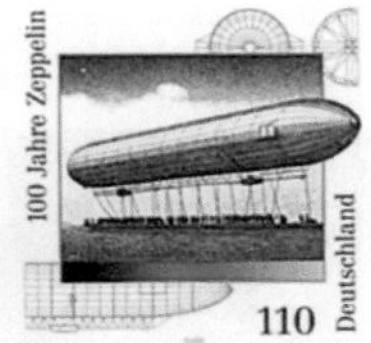

1308 LZ-1

2000. Centenary of Inaugural Flight of LZ-1 (Zeppelin airship), 1900.
2977 **1308** 110pf. multicoloured . . 1·10 95

2000. Federal State Parliament Buildings (7th series). As T **1213**. Multicoloured.
2978 110pf. Rhineland-Palatinate, Mainz . . . . 1·10 95

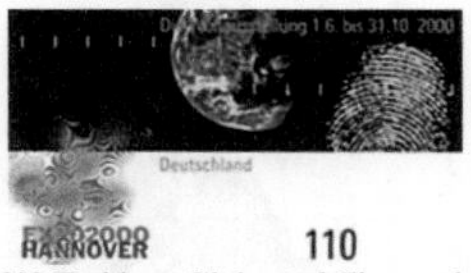

1309 Emblem, Globe and Fingerprint

2000. "EXPO 2000" World's Fair, Hanover (5th issue).
2979 **1309** 110pf. multicoloured . . 1·10 95

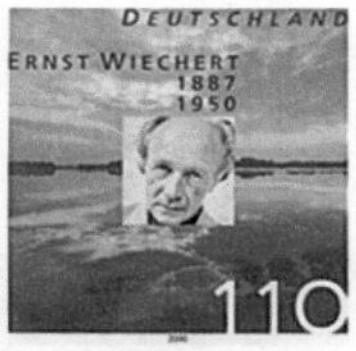

1310 Wiechert

2000. 50th Death Anniv of Ernst Wiechert (writer).
2980 **1310** 110pf. multicoloured . . 1·10 95

1311 Nietzsche (Edvard Munch)

2000. Death Centenary of Friedrich Nietzsche (philosopher).
2981 **1311** 110pf. multicoloured . . 1·10 95

1312 "For You"

2000. Greetings Stamp.
2982 **1312** 100pf. multicoloured . . 95 95

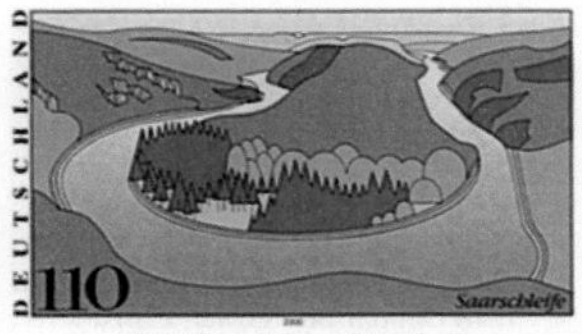

1313 Saar River, Mettlach

2000. Images of Germany.
2983 **1313** 110pf. multicoloured . . 1·10 95

1314 Adolph Kopling

2000. 150th Anniv of Kopling Society (voluntary organization).
2984 **1314** 110pf. multicoloured . . 1·10 95

1315 Building

2000. 50th Anniv of Federal Court of Justice.
2985 **1315** 110pf. multicoloured . . 1·10 95

1316 Clown's Face

2000. "For Us Children". Sheet 55 × 82 mm.
MS2986 **1316** 110pf. multicoloured 1·10 95

1317 Nocht (founder), World Map and Microscope Images of Pathogens

2000. Centenary of Bernard Nocht Institute for Tropical Medicine.
2987 **1317** 300pf. multicoloured . . 2·75 2·75

1318 Town Hall, Wernigerode **1319** National Colours

2000. Tourist Sights. Showing face values in German currency and euros.
2988 **1318** 10pf. grey, orge & slate 25 25
2989 – 20pf. orange and black 20 20
2990 – 47pf. mauve and green 45 45
2991 – 50pf. brown and red . . 55 55
2992 – 80pf. green and brown 75 75
2993 – 100pf. blue and brown 1·00 1·00
2994 – 110pf. pur, brn & orge 1·10 1·10
2997 – 220pf. blue and brown 2·00 2·00
3000 – 300pf. brown and blue 2·75 2·75
3001 – 400pf. brown and red 3·75 3·75
3002 – 440pf. black and grey 4·00 4·00
3003 – 510pf. pink and red . . 4·75 4·75
3004 – 720pf. purple & mauve 6·75 6·75
DESIGNS: 20pf. Bottcherstrasse, Bremen; 47pf. Wilhelmshohe Park, Kassel; 50pf. Ceiling decoration, Kircheim Castle; 80pf. St. Reinoldi Church, Dortmund; 100pf. Schwerin Castle, Mecklenberg; 110pf. Stone bridge, Regensburg; 220pf. St. Nikolai Cathedral, Greifswald; 300pf. Town Hall Grimma; 400pf. Wartburg Castle, Eisenach; 440pf. Cologne Cathedral; 510pf. Heidelberg Castle; 720pf. Town Hall, Hildesheim.
Nos. 2988, 2993/4 also come self-adhesive.

2000. 10th Anniv of Reunification of Germany.
3010 **1319** 110pf. black, red & yell 1·10 95

1320 Curd Jurgens

2000. Humanitarian Relief Funds. Actors. Mult.
3011 100pf.+50pf. Type **1320** . . 1·60 1·60
3012 100pf.+50pf. Lilli Palmer . . 1·60 1·60
3013 110pf.+50pf. Heinz Ruhmann . . . . 1·80 1·80
3014 110pf.+50pf. Romy Schneider . . . . 1·80 1·80
3015 300pf.+100pf. Gert Frobe 3·50 3·50

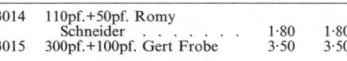

1321 Pens, Envelope and 1999 110pf. Stamp **1322** Grethe Weiser (actress and singer)

2000. Stamp Day.
3016 **1321** 110pf. multicoloured . . 1·10 1·10

2000. Famous German Women.
3017 **1322** 100pf. green and brown 90 90
3018 – 110pf. red and green . . 1·10 1·10
3019 – 220pf. brown and green 2·00 2·00
3020 – 300pf. purple and brown . . . . 2·75 2·75
DESIGNS: 110pf. Kate Strobel (politician); 200pf. Marieluise Fleisser (writer); 300pf. Nelly Sachs (writer).

2000. Federal State Parliament Buildings (8th series). As T **1213**. Multicoloured.
3025 110pf. Saarland . . . . . . 1·10 95

1323 Book Cover **1324** Bode

2000. 125th Birth Anniv of Rainer Maria Rilke (poet).
3026 **1323** 110pf. multicoloured . . 1·10 95

2000. Birth Centenary of Arnold Bode (artist).
3027 **1324** 110pf. black and red . . 1·10 95

1325 "Birth of Christ" (Conrad von Soest)

2000. Christmas. Multicoloured.
3028 100pf.+50pf. Type **1325** . . 1·50 1·50
3029 110pf.+50pf. Nativity . . . 1·80 1·80

1326 Indian Pepper (illustration from *New Book of Herbs*)

2001. 500th Birth Anniv of Leonhart Fuchs (physician and botanist).
3030 **1326** 100pf. multicoloured . . 95 95

1327 "VdK"

2001. 50th Anniv (2000) of Disabled War Veterans' Association.
3031 **1327** 110pf. multicoloured . . 1·10 95

1328 Prussian Eagle

2001. 300th Anniv of the Kingdom of Prussia.
3032 **1328** 110pf. multicoloured . . 1·10 95

1329 Lortzing and Music Score

2001. Birth Bicent of Albert Lortzing (composer).
3033 **1329** 110pf. multicoloured . . 1·10 95

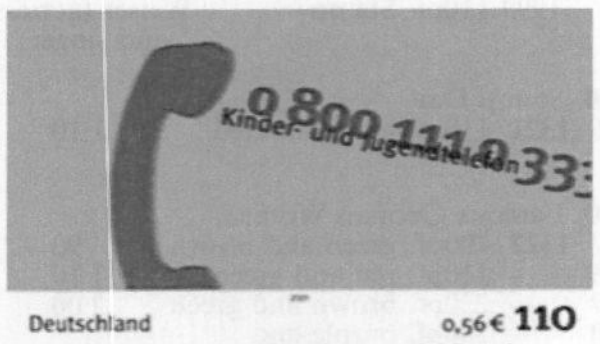

1330 Telephone Handset and Number

2001. National Federation of Child and Youth Telephone Helplines.
3034 **1330** 110pf. yellow, red & blk 1·10 95

1331 Bucer

2001. 450th Death Anniv of Martin Bucer (teacher and Protestant reformer).
3035 **1331** 110pf. multicoloured . . 1·10 95

1332 Children running

2001. Sport Promotion Fund. Multicoloured.
3036 100pf.+50pf. Type **1332** . . 1·40 1·40
3037 110pf.+50pf. Disabled and able-bodied athletes . . . 1·50 1·50
3038 110pf.+50pf. Adult and children skating . . . . . 1·50 1·50
3039 300pf.+100pf. Men playing basketball . . . . 3·75 3·75

1333 Hand holding Quill

2001. 250th Birth Anniv of Johann Heinrich Voss (writer and translator). (a) Ordinary gum.
3040 **1333** 300pf. multicoloured . . 2·75 2·75

(b) Self-adhesive gum.
3040a €1.53 multicoloured . . . 2·40 2·20

1334 Ollenhauer

2001. Birth Centenary of Erich Ollenhauer (politician).
3041 **1334** 110pf. red, black & sil 1·10 95

1335 Arnold

2001. Birth Centenary of Karl Arnold (politician).
3042 **1335** 110pf. black, green & red . . . . 1·10 95

2001. Federal State Parliament Buildings (9th series). As T **1213**. Multicoloured.
3043 110pf. Saxony . . . . . . 1·10 95

1336 Badge

2001. 50th Anniv of Federal Border Police.
3044 **1336** 110pf. multicoloured . . 1·10 95

1337 Suspension Railway

2001. Centenary of Suspension Railway, Wuppertal.
3045 **1338** 110pf.+50pf. mult . . . 1·50 1·50

1338 Rendsberg Railway Viaduct

2001. Bridges (4th series).
3046 **1338** 100pf. multicoloured . . 90 90

1339 "Post!"

2001.
3047 **1339** 110pf. multicoloured . . 1·10 95

1340 Accordion

2001. Folk Music.
3048 **1340** 110pf. multicoloured . . 1·10 95

1341 World Map

2001. 50th Anniv of Goethe Institute.
3049 **1341** 300pf. multicoloured 2·75 2·75

1342 Glass of Water

2001. Europa. Water Resources.
3050 **1342** 110pf. multicoloured . . 1·10 95

1343 Egk

2001. Birth Centenary of Werner Egk (composer and conductor).
3051 **1343** 110pf. multicoloured . . 1·10 95

2001. Federal State Parliament Buildings (10th series). As T **1213**. Multicoloured.
3052 110pf. Saxony-Anhalt . . . 1·10 95

1344 Mountain Gorilla with Young

2001. Endangered Species. Multicoloured. Ordinary or self-adhesive gum.
3053 110pf. Type **1344** . . . . . 1·10 1·10
3054 110pf. Indian rhinoceros with young . . . . 1·10 1·10

1345 Pinocchio

2001. Youth Welfare. Characters from Children's Stories. Multicoloured.
3057 100pf.+50pf. Type **1345** . . 1·40 1·40
3058 100pf.+50pf. Pippi Longstocking . . . . . . 1·40 1·40
3059 110pf.+50pf. Heidi and Peter . . . . 1·50 1·50
3060 110pf.+50pf. Jim Knopf . . 1·50 1·50
3061 300pf.+100pf. Tom Sawyer and Huckleberry Finn . . 3·50 3·50

1346 St. Catherine's Monastery and Oceanographic Chart

2001. 750th Anniv of St. Catherine's Monastery and 50th Anniv of German Oceanographic Museum, Stralsund.
3062 **1346** 110pf. multicoloured . . 1·10 95

1347 Church Exterior and Plan

2001. 250th Anniv of Catholic Court Church, Dresden.
3063 **1347** 110pf. multicoloured . . 1·10 95

2001. Federal State Parliament Buildings (11th series). As T **1213**. Multicoloured.
3064 110pf. Schleswig-Holstein . . 1·10 95

1348 Church Bell Tower, Canzow

2001.
3065 **1348** 110pf. black, blue and mauve . . . . 1·10 95

1349 Hand (circulatory disease)

2001. Health Awareness Campaign. Sheet 138 × 110 mm containing T **1349** and similar horiz designs. Multicoloured.
MS3066 110pf. Type **1349**; 110pf. Torso (cancer); 110pf. Lower body (infectious diseases); 110pf. Man holding head (depression) . . . 4·25 4·25

1350 Emblem

2001. Dragon Lancing Festival, Furth im Wald.
3067 **1350** 100pf. multicoloured . . 95 90

1351 Lime Tree, Himmelsberg

2001. Natural Heritage. Ordinary or self-adhesive gum.
3068 **1351** 110pf. multicoloured . . 1·10 95

1352 "Schoolmaster Lampel" (Wilhelm Busch) and Text

2001. Lifelong Learning.
3070 **1352** 110pf. multicoloured . . 1·10 95

1353 Felix standing on Cat

2001. "For Us Children". Sheet 110 × 66 mm.
MS3071 **1353** 110pf. multicoloured 1·10 95

2001. Federal State Parliament Buildings (12th series). As T **1213**. Multicoloured.
3072 110pf. Thuringia . . . . . 1·10 95

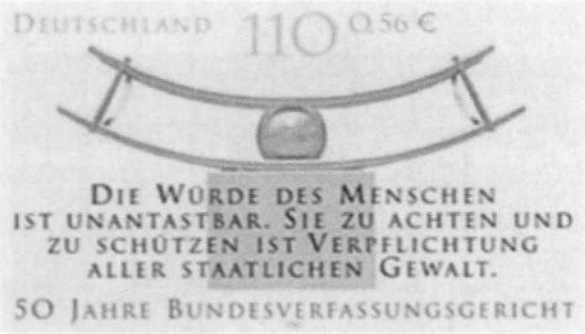

1354 "Justice" (sculpture)

2001. 50th Anniv of Federal Constitutional Court.
3073 **1354** 110pf. multicoloured . . 1·10 95

1355 Members' Flags

2001. 1st Union Network International World Congress, Berlin.
3074 **1355** 110pf. multicoloured . . 1·10 95

1356 Museum Floor Plan

2001. Jewish Museum, Berlin.
3075 **1356** 110pf. multicoloured . . 1·10 95

1357 Marilyn Monroe

2001. Humanitarian Relief Funds. Film Industry. Multicoloured.
3076 100pf.+50pf. Type **1357** . . 1·40 1·40
3077 100pf.+50pf. Charlie Chaplin . . . . 1·40 1·40
3078 110pf.+50pf. Greta Garbo 1·50 1·50
3079 110pf.+50pf. Film reel . . . 1·50 1·50
3080 300pf.+100pf. Jean Gabin 3·75 3·75
MS3080a 205 × 156 mm. As Nos. 3076/80 . . . . 9·00 9·00

1358 Ribbon and "fur Dich"

2001. Greetings Stamp.
3081 **1358** 110pf. red and black . . 1·10 95

1359 "Virgin and Child" (Alfredo Roldan)

2001. Christmas. Religious Paintings. Mult.
3082 100pf.+50pf. Type **1359** . . 1·40 1·40
3083 110pf.+50pf. "The Shepherd's Adoration" (Jusepe de Ribera) . . . . 1·50 1·50

1360 *Gauss* (survey barquentine)

2001. Centenary of German Antarctic Research. Sheet 135 × 105 mm containing T **1360** and similar horiz design. Multicoloured.
MS3084 110pf. Type **1360**; 220pf. *Polarstern* (exploration ship) 3·00 3·00

1361 Heisenberg

2001. Birth Centenary of Werner Heisenberg (physicist).
3085 **1361** 300pf. black and blue 2·75 2·75

New Currency. 100 cents = 1 euro

1362 Bautzen

2002. Millenary of Bautzen. Ordinary or self-adhesive gum.
3086 **1362** 56c. multicoloured . . . 1·10 1·10

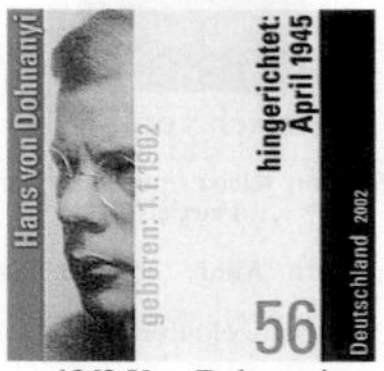

1363 Von Dohnanyi

2002. Birth Centenary of Hans von Dohnanyi (German resistance co-ordinator).
3087 **1363** 56c. multicoloured . . . 1·10 1·10

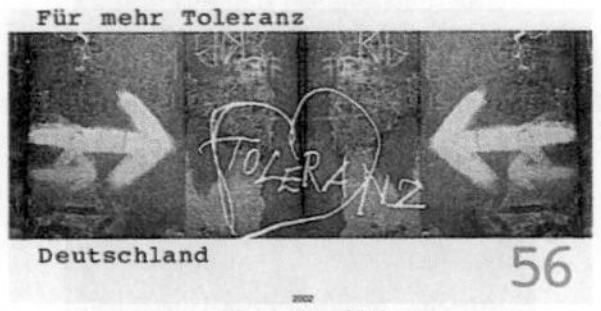

1364 Graffiti

2002. "Tolerance".
3088 **1364** 56c. multicoloured . . . 1·10 1·10

1365 "€"

2002. New Currency. Ordinary or self-adhesive gum.
3089 **1365** 56c. yellow and blue . . 1·10 1·10

1366 Mountains

2002. International Year of Mountains.
3091 **1366** 56c. + 26c. multicoloured . . . . 1·50 1·50

No. 3091 was sold with a premium towards environmental protection.

1367 Cross-country Skier (biathlon)

2002. Winter Olympic Games, Salt Lake City, U.S.A. Multicoloured.
3092 51c. + 26c. Type **1367** . . . 1·40 1·40
3093 56c. + 26c. Ice skater (speed skating) . . . . 1·50 1·50
3094 56c. + 26c. Skier (ski jumping) . . . . 1·50 1·50
3095 153c. + 51c. Man in helmet (luge) . . . . 3·75 3·75
MS3096 142 × 98 mm. As Nos. 3092/5 . . . . 8·25 8·25

Nos. 3092/**MS**3096 were sold with a premium towards "Foundation for the Promotion of Sport in Germany".

1368 Knigge and Books

2002. 250th Birth Anniv of Adolf Freiherr Knigge (author of *Uber den Umgang mit Menschen* (book on etiquette)).
3097 **1368** 56c. multicoloured . . . 1·10 1·10

1369 Front of Train Carriage

2002. Centenary of Berlin Subway.
3098 **1369** 56c. multicoloured . . . 1·10 1·10

1370 Deggendorf

2002. Millenary of Deggendorf.
3099 **1370** 56c. multicoloured . . . 1·10 1·10

1371 Mechanical Calculator (Johann Christoph Schuster)

2002. Cultural Foundation of the Federal States.
3100 **1371** 56c. multicoloured . . . 1·10 1·10

1372 Ecksberg Pilgrimage Church

2002. 150th Anniv of Ecksberg Foundation (for people with disabilities).
3101 **1372** 56c. multicoloured . . . 1·10 1·10

1373 Exhibits and Building

2002. Centenary of Freemason's Museum, Bayreuth.
3102 **1373** 56c. multicoloured . . . 1·10 1·10

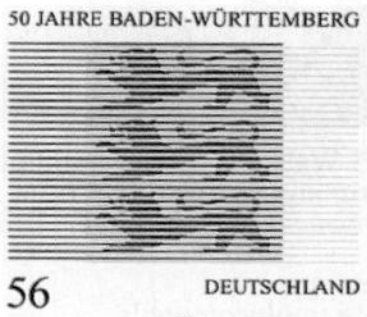

1374 Armorial Lions

2002. 50th Anniv of Baden-Württenberg State.
3103 **1374** 56c. black, gold and yellow . . . . 1·10 1·10

1375 "post"

2002.
3104 **1375** 56c. multicoloured . . . 1·10 1·10

1376 Emblem

2002. 50th Anniv of Federal Employment Services.
3105 **1376** €1.53 red and black 2·75 2·75

1377 Modern Student and Elector Friedrich the Wise (founder of Wittenberg University

2002. 500th Anniv of Martin Luther University, Halle-Wittenberg.
3106 **1377** 56c. grey, blue and mauve . . . . 1·10 1·10

1378 "KINDERGOTTESDIENST!"

2002. 150th Anniv of Children's Church Services.
3107 **1378** 56c. multicoloured . . . 95 95

1379 "Documenta11"

2002. 11th "Documenta" Modern Art Exhibition, Kassel. Sheet 100 × 70 mm.
MS3108 **1379** 56c. ultramarine, lilac and blue . . . . 1·10 1·10

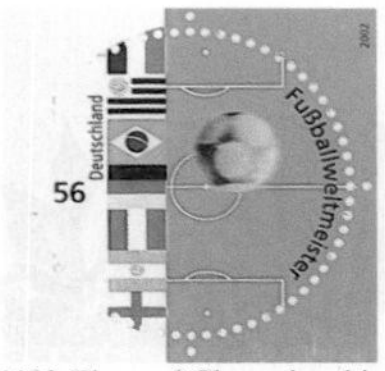

1380 Flags of Championship Winners and Football

2002. 20th-century World Cup Football Champions. Multicoloured.
3109 56c. Type **1380** . . . . . . 1·10 1·10
3110 56c. German Footballer . . 1·10 1·10

1381 Clown

2002. Europa. Circus. Ordinary or self-adhesive gum.
3111 **1381** 56c. black, red and green . . . . 1·10 1·10

1382 Dessau-Worlitz

2002. U.N.E.S.C.O. World Heritage Site. Dessau-Worlitz Gardens. Ordinary or self-adhesive gum.
3113 **1382** 56c. multicoloured . . . 1·10 1·10

1383 Thaer

2002. 250th Birth Anniv of Albrecht Daniel Thaer (agronomist).
3115 **1383** €2.25 multicoloured 4·25 4·25

1384 Desmoulin's Whorl Snail

2002. Endangered Species. Molluscs. Multicoloured.
3116 51c. Type **1384** 95 95
3117 56c. Freshwater pearl mussel 1·10 1·10

1385 Chess Pieces

2002. Youth Welfare. Toys. Multicoloured.
3118 51c. + 26c. Type **1385** . . . 1·40 1·40
3119 51c. + 26c. Wooden crane 1·40 1·40
3120 56c. + 26c. Doll . . . . . 1·50 1·50
3121 56c. + 26c. Teddy bear . . 1·50 1·50
3122 153c. + 51c. Electric train 3·75 3·75

1386 "Yellow Feather in Red"

2002. Birth Centenary of Ernst Wilhelm Nay (artist).
3123 **1386** 56c. multicoloured . . . 1·10 1·10

1387 Leaves and Silhouettes

2002. 40th Anniv of "Deutsche Welthungerhilfe" (humanitarian aid organization).
3124 **1387** 51c. multicoloured . . . 95 95

1388 "Way of Human Rights" (sculpture, Danni Karavan)

2002. 150th Anniv of National Museum of German Art and Culture, Nuremberg.
3125 **1388** 56c. multicoloured . . . 1·10 1·10

1389 Hesse

2002. 125th Birth Anniv of Hermann Hesse (writer).
3126 **1389** 56c. blue and yellow . . 1·10 1·10

1390 Trees and Rocks

2002. Hochharz National Park. Sheet 110 × 66 mm.
MS3127 **1390** 56c. multicoloured 1·10 1·10

1391 Felder

2002. 2nd Death Anniv of Josef Felder (politician and journalist).
3128 **1391** 56c. multicoloured . . . 1·10 1·10

1392 Museum Buildings

2002. U.N.E.S.C.O. World Heritage Site. Museum Island, Berlin.
3129 **1392** 56c. black and green . . 1·10 1·10

1393 Firemen fighting Fire

2002. Voluntary Fire Brigades.
3130 **1393** 56c. multicoloured . . . 1·10 1·10

1394 Building Facade

2002. 130th Anniv of Communications Museum, Berlin
3131 **1394** 153c. multicoloured . . 2·75 2·75

2002. Flood Relief. As T **1222** but with "HOCHWASSERHILFE 2002" inscribed at left and new face value.
3132 56c. + 44c. multicoloured 2·20 2·20

1395 Walls of Roman Bathhouse, Wurmlingen (illustration from *Die Alammannen* by Konrad Theiss)

2002. Archaeology.
3133 **1395** 51c. multicoloured . . . 95 95

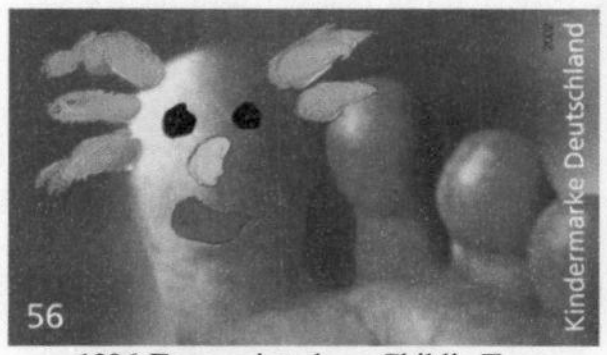

1396 Face painted on Child's Toe

2002. "For Us Children". Sheet 110 × 66 mm.
MS3134 **1396** 56c. multicoloured 1·10 1·10

1397 "Rotes Elisabeth-Ufer" (painting, Ernst Ludwig Kirchner)

2002.
3135 **1397** 112c. multicoloured . . 1·90 1·90

1398 Von Kleist (miniature, Peter Friedel)

2002. 225th Birth Anniv of Heinrich von Kleist (writer).
3136 **1398** 56c. multicoloured . . . 1·10 1·10

1399 Jochum rehearsing

2002. Birth Centenary of Eugen Jochum (conductor).
3137 **1399** 56c. multicoloured . . . 1·10 1·10

1400 Diagram of Planets (Copernicus), Horsemen and Sphere

2002. 400th Birth Anniv of Otto von Guericke (engineer and physicist).
3138 **1400** 153c. multicoloured . . 2·75 2·75

1401 Angel (detail, "The Annunciation")

2002. Christmas. Paintings by Rogier van der Weyden. Multicoloured.
3139 51c. + 26c. Type **1401** . . . 1·40 1·40
3140 56c. + 26c. The Holy Family (detail, Miraflores alterpiece) . . . . 1·50 1·50

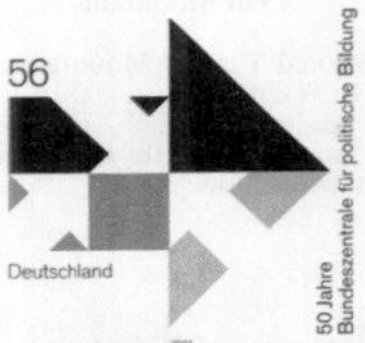

1402 Arrows

2002. 50th Anniv of Federal Agency for Civic Education.
3141 **1402** 56c. black, red and yellow . . . . 1·10 1·10

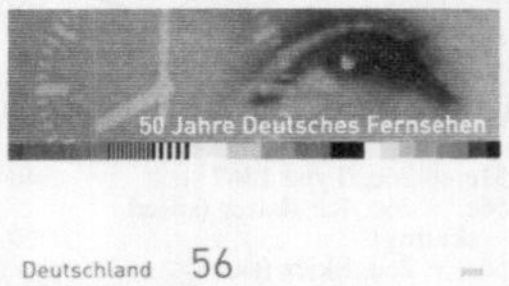

1403 Clock and Eye

2002. 50th Anniv of German Television.
3142 **1403** 56c. multicoloured . . . 1·10 1·10

1404 BMW Isetta 300

2002. Cars. Multicoloured.
3144 45c.+20c. Type **1404** 90 90
3145 55c.+25c. Volkswagen Beetle 1·10 1·10
3146 55c.+25c. Mercedes Benz 300 SL . . . . 1·10 1·10
3147 55c.+25c. VEB Sachsenring Trabant P50 . . . . . . 1·10 1·10
3148 144c.+56c. Borgward Isabella Coupe . . . . . 2·60 2·60
See also Nos. 3238/42.

1405 "Halle Market Church" (Lyonel Feininger)

2002.
3149 **1405** 55c. multicoloured . . . 75 30

2002. Tourist Sights. As T **1318** but with face value in new currency.
3150 5c. brown and green 10 10
3151 25c. olive and violet 35 15
3153 40c. multicoloured 55 25
3154 44c. yellow and black . . . 60 30
3155 45c. pink and black 60 30
3156 55c. yellow and black . . . 75 30
3157 €1 grey and black . . . . 1·30 65
3158 €1.44 pink and green . . . 2·00 1·00
3159 €1.60 grey, black and orange . . . . 2·10 1·00
3160 €1.80 green and chestnut 2·40 1·20
3161 €2 red and green . . . . 2·60 1·30
3162 €2.20 blue and black . . . 3·00 1·50
3163 €2.60 blue and red . . . 3·50 1·75
3164 €4.10 purple and blue . . . 5·50 2·20
DESIGNS: 5c. Erfuster Cathedral; 25c. J.S. Bach (statue), Leipzig; 40c. Schloss Arolsen; 44c. Philharmonic Hall, Berlin; 45c. Canal warehouse, Tonning; 55c. Old Opera House, Frankfurt; €1 Porta Niga (black gate), Trier; €1.44 Beethoven's birthplace, Bonn; €1.60 Bauhaus, Dessau; €1.80 Staatsgalerie, Stuttgart; €2 Bamberger Reister (statue); €2.20 Theodor Fontane monument, Neuruppin; €2.60 *Seute Dern* (four-mast barque), Maritime Museum, Bremerhaven; €4.10 Houses, Wismar.
Nos. 3151/2 also come self-adhesive.

2002. Famous German Women. As T **1322** but with face value in new currency.
3190 45c. green and blue 60 30
3191 55c. red and black 75 30
3192 €1 purple and blue . . . . 1·30 65
3193 €1.44 brown and blue . . . 2·00 1·00
DESIGNS: 45c. Annette von Droste-Hulshoff (writer); 55c. Hildegard Knef (actress); €1 Marie Juchacz (politician); €1.44 Esther von Kirchbach (writer).

1406 Town Buildings

2003. Millenary of Kronach.
3194 **1406** 45c. multicoloured . . . 60 30

1407 Georg Elser

2003. Birth Centenary of Georg Elser (attempted assassination of Adolf Hitler).
3195 **1407** 55c. multicoloured . . . 75 30

1408 Bridge joined by Heart

2003. 40th Anniv of German–French Co-operation Treaty.
3196 **1408** 55c. multicoloured . . . 75 30

1409 Hand and Page

2003. Year of the Bible.
3197 **1409** 55c. multicoloured . . . 75 30

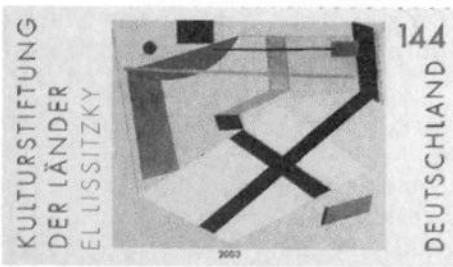

1410 "Proun 30t" (El Lissitzky)

2003. Cultural Foundation of the Federal States.
3198 **1410** €1.44 multicoloured 2·00 1·00

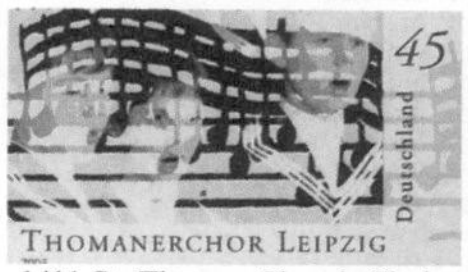

1411 St. Thomas Church Choir, Leipzig

2003. Boys' Choirs. Sheet 172 × 77 mm containing T **1411** and similar horiz designs. Multicoloured.
MS3199 45c. Type **1411**; 55c. Dresden Church choir; 100c. St. Peter's Cathedral choir, Regensburg . . . . 2·75 2·75

1412 Rose

2003. Greetings Stamp. Ordinary or self-adhesive gum.
3200 **1412** 55c. multicoloured . . . 75 30

1413 "Junger Argentier" (Max Beckman)

2003. Artists' Anniversaries. Multicoloured.
3202 55c. Type **1413** (53rd death anniv) 75 30
3203 €1 "Komposition" (Adolf Holzel) (150th birth anniv) . . . . 2·75 1·40

1414 Footballer

2003. Sports Promotion Fund. World Cup Football Championship (2006), Germany. Multicoloured.
3204 45c.+20c. Type **1414** 85 85
3205 55c.+25c. Boys playing football . . . . 1·10 1·10
3206 55c.+25c. Fan with arms raised . . . . 1·10 1·10
3207 55c.+25c. Young player heading ball . . . . . . 1·10 1·10
3208 €1.44+56c. Boy kicking ball to older man . . . . 2·75 2·75

1415 Building Facade

2003. UNESCO World Heritage Sites. Cologne Cathedral. Ordinary or self-adhesive gum.
3209 **1415** 55c. grey, red and black 75 30

1416 Flower

2003. International Horticultural Exhibition, Rostock.
3211 **1416** 45c. multicoloured . . . 60 30

1417 Oskar von Miller (founder) and Technological Symbols

2003. Centenary of Deutsches Museum, Munich.
3212 **1417** 55c. multicoloured . . . 75 30

1418 Cut-out Figures

2003. 50th Anniv of Deutscher Kinderschutzbund (children's organization).
3213 **1418** 55c. multicoloured . . . 75 30

1419 Map and Representation of Radio Waves

2003. 50th Anniv of Deutsche Welle (radio station).
3214 **1419** 55c. multicoloured . . . 75 30

1420 Aviators and Junkers W 33 Bremen

2003. 75th Anniv East–West North Atlantic Flight.
3215 **1420** 144c. + 56c. multicoloured . . . . 2·75 2·75

1421 1960s Posters

2003. Europa. Poster Art.
3216 **1421** 55c. multicoloured . . . 75 30

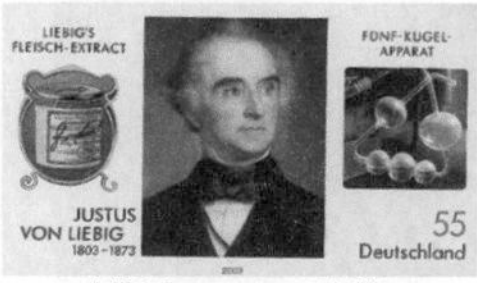

1422 Justus von Liebig

2003. Birth Bicentenary of Justus von Liebig (chemist).
3217 **1422** 55c. multicoloured . . . 75 30

1423 Reinhold Schneider and Text

2003. Birth Centenary of Reinhold Schneider (writer).
3218 **1423** 55c. multicoloured . . . 75 30

1424 Helicopter and Patrol Vehicle

2003. Centenary of ADAC (automobile association).
3219 **1424** 55c. multicoloured . . . 75 30

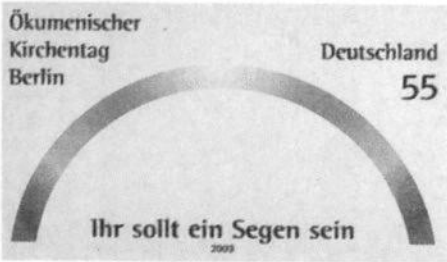

1425 Rainbow

2003. Ecumenical Church Conference, Berlin.
3220 **1425** 55c. multicoloured . . . 75 30

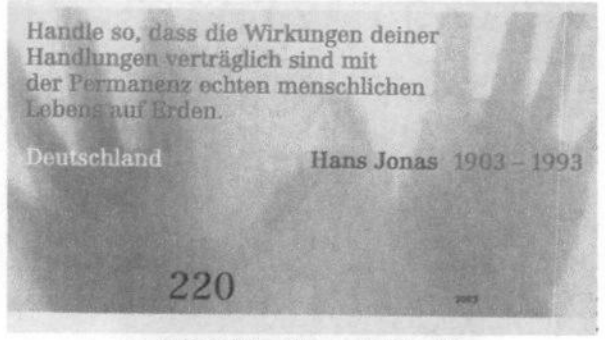

1426 Hands and Text

2003. Birth Centenary of Hans Jonas (philosopher).
3221 **1426** 220c. multicoloured . . 3·00 1·50

1427 Hand with Face and Feet

2003. 10th Anniv of Postal Codes.
3222 **1427** 55c. multicoloured . . . 75 30

1428 Bridge over Salzach River

2003. Centenary of Oberndorf–Laufen Bridge. Ordinary or self-adhesive gum.
3223 **1428** 55c. multicoloured . . . 75 30
A stamp of the same design was issued by Austria.

1429 Lake, Trees and Islands

2003. Unteres Odertal National Park. Sheet 111 × 66 mm.
MS3225 **1429** 55c. multicoloured 75 75

1430 Protesters and Tanks

2003. 50th Anniv of Uprising in East Berlin.
3226 **1430** 55c. + 25c. multicoloured . . . . 1·10 1·10

1431 Musical Notations

2003. 50th Anniv of Deutscher Musikrat (music association).
3227 **1431** €1.44 silver and blue 2·00 1·00

1432 Father chasing Son

2003. "For Us Children". "Father and Son" (cartoon by E.O. Plauen (Erich Ohser)). Sheet 111 × 191 mm containing T **1432** and similar horiz designs. Multicoloured.
MS3228 45c.+20c. Type **1432**; 55c.+25c. Father and son falling; 55c.+25c. Father looking over shoulder at son running away; 55c.+25c. Father chasing son in a circle; €1.44+56c. Father and son sliding . . . . 7·00 7·00

1433 Winding Gear and Trees

2003. Ruhr District Industrial Landscape.
3229 **1433** 55c. multicoloured . . . 75 30

1434 Andres Hermes

2003. 125th Birth Anniv of Andreas Hermes (politician).
3230 **1434** 55c. multicoloured . . . 75 30

1435 Market Stalls, Munich

2003. German Cities. Ordinary or self-adhesive gum.
3231 **1435** 45c. multicoloured . . . 60 30

1436 Petrified Forest, Chemnitz

2003.
3234 **1436** 144c. multicoloured . . 2·00 1·00

1437 Viaduct and Enz River

2003. 150th Anniv of Enztal Viaduct (railway).
3235 **1437** 55c. multicoloured . . . 75 30

1438 Theodor Adorno and Manuscript

2003. Birth Centenary of Theodor Adorno (philosopher and sociologist).
3236 **1438** 55c. multicoloured . . . 75 30

1439 Elephant and Bird

2003. "For Us Children". Sheet 111 × 65 mm.
MS3237 **1439** 55c. multicoloured 75 75

2003. Cars. As T **1404**. Multicoloured.

3238	45c. + 20c. Wartburg 311 Coupe	90	90
3239	55c. + 25c. Ford Taunus 17 M P3	1·10	1·10
3240	55c. + 25c. Porsche 356 B Coupe	1·10	1·10
3241	55c. + 25c. Opel Olympia Rekord P1	1·10	1·10
3242	144c. + 56c. Auto Union 1000 S	2·75	2·75

1440 Letter Box

2003. Post.
3243 **1440** 55c. multicoloured 75 30

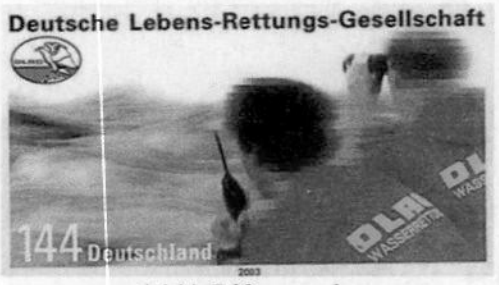

1441 Lifeguards

2003. 90th Anniv of DLRG (safety organization).
3244 **1441** 144c. multicoloured 2·00 1·00

1442 Nativity Figures (19th-century)

2003. Christmas. Multicoloured.

3245	45c. + 20c. Type **1442**	90	90
3246	55c. + 25c. Holy Family	1·10	1·10

1443 Dresden Opera House

2003. Birth Bicentenary of Gottfried Semper (architect).
3247 **1443** 55c. multicoloured 75 30

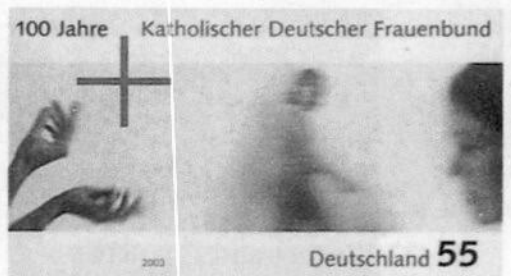

1444 Hands and Women

2003. Centenary of German Catholic Women's Federation.
3248 **1444** 55c. multicoloured 75 30

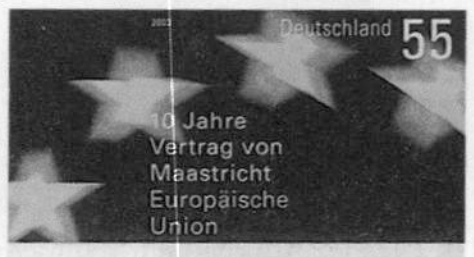

1445 Stars

2003. 10th Anniv of Maastricht Treaty.
3249 **1445** 55c. blue and yellow 75 30

1446 St. Martin's Church

2004. 800th Anniv of Landshut.
3250 **1446** 45c. multicoloured 60 30

1447 Cathedral and Images of Schleswig

2004. 1200th Anniv of Schleswig.
3251 **1447** 55c. multicoloured 75 30

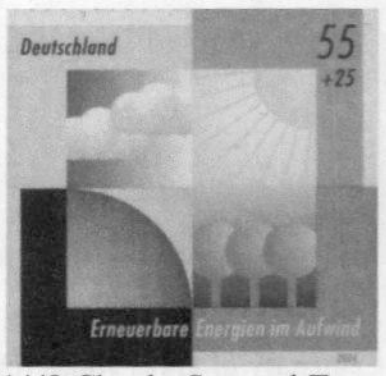

1448 Clouds, Sun and Trees

2004. Environmental Protection and Renewable Energy.
3252 **1448** 55c.+25c. multicoloured 1·10 1·10

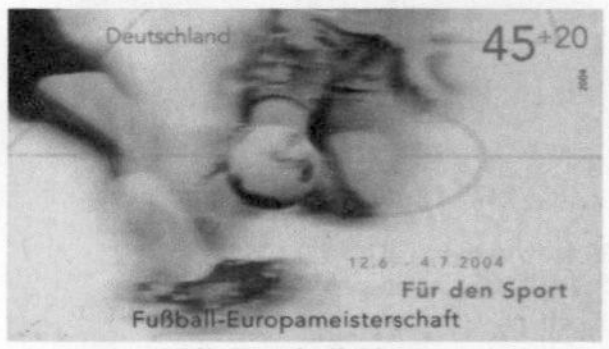

1449 Football Players

2004. Sport Promotion Fund. Multicoloured.

3253	45c.+20c. Type **1449** (European Football Championship)	90	90
3254	55c.+25c. Wheelchair athlete (Paralympics)	1·10	1·10
3255	55c.+25c. Runner (Olympic Games, Greece)	1·10	1·10
3256	55c.+25c. Footballer (50th anniv of Germany winning World Cup)	1·10	1·10
3257	144c.+56c. Hands holding trophy (Centenary of FIFA)	2·75	2·75

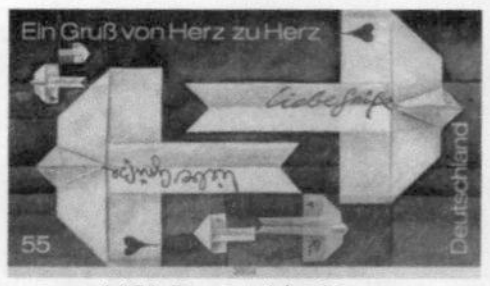

1450 Paper Airplanes

2004. Post.
3258 **1450** 55c. multicoloured 75 30

1451 Buildings

2004. 1300th Anniv of Arnstadt.
3259 **1451** 55c. multicoloured 75 30

1452 Shadow of Boy, Apple and Arrow

2004. Classic Theatre. Sheet 102 × 73 mm containing T **1452** and similar square design. Multicoloured.
MS3260 45c. Type **1452** (William Tell (Friedrich von Schiller) (200th anniv)); 100c. Faust and the devil (Faust II (Johann Wolfgang von Goethe) (150th anniv)) 2·00 2·00

1453 Joseph Schmidt

2004. Birth Centenary of Joseph Schmidt (singer).
3261 **1453** 55c. brown 75 30

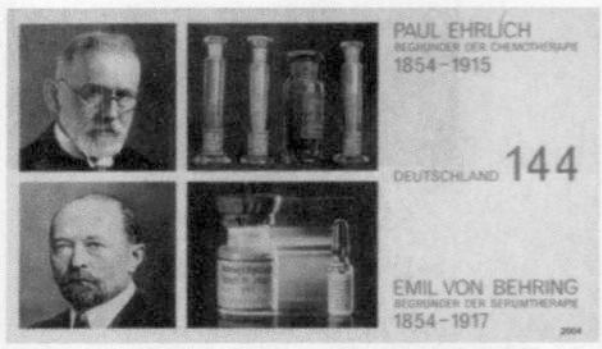

1454 Paul Ehrlich (chemistry) and Emil von Behring (medicine)

2004. 150th Birth Anniv of Nobel Prize Winners.
3262 **1454** 144c. multicoloured 2·00 1·00

1455 White Stork in Flight

2004. Endangered Species. White Stork (*Circona circona*).
3263 **1455** 55c. black, blue and red 75 30

1456 Master House, Dessau

2004. Bauhaus (design group).
3264 **1456** 55c. multicoloured 75 30

1457 Kurt Kiesinger

2004. Birth Centenary of Kurt Georg Kiesinger (politician).
3265 **1457** 55c. multicoloured 75 30

1458 Early and Modern Light Bulbs

2004. 150th Anniv of Electric Light Bulb.
3266 **1458** 220c. multicoloured 3·50 1·50

IV. WEST BERLIN

The Russian Government withdrew from the four-power control of Berlin on 1 July 1948, with the Western Sectors remaining under American, British and French control. West Berlin was constituted a "Land" of the Federal Republic on 1 September 1950. The Russian Zone issues inscribed "STADT BERLIN" (which we do not list unoverprinted in this Catalogue), were not intended for use throughout Berlin, but were for the Russian sector of the city and for Brandenburg.

The first stamps to be used in the Western Sectors were Nos. A4/5 and A7 of the Anglo-American Zones, followed by Nos. A36/52, which were on sale from 24 June to 31 August 1948, and remained valid until 19 September 1948.

1948. 100 pfennig = 1 Deutsche Mark (East).
1949. 100 pfennig = 1 Deutsche Mark (West).

1948. Pictorial issue of 1947 (Nos. 928/48) optd **BERLIN**.

B21	2pf. black	1·60	5·75
B 2	6pf. violet	1·10	5·25
B 3	8pf. red	1·10	5·50
B 4	10pf. green	1·10	1·30
B 5	12pf. grey	1·10	90
B25	15pf. brown	10·00	2·00
B 7	16pf. green	4·50	1·90
B26	20pf. blue	3·00	75
B 9	24pf. brown	1·10	55
B10	25pf. orange	22·00	60·00
B11	30pf. red	4·50	8·75
B12	40pf. mauve	6·75	8·75
B13	50pf. blue	9·75	36·00
B14	60pf. brown	2·75	45
B15	80pf. blue	10·00	29·00
B16	84pf. green	18·00	£100
B17	1m. olive	60·00	£160
B18	2m. violet	65·00	£650
B19	3m. red	90·00	£850
B20	5m. blue	£120	£850

B 2 Schoneberg

B 3 Douglas C-54 Skymaster Transport over Tempelhof Airport

1949. Inscr "DEUTSCHE POST". Berlin Views.
(a) Small size.

B35	–	1pf. grey	25	15
B36	**B 2**	4pf. brown	90	15
B36c	–	4pf. brown	7·00	5·00
B37	–	5pf. green	1·10	15
B38	–	6pf. purple	2·00	1·10
B39	**B 2**	8pf. orange	2·00	1·50
B40	–	10pf. green	90	15
B41	**B 3**	15pf. brown	17·00	75
B42	–	20pf. red	5·25	15
B42b	–	20pf. red	80·00	75
B43	–	25pf. yellow	31·00	1·20
B44	–	30pf. blue	16·00	1·20
B45	**B 2**	40pf. lake	22·00	1·10
B46	–	50pf. olive	24·00	25
B47	–	60pf. red	85·00	25
B48	–	80pf. blue	20·00	1·20
B49	–	90pf. green	22·00	1·20

(b) Large size.

B50	**B 3**	1Dm. olive	31·00	1·10
B51	–	2Dm. purple	85·00	1·50
B52	–	3Dm. red	£350	17·00
B53	–	5Dm. blue	£180	17·00

DESIGNS—As Type **B 2**: 1pf. Brandenburg Gate; 4pf. (B36c) Exhibition Building; 5, 25pf. "Tegel Schloss". 6, 50pf. Reichstag Building. 10, 30pf. "Kleistpark". 20 (B42), 80, 90pf. Technical High School; 20pf. (B42b) Olympia Stadium; 60pf. National Gallery. As Type **B 3**: 2Dm. "Gendarmenmarkt"; 3Dm. Brandenburg Gate; 5Dm. "Tegel Schloss".

For similar views inscribed "DEUTSCHE POST BERLIN" see Nos. B118/19.

B 4 Stephan Monument and Globe

B 5 Heinrich von Stephan Monument

1949. 75th Anniv of U.P.U.

B54	**B 4**	12pf. grey	33·00	8·25
B55		16pf. green	49·00	18·00
B56		24pf. orange	33·00	75
B57		50pf. olive	£200	46·00
B58		60pf. brown	£250	41·00
B59	**B 5**	1Dm. olive	£160	£140
B60		2Dm. purple	£160	85·00

B 6 Goethe and Scene from "Iphigenie"

B 9 Alms Bowl and Bear

1949. Birth Bicent of Goethe (poet). Portraits of Goethe and scenes from his works.

B61	**B 6**	10pf. green	£170	80·00
B62	–	20pf. red	£170	44·00
B63	–	30pf. blue	33·00	55·00

DESIGNS—Scenes from: 20pf. "Reineke Fuchs"; 30pf. "Faust".

1949. Numeral and pictorial issues of 1946/7 surch **BERLIN** and bold figures.

B64	**229**	5pf. on 45pf. red	4·50	25
B65	C	10pf. on 24pf. brown	18·00	25

B66 B 20pf. on 80pf. blue . . . 80·00 17·00
B67 **237** 1m. on 3m. lake . . . . £200 19·00

1949. Berlin Relief Fund.
B68 **B 9** 10pf.+5pf. green £110 £190
B69 20pf.+5pf. red £140 £190
B70 30pf.+5pf. blue £140 £300
MSB70a 111×65 mm. Nos. B68/70 (sold at 1Dm.) £900 £2500

B **10**

B **11** Harp

1950. European Recovery Programme.
B71 B **10** 20pf. red . . . . 95·00 42·00

1950. Restablishment of Berlin Philharmonic Orchestra.
B72 **B 11** 10pf.+5pf. green . . . . 60·00 40·00
B73 – 30pf.+5pf. blue £110 £100
DESIGN: 30pf. "Singing Angels" (after H. and J. van Eyck).

B **13** G. A. Lortzing

B **14** Freedom Bell

1951. Death Cent of Lortzing (composer).
B74 **B 13** 20pf. brown . . . . . . 60·00 55·00

1951. (a) Clapper at left.
B75 **B 14** 5pf. brown . . . . . . 2·20 7·75
B76 10pf. green . . . . . . 20·00 26·00
B77 20pf. red . . . . 10·00 22·00
B78 30pf. blue . . . . 70·00 80·00
B79 40pf. purple . . . . . . 13·50 43·00

(b) Clapper at right.
B82 **B 14** 5pf. green . . . . 2·20 1·90
B83 10pf. green . . . . . . 7·00 4·25
B84 20pf. red . . . . 27·00 19·00
B85 30pf. blue . . . . 70·00 55·00
B86 40pf. red . . . . 27·00 19·00

(c) Clapper in centre.
B101 **B 14** 5pf. brown . . . . . . 1·00 95
B102 10pf. green . . . . . . 2·00 1·50
B103 20pf. red . . . . 8·50 3·75
B104 30pf. blue . . . . . . 16·00 14·50
B105 40pf. violet . . . . . 70·00 41·00

B **15** Boy Stamp Collectors

B **16** Mask of Beethoven (taken from life, 1812)

1951. Stamp Day.
B80 **B 15** 10pf.+3pf. green . . . . 31·00 31·00
B81 20pf.+2pf. red . . . . . 36·00 40·00

1952. 125th Death Anniv of Beethoven (composer).
B87 **B 16** 30pf. blue . . . . 47·00 34·00

B **17** Olympic Torch

B **18** W. von Siemens (electrical engineer)

1952. Olympic Games Festival, Berlin.
B88 **B 17** 4pf. brown . . . . . . 90 1·80
B89 10pf. green . . . . . . 13·50 17·00
B90 20pf. red . . . . 18·00 25·00

1952. Famous Berliners.
B 91 – 4pf. brown 45 40
B 92 – 5pf. blue . . . . 1·30 40
B 93 – 6pf. purple . . . . . 7·00 11·50
B 94 – 8pf. brown . . . . . . 2·20 2·50
B 95 – 10pf. green . . . . . . 3·25 50
B 96 – 15pf. lilac . . . . . . 20·00 18·00
B 97 **B 18** 20pf. red . . . . . . 2·75 85
B 98 – 25pf. green . . . . . . 60·00 6·25
B 99 – 30pf. purple . . . . . 20·00 9·50
B100 – 40pf. black . . . . . . 36·00 3·25

PORTRAITS: 4pf. Zelter (musician); 5pf. Lilienthal (aviator); 6pf. Rathenau (statesman); 8pf. Fontane (writer); 10pf. Von Menzel (artist); 15pf. Virchow (pathologist); 25pf. Schinkel (architect); 30pf. Planck (physicist); 40pf. W. von Humboldt (philologist).

B **19** Church before Bombing

B **20** Chainbreaker

1953. Kaiser Wilhelm Memorial Church Reconstruction Fund.
B106 **B 19** 4pf.+1pf. brown . . . 45 16·00
B107 10pf.+5pf. green . . . 1·30 55·00
B108 – 20pf.+10pf. red . . . . 4·00 55·00
B109 – 30pf.+15pf. blue . . . 20·00 £110
DESIGN: 20pf., 30pf. Church after bombing.

1953. East German Uprising. Inscr "17. JUNI 1953".
B110 **B 20** 20pf. black . . . . . . 4·25 1·70
B111 – 30pf. red . . . . 36·00 29·00
DESIGN: 30pf. Brandenburg Gate.

B **21** Ernst Reuter

B **22** Conference Buildings

1954. Death of Ernst Reuter (Mayor of West Berlin).
B112 **B 21** 20pf. brown . . . . . 8·50 2·10

1954. Four-Power Conference, Berlin.
B113 **B 22** 20pf. red . . . . . . 9·00 4·75

B **23** O. Mergenthaler and Linotype Machine

B **25** "Germany in Bondage"

1954. Birth Cent of Mergenthaler (inventor).
B114 **B 23** 10pf. green . . . . . . 3·00 2·75

1954. West German Presidential Election. No. B103 optd **Wahl des Bundespräsidenten in Berlin 17. Juli 1954.**
B115 **B 14** 20pf. red . . . . . . 4·25 5·25

1954. 10th Anniv of Attempt on Hitler's Life.
B116 **B 25** 20pf. grey and red . . 5·75 5·00

B **26** Prussian Postilion, 1827

B **27** Memorial Library

1954. National Stamp Exhibition.
B117 **B 26** 20pf.+10pf. mult . . . 14·50 35·00

1954. Berlin Views. As Type B **2** but inscr "DEUTSCHE POST BERLIN".
B118 7pf. green . . . . 7·00 75
B119 70pf. olive . . . . £130 22·00
DESIGNS: 7pf. Exhibition building; 70pf. Grunewald hunting lodge.

1954.
B120 **B 27** 40pf. purple . . . . . 11·50 3·00

B **28** Richard Strauss

B **29** Blacksmiths forging Rail

1954. 5th Death Anniv of Strauss (composer).
B121 **B 28** 40pf. blue . . . . . . 13·50 4·25

1954. Death Cent of A. Borsig (industrialist).
B122 **B 29** 20pf. brown . . . . . 8·50 2·10

B **30** "Berlin" (liner)

B **31** Wilhelm Furtwangler (conductor)

1955.
B123 **B 30** 10pf. green . . . . . . 1·60 35
B124 25pf. blue . . . . . . 8·50 4·25

1955. 1st Death Anniv of Furtwangler.
B125 **B 31** 40pf. blue . . . . . . 22·00 21·00

B **32**

B **33** Prussian Rural Postilion, 1760

1955. Federal Parliament Session, Berlin.
B126 **B 32** 10pf. black, yell & red 45 50
B127 20pf. black, yell & red 5·75 9·50

1955. Stamp Day and Philatelic Fund.
B128 **B 33** 25pf.+10pf. mult . . . 7·00 16·00

B **34** St. Otto

B **35** Radio Tower and Exhibition Hall

1955. 25th Anniv of Berlin Bishopric.
B129 **B 34** 7pf.+3pf. brown . . . 90 3·00
B130 – 10pf.+5pf. green . . . 1·30 3·75
B131 – 20pf.+10pf. mauve . . 2·40 4·75
DESIGNS: 10pf. St. Hedwig; 20pf. St. Peter.

1956. Berlin Buildings and Monuments.
B133 – 1pf. grey 10 15
B133b – 3pf. violet 20 15
B134 – 5pf. mauve 20 15
B132 **B 35** 7pf. turquoise (A) . . 9·00 2·75
B135 – 7pf. turquoise (B) . . 20 15
B136 – 8pf. grey 55 40
B136a – 8pf. red 25 30
B137 – 10pf. green 20 15
B138 – 15pf. blue 45 25
B139 – 20pf. red 20 15
B140 – 25pf. brown 55 50
B141 – 30pf. green 90 95
B142 – 40pf. blue . . . . . 11·00 7·75
B143 – 50pf. green 90 95
B144 – 60pf. brown . . . . . 1·00 1·10
B145 – 70pf. violet . . . . . 31·00 14·00
B146 – 1Dm. green . . . . . 2·40 2·30
B146a – 3Dm. red . . . . . . 6·25 12·50

7pf. (A) Type B **35**. (B) As Type B **35** but with inscription at top.
DESIGNS—As Type B **35** (B)—HORIZ: 1pf., 3pf. Brandenburg Gate; 5pf. P.O. Headquarters; 20pf. Free University; 40pf. Charlottenburg Castle; 60pf. Chamber of Commerce and Bourse; 70pf. Schiller Theatre. VERT: 8pf. Town Hall, Neukollin; 10pf. Kaiser Wilhelm Memorial Church; 15pf. Airlift Monument; 25pf. Lilienthal Monument; 30pf. Pfaueninsel Castle; 50pf. Reuter Power-station. LARGER (24×30 mm): 1Dm. "The Great Elector" (statue, after Schluter). (29½×25 mm): 3Dm. Congress Hall, Berlin.

B **37** Eagle and Arms of Berlin

B **38**

1956. Federal Council Meeting.
B147 **B 37** 10pf. black, yell & red 1·30 45
B148 25pf. black, yell & red 5·25 4·75

1956. Centenary of German Engineers' Union.
B149 **B 38** 10pf. green . . . . . . 2·40 1·60
B150 20pf. red . . . . . . 5·75 5·75

1956. Flood Relief Fund. As No. B 77 (colour changed) surch **+10 Berlinhilfe fur die Hochwassergeschadigten DEUTSCHE BUNDESPOST-BERLIN** and bar.
B151 **B 14** 20pf.+10pf. bistre . . . 3·00 3·25

B **40** P. Lincke

B **41** Wireless Transmitter

1956. 10th Death Anniv of Lincke (composer).
B152 **B 40** 20pf. red . . . . . . 2·75 2·75

1956. Industrial Exhibition.
B153 **B 41** 25pf. brown . . . . . 6·25 10·00

B **42** Brandenburg Postilion, 1700

B **43** Spandau

1956. Stamp Day and Philatelic Fund.
B154 **B 42** 25pf.+10pf. mult . . . 3·00 4·00

1957. 725th Anniv of Spandau.
B155 **B 43** 20pf. olive and brown 55 75

B **44** Model of Hansa District

B **45** Friedrich K. von Savigny (jurist)

1957. International Building Exn, Berlin.
B156 **B 44** 7pf. brown 20 20
B157 – 20pf. red . . . . . . 1·00 90
B158 – 40pf. blue . . . . . . 2·40 2·40
DESIGNS—HORIZ: 20pf. Aerial view of Exhibition; 40pf. Exhibition Congress Hall.

1957. Portraits as Type B **45**.
B159 – 7pf. brown and green 20 15
B160 – 8pf. brown and grey 20 20
B161 – 10pf. brown and green 25 20
B162 – 15pf. sepia and blue . . 45 75
B163 – 20pf.+10pf. sepia and red 20 50
B164 – 20pf. brown and red 90 60
B165 – 25pf. sepia and lake . . 1·10 1·00
B166 **B 45** 30pf. sepia and green 2·75 2·50
B167 – 40pf. sepia and blue . . 1·10 95
B168 – 50pf. sepia and olive 5·00 7·75

PORTRAITS—VERT: 7pf. T. Mommsen (historian); 8pf. H. Zille (painter); 10pf. E. Reuter (Mayor of Berlin); 15pf. F. Haber (chemist); 20pf. (No. B164), F. Schleiermacher (theologian); 20pf. (B163), L. Heck (zoologist); 25pf. Max Reinhardt (theatrical producer); 40pf. A. von Humboldt (naturalist); 50pf. C. D. Rauch (sculptor).

The premium on No. B163 was for the Berlin Zoo. No. B167 commemorates Humboldt's death centenary.

B **46** Uta von Naumburg (statue)

B **47** "Unity Justice and Freedom"

1957. German Cultural Congress.
B169 B **46** 25pf. brown 90 95

1957. 3rd Federal Parliament Assembly.
B170 B **47** 10pf. black, ochre & red 35 80
B171 20pf. black, ochre & red . . . . 2·40 3·00

B **48** Postilion, 1897–1925

B **49** Torch of Remembrance

1957. Stamp Day.
B172 B **48** 20pf. multicoloured . . 80 85

1957. 7th World War Veterans Congress.
B173 B **49** 20pf. myrtle, yell & grn 90 70

B **50** Elly Heuss-Knapp (social worker)

B **51** Christ and Symbols of the Cosmos

1957. Mothers' Convalescence Fund.
B174 B **50** 20pf.+10pf. red . . . . 1·30 2·40

1958. German Catholics' Day.
B175 B **51** 10pf. black and green 50 50
B176 20pf. black and mauve 1·20 1·50

B **52** Otto Suhr

B **53** Pres. Heuss

1958. 1st Death Anniv of Burgomaster Otto Suhr.
B177 B **52** 20pf. red . . . . . . 1·10 1·30
See also Nos. B187 and B193.

1959.
B178 B **53** 7pf. green 20 35
B179 10pf. green 30 30
B180 20pf. red 65 30
B181 40pf. blue . . . . . . 3·00 4·75
B182 70pf. violet . . . . . 11·00 12·00

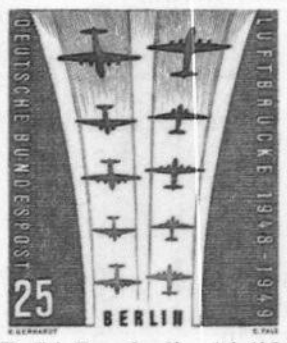

B **54** Symbolic Airlift

B **55** Brandenburg Gate, Berlin

1959. 10th Anniv of Berlin Airlift.
B183 B **54** 25pf. black and red . . 45 35

1959. 14th World Communities Congress, Berlin.
B184 B **55** 20pf. blue, red & lt blue 90 35

B **56** Schiller

B **57** Robert Koch

1959. Birth Bicentenary of Schiller (poet).
B185 B **56** 20pf. brown and red 35 35

1960. 50th Death Anniv of Robert Koch (bacteriologist).
B186 B **57** 20pf. purple 35 40

1960. 4th Death Anniv of Walther Schreiber (Mayor of Berlin, 1951–53). As Type B **52**.
B187 20pf. red 55 70
DESIGN: Portrait of Schreiber.

B **58** Boy at Window

B **59** Hans Boeckler

1960. Berlin Children's Holiday Fund. Inscr "FERIENPLATZE FUR BERLINER KINDER".
B188 B **58** 7pf.+3pf. dp brown, brown & light brown 25 40
B189 – 10pf.+5pf. deep green, olive and green . . . 25 40
B190 – 20pf.+10pf. brown, red and pink 55 75
B191 – 40pf.+20pf. deep blue, blue & light blue . . 1·30 3·75
DESIGNS: 10pf. Girl in street; 20pf. Girl blowing on Alpine flower; 40pf. Boy on beach.

1961. 10th Anniv of Hans Boeckler (politician).
B192 B **59** 20pf. black and red . . 25 25

1961. Louise Schroeder Commemoration. As Type B **52**.
B193 20pf. brown 35 25
DESIGN: Portrait of Schroeder.

B **60** Durer

B **61** "Five Crosses" Symbol and St. Mary's Church

1961. Famous Germans.
B194 5pf. olive (Magnus) 20 20
B195 7pf. brown (St. Elizabeth of Thuringia) 20 45
B196 8pf. violet (Gutenberg) . . 20 35
B197 10pf. green (Type B **60**) . . 20 20
B198 15pf. blue (Luther) 20 45
B199 20pf. red (Bach) 20 20
B200 25pf. brown (Neumann) . . 20 35
B201 30pf. brown (Kant) 20 55
B202 40pf. blue (Lessing) 65 85
B203 50pf. brown (Goethe) . . . 45 1·10
B204 60pf. red (Schiller) . . . . 45 1·20
B205 70pf. green (Beethoven) . . 45 1·10
B206 80pf. brown (Kleist) . . . . 4·00 9·25
B207 1Dm. violet (Annette von Droste-Hulshoff) . . . 1·60 3·00
B208 2Dm. green (Hauptmann) 2·20 5·00

1961. 10th Evangelical Churches' Day. Crosses in violet.
B210 B **61** 10pf. green 10 15
B211 – 20pf. purple 25 25
DESIGN: 20pf. "Five Crosses" and Kaiser Wilhelm Memorial Church.

B **62** Exhibition Emblem

1961. West Berlin Radio and Television Exn.
B212 B **62** 20pf. brown and red 25 25

B **63** "Die Linden" (1650)

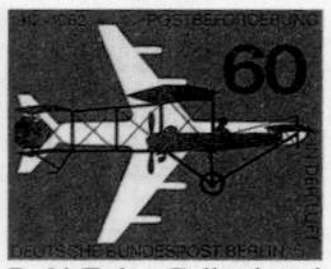

B **64** Euler Gelberhund Biplane, 1912, and Boeing 707 Airliner

1962. "Old Berlin" series.
B213 B **63** 7pf. sepia and brown 20 15
B214 – 10pf. sepia and green 20 15
B215 – 15pf. black and blue 20 15
B216 – 20pf. sepia and brown 20 15
B217 – 25pf. sepia and olive 20 30
B218 – 40pf. black and blue 35 35
B219 – 50pf. sepia and purple 35 45
B220 – 60pf. sepia and mauve 55 60
B221 – 70pf. black and purple 55 60
B222 – 80pf. sepia and red . . 70 75
B223 – 90pf. sepia and brown 80 90
B224 – 1Dm. sepia and green 90 1·20
DESIGNS: 10pf. "Waisenbrucke" (Orphans' Bridge), 1783; 15pf. Mauerstrasse, 1780; 20pf. Berlin Castle, 1703; 25pf. Potsdamer Platz, 1825; 40pf. Bellevue Castle, c. 1800; 50pf. Fischer Bridge, 1830; 60pf. Halle Gate, 1880; 70pf. Parochial Church, 1780; 80pf. University, 1825; 90pf. Opera House, 1780; 1Dm. Grunewald Lake, c. 1790.

1962. 50th Anniv of German Airmail Transport.
B225 B **64** 60pf. black and blue 55 45

B **65** Exhibition Emblem

B **66** Town Hall Schoneberg

1963. West Berlin Broadcasting Exn.
B226 B **65** 20pf. ultram, grey & bl 25 25

1964. 700th Anniv of Schoneberg.
B227 B **66** 20pf. brown 25 25

B **67** Pres. Lubke

B **68** Kaiser Wilhelm Memorial Church

1964. Re-election of Pres. Lubke.
B228 B **67** 20pf. red 20 15
B229 40pf. blue 45 30
See also Nos. B308/9.

WEST BERLIN DESIGNS. Except where illustrated the following are the same or similar designs to German Federal Republic additonaly inscr "BERLIN".

1964. Capitals of the Federal Lands. As No. 1335.
B230 20pf. multicoloured 35 30

1964. Humanitarian Relief and Welfare Funds. As Nos. 1352/5.
B231 10pf.+5pf. multicoloured . . 20 20
B232 15pf.+5pf. multicoloured . . 20 15
B233 20pf.+10pf. multicoloured 40 15
B234 40pf.+20pf. multicoloured 65 1·10

1964. Pres. Kennedy Commem. As Type **411**.
B235 40pf. blue 45 35

1964. Twelve Centuries of German Architecture. (a) Size $18\frac{1}{2} \times 22\frac{1}{2}$ mm. As Nos. 1359/66. Plain backgrounds.
B236 10pf. brown 20 15
B237 15pf. green 25 25
B238 20pf. red 25 20
B239 40pf. blue . . . . 80 1·10
B240 50pf. bistre . . . . 1·70 1·60
B241 60pf. red . . . . 1·20 1·30
B242 70pf. green . . . . 2·75 3·25
B243 80pf. brown . . . . 2·75 2·75

(b) Size $19\frac{1}{2} \times 24$ mm. As Nos. 1367/81. Coloured backgrounds.
B244 5pf. bistre 20 15
B245 8pf. red 20 15
B246 10pf. purple 20 15
B247 20pf. green 20 15
B248 30pf. olive 25 30
B249 30pf. red 25 20
B250 40pf. bistre 65 95
B251 50pf. blue 55 55
B252 60pf. red . . . . 1·80 2·20
B253 70pf. bronze . . . . 1·00 95
B254 80pf. brown . . . . 1·20 2·00
B255 90pf. black 65 95
B256 1Dm. blue 65 90
B257 1Dm.10 brown . . . . . . 1·60 1·50
B258 1Dm.30 green . . . . . . 2·75 2·30
B259 2Dm. purple . . . . 2·75 2·00
BUILDINGS: 8pf. Palatine Castle, Kaub. Others as Nos. 1359/81 of German Federal Republic.

1965. Child Welfare. As Nos. 1384/7.
B261 10pf.+5pf. Eurasian woodcock 20 15
B262 15pf.+5pf. Common pheasant 20 25
B263 20pf.+10pf. Black grouse 20 25
B264 40pf.+20pf. Western capercaillie 60 85

1965. "New Berlin". Multicoloured.
B265 10pf. Type B **68** 10 10
B266 15pf. Opera House (horiz) 10 10
B267 20pf. Philharmonic Hall (horiz) 20 10
B268 30pf. Jewish Community Centre (horiz) 25 15
B269 40pf. Regina Martyrum Memorial Church (horiz) 25 25
B270 50pf. Ernst-Reuter Square (horiz) 25 30
B271 60pf. Europa Centre . . . 35 35
B272 70pf. Technical University, Charlottenburg (horiz) . . 45 40
B273 80pf. City Motorway . . . 55 45
B274 90pf. Planetarium (horiz) 70 70
B275 1Dm. Telecommunications, Tower 80 75
B276 1Dm.10 University Clinic, Steglitz (horiz) . . . . 90 1·00

1965. Humanitarian Relief Funds. As Nos. 1406/9.
B277 10pf.+5pf. Type **425** . . . 20 20
B278 15pf.+5pf. Cinderella and birds with dress 20 20
B279 20pf.+10pf. Prince offering slipper to Cinderella . . . 25 20
B280 40pf.+20pf. Cinderella and Prince on horse 55 85

1966. As Nos. 1412/15a.
B281 10pf. brown 20 15
B282 20pf. green 20 15
B283 30pf. red 20 15
B284 50pf. blue 65 50
B284a 100pf. blue . . . . 5·25 4·50

1966. Child Welfare. As Nos. 1416/19.
B285 10pf.+5pf. Type **429** . . . 20 25
B286 20pf.+10pf. Chamois . . . 20 25
B287 30pf.+15pf. Fallow deer . . 25 25
B288 50pf.+25pf. Red deer . . . 70 85

1966. Humanitarian Relief Funds. As Nos. 1428/31.
B289 10pf.+5pf. Type **435** . . . 20 20
B290 20pf.+10pf. Frog dining with Princess 20 20
B291 30pf.+15pf. Frog Prince and Princess 35 20
B292 50pf.+25pf. In coach . . . 55 85
Designs from Grimm's "The Frog Prince".

1967. Child Welfare. As Nos. 1434/7.
B293 10pf.+5pf. Common rabbit 20 30
B294 20pf.+10pf. Stoat 20 30
B295 30pf.+15pf. Common hamster 35 30
B296 50pf.+25pf. Red fox . . . . 1·10 1·40

B **69** "Bust of a Young Man" (after C. Meit)

B **70** Broadcasting Tower and T.V. Screen

1967. Berlin Art Treasures.
B297 B **69** 10pf. sepia and bistre 20 15
B298 – 20pf. olive and blue . . 20 15
B299 – 30pf. brown and olive 25 25
B300 – 50pf. sepia and grey . . 35 35
B301 – 1Dm. black and blue 80 85
B302 – 1Dm.10 brn & chest . . 1·20 1·50
DESIGNS: 20pf. Head of "The Elector of Brandenburg" (statue by Schluter); 30pf. "St. Mark" (statue by Riemenschneider); 50pf. Head from Quadriga, Brandenburg Gate. 1Dm. "Madonna" (carving by Feuchtmayer). ($22\frac{1}{2} \times 39$ mm) 1Dm.10, "Christ and St. John" (after carving from Upper Swabia, c. 1320).

1967. West Berlin Broadcasting Exn.
B303 B **70** 30pf. multicoloured . . 25 25

1967. Humanitarian Relief Funds. As Nos. 1443/6.
B304 10pf.+5pf. multicoloured . . 20 30
B305 20pf.+10pf. multicoloured 20 30
B306 30pf.+15pf. multicoloured 25 40
B307 50pf.+25pf. multicoloured 60 85

1967. Re-election of President Lubke. As Type B **67**.
B308 B **67** 30pf. red 20 20
B309 50pf. blue 45 35

1968. Child Welfare. As Nos. 1454/7.
B310 10pf.+5pf. Wild cat 30 45
B311 20pf.+10pf. European otter 45 60
B312 30pf.+15pf. Eurasian badger 65 85
B313 50pf.+25pf. Eurasian beaver 2·00 2·20

B **71** Former Court-house

B **72** Festival Emblems

1968. 500th Anniv of Berlin Magistrates' Court.
B314 B **71** 30pf. black 25 25

1968. Athletics Festival, Berlin.
B315 B **72** 20f. red, black and grey 25 20

1968. Humanitarian Relief Funds. As Nos. 1473/6.
B316 10pf.+5pf. Doll of 1878 . . 20 25
B317 20pf.+10pf. Doll of 1850 . . 20 20
B318 30pf.+15pf. Doll of 1870 . . 20 25
B319 50pf.+25pf. Doll of 1885 . . 60 85

B 74 "The Newspaper Seller" (C. W. Allers, 1889)

B 75 Orang-Utan Family

1969. 19th-cent Berliners. Contemporary Art.

B320	– 5pf. black	20	15
B321	B 74 10pf. purple	20	15
B322	– 10pf. brown	20	15
B323	– 20pf. green	20	25
B324	– 20pf. turquoise	20	25
B325	– 30pf. brown	75	50
B326	– 30pf. brown	75	50
B327	– 50pf. blue	2·00	1·80

DESIGNS—HORIZ: 5pf. "The Cab-driver" (H. Zille, 1875). VERT: 10pf. "The Bus-driver" (C. W. Allers, 1890); 20pf. (No. B323) "The Cobblers Boy" (F. Kruger, 1839); 20pf. (No. B324) "The Cobbler" (A. von Menzel, 1833); 30pf. (No. B325) "The Borsig Forge" (P. Meyerheim, 1878); 30pf. (No. B326) "Three Berlin Ladies" (F. Kurger, 1839); 50pf. "At the Brandenburg Gate" (C. W. Allers, 1889).

1969. Child Welfare. As Nos. 1478/81.

B328	10pf.+5pf. brn, blk & yell	20	20
B329	20pf.+10pf. brown, black and buff	20	30
B330	30pf.+15pf. brn, blk & red	35	50
B331	50pf.+25pf. grey, yellow, black and blue	1·20	1·30

1969. 125th Anniv of Berlin Zoo. Sheet 99 × 74 mm containing Type B 75 and similar horiz designs.

MSB332	10pf. black and brown; 20pf. black and green; 30pf. black and purple; 50pf. black and blue (sold for 1Dm.30)	2·00	2·00

DESIGNS: 20pf. Dalmatian pelican family; 30pf. Gaur and calf; 50pf. Common zebra and foal.

B 76 Postman

B 77 J. Joachim (violinist and director, after A. von Menzel)

1969. 20th Congress of Post Office Trade Union Federation (I.P.T.T.), Berlin.

B333	B 76 10pf. olive	20	25
B334	– 20pf. brown and buff	25	25
B335	– 30pf. violet and ochre	55	55
B336	– 50pf. blue and light blue	1·20	1·00

DESIGNS: 20pf. Telephonist; 30pf. Technician; 50pf. Airmail handlers.

1969. Anniversaries. Multicoloured.

B337	30pf. Type B 77	55	40
B338	50pf. Alexander von Humboldt (after J. Stieler)	90	1·30

ANNIVERSARIES: 30pf. Centenary of Berlin Academy of Music; 50pf. Birth bicentenary of Humboldt.

B 78 Railway Carriage (1835)

B 79 T. Fontane

1969. Humanitarian Relief Funds. Pewter Models. Multicoloured. (a) Inscr "WOHLFAHRTSMARKE".

B339	10pf.+5pf. Type B 78	20	20
B340	20pf.+10pf. Woman feeding chicken (1850)	20	20
B341	30pf.+15pf. Market stall (1850)	35	35
B342	50pf.+25pf. Mounted postilion (1860)	1·20	1·10

(b) Christmas. Inscr "WEIHNACHTSMARKE".

B343	10pf.+5pf. "The Three Kings"	35	30

1970. 150th Birth Anniv of Theodor Fontane (writer).

B344	B 79 20pf. multicoloured	35	30

B 80 Heinrich von Stretlingen

B 81 Film "Title"

1970. Miniatures of Minnesingers. Mult.

B345	10pf.+5pf. Type B 80	20	25
B346	20pf.+10pf. Meinloh von Sevelingen	45	40
B347	30pf.+15pf. Burkhart von Hohenfels	60	60
B348	50pf.+25pf. Albrecht von Johannsdorf	1·40	1·50

1970. 20th International Film Festival, Berlin.

B349	B 81 30pf. multicoloured	45	40

1970. Pres. Heinemann. As Nos. 1535/55.

B350	486 5pf. black	20	15
B351	8pf. brown	90	95
B352	10pf. brown	20	15
B353	15pf. bistre	25	25
B354	20pf. green	20	15
B355	25pf. green	90	65
B356	30pf. brown	1·30	45
B357	40pf. orange	65	30
B358	50pf. blue	35	20
B359	60pf. blue	90	65
B360	70pf. brown	1·00	60
B361	80pf. green	1·10	1·00
B362	90pf. red	2·20	2·50
B363	1Dm. green	1·10	75
B364	110pf. grey	1·30	1·30
B365	120pf. brown	1·30	1·20
B366	130pf. brown	1·80	1·60
B367	140pf. green	2·00	1·80
B368	150pf. red	2·00	1·20
B369	160pf. orange	2·20	2·30
B370	170pf. orange	2·00	1·80
B371	190pf. purple	2·20	1·80
B372	2Dm. violet	2·40	1·50

B 82 Allegory of Folklore

B 83 "Caspar"

1970. 20th Berlin Folklore Week.

B373	B 82 30pf. multicoloured	55	40

1970. Humanitarian Relief Funds. Puppets. Multicoloured. (a) Relief Funds.

B374	10pf.+5pf. Type B 83	20	20
B375	20pf.+10pf. "Polichinelle"	35	30
B376	30pf.+15pf. "Punch"	55	45
B377	50pf.+25pf. "Pulcinella"	1·10	1·10

(b) Christmas.

B378	10pf.+5pf. "Angel"	25	25

B 84 L. von Ranke (after painting by J. Schrader)

1970. 175th Birth Anniv of Leopold von Ranke (historian).

B379	B 84 30pf. multicoloured	45	40

1971. Centenary of German Unification.

B380	492 30pf. black, red & orange	60	55

B 85 Class ET 165.8 Electric Train, 1933

1971. Berlin Rail Transport. Multicoloured.

B381	5pf. Class T.12 steam train, 1925	25	25
B382	10pf. Electric tram, 1890	25	20
B383	20pf. Horse tram, 1880	35	30
B384	30pf. Type B 85	55	40
B385	50pf. Electric tram, 1950	1·80	1·40
B386	1Dm. Underground train No. 2431, 1971	2·00	1·70

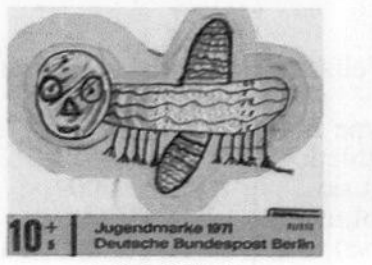
B 86 "Fly"

B 87 "The Bagpiper" (copper engraving, Durer, c. 1514)

1971. Child Welfare. Children's Drawings. Multicoloured.

B387	10pf.+5pf. Type B 86	35	35
B388	20pf.+10pf. "Fish"	25	25
B389	30pf.+15pf. "Porcupine"	45	40
B390	50pf.+25pf. "Cockerel"	1·20	1·50

1971. 500th Birth Anniv of Albrecht Durer.

B391	B 87 10pf. black and brown	35	30

B 88 Communications Tower and Dish Aerials

B 90 H. von Helmholtz (from painting by K. Morell-Kramer)

B 89 Bach and part of 2nd Brandenburg Concerto

1971. West Berlin Broadcasting Exhibition.

B392	B 88 30pf. indigo, blue & red	80	55

1971. 250th Anniv of Bach's Brandenburg Concertos.

B393	B 89 30pf. multicoloured	70	50

1971. 150th Anniv of Hermann von Helmholtz (scientist).

B394	B 90 25pf. multicoloured	55	30

B 91 "Opel" Racing-car (1921)

B 92 Dancing Men

1971. 50th Anniv of Avus Motor-racing Track. Sheet 100 × 75 mm containing horiz designs as Type B 91. Multicoloured.

MSB395	10pf. Type B 91; 25pf. "Auto-Union" (1936); 30pf. "Mercedes-Benz SSKL" (1931); 60pf. "Mercedes" racing with "Auto-Union" (1937)	1·60	1·30

1971. Accident Prevention. As Nos. 1596/1605.

B396	5pf. orange	35	30
B397	10pf. brown	30	15
B398	20pf. violet	25	20
B399	25pf. green	35	45
B400	30pf. red	70	55
B401	40pf. mauve	55	35
B402	50pf. blue	55	85
B403	60pf. blue	2·75	1·60
B404	70pf. blue and green	2·75	1·80
B405	100pf. green	1·40	1·30
B406	150pf. brown	5·50	7·50

1971. Humanitarian Relief Funds. Wooden Toys. Multicoloured. (a) Inscr "WOHLFAHRTSMARKE".

B407	10pf.+5pf. Type B 92	20	20
B408	25pf.+10pf. Horseman on wheels	35	35
B409	30pf.+15pf. Acrobat	60	60
B410	60pf.+30pf. Nurse and babies	1·20	1·10

(b) Christmas. Inscr "WEIHNACHTSMARKE".

B411	10pf.+5pf. Angel with two candles	35	30

B 93 Microscope

B 94 F. Gilly (after bust by Schadow)

1971. Birth Centenary of Material-testing Laboratory, Berlin.

B412	B 93 30pf. multicoloured	45	35

1972. Birth Bicentenary of Friedrich Gilly (architect).

B413	B 94 30pf. black and blue	55	35

B 95 Boy raiding Bird's-nest

B 97 E. T. A. Hoffman

B 96 "Grunewaldsee" (A. von Riesen)

1972. Child Welfare. Animal Protection. Multicoloured.

B414	10pf.+5pf. Type B 95	25	25
B415	25pf.+10pf. Care of kittens	35	35
B416	30pf.+15pf. Man beating watch-dog	60	55
B417	60pf.+30pf. Animals crossing road at night	1·40	1·30

1972. Paintings of Berlin Lakes. Multicoloured.

B418	10pf. Type B 96	25	25
B419	25pf. "Wannsee" (Max Liebermann)	60	55
B420	30pf. "Schlachtensee" (W. Leistikow)	1·10	75

1972. 150th Death Anniv of E. T. A. Hoffman (poet and musician).

B421	B 97 60pf. black and violet	1·10	90

B 98 Max Liebermann (self-portrait)

B 99 Stamp Printing-press

1972. 125th Birth Anniv of Max Liebermann (painter).

B422	B 98 40pf. multicoloured	70	40

1972. Stamp Day.

B423	B 99 20pf. blue, black & red	45	30

1972. Humanitarian Relief Funds. Multicoloured. (a) 19th-century Faience Chessmen. As Nos. 1636/40 of West Germany. Inscr "WOHLFAHRTSMARKE".

B424	20pf.+10pf. Knight	35	35
B425	30pf.+15pf. Rook	60	55
B426	40pf.+20pf. Queen	1·40	1·40
B427	70pf.+35pf. King	2·00	1·80

(b) Christmas. Inscr "WEIHNACHTSMARKE".

B428	20pf.+10pf. "The Holy Family"	60	50

B 100 Prince von Hardenberg (after Tischbein)

B 101 Northern Goshawk

1972. 150th Death Anniv of Karl August von Hardenberg (statesman).

B429	B 100 40pf. multicoloured	65	40

1973. Youth Welfare. Birds of Prey. Mult.

B430	20pf.+10pf. Type B 101	45	50
B431	30pf.+15pf. Peregrine falcon	80	75
B432	40pf.+20pf. Northern sparrow hawk	1·10	1·00
B433	70pf.+35pf. Golden eagle	1·90	1·70

B 102 Horse-bus, 1907

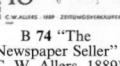

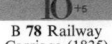

1973. Berlin Buses. Multicoloured.

B434	20pf. Type B **102**	35	30
B435	20pf. Trolley bus, 1933	35	30
B436	30pf. Motor bus, 1919	80	45
B437	30pf. Double-decker, 1970	1·20	45
B438	40pf. Double-decker, 1925	1·60	90
B439	40pf. "Standard" bus, 1973	1·60	90

B **103** L. Tieck

B **104** J. J. Quantz

1973. Birth Bicentenary of Ludwig Tieck (poet and writer).

B440	B **103** 40pf. multicoloured	70	40

1973. Death Bicentenary of Johann Quantz (composer).

B441	B **104** 40pf. black	80	60

B **105** Radio Set, 1926

1973. "50 Years of German Broadcasting". Sheet 148 × 105 mm containing horiz designs as Type B **105**.

MSB442	20pf. black and yellow; 30pf. black and green; 40pf. black and red; 70pf. black and blue (sold at 1.80Dm)	4·00	4·00

DESIGNS: 30pf. Hans Bredow and microphone of 1924; 40pf. Girl with TV and video tape-recorder; 70pf. TV camera

B **106** 17th-century Hurdy-Gurdy

B **107** G. W. Knobelsdorff

1973. Humanitarian Relief Funds. Mult. (a) Musical Instruments. Inscr "WOHLFAHRTSMARKE".

B443	20pf.+10pf. Type B **106**	35	35
B444	30pf.+15pf. 16th century drum	80	75
B445	40pf.+20pf. 18th century lute	1·00	90
B446	70pf.+35pf. 16th century organ	1·60	1·40

(b) Christmas. Inscr "WEIHNACHTSMARKE".

B447	20pf.+10pf. Christmas star	60	55

1974. 275th Birth Anniv of Georg W. von Knobelsdorff (architect).

B448	B **107** 20pf. brown	35	30

B **108** G. R. Kirchoff

B **109** A. Slaby

1974. 150th Birth Anniv of Gustav R. Kirchhoff (physicist).

B449	B **108** 30pf. green and grey	35	35

1974. 125th Birth Anniv of Adolf Slaby (radio pioneer).

B450	B **109** 40pf. black and red	60	40

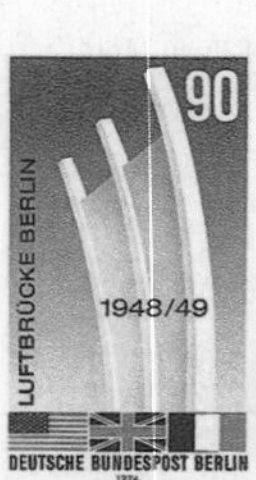
B **110** Airlift Memorial

B **111** Photography

1974. 25th Anniv of Berlin Airlift.

B451	B **110** 90pf. multicoloured	1·90	1·60

1974. Youth Welfare. Youth Activities. Multicoloured.

B452	20pf.+10pf. Type B **111**	35	35
B453	30pf.+15pf. Athletics	55	45
B454	40pf.+20pf. Music	1·00	95
B455	70pf.+35pf. Voluntary service (Nurse)	1·40	1·30

B **112** School Seal

B **113** Spring Bouquet

1974. 400th Anniv of Evangelical Grammar School, Berlin.

B456	B **112** 50pf. grey, brn & gold	70	40

1974. Humanitarian Relief Funds. Flowers. Multicoloured. (a) 25th Anniv of Humanitarian Relief Stamps. Inscr "25 JAHRE WOHLFAHRTSMARKE".

B457	30pf.+15pf. Type B **113**	35	35
B458	40pf.+20pf. Autumn bouquet	60	65
B459	50pf.+25pf. Bouquet of roses	90	75
B460	70pf.+35pf. Winter bouquet	1·60	1·40

(b) Christmas. Inscr "WEIHNACHTSMARKE."

B461	30pf.+15pf. Christmas bouquet	80	75

B **114** Tegel Airport

B **115** "Venus" (F. E. Meyer)

1974. Opening of Tegel Airport. Berlin.

B462	B **114** 50pf. violet, bl & grn	1·10	70

1974. Berlin Porcelain Figures. Mult.

B463	30pf. Type B **115**	55	35
B464	40pf. "Astronomy" (W. C. Meyer)	70	55
B465	50pf. "Justice" (J. G. Muller)	80	75

B **116** Gottfried Schadow

1975. 125th Death Anniv of Gottfried Schadow (sculptor).

B466	B **116** 50pf. brown	80	55

B **117** "Prinzess Charlotte"

1975. Berlin Pleasure Boats. Multicoloured.

B467	30pf. Type B **117**	80	40
B468	40pf. "Siegfried"	80	40
B469	50pf. "Sperber"	1·40	75
B470	60pf. "Vaterland"	1·40	75
B471	70pf. "Moby Dick"	1·80	1·50

B **118** Steam Locomotive "Drache", 1848

1975. Youth Welfare. Railway Locomotives. Multicoloured.

B472	30pf.+15pf. Type B **118**	90	85
B473	40pf.+20pf. Class 89 tank locomotive	90	90
B474	50pf.+25pf. Class 050 steam locomotive	1·80	1·50
B475	70pf.+35pf. Class 010 steam locomotive	2·75	2·50

B **119** Ferdinand Sauerbruch (surgeon)

B **120** Gymnastics Emblem

1975. Birth Cent of Ferdinand Sauerbruch.

B476	B **119** 50pf. dp brn, brn & pk	80	55

1975. Gymnaestrada (Gymnastic Games), Berlin.

B477	B **120** 40pf. black, gold and green	60	40

1975. Industry and Technology. As Nos. 1742/55.

B478	–	5pf. green	20	15
B479	–	10pf. purple	20	15
B480	–	20pf. red	25	15
B481	–	30pf. violet	35	20
B482	**572**	40pf. green	70	25
B483	–	50pf. red	70	20
B483a	–	60pf. red	1·10	35
B484	–	70pf. blue	1·20	50
B485	–	80pf. green	1·20	30
B486	–	100pf. brown	1·20	50
B486a	–	110pf. purple	1·60	1·20
B487	–	120pf. blue	1·60	1·10
B487a	–	130pf. red	2·20	1·40
B488	–	140pf. red	1·60	1·50
B488a	–	150pf. red	3·25	1·50
B489	–	160pf. green	3·50	1·50
B489a	–	180pf. brown	3·25	2·30
B489b	–	190pf. brown	3·25	2·30
B490	–	200pf. purple	2·20	60
B490a	–	230pf. purple	2·75	2·30
B490b	–	250pf. green	4·50	2·30
B490c	–	300pf. green	4·50	2·30
B491	–	500pf. black	7·00	5·25

B **121** "Lovis Corinth" (self-portrait)

B **122** Buildings in Naunynstrasse, Berlin-Kreuzberg

1975. 50th Death Anniv of Lovis Corinth (painter).

B492	B **121** 50pf. multicoloured	80	55

1975. European Architectural Heritage Year.

B493	B **122** 50pf. multicoloured	80	55

B **123** Yellow Gentian

1975. Humanitarian Relief Funds. Alpine Flowers. Multicoloured.

B494	30pf.+15pf. Type B **123**	60	40
B495	40pf.+20pf. Arnica	60	55
B496	50pf.+25pf. Cyclamen	80	75
B497	70pf.+35pf. Blue gentian	1·20	1·10

1975. Christmas. As Type B **123**, inscr "WEIHNACHTSMARKE". Mult.

B498	30pf.+15pf. Snow heather	80	75

See also Nos. B508/11, B540/3 and B557/60.

B **124** Paul Lobe

1975. Birth Cent of Paul Lobe (politician).

B499	B **124** 50pf. red	70	55

B **125** Ears of Wheat, with inscription "Grune Woche"

B **126** Putting the Shot

1976. "International Agriculture Week", Berlin.

B500	B **125** 70pf. yellow and green	80	70

1976. Youth Welfare. Training for the Olympics. Multicoloured.

B501	30pf.+15pf. Type B **126**	55	55
B502	40pf.+20pf. Hockey	55	55
B503	50pf.+25pf. Handball	90	75
B504	70pf.+35pf. Swimming	1·80	1·50

B **127** Hockey

1976. Women's World Hockey Championships.

B505	B **127** 30pf. green	70	35

B **128** Treble Clef

1976. German Choristers' Festival.

B506	B **128** 40pf. multicoloured	80	55

B **129** Fire Service Emblem

B **130** Julius Tower, Spandau

1976. 125th Anniv of Berlin Fire Service.

B507	B **129** 50pf. multicoloured	1·30	85

1976. Humanitarian Relief Funds. Garden Flowers. As Type B **123**. Multicoloured.

B508	30pf.+15pf. Iris	35	35
B509	40pf.+20pf. Wallflower	45	40
B510	50pf.+25pf. Dahlia	80	75
B511	70pf.+35pf. Larkspur	1·20	1·20

1976. Berlin Views (1st series).

B512	–	30pf. black and blue	60	40
B513	B **130**	40pf. black and brown	90	40
B514	–	50pf. black and green	1·00	60

DESIGNS: 30pf. Yacht on the Havel; 50pf. Lake and Victory Column, Tiergarten park.

See also Nos. B562/4, B605/7 and B647/9.

B **131** "Annunciation to the Shepherds" (window, Frauenkirche, Esslingen)

1976. Christmas. Sheet 71 × 101 mm.

MSB515	B **131** 30pf.+15pf. multicoloured	80	60

1977. Coil Stamps. German Castles. As Nos. 1805/12d.

B516	10pf. blue	20	15
B517	20pf. orange	20	15
B517a	25pf. red	45	35
B518	30pf. brown	25	20
B518c	35pf. red	45	40
B519	40pf. green	45	20
B519a	40pf. brown	60	30
B520	50pf. red	65	20
B520b	50pf. green	60	30
B521	60pf. brown	1·20	55
B521a	60pf. red	90	45

B522 70pf. blue . . . . 1·20 60
B522a 80pf. green 90 30
B522b 90pf. blue . . . . 1·10 85
B522c 120pf. violet . . . . . . 1·30 1·00
B523 190pf. red . . . . 2·00 1·50
B524 200pf. green . . . . . . 2·20 1·50
B524a 210pf. brown . . . . . . 2·75 1·70
B524b 230pf. green . . . . . . 2·75 1·70
B524c 280pf. blue . . . . . . 4·25 2·40
B524d 300pf. orange . . . . . . 4·25 2·10

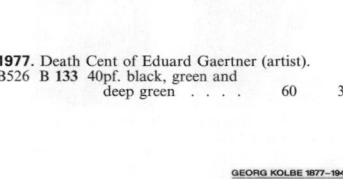

B 132 "Eugenie d'Alton" (Cristian Rauch)

B 133 "Eduard Gaertner" (self-portrait)

1977. Birth Bicentenary of Christian Daniel Rauch (sculptor).
B525 B **132** 50pf. black 80 55

1977. Death Cent of Eduard Gaertner (artist).
B526 B **133** 40pf. black, green and deep green 60 35

B 134 Bremen Kogge, 1380

B 135 Female Figure

1977. Youth Welfare. Ships. Multicoloured.
B527 30pf.+15pf. Type B **134** . . 50 50
B528 40pf.+20pf. "Helena Sloman" (steamship), 1850 . . . . 60 60
B529 50pf.+25pf. "Cap Polonio" (liner), 1914 . . . . . . 1·00 1·00
B530 70pf.+35pf. "Widar" (bulk carrier), 1971 . . . . . . 1·30 1·30

1977. Birth Cent of Georg Kolbe (sculptor).
B531 B **135** 30pf. green and black 60 35

B 136 Crosses and Text

B 137 Telephones of 1905 and 1977

1977. 17th Evangelical Churches Day.
B532 B **136** 40pf. yellow, blk & grn 60 35

1977. International Telecommunications Exhibition and Centenary of German Telephone Service.
B533 B **137** 50pf. buff, black & red . . . . 1·90 1·10

B 138 Imperial German Patent Office, Berlin-Kreuzberg

1977. Centenary of German Patent Office.
B534 B **138** 60pf. black, red & grey . . . . 1·60 70

B **139** Untitled Painting (G. Grosz)

B **141** "Madonna and Child" (stained glass window, Basilica of St. Gereon, Cologne)

B **140** Picassco Triggerfish

1977. 15th European Art Exhibition.
B535 B **139** 70pf. multicoloured 1·30 75

1977. 25th Anniv of Reopening of Berlin Aquarium. Multicoloured.
B536 20pf. Type B **140** 60 40
B537 30pf. Paddlefish 70 60
B538 40pf. Radiated tortoise . . 1·20 75
B539 50pf. Rhinoceros iguana . . 1·60 1·00

1977. Humanitarian Relief Funds. Meadow Flowers. As Type B **123**. Multicoloured.
B540 30pf.+15pf. Daisy 35 35
B541 40pf.+20pf. Marsh marigold 60 55
B542 50pf.+25pf. Sainfoin . . . 90 75
B543 70pf.+35pf. Forget-me-not 1·30 1·30

1977. Christmas. Sheet 70 × 105 mm.
MSB544 B **141** 30pf.+15pf. multicoloured 80 80

B **142** Walter Kollo

1978. Birth Cent of Walter Kollo (composer).
B545 B **142** 50pf. brown and red 1·10 60

B **143** Emblem of U.S. Chamber of Commerce

1978. 75th Anniv of U.S. Chamber of Commerce in Germany.
B546 B **143** 90pf. blue and red . . 1·30 1·00

1978. Youth Welfare. Aviation History (1st series). As T **627**. Multicoloured.
B547 30pf.+15pf. Montgolfier balloon, 1783 . . . . . 45 35
B548 40pf.+20pf. Lilienthal glider, 1891 . . . . . . 70 65
B549 50pf.+25pf. Wright Type A biplane 90 80
B550 70pf.+35pf. Etrich/Rumpler Taube, 1910 . . . . . . 1·30 1·30
See also Nos. B567/70 and B589/92.

1978. Sport Promotion Fund. As T **623**. Multicoloured.
B551 50pf.+25pf. Cycling 90 75
B552 70pf.+35pf. Fencing . . . . 1·30 1·20

B **146** Albrecht von Graefe

B **147** Friedrich Ludwig Jahn

1978. 150th Birth Anniv of Albrecht von Graefe (pioneer of medical eye services).
B553 B **146** 30pf. black and brown 70 35

1978. Birth Bicentenary of F. L. Jahn (pioneer of physical education).
B554 B **147** 50pf. red 80 55

B **148** Swimming

1978. 3rd World Swimming Championships.
B555 B **148** 40pf. multicoloured 1·10 85

B **149** "The Boat" (Karl Hofer)

1978. Birth Centenary of Karl Hofer (Impressionist painter).
B556 B **149** 50pf. multicoloured 80 55

1978. Humanitarian Relief Funds. Woodland Flowers. As Type B **123**. Multicoloured.
B557 30pf.+15pf. Solomon's seal 45 40
B558 40pf.+20pf. Wood primrose 60 55
B559 50pf.+25pf. Red helleborine 80 75
B560 70pf.+35pf. Bugle . . . . . 1·30 1·30

B **150** Prussian State Library

1978. Opening of New Prussian State Library Building.
B561 B **150** 90pf. olive and red . . 1·40 1·20

1978. Berlin Views (2nd series). As Type B **130**.
B562 40pf. black and green . . . 70 40
B563 50pf. black and purple . . . 80 60
B564 60pf. black and brown . . 1·20 75
DESIGNS: 40pf. Belvedere; 50pf. Landwehr Canal; 60pf. Village church, Lichtenrade.

B **151** "Madonna" (stained glass window, Frauenkirche, Munich)

1978. Christmas. Sheet 65 × 92 mm.
MSB565 B **151** 30pf.+15pf. multicoloured 80 80

B **152** Congress Centre

B **154** Old and New Arms

B **153** Relay Runners

1979. Opening of International Congress Centre, Berlin.
B566 B **152** 60pf. black, blue & red . . . . 1·10 70

1979. Youth Welfare. History of Aviation (2nd series). As T **627**. Multicoloured.
B567 40pf.+20pf. Vampyr glider, 1921 . . . . 55 60
B568 50pf.+25pf. Junkers Ju 52/3m D-2202 "Richthofen", 1932 . . . 80 80
B569 60pf.+30pf. Messerschmitt Bf 108 D-1010, 1934 . . 1·20 1·10
B570 90pf.+45pf. Douglas DC-3 NC-14988, 1935 . . . . 1·80 1·60

1979. Sport Promotion Fund. Multicoloured.
B571 60pf.+30pf. Type B **153** . . 1·10 90
B572 90pf.+45pf. Archers . . . . 1·30 1·30

1979. Centenary of State Printing Works, Berlin.
B573 B **154** 60pf. multicoloured 1·50 1·10

B **155** Arrows and Target

1979. World Archery Championships.
B574 B **155** 50pf. multicoloured 80 55

B **156** Television Screen

B **157** Moses Mendelssohn

1979. International Telecommunications Exhibition, Berlin.
B575 B **156** 60pf. black, grey & red . . . . 1·10 85

1979. 250th Birth Anniv of Moses Mendelssohn (philosopher).
B576 B **157** 90pf. black . . . . . 1·30 85

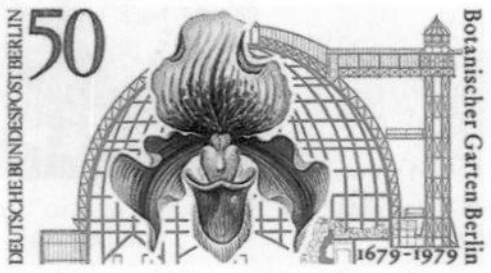

B **158** Venus Slipper Orchid and Great Tropical House

1979. 300th Anniv of Berlin Botanical Gardens.
B577 B **158** 50pf. multicoloured 80 55

B **159** Gas Lamp, Kreuzberg District

1979. 300th Anniv of Street Lighting.
B578 B **159** 10pf. green, bl & grey 45 20
B579 – 40pf. green, bis & grey 90 70
B580 – 50pf. green, brn & grey . . . . 1·20 75
B581 – 60pf. green, red & grey . . . . 1·30 1·10
DESIGNS: 40pf. Electric carbon-arc lamp, Hardenbergstrasse; 50pf. Gas Lamps, Wittenbergplatz; 60pf. Five-armed chandelier, Charlottenburg.

1979. Humanitarian Relief Funds. Woodland Flowers and Fruit. As Type B **123**, but horiz. Multicoloured
B582 40pf.+20pf. Larch 70 50
B583 50pf.+25pf. Hazelnut . . . 90 70
B584 60pf.+30pf. Horse chestnut 1·20 1·00
B585 90pf.+45pf. Blackthorn . . 1·60 1·60

B **161** Advertisement Pillar

B **162** "Nativity" (Altenberg medieval manuscript)

1979. 125th Anniv of Advertisement Pillars.
B586 B **161** 50pf. red and lilac . . 1·60 85

1979. Christmas.
B587 B **162** 40pf.+20pf. mult . . . 90 85

B 163 Map showing Wegener's Theory of Continental Drift

1980. Birth Centenary of Alfred Wegener (explorer and geophysicist).
B588 **B 163** 60pf. black, orange and blue . . . . . 1·20 1·10

1980. Youth Welfare. Aviation History (3rd series). As T **627**. Multicoloured.
B589 40pf.+20pf. Vickers Viscount 810 . . . . . . 80 75
B590 50pf.+25pf. Fokker Friendship "Condor" . . 90 85
B591 60pf.+30pf. Sud Aviation Caravelle F-BKSZ, 1955 1·10 1·00
B592 90pf.+45pf. Sikorsky S-55 helicopter OO-SHB, 1949 1·60 1·50
Nos. B589/90 are incorrectly dated.

B 164 Throwing the Javelin

1980. Sport Promotion Fund. Multicoloured.
B593 50pf.+25pf. Type **B 164** . . 70 75
B594 60pf.+30pf. Weightlifting . . 90 85
B595 90pf.+45pf. Water polo . . 1·30 1·20

B 165 Cardinal Preysing **B 166** "Operatio" (enamel medallion)

1980. 86th German Catholics Congress.
B596 **B 165** 50pf. red and black 80 55

1980. 150th Anniv of Prussian Museums. Multicoloured.
B597 40pf. Type **B 166** 80 45
B598 60pf. "Monks Reading" (oak sculpture, Ernst Barlach) . . . . 1·20 75

B 167 Robert Stolz **B 168** Von Steuben

1980. Birth Centenary of Robert Stolz (composer).
B599 **B 167** 60pf. multicoloured 1·10 85

1980. 250th Birth Anniv of Friedrich Wilhelm von Steuben (American general).
B600 **B 168** 40pf. multicoloured 1·10 55

B 169 Orlaya grandiflora

1980. Humanitarian Relief Funds. Endangered Wild Flowers. Multicoloured.
B601 40pf.+20pf. Type **B 169** . . 80 75
B602 50pf.+25pf. Yellow gagae 1·00 90
B603 60pf.+30pf. Summer pheasant's-eye . . . . . 1·00 90
B604 90p.+45pf. Venus's looking-glass . . . . 1·80 1·70
See also Nos. B622/5

1980. Berlin Views (3rd series). As Type **B 130**.
B605 40pf. black and green . . . 80 45
B606 50pf. black and brown . . 90 65
B607 60pf. black and blue . . . 1·40 85
DESIGNS: 40pf. Lilienthal Monument; 50pf. "Grosse Neugierde"; 60pf. Grunewald Tower.

B 170 "Message to the Shepherds" (Altomunster manuscript) **B 171** Von Arnim (after Strohling)

1980. Christmas.
B608 **B 170** 40pf.+20pf. mult . . . 90 85

1981. Birth Bicentenary of Achim von Arnim (poet).
B609 **B 171** 60pf. green 90 65

B 172 Von Chamisso (bronze medallion, David d'Angers)

1981. Birth Bicentenary of Adelbert von Chamisso (poet and naturalist).
B610 **B 172** 60pf. brown, deep brown and ochre 90 70

B 173 Von Gontard

1981. 250th Birth Anniv of Karl Phillipp von Gontard (architect).
B611 **B 173** 50pf. red, black & grey 90 70

B 174 Kreuzberg War Memorial **B 175** Theodolite, c. 1810

1981. Birth Bicentenary of Karl Friedrich Schinkel (architect).
B612 **B 174** 40pf. green and brown 1·10 70

1981. Youth Welfare. Optical Instruments. Multicoloured.
B613 40pf.+20pf. Type **B 175** . . 55 60
B614 50pf.+25pf. Equatorial telescope, 1820 . . . . 80 80
B615 60pf.+30pf. Microscope, 1790 . . . . 1·10 1·00
B616 90pf.+45pf. Sextant, 1830 1·80 1·70

B 176 Group Gymnastics

1981. Sport Promotion Fund. Multicoloured.
B617 60pf.+30pf. Type **B 176** . . 1·10 75
B618 90pf.+45pf. Cross-country race . . . . 1·60 1·30

B 177 "Cupid and Psyche" **B 178** Badge of Order "Pour le Merite"

1981. 150th Birth Anniv of Reinhold Begas (sculptor).
B619 **B 177** 50pf. black and blue 80 55

1981. Prussian Exhibition, Berlin-Kreuzberg.
B620 **B 178** 40pf. multicoloured 80 55

B 179 Broadcasting House, Charlottenburg **B 180** "Three Kings" (glass painting)

1981. International Telecommunications Exhibition, Berlin.
B621 **B 179** 60pf. multicoloured 1·30 85

1981. Humanitarian Relief Funds. Endangered Wild Flowers. As Type **B 169**. Multicoloured.
B622 40pf.+20pf. Common bistort 90 70
B623 50pf.+25pf. Moor-king . . 1·00 85
B624 60pf.+30pf. "Gladiolus palustris" . . . . . . 1·20 90
B625 90pf.+45pf. Siberian iris . . 2·00 1·70

1981. Christmas.
B626 **B 180** 40pf.+20pf. mult . . . 90 70

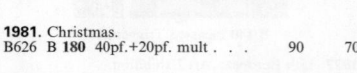

B 181 Peter Beuth **B 182** "Dancer Nijinsky" (Georg Kolbe)

1981. Birth Bicentenary of Peter Beuth (constitutional lawyer).
B627 **B 181** 60pf. black and brown 80 70

1981. 20th Century Sculptures. Mult.
B628 40pf. Type **B 182** 55 40
B629 60pf. "Mother Earth II" (Ernst Barlach) 90 60
B630 90pf. "Flora Kneeling" (Richard Scheibe) . . . . 1·40 1·20

B 183 Arms and View of Spandau, c. 1700

1982. 750th Anniv of Spandau.
B631 **B 183** 60pf. multicoloured 1·30 1·00

B 184 Daimler Steel-wheeled Car, 1889

1982. Youth Welfare Fund. Motor Cars. Multicoloured.
B632 40pf.+20pf. Type **B 184** . . 70 75
B633 50pf.+25pf. Wanderer "Puppchen", 1911 . . . 80 80
B634 60pf.+30p. Adler limousine, 1913 . . . . 1·00 95
B635 90pf.+45pf. DKW "F 1", 1913 . . . . 1·60 1·60

B 185 Sprinting

1982. Sport Promotion Fund. Multicoloured.
B636 60pf.+30pf. Type **B 185** . . 1·10 75
B637 90pf.+45pf. Volleyball . . . 1·60 1·10

B 186 Harp **B 187** "Emigrants reaching Prussian Frontier" (woodcut after drawing by Adolph von Menzel)

1982. Centenary of Berlin Philharmonic Orchestra.
B638 **B 186** 60pf. grey, red & green . . . . 1·10 70

1982. 250th Anniv of Salzburg Emigrants' Arrival in Prussia.
B639 **B 187** 50pf. stone, deep brown and brown 80 55

B 188 "Italian Stone Carriers" (Max Pechstein)

1982. Paintings. Multicoloured.
B640 50pf. Type **B 188** . . . . 1·10 75
B641 80pf. "Two Girls Bathing" (Otto Mueller) . . . . . 1·60 1·20

B 189 Floribunda-Grandiflora **B 191** "Adoration of the Kings" (detail from St. Peter altar by Master Bertram)

B 190 Castle Theatre, Charlottenburg

1982. Humanitarian Relief Funds. Roses. Multicoloured.
B642 50pf.+20pf. Type **B 189** . . 1·10 75
B643 60pf.+30pf. Hybrid tea . . 1·20 1·10
B644 80pf.+40pf. Floribunda . . 1·60 1·50
B645 120pf.+60pf. Miniature rose 2·75 2·75

1982. 250th Birth Anniv of Carl Gotthard Langhans (architect).
B646 **B 190** 80pf. red, grey and black . . . . 1·80 1·30

1982. Berlin Views (4th series). As Type **B 130**.
B647 50pf. black and blue . . . 1·10 65
B648 60pf. black and red . . . . 1·30 75
B649 80pf. black and brown . . 1·60 1·00
DESIGNS: 50pf. Villa Borsig; 60pf. Sts. Peter and Paul Church; 80pf. Villa von der Heydt.

1982. Christmas.
B650 **B 191** 50pf.+20pf. mult . . . 1·00 85

B 192 Water Pump, Klausenerplatz **B 193** Royal Prussian Telegraphy Inspectors at St. Anne's Church

1983. Street Water Pumps. Multicoloured.
B651 50pf. Type **B 192** . . . . 1·20 65
B652 60pf. Chamissoplatz . . . . 1·60 75
B653 80pf. Schloss-strasse . . . . 1·80 1·30
B654 120pf. Kuerfurstendamm . . 2·40 2·10

1983. 150th Anniv of Berlin–Coblenz Optical-Mechanical Telegraph.
B655 **B 193** 80pf. brown . . . . . 1·90 1·40

B 194 Hildebrand & Wolfmuller, 1894

1983. Youth Welfare. Motor Cycles. Mult.
B656 50pf.+20pf. Type **B 194** . . 90 65
B657 60pf.+30pf. Wanderer, 1908 1·30 90
B658 80pf.+40pf. D.K.W.-Lomos, 1922 . . . . 1·60 1·10
B659 120pf.+60pf. Mars, 1925 . . 3·25 2·20

B 195 Latin-American Dancing

1983. Sport Promotion Fund. Multicoloured.

B660	80pf.+40pf. Type B **195** . .	1·60	1·30
B661	120pf.+60pf. Ice hockey . .	2·75	2·00

B 196 "La Barbarina" (painting of Barbara Campanini)

B 197 Ringelnatz (silhouette by E. M. Engert)

1983. 300th Birth Anniv of Antoine Pesne (artist).

B662	B **196** 50pf. multicoloured	1·00	60

1983. Birth Centenary of Joachim Ringelnatz (poet and painter).

B663	B **197** 50pf. green, brn & red	1·10	75

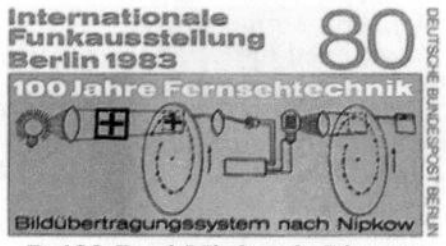

B 198 Paul Nipkow's Picture Transmission System, 1884

1983. International Broadcasting Exn, Berlin.

B664	B **198** 80pf. multicoloured	1·80	1·20

B 199 Mountain Windflower

B 200 Nigerian Yoruba Crib

1983. Humanitarian Relief Funds. Endangered Alpine Flowers. Multicoloured.

B665	50pf.+20pf. Type B **199** . .	65	65
B666	60pf.+30pf. Alpine auricula	1·10	1·10
B667	80pf.+40pf. Little primrose	2·00	1·80
B668	120pf.+60pf. Einsele's aquilegia	2·75	2·75

1983. Christmas.

B669	B **200** 50pf.+20pf. mult . . .	1·00	90

B 201 Queen Cleopatra VII (Antikenmuseum)

B 202 "Trichius Fasciatus"

1984. Art Objects in Berlin Museums. Multicoloured.

B670	30pf. Type B **201**	1·10	75
B671	50pf. Statue of seated couple from Giza Necropolis (Egyptian Museum)	1·50	1·20
B672	60pf. Goddess with pearl turban (Ethnology Museum)	1·90	1·50
B673	80pf. Majolica dish (Applied Arts Museum)	2·20	2·00

1984. Youth Welfare. Pollinating Insects. Multicoloured.

B674	50pf.+20pf. Type B **202** . .	1·20	85
B675	60pf.+30pf. "Agrumenia carniolica"	1·20	1·10
B676	80pf.+40pf. "Bombus terrestris"	1·80	1·30
B677	120pf.+60pf. "Eristalis tenax"	2·75	2·40

B 203 Hurdling

1984. Sport Promotion Fund. Multicoloured.

B678	60pf.+30pf. Type B **203** . .	1·30	1·10
B679	80pf.+40pf. Cycling	2·20	1·30
B680	120pf.+60pf. Four-seater kayaks	3·50	2·75

B 204 Klausener

B 205 "Electric Power" (K. Sutterlin)

1984. 50th Death Anniv of Dr. Erich Klausener (chairman of Catholic Action).

B681	B **204** 80pf. green & dp green	1·10	85

1984. Centenary of Berlin Electricity Supply.

B682	B **205** 50pf. yell, orge & blk	90	75

B 206 Conference Emblem

1984. 4th European Ministers of Culture Conference, Berlin.

B683	B **206** 60pf. multicoloured	1·10	70

B 207 Brehm and White Stork

1984. Death Centenary of Alfred Brehm (zoologist).

B684	B **207** 80pf. multicoloured	1·90	1·30

B 208 Heim (bust, Friedrich Tieck)

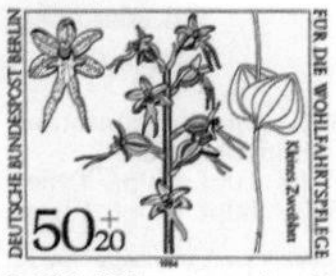

B 209 "Listera cordata"

1984. 150th Death Anniv of Ernst Ludwig Heim (medical pioneer).

B685	B **208** 50pf. black and red	1·10	85

1984. Humanitarian Relief Funds. Orchids. Multicoloured.

B686	50pf.+20pf. Type B **209** . .	1·80	1·30
B687	60pf.+30pf. "Ophrys insectifera"	2·00	1·30
B688	80pf.+40pf. "Epipactis palustris"	2·75	2·30
B689	120pf.+60pf. "Ophrys coriophora"	4·50	4·25

B 210 "Sunflowers on Grey Background"

B 211 St. Nicholas

1984. Birth Centenary of Karl Schmidt-Rottluff (artist).

B690	B **210** 60pf. multicoloured	1·10	75

1984. Christmas.

B691	B **211** 50pf.+20pf. mult . . .	1·10	1·10

B 212 Bettina von Arnim

B 213 Humboldt (statue, Paul Otto)

1985. Birth Bicentenary of Bettina von Arnim (writer).

B692	B **212** 50pf. black, brn & red	1·20	85

1985. 50th Death Anniv of Wilhelm von Humboldt (philologist).

B693	B **213** 80pf. black, blue & red	1·60	1·30

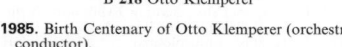

B 214 Ball in Net

1985. Sport Promotion Fund. Multicoloured.

B694	80pf.+40pf. Type B **214** (50th anniv of basketball in Germany and European championships, Stuttgart)	1·60	1·40
B695	120pf.+60pf. Table tennis (60th anniv of German Table Tennis Association)	2·75	2·30

B 215 Stylized Flower

1985. Federal Horticultural Show, Berlin.

B696	B **215** 80pf. multicoloured	1·30	1·20

B 216 Bussing Bicycle, 1868

1985. Youth Welfare. International Youth Year. Bicycles. Multicoloured.

B697	50pf.+20pf. Type B **216** . .	1·30	1·30
B698	60pf.+30pf. Child's tricycle, 1885	1·30	1·20
B699	80pf.+40pf. Jaray bicycle, 1925	1·80	1·80
B700	120pf.+60pf. Opel racing bicycle, 1925	3·75	3·50

B 217 Stock Exchange, 1863–1945

1985. 300th Anniv of Berlin Stock Exchange.

B701	B **217** 50pf. multicoloured	1·10	85

B 218 Otto Klemperer

1985. Birth Centenary of Otto Klemperer (orchestral conductor).

B702	B **218** 60pf. blue	1·30	1·20

B 219 Association Emblem

1985. 11th International Gynaecology and Obstetrics Association Congress, Berlin.

B703	B **219** 60pf. multicoloured	1·10	85

B 220 "FE 3" Television Camera, 1935

1985. International Broadcasting Exn, Berlin.

B704	B **220** 80pf. multicoloured	1·80	1·60

B 221 Seal of Brandenburg-Prussia and Preamble of Edict

1985. 300th Anniv of Edict of Potsdam (admitting Huguenots to Prussia).

B705	B **221** 50pf. lilac and black	90	70

B 222 Flowers, Strawberries and Ladybirds

1985. Humanitarian Relief Funds. Motifs from borders of medieval prayer book. Multicoloured.

B706	50pf.+20pf. Type B **222** . .	1·30	1·30
B707	60pf.+30pf. Flowers, bird and butterfly	1·60	1·60
B708	80pf.+40pf. Flowers, bee and butterfly	1·80	1·70
B709	120pf.+60pf. Flowers, berries, butterfly and snail	2·75	2·75

B 223 "Adoration of the Kings" (detail, Epiphany Altar)

B 224 Kurt Tucholsky

1985. Christmas. 500th Birth Anniv of Hans Baldung Grien (artist).

B710	B **223** 50pf.+20pf. mult . . .	1·30	1·10

1985. 50th Death Anniv of Kurt Tucholsky (writer and journalist).

B711	B **224** 80pf. multicoloured	1·80	1·20

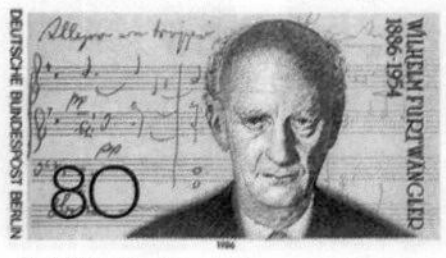

B 225 Furtwangler and Score

1986. Birth Centenary of Wilhelm Furtwangler (composer and conductor).

B712	B **225** 80pf. multicoloured	1·90	1·40

B 226 Rohe and National Gallery

1986. Birth Centenary of Ludwig Mies van der Rohe (architect).

B713	B **226** 50pf. multicoloured	1·10	1·10

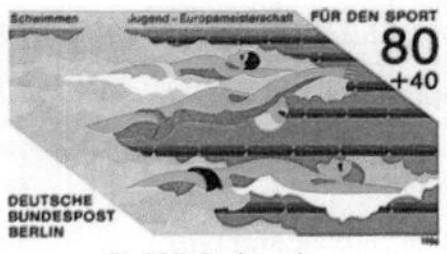

B 227 Swimming

1986. Sport Promotion Fund. Multicoloured.

B714	80pf.+40pf. Type B **227** (European Youth Championships, Berlin)	2·00	1·80
B715	120pf.+55pf. Show-jumping (World Championships, Aachen)	2·40	2·20

B 228 Glazier

1986. Youth Charity. Trades (1st series). Multicoloured.

B716	50pf.+25pf. Type B **228** . .	1·20	1·20
B717	60pf.+30pf. Locksmith . . .	1·60	1·40
B718	70pf.+35pf. Tailor	1·80	1·60
B719	80pf.+40pf. Carpenter . . .	2·20	2·10

See also Nos. B765/8.

B 229 Flags

1986. 16th European Communities Day.
B720 B 229 60pf. multicoloured 1·00 90

B 230 Ranke B 231 Benn

1986. Death Centenary of Leopold von Ranke (historian).
B721 B 230 80pf. brown and grey 1·80 1·30

1986. Birth Centenary of Gottfried Benn (poet).
B722 B 231 80pf. blue . . . . . . 1·80 1·30

B 232 Charlottenburg Gate B 233 "The Flute Concert" (detail, Adolph von Menzel)

1986. Gateways. Multicoloured.
B723 50pf. Type B 232 . . . . 1·30 1·10
B724 60pf. Griffin Gate, Glienicke Palace . . . 1·60 1·30
B725 80pf. Elephant Gate, Berlin Zoo . . . . 2·00 1·50

1986. Death Bicentenary of Frederick the Great.
B726 B 233 80pf. multicoloured 1·80 1·20

B 234 Cantharus, 1st century A.D. B 235 "Adoration of the Three Kings" (Ortenberg altarpiece)

1986. Humanitarian Relief Funds. Glassware. Multicoloured.
B727 50pf.+25pf. Type B 234 . . 3·50 1·20
B728 60pf.+30pf. Beaker, 200 A.D. . . . . 1·60 1·40
B729 70pf.+35pf. Jug, 3rd century A.D. . . . . 1·80 1·60
B730 80pf.+40pf. Diatreta 4th century A.D. . . . . . . 2·40 2·20

1986. Christmas.
B731 B 235 50pf.+25pf. mult . . . 1·00 90

1986. Famous German Women. As Nos. 2149a/54, 2158, 2161, 2166/9a.
B732 5pf. brown and grey . . 35 1·80
B733 10pf. brown and violet . . 35 1·40
B734 20pf. blue and red . . . 1·80 3·50
B735 40pf. red and blue . . . 1·30 3·75
B736 50pf. green and brown . . 1·80 2·75
B737 60pf. lilac and green . . 90 3·75
B738 80pf. brown and green . . 1·60 2·40
B739 100pf. grey and red . . . 1·80 1·50
B740 130pf. violet and blue . . 4·50 11·00
B741 140pf. brown and blue . . 4·50 12·00
B742 170pf. purple and green . . 3·00 9·25
B743 180pf. purple and blue . . 4·50 12·00
B744 240pf. brown and blue . . 3·75 12·50
B745 250pf. blue and mauve . . 8·00 20·00
B746 300pf. green and plum . . 8·50 20·00
B747 350pf. brown and black . . 6·75 15·00
B748 500pf. red and green . . . 9·00 31·00

B 236 Berlin, 1650

1987. 750th Anniv of Berlin. (a) As No. 2170.
B760 833 80pf. multicoloured . . 1·90 1·50

(b) Sheet 130 × 100 mm containing Type B 236 and similar horiz designs. Multicoloured.
MSB761 40pf. Type B 236; 50pf. Charlottenburg Castle, 1830; 60pf. Turbine Hall; 80pf. Philharmonic and Chamber Music Concert Hall 4·00 4·00

B 237 Louise Schroeder B 239 "Bohemian Refugees" (detail of relief, King Friedrich Wilhelm Monument, Berlin-Neukolln)

B 238 German Gymnastics Festival, Berlin

1987. Birth Centenary of Louise Schroeder (Mayor of Berlin).
B762 B 237 50pf. brown and orange on light brown . . . . . . 1·10 1·10

1987. Sport Promotion Fund. Multicoloured.
B763 80pf.+40pf. Type B 238 . . 1·70 1·60
B764 120pf.+55pf. World Judo Championships, Essen . . 2·75 2·50

1987. Youth Welfare. Trades (2nd series). As Type B 228. Multicoloured.
B765 50pf.+25pf. Cooper . . . . 1·20 1·30
B766 60pf.+30pf. Stonemason . . 1·30 1·30
B767 70pf.+35pf. Furrier . . . . 1·60 1·70
B768 80pf.+40pf. Painter/ lacquerer . . . . 1·80 1·70

1987. 250th Anniv of Bohemian Settlement, Rixdorf.
B769 B 239 50pf. brown and green 80 75

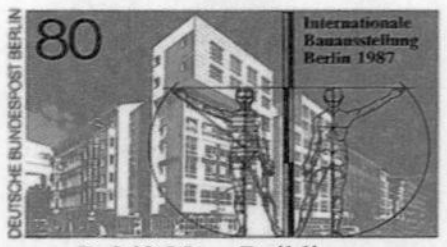

B 240 New Buildings

1987. International Building Exhibition, Berlin.
B770 B 240 80pf. silver, black & bl . . . . 1·30 1·10

B 241 Tree in Arrow Circle

1987. 14th International Botanical Congress, Berlin.
B771 B 241 60pf. multicoloured 1·00 85

B 242 Compact Disc and Gramophone

1987. International Broadcasting Exhibition, Berlin. Centenary of Gramophone Record.
B772 B 242 80pf. multicoloured 1·30 1·10

B 243 5th-century Bonnet Ornament

1987. Humanitarian Relief Funds. Precious Metal Work. Multicoloured.
B773 50pf.+25pf. Type B 243 . . 90 85
B774 60pf.+30pf. Athene plate, 1st-century B.C. . . . . 1·30 1·30
B775 70pf.+35pf. "Armilla" armlet, 1180 . . . . . 1·60 1·40
B776 80pf.+40pf. Snake bracelet, 300 B.C. . . . . 2·00 1·80

1987. Tourist Sights. As Nos. 2200/19.
B777 5pf. blue and grey 35 35
B778 10pf. blue and indigo . . . 45 35
B779 20pf. flesh and blue 45 75
B780 30pf. brown and green . . 1·10 1·10
B781 40pf. brown, red and blue 1·10 1·60
B782 50pf. ochre and blue . . . 1·60 1·00
B783 60pf. green and black . . 1·60 1·00
B784 70pf. flesh and blue . . . 1·60 2·00
B785 70pf. brown and blue . . 2·20 4·25
B786 80pf. grey and green . . . 1·60 1·00
B787 100pf. green and orange . . 1·30 1·20
B788 120pf. green and red . . 2·40 3·00
B789 140pf. bistre and yellow . . 2·75 3·50
B790 300pf. flesh and brown . . 5·25 4·00
B791 350pf. brown and blue . . 5·25 6·50

B 244 "Adoration of the Magi" (13th-century Book of Psalms) B 245 Heraldic Bear

1987. Christmas.
B797 B 244 50pf.+25pf. mult . . . 1·00 85

1988. Berlin, European City of Culture.
B798 B 245 80pf. multicoloured 1·80 1·40

B 246 Old and New Buildings

1988. Centenary of Urania Science Museum.
B799 B 246 50pf. multicoloured 1·30 1·20

B 247 "Large Pure-bred Foal" (bronze)

1988. Birth Centenary of Rene Sintenis (sculptor).
B800 B 247 60pf. multicoloured 90 75

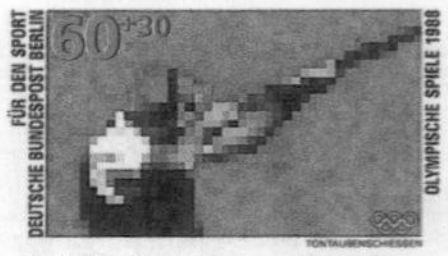

B 248 Clay-pigeon Shooting

1988. Sport Promotion Fund. Olympic Games. Multicoloured.
B801 60pf.+30pf. Type B 248 . . 1·60 1·20
B802 80pf.+40pf. Figure skating (pairs) . . . . 1·80 1·20
B803 120pf.+55pf. Throwing the hammer . . . . 2·20 2·10

B 249 Piano, Violin and Cello

1988. Youth Welfare. Music. Multicoloured.
B804 50pf.+25pf. Type B 249 . . 1·30 1·30
B805 60pf.+30pf. Wind quintet . 1·80 1·60
B806 70pf.+35pf. Guitar, recorder and mandolin . . . . . 1·80 1·70
B807 80pf.+40pf. Children's choir 2·20 2·10

B 250 Great Elector and Family in Berlin Castle Gardens B 251 Globe

1988. 300th Death Anniv of Friedrich Wilhelm, Great Elector of Brandenburg.
B808 B 250 50pf. multicoloured 1·10 1·10

1988. International Monetary Fund and World Bank Boards of Governors Annual Meetings, Berlin.
B809 B 251 70pf. multicoloured 1·10 90

B 252 First Train leaving Potsdam Station

1988. 150th Anniv of Berlin–Potsdam Railway.
B810 B 252 10pf. multicoloured 60 35

B 253 "The Collector" (bronze statue)

1988. 50th Death Anniv of Ernst Barlach (artist).
B811 B 253 40pf. multicoloured 70 55

B 254 18th-century Breast Ornament

1988. Humanitarian Relief Funds. Precious Metal Work. Multicoloured.
B812 50pf.+25pf. Type B 254 . . 1·10 1·10
B813 60pf.+30pf. 16th-century lion-shaped jug . . . . . 1·30 1·30
B814 70pf.+35pf. 16th-century goblet . . . . 1·60 1·60
B815 80pf.+40pf. 15th-century cope clasp . . . . 1·80 1·70

B 255 "Annunciation to the Shepherds" (illus from Henry the Lion's Gospel Book)

1988. Christmas.
B816 B 255 50pf.+25pf. mult . . . 1·30 1·10

B 256 Volleyball (European Championships)

1989. Sport Promotion Fund. Multicoloured.
B817 100pf.+50pf. Type B 256 2·75 2·30
B818 140pf.+60pf. Hockey (Champions Trophy) . . 3·50 3·00

B 257 Tigers and Tamer

1989. Youth Welfare. Circus. Multicoloured.
B819 60pf.+30pf. Type B 257 . . 1·80 1·90
B820 70pf.+30pf. Trapeze artistes 2·20 2·20
B821 80pf.+35pf. Sealions . . . . 2·75 2·75
B822 100pf.+50pf. Jugglers . . . 3·50 3·00

B 258 U.S. and U.K. Flags forming Airplane

1989. 40th Anniv of Berlin Airlift.
B823 B 258 60pf. multicoloured 1·30 95

B 259 Emblem

1989. 13th International Organization of Chief Accountants Congress.
B824 B **259** 80pf. multicoloured 1·30 1·30

B **260** Reuter

1989. Birth Centenary of Ernst Reuter (politician and Mayor of Berlin).
B825 B **260** 100pf. multicoloured 2·00 1·70

B **261** Satellite Radio Waves and T.V. Screen

1989. International Broadcasting Exn, Berlin.
B826 B **261** 100pf. multicoloured 1·80 1·40

B **262** Plan of Berlin Zoo and Lenne

1989. Birth Bicentenary of Peter Joseph Lenne (landscape designer).
B827 B **262** 60pf. multicoloured 1·60 1·40

B **263** Ossietzky and Masthead of "Die Weltbuhne"

1989. Birth Centenary of Carl von Ossietzky (journalist and peace activist).
B828 B **263** 100pf. multicoloured 1·80 1·70

B **264** Former School Building

1989. 300th Anniv of Berlin Lycee Francais.
B829 B **264** 40pf. multicoloured 1·00 95

B **265** St. Nicholas's Church, Berlin-Spandau

1989. 450th Anniv of Reformation.
B830 B **265** 60pf. multicoloured 1·10 1·00

B **266** 15th-century Letter Messenger

B **267** "Journalists"

1989. Humanitarian Relief Funds. Postal Deliveries. Multicoloured.
B831 60pf.+30pf. Type B **266** . . 2·40 2·40
B832 80pf.+35pf. Brandenburg mail coach, 1700 . . . . 3·50 3·00
B833 100pf.+50pf. 19th-century Prussian postal messengers . . . . 4·50 3·75

1989. Birth Centenary of Hannah Hoch (painter).
B834 B **267** 100pf. multicoloured 1·80 1·60

B **268** Angel

1989. Christmas. 16th-century Carvings by Veit Stoss, St. Lawrence's Church, Nuremberg. Multicoloured.
B835 40pf.+20pf. Type B **268** . . 1·20 1·30
B836 60pf.+30pf. "Adoration of the Magi" . . . . 2·20 2·10

B **269** Horse-drawn Passenger Vehicle

1990. 250th Anniv of Public Transport in Berlin.
B837 B **269** 60pf. multicoloured 2·00 1·50

B **270** Rudorff

1990. 150th Birth Anniv of Ernst Rudorff (founder of conservation movement).
B838 B **270** 60pf. multicoloured 2·00 1·50

1990. 500th Anniv of Regular European Postal Services. As No. 2297.
B839 **914** 100pf. deep brown, light brown and brown . . 2·40 2·00

B **271** Curtain and Theatre

1990. Cent of National Free Theatre, Berlin.
B840 B **271** 100pf. multicoloured 2·00 1·80

B **272** Facade

1990. 40th Anniv of Bundeshaus, Berlin.
B841 B **272** 100pf. multicoloured 2·75 2·10

B **273** Water Polo

1990. Sport Promotion Fund. Multicoloured.
B842 100pf.+50pf. Type B **273** 3·50 3·50
B843 140pf.+60pf. Wheelchair basketball . . . . 5·25 5·75

B **274** Moritz filling Pipe with Gunpowder

1990. Youth Welfare. 125th Anniv of Max and Moritz (characters from books by Wilhelm Busch). Multicoloured.
B844 60pf.+30pf. Type B **274** . . 1·60 1·60
B845 70pf.+30pf. Max and Moritz running off . . . 2·20 2·10
B846 80pf.+35pf. Moritz slashing sack open . . . . 2·75 2·50
B847 100pf.+50pf. Insect on Uncle Fritz's nose . . . 3·00 2·75

B **275** Poster

B **276** "Street Singer" (etching, Ludwig Knaus)

1990. 90th German Catholic Day.
B848 B **275** 60pf. multicoloured 1·80 1·50

1990. Bicentenary of Barrel-organ.
B849 B **276** 100pf. multicoloured 2·00 1·70

B **277** Pestle and Mortar and Diagram of Aspirin Molecule

B **278** Diesterweg

1990. Centenary of German Pharmaceutical Society.
B850 B **277** 100pf. multicoloured 4·00 3·00

1990. Birth Bicentenary of Adolph Diesterweg (educationist).
B851 B **278** 60pf. multicoloured 2·75 2·50

B **279** Travelling Post Office, 1900

1990. Humanitarian Relief Funds. Posts and Telecommunications. Multicoloured.
B852 60pf.+30pf. Type B **279** . . 2·40 2·20
B853 80pf.+35pf. Installing telephone lines, 1900 . . 3·00 2·75
B854 100pf.+50pf. Electric parcels van, 1930 . . . . 4·50 3·75

With the absorption of East Germany into the Federal Republic of Germany on 3 October 1990, separate issues for West Berlin ceased.

V. GERMAN DEMOCRATIC REPUBLIC (East Germany)

The German Democratic Republic was set up in October 1949 and comprised the former Russian Zone. Its stamps were used in East Berlin.

On 3 October 1990 the territory was absorbed into the German Federal Republic.

1949. 100 pfennig = 1 Deutsche mark (East).
1990. 100 pfennig = 1 Deutsche mark (West).

E **1** Pigeon and Globe

E **2** Postal Workers and Globe

1949. 75th Anniv of U.P.U.
E1 E **1** 50pf. blue and deep blue 10·00 10·00

1949. Postal Workers' Congress.
E2 E **2** 12pf. blue . . . . 10·00 8·75
E3 30pf. red . . . . 16·00 18·00

E **3** Type **1** of Bavaria and Magnifying Glass

E **4** Skier

1949. Stamp Day.
E4 E **3** 12pf.+3pf. black . . . . . 8·00 5·75

1950. 1st Winter Sports Meeting, Schierke.
E5 E **4** 12pf. violet . . . . 8·00 4·75
E6 – 24pf. blue . . . . 10·00 8·00
DESIGN: 24pf. Girl skater.

1950. Leipzig Spring Fair. As T **231** but dated "1950".
E7 24pf.+12pf. purple . . . . . 12·00 8·75
E8 30pf.+14pf. red . . . . 14·00 11·50
DESIGNS: 24pf. First Dresden China Fair, 1710; 30pf. First Sample Fair, 1894.

E **5** Globe and Sun

E **6** Wilhelm Pieck

E **7** Wilhelm Pieck

E **8** Shepherd Playing Pipes

1950. 60th Anniv of Labour Day.
E9 E **5** 30pf. red . . . . 21·00 19·00

1950.

E68 E **6** 5pf. green . . . . 13·00 4·50
E69 12pf. blue . . . . 31·00 1·70
E70 24pf. brown . . . . . . 29·00 1·60
E12 E **7** 1Dm. green . . . . . . 38·00 4·75
E13 2Dm. red . . . . 24·00 4·25
E14 5Dm. blue . . . . 9·75 1·80

For 1 and 2Dm. with different portrait of president, see Nos. E320/1 (1953).

1950. Death Bicentenary of J. S. Bach (composer).
E15 E **8** 12pf.+4pf. green . . . . 8·00 5·50
E16 – 24pf.+6pf. olive . . . . 8·00 5·50
E17 – 30pf.+8pf. red . . . . . 15·00 12·50
E18 – 50pf.+16pf. blue . . . . 24·00 16·00
DESIGNS: 24pf. Girl playing hand-organ; 30pf. Bach; 50pf. Three singers.

E **9** Dove, Globe and Stamp

E **10** L. Euler

1950. Philatelic Exhibition (DEBRIA), Leipzig.
E19 E **9** 84pf.+41pf. red . . . . . 55·00 11·50

1950. 250th Anniv of Academy of Science, Berlin.
E20 E **10** 1pf. grey . . . . 5·00 1·70
E21 – 5pf. green . . . . 7·00 5·25
E22 – 6pf. violet . . . . . . 14·00 5·25
E23 – 8pf. brown . . . . . . 22·00 11·50
E24 – 10pf. green . . . . . . 20·00 11·50
E25 – 12pf. blue . . . . 18·00 3·75
E26 – 16pf. blue . . . . 24·00 18·00
E27 – 20pf. purple . . . . . . 23·00 16·00
E28 – 24pf. red . . . . 24·00 3·75
E29 – 50pf. blue . . . . 36·00 21·00
PORTRAITS: 5pf. A. von Humboldt; 6pf. T. Mommsen; 8pf. W. von Humboldt; 10pf. H. von Helmholtz; 12pf. M. Planck; 16pf. J. Grimm; 20pf. W. Nernst; 24pf. G. W. Leibniz; 50pf. A. von Harnack.

1950. German Stamp Exhibition, "DEBRIA". Sheet 92 × 52 mm.
MSE29a Nos. E4 and E19 . . . £160 70·00

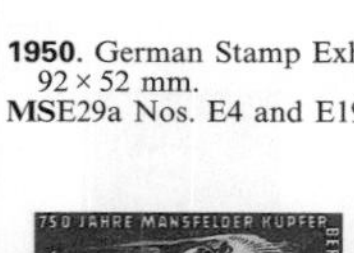

E **11** Miner

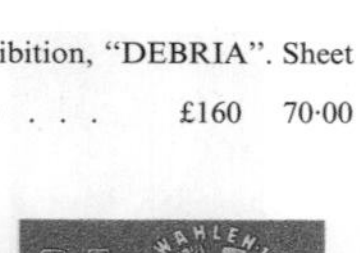

E **12** Ballot Box

1950. 750th Anniv of Mansfeld Copper Mines.
E30 E **11** 12pf. blue . . . . 7·00 8·75
E31 – 24pf. red . . . . 11·00 8·75
DESIGN: 24pf. Copper smelting.

1950. East German Elections.
E32 E **12** 24pf. brown . . . . . . 17·00 4·25

E 13 Hand, Dove and Burning Buildings

E 14 Tobogganing

1950. Peace Propaganda. Inscr "ERKAMPFT DEN FRIEDEN".

E33	–	6pf. blue	5·00	3·75
E34	E 13	8pf. brown	5·00	1·80
E35	–	12pf. blue	7·00	3·75
E36	–	24pf. red	7·00	2·00

DESIGNS (all include hand and dove): 6pf. Tank; 12pf. Atom bomb explosion; 24pf. Rows of gravestones.

1951. 2nd Winter Sports Meeting, Oberhof.

E37	E 14	12pf. blue	30·00	8·25
E38	–	24f. red (ski jumper)	14·00	10·00

E 15

1951. Leipzig Spring Fair.

E39	E 15	24pf. red	22·00	18·00
E40		50pf. blue	22·00	18·00

E 16 Presidents Pieck and Bierut

1951. Visit of Polish President to Berlin.

E41	E 16	24pf. red	25·00	21·00
E42		50pf. blue	25·00	20·00

E 17 Mao Tse-tung

E 18 Chinese Land Reform

1951. Friendship with China.

E43	E 17	12pf. green	£110	27·00
E44	E 18	24pf. red	£140	35·00
E45	E 17	50pf. blue	£110	31·00

E 19 Youth Hoisting Flag

E 20 Symbols of Agriculture & Industry

1951. 3rd World Youth Festival. Inscr as in Type E 19. On coloured papers.

E46	E 19	12pf. brown	14·50	6·50
E47	–	24pf. green and red	14·50	4·50
E48	E 19	30pf. buff and green	18·00	8·50
E49	–	50pf. red and blue	18·00	8·25

DESIGN: 24pf., 50pf. Three girls dancing.

1951. Five Year Plan.

E50	E 20	24pf. multicoloured	5·50	2·40

E 21 K. Liebknecht

E 22 Instructing Young Collectors

1951. 80th Birth Anniv of Liebknecht (revolutionary).

E51	E 21	24pf. slate and red	6·50	2·40

1951. Stamp Day.

E52	E 22	12pf. blue	5·00	2·50

E 23 P. Bykow and E. Wirth

1951. German–Soviet Friendship.

E53	E 23	12pf. blue	5·00	4·00
E54	–	24pf. red	6·25	5·75

DESIGN: 24pf. Stalin and Pres. Pieck.

E 24 Skier

E 25 Beethoven

1952. 3rd Winter Sports Meeting. Oberhof.

E55	E 24	12pf. green	7·00	4·25
E56	–	24pf. blue	7·00	4·25

DESIGN: 24pf. Ski jumper.

1952. 125th Death Anniv of Beethoven (composer).

E57	–	12pf. blue and light blue	2·40	65
E58	E 25	24pf. brown and grey	3·50	1·00

DESIGN: 12pf. Full face portrait.

E 26 President Gottwald

E 27 Bricklayers

1952. Czechoslovak–German Friendship.

E59	E 26	24pf. blue	3·50	2·10

1952. National Reconstruction Fund.

E60	–	12pf.+3pf. violet	2·00	55
E61	E 27	24pf.+6pf. red	1·80	70
E62	–	30pf.+10pf. green	2·20	90
E63	–	50pf.+10pf. blue	3·00	1·70

DESIGNS: 12pf. Workers clearing debris; 30pf. Carpenters; 50pf. Architect and workmen.

E 28 Cyclists

E 29 Handel

1952. 5th Warsaw–Berlin–Prague Cycle Race.

E64	E 28	12pf. blue	3·75	1·70

1952. Handel Festival, Halle.

E65	E 29	6pf. brown	2·20	1·70
E66	–	8pf. red	3·25	2·50
E67	–	50pf. blue	4·00	3·25

COMPOSERS: 8pf. Lortzing; 50pf. Weber.

E 31 Victor Hugo

E 32 Machinery, Dove and Globe

1952. Cultural Anniversaries.

E73	E 31	12pf. brown	4·00	5·50
E74	–	20pf. green	4·00	5·50
E75	–	24pf. red	4·00	5·00
E76	–	35pf. blue	6·25	7·50

PORTRAITS: 20pf. Leonardo da Vinci; 24pf. N. Gogol; 35pf. Avicenna.

1952. Leipzig Autumn Fair.

E77	E 32	24pf. red	3·00	1·80
E78		35pf. blue	3·00	2·50

E 33 F. L. Jahn

E 34 University Building

1952. Death Centenary of Jahn (patriot).

E79	E 33	12pf. blue	2·40	1·40

1952. 450th Anniv of Halle-Wittenberg University.

E80	E 34	24pf. green	2·40	1·30

E 35 Dove, Stamp and Flags

E 36 Dove, Globe and St. Stephen's Cathedral, Vienna

1952. Stamp Day.

E81	E 35	24pf. brown	2·40	1·40

1952. Vienna Peace Congress.

E97	E 36	24pf. red	2·00	3·25
E98		35pf. blue	2·00	4·75

E 37 President Pieck

E 38 Karl Marx

1953. President's Birthday.

E320	E 37	1Dm. olive	18·00	90
E321		2Dm. brown	3·25	1·30

1953. 70th Death Anniv of Marx.

E102	–	6pf. red and green	5·25	80
E103	–	10pf. brown and green	5·25	1·10
E104	–	12pf. red and green	90	1·10
E105	–	16pf. blue and red	3·50	2·20
E106	–	20pf. brown and yellow	1·30	1·50
E107	E 38	24pf. brown and red	3·50	1·10
E108	–	35pf. yellow and purple	3·50	3·75
E109	–	48pf. brown and green	2·50	1·10
E110	–	60pf. red and brown	5·00	3·25
E111	–	84pf. brown and blue	4·50	2·00
MSE111a		Two sheets, each 148 × 104 mm. (a) the six vert, and (b) the four horiz designs Set of 2 sheets	£400	£325

DESIGNS—VERT: 6pf. Flag and foundry; 12pf. Flag and Spassky Tower, Kremlin; 20pf. Marx reading from "Das Kapital"; 35pf. Marx addressing meeting; 48pf. Marx and Engels. HORIZ: 10pf. Marx, Engels and "Communist Manifesto"; 16pf. Marching crowd; 60pf. Flag and workers; 84pf. Marx in medallion and Stalin Avenue, Berlin.

In each case the flag shows heads of Marx, Engels, Lenin and Stalin.

E 39 Gorky

E 40 Cyclists

1953. 85th Birth Anniv of Maksim Gorky (writer).

E112	E 39	35pf. brown	35	55

1953. 6th International Cycle Race.

E113	E 40	24pf. green	3·50	2·75
E114	–	35pf. blue	1·60	1·40
E115	–	60pf. brown	2·00	2·75

DESIGNS—VERT: 35pf. Cyclists and countryside; 60pf. Cyclists in town.

E 41 H. Von Kleist

E 42 Miner

1953. 700th Anniv of Frankfurt-on-Oder.

E116	E 41	16pf. brown	2·00	2·50
E117	–	20pf. green	1·20	2·00
E118	–	24pf. red	2·00	2·75
E119	–	35pf. blue	2·00	2·75

DESIGNS—HORIZ: 20pf. St. Mary's Church; 24pf. Frankfurt from R. Oder; 35pf. Frankfurt Town Hall and coat of arms.

1953. Five Year Plan. (a) Design in minute dots.

E120	E 42	1pf. black	1·80	45
E121	–	5pf. green	2·40	1·00
E122	–	6pf. violet	2·40	85
E123	–	8pf. brown	3·25	1·00
E124	–	10pf. green	2·40	80
E125	–	12pf. blue	2·40	85
E126	–	15pf. violet	3·50	1·70
E127	–	16pf. violet	4·25	2·20
E128	–	20pf. green	4·50	2·20
E129	–	24pf. red	8·00	80
E130	–	25pf. green	6·00	3·50
E131	–	30pf. red	6·00	3·50
E132	–	35pf. blue	11·50	3·50
E133	–	40pf. red	11·50	3·25
E134	–	48pf. mauve	11·50	3·50
E135	–	60pf. blue	11·50	5·50
E136	–	80pf. turquoise	12·00	5·50
E137	–	84pf. brown	12·00	14·50

(b) Design in lines.

E153	E 42	1pf. black	80	30
E310	–	5pf. green	1·60	35
E155	–	6pf. violet	3·00	35
E156	–	8pf. brown	3·25	35
E312	–	10pf. green	2·10	35
E311	–	10pf. blue	15	30
E159	–	12pf. turquoise	3·00	35
E160	–	15pf. lilac	14·00	50
E313	–	15pf. violet	1·60	35
E162	–	16pf. violet	3·50	2·30
E163	–	20pf. green	47·00	1·50
E314	–	20pf. red	1·00	20
E165	–	24pf. red	7·00	50
E315	–	25pf. green	1·60	20
E316	–	30pf. red	1·10	20
E168	–	35pf. blue	11·00	3·75
E169	–	40pf. red	8·25	65
E317	–	40pf. mauve	85	20
E171	–	48pf. mauve	12·00	1·20
E318	–	50pf. blue	90	20
E173	–	60pf. blue	14·00	55
E319	–	70pf. brown	90	20
E175	–	80pf. turquoise	3·50	2·00
E176	–	84pf. brown	16·00	1·40

DESIGNS—VERT: 5pf. Woman turning wheel; 6pf. Workmen shaking hands; 8pf. Students; 10pf. grn Engineers; 10pf. bl and 12pf. Agricultural and industrial workers; 15pf. mve Tele-typist; 15pf. vio and 16pf. Foundry worker; 20pf. grn Workers' health centre, Elster; 20pf. red and 24pf. Stalin Avenue, Berlin; 25pf. Locomotive construction workers; 30pf. Folk dancers; 35pf. Stadium; 40pf. red, Scientist; 40pf. mve, 48pf. Zwinger, Dresden; 50pf., 60pf. Launching ship; 80pf. Farm workers; 70pf., 84pf. Workman and family.

E 43 Mechanical Grab

1953. Leipzig Autumn Fair.

E138	E 43	24pf. brown	1·80	2·75
E139	–	35pf. green	2·75	2·20

DESIGN: 35pf. Potato-harvester.

E 44 G. W. von Knobelsdorff and Opera House, Berlin

1953. German Architects.

E140	E 44	24pf. mauve	1·50	1·60
E141	–	35pf. slate	1·80	1·90

DESIGN: 35pf. B. Neumann and Wurzburg Palace.

E 45 Lucas Cranach

E 46 Nurse and Patient

1953. 400th Death Anniv of Cranach (painter).

E142	E 45	24pf. brown	3·00	1·90

1953. Red Cross.

E143	E 46	24pf. red and brown	2·75	2·20

E 47 Postman delivering Letters

E 48 Lion

1953. Stamp Day.
E144 E **47** 24pf. blue . . . . . . 2·10 85

1953. 75th Anniv of Leipzig Zoo.
E145 E **48** 24pf. brown . . . . . 2·20 90

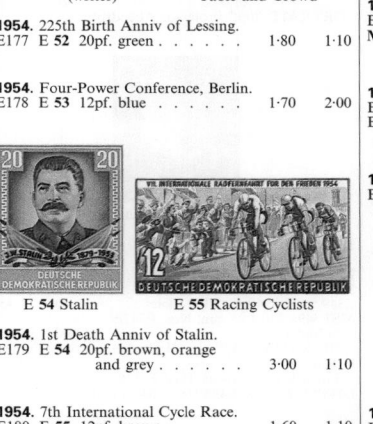

E **49** Muntzer and Peasants
E **50** Franz Schubert

1953. German Patriots.
E146 E **49** 12pf. brown . . . . . 1·40 1·40
E147 – 16pf. brown . . . . . 1·40 1·40
E148 – 20pf. red . . . . . . 1·20 60
E149 – 24pf. blue . . . . . . 1·20 60
E150 – 35pf. green . . . . . . 2·40 2·75
E151 – 48pf. sepia . . . . . . 2·50 2·30
DESIGNS: 16pf. Baron vom Stein and scroll; 20pf. Von Schill and cavalry; 24pf. Blucher and infantry; 35pf. Students marching; 48pf. Barricade, 1848 Revolution.

1953. 125th Death Anniv of Schubert.
E152 E **50** 48pf. brown . . . . . 3·00 1·90

E **52** G. E. Lessing (writer)
E **53** Conference Table and Crowd

1954. 225th Birth Anniv of Lessing.
E177 E **52** 20pf. green . . . . . . 1·80 1·10

1954. Four-Power Conference, Berlin.
E178 E **53** 12pf. blue . . . . . . 1·70 2·00

E **54** Stalin
E **55** Racing Cyclists

1954. 1st Death Anniv of Stalin.
E179 E **54** 20pf. brown, orange and grey . . . . . . 3·00 1·10

1954. 7th International Cycle Race.
E180 E **55** 12pf. brown . . . . . 1·60 1·10
E181 – 24pf. green . . . . . . 2·40 1·90
DESIGN: 24pf. Cyclists racing through countryside.

E **56** Folk Dancing
E **57** F. Reuter

1954. 2nd German Youth Assembly.
E182 E **56** 12pf. green . . . . . . 1·30 1·60
E183 – 24pf. red . . . . . . 1·30 1·50
DESIGN: 24pf. Young people and flag.

1954. 80th Death Anniv of Reuter (author).
E184 E **57** 24pf. brown . . . . . 2·40 1·90

E **58** Dam and Forest
E **59** E. Thalmann

1954. Flood Relief Fund.
E185 E **58** 24pf.+6pf. green . . . 65 1·30

1954. 10th Death Anniv of Thalmann (politician).
E186 E **59** 24pf. brown, bl & orge 1·10 95

E **60** Exhibition Buildings

1954. Leipzig Autumn Fair.
E187 E **60** 24pf. red 75 65
E188 35pf. blue 80 85

1954. (a) Nos. E155, etc surch in figures.
E189 5pf. on 6pf. violet 90 20
E190 5pf. on 8pf. brown . . . . 1·40 20
E191 10pf. on 12pf. turquoise . . 90 20
E192 15pf. on 16pf. lilac 95 20
E194 20pf. on 24pf. red . . . . . 1·30 20
E195 40pf. on 48pf. mauve . . . 3·25 20
E196 50pf. on 60pf. blue . . . . 3·00 20
E197 70pf. on 84pf. brown . . . 8·50 20

(b) No. E129 similarly surch.
E193a 20pf. on 24pf. red . . . . 1·10 70

E **62** President Pieck

1954. 5th Anniv of German Democratic Republic.
E198 E **62** 20pf. brown . . . . . 2·30 1·60
E199 35pf. blue . . . . . 2·40 1·60

E **63** Stamp of 1953
E **64** Russian Pavilion

1954. Stamp Day.
E200 E **63** 20pf. mauve . . . . . 1·60 95
MSE200b 60 × 80 mm. No. E200 imperf (sold at Dm.30) . . . . 55·00 60·00

1955. Leipzig Spring Fair.
E201 E **64** 20pf. purple 80 80
E202 – 35pf. blue (Chinese Pavilion) . . . . . 1·60 1·30

1955. Flood Relief Fund. Surch in figures.
E203 E **58** 20+5pf. on 24pf.+6pf. green 90 80

E **66** "Women of All Nations"

1955. 45th Anniv of International Women's Day.
E204 E **66** 10pf. green . . . . . . 1·00 65
E205 20pf. red . . . . . . 1·10 65

E **67** Parade of Workers
E **68** Monument to Fascist Victims, Brandenburg

1955. International Conference of Municipal Workers, Vienna.
E206 E **67** 10pf. black and red . . 1·00 1·10

1955. International Liberation Day.
E207 E **68** 10pf. blue . . . . . . 1·00 1·30
E208 20pf. mauve . . . . . 1·00 1·70
MSE208a 73 × 99 mm. Nos. E207/8 20·00 29·00

E **69** Monument to Russian Soldiers, Treptow
E **70** Schiller (poet)

1955. 10th Anniv of Liberation.
E209 E **69** 20pf. mauve . . . . . 1·40 1·00

1955. 150th Death Anniv of Schiller.
E210 E **70** 5pf. green . . . . . . 2·75 3·00
E211 – 10pf. blue 40 20
E212 – 20pf. brown 40 25
MSE212a 73 × 100 mm. Nos. E210/12 (+15pf.) . . . . . . 24·00 33·00
PORTRAITS OF SCHILLER: 10pf. Full-face; 20pf. Facing left.

E **71** Cyclists
E **72** Karl Liebknecht

1955. 8th International Cycle Race.
E213 E **71** 10pf. turquoise 60 60
E214 20pf. red 70 75

1955. German Labour Leaders.
E215 E **72** 5pf. green 25 30
E216 – 10pf. blue 50 30
E217 – 15pf. violet . . . . . 5·50 6·50
E218 – 20pf. red 60 30
E219 – 25pf. blue 60 30
E220 – 40pf. red . . . . . . 2·10 30
E221 – 60pf. brown 60 30
PORTRAITS: 10pf. A. Bebel; 15pf. F. Mehring; 20pf. E. Thalmann; 25pf. Clara Zetkin; 40pf. Wilhelm Liebknecht; 60pf. Rosa Luxemburg.

E **73** Pottery
E **74** Workers and Charter

1955. Leipzig Autumn Fair.
E222 – 10pf. blue 60 45
E223 E **73** 20pf. green 60 45
DESIGN: 10pf. Camera and microscope.

1955. 10th Anniv of Land Reform.
E224 E **74** 5pf. green . . . . . . 3·00 4·25
E225 – 10pf. blue 60 50
E226 – 20pf. red 60 45
DESIGNS—VERT: 10pf. Bricklayers at work. HORIZ: 20pf. Combine-harvesters.

E **75** "Solidarity"
E **76** Engels Speaking

1955. 10th Anniv of People's Solidarity Movement.
E227 E **75** 10pf. blue 90 45

1955. 135th Birth Anniv of Engels.
E228 E **76** 5pf. blue and yellow . . 35 15
E229 – 10pf. violet and yellow 80 15
E230 – 15pf. green and yellow 80 15
E231 – 20pf. brown and orange . . . . . . 1·70 15
E232 – 30pf. brown and grey 7·50 9·75
E233 – 70pf. green and red . . 3·00 30
MSE233a 148 × 105 mm. Nos. E228/33 . . . . 65·00 90·00
DESIGNS: 10pf. Engels and Marx; 15pf. Engels and newspaper; 20pf. Portrait facing right; 30pf. Portrait facing left; 70pf. 1848 Revolution scene.

E **77** Magdeburg Cathedral
E **78** Georg Agricola

1955. Historic Buildings.
E234 E **77** 5pf. sepia 40 45
E235 – 10pf. green 40 45
E236 – 15pf. purple 40 45
E237 – 20pf. red . . . . . . 4·00 85
E238 – 30pf. brown . . . . . 11·00 15·00
E239 – 40pf. blue . . . . . . 1·30 1·00
DESIGNS: 10pf. State Opera House, Berlin; 15pf. Old Town Hall, Leipzig; 20pf. Town Hall, Berlin; 30pf. Erfurt Cathedral; 40pf. Zwinger, Dresden.

1955. 400th Death Anniv of Agricola (scholar).
E240 E **78** 10pf. brown 90 50

E **79** "Portrait of a Young Man" (Durer)
E **80** Mozart

1955. Dresden Gallery Paintings. (1st series).
E241 E **79** 5pf. brown 80 15
E242 – 10pf. brown 80 15
E243 – 15pf. purple . . . . . 29·00 27·00
E244 – 20pf. sepia 80 15
E245 – 40pf. green 80 35
E246 – 70pf. blue . . . . . . 2·10 90
PAINTINGS: 10pf. "The Chocolate Girl" (Liotard); 15pf. "Portrait of a Boy" (Pinturicchio); 20pf. "Self-portrait with Saskia" (Rembrandt); 40pf. "Maiden with Letter" (Vermeer); 70pf. "Sistine Madonna" (Raphael).
See also Nos. E325/30 and E427/31.

1956. Birth Bicent of Mozart (composer).
E247 E **80** 10pf. green . . . . . . 13·50 10·50
E248 – 20pf. brown . . . . . 4·00 1·80
PORTRAIT: 20pf. Facing left.

E **81** Ilyushin Il-14P DDR-ABA
E **82** Heinrich Heine (poet)

1956. Establishment of East German Lufthansa Airways.
E249 – 5pf. multicoloured . . 13·00 11·00
E250 E **81** 10pf. green 90 15
E251 – 15pf. blue 90 15
E252 – 20pf. red 90 15
DESIGNS: 5pf. Lufthansa flag; 15pf. View of Ilyushin Il-14P DDR-ABF airplane from below; 20pf. Ilyushin Il-14P DDR-ABA airplane facing left.

1956. Death Centenary of Heine.
E253 E **82** 10pf. green . . . . . . 13·50 6·75
E254 – 20pf. red . . . . . . 2·40 75
PORTRAIT: 20pf. Full-face.

E **83** Mobile Cranes
E **84** E Thalmann

1956. Leipzig Spring Fair.
E255 E **83** 20pf. red 80 30
E256 35pf. blue . . . . . . 1·10 80

1956. 70th Birth Anniv of Thalmann (communist leader).
E257 E **84** 20pf. black, brn & red 55 30
MSE257a 73 × 100 mm. No. E257 10·50 27·00

E **85** Hand, Laurels and Cycle Wheel
E **86** New Buildings, Old Market-place

1956. 9th International Cycle Race.
E258 E **85** 10pf. green 80 35
E259 – 20pf. red 80 35
DESIGN: 20pf. Arms of Warsaw, Berlin and Prague and cycle wheel.

1956. 750th Anniv of Dresden.
E260 E **86** 10pf. green 30 25
E261 – 20pf. red 30 15
E262 – 40pf. violet . . . . . 1·90 2·30
DESIGNS: 20pf. Elbe Bridge; 40pf. Technical High School.

E **87** Workman

1956. 10th Anniv of Industrial Reforms.
E263 E **87** 20pf. red 55 30

E **88** Robert Schumann E **88a** Robert Schumann

1956. Death Centenary of Schumann (composer). (a) Type E **88** (wrong music).
E264 E **88** 10pf. green . . . . . . 2·50 1·90
E265 20pf. red 75 15
(b) Type E **88a** (correct music).
E266 E **88a** 10pf. green . . . . . 5·50 2·20
E267 20pf. red . . . . . . 3·00 35

E **89** Footballers E **90** T. Mann (author)

1956. 2nd Sports Festival, Leipzig.
E268 E **89** 5pf. green 20 15
E269 – 10pf. blue 20 15
E270 – 15pf. purple . . . . . 2·40 1·50
E271 – 20pf. red 20 15
DESIGNS: 10pf. Javelin thrower; 15pf. Hurdlers; 20pf. Gymnast.

1956. 1st Death Anniv of Thomas Mann.
E272 E **90** 20pf. black 90 70

E **91** J. B. Cisinski E **92** Lace

1956. Birth Centenary of Cisinski (poet).
E273 E **91** 50pf. brown . . . . . 1·10 60

1956. Leipzig Autumn Fair.
E274 E **92** 10pf. green and black 25 35
E275 – 20pf. pink and black (Sailing dinghy) . . . 40 35

E **93** Buchenwald Memorial

1956. Concentration Camp Memorials Fund.
E276 E **93** 20pf.+80pf. red . . . . 1·10 3·00
For similar stamp see No. E390.

E **94** Torch and Olympic Rings E **95**

1956. Olympic Games.
E277 E **94** 20pf. brown 45 15
E278 – 35pf. slate 90 35
DESIGN: 35pf. Greek athlete.

1956. 500th Anniv of Greifswald University.
E279 E **95** 20pf. red 55 30

E **96** Postal Carrier, 1450 E **97** E. Abbe

1956. Stamp Day.
E280 E **96** 20pf. red 60 40

1956. 110th Anniv of Zeiss Factory, Jena.
E281 E **97** 10pf. green 15 15
E282 – 20pf. brown 20 15
E283 – 25pf. blue 30 35
DESIGNS—HORIZ: 20pf. Factory buildings; 25pf. Carl Zeiss.

E **98** "Negro" E **99** Indian Elephants

1956. Human Rights Day.
E284 – 5pf. green on olive . . 1·40 1·30
E285 E **98** 10pf. brown on pink 20 15
E286 – 25pf. blue on lavender 20 15
DESIGNS: 5pf. "Chinese"; 25pf. "European".

1956. Berlin Zoological Gardens. Centres in grey.
E287 E **99** 5pf. black 20 15
E288 – 10pf. green 20 15
E289 – 15pf. purple . . . . . 4·50 3·50
E290 – 20pf. red 30 15
E291 – 25pf. brown 35 15
E292 – 30pf. blue 40 15
DESIGNS: 10pf. Greater flamingos; 15pf. Black rhinoceros; 20pf. Mouflon; 25pf. European bison; 30pf. Polar bear.

1956. Egyptian Relief Fund. No. E237 surch **HELFT AGYPTEN +10**.
E293 20pf.+10pf. red 65 35

1956. Hungarian Socialists' Relief Fund. No. E237 surch **HELFT DEM SOZIALISTISCHEN UNGARN +10.**
E294 20pf.+10pf. red 65 35

E **103** "Frieden" (freighter)

1957. Leipzig Spring Fair.
E295 E **103** 20pf. red 30 15
E296 – 25pf. blue 30 25
DESIGN: 25pf. Class E251 electric locomotive.

E **104** Silver Thistle

1957. Nature Protection Week.
E297 E **104** 5pf. brown 20 15
E298 – 10pf. green . . . . . 2·50 2·40
E299 – 20pf. brown 30 15
DESIGNS: 10pf. Green lizard; 20pf. Lady's slipper orchid.

E **105** Friedrich Froebel and Children

1957. 175th Birth Anniv of Froebel (educator).
E300 – 10pf. black and green 1·60 1·10
E301 E **105** 20pf. black and brown 20 15
DESIGN: 10pf. Children at play.

E **106** Ravensbruck Memorial E **107** Cycle Race Route

1957. Concentration Camp Memorials Fund.
E302 E **106** 5pf.+5pf. green . . . 20 15
E303 – 20pf.+10pf. red . . . 40 50
DESIGN—HORIZ: 20pf. Memorial and environs.
For similar stamp to No. E303 see No. E453.

1957. 10th International Cycle Race.
E304 E **107** 5pf. orange 40 25

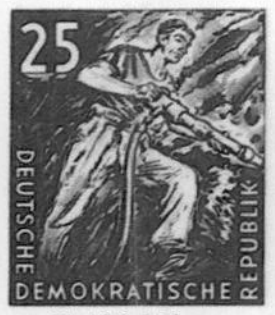

E **108** Miner E **109** Henri Dunant and Globe

1957. Coal Mining Industry.
E305 – 10pf. green 15 15
E306 – 20pf. brown 30 15
E307 E **108** 25pf. blue . . . . . . 3·00 1·10
DESIGNS (39 × 21 mm): 10pf. Mechanical shovel and coal trucks; 20pf. Gantry.

1957. Int Red Cross Day. Cross in red.
E308 E **109** 10pf. brown and green 25 30
E309 – 25pf. brown and blue 25 30
DESIGN: 25pf. H. Dunant wearing hat, and globe.

E **110** Joachim Jungius (botanist) E **111** Clara Zetkin and Flower

1957. Scientists' Anniversaries.
E322 E **110** 5pf. brown . . . . . 1·90 90
E323 – 10pf. green 20 15
E324 – 20pf. brown 20 15
PORTRAITS: 10pf. L. Euler (mathematician); 20pf. H. Hertz (physicist).

1957. Dresden Gallery Paintings (2nd series). As Type E **79**.
E325 5pf. sepia 20 15
E326 10pf. green 20 15
E327 15pf. brown 20 15
E328 20pf. red 20 15
E329 25pf. purple 35 15
E330 40pf. grey . . . . 5·50 2·40
PAINTINGS—VERT: 5pf. "The Holy Family" (Mantegna); 10pf. "The Dancer, Barbarina Campani" (Carriera); 15pf. "Portrait of Morette" (Holbein the Younger); 20pf. "The Tribute Money" (Titian); 25pf. "Saskia with a Red Flower" (Rembrandt); 40pf. "A Young Standard-bearer" (Piazetta).

1957. Birth Cent of Clara Zetkin (patriot).
E331 E **111** 10pf. green and red 65 30

E **112** Bertolt Brecht (dramatist) E **113** Congress Emblem

1957. 1st Death Anniv of Bertolt Brecht.
E332 E **112** 10pf. green 35 30
E333 25pf. blue 80 30

1957. 4th World Trade Unions Congress.
E334 E **113** 20pf. black and red 65 35

E **114** Fair Emblem E **115** Savings Bank Book

1957. Leipzig Autumn Fair.
E335 E **114** 20pf. red 30 15
E336 25pf. blue 40 15

1957. Savings Week.
E337 E **115** 10pf. black and green on grey . . . . . . 1·10 75
E338 20pf. black and mauve on grey . . 40 35

E **116** Postrider of 1563 E **117** Revolutionary's Rifle and Red Flag

1957. Stamp Day.
E339 E **116** 5pf. blue on brown 65 30

1957. 40th Anniv of Russian Revolution.
E340 E **117** 10pf. green and red 30 15
E341 25pf. blue and red . . 30 30

E **118** Artificial Satellite E **119** Professor Ramin

1957. International Geophysical Year.
E342 E **118** 10pf. blue 50 30
E343 – 20pf. red 60 15
E344 – 25pf. blue . . . . . 3·00 1·70
DESIGNS: 20pf. Stratosphere balloon; 25pf. Ship using echo-sounder.

1957. "National Prize" Composers.
E345 E **119** 10pf. black and green 1·40 1·10
E346 – 20pf. black and orange 20 15
PORTRAIT: 20pf. Professor Abendroth.

E **120** Ernst Thalmann

1957. National Memorials Fund. East German War Victims. Portraits in grey.
E347 E **120** 20pf.+10pf. mauve . . 15 15
E348 – 25pf.+15pf. blue . . . 20 15
E349 – 40pf.+20pf. violet . . 40 45
MSE349a 140 × 95 mm. Nos. E347/9 (+20pf.) . . . . 55·00 95·00
PORTRAITS: 25pf. R. Breitscheid; 40pf. Father P. Schneider.
For other stamps as Type E **120** see Nos. E374/8, E448/52, E485/7, E496/500, E540/4 and E588/92.

E **121** E **122**

1957. Air.
E350 E **121** 5pf. black and grey 1·10 15
E351 20pf. black and red 20 15
E352 35pf. black and violet 20 15
E353 50pf. black and brown 45 15
E354 E **122** 1Dm. olive and yellow 1·50 15
E355 3Dm. brown & yellow 2·75 15
E356 5Dm. blue and yellow 5·25 1·80

E **123** Fair Emblem

1958. Leipzig Spring Fair.
E357 E **123** 20pf. red 30 15
E358 25pf. blue 40 15

E **124** Transmitting Aerial and Posthorn

1958. Communist Postal Conf, Moscow.
E359 E **124** 5pf. black and grey . . 1·00 90
E360 – 20pf. red 40 15
DESIGN—HORIZ: 20pf. Aerial as in 5pf. but posthorn above figures of value.

E **125** "Zille at play"

1958. Birth Cent of Heinrich Zille (painter).
E361 E **125** 10pf. drab and green . . 2·10 1·70
E362 – 20pf. drab and red . . 70 15
DESIGN—VERT: 20pf. Self-portrait of Zille.

E **126** Max Planck

E **127** Breeding Cow

1958. Birth Cent of Max Planck (physicist).
E363 – 10pf. olive . . . . . 1·40 1·30
E364 E **126** 20pf. mauve 40 20
DESIGN—VERT: 10pf. "h" (symbol of Planck's Constant).

1958. 6th Markkleeberg Agricultural Exn. Inscr "6 Landwirtschaftsausstellung der DDR in Markkleeberg".
E365 E **127** 5pf. grey . . . . . . 2·30 1·70
E366 – 10pf. green 30 15
E367 – 20pf. red 30 15
DESIGNS (39 × 22½ mm): 10pf. Chaff-cutter; 20pf. Beet-harvester.

E **128** Charles Darwin

E **129** Congress Emblem

1958. Centenary of Darwin's Theory of Evolution and Bicentenary of Linnaeus's Plant Classification System. Portraits in black.
E368 E **128** 10pf. green . . . . . 1·30 1·30
E369 – 20pf. red 20 15
PORTRAIT—HORIZ: 20pf. Linnaeus (Carl von Linne) inscr "200 JAHRE SYSTEMA NATURAE".

1958. 5th German Socialist Unity Party Congress.
E370 E **129** 10pf. red 35 30

E **130** "The Seven Towers of Rostock", Liner and Freighters

E **131** Mare and Foal

1958. Rostock Port Reconstruction.
E371 – 10pf. green 20 15
E372 E **130** 20pf. orange 35 30
E373 – 25pf. blue . . . . . . 1·30 1·20
DESIGNS: 10pf. "Freundschaft" (freighter) at quayside; 25pf. "Frieden" (freighter) in Rostock harbour.

1958. "Resistance Fighters". As Type E **120**. Portraits in grey.
E374 5pf.+5pf. brown 30 75
E375 10pf.+5pf. green 20 75
E376 15pf.+10pf. violet . . . . . 20 3·00
E377 20pf.+10pf. brown 20 70
E378 25pf.+15pf. black . . . . . 65 12·50
PORTRAITS—VERT: 5pf. A. Kuntz; 10pf. R. Arndt; 15pf. Dr. K. Adams; 20pf. R. Renner; 25pf. W. Stoecker.

1958. "Grand Prix of the D.D.R." Horse Show.
E379 E **131** 5pf. sepia . . . . . . 2·40 2·75
E380 – 10pf. green 20 15
E381 – 20pf. brown 20 20
DESIGNS: 10pf. Horse-trotting; 20pf. Racing horses.

E **132** J. A. Komensky ("Comenius")

E **133** Camp Bugler

1958. Komensky Commem. Centres in black.
E382 E **132** 10pf. green . . . . . 1·60 1·30
E383 – 20pf. brown 20 15
DESIGN: 20pf. Komensky with pupils (from an old engraving).

1958. 10th Anniv of East German "Pioneer" Organization.
E384 E **133** 10pf.+5pf. green . . . 30 30
E385 – 20pf.+10pf. red . . . 40 30
DESIGN—VERT: 20pf. Young Pioneer saluting.

E **134** University Seal

1958. 400th Anniv of Friedrich Schiller University, Jena.
E386 E **134** 5pf. black and grey . . 1·40 1·25
E387 – 20pf. grey and red . . 30 15
DESIGN: 20pf. University building.

E **135** Model with Hamster-lined Coat, and Leipzig Central Railway Station

E **136** Soldier climbing Wall

1958. Leipzig Autumn Fair.
E388 E **135** 10pf. brown and green 20 15
E389 – 25pf. black and blue 20 25
DESIGN: 25pf. Model with Karakul fur coat, and Leipzig Old Town Hall.

1958. Concentration Camp Memorials Fund. As Type E **93** but additionally inscr "14. SEPTEMBER 1958" in black.
E390 20pf.+20pf. red 55 60

1958. 1st Summer Military Games, Leipzig.
E391 E **136** 10pf. brown and green 1·90 1·30
E392 – 20pf. yellow and brown 15 15
E393 – 25pf. red and blue . . 15 15
DESIGNS: 20pf. Games emblem; 25pf. Marching athletes with banner.

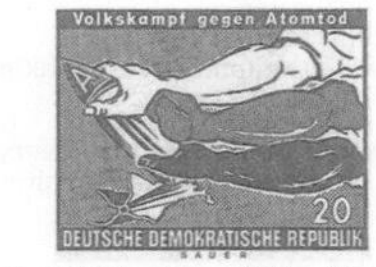

E **137** Warding off the Atomic Bomb

1958. Campaign Against Atomic Warfare.
E394 E **137** 20pf. red 20 15
E395 25pf. blue 40 25

E **138** 17th-century Mail Cart

1958. Stamp Day.
E396 E **138** 10pf. green . . . . . 1·80 1·30
E397 – 20pf. red 35 15
DESIGN: 20pf. Modern postal sorting train and Baade-Bonin 152 jetliner.

E **139** Revolutionary and Soldier

E **140** Brandenburg Gate, Berlin

1958. 40th Anniv of November Revolution.
E398 E **139** 20pf. purple and red 10·50 42·00

1958. Brandenburg Gate Commemoration.
E399 E **140** 20pf. red 45 15
E400 25pf. blue . . . . . . 2·75 1·70

E **141** "Girl's Head" (bas-relief)

E **142** Negro and European Youths

1958. Antique Art Treasures.
E401 E **141** 10pf. black and green 90 1·30
E402 – 20pf. black and red 20 15
DESIGN: 20pf. "Large Head" (from Pergamon frieze).
See also Nos. E475/8.

1958. 10th Anniv of Declaration of Human Rights.
E403 E **142** 10pf. black and green 20 15
E404 – 25pf. black and blue 1·90 1·30
DESIGN: 25pf. Chinese and European girls.

E **143** O. Nuschke

E **144** "The Red Flag" (Party Newspaper)

1958. 1st Death Anniv of Vice-Premier Otto Nuschke.
E405 E **143** 20pf. red 35 30

1958. 40th Anniv of German Communist Party.
E406 E **144** 20pf. red 50 20

E **145** Pres. Pieck

E **146** Rosa Luxemburg (revolutionary)

1959. Pres. Pieck's 83rd Birthday.
E407 E **145** 20pf. red 45 20
For 20pf. black see No. E517.

1959. 40th Death Anniv of Rosa Luxemburg and Karl Liebknecht. Centres in black.
E408 E **146** 10pf. green . . . . . 1·90 1·40
E409 – 20pf. red 20 15
DESIGN—HORIZ: 20pf. Liebknecht- (revolutionary).

E **147** Concert Hall, Leipzig

1959. 150th Birth Anniv of Felix Mendelssohn-Bartholdy (composer).
E410 E **147** 10pf. green on green 45 45
E411 – 25pf. blue on blue . . 1·80 2·75
DESIGN—HORIZ: 25pf. Opening theme of Symphony in A Major ("The Italian").

E **148** "Schwarze Pumpe" plant

E **149** Boy holding Book for Girl

1959. Leipzig Spring Fair. Inscr as in Type E **148**.
E412 E **148** 20pf. red 15 15
E413 – 25pf. blue 50 15
DESIGN—HORIZ: 25pf. Various cameras.

1959. 5th Anniv of "Youth Consecration".
E414 E **149** 10pf. black on green 1·80 1·10
E415 – 20pf. black on salmon 20 15
DESIGN: 20pf. Girl holding book for boy.

E **150** Handel's Statue, Oboe and Arms of Halle

E **151** A. von Humboldt and Jungle Scene

1959. Death Bicentenary of Handel. Centre in black.
E416 E **150** 10pf. green . . . . . 2·00 1·30
E417 – 20pf. red 20 15
DESIGN: 20pf. Portrait of Handel (after oil painting by Thomas Hudson).

1959. Death Centenary of Alexander von Humboldt (naturalist).
E418 E **151** 10pf. green . . . . . 1·80 1·30
E419 – 20pf. red 30 15
DESIGN: 20pf. As Type E **151** but with view of sleigh in forest.

E **152** Posthorn

E **153** Grey Heron

1959. Socialist Countries' Postal Ministers Conference, Berlin.
E420 E **152** 20pf. black, yell & red 20 15
E421 25pf. black, yell & bl 95 85

1959. Nature Preservation.
E422 E **153** 5pf. lilac, black & blue 20 15
E423 – 10pf. brn, sep & turq 20 15
E424 – 20pf. multicoloured 20 15
E425 – 25pf. multicoloured 45 15
E426 – 40pf. yell, blk & grey 6·00 3·50
DESIGNS: 10pf. Eurasian bittern; 20pf. Lily of the valley and "Inachis io" (butterfly); 25pf. Eurasian beaver; 40pf. "Apis mellifera" (bee) and willow catkin.

1959. Dresden Gallery Paintings as Type E **79** (3rd series).
E427 5pf. olive 20 15
E428 10pf. green 20 15
E429 20pf. orange 20 15
E430 25pf. brown 45 15
E431 40pf. red . . . . 6·75 3·50
PAINTINGS—VERT: 5pf. "The Vestal Virgin" (Kauffman); 10pf. "The Needlewoman" (Metsu); 20pf. "Mlle. Lavergne reading a letter" (Liotard); 25pf. "Old woman with a brazier" (Rubens); 40pf. "Young man in black coat" (Hals).

E **154** Great Cormorant

E **155**

1959. "Birds of the Homeland". Centres and inscriptions in black.
E432 E **154** 5pf. yellow 15 15
E433 – 10pf. green 15 15
E434 – 15pf. violet . . . . . 6·00 3·50
E435 – 20pf. pink 20 15
E436 – 25pf. blue 20 15
E437 – 40pf. red 30 15
BIRDS: 10pf. Black Stork; 15pf. Eagle Owl; 20pf. Black Grouse; 25pf. Hoopoe; 40pf. Peregrine Falcon.

1959. 7th World Youth Festival, Vienna.
E438 E **155** 20pf. red 15 15
E439 – 25pf. blue 80 65
DESIGN—HORIZ: 25pf. White girl embracing negro girl.

E **156** Hoop Exercises

1959. 3rd German Gymnastic and Sports Festival, Leipzig.
E440 E **156** 5pf.+5pf. brown . . . 15 15
E441 – 10pf.+5pf. green . . . 15 15
E442 – 20pf.+10pf. red . . . 15 15
E443 – 25pf.+10pf. blue . . . 15 15
E444 – 40pf.+20pf. purple . . 2·40 95
DESIGNS: 10pf. High jumping; 20pf. Vaulting; 25pf. Club exercises; 40pf. Fireworks over Leipzig Stadium.

E **157** Modern Leipzig Building

1959. Leipzig Autumn Fair.
E445 E **157** 20pf. grey and red . . 40 25
See also Nos. E483/4.

E **158** Glass Tea-set

1959. 75 Years of Jena Glassware.
E446 E **158** 10pf. turquoise . . . 20 25
E447 – 25pf. blue . . . . . 1·70 1·20
DESIGN—VERT: 25pf. Laboratory retorts.

1959. Ravensbruck Concentration Camp Victims. As Type E **120**. Portraits in black.
E448 5pf.+5pf. brown 15 15
E449 10pf.+5pf. green 15 15
E450 15pf.+10pf. violet 15 15
E451 20pf.+10pf. mauve . . . 15 15
E452 25pf.+15pf. blue . . . . 75 1·20
PORTRAITS: 5pf. T. Klose; 10pf. K. Niederkirchner; 15pf. C. Eisenblatter; 20pf. O. Benario-Prestes; 25pf. M. Grollmuss.

1959. Concentration Camp Memorials Fund. As No. E303 but inscr "12. SEPTEMBER 1959" in black.
E453 20pf.+10pf. red 60 30

E **159** "Russian Pennant on the Moon"

1959. Landing of Russian Rocket on the Moon.
E454 E **159** 20pf. red 75 35

E **160** E. German Flag and Combine-harvester
E **161** J. R. Becher

1959. 10th Anniv of German Democratic Republic. Designs as Type E **160** showing E. German flag in black, red and yellow. Inscriptions in black and red on coloured paper.
E455 E **160** 5pf. buff 20 15
E456 – 10pf. grey 20 15
E457 – 15pf. pale yellow . . 20 15
E458 – 20pf. lilac 20 15
E459 – 25pf. pale olive . . . 20 15
E460 – 40pf. yellow 20 15
E461 – 50pf. salmon 20 15
E462 – 60pf. turquoise . . . 20 20
E463 – 70pf. pale green . . . 20 25
E464 – 1Dm. brown 45 35
DESIGNS—East German flag and: 10pf. "Fritz Heckert" convalescent home; 15pf. Zwinger Palace, Dresden; 20pf. Steel worker; 25pf. Industrial chemist; 40pf. Leipzig Stadium; 50pf. Woman tractor-driver; 60pf. Ilyushin Il-14M airplane; 70pf. Shipbuilding; 1Dm. East Germany's first atomic reactor.

1959. 1st Death Anniv of Becher (poet).
E465 E **161** 20pf. slate and red . . 1·60 25

E **162** Schiller
E **163** 18th-century Courier and Milestone

1959. Birth Bicentenary of Schiller (poet).
E466 – 10pf. green on green 1·90 1·40
E467 E **162** 20pf. lake on pink . . 65 15
DESIGN: 10pf. Schiller's house, Weimar.

1959. Stamp Day.
E468 E **163** 10pf. green . . . . 1·60 1·25
E469 – 20pf. lake 20 15
DESIGN: 20pf. Postwoman on motor cycle.

E **164** Eurasian Red Squirrels

1959. Forest Animals.
E470 E **164** 5pf. red, brown & grey 45 10
E471 – 10pf. lt brn, brn & grn 55 10
E472 – 20pf. multicoloured 55 10
E473 – 25pf. multicoloured 65 15
E474 – 40pf. yellow, brown and blue . . . . 10·50 3·50
ANIMALS: 10pf. Brown hares; 20pf. Roe deer; 25pf. Red deer; 40pf. Lynx.

1959. Antique Art Treasures (2nd series). As Type E **141**.
E475 5pf. black and yellow . . . 15 15
E476 10pf. black and green . . . 15 15
E477 20pf. black and red 15 15
E478 25pf. black and blue . . . 1·50 90
DESIGNS: 5pf. Attic goddess (about 580 B.C.); 10pf. Princess of Tell el-Amarna (about 1360 B.C.); 20pf. Bronze horse of Toprak-Kale, Armenia (7th-century B.C.). HORIZ: (49 × 28 mm): 25pf. Altar of Zeus, Pergamon (about 160 B.C.).

E **165** Boxing

1960. Olympic Games. As Type E **165** inscr "OLYMPISCHE SOMMERSPIELE 1960" or "WINTERSPIELE" etc (20pf.). Centres and inscriptions in bistre.
E479 E **165** 5pf. brown . . . . 55 2·75
E480 – 10pf. green 15 15
E481 – 20pf. red 15 15
E482 – 25pf. blue 20 15
DESIGNS: 10pf. Running; 20pf. Ski jumping; 25pf. Sailing.

1960. Leipzig Spring Fair. As Type E **157** but inscr "LEIPZIGER FRUHJAHRSMESSE 1960".
E483 20pf. grey and red 20 15
E484 25pf. grey and blue 35 15
DESIGNS: 20pf. Northern Entrance, Technical Fair; 25pf. Ring Fair Building.

1960. Sachsenhausen Concentration Camp Victims (1st issue). As Type E **120**. Portraits in black.
E485 5pf.+5pf. drab 15 15
E486 10pf.+5pf. myrtle 15 15
E487 20pf.+10pf. purple 20 15
PORTRAITS: 5pf. L. Erdmann; 10pf. E. Schneller; 20pf. L. Horn.
See also Nos. E496/500.

E **166** Purple Foxglove
E **167** Lenin

1960. Medicinal Flowers. Background in pale drab.
E488 E **166** 5pf. red and green . . 20 15
E489 – 10pf. olive and green 20 15
E490 – 15pf. red and green 20 15
E491 – 20pf. violet & turq . . 20 15
E492 – 40pf. red, green & brn 6·25 2·75
FLOWERS: 10pf. Camomile; 15pf. Peppermint; 20pf. Poppy; 40pf. Wild Rose.

1960. 90th Birth Anniv of Lenin.
E493 E **167** 20pf. red 35 20

1960. Re-opening of Rostock Port. No. E371 optd **Inbetriebnahme des Hochsee-hafens 1. Mai 1960.**
E494 10pf. green 35 30

E **169** Russian Soldier and Liberated Prisoner

1960. 15th Anniv of Liberation.
E495 E **169** 20pf. red 35 30

1960. Sachsenhausen Concentration Camp Victims (2nd issue). As Type E **120**. Portraits in black.
E496 10pf.+5pf. green 20 15
E497 15pf.+5pf. violet . . . . 1·20 80
E498 20pf.+10pf. lake 20 15
E499 25pf.+10pf. blue 20 25
E500 40pf.+20pf. brown . . . . 2·40 2·20
PORTRAITS: 10pf. M. Lademann; 15pf. L. Breunig; 20pf. M. Thesen; 25pf. G. Sandtner; 40pf. H. Rothbarth.

E **170** Model and Plan of "Fritz Heckert" (Liner)

1960. Launching of Cruise Liner "Fritz Heckert".
E501 E **170** 5pf. slate, red & yell 15 15
E502 – 10pf.+5pf. black, red and yellow 15 15
E503 – 20pf.+10pf. black, red and blue 20 15
E504 – 25pf. black, yellow and blue . . . . 5·25 4·75
DESIGNS: 10pf. Liner under construction at Wismar; 20pf. Liner off Stubbenkammer; 25pf. Liner and Russian cruiser "Aurora" at Leningrad.

E **171** Lenin Statue, Eisleben
E **172** Masked Dancer (statuette)

1960. Lenin-Thalmann Statues.
E505 E **171** 10pf. green 30 20
E506 – 20pf. red 30 30
DESIGN: 20pf. Thalmann statue, Pushkin, U.S.S.R.

1960. 250th Anniv of Porcelain Industry, Meissen. Centres and inscriptions in blue. Figures in colours given.
E507 E **172** 5pf. orange 15 15
E508 – 10pf. green 15 15
E509 – 15pf. purple . . . . 4·25 3·50
E510 – 20pf. red 20 15
E511 – 25pf. olive 20 15
DESIGNS: 10pf. Dish inscr with swords and years "1710 1960"; 15pf. Otter; 20pf. Potter; 25pf. Coffee-pot.

E **173** Racing Cyclist

1960. World Cycling Championships.
E512 E **173** 20pf.+10pf. mult . . . 20 15
E513 – 25pf.+10pf. brown, drab and blue . . . 1·80 2·50
DESIGN ($38\frac{1}{2} \times 21$ mm): 25pf. Racing cyclists on track.

E **174** Opera House, Leipzig

1960. Leipzig Autumn Fair.
E514 E **174** 20pf. grey and red . . 25 15
E515 – 25pf. brown and blue 45 25
DESIGN: 25pf. Export goods.

E **175** Sachsenhausen Memorial
E **176** 18th-century Rook

1960. Concentration Camp Memorials Fund.
E516 E **175** 20pf.+10pf. red . . . 45 30

1960. President Pieck Mourning issue.
E517 E **145** 20pf. black 45 25
MSE517a 88 × 108 mm. No. E517. Imperf . . . . 1·90 2·10

1960. 14th Chess Olympiad, Leipzig. German Chessmen.
E518 E **176** 10pf.+5pf. green . . . 15 15
E519 – 20pf.+10pf. purple . . 15 15
E520 – 25pf.+10pf. blue . . . 1·20 2·75
DESIGNS: 20pf. 18th-century knight; 25pf. 14th-century knight.

E **177** Mail Vans

1960. Stamp Day.
E521 E **177** 20pf. yell, blk & mve 20 15
E522 – 25pf. mauve, blk & bl 1·90 1·90
DESIGN: 25pf. 19th-century railway mail coach.

E **178** Medal of 1518 showing Hans Burgkmair (painter)
E **179** Count N. von Gneisenau

1960. 400th Anniv of Dresden Art Collections.
E523 E **178** 20pf. ochre, green and buff 20 15
E524 – 25pf. black and blue 1·80 2·10
DESIGN: 25pf. "Dancing Peasants" (after Durer).

1960. Birth Bicent of Count N. von Gneisenau.
E525 E **179** 20pf. black and red . . 20 15
E526 – 25pf. blue . . . . . 1·60 1·40
DESIGN: 25pf. Similar portrait but vert.

E **180** R. Virchow

1960. 250th Anniv of Berlin Charity and 150th Anniv of Humboldt University, Berlin. Centres in black.
E527 E **180** 5pf. ochre 20 15
E528 – 10pf. green 20 15
E529 – 20pf. brown 20 15
E530 – 25pf. blue 20 15
E531 – 40pf. red . . . . . 3·00 1·80
DESIGNS—As Type E **180** (Berlin Charity); 10pf. Robert Koch; 40pf. W. Griesinger. (Humboldt University); 20pf. University building and statues of William and Alexander von Humboldt; 25pf. Plaque with profiles of Von Humboldt brothers.

E **181** Scientist with Notebook

1960. Chemical Workers' Day.
E532 E **181** 5pf. grey and red . . . 20 15
E533 – 10pf. green and orange 20 15
E534 – 20pf. red and blue . . 20 15
E535 – 25pf. blue and yellow 2·20 2·40
DESIGNS: 10pf. Chemical worker with fertiliser; 20pf. Girl worker with jar, and Trabant car; 25pf. Laboratory assistant and synthetic dress.

E **182** "Young Socialists' Express" (double-deck train)
E **183** President Pieck

1960. 125th Anniv of German Railways.
E536 E **182** 10pf. black and green 15 15
E537 – 20pf. black and red 15 15
E538 – 25pf. black and blue 4·25 5·25
DESIGNS—As Type E **182**: 25pf. Stephenson locomotive "Adler" (1835) and Class V180 diesel locomotive. (43 × 25½ mm): 20pf. Sassnitz Harbour station and train ferry "Sassnitz".

1961. 85th Birth Anniv of President Pieck.
E539 E **183** 20pf. red and black 35 30

1961. Concentration Camp Victims. As Type E **120**. Portraits in black.
E540 5pf.+5pf. green 15 15
E541 10pf.+5pf. green 15 15
E542 15pf.+5pf. violet . . . . 1·20 3·00
E543 20pf.+10pf. red 15 15
E544 25pf.+10pf. blue 15 15
PORTRAITS: 5pf. W. Kube; 10pf. H. Gunther; 15pf. Elvira Eisenschneider; 20pf. Hertha Lindner; 25pf. H. Tschape.

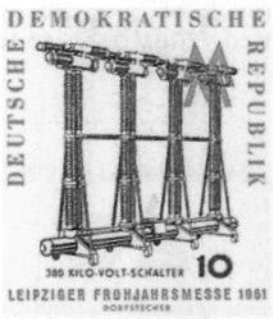

E **184** High-voltage Switchgear
E **185** Lilienstein Saxony

1961. Leipzig Spring Fair. Inscr as in Type E **184**.
E545 E **184** 10pf. slate and green 30 15
E546 – 25pf. slate and blue 50 30
DESIGN: 25pf. Fair Press Centre.

1961. Landscapes and Historical Buildings.
E547 – 5pf. grey 20 15
E548 – 10pf. green 20 15
E549 E **185** 20pf. brown 20 30
E550 – 20pf. red 20 15
E551 – 25pf. blue 20 20
DESIGNS—VERT: 5pf. Ruins of Rudelsburg; 10pf. Wartburg; 20pf. (No. E550), Town Hall, Wernigerode. HORIZ: 25pf. Brocken, Oberharz.

E **186** "Ros" (Trawler)

1961. Deep Sea Fishing Industry.
E552 E **186** 10pf. green 15 15
E553 – 20pf. purple 15 15
E554 – 25pf. blue 15 15
E555 – 40pf. violet . . . . . 2·10 1·90
DESIGNS: 20pf. Hauling nets; 25pf. "Robert Koch" (trawler); 40pf. Processing Atlantic cod.

E **187** Cosmonaut in Capsule

1961. 1st Manned Space Flight. Inscr "12.4.1961".
E556 – 10pf. red and green 65 45
E557 E **187** 20pf. red 65 45
E558 – 25pf. blue . . . . . . 4·50 5·50
DESIGNS: 10pf. Space rocket leaving globe; 25pf. Capsule's parachute descent.

E **188** Marx, Engels, Lenin and Demonstrators

1961. 15th Anniv of German Socialist Unity Party.
E559 E **188** 20pf. red 55 30

E **189** Common Zebra

1961. Centenary of Dresden Zoo.
E560 E **189** 10pf. black and green 5·50 4·75
E561 – 20pf. black and mauve 45 35
DESIGN: 20pf. Eastern black-and-white colobus.

E **190** Pioneers playing Volleyball

1961. Pioneers Meeting, Erfurt. Mult.
E562 10pf.+5pf. Type E **190** . . 15 15
E563 20pf.+10pf. Folk dancing 15 15
E564 25pf.+10pf. Model airplane construction . . . . . . 3·00 2·75

E **191** High Jump
E **192** Salt Miners and Castle

1961. 3rd European Women's Gymnastic Championships, Leipzig.
E565 E **191** 10pf. green 20 15
E566 – 20pf. mauve 20 15
E567 – 25pf. blue . . . . . . 4·75 5·00
DESIGNS—VERT: 20pf. Gymnast. HORIZ: 25pf. Exercise on parallel bars.

1961. Halle (Saale) Millenary.
E568 E **192** 10pf. black, yell & grn 2·20 1·60
E569 – 20pf. black, yell & red 20 15
DESIGN: 20pf. Scientist and Five Towers of Halle.

E **193** Canadian Canoe

1961. World Canoeing Championships.
E570 – 5pf. blue and grey . . 3·00 2·75
E571 E **193** 10pf. green and grey 20 15
E572 – 20pf. purple and grey 20 15
DESIGNS: 5pf. Folding canoe; 20pf. Canadian two-seater canoe.

E **194** Line-casting
E **195** Old Weigh-house, Leipzig

1961. World Angling Championships.
E573 E **194** 10pf. green and blue 3·00 2·10
E574 – 20pf. lake and blue . . 20 15
DESIGN: 20pf. River-fishing.

1961. Leipzig Autumn Fair.
E575 E **195** 10pf. olive and green 15 15
E576 – 25pf. blue & ultram 1·40 15
DESIGN: 25pf. Old Stock Exchange, Leipzig.
See also Nos. E612/14.

E **196** Walter Ulbricht
E **197** Dahlia

1961. Type E **196** or larger, 24 × 29 mm (Dm. values).
E577 5pf. blue 25 15
E578 10pf. green 35 15
E579 15pf. purple 40 15
E580 20pf. red 45 20
E581 25pf. turquoise 20 15
E582 30pf. red 20 15
E582a 35pf. green 30 20
E583 40pf. violet 25 15
E584 50pf. blue 30 15
E584a 60pf. green 30 25
E585 70pf. brown 35 15
E585a 80pf. blue 40 15
E586 1Dm. green 90 25
E587 2Dm. brown . . . . . . 1·60 30
See also Nos. E805/6, E1197/8 and E1255.

1961. Concentration Camps Memorials Fund. As Type E **120**. Portraits in grey and black.
E588 5pf.+5pf. green 15 15
E589 10pf.+5pf. green 15 15
E590 20pf.+10pf. mauve 20 15
E591 25pf.+10pf. blue 20 25
E592 40pf.+20pf. lake . . . . . 2·30 6·25
PORTRAITS: 5pf. C. Schonhaar; 10pf. H. Baum; 20pf. Liselotte Herrmann. HORIZ: (41 × 32½ mm): 25pf. Sophie and Hans Scholl; 40pf. Hilde and Hans Coppi.

1961. International Horticultural Exn.
E593 – 10pf. red, yellow & grn 20 15
E594 E **197** 20pf. red, yellow & brn 20 15
E595 – 40pf. red, yellow & bl 7·25 9·25
FLOWERS: 10pf. Tulip. 40pf. Rose.

E **198** Liszt and Berlioz (after Von Kaulbach and Prinzhofer)
E **199** TV Camera and Screen

1961. 150th Birth Anniv of Liszt (composer).
E596 E **198** 5pf. black 20 15
E597 – 10pf. green . . . . . 2·40 2·10
E598 – 20pf. red 20 15
E599 – 25pf. blue . . . . . . 2·75 2·40
DESIGNS: 10pf. Young hand of Liszt (from French sculpture, Liszt Museum, Budapest); 20pf. Liszt (after Rietschel); 25pf. Liszt and Chopin (after Bartolini and Bovy).

1961. Stamp Day.
E600 E **199** 10pf. black and green 1·60 2·75
E601 – 20pf. black and red 15 15
DESIGNS: 20pf. Studio microphone and radio tuning-scale.

E **200** G. S. Titov with Young Pioneers

1961. 2nd Russian Manned Space Flight.
E602 E **200** 5pf. violet and red . . 15 15
E603 – 10pf. green and red 15 15
E604 – 15pf. mauve and blue 6·50 7·75
E605 – 20pf. red and blue . . 20 15
E606 – 25pf. blue and red . . 20 15
E607 – 40pf. blue and red . . 1·60 55
DESIGNS—HORIZ: 15pf. Titov in space-suit; 20pf. Titov receiving Karl Marx Order from Ulbricht; 25pf. "Vostok 2" rocket in flight; 40pf. Titov and Ulbricht in Berlin. VERT: 10pf. Titov in Leipzig.

E **201** "Formica ruta" (Ant)

1962. Fauna Protection Campaign (1st series).
E608 E **201** 5pf. yellow, brn & blk 3·75 6·50
E609 – 10pf. brown and green 15 15
E610 – 20pf. brown and red 15 15
E611 – 40pf. yellow, blk & vio 65 35
DESIGNS: 10pf. Weasels; 20pf. Eurasian common shrews; 40pf. Common long-eared bat.
See also Nos. E699/703.

1962. Leipzig Spring Fair. As Type E **195**.
E612 10pf. sepia and green . . . 20 15
E613 20pf. black and red 45 15
E614 25pf. purple and blue . . . 70 1·10
BUILDINGS: 10pf. Zum Kaffeebaum; 20pf. Gobliser Schlosschen; 25pf. Romanus-Haus.

E **203** Pilot and Mikoyan Gurevich MiG-17 Jet Fighters

1962. 6th Anniv of East German People's Army.
E615 E **203** 5pf. blue 15 15
E616 – 10pf. green 15 15
E617 – 20pf. red 15 15
E618 – 25pf. blue 30 35
E619 – 40pf. brown . . . . . 1·60 1·75
DESIGNS: 10pf. Soldier and armoured car; 20pf. Factory guard; 25pf. Sailor and Habich I class minesweeper; 40pf. Tank and driver.

E **204** Danielle Casanova

1962. Concentration Camps Memorial Fund. Camp Victims.
E620 E **204** 5pf.+5pf. black . . . 15 15
E621 – 10pf.+5pf. green . . . 15 15
E622 – 20pf.+10pf. purple . . 20 15
E623 – 25pf.+10pf. blue . . . 30 15
E624 – 40pf.+20pf. purple . . 1·60 2·40
PORTRAITS: 10pf. Julius Fucik; 20pf. Johanna J. Schaft; 25pf. Pawel Finder; 40pf. Soja A. Kosmodemjanskaja.

E **205** Racing Cyclists and Prague Castle

1962. 15th Int Peace Cycle Race. Mult.
E625 10pf. Type E **205** 15 15
E626 20pf.+10pf. Cyclists and Palace of Culture and Science, Warsaw 20 25
E627 25pf. Cyclist and Town Hall, East Berlin . . . . 1·40 1·70

E **206** Johann Fichte

1962. Birth Bicent of Fichte (philosopher).
E628 – 10pf. green and black 1·50 2·10
E629 E **206** 20pf. red and black 20 15
DESIGN: 10pf. Fichte's birthplace, Ramenau.

E **207** Cross of Lidice
E **208** Dimitrov at Leipzig

1962. 20th Anniv of Destruction of Lidice.
E630 E **207** 20pf. red and black 20 15
E631 25pf. blue and black 1·10 1·25

1962. 80th Birth Anniv of G. Dimitrov (Bulgarian statesman).
E632 E **208** 5pf. black & turquoise 65 60
E633 – 20pf. black and red 20 15
DESIGN: 20pf. Dimitrov as Premier of Bulgaria.

E **209** Maize-planting machine

1962. 10th D.D.R. Agricultural Exhibition, Markkleeberg. Multicoloured.
E634 10pf. Type E **209** 15 15
E635 20pf. Milking shed 15 15
E636 40pf. Combine-harvester . . 1·40 1·80

E **210** "Frieden" (freighter)

1962. 5th Baltic Sea Week, Rostock.
E637 – 10pf. turquoise & blue 15 15
E638 – 20pf. red and yellow 15 15
E639 E **210** 25pf. bistre and blue 1·80 2·00
DESIGNS—HORIZ: 10pf. Map of Baltic Sea inscr "Meer des Friedens" ("Sea of Peace"). VERT: 20pf. Hochhaus, Rostock.

E **211** Brandenburg Gate, Berlin
E **212** Youth of Three Races

E **213** Folk Dancers

E **214** Youth of Three Nations

1962. World Youth Festival Games, Helsinki. Multicoloured.
E640 5pf. Type E **211** . . . . . 1·60 2·30
E641 5pf. Type E **212** . . . . . 1·70 2·30
E642 10pf.+5pf. Type E **213** . . . 45 15
E643 15pf.+5pf. Type E **214** . . . 45 15
E644 20pf. Dove . . . . 1·90 2·30
E645 20pf. National Theatre, Helsinki . . . . 1·90 2·30
Nos. 640/11 and 644/5 were issued together as a se-tenant block of four and Nos. 642/3 in horizontal pairs, both forming composite designs.

E **217** Free-style Swimming

E **218** Municipal Store, Leipzig

1962. 10th European Swimming Championships, Leipzig. Design in blue: value colours given.
E646 E **217** 5pf. orange 15 15
E647 – 10pf. blue 15 15
E648 – 20pf.+10pf. mauve . . 15 15
E649 – 25pf. blue 15 15
E650 – 40pf. violet . . . . . 1·20 1·30
E651 – 70pf. brown 15 15
DESIGNS: 10pf. Back stroke; 20pf. High diving; 25pf. Butterfly stroke; 40pf. Breast stroke; 70pf. Water-polo.
On Nos. E649/51 the value, etc, appears at the foot of the design.

1962. Leipzig Autumn Fair.
E652 E **218** 10pf. black and green 20 15
E653 – 20pf. black and red 30 15
E654 – 25pf. black and blue 1·10 75
DESIGNS: 20pf. Madler Arcade, Leipzig; 25pf. Leipzig Airport and Ilyushin Il-14M airplane.

E **219** "Transport and Communications"

E **220** Rene Blieck

E **219a** P. Popovich and A. Nikolaev

1962. 10th Anniv of "Friedrich List" Transport High School, Dresden.
E655 E **219** 5pf. black and blue 40 15

1962. "Vostok 3" and "Vostok 4" Space Flights. Sheet 89 × 108 mm.
MSE655a E **219a** 70pf. green, blue and yellow . . . . 2·40 3·00

1962. Concentration Camp Victims. Memorials Fund.
E656 E **220** 5pf.+5pf. blue . . . 15 15
E657 – 10pf.+5pf. green . . . 15 15
E658 – 15pf.+5pf. violet . . . 15 15
E659 – 20pf.+10pf. purple . . 20 15
E660 – 70pf.+30pf. brown . . 2·20 2·75
PORTRAITS—As Type E **220**: 10pf. Dr. A. Klahr; 15pf. J. Diaz; 20pf. J. Alpari. HORIZ: (39 × 21 mm): 70pf. Seven Cervi brothers.

E **221** Television Screen and Call-sign

E **222** G. Hauptmann

1962. Stamp Day and 10th Anniv of German Television.
E661 E **221** 20pf. purple and green 20 15
E662 – 40pf. purple & mauve 2·00 2·00
DESIGN: 40pf. Children with stamp album (inscr "TAG DER BRIEFMARKE 1962").

1962. Birth Centenary of Gerhart Hauptmann (author).
E663 E **222** 20pf. black and red 55 15

E **222a** Gagarin and "Vostok 1"

1962. Five Years of Russian Space Flights. Sheet 127 × 108 mm. Multicoloured.
MSE663a 5pf. Dogs "Belka" and "Strelka", 10pf. Type **E222a**; 15pf. "Sputniks 1, 2 and 3"; 20pf. Titov and "Vostok 2"; 25pf. "Luniks 1 and 2"; 30pf. Nikolaev and Popovich; 40pf. Interplanetary station and spacecraft; 50pf. "Lunik 3" . . 29·00 42·00

E **223** Pierre de Coubertin

E **224** Party Flag

1963. Birth Centenary of Pierre de Coubertin (reviver of Olympic Games).
E664 E **223** 20pf. red and grey . . 20 15
E665 – 25pf. blue and ochre 2·10 2·75
DESIGN: 25pf. Stadium.

1963. 6th Socialists Unity Party Day.
E666 E **224** 10pf. red, black & yell 35 15

E **225** Insecticide Sprayer

1963. Malaria Eradication.
E667 E **225** 20pf. black, red & orge 15 15
E668 – 25pf. multicoloured 15 15
E669 – 50pf. multicoloured 1·60 1·70
DESIGNS: 25pf. Rod of Aesculapius; 50pf. Mosquito. Map is common to all values.

E **226** Red Fox (Silver Fox race)

E **227** Barthels Hof, Leipzig (1748–1872)

1963. International Fur Auctions, Leipzig.
E670 E **226** 20pf. blue and red . . 20 15
E671 – 25pf. indigo and blue 1·80 2·40
DESIGN: 25pf. Karakul lamb.

1963. Leipzig Spring Fair.
E672 E **227** 10pf. black and yellow 20 20
E673 – 20pf. black and brown 30 25
E674 – 25pf. black and blue 1·30 1·20
LEIPZIG BUILDINGS: 20pf. New Town Hall; 25pf. Clock-tower, Karl-Marx Square.

E **227a** Laboratory Worker and Apparatus

1963. "Chemistry for Freedom and Socialism". Sheet 105 × 74 mm with Type E **227a** and similar horiz design. Imperf. No gum.
MSE674a 50pf. blue and black (E **227a**); 70pf. blue and grey (oil refinery) . . . . 4·50 11·00

E **228** J. G. Seume (poet) and Scene from "Syracuse Walk" (Birth Bicent)

1963. Cultural Anniversaries. Design and portrait in black.
E675 E **228** 5pf. yellow 15 15
E676 – 10pf. turquoise . . . 15 15
E677 – 20pf. orange 15 15
E678 – 25pf. blue . . . . . . 2·10 1·60
DESIGNS: 10pf. F. Hebbel (poet) and scene from "Mary Magdalene" (150th birth anniv); 20pf. G. Buchner (poet) and scene from "Woyzeck" (150th birth anniv); 25pf. R. Wagner (composer) and scene from "The Flying Dutchman" (150th birth anniv).

E **229** Nurse bandaging Patient

E **230** W. Bohne (runner)

1963. Centenary of Red Cross.
E679 E **229** 10pf. multicoloured 1·10 1·20
E680 – 20pf. black, grey and red 15 15
DESIGN: 20pf. Barkas type "B 1000" ambulance.

1963. Concentration Camps Memorial Fund. Sportsmen Victims (1st series). Designs in black.
E681 E **230** 5pf.+5pf. yellow . . 15 25
E682 – 10pf.+5pf. green . . 15 25
E683 – 15pf.+5pf. mauve . . 15 35
E684 – 20pf.+10pf. pink . . . 20 35
E685 – 25pf.+10pf. blue . . . 2·40 12·50
SPORTSMEN: 10pf. W. Seelenbinder (wrestler); 15pf. A. Richter (cyclist); 20pf. H. Steyer (footballer); 25pf. K. Schlosser (mountaineer).
See also Nos. E704/8.

E **231** Gymnastics

E **232** E. Pottier (lyricist) and Opening Bars of the "Internationale"

1963. 4th East German Gymnastics and Sports Festival, Leipzig. Inscr in black.
E686 E **231** 10pf.+5pf. yellow and green 20 15
E687 – 20pf.+10pf. violet and red 20 15
E688 – 25pf.+10pf. green and blue . . . . 2·75 3·50
DESIGNS: 20pf. Dederon kerchief exercises; 25pf. Relay-racing.

1963. 75th Anniv of "Internationale" (song).
E689 E **232** 20pf. black and red 20 15
E690 – 25pf. black and blue 1·10 1·40
DESIGN: 25pf. As 20pf. but portrait of P.-C. Degeyter.

E **233** V. Tereshkova

E **234** V. Bykovsky and "Vostok 6" and "Vostok 5"

1963. 2nd "Team" Manned Space Flights.
E691 E **233** 20pf. black, grey & bl 90 15
E692 E **234** 20pf. black, grey & bl 90 15
Nos. E691/2 were printed together, se-tenant, forming a composite design.

E **235** Motor Cyclist competing in "Motocross", Apolda

E **236** Treblinka Memorial

1963. World Motor Cycle Racing Championships.
E693 E **235** 10pf. emerald & green 3·75 4·25
E694 – 20pf. red and pink . . 20 15
E695 – 25pf. blue & light blue 20 15
DESIGNS—HORIZ (39 × 22 mm): 20pf. Motor cyclist; 25pf. Two motor cyclists cornering.

1963. Erection of Treblinka Memorial, Poland.
E696 E **236** 20pf. blue and red . . 35 15

E **237** Transport

E **238** Transport

1963. Leipzig Autumn Fair.
E697 E **237** 10pf. multicoloured 90 15
E698 E **238** 10pf. multicoloured 90 15
Nos. E697/8 were printed together, se-tenant, forming a composite design.

1963. Fauna Protection Campaign (2nd series). As Type E **201**. Fauna in natural colours, background colours given.
E699 10pf. green 15 15
E700 20pf. red 15 15
E701 30pf. red 20 15
E702 50pf. blue . . . . 2·75 3·75
E703 70pf. brown 45 50

DESIGNS: 10pf. Stag-beetle; 20pf. Salamander; 30pf. European pond tortoise; 50pf. Green toad; 70pf. West European hedgehogs.

1963. Concentration Camps Memorial Fund. Sportsmen Victims (2nd series). As Type E **230**. Designs in black.

E704 5pf.+5pf. yellow 15 20
E705 10pf.+5pf. green 15 20
E706 15pf.+5pf. violet 15 20
E707 20pf. 10pf. red 15 20
E708 40pf.+20pf. blue . . . . . 3·00 8·00

SPORTSMEN: 5pf. H. Tops (Gymnast); 10pf. Kate Tucholla (hockey-player); 15pf. R. Seiffert (swimmer); 20pf. E. Grube (athlete); 40pf. K. Biedermann (canoeist).

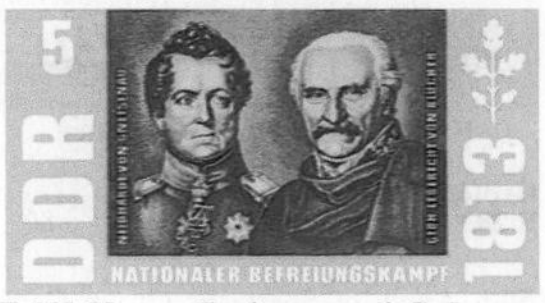

E **239** N. von Gneisenau and G. L. von Blucher

1963. 150th Anniv of German War of Liberation.

E709 E **239** 5pf. black, buff & yell 15 15
E710 – 10pf. black, buff & grn 15 15
E711 – 20pf. blk, buff & orge 20 15
E712 – 25pf. black, buff & bl 20 15
E713 – 40pf. black, buff & red . . . . 1·90 1·60

DESIGNS: 10pf. "Cossacks and (German) Soldiers in Berlin" (Ludwig Wolf); 20pf. E. M. Arndt and Baron vom Stein; 25pf. Lutzow corps in battle order (detail from painting by Hans Kohlschein); 40pf. G. von Scharnhorst and Prince Kutuzov.

E **240** V. Tereshkova

E **241** Synagogue aflame

1963. Visit of Soviet Cosmonauts to East Berlin.

E714 E **240** 10pf. green and blue 15 15
E715 – 20pf. black, red & buff 20 15
E716 – 20pf. green, red & buff 20 15
E717 – 25pf. orange and blue 3·75 2·50

DESIGNS—SQUARE: No. E717, Tereshkova in capsule. VERT: (24 × 32 mm). No. E715, Tereshkova with bouquet; No. E716, Gagarin (visit to Berlin).

1963. 25th Anniv of "Kristallnacht" (Nazi pogrom).

E718 E **241** 10pf. multicoloured 35 30

E **242** Letter-sorting Machine

1963. Stamp Day. Multicoloured.

E719 10pf. Type E **242** . . . . . 1·70 2·40
E720 20pf. Fork-lift truck loading mail train 20 15

E **243** Ski Jumper commencing Run

E **244** "Vanessa atlanta"

1963. Winter Olympic Games, Innsbruck, 1964. Rings in different colours; skier in black.

E721 E **243** 5pf. yellow 15 15
E722 – 10pf. green 15 15
E723 – 20pf.+10pf. red . . . 20 15
E724 – 25pf. blue . . . . . 1·80 2·40

DESIGNS: Ski jumper—10pf. Taking-off; 20pf. In mid-air; 25pf. Landing.

1964. Butterflies. Butterflies in natural colours; inscr in black.

E725 E **244** 10pf. olive 45 15
E726 – 15pf. lilac 45 15
E727 – 20pf. orange 45 15
E728 – 25pf. blue 45 25
E729 – 40pf. blue . . . . . 4·50 2·75

BUTTERFLIES: 15pf. "Parnassius phoebus"; 20pf. "Papilio machaon"; 25pf. "Colius croceus"; 40pf. "Nymphalis polychloros".

E **245** Shakespeare (b. 1564)

1964. Cultural Anniversaries.

E730 – 20pf. blue and pink 15 15
E731 – 25pf. purple and blue 15 15
E732 E **245** 40pf. blue and lilac . . 1·60 1·30

DESIGNS: 20pf. Quadriga, Brandenburg Gate (J. G. Schadow, sculptor, b. 1764); 25pf. Portal keystone, German Historical Museum (A. Schluter, sculptor, b. 1664).

E **246** "Elektrotecknik" Hall

1964. Leipzig Spring Fair.

E733 E **246** 10pf. black and green 1·90 25
E734 – 20pf. black and red 1·90 25

DESIGN: 20pf. Braunigkes Hof, c. 1700.

E **247** A. Saefkow

1964. Concentration Camp Victims. Memorials Fund.

E735 E **247** 5pf.+5pf. brown & bl 20 15
E736 – 10pf.+5pf. brn & ol 20 15
E737 – 15pf.+5pf. brn & vio 20 15
E738 – 20pf.+5pf. olive and red 30 15
E739 – 25pf.+10pf. blue & ol 45 25
E740 – 40pf.+10pf. ol & brn 1·60 1·70

PORTRAITS—As Type E **247**: 10pf. F. Jacob; 15pf. B. Bastlein; 20pf. H. Schulze-Boysen; 25pf. Dr. A. Kuckhoff. (49 × 27½ mm): 40pf. Dr. A. and Mildred Harnack.

E **248** Mr. Khrushchev with East German Officials

E **249** Boys and Girls

1964. Mr. Khrushchev's 70th Birthday.

E741 E **248** 25pf. blue 20 15
E742 – 40pf. black and purple 2·20 2·75

DESIGN: 40pf. Mr. Khrushchev with cosmonauts Tereshkova and Gagarin.

1964. German Youth Meeting, Berlin. Multicoloured.

E743 10pf. Type E **249** 15 15
E744 20pf. Young gymnasts . . . 15 15
E745 25pf. Youth with accordion and girl with flowers . . 1·60 1·10

E **250** Flax, Krumel and Struppi, the dog

1964. Children's Day. Multicoloured.

E746 5pf. Type E **250** 15 15
E747 10pf. Master Nadelohr . . 15 15
E748 15pf. Pittiplatsch 15 15
E749 20pf. Sandmannschen (sandman) 15 15
E750 40pf. Bummi (teddy bear) and Schnatterinchen (duckling) . . . . 1·90 1·70

The designs show characters from children's T.V. programmes.

E **251** Governess and Child (with portrait of Jenny Marx)

1964. East German Women's Congress. Mult.

E751 20pf. Type E **251** 15 15
E752 25pf. Switchboard technicians . . . . 1·30 1·10
E753 70pf. Farm girls 25 15

E **252** Cycling

E **253** Diving

1964. Olympic Games, Tokyo. Multicoloured. (a) 1st Series. As Type E **252**.

E754 5pf. Type E **252** 15 15
E755 10pf. Volleyball 15 15
E756 20pf. Judo 15 15
E757 25pf. Diving 15 15
E758 40pf.+20pf. Running . . . 45 25
E759 70pf. Horse-jumping . . . 1·90 2·00

(b) 2nd Series. As Type E **253**.

E760 10pf. Type E **253** . . . . 2·75 3·25
E761 10pf.+5pf. Horse-jumping 2·75 3·25
E762 10pf. Volleyball . . . . . 2·75 3·25
E763 10pf. Cycling . . . . . . 2·75 3·25
E764 10pf.+5pf. Running . . . . 2·75 3·25
E765 10pf. Judo . . . . 2·75 3·25

Nos. E760/5 were printed together in se-tenant blocks of six (3 × 2) within sheets of 60 (6 × 10), and with an overall pattern of the five Olympic "rings" in each block.

E **254** Young Artists

1964. 5th Young Pioneers' Meeting, East Berlin. Multicoloured.

E766 10pf.+5pf. Type E **254** . . 90 15
E767 20pf.+10pf. Planting tree . . 1·30 15
E768 25pf.+10pf. Playing with ball . . . . 2·10 2·00

E **255** Leningrad Memorial

E **256** F. Joliot-Curie

1964. Victims of Leningrad Siege Commem.

E769 E **255** 25pf. black, yellow and blue 95 15

1964. "World Peace".

E770 E **256** 20pf. sepia and red . . 20 15
E771 – 25pf. black and blue 20 15
E772 – 50pf. black and lilac 1·30 90

PORTRAITS (Campaigners for "World Peace"): 25pf. B. von Suttner; 50pf. C. von Ossietzky.

E **257** Ancient Glazier's Shop

E **258** I.W.M.A. Cachet

1964. Leipzig Autumn Fair. Multicoloured.

E773 10pf. Type E **257** 75 15
E774 15pf. Jena glass factory . . 75 15

1964. Centenary of "First International".

E775 E **258** 20pf. black and red 15 15
E776 25pf. black and blue 70 75

E **259** "Rostock Port" Stamp of 1958

E **260** Modern Buildings and Flag ("Reconstruction")

1964. National Stamp Exn, East Berlin.

E777 E **259** 10pf.+5pf. green and orange 20 15
E778 – 20pf.+10pf. blue and purple 30 15
E779 – 50pf. brown and grey 1·90 2·00

DESIGNS: 20pf., 12pf. "Peace" stamp of 1950; 50pf., 5pf. "Dresden Paintings" stamp of 1955.

1964. 15th Anniv of German Democratic Republic. Multicoloured.

E780 10pf. Type E **260** 30 20
E781 10pf. Surveyor and conveyor ("Coal") . . . 30 20
E782 10pf. Scientist and chemical works ("Chemical Industry") 30 20
E783 10pf. Guard and chemical works ("Chemical Industry") 30 20
E784 10pf. Milkmaid and dairy pen ("Agriculture") . . . 30 20
E785 10pf. Furnaceman and mills ("Steel") 30 20
E786 10pf. Student with microscope, and lecture hall ("Education") . . . 30 20
E787 10pf. Operator and lathe ("Engineering") 30 20
E788 10pf. Scientist and planetarium ("Optics") 30 20
E789 10pf. Girl with cloth, and loom ("Textiles") 30 20
E790 10pf. Docker and ship at quayside ("Shipping") . . 30 20
E791 10pf. Leipzig buildings and "businessmen" formed of Fair emblem ("Exports") 30 20
E792 10pf. Building worker and flats ("New Construction") 30 20
E793 10pf. Sculptor modelling and Dresden gateway ("Culture") 30 20
E794 10pf. Girl skier and holiday resort ("Recreation") . . . 30 20
MSE794a 210 × 285 mm. Nos. E780/94 . . . . 55·00 70·00

E **261** Monchgut (Rugen) Costume

E **262** Dr. Schweitzer and Lambarene River

1964. Provincial Costumes (1st series). Mult.

E795 5pf. Type E **261** . . . . 10·50 7·75
E796 5pf. Monchgut (male) . . . 10·50 7·75
E797 10pf. Spreewald (female) . . 45 20
E798 10pf. Spreewald (male) . . 45 20
E799 20pf. Thuringen (female) . . 45 25
E800 20pf. Thuringen (male) . . 45 25

See Nos. E932/7 and E1073/6.

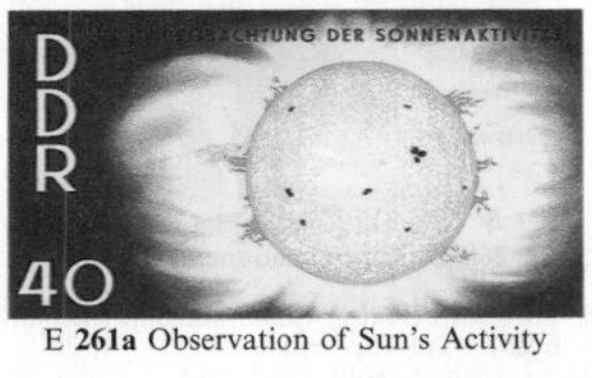

E **261a** Observation of Sun's Activity

1964. Quiet Sun Year. Three sheets, each 108 × 90 mm incorporating stamp as Type E **261a**. Multicoloured.

MSE801 (a) 25pf. Rocket over part of Earth. (b) 40pf. Type E **261a**. (c) 70pf. Earth and rocket routes 11·00 18·00

1965. 90th Birthday of Dr. Albert Schweitzer.

E802 E **262** 10pf. yellow, blk & grn 20 15
E803 – 20pf. yellow, blk & red 30 15
E804 – 25pf. yellow, blk & bl 2·75 2·75

DESIGNS: 20pf. Schweitzer and "nuclear disarmament" marchers; 25pf. Schweitzer and part of a Bach organ prelude.

1965. As Nos. E586/7 but values expressed in "MDN" (Deutschen Notenbank Marks) instead of "DM".
E805 1MDN. green 50 25
E806 2MDN. brown 55 45

E 263 A. Bebel

E 264 Fair Medal (obverse)

1965. 125th Birth Anniv of August Bebel (founder of Social Democratic Party).
E807 E 263 20pf. yellow, brn & red 40 15
See also Nos. E814/15, E839, E842 and E871.

1965. Leipzig Spring Fair and 800th Anniv of Leipzig Fair.
E808 E 264 10pf. gold and mauve 20 15
E809 – 15pf. gold and mauve 20 15
E810 – 25pf. multicoloured 65 25
DESIGNS: 15pf. Fair medal (reverse); 25pf. Chemical Works.

E 265 Giraffe

E 266 Belyaev and Leonov

1965. 10th Anniv of East Berlin Zoo.
E811 E 265 10pf. grey and green 15 15
E812 – 25pf. grey and blue 30 15
E813 – 30pf. grey and sepia 1·90 1·70
ANIMALS—HORIZ: 25pf. Iguana; 30pf. Black wildebeest.

1965. 120th Birth Anniv of W. C. Rontgen (physicist). As Type E 263 but portrait of Rontgen.
E814 10pf. yellow, brown and green 55 15

1985. 700th Birth Anniv of Dante. As Type E 263 but portrait of Dante.
E815 50pf. yellow, brown & lemon . . . . 1·50 15

1965. Space Flight of "Voskhod 2".
E816 E 266 10pf. red 30 15
E817 – 25pf. blue . . . . . . 1·90 1·80
DESIGN: 25pf. Leonov in space.

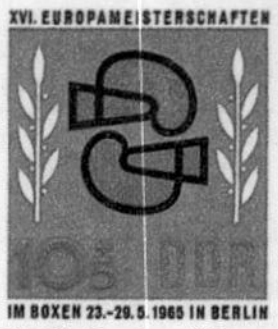

E 267 Boxing Gloves

E 269 Transmitter Aerial and Globe

E 268 Dimitrov denouncing Fascism

1965. European Boxing Championships, Berlin.
E818 E 267 10pf.+5pf. mult . . . 20 15
E819 – 20pf. gold, black and red 90 85
DESIGN: 20pf. Boxing glove.

1965. 20th Anniv of Liberation. Multicoloured.
E820 5pf.+5pf. Type E 268 . . . 15 15
E821 10pf.+5pf. Distributing "Communist Manifesto" 15 15
E822 15pf.+5pf. Soldiers of International Brigade fighting in Spain . . . 15 15
E823 20pf.+10pf. "Freedom for Ernst Thalmann" demonstration 15 15
E824 25pf.+10pf. Founding of "Free Germany" National Committee (Moscow) 20 15
E825 40pf. Ulbricht and Weinert distributing "Manifesto" on Eastern Front 20 15
E826 50pf. Liberation of concentration camps . . . 20 15
E827 60pf. Hoisting Red Flag on Reichstag . . . . 2·50 2·25
E828 70pf. Bilateral demonstration of Communist and Socialist parties 30 15

1965. 20th Anniv of East German Broadcasting Service.
E829 E 269 20pf. black, red and cerise 20 15
E830 – 40pf. black and blue 1·60 60
DESIGN: 40pf. Radio workers.

E 270 I.T.U. Emblem and Radio Circuit Diagram

E 271 F.D.G.B. Emblem

1965. Centenary of I.T.U.
E831 E 270 20pf. black, yell & ol 45 15
E832 – 25pf. black, mve & vio . . . . 1·80 60
DESIGN: 25pf. I.T.U. emblem and switch diagram.

1965. 20th Anniv of Free German (F.D.G.B.) and World Trade Unions.
E833 E 271 20pf. gold and red . . 20 15
E834 – 25pf. black, bl & gold 1·10 45
DESIGN—HORIZ (39 × 21½ mm): 25pf. Workers of "two hemispheres" (inscr "20 JAHRE WELTGEWERKSCHAFTSBUND").

E 272 Industrial Machine

E 273 Marx and Lenin

1965. 800th Anniv of Karl-Marx-Stadt (formerly Chemnitz).
E835 E 272 10pf. green and gold 20 15
E836 – 20pf. red and gold . . 20 15
E837 – 25pf. blue and gold 1·20 50
DESIGNS: 20pf. Red Tower, Chemnitz; 25pf. Town Hall, Chemnitz.

1965. Socialist Countries' Postal Ministers Conference, Peking.
E838 E 273 20pf. black, yell & red 30 15

1965. 90th Birth Anniv of Dr. Wilhelm Kulz (politician). As Type E 263 but portrait of Kulz.
E839 25pf. yellow, brown and blue . . . . 1·10 15

E 274 Congress Emblem

1965. World Peace Congress, Helsinki.
E840 E 274 10pf.+5pf. green and blue 15 15
E841 20pf.+5pf. blue and red 60 45

1965. 75th Birth Anniv of Erich Weinert (poet). As Type E 263, but portrait of Weinert.
E842 40pf. yellow, brown and red 50 15

1965. "Help for Vietnam". Surch **Hilfe fur VIETNAM +10.**
E843 E 260 10pf.+10pf. mult . . . 45 15

E 276 Rebuilt Weigh-house and Modern Buildings, Katharinenstrasse

1965. 800th Anniv of Leipzig.
E844 E 276 10pf. purple, bl & gold 15 15
E845 – 25pf. orge, sep & gold 20 15
E846 – 40pf. multicoloured 30 15
E847 – 70pf. blue and gold 1·70 95
DESIGNS: 25pf. Old Town Hall; 40pf. Opera House and new G.P.O.; 70pf. "Stadt Leipzig" Hotel.

E 277 "Praktica" and "Praktisix" Cameras

E 278 Show Jumping

1965. Leipzig Autumn Fair.
E848 E 277 10pf. blk, gold & grn 15 15
E849 – 15pf. multicoloured 15 15
E850 – 25pf. multicoloured 60 25
DESIGNS: 15pf. Clavichord and electric guitar; 25pf. "Zeiss" microscope.

1965. Leipzig Philatelic Exhibition, "INTERMESS III". Nos. E844/7 in two miniature sheets each 137 × 99 mm.
MSE851 (a) Nos. E844 and E847. (b) Nos. E845/6 (sold for 1 MDN.75) . . . . 5·75 5·75

1965. World Modern Pentathlon Championships, Leipzig. Multicoloured.
E852 10pf. Type E 278 . . . . 20 15
E853 10pf. Swimming 20 15
E854 10pf. Running . . . . . . 2·75 2·75
E855 10pf.+5pf. Fencing 20 15
E856 10pf.+5pf. Pistol-shooting 20 15

E 279 E. Leonov

E 280 Memorial at Putten, Netherlands

1965. Soviet Cosmonauts Visit to East Germany.
E857 E 279 20pf. blue, silver & red 50 70
E858 – 20pf. blue, silver & red 50 70
E859 – 25pf. multicoloured 50 70
DESIGNS—As Type E 275. No. E858, Belyaev. HORIZ (48 × 29 mm): No. E859, "Voskhod 2" and Leonov in space.

1965. Putten War Victims Commem.
E860 E 280 25pf. black, yell & bl 70 15

E 281 Stoking Furnace (from old engraving)

E 282 Red Kite

1965. Bicent of Mining School, Freiberg. Multicoloured.
E861 10pf. Type E 281 . . . . 15 15
E862 15pf. Mining ore (old engraving) 55 80
E863 20pf. Ore 15 15
E864 25pf. Sulphur 20 15

1965. Birds of Prey. Multicoloured.
E865 5pf. Type E 282 . . . . . 15 15
E866 10pf. Lammergeier 15 15
E867 20pf. Common Buzzard . . 25 15
E868 25pf. Common Kestrel . . 25 15
E869 40pf. Northern Goshawk 35 25
E870 70pf. Golden Eagle . . . . 4·25 3·75

1965. 150th Birth Anniv of A. von Menzel (painter). As Type E 263 but portrait of Menzel.
E871 10pf. yellow, brown and red 80 15

E 283 Otto Grotewohl

E 285 Ladies' Single-seater

E 284 Extract from Newsletter

1965. Grotewohl Commemoration.
E872 E 283 20f. black 80 15

1966. 50th Anniv of Spartacus Group Conference. Miniature sheet 138 × 98 mm. Type E 284 and similar horiz design.
MSE873 20pf. black and red (Type E 284); 50pf. black and red (Karl Liebknecht and Rosa Luxemburg) . . . . 2·00 3·25

1966. World Tobogganing Championships, Friedrichroda.
E874 E 285 10pf. green and olive 15 15
E875 – 20pf. blue and red . . 20 15
E876 – 25pf. indigo and blue 1·50 90
DESIGNS: 20pf. Men's double-seater; 25pf. Men's single seater.

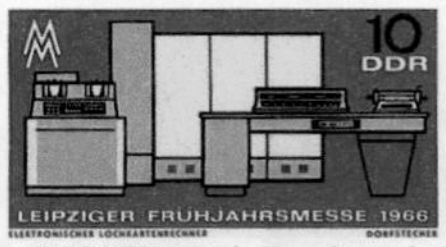

E 286 Electronic Punch-card Computer

1966. Leipzig Spring Fair. Multicoloured.
E877 10pf. Type E 286 . . . . 20 15
E878 15pf. Drilling and milling plant . . . . 1·10 15

E 287 Soldier and National Gallery, Berlin

E 288 J. A. Smoler (Sorb patriot and savant)

1966. 10th Anniv of National People's Army.
E879 E 287 5pf. black, olive & yell 15 15
E880 – 10pf. black, ol & yell 15 15
E881 – 20pf. black, ol & yell 20 15
E882 – 25pf. black, ol & yell 1·60 1·20
DESIGNS: Soldier and—10pf. Brandenburg Gate; 20pf. Industrial plant; 25pf. Combine-harvester.

1966. 150th Anniv of Jan Smoler.
E883 E 288 20pf. black, red & blue 20 15
E884 – 25pf. black, red & blue 65 50
DESIGN: 25pf. House of the Sorbs, Bautzen.

E 289 "Good Knowledge" Badge

E 290 "Luna 9" on Moon

1966. 20th Anniv of "Freie Deutsche Jugend" (Socialist Youth Movement).
E885 E 289 20pf. multicoloured 65 15

1966. Moon Landing of "Luna 9".
E886 E 290 20pf. multicoloured 1·90 30

E 291 Road Signs

1966. Road Safety.
E887 E 291 10pf. red, bl & ultram 15 15
E888 – 15pf. black, yell & grn 15 15

E889 – 25pf. black, blue & bis 20 15
E890 – 50pf. black, yell & red 1·30 75
DESIGNS: 15pf. Child on scooter crossing in front of car; 25pf. Cyclist and hand-signal; 50pf. Motor cyclist, glass of beer and ambulance.

E **292** Marx and Lenin Banner

1966. 20th Anniv of Socialist Unity Party (S.E.D.).

E891	–	5pf. multicoloured	15	15
E892	E **292**	10pf. yellow, blk & red	15	15
E893	–	15pf. black and green	20	15
E894	–	20pf. black and red	20	15
E895	–	25pf. black, yell & red	1·40	1·25

DESIGNS—VERT: 5pf. Party badge and demonstrators; 15pf. Marx, Engels and manifesto; 20pf. Pieck and Grotewohl. HORIZ: 25pf. Workers greeting Ulbricht.

E **293** W.H.O. Building

1966. Inaug of W.H.O. Headquarters, Geneva.
E896 E **293** 20pf. multicoloured 35 25

E **294** Spreewald

1966. National Parks. Multicoloured.

E897	10pf. Type E **294**	15	15
E898	15pf. Konigsstuhl (Isle of Rugen)	15	15
E899	20pf. Sachsische Schweiz	15	15
E900	25pf. Westdarss	20	15
E901	30pf. Teufelsmauer	20	15
E902	50pf. Feldberg Lakes	1·90	1·10

E **295** Lace "Flower" E **296** Lily of the Valley

1966. Plauen Lace. Floral Patterns as Type E **295**.

E903	E **295**	10pf. myrtle and green	15	15
E904	–	20pf. indigo and blue	15	15
E905	–	25pf. red and rose	20	15
E906	–	50pf. violet and lilac	2·75	1·40

1966. Int Horticultural Show, Erfurt. Mult.

E907	20pf. Type E **296**	15	15
E908	25pf. Rhododendrons	20	15
E909	40pf. Dahlias	35	25
E910	50pf. Cyclamen	4·00	3·50

E **297** Parachutist on Target

1966. 8th World Parachute Jumping Championships, Leipzig.

E911	E **297**	10pf. blue, black & bis	15	15
E912	–	15pf. multicoloured	65	70
E913	–	20pf. black, bistre & bl	20	15

DESIGNS: 15pf. Group descent; 20pf. Free fall.

E **298** Hans Kahle and Music of "The Thalmann Column"

1966. 30th Anniv of International Brigade in Spain. Multicoloured.

E914	5pf. Type E **298**	20	15
E915	10pf.+5pf. W. Bredel and open-air class	20	15
E916	15pf. H. Beimler and Madrid street-fighting	20	15
E917	20pf.+10pf. H. Rau and march-past after Battle of Brunete	20	15
E918	25pf.+10pf. H. Marchwitza and soldiers	20	15
E919	40pf.+10pf. A. Becker and Ebro battle	1·80	1·10

E **299** Canoeing

1966. World Canoeing Championships, Berlin. Multicoloured.

E920	10pf.+5pf. Type E **299**	20	15
E921	15pf. Kayak doubles	1·50	1·10

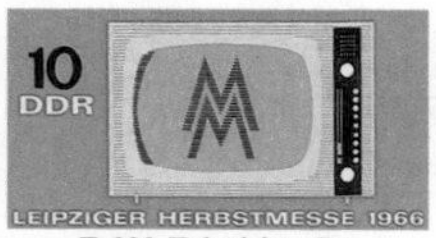

E **300** Television Set

1966. Leipzig Autumn Fair. Multicoloured.

E922	10pf. Type E **300**	45	15
E923	15pf. Electric typewriter	1·20	25

E **301** Oradour Memorial

1966. Oradour-sur-Glane War Victims Commem.
E924 E **301** 25pf. black, blue & red 35 15

E **302** "Blood Donors"

1966. International Health Co-operation.

E925	E **302**	5pf. red and green	15	15
E926	–	20pf.+10pf. red and violet	30	15
E927	–	40pf. red and blue	1·60	60

DESIGNS—HORIZ: 20pf. I.C.Y. emblem. VERT: 40pf. Health symbol.

E **303** Weightlifting ("snatch") E **304** Congress Hall

1966. World and European Weightlifting Championships, Berlin.

E928	E **303**	15pf. black and brown	1·70	1·50
E929	–	20pf.+5pf. black and blue	35	15

DESIGN: 20pf. Weightlifting ("jerk").

1966. 6th Int Journalists' Congress, Berlin.

E930	E **304**	10pf. multicoloured	55	40
E931	–	20pf. yellow and blue	20	15

DESIGN—VERT: 20pf. Emblem of Int Organization of journalists.

1966. Provincial Costumes (2nd series). As Type E **261**. Multicoloured.

E932	5pf. Altenburg (female)	35	15
E933	10pf. Altenburg (male)	35	15
E934	10pf. Mecklenburg (female)	35	15
E935	15pf. Mecklenburg (male)	35	15
E936	20pf. Magdeburger Borde (female)	2·20	2·50
E937	30pf. Magdeburger Borde (male)	2·20	2·50

E **305** "Vietnam is Invincible"

1966. Aid for Vietnam.
E938 E **305** 20pf.+5pf. black and pink 40 25

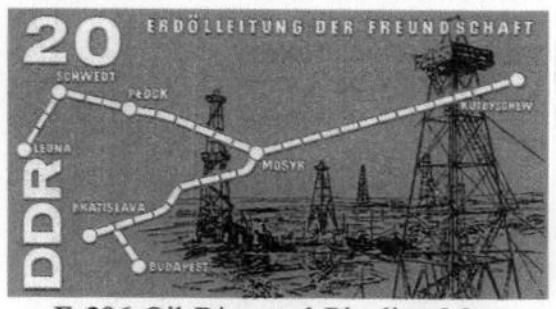

E **306** Oil Rigs and Pipeline Map

1966. Inaug of Int "Friendship" Oil Pipeline.

E939	E **306**	20pf. black and red	20	15
E940	–	25pf. black and blue	90	40

DESIGN: 25pf. "Walter Ulbricht" Oil Works, Leuna and pipeline map.

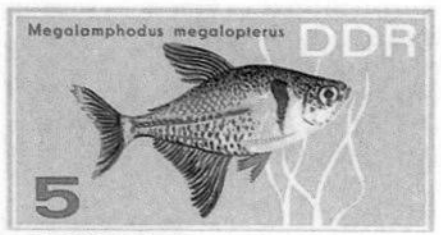

E **307** Black Phantom Tetra

1966. Aquarium Fishes. Multicoloured.

E941	5pf. Type E **307**	15	15
E942	10pf. Cardinal tetra	15	15
E943	15pf. Rio Grande cichlid	2·10	2·20
E944	20pf. Blue gularis	20	15
E945	25pf. Ramirez's dwarf cichlid	20	15
E946	40pf. Honey gourami	30	25

E **308** "Horse" (detail from Ishtar Gate)

1966. Babylonian Art Treasures, Vorderasiatisches Museum, Berlin. Multicoloured.

E947	10pf. Type E **308**	15	15
E948	20pf. Mythological animal, Ishtar Gate	15	15
E949	25pf. Lion facing right (vert)	20	15
E950	50pf. Lion facing left (vert)	80	1·20

E **309** The Wartburg from the East E **310** "Gentiana pneumonanthe"

1966. 900th Anniv of Wartburg Castle.

E951	E **309**	10pf.+5pf. slate	15	15
E952	–	20pf. green	20	15
E953	–	25pf. purple	55	45

DESIGNS: 20pf. Castle bailiwick; 25pf. Residence.

1966. Protected Plants (1st series). Mult.

E954	10pf. Type E **310**	15	15
E955	20pf. "Cephalanthera rubra"	20	15
E956	25pf. "Arnica montana"	1·60	1·00

See also Nos. E1177/82 and E1284/9.

E **311** Son leaves Home E **312** Worlitz Castle

1966. Fairy Tales (1st series). "The Wishing Table". Multicoloured.

E957	5pf. Type E **311**	20	50
E958	10pf. Setting the table	20	50
E959	20pf. The thieving inn-keeper	65	75
E960	25pf. The magic donkey	65	75
E961	30pf. The cudgel in the sack	20	50
E962	50pf. Return of the son	20	50

See also Nos. E1045/50, E1147/52, E1171/6, E1266/71, E1437/42, E1525/30, E1623/8, E1711/16, E1811/13, E1902/7, E1996/2001 and E2092/7.

1967. Principal East German Buildings. (1st series). Multicoloured.

E964	5pf. Type E **312**	15	15
E965	10pf. Stralsund Town Hall (vert)	15	15
E966	15pf. Chorin Monastery (vert)	20	15
E967	20pf. Ribbeck House, Berlin	20	15
E968	25pf. Moritzburg, Zeitz (vert)	20	15
E969	40pf. Old Town Hall, Potsdam (vert)	1·40	1·00

See also Nos. E1100/3 and E1155/60.

E **313** Rifle-shooting

1967. World Biathlon Championships, Altenburg.

E970	E **313**	10pf. blue, drab & mve	15	15
E971	–	20pf. olive, blue & grn	20	15
E972	–	25pf. green, blue & ol	80	60

DESIGNS: 20pf. Shooting on skis; 25pf. Riflemen racing on skis.

E **314** "Multilock" Loom

1967. Leipzig Spring Fair.

E973	E **314**	10pf. green, grey & pur	20	15
E974	–	15pf. bistre & blue	75	15

DESIGN: 15pf. Zeiss tracking telescope.

E **315** Mother and Child E **317** "Portrait of a Girl" (after F Hodler)

E **316** Industrial Control Desk

1967. 20th Anniv of German Democratic Women's Federation.

E975	E **315**	20pf. grey, red and purple	20	15
E976	–	25pf. brown, turquoise and brown	70	90

DESIGN: 25pf. Professional woman.

1967. Socialist Party Rally. Multicoloured.(a) 1st series.

E977	10pf. Type E **316**	15	15
E978	20pf. Ulbricht meeting workers	15	15
E979	25pf. Servicemen guarding industrial plants	20	15
E980	40pf. Agricultural workers and harvesters	60	70

Each with inset portraits of Marx, Engels and Lenin.

(b) 2nd series. As Type E **316** but vert.

E981	5pf. Agricultural worker	15	15
E982	10pf. Teacher and pupil	15	15
E983	15pf. Socialist family	50	45
E984	20pf. Servicemen	20	15

Each with inset portraits as above.

1967. Dresden Gallery Paintings (1st series). Multicoloured.

E985	20pf. Type E **317**	15	15
E986	25pf. "Peter at the Zoo" (H. Hakenbeck)	15	15
E987	30pf. "Venetian Episode" (R. Bergander)	20	15
E988	40pf. "Tahitian Women" (Gauguin) (horiz)	20	15
E989	50pf. "The Grandchild" (J. Scholtz)	1·80	1·90
E990	70pf. "Cairn in the Snow" (C. D. Friedrich) (horiz)	30	15

See also Nos. E1114/19 and E1249/54.

E **318** Barn Owl

E **319** Cycle Wheels

1967. Protected Birds. Multicoloured.

E991	5pf. Type E **318**	15	15
E992	10pf. Common Crane	15	15
E993	20pf. Peregrine Falcon	20	15
E994	25pf. Northern bullfinches	35	15
E995	30pf. River kingfisher	3·25	2·00
E996	40pf. European roller	45	15

1967. 20th Warsaw–Berlin–Prague Cycle Race.

E997	E **319**	10pf. violet, black and yellow	15	15
E998	–	25pf. red and blue	50	45

DESIGN: 25pf. Racing cyclists.

E **320** "Tom Cat"

1967. Int Children's Day. Multicoloured.

E 999	5pf. Type E **320**	15	15
E1000	10pf. "Snow White"	15	15
E1001	15pf. "Fire Brigade"	20	15
E1002	20pf. "Cockerel"	20	15
E1003	25pf. "Vase of Flowers"	20	25
E1004	30pf. "Children Playing with Ball"	1·20	85

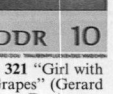

E **321** "Girl with Grapes" (Gerard Dou)

E **322** Exhibition Emblem

1967. Paintings Missing from German National Galleries (after World War II).

E1005	E **321**	5pf. blue	15	15
E1006	–	10pf. brown	15	15
E1007	–	20pf. green	20	15
E1008	–	25pf. purple	20	15
E1009	–	40pf. olive	20	15
E1010	–	50pf. sepia	1·90	1·40

DESIGNS—VERT: 25pf. "Portrait of W Schroeder-Devrient" (after K. Begas); 40pf. "Young Girl in Straw Hat" (after S. Bray); 50pf. "The Four Evangelists" (after Jordaens). HORIZ: 5pf. "Three Horsemen" (after Rubens); 20pf. "Spring Idyll" (after H. Thoma).

1967. 15th Agricultural Exn, Markkleeberg.

E1011	E **322**	20pf. red, green and yellow	30	15

E **323** Marie Curie (Birth Cent)

E **324** Jack of Diamonds

1967. Birth Anniversaries.

E1012	–	5pf. brown	15	15
E1013	E **323**	10pf. blue	15	15
E1014	–	20pf. red	20	15
E1015	–	25pf. sepia	20	15
E1016	–	40pf. green	75	70

PORTRAITS: 5pf. G. Herwegh (poet—150th); 20pf. Kathe Kollwitz (artist—cent); 25pf. J. J. Winckelmann (archaeologist—250th); 40pf. T. Storm (poet—150th).

1967. German Playing-cards. Multicoloured.

E1017	5pf. Type E **324**	15	15
E1018	10pf. Jack of Hearts	15	15
E1019	20pf. Jack of Spades	20	15
E1020	25pf. Jack of Clubs	5·25	3·25

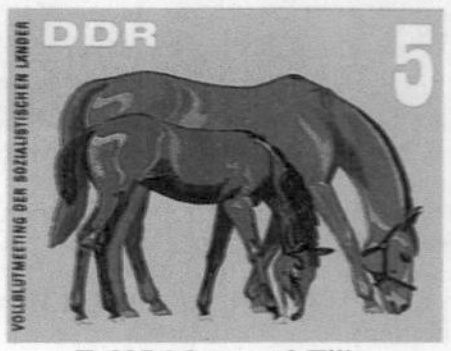

E **325** Mare and Filly

1967. Thoroughbred Horse Meeting, Berlin Multicoloured

E1021	5pf. Type E **325**	20	15
E1022	10pf. Stallion	20	15
E1023	20pf. Horse-racing	30	15
E1024	50pf. Two fillies (vert)	3·25	2·10

E **326** Kitchen Equipment

E **328** Kragujevac Memorial

E **327** Max Reichpietsch and "Friedrich der Grosse" (battleship), 1914–18

1967. Leipzig Autumn Fair. Multicoloured.

E1025	10pf. Type E **326**	45	15
E1026	15pf. Fur coat and "Interpelz" brand-mark	1·20	35

1967. 50th Anniv of Revolutionary Sailors' Movement. Multicoloured.

E1027	10pf. Type E **327**	20	15
E1028	15pf. Albin Kobis and "Prinzregent Luitpold" (battleship), 1914–18	1·60	60
E1029	20pf. Sailors' demonstration and "Seydlitz" (battle cruiser), 1914–18	45	15

1967. Victims of Kragujevac (Yugoslavia) Massacre.

E1030	E **328**	25pf. black, yellow and red	90	30

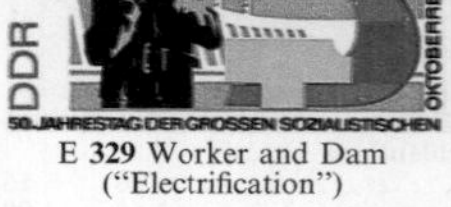

E **329** Worker and Dam ("Electrification")

E **330** Martin Luther (from engraving by Lucas Cranach the Elder)

1967. 50th Anniv of October Revolution.

E1031	–	5pf. black, orange and red	15	15
E1032	E **329**	10pf. black, red and bistre	15	15
E1033	–	15pf. black, red and grey	15	15
E1034	–	20pf. black, red and orange	30	15
E1035	–	40pf. black, red and orange	3·00	2·10

MSE1036 127 × 83 mm. Nos. E1034/5. Imperf (sold for 85pf.) 1·50 1·60

DESIGNS: 5pf. Worker and newspaper headline "Hands off Soviet Russia!"; 15pf. Treptow Memorial ("Victory over Fascism"); 20pf. German and Soviet soldiers ("Friendship"); 40pf. Lenin and "Aurora" (Russian cruiser) . Each with hammer and sickle.

1967. 450th Anniv of Reformation.

E1037	E **330**	20pf. black & mauve	20	15
E1038	–	25pf. black and blue	20	15
E1039	–	40pf. black and bistre	2·75	1·10

DESIGNS—HORIZ: 25pf. Luther's house, Wittenberg. VERT: 40pf. Castle church, Wittenberg.

E **331** Young Workers

E **332** Goethe's House, Weimar

1967. 10th "Masters of Tomorrow" Fair, Leipzig.

E1040	E **331**	20pf. black, gold and blue	85	60
E1041	–	20pf. black, gold and blue	85	60
E1042	–	25pf. multicoloured	85	60

DESIGNS—VERT: No. E1041, Young man and woman. HORIZ: (51 × 29 mm): No. E1042, Presentation of awards.

1967. Cultural Places.

E1043	E **332**	20pf. blk, brn & grey	30	15
E1044	–	25pf. olive, brn & yell	1·70	70

DESIGN: 25pf. Schiller's House, Weimar.

E **333** Queen and Courtiers

E **335** Nutcracker and Two "Smokers"

E **334** Peasants and Modern Farm Buildings

1967. Fairy Tales (2nd series). "King Thrushbeard". Designs showing different scenes.

E1045	E **333**	5pf. multicoloured	20	70
E1046	–	10pf. multicoloured	20	70
E1047	–	15pf. multicoloured	90	80
E1048	–	20pf. multicoloured	90	80
E1049	–	25pf. multicoloured	20	70
E1050	–	30pf. multicoloured	20	70

1967. 15th Anniv of Agricultural Co-operatives.

E1052	E **334**	10pf. sepia, green and olive	30	15

1967. Popular Art of the Erzgebirge. Multicoloured.

E1053	10pf. Type E **335**	90	45
E1054	20pf. "Angel" and miner with candles (carved figures)	20	15

E **336** Ice Skating

E **337** Actinometer

1968. Winter Olympic Games, Grenoble.

E1055	E **336**	5pf. blue, red and light blue	20	15
E1056	–	10pf.+5pf. blue, red and turquoise	20	15
E1057	–	15pf. multicoloured	20	15
E1058	–	20pf. ultramarine, red and blue	20	15
E1059	–	25pf. multicoloured	20	15
E1060	–	30pf. ultramarine, red and blue	2·75	1·50

DESIGNS: 10pf. Tobogganning; 15pf. Slalom; 20pf. Ice hockey; 25pf. Figure skating (pairs); 30pf. Cross-country skiing.

1968. 75th Anniv of Potsdam Meteorological Observatory and World Meteorological Day (23 March).

E1061	E **337**	10pf. blk, red & pur	90	85
E1062	–	20pf. multicoloured	90	85
E1063	–	25pf. blk, yell & grn	90	85

DESIGNS—VERT: 25pf. Cornfield by day and night. HORIZ—(50 × 28 mm): 20pf. Satellite picture of clouds.

E **338** "Venus 4"

1968. Soviet Space Achievements. Mult.

E1064	20pf. Type E **338**	20	15
E1065	25pf. Coupled satellites "Cosmos 186" and "188"	90	60

E **339** "Illegal Struggle" (man, wife and child)

E **341** Gorky

E **340** Type DE1 Diesel-electric Locomotive (built for Brazil)

1968. Stained-glass Windows, Sachsenhausen National Memorial Museum. Multicoloured.

E1066	10pf. Type E **339**	15	15
E1067	20pf. "Liberation"	20	15
E1068	25pf. "Partisans' Struggle"	60	40

1968. Leipzig Spring Fair. Multicoloured.

E1069	10pf. Type E **340**	45	15
E1070	15pf. Deep sea trawler	75	15

1968. Birth Cent of Maxim Gorky (writer).

E1071	E **341**	20pf. purple and red	20	15
E1072	–	25pf. purple and red	65	40

DESIGN: 25pf. Fulmar (from "Song of the Stormy Petrel"—poem).

1968. Provincial Costumes (3rd series). As Type E **261**. Multicoloured.

E1073	10pf. Hoyerswerda (female)	15	15
E1074	20pf. Schleife (female)	20	15
E1075	40pf. Crostwitz (female)	30	15
E1076	50pf. Spreewald (female)	2·20	1·10

E **342** Common Pheasants

E **343** Karl Marx

1968. Small Game. Multicoloured.

E1077	10pf. Type E **342**	15	15
E1078	15pf. Grey Partridges	20	15
E1079	20pf. Mallards	20	15
E1080	25pf. Greylag Geese	20	15
E1081	30pf. Wood Pigeon	20	15
E1082	40pf. Brown hares	2·20	6·00

1968. 150th Birth Anniv of Karl Marx.

E1083	–	10pf. black and green	30	55
E1084	E **343**	20pf. black, yell & red	30	55
E1085	–	25pf. blk, brn & yell	30	55

MSE1086 126 × 86 mm. Nos. E1083/5. Imperf 1·20 3·00

DESIGNS: 10pf. Title-page of "Communist Manifesto"; 25pf. Title-page of "Das Kapital".

E 344 "Fritz Heckert" (after E. Hering)

E 345 Hammer and Anvil ("The right to work")

1968. 7th Confederation of Free German Trade Unions Congress. Multicoloured.

E1087	10pf. Type E **344**	15	15
E1088	20pf. Young workers and new tenements	30	30

1968. Human Rights Year.

E1089	E **345** 5pf. mauve & purple	15	15
E1090	– 10pf. bistre & brown	15	15
E1091	– 25pf. blue & turq . .	90	55

DESIGNS: 10pf. Tree and Globe ("The right to live"); 25pf. Dove and Sun ("The right to peace").

E 346 Vietnamese Mother and Child

1968. Aid for Vietnam.

E1092	E **346** 10pf.+5pf. mult . . .	25	15

E 347 Angling (World Angling Championships, Gustrow)

1968. Sporting Events.

E1093	E **347** 20pf. blue, grn & red	50	45
E1094	– 20pf. blue, turq & grn	20	25
E1095	– 20pf. purple, red & bl	35	45

DESIGNS: No. E1094, Sculling (European Women's Rowing Championships, Berlin); No. E1095, High jumping (2nd European Youth Athletic Competitions).

E 348 Brandenburg Gate and Torch

E 349 Festival Emblem

1968. German Youth Sports Day. Mult.

E1096	10pf. Type E **348**	20	15
E1097	25pf. Stadium plan and torch	1·00	65

1968. Peace Festival, Sofia.

E1098	E **349** 20pf.+5pf. mult . . .	35	15
E1099	25pf. multicoloured	90	50

1968. Principal East German Buildings (2nd series). As Type E **312**. Multicoloured.

E1100	10pf. Town Hall, Wernigerode	15	15
E1101	20pf. Moritzburg Castle, Dresden	15	15
E1102	25pf. Town Hall, Greifswald	15	15
E1103	30pf. New Palace, Potsdam	95	1·00

DESIGN SIZES—VERT: 10pf., 25pf. (24 × 29 mm). HORIZ: 20pf., 30pf. (51½ × 29½ mm).

E 350 Walter Ulbricht

1968. 75th Birthday of Walter Ulbricht (Chairman of Council of State).

E1104	E **350** 20pf. black, red and orange	30	15

E 351 Ancient Rostock

1968. 750th Anniv of Rostock. Mult.

E1105	20pf. Type E **351**	20	15
E1106	25pf. Rostock, 1968 . . .	60	55

E 352 Dr K. Landsteiner (physician and pathologist, birth cent)

1968. Celebrities' Annivs. (1st series).

E1107	E **352** 10pf. grey	15	15
E1108	– 15pf. black	15	15
E1109	– 20pf. brown	20	15
E1110	– 25pf. blue	20	15
E1111	– 40pf. red	1·10	70

DESIGNS: 15pf. Dr. E. Lasker (chess master, birth cent); 20pf. Hans Eisler (composer, 70th birth anniv); 25pf. Ignaz Semmelweis (physician, 150th birth anniv); 40pf. Max von Pettenkofer (hygienist, 150th birth anniv).

See also Nos. E1161/4 and E1256/61.

E 353 Zlin Z-226 Trener 6 DM-WKM looping

E 354 "At the Seaside" (Womacka)

1968. Aerobatics World Championships, Magdeburg. Multicoloured.

E1112	10pf. Type E **353**	15	15
E1113	25pf. Stunt flying	70	50

1968. Dresden Gallery Paintings (2nd series). Multicoloured.

E1114	10pf. Type E **354**	20	15
E1115	15pf. "Peasants Mowing Mountain Meadow" (Egger-Lienz)	20	15
E1116	20pf. "Portrait of a Farmer's Wife" (Liebl) (vert)	20	15
E1117	40pf. "Portrait of my Daughter" (Venturelli) (vert)	25	15
E1118	50pf. "High-School Girl" (Michaelis) (vert) . . .	25	25
E1119	70pf. "Girl with Guitar" (Castelli) (vert)	2·20	1·40

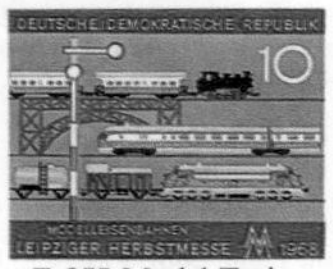

E 355 Model Trains

1968. Leipzig Autumn Fair.

E1120	E **355** 10pf. multicoloured	30	25

E 356 Spremberg Dam

1968. East German Post-War Dams. Multicoloured.

E1121	5pf. Type E **356**	15	15
E1122	10pf. Pohl Dam (vert) . .	15	15
E1123	15pf. Ohra Valley Dam (vert)	60	55
E1124	20pf. Rappbode Dam . .	25	15

E 357 Sprinting

1968. Olympic Games, Mexico. Multicoloured.

E1125	5pf. Type E **357**	15	15
E1126	10pf.+5pf. Pole-vaulting (vert)	15	15
E1127	20pf.+10pf. Football (vert)	20	15
E1128	25pf. Gymnastics (vert) . .	20	15
E1129	40pf. Water-polo (vert) . .	30	15
E1130	70pf. Sculling	1·80	1·40

E 358 Breendonk Memorial, Belgium

E 359 "Cicindela campestris"

1968. Breendonk War Victims Commem.

E1131	E **358** 25pf. multicoloured	35	15

1968. "Useful Beetles". Multicoloured.

E1132	10pf. Type E **359**	15	15
E1133	15pf. "Cychrus caraboides"	15	15
E1134	20pf. "Adalia bipunctata"	20	15
E1135	25pf. "Carabus arvensis" ("arcensis")	2·40	1·70
E1136	30pf. "Hister bipustulatus"	25	15
E1137	40pf. "Clerus mutillarius" ("Pseudoclerops mutillarius")	30	25

E 360 Lenin and Letter to Spartacus Group

1968. 50th Anniv of German November Revolution.

E1138	E **360** 10pf. black, red and yellow	15	15
E1139	– 20pf. black, red and yellow	15	15
E1140	– 25pf. black, red and yellow	55	40

DESIGNS: 20pf. Revolutionaries and title of Spartacus newspaper "Die Rote Fahne"; 25pf. Karl Liebknecht and Rose Luxemburg.

E 361 "Lailio-cattleya alba rubra" ("Maggie Raphaela")

1968. Orchids. Multicoloured.

E1141	5pf. Type E **361**	15	15
E1142	10pf. "Paphiopedilum albertianum"	15	15
E1143	15pf. "Cattleya fabia" . .	15	15
E1144	20pf. "Cattleya aclaniae"	20	15
E1145	40pf. "Sobralia macrantha"	30	25
E1146	50pf. "Dendrobium alpha"	2·50	1·70

E 362 Trying on the Boots

1968. Fairy Tales (3rd series). "Puss in Boots". As Type E **362**. Designs showing different scenes.

E1147	5pf. multicoloured	20	75
E1148	10pf. multicoloured . . .	20	75
E1149	15pf. multicoloured . . .	1·10	1·20
E1150	20pf. multicoloured . . .	1·10	1·20
E1151	25pf. multicoloured . . .	20	75
E1152	30pf. multicoloured . . .	20	75

E 363 Young Pioneers

1968. 20th Anniv of Ernst Thalmann's "Young Pioneers." Multicoloured.

E1153	10pf. Type E **363**	20	15
E1154	15pf. Young pioneers (diff)	75	30

1969. Principal East German Buildings (3rd series). As Type E **312**. Multicoloured.

E1155	5pf. Town Hall, Tangermunde (vert) . .	15	15
E1156	10pf. State Opera House, Berlin	15	15
E1157	20pf. Rampart Pavilion, Dresden Castle (vert) . .	15	15
E1158	25pf. Patrician's House, Luckau (vert)	1·30	75
E1159	30pf. Dornburg Castle . .	20	15
E1160	40pf. "Zum Stockfisch" Inn, Erfurt (vert) . . .	25	15

1969. Celebrities' Annivs. (2nd series). As Type E **352**.

E1161	10pf. olive	15	15
E1162	20pf. brown	15	15
E1163	25pf. blue	1·10	40
E1164	40pf. brown	20	15

DESIGNS: 10pf. M. A. Nexo (Danish poet—birth cent.); 20pf. O. Nagel (painter—75th birth anniv); 25pf. A. von Humboldt (naturalist—bicent. of birth); 40pf. T. Fontane (writer—150th birth anniv).

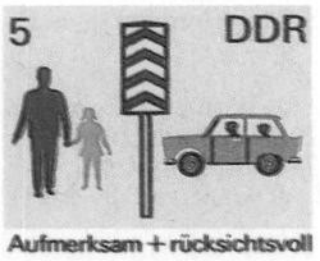

E 364 Pedestrian Crossing

1969. Road Safety. Multicoloured.

E1165	5pf. Type E **364**	15	15
E1166	10pf. Traffic lights	15	15
E1167	20pf. Class 103 electric locomotive and railway crossing sign	20	15
E1168	25pf. Motor-vehicle overtaking	65	40

E 365 "E-512" Combine- harvester

1969. Leipzig Spring Fair. Multicoloured.

E1169	10pf. Type E **365**	15	15
E1170	15pf. "Planeta-Varianii" lithograph printing-press	25	25

E 366 Jorinde and Joringel

E 367 Spring Snowflake

1969. Fairy Tales (4th series). "Jorinde and Joringel". As Type E **366**, showing different scenes.

E1171	5pf. multicoloured	20	35
E1172	10pf. multicoloured . . .	20	35
E1173	15pf. multicoloured . . .	60	55
E1174	20pf. multicoloured . . .	60	55
E1175	25pf. multicoloured . . .	20	35
E1176	30pf. multicoloured . . .	20	35

1969. Protected Plants (2nd series). Mult.

E1177	5pf. Type E **367**	15	15
E1178	10pf. Yellow pheasant's-eye ("Adonis vernalis")	15	15
E1179	15pf. Globe flower ("Trollius europaeus")	15	15
E1180	20pf. Martagon lily ("Lilium martagon") . .	20	15
E1181	25pf. Sea holly ("Eryngium maritmum")	3·50	1·90
E1182	30pf. "Dactylorchis latifolia"	35	15

See also Nos. E1284/9.

E 368 Plantation of Young Conifers

E 369 Symbols of the Societies

1969. Forest Fires Prevention. Mult.

E1183	5pf. Type E **368**	15	15
E1184	10pf. Lumber, and resin extraction	20	15

E1185 20pf. Forest stream . . . 20 15
E1186 25pf. Woodland camp . . 1·90 65

1969. 50th Anniv of League of Red Cross Societies. Multicoloured.
E1187 10pf. Type E **369** 20 15
E1188 15pf. Similar design with symbols in oblong . . . 1·40 40

E **370** Erythrite (Schneeberg)

E **371** Women and Symbols

1969. East German Minerals. Multicoloured.
E1189 5pf. Type E **370** 15 15
E1190 10pf. Fluorite (Halsbrucke) 15 15
E1191 15pf. Galena (Neudorf) . . 15 15
E1192 20pf. Smoky Quartz (Lichtenberg) 20 15
E1193 25pf. Calcite (Niederrabenstein) . . . 1·10 95
E1194 50pf. Silver (Freiberg) . . 30 25

1969. 2nd D.D.R. Women's Congress.
E1195 E **371** 20pf. red and blue 20 15
E1196 – 25pf. blue and red 1·00 40
DESIGN: 25pf. Woman and Symbols (different).

1969. As Nos. E586/7 (Ulbricht), but with face values expressed in "M" (Mark).
E1197 1M. green 35 30
E1198 2M. brown 60 50

E **372** Badge of D.D.R. Philatelists' Association

E **373** Armed Volunteers

1969. 20th Anniv of D.D.R. Stamp Exhibition, Magdeburg (1st issue).
E1199 E **372** 10pf. gold, blue and red 25 15
See also Nos. E1233/4.

1969. Aid for Vietnam.
E1200 E **373** 10pf.+5pf. mult . . . 25 15

E **374** "Development of Youth"

E **375** Inaugural Ceremony

1969. Int Peace Meeting, East Berlin. Mult.
E1201 10pf. Type E **374** 80 95
E1202 20pf.+5pf. Berlin landmarks (50 × 28 mm) 80 95
E1203 25pf. "Workers of the World" 80 95

1969. 5th Gymnastics and Athletic Meeting, Leipzig. Multicoloured.
E1204 5pf. Type E **375** 15 15
E1205 10pf.+5pf. Gymnastics . . 15 15
E1206 15pf. Athletes' parade . . 20 15
E1207 20pf.+5pf. "Sport" Art Exhibition 20 15
E1208 25pf. Athletic events . . . 1·90 50
E1209 30pf. Presentation of colours 20 15

E **376** Pierre de Coubertin (from bust by W. Forster)

E **377** Knight

1969. 75th Anniv of Pierre de Coubertin's Revival of Olympic Games' Movement.
E1210 E **376** 10pf. sepia, black & bl 15 15
E1211 – 25pf. sepia, blk & red 95 50
DESIGN: 25pf. Coubertin monument, Olympia.

1969. World Sports Championships. Mult.
E1212 E **377** 20pf. gold, red & pur 20 15
E1213 – 20pf. multicoloured 20 15
E1214 – 20pf. multicoloured 20 15
DESIGNS AND EVENTS: No. E1212, 16th World Students' Team Chess Championship, Dresden; No. E1213, Cycle Wheel (World Covered Court Cycling Championships, Erfurt); No. E1214, Ball and net (2nd World Volleyball Cup).

E **378** Fair Display Samples

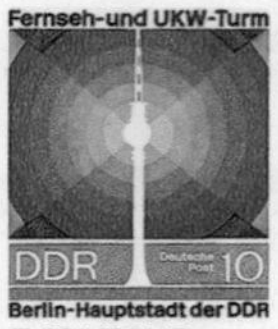

E **381** T.V. Tower, East Berlin

E **379** Rostock

1969. Leipzig Autumn Fair.
E1215 E **378** 10pf. multicoloured 20 20

1969. 20th Anniv of German Democratic Republic. (1st issue). Multicoloured.
E1216 10pf. Type E **379** 20 15
E1217 10pf. Neubrandenburg . . 20 15
E1218 10pf. Potsdam 20 15
E1219 10pf. Eisenhuttenstadt . . 20 15
E1220 10pf. Hoyerswerda 20 15
E1221 10pf. Magdeburg 20 15
E1222 10pf. Halle-Neustadt . . . 20 15
E1223 10pf. Suhl 20 15
E1224 10pf. Dresden 20 15
E1225 10pf. Leipzig 20 15
E1226 10pf. Karl-Marx Stadt . . 20 15
E1227 10pf. East Berlin 20 15
MSE1228 88 × 110 mm. 1m. East Berlin and D.D.R. emblem (30 × 52 mm) . . . . 2·10 3·25

E **380** Flags and Rejoicing Crowd (½-size illustration)

1969. 20th Anniv of German Democratic Republic (2nd issue). Sheet 110 × 154 mm.
MSE1229 E **380** 1m. multicoloured 1·70 2·20

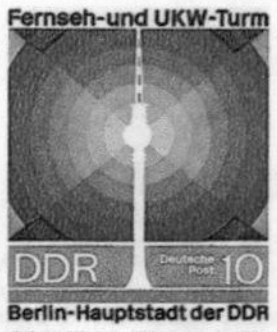

E **381** T.V. Tower, East Berlin

1969. 20th Anniv of German Democratic Republic (3rd issue). Completion of East Berlin T.V. Tower. Type E **381** and similar vert designs. Multicoloured.
E1230 10pf. Type E **381** . . . .
E1231 20pf. "Globe" of Tower on T.V. screen . . . . .
MSE1232 96 × 115 mm. 1m. T.V. Tower and receiver . . . . . 70 1·30
The design of No. **MS**E1232 is larger, 21½ × 60½ mm.

E **382** O. von Guericke Memorial, Cathedral and Hotel International, Magdeburg

1969. 20th Anniv of D.D.R. Stamp Exhibition, Magdeburg (2nd issue). Multicoloured.
E1233 20pf. Type E **382** 20 15
E1234 40pf.+10pf. Von Guericke's vacuum experiment . . . . . . 1·20 50

E **383** Ryvangen Memorial

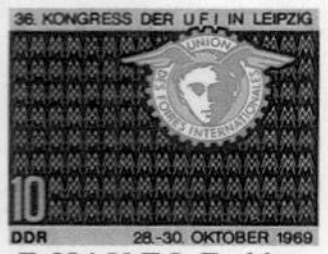

E **384** U.F.I. Emblem

1969. War Victims' Memorial, Ryvangen (Copenhagen).
E1235 E **383** 25pf. multicoloured 65 15

1969. 36th Int Fairs Union (U.F.I.) Congress, Leipzig.
E1236 E **384** 10pf. multicoloured 20 15
E1237 15pf. multicoloured 1·50 40

E **385** I.L.O. Emblem

E **386** University Seal and Building

1969. 50th Anniv of I.L.O.
E1238 E **385** 20pf. silver and green 20 15
E1239 25pf. silver & mauve 1·40 40

1969. 550th Anniv of Rostock University. Multicoloured.
E1240 10pf. Type E **386** 20 15
E1241 15pf. Steam-turbine rotor and curve (University emblem) 95 30

E **387** "Horseman" Pastry-mould

E **388** Antonov An-24B

1969. Lausitz Folk Art.
E1242 E **387** 10pf. brn, blk & flesh 1·30 1·10
E1243 – 20pf.+5pf. mult . . . 45 35
E1244 – 50pf. multicoloured 1·90 1·90
DESIGNS: 20pf. Plate; 50pf. Pastry in form of Negro couple.

1969. Interflug Aircraft. Multicoloured.
E1245 20pf. Type E **388** 15 15
E1246 25pf. Ilyushin Il-18 . . . . 1·30 1·10
E1247 30pf. Tupolev Tu-134 . . 20 15
E1248 50pf. Mil Mi-8 helicopter DM-SPA 25 15

E **389** "Siberian Teacher" (Svechnikov)

1969. Dresden Gallery Paintings (3rd series). Multicoloured.
E1249 5pf. Type E **389** 15 15
E1250 10pf. "Steel-worker" (Serov) 15 15
E1251 20pf. "Still Life" (Aslamasjan) 15 15
E1252 25pf. "A Warm Day" (Romas) . . . . 1·20 1·10
E1253 40pf. "Springtime Again" (Kabatchek) 20 15
E1254 50pf. "Man by the River" (Makovsky) 25 25

1970. Coil Stamp. As Nos. E577 etc, but value expressed in "M".
E1255 E **196** 1m. olive . . . . . 65 2·50

1970. Celebrities Annivs. (3rd series). As Type E **352**.
E1256 5pf. blue 20 15
E1257 10pf. brown 20 15
E1258 15pf. blue 20 15
E1259 20pf. purple 35 15
E1260 25pf. blue . . . . 2·10 65
E1261 40pf. red 45 15
DESIGNS: 5pf. E. Barlach (sculptor and playwright; birth cent); 10pf. J. Gutenberg (printer; 500th death anniv) (1968); 15pf. K. Tucholsky (author; 80th birth anniv); 20pf. Beethoven (birth bicent); 25pf. F. Holderlin (poet; birth bicent); 40 pf G. W. F. Hegel (philosopher; birth bicent).

E **390** Red fox

1970. Int Fur Auction, Leipzig. Mult.
E1262 10pf. Rabbit 15 15
E1263 20pf. Type E **390** 20 15
E1264 25pf. European mink . . . 2·10 15
E1265 40pf. Common hamster . . 45 25

E **391** "Little Brother and Little Sister"

1970. Fairy Tales (5th series). "Little Brother and Little Sister".
E1266 E **391** 5pf. multicoloured 45 45
E1267 – 10pf. multicoloured 45 45
E1268 – 15pf. multicoloured 65 65
E1269 – 20pf. multicoloured 65 65
E1270 – 25pf. multicoloured 20 45
E1271 – 30pf. multicoloured 20 45
DESIGNS: 10pf. to 30pf. showing different scenes.

E **392** Telephone and Electrical Switchgear

1970. Leipzig Spring Fair. Multicoloured.
E1272 10pf. Type E **392** 15 15
E1273 15pf. High-voltage transformer (vert) . . . 65 15

E **393** Horseman's Gravestone (A.D. 700)

1970. Archaeological Discoveries.
E1274 E **393** 10pf. olive, blk & grn 15 15
E1275 – 20pf. black, yell & red 15 15
E1276 – 25pf. grn, blk & yell 75 1·20
E1277 – 40pf. chestnut, black and brown 20 15
DESIGNS: 20pf. Helmet (A.D. 500); 25pf. Bronze basin (1000 B.C.); 40pf. Clay drum (2500 B.C.).

E **394** Lenin and "Iskra" (= the Spark) press

1970. Birth Centenary of Lenin. Multicoloured.
E1278 10pf. Type E **394** 15 15
E1279 20pf. Lenin and Clara Zetkin 15 15
E1280 25pf. Lenin and "State and Revolution" (book) . . 1·80 1·10

E1281 40pf. Lenin Monument, Eisleben 20 15
E1282 70pf. Lenin Square, East Berlin 30 25
MSE1283 118 × 84 mm. 1m. Lenin (vert) . . . . 2·00 3·50

1970. Protected Plants (3rd series). Vert designs as Type E **367**. Multicoloured.
E1284 10pf. Sea kale ("Crambe maritima") 15 25
E1285 20pf. Pasque flower ("Pulsatilla vulgaris") . . 15 15
E1286 25pf. Fringed gentian ("Gentiana ciliata") . . 1·80 2·00
E1287 30pf. Military orchid ("Orchis militaris") . . . 20 15
E1288 40pf. Labrador tea ("Ledum palustre") . . 25 20
E1289 70pf. Round-leaved wintergreen ("Pyrola rotundifolia") 45 30

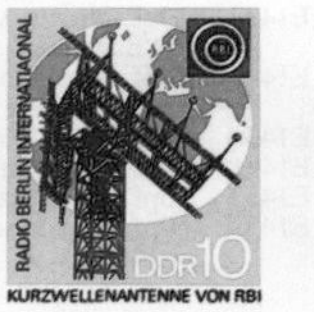

E **395** Capture of the Reichstag, 1945 E **396** Shortwave Aerial

1970. 25th Anniv of "Liberation from Fascism". Multicoloured.
E1290 10pf. Type E **395** 15 15
E1291 20pf. Newspaper headline, Kremlin and State Building, East Berlin . . 15 15
E1292 25pf. C.M.E.A. Building, Moscow and flags . . . 1·40 55
MSE1293 135 × 105 mm. 70pf. Buchenwald Monument (horiz) 2·00 1·10

1970. 25th Anniv of D.D.R. Broadcasting Service. Multicoloured.
E1294 10pf. Type E **396** 65 75
E1295 15pf. Radio Station, East Berlin (horiz) (50 × 28 mm) . . . . . 90 1·10

E **397** Globe and Ear of Corn E **398** Fritz Heckert Medal

1970. 5th World Corn and Bread Congress, Dresden. Multicoloured.
E1296 20pf. Type E **397** . . . . 1·10 95
E1297 25pf. Palace of Culture and ear of corn . . . . 1·10 95

1970. 25th Annivs of German Confederation of Trade Unions and World Trade Union Federation ("Federation Syndicale Mondiale"). Mult.
E1298 20pf. Type E **398** 15 15
E1299 25pf. F.S.M. Emblem . . 70 45

E **399** Gods Amon, Shu and Tefnut

1970. Sudanese Archaeological Excavations by Humboldt University Expedition. Multicoloured.
E1300 10pf. Type E **399** . . . 15 15
E1301 15pf. King Arnekhamani 15 15
E1302 20pf. Cattle frieze 15 15
E1303 25pf. Prince Arka . . . . 90 1·10
E1304 30pf. God Arensnuphis (vert) 15 15
E1305 40pf. War elephants and prisoners 20 15
E1306 50pf. God Apedemak . . 20 15
The above designs reproduce carvings unearthed at the Lions' Temple, Musawwarat, Sudan.

E **400** Road Patrol E **401** D.K.B. Emblem

1970. 25th Anniv of "Deutsche Volkspolizei" (police force). Multicoloured.
E1307 5pf. Type E **400** 20 15
E1308 10pf. Policewoman with children 20 15
E1309 15pf. Radio patrol car . . 20 15
E1310 20pf. Railway policeman and Class SVT18.16 diesel-hydraulic locomotive 20 15
E1311 25pf. River police in patrol boat . . . . 1·50 15

1970. 25th Anniv of "Deutscher Kulturbund" (cultural assn).
E1312 E **401** 10pf. brown, silver and blue . . . . . 2·75 2·75
E1313 – 25pf. brown, gold and blue . . . . . 2·75 2·75
DESIGN: 25pf. Johannes Becher medal.

E **402** Arms of D.D.R. and Poland

1970. 20th Anniv of Gorlitz Agreement on Oder–Neisse Border.
E1314 E **402** 20pf. multicoloured 30 15

E **403** Vaulting E **405** Cecilienhof Castle

E **404** Boy Pioneer with Neckerchief

1970. 3rd Children and Young People's Sports Days. Multicoloured.
E1315 10pf. Type E **403** 15 15
E1316 20pf.+5pf. Hurdling . . . 45 15

1970. 6th Young Pioneers Meeting. Cottbus. Multicoloured.
E1317 10pf.+5pf. Type E **404** . . 30 35
E1318 25pf.+5pf. Girl pioneer with neckerchief 30 35
Nos. E1317/18 were issued together, se-tenant, forming a composite design.

1970. 25th Anniv of Potsdam Agreement.
E1319 E **405** 10pf. yellow, red and black 20 60
E1320 – 20pf. black, red and yellow 20 60
E1321 – 25pf. black and red 20 60
DESIGNS—VERT: 20pf. "Potsdam Agreement" in four languages. HORIZ (77 × 28 mm): 25pf. Conference delegates around the table.

E **406** Pocket-watch and Wristwatch

1970. Leipzig Autumn Fair.
E1322 E **406** 10pf. multicoloured 30 15

E **407** T. Neubauer and M. Poser

1970. "Anti-Fascist Resistance".
E1323 E **407** 20pf. purple, red & bl 20 20
E1324 – 25pf. olive and red 30 30
DESIGN—VERT: 25pf. "Motherland"—detail from Soviet War Memorial, Treptow, Berlin.

E **408** Pres. Ho-Chi-Minh

1970. Aid for Vietnam and Ho-Chi-Minh. Commemoration.
E1325 E **408** 20pf.+5pf. black, red and pink 35 15

E **409** Compass and Map

1970. World "Orienteering" Championships. East Germany. Multicoloured.
E1326 10pf. Type E **409** 20 15
E1327 25pf. Runner and three map sections . . . . . 1·10 40

E **410** "Forester Scharf's Birthday" (Nagel)

1970. "The Art of Otto Nagel, Kathe Kollwitz and Ernst Barlach".
E1328 E **410** 10pf. multicoloured 15 15
E1329 – 20pf. multicoloured 15 15
E1330 – 25pf. brown & mauve . . . . . . 1·00 1·30
E1331 – 30pf. black and pink 15 15
E1332 – 40pf. black and yellow 20 15
E1333 – 50pf. black and yellow 20 15
DESIGNS: 20pf. "Portrait of a Young Girl" (Nagel); 25pf. "No More War" (Kollwitz); 30pf. "Mother and Child" (Kollwitz); 40pf. Sculptured head from Gustrow Cenotaph (Barlach); 50pf. "The Flute-player" (Barlach).

E **411** "The Little Trumpeter" (Weineck Memorial, Halle) E **413** Musk Ox

E **412** Flags Emblem

1970. 2nd National Youth Stamp Exhibition, Karl-Marx-Stadt. Multicoloured.
E1334 10pf. Type E **411** 20 30
E1335 15pf.+5pf. East German 25pf. stamp of 1959 . . 20 30

1970. "Comrades-in-Arms". Warsaw Pact Military Manoeuvres.
E1336 E **412** 10pf. multicoloured 15 15
E1337 20pf. multicoloured 25 25

1970. Animals in East Berlin "Tierpark" (Zoo). Multicoloured.
E1338 10pf. Type E **413** 35 15
E1339 15pf. Whale-headed Stork 35 15
E1340 20pf. Addax 55 30
E1341 25pf. Sun bear . . . . . 3·75 5·00

E **414** U.N. Emblem and Headquarters, New York E **415** Engels

1970. 25th Anniv of United Nations.
E1342 E **414** 20pf. multicoloured 60 20

1970. 150th Birth Anniv of Friedrich Engels.
E1343 E **415** 10pf. black, grey and orange 20 15
E1344 – 20pf. blk, grn & orge 20 15
E1345 – 25pf. blk, red & orge 1·20 80
DESIGNS: 20pf. Engels, Marx and "Communist Manifesto"; 25pf. Engels and "Anti-Duhring".

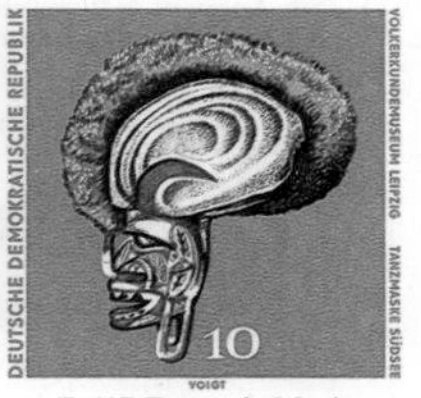

E **416** "Epiphyllum hybr" E **417** Dancer's Mask, Bismarck Archipelago

1970. Cacti Cultivation in D.D.R. Mult.
E1346 5pf. Type E **416** 15 15
E1347 10pf. "Astrophytum myriostigma" 15 15
E1348 15pf. "Echinocereus salm-dyckianus" 15 15
E1349 20pf. "Selenicereus grandiflorus" 20 15
E1350 25pf. "Hamatoc setispinus" . . . . . . 1·50 2·00
E1351 30pf. "Mamillaria boolii" 30 15

1970. Birth Bicentenary of Beethoven. As No. E1259, but colour and face value changed, in sheet 81 × 55 mm.
MSE1352 1m. green . . . . . . 1·80 2·10

1971. Exhibits from the Ethnological Museum, Leipzig.
E1353 E **417** 10pf. multicoloured 15 15
E1354 – 20pf. brown & orange 15 15
E1355 – 25pf. multicoloured 90 70
E1356 – 40pf. brown and red 30 15
DESIGNS: 20pf. Bronze head, Benin; 25pf. Tea-pot, Thailand; 40pf. Zapotec earthenware Jaguar-god, Mexico.

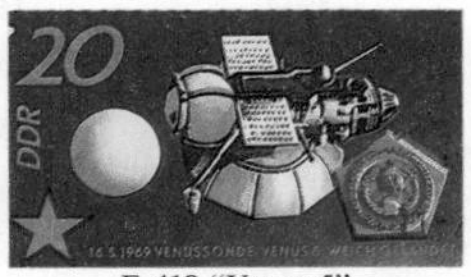

E **418** "Venus 5"

1971. Soviet Space Research. Multicoloured.
E1357 20pf. Type E **418** 20 25
E1358 20pf. Orbital space station 20 25
E1359 20pf. "Luna 10" and "Luna 16" 45 50
E1360 20pf. Various "Soyuz" spacecraft 45 50
E1361 20pf. "Proton 1" satellite and "Vostok" rocket . . 45 50
E1362 20pf. "Molniya 1" communications satellite 45 50
E1363 20pf. Gagarin and "Vostok 1" 30 30
E1364 20pf. Leonov in space . . 30 30

E **419** K. Liebknecht

E **420** J. R. Becher (poet)

1971. Birth Centenaries of Karl Liebknecht and Rosa Luxemburg (revolutionaries).
E1365 E **419** 20pf. mauve, gold and black 40 55
E1366 – 25pf. mauve, gold and black 40 55
DESIGN: 25pf. Rosa Luxemburg.

1971. Celebrities' Birth Anniversaries.
E1367 E **420** 5pf. brown 15 15
E1368 – 10pf. blue 15 15
E1369 – 15pf. black 15 15
E1370 – 20pf. purple 20 15
E1371 – 25pf. green 80 70
E1372 – 50pf. blue 30 15
DESIGNS: 5pf. (80th birth anniv); 10pf. H. Mann (writer—birth cent); 15pf. J. Heartfield (artist—80th birth anniv); 20pf. W. Bredel (70th birth anniv); 25pf. F. Mehring (politician—125th birth anniv); 50pf. J. Kepler (astronomer—400th birth anniv).
See also Nos. E1427 and E1451/5.

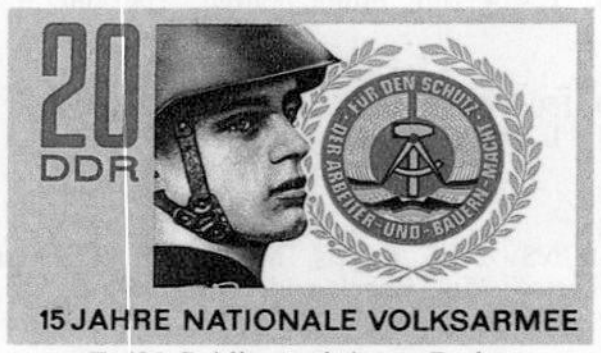

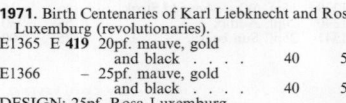

E **421** Soldier and Army Badge

1971. 15th Anniv of National People's Army.
E1373 E **421** 20pf. multicoloured 30 15

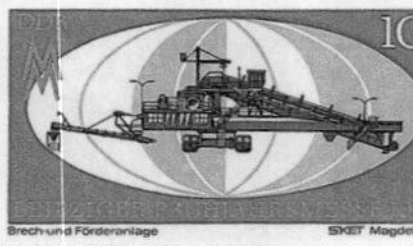
E **422** "Sket" Mobile Ore-crusher

1971. Leipzig Spring Fair. Multicoloured.
E1374 10pf. Type E **422** 15 15
E1375 15pf. Dredger "Takraf" . . 20 15

E **423** Proclamation of the Commune

E **425** St. Mary's Church

E **424** "Lunokhod 1" on Moon's Surface

1971. Centenary of Paris Commune.
E1376 E **423** 10pf. black, brown and red 15 15
E1377 – 20pf. black, brown and red 15 15
E1378 – 25pf. black, brown and red 60 65
E1379 – 30pf. black, grey and red 15 15
DESIGNS: 20pf. Women at the Place Blanche barricade; 25pf. Cover of "L'Internationale"; 30pf. Title page of Karl Marx's "The Civil War in France".

1971. Moon Mission of "Lunokhod 1".
E1380 E **424** 20pf. turquoise, blue and red 60 30

1971. Berlin Buildings. Multicoloured.
E1381 10pf. Type E **425** 15 15
E1382 15pf. Kopenick Castle (horiz) 15 15
E1383 20pf. Old Library (horiz) 20 15
E1384 25pf. Ermeler House . . . 2·40 2·30
E1385 50pf. New Guardhouse (horiz) 30 15
E1386 70pf. National Gallery (horiz) 35 25

E **426** "The Discus-thrower"

1971. 20th Anniv of D.D.R. National Olympics Committee.
E1387 E **426** 20pf. multicoloured 75 20

E **427** Handclasp and XXV Emblem

E **428** Schleife Costume

1971. 25th Anniv of Socialist Unity Party.
E1388 E **427** 20pf. black, red and gold 30 20

1971. Sorbian Dance Costumes. Mult.
E1389 10pf. Type E **428** 15 15
E1390 20pf. Hoyerswerda 15 15
E1391 25pf. Cottbus 90 85
E1392 40pf. Kamenz 20 15
For 10pf. and 20pf. in smaller size, see Nos. E1443/4.

E **429** Self-portrait, c. 1500

E **432** "Internees"

E **430** Construction Worker

E **433** Cherry stone with 180 Carved Heads

1971. 500th Birth Anniv of Albrecht Durer. Paintings. Multicoloured.
E1393 10pf. Type E **429** . . . 20 15
E1394 40pf. "The Three Peasants" 35 15
E1395 70pf. "Philipp Melanchthon" . . . . . 1·60 1·00

1971. 8th S.E.D. Party Conference.
E1396 E **430** 5pf. multicoloured 15 15
E1397 – 10pf. multicoloured 15 15
E1398 – 20pf. multicoloured 15 15
E1400 – 20pf. gold, red and mauve 30 15
E1399 – 25pf. multicoloured 55 45
DESIGNS: 10pf. Technician; 20pf. (No. E1398) Farm girl; 20pf. (No. E1400) Conference emblem (smaller, 23 × 29 mm); 25pf. Soldier.

1971. 20th Anniv of International Resistance Federation (F.I.R.). Lithographs from Fritz Cremer's "Buchenwaldzyklus".
E1401 E **432** 20pf. black & yellow 65 75
E1402 – 25pf. black and blue 65 75
DESIGN: 25pf. "Attack on Guard".

1971. Art Treasures of Dresden's Green Vaults. Multicoloured.
E1403 5pf. Type E **433** 15 15
E1404 10pf. Insignia of the Golden Fleece, c. 1730 15 15
E1405 15pf. Nuremberg jug, c. 1530 . . . . . 15 15
E1406 20pf. Mounted Moorish drummer figurine, c. 1720 . . . . 20 15
E1407 25pf. Writing-case, 1562 90 1·00
E1408 30pf. St. George medallion, c. 1570 . . . 20 15

E **434** Mongolian Arms

E **435** Child's Face

1971. 50th Anniv of Mongolian People's Republic.
E1409 E **434** 20pf. multicoloured 30 25

1971. 25th Anniv of U.N.I.C.E.F.
E1410 E **435** 20pf. multicoloured 30 15

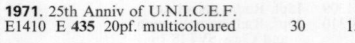

E **436** Servicemen

E **438** Vietnamese Woman and Child

E **437** "Ivan Franko" (liner)

1971. 10th Anniv of Berlin Wall. Mult.
E1411 20pf. Type E **436** 80 60
E1412 35pf. Brandenburg Gate 1·20 1·00

1971. East German Shipbuilding Industry.
E1413 E **437** 10pf. brown 15 15
E1414 – 15pf. blue and brown 15 15
E1415 – 20pf. green 15 15
E1416 – 25pf. blue . . . . . 1·20 1·30
E1417 – 40pf. brown 20 15
E1418 – 50pf. blue 25 15
DESIGNS: 15pf. "Irkutsk" (freighter); 20pf. "Rostock" freighter, 1966; 25pf. "Junge Welt" (fish-factory ship); 40pf. "Hansel" (container ship); 50pf. "Akademik Kurchatov" (research ship).

1971. Aid for Vietnam.
E1419 E **438** 10pf.+5pf. mult . . . 30 15

E **439** MAG-Butadien Plant

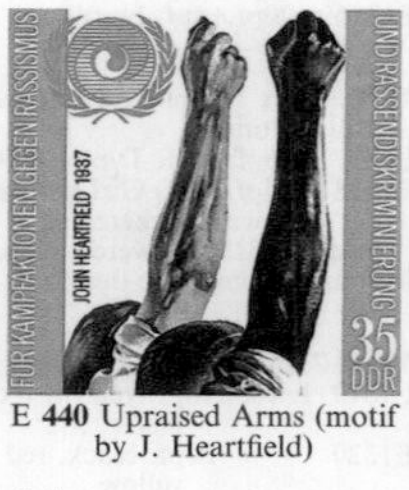

E **440** Upraised Arms (motif by J. Heartfield)

1971. Leipzig Autumn Fair.
E1420 E **439** 10pf. vio, mve & grn 15 15
E1421 – 25pf. violet, grn & bl 30 25
DESIGN: 25pf. SKL reactor plant.

1971. Racial Equality Year.
E1422 E **440** 35pf. black, sil & bl 30 15

E **441** Tupolev Tu-134 Mail Plane at Airport

1971. Philatelists' Day.
E1423 E **441** 10pf.+5pf. blue, red and green 15 15
E1424 – 25pf. red, green & bl 35 45
DESIGN: 25pf. Milestone and Zurner's measuring cart.

E **442** Wiltz Memorial, Luxembourg

E **443** German Violin

1971. Monuments. Multicoloured.
E1425 25pf. Type E **442** 25 15
E1426 35pf. Karl Marx monument, Karl-Marx-Stadt 35 15

1971. 150th Birth Anniv of R. Virchow (physician). As Type E **420**.
E1427 40pf. plum 40 20

1971. Musical Instruments in Markneukirchen Museum. Multicoloured.
E1428 10pf. North African "darbuka" 15 15
E1429 15pf. Mongolian "morin chuur" 15 15
E1430 20pf. Type E **443** 15 15
E1431 25pf. Italian mandolin . . 15 15
E1432 40pf. Bohemian bagpipes . . 20 15
E1433 50pf. Sudanese "kasso" . . 1·10 1·00

E **444** "Dahlta O 10 A" Theodolite

E **445** Donkey and Windmill

1971. 125th Anniv of Carl Zeiss Optical Works, Jena.
E1434 E **444** 10pf. black, red & bl 65 60
E1435 – 20pf. black, red & bl 65 60
E1436 – 25pf. blue, yellow and ultramarine 65 60
DESIGNS—VERT: 20pf. "Ergaval" microscope. HORIZ (52 × 29 mm) 25pf. Planetarium.

1971. Fairy Tales (6th series). As Type E **445**. "The Town Musicians of Bremen".
E1437 5pf. multicoloured . . . 35 75
E1438 10pf. multicoloured . . . 35 75
E1439 15pf. multicoloured . . . 65 95
E1440 20pf. multicoloured . . . 65 95
E1441 25pf. multicoloured . . . 35 55
E1442 30pf. multicoloured . . . 35 55

1971. Sorbian Dance Costumes. As Nos. E1389/90 but smaller, size 23 × 28 mm.
E1443 E **428** 10pf. multicoloured 20 15
E1444 – 20pf. multicoloured 60 35

E **446** Tobogganing

1971. Winter Olympic Games, Sapporo, Japan (1972).
E1445 E **446** 5pf. black, green and mauve 15 15
E1446 – 10pf.+5pf. blk, bl & mve 15 15
E1447 – 15pf.+5pf. black, grn & bl 20 15
E1448 – 20pf. black, mauve & violet 20 15
E1449 – 25pf. black, violet & mauve . . . . . . 1·70 1·40
E1450 – 70pf. black, blue and violet 30 25
DESIGNS: 10pf. Figure skating; 15pf. Speed skating; 20pf. Cross-country skiing; 25pf. Biathlon; 70pf. Ski jumping.

1972. German Celebrities. As Type E **420**.
E1451 10pf. green 15 15
E1452 20pf. mauve 15 15
E1453 25pf. blue 15 15
E1454 35pf. brown 15 15
E1455 50pf. lilac . . . . 1·40 1·30
CELEBRITIES: 10pf. J. Tralow (writer); 20pf. L. Frank (writer); 25pf. K. A. Kocor (composer); 35pf. H. Schliemann (archaeologist); 50pf. Caroline Neuber (actress).

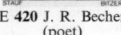

E **447** Gypsum from Eisleben

1972. Minerals. Multicoloured.

E1456	5pf. Type E **447**	15	15
E1457	10pf. Zinnwaldite, Zinnwald	15	15
E1458	20pf. Malachite, Ullersreuth	15	15
E1459	25pf. Amethyst, Wiesenbad	20	15
E1460	35pf. Halite, Merkers	20	15
E1461	50pf. Proustite, Schneeberg	1·40	1·25

E **448** Vietnamese Woman

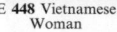

E **451** W.H.O. Emblem

E **449** Soviet Exhibition Hall

1972. Aid for Vietnam.

E1462	E **448** 10pf.+5pf. mult	30	15

1972. Leipzig Spring Fair. Multicoloured.

E1463	10pf. Type E **449**	15	15
E1464	25pf. East German and Soviet flags	25	25

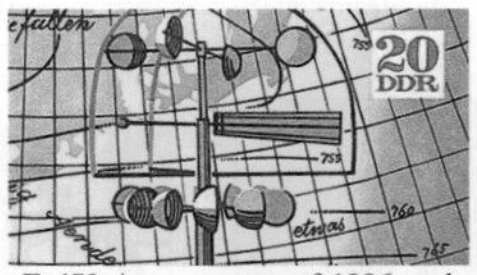

E **450** Anemometer of 1896 and Koppen's Chart of 1876

1972. International Meteorologists Meeting, Leipzig. Three sheets, each 85 × 57 mm. Multicoloured.

MSE1465	20pf. Type E **450**; 35pf. Weather station and clouds; 70pf. Satellite and weather map	2·75	2·75

1972. World Health Day.

E1466	E **451** 35pf. ultramarine, silver and blue	30	25

E **452** Kamov Ka-26 Helicopter

1972. East German Aircraft. Multicoloured.

E1467	5pf. Type E **452**	15	15
E1468	10pf. Letov Z-37 Cmelak crop-sprayer DM-SMC	15	15
E1469	35pf. Ilyushin Il-62M	25	15
E1470	1m. Ilyushin Il-62M	1·50	1·20

E **453** Wrestling

1972. Olympic Games, Munich. Mult.

E1471	5pf. Type E **453**	15	15
E1472	10pf.+5pf. High-diving	20	15
E1473	20pf. Pole-vaulting	20	15
E1474	25pf.+10pf. Rowing	20	15
E1475	35pf. Handball	35	25
E1476	70pf. Gymnastics	2·20	1·80

E **454** Soviet and East German Flags

1972. 25th Anniv of German–Soviet Friendship Society. Multicoloured.

E1477	10pf. Type E **454**	35	25
E1478	20pf. Brezhnev (U.S.S.R.) and Honecker (D.D.R.)	60	80

E **455** Steel Workers

E **456** "Karneol" Rose

1972. Trade Unions Federation Congress.

E1479	E **455** 10pf. pur, orge & brn	20	35
E1480	– 35pf. blue and brown	20	35

DESIGN: 35pf. Students.

1972. International Rose Exhibition. German Species. Multicoloured.

E1481	5pf. Type E **456**	15	15
E1482	10pf. "Berger's Rose"	15	15
E1497	10pf. "Berger's Rose"	1·20	15
E1483	15pf. "Charme"	1·40	1·90
E1484	20pf. "Izetka Spreeathen"	15	15
E1485	25pf. "Kopernicker Sommer"	20	15
E1498	25pf. "Kopernicker Sommer"	1·10	45
E1486	35pf. "Professor Knoll"	25	15
E1499	35pf. "Professor Knoll"	1·10	45

Nos. E1497/9 are smaller, size 24 × 28 mm.

E **457** "Portrait of Young Man"

1972. 500th Birth Anniv of Lucas Cranach the Elder. Multicoloured.

E1487	5pf. Type E **457**	15	15
E1488	20pf. "Mother and Child"	20	15
E1489	25pf. "Margarete Luther"	30	35
E1490	70pf. "Nymph" (horiz)	35	2·75

E **458** Compass and Motor Cyclist

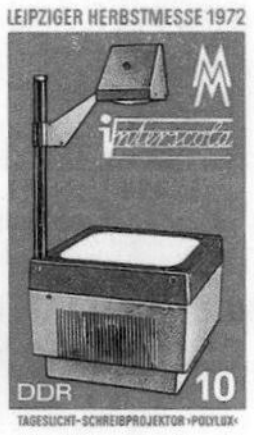

E **460** Overhead Projector

E **459** "Young Worker Reading" (J. Damme)

1972. Sports and Technical Sciences Association. Multicoloured.

E1491	5pf. Type E **458**	15	15
E1492	10pf. Light airplane and parachute	15	15
E1493	20pf. Target and obstacle race	15	15
E1494	25pf. Radio set and Morse key	70	85
E1495	35pf. "Wilhelm Pieck" (brigantine) and propeller	20	15

1972. Int Book Year.

E1496	E **459** 50pf. multicoloured	70	30

1972. Leipzig Autumn Fair.

E1500	E **460** 10pf. black and red	15	15
E1501	– 25pf. black and green	25	25

DESIGN—HORIZ: 25pf. Slide projector.

E **461** G. Dimitrov

E **462** "Catching Birds" (Egyptian relief painting, c. 2400 B.C.)

1972. 90th Birth Anniv of Georgi Dimitrov (Bulgarian statesman).

E1502	E **461** 20pf. black and red	35	15

1972. "Interartes" Stamp Exhibition, East Berlin. Multicoloured.

E1503	10pf. Type E **462**	15	15
E1504	15pf.+5pf. "Persian Spearman" (glazed tile, c. 500 B.C.)	85	90
E1505	20pf. Anatolian tapestry c. 1400 B.C	15	15
E1506	35pf.+5pf. "The Grapesellers" (Max Lingner, 1949) (horiz)	20	15

E **463** Red Cross Team and Patient

E **464** Terrestrial Globe (J. Praetorius, 1568)

1972. East German Red Cross.

E1507	E **463** 10pf. ultramarine, blue and red	25	35
E1508	– 15pf. ultramarine, blue and red	25	35
E1509	– 35pf. red, blue and ultramarine	30	35

DESIGNS—VERT: 15pf. Sea-rescue launch. HORIZ ($50\frac{1}{2}$ × 28 mm): 35pf. World map on cross, and transport.

1972. Terrestrial and Celestial Globes. Mult.

E1510	5pf. Arab celestial globe, 1279	15	15
E1511	10pf. Type E **464**	15	15
E1512	15pf. Globe clock (J. Reinhold and G. Roll, 1586)	1·60	2·40
E1513	20pf. Globe clock (J. Burgi, 1590)	20	15
E1514	25pf. Armillary sphere (J. Moeller, 1687)	20	15
E1515	35pf. Heraldic celestial globe, 1690	30	20

E **465** Monument

E **467** "Mauz and Hoppel" (Cat and Hare)

E **466** Educating Juveniles

1972. German–Polish Resistance Memorial, Berlin, Inauguration.

E1516	E **465** 25pf. multicoloured	40	20

1972. Juvenile Inventions Exhibition. Mult.

E1517	10pf. Type E **466**	20	45
E1518	25pf. Youths with welding machine	20	45

1972. Children's T.V. Characters. Mult.

E1519	5pf. Type E **467**	30	35
E1520	10pf. "Fuchs and Elster" (Fox and Magpie)	30	35
E1521	15pf. "Herr Uhu" (Eagle Owl)	60	65
E1522	20pf. "Frau Igel and Borstel" (Hedgehogs)	60	65
E1523	25pf. "Schuffel and Pieps" (Dog and Mouse)	30	35
E1524	35pf. "Paulchen" (Paul from the children's library)	30	35

E **468** "The Snow Queen"

E **469** H. Heine

1972. Fairy Tales (7th series). As Type E **468**. "The Snow Queen" (Hans Christian Andersen).

E1525	5pf. multicoloured	30	1·00
E1526	10pf. multicoloured	65	1·40
E1527	15pf. multicoloured	30	1·00
E1528	20pf. multicoloured	30	1·00
E1529	25pf. multicoloured	65	1·40
E1530	35pf. multicoloured	30	1·00

1972. 175th Birth Anniv of Heinrich Heine (poet). Sheet 60 × 86 mm.

MSE1531	E **469** 1m. black, red and green	2·00	2·00

E **470** Arms of U.S.S.R.

1972. 50th Anniv of U.S.S.R.

E1532	E **470** 20pf. multicoloured	40	15

E **471** Leninplatz, East Berlin

E **472** M. da Caravaggio

1973. (a) Size 29 × 24 mm.

E1533	– 5pf. green	25	15
E1534	– 10pf. green	55	15
E1535	– 15pf. mauve	55	15
E1536	E **471** 20pf. mauve	70	15
E1537	– 25pf. green	90	15
E1538	– 30pf. orange	20	15
E1539	– 35pf. blue	1·00	15
E1540	– 40pf. violet	45	15
E1541	– 50pf. blue	65	15
E1542	– 60pf. purple	90	15
E1543	– 70pf. brown	65	15
E1544	– 80pf. blue	90	15
E1545	– 1m. green	1·10	15
E1546	– 2m. red	1·60	15
E1546a	– 3m. mauve	2·10	45

(b) Size 22 × 18 mm.

E2197	– 5pf. green	20	15
E1548	– 10pf. green	45	15
E2198	– 10pf. green	35	10
E2199	– 15pf. mauve	40	20
E2200	E **471** 20pf. mauve	45	15
E1549a	– 25pf. green	40	20
E2202	– 30pf. orange	50	25
E2203	– 35pf. blue	55	25
E2204	– 40pf. violet	55	25
E2205	– 50pf. blue	60	25
E2206	– 60pf. purple	60	25
E2207	– 70pf. brown	65	30
E2208	– 80pf. blue	80	25
E2209	– 1m. green	85	45

E2210 – 2m. red . . . . . . 1·10 65
E2211 – 3m. mauve . . . . . 2·40 80

DESIGNS: 5pf. Eastern white pelican and Alfred Brehm House, Tierpark, Berlin; 10pf. (Nos. E1534, E1548) Neptune Fountain and Rathausstrasse, Berlin; 10pf. (No. E2198) Palace of the Republic, Berlin; 15pf. Apartment Blocks, Fishers' Island, Berlin; 25pf. TV Tower, Alexander Square, Berlin; 30 pf, Workers' Memorial, Halle; 35pf. Karl-Marx-Stadt; 40pf. Brandenburg Gate Berlin; 50pf. New Guardhouse, Berlin; 60pf. Crown Gate and Zwinger, Dresden; 70pf. Old Town Hall, Leipzig; 80pf. Rostock-Warnemunde; 1m. Soviet War Memorial, Treptow; 2, 3m. Arms of East Germany.

1973. Cultural Anniversaries.
E1551 E **472** 5pf. brown 60 90
E1552 – 10pf. green 15 15
E1553 – 20pf. purple 15 15
E1554 – 25pf. blue 15 15
E1555 – 35pf. red 20 15

PORTRAITS AND ANNIVERSARIES: 5pf. (painter, 400th birth anniv); 10pf. Friedrich Wolf (dramatist, 85th birth anniv); 20pf. Max Reger (composer, birth cent.); 25pf. Max Reinhardt (impressario, birth cent.); 35pf. Johannes Dieckmann (politician, 80th birth anniv).

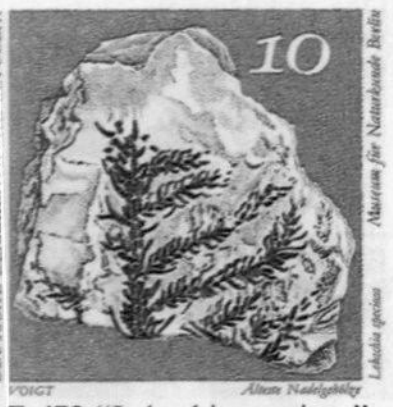

E 473 "Lebachia speciosa"

1973. Fossils in Palaeontological Collection, Berlin Natural History Museum. Multicoloured.
E1556 10pf. Type E **473** 15 15
E1557 15pf. "Spheronopteris hollandica" 15 15
E1558 20pf. "Pterodactylus kochi" 15 15
E1559 25pf. "Botryopteris" 15 15
E1560 35pf. "Archaeopteryx lithographica" 15 15
E1561 70pf. "Odontopleura ovata" . . . . . . 1·30 1·70

E 474 Copernicus (½-size illustration)

1973. 500th Birth Anniv of Copernicus.
E1562 E **474** 70pf. multicoloured 70 30

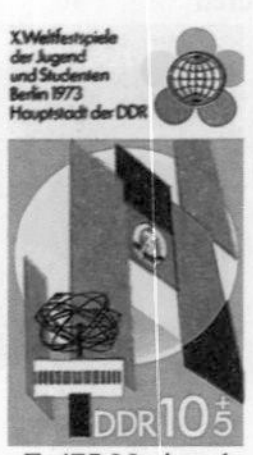

E 475 National Flags

E 476 Bobsleigh Course

1973. 10th World Youth Festival, Berlin (1st issue). Multicoloured.
E1563 10pf.+5pf. Type E **475** . . 15 15
E1564 25pf.+5pf. Youths and peace dove 25 25
See also Nos. E1592/6.

1973. 15th World Bobsleigh Championships, Oberhof.
E1565 E **476** 35pf. multicoloured 35 30

E 477 Combine Harvester

1973. Leipzig Spring Fair. Multicoloured.
E1566 10pf. Type E **477** . . . 15 15
E1567 25pf. Automatic lathe . . 25 25

E 478 Firecrests

1973. Songbirds. Multicoloured.
E1568 5pf. Type E **478** 15 15
E1569 10pf. White-winged crossbill 15 15
E1570 15pf. Bohemian waxwing 15 15
E1571 20pf. Bluethroats 15 15
E1572 25pf. Eurasian goldfinch 20 15
E1573 35pf. Golden oriole . . . 20 15
E1574 40pf. Grey wagtail . . . 25 15
E1575 60pf. Wallcreeper . . . . 3·25 2·75

E 479 Class 211 Electric Locomotive No. 200-3

1973. Railway Rolling Stock. Multicoloured.
E1576 5pf. Type E **479** 15 15
E1577 10pf. Refrigerator wagon 15 15
E1578 20pf. Long-distance passenger carriage . . . 15 15
E1579 25pf. Tank wagon 15 15
E1580 35pf. Double-deck carriage 20 15
E1581 85pf. Passenger carriage 2·10 2·30

E 480 "King Lear" (directed by W. Langhoff)

E 481 H. Matern

1973. Famous Theatrical Productions. Mult.
E1582 10pf. Type E **480** 15 15
E1583 25pf. "A Midsummer Night's Dream" (opera) (Benjamin Britten) (directed by Walter Felsenstein) 15 15
E1584 35pf. "Mother Courage" (directed by Berthold Brecht) 70 90

1973. 80th Birth Anniv of Hermann Matern (politician).
E1585 E **481** 40pf. red 50 15

E 482 Goethe and House

E 483 Firework Display

1973. Cultural Celebrities and Houses in Weimar. Multicoloured.
E1586 10pf. Type E **482** 15 15
E1587 15pf. C. M. Wieland (writer) 15 15
E1588 20pf. F. Schiller (writer) 15 15
E1589 25pf. J. G. Herder (writer) 15 15
E1590 35pf. Lucas Cranach the Elder (painter) 15 15
E1591 50pf. Franz Liszt (composer) . . . . . . 1·60 1·40

1973. World Festival of Youth and Students, East Berlin (2nd issue). Multicoloured.
E1592 5pf. Type E **483** 15 15
E1593 15pf. Students ("Int Solidarity") 15 15
E1594 20pf. Young workers ("Economic Integration") 15 15
E1595 30pf. Students ("Aid for Young Nations") . . . 85 60
E1596 35pf. Youth and Students' Emblems 15 15
MSE1597 86 × 107 mm. 50pf. Emblem and Brandenburg Gate (26.7) . . . . 1·00 1·00

E 484 W. Ulbricht

E 485 Power Network

1973. Death of Walter Ulbricht.
E1598 E **484** 20pf. black 55 25

1973. 10th Anniv of "Peace" United Energy Supply System.
E1599 E **485** 35pf. orge, pur & bl 35 30

E 486 "Leisure Activites"

1973. Leipzig Autumn Fair. Multicoloured.
E1600 10pf. Type E **486** 20 15
E1601 25pf. Yacht, guitar and power drill 40 25

E 487 Militiaman and Emblem

1973. 20th Anniv of Workers Militia. Mult.
E1602 10pf. Type E **487** 20 15
E1603 20pf. Militia guard 35 25
MSE1604 61 × 87 mm. 50pf. Militiamen (vert) 90 90

E 488 Red Flag encircling Globe

E 489 Langenstein-Zwieberge Memorial

1973. 15th Anniv of "Problems of Peace and Socialism".
E1605 E **488** 20pf. red and gold 40 20

1973. Langenstein-Zwieberge Monument.
E1606 E **489** 25pf. multicoloured 40 20

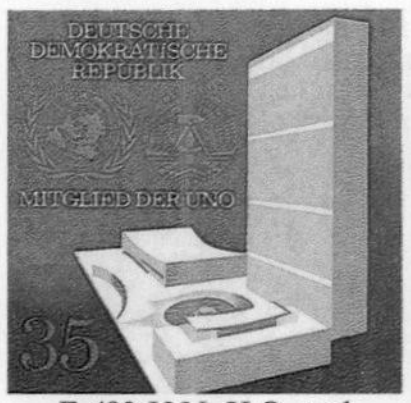

E 490 U.N. H.Q. and Emblems

E 491 "Young Couple" (G. Glombitza)

1973. Admission of German Democratic Republic to United Nations Organization.
E1607 E **490** 35pf. multicoloured 50 20

1973. Philatelists' Day and 3rd Young Philatelists' Stamp Exhibition, Halle.
E1608 E **491** 20pf.+5pf. mult . . . 30 20

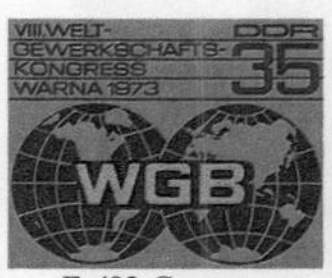

E 492 Congress Emblem

E 493 Vietnamese Child

1973. 8th World Trade Union Congress, Varna, Bulgaria.
E1609 E **492** 35pf. multicoloured 35 30

1973. "Solidarity with Vietnam".
E1610 E **493** 10pf.+5pf. mult . . . 30 25

E 494 Launching Rocket

1973. Soviet Science and Technology Days. Multicoloured.
E1611 10pf. Type E **494** 15 15
E1612 20pf. Soviet map and emblem (horiz) 15 15
E1613 25pf. Oil refinery . . . . 1·10 85

E 495 L. Corvalan

E 496 "Child with Doll" (C. L. Vogel)

1973. Solidarity with the Chilean People. Multicoloured.
E1614 10pf.+5pf. Type E **495** . . 25 25
E1615 25pf.+5pf. Pres. Allende 55 45

1973. Paintings by Old Masters. Mult.
E1616 10pf. Type E **496** 15 15
E1617 15pf. "Madonna with Rose" (Parmigianino) 15 15
E1618 20pf. "Woman with Fair Hair" (Rubens) 15 15
E1619 25pf. "Lady in White" (Titian) 20 15
E1620 35pf. "Archimedes" (D. Fetti) 20 15
E1621 70pf. "Flower Arrangement" (Jan D. de Heem) . . . . . . 3·00 1·80

E 497 Flame Emblem

E 498 "Catching the Pike"

1973. 25th Anniv of Declaration of Human Rights.
E1622 E **497** 35pf. multicoloured 60 30

1973. Fairy Tales (8th series). As Type E **498**. "At the Bidding of the Pike".
E1623 5pf. multicoloured 20 50
E1624 10pf. multicoloured . . . 90 1·20
E1625 15pf. multicoloured . . . 20 50
E1626 20pf. multicoloured . . . 20 50
E1627 25pf. multicoloured . . . 90 1·20
E1628 35pf. multicoloured . . . 20 50

E 499 E. Hoernle

E 500 Pablo Neruda

1974. Socialist Personalities.
E1629 E **499** 10pf. grey 20 15
E1630 – 10pf. lilac 20 15
E1631 – 10pf. blue 20 15
E1632 – 10pf. brown 20 15
E1633 – 10pf. green 20 15
E1634 – 10pf. brown 20 15
E1635 – 10pf. blue 20 15
E1636 – 10pf. brown 20 15

PERSONALITIES: No. E1630, Etkar Andre; E1631, Paul Merker; E1632, Hermann Duncker; E1633, Fritz Heckert; E1634, Otto Grotewohl; E1635, Wilhelm Florin; E1636, Georg Handke.
See also Nos. E1682/4.

1974. Pablo Neruda (Chilean poet) Commem.
E1637 E **500** 20pf. multicoloured 35 25

E 501 "Comecon" Emblem

E 502 "Echinopsis multiplex"

1974. 25th Anniv of Council for Mutual Economic Aid.

E1638	E 501 20pf. multicoloured	30	10

1974. Cacti. Multicoloured.

E1639	5pf. Type E 502	15	15
E1640	10pf. "Lobivia haageana"	15	15
E1641	15pf. "Parodia sanguiniflora"	2·75	2·30
E1642	20pf. "Gymnocal monvillei"	20	15
E1643	25pf. "Neoporteria rapifera"	20	20
E1644	35pf. "Notocactus concinnus"	30	30

E 503 Handball Players

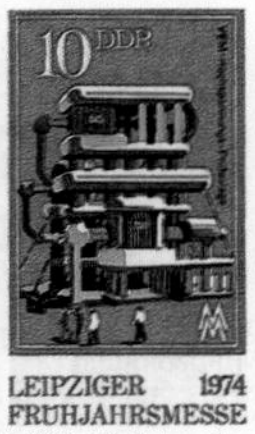

E 504 High-tension Testing Plant

1974. 8th Men's World Indoor Handball Championships.

E1645	E 503 5pf. multicoloured	40	40
E1646	– 10pf. multicoloured	40	40
E1647	– 35pf. multicoloured	40	40

Nos. E1645/7 were issued together, se-tenant, forming a composite design of a handball match.

1974. Leipzig Spring Fair. Multicoloured.

E1648	10pf. Type E 504	20	15
E1649	25pf. "Robotron" computer (horiz)	30	20

E 505 "Rhodophyllus sinuatus"

E 506 Gustav Kirchhoff

1974. Poisonous Fungi. Multicoloured.

E1650	5pf. Type E 505	15	15
E1651	10pf. "Boletus satanas"	15	15
E1652	15pf. "Amanita pantherina"	15	15
E1653	20pf. "Amanita muscaria"	15	15
E1654	25pf. "Gyromitra esculenta"	20	15
E1655	30pf. "Inocybe patouillardii"	25	25
E1656	35pf. "Amanita phalloides"	30	25
E1657	40pf. "Clitocybe dealbata"	2·10	1·60

1974. Celebrities' Birth Anniversaries.

E1658	E 506 5pf. black and grey	15	15
E1659	– 10pf. ultram & bl	15	15
E1660	– 20pf. red and pink	20	15
E1661	– 25pf. green & turq	20	15
E1662	– 35pf. choc & brn	90	75

PORTRAITS AND ANNIVERSARIES: 5pf. (physicist, 150th); 10pf. Immanuel Kant (philosopher, 250th); 20pf. Elm Welk (writer, 90th); 25pf. Johann Herder (author, 230th); 35pf. Lion Feuchtwanger (novelist, 90th).

E 507 Globe and "PEACE"

1974. 25th Anniv of 1st World Peace Congress.

E1663	E 507 35pf. multicoloured	40	30

E 508 Tractor Driver

E 509 Buk Lighthouse, 1878

1974. 25th Anniv of German Democratic Republic. Multicoloured.

E1664	10pf. Type E 508	15	15
E1665	20pf. Students	15	15
E1666	25pf. Woman worker	20	15
E1667	35pf. East German family	1·10	95

1974. Lighthouses (1st series). Multicoloured.

E1668	10pf. Type E 509	15	15
E1669	15pf. Warnemunde lighthouse, 1898	15	15
E1670	20pf. Darsser Ort lighthouse, 1848	15	15
E1671	35pf. Arkona lighthouse in 1827 and 1902	20	15
E1672	40pf. Greifswalder Oie lighthouse, 1855	1·60	1·10

See also Nos. E1760/4.

E 510 "Man and Woman looking at the Moon"

1974. Birth Bicentenary of Caspar Friedrich (painter). Multicoloured.

E1673	10pf. Type E 510	15	15
E1674	20pf. "The Stages of Life" (seaside scene)	15	15
E1675	25pf. "Heath near Dresden"	2·10	1·90
E1676	35pf. "Trees in the Elbe Valley"	30	15
MSE1677	80 × 55 mm. E 511 70pf. sepia	1·60	1·80

E 512 Lace Pattern

E 513 Show Jumping

1974. Plauen Lace.

E1678	E 512 10pf. black and violet	15	15
E1679	– 20pf. brown, black and bistre	15	15
E1680	– 25pf. black, blue and turquoise	1·50	1·40
E1681	– 35pf. black, mauve and pink	20	15

DESIGNS: Nos. E1679/81, Lace patterns similar to Type E 512.

1974. Socialist Personalities. As Type E 499.

E1682	10pf. blue	20	15
E1683	10pf. violet	20	15
E1684	10pf. brown	20	15

DESIGNS: No. E1682, R. Breitscheid; No. E1683, K. Burger; No. E1684, C. Moltmann.

1974. International Horse-breeders' Congress, Berlin. Multicoloured.

E1685	10pf. Type E 513	15	15
E1686	20pf. Horse & trap (horiz)	15	15
E1687	25pf. Haflinger draught horses (horiz)	1·70	2·00
E1688	35pf. Horse-racing (horiz)	30	20

E 514 Crane lifting Diesel Locomotive

1974. Leipzig Autumn Fair. Multicoloured.

E1689	10pf. Type E 514	20	15
E1690	25pf. Agricultural machine	35	25

E 515 "The Porcelain Shop"

E 517 Arms of East Germany and Family

E 516 Ardeatine Caves Memorial, Rome

1974. "Mon Plaisir". Exhibits in Dolls' Village, Castle Museum, Arnstadt. Mult.

E1691	5pf. Type E 515	15	15
E1692	10pf. "Fairground Crier"	15	15
E1693	15pf. "Wine-tasting in Cellar"	15	70
E1694	20pf. "Cooper and Apprentice"	15	15
E1695	25pf. "Bagpiper playing for Dancing Bear"	1·90	1·00
E1696	35pf. "Butcher's Wife and Crone"	20	20

1974. International War Memorials.

E1697	E 516 35pf. black, grn & red	45	30
E1698	– 35pf. black, bl & red	45	30

DESIGN: No. E1698, Resistance Memorial, Chateaubriant, France.

1974. 25th Anniv of German Democratic Republic. Sheet 90 × 108 mm.

MSE1699	E 517 1m. multicoloured	1·60	1·60

E 518 "James Watt" (paddle-steamer) and Modern Freighter

1974. Centenary of U.P.U. Multicoloured.

E1700	10pf. Type E 518	15	15
E1701	20pf. Steam and diesel railway locomotives	15	15
E1702	25pf. Early airliner and Tupolev Tu-134	15	15
E1703	35pf. Early mail coach and modern truck	1·30	90

E 519 "The Revolutionaries" (E. Rossdeutscher)

E 520 "The Sun shines for all" (G. Milosch)

1974. "DDR 74" Stamp Exhibition. Sculptures in Karl-Marx-Stadt. Each black, bistre and green.

E1704	10pf.+5pf. Type E 519	20	25
E1705	20pf. "The Dialectics"	20	25
E1706	25pf. "The Party"	20	25

1974. Children's Paintings. Multicoloured.

E1707	20pf. Type E 520	40	40
E1708	20pf. "My Friend Sascha" (B. Ozminski)	40	40
E1709	20pf. "Carsten the Best Swimmer" (M. Kluge)	40	40
E1710	20pf. "Me and the Blackboard" (P. Westphal)	40	40

E 521 "The Woodchopper"

E 523 Banded Jasper

E 522 "Still Life" (R. Paris)

1974. Fairy Tales (9th series). "Twittering To and Fro" by A. Tolstoi.

E1711	E 521 10pf. multicoloured	20	35
E1712	– 15pf. multicoloured	1·10	95
E1713	– 20pf. multicoloured	20	35
E1714	– 30pf. multicoloured	20	35
E1715	– 35pf. multicoloured	1·10	95
E1716	– 40pf. multicoloured	20	35

DESIGNS: Nos. E1712/16, Scenes from "Twittering To and Fro" fairy tale, similar to Type E 521.

1974. Paintings from Berlin Museums. Mult.

E1717	10pf. Type E 522	15	15
E1718	15pf. "Girl in Meditation" (W. Lachnit) (vert)	15	15
E1719	20pf. "Fisherman's House" (H. Hakenbeck) (vert)	15	15
E1720	35pf. "Girl in Red" (R. Bergander)	30	15
E1721	70pf. "Parents" (W. Sitte) (vert)	1·90	1·90

1974. Gem-stones in Freiberg Mining Academy Collection. Multicoloured.

E1722	10pf. Type E 523	15	15
E1723	15pf. Smoky quartz	15	15
E1724	20pf. Topaz	15	15
E1725	25pf. Amethyst	20	15
E1726	35pf. Aquamarine	35	15
E1727	70pf. Agate	2·10	1·90

E 524 Martha Arendsee

E 525 Peasants doing Forced Labour

1975. 90th Birth Anniv of Martha Arendsee (Socialist).

E1728	E 524 10pf. red	30	20

1975. 450th Anniv of Peasants' War.

E1729	E 525 5pf. black, green and grey	45	40
E1730	– 10pf. black, brown and grey	45	40
E1731	– 20pf. black, blue and grey	45	40
E1732	– 25pf. black, yellow and grey	60	55
E1733	– 35pf. black, lilac and grey	60	55
E1734	– 50pf. black, grey and light grey	45	40

DESIGNS: 10pf. "Paying Tithe"; 20pf. Thomas Muntzer (leader); 25pf. "Armed Peasants"; 35pf. "Liberty" flag; 50pf. Peasants on trial.

E 526 Women and Emblem

E 527 Pentakta "A-100" (microfilm camera)

1975. International Women's Year.

E1735	E 526 10pf. multicoloured	25	25
E1736	– 20pf. multicoloured	25	25
E1737	– 25pf. multicoloured	25	25

DESIGNS: 20pf., 25pf. Similar to Type E 526.

1975. Leipzig Spring Fair. Multicoloured.

E1738	10pf. Type E 527	15	15
E1739	25pf. "SKET" (cement works)	35	20

E **528** Hans Otto (actor) (1900–33)

E **529** Blue and Yellow Macaws

1975. Celebrities' Birth Anniversaries.
E1740 E **528** 5pf. blue 15 15
E1741 – 10pf. red 15 15
E1742 – 20pf. green 15 15
E1743 – 25pf. brown 20 15
E1744 – 35pf. blue . . . . . 1·20 1·00
PORTRAITS AND ANNIVERSARIES: 10pf. Thomas Mann, author (1875–1955); 20pf. Dr. A. Schweitzer (1875–1965); 25pf. Michelangelo (1475–1564); 35pf. Andre-Marie Ampere, scientist (1775–1836).

1975. Zoo Animals. Multicoloured.
E1745 5pf. Type E **529** 15 15
E1746 10pf. Orang-utan 15 15
E1747 15pf. Ibex 15 15
E1748 20pf. Indian rhinoceros (horiz) 15 15
E1749 25pf. Pygmy hippopotamus (horiz) 15 15
E1750 30pf. Grey seals (horiz) . . 20 15
E1751 35pf. Tiger (horiz) 20 15
E1752 50pf. Common zebra . . . 2·40 2·00

E **530** Soldiers, "Industry" and "Agriculture"

1975. 20th Anniv of Warsaw Treaty.
E1753 E **530** 20pf. multicoloured 1·20 20

E **531** Soviet Memorial, Berlin-Treptow

E **532** Ribbons with "Komsomol" and "F.D.J." Badges

1975. 30th Anniv of Liberation. Mult.
E1754 10pf. Type E **531** 15 15
E1755 20pf. Detail of Buchenwald memorial 15 15
E1756 25pf. Woman voluntary worker 20 15
E1757 55pf. "Socialist economic integration" 90 90
MSE1758 109 × 90 mm. 50pf. Soldier planting Red flag on Reichstag. Imperf 75 75

1975. 3rd Youth Friendship Festival, Halle.
E1759 E **532** 10pf. mult 45 20

1975. Lighthouses (2nd series). As Type E **509**. Multicoloured.
E1760 5pf. Trimmendorf lighthouse 15 15
E1761 10pf. Gellen lighthouse . . 15 15
E1762 20pf. Sassnitz lighthouse . . 15 15
E1763 25pf. Dornbusch lighthouse 20 15
E1764 35pf. Peenemunde lighthouse . . . . . . 1·30 1·00

E **533** Wilhelm Leibknecht and August Bebel

E **534** Dove and "Scientific Co-operation between Socialist Countries"

1975. Centenary of Marx's "Programmkritik" and Gotha Unity Congress.
E1765 E **533** 10pf. deep brown, brown and red . . 20 25
E1766 – 20pf. multicoloured 20 25
E1767 – 25pf. deep brown, brown and red . . 20 25
DESIGNS: 20pf. Tivoli (meeting place at Gotha) and title-page of Minutes of Unity Congress; 25pf. Karl Marx and Friedrich Engels.

1975. 25th Anniv of Eisenhuettenstadt.
E1768 E **534** 20pf. multicoloured 30 20

E **535** Construction Workers

E **536** Automatic Clock, 1585

1975. 30th Anniv of Free-German Trade Union Association.
E1769 E **535** 20pf. multicoloured 35 20

1975. Ancient Clocks. Multicoloured.
E1770 5pf. Type E **536** 15 15
E1771 10pf. Astronomical Mantlepiece clock, 1560 15 15
E1772 15pf. Automatic clock, 1600 . . . . 2·00 1·80
E1773 20pf. Mantlepiece Clock, 1720 . . . . 15 15
E1774 25pf. Mantlepiece Clock, 1700 . . . . 20 15
E1775 35pf. Astronomical Clock, 1738 . . . . 25 20

E **537** Jacob and Wilhelm Grimm's German Dictionary

1975. 275th Anniv of Academy of Science.
E1776 E **537** 10pf. black, grn & red 15 15
E1777 – 20pf. black and blue 15 15
E1778 – 25pf. blk, yell & grn 15 15
E1779 – 35pf. multicoloured 1·20 1·20
DESIGNS: 20pf. Karl Schwarzschildt observatory, Tautenberg; 25pf. Electron microscope and chemical plant; 35pf. Intercosmic satellite.

E **538** Runner with Torch

E **539** Map of Europe

1975. 5th National Youth Sports Day.
E1780 E **538** 10pf. black and pink 15 15
E1781 – 20pf. black and yellow 15 15
E1782 – 25pf. black and blue 20 15
E1783 – 35pf. black and green . . . . . 1·20 1·10
DESIGNS: 20pf. Hurdling; 25pf. Swimming; 35pf. Gymnastics.

1975. European Security and Co-operation Conference, Helsinki.
E1784 E **539** 20pf. multicoloured 35 25

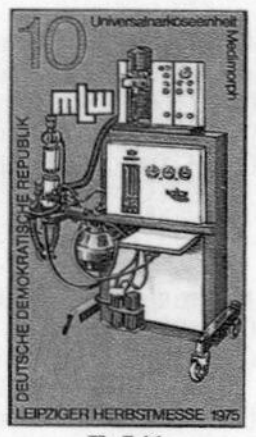

E **540** Asters

E **541** "Medimorph" (Anaesthetizing machine)

1975. Flowers. Multicoloured.
E1785 5pf. Type E **540** 15 15
E1786 10pf. Pelargoniums 15 15
E1787 20pf. Gerberas 15 15
E1788 25pf. Carnation 20 15
E1789 35pf. Chrysanthemum . . 25 15
E1790 70pf. Pansies . . . . . . 3·00 2·20

1975. Leipzig Autumn Fair. Multicoloured.
E1791 10pf. Type E **541** 20 15
E1792 25pf. Zschopau "TS-250" motor-cycle (horiz) . . . 45 25

E **542** School Crossing

1975. Road Safety. Multicoloured.
E1793 10pf. Type E **542** 15 15
E1794 15pf. Policewoman controlling traffic . . . 1·60 1·10
E1795 20pf. Policeman assisting motorist 15 15
E1796 25pf. Car having check-up 20 15
E1797 35pf. Road safety instruction 20 15

E **543** Launch of "Soyuz"

E **544** Clenched Fist and Red Star

1975. "Apollo"–"Soyuz" Space Link. Mult.
E1798 10pf. Type E **543** 15 15
E1799 20pf. Spaceships in linking manoeuvre 20 15
E1800 70pf. The completed link (88 × 33 mm) . . . . . 1·90 1·60

1975. "International Solidarity".
E1801 E **544** 10pf.+5pf. black, red and olive 30 20

E **545** "Weimar in 1650" (Merian)

1975. Millenary of Weimar.
E1802 E **545** 10pf. brown, light green and green 15 15
E1803 – 20pf. multicoloured 15 15
E1804 – 35pf. multicoloured 65 60
DESIGNS:—VERT: 20pf. Buchenwald memorial. HORIZ: 35pf. Weimar buildings (975–1975).

E **546** Vienna Memorial (F. Cremer)

E **547** Louis Braille

1975. Austrian Patriots Monument, Vienna.
E1805 E **546** 35pf. multicoloured 35 20

1975. International Braille Year. Mult.
E1806 20pf. Type E **547** 15 15
E1807 35pf. Hands reading braille 20 15
E1808 50pf. An eye-ball, eye shade and safety goggles 1·60 1·40

E **548** Post Office Gate, Wurzen

1975. National Philatelists' Day. Mult.
E1809 10pf.+5pf. Type E **548** . . 60 55
E1810 20pf. Post Office, Barenfels 15 15

E **549** Hans Christian Andersen and scene from "The Emperor's New Clothes" (½-size illustration)

1975. Fairy Tales (10th series). "The Emperor's New Clothes".
E1811 E **549** 20pf. multicoloured 55 55
E1812 – 35pf. multicoloured 90 90
E1813 – 50pf. multicoloured 55 55
DESIGNS: 35, 50pf. Different scenes.

E **550** Tobogganing

1975. Winter Olympic Games, Innsbruck (1976). Multicoloured.
E1814 5pf. Type E **550** 15 15
E1815 10pf.+5pf. Bobsleigh track 20 15
E1816 20pf. Speed-skating rink 20 15
E1817 25pf.+5pf. Ski-jump . . . 25 15
E1818 35pf. Skating-rink 25 15
E1819 70pf. Skiing . . . . 2·75 1·60
MSE1820 80 × 55 mm. 1m. Innsbruck (33 × 28 mm) . . . . 2·20 2·20

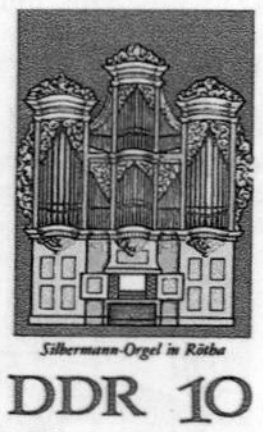

E **551** W. Pieck

E **552** Organ, Rotha

1975. Birth Cent of President Pieck (statesman).
E1821 E **551** 10pf. brown & blue 25 20

1976. Members of German Workers' Movement. As Type E **551**.
E1822 10pf. brown and red . . . 20 15
E1823 10pf. brown and green . . 20 15
E1824 10pf. brown and orange 20 15
E1825 10pf. brown and violet . . 20 15
PORTRAITS: No. E1822, Ernst Thalmann; E1823, Georg Schumann; E1824, Wilhelm Koenen; E1825, John Schehr.

1976. Gottfried Silbermann (organ builder) Commemoration. Multicoloured.
E1826 10pf. Type E **552** 15 15
E1827 20pf. Organ, Freiberg . . 15 15
E1828 35pf. Organ, Fraureuth . . 20 15
E1829 50pf. Organ, Dresden . 1·40 1·00

E **553** Richard Sorge

1976. Dr. Richard Sorge (Soviet agent) Commemoration. Sheet 82 × 65 mm.
MSE1830 E **553** 1m. black and pale olive-grey . . . . 1·80 1·80

E **554** Servicemen and Emblem

1976. 20th Anniv of National Forces (N.V.A.). Multicoloured.
E1831 10pf. Type E **554** 20 15
E1832 20pf. N.V.A. equipment 30 20

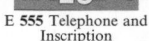

E **555** Telephone and Inscription

E **556** Block of Flats, Leipzig

1976. Centenary of Telephone.
E1833 E **555** 20pf. blue 30 15

1976. Leipzig Spring Fair. Multicoloured.
E1834 10pf. Type E **556** 20 15
E1835 25pf. "Prometey" (deep sea trawler) (horiz) . . . 45 20

E **557** Palace of the Republic, Berlin

1976. Opening of Palace of Republic, Berlin.
E1836 E **557** 10pf. multicoloured 75 15

E **558** Telecommunications Satellite Tracking Radar

E **559** Marx, Engels, Lenin and Socialist Party Emblem

1976. "Intersputnik".
E1837 E **558** 20pf. multicoloured 30 20

1976. 9th East German Socialist Party Congress.
E1838 E **559** 10pf. red, gold and deep red 20 15
E1839 – 20pf. multicoloured 35 15
MSE1840 110×91 mm. E **557** 1m. multicoloured . . . . . 1·60 1·60
DESIGN—HORIZ: 20pf. Industrial site, housing complex and emblem.

E **560** Cycling

1976. Olympic Games, Montreal. Mult.
E1841 5pf. Type E **560** 15 15
E1842 10pf.+5pf. Modern swimming pool 15 15
E1843 20pf. Modern sports hall 15 15
E1844 25pf. Regatta course . . . 20 15
E1845 35pf.+10pf. Rifle-range . . 30 15
E1846 70pf. Athletics . . . . . . 2·75 2·30
MSE1847 81×55 mm. 1m. Modern sports stadium (33×28 mm) 1·80 1·80

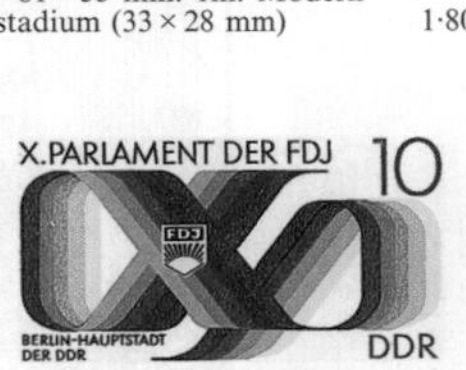

E **561** Intertwined Ribbon and Emblem

1976. 10th Youth Parliament Conference, Berlin. Multicoloured.
E1848 10pf. Type E **561** 15 15
E1849 20pf. Members of Youth Parliament and stylised industrial plant 25 25

E **562** "Himantoglossum bircinum"

E **564** Marx, Engels, Lenin and Red Flag

E **563** "Shetland Pony" (H. Drake)

1976. Flowers. Multicoloured.
E1850 10pf. Type E **562** 15 15
E1851 20pf. "Dactylorhiza incarnata" 15 15
E1852 25pf. "Anacamptis pyramidalis" 20 15
E1853 35pf. "Dactylorhiza sambucina" 25 15
E1854 40pf. "Orchis coriophora" 30 15
E1855 50pf. "Cypripedium calceolus" . . . . . . 2·50 2·10

1976. Statuettes from Berlin Museums.
E1856 E **563** 10pf. black and blue 15 15
E1857 – 20pf. black & brown 20 15
E1858 – 25pf. black & orange 20 15
E1859 – 35pf. black and green 20 15
E1860 – 50pf. black and pink 2·20 1·70
STATUETTES—VERT: 20pf. "Tanzpause" (W. Arnold); 25pf. "Am Strand" (L. Englehardt); 35pf. "Herman Duncker" (W. Howard); 50pf. "Das Gesprach" (G. Weidanz).

1976. European Communist Parties' Conference.
E1861 E **564** 20pf. blue, deep red and red 30 20

E **565** State Carriage, 1790

1976. 19th-century Horse-drawn Vehicles. Multicoloured.
E1862 10pf. Type E **565** 15 10
E1863 20pf. Russian trap, 1800 15 10
E1864 25pf. Carriage, 1840 . . . 20 10
E1865 35pf. State carriage, 1860 20 10
E1866 40pf. Stagecoach, 1850 . . 25 25
E1867 50pf. Carriage, 1889 . . . 2·75 2·40

E **566** Gera, c. 1652

1976. National Philatelists' Day, Gera. Mult.
E1868 10pf.+5pf. Type E **566** . . 20 25
E1869 20pf. Gera buildings . . . 20 30

E **567** Boxer

1976. Domestic Dogs. Multicoloured.
E1870 5pf. Type E **567** 15 15
E1871 10pf. Airedale Terrier . . 15 15
E1872 20pf. Alsatian 15 15
E1873 25pf. Collie 20 15
E1874 35pf. Schnauzer 20 25
E1875 70pf. Great Dane . . . . 3·00 2·75

E **568** Oil Refinery

1976. Autumn Fair, Leipzig. Multicoloured.
E1876 10pf. Type E **568** 20 15
E1877 25pf. Library, Leipzig . . 40 20

E **569** Templin Lake Railway Bridge

1976. East German Bridges. Multicoloured.
E1878 10pf. Type E **569** 15 15
E1879 15pf. Adlergestell Railway Bridge, Berlin 15 15
E1880 20pf. River Elbe Railway Bridge, Rosslau 15 15
E1881 25pf. Goltzschtal Viaduct 20 15
E1882 35pf. Elbe River Bridge, Magdeburg 20 15
E1883 50pf. Grosser Dreesch Bridge, Schwerin . . . . 2·20 2·00

E **570** Memorial Figures

1976. Patriots' Memorial, Budapest.
E1884 E **570** 35pf. multicoloured 40 20

E **571** Brass Jug, c. 1500

E **572** Berlin T.V. Tower

1976. Exhibits from Applied Arts Museum, Kopenick Castle, Berlin. Multicoloured.
E1885 10pf. Type E **571** 15 15
E1886 20pf. Faience covered vase, c. 1710 . . . . . 15 15
E1887 25pf. Porcelain "fruit-seller" table centre, c. 1768 . . . . . 20 15
E1888 35pf. Silver "basket-carrier" statuette, c. 1700 . . . . 20 15
E1889 70pf. Coloured glass vase, c. 1900 . . . . . 2·00 2·00

1976. "Sozphilex 77" Stamp Exhibition. East Berlin (1st issue).
E1890 E **572** 10pf.+5pf. blue, black and red . . 30 20
See also Nos. E1962/3.

E **573** Spade-tailed Guppy

E **575** The Miller and the King

E **574** Clay Pots c. 3000 B.C.

1976. Aquarium Fishes – Guppies. Mult.
E1891 10pf. Type E **573** 15 15
E1892 15pf. Lyre-tailed 15 15
E1893 20pf. Flag-tailed 15 15
E1894 25pf. Sword-tailed 20 15
E1895 35pf. Delta 20 15
E1896 70pf. Round-tailed . . . . 2·75 2·00

1976. Archaeological Discoveries in D.D.R. Multicoloured.
E1897 10pf. Type E **574** 15 15
E1898 20pf. Bronze cult vessel on wheels, c. 1300 B.C. . . 15 15
E1899 25pf. Roman gold aureus of Tetricus I, A.D. 270–273 . . . . 20 15
E1900 35pf. Viking cross-shaped pendant, 10th century A.D. 20 15
E1901 70pf. Roman glass beaker, 3rd century A.D. . . . 2·50 2·10

1976. Fairy Tales (11th series). "Rumpelstiltskin".
E1902 E **575** 5pf. multicoloured 20 30
E1903 – 10pf. multicoloured 65 60
E1904 – 15pf. multicoloured 20 30
E1905 – 20pf. multicoloured 20 30
E1906 – 25pf. multicoloured 65 60
E1907 – 30pf. multicoloured 20 30
DESIGNS: 10pf. to 30pf. Scenes from the fairy tale.

E **576** "The Air" (R. Carriera)

E **577** Arnold Zweig (author)

1976. Paintings by Old Masters from the National Art Collection, Dresden. Mult.
E1908 10pf. Type E **576** 15 15
E1909 15pf. "Madonna and Child" (Murillo) 15 15
E1910 20pf. "Viola Player" (B. Strozzi) 15 15
E1911 25pf. "Ariadne Forsaken" (A. Kauffman) 20 15
E1912 35pf. "Old Man in Black Cap" (B. Nazzari) . . . 20 15
E1913 70pf. "Officer reading a Letter" (G. Terborch) 2·75 1·90

1977. German Celebrities.
E1914 E **577** 10pf. black and pink 15 15
E1915 – 20pf. black and grey 15 15
E1916 – 35pf. black and green 20 15
E1917 – 40pf. black and blue 1·10 95
DESIGNS: 20pf. Otto von Guericke (scientist); 35pf. Albrecht D. Thaer (agriculturalist); 40pf. Gustav Hertz (physicist).

E **578** Spring near Plaue, Thuringia

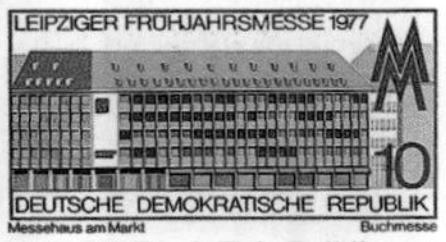

E **579** Book Fair Building

1977. Natural Phenomena. Multicoloured.
E1918 10pf. Type E **578** 15 15
E1919 20pf. Rock face near Jonsdorf 15 15
E1920 25pf. Oaks near Reuterstadt Stavenhagen 15 15
E1921 35pf. Rocky ledge near Saalburg 20 15
E1922 50pf. Erratic boulder near Furstenwalde/Spree . . 1·70 1·60

1977. Leipzig Spring Fair. Multicoloured.
E1923 10pf. Type E **579** 15 15
E1924 25pf. Aluminium casting machine 35 20

E **580** Senftenberg Costume, Zly Komorrow

E **581** Carl Friedrich Gauss

1977. Sorbian Historical Costumes. Mult.
E1925 10pf. Type E **580** 15 15
E1926 20pf. Bautzen, Budysin . . 15 15
E1927 25pf. Klitten, Kletno . . . 20 15
E1928 35pf. Nochten, Wochozy 20 15
E1929 70pf. Muskau, Muzakow 2·75 2·00

1977. Birth Bicentenary of Carl Friedrich Gauss (mathematician).
E1930 E **581** 20pf. black and blue 65 20

E **582** Start of Race

E **583** Three Flags

1977. 30th International Peace Cycle Race. Multicoloured.
E1931 10pf. Type E **582** 30 35
E1932 20pf. Spurt 30 35
E1933 35pf. Race finish 30 35

1977. 9th Congress of Free German Trade Unions Association.
E1934 E **583** 20pf. multicoloured 30 20

E **584** VKM Channel Converter and Filters

E **585** Shooting

1977. World Telecommunications Day.
E1935 E **584** 20pf. black, blue and red 30 20

1977. 25th Anniv of Sports and Technical Sciences Association.
E1936 E **585** 10pf. black, grn & red 15 15
E1937 – 20pf. black, bl & mve 15 15
E1938 – 35pf. black, pk & grn . . . . 1·00 85
DESIGNS: 20pf. Skin diving; 25pf. Radio-controlled model boat.

E **586** Accordion, 1900

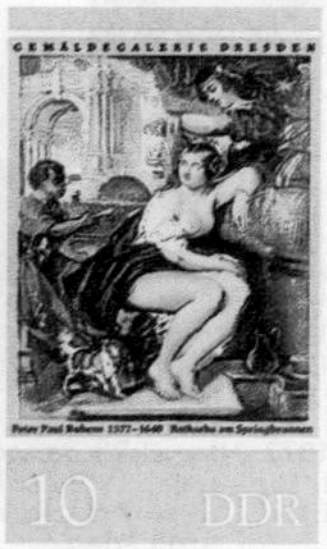

E **587** "Bathsheba at the Fountain"

1977. Old Musical Instruments from Vogtland. Multicoloured.
E1939 10pf. Type E **586** 15 15
E1940 20pf. Treble viola da gamba, 1747 . . . . . 15 15
E1941 25pf. Oboe, 1785, Clarinet, 1830, Flute, 1817 . . . 15 15
E1942 35pf. Concert zither, 1891 20 15
E1943 70pf. Trumpet, 1860 . . . 2·50 2·30

1977. 400th Birth Anniv of Peter Paul Rubens. Dresden Gallery Paintings. Multicoloured.
E1944 10pf. Type E **587** 15 15
E1945 15pf. "Mercury and Argus" (horiz) 20 15
E1946 20pf. "The Drunk Hercules" 20 15
E1947 25pf. "Diana's Return from Hunting" (horiz) 20 15
E1948 35pf. "The Old Woman with the Brazier" . . . 30 15
E1949 50pf. "Leda with the Swan" (horiz) . . . . . 3·25 2·20

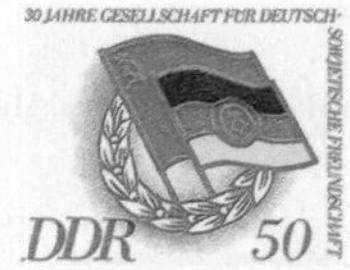

E **588** Soviet and East German Flags

1977. 30th Anniv of German-Soviet Friendship Society. Sheet 80 × 55 mm.
MSE1950 E **588** 50pf. multicoloured 1·20 1·10

E **589** Tractor and Plough

1977. Modern Agricultural Techniques. Multicoloured.
E1951 10pf. Type E **589** 15 15
E1952 20pf. Fertilizer spreader on truck 15 15
E1953 25pf. Potato digger and loader 20 15
E1954 35pf. High pressure collecting press 20 15
E1955 50pf. Milking machine . . 2·30 2·10

E **590** High Jump

E **591** "Bread for Everybody" (Wolfram Schubert)

1977. 6th Gymnastics and Athletic Meeting and 6th Children and Young People's Sports Days, Leipzig. Multicoloured.
E1956 5pf. Type E **590** 15 15
E1957 10pf.+5pf. Running . . . 15 15
E1958 20pf. Hurdling 15 15
E1959 25pf.+5pf. Gymnastics . . 20 15
E1960 35pf. Dancing 20 15
E1961 40pf. Torch bearer and flags . . . . 2·00 1·90

1977. "Sozphilex 77" Stamp Exhibition, East Berlin (2nd issue). Multicoloured.
E1962 10pf. Type E **591** 20 20
E1963 25pf. "... when Communists are Dreaming" (Walter Womacka) 55 45
MSE1964 Two sheets, each 77 × 110 mm. (a) No. E1962 × 4; (b) No. E1963 × 4 Set of 2 sheets 2·10 1·80
MSE1965 85 × 54 mm. 50pf.+20pf. "World Youth Song" (Lothar Zitzmann) (horiz) . . . . . . 1·60 1·60

E **592** "Konsument" Department Store, Leipzig

E **593** Bust of Dzerzhinsky and Young Pioneers

1977. Leipzig Autumn Fair. Multicoloured.
E1966 10pf. Type E **592** 20 15
E1967 25pf. Carved bowl and Thuringian blown-glass vases 40 20

1977. Birth Centenary of Feliks E. Dzerzhinsky (founder of Soviet Cheka). Sheet 127 × 69 mm containing Type E **593** and similar vert design. Multicoloured.
MSE1968 20pf. Type E **593**; 35pf. Portrait . . . . 1·20 1·20

E **594** Steam Locomotive "Muldenthal", 1861

1977. Transport Museum, Dresden. Mult.
E1969 5pf. Type E **594** 15 15
E1970 10pf. Dresden tram, 1896 15 15
E1971 20pf. Hans Grade's monoplane, 1909 . . . 20 15
E1972 25pf. Phanomobil tricar, 1924 . . . . 20 15
E1973 35pf. River Elbe passenger steamer, 1837 . . . . . 2·30 1·80

E **595** "Aurora" (cruiser)

1977. 60th Anniv of October Revolution. Multicoloured.
E1974 10pf. Type E **595** 20 20
E1975 25pf. Assault on Winter Palace 55 45
MSE1976 55 × 86 mm. 1m. Lenin (vert) . . . . 2·10 1·80

E **596** Soviet Memorial

E **597** Flaming Torch

1977. Soviet Memorial, Berlin-Schoenholz.
E1977 E **596** 35pf. multicoloured 40 20

1977. "Solidarity".
E1978 E **597** 10pf.+5pf. mult . . . 30 20

E **598** Ernst Meyer

E **599** H. von Kleist

1977. Socialist Personalities.
E1979 E **598** 10pf. brown 20 15
E1980 – 10pf. red 20 40
E1981 – 10pf. blue 20 15
PERSONALITIES: No. E1980, A. Frolich; No. E1981, G. Eisler.

1977. Birth Bicentenary of Heinrich von Kleist (poet). Sheet 82 × 54 mm.
MSE1982 E **599** 1m. black and red 3·00 2·20

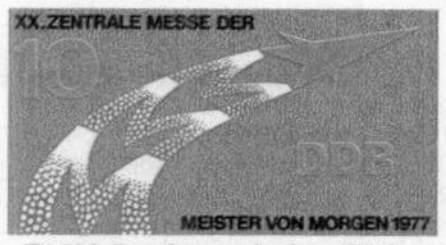

E **600** Rocket pointing Right

1977. 20th "Masters of Tomorrow" Fair, Leipzig.
E1983 E **600** 10pf. red, silver and black 20 30
E1984 – 20pf. blue, gold and black 20 30
DESIGN: 20pf. Rocket pointing left.

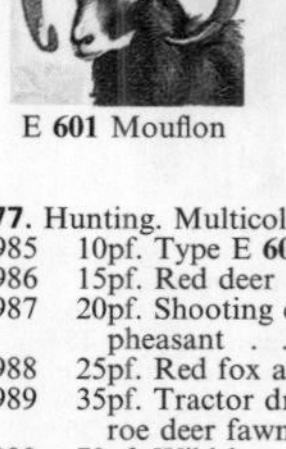

E **601** Mouflon

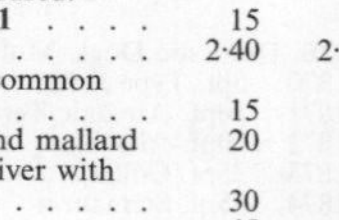

E **602** Firemen with Scaling Ladders

1977. Hunting. Multicoloured.
E1985 10pf. Type E **601** 15 15
E1986 15pf. Red deer . . . . . 2·40 2·20
E1987 20pf. Shooting common pheasant 15 15
E1988 25pf. Red fox and mallard 20 15
E1989 35pf. Tractor driver with roe deer fawn 30 15
E1990 70pf. Wild boars 45 25

1977. Fire Brigade. Multicoloured.
E1991 10pf. Type E **602** 15 15
E1992 20pf. Children visiting fire brigade (vert) 15 15
E1993 25pf. Fire engines in countryside 15 15
E1994 35pf. Artificial respiration (vert) 20 15
E1995 50pf. Fire-fighting tug . . 2·40 1·60

E **603** Traveller and King

E **605** Amilcar Cabral

E **604** Rosehips

1977. Fairy Tales (12th series). "Six World Travellers" (Brothers Grimm).
E1996 E **603** 5pf. multicoloured 20 35
E1997 – 10pf. multicoloured 1·10 80
E1998 – 20pf. multicoloured 20 35
E1999 – 25pf. multicoloured 20 35
E2000 – 35pf. multicoloured 1·10 80
E2001 – 60pf. multicoloured 20 35
DESIGNS: 10pf. to 60pf. Scenes from the fairy tale.

1978. Medicinal Plants. Multicoloured.
E2002 10pf. Type E **604** 15 15
E2003 15pf. Birch leaves 15 15
E2004 20pf. Camomile flowers . . 15 15
E2005 25pf. Coltsfoot 20 15
E2006 35pf. Lime flowers 20 15
E2007 50pf. Elder flowers . . . 2·75 2·00

1978. Amilcar Cabral (nationalist leader of Guinea-Bissau) Commemoration.
E2008 E **605** 20pf. multicoloured 35 20

E **606** Town Hall, Suhl-Heinrichs

E **608** Ear-pendant, 11th century

E **607** Post Office Van, 1921

1978. Half-timbered Buildings. Multicoloured.
E2009 10pf. Type E **606** 15 15
E2010 20pf. Farmhouse, Niederoderwitz 15 15
E2011 25pf. Farmhouse, Strassen 15 15
E2012 35pf. House, Quedlinburg 20 15
E2013 40pf. House, Eisenach . . 2·40 1·90

1978. Postal Transport. Multicoloured.
E2014 10pf. Type E **607** 20 25
E2015 20pf. Postal truck, 1978 . . 45 40
E2016 25pf. Railway mail coach, 1896 . . . . 60 55
E2017 35pf. Railway mail coach, 1978 . . . . 65 70

1978. Slavonic Treasures. Multicoloured.
E2018 10pf. Type E **608** 15 15
E2019 20pf. Ear-ring, 10th century 15 15
E2020 25pf. Bronze tag, 10th century 20 15
E2021 35pf. Bronze horse, 12th century 20 15
E2022 70pf. Arabian coin, 8th century . . . . 2·10 1·80

E **609** "Royal House" Market Square, Leipzig

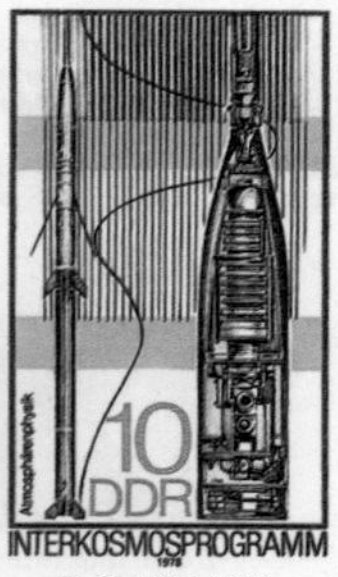

E **610** "M-100" Meteorological Rocket

1978. Leipzig Spring Fair.
E2023 E **609** 10pf. yell, blk & red 20 15
E2024 – 25pf. green, blk & red 45 25

DESIGN: 25pf. Universal measuring instrument, UMK 10/1318.

1978. "Interkosmos" Space Programme. Mult.
E2025 10pf. Type E **610** 15 15
E2026 20pf. "Interkosmos 1" satellite 15 15
E2027 35pf. "Meteor" satellite with Fourier spectrometer . . . . . 1·10 1·10
MSE2028 90 × 109 mm. 1m. "MKF-6" multispectral camera 2·75 2·75

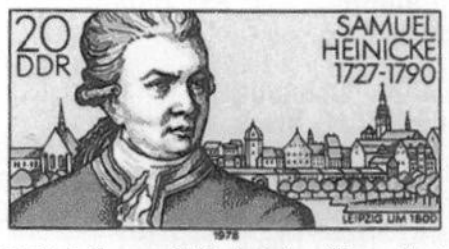

E **611** Samuel Heinicke (founder)

1978. Bicentenary of First National Deaf and Dumb Educational Institution.
E2029 20pf. Type E **611** 15 15
E2030 25pf. Child learning alphabet 75 70

E **612** Radio-range Tower, Dequede, and Television Transmission Van

E **613** Saxon miner in Gala Uniform

1978. World Telecommunications Day. Mult.
E2031 10pf. Type E **612** 15 15
E2032 20pf. Equipment in Berlin television tower and Dresden television tower 40 40

1978. 19th-Century Gala Uniforms of Mining and Metallurgical Industries. Multicoloured.
E2033 10pf. Type E **613** 15 15
E2034 20pf. Freiberg foundry worker 20 15
E2035 25pf. School of Mining academician 20 15
E2036 35pf. Chief Inspector of Mines . . . . 1·60 1·30

E **614** Lion Cub

E **615** Loading Container

1978. Centenary of Leipzig Zoo. Multicoloured.
E2037 10pf. Type E **614** 15 15
E2038 20pf. Leopard cub 15 15
E2039 35pf. Tiger cub 20 15
E2040 50pf. Snow leopard cub . . 1·60 1·30

1978. Container Goods Traffic. Multicoloured.
E2041 10pf. Type E **615** 15 15
E2042 20pf. Placing container on truck 15 15
E2043 35pf. Diesel locomotive and container wagons 20 25
E2044 70pf. Placing containers on "Boltenhagen" . . . . 2·20 1·70

E **616** Clay Ox (Egyptian Museum, Leipzig)

1978. Ancient African Works of Art in Egyptian Museums at Leipzig and Berlin. Multicoloured.
E2045 5pf. Type E **616** 15 15
E2046 10pf. Clay head of woman (Leipzig) 15 15
E2047 20pf. Gold bangle (Berlin) (horiz) 15 15
E2048 25pf. Gold ring plate (Berlin) 20 15
E2049 35pf. Gold signet-ring plate (Berlin) 20 15
E2050 40pf. Necklace (Berlin) (horiz) . . . . 1·80 1·60

E **617** Justus von Liebig (agricultural chemist, 175th birth anniv)

1978. Celebrities' Birth Anniversaries.
E2051 E **617** 5pf. black and ochre 15 15
E2052 – 10pf. black and blue 15 15
E2053 – 15pf. black and green 15 15
E2054 – 20pf. black and blue 15 15
E2055 – 25pf. black and red 20 15
E2056 – 35pf. black and green 20 15
E2057 – 70pf. black and drab 2·00 1·60
DESIGNS: 10pf. Joseph Dietzgen (writer, 150th); 15pf. Alfred Doblin (novelist, 100th); 20pf. Hans Loch (politician, 80th); 25pf. Theodor Brugsch (scientist, 100th); 35pf. Freidrich Ludwig Jahn (gymnast, 200th); 70pf. Albrecht von Graefe (ophthalmatician, 150th).

E **618** Cottbus, 1730

1978. 5th National Youth Stamp Exhibition, Cottbus. Multicoloured.
E2058 10pf.+5pf. Type E **618** . . 25 35
E2059 20pf. Modern Cottbus . . 25 35

E **619** Havana Buildings and Festival Emblem

1978. 11th World Youth and Students' Festival, Havana. Multicoloured.
E2060 20pf. Type E **619** 45 50
E2061 35pf. Festival emblem and East Berlin buildings . . 45 50

E **620** "Trooper with Halberd" (Hans Schaufelein)

E **621** "Multicar 25" Truck

1978. Drawings in Berlin State Museum. Sheet 110 × 98 mm containing Type E **620** and similar vert designs, each brownish black and stone.
MSE2062 10pf. Type E **620**; 20pf. "Woman reading a Letter" (Jean Antoine Watteau); 25pf. "Seated Boy" (Gabriel Metsu); 30pf. "Young Man cutting a Loaf" (Cornelis Saftleven); 35pf. "St. Anthony in a Landscape" (Matthias Grunewald); 50pf. "Man seated in an Armchair" (Abraham van Diepenbeeck) 3·75 3·75

1978. Leipzig Autumn Fair. Multicoloured.
E2063 10pf. Type E **621** 20 15
E2064 25pf. "Three Kings" Fair building, Petersstrasse 50 25

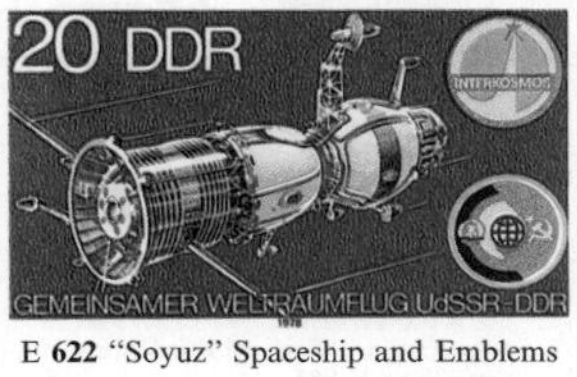

E **622** "Soyuz" Spaceship and Emblems

1978. Soviet–East German Space Flight (1st issue).
E2065 E **622** 20pf. multicoloured 35 25
See also Nos. E2069/**MS**2073.

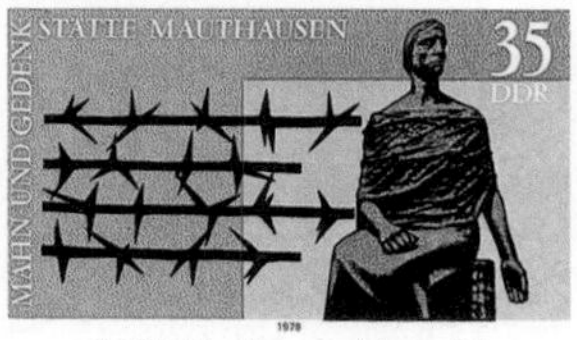

E **623** Mauthausen Memorial

1978. War Victims' Memorial, Mauthausen, Austria.
E2066 E **623** 35pf. multicoloured 35 30

E **624** W.M.S. Unit on the March

1978. 25th Anniv of Workers' Militia Squads.
E2067 20pf. Type E **624** 40 45
E2068 35pf. Members of Red Army, National People's Army and W.M.S. . . . 40 45

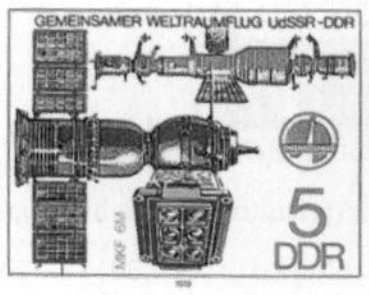

E **625** "Soyuz", "MKF 6M" Camera and Space Station

E **626** Human Pyramid

1978. Soviet–East German Space Flight (2nd issue). Multicoloured.
E2069 5pf. Type E **625** 15 15
E2070 10pf. Albert Einstein and "Soyuz" 15 15
E2071 20pf. Sigmund Jahn (first East German cosmonaut) (vert) . . . 15 15
E2072 35pf. "Salyut", "Soyuz" and Lilienthal monoplane glider . . . 1·30 1·10
MSE2073 110 × 90 mm. 1m. Space station and cosmonauts Valeri Bykovski and Jahn (54 × 32 mm) 2·20 2·10

1978. The Circus. Multicoloured.
E2074 5pf. Type E **626** 35 65
E2075 10pf. Elephant on tricycle 65 1·20
E2076 20pf. Performing horse . . 1·10 1·90
E2077 35pf. Polar bear kissing girl . . . . 2·20 3·75

E **627** African behind Barbed Wire

E **628** Construction of Natural Gas Pipe Line

1978. International Anti-Apartheid Year.
E2078 E **627** 20pf. multicoloured 35 20

1978. Construction of "Friendship Line" (Drushba-Trasse) by East German Youth.
E2079 E **628** 20pf. multicoloured 30 20

E **629** "Parides hahneli" ("Papilio hahneli")

E **631** Old Woman and Youth

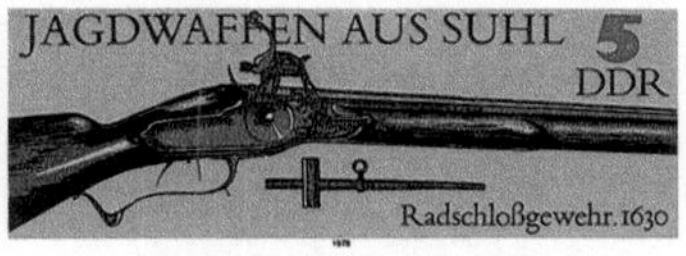

E **630** Wheel-lock Gun, 1630

1978. 250th Anniv of Dresden Scientific Museums. Multicoloured.
E2080 10pf. Type E **629** 15 15
E2081 20pf. "Agama lehmanni" 15 15
E2082 25pf. Agate 20 15
E2083 35pf. "Palaeobatrachus diluvianus" 20 15
E2084 40pf. Mantlepiece clock, c. 1720 . . . . . 20 15
E2085 50pf. Table telescope, c. 1750 . . . 3·00 2·50

1978. Sporting Guns from Suhl. Multicoloured.
E2086 5pf. Type E **630** 15 20
E2087 10pf. Double-barrelled gun, 1978 . . . . 20 20
E2088 20pf. Spring-cock gun, 1780 . . . . 30 35
E2089 25pf. Superimposed double-barrelled gun, 1978 . . . . 35 35
E2090 35pf. Percussion gun, 1850 55 60
E2091 70pf. Three-barrelled gun, 1978 . . . . 1·10 1·10

1978. Fairy Tales. "Rapunzel". Multicoloured
E2092 10pf. Type E **631** 20 35
E2093 15pf. Old Woman climbing tower on Rapunzel's hair . . . . 1·10 90
E2094 20pf. Prince calling to Rapunzel 20 35
E2095 25pf. Prince climbing through window 20 35
E2096 35pf. Old woman about to cut Rapunzel's hair . . 1·10 90
E2097 50pf. "Happy ever after" 20 35

E **632** Chaffinches

E **633** Chabo

1979. Songbirds. Multicoloured.
E2098 5pf. Type E **632** 15 15
E2099 10pf. Eurasian nuthatch 15 15
E2100 20pf. European robin . . . 15 15
E2101 25pf. Common rosefinch 20 15
E2102 35pf. Blue tit 20 20
E2103 50pf. Linnet . . . . 3·00 2·20

1979. Poultry. Multicoloured.
E2104 10pf. Type E **633** 15 15
E2105 15pf. Crows head 15 15
E2106 20pf. Porcelain-colour Feather-footed dwarf . . 15 15
E2107 25pf. Saxonian 20 15
E2108 35pf. Phoenix 20 15
E2109 50pf. Striped Italian . . . 3·00 2·00

E **634** Telephone Exchanges in 1900 and 1979

1979. Telephone and Telegraphs Communications. Multicoloured.
E2110 20pf. Type E **634** 15 15
E2111 35pf. Transmitting telegrams in 1800 and 1979 . . . . 1·00 75

E **635** Albert Einstein

E **636** Max Klinger Exhibition House, Leipzig

1979. Birth Centenary of Albert Einstein (physicist). Sheet 55 × 86 mm.
MSE2112 E **635** 1m. light brown, deep brown and brown . . . . 2·75 2·20

1979. Leipzig Spring Fair. Multicoloured.
E2113 10pf. Type E **636** 20 15
E2114 25pf. Horizontal drill and milling machine 45 25

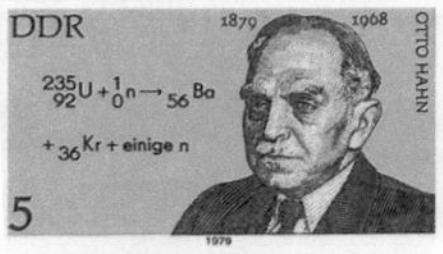

E **637** Otto Hahn (physicist, centenary)

1979. Celebrities' Birth Anniversaries.
E2115 E **637** 5pf. black and pink . . . 15 15
E2116 – 10pf. black and blue . . . 15 15
E2117 – 20pf. black and yellow 15 15
E2118 – 25pf. black and green 20 15
E2119 – 35pf. black and blue . . . 20 15
E2120 – 70pf. black and pink . . 2·20 1·80
DESIGNS: 10pf. Max von Laue (physicist, centenary); 20pf. Arthur Scheunert (physiologist, centenary); 25pf. Friedrich August Kekule (chemist, 150th); 35pf. Georg Forster (explorer and writer, 225th); 70pf. Gotth Ephraim Lessing (playwright and essayist, 250th).

E **638** "Radebeul" (container ship), "Sturmvogel" (tug) and Shipping Route Map

1979. World Navigation Day.
E2121 E **638** 20pf. multicoloured . . . 35 20

E **639** Horch "8", 1911

1979. Zwickau Motor Industry. Multicoloured.
E2122 20pf. Type E **639** 45 55
E2123 35pf. Trabant "601 S de luxe", 1978 . . . . . . 75 70

E **640** MXA Electric Train

1979. East German Locomotives and Wagons. Multicoloured.
E2124 5pf. Type E **640** 15 15
E2125 10pf. Self-discharging wagon 15 15
E2126 20pf. Diesel locomotive No. 110836.4 . . . . 15 15
E2127 35pf. Railway car transporter . . . . . . 1·20 90

E **641** Durga (18th century) E **642** Children Playing

1979. Indian Miniatures. Multicoloured.
E2128 20pf. Type E **641** 15 15
E2129 35pf. Mahavira (15th/16th century) 20 15
E2130 50pf. Todi Ragini (17th century) 30 15
E2131 70pf. Asavari Ragini (17th century) . . . . . . 2·75 2·30

1979. International Year of the Child. Multicoloured.
E2132 10pf. Type E **642** 15 15
E2133 20pf. Overseas aid for children 60 55

E **643** Construction Work on Leipziger Strasse Complex

1979. "Berlin Project" of Free German Youth Organization. Multicoloured.
E2134 10pf. Type E **643** 15 15
E2135 20pf. Berlin-Marzahn building site 50 35

E **644** Torchlight Procession of Free German Youth, 1949

1979. National Youth Festival. Mult.
E2136 10pf.+5pf. Type E **644** . . 30 35
E2137 20pf. Youth rally 30 35

E **645** Exhibition Symbol

1979. "agra 79" Agricultural Exhibition, Markkleeberg.
E2138 E **645** 10pf. multicoloured . . 30 20

E **646** "Rostock" (train ferry), 1977

1979. 70th Anniv of Sassnitz–Trelleborg Railway Ferry. Multicoloured.
E2139 20pf. Type E **646** 45 50
E2140 35pf. "Rugen" (train ferry) . . 45 50

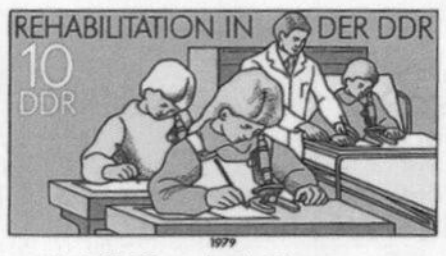

E **647** Hospital Classroom

1979. Rehabilitation. Multicoloured.
E2141 10pf. Type E **647** 15 15
E2142 35pf. Wheelchair-bound factory worker 55 55

E **648** Cycling

1979. 7th Children's and Young People's Sports Day, Berlin. Multicoloured.
E2143 10pf. Type E **648** 15 15
E2144 20pf. Roller-skating . . . 55 40

E **649** Dahlia "Rubens" E **650** Goose-thief Fountain, Dresden

1979. "iga" International Garden Exhibition, Erfurt. Dahlias. Multicoloured.
E2145 10pf. Type E **649** 15 15
E2146 20pf. "Rosalie" 15 15
E2147 25pf. "Corinna" 20 15
E2148 35pf. "Enzett-Dolli" . . . 20 15
E2149 50pf. "Enzett-Carola" . . . 30 25
E2150 70pf. "Don Lorenzo" . . . 3·25 3·00

1979. National Stamp Exhibition, Dresden. Multicoloured.
E2151 10pf.+5pf. Type E **650** . . 60 40
E2152 20pf. Dandelion fountain, Dresden 15 15
MSE2153 86 × 55 mm. 1m. Dresden buildings (horiz) . . . . 2·20 2·00

E **651** World Map and Russian Alphabet

1979. 4th International Congress of Russian Language and Literature Teachers, Berlin.
E2154 E **651** 20pf. multicoloured . . 30 20

E **652** Italian Lira de Gamba, 1592

1979. Musical Instruments in Leipzig Museum. Multicoloured.
E2155 20pf. Type E **652** . . . 20 15
E2156 25pf. French serpent, 17th/18th century 20 15
E2157 40pf. French barrel-lyre, 1750 . . . . 25 15
E2158 85pf. German tenor flugelhorn, 1850 . . . . 2·75 2·10

E **653** Horseracing

1979. 30th International Congress on Horse-breeding in Socialist Countries, Berlin. Multicoloured.
E2159 10pf. Type E **653** 15 15
E2160 25pf. Dressage (pas de deux) 95 75

E **654** Mittelbau-Dora Memorial E **655** Teddy Bear

1979. Mittelbau-Dora Memorial, Nordhausen.
E2161 E **654** 35pf. black and violet 55 30

1979. Leipzig Autumn Fair. Multicoloured.
E2162 10pf. Type E **655** 15 15
E2163 25pf. Grosser Blumenberg building, Richard Wagner Square 40 25

E **656** Philipp Dengel E **657** Building Worker and Flats

1979. Socialist Personalities.
E2164 E **656** 10pf. black, green and deep green . . 20 15
E2165 – 10pf. black, bl & ind 20 15
E2166 – 10pf. blk, stone & bis 20 15
E2167 – 10pf. black, red & brn 20 15
DESIGNS: No. E2165, Otto Buchwitz; No. E2166, Bernard Koenen; No. E2167, Heinrich Rau.

1979. 30th Anniv of German Democratic Republic. Multicoloured.
E2168 5pf. Type E **657** 15 15
E2169 10pf. Boy and girl 15 15
E2170 15pf. Soldiers 70 50
E2171 20pf. Miner and Soviet soldier 15 15
MSE2172 90 × 110 mm. 1m. Family and flats (29 × 51 mm) . . . . 1·80 1·60

E **658** Girl applying Lipstick (1966/7) E **659** Vietnamese Soldier, Mother and Child

1979. Meissen Porcelain. Multicoloured.
E2173 5pf. Type E **658** 15 20
E2174 10pf. "Altozier" coffee pot (18th cent) 20 25
E2175 15pf. "Gosser Ausschnitt" coffee pot (1973/4) . . . 30 35
E2176 20pf. Vase with lid (18th century) 45 50
E2177 25pf. Parrot with cherry (18th century) 55 60
E2178 35pf. Harlequin with tankard (18th century) . . 75 90
E2179 50pf. Flower girl (18th century) . . . . 1·10 1·20
E2180 70pf. Sake bottle (18th century) . . . . 1·60 1·80

1979. "Invincible Vietnam".
E2181 E **659** 10pf.+5pf. black and red 35 20

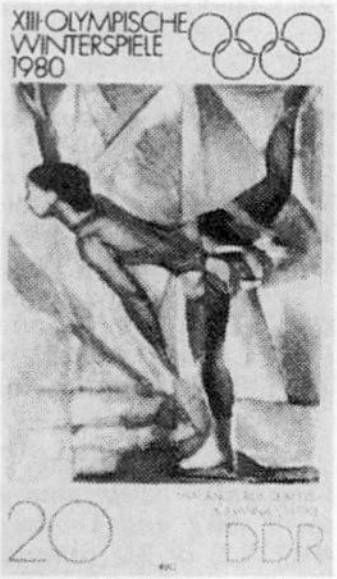

E **660** Rag-doll, 1800 E **661** "Balance on Ice" (Johanna Starke)

1979. Dolls. Multicoloured.
E2182 10pf. Type E **660** 20 35
E2183 15pf. Ceramic doll, 1960 . . 1·10 90
E2184 20pf. Wooden doll, 1780 . . 20 35
E2185 35pf. Straw puppet, 1900 . . 20 35
E2186 50pf. Jointed doll, 1800 . . 1·10 90
E2187 70pf. Tumbler-doll, 1820 . . 20 35

1980. Winter Olympic Games, Lake Placid. Multicoloured.
E2188 10pf. "Bobsleigh Start" (Gunter Rechn) (horiz) . . 20 15
E2189 20pf. Type E **661** 15 15
E2190 25pf.+10pf. "Ski jumpers" (plastic sculpture, Gunter Schultz) 20 15
E2191 35pf. "Speed Skaters at the Start" (Axel Wunsch) 1·60 1·40
MSE2192 79 × 55 mm. 1m. "Skiing Girls" (Lothar Zitmann) (29 × 24 mm) . . . . 2·20 2·20

E **662** Stille Musik Rock Garden, Grosssedlitz

1980. Baroque Gardens. Multicoloured.
E2193 10pf. Type E **662** 15 15
E2194 20pf. Belvedere Orangery, Weimar 15 15
E2195 50pf. Flower garden, Dornburg Castle 25 20
E2196 70pf. Park, Rheinsberg Castle . . . . 2·00 1·80

E **663** Cable-laying Machine and Dish Aerial

1980. Post Office Activities. Multicoloured.
E2212 10pf. Type E **663** 15 15
E2213 20pf. T.V. Tower, Berlin, and television 30 25

E **664** Johann Wolfgang Dobereiner (chemist, bicent)

1980. Celebrities' Birth Anniversaries.
E2214 E **664** 5pf. black and bistre 15 15
E2215 – 10pf. black and red 15 15
E2216 – 20pf. black and green 15 15
E2217 – 25pf. black and blue 15 15
E2218 – 35pf. black and blue 20 15
E2219 – 70pf. black and red 1·90 1·20
DESIGNS: 10pf. Frederic Joliot-Curie (physicist, and chemist, 80th anniv); 20pf. Johann Friedrich Naumann (zoologist, bicent); 25pf. Alfred Wegener (explorer and geophysicist, cent); 35pf. Carl von Clausewitz (Prussian general, bicent); 70pf. Helene Weigel (actress, 80th anniv).

E **665** Karl Marx University, Leipzig

E **666** Werner Eggerath

1980. Leipzig Spring Fair. Multicoloured.
E2220 10pf. Type E **665** 20 15
E2221 25pf. "ZT 303" tractor . . 30 25

1980. 80th Birth Anniv of Werner Eggerath (socialist).
E2222 E **666** 10pf. brown and red 45 20

E **667** Cosmonauts and "Interkosmos" Emblem

1980. "Interkosmos" Programme. Sheet 109 × 89 mm.
MSE2223 E **667** 1m. multicoloured 2·30 2·10

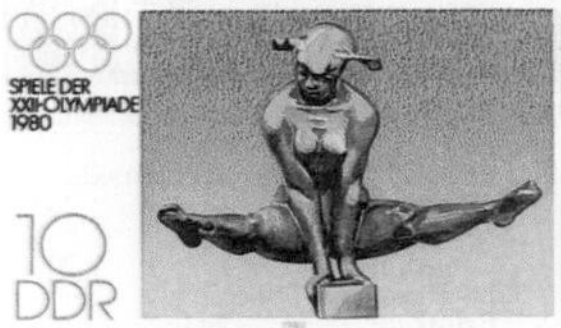

E **668** "On the Horizontal Beam" (sculpture, Erich Wurzer)

1980. Olympic Games, Moscow (1st issue). Multicoloured.
E2224 10pf. Type E **668** 15 15
E2225 20pf.+5pf. "Runners before the Winning Post" (Lothar Zitzmann) 15 15
E2226 50pf. "Coxless Four" (Wilfred Falkenthal) . . 1·40 1·20
See also Nos. E2247/9.

E **669** Flags of Member States

E **670** Co-operative Society Building (W. Gropius)

1980. 25th Anniv of Warsaw Pact.
E2227 E **669** 20pf. multicoloured 50 25

1980. Bauhaus Architecture. Multicoloured.
E2228 5pf. Type E **670** 15 15
E2229 10pf. Socialists' Memorial Place (M. v. d. Rhode) (horiz) 15 15
E2230 15pf. Monument to the Fallen of March 1922 (W. Gropius) 15 15
E2231 20pf. Steel Building 1926 (G. Muche and R. Paulick) (horiz) . . . 20 15
E2232 50pf. Trade Union school (H. Meyer) 30 20
E2233 70pf. Bauhaus building (W. Gropius) (horiz) . . 3·00 1·80

E **671** Rostock Buildings

1980. 18th Workers' Festival, Rostock. Mult.
E2234 10pf. Type E **671** 20 15
E2235 20pf. Costumed dancers 45 25

E **672** Radar Complex, Berlin-Schoenefeld Airport

1980. "Aerosozphilex 1980" International Airmail Exhibition, Berlin. Multicoloured.
E2236 20pf. Type E **672** 45 50
E2237 25pf. Ilyushin Il-62M at Schonefeld Airport . . . 45 50
E2238 35pf. PZL-106A Kruk crop-spraying airplane 65 60
E2239 70pf. Antonov An-2 aerial photography biplane and multispectrum camera . . . . 1·30 1·20
MSE2240 64 × 95 mm. 1m.+10pf. Ilyushin Il-62M jetliner and globe 2·40 2·40

E **673** Okapi

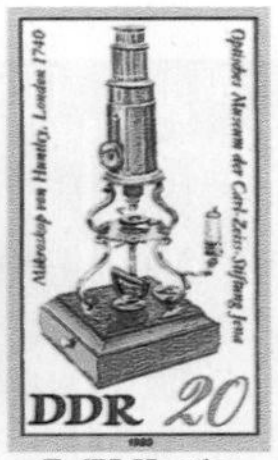

E **675** Huntley Microscope

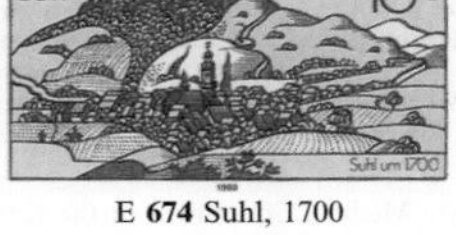

E **674** Suhl, 1700

1980. Endangered Animals. Multicoloured.
E2241 5pf. Type E **673** 15 15
E2242 10pf. Lesser pandas . . . 15 15
E2243 15pf. Maned wolf 20 15
E2244 20pf. Arabian oryx 20 15
E2245 25pf. White-eared pheasant 20 15
E2246 35pf. Musk oxen . . . . . 2·20 1·60

1980. Olympic Games, Moscow (2nd issue). As Type E **668**. Multicoloured.
E2247 10pf. "Judo" (Erhard Schmidt) 15 15
E2248 20pf.+10pf. "Swimmer" (Willi Sitte) (vert) . . . 20 20
E2249 50pf. "Spurt" (sculpture, Siegfried Schreiber) . . 1·60 1·20
MSE2250 79 × 55 mm. 1m. "Spinnakers" (Karl Raetsch) (29 × 24 mm) . . . . 2·75 2·20

1980. 6th National Youth Stamp Exhibition, Suhl. Multicoloured.
E2251 10pf.+5pf. Type E **674** . . 40 35
E2252 20pf. Modern Suhl 40 35

1980. Carl Zeiss Optical Museum, Jena. Mult.
E2253 20pf. Type E **675** 35 35
E2254 25pf. Magny microscope, 1751 . . . . 45 50
E2255 35pf. Amici microscope, 1845 . . . . 60 65
E2256 70pf. Zeiss microscope, 1873 . . . . 1·30 1·20

E **676** Majdanek Memorial

1980. War Victims' Memorial, Majdanek, Poland.
E2257 E **676** 35pf. multicoloured 60 30

E **677** Information Centre, Leipzig

1980. Leipzig Autumn Fair. Multicoloured.
E2258 10pf. Type E **677** 20 15
E2259 25pf. Carpet-knitting machine 55 25

E **678** Palace of Republic, Berlin

1980. 67th Interparliamentary Conference, Berlin.
E2260 E **678** 20pf. multicoloured 80 20

E **679** "Laughing Boy with Flute"

E **680** Clenched Fist and Star

1980. 400th Anniv of Frans Hals (artist). Multicoloured.
E2261 10pf. Type E **679** 15 15
E2262 20pf. "Portrait of Young Man in Drab Coat" . . 20 15
E2263 25pf. "The Mulatto" . . . 20 15
E2264 35pf. "Portrait of Young Man in Black Coat" . . 1·20 1·10
MSE2265 80 × 55 mm. 1m. brown (Self-portrait) (29 × 23 mm) . . 2·75 2·00

1980. "Solidarity".
E2266 E **680** 10pf.+5pf. turq & red 35 25

E **681** "Leccinum versipelle" ("Leccinum testaceo scabrum")

1980. Edible Mushrooms. Multicoloured.
E2267 5pf. Type E **681** 15 15
E2268 10pf. "Boletus miniatoporus" ("Boletus erythropus") 15 15
E2269 15pf. "Agaricus campestris" ("Agaricus campester") 20 15
E2270 20pf. "Xerocomus badius" 20 15
E2271 35pf. "Boletus edulis" . . 30 20
E2272 70pf. "Cantharellus cibarius" . . . . 2·40 2·00

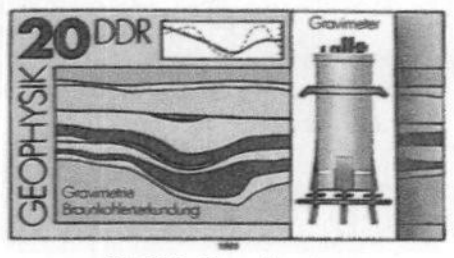

E **682** Gravimetry

1980. Geophysics. Multicoloured.
E2273 20pf. Type E **682** 35 30
E2274 25pf. Bore-hole measuring 45 45
E2275 35pf. Seismic prospecting 65 65
E2276 50pf. Seismology . . . . . 1·00 90

E **683** Radebeul–Radeburg Steam Locomotive

1980. Narrow-gauge Railways (1st series). Multicoloured.
E2277 20pf. Type E **683** 45 50
E2278 20pf. Bad Doberan–Ostseebad Kuhlungsborn steam locomotive . . . 45 50
E2279 25pf. Radebeul–Radeburg passenger carriage . . . 45 50
E2280 35pf. Bad Doberan–Ostseebad Kuhlungsborn passenger carriage . . . 45 50
See also Nos. E2342/5, E2509/12 and E2576/9.

E **684** Toy Steam Locomotive, 1850

E **685** Mozart

1980. Historical Toys. Multicoloured.
E2281 10pf. Type E **684** 20 50
E2282 20pf. Aeroplane, 1914 . . 1·10 95
E2283 25pf. Steam-roller, 1920 . . 20 30
E2284 35pf. Sailing ship, 1825 . . 20 30
E2285 40pf. Car, 1900 . . . . . 1·10 95
E2286 50pf. Balloon, 1920 . . . 20 30

1981. 225th Birth Anniv of Wolfgang Amadeus Mozart (composer). Sheet 55 × 80 mm.
MSE2287 E **685** 1m. black, carmine-rose and stone . . . 2·40 1·80

E **686** "Malus pumila"

E **687** Heinrich von Stephan

1981. Rare Plants in Berlin Arboretum. Mult.
E2288 5pf. Type E **686** 15 15
E2289 10pf. "Halesia carolina" (horiz) 15 15
E2290 20pf. "Colutea arborescens" 20 15
E2291 25pf. "Paulownia tomentosa" 25 15

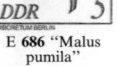

E2292 35pf. "Lonicera periclymenum" (horiz) 30 15
E2293 50pf. "Calycanthus floridus" . . . . 2·50 2·30

1981. 150th Birth Anniv of Heinrich von Stephan (founder of U.P.U.).
E2294 E **687** 10pf. black and yellow 35 20

E **688** Soldiers on Parade

1981. 25th Anniv of National People's Army. Multicoloured.
E2295 10pf. Type E **688** 20 15
E2296 20pf. Marching soldiers . . 30 15

E **689** Marx and Lenin

1981. 10th East German Socialist Party Congress (1st series).
E2297 E **689** 10pf. multicoloured 25 20
See Nos. E2309/**MS**2313.

E **690** Counter Clerks

1981. Post Office Training. Multicoloured.
E2298 5pf. Type E **690** 15 15
E2299 10pf. Telephone engineers 20 15
E2300 15pf. Radio communications 20 15
E2301 20pf. Rosa Luxemburg Engineering School, Leipzig 25 15
E2302 25pf. Freidrich List Communications School, Dresden . . . . 1·40 1·10

E **691** Erich Baron E **692** Hotel Merkur Leipzig

1981. Socialist Personalities.
E2303 E **691** 10pf. black and green 20 10
E2304 – 10pf. black and yellow 20 10
E2305 – 10pf. black and blue 20 10
E2306 – 10pf. black and brown 20 10
DESIGNS: No. E2304, Conrad Blenkle; E2305, Arthur Ewert; E2306, Walter Stoecker.

1981. Leipzig Spring Fair. Multicoloured.
E2307 10pf. Type E **692** 20 15
E2308 25pf. Open-cast mining machine 45 25

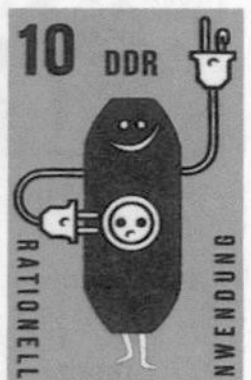

E **693** "Ernst Thalmann" (Willi Sitte) E **695** Plugs and Socket

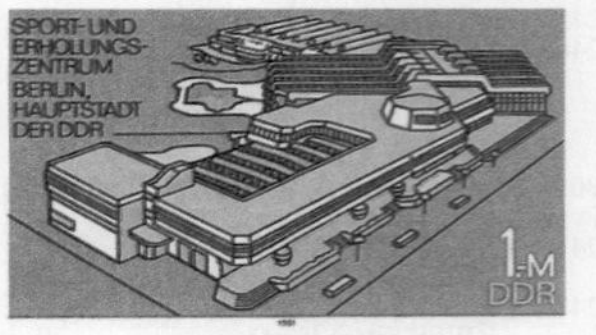

E **694** Sports Centre

1981. 10th East German Socialist Party Congress (2nd series). Multicoloured.
E2309 10pf. Type E **693** 15 15
E2310 20pf. "Brigadier" (Bernhard Heisig) . . . 15 15
E2311 25pf. "Festival Day" (Rudolf Bergander) . . 1·10 90
E2312 35pf. "Comrades in Arms" (Paul Michaelis) 20 15
MSE2313 108 × 82 mm. 1m. "When Communists are Dreaming" (Walter Womacka) . . . . . . 1·90 1·80

1981. Sports Centre, Berlin. Sheet 110 × 90 mm.
MSE2314 E **694** 1m. multicoloured 2·40 2·00

1981. Conservation of Energy.
E2315 E **695** 10pf. black & orange 25 20

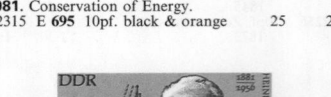

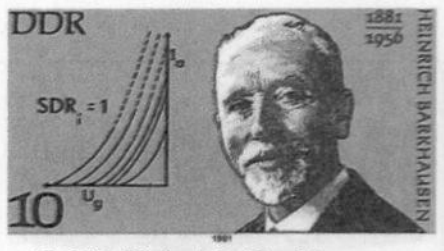

E **696** Heinrich Barkhausen

1981. Celebrities' Birth Anniversaries.
E2316 E **696** 10pf. black and blue 15 15
E2317 – 20pf. black and red 20 15
E2318 – 25pf. black and brown . . . . . . 2·75 1·80
E2319 – 35pf. black and violet 25 15
E2320 – 50pf. black and green 35 15
E2321 – 70pf. black and brown 55 25
DESIGNS: 10pf. Type E **696** (physicist, birth centenary); 20pf. Johannes R. Becher (writer, 90th birth anniv); 25pf. Richard Dedekind (mathematician, 150th birth anniv); 35pf. Georg Philipp Telemann (composer, 300th anniv); 50pf. Adelbert V. Chamisso (poet and naturalist, bicentenary); 70pf. Wilhelm Raabe (novelist, 150th birth anniv).

E **697** Free German Youth Members and Banner

1981. 11th Free German Youth Parliament. Multicoloured.
E2322 10pf. Type E **697** 25 35
E2323 20pf. Free German Youth members instructing foreign students 25 35

E **698** Worlitz Park

1981. Landscaped Parks. Multicoloured.
E2324 5pf. Type E **698** 15 15
E2325 10pf. Tiefurt Park, Weimar 15 15
E2326 15pf. Marxwalde 15 15
E2327 20pf. Branitz Park 20 15
E2328 25pf. Treptow Park, Berlin 2·20 1·50
E2329 35pf. Wiesenburg Park . . 30 25

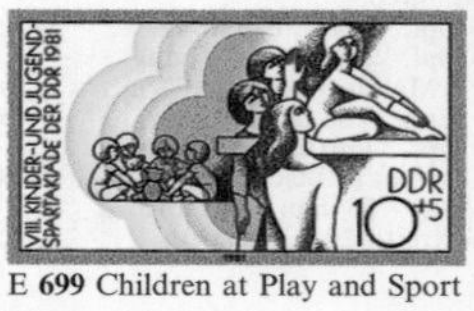

E **699** Children at Play and Sport

1981. 8th Children's and Young People's Sports Days, Berlin. Multicoloured.
E2330 10pf.+5pf. Type E **699** . . 65 45
E2331 20pf. Artistic gymnastics 30 20

E **700** Berlin Theatre

1981. Birth Bicentenary of Karl Friedrich Schinkel (architect).
E2332 E **700** 10pf. stone and black 90 15
E2333 – 25pf. stone and black 2·20 80
DESIGN: 25pf. Old Museum, Berlin.

E **701** Throwing the Javelin from a Wheel chair E **702** House, Zaulsdorf

1981. International Year of Disabled Persons. Multicoloured.
E2334 5pf. Type E **701** 25 20
E2335 15pf. Disabled people in art gallery 25 20

1981. Half-timbered Buildings. Multicoloured.
E2336 10pf. Type E **702** 15 15
E2337 20pf. "Sugar-loaf" cottage, Gross Zicker (horiz) . . 15 15
E2338 25pf. Farmhouse, Weckersdorf 20 15
E2339 35pf. House, Pillgram (horiz) 25 15
E2340 50pf. House, Eschenbach 35 25
E2341 70pf. House, Ludersdorf (horiz) . . . . 3·50 2·40

1981. Narrow-Gauge Railways (2nd series). As Type E **683**. Multicoloured.
E2342 5pf. black and red 20 30
E2343 5pf. black and red 20 30
E2344 15pf. multicoloured . . . 20 30
E2345 20pf. multicoloured . . . 20 30
DESIGNS: Nos. E2342, Freital–Kurort Kipsdorf steam locomotive; E2343, Putbus–Gohren steam locomotive; E2344, Freital–Kurort Kipsdorf luggage van; E2345, Putbus–Gohren passenger carriage.

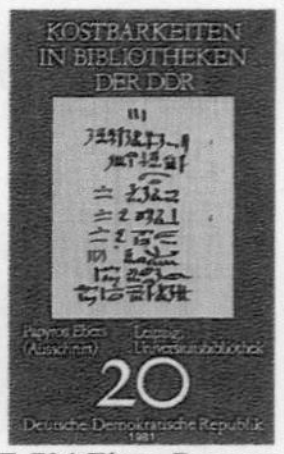

E **703** Chemical Works E **704** Ebers Papyrus (Leipzig University Library)

1981. Leipzig Autumn Fair. Multicoloured.
E2346 10pf. Type E **703** 20 15
E2347 25pf. New Draper's Hall (horiz) 45 30

1981. Precious Books from East German Libraries. Multicoloured.
E2348 20pf. Type E **704** 15 15
E2349 35pf. Maya manuscript (Dresden Library) . . 20 15
E2350 50pf. Miniature from "Les six visions Messire Francoys Petrarque" (Berlin State Library) . . 1·70 1·40

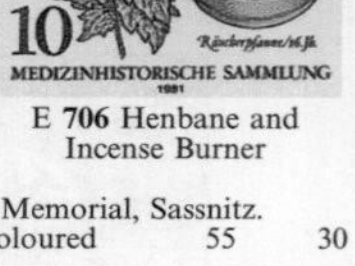

E **705** Sassnitz Memorial E **706** Henbane and Incense Burner

1981. Resistance Fighters' Memorial, Sassnitz.
E2351 E **705** 35pf. multicoloured 55 30

1981. Early Medical Equipment in the Karl-Sudhoff Institute, Leipzig. Multicoloured.
E2352 10pf. Type E **706** 15 15
E2353 20pf. Dental instruments 15 15
E2354 25pf. Forceps 20 15
E2355 35pf. Bladder knife and hernia shears 25 15

E2356 50pf. Speculum and gynaecological forceps (vert) . . . . 3·00 2·50
E2357 85pf. Triploid elevators (vert) 60 30

E **707** Letter from Friedrich Engels, 1840 E **708** African breaking Chains

1981. Stamp Day. Multicoloured.
E2358 10pf.+5pf. Type E **707** . . 1·00 35
E2359 20pf. Postcard from Karl Marx, 1878 . . . . . . 20 15

1981. "Solidarity".
E2360 E **708** 10pf.+5pf. mult . . . 30 15

E **709** Tug E **710** Windmill, Dabel

1981. Inland Shipping. Multicoloured.
E2361 10pf. Type E **709** 15 15
E2362 20pf. Tug and barges . . . 20 15
E2363 25pf. Diesel-electric paddle-ferry, River Elbe 20 15
E2364 35pf. Ice-breaker in the Oder estuary 25 15
E2365 50pf. "Schonewalde" (motor barge) 35 25
E2366 85pf. Dredger . . . . . . 3·00 2·75

1981. Windmills. Multicoloured.
E2367 10pf. Type E **710** 15 15
E2368 20pf. Pahrenz 15 15
E2369 25pf. Dresden-Gohlis . . . 15 15
E2370 70pf. Ballstadt . . . . . . 2·00 1·60

E **711** Snake, 1850 E **712** Coffee Pot, 1715

1981. Historical Toys. Multicoloured.
E2371 10pf. Type E **711** . . . 20 35
E2372 20pf. Teddy bear, 1910 . . . 20 35
E2373 25pf. Goldfish, 1935 . . . 1·30 1·10
E2374 35pf. Hobby-horse, 1850 1·30 1·10
E2375 40pf. Pull-along duck, 1800 . . . . 20 35
E2376 70pf. Clockwork frog, 1930 . . . . 20 35

1982. 300th Birth Anniv of Johann Friedrich Bottger (founder of Meissen China Works). Multicoloured.
E2377 10pf. Type E **712** 20 25
E2378 20pf. Vase decorated with flowers, 1715 . . . . 45 50
E2379 25pf. "Oberon" (figurine), 1969 . . . . 60 55
E2380 35pf. Vase "Day and Night", 1979 . . . . . 80 75
MSE2381 89 × 110 mm. 50pf. Portrait medal; 50pf. Bottger's seal 3·00 2·40

E **713** Post Office, Bad Liebenstein

1982. Post Office Building. Multicoloured.
E2382 20pf. Type E **713** 20 15
E2383 25pf. Telecommunications Centre, Berlin 20 15
E2384 35pf. Head Post Office, Erfurt 25 15
E2385 50pf. Head Post Office, Dresden 6 . . . . . . 1·90 1·60

E 714 Alpine Marmot

E 715 Silhouette of Goethe

1982. International Fur Auction, Leipzig. Multicoloured.
E2386 10pf. Type E **714** 15 15
E2387 20pf. Polecat 20 15
E2388 25pf. European mink . . . 20 15
E2389 35pf. Beech marten . . . 1·50 1·30

1982. Johann Wolfgang von Goethe and Friedrich von Schiller (writers) Commemoration. Sheet 110 × 90 mm containing Type E **715** and similar vert design. Multicoloured.
MSE2390 50pf. Type E **715** (150th death anniv); 50pf. Silhouette of Schiller (175th death (1980) and 225th birth (1984) annivs) . . . 2·75 2·40

E 716 West Entrance to Fairground

1982. Leipzig Spring Fair. Multicoloured.
E2391 10pf. Type E **716** 20 15
E2392 25pf. Seamless steel tube plant, Riesa Zeithain . . 45 25

E 717 Dr. Robert Koch E 718 Max Fechner

1982. Centenary of Discovery of Tubercle Bacillus. Sheet 80 × 55 mm.
MSE2393 E **717** 1m. multicoloured 2·40 2·30

1982. Socialist Personalities.
E2394 E **718** 10pf. brown 20 10
E2395 – 10pf. green 20 10
E2396 – 10pf. lilac 20 10
E2397 – 10pf. blue 20 10
E2398 – 10pf. green 20 10
DESIGNS: No. E2395, Ottomar Geschke; E2396, Helmut Lehmann; E2397, Herbert Warnke; E2398, Otto Winzer.

E 719 Meadow Saffron E 720 Decorative Initial "I"

1982. Poisonous Plants. Multicoloured.
E2399 10pf. Type E **719** 15 15
E2400 15pf. Bog arum 15 15
E2401 20pf. Labrador tea 20 15
E2402 25pf. Bryony 20 15
E2403 35pf. Monkshood 25 20
E2404 50pf. Henbane . . . . . 2·00 1·50

1982. International "Art of the Book" Exhibition, Leipzig.
E2405 E **720** 15pf. multicoloured 55 60
E2406 – 35pf. brn, red & blk 55 60
DESIGN: 35pf. Exhibition emblem.

E 721 "Mother with Child" (W. Womacka) E 722 Osprey

1982. 10th Free German Trade Unions Association Congress, Berlin.
E2407 E **721** 10pf. black, red and yellow 15 15
E2408 – 20pf. multicoloured 20 15
E2409 – 25pf. multicoloured 90 70
DESIGNS—HORIZ: 20pf. "Discussion by Collective of Innovators" (Willi Neubert). VERT: 25pf. "Young Couple" (Karl-Heinz Jakob).

1982. Protected Birds. Multicoloured.
E2410 10pf. Type E **722** 20 15
E2411 20pf. White-tailed sea eagle (horiz) 20 15
E2412 25pf. Little owl 20 15
E2413 35pf. Eagle owl . . . . . 1·90 1·50

E 723 Old and Modern Buildings

1982. 19th Workers' Festival, Neubrandenburg. Multicoloured.
E2414 10pf. Type E **723** 25 20
E2415 20pf. Couple in traditional costume 55 40

E 724 Memorial Medal

1982. Birth Centenary of Georgi Dimitrov (Bulgarian statesman). Sheet 80 × 55 mm.
MSE2416 E **724** 1m. multicoloured 3·00 2·10

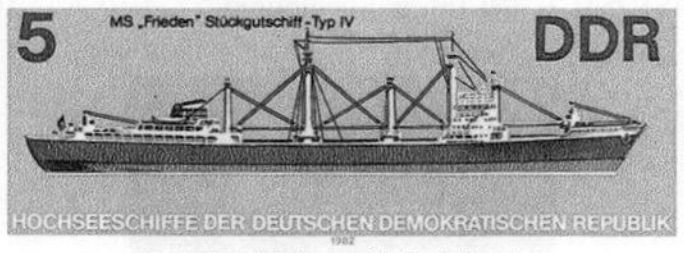

E 725 "Frieden" (freighter)

1982. Ocean-going Ships. Multicoloured.
E2417 5pf. Type E **725** 15 15
E2418 10pf. "Fichtelberg" (roll on roll off freighter) . . 15 15
E2419 15pf. "Brocken" (heavy cargo carrier) 15 15
E2420 20pf. "Weimar" (container ship) 20 15
E2421 25pf. "Vorwarts" (freighter) 20 15
E2422 35pf. "Berlin" (container ship) . . . . 1·80 1·50

E 726 Members' Activities

1982. 30th Anniv of Sports and Science Association.
E2423 E **726** 20pf. multicoloured 40 20

E 727 Bird Wedding

1982. Sorbian Folk Customs. Multicoloured.
E2424 10pf. Type E **727** 20 20
E2425 20pf. Shrove Tuesday procession 30 30
E2426 25pf. Egg rolling 45 40
E2427 35pf. Painted Easter eggs 65 60
E2428 40pf. St. John's Day riders 75 75
E2429 50pf. Distribution of Christmas gifts to hard-working children . . . . 1·00 95

E **728** Schwerin, 1640

1982. 7th National Youth Stamp Exhibition, Schwerin. Multicoloured.
E2430 10pf.+5pf. Type E **728** . . 30 40
E2431 20pf. Modern Schwerin . . 30 40

E **729** Flag and Pioneers

1982. 7th Pioneers Meeting, Dresden. Mult.
E2432 10pf.+5pf. Type E **729** . . 60 55
E2433 20pf. Trumpet and drum 20 15

E **730** "Stormy Sea" (Ludolf Backhuysen)

1982. Paintings in Schwerin State Museum. Multicoloured.
E2434 5pf. Type E **730** 15 15
E2435 10pf. "Music making at Home" (Frans van Mieris) (vert) 15 15
E2436 20pf. "The Watchman" (Carel Fabritius) (vert) 20 15
E2437 25pf. "Company of Peasants" (Adriaen Brouwer) 25 15
E2438 35pf. "Breakfast Table with Ham" (Willem Claesz Heda) 30 15
E2439 70pf. "River Landscape" (Jan van Goyen) . . . . 2·40 2·00

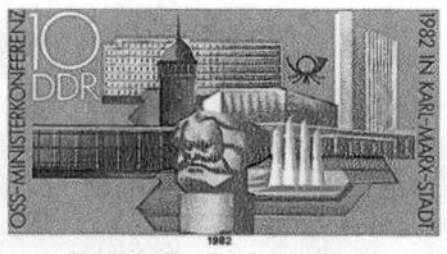

E **731** Karl-Marx-Stadt

1982. 13th Socialist Countries' Postal Ministers Conference, Karl-Marx-Stadt.
E2440 E **731** 10pf. multicoloured 30 25

E **732** Stentzlers Hof

1982. Leipzig Autumn Fair. Multicoloured.
E2441 10pf. Type E **732** 15 15
E2442 25pf. Amber box, ring and pendant 40 25

E **733** Auschwitz-Birkenau Memorial E **734** Federation Badge

1982. War Victims' Memorial, Auschwitz-Birkenau.
E2443 E **733** 35pf. blue, blk & red 35 25

1982. 9th International Federation of Resistance Fighters Congress, Berlin.
E2444 E **734** 10pf. multicoloured 35 25

E **735** "Anemone hupehensis" E **736** Palestinian Family

1982. Autumn Flowers. Multicoloured.
E2445 5pf. Type E **735** 15 15
E2446 10pf. French marigolds . . 15 15
E2447 15pf. Gazania 15 15
E2448 20pf. Sunflower 20 15
E2449 25pf. Annual chrysanthemum 25 15
E2450 35pf. Cosmea . . . . . . 2·75 1·70

1982. Solidarity with Palestinian People.
E2451 E **736** 10pf.+5pf. mult . . . 45 20

E **737** "B 1000" Ambulance E **738** Fair Emblem

1982. IFA Vehicles. Multicoloured.
E2452 5pf. Type E **737** 15 15
E2453 10pf. Road cleaner 15 15
E2454 20pf. "LD 3000" omnibus 20 15
E2455 25pf. "LD 3000" lorry . . 25 15
E2456 35pf. "W 50" lorry 30 15
E2457 85pf. "W 50" milk tanker 2·75 2·20

1982. 25th "Masters of Tomorrow" Fair, Leipzig.
E2458 E **738** 20pf. multicoloured 35 25

E **739** Aircraft and Envelope E **740** Seal of Eisleben, 1500

1982. Air.
E2459 E **739** 5pf. black and blue 15 15
E2460 15pf. black and mauve 20 20
E2461 20pf. black and orange 35 15
E2462 25pf. black and bistre 45 20
E2463 30pf. black and green 25 15
E2464 40pf. black and green 30 15
E2465 1m. black and blue 1·20 35
E2466 3m. black and brown 3·00 1·10
E2467 5m. black and red 5·00 1·20

1982. 500th Birth Anniv of Martin Luther (Protestant reformer).
E2471 10pf. Type E **740** 15 15
E2472 20pf. Luther as Junker Jog, 1521 . . . . 30 15
E2473 35pf. Seal of Wittenberg, 1500 . . . . 55 15
E2474 85pf. Luther (after Cranach) . . . . 3·25 2·10
See also No. **MS**2548.

E **741** Carpenter E **742** Johannes Brahms

1982. Mechanical Toys. Multicoloured.
E2475 10pf. Type E **741** 20 35
E2476 20pf. Shoemaker . . . . . 1·30 1·00
E2477 25pf. Baker 20 35
E2478 35pf. Cooper 20 35
E2479 40pf. Tanner . . . . 1·30 1·00
E2480 70pf. Wheelwright 20 35

1983. 150th Birth Anniv of Johannes Brahms (composer). Sheet 55 × 80 mm.
MSE2481 E **742** 1m.15, green, brown and sepia . . . . 3·75 2·40

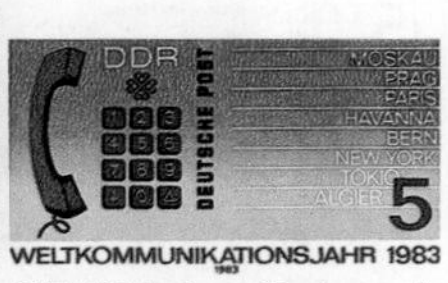

E **743** Franz Dahlem
E **744** Telephone Handset and Push-buttons

1983. Socialist Personalities.
E2482 E **743** 10pf. brown 20 15
E2483 – 10pf. green 20 15
E2484 – 10pf. green 20 15
E2485 – 10pf. lilac 20 15
E2486 – 10pf. blue 20 15
DESIGN: No. E2483, Karl Maron; E2484, Josef Miller; E2485, Fred Oelssner; E2486, Siegfried Radel.

1983. World Communications Year.
E2487 E **744** 5pf. brown, black and deep brown 20 15
E2488 – 10pf. blue, turquoise and deep blue . . 20 15
E2489 – 20pf. green, deep green and black 20 15
E2490 – 35pf. multicoloured 1·60 1·00
DESIGNS: 10pf. Aerials and tankers (Rugen Radio); 20pf. Aircraft, container ship, letter and parcel; 35pf. Optical fibre cables.

E **745** Otto Nuschke
E **746** Stolberg Town Hall

1983. Birth Cent of Otto Nuschke (politician).
E2491 E **745** 20pf. light brown, black and brown 30 20

1983. Historic Town Halls. Multicoloured.
E2492 10pf. Type E **746** 15 15
E2493 20pf. Gera (vert) 20 15
E2494 25pf. Possneck (vert) . . . 20 15
E2495 35pf. Berlin . . . . . . 1·60 1·30

E **747** Petershof

1983. Leipzig Spring Fair. Multicoloured.
E2496 10pf. Type E **747** 20 15
E2497 25pf. Robotron micro-electronic calculator . . 40 25

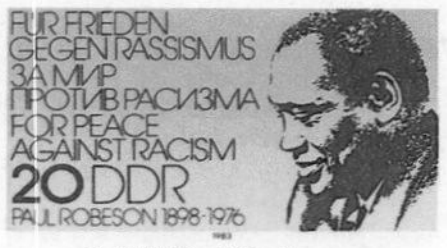

E **748** Paul Robeson

1983. 85th Birth Anniv of Paul Robeson (singer).
E2498 E **748** 20pf. multicoloured 35 25

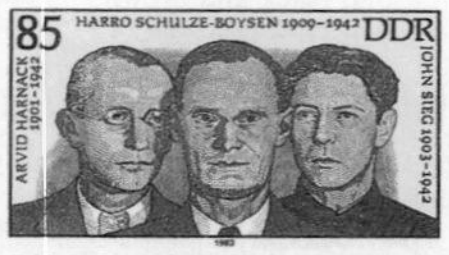

E **749** Harnack, Schulze-Boysen and Sieg

1983. 40th Death Annivs of Arvid Harnack, Harro Schulze-Boysen and John Sieg (Resistance workers). Sheet 80 × 55 mm.
MSE2499 E **749** 85pf. black and green . . . . 1·60 1·50

E **750** Karl Marx and Newspaper Mastheads

1983. Death Cent of Karl Marx. Multicoloured.
E2500 10pf. Type E **750** 15 15
E2501 20pf. Marx, Lyons silk weavers and title page of "Deutsche-Franzosische Jahrbucher" 20 15
E2502 35pf. Marx, Engels and "Communist Manifesto" 25 15
E2503 50pf. Marx and German, Russian and French versions of "Das Kapital" 30 25
E2504 70pf. Marx and part of letter to Wilhelm Bracke containing commentary on German Workers' Party Programme . . . 45 25
E2505 85pf. Globe and banner portraying Marx, Engels, Lenin . . . . . 3·00 2·75
MSE2506 81 × 56 mm. 1m.15 Karl Marx (26 × 32 mm) . . . . . 2·75 2·30

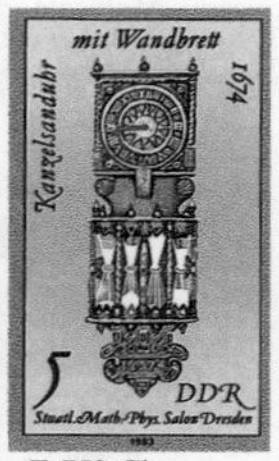

E **751** "Athene"
E **752** Chancery Hourglass with Wallmount, 1674

1983. Sculptures in State Museum, Berlin.
E2507 E **751** 10pf. brown, light brown and blue 20 15
E2508 – 20pf. brown, light brown and green 55 25
DESIGN: 20pf. "Amazon".

1983. Narrow-gauge Railways (3rd series). As Type E **683**.
E2509 15pf. grey, black and red 55 55
E2510 20pf. multicoloured . . . 55 55
E2511 20pf. grey, black and red 55 55
E2512 50pf. brown, black and grey 55 55
DESIGNS: No. E2509, Wernigerode–Nordhausen steam locomotive; E2510, Wernigerode–Nordhausen passenger carriage; E2511, Zittau–Kurort Oybin/Kurort Jonsdorf steam locomotive; E2512, Zittau–Kurort Oybin/Kurort Jonsdorf luggage van.

1983. Hourglasses and Sundials. Multicoloured.
E2513 5pf. Type E **752** 15 15
E2514 10pf. Chancery hour-glass, 1700 . . . . 15 15
E2515 20pf. Horizontal table sundial, 1611 . . . . 20 15
E2516 30pf. Equatorial sundial, 1750 . . . . 30 20
E2517 50pf. Equatorial sundial, 1760 . . . . 55 30
E2518 85pf. "Noon Gun" table sundial, 1800 . . . . 3·00 2·20

E **753** "Coryphantha elephantidens"
E **755** "Glasewaldt and Zinna defending the Barricade, Berlin, 1848" (Theodor Hosemann)

E **754** Thimo and Wilhelm

1983. Cultivated Cacti. Multicoloured.
E2519 5pf. Type E **753** 15 15
E2520 10pf. "Thelocactus schwarzii" 15 15
E2521 20pf. "Leuchtenbergia principis" 20 15
E2522 25pf. "Submatucana madisoniorum" 25 15
E2523 35pf. "Oroya peruviana" 30 20
E2524 50pf. "Copiapoa cinerea" 2·10 1·80

1983. Founders of Naumberg Cathedral. Statues in the West Choir. Multicoloured.
E2525 20pf. Type E **754** 50 45
E2526 25pf. Gepa and Gerburg 60 50
E2527 35pf. Hermann and Reglindis 65 60
E2528 85pf. Eckehard and Uta 1·80 1·50

1983. "Junior Sozphilex 1983" Stamp Exhibition, Berlin.
E2529 E **755** 10pf.+5pf. brown, black and red . . 70 55
E2530 – 20pf. multicoloured 25 15
DESIGN—HORIZ: 20pf. "Instruction at Polytechnic" (Harald Metzkes).

E **756** Simon Bolivar and Alexander von Humboldt

1983. Birth Bicentenary of Simon Bolivar.
E2531 E **756** 35pf. black, brown and deep brown 60 30

E **757** Exercise with Balls
E **758** Arms of Cottbus

1983. 7th Gymnastics and Sports Festival and 9th Children and Young People's Sports Days, Leipzig. Multicoloured.
E2532 10pf.+5pf. Type E **757** . . 55 40
E2533 20pf. Volleyball 20 25

1983. Town Arms (1st series).
E2534 E **758** 50pf. multicoloured 1·00 85
E2535 – 50pf. multicoloured 1·00 85
E2536 – 50pf. red, black and silver . . . . . . 1·00 85
E2537 – 50pf. multicoloured 1·00 85
E2538 – 50pf. black, red and silver . . . . . . 1·00 85
DESIGNS: No. E2535, Dresden; E2536, Erfurt; E2537, Frankfurt-on-Oder. (21 × 39 mm); No. E2538, Berlin.
See also Nos. E2569/73 and E2644/8.

E **759** Central Fair Palace
E **760** Militiaman

1983. Leipzig Autumn Fair. Multicoloured.
E2539 10pf. Type E **759** 20 15
E2540 25pf. Microchip 55 25

1983. 30th Anniv of Workers' Militia. Sheet 63 × 86 mm.
MSE2541 E **760** 1m. multicoloured 1·10 1·10

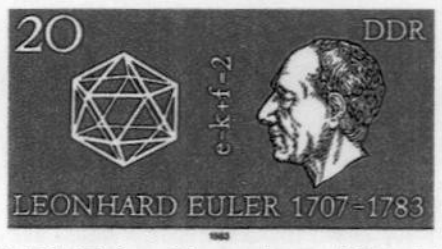

E **761** Euler, Formula and Model

1983. Death Bicentenary of Leonhard Euler (mathematician).
E2542 E **761** 20pf. blue and black 45 30

E **762** Sanssouci Castle

1983. Public Palaces and Gardens of Potsdam-Sanssouci. Multicoloured.
E2543 10pf. Type E **762** 15 15
E2544 20pf. Chinese tea house . . 25 15
E2545 40pf. Charlottenhof Palace 55 25
E2546 50pf. Film museum (former stables) . . . . 3·00 2·20

E **763** "Mother Homeland" (Yevgeni Vuzhetich)
E **765** Learning to Read and Write

E **764** "D.M.L." (Dr. Martin Luther)

1983. Vologrand War Memorial.
E2547 E **763** 35pf. blue, blk & grn 65 30

1983. 500th Birth Anniv of Martin Luther (Protestant reformer) (2nd issue). Sheet 108 × 83 mm.
MSE2548 E **764** 1m. multicoloured 3·50 3·00

1983. "Solidarity with Nicaragua".
E2549 E **765** 10pf.+5pf. mult . . . 40 25

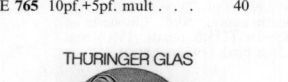

E **766** Cockerel

1983. Thuringian Glass. Multicoloured.
E2550 10pf. Type E **766** 20 15
E2551 20pf. Beaker 20 15
E2552 25pf. Vase 20 15
E2553 70pf. Goblet . . . . . . 2·40 1·80

E **767** Luge

1983. Winter Olmpic Games, Sarajevo (1984).
E2554 E **767** 10pf.+5pf. multicoloured . .
E2555 – 20pf.+10pf. multicoloured . .
E2556 – 25pf. multicoloured
E2557 – 35pf. multicoloured
MSE2558 83 × 57 mm. 85pf. blue and silver . . . . 2·10 1·70
DESIGNS: 20pf. Cross-country skiing and ski jumping; 25pf. Cross-country skiing; 35pf. Biathlion; 85pf. Olympic Centre, Sarajevo.

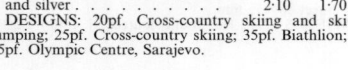

E **768** Dove and Greeting in German and English

1983. New Year. Sheet 93 × 83 mm containing Type E **768** and similar horiz designs, each showing dove and greeting in named languages. Multicoloured.
MSE2559 10pf. Type E **768**; 20pf. German and Russian; 25pf. French and German; 35pf. Spanish and German . . . . . 2·10 1·60

E **769** Dr. Otto Schott (chemist)
E **770** Friedrich Ebert

1984. Centenary of Jena Glass.
E2560 E **769** 20pf. multicoloured 35 25

1984. Socialist Personalities.
E2561 E **770** 10pf. black 20 15
E2562 – 10pf. green 20 15
E2563 – 10pf. black 20 15
DESIGNS: No. E2562, Fritz Grosse; E2563, Albert Norden.

E **771** Mendelssohn

1984. 175th Birth Anniv of Felix Mendelssohn Bartholdy (composer). Sheet 82 × 57 mm.
MSE2564 E **771** 85pf. multicoloured . . . 1·10 1·00

E **772** Milestones, Muhlau and Oederan

E **773** Old Town Hall, Leipzig

1984. Postal Milestones. Multicoloured.
E2565 10pf. Type E **772** 15 15
E2566 20pf. Milestones, Johanngeorgenstadt and Schonbrunn 20 20
E2567 35pf. Distance column, Freiberg 55 40
E2568 85pf. Distance column, Pegau . . . . 1·00 95

1984. Town Arms (2nd series). As Type E **758**.
E2569 50pf. multicoloured . . . 65 55
E2570 50pf. red, black and silver 65 55
E2571 50pf. multicoloured . . . 65 55
E2572 50pf. multicoloured . . . 65 55
E2573 50pf. multicoloured . . . 65 55
DESIGNS: No. E2569, Gera; E2570, Halle; E2571, Karl-Marx-Stadt; E2572, Leipzig; E2573, Magdeburg.

1984. Leipzig Spring Fair. Multicoloured.
E2574 10pf. Type E **773** 20 15
E2575 25pf. Body stamping press 30 25

1984. Narrow-gauge Railways (4th series). As Type E **683**.
E2576 30pf. grey, black and red 30 30
E2577 40pf. grey, black and red 40 35
E2578 60pf. multicoloured . . . 55 60
E2579 80pf. multicoloured . . . 65 80
DESIGNS: 30pf. Cranzahl–Kurort Oberwiesenthal steam locomotive; 40pf. Selketalbahn steam locomotive; 60pf. Selketalbahn passenger carriage; 80pf. Cranzahl–Kurort Oberwiesenthal passenger carriage.

E **774** Town Hall, Rostock

E **775** Telephone, Letter, Pencil and Headquarters

1984. 7th International Society for Preservation of Monuments General Assembly, Rostock and Dresden. Multicoloured.
E2580 10pf. Type E **774** 15 15
E2581 15pf. Albrecht Castle, Meissen 20 15
E2582 40pf. Gateway, Rostock (vert) 60 45
E2583 85pf. Stables, Dresden . . 1·20 1·00

1984. 25th Meeting of Posts and Telecommunications Commission of Council of Mutual Economic Aid, Cracow.
E2584 E **775** 70pf. multicoloured 70 40

E **776** Cast Iron Bowl

E **777** String Puppet

1984. Cast Iron from Lauchhammer. Multicoloured.
E2585 20pf. Type E **776** 25 20
E2586 85pf. "Climber" (Fritz Cremer) . . . . 1·00 1·00

1984. Puppets. Multicoloured.
E2587 50pf. Type E **777** 30 50
E2588 80pf. Hand puppet 60 75

E **778** Marchers with Flags

1984. National Youth Festival, Berlin. Multicoloured.
E2589 10pf.+5pf. Type E **778** . . 25 25
E2590 20pf. Young construction workers 25 35

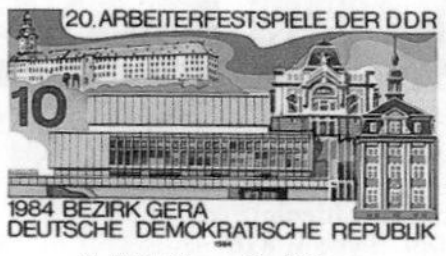

E **779** Gera Buildings

1984. 20th Workers' Festival, Gera. Multicoloured.
E2591 10pf. Type E **779** 20 20
E2592 20pf. Couple in traditional costume 35 25

E **780** Salt Carrier

E **781** Bakers' Seal, Berlin

1984. National Stamp Exhibition, Halle. Mult.
E2593 10pf.+5pf. Type E **780** . . 20 15
E2594 20pf. Citizen of Halle with his bride 30 25

1984. Historical Seals of 1442. Multicoloured.
E2595 5pf. Type E **781** 35 20
E2596 10pf. Wool weavers, Berlin 65 35
E2597 20pf. Wool weavers, Colln on Spree . . . . 1·30 50
E2598 35pf. Shoemakers, Colln on Spree . . . . 2·20 1·80

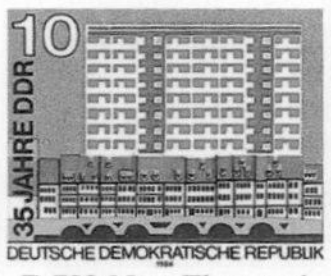

E **782** New Flats and Restored Terrace

E **783** Frege House, Katherine Street

1984. 35th Anniv of German Democratic Republic (1st issue). Multicoloured.
E2599 10pf. Type E **782** 20 15
E2600 20pf. Surface mining . . . 35 30
MSE2601 80 × 55 mm. 1m. Privy Council building . . . . 1·20 1·20
See also Nos. E2604/**MS**E2607 and E2069/**MS**E2613.

1984. Leipzig Autumn Fair. Multicoloured.
E2602 10pf. Type E **783** 20 15
E2603 25pf. Crystal jar from Olbernhau 35 25

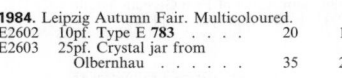

E **784** East Ironworks

1984. 35th Anniv of German Democratic Republic (2nd issue). Multicoloured.
E2604 10pf. Type E **784** 15 15
E2605 20pf. Soldiers, Mil Mi-8 helicopter, tank and warship 25 25
E2606 25pf. Petro-chemical complex, Schwedt . . . 50 40
MSE2607 110 × 90 mm. 1m. bright carmine (Family and new flats) (51 × 29 mm) . . . . 1·20 1·20

E **785** "Members of the Resistance" (Arno Wittig)

1984. Resistance Memorial, Georg-Schumann Building, Technical University of Dresden.
E2608 E **785** 35pf. multicoloured 70 30

E **786** Construction Workers

1984. 35th Anniv of German Democratic Republic (3rd issue). Multicoloured.
E2609 10pf. Type E **786** 15 15
E2610 20pf. Soldiers 25 20
E2611 25pf. Industrial workers . . 55 30
E2612 35pf. Agricultural workers 60 40
MSE2613 108 × 88 mm. 1m. Dove and national arms (vert) . . . 1·20 1·20

E **787** Magdeburg, 1551

1984. 8th National Youth Exhibition, Magdeburg. Multicoloured.
E2614 10pf.+5pf. Type E **787** . . 20 25
E2615 20pf. Modern Magdeburg 20 25

E **788** "Spring"

E **789** Entwined Cable and Red Star

1984. Statuettes by Balthasar Permoser in Green Vault, Dresden. Multicoloured.
E2616 10pf. Type E **788** 15 15
E2617 20pf. "Summer" 30 30
E2618 35pf. "Autumn" 55 45
E2619 70pf. "Winter" . . . . . 1·10 95
MSE2620 144 × 115 mm. No. E 2617 × 8 . . . . 2·20 2·20

1984. "Solidarity".
E2621 E **789** 10pf.+5pf. mult . . . 35 20

E **790** Falkenstein Castle

1984. Castles (1st series). Multicoloured.
E2622 10pf. Type E **790** 15 15
E2623 20pf. Kriebstein Castle . . 30 30
E2624 35pf. Ranis Castle 65 55
E2625 80pf. Neuenburg . . . . . 1·30 1·10
See also Nos. E2686/9 and E2742/5.

E **791** Queen and Princess

1984. Fairy Tales. "Dead Tsar's Daughter and the Seven Warriors" by Pushkin. Multicoloured.
E2626 5pf. Type E **791** 20 30
E2627 10pf. Princess and dog outside cottage 20 30
E2628 15pf. Princess and seven warriors . . . . 3·50 2·40
E2629 20pf. Princess holding poisoned apple . . . . 3·50 2·40
E2630 35pf. Princess awakened by Prince 20 30
E2631 50pf. Prince and Princess on horse 20 30

E **792** Anton Ackermann

E **794** Letter-box, 1850

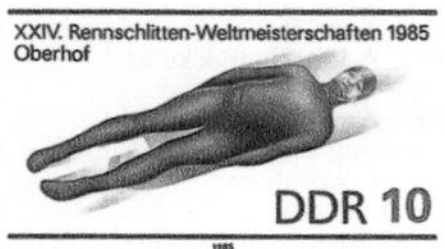

E **793** Luge

1985. Socialist Personalities.
E2632 E **792** 10pf. black 20 15
E2633 – 10pf. brown 20 15
E2634 – 10pf. purple 20 15
DESIGNS: No. E2633, Alfred Kurella; E2634, Otto Schon.

1985. 24th World Luge Championships, Oberhof.
E2635 E **793** 10pf. multicoloured 30 20

1984. Letter-boxes.
E2636 E **794** 10pf. brown and black 15 15
E2637 – 20pf. black, brown and red 20 20
E2638 – 35pf. multicoloured 45 40
E2639 – 50pf. brown, black and grey 60 55
DESIGNS: 20pf. Letter-box, 1860; 35pf. Letter-box, 1900; 50pf. Letter-box, 1920.

E **795** Semper Opera House, 1985

1985. Re-opening of Semper Opera House, Dresden. Sheet 57 × 80 mm.
MSE2640 E **795** 85pf. brown, grey and red . . . . 1·20 1·20

E **796** Bach Statue, Leipzig

E **797** Johann Sebastian Bach

1985. Leipzig Spring Fair. Multicoloured.
E2641 10pf. Type E **796** 20 15
E2642 25pf. Meissen porcelain pot 30 25

1985. 300th Birth Annivs of Bach and Handel and 400th Birth Anniv of Schutz (composers). Sheet 90 × 114 mm containing Type E **797** and similar vert designs, together with se-tenant horiz labels.
MSE2643 10pf. blue and bistre; 20pf. purple and bistre; 85pf. green and bistre . . . . 2·00 2·00
DESIGNS: 20pf. Georg Friedrich Handel; 85pf. Heinrich Schutz.

1985. Town Arms (3rd series). As Type E **758**. Multicoloured.
E2644 50pf. Neubrandenburg . . 65 55
E2645 50pf. Potsdam 65 55
E2646 50pf. Rostock 65 55
E2647 50pf. Schwerin 65 55
E2648 50pf. Suhl 65 55

E **798** Liberation Monument

E **800** Sigmund Jahn and Valeri Bykovski

E 799 Egon Erwin Kisch

1985. Liberation Monument, Seelow Heights.
E2649 E **798** 35pf. multicoloured 45 25

1985. Birth Centenary of Egon Erwin Kisch (journalist).
E2650 E **799** 35pf. multicoloured 55 45

1985. 40th Anniv of Defeat of Fascism. Multicoloured.
E2651 10pf. Type E **800** 15 15
E2652 20pf. Adolf Hennecke as miner 25 20
E2653 25pf. Agricultural workers reading paper 35 30
E2654 50pf. Laboratory technicians 80 75
MSE2655 55 × 81 mm. 1m. Soviet war memorial, Berlin-Treptow (22 × 40 mm) . . . . 1·20 1·20

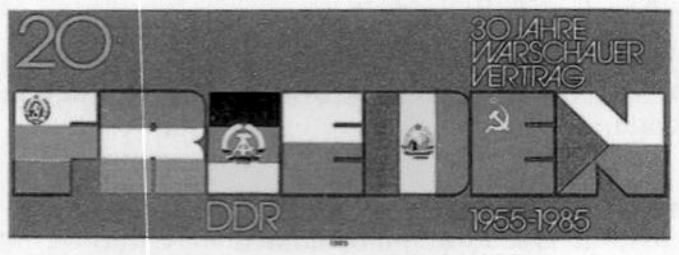

E 801 Flags forming "Frieden" (Peace)

1985. 30th Anniv of Warsaw Pact.
E2656 E **801** 20pf. multicoloured 40 25

E 802 Emblem and Berlin Buildings

1985. 12th Free German Youth Parliament, Berlin. Multicoloured.
E2657 10pf.+5pf. Type E **802** . . 20 20
E2658 20pf. Flags, Ernst Thalmann and emblem 20 20

E 803 "Solidarity" and Dove on Globe E **804** Olympic Flag

1985. "Solidarity".
E2659 E **803** 10pf.+5pf. mult . . . 30 25

1985. 90th International Olympic Committee Meeting, Berlin.
E2660 E **804** 35pf. multicoloured 65 45

E 805 "40" and Emblem E **806** Harpy Eagle

1985. 40th Anniv of Free German Trade Unions Federation.
E2661 E **805** 20pf. multicoloured 30 25

1985. Protected Animals. Multicoloured.
E2662 5pf. Type E **806** 15 15
E2663 10pf. Red-breasted geese (horiz) 15 15
E2664 20pf. Spectacled bear (horiz) 30 25
E2665 50pf. Bantengs (horiz) . . 65 55
E2666 85pf. Sunda gavial (horiz) 1·60 1·20

E 807 Support Steam-engine, Gera, 1833 E **808** Students reading

1985. Steam Engines. Multicoloured.
E2667 10pf. Type E **807** 20 15
E2668 85pf. Balance steam-engine, Frieberg, 1848 1·10 1·00

1985. 12th World Youth and Students' Festival, Moscow. Multicoloured.
E2669 20pf.+5pf. Type E **808** . . 30 35
E2670 50pf. Students with raised arms 55 60

E **809** Diver at Turning Post

1985. Second World Orienteering Diving Championship, Neuglobsow. Multicoloured.
E2671 10pf. Type E **809** 20 15
E2672 70pf. Divers . . . . 1·00 80

E **810** Bose House, Saint Thomas Churchyard E **811** Passenger Mail Coach (relief, Hermann Steinemann)

1985. Leipzig Autumn Fair. Multicoloured.
E2673 10pf. Type E **810** 20 15
E2674 25pf. J. Scherzer Bach-trumpet 45 25

1985. "Sozphilex '85" Stamp Exhibition, Berlin. Multicoloured.
E2675 5pf. Type E **811** 15 20
E2676 20pf.+5pf. Team of horses 25 25
Nos. E2675/6 were printed together, se-tenant, forming a composite design.

E **812** Electrification of Railway E **813** Gertrauden Bridge

1985. Railways. Multicoloured.
E2677 20pf. Signal box 25 20
E2678 25pf. Andreas Schubert (engineer), his steam locomotive "Saxonia", 1838, and electric locomotive Type BR250 45 25
E2679 50pf. Type E **812** 65 50
E2680 85pf. Leipzig Central Station . . . . 1·60 1·20

1985. Berlin Bridges. Multicoloured.
E2681 10pf. Type E **813** 15 15
E2682 20pf. Jungfern Bridge . . 20 25
E2683 35pf. Weidendammer Bridge 55 45
E2684 70pf. Marx-Engels Bridge 1·00 85
MSE2685 107 × 128 mm. No. E2673 × 8 . . . . 3·00 3·00

1985. Castles (2nd series). As Type E **790**. Mult.
E2686 10pf. Hohnstein Castle . . 15 15
E2687 20pf. Rochsburg 20 25
E2688 35pf. Schwarzenberg Castle 45 40
E2689 80pf. Stein Castle . . . . 1·30 1·10

E **814** Humboldt University E **815** Cecilienhof Castle and U.N. Emblem

1985. Anniversaries. Multicoloured.
E2690 20pf. Type E **814** (175th anniv of Humboldt University, Berlin) . . . 25 20
E2691 85pf. New and old Charite buildings (275th anniv of Berlin Charite (training clinic)) . . . . 1·10 1·00

1985. 40th Anniv of U.N.O.
E2692 E **815** 85pf. multicoloured 1·10 45

E **816** Elephants on Balls E **817** Grimm Brothers

1985. Circus. Multicoloured.
E2693 10pf. Type E **816** 30 30
E2694 20pf. Trapeze artiste . . . 35 45
E2695 35pf. Acrobats on monocycles . . . . . . 1·10 1·00
E2696 50pf. Tigers and trainer . . 1·60 1·40

1985. Birth Bicentenaries of Jacob and Wilhelm Grimm (folklorists). Multicoloured.
E2697 5pf. Type E **817** 20 35
E2698 10pf. "The Valiant Tailor" 20 35
E2699 20pf. "Lucky John" . . . 65 90
E2700 25pf. "Puss in Boots" . . 65 90
E2701 35pf. "The Seven Ravens" 20 35
E2702 85pf. "The Sweet Pap" . . 20 35

E **818** Water Pump, Berlin, 1900 E **819** Saxon Postilion

1986. Water Supply.
E2703 E **818** 10pf. green and red 15 15
E2704 – 35pf. deep brown, brown and green 45 35
E2705 – 50pf. purple & green 65 60
E2706 – 70pf. blue and brown 1·00 85
DESIGNS: 35pf. Water tower, Berlin-Altglienicke, 1906; 50pf. Waterworks, Berlin-Friedrichshagen, 1893; 70pf. Rappbode dam, 1959.

1986. Postal Uniforms of 1850. Multicoloured.
E2707A 10pf. Type E **819** . . . 20 15
E2708A 20pf. Prussian postman 30 25
E2709A 85pf. Prussian postal official . . . . 1·30 1·00
E2710A 1m. Postal official from Mecklenburg region 1·80 1·40

E **820** Flag

1986. 40th Anniv of Free German Youth.
E2711 E **820** 20pf. yellow, bl & blk 35 25

E **821** Flag

1986. 30th Anniv of National People's Army.
E2712 E **821** 20pf. multicoloured 60 30

E **822** Exhibition Hall

1986. Leipzig Spring Fair. Multicoloured.
E2713 35pf. Type E **822** 45 30
E2714 50pf. "Atlantik 488" (factory trawler) 60 40

E **823** Yuri Gagarin and "Vostok"

1986. 25th Anniv of Manned Space Flight. Multicoloured.
E2715 40pf. Type E **823** (first man in space) 45 50
E2716 50pf. Cosmonauts Valeri Bykovski and Sigmund Jahn, space station and "Interkosmos" emblem 55 65
E2717 70pf. Space probe "Venera", orbit around Venus and spectrometer 70 80
E2718 85pf. Reconnaissance camera MKF-6, photo, "Soyuz 22" spaceship, airplane and research ship 90 95

E **824** Marx, Engels and Lenin E **825** Memorial

1986. 11th Socialist Unity Party of Germany Day.
E2719 E **824** 10pf. black, red and silver 15 15
E2720 – 20pf. red, black and silver 20 20
E2721 – 50pf. multicoloured 65 60
E2722 – 85pf. black, red and silver . . . . . 1·30 1·10
MSE2723 80 × 55 mm. 1m. multicoloured . . . . 1·20 1·30
DESIGNS: 20pf. Ernst Thalmann (birth centenary); 50pf. Wilhelm Pieck and Otto Grotewohl, April 1946; 85pf. Family; 1m. Construction worker holding symbolic key.

1986. Opening of Ernst Thalmann Park, Berlin.
E2724 E **825** 20pf. multicoloured 35 30

E **826** Horse Tram, Dresden, 1886

1986. Trams. Multicoloured.
E2725 10pf. Type E **826** 20 15
E2726 20pf. Leipzig, 1896 . . . . 20 25
E2727 40pf. Berlin, 1919 . . . . 65 60
E2728 70pf. Halle, 1928 . . . . 1·30 1·10

E **827** Orang-utan E **828** City Seal, 1253

1986. 125th Anniv of Dresden Zoo. Multicoloured.
E2729 10pf. Type E **827** 20 15
E2730 20pf. Eastern black-and-white colobus 25 20
E2731 50pf. Mandrill 90 75
E2732 70pf. Ring-tailed lemurs 1·60 1·20

1986. 750th Anniv of Berlin (1st issue).
E2733 E **828** 10pf. deep brown, bistre and brown 20 15
E2734 – 20pf. olive, grn & brn 25 20
E2735 – 50pf. blk, brn & red 1·30 65
E2736 – 70pf. green & brown 2·40 1·40
MSE2737 54 × 80 mm. 1m. green 1·60 1·60
DESIGNS—HORIZ: 20pf. City map, 1648; 50pf. Oldest City arms. VERT: 70pf. St. Nicolas's Church, 1832; 1m. Cabinet building tower.
See also Nos. E2780/**MS**E2784 and **MS**E2828.

E **829** Couple, Tractor and House

1986. 21st Workers' Festival, Magdeburg. Mult.
E2738 20pf. Type E **829** 20 35
E2739 50pf. Port and town of Magdeburg 45 50

E **830** Berlin, 1652

1986. 9th Youth Stamp Exhibition, Berlin. Multicoloured.
E2740 10pf.+5pf. Type E **830** . . 20 30
E2741 20pf. Historic and modern Berlin buildings 20 30

E **831** Schwerin Castle

1986. Castles (3rd series). Multicoloured.
E2742 10pf. Type E **831** 15 15
E2743 20pf. Gustrow castle . . . 20 20
E2744 85pf. Rheinsberg castle . . 1·10 95
E2745 1m. Ludwigslust castle . . 1·60 1·40

E **832** Soldiers and Girl before Brandenburg Gate

1986. 25th Anniv of Berlin Wall.
E2746 E **832** 20pf. multicoloured 50 35

E **833** Doves flying from Emblem — E **834** Ring-Messehaus

1986. International Peace Year.
E2747 E **833** 35pf. multicoloured 55 30

1986. Leipzig Autumn Fair. Sheet 82 × 57 mm containing Type E **834** and similar vert design.
MSE2748 25pf. Type E **834**; 85pf. Merchants displaying cloth . . 1·60 1·60

E **835** Rostock, 1637 — E **836** Man with Rifle

1986. Coins.
E2749 E **835** 10pf. black, silver and red 20 15
E2750 – 35pf. black, silver and blue 45 40
E2751 – 50pf. multicoloured 65 55
E2752 – 85pf. black, silver and blue . . . . . 1·10 1·00
E2753 – 1m. black, silver and green . . . . . 1·30 1·20
DESIGNS: 35pf. Nordhausen, 1660; 50pf. Erfurt, 1633; 85pf. Magdeburg, 1638; 1m. Stralsund, 1622;

1986. 44th World Sports Shooting Championships, Suhl.
E2754 E **836** 20pf. black, green and grey 20 20
E2755 – 70pf. black, red and grey 90 75
E2756 – 85pf. black, blue and grey . . . . . . 1·20 1·00
DESIGNS: 70pf. Woman with pistol; 85pf. Man with double-barrelled shotgun.

E **837** Guard and Boundary Post — E **838** Hemispheres and Red Banner

1986. 40th Anniv of Border Guards.
E2757 E **837** 20pf. multicoloured 45 35

1986. 11th World Trade Unions Congress, Berlin.
E2758 E **838** 70pf. multicoloured 1·10 85

E **839** German Members Memorial, Friedrichshain — E **840** Memorial

1986. 50th Anniv of Formation of International Brigades in Spain.
E2759 E **839** 20pf. brown, black and red 35 25

1986. 25th Anniv of Sachsenhausen Memorial.
E2760 E **840** 35pf. black, grn & bl 50 30

E **841** Double-deck Train Ferry Loading Ramps

1986. Opening of Mukran–Klaipeda Railway Ferry Service. Multicoloured.
E2761 50pf. Type E **841** 55 55
E2762 50pf. "Mukran" (train ferry) 55 55
Nos. E2761/2 were printed together, se-tenant, forming a composite design.

E **842** "Help for Developing Countries"

1986. "Solidarity".
E2763 E **842** 10pf.+5pf. mult . . . 30 25

E **843** Weber (after F. Jugel)

1986. Birth Bicentenary of Carl Maria von Weber (composer). Sheet 82 × 57 mm.
MSE2764 E **843** 85pf. multicoloured 1·20 1·20

E **844** Indira Gandhi — E **845** Candle Holder, 1778

1986. 2nd Death Anniv of Indira Gandhi (Indian Prime Minister).
E2765 E **844** 10pf. stone & brown 30 25

1986. Candle Holders from the Erzgebirge. Multicoloured.
E2766 10pf. Type E **845** 20 25
E2767 20pf. Candle holder, 1796 20 25
E2768 25pf. Candle holder, 1810 65 65
E2769 35pf. Candle holder, 1821 65 65
E2770 40pf. Candle holder, 1830 20 25
E2771 85pf. Candle holder, 1925 20 25

E **846** Roland Statue, Stendal — E **847** Post Office, Freiberg

1987. Statues of Roland (1st series).
E2772 10pf. lt brown, brown & yell 15 15
E2773 20pf. lt brown, brown & bl 20 20
E2774 35pf. lt brown, brown & orge 60 50
E2775 50pf. lt brown, brown & grn 85 70
DESIGNS: Statues at—10pf. Type E **846**; 20pf. Halle; 35pf. Brandenburg; 50pf. Quedlinburg.
See also Nos. E2984/7.

1987. Post Offices.
E2776 E **847** 10pf. black, red and blue 15 15
E2777 – 20pf. multicoloured 20 20
E2778 – 70pf. multicoloured 70 70
E2779 – 1m.20 mult . . . . 1·50 1·30
DESIGNS: 20pf. Perleberg; 70pf. Weimar; 1m.20, Kirschau.

1987. 750th Anniv of Berlin (2nd issue). As Type E **828**.
E2780 20pf. brown and green . . 20 20
E2781 35pf. green and red . . . 55 45
E2782 70pf. blue and red 80 75
E2783 85pf. olive and green . . . 1·30 1·10
MSE2784 Four sheets, 75 × 108 mm (a) or 107 × 75 mm (others). (a) 10pf. As No. E2780; (b) 10pf. × 4, As No. E2781; (c) 20pf. × 4, As No. E2782; (d) 20pf. × 4, As No. E2783 . . . . 2·10 1·70
DESIGNS—VERT: 20pf. Ephraim Palace. HORIZ: 35pf. New buildings, Alt Marzahn; 70pf. Marx-Engels Forum; 85pf. Friedrichstadtpalast.

E **848** Woman with Flower in Hair — E **850** Clara Zetkin

E **849** Fair Hall 20

1987. 40th Anniv and 12th Congress (Berlin) of German Democratic Women's Federation.
E2785 E **848** 10pf. blue, red & sil 30 25

1987. Leipzig Spring Fair. Multicoloured.
E2786 35pf. Type E **849** 45 40
E2787 50pf. "Traders at Weighbridge, 1804" (Christian Geissler) . . . 65 55

1987. Socialist Personalities. Multicoloured.
E2788 E **850** 10pf. purple 20 15
E2789 – 10pf. black 20 15
E2790 – 10pf. black 20 15
E2791 – 10pf. green 20 15
DESIGNS: No. E2789, Fritz Gabler; E2790, Walter Vesper; E2791, Robert Siewert.

E **851** Construction Industry

1987. 11th Federation of Free German Trade Unions Congress, Berlin. Multicoloured.
E2792 20pf. Type E **851** 20 30
E2793 50pf. Communications industry 55 55

E **852** Flag, World Map and Doves

1987. 10th German Red Cross Congress, Dresden.
E2794 E **852** 35pf. multicoloured 50 30

E **853** Museum and Karl August Lingner (founder) (after Robert Sterl)

1987. 75th Anniv of German Hygiene Museum, Dresden.
E2795 E **853** 85pf. multicoloured 1·00 75

E **854** Old and New Farming Methods

1987. 35th Anniv of Agricultural Co-operatives.
E2796 E **854** 20pf. multicoloured 35 25

E **855** Ludwig Uhland (poet)

1987. Birth Anniversaries. Multicoloured.
E2797 10pf. Type E **855** (bicent) 15 15
E2798 20pf. Arnold Zweig (writer, centenary) . . . 20 20
E2799 35pf. Gerhart Hauptmann (writer, 125th anniv) . . 55 45
E2800 50pf. Gustav Hertz (physicist, centenary) . . 90 75

E **856** Bream

1987. Freshwater Fishes. Multicoloured.
E2801 5pf. Type E **856** 15 15
E2802 10pf. Brown trout 20 20
E2803 20pf. Wels 20 20
E2804 35pf. European grayling 45 35
E2805 50pf. Barbel 65 50
E2806 70pf. Northern pike . . . 1·10 90

E **857** Woman holding Baby — E **859** Ludwig Lazarus Zamenhof (inventor)

E **858** Horse-drawn Hand-pumped Fire Engine, 1756

1987. "Solidarity" Anti-Apartheid Campaign.
E2807 E **857** 10pf.+5pf. mult . . . 30 25

1987. Fire Engines. Multicoloured.
E2808 10pf. Type E **858** 20 15
E2809 25pf. Steam engine, 1903 20 20
E2810 40pf. Model "LF 15", 1919 . . . . 60 55
E2811 70pf. Model "LF 16-TS 8", 1971 . . . . 90 85

1987. Centenary of Esperanto (invented language). Sheet 55 × 80 mm.
MSE2812 E **859** 85pf. multicoloured 1·10 1·60

E **860** Otters

1987. Endangered Animals. European Otter. Multicoloured.
E2813 10pf. Type E **860** 20 15
E2814 25pf. Otter swimming . . 35 30
E2815 35pf. Otter 60 40
E2816 60pf. Otter's head . . . . 1·40 1·00

E **861** Tug-of-War

1987. 8th Gymnastics and Sports Festival and 11th Children and Young People's Sports Days, Leipzig. Multicoloured.
E2817 5pf. Type E **861** 15 15
E2818 10pf. Handball 15 15
E2819 20pf.+5pf. Long jumping 25 25
E2820 35pf. Table tennis 45 35
E2821 40pf. Bowling 60 55
E2822 70pf. Running . . . . . . 1·50 1·10

E **862** Association Activities

1987. 35th Anniv of Association of Sports and Technical Sciences.
E2823 E **862** 10pf. multicoloured 30 15

E **863** Head Post Office, Berlin, 1760

1987. Stamp Day. Multicoloured.
E2824 10pf.+5pf. Type E **863** . . 20 30
E2825 20pf. Wartenberg Palace 20 30

E **864** Market Scene

1987. Leipzig Autumn Fair. Sheet 80 × 58 mm containing Type E **864** and similar vert design showing "Market Scene" by Christian Geissler.
MSE2826 40pf. multicoloured; 50pf. multicoloured . . . . 1·60 1·60

E **865** Memorial Statue (Jozsef Somogyi)
E **866** Memorial, Ernst Thalmann Park

1987. War Victims' Memorial, Budapest.
E2827 E **865** 35pf. multicoloured 50 25

1987. 750th Anniv of Berlin (3rd issue). Sheet 80 × 55 mm.
MSE2828 E **866** 1m.35 black, stone and red . . . . 1·80 1·80

E **867** "Weidendamm Bridge" (Arno Mohr)

1987. 10th Art Exhibition, Dresden. Mult.
E2829 10pf. Type E **867** 15 15
E2830 50pf. "They only wanted to learn Reading and Writing (Nicaragua)" (Willi Sitte) 60 55
E2831 70pf. "Big Mourning Man" (Wieland Forster) 80 75
E2832 1m. Vase (Gerd Lucke) (horiz) . . . . 1·80 1·40

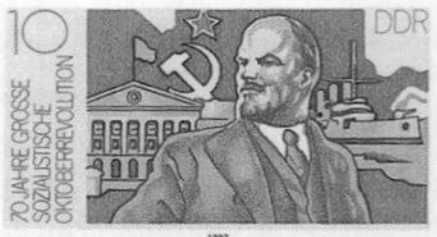

E **868** Red Flag, Smolny Building (Leningrad), "Aurora" and Lenin

1987. 70th Anniv of Russian Revolution. Multicoloured.
E2833 10pf. Type E **868** 15 15
E2834 20pf. Moscow Kremlin towers 30 15

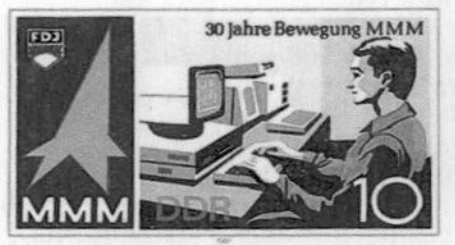

E **869** Youth using Personal Computer
E **870** Annaberg, 1810

1987. 39th "Masters of Tomorrow" Fair, Leipzig. Multicoloured.
E2835 10pf. Type E **869** 15 15
E2836 20pf. "ZIM 10-S" robot-welder 30 15

1987. Christmas Pyramids from Erzgebirge. Multicoloured.
E2837 10pf. Type E **870** 20 25
E2838 20pf. Freiberg, 1830 . . . 65 45
E2839 25pf. Neustadtel, 1870 . . 20 25
E2840 35pf. Schneeberg, 1870 . . 20 30
E2841 40pf. Lossnitz, 1880 . . . 65 60
E2842 85pf. Seiffen, 1910 . . . . 20 50

E **871** Ski Jumping

1988. Winter Olympic Games, Calgary. Mult.
E2843 5pf. Type E **871** 15 15
E2844 10pf. Speed skating . . . 20 15
E2845 20pf.+10pf. Four-man bobsleigh 35 35
E2846 35pf. Biathlon 65 55
MSE2847 80 × 55 mm. 1m.20 Two-man and single luge (horiz) . . 2·00 1·60

E **872** Berlin-Buch Post Office

1988. Postal Buildings. Multicoloured.
E2848 15pf. Type E **872** 35 25
E2849 20pf. Postal museum . . . 35 20
E2850 50pf. Berlin-Marzahn general post office . . . 1·10 60

E **873** Brecht

1988. 90th Birth Anniv of Bertholt Brecht (writer). Sheet 58 × 82 mm.
MSE2851 E **873** 70pf. grey, black and red . . . . 1·10 1·00

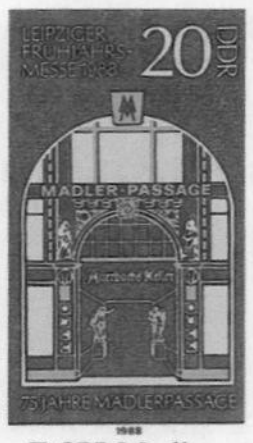

E **874** "Tillandsia macrochlamys"
E **875** Madler-passage Entrance

1988. Bromeliads. Multicoloured.
E2852 10pf. Type E **874** 20 15
E2853 25pf. "Tillandsia bulbosa" 35 25
E2854 40pf. "Tillandsia kalmbacheri" 60 40
E2855 70pf. "Guzmania blassii" 1·10 95

1988. Leipzig Spring Fair. 75th Anniv of Madler-passage (fair building). Each brown, orange and pink.
E2856 20pf. Type E **875** 20 20
E2857 70pf. "Faust and Mephistopheles" (bronze statue, Matthieu Molitor) . . . . . . 1·00 75

E **876** Eichendorff
E **877** Saddler, Muhlhausen, 1565

1988. Birth Bicentenary of Joseph von Eichendorff (writer). Sheet 82 × 55 mm.
MSE2858 E **876** 70pf. olive, drab and blue . . . . 1·40 1·10

1988. Historic Seals. Multicoloured.
E2859 10pf. Type E **877** 15 15
E2860 25pf. Butcher, Dresden, 1564 . . . . 25 25
E2861 35pf. Smith, Nauen, 16th-century 40 40
E2862 50pf. Clothier, Frankfurt on Oder, 16th-century 60 55

E **878** Georg Forster Antarctic Research Station

1988. 12th Anniv of Georg Forster Antarctic Research Station.
E2863 E **878** 35pf. multicoloured 55 25

E **879** Wismar

1988. Northern Towns of the Democratic Republic.
E2864 5pf. black, green & turquoise 15 15
E2865 10pf. black, ochre and brown 15 15
E2866 25pf. black, lightt blue & blue 35 25
E2867 60pf. black, pink and red 70 55
E2868 90pf. black, lt green & green . . . . 1·00 80
E2869 1m.20 black, brown and red . . . . 1·60 1·30
DESIGNS: 5pf. Type E **879**.; 10pf. Anklam; 25pf. Ribnitz-Damgarten; 60pf. Stralsund; 90pf. Bergen; 1m.20, Greifswald.

E **880** Hutten

1988. 500th Birth Anniv of Ulrich von Hutten (humanist). Sheet 54 × 80 mm.
MSE2870 E **880** 70pf. black, yellow and ochre . . . . 1·10 1·10

E **881** Chorin and Neuzelle Monasteries, Industrial and Agricultural Symbols

1988. 22nd Workers' Arts Festival, Frankfurt-on-Oder. Multicoloured.
E2871 20pf. Type E **881** 20 25
E2872 50pf. Buildings of Frankfurt 55 55

E **882** Cosmonauts Sigmund Jahn and Valery Bykovski

1988. 10th Anniv of U.S.S.R.–East German Manned Space Flight (1st issue). Multicoloured.
E2873 5pf. Type E **882** 20 20
E2874 10pf. "MKS-M" multi-channel spectrometer . . 20 20
E2875 20pf. "Mir"–"Soyuz" space complex 20 25
See also Nos. E2894/6.

E **883** Erfurt, 1520

1988. 10th Youth Stamp Exhibition, Erfurt and Karl-Marx-Stadt. Multicoloured.
E2876 10pf.+5pf. Type E **883** . . 15 20
E2877 20pf.+5pf. Chemnitz, 1620 25 25
E2878 25pf. Modern view of Erfurt 25 25
E2879 50pf. Modern view of Karl-Marx-Stadt (formerly Chemnitz) . . 65 60

E **884** Swearing-in Ceremony

1988. 35th Anniv of Workers' Militia Squads. Multicoloured.
E2880 5pf. Type E **884** 15 15
E2881 10pf. Tribute to Ernst Thalmann 15 15
E2882 15pf. Parade 35 30
E2883 20pf. Arms distribution . . 20 20

E **885** Balloons and Doves over Karl-Marx-Stadt

1988. 8th Pioneers Meeting, Karl-Marx-Stadt. Multicoloured.
E2884 10pf. Type E **885** 15 20
E2885 10pf.+5pf. Doves, balloons and Pioneers 20 25

E **886** Swimming

1988. Olympic Games, Seoul. Multicoloured.
E2886 5pf. Type E **886** 15 15
E2887 10pf. Handball 20 15
E2888 20pf.+10pf. Hurdling . . . 45 40
E2889 25pf. Rowing 35 30
E2890 35pf. Boxing 65 55
E2891 50pf.+20pf. Cycling . . . 65 70
MSE2892 55 × 80 mm. 85pf. Relay race . . . . 2·20 2·00

E **887** Examining Fair Goods, 1810

E **889** "'Adolph Friedrich' at Stralsund: Captain C. Leplow" (E. Laschke)

E **888** Buchenwald Memorial (Fritz Cremer)

1988. Leipzig Autumn Fair and 175th Anniv of Battle of Leipzig. Sheet 110 × 90 mm containing Type E **887** and similar vert designs. Multicoloured.
MSE2893 5pf. Type E **887**; 15pf. Battle of Leipzig Monument; 100pf. Fair, 1820 . . . . . . 1·70 1·60

1988. 10th Anniv of U.S.S.R.–East German Manned space Flight (2nd issue). As Nos. E2873/5 but values changed. Multicoloured.
E2894 10pf. Type E **882** 20 25
E2895 20pf. As No. E2874 . . . 20 25
E2896 35pf. As No. E2875 . . . 60 50

1988. War Memorials.
E2897 E **888** 10pf. green, black and brown 20 20
E2898 – 35pf. multicoloured 50 30
DESIGN: 35pf. Resistance Monument, Lake Como, Italy

1988. 500th Anniv of Stralsund Shipping Company. Captains' Paintings. Multicoloured.
E2899 5pf. Type E **889** 15 15
E2900 10pf. "'Gartenlaube' of Stralsund: Captain J. F. Kruger" (A. Luschky) 20 15
E2901 70pf. "Brigantina 'Auguste Mathilde' of Stralsund: Captain I. C. Grunwaldt" (Johnsen-Seby Bergen) . . . . . 1·00 85
E2902 1m.20 "Brig 'Hoffnung' of Cologne-on-Rhine: Captain G. A. Luther" (anon) . . . . 1·40 1·30

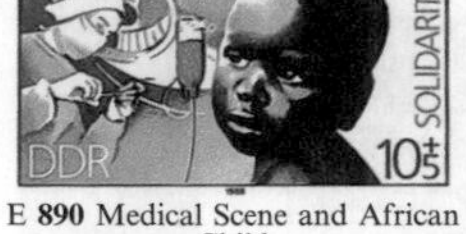

E **890** Medical Scene and African Child

1988. "Solidarity".
E2903 E **890** 10pf.+5pf. mult . . . 60 55

E **891** Magdeburg Drawbridge

E **892** Menorah

1988. Drawbridges and Ship Lifts. Mult.
E2904 5pf. Type E **891** 15 15
E2905 10pf. Lift, Magdeburg–Rothensee Canal . . . 20 15
E2906 35pf. Lift, Niederfinow . . 55 40
E2907 70pf. Bridge and lock, Altfriesack 80 75
E2908 90pf. Drawbridge, Rugendamm . . . . . 1·10 95

1988. 50th Anniv of "Kristallnacht" (Nazi pogrom).
E2909 E **892** 35pf. purple, yellow and black 50 25

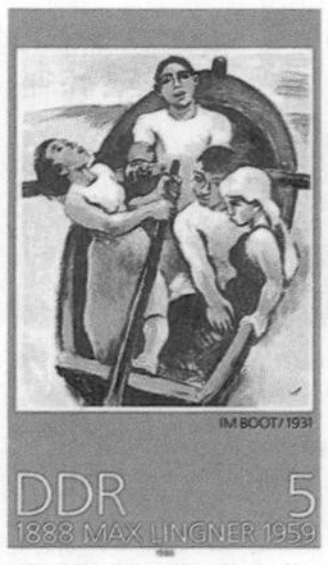

E **893** "In the Boat"

E **894** Lace (Regine Wengler)

1988. Birth Centenary of Max Lingner (artist). Multicoloured.
E2910 5pf. Type E **893** 15 15
E2911 10pf. "Mademoiselle Yvonne" 20 15
E2912 20pf. "Free, Strong and Happy" 20 20
E2913 85pf. "New Harvest" . . . 1·20 85

1988. Bobbin Lace from Erzgebirge. Pieces by lacemakers named. Each black, brown and yellow.
E2914 20pf. Type E **894** 20 25
E2915 25pf. Wally Tilp 65 45
E2916 35pf. Elisabeth Mehnert-Pfabe 20 30
E2917 40pf. Ute Siewert 20 30
E2918 50pf. Regine Siebdraht . . 65 60
E2919 85pf. Elise Schubert . . . 20 50

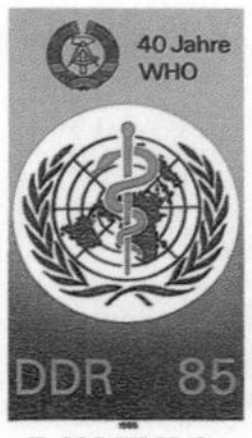

E **895** W.H.O. Emblem

E **896** Dr. Wolf

1988. 40th Anniv of W.H.O.
E2920 E **895** 85pf. silver, bl & grey . . . . . . 1·00 45

1988. Birth Centenary of Dr. Friedrich Wolf (writer). Sheet 87 × 59 mm.
MSE2921 E**896** 110pf. grey, black and vermilion . . . . 1·40 1·40

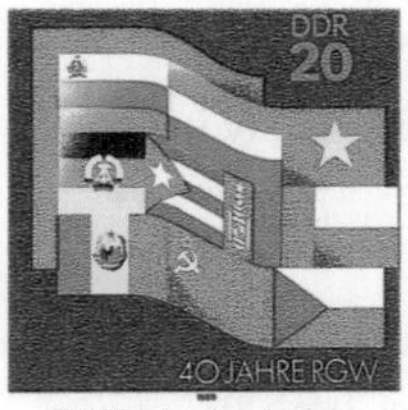

E **897** Members' Flags

1989. 40th Anniv of Council of Mutual Economic Aid.
E2922 E **897** 20pf. multicoloured 30 25

E **898** Edith Baumann

E **899** Philipp Reis Telephone, 1861

1989. Socialist Personalities.
E2923 E **898** 10pf. brown 20 15
E2924 – 10pf. green 20 15
E2925 – 10pf. brown 20 15
E2926 – 10pf. blue 20 15
DESIGNS: No. E2924, Otto Meier; E2925, Alfred Oelssner; E2926, Fritz Selbmann.

1989. Telephones. Multicoloured.
E2927 10pf. Type E **899** 20 15
E2928 20pf. Siemens & Halske wall telephone, 1882 . . 20 20
E2929 50pf. "OB 03" wall telephone, 1903 . . . . 65 60
E2930 85pf. "OB 05" desk telephone, 1905 . . . . 1·10 95

E **900** Johann Beckmann (technologist, 250th anniv)

1989. Birth Anniversaries. Multicoloured.
E2931 10pf. Type E **900** 20 15
E2932 10pf. Rudolf Mauersberger and church choir (musician, cent) 20 15
E2933 10pf. Carl von Ossietzky and masthead of "Die Weltbuhne" (journalist and peace activist, centenary) 20 15
E2934 10pf. Ludwig Renn and International Brigades flag (writer, centenary) 20 15
E2935 10pf. Adam Scharrer and cover of "Stateless People" (novelist, centenary) 20 15

E **901** Handelshof Fair Building

E **902** Muntzer (after Christoph van Stichen and Romeyn de Hooghe)

1989. Leipzig Spring Fair. Multicoloured.
E2936 70pf. Type E **901** (80th anniv) 90 80
E2937 85pf. Naschmarkt bake-house and bread shop, 1690 . . . . 1·10 95

1989. 500th Birth Anniv of Thomas Muntzer (religious reformer) (1st issue). Sheet 86 × 66 mm.
MSE2938 E **902** 110pf. black and buff . . . . 1·30 1·60
See also Nos. E2967/**MS**2972.

E **903** Friedrich List (economist and promoter of railway system)

1989. 150th Anniv of Leipzig–Dresden Railway (first German long-distance service).
E2939 E **903** 15pf. brown, pale brown and green 20 25
E2940 – 20pf. black, green and red 20 20
E2941 – 50pf. black, brown and deep brown 90 65
DESIGNS: 20pf. Dresdner Station, Leipzig, 1839; 50pf. Leipziger Station, Dresden, 1839.

E **904** Tea Caddy

E **905** Renaissance Initial "I"

1989. Meissen Porcelain. 250th Anniv of Onion Design. Each brown, blue and ultramarine.
E2942A 10pf. Type E **904** . . . 20 15
E2943A 20pf. Vase 20 20
E2944A 35pf. Bread board . . . 70 50
E2945A 70pf. Coffee pot . . . . 1·20 95

1989. 7th International Typography Exhibition, Leipzig.
E2946 E **905** 20pf. multicoloured 20 20
E2947 – 50pf. black, yellow and green 65 50
E2948 – 1m.35 red, black and grey . . . . . . 1·80 1·40
DESIGNS: 50pf. Art Nouveau initial "B"; 1m.35, Modern initial "A"s.

E **906** Chollima Statue, Pyongyang

E **907** "Princess Louise"

1989. 13th World Youth and Students' Festival, Pyongyang (E2949) and Free German Youth Whitsun Festival, Berlin (E2950). Multicoloured.
E2949 20pf. Type E **906** 20 25
E2950 20pf.+5pf. Berlin buildings 30 35

1989. 225th Birth Anniv of Johann Gottfried Schadow (sculptor). Details of "Princesses". Multicoloured.
E2951 50pf. Type E **907** 80 45
E2952 85pf. "Princess Friederike" 1·40 1·10

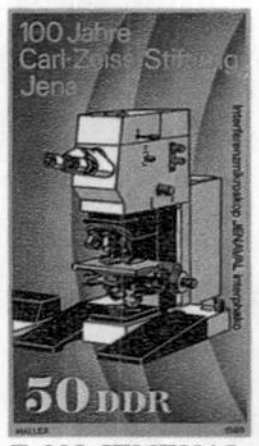

E **908** JENEVAL Interference Microscope

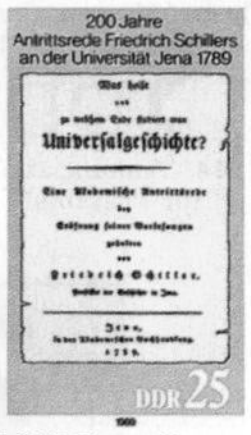

E **909** Front Page of Address

1989. Centenary of Carl Zeiss Foundation, Jena. Multicoloured.
E2953 50pf. Type E **908** 60 55
E2954 85pf. "ZKM 01-250 C" bi-coordinate measuring instrument . . . . . . 1·00 95

1989. Bicentenary of Inaugural Address to Jena University by Friedrich Schiller (writer and philosopher). Each brown, black & grey.
E2955 25pf. Type E **909** 25 35
E2956 85pf. Part of address . . . 1·00 90

E **910** A. E. Berhm

1989. 160th Birth Anniv of Alfred Edmund Brehm and 125th Death Anniv of Christian Ludwig Brehm (naturalists). Sheet 110 × 80 mm containing Type E **910** and similar vert design. Multicoloured.
MSE2957 50pf. Type E **910**; 85pf. C. L. Brehm . . . . 2·00 13·50

E **911** Storming the Bastille

1989. Bicent of French Revolution. Mult.
E2958 5pf. Type E **911** 20 15
E2959 20pf. Sans-culottes 20 20
E2960 90pf. Invading the Tuileries . . . . 1·20 95

E **912** Haflingers

1989. 40th International Horse Breeding in Socialist States Congress, Berlin. Multicoloured.
E2961 10pf. Type E **912** 15 15
E2962 20pf. English thoroughbreds (racehorses) 20 20
E2963 70pf. Heavy horses (plough team) 80 85
E2964 110pf. Thoroughbreds (dressage) . . . . 1·40 1·30

E **913** Till Eulenspiegel Fountain

1989. National Stamp Exn, Magdeburg. Fountains by Heinrich Apel. Multicoloured.

E2965	20pf. Type E **913**	20	20
E2966	70pf.+5pf. Devil's fountain	1·00	85

E **914** "Annunciation to the Peasants" E **916** African Children

E **915** New Fair Building

1989. 500th Birth Anniv of Thomas Muntzer (Protestant reformer) (2nd issue). Details of "Early Bourgeois Revolution in Germany" by Werner Tubke. Multicoloured.

E2967	5pf. Type E **914**	15	15
E2968	10pf. "Fountain of Life"	20	15
E2969	20pf. "Muntzer in the Battle"	20	20
E2970	50pf. "Lutheran Cat Battle"	80	60
E2971	85pf. "Justice, Jester"	1·30	1·10

1989. Leipzig Autumn Fair. Sheet 105×75 mm containing Type E **915** and similar horiz design. Multicoloured.

MSE2973	50pf. Type E **915**; 85pf. New fair building (different)	1·80	1·80

1989. "Solidarity".

E2974	E **916** 10pf.+5pf. mult	20	20

E **917** "Mother Group" (Fritz Cremer) E **918** "Adriana"

1989. 30th Anniv of Ravensbruck War Victims' Memorial.

E2975	E **917** 35pf. multicoloured	50	25

1989. Epiphyllums. Multicoloured.

E2976	10pf. Type E **918**	20	15
E2977	35pf. "Fire Magic"	45	30
E2978	50pf. "Franzisko"	90	75

E **919** Dove, Flag and Schoolchildren

1989. 40th Anniv of German Democratic Republic. Multicoloured.

E2979	5pf. Type E **919**	15	15
E2980	10pf. Combine harvester and agricultural workers	15	15
E2981	20pf. Political activists working together	20	20
E2982	25pf. Industrial workers	65	45
MSE2983	113×93 mm. 135pf. Construction workers (54×32 mm)	2·75	1·10

1989. Statues of Roland (2nd series). As Type E **846**. Multicoloured.

E2984	5pf. Zerbst	15	15
E2985	10pf. Halberstadt	20	15
E2986	20pf. Buch-Altmark	25	20
E2987	50pf. Perleberg	80	65

E **920** Nehru E **921** Schneeberg, 1860

1989. Birth Centenary of Jawaharlal Nehru (Indian statesman).

E2988	E **920** 35pf. brown and black	50	40

1989. Chandeliers from the Erzgebirge. Mult.

E2989	10pf. Type E **921**	20	25
E2990	20pf. Schwarzenberg, 1850	65	45
E2991	25pf. Annaberg, 1880	20	25
E2992	35pf. Seiffen, 1900	20	35
E2993	50pf. Seiffen, 1930	65	60
E2994	70pf. Annaberg, 1925	20	50

E **922** Bee on Apple Blossom E **923** "Courier" (Albrecht Durer)

1990. The Honey Bee. Multicoloured.

E2995	5pf. Type E **922**	15	15
E2996	10pf. Bee on heather	15	15
E2997	20pf. Bee on rape	20	25
E2998	50pf. Bee on clover	1·10	85

1990. 500th Anniv of Regular European Postal Services.

E2999	E **923** 35pf. chocolate, light brown and brown	55	50

E **924** Erich Weinert E **925** 19th-century Sign, Blankenburg

1990. Socialist Personalities.

E3000	E **924** 10pf. blue	30	25
E3001	– 10pf. brown	30	25

DESIGN: No. E3001, Bruno Leuschner.

1990. Posthouse Signs. Multicoloured.

E3002B	10pf. Type E **925**	15	20
E3003A	20pf. Royal Saxony sign (19th century)	25	25
E3004A	50pf. German Empire sign (1870s)	90	75
E3005A	110pf. German Empire auxiliary station sign (1900s)	1·80	1·50

E **926** Bebel E **927** Drawings by Leonardo da Vinci

1990. 150th Birth Anniv of August Bebel (politician).

E3006	E **926** 20pf. black, grey and red	40	35

1990. "Lilienthal '91" European Airmail Exhibition. Historic Flying Machine Designs. Multicoloured.

E3007	20pf. Type E **927**	25	20
E3008	35pf.+5pf. Melchior Bauer's man-powered airplane design, 1764	65	65
E3009	50pf. Albrecht Berblinger's man-powered flying machine, 1811	75	70
E3010	90pf. Otto Lilienthal's design for a monoplane glider	1·40	1·40

E **928** St. Nicholas's Church, Leipzig, and Demonstrators E **929** Warrior's Head

1990. "We Are The People".

E3011	E **928** 35pf.+15pf. mult	65	65

1990. Museum of German History, Berlin. Stone Reliefs by Andreas Schluter.

E3012	E **929** 40pf. yell, grn & blk	65	65
E3013	– 70pf. multicoloured	1·10	95

DESIGN: 70pf. Warrior's head (different).

E **930** Fair Seal, 1268 E **931** Kurt Tucholsky (writer, centenary)

1990. Leipzig Spring Fair and 825th Anniv of Leipzig. Multicoloured.

E3014	70pf. Type E **930**	1·20	85
E3015	85pf. Fair seal, 1497	1·80	1·10

1990. Birth Anniversaries.

E3016	E **931** 10pf. black, green and deep green	35	30
E3017	– 10pf. black, brown and red	35	30

DESIGN: No. E3017, Friedrich Adolph Wilhelm Diesterweg (educationist, bicent).

E **932** "Solidarity of Labour" (Walter Crane) E **933** Dicraeosaurus

1990. Centenary of Labour Day.

E3018	E **932** 10pf. grey, black and red	45	25
E3019	– 20pf. red, grey and black	90	60

DESIGN: 20pf. Red carnation.

1990. Centenary of Natural Science Museum, Berlin. Dinosaur Skeletons. Multicoloured.

E3020	10pf. Type E **933**	15	15
E3021	25pf. Kentrurosaurus	35	35
E3022	35pf. Dysalotosaurus	50	50
E3023	50pf. Brachiosaurus (vert)	65	70
E3024	85pf. Skull of brachiosaurus (vert)	1·20	1·10

E **934** Penny Black E **935** Edward Hughes and 1855 Printing Telegraph

1990. 150th Anniv of the Penny Black.

E3025	E **934** 20pf. black, mauve and magenta	45	50
E3026	– 35pf.+15pf. red, lilac and black	90	1·00
E3027	– 110pf. multicoloured	2·75	2·30

DESIGNS: 35pf. Saxony 1850 3pf. stamp; 110pf. First East Germany stamp, 1949.

1990. 125th Anniv of I.T.U. Multicoloured.

E3028	10pf. Type E **935**	20	20
E3029	20pf. Distribution rods from Berlin-Kopenick post office	25	35
E3030	25pf. Transmitting tower and radio control desk	55	60
E3031	50pf. "Molniya" communications satellite and globe	80	85
MSE3032	82×56 mm. 70pf. Philipp Reis (telephone pioneer)	2·30	2·20

E **936** Pope John Paul II

1990. Pope's 70th Birthday.

E3033	E **936** 35pf. multicoloured	60	50

E **937** Halle (18th-century)

1990. 11th National Youth Stamp Exhibition, Halle. Multicoloured.

E3034	10pf.+5pf. Type E **937**	30	35
E3035	20pf. Modern Halle	35	35

E **938** Rules of Order of Teutonic Knights, 1264 E **939** Albrechts Castle and Cathedral, Meissen

1990. Exhibits in German State Library, Berlin. Multicoloured.

E3036	20pf. Type E **938**	35	25
E3037	25pf. World map from "Rudimentum Novitiorum", 1475	80	35
E3038	50pf. "Chosrou and Schirin" by Nizami (18th century Persian manuscript)	1·10	85
E3039	110pf. Book cover from Amalia musical library	3·00	2·10

WEST GERMAN CURRENCY

On 1 July 1990 the Ostmark was abolished and replaced by the West German Deutsche Mark.

1990. Tourist Sights.

E3040	E **939** 10pf. blue	20	15
E3041	– 30pf. green	35	25
E3042	– 50pf. green	55	35
E3043	– 60pf. brown	65	55
E3044	– 70pf. brown	70	65
E3045	– 80pf. red	90	75
E3046	– 100pf. red	1·20	85
E3047	– 200pf. violet	2·00	1·70
E3048	– 500pf. green	5·25	3·75

DESIGNS: 30pf. Goethe-Schiller Monument, Weimar; 50pf. Brandenburg Gate, Berlin; 60pf. Kyffhauser Monument; 70pf. Semper Opera House, Dresden; 80pf. Sanssouci Palace, Potsdam; 100pf. Wartburg Castle, Eisenach; 200pf. Magdeburg Cathedral; 500pf. Schwerin Castle.

E **940** Different Alphabets E **942** Louis Lewandowski (choir conductor)

E **941** Letter-carrier (from playing card) and Messenger, 1486

1990. International Literacy Year.

E3049	E **940** 30pf.+5pf. on 10pf.+5pf. mult	1·00	1·30

No. E3049 was not issued without surcharge.

1990. 500th Anniv of Regular European Postal Services.

E3050	E **941** 30pf. blk, brn & grn	45	35
E3051	– 50pf. black, red and blue	65	60

E3052 – 70pf. black, brown and red 80 75
E3053 – 100pf. black, grn & bl . . . . 1·60 1·40
DESIGNS: 50pf. "Courier" (Albrecht Durer) and post rider, 1590; 70pf. Open wagon, 1595, and mail carriage, 1750; 100pf. Travelling post office vans, 1842 and 1900.

1990. Reconstruction of New Synagogue, Berlin. Multicoloured.
E3054 30pf. Type E **942** 35 30
E3055 50pf.+15pf. New Synagogue . . . . . . 1·00 90

E **943** Schliemann and Two-handled Vessel

E **944** Dresden

1990. Death Cent of Heinrich Schliemann (archaeologist). Multicoloured.
E3056 30pf. Type E **943** 35 40
E3057 50pf. Schliemann and double pot (horiz) . . . 90 75

1990. 41st International Astronautics Federation Congress, Dresden.
E3058 E **944** 30pf. black and grey 30 25
E3059 – 50pf. multicoloured 65 55
E3060 – 70pf. dp bl, grn & bl 90 75
E3061 – 100pf. multicoloured 1·40 1·40
DESIGNS: 50pf. Earth; 70pf. Moon; 100pf. Mars.

On 3 October 1990 the territory of the Democratic Republic was absorbed into the Federal Republic of Germany, whose stamps have been used since then.

OFFICIAL STAMPS

EO **58** (Cross-piece projects to left)

EO **59** (Cross-piece projects to right)

EO **84**

1954. (a) Design in minute dots.
EO185 EO **58** 5pf. green . . . . . — 10
EO186 6pf. violet . . . . — 15
EO187 8pf. brown . . . . — 10
EO188 10pf. turquoise . . — 10
EO189 12pf. blue . . . . . — 10
EO190 15pf. violet . . . . — 10
EO191 16pf. violet . . . . — 10
EO192 20pf. olive . . . . — 10
EO193 24pf. red . . . . . — 10
EO194 25pf. turquoise . . — 15
EO195 30pf. red . . . . . — 10
EO196 40pf. red . . . . . — 10
EO197 48pf. lilac . . . . . — 1·50
EO198 50pf. lilac . . . . . — 15
EO199 60pf. blue . . . . . — 15
EO200 70pf. brown . . . . — 15
EO201 84pf. brown . . . . — 3·25

(b) Design in lines.
EO202 EO **59** 5pf. green . . . . . — 20
EO203 10pf. turquoise . . — 20
EO204 12pf. turquoise . . — 20
EO205 15pf. violet . . . . — 20
EO298 20pf. olive . . . . — 20
EO212 20pf. olive . . . . — 20
EO207 25pf. green . . . . — 20
EO299 30pf. red . . . . . — 20
EO300 40pf. red . . . . . — 20
EO210 50pf. lilac . . . . . — 20
EO211 70pf. brown . . . . — 20

1956. For internal use.
EO257 EO **84** 5pf. black . . . . . — 15
EO258 10pf. black . . . . — 15
EO259 20pf. black . . . . — 15
EO260 40pf. black . . . . — 75
EO261 70pf. black . . . . — 35
Nos. EO257/61 were not on sale to the public in unused condition, although specimens of all values are available on the market. The used prices are for cancelled-to-order, with segments across the corners of the stamps. Postally used are worth more.

OFFICIAL CENTRAL COURIER SERVICE STAMPS

These were for use on special postal services for confidential mail between Government officials and state-owned enterprises.

EO **95**

1956. With or without control figures.
EO303 EO **95** 10pf. black & purple 65 25
EO304 20pf. black & purple . . . . . 2·00 25
EO305 40pf. black & purple 65 25
EO306 70pf. black & purple . . . . . 3·50 2·10

EO **123**

1958. With various control figures. (a) With one bar (thick or thin) each side of figure.
EO357 EO **123** (10pf.) red & yell 41·00 5·00
EO373 (10pf.) brown & bl 21·00 4·25
EO375 (10pf.) violet and orange . . . . 40·00 6·75
EO377 (10pf.) red and green . . . . . 44·00 5·50

(b) With two bars (thick or thin) each side of figure.
EO358 EO **123** (20pf.) red & yell 40·00 3·50
EO374 (20pf.) brown & bl 42·00 3·50
EO376 (20pf.) violet and orange . . . . 52·00 4·75
EO378 (20pf.) red and green . . . . . 43·00 3·50
Used prices for Nos. EO357/EO378 are for postally used copies.

EO **149**

1959. With various control figures. (a) With one bar each side of figure.
EO414 EO **149** (10pf.) red, violet and green . . . 8·75 6·00
EO416 (10pf.) black & bl 11·00 60·00
EO418 (10pf.) black, brown and blue 44·00 70·00

(b) With two bars each side of figure.
EO415 EO **149** (20pf.) blue, brown and yellow . . . 13·00 4·50
EO417 (20pf.) green, blue and red . . . . 18·00 6·75
EO419 (20pf.) violet, black and brown 32·00 4·50

REGISTRATION STAMPS

SELF-SERVICE POST OFFICE

These registration labels embody a face value to cover the registration fee and have franking value to this extent. They are issued in pairs from automatic machines together with a certificate of posting against a 50pf. coin. The stamps are serially numbered in pairs and inscribed with the name of the town of issue.
The procedure is to affix one label to the letter (already franked with stamps for carriage of the letter) and complete page 1 of the certificate of posting which is then placed in the box provided together with the letter. The duplicate label is affixed to the second page of the certificate and retained for production as evidence in the event of a claim. They are not obtainable over the post office counter.
Unused prices are for pairs.

ER **318**

1967.
ER992 ER **318** 50pf. red and black . . . . . 2·40

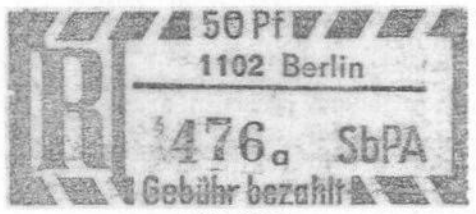

ER **319**

1968.
ER993 ER **319** 50pf. red . . . . 1·60

ER **345**

1968. For Parcel Post.
ER1089 ER **345** 50pf. black . . . 9·00

GHADAMES Pt. 6

A caravan halting place in the Libyan desert, under French administration from 1943 until 1951 when the area reverted to Libya. From 1943 to 1948 stamps of Fezzan were used.

100 centimes = 1 franc.

1 Cross of Agadem

1949.

1	**1**	4f. chestnut & brn (postage)	3·00	7·50
2		5f. green and blue	3·00	7·50
3		8f. chestnut and brown	4·25	10·00
4		10f. blue and black	4·25	10·00
5		12f. mauve and purple	6·25	20·00
6		15f. chestnut and brown	5·75	18·00
7		20f. green and brown	6·75	18·00
8		25f. blue and brown	6·00	18·00
9		50f. cerise and purple (air)	5·50	18·00
10		100f. purple and brown	6·00	18·00

GHANA Pt. 1

Formerly the British Colony of Gold Coast. Attained Dominion status on 6 March 1957, and became a republic within the British Commonwealth in 1960.

1957. 12 pence = 1 shilling;
20 shillings = 1 pound.
1965. 100 pesewas = 1 cedi.
1967. 100 new pesewas = 1 new cedi.
1972. 100 pesewas = 1 cedi = 0.8 (1967) new cedi.

CANCELLED REMAINDERS. In 1961 remainders of some issues of 1957 to 1960 were put on the market cancelled-to-order in such a way as to be indistinguishable from genuine postally used copies. Our used quotations which are indicated by an asterisk are, therefore, for cancelled-to-order copies.

29 Dr. Kwame Nkrumah, Palm-nut Vulture and Map of Africa

1957. Independence Commemoration.

166	**29**	2d. red	10	10*
167		2½d. green	10	15*
168		4d. brown	10	15*
169		1s.3d. blue	15	15*

1957. Queen Elizabeth stamps of 1952 of Gold Coast optd **GHANA INDEPENDENCE 6TH.. MARCH, 1957.**

170		½d. brown and red	10	10*
171		1d. blue	10	10*
172		1½d. green	10	10*
173		2d. brown	30	30
174		2½d. red	1·00	1·25
175		3d. mauve	30	10*
176		4d. blue	5·50	7·00
177		6d. black and orange	10	10*
178		1s. black and red	10	10*
179		2s. olive and red	60	10*
180		5s. purple and black	75	10*
181		10s. black and olive	75	60*

31 Viking Ship

1957. Inauguration of Black Star Shipping Line.

182	**31**	2½d. green	30	20
183	–	1s.3d. blue	35	1·25
184	–	5s. purple	45	3·00

DESIGNS—HORIZ: 1s.3d. Galleon; 5s. M.V. "Volta River".

34 Ambassador Hotel, Accra

1958. 1st Anniv of Independence. Flag and Coat of Arms in national colours.

185	**34**	½d. black and red	10	10
186	–	2½d. black, red and yellow	10	10
187	–	1s.3d. black and blue	30	10
188	–	2s. yellow and black	45	35

DESIGNS—HORIZ: 2½d. State Opening of Parliament; 1s.3d. National Monument. VERT: 2s. Ghana Coat of Arms.

38 Map showing the Independent African States

40 Palm-nut Vulture over Globe

41 Bristol Britannia

1958. 1st Conference of Independent African States, Accra. Star in black and yellow.

189	**38**	2½d. red and yellow	10	10
190		3d. green and brown	10	10
191	–	1s. blue, yellow and orange	20	10
192	–	2s.6d. red and purple	40	65

DESIGN—VERT: 1s., 2s.6d. Map of Africa and flaming torch.

1958. Inauguration of Ghana Airways. Inscr as in T **40/41**.

193	**40**	2½d. black, bistre and red	45	10
194	**41**	1s.3d. multicoloured	90	20
195	–	2s. multicoloured	1·00	55
196	–	2s.6d. black and bistre	1·00	95

DESIGNS—(As Type **41**): 2s. Boeing Stratocruiser and yellow-nosed albatross. (As Type **40**): 2s.6d. Palm-nut vulture and Vickers VC-10 aircraft.

1958. Prime Minister's Visit to United States and Canada. Optd **PRIME MINISTER'S VISIT, U.S.A. AND CANADA.**

197	**29**	2d. red	10	40
198		2½d. green	10	30
199		4d. brown	10	50
200		1s.3d. blue	15	25

45

46 Dr. Nkrumah and Lincoln Statue, Washington

1958. United Nations Day.

201	**45**	2½d. brown, green and black	10	10
202		1s.3d. brown, blue and black	15	10
203		2s.6d. brown, violet black	15	35

1959. 150th Birth Anniv of Abraham Lincoln.

204	**46**	2½d. pink and purple	10	10
205		1s.3d. light blue and blue	10	10
206		2s.6d. yellow and olive	15	35
MS206a		102 × 77 mm. Nos. 204/6. Imperf	55	2·00

48 Kente Cloth and Traditional Symbols

1959. Independence. Inscr "SECOND ANNIVERSARY OF INDEPENDENCE".

207	**48**	½d. multicoloured	10	10
208	–	2½d. multicoloured	10	10
209	–	1s.3d. multicoloured	15	10
210	–	2s. multicoloured	30	1·25

DESIGNS—HORIZ: 2½d. Talking drums and elephant-horn blower; 2s. Map of Africa, Ghana flag and palms. VERT: 1s.3d. "Symbols of Greeting".

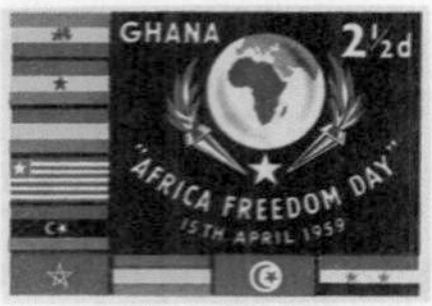

52 Globe and Flags

1959. Africa Freedom Day.

211	**52**	2½d. multicoloured	15	10
212		8½d. multicoloured	15	20

54 Nkrumah Statue, Accra

55 Ghana Timber

65a Red-fronted Gazelle

1959. Multicoloured.

213		½d. "God's Omnipotence" (postage)	10	10
213a		½d. "Gye Nyame"	30	10
214		1d. Type **54**	10	10
215		1½d. Type **55**	10	10
216		2d. Volta river	10	10
217		2½d. Cocoa bean	10	10
218		3d. "God's Omnipotence"	10	10
218a		3d. "Gye Nyame"	30	10
219		4d. Diamond and mine	4·50	65
220		6d. Red-crowned bishop (bird)	50	10
221		11d. Golden-spider lily	25	10
222		1s. Shell ginger	25	10
223		2s.6d. Giant blue turaco	2·25	15
224		5s. Tiger orchid	3·25	65
225		10s. Jewel cichlid	75	70
225a		£1 Type **65a**	3·75	4·75
226		1s.3d. Pennant-winged nightjar (air)	2·50	10
227		2s. Crowned cranes	1·75	10

SIZES—HORIZ (As Type **54**): ½d. (As Type **55**): 2d., 2½d., 3d., 4d., 6d., 1s.3d., 2s.6d. (As Type **65a**): 10s. VERT (As Type **55**): 11d., 1s., 2s., 5s.

The 3d. is a different symbolic design from the ½d.

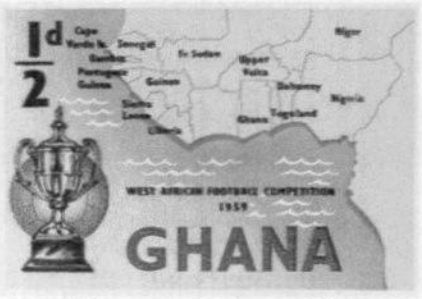

68 Gold Cup and West African Map

1959. West African Football Competition, 1959. Multicoloured.

228		½d. Type **68**	10	10*
229		1d. Footballers (vert)	10	10*
230		3d. Goalkeeper saving ball	10	10*
231		8d. Forward attacking goal	40	15*
232		2s.6d. "Kwame Nkrumah" Gold Cup (vert)	50	15*

73 Duke of Edinburgh and Arms of Ghana

1959. Visit of the Duke of Edinburgh.

233	**73**	3d. black and mauve	30	10*

74 Ghana Flag and Talking Drums

1959. U.N. Trusteeship Council. Multicoloured.

234		3d. Type **74**	10	10*
235		6d. Ghana flag and U.N. emblem (vert)	10	10*
236		1s.3d. As 6d. but emblem above flag (vert)	20	15*
237		2s.6d. "Totem pole" (vert)	25	15*

78 Eagles in Flight

85 Dr. Nkrumah

82 Flags and Map forming letter "A"

1960. 3rd Anniv of Independence. Mult.

238		½d. Type **78**	10	10*
239		3d. Fireworks	10	10*
240		1s.3d. "Third Anniversary"	30	10*
241		2s. "Ship of State"	30	15*

1960. African Freedom Day. Multicoloured.

242		3d. Type **82**	10	10*
243		6d. Letter "f"	20	10*
244		1s. Letter "d"	20	10*

1960. Republic Day. Inscr "REPUBLIC DAY 1ST JULY 1960". Multicoloured.

245		3d. Type **85**	10	10
246		1s.3d. Ghana flag	20	10
247		2s. Torch of Freedom	20	15
248		10s. Ghana arms (horiz)	50	80
MS248a		102 × 77 mm. Nos. 245/8. Imperf	40	1·50

90 Athlete

1960. Olympic Games.

249	–	3d. multicoloured	10	10
250	–	6d. multicoloured	15	10
251	**90**	1s.3d. multicoloured	25	10
252		2s.6d. multicoloured	35	60

DESIGN—VERT: 3d., 6d. Olympic torch.

91 President Nkrumah

1960. Founder's Day. Inscribed as in T **91**.

253	**91**	3d. multicoloured	10	10
254	–	6d. multicoloured	10	10
255	–	1s.3d. multicoloured	20	20

DESIGNS—VERT: 6d. President Nkrumah within star; 1s.3d. Map of Africa and column.

94 U.N. Emblem and Ghana Flag

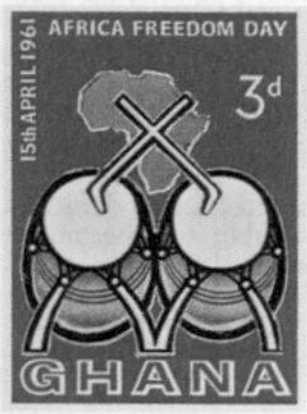

97 Talking Drums

1960. Human Rights Day.

256	**94**	3d. multicoloured	10	10
257	–	6d. yellow, black and blue	15	15
258	–	1s.3d. multicoloured	25	55

DESIGNS: U.N. Emblem with torch (6d.) or within laurel (1s.3d.).

1961. Africa Freedom Day. Inscr "15th APRIL 1961".

259	**97**	3d. multicoloured	10	10
260	–	6d. red, black and green	20	10
261	–	2s. multicoloured	50	45

DESIGNS—VERT: 6d. Map of Africa. HORIZ: 2s. Flags and map.

100 Eagle on Column

103 Dove with Olive Branch

1961. 1st Anniv of Republic. Multicoloured.
262 3d. Type **100** 10 10
263 1s.3d. "Flower" 10 10
264 2s. Ghana flags 20 90

1961. Belgrade Conference.
265 **103** 3d. green 10 10
266 – 1s.3d. blue 15 10
267 – 5s. purple . . . . 40 1·00
DESIGNS—HORIZ: 1s.3d. World map, chain and olive branch; 5s. Rostrum, Conference room.

106 President Nkrumah and Globe

1961. Founder's Day. Multicoloured.
268 3d. Type **106** 10 10
269 1s.3d. President in Kente cloth (vert) 20 10
270 5s. President in national costume (vert) . . . . . . 65 2·50
MS270a Three sheets, 106 × 86 mm (3d.) or 86 × 106 mm (others), each with Nos. 268/70 in block of four. Imperf Set of three sheets . . . 3·25 14·00

109 Queen Elizabeth II and African Map

1961. Royal Visit.
271 **109** 3d. multicoloured 15 10
272 1s.3d. multicoloured . . . 30 20
273 5s. multicoloured . . . . 65 3·50
MS273a 106 × 84 mm. No. 273 in block of 4. Imperf . . . . . . 2·25 7·50

110 Ships in Tema Harbour

1962. Opening of Tema Harbour. Multicoloured.
274 3d. Type **110** (postage) . . . 15 10
275 1s.3d. Douglas DC-8 aircraft and ships at Tema (air) . . 65 15
276 2s.6d. As No. 275 . . . . . 80 2·50

112 Africa and Peace Dove

1962. 1st Anniv of Casablanca Conference.
277 **112** 3d. multicoloured (postage) 10 10
278 1s.3d. multicoloured (air) 30 15
279 2s.6d. multicoloured . . . 40 2·00

113 Compass over Africa

115 Atomic Bomb-burst "Skull"

1962. Africa Freedom Day.
280 **113** 3d. sepia, turquoise & pur 10 10
281 6d. sepia, turquoise & brn 10 15
282 1s.3d. sepia, turq & red 15 15

1962. The Accra Assembly.
283 – 3d. black and lake 10 10
284 **115** 6d. black and red 25 45
285 – 1s.3d. turquoise 30 60
DESIGNS: 3d. Ghana Star over "five continents"; 1s.3d. Dove of Peace.

117 Patrice Lumumba

1962. 1st Death Anniv of Lumumba.
286 **117** 3d. black and yellow . . . 10 10
287 6d. black, green and slate 10 30
288 1s.3d. black, pink and green 15 35

118 Star over Two Columns

121 President Nkrumah

1962. 2nd Anniv of Republic. Inscribed "1st JULY 1962". Multicoloured.
289 3d. Type **118** 10 10
290 6d. Flaming torch 20 20
291 1s.3d. Eagle trailing flag (horiz) 40 40

1962. Founder's Day.
292 **121** 1d. multicoloured 10 10
293 – 3d. multicoloured 10 10
294 – 1s.3d. black and blue . . 30 15
295 – 2s. multicoloured . . . . 30 1·25
DESIGNS: 3d. Nkrumah medallion; 1s.3d. President and Ghana Star; 2s. Laying "Ghana" brick.

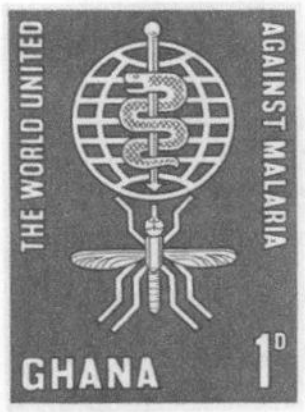

125 Campaign Emblem

126 Campaign Emblem

1962. Malaria Eradication.
296 **125** 1d. red 10 10
297 4d. green . . . . 20 1·25
298 6d. bistre 20 30
299 1s.3d. violet 25 90
MS299a 90 × 115 mm. Nos. 296/9. Imperf . . . . 75 1·50

1963. Freedom from Hunger.
300 **126** 1d. multicoloured 15 20
301 – 4d. sepia, yellow and orange . . . . 75 1·00
302 – 1s.3d. ochre, black grn . . 1·60 1·00
DESIGNS—HORIZ: 4d. Emblem in hands; 1s.3d. World map and emblem.

129 Map of Africa

133 Red Cross

1963. Africa Freedom Day.
303 **129** 1d. gold and red 10 10
304 – 4d. red, black and yellow 10 10
305 – 1s.3d. multicoloured . . . 20 10
306 – 2s.6d. multicoloured . . . 35 1·25
DESIGNS—HORIZ: 4d. Carved stool. VERT: 1s.3d. Map and bowl of fire; 2s.6d. Topi (antelope) and flag.

1963. Centenary of Red Cross. Multicoloured.
307 1d. Type **133** 40 15
308 1½d. Centenary emblem (horiz) . . . . 55 2·00
309 4d. Nurses and child (horiz) 75 20
310 1s.3d. Emblem, globe and laurel . . . . 1·75 2·00
MS310a 102 × 127 mm. Nos. 307/10. Imperf . . . . 2·75 11·00

137 "3rd Anniversary"

1963. 3rd Anniv of Republic. Multicoloured.
311 1d. Type **137** 10 10
312 4d. Three Ghanian flags . . . 10 10
313 1s.3d. Map, flag and star (vert) 20 15
314 2s.6d. Flag and torch (vert) 35 2·00

141 President Nkrumah and Ghana Flag

145 Rameses II, Abu Simbel

1963. Founder's Day.
315 **141** 1d. multicoloured 10 10
316 – 4d. multicoloured 15 10
317 – 1s.3d. multicoloured . . . 30 10
318 – 5s. yellow and mauve . . 65 75
DESIGNS—VERT: 4d. Type **141** but with larger flag behind President Nkrumah. HORIZ: 1s.3d. President Nkrumah and fireworks; 5s. Native symbol of wisdom.

1963. Preservation of Nubian Monuments. Multicoloured.
319 1d. Type **145** 15 10
320 1½d. Rock paintings (horiz) 20 65
321 2d. Queen Nefertari (horiz) 20 10
322 4d. Sphinx, Sebua 35 15
323 1s.3d. Rock Temple, Abu Simbel (horiz) 80 90

150 Class 248 Steam Locomotive and Diesel-electric Locomotive No. 1401

1963. 60th Anniv of Ghana Railway.
324 **150** 1d. multicoloured 10 10
325 6d. multicoloured 50 10
326 1s.3d. multicoloured . . . 60 60
327 2s.6d. multicoloured . . . 1·00 2·25

151 Eleanor Roosevelt and "Flame of Freedom"

154 Sun and Globe Emblem

1963. 5th Anniv of Declaration of Human Rights. Multicoloured.
328 1d. Type **151** 10 10
329 4d. Type **151** 10 30
330 6d. Eleanor Roosevelt . . . 10 10
331 1s.3d. Eleanor Roosevelt and emblems (horiz) 15 15

1964. International Quiet Sun Years.
332 **154** 3d. multicoloured 15 10
333 6d. multicoloured 25 10
334 1s.3d. multicoloured . . . 25 15
MS334a 90 × 90 mm. No. 334 in block of 4. Imperf . . . . . . 75 2·50

155 Harvesting Corn on State Farm

1964. 4th Anniv of Republic.
335 **155** 3d. olive, brown and yellow 10 10
336 – 6d. green, brown turq . . 10 10
337 – 1s.3d. red, brn salmon . . 10 10
338 – 5s. multicoloured . . . . 40 1·00
MS338a 126 × 100 mm. Nos. 335/8. Imperf . . . . 85 2·00
DESIGNS: 6d. Oil refinery, Tema; 1s.3d. "Communal Labour"; 5s. Procession headed by flag.

159 Globe and Dove

163 President Nkrumah and Hibiscus Flowers

1964. 1st Anniv of African Unity Charter.
339 **159** 3d. multicoloured 10 10
340 – 6d. green and red 10 10
341 – 1s.3d. multicoloured . . . 15 10
342 – 5s. multicoloured 45 70
DESIGNS—VERT: 6d. Map of Africa and quill pen; 5s. Planting flower. HORIZ: 1s.3d. Hitched rope on map of Africa.

1964. Founder's Day.
343 **163** 3d. multicoloured 10 10
344 6d. multicoloured 15 10
345 1s.3d. multicoloured . . . 25 10
346 2s.6d. multicoloured . . . 40 60
MS346a 90 × 122 mm. No. 346 in block of 4. Imperf . . . . . . 70 2·50

164 Hurdling

1964. Olympic Games, Tokyo. Multicoloured.
347 1d. Type **164** 10 10
348 2½d. Running . . . . 10 1·25
349 3d. Boxing (vert) 10 10
350 4d. Long-jumping (vert) . . . 10 10
351 6d. Football (vert) 15 10
352 1s.3d. Athlete holding Olympic Torch (vert) . . . 20 10
353 5s. Olympic "Rings" and flags . . . . 55 3·25
MS353a 128 × 102 mm. Nos. 351/3. Imperf . . . . 75 2·50

171 G. Washington Carver (botanist) and Plant

1964. U.N.E.S.C.O. Week.
354 **171** 6d. blue and green . . . 10 10
355 – 1s.3d. purple and blue . . 30 10
356 **171** 5s. sepia and red . . . . 50 4·00
MS356a 127 × 77 mm. Nos. 354/6. Imperf . . . . 75 2·00
DESIGN: 1s.3d. Albert Einstein (scientist) and Atomic symbol.

173 African Elephant

181 I.C.Y. Emblem

1964. Multicoloured.
357 1d. Type **173** 50 50
358 1½d. Secretary bird (horiz) . . 75 2·25
359 2½d. Purple wreath (flower) 30 2·25
360 3d. Grey parrot 75 50
361 4d. Blue-naped mousebird (horiz) 75 70
362 6d. African tulip tree (horiz) 30 30

363 1s.3d. Violet starling (horiz) 1·00 1·25
364 2s.6d. Hippopotamus (horiz) 1·00 5·50
MS364a Two sheets. (a) 150 × 86 mm. Nos. 357/9. (b) 150 × 110 mm. Nos. 360/4. Imperf
Set of 2 sheets . . . . 4·75 14·00

1965. International Co-operation Year.
365 **181** 1d. multicoloured 35 60
366 4d. multicoloured . . . . 1·00 1·40
367 6d. multicoloured . . . . 1·00 60
368 1s.3d. multicoloured . . . 1·25 2·75
MS368a 100 × 100 mm. No. 368 in block of 4. Imperf . . . . . . 2·75 5·00

182 I.T.U. Emblem and Symbols

1965. Centenary of I.T.U.
369 **182** 1d. multicoloured 15 15
370 6d. multicoloured 30 15
371 1s.3d. multicoloured . . . 55 25
372 5s. multicoloured . . . . 1·25 2·75
MS372a 132 × 115 mm. Nos. 369/72.
Imperf . . . . 7·50 10·00

183 Lincoln's Home

1965. Death Centenary of Abraham Lincoln.
373 **183** 6d. multicoloured 10 10
374 – 1s.3d. black, red and blue 15 15
375 – 2s. black, brown and yellow 15 30
376 – 5s. black and red . . . . 30 1·50
MS376a 115 × 115 mm. Nos. 373/6.
Imperf . . . . 75 3·50
DESIGNS: 1s.3d. Lincoln's inaugural address; 2s. Abraham Lincoln; 5s. Adaption of U.S. 90c. Lincoln stamp of 1869.

187 Obverse (President Nkrumah) and Reverse of 5p. Coin

1965. Introduction of Decimal Currency. Multicoloured designs showing coins expressed in the same denominations as on the stamps.
377 5p. Type **187** 20 10
378 10p. As Type **187** 25 10
379 25p. Size 63 × 39 mm . . . 55 1·00
380 50p. Size 71 × 43½ mm . . . 1·00 2·25

1965. Nos. 214/27 surch **Ghana New Currency 19th July. 1965.** and value. Multicoloured.
381 **54** 1p. on 1d. (postage) . . . 10 10
382 – 2p. on 2d. 10 10
383 – 3p. on 3d. (No. 218a) . . 1·00 5·50
384 – 4p. on 4d. . . . . 4·50 45
385 – 6p. on 6d. 50 10
386 – 11p. on 11d. 25 10
387 – 12p. on 1s. 25 10
388 – 30p. on 2s.6d. . . . . . 4·00 7·00
389 – 60p. on 5s. . . . . 4·50 70
390 – 1c.20 on 10s. . . . . . . 75 2·25
391 **65a** 2c.40 on £1 . . . . . . 1·00 6·00
392 – 15p. on 1s.3d. (air) . . . 2·50 70
393 – 24p. on 2s. . . . . 2·50 30

189 "OAU" and Flag

1965. O.A.U. Summit Conf, Accra. Mult.
394 1p. Type **189** 10 10
395 2p. "OAU" heads and flag . . 10 10
396 5p. OAU emblem and flag . . 10 10
397 6p. African map and flag (horiz) (37½ × 27½ mm) . . 10 10
398 15p. "Sunburst" and flag (horiz) (37½ × 27½ mm) . . 20 30
399 24p. "O.A.U." on map, and flag (horiz) (37½ × 27½ mm) 35 60

195 Goalkeeper saving Ball

1965. African Soccer Cup Competition. Mult.
400 6p. Type **195** 25 10
401 15p. Player with ball (vert) 40 25
402 24p. Player, ball and Soccer Cup 45 50

198 President Kennedy and Grave Memorial

1965. 2nd Death Anniv of President Kennedy.
403 **198** 6p. multicoloured 15 10
404 – 15p. violet, red and green 20 35
405 – 24p. black and purple . . 20 60
406 – 30p. purple and black . . 25 1·00
MS407 114½ × 114 mm. Nos. 403/6.
Imperf . . . . 3·00 6·50
DESIGNS: 15p. President Kennedy and Eternal Flame; 24p. President Kennedy and Memorial Inscription; 30p. President Kennedy.

202 Section of Dam and Generators

1966. Volta River Project.
408 **202** 6p. multicoloured 15 10
409 – 15p. multicoloured . . . 20 15
410 – 24p. multicoloured . . . 25 20
411 – 30p. black and blue . . 35 50
DESIGNS: 15p. Dam and Lake Volta; 24p. Word "GHANA" as Dam; 30p. "Fertility".

1965. "Black Stars" Victory in African Soccer Cup Competition. Optd **Black Stars Retain Africa Cup 21st Nov. 1966.**
412 **195** 6p. multicoloured 30 15
413 – 15p. multicoloured . . . 50 30
414 – 24p. multicoloured . . . 55 70

207 W.H.O. Building and Ghana Flag

1966. Inaug of W.H.O. Headquarters, Geneva. Mult.
415 6p. Type **207** 50 10
416 15p. Type **207** . . . . 1·25 65
417 24p. W.H.O. Building and emblem . . . . 1·40 1·60
418 30p. W.H.O. Building and emblem . . . . 1·60 3·50
MS419 120 × 101 mm. Nos. 415/18.
Imperf . . . . 18·00 19·00

209 Atlantic Herring

1966. Freedom from Hunger. Multicoloured.
420 6p. Type **209** 25 10
421 15p. Turbot 45 15
422 24p. Spadefish 50 35
423 30p. Red snapper . . . . . 50 1·10
424 60p. Blue-finned tuna . . . . 80 4·50
MS425 126 × 109 mm. No. 423 in block of 4. Imperf . . . . . . 10·00 13·00

214 African "Links" and Ghana Flag

1966. 3rd Anniv of African Charter. Multicoloured.
426 6p. Type **214** 15 10
427 15p. Flags as "quill" and diamond (horiz) 35 55
428 24p. Ship's wheel, map and cocoa bean (horiz) 40 70

217 Player heading Ball, and Jules Rimet Cup

1966. World Cup Football Championship. Multicoloured.
429 5p. Type **217** 30 10
430 15p. Goalkeeper clearing ball 70 20
431 24p. Player and Jules Rimet Cup (replica) 85 35
432 30p. Players and Jules Rimet Cup (replica) . . . . . . 1·10 1·25
433 60p. Players with ball . . . . 1·75 7·00
MS434 120 × 102 mm. No. 433 in block of 4. Imperf . . . . . . 23·00 25·00

222 U.N.E.S.C.O. Emblem

1966. 20th Anniv of U.N.E.S.C.O.
435 **222** 5p. multicoloured 50 15
436 15p. multicoloured . . . 1·25 50
437 24p. multicoloured . . . 1·50 1·00
438 30p. multicoloured . . . 1·75 2·75
439 60p. multicoloured . . . 2·50 7·00
MS440 140 × 115 mm. Nos. 435/9.
Imperf . . . . 23·00 24·00

223 Fair Emblem and Crates

1967. Ghana Trade Fair, Accra. Multicoloured.
441 5p. Type **223** 10 10
442 15p. Fair emblem and world map 15 20
443 24p. Shipping and flags . . . 25 30
444 36p. Fair emblem and hand-held hoist . . . . 40 2·50

1967. New Currency. Nos. 216/26 and 393 surch with new value.
445 1½n.p. on 2d. (postage) . . 2·00 5·50
446 3½n.p. on 4d. . . . . 7·00 3·75
447 5n.p. on 6d. . . . . 2·50 2·00
448 9n.p. on 11d. 30 30
449 10n.p. on 1s. 30 75
450 25n.p. on 2s.6d. . . . . . 3·50 6·00
451 1n.c. on 10s. . . . . 3·00 15·00
452 2n.c. on £1 . . . . 6·00 24·00
453 12½n.p. on 1s.3d. (air) . . . 4·00 3·50
454 20n.p. on 24p. on 2s. . . . 6·50 6·00

229 Ghana Eagle and Flag

1967. 1st Anniv of 24 February Revolution.
455 **229** 1n.p. multicoloured . . . 10 75
456 4n.p. multicoloured . . . 10 10
457 12½n.p. multicoloured . . 35 60
458 25n.p. multicoloured . . 65 3·25
MS459 89 × 108 mm. Nos. 455/8.
Perf or imperf . . . . 5·00 12·00

230 Maize

232 The Ghana Mace

1967. Multicoloured.
460 1n.p. Type **230** 10 10
461 1½n.p. Forest kingfisher . . . 1·00 2·75
462 2n.p. Type **232** 10 10
463 2½n.p. Commelina 35 10
464 3n.p. West African lungfish 20 40
465 4n.p. Rufous-crowned roller 1·50 10
466 6n.p. Akosombo Dam . . . 15 2·00
467 8n.p. Adomi Bridge 15 50
468 9n.p. Chameleon 75 10
469 10n.p. Tema Harbour 15 10
470 20n.p. Bush hare (blue) . . . 20 10
471 50n.p. Black-winged stilt . . 8·00 2·50
472 1n.c. Wooden stool . . . . . 2·00 1·00
473 2n.c. Frangipani . . . . . . 2·00 3·50
474 2n.c.50 Seat of State . . . . 1·75 8·00
SIZES—VERT (As Type **230**): 4n.p. (As Type **232**): 1½n.p.; 2½n.p., 20n.p., 2n.c., 2n.c.50. HORIZ (as Type **230**): 8n.p. (As Type **232**): 3n.p., 6n.p., 9n.p., 10n.p., 50n.p., 1n.c.

245 Kumasi Fort

1967. Castles and Forts
475 **245** 4n.p. multicoloured . . . 25 10
476 – 12½n.p. multicoloured . . 75 1·00
477 – 20n.p. multicoloured . . . 1·00 2·75
478 – 25n.p. multicoloured . . . 1·00 3·50
DESIGNS: 12½n.p. Christiansborg Castle and British galleon; 20n.p. Elmina Castle and Portuguese galleon; 25n.p. Cape Coast Castle and Spanish galleon.

249 "Luna 10"

255 U.N. Headquarters Building

252 Scouts and Campfire

1967. "Peaceful Use of Outer Space". Multicoloured.
479 4n.p. Type **249** 10 10
480 10n.p. "Orbiter 1" 10 45
481 12½n.p. Man in Space 20 80
MS482 140 × 90 mm. Nos. 479/81.
Imperf . . . . 1·75 4·00

1967. 50th Anniv of Ghanaian Scout Movement. Multicoloured.
483 4n.p. Type **252** 20 10
484 10n.p. Scout on march . . . 40 50
485 12½n.p. Lord Baden-Powell 50 1·75
MS486 167 × 95 mm. Nos. 483/5.
Imperf . . . . 6·00 10·00

1967. United Nations Day (24 October).
487 **255** 4n.p. multicoloured . . . 10 10
488 10n.p. multicoloured . . . 10 15
489 – 50n.p. multicoloured . . 20 70
490 – 2n.c.50 multicoloured . . 55 4·00
MS491 76 × 75 mm. No. 490. Imperf 2·25 9·50
DESIGN: 50n.p., 2n.c.50, General view of U.N. H.Q., Manhattan.

257 Leopard

1967. International Tourist Year. Multicoloured.
492 4n.p. Type **257** . . . . 1·00 20
493 12½n.p. "Papilio demodocus" (butterfly) . . . . 2·50 1·50
494 20n.p. Carmine bee eater . . 3·00 3·75
495 50n.p. Waterbuck . . . . . 3·00 9·00
MS496 126 × 126mm. Nos. 492/5. Imperf . . . . 17·00 20·00

261 Revolutionaries entering Accra

1968. 2nd Anniv of February Revolution. Mult.
497 4n.p. Type **261** 10 10
498 12½n.p. Marching troops . . 20 20
499 20n.p. Cheering people . . . 30 40
500 40n.p. Victory celebrations 50 2·25

265 Microscope and Cocoa Beans

1968. Cocoa Research.
501 **265** 2½n.p. multicoloured . . . 10 1·00
502 – 4n.p. multicoloured . . . 10 10
503 **265** 10n.p. multicoloured . . . 15 20
504 – 25n.p. multicoloured . . . 60 1·50
MS505 102 × 102 mm. Nos. 501/4. Imperf . . . . 2·25 4·50
DESIGNS: 4n.p. and 25n.p. Microscope and cocoa tree, beans and pods.

267 Kotoka and Flowers

1968. 1st Death Anniv of Lt.-Gen. E. K. Kotoka. Multicoloured.
506 4n.p. Type **267** 10 10
507 12½n.p. Kotoka and wreath 20 30
508 20n.p. Kotoka in civilian clothes 35 75
509 40n.p. Lt.-Gen. Kotoka . . . 50 2·25

271 Tobacco **277** Hurdling

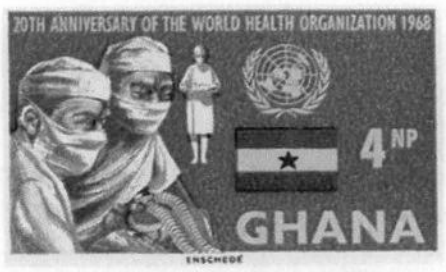

276 Surgeons, Flag and W.H.O. Emblem

1968. Flora and Fauna. Multicoloured.
510 4n.p. Type **271** 15 10
511 5n.p. North African crested porcupine 15 80
512 12½n.p. Rubber 20 75
513 20n.p. "Cymothoe sangaris" (butterfly) . . . . 1·50 2·75
514 40n.p. "Charaxes ameliae" (butterfly) . . . . 1·75 5·00
MS515 88 × 114 mm. Nos. 510 and 512/14. Imperf . . . . . . 3·25 9·00

1968. 20th Anniv of W.H.O.
516 **276** 4n.p. multicoloured . . . 20 10
517 12½n.p. multicoloured . . 40 40
518 20n.p. multicoloured . . . 60 1·25
519 40n.p. multicoloured . . . 1·00 4·25
MS520 132 × 110 mm. Nos. 516/19. Imperf . . . . 2·75 6·50

1969. Olympic Games, Mexico (1968). Multicoloured.
521 4n.p. Type **277** 10 10
522 12½n.p. Boxing 20 30
523 20n.p. Torch, Olympic Rings and flags 40 75
524 40n.p. Football . . . . . . 70 3·25
MS525 89 × 114 mm. Nos. 521/4. Imperf . . . . 3·50 7·50

281 U.N. Building **285** Dr. J. B. Danquah

1969. United Nations Day. Multicoloured.
526 4n.p. Type **281** 10 10
527 12½n.p. Native stool, staff and U.N. emblem 15 25
528 20n.p. U.N. building and emblem over Ghanian Flag 20 40
529 40n.p. U.N. emblem encircled by flags . . . . 40 2·25
MS530 127 × 117 mm. Nos. 526/9. Imperf . . . . 75 3·25

1969. Human Rights Year. Multicoloured.
531 4n.p. Type **285** 10 10
532 12½n.p. Dr. Martin Luther King 20 35
533 20n.p. As 12½n.p. 35 75
534 40n.p. Type **285** . . . . . . 50 2·50
MS535 116 × 50 mm. Nos. 531/4. Imperf . . . . 80 3·50

287 Constituent Assembly Building

1969. 3rd Anniv of Revolution. Multicoloured.
536 4n.p. Type **287** 10 10
537 12½n.p. Arms of Ghana . . . 10 15
538 20n.p. Type **287** 15 20
539 40n.p. As 12½n.p. 20 75
MS540 114 × 89 mm. Nos. 536/9. Imperf . . . . 70 2·50

1969. New Constitution. Nos. 460/74 optd **NEW CONSTITUTION 1969**.
541 **230** 1n.p. multicoloured . . . 10 2·00
542 – 1½n.p. multicoloured . . . 1·75 3·75
543 **232** 2n.p. multicoloured . . . 10 3·25
544 – 2½n.p. multicoloured . . . 10 2·00
545 – 3n.p. multicoloured . . . 1·00 2·25
546 – 4n.p. multicoloured . . . 3·00 50
547 – 6n.p. multicoloured . . . 15 2·75
548 – 8n.p. multicoloured . . . 15 2·75
549 – 9n.p. multicoloured . . . 15 3·00
550 – 10n.p. multicoloured . . . 20 2·75
551 – 20n.p. multicoloured . . . 35 2·00
552 – 50n.p. multicoloured . . . 6·50 6·00
553 – 1n.c. multicoloured . . . 1·50 7·00
554 – 2n.c. multicoloured . . . 1·50 8·50
555 – 2n.c.50 multicoloured . . . 1·50 9·50
On Nos. 541, 545, 547/50 and 552/3 the opt is horiz. The rest are vert.

290 Map of Africa and Flags **294** Red Cross and Globe

293 I.L.O. Emblem and Cogwheels

1969. Inauguration of 2nd Republic. Multicoloured.
556 4n.p. Type **290** 10 10
557 12½n.p. Figure "2", branch and Ghanaian colours . . 20 15
558 20n.p. Hands receiving egg 35 35
559 40n.p. Type **290** . . . . . . 60 1·25

1970. 50th Anniv of I.L.O.
560 **293** 4n.p. multicoloured . . . 10 10
561 12½n.p. multicoloured . . 20 55
562 20n.p. multicoloured . . . 30 1·25
MS563 117 × 89 mm. Nos. 560/2. Imperf . . . . 70 3·00

1970. 50th Anniv of League of Red Cross Societies. Multicoloured.
564 4n.p. Type **294** 20 10
565 12½n.p. Henri Dunant and Red Cross emblem (horiz) 25 25
566 20n.p. Patient receiving medicine (horiz) 30 70
567 40n.p. Patient having arm bandaged (horiz) . . . . . 35 1·75
MS568 114 × 89 mm. Nos. 564/7. Imperf . . . . 1·50 6·00

298 General Kotoka, Vickers VC-10 and Airport **302** Lunar Module landing on Moon

1970. Inauguration of Kotoka Airport. Mult.
569 4n.p. Type **298** 15 10
570 12½n.p. Control tower and tail of Vickers VC-10 . . . 25 15
571 20n.p. Aerial view of airport 40 30
572 40n.p. Airport and flags . . . 75 80

1970. Moon Landing. Multicoloured.
573 4n.p. Type **302** 30 10
574 12½n.p. Astronaut's first step onto the Moon 50 60
575 20n.p. Astronaut with equipment on Moon (horiz) . . . . 60 1·40
576 40n.p. Astronauts (horiz) . . 75 3·00
MS577 142 × 142 mm. Nos. 573/6. Imperf . . . . 2·25 12·00

306 Adult Education

1970. International Education Year. Multicoloured.
578 4n.p. Type **306** 10 10
579 12½n.p. International education 20 20
580 20n.p. "Ntesie" and I.E.Y. symbols 35 30
581 40n.p. Nursery schools . . . 60 1·00

310 Saluting March-Past

1970. 1st Anniv of Second Republic. Multicoloured
582 4n.p. Type **310** 20 10
583 12½n.p. Busia Declaration . . 15 15
584 20n.p. Doves symbol 25 30
585 40n.p. Opening of Parliament 50 1·00

314 "Crinum ornatum"

1970. Flora and Fauna. Multicoloured.
586 4n.p. Type **314** . . . . . . 1·75 25
587 12½n.p. Lioness . . . . . . 1·25 85
588 20n.p. "Ansellia africana" (flower) . . . . 1·25 1·50
589 40n.p. African elephant . . . 2·00 6·00

315 Kuduo Brass Casket

1970. Monuments and Archaeological Sites in Ghana. Multicoloured.
590 4n.p. Type **315** 15 10
591 12½n.p. Akan traditional house 30 20
592 20n.p. Larabanga Mosque . . 35 50
593 40n.p. Funerary clay head . . 50 1·10
MS594 89 × 71 mm. Nos. 590, 592 and 12½n.p. Basilica of Pompeii, 40n.p. Pistrinum of Pompeii. Imperf . . . . 6·00 9·00

316 Trade Fair Building

1971. International Trade Fair, Accra. Multicoloured.
595 4n.p. Type **316** 10 10
596 12½n.p. Cosmetic and pharmaceutical goods . . . 60 20
597 20n.p. Vehicles 65 25
598 40n.p. Construction equipment 95 95
599 50n.p. Transport and packing case (vert) . . . . 1·10 1·10

317 Christ on the Cross **318** Corn Cob

1971. Easter. Multicoloured.
600 4n.p. Type **317** 20 10
601 12½n.p. Christ and Disciples 40 55
602 20n.p. Christ blessing Disciples . . . . 50 1·25

1971. Freedom from Hunger Campaign.
603 **318** 4n.p. multicoloured . . . 10 10
604 12½n.p. multicoloured . . 30 80
605 20n.p. multicoloured . . . 40 1·75
Remainder stocks of the above stamps were optd on the occasion of the death of Lord Boyd Orr and further surch 12½, 20 and 60n.p.
It is understood that 8070 sets from the agency were overprinted locally and returned to New York. Limited remainders of these stamps (only 330 of 60n.p.) were sold at the G.P.O. We do not list these as they were not freely on sale in Ghana.

319 Guides Emblem and Ghana Flag

1971. Golden Jubilee of Ghana Girl Guides. Each design includes Guides emblem. Mult.
606 4n.p. Type **319** 20 10
607 12½n.p. Mrs E. Ofuatey-Kodjoe (founder) and guides with flags 50 50
608 20n.p. Guides laying stones 70 90
609 40n.p. Camp-fire and tent . . 1·25 1·75
610 50n.p. Signallers . . . . . . 1·50 2·00

320 Child-care Centre

1971. Y.W.C.A. World Council Meeting, Accra. Multicoloured.
612 4n.p. Type **320** 10 10
613 12½n.p. Council meeting . . . 10 15
614 20n.p. School typing class . . 15 30
615 40n.p. Building Fund Day . . 30 60
MS616 84 × 83 mm. Nos. 612/15. Imperf . . . . 70 2·00

321 Firework Display **322** Weighing Baby

1971. Christmas. Multicoloured.

617	1n.p. Type **321**	10	60
618	3n.p. African Nativity	15	70
619	6n.p. The Flight into Egypt	15	70

1971. 25th Anniv of U.N.I.C.E.F. Multicoloured.

620	5n.p. Type **322**	10	10
621	15n.p. Mother and child (horiz)	20	30
622	30n.p. Nurse	30	70
623	50n.p. Young boy (horiz)	50	2·25
MS624	111 × 120 mm. Nos. 620/3. Imperf	1·75	6·50

323 Unity Symbol and Trade Fair Emblem

1972. All African Trade Fair. Multicoloured.

625	5n.p. Type **323**	10	10
626	15n.p. Horn of Plenty	15	30
627	30n.p. Fireworks on map of Africa	20	70
628	60n.p. "Participating Nations"	25	2·00
629	1n.c. As No. 628	40	2·50

On 24 June 1972, on the occasion of the Belgian International Philatelic Exhibition, Nos. 625/9 were issued optd **BELGICA72**. Only very limited supplies were sent to Ghana (we understand not more than 900 sets), and for this reason we do not list them.

324 Books for the Blind

1972. International Book Year. Multicoloured.

630	5p. Type **324**	30	10
631	15p. Children's books	65	50
632	30p. Books for recreation	1·25	1·25
633	50p. Books for students	1·75	3·00
634	1c. Book and flame of knowledge (vert)	2·25	4·50
MS635	99 × 106 mm. Nos. 630/4. Imperf	7·00	11·00

325 "Hypoxis urceolata"

1972. Flora and Fauna. Multicoloured.

636	5p. Type **325**	30	10
637	15p. Mona monkey	65	65
638	30p. "Crinum ornatum"	3·00	4·00
639	1c. De Winton's tree squirrel	2·00	8·00

326 Football

1972. Olympic Games, Munich. Multicoloured.

640	5p. Type **326**	20	10
641	15p. Running	30	20
642	30p. Boxing	50	65
643	50p. Long-jumping	65	2·25
644	1c. High-jumping	1·10	3·50
MS645	86 × 43 mm. 40p. as No. 642 se-tenant with 60p. as No. 640	2·50	7·00

327 Senior Scout and Cub

1972. 65th Anniv of Boy Scouts. Multicoloured.

646	5p. Type **327**	30	10
647	15p. Scout and tent	55	45
648	30p. Sea scouts	80	1·25
649	50p. Leader with cubs	90	2·00
650	1c. Training school	1·25	3·50
MS651	110 × 110 mm. 40p. as 30p.; 60p. as 1c.	3·25	5·50

328 "The Holy Night" (Correggio) **330** Under 5's Clinic

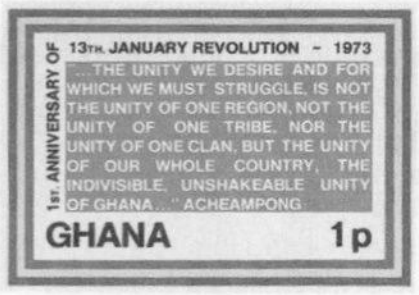

329 Extract from Speech

1972. Christmas. Multicoloured.

652	1p. Type **328**	10	30
653	3p. "Adoration of the Kings" (Holbein the Elder)	10	30
654	15p. "Madonna of the Passion" (School of Ricco)	30	30
655	30p. "King Melchior"	60	70
656	60p. "King Gaspar, Mary and Jesus"	80	2·00
657	1c. "King Balthasar"	1·00	3·25
MS658	139 × 90 mm. Nos. 655/7. Imperf	6·00	9·00

1973. 1st Anniv of 13 January Revolution. Multicoloured.

659	1p. Type **329**	10	10
660	3p. Market scene	10	10
661	5p. Selling bananas (vert)	10	10
662	15p. Farmer with hoe and produce (vert)	20	25
663	30p. Market traders	30	40
664	1c. Farmer cutting palm-nuts	70	1·40
MS665	90 × 55 mm. 40p. as 1c. and 60p. Miners	70	2·25

1973. 25th Anniv of W.H.O. Multicoloured.

666	5p. Type **330**	10	10
667	15p. Radiography	15	25
668	30p. Immunisation	25	40
669	50p. Starving child	25	80
670	1c. W.H.O. H.Q., Geneva	25	1·75

1973. World Scouting Conference, Nairobi/Addis Ababa. Nos. 646/50 optd **1st WORLD SCOUTING CONFERENCE IN AFRICA**.

671 **327**	5p. multicoloured	10	15
672 –	15p. multicoloured	30	60
673 –	30p. multicoloured	40	1·40
674 –	50p. multicoloured	55	2·00
675 –	1c. multicoloured	70	3·00
MS676	110 × 110 mm. 40p. as 30p.; 60p. as 1c.	1·75	6·50

332 Poultry Farming

1973. 10th Anniv of World Food Programme. Multicoloured.

677	5p. Type **332**	10	10
678	15p. Mechanisation	15	15
679	50p. Cocoa harvest	40	90
680	1c. F.A.O. H.Q., Rome	60	1·90
MS681	92 × 104 mm. 40p. as 15p.; 60p. as 1c.	60	2·25

333 "Green Alert"

1973. 50th Anniv of Interpol. Multicoloured.

682	5p. Type **333**	15	10
683	30p. "Red Alert"	75	80
684	50p. "Blue Alert"	1·00	1·75
685	1c. "Black Alert"	1·75	4·00

334 Handshake

1973. 10th Anniv of O.A.U. Multicoloured.

686	5p. Type **334**	10	10
687	30p. Africa Hall, Addis Ababa	15	30
688	50p. O.A.U. emblem	20	1·00
689	1c. "X" in colours of Ghana flag	35	1·50

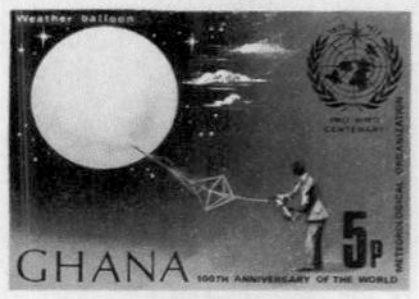

335 Weather Balloon

1973. Centenary of I.M.O./W.M.O. Multicoloured.

690	5p. Type **335**	10	10
691	15p. Satellite "Tiros"	15	20
692	30p. Computer weather map	30	65
693	1c. Radar screen	60	2·25
MS694	120 × 95 mm. 40p. as 15p.; 60p. as 30p.	1·25	3·25

336 Epiphany Scene **337** "Christ carrying the Cross" (Thomas de Kolozsvar)

1973. Christmas. Multicoloured.

695	1p. Type **336**	10	30
696	3p. Madonna and Child	10	30
697	30p. "Madonna and Child" (Murillo)	30	75
698	50p. "Adoration of the Magi" (Tiepolo)	45	1·25
MS699	77 × 103 mm. Nos. 695/8. Imperf	1·25	3·00

1974. Easter.

700 **337**	5p. multicoloured	10	10
701 –	30p. blue, silver and brown	15	35
702 –	50p. red, silver and brown	25	60
703 –	1c. green, silver and brown	35	1·25
MS704	111 × 106 mm. 15p. as No. 700; 20p. as No. 701; 25p. as No. 702. Imperf	80	1·75

DESIGNS (from 15th-century English carved alabaster): 30p. "The Betrayal"; 50p. "The Deposition"; 1c. "The Risen Christ and Mary Magdalene".

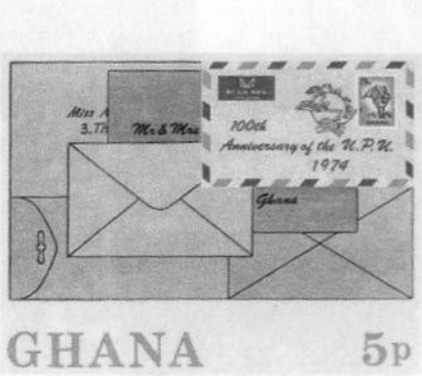

338 Letters

1974. Centenary of U.P.U. Multicoloured.

705	5p. Type **338**	10	10
706	9p. U.P.U. Monument and H.Q.	10	15
707	50p. Airmail letter	35	1·10
708	1c. U.P.U. Monument and Ghana stamp	60	2·00
MS709	108 × 90 mm. 20p. as No. 705; 30p. as No. 706; 40p. as No. 707; 60p. as No. 708	75	1·60

1974. "Internaba 1974" Stamp Exhibition. As Nos. 705/8 additionally inscr "INTERNABA 1974".

710	5p. multicoloured	10	10
711	9p. multicoloured	10	15
712	50p. multicoloured	30	1·00
713	1c. multicoloured	45	1·75
MS714	108 × 90 mm. 20p. as No. 710; 30p. as No. 711; 40p. as No. 712; 60p. as No. 713	1·50	4·00

339 Footballers

1974. World Cup Football Championship.

715 **339**	5p. multicoloured	10	10
716 –	30p. multicoloured	20	60
717 –	50p. multicoloured	25	85
718 –	1c. multicoloured	30	1·50
MS719	148 × 94 mm. 25, 40, 55 and 60p. as Nos. 715/18	1·00	3·25

DESIGNS: As Type **339** showing footballers in action.

340 Roundabout

1974. Change to Driving on the Right.

720 **340**	5p. green, red and black	10	10
721 –	15p. purple, red and black	20	35
722 –	30p. multicoloured	30	40
723 –	50p. multicoloured	40	85
724 –	1c. multicoloured	75	1·75

DESIGNS—HORIZ: 15p. Warning triangle sign. VERT: 30p. Highway arrow and slogan; 50p. Warning hands; 1c. Car on symbolic hands.

1974. West Germany's Victory in World Cup. Nos. 715/18 optd **WEST GERMANY WINNERS**.

725	5p. multicoloured	10	10
726	30p. multicoloured	20	40
727	50p. multicoloured	30	55
728	1c. multicoloured	45	1·25
MS729	148 × 94 mm. 25, 40, 55 and 60p. as Nos. 725/8	1·40	2·50

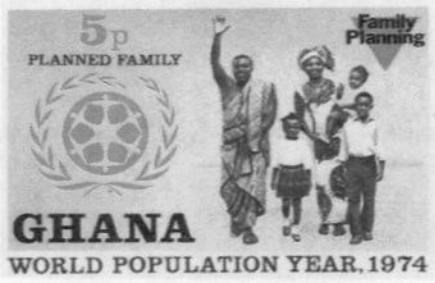

342 "Planned Family"

1974. World Population Year. Multicoloured.

730	5p. Type **342**	10	10
731	30p. Family planning clinic	25	35
732	50p. Immunization	35	60
733	1c. Population census enumeration	60	1·40

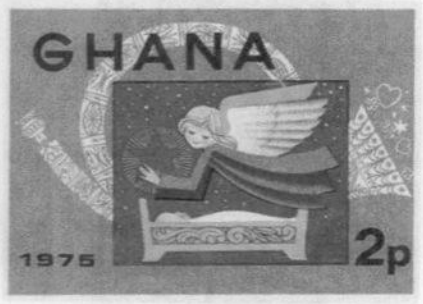

343 Angel **346** Angel

345 Tractor Driver

1974. Christmas. Multicoloured.

734	5p. Type **343**	10	10
735	7p. The Magi (diamond 47 × 47 mm)	10	10

736 9p. The Nativity 10 10
737 1c. The Annunciation . . . . . 60 1·40
MS738 128 × 128 mm. 15p. Type **343**; 30p. as 7p.; 45p. as 9p.; 60p. as 1c. Imperf . . . . . . 80 2·50

1975. "Apollo"–"Soyuz" Space Link. Nos. 715/18 optd **APOLLO SOYUZ JULY 15, 1975.**
739 **339** 5p. multicoloured 10 10
740 – 30p. multicoloured . . . 20 25
741 – 50p. multicoloured . . . 30 55
742 – 1c. multicoloured 55 80
MS743 148 × 94 mm. 25, 40, 55 and 60p. as Nos. 739/42 . . . . . 1·00 2·00

1975. International Women's Year. Multicoloured.
744 7p. Type **345** 45 10
745 30p. Motor mechanic . . . . 1·00 35
746 60p. Factory workers . . . . 1·10 80
747 1c. Cocoa research . . . . . 1·40 1·40
MS748 136 × 110 mm. 15, 40, 65 and 80p. as Nos. 744/7. Imperf . . 2·00 6·00

1975. Christmas.
749 **346** 2p. multicoloured 10 10
750 – 5p. yellow and green . . . 10 10
751 – 7p. yellow and green . . . 10 10
752 – 30p. yellow and green . . 20 20
753 – 1c. yellow and green . . . 50 1·00
MS754 98 × 87 mm. 15, 40, 65 and 80p. as Nos. 750/3. Imperf . . 90 3·00
DESIGNS: 5p. Angle with harp; 7p. Angel with lute; 30p. Angel with violin; 1c. Angel with trumpet.

347 Map Reading

1976. 14th World Scout Jamboree, Norway. Multicoloured.
755 7p. Type **347** 20 10
756 30p. Sailing 55 90
757 60p. Hiking . . . . 70 2·25
758 1c. Life-saving . . . . 80 2·50
MS759 133 × 99 mm. 15, 40, 65 and 80p. as Nos. 755/8 . . . . . . 2·25 6·50

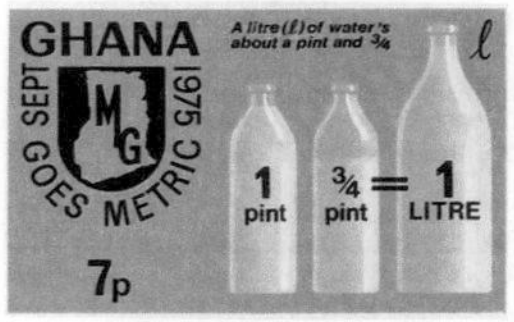

348 Bottles (litre)

1976. Metrication Publicity. Multicoloured.
760 7p. Type **348** 15 10
761 30p. Scales (kilogramme) . . 20 40
762 60p. Tape measure and bale of cloth (metre) . . . . . 40 1·00
763 1c. Ice, thermometer and kettle (temperature) . . . . 60 1·75

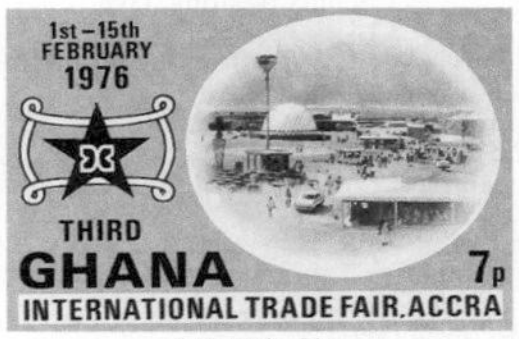

349 Fair Site

1976. International Trade Fair, Accra.
764 **349** 7p. multicoloured 10 10
765 – 30p. multicoloured . . . 15 20
766 – 60p. multicoloured . . . 25 60
767 – 1c. multicoloured . . . 40 1·00
DESIGNS: As Type **349** showing different views of the Fair.

1976. Interphil Stamp Exhibition. Nos. 755/8 optd **'INTERPHIL' 76 BICENTENNIAL EXHIBITION**.
768 **347** 7p. multicoloured 15 15
769 – 30p. multicoloured . . . 35 50
770 – 60p. multicoloured . . . 55 75
771 – 1c. multicoloured . . . 80 1·25
MS772 133 × 99 mm. 15, 40, 65 and 80p. as Nos. 768/71 . . . . . 1·25 2·50

351 Shot-put

1976. Olympic Games, Montreal. Multicoloured.
773 7p. Type **351** 15 10
774 30p. Football 30 25
775 60p. Women's 1500 m . . . 45 50
776 1c. Boxing 60 80
MS777 103 × 135 mm. 15, 40, 65 and 80p. as Nos. 773/6 . . . . . . 1·50 1·50

352 Supreme Court

1976. Centenary of Supreme Court.
778 **352** 8p. multicoloured 10 10
779 – 30p. multicoloured . . . 20 25
780 – 60p. multicoloured . . . 35 50
781 – 1c. multicoloured . . . . 60 1·00
DESIGNS: As Type **352** showing different views of the Court Buildings.

353 Examination for River Blindness

1976. Prevention of Blindness. Multicoloured.
782 7p. Type **353** 65 10
783 30p. Entomologist . . . . . 1·75 1·40
784 60p. Normal vision . . . . . 2·75 2·75
785 1c. Blackfly eradication . . . 4·25 5·00

354 Fireworks Party, Christmas Eve

1976. Christmas. Multicoloured.
786 6p. Type **354** 15 10
787 8p. Children and gifts 15 10
788 30p. Christmas feast 35 30
789 1c. As 8p. . . . . 75 1·75
MS790 122 × 98 mm. 15, 40, 65 and 80p. as Nos. 786/9. Imperf . . 1·10 4·00

355 "Gallows Frame" Telephone and Alexander Graham Bell

1976. Centenary of Telephone. Multicoloured.
791 8p. Type **355** 15 10
792 30p. Bell and 1895 telephone 30 30
793 60p. Bell and 1929 telephone 45 70
794 1c. Bell and 1976 telephone 1·00 1·25
MS795 125 × 92 mm. 15, 40, 65 and 80p. as Nos. 791/4 . . . . . . 1·00 1·40

1977. Olympic Winners. Nos. 773/6 optd **WINNERS** and country name.
796 **351** 7p. multicoloured 15 15
797 – 30p. multicoloured . . . 20 40
798 – 60p. multicoloured . . . 35 85
799 – 1c. multicoloured . . . . 40 1·50
MS800 103 × 135 mm. 15, 40, 65 and 80p. as Nos. 796/9 . . . . . 2·25 2·50
OPTD: 7p., 30p. **EAST GERMANY**; 60p. **U.S.S.R.**; 1c. **U.S.A.**

357 Dipo Dancers and Drum Ensemble

1977. 2nd World Black and African Festival of Arts and Culture, Nigeria. Multicoloured.
801 8p. Type **357** 15 15
802 30p. Arts and crafts 25 60
803 60p. Acon music and dancing priests . . . . 35 1·25
804 1c. African huts . . . . . . 40 2·00
MS805 164 × 120 mm. 15, 40, 65 and 80p. as Nos. 801/4 . . . . . . 1·00 1·50

1977. Prince Charles's Visit to Ghana. Nos. 791/94 optd **PRINCE CHARLES VISITS GHANA 17th TO 25th MARCH, 1977.**
806 8p. Type **355** 50 55
807 30p. 1895 telephone . . . . 1·25 1·00
808 60p. 1929 telephone . . . . 1·50 2·00
809 1c. 1976 telephone . . . . . 2·00 2·50
MS810 125 × 92 mm. 15, 40, 65 and 80p. as Nos. 806/9 . . . . . . 6·50 9·00

359 Olive Colobus Monkey

1977. Wildlife. Multicoloured.
811 8p. Type **359** 45 15
812 20p. Temminck's giant squirrel . . . . 1·25 80
813 30p. Hunting dog . . . . . 1·50 1·25
814 60p. African manatee (sea cow) . . . . 2·50 2·75
MS815 140 × 101 mm. 15, 40, 65 and 80p. as Nos. 811/14 . . . . . 4·00 4·50

360 "Le Chapeau de Paille" (Rubens—400th Birth Anniv)
361 The Magi, Madonna and Child

1977. Painters' Anniversaries. Multicoloured.
816 8p. Type **360** 25 10
817 30p. "Isabella of Portugal" (Titian—500th birth anniv) 40 40
818 60p. "Duke and Duchess of Cumberland" (Gainsborough—250th birth anniv) 55 65
819 1c. "Rubens and Isabella Brandt" . . . . 75 1·25
MS820 99 × 149 mm. 15, 40, 65 and 80p. as Nos. 816/19 . . . . . 2·50 2·25

1977. Christmas. Multicoloured.
821 1p. Type **361** 10 10
822 2p. Choir, St. Andrew's Anglican Church, Abossey Okai 10 10
823 6p. Methodist Church, Wesley, Accra 10 10
824 8p. Madonna and Child . . . 10 10
825 30p. Holy Spirit Cathedral, Accra 30 50
826 1c. Ebenezer Presbyterian Church, Accra . . . . . . 1·00 1·60
MS827 122 × 97 mm. 15, 40, 65 and 80p. as Nos. 822/3 and 825/6. Imperf . . . . 1·25 3·75

1978. Referendum. Nos. 821/26 optd **REFERENDUM 1978 VOTE EARLY.**
828 1p. Type **361** 10 10
829 2p. Choir, St. Andrew's Anglican Church, Abossey Okai 10 10
830 6p. Methodist Church, Wesley, Accra 10 10
831 8p. Madonna and Child . . . 10 10
832 30p. Holy Spirit Cathedral, Accra 30 50
833 1c. Ebenezer Presbyterian Church, Accra . . . . . . 1·00 1·50
MS834 122 × 97 mm. 15, 40, 65 and 80p. as Nos. 829/30 and 832/3 27·00 17·00

363 Cutting Bananas

1978. Operation "Feed Yourself". Multicoloured.
835 2p. Type **363** 10 10
836 8p. Home produce 15 10
837 30p. Market 35 35
838 60p. Fishing 70 60
839 1c. Mechanisation . . . . . 90 1·25

364 Wright Flyer III
367 "The Betrayal"

366 Players and African Cup Emblem

1978. 75th Anniv of Powered Flight.
840 **364** 8p. black, brown and ochre 20 10
841 – 30p. black, brown and green 30 30
842 – 60p. black, brown and red 40 60
843 – 1c. black, brown and blue 2·50 1·10
MS844 167 × 100 mm. 15, 40, 65 and 80p. as Nos. 840/3 . . . . . 2·00 1·40
DESIGNS: 30p. Handley Page H.P.42; 60p. De Havilland Comet 1; 1c. Concorde.

1978. "CAPEX 1978" International Stamp Exhibition, Toronto. Nos. 840/3 optd **"CAPEX 78 JUNE 9-18 1978"**.
845 **364** 8p. black, brown and ochre 15 15
846 – 30p. black, brown and green 25 25
847 – 60p. black, brown and red 50 50
848 – 1c. black, brown and blue 1·10 80
MS849 167 × 100 mm. 15, 40, 65 and 80p. as Nos. 845/8 . . . . . . 1·25 1·60

1978. Football Championships. Multicoloured.
850 8p. Type **366** 20 15
851 30p. Players and African Cup emblem (different) 25 30
852 60p. Players and World Cup emblem 40 60
853 1c. Goalkeeper and World Cup emblem . . . . 55 1·00
MS854 111 × 105 mm. 15, 40, 65 and 80p. as Nos. 850/3 . . . . . . 1·10 1·25

1978. Easter. Drawings by Durer.
855 **367** 11p. black and mauve . . 10 10
856 – 39p. black and flesh . . . 25 30
857 – 60p. black and yellow . . 35 45
858 – 1c. black and green . . . 40 65
DESIGNS: 39p. "The Crucifixion"; 60p. "The Deposition"; 1c. "The Resurrection".

1978. Football Victories of Ghana and Argentina. Nos. 850/3 and **MS**854 optd **"GHANA WINNERS"** (8, 30p.) or **"ARGENTINA WINS"** (others).
859 **366** 8p. multicoloured 45 15
860 – 30p. multicoloured . . . 45 30
861 – 60p. multicoloured . . . 70 45
862 – 1c. multicoloured 80 75
MS863 111 × 105 mm. 15, 40, 65 and 80p. as Nos. 859/62 but all optd 1·00 1·10

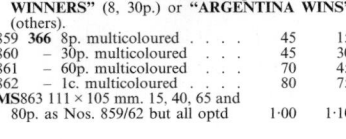

369 "Bauhinia purpurea"

1978. Flowers. Multicoloured.
864 11p. Type **369** 15 10
865 39p. "Cassia fistula" 20 55
866 60p. "Plumeria acutifolia" . . 20 70
867 1c. "Jacaranda mimosifolia" 20 1·00

370 Mail Van

1978. 75th Anniv of Ghana Railways. Multicoloured.
868 11p. Type **370** 15 10
869 39p. Pay and bank car . . . 20 65

870 60p. Steam locomotive No. 1 "Amanful", 1922 . . . . . 20 1·00
871 1c. Diesel-electric locomotive No. 1651, 1960 . . . . . 20 1·40

371 "Orbiter" Spacecraft

1979. "Pioneer" Venus Space Project. Multicoloured.
872 11p. Type **371** 15 10
873 39p. "Multiprobe" space craft 15 30
874 60p. "Orbiter" and "Multiprobe" spacecraft in Venus orbit 20 45
875 3c. Radar chart of Venus . . 30 1·40
MS876 135 × 94 mm. 15, 40, 65p. and 2c. as Nos. 872/5. Imperf 1·10 1·25

372 "O Come All Ye Faithful"

1979. Christmas. Lines and Scenes from Christmas Carols. Multicoloured.
877 8p. Type **372** 10 10
878 10p. "O Little Town of Bethlehem" 10 10
879 15p. "We Three Kings of Orient Are" 10 10
880 20p. "I Saw Three Ships come Sailing By" 10 10
881 2c. "Away In a Manger" . . 30 80
882 4c. "Ding Dong Merrily on High" . . . . . . 50 1·40
MS883 110 × 95 mm. 25, 65p., 1 and 2c. as Nos. 877, 879 and 881/2 75 1·00

373 Dr. J. B. Danquah (lawyer and nationalist)

375 Children in Classroom

374 Tribesman ringing Clack Bells

1980. Famous Ghanaians. Multicoloured.
884 20p. Type **373** 10 10
885 65p. John Mensah Sarbah (nationalist) 10 10
886 80p. Dr J. E. K. Aggrey (educationalist) 15 20
887 2c. Dr. Kwame Nkrumah (nationalist) 20 30
888 4c. G. E. (Paa) Grant (lawyer) 40 80

1980. Death Centenary of Sir Rowland Hill (1979). Multicoloured.
889 20p. Type **374** 15 15
893 25p. Type **374** 15 40
894 50p. Chieftain with Golden Elephant staff 15 40
890 65p. As 50p. 15 20
895 1c. Signalling with drums . . 20 85
891 2c. As 1c. 25 75
892 4c. Chieftain with ivory and gold staff . . . . . . 30 1·50
896 5c. As 4c. . . . . 35 3·00
MS897 115 × 86 mm. Nos. 893/6 75 1·00

1980. International Year of the Child (1979). Multicoloured.
898 20p. Type **375** 15 15
899 65p. Playing football 25 45
900 2c. Playing in a boat . . . . 40 1·00
901 4c. Mother and child . . . . 60 1·75
MS902 156 × 94 mm. 25, 50p., 1 and 3c. as Nos. 898/901 . . . . . 75 1·75

1980. "London 1980" International Stamp Exhibition. Nos. 889/96 optd **"LONDON 1980" 6th - 14th May 1980.**
903 **374** 20p. multicoloured . . . 15 15
907 – 25p. multicoloured . . . 1·25 2·50
908 – 50p. multicoloured . . . 1·50 2·75
904 – 65p. multicoloured . . . 15 50
909 – 1c. multicoloured . . . 2·25 3·25
905 – 2c. multicoloured . . . 25 1·25
906 – 4c. multicoloured . . . . 35 2·25
910 – 5c. multicoloured . . . . 4·00 5·50
MS911 115 × 86 mm. Nos. 907/10 1·00 2·00

1980. Papal Visit. Nos. 898/901 optd **"PAPAL VISIT" 8th - 9th May 1980.**
912 **375** 20p. multicoloured . . . 55 35
913 – 65p. multicoloured . . . 1·00 60
914 – 2c. multicoloured . . . . 1·75 1·40
915 – 4c. multicoloured . . . . 2·50 2·50
MS916 156 × 94 mm. 25, 50p., 1 and 3c. as Nos. 912/15 . . . . . . 9·00 7·50

378 Parliament House

1980. 3rd Republic Commemoration. Multicoloured.
917 20p. Type **378** 10 10
918 65p. Supreme Court 20 25
919 2c. The Castle 40 70
MS920 72 × 113 mm. 25p., 1 and 3c. as Nos. 917/19 . . . . . . 60 1·10

379 Boeing 737 Airliner and Map of West Africa

1980. 5th Anniv of Economic Community of West African States. Multicoloured.
921 20p. Type **379** 10 10
922 65p. Antenna and map . . . 15 20
923 80p. Cog-wheels and map . . 20 25
924 2c. Corn and map 35 50

380 "O.A.U."

381 "The Adoration of the Magi"

1980. 1st Organization of African Unity Economic Summit Conference, Nigeria.
925 **380** 20p. multicoloured . . . 10 10
926 – 65p. multicoloured . . . 15 20
927 – 80p. deep red, red and black 15 25
928 – 2c. multicoloured 20 65

DESIGNS: 65p. Maps of Africa and Ghana and banner; 80p. Map of Africa; 2c. Map of Africa, banner and Ghanaian flag.

1980. Christmas. Paintings by Fra Angelico. Multicoloured.
929 15p. Type **381** 10 10
930 20p. "The Virgin and Child, enthroned with Four Angels" 10 10
931 2c. "The Virgin and Child enthroned with Eight Angels" 35 80
932 4c. "The Annunciation" . . . 60 1·60
MS933 77 × 112 mm. 25, 50p., 1 and 3c. as Nos. 929/32 . . . . . . 75 1·25

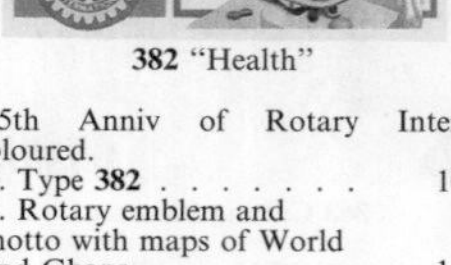

382 "Health"

1980. 75th Anniv of Rotary International. Multicoloured.
934 20p. Type **382** 10 10
935 65p. Rotary emblem and motto with maps of World and Ghana 15 30
936 2c. Rotary emblem, globe and outstretched hands . . 35 85
937 4c. "Eradication of Hunger" . . 60 1·50
MS938 121 × 93 mm. 25, 50p., 1 and 3c. as Nos. 934/7 . . . . . . 1·10 2·00

383 Narina's Trogon ("Narina Trogon")

385 Royal Yacht "Britannia"

384 Pope John Paul II, Archbishop of Canterbury and President Limann during Papal Visit

1981. Birds. Multicoloured.
939 20p. Type **383** . . . . . . 1·25 15
940 65p. White-crowned robin chat . . . . 2·00 50
941 2c. Swallow-tailed bee eater 2·50 1·75
942 4c. Rose-ringed parakeet . . 3·25 3·25
MS943 89 × 121 mm. 25, 50p., 1 and 3c. as Nos. 939/42 . . . . . . 5·00 4·00

1981. 1st Anniv of Papal Visit.
944 **384** 20p. multicoloured . . . 25 15
945 65p. multicoloured . . . 45 55
946 80p. multicoloured . . . 60 70
947 2c. multicoloured . . . . 1·10 2·00

1981. Royal Wedding. Multicoloured.
948 20p. Prince Charles and Lady Diana Spencer 10 10
952 65p. As 20p. 15 25
949 80p. Prince Charles on visit to Ghana 15 20
953 1c. As 80p. 25 35
955 2c. Type **385** . . . . . . 1·00 1·50
954 3c. Type **385** . . . . . . 70 1·10
950 4c. Type **385** 50 80
956 5c. As 20p. . . . . 1·00 2·75
MS951 95 × 85 mm. 7c. St. Paul's Cathedral . . . . 70 1·25

386 Earth Satellite Station

388 "The Betrothal of St. Catherine of Alexandria" (Lucas Cranach)

387 Pounding Fufu

1981. Commissioning of Earth Satellite Station. Mult.
957 20p. Type **386** 10 10
958 65p. Satellites beaming signals to Earth 15 15
959 80p. Satellite 15 20
960 4c. Satellite orbiting Earth . . 1·00 1·50
MS961 112 × 100 mm. 25p., 50p., 1c. and 3c. as Nos. 957/60 . . . . 70 1·40

1981. World Food Day. Multicoloured.
962 20p. Type **387** 10 10
963 65p. Plucking cocoa 25 35
964 80p. Preparing banku 35 40
965 2c. Garri processing . . . . 75 2·25
MS966 131 × 99 mm. 25p., 50p., 1c. and 3c. as Nos. 962/5 . . . . . 1·00 1·50

1981. Christmas. Details from Paintings. Multicoloured.
967 15p. Type **388** 15 10
968 20p. "Angelic Musicians play for Mary and Child" (Aachener Altares) 15 10
969 65p. "Child Jesus embracing his Mother" (Gabriel Metsu) 20 15
970 80p. "Madonna and Child" (Fra Filippo Lippi) 20 20
971 2c. "The Madonna with Infant Jesus" (Barnaba da Modena) 40 70
972 4c. "The Immaculate Conception" (Murillo) . . 45 1·10
MS973 82 × 102 mm. 6c. "Madonna and Child with Angels" (Hans Memling) . . . . 1·00 2·25

389 Blind Person

1982. International Year for Disabled Persons. Multicoloured.
974 20p. Type **389** 10 10
975 65p. Disabled person with crutches 30 35
976 80p. Blind child reading braille 40 45
977 4c. Disabled people helping one another . . . . . . 1·75 2·25
MS978 109 × 85 mm. 6c. Group of disabled people . . . . 2·75 3·00

390 African Clawless Otter

391 "Precis westermanni"

1982. Flora and Fauna. Multicoloured.
979 20p. Type **390** 25 15
980 65p. Bushbuck 40 40
981 80p. Aardvark 40 50
982 1c. Scarlet bell tree 40 60
983 2c. Glory-lilies . . . . 60 1·25
984 4c. Blue-pea . . . . 1·00 2·25
MS985 76 × 100 mm. 5c. Chimpanzee . . . . 1·25 5·00

1982. Butterflies. Multicoloured.
986 20p. Type **391** 70 15
987 65p. "Papilio menestheus" . . 1·25 1·00
988 2c. "Antanartia delius" . . . 2·00 3·50
989 4c. "Charaxes castor" . . . 2·75 4·75
MS990 98 × 123 mm. 25p., 50p., 1c. and 3c. as Nos. 986/9 . . . . 9·00 12·00

392 Scouts planting Tree

1982. 75th Anniv of Boy Scout Movement. Multicoloured.
991 20p. Type **392** 25 15
992 65p. Scouts cooking on campfire 70 65
993 80p. Sea Scouts sailing . . . 90 85
994 3c. Scouts observing African elephant . . . . 2·25 3·25
MS995 101 × 71 mm. 5c. Lord Baden-Powell (vert) . . . . . 2·25 6·50

393 Initial Stages of Construction

1982. Kpong Hydro-Electric Project. Multicoloured.
996 20p. Type **393** 65 10
997 65p. Truck removing rubble 1·25 45
998 80p. Hydro-electric turbines 2·00 65
999 2c. Aerial view of completed plant . . . . 2·75 1·60

394 Footballers

1982. World Cup Football Championship, Spain.
1000 **394** 20p. multicoloured . . . 55 10
1005 30p. multicoloured . . . 60 20
1001 – 65p. multicoloured . . . 75 35
1002 – 80p. multicoloured (Heading) 90 45

1006 – 80p. multicoloured (Three footballers) . . 75 45
1007 – 1c. multicoloured 80 55
1008 – 3c. multicoloured . . . . 1·25 1·60
1003 – 4c. multicoloured . . . . 1·75 2·00
MS1004 110 × 90 mm. 6c. multicoloured . . . . 3·75 2·75
DESIGNS: 65p. to 6c. Scenes showing footballers.

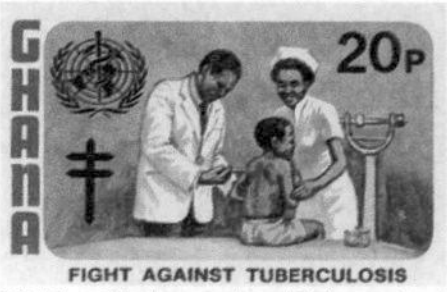

395 The Fight against Tuberculosis

1982. Centenary of Robert Koch's Discovery of Tubercle Bacillus. Multicoloured.
1009 20p. Type **395** 70 20
1010 65p. Robert Koch . . . . . 1·60 1·25
1011 80p. Robert Koch in Africa 2·00 1·75
1012 1c. Centenary of discovery of Tuberculosis . . . . . 2·25 2·75
1013 2c. Robert Koch and Nobel Prize, 1905 . . . . 3·25 4·00

396 The Shepherds worship Jesus

397 Ghana and Commonwealth Flags with Coat of Arms

1982. Christmas. Multicoloured.
1014 15p. Type **396** 10 10
1015 20p. Mary, Joseph and baby Jesus 10 10
1016 65p. The Three Kings sight star 20 30
1017 4c. Winged Angel . . . . . 70 1·75
MS1018 90 × 110 mm. 6c. The Three Kings with Jesus . . . . . . 1·00 1·75

1983. Commonwealth Day. Multicoloured.
1019 20p. Type **397** 25 15
1020 55p. Satellite view of Ghana 45 65
1021 80p. Minerals of Ghana . . 1·00 1·25
1022 3c. African fish eagle . . . 1·50 4·25

1983. Italy's Victory in World Cup Football Championships (1982). Nos. 1000/8 optd **WINNER ITALY 3–1**.
1023 20p. multicoloured 15 10
1028 30p. multicoloured 60 80
1024 65p. multicoloured 25 15
1025 80p. multicoloured 25 20
1029 80p. multicoloured . . . . 1·00 1·25
1030 1c. multicoloured . . . . . 1·10 1·40
1031 3c. multicoloured . . . . . 1·75 3·25
1026 4c. multicoloured . . . . . 1·40 1·75
MS1027 110 × 90 mm. 6c. multicoloured . . . . 1·75 1·50

1983. No. 470 surch **C1**.
1031a 1c. on 20n.p. Bush hare (blue) 40 40

399 Short-finned Pilot Whale

1983. Coastal Marine Mammals. Multicoloured.
1032 1c. Type **399** . . . . 55 1·00
1033 1c.40 Risso's dolphin . . . 60 1·10
1034 2c. False killer whale . . . 65 1·25
1035 3c. Spinner dolphin . . . . 70 1·60
1036 4c. Atlantic hump-backed dolphin . . . . 75 2·00
MS1037 117 × 76 mm. 6c. As 4c. 1·25 1·00

400 Banded Jewelfish

401 Communication Devices

1983.
1038 **400** 5p. multicoloured . . . 30 20
1039 – 10p. multicoloured . . . 30 20
1040 – 20p. multicoloured . . . 40 20
1041 – 50p. green, orange blk 40 30
1042 – 1c. orange, blue and black 50 20
1043 – 2c. multicoloured 50 30
1044 – 3c. multicoloured . . . . 1·25 30
1045 – 4c. multicoloured 40 40
1046 – 5c. multicoloured 50 40
1047 – 10c. multicoloured . . . 65 1·00
DESIGNS—HORIZ: 10p. Banded jewelfish (different); 2c. Jet airliner. VERT: 20p. "Haemanthus rupestris"; 50p. Mounted warrior; 1c. Scorpion; 3c. White-collared mangabey; 4c. Demidoff's galago; 5c. "Kaemferia nigerica"; 10c. Grey-backed camaroptera.

1983. World Communications Year. Multicoloured.
1048 1c. Type **401** 15 25
1049 1c.40 Satellite dish aerial . . 20 30
1050 2c.30 Cable and "Long Lines" (cable ship) . . . 35 55
1051 3c. Switchboard operators 40 65
1052 5c. Aircraft cockpit and air traffic controllers 55 85
MS1053 95 × 70 mm. 6c. Space satellite 30 50

402 Children receiving Presents

1983. Christmas. Multicoloured.
1054 70p. Type **402** 15 10
1055 1c. Nativity and Star of Bethlehem (vert) 15 10
1056 1c.40 Children celebrating (vert) 20 55
1057 2c.30 Family praying together (vert) . . . . . 25 1·00
1058 3c. Dancing to bongo drum 35 1·25
MS1059 70 × 90 mm. 6c. As 2c.30 30 1·50

403 Soldiers with Rifles

407 Cross and Crown of Thorns

1983. Namibia Day.
1060 **403** 50p. green and black . . 10 10
1061 – 1c. multicoloured 10 10
1062 – 1c.40 blue, lt blue blk . . 15 15
1063 – 2c.30 multicoloured . . . 20 25
1064 – 3c. multicoloured 25 30
DESIGNS: 1c. Soldiers supported by tank; 1c.40, Machete cutting chains; 2c.30, Peasant woman; 3c. Soldiers and artillery support.

1984. (a) Nos. 948/50, 952 and 954 surch.
1065 1c. on 20p. Prince Charles and Lady Diana Spencer 2·50 3·00
1066 9c. on 65p. Prince Charles and Lady Diana Spencer 3·00 4·00
1067 9c. on 80p. Prince Charles on visit to Ghana . . . . 3·00 4·00
1068 20c. on 3c. Type **385** . . . 3·50 6·00
1069 20c. on 4c. Type **385** . . . 3·50 6·00
MS1070 95 × 85 mm. 60c on 7c. St. Paul's Cathedral . . . . . 1·00 3·00

(b) Nos. 991/2 and 994 surch.
1071 10c. on 20p. Type **392** . . . 40 45
1072 19c. on 65p. Scouts cooking on campfire 80 85
1073 30c. on 3c. Scouts observing African elephant . . . . 1·50 1·50
MS1074 101 × 71 mm. 60c. on 5c. Lord Baden-Powell . . . . . 1·00 3·50

(c) Nos. 1000/3, 1005/6 and 1008 surch.
1075 **394** 1c. on 20p. multicoloured 30 30
1076 – 9c. on 65p. multicoloured 70 70
1077 – 9c. on 3c. multicoloured 70 70
1078 **394** 10c. on 30p. multicoloured 70 70
1079 – 10c. on 80p. multicoloured 70 70
1080 – 20c. on 80p. multicoloured . . . . 1·50 1·50
1081 – 20c. on 4c. multicoloured 1·50 1·50
MS1082 110 × 90 mm. 60c. on 6c. multicoloured . . . . 1·00 2·25

(d) Nos. 1019/22 surch.
1083 1c. on 20p. Type **397** . . . 10 10
1084 9c. on 55p. Satellite view of Ghana 40 45
1085 30c. on 80p. Minerals of Ghana . . . . 1·50 1·50
1086 50c. on 3c. African fish eagle . . . . 2·50 3·00

(e) Nos. 1023/6, 1028/9 and 1031 surch.
1087 **394** 1c. on 20p. multicoloured 10 10
1088 – 9c. on 65p. multicoloured 40 45
1089 – 9c. on 3c. multicoloured 40 45
1090 **394** 10c. on 30p. multicoloured 40 45
1091 – 10c. on 80p. multicoloured 40 45
1092 – 20c. on 80p. multicoloured 80 85
1093 – 20c. on 4c. multicoloured 80 85
MS1094 110 × 90 mm. 60c. on 6c. multicoloured . . . . 1·00 2·00

1984. Universal Postal Union Congress, Hamburg. Nos. 1035/6 surch **19th U.P.U. CONGRESS - HAMBURG**, emblem and new value.
1095 10c. on 3c. Spinner dolphin 40 45
1096 50c. on 5c. Atlantic humpbacked dolphin . . 2·10 2·25
MS1097 117 × 76 mm. 60c. on 6c. as No. 1096 . . . . 2·50 3·50

1984. Easter. Multicoloured.
1098 1c. Type **407** 10 10
1099 1c.40 Christ praying 10 10
1100 2c.30 The Resurrection . . 10 10
1101 3c. Palm Sunday 10 15
1102 50c. Christ on the road to Emmaus . . . . 1·10 2·25
MS1103 102 × 86 mm. 60c. Type **407** 1·00 2·50

408 Women's 400 Metre Race

409 "Amorphophallus johnsonii"

1984. Olympic Games, Los Angeles. Multicoloured.
1104 1c. Type **408** 10 10
1105 1c.40 Boxing 15 10
1106 2c.30 Hockey 20 15
1107 3c. Men's 400 metre hurdles race 20 15
1108 50c. Rhythmic gymnastics 1·75 3·50
MS1109 103 × 78 mm. 70c. Football 2·00 3·50
No. 1108 is inscribed "RYTHMIC" in error.

1984. Flowers. Multicoloured.
1110 1c. Type **409** 10 10
1111 1c.40 "Pancratium trianthum" 10 10
1112 2c.30 "Eulophia cucullata" 10 15
1113 3c. "Amorphophallus abyssinicus" 10 15
1114 50c. "Chlorophytum togoense" . . . . 1·10 5·00
MS1115 70 × 96 mm. 60c. Type **409** 1·25 3·50

410 Young Bongo

1984. Endangered Antelopes. Multicoloured.
1116 1c. Type **410** 30 20
1117 2c.30 Bongo bucks fighting 55 55
1118 3c. Bongo family 70 70
1119 20c. Bongo herd in high grass . . . . 2·25 3·50
MS1120 Two sheets, each 100 × 71 mm. (a) 70c. Head of Kob; (b) 70c. Head of Bush buck Set of 2 sheets . . . . 10·00 13·00

411 Dipo Girl

412 The Three Wise Men bringing Gifts

1984. Ghanaian Culture. Multicoloured.
1121 1c. Type **411** 10 25
1122 1c.40 Adowa dancer 10 25
1123 2c.30 Agbadza dancer . . . 10 25
1124 3c. Damba dancer 10 25
1125 50c. Dipo dancer . . . . . 90 3·50
MS1126 70 × 84 mm. 70c. Mandolin player . . . . 1·50 3·00

1984. Christmas. Multicoloured.
1127 70p. Type **412** 10 10
1128 1c. Choir of angels 10 10
1129 1c.40 Mary and shepherds at manger 10 10
1130 2c.30 The flight into Egypt 10 10
1131 3c. Simeon blessing Jesus . . 10 15
1132 50c. Holy Family and angels 90 3·00
MS1133 70 × 90 mm. 70c. Type **412** 1·50 2·75

1984. Olympic Winners. Nos. 1104/8 optd
1134 1c. Type **408** (optd **VALERIE BRISCO-HOOKS U.S.A.**) 10 10
1135 1c.40 Boxing (optd **U.S. WINNERS**) 10 10
1136 2c.30 Hockey (optd **PAKISTAN (FIELD HOCKEY)**) 10 10
1137 3c. Men's 400 metre hurdles race (optd **EDWIN MOSES U.S.A.**) 10 10
1138 50c. Rhythmic gymnastics (optd **LAURI FUNG CANADA**) . . . . 1·10 1·60
MS1139 103 × 78 mm. 70c. Football (optd **FRANCE**) . . . . 1·75 2·50

414 The Queen Mother attending Church Service

415 Moslems going to Mosque

1985. Life and Times of Queen Elizabeth the Queen Mother. Multicoloured.
1140 5c. Type **414** 10 15
1141 12c. At Ascot Races 25 30
1142 100c. At Clarence House on her 84th birthday . . . . 1·75 2·50
MS1143 56 × 84 mm. 110c. With Prince Charles at Garter ceremony 1·75 3·00
Stamps as Nos. 1140/2 but with face values of 8c., 20c. and 70c. exist from additional sheetlets with changed background colours.

1985. Islamic Festival of Id-el-Fitr. Multicoloured.
1144 5c. Type **415** 25 20
1145 8c. Moslems at prayer . . . 35 30
1146 12c. Pilgrims visiting the Dome of the Rock . . . 55 45
1147 18c. Preaching the Koran 70 60
1148 50c. Banda Nkwanta Mosque, Accra, and map of Ghana . . . . 1·75 1·60

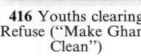

416 Youths clearing Refuse ("Make Ghana Clean")

418 Fork-tailed Flycatcher

417 Honda "Interceptor", 1984

1985. International Youth Year. Multicoloured.
1149 5c. Type **416** 10 10
1150 8c. Planting sapling ("Make Ghana Green") 15 15
1151 12c. Youth carrying bananas ("Feed Ghana") 20 25
1152 100c. Open-air class ("Educate Ghana") . . . 65 2·25
MS1153 103 × 78 mm. 110c. as 8c. 1·25 3·00

1985. Centenary of the Motorcycle. Multicoloured.
1154 5c. Type **417** 40 30
1155 8c. DKW, 1938 . . . . . . 50 40
1156 12c. BMW "R 32", 1923 . . 75 70
1157 100c. NSU, 1900 . . . . . 3·00 7·00
MS1158 78 × 108 mm. 110c. Zündapp, 1973 (vert) . . . . . 3·50 4·25

1985. Birth Bicentenary of John J. Audubon (ornithologist). Designs showing original paintings. Multicoloured.
1159 5c. Type **418** . . . . 1·25 50
1160 8c. Barred owl . . . . . . 2·25 2·00
1161 12c. Black-throated mango 2·25 2·00
1162 100c. White-crowned pigeon 6·50 9·50
MS1163 85 × 115 mm. 110c. Downy Woodpecker . . . . 6·50 3·50
No. 1159 is inscribed "York-tailed fly catcher" in error.

419 United Nations Building, New York

1985. 40th Anniv of U.N.O. Multicoloured.
1164 5c. Type **419** 10 10
1165 8c. Flags of member nations and U.N. Building . . . 10 15
1166 12c. Dove with olive branch 10 25
1167 18c. General Assembly . . . 15 35
1168 100c. Flags of Ghana and United Nations . . . . . 90 1·75
MS1169 90 × 70 mm. 110c. United Nations (New York) 1955 4c. 10th anniv stamp . . . . 75 1·75

420 Coffee

1985. 20th Anniv of United Nations Conference on Trade and Development. Designs showing export products. Multicoloured.
1170 5c. Type **420** 10 10
1171 8c. Cocoa 15 15
1172 12c. Timber 25 25
1173 18c. Bauxite . . . . 1·25 90
1174 100c. Gold . . . . 6·50 8·50
MS1175 104 × 74 mm. 110c. Agricultural produce and plate of food . . . . 1·25 2·50

421 Growth Monitoring

1985. U.N.I.C.E.F. Child Survival Campaign. Multicoloured.
1176 5c. Type **421** 30 10
1177 8c. Oral rehydration therapy 50 30
1178 12c. Breast-feeding 70 40
1179 100c. Immunization . . . . 2·50 4·50
MS1180 99 × 69 mm. 110c. Campaign logo . . . . 1·75 2·25

422 Airline Stewardess and Boys with Stamp Album

1986. "Ameripex" International Stamp Exhibition, Chicago. Multicoloured.
1181 5c. Type **422** 15 15
1182 25c. Globe and Douglas DC-10 airplane 60 45
1183 100c. Ghana Airways stewardess (vert) . . . . 2·25 3·00
MS1184 90 × 70 mm. 150c. Stamp collecting class . . . . 1·50 2·50

423 Kejetia Roundabout, Kumasi

1986. "Inter-Tourism '86" Conference. Mult.
1185 5c. Type **423** 10 10
1186 15c. Fort St. Jago, Elmina 30 30
1187 25c. Tribal warriors 45 45
1188 100c. Chief holding audience 1·75 3·25
MS1189 110 × 70 mm. 150c. African elephants . . . . 3·75 5·50

424 Tackling

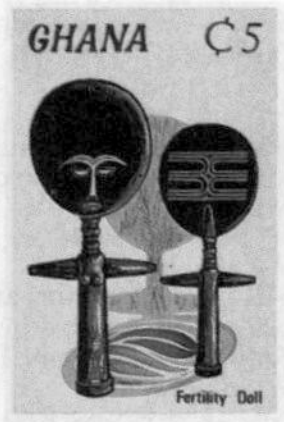

425 Fertility Doll

1987. World Cup Football Championship, Mexico (1986). Multicoloured.
1190 5c. Type **424** 20 10
1191 15c. Player taking control of ball 30 15
1192 25c. Player kicking ball . . 50 25
1193 100c. Player with ball . . . 1·50 2·25
MS1194 90 × 70 mm. 150c. Player kicking ball (different) . . . . 1·50 2·00

1987. Ghanaian Fertility Dolls. Designs showing different dolls.
1195 **425** 5c. multicoloured 10 10
1196 – 15c. multicoloured . . . 15 15
1197 – 25c. multicoloured . . . 25 25
1198 – 100c. multicoloured . . . 90 2·00
MS1199 90 × 70 mm. **425** 150c. multicoloured . . . . 1·50 2·00

426 Children of Different Races, Peace Doves and Sun

1987. International Peace Year (1986). Multicoloured.
1200 5c. Type **426** 15 10
1201 25c. Plough, peace dove and rising sun 75 25
1202 100c. Peace dove, olive branch and globe (vert) 2·50 3·00
MS1203 90 × 70 mm. 150c. Dove perched on plough (vert) . . . 1·75 2·25

427 Lumber and House under Construction

1987. "Gifex '87" International Forestry Exposition, Accra. Multicoloured.
1204 5c. Type **427** 10 10
1205 15c. Planks and furniture . . 15 15
1206 25c. Felled trees 25 25
1207 200c. Logs and wood carvings . . . . 1·60 2·25

1987. Appearance of Halley's Comet (1986). As T **151a** of Gambia. Multicoloured.
1208 5c. Mikhail Lomonosov (scientist) and Chamber of Curiosities, St. Petersburg 20 10
1209 25c. Lunar probe "Surveyor 3", 1966 . . . . 70 30
1210 200c. Wedgwood plaques for Isaac Newton, 1790 and "Apollo 11" Moon landing, 1968 . . . . . 3·25 2·25
MS1211 100 × 70 mm. 250c. Halley's Comet . . . . 4·25 2·75

428 Demonstrator and Arms breaking Shackles

1987. Solidarity with the People of Southern Africa. Multicoloured.
1212 5c. Type **428** 10 10
1213 15c. Miner and gold bars . . 40 15
1214 25c. Xhosa warriors 30 25
1215 100c. Nelson Mandela and shackles . . . . 1·25 3·00
MS1216 70 × 90 mm. 150c. Nelson Mandela . . . . 1·50 2·00

429 Aerophones

1987. Musical Instruments. Multicoloured.
1217 5c. Type **429** 10 10
1218 15c. Xylophone 15 15
1219 25c. Chordophones 30 25
1220 100c. Membranophones . . . 1·00 1·25
MS1221 90 × 70 mm. 200c. Idiophones . . . . 1·90 2·25

430 Woman filling Water Pot at Pump

1987. Int Year of Shelter for the Homeless. Mult.
1222 5c. Type **430** 10 10
1223 15c. Building house from breeze blocks 15 15
1224 25c. Modern village with stream 20 25
1225 100c. Modern houses with verandahs . . . . 75 1·25

431 Ga Women preparing Kpokpoi for Homowo Festival

1988. Ghana Festivals. Multicoloured.
1226 5c. Type **431** 10 10
1227 15c. Efute hunters with deer, Aboakyir festival 15 15
1228 25c. Fanti chief dancing at Odwira festival 25 25
1229 100c. Chief in palanquin, Yam festival . . . . . . 65 1·25

432 Port Installation

1988. 5th Anniv (1987) of 31 December Revolution. Multicoloured.
1230 5c. Type **432** . . . . 1·25 40
1231 15c. Repairing railway line 12·00 2·50
1232 25c. Planting cocoa . . . . 1·75 55
1233 100c. Miners with ore truck 13·00 14·00

433 Nurse giving Injection

435 Akwadjan Men

434 Fishing

1988. U.N.I.C.E.F. Global Immunization Campaign. Multicoloured.
1234 5c. Type **433** 20 10
1235 15c. Girl receiving injection 25 20
1236 25c. Schoolgirl crippled by polio 35 50
1237 100c. Nurse giving oral vaccine to baby . . . . . 60 2·25

1988. 10th Anniv of International Fund for Agricultural Development. Multicoloured.
1238 5c. Type **434** 85 30
1239 15c. Women harvesting crops . . . . 1·40 40
1240 25c. Cattle . . . . 1·75 50
1241 100c. Village granaries . . . 4·00 8·50

1988. Tribal Costumes. Multicoloured.
1242 5c. Type **435** 15 10
1243 25c. Banaa man 35 20
1244 250c. Agwasen woman . . . 1·50 2·00

1988. Nos. 460, 464/6, 469/70, 1031a, 1038/42, 1044 and 1046 surch.
1245 – 20c. on 50p. green, orange and black (No. 1041) 30 20
1246 – 20c. on 1c. orange, blue and black (No. 1042) 30 20
1247 – 50c. on 10n.p. mult (No. 469) 30 30
1248 – 50c. on 20n.p. deep blue and blue (No. 470) (surch **C50**) . . . . . 5·00 60
1249 – 50c. on 20n.p. deep blue and blue (No. 470) (surch **C50.00**) . . . . 5·00 60
1250 – 50c. on 10p. mult (No. 1039) 30 25
1251 – 50c. on 1c. on 20n.p. deep blue and blue (No. 1031a) (surch **C50**) . . . . . . 5·00 60
1252 – 50c. on 1c. on 20n.p. deep blue and blue (No. 1031a) (surch **C50.00**) . . . . . 5·00 60
1254 – 50c. on 1c. orange, blue and black (No. 1042) 5·00 60
1255 **230** 60c. on 1n.p. mult . . . 5·00 60
1256 – 60c. on 4n.p. mult (No. 465) . . . . . 5·00 45
1257 – 60c. on 3c. mult (No. 1044) 50 45
1258 **400** 80c. on 5p. multicoloured . . . .
1259 – 80c. on 5c. mult (No. 1046) . . . . . 7·00 7·50
1260 – 100c. on 3n.p. mult (No. 464) . . . . . . 10·00 10·00
1261 – 100c. on 20n.p. deep blue and blue (No. 470) 50 80
1262 – 100c. on 20p. mult (No. 1040) 50 80
1263 – 100c. on 3c. mult (No. 1044) 50 80
1264 – 200c. on 6n.p. mult (No. 466) . . . . . . 50 1·00

440 Boxing

1988. Olympic Games, Seoul. Multicoloured.
1265 20c. Type **440** 20 15
1266 60c. Athletics 45 55
1267 80c. Discus-throwing . . . 50 80
1268 100c. Javelin-throwing . . . 60 1·10
1269 350c. Weightlifting . . . . 1·40 3·00
MS1270 75 × 105 mm. As 80c. 4·00 3·00

441 Nutrition Lecture

443 "African Solidarity"

442 Tropical Forest

1988. 125th Anniv of Int Red Cross. Mult.
1271 20c. Type **441** 40 15
1272 50c. Red Cross volunteer with blind woman 90 90
1273 60c. Distributing flood relief supplies . . . . 1·00 1·00
1274 200c. Giving first aid . . . 2·50 3·25

1988. Christmas. Multicoloured.
1275 20c. Type **442** 15 10
1276 60c. Christ Child (vert) . . 35 35
1277 80c. Virgin and Child with Star (vert) 50 50
1278 100c. Three Wise Men following Star 60 70
1279 350c. Symbolic Crucifixion (vert) . . . . 2·00 2·50
MS1280 100 × 70 mm. 500c. Virgin and Child (vert) . . . . 2·00 2·75

1989. 25th Anniv (1988) of Organization of African Unity. Multicoloured.
1281 20c. Type **443** 10 10
1282 50c. O.A.U. Headquarters Addis Ababa 15 20
1283 60c. Emperor Haile Selassie and Ethiopian flag (horiz) 30 25
1284 200c. Kwame Nkrumah (former Ghanaian President) and flag (horiz) 60 85

444 "Amor"

1989. 500th Birth Anniv of Titian (artist). Multicoloured.

1285 20c. Type **444** 40 15
1286 60c. "The Appeal" 70 45
1287 80c. "Bacchus and Ariadne" (detail) 80 55
1288 100c. "Portrait of a Musician" . . . . . . 85 1·00
1289 350c. "Philip II seated" . . 1·75 4·00
MS1290 77 × 115 mm. 500c. "Portrait of a Gentleman" . . 2·50 2·75

1989. Olympic Medal Winners, Seoul. Nos. 1251/5 optd.

1291 20c. Type **436** (optd **A. ZUELOW DDR 60 KG**) 50 10
1292 60c. Athletics (optd **G. BORDIN ITALY MARATHON**) 65 25
1293 80c. Discus-throwing (optd **J. SCHULT DDR**) . . . 70 30
1294 100c. Javelin-throwing (optd **T. KORJUS FINLAND**) 75 35
1295 350c. Weightlifting (optd **B. GUIDIKOV BULGARIA 75 KG**) . . . . 1·75 1·10
MS1296 75 × 105 mm. 500c. As 80c. (optd **GOLD J. SCHULT DDR SILVER R. OUBARTAS USSR BRONZE R. DANNEBERG W. GERMANY** on sheet margin 2·40 2·10

1989. Various stamps surch. (a) Nos. 949/50 and 952/4.

1297 80c. on 65p. Prince Charles and Lady Diana Spencer 50 55
1298 100c. on 80p. Prince Charles on visit to Ghana . . . 60 70
1299 100c. on 1c. Prince Charles on visit to Ghana . . . 60 70
1300 300c. on 3c. Type **385** . . 1·75 2·25
1301 500c. on 4c. Type **385** . . 2·75 3·75

(b) Nos. 1048/51 and **MS**1053.

1302 60c. on 1c. Type **401** . . . 1·00 50
1303 80c. on 1c.40 Satellite dish aerial . . . . 1·10 65
1304 200c. on 2c.30 Cable and cable-laying ship . . . 2·75 2·75
1305 300c. on 3c. Switchboard operators . . . . . . 3·00 3·50
MS1306 95 × 70 mm. 500c. on 6c. Space satellite . . . . . 6·50 7·50

(c) Nos. 1104/7 and **MS**1109.

1307 60c. on 1c. Type **408** . . . 30 30
1308 80c. on 1c.40 Boxing . . . 40 45
1309 200c. on 2c.30 Hockey . . . 1·25 1·60
1310 300c. on 3c. Men's 400 metre hurdles race . . . 1·40 1·75
MS1311 103 × 78 mm. 600c. on 70c. Football . . . . 3·00 4·50

(d) Nos. 1134/7 and **MS**1139.

1312 60c. on 1c. Type **408** (optd **VALERIE BRISCO-HOOKS U.S.A.**) . . . . 1·25 1·00
1313 80c. on 1c.40 Boxing (optd **U.S. WINNERS**) . . . . 1·50 1·25
1314 200c. on 2c.30 Field hockey (optd **PAKISTAN (FIELD HOCKEY)**) . . . 4·25 4·25
1315 300c. on 3c. Men's 400 metre hurdles race (optd **EDWIN MOSES U.S.A.**) 4·25 4·75
MS1316 103 × 78 mm. 600c. on 70c. Football (optd **FRANCE**) . . . 5·00 5·50

(e) Nos. 1140/2. and **MS**1143.

1317 80c. on 5c. Type **414** . . . 35 40
1318 250c. on 12c. At Ascot Races . . . . 1·10 1·75
1319 300c. on 100c. At Clarence House on her 84th birthday . . . . 1·25 1·75
MS1320 56 × 84 mm. 500c. on 110c. With Prince Charles at Garter Ceremony . . . . 3·25 4·50

(f) Nos. 1159/61 and **MS**1163.

1321 80c. on 5c. Type **418** . . . 2·25 1·00
1322 100c. on 8c. Barred owl . . 3·50 2·50
1323 300c. on 12c. Black-throated mango . . . . 4·00 4·50
MS1324 85 × 115 mm. 500c. on 110c. Downy Woodpecker . . . . . 9·00 9·00

(g) Nos. 1190/2 and **MS**1194.

1325 60c. on 5c. Type **424** . . . 45 45
1326 200c. on 15c. Player taking control of ball . . . . . 1·50 2·00
1327 300c. on 25c. Player kicking ball . . . . 2·00 2·75
MS1328 90 × 70 mm. 600c. on 150c. Player kicking ball (different) 6·50 7·00

(h) As Nos. 1190/2 and **MS**1194 but with unissued opt **WINNERS Argentina 3 W.Germany 2**.

1329 60c. on 5c. Type **424** . . . 1·00 40
1330 200c. on 15c. Player taking control of ball . . . . . 2·00 2·50
1331 300c. on 25c. Player kicking ball . . . . 2·50 3·00
MS1332 90 × 70 mm. 600c. on 150c. Player kicking ball (different) 3·75 4·50

(i) Nos. 1208/10.

1333 60c. on 5c. Mikhail Lomonosov (scientist) and Chamber of Curiosities, St. Petersburg . . . . . 1·00 60
1334 80c. on 25c. Lunar probe "Surveyor 3", 1966 . . . 1·40 85
1335 500c. on 200c. Wedgwood plaques for Isaac Newton, 1790, and "Apollo 11" Moon landing, 1968 . . . 4·00 6·00
MS1336 100 × 70 mm. 750c. on 250c. Halley's Comet . . . . . . 4·00 5·00

(j) As Nos. 1208/10 and **MS**1211 optd **HALLEYS COMET 1985 - OFFICIAL - 1996** and emblem.

1337 60c. on 5c. Mikhail Lomonosov (scientist) and Chamber of Curiosities, St. Petersburg 50 40
1338 80c. on 25c. Lunar probe "Surveyor 3", 1966 . . . 60 50
1339 500c. on 200c. Wedgwood plaques for Isaac Newton, 1790, and "Apollo 11" Moon landing, 1968 . . . 2·75 4·75
MS1340 100 × 70 mm. 750c. on 250c. Halley's Comet . . . . 6·00 7·00

448 French Royal Standard and Field Gun

449 Storming the Bastille

1989. "Philexfrance 89" International Stamp Exhibition, Paris. Multicoloured.

1341 20c. Type **448** 60 25
1342 60c. Regimental standard, 1789, and French infantry- man . . . . . . 1·25 90
1343 80c. Revolutionary standard, 1789, and pistol . . . . . 1·50 1·00
1344 350c. Tricolour, 1794, and musket . . . . 3·75 5·50
MS1345 77 × 106 mm. 600c. Street plan of Paris, 1789 (horiz) . . 3·00 3·50

1989. Japanese Art. Portraits. As T **177a** of Gambia. Multicoloured.

1346 20c. "Minamoto-no-Yoritomo" (Fujiwara-no-Takanobu) (vert) 35 20
1347 50c. "Takami Senseki" (Watanabe Kazan) (vert) 50 30
1348 60c. "Ikkyu Sojun" (study) (Bokusai) (vert) 55 35
1349 75c. "Nakamura Kuranosuka" (Ogata Korin) (vert) 60 40
1350 125c. "Portrait of a Lady" (Kyoto branch, Kano School) (vert) 85 75
1351 150c. "Portrait of Zemmui" (anon, 12th-century) (vert) 85 80
1352 200c. "Ono no Komachi the Poetess" (Hokusai) (vert) 1·00 1·25
1353 500c. "Kobo Daisi as a Child" (anon) (vert) . . . 2·50 3·50
MS1354 Two sheets, each 102 × 77 mm. (a) 500c. "Kodai-no-Kimi" (attr Fujiwara-no-Nobuzane) (vert). (b) 500c. "Emperor Hanazono" (Fujiwara-no-Goshin) Set of 2 sheets . . 8·50 8·50

1989. Bicentenary of French Revolution. Mult.

1355 20c. Type **449** 55 20
1356 60c. Declaration of Human Rights . . . . 1·00 50
1357 80c. Storming the Bastille (horiz) . . . . 1·25 75
1358 200c. Revolution monument (horiz) . . . . 2·25 2·50
1359 350c. Tree of Liberty (horiz) 3·00 4·00

450 "Collybia fusipes"

451 "The Curse of True Love ..."

1989. Fungi (1st series). Multicoloured.

1360 20c. Type **450** 35 25
1361 50c. "Coprinus comatus" . . 50 40
1362 60c. "Xerocomus subtomentosus" 55 45
1363 80c. "Lepista nuda" 65 55
1364 150c. "Suillus placidus" . . 1·10 95
1365 200c. "Lepista nuda" (different) . . . . 1·40 1·25
1366 300c. "Marasmius oreades" 2·00 2·00
1367 500c. "Agaricus campestris" 3·25 3·25
MS1368 Two sheets, each 110 × 80 mm. (a) 600c. "*Boletus rhodoxanthus*". (b) 600c. "*Amanita rubescens*" Set of 2 sheets . . . 7·50 8·00
See also Nos. 1489/96.

1989. 425th Birth Anniv of Shakespeare. Verses and scenes from "A Midsummer Night's Dream". Multicoloured.

1369 40c. Type **451** 75 65
1370 40c. "Love looks not with the eye but with the mind" 75 65
1371 40c. "Nature here shows art" 75 65
1372 40c. "Things growing are not ripe till their season" 75 65
1373 40c. "He is defiled that draws a sword on thee" 75 65
1374 40c. "It is not enough to speak, but to speak true" 75 65
1375 40c. "Thou art as wise as thou are beautiful" . . . 75 65
1376 40c. Wildcat in wood (face value at left) 75 65
1377 40c. Man 75 65
1378 40c. Woman with flower . . 75 65
1379 40c. King and queen 75 65
1380 40c. Bottom 75 65
1381 40c. Wildcat in wood (face value at right) 75 65
1382 40c. Woman 75 65
1383 40c. Leopard 75 65
1384 40c. Tree trunk and man . . 75 65
1385 40c. Meadow flowers . . . 75 65
1386 40c. Mauve flowers 75 65
1387 40c. Plants 75 65
1388 40c. Lion 75 65
1389 40c. Fern and flowers . . . 75 65
Nos. 1369/89 were printed together, forming a composite design.

451a Bronze Mannikin

1989. Birds. Multicoloured.

1390 20c. Type **451a** 30 10
1391 50c. African pied wagtail 45 30
1392 60c. African pygmy kingfisher (inscr "Halcyon malimbicus") 1·25 1·75
1392a 60c. African pygmy kingfisher (inscr "Ispidina picta") . . . . 2·00 2·00
1393 80c. Blue-breasted kingfisher (inscr "Ispidina picta") . . . . 1·75 2·25
1393a 80c. Blue-breasted kingfisher (inscr "Halcyon malimbicus") 2·00 2·50
1394 150c. Striped kingfisher (vert) . . . . 1·10 1·25
1395 200c. Shikra (vert) . . . . 1·25 1·40
1396 300c. Grey parrot (vert) . . 1·50 1·75
1397 500c. Black kite (vert) . . 2·50 3·25
MS1398 Two sheets. (a) 128 × 83 mm. 600c. Cinnamon-breasted rock bunting and barn swallow (horiz). (b) 83 × 128 mm. 600c. Senegal puff-back flycatcher Set of 2 sheets . . . . 14·00 14·00

452 Command Module "Columbia" orbiting Moon

1989. 20th Anniv of First Manned Landing on Moon. Multicoloured.

1399 20c. Type **452** 30 15
1400 80c. Neil Armstrong's footprint on Moon . . . 50 60
1401 200c. Edwin Aldrin on Moon . . . . 1·25 1·75
1402 300c. "Apollo 11" capsule on parachutes . . . . . 1·60 2·00
MS1403 Two sheets, each 100 × 72 mm. (a) 500c. Launch of "Apollo 11". (b) 500c. Earth seen from Moon Set of 2 sheets . . 5·50 7·00

453 Desertification of Pasture

1989. World Environment Day. Multicoloured.

1404 20c. Type **453** 50 15
1405 60c. Wildlife fleeing bush fire 90 80
1406 400c. Industrial pollution . . 2·75 3·50
1407 500c. Erosion . . . . 3·00 3·75

454 "Bebearia arcadius"

1990. Butterflies. Multicoloured.

1408 20c. Type **454** 35 20
1409 60c. "Charaxes laodice" . . 50 40
1410 80c. "Euryphura porphyrion" 60 45
1411 100c. "Neptis nicomedes" 70 50
1412 150c. "Citrinophila erastus" 90 90
1413 200c. "Aethiopana honorius 1·25 1·25
1414 300c. "Precis westermanni" 1·50 1·75
1415 500c. "Cymothoe hypatha" 2·00 2·50
MS1416 Two sheets, each 104 × 72 mm. (a) 600c. "Telipna acraea". (b) 600c. "Pentila abraxas" Set of 2 sheets . . . 9·00 10·00

455 Great Ribbed Cockle

1990. Seashells. Multicoloured.

1417 20c. Type **455** 60 25
1418 60c. Elephant's snout . . . 75 40
1419 80c. Garter cone 85 80
1420 200c. Tankerville's ancilla 2·25 2·50
1421 350c. Coronate prickly-winkle . . . . 3·00 4·00

456 Nehru welcoming President Nkrumah of Ghana

1990. Birth Centenary of Jawaharlal Nehru (Indian statesman). Multicoloured.

1422 20c. Type **456** 60 25
1423 60c. Nehru addressing Bandung Conference, 1955 . . . . 75 30
1424 80c. Nehru with garland and flowers (vert) 80 55
1425 200c. Nehru releasing pigeon (vert) . . . . 1·25 1·50
1426 350c. Nehru (vert) . . . . . 1·75 2·75

457 Wyon Medal, 1838

1990. 150th Anniv of the Penny Black.

1427 **457** 20c. black and violet . . 30 20
1428 – 60c. black and green . . 55 30
1429 – 80c. black and violet . . 70 35
1430 – 200c. black and green . . 1·50 1·25
1431 – 350c. black and green . . 2·00 2·50
1432 – 400c. black and red . . . 2·00 2·50
MS1433 Two sheets, each 112 × 83 mm. (a) 600c. brown and black; (b) 600c. brown, buff and black Set of 2 sheets . . . . . 6·00 7·00

DESIGNS: 60, 600c. (**MS**1433b) Bath mail coach, 1840; 80c. Leeds mail coach, 1840; 200c. Proof of Queen's head engraved by Heath, 1840; 350c. Master die, 1840; 400c. London mail coach, 1840; 600c. (**MS**1433a) Printing the Penny Black.

458 Anniversary Emblem

1990. 10th Anniv (1989) of 4 June Revolution. Multicoloured.

1434 20c. Type **458** 15 15
1435 60c. Foodstuffs 20 20

1436 80c. Cocoa 25 30
1437 200c. Mining . . . . 1·50 1·75
1438 350c. Scales of Justice and sword . . . . 1·75 2·25

459 Map of Africa and Satellite Network

1990. 25th Anniv of Intelsat Satellite System. Multicoloured.
1439 20c. Type **459** 20 20
1440 60c. Map of Americas . . . 30 30
1441 80c. Map of Asia and Pacific 35 35
1442 200c. Map of South America and Africa . . . 90 1·00
1443 350c. Map of Indian Ocean and Pacific . . . . 1·50 2·00

460 Housewife using Telephone

1990. 2nd Anniv of Introduction of International Direct Dialling Service. Multicoloured.
1444 20c. Type **460** 25 20
1445 60c. Businessman using telephone 35 35
1446 80c. Man using phonecard telephone 40 40
1447 200c. Public telephones for internal and IDD services 90 1·00
1448 350c. Satellite station . . . 1·50 2·00

461 Blue Flycatcher

463 "Eulophia guineensis"

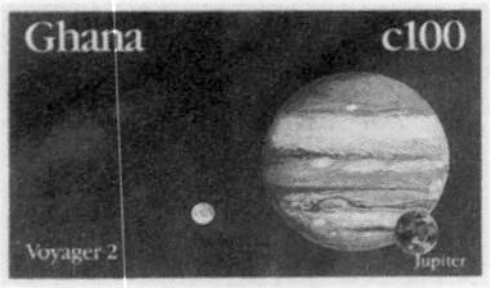
462 Jupiter

1990. African Tropical Rain Forest. Multicoloured.
1449 40c. Type **461** 80 80
1450 40c. Boomslang (snake) . . . 80 80
1451 40c. Superb sunbird 80 80
1452 40c. Bateleur 80 80
1453 40c. Yellow-casqued hornbill 80 80
1454 40c. "Salamis temora" (butterfly) 80 80
1455 40c. Potto 80 80
1456 40c. Leopard 80 80
1457 40c. Bongo 80 80
1458 40c. Grey parrot 80 80
1459 40c. Okapi 80 80
1460 40c. Gorilla 80 80
1461 40c. Flap-necked chameleon 80 80
1462 40c. West African dwarf crocodile 80 80
1463 40c. Python 80 80
1464 40c. Giant ground pangolin 80 80
1465 40c. "Pseudacraea boisduvali" (butterfly) . . 80 80
1466 40c. North African crested porcupine 80 80
1467 40c. Rosy-columned aerangis (orchid) 80 80
1468 40c. "Cymothoe sangaris" (butterfly) 80 80
MS1469 100 × 75 mm. 600c. Head of leopard (vert) . . . . 4·50 5·00

Nos. 1449/68 were printed together, se-tenant, forming a composite design.

1990. Space Flight of "Voyager 2". Multicoloured.
1470 100c. Type **462** 70 70
1471 100c. Neptune and Triton . . 70 70
1472 100c. Ariel, moon of Uranus 70 70
1473 100c. Saturn from Mimas . . 70 70
1474 100c. Saturn 70 70
1475 100c. Rings of Saturn . . . 70 70
1476 100c. Neptune 70 70
1477 100c. Uranus from Miranda 70 70
1478 100c. Volcano on Io 70 70
MS1479 Two sheets. (a) 111 × 81 mm. 600c. "Voyager 2" spacecraft (vert). (b) 80 × 111 mm. 600c. Lift off of "Voyager 2" (vert) Set of 2 sheets . . . . 4·50 5·00

1990. Orchids. Multicoloured.
1480 20c. Type **463** 45 45
1481 40c. "Eurychone rothschildiana" 60 60
1482 60c. "Bulbophyllum barbigerum" 80 80
1483 80c. "Polystachya galeata" 1·10 1·10
1484 200c. "Diaphananthe kamerunensis" . . . . . 2·00 1·75
1485 300c. "Podangis dactyloceras" . . . . . . 2·25 2·00
1486 400c. "Ancistrochilus rothschildianus" . . . . 2·50 2·00
1487 500c. "Rangaeris muscicola" 2·75 2·00
MS1488 Two sheets, each 101 × 70mm. (a) 600c. "Bolusiella imbricata". (b) "Diaphananthe rotila" Set of 2 sheets . . . . 12·00 13·00

464 "Coprinus atramentarius"

1990. Fungi (2nd series). Multicoloured.
1489 20c. Type **464** 70 45
1490 50c. "Marasmius oreades" 90 65
1491 60c. "Oudemansiella radicata" . . . . 1·00 70
1492 80c. "Boletus edulis" (Cep) 1·25 90
1493 150c. "Hebeloma crustuliniforme" . . . . . . 2·00 1·50
1494 200c. "Coprinus micaceus" 2·25 2·00
1495 300c. "Macrolepiota procera" ("Lepiota procera") . . . . 2·50 2·50
1496 500c. "Amanita phalloides" 2·75 3·00
MS1497 Two sheets, each 104 × 82 mm. (a) Nos. 1489, 1491/2 and 1496. (b) Nos. 1490 and 1493/5 Set of 2 sheets . . 8·00 9·00

465 Italian and Swedish Players chasing Ball

1990. World Cup Football Championship, Italy. Multicoloured.
1498 20c. Type **465** 45 20
1499 50c. Egyptian player penetrating Irish defence 55 30
1500 60c. Cameroon players celebrating 60 30
1501 80c. Rumanian player beating challenge 70 40
1502 100c. Russian goalkeeper Dassayev 85 65
1503 150c. Roger Milla of Cameroon (vert) . . . . 1·40 1·10
1504 400c. South Korean player challenging opponent . . 2·25 2·75
1505 600c. Klinsman of West Germany celebrating . . 2·75 3·75
MS1506 Two sheets, each 88 × 98 mm. (a) 800c. United Arab Emirates player watching ball. (b) 800c. Colombian player Set of 2 sheets . . . . 5·50 6·50

1990. 350th Death Anniv of Rubens. As T **195c** of Gambia, but vert. Multicoloured.
1507 20c. "Duke of Mantua" . . . 55 20
1508 50c. "Jan Brant" 75 30
1509 60c. "Portraits of a Young Man" 75 30
1510 80c. "Michel Ophovius" . . 90 40
1511 100c. "Caspar Gevaerts" . . 1·25 65
1512 200c. "Head of Warrior" (detail) . . . . 1·75 1·75
1513 300c. "Study of a Bearded Man" . . . . 2·25 2·75
1514 400c. "Paracelsus" . . . . 2·50 3·75
MS1515 Two sheets, each 71 × 100 mm. (a) 600c. "Warrior with two Pages" (detail). (b) 600c. "Archduke Ferdinand" (detail) Set of 2 sheets . . . . 8·00 9·00

466 Manganese Ore

467 Dance Drums

1991. Minerals. Multicoloured.
1516 20c. Type **466** 55 30
1517 60c. Iron ore 70 60
1518 80c. Bauxite ore 90 75
1519 200c. Gold ore . . . . . . 2·00 2·00
1520 350c. Diamond . . . . . . 3·00 4·00
MS1521 70 × 90 mm. 600c. Uncut and cut diamonds . . . . . . 8·50 9·00

1991. Tribal Drums. Multicoloured.
1522 20c. Type **467** 40 20
1523 60c. Message drums 85 40
1524 80c. War drums . . . . . . 1·00 50
1525 200c. Dance drums (different) . . . . 2·00 2·50
1526 350c. Ceremonial drums . . 2·50 4·00
MS1527 70 × 90 mm. 600c. Drum with carrying strap . . . . . . 6·50 7·50

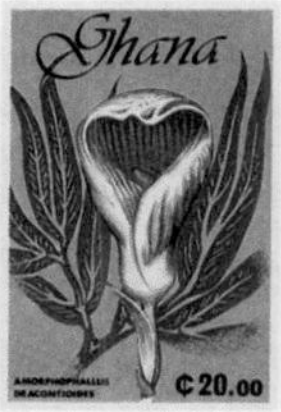
468 "Amorphophallus dracontioides"

469 Transport and Telecommunication Symbols

1991. Flowers (1st series). Multicoloured.
1528 20c. Type **468** 80 25
1529 60c. "Anchomanes difformis" . . . . 1·25 50
1530 80c. "Kaemferia nigerica" 1·50 70
1531 200c. "Aframomum sceptrum" . . . . 2·50 2·75
1532 350c. "Amorphophallus flavovirens" . . . . . . 2·75 3·75
MS1533 70 × 90 mm. 600c. "Amorphophallus flavovirens" (different) . . . . 5·50 6·00

1991. Flowers (2nd series). As T **468** but inscr "GHANA" in capitals. Multicoloured.
1534 20c. "Urginea indica" . . . 45 25
1535 60c. "Hymencallis littoralis" 85 50
1536 80c. "Crinum jagus" . . . . 1·50 70
1537 200c. "Dipcadi tacazzeanum" . . . . . . 2·00 2·75
1538 350c. "Haemanthus rupestris" . . . . 2·50 3·75
MS1539 70 × 90mm. 600c. "Urginea indica" (different) . . . . . . 5·50 6·00

1991. 40th Anniv of United Nations Development Programme. Multicoloured.
1540 20c. Type **469** 45 20
1541 60c. Agricultural research 70 40
1542 80c. Literacy 80 55
1543 200c. Advances in agricultural crop growth 1·75 2·00
1544 350c. Industrial symbols . . 2·25 3·50

470 Drawing of Scout from First Handbook

471 Women sorting Fish

1991. 50th Death Anniv of Lord Baden-Powell.
1545 **470** 20c. black and buff . . . 90 20
1546 – 50c. grey, blue and black 1·10 40
1547 – 60c. multicoloured . . . 1·10 45
1548 – 80c. black and buff . . . 1·40 55
1549 – 100c. multicoloured . . . 2·00 75
1550 – 200c. multicoloured . . . 2·50 2·00
1551 – 500c. multicoloured . . . 3·50 4·00
1552 – 600c. multicoloured . . . 3·75 5·50
MS1553 Two sheets. (a) 104 × 75 mm. 800c. multicoloured. (b) 74 × 105 mm. 800c. multicoloured Set of 2 sheets 9·00 10·00

DESIGNS—VERT: 50c. Lord Baden-Powell; 80c. Handbook illustrations by Norman Rockwell; 500c. Scout at prayer. HORIZ: 60c. Hands holding Boy Scout emblem; 100c. Mafeking Siege 1d. Goodyear stamp and African runner; 200c. Scouts with Blitz victim, London, 1944; 600c. Mafeking Siege 1d. Goodyear stamp; 800c. (**MS**1553a) Scout camp; 800c. (**MS**1553b) Envelope from Mafeking Siege.

1991. Chorkor Smoker (fish smoking process). Multicoloured.
1554 20c. Type **471** 30 20
1555 60c. Cleaning the ovens . . . 55 40
1556 80c. Washing fish 65 55
1557 200c. Laying fish on pallets 1·25 1·50
1558 350c. Stacking pallets over ovens . . . . 1·75 2·50

472 African Hind

1991. Fishes. Multicoloured.
1559 20c. Type **472** 25 25
1560 50c. Shrew squeaker 40 40
1561 80c. West African triggerfish 55 55
1562 100c. Stonehead 70 70
1563 200c. Lesser pipefish . . . . 1·50 1·50
1564 300c. Aba . . . . 1·60 1·60
1565 400c. Jewel cichlid . . . . . 1·75 1·75
1566 500c. Smooth hammerhead 1·90 1·90
MS1567 Two sheets, each 108 × 81 mm. (a) 800c. Bayad. (b) 800c. Eastern flying gurnard Set of 2 sheets . . . . 6·00 7·00

1991. Death Centenary (1990) of Vincent van Gogh (artist). As T **200b** of Gambia. Multicoloured.
1568 20c. "Reaper with Sickle" 35 25
1569 50c. "The Thresher" . . . 55 40
1570 60c. "The Sheaf-Binder" . . 60 50
1571 80c. "The Sheep-Shearers" 70 65
1572 100c. "Peasant Woman cutting Straw" 85 80
1573 200c. "The Sower" . . . . 1·60 1·75
1574 500c. "The Plough and the Harrow" (horiz) . . . . 2·25 2·50
1575 600c. "The Woodcutter" . . 2·25 2·50
MS1576 Two sheets, each 117 × 80 mm. (a) 800c. "Evening: The Watch" (horiz). (b) 800c. "Evening: The End of the Day" (horiz). Imperf Set of 2 sheets 8·50 9·00

473 Gamal Nasser (Egypt) and Conference Hall

1991. 10th Non-Aligned Ministers' Conference, Accra. Statesmen. Multicoloured.
1577 20c. Type **473** 50 30
1578 60c. Josip Tito (Yugoslavia) 55 45
1579 80c. Pandit Nehru (India) 3·50 1·25
1580 200c. Kwame Nkrumah (Ghana) . . . . 1·75 2·25
1581 350c. Achmad Sukarno (Indonesia) . . . . 1·90 3·00

474 Green-winged Pytila

1991. Birds. As T **474**. Multicoloured
1582/1629 80c. × 16, 100c. × 32 . . Set of 48 . . . . 22·00 25·00
MS1630 Three sheets, each 107 × 86 mm. (a) 800c. Marabou stork. (b) 800c. African fish eagle. (c) 800c. Saddle-bill stork Set of 3 sheets . . . . 11·00 12·00

Nos. 1582/1629 were issued together, se-tenant, as three sheetlets of 16 forming composite designs. The 80c. values show Green-winged pytilia, Orange-cheeked waxbill, African paradise flycatcher, Great blue turaco ("Blue plantain-eater"), Red bishop, Splendid glossy starling, Red-faced lovebird, African palm swift, Narina's trogon ("Narina Trogon"), Tawny eagle, Bateleur, Hoopoe, Secretary bird, African white-backed vulture, White-necked bald crow ("Bare-headed rockfowl"), Abyssinian ground hornbill, and the 100c. African open-bill stork, African spoonbill, Pink-backed pelican, Little bittern, Purple swamphen ("King reed-hen"), Saddle-bill stork, Glossy ibis, White-faced whistling duck, Black-headed heron, Hammerkop, African darter, Woolly-necked stork, Yellow-billed stork, Black-winged stilt, Goliath heron, African jacana ("Lily trotter"), Shikra, Abyssinian roller, Carmine bee eater, Pin-tailed whydah, Purple glossy starling, Yellow-mantled whydah, Pel's fishing owl, Crested touraco, Red-cheeked cordon-bleu, Olive-bellied sunbird, Red-billed hornbill, Red-billed quelea, South African crowned crane, Indian blue quail ("Blue Quail"), Egyptian vulture and Helmeted guineafowl.

475 "Nularda" (beetle)

476 Boti Falls

1991. Insects. Multicoloured.
1631 20c. Type **475** 70 20
1632 50c. "Zonocrus" (grasshopper) 85 30
1633 60c. "Gryllotalpa africana" (mole cricket) 95 30
1634 80c. Weevil . . . . 1·10 60
1635 100c. "Coenagrion" (dragonfly) . . . . . . 1·40 70
1636 150c. "Sahlbergella" (fly) . . 1·75 2·25
1637 200c. "Anthia" (ant) . . . . 2·00 2·50
1638 350c. "Megacephala" (beetle) . . . . 2·50 3·75
MS1639 106 × 79 mm. 600c. "Lacetus" (lacewing) . . . . . 8·50 9·00

1991. Multicoloured.
1639a 20c. Oil palm fruit 10 10
1640 50c. Type **476** 20 10
1641 60c. Larabanga Mosque (horiz) 20 10
1642 80c. Fort Sebastian, Shama (horiz) 20 10
1643 100c. Cape Coast Castle (horiz) . . . . 1·00 20
1644 200c. White-toothed cowrie (horiz) . . . . 1·40 35
1645 400c. True achatina (horiz) 2·25 75

1991. Christmas. Religious Paintings. As T **200c** of Gambia. Multicoloured.
1646 20c. "Adoration of the Magi" (Bosch) 55 20
1647 50c. "The Annunciation" (Campin) 75 30
1648 60c. "Virgin and Child" (detail) (Bouts) 80 30
1649 80c. "Presentation in the Temple" (Memling) . . . 1·00 50
1650 100c. "Virgin and Child enthroned with Angel and Donor" (Memling) . . . 1·25 65
1651 200c. "Virgin and Child with Saints and Donor" (Van Eyck) . . . . 2·00 2·00
1652 400c. "St. Luke painting the Virgin" (Van der Weyden) 3·00 3·75
1653 700c. "Virgin and Child" (Bouts) . . . . 4·25 6·00
MS1654 Two sheets, each 103 × 128 mm. (a) 800c. "Virgin and Child standing in a Niche" (Van der Weyden). (b) 800c. "The Annunciation" (Memling) Set of 2 sheets . . . . 7·00 8·50

477 Women collecting Water from Bore Hole

1992. Decade of Revolutionary Progress. Multicoloured.
1655 20c. Type **477** 15 10
1656 50c. Miners 40 15
1657 60c. Wood carver 30 15
1658 80c. Forestry 30 20
1659 200c. Cacao tree 60 75
1660 350c. Village electrification 1·00 1·50

478 Mount Fuji and Flying Fish

1992. "Phila Nippon '91" International Stamp Exhibition, Tokyo. Multicoloured.
1661 20c. Type **478** 65 30
1662 60c. Itsukushima Jingu Shrine 80 40
1663 80c. Geisha . . . . 1·00 50
1664 100c. Samurai house . . . . 1·40 70
1665 200c. Bonsai tree . . . . . 2·25 1·75
1666 400c. Olympic Sports Hall . 2·75 3·00
1667 500c. Great Buddha (statue) 2·75 3·25
1668 600c. Nagoya Castle . . . . 3·00 3·50
MS1669 Two sheets, each 109 × 80 mm. (a) 800c. Takamatsu Castle. (b) 800c. Heian Shrine Set of 2 sheets . . . . 11·00 12·00

479 East and West Germans celebrating

1992. Reunification of Germany. Multicoloured.
1670 20c. Type **479** 30 20
1671 60c. Signing Reunification Treaty 40 40
1672 80c. Chariot on Brandenburg Gate and fireworks 45 45
1673 1000c. Germans with unified currency . . . . 7·50 9·50
MS1674 Three sheets. (a) 109 × 78 mm. 400c. Doves and Brandenburg Gate; 400c. Chancellor Kohl and Prime Minister De Maizière. (b) 125 × 87 mm. 800c. Chancellor Kohl and members of last German Democratic Republic administration. (c) 130 × 92 mm. 300c. President Gorbachev (vert); 300c. Chancellor Kohl (vert); 300c. Map of Western Germany (face value in black) (vert); 300c. Map of Eastern Germany (face value in white) (vert) Set of 3 sheets . . 12·00 12·00

480 Steam Side-tank Locomotive, 1903

1992. Ghanaian Railways. Multicoloured.
1675 20c. Type **480** 40 30
1676 50c. AIA-AIA diesel locomotive 60 40
1677 60c. First class coach, 1931 60 45
1678 80c. Railway inspection coach No. 2212 . . . . . 70 70
1679 100c. Steam locomotive No. 401 on Kumasi turntable 90 90
1680 200c. Cocoa wagon, 1921 1·40 1·50
1681 500c. Steam locomotive No. 223 "Prince of Wales" . . . . 2·25 2·75
1682 600c. Cattle wagon . . . . 2·25 2·75
MS1683 Two sheets. (a) 106 × 76 mm. 800c. Beyer-Garratt steam locomotive No. 301, 1943. (b) 76 × 106 mm. 800c. German-built steam locomotive Set of 2 sheets . . . . 8·50 9·00

1992. Olympic Games, Albertville and Barcelona. Past Medal Winners. As T **203** of Gambia. Mutlcoloured.
1684 20c. E. Blay (Ghana) (boxing) and windmill . . 50 20
1685 60c. M. Ahey (Ghana) (athletics) and Catalan coat of arms 70 35
1686 80c. T. Wilson (U.S.A.) (70 m ski jump) and grapes 90 50
1687 100c. Four-man bobsleighing (East Germany) and passport 1·25 75
1688 200c. G. Louganis (U.S.A.) (platform diving) and decorative vase . . . . . 2·00 1·50
1689 300c. L. Visser (Netherlands) (5000 m speed skating) and wine bottle cork . . . 2·25 2·25
1690 350c. J. Passler (Italy) (biathlon) and lily . . . . 2·25 2·50
1691 400c. M. Retton (U.S.A.) (gymnastics) and silhouette of castle . . . . 2·50 2·75
1692 500c. J. Hingsen (West Germany) (decathlon) and gold and silver coins . . . 2·50 2·75
1693 600c. R. Neubert (West Germany) (heptathlon) and leather work . . . . 2·50 2·75
MS1694 Two sheets. (a) 112 × 82 mm. 800c. Silhouette of windmill. (b) 82 × 112 mm. 800c. Silhouette of folk dancer (vert) Set of 2 sheets . . . . 11·00 12·00

481 "Angides lugubris"

1992. Reptiles. Multicoloured.
1695 20c. Type **481** 20 20
1696 50c. "Kinixys erosa" (tortoise) 30 30
1697 60c. "Agama agama" (lizard) 30 30
1698 80c. "Chameleo gracilis" (chameleon) 40 40
1699 100c. "Naja melanleuca" (snake) 50 50
1700 200c. "Crocodylus niloticus" (crocodile) . . . . 90 1·10
1701 400c. "Chelonia mydas" (turtle) . . . . 1·75 2·25
1702 500c. "Varanus exanthematicus" (lizard) 1·90 2·50
MS1703 94 × 66 mm. 600c. Tortoise and snake . . . . 2·75 3·50

1992. Easter. Religious Paintings. As T **204a** of Gambia but vert designs. Multicoloured.
1704 20c. "The Four Apostles" (detail) (Durer) 40 20
1705 50c. "The Last Judgement" (detail) (Rubens) 60 30
1706 60c. "The Four Apostles" (different detail) (Durer) 60 30
1707 80c. "The Last Judgement" (different detail) (Rubens) 75 40
1708 100c. "Crucifixion" (Rubens) 90 50
1709 200c. "The Last Judgement" (different detail) (Rubens) 1·75 1·50
1710 500c. "Christum Videre" (Rubens) . . . . 2·75 3·50
1711 600c. "The Last Judgement" (different detail) (Rubens) 3·00 4·00
MS1712 Two sheets. (a) 69 × 100 mm. 800c. "Last Communion of St. Francis of Assisi" (detail) (Rubens) (vert). (b) 100 × 69 mm. 800c. "Scourging the Money Changers from the Temple" (detail) (El Greco) Set of 2 sheets . . . . 7·50 8·50

481a "Two Men at Table" (Velazquez)

1992. "Granada '92" International Stamp Exhibition, Spain. Spanish Paintings. Mult.
1713 20c. Type **481a** 40 20
1714 60c. "Christ in the House of Mary and Martha" (detail) (Velazquez) . . . 55 30
1715 80c. "The Supper at Emmaus" (Velazquez) . . 65 40
1716 100c. "Three Musicians" (Velazquez) 75 50
1717 200c. "Old Woman cooking Eggs" (Velazquez) (vert) 1·50 1·25
1718 400c. "Old Woman cooking Eggs" (detail) (Velazquez) (vert) . . . . 2·50 2·75
1719 500c. "The Surrender of Breda" (detail) (Velazquez) (vert) . . . . 2·75 3·00
1720 700c. "The Surrender of Breda" (different detail) (Velazquez) (vert) . . . . 3·00 3·75
MS1721 Two sheets. (a) 95 × 120 mm. 900c. "The Waterseller of Seville" (Velazquez) (86 × 111 mm). (b) 120 × 95 mm. 900c. "They still Say that Fish is Expensive" (Joaquín Sorolla y Bastida) (111 × 86 mm). Imperf Set of 2 sheets . . . . 9·00 9·50

482 "Danaus chrysippus"

483 Martin Pinzon and "Pinta"

1992. "Genova '92" International Thematic Stamp Exhibition. Butterflies. Mult.
1722 20c. Type **482** 50 30
1723 60c. "Papilio dardanus" . . 80 45
1724 80c. "Cynthia cardui" . . . 90 60
1725 100c. "Meneris tulbaghia" 1·00 75
1726 200c. "Salamis temora" . . 1·50 1·60
1727 400c. "Charaxes jasius" . . 2·00 2·50
1728 500c. "Precis oenone" . . . 2·25 2·50
1729 700c. "Precis sophia" . . . 2·50 2·75
MS1730 Two sheets, each 100 × 70 mm. (a) 900c. "Papilio demodocus". (b) 900c. "Precis octavia" Set of 2 sheets . . . . 7·50 8·50

1992. Prehistoric Animals. As T **207a** of Gambia. Multicoloured.
1731 20c. Iguanodon 35 25
1732 50c. Anchisaurus 50 35
1733 60c. Heterodontosaurus . . 55 35
1734 80c. Ouranosaurus 60 45
1735 100c. Anatosaurus 75 55
1736 200c. Elaphrosaurus . . . . 1·25 1·50
1737 500c. Coelophysis . . . . . 2·25 2·75
1738 600c. Rhamphorynchus . . 2·50 3·00
MS1739 Two sheets, each 100 × 70 mm. (a) 1500c. As 200c. (b) 1500c. As 500c. Set of 2 sheets 9·00 10·00

1992. World Columbian Stamp "Expo '92", Chicago. 500th Anniv of Discovery of America by Columbus. Multicoloured.
1740 200c. Type **483** . . . . . . 90 1·00
1741 200c. Vicente Pinzon and "Nina" . . . . 90 1·00
1742 200c. Columbus and Father Marchena at La Rabida 90 1·00
1743 200c. Columbus in his cabin 90 1·00
1744 200c. Fleet sights land . . . 90 1·00
1745 200c. Columbus on Samana Cay . . . . 90 1·00
1746 200c. Wreck of "Santa Maria" . . . . 90 1·00
1747 200c. Amerindians at Spanish Court . . . . . 90 1·00
MS1748 122 × 86 mm. 500c. Columbus and "Santa Maria" 3·50 4·00

484 Olive-grey Ancilla

485 "Presentation in the Temple" (Master of the Braunschweiti)

1992. Shells. Multicoloured.
1749 20c. Type **484** 20 20
1750 20c. Radula cerith 20 20
1751 60c. Rugose donex 30 30
1752 60c. Horned murex 30 30
1753 80c. Concave ear moon . . 40 40
1754 80c. Triple twella 40 40
1755 200c. "Pila africana" . . . 90 1·00
1756 200c. Rat cowrie . . . . . 90 1·00
1757 350c. "Thais hiatula" . . . 1·60 1·90
1758 350c. West African helmet 1·60 1·90
MS1759 Two sheets, each 87 × 117 mm. (a) 600c. Fanel moon ("Natica fanel"). (b) 600c. Giant hairy melongena ("Pugilina moria") Set of 2 sheets . . . . 6·00 7·00

1992. Christmas. Religious Paintings. Mult.
1760 20c. Type **485** 40 20
1761 50c. "Presentation in the Temple" (detail) (Master of St. Severin) 60 30
1762 60c. "The Visitation" (Sebastiano del Piombo) 70 30
1763 80c. "The Visitation" (detail) (Giotto) 80 40
1764 100c. "The Circumcision" (detail) (Studio of Bellini) 95 50
1765 200c. "The Circumcision" (Studio of Garofalo) . . . 1·75 1·60
1766 500c. "The Visitation" (Studio of Van der Weyden) . . . . 2·75 3·00
1767 800c. "The Visitation" (detail) (Studio of Van der Weyden) . . . . 3·25 4·25
MS1768 Two sheets, each 77 × 102 mm. (a) 900c. "Presentation in the Temple" (Bartolo di Fredi). (b) 900c. "The Visitation" (larger detail) (Giotto) Set of 2 sheets . . . . 7·50 9·00

486 "Calappa rubroguttata"

1993. Crabs. Multicoloured.
1769 20c. Type **486** 40 20
1770 60c. "Cardisoma amatum" 70 25
1771 80c. "Maia squinado" . . . 80 30
1772 400c. "Ocypoda cursor" . . 1·75 2·00
1773 800c. "Grapus grapus" . . 2·50 3·25
MS1774 127 × 97 mm. Nos. 1769/73 6·00 6·00

487 "Clerodendrum thomsoniae"

1993. Flowers. Multicoloured.
1775 20c. Type **487** 20 15
1776 20c. "Lagerstroemia flos-reginae" 20 15
1777 60c. "Cassia fistula" 35 25
1778 60c. "Spathodea campanulata" 35 25
1779 80c. "Hildegardia barteri" 40 25
1780 80c. "Mellitea ferrugenea" 40 25
1781 200c. "Petrea volubilis" 60 85
1782 200c. "Ipomoea asarifolia" 60 85
1783 350c. "Bryphyllum pinnatum" 90 1·25
1784 350c. "Ritchiea reflexa" 90 1·25
MS1785 Two sheets, each 86 × 125 mm. (a) 50c. As No. 1777; 100c. As No. 1783; 150c. As No. 1782; 300c. As No. 1779. (b) 50c. As No. 1778; 100c. As No. 1776; 150c. As No. 1780; 300c. As No. 1784 Set of 2 sheets 4·50 5·00

488 Zeppelin LZ-3 entering Floating Hangar, Lake Constance

1993. Anniversaries and Events. Multicoloured.
1786 20c. Type **488** 85 30
1787 100c. Launch of European "Ariane 4" rocket (vert) 1·25 75
1788 200c. Leopard 2·00 1·75
1789 300c. Colosseum and fruit 2·25 2·50
1790 400c. Mozart (vert) 3·75 3·25
1791 600c. Launch of Japanese "H-1" rocket (vert) 3·75 4·25
1792 800c. Zeppelin LZ-10 "Schwaben" 3·75 4·50
MS1793 Four sheets. (a) 106 × 76 mm. 900c. Count Ferdinand von Zeppelin (vert). (b) 76 × 106 mm. 900c. Launch of American space shuttle (vert). (c) 106 × 76 mm. 900c. Bongo. (d) 99 × 69 mm. 900c. Cherubino from "The Marriage of Figaro" (vert) Set of 4 sheets 16·00 16·00
ANNIVERSARIES AND EVENTS: Nos. 1786, 1792, **MS**1793a, 75th death anniv of Count Ferdinand von Zeppelin; 1787, 1791, **MS**1793b, International Space Year; 1788, **MS**1793c, Earth Summit '92, Rio; 1789, International Conference on Nutrition, Rome; 1790, **MS**1793d, Death bicentenary of Mozart.

1993. Bicentenary of the Louvre, Paris. As T **209b** of Gambia. Multicoloured.
1794 200c. "Carnival Minuet" (left detail) (Giovanni Domenico Tiepolo) 85 1·00
1795 200c. "Carnival Minuet" (centre detail) (Giovanni Domenico Tiepolo) 85 1·00
1796 200c. "Carnival Minuet" (right detail) (Giovanni Domenico Tiepolo) 85 1·00
1797 200c. "The Tooth Puller" (left detail) (Giovanni Domenico Tiepolo) 85 1·00
1798 200c. "The Tooth Puller" (right detail) (Giovanni Domenico Tiepolo) 85 1·00
1799 200c. "Rebecca at the Well" (Giovanni Battista Tiepolo) 85 1·00
1800 200c. "Presenting Christ to the People" (left detail) (Giovanni Battista Tiepolo) 85 1·00
1801 200c. "Presenting Christ to the People" (right detail) (Giovanni Battista Tiepolo) 85 1·00
MS1802 100 × 70 mm. 700c. "Chancellor Seguier" (Charles le Brun) (85 × 52 mm) 2·75 3·25

489 Energy Foods

1993. Int Conference on Nutrition, Rome. Mult.
1803 20c. Type **489** 30 15
1804 60c. Body-building foods 50 20
1805 80c. Protective foods 55 25
1806 200c. Disease prevention equipment 1·75 1·25
1807 400c. Quality control and preservation of fish products 2·25 3·00

490 Kwame Nkrumah Mausoleum

1993. Proclamation of 4th Republic. Mult.
1808 50c. Type **490** 20 15
1809 100c. Kwame Nkrumah Conference Centre 35 25
1810 200c. Book of Constitution (vert) 80 80
1811 350c. Independence Square (vert) 1·60 2·00
1812 400c. Christiansborg Castle (vert) 1·75 2·00

491 Resurrection Egg

491b Airship "Graf Zeppelin" over Alps

491a Mercedes Benz "300 SLR", Mille Migla, 1955

1993. Easter. Faberge Eggs. Multicoloured.
1813 50c. Type **491** 40 15
1814 80c. Imperial Red Cross egg with Resurrection triptych 65 25
1815 100c. Imperial Uspensky Cathedral egg 75 25
1816 150c. Imperial Red Cross egg with portraits 1·10 65
1817 200c. Orange Tree egg 1·25 1·25
1818 250c. Rabbit egg 1·25 1·50
1819 400c. Imperial Coronation egg 2·00 2·50
1820 900c. Silver-gilt enamel Easter egg 3·25 5·00
MS1821 Two sheet. (a) 73 × 100 mm. 1000c. Renaissance egg. (b) 100 × 73 mm. 1000c. Egg charms (horiz) Set of 2 sheets 8·00 9·00

1993. Centenaries of Henry Ford's First Petrol Engine (Nos. 1823/4) and Karl Benz's First Four-wheeled Car (others). Multicoloured.
1822 150c. Type **491a** 75 50
1823 400c. Ford "Depot Wagon", 1920 1·75 1·75
1824 600c. Ford "Mach 1 Mustang", 1970 2·25 2·75
1825 800c. Mercedes Benz racing car, Monaco Grand Prix, 1937 3·50 4·50
MS1826 Two sheets, each 110 × 80 mm. (a) 1000c. Mercedes Benz "Type 196" racing car, 1955 (85½ × 28½ mm). (b) 1000c. Ford "Super T", 1910 (85½ × 28½ mm) Set of 2 sheets 7·75 8·25

1993. Aviation Anniversaries. Multicoloured.
1827 50c. Type **491b** 50 30
1828 150c. Airship LZ-7 "Deutschland" (horiz) 85 55
1829 400c. Avro Vulcan jet bomber (horiz) 1·75 1·75
1830 400c. U.S. Mail Ford Trimotor (horiz) 1·75 1·75
1831 600c. Nieuport 27 biplane 2·25 2·25
1832 600c. Loading mail on "Graf Zeppelin" 2·25 2·25
1833 800c. Airship LZ-10 "Schwaben" (horiz) 3·50 4·00
MS1834 Three sheets, each 111 × 80 mm. (a) 1000c. LZ-127 "Graf Zeppelin". (b) 1000c. S.E.5A, 1918. (c) 1000c. Early airmail flight by Walter Edwards between Portland and Vancouver (57 × 42½ mm) Set of 3 sheets 14·00 14·00
ANNIVERSARIES: Nos. 1827/28, 1833, **MS**1834a, 125th birth anniv of Hugo Eckener (airship commander); 1829, 1831, **MS**1834b, 75th anniv of Royal Air Force; 1830, 1832, **MS**1834c, Bicentenary of first airmail flight.

492 African Buffalo

1993. Wild Animals. Multicoloured.
1835 20c. Type **492** 30 15
1836 50c. Giant forest hog 40 20
1837 60c. Potto 45 25
1838 80c. Bay duiker 60 30
1839 100c. Royal antelope 70 35
1840 200c. Serval 1·25 90
1841 500c. Golden cat 2·00 2·75
1842 800c. "Megaloglossus woermanni" (bat) 3·25 4·00
MS1843 Two sheets, each 68 × 98 mm. (a) 900c. Dormouse. (b) 900c. White-collared mangabey Set of 2 sheets 7·50 8·50

1993. 40th Anniv of Coronation. Nos. 1549/53 optd **40TH ANNIVERSARY OF CORONATION H.M. ELIZABETH II.**
1844 100c. multicoloured 1·25 30
1845 200c. multicoloured 2·00 1·00
1846 500c. multicoloured 4·00 4·00
1847 600c. multicoloured 4·00 4·50
MS1848 Two sheets. (a) 104 × 75 mm. 800c. multicoloured. (b) 74 × 105 mm. 800c. multicoloured Set of 2 sheets 11·00 11·00

1993. 35th Anniv of Rotary International and 60th Anniv of Ghana Red Cross Society (1992). Nos. 1562 and 1564/6 optd **35 YEARS OF ROTARY INTERNATIONAL GHANA 1958** (Nos. 1849, 1852, **MS**1853a) or **GHANA RED CROSS SOCIETY FOUNDED 1932** and cross (others).
1849 100c. Stonehead 1·10 30
1850 300c. Aba 2·75 2·75
1851 400c. Jewel cichlid 3·00 3·25
1852 500c. Smooth hammerhead 3·50 3·75
MS1853 Two sheets, each 108 × 81 mm. (a) 800c. Bayad. (b) 800c. Eastern flying gurnard Set of 2 sheets 9·50 10·00

496 "Cantharellus cibarius"

1993. Mushrooms. Multicoloured.
1854 20c. Type **496** 40 25
1855 50c. "Russula cyanoxantha" 50 30
1856 60c. "Clitocybe rivulosa" 55 30
1857 80c. "Cortinarius elatior" 60 35
1858 80c. "Mycena galericulata" 60 35
1859 200c. "Tricholoma gambosum" 1·00 1·00
1860 200c. "Boletus edulis" 1·00 1·00
1861 200c. "Lepista saeva" 1·00 1·00
1862 250c. "Gyroporus castaneus" 1·10 1·10
1863 300c. "Boletus chrysenteron" 1·25 1·25
1864 350c. "Nolanea sericea" 1·40 1·40
1865 350c. "Hygrophorus punicea" ("Hygrophorus puiceus") 1·40 1·40
1866 500c. "Gomphidius glutinosus" 1·60 1·75
1867 600c. "Russula olivacea" 1·75 2·00
1868 1000c. "Russula aurata" 2·25 2·75
MS1869 Two sheets, each 85 × 130 mm. (a) 50c. As No. 1856; 100c. As No. 1858; 150c. As No. 1860; 1000c. As No. 1864. (b) 100c. As Type **496**; 150c. As No. 1857; 300c. As No. 1859; 600c. As No. 1865 Set of 2 sheets 9·50 11·00

497 "The Actor" (Picasso)

498 Abedi Pele (Ghana)

1993. Anniversaries and Events. Multicoloured.
1870 20c. Type **497** 60 40
1871 20c. Early astronomical equipment 60 40
1872 80c. "Portrait of Allan Stein" (Picasso) 75 40
1873 200c. Modern telescope 1·25 1·50
1874 200c. "Tattoo" (Lesek Sobocki) 1·25 1·50
1875 600c. "Prison" (Sasza Blonder) 2·75 3·50
1876 800c. "Seated Male Nude" (Picasso) 3·50 4·00
MS1877 Four sheets. (a) 75 × 105 mm. 900c. "Guernica" (Picasso). (b) 75 × 105 mm. 1000c. "Bajika o Czlowieku Szczesliwym" (detail) (Antoni Mickalak) (horiz). (c) 105 × 75 mm. 1000c. Copernicus (face value at top left). (d) 105 × 75 mm. 1000c. Copernicus (face value at centre top) Set of 4 sheets 14·00 15·00
ANNIVERSARIES AND EVENTS: Nos. 1870, 1872, 1876, **MS**1877a, 20th death anniv of Picasso (artist); 1871, 1873, **MS**1877c/d, 450th death anniv of Copernicus (astronomer); 1874/5, **MS**1877b, "Polska '93" International Stamp Exhibition, Poznan.

1993. World Cup Football Championship, U.S.A. (1st issue). Multicoloured.
1878 50c. Type **498** 80 35
1879 80c. Pedro Troglio (Argentina) 90 40
1880 100c. Fernando Alvez (Uruguay) 1·00 40
1881 200c. Franco Baresi (Italy) 2·00 1·25
1882 250c. Gomez (Colombia) and Katanec (Yugoslavia) 2·00 1·75
1883 600c. Diego Maradona (Argentina) 3·50 3·50
1884 800c. Hasek (Czechoslovakia) and Wynalda (U.S.A.) 3·50 4·00
1885 1000c. Lothar Matthaeus (Germany) 4·25 4·75
MS1886 Two sheets, each 70 × 100 mm. (a) 1200c. Rabie Yassein (Egypt) and Ruud Gullit (Netherlands). (b) 1200c. Giuseppe Giannini (Italy) Set of 2 sheets 12·00 13·00
See also Nos. 2037/43.

499 Common Turkey

1993. Domestic Animals. Multicoloured.
1887 50c. Type **499** 60 25
1888 100c. Goats 80 40
1889 150c. Muscovy ducks 1·25 75
1890 200c. Donkeys 1·50 1·00
1891 250c. Red junglefowl cock 1·50 1·25
1892 300c. Pigs 1·60 1·40
1893 400c. Helmeted guineafowl 1·90 1·75
1894 600c. Dog 2·75 3·00
1895 800c. Red junglefowl hen 3·25 3·75
1896 1000c. Sheep 3·75 4·25
MS1897 Two sheets, each 133 × 106 mm. (a) 100c. As No. 1888; 250c. No. 1894; 350c. No. 1892; 500c. No. 1896. (b) 100c. No. 1893; 250c. As No. 1891; 350c. As No. 1895; 500c. Type **499** Set of 2 sheets 14·00 14·00

1993. Christmas. Religious Paintings. As T **221b** of Gambia. Black, yellow and red (Nos. 1898, 1900/1, 1905 and **MS**1906a) or multicoloured (others).
1898 50c. "Adoration of the Magi" (Durer) 60 20
1899 100c. "The Virgin and Child with St. John and an Angel" (Botticelli) 80 25
1900 150c. "Mary as Queen of Heaven" (Durer) 1·00 45
1901 200c. "Saint Anne" (Durer) 1·25 65
1902 250c. "The Madonna of the Magnificat" (Botticelli) 1·40 75
1903 400c. "The Madonna of the Goldfinch" (Botticelli) 2·25 2·50
1904 600c. "The Virgin and Child with the young St. John the Baptist" (Botticelli) 3·00 3·75
1905 1000c. "Adoration of the Shepherds" (Durer) 4·25 6·50
MS1906 Two sheets, each 102 × 128 mm. (a) 1000c. "Madonna in a Circle" (detail) (Dürer). (b) 1000c. "Mystic Nativity" (detail) (Botticelli) (horiz) Set of 2 sheets 9·00 11·00

500 Doll

501 Mickey Mouse in "Steamboat Willie", 1928

1994. Traditional Crafts. Multicoloured.
1907 50c. Type **500** 40 30
1908 50c. Pot with "head" lid 40 30
1909 200c. Bead necklace 1·00 1·00
1910 200c. Snake charmers (statuette) 1·00 1·00
1911 250c. Hoe 1·00 1·00
1912 250c. Scabbard 1·00 1·00
1913 600c. Pipe 2·25 2·75
1914 600c. Deer (carving) 2·25 2·75

1915 1000c. Mask 3·50 4·00
1916 1000c. Doll (different) 3·50 4·00
MS1917 Two sheets, each 95 × 128 mm. (a) 100c. As Type **500**; 250c. As No. 1909; 350c. As No. 1911; 500c. As No. 1913. (b) 100c. As No. 1908; 250c. As No. 1910; 350c. As No. 1912; 500c. As No. 1914 Set of 2 sheets 5·50 7·00

1994. "Hong Kong '94" International Stamp Exhibition (1st issue). As T **222a** of Gambia. Multicoloured.
1918 200c. Hong Kong 1986 50c. "Expo '86" stamp and tram 1·00 1·25
1919 200c. Ghana 1992 20c. Railways stamp and tram 1·00 1·25
Nos. 1918/19 were printed together, se-tenant, forming a complete design. See also Nos. 1920/25.

1994. "Hong Kong '94" International Stamp Exhibition (2nd issue). Imperial Palace Clocks. As T **222b** of Gambia. Multicoloured.
1920 100c. Windmill clock 1·10 1·10
1921 100c. Horse clock 1·10 1·10
1922 100c. Balloon clock 1·10 1·10
1923 100c. Zodiac clock 1·10 1·10
1924 100c. Shar-pei dog clock 1·10 1·10
1925 100c. Cat clock 1·10 1·10

1994. 65th Anniv (1993) of Mickey Mouse (Walt Disney cartoon character) (1993). Scenes from various cartoon films.
1926 50c. Type **501** 60 15
1927 100c. "The Band Concert", 1935 80 20
1928 150c. "Moose Hunters", 1937 1·10 45
1929 200c. "Brave Little Tailor", 1938 1·25 60
1930 250c. "Fantasia", 1940 1·40 80
1931 400c. "The Nifty Nineties", 1941 2·25 2·75
1932 600c. "Canine Caddy", 1941 2·75 3·25
1933 1000c. "Mickey's Christmas Carol", 1983 3·50 4·25
MS1934 Two sheets, each 127 × 102 mm. (a) 1200c. "Mickey's Elephant", 1936. (b) 1200c. "Mickey's Amateurs", 1937 Set of 2 sheets 7·50 9·00
No. 1929 is inscribed "TAYLOR" in error. The dates on Nos. 1927 and 1932 are incorrectly shown as "1937" and "1944".

501a Boy Hiker

1994. Easter. Hummel Figurines. Multicoloured.
1935 50c. Type **501a** 35 15
1936 100c. Girl with basket behind back 45 20
1937 150c. Boy with rabbits 65 35
1938 200c. Boy holding basket 75 50
1939 250c. Girl with chicks 80 70
1940 400c. Girl with lamb 1·75 2·00
1941 600c. Girl waving red handkerchief with lamb 2·00 2·25
1942 1000c. Girl with basket and posy 2·75 3·25
MS1943 Two sheets, each 93 × 126 mm. (a) 50c. As No. 1935; 150c. As No. 1942; 500c. As No. 1936; 1200c. As No. 1938. (b) 200c. As No. 1940; 300c. As No. 1939; 500c. As No. 1941; 1000c. As No. 1937 Set of 2 sheets 7·50 8·00

502 Diana Monkey with Young

1994. Wildlife. Multicoloured.
1944 50c. Type **502** 40 15
1945 100c. Bushbuck (horiz) 40 20
1946 150c. Spotted hyena (horiz) 55 35
1947 200c. Diana monkey on branch facing left 75 50
1948 500c. Diana monkey on branch facing right 1·25 1·50
1949 800c. Head of Diana monkey 1·75 2·00
1950 1000c. Aardvark (horiz) 2·00 2·50
MS1951 Two sheets, each 106 × 76 mm. (a) 2000c. Leopard. (b) 2000c. Waterbuck Set of 2 sheets 10·00 11·00

Designs of Nos. 1944 and 1947/9 include the W.W.F. Panda emblem.

503 Norwegian Forest Cat

1994. Cats. Multicoloured.
1952 200c. Type **503** 50 50
1953 200c. Blue longhair 50 50
1954 200c. Red self longhair 50 50
1955 200c. Black longhair 50 50
1956 200c. Chinchilla 50 50
1957 200c. Dilute calico longhair 50 50
1958 200c. Blue tabby and white longhair 50 50
1959 200c. Ruby Somali 50 50
1960 200c. Blue smoke longhair 50 50
1961 200c. Calico longhair 50 50
1962 200c. Brown tabby longhair 50 50
1963 200c. Balinese 50 50
1964 200c. Sorrel Abyssinian 50 50
1965 200c. Silver classic tabby 50 50
1966 200c. Chocolate-point Siamese 50 50
1967 200c. Brown tortie Burmese 50 50
1968 200c. Exotic shorthair 50 50
1969 200c. Havana brown 50 50
1970 200c. Devon rex 50 50
1971 200c. Black Manx 50 50
1972 200c. British blue shorthair 50 50
1973 200c. Calico American wirehair 50 50
1974 200c. Spotted oriental Siamese 50 50
1975 200c. Red classic tabby 50 50
MS1976 Two sheets, each 102 × 89 mm. (a) 2000c. Brown mackerel tabby Scottish fold. (b) 2000c. Seal-point colourpoint Set of 2 sheets 8·50 9·00
No. 1957 is inscribed "Dilut" in error.

504 Red-bellied Paradise Flycatcher

1994. Birds. Multicoloured.
1977 200c. Type **504** 60 60
1978 200c. Many-coloured bush shrike 60 60
1979 200c. Broad-tailed paradise whydah 60 60
1980 200c. White-crowned robin chat 60 60
1981 200c. Violet turaco ("Violet plantain-eater") 60 60
1982 200c. Village weaver 60 60
1983 200c. Red-crowned bishop 60 60
1984 200c. Common shoveler 60 60
1985 200c. Spur-winged goose 60 60
1986 200c. African crake 60 60
1987 200c. Purple swamphen ("King reed-hen") 60 60
1988 200c. White-crested tiger bittern 60 60
1989 200c. Oriole warbler ("Moho") 60 60
1990 200c. Superb sunbird 60 60
1991 200c. Blue-breasted kingfisher 60 60
1992 200c. African blue cuckoo shrike 60 60
1993 200c. Great blue turaco ("Blue plantain-eater") 60 60
1994 200c. Greater flamingo 60 60
1995 200c. African jacana ("Lily-trotter") 60 60
1996 200c. Black-crowned night heron 60 60
1997 200c. Black-winged stilt 60 60
1998 200c. White-spotted crake 60 60
1999 200c. African pygmy goose 60 60
2000 200c. African pitta 60 60
MS2001 Two sheets, each 113 × 83 mm. (a) 2000c. African spoonbill. (b) 2000c. Goliath heron Set of 2 sheets 9·00 10·00

505 Women at Stand-pipe

1994. 1st Anniv of Fourth Republic. Multicoloured.
2002 50c. Type **505** 25 15
2003 100c. Presenting certificate to farmers 35 20
2004 200c. Village electricity supply 50 35
2005 600c. Bridge 1·25 1·75
2006 800c. National Theatre 1·50 2·00
2007 1000c. Lighting perpetual flame 1·75 2·25

1994. 25th Anniv of First Manned Moon Landing. As T **326** of Antigua showing scientists. Mult.
2008 300c. Sigmund Jahn 1·00 1·00
2009 300c. Ulf Merbold 1·00 1·00
2010 300c. Hans Wilhelm Schegal 1·00 1·00
2011 300c. Ulrich Walter 1·00 1·00
2012 300c. Reinhard Furrer 1·00 1·00
2013 300c. Ernst Messerschmid 1·00 1·00
2014 300c. Mamoru Mohri 1·00 1·00
2015 300c. Klaus-Dietrich Flade 1·00 1·00
2016 300c. Chaiki Naito-Mukai 1·00 1·00
MS2017 130 × 118 mm. 2000c. Poster for "Frau im Mond" (film) by Fritz Lang 5·50 6·00

1994. Centenary of International Olympic Committee. Gold Medal Winners. As T **227b** of Gambia, but vert. Multicoloured.
2018 300c. Dieter Modenburg (Germany) (high jump), 1984 70 75
2019 400c. Ruth Fuchs (Germany) (javelin), 1972 and 1976 90 1·00
MS2020 77 × 106 mm. 1500c. Jans Weissflog (Germany) (ski jump), 1994 3·75 4·00

1994. 50th Anniv of D-Day. As T **331** of Antigua. Multicoloured.
2021 60c. H.M.S. "Roberts" (monitor) 1·50 60
2022 100c. H.M.S. "Warspite" (battleship) 1·75 1·10
2023 200c. U.S.S. "Augusta" (cruiser) 2·25 2·50
MS2024 107 × 76 mm. 1500c. U.S.S. "Nevada" (battleship) firing salvo 6·00 6·00

1994. "Philakorea '94" International Stamp Exn, Seoul. As T **227d** of Gambia. Mult.
2025 20c. Ch'unghak-dong village elder in traditional costume, (24½ × 38 mm) 15 15
2026 150c. Stone Pagoda, Punhwangsa (24½ × 38 mm) 40 40
2027 250c. Character with eggs 45 50
2028 250c. Character with pair of birds on house 45 50
2029 250c. Character with cock 45 50
2030 250c. Character with dragon and pagoda 45 50
2031 250c. Character with orange flowers 45 50
2032 250c. Character with parrot and pagoda 45 50
2033 250c. Character with plant 45 50
2034 250c. Character with fish 45 50
2035 300c. Traditional country house, Andong (24½ × 34 mm) 50 55
MS2036 100 × 70 mm. 1500c. Temple judges deliberating (42½ × 28½ mm) 4·00 4·50

506 Dennis Bergkamp (Netherlands)

1994. World Cup Football Championship, U.S.A. (2nd issue). Multicoloured.
2037 200c. Type **506** 60 70
2038 200c. Lothar Matthaus (Germany) 60 70
2039 200c. Giuseppe Signori (Italy) 60 70
2040 200c. Carlos Valderama (Colombia) 60 70
2041 200c. Jorge Campos (Mexico) 60 70
2042 200c. Tony Meola (U.S.A.) 60 70
MS2043 Two sheets, each 100 × 70 mm. (a) 1200c. Giants' Stadium, New Jersey (vert). (b) 1200c. Citrus Bowl, Orlando (vert) Set of 2 sheets 5·50 7·00

507 Common ("Crowned") Duiker

1994. Duikers (antelopes). Multicoloured.
2044 50c. Type **507** 30 15
2045 100c. Red-flanked duiker 40 25
2046 200c. Yellow-backed duiker 60 40
2047 400c. Ogilby's duiker 1·00 1·25
2048 600c. Bay duiker 1·25 1·75
2049 800c. Jentink's duiker 1·50 2·00
MS2050 Two sheets, each 106 × 76 mm. (a) 2000c. Red forest duiker. (b) 2000c. Black duiker Set of 2 sheets 8·00 9·00

1994. Christmas. Religious Paintings. As T **231a** of Gambia. Multicoloured.
2051 100c. "Madonna of the Annunciation" (Simone Martini) 60 15
2052 200c. "Madonna and Child" (Niccolo di Pietro Gerini) 90 20
2053 250c. "Virgin and Child on the Throne with Angels and Saints" (Raffaello Botticini) 1·10 60
2054 300c. "Madonna and Child with Saints" (Antonio Fiorentino) 1·40 1·10
2055 400c. "Adoration of the Magi" (Bartolo di Fredi) 1·50 1·50
2056 500c. "The Annunciation" (Cima da Congeliano) 1·75 2·00
2057 600c. "Virgin and Child with the Young St. John the Baptist" (workshop of Botticelli) 2·25 2·75
2058 1000c. "The Holy Family" (Giorgione) 2·75 3·75
MS2059 Two sheets, each 135 × 95 mm. (a) 2000c. "Adoration of the Kings" (detail showing Holy Family) (Giorgione). (b) 2000c. "Adoration of the Kings" (detail showing King and attendants) (Giorgione) Set of 2 sheets 8·50 9·00

508 Northern Region Dancer

510 Fertility Doll

509 Red Cross Stretcher-bearers

1994. Panafest '94 (2nd Pan-African Historical Theatre Festival). Multicoloured.
2060 50c. Type **508** 20 15
2061 100c. Traditional artefacts 35 25
2062 200c. Chief with courtiers 65 60
2063 400c. Woman in ceremonial costume 1·25 1·25
2064 600c. Cape Coast Castle 1·75 2·50
2065 800c. Clay figurines 2·25 3·25

1994. 75th Anniv of Red Cross. Multicoloured.
2066 50c. Type **509** 70 15
2067 200c. Worker with children 1·50 50
2068 600c. Workers erecting tents 2·50 3·50
MS2069 147 × 99 mm. Nos. 2066/7 and 1000c. As 600c. 4·25 4·75

1994. Fertility Dolls.
2070 **510** 50c. multicoloured 40 10
2071 – 100c. multicoloured 60 15
2072 – 150c. multicoloured 80 30
2073 – 200c. multicoloured 90 30
2074 – 400c. multicoloured 1·50 1·50
2075 – 600c. multicoloured 1·75 2·00
2076 – 800c. multicoloured 2·00 2·50
2077 – 1000c. multicoloured 2·25 2·75
MS2078 147 × 99 mm. Nos. 2071, 2074/5 and 250c. As 1000c. 4·50 5·00
DESIGNS: 100c. to 1000c. Different dolls.

511 Ghanaian Family

1994. International Year of the Family. Mult.
2079 50c. Type **511** 35 15
2080 100c. Teaching carpentry 55 15
2081 200c. Child care 90 25
2082 400c. Care for the elderly 1·40 1·40
2083 600c. Learning pottery 1·75 2·00
2084 1000c. Adult education students 2·25 2·75

512 Control Tower and Emblem

1995. 50th Anniv of I.C.A.O. Mult. (a) Inscr "50th Anniversary Of Ghana Civil Aviation Authority".
2085 100c. Type **512** . . . . . . 1·25
2086 400c. Communications equipment . . . . 2·50
2087 1000c. Airliner taking off . . 4·00
(b) Inscr "50th Anniversary Of The International Civil Aviation Organisation (I.C.A.O.)."
2088 100c. Type **512** 40 20
2089 400c. Communications equipment 90 90
2090 1000c. Airliner taking off . . 2·00 2·50

513 Pluto, Donald Duck and Chip n' Dale around Table

1995. 60th Anniv of Donald Duck. Walt Disney Cartoon Characters at Birthday Party. Mult.
2091 40c. Type **513** 25 15
2092 50c. Mickey Mouse and pup with banner 25 15
2093 60c. Daisy Duck with balloons 25 20
2094 100c. Goofy making cake 35 25
2095 150c. Goofy on roller blades delivering cake 45 40
2096 250c. Donald pinning donkey tail on Goofy . . 60 60
2097 400c. Ludwig von Drake singing to Pluto 90 90
2098 500c. Grandma Duck giving cake to puppies . . . . . 1·00 1·00
2099 1000c. Mickey and Minnie Mouse at piano . . . . . 1·75 2·00
2100 1500c. Pluto with bone and ball . . . . 2·50 3·25
MS2101 Two sheets. (a) 117×95 mm. 2000c. Donald blowing out birthday candles (vert). (b) 95×117 mm. 2000c. Donald wearing party hat (vert) Set of 2 sheets . . . . 9·00 9·00

514 Fort Appolonia, Beyin

1995. Forts and Castles of Ghana. Multicoloured.
2102 50c. Type **514** 30 10
2103 200c. Fort Patience, Apam 60 25
2104 250c. Fort Amsterdam, Kormantin 65 45
2105 300c. Fort St. Jago, Elmina 75 70
2106 400c. Fort William, Anomabo 90 90
2107 600c. Kumasi Fort . . . . 1·50 2·00
MS2108 Two sheets, each 102×72 mm. (a) 800c. Elmina Castle (vert). (b) 1000c. Fort St. Antonio, Axim Set of 2 sheets 4·00 4·50

515 Cochem Castle, Germany

1995. Castles of the World. Multicoloured.
2109 150c. Type **515** 40 30
2110 500c. Windsor Castle, England 70 70
2111 500c. Osaka Castle, Japan 70 70
2112 500c. Vaj Dahunyad Castle, Hungary 70 70
2113 500c. Karlstejn Castle, Czech Republic 70 70
2114 500c. Kronborg Castle, Denmark 70 70
2115 500c. Alcazar of Segovia, Spain 70 70
2116 500c. Chambourd Castle, France 70 70
2117 500c. Linderhof Castle, Germany 70 70
2118 500c. Red Fort, Delhi, India 70 70
2119 600c. Hohenzollern Castle, Germany 80 80
2120 800c. Uwajima Castle, Japan 1·00 1·00
2121 1000c. Hohenschwangau Castle, Germany . . . . 1·10 1·10
MS2122 Two sheets, each 102×72 mm. (a) 2500c. Neuschwanstein Castle, Germany. (b) 2500c. Himeji Castle, Japan Set of 2 sheets . . . . 9·00 9·00

516 European Pochard ("Eurasian Pochard")

1995. Ducks. Multicoloured.
2123 200c. Type **516** 80 35
2124 400c. African pygmy goose 90 90
2125 400c. Southern pochard . . 90 90
2126 400c. Cape teal 90 90
2127 400c. Ruddy shelduck . . . 90 90
2128 400c. Fulvous whistling duck 90 90
2129 400c. White-faced whistling duck 90 90
2130 400c. Ferruginous duck ("Ferruginous White-eye") 90 90
2131 400c. Hottentot teal . . . 90 90
2132 400c. African black duck . . 90 90
2133 400c. African yellow-bill ("Yellow-billed Duck") 90 90
2134 400c. Bahama pintail ("White-checked Pintail Duck") 90 90
2135 400c. Hartlaub's duck . . . 90 90
2136 500c. Maccoa duck . . . . 1·10 1·10
2137 800c. Cape shoveler . . . . 1·50 1·75
2138 1000c. Red-crested pochard 1·90 2·25
MS2139 Two sheets, each 104×74 mm. (a) 2500c. Roseate tern. (b) 2500c. Northern shoveler Set of 2 sheets . . . . . . 8·50 9·00
Nos. 2124/35 were printed together, se-tenant, forming a composite design.
No. 2128 is inscribed "Wistling" in error.

517 Cycling

518 "Cymothoe beckeri" (butterfly)

1995. Olympic Games, Atlanta (1996) (1st issue). Multicoloured.
2140 300c. Type **517** . . . . . . 1·00 1·00
2141 300c. Archery . . . . 1·00 1·00
2142 300c. Diving . . . . 1·00 1·00
2143 300c. Swimming . . . . . 1·00 1·00
2144 300c. Women's gymnastics 1·00 1·00
2145 300c. Fencing . . . . . . 1·00 1·00
2146 300c. Boxing . . . . . . 1·00 1·00
2147 300c. Men's gymnastics . . 1·00 1·00
2148 300c. Javelin . . . . . . 1·00 1·00
2149 300c. Tennis . . . . . . 1·00 1·00
2150 300c. Football . . . . . . 1·00 1·00
2151 300c. Equestrian . . . . . 1·00 1·00
2152 500c. Carl Lewis (U.S.A.) 1·10 1·10
2153 800c. Eric Liddell (Great Britain) . . . . . . 1·40 1·60
2154 900c. Jesse Owens (U.S.A.) 1·40 1·60
2155 1000c. Jim Thorpe (U.S.A.) 1·40 1·60
MS2156 Two sheets, each 70×100 mm. (a) 1200c. Pierre de Coubertin (founder of International Olympic Committee). (b) 1200c. John Akii Bua (Uganda) Set of 2 sheets 3·50 4·00
Nos. 2140/51 were printed together, se-tenant, forming a composite design.
See also Nos. 2334/55.

1995. Multicoloured.
2156c 300c. European goldfinch (vert) 10 10
2157 400c. Type **518** 10 10
2158 500c. "Graphium policenes" (butterfly) . . 10 10
2159 1000c. African long-tailed hawk (vert) 10 15
2159a 1100c. Kente cloth . . . 15 20
2160 2000c. Swordfish 25 30
2161 3000c. Guinean fingerfish 35 40
2162 5000c. Purple heron (vert) 60 65

519 Ghanaian Scouts

520 Trygve Lie (1946–52) and United Nations Building

1995. 18th World Scout Jamboree, Netherlands.
2163 **519** 400c. multicoloured . . . 90 1·00
2164 – 800c. multicoloured . . . 1·25 1·40
2165 – 1000c. multicoloured . . 1·25 1·40
MS2166 70×100 mm. 1200c. multicoloured . . . . 1·90 2·25
DESIGNS: 800c. to 1200c. Ghanaian scouts (different).

1995. 50th Anniv of End of Second World War in Europe. As T **237a** of Gambia. Multicoloured.
2167 400c. Winston Churchill . . 75 75
2168 400c. Gen. Dwight D. Eisenhower 75 75
2169 400c. Air Marshal Sir Arthur Tedder 75 75
2170 400c. Field-Marshal Sir Bernard Montgomery . . 75 75
2171 400c. Gen. Omar Bradley 75 75
2172 400c. Gen. Charles de Gaulle 75 75
2173 400c. French resistance fighters 75 75
2174 400c. Gen. George S. Patton 75 75
MS2175 104×74 mm. 1200c. "GIVE ME FIVE YEARS & YOU WILL NOT RECOGNISE GERMANY AGAIN" quote by Adolf Hitler in English and German (42×57 mm) 2·40 2·75

1995. 50th Anniv of United Nations. Secretary-Generals. Multicoloured.
2176 200c. Type **520** 30 40
2177 300c. Dag Hammarskjold (1953–61) 40 50
2178 400c. U. Thant (1961–71) 50 60
2179 500c. Kurt Waldheim (1972–81) 60 70
2180 600c. Javier Perez de Cuellar (1982–91) 70 90
2181 800c. Boutrous Boutrous-Ghali (1992) . . . . . 80 1·00
MS2182 104×74 mm. 1200c. U.N. flag (horiz) . . . . 1·90 2·50

521 Preserving Fish

1995. 50th Anniv of F.A.O. Multicoloured.
2183 200c. Type **521** 60 15
2184 300c. Fishermen with fish traps 75 40
2185 400c. Ox-drawn plough . . 85 80
2186 600c. Harvesting bananas 1·00 1·25
2187 800c. Planting saplings . . . 1·25 1·50
MS2188 100×70 mm. 2000c. Canoe and cattle . . . . 3·00 3·50

522 National Flag and Rotary Emblem

1995. 90th Anniv of Rotary International. Multicoloured.
2189 600c. Type **522** . . . . . . 1·00 1·25
MS2190 94×65 mm. 1200c. Ghanaian Rotary banner (vert) 1·90 2·25

1995. 95th Birthday of Queen Elizabeth the Queen Mother. As T **239a** of Gambia. Multicoloured.
2191 600c. brown, light brown and black . . . . . . 1·75 1·75
2192 600c. multicoloured . . . . 1·75 1·75
2193 600c. multicoloured . . . . 1·75 1·75
2194 600c. multicoloured . . . . 1·75 1·75
MS2195 102×127 mm. 2500c. multicoloured . . . . 4·75 4·25
DESIGNS: No. 2191, Queen Elizabeth the Queen Mother (pastel drawing); 2192, Wearing light blue hat and floral dress; 2193, At desk (oil painting); 2194, Wearing red hat and dress; **MS**2195, Wearing pale blue hat and jacket.

1995. 50th Anniv of End of Second World War in the Pacific. Medals. As T **229b** of Gambia. Mult.
2196 500c. Navy Cross and Purple Heart, U.S.A. . . 85 85
2197 500c. Air Force Cross and Distinguished Flying Cross, Great Britain . . . 85 85
2198 500c. Navy and Marine Corps Medal and Distinguished Service Cross, U.S.A. 85 85
2199 500c. Distinguished Service Medal and Distinguished Conduct Medal, Great Britain 85 85
2200 500c. Military Medal and Military Cross, Great Britain 85 85
2201 500c. Distinguished Service Cross and Distinguished Service Order, Great Britain 85 85
MS2202 108×76 mm. 1200c. Congressional Medal of Honor, U.S.A. . . . . 2·50 2·50

523 Seismosaurus

524 Arms of Otumfuo Opoku Ware II

1995. "Singapore '95" International Stamp Exhibition. Prehistoric Animals. Multicoloured.
2203 400c. Type **523** 65 65
2204 400c. Supersaurus 65 65
2205 400c. Ultrasaurus 65 65
2206 400c. Saurolophus 65 65
2207 400c. Lambeosaurus 65 65
2208 400c. Parasaurolophus . . . 65 65
2209 400c. Triceratops 65 65
2210 400c. Styracosaurus 65 65
2211 400c. Pachyrhinosaurus . . . 65 65
2212 400c. Peteinosaurus 65 65
2213 400c. Quetzalcoatlus 65 65
2214 400c. Eudimorphodon . . . 65 65
2215 400c. Allosaurus 65 65
2216 400c. Daspletosaurus . . . 65 65
2217 400c. Tarbosaurus bataar 65 65
2218 400c. Velociraptor mongoliensis 65 65
2219 400c. Herrerasaurus 65 65
2220 400c. Coelophysis 65 65
MS2221 Two sheets, each 106×76 mm. (a) 2500c. Tyrannosaurus rex (horiz). (b) 2500c. Albertosaurus (horiz) Set of 2 sheets . . . . 8·00 8·50
Nos. 2203/11 and 2212/20 respectively were printed together, se-tenant, forming composite designs.

1995. Silver Jubilee of Otumfuo Opoku Ware II (King of Ashanti). Multicoloured.
2222 50c. Type **524** 30 10
2223 100c. Silver casket 45 10
2224 200c. Golden stool 70 20
2225 400c. Busummuru sword bearer . . . . 1·10 75
2226 600c. Otumfuo Opoku Ware II . . . . 1·75 1·75
2227 800c. Otumfuo Opoku Ware II under umbrella . . 2·00 2·25
2228 1000c. Mponponsuo sword bearer . . . . 2·25 2·75

525 Nelson Mandela (1993 Peace)

1995. Centenary of Nobel Prize Trust Fund. Past Prize Winners. Multicoloured.
2229 400c. Type **525** 80 80
2230 400c. Albert Schweitzer (1952 Peace) 80 80
2231 400c. Wole Soyinka (1986 Literature) 80 80
2232 400c. Emil Fischer (1902 Chemistry) 80 80
2233 400c. Rudolf Mossbauer (1961 Physics) 80 80
2234 400c. Archbishop Desmond Tutu (1984 Peace) 80 80
2235 400c. Max Born (1954 Physics) 80 80
2236 400c. Max Planck (1918 Physics) 80 80
2237 400c. Hermann Hesse (1946 Literature) 80 80
MS2238 104×75 mm. 1200c. Paul Ehrlich (1908 Medicine) and medal . . . . 1·75 2·00

1995. Christmas. Religious Paintings. As T **245a** of Gambia. Multicoloured.
2239 50c. "The Child Jesus and the Young St. John" (Murillo) 25 10
2240 80c. "Rest on the Flight into Egypt" (Memling) 30 10

2241 300c. "Holy Family" (Van Dyck) 70 45
2242 600c. "Enthroned Madonna and Child" (Uccello) . . 1·10 1·40
2243 800c. "Madonna and Child" (Van Eyck) . . . . . . 1·25 1·75
2244 1000c. "Head of Christ" (Rembrandt) . . . . . . 1·40 2·00
MS2245 Two sheets, each 101 × 127 mm. (a) 2500c. "The Holy Family" (Pulzone). (b) 2500c. "Madonna and Child with Two Saints" (Montagna) Set of 2 sheets . . . . 7·75 8·00

526 Ernemann Camera (1903)

1995. Centenary of Cinema. Multicoloured.
2246 400c. Type **526** . . . . . . 1·00 1·00
2247 400c. Charlie Chaplin . . . 1·00 1·00
2248 400c. Rudolph Valentino . . 1·00 1·00
2249 400c. Will Rogers . . . . . 1·00 1·00
2250 400c. Greta Garbo . . . . 1·00 1·00
2251 400c. Jackie Cooper . . . . 1·00 1·00
2252 400c. Bette Davis . . . . . 1·00 1·00
2253 400c. John Barrymore . . . 1·00 1·00
2254 400c. Shirley Temple . . . . 1·00 1·00
MS2255 106 × 76 mm. 2500c. Laurel and Hardy . . . . 5·50 5·50
No. 2246 is inscribed "ERNMANN" in error.

527 John Lennon

1995. John Lennon (musician) Commemoration. Multicoloured.
2256 400c. Type **527** . . . . . . 1·10 1·10
2257 400c. Full face portrait (green background) . . . 1·10 1·10
2258 400c. With guitar . . . . . 1·10 1·10
2259 400c. Wearing glasses and caftan . . . . 1·10 1·10
2260 400c. Full face portrait (red background) . . . . . . 1·10 1·10
2261 400c. Wearing headphones 1·10 1·10
2262 400c. Wearing purple T-shirt 1·10 1·10
2263 400c. Full face portrait (blue background) . . . . . . 1·10 1·10
2264 400c. Facing right . . . . . 1·10 1·10
2265 400c. As No. 2263, but smaller (24 × 39 mm) . . 1·10 1·10
MS2266 102 × 73 mm. 2000c. John Lennon playing guitar . . . . 6·00 6·50

528 Louis Pasteur in Laboratory

529 Rat Musicians

1995. Death Centenary of Louis Pasteur (scientist). Multicoloured.
2267 600c. Type **528** . . . . . . 1·60 1·60
2268 600c. Pasteur injecting rabid dog . . . . 1·60 1·60
2269 600c. Pasteur and microscope slide . . . . 1·60 1·60
2270 600c. Laboratory equipment and birds . . . . 1·60 1·60
2271 600c. Yeast vats . . . . . 1·60 1·60

1996. Chinese New Year ("Year of the Rat").
2272 **529** 250c. brown, violet and red 60 60
2273 – 250c. brown, violet and red 60 60
2274 – 250c. brown, violet and red 60 60
2275 – 250c. brown, violet and red 60 60
MS2276 142 × 60 mm. As Nos. 2272/5, but face values and "GHANA" in red instead of white 2·00 2·00
MS2277 106 × 75 mm. 1000c. red and orange . . . . 2·00 2·00
DESIGNS:—VERT: No. 2273, Rats carrying banners; 2274, Rats carrying palanquin; 2275, Rats with offerings. HORIZ: No. **MS**2277, Four rats carrying palanquin.

1996. 125th Anniv of Metropolitan Museum of Art, New York. As T **251** of Gambia. Multicoloured.
2278 400c. "Portrait of a Man" (Van der Goes) 80 80
2279 400c. "Paradise" (detail) (Di Paolo) 80 80
2280 400c. "Portrait of a Young Man" (Messina) 80 80
2281 400c. "Tommaso Portinari" (detail) (Memling) 80 80
2282 400c. "Maria Portinari" (detail) (Memling) 80 80
2283 400c. "Portrait of a Lady" (detail) (Ghirlandaio) . . 80 80
2284 400c. "St. Christopher and the Infant Christ" (Ghirlandaio) 80 80
2285 400c. "Francesco D'Este" (detail) (Weyden) 80 80
2286 400c. "The Interrupted Sleep" (Boucher) 80 80
2287 400c. "Diana and Cupid" (detail) (Batoni) 80 80
2288 400c. "Boy blowing Bubbles" (Chardin) . . . 80 80
2289 400c. "Ancient Rome" (detail) (Pannini) 80 80
2290 400c. "Modern Rome" (detail) (Pannini) 80 80
2291 400c. "The Calmady Children" (Lawrence) . . 80 80
2292 400c. "The Triumph of Marius" (detail) (Tiepolo) 80 80
2293 400c. "Garden at Vaucression" (detail) (Vuillard) 80 80
MS2294 Two sheets, each 95 × 70 mm. (a) 2500c. "The Epiphany" (detail) (Giotto) (80 × 56 mm). (b) 2500c. "The Calling of Matthew" (detail) (Hemessen) (80 × 56 mm) Set of 2 sheets . . . . 11·00 12·00

530 Toco Toucan

1996. Wildlife of the Rainforest. Multicoloured.
2295 400c. Type **530** 80 80
2296 400c. Two-toed sloth . . . 80 80
2297 400c. Orang-utan 80 80
2298 400c. Crested hawk eagle . . 80 80
2299 400c. Tiger 80 80
2300 400c. Painted stork 80 80
2301 400c. Green-winged macaw 80 80
2302 400c. Common squirrel-monkey 80 80
2303 400c. Crab-eating macaque 80 80
2304 400c. "Cithaerias menander" and "Ithomiidae" (butterflies) 80 80
2305 400c. "Coryptophanes cristatus" and "Gekkonidae" (lizards) 80 80
2306 400c. Boa constrictor . . . 80 80
2307 400c. Hoatzin 80 80
2308 400c. Western tarsier . . . 80 80
2309 400c. Golden Lion tamarin 80 80
2310 400c. "Pteropus gouldii" (bat) 80 80
2311 400c. Guianan cock of the rock 80 80
2312 400c. Resplendent quetzal 80 80
2313 400c. Tree frog and poison-arrow frog 80 80
2314 400c. Ring-tailed lemur . . 80 80
2315 400c. Iguana 80 80
2316 400c. "Heliconius burneyi" (butterfly) 80 80
2317 400c. Vervain hummingbird 80 80
2318 400c. Verreaux's sifaka . . . 80 80
MS2319 Two sheets, each 74 × 104 mm. (a) 3000c. Raggiana bird of paradise. (b) 3000c. King vulture Set of 2 sheets . . . . 11·00 11·00

531 Pagoda of Kaiyan Si Temple, Fujian

532 Serafim Todorow (Bulgaria)

1996. "CHINA '96" 9th Asian International Stamp Exhibition. Pagodas. Multicoloured.
2320 400c. Type **531** . . . . . . 1·00 1·00
2321 400c. Kaiyuan Si Temple, Hebei . . . . 1·00 1·00
2322 400c. Fogong Si Temple, Shanxi . . . . 1·00 1·00
2323 400c. Xiangshan, Beijing . . 1·00 1·00
MS2324 Two sheets. (a) 100 × 70 mm. 1000c. Baima Si Temple, Henan. (b) 143 × 98 mm. 1000c. Gold statue (38 × 50 mm) Set of 2 sheets . . . . 4·00 4·00

1996. 70th Birthday of Queen Elizabeth II. As T **255a** of Gambia showing different photographs. Multicoloured.
2325 1000c. Queen Elizabeth II 2·00 2·00
2326 1000c. In blue hat and coat 2·00 2·00
2327 1000c. Wearing straw hat and carrying bouquet . . 2·00 2·00
MS2328 125 × 103 mm. 2500c. In open carriage at Trooping the Colour (horiz) . . . . 4·50 4·50

1996. 50th Anniv of International Amateur Boxing Association. Multicoloured.
2329 300c. Type **532** 65 55
2330 400c. Oscar de la Hoya (U.S.A.) 80 70
2331 800c. Ariel Hernandez (Cuba) . . . . 1·50 1·75
2332 1500c. Arnoldo Mesa (Cuba) . . . . 2·50 3·00
MS2333 80 × 110 mm. 3000c. Tadahiro Sasaki (Japan) . . . 4·75 5·50

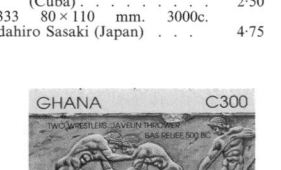

533 Ancient Greek Wrestlers

1996. Olympic Games, Atlanta (2nd issue). Previous Medal Winners. Multicoloured.
2334 300c. Type **533** 75 55
2335 400c. Aileen Riggin, 1920 (U.S.A.) 85 85
2336 400c. Pat McCormick, 1952 (U.S.A.) 85 85
2337 400c. Dawn Fraser, 1956 (Australia) 85 85
2338 400c. Chris von Saltza, 1960 (U.S.A.) 85 85
2339 400c. Anita Lonsbrough, 1960 (Great Britain) . . . 85 85
2340 400c. Debbie Meyer, 1968 (U.S.A.) 85 85
2341 400c. Shane Gould, 1972 (Australia) 85 85
2342 400c. Petra Thuemer, 1976 (Germany) 85 85
2343 400c. Marjorie Gestring, 1936 (U.S.A.) 85 85
2344 400c. Abedi Pele (Ghana) (vert) 85 85
2345 400c. Quico Navarez (Spain) (vert) 85 85
2346 400c. Heino Hanson (Denmark) (vert) 85 85
2347 400c. Mostafa Ismail (Egypt) (vert) 85 85
2348 400c. Anthony Yeboah (Ghana) (vert) 85 85
2349 400c. Jurgen Klinsmann (Germany) (vert) 85 85
2350 400c. Cobi Jones (U.S.A.) (vert) 85 85
2351 400c. Franco Baresi (Italy) (vert) 85 85
2352 400c. Igor Dobrovolski (Russia) (vert) 85 85
2353 500c. Wilma Rudolph (U.S.A.) (track and field, 1960) . . . . 1·00 1·00
2354 600c. Olympic Stadium, 1960, and Roman landmarks . . . . 1·25 1·40
2355 800c. Ladies Kayak pairs, 1960 (Soviet Union) . . . 1·50 1·75
MS2356 Two sheets, each 110 × 80 mm. (a) 2000c. Tracy Caulkins (U.S.A.) (200m freestyle, 1984). (b) 2000c. Kornelia Ender (Germany) (200m freestyle, 1976) Set of 2 sheets . . . . 8·50 8·50
Nos. 2335/43 (swimming and diving), and 2344/52 (football) respectively were printed together, se-tenant, with the backgrounds forming composite designs.

534 E. W. Agyare (35 years service with Ghana Broadcasting)

534a St. Stephen's Gate and "Jasminum mesyni"

1996. Local Broadcasting.
2357 **534** 100c. multicoloured . . . 40 40

1996. 50th Anniv of U.N.I.C.E.F. As T **258a** of Gambia. Multicoloured.
2358 400c. Ghanaian child . . . 35 35
2359 500c. Mother and child . . 45 45
2360 600c. Mother and child drinking 55 65
MS2361 74 × 104 mm. 1000c. Young child . . . . 1·10 1·25

1996. 3000th Anniv of Jerusalem. Multicoloured.
2362 400c. Type **534a** 60 40
2363 600c. The Citadel, Tower of David and "Nerium oleander" 80 80
2364 800c. Chapel of the Ascension and "Romulea bulbocodium" . . . . . 1·00 1·10
MS2365 65 × 80 mm. 2000c. Russian Orthodox Church of St. Mary Magdalene (48 × 30 mm) . . . 2·75 3·00

1996. Centenary of Radio. Entertainers. As T **259a** of Gambia. Multicoloured.
2366 500c. Frank Sinatra 45 35
2367 600c. Judy Garland 60 70
2368 600c. Bing Crosby 60 70
2369 800c. Martin and Lewis . . 80 90
MS2370 81 × 110 mm. 2000c. Edgar Bergen and Charlie McCarthy 2·25 2·75

1996. 50th Anniv of U.N.E.S.C.O. As T **273a** of Gambia. Multicoloured.
2371 400c. The Citadel, Haiti (vert) 50 25
2372 800c. Ait-Ben-Hadou (fortified village), Morocco (vert) . . . . . 90 1·00
2373 1000c. Spissky Hrad, Slovakia . . . . 1·25 1·40
MS2374 106 × 76mm. 2000c. Cape Coast Castle, Ghana . . . . . 2·25 2·75

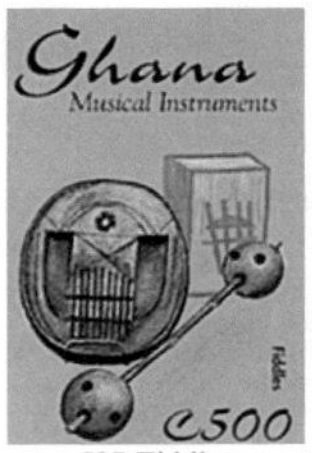

535 Fiddles

1996. Musical Insruments. Multicoloured.
2375 500c. Type **535** 75 75
2376 500c. Proverbial drum . . . 75 75
2377 500c. Double clapless bell and castanet 75 75
2378 500c. Gourd rattle 75 75
2379 500c. Horns 75 75

536 Ariel, Flounder and Sebastian

1996. Disney Friends. Disney Cartoon Characters. Multicoloured.
2380 60c. Type **536** 30 30
2381 60c. Pinocchio and Jiminy Cricket 30 30
2382 60c. Cogsworth and Lumiere 30 30
2383 60c. Copper and Tod . . . 30 30
2384 60c. Pocahontas, Meeko and Flit 30 30
2385 60c. Bambi, Flower and Thumper 30 30
2386 150c. As No. 2381 . . . . 50 50
2387 200c. Type **536** 50 50
2388 200c. As No. 2383 . . . . 50 50
2389 300c. As No. 2385 . . . . 60 60
2390 350c. As No. 2382 . . . . 60 60
2391 450c. As No. 2384 . . . . 65 65
2392 600c. Aladdin and Abu . . 70 70

2393 700c. Penny and Rufus . . 75 75
2394 800c. Mowgli and Baloo . . 80 80
MS2395 Two sheets. (a) 98 × 124 mm. 3000c. Winnie the Pooh (vert). (b) 133 × 108 mm. 3000c. Simba and Timon Set of 2 sheets . . . . 6·00 6·50

1996. 20th Anniv of Rocky (film). Sheet 143 × 182 mm, containing vert design as T **266** of Gambia. Multicoloured.
MS2396 2000c. × 3 Sylvester Stallone in "Rocky II" . . . . 5·50 6·00

537 Herd Boy and Ox

1997. Chinese New Year ("Year of the Ox"). "The Herd Boy and Weaver". Each brown, silver and black.
2397 500c. Type **537** 70 70
2398 500c. Ox and weaver in lake 70 70
2399 500c. Weaver at work . . . 70 70
2400 500c. Herd boy with dying Ox 70 70
2401 500c. Weaver flying out of window 70 70
2402 500c. Herd boy carrying children 70 70
2403 500c. Family separated by "river" 70 70
2404 500c. Petitioning the emperor 70 70
2405 500c. Family reunited . . . 70 70

538 The Tomb of Dr. Hideyo Noguchi

539 Dipo Hairstyle

1997. 120th Birth Anniv of Dr. Hideyo Noguchi (bacteriologist). Multicoloured.
2406 1000c. Type **538** . . . . . 1·25 1·40
2407 1000c. Dr. Hideyo Noguchi 1·25 1·40
2408 1000c. Birthplace of Dr. Noguchi at Sanjogarta . . . . . . 1·25 1·40
2409 1000c. Noguchi Institute, Legon . . . . 1·25 1·40
2410 1000c. Noguchi Gardens, Accra . . . . 1·25 1·40
MS2411 Two sheets, each 67 × 97 mm. (a) 3000c. Dr. Noguchi in his laboratory. (b) 3000c. Statue of Dr. Noguchi Set of 2 sheets . . . . 6·00 7·00

1997. Ghanaian Women's Hairstyle. Multicoloured.
2412 1000c. Type **539** 75 75
2413 1000c. Oduku with flowers 75 75
2414 1000c. Dansinkran 75 75
2415 1000c. Mbobom 75 75
2416 1000c. Oduku with hair pins 75 75
2417 1000c. African corn row . . . 75 75
2418 1000c. Chinese raster . . . 75 75
2419 1000c. Chinese raster with top knot 75 75
2420 1000c. Corn row 75 75
2421 1000c. Mbakaa 75 75

540 Independence Anniversary Emblem

1997. 40th Anniv of Independence. Multicoloured.
2422 200c. Type **540** 35 25
2423 200c. President J. J. Rawlings (vert) . . . . . 1·75 1·50
2424 550c. Dr. Kwane Nkrumah (first President) (vert) . . 75 80

2425 800c. Children in class . . . 1·25 1·50
2426 1100c. Akosombo Dam . . 1·75 2·00
MS2427 Two sheets. (a) 70 × 100 mm. 2000c. Dr. Nkrumah proclaiming independence (vert). (b) 101 × 141 mm. 3000c. United Nations Secretary-General Kofi Annan (37 × 50 mm) Set of 2 sheets . . . . 5·50 6·50
No. 2425 is inscribed "Acheivement" in error.

1997. 10th Anniv of Chernobyl Nuclear Disaster. As T **276b** of Gambia. Multicoloured.
2428 800c. Child's face and U.N.E.S.C.O. emblem . . 1·25 1·40
2429 1000c. As No. 2428, but inscribed "CHABAD'S CHILDREN OF CHERNOBYL" at foot 1·40 1·60

541 Deng Xiaoping

1997. Deng Xiaoping (Chinese statesman) Commemoration. Different portraits. Multicoloured.
2430 300c. Type **541** 45 30
2431 500c. Looking thoughtful . . 60 55
2432 600c. Wearing glasses . . . 70 70
2433 600c. Delivering speech . . 70 70
2434 800c. As No. 2432 . . . . 90 1·00
2435 800c. As No. 2433 . . . . 90 1·00
2436 1000c. Type **541** . . . . . 1·10 1·25
2437 1000c. As No. 2431 . . . . 1·10 1·25
MS2438 Two sheets, each 101 × 70 mm. (a) 3000c. Deng Xiaoping making speech (47 × 34 mm). (b) 4000c. Deng Xiaoping with hand raised (47 × 34 mm) Set of 2 sheets . . 6·00 7·00

1997. 50th Death Anniv of Paul Harris (founder of Rotary International). As T **276c** of Gambia. Multicoloured.
2439 2000c. Paul Harris and Egyptian patient receiving polio vaccination . . . . 2·00 2·50
MS2440 78 × 107 mm. 3000c. Paul Harris with Rotary and PolioPlus emblems . . . . 2·25 2·75

1997. Golden Wedding of Queen Elizabeth and Prince Philip. As T **276d** of Gambia. Multicoloured.
2441 800c. Queen Elizabeth II . . 90 90
2442 800c. Royal coat of arms . . 90 90
2443 800c. Queen Elizabeth and Prince Philip waving . . . 90 90
2444 800c. Queen Elizabeth and Prince Philip on official visit 90 90
2445 800c. Queen in Irish State Coach 90 90
2446 800c. Prince Philip in 1947 90 90
MS2447 100 × 71 mm. 3000c. Princess Elizabeth in 1947 . . 2·25 2·50

1997. "Pacific '97" International Stamp Exhibition, San Francisco. Death Centenary of Heinrich von Stephan (founder of the U.P.U.). As T **276e** of Gambia.
2448 1000c. blue . . . . 1·00 1·10
2449 1000c. brown . . . . 1·00 1·10
2450 1000c. red . . . . 1·00 1·10
MS2451 82 × 119 mm. 3000c. green 2·50 3·00
DESIGNS: No. 2448, Early motor car; 2449, Von Stephan and Mercury; 2450, Blanchard's balloon flight, 1784; **MS**2451, African messenger.

541a "Nihonbashi Bridge and Edobashi Bridge"

542a *"Amorphophallus flavovirens"*

1997. Birth Bicentenary of Hiroshige (Japanese painter). "One Hundred Famous Views of Edo". Multicoloured.
2452 600c. Type **541a** 70 70
2453 600c. "View of Nihonbashi Tori 1-chome" 70 70
2454 600c. "Open Garden at Fukagawa Hachiman Shrine" 70 70
2455 600c. "Inari Bridge and Minato Shrine, Teppozu" 70 70

2456 600c. "Bamboo Yards, Kyobashi Bridge" 70 70
2457 600c. "Hall of Thirty-Three Bays, Fukagawa" 70 70
MS2458 Two sheets, each 102 × 127 mm. (a) 3000c. "Sumiyoshi Festival, Tsukudajima". (b) 3000c. "Teppozu and Tsukjii Honganji Temple" Set of 2 sheets . . . 5·00 6·00

1997.
2458c 200c. Type **542a** 10 10
2458d 550c. Atumpan drums . . 10 10
2458e 800c. *Cyrestis camillus* (butterfly) 10 15

542 Jackie Gleason

1997. Famous Comedians. Multicoloured.
2459 600c. Type **542** 75 75
2460 600c. Danny Kaye 75 75
2461 600c. John Cleese 75 75
2462 600c. Lucille Ball 75 75
2463 600c. Jerry Lewis 75 75
2464 600c. Sidney James 75 75
2465 600c. Louis Defuenes . . . 75 75
2466 600c. Mae West 75 75
2467 600c. Bob Hope 75 75
MS2468 Two sheets. (a) 83 × 113 mm. 3000c. Groucho Marx. (b) 76 × 106 mm. 2000c. Professor Ajax Bukana in front of curtain; 2000c. Professor Ajax Bukana (different) (both 28 × 42 mm) Set of 2 sheets . . 4·50 5·00

543 "Gelerina calyptrata"

545 Ghanaian Players holding Trophy

544 African Pygmy Angelfish

1997. Fungi of the World. Multicoloured.
2469 200c. Type **543** 30 30
2470 300c. "Lepiota ignivolvata" 40 40
2471 400c. "Omphalotus olearius" 50 50
2472 550c. "Amanita phalloides" 60 60
2473 600c. "Entoloma conferendum" 60 60
2474 800c. "Entoloma nitidum" 70 70
2475 800c. "Coprinus picaceus" 70 70
2476 800c. "Stropharia aurantiaca" 70 70
2477 800c. "Cortinarius splendens" 70 70
2478 800c. "Gomphidius roseus" 70 70
2479 800c. "Russula sardonia" 70 70
2480 800c. "Geastrum schmidelia" 70 70
MS2481 Two sheets, each 73 × 103 mm. (a) 3000c. "Craterellus cornucopioides". (b) 3000c. "Mycena crocata" Set of 2 sheets . . . . 4·75 5·00

1997. World Football Championship, France (1998). As T **283a** of Gambia. Multicoloured.
2482 200c. Azteca Stadium, Mexico 35 30
2483 300c. The Rose Bowl, U.S.A. 45 40
2484 400c. Stadio Giuseppe Meazza, Italy 60 50
2485 500c. Olympiastadion, Germany 65 55
2486 600c. Patrick Kluivert, Netherlands 70 70
2487 600c. Roy Keane, Republic of Ireland 70 70
2488 600c. Abedi Ayew Pele, Ghana 70 70
2489 600c. Peter Schmeichel, Denmark 70 70
2490 600c. Roberto di Matteo, Italy 70 70
2491 600c. Bebeto, Brazil 70 70

2492 600c. Steve McManaman, England 70 70
2493 600c. George Oppon Weah, Liberia 70 70
2494 1000c. Maracana Stadium, Brazil . . . . 1·10 1·25
2495 2000c. Bernabeu Stadium, Spain . . . . 1·75 2·00
MS2496 Two sheets. (a) 127 × 102 mm. 3000c. David Seaman, England. (b) 102 × 127 mm. 3000c. Juninho, Brazil Set of 2 sheets . . . . . 5·50 6·00

1997. Marine Life. Multicoloured.
2497 400c. Type **544** 50 50
2498 500c. Violet-crested turaco . 55 55
2499 500c. Pied avocet 55 55
2500 500c. Bottle-nosed dolphin 55 55
2501 500c. Bottle-nosed dolphin and long-toed lapwing . . 55 55
2502 500c. Longfinned spadefish 55 55
2503 500c. Imperial angelfish and manta 55 55
2504 500c. Racoon butterflyfish and African pompano . . 55 55
2505 500c. Silvertip shark 55 55
2506 500c. Longfin banner fish 55 55
2507 500c. Longfin banner fish and manta 55 55
2508 500c. Rust parrotfish . . . 55 55
2509 500c. Coral trout 55 55
2510 600c. Angelfish 60 60
2511 800c. Broomtail wrasse . . 70 75
2512 1000c. Indian butterflyfish 85 95
MS2513 Two sheets, each 106 × 76 mm. (a) 3000c. King angelfish. (b) 3000c. Crown butterflyfish Set of 2 sheets . . 5·50 6·00
Nos. 2498/2509 were printed together, se-tenant, with the backgrounds forming a composite design.

1997. J.V.C. Under-17 World Soccer Champions (1995). Multicoloured.
2514 200c.+50c. Type **545** 40 40
2515 550c.+50c. Ghana football team (horiz) 75 75
2516 800c.+50c. Abu Iddrisu . . 90 90
2517 1000c.+50c. Emmanuel Bentil (captain) . . . . . 1·10 1·25
2518 1500c.+50c. Basiru Gambo 1·60 1·75

546 "Eurychone rothschildiana"

547 Eurasian Goldfinch

1997. Flowers of the World. Multicoloured.
2519 200c. Type **546** 40 30
2520 550c. "Bulbophyllum lepidum" 70 60
2521 800c. "Ansellia africana" . . 80 80
2522 800c. "Strophanthus preusii" (vert) 80 80
2523 800c. "Ancistrochilus rothschildlanus" (vert) . . 80 80
2524 800c. "Mussaendra arcuata" (vert) 80 80
2525 800c. "Microcoelia guyoniane" (vert) 80 80
2526 800c. "Gloriosa simplex" (vert) 80 80
2527 800c. "Brachycorythis kalbreyeri" (vert) 80 80
2528 800c. "Aframomum sceptrum" (vert) 80 80
2529 800c. "Thunbergia alata" (vert) 80 80
2530 800c. "Clerodendrum thomsoniae" (vert) . . . 80 80
2531 1100c. "Combbretum grandiflorum" . . . . . 1·25 1·50
MS2532 Two sheets, each 82 × 77 mm. (a) 3000c. "Kigelia africana" (vert). (b) 3000c. "Spathodea campanulata" (vert) Set of 2 sheets . . . . 5·50 5·50
Nos. 2522/30 were printed together, se-tenant, with the backgrounds forming a composite design.

1997. Birds of Africa. Multicoloured.
2533 200c. Type **547** 40 30
2534 300c. Cape puff-back flycatcher ("Cape Batis") 55 40
2535 400c. Double-toothed barbet ("Bearded Barbet") . . . 65 50
2536 500c. African white-necked raven ("White-necked Raven") 70 60
2537 600c. Purple grenadier . . . 80 75
2538 800c. Black bustard 80 80
2539 800c. Northern lapwing . . 80 80
2540 800c. Lichtenstein's sandgrouse ("Sandgrouse") 80 80
2541 800c. Red-crested turaco . . 80 80
2542 800c. White-browed coucal 80 80
2543 800c. Lilac-breasted roller 80 80

2544 800c. Golden pipit 80 80
2545 800c. Burchell's gonolek ("Crimson-breasted Gonolek") 80 80
2546 800c. Blackcap 80 80
2547 1000c. Zebra waxbill . . . . 1·10 1·40
MS2548 Two sheets, each 106 × 75 mm. (a) 3000c. Shaft-tailed whydah. (b) 3000c. Yellow-tufted malachite sunbird Set of 2 sheets . . . . 6·00 6·00

548 Havana Cat

1997. Cats and Dogs. Multicoloured.
2549 20c. Type **548** 25 25
2550 50c. Singapura cat 25 25
2551 80c. Papillon 30 30
2552 100c. Sphinx cat 30 30
2553 150c. British white cat . . . 30 30
2554 200c. Bulldog 30 30
2555 300c. Snowshoe cat 40 40
2556 400c. Shetland sheepdog . . 50 50
2557 500c. Schnauzer 55 55
2558 600c. Persian cat 60 60
2559 800c. Shih tzu 70 70
2560 1000c. Russian wolfhound 90 90
2561 1000c. Birman cat 90 90
2562 1000c. Basset hound 90 90
2563 1000c. Silver tabby cat . . . 90 90
2564 1000c. Afghan 90 90
2565 1000c. Burmilla cat 90 90
2566 1000c. Abyssinian cat . . . 90 90
2567 1000c. Border terrier 90 90
2568 1000c. Scottish fold cat . . 90 90
2569 1000c. Boston terrier . . . 90 90
2570 1000c. Oriental cat 90 90
2571 1000c. Keeshond 90 90
2572 2000c. Chow Chow . . . . 1·60 1·75
MS2573 Two sheets, each 73 × 100 mm. (a) 3000c. Alaskan malamute. (b) 3000c. Ragdoll cat Set of 2 sheets . . . . 6·50 6·50

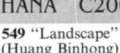

549 "Landscape" (Huang Binhong)

550 Diana, Princess of Wales

1997. Return of Hong Kong to China.
2574 **549** 200c. multicoloured . . . 30 30
2575 – 300c. multicoloured . . . 35 35
2576 – 400c. multicoloured . . . 40 40
2577 – 500c. multicoloured . . . 50 50
2578 – 600c. multicoloured . . . 60 60
2579 – 800c. multicoloured . . . 70 70
2580 – 1000c. multicoloured . . 90 95
2581 – 2000c. multicoloured . . 1·60 1·75
MS2582 138 × 105 mm. (a) 2000c. multicoloured (farm). (b) 2000c. multicoloured (mountains) (each 50 × 37 mm). P 14 × 13½ . . . 2·50 2·75
MS2583 150 × 125 mm. (a) 1000c. × 2 multicoloured (Lin Tse-Hue). (b) 1000c. × 2 multicoloured (Gwen Tian-Pei) (each 63 × 31 mm) . . . . 2·50 2·75
DESIGNS: Nos. 2575/81 and **MS**2582, Landscape paintings by Huang Binhong; **MS**2583, Historical scenes.

1997. Christmas. Paintings. As T **284a** of Gambia. Multicoloured.
2584 200c. "Cupid" (Botticelli) 25 10
2585 550c. "Zephyr and Chloris" (Botticelli) 50 25
2586 800c. "Triumphant Cupid" (Caravaggio) 75 65
2587 1100c. "The Seven Works of Mercy" (Caravaggio) . . 1·25 1·40
2588 1500c. "The Toilet of Venus" (Diego Velazquez) 1·40 1·60
2589 2000c. "Freeing of St. Peter" (Raphael) . . . 1·60 1·75
MS2590 Two sheets. (a) 95 × 105 mm. 5000c. "The Cavalcanti Annunciation" (Donatello). (b) 105 × 95 mm. 5000c. Ancient Egyptian painting of Isis and Nephthys Set of 2 sheets . . . . 8·00 8·50

1997. Diana, Princess of Wales Commemoration. Multicoloured (except Nos. 2591, 2596, 2602).
2591 1200c. Type **550** (red) . . . 80 90
2592 1200c. Wearing blue suit and holding flowers . . . 80 90
2593 1200c. Looking right . . . 80 90
2594 1200c. Sitting crossed-legged 80 90
2595 1200c. With Prince William 80 90
2596 1200c. Wearing spotted scarf (blue and black) 80 90
2597 1200c. Wearing pink shirt 80 90
2598 1200c. Wearing red dress . . 80 90
2599 1200c. Carrying bouquet . . 80 90
2600 1200c. Wearing sunglasses 80 90
2601 1200c. With children 80 90
2602 1200c. Wearing hat (brown and black) 80 90
MS2603 Two sheets. (a) 100 × 70 mm. 3000c. Diana, Princess of Wales. (b) 70 × 100 mm. 3000c. Diana, Princess of Wales (violet and black) Set of 2 sheets . . . . . 5·50 6·00

551 Horse

1998. Animals of the Chinese Lunar Calendar. Multicoloured.
2604 400c. Type **551** 10 10
2605 400c. Monkey 10 10
2606 400c. Ram 10 10
2607 400c. Cock 10 10
2608 400c. Dog 10 10
2609 400c. Ox 10 10
2610 400c. Rabbit 10 10
2611 400c. Pig 10 10
2612 400c. Snake 10 10
2613 400c. Dragon 10 10
2614 400c. Tiger 10 10
2615 400c. Rat 10 10

552 Mortie and Ferdie (January)

554 Maya Angelou

553 Union Pacific SD60M diesel Locomotive No. 6331, U.S.A.

1998. A Year in the Life of Mickey Mouse and Friends. Walt Disney cartoon characters. Multicoloured.
2616 1000c. Type **552** . . . . . 1·40 1·40
2617 1000c. Minnie on Valentine's Day (February) . . . . 1·40 1·40
2618 1000c. Goofy with kite (March) . . . . 1·40 1·40
2619 1000c. Mickey, Minnie and Pluto in rain (April) . . . 1·40 1·40
2620 1000c. Minnie with flowers (May) . . . . 1·40 1·40
2621 1000c. Daisy watering garden (June) . . . . . . 1·40 1·40
2622 1000c. Donald at Independance Day celebrations (July) . . . . 1·40 1·40
2623 1000c. Donald and Daisy on the beach (August) . . . 1·40 1·40
2624 1000c. Morty and Ferdie returning to school (September) . . . . . . 1·40 1·40
2625 1000c. Hewey, Dewey and Louie at Hallowe'en (October) . . . . 1·40 1·40
2626 1000c. Mickey on Thanksgiving Day (November) . . . . . . 1·40 1·40
2627 1000c. Mickey and Minnie at Christmas (December) 1·40 1·40
MS2628 Four sheets, each 132 × 107 mm. (a) 5000c. Mickey bottle feeding calf (Spring) (horiz). (b) 5000c. Minnie camping (Summer). (c) 5000c. Goofy sweeping leaves (Autumn). (d) 5000c. Daisy and Nephews on ice (Winter) (horiz) Set of 4 sheets 19·00 19·00

1998. Trains of the World. Multicoloured.
2629 300c. Type **553** 10 10
2630 500c. ETR 450 high-speed train, Italy 10 10
2631 800c. X200 high-speed train, Sweden 10 15
2632 800c. SPS steam locomotive, Pakistan 10 15
2633 800c. Class WP steam locomotive, India 10 15
2634 800c. Class QJ steam locomotive, China 10 15
2635 800c. Type 12 steam locomotive, Belgium . . . 10 15
2636 800c. Class P8 steam locomotive, Germany . . 10 15
2637 800c. Class "Castle" steam locomotive, Great Britain 10 15
2638 800c. Tank locomotive, Austria 10 15
2639 800c. Class P36 steam locomotive, Russia . . . 10 15
2640 800c. Steam locomotive "William Mason", U.S.A. 10 15
2641 800c. AVE high-speed train, Spain 10 15
2642 800c. Diesel locomotive No. 1602, Luxembourg 10 15
2643 800c. "Hikari" express train, Japan 10 15
2644 800c. Santa Fe Railroad GM F7 "Warbonnet" diesel locomotive, U.S.A. 10 15
2645 800c. Class E1500 diesel locomotive, Morocco . . 10 15
2646 800c. Class "Deltic" diesel locomotive, Great Britain 10 15
2647 800c. XPT high-speed train, Australia 10 15
2648 800c. Channel Tunnel shuttle train, France and Great Britain 10 15
2649 800c. Class 201 diesel locomotive, Ireland . . . 10 15
2650 1000c. TGV Duplex high-speed train, France . . . 10 15
2651 2000c. Class EL diesel locomotive, Australia . . 25 30
2652 3000c. Eurostar high-speed train, Great Britain . . . 35 40
MS2653 Two sheets, each 106 × 76 mm. (a) 5500c. Class "Duchess" steam locomotive heading the "Irish Mail", Great Britain (56 × 42 mm). (b) 5500c. TGV express train, France (56 × 42 mm) Set of 2 sheets . . 1·30 1·40

1998. Great Writers of the 20th Century. Mult.
2654 350c. Type **554** 10 10
2655 350c. Alex Haley 10 10
2656 350c. Charles Johnson . . . 10 10
2657 350c. Richard Wright . . . 10 10
2658 350c. Toni Cade Bambara 10 10
2659 350c. Henri Louis Gates Jr 10 10

555 Breguet Br 14 B2, France

1998. History of Aviation. Multicoloured.
2660 800c. Type **555** 10 15
2661 800c. Curtiss BF2C-1 Goshawk, U.S.A. 10 15
2662 800c. Supermarine Spitfire Mk IX, Great Britain . . 10 15
2663 800c. Fiat G.50, Italy . . . 10 15
2664 800c. Douglas B-18A, U.S.A. 10 15
2665 800c. Boeing FB-5, U.S.A. 10 15
2666 800c. Bristol F2B "Brisfit", Great Britain 10 15
2667 800c. Hawker Fury 1, Great Britain 10 15
2668 800c. Fiat CR-42, Italy . . 10 15
2669 800c. Messerschmitt Bf 109 E-7, Germany 10 15
2670 800c. Lockheed PV-2 Harpoon, U.S.A. 10 15
2671 800c. Airspeed Oxford Mk 1, Great Britain 10 15
2672 800c. Junkers Ju 87D-1, Germany 10 15
2673 800c. Yakovlev Yak-9D, U.S.S.R. 10 15
2674 800c. North American P-51D Mustang, U.S.A. 10 15
2675 800c. Douglas A-206 Havoc, U.S.A. 10 15
2676 800c. Supermarine Attacker F1, Great Britain 10 15
2677 800c. Mikoyan Gurevich MiG-15, U.S.S.R. 10 15
MS2678 Two sheets, each 106 × 76 mm. (a) 3000c. Supermarine Spitfires Mk 1 and Mk XIV, Great Britain (58 × 43 mm). (b) 3000c. Mitsubishi AGM8 Reisen, Japan (58 × 43 mm) Set of 2 sheets . . 75 80

556 "Empress of Ireland" (liner)

1998. Famous Ships. Multicoloured.
2679 800c. Type **556** 10 15
2680 800c. "Transylvania" (liner) 10 15
2681 800c. "Mauretania I" (liner) 10 15
2682 800c. "Reliance" (liner) . . 10 15
2683 800c. "Aquitania" (liner) . . 10 15
2684 800c. "Lapland" (liner) . . 10 15
2685 800c. "Cap Polonio" (liner) 10 15
2686 800c. "France I", 1910 (liner) 10 15
2687 800c. "Imperator" (liner) . . 10 15
2688 800c. H.M.S. "Rodney" (battleship) 10 15
2689 800c. U.S.S. "Alabama" (battleship) 10 15
2690 800c. H.M.S. "Nelson" (battleship) 10 15
2691 800c. "Ormonde" (camouflaged liner) . . . 10 15
2692 800c. U.S.S. "Radford" (destroyer) 10 15
2693 800c. "Empress of Russia" (camouflaged liner) . . . 10 15
2694 800c. Type XIV U-boat . . 10 15
2695 800c. Japanese Type A midget submarine 10 15
2696 800c. "Brin" (Italian submarine) 10 15
MS2697 Two sheets, each 100 × 75 mm. (a) 5500c. "Titanic" (liner) (43 × 57 mm). (b) 5500c. "Amistad" (slave schooner) (43 × 57 mm) Set of 2 sheets . . 1·30 1·40
No. 2681 is inscribed "MAURITANIA" in error.

1998. "Israel 98" International Stamp Exhibition, Tel-Aviv. Nos. 2362/4 optd with Emblem.
2698 400c. St. Stephen's Gate and "Jasminum mesnyi" . . . 10 10
2699 600c. The Citadel, Tower of David and "Nerium oleander" 10 10
2700 800c. Chapel of the Ascension and "Romulea bulbocodium" 10 15
MS2701 65 × 80 mm. 2000c. Russian Orthodox Church of St. Mary Magdalene (48 × 30 mm) . . . 25 30
No. **MS**2701 is additionally overprinted **ISRAEL 98 – WORLD STAMP EXHIBITION TEL-AVIV 13–21 MAY 1998** on the sheet margin.

558 "Renanthera imschootiana"

559 Elvis Presley

1998. Orchids of the World. Multicoloured.
2702 800c. Type **558** 10 15
2703 800c. "Arachnis flos-aeris" 10 15
2704 800c. "Restrepia lansbergi" 10 15
2705 800c. "Paphiopedilum tonsum" 10 15
2706 800c. "Phalaenopsis ebauche" 10 15
2707 800c. "Pleione limprichti" 10 15
2708 800c. "Phragmipedium schroderae" 10 15
2709 800c. "Zygopetalum clayii" 10 15
2710 800c. "Vanda coerulea" . . 10 15
2711 800c. "Odontonia boussole" 10 15
2712 800c. "Disa uniflora" . . . 10 15
2713 800c. "Dendrobium bigibbum" 10 15
MS2714 Two sheets, each 98 × 68 mm. (a) 5500c. "Cypripedium calceolus". (b) 5500c. "Sobralia candida" Set of 2 sheets . . . . 1·30 1·40

1998. 30th Anniv of Elvis Presley's "68 Special" Television Programme. Multicoloured.
2715 800c. Type **559** 10 15
2716 800c. Elvis in white suit . . 10 15
2717 800c. In leather jacket, holding microphone . . . 10 15
2718 800c. Wearing light blue jacket 10 15

2719 800c. Elvis with silhouetted figures in background . . 10 15
2720 800c. Elvis with guitar and microphone 10 15

560 Crest of Accra Metropolitan Assembly and Surf Boats

1998. Centenary of Accra Metropolitan Assembly. Multicoloured.
2721 200c. Type **560** 10 10
2722 550c. King Tackie Tawiah I 10 10
2723 800c. Achimota School . . 10 15
2724 1100c. Korle Bu Hospital 15 20
2725 1500c. Christianborg Castle 20 25

561 Tetteh Quarshie (cocoa industry pioneer)

1998. 50th Anniv of Ghana Cocoa Board. Multicoloured.
2726 200c. Type **561** 10 10
2727 550c. Ripe hybrid cocoa pods 10 10
2728 800c. Opening cocoa pods 10 15
2729 1100c. Fermenting cocoa beans 15 20
2730 1500c. Loading freighter with cocoa 20 25

562 Bamboo

1998. Oriental Flowers. Multicoloured.
2731 2000c. Type **562** 25 30
2732 2000c. Cherry blossom . . . 25 30
2733 2000c. Yellow chrysanthemum 25 30
2734 2000c. Orchid 25 30
2735 2000c. Green peony 25 30
2736 2000c. Red peony 25 30
2737 2000c. Pink peony 25 30
2738 2000c. White peony 25 30
MS2739 Two sheets, each 109 × 85 mm. (a) 5500c. Cherry blossom (horiz). (b) 5500c. Peonies (horiz) Set of 2 sheets . . . . 1·30 1·40

563 Two Dolphins

1998. International Year of the Ocean. Multicoloured.
2740 500c. Type **563** 10 10
2741 500c. Dolphin 10 10
2742 500c. Seagull 10 10
2743 500c. Least tern 10 10
2744 500c. Emperor angelfish . . 10 10
2745 500c. White ear (juvenile) 10 10
2746 500c. Blue shark and diver 10 10
2747 500c. Parrotfish 10 10
2748 500c. Dottyback 10 10
2749 500c. Blue-spotted stingray 10 10
2750 500c. Masked butterflyfish 10 10
2751 500c. Jackknife-fish 10 10
2752 500c. Octopus 10 10
2753 500c. Lionfish 10 10
2754 500c. Seadragon 10 10
2755 500c. Rock cod 10 10
MS2756 Two sheets. (a) 63 × 98 mm. 3000c. Great white shark. (b) 98 × 63 mm. 3000c. Devil ray Set of 2 sheets 75 80

Nos. 2740/55 were printed together, se-tenant, with the backgrounds forming a composite design.

No. 2745 is inscribed "Whit Ear" in error.

1998. Millennium Series. Famous People of the Twentieth Century. Inventors. As T **289a** of Gambia. Multicoloured.
2757 1000c. Thomas Edison . . . 10 15
2758 1000c. Peephole kinetoscope (Edison) (53 × 38 mm) . . 10 15
2759 1000c. Tesla coil (53 × 38 mm) 10 15
2760 1000c. Nikola Tesla 10 15
2761 1000c. Gottlieb Daimler . . 10 15
2762 1000c. Motorcycle (Daimler) (53 × 38 mm) 10 15
2763 1000c. Early transmitter circuit (Marconi) and dish aerial (53 × 38 mm) . . . 10 15
2764 1000c. Guglielmo Marconi 10 15
2765 1000c. Orville and Wilbur Wright 10 15
2766 1000c. "Flyer I" (Wright Brothers) (53 × 38 mm) . . 10 15
2767 1000c. Neon lights and signs (Claude) (53 × 38 mm) . . 10 15
2768 1000c. Georges Claude . . . 10 15
2769 1000c. Alexander Graham Bell 10 15
2770 1000c. Early telephone transmitter (Bell) (53 × 38 mm) 10 15
2771 1000c. Uses of lasers (Townes) (53 × 38 mm) . . 10 15
2772 1000c. Charles Townes . . . 10 15
MS2773 Two sheets, each 76 × 106 mm. (a) 5500c. Paul Ehrlich. (b) 5500c. Robert Goddard Set of 2 sheets . . . 1·30 1·40

564 British Colourpoint with Tree Decoration

1998. Christmas. Cats and Dogs. Multicoloured.
2774 500c. Type **564** 10 10
2775 600c. American shorthair kitten with basket 10 10
2776 800c. Peke-faced Persian on piano keys 10 15
2777 1000c. German spitz dog in box 10 15
2778 2000c. British shorthair Blue with antlers 25 30
2779 3000c. Persian in sleigh . . 35 40
MS2780 Two sheets, each 76 × 106 mm. (a) 5500c. English pointer puppy. (b) 5500c. Manx cat with decoration Set of 2 sheets 1·30 1·40

1999. 25th Death Anniv of Pablo Picasso (painter). As T **293a** of Gambia. Multicoloured.
2781 1000c. "Composition with Butterfly" 10 15
2782 1000c. "Mandolin and Clarinet" (vert) 10 15
2783 2000c. "Woman throwing a Stone" 25 30
MS2784 101 × 127 mm. 5500c. "Tomato Plant" (vert) 65 70

564a Lampredi

1999. Birth Centenary of Enzo Ferrari (car manufacturer). Multicoloured.
2785 2000c. Type **564a** . . . . . 1·40 1·40
2786 2000c. 250 GT Cabriolet . . 1·40 1·40
2787 2000c. 121 LM . . . . . . 1·40 1·40
MS2788 100 × 70 mm. 3000c. 365 GTS/4 Spyder (91 × 34 mm) . . 3·00 3·50

1999. 19th World Scout Jamboree, Chile. As T **291b** of Gambia. Multicoloured (except No. **MS**2792).
2789 2000c. Scout salute 25 30
2790 2000c. Scout with backpack 25 30
2791 2000c. Bowline knot 25 30
MS2792 55 × 70 mm. 5000c. Lord Baden-Powell (bistre and black) 60 65

1999. 50th Death Anniv of Mahatma Gandhi. As T **292** of Gambia. Multicoloured.
2793 2000c. Gandhi, 1931 . . . . 25 30
2794 2000c. On Salt March, 1930 (53 × 38 mm) 25 30
2795 2000c. Collecting natural salt, 1930 (53 × 38 mm) 25 30
2796 2000c. After graduating from high school, 1887 . . 25 30
MS2797 60 × 79 mm. 5500c. Mahatma Gandhi seated, 1931 65 70

1999. 80th Anniv of Royal Air Force. As T **292** of Gambia. Multicoloured.
2798 2000c. C-130 Hercules on tarmac 25 30
2799 2000c. HC2 Chinook helicopter 25 30
2800 2000c. C-130 Hercules W2 taking off 25 30
2801 2000c. Panavia Tornado F3 25 30
MS2802 Two sheets, each 90 × 70 mm. (a) 5500c. Chipmunk and EF-2000 Euro-fighter. (b) 5500c. Bristol F2B fighter and merlin (bird) Set of 2 sheets . . 1·30 1·40

1999. 1st Death Anniv of Diana, Princess of Wales. As T **293a** of Gambia.
2803 1000c. multicoloured 10 15

565 Farmer working

1999. Chinese New Year ("Year of the Rabbit"). "Farmer and the Hare" (Han Fei Tzu). Mult.
2804 1400c. Type **565** 15 20
2805 1400c. Farmer watching hare hit tree 15 20
2806 1400c. Farmer with dead hare 15 20
2807 1400c. Farmer asleep under tree 15 20

566 Shirley Temple praying

1999. 70th Birthday of Shirley Temple (actress). Showing film scenes from "Curly Top". Multicoloured.
2808 1000c. Type **566** 10 15
2809 1000c. Man looking at painting 10 15
2810 1000c. With butler 10 15
2811 1000c. As old woman in rocking chair 10 15
2812 1000c. With mother (horiz) 10 15
2813 1000c. Wearing brown coat and bowler hat (horiz) . . 10 15
2814 1000c. With cuddly toys (horiz) 10 15
2815 1000c. Pulling father's tie (horiz) 10 15
2816 1000c. With family (horiz) 10 15
2817 1000c. Watching parents (horiz) 10 15
MS2818 106 × 76 mm. 5000c. Shirley Temple on piano 60 65

567 Corythosaurus

1999. Prehistoric Animals. Multicoloured.
2819 400c. Type **567** 10 10
2820 600c. Struthiomimus 10 10
2821 800c. Pterodactylus 10 15
2822 800c. Scelidosaurus 10 15
2823 800c. Pteranodon 10 15
2824 800c. Plateosaurus 10 15
2825 800c. Ornithosuchus 10 15
2826 800c. Kentrosaurus 10 15
2827 800c. Hypsognathus 10 15
2828 800c. Erythrosuchus 10 15
2829 800c. Stegoceras 10 15
2830 800c. Ankylosaurus 10 15
2831 800c. Anatosaurus 10 15
2832 800c. Diplodocus 10 15
2833 800c. Monoclonius 10 15
2834 800c. Tyrannosaurus 10 15
2835 800c. Camptosaurus 10 15
2836 800c. Ornitholestes 10 15
2837 800c. Archaeopteryx 10 15
2838 800c. Allosaurus 10 15
2839 1000c. Lambeosaurus . . . 10 15
2840 2000c. Hesperasuchus . . . 25 30
MS2841 Two sheets, each 85 × 110 mm. (a) 5000c. Dimorphodon (vert). (b) 5000c. Apatosaurus Set of 2 sheets . . 1·20 1·30

Nos. 2821/9 and 2830/8 respectively were printed together, se-tenant, with the backgrounds forming composite designs.

568 Badgers

1999. Endangered Species. Multicoloured.
2842 200c. Type **568** 10 10
2843 400c. Azure-winged magpie 10 10
2844 600c. White stork 10 10
2845 800c. Red fox 10 15
2846 1000c. European bee eater ("Merops apiaster") . . . 10 15
2847 1000c. Hoopoe ("Upupa epops") 10 15
2848 1000c. Red deer 10 15
2849 1000c. Short-toed eagle ("Cycaetus gallicus") . . . 10 15
2850 1000c. Lacerta oceliata (lizard) 10 15
2851 1000c. Lynx 10 15
2852 1000c. Pine martin 10 15
2853 1000c. Tawny owl ("Strix aluco") 10 15
2854 1000c. Wild boar 10 15
2855 1000c. Northern goshawk ("Accipiter gentilis") . . . 10 15
2856 1000c. Garden dormouse . . 10 15
2857 1000c. Stag beetles 10 15
2858 2000c. Cinereous vulture (vert) 25 30
2859 3000c. Jay (vert) 35 40
MS2860 Two sheets, each 85 × 110 mm. (a) 5000c. Imperial eagle ("Iberian Imperial Eagle"). (b) 5000c. Wolf cub (vert) Set of 2 sheets . . . . 1·20 1·30

Nos. 2846/51 and 2852/7 respectively were printed together, se-tenant, with the backgrounds forming composite designs.

569 California Sister Butterfly

1999. "Australia '99" International Stamp Exhibition, Melbourne. Butterflies. Multicoloured.
2861 300c. Type **569** 10 10
2862 500c. Red-splashed sulphur 10 10
2863 600c. Checked white 10 10
2864 800c. Blue emperor 10 15
2865 1000c. Red admiral (vert) 10 15
2866 1000c. Buckeye (vert) . . . 10 15
2867 1000c. Desert chequered skipper (vert) 10 15
2868 1000c. Orange sulphur (vert) 10 15
2869 1000c. Tiger swallowtail (vert) 10 15
2870 1000c. Orange-bordered blue (vert) 10 15
2871 1000c. Gulf fritillary "vanillae") (vert) 10 15
2872 1000c. Monarch (vert) . . . 10 15
2873 1000c. Small tortoiseshell (vert) 10 15
2874 1000c. Brimstone (vert) . . 10 15
2875 1000c. Camberwell beauty (vert) 10 15
2876 1000c. Marbled white (vert) 10 15
2877 1000c. Purple Emperor (vert) 10 15
2878 1000c. Clouded yellow (vert) 10 15
2879 1000c. Ladoga camilla (vert) 10 15
2880 1000c. Marsh fritillary (vert) 10 15
MS2881 Two sheets, each 106 × 76 mm. (a) 5000c. Homerus swallowtail (vert). (b) 5000c. Blue copper Set of 2 sheets . . . . 1·20 1·30

Nos. 2865/72 and 2873/80 respectively were printed together, se-tenant, with the backgrounds forming composite designs.

No. 2862 is inscribed "Red-splashed Sulfer" and No. 2864 "Blue Emperorl", both in error.

571 ICE 2 (Germany), 1966

1999. Railways of the World. Multicoloured.
2883 400c. Type **571** 10 10
2884 500c. M41 No. 2112 (Hungary), 1982 . . . . . 10 10
2885 600c. DVR No. 2526 (Finland), 1963 . . . . . 10 10
2886 1000c. Class AVE 100 (Spain), 1992 . . . . . . 10 15
2887 1300c. Conrail EMD SD80 No. 4110 (U.S.A.), 1993 15 20
2888 1300c. Columbus and Greenville EMD SDP35 No. 701 (U.S.A.), 1964–6 15 20
2889 1300c. Providence and Worcester MLW M420 (U.S.A.), 1973–77 . . . . 15 20
2890 1300c. Missouri Pacific C36-7 No. 9044 (U.S.A.), 1978–85 . . . . 15 20

2891 1300c. Virginia and Maryland ALCO C-420 No. 203 (U.S.A.), 1963–68 . . . 15 20
2892 1300c. Reading EMD GP30 No. 3615 (U.S.A.), 1961–63 . . . . 15 20
2893 1300c. Illinois Terminal EMD GP7 No. 1506 (U.S.A.), 1949/54 . . . . 15 20
2894 1300c. Canadian Pacific EMD SD 38-2 (Canada), 1972–79 . . . . 15 20
2895 1300c. EMD SD 60M 500 No. 6058 (U.S.A.), 1989–96 . . . . 15 20
2896 1300c. GE U25C No. 2808 (U.S.A.), 1963–65 . . . . 15 20
2897 1300c. EMD GP 28 (U.S.A.), 1961–63 . . . . 15 20
2898 1300c. EMD SD 9 No. 162 (U.S.A.), 1954–59 . . . . 15 20
MS2899 Two sheets. (a) 85 × 110 mm. 5000c. Swiss Federal Class RE 6/6 No. 11630, 1972. (b) 110 × 85 mm. 5000c. AGP44 (U.S.A), 1990–91 Set of 2 sheets 1·20 1·30

1999. "iBRA '99" International Stamp Exhibition, Nuremberg. Multicoloured. As T **298a** of Gambia.
2900 500c. "Schomberg" (sailing ship) and Hanover 1850 1 ggr. stamp 10 10
2901 800c. Class P8 railway locomotive and Hamburg 1859 ½s. 10 15
2902 1000c. "Schomberg" (sailing ship) and Lubeck 1859 ½s. 10 15
2903 2000c. Class P8 railway locomotive and Heligoland 1867 ½s. . . . 25 30
MS2904 134 × 106 mm. 5000c. Germany 3pf. stamp on 1912 Bork-Bruck flown cover (vert) 60 65

1999. 150th Death Anniv of Katsushika Hokusai (Japanese artist). Multicoloured as T **298b** of Gambia, but horiz.
2905 1300c. "Girl picking Plum Blossoms" 15 20
2906 1300c. "Surveying a Region" 15 20
2907 1300c. "Sumo Wrestler" (bending down) 15 20
2908 1300c. "Sumo Wrestler" (dancing) 15 20
2909 1300c. "Landscape with Seaside Village" 15 20
2910 1300c. "Courtiers crossing a Bridge" 15 20
2911 1300c. "Climbing the Mountain" 15 20
2912 1300c. "Nakahara in Sagami Province" 15 20
2913 1300c. "Sumo Wrestlers" . . 15 20
2914 1300c. "An Oiran and Maid by a Fence" 15 20
2915 1300c. "Fujiwara Yoshitaka" 15 20
MS2916 Two sheets, each 100 × 70 mm. (a) 5000c. "Palanquin Bearers on a Steep Hill" (vert). (b) 5000c. "Three Ladies by a Well" (vert) Set of 2 sheets . . . . 1·20 1·30

1999. 10th Anniv of United Nations Rights of the Child Convention. Vert designs as T **298c** of Gambia. Multicoloured.
2917 3000c. Boy smiling and U.N. Headquarters Building 35 40
2918 3000c. Dove and Earth . . 35 40
2919 3000c. Mother and baby . . 35 40
MS2920 110 × 85 mm. 5000c. Boy and U.N.I.C.E.F. emblem . . 60 65
Nos. 2917/19 were printed together, se-tenant, forming a composite design.

1999. "PhilexFrance '99" International Stamp Exhibition, France. Railway Locomotives. Two sheets, each 106 × 76 mm, containing horiz designs as T **299d** of Gambia. Multicoloured.
MS2921 Two sheets. (a) 5000c. Western Railway suburban tank locomotive. (b) 5000c. National Railways Class 232-U1 Set of 2 sheets . . . . 1·20 1·30

1999. 250th Birth Anniv of Johann von Goethe (German writer). As T **298d** of Gambia. Multicoloured.
2922 2000c. Wagner entreats Faust in his study 25 30
2923 2000c. Von Goethe and Von Schiller 25 30
2924 2000c. Mephistopheles disguised as the Fool . . 25 30
MS2925 106 × 71 mm. 5000c. Faust attended by Spirits 60 65

1999. 30th Anniv of First Manned Landing on Moon. T **298e** of Gambia. Multicoloured.
2926 1300c. Command module 15 20
2927 1300c. Lunar module ascending 15 20
2928 1300c. Giant moon rock . . 15 20
2929 1300c. Lunar module's aerials and Earth from Moon 15 20
2930 1300c. Neil Armstrong . . . 15 20
2931 1300c. "One small step" (alighting on lunar surface) 15 20
MS2932 71 × 106 mm. 5000c. Earth from Moon 60 65

Nos. 2926/31 were printed together, se-tenant, forming a composite design. No. 2927 is inscribed "LUNAR MODULE ASCENSION" in error.

572 Gate of Understanding, Macao

1999. "China '99" World Philatelic Exhibition, Beijing. Return of Macao to China.
2933 **572** 1000c. multicoloured . . 10 15

1999. "Queen Elizabeth the Queen Mother's Century". As T **304a** of Gambia.
2934 2000c. black and gold . . . 25 30
2935 2000c. black and gold . . . 25 30
2936 2000c. multicoloured 25 30
2937 2000c. multicoloured 25 30
MS2938 153 × 157 mm. 5000c. multicoloured 60 65
DESIGNS: No. 2934, Lady Elizabeth Bowes-Lyon with her brother, David, 1904; 2935, Queen Mother in Rhodesia, 1957; 2936, Queen Mother seated, 1970; 2937, Queen Mother holding bouquet, 1992. (37 × 50 mm)—**MS**2938, Queen Mother in garden, 1970.

573 Dr. Ephraim Apu

1999. Birth Centenary of Dr. Ephraim Apu (traditional musicologist). Multicoloured.
2939 200c. Type **573** 10 10
2940 800c. Playing Odurugya flute 10 15
2941 1100c. Indigenious flutes . . 15 20

574 Grandma Alice and Village

1999. 25th Anniv of S.O.S. in Ghana (200, 1100c.) and 50th Anniv of S.O.S. Kinderdorf International (children's villages) (others). Multicoloured.
2942 200c. Type **574** 10 10
2943 550c. Kindergarten 10 10
2944 800c. Hermann Gneiner (founder) and Asiakwa S.O.S. building 10 15
2945 1100c. Preparing food . . . 15 20

575 Fishes inside Cloud

576 Peace Doves flying from Ghana

1999. Save the Ozone Layer Campaign. Mult.
2946 200c. Type **575** 10 10
2947 550c. African looking at diagram of ozone layer 10 10
2948 800c. Earth weeping 10 15
2949 1100c. Africans shielding Earth 15 20
2950 1500c. CFC and no-CFC appliances 25 30

1999. New Millennium. Multicoloured.
2951 300c. Type **576** 10 10
2952 700c. Kwame Nkrumah (first President) speaking (horiz) 10 10
2953 1200c. Clock tower, University of Ghana . . . 15 20

577 Liu-Yi meets Daughter of the Dragon King

2000. Chinese New Year ("Year of the Dragon"). Vert designs showing scenes from "Daughter of the Dragon King". Each design brown and silver.
2954 1600c. Type **577** 20 25
2955 1600c. Liu-Yi and Fairy Soldier 20 25
2956 1600c. Liu-Yi and the Dragon King 20 25
2957 1600c. Liu-Yi, Dragon King and Red Dragon 20 25
2958 1600c. Red Dragon and Dragon of Jing River fighting 20 25
2959 1600c. Dragon King with his daughter and brother 20 25
2960 1700c. Dragon King's brother inviting Liu-Yi to marry his niece 20 25
2961 1700c. Liu-Yi bidding farewell to Dragon King 20 25
2962 1700c. Liu-Yi with gifts from Dragon King . . . 20 25
2963 1700c. Liu-Yi with third wife 20 25
2964 1700c. Liu-Yi with third wife and son 20 25
2965 1700c. Liu-Yi realises that third wife is Daughter of the Dragon King 20 25

578 Black-faced Impala

2000. African Wildlife. Multicoloured.
2966 300c. Type **578** 10 10
2967 500c. Cheetah 10 10
2968 1000c. Wildebeest 10 15
2969 1100c. Chimpanzee (vert) . . 15 20
2970 1100c. Boomslang tree snake (vert) 15 20
2971 1100c. Ruppell's griffon ("Vulture") (vert) 15 20
2972 1100c. Leopard (vert) . . . 15 20
2973 1100c. African rhinoceros (vert) 15 20
2974 1100c. Zebra (vert) 15 20
2975 1100c. South African crowned crane ("Crowned Crane") (vert) 15 20
2976 1100c. Female lesser Kudu (vert) 15 20
2977 1200c. Rufous-crowned roller ("Purple Roller") (vert) 15 20
2978 1200c. Eastern white pelican ("Pelicans") (vert) 15 20
2979 1200c. Cattle egret ("Egrets") (vert) 15 20
2980 1200c. Zebra waxbill ("Orange-breasted Waxbill") (vert) 15 20
2981 1200c. Giraffe (vert) 15 20
2982 1200c. African buffalo (vert) 15 20
2983 1200c. Elephant (vert) . . . 15 20
2984 1200c. African lion (vert) . . 15 20
2985 3000c. Hippopotamus . . . 35 40
MS2986 Two sheets, each 76 × 106 mm. (a) 7000c. Ostrich. (b) 7000c. Young waterbuck Set of 2 sheets . . . . 1·70 1·80
Nos. 2969/76 and 2977/84 were each printed together, se-tenant, with the backgrounds forming composite designs.

579 Cape Coast Castle

2000. Tourism. Multicoloured.
2987 300c. Type **579** 10 10
2988 300c. Banda Nkwanta Mosque, Accra 10 10
2989 300c. Elephants 10 10
2990 1100c. Tribal chief 15 20
2991 1200c. Ghanaians with antelope 15 20
2992 1800c. Tribal chiefs 20 25

580 Banded ("Zebra") Duiker

2000. Fauna and Flora. Multicoloured.
2993 500c. Type **580** 10 10
2994 600c. Leopard 10 10
2995 1600c. Large spotted genet 20 25
2996 1600c. Tree pangolin . . . 20 25
2997 1600c. Bongo 20 25
2998 1600c. Elephant 20 25
2999 1600c. Flap-necked chameleon 20 25
3000 1600c. West African dwarf crocodile 20 25
3001 1600c. Lowe's monkey . . . 20 25
3002 1600c. Diana monkey . . . 20 25
3003 1600c. Potto 20 25
3004 1600c. Moustached monkey 20 25
3005 1600c. Thomas's galago . . 20 25
3006 1600c. Chimpanzee 20 25
3007 1600c. Grey parrot 20 25
3008 1600c. Hoopoe 20 25
3009 1600c. European roller . . . 20 25
3010 1600c. European bee-eater 20 25
3011 1600c. Blue-breasted kingfisher 20 25
3012 1600c. White-throated bee eater 20 25
3013 2000c. Bushbuck 25 30
3014 3000c. African wood owl . . 35 40
MS3015 Two sheets. (a) 100 × 70 mm. 6000c. Hippopotamus (vert). (b) 70 × 100 mm. 6000c. Great blue turaco (vert) Set of 2 sheets . . 1·50 1·60
Nos. 2995/3000, 3001/6 and 3007/12 were each printed together, se-tenant, with the backgrounds forming composite designs.
No. 2995 is inscribed "BLOTHED GENET" in error.

581 *Suillus luteus*

2000. African Mushrooms. Multicoloured.
3016 1500c. Type **581** 20 25
3017 1500c. *Laccaria amethystina* 20 25
3018 1500c. *Coriolus versicolor* . . 20 25
3019 1500c. *Armillaria mellea* . . 20 25
3020 1500c. *Lepiota rhacodes* . . 20 25
3021 1500c. *Russula queletil* . . . 20 25
3022 2000c. *Amanita vaginata* . . 25 30
3023 2000c. *Lycoperdon perlatum* 25 30
3024 2000c. *Schizophyllum commune* 25 30
3025 2000c. *Cantharellus cinereus* 25 30
3026 2000c. *Coprinus disseminatus* 25 30
3027 2000c. *Russula cyanoxantaha* 25 30
MS3028 Two sheets, each 53 × 81 mm. (a) 5000c. *Aleuria aurantia* (vert). (b) 5000c. *Tylopilus felleus* (vert) Set of 2 sheets . . 1·20 1·30

582 Cooking Demonstration

2000. 19th International Home Economics Congress, Accra. Multicoloured.
3029 300c. Type **582** 10 10
3030 700c. Student with home economics text book (vert) 10 10
3031 1200c. Mrs. Alberta Ollennu, Ms. Patience Adow and Association logo 15 20
3032 1800c. Congress logo (vert) 20 25

2000. 18th Birthday of Prince William. At T **312b** of Gambia. Multicoloured.
3033 2000c. In skiing gear 25 30
3034 2000c. In Eton uniform . . 25 30
3035 2000c. With Prince Harry 25 30
3036 2000c. Prince William (Royal Artillery cap in background) 25 30
MS3037 100 × 80 mm. 8000c. Prince William in blue jumper (37 × 50 mm) . . . . 95 1·00

582a "Mercury"

2000. "EXPO 2000" World Stamp Exhibition, Anaheim. Manned Spacecraft. Multicoloured.

3038 2000c. Type **582a** 25 30
3039 2000c. "Gemini" 25 30
3040 2000c. "Apollo" 25 30
3041 2000c. "Vostok" 25 30
3042 2000c. "Voskhod 2" 25 30
3043 2000c. "Soyuz" 25 30
MS3044 75 × 115 mm. 2000c. Space Shuttle *Challenger* mission emblem (vert) 25 30

Nos. 3038/43 were printed together, se-tenant, with the backgrounds forming a composite design.

582b "Apollo 18"

582c *Wetherby*, 1985

2000. 25th Anniv of "Apollo"–"Soyuz" Joint Project. Multicoloured.

3045 4000c. Type **582b** 50 55
3046 4000c. "Apollo 18" and "Soyuz 19" docking . . . 50 55
3047 4000c. "Soyuz 19" 50 55
MS3048 105 × 75 mm. 8000c. "Soyuz 19" and Earth . . . . 95 1·00

Nos. 3045/7 were printed together, se-tenant, with the backgrounds forming a composite design.

2000. 50th Anniv of Berlin Film Festival. Mult.

3049 2000c. Type **582c** 25 30
3050 2000c. *Die Frau und der Fremde*, 1985 . . . . . . 25 30
3051 2000c. *Hong Gaoliang*, 1988 . . 25 30
3052 2000c. *Skrivanci na Nitich*, 1990 . . . . 25 30
3053 2000c. *Music Box*, 1990 . . 25 30
3054 2000c. *Terma*, 1987 . . . . 25 30
MS3055 95 × 103 mm. 6000c. *Justice est Faite*, 1951 . . . . 75 80

582d Marc Seguin

2000. 175th Anniv of Stockton and Darlington Line (first public railway). Multicoloured.

3056 4000c. Type **582d** 50 55
3057 4000c. Blenkinsop's locomotive 50 55
3058 4000c. Pumping station at Dawlish 50 55

2000. Election of Albert Einstein (mathematical physicist) as *Time Magazine* "Man of the Century". Sheet 120 × 90 mm, containing vert portrait as T **312d** of Gambia.

MS3059 8000c. multicoloured . . 95 1·00

582e LZ-129 *Hindenburg*, 1936

2000. Centenary of First Zeppelin Flight. Mult.

3060 1600c. Type **582e** 20 25
3061 1600c. LZ-9 *Ersatz Deutschland*, 1911 . . . . 20 25
3062 1600c. LZ-4, 1908 . . . . . 20 25
MS3063 96 × 65 mm. 5000c. LZ-11 *Viktoria Luise*, 1912 . . . . . 60 65

Nos. 3060/2 were printed together, se-tenant, with the backgrounds forming a composite design.

582f Gymnast on Parallel Bars, Athens (1896)

2000. Olympic Games, Sydney. Multicoloured.

3064 1300c. Type **582f** 15 20
3065 1300c. Long jumping . . . 15 20
3066 1300c. Olympic Stadium, Los Angeles (1984) . . . 15 20
3067 1300c. Ancient Greek chariot racing 15 20

583 African Shorthair Cat

584 Xu Xian, White Lady and Xiao Qing

2000. Domestic Cats and Dogs. Multicoloured.

3068 1100c. Type **583** 15 20
3069 1200c. Russian blue cat . . 15 20
3070 1600c. Weimaraner (horiz) . . 20 25
3071 1800c. Keeshond (horiz) . . 20 25
3072 1800c. Fox terrier (horiz) . . 20 25
3073 1800c. Saluki (horiz) 20 25
3074 1800c. Dalmatian (horiz) . . 20 25
3075 1800c. English setter (horiz) 20 25
3076 1800c. Basenji 20 25
3077 1800c. Silver Persian (horiz) 20 25
3078 1800c. Creampoint Himalayan (horiz) 20 25
3079 1800c. British tortoiseshell shorthair (horiz) 20 25
3080 1800c. American shorthair tabby (horiz) 20 25
3081 1800c. Black Persian (horiz) 20 25
3082 1800c. Turkish van (horiz) 20 25
3083 2000c. Basset hound 20 25
MS3084 Two sheets, each 110 × 85 mm. (a) 8000c. Lilac Persian cat. (b) 8000c. Cocker spaniel Set of 2 sheets . . . . 1·90 2·00

2001. Chinese New Year ("Year of the Snake"). Showing scenes from *Tale of the White Snake* (traditional Chinese story). Each red and silver.

3085 2500c. Type **584** 30 35
3086 2500c. White Lady and Xu Xian in pharmacy 30 35
3087 2500c. Xu Xian with monk Fa Hai 30 35
3088 2500c. Xu Xian and White Lady drinking wine . . . 30 35
3089 2500c. Xu Xian having heart attack 30 35
3090 2500c. White Lady attacked by stork 30 35
3091 2500c. White Lady, Xiao Qing with swords confront Fa Hai 30 35
3092 2500c. Xiao Qing and Xu Xian on staircase 30 35
3093 2500c. Fa Hai entrapping White Lady beneath pagoda 30 35
3094 2500c. Xiao Qing, Xu Xian praying at pagoda 30 35
3095 2500c. Xiao Qing attacking Fa Hai 30 35
3096 2500c. Fa Hai turned into crab 30 35

585 Walter Gropius (architect)

2001. Twentieth Century Achievements in Architecture, Art and Medicine. Multicoloured.

3097 2500c. Type **585** 30 35
3098 2500c. Aldo Rossi 30 35
3099 2500c. Le Corbusier 30 35
3100 2500c. Antonio Gaudi . . . 30 35
3101 2500c. Paolo Soleri 30 35
3102 2500c. Mies van der Rohe . 30 35
3103 2500c. Wassily Kandinsky . 30 35
3104 2500c. Henry Moore 30 35
3105 2500c. Marc Chagall 30 35
3106 2500c. Norman Rockwell . . 30 35
3107 2500c. Antonio Lopez Garcia 30 35
3108 2500c. Frida Kahlo 30 35
MS3109 Three sheets, each 93 × 64 mm. (a) 14000c. "FRANK LLOYD WRIGHT". (b) 14000c. "Picasso". (c) 14000c. Double helix structure of DNA molecule Set of 3 sheets . . . . 5·00 5·25

586 James Cagney

586a Margie Hendrix (shoulder at bottom right)

2001. Hollywood Legends. James Cagney and Edward G. Robinson. Designs showing different portraits.

3110 **586** 4000c. green and black 50 55
3111 – 4000c. green and black 50 55
3112 – 4000c. blue and black . . 50 55
3113 – 4000c. brown and black 50 55
3114 – 4000c. mauve and black 50 55
3115 – 4000c. orange and black 50 55
3116 – 4000c. green and black 50 55
3117 – 4000c. lilac, purple and black 50 55
3118 – 4000c. purple and black 50 55
3119 – 4000c. brown and black 50 55
3120 – 4000c. brown and black 50 55
3121 – 4000c. blue and black . . 50 55

Nos. 3110/15 (Cagney) and 3116/21 (Robinson) were each printed together, se-tenant, showing a photograph of the actor.

2001. Famous Girl Pop Groups. The Cookies (Nos. 3122/4), The Ronettes (Nos. 3125/7) and The Supremes (Nos. 3128/30). Multicoloured.

3122 2700c. Type **586a** 35 40
3123 2700c. Ethel McCrea (with straight hair) 35 40
3124 2700c. Pat Lyles's head (background at bottom right) 35 40
3125 2700c. Estelle Bennett (inscr and value clear of portrait) 35 40
3126 2700c. Veronica Bennett (inscr and value touch portrait) 35 40
3127 2700c. Nedra Talley (inscr touches, value clear of portrait) 35 40
3128 2700c. Florence Ballard (left earring) 35 40
3129 2700c. Mary Wilson (two earrings) 35 40
3130 2700c. Diana Ross (right earring) 35 40

Each group forms a horizontal strip with different background colour: The Cookies cobalt, The Ronettes blue and The Supremes yellow and red.

587 Edward "Kid" Ory (trombonist)

2001. Famous American Jazz Musicians. Multicoloured.

3131 4000c. Type **587** 50 55
3132 4000c. Earl "Fatha" Hines (pianist) 50 55
3133 4000c. Lil Hardin-Armstrong (pianist) . . . 50 55
3134 4000c. John Philip Sousa (composer) 50 55
3135 4000c. James P. Johnson (pianist) 50 55
3136 4000c. Johnny St. Cyr (banjo/guitar player) . . . 50 55
3137 4000c. Scott Joplin (composer) 50 55
3138 4000c. Clarence Williams (pianist) 50 55
3139 4000c. Sidney Bechet (clarinetist/saxophonist) 50 55
3140 4000c. Willie "The Lion" Smith (pianist) 50 55
3141 4000c. Ferdinand "Jelly Roll" Morton (composer) 50 55
3142 4000c. Coleman "Bean" Hawkins (saxophonist) . . 50 55
MS3143 Two sheets, each 60 × 77 mm. (a) 14000c. Louis "Satchmo" Armstrong (cornet player). (b) 14000c. Joe "King" Oliver (cornet player) Set of 2 sheets . . . . 3·50 3·75

588 "Cranes" (Kano Eisen'in Michinobu)

2001. "Philanippon '01" International Stamp Exhibition, Tokyo. Japanese Paintings. Multicoloured.

3144 500c. Type **588** 10 10
3145 800c. "Flowers and Trees in Chen Chun's Style" (Tsubaki Chinzan) . . . 10 15
3146 1200c. "Poetry Contest of 42 Matches" (unsigned) 15 20
3147 2000c. "Cranes" (different detail) (Kano Eisen'in Michinobu) 25 30
3148 3000c. "Coming-of-Age Rite" (vert) 35 40
3149 3000c. "West Wing" (vert) 35 40
3150 3000c. "Akuta River" (vert) 35 40
3151 3000c. "Eastbound Trip: Mt. Utsu" (vert) 35 40
3152 3000c. "Eastbound Trip: Mt. Fuji" (vert) 35 40
3153 3000c. "Eastbound Trip: Black-headed Gulls" (vert) 35 40
3154 3000c. "Crossing Kawachi" (vert) 35 40
3155 3000c. "By Well Wall" (vert) 35 40
3156 4000c. "Excursion through South Gate" (vert) . . . 50 55
3157 4000c. "Excursion through East Gate" (vert) 50 55
3158 4000c. "Excursion through North Gate" (vert) . . . 50 55
3159 4000c. "Excursion through West Gate" (vert) 50 55
3160 4000c. "Sakyamuni entering Nirvana" (vert) 50 55
3161 4000c. "Animals" (vert) . . 50 55
3162 5000c. "Poetry Contest of 42 Matches" (different detail) (unsigned) 60 65
3163 12000c. "Plum Trees" (Tani Buncho) . . . . 1·50 1·60
MS3164 Four sheets, each 100 × 76 mm. (a) 14000c. "Cranes" (Kano Eisen'in Michinobu) ("GHANA" and value in red). (b) 14000c. "Cranes" (Kano Eisen'in Michinobu) ("GHANA" in yellow). (c) 14000c. "Coming-of-Age Rite" (Sumiyoshi Jokei). (d) 14000c. "Musashino Plain" (unknown artist) Set of 4 sheets 6·75 7·00

Nos. 3148/55 ("The Tales of Ise" (Sumiyoshi Jokei)) and 3156/63 ("The Story of Sakyamuni").

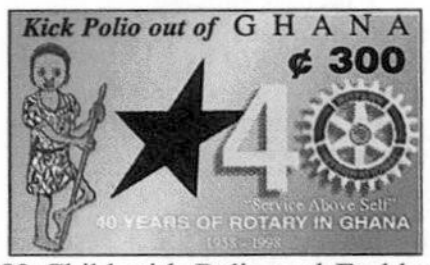

589 Child with Polio and Emblem

2001. 40th Anniv of Rotary in Ghana. Each including the Rotary International symbol. Multicoloured.

3165 300c. Type **589** 10 10
3166 1100c. Boy getting clean water from tap 15 20
3167 1200c. Paul Harris (founder of Rotary International) 15 20
3168 1800c. Man giving blood . . 20 25

590 Bentley S-Series Convertible (1950)

2001. "Belgica 2001" International Stamp Exhibition, Brussels. Twentieth-century classic Cars. Multicoloured.

3169 2000c. Type **590** 25 30
3170 3000c. Chrysler Town and Country (1948) 35 40
3171 4000c. B.M.W. 507 (1956–59) 50 55
3172 4000c. Bentley English Tourer (1934) 50 55
3173 4000c. Morris Minor (1948) 50 55
3174 4000c. Daimler SP-250 Dart (1954) 50 55
3175 4000c. DeSoto Custom Convertible (1950) 50 55
3176 4000c. Ford Thunderbird (1955–60) 50 55
3177 4000c. Porsche 356B (1959–63) 50 55
3178 4000c. Rolls-Royce Silver Cloud (1962) 50 55
3179 4000c. Austin Healey Sprite Mk 1 (1958) 50 55
3180 4000c. Mercedes 300SL (1954–57) 50 55
3181 4000c. Citroen 2cv (1949) 50 55
3182 4000c. Cadillac Series-62 (1949) 50 55
3183 5000c. Lotus Elite (1957) . . 60 65
3184 6000c. Corvette Sting Ray (1966) 75 80
MS3185 Two sheets, each 102 × 74 mm. (a) 14000c. Mercedes-Benz (1933) (85 × 28 mm). (b) 14000c. Triumph TR2 (1953–55) (85 × 28 mm) Set of 2 sheets . . . . 3·50 3·75

No. 3172 is inscribed "Bentler" and No. 3181 "Citreon", both in error.

590a Princess Victoria as a Young Girl

590b Mao in Uniform acknowledging Crowd

2001. Death Centenary of Queen Victoria. Multicoloured.
3186 5000c. Type **590a** 60 65
3187 5000c. Albert Edward, Prince of Wales 60 65
3188 5000c. Queen Victoria and Prince of Wales 60 65
3189 5000c. Queen Victoria and Prince Albert on Wedding Day 60 65
MS3190 66 × 96 mm. 12000c. Princess Victoria (The Princess Royal) . . . . 1·50 1·60
MS3190 is inscr Princess Victoria in error.

2001. 25th Death Anniv of Mao Tse-tung (Chinese leader). Multicoloured.
3191 7000c. Type **590b** 85 90
3192 7000c. Head and shoulders portrait 85 90
3193 7000c. Mao in overcoat acknowledging crowd . . 85 90
MS3194 116 × 102 mm. 12000c. Mao as a young man . . . . 1·50 1·75

590c "Zaandam"

2001. 75th Death Anniv Claude-Oscar Monet. (French painter). Multicoloured.
3195 5000c. Type **590c** 60 65
3196 5000c. "On the Seine at Bennecourt" 60 65
3197 5000c. "The Studio-boat" 60 65
3198 5000c. "Houses on the Waterfront, Zaandam" . . 60 65
MS3199 139 × 110 mm. 15000c. "Madame Gaudibert" (vert) . . 1·80 1·90

590d Queen Elizabeth in pink hat
590e Giuseppe Verdi

2001. 75th Birthday of Queen Elizabeth II. Multicoloured.
3200 4000c. Type **590d** 50 55
3201 4000c. Queen Elizabeth in white hat with flowers . . 50 55
3202 4000c. In red "trilby" . . . 50 55
3203 4000c. Wearing tiara 50 55
3204 4000c. In matching blue and pink hat and coat 50 55
3205 4000c. Queen Elizabeth in uniform for Trooping the Colour 50 55
MS3206 85 × 135 mm. 15000c. Queen Elizabeth with Duke of Edinburgh (horiz) . . . . . . 1·80 1·90

2001. Death Centenary of Giuseppe Verdi (Italian composer). Multicoloured.
3207 5000c. Type **590e** 60 65
3208 5000c. Musical scores for *Aida* and *Rigoletto* . . . 60 65
3209 5000c. Inn at Le Roncole (Verdi's birthplace) . . . 60 65
3210 5000c. Map of Italy 60 65
MS3211 76 × 106 mm. 13000c. Giuseppe Verdi . . . . 1·60 1·70
Nos. 3207/11 were printed together, se-tenant, with the backgrounds forming a composite design.

590f "Jane Avril leaving the Moulin Rouge"

2001. Death Centenary of Henri de Toulouse-Lautrec (French painter). Multicoloured.
3212 6700c. Type **590f** 80 85
3213 6700c. "Jane Avril dancing" 80 85
3214 6700c. "Jane Avril entering the Moulin Rouge" . . . 80 85

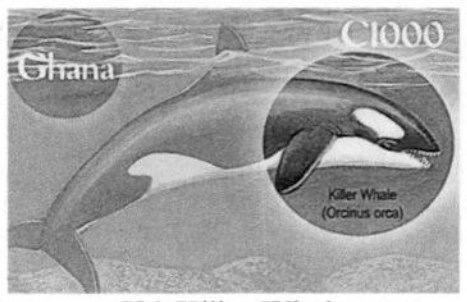

591 Killer Whale

2001. Whales and Dolphins. Multicoloured.
3215 1000c. Type **591** 10 15
3216 3000c. Narwhal 35 40
3217 4000c. Humpback whale . . 50 55
3218 4000c. Fin whale 50 55
3219 4000c. Bowhead whale . . . 50 55
3220 4000c. Grey whale 50 55
3221 4000c. Narwhal 50 55
3222 4000c. White whale ("Beluga") 50 55
3223 4000c. Head of blue whale 50 55
3224 4000c. Killer whale 50 55
3225 4000c. Northern bottlenose dolphin 50 55
3226 4000c. Sperm whale 50 55
3227 4000c. Southern right whale 50 55
3228 4000c. Pygmy right whale 50 55
3229 5000c. White whale ("Beluga") 60 65
3230 6000c. Bowhead whale . . . 75 80
MS3231 Two sheets, each 100 × 85 mm. (a) 14000c. Blue whale adult and calf. (b) 14000c. Head of sperm whale Set of 2 sheets . . . . 3·50 3·75
Nos. 3217/22 and 3223/8 were each printed together, se-tenant, the backgrounds forming composite designs.

592 *Paphiopedilum hennisianum*

2001. African Orchids. Multicoloured.
3232 1100c. Type **592** 15 20
3233 1200c. *Vuylstekeara cambria Plush* 15 20
3234 1800c. *Cymbidium Ormoulu* 20 25
3235 2000c. *Phalaenopsis Barbara Moler* 25 30
3236 4500c. *Odontocidium Tigersun* 55 60
3237 4500c. *Miltonia Emotion* . . 55 60
3238 4500c. *Odontonia sappho Excul* 55 60
3239 4500c. *Cymbidium Bulbarrow* 55 60
3240 4500c. *Dendrobium nobile* . . 55 60
3241 4500c. *Paphiopedilum insigne* 55 60
3242 4500c. *Cattleya capra* . . . 55 60
3243 4500c. *Odontoglossum rossii* 55 60
3244 4500c. *Epidendrum pseudepidendrum* 55 60
3245 4500c. *Encyclia cochleata* . . 55 60
3246 4500c. *Cymbidium Baldoyle Melbury* 55 60
3247 4500c. *Phalaenopsis asean* 55 60
MS3248 Two sheets, each 68 × 98 mm. (a) 15000c. *Calanthe vestita*. (b) 15000c. *Angraecum eburneum* Set of 2 sheets . . . 3·50 3·75

593 50th Anniversary Logo

2001. 50th Anniv of Kwame Nkrumah University of Science and Technology, Kumasi. Multicoloured.
3249 300c. Type **593** 10 10
3250 700c. Main entrance 10 10
3251 1100c. Milking cows 15 20
3252 1200c. Students in pharmacy department 15 20
3253 1800c. Halls of residence . . 20 25
MS3254 120 × 100 mm. As Nos. 3250/3, but each with a face value of 4000c. . . . . 1·90 2·00

594 Bamboo Orchestra

2001. Musical Instruments. Multicoloured.
3255 4000c. Type **594** 50 55
3256 4000c. Women playing mensuon (wind instruments) 50 55
3257 4000c. Fontomfrom (drums) 50 55
3258 4000c. Pati 50 55

595 George Olah (Chemistry Prize, 1994)

2002. Centenary of Nobel Prizes. Chemistry Prize Winners (except Nos. **MS**3277d/e). Multicoloured.
3259 4000c. Type **595** 50 55
3260 4000c. Kary Mullis (1993) 50 55
3261 4000c. Sir Harold Kroto (1996) 50 55
3262 4000c. Richard Ernst (1991) 50 55
3263 4000c. Ahmed Zewail (1999) 50 55
3264 4000c. Paul Crutzen (1995) 50 55
3265 4000c. John Walker (1997) 50 55
3266 4000c. Jens Skou (1997) . . 50 55
3267 4000c. Alan MacDiarmid (2000) 50 55
3268 4000c. Thomas Cech (1989) 50 55
3269 4000c. John Pople (1998) . . 50 55
3270 4000c. Rudolph Marcus (1992) 50 55
3271 4000c. Walter Kohn (1998) 50 55
3272 4000c. Frank Rowland (1995) 50 55
3273 4000c. Mario Molina (1995) 50 55
3274 4000c. Hideki Shirakawa (2000) 50 55
3275 4000c. Paul Boyer (1997) . . 50 55
3276 4000c. Richard Smalley (1996) 50 55
MS3277 Five sheets, each 106 × 77 mm. (a) 15000c. Svante Arrhenius (1903). (b) 15000c. Alfred Werner (1913). (c) 15000c. Peter Debye (1936). (d) 15000c. Wole Soyinka (Literature, 1986). (e) 15000c. Nelson Mandela (Peace, 1993) Set of 5 sheets . . 9·00 9·25

596 Queen Elizabeth at the Races

2002. Golden Jubilee. Multicoloured.
3278 6500c. Type **596** 80 85
3279 6500c. Queen Elizabeth on horseback 80 85
3280 6500c. Queen Elizabeth inspecting horses 80 85
3281 6500c. Queen Elizabeth in carriage with Duke of Edinburgh, Ascot races 80 85
MS3282 76 × 108 mm. 15000c. Princess Elizabeth with Duke of Edinburgh . . . . 1·80 1·90

597 Conference Logo
598 Jay Jay Okacha (Nigeria)

2002. 5th International Copyright Conference, Accra. Multicoloured.
3283 300c. Type **597** 10 10
3284 700c. Girl reading (horiz) . . 10 10
3285 1100c. Spider on web (horiz) 15 20
3286 1200c. Woven cloth in shape of Ghana (horiz) 15 20
3287 1800c. Woman playing drum (horiz) 20 25

2002. World Cup Football Championship, Japan and Korea. Multicoloured.
3288 100c. Type **598** 10 10
3289 150c. South African player 10 10
3290 300c. Pele (Brazil) 10 10
3291 400c. Roger Milla (Cameroun) 10 10
3292 500c. Bobby Charlton (England) 10 10
3293 800c. Michel Platini (France) 10 15
3294 1000c. Franz Beckenbauer (West Germany) 10 15
3295 1500c. Ulsan Munsu Stadium, Korea (horiz) 20 25
3296 2000c. German player . . . 25 30
3297 3000c. Brazilian player . . . 35 40
3298 4000c. South Korean player 50 55
3299 5000c. Yokohama International Stadium, Japan (horiz) 60 65
3300 6000c. Italian player 75 80
3301 11000c. Publicity poster, Brazil, 1950 . . . . . . 1·30 1·40
3302 12000c. Publicity poster, Italy, 1934 . . . . 1·50 1·60
MS3303 Two sheets. (a) 77 × 107 mm. 15000c. Geoff Hurst (England), 1966 (43 × 58 mm). (b) 107 × 77 mm. 15000c. Gordon Banks (England), 1970 (58 × 43 mm) Set of 2 sheets . . 3·50 3·75

599 Girl on Pony

2002. Chinese New Year ("Year of the Horse"). Multicoloured.
3304 4000c. Type **599** 50 55
3305 4000c. Girl and caparisoned pony 50 55
3306 4000c. Girl with whip and pony 50 55
3307 4000c. Girl on hobby horse 50 55

2002. No. 2159a surch **c 1000**.
3308 1000c. on 1100c. Kente cloth . . . . 2·00 2·25

2002. No. 2458e surch **c2,500**.
3309 2500c. on 800c. *Cyrestis camillus* (butterfly) . . . . 4·50 5·00

602 Crown Prince Willem-Alexander and Princess Maxima of the Netherlands

2002. "Amphilex 2002" International Stamp Exhibition, Amsterdam. Visit of Crown Prince and Princess of the Netherlands. Multicoloured.
3310 6000c. Type **602** 75 80
3311 6000c. Royal couple on wedding day 75 80
3312 6000c. Standing by windmill 75 80
3313 6000c. Serenaded by accordionist on wedding day 75 80
3314 6000c. Meeting crowds . . . 75 80
3315 6000c. Kissing on wedding day 75 80

603 "Trying to retrieve a Ball caught in a Tree"

2002. Japanese Paintings by Katsukawa Shunsho. Multicoloured.
MS3316 170 × 123 mm. 9000c. Type **603**; 9000c. "Listening to a Cuckoo in the Bedroom"; 9000c. "Holding a Cage filled with Fireflies for a Woman to read a Book" . . . . 3·25 3·50
MS3317 170 × 123 mm. 9000c. "Mother and Child taking a Tub-bath while Woman holds a Revolving Lantern"; 9000c. "Strips of Paper with Wishes and Poems are Tied on a Bamboo"; 9000c. "Women enjoying the Cool Air on a Boat" . . . . 3·25 3·50
MS3318 170 × 123 mm. 9000c. "Celebrating Feast of the Chrysanthemum"; 9000c. "Looking out for Coloured Leaves"; 9000c. "Mother reading Picture Book while sitting at a Foot-warmer" . . . . 3·25 3·50
MS3319 Four sheets, each 95 × 105 mm. (a) 15000c. "Three Women decorating a Gate with Twigs of Holly on the Day before the Setting-in of the Spring". (b) 15000c. Woman looking at flowering plant in pot. (c) 15000c. Woman at writing desk. (d) 15000c. Woman pulling down blind Set of 4 sheets . . . . . 7·25 7·50

Nos. **MS**3316/19a show details of paintings on silk "Activities of Women in the Twelve Months".
Nos. **MS**3319b/d show details from triptych "Snow, Moonlight and Flowers".

604 Scout hiking

2002. 20th World Scout Jamboree, Thailand. Multicoloured.
MS3320 109×90 mm. 6500c. Type **604**; 6500c. Scout hiking (standing on horizon); 6500c. Campfire and tent; 6500c. Scout tying knot . . . . 3·25 3·50
MS3321 99×71 mm. 15000c. Ghanian scout (vert) . . . . . 1·80 1·90

605 Mt. Tateyama, Japan

2002. International Year of Mountains. Multicoloured.
MS3322 105×90 mm. 6000c. Type **605**; 6000c. Mt. Shivling, India; 6000c. Wong Leng, Hong Kong; 6000c. Mt. Blanc, France 3·00 3·25
MS3323 100×72 mm. 15000c. Mt. Fuji, Japan . . . . 1·80 1·90

606 Lindbergh and Ryan NYP Special *Spirit of St. Louis*

2002. 75th Anniv of First Solo Trans-Atlantic Flight. Multicoloured.
MS3324 171×129 mm. 8500c. Type **606**; 8500c. Charles and Anne Lindbergh in *Spirit of St. Louis* . . . . 2·00 2·10
MS3325 114×81 mm. 15000c. Charles Lindbergh (vert) . . . 1·80 1·90

607 Variable Sunbird

609 Ice Skaters

2002. Year of Eco Tourism. Multicoloured.
MS3326 116×125 mm. 4000c. Type **607**; 4000c. Leopard; 4000c. Kob (antelope); 4000c. African buffalo; 4000c. Chimpanzee; 4000c. Lesser bushbaby . . . . . 3·00 3·25
MS3327 81×97 mm. 12000c. African elephant . . . . 1·50 1·60

2002. Queen Elizabeth the Queen Mother Commemoration. Nos. 2191/5 (95th Birthday) surch **C3000**.

3328	3000c. on 600c. brown, light brown and black	35	40
3329	3000c. on 600c. multicoloured	35	40
3330	3000c. on 600c. multicoloured	35	40
3331	3000c. on 600c. multicoloured	35	40
MS3332	102×127 mm. 20000c. on 2500c. multicoloured	2·40	2·50

The sheetlet and miniature sheet margins have black borders and are overprinted **IN MEMORIAM 1900–2002**.

2002. Winter Olympic Games, Salt Lake City. Multicoloured.

3333	7000c. Type **609**	95	1·00
3334	7000c. Skier in aerials competition	95	1·00
MS3335	88×119 mm. Nos. 3333/4	2·00	2·10

610 US Flag as Statue of Liberty with Ghana Flag

2002. "United We Stand". Support for Victims of 11 September 2001 Terrorist Attacks.
3336 **610** 7000c. multicoloured . . 95 1·00

611 Malachite Kingfisher

2002. Birds, Butterflies, Insects and Moths. Multicoloured.
MS3337 160×93 mm. 4500c. Type **611**; 4500c. Brown snake eagle ("Brown Harrier-eagle"); 4500c. Heuglin's masked weaver; 4500c. Egyptian plover; 4500c. Swallow-tailed bee eater; 4500c. Black-faced fire-finch . . . . . 3·25 3·50
MS3338 160×93 mm. 4500c. *Iolaus menas*; 4500c. *Neptis melicerta*; 4500c. *Cymothoe lucas*; 4500c. *Euphaedra francina*; 4500c. Lilac nymph; 4500c. Mocker swallowtail 3·25 3·50
MS3339 160×93 mm. 4500c. *Phymateus viridipes* (bush-hopper); 4500c. *Tomatares citrinus* (ant-lion); 4500c. *Amegilla acraensis* (digger-bee); 4500c. *Mesotopus tarandus* (stag-beetle); 4500c. *Pseudocreobotra wahlbergi* (mantis); 4500c. *Phosphorus jansoni* (longhorn beetle) . . . 3·25 3·50
MS3340 160×93 mm. 4500c. *Phiala cunina*; 4500c. *Mazuca strigicincta*; 4500c. Steindachner's emperor moth; 4500c. *Amphicallia pactolicus*; 4500c. Verdant sphinx moth; 4500c. Oleander hawk-moth 3·25 3·50
MS3341 Four sheets, each 83×86 mm. (a) 15000c. Rufous fishing owl. (b) 15000c. Giant blue swallowtail. (c) 15000c. *Pseudocreobotra wahlbergi* (mantis nymph). (d) 15000c. African moon-moth Set of 4 sheets . . 7·25 7·50

612 Casting of Net

2002. Edina Bakatue Festival. Multicoloured.

3342	1000c. Type **612**	10	15
3343	2000c. Chief in palanquin	25	30
3344	2500c. Canoe in regatta . .	30	35
3345	3000c. Fishermen in festival boat	35	40
3346	4000c. Opening ritual . . .	50	55
3347	5000c. Parade of priestesses	60	65
MS3348	160×90 mm. 4000c. As No. 3347; 4000c. As No. 3343; 4000c. As No. 3344; 4000c. As No. 3345; 4000c. As No. 3346; 4000c. Type **612**	2·50	2·60

613 Home Economics

614 Kofi Annan with Pres. Kufuor at Nobel Prize Award Ceremony

2002. 25th Anniv of Japan Overseas Co-operation Volunteers in Ghana. Multicoloured.

3349	1000c. Type **613**	10	15
3350	1000c. Public health administration	10	15
3351	2000c. Education in science and mathematics	25	30
3352	2500c. Computer technology	30	35
3353	3000c. Judo coaching . . .	35	40
MS3354	172×120 mm. 4000c. As No. 3351; 4000c. As No. 3350; 4000c. As No. 3353; 4000c. As No. 3352; 4000c. Type **613** . .	2·50	2·75

Stamps from No. **MS**3354 have the white descriptive inscriptions omitted.

2002. Kofi Annan (United Nations Secretary-General). Multicoloured.

3355	1000c. Type **614**	10	15
3356	2000c. Kofi Annan holding Citation and Nobel Peace Medal	25	30
3357	2500c. Kofi Annan	30	35
3358	3000c. In academic procession, Kwame Nkrumah University, Kumasi	35	40

615 Charlie Chaplin

616 Marlene Dietrich

2003. 25th Death Anniv of Charlie Chaplin (actor and director). Multicoloured.
MS3359 151×126 mm. 6500c. Type **615**; 6500c. Wearing dark jacket; 6500c. Wearing pinstriped dungarees; 6500c. Holding Honorary Academy Award, 1972 3·25 3·50

2003. 10th Death Anniv (2002) of Marlene Dietrich (actress and singer). Sheets containing T **616** and similar vert designs showing different portraits.
MS3360 127×178 mm. 4500c.×6 multicoloured . . . . 3·25 3·40
MS3361 76×101 mm. 15000c. Holding cigarette . . . . . . 1·80 1·90

617 Popeye alongside Canal

618 "Under the Pagoda Tree"

2003. "Popeye the Sailorman tours Amsterdam". Multicoloured.
MS3362 173×202 mm. 4500c. Type **617**; 4500c. Outside Anne Frank's House; 4500c. At Restaurant Row; 4500c. Downtown, carrying Olive Oyl; 4500c. At Central Station; 4500c. With telescope, by windmill . . 3·25 3·40
MS3363 136×93 mm. 15000c. Eating spinach (50×75 mm) 1·80 1·90

2003. Chinese New Year ("Year of the Ram").
MS3364 141×115 mm. **618** 5000c. ×4 multicoloured . . . . . . 2·40 2·50

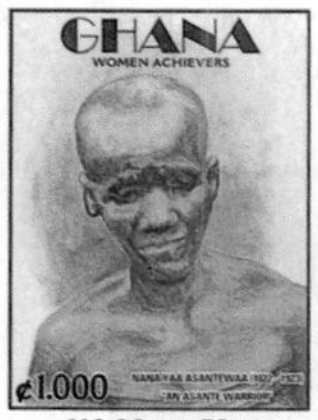

619 Nana Yaa Asantewaa (Asante warrior)

620 Children holding Drawings ("tomorrow's leaders")

2003. Women Achievers. Multicoloured.

3365	1000c. Type **619**	10	15
3366	2000c. Justice Annie Jiagge (judge)	25	30
3367	2500c. Dr. Esther Ocloo (industrialist)	30	35
3368	3000c. Dr. Efua T. Sutherland (playwright)	35	40
3369	5000c. Rebecca Dedei Aryeetay (womens rights activist)	60	65

2003. 60th Anniv of British Council in Ghana. Multicoloured.

3370	1000c. Type **620**	10	15
3371	2000c. Women holding Africawoman newspapers	25	30
3372	2500c. Singers on stage ("partners in culture") . .	30	35
3373	3000c. People reading in library ("window on the world")	35	40
3374	5000c. Footballers and coach ("leadership through sport")	60	65

621 Queen Elizabeth II wearing Diadem

623 Romain Maes (1935)

622 Ryan NYP Special *Spirit of St. Louis*

2003. 50th Anniv of Coronation. Multicoloured.
MS3375 156×94 mm. 10000c. Type **621**; 10000c. Queen wearing blue dress and hat; 10000c. Wearing Garter robes . . . . 3·60 3·75
MS3376 76×106 mm. 20000c. Wearing Garter robes (different) 2·40 2·50

2003. Centenary of Powered Flight. Multicoloured.
MS3377 185×116 mm. 7000c. Type **622**; 7000c. Lockheed Vega V *Winnie Mae* (first solo round-the-world flight, 1933); 7000c. Heinkel He 178 (first turbo-jet aircraft, 1939); 7000c. Bell XS-1 rocket airplane (first manned supersonic flight, 1947) . . . . 3·40 3·50
MS3378 106×76 mm. 20000c. Dr. Robert Goddard and first liquid-fuelled rocket . . . . . 2·40 2·50

2003. Centenary of Tour de France Cycle Race. Designs showing past winners. Multicoloured.
MS3379 Type **623**; 7000c. Sylvere Maes (1936); 7000c. Roger Lapebie (1937); 7000c. Gino Bartali (1938) . . . . 3·40 3·50
MS3380 107×75 mm. 20000c. Henri Pelissier (1923) . . . . 2·40 2·50

624 Cadillac Sixty Special (1941)

2003. Centenary of General Motors Cadillac. Multicoloured.
MS3381 126×176 mm. 7000c. Type **624**; 7000c. Eldorado (1953); 7000c. Eldorado Brougham (1957); 7000c. Eldorado Convertible (1959) . . . . . . 3·40 3·50
MS3382 90×125 mm. 20000c. Early Cadillac . . . . 2·40 2·50

625 Corvette (1962)

2003. 50th Anniv of General Motors Chevrolet Corvette. Multicoloured.

MS3383		126×152 mm. 7000c. Type **625**; 7000c. Corvette Stingray (1963); 7000c. Corvette Stingray (1964); 7000c. Corvette (1968)	3·40	3·50
MS3384		126×89 mm. 20000c. Corvette Stingray (1966)	2·40	2·50

POSTAGE DUE STAMPS

1958. Postage Due stamps of Gold Coast optd **GHANA** and bar.

D 9	D 1	1d. black	10	30
D10		2d. black	10	30
D11		3d. black	10	30
D12		6d. black	15	65
D13		1s. black	20	1·50

D 3

1958.

D14	D 3	1d. red	10	30
D15		2d. green	10	30
D16		3d. orange	10	30
D17		6d. blue	10	50
D18		1s. violet	15	2·00

1965. Surch **Ghana New Currency 19th July. 1965.** and value.

D19	D 3	1p. on 1d.	10	60
D20		2p. on 2d.	10	80
D21		3p. on 3d.	10	80
D22		6p. on 6d.	10	1·75
D23		12p. on 1s.	15	2·25

1968. Nos. D20/2 additionally surch.

D24	D 3	1½n.p. on 2p. on 2d.	5·50	4·25
D25		2½n.p. on 3p. on 3d.	1·00	5·00
D26		5n.p. on 6p. on 6d.	1·25	

1970. Inscr in new currency.

D27	D 3	1n.p. red	1·25	4·50
D28		1½n.p. green	1·50	5·00
D29		2½n.p. orange	1·75	6·50
D30		5n.p. blue	2·50	6·50
D31		10n.p. violet	3·25	8·00

1980. Currency described as "p".

D32	D 3	2p. orange	1·25	4·25
D33		3p. brown	1·25	4·25

GIBRALTAR Pt. 1

A British colony at the W. entrance to the Mediterranean.

1886. 12 pence = 1 shilling;
20 shillings = 1 pound.
1971. 100 (new) pence = 1 pound.

1886. Stamps of Bermuda (Queen Victoria) optd **GIBRALTAR**.

1	9	½d. green	13·00	7·00
2		1d. red	50·00	4·25
3		2d. purple	£100	75·00
4		2½d. blue	£140	3·25
5		4d. orange	£130	85·00
6		6d. lilac	£200	£180
7		1s. brown	£425	£350

2

7

1886. Various frames.

39	2	½d. green	6·00	1·75
40		1d. red	6·50	50
10		2d. purple	30·00	19·00
42		2½d. blue	30·00	50
12		4d. brown	75·00	75·00
13		6d. lilac	£100	£100
14		1s. brown	£190	£180

1889. Surch with new value in **CENTIMOS**.

15	2	5c. on ½d. green	6·00	19·00
16		10c. on 1d. red	12·00	9·50
17		25c. on 2d. purple	4·75	7·00
18		25c. on 2½d. blue	20·00	2·25
19		40c. on 4d. brown	50·00	70·00
20		50c. on 6d. lilac	55·00	70·00
21		75c. on 1s. brown	55·00	65·00

1889.

22	7	5c. green	4·50	80
23		10c. red	4·50	50
24		20c. green and brown	42·00	18·00
25		20c. green	11·00	70·00
26		25c. blue	18·00	70
27		40c. brown	3·75	2·75
28		50c. lilac	3·25	2·00
29		75c. green	32·00	32·00
30		1p. brown	75·00	20·00
31		1p. brown and blue	4·75	5·00
32		2p. black and red	10·00	30·00
33		5p. grey	42·00	£100

1898. As 1886.

41	2	2d. purple and blue	22·00	1·75
43		4d. brown and green	18·00	6·50
44		6d. violet and red	42·00	20·00
45		1s. brown and red	38·00	16·00

8

9

1903.

66	8	½d. green	4·00	1·75
57c		1d. purple on red	5·00	85
58a		2d. green and red	8·50	5·50
49		2½d. purple and black on blue	4·75	60
60a		6d. purple and violet	30·00	11·00
61		1s. black and red	48·00	13·00
62	9	2s. green and blue	75·00	95·00
53		4s. purple and green	80·00	£140
54		8s. purple and black on blue	£110	£140
55		£1 purple and black on red	£500	£600

1907.

67	8	1d. red	5·50	60
68		2d. grey	8·00	11·00
69		2½d. blue	5·00	1·60
70		6d. purple	£130	£375
71		1s. black on green	23·00	21·00
72	9	2s. purple and blue on blue	50·00	48·00
73		4s. black and red	£110	£140
74		8s. purple and green	£190	£190

1912. As T **8/9**, but portrait of King George V. (3d. A. Inscr "3 PENCE". B. Inscr "THREE PENCE").

89		½d. green	1·50	1·50
90		1d. red	1·75	1·00
91a		1½d. brown	1·75	30
93		2d. grey	1·25	1·25
79		2½d. blue	6·50	2·00
95a		3d. blue (A)	2·50	1·50
109		3d. blue (B)	7·50	2·00
97a		6d. purple	1·60	3·50
81		1s. black on green	9·00	3·25
102a		1s. olive and black	14·00	12·00
82		2s. purple and blue on blue	26·00	3·50
103		2s. brown and black	9·50	30·00
104		2s.6d. green and black	9·50	18·00
83		4s. black and red	32·00	55·00
105		5s. red and black	15·00	50·00
84		8s. purple and green	80·00	95·00
106		10s. blue and black	32·00	70·00
85		£1 purple and black on red	£130	£200
107		£1 orange and black	£140	£180
108		£5 violet and black	£1300	£4000

1918. Optd **WAR TAX**.

86		½d. green (No. 89)	1·00	1·75

13 The Rock of Gibraltar

1931.

110	13	1d. red	2·50	2·50
111		1½d. brown	1·75	2·25
112		2d. grey	6·50	1·75
113		3d. blue	5·50	3·00

1935. Silver Jubilee. As T **10a** of Gambia.

114		2d. blue and black	1·60	2·50
115		3d. brown and blue	3·25	3·50
116		6d. green and blue	9·50	12·00
117		1s. grey and purple	10·00	10·00

1937. Coronation. As T **10b** of Gambia.

118		½d. green	25	30
119		2d. grey	1·50	3·00
120		3d. blue	2·75	3·00

14 King George VI

15 Rock of Gibraltar

1938. King George VI.

121	14	½d. green	10	40
122b	15	1d. brown	50	60
123		1½d. red	35·00	75
123b	–	1½d. violet	75	1·50
124a	–	2d. grey	2·00	35
124c	–	2d. red	50	60
125b	–	3d. blue	50	30
125c	–	5d. orange	1·00	1·25
126b	–	6d. red and violet	4·25	1·75
127b	–	1s. black and green	3·25	4·25
128b	–	2s. black and brown	5·00	6·50
129b	–	5s. black and red	17·00	17·00
130a	–	10s. black and blue	38·00	25·00
131	14	£1 orange	38·00	45·00

DESIGNS—HORIZ: 2d. The Rock (North side); 3d., 5d. Europa Point; 6d. Moorish Castle; 1s. South-port Gate; 2s. Eliott Memorial; 5s. Government House; 10s. Catalan Bay.

1946. Victory. As T **11a** of Gambia.

132		½d. green	10	75
133		3d. blue	40	1·00

1948. Silver Wedding. As T **11b/11c** of Gambia.

134		½d. green	80	1·50
135		£1 orange	50·00	70·00

1949. U.P.U. As T **11d/11g** of Gambia.

136		2d. red	1·00	1·25
137		3d. blue	2·00	1·50
138		6d. purple	1·25	2·00
139		1s. green	1·00	3·25

1950. Inauguration of Legislative Council. Optd **NEW CONSTITUTION 1950**.

140		2d. red (No. 124c)	30	1·50
141		3d. blue (No. 125b)	65	1·00
142		6d. red and violet (No. 126b)	75	2·00
143		1s. black and green (No. 127b)	75	1·75

1953. Coronation. As T **11h** of Gambia.

144		½d. black and green	50	1·50

24 Cargo and Passenger Wharves

1953.

145	24	½d. blue and green	15	30
146	–	1d. green	1·50	40
147	–	1½d. black	1·00	1·25
148	–	2d. brown	1·75	60
149a	–	2½d. red	3·00	1·00
150	–	3d. blue	4·00	10
151	–	4d. blue	4·25	3·50
152	–	5d. purple	1·00	1·00
153	–	6d. black and blue	1·50	1·00
154a	–	1s. blue and brown	40	80
155a	–	2s. orange and violet	23·00	4·50
156	–	5s. brown	28·00	12·00
157	–	10s. brown and blue	45·00	35·00
158	–	£1 red and yellow	45·00	40·00

DESIGNS—HORIZ: 1d. South view from Straits; 1½d. Gibraltar Fish Canneries; 2d. Southport Gate; 2½d. Sailing in the Bay; 3d. Liner; 4d. Coaling wharf; 5d. Airport; 6d. Europa Point; 1s. Straits from Buena Vista; 2s. Rosia Bay and Straits; 5s. Main entrance, Government House. VERT: 10s. Tower of Homage, Moorish Castle; £1 Arms of Gibraltar.

1954. Royal Visit. As No. 150, but inscr "ROYAL VISIT 1954".

159		3d. blue	20	20

38 Gibraltar Candytuft

40 Rock and Badge of Gibraltar Regiment

1960.

160	38	½d. purple and green	15	50
161	–	1d. black and green	20	10
162	–	2d. blue and brown	70	20
163a	–	2½d. black and blue	65	30
164	–	3d. blue and orange	30	10
199	–	4d. brown and turquoise	30	1·75
166	–	6d. brown and green	70	70
167	–	7d. blue and red	1·75	1·75
168	–	9d. blue and turquoise	1·00	1·00
169	–	1s. brown and green	1·50	70
170	–	2s. brown and blue	16·00	2·75
171	–	5s. blue and green	8·00	6·00
172	–	10s. yellow and blue	20·00	13·00
173	40	£1 black and brown	15·00	12·00

DESIGNS (As Type **38**):—HORIZ: 1d. Moorish Castle; 2d. St George's Hall; 3d. The Rock by moonlight; 4d. Catalan Bay; 1s. Barbary ape; 2s. Barbary Partridge; 5s. Blue Rock Thrush. VERT: 2½d. The keys; 6d. Map of Gibraltar; 7d. Air terminal; 9d. American War Memorial; 10s. Rock lily.

1963. Freedom from Hunger. As T **20a** of Gambia.

174		9d. sepia	3·75	1·50

1963. Centenary of Red Cross. As T **20b** of Gambia.

175		1d. red and black	1·00	1·75
176		9d. red and blue	5·00	3·75

1964. 400th Birth Anniv of Shakespeare. As T **22a** of Gambia.

177		7d. bistre	50	20

1964. New Constitution. Nos. 164 and 166 optd **NEW CONSTITUTION 1964.**

178		3d. blue and orange	20	10
179		6d. sepia and green	20	60

44 I.T.U. Emblem

1965. Centenary of I.T.U.

180	44	4d. green and yellow	2·00	50
181		2s. green and blue	5·50	3·25

45 I.C.Y. Emblem

1965. I.C.Y.

182	45	½d. green and lavender	20	2·25
183		4d. purple and turquoise	70	50

The value of the ½d. stamp is shown as "1/2".

46 Winston Churchill and St. Paul's Cathedral in Wartime

1966. Churchill Commemoration.

184	46	½d. blue	20	2·25
185		1d. green	30	10
186		4d. brown	1·25	10
187		9d. violet	1·25	2·50

47 Footballer's Legs, Ball and Jules Rimet Cup

1966. World Cup Football Championships.

188	47	2½d. multicoloured	75	1·00
189		6d. multicoloured	1·00	50

53 Red Seabream

1966. European Sea Angling Championships. Gibraltar.

190	53	4d. red, blue and black	30	10
191	–	7d. red, green and black	30	70
192	–	1s. brown, green and black	50	30

DESIGNS—HORIZ: 7d. Red scorpionfish. VERT: 1s. Stone bass.

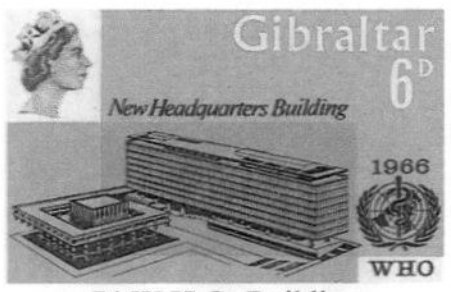

54 W.H.O. Building

1966. Inauguration of W.H.O. Headquarters, Geneva.

193	54	6d. black, green and blue	2·75	1·75
194		9d. black, purple and ochre	3·25	1·75

56 "Our Lady of Europa"

1966. Centenary of Re-enthronement of "Our Lady of Europa".

195	56	2s. blue and black	30	80

56a "Education"

56b "Science"

56c "Culture"

1966. 20th Anniv of U.N.E.S.C.O.

196	56a	2d. multicoloured	35	10
197	56b	7d. yellow, violet and olive	1·50	10
198	56c	5s. black, purple & orge	3·50	3·00

57 H.M.S. "Victory"

1967. Multicoloured.

200		½d. Type **57**	10	20
201		1d. "Arab" (early steamer)	10	10
202		2d. H.M.S. "Carmania" (merchant cruiser)	15	10
203		2½d. "Mons Calpe" (ferry)	40	30
204		3d. "Canberra" (liner)	20	10
205		4d. H.M.S. "Hood" (battle cruiser)	30	10
205a		5d. "Mirror" (cable ship)	2·00	55
206		6d. Xebec (sailing vessel)	30	50
207		7d. "Amerigo Vespucci" (Italian cadet ship)	30	60
208		9d. "Raffaello" (liner)	30	1·00
209		1s. "Royal Katherine" (galleon)	30	35
210		2s. H.M.S. "Ark Royal" (aircraft carrier, 1937)	3·50	2·50
211		5s. H.M.S. "Dreadnought" (nuclear submarine)	3·50	7·00
212		10s. "Neuralia" (liner)	14·00	23·00
213		£1 "Mary Celeste" (sailing vessel)	14·00	23·00

58 Aerial Ropeway

1967. International Tourist Year. Multicoloured.

214		7d. Type **58**	15	10
215		9d. Shark fishing (horiz)	15	10
216		1s. Skin-diving (horiz)	20	15

59 Mary, Joseph and Child Jesus

1967. Christmas. Multicoloured.

217		2d. Type **59**	15	10
218		6d. Church window (vert)	15	10

61 General Eliott and Route Map

1967. 250th Birth Anniv of General Eliott. Mult.

219		4d. Type **61**	15	10
220		9d. Heathfield Tower and Monument, Sussex	15	10
221		1s. General Eliott (vert)	15	10
222		2s. Eliott directing rescue operations (55 × 21 mm)	25	50

65 Lord Baden-Powell

1968. 60th Anniv of Gibraltar Scout Association.

223	65	4d. buff and violet	15	10
224	–	7d. ochre and green	15	20
225	–	9d. blue, orange and black	15	30
226	–	1s. yellow and green	15	30

DESIGNS: 7d. Scout flag over the Rock; 9d. Tent, Scouts and salute; 1s. Scout badges.

66 Nurse and W.H.O. Emblem

1968. 20th Anniv of W.H.O. Multicoloured.

227		2d. Type **66**	10	15
228		4d. Doctor and W.H.O. emblem	10	10

68 King John signing Magna Carta

70 Shepherd, Lamb and Star

1968. Human Rights Year.

229	68	1s. orange, brown and gold	15	10
230	–	2s. myrtle and gold	15	20

DESIGN: 2s. "Freedom" and Rock of Gibraltar.

1968. Christmas. Multicoloured.

231		4d. Type **70**	10	10
232		9d. Mary holding Holy Child	15	20

72 Parliament Houses

1969. Commonwealth Parliamentary Association Conference.

233	72	4d. green and gold	10	10
234	–	9d. violet and gold	10	10
235	–	2s. red, gold and blue	15	20

DESIGNS—HORIZ: 9d. Parliamentary emblem and outline of "The Rock". VERT: 2s. Clock Tower, Westminster (Big Ben) and Arms of Gibraltar.

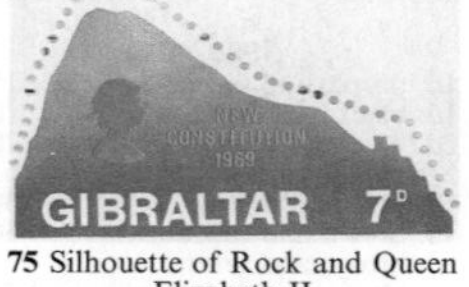

75 Silhouette of Rock and Queen Elizabeth II

1969. New Constitution.

236	75	½d. gold and orange	10	10
237		5d. silver and green	20	10
238		7d. silver and purple	20	10
239		5s. silver and blue	65	1·10

77 Soldier and Cap Badge, Royal Anglian Regiment, 1969

80 "Madonna of the Chair" (detail, Raphael)

1969. Military Uniforms (1st series). Multicoloured.

240		1d. Royal Artillery Officer, 1758, and modern cap badge	15	10
241		6d. Type **77**	20	15
242		9d. Royal Engineers' Artificer, 1786, and modern cap badge	30	15
243		2s. Private, Fox's Marines, 1704, and modern Royal Marines' cap badge	75	70

See also Nos. 248/51, 290/3, 300/303, 313/16, 331/4, 340/3 and 363/6.

1969. Christmas. Multicoloured.

244		5d. Type **80**	10	35
245		7d. "Virgin and Child" (detail, Morales)	20	35
246		1s. "The Virgin of the Rocks" (detail, Leonardo da Vinci)	20	40

83 Europa Point

88 Stamp and Rock of Gibraltar

1970. Europa Point.

247	83	2s. multicoloured	45	30

1970. Military Uniforms (2nd series). As T **77**. Multicoloured

248		2d. Royal Scots Officer (1839) and cap badge	25	10
249		5d. South Wales Borderers Private (1763) and cap badge	35	10
250		7d. Queen's Royal Regiment Private (1742) and cap badge	35	10
251		2s. Royal Irish Rangers piper (1969) and cap badge	1·00	90

1970. "Philympia 70" Stamp Exhibition, London.

252	88	1s. red and green	15	10
253	–	2s. blue and mauve	25	65

DESIGN: 2s. Stamp and Moorish Castle.

The stamps shown in the designs are well-known varieties with values omitted.

90 "The Virgin and Mary" (stained-glass window, Gabriel Loire)

1970. Christmas.

254	90	2s. multicoloured	30	40

91 Saluting Battery, Rosia

92 Saluting Battery, Rosia, Modern View

1971. Decimal Currency.

255	91	½p. multicoloured	20	30
256	92	½p. multicoloured	20	30
257	–	1p. multicoloured	80	30
258	–	1p. multicoloured	80	30
259	–	1½p. multicoloured	20	50
260	–	1½p. multicoloured	20	50
317	–	2p. multicoloured	1·25	2·00
318	–	2p. multicoloured	1·25	2·00
263a	–	2½p. multicoloured	20	50
264	–	2½p. multicoloured	20	50
265	–	3p. multicoloured	20	20
266	–	3p. multicoloured	20	20
319	–	4p. multicoloured	1·40	2·25
320	–	4p. multicoloured	1·40	2·25
269	–	5p. multicoloured	35	35
270	–	5p. multicoloured	35	35
271	–	7p. multicoloured	65	65
272	–	7p. multicoloured	65	65
273	–	8p. multicoloured	70	80
274	–	8p. multicoloured	70	80
275	–	9p. multicoloured	70	80
276	–	9p. multicoloured	70	80
277	–	10p. multicoloured	80	80
278	–	10p. multicoloured	80	80
279	–	12½p. multicoloured	1·00	1·75
280	–	12½p. multicoloured	1·00	1·75
281	–	25p. multicoloured	1·10	1·75
282	–	25p. multicoloured	1·10	1·75
283	–	50p. multicoloured	1·25	2·50
284	–	50p. multicoloured	1·25	2·50
285	–	£1 multicoloured	2·00	4·00
286	–	£1 multicoloured	2·00	4·00

DESIGNS: The two versions of each value show the same Gibraltar view taken from an early 19th-century print (first design) or modern photograph (second design): HORIZ: 1p. Prince George of Cambridge Quarters and Trinity Church; 1½p. The Wellington Bust, Alameda Gardens; 2p. Gibraltar from the North Bastion; 2½p. Catalan Bay; 3p. Convent Garden; 4p. The Exchange and Spanish Chapel; 5p. Commercial Square and Library; 7p. South Barracks and Rosia Magazine; 8p. Moorish Mosque and Castle; 9p. Europa Pass Road; 10p. South Barracks from Rosia Bay; 12½p. Southport Gates; 25p. Trooping the Colour, The Alameda. VERT: 50p. Europa Pass Gorge; £1 Prince Edward's Gate.

93

94 Regimental Arms

1971. Coil Stamps.

287	93	½p. orange	15	30
288		1p. blue	15	30
289		2p. green	50	1·10

1971. Military Uniforms (3rd series). As T **77**. Multicoloured.

290		1p. The Black Watch (1845)	35	30
291		2p. Royal Regimental of Fusiliers (1971)	55	30
292		4p. King's Own Royal Border Regiment (1704)	75	50
293		10p. Devonshire and Dorset Regiment (1801)	2·75	3·00

1971. Presentation of Colours to the Gibraltar Regiment.

294	94	3p. black, gold and red	55	30

95 Nativity Scene

1971. Christmas. Multicoloured.

295		3p. Type **95**	40	60
296		5p. Mary and Joseph going to Bethlehem	40	65

96 Soldier Artificer, 1773

97 "Our Lady of Europa"

1972. Bicentenary of Royal Engineers in Gibraltar. Multicoloured.

297		1p. Type **96**	40	60
298		3p. Modern tunneller	50	80
299		5p. Old and new uniforms and badge (horiz)	60	90

1972. Military Uniforms (4th series). As T **77**. Multicoloured.

300		1p. The Duke of Cornwall's Light Infantry, 1704	50	20
301		3p. King's Royal Rifle Corps, 1830	1·25	40

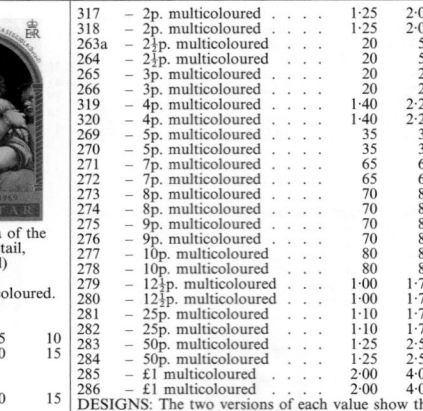

302 7p. 37th North Hampshire, Officer, 1825 . . . . . . 2·00 70
303 10p. Royal Navy, 1972 . . . 2·25 1·50

1972. Christmas.
304 **97** 3p. multicoloured 10 20
305 5p. multicoloured 10 35

98 Keys of Gibraltar and "Narcissus niveus"

1972. Royal Silver Wedding.
306 **98** 5p. red 25 20
307 7p. green 25 20

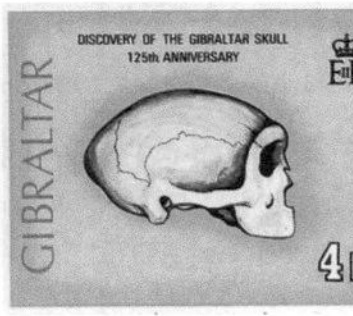

99 Flags of Member Nations and E.E.C. Symbol

100 Skull

1973. Britain's Entry into E.E.C.
308 **99** 5p. multicoloured 40 50
309 10p. multicoloured . . . . 60 1·00

1973. 125th Anniv of Gibraltar Skull Discovery. Multicoloured.
310 4p. Type **100** . . . . 1·25 50
311 6p. Prehistoric man . . . . . 1·50 70
312 10p. Prehistoric family . . . 2·00 1·25
No. 312 is size 40 × 26 mm.

1973. Military Uniforms (5th series). As T **77**. Multicoloured.
313 1p. King's Own Scottish Borderers, 1770 . . . . . 50 50
314 4p. Royal Welsh Fusiliers, 1800 . . . . 1·50 1·10
315 6p. Royal Northumberland Fusiliers, 1736 . . . . . . 2·25 2·25
316 10p. Grenadier Guards, 1898 3·00 4·50

101 "Nativity" (Danckerts)

1973. Christmas.
321 **101** 4p. violet and red 30 15
322 6p. mauve and blue . . . 40 1·10

101a Princess Anne and Captain Mark Phillips

1973. Royal Wedding.
323 **101a** 6p. multicoloured . . . 10 10
324 14p. multicoloured . . . 20 20

102 Victorian Pillar-box

103 "Madonna with the Green Cushion" (Solario)

1974. Centenary of U.P.U. Multicoloured.
325 2p. Type **102** 15 30
326 6p. Pillar-box of George VI 20 35
327 14p. Pillar-box of Elizabeth II 30 80
Nos. 325/7 also come self-adhesive from booklet panes.

1974. Military Uniforms (6th series). As T **77**. Multicoloured.
331 4p. East Lancashire Regiment, 1742 . . . . . 50 50
332 6p. Somerset Light Infantry, 1833 . . . . 70 70
333 10p. Royal Sussex Regiment, 1790 . . . . 1·00 1·40
334 16p. R.A.F. officer, 1974 . . 2·25 4·00

1974. Christmas. Multicoloured.
335 4p. Type **103** 40 30
336 6p. "Madonna of the Meadow" (Bellini) 60 95

104 Churchill and Houses of Parliament

1974. Birth Centenary of Sir Winston Churchill. Multicoloured.
337 **104** 6p. black, purple and lavender 25 15
338 – 20p. black, brown and red 35 45
MS339 114 × 93 mm. Nos. 337/8 4·50 6·50
DESIGN: 20p. Churchill and "King George V" (battleship).

1975. Military Uniforms (7th series). As T **77**. Multicoloured.
340 4p. East Surrey Regiment, 1846 . . . . 30 20
341 6p. Highland Light Infantry, 1777 . . . . 45 40
342 10p. Coldstream Guards, 1704 . . . . 60 70
343 20p. Gibraltar Regiment, 1974 . . . . 1·10 2·50

105 Girl Guides' Badge

1975. 50th Anniversary of Gibraltar Girl Guides.
346 **105** 5p. gold, blue and violet 25 55
347 7p. gold, brown and light brown 35 60
348 – 15p. silver, black and brown . . . . 50 1·25
No. 348 is as Type **105** but shows a different badge.

106 Child at Prayer

107 Bruges Madonna

1975. Christmas. Multicoloured.
349 6p. Type **106** 40 60
350 6p. Angel with lute 40 60
351 6p. Child singing carols . . . 40 60
352 6p. Three children 40 60
353 6p. Girl at prayer 40 60
354 6p. Boy and lamb 40 60

1975. 500th Birth Anniv of Michelangelo. Multicoloured.
355 6p. Type **107** 20 25
356 9p. Taddei Madonna 20 40
357 15p. Pieta . . . . 30 1·10
Nos. 355/7 also come self-adhesive from booklet panes.

108 Bicentennial Emblem and Arms of Gibraltar

109 The Holy Family

1976. Bicentenary of American Revolution.
361 **108** 25p. multicoloured . . . 50 50
MS362 85 × 133 mm. No. 361 × 4 4·50 7·00

1976. Military Uniforms (8th series). As T **24**. Multicoloured.
363 1p. Suffolk Regiment, 1795 15 20
364 6p. Northamptonshire Regiment, 1779 . . . . . 30 30
365 12p. Lancashire Fusiliers, 1793 . . . . 40 60
366 25p. Ordnance Corps, 1896 55 1·40

1976. Christmas. Multicoloured.
367 6p. Type **109** 25 15
368 9p. Madonna and Child . . . 35 25
369 12p. St. Bernard 50 60
370 20p. Archangel Michael . . . 85 1·40
Nos. 367/70 show different stained-glass windows from St. Joseph's Church, Gibraltar.

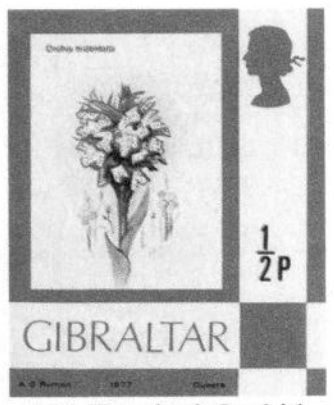

110 Queen Elizabeth II, Royal Arms and Gibraltar Arms

111 Toothed Orchid

1977. Silver Jubilee. Multicoloured.
371 **110** 6p. red 15 20
372 £1 blue . . . . 1·10 2·25
MS373 124 × 115 mm. Nos. 371/2 1·25 2·25

1977. Birds, Flowers, Fish and Butterflies. Multicoloured.
374 ½p. Type **111** . . . . 60 2·25
375 1p. Red mullet (horiz) . . . 15 70
376 2p. "Maculinea arion" (butterfly) (horiz) . . . . 30 1·75
377 2½p. Sardinian warbler . . . 1·75 2·50
378 3p. Giant squill 20 10
379 4p. Grey wrasse (horiz) . . 30 10
380 5p. "Vanessa atalanta" (butterfly) (horiz) . . . . 50 1·00
381 6p. Black kite . . . . . . 2·25 55
382 9p. Shrubby scorpion-vetch 70 70
383 10p. John dory (fish) (horiz) 40 20
384 12p. "Colias crocea" (butterfly) (horiz) . . . . 1·00 35
384b 15p. Winged asparagus pea 1·50 55
385 20p. Audouin's gull . . . . 2·00 3·00
386 25p. Barbary nut (iris) . . . 1·25 2·00
387 50p. Swordfish (horiz) . . . 2·00 1·50
388 £1 "Papilio machaon" (butterfly) (horiz) . . . . 4·25 5·00
389 £2 Hoopoe . . . . 9·00 11·00
389a £5 Arms of Gibraltar . . . 10·00 11·00

112 "Our Lady of Europa" Stamp

1977. "Amphilex '77" Stamp Exhibition, Amsterdam. Multicoloured.
390 6p. Type **112** 10 20
391 12p. "Europa Point" stamp 15 30
392 25p. "E.E.C. Entry" stamp 20 50

113 "The Annunciation" (Rubens)

1977. Christmas and 400th Birth Anniv of Rubens. Multicoloured.
393 3p. Type **113** 10 10
394 9p. "The Adoration of the Magi" 25 25
395 12p. "The Adoration of the Magi" (horiz) 30 50
396 15p. "The Holy Family under the Apple Tree" 30 55
MS397 110 × 200 mm. Nos. 393/6 2·75 4·00

114 Aerial View of Gibraltar

1978. Gibraltar from Space. Multicoloured.
398 12p. Type **114** 25 50
MS399 148 × 108 mm. 25p. Aerial view of Straits of Gibraltar . . 80 80

115 Holyroodhouse

1978. 25th Anniv of Coronation. Multicoloured.
400 6p. Type **115** 20 15
401 9p. St. James's Palace 25 15
402 12p. Sandringham 30 30
403 18p. Balmoral 40 85
406 25p. Windsor Castle . . . . 90 2·00
Nos. 402/3 also exist as self-adhesive stamps from booklet panes, No. 406 only coming in this form.

116 Short S.25 Sunderland, 1938–58

1978. 60th Anniv of Royal Air Force. Multicoloured.
407 3p. Type **116** 15 10
408 9p. Caudron G-3, 1918 . . . 35 40
409 12p. Avro Shackleton M.R.2, 1953–66 . . . . 40 55
410 16p. Hawker Hunter F.6, 1954–77 . . . . 45 1·00
411 18p. Hawker Siddeley Nimrod M.R.1, 1969–78 50 1·10

117 "Madonna with Animals"

1978. Christmas. Paintings by Durer. Multicoloured.
412 5p. Type **117** 20 10
413 9p. "The Nativity" 25 15
414 12p. "Madonna of the Goldfinch" 30 40
415 15p. "Adoration of the Magi" . . . . 35 1·00

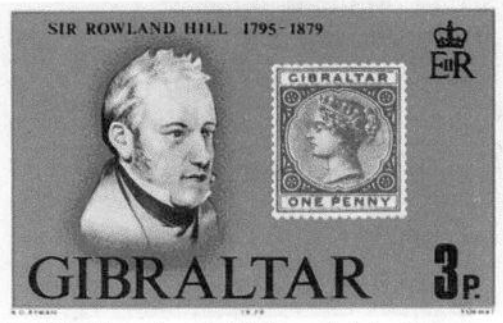

118 Sir Rowland Hill and 1d. Stamp of 1886

1979. Death Centenary of Sir Rowland Hill.
416 **118** 3p. multicoloured 10 10
417 – 9p. multicoloured 15 15
418 – 12p. multicoloured . . . 15 20
419 – 25p. black, purple yellow 25 50
DESIGNS: 9p. 1971 1p. coil stamp; 12p. 1840 Post Office Regulations; 25p. "G" cancellation.

119 Posthorn, Dish Antenna and Early Telephone

1979. Europa. Communications.
420 **119** 3p. green and pale green 15 10
421 9p. brown and ochre . . 30 90
422 12p. blue and violet . . . 35 1·25

120 African Child **121** Early Policeman

1979. Christmas. International Year of the Child. Multicoloured.
423 12p. Type **120** 25 30
424 12p. Asian child 25 30
425 12p. Polynesian child 25 30
426 12p. American Indian child 25 30
427 12p. Nativity and children of different races 25 30
428 12p. European child 25 30

1980. 150th Anniv of Gibraltar Police Force. Multicoloured.
429 3p. Type **121** 20 10
430 6p. Policemen of 1895, early 1900s and 1980 . . . . . 20 15
431 12p. Police officer and police ambulance 25 20
432 37p. Policewoman and police motor-cyclist . . . . . . 55 1·25

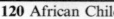

122 Peter Amigo (Archbishop) **124** "Horatio Nelson" (J. F. Rigaud)

123 Queen Elizabeth the Queen Mother

1980. Europa. Personalities. Multicoloured.
433 12p. Type **122** 20 30
434 12p. Gustavo Bacarisas (artist) 20 30
435 12p. John Mackintosh (philanthropist) 20 30

1980. 80th Birthday of The Queen Mother.
436 **123** 15p. multicoloured . . . 30 30

1980. 175th Death Anniv of Nelson. Paintings. Multicoloured.
437 3p. Type **124** 15 10
438 9p. "H.M.S. Victory' (horiz) 25 25
439 15p. "Horatio Nelson" (Sir William Beechey) 35 35
440 40p. "'H.M.S. Victory' being towed into Gibraltar" (Clarkson Stanfield) (horiz) 80 1·00
MS441 159 × 99 mm. No. 439 . . 75 1·75

125 Three Kings

1980. Christmas.
442 **125** 15p. brown and yellow . . 25 35
443 – 15p. brown and yellow . . 25 35
DESIGN: No. 443, Nativity scene.

126 Hercules creating the Mediterranean **127** Dining-room

1981. Europa. Multicoloured.
444 9p. Type **126** 20 15
445 15p. Hercules and Pillars of Hercules 25 35

1981. 450th Anniv of The Convent (Governor's Residence). Multicoloured.
446 4p. Type **127** 10 10
447 14p. King's Chapel 15 15
448 15p. The Convent 15 15
449 55p. Cloister 60 80

128 Prince Charles and Lady Diana Spencer **129**

1981. Royal Wedding.
450 **128** £1 multicoloured . . . . 1·25 1·25

1981.
451 **129** 1p. black 30 30
452 4p. blue 30 30
453 15p. green 30 30

130 Paper Airplane

1981. 50th Anniv of Gibraltar Airmail Service. Multicoloured
454 14p. Type **130** 15 15
455 15p. Airmail letters, post box and aircraft tail fin 15 15
456 55p. Jet airliner circling globe 60 80

131 Carol Singers

1981. Christmas. Children's Drawings. Multicoloured.
457 15p. Type **131** 30 15
458 55p. Postbox (vert) . . . . . 1·00 85

132 I.Y.D.P. Emblem and Stylized Faces

1981. International Year for Disabled Persons.
459 **132** 14p. multicoloured . . . 30 30

133 Douglas DC-3

1982. Aircraft. Multicoloured.
460 1p. Type **133** . . . . 25 2·00
461 2p. Vickers Viking 1B . . . 30 1·75
462 3p. Airspeed Ambassador AS.57 . . . . 30 1·75
463 4p. Vickers Viscount 800 . . 40 20
464 5p. Boeing 727-100 . . . . . 90 60
465 10p. Vickers Vanguard . . . 1·75 50
466 14p. Short Solent 2 . . . . . 1·75 3·50
467 15p. Fokker F.27 Friendship 2·75 3·50
468 17p. Boeing 737 . . . . . . 1·00 55
469 20p. B.A.C. One Eleven . . . 1·00 50
470 25p. Lockheed Constellation 4·00 4·50
471 50p. Hawker Siddeley Comet 4B . . . . 4·00 2·25
472 £1 Saro Windhover . . . . . 5·50 2·25
473 £2 Hawker Siddeley Trident 2E . . . . 6·50 5·00
474 £5 De Havilland D.H.89A Dragon Rapide . . . . . 8·00 14·00

134 Crest, H.M.S. "Opossum" **136** Gibraltar Chamber of Commerce Centenary

135 Hawker Hurricane Mk I and Supermarine Spitfires at Gibraltar

1982. Naval Crests (1st series). Multicoloured.
475 $\frac{1}{2}$p. Type **134** 10 30
476 15$\frac{1}{2}$p. H.M.S. "Norfolk" . . 30 55
477 17p. H.M.S. "Fearless" . . . 30 60
478 60p. H.M.S. "Rooke" . . . 75 2·75
See also Nos. 493/6, 510/13, 522/5, 541/4, 565/8, 592/5, 616/19 and 651/4.

1982. Europa. Operation Torch. Multicoloured.
479 14p. Type **135** 25 70
480 17p. General Giraud, General Eisenhower and Gibraltar 35 80

1982. Anniversaries. Multicoloured.
481 $\frac{1}{2}$p. Type **136** 10 65
482 15$\frac{1}{2}$p. British Forces Postal Service centenary 45 30
483 60p. 75th anniv of Gibraltar Scout Association . . . . 1·25 2·00

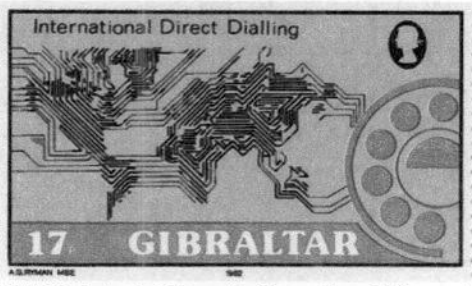

137 Printed Circuit forming Map of World

1982. International Direct Dialling.
484 **137** 17p. black, blue and orange 35 35

138 Gibraltar illuminated at Night and Holly

1982. Christmas. Multicoloured.
485 14p. Type **138** 50 30
486 17p. Gibraltar illuminated at night and mistletoe 50 35

139 Yacht Marina

1983. Commonwealth Day. Multicoloured.
487 4p. Type **139** 10 10
488 14p. Scouts and Guides Commonwealth Day Parade 20 15
489 17p. Flag of Gibraltar (vert) 25 20
490 60p. Queen Elizabeth II (from photo by Tim Graham) (vert) . . . . . 70 1·00

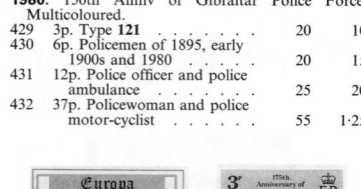

140 St. George's Hall Gallery

1983. Europa.
491 **140** 16p. black and brown . . 35 50
492 – 19p. black and blue . . . 40 75
DESIGN: 19p. Water catchment slope.

1983. Naval Crests (2nd series). As T **134**. Multicoloured.
493 4p. H.M.S. "Faulknor" . . . 30 10
494 14p. H.M.S. "Renown" . . . 70 35
495 17p. H.M.S. "Ark Royal" . . 75 40
496 60p. H.M.S. "Sheffield" . . . 1·75 1·50

141 Landport Gate, 1729

1983. Fortress Gibraltar in the 18th Century. Multicoloured.
497 4p. Type **141** 15 10
498 17p. Koehler Gun, 1782 . . . 35 30
499 77p. King's Bastion, 1779 . . 1·00 1·25
MS500 97 × 145 mm. Nos. 497/9 . 2·25 1·50

142 "Adoration of the Magi" (Raphael)

1983. Christmas. 500th Birth Anniv of Raphael. Multicoloured.
501 4p. Type **142** 25 10
502 17p. "Madonna of Foligno" (vert) 70 35
503 60p. "Sistine Madonna" (vert) . . . . 1·75 1·40

143 1932 2d. Stamp and Globe

1984. Europa, Posts and Telecommunications. Multicoloured.
504 17p. Type **143** 35 50
505 23p. Circuit board and globe 45 1·00

144 Hockey

1984. Sports. Multicoloured.
506 20p. Type **144** 70 80
507 21p. Basketball 70 80
508 26p. Rowing . . . . 70 1·25
509 29p. Football . . . . 70 1·50

1984. Naval Crests (3rd series). As T **134**. Multicoloured.
510 20p. H.M.S. "Active" . . . . 1·60 2·00
511 21p. H.M.S. "Foxhound" . . 1·60 2·25
512 26p. H.M.S. "Valiant" . . . 1·75 2·25
513 29p. H.M.S. "Hood" . . . . 1·90 2·50

145 Mississippi River Boat Float

1984. Christmas. Epiphany Floats. Multicoloured.
514 20p. Type **145** 30 30
515 80p. Roman Temple float . . 1·40 2·75

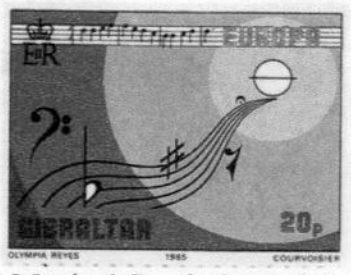

146 Musical Symbols, and Score from Beethoven's 9th (Choral) Symphony

1985. Europa. European Music Year. Multicoloured.
516 **146** 20p. multicoloured . . . 30 30
517 – 29p. multicoloured . . . 40 1·50
DESIGN: The 29p. is as T **146**, but shows different symbols.

147 Globe and Stop Polio Campaign Logo

1985. Stop Polio Campaign.
518 26p. multicoloured (Type **147**) . . . . 90 1·40
519 26p. multicoloured ("ST" visible) . . . . 90 1·40
520 26p. multicoloured ("STO" visible) . . . . 90 1·40
521 26p. multicoloured ("STOP" visible) . . . . 90 1·40
Each design differs in the position of the logo across the centre of the globe. On No. 518 only the letter "S" is fully visible, on No. 519 "ST", on No. 520 "STO" and on No. 521 "STOP". Other features of the design also differ, so that the word "Year" moves towards the top of the stamp and on No. 521 the upper logo is omitted.

1985. Naval Crests (4th series). As T **134**. Multicoloured.
522 4p. H.M.S. "Duncan" . . . 60 10
523 9p. H.M.S. "Fury" 90 50
524 21p. H.M.S. "Firedrake" . . 2·00 2·00
525 80p. H.M.S. "Malaya" . . . 4·00 6·00

148 I.Y.Y. Logo **149** St. Joseph

1985. International Youth Year. Multicoloured.
526 4p. Type **148** 35 10
527 20p. Hands passing diamond 1·40 1·10
528 80p. 75th anniv logo of Girl Guide Movement . . . . 3·25 3·75

1985. Christmas. Centenary of St. Joseph's Parish Church. Multicoloured.
529 4p. Type **149** 65 90
530 4p. St. Joseph's Parish Church 65 90
531 80p. Nativity crib . . . . . 4·00 4·75

150 "Papilio machaon" (butterfly) and The Convent

1986. Europa. Nature and the Environment. Multicoloured.
532 22p. Type **150** . . . . 1·00 50
533 29p. Herring gull and Europa Point . . . . 1·50 4·25

151 1887 Queen Victoria 6d. Stamp **152** Queen Elizabeth II in Robes of Order of the Bath

1986. Centenary of First Gibraltar Postage Stamps. Designs showing stamps. Multicoloured.
534 4p. Type **151** 30 10
535 22p. 1903 Edward VII 2½d. 1·00 1·00
536 32p. 1912 George V 1d. . . . 1·50 2·00
537 36p. 1938 George VI £1 . . . 1·60 2·50
538 44p. 1953 Coronation ½d. (29 × 46 mm) . . . . . . 2·00 3·00
MS539 102 × 73 mm. 29p. 1886 "GIBRALTAR" overprinted on Bermuda 1d. . . . . 2·50 2·75

1986. 60th Birthday of Queen Elizabeth II.
540 **152** £1 multicoloured . . . . 1·75 3·00

1986. Naval Crests (5th series). As T **134**. Multicoloured.
541 22p. H.M.S. "Lightning" . . 1·75 1·00
542 29p. H.M.S. "Hermione" . . 2·00 1·75
543 32p. H.M.S. "Laforey" . . . 2·25 3·25
544 44p. H.M.S. "Nelson" . . . 2·75 4·50

153 Prince Andrew and Miss Sarah Ferguson

1986. Royal Wedding. Sheet 115 × 85 mm.
MS545 **153** 44p. multicoloured 1·40 2·25

154 Three Kings and Cathedral of St. Mary the Crowned **155** Neptune House

1986. Christmas. International Peace Year. Multicoloured.
546 18p. Type **154** . . . . 1·00 50
547 32p. St. Andrew's Church . . 1·50 3·00

1987. Europa. Architecture. Multicoloured.
563 22p. Type **155** . . . . 1·50 50
564 29p. Ocean Heights . . . . . 2·50 4·25

1987. Naval Crests (6th series). As T **134**. Multicoloured.
565 18p. H.M.S. "Wishart" . . . 1·25 75
566 22p. H.M.S. "Charybdis" . . 1·40 1·10
567 32p. H.M.S. "Antelope" . . 1·90 3·50
568 44p. H.M.S. "Eagle" . . . . 2·50 4·50

156 13-inch Mortar, 1783 **157** Victoria Stadium

1987. Guns. Multicoloured.
569 1p. Type **156** 20 70
570 2p. 6-inch coastal gun, 1909 30 70
571 3p. 8-inch howitzer, 1783 . . 30 70
572 4p. Bofors "L40/70" AA gun, 1951 . . . . 40 10
573 5p. 100 ton rifled muzzle-loader, 1882 . . . . 40 70
574 10p. 5.25 inch heavy AA gun, 1953 . . . . 40 70
575 18p. 25-pounder gun-how, 1943 . . . . 65 1·00
576 19p. 64-pounder rifled muzzle-loader, 1873 . . . 70 1·25
577 22p. 12-pounder gun, 1758 70 50
578 50p. 10-inch rifled muzzle-loader, 1870 . . . . 1·40 3·00
579 £1 Russian 24-pounder gun, 1854 . . . . 2·50 2·50
580 £3 9.2 inch "Mk 10" coastal gun, 1935 . . . . 3·50 14·00
581 £5 24-pounder gun, 1779 . . 6·00 16·00

1987. Bicentenary of Royal Engineers' Royal Warrant. Multicoloured.
582 18p. Type **157** . . . . 1·25 65
583 32p. Freedom of Gibraltar scroll and casket . . . . . 1·75 3·00
584 44p. Royal Engineers' badge 2·50 4·00

158 The Three Kings

1987. Christmas. Multicoloured.
585 4p. Type **158** 20 10
586 22p. The Holy Family . . . 1·00 1·00
587 44p. The Shepherds . . . . 1·90 3·50

159 "Canberra" (liner) passing Gibraltar

1988. Europa. Transport and Communications. Multicoloured.
588 22p. Type **159** . . . . 1·50 2·25
589 22p. "Gibline I" (ferry), dish aerial and Boeing 737 airliner . . . . 1·50 2·25
590 32p. Horse-drawn carriage and modern coach . . . . 2·00 2·75
591 32p. Car, telephone and Rock of Gibraltar . . . . 2·00 2·75

1988. Naval Crests (7th series). As T **134**.
592 18p. multicoloured . . . . . 1·50 65
593 22p. black, brown and gold 2·00 1·25
594 32p. multicoloured . . . . . 2·25 3·50
595 44p. multicoloured . . . . . 3·00 4·75
DESIGNS: 18p. H.M.S. "Clyde"; 22p. H.M.S. "Foresight"; 32p. H.M.S. "Severn"; 44p. H.M.S. "Rodney".

160 European Bee Eater

1988. Birds. Multicoloured.
596 4p. Type **160** 75 20
597 22p. Atlantic puffin . . . . . 1·75 90
598 32p. Western honey buzzard ("Honey Buzzard") . . . . 2·25 2·50
599 44p. Blue rock thrush . . . . 2·75 3·50

161 "Zebu" (brigantine)

1989. Operation Raleigh. Multicoloured.
600 19p. Type **161** 65 60
601 22p. Miniature of Sir Walter Raleigh and logo 75 70
602 32p. "Sir Walter Raleigh" (expedition ship) and world map . . . . 1·10 2·00
MS603 135 × 86 mm. 22p. As No. 601; 44p. "Sir Walter Raleigh" (expedition ship) passing Gibraltar . . . . 4·00 4·75

162 "Snowman" (Rebecca Falero)

1988. Christmas. Children's Paintings. Multicoloured.
604 4p. Type **162** 15 10
605 22p. "The Nativity" (Dennis Penalver) 55 60
606 44p. "Father Christmas" (Gavin Key) (23 × 31 mm) 1·00 2·00

163 Soft Toys and Toy Train

1989. Europa. Children's Toys. Multicoloured.
607 25p. Type **163** . . . . 1·25 75
608 32p. Soft toys, toy boat and doll's house . . . . 1·75 2·75

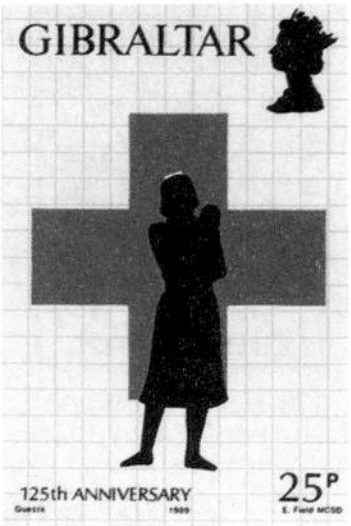

164 Port Sergeant with Keys **165** Nurse and Baby

1989. 50th Anniv of Gibraltar Regiment. Mult.
609 4p. Type **164** 40 10
610 22p. Regimental badge and colours . . . . 1·25 1·10
611 32p. Drum major . . . . . 1·75 3·00
MS612 124 × 83 mm. 22p. As No. 610; 44p. Former Gibraltar Defence Force badge . . . . . 4·50 4·75

1989. 125th Anniv of International Red Cross.
613 **165** 25p. black, red and brown 1·00 60
614 – 32p. black, red and brown 1·25 1·75
615 – 44p. black, red and brown 1·50 3·50
DESIGNS: 32p. Famine victims; 44p. Accident victims.

1989. Naval Crests (8th series). As T **134**.
616 22p. multicoloured . . . . . 1·50 75
617 25p. black and gold . . . . 1·50 1·50
618 32p. gold, black and red . . 2·00 3·25
619 44p. multicoloured . . . . . 3·00 5·00
DESIGNS: 22p. H.M.S. "Blankney"; 25p. H.M.S. "Deptford"; 32p. H.M.S. "Exmoor"; 44p. H.M.S. "Stork".

166 One Penny Coin **167** Father Christmas in Sleigh

1989. New Coinage. T **166** and similar vert designs in two miniature sheets.
MS620 72 × 94 mm. 4p. bronze, black and red (Type **166**); 4p. bronze, black and brown (two pence); 4p. silver, black and yellow (ten pence); 4p. silver, black and green (five pence) . . . . . . 1·25 1·75
MS621 100 × 95 mm. 22p. silver, black and green (fifty pence); 22p. gold, black and blue (five pounds); 22p. gold, black and brown (two pounds); 22p. gold, black and green (one pound); 22p. gold, black and violet (obverse of coin series); 22p. silver, black and blue (twenty pence) . . . . 4·75 6·50

1989. Christmas. Multicoloured.
622 4p. Type **167** 20 10
623 22p. Shepherds and sheep . . 90 70
624 32p. The Nativity . . . . . 1·40 1·75
625 44p. The Three Wise Men . . 2·25 4·00

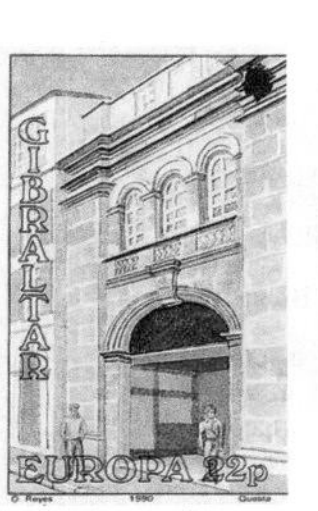

168 General Post Office Entrance **169** 19th-century Firemen

1990. Europa. Post Office Buildings. Multicoloured.
626 22p. Type **168** . . . . 1·00 1·50
627 22p. Interior of General Post Office . . . . 1·00 1·50
628 32p. Interior of South District Post Office . . . . 1·50 2·50
629 32p. South District Post Office . . . . 1·50 2·50

1990. 125th Anniv of Gibraltar Fire Service. Multicoloured.
630 4p. Type **169** 85 15
631 20p. Early fire engine (horiz) 2·00 1·10
632 42p. Modern fire engine (horiz) . . . . 2·50 3·75
633 44p. Modern fireman in breathing apparatus . . . 2·75 3·75

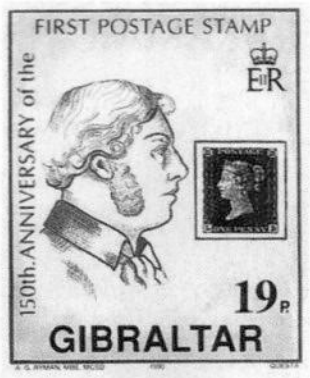

170 Henry Corbould (artist) and Penny Black

172 Candle and Holly

171 Model of Europort Development

1990. 150th Anniv of the Penny Black. Multicoloured.
634 19p. Type **170** 95 80
635 22p. Bath Royal Mail coach 1·00 90
636 32p. Sir Rowland Hill and Penny Black . . . . . . 2·25 4·00
MS637 145 × 95 mm. 44p. Penny Black with Maltese Cross cancellation . . . . 4·25 5·50

1990. Naval Crests (9th series). As T **134**. Multicoloured.
638 22p. H.M.S. "Calpe" . . . . 1·50 70
639 25p. H.M.S. "Gallant" . . . 1·60 1·75
640 32p. H.M.S. "Wrestler" . . . 2·00 3·25
641 44p. H.M.S. "Greyhound" 2·50 5·50

1990. Development Projects. Multicoloured.
642 22p. Type **171** 75 80
643 23p. Construction of building material factory . . . . . 75 1·50
644 25p. Land reclamation . . . 95 1·50

1990. Christmas. Multicoloured.
645 4p. Type **172** 15 10
646 22p. Father Christmas . . . 75 65
647 42p. Christmas tree . . . . . 1·50 2·50
648 44p. Nativity crib . . . . . 1·50 2·50

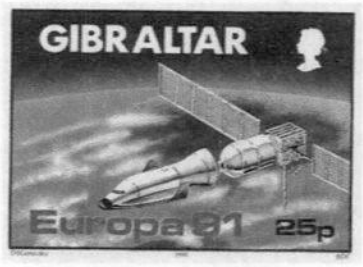

173 Space Laboratory and Spaceplane (Columbus Development Programme)

1991. Europa. Europe in Space. Multicoloured.
649 25p. Type **173** 75 75
650 32p. "ERS-1" earth resources remote sensing satellite . . 1·00 2·25

1991. Naval Crests (10th series). As T **134**.
651 4p. black, blue and gold . . 35 10
652 21p. multicoloured . . . . . 1·25 1·25
653 22p. multicoloured . . . . . 1·25 1·25
654 62p. multicoloured . . . . . 3·25 6·00
DESIGNS: 4p. H.M.S. "Hesperus"; 21p. H.M.S. "Forester"; 22p. H.M.S. "Furious"; 62p. H.M.S. "Scylla".

174 Shag

1991. Endangered Species. Birds. Multicoloured.
655 13p. Type **174** . . . . . . 85 1·25
656 13p. Barbary partridge . . . 85 1·25
657 13p. Egyptian vulture . . . . 85 1·25
658 13p. Black stork . . . . . . 85 1·25

1991. No. 580 surch **£1.05**.
659 £1.05 on £3 9.2-inch "Mk.10" coastal gun, 1935 . . . . 3·50 1·60

176 "North View of Gibraltar" (Gustavo Bacarisas)

1991. Local Paintings. Multicoloured.
660 22p. Type **176** 85 50
661 26p. "Parson's Lodge" (Elena Mifsud) . . . . 1·00 1·00
662 32p. "Governor's Parade" (Jacobo Azagury) . . . . 1·50 2·25
663 42p. "Waterport Wharf" (Rudesindo Mannia) (vert) 2·25 4·50

177 "Once in Royal David's City"

1991. Christmas. Carols. Multicoloured.
664 4p. Type **177** 30 10
665 24p. "Silent Night" . . . . . 1·50 70
666 25p. "Angels We Have Heard on High" . . . . 1·50 1·25
667 49p. "O Come All Ye Faithful" . . . . 2·25 5·00

178 "Danaus chrysippus"

1991. "Phila Nippon '91" International Stamp Exhibition, Tokyo. Sheet 116 × 91 mm.
MS668 **178** £1.05, multicoloured 3·50 4·50

179 Columbus and "Santa Maria"

1992. Europa. 500th Anniv of Discovery of America by Columbus. Multicoloured.
669 24p. Type **179** . . . . 1·25 2·00
670 24p. Map of Old World and "Nina" . . . . 1·25 2·00
671 34p. Map of New World and "Pinta" . . . . 1·50 2·50
672 34p. Map of Old World and look-out . . . . 1·50 2·50
Nos. 669/70 and 671/2 were issued together, se-tenant, each pair forming a composite design.

179a Gibraltar from North

1992. 40th Anniv of Queen Elizabeth II's Accession. Multicoloured.
673 4p. Type **179a** 15 10
674 20p. H.M.S. "Arrow" (frigate) and Gibraltar from south 60 60
675 24p. Southport Gates 75 80
676 44p. Three portraits of Queen Elizabeth . . . . 1·25 1·60
677 54p. Queen Elizabeth II . . . 1·60 1·90

180 Compass Rose, Sail, and Atlantic Map

181 Holy Trinity Cathedral

1992. Round the World Yacht Rally. Multicoloured designs, each incorporating compass rose and sail.
678 21p. Type **180** 75 80
679 24p. Map of Indonesian Archipelago (horiz) . . . . 95 1·40
680 25p. Map of India Ocean (horiz) . . . . 95 1·75
MS681 108 × 72 mm. 21p. Type **180**; 49p. Map of Mediterranean and Red Sea . . . . 2·50 3·50

1992. 150th Anniv of Anglican Diocese of Gibraltar-in-Europe. Multicoloured.
682 4p. Type **181** 20 10
683 24p. Diocesan crest and map (horiz) . . . . 1·00 65
684 44p. Construction of Cathedral and Sir George Don (horiz) . . . . 1·75 3·00
685 54p. Bishop Tomlinson . . . 2·00 3·50

182 Sacred Heart of Jesus Church

183 "Drama and Music"

1992. Christmas. Churches. Multicoloured.
686 4p. Type **182** 35 10
687 24p. Cathedral of St. Mary the Crowned . . . . . . 1·50 55
688 34p. St. Andrew's Church of Scotland . . . . 2·00 2·50
689 49p. St. Joseph's Church . . 2·50 5·50

1993. Europa. Contemporary Art. Multicoloured.
690 24p. Type **183** . . . . 1·50 2·00
691 24p. "Sculpture, Art and Pottery" . . . . 1·50 2·00
692 34p. "Architecture" . . . . 2·00 2·75
693 34p. "Printing and Photography" . . . . . . 2·00 2·75

184 H.M.S. "Hood" (battle cruiser)

1993. Second World War Warships (1st series). Sheet 120 × 79 mm, containing T **184** and similar horiz designs. Multicoloured.
MS694 24p. Type **184**; 24p. H.M.S. "Ark Royal" (aircraft carrier, 1937); 24p. H.M.A.S. "Waterhen" (destroyer); 24p. U.S.S. "Gleaves" (destroyer) . . . . 8·50 8·50
See also Nos. **MS**724, **MS**748, **MS**779 and **MS**809.

185 Landport Gate

186 £sd and Decimal British Coins (25th anniv of decimal currency)

1993. Architectural Heritage. Multicoloured.
695 1p. Type **185** . . . . 20 1·00
696 2p. St. Mary the Crowned Church (horiz) . . . . . 40 1·00
697 3p. Parsons Lodge Battery (horiz) . . . . 40 1·00
698 4p. Moorish Castle (horiz) 40 1·00
699 5p. General Post Office . . 40 30
699a 6p. House of Assembly . . 1·25 75
699b 7p. Bleak House (horiz) . . 1·25 75
699c 8p. General Eliott Memorial 1·25 75
699d 9p. Supreme Court Building (horiz) . . . . 1·25 75
700 10p. South Barracks (horiz) 40 60
700a 20p. The Convent (horiz) 2·00 75
701 21p. American War Memorial 60 80
702 24p. Garrison Library (horiz) 70 80
703 25p. Southport Gates . . . 70 80
704 26p. Casemates Gate (horiz) 70 80
704a 30p. St. Bernard's Hospital 3·00 80
704b 40p. City Hall (horiz) . . . 3·00 1·50
705 50p. Central Police Station (horiz) . . . . 1·50 2·25
706 £1 Prince Edward's Gate . . 2·00 2·75
706a £2 Church of the Sacred Heart of Jesus . . . . . 7·00 5·50
707 £3 Lighthouse, Europa Point . . . . 7·00 10·00
708 £5 Coat of Arms and fortress keys . . . . . . 10·00 14·00

1993. Anniversaries. Multicoloured.
709 21p. Type **186** 75 65
710 24p. R.A.F. crest with Handley Page 0/400 and Panavia Tornado F Mk 3 (75th anniv) . . . . 1·25 75
711 34p. Garrison Library badge and building (bicent) . . . 1·40 2·25
712 49p. Sir Winston Churchill and air raid (50th anniv of visit) . . . . 2·25 4·50

187 Mice decorating Christmas Tree

1993. Christmas. Multicoloured.
713 5p. Type **187** 20 10
714 24p. Mice pulling cracker . . 90 70
715 44p. Mice singing carols . . 1·75 2·50
716 49p. Mice building snowman 1·90 3·00

188 Exploding Atom (Lord Penney)

1994. Europa. Scientific Discoveries. Mult.
717 24p. Type **188** . . . . 1·00 1·50
718 24p. Polonium and radium experiment (Marie Curie) 1·00 1·50
719 34p. First oil engine (Rudolph Diesel) . . . . . 1·25 2·00
720 34p. Early telescope (Galileo) 1·25 2·00

189 World Cup and Map of U.S.A.

1994. World Cup Football Championship, U.S.A. Multicoloured.
721 26p. Type **189** 80 55
722 39p. Players and pitch in shape of U.S.A . . . . . 1·25 2·00
723 49p. Player's legs (vert) . . . 1·60 2·75

1994. Second World War Warships (2nd series). Sheet 112 × 72 mm, containing horiz designs as T **184**. Multicoloured.
MS724 5p. H.M.S. "Penelope" (cruiser); 25p. H.M.S. "Warspite" (battleship); 44p. U.S.S. "McLanahan" (destroyer); 49p. "Isaac Sweers" (Dutch destroyer) 7·00 8·50

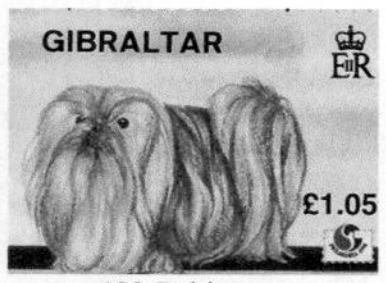

190 Pekingese

1994. "Philakorea '94" International Stamp Exhibition, Seoul. Sheet 102 × 76 mm.
MS725 **190** £1.05, multicoloured 3·00 4·00

191 Golden Star Coral

193 Great Tit

192 Throwing the Discus and Centenary Emblem

1994. Marine Life. Multicoloured.
726 21p. Type **191** 75 45
727 24p. Star fish 90 55
728 34p. Gorgonian sea-fan . . . 1·50 2·25
729 49p. Peacock wrasse ("Turkish wrasse") . . . . 2·00 3·50

1994. Centenary of Int Olympic Committee. Mult.
730 49p. Type **192** . . . . . . 1·75 2·25
731 54p. Javelin throwing and emblem . . . . 1·75 2·50

1994. Christmas. Songbirds. Multicoloured.
732 5p. Type **193** 60 10
733 24p. European robin (horiz) 1·75 70
734 34p. Blue tit (horiz) . . . . 2·00 1·50
735 54p. Eurasian goldfinch ("Goldfinch") . . . . . . 2·75 4·50

194 Austrian Flag, Hand and Star

1995. Expansion of European Union. Multicoloured.

736	24p. Type **194**	60	55
737	26p. Finnish flag, hand and star	60	60
738	34p. Swedish flag, hand and star	90	1·50
739	49p. Flags of new members and European Union emblem	1·60	3·25

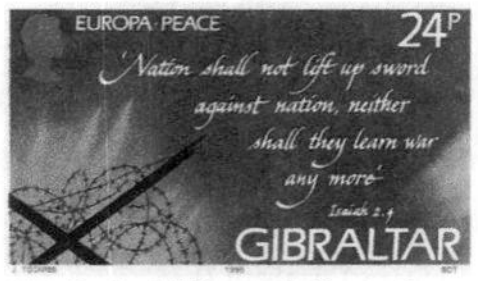

195 Barbed Wire and Quote from Isaiah Ch 2.4

1995. Europa. Peace and Freedom. Multicoloured.

740	24p. Type **195**	1·10	1·50
741	24p. Rainbow and hands releasing peace dove	1·10	1·50
742	34p. Shackles on wall and quote from Isaiah ch 61.1	1·40	2·00
743	34p. Hands and sea birds	1·40	2·00

196 Fairey Swordfish, I Class Destroyer and Rock of Gibraltar

1995. 50th Anniv of End of Second World War. Sheet 101 × 66 mm.

MS744	**196** £1.05, multicoloured	3·25	4·00

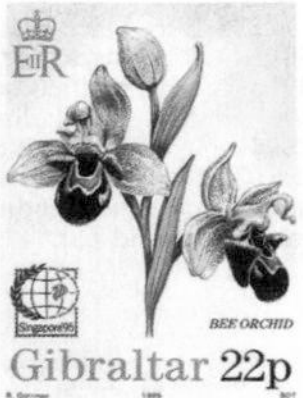

197 Yachting **198** Bee Orchid

1995. Island Games '95. Multicoloured.

745	24p. Type **197**	70	60
746	44p. Athlete on starting blocks	1·60	2·50
747	49p. Swimmer at start of race	1·60	2·50

1995. Second World War Warships (3rd series). Sheet 133 × 85 mm, containing horiz designs as T **184**. Multicoloured.

MS748	5p. H.M.S. "Calpe" (destroyer); 24p. H.M.S. "Victorious" (aircraft carrier); 44p. U.S.S. "Weehawken" (attack transport); 49p. "Savorgan de Brazza" (French destroyer)	7·50	8·00

1995. "Singapore '95" International Stamp Exhibition. Orchids. Multicoloured.

749	22p. Type **198**	1·10	1·40
750	23p. Brown bee orchid	1·10	1·40
751	24p. Pyramidal orchid	1·10	1·40
752	25p. Mirror orchid	1·10	1·40
753	26p. Sawfly orchid	1·10	1·40

199 Handshake and United Nations Emblem

1995. 50th Anniv of United Nations. Multicoloured.

754	34p. Type **199**	1·25	1·10
755	49p. Peace dove and U.N. emblem	1·50	2·50

200 Marilyn Monroe

1995. Centenary of Cinema. T **200** and similar horiz designs showing film stars. Multicoloured.

MS756	Two sheets, each 116 × 80 mm. (a) 5p. Type **200**; 25p. Romy Schneider; 28p. Yves Montand; 38p. Audrey Hepburn. (b) 24p. Ingrid Bergman; 24p. Vittorio de Sica; 24p. Marlene Dietrich; 24p. Laurence Olivier Set of 2 sheets	4·50	5·50

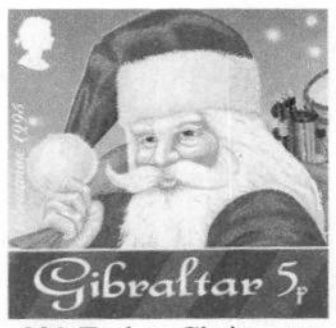

201 Father Christmas

1995. Christmas. Multicoloured.

757	5p. Type **201**	30	10
758	24p. Toys in sack	1·00	55
759	34p. Reindeer	1·50	1·25
760	54p. Sleigh over houses	2·50	4·00

202 Shih Tzu

1996. Puppies. Multicoloured.

761	5p. Type **202**	40	85
762	21p. Dalmatians	75	95
763	24p. Cocker spaniels	80	1·10
764	25p. West Highland white terriers	80	1·10
765	34p. Labrador	90	1·25
766	35p. Boxer	90	1·25

No. 762 is inscr "Dalmation" in error.

203 Princess Anne

1996. Europa. Famous Women.

767	**203** 24p. black and yellow	1·10	1·25
768	– 24p. black and green	1·10	1·25
769	– 34p. black and red	1·40	2·00
770	– 34p. black and purple	1·40	2·00

DETAILS: Nos. 768, Princess Diana; 769, Queen Elizabeth II; 770, Queen Elizabeth the Queen Mother.

204 West German Player, 1980 **205** Ancient Greek Athletes

1996. European Football Championship, England. Players from previous winning teams. Multicoloured.

771	21p. Type **204**	55	45
772	24p. French player, 1984	65	55
773	34p. Dutch player, 1988	95	1·10
774	£1.20 Danish player, 1992	3·00	4·75
MS775	135 × 91 mm. As Nos. 771/4	6·50	7·50

1996. Centenary of Modern Olympic Games.

776	**205** 34p. black, purple & orge	95	90
777	– 49p. black and brown	1·40	1·75
778	– £1.05 multicoloured	3·00	4·50

DESIGNS: 49p. Start of early race; £1.05, Start of modern race

1996. Second World War Warships (4th series). Sheet 118 × 84 mm, containing horiz designs as T **184**. Multicoloured.

MS779	5p. H.M.S. "Starling" (sloop); 25p. H.M.S. "Royalist" (cruiser); 49p. U.S.S. "Philadelphia" (cruiser); 54p. H.M.C.S. "Prescott" (corvette)	5·00	6·00

206 Asian Children

1996. 50th Anniv of U.N.I.C.E.F.

780	**206** 21p. multicoloured	60	80
781	– 24p. multicoloured	70	90
782	– 49p. multicoloured	1·25	2·00
783	– 54p. multicoloured	1·40	2·25

DESIGNS: 24p. to 54p. Children from different continents.

207 Red Kites in Flight

1996. Endangered Species. Red Kite. Multicoloured.

784	34p. Type **207**	1·10	1·50
785	34p. Red kite on ground	1·10	1·50
786	34p. On rock	1·10	1·50
787	34p. Pair at nest	1·10	1·50

208 Christmas Pudding

1996. Christmas. Designs created from "Lego" Blocks. Multicoloured.

788	5p. Type **208**	15	15
789	21p. Snowman face	70	45
790	24p. Present	80	55
791	34p. Father Christmas face	1·10	1·25
792	54p. Candle	1·50	2·75

209 "Mary Celeste" passing Gibraltar **211** "Anthocharis belia euphenoides"

210 American Shorthair Silver Tabby

1997. Europa. Tales and Legends. "The Mary Celeste". Multicoloured.

793	28p. Type **209**	80	1·00
794	28p. Boarding the "Mary Celeste"	80	1·00
795	30p. Crew leaving "Mary Celeste"	90	1·40
796	30p. "Mary Celeste" found by "Dei Gratia"	90	1·40

1997. Kittens. Multicoloured.

797	5p. Type **210**	40	1·00
798	24p. Rumpy Manx red tabby	75	1·25
799	26p. Blue point birmans	75	1·25
800	28p. Red self longhair	80	1·25
801	30p. British shorthair tortoiseshell and white	80	1·25
802	35p. British bicolour shorthairs	90	1·40
MS803	132 × 80 mm. Nos. 797/802 with "HONG KONG '97" International Stamp Exhibition logo at bottom left	7·00	8·00

1997. Butterflies. Multicoloured.

804	23p. Type **211**	70	50
805	26p. "Charaxes jasius"	85	60
806	30p. "Vanessa cardui"	95	90
807	£1.20 "Iphiclides podalirius"	3·25	5·00
MS808	135 × 90 mm. Nos. 804/7	5·25	6·50

1997. Second World War Warships (5th series). Sheet 117 × 82 mm, containing horiz designs as T **184**. Multicoloured.

MS809	24p. H.M.S. "Enterprise" (cruiser); 26p. H.M.S. "Cleopatra" (cruiser); 38p. U.S.S. "Iowa" (battleship); 50p. "Orkan" (Polish destroyer)	3·50	4·00

212 Queen Elizabeth and Prince Philip at Carriage-driving Trials

1997. Golden Wedding of Queen Elizabeth and Prince Philip. Multicoloured.

810	£1.20 Type **212**	3·50	4·00
811	£1.40 Queen Elizabeth in Trooping the Colour uniform	3·50	4·00

213 Christian Dior Evening Dress **214** "Our Lady and St. Bernard" (St. Joseph's Parish Church)

1997. Christian Dior Spring/Summer '97 Collection. Multicoloured.

812	30p. Type **213**	80	1·25
813	35p. Tunic top and skirt	1·10	1·60
814	50p. Ballgown	1·25	1·75
815	62p. Two-piece suit	1·60	2·25
MS816	110 × 90 mm. £1.20, Ballgown (different)	2·75	3·50

1997. Christmas. Stained Glass Windows. Mult.

817	5p. Type **214**	25	10
818	26p. "The Epiphany" (Our Lady of Sorrows Church)	1·00	60
819	38p. "St. Joseph" (Our Lady of Sorrows Church)	1·25	95
820	50p. "The Holy Family" (St. Joseph's Parish Church)	1·50	2·25
821	62p. "The Miraculous Medal" (St. Joseph's Parish Church)	1·75	3·25

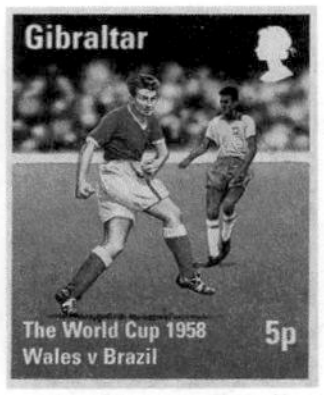

215 Sir Joshua Hassan **216** Wales v Brazil (1958)

1997. Sir Joshua Hassan (former Chief Minister) Commemoration.

822	**215** 26p. black	75	60

1998. World Football Championship, France (1998). Multicoloured.

823	5p. Type **216**	25	10
824	26p. Northern Ireland v France (1958)	1·00	60
825	38p. Scotland v Holland (1978)	1·25	90
826	£1.20 England v West Germany (1966)	2·75	4·75
MS827	153 × 96 mm. Nos. 823/6	4·75	5·50

1998. Diana, Princess of Wales Commemoration. Sheet 145 × 70 mm, containing vert designs as T **177** of Ascension. Multicoloured.

MS828	26p. Wearing jacket with white fur collar, 1988; 26p. Wearing pink checked suit and hat; 38p. Wearing black jacket, 1995; 38p. Wearing blue jacket with gold embroidery, 1987 (sold at £1.28+20p. charity premium)	3·25	3·75

216a Saro London (flying boat)

1998. 80th Anniv of Royal Air Force. Multicoloured.

829	24p. Type **216a**	70	55
830	26p. Fairey Fox	75	60

831 38p. Handley Page Halifax GR.VI . . . . 95 1·25
832 50p. Hawker Siddeley Buccaneer S.2B . . . . 1·25 2·50
MS833 110 × 77 mm. 24p. Sopwith 1½ Strutter; 26p. Bristol M.IB; 38p. Supermarine Spitfire XII; 50p. Avro York . . . . 3·50 4·50

217 Miss Gibraltar saluting

219 Nileus (dog) with Hat and Telescope

218 Striped Dolphin

1998. Europa. Festivals. National Day. Mult.
834 26p. Type **217** . . . . 70 1·00
835 26p. In black bodice and long red skirt . . . . 70 1·00
836 38p. In black bodice and short red skirt, with Gibraltar flag . . . . . . 95 1·40
837 38p. In Genoese-style costume . . . . 95 1·40

1998. International Year of the Ocean. Sheet 155 × 64 mm, containing T **218** and similar multicoloured designs.
MS838 5p. Type **218**; 5p. Common dolphin (vert); 26p. Killer whale (vert); £1.20, Blue whale . . . 4·25 5·00

1998. Bicentenary of Battle of the Nile. Multicoloured.
839 12p. Type **219** 35 30
840 26p. Rear-Admiral Sir Horatio Nelson 65 55
841 28p. Frances Nisbet, Lady Nelson . . . . 1·00 75
842 35p. H.M.S. "Vanguard" (ship of the line) . . . . . 1·25 1·50
843 50p. Battle of the Nile (47 × 29 mm) . . . . . . 1·40 2·50

220 "Love comforts like Sunshine after Rain" (William Shakespeare)

221 The Nativity

1998. Famous Quotations. Multicoloured.
844 26p. Type **220** . . . . 90 1·00
845 26p. "The price of greatness is responsibility" (Sir Winston Churchill) . . . . 90 1·00
846 38p. "Hate the sin, love the sinner" (Mahatma Gandhi) 1·10 1·50
847 38p. "Imagination is more important than knowledge" (Albert Einstein) . . . . . 1·10 1·50

1998. Christmas. Multicoloured.
848 5p. Type **221** 35 10
849 26p. Star and stable . . . . 1·25 70
850 30p. King with gold . . . . 1·40 75
851 35p. King with myrrh . . . . 1·40 1·25
852 50p. King with frankincense 1·75 2·75

222 Barbary Macaque

223 Queen Elizabeth II

1999. Europa. Parks and Gardens. Upper Rock Nature Reserve. Multicoloured.
853 30p. Type **222** . . . . 1·25 1·40
854 30p. Dartford warbler . . . 1·25 1·40
855 42p. Dusky grouper . . . . 1·50 2·00
856 42p. River kingfisher ("Common Kingfisher") . . 1·50 2·00

1999. (a) Ordinary gum.
857 **223** 1p. purple 10 10
858 2p. brown 10 10
859 4p. blue 10 10
860 5p. green 10 10
861 10p. orange 20 25
862 12p. red 25 30
863 20p. green 40 45
864 28p. mauve 55 60
865 30p. orange 60 65
866 40p. grey 80 85
867 42p. green 85 90
868 50p. bistre . . . . . 1·00 1·10
869 £1 black . . . . . . 2·00 2·10
869a £1.20 red . . . . . 2·40 2·50
869b £1.40 blue . . . . . 2·75 3·00
870 £3 blue . . . . . . 6·00 6·25

(b) Self-adhesive.
871 **223** (1st) orange 55 60
Nos. 868/71 are larger, 22 × 28 mm.
No. 871 was initially sold at 26p.

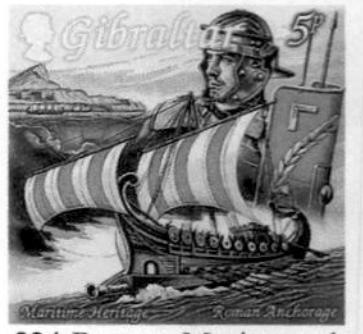

224 Roman Marine and Galley

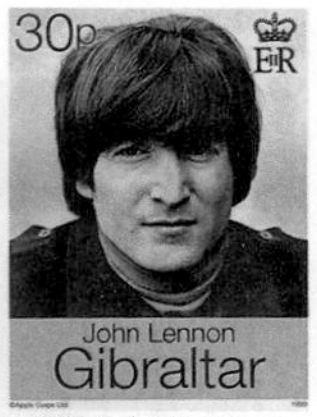

225 John Lennon (musician)

1999. Maritime Heritage. Multicoloured.
872 5p. Type **224** 25 10
873 30p. Arab sailor, medieval galley house and dhow . . 95 65
874 42p. Marine officer and British ship of the line (1779–83) . . . . 1·50 1·50
875 £1.20 Naval rating, Queen Alexandra Dry Dock and H.M.S. "Berwick" (cruiser) (1904) . . . . 3·25 4·25
MS876 116 × 76 mm. Nos. 872/5 4·50 5·50

1999. 30th Wedding Anniv of John Lennon and Yoko Ono. Designs showing John Lennon.
877 – 20p. multicoloured . . . 50 45
878 **225** 30p. black and blue . . . 75 65
879 – 40p. multicoloured . . . 95 1·25
MS880 Two sheets, each 62 × 100 mm. (a) £1 black and blue. (b) £1 multicoloured Set of 2 sheets . . . . 6·50 6·50
DESIGNS 20p. With flower over left eye; 40p. Wearing orange glasses; £1 (No. **MS**880a), Holding marriage certificate; £1 (No. **MS**880b), Standing on aircraft steps.

226 Postal Van at Dockside, 1930s

1999. 125th Anniv of U.P.U. Multicoloured.
881 5p. Type **226** 25 20
882 30p. Space shuttle and station 75 1·25

227 EF-2000 Eurofighter

1999. "Wings of Prey" (1st series). Birds of Prey and R.A.F. Fighter Aircraft. Multicoloured.
883 30p. Type **227** . . . . 1·00 1·25
884 30p. Panavia Tornado F3 . . 1·00 1·25
885 30p. BAe Harrier II GR7 . . 1·00 1·25
886 42p. Lesser kestrel . . . . . 1·00 1·25
887 42p. Peregrine falcon . . . . 1·00 1·25
888 42p. Common kestrel ("Kestrel") . . . . 1·00 1·25
MS889 Two sheets, each 105 × 86 mm. (a) Nos. 883/5. (b) Nos. 886/8 Set of 2 sheets . . 5·50 6·00
See also Nos. 943/8 and 982/7.

228 Prince Edward and Sophie Rhys-Jones

1999. Royal Wedding. Multicoloured.
890 30p. Type **228** 70 65
891 42p. Prince Edward and Sophie Rhys-Jones holding hands (vert) . . . . 1·00 90
892 54p. In carriage on wedding day . . . . 1·40 2·00
893 66p. On Chapel steps after wedding (vert) . . . . . . 1·50 2·25

229 Football

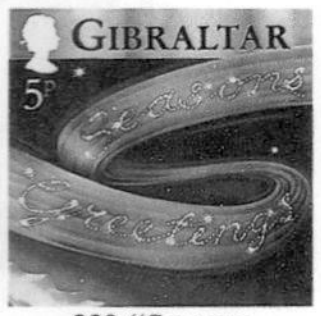

230 "Seasons Greetings"

1999. Local Sporting Centenaries. Multicoloured.
894 30p. Type **229** 75 65
895 42p. Rowing . . . . 1·00 90
896 £1.20 Cricket . . . . 3·25 4·25

1999. Christmas. Multicoloured.
897 5p. Type **230** 15 10
898 5p. "Happy Christmas" . . . 15 10
899 30p. "Happy Millennium" . . 80 80
900 30p. "Happy Christmas" and Santa with reindeer 80 80
901 42p. Santa Claus in chimney 1·25 1·75
902 54p. Santa Claus leaving presents . . . . 1·40 2·50

231 "People travelling with Environmentally-friendly Jet-packs" (Colin Grech)

2000. "Stampin' the Future" (children's stamp design competition). Multicoloured.
903 30p. Type **231** . . . . 1·25 1·50
904 42p. "Robotic Postman" (Kim Barea) . . . . 1·25 1·50
905 54p. "Living on the Moon" (Stephan Williamson-Fa) 1·25 1·50
906 66p. "Jet-powered Cars" (Michael Podesta) . . . . 1·25 1·50

232 Dutch Football Player and Flag, 1988

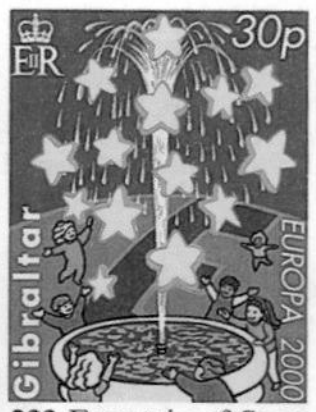

233 Fountain of Stars

2000. European Football Championship, Belgium and Netherlands. Multicoloured.
907 30p. Type **232** 85 90
908 30p. French player and flag, 1984 . . . . 85 90
909 42p. German player scoring and flag, 1996 . . . . . 1·10 1·40
910 42p. Danish player and flag, 1992 . . . . 1·10 1·40
MS911 Two sheets, each 115 × 85 mm. (a) 54p. × 4, English player and flag. (b) Nos. 907/10 Set of 2 sheets . . . . 8·50 9·00

2000. Europa. Multicoloured.
912 30p. Type **233** 80 65
913 40p. Exchanging star . . . . 1·00 1·10
914 42p. Stars and airplane . . . 1·10 1·25
915 54p. Stars and end of rainbow . . . . 1·60 2·25

234 3000 m Waterfall between Gibraltar and North African Coast, 5 Million B.C.

235 Princess Diana holding Prince William, 1982

2000. New Millennium. History of Gibraltar. Multicoloured (except Nos. 926/30).
916 5p. Type **234** 30 50
917 5p. Sabre-tooth tiger, 2 million B.C. 30 50
918 5p. Neanderthal hunting goat, and skull, 30,000 B.C. 30 50
919 5p. Phoenician traders and galley, 700 B.C. 30 50
920 5p. Roman warship, 100 B.C. 30 50
921 5p. Tarik-Ibn-Zayad, ape and Moorish Castle, 711 A.D. 30 50
922 5p. Coat of arms, 1502 . . . 30 50
923 5p. Admiral George Rooke and Union Jack, 1704 . . 30 50
924 30p. General Eliott at The Great Siege, 1779–83 . . . 80 90
925 30p. H.M.S. *Victory*, 1805 . . 80 90
926 30p. Queen Alexandra in horse-drawn carriage, 1903 (brown, silver and black) 80 90
927 30p. 100 ton gun, 1870s (grey, silver and black) . . 80 90
928 30p. Evacuees, 1940 (purple, silver and black) 80 90
929 30p. Tank and anti-aircraft gun, 1940s (brown, silver and black) 80 90
930 30p. Queen Elizabeth II in Gibraltar, 1954 (grey, silver and black) 80 90
931 30p. Aerial view of office district, 2000 . . . . . . 80 90

2000. 18th Birthday of Prince William. Multicoloured.
932 30p. Type **235** 80 65
933 42p. Prince William as a toddler . . . . 1·00 90
934 54p. Prince William with Prince Charles . . . . . 1·25 1·75
935 66p. Prince William at 18 . . 1·40 2·25
MS936 115 × 75 mm. Nos. 932/5 5·00 5·50

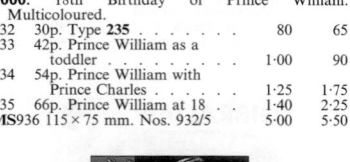

236 Lady Elizabeth Bowes-Lyon signing Book

2000. Queen Elizabeth the Queen Mother's 100th Birthday.
937 **236** 30p. black and blue . . . 85 65
938 – 42p. black and brown . . 1·10 90
939 – 54p. multicoloured . . . 1·40 1·75
940 – 66p. multicoloured . . . 1·60 2·25
MS941 115 × 75 mm. Nos. 937/40 3·75 4·00
DESIGNS: 42p. Duke and Duchess of York; 54p. Queen Mother with bouquet; 66p. Queen Mother in orange coat and hat.

237 Moorish Castle

2000.
942 **237** £5 black, silver and gold 10·00 11·00
The Queen's head on this stamp is printed in optically variable ink, which changes colour from gold to green when viewed from different angles.

2000. "Wings of Prey" (2nd series). Birds of Prey and R.A.F. Second World War Aircraft. As T **227**. Multicoloured.
943 30p. Supermarine Spitfire Mk IIA *Gibraltar* . . . . 1·25 1·40
944 30p. Hawker Hurricane Mk IIC . . . . 1·25 1·40
945 30p. Avro Lancaster BI-III *City of Lincoln* . . . . . . 1·25 1·40
946 42p. Merlin (male) . . . . . 1·40 1·60
947 42p. Merlin (female) . . . . 1·40 1·60
948 42p. Bonelli's eagle . . . . 1·40 1·60
MS949 Two sheets, each 105 × 85 mm. (a) Nos. 943/5. (b) Nos. 946/8 Set of 2 sheets . . . 4·50 5·00

238 Infant Jesus

239 Wedding of Queen Victoria and Prince Albert

2000. Christmas. Multicoloured.
950 5p. Type **238** 25 15
951 30p. Virgin Mary with infant Jesus 85 65
952 30p. Journey to Bethlehem 85 65
953 40p. Mary and Joseph with innkeeper . . . . 1·10 1·00
954 42p. The Nativity . . . . . 1·10 1·25
955 54p. Visit of the Wise Men 1·60 2·25

2001. Death Centenary of Queen Victoria.
956 **239** 30p. blue, violet and black 90 65
957 – 42p. myrtle, green & black . . . . 1·25 1·00
958 – 54p. purple, red and black 1·75 2·25
959 – 66p. brown, gold & black 1·90 2·75

DESIGNS: 42p. Victoria as Empress of India; 54p. Queen Victoria in carriage; 66p. Queen Victoria standing by chair.

240 Grass Snake

241 Long-snouted Seahorse

2001. Snakes. Multicoloured.

960	5p. Type **240**	25	40
961	5p. Ladder snake	25	40
962	5p. Montpellier snake	25	40
963	30p. Viperine snake	85	1·00
964	30p. Southern smooth snake	85	1·00
965	30p. False smooth snake	85	1·00
966	66p. Horseshoe whip snake (30 × 62 mm)	1·75	2·50
MS967	155 × 87 mm. Nos. 960/6	5·50	6·00

No. **MS**967 also commemorates the Chinese New Year "Year of the Snake".

No. 962 and **MS**967 are inscribed "MONTPELIER" in error.

2001. Europa. Water and Nature. Multicoloured.

968	30p. Type **241**	1·00	65
969	40p. Snapdragon	1·25	1·00
970	42p. Herring gull ("Yellow-legged Gull")	1·75	1·50
971	54p. Goldfish	1·75	2·50

242 Queen Elizabeth II as a Baby

243 Battle of Trafalgar, 1805

2001. 75th Birthday of Queen Elizabeth II.

972 **242**	30p. black and mauve	85	75
973 –	30p. black and violet	85	75
974 –	42p. black and red	1·25	1·50
975 –	42p. black and violet	1·25	1·50
976 –	54p. multicoloured	1·60	2·25
MS977	101 × 89 mm. £2 multicoloured	4·75	5·50

DESIGNS—HORIZ: No. 973, Queen Elizabeth as teenager; 974, On wedding day, 1947; 975, After Coronation, 1953; 976, Queen Elizabeth in blue hat. VERT: (35 × 49 mm)—No. **MS**977, Queen Elizabeth II, 2001 (photo by Fiona Hanson).

No. **MS**977 marks a successful attempt on the record for the fastest produced stamp issue. The miniature sheet was on sale in Gibraltar 10 hours and 24 minutes after the artwork was approved at Buckingham Palace.

2001. Bicentenary of *The Gibraltar Chronicle* (newspaper). Each black.

978	30p. Type **243**	1·00	65
979	42p. Invention of the telephone, 1876	1·10	90
980	54p. Winston Churchill (Victory in Second World War, 1945)	1·75	2·00
981	66p. Footprint on Moon (Moon landing, 1969)	2·00	2·75

2001. "Wings of Prey" (3rd series). Birds of Prey and Modern Military Aircraft. As T **227**. Multicoloured.

982	40p. Royal Navy Sea Harrier FA MK.2	1·00	1·25
983	40p. Western marsh harrier ("Marsh Harrier")	1·00	1·25
984	40p. R.A.F. Hawk T MK.1	1·00	1·25
985	40p. Northern sparrowhawk ("Sparrowhawk")	1·00	1·25
986	40p. R.A.F. Jaguar GR1B	1·00	1·25
987	40p. Northern hobby ("Hobby")	1·00	1·25
MS988	Two sheets, each 103 × 84 mm. (a) Nos. 982, 984 and 986. (b) Nos. 983, 985 and 987 Set of 2 sheets	5·50	6·00

244 Snoopy as Father Christmas with Woodstock

246 Joshua Grimaldi

245 One Cent Coin

2001. Christmas. Peanuts (cartoon characters by Charles Schulz). Multicoloured.

989	5p. Type **244**	20	15
990	30p. Charlie Brown and Snoopy with Christmas tree	75	65
991	40p. Snoopy asleep in wreath	1·00	1·00
992	42p. Snoopy with plate of biscuits	1·10	1·25
993	54p. Snoopy asleep on kennel	1·40	2·00
MS994	140 × 85 mm. Nos. 989/93	3·25	3·50

2002. Introduction of Euro Currency by European Union. Coins. Sheet 165 × 105 mm, containing T **245** and similar square designs showing coins. Multicoloured.

MS995	5p. Type **245**; 12p. 2 cents; 30p. 5 cents; 35p. 10 cents; 40p. 20 cents; 42p. 50 cents; 54p. 1 Euro; 66p. 2 Euros	6·50	7·00

2002. Golden Jubilee. As T **219** of Falkland Islands.

996	30p. black, red and gold	80	90
997	30p. agate, red and gold	80	90
998	30p. multicoloured	80	90
999	30p. multicoloured	80	90
1000	75p. multicoloured	1·75	2·25
MS1001	162 × 95 mm. Nos. 996/1000	5·50	6·00

DESIGNS—HORIZ: No. 996, Princess Elizabeth and Princess Margaret making radio broadcast, 1940; 997, Princess Elizabeth in Girl Guide uniform, 1942; 998, Queen Elizabeth in evening dress, 1961; 999, Queen Elizabeth in Chelsea, 1993. VERT (38 × 51 mm): No 1000, Queen Elizabeth after Annigoni.

2002. Europa. Circus. Famous Clowns. Multicoloured.

1002	30p. Type **246**	80	65
1003	40p. Karl Wettach ("Grock")	90	1·00
1004	42p. Nicolai Polakovs ("Coco")	90	1·00
1005	54p. Charlie Cairoli	1·25	1·75

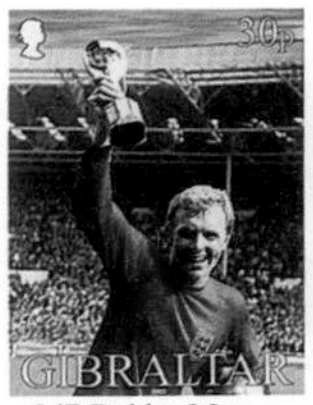

247 Bobby Moore holding Jules Rimet Trophy, 1966

248 Barbary Macaque

2002. World Cup Football Championship, Japan and Korea (2002). England's Victory, 1966. Multicoloured.

1006	30p. Type **247**	85	65
1007	42p. Kissing Trophy	1·25	90
1008	54p. Bobby Moore with Queen Elizabeth II	1·50	1·75
1009	66p. Bobby Moore in action	1·75	2·00
MS1010	135 × 90 mm. Nos. 1006/9	4·00	4·25

2002. Wildlife. Multicoloured.

1011	30p. Type **248**	60	65
1012	30p. Red fox (horiz)	60	65
1013	40p. White-toothed shrew (horiz)	80	85
1014	£1 Rabbit	2·00	2·10
MS1015	125 × 100 mm. Nos. 1011/14	4·00	4·25

249 Gibraltar from the North

250 Princess Diana holding Prince Harry

2002. Views of the Rock of Gibraltar. Multicoloured.

1016	30p. Type **249**	60	65
1017	30p. View from the south	60	65
1018	£1 View from the east (50 × 40 mm)	2·00	2·10
1019	£1 View from the west (50 × 40 mm)	2·00	2·10

Nos. 1016/19 were printed together, se-tenant, with powdered particles of the Rock sintered to their surface using thermography.

2002. 18th Birthday of Prince Harry. Multicoloured.

1020	30p. Type **250**	60	65
1021	42p. Prince Harry waving	85	90
1022	54p. Prince Harry skiing	1·10	1·25
1023	66p. Wearing dark suit	1·25	1·40
MS1024	115 × 75 mm. Nos. 1020/3	4·00	4·25

251 Crib, Cathedral of St. Mary the Crowned

2002. Christmas. Cribs from Gibraltar Cathedrals and Churches. Multicoloured.

1025	5p. Type **251**	10	10
1026	30p. St. Joseph's Parish Church	60	65
1027	40p. St. Theresa's Parish Church	80	85
1028	42p. Our Lady of Sorrows Church	85	90
1029	52p. St. Bernard's Church	1·10	1·25
1030	54p. Cathedral of the Holy Trinity	1·10	1·25

252 Archbishop of Canterbury crowning Queen Elizabeth II

254 Drama Festival Poster

253 Young Prince William with Princess Diana

2003. 50th Anniv of the Coronation. Each black, grey and purple.

1031	30p. Type **252**	60	65
1032	30p. Queen Elizabeth II in Coronation robes	60	65
1033	40p. Queen Elizabeth holding the Orb and Sceptre	80	85
1034	£1 Queen Elizabeth in Coronation Coach	2·00	2·10
MS1035	116 × 76 mm. Nos. 1031/4	4·00	4·10

2003. 21st Birthday of Prince William of Wales. Each black, grey and violet.

1036	30p. Type **253**	60	65
1037	30p. Prince William at Eton College	60	65
1038	40p. Prince William	80	85
1039	£1 Prince William in Operation Raleigh sweatshirt	2·00	2·10
MS1040	115 × 75mm. Nos. 1036/9	4·00	4·25

2003. Europa. Poster Art. Multicoloured.

1041	30p. Type **254**	60	65
1042	40p. Spring Festival poster	80	85
1043	42p. Art Festival poster	85	90
1044	54p. Dance festival poster	1·10	1·25

255 Wright Brothers' *Flyer I*, 1903

2003. Centenary of Powered Flight. Aircraft.

1045 **255**	30p. multicoloured	60	65
1046 –	40p. black and brown	80	85
1047 –	40p. black and blue	80	85
1048 –	42p. black and blue	85	90
1049 –	44p. multicoloured	90	95
1050 –	66p. multicoloured	1·25	1·40
MS1051	140 × 110 mm. Nos. 1045/50	5·25	5·50

DESIGNS—HORIZ: (37 × 28 mm) 40p. (No. 1046) Charles Lindbergh and *Spirit of St. Louis* (first Transatlantic solo flight, 1927); 40p. (No. 1047) Boeing 314 Yankee Clipper flying boat (first Transatlantic scheduled air service, 1939). (77 × 28 mm)—42p. Saunders Roe Saro A 21 Windhover amphibian (first scheduled air service between Gibraltar and Tangier, 1931); 44p. British Airways Concorde (first supersonic airliner, 1976). VERT (37 × 58 mm)—66p. Space shuttle *Columbia* (first shuttle flight in Space orbit, 1981).

256 Flag of St. George

2003. 1700th Death Anniv of St. George. Multicoloured.

1052	30p. Type **256**	60	65
1053	40p. Cross of Military Constantinian Order of St. George	80	85
1054	£1.20 "St. George and the Dragon" (stained glass window, St. Joseph's Church, Gibraltar) (32 × 63 mm)	2·40	2·50
MS1055	150 × 100 mm. Nos. 1052/4	3·75	4·00

257 Big Ben, Swift and Rock of Gibraltar

2003.

1056 **257**	(£3) multicoloured†	6·00	6·25

No. 1056 is inscribed "UK express" and was initially sold at £3.

†The Queen's head on this stamp is printed in optically variable ink which changes colour from gold to green when viewed from different angles.

258 Wood Blewit (*Lepista nuda*)

2003. Mushrooms of Gibraltar. Multicoloured.

1057	30p. Type **258**	60	65
1058	30p. Blue-green funnel-cap (*Clitocybe odora*)	60	65
1059	30p. Sulphur tuft (*Hypholoma fasciculare*)	60	65
1060	£1.20 Field mushrooms (*Agaricus campestris*)	2·40	2·50
MS1061	105 × 90mm. Nos. 1057/60	4·25	4·50

259 Daisy (Latvia), Cornflower (Estonia) and Rue (Lithuania)

2003. Enlargement of the European Union (2004). Designs showing the national flowers of new member countries. Multicoloured.

1062	30p. Type **259**	60	65
1063	40p. Rose (Cyprus) and Maltese Centaury (Malta)	80	85
1064	42p. Tulip (Hungary), Carnation (Slovenia) and Dog Rose (Slovakia)	85	90
1065	54p. Corn Poppy (Poland) and Scented Thyme (Czech Republic)	1·10	1·20

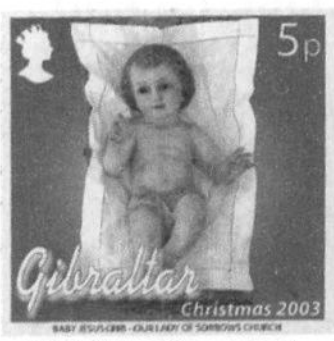

260 Baby Jesus Crib Figure, Our Lady of Sorrows Church

261 Street Cafe

2003. Christmas. Multicoloured

1066	5p. Type **260**	10	10
1067	30p. Children making Crib	60	65
1068	40p. Three Kings Cavalcade	80	80

1069	42p. Children's provisions for Santa and reindeer	85	90
1070	54p. Cathedral of St. Mary the Crowned lit for Christmas Eve Midnight Mass	1·10	1·20
MS1071	100 × 80mm. £1 Cartoon characters from Peanuts carol singing around Christmas tree (50 × 40mm)	2·00	2·10

2004. Europa. Holidays. Multicoloured.

1072	40p. Type **261**	80	85
1073	40p. St. Michael's Cave	80	85
1074	54p. Dolphins	1·10	1·10
1075	54p. Harbourside restaurant	1·10	1·10

POSTAGE DUE STAMPS

D 1

D 2

1956.

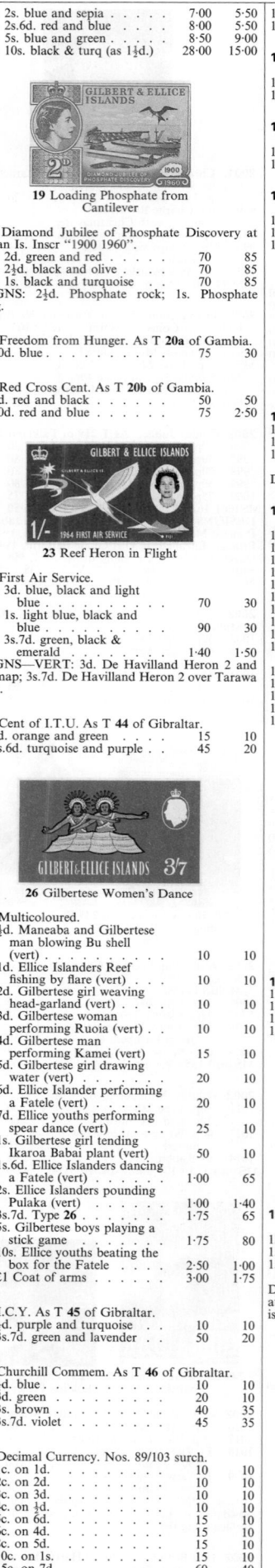

D1	D 1	1d. green	1·50	4·25
D2		2d. brown	1·50	2·75
D3		4d. blue	1·75	5·00

1971. As Nos. D1/3, but inscr in decimal currency.

D4	½p. green	25	80
D5	1p. brown	25	70
D6	2p. blue	25	1·00

1976.

D 7	D 2	1p. orange	15	60
D 8		3p. blue	15	75
D 9		5p. red	20	75
D10		7p. violet	20	75
D11		10p. green	25	75
D12		20p. green	45	1·00

D 3 Gibraltar Coat of Arms

D 4 Water Port Gates

1984.

D13	D 3	1p. black	25	50
D14		3p. red	35	50
D15		5p. blue	40	50
D16		10p. blue	50	50
D17		25p. mauve	90	1·00
D18		50p. orange	1·40	1·75
D19		£1 green	2·25	3·00

1996. Gibraltar Landmarks.

D20	D 4	1p. black, emerald and green	15	50
D21	–	10p. black and grey	50	60
D22	–	25p. black, brown and chestnut	80	80
D23	–	50p. black and lilac	1·25	1·40
D24	–	£1 black, brown and chestnut	2·75	3·00
D25	–	£2 black and blue	4·25	4·75

DESIGNS: 10p. Naval Dockyard; 25p. Military Hospital; 50p. Governor's Cottage; £1 Swans on the Laguna; £2 Catalan Bay.

D 5 Greenfinch

2002. Gibraltar Finches. Type D **5** Multicoloured.

D26	5p. Type D **5**	10	10
D27	10p. Serin	20	15
D28	20p. Siskin	40	45
D29	50p. Linnet	1·00	1·10
D30	£1 Chaffinch	2·00	2·10
D31	£2 Goldfinch	4·00	4·25

GILBERT AND ELLICE ISLANDS

Pt. 1

A British colony in the South Pacific.

1911. 12 pence = 1 shilling; 20 shillings = 1 pound.
1966. 100 cents = $1 Australian.

1911. Stamps of Fiji (King Edward VII) optd **GILBERT & ELLICE PROTECTORATE**.

1	23	½d. green	4·75	45·00
2		1d. red	45·00	28·00
3		2d. grey	8·50	15·00
4		2½d. blue	12·00	29·00
5		5d. purple and green	45·00	75·00
6		6d. purple	20·00	45·00
7		1s. black on green	20·00	60·00

2 Pandanus Pine

3

1911.

8	2	½d. green	4·25	15·00
9		1d. red	2·00	7·00
10		2d. grey	1·50	7·00
11		2½d. blue	5·00	11·00

1912.

27	3	½d. green	3·25	3·25
13		1d. red	2·25	5·00
28		1d. violet	4·50	5·50
29		1½d. red	4·50	2·00
30		2d. grey	7·00	26·00
15		2½d. blue	1·75	11·00
16		3d. purple on yellow	2·50	8·50
17		4d. black and red on yellow	75	7·00
18		5d. purple and green	1·75	7·00
19		6d. purple	1·25	7·50
20		1s. black on green	1·25	5·50
21		2s. purple and blue on blue	14·00	30·00
22		2s.6d. black and red on blue	16·00	25·00
23		5s. green and red on yellow	32·00	60·00
35		10s. green and red on green	£150	£350
24		£1 purple and black on red	£550	£1400

1918. Optd **WAR TAX**.

26	3	1d. red	50	6·50

1935. Silver Jubilee. As T **10a** of Gambia.

36	1d. blue and black	2·25	9·00
37	1½d. blue and red	1·75	3·75
38	3d. brown and blue	5·50	12·00
39	1s. grey and purple	20·00	20·00

1937. Coronation. As T**10b** of Gambia.

40	1d. violet	35	65
41	1½d. red	35	65
42	3d. blue	40	70

6 Great Frigate Bird

7 Pandanus Pine

1939.

43	6	½d. blue and green	60	1·00
44	7	1d. green and purple	30	1·50
45	–	1½d. black and red	30	1·25
46	–	2d. brown and black	75	1·00
47	–	2½d. black and green	40	70
48	–	3d. black and blue	45	1·00
49	–	5d. blue and brown	4·25	1·50
50	–	6d. green and violet	50	60
51a	–	1s. black and turquoise	5.50.00	3·25
52	–	2s. blue and red	10·00	10·00
53	–	2s.6d. blue and green	10·00	11·00
54	–	5s. red and blue	13·00	14·00

DESIGNS: 1½d. Canoe crossing reef; 2d. Canoe and boat-house; 2½d. Native house; 3d. Seascape; 5d. Ellice Is. canoe; 6d. Coconut palms; 1s. Jetty, Ocean Is.; 2s. H.M.C.S. "Nimanoa"; 2s.6d. Gilbert Is. canoe; 5s. Coat of arms.

1946. Victory. As T **11a** of Gambia.

55	1d. purple	15	40
56	3d. blue	15	40

1949. Silver Wedding. As T **11b/c** of Gambia.

57	1d. violet	40	50
58	£1 red	12·00	19·00

1949. U.P.U. As T **11d/g** of Gambia.

59	1d. purple	40	1·00
60	2d. black	2·00	2·50
61	3d. blue	50	2·25
62	1s. blue	50	2·00

1953. Coronation. As T **11h** of Gambia.

63	2d. black and grey	55	2·25

18 Great Frigate Bird

1956. As 1939 issue but with portrait of Queen Elizabeth II as in T **18** and colours changed.

64	18	½d. black and blue	65	1·25
65	7	1d. olive and violet	60	1·25
85	–	2d. green and purple	75	2·00
67	–	2½d. black and green	50	60
68	–	3d. black and red	50	60
69	–	5d. blue and orange	8·50	1·75
70	–	6d. brown and black	55	2·75
71	–	1s. black and olive	2·25	60
72	–	2s. blue and sepia	7·00	5·50
73	–	2s.6d. red and blue	8·00	5·50
74	–	5s. blue and green	8·50	9·00
75	–	10s. black & turq (as 1½d.)	28·00	15·00

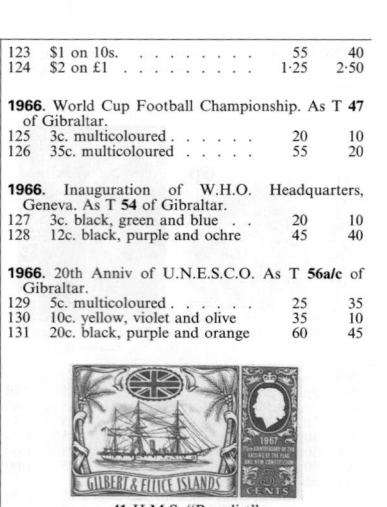

19 Loading Phosphate from Cantilever

1960. Diamond Jubilee of Phosphate Discovery at Ocean Is. Inscr "1900 1960".

76	19	2d. green and red	70	85
77	–	2½d. black and olive	70	85
78	–	1s. black and turquoise	70	85

DESIGNS: 2½d. Phosphate rock; 1s. Phosphate mining.

1963. Freedom from Hunger. As T **20a** of Gambia.

79	10d. blue	75	30

1963. Red Cross Cent. As T **20b** of Gambia.

80	2d. red and black	50	50
81	10d. red and blue	75	2·50

23 Reef Heron in Flight

1964. First Air Service.

82	–	3d. blue, black and light blue	70	30
83	23	1s. light blue, black and blue	90	30
84	–	3s.7d. green, black & emerald	1·40	1·50

DESIGNS—VERT: 3d. De Havilland Heron 2 and route map; 3s.7d. De Havilland Heron 2 over Tarawa lagoon.

1965. Cent of I.T.U. As T **44** of Gibraltar.

87	3d. orange and green	15	10
88	2s.6d. turquoise and purple	45	20

26 Gilbertese Women's Dance

1965. Multicoloured.

89	½d. Maneaba and Gilbertese man blowing Bu shell (vert)	10	10
90	1d. Ellice Islanders Reef fishing by flare (vert)	10	10
91	2d. Gilbertese girl weaving head-garland (vert)	10	10
92	3d. Gilbertese woman performing Ruoia (vert)	10	10
93	4d. Gilbertese man performing Kamei (vert)	15	10
94	5d. Gilbertese girl drawing water (vert)	20	10
95	6d. Ellice Islander performing a Fatele (vert)	20	10
96	7d. Ellice youths performing spear dance (vert)	25	10
97	1s. Gilbertese girl tending Ikaroa Babai plant (vert)	50	10
98	1s.6d. Ellice Islanders dancing a Fatele (vert)	1·00	65
99	2s. Ellice Islanders pounding Pulaka (vert)	1·00	1·40
100	3s.7d. Type **26**	1·75	65
101	5s. Gilbertese boys playing a stick game	1·75	80
102	10s. Ellice youths beating the box for the Fatele	2·50	1·00
103	£1 Coat of arms	3·00	1·75

1965. I.C.Y. As T **45** of Gibraltar.

104	½d. purple and turquoise	10	10
105	3s.7d. green and lavender	50	20

1966. Churchill Commem. As T **46** of Gibraltar.

106	½d. blue	10	10
107	3d. green	20	10
108	3s. brown	40	35
109	3s.7d. violet	45	35

1966. Decimal Currency. Nos. 89/103 surch.

110	1c. on 1d.	10	10
111	2c. on 2d.	10	10
112	3c. on 3d.	10	10
113	4c. on ½d.	10	10
114	5c. on 6d.	15	10
115	6c. on 4d.	15	10
116	8c. on 5d.	15	10
117	10c. on 1s.	15	10
118	15c. on 7d.	60	40
119	20c. on 1s.6d.	30	25
120	25c. on 2s.	30	20
121	35c. on 3s.7d.	1·00	20
122	50c. on 5s.	55	35
123	$1 on 10s.	55	40
124	$2 on £1	1·25	2·50

1966. World Cup Football Championship. As T **47** of Gibraltar.

125	3c. multicoloured	20	10
126	35c. multicoloured	55	20

1966. Inauguration of W.H.O. Headquarters, Geneva. As T **54** of Gibraltar.

127	3c. black, green and blue	20	10
128	12c. black, purple and ochre	45	40

1966. 20th Anniv of U.N.E.S.C.O. As T **56a/c** of Gibraltar.

129	5c. multicoloured	25	35
130	10c. yellow, violet and olive	35	10
131	20c. black, purple and orange	60	45

41 H.M.S. "Royalist"

1967. 75th Anniv of Protectorate.

132	41	3c. red, blue and green	30	50
133	–	10c. multicoloured	15	15
134	–	35c. sepia, yellow and green	30	50

DESIGNS: 10c. Trading post; 35c. Island family.

1968. Decimal Currency. As Nos. 89/103, but with values inscr in decimal currency.

135	–	1c. multicoloured (as 1d.)	10	15
136	–	2c. multicoloured (as 2d.)	15	10
137	–	3c. multicoloured (as 3d.)	15	10
138	–	4c. multicoloured (as ½d.)	15	10
139	–	5c. multicoloured (as 6d.)	15	10
140	–	6c. multicoloured (as 4d.)	20	10
141	–	8c. multicoloured (as 5d.)	20	10
142	–	10c. multicoloured (as 1s.)	20	10
143	–	15c. multicoloured (as 7d.)	50	20
144	–	20c. multicoloured (as 1s.6d.)	65	15
145	–	25c. multicoloured (as 2s.)	1·25	20
146	26	35c. multicoloured	1·50	20
147	–	50c. multicoloured (as 5s.)	1·50	2·50
148	–	$1 multicoloured (as 10s.)	1·50	3·75
149	–	$2 multicoloured (as £1)	4·00	3·75

45 Map of Tarawa Atoll

1968. 25th Anniversary of Battle of Tarawa.

150	3c. Type **45**	20	30
151	10c. Marines landing	20	20
152	15c. Beach-head assault	20	35
153	35c. Raising U.S. and British flags	25	50

46 Young Pupil against Outline of Abemama Island

1969. End of Inaugural Year of South Pacific University.

154	46	3c. multicoloured	10	25
155	–	10c. multicoloured	10	10
156	–	35c. black, brown and green	15	30

DESIGNS: 10c. Boy and girl students and Tarawa atoll; 35c. University graduate and South Pacific islands.

47 "Virgin and Child" in Pacific Setting

1969. Christmas

157	–	2c. multicoloured	15	20
158	47	10c. multicoloured	15	10

DESIGN: 2c. as Type **47**. but with grass foreground instead of sand.

48 "Kiss of Life"

1970. Centenary of British Red Cross.

159	**48**	10c. multicoloured	20	10
160	–	15c. multicoloured	30	45
161	–	35c. multicoloured	60	90

Nos. 160/1 are as Type **48**, but arranged differently.

49 Foetus and Patients

1970. 25th Anniversary of U.N.

162	**49**	5c. multicoloured	15	30
163	–	10c. black, grey and red	15	15
164	–	15c. multicoloured	20	30
165	–	35c. blue, green and black	30	45

DESIGNS: 10c. Nurse and surgical instruments; 15c. X-ray plate and technician; 35c. U.N. emblem and map.

53 Map of Gilbert Islands

57 "Child with Halo" (T. Collis)

1970. Centenary of Landing in Gilbert islands by London Missionary Society.

166	**53**	2c. multicoloured	15	90
167	–	10c. black and green	25	15
168	–	25c. brown and blue	20	20
169	–	35c. blue, black and red	50	70

DESIGNS—VERT: 10c. Sailing-ship "John Williams III"; 25c. Rev. S. J. Whitmee. HORIZ: 35c. M.V. "John Williams VII".

1970. Christmas. Sketches. Multicoloured.

170	2c. Type **57**	10	30
171	10c. "Sanctuary, Tarawa Cathedral" (Mrs A. Burroughs)	10	10
172	35c. "Three Ships inside Star" (Mrs. C. Barnett)	20	20

60 Casting Nets

1971. Multicoloured.

173	1c. Cutting toddy (vert)	10	10
174	2c. Lagoon fishing	15	30
175	3c. Cleaning pandanus leaves	15	15
176	4c. Type **60**	20	25
177	5c. Gilbertese canoe	45	15
178	6c. De-husking coconuts (vert)	30	45
179	8c. Weaving pandanus fronds (vert)	35	15
180	10c. Weaving a basket (vert)	40	15
181	15c. Tiger shark and fishermen (vert)	2·75	1·50
182	20c. Beating rolled pandanus leaf	1·50	90
183	25c. Loading copra	2·00	1·00
184	35c. Fishing at night	2·25	50
185	50c. Local handicrafts (vert)	1·00	1·50
186	$1 Weaving coconut screens (vert)	1·40	1·25
187	$2 Coat of arms (vert)	3·00	8·00

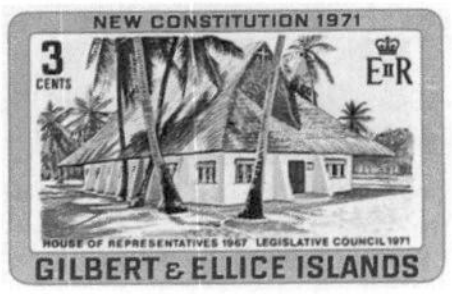

61 House of Representatives

1971. New Constitution. Multicoloured.

188	3c. Type **61**	10	20
189	10c. Maneaba Betio (Assembly hut)	20	10

62 Pacific Nativity Scene

1971. Christmas.

190	**62**	3c. black, yellow and blue	10	20
191	–	10c. black, gold and blue	10	10
192	–	35c. black, gold and red	25	35

DESIGNS: 10c. Star and palm leaves; 35c. Outrigger canoe and star.

63 Emblem and Young Boys

1971. 25th Anniv of U.N.I.C.E.F. Multicoloured.

193	3c. Type **63**	10	90
194	10c. Young boy	15	25
195	35c. Young boy's face	45	90

Nos. 193/5 include the U.N.I.C.E.F. emblem within each design.

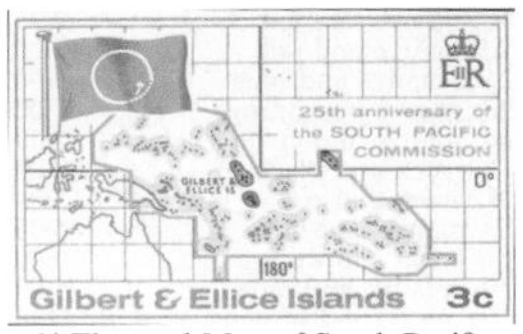

64 Flag and Map of South Pacific

1972. 25th Anniv of South Pacific Commission. Multicoloured.

196	3c. Type **64**	10	80
197	10c. Flag and native boats	15	20
198	35c. Flags of member nations	15	95

65 "Alveopora"

1972. Coral. Multicoloured.

199	3c. Type **65**	25	45
200	10c. "Euphyllia"	30	15
201	15c. "Melithea"	40	35
202	35c. "Spongodes"	80	60

66 Star of Peace

69 Dancer

68 Funafuti ("The Land of Bananas")

1972. Christmas. Multicoloured.

208	3c. Type **66**	10	10
209	10c. "The Nativity"	10	10
210	35c. Baby in "manger" (horiz)	30	30

1972. Royal Silver Wedding. As T **98** of Gibraltar, but with Floral Headdresses in background

211	3c. brown	10	15
212	35c. brown	25	15

1973. Legends of Island Names (1st series). Mult.

213	3c. Type **68**	15	50
214	10c. Butaritari ("The Smell of the Sea")	15	20
215	25c. Tarawa ("The Centre of the World")	25	50
216	35c. Abemama ("The Land of the Moon")	30	60

See also Nos. 252/5.

1973. Christmas. Multicoloured.

217	3c. Type **69**	10	15
218	10c. Canoe and lagoon	10	10
219	35c. Lagoon at evening	30	15
220	50c. Map of Christmas Island	40	1·50

1973. Royal Wedding. As T **101a** of Gibraltar. Multicoloured, background colours given.

221	3c. green	10	15
222	35c. blue	20	15

70 Meteorological Observation

1973. Centenary of I.M.O./W.M.O. Mult.

223	3c. Type **70**	30	30
224	10c. Island observing-station	30	20
225	35c. Wind-finding radar	40	25
226	50c. World weather watch stations	50	1·25

71 Te Mataaua Crest

1974. Canoe Crests. Multicoloured.

227	3c. Type **71**	10	20
228	10c. "Te Nimta-wawa"	15	10
229	35c. "Tara-tara-venei-na"	25	10
230	50c. "Te Bou-uoua"	35	1·40
MS231	154 × 130 mm. Nos. 227/30	2·00	5·50

72 £1 Stamp of 1924 and Te Koroba (canoe)

1974. Centenary of U.P.U.

232	**72**	4c. multicoloured	20	30
233	–	10c. multicoloured	20	15
234	–	25c. multicoloured	25	30
235	–	35c. multicoloured	30	40

DESIGNS: 10c. 5s. stamp of 1939 and sailing vessel "Kiakia"; 25c. $2 stamp of 1971 and B.A.C. One Eleven airplane; 35c. U.P.U. emblem.

73 Toy Canoe

1974. Christmas. Multicoloured.

236	4c. Type **73**	10	20
237	10c. Toy windmill	15	10
238	25c. Coconut "ball"	20	35
239	35c. Canoes and constellation Pleiades	25	50

74 North Front Entrance, Blenheim Palace

1974. Birth Cent of Sir Winston Churchill. Mult.

240	4c. Type **74**	10	35
241	10c. Churchill painting	10	10
242	35c. Churchill's statue, London	25	40

75 Barometer Crab

1975. Crabs. Multicoloured.

243	4c. Type **75**	40	1·25
244	10c. "Ranina ranina"	40	25
245	25c. Pelagic swimmming crab	65	90
246	35c. Ghost crab	75	1·75

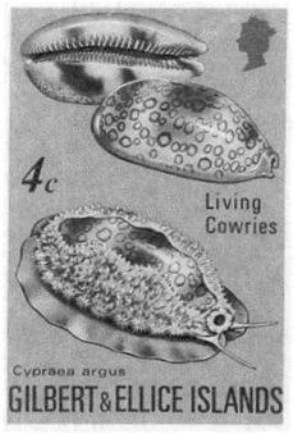

76 Eyed Cowrie

77 "Christ is Born"

1975. Cowrie Shells. Multicoloured.

247	4c. Type **76**	55	1·25
248	10c. Sieve cowrie	70	30
249	25c. Mole cowrie	1·40	1·50
250	35c. All-red map cowrie	1·60	2·50
MS251	146 × 137 mm. Nos. 247/50	14·00	17·00

1975. Legends of Island Names (2nd series). As T **68**. Multicoloured.

252	4c. Beru ("The Bud")	10	30
253	10c. Onotoa ("Six Giants")	10	15
254	25c. Abaiang ("Land to the North")	20	35
255	35c. Marakei ("Fish-trap floating on eaves")	30	50

1975. Christmas. Multicoloured.

256	4c. Type **77**	15	60
257	10c. Protestant Chapel, Tarawa	15	30
258	25c. Catholic Church, Ocean Island	25	1·00
259	35c. Fishermen and star	30	1·75

POSTAGE DUE STAMPS

D 1

1940.

D1	**D 1**	1d. green	9·00	23·00
D2		2d. red	9·50	23·00
D3		3d. brown	14·00	24·00
D4		4d. blue	16·00	30·00
D5		4d. olive	21·00	30·00
D6		6d. purple	21·00	30·00
D7		1s. violet	23·00	42·00
D8		1s.6d. green	45·00	85·00

GILBERT ISLANDS Pt. 1

On 1 January 1976 the Gilbert Islands and Tuvalu (Ellice) Islands became separate Crown Colonies. The Gilbert Islands became independent on 12 July 1979, under the name of Kiribati.

100 cents = $1.

1 Charts of Gilbert Islands and Tuvalu (formerly Ellice) Islands

1976. Separation of the Islands. Multicoloured.

1	4c. Type **1**	40	75
2	35c. Maps of Tarawa and Funafuti	70	1·50

1976. Nos. 173/87 of Gilbert and Ellice Islands optd THE GILBERT ISLANDS.

3	1c. Cutting toddy	25	30
5	2c. Lagoon fishing	50	30
12	3c. Cleaning pandanus leaves	40	1·75
7	4c. Type **60**	30	1·00
13	5c. Gilbertese canoe	50	1·00
14	6c. De-husking coconuts	50	1·00
15	8c. Weaving pandanus fronds	50	1·00
16	10c. Weaving a basket	50	1·00
17	15c. Tiger shark	2·50	1·25
18	20c. Beating a pandanus leaf	75	2·00
19	25c. Loading copra	1·25	1·25
20	35c. Fishing at night	1·75	1·75
21	50c. Local handicrafts	1·25	2·25
22	$1 Weaving coconut screens	2·25	8·00

3 "Teraaka" (training ship)

1978. Multicoloured.

23		1c. Type **3**	40	80
24		3c. "Tautunu" (inter-island freighter)	60	90
25		4c. Moorish idol (fish)	60	80
26		5c. Hibiscus	30	40
27		6c. Reef heron	1·50	1·00
28		7c. Catholic Cathedral, Tarawa	20	30
29		8c. Frangipani	20	30
30		10c. Maneaba, Bikenibeu	20	30
31		12c. Betio Harbour	35	45
32		15c. Evening scene	40	45
33		20c. Marakei Atoll	25	35
34		35c. G.I.P.C. Chapel, Tangintebu	25	40
35		40c. Flamboyant tree	40	45
36		50c. "Hypolimnas bolina", (butterfly)	1·25	1·75
37		$1 "Tabakea" (Tarawa Lagoon ferry)	75	2·50
38		$2 National flag	75	2·50

4 Church

1976. Christmas. Children's Drawings. Mult.

39		5c. Type **4**	20	15
40		15c. Feasting (vert)	30	15
41		20c. Maneaba (vert)	30	35
42		35c. Dancing	30	45

5 Porcupine Fish Helmet

6 The Queen in Coronation Robes

1976. Artefacts. Multicoloured.

43		5c. Type **5**	20	15
44		15c. Shark's teeth dagger	30	35
45		20c. Fighting gauntlet	30	40
46		35c. Coconut body armour	45	55
MS47		140 × 130 mm. Nos. 43/6	5·00	13·00

1977. Silver Jubilee. Multicoloured.

48		8c. Prince Charles' visit, 1970	10	10
49		20c. Prince Philip's visit, 1959	15	15
50		40c. Type **6**	20	35

7 Commodore Bryon and H.M.S. "Dolphin"

1977. Explorers. Multicoloured.

51		5c. Type **7**	45	1·50
52		15c. Capt. Fanning and "Betsey"	55	2·75
53		20c. Admiral Bellingshausen and "Vostok"	55	2·75
54		35c. Capt. Wilkes and U.S.S. "Vincennes"	65	4·00

8 H.M.S. "Resolution" and H.M.S. "Discovery"

9 Scout Emblem and Island Scene

1977. Christmas and Bicentenary of Capt. Cook's Discovery of Christmas Is. Mult.

55		8c. Type **8**	30	15
56		15c. Logbook entry (horiz)	30	15
57		20c. Captain Cook	40	20
58		40c. Landing party (horiz)	40	60
MS59		140 × 140 mm. Nos. 55/8	2·75	9·00

1977. 50th Anniv of Scouting in the Gilbert Is. Multicoloured.

60		8c. Type **9**	40	15
61		15c. Patrol meeting (horiz)	45	20
62		20c. Scout making mat (horiz)	50	20
63		40c. Canoeing	65	55

10 Taurus (The Bull)

11 Unicorn of Scotland

1978. The Night Sky over the Gilbert Islands.

64	**10**	10c. black and blue	45	30
65	–	20c. black and red	50	45
66	–	25c. black and green	50	50
67	–	45c. black and orange	75	80

DESIGNS: 20c. Canis Major (the Great Dog); 25c. Scorpio (the Scorpion); 45c. Orion (the Giant Warrior).

1978. 25th Anniv of Coronation.

68	**11**	45c. green, violet and silver	25	40
69	–	45c. multicoloured	25	40
70	–	45c. green, violet and silver	25	40

DESIGNS: No. 69, Queen Elizabeth II. No. 70, Great Frigate Bird.

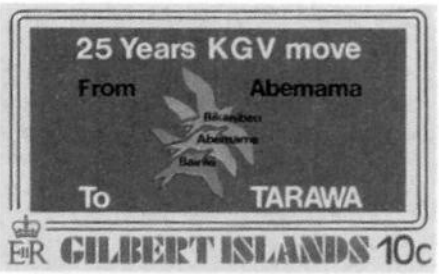

12 Birds in Flight to Tarawa

1978. 25th Anniv of Return of George V School to Tarawa. Multicoloured.

71		10c. Type **12**	10	10
72		20c. Tarawa, Abemama and school badge	20	20
73		25c. Rejoicing islanders	20	20
74		45c. King George V School on Tarawa and Abemama	35	35

13 "Te Kaue ni Maie"

1978. Christmas. Kaue (traditional head decorations). Multicoloured.

75		10c. Type **13**	10	10
76		20c. "Te Itera"	15	15
77		25c. "Te Bau"	20	20
78		45c. "Te Tai"	25	30
MS79		149 × 99 mm. Nos. 75/8	90	4·50

14 H.M.S. "Endeavour"

1979. Bicent of Captain Cook's Voyages, 1768–79.

80	**14**	10c. multicoloured	20	15
81	–	20c. multicoloured	25	30
82	–	25c. black, lilac and green	25	45
83	–	45c. multicoloured	25	80

DESIGNS: 20c. Green Turtle; 25c. Quadrant; 45c. Flaxman/Wedgwood medallion.

For later issues see **KIRIBATI**.

GOLD COAST Pt. 1

A British colony on the W. coast of Africa. For later issues after independence in 1957 see under Ghana.

12 pence = 1 shilling;
20 shillings = 1 pound.

1

4

1875.

4	**1**	½d. yellow	65·00	23·00
11a		½d. green	3·00	80
5		1d. blue	20·00	6·50
12		1d. red	3·75	50
6		2d. green	85·00	9·00
13b		2d. grey	3·75	50
14		2½d. blue and orange	4·25	70
15		3d. olive	10·00	4·50
16		4d. mauve	10·00	1·50
17		6d. orange	10·00	5·00
18a		1s. mauve	5·50	1·25
19a		2s. brown	42·00	15·00

1889. Surch **ONE PENNY.** and bar.

20	**1**	1d. on 6d. orange	£110	48·00

1889.

26	**4**	½d. mauve and green	2·50	1·00
27		1d. mauve and red	2·75	50
27b		2d. mauve and red	48·00	£140
28		2½d. mauve and blue	5·00	5·00
29		3d. mauve and orange	5·00	1·50
30		6d. mauve and violet	5·50	1·50
31		1s. green and black	10·00	16·00
32		2s. green and red	13·00	18·00
22		5s. mauve and blue	65·00	15·00
33		5s. green and mauve	50·00	29·00
23		10s. mauve and red	75·00	15·00
34		10s. green and brown	£140	50·00
24		20s. green and red	£3250	
25		20s. mauve and black on red	£160	35·00

1901. Surch **ONE PENNY.** and bar.

35	**4**	1d. on 2½d. mauve and blue	3·75	4·00
36		1d. on 6d. mauve and violet	3·25	3·50

1902. As T **4**, but with portrait of King Edward VII.

38		½d. purple and green	1·50	40
39		1d. purple and red	1·50	15
51		2d. purple and orange	5·00	50
41		2½d. purple and blue	4·50	9·00
42		3d. purple and orange	3·00	1·50
43		6d. purple and violet	3·75	1·50
44		1s. green and black	14·00	3·25
45		2s. green and red	15·00	18·00
57		2s.6d. green and yellow	28·00	£110
46		5s. green and mauve	40·00	90·00
47		10s. green and brown	55·00	£130
48		20s. purple and black on red	£130	£180

1907. As last.

59		½d. green	3·50	30
60		1d. red	7·00	40
61		2d. grey	2·25	40
62		2½d. blue	7·50	2·00
63		3d. purple on yellow	8·00	55
64a		6d. purple	3·75	3·50
65		1s. black and green	11·00	50
66		2s. purple and blue on blue	8·00	16·00
67		2s.6d. black and red on blue	28·00	90·00
68		5s. green and red on yellow	55·00	£180

8

13 King George V and Christiansborg Castle

1908.

69	**8**	1d. red	3·00	10

1913. As T **4** and **8** (1d.) but portraits of King George V.

86		½d. green	80	50
72		1d. red	1·25	10
87		1d. brown	70	10
88		1½d. red	1·75	10
89		2d. grey	1·75	30
76		2½d. blue	5·00	1·00
90		2½d. orange	75	9·00
77b		3d. purple on yellow	1·00	40
91		3d. blue	1·75	60
78		6d. purple	2·75	2·25
79e		1s. black on green	1·50	50
96		2s. purple and blue on blue	3·00	3·25
81		2s.6d. black and red on blue	5·00	13·00
98		5s. green and red on yellow	12·00	48·00
83a		10s. green and red on green	18·00	65·00
100a		15s. purple and green	£110	£300
84		20s. purple and black on red	£130	£325
102		£2 green and orange	£375	£900

1918. Surch **WAR TAX ONE PENNY.**

85		1d. on red (No. 72)	1·75	50

1928.

103	**13**	½d. green	70	40
104		1d. brown	70	10
105		1½d. red	1·25	1·50
106		2d. grey	1·25	20
107		2½d. orange	1·50	3·50
108		3d. blue	1·25	40
109		6d. black and purple	1·50	40
110		1s. black and orange	3·00	75
111		2s. black and violet	20·00	4·75
112		3s. red and olive	50·00	45·00

1935. Silver Jubilee. As T **10a** of Gambia.

113		1d. blue and black	60	50
114		3d. brown and blue	3·00	6·00
115		6d. green and blue	7·00	14·00
116		1s. grey and purple	4·75	18·00

1937. Coronation. As T **10b** of Gambia.

117		1d. brown	1·25	2·25
118		2d. grey	1·25	4·00
119		3d. blue	1·50	2·00

14

15 King George VI and Christiansborg Castle, Accra

1938.

120a	**14**	½d. green	40	50
121a		1d. brown	40	10
122a		1½d. red	40	50
123a		2d. black	40	10
124a		3d. blue	40	35
125a		4d. mauve	80	1·25
126a		6d. purple	80	20
127a		9d. orange	1·25	55
128a	**15**	1s. black and olive	1·50	65
129		1s.3d. brown and blue	2·00	50
130a		2s. blue and violet	5·00	13·00
131a		5s. olive and red	10·00	16·00
132		10s. black and violet	7·00	23·00

1946. Victory. As T **11a** of Gambia.

133a		2d. grey	10	10
134a		4d. mauve	1·50	2·75

16 Northern Territories Mounted Constabulary

1948.

135	**16**	½d. green	20	30
136	–	1d. blue	15	15
137	–	1½d. red	1·25	70
138	–	2d. brown	55	10
139	–	2½d. brown and red	2·00	3·50
140	–	3d. blue	4·00	50
141	–	4d. mauve	3·50	2·00
142	–	6d. black and orange	30	30
143	–	1s. black and red	60	30
144	–	2s. olive and red	3·25	2·00
145	–	5s. purple and black	26·00	6·00
146	–	10s. black and olive	8·00	6·00

DESIGNS—HORIZ: 1d. Christiansborg Castle; 1½d. Emblem of Joint Provincial Council; 2½d. Map showing position of Gold Coast; 3d. Nsuba manganese mine; 4d. Lake Bosumtwi; 1s. Breaking cocoa pods; 2s. Gold Coast Regt. trooping the Colour; 5s. Surfboats. VERT: 2d. Talking drums; 6d. Cocoa farmer; 10s. Forest.

1948. Silver Wedding. As T **11b/c** of Gambia.

147		1½d. red	30	30
148		10s. olive	17·00	23·00

1949. U.P.U. As T **11d/g** of Gambia.

149		2d. brown	25	20
150		2½d. orange	1·50	3·50
151		3d. blue	25	1·50
152		1s. green	25	30

1952. As 1948 but portrait of Queen Elizabeth II. Designs as for corresponding values except where stated.

153		½d. brown and red (as 2½d.)	10	20
154		1d. blue	30	10
155		1½d. green	30	1·25
156		2d. brown	30	10
157		2½d. red (as ½d.)	35	75
158		3d. mauve	75	10
159		4d. blue	35	30
160		6d. black and orange	40	15
161		1s. black and red	50	15
162		2s. olive and red	11·00	85

163		5s. purple and black	17·00	5·50
164		10s. black and olive	16·00	12·00

1953. Coronation. As T **11h** of Gambia.

165		2d. black and brown	1·00	10

POSTAGE DUE STAMPS

D 1

1923.

D1	D 1	½d. black	15·00	£110
D2		1d. black	75	1·25
D3		2d. black	13·00	5·50
D6		3d. black	2·50	20·00
D7		6d. black	1·75	8·00
D8		1s. black	1·75	65·00

For later issues see **GHANA.**

GREAT BRITAIN Pt. 1

Consisting of England, Wales, Scotland and Northern Ireland, lying to the N.W. of the European continent.

1840. 12 pence = 1 shilling;
20 shillings = 1 pound sterling.
1971. 100 (new) pence = 1 pound sterling.

1 3

1840. Letters in lower corners. Imperf.

2	1	1d. black	£450	£225
5		2d. blue	£10000	£500

1841. Imperf.

8	1	1d. brown	£250	15·00
14	3	2d. blue	£2250	70·00

In T **3** there are white lines below "POSTAGE" and above "TWO PENCE".

12 10

1847. Imperf.

59	12	6d. purple	£5250	£675
57	10	10d. brown	£4500	£900
54		1s. green	£7000	£500

1854. Perf.

29	1	1d. brown	£180	15·00
40		1d. red	40·00	9·00
34	3	2d. blue	£1750	50·00

14 18 19

1855. No letters in corners.

66a	14	4d. red	£1000	90·00
70	18	6d. lilac	£800	85·00
72	19	1s. green	£1000	£250

7 5

8 6

1858. Letters in four corners.

48	7	½d. red	85·00	15·00
43	5	1d. red	15·00	2·00
52	8	1½d. red	£350	45·00
45	6	2d. blue	£275	10·00

21 22

23 24 25

1862. Small white letters in corners.

76	21	3d. red	£1400	£225
82	22	4d. red	£1100	80·00
84	23	6d. lilac	£1250	80·00
87	24	9d. bistre	£2500	£275
90	25	1s. green	£1500	£150

30 32

1865. Designs as 1862 and T **30** and **32**, but large white letters in corners.

103	21	3d. red	£350	45·00
94	22	4d. red	£425	50·00
97	23	6d. lilac (with hyphen)	£650	75·00
109		6d. lilac (without hyphen)	£450	75·00
111	24	9d. straw	£1100	£200
112	30	10d. brown	£1850	£275
117	25	1s. green	£550	32·00
118	32	2s. blue	£1800	£125
121		2s. brown	£12000	£2500

35

38

1867.

126	35	5s. red	£4500	£550
128	–	10s. green	£35000	£2000
129	–	£1 brown	£42000	£3000
137	38	£5 orange	£7000	£3500

The 10s. and £1 are as Type **35**, but have different frames.

34

1872. Large white letters in corners.

122b	34	6d. brown	£500	45·00
125		6d. grey	£1250	£200

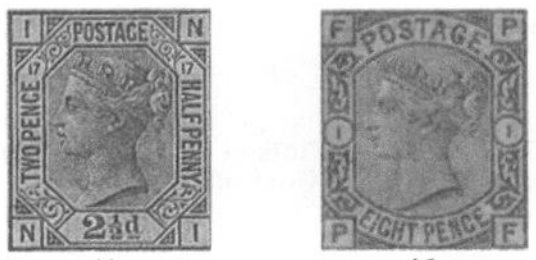
41 46

1873. Large coloured letters in corners.

141	41	2½d. mauve	£380	45·00
157		2½d. blue	£325	25·00
143	21	3d. red	£325	35·00
152	22	4d. red	£1400	£325
153		4d. green	£800	£225
160		4d. brown	£300	50·00
161	34	6d. grey	£300	55·00
156	46	8d. orange	£900	£250
150	25	1s. green	£425	70·00
163		1s. brown	£400	£110

The 3d, 4d. and 1s. are as 1862, and the 6d. as Type **34**, but all with large coloured letters.

52 53

1880. Various frames.

164	52	½d. green	40·00	10·00
187		½d. blue	20·00	7·00
166	53	1d. brown	20·00	10·00
167	–	1½d. red	£150	40·00
168	–	2d. red	£200	80·00
169	–	5d. blue	£575	£100

57 58

61

1881.

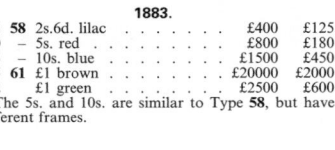

174	57	1d. lilac	2·50	1·50

1883. Types, as 1873, surch **3d.** or **6d.**

159	21	3d. on 3d. lilac	£375	£110
162	34	6d. on 6d. lilac	£400	£120

1883.

178	58	2s.6d. lilac	£400	£125
180	–	5s. red	£800	£180
183	–	10s. blue	£1500	£450
185	61	£1 brown	£20000	£2000
212		£1 green	£2500	£600

The 5s. and 10s. are similar to Type **58**, but have different frames.

62 63

1883. Various frames.

188	62	1½d. purple	90·00	35·00
189	63	2d. purple	£150	65·00
190		2½d. purple	70·00	12·00
191	62	3d. purple	£180	85·00
192		4d. green	£400	£175
193		5d. green	£400	£175
194	63	6d. green	£425	£200
195		9d. green	£800	£375
196	62	1s. green	£750	£200

71 72

73 74

75 76

77 78

79 80

81 82

1887.

197	71	½d. red	1·50	1·00
213		½d. green*	1·75	2·00
198	72	1½d. purple and green	15·00	7·00
200	73	2d. green and red	28·00	12·00
201	74	2½d. purple on blue	22·00	3·00
202	75	3d. purple on yellow	22·00	3·25
205	76	4d. green and brown	30·00	13·00
206	77	4½d. green and red	10·00	40·00
207a	78	5d. purple and blue	35·00	11·00
208	79	6d. purple on red	30·00	10·00
209	80	9d. purple and blue	60·00	40·00
210	81	10d. purple and red	45·00	38·00
211	82	1s. green	£200	60·00
214		1s. green and red	50·00	£125

*No. 213, in blue, has had the colour changed after issue.

83 90

1902. Designs not shown are as 1887 (2s.6d. to £1 as 1883) but with portrait of King Edward VII.

217	83	½d. green	2·00	1·50
219		1d. red	2·00	1·50
221	–	1½d. purple and green	35·00	18·00
291	–	2d. green and red	25·00	20·00
231	83	2½d. blue	20·00	10·00
234	–	3d. purple on yellow	35·00	15·00
238	–	4d. green and brown	40·00	18·00
240	–	4d. orange	20·00	15·00
294	–	5d. purple and blue	28·00	20·00
245	83	6d. purple	35·00	18·00
249	90	7d. grey	10·00	18·00
307	–	9d. purple and blue	60·00	60·00
311	–	10d. purple and red	60·00	60·00
314	–	1s. green and red	50·00	35·00
260	–	2s.6d. purple	£220	£120
263	–	5s. red	£350	£200
265	–	10s. blue	£600	£450
266	–	£1 green	£1500	£650

98 (Hair heavy) **99** (Lion unshaded)

1911.

325	98	½d. green	4·50	1·50
327	99	1d. red	4·50	2·50

101 (Hair light) **102** (Lion shaded)

1912.

344	101	½d. green	7·00	3·00
341	102	1d. red	5·00	2·00

104 105

106 107

108

109

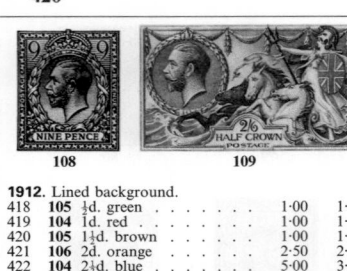

1912. Lined background.

418	105	½d. green	1·00	1·00
419	104	1d. red	1·00	1·00
420	105	1½d. brown	1·00	1·00
421	106	2d. orange	2·50	2·50
422	104	2½d. blue	5·00	3·00
376	106	3d. violet	7·00	2·00
424		4d. green	12·00	2·00
381	107	5d. brown	15·00	5·00
426a		6d. purple	3·00	1·50
387		7d. green	20·00	10·00
390		8d. black on yellow	32·00	11·00
392	108	9d. black	20·00	6·00
427		9d. green	12·00	3·50
394		10d. blue	22·00	20·00
395		1s. brown	20·00	4·00
450	109	2s.6d. brown	70·00	40·00
451		5s. red	£160	85·00
452		10s. blue	£340	8·00
403		£1 green	£1400	£850

112

1924. British Empire Exhibition. Dated "1924".

430	112	1d. red	10·00	11·00
431		1½d. brown	15·00	15·00

1925. Dated "1925".

432	112	1d. red	15·00	30·00
433		1½d. brown	40·00	70·00

113

114

115

116 St. George and the Dragon

1929. 9th U.P.U. Congress, London.

434	113	½d. green	2·25	2·25
435	114	1d. red	2·25	2·25
436		1½d. brown	2·25	1·75
437	115	2½d. blue	10·00	10·00
438	116	£1 black	£750	£550

118

119

120

121

122

123

1934. Solid background.

439	118	½d. green	50	50
440	119	1d. red	50	50
441	118	1½d. brown	50	50
442	120	2d. orange	75	75
443	119	2½d. blue	1·50	1·25
444	120	3d. violet	1·50	1·25
445		4d. green	2·00	1·25
446	121	5d. brown	6·00	2·75
447	122	9d. olive	12·00	2·25
448		10d. blue	15·00	10·00
449		1s. brown	15·00	1·25

1935. Silver Jubilee.

453	123	½d. green	75	50
454		1d. red	1·25	1·50
455		1½d. brown	75	50
456		2½d. blue	4·50	5·50

Emblems at right differ.

124 King Edward VIII

126 King George VI and Queen Elizabeth

1936.

457	124	½d. green	30	30
458		1d. red	60	50
459		1½d. brown	30	30
460		2½d. blue	30	85

1937. Coronation.

461	126	1½d. brown	30	30

128

129

130

131 King George VI

1937.

462	128	½d. green	30	25
503		½d. orange	30	30
463		1d. red	30	25
504		1d. blue	30	30
464		1½d. brown	20	25
505		1½d. green	65	60
465		2d. orange	75	50
506		2d. brown	75	40
466		2½d. blue	30	25
507		2½d. red	60	40
490		3d. violet	2·00	1·00
468	129	4d. green	60	75
508		4d. blue	2·00	1·75
469		5d. brown	2·50	85
470		6d. purple	1·25	60
471	130	7d. green	4·50	60
472		8d. red	4·00	80
473		9d. green	5·75	80
474		10d. blue	6·00	80
474a		11d. purple	2·00	2·75
475		1s. brown	7·00	75

1939.

476	131	2s.6d. brown	35·00	6·00
476a		2s.6d. green	4·50	1·50
477		5s. red	9·00	2·00
478a	–	10s. blue	20·00	5·00
478b	–	£1 brown	7·00	26·00

The 10s. and £1 values have the portrait in the centre in an ornamental frame.

134 Queen Victoria and King George VI

1940. Centenary of First Adhesive Postage Stamps.

479	134	½d. green	30	30
480		1d. red	1·00	40
481		1½d. brown	50	75
482		2d. orange	1·00	40
483		2½d. blue	2·25	50
484		3d. violet	3·00	3·50

135

1946. Victory Commemoration.

491	135	2½d. blue	20	15
492	–	3d. violet	20	40

DESIGN—HORIZ: 3d. Symbols of Peace and Reconstruction.

137

138 King George VI and Queen Elizabeth

1948. Royal Silver Wedding.

493	137	2½d. blue	35	20
494	138	£1 blue	40·00	40·00

139 Globe and Laurel Wreath

140 "Speed"

1948. Olympic Games. Inscr "OLYMPIC GAMES 1948".

495	139	2½d. blue	35	10
496	140	3d. violet	35	55
497	–	6d. purple	75	40
498	–	1s. brown	1·40	1·60

DESIGNS: 6d. Olympic symbol; 1s. Winged Victory.

143 Two Hemispheres

144 U.P.U. Monument, Berne

1949. 75th Anniv of U.P.U. Inscr as in T **143/4**.

499	143	2½d. blue	15	10
500	144	3d. violet	15	50
501	–	6d. purple	25	50
502	–	1s. brown	60	1·25

DESIGNS: 6d. Goddess Concordia, globe and points of compass; 1s. Posthorn and globe.

147 H.M.S. "Victory"

1951.

509	147	2s.6d. green	2·00	1·00
510	–	5s. red	40·00	1·50
511	–	10s. blue	10·00	8·50
512	–	£1 brown	48·00	20·00

DESIGNS: 5s. White Cliffs of Dover; 10s. St. George and dragon; £1 Royal Coat of Arms.

152 Festival Symbol

1951. Festival of Britain.

513	–	2½d. red	15	20
514	152	4d. blue	30	65

DESIGN: 2½d. Britannia, cornucopia and Mercury.

154

155

157

158

159 Queen Elizabeth II and National Emblems

1952.

570	154	½d. orange	10	10
571		1d. blue	10	10
517		1½d. green	10	20
573		2d. brown	10	10
519	155	2½d. red	15	15
575		3d. lilac	10	20
576a		4d. blue	15	15
577		4½d. brown	10	25
616c	157	5d. brown	25	35
617		6d. purple	30	30
617a		7d. green	55	50
617b	158	8d. mauve	40	45
582		9d. green	60	40
617d		10d. blue	70	60
553		11d. plum	50	1·10
617e	159	1s. brown	35	35
585		1s.3d. green	45	30
618a		1s.6d. blue	2·00	1·60

The 4d., 4½d. and 1s.3d. values are printed with colour tones reversed.

Stamps with either one or two vertical black lines on the back were issued in 1957 in connection with the Post Office automatic facing machine experiments in the Southampton area. Later the lines were replaced by almost invisible phosphor bands on the face, in the above and later issues. They are listed in the Stanley Gibbons British Commonwealth Catalogue.

For stamps as T **157**, but with face values in decimal currency, see Nos. 2031/3.

161

163

1953. Coronation. Portraits of Queen Elizabeth II.

532	161	2½d. red	20	25
533	–	4d. blue	1·10	1·90
534	163	1s.3d. green	4·25	3·00
535	–	1s.6d. blue	8·00	4·75

DESIGNS: 4d. Coronation and National Emblems; 1s.6d. Crowns and Sceptres dated "2 JUNE 1953".

166 Carrickfergus Castle

1955.

595a	166	2s.6d. brown	35	40
596a	–	5s. red	90	50
597a	–	10s. blue	4·00	4·50
762	–	£1 black	4·50	6·00

CASTLES: 5s. Caernarvon; 10s. Edinburgh; £1 Windsor.

170 Scout Badge and "Rolling Hitch"

171 "Scouts coming to Britain"

1957. World Scout Jubilee Jamboree.
557 **170** 2½d. red 15 20
558 **171** 4d. blue 35 80
559 – 1s.3d. green . . . . . . 3·50 3·50
DESIGN: 1s.3d. Globe within a compass.

1957. Inter-Parliamentary Union Conference. As No. 576a but inscr "46th PARLIAMENTARY CONFERENCE".
560 4d. blue . . . . 1·00 1·00

176 Welsh Dragon

1958. 6th British Empire and Commonwealth Games, Cardiff. Inscr as in T **176**.
567 **176** 3d. lilac 20 20
568 – 6d. mauve 40 45
569 – 1s.3d. green . . . . . . 2·25 2·40
DESIGNS: 6d. Flag and Games emblem; 1s.3d. Welsh Dragon.

180 Postboy of 1660

181 Posthorn of 1660

1960. Tercentenary of Establishment of General Letter Office.
619 **180** 3d. lilac 20 20
620 **181** 1s.3d. green . . . . . . 2·75 3·50

182 Conference Emblem

1960. 1st Anniv of European Postal and Telecommunications Conference.
621 **182** 6d. green and purple . . . 50 50
622 1s.6d. brown and blue . . 6·50 5·00

184 "Growth of Savings"

1961. Centenary of Post Office Savings Bank. Inscr "POST OFFICE SAVINGS BANK".
623A – 2½d. black and red . . . 25 25
624A **184** 3d. brown and violet . . 20 20
625A – 1s.6d. red and blue . . 2·25 2·25
DESIGNS—VERT: 2½d. Thrift plant. HORIZ: 1s.6d. Thrift plant.

186 C.E.P.T. Emblem

187 Doves and Emblem

1961. Europa.
626 **186** 2d. orange, pink and brown 15 20
627 **187** 4d. buff, mauve and blue 15 25
628 – 10d. turquoise, green bl 15 80
DESIGN: 10d. As 4d. but arranged differently.

189 Hammer Beam Roof, Westminster Hall

1961. 7th Commonwealth Parliamentary Conference.
629 **189** 6d. purple and gold . . . 25 25
630 – 1s.3d. green and blue . . 2·75 3·00
DESIGN—VERT: 1s.3d. Palace of Westminster.

191 "Units of Productivity"

1962. National Productivity Year.
631 **191** 2½d. green and red . . . 20 15
632 – 3d. blue and violet . . . 25 15
633 – 1s.3d. red, blue and green 1·50 1·75
DESIGNS: 3d. Arrows over map; 1s.3d. Arrows in formation.

194 Campaign Emblem and Family

1963. Freedom from Hunger.
634 **194** 2½d. red and pink 10 10
635 – 1s.3d. brown and yellow 1·60 1·90
DESIGN: 1s.3d. Children of three races.

196 "Paris Conference"

1963. Centenary of Paris Postal Conference.
636 **196** 6d. green and mauve . . 30 40

197 Posy of Flowers

1963. National Nature Week. Multicoloured.
637 3d. Type **197** 15 15
638 4½d. Woodland life 20 35

199 Rescue at Sea

1963. 9th International Lifeboat Conference, Edinburgh. Multicoloured.
639 2½d. Type **199** 15 20
640 4d. 19th-century lifeboat . . 40 40
641 1s.6d. Lifeboatmen . . . . . 2·40 2·50

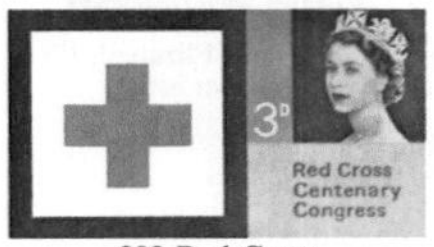

202 Red Cross

1963. Red Cross Centenary Congress.
642 **202** 3d. red and lilac 15 15
643 – 1s.3d. red, blue and grey 2·50 2·50
644 – 1s.6d. red, blue and bistre 2·50 2·50
DESIGNS: Nos. 643/4 are as Type **202** but differently arranged.

205 Commonwealth Cable

1963. COMPAC (Trans-Pacific Telephone Cable) Opening.
645 **205** 1s.6d. blue and black . . 2·00 2·25

206 Puck and Bottom ("A Midsummer Night's Dream")

210 Hamlet contemplating Yorick's Skull ("Hamlet") and Queen Elizabeth II

1964. Shakespeare Festival.
646 **206** 3d. multicoloured 15 15
647 – 6d. multicoloured 30 30
648 – 1s.3d. multicoloured . . . 70 90
649 – 1s.6d. multicoloured . . . 1·00 85
650 **210** 2s.6d. slate-purple . . . . 2·75 2·75
DESIGNS—As Type **206**: 6d. Feste ("Twelfth Night"); 1s.3d. Balcony scene ("Romeo and Juliet"); 1s.6d. "Eve of Agincourt" ("Henry V").

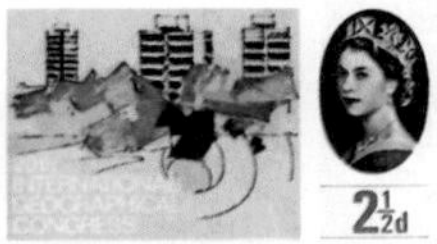

211 Flats near Richmond Park

1964. 20th Int Geographical Congress, London. Multicoloured.
651 2½d. Type **211** 10 10
652 4d. Shipbuilding yards, Belfast 30 30
653 8d. Beddgelert Forest Park, Snowdonia 65 75
654 1s.6d. Nuclear reactor, Dounreay . . . . 2·75 3·00
The designs represent "Urban development", "Industrial activity", "Forestry" and "Technological development" respectively.

215 Spring Gentian

1964. 10th Int Botanical Congress, Edinburgh. Multicoloured.
655 3d. Type **215** 10 10
656 6d. Dog rose 30 35
657 9d. Honeysuckle . . . . . . 1·60 2·25
658 1s.3d. Fringed water lily . . 2·25 2·50

219 Forth Road Bridge

1964. Opening of Forth Road Bridge.
659 **219** 3d. black, blue and violet 10 10
660 – 6d. lilac, blue and red . . 40 40
DESIGN: 6d. Forth Road and Railway Bridges.

221 Sir Winston Churchill

1965. Churchill Commemoration.
661 **221** 4d. black and drab . . . 10 10
662 – 1s.3d. black and grey . . 30 40
The 1s.3d. shows a closer view of Churchill's head.

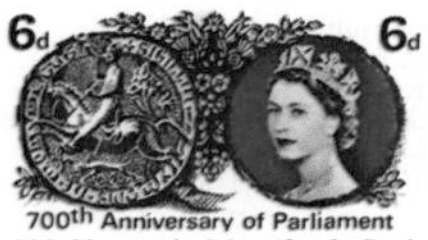

222 Simon de Montfort's Seal

1965. 700th Anniv of Simon de Montfort's Parliament.
663 **222** 6d. olive 20 20
664 – 2s.6d. black, grey and drab . . . . 80 1·00
DESIGN—(58½ × 21½ mm): 2s.6d. Parliament buildings (after engraving by Hollar, 1647).

224 Bandsmen and Banner

1965. Centenary of Salvation Army. Mult.
665 3d. Type **224** 10 15
666 1s.6d. Three Salvationists . . 65 1·00

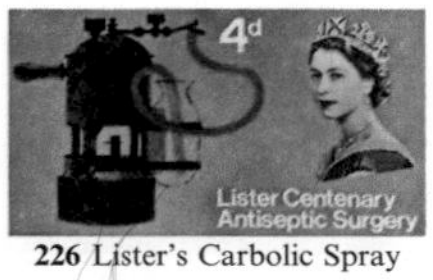

226 Lister's Carbolic Spray

1965. Centenary of Joseph Lister's Discovery of Antiseptic Surgery.
667 **226** 4d. blue, brown and grey 10 15
668 – 1s. black, purple and blue 70 1·10
DESIGN: 1s. Lister and chemical symbols.

228 Trinidad Carnival Dancers

1965. Commonwealth Arts Festival.
669 **228** 6d. black and orange . . 20 20
670 – 1s.6d. black and violet . . 80 1·10
DESIGN: 1s.6d. Canadian folk-dancers.

230 Flight of Supermarine Spitfires

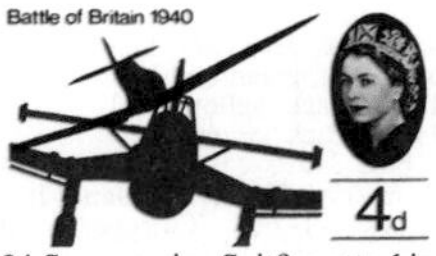

234 Supermarine Spitfire attacking Junkers Ju 878 "Stuka"

1965. 25th Anniv of Battle of Britain. Inscr "Battle of Britain 1940".
671 **230** 4d. olive and black . . . 50 70
672 – 4d. olive and black . . . 50 70
673 – 4d. multicoloured . . . 50 70
674 – 4d. olive and black . . . 50 70
675 **234** 4d. olive and black . . . 50 70
676 – 4d. multicoloured . . . 50 70
677p – 9d. violet, orange and purple . . . . 1·25 1·50
678p – 1s.3d. grey, black and blue . . . . 1·25 1·50
DESIGNS: No. 672, Pilot in Hawker Hurricane Mk I; 673, Wing-tips of Supermarine Spitfire and Messerschmitt BF 109; 674, Supermarine Spitfires attacking Heinkel HE 111H bomber; 676, Hawker Hurricanes Mk 1 over wreck of Dornier DO-17Z bomber; 9d. Anti-aircraft artillery in action; 1s.3d. Air battle over St. Paul's Cathedral.

239 Tower and "Nash" Terrace, Regent's Park

1965. Opening of Post Office Tower.
679 – 3d. yellow, blue and green 10 15
680p **239** 1s.3d. green and blue . . 30 45
DESIGN—VERT: 3d. Tower and Georgian buildings.

240 U.N. Emblem

1965. 20th Anniv of U.N.O. and International Co-operation Year.
681 **240** 3d. black, orange and blue 15 20
682 – 1s.6d. black, purple blue 75 80
DESIGN: 1s.6d. I.C.Y. Emblem.

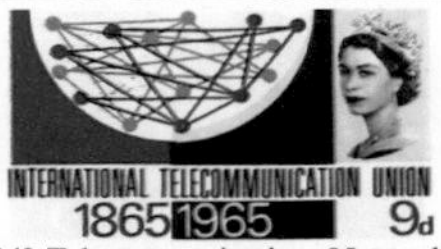

242 Telecommunications Network

1965. Centenary of I.T.U. Multicoloured.

683	9d. Type **242**	30	40
684	1s.6d. Radio waves and switchboard	1·00	1·25

244 Robert Burns (after Skirving chalk drawing)

1966. Burns Commemoration.

685	**244**	4d. black, indigo and blue	15	15
686	–	1s.3d. black, blue orange	40	70

DESIGN: 1s.3d. Robert Burns (after Nasmyth portrait).

246 Westminster Abbey

1966. 900th Anniv of Westminster Abbey.

687	**246**	3d. black, brown and blue	15	20
688	–	2s.6d. black	55	80

DESIGN: 2s.6d. Fan vaulting, Henry VII Chapel.

248 View near Hassocks, Sussex

1966. Landscapes.

689	**248**	4d. black, green and blue	10	15
690	–	6d. black, green and blue	15	20
691	–	1s.3d. black, yellow & bl	25	35
692	–	1s.6d. black, orange & blue	40	35

VIEWS: 6d. Antrim, Northern Ireland; 1s.3d. Harlech Castle, Wales; 1s.6d. Cairngorm Mountains, Scotland.

253 Goalmouth Melee

1966. World Cup Football Championship. Multicoloured.

693	4d. Players with ball (vert)	10	10
694	6d. Type **253**	15	25
695	1s.3d. Goalkeeper saving goal	50	70

255 Black-headed Gull

1966. British Birds. Multicoloured.

696	4d. Type **255**	10	20
697	4d. Blue tit	10	20
698	4d. European robin	10	20
699	4d. Blackbird	10	20

1966. England's World Cup Football Victory. As No. 693 but inscr "ENGLAND WINNERS".

700	4d. multicoloured	30	30

260 Jodrell Bank Radio Telescope

1966. British Technology.

701	**260**	4d. black and lemon . . .	10	10
702	–	6d. red, blue and orange	15	20
703	–	1s.3d. multicoloured . . .	25	40
704	–	1s.6d. multicoloured . . .	40	60

DESIGN: 6d. British motor-cars; 1s.3d. SRN 6 hovercraft; 1s.6d. Windscale reactor.

264

265

1966. 900th Anniv of Battle of Hastings. Mult.

705	4d. Type **264**	10	20
706	4d. Type **265**	10	20
707	4d. "Yellow" horse	10	20
708	4d. "Blue" horse	10	20
709	4d. "Purple" horse	10	20
710	4d. "Grey" horse	10	20
711	6d. Norman horsemen . . .	10	20
712	1s.3d. Norman horsemen attacking Harold's troops (59 × 22½ mm)	20	40

272 King of the Orient

274 Sea Freight

1966. Christmas. Multicoloured.

713	3d. Type **272**	10	10
714	1s.6d. Snowman	30	30

1967. European Free Trade Assn (EFTA).

715	9d. Type **274**	15	20
716	1s.6d. Air freight	30	45

276 Hawthorn and Bramble

282

1967. British Wild Flowers. Multicoloured.

717p	4d. Type **276**	20	20
718p	4d. Larger bindweed and viper's bugloss	20	20
719p	4d. Ox-eye daisy, coltsfoot and buttercup	20	20
720p	4d. Bluebell, red campion and wood anemone . . .	20	20
721	9d. Dog violet	20	25
722	1s.9d. Primroses	25	35

1967.

723	**282**	½d. brown	10	20
724		1d. olive	10	10
726		2d. brown	10	15
729		3d. violet	10	10
731		4d. sepia	10	10
733		4d. red	10	10
735		5d. blue	10	10
736		6d. purple	20	25
737		7d. green	40	35
738		8d. red	20	45
739		8d. turquoise	50	60
740		9d. green	40	25
741		10d. drab	50	50
742		1s. violet	45	25
743		1s.6d. blue and indigo . .	45	35
744		1s.9d. orange and black	50	45

For decimal issue, see Nos. X841 etc.

284 "Mares and Foals in a Landscape" (George Stubbs)

1967. British Paintings.

748	–	4d. multicoloured	10	10
749	**284**	9d. multicoloured	15	15
750	–	1s.6d. multicoloured . . .	25	35

PAINTINGS—VERT: 4d. "Master Lambton" (Sir Thomas Lawrence). HORIZ: 1s.6d. "Children Coming Out of School" (L. S. Lowry).

286 "Gipsy Moth IV"

1967. Sir Francis Chichester's World Voyage.

751	**286**	1s.9d. multicoloured . . .	20	20

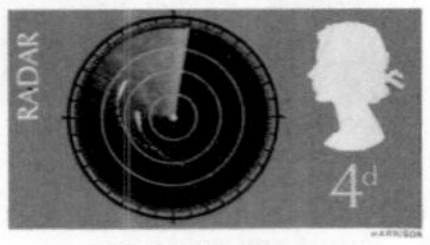

287 Radar Screen

1967. British Discovery and Invention. Mult.

752	4d. Type **287**	10	10
753	1s. "Penicillium notatum" . .	10	20
754	1s.6d. Vickers VC-10 jet engines	20	25
755	1s.9d. Television equipment	20	30

292 "Madonna and Child" (Murillo)

1967. Christmas.

756	–	3d. multicoloured	10	10
757	**292**	4d. multicoloured	10	10
758	–	1s.6d. multicoloured . . .	15	30

PAINTINGS—VERT: 3d. "The Adoration of the Shepherds" (School of Seville). HORIZ: 1s.6d. "The Adoration of the Shepherds" (Louis le Nain).

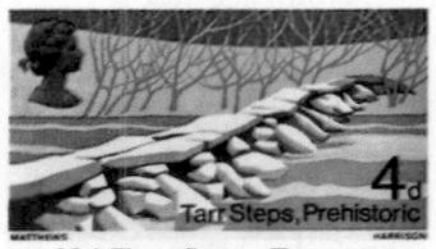

294 Tarr Steps, Exmoor

1968. British Bridges. Multicoloured.

763	4d. Type **294**	10	10
764	9d. Aberfeldy Bridge	10	15
765	1s.6d. Menai Bridge	15	25
766	1s.9d. M4 viaduct	30	30

298 "T U C" and Trades Unionists

1968. British Annivs. Events described on stamps.

767	**298**	4d. multicoloured	10	10
768	–	9d. violet, grey and black	10	15
769	–	1s. multicoloured	15	25
770	–	1s.9d. ochre and brown	35	40

DESIGNS: 9d. Mrs. Emmeline Pankhurst (statue); 1s. Sopwith Camel and English Electric Lightning fighters; 1s.9d. Captain Cook's "Endeavour" and signature.

302 "Queen Elizabeth I" (unknown artist)

1968. British Paintings.

771	**302**	4d. multicoloured	10	10
772	–	1s. multicoloured	10	20
773	–	1s.6d. multicoloured . . .	20	25
774	–	1s.9d. multicoloured . . .	25	40

PAINTINGS—VERT: 1s. "Pinkie" (Lawrence); 1s.6d. "Ruins of St. Mary Le Port" (Piper). HORIZ: 1s.9d. "The Hay Wain" (Constable).

306 Boy and Girl with Rocking Horse

1968. Christmas. Multicoloured.

775	4d. Type **306**	10	10
776	9d. Girl with doll's house (vert)	15	15
777	1s.6d. Boy with train set (vert)	15	30

310 Elizabethan Galleon

1969. British Ships. Multicoloured.

778	5d. "Queen Elizabeth 2" . .	10	15
779	9d. Type **310**	10	25
780	9d. East Indiaman	10	25
781	9d. "Cutty Sark"	10	25
782	1s. "Great Britain"	40	35
783	1s. "Mauretania I"	40	35

Nos. 778 and 782/3 are 58 × 23 mm.

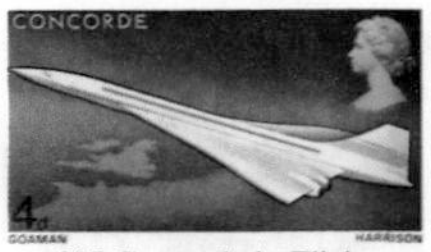

315 Concorde in Flight

1969. 1st Flight of Concorde.

784	**315**	4d. multicoloured	25	25
785	–	9d. multicoloured	55	80
786	–	1s.6d. indigo, grey and blue	85	1·10

DESIGNS: 9d. Plan and elevation views; 1s.6d. Concorde's nose and tail.

318 Queen Elizabeth II

1969.

787	**318**	2s.6d. brown	35	30
788		5s. lake	1·75	60
789		10s. blue	6·00	7·00
790		£1 black	3·25	1·50

For decimal issues see Nos. 829/31b.

No. 790 has an italic "£". For larger version with roman "£" see No. 831b.

319 Page from "Daily Mail", and Vickers Vimy Biplane

1969. Anniversary Events described on stamps.

791	**319**	5d. multicoloured	10	10
792	–	9d. multicoloured	15	20
793	–	1s. claret, red and blue . .	15	20
794	–	1s.6d. multicoloured . . .	15	25
795	–	1s.9d. turquoise, yell & sepia	20	35

DESIGNS: 9d. Europa and C.E.P.T. emblems; 1s. I.L.O. emblem; 1s.6d. Flags of N.A.T.O. countries; 1s.9d. Vickers Vimy biplane and globe showing flight route.

324 Durham Cathedral

1969. British Architecture (Cathedrals). Mult.

796	5d. Type **324**	10	20
797	5d. York Minster	10	20
798	5d. St. Giles' Cathedral, Edinburgh	10	20
799	5d. Canterbury Cathedral . .	10	20
800	9d. St. Paul's Cathedral . .	15	25
801	1s.6d. Liverpool Metropolitan Cathedral	15	25

332 Queen Eleanor's Gate, Caernarvon Castle

1969. Investiture of H.R.H. The Prince of Wales.

802	–	5d. multicoloured	10	15
803	–	5d. multicoloured	10	15
804	**332**	5d. multicoloured	10	15
805	–	9d. multicoloured	15	20
806	–	1s. black and gold	15	20

DESIGNS: No. 802, The King's Gate, Caernarvon Castle; No. 803, The Eagle Tower, Caernarvon Castle; No. 805, Celtic Cross, Margam Abbey; No. 806, H.R.H. The Prince of Wales.

335 Mahatma Gandhi

1969. Gandhi Centenary Year.

807	**335**	1s.6d. multicoloured	20	20

336 National Giro "G" Symbol

1969. Post Office Technology Commemoration.

808	**336**	5d. multicoloured	10	10
809	–	9d. green, blue and black	15	20
810	–	1s. green, lavender & black	15	20
811	–	1s.6d. purple, blue & black	15	35

DESIGNS: 9d. International subscriber dialling (Telecommunications); 1s. Pulse code modulations (Telecommunications); 1s 6d. Automatic sorting (Postal Mechanisation).

340 Herald Angel

1969. Christmas. Multicoloured.

812		4d. Type **340**	10	10
813		5d. The Three Shepherds	15	15
814		1s.6d. The Three Kings	20	30

343 Fife Harling

1970. British Rural Architecture. Multicoloured.

815		5d. Type **343**	10	10
816		9d. Cotswold limestone	10	20
817		1s. Welsh stucco	15	20
818		1s.6d. Ulster thatch	20	30

The 1s. and 1s.6d. are larger (38 × 27 mm).

347 Signing the Declaration of Arbroath

1970. Anniversaries. Events described on stamps. Multicoloured.

819		5d. Type **347**	10	10
820		9d. Florence Nightingale attending patients	15	15
821		1s. Signing of International Co-operative Alliance	20	25
822		1s.6d. Pilgrims and "Mayflower"	20	30
823		1s.9d. Sir William and Sir John Herschel, Francis Baily and Telescope	25	30

352 Mr Pickwick and Sam ("Pickwick Papers")

357 Queen Elizabeth II

1970. Literary Annivs. Death Cent of Charles Dickens (novelist) (824/7) and Birth Bicent of William Wordsworth (poet) (828). Mult.

824		5d. Type **352**	10	15
825		5d. Mr. and Mrs. Micawber ("David Copperfield")	10	15
826		5d. David Copperfield and Betsy Trotwood ("David Copperfield")	10	15
827		5d. "Oliver asking for more" ("Oliver Twist")	10	15
828		1s.6d. "Grasmere" (from engraving by J. Farrington, R.A.)	20	35

1970. Decimal Currency. Designs as T **318** but inscr in decimal currency as T **357**.

829	**357**	10p. red	50	75
830		20p. green	60	25
831		50p. blue	1·25	40
831b		£1 black	3·50	80

On No. 831b the "£" is in roman type.

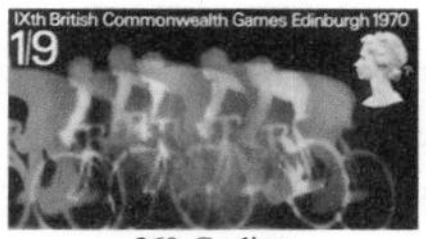

360 Cyclists

1970. 9th British Commonwealth Games. Mult.

832		5d. Runners	10	10
833		1s.6d. Swimmers	25	35
834		1s.9d. Type **360**	30	35

361 1d. Black (1840)

364 Shepherds and Apparition of the Angel

1970. "Philympia 70" Stamp Exhibition. Mult.

835		5d. Type **361**	10	10
836		9d.1s. green (1847)	20	30
837		1s.6d. 4d. red (1855)	20	45

1970. Christmas. Multicoloured.

838		4d. Type **364**	10	10
839		5d. Mary, Joseph, and Christ in the manger	10	15
840		1s.6d. The Wise Men bearing gifts	20	30

367

1971. Decimal currency. As Nos. 723, etc. but new colours and with decimal figures of value as in T **367**.

X 841	½p. blue	10	10
Y1667	1p. red	15	15
X 848	1½p. black	15	25
Y1668	2p. green	10	10
X1001	2p. light green and green	75	50
X 851	2½p. mauve	20	15
X 929	2½p. red	15	20
X 856	3p. blue	15	20
X 930	3p. mauve	20	25
X 859	3½p. grey	30	35
X 931	3½p. brown	50	60
X 861	4p. brown	20	25
Y1669	4p. blue	15	15
X 865	4½p. blue	25	30
X 866	5p. violet	20	20
Y1670	5p. brown	20	20
X 869	5½p. violet	25	30
X 870	6p. green	25	20
X 872	6½p. blue	25	20
X 875	7p. brown	25	30
X 937	7p. red	1·10	1·25
Y1672	7p. grey	35	35
Y1672a	7p. mauve	15	20
X 877	7½p. brown	25	35
X 879	8p. red	25	30
Y1673	8p. yellow	35	35
X 881	8½p. green	30	25
X 882	9p. yellow and black	45	55
X 883	9p. violet	35	25
X 884	9½p. purple	35	45
X 885	10p. brown and light brown	35	30
X 888	10p. brown	35	25
Y1674	10p. orange	30	30
X 890	10½p. yellow	40	45
X 891	10½p. blue	45	50
X 892	11p. red	40	30
X 893	11½p. drab	40	35
X 942	11½p. brown	55	55
X 896	12p. green	45	45
X 898	12½p. green	45	50
X 900	13p. brown	40	40
X 944	13p. grey	45	50
X 945	13½p. brown	60	60
X 946	14p. blue	50	50
X 947	15p. blue	50	50
X 948	15½p. violet	60	50
X 949	16p. drab	55	55
X 950	16½p. brown	80	75
X 951	17p. green	60	60
X 952	17p. blue	60	60
X 953	17½p. brown	70	75
X 954	18p. violet	70	70
X 955	18p. grey	75	60
X 913	18p. green	60	50
X 956	19p. red	80	60
Y1675	19p. bistre	60	60
X 957	19½p. grey	1·60	1·60
X 958	20p. purple	75	50
Y1678	20p. green	30	35
X 960	20p. black	1·00	1·00
X 961	20½p. blue	1·00	1·00
X 962	22p. blue	90	75
X 963	22p. green	90	80
X1016	22p. orange	80	90
X 965	23p. red	1·25	85
X 966	23p. green	90	90
X 967	24p. violet	1·60	1·50
X 968	24p. red	2·00	1·60
X 969	24p. brown	75	80
X 970	25p. purple	90	1·00
Y1752	25p. red	1·00	1·00
X 971	26p. red	1·10	60
Y1683	26p. brown	1·10	1·10
Y1683b	26p. gold	1·00	90
X 973	27p. brown	1·25	1·25
X 974	27p. violet	1·50	1·25
X 975	28p. violet	1·25	1·25
X 976	28p. ochre	1·40	1·25
X 977	28p. grey	1·40	1·25
X 978	29p. brown	1·75	1·75
X 979	29p. mauve	1·75	1·75
Y1684	29p. grey	1·25	1·25
Y1685	30p. grey	1·10	1·10
X 981	31p. purple	1·25	1·50
X 982	31p. blue	1·60	1·50
Y1686	31p. mauve	1·10	1·10
X 983	32p. blue	1·90	1·75
Y1687	33p. green	55	55
Y1687a	34p. green	55	60
X 985	34p. brown	1·75	1·75
X 986	34p. grey	2·00	1·90
X 987	34p. mauve	1·75	1·75
X 988	35p. brown	1·60	1·60
X 989	35p. yellow	1·75	1·60
Y1690	36p. blue	1·50	1·50
X 990	37p. red	2·00	1·75
Y1691	37p. mauve	1·40	1·40
Y1691a	37p. black	1·10	1·10
Y1692	38p. red	1·50	1·50
Y1693	38p. blue	1·50	1·50
Y1694	39p. mauve	1·25	1·40
Y1694b	39p. grey	80	85
Y1695	40p. blue	1·20	1·20
Y1757	41p. drab	1·75	1·75
Y1698a	42p. grey	1·20	1·20
Y1700	43p. brown	2·00	2·00
Y1700b	43p. green	85	90
Y1701	44p. brown	1·90	1·90
Y1702	45p. mauve	1·20	1·20
Y1702a	47p. green	1·20	1·20
Y1703	50p. brown	1·20	1·20
Y1758	60p. grey	2·50	2·50
Y1704	63p. green	2·00	2·00
Y1705	64p. green	2·10	2·10
Y1706	65p. blue	1·75	1·75
Y1706a	68p. brown	1·75	1·75
X 993	75p. black	2·50	1·50
X1024	75p. grey and black	9·00	8·50
Y1707	£1 violet	3·00	2·75
Y1708	£1.50 red	1·75	1·75
Y1709	£2 green	3·00	3·25
Y1801	£2 blue	3·00	2·25
Y1710	£3 mauve	4·50	4·75
Y1802	£3 violet	4·50	3·00
Y1711	£5 blue	7·50	7·50
Y1803	£5 brown	7·50	5·00

For 26p. in gold see No. 1978.

For stamps in this design but with face values expressed as 2nd, 1st or E see Nos. 1663a etc. (1989) and 1979.

368 "A Mountain Road" (T. P. Flanagan)

1971. "Ulster '71" Festival. Paintings. Mult.

881		3p. Type **368**	10	10
882		7½p. "Deer's Meadow" (Tom Carr)	40	45
883		9p. "Slieve na brock" (Colin Middleton)	45	45

371 John Keats (150th Death Anniv)

1971. Literary Anniversaries.

884	**371**	3p. black, gold and blue	10	10
885	–	5p. black, gold and green	40	45
886	–	7½p. black, gold and brown	40	50

DESIGNS AND ANNIVERSARIES: 5p. Thomas Gray (death bicentenary); 7½p. Sir Walter Scott (birth bicentenary).

374 Servicemen and Nurse of 1921

1971. British Anniversaries Events described on stamps. Multicoloured.

887		3p. Type **374**	10	10
888		7½p. Roman centurion	40	45
889		9p. Rugby football, 1871	40	45

377 Physical Sciences Building, University College of Wales, Aberystwyth

1971. British Architecture. Modern University Buildings.

890	**377**	3p. multicoloured	10	10
891	–	5p. multicoloured	25	20
892	–	7½p. ochre, black and brown	25	55
893	–	9p. multicoloured	75	80

DESIGNS: 5p. Faraday Building, Southampton University; 7½p. Engineering Department, Leicester University; 9p. Hexagon Restaurant, Essex University.

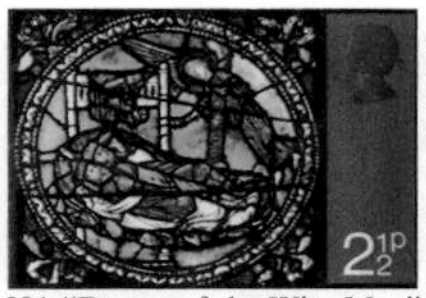

381 "Dream of the Wise Men"

1971. Christmas. Multicoloured.

894		2½p. Type **381**	10	10
895		3p. "Adoration of the Magi"	10	10
896		7½p. "Ride of the Magi"	55	75

384 Sir James Clark Ross

391 St. Andrew's Greensted-juxta-Ongar, Essex

388 Statuette of Tutankhamun

1972. British Polar Explorers. Multicoloured.

897		3p. Type **384**	10	10
898		5p. Sir Martin Frobisher	15	15
899		7½p. Henry Hudson	45	40
900		9p. Capt. Robert Scott	70	75

See also Nos. 923/7.

1972. General Anniveraries. Multicoloured.

901		3p. Type **388**	15	10
902		7½p. 19th-century Coastguard	30	45
903		9p. Ralph Vaughan Williams (composer) and score	40	50

ANNIVERSARIES: 3p. 50th anniversary of discovery of Tutankhamun's tomb; 7½p. 150th anniversary of Formation of H.M. Coastguard: 9p. Birth centenary.

1972. British Architecture. Village Churches. Multicoloured.

904		3p. Type **391**	10	10
905		4p. All Saints, Earls Barton, Northants	10	20
906		5p. St. Andrew's, Letheringsett, Norfolk	15	20
907		7½p. St. Andrew's, Helpringham, Lincs	60	75
908		9p. St. Mary the Virgin, Huish Episcopi, Somerset	60	80

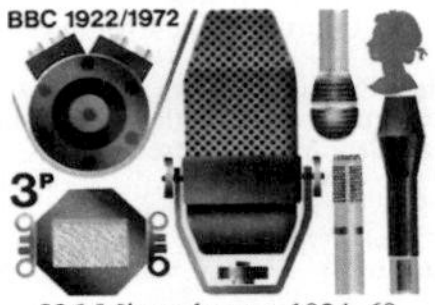

396 Microphones, 1924–69

1972. Broadcasting Anniversaries Multicoloured.

909		3p. Type **396**	10	10
910		5p. Horn loudspeaker	10	20
911		7½p. T.V. camera, 1972	45	55
912		9p. Oscillator and spark transmitter, 1897	50	65

ANNIVERSARIES: Nos. 909/11, 50th anniversary of daily broadcasting by the B.B.C.; No. 912, 75th anniversary of Marconi and Kemp's radio experiments.

400 Angel holding Trumpet

403 Queen Elizabeth and Duke of Edinburgh

1972. Christmas. Multicoloured.

913	2½p. Type **400**	10	10
914	3p. Angel playing lute . . .	10	10
915	7½p. Angel playing harp . . .	50	70

1972. Royal Silver Wedding.

916 **403**	3p. black, blue and silver	20	75
917	20p. black, purple & silver	75	70

404 "Europe"

411 W. G. Grace

405 Oak Tree

1973. Britain's Entry into European Communities.

919 **404**	3p. multicoloured	10	15
920	5p. mult (blue jigsaw) . .	25	40
921	5p. mult (green jigsaw) . .	25	40

1973. Tree Planting Year. British Trees (1st issue).

922 **405**	9p. multicoloured	35	40

See also No. 949.

1973. British Explorers. As T **384**. Mult.

923	3p. David Livingstone . . .	20	15
924	3p. H. M. Stanley	20	15
925	5p. Sir Francis Drake . . .	20	35
926	7½p. Sir Walter Raleigh . . .	20	45
927	9p. Charles Sturt	25	50

1973. County Cricket 1873–1973. Designs as T **411** showing caricatures of W. G. Grace by Harry Furniss.

928 **411**	3p. black, brown and gold	10	10
929 –	7½p. black, green and gold	65	75
930 –	9p. black, blue and gold	80	90

414 "Self-portrait" (Reynolds)

422 Palace of Westminster, seen from Whitehall

418 Court Masque Costumes

1973. British Paintings. 250th Birth Anniv of Sir Joshua Reynolds, and 150th Death Anniv of Sir Henry Raeburn. Multicoloured.

931	3p. Type **414**	10	10
932	5p. "Self-portrait" (Raeburn)	15	20
933	7½p. "Nelly O' Brien" (Reynolds)	50	45
934	9p. "Rev. R. Walker (The Skater)" (Raeburn)	60	55

1973. 400th Birth Anniv of Inigo Jones (architect and designer). Multicoloured.

935	3p. Type **418**	10	10
936	3p. St. Paul's Church, Covent Garden	10	10
937	5p. Prince's Lodging, Newmarket	35	45
938	5p. Court Masque stage scene	35	45

1973. 19th Commonwealth Parliamentary Conf.

939 **422**	8p. black, grey and stone	45	50
940 –	10p. gold and black . . .	45	50

DESIGN: 10p. Palace of Westminster, seen from Millbank.

424 Princess Anne and Capt. Mark Phillips

1973. Royal Wedding.

941 **424**	3½p. violet and silver . .	15	10
942	20p. brown and silver . .	60	75

425 "Good King Wenceslas looked out."

1973. Christmas. Multicoloured.

943	3p. Type **425**	20	25
944	3p. King and page at window	20	25
945	3p. Leaving the palace . . .	20	25
946	3p. Struggling against the wind	20	25
947	3p. Delivering gifts	20	25
948	3½p. King, page and peasant	20	25

431 Horse Chestnut

1974. British Trees (2nd issue).

949 **431**	10p. multicoloured . . .	35	35

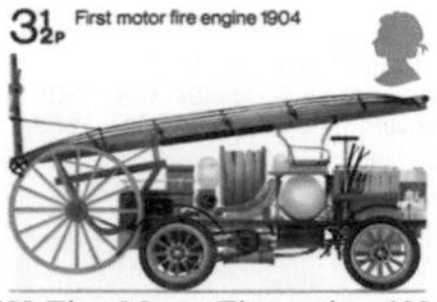

432 First Motor Fire-engine, 1904

1974. Bicentenary of Fire Prevention (Metropolis) Act. Multicoloured.

950	3½p. Type **432**	10	10
951	5½p. Prize-winning fire-engine, 1863	25	30
952	8p. First steam fire-engine, 1830	45	50
953	10p. Fire-engine. 1766 . . .	45	50

436 P.&O. Packet "Peninsular", 1888

1974. Cent of Universal Postal Union. Mult.

954	3½p. Type **436**	10	10
955	5½p. Farman H.F.III biplane, 1911	25	30
956	8p. Airmail—blue van and postbox, 1930	25	35
957	10p. Imperial Airways Short S.21 flying boat "Maia", 1937	35	40

440 Robert the Bruce

1974. Medieval Warriors. Multicoloured.

958	4½p. Type **440**	10	10
959	5½p. Owain Glyndwr	20	35
960	8p. Henry the Fifth	45	50
961	10p. The Black Prince . . .	50	50

444 Churchill in Royal Yacht Squadron Uniform

1974. Birth Centenary of Sir Winston Churchill.

962 **444**	4½p. silver, blue and green	20	15
963 –	5½p. silver, brown and grey	35	35
964 –	8p. silver, red and pink	60	55
965 –	10p. silver, brown and stone	60	55

DESIGNS: 5½p. Prime Minister, 1940; 8p. Secretary for War and Air, 1919; 10p. War correspondent, South Africa, 1899.

448 "Adoration of the Magi" (York Minster, c. 1355)

1974. Christmas. Church Roof Bosses. Multicoloured.

966	3½p. Type **448**	10	10
967	4½p. "The Nativity" (St. Helen's Church, Norwich, c. 1480)	10	10
968	8p. "Virgin and Child" (Ottery St. Mary Church, c. 1350)	30	35
969	10p. "Virgin and Child" (Worcester Cathedral, c. 1224)	40	45

452 Invalid in Wheelchair

1975. Health and Handicap Funds.

970 **452**	4½p.+1½p. blue and azure	25	25

453 "Peace—Burial at Sea"

1975. Birth Bicentenary of J. M. W. Turner (painter). Multicoloured.

971	4½p. Type **453**	10	10
972	5½p. "Snowstorm—Steamer off a Harbour's Mouth"	15	20
973	8p. "The Arsenal, Venice" . .	25	35
974	10p. "St. Laurent"	40	40

457 Charlotte Square, Edinburgh

1975. European Architectural Heritage Year. Multicoloured.

975	7p. Type **457**	25	25
976	7p. The Rows, Chester . . .	25	25
977	8p. Royal Observatory, Greenwich	25	30
978	10p. St. George's Chapel, Windsor	25	30
979	12p. National Theatre, London	25	35

462 Sailing Dinghies

1975. Sailing. Multicoloured.

980	7p. Type **462**	15	10
981	8p. Racing keel yachts . . .	30	30
982	10p. Cruising yachts	30	35
983	12p. Multihulls	50	50

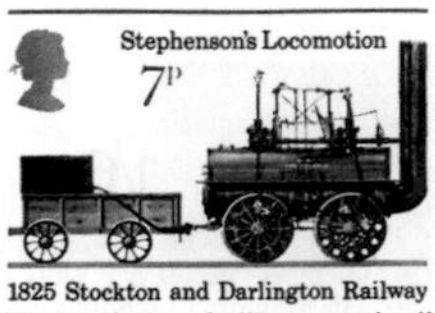

466 Stephenson's "Locomotion", 1825

1975. 150th Anniv of Public Railways. Mult.

984	7p. Type **466**	25	20
985	8p. "Abbotsford", 1876 . . .	35	40
986	10p. "Caerphilly Castle", 1923	45	45
987	12p. High Speed Train, 1975	50	50

470 Palace of Westminster

1975. 62nd Inter-Parliamentary Union Conference.

988 **470**	12p. multicoloured . . .	35	40

471 Emma and Mr. Woodhouse ("Emma")

1975. Birth Bicentenary of Jane Austen (novelist). Multicoloured.

989	8½p. Type **471**	15	10
990	10p. Catherine Morland ("Northanger Abbey") . .	40	35
991	11p. Mr. Darcy ("Pride and Prejudice")	40	35
992	13p. Mary and Henry Crawford ("Mansfield Park")	45	50

475 Angels with Harp and Lute

1975. Christmas. Multicoloured.

993	6½p. Type **475**	15	15
994	8½p. Angel with mandolin . .	25	30
995	11p. Angel with horn	40	40
996	13p. Angel with trumpet . .	40	40

479 Housewife

1976. Centenary of Telephone. Multicoloured.

997	8½p. Type **479**	15	10
998	10p. Policeman	30	30
999	11p. District nurse	40	40
1000	13p. Industrialist	45	45

483 Hewing Coal (Thomas Hepburn)

1976. Social Reformers. Multicoloured.

1001	8½p. Type **483**	20	10
1002	10p. Machinery (Robert Owen)	35	30
1003	11p. Chimney cleaning (Lord Shaftesbury) . . .	40	35
1004	13p. Hands clutching prison bars (Elizabeth Fry) . . .	40	35

487 Benjamin Franklin (bust by Jean-Jacques Caffieri)

488 "Elizabeth of Glamis"

1976. Bicentenary of American Revolution.

1005	487	11p. multicoloured	35	35

1976. Centenary of Royal National Rose Society. Multicoloured.

1006	8½p. Type **488**	15	10
1007	10p. "Grandpa Dickson"	25	30
1008	11p. "Rosa Mundi"	40	40
1009	13p. "Sweet Briar"	50	50

492 Archdruid

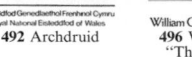

496 Woodcut from "The Canterbury Tales"

1976. British Cultural Traditions. Multicoloured.

1010	8½p. Type **492**	15	10
1011	10p. Morris dancing	30	30
1012	11p. Scots piper	40	40
1013	13p. Welsh harpist	45	45

The 8½p. and 13p. commemorate the 800th Anniv of the Royal National Eisteddfod.

1976. 500th Anniv of British Printing. Multicoloured.

1014	8½p. Type **496**	20	10
1015	10p. Extract from "The Tretyse of Love"	35	30
1016	11p. Woodcut from "The Game and Playe of Chesse" by William Caxton	40	40
1017	13p. Early printing press	40	45

500 Virgin and Child

1976. Christmas. English Medieval Embroidery. Multicoloured.

1018	6½p. Type **500**	15	15
1019	8½p. Angel with crown	30	20
1020	11p. Angel appearing to Shepherds	35	40
1021	13p. The Three Kings	40	45

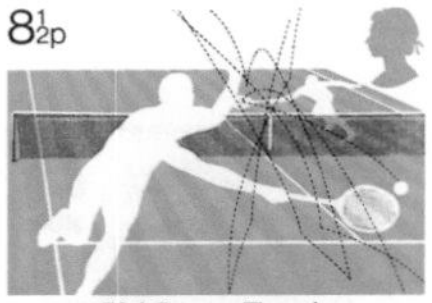

504 Lawn Tennis

1977. Racket Sports. Multicoloured.

1022	8½p. Type **504**	15	10
1023	10p. Table tennis	30	30
1024	11p. Squash	40	40
1025	13p. Badminton	40	45

508

1977.

1026	508	£1 green and olive	3·00	25
1026b		£1.30 brown and blue	5·50	6·00
1026c		£1.33 mauve and black	7·50	7·00
1026d		£1.41 brown and blue	8·00	8·50
1026e		£1.50 olive and black	6·00	5·00
1026f		£1.60 brown and blue	6·00	7·00
1027		£2 green and brown	12·00	50
1028		£5 pink and blue	29·00	3·00

509 Steroids—Conformational Analysis

1977. Centenary of Royal Insitute of Chemistry. Multicoloured.

1029	8½p. Type **509**	15	10
1030	10p. Vitamin C—synthesis	35	40
1031	11p. Starch—chromatography	35	40
1032	13p. Salt—crystallography	35	40

513

1977. Silver Jubilee. Multicoloured.

1033	8½p. Type **513**	15	15
1034	9p. Type **513**	25	15
1035	10p. "Leaf" initials	30	25
1036	11p. "Star" initials	40	35
1037	13p. "Oak" initials	45	40

517 "Gathering of Nations"

518 West European Hedgehog

1977. Commonwealth Heads of Government Meeting, London.

1038	517	13p. multicoloured	35	35

1977. British Wildlife. Multicoloured.

1039	9p. Type **518**	25	25
1040	9p. Brown hare	25	25
1041	9p. Eurasian red squirrel	25	25
1042	9p. European otter	25	25
1043	9p. Eurasian badger	25	25

523 "Three French Hens, Two Turtle Doves and a Partridge in a Pear Tree"

1977. Christmas. "The Twelve Days of Christmas". Multicoloured.

1044	7p. Type **523**	20	15
1045	7p. "Six Geese a-laying, Five Gold Rings, Four Colly Birds"	20	15
1046	7p. "Eight Maids a-milking, Seven Swans a-Swimming"	20	15
1047	7p. "Ten Pipers piping, Nine Drummers drumming"	20	10
1048	7p. "Twelve Lords a-leaping, Eleven Ladies dancing"	20	15
1049	9p. "A Partridge in a Pear Tree"	20	15

529 Oil—North Sea Production Platform

537 State Coach

533 The Tower of London

1978. Energy Resources. Multicoloured.

1050	9p. Type **529**	20	10
1051	10½p. Coal—modern pithead	25	25
1052	11p. Natural gas—flame rising from sea	35	35
1053	13p. Electricity—nuclear power station and uranium atom	40	40

1978. British Architecture. Historic Buildings. Multicoloured.

1054	9p. Type **533**	25	10
1055	10½p. Holyroodhouse	25	30
1056	11p. Caernarvon Castle	35	35
1057	13p. Hampton Court Palace	35	35
MS1058	121 × 90mm. Nos. 1054/7	1·40	1·40

1978. 25th Anniv of Queen's Coronation.

1059	537	9p. gold and blue	25	15
1060	–	10½p. gold and red	30	35
1061	–	11p. gold and green	30	35
1062	–	13p. gold and violet	40	45

DESIGNS: 10½p. St. Edward's Crown; 11p. The Sovereign's Orb; 13p. Imperial State Crown.

541 Shire Horse

1978. Horses. Multicoloured.

1063	9p. Type **541**	20	10
1064	10½p. Shetland pony	35	40
1065	11p. Welsh pony	35	45
1066	13p. Thoroughbred	45	50

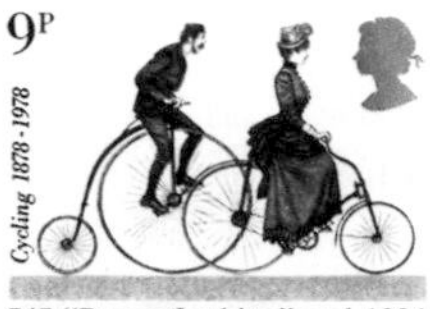

545 "Penny-farthing" and 1884 Safety Bicycle

1978. Centenaries of Cyclists' Touring Club and British Cycling Federation. Multicoloured.

1067	9p. Type **545**	20	10
1068	10½p. 1920 Touring bicycles	30	35
1069	11p. Modern small-wheeled bicycles	35	40
1070	13p. 1978 Road-racers	40	40

549 Singing Carols round the Christmas Tree

1978. Christmas. Carol-singing. Mult.

1071	7p. Type **549**	15	10
1072	9p. The Waits	30	15
1073	11p. 18th-century carol singers	35	40
1074	13p. "The Boar's Head Carol"	40	45

553 Old English Sheepdog

1979. Dogs. Multicoloured.

1075	9p. Type **553**	15	10
1076	10½p. Welsh springer spaniel	35	30
1077	11p. West Highland terrier	35	40
1078	13p. Irish setter	35	40

557 Primrose

1979. Spring Wild Flowers. Multicoloured.

1079	9p. Type **557**	15	10
1080	10½p. Daffodil	30	35
1081	11p. Bluebell	40	35
1082	13p. Snowdrop	40	30

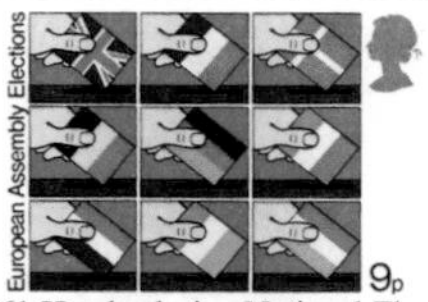

561 Hands placing National Flags into Ballot Boxes

1979. First Direct Elections to European Assembly.

1083	561	9p. multicoloured	15	10
1084	–	10½p. multicoloured	30	30
1085	–	11p. multicoloured	35	35
1086	–	13p. multicoloured	40	35

DESIGNS: Nos. 1084/6 differ from Type **561** in the position of the hands and flags.

565 "Saddling 'Mahmoud' for the Derby, 1936" (Sir Alfred Munnings)

1979. Horse-racing Paintings. Bicentenary of the Derby (9p). Multicoloured.

1087	9p. Type **565**	20	10
1088	10½p. "The Liverpool Great National Steeple Chase, 1839" (aquatint, F. C. Turner)	30	30
1089	11p. "The First Spring Meeting, Newmarket, 1793" (J. N. Sartorius)	35	35
1090	13p. "Racing at Dorsett Ferry, Windsor, 1684" (Francis Barlow)	35	35

569 "The Tale of Peter Rabbit" (Beatrix Potter)

573 Sir Rowland Hill

1979. International Year of the Child. Multicoloured.

1091	9p. Type **569**	30	35
1092	10½p. "The Wind in the Willows" (Kenneth Grahame)	35	35
1093	11p. "Winnie-the-Pooh" (A. A. Milne)	40	40
1094	13p. "Alice's Adventures in Wonderland" (Lewis Carroll)	60	60

1979. Death Cent of Sir Rowland Hill. Mult.

1095	10p. Type **573**	25	15
1096	11½p. Postman, c. 1839	30	30
1097	13p. London postman, c. 1839	35	40
1098	15p. Woman and young girl with letters, 1840	60	45
MS1099	82 × 121mm. Nos. 1095/8	1·40	1·25

577 Policeman on the Beat

1979. 150th Anniv of Metropolitan Police. Mult.

1100	10p. Type **577**	25	10
1101	11½p. Policeman directing traffic	30	35
1102	13p. Mounted policewoman	40	45
1103	15p. River patrol boat	60	45

581 The Three Kings

1979. Christmas. Multicoloured.

1104	8p. Type **581**	15	15
1105	10p. Angel appearing to the Shepherds	20	25
1106	11½p. The Nativity	30	35
1107	13p. Mary and Joseph travelling to Bethlehem	50	40
1108	15p. The Annunciation	55	45

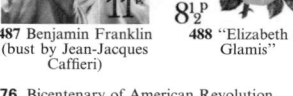

586 River Kingfisher ("Kingfisher")

1980. Cent of Wild Bird Protection Act. Mult.

1109	10p. Type **586**	20	10
1110	11½p. White-throated dipper ("Dipper")	40	35
1111	13p. Moorhen	50	45
1112	15p. Yellow wagtails	50	45

590 "Rocket" approaching Moorish Arch, Liverpool

1980. 150th Anniv of Liverpool and Manchester Railway. Multicoloured.

1113	12p. Type **590**	20	20
1114	12p. First and Second Class carriages passing through Olive Mount cutting	20	20
1115	12p. Third Class carriage and sheep truck crosssing Chat Moss	20	20
1116	12p. Horsebox and carriage truck near Bridgewater Canal	20	20
1117	12p. Truck and mail coach at Manchester	20	20

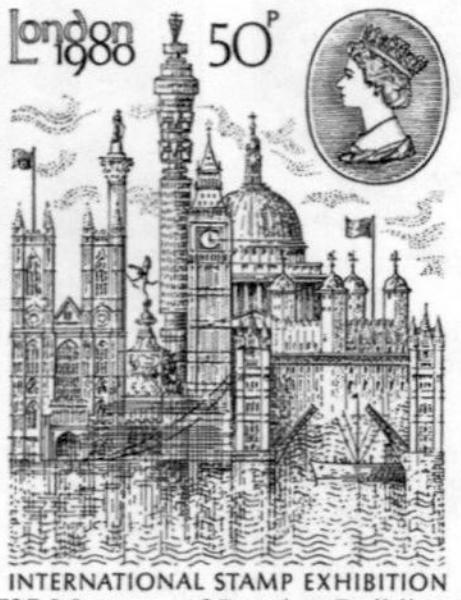

595 Montage of London Buildings

1980. "London 1980" International Stamp Exn.

1118 **595**	50p. brown	1·25	1·10
MS1119	90 × 123 mm. No. 1118 (sold at 75p.)	1·40	1·50

596 Buckingham Palace **605** Queen Elizabeth the Queen Mother

601 Charlotte Bronte ("Jane Eyre")

1980. London Landmarks. Multicoloured.

1120	10½p. Type **596**	25	10
1121	12p. The Albert Memorial	25	15
1122	13½p. Royal Opera House	35	40
1123	15p. Hampton Court	45	50
1124	17½p. Kensington Palace	60	50

1980. Famous Authoresses. Multicoloured.

1125	12p. Type **601**	25	10
1126	13½p. George Eliot ("The Mill on the Floss")	30	35
1127	15p. Emily Bronte ("Wuthering Heights")	40	35
1128	17½p. Elizabeth Gaskell ("North and South")	50	40

1980. 80th Birthday of The Queen Mother.

1129 **605**	12p. multicoloured	75	75

606 Sir Henry Wood **610** Running

1980. British Conductors. Multicoloured.

1130	12p. Type **606**	20	10
1131	13½p. Sir Thomas Beecham	35	45
1132	15p. Sir Malcolm Sargent	40	40
1133	17½p. Sir John Barbirolli	45	40

1980. Sport Centenaries. Multicoloured.

1134	12p. Type **610**	20	10
1135	13½p. Rugby	40	40
1136	15p. Boxing	35	35
1137	17½p. Cricket	45	40

CENTENARIES: 12p. Amateur Athletics Association; 13½p. Welsh Rugby Union; 15p. Amateur Boxing Association; 17½p. First England–Australia Test Match.

614 Christmas Tree

1980. Christmas. Multicoloured.

1138	10p. Type **614**	20	10
1139	12p. Candles	20	20
1140	13½p. Mistletoe and apples	40	40
1141	15p. Crown, chains and bell	55	55
1142	17½p. Holly wreath	55	55

619 St. Valentine's Day

1981. Folklore. Multicoloured.

1143	14p. Type **619**	25	10
1144	18p. Morris dancers	35	50
1145	22p. Lammastide	60	55
1146	25p. Medieval mummers	70	65

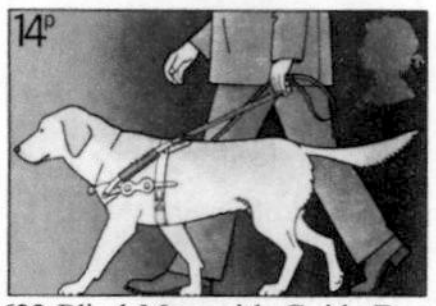

623 Blind Man with Guide Dog

1981. Int Year of Disabled Persons. Mult.

1147	14p. Type **623**	35	20
1148	18p. Hands spelling "Deaf" in sign language	45	60
1149	22p. Disabled man in wheelchair	60	75
1150	25p. Disabled artist painting with foot	70	85

627 "Aglais urticae" **636** Prince Charles and Lady Diana Spencer

631 Glenfinnan, Scotland

1981. Butterflies. Multicoloured.

1151	14p. Type **627**	25	20
1152	18p. "Maculinea arion"	55	60
1153	22p. "Inachis io"	65	70
1154	25p. "Carterocephalus palaemon"	70	75

1981. 50th Anniv of National Trust for Scotland. British Landscapes. Multicoloured.

1155	14p. Type **631**	30	15
1156	18p. Derwentwater, England	45	45
1157	20p. Stackpole Head, Wales	65	70
1158	22p. Giant's Causeway, Northern Ireland	70	75
1159	25p. St. Kilda, Scotland	80	90

1981. Royal Wedding.

1160 **636**	14p. multicoloured	65	40
1161	25p. multicoloured	1·25	1·60

637 "Expeditions"

1981. 25th Anniv of Duke of Edinburgh Award Scheme. Multicoloured.

1162	14p. Type **637**	25	10
1163	18p. "Skills"	45	50
1164	22p. "Service"	70	70
1165	25p. "Recreation"	80	80

641 Cockle-dredging from "Linsey II"

1981. Fishing Industry. Multicoloured.

1166	14p. Type **641**	25	10
1167	18p. Hauling in trawl net	45	50
1168	22p. Lobster potting	65	50
1169	25p. Hoisting seine net	75	60

645 Father Christmas

1981. Christmas. Children's Pictures. Mult.

1170	11½p. Type **645**	25	20
1171	14p. Jesus Christ	35	20
1172	18p. Flying angel	50	60
1173	22p. Joseph and Mary arriving at Bethlehem	75	70
1174	25p. Three Kings approaching Bethlehem	85	75

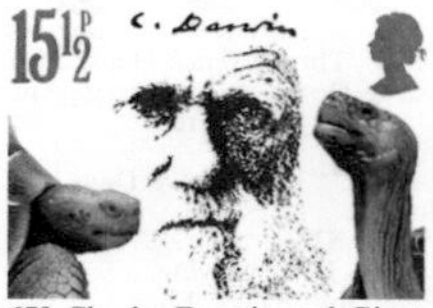

650 Charles Darwin and Giant Tortoises

1982. Death Cent of Charles Darwin. Mult.

1175	15½p. Type **650**	40	20
1176	19½p. Darwin and Marine iguanas	50	60
1177	26p. Darwin and cactus ground finch and large ground finch	65	85
1178	29p. Darwin and prehistoric skulls	70	90

654 Boys' Brigade **658** Ballerina

1982. Youth Organizations. Multicoloured.

1179	15½p. Type **654**	25	15
1180	19½p. Girls' Brigade	45	55
1181	26p. Boy Scout Movement	60	75
1182	29p. Girl Guides Movement	75	80

1982. Europa. British Theatre. Multicoloured.

1183	15½p. Type **658**	25	15
1184	19½p. Harlequin	40	50
1185	26p. Hamlet	70	70
1186	29p. Opera singer	75	90

662 Henry VIII and "Mary Rose"

1982. Maritime Heritage. Multicoloured.

1187	15½p. Type **662**	35	20
1188	19½p. Admiral Blake and "Triumph"	50	50
1189	24p. Lord Nelson and H.M.S. "Victory"	65	75
1190	26p. Lord Fisher and H.M.S. "Dreadnought"	80	85
1191	29p. Viscount Cunningham and H.M.S. "Warspite"	85	90

667 "Strawberry Thief" (William Morris)

1982. British Textiles. Multicoloured.

1192	15½p. Type **667**	25	10
1193	19½p. Untitled (Steiner and Co.)	50	55
1194	26p. "Cherry Orchard" (Paul Nash)	65	75
1195	29p. "Chevron" (Andrew Foster)	75	90

671 Development of Communications (⅔-size illustration)

1982. Information Technology. Multicoloured.

1196	15½p. Type **671**	40	10
1197	26p. Modern technological aids	60	90

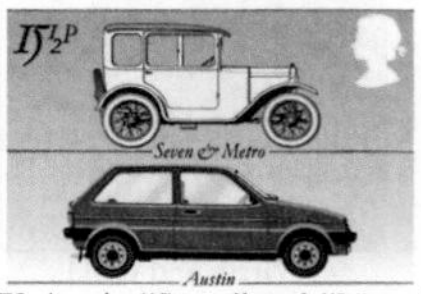

673 Austin "Seven" and "Metro"

1982. British Motor Industry. Multicoloured.

1198	15½p. Type **673**	30	10
1199	19½p. Ford "Model T" and "Escort"	55	55
1200	26p. Jaguar "SS1" and "XJ6"	65	70
1201	29p. Rolls-Royce "Silver Ghost" and "Silver Spirit"	1·00	90

677 "While Shepherds Watched"

1982. Christmas. Carols. Multicoloured.

1202	12½p. Type **677**	25	20
1203	15½p. "The Holly and the Ivy"	35	20
1204	19½p. "I saw Three Ships"	65	70
1205	26p. "We Three Kings"	75	80
1206	29p. "Good King Wenceslas"	80	90

682 Atlantic Salmon

1983. British River Fishes. Multicoloured.

1207	15½p. Type **682**	30	10
1208	19½p. Northern pike	60	60
1209	26p. Brown trout	75	75
1210	29p. Eurasian perch	90	90

686 Tropical Island

1983. Commonwealth Day. Geographical Regions. Multicoloured.

1211	15½p. Type **686**	30	10
1212	19½p. Desert	55	60
1213	26p. Temperate farmland	75	80
1214	29p. Mountain range	85	85

690 Humber Bridge

1983. Europa. Engineering Achievements. Multicoloured.

1215	16p. Type **690**	30	10
1216	20½p. Thames Flood Barrier	80	1·00
1217	28p. "Iolair" (oilfield emergency support vessel)	90	1·00

693 Musketeer and Pikeman, The Royal Scots (1633)

698 20th-century Garden, Sissinghurst

1983. British Army Uniforms. Multicoloured.

1218	16p. Type **693**	30	10
1219	20½p. Fusilier and Ensign, The Royal Welsh Fusiliers (mid-18th century)	45	60
1220	26p. Riflemen, 95th Rifles (The Royal Green Jackets) (1805)	70	90
1221	28p. Sergeant (khaki service uniform) and Guardsman (full dress), The Irish Guards (1900)	75	90
1222	31p. Paratroopers, The Parachute Regiment (1983)	75	80

1983. British Gardens. Multicoloured.

1223	16p. Type **698**	30	10
1224	20½p. 19th-century garden, Biddulph Grange	40	55
1225	28p. 18th-century garden, Blenheim	75	90
1226	31p. 17th-century garden. Pitmedden	80	90

702 Merry-go-round

1983. British Fairs. Multicoloured.

1227	16p. Type **702**	35	15
1228	20½p. Big wheel, helter-skelter and performing animals	60	70
1229	28p. Side shows	75	80
1230	31p. Early produce fair	85	85

706 "Christmas Post" (pillar-box)

1983. Christmas. Multicoloured.

1231	12½p. Type **706**	25	10
1232	16p. "The Three Kings" (chimney pots)	30	10
1233	20½p. "World at Peace" (dove and blackbird)	55	75
1234	28p. "Light of Christmas" (street lamp)	75	80
1235	31p. "Christmas Dove" (hedge sculpture)	90	1·00

711 Arms of College of Arms

1984. 500th Anniv of College of Arms. Mult.

1236	16p. Type **711**	35	15
1237	20½p. Arms of King Richard III (founder)	45	65
1238	28p. Arms of Earl Marshal of England	90	90
1239	31p. Arms of City of London	1·00	1·00

715 Highland Cow

1984. Cattle. Multicoloured.

1240	16p. Type **715**	35	15
1241	20½p. Chillingham wild bull	55	60
1242	26p. Hereford bull	75	75
1243	28p. Welsh black bull	75	85
1244	31p. Irish moiled cow	1·00	90

720 Garden Festival Hall, Liverpool

1984. Urban Renewal. Multicoloured.

1245	16p. Type **720**	30	10
1246	20½p. Milburngate Centre, Durham	50	60
1247	28p. Bush House, Bristol	90	1·00
1248	31p. Commercial Street development, Perth	1·00	1·00

725 Abduction of Europa

1984. 25th Anniv of C.E.P.T. (Europa) (Nos. 1249, 1251), and Second Election to European Parliament (others).

1249	–	16p. grey, blue and gold	30	15
1250	725	16p. grey, black, and gold	30	15
1251	–	20½p. red, purple and gold	70	75
1252	725	20½p. red, pur, blk gold	70	75

DESIGN: Nos. 1249 and 1251, Bridge (C.E.P.T. 25th anniv logo).

726 Lancaster House

727 View of Earth from "Apollo 11"

1984. London Economic Summit Conference.

1253	726	31p. multicoloured	85	85

1984. Centenary of Greenwich Meridian. Mult.

1254	16p. Type **727**	40	10
1255	20½p. Navigational chart of the English Channel	75	55
1256	28p. Greenwich Observatory	85	75
1257	31p. Sir George Airey's Transit Telescope	1·10	90

731 Bath Mail Coach leaving London, 1784

1984. Bicentenary of First Mail Coach Run, Bath and Bristol to London. Multicoloured.

1258	16p. Type **731**	40	35
1259	16p. Attack on Exeter Mail, 1816	40	35
1260	16p. Norwich Mail in thunderstorm, 1827	40	35
1261	16p. Holyhead and Liverpool Mails leaving London, 1828	40	35
1262	16p. Edinburgh Mail snowbound, 1831	40	35

736 Nigerian Clinic

1984. 50th Anniv of British Council. Mult.

1263	17p. Type **736**	35	10
1264	22p. Violinist and Acropolis, Athens	55	75
1265	31p. Building project, Sri Lanka	70	1·00
1266	34p. British Council library, Middle East	75	90

740 The Holy Family

1984. Christmas. Multicoloured.

1267	13p. Type **740**	25	20
1268	17p. Arrival in Bethlehem	45	25
1269	22p. Shepherd and Lamb	55	80
1270	31p. Virgin and Child	75	1·00
1271	34p. Offering of Frankincense	1·00	1·10

745 "Flying Scotsman"

1985. Famous Trains. Multicoloured.

1272	17p. Type **745**	50	20
1273	22p. "Golden Arrow"	80	80
1274	29p. "Cheltenham Flyer"	90	1·00
1275	31p. "Royal Scot"	1·10	1·20
1276	34p. "Cornish Riviera"	1·40	1·20

750 "Bombus terrestris" (bee)

755 "Water Music" (George Frideric Handel)

1985. Insects. Multicoloured.

1277	17p. Type **750**	40	10
1278	22p. "Coccinella septempunctata" (ladybird)	65	55
1279	29p. "Decticus verrucivorus" (bush-cricket)	85	90
1280	31p. "Lucanus cervus" (stag beetle)	1·10	1·00
1281	34p. "Anax imperator" (dragonfly)	1·10	90

1985. Europa. European Music Year. British Composers. Mutlicoloured.

1282	17p. Type **755**	55	10
1283	22p. "The Planets" Suite (Gustav Holst)	75	90
1284	31p. "The First Cuckoo" (Frederick Delius)	1·40	1·25
1285	34p. "Sea Pictures" (Edward Elgar)	1·40	1·25

759 R.N.L.I. Lifeboat and Signal Flags

1985. Safety at Sea. Multicoloured.

1286	17p. Type **759**	40	15
1287	22p. Beachy Head Lighthouse and chart	60	70
1288	31p. "Marecs A" communications satellite and dish aerials	90	1·00
1289	34p. Buoys	1·00	1·20

763 Datapost Motorcyclist, City of London

771 Peter Sellers (from photo by Bill Brandt)

767 King Arthur and Merlin

1985. 350 Years of Royal Mail Public Postal Service. Multicoloured.

1290	17p. Type **763**	35	10
1291	22p. Rural postbus	55	70
1292	31p. Parcel delivery in winter	80	1·00
1293	34p. Town letter delivery	1·00	1·00

1985. Arthurian Legends. Multicoloured.

1294	17p. Type **767**	35	10
1295	22p. Lady of the Lake	55	70
1296	31p. Queen Guinevere and Sir Lancelot	90	1·10
1297	34p. Sir Galahad	1·00	1·10

1985. British Film Year. Multicoloured.

1298	17p. Type **771**	45	10
1299	22p. David Niven (from photo by Cornell Lucas)	60	70
1300	29p. Charlie Chaplin (from photo by Lord Snowdon)	1·0	1·10
1301	31p. Vivien Leigh (from photo by Angus McBean)	1·10	1·25
1302	34p. Alfred Hitchcock (from photo by Howard Coster)	1·40	1·40

776 Principal Boy

1985. Christmas. Pantomime Characters. Mult.

1303	12p. Type **776**	35	15
1304	17p. Genie	40	25
1305	22p. Dame	65	90
1306	31p. Good fairy	1·00	1·10
1307	34p. Pantomime cat	1·10	1·25

781 Light Bulb and North Sea Oil Drilling Rig (Energy)

1986. Industry Year. Multicoloured.

1308	17p. Type **781**	40	10
1309	22p. Thermometer and pharmaceutical laboratory (Health)	60	70
1310	31p. Garden hoe and steelworks (Steel)	1·10	1·10
1311	34p. Loaf of bread and cornfield (Agriculture)	1·40	1·25

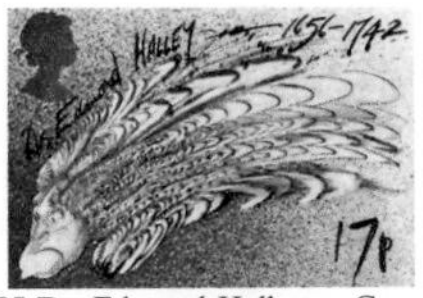

785 Dr. Edmond Halley as Comet

1986. Appearance of Halley's Comet. Multicoloured.

1312	17p. Type **785**	35	10
1313	22p. "Giotto" spacecraft approaching comet	60	75
1314	31p. "Twice in a lifetime"	90	1·00
1315	34p. Comet orbiting sun and planets	1·10	1·10

789 Queen Elizabeth II in 1928, 1942 and 1952

1986. 60th Birthday of Queen Elizabeth II. Multicoloured.
1316 17p. Type **789** 60 50
1317 17p. Queen Elizabeth II in 1958, 1973 and 1982 . . . 60 50
1318 34p. Type **789** . . . . . . 1·40 1·75
1319 34p. As No. 1317 . . . . . 1·40 1·75

791 Barn Owl

1986. Europa. Nature Conservation. Endangered Species. Multicoloured.
1320 17p. Type **791** 40 10
1321 22p. Pine marten . . . . . 80 1·00
1322 31p. Wild cat . . . . 1·25 1·25
1323 34p. Natterjack toad . . . . 1·40 1·40

795 Peasants working in Fields

1986. 900th Anniv of Domesday Book. Mult.
1324 17p. Type **795** 40 10
1325 22p. Freemen working at town trades 70 35
1326 31p. Knights and retainers 1·10 1·40
1327 34p. Lord at banquet . . . 1·25 1·40

799 Athletics

1986. 13th Commonwealth Games, Edinburgh, and World Hockey Cup for Men, London. Multicoloured.
1328 17p. Type **799** 40 10
1329 22p. Rowing 55 70
1330 29p. Weightlifting 75 80
1331 31p. Rifle shooting . . . . 1·00 1·10
1332 34p. Hockey . . . . 1·25 1·25

804 Prince Andrew and Miss Sarah Ferguson (from photo by Gene Nocon)

806 Stylized Cross on Ballot Paper

1986. Royal Wedding.
1333 **804** 12p. multicoloured . . . 50 30
1334 – 17p. multicoloured . . . 1·00 95
DESIGN: 17p. As Type **804** but with naval motif at foot.

1986. 32nd Commonwealth Parliamentary Association Conference.
1335 **806** 34p. multicoloured . . . 1·00 1·00

807 Lord Dowding and Hawker Hurricane Mk I

1986. History of Royal Air Force. Multicoloured.
1336 17p. Type **807** 70 10
1337 22p. Lord Tedder and Hawker Typhoon IB . . 90 95
1338 29p. Lord Trenchard and De Havilland D.H.9A . . 1·25 1·10
1339 31p. Sir Arthur Harris and Avro Type 683 Lancaster 1·50 1·40
1340 34p. Lord Portal and De Havilland D.H.98 Mosquito . . . . 1·75 1·50
Nos. 1336/40 were issued to celebrate 50th anniv of the first R.A.F. Commands.

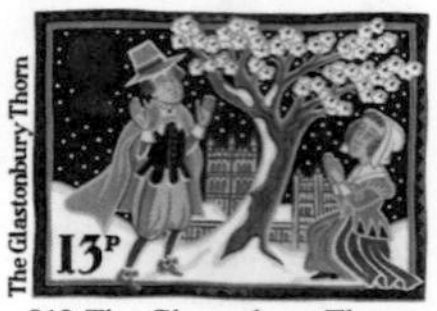

812 The Glastonbury Thorn

1986. Christmas. Folk Customs. Multicoloured.
1341 12p. Type **812** 50 30
1342 13p. Type **812** 25 10
1343 18p. The Tanad Valley Plygain 45 10
1344 22p. The Hebrides Tribute 80 95
1345 31p. The Dewsbury Church Knell . . . . 90 1·00
1346 34p. The Hereford Boy Bishop . . . . 1·25 1·10

817 North American Blanket Flower

821 "Principia Mathematica"

1987. Flower Photographs by Alfred Lammer. Multicoloured.
1347 18p. Type **817** 40 10
1348 22p. Globe thistle 70 85
1349 31p. "Echeveria" . . . . . 1·00 1·25
1350 34p. Autumn crocus . . . . 1·10 1·25

1987. 300th Anniv of "Principia Mathematica" by Sir Isaac Newton. Multicoloured.
1351 18p. Type **821** 60 15
1352 22p. "Motion of Bodies in Ellipses" 85 90
1353 31p. "Optick Treatise" . . . 1·40 1·60
1354 34p. "The System of the World" . . . . 1·50 1·50

825 Willis Faber Dumas Building, Ipswich

1987. Europa. British Architects in Europe.
1355 18p. Type **825** 55 15
1356 22p. Pompidou Centre, Paris 80 90
1357 31p. Staatsgalerie, Stuttgart 1·40 1·50
1358 34p. European Investment Bank, Luxembourg . . . 1·50 1·50

829 Brigade Members with Ashford Litter, 1887

833 Arms of the Lord Lyon, King of Arms

1987. Centenary of St. John Ambulance Brigade. Multicoloured.
1359 18p. Type **829** 40 10
1360 22p. Bandaging blitz victim, 1940 . . . . 60 70
1361 31p. Volunteer with fainting girl, 1965 . . . . . . 1·00 1·10
1362 34p. Transport of transplant organ by Air Wing, 1987 1·25 1·25

1987. 300th Anniv of Revival of Order of the Thistle. Multicoloured.
1363 18p. Type **833** 50 10
1364 22p. Scottish heraldic banner of Prince Charles 75 90
1365 31p. Arms of Royal Scottish Academy of Painting, Sculpture and Architecture . . . . . . 1·40 1·40
1366 34p. Arms of Royal Society of Edinburgh . . . . . . 1·50 1·40

837 Crystal Palace, "Monarch of the Glen" (Landseer) and Grace Darling

1987. 150th Anniv of Queen Victoria's Accession. Multicoloured.
1367 18p. Type **837** 50 10
1368 22p. "Great Eastern", "Beeton's Book of Household Management" and Prince Albert 80 90
1369 31p. Albert Memorial, ballot box and Disraeli . . . . 1·50 1·50
1370 34p. Diamond Jubilee emblem, newspaper placard for Relief of Mafeking and morse key 1·60 1·60

841 Pot by Bernard Leach

1987. Studio Pottery. Multicoloured.
1371 18p. Type **841** 50 10
1372 26p. Pot by Elizabeth Fritsch 70 70
1373 31p. Pot by Lucie Rie . . . 1·25 1·10
1374 34p. Pot by Hans Coper . . 1·40 1·40

845 Decorating the Christmas Tree

1987. Christmas. Multicoloured.
1375 13p. Type **845** 30 10
1376 18p. Waiting for Father Christmas 40 20
1377 26p. Sleeping child and Father Christmas in sleigh 80 1·00
1378 31p. Child reading . . . . 1·10 1·50
1379 34p. Child playing recorder and snowman . . . . . 1·25 1·50

850 Short-spined Seascorpion ("Bull-rout") (Jonathan Couch)

1988. Bicentenary of Linnean Society. Archive Illustrations. Multicoloured.
1380 18p. Type **850** 55 10
1381 26p. Yellow Waterlily (Major Joshua Swatkin) 85 1·00
1382 31p. Tundra swan ("Bewick's Swan") (Edward Lear) . . . . . 1·10 1·25
1383 34p. "Morchella esculenta" (James Sowerby) . . . . 1·25 1·40

854 Revd. William Morgan (Bible translator, 1588)

1988. 400th Anniversary of Welsh Bible. Mult.
1384 18p. Type **854** 40 10
1385 26p. William Salesbury (New Testament translator, 1567) 70 95
1386 31p. Bishop Richard Davies (New Testament translator, 1567) . . . . 1·25 1·25
1387 34p. Bishop Richard Parry (editor of Revised Welsh Bible, 1620) . . . . . . 1·40 1·25

858 Gymnastics (Cent of British Amateur Gymnastics Association)

1988. Sports Organizations. Multicoloured.
1388 18p. Type **858** 40 15
1389 26p. Downhill skiing (Ski Club of Great Britain) . . 70 80
1390 31p. Tennis (centenary of Lawn Tennis Association) 1·10 1·25
1391 34p. Football (centenary of Football League) . . . . 1·25 1·25

862 "Mallard" and Mailbags on Pick-up Arms

1988. Europa. Transport and Mail Services in 1930s. Multicoloured.
1392 18p. Type **862** 50 15
1393 26p. Loading transatlantic mail on liner "Queen Elizabeth" . . . . 1·00 1·00
1394 31p. Glasgow tram No. 1173 and pillar box 1·25 1·60
1395 34p. Imperial Airways Handley Page "Horatius" and airmail van . . . . . 1·60 1·75

866 Early Settler and Sailing Clipper

1988. Bicentenary of Australian Settlement. Mult.
1396 18p. Type **866** 50 25
1397 18p. Queen Elizabeth II with British and Australian Parliament Buildings . . . 50 25
1398 34p. W. G. Grace (cricketer) and tennis racquet . . . . 1·00 80
1399 34p. Shakespeare, John Lennon (entertainer) and Sydney Opera House . . 1·00 80
Stamps in similar designs were also issued by Australia.

870 Spanish Galeasse off The Lizard

1988. 400th Anniv of Spanish Armada. Mult.
1400 18p. Type **870** 70 40
1401 18p. English Fleet leaving Plymouth 70 40
1402 18p. Engagement off Isle of Wight 70 40
1403 18p. Attack of English fire-ships, Calais 70 40
1404 18p. Armada in storm, North Sea 70 40
Nos. 1400/4 were printed together, se-tenant, forming a composite design.

875 "The Owl and the Pussy-cat"

1988. Death Centenary of Edward Lear (artist and author).
1405 **875** 19p. black, cream and red 65 20
1406 – 27p. black, cream yellow 1·00 1·00

1407 – 32p. black, cream green 1·25 1·40
1408 – 35p. black, cream and blue 1·40 1·40
MS1409 122 × 90 mm. Nos. 1405/8 (sold at £1.35) 7·00 7·50

DESIGNS: 27p. "Edward Lear as a Bird" (self-portrait); 32p. "Cat" (from alphabet book); 35p. "There was a Young Lady whose Bonnet ..." (limerick).

The premium on No. **MS**1409 was used to support the "Stamp World London 90" International Stamp Exhibition.

CARRICKFERGUS CASTLE
879 Carrickfergus Castle

1988.

1410 **879** £1 green 3·25 60
1411 – £1.50 red 4·50 1·25
1412 – £2 blue 8·00 1·50
1413 – £5 brown 25·00 5·50

DESIGNS: £1.50, Caernarfon Castle; £2, Edinburgh Castle; £5, Windsor Castle.

For similar designs, but with silhouette of Queen's head, see Nos. 1611/14.

883 Journey to Bethlehem

1988. Christmas. Christmas Cards. Multicoloured.
1414 14p. Type **883** 45 20
1415 19p. Shepherds and Star 50 20
1416 27p. Three Wise Men 90 1·00
1417 32p. Nativity 1·10 1·10
1418 35p. The Annunciation 1·40 1·10

888 Atlantic Puffin

1989. Centenary of Royal Society for the Protection of Birds. Multicoloured.
1419 19p. Type **888** 45 20
1420 27p. Pied avocet ("Avocet") 1·25 1·25
1421 32p. Oystercatcher 1·25 1·25
1422 35p. Northern gannet ("Gannet") 1·40 1·40

892 Rose

1989. Greetings Stamps. Multicoloured.
1423 19p. Type **892** 5·50 5·50
1424 19p. Cupid 5·50 5·50
1425 19p. Yachts 5·50 5·50
1426 19p. Fruit 5·50 5·50
1427 19p. Teddy bear 5·50 5·50

897 Fruit and Vegetables

1989. Food and Farming Year. Multicoloured.
1428 19p. Type **897** 45 15
1429 27p. Meat products 90 85
1430 32p. Dairy produce 1·25 1·40
1431 35p. Cereal products 1·40 1·50

901 Mortar Board

905 Toy Train and Airplane

1989. Anniversaries. Multicoloured.
1432 19p. Type **901** (150th anniv of Public Education in England) 1·00 50
1433 19p. Cross on Ballot paper (3rd Direct Elections to European Parliament) 1·00 50
1434 35p. Posthorn (26th Postal, Telegraph and Telephone International Congress, Brighton) 1·50 1·75
1435 35p. Globe (Inter-Parliamentary Union Centenary Conference, London) 1·50 1·75

1989. Europa. Games and Toys. Multicoloured.
1436 19p. Type **905** 65 20
1437 27p. Building bricks 95 1·00
1438 32p. Dice and board games 1·40 1·40
1439 35p. Toy robot, boat and doll's house 1·50 1·50

909 Ironbridge, Shropshire

913

1989. Industrial Archaeology. Multicoloured.
1440 19p. Type **909** 60 15
1441 27p. Tin Mine, St. Agnes Head, Cornwall 1·00 1·10
1442 32p. Cotton Mills, New Lanark, Strathclyde 1·10 1·25
1443 35p. Pontcysyllte Aqueduct, Clwyd 1·25 1·50
MS1444 122 × 90 mm. 19p., 27p., 32p. and 35p. each multicoloured (horiz) (sold at £1.40) 5·50 5·50

The premium on **MS**1444 was used to support "Stamp World London 90" International Stamp Exhibition.

1989.

1663a **913** (2nd) blue 90 90
1447 (1st) black 1·75 1·75
1664a (1st) red 90 90
1664b (1st) gold 45 45
1664c (E) blue 65 65

The above were sold at the current rate for the day. No. 1664c was valid for the basic European airmail rate.

The 2nd blue and 1st red exist with ordinary or self-adhesive gum.

For 1st class in gold see No. 1979.

915 Snowflake (× 10)

919 Royal Mail Coach

1989. 150th Anniv of Royal Microscopical Society. Multicoloured.
1453 19p. Type **915** 45 15
1454 27p. "Calliphora erythrocephala" (fly) (× 5) 95 1·10
1455 32p. Blood cells (× 500) 1·10 1·40
1456 35p. Microchip (× 600) 1·25 1·40

1989. Lord Mayor's Show, London. Multicoloured.
1457 20p. Type **919** 70 40
1458 20p. Escort of Blues and Royals 70 40
1459 20p. Lord Mayor's Coach 70 40
1460 20p. Coach team passing St. Paul's 70 40
1461 20p. Blues and Royals drum horse 70 40

This issue commemorates the 800th anniv of the installation of the first Lord Mayor of London.

924 14th-century Peasants from Stained-glass Window

1989. Christmas. 800th Anniv of Ely Cathedral.
1462 **924** 15p. gold, silver and blue 40 15
1463 – 15p.+1p. gold, silver and blue 50 40
1464 – 20p.+1p. gold, silver and red 65 80
1465 – 34p.+1p. gold, silver and green 1·25 1·75
1466 – 37p.+1p. gold, silver and green 1·40 1·90

DESIGNS: 15p.+1p. Arches and roundels, West Front; 20p.+1p. Octagon Tower; 34p.+1p. Arcade from West Transept; 37p.+1p. Triple arch from West Front.

929 Queen Victoria and Queen Elizabeth II

930 Kitten

1990. 150th Anniv of the Penny Black.
1467 **929** 15p. blue 80 80
1469 20p. black and cream 80 80
1471 29p. mauve 1·75 1·75
1473 34p. grey 2·00 2·00
1474 37p. red 2·25 2·25

For this design with "1st" face value see No. 2133.

1990. 150th Anniv of Royal Society for Prevention of Cruelty to Animals. Multicoloured.
1479 20p. Type **930** 60 15
1480 29p. Rabbit 1·10 1·10
1481 34p. Duckling 1·25 1·25
1482 37p. Puppy 1·40 1·40

934 Teddy Bear

1990. Greetings Stamps. "Smiles". Multicoloured (except No. 1492).
1483 20p. Type **934** 3·50 2·50
1484 20p. Dennis the Menace 3·50 2·50
1485 20p. Punch 3·50 2·50
1486 20p. Cheshire Cat 3·50 2·50
1487 20p. The Man in the Moon 3·50 2·50
1488 20p. The Laughing Policeman 3·50 2·50
1489 20p. Clown 3·50 2·50
1490 20p. Mona Lisa 3·50 2·50
1491 20p. Queen of Hearts 3·50 2·50
1492 20p. Stan Laurel (comedian) (gold and black) 3·50 2·50

See also Nos. 1550/9.

944 Alexandra Palace ("Stamp World London 90" Exhibition)

948 Export Achievement Award

1990. Europa (Nos. 1493 and 1495) and "Glasgow 1990 European City of Culture" (Nos. 1494 and 1496). Multicoloured.
1493 20p. Type **944** 60 20
1494 20p. Glasgow School of Art 60 20
1495 29p. British Philatelic Bureau, Edinburgh 1·40 1·60
1496 37p. Templeton Carpet Factory, Glasgow 1·50 1·60

1990. 25th Anniv of Queen's Awards for Export and Technology. Multicoloured.
1497 20p. Type **948** 70 45
1498 20p. Technological Achievement Award 70 45
1499 37p. Type **948** 1·25 1·25
1500 37p. As No. 1498 1·25 1·25

1990. "Stamp World London 90" International Stamp Exhibition, London. Sheet 122 × 90 mm, containing No. 1469.
MS1501 **929** 20p. black and cream (sold at £1) 4·50 4·50

The premium on No. **MS**1501 was used to support the "Stamp World London 90" International Stamp Exhibition.

950 Cycad and Sir Joseph Banks Building

954 Thomas Hardy and Clyffe Clump, Dorset

1990. 150th Anniv of Kew Gardens. Mult.
1502 20p. Type **950** 55 15
1503 29p. Stone pine and Princess of Wales Conservatory 90 1·00
1504 34p. Willow tree and Palm House 1·40 1·60
1505 37p. Cedar tree and Pagoda 1·60 1·50

1990. 150th Anniv of Thomas Hardy (author).
1506 **954** 20p. multicoloured 80 70

955 Queen Elizabeth the Queen Mother

959 Victoria Cross

1990. 90th Birthday of Queen Elizabeth the Queen Mother. Multicoloured.
1507 20p. Type **955** 95 20
1508 29p. Queen Elizabeth 1·40 1·50
1509 34p. Elizabeth, Duchess of York 2·00 2·10
1510 37p. Lady Elizabeth Bowes-Lyon 2·25 2·20

1990. Gallantry Awards. Multicoloured.
1517 20p. Type **959** 80 65
1518 20p. George Cross 80 65
1519 20p. Distinguished Service Cross and Distinguished Service Medal (horiz) 80 65
1520 20p. Military Cross and Military Medal (horiz) 80 65
1521 20p. Distinguished Flying Cross and Distinguished Flying Medal (horiz) 80 65

964 Armagh Observatory, Jodrell Bank Radio Telescope and La Palma Telescope

1990. Astronomy. Multicoloured.
1522 22p. Type **964** 65 15
1523 26p. Newton's moon and tides diagram with early telescopes 1·00 1·10
1524 31p. Greenwich Old Observatory and early astronomical equipment 1·25 1·40
1525 37p. Stonehenge, gyroscope and navigating by stars 1·50 1·40

Nos. 1522/5 commemorate the Centenary of the British Astronomical Association and the Bicentenary of the Armagh Observatory.

968 Building a Snowman

1990. Christmas. Multicoloured.
1526 17p. Type **968** 50 15
1527 22p. Fetching the Christmas tree 70 20
1528 26p. Carol singing 95 1·10
1529 31p. Tobogganing 1·25 1·50
1530 37p. Ice-skating 1·40 1·50

973 "King Charles Spaniel"

988 Michael Faraday. (inventor of electric motor) (birth bicentenary)

978 Song Thrush's Nest

1991. Dogs. Paintings by George Stubbs. Mult.

1531	22p. Type **973**	85	15
1532	26p. "A Pointer"	1·10	1·25
1533	31p. "Two Hounds in a Landscape"	1·25	1·25
1534	33p. "A Rough Dog"	1·40	1·40
1535	37p. "Fino and Tiny"	1·50	1·40

1991. Greetings Stamps. "Good Luck". Mult.

1536	(1st) Type **978**	1·90	1·90
1537	(1st) Shooting star and rainbow	1·90	1·90
1538	(1st) Black-billed magpies and charm bracelet	1·90	1·90
1539	(1st) Black cat	1·90	1·90
1540	(1st) River kingfisher with key	1·90	1·90
1541	(1st) Mallard and frog	1·90	1·90
1542	(1st) Four-leaf clover in boot and match box	1·90	1·90
1543	(1st) Pot of gold at end of rainbow	1·90	1·90
1544	(1st) Heart-shaped butterflies	1·90	1·90
1545	(1st) Wishing well and sixpence	1·90	1·90

The background of the stamps forms a composite design.

Nos. 1536/45 were sold at the current rate.

1991. Scientific Achievements. Multicoloured.

1546	22p. Type **988**	60	30
1547	22p. Charles Babbage (computer science pioneer) (birth bicentenary)	60	30
1548	31p. Radar sweep of East Anglia (50th anniv of operational radar network)	1·20	1·40
1549	37p. Gloster Whittle E28/39 airplane over East Anglia (50th anniv of first flight of Sir Frank Whittle's jet engine)	1·40	1·75

992 Teddy Bear

1991. Greetings Stamps. "Smiles". As Nos. 1483/92, but inscr "1st" as in T **992**. Multicoloured (except No. 1559).

1550	(1st) Type **992**	1·25	1·50
1551	(1st) Dennis the Menace	1·25	1·50
1552	(1st) Punch	1·25	1·50
1553	(1st) Cheshire Cat	1·25	1·50
1554	(1st) The Man in the Moon	1·25	1·50
1555	(1st) The Laughing Policeman	1·25	1·50
1556	(1st) Clown	1·25	1·50
1557	(1st) Mona Lisa	1·25	1·50
1558	(1st) Queen of Hearts	1·25	1·50
1559	(1st) Stan Laurel (comedian) (gold and black)	1·25	1·50

Nos. 1550/9 were sold at the current rate.

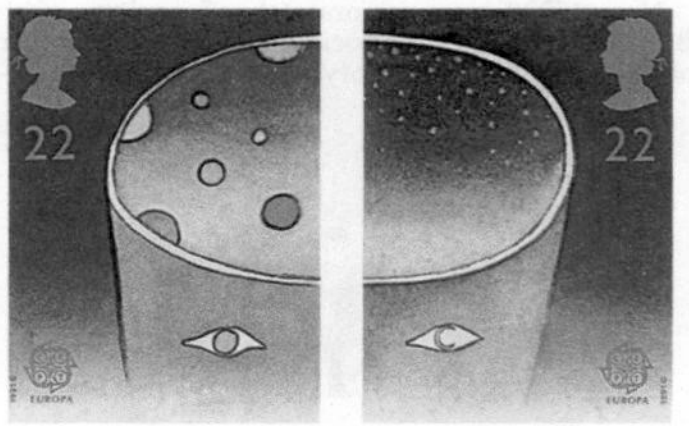

993/4 Man looking at Space

1991. Europa. Europe in Space. Multicoloured.

1560	22p. Type **993**	75	50
1561	22p. Type **994**	75	50
1562	37p. Space looking at Man (Queen's head on left)	2·00	1·40
1563	37p. Similar to No. 1562 (Queen's head on right)	2·00	1·40

Stamps of the same value were printed together in horizontal pairs, each pair forming a composite design.

997 Fencing

1001 "Silver Jubilee"

1991. World Student Games, Sheffield (Nos. 1564/6) and World Cup Rugby Championship (No. 1567).

1564	22p. Type **997**	60	20
1565	26p. Hurdling	1·00	1·00
1566	31p. Diving	1·25	1·25
1567	37p. Rugby	1·50	1·50

1991. 9th World Congress of Roses, Belfast. Multicoloured.

1568	22p. Type **1001**	95	20
1569	26p. "Mme Alfred Carriere"	1·10	1·25
1570	31p. "Rosa moyesii"	1·25	1·25
1571	33p. "Harvest Fayre"	1·50	1·50
1572	37p. "Mutabilis"	1·60	1·50

1006 Iguanodon

1991. 150th Anniv of Dinosaurs' Identification by Owen. Multicoloured.

1573	22p. Type **1006**	90	20
1574	26p. Stegosaurus	1·10	1·25
1575	31p. Tyrannosaurus	1·25	1·25
1576	33p. Protoceratops	1·50	1·50
1577	37p. Triceratops	1·60	1·50

1011 Map of 1816

1991. Bicentenary of Ordnance Survey. Maps of Hamstreet, Kent.

1578 **1011**	24p. black, mauve and cream	60	20
1579 –	28p. multicoloured	1·00	95
1580 –	33p. multicoloured	1·25	1·40
1581 –	39p. multicoloured	1·50	1·40

DESIGNS: 28p. Map of 1906; 33p. Map of 1959; 39p. Map of 1991.

1015 Adoration of the Magi

1991. Christmas. Illuminated Letters from "Acts of Mary and Jesus" Manuscript in Bodleian Library, Oxford. Multicoloured.

1582	18p. Type **1015**	75	10
1583	24p. Mary and Baby Jesus in the Stable	90	10
1584	28p. The Holy Family and Angel	95	1·25
1585	33p. The Annunciation	1·10	1·40
1586	39p. The Flight into Egypt	1·25	1·60

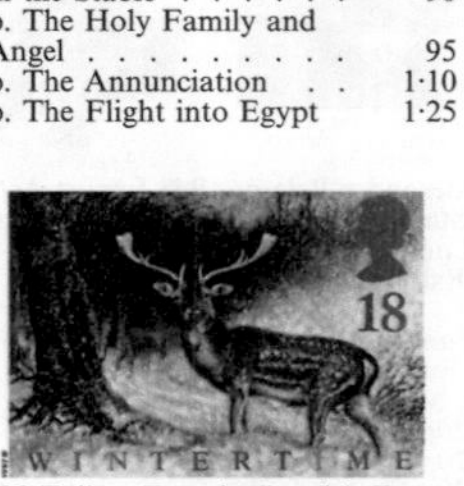

1020 Fallow Deer in Scottish Forest

1992. The Four Seasons. Wintertime. Multicoloured.

1587	18p. Type **1020**	55	15
1588	24p. Hare on North Yorkshire moors	75	20
1589	28p. Fox in the Fens	1·00	1·10
1590	33p. Redwing and Home Counties village	1·25	1·40
1591	39p. Welsh mountain sheep in Snowdonia	1·40	1·60

1025 Flower Spray

1992. Greetings Stamps. "Memories". Multicoloured.

1592	(1st) Type **1025**	1·40	1·40
1593	(1st) Double locket	1·40	1·40
1594	(1st) Key	1·40	1·40
1595	(1st) Model car and cigarette cards	1·40	1·40
1596	(1st) Compass and map	1·40	1·40
1597	(1st) Pocket watch	1·40	1·40
1598	(1st) 1854 1d. Red stamp and pen	1·40	1·40
1599	(1st) Pearl necklace	1·40	1·40
1600	(1st) Marbles	1·40	1·40
1601	(1st) Bucket, spade and starfish	1·40	1·40

Nos. 1592/1601 were issued together, se-tenant, the backgrounds forming a composite design.

1035 Queen Elizabeth in Coronation Robes and Parliamentary Emblem

1992. 40th Anniv of Accession. Multicoloured.

1602	24p. Type **1035**	1·10	1·10
1603	24p. Queen Elizabeth in Garter robes and archiepiscopal arms	1·10	1·10
1604	24p. Queen Elizabeth with baby Prince Andrew and Royal Arms	1·10	1·10
1605	24p. Queen Elizabeth at Trooping the Colour	1·10	1·10
1606	24p. Queen Elizabeth and Commonwealth emblem	1·10	1·10

1040 Tennyson in 1888 and "The Beguiling of Merlin" (Sir Edward Burne-Jones)

1992. Death Centenary of Alfred, Lord Tennyson (poet). Multicoloured.

1607	24p. Type **1040**	60	20
1608	28p. Tennyson in 1856 and "April Love" (Arthur Hughes)	85	85
1609	33p. Tennyson in 1864 and "I am Sick of the Shadows" (John Waterhouse)	1·40	1·60
1610	39p. Tennyson as a young man and "Mariana" (Dante Gabriel Rossetti)	1·50	1·60

1044 Carrickfergus Castle

1992. Designs as Nos. 1410/13, but showing Queen's head in silhouette as T **1044**.

1611 **1044**	£1 green and gold	5·50	1·00
1612 –	£1.50 purple and gold	5·00	1·00
1613 –	£2 blue and gold	6·75	1·00
1995 **1044**	£3 violet and gold	20·00	3·50
1614 –	£5 brown and gold	17·00	3·00

The Queen's head on these stamps is printed in optically variable ink which changes colour from gold to green when viewed from different angles.

1045 British Olympic Association Logo (Olympic Games, Barcelona)

1992. Europa. International Events. Mult.

1615	24p. Type **1045**	1·00	65
1616	24p. British Paralympic Association symbol (Paralympics 92, Barcelona)	1·00	65
1617	24p. "Santa Maria" (500th anniv of discovery of America by Columbus)	1·00	55
1618	39p. "Kaisei" (Japanese cadet brigantine) (Grand Regatta Columbus, 1992)	1·25	1·40
1619	39p. British Pavilion, "EXPO '92", Seville	1·40	1·40

1050 Pikeman

1992. 350th Anniv of the Civil War. Multicoloured.

1620	24p. Type **1050**	60	20
1621	28p. Drummer	85	85
1622	33p. Musketeer	1·40	1·40
1623	39p. Standard Bearer	1·50	1·50

1054 "The Yeomen of the Guard"

1992. 150th Birth Anniv of Sir Arthur Sullivan (composer). Gilbert and Sullivan Operas. Multicoloured.

1624	18p. Type **1054**	50	20
1625	24p. "The Gondoliers"	80	20
1626	28p. "The Mikado"	95	1·00
1627	33p. "The Pirates of Penzance"	1·50	1·60
1628	39p. "Iolanthe"	1·60	1·60

1059 "Acid Rain Kills"

1992. Protection of the Environment. Children's Paintings. Multicoloured.

1629	24p. Type **1059**	70	20
1630	28p. "Ozone Layer"	1·10	1·10
1631	33p. "Greenhouse Effect"	1·25	1·25
1632	39p. "Bird of Hope"	1·40	1·25

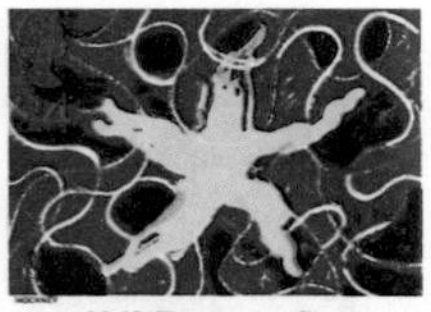
1063 European Star

1992. Single European Market.

1633 **1063**	24p. multicoloured	90	80

1064 "Angel Gabriel", St. James's, Pangbourne

1992. Christmas. Stained Glass Windows. Multicoloured.

1634	18p. Type **1064**	45	15
1635	24p. "Madonna and Child", St. Mary's, Bibury	75	15
1636	28p. "King with Gold", Our Lady and St. Peter, Leatherhead	90	1·10
1637	33p. "Shepherds", All Saints, Porthcawl	1·10	1·40
1638	39p. "Kings with Frankincense and Myrrh", Our Lady and St. Peter, Leatherhead	1·25	1·50

1069 Mute Swan Cob and St. Catherine's Chapel, Abbotsbury

1993. 600th Anniv of Abbotsbury Swannery. Multicoloured.

1639	18p. Type **1069**	1·25	30
1640	24p. Cygnet and decoy	1·10	30
1641	28p. Swans and cygnet	1·40	1·90
1642	33p. Eggs in nest and tithe barn, Abbotsbury	1·75	2·40
1643	39p. Young swan and the Fleet	1·90	2·40

1074 Long John Silver and Parrot ("Treasure Island")

1993. Greetings Stamps. "Gift Giving". Gold, cream and black (No. 1645) or multicoloured (others).

1644	(1st) Type **1074**	1·25	1·25
1645	(1st) Tweedledum and Tweedledee ("Alice Through the Looking Glass")	1·25	1·25
1646	(1st) William ("William" books)	1·25	1·25
1647	(1st) Mole and Toad ("The Wind in the Willows")	1·25	1·25
1648	(1st) Teacher and Wilfrid ("The Bash Street Kids")	1·25	1·25
1649	(1st) Peter Rabbit and Mrs. Rabbit ("The Tale of Peter Rabbit")	1·25	1·25
1650	(1st) Snowman ("The Snowman") and Father Christmas ("Father Christmas")	1·25	1·25
1651	(1st) The Big Friendly Giant and Sophie ("The BFG")	1·25	1·25
1652	(1st) Bill Badger and Rupert Bear	1·25	1·25
1653	(1st) Aladdin and the Genie	1·25	1·25

1084 Decorated Enamel Dial

1993. 300th Birth Anniv of John Harrison (inventor of the marine chronometer). Details of "H4" Clock. Multicoloured.

1654	24p. Type **1084**	60	20
1655	28p. Escapement, remontoire and fusee	1·00	1·10
1656	33p. Balance, spring and temperature compensator	1·40	1·25
1657	39p. Back of movement	1·50	1·40

1088 "Britannia"

1993.

1658	**1088** £10 multicoloured	28·00	12·00

1089 "Dendrobium hellwigianum"

1993. 14th World Orchid Conference, Glasgow. Multicoloured.

1659	18p. Type **1089**	45	20
1660	24p. "Paphiopedilum" Maudiae "Magnificum"	75	20
1661	28p. "Cymbidium lowianum"	1·00	1·10
1662	33p. "Vanda" Rothschildiana	1·25	1·50
1663	39p. "Dendrobium vexillarius var albiviride"	1·60	1·40

1094 "Family Group" (bronze sculpture) (Henry Moore)

1993. Europa. Contemporary Art. Multicoloured.

1767	24p. Type **1094**	60	20
1768	28p. "Kew Gardens" (lithograph) (Edward Bawden)	90	1·00
1769	33p. "St. Francis and the Birds" (Stanley Spencer)	1·25	1·40
1770	39p. "Still Life: Odyssey I" (Ben Nicholson)	1·40	1·40

1098 Emperor Claudius (from gold coin)

1993. Roman Britain. Multicoloured.

1771	24p. Type **1098**	60	20
1772	28p. Emperor Hadrian (bronze head)	90	1·00
1773	33p. Goddess Roma (from gemstone)	1·25	1·40
1774	39p. Christ (Hinton St. Mary mosaic)	1·40	1·40

1102 "Midland Maid" and other Narrow Boats, Grand Junction Canal

1993. Inland Waterways. Multicoloured.

1775	24p. Type **1102**	60	20
1776	28p. "Yorkshire Lass" and other Humber keels, Stainforth and Keadby Canal	95	1·00
1777	35p. "Valley Princess" and other horse-drawn barges, Brecknock and Abergavenny Canal	1·25	1·25
1778	39p. Steam barges, including "Pride of Scotland", and fishing boats, Crinan Canal	1·50	1·40

Nos. 1775/8 commemorate the bicentenary of the Acts of Parliament authorizing the canals depicted.

1106 Horse Chestnut

1993. The Four Seasons. Autumn. Fruits and Leaves. Multicoloured.

1779	18p. Type **1106**	50	20
1780	24p. Blackberry	75	20
1781	28p. Hazel	1·10	1·25
1782	33p. Rowan	1·40	1·50
1783	39p. Pear	1·50	1·50

1111 "The Reigate Squire"

1116

1993. Sherlock Holmes. Centenary of the Publication of "The Final Problem". Multicoloured.

1784	24p. Type **1111**	1·10	1·10
1785	24p. "The Hound of the Baskervilles"	1·10	1·10
1786	24p. "The Six Napoleons"	1·10	1·10
1787	24p. "The Greek Interpreter"	1·10	1·10
1788	24p. "The Final Problem"	1·10	1·10

1993. Self-adhesive.

1976	**1116** (2nd) blue	2·00	2·50
1789	(1st) red	1·25	1·40

Nos. 1976/7 were sold at the current rates.

1117 Bob Cratchit and Tiny Tim

1993. Christmas. 150th Anniv of Publication of "A Christmas Carol" by Charles Dickens. Multicoloured.

1790	19p. Type **1117**	60	15
1791	25p. Mr. and Mrs. Fezziwig	90	15
1792	30p. Scrooge	1·25	1·50
1793	35p. The prize turkey	1·40	1·60
1794	41p. Mr. Scrooge's nephew	1·50	1·60

1122 Class 5 No. 44957 and Class B1 No. 61342 on West Highland Line

1994. The Age of Steam. Railway Photographs by Colin Gifford.

1795	**1122** 19p. green, grey black	55	25
1796	– 25p. lilac, grey and black	90	95
1797	– 30p. brown, grey & black	1·40	1·40
1798	– 35p. purple, grey & black	1·50	1·60
1799	– 41p. blue, grey and black	1·50	1·50

DESIGNS: 25p. Class A1 No. 60149 "Amadis" at Kings Cross; 30p. Class 4 No. 43000 on turntable at Blyth North; 35p. Class No. 42455 near Wigan Central; 41p. Class "Castle" No. 7002 "Devizes Castle" on bridge crossing Worcester and Birmingham Canal.

1127 Dan Dare and the Mekon

1994. Greetings Stamps. "Messages". Mult.

1800	(1st) Type **1127**	1·00	90
1801	(1st) The Three Bears	1·00	90
1802	(1st) Rupert Bear	1·00	90
1803	(1st) Alice ("Alice in Wonderland")	1·00	90
1804	(1st) Noggin and The Ice Dragon	1·00	90
1805	(1st) Peter Rabbit posting a letter	1·00	90
1806	(1st) Red Riding Hood and wolf	1·00	90
1807	(1st) Orlando the Marmalade Cat	1·00	90
1808	(1st) Biggles	1·00	90
1809	(1st) Paddington Bear on station	1·00	90

1137 Castell Y Waun (Chirk Castle), Clwyd, Wales

1994. 25th Anniv of Investiture of the Prince of Wales. Paintings by Prince Charles. Multicoloured.

1810	19p. Type **1137**	55	20
1811	25p. Ben Arkle, Sutherland, Scotland	1·00	20
1812	30p. Mourne Mountains, County Down, Northern Ireland	1·10	1·40
1813	35p. Dersingham, Norfolk, England	1·40	1·50
1814	41p. Dolwyddelan, Gwynedd, Wales	1·50	1·50

1142 Bather at Blackpool

1994. Centenary of Picture Postcards. Mult.

1815	19p. Type **1142**	60	20
1816	25p. "Where's my Little Lad?"	90	20
1817	30p. "Wish You were Here!"	1·10	1·25
1818	35p. Punch and Judy show	1·40	1·50
1819	41p. "The Tower Crane" machine	1·50	1·50

1147 British Lion and French Cockerel over Tunnel

1994. Opening of Channel Tunnel. Multicoloured.

1820	25p. Type **1147**	80	70
1821	25p. Symbolic hands over train	80	70
1822	41p. Type **1147**	1·50	1·50
1823	41p. As No. 1821	1·50	1·50

1149 Groundcrew replacing Smoke Canisters on Douglas Boston of 88 Sqn

1994. 50th Anniv of D-Day. Multicoloured.

1824	25p. Type **1149**	1·00	1·10
1825	25p. H.M.S. "Warspite" (battleship) shelling enemy positions	1·00	1·10
1826	25p. Commandos landing on Gold Beach	1·00	1·10
1827	25p. Infantry regrouping on Sword Beach	1·00	1·10
1828	25p. Tank and infantry advancing, Ouistreham	1·00	1·10

1154 The Old Course, St. Andrews

1994. Scottish Golf Courses. Multicoloured.

1829	19p. Type **1154**	50	20
1830	25p. The 18th Hole, Muirfield	75	20
1831	30p. The 15th Hole ("Luckyslap"), Carnoustie	1·10	1·40
1832	35p. The 8th Hole ("The Postage Stamp"), Royal Troon	1·25	1·40
1833	41p. The 9th Hole, Turnberry	1·40	1·40

Nos. 1829/33 commemorate the 250th anniversary of golf's first set of rules produced by the Honourable Company of Edinburgh Golfers.

1159 Royal Welsh Show, Llanelwedd

1994. The Four Seasons. Summertime. Multicoloured.

1834	19p. Type **1159**	50	20
1835	25p. All England Tennis Championships, Wimbledon	75	20
1836	30p. Cowes Week	1·10	1·25

1837 35p. Test Match, Lord's . . 1·25 1·60
1838 41p. Braemar Gathering . . 1·40 1·60

1164 Ultrasonic Imaging

1994. Europa. Medical Discoveries. Multicoloured.
1839 25p. Type **1164** 80 20
1840 30p. Scanning electron microscopy . . . . 1·25 1·10
1841 35p. Magnetic resonance imaging . . . . 1·25 1·40
1842 41p. Computed tomography 1·50 1·40

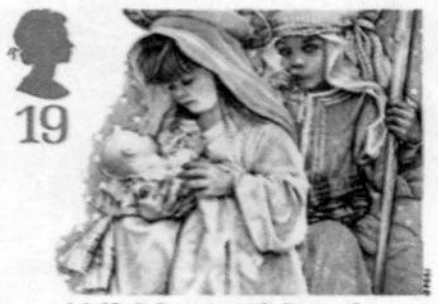
1168 Mary and Joseph

1994. Christmas. Children's Nativity Plays. Multicoloured.
1843 19p. Type **1168** 65 15
1844 25p. Three Wise Men . . . 90 15
1845 30p. Mary with doll . . . . 1·10 1·40
1846 35p. Shepherds . . . . . . 1·25 1·40
1847 41p. Angels . . . . 1·50 1·40

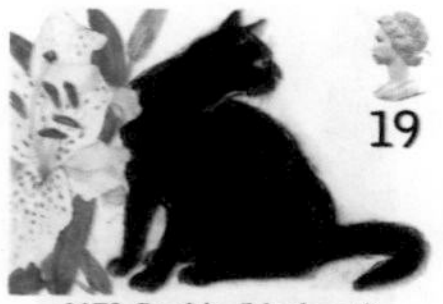
1173 Sophie (black cat)

1995. Cats. Multicoloured.
1848 19p. Type **1173** 80 20
1849 25p. Puskas (Siamese) and Tigger (tabby) 95 25
1850 30p. Chloe (ginger cat) . . . 1·10 1·40
1851 35p. Kikko (tortoiseshell) and Rosie (Abyssinian) 1·25 1·50
1852 41p. Fred (black and white cat) . . . . 1·60 1·60

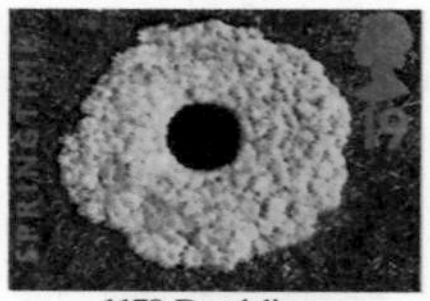
1178 Dandelions

1995. The Four Seasons. Springtime. Plant Sculptures by Andy Goldsworthy. Multicoloured.
1853 19p. Type **1178** 80 15
1854 25p. Sweet chestnut leaves 95 15
1855 30p. Garlic leaves . . . . . 1·25 1·40
1856 35p. Hazel leaves . . . . . 1·25 1·40
1857 41p. Spring grass . . . . . 1·60 1·60

1183 "La Danse a la Campagne" (Renoir)

1995. Greetings Stamps. "Greetings in Art".
1858 **1183** (1st) multicoloured . . 1·00 80
1859 – (1st) multicoloured . . 1·00 80
1860 – (1st) multicoloured . . 1·00 80
1861 – (1st) multicoloured . . 1·00 80
1862 – (1st) multicoloured . . 1·00 80
1863 – (1st) multicoloured . . 1·00 80
1864 – (1st) brown and silver 1·00 80
1865 – (1st) multicoloured . . 1·00 80
1866 – (1st) multicoloured . . 1·00 80
1867 – (1st) black, yellow and silver . . . . 1·00 80
DESIGNS: No. 1859, "Troilus and Criseyde" (Peter Brookes); 1860, "The Kiss" (Rodin); 1861, "Girls on the Town" (Beryl Cook); 1862, "Jazz" (Andrew Mockett); 1863, "Girls performing a Kathak Dance" (Aurangzeb period); 1864, "Alice Keppel with her Daughter" (Alice Hughes); 1865, "Children Playing" (L. S. Lowry); 1866, "Circus Clowns" (Emily Firmin and Justin Mitchell); 1867, Decoration from "All the Love Poems of Shakespeare" (Eric Gill).

1193 Fireplace Decoration, Attingham Park, Shropshire

1198 British Troops and French Civilians celebrating

1995. Centenary of The National Trust. Multicoloured.
1868 19p. Type **1193** 60 20
1869 25p. Oak seedling 80 20
1870 30p. Carved table leg, Attingham Park . . . . . 1·00 1·25
1871 35p. St. David's Head, Dyfed, Wales . . . . . . 1·25 1·50
1872 41p. Elizabethan window, Little Moreton Hall, Cheshire . . . . 1·40 1·50

1995. Europa. Peace and Freedom.
1873 **1198** 19p. silver, brown and black 70 40
1874 – 19p. multicoloured . . 70 40
1875 – 25p. silver, blue and black . . . . 1·00 60
1876 – 25p. multicoloured . . 1·00 60
1877 – 30p. multicoloured . . 1·25 1·75
DESIGNS: No. 1874, Symbolic hands and Red Cross; 1875, St. Paul's Cathedral and searchlights; 1876, Symbolic hand releasing peace dove; 1877, Symbolic hands.
Nos. 1873 and 1875 commemorate the 50th anniversary of the end of the Second World War, No. 1874 the 125th anniversary of the British Red Cross Society and Nos. 1876/7 the 50th anniversary of the United Nations.
Nos. 1876/7 include the "EUROPA" emblem.

1203 "The Time Machine"

1995. Science Fiction. Novels by H. G. Wells. Multicoloured.
1878 25p. Type **1203** 95 25
1879 30p. "The First Men in the Moon" . . . . 1·40 1·50
1880 35p. "The War of the Worlds" . . . . 1·50 1·60
1881 41p. "The Shape of Things to Come" . . . . 1·60 1·60
Nos. 1878/81 commemorate the centenary of publication of Wells's "The Time Machine".

1207 The Swan, 1595

1995. Reconstruction of Shakespeare's Globe Theatre. Multicoloured.
1882 25p. Type **1207** 90 90
1883 25p. The Rose, 1592 . . . 90 90
1884 25p. The Globe, 1599 . . . 90 90
1885 25p. The Hope, 1613 . . . 90 90
1886 25p. The Globe, 1614 . . . 90 90
Nos. 1882/6 were printed together, se-tenant, forming a composite design.

1212 Sir Rowland Hill and Uniform Penny Postage Petition

1995. Pioneers of Communications.
1887 **1212** 19p. silver, red and black 65 30
1888 – 25p. silver, brown and black 90 35
1889 – 41p. silver, green and black . . . . 1·50 1·60
1890 – 60p. silver, blue and black . . . . 1·75 1·90
DESIGNS: 25p. Hill and Penny Black; 41p. Guglielmo Marconi and early wireless; 60p. Marconi and sinking of "Titanic" (liner).

Nos. 1887/8 mark the birth bicentenary of Sir Rowland Hill and Nos. 1889/90 the centenary of the first radio transmissions.

1216 Harold Wagstaff

1995. Centenary of Rugby League. Multicoloured.
1891 19p. Type **1216** 85 25
1892 25p. Gus Risman . . . . . 1·00 30
1893 30p. Jim Sullivan . . . . . 1·25 1·50
1894 35p. Billy Batten . . . . . 1·25 1·60
1895 41p. Brian Bevan . . . . . 1·60 1·75

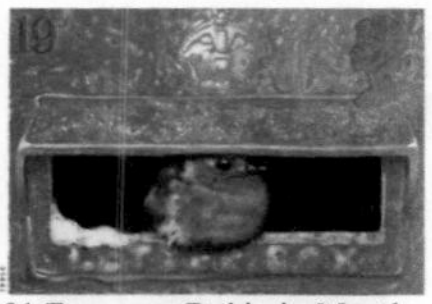
1221 European Robin in Mouth of Pillar Box

1995. Christmas. Christmas Robins. Multicoloured.
1896 19p. Type **1221** 60 20
1897 25p. European robin on railings and holly 85 30
1898 30p. European robin on snow-covered milk bottles 1·25 1·40
1899 41p. European robin on road sign . . . . 1·60 1·60
1900 60p. European robin on door knob and Christmas wreath . . . . 1·75 1·90

1226 Opening Lines of "To a Mouse" and Fieldmouse

1996. Death Bicent of Robert Burns (Scottish poet).
1901 **1226** 19p. cream, brown and black 60 25
1902 – 25p. multicoloured . . 90 30
1903 – 41p. multicoloured . . 1·40 1·50
1904 – 60p. multicoloured . . 1·75 1·90
DESIGNS: 25p. "O my Luve's like a red, red rose" and wild rose; 41p. "Scots, wha hae wi Wallace bled" and Sir William Wallace; 60p. "Auld Lang Syne" and highland dancers.

1230 "MORE! LOVE" (Mel Calman)

1996. Greetings Stamps. Cartoons.
1905 **1230** (1st) black and mauve 80 75
1906 – (1st) black and green 80 75
1907 – (1st) black and blue . . 80 75
1908 – (1st) black and violet 80 75
1909 – (1st) black and red . . 80 75
1910 – (1st) black and blue . . 80 75
1911 – (1st) black and red . . 80 75
1912 – (1st) black and violet 80 75
1913 – (1st) black and green 80 75
1914 – (1st) black and mauve 80 75
DESIGNS: No. 1906, "Sincerely" (Charles Barsotti); 1907, "Do you have something for the HUMAN CONDITION?" (Mel Calman); 1908, "MENTAL FLOSS" (Leo Cullum); 1909, "4.55 P.M." (Charles Barsotti); 1910, "Dear lottery prize winner" (Larry); 1911, "I'm writing to you because ..." (Mel Calman); 1912, "FETCH THIS, FETCH THAT" (Charles Barsotti); 1913, "My day starts before I'm ready for it" (Mel Calman); 1914, "THE CHEQUE IN THE POST" (Jack Ziegler).
Nos. 1905/14 were sold at the current rate.

1240 "Muscovy Duck"

1996. 50th Anniv of the Wildfowl and Wetlands Trust. Bird paintings by C. F. Tunnicliffe. Multicoloured.
1915 19p. Type **1240** 70 25
1916 25p. "Lapwing" 90 30
1917 30p. "White-fronted Goose" 1·00 1·25
1918 35p. "Bittern" . . . . . . 1·10 1·25
1919 41p. "Whooper Swan" . . . 1·50 1·60

1245 The Odeon, Harrogate

1996. Centenary of Cinema.
1920 **1245** 19p. multicoloured . . 50 25
1921 – 25p. multicoloured . . 70 30
1922 – 30p. multicoloured . . 90 1·10
1923 – 35p. black, red and silver . . . . 1·25 1·25
1924 – 41p. multicoloured . . 1·60 1·60
DESIGNS: 25p. Laurence Olivier and Vivien Leigh in "Lady Hamilton" (film); 30p. Old cinema ticket; 35p. Pathe News still; 41p. Cinema sign, The Odeon, Manchester.

1250 Dixie Dean

1996. European Football Championship. Multicoloured.
1925 19p. Type **1250** 40 20
1926 25p. Bobby Moore 70 20
1927 35p. Duncan Edwards . . . 1·25 1·60
1928 41p. Billy Wright . . . . . 1·40 1·60
1929 60p. Danny Blanchflower 1·75 1·90

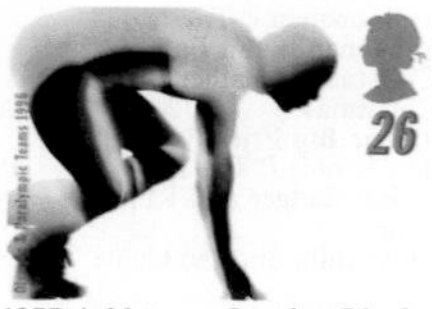

1255 Athlete on Starting Blocks

1996. Olympic and Paralympic Games, Atlanta. Multicoloured.
1930 26p. Type **1255** . . . . . . 1·10 1·00
1931 26p. Throwing the javelin 1·10 1·00
1932 26p. Basketball . . . . . . 1·10 1·00
1933 26p. Swimming . . . . . . 1·10 1·00
1934 26p. Athlete celebrating and Olympic Rings . . . . . 1·10 1·00

1260 Prof. Dorothy Hodgkin (scientist)

1996. Europa. Famous Women.
1935 **1260** 20p. green, grey and black 60 25
1936 – 26p. mauve, grey & black 75 75
1937 – 31p. bronze, grey and black . . . . 95 1·10
1938 – 37p. silver, grey and black . . . . 1·25 1·40
1939 – 43p. gold, grey and black . . . . 1·40 1·50
DESIGNS: 26p. Dame Margot Fonteyn (ballerina); 31p. Dame Elisabeth Frink (sculptress); 37p. Dame Daphne du Maurier (novelist); 43p. Dame Marea Hartman (sports administrator).
Nos. 1936/7 include the "EUROPA" emblem.

1265 "Muffin the Mule"

1996. 50th Anniv of Children's Television. Multicoloured.
1940 20p. Type **1265** 55 20
1941 26p. "Sooty" 80 20
1942 31p. "Stingray" . . . . . . 1·00 1·50
1943 37p. "The Clangers" . . . 1·40 1·60
1944 43p. "Dangermouse" . . . 1·60 1·75

1270 Triumph TR3

1996. Classic Sports Cars. Multicoloured.

1945	20p. Type **1270**	55	20
1946	26p. MG TD	80	20
1947	37p. Austin-Healey 100	1·40	1·50
1948	43p. Jaguar XK120	1·40	1·50
1949	63p. Morgan Plus 4	1·75	1·50

1275 The Three Kings

1996. Christmas. Multicoloured.

1950	(2nd.) Type **1275**	75	20
1951	(1st) The Annunciation	1·00	35
1952	31p. The Journey to Bethlehem	1·10	1·50
1953	43p. The Nativity	1·25	1·50
1954	63p. The Shepherds	1·60	1·75

1280 "Gentiana acaulis" (Georg Ehret)

1997. Greeting Stamps. 19th-century Flower Paintings. Multicoloured.

1955	(1st) Type **1280**	85	90
1956	(1st) "Magnolia grandiflora" (Ehret)	85	90
1957	(1st) "Camellia japonica" (Alfred Chandler)	85	90
1958	(1st) "Tulipa" (Ehret)	85	90
1959	(1st) "Fuchsia" "Princess of Wales" (Augusta Withers)	85	90
1960	(1st) "Tulipa gesneriana" (Ehret)	85	90
1961	(1st) "Guzmania splendens" (Charlotte Sowerby)	85	90
1962	(1st) "Iris latifolia" (Ehret)	85	90
1963	(1st) "Hippeastrum rutilum" (Pierre-Joseph Redoute)	85	90
1964	(1st) "Passiflora coerulea" (Ehret)	85	90

1290 "King Henry VIII"

1997. 450th Death Anniv of King Henry VIII. Multicoloured.

1965	26p. Type **1290**	1·00	90
1966	26p. "Catherine of Aragon"	1·25	1·00
1967	26p. "Anne Boleyn"	1·25	1·00
1968	26p. "Jane Seymour"	1·25	1·00
1969	26p. "Anne of Cleves"	1·25	1·00
1970	26p. "Catherine Howard"	1·25	1·00
1971	26p. "Catherine Parr"	1·25	1·00

1297 St. Columba in Boat

1303 "Dracula"

1997. Religious Anniversaries. Multicoloured.

1972	26p. Type **1297**	75	35
1973	37p. St. Columba on Iona	1·10	1·50
1974	43p. St. Augustine with King Ethelbert	1·50	1·50
1975	63p. St. Augustine with Model of Cathedral	2·00	2·10

Nos. 1972/3 commemorate the 1400th death anniversary of St. Columba and Nos. 1974/5 the 1400th anniversary of the arrival of St. Augustine of Canterbury in Kent.

1997. Europa. Tales and Legends. Horror Stories. Multicoloured.

1980	26p. Type **1303**	1·00	40
1981	31p. "Frankenstein"	1·10	1·40
1982	37p. "Dr. Jekyll and Mr. Hyde"	1·40	1·50
1983	43p. "The Hound of the Baskervilles"	1·75	1·60

Nos. 1980/3 commemorate the birth bicentenary of Mary Shelley (creator of Frankenstein) with the 26p. and 31p. values incorporating the "EUROPA" emblem.

1307 Reginald Mitchell and Supermarine Spitfire Mk IIA

1997. British Aircraft Designers. Multicoloured.

1984	20p. Type **1307**	75	40
1985	26p. Roy Chadwick and Avro Lancaster Mk I	1·10	1·10
1986	37p. Ronald Bishop and De Havilland Mosquito B Mk XVI	1·40	1·10
1987	43p. George Carter and Gloster Meteor T Mk 7	1·50	1·40
1988	63p. Sir Sidney Camm and Hawker Hunter FGA Mk 9	2·00	1·90

1312 Carriage Horse and Coachman

1997. "All the Queen's Horses". 50th Anniv of the British Horse Society. Multicoloured.

1989	20p. Type **1312**	80	45
1990	26p. Lifeguards horse and trooper	1·10	1·40
1991	43p. Blues and Royals drum horse and drummer	1·50	1·50
1992	63p. Duke of Edinburgh's horse and groom	2·00	2·00

1316 Haroldswick, Shetland

1997. Sub-Post Offices. Multicoloured.

1997	20p. Type **1316**	75	50
1998	26p. Painswick, Gloucestershire	1·00	60
1999	43p. Beddgelert, Gwynedd	1·50	1·50
2000	63p. Ballyroney, County Down	2·25	2·10

Nos. 1997/2000 were issued on the occasion of the Centenary of The National Federation of Sub-Postmasters.

1320 "Noddy"

1997. Birth Centenary of Enid Blyton (children's author). Multicoloured.

2001	20p. Type **1320**	60	45
2002	26p. "Famous Five"	1·00	1·25
2003	37p. "Secret Seven"	1·25	1·25
2004	43p. "Faraway Tree"	1·50	1·50
2005	63p. "Malory Towers"	2·00	2·00

1325 Children and Father Christmas pulling Cracker

1997. Christmas. 150th Anniv of the Christmas Cracker. Multicoloured.

2006	(2nd.) Type **1325**	75	20
2007	(1st) Father Christmas with traditional cracker	90	30
2008	31p. Father Christmas riding cracker	1·00	1·60
2009	43p. Father Christmas on snowball	1·25	1·75
2010	63p. Father Christmas and chimney	1·60	1·90

1330 Wedding Photograph, 1947

1997. Royal Golden Wedding.

2011	**1330**	20p. gold, brown and black	85	45
2012	–	26p. multicoloured	1·10	70
2013	**1330**	43p. gold, green and black	1·90	2·25
2014	–	63p. multicoloured	2·50	3·00

DESIGNS: 26p. and 63p. Queen Elizabeth II and Prince Philip, 1997.

1332 Common Dormouse

1338 Diana, Princess of Wales (photo by Lord Snowdon)

1998. Endangered Species. Multicoloured.

2015	20p. Type **1332**	60	40
2016	26p. Lady's slipper orchid	70	40
2017	31p. Song thrush	1·00	1·00
2018	37p. Shining ram's-horn snail	1·25	1·10
2019	43p. Mole cricket	1·40	1·25
2020	63p. Devil's bolete	1·90	1·75

1998. Diana, Princess of Wales Commemoration. Multicoloured.

2021	26p. Type **1338**	90	90
2022	26p. At British Lung Foundation Function, April 1997 (photo by John Stillwell)	90	90
2023	26p. Wearing tiara, 1991 (photo by Lord Snowdon)	90	90
2024	26p. On visit to Birmingham, October 1995 (photo by Tim Graham) (checked suit)	90	90
2025	26p. In evening dress, 1987 (photo by Terence Donovan)	90	90

1343 Lion of England and Griffin of Edward III

1348

1998. 650th Anniv of the Order of the Garter. The Queen's Beasts. Multicoloured.

2026	26p. Type **1343**	90	90
2027	26p. Falcon of Plantagenet and Bull of Clarence	90	90
2028	26p. Lion of Mortimer and Yale of Beaufort	90	90
2029	26p. Greyhound of Richmond and Dragon of Wales	90	90
2030	26p. Unicorn of Scotland and Horse of Hanover	90	90

1998. As Type **157** (Wilding definitive of 1952–54) but with face values in decimal currency as Type **1348**.

2031	**1348**	20p. green	70	75
2032		26p. brown	90	95
2033		37p. purple	2·75	2·75

See also Nos. 2295/8.

1349 St. John's Point Lighthouse, County Down

1998. 300th Anniv of the 1st Lighthouse and Final Year of Manned Lighthouses. Multicoloured.

2034	20p. Type **1349**	50	40
2035	26p. Smalls Lighthouse, Pembrokeshire	75	50
2036	37p. Needles Rock Lighthouse, Isle of Wight, c. 1900	1·10	1·25
2037	43p. Bell Rock Lighthouse, Arbroath, mid-19th century	1·50	1·50
2038	63p. Eddystone Lighthouse, Plymouth, 1698	2·10	2·10

1354 Tommy Cooper

1998. Comedians. Multicoloured.

2041	20p. Type **1354**	50	50
2042	26p. Eric Morecambe	90	90
2043	37p. Joyce Grenfell	1·25	1·25
2044	43p. Les Dawson	1·50	1·50
2045	63p. Peter Cook	2·10	2·10

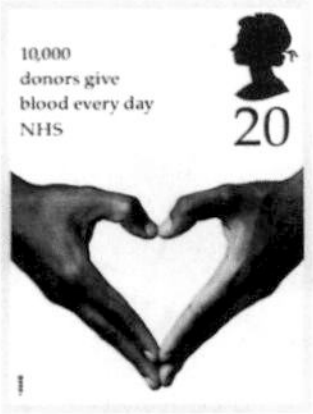

1359 Hands forming Heart

1998. 50th Anniv of the National Health Service. Multicoloured.

2046	20p. Type **1359**	50	50
2047	26p. Adult and child holding hands	90	90
2048	43p. Hands forming cradle	1·50	1·50
2049	63p. Hand taking pulse	2·10	2·10

1363 "The Hobbit" (J. R. R. Tolkien)

1998. Famous Children's Fantasy Novels. Multicoloured.

2050	20p. Type **1363**	50	45
2051	26p. "The Lion, The Witch and the Wardrobe" (C. S. Lewis)	85	55
2052	37p. "The Phoenix and the Carpet" (E. Nesbit)	1·25	1·50
2053	43p. "The Borrowers" (Mary Norton)	1·40	1·50
2054	63p. "Through the Looking Glass" (Lewis Carroll)	2·10	2·00

Nos. 2050/4 commemorate the birth centenary of C. S. Lewis and the death centenary of Lewis Carroll.

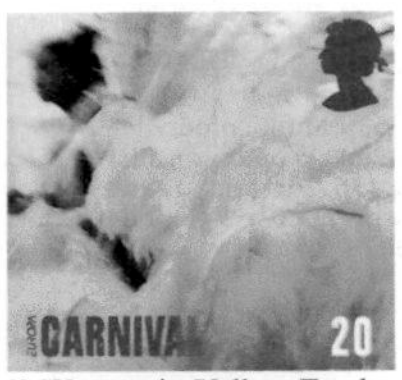

1368 Woman in Yellow Feathered Costume

1998. Europa. Festivals. Notting Hill Carnival. Multicoloured.

2055	20p. Type **1368**	75	45
2056	26p. Woman in blue costume and headdress	95	55
2057	43p. Group of children in white and gold robes	1·50	1·60
2058	63p. Child in "Tree" costume	2·00	2·10

The 20p. and 26p. incorporate the "EUROPA" emblem.

1372 Sir Malcolm Campbell's "Bluebird", 1925

1998. British Land Speed Record Holders. Multicoloured.

2059	20p. Type **1372**	70	25
2060	26p. Sir Henry Segrave's "Sunbeam", 1926	85	30
2061	30p. John G. Parry Thomas's "Babs", 1926	1·25	1·50
2062	43p. John R. Cobb's "Railton Mobil Special", 1947	1·50	1·60
2063	63p. Donald Campbell's "Bluebird CN7", 1964	2·25	2·40

Nos. 2059/63 commemorate the 50th death anniversary of Sir Malcolm Campbell.

1377 Angel with Hands raised in Blessing

1998. Christmas. Angels. Multicoloured.

2064	20p. Type **1377**	70	50
2065	26p. Angel praying	85	60
2066	30p. Angel plaing flute	1·25	1·50
2067	43p. Angel playing lute	1·40	1·60
2068	63p. Angel praying (different)	2·00	2·25

1382 Greenwich Meridian and Clock (John Harrison's chronometer)

1999. Millennium Series. The Inventors' Tale. Multicoloured.

2069	20p. Type **1382**	70	70
2070	26p. Industrial worker and blast furnace (James Watt's discovery of steam power)	95	1·00
2071	43p. Early photos of leaves (Henry Fox-Talbot's photographic experiments)	1·50	1·60
2072	63p. Computer inside human head (Alan Turing's work on computers)	2·25	2·40

1386 Airliner hugging Globe (International air travel)

1999. Millennium Series. The Travellers' Tale.

2073	**1386**	20p. multicoloured	75	70
2074	–	26p. multicoloured	95	1·00
2075	–	43p. black, stone and bronze	1·50	1·60
2076	–	63p. multicoloured	2·25	2·40

DESIGNS: 26p. Women on bicycle (development of the bicycle); 43p. Victorian railway station (growth of public transport); 63p. Captain Cook and Maori (Captain James Cook's voyages).

1390

1999. (a) Self-adhesive.

2077	**1390**	(1st) grey (face value) (Queen's head in colourless relief)	2·25	2·25

(b) Ordinary gum.

2078	**1390**	(1st) black	2·25	2·25

1391 Vaccinating Child (pattern in cow markings) (Jenner's development of smallpox vaccine)

1999. Millennium Series. The Patients' Tale. Multicoloured.

2080	20p. Type **1391**	75	70
2081	26p. Patient on trolley (nursing care)	95	1·00
2082	43p. Penicillin mould (Fleming's discovery of penicillin)	1·50	1·60
2083	63p. Sculpture of test-tube baby (development of in-vitro fertilization)	2·25	2·40

1395 Dove and Norman Settler (medieval migration to Scotland)

1999. Millennium Series. The Settlers' Tale. Multicoloured.

2084	20p. Type **1395**	75	70
2085	26p. Pilgrim Fathers and Red Indian (17th-century migration to America)	95	1·00
2086	43p. Sailing ship and aspects of settlement (19th-century migration to Australia)	1·50	1·60
2087	63p. Hummingbird and superimposed stylized face (20th-century migration to Great Britain)	2·25	2·40

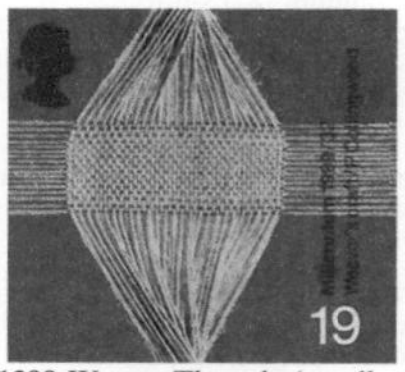

1399 Woven Threads (woollen industry)

1999. Millennium Series. The Workers' Tale. Multicoloured.

2088	19p. Type **1399**	75	70
2089	26p. Salts Mill, Saltaire (cotton industry)	95	1·00
2090	44p. Hull on slipway (shipbuilding)	1·50	1·60
2091	64p. Lloyd's Building (City of London finance centre)	2·25	2·40

1403 Freddie Mercury (lead singer of pop group Queen) ("Popular Music")

1999. Millennium Series. The Entertainers' Tale. Multicoloured.

2092	19p. Type **1403**	75	70
2093	26p. Bobby Moore with World Cup, 1966 ("Sport")	95	1·00
2094	44p. Dalek from "Dr. Who" (science-fiction series) ("Television")	1·50	1·60
2095	64p. Charlie Chaplin (film star) ("Cinema")	2·25	2·40

1407 Prince Edward and Miss Sophie Rhys-Jones (from photo by John Swannell)

1999. Royal Wedding. Multicoloured.

2096	26p. Type **1407**	85	85
2097	64p. Couple in profile	1·90	1·90

1409 Suffragette behind Prison Window (Equal Rights for Women)

1999. Millennium Series. The Citizens' Tale. Multicoloured.

2098	19p. Type **1409**	75	70
2099	26p. Water tap (Right to Health)	95	1·00
2100	44p. Generations of school children (Right to Education)	1·50	1·60
2101	64p. "MAGNA CARTA" (Human Rights)	2·25	2·40

1413 Molecular Structures (DNA Decoding)

1999. Millennium Series. The Scientists' Tale. Multicoloured.

2102	19p. Type **1413**	75	70
2103	26p. Large ground finch and fossilized skeleton (Darwin's Theory of Evolution)	95	1·00
2104	44p. Rotation of polarized light by magnetism (Faraday's work on electricity)	1·50	1·60
2105	64p. Saturn (development of astronomical telescopes)	2·25	2·50

1999. Solar Eclipse. Sheet 89 × 101 mm.

MS2106	No. 2105 × 4 (sold at £2.56)	18·00	18·00

1417 Upland Landscape (Strip Farming)

1999. Millennium Series. The Farmers' Tale. Multicoloured.

2107	19p. Type **1417**	75	70
2108	26p. Horse-drawn plough (Mechanical Farming)	95	1·00
2109	44p. Man peeling potato (food imports)	1·50	1·60
2110	64p. Aerial view of combine harvester (Satellite Agriculture)	2·25	2·40

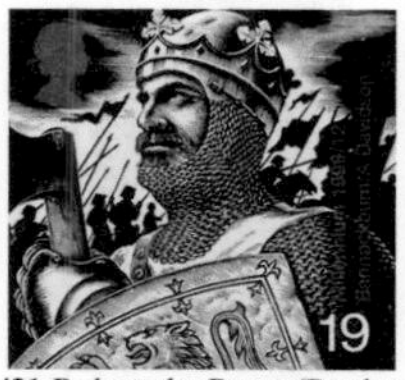

1421 Robert the Bruce (Battle of Bannockburn, 1314)

1999. The Millennium Series. The Soldiers' Tale.

2111	**1421**	19p. black, stone and silver	75	70
2112	–	26p. multicoloured	95	1·00
2113	–	44p. grey, black and silver	1·50	1·60
2114	–	64p. multicoloured	2·25	2·40

DESIGNS: 26p. Cavalier and horse (English Civil War); 44p. War Graves Cemetery, The Somme (World Wars); 64p. Soldiers with boy (Peace-keeping).

1425 "Hark the herald angels sing" and Hymnbook (John Wesley)

1999. Millennium Series. The Christians' Tale. Multicoloured.

2115	19p. Type **1425**	75	70
2116	26p. King James I and Bible (Authorised version of Bible)	95	1·00
2117	44p. St. Andrews Cathedral, Fife ("Pilgrimage")	1·50	1·60
2118	64p. Nativity ("First Christmas")	2·25	2·40

1429 "World of the Stage" (Allen Jones)

1999. The Millennium Series. The Artists' Tale. Multicoloured.

2119	19p. Type **1429**	70	75
2120	26p. "World of Music" (Bridget Riley)	90	1·00
2121	44p. "World of Literature" (Lisa Milroy)	1·50	1·60
2122	64p. "New Worlds" (Sir Howard Hodgkin)	2·25	2·50

1433 Clock Face and Map of North America

1434 Clock Face and Map of Asia

1435 Clock Face and Map of Middle East

1436 Clock Face and Map of Europe

1999. Millennium Series. "Millennium Timekeeper". Sheet 120 × 89 mm. Multicoloured.

MS2123	64p. Type **1433**; 64p. Type **1434**; 64p. Type **1435**; 64p. Type **1436**	17·00	17·00

No. **MS**2123 also exists overprinted **EARLS COURT, LONDON 22–28 MAY 2000 THE STAMP SHOW 2000** from Exhibition Premium Passes, costing £10, available from 1 March 2000.

1437 Queen Elizabeth II   **1438** Barn Owl (World Owl Trust, Muncaster)

2000. New Millennium.
2124 **1437** (1st) brown 80 90

2000. Millennium Projects (1st series). "Above and Bend".
2125 19p. Type **1438** 70 75
2126 26p. Night sky (National Space Science Centre, Leicester) . . . . 90 1·00
2126a (1st) As No. 2126 . . . . 3·50 3·50
2127 44p. River Goyt and textile mills (Torrs Walkway, New Mills) . . . . . . 1·50 1·60
2128 64p. Cape gannets (Seabird Centre, North Berwick) 2·25 2·40

1442 Millennium Beacon (Beacons across The Land)

2000. Millennium Projects (2nd series). "Fire and Light". Multicoloured.
2129 19p. Type **1442** 70 75
2130 26p. Garratt steam locomotive No. 143 pulling train (Rheilffordd Eryri, Welsh Highland Railway) . . . . 90 1·00
2131 44p. Lightning (Dynamic Earth Centre, Edinburgh) 1·50 1·60
2132 64p. Multicoloured lights (Lighting Croydon's Skyline) . . . . 2·25 2·40

2000. As T **929** but with "1st" face value.
2133 (1st) black and cream . . . 1·10 1·25

1447 Beach Pebbles (Turning the Tide, Durham Coast)

2000. Millennium Projects (3rd series). "Water and Coast".
2134 19p. Type **1447** 70 75
2135 26p. Frog's legs and water lilies (National Pondlife Centre, Merseyside) . . . 90 1·00
2136 44p. Cliff Boardwalk (Parc Arfordirol, Llanelli Coast) 1·50 1·60
2137 64p. Reflections in water (Portsmouth Harbour Development) . . . . . . 2·00 2·25

1451 Reed Beds, River Braid (ECOS, Ballymena)

2000. Millennium Projects (4th series). "Life and Earth".
2138 (2nd.) Type **1451** 70 75
2139 (1st) South American leaf-cutter ants ("Web of Life" Exhibition, London Zoo) 95 1·00
2140 44p. Solar sensors (Earth Centre, Doncaster) . . . 1·50 1·60
2141 64p. Hydroponic leaves (Project SUZY, Teesside) 2·25 2·40

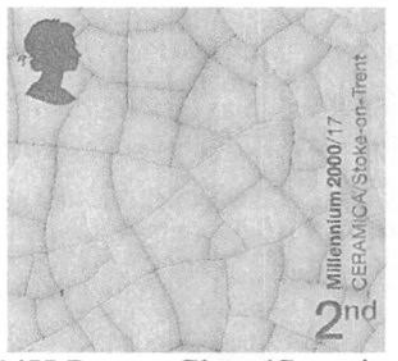

1455 Pottery Glaze (Ceramica Museum, Stoke-on-Trent)

2000. Millennium Projects (5th series). "Art and Craft".
2142 (2nd.) Type **1455** 70 75
2143 (1st) Bankside Galleries (Tate Modern, London) 90 1·00
2144 45p. Road marking (Cycle Network Artworks) . . . 1·50 1·60
2145 65p. People of Salford (Lowry Centre, Salford) 2·25 2·40

2000. "Stamp Show 2000" International Stamp Exhibition, London. Jeffrey Matthews Colour Palette. Sheet 124×70 mm, containing stamps as T **367**.
MS2146 4p. blue; 5p. brown; 6p. green; 10p. orange; 31p. mauve; 39p. mauve; 64p. green; £1 violet 13·00 12·00

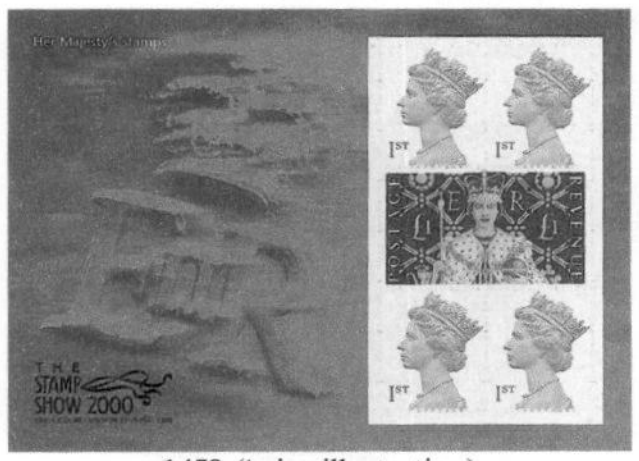

1459 (½-size illustration)

2000. "Stamp Show 2000" International Stamp Exhibition, London. "Her Majesty's Stamps". Sheet 121×89 mm.
MS2147 **1459** (1st) brown (Type **1437**) × 4; £1 green (as Type **163**) . . . . 18·00 12·00
The £1 value is an adaptation of the 1953 Coronation 1s.3d. stamp originally designed by Edmund Dulac.

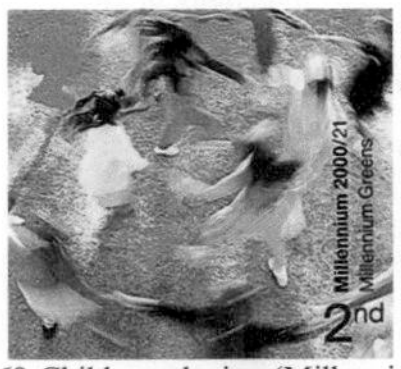

1460 Children playing (Millennium Greens Project)

2000. Millennium Projects (6th series). "People and Places". Multicoloured.
2148 (2nd.) Type **1460** 75 70
2149 (1st) Millennium Bridge, Gateshead . . . . 95 1·00
2150 45p. Daisies (Mile End Park, London) . . . . . 1·50 1·60
2151 65p. African Hut and Thatched Cottage ("On the Meridian Line" Project) . . . . 2·25 2·40

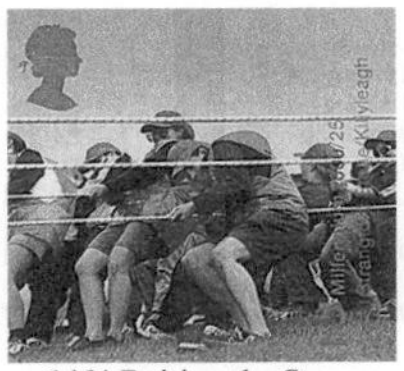

1464 Raising the Stone (Strangford Stone, Killyleagh)

2000. Millennium Projects (7th series). "Stone and Soil".
2152 **1464** (2nd.) blk, grey & silver 75 70
2153 – (1st) multicoloured . . 90 1·00
2154 – 45p. multicoloured . . 1·50 1·60
2155 – 65p. multicoloured . . 2·25 2·40
DESIGNS: No. 2153, Horse's Hooves (Trans Pennine Trail, Derbyshire); 2154 Cyclist (Kingdom of Fife Cycle Ways, Scotland); 2155, Bluebell Wood (Groundwork's "Changing Places" Project).

1468 Tree Roots ("Yews for the Millennium" Project)

2000. Millennium Projects (8th series). "Tree and Leaf". Multicoloured.
2156 (2nd.) Type **1468** 75 70
2157 (1st) Sunflower ("Eden" Project, St. Austell) . . . 90 1·00
2158 45p. Sycamore seeds (Millennium Seed Bank, Wakehurst Place, Surrey) 1·50 1·60
2159 65p. Forest, Doire Dach ("Forest for Scotland") 2·25 2·40

1472 Queen Elizabeth the Queen Mother

1472a Royal Family on Queen Mother's 99th Birthday (½-size illustration)

2000. Queen Elizabeth the Queen Mother's 100th Birthday. Multicoloured.
2160 27p. Type **1472** . . . . . . 2·50 2·50
MS2161 121×89 mm. **1427a** multicoloured . . . . 10·00 10·00

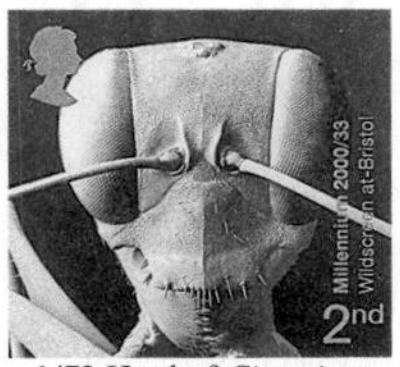

1473 Head of *Gigantiops destructor* (Ant) (Wildscreen at Bristol)

2000. Millennium Projects (9th series). "Mind and Matter". Multicoloured.
2162 (2nd.) Type **1473** 75 70
2163 (1st) Gathering water lilies on Broads (Norfolk and Norwich Project) . . . . 90 1·00
2164 45p. X-ray of hand holding computer mouse (Millennium Point, Birmingham) . . . . . . 1·50 1·60
2165 65p. Tartan wool holder (Scottish Cultural Resources Access Network) . . . . 2·25 2·40

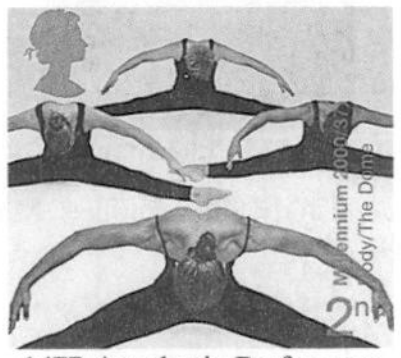

1477 Acrobatic Performers (Millennium Dome)

2000. Millennium Projects (10th series). "Body and Bone".
2166 **1477** (2nd.) black, blue & silver 75 70
2167 – (1st) multicoloured . . 90 1·00
2168 – 45p. multicoloured . . 1·50 1·60
2169 – 65p. multicoloured . . 2·25 2·40
DESIGNS: No. 2167, Football players (Hampden Park, Glasgow); 2168, Bather (Bath Spa Project); 2169, Hen's egg under magnification (Centre for Life, Newcastle).

1481 Virgin and Child Stained Glass Window, St. Edmundsbury Cathedral (Suffolk Cathedral Millennium Project)

2000. Millennium Projects (11th series). "Spirit and Faith". Multicoloured.
2170 (2nd.) Type **1481** 75 70
2171 (1st) Floodlit church of St. Peter and St. Paul, Overstowey (Church Floodlighting Trust) . . . 95 1·00
2172 45p. 12th-cent Latin Gradual (St. Patrick Centre, Downpatrick) . . 1·50 1·60
2173 65p. Chapter House ceiling, York Minster (York Millennium Mystery Plays) . . . . 2·25 2·40

1485 Church Bells (Ringing in the Millennium)

2000. Millennium Projects (12th series). "Sound and Vision". Multicoloured.
2174 (2nd.) Type **1485** 75 70
2175 (1st) Eye (Year of the Artist) . . . . 95 1·00
2176 45p. Top of harp (Canolfan Mileniwm, Cardiff) . . . 1·50 1·60
2177 65p. Silhouetted figure within latticework (TS2K Creative Enterprise Centres, London) . . . . 2·25 2·40

1489 "Flower" ("Nurture Children")

2001. New Millennium. Rights of the Child, Face Paintings. Multicoloured.
2178 (2nd.) Type **1489** 75 75
2179 (1st) "Tiger" ("Listen to Children") . . . . . . 1·00 1·10
2180 45p. "Owl" ("Teach Children") . . . . 1·60 1·75
2181 65p. "Butterfly" ("Ensure Children's Freedom") . . 2·40 2·50

1493 "Love"

2001. "Occasions" Greetings Stamps. Multicoloured.
2182 (1st) Type **1493** 90 90
2183 (1st) "THANKS" 90 90
2184 (1st) "abc" "New Baby" . . 90 90
2185 (1st) "WELCOME" 90 90
2186 (1st) "Cheers" 90 90
The silver-grey backgrounds are printed in Iriodin ink which gives a shiny effect.

1498 Dog and Owner on Bench

2001. Cats and Dogs. Self-adhesive.
2187 **1498** (1st) black, grey & silver . . . . 1·50 1·00
2188 – (1st) black, grey & silver . . . . 1·50 1·00
2189 – (1st) black, grey & silver . . . . 1·50 1·00
2190 – (1st) black, grey & silver . . . . 1·50 1·00
2191 – (1st) black, grey & silver . . . . 1·50 1·00
2192 – (1st) black, grey & silver . . . . 1·50 1·00
2193 – (1st) black, grey & silver . . . . 1·50 1·00
2194 – (1st) black, grey & silver . . . . 1·50 1·00
2195 – (1st) black, grey & silver . . . . 1·50 1·00
2196 – (1st) black, grey & silver . . . . 1·50 1·00
DESIGNS: No. 2188 Dog in bath; 2189, Boxer at dog show; 2190, Cat in handbag; 3192, Dog in car; 2193, Cat at window; 2194, Dog behind fence; 2195, Cat watching bird; 2196, Cat in washbasin.

1508 "RAIN"

2001. The Weather. Multicoloured.

2197	19p. Type **1508**	70	75
2198	27p. "FAIR"	85	90
2199	45p. "STORMY"	1·50	1·60
2200	65p. "VERY DRY"	2·40	2·50
MS2201	105 × 105 mm. Nos. 2197/2200	11·50	9·00

The violet on the 27p. and miniature sheet is printed in thermochromic ink, which changes from violet to blue when exposed to heat.

1512 *Vanguard* Class Submarine, 1992

2001. Centenary of Royal Navy Submarine Service. Multicoloured. (a) Ordinary gum.

2202	(2nd) Type **1512**	70	75
2203	(1st) *Swiftsure* Class Submarine, 1973	85	90
2204	45p. *Unity* Class Submarine, 1939	1·50	1·60
2205	65p. "Holland" Type Submarine, 1901 . .	2·40	2·50
MS2206	92 × 97 mm. (a) (1st) White Ensign; (b) (1st) Union Jack; (c) (1st) Jolly Roger flown by H.M.S. *Proteus* (submarine); (d) (1st) Flag of Chief of Defence Staff . . .	7·50	6·00

(b) Self-adhesive.

2207	(1st) *Swiftsure* Class Submarine, 1973	25·00	20·00
2208	(1st) White Ensign	8·50	7·50
2209	(1st) Jolly Roger Flown by H.M.S. *Proteus* (submarine)	8·50	7·50

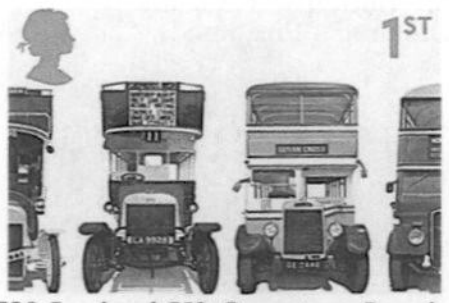

1520 Leyland X2 Open-top, London General B Type, Leyland Titan TD1 and AEC Regent 1

1521 AEC Regent 1, Daimler COG5, Utility Guy Arab Mk II and AEC Regent III RT Type

1522 AEC Regent III RT Type, Bristol KSW5G Open-top, AEC Routemaster and Bristol Lodekka FSF6G

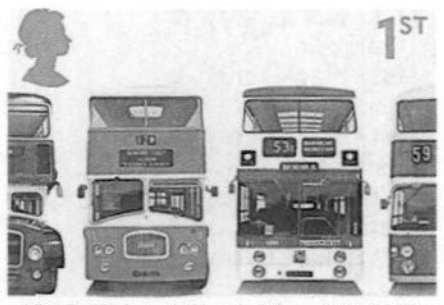

1523 Bristol Lodekka FSF6G, Leyland Titan PD3/4, Leyland Atlantean PDR1/1 and Daimler Fleetline CRG6LX-33

1524 Daimler Fleetline CRG6LX-33, MCW Metrobus DR102/43, Leyland Olympian ONLXB/1R and Dennis Trident

2001. 150th Anniv of First Double-decker Bus.

2210	**1520** (1st) multicoloured . .	1·10	1·10
2211	**1521** (1st) multicoloured . .	1·10	1·10
2212	**1522** (1st) multicoloured . .	1·10	1·10
2213	**1523** (1st) multicoloured . .	1·10	1·10
2214	**1524** (1st) multicoloured . .	1·10	1·10
MS2215	120 × 105 mm. Nos. 2210/14	8·25	8·25

In No. **MS**2215 the illustrations of the AEC Regent III RT Type and the Daimler Fleetline CRG6LX-33 appear twice.

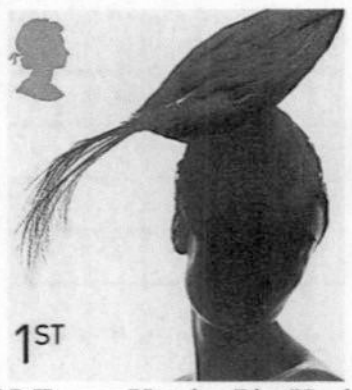

1525 Toque Hat by Pip Hackett

2001. Fashion Hats. Multicoloured.

2216	(1st) Type **1525**	85	90
2217	(E) Butterfly hat by Dai Rees	1·10	1·25
2218	45p. Top hat by Stephen Jones	1·50	1·60
2219	65p. Spiral hat by Philip Treacy	2·40	2·50

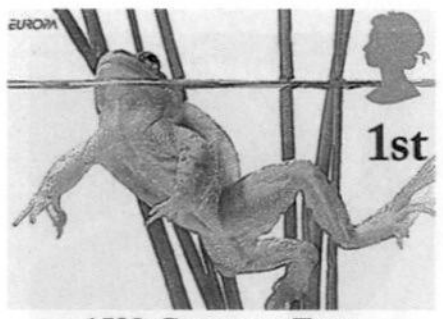

1529 Common Frog

2001. Europa. Pond Life. Multicoloured.

2220	(1st) Type **1529**	75	85
2221	(E) Great diving beetle . . .	95	1·00
2222	45p. Three-spined stickleback	1·25	1·40
2223	65p. Southern hawker dragonfly	2·00	2·10

The 1st and E values incorporate the "EUROPA" emblem.

1533 Policeman

2001. Punch and Judy Show Puppets. Multicoloured. (a) Ordinary Gum.

2224	(1st) Type **1533**	80	75
2225	(1st) Clown	80	75
2226	(1st) Mr. Punch	80	75
2227	(1st) Judy	80	75
2228	(1st) Beadle	80	75
2229	(1st) Crocodile	80	75

(b) Self-adhesive.

2230	(1st) Mr. Punch	7·50	7·50
2231	(1st) Judy	7·50	7·50

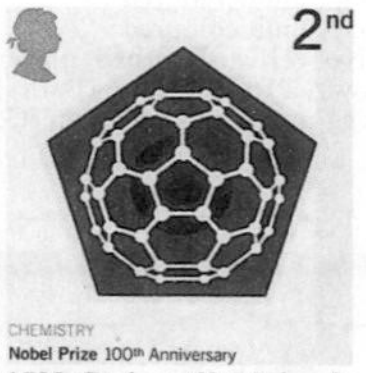

1539 Carbon 60 Molecule (Chemistry)

2001. Centenary of Nobel Prizes.

2232	**1539** (2nd) black, silver and grey	60	55
2233	– (1st) multicoloured . .	80	90
2234	– (E) black, silver and green	1·00	1·10
2235	– 40p. multicoloured . .	1·00	1·10
2236	– 45p. multicoloured . .	1·40	1·50
2237	– 65p. black and silver . .	2·10	2·25

DESIGNS: No. 2233, Globe (Economic Sciences); 2234, Embossed Dove (Peace); 2235, Crosses (Physiology or Medicine); 2236, Poem "The Addressing of Cats" by T. S. Eliot in Open Book (Literature); 2237, Hologram of Boron Molecule (Physics).

The grey on No. 2232 is printed in thermochromic ink which temporarily changes to pale grey when exposed to heat.

The centre of No. 2235 is coated with a eucalyptus scent.

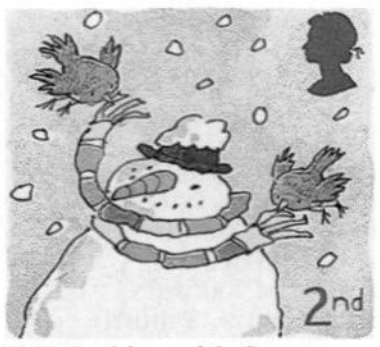

1545 Robins with Snowman

2001. Christmas. Robins. Self-adhesive. Multicoloured.

2238	(2nd) Type **1545**	75	70
2239	(1st) Robins on bird table	95	1·00
2240	(E) Robins skating on bird bath	1·00	1·10
2241	45p. Robins with Christmas pudding	1·40	1·50
2242	65p. Robins in paper chain nest	2·10	2·25

1550 "How the Whale got his Throat"

2002. Centenary of Publication of Rudyard Kipling's *Just So Stories.* Multicoloured. Self-adhesive.

2243	(1st) Type **1550**	95	85
2244	(1st) "How the Camel got his Hump"	95	85
2245	(1st) "How the Rhinoceros got his Skin"	95	85
2246	(1st) "How the Leopard got his Spots"	95	85
2247	(1st) "The Elephant's Child"	95	85
2248	(1st) "The Sing-Song of Old Man Kangaroo"	95	85
2249	(1st) "The Beginning of the Armadillos"	95	85
2250	(1st) "The Crab that played with the Sea"	95	85
2251	(1st) "The Cat that walked by Himself"	95	85
2252	(1st) "The Butterfly that stamped"	95	85

1560 Queen Elizabeth II, 1952 (Dorothy Wilding)

1566

2002. Golden Jubilee. Studio portraits of Queen Elizabeth II by photographers named. Multicoloured.

2253	(2nd) Type **1560**	55	55
2254	(1st) Queen Elizabeth II, 1968 (Cecil Beaton) . . .	80	80
2255	(E) Queen Elizabeth II, 1978 (Lord Snowdon)	1·00	1·00
2256	45p. Queen Elizabeth II, 1984 (Yousef Karsh) . . .	1·40	1·40
2257	65p. Queen Elizabeth II, 1996 (Tim Graham) . . .	2·10	2·00

2002. As T **154/5** (Wilding definitive of 1952–54), but with service indicator as T **1566**.

2258	**1566** (2nd) red	1·00	1·00
2259	– (1st) green	1·25	1·25

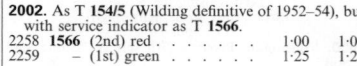

1567 Rabbits ("a new baby")

2002. "Occasions". Greetings Stamps. Mult.

2260	(1st) Type **1567**	80	90
2261	(1st) "LOVE"	80	90
2262	(1st) Aircraft sky-writing "hello"	80	90
2263	(1st) Bear pulling potted topiary tree (Moving Home)	80	90
2264	(1st) Flowers ("best wishes")	80	90

No. 2262 also comes self-adhesive.

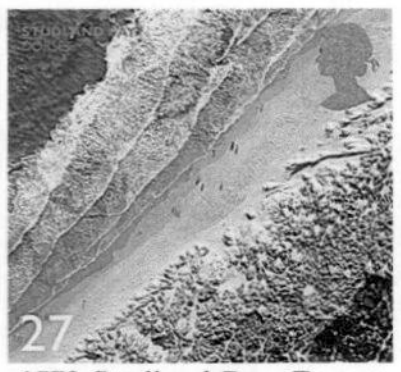

1572 Studland Bay, Dorset

2002. British Coastlines. Multicoloured.

2265	27p. Type **1572**	75	80
2266	27p. Luskentyre, South Harris	75	80
2267	27p. Cliffs, Dover, Kent . .	75	80
2268	27p. Padstow Harbour, Cornwall	75	80
2269	27p. Broadstairs, Kent . . .	75	80
2270	27p. St. Abbs Head, Scottish Borders	75	80
2271	27p. Dunster Beach, Somerset	75	80
2272	27p. Newquay Beach, Cornwall	75	80
2273	27p. Portrush, County Antrim	75	80
2274	27p. Sand-spit, Conwy . . .	75	80

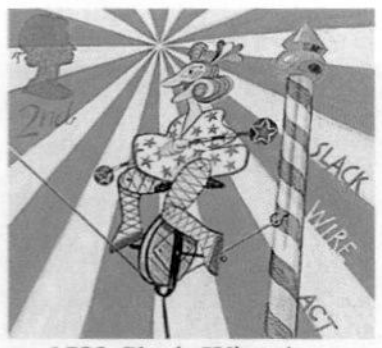

1582 Slack Wire Act

2002. Circus. Multicoloured.

2275	(2nd) Type **1582**	55	60
2276	(1st) Lion tamer	75	85
2277	(E) Trick tri-cyclists	1·00	1·10
2278	45p. Krazy kar	1·25	1·40
2279	65p. Equestrienne	1·90	2·00

1587 Queen Elizabeth the Queen Mother

2002. Queen Elizabeth the Queen Mother Commemoration. As Nos. 1507/10 with changed face values and showing both the Queen's head and frame in black.

2280	**1587** (1st) multicoloured . .	75	85
2281	(E) black and blue . .	1·00	1·10
2282	45p. multicoloured . .	1·25	1·40
2283	65p. black, stone and brown	1·90	2·00

1588 Airbus A340-600 (2002)

2002. 50th Anniv of Passenger Jet Aviation. Airliners. Multicoloured.

2284	(2nd) Type **1588**	55	55
2285	(1st) Concorde (1976) . . .	70	80
2286	(E) Trident (1964)	90	1·00
2287	45p. VC 10 (1964)	1·25	1·40
2288	65p. Comet (1952)	1·90	2·00
MS2289	120 × 105mm. Nos. 2284/8	5·00	5·50

No. 2285 also comes self-adhesive.

1593 Crowned Lion with Shield of St. George

1594 Top Left Quarter of English Flag, and Football

1595 Top Right Quarter of English Flag, and Football

1596 Bottom Left Quarter of English Flag, and Football

1597 Bottom Right Quarter of English Flag, and Football

2002. World Cup Football Championship, Japan and Korea (2002).

2291 **1593** (1st) blue, red and silver 1·50 1·25
MS2292 145 × 74 mm. No. 2291; **1594** (1st) multicoloured; **1595** (1st) multicoloured, **1596** (1st) multicoloured; **1597** (1st) multicoloured . . . . 3·00 4·00

(b) Self-adhesive.

2293 **1594** (1st) multicoloured . . 1·50 1·50
2294 **1595** (1st) multicoloured . . 1·50 1·50

2002. Self-adhesive.

2295 **914** (1st) gold 45 50
2296 **1093a** (E) blue 60 65
2297 **367a** 42p. grey 65 70
2298 68p. brown . . . . . 1·10 1·25

No. 2295 was initially sold for 27p.

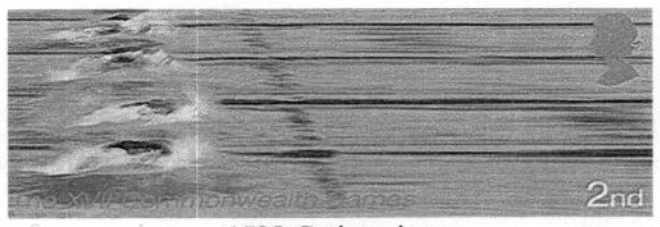

1598 Swimming

2002. 17th Commonwealth Games, Manchester. Multicoloured.

2299 (2nd) Type **1598** 50 55
2300 (1st) Running 70 80
2301 (E) Cycling . . . . 90 1·00
2302 47p. Long jumping . . . . 1·25 1·40
2303 68p. Wheelchair racing . . . 1·90 2·00

1603 Tinkerbell

2002. 150th Anniv of Great Ormond Street Children's Hospital. *Peter Pan* by Sir James Barrie. Multicoloured.

2304 (2nd) Type **1063** 50 55
2305 (1st) Wendy, John and Michael Darling in front of Big Ben 70 80
2306 (E) Crocodile and alarm clock . . . . 90 1·00
2307 47p. Captain Hook . . . . 1·25 1·40
2308 68p. Peter Pan . . . . . . 1·90 2·00

1608 Millennium Bridge, 2001

2002. Bridges of London. Multicoloured.

2309 (2nd) Type **1608** 50 55
2310 (1st) Tower Bridge, 1894 . . 70 80
2311 (E) Westminster Bridge, 1864 . . . . 90 1·00
2312 47p. "Blackfriars Bridge, c 1800" (William Marlow) 1·25 1·40
2313 68p. "London Bridge, c 1670" (Wenceslaus Hollar) . . . . 1·90 2·00

No. 2310 also comes self-adhesive.

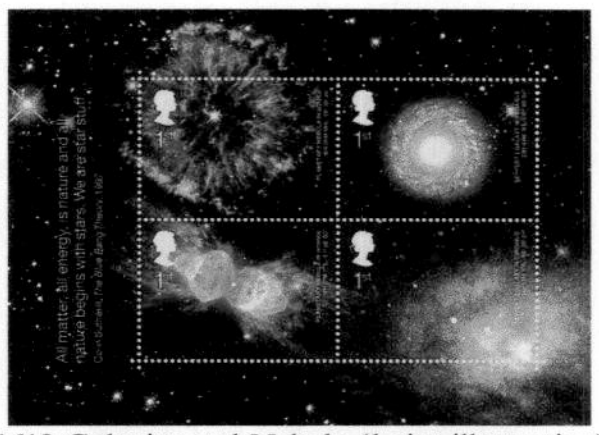

1613 Galaxies and Nebula (½-size illustration)

2002. Astronomy. Sheet 120 × 89 mm. Multicoloured.

MS2315 **1613** (1st) Planetary nebula in Aquila; (1st) Seyfert 2 galaxy in Pegasus; (1st) Planetary nebula in Norma; (1st) Seyfert 2 galaxy in Circinus . . . . 2·75 3·00

1614 Green Pillar Box, 1857

1619 Blue Spruce Star

2002. 150th Anniv of the First Pillar Box.

2316 (2nd) Type **1614** 50 55
2317 (1st) Horizontal Aperture Box, 1874 . . . . 70 80
2318 (E) Air Mail Box, 1934 . . 90 1·00
2319 47p. Double Aperture Box, 1939 . . . . 1·25 1·40
2320 68p. Modern Style Box, 1980 . . . . 1·90 2·00

2002. Christmas. Self-adhesive.

2321 (2nd) Type **1619** 50 55
2322 (1st) Holly 70 80
2323 (E) Ivy . . . . 90 1·00
2324 47p. Mistletoe . . . . . . 1·25 1·40
2325 68p. Pine cone . . . . . . 1·90 2·00

2002. 50th Anniv of Wilding Definitives (1st issue). Sheet 124 × 70 mm, containing designs as T **154/5** and **157/60** (1952–54 issue), but with values in decimal currency as T **1348** or with service indicator as T **1566**, printed on cream.

MS2326 1p. red; 2p. blue; 5p. brown; (2nd) red; (1st) green; 33p. brown; 37p. mauve; 47p. brown; 50p. green . . . . 6·25 6·50

See also No. **MS**2367.

1624 Barn Owl landing

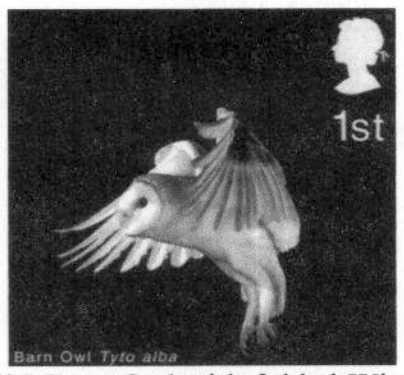

1625 Barn Owl with folded Wings and Legs down

1626 Barn Owl with extended Wings and Legs down

1627 Barn Owl in Flight with Wings lowered

1628 Barn Owl in Flight with Wings raised

1629 Kestrel with Wings folded

1630 Kestrel with Wings fully extended upwards

1631 Kestrel with Wings horizontal

1632 Kestrel with Wings partly extended downwards

1633 Kestrel with Wings fully extended downwards

2003. Birds of Prey.

2327 **1624** (1st) multicoloured . . 70 80
2328 **1625** (1st) multicoloured . . 70 80
2329 **1626** (1st) multicoloured . . 70 80
2330 **1627** (1st) multicoloured . . 70 80
2331 **1628** (1st) multicoloured . . 70 80
2332 **1629** (1st) multicoloured . . 70 80
2333 **1630** (1st) multicoloured . . 70 80
2334 **1631** (1st) multicoloured . . 70 80
2335 **1632** (1st) multicoloured . . 70 80
2336 **1633** (1st) multicoloured . . 70 80

1634 "Gold star, See me, Playtime"

2003. "Occasions" Greetings Stamps.

2337 **1634** (1st) yellow and blue 70 80
2338 – (1st) red and blue . . . 70 80
2339 – (1st) purple and green 70 80
2340 – (1st) green and red . . 70 80
2341 – (1st) blue and yellow 70 80
2342 – (1st) blue and purple 70 80

DESIGNS: No. 2338, "I U, XXXX, S.W.A.L.K."; 2239, "Angel, Poppet, Little terror"; 2340, "Yes, No, Maybe"; 2341, "Oops!, Sorry, Will try harder"; 2342, "I did it!, You did it!, We did it!".

1640 Completing the Genome Jigsaw

2003. 50th Anniv of Discovery of DNA. Multicoloured.

2343 (2nd) Type **1640** 50 55
2344 (1st) Ape with Moustache and Scientist 70 80
2345 (E) DNA Snakes and Ladders . . . . 90 1·00
2346 47p. "Animal Scientists" . . 1·25 1·40
2347 68p. Genome Crystal Ball 1·90 2·00

1645 Strawberry

2003. Fruit and Vegetables. Self-adhesive.

2348 (1st) Type **1645** 70 80
2349 (1st) Potato 70 80
2350 (1st) Apple 70 80
2351 (1st) Red pepper 70 80
2352 (1st) Pear 70 80
2353 (1st) Orange 70 80
2354 (1st) Tomato 70 80
2355 (1st) Lemon 70 80
2356 (1st) Cabbage 70 80
2357 (1st) Aubergine 70 80

Nos. 2348/57 are accompanied by a similar-sized pane of self-adhesive labels showing ears, eyes, mouths, hats etc which are intended for the adornment of fruit and vegetables depicted.

1655

2003. Overseas Stamps. Self-adhesive.

2358 **1655** (Europe) blue and red 80 85
2359 (Worldwide) red and blue . . . . 1·60 1·75
2359a (Worldwide postcard) black, red and blue 80 85

Nos. 2358/9 were intended to pay postage on mail up to 40 grams to either Europe (52p.) or foreign destinations outside Europe (£1.12). No. 2359a was intended to pay postcard rate to foreign destination (43p.)

1656 Amy Johnson (pilot) and Bi-plane

2003. Extreme Endeavours. (British Explorers).

2360 (2nd) Type **1656** 45 50
2361 (1st) Members of 1953 British Team on Everest 70 75
2362 (E) Freya Stark (traveller and writer) and desert . . 90 95
2363 42p. Ernest Shackleton (Antarctic explorer) and wreck of *Endurance* . . . 1·00 1·10
2364 47p. Francis Chichester (yachtsman) and *Gipsy Moth IV* . . . . 1·10 1·20
2365 68p. Robert Falcon Scott (Antarctic explorer) and Norwegian Expedition at the Pole . . . . 1·60 1·80

No. 2361 also comes self-adhesive.

2003. 50th Anniv of Wilding Definitives (2nd issue). Sheet 124 × 70 mm, containing designs as Nos. 519, 575, 617b and 585 (1952–54 issue), but with values in decimal currency as T **1348** or with service indicator as T **1566**, printed on cream.

MS2367 4p. lilac; 8p. blue; (1st) purple; 20p. green; 28p. green; 34p. purple; (1st) chestnut; 42p. blue; 68p. blue . . . . 9·50 9·75

1662 Guardsmen in Coronation Procession

2003. 50th Anniv of Coronation.

2368	**1662** (1st) multicoloured	45	50
2369	– (1st) black and gold	45	50
2370	– (1st) multicoloured	45	50
2371	– (1st) black and gold	45	50
2372	– (1st) multicoloured	45	50
2373	– (1st) black and gold	45	50
2374	– (1st) multicoloured	45	50
2375	– (1st) black and gold	45	50
2376	– (1st) multicoloured	45	50
2377	– (1st) black and gold	45	50

DESIGNS: No. 2369, East End children reading Coronation party poster; 2670, Queen Elizabeth II in Coronation Chair with Bishops of Durham and Bath & Wells; 2671, Children in Plymouth working on Royal Montage; 2672, Queen Elizabeth II in Coronation Robes (photograph by Cecil Beaton); 2673, Childrens Race at East End Street Party; 2674, Coronation Coach passing through Marble Arch; 2675, Children in Fancy Dress; 2676, Coronation Coach outside Buckingham Palace; 2677, Children eating at London street party.

No. 2372 does not show a silhouette of the Queens head in gold as do the other nine designs.

2003. 50th Anniv of Coronation. Designs as Nos. 585, 534 (Wilding definitive of 1952) and **163** (Coronation commemorative of 1953), but with values in decimal currency as T **1348**.

2378	47p. brown	2·50	2·50
2379	68p. blue	2·50	2·50
2380	£1 green	45·00	45·00

1672 Prince William in September 2001 (Brendan Beirne)

2003. 21st Birthday of Prince William of Wales.

2381	**1672** 28p. multicoloured	45	50
2382	– (E) mauve, black and green	60	65
2383	– 47p. multicoloured	75	80
2384	– 68p. deep green, black and green	1·10	1·20

DESIGNS: No. 2382, Prince William in September 2000 (Tim Graham); 2383, Prince William in September 2001 (Camera Press); 2384, Prince William in September 2001 (Tim Graham).

1676 Loch Assynt, Sutherland

2003. A British Journey: Scotland. Multicoloured.

2385	(2nd) Type **1676**	30	35
2386	(1st) Ben More, Isle of Mull	45	50
2387	(E) Rothiemurchus, Cairngorms	60	65
2388	42p. Dalveen Pass, Lowther Hills	65	70
2389	47p. Glenfinnan Viaduct, Lochaber	75	80
2390	68p. Papa Little, Shetland Islands	1·10	1·20

No. 2386 also comes self-adhesive.

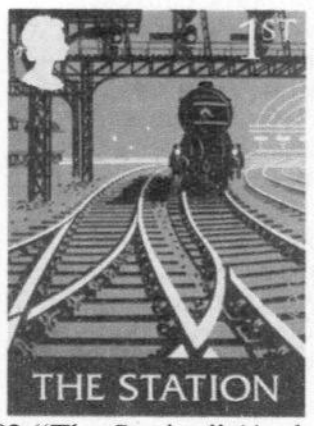

1682 "The Station" (Andrew Davidson)

2003. British Pub Signs. Multicoloured.

2392	(1st) Type **1682**	45	50
2393	(E) "Black Swan" (Stanley Chew)	60	65
2394	42p. "The Cross Keys" (George Mackenney)	65	70
2395	47p. "The Mayflower" (Ralph Ellis)	75	80
2396	68p. "The Barley Sheaf" (Joy Cooper)	1·10	1·20

1687 Meccano Constructor Biplane, c. 1931

2003. Classic Transport Toys. Multicoloured.

2397	(1st) Type **1687**	45	50
2398	(E) Wells-Brimtoy Clockwork Double-decker Omnibus, c. 1938	60	65
2399	42p. Hornby M1 Clockwork Locomotive and Tender, c. 1948	65	70
2400	47p. Dinky Toys Ford Zephyr, c. 1956	75	80
2401	68p. Mettoy Friction Drive Space Ship Eagle, c. 1960	1·10	1·20
MS2402	115 × 105 mm. Nos. 2397/401	3·50	3·75

No. 2397 also comes self-adhesive.

1692 Coffin of Denytenamun, Egyptian, c. 900BC

2003. 250th Anniv of the British Museum. Multicoloured.

2404	(2nd) Type **1692**	30	35
2405	(1st) Alexander the Great, Greek, c. 200BC	45	50
2406	(E) Sutton Hoo Helmet, Anglo-Saxon, c. AD600	60	65
2407	42p. Sculpture of Parvati, South Indian, c. AD1550	65	70
2408	47p. Mask of Xiuhtecuhtli, Mixtec-Aztec, c. AD1500	75	80
2409	68p. Hoa Hakananai'a, Easter Island, c. AD1000	1·10	1·20

1698 Ice Spiral

2003. Christmas. Ice Sculptures by Andy Goldsworthy. Multicoloured.

2410	(2nd) Type **1698**	30	35
2411	(1st) Icicle Star	45	50
2412	(E) Wall of Ice Blocks	60	65
2413	53p. Ice Ball	80	85
2414	68p. Ice Hole	1·10	1·20
2415	£1.12 Snow Pyramids	1·60	1·70

1704 (½-size illustration)

2003. England's Victory in Rugby World Cup Championship, Australia. Sheet 115 × 85 mm. Multicoloured.

MS2416	**1704** (1st) England flags and fans; (1st) England team standing in circle before match; 68p. World Cup trophy; 68p. Victorious England players after match	4·50	4·50

1705 Dolgoch, Rheilffordd Talyllyn Railway, Gwynedd

2004. Classic Locomotives. Multicoloured.

2417	20p. Type **1705**	30	35
2418	28p. CR Class 439, Bo'ness and Kinneil Railway, West Lothian	45	50
2419	(E) GCR Class 8K, Leicestershire	60	65
2420	42p. GWR Manor Class *Bradley Manor*, Severn Valley Railway, Worcestershire	65	70
2421	47p. SR West Country class *Blackmoor Vale*, Bluebell Railway, East Sussex	75	80
2422	68p. (1710 BR Standard class, Keighley & Worth Valley Railway, Yorkshire)	1·10	1·20
MS2423	190 × 67 mm. Nos. 2417/22	3·75	4·25

1711 Postman

2004. Occasions.

2424	**1711** (1st) mauve and black	45	50
2425	– (1st) magenta and black	45	50
2426	– (1st) lemon and black	45	50
2427	– (1st) green and black	45	50
2428	– (1st) blue and black	45	50

DESIGNS: No. 2425, Face; 2426, Duck; 2427, Baby; 2428, Aircraft.

1716 Map showing Middle Earth

2004. 50th Anniv of Publication of *The Fellowship of the Ring* and *The Two Towers* by J. R. R. Tolkien. Multicoloured.

2429	(1st) Type **1716**	45	50
2430	(1st) Forest of Lothlorien in Spring	45	50
2431	(1st) Dust-jacket for *The Fellowship of the Ring*	45	50
2432	(1st) Rivendell	45	50
2433	(1st) The Hall at Bag End	45	50
2434	(1st) Orthanc	45	50
2435	(1st) Doors of Durin	45	50
2436	(1st) Barad-dur	45	50
2437	(1st) Minas Tirth	45	50
2438	(1st) Fangorn Forest	45	50

1726 Ely Island, Lower Lough Erne

2004. A British Journey: Northern Ireland. Multicoloured.

2439	(2nd) Type **1726**	30	35
2440	(1st) Giant's Causeway, Antrim Coast	45	50
2441	(E) Slemish, Antrim Mountains	60	65
2442	42p. Banns Road, Mourne Mountains	65	70
2443	47p. Glenelly Valley, Sperrins	75	80
2444	68p. Islandmore, Strangford Lough	1·10	1·20

No. 2440 also comes self-adhesive.

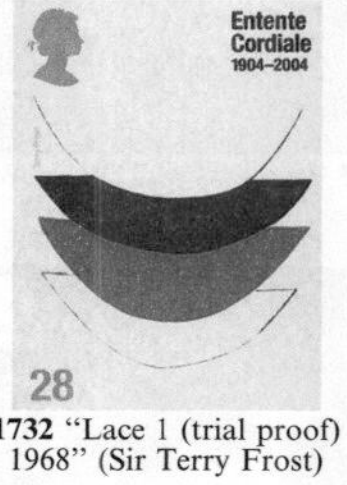

1732 "Lace 1 (trial proof) 1968" (Sir Terry Frost)

2004. Centenary of the Entente Cordiale. Contemporary Paintings.

2446	**1732** 28p. grey, black and red	55	60
2447	– 57p. multicoloured	90	95

DESIGN: No. 1733, "Coccinelle" (Sonia Delaunay)

Stamps in similar designs were issued by France.

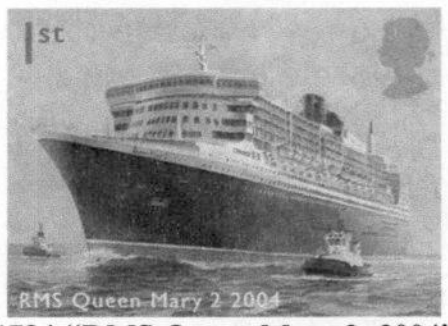

1734 "RMS Queen Mary 2, 2004" (Edward D. Walker)

2004. Ocean Liners. Multicoloured.

2448	(1st) Type **1734**	45	50
2449	(E) "SS Canberra 1961" (David Cobb)	60	65
2450	42p. "RMS Queen Mary 1936" (Charles Pears)	65	70
2451	47p. "RMS Mauretania, 1907" (Thomas Henry)	75	80
2452	57p. "SS City of New York, 1888" (Raphael Monleaon y Torres)	90	95
2453	68p. "PS Great Western, 1838" (Joseph Walter)	1·10	1·20
MS2454	114 × 104 mm. Nos. 2448/53	4·50	4·75

No.2448 also comes self-adhesive.

Nos. 2448/55 commemorate the introduction to service of the *Queen Mary 2*.

1740 Dianthus Allwoodii Group

2004. Bicentenary of the Royal Horticultural Society (1st issue). Multicoloured.

2456	(2nd) Type **1740**	30	35
2457	(1st) Dahlia "Garden Princess"	45	50
2458	(E) Clematis "Arabella"	60	65
2459	42p. Miltonia "French Lake"	65	70
2460	47p. Lilium "Lemon Pixie"	75	80
2461	68p. Delphinium "Clifford Sky"	1·10	1·20
MS2462	115 × 105 mm. Nos. 2456/61	4·50	4·75

2004. Bicentenary of the Royal Horticultural Society (2nd issue). Designs as Nos. 1955, 1958 and 1962 (1997 Greeting Stamps 19th-century Flower Paintings). Multicoloured.

2463	(1st) Type **1280**	45	50
2464	(1st) "Tulipa" (Ehret)	45	50
2465	(1st) "Iris latifolia" (Ehret)	45	50

REGIONAL ISSUES

I. CHANNEL ISLANDS.

Islands in the English Channel off N.W. coast of France. Occupied by German forces from June 1940 to May 1945, when separate issues for both islands were made.

C **1** Gathering Vraic (seaweed)

1948. 3rd Anniversary of Liberation.

C1	C **1** 1d. red	25	30
C2	– 2½d. blue	25	30

DESIGN: 2½d. Islanders gathering vraic.

II. GUERNSEY.

2

3

1958.

6	**2** 2½d. red	35	40
7p	**3** 3d. lilac	15	20
9	4d. blue	10	20
10	4d. sepia	10	15
11	4d. red	25	25
12	5d. blue	20	30

For War Occupation issues and issues of independent postal administration from 1967 see **GUERNSEY**.

III. ISLE OF MAN.

1

2

3

1958.

1	1	2½d. red	40	1·25
2	2	3d. lilac	20	20
3p		4d. blue	20	30
5		4d. sepia	25	40
6		4d. red	45	75
7		5d. blue	45	75

1971. Decimal Currency.

8	3	2½p. red	20	15
9		3p. blue	20	15
10		5p. violet	40	60
11		7½p. brown	40	75

For issues of independent postal administration from 1973 see **ISLE OF MAN**.

IV. JERSEY.

8

9

1958.

9	8	2½d. red	20	45
10p	9	3d. lilac	15	15
11p		4d. blue	15	25
12		4d. sepia	15	25
13		4d. red	15	25
14		5d. blue	15	50

For War Occupation issues and issues of independent postal administration from 1969 see **JERSEY**.

V. ENGLAND

EN **1** Three Lions

2001.

EN1	EN **1**	(2nd) green and silver	30	35
EN2	–	(1st) brown and silver	45	50
EN3	–	(E) green and silver	60	65
EN4	–	65p. lilac and silver	1·60	1·75
EN5		68p. lilac and silver	1·10	1·25

DESIGNS: No. EN2, Crowned Lion with Shield of St. George; EN3, Oak Tree; EN4/5, Tudor Rose.

Nos EN1/3 were initially sold at 19p., 27p. and 36p., the latter representing the basic European airmail rate.

2003. As Nos. EN1/3 and EN5 but with white borders.

EN6	EN **1**	(2nd) green and silver	30	35
EN7	–	(1st) brown and silver	45	50
EN8	–	(E) green and silver	60	65
EN9	–	68p. lilac and silver	1·10	1·20

VI. NORTHERN IRELAND.

N 1

N 2

N 3

N 4

1958.

NI 1	N **1**	3d. lilac	15	10
NI 2		4d. blue	15	15
NI 8		4d. sepia	15	15
NI 9		4d. red	20	20
NI10		5d. blue	20	20
NI 3	N **2**	6d. purple	20	25
NI 4		9d. green	30	70
NI 5	N **3**	1s.3d. green	30	70
NI 6		1s.6d. blue	30	70

1971.

NI12	N **4**	2½p. mauve	70	45
NI14		3p. blue	20	15
NI15		3½p. grey	20	25
NI17		4½p. blue	30	25
NI18		5p. violet	1·25	1·25
NI19		5½p. violet	20	20
NI21		6½p. blue	20	20
NI22		7p. brown	35	25
NI23		7½p. brown	1·75	1·75
NI24		8p. red	35	40
NI25		8½p. green	35	40
NI26		9p. violet	40	40
NI27		10p. brown	40	50
NI29		10½p. blue	40	50
NI30		11p. red	50	50
NI34		11½p. drab	85	85
NI31		12p. green	50	50
NI36		12½p. green	60	60
NI37Ea		13p. brown	1·00	30
NI32		13½p. brown	60	70
NI38		14p. blue	75	75
NI33		15p. blue	60	70
NI41		15½p. violet	80	80
NI42		16p. brown	1·00	1·00
NI43		17p. blue	90	95
NI45		18p. violet	1·00	1·00
NI46		18p. grey	1·00	90
NI47		18p. green	1·00	95
NI49		19p. red	1·00	1·00
NI69		19p. bistre	90	80
NI50		19½p. grey	1·90	1·90
NI51		20p. black	1·00	80
NI79		20p. green	75	70
NI52		20½p. blue	3·00	3·50
NI53		22p. blue	1·10	1·10
NI54		22p. green	1·10	1·10
NI55		22p. red	1·25	90
NI56		23p. green	1·25	1·10
NI57		24p. red	1·50	90
NI58		24p. brown	1·10	90
NI72		25p. red	75	75
NI60		26p. red	1·25	1·25
NI61		26p. drab	1·50	1·25
NI81		26p. brown	1·25	1·00
NI62		28p. blue	1·40	1·25
NI63		28p. grey	1·60	1·40
NI74		30p. grey	1·50	1·40
NI64		31p. purple	1·60	1·60
NI65		32p. blue	1·75	1·75
NI66		34p. grey	1·90	1·90
NI67		37p. red	1·90	1·90
NI82		37p. mauve	1·50	1·25
NI83		38p. blue	2·10	2·10
NI68		39p. mauve	1·90	1·90
NI84		40p. blue	1·10	1·100
NI76		41p. brown	2·25	2·25
NI85		63p. green	2·40	2·25
NI86		64p. green	2·25	2·10
NI87		65p. blue	2·00	2·00

2000. As Type N **4** but with "1st" face value.

NI88	(1st) bright red	1·90	1·90

N **6** Basalt Columns, Giant's Causeway

2001.

NI89	N **6**	(2nd) multicoloured	30	35
NI90	–	(1st) black, blue & yellow	45	50
NI91	–	(E) black, blue & orange	60	70
NI92	–	65p. black, mauve & yell	1·60	1·75
NI93		68p. black, mauve and yellow	1·10	1·25

DESIGNS: NI90, Aerial view of patchwork fields; NI91, Linen pattern; NI92/3, Vase pattern from Belleck.

Nos. NI89, NI90 and NI91 were initially sold at 19p., 27p. and 36p., the latter representing the basic European airmail rate.

2003. As Nos. NI89/91 and NI93 but with white borders.

NI94	N **6**	(2nd) multicoloured	30	35
NI95	–	(1st) black, blue and yellow	45	50
NI96	–	(E) black and blue	60	65
NI97	–	68p. black, mauve and yellow	1·10	1·20

VII. SCOTLAND.

S 1

S 2

S 3

S 4

1958.

S 7	S **1**	3d. lilac	10	15
S 8		4d. blue	10	15
S 9		4d. sepia	10	10
S10		4d. red	10	10
S11		5d. blue	20	10
S 3	S **2**	6d. purple	20	15
S 4		9d. green	35	40
S 5	S **3**	1s.3d. green	40	40
S 6		1s.6d. blue	45	50

1971. Decimal Currency.

S14	S **4**	2½p. mauve	20	20
S16		3p. blue	15	15
S17		3½p. grey	20	25
S19		4½p. blue	30	25
S20		5p. violet	85	1·00
S21		5½p. violet	20	20
S23		6½p. blue	20	20
S24		7p. brown	30	30
S25		7½p. brown	95	1·25
S26		8p. red	45	40
S27		8½p. green	40	40
S28		9p. violet	40	40
S30		10p. brown	40	50
S31		10½p. blue	45	50
S32		11p. red	50	50
S36		11½p. drab	80	80
S33		12p. green	55	50
S38		12½p. green	60	70
S39		13p. brown	75	75
S34		13½p. brown	70	80
S54		14p. blue	60	70
S35		15p. blue	60	70
S41		15½p. violet	80	80
S42		16p. drab	80	85
S58		17p. blue	1·00	1·10
S44		18p. violet	80	80
S59		18p. grey	1·10	85
S60		18p. green	1·25	90
S62		19p. red	70	70
S81		19p. bistre	80	70
S45		19½p. grey	1·50	1·50
S64		20p. black	95	95
S90		20p. green	60	60
S46		20½p. blue	3·75	3·75
S47		22p. blue	1·10	1·10
S65		22p. green	1·40	1·50
S66		22p. red	1·25	90
S67		23p. green	1·25	1·10
S69		24p. red	1·50	1·00
S70		24p. brown	1·40	1·25
S84		25p. red	1·25	1·00
S49		26p. red	1·25	1·25
S73		26p. drab	1·25	1·25
S91		26p. brown	1·00	1·00
S74		28p. blue	1·25	1·25
S75		28p. grey	1·25	1·25
S86		30p. grey	1·50	1·25
S76		31p. purple	1·50	1·40
S77		32p. blue	1·75	1·60
S78		34p. grey	1·90	1·90
S79		37p. red	1·90	1·90
S92		37p. mauve	1·25	90
S80		39p. mauve	2·00	1·90
S88		41p. brown	1·90	1·90
S93		63p. green	2·25	2·00

S **5** Scottish Flag

1999.

S94	S **5**	(2nd) blue, deep blue and silver	30	35
S95	–	(1st) multicoloured	40	45
S96	–	(E) lilac, deep lilac and silver	60	70
S97	–	64p. multicoloured	3·00	2·25
S98		65p. multicoloured	1·60	1·75
S99		68p. multicoloured	1·10	1·25

DESIGNS: No. S95, Scottish Lion; S96, Thistle; S97/9, Tartan.

Nos. S94, S95 and S96 were initially sold at 19p., 26p. and 30p., the latter representing the basic European airmail rate.

2000. As Type S **4** but with "1st" face value.

S108	(1st) bright red	2·00	2·00

2003. As Nos. S94/6 and S99 but with white borders.

S109	S **5**	(2nd) blue, deep blue and silver	30	35
S110	–	(1st) multicoloured	45	50
S111	–	(E) lilac, deep lilac and silver	60	65
S112	–	68p. multicoloured	1·10	1·20

VIII. WALES.

W 1

W 2

W 3

W 4

1958.

W 1	W **1**	3d. lilac	15	15
W 8		4d. blue	10	15
W 9		4d. sepia	15	15
W10		4d. red	15	15
W11		5d. blue	15	15
W 3	W **2**	6d. purple	35	30
W 4		9d. green	40	35
W 5	W **3**	1s.3d. green	40	40
W 6		1s.6d. blue	50	40

1971. Decimal Currency.

W13	W **4**	2½p. mauve	20	20
W14		3p. blue	25	20
W16		3½p. grey	20	30
W18		4½p. blue	30	30
W19		5p. violet	1·00	1·10
W20		5½p. violet	25	30
W22		6½p. blue	20	20
W23		7p. brown	25	25
W24		7½p. brown	90	1·25
W25		8p. red	30	35
W26		8½p. green	30	35
W27		9p. violet	40	40
W29		10p. brown	40	40
W30		10½p. blue	40	45
W31		11p. red	40	45
W35		11½p. drab	90	80
W32		12p. green	40	50
W37		12½p. green	70	70
W38		13p. brown	60	60
W33		13½p. brown	60	70
W40		14p. blue	70	70
W34		15p. blue	60	70
W42		15½p. violet	75	75
W43		16p. drab	1·50	1·60
W44		17p. blue	70	80
W46		18p. violet	1·00	95
W47		18p. grey	95	90
W48		18p. green	75	75
W50		19p. red	1·00	80
W70		19p. bistre	80	70
W51		19½p. grey	1·50	1·50
W52		20p. black	90	90
W72		20p. green	1·25	1·40
W53		20½p. blue	3·25	3·25
W54		22p. blue	1·10	1·10
W55		22p. green	95	1·10
W56		22p. red	1·00	1·10
W57		23p. green	1·00	1·25
W58		24p. red	95	1·10
W59		24p. brown	75	75
W73		25p. red	1·25	1·00
W61		26p. red	1·10	1·10
W62		26p. drab	1·40	1·40
W74		26p. brown	1·60	1·50
W63		28p. blue	1·25	1·25
W64		28p. grey	1·50	1·40
W75		30p. grey	1·10	1·25
W65		31p. purple	1·40	1·40
W66		32p. blue	1·60	1·40
W67		34p. grey	1·60	1·60
W68		37p. red	1·90	1·90
W76		37p. mauve	2·40	2·40
W69		39p. mauve	2·00	2·00
W77		41p. brown	1·75	1·90
W78		63p. green	3·75	3·75

W **5** Without "p"

1997.

W79	W **5**	20p. green	80	80
W80		26p. brown	1·10	1·00
W81		37p. mauve	1·75	1·75
W82		63p. green	2·50	2·50

W **6** Leek

1999.

W83	W **6**	(2nd) brown, orange and black	30	35
W84	–	(1st) multicoloured	40	45
W85	–	(E) multicoloured	60	70
W86	–	64p. multicoloured	2·75	2·40
W87		65p. multicoloured	1·60	1·75
W88		68p. multicoloured	1·10	1·25

DESIGNS: No. W84, Welsh Dragon; W85, Daffodil; W86/8, Prince of Wales Feathers.

Nos. W83, W84 and W85 were initially sold at 19p., 26p. and 30p., the latter representing the basic European airmail rate.

2000. As Type W **5** but with "1af/st" face value.

W97	(1st) bright red	1·75	1·75

2003. As Nos. W83, W84/5 and W88, but with white borders.

W 98	W **6**	(2nd) orange, brown and black	30	35
W 99	–	(1st) multicoloured	45	50
W100	–	(E) blue, deep blue and black	60	65
W101	–	68p. multicoloured	1·10	1·20

OFFICIAL STAMPS
(for Government Departments)

ADMIRALTY

Overprinted **ADMIRALTY OFFICIAL**.

1903. Stamps of King Edward VII.

O101	**83**	½d. turquoise	15·00	12·00
O102	–	1d. red	10·00	6·00
O103	–	1½d. purple and green	£110	70·00
O104	–	2d. green and red	£185	85·00
O105	**83**	2½d. blue	£200	70·00
O106	–	3d. purple on yellow	£185	70·00

ARMY
Overprinted **ARMY OFFICIAL**.

1896. Stamps of Queen Victoria.

O41	**71**	½d. red	3·50	1·50
O42		½d. green	3·50	6·00
O43	**57**	1d. lilac	3·50	2·50
O44	**74**	2½d. purple on blue	15·00	8·00
O45	**79**	6d. purple on red	50·00	30·00

1902. Stamps of King Edward VII.

O48	**83**	½d. turquoise	5·00	2·00
O49		1d. red	5·00	2·00
O50		6d. purple	£120	50·00

BOARD OF EDUCATION
Overprinted **BOARD OF EDUCATION**.

1902. Stamps of Queen Victoria.

O81	**78**	5d. purple on blue	£1000	£225
O82	**82**	1s. green and red	£3000	£1800

1902. Stamps of King Edward VII.

O83	**83**	½d. turquoise	£100	35·00
O84		1d. red	£100	35·00
O85		2½d. blue	£1500	£110
O86	–	5d. purple and blue	£6000	£2000
O87	–	1s. green and red	£60000	

GOVERNMENT PARCELS
Overprinted **GOVT. PARCELS**.

1883. Stamps of Queen Victoria.

O61	**62**	1½d. purple	£200	45·00
O62	–	6d. green (No. 194)	£1200	£400
O63	–	9d. green (No. 195)	£1000	£400
O64	**25**	1s. brown (No. 163)	£850	£125

1887. Stamps of Queen Victoria.

O69	**57**	1d. lilac	50·00	10·00
O65	**72**	1½d. purple and green	50·00	5·00
O70	**73**	2d. green and red	£100	15·00
O71	**77**	4½d. green and red	£160	£125
O66	**79**	6d. purple on red	£100	18·00
O67	**80**	9d. purple and blue	£150	25·00
O68	**82**	1s. green	£250	£100
O72		1s. green and red	£250	90·00

1902. Stamps of King Edward VII.

O74	**83**	1d. red	30·00	12·00
O75	–	2d. green and red	90·00	22·00
O76	**83**	6d. purple	£160	25·00
O77	–	9d. purple and blue	£350	75·00
O78	–	1s. green and red	£550	£125

INLAND REVENUE
Overprinted **I.R. OFFICIAL**.

1882. Stamps of Queen Victoria.

O 1	**52**	½d. green	60·00	20·00
O 5		½d. blue	60·00	22·00
O 3	**57**	1d. lilac	4·00	2·00
O 6	–	2½d. purple (No.3 190)	£250	80·00
O 4	**34**	6d. grey (No. 161)	£250	65·00
O 7	–	1s. green (No. 196)	£3500	£850
O 9	–	5s. red (No. 181)	£2500	£750
O10	–	10s. blue (No. 183)	£3750	£1000
O11	**61**	£1 brown	£32000	£14000

1888.

O13	**71**	½d. red	5·00	2·00
O17		½d. green	10·00	6·00
O14	**74**	2½d. purple on blue	10·00	10·00
O18	**79**	6d. purple on red	£250	60·00
O15	**89**	1s. green	£350	£125
O19		1s. green and red	£1400	£450
O16	**61**	£1 green	£5500	£950

1902. Stamps of King Edward VII.

O20	**83**	½d. turquoise	22·00	3·00
O21		1d. red	15·00	2·00
O22		2½d. blue	£500	£125
O23		6d. purple	£120000	
O24	–	1s. green and red	£1250	£250
O25	–	5s. red	£7500	£4500
O26	–	10s. blue	£35000	£18000
O27	–	£1 green	£25000	£12000

OFFICE OF WORKS
Overprinted **O.W. OFFICIAL**.

1896. Stamps of Queen Victoria.

O31	**71**	½d. red	£150	75·00
O32		½d. green	£200	£100
O33	**57**	1d. lilac	£250	75·00
O34	**78**	5d. purple and blue	£1250	£400
O35	**81**	10d. purple and red	£2000	£600

1902. Stamps of King Edward VII.

O36	**83**	½d. turquoise	£500	£150
O37	–	1d. red	£500	£150
O38	–	2d. green and red	£1000	£300
O39	**83**	2½d. blue	£1200	£500
O40	–	10d. purple and red	£12000	£4250

ROYAL HOUSEHOLD
Overprinted **R.H. OFFICIAL**.

1902. Stamps of King Edward VII.

O91	**83**	½d. turquoise	£200	£140
O92		1d. red	£175	£120

POSTAGE DUE STAMPS

D 1

D 4

1914.

D 1	**D 1**	½d. green	50	25
D56		½d. orange	15	1·25
D 2		1d. red	50	25
D57		1d. blue	15	50
D 3		1½d. brown	48·00	20·00
D58		1½d. green	90	3·50
D69		2d. black	25	75
D60		3d. violet	30	30
D15		4d. green	15·00	3·00
D61		4d. blue	30	30
D62		5d. brown	45	60
D63		6d. purple	50	30
D76		8d. red	1·25	1·00
D17		1s. blue	10·00	1·00
D64		1s. brown	90	30
D65		2s.6d. purple on yellow	4·75	75
D66		5s. red on yellow	6·50	1·00
D67		10s. blue on yellow	10·00	5·50
D68		£1 black on yellow	40·00	7·50

On the 2s.6d. to £1 the inscription reads "TO PAY".

1970. Decimal Currency.

D77	–	½p. blue	15	50
D78	–	1p. purple	15	15
D79	–	2p. green	20	15
D80	–	3p. blue	20	15
D81	–	4p. brown	25	15
D82	–	5p. violet	25	15
D83	–	7p. brown	35	80
D84	**D 4**	10p. red	30	30
D85		11p. green	50	1·00
D86		20p. brown	60	25
D87		50p. blue	1·75	25
D88		£1 black	3·25	50
D89		£5 yellow and black	35·00	1·50

DESIGN: ½p. to 7p. similar to Type D 4, but with "TO PAY" reading vertically upwards at the left.

D 5

D 7

1982.

D 90	**D 5**	1p. red	10	30
D 91		2p. blue	30	30
D 92		3p. mauve	15	30
D 93		4p. blue	15	25
D 94		5p. brown	20	25
D 95	–	10p. brown	30	40
D 96	–	20p. green	50	60
D 97	–	25p. blue	80	90
D 98	–	50p. black	1·50	1·10
D 99	–	£1 red	3·00	1·25
D100	–	£2 blue	6·00	2·40
D101	–	£5 orange	14·00	2·00

DESIGNS: 10p. to £5, as Type D 5 but with "TO PAY" horizontal.

1994.

D102	**D 7**	1p. red, yellow and black	10	50
D103		2p. mauve, purple blk	10	50
D104		5p. yellow, brown blk	15	35
D105		10p. yellow, green blk	30	45
D106		20p. green, violet blk	50	70
D107		25p. mauve, red black	70	75
D108		£1 violet, mauve black	3·00	2·50
D109		£1.20 blue, green blk	3·75	3·50
D110		£5 dp green, green blk	14·00	12·00

GREAT COMORO Pt. 6

A French island north west of Madagascar. From 1914 to 1950 the stamps of Madagascar were used. In 1950 it became part of the Comoro Islands.

100 centimes = 1 franc.

1897. "Tablet" key-type inscr "GRANDE COMORE" in red or blue.

1	D	1c. black on blue	1·00	1·25
2		2c. brown on buff	75	1·40
3		4c. brown on grey	1·75	2·25
4		5c. green on light green	2·75	1·40
5		10c. black on lilac	3·25	4·00
14		10c. red	10·50	13·00
6		15c. blue	19·00	7·25
15		15c. grey	11·50	15·00
7		20c. red on green	8·00	13·00
8		25c. black on pink	4·00	6·00
16		25c. blue	12·00	13·00
9		30c. brown on drab	10·00	13·50
17		35c. black on yellow	17·00	19·00
10		40c. red on yellow	15·00	15·00
18		45c. black on green	60·00	60·00
11		50c. red on pink	18·00	19·00
19		50c. brown on blue	32·00	35·00
12		75c. brown on blue	35·00	38·00
13		1f. green	15·00	22·00

1912. Surch.

20	D	05 on 2c. brown on buff	45	35
21		05 on 4c. brown on grey	40	35
22		05 on 15c. blue	1·00	85
23		05 on 20c. red on green	15	2·50
24		05 on 25c. black on pink	60	85
25		05 on 30c. brown on drab	50	85
26		10 on 40c. red on yellow	95	1·75
27		10 on 45c. black on green	1·25	1·75
28		10 on 50c. red on pink	20	85
29		10 on 75c. brown on orange	1·75	3·25

GREECE Pt. 3

A country in the S.E. of Europe, under Turkish rule till 1830, when it became a kingdom. A republic was established from 1924 to 1935 when the monarchy was restored. The country was under German occupation from April 1941 to October 1944. The monarchy was once again abolished during 1973 and a republic set up.

1861. 100 lepta = 1 drachma.
2002. 100 cents = 1 euro.

1 Hermes

2

1861. Imperf or perf.

62	**1**	1l. brown	4·00	3·25
17		2l. buff	8·75	20·00
55		5l. green	12·50	2·75
19b		10l. orange on blue	£190	14·00
56		10l. orange	12·50	2·75
20		20l. blue	£170	4·75
59a		20l. red	2·50	2·20
53		30l. brown	37·00	4·75
60		30l. blue	£120	7·50
28		40l. mauve on blue	£250	13·00
37		40l. orange on green	£425	37·00
43d		40l. bistre on blue	14·00	27·00
43f		40l. green on blue	14·00	27·00
50		40l. buff	14·00	35·00
61		40l. mauve	35·00	9·75
52		60l. green on green	17·00	50·00
54		60l. green	£300	30·00
22		80l. red	50·00	15·00

1886. Imperf.

73	**2**	1l. brown	85	1·10
86		2l. buff	1·60	1·60
87b		5l. green	3·50	1·60
76		10l. orange	5·75	2·50
89c		20l. red	3·75	75
90d		25l. blue	47·00	1·60
91		25l. purple	4·25	1·50
79		40l. purple	50·00	21·00
93		40l. blue	6·00	1·70
80		50l. green	2·50	1·70
81		1d. grey	44·00	1·80

1886. Perf.

100	**2**	1l. brown	1·70	1·20
96		2l. buff	1·10	1·10
102		5l. green	4·75	1·50
103b		10l. orange	9·00	1·40
104		20l. red	2·50	45
105d		25l. blue	44·00	1·80
106a		25l. purple	4·25	1·30
107		40l. purple	60·00	25·00
108		40l. blue	10·00	2·50
83		50l. green	10·00	3·75
84		1d. grey	85·00	5·25

3 Wrestlers

4 Discus thrower

5 Vase depicting Pallas Athene

6 Quadriga of Chariot driving

1896. 1st International Olympic Games. Perf.

110	**3**	1l. yellow	1·20	50
111		2l. red	1·30	50
112	**4**	5l. mauve	3·25	90
113		10l. grey	3·50	1·00
114	**5**	20l. brown	13·50	45
115	**6**	25l. red	18·00	80
116	**5**	40l. violet	9·00	3·50
117	**6**	60l. black	25·00	15·00
118	–	1d. blue	60·00	11·00
119	–	2d. olive	£150	41·00
120	–	5d. green	£375	£180
121	–	10d. brown	£400	£225

DESIGNS—As Type **6**—HORIZ: 1d. Acropolis and Stadium; 10d. Acropolis with Parthenon. VERT: 2d. "Hermes" (after statue by Praxiteles); 5d. "Victory" (after statue by Paeonius).

1900. Surch. Imperf.

122	**2**	20l. on 25l. blue	2·50	1·00
130	**1**	30l. on 40l. purple	5·00	4·00
131		40l. on 2l. buff	6·50	5·50
132		50l. on 40l. buff	5·00	5·00
123	**2**	1d. on 40l. purple	12·50	7·25
124		2d. on 40l. purple	£170	
133	**1**	3d. on 10l. orange	44·00	34·00
134		5d. on 40l. purple on blue	£110	£120

1900. Surch. Perf.

125	**2**	20l. on 25l. blue	2·50	2·75
135	**1**	30l. on 40l. purple	7·50	6·50
136		40l. on 2l. buff	9·25	4·75
137		50l. on 40l. buff	8·00	5·75
126	**2**	1d. on 40l. purple	17·00	8·50
127a		2d. on 40l. purple	8·50	10·00
138	**1**	3d. on 10l. orange	47·00	47·00
139		5d. on 40l. purple on blue	£120	£120

1900. Surch **AM** and value.

140	**2**	25l. on 40l. purple (No. 79)	4·25	7·25
142		25l. on 40l. purple (No. 107)	8·50	9·50
141		50l. on 25l. blue (No. 90d)	20·00	20·00
143		50l. on 25l. blue (No. 105)	44·00	25·00
144	**1**	1d. on 40l. brown on blue (No. 43d)	85·00	£100
146		1d. on 40l. brown on blue (Perf)	£120	£140
145		2d. on 5l. green (No. 55)	12·50	16·00
147		2d. on 5l. green (No. 102)	16·00	15·00

1900. Olympic Games stamps surch **AM** and value.

148	–	5l. on 1d. blue	8·25	8·00
149	**5**	25l. on 40l. violet	65·00	55·00
150	–	50l. on 2d. olive	75·00	55·00
151	–	1d. on 5d. green	£275	£150
152	–	2d. on 10d. brown	70·00	70·00

15

16 Hermes after the "Mercury" of Giovanni da Bologna

17

1901.

167	**15**	1l. brown	60	25
168		2l. grey	60	25
169		3l. orange	70	35
170	**16**	5l. green	70	25
171		10l. red	2·10	30
172	**15**	20l. mauve	4·25	25
173	**16**	25l. blue	5·00	30
160	**15**	30l. purple	8·75	1·50
175		40l. brown	24·00	2·50
176		50l. lake	17·00	1·70
163	**17**	1d. black	44·00	2·00
164		2d. bronze	9·25	7·50
165		3d. silver	8·50	8·00
166		5d. gold	8·50	10·50

19 Head of Hermes

20 Athlete throwing Discus

21 Jumper

23 Atlas offering the Apples of Hesperides to Hercules

1902.

178	**19**	5l. orange	2·10	1·20
179		25l. green	25·00	4·00
180		50l. blue	25·00	4·00
181		1d. red	25·00	10·00
182		2d. brown	44·00	30·00

1906. Olympic Games. Dated "1906".

183	**20**	1l. brown	1·10	60
184		2l. black	1·10	60
185	**21**	3l. orange	1·50	60
186		5l. green	2·20	50
187	–	10l. red	3·00	60
188	**23**	20l. red	9·50	65
189	–	25l. blue	18·00	1·10
190	–	30l. purple	15·00	4·25
191	–	40l. brown	7·25	3·50
192	**23**	50l. purple	18·00	4·25
193	–	1d. black	50·00	12·00
194	–	2d. red	75·00	25·00
195	–	3d. yellow	£110	95·00
196	–	5d. blue	£110	95·00

DESIGNS—As Type **20**: 10l. Victory; 20l. Wrestlers; 40l. "Daemon" or God of the Games. As Type **23**: 25l. Hercules and Antaeus; 1d., 2d., 3d. Race, Ancient Greeks; 5d. Olympic Offerings.

29 Head of Hermes

30 Iris

31 Hermes

32 Hermes and Arcas

ΕΛΛΗΝΙΚΗ
ΔΙΟΙΚΗΣΙΣ

(**34**) "Greek Administration"

1911. Roul.

213	**29**	1l. green	20	20
214	**30**	2l. red	20	20
215	**29**	3l. red	30	20
216	**31**	5l. green	55	15
217	**29**	10l. red	35	15
218	**30**	15l. blue	35	20
219		20l. lilac	25	40
220		25l. blue	2·50	40
221	**31**	30l. red	1·00	55
222	**30**	40l. blue	3·25	1·60
223	**31**	50l. purple	3·50	90
224		80l. purple	5·50	70
225	**32**	1d. blue	4·75	25
226		2d. red	5·50	40
227		3d. red (20 × 26½ mm)	10·00	50
209		3d. red (20¼ × 25¼ mm)	22·00	90
228		5d. blue (20 × 26½ mm)	16·00	50
210		5d. blue (20¼ × 25¼ mm)	27·00	4·25
229		10b. blue (20 × 26½ mm)	11·50	75
211b		10d. blue (20¼ × 25¼ mm)	34·00	25·00
212	–	25d. blue	50·00	33·00
230	–	25d. slate	14·50	2·75

The 25d. is as Type **29** but larger (24 × 31 mm).

1912. Optd with T **34**.

232A	**29**	1l. green	80	80
233	**30**	2l. red	80	70
234	**29**	3l. red	70	80
249B	**31**	5l. green	80	80
236A	**29**	10l. red	1·70	1·30
237A	**30**	20l. lilac	2·50	2·20
231	**15**	20l. mauve	2·20	2·50
238A	**30**	25l. blue	2·50	2·50
239A	**31**	30l. red	2·50	2·50
240B	**30**	40l. blue	2·75	4·00
241A	**31**	50l. purple	4·00	4·00
242A	**32**	1d. blue	10·00	2·50
243A		2d. red	38·00	21·00
244B		3d. red	30·00	21·00
245A		5d. blue	20·00	18·00
246B		10d. blue	34·00	22·00
247d	–	25d. blue (No. 212)	41·00	42·00

35 Vision of Constantine over Athens and Salamis

36 Victorious Eagle over Mt. Olympus

1913. Occupation of Macedonia, Epirus and the Aegean Islands. Rouletted.

252	**35**	1l. brown	45	35
253	**36**	2l. red	45	35
254		3l. orange	35	40
255	**35**	5l. green	1·00	35
256		10l. red	7·50	25
257		20l. violet	20·00	2·75
258	**36**	25l. blue	2·50	60
259	**35**	30l. green	44·00	1·90
260	**36**	40l. blue	11·50	4·25
261	**35**	50l. blue	4·25	2·50
262	**36**	1d. purple	6·75	2·75
263	**35**	2d. brown	41·00	6·50
264	**36**	3d. blue	£150	21·00
265	**35**	5d. grey	£120	29·00
266	**36**	10d. red	£120	£170
267	**35**	25d. black	£120	£170

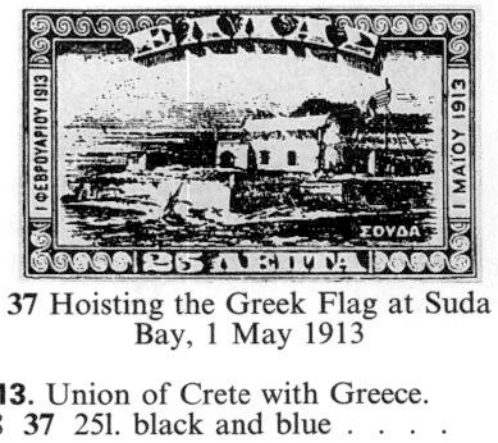

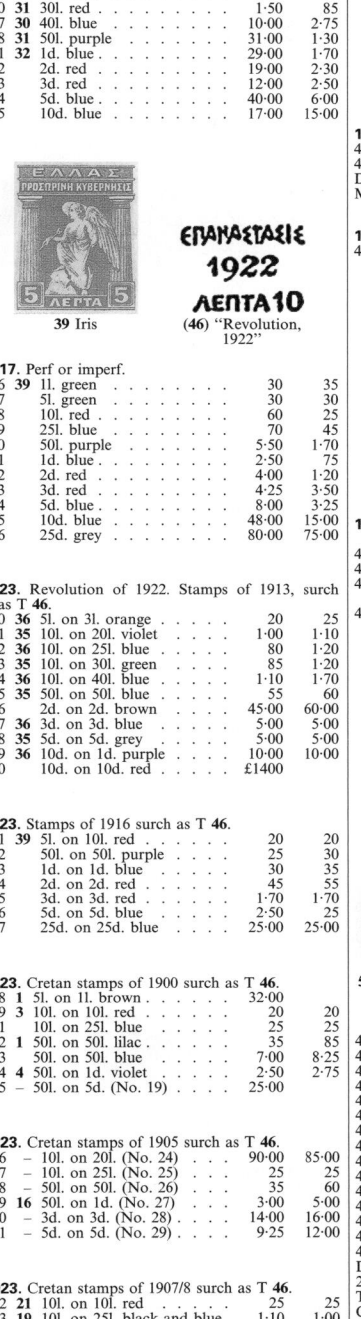

37 Hoisting the Greek Flag at Suda Bay, 1 May 1913

(**38**)

1913. Union of Crete with Greece.

268	**37**	25l. black and blue	6·50	3·25

1916. Stamps of 1911 optd with T **38**.

269	**29**	1l. green	20	20
270	**30**	2l. red	30	25
271	**29**	3l. red	35	35
272	**31**	5l. green	40	30
273	**29**	10l. red	85	25
274	**30**	20l. lilac	1·20	25
275		25l. blue	1·20	25
280	**31**	30l. red	1·50	85
277	**30**	40l. blue	10·00	2·75
278	**31**	50l. purple	31·00	1·30
281	**32**	1d. blue	29·00	1·70
282		2d. red	19·00	2·30
283		3d. red	12·00	2·50
284		5d. blue	40·00	6·00
285		10d. blue	17·00	15·00

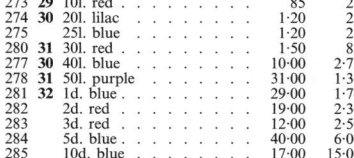

39 Iris

ΕΠΑΝΑΣΤΑΣΙΣ
1922
ΛΕΠΤΑ 10

(**46**) "Revolution, 1922"

1917. Perf or imperf.

286	**39**	1l. green	30	35
287		5l. green	30	30
288		10l. red	60	25
289		25l. blue	70	45
290		50l. purple	5·50	1·70
291		1d. blue	2·50	75
292		2d. red	4·00	1·20
293		3d. red	4·25	3·50
294		5d. blue	8·00	3·25
295		10d. blue	48·00	15·00
296		25d. grey	80·00	75·00

1923. Revolution of 1922. Stamps of 1913, surch as T **46**.

340	**36**	5l. on 3l. orange	20	25
341	**35**	10l. on 20l. violet	1·00	1·10
342	**36**	10l. on 25l. blue	80	1·20
343	**35**	10l. on 30l. green	85	1·20
344	**36**	10l. on 40l. blue	1·10	1·70
345	**35**	50l. on 50l. blue	55	60
346		2d. on 2d. brown	45·00	60·00
347	**36**	3d. on 3d. blue	5·00	5·00
348	**35**	5d. on 5d. grey	5·00	5·00
349	**36**	10d. on 1d. purple	10·00	10·00
350		10d. on 10d. red	£1400	

1923. Stamps of 1916 surch as T **46**.

351	**39**	5l. on 10l. red	20	20
352		50l. on 50l. purple	25	30
353		1d. on 1d. blue	30	35
354		2d. on 2d. red	45	55
355		3d. on 3d. red	1·70	1·70
356		5d. on 5d. blue	2·50	25
357		25d. on 25d. blue	25·00	25·00

1923. Cretan stamps of 1900 surch as T **46**.

358	**1**	5l. on 1l. brown	32·00	
359	**3**	10l. on 10l. red	20	20
361		10l. on 25l. blue	25	25
362	**1**	50l. on 50l. lilac	35	85
363		50l. on 50l. blue	7·00	8·25
364	**4**	50l. on 1d. violet	2·50	2·75
365	–	50l. on 5d. (No. 19)	25·00	

1923. Cretan stamps of 1905 surch as T **46**.

366	–	10l. on 20l. (No. 24)	90·00	85·00
367	–	10l. on 25l. (No. 25)	25	25
368	–	50l. on 50l. (No. 26)	35	60
369	**16**	50l. on 1d. (No. 27)	3·00	5·00
370	–	3d. on 3d. (No. 28)	14·00	16·00
371	–	5d. on 5d. (No. 29)	9·25	12·00

1923. Cretan stamps of 1907/8 surch as T **46**.

372	**21**	10l. on 10l. red	25	25
373	**19**	10l. on 25l. black and blue	1·10	1·00
374		50l. on 1d. (No. 31)	4·00	6·00

No. 372 is as Crete No. 36 but without "HELLAS" optd. No. 377 is the optd stamp.

1923. Optd stamps of Crete surch as T **46**.

375	**1**	5l. on 1l. brown (No. 32)	20	20
376	–	5l. on 5l. green (No. 34)	25	25
377	**21**	10l. on 10l. red (No. 36)	25	25
378	–	10l. on 20l. (No. 37)	25	25
379	–	10l. on 25l. (No. 30)	30	35
381	–	50l. on 50l. (No. 39)	45	45
382	**16**	50l. on 1d. (No. 40)	5·00	6·75
384	–	3d. on 3d. (No. 42)	10·00	16·00
385	–	5d. on 5d. (No. 43)	£200	£250

1923. Postage Due stamps of Crete of 1900 surch as T **38**.

386	D **8**	5l. on 5l. red	20	25
387		5l. on 10l. red	20	25
388		10l. on 20l. red	10·50	10·00
389		10l. on 40l. red	30	85
390		50l. on 50l. red	35	80
391		50l. on 1d. red	50	1·20
392		50l. on 1d. on 1d. red	8·50	9·50
393		2d. on 2d. red	85	1·10

1923. Postage Due stamps of Crete of 1908 with opt, surch as T **46**.

397	D **8**	5l. on 5l. red	20	20
398		5l. on 10l. red	20	20
399		10l. on 20l. red	35	30
400		50l. on 50l. red	60	60
401		50l. on 1d. red	2·40	2·75
402		2d. on 2d. red	5·50	5·50

47 Lord Byron

49 Grave of Marco Botzaris

1924. Byron Centenary.

403	**47**	80l. blue	70	25
404	–	2d. black and violet	1·80	80

DESIGN—HORIZ: (45 × 30 mm): 2d. Byron at Missolonghi.

1926. Centenary of Fall of Missolonghi. Roul.

405	**49**	25l. mauve	80	35

50 Savoia Marchetti S-55C Flying Boat over Fortress

1926. Air. Each showing Savoia Marchetti S-55C flying boat. Multicoloured.

406		2d. Type **50**	2·00	1·10
407		3d. Acropolis	12·50	8·25
408		5d. Map of Greece and Mediterranean	2·50	1·10
409		10d. Colonnade	13·50	8·75

51 Corinth Canal

52 Dodecanese Costume

53 Temple of Theseus, Athens

54 Acropolis

1927.

410	**51**	5l. green	20	10
411	**52**	10l. red	35	10
412	–	20l. violet	40	10
413	–	25l. green	45	10
414	–	40l. green	60	10
415	**51**	50l. violet	1·60	10
416		80l. black and blue	1·30	25
417	**53**	1d. brown and blue	1·60	10
418b	–	2d. black and green	4·75	25
419d	–	3d. black and violet	5·25	20
419e	–	4d. brown	17·00	75
420	–	5d. black and orange	13·50	90
421	–	10d. black and red	32·00	5·00
422	–	15d. black and green	47·00	8·00
423a	**54**	25d. black and green	31·00	9·75

DESIGNS—As Type **52**: 20l. Macedonian costume; 25l. Monastery of Simon Peter, Athos; 40l. White Tower, Salonika. As Type **53**: 2d. Acropolis; 3d. Cruiser "Averoff"; 4d. Mistra Cathedral. As Type **54**: 5, 15d. The Academy of Sciences, Athens; 10d. Temple of Theseus.

55 General Favier and Acropolis

1927. Centenary of Liberation of Athens.

424	**55**	1d. red	55	20
425		3d. blue	3·00	50
426		6d. green	15·00	8·50

56 Navarino Bay and Pylos

58 Sir Edward Codrington

1927. Centenary of Battle of Navarino.

427	**56**	1d.50 green	1·75	30
428	–	4d. blue	11·50	1·10
429	**58**	5d. black and brown (A)	7·00	3·50
430	–	5d. black and brown (B)	37·00	7·75
431	–	5d. black and blue	36·00	6·25
432	–	5d. black and red	17·50	6·75

DESIGNS: 4d. Battle of Navarino; 5d. (No. 429) "Sir Codrington" (A); 5d. (No. 430) "Sir Edward Codrington" (B); 5d. (No. 431) De Rigny; 5d. (No. 432) Van der Heyden.

59 Righas Ferreo

64 Monastery of Arkadi, Crete, and Abbott Gabriel

1930. Centenary of Independence.

433	**59**	10l. brown	20	10
434	–	20l. black	20	15
435	–	40l. green	25	20
436	–	50l. red	30	25
437	–	50l. blue	30	25
438	–	1d. red	30	25
439	–	1d. orange	30	25
440	–	1d.50 blue	65	15
441	–	1d.50 red	60	20
442	–	2d. orange	70	25
443	–	3d. brown	1·30	45
444	–	4d. blue	5·50	45
445	–	5d. purple	2·20	95
446	–	10d. black	12·00	4·50
447	–	15d. green	16·00	7·25
448	–	20d. blue	17·00	10·00
449	–	25d. black	15·00	12·00
450	–	50d. brown	30·00	42·00

DESIGNS as Type **59**: 20l. Patriarch Gregory V; 40l. A. Ypsilanti; 50l. (No. 436) L. Bouboulina; 50l. (437), Ath. Diakos; 1d. (438), Th. Colocotroni; 1d. (439), C. Kanaris; 1d.50, (440), Karaiskakes; 1d.50 (441), M. Botzaris; 2d. A. Miaoulis; 3d. L. Kondouriotis; 5d. Capo d'Istria; 10d. P. Mavromichalis; 15d. Solomos; 20d. Corais. (27½ × 40 mm): 4d. Map of Greece. (27 × 44 mm): 50d. Sortie from Missolonghi. (43 × 28½ mm): 25d. Declaration of Independence.

1930.

451	**64**	8d. violet	26·00	65

1932. Stamps of 1927 surch.

452	–	1d.50l. on 5d. black and blue (No. 431)	2·75	20
453	–	1d.50l. on 5d. black and red (No. 432)	2·75	20
454	**55**	2d. on 3d. blue	3·25	35
455	**58**	2d. on 5d. black and brown (No. 429)	2·75	25
456	–	2d. on 5d. black and brown (No. 430)	8·25	25
457	**55**	4d. on 6d. green	3·25	80

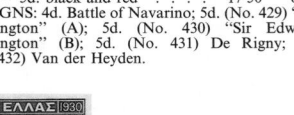

66 "Graf Zeppelin" and Acropolis

1933. Air.

458	**66**	30d. red	19	9·75
459		100d. blue	85·00	41·00
460		120d. brown	80·00	65·00

67 Swinging the Propeller

68 "Flight"

1933. Air. Aeroespresso Company issue.

461	**67**	50l. orange and green	50	40
462	–	1d. orange and blue	80	50
463	–	3d. brown and purple	1·10	85
464	**68**	5d. blue and orange	8·50	7·50
465	–	10d. black and red	1·80	2·20
466	–	20d. green and black	12·00	7·75
467	–	50d. blue and brown	80·00	60·00

DESIGNS—HORIZ: 1d. Temple of Neptune, Corinth; 3d. Marina Fiat MF.5 flying boat over Hermoupolis; 10d. Map of Italy–Greece–Rhodes–Turkey air routes. VERT: 20d. Hermes and Marina Fiat MF.5 flying boat; 50d. Woman and Marina Fiat MF.5 flying boat.

71 Greece

1933. Air. Government issue.
468 **71** 50l. green 55 45
469 1d. red . . . . 1·40 60
470 – 2d. violet . . . . 1·60 1·10
471 – 5d. blue . . . . 6·75 4·75
472 – 10d. red . . . . 19·00 11·50
473 **71** 25d. blue . . . . 35·00 19·00
474 – 50d. brown . . . . 50·00 45·00
DESIGNS—VERT: 2, 10d. Ikarian Islands. HORIZ: 5, 50d. Junkers G.24 airplane and Acropolis.

74 Admiral Kondouriotis and Cruiser "Averoff" **75** "Greece"

1933.
475 **74** 50d. blue and black . . . 80·00 3·00
476 **75** 75d. purple and black . . . £120 £120
477 – 100d. green and brown . . £475 30·00
DESIGN—VERT: 100d. Statue (Youth of Marathon).

78 Athens Stadium, Entrance

1934.
479 **78** 8d. blue . . . . 85·00 90

79 Sun Chariot **83** King Constantine

1935. Air. Mythological designs.
488a **79** 1d. red . . . . 1·00 3·00
488b – 2d. blue . . . . 2·00 55
488c – 5d. mauve . . . . 20·00 4·25
488d – 7d. blue . . . . 30·00 10·00
484 – 10d. brown . . . . 8·25 2·50
488e – 10d. orange . . . . . . 4·00 3·75
485 – 25d. red . . . . 9·00 10·50
486 – 30d. green . . . . 1·40 2·75
487 – 50d. mauve . . . . . . 5·50 9·25
488 – 100d. brown . . . . . . 3·00 3·75
DESIGNS—HORIZ: 2d. Iris; 30d. Triptolemus; 100d. Phrixus and Helle. VERT: 5d. Daedalus and Icarus; 7d. Minerva; 10d. Hermes; 25d. Zeus and Ganymede; 50d. Bellerophon on Pegasus.

(81)

(82)

1935. Restoration of Greek Monarchy. Surch with T **81** (489/91) or **82** (492/3).
489 D **20** 50l. on 40l. blue 35 25
490 3d. on 3d. red 85 80
492 – 5d. on 100d. green and brown (No. 477) . . . 2·00 1·00
493 **75** 15d. on 75d. pur & blk 8·75 5·50

1936. Re-interment of King Constantine and Queen Sophia.
494 **83** 3d. brown and black . . . 50 20
495 8d. blue and black . . . . 1·70 1·30

85 Pallas Athene (Minerva) **86** Bull-leaping

89 King George II **89a** Statue of King Constantine

1937. Cent of Athens University.
496 **85** 3d. brown 75 35

1937.
497 **86** 5l. blue and brown . . . 10 15
498 – 10l. brown and blue . . . 10 10
499 – 20l. green and black . . . 10 10
500 – 40l. black and green . . . 10 10
501 – 50l. black and brown . . . 10 10
502 – 80l. brown and violet . . 10 10
503 **89** 1d. green 20 10
515 **89a** 1d.50 green 55 15
504 – 2d. blue 20 15
505 **89** 3d. brown 35 10
506 – 5d. red 20 15
507 – 6d. olive 20 20
508 – 7d. brown 80 65
509 **89** 8d. blue . . . . 1·20 35
510 – 10d. brown 20 15
511 – 15d. green 25 25
512 – 25d. blue 20 30
516 **89a** 30d. red . . . . 3·50 3·50
513 **89** 100d. red . . . . 13·50 11·00
DESIGNS—(Size as Type **89a**). VERT: 10l. Court Lady of Tiryns; 20l. Zeus and Thunderbolt; 80l. Venus of Milo; 25d. "Glory" of Psara. HORIZ: 40l. Amphictyonic Coin; 50l. Chairing Diagoras of Rhodes; 2d. Battle of Salamis; 5d. Panathenaic chariot; 6d. Alexander the Great at Battle of Issus; 7d. St. Paul on Mt. Areopagus; 10d. Temple of St. Demetrius, Salonica; 15d. Leo III (the Isaurian) destroying Saracens.

93 Prince Paul and Princess Frederika Louise

1938. Royal Wedding.
517 **93** 1d. green 20 20
518 3d. brown 60 20
519 8d. blue . . . . 75 1·10

94 Arms of Greece, Rumania, Turkey and Yugoslavia

1938. Balkan Entente.
520 **94** 6d. blue . . . . 6·25 2·20

1938. Air. Postage Due stamp optd with Junkers G.24 airplane. Perf or rouletted.
521 D **20** 50l. brown 20 25

96 Arms of Ionian Islands **97** Corfu Bay and Citadel

1939. 75th Anniv of Cession of Ionian Islands.
523 **96** 1d. blue . . . . 2·10 45
524 **97** 4d. green . . . . 5·25 1·60
525 – 20d. orange . . . . 25·00 20·00
526 – 20d. blue . . . . 25·00 20·00
527 – 20d. red . . . . 25·00 20·00
DESIGN—HORIZ: 20d. As Type **1** of Ionian Is. but with portraits of George I of Greece and Queen Victoria.

99 Javelin Thrower **100** Arms of Greece, Rumania, Turkey and Yugoslavia

1939. 10th Pan-Balkan Games, Athens.
528 – 50l. green 30 35
529 **99** 3d. red 60 35
530 – 6d. brown on orange . . . 4·00 2·75
531 – 8d. blue on grey . . . . . 4·00 4·00
DESIGNS: 50l. Runner; 6d. Discus-thrower; 8d. Jumper.

1940. Balkan Entente.
532 **100** 6d. blue . . . . 7·25 1·40
533 8d. slate . . . . 6·50 1·50

101 Greek Youth Badge **103** Meteora Monasteries

1940. 4th Anniv of Greek Youth Organization. (a) Postage.
534 **101** 3d. blue, red and silver . . 85 1·10
535 – 5d. black and blue . . . 4·75 2·75
536 – 10d. black and orange . . 6·00 4·50
537 – 15d. black and green . . 44·00 48·00
538 – 20d. black and red . . . 35·00 30·00
539 – 25d. black and blue . . . 40·00 33·00
540 – 30d. black and purple . . 40·00 33·00
541 – 50d. black and red . . . 50·00 39·00
542 – 75d. gold, brown and blue 50·00 38·00
543 **101** 100d. blue, red and silver 65·00 47·00
DESIGNS—VERT: 5d. Boy member; 10d. Girl member; 15d. Javelin thrower; 20d. Youths in column formation; 25d. Standard bearer and buglers; 30d. Three youths in uniform; 50d. Youths on parade; 75d. Coat of arms.

(b) Air.
544 **103** 2d. black and orange . . 80 75
545 – 4d. black and green . . . 3·25 2·50
546 – 6d. black and red . . . . 6·00 5·00
547 – 8d. black and blue . . . 9·25 9·25
548 – 16d. black and violet . . 22·00 18·00
549 – 32d. black and orange . . 41·00 42·00
550 – 45d. black and green . . 41·00 42·00
551 – 55d. black and red . . . 50·00 47·00
552 – 65d. black and blue . . . 47·00 46·00
553 – 100d. black and violet . . 60·00 46·00
DESIGNS (views and aircraft): 4d. Simon Peter Monastery, Mt. Athos; 6, 16d. Isle of Santorin; 8d. Church at Pantanassa; 32d. Ponticonissi, Corfu; 45d. Acropolis; 55d. Erechtheum; 65d. Temple of Nike; 100d. Temple of Zeus.

1941. Postage Due stamps optd with Junkers G.24 airplane, No. 556 also surch. Perf (558/60), perf or rouletted (556/7).
556 D **20** 1d. on 2d. red 25 25
557 5d. blue . . . . 1·60 25
558 10d. green 10 35
559 25d. red . . . . 70 1·60
560 50d. orange . . . . . . 95 2·00

105 "Boreas" (North Wind)

1942. Air. Winds. (Symbolic designs).
561 **105** 2d. emerald and green . . 15 30
562 – 5d. orange and red . . . 20 30
563 – 10d. red and brown . . . 25 35
567 – 10d. red and orange . . . 20 55
564 – 20d. ultramarine and blue 45 55
565 – 25d. orange & light orange 30 90
568 – 25d. green and grey . . . 15 20
566 – 50d. black and grey . . . 95 1·60
569 – 50d. violet and blue . . . 15 20
570 **105** 100d. black and grey . . 15 20
571 – 200d. red and pink . . . 15 20
572 – 400d. green and blue . . 15 25
DESIGNS: 5d. "Notos" (South); 10d. "Apiliotis" (East); 20d. "Lips" (South-west); 25d. "Zephyr" (West); 50d. "Kekias" (North-east); 200d. "Evros" (South-east); 400d. "Skiron" (North-west).

106 Windmills on Mykonos Is.

1942.
573 **106** 2d. brown 10 20
574 – 5d. green 10 15
575 – 10d. blue 10 15
576 – 15d. purple 10 15
577 – 25d. orange 10 15
578 – 50d. blue 10 15
579 – 75d. red 10 15
580 – 100d. black 10 15
581 – 200d. blue 10 15
582 – 500d. brown 10 15
583 – 1000d. brown 10 15
584 – 2000d. blue 10 15
585 – 5000d. red 10 15
586 – 15,000d. purple 10 15
587 – 25,000d. green 10 15
588 – 500,000d. blue 20 30
589 **106** 2,000,000d. green . . . 20 30
590 – 5,000,000d. red 20 30
DESIGNS: 5d., 5,000,000d. Burzi Fortress, Nauplion; 10d., 500,000d. Katokhi on Aspropotamos River; 15d. Heraklion, Crete; 25d. Houses on Hydra Is; 50d., Meteora Monastery; 75d. Edessa; 100d., 200d. Monastery on Mt. Athos; 500d., 5000d. Konitza Bridge; 1000d., 15,000d. Ekatontapiliani Church; 2000d., 25,000d. Kerkyra (Corfu) Is.

110 Child

1943. Children's Welfare Fund.
592 **110** 25d.+25d. green 10 15
593 – 100d.+50d. purple 10 15
594 – 200d.+100d. brown . . . 10 20
DESIGN: 100d. Mother and child; 200d. Madonna and child.

(112)

1944. Children's Convalescent Camp Fund. Surch as T **112**.(a) Postage.
595 **106** 50,000d.+450,000d. on 2d. brown 55 75
596 – 50,000d.+450,000d. on 5d. green (No. 574) 55 75
597 – 50,000d.+450,000d. on 10d. blue (No. 575) . . 55 75
598 – 50,000d.+450,000d. on 15d. purple (No. 576) 55 75
599 – 50,000d.+450,000d. on 25d. orange (No. 577) 55 75

(b) Air.
600 – 50,000d.+450,000d. on 10d. red (No. 567). . . 55 75
601 – 50,000d.+450,000d. on 25d. green (No. 568) . . 55 75
602 – 50,000d.+450,000d. on 50d. blue (No. 569) . . 55 75
603 **106** 50,000d.+450,000d. on 100d. black 55 75
604 – 50,000d.+450,000d. on 200d. claret (No. 571) 55 75

ΔΡΑΧΜΑΙ ΝΕΑΙ
(**113**) (Trans "New drachmas")

1944. Optd as T **113**.
605 – 50l. black and brown (No. 501) 10 20
606 – 2d. blue (No. 504) 10 10
607 – 5d. red (No. 506) 10 15
608 – 6d. olive (No. 507) 10 20

92 "Glory" of Psara **114** "OXI" = No

1945.
609 **92** 1d. purple 10 20
610 3d. red 20 15
611 5d. blue 20 15
612 10d. brown 25 15
613 20d. violet 35 15
614 50d. green 80 30
615 100d. blue . . . . 6·50 6·75
616 200d. green . . . . . . 5·00 1·60
For 25d. in Type **92** but larger, see No. 512.

1945. Resistance to Italian Ultimatum.
617 **114** 20d. orange 25 20
618 40d. blue 25 20

115 President Roosevelt

(**116**)

1945. Roosevelt Mourning Issue. Black borders.
619 **115** 30d. purple 25 15
620 60d. grey 25 20
621 200d. violet 25 20

1946. Surch as T **116**.
622 – 10d. on 10d. (No. 567) . . 25 20
623 – 10d. on 2000d. (No. 584) 25 20

624	–	20d. on 50d. (No. 569)	25	20
625	–	20d. on 500d. (No. 582)	25	20
626	–	20d. on 1000d. (No. 583)	25	20
627	–	30d. on 5d. (No. 574)	25	20
628	–	50d. on 50d. (No. 578)	25	20
629	–	50d. on 25,000d. (No. 587)	45	20
630	–	100d. on 10d. (No. 575)	1·50	20
631	106	100d. on 2,000,000d.	85	20
632	–	130d. on 20l. (No. 499)	85	20
633	–	250d. on 20l. (No. 499)	85	20
634	–	300d. on 80l. (No. 502)	50	30
635	–	450d. on 75d. (No. 579)	1·70	35
636	–	500d. on 5,000,000d. (No. 590)	2·50	40
637	–	1000d. on 500,000d. (No. 588)	10·00	1·10
638	–	2000d. on 5,000d. (No. 585)	32·00	3·50
639	–	5000d. on 15,000d. (No. 586)	£120	24·00

117 E. Venizelos

1946. 10th Anniv of Death of Venizelos (statesman).

640	117	130d. green	25	20
641		300d. brown	25	20

1946. Restoration of Monarchy. Surch with value in circle and date **1-9-1946**.

642	89	50d. on 1d. green	50	15
643		250d. on 3d. brown	85	15
644		600d. on 8d. blue	6·75	85
645		3000d. on 100d. red	17·00	1·00

119 Women carrying Munitions, Pindos Mountains   **121** Panayiotis Tsaldaris

1946. Victory. War Scenes.

646	–	50d. green	25	45
647	–	100d. blue	35	20
648	119	250d. green	50	15
649	–	500d. brown	85	15
650	–	600d. brown	1·40	70
651	–	1000d. violet	3·50	35
682	–	1000d. green	5·00	55
652	–	2000d. blue	14·00	1·90
653	–	5000d. red	26·00	1·40

DESIGNS—HORIZ: 50d. Convoy; 500d. Infantry column; 1000d. (No. 651) Supermarine Spitfire Mk IIB and pilot; 1000d. (No. 682) Battle of Crete; 2000d. Torpedo boat "Hyacinth" towing submarine "Perla". VERT: 100d. Torpedoing of Cruiser "Helle"; 600d. Badge, Alpine troops and map of Italy; 5000d. War Memorial at El Alamein.

1946. 10th Death Anniv of P. Tsaldaris (statesman).

654	121	250d. brown and pink	3·00	75
655		600d. blue	3·00	1·20

1947. King George II Mourning issue. Surch with value in circle in corner and black border.

656	89	50d. on 1d. green	45	20
657		250d. on 3d. brown	1·20	20
658		600d. on 8d. blue	3·00	65

124 Castelrosso Fortress   **126** Apollo (T **1** of Dodecanese Is.)

1947. Restoration of Dodecanese Is. to Greece.

659	124	20d. blue	25	15
660	–	30d. pink and black	25	15
661	–	50d. blue	25	10
662	–	100d. green and olive	25	10
663	–	200d. orange	85	10
664	–	250d. grey	85	10
665	–	300d. orange	70	10
666	–	400d. blue	1·70	10
667	126	450d. blue	2·20	10
668	–	450d. blue	1·70	10
669	126	500d. red	1·20	10
670	–	600d. purple	1·20	20
671	–	700d. mauve	2·20	20
672	–	700d. green	17·00	15
673	–	800d. green and violet	3·50	15
674	–	1000d. olive	85	15
675	126	1300d. red	13·00	15
676	124	1500d. brown	55·00	30
677	–	1600d. blue	6·50	30
678	–	2000d. red and brown	37·00	20
679	–	2600d. green	8·50	50
680	–	5000d. violet	50·00	60
681	–	10,000d. blue	65·00	55

DESIGNS—HORIZ: 100, 400d. St. John's Convent, Patmos. VERT: 30, 1600, 2000d. Dodecanese vase; 50, 300d. Woman in national costume; 200, 250d. E. Xanthos; 450 (No. 668), 800d. Casos Is. and 19th-century frigate; 600, 700 (2), 5000d. Statue of Hippocrates; 1000, 2600, 10,000d. Colossus of Rhodes.

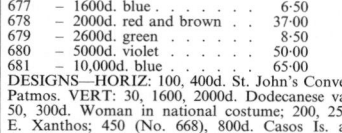

129 Column of Women and Children

1949. Abduction of Greek Children to neighbouring Countries.

683	129	450d. violet	3·00	19·00
684	–	1000d. brown	5·50	1·50
685	–	1800d. red	5·75	1·50

DESIGNS—VERT: 1000d. Captive children and map of Greece; 1800d. Hand menacing woman and child.

130 Maps and Flags

1950. Battle of Crete.

686	130	1000d. blue	6·75	25

131 "Youth of Marathon"

1950. 75th Anniv of U.P.U. Inscr "1874–1949" in white figures at top.

687	131	1000d. green on buff	85	30

133 St. Paul   **134** St. Paul

1951. 19th Cent of St. Paul's Travels in Greece.

688	–	700d. purple	2·00	70
689	133	1600d. blue	7·25	2·00
690	134	2600d. brown	11·00	2·40
691	–	10,000d. brown	95·00	55·00

DESIGNS—As Type **134**: 700d. Sword and altar (horiz); 10,000d. St. Paul preaching to Athenians (vert).

135 "Industry"   **136** Blessing before Battle

1951. Reconstruction Issue.

692	135	700d. orange	1·90	20
693	–	800d. green	4·50	25
694	–	1300d. blue	6·00	25
695	–	1600d. olive	18·00	25
696	–	2600d. violet	47·00	1·20
697	–	5000d. purple	47·00	35

DESIGNS—VERT: 800d. Fish and trident; 1300d. Workmen and column; 1600d. Ceres and tractors; 2600d. Women and loom; 5000d. Map and stars ("Electrification").

1952. Air. Anti-Communist Campaign.

698	136	1,000d. blue	1·00	25
699	–	1,700d. turquoise	4·25	70
700	–	2,700d. brown	10·50	2·75
701	–	7,000d. green	30·00	12·50

DESIGNS—VERT: 1,700d. "Victory" over mountains; 2,700d. Infantry attack; 7,000d. "Victory" and soldiers.

137 King Paul   **138** "Spirit of Greece"

1952. 50th Birthday of King Paul.

702	137	200d. green	85	25
703		1,000d. red	2·00	25
704	138	1,400d. blue	9·00	85
705	137	10,000d. purple	31·00	7·75

139 "Oranges"

1953. National Products.

706	139	500d. orange and red	1·10	15
707	–	700d. yellow and brown	1·10	15
708	–	1,000d. green and blue	1·80	15
709	–	1,300d. buff and purple	3·00	25
710	–	2,000d. green and brown	9·25	25
711	–	2,600d. bistre and violet	17·00	60
712	–	5,000d. green and brown	20·00	45

DESIGNS—VERT: 700d. "Tobacco" (tobacco plant); 1,300d. "Wine" (wineglass and vase); 2,000d. "Figs" (basket of figs); 2,600d. "Dried Fruit" (grapes and currant bread); 5,000d. "Grapes" (male figure holding grapes). HORIZ: 1,000d. "Olive Oil" (Pallas Athene and olive branch).

140 Bust of Pericles   **141** Alexander the Great

1954. Ancient Greek Art. Sculptures, etc.

713	140	100d. brown	25	10
714	–	200d. black	25	10
715	–	300d. violet	40	15
716	–	500d. green	60	10
717	–	600d. red	1·10	10
718	141	1,000d. black and blue	1·80	10
719	–	1,200d. olive	1·70	10
720	–	2,000d. brown	5·25	20
721	–	2,400d. blue	5·50	35
722	–	2,500d. green	6·25	25
723	–	4,000d. red	17·00	25
724	–	20,000d. purple	£110	1·00

DESIGNS—As Type **140**: VERT: 200d. Mycenaean oxhead vase; 1,200d. Head of charioteer of Delphi; 2,000d. Vase of Dipylon; 2,500d. Man carrying calf; 20,000d. Two pitcher bearers. HORIZ: 2,400d. Hunting wild boar. As Type **141**: VERT: 300d. Bust of Homer; 500d. Zeus of Istiaca; 600d. Youth's head; 4,000d. Dish depicting voyage of Dionysus.

See also Nos. 733a/41.

143 Athlete Bearing Torch

1954. Air. 5th Anniv of N.A.T.O. Inscr "NATO".

725	143	1,200d. orange	3·25	20
726	–	2,400d. green	37·00	1·80
727	–	4,000d. blue	55·00	2·50

DESIGNS—VERT: 2,400d. Amphictyonic coin; 4,000d. Pallas Athene.

Currency revalued.
1000 old drachma = one new drachma.

144 Extracts from "Hansard" (Parliamentary Debates)   **145** Samian Coin Depicting Pythagoras

1954. "Enosis" (Union of Cyprus with Greece).

728	144	1.20d. black and yellow	2·75	30
729		2d. black and salmon	8·00	2·30
730		2d. black and blue	8·00	2·30
731		2.40d. black and lavender	8·00	1·60
732		2.50d. black and pink	8·50	1·40
733		4d. black and lemon	28·00	2·30

On No. 728 the text is in Greek, on Nos. 730/1 in French and on the remainder in English.

1955. As Nos. 713/24 but new colours and values.

733a	140	10l. green	20	10
734	–	20l. myrtle (No. 714)	25	15
734a	–	20l. purple (No. 714)	20	15
735	140	30l. brown	35	10
736	–	50l. lake (No. 716)	70	15
736a	–	50l. green (No. 716)	45	10
736b	–	70l. orange (No. 719)	20	15
737	–	1d. green (No. 717)	1·20	10
737a	–	1d. brown (No. 717)	1·70	10
737b	–	1d.50 blue (No. 724)	10·00	20
738	141	2d. black and brown	8·00	10
738a		2d.50 black and mauve	10·00	10
739	–	3d. orange (No. 721)	6·50	20
739a	–	3d. blue (No. 722)	1·70	20
740	–	3d.50 red (No. 715)	7·50	45
741	–	4d. blue (No. 723)	50·00	25

1955. Pythagorean Congress.

742	145	2d. green	1·80	30
743	–	3d.50 black	4·25	1·90
744	145	5d. purple	32·00	1·40
745	–	6d. blue	26·00	23·00

DESIGNS—VERT: 3d.50, Representation of Pythagoras theorem. HORIZ: 6d. Map of Samos.

146 Rotary Emblem and Globe   **147** King George I

1956. 50th Anniv of Rotary International.

746	146	2d. blue	7·50	40

1956. Royal Family.

747	–	10l. violet	20	10
748	–	20l. purple	15	10
749	147	30l. brown	25	10
750	–	50l. brown	25	10
751	–	70l. blue	35	15
752	–	1d. blue	50	15
753	–	1d.50 grey	1·30	25
754	–	2d. black	1·40	15
755	–	3d. brown	1·60	10
756	–	3d.50 brown	6·00	20
757	–	4d. green	6·00	15
758	–	5d. red	4·00	15
759	–	7d.50 blue	5·25	1·20
760	–	10d. blue	19·00	50

PORTRAITS—HORIZ: 10l. King Alexander; 5d. King Paul and Queen Frederika; 10d. King and Queen and Crown Prince Constantine. VERT: 20l. Crown Prince Constantine; 50l. Queen Olga; 70l. King Otto; 1d. Queen Amalia; 1d.50, King Constantine; 2d. King Paul; 3d. King George II; 3d.50, Queen Sophia; 4d. Queen Frederika; 7d.50, King Paul.

See also Nos. 764/77.

148 Dionysios Solomos   **149** "Argo" (5th Century B.C.)

1957. Death Centenary of D. Solomos (national poet).

761	–	2d. yellow and brown	3·50	30
762	148	3d.50 grey and blue	3·50	1·80
763	–	5d. bistre and green	4·25	5·00

DESIGNS—HORIZ: 2d. Solomos and K. Mantzaros (composer); 5d. Zante landscape and Solomos.

1957. As Nos. 747/60. Colours changed.

764	–	10l. red	10	40
765	–	20l. orange	10	40
766	147	30l. black	15	40
767	–	50l. green	20	40
768	–	70l. purple	45	35
769	–	1d. red	65	10

770 – 1d.50 green . . . . 1·60 10
771 – 2d. red . . . . 2·00 10
772 – 3d. blue . . . . 2·10 15
773 – 3d.50 purple . . . . . . 5·50 20
774 – 4d. brown . . . . 7·50 15
775 – 5d. blue . . . . 6·00 20
776 – 7d.50 yellow . . . . . . 1·60 1·00
777 – 10d. green . . . . 34·00 60

1958. Greek Merchant Marine Commemoration. Ship designs.
778 – 50l. multicoloured 10 10
779 – 1d. ochre, black and blue 20 15
780 – 1d.50 red, black and blue 90 1·00
781 – 2d. multicoloured 35 30
782 – 3d.50 black, red and blue 1·10 1·30
783 **149** 5d. multicoloured . . . . 7·50 7·75
SHIPS: 50l. "Michael Carras" (tanker); 1d. "Queen Frederika" (liner); 1d.50, Full-rigged sailing ship, 1821; 2d. Byzantine galley; 3d.50, 6th-century B.C. galley.

150 The Piraeus (Port of Athens) **151** "Narcissus" and Flower

1958. Air. Greek Ports.
784 **150** 10d. multicoloured . . . 11·00 15
785 – 15d. multicoloured . . . 1·80 20
786 – 20d. multicoloured . . . 11·00 15
787 – 25d. multicoloured . . . 1·80 40
788 – 30d. multicoloured . . . 1·80 40
789 – 50d. blue, black and brown . . . . 5·00 40
790 – 100d. blue, black & brown . . . . 30·00 2·00
PORTS: 15d. Salonika; 20d. Patras; 25d. Hermoupolis (Syra); 30d. Volos (Thessaly); 50d. Kavalla; 100d. Heraklion (Crete).

1958. International Congress for Protection of Nature, Athens. Mythological and Floral designs. Multicoloured.
791 20l. Type **151** 10 15
792 30l. "Daphne and Apollo" 10 45
793 50l. "Venus and Adonis" (Venus and hibiscus) . . . 10 45
794 70l. "Pan and the Nymph" (Pan and pine cones) . . . 25 45
795 1d. Crocus (21½ × 26 mm) . . 45 50
796 2d. Iris (22 × 32 mm) 55 30
797 3d.50 Tulip (22 × 32 mm) . . 25 35
798 5d. Cyclamen (22 × 32 mm) 2·10 2·50

152 Jupiter's Head and Eagle (Olympia 4th-century B.C. coin)

1959. Ancient Greek Coins. Designs as T **152** showing both sides of each coin. Inscriptions in black.
799 **152** 10l. green and brown . . 10 15
800 – 20l. grey and blue 20 10
801 – 50l. grey and purple . . . 25 10
802 – 70l. grey and blue 35 20
803 – 1d. drab and red 65 10
804 – 1d.50 grey and ochre . . 1·00 10
805 – 2d.50 drab and mauve . . 1·50 10
806 – 4d.50 grey and green . . 5·50 35
807 – 6d. blue and olive . . . . 15·00 25
808 – 8d.50 drab and red . . . 2·30 1·40
COINS—HORIZ: 20l. Athene's head and owl (Athens 5th cent. B.C.); 50l. Nymph Arethusa and chariot (Syracuse 5th cent. B.C.); 70l. Hercules and Jupiter (Alexander the Great 4th cent. B.C.); 1d.50, Griffin and squares (Abdera, Thrace 5th cent. B.C.); 2d.50, Apollo and lyre (Chalcidice, Macedonia 4th cent. B.C.). VERT: 1d. Helios and rose (Rhodes 4th cent. B.C.); 4d.50, Apollo and labyrinth (Crete 3rd cent. B.C.); 6d. Venus and Apollo (Paphos, Cyprus 4th cent. B.C.); 8d.50, Ram's heads and incised squares (Delphi 5th cent. B.C.).
See also Nos. 909/17.

153 Amphitheatre, Delphi **154** "Victory" and Greek Soldiers through the Ages

1959. Ancient Greek Theatre.
809 – 20l. multicoloured 20 20
810 – 50l. brown and olive . . . 25 20
811 – 1d. multicoloured 30 25
812 – 2d.50 brown and blue . . 45 20
813 **153** 3d.50 multicoloured . . . 8·75 8·75
814 – 4d.50 brown and black . . 1·30 60
815 – 6d. brown, grey and black 1·20 90
DESIGNS—VERT: 20l. Ancient theatre audience (after a Pharsala Thessaly vase of 580 B.C.); 50l. Clay mask of 3rd century B.C.); 1d. Flute, drum and lyre; 2d.50, Actor (3rd century statuette); 6d. Performance of a satirical play (after a mixing-bowl of 410 B.C.). HORIZ: 4d.50, Performance of Euripides' "Andromeda" (after a vase of 4th century B.C.).

1959. 10th Anniv of Greek Anti-Communist Victory.
816 **154** 2d.50 blue, black & brn 2·10 30

155 "The Good Samaritan" **156** Imre Nagy (formerly Prime Minister of Hungary)

1959. Red Cross Commem. Cross in red.
817 – 20l. multicoloured 20 20
818 – 50l. grey, red and blue . . 30 25
819 – 70l. black, brown, bis & bl 40 35
820 – 2d.50 blk, brn, grey & red 60 25
821 – 3d. multicoloured . . . . 5·00 5·75
822 – 4d.50 orange and red . . 95 95
823 **155** 6d. multicoloured 90 70
DESIGNS—HORIZ: 20l. Hippocrates Tree, Cos. VERT: 50l. Bust of Aesculapius; 70l. St. Basil (after mosaic in Hosios Loukas Monastery, Boeotia); 2d.50, Achilles and Patroclus (from vase of 6th cent B.C.); 3d. (32 × 47½ mm) Red Cross, globe, infirm people and nurses; 4d.50, J. H. Dunant.

1959. 3rd Anniv of Hungarian Revolt.
824 **156** 4d.50 sepia, brown & red 1·10 95
825 6d. black, blue & ultram 1·10 95

157 Kostes Palamas **158** Brig in Storm

1960. Birth Cent of Palamas (poet).
826 **157** 2d.50 multicoloured . . . 1·90 35

1960. World Refugee Year. Multicoloured.
827 2d.50 Type **158** 30 20
828 4d.50 Brig in calm waters . . 55 75

159 Scout emulating St. George **160** Sprinting

1960. 50th Anniv of Greek Boy Scout Movement. Multicoloured.
829 20l. Type **159** 10 20
830 30l. Ephebi Oath and Scout Promise 10 20
831 40l. Fire rescue work (horiz) 10 20
832 50l. Planting tree (horiz) . . 25 20
833 70l. Map reading (horiz) . . 10 20
834 1d. Scouts on beach (horiz) 30 25
835 2d.50 Crown Prince Constantine in uniform . . 85 45
836 6d. Greek Scout Flag and Medal (horiz) . . . . . . 1·00 1·10

1960. Olympic Games.
837 – 20l. brown, black and blue 10 20
838 – 50l. brown and black . . 10 20
839 – 70l. brown, black & green 10 20
840 – 80l. multicoloured 15 20
841 – 1d. multicoloured 30 25
842 – 1d.50 brown, blk & orge 30 30
843 – 2d.50 brown, black & bl 75 35
844 **160** 4d.50 multicoloured . . . 70 65
845 – 5d. multicoloured . . . . 1·60 1·00
846 – 6d. brown, black & violet 1·80 1·00
847 – 12d.50 multicoloured . . 6·75 6·75
DESIGNS—VERT: 20l. "Armistice" (official holding plaque); 70l. Athlete taking oath; 2d.50, Discus-throwing; 5d. Javelin-throwing. HORIZ: 50l. Olympic flame; 80l. Cutting branches from crown-bearing olive tree; 1d. Entrance of chief judges; 1d.50 Long jumping; 6d. Crowning the victor; 12d.50, Quadriga or chariot-driving (entrance of the victor).

1960. 1st Anniv of European Postal and Telecommunications Conf. As T **371a** of Italy.
848 4d.50 blue . . . . 2·50 1·40

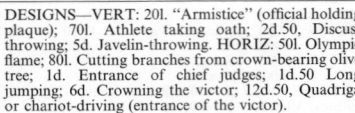

162 Crown Prince Constantine and "Nirefs"

1961. Victory of Crown Prince Constantine in Dragon-class Yacht Race, Olympic Games.
849 **162** 2d.50 multicoloured . . . 40 25

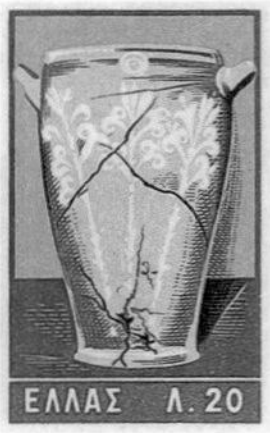

163 Kastoria **164** Lilies Vase of Knossos

1961. Tourist Publicity Issue.
850 **163** 10l. blue 10 10
851 – 20l. plum 10 10
852 – 50l. blue 15 10
853 – 70l. purple 20 10
854 – 80l. blue 30 25
855 – 1d. brown 55 10
856 – 1d.50 green 60 10
857 – 2d.50 red . . . . 1·90 10
858 – 3d.50 violet 70 30
859 – 4d. green . . . . 4·50 15
860 – 4d.50 blue 80 10
861 – 5d. lake . . . . 4·00 10
862 – 6d. myrtle . . . . 1·50 10
863 – 7d.50 black 65 20
864 – 8d. blue . . . . 2·50 30
865 – 8d.50 orange . . . . . 2·75 40
866 – 12d.50 sepia . . . . . 1·20 50
DESIGNS—HORIZ: 20l. The Meteora (Monasteries); 50l. Hydra; 70l. Acropolis, Athens; 80l. Mykonos. 1d. Salonika; 1d.50, Olympia; 2d.50, Knossos; 3d.50, Rhodes; 4d. Epidavros; 4d.50, Sounion; 5d. Temple of Zeus, Athens; 7d.50, Yannina; 12d.50, Delos, VERT: 6d. Delphi; 8d. Mount Athos; 8d.50, Santorini (Thira).

1961. Minoan Art.
867 **164** 20l. multicoloured 15 20
868 – 50l. multicoloured 25 20
869 – 1d. multicoloured 30 20
870 – 1d.50 multicoloured . . . 60 25
871 – 2d.50 multicoloured . . . 3·25 20
872 – 4d.50 multicoloured . . . 1·60 1·50
873 – 6d. multicoloured . . . . 5·50 1·10
874 – 10d. multicoloured . . . 5·00 6·25
DESIGNS—VERT: 1d.50, Knossos rhyton-bearer; 4d.50, Part of Hagia trias sarcophagus. HORIZ: 50l. Partridges and fig-pecker (Knossos frieze); 1d. Kamares fruit dish; 2d.50, Ladies of Knossos Palace (painting); 6d. Knossos dancer (painting); 10d. Kamares prochus and pithos with spout.

165 Reactor Building

1961. Inauguration of "Democritus" Nuclear Research Centre, Aghia Paraskevi.
875 **165** 2d.50 purple and mauve 30 25
876 – 4d.50 blue and grey . . . 60 60
DESIGN: 4d.50, Democritus and atomic symbol.

166 Doves **167** Emperor Nicephorus Phocas

1961. Europa.
877 **166** 2d.50 red and pink . . . 10 20
878 4d.50 ultramarine & blue 15 25

1961. Millenary of Liberation of Crete from the Saracens.
879 **167** 2d.50 multicoloured . . . 35 35

168 "Hermes" 1l. Stamp of 1861

1961. Centenary of First Greek Postage Stamps. "Hermes" stamps of 1861. Multicoloured.
880 20l. Type **168** 10 15
881 50l. "2l." 10 10
882 1d.50 "5l." 15 10
883 2d.50 "10l." 20 20
884 4d.50 "20l." 35 25
885 6d. "40l." 45 45
886 10d. "80l." . . . . 95 1·00

169 Ptolemais Steam Plant

1962. Electrification Project. Multicoloured.
887 20l. Tauropos dam (vert) . . 10 20
888 50l. Ladhon River hydro-electric plant (vert) 20 20
889 1d. Type **169** 20 25
890 1d.50 Louros River dam . . 20 20
891 2d.50 Aliverion steam plant 70 20
892 4d.50 Salonika hydro-electric sub-station 65 75
893 6d. Agra River power station 1·90 1·90

170 Zappion Building

1962. N.A.T.O. Ministers' Conference, Athens.
894 **170** 2d.50 multicoloured . . . 20 10
895 – 3d. sepia, brown and buff 20 10
896 – 4d.50 black and blue . . 25 35
897 – 6d. black and red 25 30
DESIGNS—VERT: 3d. Ancient Greek warrior with shield; 4d.50, Soldier kneeling (after Marathon tomb); 6d. (21 × 37 mm), Soldier (statue in Temple of Aphea, Aegina).

171 Europa "Tree"

1962. Europa.
898 **171** 2d.50 red and black . . . 35 20
899 4d.50 blue and black . . 1·00 60

172 "Protection" **173** Demeter, Goddess of Corn

1962. Greek Farmers' Social Insurance Scheme.
900 **172** 1d.50 black, brown & red 25 10
901 2d.50 black, brown & grn 35 20

1963. Freedom from Hunger. Multicoloured.
902 2d.50 Type **173** 25 20
903 4d.50 Wheat ears and globe 45 45

174 Kings of the Greek Dynasty

1963. Cent of Greek Royal Dynasty.

904 **174**	50l. red	20	10
905	1d.50 green	30	15
906	2d.50 brown	60	15
907	4d.50 blue	1·10	75
908	6d. violet	1·50	25

1963. Ancient Greek Coins. As Nos. 799/808 but colours changed and some designs rearranged. Inscr in black; coins in black and drab or grey; background colours given.

909	50l. blue (As No. 801)	20	10
910	80l. purple (As 802)	20	20
911	1d. green (As 803)	30	10
912	1d.50 red (As 804)	50	10
913	3d. olive (As 799)	35	10
914	3d.50 red (As 800)	35	25
915	4d.50 brown (As 806)	35	15
916	6d. turquoise (As 807)	35	20
917	8d.50 blue (As 808)	1·00	55

175 "Athens at Dawn" (after watercolour by Lord Baden-Powell) **176** Delphi

1963. 11th World Scout Jamboree, Marathon.

918 **175**	1d. multicoloured	10	20
919 –	1d.50 orange, black & bl	10	20
920 –	2d.50 multicoloured	50	25
921 –	3d. black, brown & green	30	25
922 –	4d.50 multicoloured	60	50

DESIGNS—HORIZ: 3d. A. Lefkadites (founder of Greek Scout Movement) and Lord Baden-Powell. VERT: 1d.50, Jamboree Badge; 2d.50, Crown Prince Constantine, Chief Scout of Greece; 4d.50, Scout bugling with Atlantic trumpet triton shell.

1963. Red Cross Centenary. Multicoloured.

923	1d. Type **176**	25	15
924	2d. Centenary emblem	15	10
925	2d.50 Queen Olga	15	20
926	4d.50 Henri Dunant	45	50

177 "Co-operation"

1963. Europa.

927 **177**	2d.50 green	1·70	20
928	4d.50 purple	2·75	2·00

178 Great Lavra Church **179** King Paul

1963. Millenary of Mt. Athos Monastic Community. Multicoloured.

929	30l. Vatopediou Monastery (horiz)	10	20
930	80l. Dionysion Monastery (horiz)	10	20
931	1d. Protaton Church, Karyae	10	20
932	2d. Stavronikita Monastery (horiz)	35	10
933	2d.50 Cover of Nicephorus Phocas Gospel, Great Lavra Church (horiz)	1·10	20
934	3d.50 St. Athanasius the Anthonite (fresco) (horiz)	45	60
935	4d.50 11th-century papyrus, Iviron Monastery (horiz)	40	40
936	6d. Type **178**	45	35

1964. Death of Paul I.

937 **179**	30l. brown	10	10
938	50l. violet	10	10
939	1d. green	65	10
940	1d.50 orange	20	10
941	2d. blue	50	10
942	2d.50 sepia	55	10
943	3d.50 purple	45	20
944	4d. blue	1·10	30
945	4d.50 blue	1·20	65
946	6d. red	2·10	35

180 Gold Coin **181** Trident of Paxi

1964. Byzantine Art Exn, Athens. Mult.

947	1d. Type **180**	15	10
948	1d.50 "Two Saints"	15	20
949	2d. "Archangel Michael"	15	10
950	2d.50 "Young Lady"	20	15
951	4d.50 "Angel"	50	60

DESIGN origins: 1d. reign of Emperor Basil II (976–1025); 1d.50, from Harbaville's 10th cent ivory triptych (Louvre); 2d. 14th cent Constantinople icon (Byzantine Museum, Athens); 2d.50, from 14th cent fresco "The Birth of the Holy Virgin" by Panselinos (Protaton Church, Mt. Athos); 4d.50, from 11th cent mosaic (Daphne Church, Athens).

1964. Centenary of Union of Ionian Islands with Greece. Inscr "1864–1964".

952 **181**	20l. grey, slate and green	10	15
953 –	30l. multicoloured	10	10
954 –	1d. lt brn, brn & red-brn	10	10
955 –	2d. multicoloured	10	10
956 –	2d.50 pale green, deep green and green	20	20
957 –	4d.50 multicoloured	55	65
958 –	6d. multicoloured	35	25

DESIGNS: 30l. Venus of Cythera; 1d. Ulysses of Ithaca; 2d. St. George of Levkas; 2d.50, Zakynthos of Zante; 4d.50, Cephalus of Cephalonia; 6d. War galley emblem of Corfu.

182 Greek Child **183** Europa "Flower"

1964. 50th Anniv of National Institution of Social Welfare (P.I.K.P.A.).

959 **182**	2d.50 multicoloured	40	20

1964. Europa.

960 **183**	2d.50 red and green	95	30
961	4d.50 brown and drab	1·40	85

184 King Constantine II and Queen Anne-Marie **185** Peleus and Atlanta (amphora)

1964. Royal Wedding.

962 **184**	1d.50 green	20	25
963	2d.50 red	10	10
964	4d.50 blue	20	30

1964. Olympic Games, Tokyo. Multicoloured.

965	10l. Type **185**	10	20
966	1d. Running (bowl) (horiz)	10	20
967	2d. Jumping (pot) (horiz)	10	20
968	2d.50 Throwing the discus	20	20
969	4d.50 Chariot-racing (sculpture) (horiz)	35	45
970	6d. Boxing (vase) (horiz)	20	25
971	10d. Apollo (part of frieze, Zeus Temple, Olympia)	30	30

186 "Christ stripping off His garments" **187** Aesculapius Theatre, Epidavros

1965. 350th Death Anniv of El Greco. Mult.

972	50l. Type **186**	10	10
973	1d. "Angels' Concert"	10	15
974	1d.50 El Greco's signature (horiz)	10	15
975	2d.50 Self-portrait	10	10
976	4d.50 "Storm-lashed Toledo"	35	35

1965. Greek Artistic Festivals. Mult.

977	1d.50 Type **187**	10	10
978	4d.50 Herod Atticus Theatre, Athens	30	25

188 ITU Emblem and Symbols

1965. Centenary of I.T.U.

979 **188**	2d.50 red, blue and grey	35	15

189 "New Member making Affirmation" (after Tsokos)

1965. 150th Anniv of "Philiki Hetaeria" ("Friends' Society"). Multicoloured.

980	1d.50 Type **189**	10	10
981	4d.50 Society flag	30	25

190 AHEPA Emblem **191** Venizelos as Revolutionary

1965. American Hellenic Educational Progressive Assn (AHEPA) Congress, Athens.

982 **190**	6d. black, olive and blue	35	25

1965. Birth Cent of E. Venizelos (statesman).

983 **191**	1d.50 green	20	20
984 –	2d. blue	25	40
985 –	2d.50 brown	20	20

DESIGNS: 2d. Venizelos signing Treaty of Sevres (1920); 2d.50, Venizelos.

192 Games' Flag **193** Symbols of the Planets

1965. Balkan Games, Athens. Multicoloured.

986	1d. Type **192**	10	20
987	2d. Victor's medal (vert)	10	20
988	6d. Karaiskakis Stadium, Athens	25	25

1965. Int Astronautic Conference Athens. Mult.

989	50l. Type **193**	10	20
990	2d.50 Astronaut in space	20	20
991	6d. Rocket and space-ship	25	25

194 Europa "Sprig"

1965. Europa.

992 **194**	2d.50 blue, black and grey	30	15
993	4d.50 green, black & olive	75	60

195 Hipparchus (astronomer) and Astrolabe

1965. Opening of Evghenides Planetarium, Athens.

994 **195**	2d.50 black, red and green	30	20

196 Carpenter Ants **197** St. Andrew's Church, Patras

1965. 50th Anniv of P.O. Savings Bank. Multicoloured.

995	10l. Type **196**	10	10
996	2d.50 Savings Bank and book	30	20

1965. Restoration of St. Andrew's Head to Greece. Multicoloured.

997	1d. Type **197**	10	10
998	5d. St. Andrew, after 11th-cent mosaic, Hosios Loukas Monastry, Boeotia	25	20

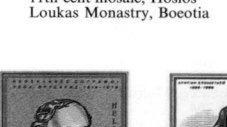

198 T. Brysakes **200** Geannares (revolutionary leader)

199 Greek 25d. Banknote of 1867

1966. Modern Greek Painters. Multicoloured.

999	80l. Type **198**	10	20
1000	1d. N. Lytras	10	10
1001	2d.50 C. Volonakes	10	10
1002	4d. N. Gyses	15	15
1003	5d. G. Jacobides	20	20

1966. 125th Anniv of Greek National Bank.

1004 –	1d.50 green	10	10
1005 –	2d.50 brown	10	20
1006 –	4d. blue	10	10
1007 **199**	6d. black	30	25

DESIGNS—VERT: (23 × 33½ mm): 1d.50, J.-G. Eynard; 2d.50, G. Stavros (founders). HORIZ: (As Type **199**): 4d. National Bank Headquarters, Athens.

1966. Centenary of Cretan Revolt. Mult.

1008	2d. Type **200**	10	10
1009	2d.50 Explosion of gunpowder machine, Arkadi Monastery (horiz)	10	20
1010	4d.50 Map of Crete (horiz)	20	25

201 "Movement of Water" (Decade of World Hydrology) **202** Tragedian's Mask of 4th Century, B.C.

1966. U.N.O. Events.

1011 **201**	1d. blue, brown and black	10	10
1012 –	3d. multicoloured	10	10
1013 –	3d. black, blue and red	20	25

DESIGNS—VERT: 3d. U.N.E.S.C.O. emblem (20th anniv); 5d. W.H.O. Building (inauguration of H.Q., Geneva).

1966. 2,500th Anniv of Greek Theatre.

1014 **202**	1d. multicoloured	10	20
1015 –	1d.50 black, red & brn	10	20
1016 –	2d.50 black, grn & lt grn	10	20
1017 –	4d.50 multicoloured	25	25

DESIGNS—HORIZ: 1d.50, Dionysus in a Thespian ship-chariot (vase painting, 500–480 B.C.); 2d.50, Theatre of Dionysus, Athens. VERT: 4d.50, Dionysus dancing (after vase painting by Kleophredes, c. 500 B.C.).

203 Boeing 707 Jetliner crossing Atlantic Ocean

1966. Inauguration of Greek Airways Transatlantic Flights.
1018 **203** 6d. indigo, blue & lt blue 35 30

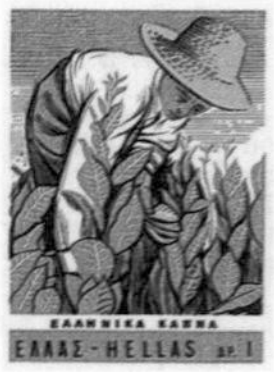

204 Tending Plants

1966. Greek Tobacco. Multicoloured.
1019 1d. Type **204** 15 15
1020 5d. Sorting leaf 35 30

205 Europa "Ship" **206** Horseman (embroidery)

1966. Europa.
1021 **205** 1d.50 black, olive & grn 30 20
1022 4d.50 deep brown, brown and light brown 60 50

1966. Greek "Popular" Art. Multicoloured.
1023 10l. Knitting-needle boxes (vert) 10 10
1024 30l. Type **206** 10 10
1025 50l. Cretan lyre (vert) 10 10
1026 1d. "Massa" (Musical instrument) (vert) 10 10
1027 1d.50 "Cross and Angels" (bas-relief after Melios) (vert) 10 10
1028 2d. "Sts. Constantine and Helen" (icon) (vert) 70 10
1029 2d.50 Carved altar-screen, St. Nicholas' Church, Galaxidion (vert) 15 10
1030 3d. 19th-century ship of Skyros (embroidery) 20 10
1031 4d. "Psiki" (wedding procession) (embroidery) 60 10
1032 4d.50 Distaff (vert) 25 15
1033 5d. Earrings and necklace (vert) 45 10
1034 20d. Detail of handwoven cloth 85 35

207 Princess Alexia **208** "Woodcutter" (after D. Filippotes)

1966. Princess Alexia's First Birthday.
1035 **207** 2d. green 10 10
1036 – 2d.50 brown 15 10
1037 – 3d.50 blue 25 25
PORTRAITS: 2d.50, Royal Family; 3d.50, Queen Anne-Marie with Princess Alexia.

1967. Greek Sculpture. Multicoloured.
1038 20l. "Night" (I. Cossos) (vert) 10 20
1039 50l. "Penelope" (L. Drossos) (vert) 10 20
1040 80l. "Shepherd" (G. Phitalis) (vert) 10 4·25
1041 2d. "Woman's Torso" (K. Demetriades) (vert) 20 20
1042 2d.50 "Kolokotronis" (L. Sochos) (vert) 10 20
1043 3d. "Girl Sleeping" (I. Halepas) 35 30
1044 10d. Type **208** 20 25

209 Olympic Rings ("Olympic Day") **210** Cogwheels

1967. Sports Events. Multicoloured.
1045 1d. Type **209** 10 15
1046 1d.50 Marathon Cup, first Olympics (1896) 10 20
1047 2d.50 Hurdling 15 10
1048 5d. "The Discus-thrower" after C. Demetriades 30 25
1049 6d. Ancient Olympic stadium 35 15
The 2d.50, commemorates the European Athletics Cup, 1967. 5d. (vert), The European Highest Award Championships, 1968. 6d. The Inaug of "International Academy" buildings, Olympia.

1967. Europa.
1050 **210** 2d.50 multicoloured 45 25
1051 4d.50 multicoloured 90 60

211 "Lonchi" (destroyer) and Sailor **212** The Plaka, Athens

1967. Nautical Week. Multicoloured.
1052 20l. Type **211** 10 15
1053 1d. "Eugene Eugenides" (cadet ship) (vert) 10 10
1054 2d.50 Merchant Marine Academy, Aspropyrgos, Attica 10 10
1055 3d. "Averoff" (cruiser) and Naval School, Poros 35 25
1056 6d. "Australis" (liner) and figurehead 35 25

1967. International Tourist Year. Multicoloured.
1057 2d.50 Island of Skopelos (horiz) 10 10
1058 4d.50 Apollo's Temple, Bassai, Peleponnese (horiz) 40 25
1059 6d. Type **212** 35 20

213 Soldier and Phoenix **214** Industrial Skyline

1967. National Revolution of April 21st (1967).
1060 **213** 2d.50 multicoloured 10 10
1061 3d. multicoloured 10 10
1062 4d.50 multicoloured 30 25

1967. 1st Convention of U.N. Industrial Development Organisation, Athens.
1063 **214** 4d.50 ultramarine, black and blue 20 25

215 "Seaside Scene" (A. Pelaletos)

1967. Children's Drawings. Multicoloured.
1064 20l. Type **215** 10 10
1065 1d.50 "Steamer and Island" (L. Tsirikas) 10 10
1066 3d.50 "Country Cottage" (K. Ambeliotis) 20 25
1067 6d. "The Church on the Hill" (N. Frangos) 20 20

216 Throwing the Javelin **217** F.I.A. and E.L.P.A. Emblems

1968. Sports Events, 1968. Multicoloured.
1068 50l. Type **216** 10 10
1069 1d. Long jumping 10 10
1070 1d.50 "Apollo's Head", Temple of Zeus (vert) 10 10
1071 2d.50 Olympic scene on Attic vase (vert) 15 10
1072 4d. Olympic rings (Olympic Day) 20 20
1073 4d.50 "Throwing the Discus", sculpture by Demetriades (European Athletic Championships, 1969) (vert) 35 35
1074 6d. Long-distance running (vert) 15 20
The 50l., 1d. and 6d. represent the Balkan Games, and the 1d.50 and 2d.50, the Olympic Academy Meeting.

1968. General Assembly of International Automobile Federation (F.I.A.), Athens.
1075 **217** 5d. blue and brown 40 30

218 Europa "Key"

1968. Europa.
1076 **218** 2d.50 multicoloured 55 25
1077 4d.50 multicoloured 1·30 75

219 "Athene defeats Alkyoneus" (from frieze, Altar of Zeus, Pergamos)

1968. "Hellenic Fight for Civilization" Exhibition, Athens. Multicoloured.
1078 10l. Type **219** 10 10
1079 20l. Athene attired for battle (bronze from Piraeus) (vert) (24 × 37 mm) 10 10
1080 50l. Alexander the Great (from sarcophagus of Alexander of Sidon) (vert) (24 × 37 mm) 10 10
1081 1d.50 Emperors Constantine and Justinian making offerings to the Holy Mother (Byzantine mosaic) 15 15
1082 2d.50 Emperor Constantine Paleologos (lithograph by D. Tsokos) (vert) (24 × 37 mm) 15 10
1083 3d. "Greece in Missolonghi" (painting by Delacroix) (vert) (28 × 40 mm) 15 15
1084 4d.50 "Evzone" (Greek soldier, painting by G. B. Scott) (vert) (28 × 40 mm) 30 25
1085 6d. "Victory of Samothrace" (statue) (vert) (28 × 40 mm) 35 35

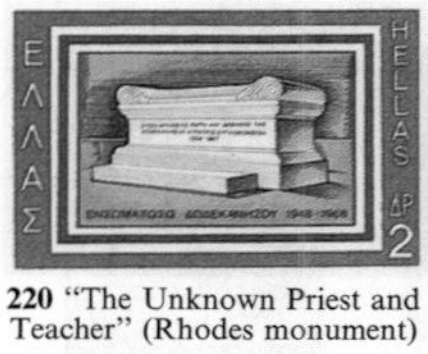

220 "The Unknown Priest and Teacher" (Rhodes monument) **221** Congress Emblem

1968. 20th Anniv of Dodecanese Union with Greece. Multicoloured.
1086 2d. Type **220** 20 10
1087 5d. Greek flag on map (vert) 70 60

1968. 19th Biennial Congress of Greek Orthodox Archdiocese of North and South America.
1088 **221** 6d. multicoloured 35 30

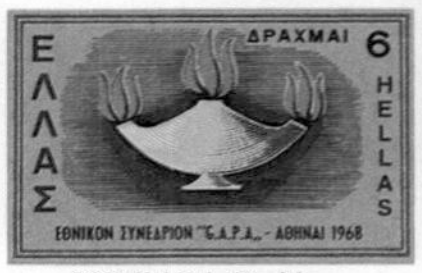

222 GAPA Emblem **223** "Hand of Aesculapius" (fragment of bas-relief from Asclepios' Temple, Athens)

1968. Regional Congress of Greek-American Progressive Association (GAPA).
1089 **222** 6d. multicoloured 35 30

1968. 5th European Cardiological Congress. Athens.
1090 **223** 4d.50 black, yell & lake 85 75

224 Panathenaic Stadium **226** Goddess "Hygeia"

225 Westland Lysander Mk 1 ramming Savoia Marchetti S.M.79–11 Sparviero Bomber

1968. Olympic Games, Mexico. Multicoloured.
1091 2d.50 Type **224** 15 10
1092 5d. Ancient Olympia 45 15
1093 10d. One of Pindar's odes 75 65
The 10d. is 28 × 40 mm.

1968. Royal Hellenic Air Force. Mult.
1094 2d.50 Type **225** 70 50
1095 3d.50 Mediterranean Flight in Breguet 19 bomber, 1928 20 25
1096 8d. Farman H.F.III biplane and Lockheed Super Starfighter (vert) 55 50

1968. 20th Anniv of World Health Organization.
1097 **226** 5d. multicoloured 40 25

227 St. Zeno, the Letter-carrier **228** "Workers' Festival Parade" (detail from Minoan vase)

1969. Greek Post Office Festival.
1098 **227** 2d.50 multicoloured 35 20

1969. 50th Anniv of I.L.O. Multicoloured.
1099 1d.50 "Hephaestus and Cyclops" (detail from ancient bas-relief) 15 10
1100 10d. Type **228** 55 50

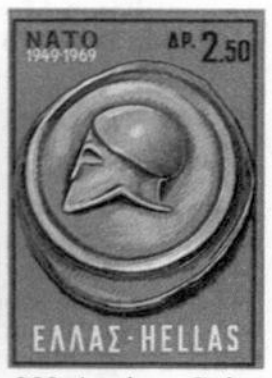

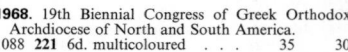

229 Yacht Harbour, Vouliagmeni **230** Ancient Coin of Kamarina

1969. Tourism. Multicoloured.
1101 1d. Type **229** 10 10
1102 5d. "Chorus of Elders" (Ancient drama) (vert) . . 40 40
1103 6d. View of Astypalia . . . 20 20

1969. 20th Anniv of N.A.T.O. Multicoloured.
1104 2d.50 Type **230** 20 10
1105 4d.50 "Going into Battle" (from Corinthian vase) (horiz) 55 50

231 Colonnade

232 Gold Medal

1969. Europa.
1106 **231** 2d.50 multicoloured . . 1·10 25
1107 4d.50 multicoloured . . 1·60 95

1969. 9th European Athletic Championships, Athens. Multicoloured.
1108 20l. Type **232** 10 10
1109 3d. Pole-vaulting, and ancient pentathlon contest 15 15
1110 5d. Relay-racing, and Olympic race c. 525 B.C. (horiz) 20 20
1111 8d. Throwing the discus, modern and c. 480 B.C. 55 60

233 "19th-century Brig and Steam-ship" (I. Poulakas)

234 Raising the Flag on Mt. Grammos

1969. Navy Week and Merchant Marine Year. Multicoloured.
1112 80l. Type **233** 20 20
1113 2d. "Olympic Garland" (tanker) (horiz) 10 10
1114 2d.50 "Themistodes and Karteria, War of Independence, 1821" (anon) (41 × 29 mm) . . . 20 10
1115 4d.50 "Velos" (modern destroyer) (horiz) 45 35
1116 6d. "The Battle of Salamis" (K. Volonakis) (41 × 29 mm) 70 60

1969. 20th Anniv of Communists' Defeat on Mounts Grammos and Vitsi.
1117 **234** 2d.50 multicoloured . . 50 25

235 Athena Promachos

236 Demetrius Karatasios (statue by G. Demetriades)

1969. 25th Anniv of Liberation. Multicoloured.
1118 4d. Type **235** 15 10
1119 5d. "Resistance" (21 × 37 mm) 60 55
1120 6d. Map of Eastern Mediterranean theatre . . 20 10

1969. Heroes of Macedonia's Fight for Freedom. Multicoloured.
1121 1d.50 Type **236** 10 10
1122 2d.50 Emmanuel Pappas (statue by N. Perantinos) 10 10
1123 3d.50 Pavlos Melas (from painting by P. Mathiopoulos) 20 20
1124 4d.50 Capetan Kotas . . . 55 55

237 Dolphin Mosaic, Delos (110 B.C.)

1970. Greek Mosaics. Multicoloured.
1125 20l. "Angel of the Annunciation", Daphne (11th-century) (vert) (23 × 34 mm) 10 10
1126 1d. Type **237** 10 10
1127 1d.50 "The Holy Ghost", Hosios Loukas Monastery (11th-century) (vert) (23 × 34 mm) 20 20
1128 2d. "Hunter", Pella (4th-century B.C.) (vert) (23 × 34 mm) 25 15
1129 5d. "Bird", St. George's Church, Salonika (5th-century) (vert) (23 × 34 mm) 30 25
1130 6d. "Christ", Nea Moni Church, Khios (5th-century) 55 65

238 Overwhelming the Cretan Bull (sculpture)

1970. "The Labours of Hercules".
1131 **238** 20l. multicoloured . . . 10 20
1132 – 30l. multicoloured . . . 10 20
1133 – 1d. black, blue and slate 15 10
1134 – 1d.50 brn, grn & ochre 15 10
1135 – 2d. multicoloured . . . 1·20 10
1136 – 2d.50 brown, red & buff 20 10
1137 – 3d. multicoloured . . . 1·20 10
1138 – 4d.50 multicoloured . . 25 15
1139 – 5d. multicoloured . . . 25 10
1140 – 6d. multicoloured . . . 25 10
1141 – 20d. multicoloured . . . 1·10 50
DESIGNS—HORIZ: 30l. Hercules and Cerberus (from decorated pitcher); 1d.50, The Lernean Hydra (from stamnos); 2d. Hercules and Geryon (from amphora); 4d.50, Combat with the River-god Achelous (from pitcher); 5d. Overwhelming the Nemean Lion (from amphora); 6d. The Stymphalian Birds (from vase); 20d. Wrestling with Antaeus (from bowl). VERT: 1d. Golden Apples of the Hesperides (sculpture); 2d.50, The Erymanthine Boar (from amphora); 3d. The Centaur Nessus (from vase).

239 "Flaming Sun"

1970. Europa.
1142 **239** 2d.50 yellow and red . . 1·60 25
1143 – 3d. blue and light blue 90 35
1144 **239** 4d.50 yellow and blue . . 2·50 1·50
DESIGN—VERT: 3d. "Owl" and CEPT emblem.

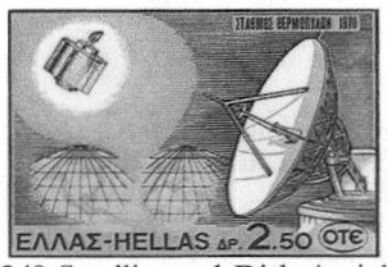
240 Satellite and Dish Aerial

1970. Satellite Earth Telecommunications Station, Thermopylae.
1145 **240** 2d.50 multicoloured . . 20 20
1146 4d.50 multicoloured . . 70 70

241 Saints Cyril and Methodius with Emperor Michael III, (from 12th-cent wall-painting)

1970. Saints Cyril and Methodius Commemoration. Multicoloured.
1147 50l. Saints Demetrius, Cyril and Methodius (mosaic) (21 × 37 mm) 10 15
1148 2d. St. Cyril (Russian miniature) (25 × 32 mm) 35 50
1149 5d. Type **241** 35 20
1150 10d. St. Methodius (Russian miniature) (25 × 32 mm) 45 55
Nos. 1148 and 1150 were issued together, se-tenant, forming a composite design.

242 Cephalonian Fir

244 New U.P.U. Headquarters Building, Berne (Opening)

243 "Cultural Links"

1970. Nature Conservation Year. Mult.
1151 80l. Type **242** 25 25
1152 2d.50 "Jankaea heldreichii" (plant) (23 × 34 mm) . . . 85 15
1153 6d. Rock Partridge (horiz) 1·30 40
1154 8d. Wild goat . . . . 1·40 1·80

1970. American–Hellenic Education Progressive Association Congress, Athens.
1155 **243** 6d. multicoloured . . . 60 25

1970. Anniversaries. Multicoloured.
1156 50l. Type **244** 10 10
1157 2d.50 Emblem (Int Education Year) (vert) (28½ × 41 mm) 20 10
1158 3d.50 Mahatma Gandhi (birth cent) (vert) 20 20
1159 4d. "25" (25th Anniv of United Nations) (vert) . . 40 20
1160 4d.50 Beethoven (birth bicent) (vert) (28½ × 41 mm) . . . . . 1·00 1·00

245 "The Nativity"

1970. Christmas. Scenes from "The Mosaic of the Nativity", Hosios Loukas Monastery. Mult.
1161 2d. "The Shepherds" (vert) 15 20
1162 4d.50 "The Magi" (vert) . . 25 25
1163 6d. Type **245** 60 60

246 "Death of Bishop of Salona in Battle, Alamana" (lithograph)

1971. 150th Anniv of War of Independence (1st issue). The Church. Multicoloured.
1164 50l. Warriors taking the oath (medal) (vert) . . . 10 20
1165 2d. Patriarch Gregory V (statue by Phitalis) (vert) 10 20
1166 4d. Type **246** 20 20
1167 10d. "Bishop Germanos blessing the Standard" (Vryzakis) 65 50
See also Nos. 1168/73, 1178/80, 1181/6 and 1187/89.

1971. 150th Anniv of War of Independence (2nd issue). The War at Sea. As T **246**. Multicoloured.
1168 20l. "Leonidas" (warship) (37 × 24 mm) 10 20
1169 1d. "Pericles" (warship) (37 × 24 mm) 20 20
1170 1d.50 "Terpsichore" (warship) (from painting by Roux) (37 × 24 mm) 20 20
1171 2d.50 "Karteria" (warship) (from painting by Hastings) (37 × 24 mm) 20 20
1172 3d. "Battle of Samos" (contemporary painting) (40 × 28 mm) 50 35
1173 6d. "Turkish Frigate ablaze, Battle of Yeronda" (Michalis) (40 × 28 mm) 1·10 75

247 Spyridon Louis winning Marathon, Athens, 1896

1971. 75th Anniv of Olympic Games Revival. Multicoloured.
1174 3d. Type **247** 25 10
1175 8d. P. de Coubertin and Memorial, Olympia (vert) 80 65

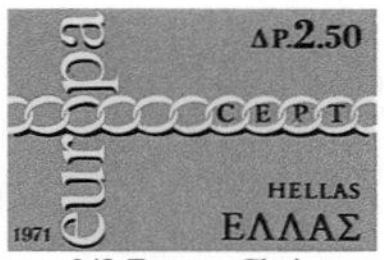
248 Europa Chain

1971. Europa.
1176 **248** 2d.50 yellow, grn & blk 1·20 25
1177 5d. yellow, orange & blk 3·00 1·40

1971. 150th Anniv of War of Independence (3rd issue). "Teaching the People". As T **246**. Multicoloured.
1178 50l. Eugenius Voulgaris (vert) 20 10
1179 2d.50 Dr. Adamantios Korais (vert) 20 20
1180 15d. "The Secret School" (N. Ghyzis) (horiz) . . . 70 70
SIZES: 50l., 2d.50, 23 × 34 mm. 15d. as Type **246**.

1971. 150th Anniv of War of Independence (4th issue). The War on Land. As T **246**. Mult.
1181 50l. "Battle of Corinth" (Krazeisen) (vert) 70 10
1182 1d. "Sacrifice of Kapsalia" (Vryzakis) (vert) 70 20
1183 2d. "Suliot Women in Battle" (Deneuville) (horiz) 20 10
1184 5d. "Battle of Athens" (Zographos) (vert) 25 20
1185 6d.50 "Battle of Maniaki" (lithograph) (horiz) . . . 30 20
1186 9d. "Death of Markos Botsaris at Karpenisi" (Vryzakis) (horiz) 55 70
SIZES: 50l., 1d., 5d.25 × 40 mm. 2d.40 × 25 mm. 6d.50, 9d. as Type **246**.

249 Kaltetsi Monastery and Seal of Peloponnesian Senate

1971. 150th Anniv of War of Independence (5th issue). Government.
1187 **249** 2d. black, green & brown 35 20
1188 – 2d.50 black, lt blue & bl 20 20
1189 – 20d. black, yellow & brn 1·20 1·10
DESIGNS: 2d.50, National Assembly Memorial, Epidavros, and Seal of Provincial Administration; 20d. Signature and seal of John Capodistria, first President of Greece.

250 Hosios Loukas Monastery, Boeotia

1972. Greek Monasteries and Churches. Mult.
1190 50l. Type **250** 10 15
1191 1d. Daphni Church, Attica 10 10
1192 2d. St. John the Divine, Patmos 15 15
1193 2d.50 Panaghia Koumbelidiki Church, Kastoria 20 15
1194 4d.50 Panaghia ton Chalkeon, Saloniki . . . 25 15
1195 6d.50 Panaghia Paregoritissa Church, Arta 30 20
1196 8d.50 St. Paul's Monastery, Mount Athos . . . . . . 85 1·00

251 Cretan Costume

252 Flag and Map

1972. Greek Costumes (1st series). Mult.
1197 50l. Type **251** 10 10
1198 1d. Pindus bride 10 10
1199 2d. Warrior-chief Missolonghi 20 10
1200 2d.50 Sarakatsana woman, Attica 10 10
1201 3d. Nisiros woman 15 10
1202 4d.50 Megara woman . . . 15 15
1203 6d.50 Trikeri (rural) 25 20
1204 10d. Pylaia woman, Macedonia . . . . 1·60 95
See also Nos. 1232/48 and 1282/96.

1972. 5th Anniv of 1967 Revolution. Mult.
1205 2d.50 Commemorative medal (horiz) 15 10
1206 4d.50 Type **252** 20 20
1207 5d. Facets of modern development 30 30

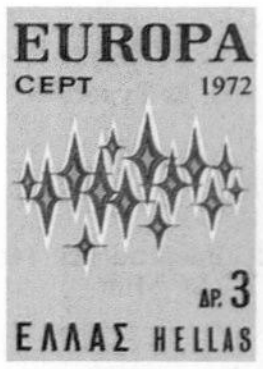

253 "Communications"

254 Acropolis, Athens

1972. Europa.
1208 **253** 3d. multicoloured . . . 55 25
1209 4d.50 multicoloured . . 1·80 1·10

1972. 20th Anniv of Acropolis Motor Rally. Multicoloured.
1210 4d.50 Type **254** 40 45
1211 5d. Emblem and map . . . 40 45

255 "Gaia delivering Erecthonius to Athene"

1972. Greek Mythology. Museum Pieces (1st series).
1212 **255** 1d.50 black and green 15 15
1213 – 2d. black and blue . . . 20 20
1214 – 2d.50 black and brown 20 25
1215 – 5d. black and brown . . 45 35
DESIGNS: 2d. "Uranus" (altar piece); 2d.50, "The Gods repulsing the Giants"; 5d. "Zeus".
See also Nos. 1252/5 and 1271/4.

256 "Young Athlete" (statue)

1972. Olympic Games, Munich. Ancient Olympics. Multicoloured.
1216 50l. Type **256** 10 15
1217 1d.50 "Wrestlers" (bas-relief) (horiz) 10 10
1218 3d.50 "Female athlete" (statuette) 15 20
1219 4d.50 "Ballgame" (bas-relief) (horiz) 25 25
1220 10d. "Runners" (amphora) (horiz) 80 55

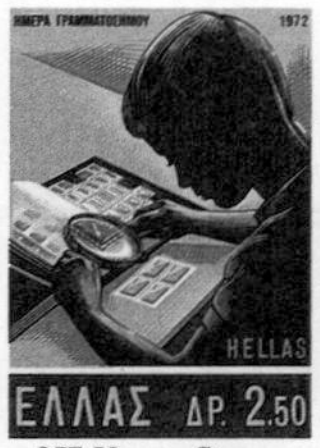

257 Young Stamp Collector

258 "The Birth of Christ"

1972. Stamp Day.
1221 **257** 2d.50 multicoloured . . 15 25

1972. Christmas. Multicoloured.
1222 2d.50 "Pilgrimage of the Magi" 15 20
1223 4d.50 Type **258** 20 20
Nos. 1222/3 were issued together, se-tenant, forming a composite design.

259 University Buildings

1973. Cent of Nat Polytechnic University, Athens.
1224 **259** 2d.50 multicoloured . . 15 20

260 "Spring" (wall fresco)

1973. Archaeological Discoveries, Island of Thera. Multicoloured.
1225 10l. Type **260** 10 20
1226 20l. "Barley" jug 10 10
1227 30l. "Blue Apes" fresco (horiz) 10 10
1228 1d.50 "Bird" (jug) 10 10
1229 2d.50 "Swallows" (detail, "Spring" fresco) (horiz) 20 20
1230 5d. "Wild Goats" fresco (horiz) 20 25
1231 6d.50 "Wrestlers" (detail, fresco) (horiz) 30 30

1973. Greek Regional Costumes (2nd series). As Type **251**. Multicoloured.
1232 10l. Peloponnese 10 20
1233 20l. Central Greece 10 20
1234 30l. Locris (Livanates) . . . 10 20
1235 50l. Skyros (male) 10 20
1236 1d. Spetsai 10 20
1237 1d.50 Almyros 10 20
1238 2d.50 Macedonia (Roumlouki) 10 10
1239 3d.50 Salamis 10 20
1240 4d.50 Epirus (Souli) 10 10
1241 5d. Lefkas (Santa Maura) 10 10
1242 6d.50 Skyros (female) . . . 20 10
1243 8d.50 Corinth 20 20
1244 10d. Corfu (Garitsa) 30 10
1245 15d. Epirus 40 10
1246 20d. Thessaly (Karagouniko) 65 10
1247 30p. Macedonia (Episkopi) 75 30
1248 50d. Thrace (Makra Gefyra) 1·75 65

261 Europa "Posthorn"

1973. Europa.
1249 **261** 2d.50 blue and light blue 25 25
1250 3d. red, orange and lake 30 25
1251 4d.50 brown, bronze and green 40 40

262 "Olympus" (from photograph by Boissonnas)

1973. Greek Mythology (2nd series).
1252 **262** 1d. black and grey . . . 10 20
1253 – 2d. multicoloured . . . 20 25
1254 – 2d.50 black, grey & brn 20 20
1255 – 4d.50 multicoloured . . 40 40
DESIGNS: 2d. "Zeus in combat with Typhoeus" (amphora); 2d.50, "Zeus at Battle of Giants" (altar relief); 4d.50, The "Punishment of Atlas and Prometheus" (vase).

263 Dr. G. Papanicolaou

264 "Our Lady of the Annunciation"

1973. Honouring Dr. George Papanicolaou (cancer specialist).
1256 **263** 2d.50 multicoloured . . 10 10
1257 6d.50 multicoloured . . 20 25

1973. 150th Anniv of Discovery of Miraculous Icon of our Lady of the Annunciation, Tinos.
1258 **264** 2d.50 multicoloured . . 40 25

265 "Triptolemus in a Chariot" (vase)

267 G. Averof

266 Child examining Stamp

1973. European Transport Ministers Conference, Athens.
1259 **265** 4d.50 multicoloured . . 25 25

1973. Stamp Day.
1260 **266** 2d.50 multicoloured . . 25 25

1973. National Benefactors (1st series).
1261 **267** 1d.50 brown 10 20
1262 – 2d. red 10 20
1263 – 2d.50 green 10 20
1264 – 4d. lilac 10 20
1265 – 6d.50 black 20 25
DESIGNS: 2d. A. Arsakis; 2d.50, C. Zappas; 4d. A. Syngros; 6d.50, I. Varvakis.
See also Nos. 1315/18.

268 "Lord Byron in Suliot costume" (by Thomas Phillips)

269 "Harpist of Keros"

1974. 150th Death Anniv of Lord Byron. Multicoloured.
1266 2d.50 Type **268** 10 15
1267 4d.50 "Byron taking the Oath at Grave of Markos Botsaris" (lithograph) . . 10 15

1974. Europa. Ancient Greek Sculptures. Multicoloured.
1268 3d. Type **269** 15 10
1269 4d.50 "Athenian Maiden" 25 20
1270 6d.50 "Charioteer of Delphi" (bronze) 50 55

270 "Theocracy of Zeus" (vase)

271 U.P.U. Emblem within Mycenaean Vase Design

1974. Greek Mythology (3rd series).
1271 **270** 1d.50 black and orange 10 15
1272 – 2d. brown, red & orange 10 10
1273 – 2d.50 black, brn & orge 10 15
1274 – 10d. brown, red & orange 20 20
DESIGNS—HORIZ: 2d. "Athena's Birth" (vase); 2d.50, "Artemis, Apollo and Lito" (vase). VERT: 10d. "Hermes" (vase).

1974. Centenary of U.P.U. Multicoloured.
1275 2d. Type **271** 10 20
1276 4d.50 Hermes (horiz) . . . 10 30
1277 6d.50 Woman reading letter 15 60

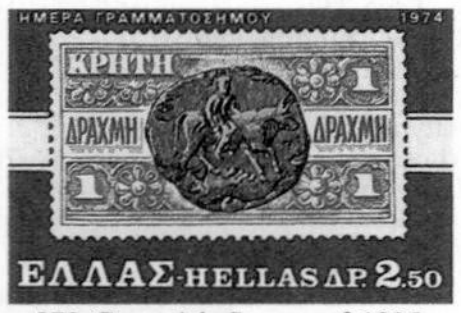

272 Crete 1d. Stamp of 1905

1974. Stamp Day.
1278 **272** 2d.50 black, red & violet 15 20

273 Joseph

274 Secret Assembly, Vostitsa

1974. Christmas. Multicoloured.
1279 2d. Type **273** 10 15
1280 4d.50 Virgin and Child on donkey 10 15
1281 8d.50 Jacob 10 15
Nos. 1279/81 were issued together, se-tenant, forming a composite design.

1974. Greek Costumes (3rd series). As T **251**. Multicoloured.
1282 20l. Megara 10 15
1283 30l. Salamis 10 15
1284 50l. Edipsos 10 15
1285 1d. Kymi 10 15
1286 1d.50 Sterea Hellas 10 15
1287 2d. Desfina 10 10
1288 3d. Epirus 10 10
1289 3d.50 Naousa 10 10
1290 4d. Hasia 10 15
1291 4d.50 Thasos 10 10
1292 5d. Skopelos 10 10
1293 6d.50 Epirus 10 10
1294 10d. Pelion 15 15
1295 25d. Kerkyra 25 20
1296 30d. Boeotia (Tanagra) . . 80 65

1975. 150th Death Anniv of Girgorios Dikeos Papaflessas (Soldier).
1297 **274** 4d. black, brown & stone 10 10
1298 – 7d. multicoloured . . . 10 10
1299 – 11d. multicoloured . . . 15 25
DESIGNS—VERT: 7d. Papaflessas in uniform. HORIZ: 11d. Aghioi Apostoli (chapel), Kalamala.

275 Roses in Vase

277 Neolithic Goddess

276 Mansion, Kastoria

1975. Europa. Multicoloured.
1300 4d. Type **275** 15 20
1301 7d. Erotokritos and Aretussa 25 30
1302 11d. Girl and sheep . . . . 1·10 60

1975. National Architecture.
1303 **276** 10l. black and blue . . . 10 15
1304 – 40l. black and red . . . 10 15
1305 – 4d. black and brown . . 10 15
1306 – 6d. black and blue . . . 10 15
1307 – 11d. black and orange 20 25
DESIGNS: 40l. House, Arnea, Halkidiki; 4d. House, Veria; 6d. Mansion, Siatista; 11d. Mansion, Amelakia, Thessaly.

1975. International Women's Year.
1308 **277** 1d.50 brown, deep mauve and mauve . . 10 15
1309 – 8d.50 black, red and ochre 10 15
1310 – 11d. black, dp blue & bl 15 20
DESIGNS: 8d.50, Confrontation between Antigone and Creon; 11d. Women "Looking to the Future".

278 Alexandros Papanastasiou (founder) and University Buildings

1975. 50th Anniv of Thessaloniki University.
1311 **278** 1d.50 sepia and brown 10 15
1312 – 4d. multicoloured . . . 10 15
1313 – 11d. multicoloured . . . 15 25
DESIGNS: 4d. Original University building; 11d. Plan of University city.

279 Greek 100d. Stamp of 1933

281 Pontos Lyre

280 Evangelos Zappas and Zappeion Building

1975. Stamp Day.
1314 **279** 11d. brown, cream & grn 15 20

1975. National Benefactors (2nd series).
1315 **280** 1d. black, grey and green 10 15
1316 – 4d. black, grey and brown 10 10
1317 – 6d. black, brown & orge 10 10
1318 – 11d. black, grey and red 20 25
DESIGNS: 4d. Georgios Rizaris and Rizarios Ecclesiastical School; 6d. Michael Tositsas and Metsovion Technical University; 11d. Nicolaos Zosimas and Zosimea Academy.

1975. Musical Instruments. Multicoloured.
1319 10l. Type **281** 10 10
1320 20l. Musicians (Byzantine mural) 10 15
1321 1d. Cretan lyre 10 10
1322 1d.50 Tambourine 10 10
1323 4d. Cithern-player (from amphora) (horiz) 10 10
1324 6d. Bagpipes 10 10
1325 7d. Lute 10 10
1326 10d. Barrel-organ 10 10
1327 11d. Pipes and zournades 10 10
1328 20d. "Praise God" (Byzantine mural) (horiz) 20 10
1329 25d. Drums 20 15
1330 30d. Kanonaki (horiz) . . . 55 35

282 Early telephone

1976. Telephone Centenary. Multicoloured.
1331 7d. Type **282** 15 20
1332 11d. Modern telephone and globe 20 20
Nos. 1331/2 were issued together, se-tenant, forming a composite design.

283 Battle of Missolonghi

1976. 150th Anniv of Fall of Missolonghi.
1333 **283** 4d. multicoloured . . . 10 20

284 Florina Jug

285 Lion attacking Bull

1976. Europa. Multicoloured.
1334 7d. Type **284** 20 20
1335 8d.50 Plate with birds design (25 × 30 mm) 20 20
1336 11d. Egina pitcher 45 40

1976. Ancient Sealing-stones. Multicoloured.
1337 2d. Type **285** 10 10
1338 4d.50 Water birds 10 10
1339 7d. Wounded bull 10 15
1340 8d.50 Head of Silenus (27 × 40 mm) 10 15
1341 11d. Cow feeding calf (40 × 27 mm) 15 25

286 Long-jumping

287 Lemnos

1976. Olympic Games, Montreal. Mult.
1342 50l. Type **286** 10 15
1343 2d. Handball 10 10
1344 3d.50 Wrestling 10 10
1345 4d. Swimming 15 15
1346 11d. Athens and Montreal stadiums (52 × 37 mm) . . 20 20
1347 25d. The Olympic flame . . 45 45

1976. Tourist Publicity. Multicoloured.
1348 30d. Type **287** 30 10
1349 50d. Lesbos (horiz) 55 25
1350 75d. Chios (horiz) 70 25
1351 100d. Samos (horiz) . . . . 95 1·00

288 "The Magi speaking to the Jews"

289 Lascaris Book of Grammar, 1476

1976. Christmas. Illustrations from manuscripts at Esfigmenou Monastery. Multicoloured.
1352 4d. Type **288** 10 15
1353 7d. "The Adoration of the Magi" 20 20

1976. 500th Anniv of Printing of First Greek Book.
1354 **289** 4d. multicoloured . . . 10 15

290 Heinrich Schliemann

291 "Patients visiting Aesculapius" (relief)

1976. Centenary of Schliemann's Excavation of the Royal Graves, Mycenae. Multicoloured.
1355 2d. Type **290** 10 10
1356 4d. Gold bracelet (horiz) . . 10 10
1357 5d. Silver and gold brooch 10 15
1358 7d. Gold diadem (horiz) . . 10 15
1359 11d. Gold mask 20 25

1977. International Rheumatism Year.
1360 **291** 50l. black, stone and red 10 15
1361 – 1d. black, orange and red 10 10
1362 – 1d.50 black, stone and red 10 10
1363 – 2d. black, orange and red 10 10
1364 – 20d. black, stone and red 15 25
DESIGNS—(22 × 27 mm): 1d. Ancient clinic; 1d.50, "Aseculapius curing a young man" (relief); 2d. Hercules and nurse. (23 × 34 mm): 20d. "Cured patient offering model of leg" (relief).

292 Fortresses of Mani

1977. Europa. Multicoloured.
1365 5d. Type **292** 15 15
1366 7d. Santorin (vert) 15 20
1367 15d. Lassithi Plain, Crete . . 60 50

293 Emblem and Transport

1977. 45th European Conference of Ministers of Transport.
1368 **293** 7d. multicoloured . . . 10 15

294 Alexandria Lighthouse (Roman coin)

1977. "The Civilizing Influence of Alexander the Great". Multicoloured.
1369 50l. Type **294** 10 20
1370 1d. "Placing the Works of Homer in Achilles' tomb" (fresco, Raphael) 10 10
1371 1d.50 Descending to sea bed in special ship (Flemish miniature) 10 10
1372 3d. In search of the water of life (Hindu plate) 10 15
1373 7d. Alexander the Great on horseback (Coptic carpet) 10 15
1374 11d. Listening to oracle (Byzantine manuscript) . . 20 25
1375 30d. Death of Alexander the Great (Persian miniature) 25 30

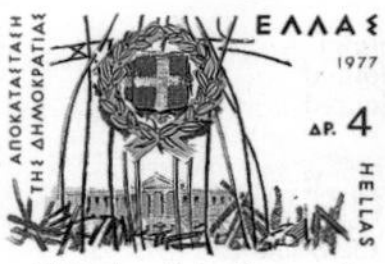

295 Wreath in Front of University

296 Archbishop Makarios

1977. Restoration of Democracy.
1376 **295** 4d. blue, green and black 10 10
1377 – 7d. multicoloured . . . 10 10
1378 – 20d. multicoloured . . . 20 25
DESIGNS—HORIZ: (26 × 22 mm) 7d. Demonstrators at University. VERT: (22 × 26 mm) 20d. Hand with olive branch, University and flags.

1977. Archbishop Makarios Commemoration.
1379 **296** 4d. black and grey . . . 10 15
1380 – 7d. black, brown & stone 10 15
DESIGN: 7d. Makarios and map of Cyprus.

297 Melas Building, Athens (former post office)

1977. 19th-century Hellenic Architecture.
1381 **297** 50l. black, stone and red 10 10
1382 – 1d. black, stone & green 10 10
1383 – 1d.50 black, stone & bl 10 10
1384 – 2d. black, stone & green 10 10
1385 – 5d. black, stone & yellow 10 10
1386 – 50d. black, stone & orge 25 45
DESIGNS: 1d. Institution for the Blind, Thessalonika; 1d.50, Town Hall of Hermoupolis, Syros; 2d. Branch Office of National Bank, Piraeus; 5d. Ilissia (Palace of Duchess of Plakentia), Athens; 50d. Municipal Theatre, Patras.

298 The Battle of Navarino

1977. 150th Anniv of Battle of Navarino.
1387 **298** 4d. yellow, black & brn 10 15
1388 – 7d. multicoloured . . . 15 20
DESIGN: 7d. Admirals Van der Heyden, Sir Edward Codrington and Comte de Rigny.

299 Parthenon and Industrial Complex

1977. Environmental Protection. Mult.
1389 3d. Type **299** 10 10
1390 4d. Birds and fish (horiz) . . 10 10
1391 7d. Living and dead trees (horiz) 10 15
1392 30d. Head of Erechtheum caryatid and chimneys . . 25 35

300 Map of Greece and Ships

1977. "Greeks Abroad". Multicoloured.
1393 4d. Type **300** 10 10
1394 5d. Globe and Greek flag 10 10
1395 7d. Globe and swallows . . 10 15
1396 11d. Envelope with flags . . 15 15
1397 13d. Map of the World . . 20 30

301 "The Port of Kalamata" (C. Parthenis)

1977. Greek Paintings. Multicoloured.
1398 1d.50 Type **301** 15 20
1399 2d.50 "Arsanas" (S. Papaloucas) (vert) . . 10 15
1400 4d. "Santorin" (C. Maleas) 10 10
1401 7d. "The Engagement" (N. Gyzis) 10 15
1402 11d. "The Straw Hat" (N. Lytras) (vert) 15 15
1403 15d. "Spring" (G. Iacovidis) 20 25

302 "Ebenus cretica"

303 Horse Postman and Pre-stamp Cancel

1978. Greek Flora. Multicoloured.
1404 1d.50 Type **302** 10 15
1405 2d.50 "Fritillaria rhodokanakis" 10 10
1406 3d. "Campanula oreadum" 10 10
1407 4d. "Lilium heldreichii" . . 15 15
1408 7d. "Viola delphinantha" . . 15 20
1409 25d. "Paeonia rhodia" . . . 25 30

1978. 150th Anniv of Postal Service. Mult.
1410 4d. Type **303** 10 10
1411 5d. "Maximilianos" (passenger steamer) and Greek "Hermes" stamp 15 10
1412 7d. Steam mail train and 1896 Olympic Games stamp 15 20
1413 30d. Postmen on motor cycles and 1972 "Stamp Day" commemorative . . 20 35
MS1414 101 × 92 mm. Nos. 1410/13 (sold at 60d.) 95 60

304 Lighting the Olympic Flame

305 St. Sophia, Salonika

1978. 80th International Olympic Committee Session, Athens. Multicoloured.
1415 7d. Type **304** 20 15
1416 13d. Start of 100 m race . . 45 40

1978. Europa. Multicoloured.
1417 4d. Type **305** 25 25
1418 7d. Lysicrates' Monument, Athens 35 35

306 Bust of Aristotle

307 Rotary Emblem (50th anniv)

1978. 2300th Death Anniv of Aristotle. Multicoloured.
1419 2d. Type **306** 10 15
1420 4d. "The School of Athens" (detail Raphael) 10 15
1421 7d. Map of Chalkidiki and statue plinth 10 15
1422 20d. "Aristotle the Wise" (Byzantine fresco) (21 × 37 mm) 20 30

1978. Anniversaries and Events. Mult.
1423 1d. Type **307** 10 15
1424 1d.50 Surgery (11th Greek Surgery Congress) (vert) 10 15
1425 2d.50 Ugo Foscolo (poet, birth bicentenary) . . . 10 15
1426 5d. Bronze head (25th anniv of European Convention on Human Rights) . . . 10 15
1427 7d. Hand with reins (Conference of Ministers of Culture of Council of Europe countries) (vert) 10 15
1428 13d. Wright Flyer I with Daedalus and Icarus (75th anniv of first powered flight) (vert) 20 30

308 The Poor Woman with Five Children

1978. "The Twelve Months" (Greek fairy tale). Multicoloured.
1429 2d. Type **308** 10 10
1430 3d. The poor woman and the twelve months 10 15
1431 4d. The poor woman and the gold coins 10 15
1432 20d. The poor woman with her children and the rich woman with the snakes 20 25

309 Grafted Plant and Circulation Diagram

1978. Transplants. Multicoloured.
1433 4d. Type **309** 10 10
1434 10d. "Miracle of Sts. Cosmas and Damian" (Alonso de Sedano) . . . 10 15

310 "Virgin and Child"

311 First Academy, Nauplion, and Cadet

1978. Christmas. Icons from Stavronikita Monastery, Mount Athos. Multicoloured.
1435 4d. Type **310** 10 10
1436 7d. "The Baptism of Christ" 10 15

1978. 150th Anniv of Military Academy. Multicoloured.
1437 1d.50 Type **311** 10 15
1438 2d. Academy coat of arms (vert) 10 10
1439 10d. Modern Academy, Athens, and cadet 20 25

312 "Antipliarchos Laskos" (destroyer)

1978. Greek Naval Ships. Multicoloured.
1440 50l. Type **312** 10 10
1441 1d. "Andromeda" (motor torpedo-boat) 10 10
1442 2d.50 "Papanicolis" (submarine) 10 10
1443 4d. "Psara" (cruiser) 10 10
1444 5d. "Madonna of Hydra" (armed sailing caique) . . 15 10
1445 7d. Byzantine dromon . . . 15 15
1446 50d. Athenian trireme . . . 70 45

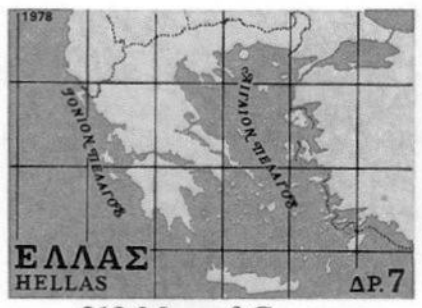
313 Map of Greece

314 Kitsos Tsavellas

1978. The Greek State.
1447 **313** 7d. multicoloured . . . 10 10
1448 11d. multicoloured . . . 15 10
1449 13d. multicoloured . . . 20 25

1979. "The Struggle of the Souliots".
1450 **314** 1d.50 lt brn, blk & brn 10 10
1451 – 3d. multicoloured . . . 10 10
1452 – 10d. multicoloured . . . 10 15
1453 – 20d. ochre, black and brown 15 20
DESIGNS—HORIZ: 3d. Souli Castle; 10d. Fighting Souliots. VERT: 20d. The dance of Zalongo.

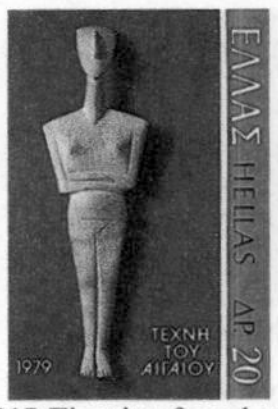
315 Figurine found at Amorgos

316 Cretan Postmen

1979. Art of the Aegean.
1454 **315** 20d. multicoloured . . . 20 25

1979. Europa. Multicoloured.
1455 4d. Type **316** 10 15
1456 7d. Mounted postman . . . 15 1·60
Nos. 1454/5 were issued in se-tenant pairs, forming a composite design.

317 Nicolas Skoufas

318 Flags of Member States forming Ear of Wheat

1979. Anniversaries and Events. Mult.
1457 1d.50 Type **317** (founder of Friendly Society, birth bicentenary) 10 25
1458 2d. Steam and diesel locomotives (75th anniv of railway) (horiz) 10 20
1459 3d. Basketball (European Basketball Championship) 10 20
1460 4d. Fossil moonfish "Mene psarianos" (7th International Congress of Mediterranaen Neogene) (horiz) 10 20
1461 10d. Greek church (Balkan Tourist Year) 10 20
1462 20d. Victory of Paeonius and flags (50th anniv of Balkan Sports) 20 30

1979. Signing of Treaty, Accession of Greece to European Community. Multicoloured.
1463 7d. Type **318** 10 10
1464 30d. European Parliament (horiz) 15 35

319 "Girl with Dove" (classic statue)

320 Head of Philip of Macedonia

1979. International Year of the Child. Multicoloured.
1465 5d. Type **319** 10 10
1466 8d. Girl with doves 10 15
1467 20d. "Mother and Children" (detail, Iacovides) 20 25

1979. Archaeological Discoveries from Vergina. Multicoloured.
1468 6d. Type **320** 10 10
1469 8d. Gold Wreath 10 15
1470 10d. Copper vessel 10 10
1471 14d. Golden casket (horiz) 10 15
1472 18d. Silver ewer 10 25
1473 20d. Gold quiver 20 20
1474 30d. Iron cuirass 35 50

321 Purple Heron

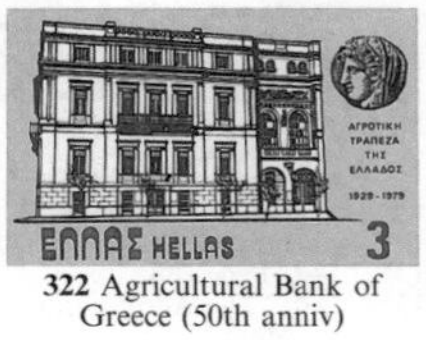
322 Agricultural Bank of Greece (50th anniv)

1979. Endangered Birds. Multicoloured.
1475 6d. Type **321** 15 20
1476 8d. Audouin's gull 30 20
1477 10d. Eleonora's falcon (horiz) 30 20
1478 14d. River kingfisher (horiz) 35 30
1479 20d. Eastern white pelican 85 80
1480 25d. White-tailed sea eagle 1·10 85

1979. Anniversaries and Events.
1481 **322** 3d. black, yellow & olive 10 15
1482 – 4d. multicoloured . . . 10 15
1483 – 6d. multicoloured . . . 10 15
1484 – 8d. multicoloured . . . 10 15
1485 – 10d. multicoloured . . . 15 20
1486 – 12d. multicoloured . . . 15 20
1487 – 14d. multicoloured . . . 20 20
1488 – 18d. multicoloured . . . 20 20
1489 – 25d. multicoloured . . . 40 45
DESIGNS—HORIZ: 10d. Ionic capital and map of Balkans ("Balkanfila '79" Stamp Exhibition); 25d. Parliamentary Meeting (104th anniv of Greek Parliament). VERT: 4d. Cosmas the Aetolian (monk and martyr) (death bicent.); 6d. Basil the Great (1600th death anniv); 8d. Magnifying glass and map of Balkan countries ("Balkanfila '79" Stamp Exhibition); 12d. Aristolelis Valaoritis (poet) (death centenary); 14d. Golfer (World Golfing Championship); 18d. Bust of Hippocrates (International Hippocratic Foundation, Kos).

323 Parnassos

324 Gate of Galerius

1979. Landscapes. Multicoloured.
1490 50l. Type **323** 10 10
1491 1d. Tempi (horiz) 10 10
1492 2d. Milos 10 10
1493 4d. Vikos Gorge 10 10
1494 5d. Misolonghi (horiz) . . . 10 10
1495 6d. Louros Aqueduct . . . 10 10
1496 7d. Samothraki 10 10
1497 8d. Sithonia, Chalkidike (horiz) 10 10
1498 10d. Samaria Gorge 10 10
1499 12d. Sifnos 10 10
1500 14d. Kymi (horiz) 10 15
1501 18d. Ios 10 15
1502 20d. Thasos 15 15
1503 30d. Paros (horiz) 20 15
1504 50d. Cephalonia 55 60

1980. 1st Hellenic Nephrology Congress, Thessalonika.
1505 **324** 8d. blue, black and red 15 15

325 Aegosthena Castle

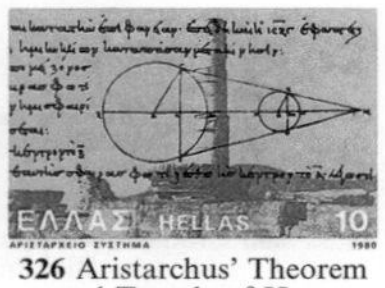
326 Aristarchus' Theorem and Temple of Hera

1980. Castles, Caves and Bridges. Mult.
1506 4d. Type **325** 10 15
1507 6d. Byzantine castle, Thessalonika (horiz) . . . 10 15
1508 8d. Perama cave, Ioannina 10 10
1509 10d. Dyros cave, Mani . . . 10 10
1510 14d. Arta bridge (horiz) . . 10 10
1511 20d. Kalogiros bridge, Epirus (horiz) 25 30

1980. 2300th Birth Anniv of Aristarchus of Samos (astronomer).
1512 **326** 10d. pink, black & brown 15 15
1513 – 20d. multicoloured . . . 20 35
DESIGN: 20d. Heliocentric system.

327 George Seferis (writer)

1980. Europa.
1514 **327** 8d. brown, blue & black 15 15
1515 – 14d. brn, blk and cream 25 35
DESIGN: 14d. Maria Callas (opera singer).

328 Open Book

1980. Energy Conservation. Multicoloured.
1516 8d. Type **328** 10 15
1517 20d. Lightbulb and candle (vert) 10 25

329 Fire-fighting

1980. Anniversaries and Events. Mult.
1518 4d. Type **329** (50th anniv of fire brigade) 10 20
1519 6d. St. Demetrius (mosaic) (1700th birth anniv) (vert) 10 20
1520 8d. Revolutionaries (Theriso revolution, 75th anniv) . . 10 20
1521 10d. Ancient vase and olive branch (World Olive Oil Year) (vert) 10 20
1522 14d. International press emblem (15th International Journalists Federation Congress) (vert) 15 20
1523 20d. Constantinos Ikonomos (cleric and scholar), (birth bicent.) (vert) 15 25

330 Olympia and Coin of Elia

1980. Olympic Games, Moscow. Designs showing Greek stadia. Multicoloured.
1524 8d. Type **330** 10 10
1525 14d. Delphi and Delphic coin 20 30
1526 18d. Epidaurus and coin of Olympia 15 20
1527 20d. Rhodes and coin of Kos 15 15
1528 50d. Panathenaic stadium and First Olympic Games medal 50 55

331 Asbestos

1980. Minerals. Multicoloured.
1529 6d. Type **331** 10 10
1530 8d. Gypsum (vert) 10 10
1531 10d. Copper 10 10
1532 14d. Barite (vert) 20 30
1533 18d. Chromite 10 15
1534 20d. Mixed sulphides (vert) 10 15
1535 30d. Bauxite (vert) 30 30

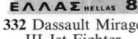

332 Dassault Mirage III Jet Fighter

333 Left Detail of Poulakis' Painting

1980. Anniversaries and Events. Mult.
1536 6d. Breakdown truck (20th anniv of Automobile and Touring Club of Greece road assistance service) (horiz) 10 20
1537 8d. Type **332** (50th anniv of Air Force) 10 20
1538 12d. Piper Super Cub light airplane outside hangar (50th anniv of Thessalonika Flying Club) (horiz) 15 20
1539 20d. Harbour scene (50th anniv of Piraeus Port Organization) 30 30
1540 25d. Association for Macedonian Studies Headquarters (40th anniv) 25 35

1980. Christmas. Details from "He is Happy Thanks to You" by T. Poulakis (in St. John's Monastery, Pataros). Multicoloured.
1541 6d. Type **333** 10 20
1542 14d. Virgin and Child (centre) 10 20
1543 20d. Right detail 20 30
Nos. 1541/3 were issued together, se-tenant, forming a composite design.

334 Fresh and Canned Vegetables

1981. Exports. Multicoloured.
1544 9d. Type **334** 10 10
1545 17d. Fruit 15 15
1546 20d. Cotton 15 15
1547 25d. Marble 20 30

335 "Kira Maria" (Alexandrian folk dance)

1981. Europa. Multicoloured.
1548 12d. Type **335** 15 15
1549 17d. "Sousta" (Cretan dance) 35 35

336 Olympic Stadium, Kalogreza

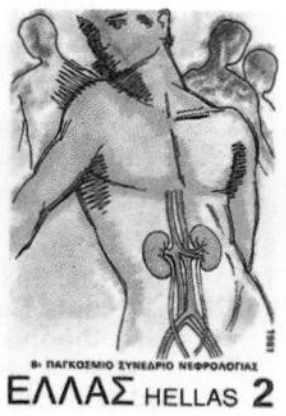

337 Human Figure showing Kidneys

1981. European Athletic Championships, Athens (1982) (1st issue).
1550 **336** 12d. blue, black & lt blue 10 10
1551 – 17d. multicoloured . . . 20 30
DESIGN: 17d. Athletes converging on Greece.
See also Nos. 1586/8.

1981. Anniversaries and Events.
1552 **337** 2d. multicoloured . . . 10 20
1553 – 3d. multicoloured . . . 10 20
1554 – 6d. multicoloured . . . 10 20
1555 – 9d. yellow, black & brn 10 20
1556 – 12d. multicoloured . . . 25 20
1557 – 21d. multicoloured . . . 15 25
1558 – 40d. red, blue & dp blue 20 50
DESIGNS AND EVENTS—VERT: 2d. Type **337** (8th World Nephrology Conference, Athens); 3d. Parachutist, glider, Potez 25 biplane and boy with model glider (50th anniv of Greek National Air Club); 6d. Meteora Monasteries, Thessaly, and Konitsa Bridge, Epirus (International Historical Symposium, Volos, and centenary of incorporation of Thessaly and Epirus into Greece); 12d. Oil rig (first Greek oil production); 40d. Heart (15th World Cardiovascular Surgery Conference Athens). HORIZ: 9d. Bowl with "eye" decoration (50th anniv of Greek Ophthalmological Society); 21d. Globes, plant and coin (Foundation in Athens of World Association for International Relations).

338 Variable Scallops

339 Aegean Island Bell Tower

1981. Shells, Fishes and Butterflies. Mult.
1559 4d. Type **338** 15 20
1560 5d. Painted comber (fish) . . 15 20
1561 12d. Mediterranean parrotfishes 15 20
1562 15d. Dentex (fish) 15 20
1563 17d. Apollo (butterfly) . . . 20 50
1564 50d. Pale clouded yellow (butterfly) 55 70

1981. Bell Towers and Altar Screens. Mult.
1565 4d. Type **339** 10 20
1566 6d. Altar gate, St. Paraskevi Church, Metsovo 10 20
1567 9d. Altar gate, Pelion (horiz) 10 10
1568 12d. Bell tower, Saints Constantine and Helen Church, Halkiades, Epirus 10 10
1569 17d. Altar screen, St. Nicholas Church, Velvendos (horiz) 15 20
1570 30d. Icon of St. Jacob and stand, Alexandroupolis Church Museum 20 20
1571 40d. Upper section of altar gate, St. Nicholas Church, Makrinitsa 40 50

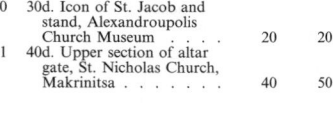

340 Town Scene

1981. Anniversaries and Events. Mult.
1572 3d. Type **340** (Council of Europe Urban Renaissance campaign) . . 10 20
1573 9d. St. Simeon, Archbishop of Thessalonika (Canonization by Greek Orthodox Church) (vert) 10 20
1574 12d. Child Jesus (detail from Byzantine icon) (Breast feeding campaign) (vert) 10 20
1575 17d. Gina Bachauer (pianist, 5th death anniv) (vert) . . 15 20
1576 21d. Constantine Broumidis (artist, 175th birth anniv) (vert) 15 20
1577 50d. "Phoenix" banknotes 1831 (first banknotes, 150th anniv) 25 50

341 Old Parliament Building (museum)

342 "Flight from Missolonghi"

1982. Anniversaries and Events. Mult.
1578 2d. Type **341** (centenary of Historical and Ethnological Society) . . 10 20
1579 9d. Angelos Sikelianos (poet, 31st death anniv) (vert) 15 10
1580 15d. Harilaos Tricoupis (politician, 150th birth anniv) (vert) 10 20
1581 21d. Mermaid (History of Aegean Islands Exhibition) (vert) 10 20
1582 30d. Airbus Industrie A300 jetliner and emblem (25th anniv of Olympic Airways) 20 30
1583 50d. Skull of Petralona man and Petralona cave (3rd European Congress of Anthropology, Petralona) (vert) 35 55

1982. Europa. Multicoloured.
1584 21d. Bust of Miltiades and shield (Battle of Marathon) 45 20
1585 30d. Type **342** . . . . . . 1·00 70

343 Pole-vaulter and Wreath

1982. European Athletic Championships (2nd issue). Multicoloured.
1586 21d. Type **343** 15 20
1587 25d. Women runners (vert) 15 20
1588 40d. Athletes at start of race, shot putter, high jumper and hurdler . . . 45 40

344 Lectionary Heading

1982. Byzantine Book Illustrations. Mult.
1589 4d. Type **344** 10 10
1590 6d. Initial letter E (vert) . . 10 10
1591 12d. Initial letter T (vert) . . 10 10
1592 15d. Canon-table of Gospel readings (vert) 15 15
1593 80d. Heading from zoology book 40 60

345 "Karaiskakis' Camp in Piraeus" (detail, von Krazeisen)

346 Cypriot "Disappearances" Demonstration

1982. Birth Bicentenary of Georges Karaiskakis (revolutionary leader).
1594 **345** 12d. green, black & blue 15 10
1595 – 50d. multicoloured . . . 50 60
DESIGN: 50d. Karaiskakis meditating.

1982. Amnesty International Year of the "Disappearances". Multicoloured.
1596 15d. Type **346** 10 15
1597 75d. Victims, barbed wire and candle 50 75

347 "Demonstration in Athens, 25 March 1942–44" (P. Zachariou.)

1982. National Resistance, 1941–44. Mult.
1598 1d. Type **347** 10 10
1599 2d. "Kalavryta's Sacrifice" (S. Vasillou) 10 10
1600 5d. "Resistance in Thrace" (A. Tassos) (vert) 10 10
1601 9d. "The Onset of the Struggle in Crete" (P. Gravalos) (vert) . . . 10 10
1602 12d. Resistance Fighters (vert) 15 10
1603 21d. "Gorgopotamos" (A. Tassos) (vert) 30 25
1604 30d. "Kaisariani, Athens" (G. Sikeliotis) 25 25
1605 50d. "The Struggle in Northern Greece" (V. Katraki) 55 40
MS1606 Two sheets (a) 90 × 81 mm. Nos. 1598/9 and 1604/5; (b) 81 × 90 mm. Nos. 1600/3 . . . 3·00 2·25

348 Mary and Jesus

1982. Christmas. Early Christian Bas-reliefs. Multicoloured.
1607 9d. Type **348** 10 20
1608 21d. Jesus in manger . . . 20 50

349 Figurehead from Tsamados's "Ares" (brig)

1983. 25th Anniv of International Maritime Organization. Ships' Figureheads. Mult.
1609 11d. Type **349** 15 30
1610 15d. Miaoulis's "Ares" (full-rigged ship) (vert) 15 10
1611 18d. Topsail schooner from Sphakia (vert) 20 10
1612 25d. Bouboulina's "Spetses" (full-rigged ship) (vert) . . 25 20
1613 40d. Babas's "Epameinondas" (brig) (vert) 40 30
1614 50d. "Carteria" (steamer) 70 55

350 Letter and Map of Greece showing Postcode Districts

351 Archimedes

1983. Inauguration of Postcode. Multicoloured.
1615 15d. Type **350** 15 10
1616 25d. Hermes' head within posthorn 30 25

1983. Europa. Multicoloured.
1617 25d. Acropolis, Athens (49 × 34 mm) 50 35
1618 80d. Type **351** . . . . . . 1·10 1·10

352 Rowing

353 Marinos Antypas (farmers' leader)

1983. Sports. Multicoloured.
1619 15d. Type **352** 10 20
1620 18d. Water skiing (vert) . . 30 20
1621 27d. Windsurfing (vert) . . 50 40
1622 50d. Ski lift (vert) 30 30
1623 80d. Skiing 70 95

1983. Personalities. Multicoloured.
1624 **353** 6d. multicoloured . . . 10 10
1625 – 9d. multicoloured . . . 10 10
1626 – 15d. multicoloured . . . 10 10
1627 – 20d. multicoloured . . . 15 10
1628 – 27d. multicoloured . . . 20 15
1629 – 32d. multicoloured . . . 30 30
1630 – 40d. yellow, brown & blk 35 30
1631 – 50d. multicoloured . . . 55 55
DESIGNS: 9d. Nicholas Plastiras (soldier and statesman); 15d. George Papandreou (statesman); 20d. Constantin Cavafy (poet); 27d. Nikos Kazantzakis (writer); 32d. Manolis Calomiris (composer); 40d. George Papanicolaou (medical researcher); 50d. Despina Achladioti, "Matron of Rho" (patriot).

354 Democritus

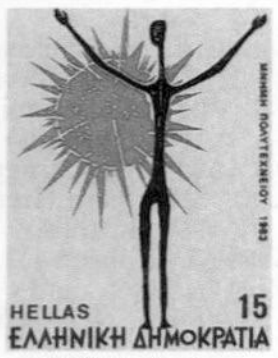

355 Poster by V. Katraki

1983. 1st Int Democritus Congress, Xanthe.
1632 **354** 50d. multicoloured . . . 35 35

1983. 10th Anniv of Polytechnic School Uprising. Multicoloured.
1633 15d. Type **355** 10 10
1634 30d. Students leaving Polytechnic 25 30

356 The Deification of Homer

357 Horse's Head, Chariot of Seline

1983. Homeric Odes. Multicoloured.
1635 **356** 2d. sepia and brown . . 10 10
1636 – 3d. brown, lt orge & orge 10 10
1637 – 4d. yellow, brn & dp brn 10 10
1638 – 5d. multicoloured . . . 10 10
1639 – 6d. orange and brown 10 10
1640 – 10d. lt orge, brn & orge 10 10
1641 – 14d. orge, lt orge & brn 10 10
1642 – 15d. lt orge, orge & brn 10 10
1643 – 20d. bistre, black & brn 20 10
1644 – 27d. brown, pale orange and orange 20 10
1645 – 30d. brown, pale orange and orange 20 10
1646 – 32d. orge, brn & lt orge 35 20
1647 – 50d. brn, lt orge & orge 35 20
1648 – 75d. brown, orange & red 45 20
1649 – 100d. sepia, green & brn 1·00 65
DESIGN—HORIZ: 3d. Abduction of Helen by Paris (pot); 4d. Wooden horse; 5d. Achilles throwing dice with Ajax (jar); 14d. Battle between Ajax and Hector (dish); 15d. Priam requesting body of Hector (pot); 27d. Ulysses escaping from Polyphemus's cave; 32d. Ulysses and Sirens; 50d. Ulysses slaying suitors; 75d. Heroes of Iliad (cup). VERT: 6d. Achilles; 10d. Hector receiving arms from his parents (vase); 20d. Binding of Polyphemus; 30d. Ulysses meeting Nausica; 100d. Homer (bust).

1984. Parthenon Marbles. Multicoloured.
1650 14d. Type **357** 20 20
1651 15d. Dionysus 20 20
1652 20d. Hestia, Dione and Aphrodite 30 30
1653 27d. Ilissus 35 30
1654 32d. Lapith and Centaur . . 75 80
MS1655 105 × 81 mm. 15d. Horseman (left); 21d. Horeman (right); 27d. Heroes (left); 32d. Heroes (right) . . . . 3·50 2·25

358 Bridge

359 Ancient Stadium, Olympia

1984. Europa. 25th Anniv of C.E.P.T.
1656 **358** 15d. multicoloured . . . 30 25
1657 27d. multicoloured . . . 95 1·00

1984. Olympic Games, Los Angeles. Multicoloured.
1658 14d. Type **359** 20 20
1659 15d. Athletes preparing for training 20 20
1660 20d. Flute player, discus thrower and long jumper 35 20
1661 32d. Athletes training . . . 50 45
1662 80d. K. Vikelas and Panathenaic Stadium . . 1·20 1·10

360 Tank on Map of Cyprus

361 Pelion Steam Train

1984. 10th Anniv of Turkish Invasion of Cyprus. Multicoloured.
1663 20d. Type **360** 30 20
1664 32d. Hand grasping barbed wire and map of Cyprus 45 40

1984. Railway Centenary. Multicoloured.
1665 15d. Type **361** 35 25
1666 20d. Steam goods train on Papadia Bridge (vert) . . 80 70
1667 30d. Piraeus-Peloponnese steam train 55 35
1668 50d. Cogwheel railway, Kalavryta (vert) . . . . . 1·40 95

362 Athens 5th Cent B.C. Silver Coin on Plan of City

363 "10" enclosing Arms

1984. 150th Anniv of Athens as Capital. Multicoloured.
1669 15d. Type **362** 35 20
1670 100d. Symbols of ancient Athens and skyline of modern Athens 40 85

1984. 10th Anniv of Revolution.
1671 **363** 95d. multicoloured . . . 85 35

364 "Annunciation"

365 Running

1984. Christmas. Multicoloured.
1672 14d. Type **364** 40 25
1673 20d. "Nativity" 45 25
1674 25d. "Presentation in the Temple" 50 45
1675 32d. "Baptism of Christ" . . 60 60
Nos. 1672/5 show scenes from Hagion Panton icon by Athanasios Tountas.

1985. 16th European Indoor Athletics Championships, New Phaleron. Multicoloured.
1676 12d. Type **365** 20 20
1677 15d. Putting the shot . . . 20 15
1678 20d. Sports stadium (37 × 24 mm) 35 20
1679 25d. Hurdling 35 20
1680 80d. High jumping 85 70

366 Catacomb Niche

1985. Catacombs of Melos. Multicoloured.
1681 15d. Type **366** 20 10
1682 20d. Martyrs' altars and niches central passageway 30 15
1683 100d. Niches 70 60

367 Apollo and Marsyas

1985. Europa. Multicoloured.
1684 27d. Type **367** 55 45
1685 80d. Dimitris Mitropoulos and Nikos Skalkotas (composers) 80 60

368 Coin (315 B.C.) and "Salonika" (relief)

1985. 2300th Anniv of Salonika. Mult.
1686 1d. Type **368** 10 20
1687 5d. Saints Demetrius and Methodius (mosaics) (49 × 34 mm) 15 20
1688 15d. Galerius's Arch (detail) (Roman period) 10 10
1689 20d. Salonika's eastern walls (Byzantine period) 25 10
1690 32d. Upper City, Salonika 25 20
1691 50d. Greek army liberating Salonika, 1912 . . . . . 70 20
1692 80d. Soldier's legs and Salonika (German occupation 1941–44) . . . 70 30
1693 95d. Contemporary views of Salonika (60th anniv of Aristotelian University and International Trade Fair) (49 × 34 mm) . . . 1·10 1·00

369 Urn on Map of Cyprus

370 "Democracy crowning the City" (relief)

1985. 25th Anniv of Republic of Cyprus.
1694 **369** 32d. multicoloured . . . 35 35

1985. Athens, "Cultural Capital of Europe".
1695 **370** 15d. multicoloured . . . 15 10
1696 – 20d. black, grey and blue 20 20
1697 – 32d. multicoloured . . . 55 30
1698 – 80d. multicoloured . . . 80 85
DESIGNS—HORIZ: 20d. Tritons and dolphins (mosaic floor, Roman baths, Hieratis); 80d. Capodistrian University, Athens. VERT: 32d. Angel (fresco, Pentelis Cave).

371 Children of different Races

373 Folk Dance

372 Girl with Flower Crown

1985. International Youth Year (1st issue) (15, 25d.) and 40th Anniv of United Nations Organization (27, 100d.). Multicoloured.
1699 15d. Type **371** 10 10
1700 25d. Doves and youths . . . 25 20
1701 27d. Interior of U.N. General Assembly 55 20
1702 100d. U.N. Building, New York, and U.N. emblem 75 90
See also No. **MS**1703.

1985. International Youth Year (2nd issue). "Piraeus '85" Stamp Exhibition. Sheet 87 × 62 mm.
MS1703 **372** 100d. multicoloured 1·10 1·10

1985. Pontic Culture. Multicoloured.
1704 12d. Type **373** 20 20
1705 15d. Monastery of Our Lady of Soumela 30 20
1706 27d. Women's costumes (vert) 45 25
1707 32d. Trapezus High School 50 25
1708 80d. Sinope Castle 75 75

374 Hestia

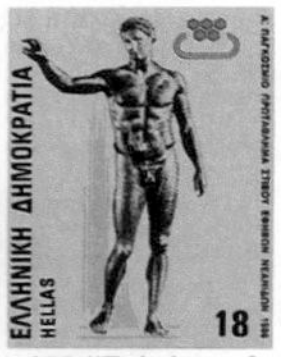

375 "Ephebos of Antikythera"

1986. Gods of Olympus.
1709 **374** 5d. orange, black & brn 10 15
1710 – 18d. orange, black & brn 20 15
1711 – 27d. orange, black & bl 35 15
1712 – 32d. orange, black & red 45 25
1713 – 35d. orange, black & brn 45 25
1714 – 40d. orange, black & red 60 20
1715 – 50d. orange, black & grey 75 25
1716 – 110d. orange, blk & brn 95 25
1717 – 150d. orange, blk & grey 1·40 25
1718 – 200d. orange, black & bl 1·60 35
1719 – 300d. orange, black & bl 2·20 90
1720 – 500d. orange, black & bl 5·50 2·50
DESIGNS: 18d. Hermes; 27d. Aphrodite; 32d. Ares; 35d. Athene; 40d. Hephaestus; 50d. Artemis; 110d. Apollo; 150d. Demeter; 200d. Poseidon; 300d. Hera; 500d. Zeus.

1986. Sports Events and Anniversaries.
1721 **375** 18d. green, black & grey 20 20
1722 – 27d. yellow, black & red 40 30
1723 – 32d. multicoloured . . . 60 45
1724 – 35d. green, black & bis 90 70
1725 – 40d. multicoloured . . . 75 60
1726 – 50d. multicoloured . . . 75 40
1727 – 110d. multicoloured . . 2·10 1·50
DESIGNS—VERT: 18d. Type **375** (1st World Junior Athletics Championships); 32d. Footballers (Pan-European Junior Football Finals); 35d. "Wrestlers" (sculpture) (Pan-European Freestyle and Greco-Roman Wrestling Championships); 50d. Cyclists (6th International Round Europe Cycling Meet.). HORIZ: 27d. "Diadoumenos" (sculpture by Polycleitus) (1st World Junior Athletics Championships); 40d. Volleyball players (Men's World Volleyball Championships); 110d. "Victory" (unadopted design by Nikephoros Lytras for first Olympic Games commemoratives, 1896) (90th anniv of modern Olympic Games).

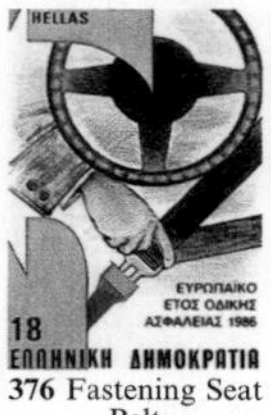

376 Fastening Seat Belt

377 Intelpost

1986. European Road Safety Year. Mult.
1728 18d. Type **376** 30 10
1729 27d. Motorcyclist in traffic 70 45
1730 110d. Child strapped in back seat of car and speed limit signs . . . . 1·40 80

1986. New Postal Services. Multicoloured.
1731 18d. Type **377** 25 20
1732 110d. "Express Mail" banner around globe . . 85 95

378 Sapling between Hands and burning Forest

1986. Europa.
1733 **378** 35d. green, black & orge 1·80 1·70
1734 – 110d. blue, black & grn 2·10 2·20
DESIGN: 110d. Dalmatian pelicans on Prespa Lake.

379 Victims' Memorial and Workers

1986. Centenary of Chicago May Day Strike.
1735 **379** 40d. multicoloured . . . 45 35

380 Swearing-in of Venizelos Government

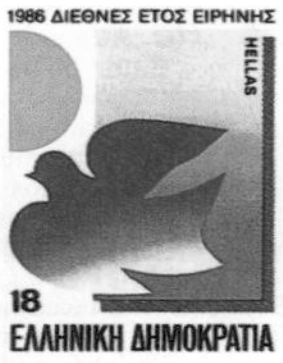

381 Dove and Sun

1986. 50th Death Anniv of Eleftherios Venizelos (politician) (18d.) and 6th International Crete Conference, Hania (110d.). Multicoloured.
1736 18d. Type **380** 25 20
1737 110d. Hania harbour . . . 1·00 85

1986. International Peace Year. Multicoloured.
1738 18d. Type **381** 20 20
1739 35d. Dove holding olive branch with flags as leaves 45 35
1740 110d. Dove with olive branch flying out of globe (horiz) 80 95

382 "Madonna and Child"

383 "The Fox and the Grapes"

1986. Christmas. Designs showing icons. Multicoloured.
1741 22d. Type **382** 20 10
1742 46d. "Adoration of the Magi" (24 × 32 mm) . . . 50 55
1743 130d. "Christ enthroned with St. John the Evangelist" 90 65

1987. Aesop's Fables. Multicoloured.
1744A 2d. Type **383** 15 20
1745A 5d. "The North Wind and the Sun" 15 20
1746A 10d. "The Stag at the Spring and the Lion" 30 20
1747A 22d. "Zeus and the Snake" 50 20
1748A 32d. "The Crow and the Fox" 60 25
1749A 40d. "The Woodcutter and Hermes" 95 65
1750A 46d. "The Ass in a Lion's Skin and the Fox" . . . 1·40 75
1751A 130d. "The Hare and the Tortoise" . . . . 2·50 90

384 "Composition" (Archilleas Apergis)

385 Player shooting Goal and Indoor Court

1987. Europa. Sculptures. Multicoloured.
1752b 40d. Type **384** . . . . . 1·50 1·50
1753a 130d. "Delphic Light" (Gerassimos Sklavos) . . 1·70 1·80

1987. 25th European Men's Basketball Championships, Athens. Multicoloured.
1754 22d. Type **385** 35 50
1755 25d. Emblem and spectators (32 × 24 mm) 25 10
1756 130d. Players . . . . 1·00 1·20
MS1757 113 × 63 mm. 40d. Players; 60d. Players around goal; 100d. Player shooting goal (each 28 × 40 mm) . . . . 2·00 1·60

386 Banner and Students

1987. 150th Annivs. of Athens University (3, 23d.) and National Metsovio Polytechnic Institute (others). Multicoloured.
1758 3d. Type **386** 15 15
1759 23d. Medal and owl 25 15
1760 40d. Building facade, measuring instruments and computer terminal (vert) 35 35
1761 60d. Students outside building (vert) 80 85

387 Ionic and Corinthian Capitals, Temple of Apollo, Phigaleia-Bassae

1987. Classical Architecture Capitals. Mult.
1762 2d. Type **387** 10 10
1763 26d. Doric capital, Parthenon 20 20
1764 40d. Ionic capital, The Erechtheum 30 25
1765 60d. Corinthian capital, The Tholos, Epidaurus . . . . 1·10 1·00

388 Hands holding Cup Aloft

389 Diploma Engraving (Yiannis Kephalinos)

1987. Greek Victory in European Basketball Championship.
1766 **388** 40d. multicoloured . . . 60 60

1987. 150th Anniv of Fine Arts High School (1767) and 60th Anniv of Panteios Political Science High School (1768). Multicoloured.
1767 26d. Type **389** 20 10
1768 60d. School campus (horiz) 65 65

390 Angel and Christmas Tree (left half)

391 Eleni Papadaki in "Hecuba" (Euripides) and Philippi Amphitheatre

1987. Christmas.
1769 26d. Type **390** 35 30
1770 26d. Angel and Christmas tree (right half) 35 30
Nos. 1769/70 were printed together, se-tenant, forming a composite design.

1987. Greek Theatre. Multicoloured.
1771 2d. Type **391** 10 20
1772 4d. Christopher Nezer in "The Wasps" (Aristophanes) and Dodona amphitheatre . . 10 20
1773 7d. Emilios Veakis in "Oedipus Rex" (Sophocles) and Delphi amphitheatre 15 20
1774 26d. Marika Kotopouli in "The Shepherdess's Love" (Dimitris Koromilas) . . 25 25
1775 40d. Katina Paxinou in "Abraham's Sacrifice" (Vitzentzos Cornaros) . . 40 20
1776 50d. Kyveli in "Countess Valeraina's Secret" (Gregory Xenopoulos) . . 50 20
1777 60d. Karolos Koun and stage set 60 60
1778 100d. Dimitris Rontiris teaching National Theatre dancers an ancient dance 1·30 40

392 "Codonellina sp." (polyzoan)

394 Satellite and Fax Machine

393 Ancient Olympia

1988. Marine Life. Multicoloured.
1779A 30d. Type **392** 55 40
1780A 40d. "Diaperoecia major" (polyzoan (clump-forming animals)) . . . 60 40
1781A 50d. "Artemia" (marine animal) 85 55
1782A 60d. "Posidonia oceanica" (plant) and Marmora sea-bream . . . . . . 1·60 1·20
1783A 100d. "Padina pavonica" (plant) . . . . 2·75 1·20

1988. Olympic Games, Seoul. Multicoloured.
1784A 4d. Type **393** 30 25
1785A 20d. Ancient athletes in Gymnasium 70 40
1786A 30d. Modern Olympics centenary emblem . . . 1·20 65
1787A 60d. Ancient athletes training . . . . 3·00 2·20
1788A 170d. Runner with Olympic flame . . . . 4·75 1·70

1988. Europa. Transport and Communications. Multicoloured.
1789B 60d. Type **394** . . . . . 4·00 1·30
1790B 150d. Modern express and commuter trains . . . . 5·00 1·90

395 Katarraktis Falls

396 Emblems

1988. European Campaign for Rural Areas. Waterfalls. Multicoloured.
1791A 10d. Type **395** . . . . . 1·10 45
1792A 60d. Edessa waterfalls . . 3·00 1·60
1793A 100d. River Edessaios cascades . . . . 4·75 1·50

1988. 20th European Postal Workers Trade Unions Congress.
1794A **396** 60d. multicoloured . . 4·00 2·10

397 Mytilene Harbour, Lebos (painting by Theophilos)

398 Eleftherios Venizelos, Map and Flag

1988. Prefecture Capitals (1st series). Mult.
1795B 2d. Type **397** 10 10
1796B 3d. Alexandroupolis lighthouse, Evros (vert) 10 10
1797B 4d. St. Nicholas's bell-tower, Kozani (vert) . . 10 10
1798B 5d. Workmen's centre, Hermoupolis, Cyclades (vert) 10 10
1799B 7d. Sparta Town Hall, Lakonia 10 10
1800B 8d. Pegasus, Leukas . . . 15 10
1801B 10d. Castle of the Knights, Rhodes, Dodecanese (vert) 15 10
1802B 20d. Acropolis, Athens (vert) 15 10
1803B 25d. Aqueduct, Kavala . . 20 15
1804B 30d. Castle and statue of Athanasios Diakos, Lamia, Phthiotis (vert) 20 15
1805B 50d. Preveza Cathedral bell-tower and clock (vert) 35 15
1806B 60d. Esplanade, Corfu . . 50 35
1807B 70d. Aghios Nicholaos, Lassithi 55 30
1808B 100d. Six Springheads, Poligiros, Khalkidiki . . 1·20 25
1809B 200d. Church of Paul the Apostle, Corinth, Corinthia . . . . 2·75 40
See also Nos. 1848/62, 1911/22 and 1955/64.

1988. 75th Annivs. of Union of Crete and Greece (30d.) and Liberation of Epirus and Macedonia (70d.). Multicoloured.
1810A 30d. Type **398** 60 30
1811A 70d. Flags, map and "Liberty" . . . . 1·50 80

399 "Adoration of the Magi" (El Greco)

400 Map of E.E.C. and Castle of Knights, Rhodes

1988. Christmas. Multicoloured.
1812 30d. Type **399** 55 35
1813 70d. "The Annunciation" (Kostas Parthenis) (horiz) 1·00 75

1988. European Economic Community. Meeting of Heads of State, Rhodes. Multicoloured.
1814A 60d. Type **400** . . . . . 1·20 1·00
1815A 100d. Members' flags and coin . . . . 1·10 85

401 Ancient Olympia and High Jumper

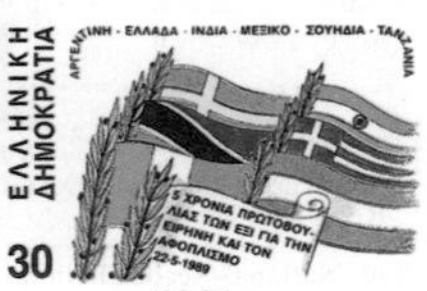

402 Flags

1989. Centenary (1996) of Modern Olympic Games (1st issue). Multicoloured.
1816A 30d. Type **401** 25 30
1817A 60d. Wrestlers and Delphi 1·00 80
1818A 70d. Acropolis, Athens, and swimmers . . . . . 1·10 1·00
1819A 170d. Stadium and Golden Olympics emblem . . . 2·20 1·50
See also Nos. 1863/7, **MS**1995 and 1998/2001.

1989. International Anniversaries. Mult.
1820A 30d. Type **402** (5th anniv of Six-nation Initiative for Peace and Disarmament) 50 40
1821A 50d. Flag and "Liberty" (bicentenary of French Revolution) 55 45
1822A 60d. Flag and ballot box (third direct European Parliament elections) . . 1·70 1·40
1823A 70d. Coins (cent of Interparliamentary Union) . . . . 1·70 1·50
1824A 200d. Flag (40th anniv of Council of Europe) . . 3·25 1·10

403 Whistling Bird

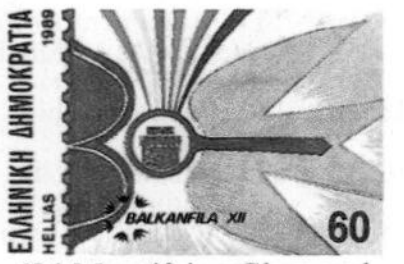

404 Magnifying Glass and Bird

1989. Europa. Children's Toys. Multicoloured.
1825B 60d. Type **403** . . . . . 2·20 1·50
1826B 170d. Butterfly . . . . . 2·50 1·20

1989. "Balkanfila XII" International Stamp Exhibition, Salonica. Multicoloured.
1827 60d. Type **404** 55 40
1828 70d. Eye looking through magnifying glass 55 55
MS1829 86 × 61 mm. 200d. Stamp collectors (42 × 30 mm) . . . . 1·75 1·75

405 Dog Roses

1989. Wild Flowers. Multicoloured.
1830 8d. Type **405** 15 10
1831 10d. Common myrtle . . . 15 10

1832 20d. Common poppies . . . 20 20
1833 30d. Anemones 30 25
1834 60d. Dandelions and chicory 45 35
1835 70d. Mallow 60 50
1836 200d. Thistles . . . . 1·10 1·20

406 Brown Bear

407 Gregoris Lambrakis

1990. Endangered Animals. Multicoloured.
1837 40d. Type **406** 35 20
1838 70d. Loggerhead turtle . . . 60 35
1839 90d. Mediterranean monk seal 75 50
1840 100d. Lynx 90 90

1990. Politicians' Death Anniversaries. Mult.
1841 40d. Type **407** (27th anniv) 40 35
1842 40d. Pavlos Bakoyiannis (first anniv) 40 35

408 Clasped Hands, Roses and Flag

409 Old Central Post Office Interior

1990. National Reconciliation. Multicoloured.
1843 40d. Type **408** 30 20
1844 70d. Dove with banner . . . 50 40
1845 100d. Map and hands holding roses 95 95

1990. Europa. Post Offices Buildings. Mult.
1846 70d. Type **409** . . . . . . 1·30 1·20
1847 210d. Exterior of modern post office . . . . 1·90 1·70

410 "Animal Fair" (D. Gioldassi) (Karditsa)

411 Yachting

1990. Prefecture Capitals (2nd series). Mult.
1848B 2d. Type **410** 10 10
1849B 5d. Fort, Trikala (horiz) 10 10
1850B 8d. Street, Veroia (Imathia) 10 10
1851B 10d. Monument to Fallen Heroes, Missolonghi (Aetolia) (horiz) 10 10
1852B 15d. Harbour, Chios (horiz) 10 15
1853B 20d. Street, Tripolis (Arcadia) (horiz) 10 10
1854B 25d. "City and Town Hall" (woodcut, A. Tassos) (Volos, Magnesia) (horiz) . . . 30 20
1855B 40d. Town Hall, Kalamata (Messenia) (horiz) . . . 20 20
1856B 50d. Market, Pyrgos (Elia) (horiz) 30 25
1857B 70d. Lake and island, Yannina (horiz) 35 30
1858B 80d. Harhour sculpture, Rethymnon 55 25
1859B 90d. Argostolion (Cephalonia) (horiz) . . 55 50
1860B 100d. Citadel and islet, Nauplion (Argolis) (horiz) 75 40
1861B 200d. Lighthouse, Patras (Akhaia) . . . . . . 1·50 55
1862B 250d. Street, Florina (horiz) . . . . 2·30 1·10

1990. Centenary (1996) of Modern Olympic Games (2nd issue). Multicoloured.
1863 20d. Type **411** 20 20
1864 50d. Wrestling 45 35
1865 80d. Running 85 80
1866 100d. Handball 90 60
1867 250d. Football . . . . . . 2·75 95

412 Schliemann and Lion Gate, Mycenae

413 "Woman knitting" (lithograph, Vasso Katraki)

1990. Death Cent of Heinrich Schliemann (archaeologist).
1868 **412** 80d. multicoloured . . . 2·40 1·20

1990. 50th Anniv of Greek–Italian War. Mult.
1869 50d. Type **413** 30 20
1870 80d. "Virgin Mary protecting Army" (lithograph, George Gounaropoulou) 50 50
1871 100d. "Women's War Work" (lithograph, Kosta Grammatopoulou) . . . 75 60

414 Hermes

1990. Stamp Day. Sheet 87 × 62 mm.
MS1872 **414** 300d. multicoloured 7·50 7·50

415 Calliope, Euterpe and Erato

1991. The Nine Muses. Multicoloured.
1873 50d. Type **415** 45 25
1874 80d. Terpsichore, Polyhymnia and Melpomene 85 45
1875 250d. Thalia, Clio and Urania . . . . 2·10 95

416 Battle Scene (Ioannis Anousakis)

1991. 50th Anniv of Battle for Crete. Mult.
1876 60d. Type **416** 90 50
1877 300d. Map and flags of allied nations (32 × 24 mm) . . . . . . 1·90 1·10

417 Icarus pushing Satellite

418 Swimming

1991. Europa. Europe in Space. Mult.
1878 80d. Type **417** . . . . . 1·40 95
1879 300d. Chariot of the Sun . . 2·75 1·90

1991. 11th Mediterranean Games, Athens. Multicoloured.
1880 10d. Type **418** 20 15
1881 60d. Basketball 40 25
1882 90d. Gymnastics 60 25
1883 130d. Weightlifting 80 50
1884 300d. Throwing the hammer 2·10 1·60

419 Pillar of Democracy

421 Pres Konstantinos Karamanlis signing Treaty of Athens

1991. 2500th Anniv of Birth of Democracy.
1885 **419** 100d. black, stone & blue 95 55

1991. 10th Anniv of Greek Admission to European Community. Multicoloured.
1887 50d. Type **421** 35 30
1888 80d. Map of Europe and Pres. Karamanlis 55 45

422 Emblem and Speed Skaters

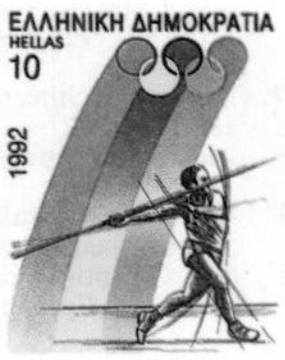

423 Throwing the Javelin

1991. Winter Olympic Games, Albertville. Multicoloured.
1889 80d. Type **422** 90 80
1890 300d. Slalom skier . . . . . 2·00 1·30

1992. Olympic Games, Barcelona. Mult.
1891 10d. Type **423** 20 15
1892 60d. Show jumping 65 30
1893 90d. Runner (37 × 24 mm) 1·00 65
1894 120d. Gymnastics . . . . . 1·30 50
1895 340d. Runners' heads forming Olympic rings (37 × 24 mm) . . . . . . 2·75 1·30

424 Couple beneath Umbrella

425 "Santa Maria", Map and Columbus

1992. Health. Multicoloured.
1896 60d. Type **424** (anti-AIDS campaign) 20 25
1897 80d. Doctor examining child (1st European Gastroenterology Week) 65 30
1898 90d. Crab killing flower on healthy plant (anti-cancer campaign) 75 35
1899 120d. Hephaestus's forge (from 6th-century B.C. urn) (European Year of Social Security, Hygiene and Health in the Workplace) 85 55
1900 280d. Alexandros Onassis Cardiosurgical Centre . . 2·75 1·20

1992. Europa. 500th Anniv of Discovery of America by Columbus. Multicoloured.
1901 90d. Type **425** . . . . . . 1·30 1·30
1902 340d. Chios in late 15th century . . . . 3·25 1·80

426 Proetus, Bellerophon and Pegasus

1992. European Transport Ministers' Conference, Athens. Sheet 85 × 59 mm.
MS1903 **426** 300d. multicoloured 4·00 4·00

427 Head of Hercules with Lion Skin (relief)

428 Piraeus

1992. Macedonia. Multicoloured.
1904 10d. Type **427** 20 15
1905 20d. Map of Macedonia and bust of Aristotle (horiz) 25 15
1906 60d. Alexander the Great at Battle of Issus (mural) (horiz) 55 20
1907 80d. Tomb of Philip II at Vergina, and Manolis Andronikos (archaeologist) 95 35
1908 90d. Deer hunt (mosaic, Pella) . . . . 1·00 35
1909 120d. Macedonian coin . . 1·40 70
1910 340d. 4th-century Church. Philippi, and Apostle Paul 4·00 1·70

1992. Prefecture Capitals (3rd series). Mult.
1911B 10d. Type **428** 10 10
1912B 20d. Amphissa (Phocis) . . 10 10
1913B 30d. The Heraion, Samos 20 15
1914B 40d. Canea 25 15
1915B 50d. Zakynthos 35 25
1916B 60d. Karpenisi (Evrytania) 35 25
1917B 70d. Cave, Kilkis (vert) . . 50 35
1918B 80d. Door of Town Hall Xanthi (vert) 55 35
1919B 90d. Macedonian Struggle Museum, Thessaloniki 75 40
1920B 120d. Tsanakleous School, Komotini (Rhodope) . . 1·00 50
1921B 340d. Spring, Drama . . . 2·50 95
1922B 400d. Pinios Bridge, Larissa . . . . 2·40 1·30

429 Column, Map, Flags and European Community Emblem

1992. Single European Market.
1923 **429** 90d. multicoloured . . . 70 1·50

430 Headstone (4th century B.C.)

431 Georgakis Olympios at Sekkou Monastery, 1821

1993. 2400th Anniv of Rhodes. Multicoloured.
1924 60d. Type **430** 50 25
1925 90d. "Aphrodite bathing" (statue) . . . . 1·10 40
1926 120d. "St. Irene" (from St. Catherine's church) . . 1·00 60
1927 250d. St. Paul's Gate, Naillac Mole . . . . . . 2·75 1·70

1993. Historical Events. Multicoloured.
1928 10d. Type **431** (War of Independence) 20 15
1929 30d. Theodore Kolokotronis (War of Independence) . . 25 20
1930 60d. Pavlos Melas (military hero) 50 25
1931 90d. "Glory crowns the Casualties" (Balkan Wars, 1912–13) . . . . 1·20 65
1932 120d. Soldiers of Sacred Company, El Alamein, 1942 (horiz) . . . . . . 1·90 80
1933 150d. Sacred Company on Aegean Islands, 1943–45 (horiz) . . . . 1·90 95
1934 200d. Victims' Monument, Kalavryta (destruction of village, 1943) . . . . . . 2·75 1·60

432 "The Benefits of Transportation" (Konstantinus Parthenis) (left half)

1993. Europa. Contemporary Art. Mult.

1935	90d. Type **432**	1·30	1·20
1936	350d. "The Benefits of Transportation" (right half)	3·50	3·25

Nos. 1935/6 were issued together, se-tenant, forming a composite design.

433 Athens Concert Hall

1993. Modern Athens. Multicoloured.

1937	30d. Type **433**	30	20
1938	60d. Iliou Melathron (former house of Heinrich Schliemann (archaeologist), now Numismatic Museum)	55	35
1939	90d. National Library	90	50
1940	200d. Athens Eye Hospital	1·90	1·20

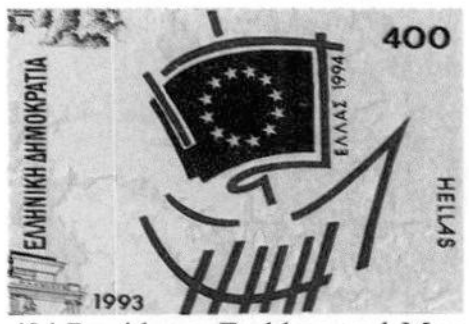

434 Presidency Emblem and Map

1993. Greek Presidency (1994) of European Union (1st issue). Sheet 84 × 60 mm.

MS1941	**434** 400d. multicoloured	4·00	4·00

See also Nos. 1953/4.

435 "Hermes leading Selene's Chariot" (Boeotian vase)

436 "Last Supper" (icon by Michael Damaskinou, St. Catherine's Church, Heraklion, Crete)

1994. 2nd Pan-European Transport Conf.

1942	**435** 200d. multicoloured	1·50	80

1994. Easter. Multicoloured.

1943	30d. Type **436**	20	15
1944	60d. "Crucifixion" (detail of wall painting, Great Meteoron)	35	10
1945	90d. "Burial of Christ" (icon, Church of the Presentation of the Lord, Patmos) (horiz)	60	35
1946	150d. "Resurrection" (detail, illuminated manuscript from Mt. Athos) (horiz)	1·30	85

437 Thales of Miletus (philosopher)

438 Demetrios Vikelas (first president, after G. Roilos)

1994. Europa. Discoveries. Multicoloured.

1947	90d. Type **437**	1·00	80
1948	350d. Konstantinos Karatheodoris (mathematician) and equations	2·75	1·70

1994. Sports Events and Anniversary. Mult.

1949	60d. Type **438** (centenary of International Olympic Committee)	40	25
1950	90d. Modern footballer and ancient relief (World Cup Football Championship, U.S.A.) (horiz)	60	50
1951	120d. Ball, net and laurel (World Volleyball Championship, Piraeus and Salonika)	1·00	45
MS1952	68 × 70 mm. 400d. Modern footballers, Statue of Liberty and ancient relief (World Cup) (41 × 51 mm)	3·00	3·00

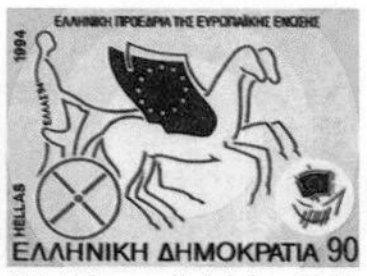

439 "Greece" driving E.U. Chariot

1994. Greek Presidency of European Union. Multicoloured.

1953	90d. Type **439**	75	55
1954	120d. Doric columns and E.U. flag	1·10	65

440 Parigoritissas Byzantine Church, Arta

441 "Declaration of Constitution" (detail, Carl Haupt)

1994. Prefecture Capitals (4th series). Mult.

1955B	10d. Tsalopoulou mansion house, Katerini (Pieria) (vert)	10	10
1956B	20d. Type **440**	10	10
1957B	30d. Bridge and tower, Levadia (Boeotia) (vert)	20	15
1958B	40d. Koumbelidikis church Kastoria	20	20
1959B	50d. Outdoor theatre, Grevena	20	20
1960B	60d. Waterfall, Edessa (Pella)	30	20
1961B	80d. Red House, Chalkida (Euboea)	55	35
1962B	90d. Government House, Serres	70	35
1963B	120d. Town Hall, Heraklion	75	45
1964B	150d. Church of our Lady of the Annunciation, Igoumenitsa (Thesprotia) (vert)	1·00	55

1994. 150th Anniv of Constitution. Mult.

1965	60d. Type **441**	35	20
1966	150d. Ioannis Makrygiannis, Andreas Metaxas and Dimitrios Kallergis (from "Neos Aristophanes" (magazine))	25	40
1967	200d. "The Night of 3rd September 1843" (anon) (horiz)	1·70	95
1968	340d. Article 107 of 1844 Constitution and Parliament Seal (horiz)	2·75	2·00

442 Mercouri and Demonstrators (fighter for Democracy)

1995. Melina Mercouri (actress and Minister of Culture) Commemoration. Multicoloured.

1969	60d. Type **442**	65	20
1970	90d. Mercouri and Acropolis (politician)	75	35
1971	100d. Mercouri in three roles (actress)	1·40	55
1972	340d. Mercouri with flowers (vert)	4·00	1·10

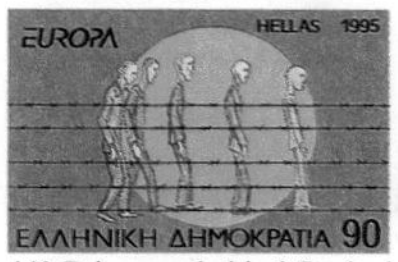

443 Prisoners behind Barbed Wire

444 Emblem

1995. Europa. Peace and Freedom. Mult.

1973	90d. Type **443**	1·30	1·60
1974	340d. Doves flying from crushed barbed wire	3·50	2·00

Nos. 1973/4 were issued together, se-tenant, forming a composite design.

1995. Anniversaries and Events. Mult.

1975	10d. Type **444** (5th World Junior Basketball Championship)	25	10
1976	70d. Agriculture University, Athens (75th anniv) (horiz)	60	25
1977	90d. Delphi (50th anniv of U.N.O.)	85	25
1978	100d. Greek flag and returning soldier (50th anniv of end of Second World War)	1·10	45
1979	120d. "Peace" (statue by Kifissodotos) (50th anniv of U.N.O.)	1·20	65
1980	150d. Dolphins (European Nature Conservation Year) (horiz)	1·60	65
1981	200d. Old telephone and modern key-pad (cent of telephone in Greece)	2·10	95
1982	300d. Owl sitting on ball (29th European Basketball Championship)	3·75	1·20

445 "The First Vision of the Apocalypse" (icon, Thomas Bathas)

1995. 1900th Anniv of the Apocalypse of St. John. Multicoloured.

1983	80d. Type **445**	95	65
1984	110d. St. John dictating to Prochoros in front of the Cave of the Apocalypse (miniature from the Four Gospels, Codex 81 of library of Patmos Monastery)	1·00	70
1985	300d. Trumpet of the First Angel (gilded Gospel cover) (horiz)	2·50	1·50

446 Goddess Athene with Argonauts

447 Psyttaleia

1995. Jason and the Argonauts. Mult.

1986	80d. Type **446**	45	40
1987	120d. Phineas (blind seer), god Hermes and the Voreadae pursuing Harpies	95	80
1988	150d. Medea, Nike and Jason taming bull	1·10	90
1989	200d. Jason and Medea killing snake and taking the Golden Fleece	1·50	1·20
1990	300d. Jason presenting Golden Fleece to Pelias	2·50	1·50

1995. Lighthouses. Multicoloured.

1991	80d. Type **447**	65	45
1992	120d. Sapienza	95	65
1993	150d. Kastri, Othonoi	1·40	85
1994	500d. Zourva, Hydra	4·00	2·00

448 1l. Stamp

1996. Centenary of Modern Olympic Games (3rd issue). Reproduction of Olympic Games issue of 1896. Three sheets each 88 × 88 mm, containing designs as T **448**. Inscriptions in brown, backgrounds flesh; colour of reproductions listed below.

MS1995	3 sheets (a) 80d. ochre (Type **448**); 120d. pink (2l.); 150d. brown (5l.); 650d. olive (10d.). (b) 80d. red (25l.); 120d. black (60l.); 150d. blue (1d.); 650d. reddish brown (10d.). (c) 80d. brown (20l.); 120d. lilac (40l.); 150l. brown (2d.); 650d. green (5d.) Set of 3 sheets	16·00	16·00

449 Sappho (poet)

450 Running

1996. Europa. Famous women.

1996	**449** 120d. multicoloured	1·10	1·20
1997	– 430d. brown, black & bl	4·25	3·25

DESIGN: 430d. Amalia Fleming.

1996. Centenary of Modern Olympic Games (3rd issue). Mult.

1998	10d. Type **450**	45	10
1999	80d. Throwing the discus	70	45
2000	120d. Weightlifting	1·20	60
2001	200d. Wrestling (horiz)	1·70	1·30

451 Hippocrates

452 Mytilene

1996. 1st Int Medical Olympiad, Athens.

2002	**451** 80d. brown, pink & black	85	70
2003	– 120d. brown, green & blk	1·40	1·10

DESIGN: 120d. Galen.

1996. Castles (1st series). Multicoloured.

2004B	10d. Type **452**	15	10
2005B	20d. Lindos	20	10
2006B	30d. Rethymnon	25	15
2007B	70d. Assos Cephalonia	35	40
2008B	80d. Castle of the Serbs	60	50
2009B	120d. Monemvasia	1·10	55
2010B	200d. Didimotihon	1·50	70
2011B	430d. Vonitsas	3·00	1·50
2012B	1000d. Nikopolis	8·25	4·00

See also Nos. 2069/78.

453 Puppets

1996. Shadow Puppets. Multicoloured.

2013	80d. Type **453**	60	35
2014	100d. Men courting woman	65	55
2015	120d. Soldiers	1·10	65
2016	200d. Men fighting dragon	1·90	1·20

454 Inscription on Wine Jug (720 B.C.)

456 St Dimitrios (patron saint) (fresco, Aghios Nikolaos Orphanos Church)

455 Papandreou, Cap, Degree and Books

1996. The Greek Language. Multicoloured.

2017	80d. Type **454**	60	25
2018	120d. Homer's "Iliad" (papyrus scroll, 436–45)	95	50
2019	150d. Psalm (6th century)	1·00	65
2020	350d. Dionysios Solomos (writer) and verse of poem (1824)	3·25	1·60

1997. Andreas Papandreou (Prime Minister, 1981–89 and 1993–96) Commemoration. Multicoloured.

2021	80d. Type **455** (Doctorate in Economics, Harvard University, 1943)	55	35
2022	120d. Return from exile, 1974, and smoking pipe	80	45
2023	150d. Parliament building and Papandreou	1·20	70
2024	500d. State flag, dove and Papandreou wearing glasses	3·25	2·50

1997. Thessaloniki, Cultural Capital of Europe. Multicoloured.

2025	80d. Type **456**	55	35
2026	100d. Hippocratic Hospital (horiz)	85	40
2027	120d. Marble statue pedestal (2nd century) and circular relief of woman's head	1·00	60
2028	150d. Mosaic (detail) in cupola of Rotunda	1·30	80
2029	300d. 14th-century chalice (horiz)	3·00	1·20

457 Trikomo

1997. Macedonian Bridges. Multicoloured.

2030	80d. Type **457**	55	35
2031	120d. Portitsa	1·00	60
2032	150d. Ziakas	1·20	75
2033	350d. Kastro	3·00	1·40

458 Prometheus the Fire-stealer

1997. Europa. Tales and Legends. Mult.

2034	120d. Type **458**	1·10	85
2035	430d. Knights (Digenes Akritas)	3·50	2·20

459 Running

1997. 6th World Athletics Championships, Athens. Multicoloured.

2036	20d. Type **459**	20	15
2037	100d. "Nike" (statue)	50	35
2038	140d. High jumping	95	55
2039	170d. Hurdling	1·20	90
2040	500d. Stadium, Athens	4·25	2·10

460 Alexandros Panagoulis (resistance leader)

461 Vassilis Avlonitis

1997. Anniversaries. Multicoloured.

2041	20d. Type **460** (20th death anniv (1996))	20	10
2042	30d. Grigorios Xenopoulos (writer, 130th birth anniv)	20	10
2043	40d. Odysseas Elytis (poet, first death anniv) (horiz)	25	25
2044	50d. Panayiotis Kanellopoulos (Prime Minister, 1945 and 1967, tenth death anniv (1996))	30	20
2045	100d. Harilaos Trikoupis (Prime Minister 1881–85, death centenary (1996)) (horiz)	95	40
2046	170d. Maria Callas (opera singer, 20th death anniv) (horiz)	1·40	80
2047	200d. Rigas Velestinlis-Feraios (revolutionary writer, death bicent (1998))	1·90	1·30

1997. Greek Actors. Multicoloured.

2048	20d. Type **461**	20	10
2049	30d. Vassilis Argyropoulos	20	10
2050	50d. Georgia Vassileiadou	45	20
2051	70d. Lambros Constantaras	55	30
2052	100d. Vassilis Logothetidis	85	35
2053	140d. Dionysis Papagiannopoulos	1·20	55
2054	170d. Nikos Stavrides	1·30	65
2055	200d. Mimis Fotopoulos	1·90	70

462 "Greece", Greek Flag and Colossus of Rhodes

463 Aghia Sofia Hospital, Athens

1998. 50th Anniv of Incorporation of Dodecanese Islands into Greece. Multicoloured.

2056	100d. German commander signing surrender to British and Greek military authorities at Simi, 1945	60	45
2057	140d. Type **462**	1·10	85
2058	170d. Greek and British military representatives at transfer ceremony, Rhodes, 1947	1·50	90
2059	500d. Raising Greek flag, Kasos, 1947	3·50	95

1998. Anniversaries and Events. Mult.

2060	20d. Type **463** (cent of Aghia Sofia Children's Hospital)	20	15
2061	100d. St. Xenophon's Monastery (millenary) (vert)	65	40
2062	140d. Woman in traditional costume (4th International Thracian Congress, Nea Orestiada) (vert)	1·20	70
2063	150d. Parthenon and congress emblem (International Cardiography Research Congress, Rhodes)	1·30	85
2064	170d. Sculpture of man and young boy (Cardiography Congress) (vert)	1·50	80
2065	500d. Emblem (50th anniv of Council of Europe) (vert)	3·50	1·60

464 Ancient Theatre, Epidavros

1998. Europa. National Festivals. Mult.

2066	140d. Type **464**	1·10	80
2067	500d. Festival in Herod Atticus Theatre, Athens	4·25	3·00

466 Ierapetra, Crete

1998. Castles (2nd series). Multicoloured.

2069	30d. Type **466**	20	10
2070	50d. Corfu	30	15
2071	70d. Limnos	35	25
2072	100d. Argolis	70	30
2073	150d. Iraklion, Crete	95	55
2074	170d. Naupaktos (vert)	1·10	70
2075	200d. Ioannina (vert)	1·40	90
2076	400d. Platamona	3·00	1·70
2077	550d. Karitainas (vert)	4·00	2·30
2078	600d. Fragkokastello, Crete	4·75	2·50

467 "Church of St. George of the Greeks" (18th-century copperplate)

1998. 500th Anniv of Greek Orthodox Community in Venice. Multicoloured.

2079	30d. Type **467**	20	20
2080	40d. "Christ Pantocrator" (icon) (vert)	25	20
2081	140d. Illuminated script of hymn "Epi Soi hairei" by Georgios Klontzas (vert)	80	65
2082	230d. "St. George of the Greeks" (illuminated manuscript, 1640)	2·20	75·00

468 Homer (poet)

1998. Ancient Greek Writers.

2083	**468**	20d. brown and gold	20	20
2084	–	100d. brown and gold	75	50
2085	–	140d. red and gold	95	85
2086	–	200d. black and gold	1·20	95
2087	–	250d. brown and gold	2·10	1·40

DESIGNS: No. 2084, Sophocles (poet); 2085, Thucydides (historian); 2086, Plato (philosopher); 2087, Demosthenes (orator).

469 Ancient Trireme and Circulation of Mediterranean Sea Currents

1999. International Year of the Ocean. Multicoloured.

2088	40d. Type **469**	20	20
2089	100d. Galleon (detail of icon "Thou art Great, O Lord" by I. Kornaros)	45	45
2090	200d. "Aigaio" (oceanographic vessel), astrolabe and seismic sounding of seabed	1·30	95
2091	500d. Apollo on ship (3rd-century B.C. silver tetradrachmon coin of Antigonus Dosonos)	2·10	2·50

470 Karamanlis

1999. 1st Death Anniv of Konstantinos Karamanlis (Prime Minister 1955–63 and 1974; President 1980–85 and 1990–95). Multicoloured.

2092	100d. Type **470**	55	40
2093	170d. Karamanlis and jubilant crowd, 1974	1·00	70
2094	200d. Karamanlis and Council of Europe emblem, 1979	1·30	80
2095	500d. Karamanlis and Greek flag (vert)	2·10	2·10

471 Mt. Olympus and Flowers

1999. Europa. Parks and Gardens. Multicoloured.

2096	170d. Type **471**	1·10	55
2097	550d. Mt. Olympus and flowers (different)	2·10	1·70

Nos. 2096/7 were issued together, se-tenant, forming a composite design.

472 Ancient Greek and Japanese Noh Theatre Masks

1999. Centenary of Diplomatic Relations between Greece and Japan.

2098	**472**	120d. multicoloured	55	40

473 Temple of Hylates Apollo, Kourion

1999. Cyprus–Greece Joint Issue. 4000 Years of Greek Culture. Multicoloured.

2099	120d. Type **473**	55	40
2100	120d. Mycenaean pot depicting warriors (Athens)	55	40
2101	120d. Mycenaean crater depicting horse (Nicosia)	55	40
2102	120d. Temple of Apollo, Delphi	55	30

474 Trains

1999. Fifth Anniv of Community Support Programme. Multicoloured.

2103	20d. Type **474** (modernization of railways)	10	30
2104	120d. Bridge over River Antirrio	50	60
2105	140d. Compact disk, delivery lorries and conveyor belt (modernization of Post Office)	70	75
2106	250d. Athens underground train	1·40	2·00
2107	500d. Control tower, Eleftherios Venizelos airport, Athens	2·20	2·40

475 Helicopter and Commandos in Inflatable Boat

1999. Armed Forces. Multicoloured.

2108	20d. Type **475**	10	15
2109	30d. Missile corvette	15	20
2110	40d. Two F-16 aircraft	20	25
2111	50d. CL-215 aircraft dispersing water on forest fire	20	20
2112	70d. Destroyer	30	30
2113	120d. Forces distributing aid in Bosnia	60	55
2114	170d. Dassault Mirage 2000 jet fighter above Aegean	85	85
2115	250d. Helicopters, tanks and soldiers on joint exercise	1·30	1·30
2116	600d. Submarine "Okeanos"	2·40	3·00

476 Birth of Christ

2000. Birth Bimillenary of Jesus Christ. Icons. Mult.

2117	20d. Type **476**	10	20
2118	50d. Discussion between men of different denominations	25	25
2119	120d. Angels praising God	60	60
2120	170d. Epiphany (horiz)	85	85
2121	200d. Communion (35 × 35 mm)	1·00	1·00
2122	500d. Heavenly beings above priests and worshippers (27 × 57 mm)	2·50	2·50

477 "Building Europe"

478 *Ilissos* (steamship)

2000. Europa.

2123	**477** 170d. multicoloured	85	1·00

2000. Ships. Multicoloured.

2124	10d. Type **478**	10	10
2125	120d. *Adrias* (destroyer)	60	60
2126	170d. *Ia II* (steamship)	85	85
2127	400d. *Vas Olga* (destroyer)	2·10	1·50

479 Rainbow over Village (Spyros Dalakos)

2000. "Stampin' the Future". Winning Entries in Children's International Painting Competition. Mult.

2128	130d. Type **479**	75	50
2129	180d. Robots (Moshovaki-Chaiger Ornella)	90	90
2130	200d. Cars and house (Zisis Zariotis)	1·00	1·00
2131	620d. Children astride rocket (Athina Limioudi)	3·00	2·50

480 Torch and Flag

481 Emblem and Olympic Rings

2000. Olympic Games, Sydney. Multicoloured.

2132	200d. Type **480**	90	95
2133	650d. Torch, flag and Sydney Opera House	2·75	2·20

2000. Olympic Games, Athens (2004) (1st issue).

2134	**481** 10d. multicoloured	10	10
2135	50d. multicoloured	40	35
2136	130d. multicoloured	65	65
2137	180d. multicoloured	90	90
2138	200d. multicoloured	1·20	1·10
2139	650d. multicoloured	3·25	2·75

See also Nos. **MS**2169, 2191/**MS**2196, 2207/10, **MS**2211, 2216/21, **MS**2222, 2234/8, **MS**2239, 2246/51, 2252/**MS**2258, 2259/63, 2264/**MS**2270, **MS**2271 and **MS**2272.

483 Orpheus Christ (sculpture)

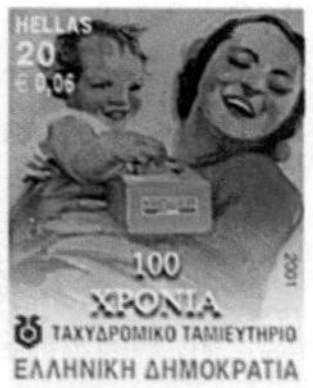

484 Mother and Child holding Money Box

2000. Birth Bimillenary of Jesus Christ. Mult.

2141	20d. Type **483**	10	10
2142	30d. The Good Shepherd (sculpture)	15	20
2143	40d. Christ Pantocrator (mosaic, Holy Monastery of Sina)	25	25
2144	100d. Anapeson in the Protato of Mount Athos (fresco, Manuel Panselinos) (horiz)	65	60
2145	130d. Christ (icon)	90	90
2146	150d. Christ (icon)	1·20	1·20
2147	180d. Christ Pantocrator (Encaustic icon)	1·50	1·50
2148	1000d. Christ Pantocrator (Byzantine coin) (horiz)	6·75	6·75

2001. Anniversaries and Events. Multicoloured.

2149	20d. Type **484** (centenary of Post Office Savings Bank)	10	10
2150	130d. Euro currency and emblem (centenary of Post Office Savings Bank) (horiz)	75	75
2151	140d. Refugees (50th anniv of United Nations High Commissioner for Refugees) (horiz)	90	90
2152	180d. Emblem and crowd (75th anniv of Thessalonika International Trade Fair)	90	55
2153	200d. University facade (75th anniv of Aristotle University, Thessalonika) (horiz)	90	55
2154	500d. Academy building (75th anniv of Academy of Athens) (horiz)	1·90	95
2155	700d. Ioannis Zigdis (politician, third death anniv)	3·25	1·90

485 Dried Earth

2001. Europa. Water Resources. Multicoloured.

2156	180d. Type **485**	95	45
2157	650d. Pool of water and droplet	2·75	1·10

486 Little Egret

2001. Flora and Fauna. Multicoloured.

2158	20d. Type **486**	10	20
2159	50d. White storks	30	25
2160	100d. Bearded vulture	60	35
2161	140d. Orchid (vert)	85	45
2162	150d. Dalmatian pelican (vert)	1·00	45
2163	200d. Lily, Plastina Lake, Karditsa	1·20	55
2164	700d. Egyptian vulture	2·40	1·90
2165	850d. Black vulture	3·75	2·50

487 Emblem

2001. New Name of Hellenic Post.

2166	**487** 140d. blue and yellow	85	85
2167	200d. blue	1·20	1·20

490 Kamakaki, Salamina

2002. Traditional Dances. Multicoloured.

2170	2c. Type **490**	10	10
2171	3c. Prikia (bride's dowry)	10	10
2172	5c. Zagorissios, Epirus (vert)	10	10
2173	10c. Balos, Aegean Islands	15	10
2174	15c. Synkathistos, Thrace	20	10
2175	20c. Tsakonikos, Peloponnese (vert)	30	15
2176	30c. Pyrrichios (Sera) (Pontian Greek)	40	20
2177	35c. Fourles, Kythnos (vert)	50	25
2178	40c. Apokriatos, Skyros	55	30
2179	45c. Kotsari (Pontian Greek)	50	30
2180	50c. Pentozalis, Crete (vert)	70	35
2181	55c. Karagouna, Thessaly	75	40
2182	60c. Hassapiko, Smyrneikos	85	40
2183	65c. Zalistos, Naoussa	90	45
2184	85c. Pogonissios, Epirus	1·20	60
2185	€1 Kalamtianos, Peloponnese	1·40	70
2186	€2 Maleviziotis, Crete	2·75	1·40
2187	€2.15 Tsamikos, Roumeli	3·00	1·50
2188	€2.60 Zeibekikos (vert)	3·50	1·80
2189	€3 Nyfiatikos, Corfou	4·25	2·10
2190	€4 Paschaliatikos	5·50	2·75

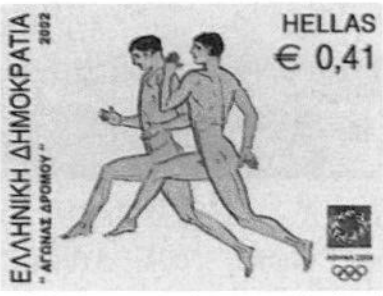

491 Runners (vase painting)

2002. Olympics Games, Athens (2004) (3rd issue). Multicoloured.

2191	41c. Type **491**	55	30
2192	59c. Charioteer (8th-century bronze statuette) (vert)	80	40
2193	80c. Javelin thrower (vase painting)	1·10	55
2194	€2.05 Doryphoros ("Spear Bearer") (statue, Polycleitos) (vert)	2·75	1·40
2195	€2.35 Weightlifter (vase painting)	3·25	1·60
MS2196	121 × 80 mm. €5 "Crypt of the ancient Olympic stadium, Olympia" (49 × 29 mm).	7·00	7·00

492 Performing Elephant

2002. Europa. Circus. Multicoloured.

2197	60c. Type **492**	85	40
2198	€2.60 Equestrian acrobat	3·75	1·80

493 Navy Scout

2002. Scouts. Multicoloured.

2199	45c. Type **493**	60	30
2200	60c. Scout and World Conference emblem	85	40
2201	70c. Air scout and Cub scouts planting tree	1·00	50
2202	€2.15 Scouts, mountains and map	3·00	1·50

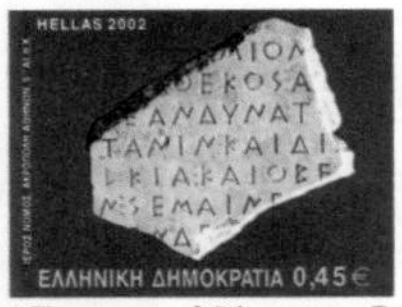

494 Fragment of 5th-century B.C. Tablet, Acropolis, Athens

2002. The Greek Language. Multicoloured.

2203	45c. Type **494**	60	30
2204	60c. 13th-century B.C. Linear B script tablet, Glay	85	40
2205	90c. Manuscript and General Makrygiannis (writer)	1·30	65
2206	€2.15 Manuscript and page from 11th-century Byzantine manuscript, Mount Athos	3·00	1·50

495 Man wearing Olive Wreath holding Two Ears of Corn

2002. Olympics Games, Athens (2004) (4th issue). Multicoloured.

2207	45c. Type **495**	60	30
2208	60c. Man wearing wreath and chewing ear of corn	85	40
2209	€2.15 Man beside column wearing wreath and chewing ear of corn	3·00	1·50
2210	€2.60 Man beside tilted column holding wreath	3·50	1·80

496 Facade

2002. Olympics Games, Athens (2004) (5th issue). Early Stadia. Sheet 120 × 75 mm.

MS2211	**496** €6 multicoloured	8·50	5·50

497 Chrysostomos Papadopoulos (1923–38)

2002. Archbishops of Athens. Multicoloured.

2212	10c. Type **497**	15	10
2213	45c. Chrysanthos Philippides (1938–41)	60	30
2214	€2.15 Damaskinos Papandreou (1941–49)	3·00	1·50
2215	€2.60 Seraphem Tikas (1974–98)	3·50	1·80

498 Discus

499 Athena (Girl Mascot)

2003. Olympic Games, Athens (2004) (6th issue). Multicoloured.

2216	2c. Type **498**	10	10
2217	5c. Shot put	10	10
2218	47c. Javelin	60	30
2219	65c. High jump	85	40
2220	€2.17 Hurdles	3·00	1·50
2221	€2.85 Dumbbells	4·00	2·00

2003. Olympic Games, Athens (2004) (7th issue). Sheet 128 × 82 mm containing T **499** and similar horiz design. Multicoloured.

MS2222	€2.50 Type **499**; €2.85 Phevos (boy mascot)	7·50	3·75

500 Globe

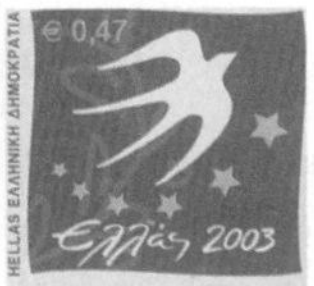

501 Swallow and European Stars

2003. Greetings Stamps. Sheet 123 × 124 containing T **500** and similar square designs. Multicoloured.
MS2223 47c. (a) Type **500** (corporate); 47c. (b) 2004 Olympics emblem (sponsor); 47c. (c) Man wearing wreath (Greece); 47c. (d) Roses (wedding); 47c. (e) Grid and skyline (corporate); 47c. (f) Stylized train (children); 47c. (g) Couple (social occasion); 65c. (h) Statue head (Greece); 65c. (i) Acropolis (Greece) . . . . . . 6·25 6·50

2003. Greek Presidency of the European Union. Multicoloured.
2224 47c. Type **501** 60 30
2225 65c. White Tower, Thessaloniki formed from letters 85 40
2226 €2.17 Swallows (fresco, Thera) . . . . 2·00 1·00
2227 €2.85 Stars and flags of member countries as jigsaw puzzle . . . . . . 4·00 2·00

502 Stylized Figure

2003. Europa. Poster Art. Multicoloured.
2228 65c. Type **502** 85 40
2229 €2.85 House with flag pole and veranda . . . . . . 4·00 2·00

503 Apple floating in Space and Trees

2003. Environmental Protection. Multicoloured.
2230 15c. Type **503** 20 10
2231 47c. Apple floating in water . . 60 30
2232 65c. Wreath above waves . . 85 40
2233 €2.85 Planet above apple tree . . . . 4·00 2·00

504 High Jump

2003. Olympic Games, Athens (2004) (8th issue). Multicoloured.
2234 5c. Type **504** 10 10
2235 47c. Wrestlers 60 30
2236 65c. Runners 85 40
2237 80c. Cyclists (vert) . . . . . 1·10 55
2238 €4 Windsurfer (vert) . . . . 5·75 2·75

505 Athena (Girl Mascot)

2003. Olympic Games, Athens (2004) (9th issue). Sheet 128 × 80 mm containing T **505** and similar horiz design. Multicoloured.
MS2239 €2.50 Type **505**; €2.85 Phevos (boy mascot) . . . . . 7·50 3·75

506 Stair Maker

2003. Traditional Trades and Crafts. Multicoloured.
2240 3c. Type **506** 10 10
2241 10c. Shoemaker 15 10
2242 50c. Smith 65 30
2243 €1 Type setter . . . . . . 1·40 70
2244 €1.40 Sponge diver . . . . 1·90 95
2245 €4 Hand weaver . . . . 5·75 2·75

507 Weightlifting

2003. Olympic Games 2004, Athens (10th issue). Athletes. Multicoloured.
2246 20c. Type **507** 25 10
2247 30c. Throwing javelin . . . 40 20
2248 40c. Charioteers 55 25
2249 47c. Soldier carrying spear and shield 60 30
2250 €2 Running . . . . 2·75 1·30
2251 €2.85 Throwing discus . . 4·00 2·00

508 Volos

2004. Olympic Games 2004, Athens (11th issue). Cities. Multicoloured.
2252 1c. Type **508** 10 10
2253 2c. Patra 10 10
2254 5c. Herakleio, Crete 10 10
2255 47c. Athens 60 30
2256 €1.40 Thessalonika . . . . 1·90 95
2257 €4 Athens . . . . 5·75 2·75
MS2258 120 × 135 mm. Nos. 2252/7 8·50 4·25

509 Spiros Louis

2004. Olympic Games 2004, Athens (12th issue). Greek Olympic Champions. Multicoloured.
2259 3c. Type **509** (marathon, 1896) 10 10
2260 10c. Aristides Konstantinides (cycling, 1896) 15 10
2261 €2 Ioannis Fokianos (modern Olympic pioneer) 2·75 1·30
2262 €2.17 Ioannis Mitropoulos (gymnast, 1896) . . . . . 3·00 1·40
2263 €3.60 Konstantinos Tsiklitiras (long jump, 1912) . . . . 5·00 5·25

510 Swimming

2004. Olympic Games 2004, Athens (13th issue). Sport Disciplines. Multicoloured.
2264 5c. Type **510** 10 10
2265 10c. Hands applying rosin 15 10
2266 20c. Canoeing 25 10
2267 47c. Relay race 60 30
2268 €2 Gymnastics floor exercise (vert) . . . . . . 2·75 1·30
2269 €5 Gymnastics ring exercise (vert) . . . . 3·25 1·60
MS2270 162 × 140 mm. Nos. 2264/9 7·00 3·50

511 Woman holding Torch

513 Yacht

512 Dove and Olympic Rings

2004. Olympic Games 2004, Athens (14th issue). Greetings Stamps. Sheet 90 × 75 mm containing T **511** and similar square design. Multicoloured.
MS2271 47c. Type **511**; €2.50 Woman and buildings . . . . 4·00 4·00

2004. Olympic Games 2004, Athens (15th issue). Sheet 128 × 81 mm containing T **512** and similar horiz design. Multicoloured.
MS2272 47c. Type **512**; €2.50 Dove and children . . . . 4·50 4·50

2004. Europa. Holidays. Multicoloured.
2273 65c. Type **513** 85 40
2274 €2.85 Hot air balloon . . . 4·00 2·00

CHARITY TAX STAMPS

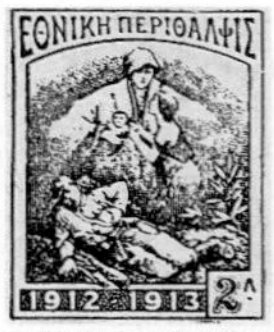

C **38** Dying Soldier, Widow and Child

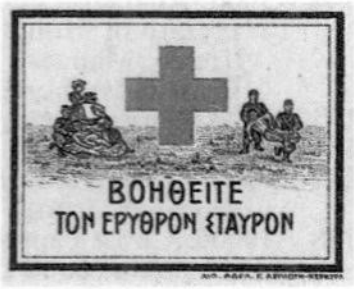

C **39** Red Cross, Nurses, Wounded and Bearers

1914. Roul.
C269 C **38** 2l. red 40 30
C270 5l. blue 55 45

1915. Red Cross. Roul.
C271 C **39** (5l.) red and blue . . . 13·50 1·60

C **40** Greek Women's Patriotic League Badge

1915. Greek Women's Patriotic League.
C272 C **40** (5l.) red and blue . . . 90 80

Κ. Π.
λεπτοῦ
1
(C 42)

C 43

Κ. Π.
λεπτοῦ
1
(C 44)

Κ.Π.
10 ΛΕΠΤΑ 10
(C 46)

1917. Surch as Type C 42.
C297 **15** 1 on 1l. brown . . . . . 1·50 1·60
C303 1 on 3l. orange 30 30
C299 5 on 1l. brown . . . . . 1·40 1·50
C300 5 on 20l. mauve 55 55
C307 **36** 5 on 25l. blue 60 60
C304 **15** 5 on 40l. brown 55 55
C308 **36** 5 on 40l. blue 30 30
C305 **15** 5 on 50l. lake 55 60
C309 **35** 5 on 50l. blue 30 30
C306 **17** 5 on 1d. black . . . . . 1·40 1·40
C301 **15** 10 on 30l. purple 80 80
C302 30 on 30l. purple . . . . 1·40 1·10

1917. Fiscal stamps surch as Type C **44**. Roul.
C310 C **43** 1l. on 10l. blue 70 70
C328 1l. on 50l. purple . . . 70 70
C311 1l. on 80l. blue 60 60
C330 5l. on 10l. purple . . . 70 60
C329 5l. on 10l. blue 80 60
C312 5l. on 60l. blue . . . . 4·00 2·75
C313 5l. on 80l. blue . . . . 2·75 2·20
C331 10l. on 50l. purple . . 6·50 7·50
C326 10l. on 70l. blue . . . 6·50 5·50
C315 10l. on 90l. blue . . . 9·75 7·75
C316 20l. on 20l. blue . . . £1500 £700
C317 20l. on 30l. blue . . . 3·25 3·25
C318 20l. on 40l. blue . . . 12·00 12·00
C319 20l. on 50l. blue . . . 5·50 5·00
C320 20l. on 60l. blue . . . £275 £180
C321 20l. on 80l. blue . . . 55·00 33·00
C322 20l. on 90l. blue . . . 3·00 2·40
C333 20l. on 2d. blue . . . 7·25 5·50

1917. Fiscal stamps surch as Type C **46**. Roul.
C334 C **43** 1l. on 10l. blue . . . . 1·10 1·00
C341 5l. on 10l. purple & red 6·75 2·75
C335 5l. on 50l. blue . . . . 31·00 31·00
C338 10l. on 50l. blue . . . 7·25 6·25
C339 20l. on 50l. blue . . . 15·00 15·00
C340 30l. on 50l. blue . . . 10·50 9·25

C **48** Wounded Soldier

C **77** St. Demetrius

C **49**

1918. Red Cross. Roul.
C342 C **48** 5l. red, blue and yellow 5·25 2·00

1918. Optd **P.I.P.** in Greek.
C343 C **48** 5l. red, blue and yellow 6·25 1·50

1922. Greek Women's Patriotic League. Surch as in Type C **49**.
C344 C **49** 5l. on 10l. red and blue £190 7·00
C345 5l. on 20l. red and blue 31·00 28·00
C346 5l. on 50l. red and blue £160 80·00
C347 5l. on 1d. red and blue 2·75 32·00
Nos. C344/7 were not issued without surcharge.

1924. Red Cross. As Type C **48** but wounded soldier and family.
C406 10l. red, blue and yellow . . 1·10 60

1934. Salonika Int Exn Fund.
C478 C **77** 20l. brown 20 10

C **78** Allegory of Health

ΠΡΟΝΟΙΑ
(C **85**)

1934. Postal Staff Anti-tuberculosis Fund.
C480 C **78** 10l. orange and green 10 10
C481 20l. orange and blue 30 30
C482 50l. orange and green 1·40 45

1935. As Type C **78** but with country inscription at top.
C494 10l. orange and green . . . 35 10
C495 20l. orange and blue . . . 35 20
C496 50l. orange and green . . . 55 20
C497 50l. orange and brown . . 90 25

1937. Nos. D273 and 415 optd with Type C **85**.
C498 D **20** 10l. red 35 25
C500 **51** 50l. violet 45 15

λ.50
ΠΡΟΝΟΙΑ
(C **95**)

C **96** Queens Olga and Sophia

1938. Surch with Type C **95**.
C521 D **20** 50l. on 5l. green . . . 80 45
C522 50l. on 20l. slate . . . 5·50 1·10
C523 **52** 50l. on 20l. violet . . . 55 10

1939.
C524 C **96** 10l. red 10 10
C525 50l. green 10 10
C526 1d. blue 20 20

ΠΡΟΣΤΑΣΙΑ ΦΥΜΑΤΙΚΩΝ ΤΤΤ
(C **104**)

1940. Postal staff Anti-tuberculosis Fund. Optd with Type C **104**.
C554 C **96** 50l. green 25 30

Κ.Π.
λεπτῶν
50
(C **105**)

ΔΡ.1
(C **107**)

1941. Social Funds. No. 410 surch with Type C **105**.

C561	**51**	50l. on 5l. green	20	10

1941. Postal Staff Anti-tuberculosis Fund. Surch **50** and bars.

C562	C **78**	50l. on 10l.	75	95
C563	–	50l. on 10l. (No. C494)	30	10

1942. Sample Fair, Salonika. No. C478 surch with Type C **107**.

C573	C **77**	1d. on 20l. brown	30	10

(C **109**)

(C **111**)

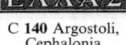

1942. Postal Staff Anti-tuberculosis Fund. Nos. 410 and 413 surch with Type C **109**.

C591	**51**	10d. on 5l. green	10	10
C592		10l. on 25l. green	20	10

1944. Postal Staff Anti-tuberculosis Fund. No. 580 optd with Type C **111**.

C599		100d. black	10	10

(C **112**)

1944. Postal Staff Anti-tuberculosis Fund. No. 579 surch with Type C **112**.

C600		5000d. on 75d. red	10	10

(C **113**)

1944. Postal Staff Anti-tuberculosis Fund. Surch as Type C **113**.

C619	–	1d. on 40l. (No. 500)	10	10
C620	–	2d. on 40l. (No. 500)	10	10
C605	**106**	25,000d. on 2d.	30	30

(C **117**)

C **127** St. Demetrius

(C **123**)

1946. Postal Staff Anti-tuberculosis Fund. Surch as Type C **117**.

C640	C **117**	20d. on 5l.	1·40	30
C641		20d. on 40l. (No. 500)	60	10

1946. Red Cross. Surch as Type C **117**.

C642	C **96**	50d. on 50l. (No. C525)	60	10

1946. Social Funds. Surch as Type C **117**.

C643	C **96**	50d. on 1d. (No. C526)	30	10

1947. Postal Staff Anti-tuberculosis Fund. Additionally surch with T C **123**.

C659	C **96**	50d. on 50l. (C525)	38·00	–
C660		50l. on 50d. (C554)	1·25	10

1948. Church Restoration Fund.

C682	C **127**	50d. brown	45	20

1950. Postal Staff Anti-tuberculosis Fund. Surch with Type C **117**.

C686		50d. on 10l. (No. 498)	95	10

(C **136**)

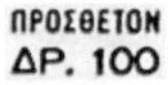

(C **139**)

1951. Postal Staff Welfare Fund. Surch with Type C **136**.

C698	**86**	50d. on 5l. blue & brown	1·60	10

1951. Postal Staff Anti-tuberculosis Fund. Surch with Cross of Lorraine and **50**.

C699	**89**	50d. on 3d. brown	1·40	10

1952. State Welfare Fund. No. 509 surch with Type C **139**.

C706	**89**	100d. on 8d. blue	80	10

C **140** Argostoli, Cephalonia

C **148** Zeus (Macedonian Coin of Philip II)

1953. Ionian Is. Earthquake Fund.

C713	–	300d. slate	90	10
C714	C **140**	500d. brown & yellow	2·75	75

DESIGN: 300d. Church of Faneromeni, Zante.

1956. Macedonian Cultural Fund.

C761	C **148**	50l. red	95	25
C762	–	1d. blue (Aristotle)	4·25	1·20

POSTAGE DUE STAMPS

D **2**

D **20**

1875.

D73	D **2**	1l. green and black	75	75
D74		2l. green and black	75	75
D75		5l. green and black	90	1·00
D88		10l. green and black	90	1·00
D89		20l. green and black	90	1·00
D78		40l. green and black	5·75	5·50
D91		60l. green and black	5·75	5·50
D80		70l. green and black	6·25	6·00
D81		80l. green and black	9·00	8·25
D82		90l. green and black	7·50	6·75
D95		100l. green and black	7·25	6·75
D96		200l. green and black	9·75	6·75
D83		1d. green and black	9·75	6·75
D84		2d. green and black	10·00	8·00

1902.

D183	D **20**	1l. brown	35	25
D184		2l. grey	35	25
D185		3l. orange	35	25
D186		5l. green	35	25
D273		10l. red	25	25
D188		20l. mauve	25	25
D275		25l. blue	15	10
D190		30l. purple	45	30
D191		40l. brown	20	35
D451		50l. brown	10	10
D193		1d. black	1·10	85
D194		2d. bronze	2·20	1·20
D195		3d. silver	2·75	1·70
D196		5d. gold	6·25	4·25

1912. Optd with T **34**.

D252A	D **20**	1l. brown	50	50
D253A		2l. grey	50	50
D254A		3l. orange	35	35
D255A		5l. green	45	45
D256A		10l. red	80	80
D257D		20l. mauve	65	65
D258		30l. purple	2·75	2·50
D259D		40l. brown	75	75
D260		50l. brown	60	60
D261D		1d. black	6·25	6·00
D262D		2d. bronze	7·50	7·25
D263D		3d. silver	11·50	11·50
D264D		5d. gold	22·00	21·00

1913. Perf or roul.

D269	D **20**	1l. green	10	10
D270		2l. red	10	10
D271		3l. red	10	10
D274		20l. slate	20	15
D276		30l. red	10	15
D277		40l. blue	20	20
D279		80l. purple	45	40
D452		1d. blue	35	25
D453		2d. red	10	10
D282		3d. red	4·25	2·25
D455		5d. blue	10	10
D456		10d. green	10	10
D595		10d. orange	15	15
D457		15d. brown	20	20
D458		25d. red	45	70
D596		25d. blue	10	20
D480		50d. orange	20	40
D481		100d. green	25	40
D597		100d. brown	10	10
D598		200d. violet	10	10

1942. Surch **50**.

D564	D **20**	50l. on 30l. red	45	60

GREEK WAR ISSUES, 1912–1913

For provisional issues used in territories occupied by Greece during the Balkan War, see Stanley Gibbons Part 3 (Balkans) Catalogue.

GREEK OCCUPATION OF ALBANIA — Pt. 3

100 lepta = 1 drachma.

Stamps of Greece optd with T **1**.

(**1**)

1940. Stamps of 1937.

1	**86**	5l. blue and brown	15	15
2	–	10l. brown & blue (No. 498)	15	15
3	–	20l. green & blk (No. 499)	15	15
4	–	40l. black & grn (No. 500)	15	15
5	–	50l. black & brn (No. 501)	15	15
6	–	80l. brown & vio (No. 502)	15	15
7	**89**	1d. green	25	25
8	–	2d. blue (No. 504)	25	25
9	**89**	3d. brown	25	25
10	–	5d. red (No. 506)	40	40
11	–	6d. olive (No. 507)	40	40
12	–	7d. brown (No. 508)	50	50
13	**89**	8d. blue	50	50
14	–	10d. brown (No. 510)	1·00	1·00
15	–	15d. green (No. 511)	75	75
16	–	25d. blue (No. 512)	2·50	2·50
17	**89a**	30d. red	5·00	5·00

1940. Charity Tax Stamps of 1939.

18	C **96**	10l. red on rose	15	15
19		50l. green on green	15	15
20		1d. blue on blue	25	25

1940. Nos. 534/53 (Youth Organization).

26	**101**	3d. blue, red & sil (postage)	75	75
27	–	5d. black and blue	3·50	3·50
28	–	10d. black and orange	5·75	5·75
29	–	15d. black and green	12·50	12·50
30	–	20d. black and red	7·75	7·75
31	–	25d. black and blue	7·75	7·75
32	–	30d. black and violet	9·50	9·50
33	–	50d. black and red	12·00	12·00
34	–	75d. gold, blue and brown	12·50	12·50
35	**101**	100d. blue, red and silver	16·00	16·00
36	**103**	2d. black and orange (air)	25	25
37	–	4d. black and green	1·30	1·00
38	–	6d. black and red	2·00	1·80
39	–	8d. black and blue	3·75	3·50
40	–	16d. black and violet	6·50	6·25
41	–	32d. black and orange	11·50	11·00
42	–	45d. black and green	11·50	11·50
43	–	55d. black and red	12·00	11·00
44	–	65d. black and blue	12·50	11·00
45	–	100d. black and violet	17·00	13·50

POSTAGE DUE STAMPS

1940. Postage Due stamps of 1913.

D21	D **20**	2d. red	25	25
D22		5d. blue	65	65
D23		10d. green	90	90
D24		15d. brown	1·00	1·00

1940. Postage Due stamp surch also.

D25	D **20**	50l. on 25d. red	1·00	1·00

GREENLAND — Pt. 11

A Danish possession N.E. of Canada. On 5 June 1963, Greenland became an integral part of the Danish Kingdom.

100 ore = 1 krone.

1 Christian X

2 Polar Bear

1938.

1	**1**	1ore green	15	25
2		5ore red	1·40	1·00
3		7ore green	1·90	2·30
4		10ore violet	85	45
5		15ore red	85	60
5a		20ore red	1·30	90
6	**2**	30ore blue	7·00	5·75
6a		40ore blue	23·00	5·25
7		1k. brown	8·50	6·75

3 Harp Seal

4 King Christian X

5 Eskimo Kayak

1945.

8	**3**	1ore violet and black	24·00	22·00
9		5ore buff and violet	24·00	22·00
10		7ore black and green	24·00	22·00
11	**4**	10ore olive and purple	22·00	22·00
12		15ore blue and red	22·00	22·00
13	–	30ore brown and blue	22·00	22·00
14	–	1k. grey and brown	22·00	22·00
15	**5**	2k. green and brown	23·00	22·00
16	–	5k. brown and purple	28·00	22·00

DESIGNS—HORIZ: As Type **5**: 30ore Dog team; 1k. Polar bear; 5k. Eider.

1945. Liberation of Denmark. Nos. 8/16 optd **DANMARK BEFRIET 5 MAJ 1945**.

17	**3**	1ore violet and black	65·00	41·00
18		5ore buff and violet	65·00	41·00
19		7ore black and green	65·00	41·00
20	**4**	10ore olive and purple	65·00	75·00
21		15ore blue and red	65·00	75·00
22	–	30ore brown and blue	65·00	75·00
23	–	1k. grey and brown	65·00	75·00
24	**5**	2k. green and brown	65·00	75·00
25	–	5k. brown and purple	65·00	75·00

7 King Frederik IX

8 Polar Ship "Gustav Holm"

1950.

26	**7**	1ore green	25	15
27		5ore red	35	20
28		10ore green	40	20
29a		15ore violet	55	40
30		25ore red	1·90	85
31		30ore blue	23·00	1·40
32		30ore red	65	30
33	**8**	50ore blue	42·00	11·00
34		1k. brown	14·50	1·80
35		2k. red	6·25	1·70
36		5k. grey	3·50	1·20

1956. Nos. 6a and 7 surch **60 ore**.

37	**2**	60ore on 40ore blue	6·25	90
38		60ore on 1k. brown	45·00	5·50

10 "The Boy and the Fox"

12 Hans Egede (after J. Horner)

14 Knud Rasmussen (founder of Thule)

1957. Greenland Legends.

39	**10**	50ore red	1·80	70
40	–	60ore blue	1·80	75
41	–	80ore brown	1·90	90
42	–	90ore blue	2·50	2·20

DESIGNS: 60ore "Mother of the Sea"; 80ore "The Girl and the Eagle"; 90ore "Great Northern Diver and Raven".

1958. Royal Tuberculosis Relief Fund. No. 33 surch with Cross of Lorraine and **30+10**.

43	**8**	30ore+10ore on 50ore blue	2·10	90

1958. Death Bicent of Hans Egede (missionary).

44	**12**	30ore red	6·50	95

1959. Greenland Fund. Surch **Gronlandsfonden 30+10** and bars.

45	**7**	30ore+10ore on 25ore red	4·50	3·25

The note below No. 413 of Denmark also applies here.

1960. 50th Anniv of Thule Settlement.

46	**14**	30ore red	1·20	85

15 Drum Dance

16 Northern Lights

17 Frederik IX

18 Polar Bear

1961.
47 **15** 35ore green 90 50

1963.
48 **16** 1ore green 20 15
49 5ore red 25 20
50 10ore green 45 30
51 12ore green 35 35
52 15ore purple 80 60
53 **17** 20ore blue . . . . 2·50 2·20
54 25ore brown 40 30
54a 30ore green 35 30
55 35ore red 35 30
56 40ore grey 40 30
57 50ore blue . . . . 7·00 5·25
57a 50ore red 45 30
57b 60ore red 50 25
58 80ore orange 65 60
59 **18** 1k. brown 70 25
60 2k. red . . . . 2·30 55
61 5k. blue . . . . 2·30 95
62 10k. green . . . . 3·00 55

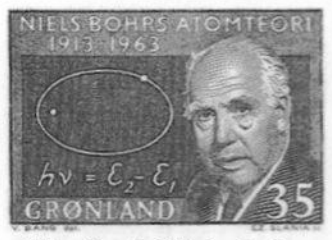

18a Prof. Niels Bohr

19 S. Kleinschmidt

1963. 50th Anniv of Bohr's Atomic Theory.
63 **18a** 35ore red 30 30
64 60ore blue . . . . 2·50 2·40

1964. 150th Birth Anniv of S. Kleinschmidt (philologist).
65 **19** 35ore brown 60 60

20a Princess Margrethe and Prince Henri de Monpezat

21a "The Children in the Round Tower" (legend)

1967. Royal Wedding.
66 **20a** 50ore red . . . . 2·40 2·10

1968. Child Welfare.
67 **21a** 60ore+10ore red 65 65

22 King Frederik IX and Map of Greenland

1969. King Frederik's 70th Birthday.
68 **22** 60ore red . . . . 1·10 95

24 Musk Ox

25 Celebrations at Jakobshavn

1969.
69 – 1k. blue 55 45
70 – 2k. green 75 40
71 – 5k. blue . . . . 1·50 60
72 – 10k. brown . . . . 2·75 1·20
73 **24** 25k. olive . . . . 6·50 1·90
DESIGN—HORIZ: 1k. Bowhead whale and coastline; 2k. Narwhal; 5k. Polar bear; 10k. Walruses.

1970. 25th Anniv of Denmark's Liberation.
74 **25** 60ore red . . . . 1·60 1·50

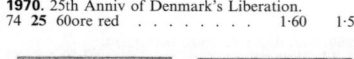

26 Egede and Gertrud Rask aboard the "Haabet"

27 Mail Kayaks

1971. 250th Anniv of Hans Egede's Arrival in Greenland.
75 **26** 60ore red . . . . 1·00 1·00
76 – 60ore+10ore red . . . . . 1·20 1·30

DESIGN: No. 76, Hans Egede and Gertrud Rask meeting Greenlanders.
The premium on No. 76 was for the Greenland Church Building Fund.

1971. Greenland Mail Transport.
77 **27** 50ore green 25 25
78 – 70ore red 35 25
79 – 80ore black 40 40
80 – 90ore blue 35 30
81 – 1k. red 55 50
82 – 1k.30 blue 55 45
83 – 1k.50 green 80 45
84 – 2k. blue 75 50
DESIGNS: 70 ore Umiak (women's boat); 80 ore Consolidated Catalina amphibian; 90 ore Mail dog-sledge; 1k. "Kununhuak" (coaster) and "Dlik" (tug); 1k.30 "Sokongen" (schooner); 1k.50 "Karen" (sailing longboat); 2k. Sikorsky S-61N helicopter.

28 King Frederik IX and Royal Yacht "Dannebrog"

29 Queen Margrethe

1972. King Frederik IX's and Queen Ingrid's Fund.
85 **28** 60ore+10ore red 75 65

1973.
86 **29** 10ore green 25 20
87 60ore brown 30 35
88 90ore brown 50 45
88a 100ore red 40 25
89 120ore blue 65 60
89a 130ore blue 50 50
For values inscribed "KALAALLIT NUNAAT" at top, see Nos. 99/104.

30 Heimaey Eruption

1973. Aid for Victims of Heimaey (Iceland) Eruption.
90 **30** 70ore+20ore blue and red . . . 90 85

31 "Carl Egede" (trawler) and Kayaks

32 Gyr Falcon and Radio Aerial

1974. Bicentenary of Royal Greenland Trade Department.
91 **31** 1k. brown 65 50
92 – 2k. brown 65 45
DESIGN—VERT: 2k. Trade Department Headquarters, Trangraven, Copenhagen.

1975. 50th Anniv of Greenland's Telecommunications Service.
93 **32** 90ore red 45 45

33 Sirius Sledge Patrol

1975. 25th Anniv of Sirius Sledge Patrol.
94 **33** 1k.20 brown 45 45

34 Arm-wrestling (after H. Egede)

35 Inuit Carved Mask

1976. Greenland Sports Publicity.
95 **34** 100ore+20ore brown and green on stone 45 45

1977. Eskimo Mask.
96 **35** 9k. grey . . . . 2·30 2·00

36 Bronlund and Disko Bay, Jakobshavn

37 Cape York Meteorite and "Ulo" (woman's knife)

1977. Birth Cent of Jorgen Bronlund (explorer).
97 **36** 1k. brown 35 30

1978. Centenary of Commission for Scientific Researches in Greenland.
98 **37** 1k.20 brown 45 35

38 Queen Margrethe

1978.
99 **38** 5ore red 25 15
100 80ore brown 30 25
101 120ore brown 45 40
102 130ore red 45 30
103 160ore blue 50 50
104 180ore green 60 50

39 Sun rising over Mountains

1978. 25th Anniv of Constitution.
105 **39** 1k.50 blue 40 40

40 Foundation Ceremony

41 Tupilak (imaginary animal)

1978. 250th Anniv of Godthab.
106 **40** 2k.50 brown 70 45

1978. Folk Art.
107 **41** 6k. red . . . . 1·50 1·30
108 – 7k. green . . . . 1·70 1·30
109 – 8k. blue . . . . 1·90 1·50
DESIGNS: 7k. Soapstone figure (Simon Kristoffersen; 8k. "Eskimo Family" (driftwood sculpture by Johannas Kreutzamann).

42 Helmsman

43 Rasmussen with Eskimos

1979. Internal Autonomy.
110 **42** 1k.10 brown 45 30

1979. Birth Centenary of Knud Rasmussen (polar explorer).
111 **43** 1k.30+20ore red 45 40

45 Eskimo Child

47 Queen Margrethe and Map of Greenland

1979. International Year of the Child.
112 **45** 2k. green 65 45

1980.
113 **47** 50ore violet 30 25
114 80ore brown 45 35
115 1k.30 red 50 45
116 1k.50 blue 60 55
117 1k.60 blue 65 50
118 1k.80 red 75 70
119 2k.30 green 65 65
120 2k.50 red 75 50
121 2k.80 brown . . . . . . 1·10 70
122 3k. red . . . . . . 1·20 75
122a 3k.20 red . . . . . . 1·20 65
123 3k.80 black . . . . . . 1·20 1·20
124 4k.10 blue . . . . . . 1·50 1·40
124a 4k.40 blue . . . . . . 1·70 1·40

48 Eskimos and Rasmus Berthelsen in Library

49 "Reindeer Sledge and the Larva" (drawing, Jens Kreutzmann)

1980. 150th Anniv of Greenland Public Libraries.
125 **48** 2k. brown on yellow . . . 60 45

1980. Greenland Art.
126 **49** 1k.60 red 45 45
127 – 2k.70 violet 75 80
128 – 3k. black 80 65
DESIGNS: 2k.70 "Harpooning Walrus" (printing by Jakob Danielsen); 3k. "Foot Race between Quloqutsuk and Aqigssia (woodcut by Aron from Kangeq).

50 Mikkelsen and Eskimo

52 Atlantic Cod

1980. Birth Centenary of Ejnar Mikkelsen (Inspector of East Greenland).
129 **50** 4k. green . . . . 1·00 85

1981.
130 **52** 25k. brown and blue . . . 5·75 3·75

53 Stone Tent Ring, Wolf and King Eiders

54 Reindeer and Hunter (Saqqaq culture, 2000 B.C.)

1981. Peary Land Expeditions.
131 **53** 1k.60+20ore brown 65 65

1981. Greenland Prehistory.
132 **54** 3k.50 blue 90 90
133 – 5k. brown . . . . 1·30 1·20
DESIGN: 5k. Hunters dragging walrus (Tunit-Dorset culture, 50 B.C.).

55 Shrimps

57 Eric the Red discovering Greenland, 982

1982.
134 **55** 10k. blue and red . . . . 2·50 1·50

1982. Millenary of Greenland (1st issue).
135 **57** 2k.+40ore brown 85 80
See also Nos. 136/7, 140/2, 145/7 and 152/3.

58 Eskimos hunting Bowhead Whale (1000–1100)

1982. Millenary of Greenland (2nd issue).
136 **58** 2k. red 55 50
137 – 2k.70 blue 80 75
DESIGN: 2k.70, Bishop Joen Smyrill's staff and house at Gardar (1100–1200).

59 Atlantic Salmon

60 Blind Person, Armband, Cassette and White Stick

1983.
138 **59** 50k. black and blue . . . 11·00 5·50

1983. Welfare of the Blind.
139 **60** 2k.50+40ore red 85 95

61 Eskimos and Northerners bartering (1200–1300)

62 Herrnhut Bandsmen

1983. Millenary of Greenland (3rd issue).
140 **61** 2k.50 brown 70 65
141 – 3k.50 brown 75 90
142 – 4k.50 blue . . . . 1·20 1·20
DESIGNS: 3k.50, Mummy of Eskimo boy (1300–1400); 4k.50, Hans Pothorst's expedition to America (1400–1500).

1983. 250th Anniv of Herrnhut Moravian Brethren Settlement.
143 **62** 2k.50 brown 70 75

63 "Polar Bear killing Seal Hunter"

64 Bowhead Whales and Glass Beads (trading goods) (1500–1600)

1984. 50th Death Anniv of Karale Andreassen (writer and artist).
144 **63** 3k.70 black . . . . 1·10 1·00

1984. Millenary of Greenland (4th issue).
145 **64** 2k.70 brown 85 90
146 – 3k.70 blue 95 95
147 – 5k.50 brown . . . . 1·40 1·30
DESIGNS: 3k.70 Greenlanders in European dress and apostle spoons (1600–1700); 5k.50, Hans Egede's mission station, Godthab, and key (1700–1800).

65 Prince Henrik of Denmark

66 Danish Grenadier, 1734

1984. Prince Henrik's 50th Birthday.
148 **65** 2k.70 brown . . . . 1·10 1·10

1984. 250th Anniv of Christianshab.
149 **66** 3k.70 brown . . . . 1·00 90

67 Lund

68 Spotted Wolffish

1984. 36th Death Anniv of Henrik Lund (composer).
150 **67** 5k. green . . . . 1·70 1·50

1984.
151 **68** 10k. black and blue . . . 3·00 2·75

69 "Hvalfisken" (brig) (1800–1900)

70 Queen Ingrid and "Chrysanthemum frutescens" "Sofiero"

1985. Millenary of Greenland (5th issue).
152 **69** 2k.80 purple . . . . 1·10 1·00
153 – 6k. black . . . . 1·30 1·40
DESIGN: 6k. Communications satellite and globe (1900–2000).

1985. 50th Anniv of Queen Ingrid's Arrival in Denmark.
154 **70** 2k.80 multicoloured . . . 70 75

71 Nesting Birds and I.Y.Y. Emblem

72 "Hare Hunt"

1985. International Youth Year.
155 **71** 3k.80 multicoloured . . . 90 90

1985. 130th Birth Anniv of Gerhard Kleist (artist).
156 **72** 9k. green . . . . 2·20 2·00

73 Greenland Halibut

74 Post Office Flags

1985.
157 **73** 10k. brown and blue . . . 2·40 2·40

1986. Postal Independence.
158 **74** 2k.80 red 70 65

75 Towing Man on Bladder (traditional sport)

76 Needle Case and Combs

1986. Greenland Athletic Federation.
159 **75** 2k.80+50ore mult . . . . 1·20 1·10

1986. Local Craft Artefacts.
160 **76** 2k.80 brown and red . . . 90 80
161 – 3k. violet and red 90 65
162 – 3k.80 black and blue . . . 1·00 95
163 – 3k.80 purple and blue . . . 1·40 1·20
164 – 5k. brown and green . . . 1·50 1·30
165 – 6k.50 brown and green . . 1·90 1·70
166 – 10k. brown and purple . . 3·00 2·40
DESIGNS: 3k. Tubs; 3k.80, (No. 162) Ulos (knives for working sealskins); 3k.80, (No. 163) Eye masks; 5k. Harpoon heads; 6k.50, Lard lamps; 10k. Masks.

77 "Daily Life in Thule" (collage by Aninaaq)

78 Capelin

1986. Art from Thule.
167 **77** 2k.80 brown 80 85

1986.
168 **78** 10k. brown and green . . . 2·75 2·30

79 Fulmar and Iceberg

1987. "Hafnia 87" International Stamp Exhibition, Copenhagen (1st issue). Sheet 95 × 70 mm containing T **79** and similar vert designs showing coastal view of Greenland from sketch by Jens Lorentzen. Multicoloured.
MS169 2k.80 Type **79**; 3k.80 Uummannaq Mountain and ice floes; 6k.50 Fulmars swimming and steamer in bay (sold at 19k.50) 6·25 7·25
See also No. **MS**193.

80 "Ammassalik Fjord" (Peter Rosing)

81 Father and Son on Ice-floe

1987. Greenland Art.
170 **80** 2k.80 brown 80 75

1987. Fishing, Sealing and Whaling Industries Year.
171 **81** 3k.80 multicoloured . . . 1·00 1·00

83 Rock Ptarmigans

84 Uummannaq Mountain

1988. Birds. Multicoloured.
172 3k. Gyr falcons . . . . . . 1·50 85
173 3k.20 Long-tailed ducks . . . 1·10 80
174 4k. Snow geese . . . . . . 1·60 85
175 4k.10 Common ravens . . . 1·40 1·20
176 4k.40 Snow buntings . . . . 1·60 1·30
177 5k. Type **83** . . . . 1·60 1·20
178 5k.50 White-tailed sea eagles 2·10 1·80
179 5k.50 Black guillemots . . . 1·70 1·50
180 6k.50 Brunnich's guillemots 2·30 1·80
181 7k. Great northern divers . . 2·40 1·90
182 7k.50 Long-tailed skuas . . . 2·30 1·90
183 10k. Snowy owl . . . . . . 2·75 2·00

1987. "Hafnia 87" International Stamp Exhibition, Copenhagen (2nd issue). Sheet 94 × 68 mm.
MS193 **84** 2k.80 blue and red (sold at 4k.) . . . . 2·30 2·50

85 Telefax, Sledge and De Havilland Dash Seven

1988. 50 Years of Greenland Postal Administration.
194 **85** 3k.+50ore multicoloured 1·30 1·50

87 National Flag

1989. 10th Anniv of Internal Autonomy. Mult.
195 3k.20 Type **87** 85 70
196 4k.40 National arms . . . . 1·30 1·20

88 Cotton Grass

89 Queen Margrethe

1989. Flowers. Multicoloured.
197 4k. Bellflower (vert) . . . . 1·20 90
198 4k. Hairy lousewort (vert) . . 1·30 1·20
199 5k. Type **88** . . . . 1·50 1·20
200 5k.50 Labrador tea . . . . . 1·60 1·30
201 6k.50 Arctic white heather . . 2·20 1·80
202 7k.25 Purple saxifrage . . . 2·75 2·20
203 10k. Arctic poppy (vert) . . . 2·75 2·20

1990.
210 **89** 25ore green 25 15
213 1k. brown 40 35
218 4k. red . . . . 1·10 80
219 4k.25 red . . . . 1·30 1·00
221 6k.50 blue . . . . 1·90 1·70
222 7k. violet . . . . 2·10 1·80

90 Chained Sledge Dog and nesting Eiders

91 Frederik Lynge

1990. Greenland Environmental Foundation.
225 **90** 400ore+50ore mult . . . . 2·20 2·00

1990. Augo and Frederik Lynge (Greenland Members of Danish Folketing).
226 **91** 10k. red and blue . . . . 3·00 2·10
227 – 25k. purple and blue . . . 6·75 3·75
DESIGN: 25k. Augo Lynge.

92 Ringed Seal ("Phoca hispida")

93 Dogs and Fisherman

1991. Marine Mammals. Multicoloured.
228 4k. Type **92** . . . . 1·30 1·20
229 4k. Harp seals ("Pagophilus groenlandicus") . . . . 1·30 1·20
230 7k.25 Hooded seals ("Cystophora cristata") . . 1·90 1·70
231 7k.25 Walrus ("Odobenus rosmarus") . . . . 1·90 1·70
232 8k.50 Bearded seal ("Erignatus barbatus") . . 2·20 1·90
233 8k.50 Common seal ("Phoca vitulina") . . . . 2·20 1·90
MS234 142 × 86 mm. Nos. 228/33 12·00 13·00

1991. 250th Anniv of Ilulissat (Jakobshavn).
235 **93** 4k. multicoloured . . . . 1·30 1·20

94 Iceberg and Summer Flowers

1991. Nordic Countries' Postal Co-operation. Tourism. Multicoloured.
236 4k. Type **94** . . . . 1·10 1·00
237 8k.50 Ski party and dog sled in winter . . . . 2·30 2·30

95 Birds

96 Jonathan Petersen (composer, 110th anniv)

1991. 75th Anniv of Blue Cross (health education organization)
238 **95** 4k.+50ore multicoloured 4·25 6·50

1991. Birth Anniversaries.
239 **96** 10k. black and blue . . . 3·00 2·00
240 – 50k. brown and blue . . . 11·50 11·50
DESIGN: 50k. Hans Lynge (writer and artist, 85th anniv).

97 Arms and Paamiut

1992. Bicentenary of Paamiut (Fredrikshaab).
241 **97** 7k.25 brown and blue . . . 2·10 2·00

98 Royal Couple in 1992 and in Official Wedding Photograph

1992. Silver Wedding of Queen Margrethe and Prince Henrik.
242 **98** 4k. multicoloured . . . . 1·70 1·40

99 Moller and Drawing of Godthab Church

100 Rainbow and Landscape

1992. 150th Birth Anniv of Lars Moller (editor and printer).
243 **99** 100k. red and blue . . . . 22·00 19·00

1992. Neriuffik Cancer Research Organization.
244 **100** 4k.+50ore multicoloured 3·00 2·50

101 Mother and Child with Father Christmas

102 Flame and Laurel Wreath framed by Dance Drum

1992. Christmas.
245 **101** 4k. multicoloured . . . . 1·70 1·20

1993. Int Year of Indigenous Peoples.
246 **102** 4k. multicoloured . . . . 1·30 1·10

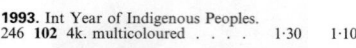

103 Flat Crab

1993. Crabs.
247 **103** 4k. red, yellow and green 1·20 90
248 – 7k.25 brown and blue . . 2·40 2·30
249 – 8k.50 multicoloured . . . 2·40 2·40
DESIGNS: 7k.25, Sand crab; 8k.50, Stone crabs.

104 Ummannaq Church

1993. Nordic Countries' Postal Co-operation. Churches. Multicoloured.
250 4k. Type **104** . . . . 1·00 1·20
251 8k.50 Hvalso church ruins . . 2·30 4·50

105 Children in Tent

1993. Anniversaries.
252 **105** 4k.+50ore multicoloured 1·60 1·80
253 – 4k.+50ore red and violet 1·60 1·80
MS254 140 × 80 mm. Nos. 252/3 each × 2 . . . . 14·50 16·00
DESIGNS: No. 252 Type **105** (50th anniv of scouts in Greenland); 253, Birds, crosses and landscape (70th anniv of Red Cross in Greenland).

106 Corpuscles and "AIDS"

1993. Anti-AIDS Campaign.
255 **106** 4k. multicoloured . . . . 1·20 1·10

107 Wolf

108 Dog Sled

1993. Animals. Multicoloured.
256 4k. Polar bear . . . . 1·40 1·30
257 5k. Type **107** . . . . 1·50 1·50
258 5k.50 Ermine . . . . 1·60 1·60
259 7k.25 Arctic lemmings . . . 1·70 1·90
260 7k.25 Wolverine . . . . . . 2·30 2·30
261 7k.50 Musk ox . . . . . . 2·50 2·75
262 8k.50 Arctic fox . . . . . . 2·40 2·50
263 9k. Mountain hare . . . . . 2·50 2·75
264 10k. Reindeer . . . . 2·75 3·00

1993. Christmas.
265 **108** 4k. multicoloured . . . . 1·40 1·30

109 Skiers

111 First Church

110 Transmission Line

1994. Winter Olympic Games, Lillehammer, Norway.
266 **109** 4k.+50ore multicoloured 1·90 1·40
MS267 140 × 80 mm. No. 266 × 4 13·00 10·50

1994. Inauguration of Buksefjorden Hydroelectric Power Station.
268 **110** 4k. multicoloured . . . . 1·20 1·10

1994. Centenary of Ammassalik.
269 **111** 7k.25 blue, brown & grn 2·10 1·90

112 "Danmark" (sail/steam barque)

1994. Europa. Discoveries. "Danmark" Expedition to North-east Coast, 1906–08. Multicoloured.
270 4k. Type **112** . . . . 1·20 1·10
271 7k.25 "Danmark" and dogs following ELG Mobil car 2·10 2·00

113 "Ceres" (William Moen)

1994. Figureheads from Greenlandic Ships (1st series). Multicoloured.
272 4k. Type **113** . . . . 1·10 1·10
273 8k.50 "Nordlyset" (Johan Heldt) . . . . 2·20 2·30
See also Nos. 287/8 and 306/7.

114 Christmas Visiting

1994. Christmas. Multicoloured.
274 4k. Type **114** . . . . 1·10 1·10
275 5k. Santa Claus outside igloo 1·40 1·30

115 "Listera cordata"

116 Teacher and Student

1995. Arctic Orchids (1st series). Multicoloured.
276 4k. Type **115** . . . . 1·10 1·00
277 7k.25 "Leucorchis albida" . . 2·00 1·90
See also Nos. 293/5.

1995. 150th Anniv of Nuuk Training College.
278 **116** 4k. multicoloured . . . . 1·20 1·10

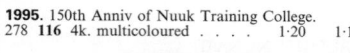

116a U.N. Emblem and "50"

1995. 50th Anniv of United Nations.
279 **116a** blue, green and red . . . 2·10 2·00

117 Iceberg and Meadow

1995. Nordic Countries' Postal Co-operation. Tourism.
280 4k. Type **117** . . . . 1·20 1·20
281 8k.50 Mountains and valleys 2·20 2·30

118 Airmail Envelope

1995. Europa. Peace and Freedom. Multicoloured.
282 4k. Type **118** . . . . 1·50 1·10
283 8k.50 Doves and seascape . . 2·75 2·30

119 King Christian X

1995. 50th Anniv of Liberation. Three sheets each 140 × 80 mm, containing reproductions of 1945 "American Series", surcharged in red. Multicoloured.
MS284 (a) 5k. on 10ore Type **119**; 5k. on 15ore Type **119**; (b) 1k. on 1ore Seal; 5k. on 5ore Seal; 7k. on 7ore Seal; (c) 4k. on 30ore Dog team; 4k. on 1k. Polar bear; 4k. on 2k. Eskimo kayak; 4k. on 5k. Eider Set of 3 sheets . . . . . 22·00 21·00

120 Children with Flag

121 Boy running with Lamps

1995. 10th Anniv of National Flag.
285 **120** 4k.+50ore multicoloured 2·10 1·60
MS286 80 × 140 m. No. 285 × 4 13·50 10·50
The premium was for the benefit of the Greenland Flag Society.

1995. Figureheads from Greenlandic Ships (2nd series). As T **113**. Multicoloured.
287 4k. "Hvalfisken" (H. J. Moen) (vert) . . . . 1·50 1·10
288 8k.50 "Tjalfe" . . . . 2·50 2·40

1995. Christmas. Multicoloured.
289 4k. Type **121** . . . . 1·50 1·00
290 5k. Boy running with lamp and moon . . . . 1·80 1·20

1995. Nos. 210 and 213 surch.
291 **89** 4k.25 on 25ore green . . . 2·50 1·80
292 4k.50 on 1k. brown . . . 3·00 2·10

1996. Arctic Orchids (2nd series). As T **115**. Multicoloured.
293 4k.25 Early coral-root . . . 1·30 1·00
294 4k.50 Round-leaved orchid 1·50 1·20
295 7k.50 Northern green orchid 2·30 2·20

124 Killer Whale

1996. Whales (1st series). Each black, red and blue.
296 25ore Type **124** 45 40
297 50ore Humpback whale . . . 45 45
298 1k. Beluga 60 50
299 4k.50 Sperm whale . . . . . 1·20 1·30
300 6k.50 Bowhead whale . . . . 1·90 1·70
301 9k.50 Minke whale . . . . . 1·80 2·30
See also Nos. 318/22.

125 Arnarulunnguaq (Eskimo traveller)

1996. Europa. Famous Women.
303 **125** 4k.50 blue . . . . 2·10 1·20

126 Man in Wheelchair at Sea Shore

1996. Greenland Society of Handicapped and Disabled.
304 **126** 4k.25+50ore mult . . . . 1·50 1·40
MS305 140 × 81 mm. No. 304 × 4 7·25 5·50

1996. Figureheads from Greenlandic Ships (3rd series). As T **113**. Multicoloured.
306 15k. "Blaa Hejren" . . . . . 4·00 3·75
307 20k. "Gertrud Rask" (horiz) 5·00 5·50

127 Child and Angels

1996. Christmas. Multicoloured.
308 4k.25 Type **127** . . . . . . 1·20 1·20
309 4k.50 Star and children . . . 1·20 1·30

128 Arctic Fritillary

129 Queen Margrethe in Greenlandic Costume

1997. Butterflies. Multicoloured.
310 2k. Type **128** 65 55
311 3k. Northern clouded yellow 95 85
312 4k.75 Arctic blue . . . . . . 1·40 1·20
313 8k. Small copper . . . . . . 2·10 2·00

1997. Silver Jubilee of Queen Margrethe.
314 **129** 4k.50 multicoloured . . . 1·20 95

130 Globe and Musicians

1997. Opening of Katuaq Cultural Centre, Nuuk.
315 **130** 4k.50+50ore mult . . . . 1·40 1·50
MS316 140 × 82 mm. No. 315 × 4 6·50 7·00

131 Bear of the Sea inhaling Umiak (boat)

1997. Europa. Tales and Legends.
317 **131** 4k.75 blue . . . . 1·90 1·70

1997. Whales (2nd series). As T **124**. Mult.
318 5k. Blue whale . . . . 1·40 1·40
319 5k.75 Fin whale . . . . . . 1·50 1·60
320 6k. Sei whale . . . . 1·50 1·50
321 8k. Narwhal . . . . 1·80 1·90
MS322 140 × 81 mm. Nos. 318/21 6·00 7·00

132 Dancing Children and Church

1997. Bicentenary of Nanortalik.
323 **132** 4k.50 multicoloured . . . 1·30 1·20

133 "Drum Dancer"

1997. Greenland Art (1st series). 20th Death Anniv of Aage Gitz-Johansen. Multicoloured.
324 10k. Type **133** . . . . . 2·40 2·50
325 16k. "Ammassalik Woman" 3·75 3·75
See also Nos. 342/3 and 353/4.

134 Boy with Huskies

1997. Christmas. Multicoloured.
326 4k.50 Type **134** . . . . . . 1·50 1·50
327 4k.75 Family on sledge and father disentangling traces 1·50 1·30

135 Common Porpoise

1998. International Year of the Ocean. Cetaceans. Multicoloured.
328 2k. Type **135** 75 65
329 3k. White-beaked dolphin . . 85 85
330 4k.50 Long-finned pilot whale ("Globicephala melaena") 1·10 1·10
331 4k.50 Northern bottle-nosed whale ("Hyperoodon ampullatus") . . . . . . 1·10 1·10
332 4k.75 Atlantic white-sided dolphin ("Lagenorhynchus acutus") . . . . 1·10 1·10
333 4k.75 Black right whale ("Eubalaena glacialis") . . 1·10 1·10
MS334 141 × 81 mm. Nos. 328/33 6·50 6·00

136 Augo and Frederik Lynge (first Greenland members of Danish Parliament)

137 Kathrine Chemnitz

1998. New Order, 1950 (redefinition of Greenland's status).
335 **136** 4k.50 blue, lilac and red 1·10 1·20

1998. 20th Death Anniv of Kathrine Chemnitz (founder) and 50th Anniv of Women's Society of Greenland.
336 **137** 4k.50+50ore mult . . . . 1·20 1·30
MS337 80 × 140 mm. No. 336 × 4 5·25 5·25

138 "Children's Faces" (Class 4B, Atuarfik Ukaliusaq School)

139 "Gertrud Rask" (sailing coaster)

1998. Europa. National Festivals. Children's Day. Multicoloured.
338 4k.75 Type **138** . . . . . . 1·50 1·50
339 10k. "Children playing" (Class 5A, Edvard Kruse-p Atuarfia School) . . . . . 2·40 2·30

1998. Nordic Countries' Postal Co-operation. Sailing Ships. Multicoloured.
340 4k.50 Type **139** . . . . . . 1·90 1·20
341 4k.75 "Hans Egede" (sailing coaster) . . . . 1·50 1·30

140 "Breastfeeding Older Brother"

1998. Greenland Art (2nd series). 10th Death Anniv of Hans Lynge (artist). Multicoloured.
342 11k. Type **140** . . . . . . 2·50 2·75
343 25k. "Refuelling" . . . . . 5·75 6·00

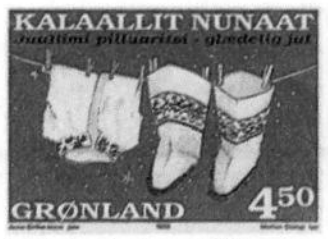
141 Jacket and Slippers on Line

142 Owl with Chicks

1998. Christmas. Multicoloured.
344 4k.50 Type **141** . . . . . . 1·30 1·20
345 4k.75 Hat and slippers on line . . . . 1·30 1·30

1999. Endangered Species. The Snowy Owl Multicoloured.
346 1k. Type **142** 60 55
347 4k.75 Owl in flight . . . . . 1·00 1·20
348 5k.50 Male and female owls 1·00 1·30
349 5k.75 Owl on rock . . . . . 2·10 1·70

143 Ammassalik Pincushion

144 Polar Bear

1999. Greenland National Museum and Archives.
350 **143** 4k.50+50ore black, blue and red . . . . 1·40 1·40
MS351 80 × 141 mm. No. 350 × 4 5·75 5·75

1999. Europa. Parks and Gardens.
352 **144** 6k. multicoloured . . . . 2·00 1·90

145 "The Man from Aluk"

1999. Greenland Art (3rd series). Paintings by Peter Rosing. Multicoloured.
353 7k. Type **145** . . . . 1·90 1·90
354 20k. "Homecoming" . . . . 5·00 5·00

146 Viking Longship

1999. Greenland Vikings (1st series).
355 **146** 4k.50 green and blue . . 1·20 1·20
356 – 4k.75 green and blue . . 1·20 1·30
357 – 5k.75 brown and blue . . 1·50 1·50
358 – 8k. brown and blue . . . 1·80 1·90
MS359 140 × 80 mm. Nos. 355/8 5·50 5·75
DESIGNS: 4k.75, Man collecting driftwood; 5k.75, Arrowhead and coins; 8k. Tjodhilde's Church, Brottal.
See also Nos. 363/7 and 390/4.

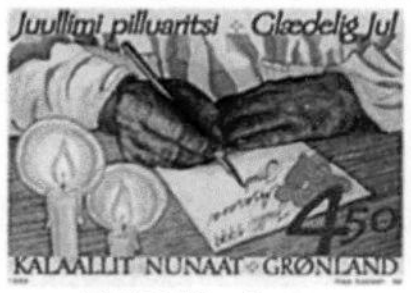
147 Writing Letter

1999. Christmas. Multicoloured.
360 4k.50 Type **147** . . . . . . 1·20 1·10
361 4k.75 Candles and clasped hands . . . . 1·20 1·20

148 Ice Cap

1999. New Millennium.
362 **148** 5k.75 multicoloured . . . 1·60 1·60

2000. Greenland Vikings (2nd series). As T **146**.
363 25ore brown and blue . . . 80 60
364 3k. brown and blue . . . . 1·20 1·10
365 5k.50 blue . . . . 1·60 1·60
366 21k. blue . . . . 3·50 4·25
MS367 140 × 81 mm. Nos. 363/6 7·00 7·25
DESIGNS: 25ore Walruses; 3k. Story teller and model of great northern diver; 5k.50, Dog chasing reindeer; 21k. Viking with gyr falcon, polar bear, walrus tusks and straps and bag of ship's tar (trading goods).

149 Huskies pulling Sledge

2000. 50th Anniv of "Sirius" (naval sledge patrol).
368 **149** 10k. multicoloured . . . 2·50 2·50

150 Queen Margrethe II (from photograph by Rigmor Mydtskov)

151 "Building Europe"

2000.
372 **150** 25ore blue and black . . 25 15
373 50ore blue and brown . . 75 55
374 4k.50 blue and red . . . 1·20 1·10
375 4k.75 blue & ultramarine 1·20 1·20
378 8k. blue and bistre . . . 2·00 1·90
379 10k. blue and green . . . 2·00 2·00
380 12k. blue and purple . . . 2·75 2·75

2000. Europa.
381 **151** 4k.75 multicoloured . . . 1·80 1·60

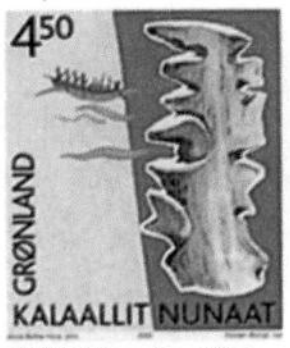
152 Wooden Map

153 Drum Dance

2000. Cultural Heritage (1st series). Multicoloured.
382 4k.50 Type **152** . . . . . . 1·10 1·20
383 4k.75 Sealskin . . . . 1·40 1·40
See also Nos. 395/6, 408/9 and 428/9.

2000. "Hafnia 01" International Stamp Exhibition, Copenhagen.
384 **153** 4k.50+1k. multicoloured 1·50 1·30
MS385 80 × 141 mm. No. 384 × 4

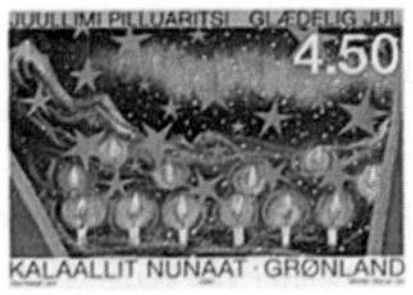
154 Candles and Stars

2000. Christmas. Multicoloured.
386 4k.50 Type **154** . . . . . . 1·30 1·40
387 4k.75 Winter landscape and star . . . . 1·60 1·40

155 Gymnast and Map

2001. Arctic Winter Games, Nunavut.
388 **155** 4k. 50+50 multicoloured 1·60 1·40
MS389 81 × 140 mm. No. 388 × 4 5·75 5·75

2001. Greenland Vikings (3rd series). As T **146**.
390 1k. red and blue 95 80
391 4k.50 ultramarine and blue 1·40 1·10
392 5k. ultramarine and blue . . 1·40 1·40
393 10k. red and blue . . . . . 2·50 2·10
MS394 141 × 81 mm. Nos. 390/3 5·00 5·00
DESIGNS: 1k. Fisherman and seals; 4k.50, Mouse sitting on food; 5k. Man with packhorses; 10k. Stone wall and common raven.

2001. Cultural Heritage (2nd series). As T **152**. Multicoloured.
395 4k.50 Preserving trout . . . 1·20 1·10
396 4k.75 Fishing spear . . . . . 1·10 2·50

156 Krill

2001. Europa. Water Resources.
397 **156** 15k. multicoloured . . . 3·00 3·25

157 Rock Ptarmigan and Berries

2001. Christmas. Multicoloured.
398 4k.50 Type **157** . . . . . . 1·10 1·10
399 4k.75 Doves flying . . . . . 1·30 1·30

158 Northern Lights

2001. Essays by Harry Nielsen for First Greenland Stamps. Each black and brown.
400 5k.75 Type **158** . . . . . . 1·80 1·70
401 8k. Seal . . . . 3·50 3·50
402 21k. Polar bear . . . . . . 6·25 5·75
MS403 142 × 80 mm. Nos. 400/2 6·25 7·00

159 Detail of "Stone and Man"

160 Banner, Igloo Builders and Polar Bears

2002. Nordic Countries' Postal Co-operation. Modern Art. Multicoloured.
404 1k. Type **159** (sculpture project, Aka Hoegh and others) 25 25
405 31k. Snow Sculpture (Nuuk Snow Festival, 2001) . . . 6·25 6·75

2002. "Children are People Too" (child welfare project).
406 **160** 4k.50 +50ore multicoloured . . . . . 1·20 1·20
MS407 81 × 140 mm. No. 406 × 4 4·50 3·50

2002. Cultural Heritage (3rd series). As T **152**. Multicoloured.
408 4k.50 Drum, Thule 65 95
409 4k.75 Inuit carved mask . . . 1·30 1·30

161 *Nordlyset* (sailing barque)

2002. Ships (1st series). Multicoloured.
410 2k. Type **161** 65 55
411 4k. *Hvidbjornen* (steam/sailing barque) . . . . 1·60 90
412 6k. *Staerkodder* (sloop) . . . 1·30 1·30
413 16k. *Haabet* (crayer) . . . . 3·75 4·00
See also Nos. 438/41.

162 Clown, Child and Snow Scene

2002. Europa. Circus.
414 **162** 11k. multicoloured . . . 2·75 2·75

163 Man carrying Gifts and Children on Sledge

2002. Christmas. (a) Ordinary gum.
415 4k.50 Type **163** . . . . . . 1·00 1·00
416 4k.75 Mother with child and carol singers . . . . 1·10 1·10
(b) Self-adhesive gum.
417 4k.50 No. 414 . . . . 1·00 1·10
418 4k.75 No. 416 . . . . 1·10 1·10
Nos. 417/18 form a composite design.

164 Cliffs and Greenland Shark (*Somniosus microcephalus*)

2002. Centenary of International Council for the Exploration of the Sea. Multicoloured.
419 7k. Type **164** . . . . 1·60 1·60
420 19k. Deepwater redfish (*Sebates mentella*) . . . . 4·25 4·50
MS421 185 × 60 mm Nos. 419/20 5·75 6·00
Stamps of a similar design were issued by Denmark and Faroe Islands.

165 Puppies

2003. Sled Dogs. Each black.
422 4k.50 Type **165** 85 80
423 4k.75 Adult . . . . 95 1·00
424 6k. Adult wearing harness . . 2·50 2·40

166 Tents and mountains

2003. Centenary of the Danish Literary Expedition to Greenland.
425 **166** 15k. agate, green and blue 4·00 4·00
426 – 21k. blue (28 × 22 mm) . . 3·75 3·75
MS427 166 × 61 mm Nos. 424/5 plus label . . . . 6·25 6·25
DESIGN: 21k. Knud Ramussen Stamps of a similar design were issued by Denmark.

2003. Cultural Heritage (4th series). As T **152**. Multicoloured.
428 25ore Comb, East Greenland 20 20
429 1k. Water bucket, East Greenland 25 25

167 Silamiut Theatre Poster

168 Narwhals and Cliffs

2003. Europa. Poster Art.
430 **167** 5k.50 multicoloured . . . 1·60 1·40

2003. 50th Anniv of Qaanaaq (settlement).
431 **168** 15k. multicoloured . . . 1·90 2·75

169 Children around Christmas Tree

170 Santa Claus inside Bauble

2003. Christmas. Ordinary or self-adhesive gum.
432 5k. Type **169** 90 90
433 5k.50 Family entering church 1·00 1·00
Nos. 434/5 were issued togethert, se-tenant, forming a composite design.

2003. Santa Claus of Greenland.
436 **170** 5k.+50ore multicoloured 1·00 1·00
MS437 81 × 140 mm. No. 436 × 4 4·00 4·00

2003. Ships (2nd series). As T **161**. Multicoloured.
438 6k.75 *Emma* (galleass) . . . 1·25 1·25
439 7k.75 *Gamle Fox* (screw-propelled schooner) . . . . 1·40 1·40
440 8k.75 *Godthaab* (screw-propelled barquentine) . . 1·60 1·60
441 26k. *Sonja* (whaling steamer) 4·75 4·75

171 Moon Man

172 Route Map

2004. Nordic Mythology. Multicoloured.
442 5k.50 Type **171** . . . . . 1·00 1·00
443 6k.50 Northern lights . . . . 1·10 1·10
MS444 106 × 70 mm. Nos. 442/3 2·10 2·10
Stamps of a similar theme were issued by Aland Island, Denmark, Faeroe Islands, Finland, Iceland, Norway and Sweden.

2004. 50th Anniv of First Scheduled Flight from Denmark to Greenland.
445 **172** 8k.75 multicoloured . . . 1·60 1·60

173 National Arms

174 Rowing Boat attempting Landing on Island

2004. 50th Anniv of Home Rule.
446 **173** 11k. multicoloured . . . 2·00 2·00

2004. 150th Birth Anniv of Otto Sverdrup (polar explorer).
447 **174** 17k.50 purple and buff . . 2·75 2·75
MS448 165 × 60 mm. No. 447 plus 2 labels . . . . 2·75 2·75
No. **MS**448 was issued with two stamp-sized labels showing designs of Canada and Norway stamps. Stamps of similar designs were issued by Norway and Canada.

PARCEL POST STAMPS

P 1 Arms of Greenland

1905.
P 4A **P 1** 1ore green . . . . . . 50·00 39·00
P 5A 2ore yellow . . . . . . £375 80·00
P 6A 5ore brown . . . . . . £130 90·00
P 7A 10ore blue . . . . . . 44·00 41·00
P 8A 15ore violet £200 £130
P 9A 20ore red . . . . 8·75 6·25
P13 70ore violet £120 £120
P14 1k. yellow . . . . . 42·00 60·00
P12A 3k. brown £100 £140
Prices for used stamps are for rubber stamp cancellations applied in Copenhagen, the various Greenland cancellations being worth much more. Stamps with numeral cancellations have been used as saving stamps.

GRENADA Pt. 1

One of the Windward Is., Br. W. Indies. Ministerial Government was introduced on 1 January 1960. Achieved Associated Statehood on 3 March 1967 and Independence on 7 February 1974.

1861. 12 pence = 1 shilling;
20 shillings = 1 pound.
1949. 100 cents = 1 West Indian dollar.

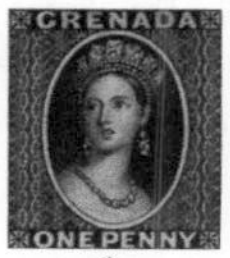

1

5

1861.
14 **1** 1d. green . . . . 75·00 7·50
6 6d. red . . . . £600 13·00

1875. Surch **POSTAGE** and value in words.
21 **5** ½d. mauve . . . . 11·00 5·50
22 2½d. lake . . . . 60·00 7·00
23 4d. blue . . . . £100 8·00
13 1s. mauve . . . . £650 11·00

1883. Revenue stamp surch crown and value (in green) optd **POSTAGE**.
27 **5** 1d. orange . . . . £325 55·00

1883. Revenue stamp as last but optd **POSTAGE** diagonally on each half.
29 **5** Half of 1d. orange £275 £110

13

21

1883.
30 **13** ½d. green . . . . 1·25 1·00
31 1d. red . . . . 70·00 3·25
32 2½d. blue . . . . 7·00 1·00
33 4d. grey . . . . 5·50 1·75
34 6d. mauve . . . . 3·25 4·00
35 8d. brown . . . . 9·00 12·00
36 1s. violet . . . . £120 55·00

1886. Revenue stamps as No. 27 but surch **POSTAGE**. and value in words or figures.
43 **5** ½d. on 2s. orange . . . . . 12·00 20·00
37 1d. on 1½d. orange . . . . 42·00 30·00
39 1d. on 4d. orange . . . . . £160 90·00
38 1d. on 1s. orange . . . . . 38·00 30·00
41 4d. on 2s. orange . . . . . 38·00 18·00

1887. As T **13**, but inscr "GRENADA POSTAGE & REVENUE" at top.
40 **13** 1d. red . . . . 1·50 1·25

1890. Revenue stamp as No. 27 but surch **POSTAGE AND REVENUE 1d.**
45 **5** 1d. on 2s. orange . . . . . 60·00 55·00

1891. Surch **POSTAGE AND REVENUE 1d.**
46 **13** 1d. on 8d. brown . . . . . 10·00 13·00

1891. Surch **2½d.**
47 **13** 2½d. on 8d. brown . . . . 8·00 11·00

1895.
48 **21** ½d. mauve and green . . . 2·50 1·75
49 1d. mauve and red . . . . 4·50 75
50 2d. mauve and brown . . . 40·00 32·00
51 2½d. mauve and blue . . . 5·50 1·50
52 3d. mauve and orange . . . 6·50 16·00
53 6d. mauve and green . . . 12·00 30·00
54 8d. mauve and black . . . 12·00 45·00
55 1s. green and orange . . . . 19·00 40·00

23 Flagship of Columbus (Columbus named Grenada "La Concepcion")

1898. 400th Anniv of Discovery of Grenada by Columbus.
56 **23** 2½d. blue . . . . 14·00 6·00

1902. As T **21**, but portrait of King Edward VII.
57 ½d. purple and green . . . . . 3·25 1·25
58 1d. purple and red . . . . . 4·50 30
59 2d. purple and brown . . . . 3·00 10·00
60 2½d. purple and blue . . . . 3·50 2·75
61 3d. purple and orange . . . . 3·75 9·00
72 6d. purple and green . . . . . 5·50 13·00
63 1s. green and orange . . . . 4·00 27·00
64 2s. green and blue . . . . . 21·00 55·00
65 5s. green and red . . . . . . 42·00 60·00
66 10s. green and purple £120 £250

26 Badge of the Colony

28

1906.
77 **26** ½d. green . . . . 4·50 30
78 1d. red . . . . 6·50 10
79 2d. orange . . . . 3·00 3·00
80 2½d. blue . . . . 6·00 1·75
84 3d. purple on yellow . . . . 4·75 1·75
85 6d. purple . . . . 20·00 23·00
86 1s. black on green . . . . . 7·00 4·50
87 2s. blue and purple on blue 19·00 12·00
88 5s. green and red on yellow 60·00 70·00
83 10s. green and red on green 90·00 £180

1913.
112 **28** ½d. green . . . . 1·25 30
113 1d. red 80 75
114 1d. brown . . . . 1·50 30
115 1½d. red . . . . 1·50 1·50
116 2d. orange . . . . 1·25 30
117 2d. grey . . . . 2·50 2·75
94 2½d. blue . . . . 1·75 3·50
118 2½d. grey . . . . 1·00 9·00
96 3d. purple on yellow . . . 65 85
121 3d. blue . . . . 1·25 11·00
123 4d. black and red on yellow . . . . 1·00 3·75
124 5d. purple and green . . . 1·50 4·25
97 6d. purple . . . . 1·50 9·00
126 6d. black and red . . . . 2·25 2·50
127 9d. purple and black . . . 2·25 9·50
98a 1s. black on green . . . . 1·25 7·50
129 1s. brown . . . . 3·00 10·00
99 2s. purple and blue on blue . . . . 6·50 12·00
131 2s.6d. black & red on blue 7·00 20·00
132 3s. green and violet . . . 6·00 27·00
133 5s. green and red on yellow . . . . 12·00 35·00
101 10s. green and red on green . . . . 55·00 90·00

1916. Optd **WAR TAX**.
111 **28** 1d. red 30 20

31 Grand Anse Beach

32 Badge of the Colony

1934.
135 **31** ½d. green . . . . 15 1·25
136a **32** 1d. black and brown . . . 65 35
137a – 1½d. black and red . . . 1·25 55
138 **32** 2d. black and orange . . 1·00 75
139 – 2½d. blue 50 50
140 **32** 3d. black and olive . . . 1·00 2·75
141 6d. black and purple . . . 2·00 1·75
142 1s. black and brown . . . 2·00 4·00
143 2s.6d. black and blue . . 8·00 28·00
144 5s. black and violet . . . 38·00 50·00
DESIGNS—VERT: 1½d. Grand Etang; 2½d. St. George's.

1935. Silver Jubilee. As T **10a** of Gambia.
145 ½d. black and green . . . . 80 1·25
146 1d. blue and grey . . . . . 80 1·75

147		1½d. blue and red	80	2·25
148		1s. grey and purple	6·50	19·00

1937. Coronation. As T **10b** of Gambia.

149	1d. violet	40	1·00
150	1½d. red	40	40
151	2½d. blue	80	1·00

35 King George VI

40 Badge of the Colony

1937.

152b	**35**	½d. brown	20	80

1938. As 1934, but with portrait of King George VI.

153a	**31**	½d. green	60	1·25
154a	**32**	1d. black and brown	50	50
155	–	1½d. black and red	50	85
156	**32**	2d. black and orange	30	50
157	–	2½d. blue	30	30
158ab	**32**	3d. black and olive	30	80
159		6d. black and purple	1·25	40
160		1s. black and brown	2·25	40
161		2s. black and blue	19·00	1·75
162		5s. black and violet	3·75	2·00
163e	**40**	10s. blue and red	27·00	8·50

1946. Victory. As T **11a** of Gambia.

164	1½d. red	10	30
165	3½d. blue	10	70

1948. Silver Wedding. As T **11b/c** of Gambia.

166	1½d. red	15	10
167	10s. grey	12·00	17·00

1949. U.P.U. As T **11d/g** of Gambia.

168	5c. blue	15	10
169	6c. olive	1·50	2·25
170	12c. mauve	15	30
171	24c. brown	15	30

41 King George VI

42 Badge of the Colony

1951.

172	**41**	½c. black and brown	15	1·60
173		1c. black and green	15	25
174		2c. black and brown	15	50
175		3c. black and red	15	10
176		4c. black and orange	35	40
177		5c. black and violet	20	10
178		6c. black and olive	30	60
179		7c. black and blue	1·75	10
180		12c. black and purple	2·25	30
181	**42**	25c. black and brown	2·25	80
182		50c. black and blue	6·50	40
183		$1.50 black and orange	7·50	7·00
184		$2.50 slate and red	5·50	5·50

No. 184 is larger, 24½ × 30½ mm.

43a Arms of University

43b Princess Alice

1951. Inauguration of B.W.I. University College.

185	**43a**	3c. black and red	45	1·00
186	**43b**	6c. black and olive	45	40

1951. New Constitution. Nos. 175/7 and 180 optd **NEW CONSTITUTION 1951**.

187	**41**	3c. black and red	15	60
188		4c. black and orange	15	60
189		5c. black and violet	10	70
190		12c. black and purple	15	70

1953. Coronation. As T **11h** of Gambia.

191	3c. black and red	20	10

1953. As T **41**, but with portrait of Queen Elizabeth II, and T **42**, but Royal Cypher changed.

192	**41**	½c. black and brown	10	10
193		1c. black and green	10	10
214		2c. black and brown	10	10
195		3c. black and red	10	10
196		4c. black and orange	10	10
197		5c. black and violet	10	10
198		6c. black and olive	45	1·25
199		7c. black and blue	1·25	10
219		12c. black and purple	20	10
201	**42**	25c. black and brown	1·25	20
202		50c. black and blue	5·50	40
203		$1.50 black and orange	11·00	14·00
204		$2.50 slate and red	18·00	10·00

No. 204 is larger, 24½ × 30½ mm.

47a Federation Map

1958. British Caribbean Federation.

205	**47a**	3c. green	35	10
206		6c. blue	45	60
207		12c. red	55	10

48 Queen Victoria, Queen Elizabeth II, Mail Van and Post Office, St. George's

1961. Grenada Stamp Centenary.

208	**48**	3c. red and black	25	10
209	–	8c. blue and orange	55	25
210	–	25c. lake and blue	55	25

DESIGNS (incorporating Queen Victoria and Queen Elizabeth II): 8c. Flagship of Columbus; 25c. "Solent I" (paddle-steamer) and Douglas DC-3 aircraft.

1963. Freedom from Hunger. As T **20a** of Gambia.

211	8c. green	30	15

1963. Centenary of Red Cross. As T **20b** of Gambia.

212	3c. red and black	20	15
213	25c. red and blue	40	15

1965. Centenary of I.T.U. As T **44** of Gibraltar.

221	2c. orange and olive	10	10
222	50c. yellow and red	25	20

1965. I.C.Y. As T **45** of Gibraltar.

223	1c. purple and turquoise	10	15
224	25c. green and lavender	20	15

1966. Churchill Commem. As T **46** of Gibraltar.

225	1c. blue	10	15
226	3c. green	10	15
227	25c. brown	15	10
228	35c. violet	25	15

49 Queen Elizabeth II and Duke of Edinburgh

1966. Royal Visit.

229	**49**	3c. black and blue	25	15
230		35c. black and mauve	65	15

52 Hillsborough, Carriacou

1966. Multicoloured.

231	1c. Type **52**	20	1·25
232	2c. Bougainvillea	20	10
233	3c. Flamboyant plant	1·00	1·00
234	5c. Levera Beach	1·25	10
235	6c. Carenage, St. George's	1·00	10
236	8c. Annandale Falls	1·00	10
237	10c. Cocoa pods	50	10
238	12c. Inner Harbour	30	1·25
239	15c. Nutmeg	30	1·25
240	25c. St. George's	30	10
241	35c. Grand Anse beach	30	10
242	50c. Bananas	1·25	1·75
243	$1 Badge of the Colony (vert) (25 × 39 mm)	7·00	3·75
244	$2 Queen Elizabeth II (vert) (25 × 39 mm)	5·00	7·50
245	$3 Map of Grenada (vert) (25 × 39 mm)	4·50	14·00

1966. World Cup Football Championship. As T **47** of Gibraltar.

246	5c. multicoloured	10	10
247	50c. multicoloured	40	90

1966. Inauguration of W.H.O. Headquarters, Geneva. As T **54** of Gibraltar.

248	8c. black, green and blue	20	10
249	25c. black, purple and ochre	45	20

1966. 20th Anniv of U.N.E.S.C.O. As T **56a/c** of Gibraltar.

250	2c. multicoloured	10	10
251	15c. yellow, violet and orange	15	10
252	50c. black, purple and orange	30	90

1967. Statehood. Nos. 232/3, 236 and 240 optd **ASSOCIATED STATEHOOD 1967**.

253	2c. multicoloured	10	15
254	3c. multicoloured	10	10
255	8c. multicoloured	15	10
256	25c. multicoloured	15	15

1967. World Fair, Montreal. Nos. 232, 237, 239 and 243/4 surch or optd **expo67 MONTREAL CANADA** and emblem.

257	1c. on 15c. multicoloured	10	20
258	2c. multicoloured	10	20
259	3c. on 10c. multicoloured	10	20
260	$1 multicoloured	30	25
261	$2 multicoloured	45	30

1967. Nos. 231/45 optd **ASSOCIATED STATEHOOD**.

262	**52**	1c. multicoloured	10	10
263	–	2c. multicoloured	10	10
264	–	3c. multicoloured	10	10
265	–	5c. multicoloured	10	10
266	–	6c. multicoloured	10	10
267	–	8c. multicoloured	10	10
268	–	10c. multicoloured	10	10
269	–	12c. multicoloured	10	10
270	–	15c. multicoloured	15	10
271	–	25c. multicoloured	20	10
272	–	35c. multicoloured	55	10
273	–	50c. multicoloured	1·00	20
274	–	$1 multicoloured	1·50	60
275	–	$2 multicoloured	1·25	3·75
276	–	$3 multicoloured	2·25	5·50

70 Kennedy and Local Flower

1968. 50th Birth Anniv of Pres. Kennedy. Multicoloured.

277	1c. Type **70**	10	15
278	15c. Type **70**	10	10
279	25c. Kennedy and strelitzia	10	10
280	35c. Kennedy and roses	10	10
281	50c. As 25c.	15	20
282	$1 As 35c.	25	60

73 Scout Bugler

1968. World Scout Jamboree, Idaho. Mult.

283	1c. Type **73**	10	10
284	2c. Scouts camping	10	10
285	3c. Lord Baden-Powell	10	10
286	35c. Type **73**	25	10
287	50c. As 2c.	35	20
288	$1 As 3c.	50	55

76 "Near Antibes"

1968. Paintings by Sir Winston Churchill. Multicoloured.

289	10c. Type **76**	10	10
290	12c. "The Mediterranean"	15	10
291	15c. "St. Jean, Cap Ferratt"	15	10
292	25c. Type **76**	20	10
293	35c. As No. 291	25	10
294	50c. Sir Winston painting	35	25

1968. No. 275 surch **$5**.

295	$5 on $2 multicoloured	1·50	2·25

1968. "Children Need Milk". Surch **CHILDREN NEED MILK** and value. (a) Nos. 244/5.

296	2c.+3c. on $2 multicoloured	10	10
297	3c.+3c. on $3 multicoloured	10	10

(b) Nos. 243/4.

298	1c.+3c. on $1 multicoloured	10	40
299	2c.+3c. on $2 multicoloured	13·00	55·00

83 Edith McGuire (U.S.A.)

1968. Olympic Games, Mexico.

300	**83**	1c. brown, black and blue	10	30
301	–	2c. multicoloured	10	30
302	–	3c. scarlet, brown and green	10	30
303	**83**	10c. multicoloured	15	30
304	–	50c. multicoloured	55	75
305	–	60c. red, brown and orange	60	80

DESIGNS: 2c., 50c. Arthur Wint (Jamaica); 3c., 60c. Ferreira da Silva (Brazil).

86 Hibiscus

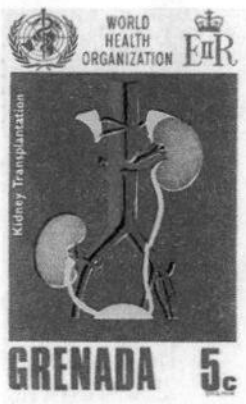

102 Kidney Transplant

1968. Multicoloured.

306	1c. Type **86**	10	10
307	2c. Strelitzia	10	10
308	3c. Bougainvillea	10	10
309	5c. Rock hind (horiz)	10	10
310	6c. Sailfish	10	10
311	8c. Red snapper (horiz)	10	30
312	10c. Marine toad (horiz)	10	10
313	12c. Turtle	15	10
314	15c. Tree boa (horiz)	1·00	60
314a	15c. Thunbergia	2·75	2·50
315	25c. Greater Trinidadian murine opossum	30	10
316	35c. Nine-banded armadillo (horiz)	35	10
317	50c. Mona monkey	45	25
317a	75c. Yacht in St. George's Harbour (horiz)	14·00	8·50
318	$1 Bananaquit	3·00	1·50
319	$2 Brown pelican	8·00	11·00
320	$3 Magnificent frigate bird	4·50	5·00
321	$5 Bare-eyed thrush	10·00	22·00

Nos. 318/21 are larger, 25½ × 48 mm.

1968. 20th Anniv of W.H.O. Multicoloured.

322	5c. Type **102**	20	10
323	25c. Heart transplant	30	10
324	35c. Lung transplant	30	10
325	50c. Eye transplant	35	50

106 "The Adoration of the Kings" (Veronese)

114 Dame Hylda Bynoe

111 Dame Hylda Bynoe (Governor) and Island Scene

1968. Christmas.

326	**106**	5c. multicoloured	10	10
327	–	15c. multicoloured	10	10
328	–	35c. multicoloured	10	10
329	–	$1 multicoloured	30	40

DESIGNS: 15c. "Madonna and Child with Saints John and Catherine" (Titian); 35c. "The Adoration of the Kings" (Botticelli); $1 "A Warrior Adoring" (Catena).

1969. Caribbean Free Trade Area Exhibition. Nos. 300/5 surch **VISIT CARIFTA EXPO '69 April 5-30** and value.

330 **83**	5c. on 1c.	10	10
331 –	8c. on 2c.	10	10
332 –	25c. on 3c.	10	10
333 **83**	35c. on 10c.	10	10
334 –	$1 on 50c.	20	30
335 –	$2 on 60c.	35	60

1969. Carifta Expo '69. Multicoloured.

336	5c. Type **111**	10	10
337	15c. Premier E. M. Gairy and island scene	10	10
338	50c. Type **111**	10	30
339	60c. Emblems of 1958 and 1967 World's Fairs	10	65

1969. Human Rights Year. Multicoloured.

340	5c. Type **114**	10	10
341	25c. Dr. Martin Luther King	15	10
342	35c. As 5c.	15	10
343	$1 "Balshazzar's Feast" (Rembrandt) (horiz)	30	45

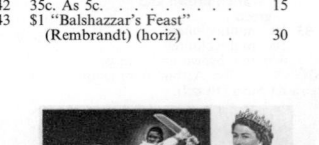

117 Batsman and Wicket-keeper

1969. Cricket.

344 **117**	3c. yellow, brown and blue	25	1·00
345 –	10c. multicoloured	25	40
346 –	25c. brown, ochre & green	45	85
347 –	35c. multicoloured	65	90

DESIGNS: 10c. Batsman playing defensive stroke; 25c. Batsman sweeping ball; 35c. Batsman playing on-drive.

129 Astronaut handling Moon Rock

1969. First Man on the Moon. Multicoloured.

348	$\frac{1}{2}$c. As Type **129** but larger (56 × 35 mm)	10	10
349	1c. Moon rocket and moon	10	10
350	2c. Module landing	10	10
351	3c. Declaration left on the moon	10	10
352	8c. Module leaving rocket	10	10
353	25c. Rocket lifting-off (vert)	25	10
354	35c. Spacecraft in orbit (vert)	25	10
355	50c. Capsule with parachutes (vert)	35	30
356	$1 Type **129**	50	1·25
MS357	115 × 90 mm. Nos. 351 and 356. Imperf	1·00	2·75

130 Gandhi

1969. Birth Cent of Mahatma Gandhi. Mult.

358	6c. Type **130**	15	20
359	15c. Gandhi standing	20	10
360	25c. Gandhi walking	25	10
361	$1 Head of Gandhi	50	75
MS362	155 × 122 mm. Nos. 358/61. Imperf	1·75	3·50

1969. Christmas. Nos. 326/9 optd **1969** and surch (No. 363).

363 –	2c. on 15c. multicoloured	10	90
364 **106**	5c. multicoloured	10	10
365 –	35c. multicoloured	20	10
366 –	$1 multicoloured	80	1·90

135 "Blackbeard" (Edward Teach)

1970. Pirates.

367 **135**	15c. black	35	10
368 –	25c. green	50	10
369 –	50c. lilac	90	20
370 –	$1 carmine	1·50	75

DESIGNS: 25c. Anne Bonney; 50c. Jean Lafitte; $1 Mary Read.

1970. No. 348 surch **5c.**

371	5c. on $\frac{1}{2}$c. multicoloured	10	10

141/2 "The Last Supper" (detail, Del Sarto)

1970. Easter. Paintings.

372 **141**	5c. multicoloured	10	30
373 **142**	5c. multicoloured	10	30
374 –	15c. multicoloured	15	35
375 –	15c. multicoloured	15	35
376 –	25c. multicoloured	15	35
377 –	25c. multicoloured	15	35
378 –	60c. multicoloured	20	60
379 –	60c. multicoloured	20	60
MS380	120 × 140 mm. Nos. 376/9	75	1·75

DESIGNS: 15c. "Christ crowned with Thorns" (detail, Van Dyck); 25c. "The Passion of Christ" (detail, Memling); 60c. "Christ in the Tomb" (detail, Rubens).

Each value was issued in sheets containing the two stamps se-tenant. Each design is spread over two stamps as in Types **141/2**.

149 Girl with Kittens in Pram

1970. Birth Bicentenary of Wordsworth. "Children and Pets". Multicoloured.

381	5c. Type **149**	15	15
382	15c. Girl with puppy and kitten	25	15
383	30c. Boy with fishing-rod and cat	30	30
384	60c. Boys and girls with cats and dogs	40	1·50
MS385	Two sheets, each 114 × 126 mm. Nos. 381, 383 and Nos. 382, 384. Imperf	1·00	2·00

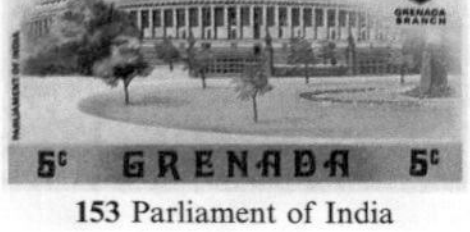

153 Parliament of India

1970. 7th Regional Conference of Commonwealth Parliamentary Association. Parliament Buildings. Multicoloured.

386	5c. Type **153**	10	10
387	25c. Great Britain	10	10
388	50c. Canada	20	15
389	60c. Grenada	20	15
MS390	126 × 90 mm. Nos. 386/9	50	90

157 Tower of the Sun

1970. World Fair, Osaka. Multicoloured.

391	1c. Type **157**	10	35
392	2c. Livelihood and Industry Pavilion (horiz)	10	35
393	3c. Flower painting, 1634	10	35
394	10c. "Adam and Eve" (Tintoretto) (horiz)	10	10
395	25c. Organization For Economic Co-operation and Development (O.E.C.D.) Pavilion (horiz)	15	10
396	50c. San Francisco Pavilion	30	1·60
MS397	121 × 91 mm. $1 Japanese Pavilion (56 × 34 mm)	55	1·50

164 Roosevelt and "Raising U.S. Flag on Iwo Jima"

1970. 25th Anniv of Ending of World War II. Multicoloured.

398	$\frac{1}{2}$c. Type **164**	10	80
399	5c. Zhukov and "Fall of Berlin"	70	30
400	15c. Churchill and "Evacuation at Dunkirk"	1·50	45
401	25c. De Gaulle and "Liberation of Paris"	1·25	45
402	50c. Eisenhower and "D-Day Landing"	1·50	1·50
403	60c. Montgomery and "Battle of Alamein"	1·50	3·25
MS404	163 × 113 mm. Nos. 398, 400, 402/3	2·75	7·00

1970. "Philympia 1970" Stamp Exhibition, London. Nos. 353/6 optd **PHILYMPIA LONDON 1970.**

405 –	25c. multicoloured	10	10
406 –	35c. multicoloured	10	10
407 –	50c. multicoloured	15	15
408 **129**	$1 multicoloured	20	30

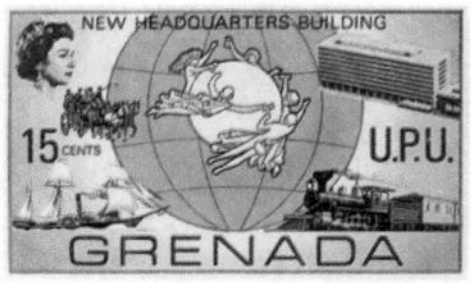

170 U.P.U. Headquarters Building and Transport

1970. New U.P.U. Headquarters Building. Multicoloured.

409	15c. Type **170**	60	20
410	25c. As Type **170**, but modern transport	60	20
411	50c. Sir Rowland Hill and U.P.U. Building (vert)	35	35
412	$1 Abraham Lincoln and U.P.U. Building (vert)	40	1·75
MS413	79 × 85 mm. Nos. 411/12	1·00	3·50

171 "The Madonna of the Goldfinch" (Tiepolo)

1970. Christmas. Multicoloured.

414	$\frac{1}{2}$c. Type **171**	10	35
415	$\frac{1}{2}$c. "The Virgin and Child with St. Peter and St. Paul" (Bouts)	10	35
416	$\frac{1}{2}$c. "The Virgin and Child" (Bellini)	10	35
417	2c. "The Madonna of the Basket" (Correggio)	10	35
418	3c. Type **171**	10	35
419	35c. As No. 415	20	10
420	50c. As 2c.	30	40
421	$1 As No. 416	50	1·60
MS422	102 × 87 mm. Nos. 420/1	1·00	3·00

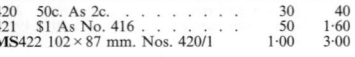

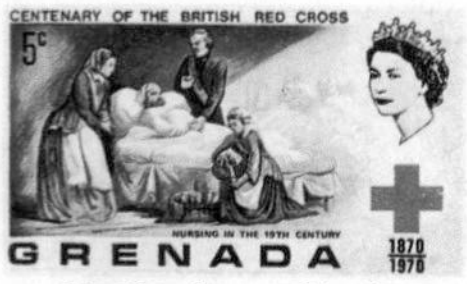

172 19th-Century Nursing

1970. Cent of British Red Cross. Multicoloured.

423	5c. Type **172**	20	10
424	15c. Military ambulance, 1918	25	10
425	25c. First-aid post, 1941	35	10
426	60c. Red Cross transport, 1970	90	1·25
MS427	113 × 82 mm. Nos. 423/6	2·00	1·60

173 John Dewey and Art Lesson

1971. Int Education Year. Multicoloured.

428	5c. Type **173**	10	10
429	10c. Jean-Jacques Rousseau and "Alphabetization"	15	10
430	50c. Maimonides and laboratory	50	15
431	$1 Bertrand Russell and mathematics class	95	40
MS432	90 × 98 mm. Nos. 430/1	1·00	2·00

174 Jennifer Hosten and Outline of Grenada

1971. Winner of "Miss World" Competition (1970).

433 **174**	5c. multicoloured	10	10
434	10c. multicoloured	10	10
435	15c. multicoloured	15	10
436	25c. multicoloured	15	10
437	35c. multicoloured	15	10
438	50c. multicoloured	35	55
MS439	92 × 89 mm. **174** 50c. multicoloured. Printed on silk. Imperf	75	1·75

175 French and Canadian Scouts

1971. 13th World Scout Jamboree, Asagiri, Japan. Multicoloured.

440	5c. Type **175**	10	10
441	35c. German and American scouts	25	25
442	50c. Australian and Japanese scouts	30	50
443	75c. Grenada and British scouts	35	1·00
MS444	101 × 114 mm. Nos. 442/3	1·25	2·50

176 "Napoleon reviewing the Guard" (E. Detaille)

1971. 150th Death Anniv of Napoleon Bonaparte. Paintings. Multicoloured.
445 5c. Type **176** 15 15
446 15c. "Napoleon before Madrid" (Vernet) 20 15
447 35c. "Napoleon crossing Mt. St. Bernard" (David) . . . 25 15
448 $2 "Napoleon in his Study" (David) . . . . 50 1·50
MS449 101 × 76 mm. No. 447. Imperf . . . . 1·25 1·60

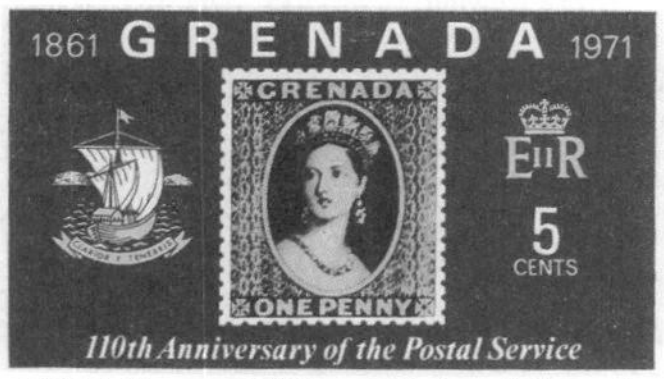

177 1d. Stamp of 1861 and Badge of Grenada

1971. 110th Anniv of the Postal Service. Mult.
450 5c. Type **177** 20 20
451 15c. 6d. stamp of 1861 and Queen Elizabeth II 25 15
452 35c. 1d. and 6d. stamps of 1861 and badge of Grenada 40 20
453 50c. Scroll and 1d. stamp of 1861 . . . . 50 2·00
MS454 96 × 114 mm. Nos. 452/3 1·00 1·00

178 Apollo Splashdown

1971. Apollo Moon Exploration Series. Mult.
455 1c. Type **178** 10 35
456 2c. Recovery of "Apollo 13" 10 35
457 3c. Separation of Lunar Module from "Apollo 14" 10 35
458 10c. Shepard and Mitchell taking samples of moon rock 25 10
459 25c. Moon Buggy 75 20
460 $1 "Apollo 15" blast-off (vert) . . . . 2·00 3·50
MS461 77 × 108 mm. 50c. as $1 1·40 1·50

179 67th Regt. of Foot, 1787

1971. Military Uniforms. Multicoloured.
462 ½c. Type **179** 10 10
463 1c. 45th Regt. of Foot, 1792 10 10
464 2c. 29th Regt. of Foot, 1794 10 10
465 10c. 9th Regt. of Foot, 1801 45 10
466 25c. 2nd Regt. of Foot, 1815 85 20
467 $1 70th Regt. of Foot, 1764 2·50 2·00
MS468 108 × 99 mm. Nos. 466/7 2·25 2·75

180 "The Adoration of the Kings" (Memling)

1972. Christmas (1971). Multicoloured.
469 15c. Type **180** 15 10
470 25c. "Madonna and Child" (Michelangelo) 20 10
471 35c. "Madonna and Child" (Murillo) 25 10
472 50c. "The Virgin with the Apple" (Memling) . . . . 30 2·00
MS473 105 × 80 mm. $1 "The Adoration of the Kings" (Mostaert) . . . . 75 1·25

1972. Winter Olympic Games, Sapporo, Japan. Nos. 462/4 surch **WINTER OLYMPICS FEB. 3-13, 1972 SAPPORO, JAPAN**, Olympic rings and premium. Nos. 476/7 additionally optd **AIR MAIL**.
474 $2 on 2c. mult (postage) . . 50 90
476 35c. on ½c. multicoloured (air) 15 25
477 50c. on 1c. multicoloured . . 15 35
MS475 108 × 99 mm. Nos. 466/7 1·00 1·25

1972. General Election. Nos. 307/8, 310 and 315 optd **VOTE FEB. 28 1972**.
478 2c. multicoloured 20 50
479 3c. multicoloured 20 50
480 6c. multicoloured 30 50
481 25c. multicoloured 50 30

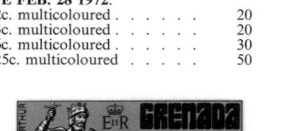

183 King Arthur

1972. U.N.I.C.E.F. Multicoloured.
482 ½c. Type **183** 10 20
483 1c. Robin Hood 10 20
484 2c. Robinson Crusoe (vert) 10 20
485 25c. Type **183** 10 10
486 50c. As 1c. 25 40
487 75c. As 2c. . . . . 30 1·10
488 $1 Mary and her little lamb (vert) . . . . 45 1·25
MS489 65 × 98 mm. No. 488 . . 55 80

1972. "Interpex" Stamp Exbn, New York. Nos. 433/8 optd **INTERPEX 1972**.
490 **174** 5c. multicoloured 10 10
491 10c. multicoloured 10 10
492 15c. multicoloured 10 10
493 25c. multicoloured 10 10
494 35c. multicoloured 15 15
495 50c. multicoloured 25 30
MS496 92 × 89 mm. **174** 50c. multicoloured. Printed on silk. Imperf . . . . 6·00 11·00

1972. Nos. 306/8 and 433 surch **12c**.
497 – 12c. on 1c. multicoloured 40 70
498 – 12c. on 2c. multicoloured 40 70
499 – 12c. on 3c. multicoloured 40 70
500 **174** 12c. on 5c. multicoloured 40 70

1972. Air. Optd **AIR MAIL** or surch in addition.
501 – 5c. mult (No. 309) 10 10
518 **175** 5c. multicoloured . . . . 1·10 10
502 – 8c. mult (No. 311) 15 10
503 – 10c. mult (No. 312) 15 10
504 – 15c. mult (No. 314a) . . . 30 10
505 – 25c. mult (No. 315) . . . 35 20
506 – 30c. on 1c. mult (No. 306) 40 25
507 – 35c. mult (No. 316) . . . 40 25
519 – 35c. mult (No. 441) . . . 2·50 30
508 – 40c. on 2c. mult (No. 307) 50 25
509 – 45c. on 3c. mult (No. 308) 55 35
510 – 50c. mult (No. 317) . . . 55 35
520 – 50c. mult (No. 442) . . . 2·50 45
511 – 60c. on 5c. mult (No. 309) 60 40
512 – 70c. on 6c. mult (No. 310) 70 50
521 – 75c. mult (No. 443) . . . 3·50 1·50
513 – $1 multicoloured (No. 318) . . . . . . 7·00 1·00
514 – $1.35 on 8c. mult (No. 311) . . . . . . 3·50 2·25
515 – $2 multicoloured (No. 319) . . . . . . 9·50 9·50
516 – $3 multicoloured (No. 320) . . . . . . 10·00 9·50
517 – $5 multicoloured (No. 321) . . . . . . 12·00 17·00

187 Yachting

1972. Olympic Games, Munich. Multicoloured.
522 ½c. Type **187** (postage) . . . 10 10
523 1c. Show-jumping 10 10
524 2c. Running (vert) 10 10
525 35c. As 2c. 30 10
526 50c. As 1c. 40 40
527 25c. Boxing (air) 25 10
528 $1 As 25c. 65 85
MS529 82 × 85 mm. 60c. as 25c. and 70c. as 1c. . . . . 1·00 1·40

1972. Royal Silver Wedding. As T **98** of Gibraltar, but with Badge of Grenada and Nutmegs in background.
530 8c. brown 10 10
531 $1 blue 45 55

189 Boy Scout Saluting

1972. 65th Anniv of Boy Scouts. Multicoloured.
532 ½c. Type **189** (postage) . . . 10 10
533 1c. Scouts knotting ropes . . 10 10
534 2c. Scouts shaking hands . . 10 10
535 3c. Lord Baden-Powell . . . 10 10
536 75c. As 2c. . . . . 70 2·75
537 $1 As 3c. . . . . 75 2·75
538 25c. Type **189** (air) 40 20
539 35c. As 1c. 50 20
MS540 87 × 88 mm. 60c. as 3c. and 70c. as 2c. . . . . 1·50 1·50

190 Madonna and Child

1972. Christmas. Multicoloured.
541 1c. Type **190** 10 25
542 3c. The Three Kings 10 25
543 5c. The Nativity 10 10
544 25c. Type **190** 15 10
545 35c. As 3c. 15 10
546 $1 As 5c. . . . . 40 1·00
MS547 102 × 76 mm. 60c. Type **190** and 70c. as 3c. 60 80

191 Greater Flamingos

1973. National Zoo. Multicoloured.
548 25c. Type **191** 70 35
549 35c. Brazilian tapir 40 35
550 60c. Blue and yellow macaws 1·25 1·75
551 70c. Ocelot . . . . 70 2·00

192 Class II Racing Yacht

1973. Yachting. Multicoloured.
552 25c. Type **192** 25 10
553 35c. Harbour, St. George's 30 10
554 60c. Yacht "Bloodhound" . . 45 65
555 70c. St. George's 50 75

193 Helios (Greek god) and Earth orbiting the Sun

1973. Centenary of I.M.O./W.M.O. Greek Gods. Multicoloured.
556 ½c. Type **193** 10 10
557 1c. Poseidon and "Normad" storm detector 10 10
558 2c. Zeus and radarscope . . 10 10
559 3c. Iris and weather ballon 10 10
560 35c. Hermes and "ATS-3" satellite 25 10
561 50c. Zephyrus and diagram of pressure zones 30 30
562 75c. Demeter and space photo 30 60
563 $1 Selene and rainfall diagram . . . . 30 1·00
MS564 123 × 92 mm. $2 Computer weather map (42 × 31 mm.) . . 1·00 1·25

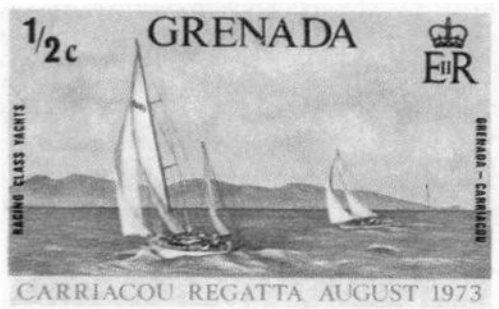

194 Racing Class Yachts

1973. Carriacou Regatta. Multicoloured.
565 ½c. Type **194** 10 10
566 1c. Cruising Class yacht . . . 10 10
567 2c. Open-decked sloops . . . 10 10
568 35c. "Mermaid" (sloop) . . . 30 10
569 50c. St. George's Harbour . . 35 25
570 75c. Map of Carriacou . . . 40 55
571 $1 Boat-building 55 70
MS572 109 × 88 mm. $2 End of race 1·00 1·75

195 Ignatius Semmelweis (obstetrician)

197 "Virgin and Child" (Maratti)

196 Princess Anne and Capt. Mark Phillips

1973. 25th Anniv of W.H.O. Multicoloured.
573 ½c. Type **195** 10 35
574 1c. Louis Pasteur 10 35
575 2c. Edward Jenner 10 35
576 3c. Sigmund Freud 10 35
577 25c. Emil von Behring (bacteriologist) 65 10
578 35c. Carl Jung 75 20
579 50c. Charles Calmette (bacteriologist) . . . . . . 1·10 1·00
580 $1 William Harvey . . . . . 1·40 2·50
MS581 105 × 80 mm. $2 Marie Curie 1·25 1·60

1973. Royal Wedding.
582 **196** 25c. multicoloured 10 10
583 $2 multicoloured 30 45
MS584 79 × 100 mm. 75c. and $1 as Nos. 582/3 . . . . 40 30

1973. Christmas. Multicoloured.
585 ½c. Type **197** 10 10
586 1c. "Madonna and Child" (Crivelli) 10 10
587 2c. "Virgin and Child with two Angels" (Verrocchio) 10 10
588 3c. "Adoration of the Shepherds" (Roberti) . . . 10 10
589 25c. "The Holy Family with the Infant Baptist" (Baroccio) 15 10
590 35c. "The Holy Family" (Bronzino) 15 10
591 75c. "Mystic Nativity" (Botticelli) 20 20
592 $1 "Adoration of the Kings" (Geertgen) 25 30
MS593 89 × 89 mm. $2 "Adoration of the Kings" (Mostaert) (30 × 45 mm) . . . . 1·00 1·10

1974. Independence. Nos. 306/9, 311/13, 315/16 and 317a/21 optd **INDEPENDENCE 7TH FEB. 1974**.
594 **86** 1c. multicoloured 10 50
595 – 2c. multicoloured 10 50
596 – 3c. multicoloured 10 50
597 – 5c. multicoloured 10 10
598 – 8c. multicoloured 15 10
599 – 10c. multicoloured 20 15
600 – 12c. multicoloured 20 15
601 – 25c. multicoloured 45 25
602 – 35c. multicoloured 75 25
603 – 75c. multicoloured . . . . 2·00 1·50
604 – $1 multicoloured . . . . . 3·75 1·75
605 – $2 multicoloured . . . . . 6·00 6·50
606 – $3 multicoloured . . . . . 8·00 8·50
607 – $5 multicoloured . . . . . 12·00 17·00

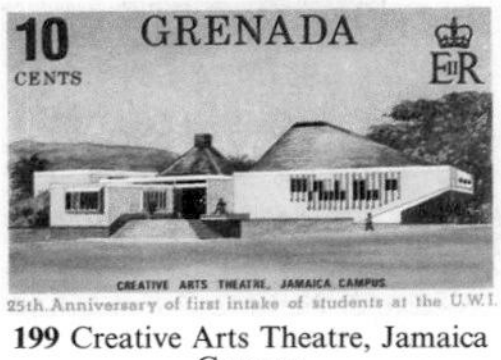

199 Creative Arts Theatre, Jamaica Campus

1974. 25th Anniv of University of West Indies. Multicoloured.
608 10c. Type **199** 10 10
609 25c. Marryshow House 10 10
610 50c. Chapel, Jamaica Campus (vert) 20 10
611 $1 University arms (vert) 30 30
MS612 69 × 86 mm. $2 as No. 611 50 1·00

200 Nutmeg Pods and Scarlet Mace

201 Footballers (West Germany v. Chile)

1974. Independence. Multicoloured.
613 3c. Type **200** 10 10
614 8c. Map of Grenada 10 10
615 25c. Prime Minister Eric Gairy 15 10
616 35c. Grand Anse Beach and flag 15 10
617 $1 Coat of arms 35 40
MS618 91 × 125 mm. $2 as $1 55 1·00

1974. World Cup Football Championship, West Germany. Multicoloured.
619 ½c. Type **201** 10 10
620 1c. East Germany v. Australia 10 10
621 2c. Yugoslavia v. Brazil 10 10
622 10c. Scotland v. Zaire 10 10
623 25c. Netherlands v. Uruguay 15 10
624 50c. Sweden v. Bulgaria 20 10
625 75c. Italy v. Haiti 35 15
626 $1 Poland v. Argentina 50 25
MS627 114 × 76 mm. $2 Country flags 1·00 1·75

202 Early U.S. Mail-trains and Concorde

1974. Centenary of U.P.U. Multicoloured.
628 ½c. Type **202** 10 10
629 1c. "Caesar" (snow) (1839) and Westland Wessex HU Mk 5 helicopter 10 10
630 2c. Airmail transport 10 10
631 8c. Pigeon post (1480) and telephone dial 15 10
632 15c. 18th-century bellman and tracking antenna 30 10
633 25c. Messenger (1450) and satellite 35 10
634 35c. French pillar-box (1850) and mail-boat 50 10
635 $1 18th-century German postman and British Advanced Passenger Train 1·50 85
MS636 105 × 66 mm. $2 St. Gotthard mail-coach (1735) 1·00 1·75

203 Sir Winston Churchill

1974. Birth Centenary of Sir Winston Churchill.
637 **203** 35c. multicoloured 15 10
638 $2 multicoloured 45 1·00
MS639 126 × 96 mm. 75c. as 35c. and $1 as $2 75 75

204 "Madonna and Child of the Eucharist" (Botticelli)

1974. Christmas. "Madonna and Child" paintings by named artists. Multicoloured.
640 ½c. Type **204** 10 10
641 1c. Niccolo di Pietro 10 10
642 2c. Van der Weyden 10 10
643 3c. Bastiani 10 10
644 10c. Giovanni 10 10
645 25c. Van der Weyden 20 10
646 50c. Botticelli 25 20
647 $1 Mantegna 35 50
MS648 117 × 96 mm. $2 as 1c. 60 1·00

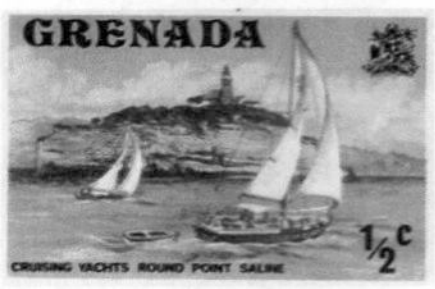

205 Yachts, Point Saline

1975. Multicoloured.
649 ½c. Type **205** 10 85
650 1c. Yacht Club race 10 10
651 2c. Carenage taxi 10 10
652 3c. Large working boats 10 10
653a 5c. Deep-water dock 10 15
654 6c. Cocoa beans in drying trays 10 10
655 8c. Nutmegs 1·25 10
656 10c. Rum distillery, River Antoine Estate, c. 1785 10 10
657 12c. Cocoa tree 30 10
658 15c. Fishermen at Fontenoy 10 10
659 20c. Parliament Building 15 15
660 25c. Fort George cannons 20 15
661 35c. Pearls Airport 20 15
662 50c. General Post Office 15 30
663 75c. Carib's Leap, Sauteurs Bay 45 50
664 $1 Carenage, St. George's 50 70
665 $2 St. George's Harbour by night 50 1·50
666 $3 Grand Anse Beach 55 2·00
667 $5 Canoe Bay and Black Bay 65 3·00
668 $10 Sugar-loaf Island 1·25 6·50
Nos. 663/8 are size 45 × 28 mm.

206 Sailfish

1975. Big Game Fishing. Multicoloured.
669 ½c. Type **206** 10 10
670 1c. Blue marlin 10 10
671 2c. White marlin 10 10
672 10c. Yellow-finned tuna 10 10
673 25c. Wahoo 25 10
674 50c. Dolphin (fish) 40 15
675 70c. Giant grouper 60 20
676 $1 Great barracuda 80 35
MS677 107 × 80 mm. $2 Short-finned mako 1·25 1·25

207 Granadilla Barbadine

1975. Flowers. Multicoloured.
678 ½c. Type **207** 10 10
679 1c. Bleeding Heart (Easter Lily) 10 10
680 2c. Poinsettia 10 10
681 3c. Cocoa flower 10 10
682 10c. Gladioli 10 10
683 25c. Redhead/Yellowhead 20 10
684 50c. Plumbago 30 15
685 $1 Orange flower 50 25
MS686 102 × 82 mm. $2 Barbados gooseberry 1·10 1·25

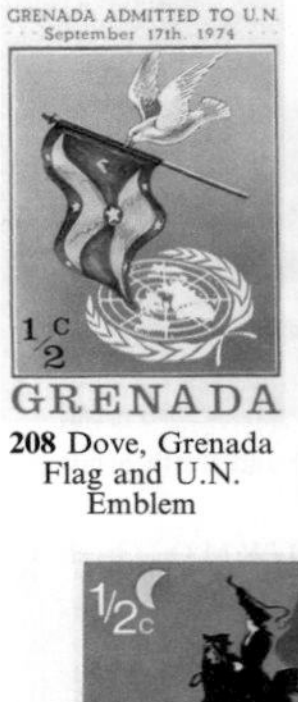

208 Dove, Grenada Flag and U.N. Emblem

210 "Blood of the Redeemer" (G. Bellini)

209 Paul Revere's Midnight Ride

1975. Grenada's Admission to the U.N. (1974). Multicoloured.
687 ½c. Type **208** 10 10
688 1c. Grenada and U.N. flags 10 10
689 2c. Grenada coat of arms 10 10
690 35c. U.N. emblem over map of Grenada 15 10
691 50c. U.N. buildings and flags 20 15
692 $2 U.N. emblem and scroll 45 45
MS693 122 × 91 mm. 75c. Type **208** and $1 as 2c. 65 90

CANCELLED REMAINDERS*. Some of the following issues have been remaindered, cancelled to order, at a fraction of their face value. For all practical purposes these are indistinguishable from genuine postally used copies. Our used quotations, which are indicated by an asterisk, are the same for cancelled-to-order or postally used copies.

1975. Bicentenary of American Revolution (1st issue). Multicoloured.
694 ½c. Type **209** (postage) 10 10*
695 1c. Crispus Attucks 10 10*
696 2c. Patrick Henry 10 10*
697 3c. Franklin visits Washington 10 10*
698 5c. Rebel troops 10 10*
699 10c. John Paul Jones 10 10*
700 40c. "John Hancock" (Copley) (vert) (air) 25 10*
701 50c. "Benjamin Franklin" (Roslin) (vert) 40 15*
702 75c. "John Adams" (Copley) (vert) 55 15*
703 $1 "Lafayette" (Casanova) (vert) 60 20*
MS704 Two sheets, each 131 × 102 mm: $2 Grenada arms and U.S. seal; $2 Grenada and U.S. flags 1·00 60*
Stamps from No. **MS**704 are horiz and larger: 47½ × 35 mm.
See also Nos. 785/92.

1975. Easter. Multicoloured.
705 ½c. Type **210** 10 10*
706 1c. "Pieta" (Bellini) 10 10*
707 2c. "The Entombment" (Van der Weyden) 10 10*
708 3c. "Pieta" (Bellini) 10 10*
709 35c. "Pieta" (Bellini) 20 10*
710 75c. "The Dead Christ" (Bellini) 25 10*
711 $1 "The Dead Christ supported by Angels" (Procaccini) 30 10*
MS712 117 × 100 mm. $2 "Pieta" (Botticelli) 75 30*

211 Wildlife Study

1975. 14th World Scout Jamboree, Norway. Multicoloured.
713 ½c. Type **211** 10 10*
714 1c. Sailing 10 10*
715 2c. Map-reading 10 10*
716 35c. First-aid 40 10*
717 40c. Physical training 40 10*
718 75c. Mountaineering 50 10*
719 $2 Sing-song 85 20*
MS720 106 × 80 mm. $1 Boat-building 1·00 30*

212 Leafy Jewel Box

213 "Lycorea ceres"

1975. Sea Shells. Multicoloured.
721 ½c. Type **212** 10 10*
722 1c. Emerald nerite 10 10*
723 2c. Yellow American cockle 10 10*
724 25c. Common purple janthina 85 10*
725 50c. Atlantic turkey wing 1·75 15*
726 75c. West Indian fighting conch 2·25 20*
727 $1 Noble wentletrap 2·25 20*
MS728 102 × 76 mm. $2 Music volute 2·00 80*

1975. Butterflies. Multicoloured.
729 ½c. Type **213** 10 10*
730 1c. "Adelpha cytherea" 10 10*
731 2c. "Atlides polybe" 10 10*
732 35c. "Anteos maerula" 80 10*
733 45c. "Parides neophilus" 85 10*
734 75c. "Nymula orestes" 1·25 15*
735 $2 "Euptychia cephus" 1·75 20*
MS736 108 × 83 mm. $1 "Papilio astyalus" (sub-species "lycophron") 1·25 40*

214 Rowing

215 "The Boy David" (Michelangelo)

1975. Pan-American Games, Mexico City. Mult.
737 ½c. Type **214** 10 10*
738 1c. Swimming 10 10*
739 2c. Show-jumping 10 10*
740 35c. Gymnastics 15 10*
741 45c. Football 15 10*
742 75c. Boxing 25 15*
743 $2 Cycling 65 20*
MS744 106 × 81 mm. $1 Yachting 1·00 40*

1975. 500th Birth Anniv of Michelangelo. Multicoloured.
745 ½c. Type **215** 10 10*
746 1c. "Young Man" (detail) 10 10*
747 2c. "Moses" 10 10*
748 40c. "Prophet Zachariah" 30 10*
749 50c. "St. John the Baptist" 30 15*
750 75c. "Judith and Holofernes" 40 20*
751 $2 "Doni Madonna" (detail from "Holy Family") 70 25*
MS752 104 × 89 mm. $1 "Madonna" (head from Pieta) 1·00 30*

216 "Madonna and Child" (Filippino Lippi)

217 Bananaquit

1975. Christmas. "Virgin and Child" paintings by artists named. Multicoloured.
753 ½c. Type **216** 10 10*
754 1c. Mantegna 10 10*
755 2c. Luis de Morales 10 10*
756 35c. G. M. Morandi 15 10*
757 50c. Antonello da Messina 15 10*
758 75c. Durer 20 10*
759 $1 Velasquez 25 10*
MS760 125 × 95 mm. $2 Bellini 1·00 30*

1976. Flora and Fauna. Multicoloured.
761 ½c. Type **217** 10 10*
762 1c. Brazilian agouti 10 10*
763 2c. Hawksbill turtle (horiz) 10 10*
764 5c. Dwarf poinciana 10 10*
765 35c. Black-finned tuna ("Albacore") (horiz) 90 10*
766 40c. Cardinal's guard 95 10*
767 $2 Nine-banded armadillo (horiz) 2·50 30*
MS768 82 × 89 mm. $1 Belted kingfisher 7·50 90*

218 Carnival Time

1976. Tourism. Multicoloured.
769 ½c. Type **218** 10 10*
770 1c. Scuba diving 10 10*
771 2c. Liner "Southward" at St. George's 10 10*
772 35c. Game fishing 65 10*
773 50c. St. George's Golf Course 2·25 20*
774 75c. Tennis 2·50 25*
775 $1 Ancient rock carvings at Mount Rich 2·75 25*
MS776 100 × 73 mm. $2 Small boat sailing 1·75 60*

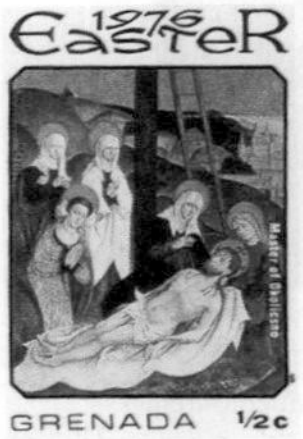

219 "Pieta" (Master of Okolicsno)

220 Sharpshooters

1976. Easter. Paintings by artists named. Multicoloured.
777 ½c. Type **219** 10 10*
778 1c. Correggio 10 10*
779 2c. Van der Weyden 10 10*
780 3c. Durer 10 10*
781 35c. Master of the Holy Spirit 15 10*
782 75c. Raphael 30 15*
783 $1 Raphael 35 20*
MS784 108 × 86 mm. $2 Crespi 1·00 60*

1976. Bicentenary of American Revolution (2nd issue). Multicoloured.
785 ½c. Type **220** 10 10*
786 1c. Defending the Liberty Pole 10 10*
787 2c. Loading muskets 10 10*
788 35c. The Fight for Liberty 30 10*
789 50c. Peace Treaty, 1783 35 10*
790 $1 Drummers 50 20*
791 $3 Gunboat 90 30*
MS792 93 × 79 mm. 75c. as 35c. and $2 as 50c. 75 60*

221 Nature Study

222 Volleyball

1976. 50th Anniv of Girl Guides in Grenada. Multicoloured.
793 ½c. Type **221** 10 10*
794 1c. Campfire cooking 10 10*
795 2c. First aid 10 10*
796 50c. Camping 50 10*
797 75c. Home economics 65 15*
798 $2 First aid 90 25*
MS799 111 × 85 mm. $1 Painting 1·00 70*

1976. Olympic Games, Montreal. Multicoloured.
800 ½c. Type **222** 10 10*
801 1c. Cycling 10 10*
802 2c. Rowing 10 10*
803 35c. Judo 30 10*
804 45c. Hockey 60 10*
805 75c. Gymnastics 60 20*
806 $1 High jump 60 20*
MS807 106 × 81 mm. $3 Equestrian event 1·00 80*

223 "Cha-U-Kao at the Moulin Rouge"

225 Satellite Assembly

224 Piper Apache 235

1976. 75th Death Anniv of Toulouse-Lautrec. Multicoloured.
808 ½c. Type **223** 10 10*
809 1c. "Quadrille of the Moulin Rouge" 10 10*
810 2c. "Profile of a Woman" 10 10*
811 3c. "Salon in the Rue des Moulins" 10 10*
812 40c. "The Laundryman" 55 10*
813 50c. "Marcelle Lender dancing the Bolero" 65 10*
814 $2 "Signor Boileau at the Cafe" 1·75 25*
MS815 152 × 125 mm. $1 "Woman with Boa" 2·25 70*

223a Map of the Caribbean

1976. West Indian Victory in World Cricket Cup.
816 35c. Type **223a** 1·00 35
817 $1 The Prudential Cup 1·50 5·00

1976. Airplanes. Multicoloured.
818 ½c. Type **224** 10 10*
819 1c. Beech 50 Twin Bonanza 10 10*
820 2c. De Havilland Twin Otter 100 10 10*
821 40c. Britten Norman Islander 60 10*
822 50c. De Havilland Heron 2 65 10*
823 $2 Hawker Siddeley H.S.748 2·00 50*
MS824 75 × 83 mm. $3 B.A.C. One Eleven 500 1·50 80*

1976. Viking and Helios Space Missions. Multicoloured.
825 ½c. Type **225** 10 10*
826 1c. Helios satellite 10 10*
827 2c. Helios encapsulation 10 10*
828 15c. Systems test 10 10*
829 45c. Viking lander (horiz) 20 10*
830 75c. Lander on Mars 30 15*
831 $2 Viking encapsulation 60 25*
MS832 110 × 85 mm. $3 Orbiter and lander 1·00 75*

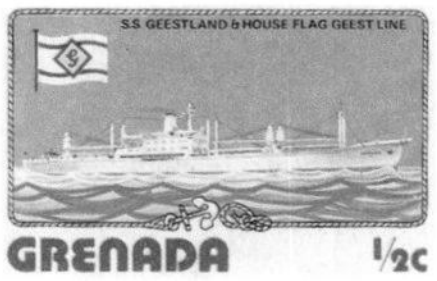

226 S.S. "Geestland"

1976. Ships. Multicoloured.
833 ½c. Type **226** 10 10*
834 1c. M.V. "Federal Palm" 10 10*
835 2c. H.M.S "Blake" 10 10*
836 25c. M.V. "Vistafjord" 45 10*
837 75c. S.S. "Canberra" 80 15*
838 $1 S.S. "Regina" 90 20*
839 $5 S.S. "Arandora Star" 1·75 40*
MS840 91 × 78 mm. $2 "Santa Maria" 1·60 4·00

227 "San Barnaba Altarpiece" (Botticelli)

1976. Christmas. Multicoloured.
841 ½c. Type **227** 10 10*
842 1c. "Annunciation" (Botticelli) 10 10*
843 2c. "Madonna of Chancellor Rolin" (Jan van Eyck) 10 10*
844 35c. "Annunciation" (Fra Filippo Lippi) 15 10*
845 50c. "Madonna of the Magnificat" (Botticelli) 20 10*
846 75c. "Madonna of the Pomegranate" (Botticelli) 30 15*
847 $3 "Madonna with St. Cosmas and other Saints" (Botticelli) 70 25*
MS848 71 × 57 mm. $2 "Gypsy Madonna" (Titian) 1·00 60*

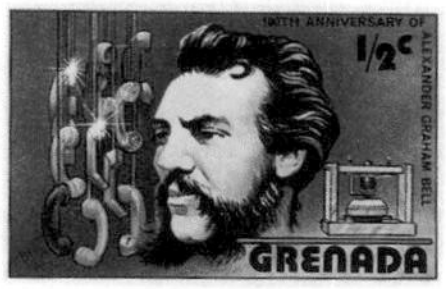

228 Alexander Graham Bell and Telephones

1976. Centenary of First Telephone. Multicoloured.
849 ½c. Type **228** 10 10*
850 1c. Telephone users within globe 10 10*
851 2c. Telephone satellite 10 10*
852 18c. Telephone viewer and console 20 10*
853 40c. Satellite and tracking stations 25 10*
854 $1 Satellite transmitting to ships 35 15*
855 $2 Dish aerial and modern telephone 55 25*
MS856 107 × 80 mm. $5 Globe encircled by flags 1·25 75*

229 Coronation Scene

1977. Silver Jubilee. Multicoloured.(a) Perf.
857 ½c. Type **229** 10 10*
858 1c. Sceptre and orb 10 10*
859 35c. The Queen on horseback 10 10*
860 $2 Spoon and ampulla 25 15*
861 $2.50 The Queen and Prince Philip 25 15*
MS862 103 × 79 mm. $5 Royal Visit to Grenada 75 60*

(b) Roul. Self-adhesive.
863 35c. As $2.50 50 15
864 50c. As $2 25 1·00
865 $1 As 1c. 50 1·40
866 $3 As 35c. 1·25 2·75

230 Water Skiing

1977. Easter Water Parade. Multicoloured.
867 ½c. Type **230** 10 10*
868 1c. Speedboat race 10 10*
869 2c. Row boat race 10 10*
870 22c. Swimming 20 10*
871 35c. Work boat race 30 10*
872 75c. Water polo 50 15*
873 $2 Game fishing 1·00 25*
MS874 115 × 85 mm. $3 Yacht race 1·25 75*

231 Meeting Place, Grand Anse Beach

1977. 7th Meeting of Organization of American States.
875 **231** 35c. multicoloured 10 10
876 $1 multicoloured 25 60
877 $2 multicoloured 40 1·75

232 Rafting

1977. Caribbean Scout Jamboree, Jamaica. Multicoloured.
878 ½c. Type **232** 10 10*
879 1c. Tug-of-war 10 10*
880 2c. Sea Scouts regatta 10 10*
881 18c. Camp fire 20 10*
882 40c. Field kitchen 25 10*
883 $1 Scouts and sea scouts 55 15*
884 $2 Hiking and map reading 75 25*
MS885 107 × 85 mm. $3 Semaphore 2·00 80*

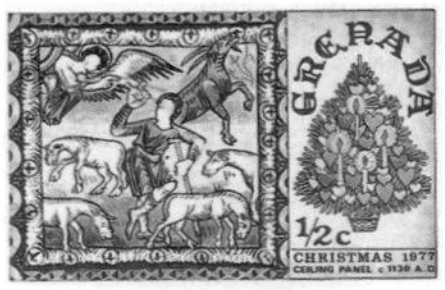

233 Angel and Shepherd

1977. Christmas. Ceiling Panels from Church of St. Martin, Zillis. Multicoloured.
886 ½c. Type **233** 10 10*
887 1c. St. Joseph 10 10*
888 2c. Virgin and Child fleeing to Egypt 10 10*
889 22c. Angel 10 10*
890 35c. Magus on horseback 10 10*
891 75c. Three horses 15 15*
892 $2 Virgin and Child 40 25*
MS893 85 × 112 mm. $3 Magus offering gift 1·00 70*

1977. Royal Visit. Nos. 857/61 optd **Royal Visit W.I. 1977.**
894 ½c. Type **229** 10 10
895 1c. Sceptre and Orb 10 10
896 35c. Queen on horseback 10 10
897 $2 Spoon and ampulla 30 40
898 $2.50 The Queen and Prince Philip 35 45
MS899 103 × 79 mm. $5 Royal visit to Grenada 70 80

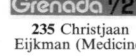

235 Christjaan Eijkman (Medicine)

237 Rocket Launching

236 Count von Zeppelin and First Zeppelin Airship LZ-1

1978. Nobel Prize Winners. Multicoloured.
900 ½c. Type **235** 10 10*
901 1c. Sir Winston Churchill (Literature) 30 10*
902 2c. Woodrow Wilson (Peace) 10 10*
903 35c. Frederic Passy (Peace) 15 10*
904 $1 Albert Einstein (Physics) 1·00 20*
905 $3 Carl Bosch (Chemistry) 1·75 35*
MS906 114 × 99 mm. $2 Alfred Nobel 70 60*

1978. 75th Anniv of First Zeppelin Flight and 50th Anniv of Lindbergh's Transatlantic Flight. Multicoloured.
907 ½c. Type **236** 10 10*
908 1c. Lindbergh with "Spirit of St. Louis" 10 10*
909 2c. Airship "Deutschland" 10 10*
910 22c. Lindbergh's arrival in France 30 10*
911 75c. Lindbergh and "Spirit of St. Louis" in flight 60 10*
912 $1 "Graf Zeppelin" over Alps 65 15*
913 $3 "Graf Zeppelin" over White House 1·40 25*
MS914 103 × 85 mm. Lindbergh in cockpit; $2 Count von Zeppelin and airship LZ-5 1·00 60*

1978. Space Shuttle. Multicoloured.
915 ½c. Type **237** 10 10*
916 1c. Booster jettison 10 10*
917 2c. External tank jettison 10 10*
918 18c. Space Shuttle in orbit 30 10*
919 75c. Satellite placement 65 10*
920 $2 Landing approach 1·40 20*
MS921 103 × 85 mm. $3 Shuttle after landing 1·40 60*

238 Black-headed Gull

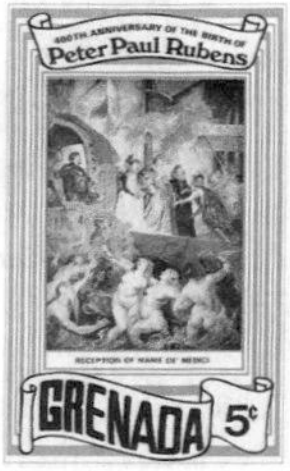

239 "The Landing of Marie de Medici at Marseilles"

1978. Wild Birds of Grenada. Multicoloured.
922 ½c. Type **238** 10 10*
923 1c. Wilson's storm petrel ("Wilsons Petrel") 10 10*
924 2c. Killdeer plover ("Killdeer") 10 10*
925 50c. White-necked jacobin 1·50 10*
926 75c. Blue-faced booby 1·75 15*
927 $1 Broad-winged hawk 2·50 20*
928 $2 Red-necked pigeon 3·00 30*
MS929 103 × 94 mm. $3 Scarlet ibis 6·00 1·00*

1978. 400th Birth Anniv of Peter Paul Rubens. Multicoloured.
930 5c. Type **239** 10 10*
931 15c. "Rubens and Isabella Brandt" 10 10*
932 18c. "Marchesa Brigida Spindola-Doria" 10 10*
933 25c. "Ludovicus Nonninus" 10 10*
934 45c. "Helene Fourment and her Children" 15 10*
935 75c. "Clara Serena Rubens" 25 10*
936 $3 "Le Chapeau de Paille" 60 20*
MS937 65 × 100 mm. $5 "Self Portrait" 1·00 60*

240 Ludwig van Beethoven

241 King Edward's Chair

1978. 150th Death Anniv of Beethoven. Mult.
938 5c. Type **240** 10 10*
939 15c. Woman violinist (horiz) 15 10*
940 18c. Musical instruments (horiz) 20 10*
941 22c. Piano (horiz) 20 10*
942 50c. Violins 40 10*

943 75c. Piano and sonata score 50 15*
944 $3 Beethoven's portrait and home (horiz) 1·25 25*
MS945 83 × 62 mm. $2 Beethoven and score 1·10 60*

1978. 25th Anniv of Coronation. Mult.(a) Perf.
946 35c. Type **241** 10 10
947 $2 Queen with regalia 30 35
948 $2.50 St. Edward's Crown 30 40
MS949 102 × 76 mm. $5 Queen and Prince Philip 80 80

(b) Roul × imperf. Self-adhesive.
950 25c. Queen Elizabeth II taking salute, Trooping the Colour 15 15
951 35c. Queen at Maundy Thursday ceremony 15 25
952 $5 Queen and Prince Philip at Opening of Parliament 1·50 2·50

243 Goalkeeper reaching for Ball

1978. World Cup Football Championship, Argentina.
953 **243** 40c. multicoloured 10 10
954 – 60c. multicoloured 15 20
955 – 90c. multicoloured 25 30
956 – $2 multicoloured 60 60
MS957 130 × 97 mm. $2.70, multicoloured 1·10 1·10
DESIGNS: 60c. to $2.70, Designs similar to Type **243** with goalkeeper reaching for ball.

244 Aerial Phenomena, Germany, 1561 and U.S.A., 1952

1978. U.F.O. Research. Multicoloured.
958 5c. Type **244** 15 10
959 35c. Various aerial phenomena, 1950 35 25
960 $3 U.F.O.s, 1965 2·00 1·75
MS961 112 × 89 mm. $2 Sir Eric Gairy and U.F.O. research laboratory 1·25 1·25

245 Wright Flyer III, 1902

1978. 75th Anniv of Powered Flight. Mult.
962 5c. Type **245** 10 10
963 15c. Wright Flyer I, 1903 10 10
964 18c. Wright Type A 10 10
965 22c. Wright Flyer I from above 15 10
966 50c. Orville Wright and Wright Type A 20 20
967 75c. Wright Type A, Pau, France, 1908 25 25
968 $3 Wilbur Wright and Wright glider No. IV 80 70
MS969 114 × 85 mm. $2 Wright glider No. III 1·00 75

246 Cook and Hawaiian Feast

1978. 250th Birth Anniv of Captain James Cook and Bicentenary of Discovery of Hawaii. Multicoloured.
970 18c. Type **246** 60 20
971 35c. Cook and Hawaiian dance 75 25
972 75c. Cook and Honolulu harbour 1·25 1·00
973 $3 Cook's statue and H.M.S. "Resolution" 1·75 5·50
MS974 116 × 88 mm. $4 Cook and death scene 3·00 1·50

247 "Paumgartner Altarpiece" (detail)

248 National Convention and Cultural Centre (interior)

1978. Christmas. Paintings by Durer. Multicoloured.
975 40c. Type **247** 20 15
976 60c. "The Adoration of the Magi" 25 20
977 90c. "Virgin and Child" 30 20
978 $2 "Virgin and Child with St. Anne" (detail) 55 55
MS979 113 × 83 mm. $4 "Madonna and Child" 1·10 1·50

1979. 5th Anniv of Independence.
980 5c. Type **248** 10 10
981 18c. National Convention and Cultural Centre (exterior) 10 10
982 22c. Easter Water Parade, 1978 10 10
983 35c. Sir Eric M. Gairy (Prime Minister) 10 10
984 $3 The Cross, Fort Frederick 45 60

249 "Acalypha hispida"

250 Birds in Flight

1979. Flowers. Multicoloured.
985 18c. Type **249** 10 10
986 50c. "Hibiscus rosa sinensis" 20 15
987 $1 "Thunbergia grandiflora" 30 25
988 $3 "Nerium oleander" 80 1·10
MS989 115 × 90 mm. $2 "Lagerstroemia speciosa" 75 1·00

1979. 30th Anniv of Declaration of Human Rights. Multicoloured.
990 15c. Type **250** 10 10
991 $2 Bird in Flight 55 65

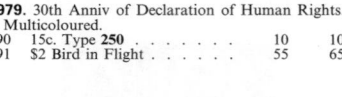

251 Children playing Cricket

1979. Int Year of the Child (1st issue). Mult.
992 18c. Type **251** 1·00 50
993 22c. Children playing baseball 40 30
994 $5 Children playing in a tree 3·25 7·00
MS995 114 × 92 mm. $4 Children with model spaceship 1·25 2·25
See also Nos. 1006/7 and 1025/34.

252 "Around the World in 80 Days"

1979. 150th Birth Anniv of Jules Verne. Mult.
996 18c. Type **252** 35 20
997 35c. "20,000 Leagues under the Sea" 50 20
998 75c. "From the Earth to the Moon" 60 50
999 $3 "Master of the World" 1·40 2·00
MS1000 110 × 85 mm. $4 "Clipper of the Clouds" 1·25 1·25

253 Mail Runner, Africa (early 19th-century)

1979. Death Cent of Sir Rowland Hill. Mult.
1001 20c. Type **253** 10 10
1002 40c. Pony Express, America (mid 19th-century) 10 10
1003 $1 Pigeon post 15 25
1004 $3 Mail coach, Europe (18–19th century) 40 80
MS1005 127 × 100 mm. $5 Sir Rowland Hill and 1891 1d. on 8d. × 4 75 1·10

254 "The Pistol of Peace" (vaccination gun), Map of Grenada and Children

1979. International Year of the Child (2nd issue). "Grenada—First Nation 100% Immunized"
1006 **254** 5c. multicoloured 25 75
1007 $1 multicoloured 75 2·50

255 Reef Shark

1979. Marine Wildlife. Multicoloured.
1008 40c. Type **255** 40 30
1009 45c. Spotted eagle ray 40 30
1010 50c. Many-toothed conger 45 40
1011 60c. Golden olive (shell) 70 85
1012 70c. West Indian murex (shell) 85 1·00
1013 75c. Giant tun (shell) 90 1·10
1014 90c. Brown booby 2·25 2·25
1015 $1 Magnificent frigate bird 2·25 2·25
MS1016 109 × 78 mm. $2.50, Sooty tern 2·50 2·00

256 The Flight into Egypt

1979. Christmas. Tapestries. Multicoloured.
1017 6c. Type **256** 10 10
1018 25c. The Flight into Egypt (detail) 10 10
1019 30c. Angel (vert) 10 10
1020 40c. (Doge Marino Grimani) (detail) (vert) 10 10
1021 90c. The Annunciation to the Shepherds (vert) 15 15
1022 $1 The Flight into Egypt (Rome) (vert) 15 15
1023 $2 The Virgin in Glory (vert) 25 40
MS1024 111 × 148 mm. $4 Doge Marino Grimani (vert) 70 1·00

257 Mickey Mouse playing Baseball

258 Paul Harris (founder)

1979. International Year of the Child (3rd issue). Disney cartoon characters. Multicoloured.
1025 ½c. Type **257** 10 10
1026 1c. Donald Duck high-jumping 10 10
1027 2c. Goofy playing basketbal 10 10
1028 3c. Goofy hurdling 10 10
1029 4c. Donald Duck playing golf 10 10
1030 5c. Mickey Mouse playing cricket 10 10
1031 10c. Mickey Mouse playing football 10 10
1032 $2 Mickey Mouse playing tennis 1·75 3·50
1033 $2.50 Minnie Mouse riding horse 1·75 3·50
MS1034 125 × 100 mm. $3 Goofy in riding gear 1·25 1·50

1980. 75th Anniv of Rotary International. Mult.
1035 6c. Type **258** 10 10
1036 30c. "Health" 10 15
1037 90c. "Hunger" 15 30
1038 $2 "Humanity" 40 80
MS1039 104 × 89 mm. $4 Rotary International emblem 1·00 1·60

1980. 1st Anniv of Revolution (1st issue). Nos. 651/2, 654/7, 659/60 and 662/8 optd **PEOPLE'S REVOLUTION 13 MARCH 1979**.
1040 2c. Carenage taxi 10 40
1041 3c. Large working boats 10 40
1042 6c. Cocoa beans in drying trays 10 10
1043 8c. Nutmegs 10 10
1044 10c. Rum distillery, River Antoine Estate, c. 1785 10 10
1045 12c. Cocoa tree 10 10
1046 20c. Parliament Building 10 15
1047 25c. Fort George cannons 30 30
1048 50c. General Post Office 30 30
1049 75c. Carib's Leap, Sauteurs Bay 50 40
1050 $1 Carenage, St. George's 60 60
1051 $2 St. George's Harbour by night 1·25 2·00
1052 $3 Grand Anse Beach 1·50 3·25
1053 $5 Canoe Bay and Black Bay 2·00 5·50
1054 $10 Sugar-loaf Island 3·25 8·00
See also Nos. 1069/72.

260 Boxing

1980. Olympic Games, Moscow. Multicoloured.
1055 25c. Type **260** 10 10
1056 40c. Cycling 15 10
1057 90c. Show-jumping 20 30
1058 $2 Running 40 1·00
MS1059 128 × 95 mm. $4 Sailing 1·00 1·40

261 Tropical Kingbird

1980. Wild Birds. Multicoloured.
1060 20c. Type **261** 85 20
1061 40c. Rufous-breasted hermit 1·25 25
1062 $1 Troupial 1·75 1·75
1063 $2 Ruddy quail dove 2·25 4·00
MS1064 85 × 114 mm. $3 Prarie warbler 3·75 1·75

1980. "London 1980" International Stamp Exhibition. Nos. 1001/4 optd **LONDON 1980**.
1065 20c. Type **253** 15 15
1066 40c. Pony Express, America 20 15
1067 $1 Pigeon post 30 30
1068 $3 Mail coach, Europe 85 90

263 Free Hot Lunch at Schools

1980. 1st Anniv of Revolution (2nd issue). Multicoloured.
1069 10c. Type **263** 10 10
1070 40c. "From tree to can" (agro-industry) 15 15
1071 $1 National Health care 30 30
1072 $2 New housing projects 50 70
MS1073 110 × 85 mm. $5 Prime Minister Maurice Bishop (vert) 75 85

264 Jamb Statues, West Portal, Chartres Cathedral

1980. Famous Works of Art. Multicoloured.
1074 8c. Type **264** 10 10
1075 10c. "Les Demoiselles d' Avignon" (painting, Picasso) 10 10
1076 40c. Winged Victory of Samothrace (statue) . . . 15 15
1077 50c. "The Night Watch" (painting, Rembrandt) . . 15 15
1078 $1 "Portrait of Edward VI as a Child" (painting, Holbein the Younger) . . 25 25
1079 $3 Portrait head of Queen Nefertiti (carving) 70 70
MS1080 101 × 101 mm. $4 "Weier Haws" (detail of painting by Durer) (vert) 75 75

265 Carib Canoes

1980. Shipping. Multicoloured.
1081A ½c. Type **265** 10 40
1082A 1c. Boat building 10 40
1083A 2c. Small working boat . . 15 40
1084A 4c. Columbus's "Santa Maria" 40 40
1085A 5c. West Indiaman barque, c. 1840 . . . . 40 30
1086A 6c. "Orinoco" (paddle-steamer), c. 1851 . . . 40 40
1087A 10c. Working schooner . . 50 10
1088A 12c. Trimaran at Grand Anse anchorage . . . . 1·00 55
1089A 15c. Spice Island cruising yacht "Petite Amie" . . 50 10
1090A 20c. Fishing pirogue . . . 1·00 20
1091A 25c. Harbour police launch . . . . 2·00 30
1092A 30c. Grand Anse speedboat . . . . . . 1·50 30
1093A 40c. "Seimstrand" (freighter) . . . . . . 2·00 35
1094B 50c. "Ariadne" (cadet schooner) 50 50
1095A 90c. "Geestide" (freighter) 1·75 50
1096A $1 "Cunard Countess" (liner) . . . . 3·00 80
1097A $3 Rum-runner . . . . . 2·50 4·25
1098A $5 "Statendam" (liner) off St. George's . . . . . 3·50 7·50
1099B $10 Coastguard patrol boat . . . . 3·75 8·50

Nos. 1081/99 come with and without date imprint.

1980. Christmas. Scenes from Walt Disney's "Snow White and the Seven Dwarfs". As T **257**. Multicoloured.
1100 ½c. Snow White at well . . 10 10
1101 1c. The Wicked Queen . . . 10 10
1102 2c. Snow White singing to animals 10 10
1103 3c. Snow White doing housework for Dwarfs . . 10 10
1104 4c. The Seven Dwarfs . . . 10 10
1105 5c. Snow White with Dwarfs 10 10
1106 10c. Witch offering Snow White apple 10 10
1107 $2.50 Snow White with Prince and Dwarfs . . . 3·25 1·75
1108 $3 Snow White and Prince 3·75 2·00
MS1109 127 × 102 mm. $4 Snow White sleeping (vert) . . . . . 4·25 1·50

1981. 50th Anniv of Walt Disney's Pluto (cartoon character). As T **257**. Multicoloured.
1110 $2 Pluto with birthday cake 1·00 1·00
MS1111 127 × 102 mm. $4 Pluto in scene from film "Pueblo Pluto" 1·25 1·00

266 Revolution and Grenada Flags

1981. Festival of the Revolution. Multicoloured.
1112 5c. Type **266** 10 10
1113 10c. Teacher, pupil, book and pencil ("education") 10 10
1114 15c. Food processing plant ("industry") 10 10
1115 25c. Selection of fruits and farm scene ("agriculture") 15 10
1116 40c. Crawfish and boat ("fishing") 20 15
1117 90c. "Cunard Countess" arriving at St. George's Harbour ("shipping") . . 50 30
1118 $1 Straw-work ("native handicrafts") 60 40
1119 $3 Map of Caribbean with expanded view of Grenada . . . . 1·75 1·75

1981. Easter. Walt Disney cartoon characters. As T **257**. Multicoloured.
1120 35c. Mickey Mouse and Goofy 30 15
1121 40c. Donald Duck, Chip and Daisy Duck 30 15
1122 $2 Minnie Mouse . . . . . 75 1·00
1123 $2.50 Pluto and Mickey Mouse . . . . 75 1·10
MS1124 127 × 101 mm. $4 Goofy 1·75 1·50

267 "Woman-Flower"

268 Prince Charles playing Polo

1981. Birth Centenary of Picasso. Multicoloured.
1125 25c. Type **267** 15 10
1126 30c. "Portrait of Madame" 15 10
1127 90c. "Cavalier with Pipe" 25 30
1128 $4 "Large Heads" . . . . . 70 1·00
MS1129 128 × 103 mm. $5 "Woman on the Banks of the Seine" (after Courbet). Imperf . . . . . . 2·50 1·40

1981. Royal Wedding (1st issue). Multicoloured.
1134 30c. Prince Charles and Lady Diana Spencer . . . 20 20
1135 40c. Holyrood House . . . 30 30
1130 50c. As 30c. 10 10
1131 $2 As 40c. 35 50
1132 $4 Type **268** 50 75
MS1133 98 × 94 mm. $5 Glass Coach 75 75

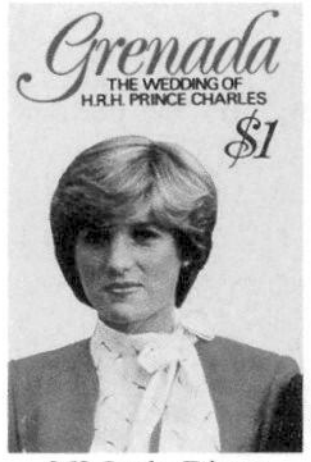

269 Lady Diana Spencer

270 "The Bath" (Mary Cassatt)

1981. Royal Wedding (2nd issue). Multicoloured. Self-adhesive.
1136 $1 Type **269** 30 65
1137 $2 Prince Charles 30 65
1138 $5 Prince Charles and Lady Diana Spencer . . . . . 1·00 1·75

1981. "Decade for Women". Paintings. Mult.
1139 15c. Type **270** 10 10
1140 40c. "Mademoiselle Charlotte du Val d'Ognes" (Constance Marie Charpentier) . . . 20 10
1141 60c. "Self-portrait" (Mary Beale) 30 20
1142 $3 "Woman in White Stockings" (Suzanne Valadon) . . . . 1·25 1·00
MS1143 101 × 77 mm. $5 "The Artist hesitating between the Arts of Music and Painting" (Angelica Kauffman) (horiz) . . . . . . 1·75 2·00

1981. Christmas. As T **257** showing scenes from Walt Disney's cartoon film "Cinderella".
1144 ½c. multicoloured 10 10
1145 1c. multicoloured 10 10
1146 2c. multicoloured 10 10
1147 3c. multicoloured 10 10
1148 4c. multicoloured 10 10
1149 5c. multicoloured 10 10
1150 10c. multicoloured 15 10
1151 $2.50 multicoloured . . . . 3·50 2·50
1152 $3 multicoloured . . . . . 3·50 2·75
MS1153 127 × 103 mm. $5 multicoloured . . . . 5·50 3·25

271 Landing

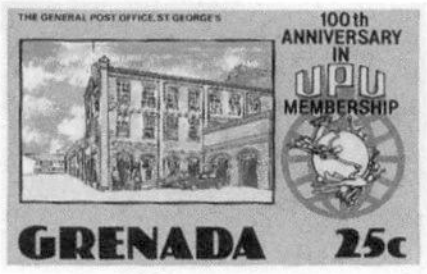

273 General Post Office, St. George's

272 West German Footballer and Flag

1981. Space Shuttle Project. Multicoloured.
1154 30c. Type **271** 20 15
1155 60c. Working in space . . . 40 30
1156 70c. Lift off 45 35
1157 $3 Separation . . . . . . 1·10 1·25
MS1158 117 × 89 mm. $5 In orbit 1·75 1·25

1981. World Cup Football Championship, Spain (1982). Multicoloured.
1159 25c.+10c. Type **272** 75 30
1160 40c.+20c. Argentinian footballer and flag 90 40
1161 50c.+25c. Brazilian footballer and flag . . . . 1·00 50
1162 $1+50c. English footballer and flag . . . . 1·50 95
MS1163 141 × 128 mm. $5+50c. Spanish orange mascot and Jules Rimet Trophy (vert) . . . . . 3·50 2·00

1981. Cent of U.P.U. Membership. Mult.
1164 25c. Type **273** 25 15
1165 30c. 1861 1d. stamp 30 20
1166 90c. New U.P.U. Headquarters Building 25c. commemorative . . . 70 50
1167 $4 1961 Stamp Centenary 25c. commemorative . . . 1·25 2·00
MS1168 137 × 87 mm. $5 1974 Centenary of U.P.U. ½c. commemorative . . . . 3·25 3·75

274 Artist without Hands

276 "Dryas julia"

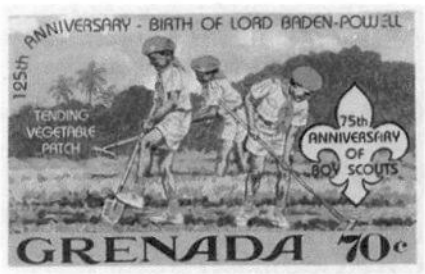

275 Tending Vegetable Patch

1982. International Year for the Disabled (1981). Multicoloured.
1169 30c. Type **274** 20 10
1170 40c. Computer operator without hands 20 10
1171 70c. Blind schoolteacher teaching braille 50 15
1172 $3 Midget playing drums . . 1·10 80
MS1173 101 × 72 mm. $4 Auto mechanic confined to wheelchair 3·00 3·25

1982. 75th Anniv of Boy Scout Movement and 125th Birth Anniv of Lord Baden-Powell. Multicoloured.
1174 70c. Type **275** 50 45
1175 90c. Map-reading 55 55
1176 $1 Bee-keeping 65 65
1177 $4 Hospital reading . . . . 2·25 2·75
MS1178 100 × 71 mm. $5 Presentation of trophies . . . 1·25 1·00

1982. Butterflies. Multicoloured.
1179 10c. Type **276** 75 30
1180 60c. "Phoebis agarithe" . . 2·50 1·50
1181 $1 "Anartia amathea" . . . 3·00 2·00
1182 $3 "Battus polydamas" . . . 4·25 7·00
MS1183 111 × 85 mm. $5 "Junonia evarete" . . . . 6·00 2·25

277 "Saying Grace"

278 Kensington Palace

1982. Norman Rockwell (painter) Commemoration. Multicoloured.
1184 15c. Type **277** 40 10
1185 30c. "Nothing Up His Sleeve" (inscr "Card Tricks") 65 15
1186 60c. "Pharmacist" 85 25
1187 70c. "Hobo" (inscr "Pals") 90 35

1982. 21st Birthday of Princess of Wales. Multicoloured.
1188 50c. Type **278** . . . . . . 90 1·00
1189 60c. Type **278** . . . . . . 1·50 50
1190 $1 Prince and Princess of Wales . . . . 1·50 1·75
1191 $2 As $1 . . . . 2·75 1·50
1192 $3 Princess of Wales . . . . 2·75 2·75
1193 $4 As $3 . . . . 3·00 2·50
MS1194 103 × 75 mm. $5 Princess Diana (different) . . . . 3·00 1·50

279 Mary McLeod Bethune appointed Director of Negro Affairs, 1942

1982. Birth Centenary of Franklin D. Roosevelt. Multicoloured.
1195 10c. Type **279** 10 10
1196 60c. Huddie Ledbetter "Leadbelly" in concert (Works Progress administration) 30 20
1197 $1.10 Signing bill No. 8802, 1941 (Fair Employment committee) 40 25
1198 $3 Farm Security administration 55 60
MS1199 100 × 70 mm. $5 William Hastie, first Negro Judicial appointee . . . . 1·25 1·25

1982. Birth of Prince William of Wales. Nos. 1188/93 optd **ROYAL BABY 21.6.82.**
1200 50c. Type **278** . . . . . . 30 1·00
1201 60c. Type **278** 35 35
1202 $1 Prince and Princess of Wales . . . . 55 1·25
1203 $2 As $1 . . . . 1·00 1·00
1204 $3 Princess of Wales . . . . 1·75 2·25
1205 $4 As $3 . . . . 1·90 1·90
MS1206 103 × 75 mm. $5 Princess Diana (different) . . . . 2·00 1·25

280 Apostle and Tormentor

1982. Easter. Details from Painting "The Way to Calvary" by Raphael. Multicoloured.
1207 40c. Type **280** 25 10
1208 70c. Captain of the guards (vert) 30 15
1209 $1.10 Christ and apostle (vert) 35 25
1210 $4 Mourners (vert) . . . . 70 1·25
MS1211 102 × 126 mm. $5 Christ falls beneath the cross (vert) . . 1·50 1·50

281 "Orient Express"

1982. Famous Trains of the World. Mult.
1212 30c. Type **281** 50 35
1213 60c. "Trans-Siberian Express" 60 70
1214 70c. "Fleche d'Or" 70 80
1215 90c. "Flying Scotsman" . . 85 1·00

1216	$1 German Federal Railways steam locomotive	1·00	1·25
1217	$3 German National Railways Class 05 steam locomotive	2·25	4·00
MS1218	109 × 81 mm. $5 "20th Century Limited"	2·00	2·00

282 Footballers

1982. World Cup Football Championship Winners.

1219 **282**	60c. multicoloured	35	35
1220	$4 multicoloured	2·00	2·00
MS1221	93 × 119 mm. $5 multicoloured	2·50	2·25

1982. Christmas. Scenes from Walt Disney's cartoon film "Robin Hood". As T **257**, but horiz.

1222	½c. multicoloured	10	10
1223	1c. multicoloured	10	10
1224	2c. multicoloured	10	10
1225	3c. multicoloured	10	10
1226	4c. multicoloured	10	10
1227	5c. multicoloured	10	10
1228	10c. multicoloured	10	10
1229	$2.50 multicoloured	3·00	3·50
1230	$3 multicoloured	3·00	3·50
MS1231	121 × 96 mm. $5 multicoloured	6·50	4·00

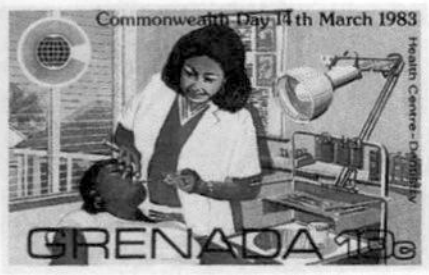

283 Killer Whale **285** Dentistry at Health Centre

284 "Construction of Ark"

1983. Save the Whales. Multicoloured.

1232	15c. Type **283**	1·00	30
1233	40c. Sperm whale	2·25	90
1234	70c. Blue whale	2·75	2·75
1235	$3 Common dolphin	3·50	6·50
MS1236	84 × 74 mm. $5 Humpback whales	6·50	4·00

1983. 500th Birth Anniv of Raphael. Mult.

1237	25c. Type **284**	20	10
1238	30c. "Jacob's Vision"	20	10
1239	90c. "Joseph interprets the Dreams of his Brothers"	40	30
1240	$4 "Joseph interprets Pharaoh's dreams"	1·10	1·40
MS1241	128 × 100 mm. $5 "Creation of the Animals"	1·25	1·75

1983. Commonwealth Day. Multicoloured.

1242	10c. Type **285**	10	10
1243	70c. Airport runway construction	35	35
1244	$1.10 Tourism	40	55
1245	$3 Boat-building	80	1·40

286 Maritime Communications via Satellite

1983. World Communications Year. Multicoloured.

1246	30c. Type **286**	15	15
1247	40c. Rural telephone installation	20	15
1248	$2.50 Satellite weather map	60	1·00
1249	$4 Airport control room	60	1·10
MS1250	111 × 85 mm. $5 Communications satellite	1·25	1·25

287 Franklin Sport Sedan, 1928

1983. 75th Anniv of Model "T" Ford Car. Multicoloured.

1251	6c. Type **287**	15	20
1252	10c. Delage "D8", 1933	20	10
1253	40c. Alvis, 1938	35	25
1254	60c. Invicta "S-type" tourer, 1931	45	45
1255	70c. Alfa-Romeo "1750 Gran Sport", 1930	55	55
1256	90c. Isotta Fraschini, 1930	60	75
1257	$1 Bugatti "Royale Type 41"	70	75
1258	$2 BMW "328", 1938	1·40	1·75
1259	$3 Marmon "V16", 1931	1·60	2·50
1260	$4 Lincoln "K8" saloon, 1932	1·90	3·00
MS1261	114 × 90 mm. $5 Cougar "TR 7", 1972	1·50	2·00

288 Airship N.1 "Norge"

1983. Bicentenary of Manned Flight. Multicoloured.

1262	30c. Type **288**	60	30
1263	60c. Gloster VI seaplane	1·00	1·00
1264	$1.10 Curtiss NC-4 flying boat	1·60	1·75
1265	$4 Dornier Do 18 flying boat "Aeolus"	3·50	4·50
MS1266	114 × 85 mm. $5 Modern hot-air balloon (vert)	1·50	1·50

289 Morty **291** William I

290 Daisy Duck on Pommel Horse

1983. Christmas. Multicoloured.

1267	½c. Type **289**	10	10
1268	1c. Ludwig von Drake	10	10
1269	2c. Gyro Gearloose	10	10
1270	3c. Pluto and Figaro	10	10
1271	4c. Morty and Ferdie	10	10
1272	5c. Mickey Mouse and Goofy	10	10
1273	10c. Chip n'Dale	10	10
1274	$2.50 Mickey and Minnie Mouse	2·25	3·50
1275	$3 Donald and Grandma Duck	2·25	3·50
MS1276	127 × 102 mm. $5 Goofy with Christmas tree	4·50	4·50

Nos. 1267/75 show Disney cartoon characters in scenes from "It's beginning to look a lot like Christmas" (song).

1984. Olympic Games. Los Angeles. Multicoloured.

A. Inscr "1984 LOS ANGELES"

1277A	½c. Type **290**	10	10
1278A	1c. Mickey Mouse boxing	10	10
1279A	2c. Daisy Duck in archery event	10	10
1280A	3c. Clarabelle Cow on uneven bars	10	10
1281A	4c. Mickey and Minnie Mouse in hurdles race	10	10
1282A	5c. Donald Duck with Chip'n'Dale weightlifting	10	10
1283A	$1 Little Hiawatha in single kayak	2·50	2·25
1284A	$2 The Tortoise and the Hare in marathon	3·00	3·75
1285A	$3 Mickey Mouse polevaulting	3·50	4·00
MS1286A	127 × 101 mm. $5 Donald Duck in medley relay (vert)	5·50	3·50

B. Inscr "1984 OLYMPICS LOS ANGELES" and Olympic Emblem.

1227B	½c. Type **290**	10	10
1278B	1c. Mickey Mouse boxing	10	10
1279B	2c. Daisy Duck in archery event	10	10
1280B	3c. Clarabelle Cow on uneven bars	10	10
1281B	4c. Mickey and Minnie Mouse in hurdles race	10	10
1282B	5c. Donald Duck with Chip'n'Dale weightlifting	10	10
1283B	$1 Little Hiawatha in single kayak	2·50	2·25
1284B	$2 The Tortoise and the Hare in marathon	3·00	3·75
1285B	$3 Mickey Mouse polevaulting	3·50	4·00
MS1286B	127 × 100 mm. $5 Donald Duck in medley relay (vert)	6·50	5·50

1984. English Monarchs. Multicoloured.

1287	$4 Type **291**	2·00	2·75
1288	$4 William II	2·00	2·75
1289	$4 Henry I	2·00	2·75
1290	$4 Stephen	2·00	2·75
1291	$4 Henry II	2·00	2·75
1292	$4 Richard I	2·00	2·75
1293	$4 John	2·00	2·75
1294	$4 "Henry III"	2·00	2·75
1295	$4 Edward I	2·00	2·75
1296	$4 Edward II	2·00	2·75
1297	$4 Edward III	2·00	2·75
1298	$4 Richard II	2·00	2·75
1299	$4 Henry IV	2·00	2·75
1300	$4 Henry V	2·00	2·75
1301	$4 Henry VI	2·00	2·75
1302	$4 Edward IV	2·00	2·75
1303	$4 Edward V	2·00	2·75
1304	$4 Richard III	2·00	2·75
1305	$4 Henry VII	2·00	2·75
1306	$4 Henry VIII	2·00	2·75
1307	$4 Edward VI	2·00	2·75
1308	$4 Jane Grey	2·00	2·75
1309	$4 Mary I	2·00	2·75
1310	$4 Elizabeth I	2·00	2·75
1311	$4 James I	2·00	2·75
1312	$4 Charles I	2·00	2·75
1313	$4 Charles II	2·00	2·75
1314	$4 James II	2·00	2·75
1315	$4 William III	2·00	2·75
1316	$4 Mary II	2·00	2·75
1317	$4 Anne	2·00	2·75
1318	$4 George I	2·00	2·75
1319	$4 George II	2·00	2·75
1320	$4 George III	2·00	2·75
1321	$4 George IV	2·00	2·75
1322	$4 William IV	2·00	2·75
1323	$4 Victoria	2·00	2·75
1324	$4 Edward VII	2·00	2·75
1325	$4 George V	2·00	2·75
1326	$4 Edward VIII	2·00	2·75
1327	$4 George VI	2·00	2·75
1328	$4 Elizabeth II	2·00	2·75

Although inscribed "Henry III" the portrait on No. 1294 is actually of Edward II.

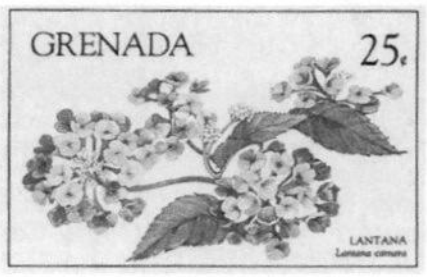

292 Lantana

1984. Flowers. Multicoloured.

1329	25c. Type **292**	20	15
1330	30c. Plumbago	25	15
1331	90c. Spider lily	60	35
1332	$4 Giant alocasia	1·50	2·75
MS1333	108 × 90 mm. $5 Orange trumpet vine	1·00	1·50

293 Blue Parrotfish

1984. Coral Reef Fishes. Multicoloured.

1334	10c. Type **293**	1·40	45
1335	30c. Flame-backed angelfish	2·75	1·10
1336	70c. Painted wrasse	4·00	3·25
1337	90c. Rosy razorfish	4·75	3·50
MS1338	81 × 85 mm. $5 Spanish hogfish	6·50	4·75

1984. Universal Postal Union Congress, Hamburg. Nos. 1331/2 optd **19TH U.P.U CONGRESS HAMBURG**.

1339	90c. Spider lily	60	65
1340	$4 Giant alocasia	2·00	2·50
MS1341	108 × 90 mm. $5 Orange trumpet vine	1·50	2·50

295 Freighter

1984. Ships. Multicoloured.

1342	40c. Type **295**	1·25	55
1343	70c. "Queen Elizabeth 2"	1·50	1·50
1344	90c. Sailing boats	1·60	2·00
1345	$4 "Amerikanis"	3·50	8·00
MS1346	107 × 80 mm. $5 Spanish galleon	5·00	7·00

296 "The Night" (detail) (Correggio)

1984. 450th Death Anniv of Correggio (painter). Multicoloured.

1347	10c. Type **296**	45	15
1348	30c. "The Virgin adoring the Child"	80	50
1349	40c. "The Mystical Marriage of St. Catherine with St. Sebastian"	2·00	1·75
1350	$4 "The Madonna and the Fruit Basket"	4·50	5·50
MS1351	54 × 73 mm. $5 "The Madonna at the Spring"	4·25	3·00

297 "L'Absinthe" (Degas) **298** Train on Puffing Billy Line, Victoria

1984. 150th Birth Anniv of Edgar Degas (painter). Multicoloured.

1352	25c. Type **297**	80	30
1353	70c. "Pouting" (horiz)	1·50	1·25
1354	$1.10 "The Millinery Shop"	2·00	2·00
1355	$3 "The Bellelli Family" (horiz)	3·75	4·25
MS1356	84 × 54 mm. $5 "The Cotton Market"	4·25	3·00

1984. "Ausipex" International Stamp Exhibition, Melbourne. Multicoloured.

1357	$1.10 Type **298**	2·25	1·75
1358	$4 Yacht "Australia II" (winner of America's Cup)	4·75	5·25
MS1359	107 × 76 mm. $5 Melbourne tram	4·25	4·00

299 George Stephenson's "Locomotion" (1825)

1984. Railway Locomotives. Multicoloured.

1360	30c. Type **299**	80	35
1361	40c. Braithwaite and Ericsson's "Novelty" (1829)	95	40
1362	60c. William Norris's "Washington Farmer" (1836)	1·00	75
1363	70c. French Crampton type (1859)	1·00	1·00
1364	90c. Dutch State Railways (1873)	1·10	1·50
1365	$1.10 "Champion", U.S.A. (1882)	1·25	2·00

1366 $2 Webb Compound type (1893) . . . . 1·75 3·25
1367 $4 Berlin "No. 74" (1900) 2·75 5·50
MS1368 Two sheets, each 100 × 70 mm. (a) $5 Crampton "Phoenix" (1863); (b) $5 Mikado type, Japan (1897) Set of 2 sheets 6·00 6·50

1984. Opening of Point Saline International Airport (1st issue). Nos. 1247 and 1249 optd **OPENING OF POINT SALINE INT'L AIRPORT**.
1369 40c. Rural telephone installation 30 30
1370 $3 Airport control room . . 2·00 2·00
MS1371 111 × 85 mm. $5 Communications satellite . . . 3·50 3·25
See also Nos. 1399/6.

301 Donald Duck as Father Christmas looking into Mirror

1984. Christmas. Walt Disney cartoon characters. Multicoloured.
1372 45c. Type **301** . . . . . . 1·25 40
1373 60c. Donald Duck filling stocking with presents . . 1·50 55
1374 90c. As Father Christmas pulling a sleigh . . . . . 2·00 1·10
1375 $2 As Father Christmas decorating Christmas tree 3·50 3·75
1376 $4 Donald Duck and nephews singing carols . . 5·00 6·00
MS1377 127 × 102 mm. $5 Father Christmas in sleigh . . . . . . 7·00 8·00

1985. Birth Bicentenary of John J. Audubon (ornithologist) (1st issue). As T **418** of Ghana. Multicoloured.
1378 50c. Clapper rail (vert) . . . 2·00 75
1379 70c. Hooded warbler (vert) 2·25 1·50
1380 90c. Common flicker (vert) 2·75 1·75
1381 $4 Bohemian waxwing (vert) 5·50 8·00
MS1382 82 × 112 mm. $5 Merlin ("Pigeon Hawk") . . . . . . 9·00 4·50
See also Nos. 1480/4.

302 Honda "XL500R"

1985. Centenary of the Motor Cycle. Multicoloured.
1383 25c. Type **302** . . . . . . 1·00 50
1384 50c. Suzuki "GS1100ES" . . 1·50 1·00
1385 90c. Kawasaki "KZ700" . . 2·00 2·25
1386 $4 BMW "K100" . . . . . 6·00 6·50
MS1387 109 × 81 mm. $5 Yamaha "500CC V Four" . . . . . . 7·50 5·00

303 "Explorer"

1985. 75th Anniv of Girl Guide Movement. Designs showing work for Guide badges. Multicoloured.
1388 25c. Type **303** 55 30
1389 60c. "Cook" 90 65
1390 90c. "Musician" . . . . . 1·50 1·10
1391 $3 "Home nurse" . . . . . 3·00 4·50
MS1392 97 × 70 mm. $5 Flags of Girl Guides and Grenada . . . 2·50 2·50

304 Hawker Siddeley H.S.748 on Inaugural Flight from Barbados

1985. Opening of Point Saline International Airport (1984) (2nd issue). Multicoloured.
1393 70c. Type **304** . . . . . . 2·50 1·00
1394 $1 Lockheed TriStar 500 on inaugural flight from New York . . . . 3·25 1·50
1395 $4 Lockheed TriStar 500 on inaugural flight to Miami 6·50 8·50
MS1396 101 × 72 mm. $5 Point Saline Airport terminal and Hawker Siddeley H.S.748 on tarmac . . . . 5·50 3·75

305 Douglas DC-8-61

1985. 40th Anniv of International Civil Aviation Organization. Multicoloured.
1397 10c. Type **305** 40 20
1398 50c. Lockheed Starliner (inscr "Super Constellation") . . . . . 1·00 75
1399 60c. Vickers 952 Cargoliner 1·25 85
1400 $4 De Havilland Twin Otter 200/300 . . . . 4·50 7·00
MS1401 102 × 64 mm. $5 Hawker Siddeley H.S.748 turboprop . . 3·00 3·00

306 Model Boat Racing

1985. Water Sports. Multicoloured.
1402 10c. Type **306** 25 10
1403 50c. Scuba diving, Carriacou 55 35
1404 $1.10 Windsurfers on Grand Anse Beach . . . . . . 85 1·25
1405 $4 Windsurfing . . . . . 2·00 6·00
MS1406 107 × 77 mm. $5 Beach scene . . . . 2·25 2·75

307 Bird of Paradise (flower)

1985. Native Flowers. Multicoloured.
1407 ½c. Type **307** 50 60
1408 1c. Passion flower 50 60
1409 2c. Oleander 50 60
1410a 4c. Bromeliad 80 60
1411a 5c. Anthurium 80 40
1412a 6c. Bougainvillea 80 50
1413a 10c. Hibiscus 80 30
1414a 15c. Ginger . . . . 1·25 30
1415a 25c. Poinsettia . . . . . 1·25 30
1425d 30c. Mexican creeper . . . 30 60
1417a 40c. Angel's trumpet . . . 1·00 50
1425e 50c. Amaryllis 40 75
1425f 60c. Prickly pear . . . . 50 1·25
1420a 70c. Chenille plant . . . 1·50 1·50
1420b 75c. Cordia . . . . 1·50 2·00
1425g $1 Periwinkle . . . . . . 50 1·25
1422a $1.10 Ixora . . . . . . 2·50 2·75
1423a $3 Shrimp plant . . . . 3·00 6·50
1424a $5 Plumbago . . . . . . 2·50 7·00
1425a $10 "Lantana camara" . . 4·00 10·00
1425b $20 Peregrina . . . . . . 8·50 16·00

308 The Queen Mother at Royal Opera House, London

309 Youth Gardening (Horticulture)

1985. Life and Times of Queen Elizabeth the Queen Mother. Multicoloured.
1426 $1 Type **308** 40 60
1427 $1.50 The Queen Mother playing snooker at London Press Club (horiz) 55 85
1428 $2.50 At Epsom Races, 1960 95 1·50
MS1429 56 × 85 mm. $5 With Prince of Wales on 80th Birthday . . 1·75 3·00
Stamps as Nos. 1426/8 but with face values of 90c., $1 and $3 exist from additional sheetlets with changed background colours.

1985. International Youth Year. Multicoloured.
1430 25c. Type **309** 25 20
1431 50c. Young people on beach (Leisure) 35 40
1432 $1.10 Girls in classroom (Education) . . . . . . 60 1·10
1433 $3 Nurse and young patient (Health Care) . . . . . . 1·50 2·50
MS1434 111 × 80 mm. $5 Children of different races . . . . . . 1·50 3·00

309a Crumhorn

1985. 300th Birth Anniv of Johann Sebastian Bach (composer).
1435 **309a** 25c. multicoloured . . . 80 20
1436 – 70c. multicoloured . . . 1·50 85
1437 – $1 multicoloured . . . 2·00 1·25
1438 – $3 multicoloured . . . 3·00 5·00
MS1439 104 × 74 mm. $5 black, grey and cinnamon . . . . 3·50 3·75
DESIGNS: 70c. Oboe d'amore; $1 Violin; $3 Harpsichord; $5 Johann Sebastian Bach.

310 Cub Scouts Camping

1985. 4th Caribbean Cuboree. Multicoloured.
1440 10c. Type **310** 30 15
1441 50c. Cub scouts swimming ("Physical Fitness") . . . 65 40
1442 $1 Stamp collecting . . . . 1·50 80
1443 $4 Birdwatching . . . . . 3·50 3·00
MS1444 103 × 75 mm. $5 Cub scouts saluting leader (vert) . . . . . 3·25 3·75

310a Flags of Great Britain and Grenada

1985. Royal Visit. Multicoloured.
1445 50c. Type **310a** . . . . . . 1·00 40
1446 $1 Queen Elizabeth II (vert) 1·00 1·25
1447 $4 Royal Yacht "Britannia" 2·75 5·00
MS1448 111 × 85 mm. $5 Map of Grenada . . . . 1·75 3·25

1985. 150th Birth Anniv of Mark Twain (author). As T **145a** of Gambia. Design showing Walt Disney cartoon characters in scenes from "The Prince and the Pauper". Multicoloured.
1449 25c. Mortie as Tom meeting the Prince (Ferdie) . . . 60 20
1450 50c. Tom and the Prince exchanging clothes . . . 80 50
1451 $1.10 The Prince with John Cantry . . . . 1·75 1·75
1452 $1.50 The Prince knights Mike Hendon (Goofy) . . 2·25 2·75
1453 $2 Tom and the Whipping Boy . . . . 2·50 3·00
MS1454 124 × 100 mm. $5 The Prince, Tom and Mike Hendon 6·00 6·00

1985. Birth Bicentenaries of Grimm Brothers (folklorists). As T **145b** of Gambia, showing Walt Disney cartoon characters in scenes from "The Fisherman and his Wife". Multicoloured.
1455 30c. The Fisherman (Goofy) catching enchanted fish 85 30
1456 60c. The Fisherman scolded by his Wife (Clarabelle) 1·25 80
1457 70c. The Fisherman's Wife with dream cottage . . . 1·40 95
1458 $1 The Fisherman's Wife as King . . . . 2·25 1·50
1459 $3 The Fisherman and Wife in their original shack . . 3·75 4·50
MS1460 126 × 100 mm. $5 The Fisherman in boat . . . . . . 6·00 6·00

311 Red-spotted Hawkfish

1985. Marine Life. Multicoloured.
1461 25c. Type **311** . . . . . . 1·50 55
1462 50c. Spot-finned butterflyfish 2·25 1·10
1463 $1.10 Fire coral and orange sponges . . . . 3·75 3·25
1464 $3 Pillar coral . . . . . . 6·00 7·50
MS1465 127 × 100 mm. $5 Bigeye 3·75 4·50

311a Mary McLeod Bethune (educationist) and 1975 International Women's Year 10c.

1985. 40th Anniv of U.N.O. Designs showing United Nations (New York) stamps. Mult.
1466 50c. Type **311a** 30 30
1467 $2 Maimonides (physician) and 1966 W.H.O. 5c. . . 2·50 3·50
1468 $2.50 Alexander Graham Bell (telephone inventor) and 1956 I.T.U. 3c. . . . 2·00 4·00
MS1469 110 × 85 mm. $5 Dag Hammarskjold (Secretary-General) (vert) . . . . 1·25 2·00

312 "Adoration of the Shepherds" (Mantegna)

1985. Christmas. Religious Paintings. Multicoloured.
1470 25c. Type **312** 20 15
1471 60c. "Journey of the Magi" (Sassetta) 30 40
1472 90c. "Madonna and Child enthroned with Saints" (Raphael) 35 70
1473 $4 "Nativity" (Monaco) . . 1·00 4·25
MS1474 107 × 81 mm. $5 "Madonna and Child enthroned with Saints" (Gaddi) . . . . 1·50 2·50

312a Columbus Monument, 1893

312b Snowy Egret

1986. Centenary of Statue of Liberty (1st issue). Multicoloured.
1475 5c. Type **312a** 15 20
1476 25c. Columbus Monument, 1986 . . . . 30 20
1477 40c. Mounted police, Central Park, 1895 (horiz) 1·75 1·10
1478 $4 Mounted police, 1986 (horiz) . . . . 5·00 8·00
MS1479 104 × 76 mm. $5 Statue of Liberty (vert) . . . . 2·75 2·75
See also Nos. 1644/52.

1986. Birth Bicentenary of John J. Audubon (ornithologist) (2nd issue). Multicoloured.
1480 50c. Type **312b** . . . . . . 2·00 80
1481 90c. Greater flamingo . . . 2·75 2·00
1482 $1.10 Canada goose . . . . 2·75 2·50
1483 $3 Smew . . . . 4·50 6·00
MS1484 103 × 72 mm. $5 Brent goose (horiz) . . . . 13·00 13·00

1986. Visit of President Reagan. Nos. 1418 and 1424 optd **VISIT OF PRES REAGAN 20 FEB. 1986.**
1485 50c. Amaryllis 50 50
1486 $5 Plumbago . . . . 3·00 5·00

314 Methodist Church, St. George's

1986. Bicentenary of Methodist Church in Grenada. Multicoloured.
1487 60c. Type **314** . . . . . . 70 1·00
MS1488 102 × 73 mm. $5 St. Georges . . . . 1·00 3·00

315 Player with Ball

316 Brown-lined Latirus

1986. World Cup Football Championship, Mexico. Multicoloured.
1489 50c. Type **315** 80 55
1490 70c. Player heading ball . . 1·00 1·00
1491 90c. Player controlling ball 1·50 1·50
1492 $4 Player controlling ball with right foot . . . . . 5·50 7·00
MS1493 103 × 71 mm. $5 Player tackling . . . . 4·25 5·00

1986. Appearance of Halley's Comet (1st issue). As T **151a** of Gambia. Multicoloured.
1494 5c. Clyde Tombaugh (astronomer) and Dudley Observatory, New York 40 40
1495 20c. N.A.S.A. – U.S.A.F. "X-24B" Space Shuttle prototype, 1973 . . . . . 50 30
1496 40c. German comet medal, 1618 . . . . 70 45
1497 $4 Destruction of Sodom and Gomorrah, 1949 B.C. 3·50 4·50
MS1498 102 × 70 mm. $5 Halley's Comet over Grenada . . . . . 6·50 7·00
See also Nos. 1533/7 and 1980/4.

1986. 60th Birthday of Queen Elizabeth II. As T **151b** of Gambia.
1499 2c. black and yellow 10 15
1500 $1.50 multicoloured 80 80
1501 $4 multicoloured . . . . . 1·60 2·50
MS1502 120 × 85 mm. $5 black and brown . . . . 1·75 3·25
DESIGNS: 2c. Princess Elizabeth in 1951; $1.50, Queen presenting trophy at polo match, Windsor, 1965; $4 at Epsom, Derby Day, 1977; $5 King George VI and family, 1939.

315a Goofy as Pitcher

1986. "Ameripex" International Stamp Exhibition, Chicago. Designs showing Walt Disney cartoon characters playing baseball. Multicoloured.
1503 1c. Type **315a** 10 10
1504 2c. Goofy as catcher 10 10
1505 3c. Mickey Mouse striking ball and Donald Duck as catcher 10 10
1506 4c. Huey forcing out Dewey 10 10
1507 5c. Chip n'Dale chasing flyball 10 10
1508 6c. Mickey Mouse, Donald Duck and Clarabelle in argument 10 10
1509 $2 Minnie Mouse and Donald Duck reading baseball rules . . . . . . 1·75 2·75
1510 $3 Ludwig von Drake as umpire with Goofy and Pete colliding . . . . . 2·25 3·25
MS1511 Two sheets, each 126 × 101 mm. (a) $5 Donald Duck striking ball. (b) $5 Minnie and Mickey Mouse running between bases Set of 2 sheets 11·00 13·00

1986. Royal Wedding. As T **153b** of Gambia. Multicoloured.
1512 2c. Prince Andrew and Miss Sarah Ferguson 10 30
1513 $1.10 Prince Andrew . . . 70 80
1514 $4 Prince Andrew with H.M.S. "Brazen's" Westland Lynx helicopter 3·50 3·50
MS1515 88 × 88 mm. $5 Prince Andrew and Miss Sarah Ferguson (different) . . . . 4·50 5·00

1986. Sea Shells. Multicoloured.
1516 25c. Type **316** 45 25
1517 60c. Lamellose wentletrap 75 90
1518 70c. Turkey wing . . . . . 85 1·00
1519 $4 Rooster tail conch . . . 2·00 5·00
MS1520 110 × 75 mm. $5 Angular triton . . . . 2·75 6·00

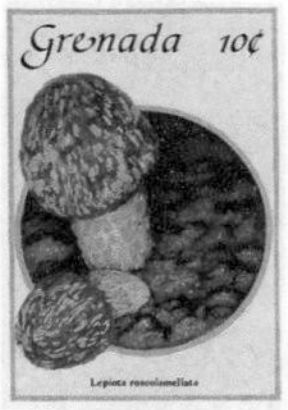

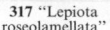

317 "Lepiota roseolamellata"

318 Dove on Rifles and Mahatma Gandhi (Disarmament Week)

1986. Mushrooms. Multicoloured.
1521 10c. Type **317** 60 40
1522 60c. "Lentinus bertieri" . . 1·75 1·75
1523 $1 "Lentinus retinervis" . . 2·50 2·50
1524 $4 "Eccilia cystiophorus" 5·75 7·50
MS1525 127 × 100 mm. $5 "Cystolepiota eriophora" . . . 10·00 13·00

1986. World Cup Football Championship Winners, Mexico. Nos. 1489/92 optd **WINNERS Argentina 3 W. Germany 2**.
1526 50c. Type **315** 85 85
1527 70c. Player heading ball . . 1·00 1·00
1528 90c. Player controlling ball 1·40 1·60
1529 $4 Player controlling ball with right foot . . . . . 4·50 5·00
MS1530 101 × 71 mm. $5 Player tackling . . . . 3·50 4·50

1986. International Events. Multicoloured.
1531 60c. Type **318** 50 50
1532 $4 Hands passing olive branch and Martin Luther King (International Peace Year) (horiz) . . . . . . 1·50 3·00

1986. Appearance of Halley's Comet (2nd issue). Nos. 1494/7 optd with T **447a** of Ghana.
1533 5c. Clyde Tombaugh (astronomer) and Dudley Observatory, New York 60 60
1534 20c. N.A.S.A. – U.S.A.F. "X-24B" Space Shuttle prototype, 1973 . . . . . 85 60
1535 40c. German comet medal, 1618 . . . . 1·25 70
1536 $4 Destruction of Sodom and Gomorrah, 1949 B.C. 5·00 7·00
MS1537 102 × 70 mm. $5 Halley's Comet over Grenada . . . . 3·50 4·25

318a Mickey Mouse asleep in Armchair

1986. Christmas. Multicoloured.
1538 30c. Type **318a** 35 25
1539 45c. Young Mickey Mouse with Father Christmas . . 45 30
1540 60c. Donald Duck with toy telephone (horiz) 60 50
1541 70c. Pluto with pushcart (horiz) 70 70
1542 $1.10 Daisy Duck with doll (horiz) . . . . 1·00 1·25
1543 $2 Goofy as Father Christmas . . . . 1·75 2·00
1544 $2.50 Goofy singing carols at piano . . . . 2·00 2·50
1545 $3 Mickey Mouse, Donald Duck and nephew riding toy train (horiz) . . . . . 2·25 3·00
MS1546 Two sheets, each 127 × 101 mm. (a) $5 Donald Duck, Goofy and Mickey Mouse delivering presents (vert). (b) $5 Father Christmas playing toy piano Set of 2 sheets . . . . . 7·00 11·00

319 Cockerel and Hen

1986. Fauna and Flora. Multicoloured.
1547 10c. Type **319** 20 10
1548 30c. Fish-eating bat 35 20
1549 60c. Goat 55 45
1550 70c. Cow 60 50
1551 $1 Anthurium . . . . . . 1·50 1·25
1552 $1.10 Royal poinciana . . . 1·50 1·25
1553 $2 Frangipani . . . . . . 2·50 3·25
1554 $4 Orchid . . . . 8·50 9·50
MS1555 Two sheets, each 104 × 73 mm. (a) $5 Grenada landscape. (b) $5 Horse Set of 2 sheets . . . . 12·00 13·00

320 Maserati "Biturbo" (1984)

1986. Centenary of Motoring. Multicoloured.
1556 10c. Type **320** 25 25
1557 30c. AC "Cobra" (1960) . . 40 40
1558 60c. Corvette (1963) 60 60
1559 70c. Dusenberg "SJ7" (1932) 70 70
1560 90c. Porsche (1957) . . . . 85 1·00
1561 $1 Stoewer (1930) . . . . . 1·00 1·25
1562 $2 Volkswagen "Beetle" (1957) . . . . 1·60 2·00
1563 $3 Mercedes "600 Limo" (1963) . . . . 1·90 2·50
MS1564 Two sheets, each 106 × 77 mm. (a) $5 Stutz (1914). (b) $5 Packard (1941) Set of 2 sheets . . . . 5·50 7·00

321 Pole Vaulting

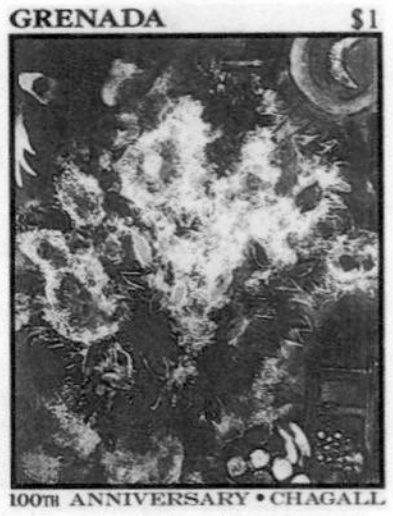

321a Painting by Chagall

1986. Olympic Games, Seoul, South Korea (1988). Multicoloured.
1565 10c.+5c. Type **321** 10 30
1566 50c.+20c. Gymnastics . . . 35 60
1567 70c.+30c. Putting the shot 50 85
1568 $2+$1 High jumping . . . . 1·00 2·25
MS1569 80 × 100 mm. $3+$1 Swimming . . . . 1·50 3·25
The premiums on Nos. 1565/9 were to support the participation of the Grenada team.

1986. Birth Centenary of Marc Chagall (artist). Designs showing various paintings.
1570/1609 $1 × 40 multicoloured Set of 40 . . . . . . 24·00 26·00
MS1610 Ten sheets, each 110 × 95 mm. $5 × 10 multicoloured (each 104 × 89 mm). Imperf Set of 10 sheets . . . . 24·00 26·00

321b "Columbia", 1958

1987. America's Cup Yachting Championship. Multicoloured.
1611 10c. Type **321b** 25 20
1612 60c. "Resolute", 1920 . . . 55 60
1613 $1.10 "Endeavor", 1934 . . 85 1·25
1614 $4 "Rainbow", 1934 . . . . 1·75 3·50
MS1615 113 × 84 mm. $5 "Weatherly", 1962 . . . . . . 2·25 4·00

322 Virgin Mary and Outline Map of Grenada

323 Black Grouper

1987. 500th Anniv (1992) of Discovery of America by Christopher Columbus (1st issue). Multicoloured.
1616 10c. Type **322** 30 20
1617 30c. "Santa Maria", "Pinta" and "Nina" (horiz) . . . 80 35
1618 50c. Columbus and outline map of Grenada 90 45
1619 60c. Christopher Columbus 90 55
1620 90c. King Ferdinand and Queen Isabella of Spain (horiz) 90 80
1621 $1.10 Map of Antilles by Columbus . . . . 1·25 1·00
1622 $2 Caribs with sailing raft (horiz) . . . . 1·40 2·50
1623 $3 Columbus in the New World, 1493 (contemporary drawing) 1·60 2·50
MS1624 Two sheets, each 104 × 72 mm. (a) $5 Route map and Colombus' signature. (b) $5 Columbus carrying Christ Child Set of 2 sheets . . . . . . 5·00 7·50
See also Nos. 2051/5, 2091/9, 2222/30, 2389/95 and 2423/4.

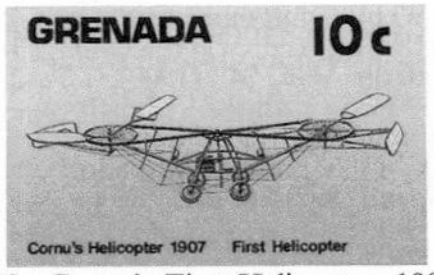

322a Cornu's First Helicopter, 1907

1987. Milestones of Transportation. Multicoloured.
1625 10c. Type **322a** . . . . . . 1·25 65
1626 15c. "Monitor" and "Merrimack" (first battle between ironclad warships), 1862 . . . . . 1·25 65
1627 30c. LZ1 (first Zeppelin), 1900 . . . . 1·40 80
1628 50c. "Sirius" (first transatlantic paddle-steamer crossing), 1838 1·50 85
1629 60c. Steam locomotive on Trans-Siberian Railway (longest line) . . . . . . 1·75 1·00
1630 70c. U.S.S "Enterprise" (largest aircraft carrier), 1960 . . . . 1·75 1·25
1631 90c. Blanchard and Jeffries' balloon (first balloon across English Channel), 1785 . . . . 1·75 1·40
1632 $1.50 U.S.S. "Holland I" (first steam-powered submarine), 1900 . . . . 2·50 2·50
1633 $2 "Oceanic I" (first luxury liner), 1871 . . . . . . 3·00 3·00
1634 $3 Lamborghini "Countach" (fastest commercial car), 1984 . . . . 3·25 3·50

1987. "Capex '87" International Stamp Exhibition, Toronto. Game Fishes. Multicoloured.
1635 10c. Type **323** 35 15
1636 30c. Blue marlin (horiz) . . 50 15
1637 60c. White marlin 70 55
1638 70c. Bigeye threshershark (horiz) 80 70
1639 $1 Bonefish (horiz) . . . . 1·10 1·00
1640 $1.10 Wahoo (horiz) . . . . 1·25 1·25
1641 $2 Sailfish (horiz) . . . . . 2·00 2·50
1642 $4 Albacore (horiz) . . . . 3·00 3·75
MS1643 Two sheets, each 100 × 70 mm. (a) $5 Yellow-finned tuna. (b) $5 Great barracuda (horiz) Set of 2 sheets . . . . 8·00 11·00

323a Computer Projections on Statue and Base

1987. Centenary of Statue of Liberty (2nd issue). Multicoloured.
1644 10c. Type **323a** 15 15
1645 25c. Statue and fireworks . . 20 15
1646 50c. Statue and fireworks (different) 35 35
1647 60c. Statue and boats (vert) 45 45
1648 70c. Computer projection of top of Statue 50 50
1649 $1 Rear view of Statue and fireworks (vert) 80 80
1650 $1.10 Aerial view of Statue (vert) . . . . 95 1·25
1651 $2 Statue and flotilla (vert) 2·00 2·25
1652 $4 "Queen Elizabeth 2" in New York Harbour (vert) 3·50 4·00

324 Alice and the Rabbit Hole

1987. 50th Anniv of First Full-Length Disney Cartoon Film. Nos. 1653/1706 show scenes from various films and No. **MS**1707 depict scenes from "Alice in Wonderland", "Cinderella", "Peter Pan", "Pinocchio", "Sleeping Beauty" and "Snow White and the Seven Dwarfs".
1653/1706 30c. × 54 multicoloured Set of 54 . . . . . . 17·00 18·00
MS1707 Six sheets, each 127 × 102 mm. $5 × 6 multicoloured Set of 6 sheets 30·00 30·00

325 Isaac Newton holding Apple (Law of Gravity)

1987. Great Scientific Discoveries. Multicoloured.
1708 50c. Type **325** 85 85
1709 $1.10 John Jacob Berzelius and symbols of chemical elements . . . . 1·75 1·75
1710 $2 Robert Boyle (law of Pressure and Volume) . . 2·50 3·25
1711 $3 James Watt and drawing of steam engine . . . . . 4·75 5·00
MS1712 105 × 75 mm. $5 "Voyager" (experimental aircraft) and Wright glider No. IV . . . . 3·00 4·00
No. 1711 is inscribed "RUDOLF DIESEL" and No. **MS**1712 "Flyer I", both in error.

326 Wade Boggs (Boston Red Sox)

1987. All-star Baseball Game, Oakland, California. Sheet 114 × 82 mm, containing T **326** and similar horiz design. Multicoloured.
MS1713 $1 Type **326**; $1 Eric Davis (Cincinnati Reds) . . . . . . 75 1·50

1987. 60th Anniv of International Social Security Association. Nos. 1413, 1418 and 1423 optd **INTERNATIONAL SOCIAL SECURITY ASSOCIATION** and emblem.
1714 10c. Hibiscus 10 15
1715 50c. Amaryllis 25 35
1716 $3 Shrimp plant . . . . . . 1·40 2·25

327a Independance Hall, Philadelphia

1987. Bicentenary of U.S. Constitution. Mult.
1717 15c. Type **327a** 10 10
1718 50c. Benjamin Franklin (Pennsylvania delegate) 25 35
1719 60c. State Seal, Massachusetts (horiz) . . 25 35
1720 $4 Robert Morris (Pennsylvania delegate) 1·75 2·75
MS1721 105 × 75 mm. $5 James Madison (Virginia delegate) (vert) 1·50 3·50

328 Goofy in "The Shadow"

329 "The Annunciation" (Fra Angelico)

1987. "Hafnia '87" International Stamp Exhibition. Walt Disney cartoon characters in scenes from Hans Christian Andersen's fairy tales. Multicoloured.
1722 25c. Type **328** 50 30
1723 30c. Mother Stork and brood in "The Storks" . . 50 30
1724 50c. King Richard, Robin Hood and Little John (from Robin Hood) in "The Emperor's New Clothes" 75 55
1725 60c. Goofy and Pluto in "The Tinderbox" 75 55
1726 70c. Daisy and Donald Duck in "The Shepherdess and the Chimney Sweep" 80 70
1727 $1.50 Mickey and Minnie Mouse in "The Little Mermaid" . . . . 1·60 1·75
1728 $3 Clarabelle and Goofy in "The Princess and the Pea" . . . . 2·50 3·50
1729 $4 Minnie Mouse and Pegleg Pete in "The Marsh King's Daughter" 2·50 3·50
MS1730 Two sheets, each 127 × 102 mm. (a) $5 Goofy in "The Flying Trunk". (b) $5 Goofy as "The Sandman" Set of 2 sheets 12·00 14·00

1987. Christmas. Religious Paintings. Multicoloured.
1731 15c. Type **329** 55 10
1732 30c. "The Annunciation" (attr. Hubert van Eyck) 90 30
1733 60c. "The Adoration of the Magi" (Januarius Zick) 1·75 1·40
1734 $4 "The Flight into Egypt" (Gerard David) . . . . . 5·50 7·00
MS1735 99 × 75 mm. $5 "The Circumcision" (Giovanni Bellini studio) . . . . 7·00 8·00

330 T. Albert Marryshow

1988. Birth Centenary of T. Albert Marryshow (nationalist).
1736 **330** 25c. brown, lt brn & red 30 30

330a Wedding Photograph, 1947

332 Scout fishing from Boat

331 Goofy and Daisy Duck lighting Olympic Torch, Olympia

1988. Royal Ruby Wedding. Multicoloured.
1737 **330a** 15c. brown, black & bl 45 10
1738 – 50c. multicoloured . . . 80 50
1739 – $1 brown and black . . 1·40 1·00
1740 – $4 multicoloured . . . 3·25 4·00
MS1741 76 × 100 mm. $5 multicoloured . . . . 2·25 3·25
DESIGNS: 50c. Queen Elizabeth II with Prince Charles and Princess Anne, c. 1955; $1 Queen with Princess Anne, c. 1957; $4 Queen Elizabeth (from photo by Tim Graham), 1980; $5 Princess Elizabeth in wedding dress, 1947.

1988. Olympic Games, Seoul. Designs showing Walt Disney cartoon characters. Multicoloured.
1742 1c. Type **331** 10 10
1743 2c. Donald and Daisy Duck carrying Olympic torch 10 10
1744 3c. Donald Duck, Goofy and Mickey Mouse carrying flags of U.S., Korea and Spain 10 10
1745 4c. Donald Duck releasing doves 10 10
1746 5c. Mickey Mouse flying with rocket belt 10 10
1747 10c. Morty and Ferdie carrying banner with Olympic motto 10 10
1748 $6 Donald Duck, Minnie Mouse and Hodori the Tiger (mascot of Seoul Games) . . . . 6·00 5·50
1749 $7 Pluto. Hodori and old post office, Seoul . . . . 6·00 5·50
MS1750 Two sheets, each 127 × 101 mm. (a) $5 Mickey Mouse taking athlete's oath. (b) $5 Donald and Daisy Duck as athletes at Closing Ceremony Set of 2 sheets . . . . 8·50 10·00

1988. Stamp Exhibitions. Nos. 1631/4 optd.
1751 90c. Blanchard and Jeffries' balloon, 1785 (optd **OLYMPHILEX '88**, Seoul) . . . . 1·25 90
1752 $1.50 U.S.S "Holland I", 1900 (optd **INDEPENDENCE 40**, Israel) . . . . 1·75 1·50
1753 $2 "Oceanic I", 1871 (optd **FINLANDIA 88**, Helsinki) . . . . 2·25 2·25
1754 $3 Lamborghini "Countach", 1984 (optd **PRAGA 88**, Prague) . . . 2·75 2·75

1988. World Scout Jamboree, Australia. Mult.
1755 20c. Type **332** 40 15
1756 70c. Scouts hiking through forest (horiz) . . . . . . 1·00 1·00
1757 90c. Practising first aid (horiz) . . . . 1·40 1·40
1758 $3 Shooting rapids in inflatable canoe . . . . . 3·00 3·75
MS1759 114 × 80 mm. $5 Scout with koala . . . . 2·10 3·00

333 "Santa Maria de Guia" (Columbus), 1498 and Map of Rotary District

1988. Rotary District 405 Conference, St. George's. Multicoloured.
1760 $2 Type **333** . . . . 80 1·00
MS1761 133 × 90 mm. $10 Rotary emblem (horiz) . . . . 4·25 6·00

334 Roseate Tern

335 Vauxhall Type "OE 30/98", 1925

1988. Birds. Multicoloured.
1762 10c. Type **334** 80 30
1763 25c. Laughing gull . . . . 1·00 30
1764 50c. Osprey . . . . 1·60 70
1765 60c. Rose-breasted grosbeak 1·60 70
1766 90c. American purple gallinule ("Purple Gallinule") . . . . 1·60 90
1767 $1.10 White-tailed tropic bird . . . . 1·60 1·00
1768 $3 Blue-faced booby . . . . 2·25 2·75
1769 $4 Common shoveler . . . 2·25 3·00
MS1770 Two sheets, each 100 × 71 mm. (a) $5 Belted kingfisher. (b) $5 Grenada flycatcher ("Rusty-tailed Flycatcher") Set of 2 sheets . . 7·00 9·00

1988. Cars. Multicoloured.
1771 $2 Type **335** . . . . 1·25 1·25
1772 $2 Wills "Sainte Claire", 1926 . . . . 1·25 1·25
1773 $2 Bucciali, 1928 . . . . . 1·25 1·25
1774 $2 Irving Napier "Golden Arrow", 1929 . . . . . . 1·25 1·25
1775 $2 Studebaker "President", 1930 . . . . 1·25 1·25
1776 $2 Thomas "Flyer", 1907 . . 1·25 1·25
1777 $2 Isotta-Franschini "Tipo J", 1908 . . . . 1·25 1·25
1778 $2 Fiat 10/14HP, 1910 . . . 1·25 1·25
1779 $2 Mercer "Type 35 Raceabout", 1911 . . . . 1·25 1·25
1780 $2 Marmon "Model 34 Cloverleaf", 1917 . . . . 1·25 1·25
1781 $2 Tatra "Type 77", 1934 . . 1·25 1·25
1782 $2 Rolls-Royce "Phantom III", 1938 . . . . 1·25 1·25
1783 $2 Studebaker "Champion Starlight", 1947 . . . . . 1·25 1·25
1784 $2 Porsche "Gmund", 1948 . . 1·25 1·25
1785 $2 Tucker, 1948 . . . . . . 1·25 1·25
1786 $2 Peerless "V-16", 1931 . . 1·25 1·25
1787 $2 Minerva "AL", 1931 . . 1·25 1·25
1788 $2 Reo "Royale", 1953 . . 1·25 1·25
1789 $2 Pierce Arrow "Silver Arrow", 1933 . . . . . . 1·25 1·25
1790 $2 Hupmobile "Aerodynamic", 1934 . . 1·25 1·25
1791 $2 Peugeot "404", 1965 . . 1·25 1·25
1792 $2 Ford "Capri", 1969 . . . 1·25 1·25
1793 $2 Ferrari "312T", 1975 . . 1·25 1·25
1794 $2 Lotus "T-79", 1978 . . . 1·25 1·25
1795 $2 Williams-Cosworth "FW07", 1979 . . . . . 1·25 1·25
1796 $2 H.R.G. "1500 Sports", 1948 . . . . 1·25 1·25
1797 $2 Crosley "Hotshot", 1949 1·25 1·25
1798 $2 Volvo "PV444", 1955 . . 1·25 1·25
1799 $2 Maserati "Tipo 61", 1960 1·25 1·25
1800 $2 Saab "96", 1963 . . . . 1·25 1·25

1988. 500th Birth Anniv of Titian (artist). As T **166a** of Gambia. Multicoloured.
1801 10c. "Lavinia Vecellio" . . 10 10
1802 20c. "Portrait of a Man" . . 10 10
1803 25c. "Andrea de Franceschi" 10 15
1804 90c. "Head of a Soldier" . . 40 45
1805 $1 "Man with a Flute" . . 45 50
1806 $2 "Lucrezia and Tarquinius" . . . . . . 80 1·00
1807 $3 "Duke of Mantua with Dog" . . . . 1·25 1·60
1808 $4 "La Bella di Tiziano" . . 1·60 2·00
MS1809 Two sheets, each 110 × 95 mm. (a) $5 "Allegory of Alfonso D'Avalos (detail). (b) $5 "Fall of Man" (detail) (horiz) Set of 2 sheets . . . . 4·25 5·50

336 "Graf Zeppelin" over Chicago World's Fair, 1933

338 Pineapple

337 Tasmanian Wolf, Mickey Mouse and Pluto

1988. Airships. Multicoloured.
1810 10c. Type **336** 50 20
1811 15c. LZ-1 over Lake Constance, 1901 (horiz) 60 25
1812 25c. "Washington" (balloon) and "George Washington Curtis" (balloon barge), 1862 . . . . 70 30
1813 45c. "Hindenburg" and Maybach "Zeppelin" car (horiz) 80 40
1814 50c. Goodyear Aerospace airship in Statue of Liberty Centenary Race, 1986 . . . . 80 40
1815 60c. "Hindenburg" over Statue of Liberty, 1937 (horiz) 90 50
1816 90c. Heinkel biplane docking experiment with "Hindenburg", 1936 (horiz) . . . . 1·40 80
1817 $2 "Hindenburg" over Olympic Stadium, Berlin, 1936 . . . . 2·00 2·00
1818 $3 "Hindenburg" over Christ of the Andes Monument, 1937 . . . . 2·50 2·50
1819 $4 "Hindenburg" and "Bremen" (liner), 1936 (horiz) . . . . 2·75 2·75
MS1820 Two sheets. (a) 75 × 95 mm. $5 LZ-127 "Graf Zeppelin", 1930 (horiz). (b) 95 × 75 mm. $5 LZ-129 "Hindenburg", 1935 (horiz) Set of 2 sheets . . . . 4·75 5·50

1988. "Sydpex '88". National Stamp Exhibition, Sydney and 60th Birthday of Mickey Mouse. Multicoloured.
1821 1c. Type **337** 10 10
1822 2c. Mickey Mouse feeding wallabies 10 10
1823 3c. Mickey Mouse and Goofy with kangaroo . . 10 10
1824 4c. Mickey and Minnie Mouse riding emus . . . 10 10
1825 5c. Mickey and Minnie Mouse with wombat . . . 10 10
1826 10c. Mickey Mouse and Donald Duck watching platypus 10 10
1827 $5 Mickey Mouse and Goofy photographing blue-winged kookaburra 5·50 5·50
1828 $6 Mickey Mouse and Koala on map of Australia . . . . 5·50 5·50
MS1829 Two sheets, each 127 × 102 mm. (a) $5 Mickey Mouse with birthday cake. (b) $5 Mickey and Minnie Mouse with rainbow lories Set of 2 sheets 12·00 13·00

1988. 10th Anniv of International Fund for Agricultural Development. Multicoloured.
1830 25c. Type **338** 35 15
1831 75c. Bananas 70 60
1832 $3 Mace and nutmeg (horiz) 2·50 2·75

339 Lignum Vitae

1988. Flowering Trees and Shrubs. Mult.

1833 15c. Type **339** 15 15
1834 25c. Saman 20 15
1835 35c. Red frangipani 25 20
1836 45c. Flowering maple . . . 30 25
1837 60c. Yellow poui 40 40
1838 $1 Wild chestnut 60 70
1839 $3 Mountain immortelle . . 1·50 2·25
1840 $4 Queen of flowers . . . . 1·75 2·50
MS1841 Two sheets, each 117 × 88 mm. (a) $5 Flamboyant. (b) $5 Orchid tree Set of 2 sheets 4·25 5·50

340 Mickey Mantle (New York Yankees)

1988. Major League Baseball Players (1st series). Designs showing portraits or league emblems.

1842/1922 30c. × 81 multicoloured Set of 81 . . . . . . 12·00 14·00

340a Donald Duck's Nephew on Mantelpiece

1988. Christmas. "Mickey's Christmas Eve". Designs showing Walt Disney cartoon characters. Multicoloured.

1923 $1 Type **340a** 65 65
1924 $1 Goofy with string of popcorn 65 65
1925 $1 Chip'n'Dale decorating Christmas tree 65 65
1926 $1 Father Christmas in sleigh 65 65
1927 $1 Donald's nephew with stocking 65 65
1928 $1 Donald's nephew unpacking decorations . . 65 65
1929 $1 Donald Duck with present 65 65
1930 $1 Mickey Mouse with present 65 65
MS1931 Two sheets, each 127 × 102 mm. (a) $5 Ferdie leaving drink for Father Christmas. (b) $5 Mordie and Ferdie asleep Set of 2 sheets . . 7·00 8·50

341 Tina Turner

1988. Entertainers. Multicoloured.

1932 10c. Type **341** 30 20
1933 25c. Lionel Ritchie 30 20
1934 45c. Whitney Houston . . . 45 30
1935 60c. Joan Armatrading . . . 60 45
1936 75c. Madonna 90 60
1937 $1 Elton John . . . . . . 1·00 80
1938 $3 Bruce Springsteen . . . 2·00 2·75
1939 $4 Bob Marley . . . . . . 4·00 4·00
MS1940 115 × 155 mm. 55c. × 2 Yoko Minamino; $1 × 2 Yoko Minamino (different) . . . . . 1·90 2·75
No. 1935 is incorrectly inscribed "JOAN AMMERTRADING".

342 Atlantic Railway No. 2, 1889, Canada

343 Women's Long Jump (Jackie Joyner-Kersee, U.S.A.)

1989. North American Railway Locomotives. Mult.

1941 $2 Type **342** . . . . 1·25 1·25
1942 $2 Virginia & Truckee Railroad "J. W Bowker" type, 1875, U.S.A. . . . . 1·25 1·25
1943 $2 Philadelphia & Reading Railway "Ariel", 1872, U.S.A. . . . . 1·25 1·25
1944 $2 Chicago & Rock Island Railroad "America" type, 1867, U.S.A. . . . . . . 1·25 1·25
1945 $2 Lehigh Valley Railroad Consolidation No. 63, 1866, U.S.A. . . . . . . 1·25 1·25
1946 $2 Great Western Railway "Scotia", 1860, Canada . . 1·25 1·25
1947 $2 Grand Trunk Railway Class "Birkenhead", 1854, Canada . . . . 1·25 1·25
1948 $2 Camden & Amboy Railroad "Monster", 1837, U.S.A. . . . . . . 1·25 1·25
1949 $2 Baltimore & Ohio Railroad Class "Grasshopper", 1834, U.S.A. . . . . 1·25 1·25
1950 $2 Peter Cooper's "Tom Thumb", 1829, Baltimore & Ohio Railroad, U.S.A. . 1·25 1·25
1951 $2 United Railways of Yucatan "Yucatan", 1925, Mexico . . . . 1·25 1·25
1952 $2 Canadian National Railways Class T2, 1924 . 1·25 1·25
1953 $2 St. Louis–San Francisco Railroad Class "Light Mikado", 1919, U.S.A. . 1·25 1·25
1954 $2 Atlantic Coast Line Railroad Class "Light Pacific", 1919, U.S.A. . . 1·25 1·25
1955 $2 Edaville Railroad No. 7, 1913, U.S.A. . . . . . . 1·25 1·25
1956 $2 Denver & Rio Grande Western Railroad Class K 27, 1903, U.S.A. . . . . 1·25 1·25
1957 $2 Pennsylvania Railroad Class E-2 No. 7002, 1902, U.S.A. . . . . 1·25 1·25
1958 $2 Pennsylvania Railroad Class H6, 1899, U.S.A. . 1·25 1·25
1959 $2 John Jarvis's "De Witt Clinton", 1831, Mohawk Hudson Railroad, U.S.A. 1·25 1·25
1960 $2 St. Clair Tunnel Company No. 598, 1891, Canada . . . . 1·25 1·25
1961 $2 Chesapeake & Ohio Railroad Class M-I steam turbine electric locomotive No. 500, 1947, U.S.A. . . 1·25 1·25
1962 $2 Rutland Railroad steam locomotive No. 93, 1946, U.S.A. . . . . 1·25 1·25
1963 $2 Pennsylvania Railroad Class T1, 1942, U.S.A. . . 1·25 1·25
1964 $2 Chesapeake & Ohio Railroad Class H-8, 1942, U.S.A. . . . . 1·25 1·25
1965 $2 Atchison, Topeka & Santa Fe Railway Model FT diesel, 1941, U.S.A. . 1·25 1·25
1966 $2 Gulf, Mobile & Ohio Railroad Models S-I and S-2 diesels, 1940, U.S.A. 1·25 1·25
1967 $2 New York, New Haven & Hartford Railroad Class 15, 1937, U.S.A. . . 1·25 1·25
1968 $2 Seaboard Air Line Railroad Class R, 1936, U.S.A. . . . . 1·25 1·25
1969 $2 Newfoundland Railway Class R-2, 1930 . . . . . 1·25 1·25
1970 $2 Canadian National Railway diesel No. 9000, 1928 . . . . 1·25 1·25

1989. Olympic Gold Medal Winners, Seoul (1988). Multicoloured.

1971 10c. Type **343** 30 20
1972 25c. Women's Singles Tennis (Steffi Graf, West Germany) 70 35
1973 45c. Men's 1500 m (Peter Rono, Kenya) 80 40
1974 75c. Men's 1000 m single kayak (Greg Barton, U.S.A.) 90 60
1975 $1 Women's team foil (Italy) 1·10 75
1976 $2 Women's 100 m freestyle swimming (Kristin Otto, East Germany) . . . . . 2·25 2·25
1977 $3 Men's still rings gymnastics (Holger Behrendt, East Germany) 2·50 2·75
1978 $4 Synchronized swimming pair (Japan) . . . . . . 2·75 3·00
MS1979 Two sheets, each 76 × 100 mm. (a) $6 Olympic flame. (b) $6 Runner with Olympic torch Set of 2 sheets . . . . . 8·50 9·50

344 Nebulae

1989. Appearance of Halley's Comet (1986) (3rd issue).

1980 **344** 25c.+5c. multicoloured 70 80
1981 – 75c.+5c. black & green 1·10 1·40
1982 – 90c.+5c. multicoloured 1·25 1·60
1983 – $2+5c. multicoloured . . 1·75 2·50
MS1984 111 × 78 mm. $5+5c. multicoloured. Imperf . . . . 4·00 5·00

DESIGNS: 75c.+5c. Marine astronomical experiments; 90c.+5c. Moon's surface; $2+5c. Edmond Halley, Sir Isaac Newton and his book "Principia". (102 × 69 mm)—$5+5c. 17th-century warships and astrological signs.

1989. Japanese Art. Paintings by Hiroshige. As T **177a** of Gambia. Multicoloured.

1985 10c. "Shinagawa on Edo Bay" 30 20
1986 25c. "Pine Trees on the Road to Totsuka" 40 30
1987 60c. "Kanagawa on Edo Bay" 60 50
1988 75c. "Crossing Banyu River to Hiratsuka" 65 55
1989 $1 "Windy Shore at Odawara" 80 70
1990 $2 "Snow-Covered Post Station of Mishima" . . . 1·40 1·75
1991 $3 "Full Moon at Fuchu" 1·60 2·00
1992 $4 "Crossing the Stream at Okitsu" . . . . 2·25 2·50
MS1993 Two sheets, each 102 × 76 mm. (a) $5 "Mountain Pass at Nissaka". (b) $5 "Mt Uzu at Okabe" Set of 2 sheets . . . 4·25 5·50

345 Great Blue Heron

1989. Birds. Multicoloured.

1994 5c. Type **345** . . . . . . 90 1·00
1995a 10c. Green-backed heron ("Green Heron") 90 70
1996a 15c. Ruddy turnstone . . . 1·00 75
1997a 25c. Blue-winged teal . . . 1·10 30
1998a 35c. Little ringed plover ("Ring-necked Plover") (vert) . . . . 1·25 30
1999a 45c. Green-throated carib ("Emerald-throated Hummingbird") (vert) 1·25 40
2000a 50c. Rufous-breasted hermit ("Hairy Hermit") (vert) . . . . 1·40 45
2001a 60c. Lesser Antillean bullfinch (vert) . . . . . 1·50 65
2002a 75c. Brown pelican (vert) 1·75 75
2003a $1 Black-crowned night heron (vert) . . . . . . 2·00 1·00
2004a $3 American kestrel ("Sparrow Hawk") (vert) 3·00 3·25
2005a $5 Barn swallow (vert) . . 4·00 4·75
2006 $10 Red-billed tropic bird (vert) . . . . 6·00 8·50
2007 $20 Barn owl (vert) . . . . 12·00 15·00

345a Scotland Player

1989. World Cup Football Championship, Italy (1990) (1st issue). Multicoloured.

2008 10c. Type **345a** 40 20
2009 25c. England and Brazil players 50 30
2010 60c. Paolo Rossi (Italy) . . 75 55
2011 75c. Jairzinho (Brazil) . . . 90 70
2012 $1 Sweden striker . . . . . 1·10 90
2013 $2 Pele (Brazil) . . . . . . 2·25 2·00
2014 $3 Mario Kempes (Argentina) . . . . 3·00 2·75
2015 $4 Pat Jennings (Northern Ireland) . . . . 3·25 3·00
MS2016 Two sheets. (a) 70 × 93 mm. $6 Players jumping for ball. (b) 82 × 71 mm. $6 Goalkeeper Set of 2 sheets . . . . 8·50 10·00
See also Nos. 2174/8 and **MS**2179.

346 Xebec and Sugar Cane

1989. "Philexfrance '89" International Stamp Exhibition, Paris. Designs showing French sailing vessels and plantation crops. Mult.

2017 25c. Type **346** . . . . . . 1·00 30
2018 75c. Lugger and cotton . . 1·60 85
2019 $1 Full-rigged ship and cocoa . . . . 1·75 1·10
2020 $4 Ketch and coffee . . . . 3·50 5·50
MS2021 114 × 70 mm. $6 "View of Fort and Town of St. George, 1779" (105 × 63 mm). Imperf 5·50 7·00

347 Alan Shepard and "Freedom 7" Spacecraft, 1961 (first American in Space)

1989. 20th Anniv of First Manned Landing on Moon. Multicoloured.

2022 15c. Type **347** 70 40
2023 35c. "Friendship 7" spacecraft, 1962 (first manned earth orbit) . . . 90 55
2024 45c. "Apollo 8" orbiting Moon, 1968 (first manned lunar orbit) . . . . 1·00 65
2025 70c. "Apollo 15" lunar rover, 1972 . . . . . . 1·50 85
2026 $1 "Apollo 11" emblem and lunar module "Eagle" on Moon, 1969 . . . . . . 1·75 1·10
2027 $2 "Gemini 8" and "Agena" rocket, 1966 (first space docking) . . . . 3·00 2·25
2028 $3 Edward White in space, 1965 (first U.S. space walk) . . . . 3·25 3·00
2029 $4 "Apollo 7" emblem . . . 3·75 3·50
MS2030 Two sheets, each 101 × 71 mm. (a) $5 Moon and track of "Apollo 11", 1969. (b) $5 Armstrong and Aldrin raising U.S. flag on Moon, 1969 Set of 2 sheets 12·00 10·00

348 "Hygrocybe occidentalis"

349 Y.W.C.A. Logo and Grenada Scenery

1989. Fungi. Multicoloured.

2031 15c. Type **348** 50 40
2032 40c. "Marasmius haematocephalus" 65 55
2033 50c. "Hygrocybe hypohaemacta" 75 65
2034 70c. "Lepiota pseudoignicolor" . . . . 1·00 90
2035 90c. "Cookeina tricholoma" 1·25 1·25
2036 $1.10 "Leucopaxillus gracillimus" . . . . . . 1·50 1·50
2037 $2.25 "Hygrocybe nigrescens" . . . . 2·75 3·00
2038 $4 "Clathrus crispus" . . . 3·75 4·00
MS2039 Two sheets, each 57 × 70 mm. (a) $6 "Mycena holoporphyra". (b) $6 "Xeromphalina tenuipes" Set of 2 sheets . . . . 12·00 13·00

1989. Centenary of Young Women's Christian Association. Multicoloured.

2040 50c. Type **349** 45 45
2041 75c. Y.W.C.A. logo and town (horiz) 80 80

350 "Historis odius"

1989. Butterflies. Multicoloured.
2042 6c. Type **350** 30 30
2043 30c. "Marpesia petreus" . . 55 55
2044 40c. "Danaus gilippus" . . 60 60
2045 60c. "Dione juno" 80 80
2046 $1.10 "Agraulis vanillae" . . 1·25 1·25
2047 $1.25 "Danaus plexippus" 1·50 1·50
2048 $4 "Papilio androgeus . . . 3·25 3·25
2049 $5 "Dryas julia" . . . . . 3·25 3·25
MS2050 Two sheets, each 87 × 115 mm. (a) $6 "Anartia jatrophae". (b) $6 "Strymon simaethis" Set of 2 sheets . . . 9·50 11·00

351 Amerindian Hieroglyph

1989. 500th Anniv (1992) of Discovery of America by Columbus (2nd issue). Designs showing different hieroglyphs.
2051 **351** 45c. brown, black & blue 80 50
2052 – 60c. brown, black & grn 90 60
2053 – $1 brown, black and violet . . . . 1·60 1·00
2054 – $4 dp brown, black & brn . . . . 4·25 4·75
MS2055 74 × 86 mm. $6 brown, black and red . . . . 4·00 5·50

352 Amos leaving Home

1989. "World Stamp Expo '89" International Stamp Exhibition, Washington. Designs showing Walt Disney cartoon characters in scenes from "Ben and Me". Multicoloured.
2056 1c. Type **352** 10 10
2057 2c. Meeting of Benjamin Franklin and Amos . . . 10 10
2058 3c. The Franklin stove . . . 10 10
2059 4c. Ben and Amos with bi-focals 10 10
2060 5c. Amos on page of "Pennsylvania Gazette" 10 10
2061 6c. Ben working printing press 10 10
2062 10c. Conducting experiment with electricity 10 10
2063 $5 Ben disembarking in England . . . . 5·00 5·50
2064 $6 Ben with Document of Agreement . . . . 5·50 6·00
MS2065 Two sheets, each 127 × 101 mm. (a) $6 Benjamin Franklin teaching (vert). (b) $6 Signatories of Declaration of Independence Set of 2 sheets 8·00 10·00

352a "Christ in the House of Mary and Martha"

1990. Christmas. Paintings by Rubens. Multicoloured.
2066 20c. Type **352a** 50 25
2067 35c. "The Circumcision" . . 65 40
2068 60c. "Trinity adored by Duke of Mantua and Family" . . . . 1·00 65
2069 $2 "Holy Family with St. Francis" . . . . . . 2·75 2·75
2070 $3 "The Ildefonso Altarpiece" . . . . 3·25 3·50
2071 $4 "Madonna and Child with Garland and Putti" 3·75 4·00
MS2072 Two sheets, each 70 × 95 mm. (a) $5 "Adoration of the Magi". (b) $5 "Virgin and Child adored by Angels" Set of 2 sheets . . . . 7·50 9·00

353 Alexander Graham Bell and Early Telephone System (150th anniv of invention)

1990. Anniversaries. Multicoloured.
2073 10c. Type **353** 30 20
2074 25c. George Washington and Capitol (bicentenary of presidential inauguration) 30 20
2075 35c. Shakespeare and birthplace, Stratford (425th birth anniv) . . . 1·50 35
2076 75c. Nehru and Gandhi (birth cent of Nehru) . . 3·50 1·50
2077 $1 Dr. Hugo Eckener, Ferdinand von Zeppelin and airship "Graf Zeppelin" (80th anniv of first passenger Zeppelin) 2·00 1·25
2078 $2 Charlie Chaplin (birth cent) . . . . 5·00 3·00
2079 $3 Container ship in Hamburg Harbour (800th anniv) . . . . 2·75 3·50
2080 $4 Friedrich Ebert (first President) and Heidelberg gate (70th anniv of German Republic) . . . . 2·75 3·50
MS2081 Two sheets, each 100 × 72 mm. (a) $6 13th-century ships in Hamburg Harbour (vert) (800th anniv). (b) $6 Concorde (20th anniv of first test flight) Set of 2 sheets . . . . 8·50 10·00
No. 2080 is inscribed "40th Anniversary of German Republic" in error.

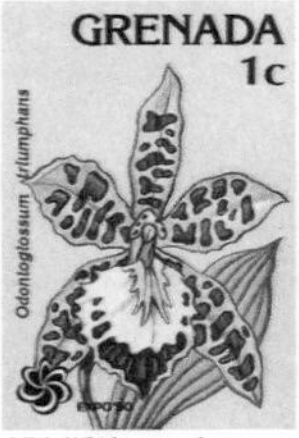

354 "Odontoglossum triumphans" **354a** "Marpesia petreus"

1990. "EXPO '90" International Garden and Greenery Exhibition, Osaka. Caribbean Orchids. Multicoloured.
2082 1c. Type **354** 10 10
2083 25c. "Oncidium splendidum" 30 20
2084 60c. "Laelia anceps" 60 60
2085 75c. "Cattleya trianaei" . . 75 75
2086 $1 "Odontoglossum rossii" 1·00 1·00
2087 $2 "Brassia gireoudiana" . . 1·75 1·75
2088 $3 "Cattleya dowiana" . . . 2·25 2·25
2089 $4 "Sobralia macrantha" . . 2·50 2·50
MS2090 Two sheets, each 97 × 68 mm. (a) $6 "Oncidium lanceanum". (b) $6 "Laelia rubescens" Set of 2 sheets . . . 8·50 9·50

1990. 500th Anniv (1992) of Discovery of America by Columbus (3rd issue). New World Natural History—Butterflies. Multicoloured.
2091 15c. Type **354a** 65 20
2092 25c. "Junonia evarete" . . . 80 25
2093 75c. "Siproeta stelenes" . . . 1·40 70
2094 90c. "Historis odius" . . . 1·60 85
2095 $1 "Mestra cana" . . . . . 1·60 90
2096 $2 "Biblis hyperia" . . . . 2·50 2·75
2097 $3 "Dryas julia" . . . . . 3·00 3·50
2098 $4 "Anartia amathea" . . . 3·00 3·75
MS2099 Two sheets, each 101 × 69 mm. (a) $6 "Pseudolycaena marsyas". (b) $6 "Phoebis philea" Set of 2 sheets 12·00 13·00

354b Caribbean Monk Seal

1990. Local Fauna. Multicoloured.
2100 10c. Type **354b** 50 30
2101 15c. Little brown bat . . . 60 30
2102 45c. Brown rat 70 50
2103 60c. Common rabbit 80 60
2104 $1 Water opossum . . . . 1·25 95
2105 $2 White-nosed ichneumon 1·75 1·75
2106 $3 Little big-eared bat (vert) 2·25 2·50
2107 $4 Mouse opossum . . . . 2·25 2·50
MS2108 Two sheets, each 107 × 80 mm. (a) $6 Common rabbit (different). (b) $6 Water opossum (different) Set of 2 sheets 8·50 10·00

354c British Tanks during Operation Battleaxe, 1941

1990. 50th Anniv of Second World War. Mult.
2109 25c. Type **354c** 30 30
2110 35c. Allied tank in southern France, 1944 . . . . . . 40 40
2111 45c. U.S. forces landing on Guadalcanal, 1942 . . . 45 45
2112 50c. U.S. attack in New Guinea, 1943 . . . . . . 50 50
2113 60c. Hoisting U.S. flag on Leyte, Phillippines, 1944 60 60
2114 75c. U.S. tanks entering Cologne, 1945 . . . . . 75 75
2115 $1 Anzio offensive, 1944 . . 95 95
2116 $2 Battle of the Bismarck Sea, 1943 . . . . 1·75 1·75
2117 $3 U.S.S. "Langley" and U.S.S. "Ticonderoga" (aircraft carriers), 1944 . . 2·25 2·25
2118 $4 Focke Wulf Fw 190A fighter attacking Salerno landing, 1943 . . . . . . 2·50 2·50
MS2119 111 × 83 mm. $6 German "U-30" submarine, 1939 . . . 3·50 4·00

1990. "Stamp World London '90" International Stamp Exhibition (1st issue). As T **193** of Gambia, but horiz showing Walt Disney cartoon characters and British trains.
2120 5c. Mickey Mouse driving S.R. "King Arthur" class locomotive, 1925 . . . . 30 10
2121 10c. Mickey and Minnie Mouse with "Puffing Billy", 1813 . . . . . . 30 10
2122 20c. Mickey Mouse with Pluto pulling Durham colliery wagon, 1765 . . . 50 15
2123 45c. Mickey Mouse timing L.N.E.R. locomotive No. 2509 "Silver Link", 1935 . . . . 80 25
2124 $1 Mickey Mouse and Donald Duck with locomotive No. 60149 "Amadis", 1948 . . . . . 1·75 1·00
2125 $2 Goofy and Mickey Mouse with Liverpool & Manchester Railway locomotive, 1830 . . . . 2·50 2·75
2126 $4 Goofy and Donald Duck with Great Northern locomotive No. 1, 1870 3·25 4·00
2127 $5 Mickey Mouse and Gyro the Mechanic with Advanced Passenger Train, 1972 . . . . . . 3·25 4·00
MS2128 Two sheets, each 127 × 101 mm. (a) $6 Minnie Mouse, Donald and Daisy Duck in Trevithick's Catch-Me-Who-Can, 1808 (horiz). (b) $6 Donald Duck and Locomotion, 1825 Set of 2 sheets . . . . 12·00 13·00
No. 2126 is inscribed "Flying Scotsman" in error.
See also No. **MS**2146.

355 U.S. Paratroop Drop over Grenada

1990. 50th Anniv of United States Airborne Forces.
2129 75c. Type **355** . . . . . . 1·25 1·25
MS2130 Two sheets, each 115 × 87 mm. (a) $2.50, Paratrooper landing. (b) $6 Paratroop uniforms of 1940 and 1990 Set of 2 sheets . . . . . 5·50 6·50

1990. 90th Birthday of Queen Elizabeth the Queen Mother. As T **194** of Gambia showing photographs from the 1960s. Multicoloured.
2131 $2 Queen Mother in coat and hat . . . . 1·75 1·75
2132 $2 Queen Mother in evening dress . . . . 1·75 1·75
2133 $2 Queen Mother in Garter robes . . . . 1·75 1·75
MS2134 90 × 75 mm. $6 Queen Mother (as No. 2131) . . . . 3·50 4·00

1990. Olympic Games, Barcelona (1992) (1st issue). As T **195a** of Gambia. Multicoloured.
2135 10c. Men's steeplechase . . 30 20
2136 15c. Dressage 45 30
2137 45c. Men's 200 m. butterfly swimming 50 45
2138 50c. Men's hockey . . . . 1·50 60
2139 65c. Women's beam gymnastics 60 60
2140 75c. "Flying Dutchman" class sailing . . . . . . 1·00 80
2141 $2 Freestyle wrestling . . . 1·75 1·75
2142 $3 Men's springboard diving 2·25 2·75
2143 $4 Women's 1000 m. sprint cycling . . . . 3·75 3·75
2144 $5 Men's basketball . . . . 4·50 4·50
MS2145 Two sheets, each 101 × 70 mm. (a) $8 Equestrian three-day event. (b) $8 Men's 10000 metres Set of 2 sheets . . 9·50 11·00
See also Nos. 2414/22.

356 Map of North America and Logo

1990. "Stamp World London 90" International Stamp Exhibition (2nd issue). Sheet 97 × 75 mm.
MS2146 **356** $6 mauve . . . . . 4·25 5·50

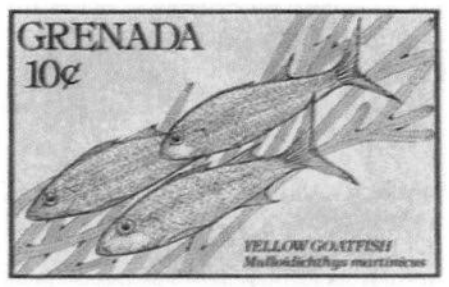

357 Yellow Goatfish

1990. Coral Reef Fishes. Multicoloured.
2147 10c. Type **357** 30 30
2148 25c. Black margate 45 35
2149 65c. Blue-headed wrasse . . 85 75
2150 75c. Puddingwife 95 85
2151 $1 Four-eyed butterflyfish 1·10 95
2152 $2 Honey damselfish . . . . 2·00 2·00
2153 $3 Queen angelfish . . . . 2·50 2·50
2154 $5 Cherub angelfish . . . . 3·00 3·50
MS2155 Two sheets, each 103 × 72 mm. (a) $6 Smooth trunkfish. (b) $6 Sergeant major Set of 2 sheets . . . . 8·00 9·00

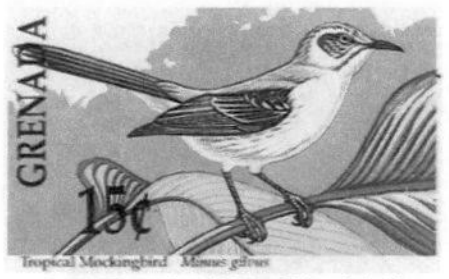

358 Tropical Mockingbird

1990. Birds. Multicoloured.
2156 15c. Type **358** 30 30
2157 25c. Grey kingbird 35 35
2158 65c. Bare-eyed thrush . . . 75 75
2159 75c. Antillean crested hummingbird 85 85
2160 $1 House wren . . . . . . 1·00 1·00
2161 $2 Purple martin . . . . . 1·75 1·75
2162 $4 Lesser Antillian tanager ("Hooded Tanager") . . 2·50 2·50
2163 $5 Scaly-breasted ground dove . . . . 3·00 3·00
MS2164 Two sheets, each 101 × 72 mm. (a) $6 Fork-tailed flycatcher. (b) $6 Smooth-billed ani Set of 2 sheets . . . . . . 12·00 13·00

359 Coral Crab

1990. Crustaceans. Multicoloured.
2165 5c. Type **359** 20 30
2166 10c. Smoothtail spiny lobster 20 30
2167 15c. Flamestreaked box crab 20 30
2168 25c. Spotted swimming crab 30 25
2169 75c. Sally lightfoot rock crab 70 60
2170 $1 Spotted spiny lobster . . 90 80
2171 $3 Longarm spiny lobster 2·00 2·50
2172 $20 Caribbean spiny lobster 13·00 18·00
MS2173 Two sheets, 106 × 75 mm. (a) $6 Copper lobster. (b) $6 Spanish lobster Set of 2 sheets 8·00 9·00

360 Cameroon Player

1990. World Cup Football Championship, Italy (2nd issue). Multicoloured.
2174 10c. Type **360** 20 15
2175 25c. Michel (Spain) 25 15
2176 $1 Brehme (West Germany) 85 85
2177 $5 Nevin (Scotland) . . . . 3·00 4·00
MS2178 Two sheets, each 95 × 90 mm. (a) $6 Giannini (Italy). (b) $6 Perdomo (Uruguay) Set of 2 sheets . . . . 9·50 11·00

1990. World Cup Football Championship, Italy (1990) (3rd issue). No. **MS**2016a optd **1990 W GERMANY 1 ARGENTINA 0.**
MS2179 70 × 93 mm. $6 Players jumping for ball . . . . 6·50 7·50

1990. Christmas. Paintings by Raphael. As T **195b** of Gambia. Multicoloured.
2180 10c. "The Ansidei Madonna" 20 10
2181 15c. "The Sistine Madonna" 20 10
2182 $1 "The Madonna of the Baldacchino" . . . . . . 1·50 70
2183 $2 "The Large Holy Family" (detail) . . . . . 2·50 2·75
2184 $5 "Madonna in the Meadow" . . . . 4·00 6·00
MS2185 Two sheets, each 71 × 101 mm. (a) $6 "Madonna of the Diadem" (detail). (b) $6 "The Madonna of the Veil" (detail) Set of 2 sheets . . . . 13·00 14·00

1991. 350th Death Anniv of Rubens. As T **195c** of Gambia. Multicoloured.
2186 5c. "The Brazen Serpent" (detail) 20 10
2187 10c. "The Garden of Love" 20 10
2188 25c. "Head of Cyrus" (detail) 40 20
2189 75c. "Tournament in Front of a Castle" . . . . . . 1·00 60
2190 $1 "The Brazen Serpent" (different detail) . . . . . 1·10 75
2191 $2 "Judgement of Paris" (detail) . . . . 1·75 2·00
2192 $4 "The Brazen Serpent" . . 2·50 3·50
2193 $5 "The Karmesse" (detail) 3·00 3·50
MS2194 Two sheets, each 101 × 70 mm. (a) $6 "Anger of Neptune" (detail). (b) $6 "The Prodigal son" (detail) Set of 2 sheets . . . . 12·00 13·00

362 "The Sorcerer's Apprentice"

1991. 50th Anniv of "Fantasia" (cartoon film). Multicoloured.
2195 5c. Type **362** 50 20
2196 10c. Dancing mushrooms ("The Nutcracker Suite") 50 20
2197 20c. Pterodactyls ("The Rite of Spring") 90 20
2198 45c. Centaurs ("The Pastoral Symphony") . . 1·50 40
2199 $1 Bacchus and Jacchus ("The Pastoral Symphony") . . . . . . 2·50 1·25
2200 $2 Dancing ostrich ("Dance of the Hours") . . . . . 3·25 3·25
2201 $4 Elephant ballet ("Dance of the Hours") . . . . . 4·25 4·75
2202 $5 Diana ("The Pastoral Symphony") . . . . . . 4·25 4·75
MS2203 Two sheets, each 122 × 102 mm. (a) $6 Mickey Mouse as the Sorcerer's Apprentice. (b) $6 Mickey Mouse with Leopold Stokowski (conductor) Set of 2 sheets . . . 13·00 14·00
MS2204 176 × 213 mm. $12 Mickey Mouse as the Sorcerer's Apprentice (vert) . . . . . . 13·00 14·00

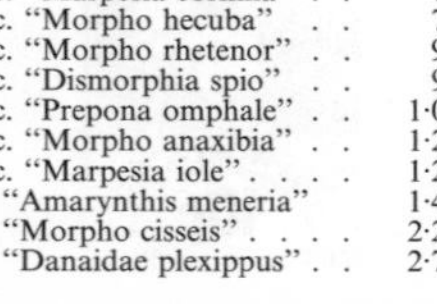

363 "Adelpha iphicla"

1991. Butterflies. Multicoloured.
2205 5c. Type **363** 50 50
2206 10c. "Nymphalidae claudina" 50 40
2207 15c. "Brassolidae polyxena" 60 30
2208 20c. "Zebra Longwing" . . 70 30
2209 25c. "Marpesia corinna" . . 70 25
2210 30c. "Morpho hecuba" . . 70 30
2211 45c. "Morpho rhetenor" . . 90 45
2212 50c. "Dismorphia spio" . . 95 55
2213 60c. "Prepona omphale" . . 1·00 65
2214 70c. "Morpho anaxibia" . . 1·25 75
2215 75c. "Marpesia iole" . . . . 1·25 80
2216 $1 "Amarynthis meneria" . . 1·40 1·00
2217 $2 "Morpho cisseis" . . . . 2·25 2·50
2218 $3 "Danaidae plexippus" . . 2·75 3·00
2219 $4 "Morpho achilleana" . . 3·25 4·00
2220 $5 "Calliona argenissa" . . 3·75 4·25
MS2221 Four sheets, each 118 × 80 mm. (a) $6 "Anteos clorinde". (b) $6 "Haetera piera". (c) $6 "Papilio cresphontes". (d) $6 "Prepona pheridames" Set of 4 sheets . . . . 17·00 19·00

363a Vitus Bering in Bering Sea, 1728–9

1991. 500th Anniv (1992) of Discovery of America by Columbus. History of Exploration. Mult.
2222 5c. Type **363a** 60 50
2223 10c. De Bougainville off Pacific island, 1766–69 . . 60 40
2224 25c. Polynesian canoe . . . 45 30
2225 50c. De Mendana off Solomon Islands, 1567–69 1·25 50
2226 $1 Darwin's H.M.S. "Beagle". 1831–35 . . . . 2·25 1·25
2227 $2 Cook's H.M.S. "Endeavour", 1768–71 . . 3·75 3·25
2228 $4 William Schouten in LeMaire Strait, 1615–17 3·75 4·25
2229 $5 Tasman off New Zealand, 1642–44 . . . . 3·75 4·25
MS2230 Two sheets, each 116 × 77 mm. (a) $6 "Santa Maria" sinking. (b) $6 Bow of "Santa Maria" (vert) Set of 2 sheets . . . . 8·50 9·50

1991. "Phila Nippon '91" International Stamp Exhibition, Tokyo. Horiz designs as T **198c** of Gambia showing Walt Disney cartoon characters at Japanese festivals. Multicoloured.
2231 5c. Minnie Mouse and Daisy Duck at Dolls festival 35 20
2232 10c. Morty and Ferdie with Boys' Day display 35 20
2233 20c. Mickey and Minnie Mouse at Star festival . . 60 20
2234 45c. Minnie and Daisy folk-dancing . . . . 1·00 35
2235 $1 Huey, Dewey and Louie wearing Eboshi headdresses . . . . 1·75 85
2236 $2 Mickey and Goofy pulling decorated car at Gion festival . . . . . . 3·25 3·25
2237 $4 Minnie and Daisy preparing rice broth, Seven Plants festival . . . 4·00 4·25
2238 $5 Huey and Dewey with straw boat at Lanterns festival . . . . 4·00 4·25
MS2239 Three sheets, each 127 × 101 mm. (a) $6 Minnie Mouse in kimono. (b) $6 Mickey taking photo (horiz). (c) $6 Goofy behind fair stall (horiz) Set of 3 sheets . . . . 14·00 15·00

1991. Death Centenary (1990) of Vincent van Gogh (artist). As T **200b** of Gambia. Multicoloured.
2240 20c. "Blossoming Almond Branch in Glass" (vert) 50 25
2241 25c. "La Mousme sitting" (vert) 50 25
2242 30c. "Still Life with Red Cabbages and Onions" 55 30
2243 40c. "Japonaiserie: Flowering Plum Tree" (vert) 70 40
2244 45c. "Japonaiserie: Bridge in the Rain" (vert) 70 40
2245 60c. "Still Life with Basket of Apples" . . . . 1·00 60
2246 75c. "Italian Woman" (vert) 1·10 70
2247 $1 "The Painter on his Way to Work" (vert) . . . . . 1·60 1·00
2248 $2 "Portrait of Pere Tanguy" (vert) . . . . . 2·50 2·25
2249 $3 "Still Life with Plaster Statuette, a Rose and Two Novels" (vert) . . . 3·25 3·25
2250 $4 "Still Life: Bottle, Lemons and Oranges" . . 3·50 3·75
2251 $5 "Orchard with Blossoming Apricot Trees" . . . . 3·50 3·75
MS2252 Five sheets. (a) 76 × 102 mm. $6 "Roubine du Roi Canal with Washerwoman" (73 × 99 mm). (b) 102 × 76 mm. $6 "Farmhouse in a Wheatfield" (99 × 73 mm). (c) 102 × 76 mm. $6 "The Gleize Bridge over the Vigueirat Canal" (99 × 73 mm). (d) 102 × 76 mm. $6 "Rocks with Oak Tree" (99 × 73 mm). (e) 76 × 102 mm. $6 "Japonaiserie: Oiran" (73 × 99 mm). Imperf. Set of 5 sheets . . . . 22·00 24·00

364 "Psilocybe cubensis"

1991. Fungi. Multicoloured.
2253 15c. Type **364** 70 30
2254 25c. "Leptonia caeruleocapitata" 80 30
2255 65c. "Cystolepiota eriophora" . . . . 1·40 85
2256 75c. "Chlorophyllum molybdites" . . . . . . 1·40 1·00
2257 $1 "Xerocomus hypoxanthus" . . . . . 1·60 1·25
2258 $2 "Volvariella cubensis" . . 2·50 2·75
2259 $4 "Xerocomus coccolobae" 3·25 4·00
2260 $5 "Pluteus chrysophlebius" 3·25 4·00
MS2261 Two sheets, each 100 × 70 mm. (a) $6 "Psathyrella tuberculata". (b) $6 "Hygrocybe miniata" Set of 2 sheets . . . 14·00 14·00

365 Johannes Kepler (astronomer)

1991. Exploration of Mars. Designs showing astronomers, spacecraft and Martian landscapes. Multicoloured.
2262/97 75c. × 9, $1.25 × 9, $2 × 9, $7 × 9 Set of 36 . . . . 48·00 48·00
MS2298 Three sheets, each 112 × 92 mm. (a) $6 Projected spacecraft. (b) $6 Mars and part of spacecraft. (c) $6 Phobos satellite over Mars Set of 3 sheets . . . 11·00 12·00

1991. 65th Birthday of Queen Elizabeth II. As T **198a** of Gambia. Multicoloured.
2299 15c. Royal Family on balcony after Trooping the Colour, 1985 . . . . 50 15
2300 40c. Queen and Prince Philip at Peterborough, 1988 . . . . 75 35
2301 $2 Queen and Queen Mother at Windsor, 1986 2·50 1·75
2302 $4 Queen and Prince Philip on visit to United Arab Emirates . . . . 3·00 3·00
MS2303 68 × 90 mm. $5 Separate photographs of the Queen and Prince Philip . . . . 3·50 4·25

1991. 10th Wedding Anniv of the Prince and Princess of Wales. As T **198b** of Gambia. Multicoloured.
2304 10c. Prince and Princess in July 1985 . . . . 60 10
2305 50c. Separate photographs of Prince, Princess and sons . . . . 1·25 45
2306 $1 Prince Henry at Trooping the Colour and Prince William in Majorca 1·50 1·00
2307 $5 Separate photographs of Prince Charles and Princess Diana . . . . . 4·25 4·50
MS2308 68 × 90 mm. $5 Prince, Princess and sons on holiday in Majorca . . . . 6·00 5·50

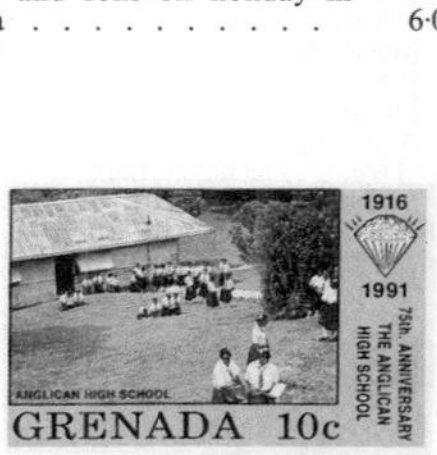

366 Anglican High School Pupils

1991. 75th Anniv of Anglican High School (10, 25c.) and 40th Anniv of University of the West Indies (45, 50c.). Multicoloured.
2309 10c. Type **366** 35 20
2310 25c. Artist's impression of new Anglican High School 60 20
2311 45c. Marryshow House, Grenada 85 55
2312 50c. University Administrative Building, Barbados . . . . 90 1·00

367 George Stephenson's First Locomotive, 1814 (Great Britain)

1991. Great Railways of the World. Mult.
2313 75c. Type **367** 60 60
2314 75c. George Stephenson . . 60 60
2315 75c. Killingworth locomotive, 1816 (Great Britain) 60 60
2316 75c. George Stephenson's "Locomotion", 1825 (Great Britain) 60 60
2317 75c. "Locomotion" in Darlington, 1825 (Great Britain) 60 60
2318 75c. Opening of Stockton & Darlington Railway, 1825 60 60
2319 75c. Timothy Hackworth's "Royal George", 1827 (Great Britain) 60 60
2320 75c. Northumbrian T831 (Great Britain) 60 60
2321 75c. "Planet", 1830 (Great Britain) 60 60
2322 $1 "Old Ironsides", 1832 (U.S.A.) 80 80
2323 $1 "Wilberforce", 1832 (Great Britain) 80 80
2324 $1 "Adler", 1835 (Germany) 80 80
2325 $1 "North Star", 1837 (Great Britain) 80 80
2326 $1 London & Birmingham Railway No. 1, 1838 (Great Britain) 80 80
2327 $1 Stephenson's "Austria", 1838 (Austria) 80 80
2328 $1 Baltimore & Ohio Railroad No. 378 "Muddigger", 1840 (U.S.A.) 80 80
2329 $1 Baltimore & Ohio Railroad Norris, 1840 (U.S.A.) 80 80
2330 $1 "Centaur", 1840 (Great Britain) 80 80
2331 $2 "Lion", 1841 (Great Britain) . . . . 1·50 1·50
2332 $2 "Beuth", 1843 (Germany) 1·50 1·50
2333 $2 "Derwent", 1845 (Great Britain) . . . . 1·50 1·50
2334 $2 "Bets", 1846 (Hungary) 1·50 1·50
2335 $2 Opening of Budapest to Vac railway, 1846 (Hungary) . . . . 1·50 1·50
2336 $2 Carriages, Stockton & Darlington Railway, 1846 (Great Britain) . . . . . 1·50 1·50
2337 $2 "Long Boiler" type, 1847 (France) . . . . 1·50 1·50
2338 $2 Baldwin locomotive, 1850 (U.S.A.) . . . . 1·50 1·50
2339 $2 Steam locomotive, 1850 (Germany) . . . . 1·50 1·50
MS2340 Two sheets, each 116 × 86 mm. (a) $6 Part of Stephenson's "Locomotion", 1825 (Great Britain). (b) $6 Train on Liverpool & Manchester Railway, 1833 (Great Britain) Set of 2 sheets 14·00 15·00

368 Barbu

1991. Marine Life of the Sandflats. Mult.
2341 50c. Type **368** 80 80
2342 50c. Beau Gregory 80 80
2343 50c. Porcupinefish 80 80
2344 50c. Queen or pink conch and conchfish 80 80
2345 50c. Hermit crab 80 80
2346 50c. Bluestripe lizardfish . . 80 80
2347 50c. Spot-finned mojarra . . 80 80
2348 50c. Southern stingray . . . 80 80
2349 50c. Long-spined sea urchin and slippery dick 80 80
2350 50c. Peacock flounder . . . 80 80
2351 50c. West Indian sea star . . 80 80
2352 50c. Spotted goatfish . . . 80 80
2353 50c. Netted olive and West Indian sea egg 80 80
2354 50c. Pearly razorfish 80 80
2355 50c. Spotted jawfish and yellow-headed jawfish . . 80 80
MS2356 105 × 76 mm. $6 Short-nosed batfish . . . . 11·00 12·00
Nos. 2341/55 were printed together, se-tenant, forming a composite design.

1991. Christmas. Religious Paintings by Albrecht Durer. As T **200c** of Gambia. Mult.
2357 10c. "Adoration of the Magi" (detail) 60 10
2358 35c. "Madonna with the Siskin" (detail) 90 25
2359 50c. "Feast of the Rose Garlands" (detail) . . . . 1·25 45
2360 75c. "Virgin with the Pear" (detail) . . . . 1·75 80

2361 $1 "Virgin in Half-length" (detail) 2·25 1·00
2362 $2 "Madonna and Child" (detail) 3·25 3·25
2363 $4 "Virgin and Child with St. Anne" (detail) 3·75 5·00
2364 $5 "Virgin and Child" (detail) 3·75 5·00
MS2365 Two sheets, each 102 × 127 mm. (a) $6 "Virgin with a Multitude of Animals" (detail). (b) $6 "The Nativity" (detail). P 14½ × 14 Set of 2 sheets 13·00 14·00

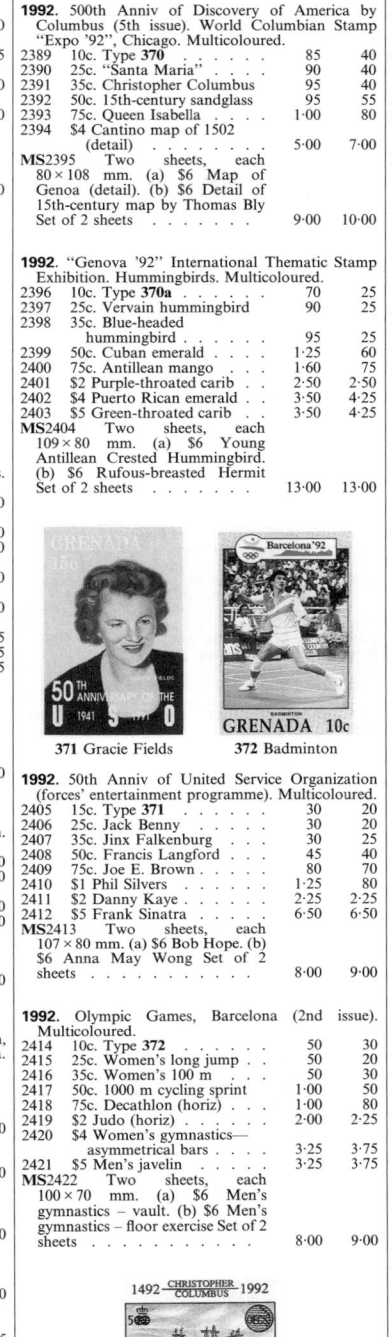

369 Goofy windsurfing

1992. Thrill Sports. Walt Disney cartoon characters. Multicoloured.
2366 5c. Type **369** 40 30
2367 10c. Mickey Mouse skateboarding 50 30
2368 20c. Daisy Duck gliding 80 30
2369 45c. Mickey's nephews stunt kite flying 1·25 30
2370 $1 Donald Duck mountain biking 2·00 1·10
2371 $2 Donald and Chipmunk parachuting 2·75 2·75
2372 $4 Mickey go-karting 4·00 4·75
2373 $5 Minnie water skiing 4·00 4·75
MS2374 Four sheets, each 128 × 102 mm. (a) $6 Mickey bungee jumping (vert). (b) $6 Mickey and Minnie river rafting. (c) $6 Donald's nephews playing roller hockey. (d) $6 Mickey hang-gliding Set of 4 sheets 16·00 17·00

1992. 40th Anniv of Queen Elizabeth II's Accession. As T **202a** of Gambia. Mult.
2375 10c. Waterfall 65 20
2376 50c. Street in St. George's 75 40
2377 $1 Colonial-style houses, St. George's 1·40 80
2378 $5 St. George's from the sea 4·25 4·50
MS2379 Two sheets, each 75 × 96 mm. (a) $6 Village on hillside. (b) $6 Yacht at anchor off village Set of 2 sheets 11·00 11·00

1992. "Granada '92" International Stamp Exhibition, Spain. Spanish Paintings. As T **481a** of Ghana. Multicoloured.
2380 10c. "The Corpus Christi Procession in Seville" (Manuel Cabral y Aguado) (horiz) 40 20
2381 35c. "The Mancorbo Channel" (Carlos de Haes) 55 20
2382 50c. "Amalia de Llano y Dotres, Countess of Vilches" (Federico de Madrazo y Kuntz) 75 40
2383 75c. "Conchita Serrano y Dominguez, Countess of Santovenia" (Eduardo Rosales Gallina) 1·00 70
2384 $1 "Queen Maria Isabel de Braganza" (Bernardo Lopez Piquer) 1·40 85
2385 $2 "The Presentation of Don John of Austria to Charles V" (detail) (Gallina) 2·25 2·25
2386 $4 "The Presentation of Don John of Austria to Charles V" (different detail) (Gallina) 3·50 4·25
2387 $5 "The Testament of Isabella the Catholic" (Gallina) (horiz) 3·50 4·25
MS2388 Two sheets, each 120 × 95 mm. (a) $6 "The Horse Corral in the Old Madrid Bullring" (Manuel Castellano) (111 × 85 mm). (b) $6 "Meeting of Poets in Antonio Mariá Esquivel's Studio" (Antonia Mariá Esquivel y Suárez de Urbina) (111 × 85 mm). Imperf Set of 2 sheets 8·00 9·00

370 Green-winged Macaw

370a Ruby-throated Hummingbird

1992. 500th Anniv of Discovery of America by Columbus (5th issue). World Columbian Stamp "Expo '92", Chicago. Multicoloured.
2389 10c. Type **370** 85 40
2390 25c. "Santa Maria" 90 40
2391 35c. Christopher Columbus 95 40
2392 50c. 15th-century sandglass 95 55
2393 75c. Queen Isabella 1·00 80
2394 $4 Cantino map of 1502 (detail) 5·00 7·00
MS2395 Two sheets, each 80 × 108 mm. (a) $6 Map of Genoa (detail). (b) $6 Detail of 15th-century map by Thomas Bly Set of 2 sheets 9·00 10·00

1992. "Genova '92" International Thematic Stamp Exhibition. Hummingbirds. Multicoloured.
2396 10c. Type **370a** 70 25
2397 25c. Vervain hummingbird 90 25
2398 35c. Blue-headed hummingbird 95 25
2399 50c. Cuban emerald 1·25 60
2400 75c. Antillean mango 1·60 75
2401 $2 Purple-throated carib 2·50 2·50
2402 $4 Puerto Rican emerald 3·50 4·25
2403 $5 Green-throated carib 3·50 4·25
MS2404 Two sheets, each 109 × 80 mm. (a) $6 Young Antillean Crested Hummingbird. (b) $6 Rufous-breasted Hermit Set of 2 sheets 13·00 13·00

371 Gracie Fields

372 Badminton

1992. 50th Anniv of United Service Organization (forces' entertainment programme). Multicoloured.
2405 15c. Type **371** 30 20
2406 25c. Jack Benny 30 20
2407 35c. Jinx Falkenburg 30 25
2408 50c. Francis Langford 45 40
2409 75c. Joe E. Brown 80 70
2410 $1 Phil Silvers 1·25 80
2411 $2 Danny Kaye 2·25 2·25
2412 $5 Frank Sinatra 6·50 6·50
MS2413 Two sheets, each 107 × 80 mm. (a) $6 Bob Hope. (b) $6 Anna May Wong Set of 2 sheets 8·00 9·00

1992. Olympic Games, Barcelona (2nd issue). Multicoloured.
2414 10c. Type **372** 50 30
2415 25c. Women's long jump 50 20
2416 35c. Women's 100 m 50 30
2417 50c. 1000 m cycling sprint 1·00 50
2418 75c. Decathlon (horiz) 1·00 80
2419 $2 Judo (horiz) 2·00 2·25
2420 $4 Women's gymnastics—asymmetrical bars 3·25 3·75
2421 $5 Men's javelin 3·25 3·75
MS2422 Two sheets, each 100 × 70 mm. (a) $6 Men's gymnastics – vault. (b) $6 Men's gymnastics – floor exercise Set of 2 sheets 8·00 9·00

372a Columbus meeting Amerindians

1992. 500th Anniv of Discovery of America by Columbus (6th issue). Organization of East Caribbean States. Multicoloured.
2423 $1 Type **372a** 70 70
2424 $2 Ships approaching island 1·40 1·60

372b "The Blue Comet" Locomotive, Boucher (1933)

1992. Toy Trains from American Manufacturers. Multicoloured.
2425 10c. Type **372b** 40 20
2426 35c. No. 2220 switching locomotive, Voltamp (1906) 50 25
2427 40c. No. 221 tunnel locomotive, Knapp (1905) 50 30
2428 75c. "Grand Canyon" locomotive, American Flyer (1931) 80 55
2429 $1 "Streamliner" tin locomotive, Hafner (1930s) 1·10 80
2430 $2 No. 237 switching locomotive, Elektoy (1911) 2·00 2·25
2431 $4 Parlor car, Ives (1928) 3·50 4·00
2432 $5 "Improved President's Special" locomotive, American Flyer (1927) 3·50 4·00
MS2433 Two sheets, each 133 × 103 mm. (a) $6 No. 1122 locomotive, Ives (1921) (38½ × 50 mm). (b) $6 No. 3239 locomotive, Ives (1912) (50 × 38½ mm) Set of 2 sheets 8·00 9·00

1992. Postage Stamp Mega Event, New York. Sheet 100 × 70 mm, containing multicoloured design as T **207a** of Gambia.
MS2434 $6 Guggenheim Museum 3·50 4·25

373 "Matador" (yacht), Newport News Regatta

1992. World Regattas. Multicoloured.
2435 15c. Type **373** 20 20
2436 25c. "Awesome", Antigua 25 25
2437 35c. "Mistress Quickly", Bermuda 30 30
2438 50c. "Emeraude", St. Tropez 50 50
2439 $1 "Diva G", German Admirals Cup 80 80
2440 $2 "Lady Be", French Admirals Cup 1·50 1·75
2441 $4 "Midnight Sun", Admirals Cup 2·75 3·50
2442 $5 "CARAT", Sardinia Cup 2·75 3·50
MS2443 Two sheets, each 113 × 85 mm. (a) $6 Yachts, Grenada Regatta (horiz). (b) $6 Fastnet Race, 1979 (horiz) Set of 2 sheets 9·00 11·00

1992. Christmas. Religious Paintings. As T **207b** of Gambia. Multicoloured.
2444 10c. "Adoration of the Magi" (detail) (Fra Filippo Lippi) 45 15
2445 15c. "Madonna adoring Child in a Wood" (Lippi) 55 20
2446 25c. "Adoration of the Magi" (detail) (Botticelli) 70 20
2447 35c. "The Epiphany—Adoration of the Magi" (detail) (Hieronymus Bosch) 75 20
2448 50c. "Adoration of the Magi" (detail) (Giovanni de Paolo) 1·00 45
2449 75c. "Adoration of the Magi" (Gentile da Fabriano) 1·50 60
2450 90c. "Adoration of the Magi" (detail) (Juan Batista Maino) 1·75 70
2451 $1 "Adoration of the Child" (Master of Liesborn) 1·75 90
2452 $2 "Adoration of the Kings" (Master of Liesborn) 2·75 2·75
2453 $3 "Adoration of the Three Wise Men" (Pedro Berruguete) 3·00 3·50
2454 $4 "Adoration of the Child" (Lippi) 3·75 4·50
2455 $5 "Adoration of the Child" (Correggio) 3·75 4·50
MS2456 Three sheets, each 72 × 97 mm. (a) $6 "Adoration of the Magi" (detail) (Andrea Mantegna). (b) $6 "Adoration of the Magi" (detail) (Hans Memling). (c) $6 "Adoration of the Shepherds" (La Tour) Set of 3 sheets 15·00 16·00
No. 2447 is inscribed "Hieronymous" in error.

374 Cher

375 Grenada Dove

1992. Gold Record Award Winners. Mult.
2457 90c. Type **374** 1·25 1·25
2458 90c. Michael Jackson 1·25 1·25
2459 90c. Elvis Presley 1·25 1·25
2460 90c. Dolly Parton 1·25 1·25
2461 90c. Johnny Mathis 1·25 1·25
2462 90c. Madonna 1·25 1·25
2463 90c. Nat King Cole 1·25 1·25
2464 90c. Janice Joplin 1·25 1·25
MS2465 Two sheets, each 100 × 70 mm. (a) $3 Chuck Berry; $3 James Brown. (b) $3 Frank Sinatra; $3 Perry Como Set of 2 sheets 12·00 12·00
Nos. 2457/64 were printed together, se-tenant, with a composite background design.

1992. Anniversaries and Events. Mult.
2466 10c. Type **375** 1·00 65
2467 25c. Airship LZ-1 on maiden flight, 1900 (horiz) 1·00 30
2468 50c. ENDOSAT (robot plane) project (horiz) 1·25 55
2469 75c. Konrad Adenauer (German statesman) and industrial skyline (horiz) 1·25 70
2470 $1.50 Golden lion tamarin (horiz) 2·75 2·00
2471 $2 Mountain gorilla (horiz) 3·50 2·75
2472 $2 Outline of man and heart (horiz) 3·25 2·75
2473 $3 Wolfgang Amadeus Mozart 4·50 3·75
2474 $4 "Voyager 2" and Neptune (horiz) 4·50 4·50
2475 $4 Adenauer with flag and map of West Germany (horiz) 4·50 4·50
2476 $5 Count von Zeppelin and "Graf Zeppelin" (horiz) 4·50 4·75
2477 $6 Admiral Richard Byrd (polar explorer) (horiz) 4·50 4·75
MS2478 Five sheets. (a) 110 × 80 mm. $6 Count von Zeppelin (horiz). (b) 110 × 80 mm. $6 Space shuttle recovering "Intelsat 6" satellite. (c) 110 × 80 mm. $6 Konrad Adenauer (horiz). (d) 95 × 70 mm. $6 Spotted Little Owl (horiz). (e) 100 × 70 mm. $6 Papageno costume from "The Magic Flute" Set of 5 sheets 24·00 25·00
ANNIVERSARIES AND EVENTS: No. 2466, National bird; 2467, 2476, **MS**2478a, 75th death anniv of Count Ferdinand von Zeppelin; 2468, 2475, **MS**2478b, International Space Year; 2469, 2475, **MS**2478c, 25th death anniv of Konrad Adenauer; 2470/1, **MS**2478d, Earth Summit '92, Rio; 2472, United Nations World Health Organization Projects; 2473, **MS**2478e, Death bicentenary of Mozart; 2477, 75th anniv of International Association of Lions Clubs.

376 Care Bear on Beach

1992. Ecology.
2479 75c. Type **376** 1·00 60
MS2480 71 × 101 mm. $2 Care Bear and butterfly (vert) 2·25 2·25

377 Samoyed and St. Basil's Cathedral, Moscow

1993. Dogs of the World. Multicoloured.
2481 10c. Type **377** 70 40
2482 15c. Chow and Ling Yin Monastery, China 85 40
2483 25c. Boxer and Tower of London 90 30
2484 90c. Basenji and Yamma Mosque, Niger 1·60 75
2485 $1 Golden labrador and Parliament Building, Ottawa 1·60 80
2486 $3 St. Bernard and Parsenn, Switzerland 2·75 3·00
2487 $4 Rhodesian ridgeback and Melrose House, South Africa 3·00 3·50
2488 $5 Afghan hound and Mazar-i-Sharif, Afghanistan 3·00 3·50
MS2489 Two sheets, each 100 × 70 mm. (a) $6 Australian cattle dog. (b) $6 Alaskan malamute Set of 2 sheets 10·00 10·00
No. **MS**2489a is inscribed "Austrailian" in error.

1993. Bicentenary of the Louvre, Paris. Paintings by Jean-Antoine Watteau. As T **209b** of Gambia. Multicoloured.
2490 $1 "The Faux-pas" 95 95
2491 $1 "Portrait of a Gentleman" 95 95
2492 $1 "Young Lady with Archlute" 95 95
2493 $1 "Young Man Dancing" 95 95
2494 $1 "Autumn, Pamona and a Cherub" 95 95
2495 $1 "Judgement of Paris" 95 95

2496 $1 "Pierrot" (detail) 95 95
2497 $1 "Pierrot" (different detail) 95 95
MS2498 100 × 70 mm. $6 "The Embarkation for Cythère" (85 × 52 mm). . . . . 4·25 5·00

378 Baha'i Shrine, Haifa

1993. Centenary of Baha'i Faith.
2499 **378** 75c. multicoloured . . . 1·50 1·00

379 "Citheronia magnifica"

1993. Moths. Multicoloured.
2500 10c. Type **379** 25 25
2501 35c. "Automeris metali" . . 40 25
2502 45c. "Thysania zenobia" . . 50 30
2503 75c. "Agrius cingulatus" . . 70 55
2504 $1 "Composia fidelissima" 80 65
2505 $2 "Synchlora xysteraria" 1·50 1·75
2506 $4 "Eumorpha labruscae" 2·50 2·75
2507 $5 "Ascalapha odorata" . . 2·50 2·75
MS2508 Two sheets, each 100 × 70 mm. (a) $6 "Epimecis detexta" (vert). (b) $6 "Xylophanes titana" (vert) Set of 2 sheets . . . . 7·50 8·50

380 Heliconia

381 "Woman with Loaves" (Picasso)

1993. Flowers. Multicoloured.
2509 10c. Type **380** 25 25
2510 35c. Pansy 40 25
2511 45c. Water lily 50 30
2512 75c. Bougainvillea 70 55
2513 $1 Calla lily 80 65
2514 $2 California poppy . . . . 1·50 1·75
2515 $4 Red ginger . . . . . . 2·50 3·00
2516 $5 Anthurium . . . . . . 2·50 3·00
MS2517 Two sheets, each 70 × 100 mm. (a) $6 Christmas rose (horiz). (b) $6 Moth orchid (horiz) Set of 2 sheets . . . . 7·50 8·50

1993. 40th Anniv of Coronation. As T **215a** of Gambia.
2518 35c. multicoloured 70 75
2519 70c. multicoloured 80 85
2520 $1 brown and black 85 90
2521 $5 multicoloured . . . . . 2·25 2·50
MS2522 70 × 100 mm. $6 multicoloured . . . . 5·50 6·00
DESIGNS: 35c. Queen Elizabeth II at Coronation (photograph by Cecil Beaton); 70c. Sceptres; $1 Queen Elizabeth receiving sceptre from Archbishop of Canterbury; $5 Queen and Prince Philip with their children, 1960s. (28½ × 42½ mm)—$6 "Queen Elizabeth II, 1965" (detail) (Peter Greenham).

1993. Anniversaries and Events. Each brown, deep brown and black (Nos. 2527, 2535, **MS**2536d) or multicoloured (others).
2523 25c. Type **381** 30 20
2524 35c. 16th-century telescope 35 20
2525 35c. Public Library building 35 20
2526 35c. Gaetan Boucher (speed skating, 1984) 35 20
2527 50c. Willy Brandt with Senator Edward Kennedy (horiz) 40 30
2528 75c. Carnival float (horiz) 50 40
2529 90c. "Weeping Woman" (Picasso) 65 45
2530 $1 "Marii Prohaska" (Tyrus Czyzewski) 70 50
2531 $3 "Marysia et Burek a Geylan" (S. Wirkiewicz) 2·25 2·25
2532 $4 "Woman seated in Airchair" (Picasso) . . . 2·75 2·75
2533 $4 Astronaut on Moon . . 2·75 2·75
2534 $5 Norbert Schramm (figure skating, 1984) . . . . . 2·75 2·75
2535 $5 Willy Brandt and Kurt Waldheim (horiz) . . . . 2·75 2·75
MS2536 Five sheets. (a) 76 × 107 mm. $5 Copernicus. (b) 75 × 105 mm. $6 "Three Women at the Spring" (detail) (Picasso). (c) 76 × 105 mm. $6 Women's Super G skiing medal winners, 1988 (horiz). (d) 105 × 75 mm. $6 Newspaper headline, 1974. (e) 105 × 76 mm. $6 "Parting" (detail) (Witold Wojtkiewicz) Set of 5 sheets . . . . 17·00 18·00
ANNIVERSARIES AND EVENTS: Nos. 2523, 2529, 2532, **MS**2536b, 20th death anniv of Picasso (artist); 2524, 2533, **MS**2536a, 450th death anniv of Copernicus (astronomer); 2525, Centenary (1992) of Grenada Public Library; 2526, 2534, **MS**2536c, Winter Olympic Games '94, Lillehammer; 2527, 2535, **MS**2536d, 80th birth anniv (1992) of Willy Brandt (German politician); 2528, Grenada Carnival; 2530/1, **MS**2536e, "Polska '93" International Stamp Exhibition, Poznan.

382 Yellow-green Vireo ("Red-eyed Vireo")

1993. Songbirds. Multicoloured.
2537 15c. Type **382** 60 60
2538 25c. Fork-tailed flycatcher ("Scissor-tailed Flycatcher") 65 65
2539 35c. Palm chat 75 75
2540 35c. Chaffinch 75 75
2541 45c. Yellow wagtail 80 80
2542 45c. Painted bunting 80 80
2543 50c. Short-tailed pygmy tyrant ("Short-tailed Pygmy Flycatcher") . . . 80 80
2544 65c. Orange-breasted bunting ("Rainbow Bunting") 90 90
2545 75c. Red crossbill 90 90
2546 75c. Kauai akialoa 90 90
2547 $1 Yellow-throated longclaw ("Yellow-throated Wagtail") . . . . 1·00 1·00
2548 $4 Barn swallow . . . . . 2·50 2·75
MS2549 Two sheets, each 105 × 86 mm. (a) $6 Song thrush. (b) $6 White-crested laughing thrush Set of 2 sheets . . . . 7·00 8·00
Nos. 2537/48 were printed together, se-tenant, with the backgrounds forming a composite design.

383 Atlantic Grey Cowrie and Atlantic Yellow Cowrie

1993. Seashells. Multicoloured.
2550 15c. Type **383** 55 55
2551 15c. Candy-stick tellin and sunrise tellin 55 55
2552 25c. Caribbean vase 60 60
2553 35c. Lightning venus and royal comb venus 70 70
2554 35c. Crown cone 70 70
2555 45c. Reticulated cowrie-helmet 80 80
2556 50c. Barbados mitre and variegated turret shell . . 80 80
2557 50c. Common egg cockle and Atlantic strawberry cockle 80 80
2558 75c. Measled cowrie 90 90
2559 75c. Rooster-tail conch . . . 90 90
2560 $1 Lion's-paw scallop and Antillean scallop . . . . 1·00 1·00
2561 $4 Dog-head triton . . . . 2·25 2·75
MS2562 Two sheets, each 76 × 106 mm. (a) $6 Dyson's keyhole limpet. (b) $6 Virgin nerite and Emerald nerite Set of 2 sheets 11·00 11·00
Nos. 2550/61 were printed together, se-tenant, with the backgrounds forming a composite design.

1993. Asian International Stamp Exhibitions. As T **219a** of Gambia. Mult. (a) "Indopex '93", Surabaya, Indonesia.
2563 35c. Megalithic carving, Sumba Island 35 25
2564 45c. Entrance to Gao Gajah, Bali 45 30
2565 $1.50 Statue of kris holder 1·00 1·00
2566 $1.50 Hanuman protecting Sita . . . . 1·00 1·00
2567 $1.50 Sendi of Visu mounted on Garuda . . . 1·00 1·00
2568 $1.50 Wahana (votif figure) 1·00 1·00
2569 $1.50 Hanuman (different) 1·00 1·00
2570 $1.50 Singa (symbolic lion) 1·00 1·00
2571 $2 Loving-mother Bridge, Taroko Gorge National Park . . . . 1·40 1·50
2572 $4 Head of Kala over temple gateway, Northern Bali . . . . 2·50 3·00
MS2573 104 × 134 mm. $6 Slow loris 3·75 4·25

(b) "Taipei '93", Taiwan.
2574 35c. Fire-breathing dragon, New Year's Fair, Chongqing 35 25
2575 45c. Stone elephant, Ming Tomb, Nanjing 45 30
2576 $1.50 "Ornamental Cock" (Han Meilin) . . . . . 1·00 1·00
2577 $1.50 "He's even afraid of Cows" (Meilin) . . . . . 1·00 1·00
2578 $1.50 "On a Moonlit Night" (Meilin) . . . . 1·00 1·00
2579 $1.50 "Eyes that see in the Dark" (Meilin) . . . . . 1·00 1·00
2580 $1.50 "He's well behaved" (Meilin) . . . . 1·00 1·00
2581 $1.50 "He doesn't Bite" (Meilin) . . . . 1·00 1·00
2582 $2 Marble peifang, Ming 13 Tombs, Beijing . . . . . 1·40 1·50
2583 $4 Stone pillar, Nanjing . . 2·50 3·00
MS2584 104 × 134 mm. $6 Orang-utan, Mt. Lesuser National Park 3·75 4·25

(c) "Bangkok 1993", Thailand.
2585 35c. Nora Nair, Prasad Phra Thepidon, Wat Phra Kaew 35 25
2586 45c. Stucco deities at Library of Wat Phra Singh 45 30
2587 $1.50 Wooden carved horses 1·00 1·00
2588 $1.50 Wheel of the law . . . 1·00 1·00
2589 $1.50 Lanna bronze elephant . . . . 1·00 1·00
2590 $1.50 Kendi in the form of elephant . . . . 1·00 1·00
2591 $1.50 Bronze duck . . . . 1·00 1·00
2592 $1.50 Horseman . . . . . 1·00 1·00
2593 $2 Naga snake, Chiang Mai's Temple . . . . . . 1·40 1·50
2594 $4 Stucco figures, Wat Chang Lom . . . . 2·50 3·00
MS2595 134 × 104 mm. $6 Elephant calf (horiz) . . . . 3·75 4·25
No. 2590 is incorrectly inscribed "Kendi in the form of an Elphant".

1993. World Cup Football Championship, U.S.A. (1994) (1st issue). As T **221a** of Gambia. Mult.
2596 10c. Nikolai Larionov (Russia) 35 30
2597 25c. Andrea Carnevale (Italy) 60 25
2598 35c. Enzo Schifo (Belgium) and Soon-Ho Choi (South Korea) 70 25
2599 45c. Gary Lineker (England) 1·00 30
2600 $1 Diego Maradona (Argentina) . . . . 1·50 80
2601 $2 Lothar Mattaeus (Germany) . . . . 1·75 2·00
2602 $4 Jan Karas (Poland) and Julio Cesar Silva (Brazil) 2·50 3·25
2603 $5 Claudio Caniggia (Argentina) . . . . 2·50 3·25
MS2604 Two sheets, each 75 × 104 mm. (a) $6 Wlodzimierz (Poland). (b) $6 José Basualdo (Argentina) Set of 2 sheets . . 7·00 8·00
See also Nos. 2743/9.

384 James K. Spensley

1993. Centenary of Italian Football. Past and present Genoa players. Each blue, red and black.
2605 $3 Type **384** . . . . . . 2·50 2·50
2606 $3 Renzo de Vecchi . . . . 2·50 2·50
2607 $3 Giovanni de Pra' . . . . 2·50 2·50
2608 $3 Luigi Burlando . . . . . 2·50 2·50
2609 $3 Felice Levratto . . . . . 2·50 2·50
2610 $3 Guglielmo Stabile . . . . 2·50 2·50
2611 $3 Vittorio Sardelli . . . . 2·50 2·50
2612 $3 Juan Carlos Verdeal . . 2·50 2·50
2613 $3 Fosco Becattini . . . . 2·50 2·50
2614 $3 Julio Cesar Abadie . . . 2·50 2·50
2615 $3 Luigi Meroni . . . . . 2·50 2·50
2616 $3 Roberto Pruzzo . . . . 2·50 2·50
MS2617 Two sheets. (a) 100 × 75 mm. $15 Genoa Football Club badge (29 × 45 mm). (b) 129 × 106 mm. $15 Genoa team of 1991–92 (48 × 35 mm) Set of 2 sheets . . . . 22·00 22·00

385 "The Band Concert", 1935

1993. 65th Anniv of Mickey Mouse. Scenes from Walt Disney cartoon films. Multicoloured.
2618 25c. Type **385** 90 20
2619 35c. "Mickey's Circus", 1936 . . . . 1·00 20
2620 50c. "Magician Mickey", 1937 . . . . 1·25 35
2621 75c. "Moose Hunters", 1937 1·60 60
2622 $1 "Mickey's Amateurs", 1937 . . . . 1·75 80
2623 $2 "Tugboat Mickey", 1940 2·50 2·50
2624 $4 "Orphan's Benefit", 1941 3·50 4·25
2625 $5 "Mickey's Christmas Carol", 1983 . . . . . . 3·50 4·25
MS2626 Two sheets, each 127 × 102 mm. (a) $6 "Mickey's Birthday Party", 1942. (b) $6 "Mickey's Trailer", 1938 (vert) Set of 2 sheets . . . . 11·00 11·00
No. 2624 is inscribed "Oprhan's Benefit" in error.

1993. Christmas. Religious Paintings. As T **221b** of Gambia. Black, yellow and red (Nos. 2627/8, 2632 and 2634, **MS**2635a) or multicoloured (others).
2627 10c. "The Nativity" (Durer) 25 15
2628 25c. "The Annunciation" (Durer) 35 15
2629 35c. "The Litta Madonna" (Da Vinci) 40 20
2630 60c. "The Virgin and Child with St. John the Baptist and St. Anne" (Da Vinci) 50 40
2631 90c. "The Madonna with the Carnation" (Da Vinci) 65 65
2632 $1 "Adoration of the Magi" (Durer) 75 75
2633 $4 "The Benois Madonna" (Da Vinci) . . . . 2·50 3·25
2634 $5 "The Virgin Mary in the Sun" (Durer) . . . . . . 2·50 3·25
MS2635 Two sheets, each 102 × 128 mm. (a) $6 "The Holy Family with Three Hares" (detail) (Dürer). (b) $6 "Adoration of the Magi" (detail) (Da Vinci) Set of 2 sheets . . . . 8·00 9·00
Nos. 2629/31, 2633 and **MS**2635b are inscribed "LEONARDO DI VINCI" in error.

386 Blanchard's Balloon over Walnut St. Prison

1993. Aviation Anniversaries. Multicoloured.
2636 35c. Airship "Graf Zeppelin" over Vienna at night 35 20
2637 45c. Type **386** 20 25
2638 50c. Lysander 50 35
2639 75c. "Graf Zeppelin" over Pyramids 75 55
2640 $2 Blanchard waving hat from balloon (vert) . . . 90 95
2641 $3 Hawker Typhoon . . . . 2·00 2·50
2642 $5 "Graf Zeppelin" over Rio de Janeiro . . . . . 3·25 3·75
MS2643 Three sheets, each 106 × 77 mm. (a) $6 "Graf Zeppelin". (b) Blanchard's balloon (vert). (c) $6 Hawker Hurricane Set of 3 sheets . . . . 10·50 11·00
ANNIVERSARIES: Nos. 2636, 2639, 2642, **MS**2643a, 125th birth anniv of Hugo Eckener (airship commander); 2637, 2640, **MS**2643b, Bicentenary of first airmail flight; 2638, 2641, **MS**2643c, 75th anniv of Royal Air Force.

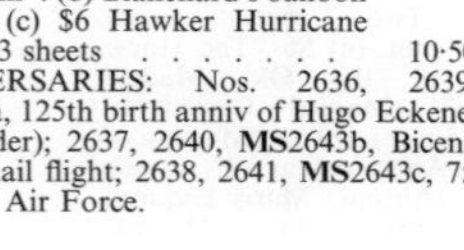

387 Mercedes Benz "370 S" Cabriolet, 1932

1993. Centenaries of Henry Ford's First Petrol Engine (Nos. 2645/6, **MS**2648b) and Karl Benz's First Four-wheeled Car (others). Multicoloured.
2644 35c. Type **387** 55 20
2645 45c. Ford "Mustang", 1966 65 30

2646 $3 Ford "Model A" Phaeton, 1930 3·25 3·75
2647 $4 Mercedes Benz "300 Sl" Gullwing 3·50 4·00
MS2648 Two sheets, each 76 × 106 mm. (a) $6 Mercedes Benz "290", 1934. (b) $6 Ford "Model A", 1903 Set of 2 sheets 8·00 9·00

1993. Famous Paintings by Rembrandt and Matisse. As T **221c** of Gambia. Multicoloured.
2649 15c. "Self-portrait", 1900 (Matisse) 30 20
2650 35c. "Self-portrait", 1629 (Rembrandt) 35 20
2651 45c. "Self-portrait", 1918 (Matisse) 40 25
2652 50c. "Self-portrait", 1640 (Rembrandt) 50 35
2653 75c. "Self-portrait", 1652 (Rembrandt) 65 55
2654 $2 "Self-portrait", 1906 (Matisse) 1·40 1·75
2655 $4 "Self-portrait", 1900 (different) (Matisse) 2·50 3·50
2656 $5 "Self-portrait", 1625–31 (Rembrandt) 2·75 3·50
MS2657 Two sheets. (a) 100 × 125 mm. $6 "The Painter in his Studio" (detail) (Matisse). P 13½ × 14. (b) 125 × 100 mm. $6 "The Sampling Officials of the Drapers' Guild" (detail) (Rembrandt) (horiz). P 14 × 13½ Set of 2 sheets 7·00 8·00

388 Fishermen with Blue Marlin

389 National Flag and Ketch in Bay

1994. 25th Anniv of Spice Island Billfish Tournament. Multicoloured.
2658 15c. Type **388** 50 30
2659 25c. Sailfish with angler 55 30
2660 35c. Yellow-finned tuna with angler 65 30
2661 50c. White marlin with angler 75 60
2662 75c. Catching a sailfish 85 1·00

1994. 25th Anniv of Independence.
2663 35c. Type **389** 75 40
MS2664 76 × 106 mm. $6 Map of Grenada 4·00 5·00

1994. "Hong Kong '94" International Stamp Exhibition (1st issue). As T **222a** of Gambia. Multicoloured.
2665 40c. Hong Kong 1971 Scouting 50c. stamp and "Hong Kong Post Office, 1846" (left detail) (M. Bruce) 50 65
2666 40c. Grenada 1988 Rotary $2 and "Hong Kong Post Office, 1846" (right detail) (M. Bruce) 50 65
Nos. 2665/6 were printed together, se-tenant, with the centre part of each pair forming the complete painting.
See also Nos. 2667/72.

1994. "Hong Kong '94" International Stamp Exhibition (2nd issue). Qing Dynasty Porcelain. As T **222b** of Gambia. Multicoloured.
2667 45c. Vase with dragon decoration 60 60
2668 45c. Hat stand with brown base 60 60
2669 45c. Gourd-shaped vase 60 60
2670 45c. Rotating vase with openwork 60 60
2671 45c. Candlestick with dogs 60 60
2672 45c. Hat stand with orange base 60 60

390 "Hygrocybe acutoconica"

1994. Fungi. Multicoloured.
2673 35c. Type **390** 50 30
2674 45c. "Leucopaxillus gracillimus" 55 30
2675 50c. "Leptonia caeruleocapitata" 55 30
2676 75c. "Leucocoprinus birnbaumii" 70 50
2677 $1 "Marasmius atrorubens" 85 75
2678 $2 "Boletellus cubensis" 1·40 1·50
2679 $4 "Chlorophyllum molybdites" 2·25 2·75
2680 $5 "Psilocybe cubensis" 2·25 2·75
MS2681 Two sheets, each 100 × 70 mm. (a) $6 "Mycena pura". (b) $6 "Pyrrhoglossum lilaceipes" Set of 2 sheets 9·00 9·00

391 Quetzalcoatlus

1994. Prehistoric Animals. Multicoloured.
2682 75c. Type **391** 70 65
2683 75c. Pteranodon ingens 70 65
2684 75c. Tropeognathus 70 65
2685 75c. Phobetor 70 65
2686 75c. Alamosaurus 70 65
2687 75c. Triceratops 70 65
2688 75c. Tyrannosaurus rex 70 65
2689 75c. Head of Tyrannosaurus rex 70 65
2690 75c. Lambeosaurus 70 65
2691 75c. Spinosaurus 70 65
2692 75c. Parasaurolophus 70 65
2693 75c. Hadrosaurus 70 65
2694 75c. Germanodactylus 70 65
2695 75c. Dimorphodon 70 65
2696 75c. Ramphorynchus 70 65
2697 75c. Apatosaurus 70 65
2698 75c. Pterodactylus 70 65
2699 75c. Stegosaurus 70 65
2700 75c. Brathiosaurus 70 65
2701 75c. Allosaurus 70 65
2702 75c. Plesiosaurus 70 65
2703 75c. Ceratosaurus 70 65
2704 75c. Compsognathus 70 65
2705 75c. Elaphosaurus 70 65
MS2706 Two sheets. (a) 100 × 70 mm. $6 Pteranodon ingens (different). (b) 70 × 100 mm. $6 Head of Plateosaurus (vert) Set of 2 sheets 8·50 9·00
Nos. 2682/93 and 2694/2705 respectively were printed together, se-tenant, forming composite designs.

1994. 25th Anniv of First Manned Moon Landing. Space Shuttle "Challenger". As T **227a** of Gambia. Multicoloured
2707 $2 Space shuttle "Challenger" 1·25 1·40
2708 $2 Judith Resnick (astronaut) 1·25 1·40
2709 $2 Aircraft in memorial fly past 1·25 1·40
2710 $2 Dick Scobee (astronaut) 1·25 1·40
2711 $2 Mission logo 1·25 1·40
2712 $2 Michael Smith (astronaut) 1·25 1·40
MS2713 107 × 76 mm. $6 "Challenger" crew 3·75 4·50

1994. Centenary of International Olympic Committee. Gold Medal Winners. As T **227b** of Gambia. Multicoloured.
2714 50c. Heike Drechsler (Germany) (long jump), 1992 50 30
2715 $1.50 Nadia Comaneci (Rumania) (gymnastics), 1976 and 1980 1·90 1·90
MS2716 107 × 76 mm. $6 Dan Jansen (U.S.A.) (1000 metre speed skating), 1994 3·75 4·25

391a Grenadian Family

1994. International Year of the Family.
2717 **391a** $1 multicoloured 80 80

1994. 50th Anniv of D-Day. As T **227c** of Gambia. Multicoloured.
2718 40c. Sherman amphibious tank leaving landing craft 75 30
2719 $2 Tank on Churchill "Ark" bridging vehicle 2·25 2·00
2720 $3 Churchill "Bobbin" tank laying roadway 2·50 2·50
MS2721 107 × 76 mm. $6 Churchill AVRE with fascine 3·50 4·00

1994. "Philakorea '94" International Stamp Exhibition, Seoul. As T **227d** of Gambia. Multicoloured.
2722 40c. Wonson Park (horiz) 30 25
2723 $1 Pusan (horiz) 55 60
2724 $1 "Lady in a Hooded Cloak" (left detail) (Sin Yunbok) 55 60
2725 $1 "Lady in a Hooded Cloak" (right detail) 55 60
2726 $1 "Kiaseng House" (left detail) (Sin Yunbok) 55 60
2727 $1 "Kiaseng House" (right detail) 55 60
2728 $1 "Amorous Youth on a Picnic" (left detail) (Sin Yunbok) 55 60
2729 $1 "Amorous Youth on a Picnic" (right detail) 55 60
2730 $1 "Chasing a Cat" (left detail) (Sin Yunbok) 55 60
2731 $1 "Chasing a Cat" (right detail) 55 60
2732 $4 Korean orchestra, National Theatre, Seoul (horiz) 2·00 2·50
MS2733 70 × 102 mm. $6 "Roof Tiling" (detail) (Kim Hongdo) 3·25 3·50
Nos. 2724/31 were printed together, se-tenant, forming composite designs of each painting.

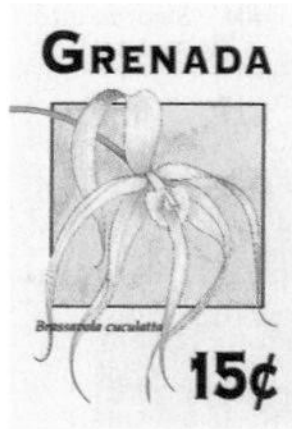
392 "Brassavola cuculatta"

393 Tony Meola (U.S.A.)

1994. Orchids. Multicoloured.
2734 15c. Type **392** 30 20
2735 25c. "Comparettia falcata" 40 20
2736 45c. "Epidendrum ciliare" 50 30
2737 75c. "Epidendrum cochleatum" 70 50
2738 $1 "Ionopsis utricularioides" 80 70
2739 $2 "Onicidium ceboletta" 1·25 1·40
2740 $4 "Onicidium luridium" 2·25 2·50
2741 $5 "Rodriquezia secunda" 2·25 2·50
MS2742 Two sheets, each 100 × 70 mm. (a) $6 "Ionopsis utriculariodes" (different). (b) $6 "Onicidium luridium" (different) Set of 2 sheets 8·00 8·50
No. **MS**2742b is inscribed "Onicium luridum" in error.

1994. World Cup Football Championship, U.S.A. (2nd issue). Multicoloured.
2743 75c. Type **393** 80 80
2744 75c. Steve Mark (Grenada) 80 80
2745 75c. Gianluigi Lentini (Italy) 80 80
2746 75c. Belloumi (Algeria) 80 80
2747 75c. Nunoz (Spain) 80 80
2748 75c. Lothar Matthaus (Germany) 80 80
MS2749 Two sheets. (a) 99 × 70 mm. $6 World Cup Championship poster, 1930. (b) 70 × 114 mm. $6 Steve Mark (Grenada) (different) Set of 2 sheets 7·50 8·00

393a Sir Shridath Ramphal

1994. 1st Recipients of Order of the Caribbean Community. Multicoloured.
2750 15c. Type **393a** 10 10
2751 65c. William Demas 40 40
2752 $2 Derek Walcott 1·75 1·75

394 Yellow-tailed Snapper

1994. Fishes. Multicoloured.
2753 15c. Type **394** 40 20
2754 20c. Blue tang 40 20
2755 25c. Porkfish (vert) 40 20
2756 75c. Four-eyed butterflyfish 75 50
2757 $1 Reid's seahorse (vert) 85 70
2758 $2 Spotted moray (vert) 1·50 1·60
2759 $4 Royal gramma ("Fairy basslet") 2·50 2·75
2760 $5 Queen triggerfish (vert) 2·50 2·75
MS2761 Two sheets, each 106 × 76 mm. (a) $6 Queen angelfish. (b) $6 Long-spined squirrelfish Set of 2 sheets 7·50 8·00

395 Mickey Mouse bathing Pluto

1994. Chinese New Year ("Year of the Dog"). Walt Disney cartoon characters. Multicoloured.
2762 2c. Type **395** 15 10
2763 3c. Dog taking mouthwash 15 10
2764 4c. Dog with curlers in tail 15 10
2765 5c. Brushing dog's eyelashes 15 10
2766 10c. Giving dog manicure 25 10
2767 15c. Mickey spraying Pluto with flea powder 40 15
2768 20c. Dogs on display 40 20
2769 $4 Judge checking Pluto's teeth 4·50 4·75
2770 $5 Pluto wearing "1st Prize" rosette 4·50 4·75
MS2771 Three sheets, each 127 × 102 mm. (a) $6 King Charles Spaniel rubbing against judge's leg. (b) $6 Pluto holding rosette. (c) $6 Pluto with No. 13 on coat Set of 3 sheets 11·00 12·00

396 "Anartia amathea"

1994. Butterflies. Multicoloured.
2772A 10c. Type **396** 30 20
2773A 15c. "Marpesia petreus" 30 20
2774B 25c. "Hylephila phylaeus" 40 20
2775B 35c. "Junonia evarete" 45 25
2776A 45c. "Pseudolycaena marsyas" 50 30
2777A 50c. "Heliconius charitonius" 50 30
2778A 75c. "Hypolimnas misippus" 70 45
2778cB 90c. "Purgus oilcus" 45 50
2779A $1 "Cepheuptychia cephus" 75 55
2779cB $1.50 "Allosmaitia piplea" 80 85
2780A $2 "Historis odius" 1·75 1·50
2781A $3 "Phoebis philea" 2·50 2·75
2782A $4 "Urbanus proteus" 3·25 3·75
2783A $5 "Battus polydamas" 3·50 4·00
2784A $10 "Philaethria dido" 6·00 7·50
2785A $20 "Hamadryas arethusa" 10·00 13·00

1994. Christmas. Religious Paintings by Francisco de Zurbaran. As T **231a** of Gambia. Multicoloured.
2786 10c. "The Virgin and Child with St. John" (1658) 20 15
2787 15c. "The Circumcision" 30 20
2788 25c. "Adoration of St. Joseph" 30 20
2789 35c. "Adoration of the Magi" 30 20
2790 75c. "The Portiuncula" 60 45
2791 $1 "The Virgin and Child with St. John" (1662) 75 60
2792 $2 "The Virgin and Child with St. John" (1658/64) 1·25 1·75
2793 $4 "The Flight into Egypt" 2·25 3·25
MS2794 Two sheets. (a) 74 × 86 mm. $6 "Our Lady of Ransom and Two Mercedarians" (detail). (b) 114 × 100 mm. $6 "Adoration of the Shepherds" (detail) (horiz) Set of 2 sheets 7·50 8·00

397 Grenada Dove on Nest

1995. Birds. Multicoloured.
2795 25c. Type **397** 1·10 50
2796 35c. Pair of Grenada doves at nest 1·10 50
2797 45c. Cuban tody (vert) 1·25 50
2798 75c. Grenada dove on branch (vert) 1·50 1·50
2799 75c. Painted bunting 1·50 1·50
2800 $1 Grenada dove in flight (vert) 1·60 1·60
2801 $1 Red-legged honeycreeper 1·60 1·60
2802 $5 Green jay 3·50 4·25
MS2803 Two sheets, each 101 × 71 mm. (a) $6 Chaffinch. (b) $6 Chestnut-sided shrike vireo Set of 2 sheets 7·50 8·00
Nos. 2795/6, 2798 and 2800 also show the W.W.F. Panda emblem.

397a Junior Murray (West Indies)

1995. Centenary of First English Cricket Tour to the West Indies. Multicoloured.

2804 25c. Type **397a** 40 30
2805 35c. Richie Richardson (West Indies) 45 30
2806 $2 Alec Stewart (England) and Wisden Trophy (horiz) . . . . 1·60 1·75
MS2807 75 × 95 mm. $3 West Indian team, 1994 . . . . 2·25 2·25

398 Hooded Merganser

1995. Water Birds of the World. Multicoloured.

2808 25c. Type **398** 30 30
2809 35c. Green-winged teal . . . 35 30
2810 75c. King eider 70 75
2811 75c. Common shoveler . . . 70 75
2812 75c. Long-tailed duck . . . 70 75
2813 75c. Chiloe wigeon 70 75
2814 75c. Red-breasted merganser 70 75
2815 75c. Falcated teal 70 75
2816 75c. Vericolor teal 70 75
2817 75c. Smew 70 75
2818 75c. Red-crested pochard . . 70 75
2819 75c. Pintail 70 75
2820 75c. Barrow's goldeneye . . 70 75
2821 75c. Stellar's eider 70 75
2822 $1 Harlequin duck 75 75
2823 $3 European wigeon . . . . 1·75 2·00
MS2824 Two sheets, each 74 × 104 mm. (a) $5 Common shelduck ("European Wigeon"). (b) $6 Egyptian goose Set of 2 sheets . . . . 6·50 7·50

Nos. 2810/21 were printed together, se-tenant, forming a composite design.

No. 2811 is inscribed "Shobeler" in error.

399 Pig Priest, China

1995. Chinese New Year ("Year of the Pig"). Ornaments. Multicoloured.

2825 50c. Type **399** 45 55
2826 75c. Porcelain pig, Scotland 55 65
2827 $1 Seated porcelain pig, Italy 60 75
MS2828 107 × 77 mm. $2 Jade pig, China . . . . 1·25 1·40

400 Yellow-tailed Damselfish

1995. Marine Life. Multicoloured.

2829 $1 Type **400** 75 75
2830 $1 Blue-headed wrasse . . . 75 75
2831 $1 Balloonfish 75 75
2832 $1 Shy hamlet 75 75
2833 $1 Orange tube coral . . . 75 75
2834 $1 Rock beauty 75 75
2835 $1 Creole wrasse 75 75
2836 $1 Queen angelfish 75 75
2837 $1 Trumpetfish 75 75
2838 $1 Barred hamlet 75 75
2839 $1 Tube sponge 75 75
2840 $1 Porcupine fish 75 75
2841 $1 Firecoral 75 75
2842 $1 Royal gramma ("Fairy basslet") 75 75
2843 $1 Sea anemone 75 75
MS2844 Two sheets, each 106 × 76 mm. (a) $5 Seahorse. (b) $6 Elkhorn coral Set of 2 sheets 6·00 7·00

Nos. 2829/34 and 2835/43 respectively were printed together, se-tenant, forming composite designs.

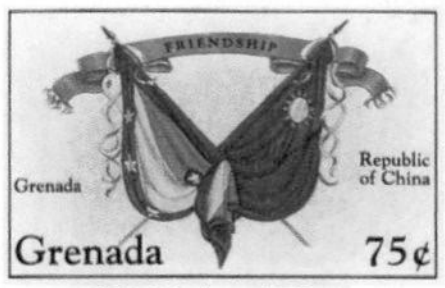

401 National Flags

1995. Grenada–Taiwan (Republic of China) Friendship. Multicoloured.

2845 75c. Type **401** . . . . . . 1·00 75
2846 $1 Prime Minister Brathwaite and President Lee Teng-hui . . . . . . 1·00 80
MS2847 76 × 106 mm. Nos. 2845/6 2·00 1·75

402 Cocker Spaniel

404 "Swords into Ploughshares"

403 Grenadian Scout

1995. Domestic Animals. Multicoloured.

2848 10c. Type **402** 50 30
2849 15c. Pinto (horse) 60 30
2850 25c. Rottweiler 70 20
2851 35c. German shepherd . . . 75 20
2852 45c. Persian (cat) 80 25
2853 50c. Snowshoe (cat) 80 30
2854 75c. Percheron (horse) . . . 1·25 60
2855 $1 Scottish fold (cat) . . . 1·25 70
2856 $2 Arabian (horse) . . . . 2·00 2·00
2857 $3 Andalusian (horse) . . . 2·25 2·50
2858 $4 C.P. Shorthair (cat) . . . 2·50 3·00
2859 $5 Chihuahua . . . . . . 3·00 3·25
MS2860 Three sheets, each 100 × 71 mm. (a) $5 Manx (cat). (b) $5 Donkey. (c) $6 Shar Pei Set of 3 sheets . . . . 8·00 9·00

1995. Centenary (1992) of Sierra Club (environmental protection society). Endangered Species. As T **224a** of Gambia. Multicoloured.

2861 $1 Head of margay at night 70 70
2862 $1 Margay sitting 70 70
2863 $1 Head of margay in daylight 70 70
2864 $1 Head of Andean condor 70 70
2865 $1 Andean condor facing right 70 70
2866 $1 Andean condor facing left 70 70
2867 $1 White-faced saki on branch 70 70
2868 $1 White-faced saki showing mane 70 70
2869 $1 Patagonia landscape . . 70 70
2870 $1 Lesser rheas feeding (horiz) 70 70
2871 $1 Pair of lesser rheas (horiz) 70 70
2872 $1 Lesser rhea (horiz) . . . 70 70
2873 $1 Sunset over snow-covered mountains, Patagonia (horiz) 70 70
2874 $1 Volcanic eruption, Patagonia (horiz) 70 70
2875 $1 White-faced Saki (horiz) 70 70
2876 $1 Common caracara on branch (horiz) 70 70
2877 $1 Pair of common caracaras at nest (horiz) 70 70
2878 $1 Common caracara facing left (horiz) 70 70

1995. 18th World Scout Jamboree, Netherlands. Multicoloured.

2879 75c. Type **403** 45 50
2880 $1 Scout abseiling 55 60
2881 $2 Scout saluting and national flag . . . . . . 85 1·00
MS2882 107 × 77 mm. $6 Scout in canoe . . . . 3·00 3·50

1995. 50th Anniv of End of Second World War in Europe. Fighter Aircraft. As T **237a** of Gambia. Multicoloured.

2883 $2 Lavochkin La-7 (fighter) 1·50 1·40
2884 $2 Hawker Hurricane . . . 1·50 1·40
2885 $2 North American P-51D Mustang . . . . 1·50 1·40
2886 $2 Messerschmitt Bf 109 . . 1·50 1·40
2887 $2 Bristol Type 152 Beaufighter . . . . 1·50 1·40
2888 $2 Messerschmitt Me 262 1·50 1·40
2889 $2 Republic P-47 Thunderbolt . . . . . . 1·50 1·40
2890 $2 Hawker Tempest . . . . 1·50 1·40
MS2891 106 × 76 mm. $6 Nose of Republic P-47 Thunderbolt . . 3·50 3·75

1995. 50th Anniv of United Nations. Multicoloured.

2892 75c. Type **404** 40 50
2893 $1 Globe and dove 50 60
2894 $2 U.N. Building, New York . . . . 85 1·10
MS2895 101 × 71 mm. $6 Anniversary logo (horiz) . . . 2·50 3·00

405 Woman with Baskets

406 National Flag and Rotary Logo

1995. 50th Anniv of F.A.O. Multicoloured.

2896 75c. Type **405** 40 50
2897 $1 Boy with basket on head 50 60
2898 $2 Men harvesting bananas 85 1·10
MS2899 72 × 102 mm. $6 F.A.O. logo . . . . 2·50 3·00

1995. 90th Anniv of Rotary International. Multicoloured.

2900 $5 Type **406** . . . . 2·10 2·40
MS2901 76 × 106 mm. $6 Paul Harris (founder) and logo . . 2·75 3·25

1995. 95th Birthday of Queen Elizabeth the Queen Mother. As T **239a** of Gambia.

2902 $1.50 brown, lt brown & blk 1·60 1·60
2903 $1.50 multicoloured . . . . 1·60 1·60
2904 $1.50 multicoloured . . . . 1·60 1·60
2905 $1.50 multicoloured . . . . 1·60 1·60
MS2906 127 × 102 mm. $6 multicoloured . . . . 6·00 6·00

DESIGNS: No. 2902, Queen Elizabeth the Queen Mother (pastel drawing); 2903, Holding rose; 2904, At desk (oil painting); 2905, In blue hat and white coat; **MS**2906, Wearing floral hat.

1995. 50th Anniv of End of Second World War in the Pacific. As T **239b** of Gambia. Multicoloured.

2907 $2 Dogfight over the Marianas . . . . 1·40 1·40
2908 $2 U.S. dive-bomber and burning aircraft carrier, Battle of Midway . . . . 1·40 1·40
2909 $2 U.S. aircraft attacking Japanese transport, Battle of the Bismarck Sea . . . 1·40 1·40
2910 $2 "Mushashi" (Japanese battleship) on fire in Leyte Gulf . . . . 1·40 1·40
2911 $2 U.S. aircraft taking off from Henderson Field . . 1·40 1·40
2912 $2 Battleships at Guadalcanal . . . . . . 1·40 1·40
MS2913 108 × 77 mm. $6 U.S. bomber . . . . 3·50 3·75

407 Tian Bingyi (China) (badminton)

408 Junior Murray (West Indies)

1995. Olympic Games, Atlanta (1996) (1st issue). Multicoloured.

2914 75c. Type **407** 80 80
2915 75c. Waldemar Leigien (Poland) and Frank Wieneke (West Germany) (judo) 80 80
2916 75c. Nelli Kim (U.S.S.R.) (gymnastics) 80 80
2917 75c. Alessandro Andri (Italy) (shot put) 80 80
2918 $2 Jackie Joyner (U.S.A.) (heptathlon) . . . . . . 1·75 1·75
2919 $2 Mitsuo Tsukahara (Japan) (gymnastics) . . . 1·75 1·75
2920 $2 Flo Hyman (U.S.A.) and Zhang Rung Fang (China) (volleyball) . . . 1·75 1·75
2921 $2 Steffi Graf (West Germany) (tennis) . . . . 1·75 1·75
MS2922 Two sheets, each 72 × 102 mm. (a) $6 Wilma Rudolph (U.S.A.) (athletics). (b) $6 Soling class yacht Set of 2 sheets . . . . 7·00 8·00

No. **MS**2922b is inscribed "Sailing" in error.

See also Nos. 3102/24.

1995. Anniversaries and Events. Multicoloured.

2923 25c. Type **408** (centenary of first English cricket tour to the West Indies) . . . 1·25 50
2924 75c. Nutmeg (opening of Grenada Spice Factory) 90 75
2925 $1 Sendall Tunnel (centenary (1994)) . . . . 95 1·10
2926 $1 Caribbean Development Bank building (25th anniv) . . . . 95 1·10

409 Ajamu

410 Elvis Presley and Signature

1995. Local Entertainers. Multicoloured.

2927 35c. Type **409** 50 50
2928 35c. Mighty Sparrow . . . 50 50
2929 50c. Mighty Sparrow in evening dress 60 60
2930 75c. Ajamu (different) . . . 75 75

1995. Entertainment Legends. Multicoloured.

2931 75c. Type **410** 65 65
2932 75c. Marilyn Monroe . . . 65 65

411 Elvis Presley

1995. 60th Birth Anniv of Elvis Presley (singer). Multicoloured.

2933 $1 Type **411** 70 70
2934 $1 With beard 70 70
2935 $1 With long hair and microphone 70 70
2936 $1 Wearing white shirt . . . 70 70
2937 $1 Wearing pink shirt and purple jacket 70 70
2938 $1 With short hair and microphone 70 70
2939 $1 Wearing magenta shirt 70 70
2940 $1 Wearing orange shirt . . 70 70
2941 $1 Wearing purple shirt . . 70 70

412 Film Reel and Oscar Statuette

1995. Centenary of Cinema. Multicoloured.

2942 $1 Type **412** 90 85
2943 $1 "HOLLYWOOD" sign 90 85
2944 $1 Charlie Chaplin 90 85
2945 $1 Shirley Temple 90 85
2946 $1 Spencer Tracy and Katherine Hepburn . . . 90 85
2947 $1 Marilyn Monroe 90 85
2948 $1 John Wayne 90 85
2949 $1 Marlon Brando 90 85
2950 $1 Tom Cruise 90 85
MS2951 107 × 77 mm. $5 Orson Welles (horiz) . . . . 7·00 7·00

Nos. 2942/50 were printed together, se-tenant, forming a composite design.

413 "B1 Level Vista Dome" Electric Locomotive, Japan

1995. Trains of the World (1st series). Multicoloured.

2952 $1 Type **413** . . . . 1·00 90
2953 $1 Rolios Rail Class 25NC steam locomotive, South Africa . . . . 1·00 90
2954 $1 Class 460 electric locomotive, Switzerland 1·00 90
2955 $1 Central Railway diesel locomotive No. 605, Peru 1·00 90
2956 $1 X2000 tilt body train, Sweden . . . . 1·00 90
2957 $1 Via Rail Toronto to Vancouver observation car, Canada . . . . . . 1·00 90
2958 $1 Intercity 125 diesel locomotive, Great Britain 1·00 90

2959 $1 "The Flying Scotsman" steam locomotive, Great Britain . . . . 1·00 90
2960 $1 "Indian Pacific" diesel locomotive, Australia . . 1·00 90
2961 $1 ETR 450 electric train, Italy . . . . 1·00 90
2962 $1 Isparta to Bozanonu Line steam locomotive, Turkey 1·00 90
2963 $1 TGV train, France . . . 1·00 90
2964 $1 ICE train, Germany . . 1·00 90
2965 $1 Nishi Line electric locomotive, Japan . . . . 1·00 90
2966 $1 "Hikari" train, Japan . . 1·00 90
2967 $1 Central Pacific Jupiter steam locomotive, U.S.A. 1·00 90
2968 $1 Amtrak Type 900 electric locomotive, U.S.A. . . . 1·00 90
2969 $1 "Sir Nigel Gresley" steam locomotive, Great Britain . . . . 1·00 90
MS2970 Two sheets, each 106 × 76 mm. (a) $5 Diesel hydraulic train, Korea. (b) $6 Peking–Ulan Bator express, Mongolia Set of 2 sheets . . . 7·00 8·00

See also Nos. 3167/83.

414 Teresa Teng

1995. Teresa Teng (Chinese actress) Commem. Different portraits. Multicoloured unless otherwise indicated.

2971 35c. Type **414** 50 50
2972 35c. As a child (brown, ochre and yellow) 50 50
2973 35c. Wearing feather boa (black, grey and yellow) 50 50
2974 35c. With motor scooter . . 50 50
2975 35c. Holding microphone . . 50 50
2976 35c. In white sweater . . . 50 50
2977 35c. Playing flute 50 50
2978 35c. With hand to hair (black, grey and yellow) 50 50
2979 35c. Wearing gold decorated dress 50 50
2980 35c. With fan 50 50
2981 35c. As South-sea islander 50 50
2982 35c. With hands clasped . . 50 50
2983 35c. In kimono 50 50
2984 35c. Holding bow tie . . . 50 50
2985 35c. Wearing black blouse 50 50
2986 35c. Resting on chair arm 50 50
2987 75c. In army uniform . . . 65 65
2988 75c. In navy uniform . . . 65 65
2989 75c. In air force uniform . . 65 65
2990 75c. Singing with hand out stretched (black, grey and yellow) 65 65
2991 75c. Singing with flowers in hair 65 65
2992 75c. Singing in blue floral dress 65 65
2993 75c. With pink scarf 65 65
2994 75c. In fringed dress 65 65
2995 75c. In pale green sweater 65 65
2996 75c. With hands to face . . 65 65

Nos. 2987/96 are larger, 34 × 46 mm.

415 Mickey Mouse fighting Big Pete

1995. Mickey's Pirate Adventure. Walt Disney cartoon characters. Multicoloured.

2997 15c. Type **415** 30 20
2998 25c. Mickey with treasure chest 30 20
2999 35c. Minnie Mouse trying on plunder 30 20
3000 75c. Goofy with telescope and Mickey swimming with barrel 55 40
3001 $3 Big Pete . . . . 2·00 2·25
3002 $5 Mickey with monkey, seagull and handkerchief 2·50 3·00
MS3003 Two sheets, each 108 × 103 mm. (a) $6 Sea rat pirate. (b) $6 Minnie being thrown overboard by pirates Set of 2 sheets . . . . 8·00 8·50

416 Albert Michelson (1907 Physics)

1995. Centenary of Nobel Trust Fund. Multicoloured.

3004 $1 Type **416** 95 85
3005 $1 Ralph Bunche (1950 Peace) 95 85
3006 $1 Edwin Neher (1991 Medicine) 95 85
3007 $1 Klaus Vonklitzing (1985 Physics) 95 85
3008 $1 Johann Deisenhofer (1988 Chemistry) 95 85
3009 $1 Max Delbruck (1969 Medicine) 95 85
3010 $1 J. Georg Bednorz (1987 Physics) 95 85
3011 $1 Feodor Lynen (1964 Medicine) 95 85
3012 $1 Walther Bothe (1954 Physics) 95 85
3013 $1 James Franck (1925 Physics) 95 85
3014 $1 Gustav Hertz (1925 Physics) 95 85
3015 $1 Friedrich Bergius (1931 Chemistry) 95 85
3016 $1 Otto Loewi (1936 Medicine) 95 85
3017 $1 Fritz Lipmann (1953 Medicine) 95 85
3018 $1 Otto Meyerhof (1922 Medicine) 95 85
3019 $1 Paul Heyse (1910 Literature) 95 85
3020 $1 Jane Addams (1931 Peace) 95 85
3021 $1 Carl Braun (1909 Physics) 95 85
3022 $1 Hans Dehmelt (1989 Physics) 95 85
3023 $1 Heinrich Boll (1972 Literature) 95 85
3024 $1 Georges Kohler (1984 Medicine) 95 85
3025 $1 Wolfgang Pauli (1945 Physics) 95 85
3026 $1 Sir Bernard Katz (1970 Medicine) 95 85
3027 $1 Ernest Ruska (1986 Physics) 95 85
3028 $1 William Golding (1983 Literature) 95 85
3029 $1 Hartmut Michel (1988 Chemistry) 95 85
3030 $1 Hans Bethe (1967 Physics) 95 85
MS3031 Three sheets, each 105 × 76 mm. (a) $6 Theodore Roosevelt (1906 Peace). (b) $6 Woodrow Wilson (1919 Peace). (c) $6 Sir Winston Churchill (1953 Literature) Set of 3 sheets . . . 11·00 12·00

Nos. 3004/12, 3013/21 and 3022/30 respectively were printed together, se-tenant, forming composite designs.

No. 3015 is inscribed "Freidrich" in error.

1995. Christmas. Religious Paintings. As T **245a** of Gambia. Multicoloured.

3032 15c. "The Madonna" (Bartolommeo Montagna) 20 10
3033 25c. "Sacred Conversation Piece" (Bonifacio dei Pitati) 20 10
3034 35c. "Nativity" (Van Loo) 25 10
3035 75c. "Madonna of the Fountain" (Van Eyck) . . 45 40
3036 $2 "The Apparition of the Virgin to St. Philip Neri" (Giovanni Tiepolo) . . . 1·25 1·50
3037 $5 "The Holy Family" (Ribera) . . . . 2·50 3·50
MS3038 Two sheets. (a) 127 × 101 mm. $6 "Madonna and Child" (detail) (Van Dyck). (b) 101 × 127 mm. $6 "The Vision of St. Anthony" (detail) (Van Dyck) Set of 2 sheets . . . . 7·50 8·50

417 Pres. Ronald Reagan at Fort George

1995. 12th Anniv of Liberation of Grenada (1st issue). Multicoloured.

3039 75c. Type **417** 60 70
3040 75c. Pres. Reagan with U.S. and Grenadian flags . . . 60 70
3041 75c. St. George's 60 70
MS3042 Two sheets, each 70 × 100 mm. (a) $5 Pres. Reagan and beach. (b) $6 Pres. Reagan and waterfall Set of 2 sheets . . 6·00 7·00

Nos. 3039/41 were printed together, se-tenant, forming a composite design.

See also Nos. 3043/51.

418 Pres. Ronald Reagan

419 Pope John Paul II and Statue of Liberty

1995. 12th Anniv of Liberation of Grenada (2nd issue). Designs showing Pres. Ronald Reagan. Multicoloured.

3043 $1 With wife 95 85
3044 $1 Type **418** 95 85
3045 $1 With microphones . . . 95 85
3046 $1 Wearing stetson 95 85
3047 $1 In front of U.S. flag . . 95 85
3048 $1 In front of Brandenburg Gate, Berlin 95 85
3049 $1 Saluting by helicopter . . 95 85
3050 $1 On horseback 95 85
3051 $1 Addressing troops . . . 95 85

1995. Papal Visit to New York. Multicoloured.

3052 $1 Type **419** 80 80
3053 $1 Pope John Paul II and cathedral 80 80
MS3054 105 × 76 mm. $6 Pope John Paul II . . . . 3·50 3·75

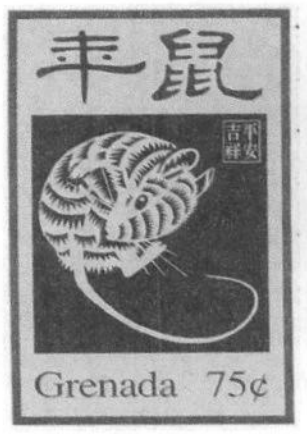

420 Rat asleep

421 "Young Woman" (Durer)

1996. Chinese New Year ("Year of the Rat").

3055 **420** 75c. buff, green and brown 60 60
3056 – 75c. orange, red and violet 60 60
3057 – 75c. buff, red and green 60 60
MS3058 95 × 58 mm. Nos. 3055/7 1·50 1·75
MS3059 76 × 106 mm. $1 multicoloured 75 85

DESIGNS—VERT: No. 3056, Rat eating; 3057, Rat asleep (T **420** reversed). HORIZ: No. **MS**3059, Two rats.

1996. Famous Drawings and Paintings by Durer and Rubens. Multicoloured.

3060 15c. Type **421** 40 20
3061 25c. "Four Horsemen of the Apocalypse" (Durer) . . 45 20
3062 35c. "Assumption and Coronation of the Virgin" (Durer) 50 20
3063 75c. "Mulay Ahmed" (Rubens) 80 50
3064 $1 "Anthony van Dyck aged 15" (Rubens) 90 60
3065 $2 "Head of a Young Monk" (Rubens) . . . . 1·75 1·75
3066 $3 "A Scholar inspired by Nature" (Rubens) . . . . 2·00 2·25
3067 $5 "Hanns Durer" (Durer) 3·00 3·50
MS3068 Two sheets, each 102 × 127 mm. (a) $5 "Martyrdom of St. Ursula" (detail) (Rubens). (b) $6 "The Death of the Virgin" (detail) (Durer) Set of 2 sheets 10·00 10·00

422 Goofy Tap-dancing

1996. Famous Dances. Walt Disney cartoon characters Dancing. Multicoloured.

3069 35c. Type **422** 70 20
3070 45c. Donald Duck doing Mexican hat dance (horiz) 80 25
3071 75c. Daisy Duck as hula dancer . . . . 1·25 55
3072 90c. Mickey and Minnie Mouse doing the tango (horiz) . . . . 1·25 70
3073 $1 Donald and Daisy doing the jitterbug . . . . . . 1·40 85
3074 $2 Mickey and Minnie performing Ukrainian folk dance (horiz) . . . . . . 2·25 2·50
3075 $3 Goofy and Pluto as ballet dancers (horiz) . . 2·50 2·75
3076 $4 Mickey and Minnie line-dancing . . . . 2·50 2·75
MS3077 Two sheets, each 133 × 109 mm. (a) $5 Minnie doing the can-can (horiz). (b) $6 Scrooge McDuck doing the Scottish sword dance Set of 2 sheets . . . . . 6·50 7·50

1996. 70th Birthday of Queen Elizabeth II. As T **255a** of Gambia showing different photographs. Multicoloured.

3078 35c. As Type **255a** of Gambia 50 25
3079 75c. Wearing white hat . . 85 55
3080 $4 With bouquet . . . . . 3·00 3·50
MS3081 103 × 125 mm. $6 Queen and Prince Philip . . . . . . 5·00 5·50

423 Ferrari "125 F1"

1996. Ferrari Racing Cars. Multicoloured.

3082 $1.50 Type **423** . . . . . . 1·25 1·25
3083 $1.50 "Tipo 625" . . . . . 1·25 1·25
3084 $1.50 "P4" . . . . 1·25 1·25
3085 $1.50 "312P" . . . . 1·25 1·25
3086 $1.50 "312" Formula 1 . . 1·25 1·25
3087 $1.50 "312B" . . . . 1·25 1·25
MS3088 100 × 71 mm. $6 "F333 SP" (84 × 28 mm) . . . . 4·00 4·00

1996. 50th Anniv of U.N.I.C.E.F. As T **258a** of Gambia. Multicoloured.

3089 35c. Child writing in book (horiz) 20 25
3090 $2 Child planting seedling (horiz) . . . . 1·00 1·25
3091 $3 Children and U.N.I.C.E.F. emblem (horiz) . . . . 1·50 2·00
MS3092 75 × 106 mm. $5 Young boy 2·50 3·00

424 Lions' Gate, Jerusalem

1996. 3000th Anniv of Jerusalem. Multicoloured.

3093 75c. Type **424** 60 45
3094 $2 New Gate . . . . 1·40 1·40
3095 $3 Dung Gate . . . . . . 1·75 2·00
MS3096 114 × 74 mm. $5 The Old City (horiz) . . . . 3·25 3·25

1996. Centenary of Radio. Entertainers. As T **259a** of Gambia. Multicoloured.

3097 35c. Jack Benny 35 25
3098 75c. Gertrude Berg 55 45
3099 $1 Eddie Cantor 65 60
3100 $2 Groucho Marx . . . . . 1·25 1·50
MS3101 70 × 100 mm. $6 George Burns and Gracie Allen (horiz) 3·75 3·75

425 Olympic Stadium, Athens, 1896

1996. Olympic Games, Atlanta (2nd issue). Previous Medal Winners. Multicoloured.

3102 35c. Gold medal of 1896 (vert) 40 25
3103 75c. Type **425** 65 45
3104 $1 Boughera el Quafi (France) (Gold, 1928) . . 70 70
3105 $1 Gustav Jansson (Sweden) (Bronze, 1952) 70 70
3106 $1 Spiridon Louis (Greece) (Gold, 1896) 70 70
3107 $1 Basil Heatley (Great Britain) (Silver, 1964) . . 70 70
3108 $1 Emil Zatopek (Czechoslovakia) (Gold, 1952) 70 70
3109 $1 Frank Shorter (U.S.A.) (Gold, 1972) 70 70
3110 $1 Alain Minoun O'Kacha (France) (Gold, 1956) . . 70 70

3111 $1 Kokichi Tsu Uraya (Japan) (Bronze, 1964) . . 70 70
3112 $1 Delfo Cabrera (Argentina) (Gold, 1948) 70 70
3113 $1 Harald Sakata (U.S.A.) (Silver—light heavyweight, 1948) 70 70
3114 $1 Tom Kono (U.S.A.) (Gold—middleweight, 1952 and 1956) 70 70
3115 $1 Naim Suleymanoglu (Turkey) (Gold—featherweight, 1988) . . . 70 70
3116 $1 Lee Hyung Kun (South Korea) (Gold—light heavyweight, 1988) . . . 70 70
3117 $1 Vassily Alexeyev (U.S.S.R.) (Gold—super heavyweight, 1972 and 1976) 70 70
3118 $1 Chen Weiqiang (China) (Gold—featherweight, 1984) 70 70
3119 $1 Ye Huanming (China) (Gold—featherweight, 1988) 70 70
3120 $1 Manfred Nerlinger (Germany) (Silver—super heavyweight, 1988) . . . 70 70
3121 $1 Joseph Depietro (U.S.A.) (Gold—bantamweight, 1948) 70 70
3122 $2 Ancient Greek runners 1·50 1·60
3123 $3 Spiridon Louis (Greece) (Gold—marathon, 1896) 2·00 2·25
MS3124 Two sheets, each 75 × 105 mm. (a) $5 Manfred Nerlinger (Germany) (Silver – super heavyweight weightlifting, 1988) (vert). (b) $6 Thomas Hicks (U.S.A.) (Gold – marathon, 1904) (vert) Set of 2 sheets . . . . . 7·00 8·00

Nos. 3104/12 (marathon runners) and 3113/21 (weightlifters) respectively were printed together, se-tenant, with the backgrounds forming composite designs.

426 Mercedes-Benz, 1929

1996. Classic Cars. Multicoloured.
3125 35c. Type **426** 35 25
3126 50c. Bugatti Type 35, 1927 45 30
3127 75c. J. Dusenberg, 1935 . . 65 45
3128 $1 Mercer, 1914 . . . . . 70 70
3129 $1 Type 57C Atalante, 1939 70 70
3130 $1 Cannstatt-Daimler, 1900 70 70
3131 $1 Delage, 1925 . . . . . 70 70
3132 $1 Coventry Daimler, 1899 70 70
3133 $1 Vauxhall, 1900 . . . . . 70 70
3134 $1 T-15 Hispano-Suza, 1912 70 70
3135 $2 Alfa Romeo, 1929 . . . 1·50 1·60
3136 $3 Rolls Royce, 1910 . . . 1·90 2·25
MS3137 Two sheets, each 66 × 96 mm. (a) $6 L-Head Mercer, 1915 (56 × 42 mm). (b) $6 Mercedes, 1937 (56 × 42 mm) Set of 2 sheets . . . . 8·00 9·00

427 "Gorch Fock" (cadet barque), Germany, 1916

1996. Ships. Multicoloured.
3138 $1 Type **427** 75 75
3139 $1 "Henry B. Hyde", U.S.A., 1886 . . . . . 75 75
3140 $1 "Resolution" (galleon), Great Britain, 1652 . . . 75 75
3141 $1 U.S.S. "Constitution" (frigate), U.S.A., 1797 . . 75 75
3142 $1 "Nippon Maru" (cadet ship), Japan, 1930 . . . . 75 75
3143 $1 "Preussen" (full-rigged sailing ship), Germany, 1902 . . . . 75 75
3144 $1 "Taeping" (clipper), Great Britain, 1852 . . . 75 75
3145 $1 "Chariot of Fame" (clipper), U.S.A., 1853 . . 75 75
3146 $1 "Star of India" (clipper), U.S.A., 1861 . . . . . 75 75
3147 $1 H.M.S. "Bounty" . . . 75 75
3148 $1 "Bismark" (German battleship) 75 75
3149 $1 "Chuii Apoo" and two junks 75 75
3150 $1 "Lubeck" (German frigate) 75 75
3151 $1 Dutch galleon 75 75
3152 $1 "Augsburg" (German frigate) 75 75
3153 $1 "Henri Grace a Dieu" (British galleon) 75 75
3154 $1 H.M.S. "Prince of Wales" (battleship) . . . 75 75
3155 $1 "Santa Anna" (Spanish carrack) 75 75
MS3156 Two sheets, each 104 × 74 mm. (a) $5 H.M.S. "Victory" (ship of the line), Great Britain, 1805. (b) $6 "Cutty Sark" (clipper), Great Britain, 1869 Set of 2 sheets . . . . 7·50 8·00

No. 3151 is inscribed "BARBARY CORSAIR" and No. 3153 is stated to be French, both in error.

428 Jacqueline Kennedy

1996. Jacqueline Kennedy Onassis Commemoration. Multicoloured.
3157 $1 Type **428** 70 70
3158 $1 Wearing mauve blouse 70 70
3159 $1 In evening dress (inscr at right) 70 70
3160 $1 In evening dress (inscr at left) 70 70
3161 $1 Wearing pink dress . . . 70 70
3162 $1 Wearing blue dress with collar embroidered . . . 70 70
3163 $1 Wearing white jacket and brooch 70 70
3164 $1 In yellow jacket and green shirt 70 70
3165 $1 Wearing black jacket . . 70 70
MS3166 76 × 106 mm. $6 Jacqueline Kennedy Onassis (different) . . 3·50 4·25

429 Class C51 Locomotive of Imperial Train, Japan

1996. Trains of the World (2nd series). Multicoloured.
3167 35c. Type **429** 50 25
3168 75c. "Rheingold" express, Germany 75 45
3169 $1 Atlantic Coast Line locomotive No. 153, 1894, U.S.A. 75 75
3170 $1 Smith Compound No. 1619, Great Britain 75 75
3171 $1 Trans-Siberian Soviet Railways 75 75
3172 $1 Palatinate Railway Krauss locomotive, 1898, Germany 75 75
3173 $1 Paris, Lyons and Mediterranean line, France 75 75
3174 $1 Diesel-electric 0341 locomotive, Italy 75 75
3175 $1 Class C62 locomotive, Japan 75 75
3176 $1 Shantung Railways locomotive, China 75 75
3177 $1 Class C57 locomotive, Japan 75 75
3178 $1 Diesel express train, Japan 75 75
3179 $1 Shanghai–Nanking Railway locomotive, China 75 75
3180 $1 Class D51 locomotive, Japan 75 75
3181 $2 "Pioneer", 1851, U.S.A. 1·50 1·60
3182 $3 "France", France . . . . 1·90 2·25
MS3183 Two sheets, each 105 × 73 mm. (a) $5 Baden State Railways locomotive, Germany. (b) $6 Class C11 locomotive, Japan Set of 2 sheets . . . . . 8·00 9·00

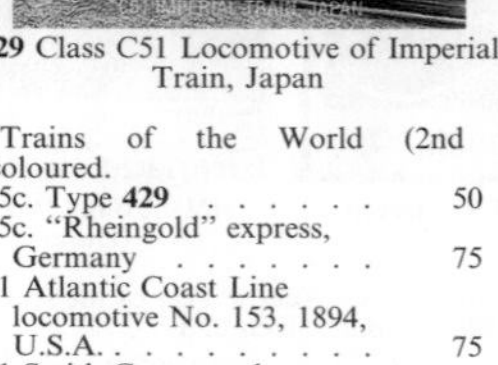

430 Winter Jasmine

1996. Flowers. Multicoloured.
3184 $1 Type **430** 70 70
3185 $1 Chrysanthemum 70 70
3186 $1 Lilac 70 70
3187 $1 Japanese iris 70 70
3188 $1 Hibiscus 70 70
3189 $1 Sacred lotus 70 70
3190 $1 Apple blossom 70 70
3191 $1 Gladiolus 70 70
3192 $1 Japanese quince 70 70
3193 $1 Canterbury bell (vert) . . 70 70
3194 $1 Rose (vert) 70 70
3195 $1 Nasturtium (vert) 70 70
3196 $1 Daffodil (vert) 70 70
3197 $1 Tulip (vert) 70 70
3198 $1 Snapdragon (vert) . . . 70 70
3199 $1 Zinnia (vert) 70 70
3200 $1 Sweetpea (vert) 70 70
3201 $1 Pansy (vert) 70 70
MS3202 Two sheets. (a) 104 × 74 mm. $5 Aster. (b) 74 × 104 mm. $6 Peony (vert) Set of 2 sheets . . . . 8·00 9·00

Nos. 3184/92 and 3193/3201 respectively were printed together, se-tenant, with the backgrounds forming a composite design.

431 Zeppelin L-31 (Germany)

1996. Airships. Multicoloured.
3203 30c. Type **431** 40 40
3204 30c. Zeppelin L-35 (Germany) 40 40
3205 50c. Zeppelin L-30 (Germany) 55 45
3206 75c. Zeppelin L-2 10 (Germany) 75 55
3207 $1.50 Zeppelin L-21 (Germany) . . . . 1·25 1·40
3208 $1.50 Zodiac Type 13 Spiess (France) . . . . 1·25 1·40
3209 $1.50 N1 "Norge" (Roald Amundsen) . . . . 1·25 1·40
3210 $1.50 LZ-127 "Graf Zeppelin" (Germany) . . 1·25 1·40
3211 $1.50 LZ-129 "Hindenburg" (Germany) . . . . 1·25 1·40
3212 $1.50 Zeppelin NT (Germany) . . . . 1·25 1·40
3213 $3 Zeppelin L-3 (Germany) 2·00 2·25
3214 $3 Beardmore No. 24 (Great Britain) . . . . 2·00 2·25
MS3215 Two sheets, each 104 × 74 mm. (a) $6 Zeppelin ZT (Germany). (b) $6 Zeppelin L-13 (Germany) Set of 2 sheets . . . 8·00 8·00

432 Horned Guan

1996. West Indian Birds. Multicoloured.
3216 $1.50 Type **432** . . . . . 1·40 1·40
3217 $1.50 St. Lucia amazon ("St. Lucia Parrot") . . . 1·40 1·40
3218 $1.50 Highland guan ("Black Penelopina") . . 1·40 1·40
3219 $1.50 Grenada dove . . . . 1·40 1·40
3220 $1.50 St. Vincent amazon ("St. Vincent Parrot") . . 1·40 1·40
3221 $1.50 White-breasted trembler . . . . 1·40 1·40
MS3222 Two sheets, each 100 × 70 mm. (a) $5 Semper's warbler. (b) $6 Yellow warbler ("Barbados Yellow Warbler") Set of 2 sheets . . . . 8·00 9·00

The inscriptions on Nos. **MS**3222a and **MS**3222b are transposed in error.

Nos. 3216/21 were printed together, se-tenant, with the backgrounds forming a composite design.

433 Blue Whale

1996. Whales and Turtles. Multicoloured.
3223 $1.50 Type **433** . . . . . 1·40 1·40
3224 $1.50 Humpback whale . . 1·40 1·40
3225 $1.50 Right whale . . . . . 1·40 1·40
3226 $1.50 Hawksbill turtle . . . 1·40 1·40
3227 $1.50 Leatherback turtle . . 1·40 1·40
3228 $1.50 Green turtle . . . . . 1·40 1·40

434 Killer Whale

1996. Marine Life. Multicoloured.
3229 $1 Type **434** 75 75
3230 $1 Dolphin 75 75
3231 $1 Two dolphins 75 75
3232 $1 Sea lion and regal angelfish 75 75
3233 $1 Dolphins and hawksbill turtle 75 75
3234 $1 Three hawksbill turtles 75 75
3235 $1 Regal angelfish and pennant coralfish 75 75
3236 $1 Pennant coralfish 75 75
3237 $1 Sea lion and squirrelfish 75 75
3238 $1 Brown pelican 75 75
3239 $1 Killer whale (different) 75 75
3240 $1 Whale 75 75
3241 $1 Dolphins and sea lion . . 75 75
3242 $1 Shortfin pilot whale, blue-ringed octopus and sea lion 75 75
3243 $1 Hammerhead sharks and sea lion 75 75
3244 $1 Blue-striped grunts . . . 75 75
3245 $1 Stingray and Van Gogh fusilier 75 75
3246 $1 Van Gogh fusilier, ribbon moray and percoid fish 75 75
MS3247 Two sheets, each 106 × 76 mm. (a) $6 Pair of sea lions (horiz). (b) $6 Pair of dolphins (horiz) Set of 2 sheets 8·00 9·00

Nos. 3229/37 and 3238/46 respectively were printed together, se-tenant, with the backgrounds forming a composite design.

1996. Christmas. Religious Paintings. As T **245a** of Gambia. Multicoloured.
3248 25c. "The Visitation" (Tintoretto) 40 20
3249 35c. "Virgin with the Child" (Palma Vecchio) 45 25
3250 50c. "The Adoration of the Magi" (Botticelli) 55 30
3251 75c. "The Annunciation" (Titian) 75 45
3252 $1 "The Flight into Egypt" (Tintoretto) 90 65
3253 $3 "The Holy Family with the Infant Saint John" (Andrea del Sarto) . . . 2·00 2·50
MS3254 Two sheets, each 106 × 76 mm. (a) $6 "Adoration of the Magi" (Paolo Schiavo). (b) $6 "Madonna and Child with Saints" (Vincenzo Ponna) Set of 2 sheets 8·00 8·50

No. 3250 is inscr "Botticceli" in error.

1996. 20th Anniv of Rocky (film). Sheet 143 × 182 mm, containing vert design as T **266** of Gambia. Multicoloured.
MS3255 $2 × 3, Sylvester Stallone in "Rocky V" . . . . 3·50 4·00

435 Ox

1997. Chinese New Year ("Year of the Ox"). Sheet 150 × 75 mm, containing T **435** and similar triangular designs. Multicoloured. Self-adhesive on silver foil.
MS3256 $2 Type **435** ("GRENADA" in black); $2 Ox ("GRENADA" in pink); $2 Ox ("GRENADA" in blue) . . . 4·00 4·00

436 Mickey at Tram Stop

1997. "HONG KONG '97" International Stamp Exhibition. Mickey in Hong Kong. Disney cartoon characters. Multicoloured.
3257 35c. Type **436** 80 90
3258 50c. Mickey and Donald fishing at Victoria Harbour 80 90
3259 75c. Donald and Mickey parachuting . . . . . . 1·00 1·10
3260 90c. Mickey and Minnie visiting Bank of China . . 1·00 1·10
3261 $1 Mickey with pet parrot 1·10 1·25
3262 $1 Mickey drinking Kung-fu Tea . . . . 1·10 1·25
3263 $1 Mickey, Minnie and Goofy shopping at Chinese Wet Market . . . 1·10 1·25
3264 $1 Mickey, Minnie and Goofy with grasshoppers 1·10 1·25

3265 $1 Mickey and Goofy with lanterns . . . . 1·10 1·25
3266 $1 Mickey and Minnie practising Tai-chi . . . . 1·10 1·25
3267 $2 Goofy delivering bottled gas . . . . 1·25 1·40
3268 $3 Mickey, Minnie and Donald at "Jumbo" floating restaurant . . . . 1·40 1·50
MS3269 Four sheets, each 132 × 108 mm. (a) $3 Mickey and skyscrapers (vert). (b) $4 Mickey and Minnie dancing (vert). (c) $5 Mickey pulling rickshaw (vert). (d) $6 Mickey with noodles (vert) Set of 4 sheets . . . . 13·00 14·00

1997. 50th Anniv of U.N.E.S.C.O. As T **273a** of Gambia. Multicoloured.
3270 35c. Temple, Kyoto, Japan 40 25
3271 75c. Timbered houses, Quedlinburg, Germany . . 60 45
3272 90c. View from walls, Dubrovnik, Croatia . . . 70 55
3273 $1 Ruins at Delphi, Greece 75 75
3274 $1 Bryggen Wharf, Bergen, Norway (vert) 75 75
3275 $1 Old city, Berne, Switzerland (vert) 75 75
3276 $1 Warsaw, Poland (vert) 75 75
3277 $1 Fortress walls, Luxembourg (vert) . . . 75 75
3278 $1 Interior of Drottningholm Palace, Sweden (vert) 75 75
3279 $1 Petajavesi Church, Finland (vert) 75 75
3280 $1 Vilnius, Lithuania (vert) 75 75
3281 $1 Jelling Church, Denmark (vert) 75 75
3282 $1 Entrance to caves, Desert of Taklamakan, China (vert) 75 75
3283 $1 House, Desert of Taklamakan, China (vert) 75 75
3284 $1 Monument, Desert of Taklamakan, China (vert) 75 75
3285 $1 Palace of Cielos Purpuras, Wudang, China (vert) 75 75
3286 $1 House, Wudang, China (vert) 75 75
3287 $1 Stone Guardian, The Great Wall, China (vert) 75 75
3288 $1 Ming Dynasty statue, Wudang, China (vert) . . 75 75
3289 $1 The Great Wall, China (vert) 75 75
3290 $1.50 Segovia Cathedral, Spain . . . . 1·10 1·25
3291 $1.50 Wurtzburg, Germany 1·10 1·25
3292 $1.50 Plitvice Lakes, Croatia 1·10 1·25
3293 $1.50 Batalha Monastery, Portugal . . . . 1·10 1·25
3294 $1.50 River Seine, Paris, France . . . . 1·10 1·25
3295 $2 Tomar, Portugal . . . . 1·40 1·60
3296 $3 Palace of Chaillot, Paris, France . . . . 1·90 2·25
MS3297 Three sheets, each 127 × 102 mm. (a) $6 Popocatepetl Monastery, Mexico. (b) $6 Woodland path, Shirakami-Sanchi, Japan. (c) $6 Interior of the Hieronymites' Monastery, Portugal Set of 3 sheets . . . 12·00 14·00

437 Devon Rex

1997. Cats and Dogs. Multicoloured.
3298 35c. Type **437** 50 25
3299 75c. King Charles spaniel 70 45
3300 90c. Japanese bobtail . . . 75 50
3301 $1 Afghan hound 75 75
3302 $1 Turkish van 75 75
3303 $1 Ragdoll 75 75
3304 $1 Siberian 75 75
3305 $1 Egyptian mau 75 75
3306 $1 American shorthair . . . 75 75
3307 $1 Benegal 75 75
3308 $1 Asian longhair 75 75
3309 $1 Somali 75 75
3310 $1 Turkish angora 75 75
3311 $1 Lhasa apso 75 75
3312 $1 Rough collie 75 75
3313 $1 Norwich terrier 75 75
3314 $1 American cocker spaniel 75 75
3315 $1 Chinese crested dog . . . 75 75
3316 $1 Old English sheepdog . . 75 75
3317 $1 Standard poodle 75 75
3318 $1 German shepherd 75 75
3319 $1 German shorthair pointer 75 75
3320 $2 Cornish rex . . . . . . 1·40 1·60
3321 $3 Pekingese . . . . 1·90 2·25
MS3322 Two sheets, each 106 × 76 mm. (a) $6 Singapura. (b) $6 Bernese mountain dog Set of 2 sheets . . . . 8·50 9·00

438 Dunkleosteus

1997. Dinosaurs. Multicoloured.
3323 35c. Type **438** 60 30
3324 75c. Tyrannosaurus rex . . 1·00 55
3325 $1.50 Sordes . . . . 1·25 1·40
3326 $1.50 Dimorphodon . . . . 1·25 1·40
3327 $1.50 Diplodocus . . . . . 1·25 1·40
3328 $1.50 Allosaurus . . . . . 1·25 1·40
3329 $1.50 Pentaceratops . . . . 1·25 1·40
3330 $1.50 Protoceratops . . . . 1·25 1·40
3331 $2 Askeptosaurus (vert) . . 1·40 1·60
3332 $3 Triceratops (vert) . . . . 1·90 2·25
MS3333 Two sheets, each 103 × 74 mm. (a) $6 Tristychius (vert). (b) $6 Maiasaura (vert) Set of 2 sheets . . . . 9·00 9·50
Nos. 3325/30 were printed together, se-tenant, with the backgrounds forming a composite design.

439 Porcelain Crab

1997. Marine Life. Multicoloured.
3334 45c. Type **439** 45 30
3335 75c. Humpback whale . . . 90 45
3336 90c. Hermit crab 75 50
3337 $1 Great white shark . . . 1·00 70
3338 $1.50 Octopus (vert) . . . . 1·25 1·40
3339 $1.50 Lei triggerfish (vert) 1·25 1·40
3340 $1.50 Lionfish (vert) . . . . 1·25 1·40
3341 $1.50 Harlequin wrasse (vert) . . . . 1·25 1·40
3342 $1.50 Clown fish (vert) . . . 1·25 1·40
3343 $1.50 Moray eel (vert) . . . 1·25 1·40
3344 $3 Green sea turtle . . . . 1·90 2·25
3345 $4 Whale shark . . . . . . 2·50 2·75
MS3346 Two sheets, each 106 × 76 mm. (a) $6 Pacific barracudas. (b) $6 Scalloped hammerhead shark Set of 2 sheets 8·50 9·00
Nos. 3338/43 were printed together, se-tenant, with the backgrounds forming a composite design.

1997. 300th Anniv of Mother Goose Nursery Rhymes. Sheet 72 × 102 mm, containing multicoloured design as T **276a** of Gambia.
MS3347 $5 Boy holding umbrella ("Rain") (vert) . . . . 3·50 4·00

1997. 10th Anniv of Chernobyl Nuclear Disaster. As T **276a** of Gambia. Multicoloured.
3348 $2 As Type **276b** of Gambia 1·40 1·60
3349 $2 As No. 3348, but inscribed "CHABAD'S CHILDREN OF CHERNOBYL" at foot 1·40 1·60

1997. 50th Death Anniv of Paul Harris (founder of Rotary International). As T **276c** of Gambia. Multicoloured.
3350 $3 Paul Harris and vocational training programme, Philippines 1·75 2·00
MS3351 78 × 107 mm. $6 Hands holding globe and doves . . . 3·25 3·75

1997. Golden Wedding of Queen Elizabeth and Prince Philip. As T **276d** of Gambia. Multicoloured.
3352 $1 Queen Elizabeth and Prince Philip waving . . . 75 75
3353 $1 Royal coat of arms . . . 75 75
3354 $1 Queen Elizabeth with Prince Philip in naval uniform 75 75
3355 $1 Queen Elizabeth and Prince Philip at Buckingham Palace . . . 75 75
3356 $1 Windsor Castle 75 75
3357 $1 Prince Philip 75 75
MS3358 100 × 70 mm. $6 Queen Elizabeth with Prince Philip in naval uniform (different) . . . 4·25 4·50

1997. "Pacific '97" International Stamp Exhibition, San Francisco (1st issue). Death Centenary of Heinrich von Stephan (founder of the U.P.U.). As T **276e** of Gambia.
3359 $2 green and black . . . . 1·25 1·40
3360 $2 brown . . . . 1·25 1·40
3361 $2 blue . . . . 1·25 1·40
MS3362 82 × 119 mm. $6 violet and black . . . . 3·50 4·25
DESIGNS: No. 3359, Postman on motorcycle; 3360, Von Stephan and Mercury; 3361, Postman on skis, Rocky Mountains, 1900s; **MS**3362, Von Stephan and Chinese letter carrier.
See also Nos. 3392/3409.

1997. Birth Bicentenary of Hiroshige (Japanese painter). As T **541a** of Ghana. Multicoloured.
3363 $1.50 "Nihon Embankment, Yoshiwara" . . . . . . 1·25 1·25
3364 $1.50 "Asakusa Ricefields and Torinomachi Festival" . . . . 1·25 1·25
3365 $1.50 "Senju Great Bridge" 1·25 1·25
3366 $1.50 "Dawn inside the Yoshiwara" . . . . . . 1·25 1·25
3367 $1.50 "Tile Kilns and Hasiba Ferry, Sumida River" . . . . 1·25 1·25
3368 $1.50 "View from Massaki of Suijin Shrine, Uchigawa Inlet and Sekiya" . . . . 1·25 1·25
MS3369 Two sheets, each 102 × 127 mm. (a) $6 "Kinryuzan Temple, Asakusa". (b) $6 "Night view of Saruwaka-machi" Set of 2 sheets . . . . 8·50 9·00

1997. 175th Anniv of Brothers Grimm's Third Collection of Fairy Tales. Snow White. As T **277a** of Gambia. Multicoloured.
3370 $2 Queen looking in mirror 1·50 1·50
3371 $2 Snow White and the Seven Dwarfs . . . . . . 1·50 1·50
3372 $2 Snow White and Prince 1·50 1·50
MS3373 124 × 96 mm. $6 Witch with apple . . . . 4·00 4·25

440 One-man Luge

1997. Winter Olympic Games, Nagano, Japan. Multicoloured.
3374 45c. Type **440** 45 30
3375 75c. Men's speed skating . . 65 45
3376 $1 One-man luge (different) 75 75
3377 $1 Ski jumping (blue ski suit) 75 75
3378 $1 Downhill skiing 75 75
3379 $1 Speed skating 75 75
3380 $1 Two-man bobsleigh . . . 75 75
3381 $1 Women's figure skating 75 75
3382 $1 Alpine combined 75 75
3383 $1 Ice hockey 75 75
3384 $1 Ski jumping (yellow ski suit) 75 75
3385 $2 Men's figure skating . . 1·40 1·60
3386 $3 Slalom . . . . 1·90 2·25
MS3387 Two sheets, each 96 × 69 mm. (a) $6 Four-man bobsleigh. (b) $6 Downhill skiing (vert) Set of 2 sheets . . . . . 8·50 9·00

441 Bank of China

1997. Return of Hong Kong to China. Multicoloured.
3388 90c. Type **441** 65 50
3389 $1 Skyscrapers 75 55
3390 $1.75 "Hong Kong '97" on modern buildings (63 × 32 mm) . . . . . . 1·40 1·60
3391 $2 Deng Xiaoping and Hong Kong (63 × 32 mm) 1·60 1·75

442 Minnie Mouse dancing the Hula

1997. "Pacific '97" International Stamp Exhibition, San Francisco (2nd issue). Centenary of the Cinema. Minnie Mouse in "Hawaiian Holiday". Multicoloured.
3392 50c. Type **442** (Frame 1) . . 60 60
3393 50c. Frame 2 . . . . 60 60
3394 50c. Frame 3 . . . . 60 60
3395 50c. Frame 4 . . . . 60 60
3396 50c. Frame 5 . . . . 60 60
3397 50c. Frame 6 . . . . 60 60
3398 50c. Frame 7 . . . . 60 60
3399 50c. Frame 8 . . . . 60 60
3400 50c. Frame 9 . . . . 60 60
3401 50c. Frame 10 . . . . . . 60 60
3402 50c. Frame 11 . . . . . . 60 60
3403 50c. Frame 12 . . . . . . 60 60
3404 50c. Frame 13 . . . . . . 60 60
3405 50c. Frame 14 . . . . . . 60 60
3406 50c. Frame 15 . . . . . . 60 60
3407 50c. Frame 16 . . . . . . 60 60
3408 50c. Frame 17 . . . . . . 60 60
MS3409 110 × 130 mm. $6 Frame 18 6·50 7·00

443 Hercules lifting Rock

1997. "Hercules" (cartoon film) (1st series). Multicoloured.
3410 $1 Type **443** 90 90
3411 $1 Pegasus 90 90
3412 $1 Megara 90 90
3413 $1 Philoktetes 90 90
3414 $1 Nessus 90 90
3415 $1 Hydra 90 90
3416 $1 Pain and Panic 90 90
3417 $1 Hades 90 90
MS3418 Two sheets. (a) 131 × 104 mm. $6 Hercules as a boy. (b) 104 × 131 mm. $6 The Muses Set of 2 sheets . . . . 9·00 10·00
See also Nos. 3561/85.

1997. World Cup Football Championship, France (1998). As T **283a** of Gambia. Multicoloured (except Nos. 3422/3 and 3428).
3419 15c. West German and Italian Players, 1982 (vert) 35 20
3420 75c. Italian player holding World Cup, 1982 (vert) 70 45
3421 90c. West German and Italian players wearing "20" shirts, 1982 (vert) . . 75 50
3422 $1 Uruguay team, 1950 (brown) 75 75
3423 $1 Brazilian team, 1958 (brown) 75 75
3424 $1 West German team, 1974 75 75
3425 $1 Argentine team, 1986 . . 75 75
3426 $1 Italian team, 1982 . . . 75 75
3427 $1 West German team, 1990 75 75
3428 $1 Italian team, 1934 (brown) 75 75
3429 $1 Brazilian team, 1970 . . 75 75
3430 $1 Seaman, England 75 75
3431 $1 Klinsmann, Germany . . 75 75
3432 $1 Berger, Czech Republic 75 75
3433 $1 McCoist, Scotland . . . 75 75
3434 $1 Gascoigne, England . . . 75 75
3435 $1 Djorkaeff, France . . . 75 75
3436 $1 Sammer, Germany . . . 75 75
3437 $1 Futre, Portugal 75 75
3438 $2 Italian player beating goal keeper, 1982 (vert) 1·40 1·60
3439 $3 Goal-mouth melee, 1982 (vert) . . . . 1·90 2·25
3440 $4 Two West German players tackling Italian player (vert) . . . . . . 2·50 2·75
MS3441 Two sheets. (a) 102 × 127 mm. $6 Beckenbaur holding World Cup, Germany (vert). (b) 127 × 102 mm. $6 Moore, England Set of 2 sheets 9·00 10·00

444 Peacock

1997. Butterflies and Moths. Multicoloured.
3442 45c. Type **444** 50 30
3443 75c. Orange flambeau . . . 70 45
3444 90c. Eastern tailed blue . . 75 50
3445 $1 Brimstone 75 75
3446 $1 Mocker swallowtail . . . 75 75
3447 $1 American painted lady 75 75
3448 $1 Tiger swallowtail 75 75
3449 $1 Long wing 75 75
3450 $1 Sunset moth 75 75
3451 $1 Australian Blue Mountain swallowtail . . 75 75
3452 $1 Bird wing 75 75
3453 $2 Black and red . . . . . 1·40 1·60
3454 $3 Large white . . . . . . 1·90 2·25
3455 $4 Oriental swallowtail . . . 2·50 2·75
MS3456 Two sheets, each 76 × 106 mm. (a) $5 Monarch. (b) $5 Blue morpho Set of 2 sheets 8·00 9·00

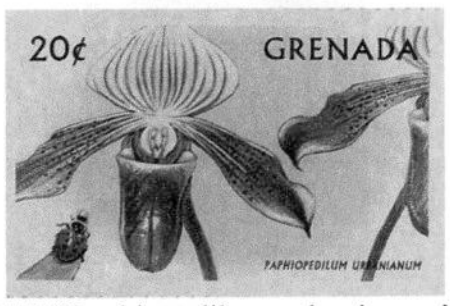

445 "Paphiopedilum urbanianum"

1997. Orchids of the World. Multicoloured.
3457 20c. Type **445** 45 20
3458 35c. "Trichoceros parviflorus" 60 25
3459 45c. "Euanthe sanderiana" (vert) 65 30
3460 75c. "Oncidium macranthum" (vert) . . . 75 45

3461 90c. "Psychopsis kramerianum" (vert) . . . 80 55
3462 $1 "Oncidium hastatum" (vert) . . . 85 60
3463 $2 "Broughtonia sanguinea" (vert) . . . 1·40 1·50
3464 $2 "Anguloa virginalis" (vert) . . . 1·40 1·50
3465 $2 "Dendrobium bigibbum" (vert) . . . 1·40 1·50
3466 $2 "Lucasiana" (vert) . . . 1·40 1·50
3467 $2 "Cymbidium" (vert) . . 1·40 1·50
3468 $2 "Cymbidium" and vase (vert) . . . 1·40 1·50
3469 $2 "Odontoglossum crispum" (vert) . . . 1·40 1·50
3470 $2 "Cattleya brabantiae" (vert) . . . 1·40 1·50
3471 $2 "Cattleya bicolor" (vert) 1·40 1·50
3472 $2 "Trichopilia suavia" (vert) . . . 1·40 1·50
3473 $2 "Encyclia mariae" (vert) 1·40 1·50
3474 $2 "Angraecum leonis" (vert) . . . 1·40 1·50
3475 $3 "Masdevallia saltatix" (vert) . . . 1·90 2·25
3476 $4 "Cattleya luteola" . . . 2·50 2·75
MS3477 Two sheets. (a) 76 × 106 mm. $6 "Laelia milleri". (b) 106 × 76 mm. $6 "Oncidium onustum" Set of 2 sheets . . . 9·00 10·00

Nos. 3463/8 and 3469/74 respectively were printed together, se-tenant, with the backgrounds forming composite designs.

446 "Boletus erythropus"

1997. Fungi of the World. Multicoloured.

3478 35c. Type **446** . . . 60 25
3479 75c. "Armillariella mellea" 70 45
3480 90c. "Amanita flavorubens" 80 50
3481 $1 Indigo milky . . . 85 55
3482 $1.50 "Agaricus solidipes" 1·25 1·40
3483 $1.50 Salmon waxy cap . . 1·25 1·40
3484 $1.50 Fused maramius . . . 1·25 1·40
3485 $1.50 Shellfish-scented russula . . . 1·25 1·40
3486 $1.50 Red-capped scaber stalk . . . 1·25 1·40
3487 $1.50 "Calocybe gambosum" . . . 1·25 1·40
3488 $1.50 "Boletus parasiticus" 1·25 1·40
3489 $1.50 "Frostis bolete" . . . 1·25 1·40
3490 $1.50 "Amanita myscara flavilolvata" . . . 1·25 1·40
3491 $1.50 "Volvariella volvacea" 1·25 1·40
3492 $1.50 Stuntz's blue legs . . 1·25 1·40
3493 $1.50 Orange-latex milky . . 1·25 1·40
3494 $2 "Tylopilus balloui" . . . 1·40 1·90
3495 $4 "Boletus parasiticus" . . . 2·50 2·75
MS3496 Two sheets, each 97 × 67 mm. (a) $6 "Agaricus argenteus". (b) $6 "Omphalotus illudens" Set of 2 sheets . . . 8·50 9·50

447 Princess Diana with Landmine Victims

1997. Diana, Princess of Wales Commemoration. Multicoloured.

3497 $1.50 Type **447** . . . 1·25 1·25
3498 $1.50 With sick child . . 1·25 1·25
3499 $1.50 With young boy on crutches . . . 1·25 1·25
3500 $1.50 With leper . . . 1·25 1·25
3501 $1.50 Holding baby . . . 1·25 1·25
3502 $1.50 Walking through minefield . . . 1·25 1·25
MS3503 76 × 106 mm. $5 With Mother Teresa . . . 3·75 3·75

448 "Angel" (Matthias Grunewald)

1997. Christmas. Religious Paintings. Multicoloured.

3504 35c. Type **448** . . . 45 25
3505 50c. "St. Demetrius" (icon) 60 30
3506 75c. Three-panelled reliquary . . . 75 45
3507 $1 "Angel of the Annunciation" (Jan van Eyck) . . . 85 55
3508 $3 "The Annunciation" (Simone Martini) . . . 2·25 2·50
3509 $4 "St. Michael" (icon) . . 2·50 3·00
MS3510 Two sheets. (a) 104 × 114 mm. $6 "The Coronation of the Virgin" (Fra Angelico). (b) 114 × 104 mm. $6 "The Annunciation" (Titian) (horiz) Set of 2 sheets . . . 9·00 10·00

1998. Chinese New Year ("Year of the Tiger"). Sheet 150 × 75 mm, containing triangular designs as T **435** showing tigers. Multicoloured. Self-adhesive on silver foil.

MS3511 $1.50, "GRENADA" in pink; $1.50, "GRENADA" in gold; $1.50, "GRENADA" in bronze . . . 1·80 1·90

No. **MS**3511 also exists on gold foil.

449 Black-tailed Damselfish

1998. Fishes. Multicoloured.

3512 65c. Type **449** . . . 55 40
3513 90c. Yellow sweetlips . . . 75 50
3514 $1 Common squirrelfish . . 80 55
3515 $1.50 Blue tang . . . 1·00 1·10
3516 $1.50 Porkfish . . . 1·00 1·10
3517 $1.50 Banded butterflyfish . 1·00 1·10
3518 $1.50 Thread-finned butterflyfish . . . 1·00 1·10
3519 $1.50 Hooded butterflyfish ("Red-headed") . . . 1·00 1·10
3520 $1.50 Emperor angelfish . . 1·00 1·10
3521 $1.50 Duboulay's angelfish ("Scribbled Anglefish") 1·00 1·10
3522 $1.50 Lemon-peel angelfish 1·00 1·10
3523 $1.50 Bandit angelfish . . . 1·00 1·10
3524 $1.50 Bicoloured angelfish ("Biclor Cherub") . . . 1·00 1·10
3525 $1.50 Palette surgeonfish ("Regal Tang") . . . 1·00 1·10
3526 $1.50 Yellow tang . . . 1·00 1·10
3527 $2 Powder-blue surgeonfish 1·25 1·40
MS3528 Two sheets, each 110 × 80 mm. (a) $6 Two-banded anemonefish. (b) $6 Forceps butterflyfish ("Long-nosed Butterflyfish") . . . 9·00 10·00

Nos. 3515/20 and 3521/6 respectively were printed together, se-tenant, with the backgrounds forming composite designs.

450 "Sophronitis grandiflora"

1998. Flowers of the World. Multicoloured.

3529 $1.50 Type **450** . . . 60 65
3530 $1.50 "Phalaenopsis amboinensis" . . . 60 65
3531 $1.50 "Zygopetalum intermedium" . . . 60 65
3532 $1.50 "Paphiopedilum purpuratum" . . . 60 65
3533 $1.50 "Miltonia regnellii" 60 65
3534 $1.50 "Dendrobium parishii" . . . 60 65
3535 $1.50 "Arachnis clarkei" . . 60 65
3536 $1.50 "Cymbidium eburneum" . . . 60 65
3537 $1.50 "Dendrobium chrysotoxum" . . . 60 65
3538 $1.50 "Paphiopedilum insigne" . . . 60 65
3539 $1.50 "Paphiopedilum venustum" . . . 60 65
3540 $1.50 "Renanthera imschootiana" . . . 60 65
MS3541 Two sheets, each 104 × 72 mm. (a) $6 "Pleione maculata". (b) $6 "Lycaste aromatica" Set of 2 sheets . . 4·75 5·00

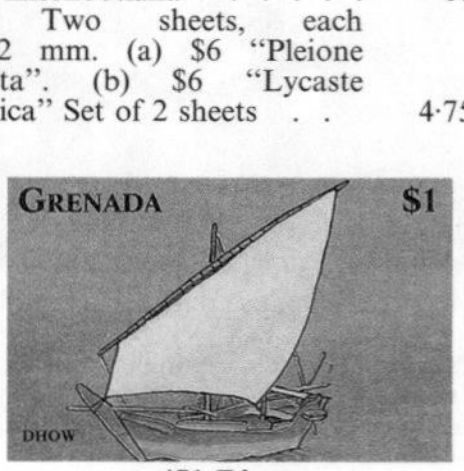

451 Dhow

1998. Famous Ships. Multicoloured.

3542 $1 Type **451** . . . 40 45
3543 $1 Galleon . . . 40 45
3544 $1 Felucca . . . 40 45
3545 $1 Schooner . . . 40 45
3546 $1 Aircraft carrier . . . 40 45
3547 $1 Knau . . . 40 45
3548 $1 Destroyer . . . 40 45
3549 $1 Viking longship . . . 40 45
3550 $1 "Queen Elizabeth 2" (liner) . . . 40 45
3551 $1 Brig . . . 40 45
3552 $1 Clipper . . . 40 45
3553 $1 Caique . . . 40 45
3554 $1 Mississippi riverboat . . 40 45
3555 $1 Luxury liner . . . 40 45
3556 $1 "Mayflower" (Pilgrim Fathers) . . . 40 45
3557 $1 Frigate . . . 40 45
3558 $1 Janggolan . . . 40 45
3559 $1 Junk . . . 40 45
MS3560 Two sheets, each 100 × 75 mm. (a) $6 Nuclear submarine (58 × 43 mm). (b) $6 "Lusitania" (liner) (86 × 29 mm) Set of 2 sheets . . . 4·75 5·00

Nos. 3542/50 and 3551/9 were printed together, se-tenant, forming composite background designs.

1998. "Hercules" (cartoon film) (2nd series). As T **443** showing Disney cartoon characters. Multicoloured.

3561/8 10c. × 8 Hercules and giant statue; Hercules, Pegasus and Philoktetes; Hercules and Philoktetes with shield and arrows; Hercules swinging from blades; Nessus carrying off Megara; Hercules fighting Nessus; Hercules fighting giant lion; Hercules and Pegasus leaving prints on pavement . . .
3569/76 $1 × 8 Baby Hercules with Zeus and Alcmene; Baby Hercules with Hades; Hades in the Underworld; Baby Hercules and young Pegasus; Baby Hercules with Pain and Panic; Baby Hercules with mortal parents; Hercules towing hay waggon; Hercules receiving gold medallion . . .
3577/84 $1 × 8 Hercules and Megara; Megara and Hades; Hercules training with Philoktetes; Hercules confronting Hades; Giant destroying city; Zeus; Hercules saving Megara by lifting pillar; Hercules diving into sea
3561/84 Set of 24 . . . 18·00 20·00
MS3585 Six sheets, each 127 × 102 mm. (a) $6 Hades. (b) $6 Baby Pegasus. (c) $6 Hercules with sword. (d) $6 Hades on fire. (e) $6 Zeus and Hercules (horiz). (f) $6 Hercules and Megara riding Pegasus (horiz) Set of 6 sheets 27·00 30·00

452 Arctic Skua

1998. Seabirds. Multicoloured.

3586 90c. Type **452** . . . 35 40
3587 $1 Fulmar ("Northern Fulmar") (horiz) . . . 40 45
3588 $1 Black-legged kittiwake (horiz) . . . 40 45
3589 $1 Pintado petrel ("Cape Petrel") (horiz) . . . 40 45
3590 $1 Mediterranean gull (horiz) . . . 40 45
3591 $1 Brandt's cormorant (horiz) . . . 40 45
3592 $1 Greater shearwater (horiz) . . . 40 45
3593 $1 Black-footed albatross (horiz) . . . 40 45
3594 $1 Red-necked phalarope (horiz) . . . 40 45
3595 $1 Black skimmer (horiz) . . 40 45
3596 $1.10 Humboldt penguin . . 45 50
3597 $2 Herring gull . . . 80 85
3598 $3 Red knot . . . 1·20 1·30
MS3599 Two sheets, each 100 × 70 mm. (a) $5 Black-browed albatross. (b) $5 King penguin Set of 2 sheets . . . 4·00 4·25

Nos. 3587/95 were printed together, se-tenant, with the backgrounds forming a composite design.

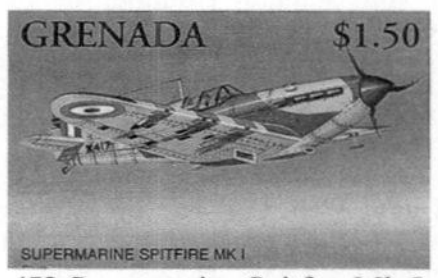

453 Supermarine Spitfire Mk I

1998. History of the Supermarine Spitfire (aircraft). Designs showing different versions. Multicoloured.

3600 $1.50 Type **453** . . . 60 65
3601 $1.50 Mark VIII . . . 60 65
3602 $1.50 Mark III . . . 60 65
3603 $1.50 Mark XVI . . . 60 65
3604 $1.50 Mark V . . . 60 65
3605 $1.50 Mark XIX . . . 60 65
3606 $1.50 Mark IX . . . 60 65
3607 $1.50 Mark XIV . . . 60 65
3608 $1.50 Mark XII . . . 60 65
3609 $1.50 Mark XI . . . 60 65
3610 $1.50 H.F. Mark VIII . . . 60 65
3611 $1.50 Mark VB . . . 60 65
MS3612 Two sheets, each 80 × 106 mm. (a) $6 Mark IA. (b) $6 Mark IX (different) (both 56 × 41 mm) Set of 2 sheets . . 4·75 5·00

454 Walrus

1998. International Year of the Ocean. Multicoloured.

3613 75c. Type **454** . . . 30 35
3614 75c. Jackass penguins ("African Black-footed Penguin") . . . 30 35
3615 75c. Jackass penguin ("African Black-footed Penguin") . . . 30 35
3616 75c. California sealion . . . 30 35
3617 75c. Green turtle . . . 30 35
3618 75c. Redfin anthias . . . 30 35
3619 75c. Sperm whale . . . 30 35
3620 75c. French angelfish and Australian sealion . . . 30 35
3621 75c. Jellyfish . . . 30 35
3622 75c. Sawfish . . . 30 35
3623 75c. Cuckoo wrasse . . . 30 35
3624 75c. Garibaldi . . . 30 35
3625 75c. Spinecheek anemonefish 30 35
3626 75c. Leafy seadragon . . . 30 35
3627 75c. Blue-spotted goatfish 30 35
3628 75c. Two-spot gobies . . . 30 35
MS3629 Two sheets, each 98 × 68 mm. (a) $5 Atlantic spotted dolphins. (b) $6 Octopus Set of 2 sheets . . . 4·50 4·75

Nos. 3613/28 were printed together, se-tenant, with the backgrounds forming a composite design.

454a Flags of Grenada and CARICOM

1998. 25th Anniv of Caribbean Community.

3630 **454a** $1 multicoloured . . . 40 45

454b Stylized Americas

1998. 50th Anniv of Organization of American States.

3631 **454b** $1 multicoloured . . . 40 45

1998. 25th Death Anniv of Pablo Picasso (painter). As T **291a** of Gambia. Multicoloured.

3632 45c. "The Bathers" (vert) . . 20 25
3633 $2 "Luncheon on the Grass" . . . 80 85
3634 $3 "The Swimmer" . . . 1·20 1·30
MS3635 102 × 127 mm. $5 "Tomato Plant" (vert) . . . 2·00 2·10

1998. Birth Centenary of Enzo Ferrari (car manufacturer). As T **564a** of Ghana. Multicoloured.

3636 $2 250 GT Berlinetta Lusso 1·50 1·50
3637 $2 250 GTO . . . 1·50 1·50
3638 $2 250 GT Boano/Ellena cabriolet . . . 1·50 1·50
MS3639 104 × 70 mm. $5 246 GTS Dino (91 × 34 mm) . . . 4·00 4·50

454c Scout Saluting

454d Mahatma Gandhi

1998. 19th World Scout Jamboree, Chile. Multicoloured.
3640 $2 Type **454c** 80 85
3641 $3 International scout flag 1·20 1·30
3642 $4 Applying first aid . . . 1·60 1·70
MS3643 106 × 76 mm. $6 International scout flag . . . . 2·40 2·50

1998. 50th Death Anniv of Mahatma Gandhi.
3644 **454d** $1 black, grey and mauve 40 45
MS3645 70 × 100 mm. $6 multicoloured . . . . 2·40 2·50
DESIGN: $6, Gandhi and spinning wheel.

1998. 80th Anniv of Royal Air Force. As T **292a** of Gambia. Multicoloured.
3646 $2 Supermarine Spitfire Mk IIa 80 85
3647 $2 Supermarine Spitfire Mk IXb from above . . . 80 85
3648 $2 Supermarine Spitfire Mk IXb from side 80 85
3649 $2 Hawker Hurricane Mk IIC of Battle of Britain Memorial Flight 80 85
3650 $2 EF-2000 Eurofighter above clouds 80 85
3651 $2 Nimrod MR2P (maritime reconnaissance) 80 85
3652 $2 EF-2000 Eurofighter at low level 80 85
3653 $2 C-47 Dakota (transport) 80 85
MS3654 Four sheets, each 93 × 70 mm. (a) $6 Bristol F2B fighter and head of falcon. (b) $6 Bristol F2B fighter and northern goshawk (bird). (c) $6 Jet Provost (trainer) and EF-2000 Eurofighter. (d) $6 VC10 (transport) and EF-2000 Eurofighter Set of 4 sheets . . . . 9·75 10·00

455 "Knights in Combat"

1998. Birth Bicentenary of Eugene Delacroix (painter). Multicoloured.
3655 $1 Type **455** 40 45
3656 $1 "Murder of Bishop of Liege" 40 45
3657 $1 "Still Life" 40 45
3658 $1 "Battle of Nancy" . . . 40 45
3659 $1 "Shipwreck of Don Juan" 40 45
3660 $1 "The Death of Ophelia" 40 45
3661 $1 "Attila the Hun" 40 45
3662 $1 "Arab Entertainers" . . 40 45
MS3663 100 × 92 mm. $5 "The Capture of Constantinople" . . 2·00 2·10

1998. 1st Death Anniv of Diana, Princess of Wales. As T **293a** of Gambia. Multicoloured.
3664 $1 Diana, Princess of Wales 40 45

456 Arthur Ashe

1998. Famous Tennis Players. Multicoloured.
3665 45c. Type **456** 20 25
3666 75c. Martina Hingis 30 35
3667 90c. Chris Evert 35 40
3668 $1 Steffi Graf 40 45
3669 $1.50 A. Sanchez Vicario . . 60 65
3670 $2 Monica Seles 80 85
3671 $3 Martina Navratilova . . 1·20 1·30
MS3672 81 × 108 mm. $6 Martina Hingis (different) . . . . . . 2·40 2·50

457 Dove of Peace with Stars and Streamers

458 "The Angel's parting from Tobias" (Jean Bilevelt)

1998. Grenada's Participation in U.N. Peacekeeping Operations, Beirut, 1982–4.
3673 **457** $1 multicoloured 40 45

1998. Christmas. Religious Paintings. Multicoloured.
3674 35c. Type **458** 15 20
3675 45c. "Allegory of Faith" (Moretto Da Brescia) . . 20 25
3676 90c. "Crucifixion" (Ugolino Di Tedice) 35 40
3677 $1 "The Triumphal Entry into Jerusalem" (Master of the Thuison Altarpiece) 40 45

459 Antillean Euphonia ("Blue-hooded Euphonia")

1998. Christmas. Birds. Multicoloured.
3678 45c. Type **459** 20 25
3679 75c. Red-billed whistling duck ("Black-bellied Whistling Duck") 30 35
3680 90c. Caribbean martin ("Purple Martin") 35 40
3681 $1 Imperial amazon ("Imperial Parrot") . . . 40 45
3682 $2 Adelaide's warbler . . . 80 85
3683 $3 Greater flamingo ("Roseate Flamingo") . . 1·20 1·30
MS3684 Two sheets, each 97 × 84 mm. (a) $5 Green-throated carib. (b) $6 Purple-throated carib and Canada 1898 Imperial Penny Postage 2c. stamp (37 × 60 mm) Set of 2 sheets . . . . 4·50 4·75

1999. Chinese New Year ("Year of the Rabbit"). Sheet 150 × 75 mm, containing triangular designs as T **435** showing rabbits. Multicoloured. Self-adhesive on silver foil.
MS3685 $1 "GRENADA" in green; $1 "GRENADA" in orange; $1 "GRENADA" in pink . . . . 1·20 1·30

1999. Millennium Series. Famous People of the Twentieth Century. Great Thinkers of the Past and Present. Designs as T **289a** of Gambia. Mult.
3686 $1 Martin Luther King Jr (civil rights leader) . . . 40 45
3687 $1 Socrates (Greek philosopher) (56 × 41 mm) 40 45
3688 $1 Sir Thomas More (English scholar) (56 × 41 mm) 40 45
3689 $1 Chaim Weizmann (first President of Israel) . . . 40 45
3690 $1 Alexander Solzhenitsyn (Russian writer) 40 45
3691 $1 Galileo Galilei (Italian astronomer) (56 × 41 mm) 40 45
3692 $1 Michael Servetus (Spanish theologian) (56 × 41 mm) 40 45
3693 $1 Salman Rushdie (British novelist) 40 45
MS3694 106 × 76 mm. $6 Mother Teresa (founder of Missionaries of Charity) . . . . 2·40 2·50
No. 3692 is inscribed "MICHAEL SERVENTUS" in error.

460 Robert H. Goddard (rocket scientist)

1999. Space Exploration. Multicoloured.
3695 $1.50 Type **460** 60 65
3696 $1.50 Wernher von Braun (rocket scientist) 60 65
3697 $1.50 Yuri A. Gagarin (first cosmonaut to orbit Earth, 1961) 60 65
3698 $1.50 "Freedom 7" (first American manned Space flight, 1961) 60 65
3699 $1.50 Aleksei Leonov (first Russian to walk in Space, 1965) 60 65
3700 $1.50 Neil Armstrong and Edwin Aldrin (first astronauts on Moon, 1969) 60 65
3701 $1.50 "Mariner 9" (first spacecraft to orbit Mars, 1971) 60 65
3702 $1.50 "Voyager 1" (Jupiter probe, 1979) 60 65
3703 $1.50 Bruce McCandless (first astronaut to work in Space unattached, 1984) 60 65
3704 $1.50 "Giotto" probe (study of Halley's Comet, 1986) 60 65
3705 $1.50 Space Shuttle "Atlantis" (launch of "Galileo" probe, 1989) . . 60 65
3706 $1.50 "Magellan" (Venus probe, 1990) 60 65
MS3707 Two sheets, each 60 × 76 mm. (a) $6 John Glenn (first American to orbit Earth, 1962). (b) $6 Neil Armstrong (first astronaut to walk on Moon, 1969) Set of 2 sheets . . . . 4·75 5·00
Nos. 3695/3700 and 3701/6 were respectively printed together, se-tenant, with the backgrounds forming composite designs.

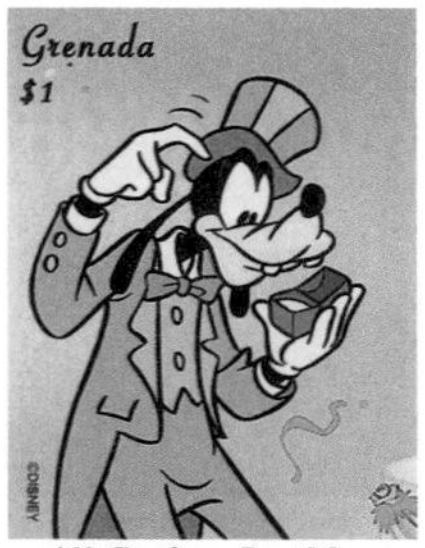

461 Goofy as Best Man

1999. 70th Birthday of Mickey Mouse. Mickey's Dream Wedding. Walt Disney cartoon characters. Multicoloured.
3708 $1 Type **461** 80 80
3709 $1 Mickey as groom 80 80
3710 $1 Minnie as bride 80 80
3711 $1 Daisy Duck as bridesmaid 80 80
3712 $1 Donald Duck 80 80
3713 $1 Pluto in love 80 80
3714 $1 Huey, Duey and Louie 80 80
3715 $1 Lady (Pekingese) 80 80
MS3716 Two sheets. (a) 102 × 127 mm. $6 Mickey's nephew eating cake. (b) 127 × 102 mm. $6 Mickey and Minnie in carriage (horiz) Set of 2 sheets . . . . 9·00 9·50
Nos. 3708/15 were printed together, se-tenant, with the backgrounds forming a composite design.

462 Grand Trunk Western, U.S.A.

1999. Trains of the World. Multicoloured.
3717 25c. Type **462** 10 15
3718 35c. Louisville & Nashville, U.S.A. 15 20
3719 45c. Gulf, Mobile and Ohio, U.S.A. 20 25
3720 75c. Missouri Pacific, U.S.A. 30 35
3721 90c. "RTG" National Railway, France 35 40
3722 $1 Florida East Coast, U.S.A. 40 45
3723 $1.50 Rio Grande, U.S.A. 60 65
3724 $1.50 Erie Lackawanna, U.S.A. 60 65
3725 $1.50 New York Central, U.S.A. 60 65
3726 $1.50 Pennsylvania, U.S.A. 60 65
3727 $1.50 Milwaukee Road, U.S.A. 60 65
3728 $1.50 Illinois Central, U.S.A. 60 65
3729 $1.50 Burlington Route, U.S.A. 60 65
3730 $1.50 "Texas Special", Missouri, Kansas and Texas, U.S.A. 60 65
3731 $1.50 City of Los Angeles, U.S.A. 60 65
3732 $1.50 Northwestern, U.S.A. 60 65
3733 $1.50 Canadian National . . 60 65
3734 $1.50 Rock Island, U.S.A. 60 65
3735 $1.50 TGV, French National Railways . . . 60 65
3736 $1.50 HST, British Railways 60 65
3737 $1.50 TEE, Trans Europe Express 60 65
3738 $1.50 Ancona Express, Italy 60 65
3739 $1.50 XPT, Australia . . . 60 65
3740 $1.50 APT-P, British Railways 60 65
3741 $1.50 Western Pacific, U.S.A. 60 65
3742 $1.50 Union Pacific, U.S.A. 60 65
3743 $1.50 Chesapeake and Ohio, U.S.A. 60 65
3744 $1.50 Southern Pacific, U.S.A. 60 65
3745 $1.50 Baltimore and Ohio, U.S.A. 60 65
3746 $1.50 Wabash, U.S.A. . . . 60 65
3747 $3 Kansas City Southern, U.S.A. . . . . 1·20 1·30
3748 $4 New Haven, U.S.A. . . 1·60 1·70
MS3749 Four sheets, each 98 × 68 mm. (a) $6 Eld 4, Netherlands. (b) $6 "Hikari" express train, Japan. (c) $6 Santa Fe, U.S.A. (d) $6 Inter City express, Germany Set of 4 sheets 9·75 10·00
Nos. 3723/8, 3729/34, 3735/40 and 3741/6 respectively were printed together, se-tenant, with the backgrounds forming composite designs.

463 "Papilio blumei" (butterfly)

1999. "Australia '99" World Stamp Exhibition, Melbourne. Wildlife. Multicoloured.
3750 75c. Type **463** 30 35
3751 75c. Great egret ("Egret") 30 35
3752 75c. Kumarahou (flower) . . 30 35
3753 75c. Javan rhinoceros . . . 30 35
3754 75c. Grey-backed white-eye ("Silver-eye") (bird) . . . 30 35
3755 75c. Kiore (rodent) 30 35
3756 75c. "Cyclorana novaehollandiae" (frog) 30 35
3757 75c. Caterpillar 30 35
3758 75c. Pacific black duck ("Grey Duck") 30 35
3759 75c. Honey blue-eye (fish) 30 35
3760 75c. Krefft's turtle 30 35
3761 75c. Archer fish 30 35
3762 75c. Binturong (vert) . . . 30 35
3763 75c. Two Indian elephants (vert) 30 35
3764 75c. Indian elephant (vert) 30 35
3765 75c. Chestnut-capped laughing thrush ("Garkulax mitratus") (vert) 30 35
3766 75c. "Vanda hookeriana" (orchid) (vert) 30 35
3767 75c. Grey heron ("Heron") (vert) 30 35
3768 75c. Fur seal (vert) 30 35
3769 75c. Black-faced cormorant ("Shag") (bird) (vert) . . 30 35
3770 75c. Round batfish (vert) . . 30 35
3771 75c. Loggerhead turtle (vert) 30 35
3772 75c. Three harlequin sweetlips (vert) 30 35
3773 75c. Two harlequin sweetlips (vert) 30 35
3774 $1 Orang-utan 40 45
3775 $2 Douroucouli (monkey) 80 85
3776 $3 Black caiman (alligator) 1·20 1·30
3777 $4 Panther ("Black Leopard") (vert) . . . . 1·60 1·70
MS3778 Two sheets. (a) 110 × 85 mm. $6 Impala. (b) 85 × 110 mm. $6 Ring-tailed lemur Set of 2 sheets . . . . 4·75 5·00
Nos. 3750/61 and 3762/73 respectively were printed together, se-tenant, with the backgrounds forming composite designs.
Nos. 3753 and 3775 were inscribed "JAUAN RHINOCEROS" and "DOUROCOULI" in error.

1999. "iBRA '99" International Stamp Exhibition, Nuremberg. Horiz designs as T **298a** of Gambia. Multicoloured.
3779 75c. Railway locomotive, 1893, and Prussia 1860 ½sgr. stamp 30 35
3780 90c. "Humboldt" (sailing ship) and Mecklenburg-Schwerin 1856 4 × ⅓s. . . 35 40
3781 $1 Railway locomotive, 1893, and Saxony 1850 3pf. 40 45
3782 $2 "Humboldt" (sailing ship) and Mecklenburg-Strelitz 1864 ⅓sgr. 80 85
MS3783 121 × 104 mm. $6 Saxony 1850 3pf. with Leipzig postmark 2·40 2·50

1999. 150th Death Anniv of Katsushika Hokusai (Japanese artist). As T **298b** of Gambia. Multicoloured.
3784 $1.50 "The Actor Ichikawa Danjuro Danjuro as Tomoe Gozen" 60 65
3785 $1.50 "Washing Clothes" (drawing) 60 65
3786 $1.50 "The Prostitute of Eguchi" 60 65
3787 $1.50 "Sudden Shower from a Fine Sky" 60 65
3788 $1.50 "Hanging Clothes out to dry" (drawing) 60 65
3789 $1.50 "Shimada" 60 65
3790 $1.50 "Head of Old Man" 60 65
3791 $1.50 "Piebald Horse" (drawing) 60 65
3792 $1.50 "Girl making Cord for binding Hats" 60 65
3793 $1.50 "Li Po admiring Waterfall of Lo-shan" . . 60 65
3794 $1.50 "Bay Horse" (drawing) 60 65
3795 $1.50 "Potted Dwarf Pine with Basin" 60 65
MS3796 Two sheets, each 72 × 102 mm. (a) $6 "The Guardian God Fudo Myoo and his Attendants". (b) $6 "Women on the Beach at Enoshima" Set of 2 sheets . . . . 4·75 5·00
No. 3788 is inscribed "DRAWINFS" in error.

1999. 10th Anniv of United Nations Rights of the Child Convention. As T **298c** of Gambia. Multicoloured.
3797 $3 Eskimo girl and Russian boy . . . . 1·20 1·30
3798 $3 American girl . . . . . 1·20 1·30
3799 $3 African boy and Indian girl . . . . 1·20 1·30
MS3800 110 × 85 mm. $6 Young boy 2·40 2·50
Nos. 3797/9 were printed together, se-tenant, forming a composite design.

1999. "PhilexFrance '99" International Stamp Exhibition, Paris. Railway Locomotives. Two sheets containing horiz designs as T **299d** of Gambia. Multicoloured.
MS3801 (a) 106 × 76 mm. $6 Paris, Lyons and Mediterranean Railway Compound Pacific. (b) 106 × 81 mm. $6 French heavy freight locomotive Set of 2 sheets . . . 4·75 5·00

1999. 250th Birth Anniv of Johann von Goethe (German poet and dramatist). Multicoloured designs as T **298d** of Gambia.
3802 $3 mauve, purple and black . . . 1·20 1·30
3803 $3 blue, lilac and black . . . 1·20 1·30
3804 $3 violet, deep violet and black . . . 1·20 1·30
MS3805 76 × 106 mm. $6 orange, brown and black . . . 2·40 2·50
DESIGNS—HORIZ: No. 3802, Faust contemplating Moon; 3803, Goethe and Friedrich von Schiller (dramatist); 3804, Faust talking with Wagner. VERT: No. **MS**3805, Margaret (from "Faust").

1999. 30th Anniv of First Manned Landing on Moon. Horiz designs as T **298e** of Gambia. Multicoloured.
3806 $1.50 The Moon . . . 60 65
3807 $1.50 Edward White on first space walk . . . 60 65
3808 $1.50 Edwin "Buzz" Aldrin . . . 60 65
3809 $1.50 The Earth . . . 60 65
3810 $1.50 Michael Collins . . . 60 65
3811 $1.50 Neil Armstrong . . . 60 65
3812 $1.50 Footprint on the Moon . . . 60 65
3813 $1.50 V2 rocket . . . 60 65
3814 $1.50 Command module "Columbia" . . . 60 65
3815 $1.50 Lunar Rover . . . 60 65
3816 $1.50 Lunar module "Eagle" . . . 60 65
3817 $1.50 Command module re-entering Earth's atmosphere . . . 60 65
MS3818 Two sheets. (a) 110 × 85 mm. $6 Neil Armstrong with American flag. (b) 85 × 111 mm. $6 Launch of "Apollo 11" (vert) Set of 2 sheets . . . 4·75 5·00

464 Astronaut with Letter

1999. 125th Anniv of Universal Postal Union. Space Mail. Multicoloured.
3819 $2 Type **464** . . . 80 85
3820 $2 Supply spaceship "Progress" . . . 80 85
3821 $2 Postmark of space station "MIR" . . . 80 85
3822 $2 Buran shuttle and "MIR" . . . 80 85
MS3823 104 × 75 mm. $6 Space station "MIR" . . . 2·40 2·50

465 "Carry On Doctor"

1999. 50th Anniv of the Variety Club of Great Britain. Scenes from "Carry On" Films. Multicoloured.
3824 $1 "Carry On Dick" . . . 40 45
3825 $1 Type **465** . . . 40 45
3826 $1 "Carry On England" . . . 40 45
3827 $1 "Carry On Matron" . . . 40 45
3828 $1 "Carry On Round The Bend" . . . 40 45
3829 $1 "Carry On Up The Jungle" . . . 40 45
3830 $1 "Carry On Loving" . . . 40 45
3831 $1 "Carry On Up The Khyber" . . . 40 45
MS3832 110 × 86 mm. $6 Actors from "Carry On" films . . . 2·40 2·50

1999. Royal Wedding. As T **298** of Gambia. Multicoloured.
3833 $3 Prince Edward . . . 1·20 1·30
3834 $3 Sophie and Prince Edward . . . 1·20 1·30
3835 $3 Sophie Rhys-Jones . . . 1·20 1·30
MS3836 78 × 108 mm. $6 Prince Edward and Sophie Rhys-Jones . . . 2·40 2·50

466 "U.S.S. Enterprise NCC-1701" (from original series)

1999. Spacecraft of "Star Trek". Multicoloured.
3837 $1.50 Type **466** . . . 60 65
3838 $1.50 Klingon battle cruiser (blue and orange planets in background) (Voyager series) . . . 60 65
3839 $1.50 "U.S.S. Enterprise" 1701 (green planet in background) (Next Generation series) . . . 60 65
3840 $1.50 Warbird "Voyager" (below blue planet) . . . 60 65
3841 $1.50 U.S.S. "Romulan" (in front of orange planet) (original series) . . . 60 65
3842 $1.50 "U.S.S. Enterprise" 1701 (pink planet in background) (original series) . . . 60 65
3843 $1.50 "Borg Cube" (Next Generation series) . . . 60 65
3844 $1.50 "U.S.S. Enterprise NCC" 1701 (in front of multicoloured flames) . . . 60 65
3845 $1.50 Klingon "Bird of Prey" (original series) . . . 60 65

1999. "Queen Elizabeth the Queen Mother's Century". As T **304a** of Gambia.
3846 $2 black and gold . . . 80 85
3847 $2 multicoloured . . . 80 85
3848 $2 black and gold . . . 80 85
3849 $2 multicoloured . . . 80 85
MS3850 154 × 157 mm. $6 multicoloured . . . 2·40 2·50
DESIGNS: No. 3846, Queen Mother with Prince Charles, 1948; 3847, Queen Mother in pink outfit, 1970; 3848, Queen Mother in Australia, 1958; 3849, Queen Mother waving. (37 × 50 mm)—**MS**3850, Queen Mother in Coronation robes, 1953.
No. **MS**3850 also shows the Royal Arms embossed in gold, and inscr "Good Health and Happiness to Her Majesty The Queen Mother on her 101st Birthday".

467 George Gershwin

1999. American Entertainers. Multicoloured.
3851 $1 Type **467** . . . 40 45
3852 $1 Florence Mills . . . 40 45
3853 $1 Sam Beckett . . . 40 45
3854 $1 Bessie Smith . . . 40 45
3855 $1 Billie Holiday . . . 40 45
3856 $1 Bert Williams . . . 40 45
3857 $1 Cole Porter . . . 40 45
3858 $1 Sofie Tucker . . . 40 45
3859 $1 Lon Chaney . . . 40 45
3860 $1 Buster Keaton . . . 40 45
3861 $1 Norma Shearer . . . 40 45
3862 $1 James Cagney . . . 40 45
3863 $1 Hedda Hopper . . . 40 45
3864 $1 Jean Harlow . . . 40 45
3865 $1 Marlene Dietrich . . . 40 45
3866 $1 Ramon Novarro . . . 40 45
MS3867 Two sheets, each 76 × 86 mm. (a) $6 Clark Gable. (b) $6 Louis Armstrong Set of 2 sheets . . . 4·75 5·00
Nos. 3885/8 and 3859/66 respectively were printed together, se-tenant, with the backgrounds forming composite designs.

468 Ouranosaurus

1999. Prehistoric Animals. Multicoloured.
3868 35c. Type **468** . . . 15 20
3869 45c. Struthiomimus (vert) . . . 20 25
3870 75c. Parasaurolophus (vert) . . . 30 35
3871 $1 Archaeopteryx . . . 40 45
3872 $1 Brachiosaurus . . . 40 45
3873 $1 Dilophosaurus . . . 40 45
3874 $1 Dimetrodon . . . 40 45
3875 $1 Psittacosaurus . . . 40 45
3876 $1 Acrocanthosaurus . . . 40 45
3877 $1 Stenonychosaurus . . . 40 45
3878 $1 Dryosaurus . . . 40 45
3879 $1 Campsognathus . . . 40 45
3880 $1 Agathaumus . . . 40 45
3881 $1 Camarosaurus . . . 40 45
3882 $1 Quetzalcoatlus . . . 40 45
3883 $1 Alioramus . . . 40 45
3884 $1 Camptosaurus . . . 40 45
3885 $1 Albertosaurus . . . 40 45
3886 $1 Anatosaurus . . . 40 45
3887 $1 Spinosaurus . . . 40 45
3888 $1 Centrosaurus . . . 40 45
3889 $2 Triceratops . . . 80 85
3890 $3 Stegoceras . . . 1·20 1·30
3891 $4 Stegosaurus . . . 1·60 1·70
MS3892 Two sheets, each 85 × 110 mm. (a) $6 Velociraptor (vert). (b) $6 Tyrannosaurus (vert) Set of 2 sheets . . . 4·75 5·00
Nos. 3871/9 and 3880/8 were printed together, se-tenant, with the backgrounds forming a composite design.
No. 3871 is inscribed "ARCHEOPTERYX" in error.

469 Christmas Rose

1999. Christmas. Multicoloured.
3893 20c. Type **469** . . . 10 15
3894 75c. Tulip . . . 30 35
3895 90c. Pear . . . 35 40
3896 $1 Hibiscus . . . 40 45
3897 $4 Lily . . . 1·60 1·70
MS3898 106 × 91 mm. $6 "The Nativity" (Botticelli) (horiz) . . . 2·40 2·50

1999. Faces of the Millennium: Diana, Princess of Wales. Vert designs as T **307** of Gambia showing collage of miniature flower photographs. Multicoloured.
3899 $1 Top of head (face value at left) . . . 40 45
3900 $1 Top of head (face value at right) . . . 40 45
3901 $1 Ear (face value at left) . . . 40 45
3902 $1 Eye and temple (face value at right) . . . 40 45
3903 $1 Cheek (face value at left) . . . 40 45
3904 $1 Cheek (face value at right) . . . 40 45
3905 $1 Blue background (face value at left) . . . 40 45
3906 $1 Chin (face value at right) . . . 40 45
Nos. 3899/906 were printed together, se-tenant, and when viewed as a whole, form a portrait of Diana, Princess of Wales.

470 Green Dragon

2000. Chinese New Year ("Year of the Dragon"). Multicoloured.
3907 $2 Type **470** . . . 80 85
3908 $2 Dragon ("GRENADA" in red) . . . 80 85
3909 $2 Dragon ("GRENADA" in violet) . . . 80 85

471 Roseate Spoonbill

2000. Birds of Grenada. Multicoloured.
3910 75c. Type **471** . . . 30 35
3911 90c. Scarlet ibis . . . 35 40
3912 $1 Adelaide's warbler . . . 40 45
3913 $1 Hispaniolan trogon . . . 40 45
3914 $1 Sun conure ("Sun Parakeet") . . . 40 45
3915 $1 Black-necked stilt . . . 40 45
3916 $1 Sora crake ("Sora") . . . 40 45
3917 $1 Fulvous whistling duck ("Fulvous Tree Duck") . . . 40 45
3918 $1 Blue-headed parrot . . . 40 45
3919 $1 Tropical mockingbird . . . 40 45
3920 $1 Antillean euphonia ("Blue-hooded Euphonia") . . . 40 45
3921 $1 Troupial . . . 40 45
3922 $1 Brown-throated conure ("Caribbean Parakeet") . . . 40 45
3923 $1 Forest thrush . . . 40 45
3924 $1 Lesser Antillean tanager ("Hooded Tanager") . . . 40 45
3925 $1 Stripe-headed tanager . . . 40 45
3926 $1 Ringed kingfisher . . . 40 45
3927 $1 Zenaida dove . . . 40 45
3928 $1.50 Sparkling violetear . . . 60 65
3929 $2 Northern jacana . . . 80 85
MS3930 Two sheets, each 70 × 97 mm. (a) $6 Cedar waxwing (37 × 50 mm). (b) $6 Antillean siskin (50 × 37 mm) Set of 2 sheets . . . 4·75 5·00
Nos. 3912/19 and 3920/7 were each printed together, se-tenant, with the backgrounds forming composite designs.
No. 3912 is inscribed "Ade; aode's Warbler" and No. 3919 "Tropical Mockinbird", both in error.

471a Jan Vermeer (Dutch painter) (died 1675)

472 *Clitcybe geotropa*

2000. New Millennium. People and Events of Seventeenth Century (1650–1700). Multicoloured.
3931 50c. Type **471a** . . . 20 25
3932 50c. Antoni van Leeuwenhoek (discovered micro-organisms, 1674) . . . 20 25
3933 50c. Salem Witch Trials, Massachusetts, 1692 . . . 20 25
3934 50c. Sir Isaac Newton and reflecting telescope, 1668 . . . 20 25
3935 50c. Voltaire (French writer and historian) (born 1694) . . . 20 25
3936 50c. Ivan V and Peter I (joint rulers of Russia, 1682) . . . 20 25
3937 50c. Shun Zhi, first Chinese Emperor of Qing Dynasty (died 1662) . . . 20 25
3938 50c. Christian Huggens and Saturn, 1655 . . . 20 25
3939 50c. Microscopic mite (Robert Hooke's experiments in cytology, 1665) . . . 20 25
3940 50c. "Verdant Peaks" (Wang Shih-rnin), 1672 . . . 20 25
3941 50c. Rene Descartes (French philosopher) (died 1650) . . . 20 25
3942 50c. Completion of Canal du Midi, 1681 . . . 20 25
3943 50c. William of Orange and Bill of Rights, 1688 . . . 20 25
3944 50c. William III on horseback (end of King William's War), 1697) . . . 20 25
3945 50c. Cassini (French astronomer) and images of Mars, 1666 . . . 20 25
3946 50c. Sir Isaac Newton and apples (law of gravity, 1666) (59 × 39 mm) . . . 20 25
3947 50c. Jupiter's Moons (Olaus Roemer) (Danish astronomer) (discovered finite speed of light, 1676) . . . 20 25
No. 3936 is dated "1694" in error.

2000. 400th Birth Anniv of Sir Anthony Van Dyck (Flemish painter). As T **312a** of Gambia. Mult.
3948 $1 "King Charles I on Horseback" . . . 40 45
3949 $1 "St. Martin dividing his Cloak" . . . 40 45
3950 $1 "Gio. Paolo Babli on Horseback" . . . 40 45
3951 $1 "Marchese Anton Giulio Brignole-Sale on Horseback" . . . 40 45
3952 $1 "Study of a Horse" . . . 40 45
3953 $1 "Oriental on Horseback" . . . 40 45
3954 $1 "Young Woman resting Head on Hand" . . . 40 45
3955 $1 "Self-portrait", 1613–14 . . . 40 45
3956 $1 "Woman looking Upwards" . . . 40 45
3957 $1 "Head of an Old Man", c. 1621 . . . 40 45
3958 $1 "Head of a Boy" . . . 40 45
3959 $1 "Head of an Old Man", 1616–18 . . . 40 45
3960 $1.50 "Portrait of a Man" . . . 60 65
3961 $1.50 "Portrait of a Man aged Seventy" . . . 60 65
3962 $1.50 "Portrait of a Woman" . . . 60 65
3963 $1.50 "Elderly Man" . . . 60 65
3964 $1.50 "Portrait of a Young Man" . . . 60 65
3965 $1.50 "Man with a Glove" . . . 60 65
3966 $1.50 "St. John the Baptist" . . . 60 65
3967 $1.50 "St. Anthony of Padua and the Ass of Rimini" . . . 60 65
3968 $1.50 "The Stoning of St. Stephen" . . . 60 65
3969 $1.50 "The Martyrdom of St. Sebastian" . . . 60 65
3970 $1.50 "St. Sebastian bound for Martyrdom" . . . 60 65
3971 $1.50 "St. Jerome" . . . 60 65
3972 $1.50 "Portrait of Anthony Van Dyck", 1614–15 . . . 60 65
3973 $1.50 "Self-portrait" (after Rubens) . . . 60 65
3974 $1.50 "Isabella Brant" . . . 60 65
3975 $1.50 "The Penitent Apostle Peter" . . . 60 65

3976 $1.50 "Head of a Robber" (used by Rubens in his "Coup de Lance") 60 65
3977 $1.50 "Heads of the Apostles" (detail from Ruben's "Feast at the House of Simon the Pharisee") 60 65
MS3978 Six sheets. (a) 103 × 127 mm. $5 "Prince Thomas-Francis of Savoy on Horseback". (b) 102 × 127 mm. $5 "Emperor Theodosius refused Entry in Milan Cathedral" (horiz). (c) 102 × 127 mm. $5 "King Charles I on Horseback". (d) 127 × 102 mm, $6 "St. Jerome in the Wilderness". (e) 102 × 127 mm. $6 "St. Martin" (horiz). (f) 127 × 102 mm. $6 Detail of "Portrait of a Man and His Wife" (horiz) Set of 6 sheets 13·50 14·00

No. **MS**3978b is inscribed "Emperor Theoddosius" in error.

2000. Fungi. Multicoloured.

3979 35c. Type **472** 15 20
3980 45c. *Psalliota augusta* 20 25
3981 $1 *Amanita rubescens* 40 45
3982 $1.50 *Pholiota spectabilis* 60 65
3983 $1.50 *Mycena polygramma* 60 65
3984 $1.50 *Collybia iocephala* 60 65
3985 $1.50 *Corinus comatus* 60 65
3986 $1.50 *Amanita muscaria sp.* 60 65
3987 $1.50 *Boletus aereus* 60 65
3988 $1.50 *Ungulina marginata* 60 65
3989 $1.50 *Pleurotus ostreatus* 60 65
3990 $1.50 *Flammula penetrans* 60 65
3991 $1.50 *Morchella crassipes* 60 65
3992 $1.50 *Lepiota procera* 60 65
3993 $1.50 *Tricholoma aurantium* 60 65
3994 $4 *Boletus satanas* 1·60 1·70
MS3995 Two sheets. (a) 82 × 112 mm. $6 *Daedala quercina*. (b) 112 × 82 mm. $6 *Lepiota acutesquamosa* Set of 2 sheets 4·75 5·00

Nos. 3982/7 and 3988/93 were each printed together, se-tenant, with the backgrounds forming composite designs.

No. 3986 is inscribed "Aminita muscaria" in error.

2000. 18th Birthday of Prince William. As T **312b** of Gambia. Multicoloured.

3996 $1.50 Prince William wearing blue and white tie 60 65
3997 $1.50 With Prince of Wales 60 65
3998 $1.50 Prince William waving 60 65
3999 $1.50 In skiing gear 60 65
MS4000 100 × 80 mm. $6 Prince William (37 × 50 mm) 2·40 2·50

2000. "EXPO 2000" World Stamp Exhibition, Anaheim, U.S.A. Spacecraft. As T **582a** of Ghana. Multicoloured.

4001 $1.50 "Lunik 4" 60 65
4002 $1.50 "Clemintine" 60 65
4003 $1.50 "Luna 12" 60 65
4004 $1.50 "Luna 16" 60 65
4005 $1.50 Lunar Module *Eagle* from "Apollo 11" 60 65
4006 $1.50 "Ranger 7" 60 65
MS4007 117 × 84 mm. $6 "Apollo 13" 2·40 2·50

Nos. 4001/6 were printed together, se-tenant, with the backgrounds forming a composite design.

2000. 25th Anniv of "Apollo–Soyuz" Joint Project. As T **582b** of Ghana. Multicoloured.

4008 $3 Russian "A-2" rocket 1·20 1·30
4009 $3 "Soyuz 19" 1·20 1·30
4010 $3 "Apollo 18" command module docked with "Soyuz 19" 1·20 1·30
MS4011 88 × 70 mm. $6 Valeri Kubasov ("Soyuz" engineer) and Thomas Stafford ("Apollo" commander) (horiz) 2·40 2·50

2000. 50th Anniv of Berlin Film Festival. As T **582c** of Ghana. Multicoloured.

4012 $1.50 *Alphaville*, 1965 60 65
4013 $1.50 Rod Steiger, 1964 60 65
4014 $1.50 *Os Fuzis*, 1964 60 65
4015 $1.50 Jean-Pierre Leaud, 1966 60 65
4016 $1.50 *Cul-de-sac*, 1966 60 65
4017 $1.50 *Ikiru*, 1961 60 65
MS4018 97 × 103 mm. $6 *His Yen*, 1993 2·40 2·50

No. 4012 is inscribed "ALPHAVILE" and No. 4016 "CUL-DELSAC", both in error.

2000. 175th Anniv of Stockton and Darlington Line (first public railway). As T **582d** of Ghana. Multicoloured.

4019 $3 As Type **582d** of Ghana 1·20 1·30
4020 $3 Robert Stephenson's John Bull locomotive, 1831 1·20 1·30

2000. 250th Death Anniv of Johann Sebastian Bach (German composer). Sheet 77 × 89 mm, containing vert portrait (24 × 40 mm) as T **312c** of Gambia.

MS4021 $6 multicoloured 2·40 2·50

2000. Election of Albert Einstein (mathematical physicist) as *Time Magazine* "Man of the Century". Sheet 117 × 91 mm, containing vert portrait as T **312d** of Gambia.

MS4022 $6 multicoloured 2·40 2·50

2000. Centenary of First Zeppelin Flight. As T **582e** of Ghana, each incorporating a different portrait of Count Ferdinand von Zeppelin. Multicoloured.

4023 $3 LZ-130 *Graf Zeppelin II* 1·20 1·30
4024 $3 LZ-2, 1906 1·20 1·30
4025 $3 LZ-127 *Graf Zeppelin*, 1928 1·20 1·30
MS4026 119 × 76 mm. $6 LZ-129 *Hindenburg*, 1936 (50 × 37 mm) 2·40 2·50

2000. Olympic Games, Sydney. As T **582f** of Ghana. Multicoloured.

4027 $2 Archibald Hahn (athletics), St. Louis (1904) 80 85
4028 $2 Showjumping 80 85
4029 $2 Sports Palace, Rome (1960) and Italian flag 80 85
4030 $2 Ancient Greek chariot racing 80 85

472a Junior Murray

473 *Brassolaelio cattleya*

2000. West Indies Cricket Tour and 100th Test Match at Lord's. Multicoloured.

4031 90c. Type **472a** 35 40
4032 $5 Rawl Lewis 2·00 2·10
MS4033 120 × 105 mm. $6 Lord's Cricket Ground (horiz) 2·40 2·50

2000. Orchids. Multicoloured.

4034 75c. Type **473** 30 35
4035 90c. *Maxilbera* 35 40
4036 $1 *Isochilius* 40 45
4037 $1.50 *Lycaste* 60 65
4038 $1.50 *Cochleanthes* 60 65
4039 $1.50 *Brassocattleya* 60 65
4040 $1.50 *Brassolaelio cattleya* 60 65
4041 $1.50 *Iwanagaara* 60 65
4042 $1.50 *Sophrocattleya* 60 65
4043 $1.50 *Laeliocattleya* 60 65
4044 $1.50 *Saphrocattleya* 60 65
4045 $1.50 *Epidendrum* 60 65
4046 $1.50 *Cattleya* 60 65
4047 $1.50 *Ionopsis* 60 65
4048 $1.50 *Brassoepidendrum* 60 65
4049 $2 *Oncidium* 80 85
MS4050 Two sheets, each 73 × 103 mm. (a) $6 *Brassocattleya*. (b) $6 *Vanilla* Set of 2 sheets 4·75 5·00

474 Sir Donald Bradman playing a Stroke

475 Maine Coon

2000. Famous Cricketers. Six sheets, each 290 × 165 mm, containing T **474** and similar vert designs. Multicoloured.

MS4051 (a) $1 × 8, Type **474** and similar shots in sequence. (b) $1 × 8, Sequence of Shane Warne bowling. (c) $2 × 4, Sir Garfield Sobers bowling (two different) or batting (two different). (d) $2 × 4, Different shots of Sir Jack Hobbs batting. (e) $2 × 4, Different shots of Sir Viv Richards batting. (f) $2 × 5, Bradman, Sobers, Hobbs, Warne and Richards Set of 6 sheets 20·00 21·00

2000. Cats and Dogs. Multicoloured.

4052 75c. Type **475** 30 35
4053 90c. Selkirk rex cat 35 40
4054 $1.50 Spotted tabby British shorthair (horiz) 60 65
4055 $1.50 Burmilla (horiz) 60 65
4056 $1.50 British blue shorthair (horiz) 60 65
4057 $1.50 Siamese (horiz) 60 65
4058 $1.50 Japanese bobtail (horiz) 60 65
4059 $1.50 Oriental shorthair (horiz) 60 65
4060 $1.50 Labrador retriever (horiz) 60 65
4061 $1.50 Standard poodle (horiz) 60 65
4062 $1.50 Boxer (horiz) 60 65
4063 $1.50 Rough-coated jack russell terrier (horiz) 60 65
4064 $1.50 Tibetan terrier (horiz) 60 65
4065 $1.50 Welsh corgi (horiz) 60 65
4066 $2 Shetland sheepdog 80 85
4067 $3 Central Asian sheepdog 1·20 1·30
MS4068 Two sheets, each 106 × 76 mm. (a) $6 Scottish fold cat. (b) $6 Irish red and white setter (horiz) Set of 2 sheets 4·75 5·00

Nos. 4054/9 (cats) and 4060/5 (dogs) were each printed together, se-tenant, with the backgrounds forming composite designs.

476 *Marpesia eleuchea bahamaensis*

2000. Butterflies. Multicoloured.

4069 45c. Type **476** 20 25
4070 75c. *Pterourus palamedes* 30 35
4071 90c. *Dryas julia framptonii* 35 40
4072 $1 *Hypna clytemnestra iphegenia* 40 45
4073 $1.50 *Danaus plexippus* 60 65
4074 $1.50 *Anartia amathea* 60 65
4075 $1.50 *Colobura dirce* 60 65
4076 $1.50 *Parides gundiachianus* 60 65
4077 $1.50 *Spiroeta stelenes* 60 65
4078 $1.50 *Hammadryas feronia* 60 65
4079 $1.50 *Merchantis isthmia* 60 65
4080 $1.50 *Colias eurytheme* 60 65
4081 $1.50 *Papilio troilus* 60 65
4082 $1.50 *Junonia coenia* 60 65
4083 $1.50 *Doxocopa laure* 60 65
4084 $1.50 *Pierella hyalinus* 60 65
MS4085 Two sheets, each 95 × 68 mm. (a) $6 *Danaus gilippus*. (b) $6 *Agraulis vanilae insularis* Set of 2 sheets 4·75 5·00

Nos. 4073/8 and 4079/84 were each printed together, se-tenant, with the backgrounds forming composite designs.

477 Grenada National Cricket Stadium

2000. New National Cricket Stadium. Multicoloured.

4086 $2 Type **477** 80 85
MS4087 102 × 79 mm. $1 West Indies and New Zealand Test teams; $1 Cricket match in progress 80 85

478 Vanderhaeghe (Belgian player)

2000. "Euro 2000" Football Championship. Multicoloured.

4088 $1.50 Type **478** 60 65
4089 $1.50 Belgian team 60 65
4090 $1.50 Ronny Gaspercic (Belgian player) 60 65
4091 $1.50 Lorenzo Staelens (Belgian player) 60 65
4092 $1.50 Koning Boudewijn Stadium 60 65
4093 $1.50 Strupar and Mpenza (Belgian player and coach) 60 65
4094 $1.50 Sergi Barjuan (Spanish player) 60 65
4095 $1.50 Spanish team 60 65
4096 $1.50 Luis Enrique (Spanish player) 60 65
4097 $1.50 Hierro (Spanish player) 60 65
4098 $1.50 De Kuip Stadium, Rotterdam 60 65
4099 $1.50 Raul Gonzales (Spanish player) 60 65
4100 $1.50 Dejan Savicevic (Yugoslav player) 60 65
4101 $1.50 Yugoslav team 60 65
4102 $1.50 Predrag Migatovic (Yugoslav player) 60 65
4103 $1.50 Savo Milosevic (Yugoslav player) 60 65
4104 $1.50 Jan Breydel Stadium, Bruges 60 65
4105 $1.50 Darko Kovacevic (Yugoslav player) 60 65
MS4106 Three sheets, each 145 × 95 mm. (a) $6 Robert Waseige (Belgian trainer) (vert). (b) $6 José Antonio Camacho (Spanish trainer) (vert). (c) $6 Vujadin Boskov (Yugoslav trainer) (vert) Set of 3 sheets 7·25 7·50

479 Porkfish

2000. Tropical Fish. Multicoloured.

4107 45c. Type **479** 20 25
4108 75c. Short bigeye 30 35
4109 90c. Red snapper 35 40
4110 $1 Creole wrasse 40 45
4111 $1 Hawksbill turtle 40 45
4112 $1 Foureye butterflyfish 40 45
4113 $1 Porcupinefish 40 45
4114 $1 Yellowtail damselfish 40 45
4115 $1 Adult French angelfish 40 45
4116 $1 Yellow goatfish 40 45
4117 $1 Blue-striped grunt 40 45
4118 $1 Spanish grunt 40 45
4119 $1 Queen triggerfish 40 45
4120 $1 Juvenile French angelfish 40 45
4121 $1 Beaugregory 40 45
4122 $1 Queen angelfish 40 45
4123 $1 Sergeant major 40 45
4124 $1 Bank butterflyfish 40 45
4125 $1 Spanish hogfish 40 45
4126 $1 Porkfish (different) 40 45
4127 $1 Banded butterflyfish 40 45
4128 $1 Longsnout seahorse 40 45
4129 $2 Indigo hamlet 80 85
4130 $3 Blue tang 1·20 1·30
MS4131 Two sheets, each 102 × 73 mm. (a) $6 Blue tang (different). (b) $6 Queen angelfish (different) Set of 2 sheets 4·75 5·00

Nos. 4111/19 and 4120/8 were each printed together, se-tenant, with the backgrounds forming composite designs.

No. 4126 is inscribed "Poskfish" in error.

2000. Monarchs of the Millenium. As T **314a** of Gambia.

4132 $1.50 multicoloured 60 65
4133 $1.50 multicoloured 60 65
4134 $1.50 lilac, stone and brown 60 65
4135 $1.50 lilac, stone and brown 60 65
MS4136 116 × 136 mm. $6 multicoloured 2·40 2·50

DESIGNS: No. 4132, King George III of Great Britain; 4133, King George IV of Great Britain; 4134, Duchess Charlotte of Luxembourg; 4135, Duke Jean of Luxembourg; **MS**4136 King Charles VIII of France.

2000. Popes of the Millennium. As T **314b** of Gambia. Multicoloured (except **MS**4143).

4137 $1.50 Stephen VIII 60 65
4138 $1.50 Theodore 60 65
4139 $1.50 Theodore II 60 65
4140 $1.50 Valentine 60 65
4141 $1.50 Vitalian 60 65
4142 $1.50 Zacharias 60 65
MS4143 116 × 136 mm. $6 Sylvester II (grey, black and stone) 2·40 2·50

480 500 Mondial Sports Car, 1953

2000. Ferrari Cars. Multicoloured.

4144 20c. Type **480** 10 15
4145 45c. 166 Inter saloon, 1948 20 25
4146 75c. 340 MM sports car, 1953 30 35
4147 90c. 500 Superfast saloon, 1964 35 40
4148 $1 166 MM sports car, 1948 40 45
4149 $1.50 250 S saloon, 1952 60 65

4150 $2 250 California convertible, 1957 . . . . 80 85
4151 $3 365 California convertible, 1966 . . . . 1·20 1·30

481 Marmon Model 34, 1921

2000. Classic Cars. Multicoloured.
4152 45c. Type **481** 20 25
4153 75c. Buick D44, 1917 . . . 30 35
4154 90c. Hudson Runabout Landau, 1918 . . . . . 35 40
4155 $1 Chevrolet Royal Mail, 1915 . . . . 40 45
4156 $1.50 Rolls Royce, 1929 . . 60 65
4157 $1.50 Graham Convertible, 1932 . . . . 60 65
4158 $1.50 Mercedes-Benz 540K, 1937 . . . . 60 65
4159 $1.50 Jaguar Mk V, 1948 60 65
4160 $1.50 Lagonda Drophead Coupe, 1939 . . . . 60 65
4161 $1.50 Alfa Romeo Gran Sport, 1930 . . . . . . 60 65
4162 $1.50 Cadillac V63, 1925 . . 60 65
4163 $1.50 Plymouth, 1939 . . . 60 65
4164 $1.50 Franklin Club Sedan, 1934 . . . . 60 65
4165 $1.50 Fiat Ardita, 1933 . . 60 65
4166 $1.50 Essex Speedabout, 1929 . . . . 60 65
4167 $1.50 Stutz Bearcat, 1932 . . 60 65
4168 $2 Kissel Speedster, 1925 . . 80 85
4169 $3 Ford Model T, 1915 . . 1·20 1·30
MS4170 Two sheets, each 94 × 67 mm. (a) $6 Dodge Tourer, 1915. (b) $6 Chrysler, 1924 Set of 2 sheets . . . . 4·75 5·00

482 Borsig Standard Locomotive, 1863

2000. German Railway Locomotives. Mult.
4171 $1.50 Type **482** 60 65
4172 $1.50 German Federal Railway Austerity Class 52, 1940s 60 65
4173 $1.50 Stephenson locomotive *Adler* without tender, 1835 . . . . 60 65
4174 $1.50 Crampton locomotive *Bardenia*, 1863 . . . . . 60 65
4175 $1.50 Drache, 1848 . . . . 60 65
4176 $1.50 Stephenson locomotive *Adler* with tender, 1835 60 65
4177 $1.50 German Federal Railway Class 10, 1956 60 65
4178 $1.50 German Federal Railway Class E10 electric locomotive, 1957 . . . . 60 65
4179 $1.50 German Federal Railway Class 23, 1953 60 65
4180 $1.50 German Federal Railway tank locomotive, 1950s 60 65
4181 $1.50 East German State Railway rebuilt Class 01 Pacific, 1950s 60 65
4182 $1.50 East German State Railway diesel railcar on Berlin–Schonefeld service, 1950s 60 65
MS4183 Two sheets, each 80 × 72 mm. (a) $6 Borsig locomotive of Berlin and Anhalt Railway, 1841. (b) $6 German Federal Railway V.200 diesel-hydraulic locomotive, 1952 Set of 2 sheets . . . . 4·75 5·00

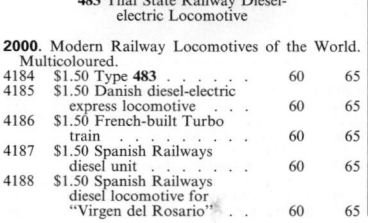

483 Thai State Railway Diesel-electric Locomotive

2000. Modern Railway Locomotives of the World. Multicoloured.
4184 $1.50 Type **483** 60 65
4185 $1.50 Danish diesel-electric express locomotive . . . 60 65
4186 $1.50 French-built Turbo train 60 65
4187 $1.50 Spanish Railways diesel unit 60 65
4188 $1.50 Spanish Railways diesel locomotive for "Virgen del Rosario" . . 60 65
4189 $1.50 Malayan Railways Class 22 diesel-electric locomotive 60 65
4190 $1.50 British Railways Class 87 electric locomotive . . 60 65
4191 $1.50 Iraqi Railway diesel-electric locomotive 60 65
4192 $1.50 Austrian Railways electric locomotive 60 65
4193 $1.50 South Australia Railways diesel locomotive 60 65
4194 $1.50 Black Mesa and Lake Powell Railroad electric locomotive 60 65
4195 $1.50 Yugoslav Railways diesel-electric unit 60 65
MS4196 Four sheets, each 96 × 66 mm. (a) $6 Netherlands Railway Inter-city electric train. (b) $6 Swiss Railways Suburban electric unit. (c) $6 T.E.E. diesel locomotive for "Parsifal". (d) $6 New Zealand Railways "Silver Fern" diesel railcar unit Set of 4 sheets . . . . 9·75 10·00

484 Girl at Skylight

2000. Nursery Rhymes. Multicoloured.
4197 $1.50 Type **484** 60 65
4198 $1.50 Woman and rainbow 60 65
4199 $1.50 Cow and rainbow . . 60 65
4200 $1.50 Boy in nightshirt . . . 60 65
4201 $1.50 Old Woman with baby 60 65
4202 $1.50 Boy on show 60 65
4203 $1.50 Bird in tree and crook 60 65
4204 $1.50 Little Bo-Peep 60 65
4205 $1.50 Sheep 60 65
4206 $1.50 Goose and fence . . . 60 65
4207 $1.50 Goose and Little Bo-Peep 60 65
4208 $1.50 Dog 60 65
4209 $1.50 Sheep and cottage . . 60 65
4210 $1.50 Sun and lane 60 65
4211 $1.50 Cow and haystack . . 60 65
4212 $1.50 Two geese 60 65
4213 $1.50 Dog and Boy Blue's leg 60 65
4214 $1.50 Little Boy Blue asleep 60 65
4215 $1.50 Dove and tower . . . 60 65
4216 $1.50 Cow jumping over moon 60 65
4217 $1.50 Spoon 60 65
4218 $1.50 Dog laughing 60 65
4219 $1.50 Cat playing fiddle . . 60 65
4220 $1.50 Dish 60 65
MS4221 Four sheets, each 106 × 77 mm. (a) $6 Old Woman and shoe (horiz). (b) $6 Little Bo-Peep (horiz). (c) $6 Little Boy Blue asleep (horiz). (d) $6 Cow jumping over moon (horiz) Set of 4 sheets 9·75 10·00

Nos. 4197/202 (Old Woman that lived in a Shoe), 4203/8 (Little Bo-Peep), 4209/14 (Little Boy Blue) and 4215/20 (The Cat and the Fiddle) were each printed together, se-tenant, with the backgrounds forming composite designs.

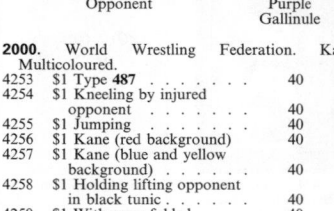

485 Heidi walking with Governess

2000. Shirley Temple in *Heidi*. Showing scenes from the film. Multicoloured.
4222 $1.50 Type **485** 60 65
4223 $1.50 Heidi with grandfather 60 65
4224 $1.50 Heidi with Peter the Goat Boy 60 65
4225 $1.50 Heidi with doves . . . 60 65
4226 $1.50 Heidi with grandfather tying knot 60 65
4227 $1.50 Heidi and governess sitting on bench 60 65
4228 $1.50 Heidi in bed 60 65
4229 $1.50 Heidi with Klara Sesemann 60 65
4230 $1.50 Heidi with Andrews the butler 60 65
4231 $1.50 Heidi unwrapping Christmas presents with the Sesemanns 60 65
MS4232 105 × 75 mm. $6 Heidi sitting on log . . . . 2·40 2·50

486 Betty Boop sitting in Sports Car, Hollywood

2000. Betty Boop (cartoon character). Twelve sheets containing vert designs as T **486** showing geographical locations. Multicoloured.
MS4233 (a) 110 × 90 mm. $6 Type **486**. (b) 110 × 90 mm. $6 Riding horse, Argentina. (c) 110 × 90 mm. $6 Sitting on camel, Turkey. (d) 110 × 90 mm. $6 As flamenco dancer, Spain. (e) 110 × 90 mm. $6 Drinking champagne, France. (f) 110 × 90 mm. $6 Fishing, South Pacific. (g) 110 × 90 mm. $6 As belly dancer, Eygpt. (h) 90 × 110 mm. $6 With guardsman outside Buckingham Palace, London. (i) 90 × 110 mm. $6 In floral hat, Switzerland. (j) 90 × 110 mm. $6 In kimono, Japan. (k) 90 × 110 mm. $6 As Statue of Liberty, New York. (l) 90 × 110 mm. $6 Wearing lei, Hawaii Set of 12 sheets . . . . 29·00 30·00

2000. Scenes from *The Three Stooges* (American T.V. comedy series). As T **310** of Gambia. Multicoloured.
4234 $1 Moe pointing bottle at Curly Joe 40 45
4235 $1 Eating straw with horse 40 45
4236 $1 Larry holding flowers . . 40 45
4237 $1 Reading letter 40 45
4238 $1 Looking in saucepan . . 40 45
4239 $1 Holding wads of notes 40 45
4240 $1 Moe in breastplate (guard behind in purple and green) 40 45
4241 $1 Indoors with horse . . . 40 45
4242 $1 Larry in breastplate (guard behind in lilac and yellow) 40 45
4243 $1 Western bar brawl . . . 40 45
4244 $1 As "DELIGATES" . . . 40 45
4245 $1 In Victorian dress (two as women) 40 45
4246 $1 Moe pointing gun . . . 40 45
4247 $1 Holding certificate . . . 40 45
4248 $1 Moe using secateurs near Curly's nose 40 45
4249 $1 Larry (picture at right) 40 45
4250 $1 Moe in front of picture 40 45
4251 $1 Curly 40 45
MS4252 Twelve sheets. (a) 108 × 87 mm. $5 Curly in green shirt holding Moe's arm (vert). (b) 108 × 87 mm. $5 In evening dress with girl. (c) 108 × 87 mm. $5 Moe with Larry holding woman's hand (vert). (d) 91 × 137 mm. $5 With secretary from *He Cooked His Goose* (vert). (e) 108 × 87 mm. $5 As No. 4243. (f) 108 × 89 mm. $5 Having heads banged together by cowboy. (g) 97 × 118 mm. $5 Putting Larry in a jet engine (vert). (h) 98 × 125 mm. $5 Curly Joe with cigar (vert). (i) 107 × 88 mm. $5 Listening to jet engine. (j) 107 × 88 mm. $5 Swinging propeller. (k) 130 × 100 mm. $6 Larry and Moe in breastplates. (l) 130 × 100 mm. $6 Curly with hand in mangle Set of 12 sheets . . 25·00 26·00

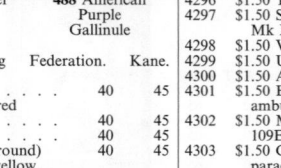

487 Kane jumping over Opponent

488 American Purple Gallinule

2000. World Wrestling Federation. Kane. Multicoloured.
4253 $1 Type **487** 40 45
4254 $1 Kneeling by injured opponent 40 45
4255 $1 Jumping 40 45
4256 $1 Kane (red background) 40 45
4257 $1 Kane (blue and yellow background) 40 45
4258 $1 Holding lifting opponent in black tunic 40 45
4259 $1 With arms folded 40 45
4260 $1 Lifting opponent in black and white trousers 40 45
4261 $1 Lifting opponent No. 59 40 45
MS4262 Two sheets, each 77 × 118 mm. (a) $5 With black glove on right hand. (b) $5 Lifting opponent Set of 2 sheets . . . 4·00 4·25

2000. "Espana 2000" International Stamp Exhibition, Madrid. Paintings from the Prado Museum. As T **326a** of Gambia. Multicoloured.
4263 $1.50 King Ferdinand and priest from "The Virgin of the Catholic Monarchs" (anon) 60 65
4264 $1.50 Virgin and Child from "The Virgin of the Catholic Monarchs" . . . 60 65
4265 $1.50 Queen Isabella and priest from "The Virgin of the Catholic Monarchs" 60 65
4266 $1.50 "The Flagellation" (Alejo Fernandez) 60 65
4267 $1.50 "The Virgin and Souls in Purgatory" (Pedro Machuca) 60 65
4268 $1.50 "The Holy Trinity" (El Greco) 60 65
4269 $1.50 "The Saviour's Blessing" (Francisco de Zurbaran) 60 65
4270 $1.50 "St. John the Baptist" (Francesco Solimena) . . 60 65
4271 $1.50 "Noli Me Tangere" (Correggio) 60 65
4272 $1.50 "St. Casilda" (Francisco de Zurbaran) 60 65
4273 $1.50 "Nicolas Omazur" (Murillo) 60 65
4274 $1.50 "Juan Martinez Montanes" (Velazquez) 60 65
4275 $1.50 "Playing at Giants" (Goya) 60 65
4276 $1.50 "The Holy Family with Oak Tree" (Raphael and Giulio Romano) . . 60 65
4277 $1.50 "Don Gaspar Melchor de Jovellanos" (Goya) . . 60 65
4278 $1.50 Courtier from "Joseph in Pharaoh's Palace" (Jacopo Amiconi) 60 65
4279 $1.50 Pharaoh and Joseph from "Joseph in Pharaoh's Palace" 60 65
4280 $1.50 Servant with hat from "Joseph in Pharaoh's Palace" 60 65
MS4281 Three sheets. (a) 90 × 110 mm. $6 "The Virgin of the Catholic Monarchs" (anon). (b) 90 × 110 mm. $6 "St. Anne, the Virgin, St. Elizabeth, St. John and the Christ Child" (Fernando Yanez de la Almedina). (c) 110 × 90 mm. $6 "Joseph in Pharoah's Palace" (Jacopo Amiconi) (horiz) Set of 3 sheets 7·25 7·50

2000. Birds of the Caribbean. Multicoloured.
4282 25c. Type **488** 10 15
4283 40c. Limpkin 15 20
4284 50c. Black-necked stilt . . . 20 25
4285 60c. Painted bunting 25 30
4286 75c. Yellow-breasted flycatcher warbler ("Yellow-breasted Warbler") 30 35
4287 $1 Blackburnian warbler . . 40 45
4288 $1.25 Blue grosbeak 50 55
4289 $1.50 Black and white warbler 60 65
4290 $1.60 Himalayan whistling thrush ("Blue Whistling Thrush") 65 70
4291 $3 Common yellowthroat 1·20 1·30
4292 $4 Indigo bunting . . . . . 1·60 1·70
4293 $5 Catbird . . . . 2·00 2·25
4294 $10 Bananaquit . . . . . . 4·00 4·25
4295 $20 Blue-grey gnatcatcher 8·00 8·25

489 Messerschmitt Bf 109E under Attack

2000. 60th Anniv of Battle of Britain. Multicoloured.
4296 $1.50 Type **489** 60 65
4297 $1.50 Supermarine Spitfire Mk XI 60 65
4298 $1.50 V1 flying bomb . . . 60 65
4299 $1.50 U-Boat under attack . 60 65
4300 $1.50 Anti-aircraft gun . . . 60 65
4301 $1.50 Bedford army ambulance 60 65
4302 $1.50 Messerschmitt Bf 109E 60 65
4303 $1.50 German pilot parachuting 60 65
4304 $1.50 Hawker Hurricane MkI 60 65
4305 $1.50 British airfield under attack 60 65

4306 $1.50 Heinkel He 111H on fire 60 65
4307 $1.50 R.A.F. emblem on Supermarine Spitfire Mk XI 60 65
MS4308 Two sheets, each 99 × 71 mm. (a) $6 Supermarine Spitfire Mk IX. (b) $6 Hawker Hurricane Mk 1s on tarmac Set of 2 sheets . . . . 4·75 5·00
No. 4304 is inscribed "Hanker Hurricane HK1" and No. **MS**4308 "HK1", both in error.

2000. Queen Elizabeth the Queen Mother's 100th Birthday. As T **318** of Gambia. Multicoloured.
4309 $1.50 Queen Mother in grey hat 60 65

2000. Faces of the Millennium: Queen Elizabeth the Queen Mother's 100th Birthday. As T **307a** of Gambia showing collage of miniature flower photographs. Multicoloured.
4310 $1 Top of head (face value at left) 40 45
4311 $1 Top of head (face value at right) 40 45
4312 $1 Eye and temple (face value at left) 40 45
4313 $1 Temple (face value at right) 40 45
4314 $1 Cheek (face value at left) 40 45
4315 $1 Cheek (face value at right) 40 45
4316 $1 Chin (face value at left) 40 45
4317 $1 Neck (face value at right) 40 45
Nos. 4310/17 were printed together, se-tenant, in sheetlets of 8 with the stamps arranged in two vertical columns separated by a gutter also containing miniature photographs. When viewed as a whole the sheetlet forms a portrait of the Queen Mother.

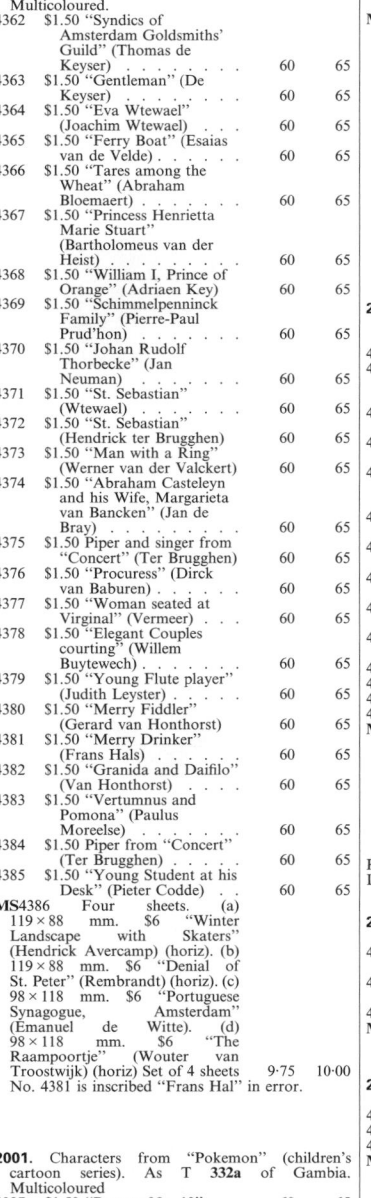

490 *Brassavola nodosa*

491 Angel in Red

2000. Caribbean Flowers. Multicoloured.
4318 25c. Type **490** 10 15
4319 35c. *Laelia anceps* (horiz) . . 15 20
4320 75c. *Plumeria rubra* (horiz) 30 35
4321 $1 *Bougainvillea glabra* (horiz) 40 45
4322 $1 *Allamanda catharticia* . . 40 45
4323 $1.50 *Cassia alata* 60 65
4324 $1.50 *Anthurium andreanum* 60 65
4325 $1.50 *Ipomea crassicaulis* . . 60 65
4326 $1.50 *Laelia anceps* 60 65
4327 $1.50 *Galeandra baueri* . . . 60 65
4328 $1.50 *Hibiscus rosa-sinensis* 60 65
4329 $1.50 *Alpinia purpurata* . . 60 65
4330 $1.50 *Strelitzia reginae* . . . 60 65
4331 $1.50 *Psychlis atropurpurea* 60 65
4332 $1.50 *Cattleya velutina* . . . 60 65
4333 $1.50 *Caularthron bicornutum* 60 65
4334 $1.50 *Cattleya warneri* . . . 60 65
4335 $1.50 *Mandevilla splendens* 60 65
4336 $1.50 *Tithonia rotundifolia* 60 65
4337 $1.50 *Lagerstromia speciosa* 60 65
4338 $1.50 *Columnea argentea* . . 60 65
4339 $1.50 *Brunfelsia calycina* . . 60 65
4340 $1.50 *Portlandia albiflora* . . 60 65
4341 $1.50 *Pachira insignis* . . . 60 65
4342 $1.50 *Jatropha integerrima* 60 65
4343 £1.50 *Jacaranda filicifolia* . . 60 65
4344 $1.50 *Cordia sebestena* . . . 60 65
4345 $1.50 *Allamanda cathartica* 60 65
4346 $1.50 *Samanea saman* . . . 60 65
4347 $2 *Lisianthius nigrescens* (horiz) 80 85
4348 $2 *Aspasia epidendroides* . . 80 85
4349 $3 *Oncidium splendidum* . . 1·20 1·30
MS4350 Four sheets. (a) 68 × 97 mm. $6 *Anthurium scherzerianum* (horiz). (b) 68 × 97 mm. $6 *Ipomea learii* (horiz). (c) 94 × 61 mm. $6 *Fuchsia* (horiz). (d) 94 × 61 mm. $6 *Heliconia psittaconia* Set of 4 sheets . . . . 9·75 10·00
Nos. 4323/8, 4329/34, 4335/40 and 4341/6 were each printed together, se-tenant, each forming a composite floral design.
No. 4320 is inscribed "Plumieria", 4341 "Pachira insigis", 4343 "Jacarancla filicifolia" and 4345 "Corclia filicifolia", all in error.

2000. Christmas. Holy Year. Multicoloured.
4351 15c. Type **491** 10 10
4352 25c. Angel praying 10 15
4353 50c. Type **491** 20 25
4354 $2 As 25c 80 85
4355 $2 Type **491** 80 85
4356 $5 As 25c . . . . 2·00 2·10
MS4357 110 × 120 mm. $6 Holy Child (horiz) . . . . 2·40 2·50

2001. Chinese New Year. ("Year of the Snake"). As T **470**. Multicoloured.
4358 $2 Blue and yellow snake 80 85
4359 $2 Green snake (inverted triangle) 80 85
4360 $2 Red snake 80 85

491a Lucy and Desi with Friends

2001. Scenes from *I Love Lucy* (American T.V. comedy series). Eight sheets, each containing multicoloured design as T **491a**.
MS4361 (a) 80 × 112 mm. $6 Type **491a**. (b) 80 × 110 mm. $6 Lucy and Desi dancing. (c) 88 × 127 mm. $6 Lucy in checked jacket. (d) 92 × 124 mm. $6 Lucy in checked jacket dancing with Desi. (e) 98 × 120 mm. $6 Desi laughing with William Frawley. (f) 118 × 92 mm. $6 Lucy leaning on mantelpiece. (g) 118 × 100 mm. $6 Lucy sitting at desk. (h) 92 × 124 mm. $6 William Frawley and Desi at desk (horiz) Set of 8 sheets . . . . 19·00 20·00

2001. Bicentenary of Rijksmuseum, Amsterdam. Dutch Paintings. As T **330a** of Gambia. Multicoloured.
4362 $1.50 "Syndics of Amsterdam Goldsmiths' Guild" (Thomas de Keyser) 60 65
4363 $1.50 "Gentleman" (De Keyser) 60 65
4364 $1.50 "Eva Wtewael" (Joachim Wtewael) . . . 60 65
4365 $1.50 "Ferry Boat" (Esaias van de Velde) 60 65
4366 $1.50 "Tares among the Wheat" (Abraham Bloemaert) 60 65
4367 $1.50 "Princess Henrietta Marie Stuart" (Bartholomeus van der Heist) 60 65
4368 $1.50 "William I, Prince of Orange" (Adriaen Key) 60 65
4369 $1.50 "Schimmelpenninck Family" (Pierre-Paul Prud'hon) 60 65
4370 $1.50 "Johan Rudolf Thorbecke" (Jan Neuman) 60 65
4371 $1.50 "St. Sebastian" (Wtewael) 60 65
4372 $1.50 "St. Sebastian" (Hendrick ter Brugghen) 60 65
4373 $1.50 "Man with a Ring" (Werner van der Valckert) 60 65
4374 $1.50 "Abraham Casteleyn and his Wife, Margarieta van Bancken" (Jan de Bray) 60 65
4375 $1.50 Piper and singer from "Concert" (Ter Brugghen) 60 65
4376 $1.50 "Procuress" (Dirck van Baburen) 60 65
4377 $1.50 "Woman seated at Virginal" (Vermeer) . . . 60 65
4378 $1.50 "Elegant Couples courting" (Willem Buytewech) 60 65
4379 $1.50 "Young Flute player" (Judith Leyster) 60 65
4380 $1.50 "Merry Fiddler" (Gerard van Honthorst) 60 65
4381 $1.50 "Merry Drinker" (Frans Hals) 60 65
4382 $1.50 "Granida and Daifilo" (Van Honthorst) 60 65
4383 $1.50 "Vertumnus and Pomona" (Paulus Moreelse) 60 65
4384 $1.50 Piper from "Concert" (Ter Brugghen) 60 65
4385 $1.50 "Young Student at his Desk" (Pieter Codde) . . 60 65
MS4386 Four sheets. (a) 119 × 88 mm. $6 "Winter Landscape with Skaters" (Hendrick Avercamp) (horiz). (b) 119 × 88 mm. $6 "Denial of St. Peter" (Rembrandt) (horiz). (c) 98 × 118 mm. $6 "Portuguese Synagogue, Amsterdam" (Emanuel de Witte). (d) 98 × 118 mm. $6 "The Raampoortje" (Wouter van Troostwijk) (horiz) Set of 4 sheets 9·75 10·00
No. 4381 is inscribed "Frans Hal" in error.

2001. Characters from "Pokemon" (children's cartoon series). As T **332a** of Gambia. Multicoloured
4387 $1.50 "Rattata No. 19" . . 60 65
4388 $1.50 "Sandshrew No. 27" 60 65
4389 $1.50 "Wartortle No. 08" 60 65
4390 $1.50 "Primeape No. 57" . . 60 65
4391 $1.50 "Golduck No. 55" . . 60 65
4392 $1.50 "Persian No. 53" . . 60 65
MS4393 74 × 115 mm. $6 "Jolteon No. 135" . . . . 2·40 2·50

492 African Pygmy Goose

2001. "Hong Kong 2001" International Stamp Exhibition. Ducks of the World. Multicoloured.
4394 $1.25 Type **492** 50 55
4395 $1.25 Versicolor teal ("Silver Teal") 50 55
4396 $1.25 Marbled teal 50 55
4397 $1.25 Garganey 50 55
4398 $1.25 Wandering whistling duck 50 55
4399 $1.25 Northern shoveler . . 50 55
4400 $1.25 Flying steamer duck ("Flightless Steamer Duck") 50 55
4401 $1.25 Radjah shelduck . . . 50 55
4402 $1.25 Cape teal 50 55
4403 $1.25 Hartlaub's duck . . . 50 55
4404 $1.25 Ruddy shelduck . . . 50 55
4405 $1.25 Bahama pintail ("White-cheeked Pintail") 50 55
4406 $1.25 Fulvous whistling duck (vert) 50 55
4407 $1.25 African black duck (vert) 50 55
4408 $1.25 Madagascar pochard ("Madagascan White-eye") (vert) 50 55
4409 $1.25 African pygmy goose ("Pygmy Goose") (vert) 50 55
4410 $1.25 Wood duck (female) (vert) 50 55
4411 $1.25 Wood duck (male) (vert) 50 55
MS4412 Three sheets, each 100 × 70 mm. (a) $6 Flying steamer duck. (b) $6 Flightless steamer duck. (c) $6 Australian shelduck (vert) Set of 3 sheets 7·25 7·50

493 "Daily Life in Edo" (Miyagawa Choshum)

2001. "Philanippon '01" International Stamp Exhibition, Tokyo. Japanese Paintings. Multicoloured.
4413 75c. Type **493** 30 35
4414 90c. "Twelve Famous Places in Japan" (Kano Isen'in Naganobu) 35 40
4415 $1 "After the Rain" (Kawai Gyokudo) 40 45
4416 $1.25 "Ryogoku Bridge" (Kano Kyuei) 50 55
4417 $2 "Courtesan of Fukagawa" (Katsukawa Shun'ei) 80 85
4418 $2 "Yugao Chapter" (85 × 28 mm) 80 85
4419 $2 "Suetsumuhana Chapter" (85 × 28 mm) 80 85
4420 $2 "Wakamurasaki Chapter" (85 × 28 mm) . . 80 85
4421 $2 "Momiji-no-ga Chapter" (85 × 28 mm) 80 85
4422 $2 Praying in the woods (vert) 80 85
4423 $2 Lady with servants (vert) 80 85
4424 $2 Fire by river (vert) 80 85
4425 $2 Pagoda by river (vert) . . 80 85
4426 $3 "Bear Killing" (unsigned) 1·20 1·30
MS4427 Two sheets. (a) 93 × 81 mm. $6 "Pomegranates and a Small Bird" (Onishi Keisai). (b) 97 × 76 mm. $6 from "Bodhisattva: Never Despise" (Enryaku-ji) (vert). Nos. 4418/21 depict "Tale of Genji" Set of 2 sheets . . . . 4·75 5·00
Nos. 4418/21 depict "Tale of Genji" (Kano Ryusetsu Hidenobu), and Nos. 4422/5 illustrates "The Lotus Sutra—Tactfulness" (Hompo-ji).

2001. Death Centenary of Queen Victoria. As T **590a** of Ghana. Multicoloured.
4428 $3 Princess Victoria as a young girl . . . . . . 1·20 1·30
4429 $3 Young Queen Victoria wearing crown . . . . . 1·20 1·30
4430 $3 In old age . . . . 1·20 1·30
MS4431 77 × 107 mm. $6 Queen Victoria on throne . . . . . . 2·40 2·50

2001. 25th Death Anniv of Mao Tse-tung (Chinese leader). As T **590b** of Ghana. Multicoloured.
4432 $2 Mao Tse-tung in 1936 . . 80 85
4433 $2 In 1919 . . . . 80 85
4434 $2 In 1945 . . . . 80 85
MS4435 133 × 126 mm. $3 Mao Tse-tung encouraging troops in 1938 1·20 1·30

2001. 75th Death Anniv of Claude-Oscar Monet (French painter). As T **590c** of Ghana. Multicoloured.
4436 $2 "Boats in Winter Quarters, Etretat" 80 85
4437 $2 "Regatta at Sainte Adresse" 80 85
4438 $2 "Bridge at Bougival" . . 80 85
4439 $2 "Beach at Sainte Adresse" 80 85
MS4440 136 × 111 mm. $6 "Monet's Garden at Vetheuil" (vert) . . 2·40 2·50

2001. 75th Birthday of Queen Elizabeth II. As T **590d** of Ghana. Multicoloured.
4441 $2 Queen in straw boater . . 80 85
4442 $2 Queen in red hat 80 85
4443 $2 Wearing multicoloured pastel hat 80 85
4444 $2 Wearing mauve turban-style hat 80 85
MS4445 76 × 100 mm. $6 Queen wearing mauve hat and coat (37 × 50 mm) . . . . 2·40 2·50

2001. Death Centenary of Giuseppe Verdi (Italian composer). As T **590e** of Ghana. Multicoloured.
4446 $2 Character from Ernani (opera) 80 85
4447 $2 Score from Ernani . . . 80 85
4448 $2 Verdi as a young man . . 80 85
4449 $2 La Scala Opera House, Milan 80 85
MS4450 76 × 106 mm. $6 Verdi in old age . . . . 2·40 2·50

2001. Death Centenary of Henri de Toulouse-Lautrec (French painter). As T **590f** of Ghana. Multicoloured.
4451 $2 "Alone" 80 85
4452 $2 "Two Half-naked Women" 80 85
4453 $2 "The Toilette" 80 85
4454 $2 "Justine Dieuhl" 80 85
MS4455 66 × 84 mm. $6 "Mademoiselle Dihau at the Piano" . . . . 2·40 2·50

494 Woman on Beach

2001. United Nations Women's Human Rights Campaign. Multicoloured.
4456 90c. Type **494** 35 40
4457 $1 "Caribbean Woman II" 40 45

495 Marlene Dietrich smoking

2001. Birth Centenary of Marlene Dietrich (actress and singer).
4458 **495** $2 multicoloured 80 85
4459 – $2 black, purple and red 80 85
4460 – $2 black, purple and red 80 85
4461 – $2 black, purple and red 80 85
DESIGNS No. 4459, Marlene Dietrich on stage with microphone; 4460, Wearing feather boa; 4461, Sitting in armchair.

496 Phoenician Merchant Ship

2001. "Belgica 2001" International Stamp Exhibition, Brussels. Sailing Ships. Mult.
4462 45c. Type **496** 20 25
4463 75c. Portuguese caravel . . 30 35
4464 90c. Marblehead schooner 35 40
4465 $1 Mala pansi 40 45
4466 $1 English cog 40 45
4467 $1 Roman merchantman . . 40 45
4468 $1 Greek war galley 40 45
4469 $1 Greek merchantman . . 40 45
4470 $1 Oseberg Viking longship 40 45
4471 $1 Egyptian sailing craft . . 40 45
4472 $1 Egyptian galley 40 45
4473 $1 16th-century galleass . . 40 45
4474 $1 Norman ship 40 45
4475 $1 English carrack 40 45
4476 $1 Mediterranean carrack 40 45
4477 $1 Spanish galleon 40 45
4478 $1 Elizabethan Grumster . . 40 45
4479 $1 British East Indiaman . . 40 45
4480 $1 Clipper 40 45
4481 $1 British ship of the line 40 45
4482 $1 British gun boat 40 45
4483 $1 English hoy 40 45

4484 $1 Gloucester fishing schooner 40 45
4485 $1 Sloop-rigged yacht . . . 40 45
4486 $1 Chinese junk 40 45
4487 $1 Sambuk 40 45
4488 $1 Baltimore clipper schooner 40 45
4489 $1 Schooner-rigged yacht . . 40 45
4490 $1 American clipper 40 45
4491 $1 American frigate 40 45
4492 $1 Sail/steam mail packet . . 40 45
4493 $1.50 American corvette . . 60 65
4494 $2 Racing schooner 80 85
MS4495 Two sheets, each 60 × 44 mm. (a) $6 *Suhaili* (yacht), 1968. (b) $6 *Gulf Streamer* (trimaran) and Polynesian outrigger Set of 2 sheets . . . 4·75 5·00

No. 4481 is inscribed "BRITISH GUN SHIP", 4482 "BRITISH FLAGSHIP" and 4484 "GLOUSTER", all in error.

497 Montauk Point Lighthouse, New York

497a Anatoly Karpov

2001. Lighthouses. Multicoloured.
4496 25c. Type **497** 10 15
4497 50c. Alcatraz lighthouse, San Francisco 20 25
4498 $1 Barnegat lighthouse, New Jersey 40 45
4499 $1.50 Point Amour lighthouse, Canada . . . 60 65
4500 $1.50 Inubo-Saki lighthouse, Japan 60 65
4501 $1.50 Belle-Ile lighthouse, France 60 65
4502 $1.50 Faerder lighthouse, Norway 60 65
4503 $1.50 Cape Agulhas lighthouse, South Africa 60 65
4504 $1.50 Minicoy lighthouse, India 60 65
4505 $1.50 Admiralty lighthouse, Washington 60 65
4506 $1.50 Hooper's Strait lighthouse, Maryland . . 60 65
4507 $1.50 Hunting Island lighthouse, South Carolina 60 65
4508 $1.50 Key West Lighthouse Museum, Florida 60 65
4509 $1.50 Old Point Loma lighthouse, California . . 60 65
4510 $1.50 Old Makinac Point lighthouse, Michigan . . 60 65
4511 $1.50 Keri lighthouse, Estonia 60 65
4512 $1.50 Anholt lighthouse, Denmark 60 65
4513 $1.50 Porer lighthouse, Croatia 60 65
4514 $1.50 Laotieshan lighthouse, China 60 65
4515 $1.50 Sapienza Methoni lighthouse, Greece 60 65
4516 $1.50 Arkona lighthouse, Germany 60 65
4517 $2 St. Augustine lighthouse, Florida 80 85
MS4518 Four sheets, each 70 × 98 mm. (a) $6 Kvitsoy lighthouse, Norway. (b) $6 Mahota Pagoda lighthouse, China. (c) $6 Boston lighthouse, Massachusetts. (d) $6 Pellworm lighthouse, Germany. . . . . 9·75 10·00

Nos. 4503 and 4515 are inscribed "Africca" or "Sapientza", both in error.

2001. First e-World Chess Championship. Sheet 88 × 103 mm.
MS4518a **497a** $20 multicoloured 8·00 8·25

498 Commerson's Dolphin

2001. Whales and Dolphins. Multicoloured.
4519 25c. Type **498** 10 15
4520 50c. Pacific white-sided dolphin 20 25
4521 $1.50 Risso's dolphin . . . 60 65
4522 $1.50 Fraser's dolphin . . . 60 65
4523 $1.50 Dall's porpoise . . . 60 65
4524 $1.50 Right whale 60 65
4525 $1.50 Grey whale 60 65
4526 $1.50 Minke whale 60 65
4527 $1.50 Common dolphin . . . 60 65
4528 $1.50 Antillean beaked whale 60 65
4529 $1.50 Killer whale's tail and divers 60 65
4530 $1.50 Bryde's whale 60 65
4531 $1.50 Cuvier's beaked whale 60 65
4532 $1.50 Sei whale 60 65
4533 $1.50 Harbour porpoise . . 60 65
4534 $1.50 Beluga 60 65
4535 $1.50 White-beaked dolphin 60 65
4536 $1.50 Narwhal 60 65
4537 $1.50 Bowhead whale . . . 60 65
4538 $1.50 Fin whale 60 65
4539 $2 Northern bottlenosed whale 80 85
4540 $3 Baird's beaked whale . . 1·20 1·30
MS4541 Four sheets, each 75 × 52 mm. (a) $6 Humpback whale and calf. (b) $6 Sperm whale calf. (c) $6 Blue whale with calf. (d) $6 Southern right whale . . 9·75 10·00

Nos. 4521/6, 4527/32 and 4533/8 were printed together, se-tenant, with the backgrounds forming composite designs.

499 World Cup Publicity Poster, Brazil, 1950

2001. World Cup Football Championship, Japan and Korea (2002). Multicoloured.
4542 $1.50 Type **499** 60 65
4543 $1.50 West German players, Switzerland, 1954 . . . . 60 65
4544 $1.50 Just Fontaine (France), Sweden, 1958 60 65
4545 $1.50 Garrincha (Brazil), Chile, 1962 . . . . 60 65
4546 $1.50 Bobby Moore (England), England, 1966 60 65
4547 $1.50 Pele (Brazil), Mexico, 1970 . . . . 60 65
4548 $1.50 Osvaldo Ardiles (Argentina), Argentina, 1978 . . . . 60 65
4549 $1.50 Lakhdar Belloumi (Algeria), Spain, 1982 . . 60 65
4550 $1.50 Diego Maradona (Argentina), Mexico, 1986 60 65
4551 $1.50 Lothar Matthaus and Rudi Voller (West Germany), Italy, 1990 . . 60 65
4552 $1.50 Seo Jung Won (South Korea), U.S.A., 1994 . . 60 65
4553 $1.50 Ronaldo (Brazil), France, 1998 . . . . . . 60 65
MS4554 Two sheets, each 88 × 75 mm. (a) $6 Detail of Jules Rimet Trophy, Uruguay, 1930. (b) $6 Detail of World Cup Trophy, Japan–Korea, 2002 . . . . . 4·75 5·00

500 Arsenal Football Stadium, Highbury

2001. British Football Clubs (1st series). Multicoloured.
4555 $1.50 Type **500** 60 65
4556 $1.50 Players celebrating European Cup Winners' Cup success, 1994 . . . 60 65
4557 $1.50 Players celebrating Premiership success, 1998 60 65
4558 $1.50 Entrance to Highbury 60 65
4559 $1.50 Dressing room 60 65
4560 $1.50 Arsenal defenders with trophies and shield, 1998 60 65
4561 $1.50 Aston Villa emblem at Villa Park 60 65
4562 $1.50 Villa Park stands at night 60 65
4563 $1.50 Stands and boxes . . . 60 65
4564 $1.50 Trinity Road Stand, Villa Park 60 65
4565 $1.50 Holte End Stand, Villa Park 60 65
4566 $1.50 Aston Villa supporters 60 65
4567 $1.50 Reebok Stadium, Bolton (empty) 60 65
4568 $1.50 Players celebrating Division 1 play-off success, 2001 . . . . . . 60 65
4569 $1.50 Fan holding banner 60 65
4570 $1.50 Fans celebrating promotion 60 65
4571 $1.50 Team with Division 1 Cup, 2001 . . . . 60 65
4572 $1.50 Reebok Stadium during match 60 65
4573 $1.50 Everton squad, 2001–02 . . . . 60 65
4574 $1.50 Manager Duncan Ferguson, 2000 . . . . . 60 65
4575 $1.50 Statue of Dixie Dean (former player) 60 65
4576 $1.50 Everton supporters watching match 60 65
4577 $1.50 Goodison Park Stadium 60 65
4578 $1.50 Everton squad, League champions, 1969–70 . . . . 60 65
4579 $1.50 Ipswich Town players and Division 1 Cup, 2000 60 65
4580 $1.50 Ipswich Town squad, 2001–02 . . . . 60 65
4581 $1.50 Manager George Burley shaking hands with David Sheepshanks (chairman) 60 65
4582 $1.50 Pablo Counago running 60 65
4583 $1.50 Matt Holland (captain), 2001 . . . . . 60 65
4584 $1.50 George Burley with Manager of the Year Award, 2001 . . . . . . 60 65
4585 $1.50 Anfield Stadium, Liverpool 60 65
4586 $1.50 Players celebrating Worthington Cup victory, 2000–01 . . . . 60 65
4587 $1.50 Players celebrating F.A. Cup victory, 2000–01 60 65
4588 $1.50 Supporters watching match 60 65
4589 $1.50 Victorious U.E.F.A. Cup Team, 2000–01 . . . 60 65
4590 $1.50 Players, manager and fans, Treble victory parade, 2001 . . . . . . 60 65
4591 $1.50 Billy Meredith, Denis Law and Bobby Charlton (former players) 60 65
4592 $1.50 Treble Trophies, 1998–9 . . . . 60 65
4593 $1.50 Different views of Old Trafford before 1950s . . 60 65
4594 $1.50 Different views of Old Trafford since 1974 . . . 60 65
4595 $1.50 Players celebrating third successive Premiership title, 2000–01 60 65
4596 $1.50 George Best, Bryan Robson and David Beckham (players) 60 65
4597 $1.50 Exterior of Ibrox Stadium, Glasgow 60 65
4598 $1.50 Rangers' European Cup winning team, 1972 60 65
4599 $1.50 Scottish F.A. and Premier League trophies, 2000 . . . . 60 65
4600 $1.50 Ibrox Stadium from the air 60 65
4601 $1.50 Match in progress at Ibrox Stadium 60 65
4602 $1.50 Scottish flag and emblem celebrating ninth consecutive league victory, 1997 . . . . 60 65

501 Father Christmas and House

2001. Christmas. Father Christmas. Multicoloured.
4603 15c. Type **501** 10 10
4604 50c. Father Christmas with snowman and fir trees . . 20 25
4605 $1 Father Christmas ice-skating 40 45
4606 $4 Father Christmas with children . . . . 1·60 1·70
MS4607 107 × 76 mm. $6 Father Christmas eating mince pie . . 2·40 2·50

502 Princess Diana wearing Blue Dress and Tiara

2001. 40th Birth Anniv of Diana, Princess of Wales. Multicoloured.
4608 $1.50 Type **502** 60 65
4609 $1.50 Wearing white evening dress 60 65
4610 $1.50 In red dress and tiara 60 65
MS4611 80 × 102 mm. $6 Wearing pearl choker . . . . 2·40 2·50

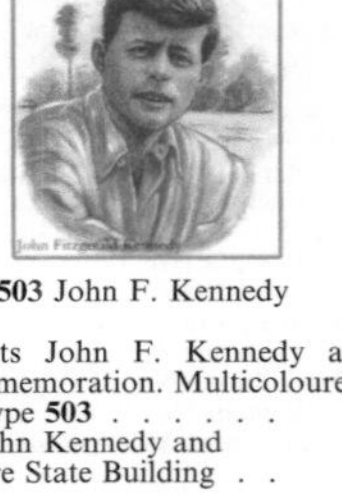

503 John F. Kennedy

2001. Presidents John F. Kennedy and Ronald Reagan Commemoration. Multicoloured.
4612 $1.50 Type **503** 60 65
4613 $1.50 John Kennedy and Empire State Building . . 60 65
4614 $1.50 John Kennedy with aircraft 60 65
4615 $1.50 Ronald Reagan in *Hellcats of the Navy* (film) 60 65
4616 $1.50 Wearing dark suit and red tie 60 65
4617 $1.50 Ronald Reagan with American flag 60 65
MS4618 Two sheets. (a) 67 × 83 mm. $6 John F. Kennedy. (b) 78 × 105 mm. $6 Ronald Reagan on telephone . . . . 4·75 5·00

2001. Centenary of Nobel Prizes. Prize Winners of 1901 (Nos. 4619/22 and 4629/30) and 1921 (others). As T **595** of Ghana. Multicoloured.
4619 75c. Emil von Behring (Medicine) 30 35
4620 90c. Wilhelm Rontgen (Physics) 35 40
4621 $1 Jacobus van't Hoff (Chemistry) 40 45
4622 $1.50 Frederic Passy (Peace) 60 65
4623 $1.50 Albert Einstein as a young man (horiz) . . . 60 65
4624 $1.50 Smoking a pipe (horiz) 60 65
4625 $1.50 Wearing grey (horiz) 60 65
4626 $1.50 In pink jumper (horiz) 60 65
4627 $1.50 Wearing black jacket (horiz) 60 65
4628 $1.50 In blue jumper (horiz) 60 65
4629 $2 Jean-Henri Dunant (Peace) 80 85
4630 $3 Rene Sully-Prudhomme (Literature) . . . . 1·20 1·30
MS4631 65 × 87 mm. $6 Albert Einstein wearing Panama hat 2·40 2·50

504 Brown Horse with Pale Mane

2001. Chinese New Year ("Year of the Horse"). Tang Dynasty Ceramic Horses. Multicoloured.
4632 $1.50 Type **504** 60 65
4633 $1.50 Purple dappled horse 60 65
4634 $1.50 Blue horse 60 65
4635 $1.50 Brown horse with short mane 60 65
MS4636 100 × 70 mm. $4 Brown horse with flowers on bridle . . 1·60 1·70

505 Ruby

506 U.S. Flag as Statue of Liberty with Grenada Flag

2001. Precious Stones and Minerals. Multicoloured.
4637 $1.50 Type **505** 60 65
4638 $1.50 Sardonyx 60 65
4639 $1.50 Sapphire 60 65
4640 $1.50 Opal 60 65
4641 $1.50 Topaz 60 65
4642 $1.50 Turquoise 60 65
4643 $1.50 Garnet 60 65
4644 $1.50 Amethyst 60 65
4645 $1.50 Aquamarine 60 65
4646 $1.50 Diamond 60 65
4647 $1.50 Emerald 60 65
4648 $1.50 Pearl 60 65
4649 $1.50 Ruby (horiz) 60 65
4650 $1.50 Diamond (horiz) . . . 60 65
4651 $1.50 Sapphire (horiz) . . . 60 65
4652 $1.50 Opal (horiz) 60 65
4653 $1.50 Turquoise (horiz) . . 60 65
4654 $1.50 Jade (horiz) 60 65
MS4655 Three sheets. (a) 82 × 76 mm. $6 Uraninite (horiz). (b) 92 × 56 mm. $6 Calcite (horiz). (c) $6 68 × 78 mm. $6 Quartz 7·25 7·50

Nos. 4637/42 (polished gem stones), 4643/8 (polished gem stones) and 4649/54 (raw stones).

2002. "United We Stand". Support for Victims of 11 September 2001 Terrorist Attacks.
4656 **506** $2 multicoloured 80 85

507 Queen Elizabeth with Prince Philip

2002. Golden Jubilee. Multicoloured.
4657 $2 Type **507** 80 85
4658 $2 Queen Elizabeth in open carriage 80 85
4659 $2 Queen Elizabeth in evening dress 80 85
4660 $2 Queen Elizabeth on bridge 80 85
MS4661 76 × 109 mm. $6 Queen Elizabeth in Grenadier uniform 2·40 2·50

508 Dale Earnhardt and Car, 1980, within "1"

2002. Dale Earnhardt (stock car driver) Commemoration. Designs each within figures commemorating his seven Winston Cup victories. Multicoloured.
4662 $2 Type **508** 80 85
4663 $2 With Winston Cup and car, 1986 . . . . 80 85
4664 $2 With Winston Cup, 1987 80 85
4665 $2 With Winston Cup, 1990 80 85
4666 $2 With Winston Cup, 1991 80 85
4667 $2 With Winston Cup, 1993 80 85
4668 $2 With Winston Cup, 1994 80 85

509 Cannon on C.S.S. *Teaser* (gunboat)

2002. Naval Campaigns of the American Civil War.
4669 **509** $1 deep brown, brown and black 40 45
4670 – $1 deep brown, brown and black 40 45
4671 – $1 deep brown, brown and black 40 45
4672 – $1 deep brown, brown and black 40 45
4673 – $1 deep brown, brown and black 40 45
4674 – $1 deep brown, brown and black 40 45
4675 – $1.25 brown, ochre and black 50 55
4676 – $1.25 brown, ochre and black 50 55
4677 – $1.25 brown, ochre and black 50 55
4678 – $1.25 brown, ochre and black 50 55
4679 – $1.25 brown, ochre and black 50 55
4680 – $1.25 brown, ochre and black 50 55
4681 – $1.50 deep brown, brown and black 60 65
4682 – $1.50 deep brown, brown and black 60 65
4683 – $1.50 deep brown, brown and black 60 65
4684 – $1.50 deep brown, brown and black 60 65
4685 – $1.50 deep brown, brown and black 60 65
4686 – $1.50 deep brown, brown and black 60 65
4687 – $1.50 brown, yellow and black 60 65
4688 – $1.50 brown, yellow and black 60 65
4689 – $1.50 brown, yellow and black 60 65
4690 – $1.50 brown, yellow and black 60 65
4691 – $1.50 brown, yellow and black 60 65
4692 – $1.50 brown, yellow and black 60 65
MS4693 Four sheets, each 72 × 94 mm. (a) $6 blue, violet and black. (b) $6 violet, blue and black. (c) $6 deep blue, blue and black. (d) $6 deep blue, blue and black . . . . 9·75 10·00

DESIGNS: No. 4669, Type **509**; 4670, U.S. gunboats on James River, 1862; 4671, U.S.S. *Tyler* (river gunboat); 4672, U.S.S. *Maratanza* (steam gunboat); 4673, U.S.S. *Metacomet* (steam gunboat); 4674, U.S.S. *Rattler* (river gunboat); 4675, C.S.S. *Tennessee* (ironclad); 4676, U.S.S. *Hartford* (Federal flagship) engaging the *Tennessee*; 4677, U.S.S. *Chickasaw* (river monitor); 4678, U.S.S. *Ossipee* (steam sloop); 4679, Battle of Mobile Bay; 4680, U.S.S. *Chickasaw* in action at Mobile Bay; 4681, C.S.S. *Alabama* (commerce raider); 4682, U.S.S. *Kearsarge* engaging the *Alabama*; 4683, U.S.S. *Hatteras* (paddle gunboat); 4684, C.S.S. *Alabama* attacking merchant ships; 4685, C.S.S. *Sumte* (cruiser); 4686, U.S.S. *Kearsarge* (steam sloop); 4687, C.S.S. *H.L. Hunley* (submarine); 4688, U.S.S. *Cumberland* (frigate); 4689, C.S.S. *Old Dominion* (blockade runner); 4890, U.S.S. *Housatonic* (steam sloop); 4691, U.S.S. *Hartford*; 4692, U.S.S. *Essex* (river gunboat); **MS**4693a U.S.S. *Monitor* (monitor); **MS**4693b Captain Semmes of C.S.S. *Alabama*; **MS**4693c C.S.S. *Tennessee*; **MS**4693d C.S.S. *Florida* (steam corvette).

510 Mickey Mouse

2002. Birth Centenary (2001) of Walt Disney. Mickey Mouse. Multicoloured.
4694 $1 Type **510** 40 45
4695 $1 In "The Nifty Nineties", 1941 . . . . 40 45
4696 $1 In "Magician Mickey", 1937 . . . . 40 45
4697 $1 In "Steamboat Willie", 1928 . . . . 40 45
4698 $1 In "Fantasia", 1940 . . . 40 45
4699 $1 In "Mickey Mouse Club", 1955 . . . . . . 40 45
4700 $1 In "Cactus Kid", 1930 40 45
4701 $1 In "The Prince and the Pauper", 1990 . . . . . 40 45
4702 $1 In "Brave Little Tailor", 1938 . . . . 40 45
4703 $1 In "Canine Caddy", 1941 40 45

511 Chiune Sugihara

2002. Chiune Sugihara (Japanese Consul-general in Lithuania who rescued Jews, 1939–40) Commemoration.
4704 **511** $2 multicoloured 80 85

512 Mawensi Peak, Kilimanjaro, Kenya

2002. International Year of Mountains. Multicoloured.
4705 $2 Type **512** 80 85
4706 $2 Mt. Stanley, Uganda . . 80 85
4707 $2 Mt. Taweche, Nepal . . 80 85
4708 $2 Mt. San Exupery, Argentina 80 85
MS4709 100 × 70 mm. $6 Mt. Aso, Japan . . . . 2·40 2·50
No. 4708 is inscribed "Exuprey" in error.

513 Church and Bunting

2002. Year of Eco Tourism. Multicoloured.
4710 $1 Type **513** 40 45
4711 $1 Little ringed plover . . . 40 45
4712 $1 Relaxing on the patio . . 40 45
4713 $1 Scuba diver and grouper 40 45
4714 $1 Two red snappers . . . 40 45
4715 $1 Four yachts 40 45
MS4716 75 × 75 mm. $6 Purple martin over Grenada . . . . . 2·40 2·50

514 Downhill Skiing

2002. Winter Olympic Games, Salt Lake City. Multicoloured.
4717 $2 Type **514** 80 85
4718 $2 Slalom skiing 80 85
MS4719 82 × 102 mm. Nos. 4717/18 1·60 1·70

515 Scout in Canoe

2002. 20th World Scout Jamboree, Thailand. Multicoloured.
4720 $2 Type **515** 80 85
4721 $2 Paddling canoe 80 85
4722 $2 Scout blowing bugle . . 80 85
4723 $2 Scout saluting 80 85
MS4724 100 × 74 mm. $6 Thai scout saluting . . . . 2·40 2·50
Nos. 4720/3 were printed together, se-tenant, with the backgrounds forming a composite design.

516 Heidi Klum (model)

517 Army Bear

2002. APS Stampshow 2002, Atlantic City, U.S.A. Designs showing Heidi Klum. Multicoloured.
4725 $1.50 Type **516** 60 65
4726 $1.50 Wearing chain earrings 60 65
4727 $1.50 Close-up of face . . . 60 65

2002. Centenary of the Teddy Bear (1st issue). Multicoloured.
4728 $2 Type **517** 80 85
4729 $2 Navy bear 80 85
4730 $2 Air Force bear 80 85
4731 $2 Marines bear 80 85
4732 $2 Basketball bear (38 × 50 mm) 80 85
4733 $2 Judo bear (38 × 50 mm) 80 85
4734 $2 Golf bear (38 × 50 mm) 80 85
4735 $2 Baseball bear (38 × 50 mm) 80 85
4736 $5 Bear with red hat and pink bow . . . . 2·00 2·10
4737 $5 Bear with clogs . . . . . 2·00 2·10
4738 $5 Bear with black hat and scarf . . . . 2·00 2·10
4739 $5 Bear with cheeses . . . . 2·00 2·10
Nos. 4728/31 (armed forces bears), 4732/5 (sports bears) and 4736/9 (Dutch bears).
See also Nos. 4851/**MS**4852.

518 "Mareep No. 179"

2002. Pokémon (children's cartoon series). Multicoloured.
4740 $1.50 Type **518** 60 65
4741 $1.50 "Sunkern No. 191" 60 65
4742 $1.50 "Teddiursa No. 216" 60 65
4743 $1.50 "Swinub No. 220" . . 60 65
4744 $1.50 "Murkrow No. 198" 60 65
4745 $1.50 "Snubbull No. 209" 60 65
MS4746 66 × 91 mm. $6 "Togepi No. 175" . . . . 2·40 2·50

518a Elvis Presley wearing Stetson

2002. 25th Death Anniv of Elvis Presley.
4747 **518a** $1 multicoloured . . . 40 45

518b Axel, Zeeland

2002. "Amphilex '02" International Stamp Exhibition, Amsterdam (1st issue). Dutch Women's Traditional Costumes. Sheet, 120 × 140 mm, containing vert designs, each 37 × 51 mm. Multicoloured.
MS4748 $3 Type **518b**; $3 Eerde, Noord-Brabant; $3 Volendam, Noord-Holland . . . . 3·50 3·75

518c Jacobus van't Hoff (Chemistry, 1901)

2002. "Amphilex '02" International Stamp Exhibition, Amsterdam (2nd issue). (a) Dutch Nobel Prize Winners. Sheet 150 × 100 mm.
MS4749 $1.50 Type **518c** (black and green); $1.50 Peace Prize medal (black and blue); $1.50 Pieter Zeeman (Physics, 1902) (black and mauve); $1.50 Johannes van der Waals (Physics, 1910) (black and cinnamon); $1.50 Tobias Asser (Peace, 1911) (black and lilac); $1.50 Heike Kamerlingh Onnes (Physics, 1913) black and green 3·50 3·75

(b) Dutch Lighthouses. Sheet 128 × 148 mm. Multicoloured
MS4750 $1.50 Schiermonnikoog; $1.50 Texel; $1.50 Egmond; $1.50 Scheveningen; $1.50 Schouwen; $1.50 Hellevoetsluis . . . . . 3·50 3·75

519 Molly Middleton and Father

2002. Shirley Temple in *Our Little Girl.* Showing scenes from film. Multicoloured.
4751 $1.50 Type **519** 60 65
4752 $1.50 Family picnic 60 65
4753 $1.50 Molly with Sniff (dog), talking to park keeper 60 65
4754 $1.50 Molly with parents and another man 60 65
4755 $1.50 Molly and Sniff on see-saw 60 65
4756 $1.50 Molly with Sniff in pink bonnet 60 65
4757 $2 Molly with mother (vert) 80 85
4758 $2 Molly watching clown (vert) 80 85
4759 $2 Molly at prayer (vert) . . 80 85
4760 $2 Leaning on father's knee (vert) 80 85
MS4761 105 × 76 mm. $6 Molly wearing pink dress . . . . . . 2·40 2·50

520 World Trade Center

2002. 1st Anniv of 11 September 2001 Attacks. Sheet 140 × 98 mm.
MS4762 **520** $6 multicoloured . . 2·40 2·40

521 Popeye at Santa Croce Basilica, Florence

2002. "Popeye" (cartoon character). Multicoloured.

4763	$1.50 Type **521**	60	65
4764	$1.50 With Brutus at Eiffel Tower, Paris	60	65
4765	$1.50 On steps of Parthenon, Athens . . .	60	65
4766	$1.50 With Olive Oyl near Rialto Bridge, Venice . .	60	65
4767	$1.50 Near Big Ben, London	60	65
4768	$1.50 In front of traditional wooden building, Norway	65	65
4769	$2 Sweet Pea on footballer's back (29 × 44 mm) . . .	80	85
4770	$2 Jeep (dog) tugging footballer's shorts (29 × 44 mm)	80	85
4771	$2 Popeye in football kit (29 × 44 mm)	80	85
4772	$2 Brutus being kicked by Popeye (29 × 44 mm) . .	80	85

MS4773 Three sheets. (a) $6 Brutus heading ball (44 × 29 mm). (b) $6 Popeye celebrating with footballers (44 × 29 mm). (c) $6 Popeye and Leaning Tower of Pisa (50 × 78 mm) . . . . 7·25 7·50

Nos. 4769/72 were issued together, se-tenant, with the backgrounds forming a composite design.

522 Common Morpho

523 Norman Wisdom

2002. Flora and Fauna. Multicoloured.

4774	$1.50 Type **522**	60	65
4775	$1.50 Blue night butterfly	60	65
4776	$1.50 Small flambeau . . .	60	65
4777	$1.50 Grecian shoemaker . .	60	65
4778	$1.50 Orange-barred sulphur	60	65
4779	$1.50 Cramer's mesene . . .	60	65
4780	$1.50 Honey bee	60	65
4781	$1.50 Dragonfly	60	65
4782	$1.50 Milkweed bug	60	65
4783	$1.50 Bumble bee	60	65
4784	$1.50 Migratory grasshopper	60	65
4785	$1.50 Monarch caterpillar	60	65
4786	$1.50 *Boletus crocipodius* . .	60	65
4787	$1.50 *Boletus edulis*	60	65
4788	$1.50 *Flammulina velutipes*	60	65
4789	$1.50 *Amanita phalloides* . .	60	65
4790	$1.50 *Tricholoma aurantium*	60	65
4791	$1.50 *Amanita muscaria* . .	60	65
4792	$1.50 Blue whale and calf	60	65
4793	$1.50 Pygmy sperm whale	60	65
4794	$1.50 Humpback whale . .	60	65
4795	$1.50 Killer whale	60	65
4796	$1.50 Bowhead whale . . .	60	65
4797	$1.50 Grey whale	60	65

MS4798 Four sheets, each 105 × 76 mm. (a) $6 Figure of eight butterfly. (b) $6 Hercules beetle. (c) $6 Sharp-scaled parasol (fungus). (d) $6 Blue whale . . 9·75 10·00

Nos. 4780/5 (butterflies), 4775/80 (insects), 4781/6 (fungi) and 4787/92 (whales) were each printed together, se-tenant, with the backgrounds forming composite designs.

Nos. 4792/7 and 4791 are inscribed "Flammula" or "Aminita", both in error.

2002. Sir Norman Wisdom (comedian and actor).
4799 **523** $1.50 multicoloured . . 60 65

523a Madonna and Child, Four Angels and St. Francis (Cimabue)

2002. Christmas. Religious Paintings. Multicoloured.

4800	15c. Type **523a**	10	10
4801	25c. "Madonna and Child and Two Angels" (Cimabue) (vert)	10	15
4802	50c. "Madonna Enthroned" (detail) (Cimabue) (vert)	20	25
4803	$1 "Madonna Enthroned" (Cimabue) (vert)	40	45
4804	$4 "Madonna and Child, Four Angels and St. Francis" (Cimabue) (vert)	1·60	1·75

MS4805 72 × 98 mm. $6 "Nativity" (Perugino) (vert) . . . . 2·40 2·50

524 Sextant

2002. 550th Birth Anniv of Amerigo Vespucci (explorer). Sheets containing T **524** and similar multicoloured designs.
MS4806 Two sheets. (a) 98 × 147 mm. $3 Type **524**; $3 Amerigo Vespucci; $3 Caravel (b) 138 × 90 mm. $3 Map of South America and caravel (horiz); $3 Compass and caravels (horiz); $3 Map of Africa and Europe (horiz) Set of 2 sheets . . . . 7·25 7·50
MS4807 Two sheets. (a) 78 × 85 mm. $6 Compass rose (28 × 42 mm). (b) 85 × 78 mm. $6 Globe and scroll (28 × 42 mm) Set of 2 sheets . . 4·75 5·00

525 Arsenal Stadium

2002. Arsenal Football Club -- FA Community Shield Winners. Sheet 125 × 125 mm containing T **525** and similar horiz designs. Multicoloured.
MS4808 $1.50 Type **525**; $1.50 Footballers celebrating after winning goal; $1.50 Winning team with FA Shield; $1.50 Arsenal 2002/3 squad with trophies; $1.50 Gilberto with FA Shield; $1.50 Arsenal FC, Stadium and new crest . . . . 3·50 3·75

2002. British Football Clubs. Eight sheets, each 125 × 125 mm, containing horiz designs as T **525**. Multicoloured.
MS4809 Arsenal 2001/2 $1.50 Team with FA Cup, Millennium Stadium, Cardiff; $1.50 Winning team with Championship banners; $1.50 Premiership Trophy winning team; $1.50 Winning team with Premiership trophy on rostrum; $1.50 Players celebrating FA Cup winning goal; $1.50 Arsene Wenger (Manager) and Tony Adams (captain) with trophies 4·00 4·25
MS4810 Celtic $1.50 Celtic Park Stadium; $1.50 Martin O'Neill with SPL Trophy; $1.50 Henrik Larsson; $1.50 Celtic squad of 2002/3; $1.50 Celtic scoring goal; $1.50 Celtic Park . . . . . . 4·00 4·25
MS4811 Chelsea $1.50 Crowd watching floodlit match; $1.50 Cup Winners' Cup winning team with trophy, 1988; $1.50 Chelsea supporters at match; $1.50 "The Shed End" at Stamford Bridge ground; $1.50 Stamford Bridge stadium; $1.50 Winning team with FA Cup, 2000 . . . . 4·00 4·25
MS4812 Liverpool $1.50 Anfield's Centenary stand seen from main stand; $1.50 First team squad, 2002/3; $1.50 Gerard Houllier and Phil Thompson; $1.50 Milan Baros; $1.50 Vladimir Smicer and Danny Murphy; $1.50 The Kop seen from Anfield Road end 4·00 4·25
MS4813 Manchester City $1.50 Maine Road stadium (from above); $1.50 Fans with Division One Champions flags; $1.50 Kevin Keegan (manager) with Division 1 trophy; $1.50 Winning Division 1 with trophy; $1.50 Winning team with medals; $1.50 Maine Road stadium (from stands) . . . . 4·00 4·25
MS4814 Manchester United $1.50 David Beckham; $1.50 First team squad, 2002/3; $1.50 Old Trafford stadium (aerial view); $1.50 Players after Ole Gunnar Solskjaer's 100th goal; $1.50 Manchester United fans; $1.50 North stand, Old Trafford . . 4·00 4·25
MS4815 Norwich City $1.50 Players at The Nest (NCFC ground 1908–35); $1.50 Norwich City players,1971/2; $1.50 With Milk Cup trophy, 1985; $1.50 Carrow Road stadium; $1.50 Winning UEFA Cup,1993; $1.50, Match of 1958/9 . . . . 4·00 4·25
MS4816 Tottenham Hotspur $1.50 Fans watching match; $1.50 Spurs v. Fulham match, 2001; $1.50 Spurs v. Liverpool match, 2002; $1.50 Winning UEFA Cup team, 1972; $1.50 Players celebrating win against Chelsea, 2002; $1.50 Club Shield and White Hart Lane stadium . . . . 4·00 4·25

526 Johan Mjallby (Sweden)

528 Princess Diana wearing Bow Tie

527 Foundation Logo and US Flag

2002. World Cup Football Championship, Japan and Korea. Miniature sheets containing T **526** and similar vert designs. Multicoloured.
MS4817 165 × 82 mm. $1.50 Type **526**; $1.50 Magnus Hedman (Sweden); $1.50 Fredrik Ljungberg (Sweden); $1.50 Khalilou Fadiga (Senegal); $1.50 El Hadji Diouf (Senegal); $1.50 Papa Bouba Diop (Senegal) . . . . 2·40 2·50
MS4818 165 × 82 mm. $1.50 Roberto Carlos (Brazil); $1.50 Juninho Paulista (Brazil); $1.50 Ronaldinho (Brazil); $1.50 Johan Walem (Belgium); $1.50 Marc Wilmots (Belgium); $1.50 Bart Goor (Belgium) . . 3·50 3·75
MS4819 Four sheets, each 82 × 82 mm. (a) $3 Henrik Larsson (Sweden); $3 Niclas Alexandersson (Sweden). (b) $3 Khalilou Fadiga (Senegal); $3 Bruno Metsou (coach, Senegal). (c) $3 Luiz Felipe Scolari (coach, Brazil); $3 Ronaldo (Brazil). (d) $3 Wesley Sonck (Belgium); $3 Robert Waseige (coach, Belgium) Set of 4 sheets . . . . 9·50 9·75

2002. National Law Enforcement and Firefighters Children's Foundation. Sheet 75 × 115 mm.
MS4820 **527** $6 multicoloured . . 2·40 2·50

2002. 5th Death Anniv of Diana, Princess of Wales. Two sheets containing T **528** and similar vert designs. Multicoloured.
MS4821 137 × 120 mm. $2 Type **528**; $2 Wearing blue dress; $2 Wearing red and white jacket and hat; $2 Wearing pink dress . . . . . 2·40 2·50
MS4822 70 × 100 mm. $6 Wearing headset . . . . 2·40 2·50

529 Pres Reagan on the DMZ in Korea, 1983

2002. Presidents Ronald Reagan and John F. Kennedy. Four sheets containing T **529** and similar multicoloured designs.
MS4823 175 × 117 mm. $1.50 Type **529**; $1.50 Pres Reagan with Prime Minister Margaret Thatcher; $1.50 Speaking at the Berlin Wall, 1987; $1.50 Signing INF Treaty with Soviet Secretary General Gorbachev; $1.50 With Egyptian President Sadat, 1981; $1.50 At home with horse Set of 4 sheets . . . . 4·25 4·50
MS4824 175 × 117 mm. $1.50 Pres Kennedy meeting with Cabinet; $1.50 Signing a bill into law; $1.50 Meeting Civil Rights leaders; $1.50 With astronaut John Glenn; $1.50 On the campaign trail; $1.50 With Jacqueline Kennedy arriving in Dallas, 1963 . . . . 4·25 4·50
MS4825 Two sheets, each 82 × 115 mm. (a) $6 Pres. Reagan making speech. (b) Pres. Kennedy making speech (vert) Set of 2 sheets . . . . 4·75 5·00

530 Magnifying Glass and Globe

2002. 50th Anniv of International Federation of Stamp Dealers' Associations. P 14.
4826 **530** $2 multicoloured 80 85

531 Ram

2003. Chinese New Year ("Year of the Ram").
MS4827 130 × 123 mm. **531** $1.25 × 4, multicoloured . . . 2·00 2·10

532 Toy Airplane

2003. Learning Resources (1st series). M Gears Childrens' Construction Sets. Sheet 222 × 152 mm containing T **532** and similar horiz designs showing toys. Multicoloured.
MS4828 $2 Type **532**; $2 Dune buggy; $2 Robot; $2 Racing car 3·25 3·50
See also **MS**4853.

533 David Brown

2003. *Columbia* Space Shuttle Commemoration. Sheet 184 × 145 mm, containing T **533** and similar vert designs showing crew members. Multicoloured.
MS4829 $1 Type **533**; $1 Commander Rick Husband; $1 Laurel Clark; $1 Kalpana Chawla; $1 Payload Commander Michael Anderson; $1 Pilot William McCool; $1 Ilan Ramon . . . 2·40 2·50

534 Grenada Dove and "CC" Emblem

2003. 30th Anniv of CARICOM.
4830 **534** $1 multicoloured 45 50

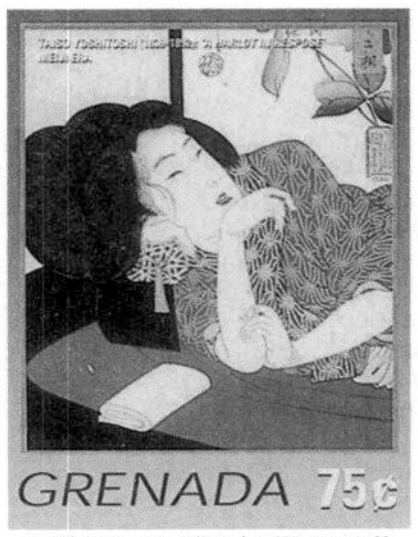

535 "A Harlot in Repose"

2003. Japanese Art. Paintings of Women by Taiso Yoshitoshi. Multicoloured.
4831 75c. Type **535** 30 35
4832 $1 "A 'Shakuni' or Geisha, who serves Wine or Sake" 45 50
4833 $1.25 "A 'Joro', or Low Ranking Prostitute, having a Snack" 50 55
4834 $3 "A Geisha known as a 'Geiko' or Entertainer relaxing" . . . . 1·20 1·40
MS4835 175 × 135 mm. $2 "Enjoying a Cool Evening Breeze in a Pleasure Boat"; $2 "A Fukagawa Waitress carrying a Wooden Table laden with Food"; $2 "A Spoiled Unmarried Woman pretending to be displeased with an Admirer"; $2 "A Coy Young Girl biting her Sleeve pretending to be Embarrassed" . . . . . 3·25 3·50
MS4836 66 × 132 mm. $6 "A Geisha about to Board a Party-Boat" (detail) . . . . 2·40 2·50

536 "St. Catherine Altarpiece" (detail of St. Dorothy, St. Agnes and St. Cunigonde)

2003. 450th Death Anniv of Lucas Cranach the Elder (artist). Multicoloured.
4837 50c. Type **536** 20 25
4838 75c. "The St. Catherine Altarpiece" (detail of St. Margaret) (vert) . . . 30 35
4839 $1.25 "The St. Catherine Altarpiece" (detail of St. Barbara) (vert) 50 55
4840 $3 "The St. Catherine Altarpiece" (detail of young girl) (vert) . . . . 1·20 1·40
MS4841 158 × 191 mm. $2 "Lot and his Daughters" (detail); $2 "David and Bathsheba" (detail); $2 "The Agony in the Garden" (detail); $2 "The Adoration of the Magi" 3·25 3·50
MS4842 120 × 100 mm. $6 "Samson and Delilah" (detail) (vert) . . 2·40 2·40

537 "Jardin Aux Tournesols"

2003. 85th Death Anniv of Gustav Klimt (artist). Multicoloured.
4843 15c. Type **537** 10 15
4844 25c. "L'allee Aux Poulets" 10 15
4845 75c. "Allee Dans Le Parc Du Schloss Kammer" . . 30 35
4846 $1 "Portrait de Johanna Staude" 40 45
4847 $1.25 "Portrait de Friederike Maria Beer" 50 55
4848 $3 "Portrait de Mada Primavesi" . . . . 1·20 1·40
MS4849 180 × 105 mm. $2 "La Jeune Fille"; $2 "Les Amies"; $2 "Le Berceau"; $2 "La Vie et la Mort" . . . . 3·25 3·50
MS4850 81 × 102 mm. $6 "Portrait de Margaret Stonborough-Wittgenstein". Imperf . . . . 2·40 2·50

538 Embroidery Teddy Bear

2003. Centenary of the Teddy Bear (2nd issue). Embroidered Fabric Teddy Bears. Self-adhesive. Imperf.
4851 **538** $15 ochre, silver and rose-red . . . . 6·00 6·00
MS4852 126 × 157 mm. No. 4850 × 4 25·00 24·00

539 Children reading Books

2003. Learning Resources (2nd series). Reading Rods. Sheet 222 × 156 mm containing T **539** and similar horiz designs. Multicoloured. .
MS4853 $2 Type **539**; $2 Girl playing with reading rods; $2 Children writing; $2 Teacher and children with book . . . . . . 3·25 3·50

540 Silvere Maes

2003. Centenary of Tour de France Cycle Race. Designs showing past winners. Multicoloured.
MS4854 160 × 100 mm. $2 Type **540**; $2 Jean Lazarides (1946); $2 Jean Robic (1947); $2 Gino Bartali (1948) . . . . 3·25 3·50
MS4855 160 × 100 mm. $2 Fausto Coppi (1949); $2 Ferdinand Kubler (1950); $2 Hugo Koblet (1951); $2 Fausto Coppi (1952) 3·25 3·50
MS4856 160 × 100 mm. $2 Roger Walkowiak (1956); $2 Jacques Anquetil (1957); $2 Charly Gaul (1958); $2 Federico Bahamontes (1959) . . . . 3·25 3·50
MS4857 Three sheets, each 100 × 70 mm. (a) $6 Fausto Coppi (1949). (b) $6 Ferdinand Kubler (1950). (c) $6 Jacques Anquetil (1964) Set of 3 sheets . . . . 7·25 7·50

541 Louis Bleriot and *Bleriot* XI (first powered flight across English Channel, 1909)

2003. Centenary of Powered Flight. Multicoloured.
MS4858 128 × 150 mm. $2 Type **541**; $2 Johnnie Johnson (World War II Ace pilot) and aircraft; $2 Wright Brothers and *Flyer I* (first powered flight, 1903); $2 Jacqueline Cochran and aircraft (first woman to break sound barrier) . . . . 3·25 3·50
MS4859 119 × 119 mm. $2 Alcock and Brown and Vickers FB-27 *Vimy* (first non-stop transatlantic flight, 1919); $2 Amelia Earhart and aircraft; $2 Chuck Yeager and Bell XS-1 rocket airplane (first manned supersonic flight, 1947); $2 Charles Lindbergh and Ryan NYP Special *Spirit of St. Louis* (first solo non-stop transatlantic flight, 1927) . . . . 3·25 3·50

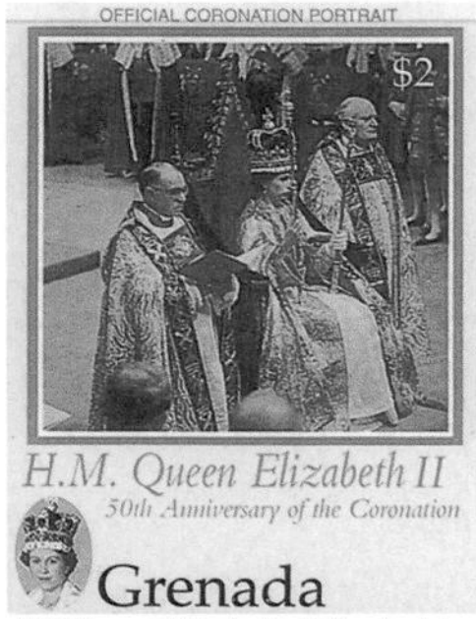

542 Queen Elizabeth II flanked by Bishops

2003. 50th Anniv of Coronation. Multicoloured.
4860 $2 Type **542** 80 85
4861 $2 Holy Communion . . . 80 85
4863 $2 Enthronement of Queen 80 85
4864 $2 Queen and Duke of Edinburgh 80 85
4865 $2 Queen leaving Westminster Abbey in Coronation Coach . . . 80 85
4866 $2 Queen and family on Palace balcony 80 85
4867 $2 Westminster Abbey . . . 80 85
MS4868 106 × 76 mm. $6 Queen in Coronation Coach . . . . . . 2·40 2·50
No. 4867 is inscr "Floodlit Mall" in error.

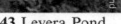

543 Levera Pond

544 Clive Andrews

2003. International Year of Freshwater. Multicoloured.
MS4869 150 × 88 mm. $2 Type **543**; $2 Concord Falls; $2 Lake Antoine . . . . 2·40 2·50
MS4870 100 × 70 mm. $6 Lake Grand Etang . . . . 2·40 2·50

2003. Centenary of Circus Clowns. Multicoloured.
MS4871 119 × 194 mm. $2 Type **544**; $2 Bell Bozo; $2 Bumpsy; $2 Anne Fratellini . . . . 3·25 3·50
MS4872 146 × 218 mm. $2 Stag (acrobat); $2 Olga and Regina Kolpensky with white poodles; $2 Brad Byers; $2 Tiger . . . . . 3·25 3·50
No. **MS**4871 shows clowns and is cut in the shape of a clown. No. **MS**4872 shows other circus performers and is cut in the shape of a circus elephant.

545 Aerial View of Campus

2003. St. George's University School of Medicine. Multicoloured.
4873 75c. Type **545** 30 35
4874 $1 University buildings . . . 40 45

546 General Sir Mike Jackson and Tank

2003. Operation "Iraqi Freedom". Showing commanders of British armed forces in Iraq (**MS**4875) or British aircraft, tanks and ships (**MS**4876). Multicoloured.
MS4875 186 × 130 mm. $1 Type **546**; $1 Air Vice-Marshal Glenn Torpy and RAF Jaguar fighter; $1 Air Marshal Brian Burridge and RAF Harrier GR7 fighter; $1 Major General Tony Milton and warship; $1 Major General Peter Wall and soldiers; $1 Major General Barney White-Spunner ; $1 Admiral Sir Alan West and aircraft carrier; $1 Air Chief Marshal Peter Squire and surveillance aircraft . . . . . 3·25 3·50
MS4876 186 × 130 mm. $1 Royal Marine Gazelle helicopter; $1 Royal Marine hovercraft; $1 RAF Jaguar fighter; $1 HMS *Liverpool*; $1 RAF Harrier GR7; $1 Challenger 2 tank; $1 RAF Chinook helicopter; $1 RAF Tornado F3 . . . . 3·25 3·50

547 Prince William with Bouquet

2003. 21st Birthday of Prince William of Wales. Multicoloured.
MS4877 79 × 145 mm. $3 Type **547**; $3 Wearing blue T-shirt; $3 In close-up, looking down . . . . 4·25 4·50
MS4878 105 × 76 mm. $6 Prince William (horiz) . . . . 2·40 2·40

548 Yellow Allamanda

2003. Birds, Fish and Flowers of the Caribbean. Multicoloured.
4879 25c. Type **548** 10 15
4880 50c. Queen of the Night (flower) 20 15
4881 75c. Anthurium 30 35
4882 $1 Smallmouthed grunt (fish) 40 45
4883 $1 Spotfinned butterflyfish 40 45
4884 $1 Gold coney (fish) 40 45
4885 $1.25 Osprey 50 55
4886 $1.25 Red-eyed vireo (bird) 50 55
4887 $1.25 Northern oriole . . . 50 55
4888 $3 Oleander . . . . 1·20 1·40
4889 $3 Night sergeant (fish) . . 1·20 1·40
4890 $3 Bahama pintail (duck) 1·20 1·40
MS4891 105 × 85 mm. $2 Blue passion flower; $2 Chinese hibiscus; $2 Poinsettia; $2 Bird of Paradise (flower) . . . . . .
MS4892 105 × 85 mm. $2 Spot-finned hogfish ("Cuban Hogfish"); $2 Blueheaded wrasse; $2 Black-capped basslet ("Black Cap Gramma"); $2 Cherub angelfish ("Cherubfish") . . . .
MS4893 105 × 85 mm. $2 Slaty-capped shrike vireo; $2 Common flicker ("Northern Flicker"); $2 Blackburnian warbler; $2 Common tody flycatcher . . . 3·25 3·50
MS4894 Three sheets, each 96 × 66 mm. (a) $6 Shrimp plant. (b) $6 Banded butterflyfish. (c) $6 Blue grosbeak (vert) Set of 3 sheets 7·25 7·50

549 Spinosaurus

2003. Prehistoric Animals. Multicoloured.
MS4895 178 × 117 mm. $2 Type **549**; $2 Herrerasaurus; $2 Protarchaeopteryx; $2 Sinosauropteryx . . . . 3·25 3·50
MS4896 178 × 117 mm. $2 Allosaurus; $2 Crylophosaurus; $2 Eoraptor; $2 Caudipteryx . . . 3·25 3·50
MS4897 Two sheets, each 98 × 68 mm. (a) $6 Triceratops (vert). (b) $6 Archaeopteryx (vert) Set of 2 sheets . . . . 4·75 5·00

550 "Madonna and Child" (detail) (Giotto) from Church of Ognissanti

2003. Christmas. Multicoloured.
4898 35c. Type **550** 15 20
4899 75c. "The Ognissanti Madonna" (detail) (Giotto) 30 35
4900 $1 "Madonna of the Angels" (detail) (Giotto) 40 45
4901 $4 "Madonna and Child" (Giotto) from Florentine Church of San Giorgio alla Costa . . . . 1·60 1·75
MS4902 74 × 95 mm. $6 "Holy Family with John the Baptist and St. Elizabeth" (Nicolas Poussin) (horiz) . . . . 2·40 2·50

551 "At the Palmist's" (Jean-Baptiste Le Prince)

2003. 300th Anniv of St. Petersburg. "Treasures of the Hermitage". Multicoloured.
4903 45c. Type **551** 20 25
4904 $1 "A Visit to Grandmother" (Louis Le Nain) (horiz) 40 45
4905 $1.50 "Musicale" (Dirck Hals) (horiz) 60 65
4906 $3 "A Young Woman in the Morning" (Frans van Mieris the Elder) . . . . 1·20 1·40
MS4907 118 × 181 mm. $2 "Louis, Grand Dauphin de France" (Louis Tocqué); $2 "Count P. A. Stroganov as a Child" (Jean-Baptiste Greuze); $2 "A Boy with a Book" (Jean- Baptiste Perroneau); $2 "A Girl with a Doll" (Jean-Baptiste Greuze) 3·25 3·50
MS4908 (a) 78 × 65 mm. $6 "The Lute Player" (Caravaggio). Imperf. (b) 67 × 77 mm. $6 "The Spoiled Child" (Jean-Baptiste Greuze). Imperf . . . . 4·75 5·00

552 "The Spring Tonic"

2003. 25th Death Anniv of Norman Rockwell. Multicoloured.
MS4909 149 × 179 mm. $2 Type **552**; $2 "The Facts of Life"; $2 "The Proper Gratuity"; $2 "The Runaway" . . . . 3·25 3·50
MS4910 91 × 99 mm. $6 "Boy with Carriage" (detail) (horiz) . . . 2·40 2·50

553 "Claude Drawing"

2003. 30th Death Anniv of Pablo Picasso (artist). Multicoloured.
MS4911 132 × 168 mm. $2 Type **553**; $2 "Claude and Paloma at Play" (detail); $2 "Paloma at Three Years Old"; $2 "Paloma with an Orange" . . . . 3·25 3·50
MS4912 72 × 99 mm. $6 "Paloma in Blue". Imperf . . . . 2·40 2·50

554 Brown and White Monkey

556 Chinese Lady

555 *Lissy* (sail training ship) on River Weser

2004. Chinese New Year ("Year of the Monkey"). Multicoloured.
MS4913 116 × 141 mm. $1.50 Type **554**; $1.50 Proboscis monkey; $1.50 Light brown monkey; $1.50 Grey monkey . . . . 2·40 2·50

2004. Opening of Weser Tunnel, Germany. Sheet 113 × 82 mm.
MS4914 **555** $6 multicoloured . . 2·40 2·50

2004. Hong Kong 2004 International Stamp Exhibition. Paintings by Pu Hsin-yu. Multicoloured.
MS4915 156 × 112 mm. $1.50 Type **556**; $1.50 Two monkeys in tree; $1.50 Mountain landscape with temple and waterfall; $1.50 Bird in tree with red flower; $1.50 Man sat by gnarled tree; $1.50 Man in red . . . . 4·25 4·50
MS4916 107 × 105 mm. $3 Branch; $3 Bearded man . . . . 2·40 2·50

557 Muffy

2004. Arthur the Aardvark and Friends. Multicoloured.
MS4917 165 × 134 mm. $1.50 Type **557**; $1.50 Francine; $1.50 Brain with potted plants; $1.50 D.W. as astronaut in space; $1.50 Sue Ellen with insects in jam jars; $1.50 Arthur with model of solar system . . . . 2·40 2·50
MS4918 150 × 184 mm. $2 Arthur as Robin Hood; $2 Arthur as Rumpelstiltskin; $2 Arthur with sword; $2 Arthur as King Arthur 3·25 3·50

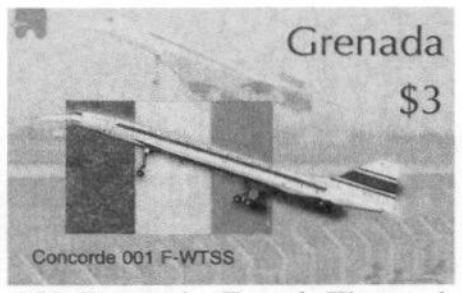

558 Concorde, French Flag and Concorde at Take-off

2004. Last Flight of Concorde (2003). Multicoloured.
MS4919 88 × 129 mm. $3 Type **558**; $3 Concorde, French flag and spectators at perimeter fence; $3 Concorde, French flag and control panel (first flight, Toulouse, Fran, 1969) . . . . 4·25 4·00
MS4920 88 × 129 mm. $3 Concorde, Union Jack, Singapore flag and roof of building; $3 Concorde, Union Jack, Singapore flag and skyscraper; $3 Concorde, Union Jack, Singapore flag and street (London to Singapore flights, 1977) . . . . 4·25 4·00
MS4921 88 × 129 mm. $3 Concorde and dome of US Capitol; $3 Concorde, Capitol building and top of statue; $3 Concorde, Capitol and plinth of statue (last flight, Paris to Washington, 2003) 4·25 4·50

OFFICIAL STAMPS

1982. Optd **P.R.G.** (a) Nos. 1085/97 and 1099.
O 1 5c. West Indiaman barque, c. 1840 . . . . . 30 40
O 2 6c. R.M.S.P. "Orinoco", c. 1851 . . . . 30 40
O 3 10c. Working schooner . . . 30 30
O 4 12c. Trimaran at Grand Anse anchorage 30 30
O 5 15c. Spice Island cruising yacht "Petite Amie" . . . 30 30
O 6 20c. Fishing pirogue 35 30
O 7 25c. Harbour police launch 40 30
O 8 30c. Grand Anse speedboat 40 30
O 9 40c. M.V. "Seimstrand" . . 50 30
O10 50c. Three-masted schooner "Ariadne" 60 40
O11 90c. M.V. "Geestide" . . . 90 1·00
O12 $1 M.V "Cunard Countess" 90 1·00
O13 $3 Rum-runner . . . . . . 2·25 4·25
O14 $10 Coast-guard patrol boat 6·00 12·00

(b) Nos. 1130/2 and 1134/5.
O15 30c. Prince Charles and Lady Diana Spencer . . . 1·50 2·25
O16 40c. Holyrood House . . . 2·25 2·75
O17 50c. Prince Charles and Lady Diana Spencer . . . 1·25 2·00
O18 $2 Holyrood House . . . . 2·25 3·50
O19 $4 Type **268** . . . . 5·00 8·00

POSTAGE DUE STAMPS

D 1

1892.
D 8 D 1 1d. black . . . . 3·50 7·50
D 9 2d. black . . . . 11·00 1·75
D10 3d. black . . . . 13·00 6·00

1892. Surch **SURCHARGE POSTAGE** and value.
D4 13 1d. on 6d. mauve . . . . . 80·00 1·25
D5 1d. on 8d. brown . . . . . £750 3·25
D6 2d. on 6d. mauve . . . . . £150 2·50
D7 2d. on 8d. brown . . . . . £1500 10·00

1921. As Type D 1 but inscr "POSTAGE DUE" instead of "SURCHARGE POSTAGE".
D11 D 1 1d. black . . . . 1·25 1·00
D12 1½d. black . . . . 8·50 21·00
D13 2d. black . . . . 2·00 1·75
D14 3d. black . . . . 2·00 4·50

1952. As last, but currency changed.
D15 D 1 3c. black . . . . 30 7·00
D16 4c. black . . . . 30 13·00
D17 6c. black . . . . 45 12·00
D18 8c. black . . . . 75 12·00

GRENADINES OF GRENADA (CARRIACOU AND PETITE MARTINIQUE) Pt. 1

The southern part of the group, attached to Grenada. Main islands Petit Martinique and Carriacou. From 1999 stamps were inscribed "Grenada Carriacou and Petite Martinique".

100 cents = 1 dollar.

1973. Royal Wedding. Nos. 582/3 of Grenada optd **GRENADINES.**
1 **196** 25c. multicoloured 15 10
2 $2 multicoloured 45 50

1974. Stamps of Grenada optd **GRENADINES**.
4 1c. multicoloured (No. 306) . . 10 10
5 2c. multicoloured (No. 307) . . 10 10
6 3c. multicoloured (No. 308) . . 10 10
7 5c. multicoloured (No. 309) . . 15 10
8 8c. multicoloured (No. 311) . . 15 10
9 10c. multicoloured (No. 312) 15 10
10 12c. multicoloured (No. 313) 20 10
11 25c. multicoloured (No. 315) 45 10
12 $1 multicoloured (No. 318) . . 2·50 60
13 $2 multicoloured (No. 319) . . 3·00 1·50
14 $3 multicoloured (No. 320) . . 3·00 1·75
15 $5 multicoloured (No. 321) . . 3·75 2·25

1974. World Cup Football Championship. As Nos. 619/27 of Grenada, but inscr "GRENADA GRENADINES".
16 ½c. multicoloured 10 10
17 1c. multicoloured 10 10
18 2c. multicoloured 10 10
19 10c. multicoloured 20 10
20 25c. multicoloured 25 10
21 50c. multicoloured 30 15
22 75c. multicoloured 30 20
23 $1 multicoloured 35 25
MS24 114 × 76 mm. $2 multicoloured 75 80

1974. Cent of U.P.U. As Nos. 628 etc of Grenada, but inscr "GRENADA GRENADINES".
25 8c. multicoloured 10 10
26 25c. multicoloured 15 10
27 35c. multicoloured 15 10
28 $1 multicoloured 70 40
MS29 172 × 109 mm. $1 as 15c. and $2 as $1 . . . . 1·00 1·00

1974. Birth Cent of Sir Winston Churchill. As Nos. 637/9 of Grenada, but inscr "GRENADA GRENADINES".
30 35c. multicoloured 15 10
31 $2 multicoloured 40 45
MS32 129 × 96 mm. 75c. as 35c. and $1 as $2 . . . . 35 80

1974. Christmas. As Nos. 640/8 of Grenada, but inscr "GRENADA GRENADINES" and background colours changed.
33 **204** ½c. multicoloured 10 10
34 – 1c. multicoloured 10 10
35 – 2c. multicoloured 10 10
36 – 3c. multicoloured 10 10
37 – 10c. multicoloured 10 10

38 – 25c. multicoloured 10 10
39 – 50c. multicoloured 15 15
40 – $1 multicoloured 30 25
MS41 117 × 96 mm. $2 as 1c. 45 60

1975. Big Game Fishing. As Nos. 669 etc of Grenada, but inscr "GRENADA GRENADINES" and background colours changed.
42 ½c. multicoloured 10 10
43 1c. multicoloured 10 10
44 2c. multicoloured 10 10
45 10c. multicoloured 15 10
46 25c. multicoloured 20 10
47 50c. multicoloured 20 15
48 70c. multicoloured 25 20
49 $1 multicoloured 35 35
MS50 107 × 80 mm. $2 multicoloured 60 90

1975. Flowers. As Nos. 678 etc of Grenada, but inscr "GRENADINES".
51 ½c. multicoloured 10 10
52 1c. multicoloured 10 10
53 2c. multicoloured 10 10
54 3c. multicoloured 10 10
55 10c. multicoloured 10 10
56 25c. multicoloured 10 10
57 50c. multicoloured 20 15
58 $1 multicoloured 30 20
MS59 102 × 82 mm. $2 multicoloured 60 70

CANCELLED REMAINDERS*. Some of the following issues have been remaindered, cancelled-to-order, at a fraction of their face value. For all practical purposes these are indistinguishable from genuine postally used copies. Our used quotations, which are indicated by an asterisk, are the same for cancelled-to-order or postally used copies.

3 "Christ Crowned with Thorns" (Titian)

4 "Dawn" (detail from Medici Tomb)

1975. Easter. Paintings showing Crucifixion and Deposition by artists listed. Multicoloured.
60 ½c. Type **3** 10 10*
61 1c. Giotto 10 10*
62 2c. Tintoretto 10 10*
63 3c. Cranach 10 10*
64 35c. Caravaggio 15 10*
65 75c. Tiepolo 20 10*
66 $2 Velasquez 40 15*
MS67 105 × 90 mm. $1 Titian 60 30

1975. 500th Anniv of Michelangelo. Multicoloured.
68 ½c. Type **4** 10 10*
69 1c. "Delphic Sibyl" 10 10*
70 2c. "Giuliano de Medici" 10 10*
71 40c. "The Creation" (detail) 15 10*
72 50c. "Lorenzo de Medici" 15 10*
73 75c. "Persian Sibyl" 20 10*
74 $2 "Head of Christ" 30 15*
MS75 118 × 96 mm. $1 "The Prophet Jeremiah" 75 50

1975. Butterflies. As T **213** of Grenada, but inscr "GRENADINES". Multicoloured.
76 ½c. "Morpho peleides" 10 10*
77 1c. "Danaus eresimus" ("Danaus gilippus") 10 10*
78 2c. "Dismorphia amphione" 10 10*
79 35c. "Hamadryas feronia" 35 10*
80 45c. "Philaethria dido" 45 10*
81 75c. "Phoebis argante" 70 15*
82 $2 "Prepona laertes" 1·40 30*
MS83 104 × 77 mm. $1 "Siproeta stelenes" 3·00 3·25

5 Progress "Standard" Badge

1975. 14th World Scout Jamboree, Norway. Multicoloured.
84 ½c. Type **5** 10 10*
85 1c. Boatman's badge 10 10*
86 2c. Coxswain's badge 10 10*
87 35c. Interpreter's badge 15 10*
88 45c. Ambulance badge 20 10*
89 75c. Chief Scout's award 25 10*
90 $2 Queen's Scout award 35 15*
MS91 106 × 80 mm. $1 Venture award 55 30*

6 The Surrender of Lord Cornwallis

1975. Bicentenary of American Revolution (1976) (1st issue). Multicoloured.
92 ½c. Type **6** 10 10*
93 1c. Minute-men 10 10*
94 2c. Paul Revere's ride 10 10*
95 3c. Battle of Bunker Hill 10 10*
96 5c. Fifer and drummers 10 10*
97 45c. Backwoodsman 15 10*
98 75c. Boston Tea Party 20 10*
99 $2 Naval engagement 45 10*
100 $2 George Washington 45 35
101 $2 White House and flags 45 35
MS102 Two sheets 113 × 128 mm containing No. 100, and 128 × 113 mm containing No. 101. Imperf 1·10 1·40
Nos. 100/1 are larger, 35 × 60 mm.
See also Nos. 176/**MS**183

7 Fencing

1975. Pan-American Games, Mexico City. Multicoloured.
103 ½c. Type **7** 10 10*
104 1c. Hurdling 10 10*
105 2c. Pole-vaulting 10 10*
106 35c. Weightlifting 15 10*
107 45c. Throwing the javelin 15 10*
108 75c. Throwing the discus 15 10*
109 $2 Diving 35 15*
MS110 78 × 104 mm. $1 Sprinter 40 20*

1975. Nos. 649/68 of Grenada additionally inscr "GRENADINES".
111 ½c. Yachts, Point Saline 10 30
112 1c. Yacht Club race, St. George's 10 15
113 2c. Carenage taxi 10 15
114 3c. Large working boats 10 15
115 5c. Deep-water dock, St. George's 10 15
116 6c. Cocoa beans in drying trays 10 15
117 8c. Nutmegs 10 15
118 10c. Rum distillery, River Antoine Estate, c. 1785 10 15
119 12c. Cocoa tree 10 15
120 15c. Fishermen at Fontenoy 10 15
121 20c. Parliament Building 10 60
122 25c. Fort George cannons 10 15
123 35c. Pearls Airport 75 15
124 50c. General Post Office 20 90
125 75c. Carib's Leap, Sauteurs Bay 40 60
126 $1 Carenage, St. George's 60 85
127 $2 St. George's Harbour by night 90 2·00
128 $3 Grand Anse beach 1·10 2·50
129 $5 Canoe Bay and Black Bay 1·25 5·00
130 $10 Sugar-loaf Island 2·25 5·50

8 Virgin and Child" (Durer)

1975. Christmas. "Virgin and Child" paintings by Artists named.
131 ½c. Type **8** 10 10*
132 1c. Durer 10 10*
133 2c. Correggio 10 10*
134 40c. Botticelli 15 10*
135 50c. Niccolo da Cremona 15 10*
136 75c. Correggio 15 10*
137 $2 Correggio 30 15*
MS138 114 × 120 mm. $1 Bellini 60 50*

9 Bleeding Tooth

1976. Shells. Multicoloured.
139 ½c. Type **9** 10 10*
140 1c. Toothed donax 10 10*
141 2c. Hawk-wing conch 10 10*
142 3c. Atlantic distorsio 10 10*
143 25c. Scotch bonnet 40 10*
144 50c. King helmet 50 10*
145 75c. Queen or pink conch 75 15*
MS146 79 × 105 mm. $2 Atlantic trumpet triton 1·00 70*

10 Cocoa Thrush

1976. Flora and Fauna. Multicoloured.
147 ½c. "Lignum vitae" 10 10*
148 1c. Type **10** 10 10*
149 2c. "Eurypelma sp." (spider) 10 10*
150 35c. Lesser Antillean Tanager ("Hooded Tanager") 1·25 10*
151 50c. "Nyctaginaceae" 1·00 15*
152 75c. Grenada dove 2·50 25*
153 $1 Marine toad 2·50 25*
MS154 108 × 84 mm. $2 Blue-hooded euphonia 4·00 1·00*

11 Hooked Sailfish

1976. Tourism. Multicoloured.
155 ½c. Type **11** 10 10*
156 1c. Careened schooner, Carriacou 10 10*
157 2c. Carriacou Annual Regatta 10 10*
158 18c. Boat building on Carriacou 20 10*
159 22c. Workboat race, Carriacou Regatta 20 10*
160 75c. Cruising off Petit Martinique 30 20*
161 $1 Water skiing 40 20*
MS162 105 × 87 mm. $2 Yacht racing at Carriacou 70 75*

12 Making a Camp Fire

1976. 50th Anniv of Girl Guides in Grenada. Multicoloured.
163 ½c. Type **12** 10 10*
164 1c. First aid 10 10*
165 2c. Nature study 10 10*
166 50c. Cookery 50 15*
167 $1 Sketching 75 25*
MS168 85 × 110 mm. $2 Guide playing guitar 1·00 75*

13 "Christ Mocked" (Bosch)

1976. Easter. Multicoloured.
169 ½c. Type **13** 10 10*
170 1c. "Christ Crucified" (Antonello da Messina) 10 10*
171 2c. "Adoration of the Trinity" (Durer) 10 10*
172 3c. "Lamentation of Christ" (Durer) 10 10*
173 35c. "The Entombment" (Van der Weyden) 15 10*
174 $3 "The Entombment" (Raphael) 60 30*
MS175 57 × 72 mm. $2 "Blood of the Redeemer" (G. Bellini) 65 70*

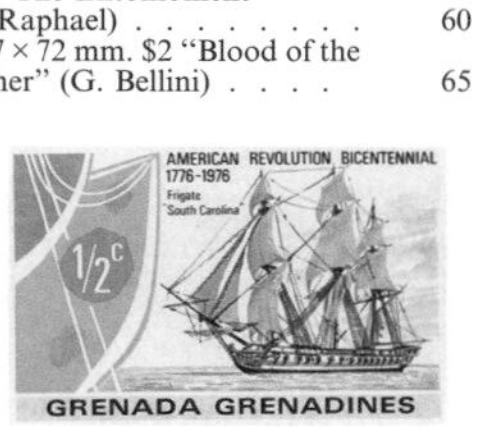

14 "South Carolina" (frigate)

1976. Bicentenary of American Revolution (2nd issue). Multicoloured.
176 ½c. Type **14** 10 10*
177 1c. "Lee" (schooner) 10 10*
178 2c. H.M.S. "Roebuck" (frigate) 10 10*
179 35c. "Andrew Doria" (brig) 40 10*
180 50c. "Providence" (sloop) 50 15*
181 $1 "Alfred" (frigate) 75 20*
182 $2 "Confederacy" (frigate) 1·25 30*
MS183 72 × 85 mm. $3 "Revenge" (cutter) 1·00 1·00*

15 Piper Apache

1976. Aircraft. Multicoloured.
184 ½c. Type **15** 10 10*
185 1c. Beech 50 Twin Bonanza 10 10*
186 2c. De Havilland Twin Otter 10 10*
187 40c. Britten Norman Islander 30 10*
188 50c. De Havilland Heron 2 40 10*
189 $2 Hawker Siddeley H.S.748 1·25 25*
MS190 71 × 85 mm. $3 B.A.C. One-Eleven 500 1·00 1·00*

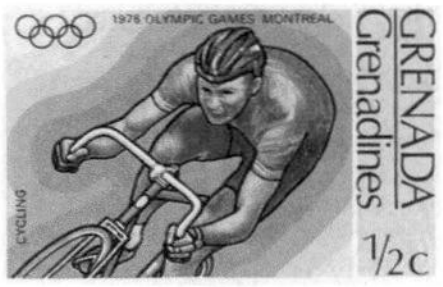

16 Cycling

1976. Olympic Games, Montreal. Multicoloured.
191 ½c. Type **16** 10 10*
192 1c. Pommel horse 10 10*
193 2c. Hurdling 10 10*
194 35c. Shot putting 10 10*
195 45c. Diving 15 10*
196 75c. Sprinting 15 10*
197 $2 Rowing 35 25*
MS198 101 × 76 mm. $3 Sailing 80 75*

17 "Virgin and Child" (Cima)

1976. Christmas. Multicoloured.
199 ½c. Type **17** 10 10*
200 1c. "The Nativity" (Romanino) 10 10*
201 2c. "The Nativity" (Romanino) (different) 10 10*
202 35c. "Adoration of the Kings" (Bruegel) 15 10*
203 50c. "Madonna and Child" (Girolamo) 20 10*
204 75c. "Adoration of the Magi" (Giorgione) (horiz) 20 15*
205 $2 "Adoration of the Kings" (School of Fra Angelico) (horiz) 40 25*
MS206 120 × 100 mm. $3 "The Holy Family" (Garofalo) 60 2·25

18 Alexander Graham Bell and First Telephone

1977. Centenary of First Telephone Transmission. Designs showing Alexander Graham Bell and telephone. Multicoloured.
207 ½c. Type **18** 10 10*
208 1c. 1895 telephone 10 10*
209 2c. 1900 telephone 10 10*
210 35c. 1915 telephone 15 10*
211 75c. 1920 telephone 20 10*
212 $1 1929 telephone 25 15*
213 $2 1963 telephone 35 25*
MS214 107 × 78 mm. $3 Telephone, 1976 1·10 75*

19 Coronation Coach

1977. Silver Jubilee. Multicoloured. (a) Perf.
215 35c. Type **19** 10 10*
216 $2 Queen entering Abbey 20 10*

217 $4 Queen crowned 35 25*
MS218 100 × 70 mm. $5 The Mall on Coronation Night . . . . . . 60 1·25

(b) Imperf × roul. Self-adhesive.
219 35c. Royal visit 15 20
220 50c. Crown of St. Edward . . 30 80
221 $2 The Queen and Prince Charles . . . . 50 1·60
222 $5 Royal Standard . . . . . 60 1·75
Nos. 219/22 come from booklets.

21 "Disrobing of Christ" (Fra Angelico)

22 "The Virgin adoring the Child" (Correggio)

1977. Easter. Paintings by artists named. Mult.
223 ½c. Type **21** 10 10*
224 1c. Fra Angelico 10 10*
225 2c. El Greco 10 10*
226 18c. El Greco 10 10*
227 35c. Fra Angelico 15 10*
228 50c. Giottino 15 10*
229 $2 Antonello da Messina . . 35 25*
MS230 121 × 94 mm. $3 Fra Angelico 65 65*

1977. Christmas. Multicoloured.
231 ½c. Type **22** 10 10*
232 1c. "Virgin and Child" (Giorgione) 10 10*
233 2c. "Virgin and Child" (Morales) 10 10*
234 18c. "Madonna della Tenda" (Raphael) 10 10*
235 35c. "Rest on the Flight into Egypt" (Van Dyck) 15 10*
236 50c. "Madonna and Child" (Lippi) 15 10*
237 $2 "Virgin and Child" (Lippi) (different) 35 25*
MS238 114 × 99 mm. $3 "Virgin and Child with Angels and Saints" (Ghirlandaio) 65 65*

1977. Royal Visit. Nos. 215/17 optd **ROYAL VISIT W.I. 1977**.
239 35c. Type **19** 10 10
240 $2 Queen entering Abbey . . 35 20
241 $4 Queen crowned 70 30
MS242 100 × 70 mm. $5 The Mall on Coronation Night 70 90

24 Life-saving

1977. Caribbean Scout Jamboree, Jamaica. Multicoloured.
243 ½c. Type **24** 10 10*
244 1c. Overnight hike 10 10*
245 2c. Cubs tying knots 10 10*
246 22c. Erecting a tent 15 10*
247 35c. Gang show limbo dance . 25 10*
248 75c. Campfire cooking . . . 40 15*
249 $3 Sea Scouts in "Mirror" dinghies 80 30*
MS250 109 × 85 mm. $2 Pioneering project—Spring bridge . . . . 1·10 90*

25 Blast-off

1977. Space Shuttle. Multicoloured.
251 ½c. Type **25** 10 10*
252 1c. Booster jettison 10 10*
253 2c. External tank jettison . . 10 10*
254 22c. Working in orbit 15 10*
255 50c. Shuttle re-entry 25 10*
256 $3 Shuttle landing 85 30*
MS257 85 × 103 mm. $2 Shuttle being towed 60 70*

26 Alfred Nobel and Physiology/ Medicine Medal

1978. Nobel Prize Awards. Multicoloured.
258 ½c. Type **26** 10 10*
259 1c. Physics and Chemistry medal 10 10*
260 2c. Peace medal (reverse) . . 10 10*
261 22c. Nobel Institute, Oslo . . 25 10*
262 75c. Peace Prize committee . 50 15*
263 $3 Literature medal . . . . 1·50 30*
MS264 127 × 103 mm. $2 Peace medal and Nobel's will 50 60*

27 German Zeppelin Stamp, 1930

1978. 75th Anniv of First Zeppelin Flight and 50th Anniv of Lindbergh's Transatlantic Flight. Multicoloured.
265 5c. Type **27** 20 10*
266 15c. French Concorde stamp, 1970 . . . . 60 10*
267 25c. Liechtenstein Zeppelin stamp, 1931 . . . . . . 20 10*
268 35c. Panama Lindbergh stamp, 1928 . . . . 20 10*
269 50c. Russia Airship stamp, 1931 . . . . 25 10*
270 $3 Spanish Lindbergh stamp, 1930 . . . . 75 30*
MS271 140 × 79 mm. 75c. U.S.A. Lindbergh stamp, 1927; $2 German LZ-129 *Hindenburg* stamp, 1936 . . . . 1·10 90*

28 Coronation Ring

1978. 25th Anniv of Coronation. Multicoloured.
(a) Horiz designs. Perf.
272 50c. Type **28** 10 10
273 $2 The Orb 25 30
274 $2.50 Imperial State Crown 30 35
MS275 97 × 67 mm. $5 Queen Elizabeth II 60 60

(b) Vert designs. Roul × imperf. Self-adhesive.
276 18c. Drummer, Royal Regiment of Fusiliers . . . 15 35
277 50c. Drummer, Royal Anglian Regiment 15 45
278 $5 Drum Major, Queen's Regiment . . . . 1·00 3·00

30 "Le Chapeau de Paille"

32 Audubon's Shearwater

31 Wright Flyer I

1978. 400th Birth Anniv of Rubens. Mult.
279 5c. Type **30** 10 10
280 15c. "Archilles slaying Hector" 15 10
281 18c. "Helene Fourment and her Children" 15 10
282 22c. "Rubens and Isabella Brandt" 15 10
283 35c. "The Ildefonso Altarpiece" 20 10
284 $3 "Heads of Negroes" (detail) . . . . 75 1·00
MS285 85 × 127 mm. $2 "Self-portrait" . . . . 70 1·00

1978. 75th Anniv of Powered Flight.
286 **31** 5c. black, blue and brown 10 10
287 – 15c. black, brown and red 10 10
288 – 18c. black, brown and red 10 10
289 – 25c. black, yellow and green 10 10
290 – 35c. black, pink and purple 15 10
291 – 75c. black, lilac and yellow 25 25
292 – $3 black, violet and mauve 75 75
MS293 126 × 83 mm. $2 black, blue and green . . . . 75 1·00

DESIGNS—HORIZ: 25c. Wright Flyer III, 1905; 35c. Wright glider No. 1; 75c. Wright Flyer I (different); $2 Various Wright aircraft; $3 Wright Type A. VERT: 15c. Orville Wright; 18c. Wilbur Wright.

1978. Birds. Multicoloured.
294 5c. Type **32** 50 15
295 10c. Semi-palmated plover ("Northern Ring-necked Plover") 70 15
296 18c. Purple-throated carib ("Garnet-throated Hummingbird") (horiz) . . 1·00 15
297 22c. Red-billed whistling duck ("Black-bellied Tree Duck") (horiz) . . . . . . 1·00 20
298 40c. Caribbean martin (horiz) 1·50 35
299 $1 White-tailed tropic bird ("Yellow-tailed Tropicbird") . . . . 2·25 50
300 $2 Long-billed curlew . . . . 3·25 75
MS301 78 × 78 mm. $5 Snowy egret 5·00 2·75

33 Players with Ball

1978. World Cup Football Championship, Argentina. Multicoloured.
302 15c. Type **33** 10 10
303 35c. Running with ball . . . 20 10
304 50c. Player with ball 25 20
305 $3 Heading 80 80
MS306 114 × 85 mm. $2 Player with ball (different) . . . . 80 1·25

34 Captain Cook and Kalaniopu (King of Hawaii), 1778

1978. 250th Birth Anniv of Captain James Cook. Multicoloured.
307 18c. Type **34** 45 10
308 22c. Cook and native of Hawaii 60 15
309 50c. Cook and death scene, 1779 . . . . 1·00 30
310 $3 Cook and offering ceremony . . . . 2·25 1·75
MS311 117 × 113 mm. $4 H.M.S. "Resolution" (vert) . . . . . 1·50 1·00

35 "Virgin at Prayer"

36 "Strelitzia reginae"

1978. Christmas. Paintings by Durer. Multicoloured.
312 40c. Type **35** 15 10
313 60c. "The Dresden Altarpiece" 20 15
314 90c. "Madonna and Child with St. Anne" 20 15
315 $2 "Madonna and Child with Pear" 50 50
MS316 114 × 84 mm. $4 "Salvator Mundi" . . . . 1·00 1·40

1979. Flowers. Multicoloured.
317 22c. Type **36** 15 10
318 40c. "Euphorbia pulcherrima" 25 15
319 $1 "Heliconia humilis" . . . 45 30
320 $3 "Thunbergia alata" . . . 80 80
MS321 114 × 90 mm. $2 "Bougainvillaea glabra" . . . 75 1·00

37 Children with Pig

1979. International Year of the Child. Multicoloured.
322 18c. Type **37** 10 10
323 50c. Children with donkey . . 20 25
324 $1 Children with goats . . . 25 30
325 $3 Children fishing 65 80
MS326 104 × 86 mm. $4 Child with coconuts . . . . 1·00 1·90

38 "20,000 Leagues under the Sea"

1979. 150th Birth Anniv of Jules Verne (author). Multicoloured.
327 18c. Type **38** 40 10
328 38c. "From the Earth to the Moon" 45 20
329 75c. "From the Earth to the Moon" (different) 55 35
330 $3 "Five Weeks in a Balloon" . . . . 1·00 1·00
MS331 111 × 86 mm. $4 "Around the World in 80 Days" . . . . 1·00 1·60

39 Sir Rowland Hill and Mail Van

1979. Death Centenary of Sir Rowland Hill. Multicoloured.
332 15c. Type **39** 10 10
333 $1 "Britanis" (cargo liner) . . 20 20
334 $2 Diesel mail train 30 30
335 $3 Concorde 90 70
MS336 85 × 67 mm. $4 Sir Rowland Hill . . . . 75 1·00

40 "Virgin and Child Enthroned" (11th-century Byzantine)

1979. Christmas. Sculptures. Multicoloured.
337 6c. Type **40** 10 10
338 25c. "Presentation in the Temple" (Andre Beauneveu) 10 10
339 30c. "Flight to Egypt" (Utrecht, c. 1510) 10 10
340 40c. "Madonna and Child" (Jacopo della Quercia) . . 10 10
341 90c. "Madonna della Mela" (Luca della Robbia) . . . 15 15
342 $1 "Madonna and Child" (Antonio Rossellino) . . . 20 20
343 $2 "Madonna and Child" (Antwerp, 1700) 35 35
MS344 125 × 95 mm. $4 "Virgin", Krumau . . . . 65 1·00

41 Great Hammerhead

1979. Marine Wildlife. Multicoloured.
345 40c. Type **41** 40 30
346 45c. Spot-finned butterflyfish 45 30
347 50c. Permit (fish) 45 40
348 60c. Threaded turban (shell) 65 55
349 70c. Milk conch 75 75
350 75c. Great blue heron . . . . 1·25 90
351 90c. Colourful Atlantic moon (shell) . . . . 95 1·00
352 $1 Red-footed booby . . . . 1·75 1·75
MS353 99 × 86 mm. $2.50 Collared plover . . . . 2·00 1·10

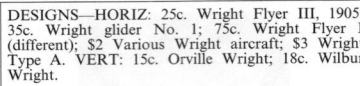

42 Doctor Goofy

1979. International Year of the Child. Walt Disney cartoon characters. Multicoloured.
354 ½c. Type **42** 10 10
355 1c. Admiral Mickey Mouse 10 10
356 2c. Fireman Goofy 10 10
357 3c. Nurse Minnie Mouse 10 10
358 4c. Drum Major Mickey Mouse 10 10
359 5c. Policeman Donald Duck 10 10
360 10c. Pilot Donald Duck 10 10
361 $2 Postman Goofy (horiz) 2·25 2·25
362 $2.50 Train driver Donald Duck (horiz) 2·25 2·25
MS363 128 × 102 mm. $3 Mickey Mouse as fireman 1·75 2·00

1980. 1st Anniv of Revolution. Nos. 116 and 119/30 optd **PEOPLE'S REVOLUTION 13 MARCH 1979.**
364 6c. Cocoa beans in drying trays 10 10
365 12c. Cocoa tree 10 10
366 15c. Fishermen at Fontenoy 10 10
367 20c. Parliament Building, St. George's 10 10
368 25c. Fort George cannons 15 10
369 35c. Pearls Airport 20 10
370 50c. General Post Office 35 15
371 75c. Carib's Leap, Sauteurs Bay 40 20
372 $1 Carenage, St. George's 55 30
373 $2 St. George's Harbour by night 85 70
374 $3 Grand Anse Beach 1·60 1·60
375 $5 Canoe Bay and Black Bay 2·25 2·50
376 $10 Sugar-loaf Island 3·75 4·25

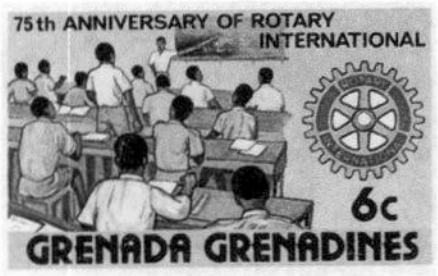

43 Classroom

1980. 75th Anniv of Rotary International. Multicoloured.
377 6c. Type **43** 10 10
378 30c. Different races encircling Rotary emblem 20 10
379 60c. Rotary executive presenting doctor with cheque 35 20
380 $3 Nurses with young patients 1·25 75
MS381 85 × 72 mm. $4 Paul P. Harris (founder) 1·00 1·60

44 Yellow-bellied Seedeater

1980. Wild Birds. Multicoloured.
382 25c. Type **44** 50 15
383 40c. Blue-hooded euphonia 55 20
384 90c. Yellow warbler 1·25 65
385 $2 Tropical mockingbird 1·75 1·25
MS386 83 × 110 mm. $3 Barn Owl 4·00 1·50

45 Running

1980. Olympic Games, Moscow. Multicoloured.
387 30c. Type **45** 20 15
388 40c. Football 15 20
389 90c. Boxing 35 35
390 $2 Wrestling 70 75
MS391 104 × 75 mm. $4 Athletes in silhouette 75 1·10

1980. "London 1980" International Stamp Exhibition. Nos. 332/5 optd **LONDON 1980.**
392 15c. Mail van 15 15
393 $1 "Britanis" (cargo liner) 75 35
394 $2 Diesel mail train 1·50 1·00
395 $3 Concorde 2·50 2·00

47 Long-jawed Squirrelfish

1980. Fishes. Multicoloured.
396A ½c. Type **47** 10 10
397A 1c. Blue chromis 10 10
398A 2c. Four-eyed butterflyfish 10 10
399A 4c. Sergeant major 10 10
400A 5c. Yellow-tailed snapper 10 10
401A 6c. Mutton snapper 10 10
402A 10c. Cocoa damselfish 10 10
403A 12c. Royal gramma 10 10
404A 15c. Cherub angelfish 10 10
405A 20c. Black-barred soldierfish 15 10
406A 25c. Mottled grouper 15 15
407A 30c. Caribbean long-nosed butterflyfish 15 20
408A 40c. Puddingwife 20 25
409A 50c. Midnight parrotfish 25 35
410A 90c. Red-spotted hawkfish 40 55
411A $1 Hogfish 45 60
412A $3 Beau Gregory 1·25 1·50
413A $5 Rock beauty 1·75 1·75
414A $10 Barred hamlet 2·75 2·75

1980. Christmas. Scenes from Walt Disney's "Bambi". As T **42**. Multicoloured.
415 ½c. Bambi with mother 10 10
416 1c. Bambi with quails 10 10
417 2c. Bambi meets Thumper the rabbit 10 10
418 3c. Bambi meets Flower the skunk 10 10
419 4c. Bambi and Faline 10 10
420 5c. Bambi with his father 10 10
421 10c. Bambi on ice 10 10
422 $2.50 Faline with foals 1·75 1·25
423 $3 Bambi and Faline 1·75 1·25
MS424 127 × 102 mm. $4 Bambi as Prince of the Forest (vert) 2·00 2·00

48 "The Unicorn in Captivity" (15th century unknown artist)

49 "Bust of a Woman"

1981. Art Masterpieces. Multicoloured.
425 6c. Type **48** 10 10
426 10c. "The Fighting 'Temeraire'" (Turner) (horiz) 10 10
427 25c. "Sunday Afternoon on the Ile de la Grande Jatte" (Seurat) (horiz) 15 15
428 90c. "Max Schmitt in a Single Scull" (Eakins) (horiz) 45 45
429 $2 "The Burial of the Count of Orgaz" (El Greco) 85 85
430 $3 "Portrait of George Washington" (Stuart) 1·10 1·10
MS431 66 × 101 mm. $5 "Kaiser Karl de Grosse" (detail Durer) 1·75 2·00

1981. 50th Anniv of Walt Disney's Pluto (cartoon character). As T **42**.
432 $2 Mickey Mouse serving birthday cake to Pluto 1·00 80
MS433 127 × 101 mm. $4 Pluto in scene from film "Pluto's Dream House" 1·50 1·50

1981. Easter. Walt Disney cartoon characters. As T **42**. Multicoloured.
434 35c. Chip 20 20
435 40c. Dewey 20 20
436 $2 Huey 60 60
437 $2.50 Mickey Mouse 75 75
MS438 126 × 102 mm. $4 Jimmy Cricket 1·50 1·50

1981. Birth Centenary of Picasso. Mult.
439 6c. Type **49** 10 10
440 40c. Woman (study for "Les Demoiselles d'Avignon") 20 15
441 90c. "Nude with raised Arms (The Dancer of Avignon)" 30 20
442 $4 "The Dryad" 75 75
MS443 103 × 128 mm. $5 "Les Demoiselles d'Avignon". Imperf 1·40 1·25

50 Balmoral Castle

51 Lady Diana Spencer

1981. Royal Wedding (1st issue). Multicoloured.
448 30c. Prince Charles and Lady Diana Spencer 35 20
444 40c. As 30c. 15 15
449 40c. Type **50** 45 35
445 $2 Type **50** 50 50
446 $4 Prince Charles as parachutist 90 90
MS447 97 × 84 mm. $5 Royal Coach 70 70

1981. Royal Wedding (2nd issue). Multicoloured. Self-adhesive.
450 $1 Type **51** 20 35
451 $2 Prince Charles 25 50
452 $5 Prince Charles and Lady Diana Spencer (horiz) 1·25 2·00

52 Amy Johnson (1st solo flight, Britain to Australia by Woman, May 1930)

54 Footballer

53 Boeing 747 SCA Carrier

1981. "Decade for Women". Famous Female Aviators. Multicoloured.
453 30c. Type **52** 45 15
454 70c. Mme. La Baronne de Laroche (1st qualified woman pilot, March 1910) 70 30
455 $1.10 Ruth Nichols (solo Atlantic flight attempt, June 1931) 80 40
456 $3 Amelia Earhart (1st North Atlantic solo flight by woman, May 1932) 1·75 1·10
MS457 90 × 85 mm. $5 Valentina Nikolayeva-Tereshkova (1st woman in space, June 1963) 1·25 1·40

1981. Christmas. Designs as T **42** showing scenes from Walt Disney's cartoon film "Lady and the Tramp".
458 ½c. multicoloured 10 10
459 1c. multicoloured 10 10
460 2c. multicoloured 10 10
461 3c. multicoloured 10 10
462 4c. multicoloured 10 10
463 5c. multicoloured 10 10
464 10c. multicoloured 10 10
465 $2.50 multicoloured 3·25 1·50
466 $3 multicoloured 3·25 1·50
MS467 128 × 103 mm. $5 multicoloured 5·00 3·00

1981. Space Shuttle Project. Multicoloured.
468 10c. Type **53** 30 10
469 40c. Re-entry 65 15
470 $1.10 External tank separation 1·25 45
471 $3 Touchdown 1·75 1·00
MS472 117 × 98 mm. $5 Launch 2·50 1·60

1981. World Cup Football Championship, Spain (1982).
473 **54** 20c. multicoloured 15 10
474 – 40c. multicoloured 20 15
475 – $1 multicoloured 35 30
476 – $2 multicoloured 65 55
MS477 106 × 128 mm. $4 multicoloured 1·40 1·60
DESIGNS: 40c. to $4 various designs showing footballers.

55 Mail Van and Stagecoach

1982. Cent of U.P.U. Membership. Multicoloured.
478 30c. Type **55** 30 15
479 40c. U.P.U. emblem 30 15
480 $2.50 "Queen Elizabeth 2" (liner) and sailing ship 1·50 70
481 $4 Concorde and De Havilland D.H.9 biplane 2·25 1·25
MS482 117 × 78 mm. $5 British Advanced Passenger Train and steam mail trains 3·00 2·25

56 National Sports Meeting

1982. 75th Anniv of Boy Scout Movement and 125th Birth Anniv of Lord Baden-Powell. Multicoloured.
483 6c. Type **56** 15 10
484 90c. Sea scouts sailing 50 30
485 $1.10 Handicraft 65 60
486 $3 Animal tending 1·40 1·40
MS487 100 × 71 mm. $5 Music around campfire 1·40 1·75

57 "Anartia jatrophae"

1982. Butterflies. Multicoloured.
488 30c. Type **57** 75 30
489 40c. "Chioides vintra" 80 35
490 $1.10 "Cynthia cardui" 1·75 75
491 $3 "Historis odius" 2·75 1·60
MS492 103 × 77 mm. $5 "Dione juno" 3·25 2·50

58 Prince and Princess of Wales

60 "Presentation of Christ in the Temple"

59 "New Deal"—Soil Conservation

1982. 21st Birthday of Princess of Wales. Multicoloured.
493 50c. Blenheim Palace 1·25 1·75
494 60c. As 50c. 75 75
495 $1 Type **58** 1·75 2·25
496 $2 Type **58** 1·75 2·00
497 $3 Princess of Wales 2·50 2·75
498 $4 As $3 2·50 2·75
MS499 103 × 75 mm. $5 Princess Diana (different) 5·50 2·50

1982. Birth Centenary of Franklin D. Roosevelt. Multicoloured.
500 30c. Type **59** 25 10
501 40c. Roosevelt and George Washington Carver (scientist) 25 10
502 70c. Civilian conservation corps (reafforestation) 30 20
503 $3 Roosevelt with Pres. Barclay of Liberia, Casablanca Conference, 1943 70 80
MS504 100 × 72 mm. $5 Roosevelt delivering address at Howard University 1·75 1·75

1982. Birth of Prince William of Wales. Nos. 493/8 optd **ROYAL BABY 21.6.82.**
505 50c. Blenheim Palace 50 75
506 60c. As 50c. 55 60
507 $1 Type **58** 70 1·00
508 $2 Type **58** 1·00 1·25
509 $3 Princess of Wales 1·25 1·75
510 $4 As $3 1·50 1·75
MS511 103 × 75 mm. $5 Princess Diana (different) 2·10 2·25

1982. Easter. Easter Paintings by Rembrandt. Multicoloured.
512 30c. Type **60** 25 10
513 60c. "Descent from the Cross" 30 10

514 $2 "Raising of the Cross" . . 45 60
515 $4 "Resurrection of Christ" 80 1·25
MS516 101 × 126 mm. $5 "The Risen Christ" . . . . 2·40 2·00

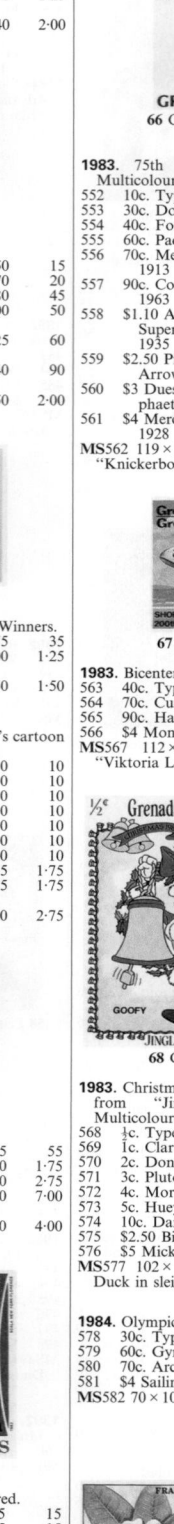

61 "Santa Fe", U.S.A.

1982. Famous Trains of the World. Mult.
517 10c. Type **61** 50 15
518 40c. "Mistral", France . . . 70 20
519 70c. "Rheingold", Germany 80 45
520 $1 "ET 403", France . . . . 1·00 50
521 $1.10 Steam locomotive "Mallard", Great Britain 1·25 60
522 $2 Tokaido Shinkansen "Hikari", Japan . . . . . 1·40 90
MS523 121 × 95 mm. $5 "Settebello", Italy . . . . . . 1·50 2·00

62 Footballers

1982. World Cup Football Championship Winners.
524 **62** 60c. multicoloured 75 35
525 $4 multicoloured . . . . . 2·00 1·25
MS526 92 × 134 mm. $5 multicoloured . . . . 1·50 1·50

1982. Christmas. Scenes from Walt Disney's cartoon film "The Rescuers". As T **42**, but horiz.
527 ½c. multicoloured 10 10
528 1c. multicoloured 10 10
529 2c. multicoloured 10 10
530 3c. multicoloured 10 10
531 4c. multicoloured 10 10
532 5c. multicoloured 10 10
533 10c. multicoloured 10 10
534 $2.50 multicoloured . . . . 2·75 1·75
535 $3 multicoloured . . . . . . 2·75 1·75
MS536 120 × 96 mm. $5 multicoloured . . . . 5·00 2·75

63 Short-finned Pilot Whale

1982. Save the Whale. Multicoloured.
537 10c. Type **63** 85 55
538 60c. Dall's porpoise . . . . 2·00 1·75
539 $1.10 Humpback whale . . . 3·50 2·75
540 $3 Bowhead whale . . . . . 6·00 7·00
MS541 113 × 84 mm. $5 Spotted dolphin . . . . 4·50 4·00

64 "David and Goliath"

1983. 500th Anniv of Raphael. Multicoloured.
542 25c. Type **64** 15 15
543 30c. "David sees Bathsheba" 15 15
544 90c. "Triumph of David" . . 30 35
545 $4 "Anointing of Solomon" 70 90
MS546 126 × 101 mm. $5 "Anointing of David" . . . . 80 1·10

65 Voice and Visual Communication

1983. World Communications Year. Mult.
547 30c. Type **65** 10 10
548 60c. Ambulance 25 20
549 $1.10 Westland Whirlwind helicopters 45 45
550 $3 Satellite . . . . 1·00 1·00
MS551 127 × 85 mm. $5 Diver and bottle-nosed dolphin . . . . . 2·50 2·00

66 Chrysler "Imperial Roadster", 1931

1983. 75th Anniv of Model "T" Ford Car. Multicoloured.
552 10c. Type **66** 15 15
553 30c. Doble steam car, 1925 25 25
554 40c. Ford "Mustang", 1965 25 30
555 60c. Packard tourer, 1930 . . 35 40
556 70c. Mercer "Raceabout", 1913 . . . . 35 40
557 90c. Corvette "Stingray", 1963 . . . . 35 40
558 $1.10 Auburn "851 Supercharger Speedster", 1935 . . . . 40 45
559 $2.50 Pierce-Arrow "Silver Arrow", 1933 . . . . . 65 95
560 $3 Duesenberg dual cowl phaeton, 1929 . . . . . 75 1·25
561 $4 Mercedes-Benz "SSK", 1928 . . . . 75 1·50
MS562 119 × 90 mm. $5 McFarlan "Knickerbocker" cabriolet, 1923 1·50 2·50

67 Short Solent 2 Flying Boat

1983. Bicentenary of Manned Flight. Mult.
563 40c. Type **67** 85 20
564 70c. Curtiss R3C-2 seaplane 1·00 35
565 90c. Hawker Nimrod biplane 1·25 40
566 $4 Montgolfier balloon . . . 3·25 2·75
MS567 112 × 85 mm. $5 LZ-11 "Viktoria Luise" (airship) . . . 1·75 2·00

68 Goofy

69 Weightlifting

1983. Christmas Disney cartoon characters in scenes from "Jingle Bells" (Christmas carol). Multicoloured.
568 ½c. Type **68** 10 10
569 1c. Clarabelle Cow 10 10
570 2c. Donald Duck 10 10
571 3c. Pluto 10 10
572 4c. Morty and Ferdie 10 10
573 5c. Huey, Dewey and Louie 10 10
574 10c. Daisy and Chip n'Dale 10 10
575 $2.50 Big Bad Wolf . . . . 4·75 5·00
576 $5 Mickey Mouse . . . . . 5·00 5·50
MS577 102 × 124 mm. $5 Donald Duck in sleigh . . . . 8·00 8·50

1984. Olympic Games, Los Angeles. Mult.
578 30c. Type **69** 20 15
579 60c. Gymnastics 45 35
580 70c. Archery 50 40
581 $4 Sailing . . . . 1·90 1·90
MS582 70 × 102 mm. $5 Basketball 2·25 2·25

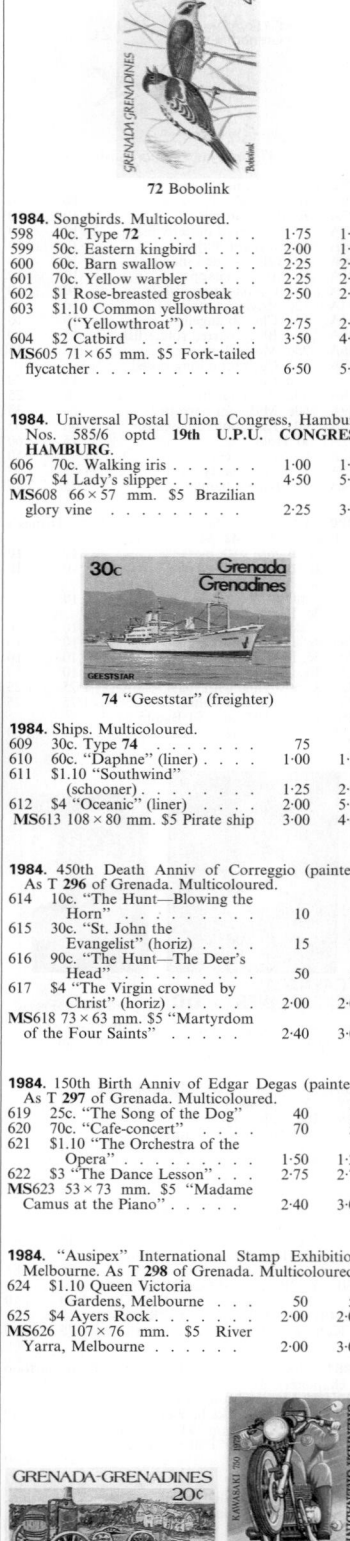

70 Frangipani

71 Goofy

1984. Flowers. Multicoloured.
583 15c. Type **70** 15 10
584 40c. Dwarf poinciana 30 25
585 70c. Walking iris 55 45
586 $4 Lady's slipper . . . . . 1·75 2·50
MS587 66 × 57 mm. $5 Brazilian glory vine . . . . 1·50 2·50

1984. Easter. Multicoloured.
588 ½c. Type **71** 10 10
589 1c. Chip and Dale 10 10
590 2c. Daisy Duck and Huey . . 10 10
591 3c. Daisy Duck 10 10
592 4c. Donald Duck 10 10
593 5c. Merlin and Madam Mim 10 10
594 10c. Flower 10 10
595 $2 Minnie and Mickey Mouse . . . . 1·25 2·00
596 $4 Minnie Mouse . . . . . 1·75 2·75
MS597 126 × 100 mm. $5 Minnie Mouse (different) . . . . . . 3·00 3·75

72 Bobolink

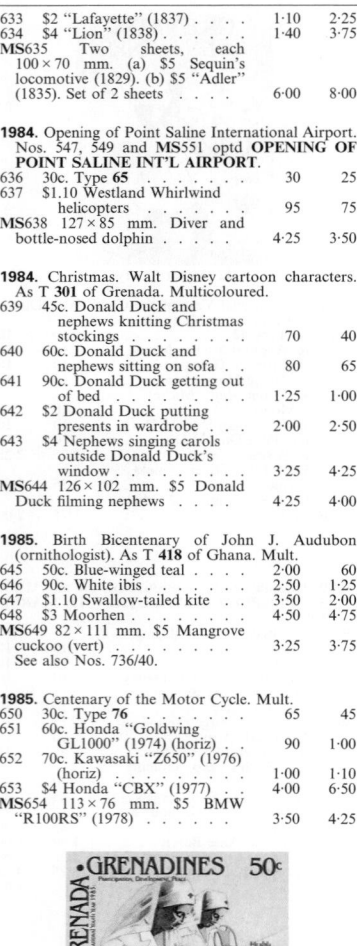

1984. Songbirds. Multicoloured.
598 40c. Type **72** . . . . 1·75 1·50
599 50c. Eastern kingbird . . . . 2·00 1·60
600 60c. Barn swallow . . . . . 2·25 2·00
601 70c. Yellow warbler . . . . 2·25 2·00
602 $1 Rose-breasted grosbeak 2·50 2·50
603 $1.10 Common yellowthroat ("Yellowthroat") . . . . . 2·75 2·75
604 $2 Catbird . . . . 3·50 4·50
MS605 71 × 65 mm. $5 Fork-tailed flycatcher . . . . 6·50 5·00

1984. Universal Postal Union Congress, Hamburg. Nos. 585/6 optd **19th U.P.U. CONGRESS HAMBURG**.
606 70c. Walking iris . . . . . . 1·00 1·00
607 $4 Lady's slipper . . . . . 4·50 5·00
MS608 66 × 57 mm. $5 Brazilian glory vine . . . . 2·25 3·00

74 "Geeststar" (freighter)

1984. Ships. Multicoloured.
609 30c. Type **74** 75 75
610 60c. "Daphne" (liner) . . . . 1·00 1·25
611 $1.10 "Southwind" (schooner) . . . . 1·25 2·00
612 $4 "Oceanic" (liner) . . . . 2·00 5·50
MS613 108 × 80 mm. $5 Pirate ship 3·00 4·00

1984. 450th Death Anniv of Correggio (painter). As T **296** of Grenada. Multicoloured.
614 10c. "The Hunt—Blowing the Horn" 10 10
615 30c. "St. John the Evangelist" (horiz) 15 15
616 90c. "The Hunt—The Deer's Head" 50 50
617 $4 "The Virgin crowned by Christ" (horiz) . . . . . 2·00 2·00
MS618 73 × 63 mm. $5 "Martyrdom of the Four Saints" . . . . . 2·40 3·00

1984. 150th Birth Anniv of Edgar Degas (painter). As T **297** of Grenada. Multicoloured.
619 25c. "The Song of the Dog" 40 15
620 70c. "Cafe-concert" 70 50
621 $1.10 "The Orchestra of the Opera" . . . . 1·50 1·25
622 $3 "The Dance Lesson" . . . 2·75 2·75
MS623 53 × 73 mm. $5 "Madame Camus at the Piano" . . . . . 2·40 3·00

1984. "Ausipex" International Stamp Exhibition, Melbourne. As T **298** of Grenada. Multicoloured.
624 $1.10 Queen Victoria Gardens, Melbourne . . . 50 50
625 $4 Ayers Rock . . . . 2·00 2·00
MS626 107 × 76 mm. $5 River Yarra, Melbourne . . . . . . 2·00 3·00

75 Col. Steven's Model (1825)

76 Kawasaki "750" (1972)

1984. Railway Locomotives. Multicoloured.
627 20c. Type **75** 55 25
628 50c. "Royal George" (1827) 70 50
629 60c. "Stourbridge Lion" (1829) 75 65
630 70c. "Liverpool" (1830) . . . 80 85
631 90c. "South Carolina" (1832) 90 1·25
632 $1.10 "Monster" (1836) . . . 90 1·50
633 $2 "Lafayette" (1837) . . . . 1·10 2·25
634 $4 "Lion" (1838) . . . . . . 1·40 3·75
MS635 Two sheets, each 100 × 70 mm. (a) $5 Sequin's locomotive (1829). (b) $5 "Adler" (1835). Set of 2 sheets . . . . 6·00 8·00

1984. Opening of Point Saline International Airport. Nos. 547, 549 and **MS551** optd **OPENING OF POINT SALINE INT'L AIRPORT**.
636 30c. Type **65** 30 25
637 $1.10 Westland Whirlwind helicopters 95 75
MS638 127 × 85 mm. Diver and bottle-nosed dolphin . . . . . 4·25 3·50

1984. Christmas. Walt Disney cartoon characters. As T **301** of Grenada. Multicoloured.
639 45c. Donald Duck and nephews knitting Christmas stockings 70 40
640 60c. Donald Duck and nephews sitting on sofa . . 80 65
641 90c. Donald Duck getting out of bed . . . . 1·25 1·00
642 $2 Donald Duck putting presents in wardrobe . . . 2·00 2·50
643 $4 Nephews singing carols outside Donald Duck's window . . . . 3·25 4·25
MS644 126 × 102 mm. $5 Donald Duck filming nephews . . . . 4·25 4·00

1985. Birth Bicentenary of John J. Audubon (ornithologist). As T **418** of Ghana. Mult.
645 50c. Blue-winged teal . . . . 2·00 60
646 90c. White ibis . . . . 2·50 1·25
647 $1.10 Swallow-tailed kite . . 3·50 2·00
648 $3 Moorhen . . . . 4·50 4·75
MS649 82 × 111 mm. $5 Mangrove cuckoo (vert) . . . . 3·25 3·75
See also Nos. 736/40.

1985. Centenary of the Motor Cycle. Mult.
650 30c. Type **76** 65 45
651 60c. Honda "Goldwing GL1000" (1974) (horiz) . . 90 1·00
652 70c. Kawasaki "Z650" (1976) (horiz) . . . . 1·00 1·10
653 $4 Honda "CBX" (1977) . . . 4·00 6·50
MS654 113 × 76 mm. $5 BMW "R100RS" (1978) . . . . . . 3·50 4·25

77 Nursing Cadets folding Bandages (Health)

1985. International Youth Year. Mult.
655 50c. Type **77** 70 45
656 70c. Scuba diver and turtle (Environment) . . . . . 1·00 80
657 $1.10 Yachting (Leisure) . . 1·60 1·50
658 $3 Boys playing chess (Education) . . . . 8·00 8·00
MS659 98 × 70 mm. $5 Hands touching globe . . . . 2·75 3·00

1985. 40th Anniv of International Civil Aviation Organization. As T **305** of Grenada. Multicoloured.
660 5c. Lockheed Lodestar . . . 40 20
661 70c. Hawker Siddeley H.S.748 . . . . 1·75 55
662 $1.10 Boeing 727-200 . . . . 2·25 90
663 $4 Boeing 707 . . . . 3·50 2·50
MS664 87 × 68 mm. $4 Pilatus Britten Norman Islander . . . 3·50 3·00

78 Lady Baden-Powell (founder) and Grenadian Guide Leaders

1985. 75th Anniv of Girl Guide Movement. Multicoloured.
665 30c. Type **78** 50 20
666 50c. Guide leader and guides on botany field trip . . . . 1·00 30
667 70c. Guide leader and guides camping (vert) . . . . . . 1·00 45
668 $4 Guides sailing (vert) . . . 4·00 2·25
MS669 100 × 73 mm. $5 Lord and Lady Baden-Powell (vert) . . . 3·75 4·25

79 "Chiomara asychis"

1985. Butterflies. Multicoloured.
670 ½c. Type **79** 10 20
671 1c. "Anartia amathea" . . . 10 20
672 2c. "Pseudolycaena marsyas" 10 20

673 4c. "Urbanus proteus" . . . 10 20
674 5c. "Polygonus manueli" . . 15 20
675a 6c. "Battus polydamas" . . 20 15
676 10c. "Eurema daira" . . . 30 15
677 12c. "Phoebis agarithe" . . 45 20
678 15c. "Aphrissa statira" . . . 45 20
679 20c. "Strymon simaethis" 60 20
680 25c. "Mestra cana" 60 25
681 30c. "Agraulis vanillae" . . 60 30
682 40c. "Junonia evarete" . . . 75 45
683 60c. "Dryas julia" . . . . . 1·00 65
684 70c. "Philaethria dido" . . 1·10 75
685 $1.10 "Hamadryas feronia" 1·75 1·25
686 $2.50 "Strymon rufofusca" 3·25 3·00
687 $5 "Appias drusilla" . . . . 5·00 4·75
688 $10 "Polites dictynna" . . . 8·00 9·00
688b $20 "Euptychia cephus" . . 12·00 17·00

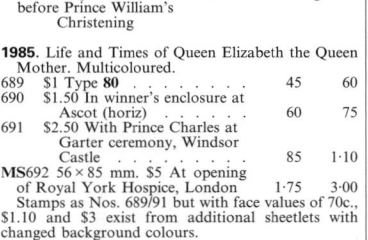

80 The Queen Mother before Prince William's Christening

81 Scuba Diving

1985. Life and Times of Queen Elizabeth the Queen Mother. Multicoloured.
689 $1 Type **80** 45 60
690 $1.50 In winner's enclosure at Ascot (horiz) 60 75
691 $2.50 With Prince Charles at Garter ceremony, Windsor Castle . . . . 85 1·10
MS692 56 × 85 mm. $5 At opening of Royal York Hospice, London 1·75 3·00
Stamps as Nos. 689/91 but with face values of 70c., $1.10 and $3 exist from additional sheetlets with changed background colours.

1985. Water Sports. Multicoloured.
693 15c. Type **81** 30 10
694 70c. Boys playing in waterfall 60 45
695 90c. Water skiing 70 55
696 $4 Swimming . . . . 2·75 2·25
MS697 103 × 78 mm. $5 Scuba diver 2·75 3·25

82 Queen or Pink Conch

1985. Marine Life. Multicoloured.
698 60c. Type **82** 75 40
699 90c. Porcupinefish and fire coral 95 60
700 $1.10 Ghost crab . . . . . . 1·25 1·00
701 $4 West Indies spiny lobster 2·75 4·00
MS702 299 × 70 mm. $5 Long-spined urchin . . . . 5·00 4·00

1985. 300th Birth Anniv of Johann Sebastian Bach (composer). As T **309a** of Grenada. Multicoloured.
703 15c. Natural trumpet 50 10
704 60c. Bass viol 85 40
705 $1.10 Flute . . . . 1·50 70
706 $3 Double flageolet . . . . . 2·25 1·75
MS707 110 × 75 mm. $5 Johann Sebastian Bach . . . . 3·25 3·50

1985. Royal Visit. As T **310a** of Grenada. Mult.
708 10c. Arms of Great Britain and Grenada 20 20
709 $1 Queen Elizabeth II (vert) 1·00 1·75
710 $4 Royal Yacht "Britannia" 3·00 4·75
MS711 111 × 83 mm. $5 Map of Grenada Grenadines . . . . . 3·00 3·75

1985. 40th Anniv of United Nations Organization. Designs as T **311a** of Grenada showing United Nations (New York) stamps. Multicoloured.
712 $1 Neil Armstrong (first man on Moon) and 1982 Peaceful Uses of Outer Space 20c. . . . . 1·25 1·10
713 $2 Gandhi and 1971 Racial Equality Year 13c. . . . . 3·75 4·50
714 $2.50 Maimonides (physician) and 1956 World Health Organization 3c. . . . . 5·00 6·00
MS715 110 × 85 mm. $5 U.N. Under-Secretary . . . . 2·50 3·00

1985. 150th Birth Anniv of Mark Twain (author). As T **145a** of Gambia showing Walt Disney cartoon characters illustrating scenes from "Letters from Hawaii". Multicoloured.
716 25c. Minnie Mouse dancing the hula 60 30
717 50c. Donald Duck surfing . . 90 65
718 $1.50 Donald Duck roasting marshmallow in volcano 2·25 2·25
719 $3 Mickey Mouse and Chip n'Dale canoeing . . . . . 3·75 4·00
MS720 127 × 120 mm. $5 Mickey Mouse with cat . . . . 4·75 3·75

1985. Birth Bicentenaries of Grimm Brothers (folklorists). As T **145b** of Gambia, but vert, showing Walt Disney cartoon characters in scenes from "The Elves and the Shoemaker". Multicoloured.
721 30c. Mickey Mouse as the unsuccessful Shoemaker . . 70 40
722 60c. Two elves making shoes 1·10 85
723 70c. The Shoemaker discovering the new shoes 1·40 1·00
724 $4 The Shoemaker's wife (Minnie Mouse) making clothes for the elves . . . 4·25 5·00
MS725 126 × 101 mm. $5 The Shoemaker and his wife waving 5·50 5·00

83 "Madonna and Child" (Titian)

85 Two Footballers

1985. Christmas. Religious Paintings. Mult.
726 50c. Type **83** 45 35
727 70c. "Madonna and Child with St. Mary and John the Baptist" (Bugiardini) 55 50
728 $1.10 "Adoration of the Magi" (Di Fredi) . . . . 80 1·40
729 $3 "Madonna and Child with Young St. John the Baptist" (Bartolomeo) . . 1·25 3·75
MS730 112 × 81 mm. $5 "The Annunciation" (Botticelli) . . . 2·75 6·00

1986. Centenary of Statue of Liberty (1st issue). As T **312a** of Grenada. Multicoloured.
731 5c. Croton Reservoir, New York (1875) 10 10
732 10c. New York Public Library (1986) 10 10
733 70c. Old Boathouse, Central Park (1894) 25 40
734 $4 Boating in Central Park (1986) . . . . 1·40 2·25
MS735 103 × 76 mm. $5 Statue of Liberty (vert) . . . . 3·75 4·25
See also Nos. 892/903.

1986. Birth Bicentenary of John J. Audubon (ornithologist) (2nd issue). As T **312b** of Grenada. Multicoloured.
736 50c. Louisiana heron . . . . 2·00 1·00
737 70c. Black-crowned night heron . . . . 2·50 1·50
738 90c. American bittern . . . . 2·75 2·00
739 $4 Glossy ibis . . . . 5·00 6·50
MS740 103 × 74 mm. $5 King eider 6·50 8·50

1986. Visit of President Reagan of U.S.A. Nos. 684 and 687, optd **VISIT OF PRES. REAGAN 20 FEBRUARY 1986.**
741 70c. "Philaethria dido" . . . 1·50 1·25
742 $5 "Appias drusilla" . . . . 6·50 8·00

1986. World Cup Football Championship, Mexico. Designs showing footballers.
743 **85** 10c. multicoloured 60 40
744 – 70c. multicoloured . . . . 1·75 1·25
745 – $1 multicoloured . . . . . 2·00 1·75
746 – $4 multicoloured . . . . . 5·00 6·50
MS747 86 × 104 mm. $5 multicoloured . . . . 5·50 5·50

1986. Appearance of Halley's Comet (1st issue). As T **151a** of Gambia. Multicoloured.
748 5c. Nicholas Copernicus (astronomer) and Earl of Rosse's six foot reflector telescope 40 40
749 20c. "Sputnik I" (first satellite) orbiting Earth, 1957 . . . . 60 40
750 40c. Tycho Brahe's notes and sketch of 1577 Comet . . . 80 60
751 $4 Edmond Halley and 1682 Comet . . . . 3·75 4·50
MS752 101 × 70 mm. $5 Halley's Comet . . . . 3·00 3·50
See also Nos. 790/4.
The captions of Nos. 750/1 are transposed.

1986. 60th Birthday of Queen Elizabeth II. As T **151b** of Gambia.
753 2c. black and yellow 10 15
754 $1.50 multicoloured . . . . 80 1·00
755 $4 multicoloured . . . . . . 2·00 2·75
MS756 120 × 85 mm. $5 black and brown . . . . 2·00 3·50
DESIGNS: 2c. Princesses Elizabeth and Margaret, Windsor Park, 1933; $1.50, Queen Elizabeth; $4 In Sydney, Australia, 1970; $5 The Royal Family, Coronation Day, 1937.

1986. "Ameripex '86" International Stamp Exhibition, Chicago. As T **315a** of Grenada. Multicoloured.
757 30c. Donald Duck riding mule in Grand Canyon . . 60 45
758 60c. Daisy Duck, Timothy Mouse and Dumbo on Golden Gate Bridge, San Francisco . . . . 85 1·00
759 $1 Mickey Mouse and Goofy in fire engine and Chicago Watertower . . . . 1·50 1·75
760 $3 Mickey Mouse as airmail pilot and White House . . 3·00 4·00
MS761 126 × 101 mm. $5 Donald Duck and Mickey Mouse watching Halley's Comet over Statue of Liberty . . . . . . 3·75 7·50

1986. Royal Wedding. As T **153b** of Gambia. Multicoloured.
762 60c. Prince Andrew and Miss Sarah Ferguson 55 45
763 70c. Prince Andrew in car . . 65 55
764 $4 Prince Andrew with Westland Lynx naval helicopter . . . . 2·75 3·50
MS765 88 × 88 mm. $5 Prince Andrew and Miss Sarah Ferguson (different) . . . . 4·00 5·50

86 "Hygrocybe firma"

87 Giant Atlantic or Dolobrate Pyram

1986. Mushrooms of the Lesser Antilles. Mult.
766 15c. Type **86** 80 40
767 50c. "Xerocomus coccolobae" 1·75 1·25
768 $2 "Volvariella cubensis" . . 3·50 4·00
769 $3 "Lactarius putidus" . . . 4·50 5·00
MS770 76 × 80 mm. $5 "Leptonia caeruleopitata" . . . . 9·00 12·00

1986. Sea Shells. Multicoloured.
771 15c. Type **87** 90 50
772 50c. Beau's murex . . . . . 2·00 1·25
773 $1.10 West Indian fighting conch . . . . 2·25 2·75
774 $4 Alphabet conch . . . . . 3·75 7·00
MS775 109 × 75 mm. $5 Brown-lined paper bubble . . . . 6·50 8·50

1986. World Cup Football Championship Winners, Mexico. Nos. 743/6 optd **WINNERS Argentina 3 W. Germany 2.**
776 **85** 10c. multicoloured 65 40
777 – 70c. multicoloured . . . . 1·40 1·10
778 – $1 multicoloured . . . . . 1·75 1·40
779 – $4 multicoloured . . . . . 4·00 5·50
MS780 86 × 104 mm. $5 multicoloured . . . . 8·00 10·00

88 Common Opossum

89 Cycling

1986. Wildlife. Multicoloured.
781 10c. Type **88** 20 20
782 30c. Giant toad 40 40
783 60c. Land tortoise 80 80
784 70c. Murine opossum (vert) 85 85
785 90c. Burmese mongoose (vert) 90 1·00
786 $1.10 Nine-banded armadillo 1·00 1·25
787 $2 Agouti . . . . 1·75 2·50
788 $3 Humpback whale . . . . 4·50 5·00
MS789 Two sheets, each 103 × 72 mm. (a) $5 Mona monkey (vert). (b) $5 Iguana. Set of 2 sheets . . . . 11·00 14·00

1986. Appearance of Halley's Comet (2nd issue). Nos. 748/51 optd with T **447a** of Ghana.
790 5c. Nicholas Copernicus (astronomer) and Earl of Rosse's six foot reflector telescope 60 60
791 20c. "Sputnik I" orbiting Earth, 1957 . . . . 80 50
792 40c. Tycho Brahe's notes and sketch of 1577 Comet . . . 1·00 60
793 $4 Edmond Halley and 1682 Comet . . . . 5·00 6·00
MS794 102 × 70 mm. $5 Halley's Comet . . . . 4·00 5·50

1986. Christmas. As T **318a** of Grenada showing Walt Disney cartoon characters. Multicoloured.
795 25c. Chip n'Dale with hummingbird 40 15
796 30c. Robin delivering card to Mickey Mouse (vert) . . . 40 20
797 50c. Piglet, Pooh and Jose Carioca on beach 55 30
798 60c. Grandma Duck feeding birds (vert) 65 40
799 70c. Cinderella and birds with mistletoe (vert) 70 50
800 $1.50 Huey, Dewey and Louie windsurfing . . . . 1·25 2·00
801 $3 Mickey Mouse and Morty on beach with turtle . . . 1·50 3·25
802 $4 Kittens playing on piano (vert) . . . . 2·00 3·75
MS803 Two sheets, each 127 × 102 mm. (a) $5 Mickey Mouse and Willie the Whale. (b) $5 Bambi, Thumper and Blossom in snow (vert). Set of 2 sheets 8·00 11·50

1986. Olympic Games, Seoul, South Korea (1988). Multicoloured.
804 10c.+5c. Type **89** 75 40
805 50c.+20c. Sailing 75 90
806 70c.+30c. Gymnastics . . . . 75 1·10
807 $2+$1 Horse trials . . . . . 2·00 3·00
MS808 80 × 100 mm. $3+$1 Marathon . . . . . . 2·50 4·50

90 Aston-Martin "Volante" (1984)

1986. Centenary of Motoring. Multicoloured.
809 10c. Type **90** 25 25
810 30c. Jaguar "MK V" (1948) 45 45
811 60c. Nash "Ambassador" (1956) 60 65
812 70c. Toyota "Supra" (1984) 60 70
813 90c. Ferrari "Testarosa" (1985) 70 90
814 $1 BMW "501B" (1955) . . 70 95
815 $2 Mercedes-Benz "280 SL" (1968) . . . . 1·00 2·00
816 $3 Austro-Daimler "ADR8" (1932) . . . . 1·25 2·50
MS817 Two sheets, each 116 × 85 mm. (a) $5 Morgan "+8" (1977). (b) $5 Checker taxi. Set of 2 sheets . . . . 5·50 11·00

1986. Birth Centenary of Marc Chagall (artist). As T **321a** of Grenada, showing various paintings.
818/57 $1.10 × 40 multicoloured. Set of 40 . . . . 28·00 28·00
MS858 Two sheets, each 110 × 95 mm. $5 × 10 multicoloured (each 104 × 89 mm). Imperf. Set of 10 sheets . . . . 28·00 28·00

1987. America's Cup Yachting Championship. As T **321b** of Grenada. Multicoloured.
859 25c. "Defender", 1895 . . . 60 40
860 45c. "Galatea", 1886 . . . . 80 60
861 70c. "Azzurra", 1981 . . . . 1·00 1·00
862 $4 "Australia II", 1983 . . . 2·00 3·50
MS863 113 × 83 mm. $5 "Columbia" defeating "Shamrock", 1899 (horiz) . . . . 5·00 7·00

1987. 500th Anniv (1992) of Discovery of America by Christopher Columbus (1st issue). As T **322** of Grenada. Multicoloured.
864 15c. Christopher Columbus 35 25
865 30c. Queen Isabella of Castile 40 30
866 50c. "Santa Maria" 60 50
867 60c. Claiming the New World for Spain 60 60
868 90c. Early Spanish map of Lesser Antilles 80 75
869 $1 King Ferdinand of Aragon 80 80
870 $2 Fort La Navidad (drawing by Columbus) . . . . . . 1·50 2·00
871 $3 Galley and Caribs, Hispaniola (drawing by Columbus) . . . . 2·00 2·50
MS872 Two sheets, 104 × 72 mm. (a) $5 Caribs pearl fishing. (b) $5 "Santa Maria" at anchor. Set of 2 sheets . . . . 8·00 11·00
See also Nos. 1191/5, 1224/32, 1366/74, 1494/1500 and 1519/20.

1987. Milestones of Transportation. As T **322a** of Grenada. Multicoloured.
873 10c. Saunders Roe "SRN1" (first hovercraft), 1959 . . 65 30
874 15c. Bugatti "Royale" (largest car), 1931 . . . . 70 35
875 30c. Aleksei Leonov and "Voskhod II" (first spacewalk), 1965 . . . . . 90 55
876 50c. C.S.S "Hunley" (first submarine to sink enemy ship), 1864 . . . . 1·25 75

877 60c. Rolls Royce "Flying Bedstead" (first VTOL aircraft), 1954 . . . . . . 1·50 85
878 70c. "Jenny Lind" (first mass produced locomotive class), 1847 . . . . 1·60 1·25
879 90c. Duryea "Buggvaut" (first U.S petrol-driven car), 1893 . . . . 1·75 1·25
880 $1.50 Steam locomotive, Metropolitan Railway, London (first underground line), 1863 . . . . 2·50 2·75
881 $2 S.S. "Great Britain" (first transatlantic crossing by screw-steamship), 1843 . . 3·00 3·25
882 $3 "Budweiser Rocket" (fastest car), 1979 . . . . 3·25 3·75

1987. "Capex '87" International Stamp Exhibition, Toronto. Game Fishes. As T **323** of Grenada but horiz. Multicoloured.
883 6c. Yellow chub 15 15
884 30c. King mackerel 40 30
885 50c. Short-finned mako . . . 55 55
886 60c. Dolphin (fish) 60 60
887 90c. Skipjack tuna ("Bonito") 75 75
888 $1.10 Cobia . . . . 1·00 1·25
889 $3 Tarpon . . . . 2·25 2·75
890 $4 Swordfish . . . . 2·50 3·25
MS891 Two sheets, each 100 × 70 mm. (a) $5 Spotted jewfish. (b) $5 Amberjack. Set of 2 sheets . . . . 8·00 11·00

1987. Centenary of Statue of Liberty (1986) (2nd issue). As T **323a** of Grenada. Multicoloured.
892 10c. Cleaning face of statue 20 20
893 15c. Commemorative lapel badges 30 30
894 25c. Band playing and statue 40 40
895 30c. Band on parade and statue 45 45
896 45c. Face of statue 50 50
897 50c. Cleaning head of statue (horiz) 55 55
898 60c. Models of statue (horiz) 65 65
899 70c. Small boat flotilla (horiz) 75 85
900 $1 Unveiling ceremony . . . 85 90
901 $1.10 Statue and Manhattan skyline . . . . 90 1·00
902 $2 Parade of warships . . . 1·75 2·00
903 $3 Making commemorative flags . . . . 1·90 2·25

1987. Great Scientific Discoveries. As T **325** of Grenada. Multicoloured.
904 60c. Newton medal . . . . . 1·00 80
905 $1 Louis Daguerre (inventor of daguerreotype) . . . . 1·25 1·00
906 $2 Antoine Lavoisier and apparatus . . . . 2·25 3·00
907 $3 Rudolf Diesel and first oil engine . . . . 6·00 5·00
MS908 105 × 75 mm. $5 Halley's Comet . . . . 6·00 7·50
No. 907 is inscribed "JAMES WATT" in error.

1987. Bicentenary of U.S. Constitution. As T **327a** of Grenada. Multicoloured.
909 10c. Washington addressing delegates, Constitutional Convention 25 20
910 50c. Flag and State Seal, Georgia 85 75
911 60c. Capitol, Washington (vert) 85 80
912 $4 Thomas Jefferson (statesman) (vert) . . . . . 3·25 6·00
MS913 105 × 75 mm. $5 Alexander Hamilton (New York delegate) (vert) . . . . 2·25 4·00

1987. "Hafnia '87" International Stamp Exhibition, Copenhagen. Designs as T **328** of Grenada, but horiz, illustrating Hans Christian Andersen's fairy tales. Multicoloured.
914 25c. Donald and Daisy Duck in "The Swineherd" . . . 50 30
915 30c. Mickey Mouse, Donald and Daisy Duck in "What the Good Man Does is Always Right" 55 35
916 50c. Mickey and Minnie Mouse in "Little Tuk" . . 75 75
917 60c. Minnie Mouse and Ferdie in "The World's Fairest Rose" 75 75
918 70c. Mickey Mouse in "The Garden of Paradise" . . . 80 80
919 $1.50 Goofy and Mickey Mouse in "The Naughty Boy" . . . . 2·00 2·25
920 $3 Goofy in "What the Moon Saw" . . . . 2·75 3·00
921 $4 Alice as "Thumbelina" . . 3·25 3·50
MS922 Two sheets, each 127 × 101 mm. (a) $5 Daisy Duck in "Hans Clodhopper". (b) $5 Aunt Matilda and Mickey Mouse in "Elder-Tree Mother". Set of 2 sheets . . . . 11·00 12·00

91 "The Virgin and Child with Saints Martin and Agnes"
92 Scout signalling with Semaphore Flags

1987. Christmas. Religious Paintings by El Greco. Multicoloured.
923 10c. Type **91** 40 15
924 50c. "St. Agnes" (detail from "The Virgin and Child with Saints Martin and Agnes") . . . . 1·25 75
925 60c. "The Annunciation" . . 1·25 75
926 $4 "The Holy Family with St. Anne" . . . . 4·75 7·25
MS927 75 × 101 mm. $5 "The Adoration of the Shepherds" 7·50 8·50

1988. Royal Ruby Wedding. As T **330a** of Grenada. Multicoloured.
928 20c. brown, black and green 50 15
929 30c. brown and black 50 20
930 $2 multicoloured . . . . . . 2·25 2·50
931 $3 multicoloured . . . . . . 2·50 3·25
MS932 76 × 100 mm. $5 multicoloured . . . . 4·50 5·00
DESIGNS: 20c. Queen Elizabeth II with Princess Anne, c. 1957; 30c. Wedding photograph, 1947; $2 Queen with Prince Charles and Princess Anne, c. 1955; $3 Queen Elizabeth (from photo by Tim Graham), 1980; $5 Princess Elizabeth in wedding dress, 1947.

1988. Olympic Games, Seoul. As T **331** of Grenada showing Walt Disney cartoon characters as Olympic competitors. Multicoloured.
933 1c. Minnie Mouse as rhythmic gymnast (horiz) 10 10
934 2c. Pete and Goofy as pankration wrestlers (horiz) 10 10
935 3c. Huey and Dewey as synchronized swimmers (horiz) 10 10
936 4c. Huey, Dewey and Louie in hoplite race (horiz) . . . 10 10
937 5c. Clarabelle and Daisy Duck playing baseball (horiz) 10 10
938 10c. Goofy and Donald Duck in horse race (horiz) . . . 10 10
939 $6 Donald Duck and Uncle Scrooge McDuck windsurfing (horiz) . . . . 4·50 5·50
940 $7 Mickey Mouse in chariot race (horiz) . . . . . . 4·75 5·50
MS941 Two sheets, each 127 × 101 mm. (a) $5 Mickey Mouse throwing discus in pentathalon. (b) $5 Donald Duck playing tennis. Set of 2 sheets 7·50 9·00

1988. World Scout Jamboree, Australia. Mult.
942 50c. Type **92** 50 35
943 70c. Canoeing 60 50
944 $1 Cooking over campfire (horiz) 70 65
945 $3 Scouts around campfire (horiz) . . . . 2·00 3·00
MS946 110 × 77 mm. $5 Erecting tent (horiz) . . . . 4·00 4·50

1988. Birds. As T **334** of Grenada. Mult.
947 20c. Yellow-crowned night heron 30 25
948 25c. Brown pelican 30 25
949 45c. Audubon's shearwater . 40 35
950 60c. Red-footed booby . . . 50 45
951 70c. Bridled tern 55 50
952 90c. Red-billed tropic bird . . 70 70
953 $3 Blue-winged teal . . . . . 1·75 2·25
954 $4 Sora crake ("Sora") . . . 2·00 2·75
MS955 Two sheets, each 105 × 75 mm. (a) $5 Purple-throated carib. (b) $5 Little blue heron. Set of 2 sheets . . . . 6·00 6·50

1988. 500th Birth Anniv of Titian (artist). As T **166a** of Gambia. Multicoloured.
956 15c. "Man with Blue Eyes" 15 15
957 30c. "The Three Ages of Man" (detail) 20 20
958 60c. "Don Diego Mendoza" 35 35
959 75c. "Emperor Charles V seated" 50 50
960 $1 "A Young Man in a Fur" 60 60
961 $2 "Tobias and the Angel" 1·10 1·40
962 $3 "Pietro Bembo" . . . . . 1·60 1·90
963 $4 "Pier Luigi Farnese" . . . 1·75 2·25
MS964 110 × 95 mm. (a) $5 "Sacred and Profane Love" (detail). (b) $5 "Venus and Adonis" (detail). Set of 2 sheets . . . . 7·00 8·00

1988. Airships. As T **336** of Grenada. Multicoloured.
965 10c. "Hindenburg" over Sugarloaf Mountain, Rio de Janeiro, 1937 (horiz) . . 60 30
966 20c. "Hindenburg" over New York, 1937 (horiz) 75 30
967 30c. U.S. Navy "K" Class airships on Atlantic escort duty, 1944 (horiz) 85 35
968 40c. "Hindenburg" approaching Lakehurst, 1937 . . . . 90 45
969 60c. "Graf Zeppelin" and "Hindenburg" over Germany, 1936 . . . . . 1·10 60
970 70c. "Hindenburg" and "Los Angeles" moored at Lakehurst, 1936 (horiz) . . 1·10 70
971 $1 "Graf Zeppelin II" over Dover, 1939 . . . . 1·10 85
972 $2 "Ersatz Deutschland" on scheduled passenger flight, 1912 (horiz) . . . . 1·50 1·60
973 $3 "Graf Zeppelin" over Dome of the Rock, Jerusalem, 1931 (horiz) . . 2·00 2·25
974 $4 "Hindenburg" over Olympic stadium, Berlin, 1936 (horiz) . . . . . . 2·25 2·25
MS975 Two sheets (a) 76 × 95 mm. $5 LZ-127 "Graf Zeppelin", 1933. (b) 95 × 76 mm. $5 LZ-127 "Graf Zeppelin", 1931 (horiz). Set of 2 sheets . . . . 8·00 10·00

93 Bambi and his mother

1988. Disney Animal Cartoon Films.
976/1029 30c. × 54 multicoloured. Set of 54 . . . . 17·00 15·00
MS1030 Six sheets, each 127 × 102 mm. $5 × 6 multicoloured. Set of 6 sheets 28·00 30·00
DESIGNS: Scenes from "Bambi", "Dumbo" $5 (vert), "Lady and the Tramp" $5 (vert), "The Aristocats", "The Fox and the Hound" and "101 Dalmatians".

1988. "Sydpex '88" National Stamp Exhibition, Sydney and 60th Birthday of Mickey Mouse. As T **337** of Grenada. Multicoloured.
1031 1c. Mickey Mouse conducting at Sydney Opera House 10 10
1032 2c. Mickey Mouse and Donald Duck at Ayers Rock 10 10
1033 3c. Goofy and Mickey Mouse on sheep station 10 10
1034 4c. Goofy and Mickey Mouse at Lone Pine Koala Sanctuary 10 10
1035 5c. Mickey Mouse, Donald Duck and Goofy playing Australian football . . . 10 10
1036 10c. Mickey Mouse and Goofy camel racing . . . 10 10
1037 $5 Donald Duck and his nephews bowling . . . . 4·50 5·00
1038 $6 Mickey Mouse with America's Cup trophy and "Australia II" (yacht) 5·50 6·00
MS1039 Two sheets, each 127 × 102 mm. (a) $5 Goofy diving on Great Barrier Reef. (b) $5 Donald Duck, Mickey and Minnie Mouse at beach barbecue. Set of 2 sheets . . . . 7·50 9·50

1988. Flowering Trees and Shrubs. As T **339** of Grenada. Multicoloured.
1040 10c. Potato tree (vert) . . . 15 15
1041 20c. Wild cotton 15 15
1042 30c. Shower of gold (vert) 20 20
1043 60c. Napoleon's button (vert) 35 30
1044 90c. Geiger tree 60 70
1045 $1 Fern tree 70 80
1046 $2 French cashew . . . . . 1·25 2·00
1047 $4 Amherstia (vert) . . . . 2·00 3·00
MS1048 Two sheets, each 117 × 88 mm. (a) $5 African tulip tree (vert). (b) $5 Swamp immortelle. Set of 2 sheets . . 4·25 5·50

1988. Cars. As T **335** of Grenada. Mult.
1049 $2 Doble "Series E", 1925 1·40 1·25
1050 $2 Alvis "12/50", 1926 . . 1·40 1·25
1051 $2 Sunbeam 3-litre, 1927 . . 1·40 1·25
1052 $2 Franklin "Airman", 1928 1·40 1·25
1053 $2 Delage "D8S", 1929 . . 1·40 1·25
1054 $2 Mors, 1897 . . . . . . 1·40 1·25
1055 $2 Peerless "Green Dragon", 1904 . . . . . 1·40 1·25
1056 $2 Pope-Hartford, 1909 . . 1·40 1·25
1057 $2 Daniels "Submarine Speedstar", 1920 . . . . 1·40 1·25
1058 $2 McFarlan 9.3 litre, 1922 1·40 1·25
1059 $2 Frazer Nash "Lemans" replica, 1949 . . . . . . 1·40 1·25
1060 $2 Pegaso "Z102", 1953 . . 1·40 1·25
1061 $2 Siata "Spyder V-8", 1953 1·40 1·25
1062 $2 Kurtis-Offenhauser, 1953 1·40 1·25
1063 $2 Kaiser-Darrin, 1954 . . . 1·40 1·25
1064 $2 Tracta, 1930 . . . . . . 1·40 1·25
1065 $2 Maybach "Zeppelin", 1932 . . . . 1·40 1·25
1066 $2 Railton "Light Sports", 1934 . . . . 1·40 1·25
1067 $2 Hotchkiss, 1936 . . . . 1·40 1·25
1068 $2 Mercedes-Benz "W163", 1939 . . . . 1·40 1·25
1069 $2 Aston-Martin "Vantage V8", 1982 . . . . . . 1·40 1·25
1070 $2 Porsche "956", 1982 . . 1·40 1·25
1071 $2 Lotus "Esprit Turbo", 1983 . . . . 1·40 1·25
1072 $2 McLaren "MP4/2", 1984 1·40 1·25
1073 $2 Mercedes-Benz "190E 2.3-16", 1985 . . . . . . 1·40 1·25
1074 $2 Ferrari "250 GT Lusso", 1963 . . . . 1·40 1·25
1075 $2 Porsche "904", 1964 . . 1·40 1·25
1076 $2 Volvo "P1800", 1967 . . 1·40 1·25
1077 $2 McLaren-Chevrolet "M8D", 1970 . . . . . . 1·40 1·25
1078 $2 Jaguar "XJ6", 1981 . . . 1·40 1·25

1988. "Mickey's Christmas Parade". As T **340a** of Grenada showing Walt Disney cartoon characters. Multicoloured.
1079 $1 Dumbo 65 65
1080 $1 Goofy as Father Christmas 65 65
1081 $1 Minnie Mouse waving from window 65 65
1082 $1 Clarabelle, Mordie and Ferdie watching parade 65 65
1083 $1 Donald Duck's nephews 65 65
1084 $1 Donald Duck as drummer 65 65
1085 $1 Toy soldiers 65 65
1086 $1 Mickey Mouse on wooden horse 65 65
MS1087 Two sheets, each 127 × 102 mm. (a) $7 Peter Pan and Captain Hook on float (horiz). (b) $7 Mickey Mouse as Father Christmas and Donald Duck in carnival train (horiz). Set of 2 sheets . . . . 10·00 11·00

94 Middleweight Boxing (Gold, Henry Maske, East Germany)

1989. Olympic Medal Winners, Seoul (1988). Multicoloured.
1088 15c. Type **94** 40 20
1089 50c. Freestyle wrestling (130 kg) (Bronze, Andreas Schroeder, East Germany) 60 40
1090 60c. Women's team gymnastics (Bronze, East Germany) 70 50
1091 75c. Platform diving (Gold, Greg Louganis, U.S.A.) 80 60
1092 $1 Freestyle wrestling (52 kg) (Gold, Mitsuru Sato, Japan) 90 80
1093 $2 Men's freestyle 4 × 200 m relay swimming (Bronze, West Germany) 1·40 1·40
1094 $3 Men's 5000 m (Silver, Dieter Baumann, West Germany) . . . . 1·60 2·00
1095 $4 Women's heptathlon (Gold, Jackie Joyner-Kersee, U.S.A.) . . . . . 2·00 2·50
MS1096 Two sheets, each 70 × 100 mm. (a) $6 Weightlifting (67.5 kg) (Gold, Joachim Kunz, East Germany). (b) $6 Team Three-Day Event (Gold, West Germany). Set of 2 sheets . . . 6·50 8·50

1989. Japanese Art. Paintings by Hiroshige. As T **177a** of Gambia. Multicoloured.
1097 15c. "Crossing the Oi at Shimada by Ferry" . . . 25 25
1098 20c. "Daimyo and Entourage at Arai" . . . 30 30
1099 45c. "Cargo Portage through Goyu" 50 50
1100 75c. "Snowfall at Fujigawa" 75 75
1101 $1 "Horses for the Emperor at Chirifu" 85 85
1102 $2 "Rainfall at Tsuchiyama" 1·60 1·60
1103 $3 "An Inn at Ishibe" . . . 2·25 2·25
1104 $4 "On the Shore of Lake Biwa at Otsu" . . . . . 2·75 2·75
MS1105 Two sheets, each 102 × 78 mm. (a) $5 "Fishing Village of Yokkaichi on the Mie". (b) $5 "Pilgrimage to Atsuta Shrine at Miya". Set of 2 sheets 4·75 7·00

1989. World Cup Football Championship, Italy (1990) (1st issue). As T **345a** of Grenada. Mult.
1106 15c. World Cup trophy . . 50 20
1107 20c. Flags of Argentina (winners 1986) and International Federation of Football Associations (FIFA) (horiz) . . . . . 1·00 20
1108 45c. Franz Beckenbauer (West Germany) with World Cup, 1974 . . . . 1·00 35
1109 75c. Flags of Italy (winners 1982) and FIFA (horiz) 1·50 55
1110 $1 Pele (Brazil) with Jules Rimet trophy . . . . . . 1·50 85
1111 $2 Flags of West Germany (winners 1974) and FIFA (horiz) . . . . 2·00 2·00

1112 $3 Flags of Brazil (winners 1970) and FIFA (horiz) 2·00 2·75
1113 $4 Jules Rimet trophy and Brazil players . . . . . . 2·00 2·75
MS1114 (a) 100 × 81 mm. $6 Goalkeeper (horiz). (b) 66 × 95 mm. $6 Péle with Jules Rimet trophy. Set of 2 sheets 8·50 9·00
See also Nos. 1285/9.

1989. North American Railway Locomotives. As T **342** of Grenada. Multicoloured.
1115 $2 Morris & Essex Railroad "Dover", 1841, U.S.A. . . 1·50 1·50
1116 $2 Baltimore & Ohio Railroad No. 57 "Memnon", 1848, U.S.A. 1·50 1·50
1117 $2 Camden & Amboy Railroad "John Stevens", 1849, U.S.A. . . . . . . 1·50 1·50
1118 $2 Lawrence Machine Shop "Lawrence", 1853, U.S.A. 1·50 1·50
1119 $2 South Carolina Railroad "James S. Corry", 1859, U.S.A. . . . . 1·50 1·50
1120 $2 Mine Hill & Schuylkill Haven Railroad flexible beam No. 3, 1860, U.S.A. 1·50 1·50
1121 $2 Delaware, Lackawanna & Western Railroad "Montrose", 1861, U.S.A. 1·50 1·50
1122 $2 Central Pacific Railroad No. 68 "Pequop", 1868, U.S.A. . . . . 1·50 1·50
1123 $2 Boston & Providence Railroad "Daniel Nason", 1863, U.S.A. . . . . . . 1·50 1·50
1124 $2 Morris & Essex Railroad "Joe Scranton", 1870, U.S.A. . . . . 1·50 1·50
1125 $2 Central Railroad of New Jersey No. 124, 1871, U.S.A. . . . . 1·50 1·50
1126 $2 Baldwin tramway steam locomotive, 1876, U.S.A. 1·50 1·50
1127 $2 Lackawanna & Bloomsburg Railroad "Luzerne", 1878, U.S.A. 1·50 1·50
1128 $2 Central Mexican Railroad No. 150, 1892 1·50 1·50
1129 $2 Denver South Park & Pacific Railroad No. 15, Breckenridge, 1879, U.S.A. . . . . 1·50 1·50
1130 $2 Miles Planting & Manufacturing Company plantation locomotive "Daisy", 1894, U.S.A. . . 1·50 1·50
1131 $2 Central of Georgia Railroad Baldwin 854 No. 1136, 1895, U.S.A. 1·50 1·50
1132 $2 Savannah, Florida & Western Railroad No. 111, 1900, U.S.A. . . 1·50 1·50
1133 $2 Douglas, Gilmore & Company contractors locomotive No. 3, 1902, U.S.A. . . . . 1·50 1·50
1134 $2 Lehigh Valley Coal Company compressed air locomotive No. 900, 1903, U.S.A. . . . . 1·50 1·50
1135 $2 Louisiana & Texas Railroad McKeen motor locomotive, 1908, U.S.A. 1·50 1·50
1136 $2 Clear Lake Lumber Company Type B Climax locomotive No. 6, 1910, U.S.A. . . . . 1·50 1·50
1137 $2 Blue Jay Lumber Company Heisler locomotive No. 10, 1912, U.S.A. . . . . 1·50 1·50
1138 $2 Stewartstown Railroad petrol locomotive No. 6, 1920s, U.S.A. . . . . . . 1·50 1·50
1139 $2 Bangor & Aroostock Railroad Class G No. 186, 1921, U.S.A. . . 1·50 1·50
1140 $2 Hammond Lumber Company Mallet locomotive, No. 6, 1923, U.S.A. . . . . 1·50 1·50
1141 $2 Central Railway of New Jersey diesel locomotive No. 1000, 1925, U.S.A. 1·50 1·50
1142 $2 Atchison Topeka & Santa Fe Railroad "Super Chief" diesel express, 1935, U.S.A. . . . . . . 1·50 1·50
1143 $2 Norfolk & Western Railroad Class Y-6, 1948, U.S.A. . . . . 1·50 1·50
1144 $2 Boston & Maine Railroad Budd diesel railcar, 1949, U.S.A. . . . 1·50 1·50

94a Mickey Mouse and Donald Duck at Ecole Militaire Inflating Balloon

1989. "Philexfrance '89" International Stamp Exn, Paris. Designs showing Walt Disney cartoon characters in Paris. Multicoloured.
1145 1c. Type **94a** 10 10
1146 2c. Mickey and Minnie Mouse on river boat passing Conciergerie . . . 10 10
1147 3c. Mickey Mouse at Hotel de Ville (vert) 10 10
1148 4c. Mickey Mouse at Genie of the Bastille monument (vert) 10 10
1149 5c. Mickey and Minnie Mouse arriving at Opera House 10 10
1150 10c. Mickey and Minnie Mouse on tandem in Luxembourg Gardens . . 10 10
1151 $5 Mickey Mouse in aeroplane over L'Arch de La Defense (vert) . . . . 5·50 6·50
1152 $6 Mickey Mouse at Place Vendome (vert) . . . . . 5·50 6·50
MS1153 Two sheets, each 127 × 102 mm. (a) $6 Mickey and Minnie Mouse on scooter in Place de la Concorde. (b) $6 Donald Duck, Mickey and Minnie Mouse in balloon over Versailles. Set of 2 sheets . . . . 11·00 13·00

95 Launch of "Apollo 11"

97 Buddy Holly

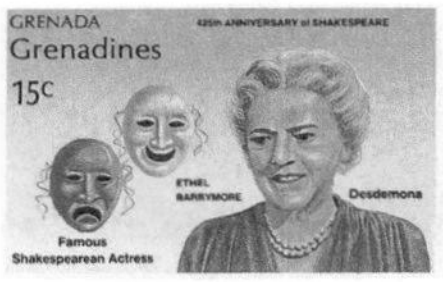

96 Ethel Barrymore

1989. 20th Anniv of First Manned Landing on Moon. Multicoloured.
1154 25c. Type **95** 30 30
1155 50c. Splashdown (horiz) . . 50 50
1156 60c. Modules in space . . . 60 60
1157 75c. Aldrin setting up experiment (horiz) 70 70
1158 $1 "Apollo 11" leaving Earth orbit (horiz) . . . 80 80
1159 $2 Moving "Apollo 11" to launch site . . . . 1·60 1·90
1160 $3 Lunar module "Eagle" leaving Moon (horiz) . . 2·00 2·50
1161 $4 "Eagle" landing on Moon . . . . 2·25 2·75
MS1162 (a) 71 × 100 mm. $5 Armstrong stepping onto Moon. (b) 101 × 72 mm. $5 Armstrong's footprint on Moon. Set of 2 sheets 6·50 8·00

1989. Fungi. As T **348** of Grenada. Mult.
1163 6c. "Agaricus purpurellus" (incorrectly inscr "Collybia aurea") 35 25
1164 10c. "Podaxis pistillaris" . . 35 25
1165 20c. "Hygrocybe firma" . . 55 45
1166 30c. "Agaricus rufoaurantiacus" 65 55
1167 75c. "Leptonia howellii" . . 1·40 1·40
1168 $2 "Marasmiellus purpureus" . . . . 2·50 2·75
1169 $3 "Marasmius trinitatis" 3·00 3·25
1170 $4 "Collybia aurea" (incorrectly inscr "Hygrocybe martinicensis") . . . . . 3·25 3·50
MS1171 Two sheets, each 56 × 71 mm. (a) $6 "Lentinus crinitus" (incorrectly inscr "Agaricus purpurellus"). (b) $6 "Hygrocybe martinicensis" (incorrectly inscr "Lentinus crinitus"). Set of 2 sheets . . . 12·00 13·00

1989. Butterflies. As T **350** of Grenada. Mult.
1172 25c. "Battus polydamas" (inscr "Papilio androgeus") 40 40
1173 35c. "Phoebis sennae" . . . 45 45
1174 45c. "Hamadryas feronia" 55 55
1175 50c. "Cynthia cardui" . . . 55 55
1176 75c. "Ascia monuste" . . . 80 80
1177 90c. "Eurema lisa" 90 90
1178 $2 "Aphrissa statira" . . . 2·00 2·00
1179 $3 "Hypolimnas misippus" 2·50 2·50
MS1180 Two sheets, each 87 × 115 mm. (a) $6 "Anartia amathea". (b) $6 "Pseudolycaena marsyas". Set of 2 sheets . . . 9·00 11·00

1989. 425th Birth Anniv of Shakespeare. Shakespearean Actors. Multicoloured.
1181 15c. Type **96** 35 25
1182 $1.10 Richard Burton . . . 1·50 1·25
1183 $2 John Barrymore . . . . 2·25 2·25
1184 $3 Paul Robeson . . . . . 2·50 2·75
MS1185 103 × 77 mm. $6 Bando Tamasaburo and Nakamura Kanzaburo . . . . 4·50 5·50

1989. Musicians. Multicoloured.
1186 10c. Type **97** 35 25
1187 25c. Jimmy Hendrix 55 40
1188 75c. Mighty Sparrow . . . 70 70
1189 $4 Katsutoji Kineya . . . . 3·00 4·00
MS1190 103 × 77 mm. $6 Kurt Weill 4·25 4·75

97a Arawaks canoeing

1989. 500th Anniv (1992) of Discovery of America by Columbus (2nd issue). Pre-Columbian Arawak Society. As T **247** of Antigua. Multicoloured.
1191 15c. Type **97a** 25 25
1192 75c. Family and campfire 75 75
1193 90c. Using stone tools . . . 95 95
1194 $3 Eating and drinking . . 2·50 3·00
MS1195 84 × 87 mm. $6 Making fire 3·50 4·25

1989. "World Stamp Expo '89" International Stamp Exhibition, Washington. Designs showing Walt Disney cartoon characters illustrating proverbs from "Poor Richard's Almanack". As T **352** of Grenada. Multicoloured.
1196 1c. Uncle Scrooge McDuck with gold coins in sinking boat 10 10
1197 2c. Robin Hood shooting apple off Friar Tuck . . . 10 10
1198 3c. Winnie the Pooh with honey 10 10
1199 4c. Goofy, Minnie Mouse and Donald Duck exercising 10 10
1200 5c. Pinnochio holding Jimminy Cricket 10 10
1201 6c. Huey and Dewey putting up wallpaper 10 10
1202 8c. Mickey Mouse asleep in storm 15 10
1203 10c. Mickey Mouse as Benjamin Franklin selling "Pennsylvania Gazette" 15 10
1204 $5 Mickey Mouse with chicken, recipe book and egg . . . . 4·00 5·00
1205 $6 Mickey Mouse missing carriage . . . . 4·50 5·00
MS1206 Two sheets, each 127 × 102 mm. (a) $6 Mickey Mouse bowing. (b) $6 Mickey Mouse delivering basket of food (vert). Set of 2 sheets . . . . . 10·50 11·00

1990. Christmas. Paintings by Rubens. As T **352a** of Grenada. Multicoloured.
1207 10c. "The Annunciation" . . 35 15
1208 15c. "The Flight of the Holy Family into Egypt" . . . 40 15
1209 25c. "The Presentation in the Temple" 55 15
1210 45c. "The Holy Family under the Apple Tree" . . 70 25
1211 $2 "Madonna and Child with Saints" . . . . . . 2·00 2·50
1212 $4 "The Virgin and Child enthroned with Saints" . . 3·00 4·00
1213 $5 "The Holy Family" . . . 3·00 4·00
MS1214 Two sheets, each 70 × 95 mm. (a) $5 "The Adoration of the Magi" (sketch). (b) $5 "The Adoration of the Magi". Set of 2 sheets . . . . 12·00 14·00

1990. "EXPO '90" International Garden and Greenery Exhibition, Osaka. Caribbean Orchids. As T **354** of Grenada. Multicoloured.
1215 15c. "Brassocattleya" Thalie 30 30
1216 20c. "Odontocidium" Tigersun 35 35
1217 50c. "Odontioda" Hambuhren 55 55
1218 75c. "Paphiopedium" Delrosi 75 75
1219 $1 "Vuylstekeara" Yokara 95 95
1220 $2 "Paphiopedilum" Geelong . . . . 1·75 2·00
1221 $3 "Wilsonara" Tigerwood 2·00 2·25
1222 $4 "Cymbidium" Ormoulu 2·50 2·75
MS1223 Two sheets, each 98 × 68 mm. (a) $6 "Odontonia" Sappho. (b) $6 "Cymbidium" Vieux Rose. Set of 2 sheets . . 11·00 11·50

1990. 500th Anniv (1992) of Discovery of America by Columbus (3rd issue). New World Natural History—Insects. As T **354a** of Grenada. Mult.
1224 35c. "Dynastes hercules" (beetle) 35 35
1225 40c. "Chalcolepidius porcatus" (beetle) 35 35
1226 50c. "Acrocinus longimanus" (beetle) . . . 40 40
1227 60c. "Battus polydamas" (butterfly) 75 75
1228 $1 "Orthemis ferruginea" (skimmer) 95 95
1229 $2 "Psiloptera variolosa" (beetle) . . . . 1·60 1·75
1230 $3 "Hypolimnas misippus" (butterfly) . . . . . . 2·50 2·75
1231 $4 Scarab beetle . . . . . 2·50 2·75
MS1232 Two sheets, each 102 × 70 mm. (a) $6 "Calpodes ethlius" (butterfly). (b) "Danaus plexippus" (butterfly). Set of 2 sheets . . . . 8·50 9·50

1990. Wildlife. As T **254** of Antigua. Mult.
1233 5c. West Indies giant rice rat 20 20
1234 25c. Agouti 35 35
1235 30c. Humpback whale . . . 70 65
1236 40c. Pilot whale 70 65
1237 $1 Spotted dolphin 95 95
1238 $2 Egyptian mongoose . . . 1·75 2·00
1239 $3 Brazilian tree porcupine 2·25 2·75
1240 $4 American manatee . . . 2·50 3·00
MS1241 Two sheets, each 107 × 80 mm. (a) $6 Caribbean monk seal. (b) $6 Egyptian mongoose (different). Set of 2 sheets . . . . 8·00 9·00

1990. 50th Anniv of Second World War. As T **354b** of Grenada. Multicoloured.
1242 6c. British tanks in France, 1939 . . . . 30 30
1243 10c. Operation "Crusader", North Africa, 1941 . . . 30 30
1244 20c. Retreat of the Afrika Corps, 1942 . . . . . . 40 40
1245 45c. American landing on Aleutian Islands, 1943 . . 50 50
1246 50c. U.S marines landing on Tarawa, 1943 . . . . . . 55 55
1247 60c. U.S army entering Rome, 1944 . . . . . . 60 60
1248 75c. U.S tanks crossing River Seine, 1944 . . . . 70 70
1249 $1 Battle of the Bulge, 1944 95 95
1250 $5 American infantry in Italy, 1945 . . . . 3·00 3·50
1251 $6 B-29 "Enola Gay" dropping atomic bomb on Hiroshima, 1945 . . . . 3·50 3·50
MS1252 112 × 84 mm. $6 St. Paul's Cathedral in London Blitz, 1940 4·00 5·00

1990. "Stamp World London '90" International Stamp Exhibition. As T **193** of Gambia showing Walt Disney cartoon characters at Shakespeare sites. Multicoloured.
1253 15c. Daisy Duck at Ann Hathaway's Cottage (horiz) 40 20
1254 30c. Minnie and Bill Mouse at Shakespeare's birthplace, Stratford . . . 55 35
1255 50c. Minnie Mouse in front of Mary Arden's house, Wilmcote 75 70
1256 60c. Mickey Mouse leaning on hedge in New Place gardens, Stratford (horiz) 90 90
1257 $1 Mickey Mouse walking in New Place gardens, Stratford (horiz) . . . . 1·25 1·25
1258 $2 Mickey Mouse carrying books in Scholars Lane, Stratford . . . . 2·25 2·50
1259 $4 Mickey Mouse and Royal Shakespeare Theatre, Stratford . . . . 3·25 4·00
1260 $5 Ludwig von Drake teaching Mickey Mouse at the Stratford Grammar School (horiz) . . . . . 3·25 4·00
MS1261 Two sheets, each 126 × 101 mm. (a) $6 Mickey Mouse as Shakespeare. (b) $6 Mickey and Minnie Mouse in rowing boat on River Avon, Stratford (horiz). Set of 2 sheets 11·00 12·00

1990. 90th Birthday of Queen Elizabeth the Queen Mother. As T **194** of Gambia, showing photographs 1970–79.
1262 $2 Queen Mother wearing pink hat and coat . . . . 1·10 1·40
1263 $2 Prince Charles and Queen Mother at Garter ceremony . . . . 1·10 1·40
1264 $2 Queen Mother in blue floral outfit . . . . 1·10 1·40
MS1265 90 × 75 mm. $6 Queen Mother in Garter robes . . . . 4·25 5·00

1990. Birds. As T **358** of Grenada, but vert. Multicoloured.
1267 25c. Yellow-bellied seedeater 30 30
1268 45c. Carib grackle 50 50
1269 50c. Black-whiskered vireo 55 55
1270 75c. Bananaquit 70 70
1271 $1 White-collared swift . . . 95 95
1272 $2 Yellow-bellied elaenia . . 1·50 1·50
1273 $3 Blue-hooded euphonia 2·00 2·00
1274 $5 Eared dove . . . . . . 3·25 3·25
MS1275 Two sheets, each 101 × 72 mm. (a) $6 Mangrove cuckoo. (b) $6 Scaly-breasted thrasher. Set of 2 sheets . . . 8·50 10·00

1990. Crustaceans. As T **359** of Grenada. Mult.
1276 10c. Slipper lobster 20 20
1277 25c. Green reef crab 30 30
1278 65c. Caribbean lobsterette 60 60
1279 75c. Blind deep sea lobster 70 70
1280 $1 Flattened crab 95 95
1281 $2 Ridged slipper lobster . . 1·75 2·00

1282 $3 Land crab 2·25 2·75
1283 $4 Mountain crab 2·50 2·75
MS1284 Two sheets, each 108×76 mm. (a) $6 Caribbean king crab. (b) $6 Purse crab. Set of 2 sheets 8·00 10·00

98 Lineker, England

1990. World Cup Football Championship, Italy (2nd issue). Multicoloured.
1285 15c. Type **98** 25 25
1286 45c. Burruchaga, Argentina 45 45
1287 $2 Hysen, Sweden 1·75 2·25
1288 $4 Sang Ho, South Korea 2·75 3·75
MS1289 Two sheets, each 76×90 mm. (a) $6 Ramos, U.S.A. (b) $6 Stojkovic, Yugoslavia. Set of 2 sheets 8·50 9·50

1990. Olympic Games, Barcelona (1992). As T **195a** of Gambia. Multicoloured.
1290 10c. Boxing 10 10
1291 25c. Olympic flame 20 20
1292 50c. Football 40 40
1293 75c. Discus throwing 60 60
1294 $1 Pole vaulting 85 85
1295 $2 Show jumping 1·75 2·00
1296 $4 Women's basketball 3·50 3·75
1297 $5 Men's gymnastics 3·00 3·75
MS1298 Two sheets. (a) 101×70 mm. $6 Sailboards. (b) 70×101 mm. $6 Decathlon. Set of 2 sheets 8·50 9·50

1991. 350th Death Anniv of Rubens. As T **195c** of Gambia. Multicoloured.
1299 5c. "Adam and Eve" (Eve detail) (vert) 25 20
1300 15c. "Esther before Ahasuerus" (detail) 40 20
1301 25c. "Adam and Eve" (Adam detail) (vert) 50 25
1302 50c. "Expulsion from Eden" 80 60
1303 $1 "Cain slaying Abel" (detail) (vert) 1·40 1·10
1304 $2 "Lot's Flight" 2·00 2·25
1305 $4 "Samson and Delilah" (detail) 3·00 4·00
1306 $5 "Abraham and Melchizedek" 3·50 4·00
MS1307 Two sheets, each 101×71 mm. (a) $6 "The Meeting of David and Abigail" (detail). (b) $6 "Daniel in the Lions' Den" (detail). Set of 2 sheets 10·00 12·00

1991. Coral Reef Fishes. As T **357** of Grenada. Multicoloured.
1308 15c. Barred hamlet 50 25
1309 35c. Long-spined squirrelfish 80 50
1310 45c. Red-spotted hawkfish 85 60
1311 75c. Bigeye 1·25 1·00
1312 $1 Balloonfish ("Spiny puffer") 1·50 1·25
1313 $2 Small-mouth grunt 2·25 2·50
1314 $3 Harlequin bass 2·75 3·25
1315 $4 Creole fish 3·00 3·50
MS1316 Two sheets, each 103×72 mm. (a) $6 Copper sweeper. (b) $6 Royal gramma ("Fairy Basslet"). Set of 2 sheets 8·50 10·00

99 Angel with Star and Lantern

100 "Brassia maculata"

1991. Christmas (1990). Hummel Figurines. Multicoloured.
1317 10c. Type **99** 30 10
1318 15c. Christ Child and Angel playing mandolin 40 15
1319 25c. Shepherd 55 25
1320 50c. Angel with trumpet and lantern 1·00 50
1321 $1 Nativity scene 1·60 95
1322 $2 Christ Child and Angel holding candle 2·50 2·50
1323 $4 Angel with baskets 3·50 4·25
1324 $5 Angels singing 3·75 4·25
MS1325 Two sheets, each 99×122 mm. (a) 5c. As No. 1318; 40c. As No. 1320; 60c. As No. 1321; $3 As No. 1324. (b) 20c. As Type **99**; 30c. As No. 1319; 75c. As No. 1322; $6 As No. 1323. Set of 2 sheets 10·00 11·00

1991. Orchids. Multicoloured.
1326 5c. Type **100** 30 30
1327 10c. "Oncidium lanceanum" 30 30
1328 15c. "Broughtonia sanguinea" 35 20
1329 25c. "Diacrium bicornutum" 40 20
1330 35c. "Cattleya labiata" 40 20
1331 45c. "Epidendrum fragrans" 50 25
1332 50c. "Oncidium papilio" 55 30
1333 75c. "Neocogniauxia monophylla" 70 50
1334 $1 "Epidendrum polybulbon" 80 70
1335 $2 "Spiranthes speciosa" 1·40 1·40
1336 $4 "Epidendrum ciliare" 2·25 2·75
1337 $5 "Phais tankervilliae" 2·50 3·00
1338 $10 "Brassia caudata" 4·50 5·00
1339 $20 "Brassavola cordata" 9·25 11·00

1991. Butterflies. As T **363** of Grenada. Mult.
1340 5c. Crimson-patched longwing 40 30
1341 10c. "Morpho helena" 40 30
1342 15c. "Morpho sulkowskyi" 55 35
1343 20c. "Dynastor napoleon" 60 40
1344 25c. "Pieridae callinira" 60 45
1345 30c. "Anartia amathea" 65 50
1346 35c. "Heliconiidae dido" 65 50
1347 45c. "Papilionidae columbus" 75 65
1348 50c. "Nymphalidae praeneste" 85 70
1349 60c. "Panacea prola" 1·00 80
1350 75c. "Dryas julia" 1·00 90
1351 $1 "Papilionidae orthosilaus" 1·25 1·10
1352 $2 "Pyrrhopyge cometes" 1·75 2·00
1353 $3 "Papilionidae paeon" 2·00 2·50
1354 $4 "Morpho cypris" 2·50 3·00
1355 $5 Choringa 3·00 3·25
MS1356 Four sheets, each 118×80 mm. (a) $6 "Danaus plexippus". (b) $6 "Caligo idomenides". (c) $6 "Nymphalidae amydon". (d) $6 "Papilio childrenae". Set of 4 sheets 15·00 15·00

101 Donald and Daisy Duck with Solar-powered Car

1991. Ecology Conservation. Walt Disney cartoon characters. Multicoloured.
1357 10c. Type **101** 60 20
1358 15c. Goofy saving water 70 20
1359 25c. Donald and Daisy on nature hike 90 35
1360 45c. Donald Duck returning chick to nest 1·25 55
1361 $1 Donald Duck and balloons 2·00 1·25
1362 $2 Minnie Mouse and Daisy Duck on hot day 3·00 2·75
1363 $4 Mickey's nephews cleaning beach 3·75 4·25
1364 $5 Donald Duck on pedal generator 3·75 4·25
MS1365 Three sheets, each 127×102 mm. (a) $6 Hiawatha and felled forest. (b) $6 Donald Duck recycling (vert). (c) $6 Mickey Mouse with Arbor Day notice. Set of 3 sheets 14·00 15·00

1991. 500th Anniv (1992) of Discovery of America by Columbus (4th issue). History of Exploration. As T **363a** of Grenada. Multicoloured.
1366 15c. Magellan's "Vitoria" rounding Cape Horn, 1519–21 1·00 50
1367 20c. Drake's Golden Hind, 1577–80 1·40 50
1368 50c. Cook's H.M.S "Resolution", 1768–71 2·00 90
1369 60c. Douglas World Cruiser seaplane, 1924 2·00 80
1370 $1 "Sputnik I" satellite, 1957 2·00 1·00
1371 $2 Gagarin's space flight, 1961 2·25 2·25
1372 $4 Glenn's space flight, 1962 2·50 3·50
1373 $5 Space shuttle, 1981 3·00 3·50
MS1374 Two sheets. (a) 105×78 mm. $6 Bow of "Pinta" (vert). (b) 78×105 mm. $6 Fleet of Columbus. Set of 2 sheets 8·00 10·00

1991. "Phila Nippon '91" International Stamp Exhibition, Tokyo. As T **198c** of Gambia but horiz showing Walt Disney cartoon characters in Japanese scenes. Multicoloured.
1375 15c. Minnie Mouse with silkworms 65 20
1376 30c. Mickey, Minnie, Morty and Ferdie at Torii Gate 85 35
1377 50c. Donald Duck and Mickey Mouse trying origami 1·25 60
1378 60c. Mickey and Minnie diving for pearls 1·40 70
1379 $1 Minnie Mouse in kimono 2·00 1·10
1380 $2 Mickey making masks 2·75 2·50
1381 $4 Donald and Mickey making paper 3·50 3·75
1382 $5 Minnie and Pluto making pottery 3·75 4·00
MS1383 Four sheets, each 122×102 mm. (a) $6 Mickey flower-arranging. (b) $6 Mickey carving a netsuke. (c) $6 Mickey at tea ceremony. (d) $6 Mickey making printing plate. Set of 4 sheets 16·00 16·00

1991. Fungi. As T **364** of Grenada. Multicoloured.
1384 5c. "Pyrrhoglossum pyrrhum" 35 25
1385 45c. "Agaricus purpurellus" 85 50
1386 50c. "Amanita craseoderma" 85 55
1387 90c. "Hygrocybe acutoconica" 1·50 1·25
1388 $1 "Limacella guttata" 1·50 1·25
1389 $2 "Lactarius hygrophoroides" 2·00 2·00
1390 $4 "Boletellus cubensis" 3·25 3·50
1391 $5 "Psilocybe caerulescens" 3·25 3·50
MS1392 Two sheets, each 100×70 mm. (a) $6 "Marasmius haematocephalus". (b) $6 "Lepiota spiculata". Set of 2 sheets 12·00 13·00

1991. 65th Birthday of Queen Elizabeth II. As T **198a** of Gambia. Multicoloured.
1393 20c. Queen, Prince Philip, Prince Charles and Prince William at Trooping the Colour, 1990 30 20
1394 25c. Queen and Prince Charles at polo match, 1985 30 20
1395 $2 Queen and Prince Philip at Maundy service, 1989 2·00 2·50
1396 $4 Queen with Queen Mother on her 87th birthday, 1987 3·25 3·75
MS1397 68×90 mm. $5 The Queen at Caen Hill, 1990, and Prince Philip at R.A.F. Benson, 1989 3·75 4·50

1991. 10th Wedding Anniv of Prince and Princess of Wales. As T **198b** of Gambia. Multicoloured.
1398 5c. Prince and Princess of Wales kissing, 1987 60 25
1399 60c. Portraits of Prince, Princess and sons 1·25 70
1400 $1 Prince Harry in 1988 and Prince William in 1987 1·25 1·10
1401 $5 Princess Diana in 1990 and Prince Charles in 1988 5·00 4·75
MS1402 68×90 mm. $5 Princess with Prince Harry in Majorca, and Prince and Princess with Prince Harry at polo match 5·50 5·00

1991. Death Centenary (1990) of Vincent van Gogh (artist). As T **200b** of Gambia. Multicoloured.
1403 5c. "Two Thistles" 50 30
1404 10c. "Baby Marcelle Roulin" 55 30
1405 15c. "Still Life: Basket with Six Oranges" (horiz) 65 20
1406 25c. "Orchard in Blossom" 80 20
1407 45c. "Armand Roulin" 1·00 35
1408 50c. "Wood Gatherers in Snow" (detail) (horiz) 1·00 50
1409 60c. "Almond Tree in Blossom" 1·25 50
1410 $1 "An Old Man" 1·75 1·25
1411 $2 "The Seine Bridge at Asnieres" (horiz) 2·50 2·50
1412 $3 "Vase with Lilacs, Daises and Anemones" 2·75 3·00
1413 $4 "Self Portrait" 3·00 3·50
1414 $5 "Patience Escalier" 3·00 3·50
MS1415 Three sheets. (a) 127×102 mm. $6 "Quay with Men unloading Sand Barges" (horiz). (b) 127×102 mm. $6 "Sunset: Wheat Fields near Arles" (horiz). (c) 102×127 mm. "Les Alyscamps". Imperf. Set of 3 sheets 12·00 13·00

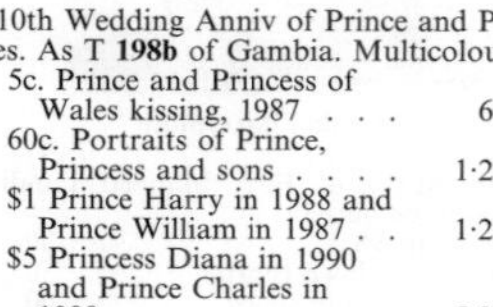

102 Sargassum Triggerfish

1991. Reef Fishes. Multicoloured.
1416 50c. Type **102** 90 90
1417 50c. Tobaccofish 90 90
1418 50c. Caribbean long-nosed butterflyfish 90 90
1419 50c. Cherub angelfish 90 90
1420 50c. Black jack 90 90
1421 50c. Masked goby and black jack 90 90
1422 50c. Spot-finned hogfish 90 90
1423 50c. Royal gramma ("Fairy basslet") 90 90
1424 50c. Orange-backed bass 90 90
1425 50c. Candy basslet 90 90
1426 50c. Black-capped basslet 90 90
1427 50c. Long-jawed squirrelfish 90 90
1428 50c. Jackknife-fish 90 90
1429 50c. Bigeye 90 90
1430 50c. Short bigeye 90 90
MS1431 106×66 mm. $6 Caribbean flashlight fish 9·00 11·00
Nos. 1416/30 were printed together, se-tenant, forming a composite design.

1991. Christmas. Religious Paintings by Martin Schongauer. As T **200c** of Gambia.
1432 10c. black and brown 60 15
1433 35c. multicoloured 1·00 30
1434 50c. multicoloured 1·40 50
1435 75c. multicoloured 1·75 80
1436 $1 multicoloured 1·90 1·25
1437 $2 multicoloured 3·00 3·00
1438 $4 black and brown 3·75 4·25
1439 $5 black, grey and red 3·75 4·50
MS1440 Two sheets, each 102×127 mm. (a) $6 multicoloured. (b) $6 multicoloured. Set of 2 sheets 9·50 11·00
DESIGNS: 10c. "Angel of the Annunciation"; 35c. "Madonna of the Rose Hedge" (detail); 50c. "Madonna of the Rose Hedge" (different detail); 75c. "Nativity" (detail); $1 "Adoration of the Shepherds" (detail); $2 "The Nativity"; $4 "Nativity" (different); $5 "Symbol of St. Matthew"; $6 (No. **MS**1440a) "Adoration of the Shepherds" (different detail); $6 (No. **MS**1440b) "Nativity".

1992. Great Railways of the World. As T **367** of Grenada. Multicoloured.
1441 75c. Medoc locomotive No. J-S 58, 1857 (Switzerland) 1·10 1·10
1442 75c. Stirling single locomotive No. 1, 1870 (Great Britain) 1·10 1·10
1443 75c. Paris–Lyon–Mediterranee locomotive No. 90, 1877 (France) 1·10 1·10
1444 75c. Standard type, 1880 (U.S.A.) 1·10 1·10
1445 75c. Class 650 "Vittorio Emanuel II", 1884 (Italy) 1·10 1·10
1446 75c. Johnson single, 1887 (Great Britain) 1·10 1·10
1447 75c. Locomotive No. 999, 1893 (U.S.A.) 1·10 1·10
1448 75c. Class Q1, 1896 (Great Britain) 1·10 1·10
1449 75c. "Claud Hamilton", 1900 (Great Britain) 1·10 1·10
1450 $1 Class P8, 1906 (Germany) 1·10 1·10
1451 $1 Class P, 1910 (Denmark) 1·10 1·10
1452 $1 Southern Railway Ps4, 1926 (U.S.A.) 1·10 1·10
1453 $1 "Kestrel", 1932 (Ireland) 1·10 1·10
1454 $1 Southern Pacific Class GS2, 1937 (U.S.A.) 1·10 1·10
1455 $1 Class 12, 1938 (Belgium) 1·10 1·10
1456 $1 Norfolk and Western Railroad Class J No. 600, 1941 (U.S.A.) 1·10 1·10
1457 $1 Alco PA series diesel, 1946 (U.S.A.) 1·10 1·10
1458 $1 Class 4E electric, 1954 (South Africa) 1·10 1·10
1459 $2 Trans Europe Express train, 1957 1·50 1·50
1460 $2 New Haven Railroad Type FL9 diesel, 1960 (U.S.A.) 1·50 1·50
1461 $2 "Hikari" train, 1964 (Japan) 1·50 1·50
1462 $2 Class 103.1 electric, 1970 (Germany) 1·50 1·50
1463 $2 RTG diesel, 1972 (France) 1·50 1·50
1464 $2 ETR 401 Pendolino train, 1976 (Italy) 1·50 1·50
1465 $2 Advanced Passenger Train Class 370, 1981 (Great Britain) 1·50 1·50
1466 $2 Via Rail LRC diesel, 1982 (Canada) 1·50 1·50
1467 $2 MAV BZMOT 601, 1983 (Hungary) 1·50 1·50
MS1468 Two sheets, each 120×80 mm. (a) $6 Werner von Siemens's electric locomotive, 1879 (Germany). (b) ETR 401 Pendolino train, 1976 (Italy). Set of 2 sheets 11·00 11·00

1992. 40th Anniv of Queen Elizabeth II's Accession. As T **202a** of Gambia. Multicoloured.
1469 60c. Swimming jetty on beach 1·00 40
1470 75c. View of Grenadines 1·10 45
1471 $2 Surf on beach 2·25 1·75
1472 $4 Secluded bay 3·50 3·25
MS1473 Two sheets, each 74×92 mm. (a) $6 Plantation house. (b) $6 St. George's. Set of 2 sheets 9·00 9·50

1992. Olympic Games, Barcelona. As T **372** of Grenada. Multicoloured.
1474 10c. Women's backstroke swimming 60 30
1475 15c. Women's handball 65 30
1476 25c. Men's 4×100 m relay 75 30
1477 35c. Men's hammer throw 80 35
1478 50c. Men's 110 m hurdles 90 60
1479 75c. Men's pole vault 1·25 80
1480 $1 Men's volleyball 1·40 1·00
1481 $2 Men's weightlifting 2·50 2·75

1482 $5 Men's gymnastics . . . . 3·25 4·00
1483 $6 Football . . . . 3·75 4·25
MS1484 Two sheets, each 100 × 70 mm. (a) $15 Finn class single-handed dinghy sailing. (b) $15 Baseball. Set of 2 sheets 16·00 17·00

1992. Granada '92 Int Stamp Exn, Spain. Spanish Paintings. As T **481a** of Ghana. Mult.
1485 10c. "The Surrender of Seville" (Zurbaran) . . . 30 20
1486 35c. "The Liberation of St. Peter by an Angel" (Antonio de Pereda) . . . 50 35
1487 50c. "Joseph explains the Dreams of the Pharaoh" (Antonio del Castillo Saavedra) (horiz) 75 60
1488 75c. "The Flower Vase" (Juan de Arellano) . . . 1·00 70
1489 $1 "The Duke of Pastrana" (Juan Carreno de Miranda) . . . . 1·25 90
1490 $2 "The Annunciation" (detail) (Francisco Rizi) 2·00 2·00
1491 $4 "The Annunciation" (different detail) (Rizi) . . 3·00 3·50
1492 $5 "Old Women Seated" (attr Antonio Puga) . . . 3·00 3·50
MS1493 Two sheets. (a) 95 × 120 mm. $6 "The Triumph of Saint Hermenegildo" (Francisco de Herrera the younger) (86 × 111 mm). (b) 120 × 95 mm. $6 "Relief of Genoa" (De Pereda) (110 × 84 mm). Imperf. Set of 2 sheets . . . . 7·00 8·00

103 Don Isaac Abarbanel, Minister of Finance

1992. 500th Anniv of Discovery of America by Columbus (5th issue). World Columbian Stamp Expo '92, Chicago. Multicoloured.
1494 10c. Type **103** 15 15
1495 25c. Columbus on voyage 25 25
1496 35c. Look-out sighting land 30 30
1497 50c. King Ferdinand and Queen Isabella of Spain 50 50
1498 60c. Columbus showing map to Queen Isabella 55 55
1499 $5 "Santa Maria" and bird 4·00 5·50
MS1500 Two sheets, each 100 × 71 mm. (a) $6 Christopher Columbus. (b) $6 Columbus with hand to face. Set of 2 sheets 7·00 8·00

1992. "Genova '92" International Thematic Stamp Exhibition. Hummingbirds. As T **370a** of Grenada. Multicoloured.
1501 5c. Male blue-headed hummingbird 25 30
1502 10c. Female rufous-breasted hermit 25 25
1503 20c. Female blue-headed hummingbird 30 25
1504 45c. Male green-throated carib 45 30
1505 90c. Male Antillean crested hummingbird 60 70
1506 $2 Male purple-throated carib . . . . 1·40 1·60
1507 $4 Female purple-throated carib . . . . 2·40 2·75
1508 $5 Female Antillean crested hummingbird . . . . . . 2·50 2·75
MS1509 Two sheets, each 104 × 75 mm. (a) $6 Male Rufous-breasted Hermit. (b) $6 Female Green-throated Carib. Set of 2 sheets . . . . 9·50 11·00

1992. 50th Anniv of United Service Organization (forces' entertainment programme). As T **371** of Grenada. Multicoloured.
1510 10c. James Cagney 60 25
1511 15c. Anne Sheridan 60 25
1512 35c. Jerry Colonna 60 25
1513 50c. Spike Jones 70 40
1514 75c. Edgar Bergen 90 55
1515 $1 The Andrews Sisters . . 1·40 80
1516 $2 Dinah Shore . . . . . . 2·00 2·00
1517 $5 Bing Crosby . . . . . . 4·50 4·50
MS1518 Two sheets, each 107 × 80 mm. (a) $6 Fred Astaire. (b) $6 Marlene Dietrich. Set of 2 sheets . . . . 7·00 7·50
No. 1515 is incorrectly inscribed "THE ANDREW SISTERS".

1992. 500th Anniv of Discovery of America by Columbus (6th issue). Organization of East Caribbean States. As Nos. 2423/4 of Grenada.
1519 $1 Columbus meeting Amerindians 65 65
1520 $2 Ships approaching island 1·25 1·50

1992. Toy Trains from American Manufacturers. As T **372b** of Grenada. Multicoloured.
1521 15c. No. 2220 switcher locomotive, Voltamp (1910) 25 15
1522 25c. Clockwork locomotive of Bridge Port Line, American Miniature Railroad (1907) 35 20
1523 50c. First electric toy locomotive, Ives (1910) . . 60 40
1524 75c. "J.C. Penney Special" locomotive, American Flyer (1920s) 80 60
1525 $1 Clockwork cast-metal locomotive, Hafner (1916) 90 80
1526 $2 Pull toy copper-plated locomotive, probably Hubley (1900) . . . . . 1·75 2·25
1527 $4 "Mayflower" locomotive, American Flyer (1928) . . 3·00 3·50
1528 $5 "Olympian" locomotive, Ives (1929) . . . . 3·00 3·50
MS1529 Two sheets. (a) 128 × 93 mm. $6 Clockwork locomotive, Ives (1910) (50 × 38½ mm). (b) 142 × 95 mm. $6 "Statesman" locomotive, American Flyer (50 × 38½ mm). P 13. Set of 2 sheets . . . . . . 7·50 8·50

1992. Postage Stamp Mega Event, New York. Sheet 100 × 70 mm containing multicoloured design as T **207a** of Gambia.
MS1530 $6 Brooklyn Bridge . . 3·50 4·25

1992. Christmas. Religious Paintings. "The Annunciation" by various artists. As T **207b** of Gambia. Multicoloured.
1531 5c. Robert Campin 15 10
1532 15c. Melchior Broederlam 25 10
1533 25c. Fra Filippo Lippi (two-panel diptych) 30 15
1534 35c. Simone Martini . . . 40 20
1535 50c. Lippi (detail from left panel) 55 45
1536 75c. Lippi (detail from right panel) 70 60
1537 90c. Albert Bouts 80 80
1538 $1 D. di Michelino 90 90
1539 $2 Rogier van der Weyden 1·75 2·00
1540 $3 Sandro Botticelli (detail of angel) . . . . 2·25 2·75
1541 $4 Botticelli (detail of Virgin Mary) . . . . 2·75 3·50
1542 $5 Bernardo Daddi (horiz) 2·75 3·50
MS1543 Three sheets, each 72 × 97 mm. (a) $6 Van der Weyden (different). (b) $6 Botticelli (as $3). (c) $6 Hubert van Eyck. Set of 3 sheets . . . . . 10·50 12·00

1992. Gold Record Award Winners. As T **374** of Grenada. Multicoloured.
1544 90c. Leonard Bernstein . . 1·50 1·25
1545 90c. Ray Charles . . . . . 1·50 1·25
1546 90c. Bob Dylan . . . . . . 1·50 1·25
1547 90c. Barbra Streisand . . . 1·50 1·25
1548 90c. Frank Sinatra . . . . 1·50 1·25
1549 90c. Harry Belafonte . . . 1·50 1·25
1550 90c. Aretha Franklin . . . 1·50 1·25
1551 90c. Garth Brooks . . . . 1·50 1·25
MS1552 Two sheets, each 100 × 70 mm. (a) $3 Charlie Parker; $3 Miles Davis. (b) $3 Johnny Cash; $3 Willie Nelson. Set of 2 sheets . . . . 7·00 8·00
Nos. 1544/51 were printed together, se-tenant, with a composite background design.

1992. 60th Anniv of Goofy (Disney cartoon character). Scenes from various cartoon films. As T **207c** of Gambia. Multicoloured.
1553 5c. "Father's Day Off", 1953 . . . . 30 20
1554 10c. "Cold War", 1951 . . 35 20
1555 15c. "Home Made Home", 1951 . . . . 40 20
1556 25c. "Get Rich Quick", 1951 . . . . 50 25
1557 50c. "Man's Best Friend", 1952 . . . . 70 40
1558 75c. "Aquamania", 1961 . . 1·00 55
1559 90c. "Tomorrow We Diet", 1951 . . . . 1·10 65
1560 $1 "Teachers Are People", 1952 . . . . 1·25 75
1561 $2 "The Goofy Success Story", 1955 . . . . . 2·00 1·75
1562 $3 "Double Dribble", 1946 2·50 3·00
1563 $4 "Hello Aloha", 1952 . . 2·75 3·25
1564 $5 "Father's Lion", 1952 . . 3·00 3·50
MS1565 Three sheets, each 128 × 102 mm. (a) $6 "Motor Mania", 1956. (b) $6 "Hold that Pose", 1950 (vert). (c) $6 "Father's Weekend", 1953 (vert). Set of 3 sheets . . . . 12·00 13·00

1992. Anniversaries and Events. As T **375** of Grenada. Multicoloured, except No. 1571.
1566 25c. Zeppelin "Viktoria Luise" over Kiel Harbour (horiz) 75 30
1567 50c. Space shuttle "Columbia" landing (horiz) 85 35
1568 75c. German Federal Republic flag and arms (horiz) 85 50
1569 $1.50 Giant anteater (horiz) 1·00 1·00
1570 $2 Scarlet macaw . . . . . 2·75 2·00
1571 $2 W.H.O. emblem (black and blue) (horiz) . . . . 1·50 1·50
1572 $3 Wolfgang Amadeus Mozart . . . . 4·00 3·00
1573 $4 The Berlin Airlift (horiz) 3·25 3·50
1574 $4 Repairing "Intelsat VI" satellite in space (horiz) 3·25 3·50
1575 $5 Zeppelin "Hindenburg" on fire (horiz) . . . . . . 3·25 3·50
1576 $5 Admiral Richard Byrd's Ford Trimotor aircraft (horiz) . . . . 3·25 3·50
MS1577 Five sheets. (a) 110 × 80 mm. $6 Zeppelin LZ-4, 1913 (51½ × 39½ mm). (b) 110 × 80 mm. $6 First flight of space shuttle "Endeavour" (51½ × 39½ mm). (c) 110 × 80 mm. $6 Map of West Germany (39½ × 51½ mm). (d) 110 × 80 mm. $6 Jaguar (51½ × 39½ mm). (e) 98 × 67 mm. $6 Figaro costume from "The Marriage of Figaro". Set of 5 sheets . . . . 18·00 20·00
ANNIVERSARIES AND EVENTS: Nos. 1566, 1575, **MS**1577a, 75th death anniv of Count Ferdinand von Zeppelin; 1567, 1574, **MS**1577b, International Space Year; 1568, 1573, **MS**1577c, 25th death anniv of Konrad Adenauer (German statesman); 1569/70, **MS**1577d, Earth Summit '92, Rio; 1571, United Nations World Health Organization Projects; 1572, **MS**1577e, Death bicentenary of Mozart; 1576, 75th anniv of International Association of Lions Clubs.

104 "Atalanta" and "Mischief" (yachts), 1881

105 "Battus polydamus"

1992. History of The Americas Cup Challenge Trophy. Multicoloured.
1578 15c. Type **104** 60 20
1579 25c. "Valkyrie III" and "Defender", 1895 . . . . 75 30
1580 35c. "Shamrock IV" and "Resolute", 1920 . . . . 90 45
1581 75c. "Endeavour II" and "Ranger", 1937 . . . . . 1·40 70
1582 $1 "Sceptre" and "Columbia", 1958 . . . . 1·60 85
1583 $2 "Australia II" and "Liberty", 1983 . . . . . 2·25 2·25
1584 $4 "Stars & Stripes" and "Kookaburra III", 1987 3·25 4·00
1585 $5 "New Zealand" and "Stars & Stripes", 1988 3·25 4·00
MS1586 Two sheets, each 114 × 85 mm. (a) $6 "America" (schooner), 1851 (57 × 43 mm). (b) $6 Americas Cup emblems (57 × 43 mm). Set of 2 sheets 10·00 11·00

1993. Dogs of the World. As T **377** of Grenada, but vert. Multicoloured.
1587 35c. Irish setter and Glendalough, Ireland . . 50 25
1588 50c. Boston terrier and Boston State House, U.S.A. 70 50
1589 75c. Beagle and Temple to Athena, Greece . . . . 1·00 60
1590 $1 Weimaraner and Nesselwang, Germany . . 1·25 85
1591 $3 Norwegian elkhound and Urnes Stave Church, Norway . . . . 2·50 3·00
1592 $4 Mastiff and Sphinx, Egypt . . . . 2·75 3·00
1593 $5 Akita and Torii Temple, Kyoto, Japan . . . . . 2·75 3·00
1594 $5 Saluki and Rub'al Khali, Saudi Arabia . . . . . . 2·75 3·00
MS1595 Two sheets, each 99 × 71 mm. (a) $6 Bull dog, Great Britain. (b) $6 Shar Pei, China. Set of 2 sheets . . . . 7·50 8·50

1993. Bicentenary of the Louvre, Paris. As T **209b** of Gambia. Multicoloured (except No. 1599).
1596 $1 "Madonna and Child with the young John the Baptist" (Botticelli) . . . 1·00 1·00
1597 $1 "The Buffet" (Chardin) 1·00 1·00
1598 $1 "Return from Market" (Chardin) . . . . 1·00 1·00
1599 $1 "Erasmus" (Durer) (black and grey) . . . . 1·00 1·00
1600 $1 "Self-portrait with Eryngium" (Durer) . . . 1·00 1·00
1601 $1 "Jeanne of Aragon" (Raphael) . . . . 1·00 1·00
1602 $1 "La Belle Jardiniere" (detail) (Raphael) . . . . 1·00 1·00
1603 $1 "La Belle Jardiniere" (different detail) (Raphael) 1·00 1·00
MS1604 70 × 100 mm. $6 "King Charles I Hunting" (Van Dyck) (52 × 85 mm) . . . . 3·75 4·50

1993. Butterflies. Multicoloured.
1605 15c. Type **105** 40 20
1606 35c. "Astraptes talus" . . . 55 20
1607 45c. "Pseudolycaena marsyas" 55 25
1608 75c. "Siproeta stelenes" . . 70 50
1609 $1 "Phoebis sennae" 80 60
1610 $2 "Dione juno" . . . . . 1·40 1·40
1611 $4 "Chlorostrymon simaethis" . . . . 2·25 2·75
1612 $5 "Urbanus proteus" . . . 2·50 2·75
MS1613 Two sheets, each 100 × 70 mm. (a) $6 "Historis odius" ("Orion"). (b) $6 "Heliconius charithonia" ("Zebra"). Set of 2 sheets . . . 7·00 8·00

1993. Flowers. As T **380** of Grenada. Mult.
1614 35c. Hibiscus 50 20
1615 35c. Columbine 50 20
1616 45c. Red ginger 50 25
1617 75c. Bougainvillea 70 50
1618 $1 Crown imperial 80 60
1619 $2 Fairy orchid . . . . . . 1·40 1·40
1620 $4 Heliconia . . . . 2·25 2·75
1621 $5 Tulip . . . . 2·50 2·75

1993. 40th Anniv of Coronation. As T **215a** of Gambia.
1623 35c. multicoloured 30 55
1624 50c. multicoloured 40 60
1625 $2 green and black . . . . 1·10 1·40
1626 $4 multicoloured . . . . . 1·90 2·00
MS1627 70 × 100 mm. $6 multicoloured . . . . 6·00 6·50
DESIGNS—(38 × 27 mm): 35c. Queen Elizabeth II at Coronation (photograph by Cecil Beaton); 50c. Ampulla and spoon; $2 Queen Elizabeth II leaving for Coronation; $4 Prince Harry's christening. (28½ × 42½ mm)—$6 "Queen Elizabeth II, 1954" (detail) (Pietro Annigoni).

1993. Anniversaries and Events. As T **381** of Grenada. Multicoloured.
1628 15c. "Painter and Model" (Picasso) (horiz) 55 30
1629 35c. Keith Tkachuk and Dmitri Mironov (ice hockey, 1992) (horiz) . . 1·00 40
1630 50c. Early telescope 85 50
1631 75c. "Gra w Gudziki" (Ludomir Slerdinski) (horiz) 90 90
1632 75c. Willy Brandt and Lyndon Johnson, 1961 (horiz) 90 90
1633 $1 "Artist and his Model" (Picasso) (horiz) . . . . 1·00 1·00
1634 $2 "Pocalunek Mongolskiego Ksiecia" (S. Wirkiewicz) (horiz) . . 1·40 1·75
1635 $4 "The Drawing Lesson" (Picasso) (horiz) . . . . . 2·25 2·75
1636 $4 Radio telescope . . . . 2·25 2·75
1637 $5 Alberto Tomba (Giant Slalom, 1984) (horiz) . . 2·25 2·75
1638 $5 Willy Brandt and Eleanor Hulles, 1957 (horiz) . . . . 2·25 2·75
MS1639 Five sheets. (a) 105 × 75 mm. $5 Copernicus. (b) 105 × 75 mm. $6 Picasso (horiz). (c) 75 × 105 mm. $6 Emil Zogragski (70 metre ski jump, 1984). (d) 75 × 105 mm. $6 "Allegory" (detail) (Jan Wydra). (e) 105 × 75 mm. $6 Willy and Rut Brandt (grey and black) (horiz) Set of 5 sheets . . . . . . 17·00 19·00
ANNIVERSARIES AND EVENTS: Nos. 1628, 1633, 1635, **MS**1639b, 20th death anniv of Picasso (artist); 1629, 1637, **MS**1639c, Winter Olympic Games '94, Lillehammer; 1630, 1636, **MS**1639a, 450th death anniv of Copernicus (astronomer); 1631, 1634, **MS**1639d, Polska '93 International Stamp Exhibition, Poznan; 1632, 1638, **MS**1639e, 80th birth anniv of Willy Brandt (German politician).

1993. Songbirds. As T **382** of Grenada. Multicoloured.
1640 15c. Painted bunting 60 60
1641 15c. White-throated sparrow 60 60
1642 25c. Common grackle . . . 70 70
1643 25c. Royal flycatcher . . . 70 70
1644 35c. Swallow tanager . . . 75 75
1645 35c. Vermilion flycatcher . . 75 75
1646 45c. Black-headed bunting 80 80
1647 50c. Rose-breasted grosbeak 80 80
1648 75c. Corn bunting 80 80
1649 75c. Rose-breasted thrush tanager 80 80
1650 $1 Buff-throated saltator . . 90 90
1651 $4 Plush-capped finch . . . 2·25 2·25
MS1652 Two sheets, each 115 × 86 mm. (a) $6 Pine grosbeak. (b) $6 Bohemian waxwing. Set of 2 sheets . . . . 12·00 12·00
Nos. 1640/51 were printed together, se-tenant, with the backgrounds forming a composite design.
Nos. 1645/6 show the scientific inscriptions transposed between the designs.

1993. Shells. As T **383** of Grenada. Mult.
1653 15c. Hawk-wing conch . . . 35 35
1654 15c. Music volute 35 35
1655 25c. Globe vase and deltoid rock shell 40 40
1656 35c. Spiny Caribbean vase 40 40
1657 35c. American common sundial and common purple janthina 40 40
1658 45c. Toothed donax and gaudy asaphis 40 40
1659 45c. Mouse cone 40 40
1660 50c. Gold-mouthed triton 50 50
1661 75c. Tulip mussel and trigonal tivela 60 60
1662 75c. Common dove shell and chestnut latirus . . . 60 60

1663 $1 Wide-mouthed purpura 70 70
1664 $4 American thorny oyster and Atlantic wing oyster 2·25 2·25
MS1665 Two sheets, each 70 × 106 mm. (a) $6 Atlantic turkey wing. (b) $6 Zebra or zigzag periwinkle. Set of 2 sheets 10·00 10·00
Nos. 1653/64 were printed together, se-tenant, with the backgrounds forming a composite design.

1993. Asian International Stamp Exhibitions. As T **219a** of Gambia. Multicoloured. (a) "Indopex '93", Surabaya, Indonesia.
1666 35c. National Museum, Central Jakarta (horiz) 40 20
1667 45c. Sacred wheel and deer (horiz) 45 25
1668 $1 Ramayana relief, Panataran Temple (horiz) 70 60
1669 $1.50 "Bullock Carts" (Batara Lubis) (horiz) 1·25 1·25
1670 $1.50 "Surat Irsa II" (A. D. Pirous) (horiz) 1·25 1·25
1671 $1.50 "Self-portrait with Goat" (Kartika) (horiz) 1·25 1·25
1672 $1.50 "The Cow-est Cow" (Ivan Sagito) (horiz) 1·25 1·25
1673 $1.50 "Rain Storm" (Sudjana Kerton) (horiz) 1·25 1·25
1674 $1.50 "Story of Pucuk Flower" (Effendi) (horiz) 1·25 1·25
1675 $5 Candi Tikus, Trawulan, East Java (horiz) 2·50 3·00
MS1676 134 × 105 mm. $6 Banteng cattle (horiz) 3·50 4·00

(b) "Taipei '93", Taiwan.
1677 35c. Macau Palace Casino, Hong Kong (horiz) 40 20
1678 45c. Stone lion, Ming Tomb, Nanjing (horiz) 45 25
1679 $1 Stone camels, Ming Tomb, Nanjing (horiz) 70 60
1680 $1.50 Nesting quail incense burner (horiz) 1·25 1·25
1681 $1.50 Standing quail incense burner (horiz) 1·25 1·25
1682 $1.50 Seated qilin incense burner (horiz) 1·25 1·25
1683 $1.50 Pottery horse, Han period (horiz) 1·25 1·25
1684 $1.50 Seated caparisoned elephant (horiz) 1·25 1·25
1685 $1.50 Cow in imitation of Delft faience (horiz) 1·25 1·25
1686 $5 Stone lion and elephant, Ming Tomb, Nanjing (horiz) 2·50 3·00
MS1687 134 × 105 mm. $6 Sumatran tiger, Mt. Leuser National Park 3·50 4·00

(c) "Bangkok 1993", Thailand.
1688 35c. Three Naga snakes, Chiang Mai's Temple (horiz) 40 20
1689 45c. Sri Mariamman Temple, Singapore (horiz) 45 25
1690 $1 Topiary, Hua Hin Resort (horiz) 70 60
1691 $1.50 "Buddha's Victory over Mara" (horiz) 1·25 1·25
1692 $1.50 "Mythological Elephant" (horiz) 1·25 1·25
1693 $1.50 "Battle with Mara" (Thon Buri) (horiz) 1·25 1·25
1694 $1.50 "Untitled" (Panya Wijinthanasarn) (horiz) 1·25 1·25
1695 $1.50 "Temple Mural" (horiz) 1·25 1·25
1696 $1.50 "Elephants in Pahcekha Buddha's Heaven" (horiz) 1·25 1·25
1697 $5 Pak Tai Temple, Cheung Chau Island (horiz) 2·50 3·00
MS1698 134 × 105 mm. $6 Monkey from Chiang Kong 3·50 4·00

1993. World Cup Football Championship, U.S.A. (1994) (1st issue). As T **221a** of Gambia. Mult.
1699 15c. McCall (Scotland) and Verri (Brazil) (horiz) 70 20
1700 25c. Verri (Brazil) and Maradona (Argentina) (horiz) 75 20
1701 35c. Schillaci (Italy) and Saldana (Uruguay) (horiz) 80 25
1702 45c. Gullit (Holland) and Wright (England) (horiz) 90 35
1703 $1 Verri (Brazil) and Maradona (Argentina) (different) (horiz) 1·25 80
1704 $2 Zubizarreta and Fernandez (Spain) with Albert (Belgium) (horiz) 1·75 1·75
1705 $4 Hagi (Rumania) and McGrath (Ireland) (horiz) 2·50 3·25
1706 $5 Gorriz (Spain) and Scifo (Belgium) (horiz) 2·50 3·25
MS1707 Two sheets, each 104 × 75 mm. (a) $6 Foxboro Stadium, Massachusetts (horiz). (b) $6 Rudi Voeller (Germany). Set of 2 sheets 8·00 9·00
See also Nos. 1810/16.

1993. 65th Anniv of Mickey Mouse. Scenes from Walt Disney cartoon films. As T **385** of Grenada.
1708 15c. "Mickey's Rival", 1936 55 25
1709 35c. "The Worm Turns", 1937 70 25
1710 50c. "The Pointer", 1939 85 55
1711 75c. "Society Dog Show", 1939 1·25 90
1712 $1 "A Gentleman's Gentleman", 1941 1·40 1·00
1713 $2 "The Little Whirlwind", 1941 2·00 2·25
1714 $4 "Mickey Down Under", 1948 2·75 3·25
1715 $5 "R'coon Dawg", 1951 2·75 3·25
MS1716 Two sheets, each 127 × 102 mm. (a) $6 "Lonesome Ghosts", 1937. (b) $6 "Mickey's Garden", 1935 (vert). Set of 2 sheets 8·00 8·50

1993. Christmas. Religious Paintings. As T **211b** of Gambia. Black, yellow and red (Nos. 1717, 1721/3 and MS1725a) or multicoloured (others).
1717 10c. "Adoration of the Shepherds" (detail) (Durer) 30 20
1718 25c. "Adoration of the Magi" (detail) (Raphael) 40 20
1719 35c. "Presentation at the Temple" (detail) (Raphael) 45 20
1720 50c. "Adoration of the Magi" (different detail) (Raphael) 55 35
1721 75c. "Adoration of the Shepherds" (different detail) (Durer) 90 60
1722 $1 "Adoration of the Shepherds" (different detail) (Durer) 1·00 85
1723 $4 "Adoration of the Shepherds" (different detail) (Durer) 2·50 3·25
1724 $5 "Presentation at the Temple" (different detail) (Raphael) 2·50 3·25
MS1725 Two sheets. (a) 102 × 128 mm. $6 "Adoration of the Shepherds" (different detail) (Dürer) (horiz). (b) 128 × 102 mm. $6 "Annunciation" (detail) (Raphael). Set of 2 sheets 7·00 8·00

1993. Aviation Anniversaries. As T **386** of Grenada. Multicoloured.
1726 15c. Avro Lancaster 30 25
1727 35c. Blanchard's balloon crossing the River Delaware 40 25
1728 50c. Airship "Graf Zeppelin" over Rio de Janeiro 50 35
1729 75c. Hugo Eckener 65 50
1730 $3 Pres. Washington handing passport to Blanchard 1·40 1·75
1731 $5 Short Sunderland flying boat 2·50 3·00
1732 $5 Eckener in "Graf Zeppelin" 2·50 3·00
MS1733 Three sheets. (a) 76 × 107 mm. $6 Supermarine Spitfire. (b) 107 × 76 mm. $6 Blanchard's balloon (vert). (c) 107 × 76 mm. $6 Eckener with Pres. Hoover. Set of 3 sheets 11·50 12·50
ANNIVERSARIES: Nos. 1726, 1731, MS1733a, 75th anniv of Royal Air Force; 1727, 1730, MS1733b. Bicentenary of first airmail flight; 1728/9, 1732, MS1733c, 125th birth anniv of Hugo Eckener (airship commander).

1993. Centenaries of Henry Ford's First Petrol Engine (Nos. 1735/6) and Karl Benz's First Four-wheeled Car (others). As T **387** of Grenada. Multicoloured.
1734 25c. Mercedes Benz "300 SLR", 1955 85 25
1735 45c. Ford "Thunderbird", 1957 1·00 25
1736 $4 Ford "150-A" station wagon, 1929 3·50 3·75
1737 $5 Mercedes Benz "540 K" 3·50 3·75
MS1738 Two sheets, 76 × 107 mm. (a) $6 Mercedes Benz "SSK", 1929. (b) $6 Ford "Model T", 1924. Set of 2 sheets 8·00 9·00

1993. Famous Paintings by Rembrandt and Matisse. As T **221c** of Gambia. Multicoloured.
1739 15c. "Hendrickje Stoffels as Flora" (Rembrandt) 40 25
1740 35c. "Lady and Gentleman in Black" (Rembrandt) 50 25
1741 50c. "Aristotle with the Bust of Homer" (Rembrandt) 60 40
1742 75c. "Interior: Flowers and Parakeets" (Matisse) 85 60
1743 $1 "Goldfish" (Matisse) 1·00 85
1744 $2 "The Girl with Green Eyes" (Matisse) 1·75 2·25
1745 $3 "Still Life with a Plaster Figure" (Matisse) 2·00 2·75
1746 $5 "Christ and the Woman of Samaria" (Rembrandt) 2·50 3·25
MS1747 Two sheets. (a) 100 × 125 mm. $6 "Anna accused of stealing the Kid" (detail) (Rembrandt). (b) 125 × 100 mm. $6 "Tea in the Garden" (detail) (Matisse) (horiz). Set of 2 sheets 8·00 9·00

1994. "Hong Kong '94" International Stamp Exhibition (1st issue). As T **222a** of Gambia. Multicoloured.
1748 40c. Hong Kong 1984 $5 aviation stamp and airliner at Kai Tak Airport 80 85
1749 40c. Grenada Grenadines 1988 20c. airships stamp and junk in Kowloon Bay 80 85
Nos. 1748/9 were printed together, se-tenant, forming a composite design.
See also Nos. 1750/5.

1994. "Hong Kong '94" International Stamp Exhibition (2nd issue). Jade Sculptures. As T **222b** of Gambia, but horiz. Multicoloured.
1750 45c. White jade brush washer 60 60
1751 45c. Archaic jade brush washer 60 60
1752 45c. Dark green jade brush washer 60 60
1753 45c. Green jade almsbowl 60 60
1754 45c. Archaic jade dog 60 60
1755 45c. Yellow jade brush washer 60 60

1994. Fungi. As T **390** of Grenada, but with white backgrounds. Multicoloured.
1756 35c. "Hygrocybe hypohaemacta" 45 30
1757 45c. "Cantharellus cinnabarinus" 55 35
1758 50c. "Marasmius haematocephalus" 60 40
1759 75c. "Mycena pura" 80 60
1760 $1 "Gymnopilus russipes" 90 80
1761 $2 "Calocybe cyanocephala" 1·40 1·75
1762 $4 "Pluteus chrysophlebius" 2·50 3·00
1763 $5 "Chlorophyllum molybdites" 2·50 3·00
MS1764 Two sheets, each 100 × 70 mm. (a) $6 "Xeromphalina tenuipes". (b) "Collybia fibrosipes". Set of 2 sheets 7·50 8·00
No. 1757 is inscribed "Cantherellus cinnabarinus" and No. 1762 "Pleuteus chrysophlebius", both in error.

1994. Prehistoric Animals. As T **391** of Grenada. Multicoloured.
1765 15c. Spinosaurus 30 25
1766 35c. Apatosaurus (Brontosaurus) 45 30
1767 45c. Tyrannosaurus rex 50 35
1768 55c. Triceratops 50 40
1769 $1 Pachycephalosaurus 85 75
1770 $2 Pteranodon 1·40 1·75
1771 $4 Parasaurolophus 2·50 3·00
1772 $5 Brachiosaurus 2·50 3·00
MS1773 Two sheets, each 100 × 70 mm. (a) $6 Head of Brachiosaurus (vert). (b) $6 Spinosaurus and Tyrannosaurus rex fighting (vert). Set of 2 sheets 7·50 8·00

1994. 25th Anniv of First Manned Moon Landing. Space Shuttle "Challenger". As T **227a** of Gambia. Multicoloured.
1774 $1.10 "Challenger" crew in training 1·00 1·25
1775 $1.10 Christa McAuliffe (astronaut) 1·00 1·25
1776 $1.10 "Challenger" on launch pad 1·00 1·25
1777 $1.10 Gregory Jarvis (astronaut) 1·00 1·25
1778 $1.10 Ellison Onizuka (astronaut) 1·00 1·25
1779 $1.10 Ronald McNair (astronaut) 1·00 1·25
MS1780 107 × 76 mm. $6 Judith Resnick (astronaut) (vert) 4·00 4·50

1994. Centenary of International Olympic Committee. Gold Medal Winners. As T **227b** of Gambia. Multicoloured.
1781 50c. Silke Renk (Germany) (javelin), 1992 35 35
1782 $1.50 Mark Spitz (U.S.A.) (swimming), 1972 90 1·40
MS1783 106 × 77 mm. $6 Japanese team (Nordic skiing), 1994 3·25 3·75

1994. International Year of the Family. As T **391a** of Grenada. Multicoloured.
1784 $1 Grenadines family 60 60

1994. 50th Anniv of D-Day. As T **227c** of Gambia. Multicoloured.
1785 40c. Churchill bridge-laying tank 35 30
1786 $2 Sherman "Firefly" tank leaving landing craft 1·00 1·50
1787 $3 Churchill "Crocodile" flame-thrower 1·60 2·00
MS1788 107 × 76 mm. $6 Sherman "Crab" flail tank 3·25 3·75

1994. "Philakorea '94" International Stamp Exhibition, Seoul (1st issue). As T **227d** of Gambia. Multicoloured.
1789 40c. Onung Tomb (horiz) 30 30
1790 $1 Stone pagoda, Mt. Namsam (horiz) 55 65
1791 $1 "Admiring Spring in the Country" (left detail) (Sin Yunbok) 55 65
1792 $1 "Admiring Spring in the Country" (right detail) 55 65
1793 $1 "Woman on Dano Day" (left detail) (Sin Yunbok) 55 65
1794 $1 "Woman on Dano Day" (right detail) 55 65
1795 $1 "Enjoying Lotuses while Listening to Music" (left detail) (Sin Yunbok) 55 65
1796 $1 "Enjoying Lotuses while Listening to Music" (right detail) 55 65
1797 $1 "Women by a Crystal Stream" (left detail) (Sin Yunbok) 55 65
1798 $1 "Women by a Crystal Stream" (right detail) 55 65
1799 $4 Pusan (horiz) 2·25 2·75
MS1800 70 × 102 mm. $6 "Blacksmith Shop" (detail) (Kim Duksin) 3·25 3·75
The two details of each painting on Nos. 1791/8 were printed together, se-tenant, each pair forming a composite design.
See also Nos. 1817/31.

1994. Orchids. As T **392** of Grenada. Multicoloured.
1801 15c. "Cattleya aurantiaca" 35 25
1802 25c. "Blettia patula" 40 25
1803 45c. "Sobralia macrantha" 50 30
1804 75c. "Encyclia belizensis" 70 55
1805 $1 "Sophrolaeliocattleya" 85 75
1806 $2 "Encyclia fragrans" 1·40 1·75
1807 $4 "Schombocattleya" 2·50 3·00
1808 $5 "Brassolaeliocattleya" 2·50 3·00
MS1809 Two sheets, each 100 × 70 mm. (a) $6 "Ornithidium coccineum" (horiz). (b) $6 "Brassavola nodosa" (horiz). Set of 2 sheets 8·50 9·00

1994. World Cup Football Championship, U.S.A. (2nd issue). As T **393** of Grenada. Multicoloured.
1810 75c. Steve Mark (Grenada) 70 70
1811 75c. Jurgen Kohler (Germany) 70 70
1812 75c. Almir (Brazil) 70 70
1813 75c. Michael Windiscmann (U.S.A.) 70 70
1814 75c. Guiseppe Giannini (Italy) 70 70
1815 75c. Rashidi Yekini (Nigeria) 70 70
MS1816 Two sheets, each 90 × 70 mm. (a) $6 Kemari (ancient Japanese game). (b) Hand holding trophy. Set of 2 sheets 7·50 8·50

106 Mickey Mouse and Unjin Miruk Window from Kwanch Ok Temple

1994. "Philakorea '94" International Stamp Exhibition, Seoul (2nd issue). Walt Disney cartoon characters. Multicoloured.
1817 3c. Type **106** 30 40
1818 4c. Goofy imitating statue of Admiral Yi, Chonju 30 40
1819 5c. Cousin Gus and Donald Duck eating dinner 30 40
1820 10c. Mickey playing flute 45 35
1821 15c. Goofy with Tolharubang (statue) 60 20
1822 15c. Type **106** 60 20
1823 20c. Mickey and Minnie at Hyang-Wonjong 60 20
1824 35c. As 4c. 75 25
1825 50c. As 5c. 90 35
1826 75c. As 10c. 1·10 65
1827 $1 As 15c. 1·40 90
1828 $2 As 20c. 2·25 2·50
1829 $4 Mickey as Somori-Kut shaman 3·00 3·50
1830 $5 Minnie holding ceremonial fan 3·00 3·50
MS1831 Two sheets, each 130 × 103 mm. (a) $6 Minnie beating Buk drum (vert). (b) $6 Mickey in swimming pool at Pugok Hawaii (vert). Set of 2 sheets 8·00 9·00

1994. 1st Recipients of Order of the Caribbean Community. As Nos. 2750/2 of Grenada. Multicoloured.
1832 25c. Sir Shridath Ramphal 10 10
1833 50c. William Demas 25 30
1834 $2 Derek Walcott 2·50 2·50

1994. Fishes. As T **394** of Grenada. Multicoloured.
1835 75c. Porkfish 85 80
1836 75c. Blue chromis 85 80
1837 75c. Caribbean reef shark (facing left) 85 80
1838 75c. Long-spined squirrelfish 85 80
1839 75c. Four-eyed butterflyfish 85 80
1840 75c. Blue head 85 80
1841 75c. Royal gramma 85 80
1842 75c. Sharp-nosed puffer 85 80
1843 75c. Reid's seahorse 85 80
1844 75c. Black-barred soldierfish 85 80
1845 75c. Red-lipped blenny 85 80
1846 75c. Painted wrasse 85 80
1847 75c. Yellow-tailed snapper 85 80
1848 75c. Caribbean reef shark (facing right) 85 80
1849 75c. Great barracuda 85 80
1850 75c. Red-tailed parrotfish 85 80
1851 75c. Blue tang 85 80
1852 75c. Queen angelfish 85 80
1853 75c. Red hind 85 80
1854 75c. Rock beauty 85 80
1855 75c. Queen parrotfish 85 80
1856 75c. Spanish hogfish 85 80
1857 75c. Spotted moray 85 80
1858 75c. Queen triggerfish 85 80
MS1859 Two sheets, each 102 × 72 mm. (a) $6 Head of queen angelfish. (b) $6 Head of painted wrasse. Set of 2 sheets 8·00 9·00

Nos. 1835/46 and 1847/58 respectively were printed together, se-tenant, forming composite designs.

1994. Christmas. Religious Paintings by Bartolome Murillo. As T **231a** of Gambia. Multicoloured.
1860 15c. "The Annunciation" . . 30 20
1861 35c. "The Adoration of the Shepherds" 40 20
1862 50c. "Virgin and Child with St. Rose" 50 30
1863 50c. "Flight into Egypt" . . 50 30
1864 75c. "Virgin and Child" . . 70 45
1865 $1 "Virgin of the Rosary" 85 70
1866 $4 "The Holy Family" . . . 2·50 3·25
MS1867 Two sheets. (a) 85 × 95 mm. $6 "Adoration of the Shepherds" (different) (detail). (b) 95 × 125 mm. $6 "The Holy Family with a Little Bird" (detail). Set of 2 sheets . . . . 7·50 8·00

1995. Birds. As T **397** of Grenada. Multicoloured.
1868 25c. Scaly-breasted ground dove ("Ground Dove") (vert) 80 40
1869 50c. White-winged dove . . 1·25 60
1870 $2 Inca dove (vert) . . . . 2·25 2·25
1871 $4 Mourning dove . . . . 3·25 4·50

1995. Centenary of First English Cricket Tour to the West Indies. As T **397a** of Grenada. Multicoloured.
1872 50c. Mike Atherton (England) and Wisden Trophy 85 55
1873 75c. Curtly Ambrose (West Indies) (vert) . . . . . . 1·00 90
1874 $1 Brian Lara (West Indies) (vert) . . . . 1·25 1·25
MS1875 75 × 95 mm. $3 West Indian team, 1994 . . . . 2·75 2·75

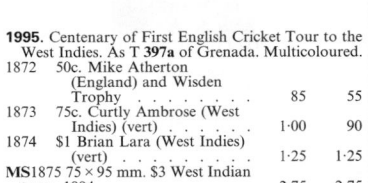

107 Aspects of London, National Flag and Map

108 Pig

1995. Capitals of the World. Aspects of various cities, national flags and maps. Multicoloured.
1876 $1 Type **107** 65 70
1877 $1 Cairo 65 70
1878 $1 Vienna 65 70
1879 $1 Paris 65 70
1880 S1 Rome 65 70
1881 $1 Budapest 65 70
1882 $1 Moscow 65 70
1883 $1 Peking ("Beijing") . . . 65 70
1884 $1 Tokyo 65 70
1885 $1 Washington 65 70

1995. Chinese New Year ("Year of the Pig"). Multicoloured designs showing "GRENADA GRENADINES" in colours indicated.
1886 75c. Type **108** (violet) . . . 50 60
1887 75c. Pig (carmine) 50 60
1888 75c. Pig (brown) 50 60
1889 75c. Pig (vermilion) 50 60
MS1890 Two sheets. (a) 106 × 77 mm. $2 Two pigs (horiz). (b) 67 × 83 mm. Nos. 1886/9. Set of 2 sheets . . . . 3·25 3·50

109 Bull Shark and Diver

1995. Marine Life of the Caribbean. Multicoloured.
1891 $1 Type **109** 75 75
1892 $1 Great white shark . . . 75 75
1893 $1 Octopus and shoal of fish 75 75
1894 $1 Great barracuda 75 75
1895 $1 Green moray 75 75
1896 $1 Spotted eagle ray 75 75
1897 $1 Sea snake 75 75
1898 $1 Stingray 75 75
1899 $1 Grouper 75 75
1900 $1 Dolphins 75 75
1901 $1 Lionfish 75 75
1902 $1 Sea turtle and rock beauty (fish) 75 75
1903 $1 Blue-cheeked butterflyfish and nurse shark 75 75
1904 $1 Queen angelfish 75 75
1905 $1 Grouper and coney . . . 75 75
1906 $1 Rainbow eel and spotted moray 75 75
1907 $1 Sun flower-star and coral crab 75 75
1908 $1 Octopus on sea bed . . . 75 75
MS1909 Two sheets each 107 × 77 mm. (a) $5 French angelfish. (b) $6 Smooth hammerhead. Set of 2 sheets 6·50 7·00

110 Suffolk Punch

1995. Domestic Animals. Multicoloured.
1910 15c. Type **110** 60 40
1911 25c. Shetland pony 60 40
1912 75c. Blue persian (cat) . . . 60 65
1913 75c. Sorrel abyssinian (cat) 60 65
1914 75c. White angora (cat) . . 60 65
1915 75c. Brown Burmese (cat) 60 65
1916 75c. Red tabby exotic shorthair (cat) 60 65
1917 75c. Seal-point birman (cat) 60 65
1918 75c. Korat (cat) 60 65
1919 75c. Norwegian forest cat 60 65
1920 75c. Lilac-point Balinese (cat) 60 65
1921 75c. British shorthair (cat) 60 65
1922 75c. Red self longhair (cat) 60 65
1923 75c. Calico Manx (cat) . . . 60 65
1924 75c. Shetland sheepdog . . 60 65
1925 75c. Bull terrier 60 65
1926 75c. Afghan hound 60 65
1927 75c. Scottish terrier 60 65
1928 75c. Labrador retriever . . 60 65
1929 75c. English springer spaniel 60 65
1930 75c. Samoyed (dog) 60 65
1931 75c. Irish setter 60 65
1932 75c. Border collie 60 65
1933 75c. Pekingese 60 65
1934 75c. Dachshund 60 65
1935 75c. Weimaraner (dog) . . . 60 65
1936 $1 Arab 85 85
1937 $3 Shire horse . . . . . . 1·75 2·00
MS1938 Two sheets, each 105 × 75 mm. (a) $6 Seal-point colourpoint (cat). (b) $6 English setter. Set of 2 sheets . . . . . 7·00 7·50

1995. Centenary (1992) of Sierra Club (environmental protection society). Endangered Species. As T **224a** of Gambia. Multicoloured.
1939 $1 Spotted owl ("Northern Spotted Owl") 80 80
1940 $1 Brown pelican on perch 80 80
1941 $1 Head of brown pelican 80 80
1942 $1 Head of jaguarundi . . . 80 80
1943 $1 Jaguarundi looking over shoulder 80 80
1944 $1 Maned wolf in undergrowth 80 80
1945 $1 American wood stork ("Wood Stork") standing on two legs 80 80
1946 $1 American wood stork standing on one leg . . . 80 80
1947 $1 Close-up of maned wolf 80 80
1948 $1 Brown pelican (horiz) . . 80 80
1949 $1 Close-up of spotted owl ("Northern Spotted Owl") (horiz) 80 80
1950 $1 Spotted owl ("Northern Spotted Owl") chick (horiz) 80 80
1951 $1 Jaguarundi (horiz) . . . 80 80
1952 $1 Central American spider monkey sitting with young (horiz) 80 80
1953 $1 Central American spider monkey carrying young (horiz) 80 80
1954 $1 Central American spider monkey swinging from branch (horiz) 80 80
1955 $1 American wood stork ("Wood Stork") (horiz) 80 80
1956 $1 Pair of maned wolfs (horiz) 80 80

1995. 18th World Scout Jamboree, Netherlands. As T **403** of Grenada. Multicoloured.
1957 75c. Grenadian scout on beach 60 70
1958 $1 Scout with staff on hill 80 90
1959 $2 Scout saluting and national flag . . . . . . 1·10 1·50
MS1960 107 × 77 mm. $6 Scout snorkelling . . . . 3·50 4·00

1995. 50th Anniv of End of Second World War in Europe. Bombers. As T **237a** of Gambia. Mult.
1961 $2 Avro Type **683** Lancaster 1·50 1·50
1962 $2 Junkers Ju 88 . . . . . 1·50 1·50
1963 $2 North American B-25 Mitchell . . . . 1·50 1·50
1964 $2 Boeing B-17 Flying Fortress . . . . 1·50 1·50
1965 $2 Petlyakov Pe-2 . . . . . 1·50 1·50
1966 $2 Martin B-26 Marauder 1·50 1·50
1967 $2 Heinkel He 111H . . . . 1·50 1·50
1968 $2 Consolidated B-24 Liberator . . . . 1·50 1·50
MS1969 105 × 75 mm. $6 Pres. Truman and newspaper headline (57 × 43 mm) . . . . 3·00 3·50

1995. 50th Anniv of United Nations. As T **404** of Grenada. Multicoloured.
1970 75c. U.N. Headquarters, New York, and flag . . . 60 90
1971 $1 Trygve Lie (first Secretary-General) . . . . 80 1·10
1972 $2 U.N. soldier . . . . . . 1·10 1·40
MS1973 101 × 76 mm. $6 Peace dove over emblem . . . . 2·50 3·00

Nos. 1970/2 were printed together, se-tenant, forming a composite design.

1995. 50th Anniv of F.A.O. As T **405** of Grenada. Multicoloured.
1974 75c. Man hoeing 60 90
1975 $1 Woman hoeing . . . . . 80 1·10
1976 $2 Man and woman hoeing 1·10 1·40
MS1977 106 × 76 mm. $6 Child eating with chopsticks . . . . 2·50 3·00
Nos. 1974/6 were printed together, se-tenant, forming a composite design.

1995. 90th Anniv of Rotary International. As T **406** of Grenada. Multicoloured.
1978 $5 Paul Harris (founder) and logo (horiz) . . . . . 2·50 3·00
MS1979 106 × 76 mm. $6 Rotary Club and International logos (horiz) . . . . 2·75 3·25

1995. 95th Birthday of Queen Elizabeth the Queen Mother. As T **239a** of Gambia.
1980 $1.50 brown, light brown and black . . . . 1·40 1·40
1981 $1.50 multicoloured . . . . 1·40 1·40
1982 $1.50 multicoloured . . . . 1·40 1·40
1983 $1.50 multicoloured . . . . 1·40 1·40
MS1984 102 × 127 mm. $6 multicoloured . . . . 6·00 5·50
DESIGNS: No. 1980, Queen Elizabeth the Queen Mother (pastel drawing); 1981, At Remembrance Day service; 1982, At desk (oil painting); 1983, Wearing green hat; **MS**1984, Unveiling memorial to Blitz victims.

1995. 50th Anniv of End of Second World War in the Pacific. As T **239b** of Gambia. Multicoloured.
1985 $2 Mitsubishi G4M1 "Betty" (bomber) . . . . 1·40 1·50
1986 $2 Japanese submarine "I 14" with seaplane on catapault . . . . 1·40 1·50
1987 $2 Mitsubishi GM31 "Nell" (bomber) . . . . 1·40 1·50
1988 $2 "Akizuki" (Japanese destroyer) . . . . 1·40 1·50
1989 $2 "Kirishima" (Japanese battleship) . . . . 1·40 1·50
1990 $2 "Asigari" (Japanese cruiser) . . . . 1·40 1·50
MS1991 108 × 76 mm. $6 Japanese Aichi D3A1 "Val" dive bomber 3·50 3·75

1995. Olympic Games, Atlanta (1996). As T **407** of Grenada. Multicoloured.
1992 15c. Rosemary Ackerman (East Germany) (high jump) (horiz) 50 60
1993 15c. Li Ning (China) (gymnastics) (horiz) . . . 50 60
1994 15c. Denise Parker (U.S.A.) (archery) (horiz) . . . 50 60
1995 $3 Terry Carlisle (U.S.A.) (skeet shooting) (horiz) . . 2·00 2·50
1996 $3 Kathleen Nord (East Germany) (swimming) (horiz) . . . . 2·00 2·50
1997 $3 Brigit Schmidt (East Germany) (canoeing) (horiz) . . . . 2·00 2·50
MS1998 Two sheets, each 102 × 72 mm. (a) $6 Dan Gable (U.S.A.) and Kikuo Wada (Japan) (wrestling). (b) $6 George Foreman (U.S.A.) (boxing). Set of 2 sheets . . . . 7·00 8·00

111 Brown Pelican

1995. Birds of the Caribbean. Multicoloured.
1999 10c. Type **111** 40 40
2000 15c. Black-necked stilt ("Common Stilt") 50 40
2001 25c. Cuban trogon ("Cuban Trogan") 55 30
2002 35c. Greater flamingo ("Flamingo") 60 30
2003 75c. Imperial amazon ("Parrot") 80 45
2004 $1 Pintail ("Pintail Duck") 90 1·00
2005 $1 Great blue heron . . . . 90 1·00
2006 $1 Jamaican tody . . . . . 90 1·00
2007 $1 Laughing gull . . . . . 90 1·00
2008 $1 Purple-throated carib . . 90 1·00
2009 $1 Red-legged thrush . . . 90 1·00
2010 $1 Ruddy duck . . . . . . 90 1·00
2011 $1 Common shoveler ("Shoveler Duck") . . . 90 1·00
2012 $1 Great red-bellied woodpecker ("West Indian Red-bellied Woodpecker") . . . . . 90 1·00
2013 $2 Ringed kingfisher . . . . 1·40 1·75
2014 $3 Strip-headed tanager . . 1·75 2·25
MS2015 Two sheets, each 104 × 73 mm. (a) $5 Village weaver. (b) $5 Blue-hooded euphonia. Set of 2 sheets . . . 7·00 7·50
No. 2001 is inscr "Cuban Trogan", No. 2008 "Purple-throated Carb" and No. 2013 "Ringed King Fisher", all in error.

No. **MS**2015, carry the "Singapore '95" exhibition logo.

1995. Mickey's Pirate Adventure. Walt Disney cartoon characters. As T **415** of Grenada. Multicoloured.
2016 10c. Goofy and Donald Duck with treasure chests (horiz) 35 25
2017 35c. Mickey and Minnie Mouse at ship's wheel (horiz) 55 25
2018 75c. Mickey, Donald and Goofy opening chest (horiz) 90 55
2019 $1 Big Pete and rats confronting Mickey (horiz) . . . . 1·00 75
2020 $2 Mickey, Goofy and Donald in boat (horiz) . . 1·75 2·00
2021 $5 Goofy fighting rat pirate with mop (horiz) . . . . 3·25 4·25
MS2022 Two sheets, each 108 × 130 mm. (a) $6 Goofy and cannon-balls. (b) $6 Monkey pinching Mickey's nose. P 13½ × 14. Set of 2 sheets . . . 7·50 8·00

1995. Centenary of Nobel Trust Fund. As T **416** of Gambia. Multicoloured.
2023/51 75c. × 2, $1 × 27 . . . . Set of 29 . . . . 16·00 18·00
MS2052 Three sheets, each 105 × 76 mm. (a) $6 Sir Winston Churchill (1953 Literature). (b) $6 Willy Brandt (1971 Peace). (c) $6 Albert Schweitzer (1952 Peace). Set of 3 sheets . . . . 15·00 14·00
DESIGNS: 75c. W. Arthur Lewis (1979 Economics); Derek Walcott (1992 Literature); $1 Jules Border (1919 Medicine); Rene Cassin (1968 Peace); Verner von Heidenstam (1916 Literature); Jose Echegaray (1904 Literature); Otto Wallach (1910 Chemistry); Corneille Heymans (1938 Medicine); Ivar Giaever (1973 Physics); Sir William Cremer (1903 Peace); John Strutt (1904 Physics); James Franck (1925 Physics); Tobias Asser (1911 Peace); Carl Spitteler (1919 Literature); Christiaan Eijkman (1929 Medicine); Ragnar Granit (1967 Medicine); Frederic Passy (1901 Peace); Louis Neel (1970 Physics); Sir William Ramsay (1904 Chemistry); Philip Noel-Baker (1959 Peace); Heike Onnes (1913 Physics); Fridtjof Nansen (1922 Peace); Sir Ronald Ross (1902 Medicine); Paul Muller (1948 Medicine); Allvar Gullstrand (1911 Medicine); Gerhart Hauptmann (1912 Literature); Hans Spemann (1935 Medicine); Cecil Powell (1950 Physics); Walther Bothe (1954 Physics).
Nos. 2025/33, 2034/42 and 2043/51 respectively were printed together, se-tenant, forming composite designs.
No. 2027 (Von Heidenstam) is inscribed "1906" and No. 2044 "Fridtjof Nanser", both in error.

112 Nita Naldi and Rudolph Valentino

114 Symbolic Rat and Candle

113 Man on Donkey

1995. Centenary of Cinema. Multicoloured.
2053 $1 Type **112** 75 75
2054 $1 Ramon Novaro and Alice Terry 75 75
2055 $1 Frederic March and Joan Crawford 75 75
2056 $1 Clark Gable and Vivien Leigh 75 75
2057 $1 Barbara Stanwyck and Burt Lancaster 75 75
2058 $1 Warren Beatty and Natalie Wood 75 75
2059 $1 Spencer Tracy and Katharine Hepburn . . . 75 75
2060 $1 Humphrey Bogart and Lauren Bacall 75 75
2061 $1 Omar Sharif and Julie Christie 75 75
2062 $1 Marion Davies 75 75
2063 $1 Marlene Dietrich 75 75
2064 $1 Lillian Gish 75 75
2065 $1 Bette Davis 75 75
2066 $1 Elizabeth Taylor 75 75
2067 $1 Veronica Lake 75 75
2068 $1 Ava Gardner 75 75
2069 $1 Grace Kelly 75 75
2070 $1 Kim Novak 75 75
MS2071 Two sheets. (a) 72 × 102 mm. $6 Sophia Loren. (b) 102 × 72 mm. $6 Greta Garbo and John Gilbert (horiz). Set of 2 sheets . . . . 7·00 8·00

Nos. 2053/61 and 2062/70 respectively were printed together, se-tenant, forming composite designs.

1995. Racing Cars. As T **423** of Grenada. Multicoloured.

2072 10c. Williams-Renault Formula 1, 1990s 30 20
2073 25c. Porsche "956", Le Mans, 1980s 45 20
2074 35c. Lotus "John Player Special", 1970s 50 20
2075 75c. Ford "GT-40", 1960s 75 45
2076 $2 Mercedes-Benz "W196", 1950s . . . . 1·50 2·00
2077 $3 Mercedes "SSK", 1920s 2·00 2·50
MS2078 103 × 73 mm. $6 Jackie Stewart in Tyrell-Ford, 1971 (vert) 3·75 4·00

1995. Local Transport. Multicoloured.

2079 35c. Type **113** 30 20
2080 75c. Local bus 70 60

1995. Evolution of Sailing Ships. As T **427** of Grenada. Multicoloured.

2081 $1 "Preussen" (full-rigged ship) . . . . 90 1·00
2082 $1 Japanese junk . . . . . 90 1·00
2083 $1 Caribbean pirate ship . . 90 1·00
2084 $1 "Mayflower" (Pilgrim Fathers) . . . . 90 1·00
2085 $1 Chinese junk . . . . . . 90 1·00
2086 $1 "Santa Maria" (Columbus) . . . . 90 1·00
MS2087 103 × 73 mm. $5 Spanish galleon (56 × 41 mm) . . . . . 3·25 3·50

1995. Christmas. Religious Paintings. As T **245a** of Gambia. Multicoloured.

2088 10c. "Immaculate Conception" (Piero di Cosimo) 30 20
2089 15c. "St. Michael dedicating Arms to the Madonna" (Le Nain) 35 20
2090 35c. "Annunciation" (Lorenzo di Credi) . . . 55 20
2091 50c. "The Holy Family" (Jacob Jordaens) 70 30
2092 $3 "Madonna and Child" (Lippi) . . . . 2·25 3·00
2093 $5 "Madonna and Child with Ten Saints" (Fiorentino) . . . . . . 3·25 4·00
MS2094 102 × 127 mm. (a) $6 "Adoration of the Shepherds" (detail) (Van Oost). (b) $6 "Holy Family" (detail) (Del Start). Set of 2 sheets . . . . 7·50 8·00

1996. Chinese New Year ("Year of the Rat"). Multicoloured, background colours given.

2095 **114** 75c. blue 55 60
2096 75c. lilac 55 60
2097 75c. brown 55 60
2098 75c. green 55 60
MS2099 69 × 84 mm. Nos. 2095/8 1·60 1·75
MS2100 76 × 106 mm. $2 Two rats (horiz) . . . . 1·40 1·50

The four designs show different Chinese characters.

1996. Works of Art by Durer and Rubens. As T **421** of Grenada. Multicoloured.

2101 15c. "The Centaur Family" (Durer) 30 20
2102 35c. "Oriental Ruler Seated" (Durer) 40 20
2103 50c. "The Entombment" (Durer) 55 30
2104 75c. "Man in Armour" (Rubens) 70 50
2105 $1 "Peace embracing Plenty" (Rubens) 85 75
2106 $2 "Departure of Lot" (Rubens) . . . . 1·50 1·75
2107 $3 "The Four Evangelists" (Rubens) . . . . 1·75 2·25
2108 $5 "Knight, Death and Devil" (Durer) . . . . . 3·00 3·75
MS2109 Two sheets, each 101 × 127 mm. (a) $5 "The Fathers of the Church" (detail) (Rubens). (b) $6 "St. Jerome" (detail) (Durer). Set of 2 sheets . . . . 6·50 7·50

115 Mickey and Minnie at New Year's Day "Hopping John" Tradition

1996. Traditional Holidays. Walt Disney cartoon characters. Multicoloured.

2110 25c. Type **115** 40 15
2111 50c. Disney characters dancing around maypole 60 30
2112 75c. Mickey, Minnie and Pluto watching Independence Day fireworks 85 40
2113 90c. Gyro Gearloose and Donald's nephews in Halloween costumes . . . 90 55
2114 $3 Donald Duck as Puritan and nephews as Indians on Thanksgiving Day . . 2·50 3·00
2115 $4 Huey and Dewey with Hanukkah dreidle . . . . 2·50 3·25
MS2116 Two sheets, each 124 × 98 mm. (a) $6 Mickey, Minnie and Donald taking part in Caribbean carnival. (b) $6 Traditional pot of gold in St. Patrick's Day parade (vert). Set of 2 sheets . . . . 8·50 9·00

116 Gateway in Imperial Palace, Peking (½-size illustration)

1996. "CHINA '96" 9th Asian International Stamp Exhibition, Peking. Multicoloured.

2117 $1 Type 116 . . . . 65 70
2118 $1 Eastern end of Great Wall at Shanhaiguan . . 65 70
2119 $1 Great Wall fortress, Shanhaiguan 65 70
2120 $1 Gate of Heavenly Peace, Peking 65 70
2121 $1 Sun Yat-sen's Mausoleum, Nanjing . . 65 70
2122 $1 Summer Palace, Peking 65 70
2123 $1 Temple of Heaven, Peking 65 70
2124 $1 Hall of Supreme Harmony, Forbidden City, Peking 65 70
MS2125 Three sheets. (a) 150 × 100 mm. $2 Traditional Chinese painting (39 × 50 mm). (b) 90 × 68 mm. $6 Great Wall of China from the air (39 × 50 mm). (c) 90 × 68 mm. $6 Marble Boat, Summer Palace, Peking (50 × 39 mm). Set of 3 sheets 7·00 7·50

1996. 70th Birthday of Queen Elizabeth II. As T **255a** of Gambia. Multicoloured.

2126 35c. As Type **255a** of Gambia 40 25
2127 $2 Queen wearing tiara and green dress . . . . 1·25 1·40
2128 $4 Windsor Castle . . . . . 2·50 2·75
MS2129 103 × 125 mm. $6 Queen Elizabeth at Windsor . . . . . 3·75 4·00

1996. Flowers. As T **430** of Grenada. Multicoloured.

2130 35c. "Camellia" "Apple Blossom" 40 25
2131 75c. "Odontoglossum" . . . 60 60
2132 75c. "Cattleya" 60 60
2133 75c. "Paphiopedilum" "Venus's Slipper" 60 60
2134 75c. "Laeliocattleya" "Marysville" 60 60
2135 75c. Fuchsia "Citation" . . . 60 60
2136 75c. Fuchsia "Amy Lye" . . 60 60
2137 75c. "Clysonimus" (butterfly) and temple . . 60 60
2138 75c. Foxglove ("Digitalis purpurea") 60 60
2139 75c. Martagon lily ("Lilium martagon") 60 60
2140 75c. "Tulipa" "Couleur Cardinal" 60 60
2141 75c. Snowdrop ("Galanthus nivalis") 60 60
2142 75c. "Rosa" "Superstar" . . 60 60
2143 75c. Crocus "Dutch Yellow Mammoth" 60 60
2144 75c. Japanese lily ("Lilium speciosum") 60 60
2145 75c. "Lilium" "Joan Evans" 60 60
2146 75c. "Rosa" "Rosemary Harkness" 60 60
2147 90c. "Camellia japonica" "Extravaganza" 65 65
2148 $1 Chrysanthemum "Primrose Dorothy Else" 75 75
2149 $2 Dahlia "Brandaris" . . . 1·25 1·40
MS2150 Two sheets, each 68 × 98 mm. (a) $5 Narcissus "Rembrandt". (b) $6 Gladiolus "Flowersong". Set of 2 sheets 6·50 7·50

Nos. 2135/46 were printed together, se-tenant, with the backgrounds forming a composite design.

No. 2135 is inscribed "Fuschcia", No. 2133 "Mammouth" and **MS**2150b "Gladiollus", all in error.

1996. 50th Anniv of UNICEF. As T **258a** of Gambia. Multicoloured.

2151 75c. Child's face (horiz) . . 55 45
2152 $2 Child with spoon (horiz) 1·10 1·40
2153 $3 Girl sewing (horiz) . . . 1·60 1·90
MS2154 105 × 75 mm. $6 Mother carrying child . . . . 3·00 3·50

1996. 3000th Anniv of Jerusalem. Multicoloured designs as T **424** of Grenada, but horiz.

MS2155 137 × 47 mm. $1 Pool of Bethesda and "Papaver rhoeas"; $2 Damascus Gate and "Chrysanthemum coronarium"; $3 Church of All Nations and "Myrtus communis". . . . . . 4·00 3·75
MS2156 82 × 62 mm. $6 Church of the Holy Sepulchre . . . . . 4·00 3·75

1996. Centenary of Radio. Entertainers. As T **259a** of Gambia. Multicoloured.

2157 35c. Ed Wynn 35 25
2158 75c. Red Skelton 55 45
2159 $1 Joe Penner 65 55
2160 $3 Jerry Colonna . . . . . 1·75 2·00
MS2161 70 × 99 mm. $6 Bob Elliot and Ray Goulding (horiz) . . 3·25 3·75

1996. Olympic Games, Atlanta. Previous Medal Winners. As T **425** of Grenada. Multicoloured.

2162 35c. Los Angeles Memorial Coliseum 35 25
2163 75c. Connie Carpenter-Phinney (U.S.A.) (Cycling) 75 55
2164 $1 Josef Neckermann (Germany) (vert) 70 70
2165 $1 Harry Boldt (Germany) (vert) 70 70
2166 $1 Elena Petouchkova (Russia) (vert) 70 70
2167 $1 Alwin Schockemoehle (Germany) (vert) 70 70
2168 $1 Hans Winkler (Germany) (vert) 70 70
2169 $1 Joe Fargis (U.S.A.) (vert) 70 70
2170 $1 David Broome (Great Britain) (vert) 70 70
2171 $1 Reiner Klimke (Germany) (vert) 70 70
2172 $1 Richard Meade (Great Britain) (vert) 70 70
2173 $1 Julianne McNamara (U.S.A.) (vert) 70 70
2174 $1 Takuti Hayata (Japan) (vert) 70 70
2175 $1 Nikolai Adriana (Russia) (vert) 70 70
2176 $1 Mitch Gaylord (U.S.A.) (vert) 70 70
2177 $1 Ludmilla Tourischeva (Russia) (vert) 70 70
2178 $1 Karin Janz (Germany) (vert) 70 70
2179 $1 Peter Kormann (U.S.A.) (vert) 70 70
2180 $1 Sawoo Kato (Japan) (vert) 70 70
2181 $1 Nadia Comaneci (Rumania) (vert) 70 70
2182 $2 Mohamed Bouchighe (Algeria) (Boxing) (vert) 1·25 1·40
2183 $3 Jackie Joyner Kersee (U.S.A.) (Javelin) . . . . 1·75 1·90
MS2184 Two sheets, each 103 × 74 mm. (a) $5 Child waving flag (vert). (b) $6 William Steinkraus (U.S.A.) (Show jumping). Set of 2 sheets . . . 6·50 7·00

Nos. 2164/72 (equestrians) and 2173/81 (gymnasts) respectively were printed together, se-tenant, with the backgrounds forming composite designs.

1996. Classic Cars. As T **426** of Grenada. Multicoloured.

2185 35c. Chevrolet Belair convertible 40 25
2186 50c. V.I.P. car 55 30
2187 75c. Rolls-Royce Torpedo 65 45
2188 $1 Nissan "Cepric" type . . 70 70
2189 $1 Delaunay-Belleville HB6 70 70
2190 $1 Bugatti Type-15 . . . . 70 70
2191 $1 Mazda Type 800 . . . . 70 70
2192 $1 Mercedes 24/100/140 Sport 70 70
2193 $1 MG K3 Rover 70 70
2194 $1 Plymouth Fury 70 70
2195 $2 Mercedes-Benz 500K . . 1·25 1·40
2196 $3 Bugatti Type-13 . . . . 1·75 1·90
MS2197 Two sheets, each 106 × 76 mm. (a) $5 Bugatti "Roadster" Type-55. (b) $6 Lincoln Type-L. Set of 2 sheets 6·50 7·00

1996. Ships. As T **427** of Grenada. Multicoloured.

2198 35c. Grenada schooner . . . 50 25
2199 75c. Grenada schooner (different) 75 45
2200 $1 Athenian triremes, 1000 B.C. 80 80
2201 $1 Egyptian Nile galley, 30 B.C. 80 80
2202 $1 Bangladesh dinghi, 310 B.C. 80 80
2203 $1 Warship of Queen Hatshepsut, 476 B.C. . . 80 80
2204 $1 Chinese Junk, 200 B.C. 80 80
2205 $1 Polynesian ocean-going canoe, 600 B.C 80 80
2206 $1 "Europa" (liner), 1957 80 80
2207 $1 "Lusitania" (liner), 1906 80 80
2208 $1 "Queen Mary" (liner), 1936 . . . . 80 80
2209 $1 "Bianca C" (liner) . . . 80 80
2210 $1 "France" (liner), 1952 . . 80 80
2211 $1 "Orion" (liner), 1915 . . 80 80
MS2212 Two sheets, each 104 × 74 mm. (a) $5 "Queen Elizabeth 2" (liner), 1969 (56 × 42 mm). (b) $6 Viking longship, 610 (42 × 56 mm). Set of 2 sheets . . . . 6·50 7·00

117 Felix Mendelssohn

1996. Composers. Multicoloured.

2213 $1 Type **117** 80 70
2214 $1 Franz Schubert 80 70
2215 $1 Franz Joseph Haydn . . 80 70
2216 $1 Robert Schumann . . . 80 70
2217 $1 Ludwig van Beethoven 80 70
2218 $1 Gioacchino Rossini . . . 80 70
2219 $1 George Frederick Handel 80 70
2220 $1 Pyotr Tchaikovsky . . . 80 70
2221 $1 Frederic Chopin 80 70
2222 $1 Bela Bartok 80 70
2223 $1 Giacomo Puccini 80 70
2224 $1 George Gershwin 80 70
2225 $1 Leonard Bernstein . . . 80 70
2226 $1 Kurt Weill 80 70
2227 $1 John Cage 80 70
2228 $1 Aaron Copland 80 70
2229 $1 Sergei Prokofiev 80 70
2230 $1 Igor Stravinsky 80 70
MS2231 Two sheets, each 74 × 104 mm. (a) $5 Richard Strauss. (b) $6 Wolfgang Amadeus Mozart. Set of 2 sheets . . . . 8·50 7·50

Nos. 2213/21 and 2222/30 respectively were printed together, se-tenant, with the backgrounds forming composite designs.

1996. Railway Steam Locomotives. As T **429** of Grenada. Multicoloured.

2232 $1.50 Class 38 No. 382, Germany . . . . 1·10 1·10
2233 $1.50 "Duchess of Hamilton", Great Britain 1·10 1·10
2234 $1.50 Class W.P., India . . 1·10 1·10
2235 $1.50 Class 141R "Americaine", France . . 1·10 1·10
2236 $1.50 Class A4 "Mallard", Great Britain . . . . . 1·10 1·10
2237 $1.50 Class 18 No. 201, Germany . . . . 1·10 1·10
2238 $1.50 Class A2 "Blue Peter", Great Britain . . 1·10 1·10
2239 $1.50 Class P36, Russia . . 1·10 1·10
2240 $1.50 Class QJ, China . . . 1·10 1·10
2241 $1.50 Class 12, Belgium . . 1·10 1·10
2242 $1.50 Class "Challenger", U.S.A. . . . . 1·10 1·10
2243 $1.50 Class 25, South Africa 1·10 1·10
MS2244 Two sheets, each 100 × 70 mm. (a) $5 Class "King", Great Britain. (b) $6 Class "Royal Scot", Great Britain. Set of 2 sheets . . . . 7·00 7·50

1996. Christmas. Religious Paintings. As T **245a** of Gambia. Showing different details from "Suffer Little Children to Come Unto Me" by Van Dyck.

2245 15c. multicoloured 40 20
2246 25c. multicoloured 40 20
2247 $1 multicoloured . . . . . 1·00 65
2248 $1.50 multicoloured . . . . 1·25 1·25
2249 $2 multicoloured . . . . . 1·60 1·60
2250 $4 multicoloured . . . . . 2·50 3·25
MS2251 Two sheets, each 106 × 76 mm. (a) $6 "Suffer Little Children to Come Unto Me" (detail) (Van Dyck) (horiz). (b) $6 "Adoration of the Magi" (Rembrandt) (horiz). Set of 2 sheets . . . . 7·50 8·50

118 Man Ho Temple, 1841

1997. "HONG KONG '97" International Stamp Exhibition. Hong Kong Past and Present. T **118** and similar horiz designs. Multicoloured. P 14.

MS2252 Five sheets, each 120 × 96 mm. (a) $3 Type **118**; $3 Man Ho Temple, 1983. (b) $3 St. John's Cathedral, Victoria 1886; $3 St. John's Cathedral, Victoria 1983. (c) $3 Victoria Harbour, 1858; $3 Victoria Harbour, 1983. (d) $3 Waterfront skyscraper; $3 Aerial view of central Victoria. (e) $3 Signing of Treaty of Nanking, 1852. $3 Margaret Thatcher signing The Joint Declaration, 1984. Set of 5 sheets . . . . 22·00 20·00

1997. 50th Anniv of UNESCO. As T **273a** of Gambia. Multicoloured.

2253 15c. Temple, Kyoto, Japan 40 20
2254 25c. Roman ruins, Trier, Germany 40 20
2255 $1 Gateway, Mount Taishan, China 80 80
2256 $1 Temple guardian, Kyoto, Japan (vert) 80 80
2257 $1 Temple deity, Kyoto, Japan (vert) 80 80
2258 $1 Temple lamp, Kyoto, Japan (vert) 80 80
2259 $1 Ayutthaya, Thailand (vert) 80 80
2260 $1 Statue, Borobudur Temple, Indonesia (vert) 80 80
2261 $1 Monuments at Pattadakal, India (vert) 80 80
2262 $1 Sleeping buddha, Polonnaruwa, Sri Lanka (vert) 80 80
2263 $1 Sagarmatha National Park, Nepal (vert) 80 80
2264 $1 Congonhas Sanctuary, Brazil (vert) 80 80
2265 $1 Cartagena, Colombia (vert) 80 80
2266 $1 Pueblo, Guatemala (vert) 80 80
2267 $1 Maya statue, Honduras (vert) 80 80
2268 $1 Popocatepetl Monastery, Mexico (vert) 80 80
2269 $1 Galapagos Islands, Ecuador (vert) 80 80
2270 $1 Waterfall, Costa Rica (vert) 80 80
2271 $1 Glaciares National Park, Argentina (vert) 80 80
2272 $1.50 Notre Dame Cathedral, Paris, France 1·10 1·10
2273 $1.50 Timbered house, Maulbronn, Germany . . 1·10 1·10
2274 $1.50 Gateway, Himeji-jo, Japan . . . . 1·10 1·10
2275 $1.50 Lion statues, Delphi, Greece . . . . 1·10 1·10
2276 $1.50 Palace of Fontainebleau, France . . 1·10 1·10
2277 $1.50 Scandola Nature Reserve, France . . . . . 1·10 1·10
2278 $2 Citadel, Dubrovnik, Croatia . . . . 1·50 1·60
2279 $4 Angra do Heroismo, Portugal . . . . 2·50 3·00

MS2280 Three sheets, each 127 × 102 mm. (a) $6 Mont St. Michel, France. (b) $6 Ruins of Teotihuacau, Mexico. (c) $6 Temple, Chengde, China. Set of 3 sheets . . . . 10·00 11·00

119 Springer Spaniel

1997. Cats and Dogs. Multicoloured.

2281 35c. Type **119** 50 25
2282 45c. Abyssinian blue 50 30
2283 50c. Burmese cream (vert) 50 30
2284 75c. Doberman pinscher . . 75 50
2285 90c. Persian tortoiseshell and white 75 50
2286 $1 Italian spinone (vert) . . 85 55
2287 $1.50 Siamese chocolate point . . . . 1·10 1·10
2288 $1.50 Oriental shorthair white . . . . 1·10 1·10
2289 $1.50 Burmese sable . . . . 1·10 1·10
2290 $1.50 Abyssinian tabby . . 1·10 1·10
2291 $1.50 Persian shaded silver 1·10 1·10
2292 $1.50 Tonkinese natural mink . . . . 1·10 1·10
2293 $1.50 Leonberger . . . . . . 1·10 1·10
2294 $1.50 Newfoundland . . . . 1·10 1·10
2295 $1.50 Boxer . . . . 1·10 1·10
2296 $1.50 St. Bernard . . . . . 1·10 1·10
2297 $1.50 Silky terrier . . . . . 1·10 1·10
2298 $1.50 Miniature schnauzer 1·10 1·10
2299 $2 Cocker spaniel (vert) . . 1·50 1·60
2300 $3 Oriental shorthair agouti (vert) . . . . 2·00 2·25

MS2301 Two sheets. (a) 75 × 105 mm. $6 Sphynx (vert). (b) 105 × 75 mm. $6 Golden retriever puppy. Set of 2 sheets . . . 7·50 8·00

Nos. 2287/92 (cats) and Nos. 2293/8 (dogs) respectively were printed together, se-tenant, with the backgrounds forming composite designs.

1997. Dinosaurs. As T **438** of Grenada. Mult.

2302 45c. Stegosaurus 60 30
2303 90c. Diplodocus 80 50
2304 $1 Pteranodon (vert) 80 55
2305 $1.50 Rhamphorhynchus and head of Brachiosaurus . . . . . 1·10 1·10
2306 $1.50 Archaeopteryx . . . . 1·10 1·10
2307 $1.50 Anurognathus and body of Brachiosaurus . . 1·10 1·10
2308 $1.50 Head of Albertosaurus 1·10 1·10
2309 $1.50 Herrerasaurus and legs of Brachiosaurus . . 1·10 1·10
2310 $1.50 Platyhystrix and body of Albertosaurus . . . . 1·10 1·10
2311 $2 Deinonychus and Ankylasaurus (vert) . . . 1·50 1·60

MS2312 Two sheets, each 103 × 74 mm. (a) $6 Allosaurus (vert). (b) $6 Hydacrosaurus. Set of 2 sheets . . . . 8·00 8·50

Nos. 2305/10 were printed together, se-tenant, with the backgrounds forming a composite design.

1997. 300th Anniv of Mother Goose Nursery Rhymes. Sheet 72 × 102 mm containing vert design as T **276a** of Gambia. Multicoloured.

MS2313 $6 Girl and sheep ("Baa, Baa, Black Sheep") . . . . . 3·50 4·00

1997. 50th Death Anniv of Paul Harris (founder of Rotary International). As T **276b** of Gambia. Multicoloured.

2314 $3 Paul Harris and village women with water pump, Burkina Faso . . . . . . 1·50 2·00

MS2315 78 × 108 mm. $6 Early Rotary parade float . . . . . 3·00 3·50

1997. Golden Wedding of Queen Elizabeth and Prince Philip. As T **276c** of Gambia. Multicoloured (except Nos. 2318/19).

2316 $1 Engagement photograph, 1947 . . . . 80 80
2317 $1 Royal coat of arms . . . 80 80
2318 $1 Queen Elizabeth and Duke of Edinburgh, 1953 (brown) 80 80
2319 $1 Formal portrait of Queen Elizabeth with Prince Philip in uniform (brown) 80 80
2320 $1 Sandringham House . . 80 80
2321 $1 Queen Elizabeth and Prince Philip in carriage 80 80

MS2322 100 × 70 mm. $6 Wedding photograph, 1947 . . . . . . 3·50 3·75

1997. "Pacific '97" International Stamp Exhibition, San Francisco. Death Centenary of Heinrich von Stephan (founder of the U.P.U.). As T **276d** of Gambia.

2323 $1.50 green . . . . 1·10 1·10
2324 $1.50 brown . . . . 1·10 1·10
2325 $1.50 violet . . . . 1·10 1·10

MS2326 82 × 118 mm. $6 blue and black . . . . 3·25 3·75

DESIGNS: No. 2323, Pony Express, 1860; 2324, Von Stephan and Mercury; 2325, American steam locomotive; MS2326 Von Stephan and camel courier, Baghdad.

1997. Birth Bicentenary of Hiroshige (Japanese painter). "100 Famous Views of Edo". As T **541a** of Ghana but horiz. Multicoloured.

2327 $1.50 "Koume Embankment" . . . . . 1·00 1·00
2328 $1.50 "Azuma Shrine and the Entwined Camphor" 1·00 1·00
2329 $1.50 "Yanagishima" . . . 1·00 1·00
2330 $1.50 "Inside Akiba Shrine, Ukeji" . . . . 1·00 1·00
2331 $1.50 "Distant View of Kinryuzan Temple and Azuma Bridge" . . . . . 1·00 1·00
2332 $1.50 "Night View of Matsuchiyama and the San'ya Canal" . . . . . 1·00 1·00

MS2333 Two sheets, each 102 × 127 mm. (a) $6 "Five Pines, Onagi Canal". (b) $6 "Spiral Hall, Five Hundred Rakan Temple". Set of 2 sheets . . . . 7·00 7·50

1997. 175th Anniv of Brothers Grimm's Third Collection of Fairy Tales. "The Fox and the Geese". As T **277a** of Gambia. Multicoloured.

2334 $2 Fox and geese . . . . . 1·60 1·60
2335 $2 Fox with knife and fork and geese . . . . 1·60 1·60
2336 $2 Fox asleep and singing geese . . . . 1·60 1·60

MS2337 124 × 96 mm. $6 Fox (horiz) 3·75 4·00

1997. Winter Olympic Games, Nagano, Japan. As T**440** of Grenada. Multicoloured.

2338 90c. Slalom 65 50
2339 $1 Downhill skiing 70 70
2340 $1 Freestyle ski-jumping (blue and green ski suit) 70 70
2341 $1 Curling 70 70
2342 $1 Ski-jumping (pink ski suit) 70 70
2343 $1 Four-man bobsleigh . . 70 70
2344 $1 Nordic combined 70 70
2345 $1 Speed skating 70 70
2346 $1 Ice hockey 70 70
2347 $1 Cross-country skiing . . 70 70
2348 $2 One-man luge . . . . . 1·25 1·40
2349 $3 Men's figure-skating . . 1·75 1·90
2350 $5 Speed skating (different) 2·75 3·00

MS2351 Two sheets, each 97 × 67 mm. (a) $6 Figure skating. (b) $6 One-man luge (vert). Set of 2 sheets . . . . 7·00 7·50

120 Hong Kong

1997. Return of Hong Kong to China. Multicoloured.

2352 **120** $1 multicoloured 70 60
2353 – $1.25 multicoloured . . 80 80
2354 – $1.50 mult (63 × 32 mm) 95 1·00
2355 – $2 mult (63 × 32 mm) . . 1·25 1·40

DESIGNS: $1.25 to $2 Modern Hong Kong shown through inscriptions.

1997. Marine Life. As T **439** of Grenada. Mult.

2356 10c. Wimplefish 10 10
2357 15c. Clown triggerfish . . . 10 10
2358 25c. Ringed emperor angelfish 10 15
2359 35c. Hooded butterflyfish . . 15 20
2360 45c. Semicircle angelfish . . 20 25
2361 75c. Scribbled angelfish . . 30 35
2362 90c. Threadfin butterflyfish 35 40
2363 $1 Clown surgeonfish . . . 40 45
2364 $2 Bottle-nosed dolphin . . 80 85
2365 $5 Triggerfish . . . . 2·00 2·10
2366 $10 Lionfish . . . . 4·00 4·25
2367 $20 Jackknifefish . . . . . 8·00 8·25

121 Winnie the Pooh as Monday's Child

1997. "Monday's Child" (poem). Disney cartoon characters from Winnie the Pooh illustrating various verses. Multicoloured.

2368 $1 Type **121** . . . . 1·25 1·25
2369 $1 Kanga as Tuesday's child 1·25 1·25
2370 $1 Eeyore as Wednesday's child . . . . 1·25 1·25
2371 $1 Tigger as Thursday's child . . . . 1·25 1·25
2372 $1 Piglet as Friday's child 1·25 1·25
2373 $1 Rabbit as Saturday's child . . . . 1·25 1·25

MS2374 128 × 107 mm. $6 Christopher Robin as Sunday's child . . . . 5·50 5·50

122 Snow White kissing Grumpy

1997. Disney Sweethearts. Disney cartoon characters kissing. Multicoloured.

2375 $1 Type **122** . . . . 1·10 1·10
2376 $1 Figaro the Cat and Cleo the Fish . . . . 1·10 1·10
2377 $1 Peter Pan and Wendy . . 1·10 1·10
2378 $1 Cinderella and the Prince 1·10 1·10
2379 $1 Ariel and Eric . . . . . . 1·10 1·10
2380 $1 Beauty and the Prince . . 1·10 1·10
2381 $1 Aladdin and Jasmine . . 1·10 1·10
2382 $1 Pocahontas and Captain John Smith . . . . 1·10 1·10
2383 $1 Phoebus and Esmeralda 1·10 1·10

MS2384 127 × 102 mm. $6 Georges Hautecourt kissing cats tail (vert) 5·50 5·50

1997. World Cup Football Championship, France (1998). As T **283a** of Gambia.

2385 10c. blue 25 25
2386 20c. multicoloured 30 30
2387 45c. brown 40 30
2388 $1 black 70 70
2389 $1 brown 70 70
2390 $1 black 70 70
2391 $1 brown 70 70
2392 $1 multicoloured 70 70
2393 $1 multicoloured 70 70
2394 $1 black 70 70
2395 $1 brown 70 70
2396 $1 multicoloured 70 70
2397 $1 black 70 70
2398 $1 black 70 70
2399 $1 black 70 70
2400 $1 black 70 70
2401 $1 black 70 70
2402 $1 black 70 70
2403 $1 black 70 70
2404 $1 black 70 70
2405 $1.50 multicoloured . . . . 95 1·00
2406 $5 black . . . . 2·75 3·00

MS2407 Two sheets. (a) 127 × 102 mm. $6 black. (b) 102 × 127 mm. $6 black. Set of 2 sheets . . . . 8·50 9·00

DESIGNS—HORIZ: No. 2385, Italian team, 1934; 2386, Angolan team; 2387, Brazilian team, 1958; 2388, Uruguay team, 1950; 2389, Winning England team, 1966; 2390, West German team, 1954; 2391, Uruguyan officials with Jules Rimet trophy, 1930; 2392, West German players celebrating, 1990; 2393, Maradona (Argentine player), 1986; 2394, Brazilian players, 1994; 2395, Argentine players, 1978; 2396, West German player holding World Cup, 1974; 2405, West German team, 1974; 2406, Italian team, 1938; MS2407b, Paulao, Angola. VERT: No. 2397, Ademir, Brazil; 2398, Kocsis, Hungary; 2399, Leonidas, Brazil; 2400, Nejedly, Czechoslavakia; 2401, Schiavio, Italy; 2402, Stabile, Uruguay; 2403, Pele, Brazil; 2404, Fritzwalter, West Germany; MS2407a, Shearer, England.

1997. Butterflies. As T **444** of Grenada. Mult.

2408 75c. "Polyura dehaani" . . 65 45
2409 90c. "Polyura dolon" . . . 70 50
2410 $1 "Charaxes candiope" . . 70 55
2411 $1.50 "Pantaporia punctata" 95 95
2412 $1.50 "Euthalia confucius" 95 95
2413 $1.50 "Euthalia kardama" 95 95
2414 $1.50 "Limenitis albomaculata" 95 95
2415 $1.50 "Hestina assimilis" . . 95 95
2416 $1.50 "Kallima inachus" . . 95 95
2417 $1.50 "Euthalia teutoides" 95 95
2418 $1.50 "Euphaedra francina" 95 95
2419 $1.50 "Euphaedra eleus" . . 95 95
2420 $1.50 "Euphaedra harpalyce" 95 95
2421 $1.50 "Euphaedra cyparissa" 95 95
2422 $1.50 "Euphaedra gausape" 95 95
2423 $1.50 "Euphaedra imperialis" 95 95
2424 $2 "Charaxes etesippe" . . 1·25 1·40
2425 $3 "Charaxes castor" . . . 1·75 1·90

MS2426 Two sheets, each 106 × 76 mm. (a) $5 "Charaxes nobilis" (vert). (b) $6 "Charaxes numenes" (vert). Set of 2 sheets 6·50 7·00

Nos. 2412/17 and 2418/23 respectively were printed together, se-tenant, with the backgrounds forming composite designs.

123 James Dean

1997. James Dean (actor) Commemoration. Different portaits. Multicoloured.

2427 $1 Type **123** 70 70
2428 $1 Wearing purple jumper 70 70
2429 $1 Wearing stetson and smoking 70 70
2430 $1 Wearing dinner jacket and tie 70 70
2431 $1 Full-face portrait 70 70
2432 $1 Grimacing 70 70
2433 $1 Wearing stetson 70 70
2434 $1 Leaning on arms 70 70
2435 $1 Smoking 70 70

124 "Symphyglossum sanguineum"

1997. Orchids of the World. Multicoloured.

2436 35c. Type **124** 40 25
2437 45c. "Doritaenopsis" "Mythic Beauty" . . . 50 30
2438 75c. "Odontoglossum cervantesii" 65 45
2439 90c. "Cattleya" "Pumpernickel" . . . 70 50
2440 $1 "Vanda" "Patricia Low" 70 55

2441/9	$1 × 9 (“Lycaste” “Aquila”; “Brassolaeliocattleya” “Dorothy Bertsch”; “Phalaenopsis” “Zuma Urchin”; “Promenaea xanthina”; “Amesiella philippinensis”; “Brassocattleya” “Angel Lace”; “Brassoepidendrum” “Peggy Ann”; “Miltonia seine”; “Sophralaeliocattleya” “Precious Stones”)	5·50	
2450/8	$1 × 9 (“Cymbidium” “Showgirl”; “Disa blackii”; “Phalaenopsis aphrodite”; “Iwanagaara” “Apple Blossom”; “Masdevallia” “Copper Angel”; “Paphiopedilum micranthum”; “Paphiopedilum” “Clare de Lune”; “Cattleya forbesii”; “Dendrobium” “Dawn Maree”)	5·50	
2459	$1.50 “Odontonia” “Debutante”	1·00	1·00
2460/5	$1.50 × 6 (“Miltoniopsis” “Jean Sabourin”; “Cymbidium” “Red Beauty”; “Brassocattleya” “Green Dragon”; “Phalaenopsis” hybrid; “Laeliocattleya” “Mary Ellen Carter”; “Disa” hybrid)	5·50	
2466/71	$1.50 × 6 (“Lycaste macrobulbon”; “Cochleanthes discolor”; “Cymbidium” “Nang Carpenter”; “Paphiopedilum” “Claire de Lune”; “Masdevallia caudata”; “Cymbidium” “Showgirl”)	5·50	
2472	$2 “Laeliocattleya” “Mini Purple”	1·25	1·40
2473	$3 “Phragmipedium dominiarum”	1·75	1·90
MS2474	Two sheets, each 76 × 106 mm. (a) $5 “Phalenopsis” “Medford Star”. (b) $6 “Brassolaelio-cattleya” “Dorothy Bertsch”. Set of 2 sheets	7·00	7·50

Nos. 2460/5 and 2466/71 respectively were printed together, se-tenant, with the backgrounds forming composite designs.

125 “Clitocybe metachroa”

1997. Fungi. Multicoloured.

2475	75c. Type **125**	60	45
2476	90c. “Clavulinopsis helvola”	70	50
2477	$1 “Lycoperdon pyriforme”	70	55
2478	$1.50 “Auricularia auricula-judae”	95	95
2479	$1.50 “Entoloma incanum”	95	95
2480	$1.50 “Coprinus atramentarius”	95	95
2481	$1.50 “Mycena polygramma”	95	95
2482	$1.50 “Lepista nuda”	95	95
2483	$1.50 “Pleurotis cornucopiae”	95	95
2484	$1.50 “Laccaria amethystina”	95	95
2485	$2 “Clathrus archeri”	1·25	1·40
2486	$3 “Lactarius trivialis”	1·75	1·90
MS2487	Two sheets, each 106 × 76 mm. (a) $6 “Morchella esculenta”. (b) $6 “Amanita muscaria”. Set of 2 sheets	7·50	8·00

126 Ludwig van Beethoven

1997. Classical Composers. Multicoloured.

2488	$1 Type **126**	80	80
2489	$1 Pyotr Tchaikovsky	80	80
2490	$1 Johann Christian Bach	80	80
2491	$1 Frederic Chopin	80	80
2492	$1 Igor Stravinsky	80	80
2493	$1 Franz Joseph Haydn	80	80
2494	$1 Gustav Mahler	80	80
2495	$1 Gioacchino Antonio Rossini	80	80
MS2496	Two sheets, each 106 × 76 mm. (a) $6 Wolfgang Amadeus Mozart. (b) $6 Franz Schubert. Set of 2 sheets	8·50	9·00

127 Diana, Princess of Wales and Buckingham Palace

1997. Diana, Princess of Wales Commemoration. Multicoloured.

2497	$1.50 Type **127**	1·10	1·10
2498	$1.50 Princess Diana and lake at Althorp	1·10	1·10
2499	$1.50 Princess Diana and Westminster Abbey	1·10	1·10
2500	$1.50 Princess Diana and gates to Althorp	1·10	1·10
2501	$1.50 Princess Diana in pink hat and gates to Kensington Palace	1·10	1·10
2502	$1.50 Princess Diana and Althorp House	1·10	1·10
MS2503	115 × 80 mm. $6 Holding bouquet (60 × 40 mm)	3·75	4·00

1997. Christmas. Religious Paintings. As T **448** of Grenada. Multicoloured.

2504	20c. “Choir of Angels (Simon Marmion)	30	15
2505	75c. “The Annunciation” (Giotto)	65	45
2506	90c. “Festival of the Rose Garlands” (Albrecht Durer)	70	50
2507	$1.50 “Madonna with Two Angels” (Hans Memling)	95	1·00
2508	$2 “The Ognissanti Madonna” (Giotto)	1·25	1·40
2509	$3 “Angel with Candlestick” (Michelangelo)	1·75	1·90
MS2510	Two sheets, each 114 × 104 mm. (a) $6 “The Rising of the Sun” (detail) (horiz) (Francois Boucher). (b) $6 “Cupid” (detail) (horiz) (Jean-Baptiste Huet). Set of 2 sheets	7·50	7·50

No. 2506 is inscribed “DUER” in error.

1998. Fishes. As T **449** of Grenada. Multicoloured.

2511	$1 Queen angelfish	75	75
2512	$1 Clown triggerfish	75	75
2513	$1 Four-spot butterflyfish	75	75
2514	$1 Yellow-tailed damselfish	75	75
2515	$1 Yellow-headed wrasse	75	75
2516	$1 Royal gramma	75	75
2517	$1 Candy basslet	75	75
2518	$1 Smooth trunkfish	75	75
2519	$1 Coral hind	75	75
MS2520	Two sheets. (a) 102 × 72 mm. $6 Black-finned reef shark. (b) 72 × 102 mm. $6 Yellow-headed jawfish (vert). Set of 2 sheets	8·50	8·50

Nos. 2511/19 were printed together, se-tenant , with the backgrounds forming a composite design.

128 Tiger (hologram)

1998. Chinese New Year (“Year of the Tiger”).

2521	**128** $1.50 black on silver foil	60	65
MS2522	64 × 76 mm. 128 $3 black on silver foil (52 × 65 mm)	1·20	1·30

129 “Alabama” (Confederate warship)

1998. Famous Ships. Multicoloured. (a) Ships of the 1860s.

2523	75c. Type **129**	65	65
2524	75c. “Persia” (paddle-steamer)	65	65
2525	75c. “Ariel” (clipper)	65	65
2526	75c. “Florida” (Confederate warship)	65	65
2527	75c. “Great Eastern” (paddle-steamer)	65	65
2528	75c. “Jacob Bell” on fire	65	65
2529	75c. “Star of India” (clipper)	65	65
2530	75c. “Robert E. Lee” (Mississippi paddle-steamer)	65	65
2531	75c. U.S.S. “Passaic” (monitor)	65	65
2532	75c. “Madagascar” (clipper)	65	65
2533	75c. H.M.S. “Devastation” (battleship)	65	65
2534	75c. “General Grant” (clipper)	65	65

(b) Ships of the American Civil War.

2535	$1 Clark Gable as Rhett Butler in “Gone with the Wind” (vert)	75	75
2536	$1 Crew abandoning blockade runner wrecked on Sullivan’s Island (vert)	75	75
2537	$1 Margaret Mitchell (author of “Gone with the Wind”) (vert)	75	75
2538	$1 George Alfred Trenholm (ship owner) (vert)	75	75
2539	$1 Dock Street Theatre, Charleston (vert)	75	75
2540	$1 “Howlett” (paddle-steamer) sinking (vert)	75	75
2541	$1 U.S.S. “Tecumseh” on fire (vert)	75	75
2542	$1 City Jail, Charleston (vert)	75	75
MS2543	Two sheets, each 106 × 76 mm. (a) $6 “Nashville” sinking Union clipper “Harvey Birch” (57 × 42 mm). (b) $6 “Hatteras” (paddle-steamer) on fire (42 × 57 mm). Set of 2 sheets	8·00	8·50

130 Concept Strike Fighter

1998. Aircraft Designs of the Future. Multicoloured.

2544	70c. Type **130**	30	35
2545	90c. Concept space shuttle	35	40
2546	$1 Velocity 173 RG Elite	40	45
2547	$1 Davis DA-9	40	45
2548	$1 Concorde	40	45
2549	$1 Voyager	40	45
2550	$1 Factimobile	40	45
2551	$1 RAF 2000	40	45
2552	$1 Boomerang	40	45
2553	$1 N1M Flying Wing	40	45
2554	$2 Concept air and space jet	80	85
2555	$3 V Jet II	1·20	1·30
MS2556	Two sheets, each 100 × 70 mm. (a) $6 Concept aeropod. (b) $6 Delmar. Set of 2 sheets	4·75	5·00

131 “Lycaste deppei”

1998. Orchids of the World. Multicoloured.

2557	$1 Type **131**	40	45
2558	$1 “Dendrobium victoriae”	40	45
2559	$1 “Dendrobium nobile”	40	45
2560	$1 “Cymbidium dayanum”	40	45
2561	$1 “Cymbidium” “Starbright”	40	45
2562	$1 “Cymbidium giganteum”	40	45
2563	$1 “Chysis aurea”	40	45
2564	$1 “Broughtonia sanguinea”	40	45
2565	$1 “Cattleya guttata”	40	45
2566	$1 “Calanthe vestita”	40	45
2567	$1 “Cattleya bicolor”	40	45
2568	$1 “Laelia anceps”	40	45
2569	$1 “Epidendrum prismatocarpum”	40	45
2570	$1 “Coelogyne ochracea”	40	45
2571	$1 “Doritaenopsis eclantant”	40	45
2572	$1 “Laelia gouldiana”	40	45
2573	$1 “Encyclia vitellina”	40	45
2574	$1 “Maxillaria praestans”	40	45
2575	$1 “Laelia tenebrosa”	40	45
2576	$1.50 “Phragmipedium besseae”	60	65
2577	$2 “Pschopsis papilio”	80	85
2578	$3 “Masdevallia coccinea”	1·20	1·30
MS2579	Two sheets, each 29 × 43 mm. (a) $6 “Masdevallia ignea”. (b) $6 “Encyclia brassavolae”. Set of 2 sheets	4·75	5·00

1998. Seabirds. As T **452** of Grenada. Multicoloured.

2580	75c. Bonaparte’s gull (horiz)	30	35
2581	90c. Western sandpiper (horiz)	35	40
2582	$1.50 Common tern (horiz)	60	65
2583	$1.50 Brown pelican (horiz)	60	65
2584	$1.50 Black-legged kittiwake and white tern (horiz)	60	65
2585	$1.50 Herring gull (horiz)	60	65
2586	$1.50 Lesser noddy (horiz)	60	65
2587	$1.50 Black-legged kittiwake (horiz)	60	65
2588	$1.50 Whimbrel (horiz)	60	65
2589	$1.50 Golden white-tailed tropic bird (horiz)	60	65
2590	$1.50 Arctic tern (horiz)	60	65
2591	$1.50 Ruddy turnstone	60	65
2592	$1.50 Blue-eyed cormorant (“Imperial Shag”) (horiz)	60	65
2593	$1.50 Magellan gull (horiz)	60	65
2594	$2 Great black-backed gull (horiz)	80	85
2595	$3 Dotterell (horiz)	1·20	1·30
MS2596	Two sheets, each 100 × 70 mm. (a) $5 Broad-billed prion (horiz). (b) $5 Yellow-nosed albatross. Set of 2 sheets	4·00	4·25

1998. International Year of the Ocean. As T **454** of Grenada. Multicoloured.

2597	75c. Great black-backed gull	30	35
2598	75c. Common dolphin	30	35
2599	75c. Seal	30	35
2600	75c. Amazonian catfish	30	35
2601	75c. Shark	30	35
2602	75c. Goldfish	30	35
2603	75c. Cyathopharynx	30	35
2604	75c. Killer whale	30	35
2605	75c. Telmatochromis	30	35
2606	75c. Crab	30	35
2607	75c. Octopus	30	35
2608	75c. Turtle	30	35
2609	90c. Two dolphins	35	40
2610	90c. Seal	35	40
2611	90c. Turtle on rock	35	40
2612	90c. Leopard shark	35	40
2613	90c. Flame angelfish	35	40
2614	90c. Syndontis	35	40
2615	90c. Lamprologus	35	40
2616	90c. “Krptopterus bicirrhus”	35	40
2617	90c. “Pterophyllum scalare”	35	40
2618	90c. Swimming pancake	35	40
2619	90c. Cowfish	35	40
2620	90c. Seahorse	35	40
MS2621	Two sheets, each 98 × 68 mm. (a) $6 “Tetraodon mbu”. (b) $6 Goldfish. Set of 2 sheets	4·75	5·00

Nos. 2597/2608 and 2609/20 respectively were printed together, se-tenant, with the backgrounds forming composite designs.

1998. 50th Anniv of Organization of American States. As T **454a** of Grenada.

2622	$1 violet, orange and black	40	45

1998. 25th Death Anniv of Pablo Picasso (painter). As T **291a** of Gambia. Multicoloured.

2623	45c. “Bust of a Woman” (vert)	20	25
2624	$2 “Three Musicians”	80	85
2625	$3 “Studio at La Californie”	1·20	1·30
MS2626	102 × 127 mm. $5 “Woman with a Blue Hat”	2·00	2·10

1998. Birth Centenary of Enzo Ferrari (car manufacturer). As T **454b** of Grenada. Multicoloured.

2627	$2 275 GTB	1·50	1·50
2628	$2 340 MM	1·50	1·50
2629	$2 250 GT SWB Berlinetta “Hot Rod”	1·50	1·50
MS2630	104 × 72 mm. $5 First Ferrari cabriolet (91 × 34 mm). P 14 × 14½	3·50	3·75

1998. 19th World Scout Jamboree, Chile. As T **455** of Grenada. Multicoloured.

2631	90c. Scout greeting	35	40
2632	$1.50 Lord Baden-Powell	60	65
2633	$5 Scout salute	2·00	2·10
MS2634	76 × 106 mm. $6 Lord Baden-Powell (vert)	2·40	2·50

1998. 50th Death Anniv of Mahatma Gandhi. As T **455a** of Grenada.

2635	$1 grey, brown and black	40	45
MS2636	100 × 70 mm. $6 grey, brown and black	2·40	2·50

1998. 80th Anniv of Royal Air Force. As T **292a** of Gambia. Multicoloured.

2637	$2 Tornado GR1	80	85
2638	$2 BAe Hawk T1A	80	85
2639	$2 Sepecat Jaguar GR1	80	85
2640	$2 Harrier GR7	80	85
2641	$2 Chinook helicopter carrying three loads	80	85
2642	$2 Silhouette of BAe Harrier GR5	80	85
2643	$2 Panavia Tornado F3 ADV at sunset	80	85
2644	$2 Chinook HC2 carrying 105 mm light gun	80	85
MS2645	Four sheets, each 93 × 70 mm. (a) $6 Bristol F2B fighter and head of golden eagle (bird). (b) $6 Bristol F2B fighter and montagu’s harrier in flight. (c) $6 Hawker Hunter and EF-2000 Eurofighter. (d) $6 Tornado and EF-2000 Eurofighter. Set of 4 sheets	9·75	10·00

1998. Birth Bicentenary of Eugene Delacroix (painter). As T **294** of Gambia. Multicoloured.

2646	$1 “The Natchez”	40	45
2647	$1 “Christ and His Disciples Crossing the Sea of Galilee”	40	45
2648	$1 “Sunset”	40	45
2649	$1 “Moroccans outside the Walls of Tangier”	40	45
2650	$1 “The Fireplace”	40	45
2651	$1 “Forest View with an Oak Tree”	40	45

2652 $1 "View of the Harbour at Dieppe" 40 45
2653 $1 "Arab Tax Collectors" 40 45
MS2654 85 × 105 mm. $5 "Young Orphan" 2·00 2·10

1998. 1st Death Anniv of Diana, Princess of Wales. As T **293a** of Gambia.
2655 $1.50 multicoloured 60 65

132 Father Christmas and Hare

1998. Disney's Christmas Trains. Walt Disney cartoon characters in train carriages. Multicoloured.
2656 $1 Type **132** 85 85
2657 $1 Giraffe, elephant and tiger 85 85
2658 $1 Three Pigs and Wolf 85 85
2659 $1 Pied Piper, Jiminy Cricket, penguins and children 85 85
2660 $1 Swans, Little Hiawatha and tortoise 85 85
2661 $1 Mickey Mouse as train driver 85 85
2662 $1 Pluto, Chip and Dale 85 85
2663 $1 Donald and Daisy Duck 85 85
2664 $1 Goofy, Huey, Dewey and Louie 85 85
2665 $1 Minnie Mouse and presents 85 85
2666 $1 Piglet as train driver 85 85
2667 $1 Winnie the Pooh and honey 85 85
2668 $1 Rabbit and Owl 85 85
2669 $1 Kanga, Roo and Christopher Robin 85 85
2670 $1 Eeyore and Tigger 85 85
MS2671 Three sheets, each 133 × 109 mm. (a) $6 Father Christmas and toy train. (b) $6 Mickey Mouse as train driver. (c) $6 Rabbit, Winnie the Pooh, Piglet and Eeyore. Set of 3 sheets 12·00 13·00

1999. Chinese New Year ("Year of the Rabbit"). Sheet 150 × 76 mm, containing triangular designs as T **435** of Grenada each showing rabbits. Multicoloured. Self-adhesive on gold foil.
MS2672 $1.50, "GRENADA GRENADINES" in green; $1.50 "GRENADA GRENADINES" in orange; $1.50 "GRENADA GRENADINES" in red 1·80 1·90

133 Troodon

1999. "Australia '99" World Stamp Exhibition, Melbourne. Prehistoric Animals. Multicoloured.
2673 $1 Type **133** 40 45
2674 $1 Camptosaurus 40 45
2675 $1 Parasaurolophus 40 45
2676 $1 Dryosaurus 40 45
2677 $1 Gallimimus 40 45
2678 $1 Camarasaurus 40 45
2679 $1.50 Duckbill (horiz) 60 65
2680 $1.50 Lambeosaurus (horiz) 60 65
2681 $1.50 Igaunodon (horiz) 60 65
2682 $1.50 Euoplocephalus (horiz) 60 65
2683 $1.50 Triceratops (horiz) 60 65
2684 $1.50 Brachiosaurus (horiz) 60 65
2685 $1.50 Ponoptosaurus (horiz) 60 65
2686 $1.50 Stegosaurus (horiz) 60 65
MS2687 Three sheets. (a) 106 × 76 mm. $6 Edmontosaurus (horiz). (b) 76 × 106 mm. $6 "Tyrannosaurus Rex". (c) 76 × 106 mm. $6 Halticosaurus. Set of 3 sheets 7·25 7·50

134 Great Indian Peninsula Passenger and Mail Locomotive

1999. Steam Trains of the World. Multicoloured.
2688 15c. Type **134** 10 10
2689 75c. Midland Great Western passenger locomotive (Ireland) 30 35
2690 90c. Canada Pacific express locomotive 35 40
2691 $1.50 East Indian Railway express locomotive 60 65
2692 $2 Victorian Railways suburban tank locomotive (Australia) 80 85
2693 $2 Eastern Railways compound locomotive (France) 80 85
2694 $2 Govt Railways Class WF tank locomotive (New Zealand) 80 85
2695 $2 Burma Railways oil-burning tank locomotive, 1899 80 85
2696 $2 Federated Malay States Railway Class G steam locomotive, 1899 80 85
2697 $2 Belfast and Northern Counties Railway narrow-gauge tank locomotive 80 85
2698 $2 Shunting tank locomotive (Russia) 80 85
2699 $2 G.N.R. Ivatt large-boilered "Atlantic" type 80 85
2700 $2 Palatine Railway "Atlantic" type express locomotive (Germany) 80 85
2701 $2 Belgian State Railways "Dunalastair" type locomotive 80 85
2702 $2 Swedish State Railways Class Cc locomotive 80 85
2703 $2 Antofagasta and Bolivian Railway tank locomotive (Chile) 80 85
2704 $2 Bolivian State Fairlie type locomotive 80 85
2705 $2 Belgian State Railways express locomotive 80 85
2706 $2 London and South Western Railway Drummond's mixed traffic locomotive 80 85
2707 $2 Belfast and Northern Counties Railways Compound locomotive 80 85
2708 $2 Dutch State Railway express passenger locomotive 80 85
2709 $2 Gothard Railway heavy freight locomotive (Switzerland) 80 85
2710 $2 Waterford, Limerick and Western railway goods locomotive (Ireland) 80 85
2711 $2 Atchison, Topeka and Santa Fe railway tandem compound express locomotive (U.S.A.) 80 85
2712 $2 Midland Railway Class "Princess of Wales" locomotive (Great Britain) 80 85
2713 $3 Glasgow and South Western Railway Stirling type locomotive 1·20 1·30
MS2714 Two sheets, each 100 × 70 mm. (a) $6 Paris, Lyons and Mediterranean compound locomotive (France). (b) $6 Italian Southern Railway compound locomotive. Set of 2 sheets 4·75 5·00
No. 2701 is inscribed "Dunalastiar" in error.

135 Porkfish

1999. Fauna and Flora. Multicoloured.
2715 75c. Type **135** 30 35
2716 90c. Leatherback turtle 35 40
2717 $1 Red-billed tropic bird ("White-tailed Tropicbird") (vert) 40 45
2718 $1 Laughing gull (vert) 40 45
2719 $1 Palm tree (vert) 40 45
2720 $1 Humpback whale (vert) 40 45
2721 $1 Painted bunting (vert) 40 45
2722 $1 Common grackle (vert) 40 45
2723 $1 Green anole (lizard) (vert) 40 45
2724 $1 "Morpho peleides" (butterfly) (vert) 40 45
2725 $1 "Prepona meander" (butterfly) (vert) 40 45
2726 $1 Common dolphin (vert) 40 45
2727 $1 "Catonephele numilia" (butterfly) (vert) 40 45
2728 $1 Sooty tern (vert) 40 45
2729 $1 Vermilion flycatcher (vert) 40 45
2730 $1 Blue grosbeak (vert) 40 45
2731 $1 Great egret (vert) 40 45
2732 $1 "Actinate pellenea" (butterfly) (vert) 40 45
2733 $1 "Anteos clorinde" (butterfly) (vert) 40 45
2734 $1 Common iguana (vert) 40 45
2735 $1.50 Ruby-throated hummingbird 60 65
2736 $2 "Theope eudocia" (butterfly) 80 85
MS2737 Two sheets, each 85 × 110 mm. (a) $6 Bananaquit. (b) $6 Beaugregory (fish). Set of 2 sheets 4·75 5·00
Nos. 2717/25 and 2726/34 respectively were printed together, se-tenant, with the backgrounds forming composite designs.
No. 2727 is inscribed "numili" in error.

136 John H. Glenn (astronaut), 1998

1999. John Glenn's (first American to orbit Earth) Return to Space. Multicoloured, except Nos. 2716, 2718 and 2720/1.
2738 $1 Type **136** 40 45
2739 $1 Glenn and Pres. John F. Kennedy (brown and red) 40 45
2740 $1 Inside "Discovery", 1998 40 45
2741 $1 Climbing from "Friendship 7" capsule, 1962 (brown and red) 40 45
2742 $1 Medical checkup 40 45
2743 $1 Climbing into space capsule, 1962 (brown and red) 40 45
2744 $1 As Democratic Senator for Ohio, 1974 (vert) (brown and red) 40 45
2745 $1 In space suit, 1962 (vert) 40 45
2746 $1 Smiling during suit up test, 1998 (vert) 40 45
2747 $1 Preparing for "Discovery" flight (vert) 40 45
2748 $1 At press conference (with microphone) (vert) 40 45
2749 $1 Smiling at camera (wearing glasses) (vert) 40 45
2750 $1 Participating in medical research (vert) 40 45
2751 $1 Posing in space suit, 1998 (vert) 40 45
No. 2744 was inscribed "Junior Senator form Ohio (1974)" in error.

1999. "iBRA '99" International Stamp Exhibition, Nuremberg. As T **298a** of Gambia. Multicoloured.
2752 35c. "Luckenbach" (full-rigged ship) and Thurn and Taxis Northern District 1852 ¼sgr. stamp 15 20
2753 45c. Leipzig–Dresden Railway carriage and Schleswig-Holstein 1850 1s. 20 25
2754 $1.50 Leipzig–Dresden Railway carriage and Oldenburg 1852 ⅓sgr. 60 65
2755 $3 "Luckenbach" (full-rigged ship) and North German Confederation 1868 ¼g. 1·20 1·30
MS2756 154 × 86 mm. $6 Thurn and Taxis Northern District 1865 ¼sgr. rouletted pair used on cover 2·40 2·50

1999. 150th Death Anniv of Katsushika Hokusai (Japanese artist). As T **298b** of Gambia. Multicoloured.
2757 $1.50 "Fuchu" 60 65
2758 $1.50 "Doll Fair at Fikkendana" 60 65
2759 $1.50 "Sumo Wrestlers" (in arm hold) 60 65
2760 $1.50 "Sumo Wrestlers" (in head lock) 60 65
2761 $1.50 "Sojo Henjo" 60 65
2762 $1.50 "Twin Gardens Gateway of Asakusa Kannon Temple" 60 65
2763 $1.50 "A Breeze on a Fine Day" 60 65
2764 $1.50 "Ejiri" 60 65
2765 $1.50 "Horse Drawings" (galloping) 60 65
2766 $1.50 "Horse Drawings" (stationary) 60 65
2767 $1.50 "View along Bank of Sumida River" 60 65
2768 $1.50 "Thunderstorm Below the Mountain" 60 65
MS2769 Two sheets, each 102 × 72 mm. (a) $6 "Stretching Cloth" (vert). (b) $6 "Kobo Daishi exorcising Demon that causes Sickness" (vert). Set of 2 sheets 4·75 5·00
No. 2762 is inscribed "TWIN GARDAINS GATEWAY" in error.

1999. 10th Anniv of United Nations Rights of the Child Convention. As T **298c** of Gambia. Multicoloured.
2770 $3 African boy 1·20 1·30
2771 $3 Liv Ullman (UNICEF's first female ambassador) 1·20 1·30
2772 $3 African woman in head scarf 1·20 1·30
MS2773 110 × 84 mm. $6 Maurice Pate (Founding Director of UNICEF) 2·40 2·50
Nos. 2770/2 were printed together, se-tenant, forming a composite design.

1999. "PhilexFrance '99" International Stamp Exhibition, Paris. Railway Locomotives. Two sheets containing horiz designs as T **299d** of Gambia. Multicoloured.
MS2774 (a) 106 × 81 mm. $6 Paris, Orleans and Mediterranean Railway Cha Pelon type steam locomotive. (b) 106 × 76 mm. $6 French National Railways Class 7000 high speed electric locomotive. Set of 2 sheets 4·75 5·00

1999. 250th Birth Anniv of Johann von Goethe (German writer). As T **298d** of Gambia.
2775 $3 multicoloured 1·20 1·30
2776 $3 blue and black 1·20 1·30
2777 $3 blue, violet and black 1·20 1·30
MS2778 71 × 106 mm. $6 brown, chestnut and black 2·40 2·50
DESIGNS—HORIZ: No. 2775, Peasants dancing under linden-tree; 2776, Goethe and Schiller; 2777, Faust dreams of soaring above the mortal. VERT: **MS**2778, Johann von Goethe.

1999. Royal Wedding. As T **298** of Gambia. Multicoloured.
2779 $3 Sophie Rhys-Jones 1·20 1·30
2780 $3 Sophie and Prince Edward 1·20 1·30
2781 $3 Prince Edward 1·20 1·30
MS2782 78 × 108 mm. $6 Sophie and Prince Edward on wedding day 2·40 2·50

1999. "Queen Elizabeth the Queen Mother's Century". As T **304a** of Gambia.
2783 $2 black and gold 80 85
2784 $2 multicoloured 80 85
2785 $2 black and gold 80 85
2786 $2 multicoloured 80 85
MS2787 153 × 157 mm. $6 multicoloured 2·40 2·50
DESIGNS: No. 2783, Lady Elizabeth Bowes-Lyon as a child; 2784, Queen Mother in Rhodesia, 1957; 2785, Queen Mother with Princesses Elizabeth and Anne, 1950; 2786, Queen Mother, 1988. (37 × 50 mm)—**MS**2787, Queen Mother reviewing Black Watch, Berlin.

138 George Raft

140 Kirk Douglas

139 "Sputnik I", 1957

1999. Early Cinema Actors.
2788 **138** $1 multicoloured 40 45
2789 – $1 grey and black 40 45
2790 – $1 grey and black 40 45
2791 – $1 multicoloured 40 45
2792 – $1 multicoloured 40 45
2793 – $1 black and grey 40 45
2794 – $1 black, blue and grey 40 45
2795 – $1 multicoloured 40 45
2796 – $2 multicoloured 80 85
2797 – $2 black and grey 80 85
2798 – $2 multicoloured 80 85
2799 – $2 black and grey 80 85
MS2800 $6 multicoloured 2·40 2·50
DESIGNS: No. 2791, Fatty Arbuckle; 2792, Buster Keaton; 2795, Harold Lloyd; 2796, James Cagney; 2798, Edward G. Robinson; **MS**2800, Charlie Chaplin. (53 × 39 mm): No. 2789, George Raft in "Scarface"; 2790, Fatty Arbuckle with nurse; 2793, Buster Keaton on locomotive cow-catcher; 2794, Harold Lloyd hanging on clockface; 2797, James Cagney in "The Public Enemy"; 2799, Edward G. Robinson in "Little Caesar".

1999. Space Exploration. Multicoloured.
2801 $1.50 Type **139** 60 65
2802 $1.50 "Explorer I", 1958 60 65
2803 $1.50 "Telstar I" satellite, 1962 60 65
2804 $1.50 "Maristat I", 1976 60 65
2805 $1.50 Long Duration Exposure facility, 1984 60 65
2806 $1.50 Hubble Space Telescope, 1990 60 65
2807 $1.50 X-15 rocket plane, 1960 (vert) 60 65
2808 $1.50 "Freedom 7" rocket, 1961 (vert) 60 65
2809 $1.50 "Friendship 7", 1962 (vert) 60 65
2810 $1.50 "Gemini 4" rocket and Edward H. White, 1965 (vert) 60 65

2811	$1.50 Saturn V rocket and Edwin E. Aldrin stepping onto Moon, 1969 (vert)	60	65
2812	$1.50 Lunar Rover, "Apollo 15" mission, 1971 (vert)	60	65
MS2813	Two sheets, each 110×85 mm. (a) $6 "Mars Pathfinder", 1997 (55×42 mm); (b) $6 Space shuttle "Columbia", 1981 (55×42 mm). Set of 2 sheets	4·75	5·00

Nos. 2801/6 and 2807/12 were each printed together, se-tenant, with the backgrounds forming composite designs.

1999. Kirk Douglas (American actor). Multicoloured.

2814	$1.50 Type **140**	60	65
2815	$1.50 As a boxer in "Champion"	60	65
2816	$1.50 As Van Gogh in "Lust for Life"	60	65
2817	$1.50 With white hair and wearing black shirt	60	65
2818	$1.50 In French uniform for "Paths of Glory"	60	65
2819	$1.50 As a cowboy in "The Bad and the Beautiful"	60	65
MS2820	93×106 mm. $6 As Spartacus	2·40	2·50

141 Elvis Presley

1999. Elvis Presley Commemoration. Each grey, silver and black.

2821	$1.50 Type **141**	60	65
2822	$1.50 Resting chin on hand	60	65
2823	$1.50 Wearing roll-neck sweater	60	65
2824	$1.50 Leaning against brick wall	60	65
2825	$1.50 Singing into microphone	60	65
2826	$1.50 Singing with eyes closed	60	65

141a Howard Thurston (magician)

142 Poinsettia and Candle

1999. Famous Magicians. Multicoloured.

2826a	$1.50 Type **141a**	60	65
2826b	$1.50 Harry Houdini	60	65
2826c	$1.50 Harry Kellar	60	65

1999. Christmas. Foliage and Candles. Mult.

2827	15c. Type **142**	10	10
2828	35c. Holly	15	20
2829	75c. Fir tree	30	35
2830	$1.50 Ivy	60	65
2831	$3 Geranium	1·20	1·30
MS2832	83×108 mm. $6 "The Adoration of the Magi" (horiz)	2·40	2·50

No. 2829 is inscribed "FUR TREE" in error.

2000. New Millennium. People and Events of Fourteenth Century (1300–30). As T **417a** of Grenada. Multicoloured.

2833	50c. Robert the Bruce, King of Scotland, 1306	20	25
2834	50c. Fresco by Giotto, 1306	20	25
2835	50c. Mansa Musa, ruler of Mali, 1307	20	25
2836	50c. Dante and *The Divine Comedy*, 1321	20	25
2837	50c. Noh Theatre masks, Japan, 1325	20	25
2838	50c. Staircase, Tenochtitlan (Aztec capital, founded 1325)	20	25
2839	50c. Ibn Batuta on camel (start of journey, 1325)	20	25
2840	50c. Great Munich Fire, 1327	20	25
2841	50c. Grand Duke Ivan I (transfer of capital to Moscow, 1328)	20	25
2842	50c. Archers and castle (beginning of Hundred Years War, 1337)	20	25
2843	50c. Cannon at siege of Calais, 1346 (first recorded use of cannon)	20	25
2844	50c. "Death" (Black Death in Europe, 1348)	20	25
2845	50c. Boccaccio composing *The Decameron*, 1348	20	25
2846	50c. Early Italian spectacles, 1350	20	25
2847	50c. Knight (introduction of plate armour, 1350)	20	25
2848	50c. Junks (completion of Grand Canal of China, 1326) (59×39 mm)	20	25
2849	50c. Maori canoe (Maori migration to New Zealand, 1350)	20	25

143 Dragon

2000. Chinese New Year ("Year of the Dragon"). Sheet 79×60 mm.

MS2850	**143** $4 multicoloured	1·60	1·70

144 Barn Swallow

2000. Birds. Multicoloured.

2851	75c. Type **144**	30	35
2852	90c. Caribbean coot	35	40
2853	$1 Turquoise parrot	40	45
2854	$1 Scarlet-chested parrot	40	45
2855	$1 Red-capped parrot	40	45
2856	$1 Eastern rosella	40	45
2857	$1 Budgerigar	40	45
2858	$1 Superb parrot ("Orange-Flanked Parakeet")	40	45
2859	$1 Mallee ringneck parrot	40	45
2860	$1 Red-rumped parrot	40	45
2861	$1 Yellow-fronted parakeet	40	45
2862	$1 Rainbow lory ("Red-collared Lorikeet")	40	45
2863	$1 Lesser sulphur-crested cockatoo ("Citron-crested Cockatoo")	40	45
2864	$1 Papuan lory ("Stella's Lorikeet")	40	45
2865	$1 Major Mitchell's cockatoo ("Leadbeator's Cockatoo")	40	45
2866	$1 Golden conure	40	45
2867	$1 Red-spotted lorikeet	40	45
2868	$1 Red-shouldered macaw ("Nobel macaw")	40	45
2869	$1 Goffin's cockatoo	40	45
2870	$1 Sun conure	40	45
2871	$1.50 Puerto Rican emerald	60	65
2872	$1.50 Green mango	60	65
2873	$1.50 Red-legged thrush	60	65
2874	$1.50 Green-cheeked amazon ("Red-crowned Parrot")	60	65
2875	$1.50 Hispaniolan amazon ("Hispaniolan Parrot")	60	65
2876	$1.50 Yellow-headed parrot ("Yellow-crowned Parrot")	60	65
2877	$1.50 Yellow-shouldered blackbird	60	65
2878	$1.50 Troupial	60	65
2879	$1.50 Green-throated carib	60	65
2880	$1.50 Nanday conure ("Black-hooded Parakeet")	60	65
2881	$1.50 Scarlet tanager	60	65
2882	$1.50 Golden bishop ("Yellow-crowned Bishop")	60	65
2883	$2 Moorhen ("Common Moorhen")	80	85
2884	$3 Orange-winged amazon ("Orange-winged Parrot")	1·20	1·30
MS2885	Four sheets. (a) 74×98 mm. $6 Crimson rosella ("Pennant's Parakeet"). (b) 74×98 mm. $6 Scarlet macaw (vert). (c) 75×107 mm. $6 Puerto Rican lizard cuckoo. (d) 75×107 mm. $6 Pin-tailed whydah (vert). Set of 4 sheets	9·75	10·00

Nos. 2853/61, 2862/70, 2871/6 and 2877/82 were each printed together, se-tenant, with the backgrounds forming composite designs.

No. 2859 is inscribed "Rigneck", No. 2863 "Cocatoo", No. 2865 "Cockatto" and No. 2869 "GoffinsCocatto", all in error.

145 *Cantharellus cinnabarinus*

146 Ferdinand Magellan (Spanish navigator)

2000. Fungi. Multicoloured.

2886	$2 Type **145**	80	85
2887	$2 *Hygrocybe conica*	80	85
2888	$2 *Cortinarius violaceus*	80	85
2889	$2 *Leccinum versipelle*	80	85
2890	$2 *Russula xerampelina*	80	85
2891	$2 *Entoloma nitidum*	80	85
2892	$2 *Lentinus tigrinus*	80	85
2893	$2 *Mycena flavoalba*	80	85
2894	$2 *Boletus legaliae* (horiz)	80	85
2895	$2 *Russula emetica* (horiz)	80	85
2896	$2 *Cortinarius alboviolaceus* (horiz)	80	85
2897	$2 *Volvariella bombycina* (horiz)	80	85
MS2898	Two sheets, each 103×81 mm. (a) $6 *Gomphus floccosus* (horiz). (b) $6 *Collybia dryophila* (horiz). Set of 2 sheets	4·75	5·00

No. 2886 is inscribed "Canharellus", No. 2889 "Lecinum", and No. **MS**2898 (a) "Comphus", all in error.

2000. New Millennium. Sea Exploration. Mult.

2899	50c. Type **146**	20	25
2900	50c. Ship in storm	20	25
2901	50c. Queen Elizabeth I's hand on globe	20	25
2902	50c. Two wandering albatrosses ("Albatrosses")	20	25
2903	50c. Emperor penguins	20	25
2904	50c. Tahitian woman	20	25
2905	50c. Breadfruit	20	25
2906	50c. Moai (carved statue) on Easter Island	20	25
2907	50c. Maori carving	20	25
2908	50c. Lobster	20	25
2909	50c. Orchid	20	25
2910	50c. Walrus	20	25
2911	50c. Kangaroo	20	25
2912	50c. H.M.S. *Beagle* (Charles Darwin) careened	20	25
2913	50c. Magnificent frigate bird ("Frigatebird")	20	25
2914	50c. Ship and boats in the Strait of Magellan (59×39 mm)	20	25
2915	50c. Captain James Cook (English navigator)	20	25

146a Salvador Allende elected President of Chile, 1970

2000. New Millennium. People and Events of Twentieth Century (1970–79). Multicoloured.

2916	20c. Type **146a**	10	15
2917	20c. Cartoon characters around globe (introduction of Earth Day holiday, 1970)	10	15
2918	20c. Computerized Axial Tomography (CAT) scanner, 1971	10	15
2919	20c. Pres. Richard Nixon in China (re-opening of U.S. relations with People's Republic, 1972)	10	15
2920	20c. Terrorist and flag (murder of Israeli athletes at Munich Olympics 1972)	10	15
2921	20c. Petrol ration sign (OPEC oil price rises, 1973)	10	15
2922	20c. Sydney Opera House, 1973	10	15
2923	20c. Pres. Richard Nixon leaving helicoptor (resignation 1974)	10	15
2924	20c. Stylized black hole (new theory, 1974)	10	15
2925	20c. U.S. Bicentennial celebrations, 1976	10	15
2926	20c. Louise Brown, first test tube baby, born (born 1978)	10	15
2927	20c. Pope John Paul II visiting Poland, 1978	10	15
2928	20c. Ayatollah Khomeini (Iran's Islamic Revolution, 1978)	10	15
2929	20c. Concorde (first flight, 1979)	10	15
2930	20c. Charles de Gaulle (died 1970) and Eiffel Tower	10	15
2931	20c. Pres. Sadat, Prime Minister Begin and Pres. Carter (Camp David Talks 1978/9) (59×39 mm)	10	15
2932	20c. Mother Teresa (Nobel Peace Prize, 1979)	10	15

No. 2932 is inscribed "Noble Peace Prize" in error.

147 Elongate Mbuna ("Slender Mbuna")

2000. Tropical Fish. Multicoloured.

2933	35c. Type **147**	15	20
2934	45c. *Pygoplites diacanthus*	20	25
2935	75c. *Pomacanthus semicirclatus*	30	35
2936	75c. Siamese fighting fish	30	35
2937	90c. *Zanclus canescens*	35	40
2938	$1 *Xiphophorus maculatus*	40	45
2939	$1 Dwarf pencilfish	40	45
2940	$1 Bumblebee goby	40	45
2941	$1 Black-headed blenny	40	45
2942	$1 Velvet boarfish	40	45
2943	$1 Red-tailed surgeonfish ("Achilles Tang")	40	45
2944	$1 Swordtail	40	45
2945	$1 Moorish idol	40	45
2946	$1 Banded pipefish	40	45
2947	$1 Striped catfish	40	45
2948	$1 Emperor angelfish	40	45
2949	$1 Magenta dottyback ("Strawberryfish")	40	45
2950	$1 Jackknife-fish	40	45
2951	$1 Flame angelfish	40	45
2952	$1 Yellow-tailed ("Clarke's") anemonefish	40	45
2953	$1 Flash-back dottyback	40	45
2954	$1 Coral trout	40	45
2955	$1 Foxface	40	45
2956	$1.65 *Bodianus rufus*	65	70
2957	$1.65 *Coris aygula*	65	70
2958	$1.65 *Centropyge bicolor*	65	70
2959	$1.65 *Balistoides conspicillum*	65	70
2960	$1.65 *Poecilia reticulata*	65	70
2961	$1.65 *Heniochus acuminatus*	65	70
2962	$1.65 *Plectorhinchus chaetodonoides*	65	70
2963	$1.65 *Bodianus pulchellus*	65	70
2964	$1.65 *Acanthurus leucosternon*	65	70
2965	$1.65 *Chromileptis altivelis*	65	70
2966	$1.65 *Pterophyllum scalare*	65	70
2967	$1.65 *Premnas biaculeatus*	65	70
2968	$2 Pennant coralfish ("Wimplefish")	80	85
2969	$2 *Gramma loreto*	80	85
2970	$3 *Zebrasoma xanthurum*	1·20	1·30
MS2971	Four sheets. (a) 97×68 mm. $6 Harlequin Tuskfish. (b) 97×68 mm. $6 Purple Queen. (c) 93×65 mm. $6 *Equetus punctatus*. (d) 93×65 mm. $6 *Pomacanthus imperator* (vert). Set of 4 sheets	9·75	10·00

Nos. 2940/7, 2948/55, 2956/61 and 2962/7 were each printed together, se-tenant, with the backgrounds forming composite designs.

No. 2942 is inscribed "CCAPROS APER", No. 2949 "PSEUDOCHROMIS ORPHYREUS", No. 2954 "CEPHALOPHELIS MINIATUS", No. 2962 "PLECTORHYNCHUS CHAETODONOIDS" and No. 2963 "BODIANUS PUCHELLUS", all in error.

2000. 400th Birth Anniv of Sir Anthony Van Dyck (Flemish painter). As T **312a** of Gambia. Mult.

2972	$1.50 "Portrait of an Elderly Woman"	60	65
2973	$1.50 "Head of a Young Woman"	60	65
2974	$1.50 "Portrait of a Man"	60	65
2975	$1.50 "Jan van den Wouwer"	60	65
2976	$1.50 "Portrait of a Young Man"	60	65
2977	$1.50 "Everhard Jabach"	60	65
2978	$1.50 "Man in Armour"	60	65
2979	$1.50 "Portrait of a Young General"	60	65
2980	$1.50 "Emanuele Filiberto, Prince of Savoy"	60	65
2981	$1.50 "Donna Polixena Spinola Guzman de Leganes"	60	65
2982	$1.50 "Luigia Cattaneo Gentile"	60	65
2983	$1.50 "Giovanni Battista Cattaneo"	60	65
2984	$1.50 "Marchesa Paolina Adorno Brignole-Sale" (1623–25)	60	65
2985	$1.50 "Marchesa Geronima Spinola"	60	65
2986	$1.50 "Marchesa Paolina Adorna Brignole-Sale" (1627)	60	65
2987	$1.50 "Marcello Durazzo"	60	65
2988	$1.50 "Marchesa Grimaldi Cattaneo with a Black Page"	60	65
2989	$1.50 "Young Man of the House of Spinola"	60	65
2990	$1.50 "Cardinal Bentivoglio"	60	65
2991	$1.50 "Cardinal Infante Ferdinand"	60	65

2992 $1.50 "Cesare Alessandro Scaglia, Abbe of Staffarda and Mandanici" 60 65
2993 $1.50 "A Roman Clergyman" 60 65
2994 $1.50 "Jean-Charles della Faille" 60 65
2995 $1.50 "Cardinal Domenico Rivarola" 60 65
MS2996 Six sheets. (a) 100 × 123 mm. $5 "Hendrick van der Bergh". (b) 100 × 123 mm. $5 "Jaques le Roy". (c) 100 × 123 mm. $6 "Justus van Meerstraeten". (d) 100 × 123 mm. $6 "Frederik Hendrik, Prince of Orange". (e) 100 × 123 mm. $6 "Maria Louisa de Tassis" (horiz). (f) 123 × 100 mm. $6 "Abbot Scaglia adoring the Virgin and Child" (horiz). Set of 6 sheets 13·50 14·00

Nos. 2972/3 are inscribed "Women", No. 2983 "Cattanaeo" and No. 2992 "Stafford", all in error.

2000. 18th Birthday of Prince William. As T **312b** of Gambia. Multicoloured.
2997 $1.50 Prince William with birthday gift 60 65
2998 $1.50 In Eton uniform . . . 60 65
2999 $1.50 Wearing checked shirt 60 65
3000 $1.50 Wearing grey suit . . 60 65
MS3001 100 × 80 mm. $6 Wearing blue jumper (37 × 50 mm) . . . 2·40 2·50

2000. "EXPO 2000" World Stamp Exhibition, Anaheim, U.S.A. Spacecraft. As T **582a** of Ghana. Multicoloured.
3002 $1.50 "Foton" and comet 60 65
3003 $1.50 "Sub-Satellite" and rock particle 60 65
3004 $1.50 Satellite near Eros . . 60 65
3005 $1.50 "Explorer 16" 60 65
3006 $1.50 Space Shuttle *Challenger* 60 65
3007 $1.50 Giotto facing right and Halley's Comet . . . 60 65
3008 $1.50 Circular satellite with aerial (inscr "Foton") . . 60 65
3009 $1.50 Giotto facing left (inscr "Sub-Satellite") . . 60 65
3010 $1.50 Satellite with solar panels extended (inscr "Near Eros") 60 65
3011 $1.50 Satellite over planet surface (inscr "Explorer XVI") 60 65
3012 $1.50 Satellite with folded solar panels (inscr "Astro Challenger") 60 65
3013 $1.50 Circular satellite with cones on base (inscr "Giotto Halley's Comet") 60 65
MS3014 Two sheets. (a) 76 × 106 mm. $6 "Pegasus" over Saturn. (b) 106 × 76 mm. $6 "Lunar Prospector". Set of 2 sheets . . . . 4·75 5·00

Nos. 3002/7 and 3008/13 were each printed together, se-tenant, with the backgrounds forming composite designs.

Inscriptions on Nos. 3008/13 repeat those of Nos. 3002/7 in error.

2000. 25th Anniv of "Apollo–Soyuz" Joint Project. As T **582b** of Ghana. Multicoloured.
3015 $3 Thomas P. Stafford (Commander of "Apollo 18") . . . . . . 1·20 1·30
3016 $3 Joint Mission Badge . . 1·20 1·30
3017 $3 Donald D. Slayton ("Apollo 18") . . . . . 1·20 1·30
MS3018 70 × 88 mm. $6 Alexei Leonov (Commander of "Soyuz 19") . . . . 2·40 2·50

2000. 50th Anniv of Berlin Film Festival. As T **582c** of Ghana. Multicoloured.
3019 $1.50 James Stewart in *Mr. Hobbs takes a Vacation*, 1962 . . . . 60 65
3020 $1.50 Sachiko Hidari in *Kanojo To Kare*, 1964 . . 60 65
3021 $1.50 Juliette Mayniel in *Kirmes*, 1960 . . . . . . 60 65
3022 $1.50 *Le Bonheur*, 1965 . . . 60 65
3023 $1.50 *La Notte*, 1961 . . . 60 65
3024 $1.50 Lee Marvin in *Cat Ballou*, 1965 . . . . . . 60 65
MS3025 97 × 103 mm. $6 *The Thin Red Line*, 1999 . . . . 2·40 2·50

2000. 175th Anniv of Stockton and Darlington Line (first public railway). As T **582d** of Ghana. Multicoloured.
3026 $3 As Type **582d** of Ghana 1·20 1·30
3027 $3 George Stephenson's *Rocket* . . . . 1·20 1·30

2000. 250th Death Anniv of Johann Sebastian Bach (German composer). Sheet, 75 × 88 mm, containing vert design as T **312c** of Gambia. Multicoloured.
MS3028 $6 Statue of Johann Sebastian Bach . . . . 2·40 2·50

2000. Election of Albert Einstein (mathematical physicist) as *Time Magazine* "Man of the Century". Sheet, 117 × 90 mm, containing vert design as T **312d** of Gambia. Multicoloured.
MS3029 $6 Albert Einstein . . . 2·40 2·50

2000. Centenary of First Zeppelin Flight. As T **582e** of Ghana, each incorporating a portrait of Count Ferdinand von Zeppelin. Multicoloured.
3030 $3 LZ-3, 1906 . . . . . . 1·20 1·30
3031 $3 LZ-56, 1915 . . . . . . 1·20 1·30
3032 $3 LZ-88, 1917 . . . . . . 1·20 1·30
MS3033 118 × 75 mm. $6 LZ-1, 1900 (50 × 37 mm) . . . . 2·40 2·50

2000. Olympic Games, Sydney. As T **582f** of Ghana. Multicoloured.
3034 $2 Frantz Reichel (rugby), Paris (1900) 80 85
3035 $2 Modern discus-thrower 80 85
3036 $2 Seoul Sports Complex (1988) and South Korean flag 80 85
3037 $2 Ancient Greek wrestlers 80 85

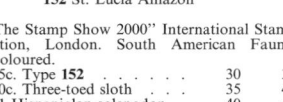

148 *Euplagia quadripunctaria*

2000. Butterflies and Moths. Multicoloured.
3038 $1.50 Type **148** 60 65
3039 $1.50 *Oenosandra boisduvalii* 60 65
3040 $1.50 *Thinopteryx erocopterata* 60 65
3041 $1.50 *Euschemon rafflesia* . . 60 65
3042 $1.50 *Milionia isodoxa* . . . 60 65
3043 $1.50 *Oysphania euprina* . . 60 65
3044 $1.50 *Thaloina clara* 60 65
3045 $1.50 *Zerynthia rumina* . . 60 65
3046 $1.50 *Attacus atlas* 60 65
3047 $1.50 *Lasiocampa quercus* 60 65
3048 $1.50 *Pararge schakra* . . . 60 65
3049 $1.50 *Arhopala amantes* . . 60 65
3050 $1.50 *Heliconius charithonia* 60 65
3051 $1.50 *Dismorphia amphione* 60 65
3052 $1.50 *Theela coronata* . . . 60 65
3053 $1.50 *Cithaerias esmeralda* 60 65
3054 $1.50 *Zerene eurydice* . . . 60 65
3055 $1.50 *Theela eudoela* 60 65
3056 $1.50 *Catonephele numilia* 60 65
3057 $1.50 *Diaethria clymena* . . 60 65
3058 $1.50 *Mesene phareus* . . . 60 65
3059 $1.50 *Estigmene aerea* . . . 60 65
3060 $1.50 *Marpesia petreus* . . . 60 65
3061 $1.50 *Cepheuptychia cephus* 60 65
MS3062 Six sheets. (a) 70 × 95 mm. $6 *Tajuria cippus*. (b) 78 × 97 mm. $6 *Ecpantheria serifonia*. (c) 75 × 105 mm. $6 *Ornithoptera alexandrae*. (d) 127 × 100 mm. $6 *Hyalophora cecropia* (vert). (e) 100 × 73 mm. $2 *Cyrestis thyodamos*; $2 *Papilionidae*; $2 *Apatura iris*; $2 *Crypsiphona ocyltaria*. (f) 100 × 73 mm. $2 *Hemaris thysbe*; $2 *Helicopis cupido*; $2 *Aretia eaja*; $2 *Erateina staudingeri*. Set of 6 sheets . . 16·00 17·00

Nos. 3038/43, 3044/9, 3050/5 and 3056/61 were each printed together, se-tenant, with the backgrounds forming composite designs.

No. 3038 is inscribed "quadripunctama", No. 3041 "Eusehemon zafflesia", No. 3045 "Zerynthia", No. 3048 "Parage", No. 3050 "charitonius", No. 3056 "numili", **MS**3062 (d) "Hyalophor", all in error.

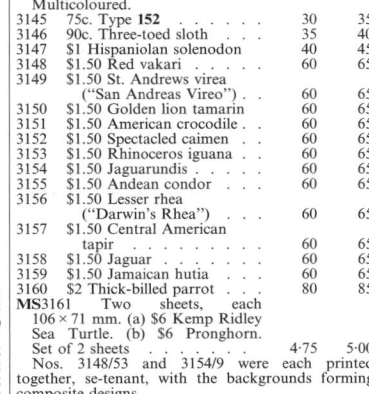

150 Golsdorf Compound Tank Locomotive, Vienna Metropolitan Railway

2000. Railways of the World. Multicoloured.
3066 90c. Type **150** 35 40
3067 $1 Vauxhall, Dublin and Kingstown Railway . . . 40 45
3068 $1.50 Electric railcar, South Jersey Transit 60 65
3069 $1.50 "Metroliner", Amtrak 60 65
3070 $1.50 Maglev train, H.S.S.T. 60 65
3071 $1.50 Model E60C electric locomotive, Amtrak . . . 60 65
3072 $1.50 "Parsifal" diesel express, T.E.E. 60 65
3073 $1.50 Class G.G.I. electric locomotive, Pennsylvania 60 65
3074 $1.50 Electric locomotive, Norwegian State Railways 60 65
3075 $1.50 Diesel-electric locomotive, Jamaica Railway 60 65
3076 $1.50 Diesel-electric locomotive, China 60 65
3077 $1.50 Electric locomotive, Portuguese Railways . . . 60 65
3078 $1.50 "Re-6/6" electric locomotive, Swiss Federal Railways 60 65
3079 $1.50 Dual-purpose electric locomotive, Turkish State Railways 60 65
3080 $1.50 Passenger steam locomotive, Perak Govt Railway 60 65
3081 $1.50 Tank locomotive, Rhondda & Swansea Railway 60 65
3082 $1.50 Aspinal tank locomotive, Lancashire & Yorkshire Railway . . . 60 65
3083 $1.50 Tank locomotive, Northwestern Railway, India 60 65
3084 $1.50 Imperial Mail locomotive, Shanghai–Nanking Railway 60 65
3085 $1.50 Passenger tank locomotive, Danish State Railway 60 65
3086 $1.50 Braithwait steam locomotive, Eastern Counties Railway 60 65
3087 $1.50 *Philadelphia*, Austria 60 65
3088 $1.50 Stephenson locomotive of 1836 . . . . 60 65
3089 $1.50 *Aigle* locomotive, Western Railway, France 60 65
3090 $1.50 Borsig Standard steam locomotive, Germany . . 60 65
3091 $1.50 *Ajax*, Great Western Railway 60 65
3092 $2 Metro-Cammell diesel-electric locomotive, Nigerian Railways 80 85
3093 $3 T.G.V. 001 high-speed turbo train, French National Railways . . . 1·20 1·30
MS3094 Four sheets, each 81 × 57 mm. (a) $6 *The Experiment*, U.S.A. (b) $6 Freight steam locomotive, South African Railway. (c) $6 Diesel-electric locomotive, South African Railway. (d) $6 "Prospector" diesel railcar, Western Australia. Set of 4 sheets . . . . 9·75 10·00

151 Irish Setter

2000. Cats and Dogs. Multicoloured.
3095 45c. Type **151** 20 25
3096 75c. Blue point snowshoe 30 35
3097 90c. Dalmatian 35 40
3098 $1.50 California spangled cat 60 65
3099 $1.50 Russian blue 60 65
3100 $1.50 Seal point Siamese . . 60 65
3101 $1.50 Black Devon rex . . . 60 65
3102 $1.50 Silver tabby British shorthair 60 65
3103 $1.50 Tricolour Japanese bobtail 60 65
3104 $1.50 Great Dane 60 65
3105 $1.50 Newfoundland 60 65
3106 $1.50 Rottweiler 60 65
3107 $1.50 Bulldog 60 65
3108 $1.50 Japanese spitz 60 65
3109 $1.50 Bull terrier 60 65
3110 $1.50 British white shorthair 60 65
3111 $1.50 Blue-cream American shorthair 60 65
3112 $1.50 Bombay 60 65
3113 $1.50 Red Burmese 60 65
3114 $1.50 Sorrel Abyssinian . . 60 65
3115 $1.50 Ocicat 60 65
3116 $1.50 Alaskan malamute . . 60 65
3117 $1.50 Golden retriever . . . 60 65
3118 $1.50 Afghan hound 60 65
3119 $1.50 Long-haired dachshund 60 65
3120 $1.50 Irish terrier 60 65
3121 $1.50 Miniature poodle . . 60 65
3122 $2 German shepherd . . . 80 85
3123 $3 Black and white maine coon . . . . 1·20 1·30
3124 $4 Brown tabby British shorthair . . . . 1·60 1·70
MS3125 Four sheets. (a) 106 × 76 mm. $5 Silver Classic Tabby Persian (horiz). (b) 76 × 106 mm. $5 Red-white Bicolor British Shorthair. (c) 106 × 76 mm. $6 Basset Hound (horiz). (d) 76 × 106 mm. $6 Labrador Retriever. Set of 4 sheets 9·00 9·25

Nos. 3098/103 (cats), 3104/9 (dogs), 3110/15 (cats) and 3116/21 (dogs) were each printed together, se-tenant, with the backgrounds forming composite designs.

No. 3108 is inscribed "Sptz" and No. 3121 "Minature", both in error.

2000. "Euro 2000" Football Championship. As T **479** of Grenada. Multicoloured.
3126 $1.50 Tofting (Danish player) 60 65
3127 $1.50 Danish team 60 65
3128 $1.50 Michael Laudrup (Danish player) 60 65
3129 $1.50 Jorgensen (Danish player) 60 65
3130 $1.50 Philips Stadium, Eindhoven 60 65
3131 $1.50 Moller (Danish player) 60 65
3132 $1.50 Thuram (French player) 60 65
3133 $1.50 French team 60 65
3134 $1.50 Barthez (French player) 60 65
3135 $1.50 Zidane (French player) 60 65
3136 $1.50 Jan Breydel Stadium, Bruges 60 65
3137 $1.50 Michel Platini (French player) 60 65
3138 $1.50 Giovanni van Bronckhorst (Dutch player) 60 65
3139 $1.50 Dutch team 60 65
3140 $1.50 Patrick Kluivert (Dutch player) 60 65
3141 $1.50 Johan Cruyff (Dutch player) 60 65
3142 $1.50 Amsterdam Arena Stadium 60 65
3143 $1.50 Zenden (Dutch player) 60 65
MS3144 Three sheets, each 145 × 96 mm. (a) $6 Bo Johansson (Danish trainer) (vert). (b) $6 Roger Lemerre (French trainer) (vert). (c) $6 Frank Rijkaard (Dutch trainer) (vert). Set of 3 sheets . . . . 7·25 7·50

152 St. Lucia Amazon

2000. "The Stamp Show 2000" International Stamp Exhibition, London. South American Fauna. Multicoloured.
3145 75c. Type **152** 30 35
3146 90c. Three-toed sloth . . . 35 40
3147 $1 Hispaniolan solenodon 40 45
3148 $1.50 Red vakari 60 65
3149 $1.50 St. Andrews virea ("San Andreas Vireo") . . 60 65
3150 $1.50 Golden lion tamarin 60 65
3151 $1.50 American crocodile . . 60 65
3152 $1.50 Spectacled caimen . . 60 65
3153 $1.50 Rhinoceros iguana . . 60 65
3154 $1.50 Jaguarundis 60 65
3155 $1.50 Andean condor . . . 60 65
3156 $1.50 Lesser rhea ("Darwin's Rhea") . . . 60 65
3157 $1.50 Central American tapir 60 65
3158 $1.50 Jaguar 60 65
3159 $1.50 Jamaican hutia . . . 60 65
3160 $2 Thick-billed parrot . . . 80 85
MS3161 Two sheets, each 106 × 71 mm. (a) $6 Kemp Ridley Sea Turtle. (b) $6 Pronghorn. Set of 2 sheets . . . . 4·75 5·00

Nos. 3148/53 and 3154/9 were each printed together, se-tenant, with the backgrounds forming composite designs.

2000. Monarchs of the Millennium. As T **314a** of Gambia. Multicoloured (except Nos. 3162 and 3166).
3162 $1.50 King Louis XVI of France (lilac, green and brown) 60 65
3163 $1.50 King Louis XVIII of France 60 65
3164 $1.50 Kublai Khan's Empress, China 60 65
3165 $1.50 Queen Mary I of England 60 65
3166 $1.50 Mohammed Ali, Shah of Iran (black, green and brown) 60 65
3167 $1.50 Emperor Qianlong of China 60 65
MS3168 116 × 136 mm. $6 Grand Duke Vladimir I of Kiev . . . 2·40 2·50

2000. Popes of the Millennium. As T **314b** of Gambia. Multicoloured (except No. **MS**3173).
3169 $1.50 Adrian VI 60 65
3170 $1.50 Paul II 60 65
3171 $1.50 Callistus III 60 65
3172 $1.50 Eugene IV 60 65
MS3173 116 × 136 mm. $6 Gregory XI (grey, black and green) . . 2·40 2·50

153 "Wind"

154 David Copperfield (portrait at left with levitating legs at right)

2000. "The Storm Riders" (Chinese comic series by Ma Wing Sing). Multicoloured.
3174 $4 Type **153** . . . . . . 1·60 1·70
3175 $4 "Cloud" with sword . . 1·60 1·70
3176 $4 "Cloud" with dragon . . 1·60 1·70
3177 $4 "Wind" with waves . . 1·60 1·70

2000. David Copperfield (conjurer). Multicoloured.
3178 $1.50 Type **154** 60 65
3179 $1.50 Portrait at right with levitating body at left . . 60 65

3180 $1.50 Portrait at right with levitating legs at left . . . 60 65
3181 $1.50 Portrait at left with levitating body at right . . 60 65

2000. "Espana 2000" International Stamp Exhibition, Madrid. Paintings from the Prado. As T **326a** of Gambia. Multicoloured.

3182 $1.50 "St. John the Baptist and the Franciscan Maestro, Henricus Werl" (Robert Campin) 60 65
3183 $1.50 "Justice and Peace" (Corrado Giaquinto) . . . 60 65
3184 $1.50 "St. Barbara" (Robert Campin) 60 65
3185 $1.50 "John Fane, 10th Earl of Westmoreland" (Thomas Lawrence) . . . 60 65
3186 $1.50 "The Marchioness of Manzanedo" (Jean-Louis-Ernest Meissonier) 60 65
3187 $1.50 "Mr. Storer" (Martin Archer Shee) 60 65
3188 $1.50 "Isabella Carla Eugenia" (Alonso Sanchez Coello) 60 65
3189 $1.50 "Nobleman with his Hand on his Chest" (El Greco) 60 65
3190 $1.50 "King Philip III" (Juan Pantoja de la Cruz) 60 65
3191 $1.50 Madonna and Child from "The Holy Family with Sts. Ildefonsus and John the Evangelist, and the Master Alonso de Villegas" (Blas del Prado) 60 65
3192 $1.50 "The Last Supper" (Bartolme Carducci) . . . 60 65
3193 $1.50 St. John from "The Holy Family with Sts. Ildefonsus and John the Evangelist, and the Master Alonso de Villegas" 60 65
3194 $1.50 "St. Dominic of Silos" (Bartolome Bermejo) . . 60 65
3195 $1.50 "Head of a Prophet" (Jaume Huguet) 60 65
3196 $1.50 "Christ giving His Blessing" (Fernando Gallego) 60 65
3197 $1.50 "The Mystic Marriage of St. Catherine" (Alonso Sanchez Coello) 60 65
3198 $1.50 "St. Catherine of Alexandria" (Fernando Yanez de la Almedina) . . 60 65
3199 $1.50 "Virgin and Child" (Luis de Morales) 60 65
MS3200 Three sheets, each 110 × 90 mm. (a) $6 As No. 3192 (horiz). (b) $6 "The Coronation of the Virgin" (El Greco) (horiz). (c) $6 As No. 3191. Set of 3 sheets 7·25 7·50

155 Barbara Taylor Bradford

2000. Great Writers of the 20th Century: Barbara Taylor Bradford. Sheet 126 × 87 mm.

MS3201 **155** $6 multicoloured . . 2·40 2·50

2000. 60th Anniv of Battle of Britain. As T **327** of Gambia. Multicolourred.

3202 $1 R.A.F. Pilots running to their planes 40 45
3203 $1 Barrage balloons 40 45
3204 $1 Supermarine Spitfire B aircraft (fighter) 40 45
3205 $1 Princess Elizabeth broadcasting, 1940 . . . 40 45
3206 $1 Fire Watcher and auxilary fireman 40 45
3207 $1 Painting white bands round posts 40 45
3208 $1 Bombed building 40 45
3209 $1 Air Raid Wardens and auxilary policewoman . . 40 45
3210 $1 Women fire-fighters . . . 40 45
3211 $1 Family leaving bombed home 40 45
3212 $1 Searchlight 40 45
3213 $1 Winston Churchill inspecting bomb damage in Coventry 40 45
3214 $1 Rescue team evacuating casualty 40 45
3215 $1 Re-united family 40 45
3216 $1 After air raid on Buckingham Gate 40 45
3217 $1 Aftermath of air raid on Coventry 40 45
MS3218 Two sheets, each 106 × 76 mm. (a) $6 Hawker Hurricane (fighter). (b) $6 British family outside air raid shelter (vert). Set of 2 sheets . . . . 4·75 5·00

No. 3215 is inscribed "RESCUSE" in error.

156 Queen Elizabeth, the Queen Mother

157 Rat Snake

2000. 100th Birthday of Queen Elizabeth, the Queen Mother.

3219 **156** $1.50 multicoloured . . 60 65

2000. Faces of the Millennium: Queen Elizabeth the Queen Mother. As T **307a** of Gambia showing collage of miniature flower photographs. Multicoloured.

3220 $1 Top of head (face value at left) 40 45
3221 $1 Top of head (face value at right) 40 45
3222 $1 Eye and temple (face value at left) 40 45
3223 $1 Temple (face value at right) 40 45
3224 $1 Cheek (face value at left) 40 45
3225 $1 Cheek (face value at right) 40 45
3226 $1 Chin (face value at left) 40 45
3227 $1 Neck (face value at right) 40 45

Nos. 3220/7 were printed together, se-tenant, in sheetlets of 8 with the stamps arranged in two vertical columns separated by a gutter also containing miniature photographs. When viewed as a whole the sheetlet forms a portrait of the Queen Mother.

2000. Faces of the Millennium: Pope John Paul II. As T **307a** of Gambia showing collage of miniature religious photographs. Multicoloured.

3228 $1 Top of head (face value at left) 40 45
3229 $1 Top of head (face value at right) 40 45
3230 $1 Ear (face value at left) 40 45
3231 $1 Temple and eye (face value at right) 40 45
3232 $1 Neck and collar (face value at left) 40 45
3233 $1 Cheek and fingertips (face value at right) . . . 40 45
3234 $1 Shoulder (face value at left) 40 45
3235 $1 Hands (face value at right) 40 45

Nos. 3228/35 were printed together, se-tenant, in sheetlets of 8 with the stamps arranged in two vertical columns separated by a gutter also containing miniature photographs. When viewed as a whole the sheetlet forms a portrait of Pope John Paul II.

2001. Chinese New Year. "Year of the Snake". Multicoloured.

3236 90c. Type **157** 35 40
3237 90c. Mangrove snake . . . 35 40
3238 90c. Boomslang 35 40
3239 90c. Emerald tree boa . . . 35 40
3240 90c. African egg-eating snake 35 40
3241 90c. Chinese green tree viper 35 40
MS3242 74 × 88 mm. $4 King Cobra 1·60 1·70

2001. Bicentenary of Rijksmuseum, Amsterdam. Dutch Paintings. As T **330a** of Gambia. Multicoloured.

3243 $1.50 Harpist from "A Music Party" (Rembrandt) 60 65
3244 $1.50 Woman singing from "A Music Party" 60 65
3245 $1.50 Boy and girl from "Rutger Jan Schimmelpenninck with his Wife and Children" (Pierre-Paul Prud'hon) . . 60 65
3246 $1.50 Girl from "Rutger Jan Schimmelpenninck with his Wife and Children" 60 65
3247 $1.50 "The Syndics" (Thomas de Keyser) . . . 60 65
3248 $1.50 "Marriage Portrait of Isaac Massa and Beatrix van der Laen" (Frans Hals) 60 65
3249 $1.50 Bride from "Marriage Portrait of Isaac Massa and Beatrix van der Laen" 60 65
3250 $1.50 "Winter Landscape with Ice Skaters" (Hendrick Avercamp) . . 60 65
3251 $1.50 Woman and clerk from "The Spendthrift" (Cornelis Troost) 60 65
3252 $1.50 Beggars from "The Spendthrift" 60 65
3253 $1.50 Two men and a Woman from "The Art Gallery of Jan Gildemeester Jansz" (Adriaan de Lelie) 60 65
3254 $1.50 Man examining painting from "The Art Gallery of Jan Gildemeester Jansz" . . 60 65
3255 $1.50 Couple with musicians from "Garden Party" (Dirck Hals) 60 65
3256 $1.50 "Still Life with Gilt Goblet" (Willem Claesz Heda) 60 65
3257 $1.50 Two men arguing from "Orestes and Pylades disputing at the Altar" (Pieter Lastman) 60 65
3258 $1.50 Women at altar from "Orestes and Pylades disputing at the Altar" . . 60 65
3259 $1.50 "Self-portrait in a Yellow Robe" (Jan Lievens) 60 65
3260 $1.50 Couples with monkey from "Garden Party" . . 60 65
3261 $1.50 Goatherd and goats from "Dune Landscape" (Jan van Goyen) 60 65
3262 $1.50 "The Raampoortje" (Wouter Johannes van Troostwijk) 60 65
3263 $1.50 Houses from "The Ferryboat" (Esaias van de Velde) 60 65
3264 $1.50 "The Departure of a Dignitary from Middleburg" (Adriaen van de Venne) 60 65
3265 $1.50 Cart on ferry from "The Ferryboat" 60 65
3266 $1.50 Group of peasants by fence from "Dune Landscape" 60 65
MS3267 Four sheets. (a) 87 × 118 mm. $6 "Anna accused by Tobit of Stealing a Kid" (Rembrandt). (b) 118 × 87 mm. $6 "Cleopatra's Banquet" (Gerard Lairesse) (horiz). (c) 118 × 87 mm. $6 "View of Tivoli" (Isaac de Moucheron) (horiz). (d) 87 × 118 mm. $6 "A Music Party" (Rembrandt). Set of 4 sheets 9·75 10·00

No. 3248 is inscribed "Marraige" and "dr" in error.

158 Greater Flamingo

2001. Tropical Fauna. Multicoloured.

3268 75c. Type **158** 30 35
3269 90c. Cuban crocodile (horiz) 35 40
3270 $1 Jaguarundi 40 45
3271 $1.50 Red-breasted toucan 60 65
3272 $1.50 Mexican black howler monkey 60 65
3273 $1.50 Fieck's pygmy boa . . 60 65
3274 $1.50 Red-eyed tree frog . . 60 65
3275 $1.50 Caimen 60 65
3276 $1.50 Jaguar 60 65
3277 $1.50 Cuban pygmy owl . . 60 65
3278 $1.50 Woody spider monkey 60 65
3279 $1.50 Bee hummingbirds . . 60 65
3280 $1.50 Dragonfly, leaf frog and poison dart frog . . 60 65
3281 $1.50 Red brocket deer . . 60 65
3282 $1.50 Cuban stream anole 60 65
3283 $2 Wedge-capped capuchin monkey (horiz) 80 85
MS3284 Two sheets. (a) 72 × 104 mm. $6 Ocelot. (b) 72 × 98 mm. $6 Western knight anole. Set of 2 sheets . . . . 4·75 5·00

Nos. 3271/6 and 3277/82 were each printed together, se-tenant, with the backgrounds forming composite designs.

No. 3271 is inscribed "Red-Breated" in error.

2001. Characters from "Pokemon" (children's cartoon series). As T **332a** of Gambia. Multicoloured.

3285 $1.50 "Bellsprout No. 69" 60 65
3286 $1.50 "Vulpix No. 37" . . . 60 65
3287 $1.50 "Dewgong No. 87" 60 65
3288 $1.50 "Oddish No. 43" . . 60 65
3289 $1.50 "Dratini No. 147" . . 60 65
3290 $1.50 "Jigglypuff No. 39" 60 65
MS3291 74 × 114 mm. $6 "Pikachu No. 25" . . . . 2·40 2·50

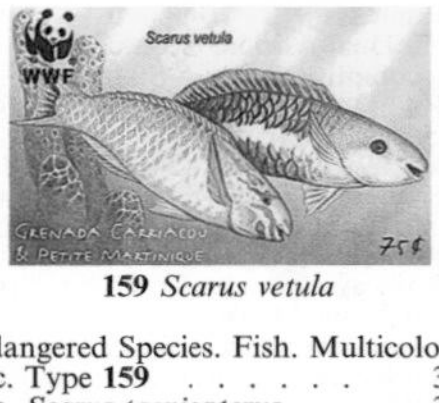

159 *Scarus vetula*

2001. Endangered Species. Fish. Multicoloured.

3292 75c. Type **159** 30 35
3293 75c. *Scarus taeniopterus* . . 30 35
3294 75c. *Sparisoma viride* . . . 30 35
3295 75c. *Sparisoma rubripinne* 30 35

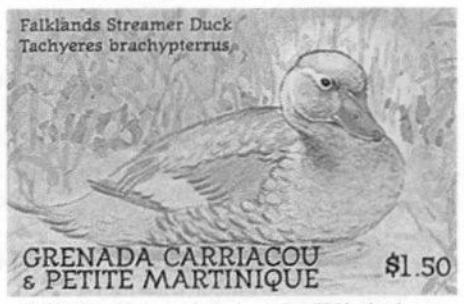

160 Falkland Islands Flightless Streamer Duck ("Falklands Streamer Duck")

2001. Caribbean Ducks and Waterfowl. Mult.

3296 $1.50 Type **160** 60 65
3297 $1.50 Black-crowned night heron 60 65
3298 $1.50 Muscovy duck 60 65
3299 $1.50 Ruddy duck 60 65
3300 $1.50 Northern screamer ("Black necked Screamer") 60 65
3301 $1.50 White-faced whistling duck 60 65
MS3302 60 × 93 mm. $6 Great egret (vert) . . . . 2·40 2·50

Nos. 3296/301 were printed together, se-tenant, with the backgrounds forming a composite design.

161 Virgie Cary (Shirley Temple) sitting on Chair

2001. Shirley Temple in *The Littlest Rebel*. Showing scenes from the film. Multicoloured.

3303 $2 Type **161** 80 85
3304 $2 Virgie with her mother (Karen Morley) 80 85
3305 $2 Virgie with her father, Captain Cary (John Boles) 80 85
3306 $2 Virgie comforting her mother 80 85
3307 $2 Virgie with Uncle Billy (Bill Robinson) and Col. Morrison (Jack Holt) . . 80 85
3308 $2 Virgie hugging her father 80 85
3309 $2 Virgie being admonished by Col. Morrison (horiz) 80 85
3310 $2 Virgie disguised as a negro slave (horiz) . . . 80 85
3311 $2 Virgie escaping with her father in buggy (horiz) . . 80 85
3312 $2 Virgie with Abraham Lincoln (Frank McGlynn Sr.) (horiz) 80 85
MS3313 105 × 75 mm. $6 Virgie tap dancing with Uncle Billy . . . 2·40 2·50

2001. Betty Boop (cartoon character). As T **486** of Grenada showing Betty in various geographical locations. Multicoloured.

3314 $1 Flamenco dancing, Spain 40 45
3315 $1 In national dress, Turkey 40 45
3316 $1 Wearing lei, Hawaii . . . 40 45
3317 $1 As belly-dancer, Egypt 40 45
3318 $1 With flower in hair, South Pacific 40 45
3319 $1 Riding horse, Argentina 40 45
3320 $1 Drinking champagne, France 40 45
3321 $1 Sitting in sports car, Hollywood 40 45
3322 $1 As Statue of Liberty, New York 40 45
MS3323 Two sheets, each 90 × 110 mm. (a) $6 On a gondola, Venice. (b) $6 By river, India. Set of 2 sheets . . . . 4·75 5·00

162 Clark Gable smoking Cigar

2001. Birth Centenary of Clark Gable (American film star). Multicoloured.

3324 $1.50 Type **162** 60 65
3325 $1.50 In *Gone With the Wind* 60 65
3326 $1.50 Sitting in director's chair 60 65
3327 $1.50 Signing autograph . . 60 65
3328 $1.50 Wearing checked tie 60 65
3329 $1.50 In pin-stripe suit with legs crossed 60 65
3330 $1.50 Seated in car 60 65
3331 $1.50 In grey suit 60 65
3332 $1.50 In casual dress . . . 60 65

3333 $1.50 Arm resting on knee 60 65
3334 $1.50 On telephone 60 65
3335 $1.50 In evening dress . . . 60 65
MS3336 Two sheets. (a) 114 × 88 mm. $6 Wearing U.S. Air Force uniform. (b) 98 × 110 mm. $6 As Rhett Butler in *Gone With the Wind*. Set of 2 sheets . . . 4·75 5·00

2001. "Philanippon '01" International Stamp Exhibition, Tokyo. Japanese Paintings. As T **493** of Grenada. Multicoloured

3337 75c. "Daily Life in Edo" (Miyagawa Choshun) . . 30 35
3338 90c. "Twelve Famous Places in Japan" (Kani Isen'in Naganobu) 35 40
3339 $1 "Along the Sumida River" (Kano Kyuei) . . 40 45
3340 $1.25 "Cranes" (Kano Eisen'in Michinobu) . . . 50 55
3341 $2 "Courtesan of Yoshiwara" (Katsukawa Shun'ei) 80 85
3342 $2 "Kiritsubo Chapter" (86 × 28 mm) 80 85
3343 $2 "Akahsi Chapter" (86 × 28 mm) 80 85
3344 $2 "Hatsune Chapter" (86 × 28 mm) 80 85
3345 $2 "E-Awase Chapter" (86 × 28 mm) 80 85
3346 $2 Buddha on golden elephant (vert) 80 85
3347 $2 Buddha on white elephant (vert) 80 85
3348 $2 Buddha on elephant and temple (vert) 80 85
3349 $2 Buddha on elephant with crowd (vert) 80 85
3350 $3 "Bear killing" (unsigned) 1·20 1·30
MS3351 Two sheets. (a) 86 × 74 mm. $6 "Sage pointing to the Moon" (Katagiri Ranseki). (b) 97 × 77 mm. $6 Frontispiece from "Devadatta" (Itsukushima-Jinja) (vert). Set of 2 sheets . . . . . 4·75 5·00

Nos. 3342/5 depicts "Tale of Genji" (Kano Ryusetsu Hidenobu), and 3346/9 illustrates "The Lotus Sutra".

2001. Death Centenary of Queen Victoria. As **590a** of Ghana. Multicoloured.

3352 $3 Queen Victoria at her Coronation . . . . 1·20 1·30
3353 $3 Princess Victoria as a young girl, standing . . . 1·20 1·30
3354 $3 In old age . . . . 1·20 1·30
MS3355 107 × 77 mm. $6 Queen Victoria within royal arms . . 2·40 2·50

2001. 25th Death Anniv of Mao Tse-tung (Chinese leader). As T **590b** of Ghana. Multicoloured

3356 $1.50 Young Mao Tse-tung on steps (horiz) 60 65
3357 $1.50 Mao talking with country people on the Long March (horiz) . . . 60 65
3358 $1.50 Visiting a rural market place (horiz) 60 65
3359 $1.50 Explaining doctrines to soldiers (horiz) 60 65
MS3360 93 × 134 mm. $3 Mao Tse-tung in 1939 proclaiming the People's Republic of China . . 1·20 1·30

2001. 75th Death Anniv of Claude-Oscar Monet (French painter). As T **590c** of Ghana. Mult.

3361 $1 "The Magpie" 40 45
3362 $1 "La Pointe de la Heve at Low Tide" 40 45
3363 $1 "Regatta at Argenteuil" 40 45
3364 $1 "La Grenouillere (the Frog Pond)" 40 45
MS3365 138 × 110 mm. $6 "J. F. Jacquemart with Parasol" (vert) 2·40 2·50

2001. 75th Birthday of Queen Elizabeth II. As T **590d** of Ghana. Multicoloured.

3366 $1.25 Princess Elizabeth wearing pearl necklace . . 50 55
3367 $1.25 Queen in blue coat with brooch 50 55
3368 $1.25 Wearing tiara 50 55
3369 $1.25 Queen Elizabeth in pink 50 55
3370 $1.25 Queen in Order of the Bath robes 50 55
3371 $1.25 Wearing blue hat and coat 50 55
3372 $2 Young Queen in red hat with feathers 80 85
3373 $2 Queen Elizabeth in evening dress with orders 80 85
3374 $2 Young Queen wearing tiara 80 85
MS3375 119 × 147 mm. $5 Queen Elizabeth at Coronation (38 × 51 mm) . . . . 2·00 2·10

2001. Death Centenary of Giuseppe Verdi (Italian composer). As T **590e** of Ghana. Showing various portraits of the composer.

3376 25c. multicoloured 10 15
3377 75c. multicoloured 30 35
3378 $2 multicoloured 80 85
3379 $3 multicoloured . . . . . 1·20 1·30
MS3380 78 × 112 mm. $6 multicoloured . . . . 2·40 2·50

Nos. 3376/9 were printed together, se-tenant, with the backgrounds forming a composite design.

2001. Death Centenary of Henri de Toulouse-Lautrec (French painter). As T **590f** of Ghana. Multicoloured.

3381 $1 "Helene V" (horiz) . . . 40 45
3382 $1 "Clownesse" (horiz) . . 40 45
3383 $1 "Madame Berthe Bady" (horiz) 40 45
3384 $1 "Woman with the Black Boa" (horiz) 40 45
MS3385 55 × 85 mm. $6 "Loie Fuller at the Folies Bergere" . . . . 2·40 2·50

2001. Birth Centenary of Marlene Dietrich (German actress). As T **495** of Grenada. Multicoloured.

3386 $2 Singing on stage 80 85
3387 $2 With feather boa 80 85
3388 $2 In floral dress 80 85
3389 $2 Wearing hat, coat and gloves 80 85

163 *Creole* (racing schooner), 1927

2001. Ships. Multicoloured.

3390 90c. Type **163** 35 40
3391 $1 *Britannia* (steamer), 1887 40 45
3392 $1.25 *Santa Maria* and Christopher Columbus, 1492 . . . . 50 55
3393 $1.25 *Sao Gabriel* and Vasco da Gama, 1498 . . . . . 50 55
3394 $1.25 *Vitoria* and Ferdinand Magellan, 1519 . . . . . 50 55
3395 $1.25 *Golden Hind* and Sir Francis Drake, 1577 . . . 50 55
3396 $1.25 H.M.S. *Endeavour* and Captain James Cook, 1768 . . . . 50 55
3397 $1.25 H.M.S. *Erebus* and John Franklin 50 55
3398 $1.25 *William Fawcett* (paddle steamer), 1829 . . 50 55
3399 $1.25 *Sirius* (paddle steamer), 1838 . . . . . . 50 55
3400 $1.25 *Great Britain* (steam/sail vessel), 1843 . . . . 50 55
3401 $1.25 *Oriental* (American clipper), 1849 . . . . . . 50 55
3402 $1.25 *Lightning* (clipper), 1854 . . . . 50 55
3403 $1.25 *Great Eastern* (paddle steamer), 1858 . . . . . 50 55
3404 $1.25 *Mayflower* (Pilgrim Fathers), 1620 (vert) . . . 50 55
3405 $1.25 *Sv. Petr* (Bering), 1728 (vert) 50 55
3406 $1.25 H.M.S. *Beagle* (Darwin), 1825 (vert) . . 50 55
3407 $1.25 H.M.S. *Challenger* (survey ship), (vert) . . . 50 55
3408 $1.25 *Vega* (Nordenskjold), 1872 (vert) 50 55
3409 $1.25 *Fram* (Amundsen and Nansen), 1892 (vert) . . . 50 55
3410 $2 *Ariel* (clipper), 1865 . . . 80 85
3411 $3 *Sindia* (barque), 1887 . . 1·20 1·30
MS3412 Two sheets, each 60 × 45 mm. (a) $6 *Cutty Sark* (clipper), 1869. (b) $6 *Challenger* (American clipper), 1851. Set of 2 sheets . . . . 4·75 5·00

No. 3405 is inscribed "GABRIEL" in error. The same stamp shows two different incorrect spellings of Bering.

No. 3407 is inscribed "1852" in error.

164 *Vanda Singapore* (orchid)

2001. Orchids. Multicoloured.

3413 25c. Type **164** 10 15
3414 50c. *Vanda Joan Warne* . . 20 25
3415 75c. *Vanda lamellata* 30 35
3416 $1.50 *Papilionanthe teres* . . 60 65
3417 $1.50 *Vanda flabellata* . . . 60 65
3418 $1.50 *Vanda tessellata* (name bottom left) 60 65
3419 $1.50 *Vanda pumila* 60 65
3420 $1.50 *Rhynchostylis gigantea* 60 65
3421 $1.50 *Vandopsis gigantea* . . 60 65
3422 $1.50 *Vanda tessellata* (name centre left) 60 65
3423 $1.50 *Vanda helvola* 60 65
3424 $1.50 *Vanda brunnea* 60 65
3425 $1.50 *Vanda stageana* . . . 60 65
3426 $1.50 *Vanda limbata* 60 65
3427 $1.50 *Vandopsis tricolor* . . 60 65
3428 $2 *Vanda merrillii* 80 85
MS3429 Two sheets, each 68 × 97 mm. (a) $6 *Vanda insignis*. (b) $6 *Vandopsis lissochiloides*. Set of 2 sheets . . . . 4·75 5·00

No. 3425 is inscribed "STANGEANA" in error.

165 Richard Petty (stock car driver)

2001. Richard Petty (stock car driver). Two sheets each containing vert designs as T **165**. Multicoloured.

MS3430 (a) 92 × 130 mm. $6 Type **165**. (b) 92 × 135 mm. $6 Richard Petty being interviewed. Set of 2 sheets . . . . 4·75 5·00

166 Dale Earnhardt in Yellow Overalls, 1980

2001. Dale Earnhardt (stock car driver) Commemoration. Multicoloured.

3431 $2 Type **166** 80 85
3432 $2 With Winston Cup, 1986 80 85
3433 $2 With Winston Cup, 1987 80 85
3434 $2 With Winston Cup, 1990 80 85
3435 $2 With Winston Cup, 1991 80 85
3436 $2 With Winston Cup, 1993 80 85
3437 $2 With Winston Cup, 1994 80 85
3438 $4 Dale Earnhardt's Chevrolet cars (76 × 52 mm) . . . . . . 1·60 1·70

167 Ferrari F1 86, 1986

2001. Ferrari Formula 1 Racing Cars. Multicoloured.

3439 $1.50 Type **167** 60 65
3440 $1.50 Ferrari F1 89, 1989 60 65
3441 $1.50 Ferrari F92A, 1992 60 65
3442 $1.50 Ferrari F1 93, 1993 60 65
3443 $1.50 Ferrari 412T1, 1994 60 65
3444 $1.50 Ferrari F310, 1996 . . 60 65

168 World Cup Publicity Poster, Brazil, 1950

169 "Coronation of the Virgin" (Filipo Lippi)

2001. World Cup Football Championship, Japan and Korea (2002). Designs showing publicity posters and badges from previous World Cups. Multicoloured.

3445 $1.50 Type **168** 60 65
3446 $1.50 Switzerland, 1954 . . 60 65
3447 $1.50 Sweden, 1958 . . . . 60 65
3448 $1.50 Chile, 1962 . . . . . 60 65
3449 $1.50 England, 1966 . . . . 60 65
3450 $1.50 Mexico, 1970 . . . . 60 65
3451 $1.50 Argentina, 1978 . . . 60 65
3452 $1.50 Spain, 1982 . . . . . 60 65
3453 $1.50 Mexico, 1986 . . . . 60 65
3454 $1.50 Italy, 1990 . . . . . 60 65
3455 $1.50 U.S.A., 1994 . . . . 60 65
3456 $1.50 France, 1998 . . . . 60 65
MS3457 Two sheets, 88 × 75 mm. (a) $6 Uruguay, 1930. (b) $6 Detail of World Cup trophy, Japan-Korea, 2002. Set of 2 sheets . . . . . 4·75 5·00

2001. Christmas. Italian Renaissance Religious Paintings. Multicoloured.

3458 25c. Type **169** 10 15
3459 75c. "Virgin and Child" (Andrea Mantegna) . . . 30 35
3460 $1.50 "Madonna and Child" (Tommaso Masaccio) . . 60 65
3461 $3 "Madonna and Child" (Raffaelo Sanzio) . . . . 1·20 1·30
MS3462 96 × 136 mm. $6 "Virgin and Child enthroned with Angels" (Mantegna) . . . . 2·40 2·50

170 "Battle of Solebay, 1672"

2001. Royal Navy Commemoration. Marine Paintings. Multicoloured.

3463 75c. "H.M.S. Renown (battle cruiser), Portsmouth Harbour, 1922" (vert) 30 35
3464 90c. "Battle of the Saintes, 1782" (vert) 35 40
3465 $1.50 Type **170** 60 65
3466 $1.50 "Royal Prince, 1679" 60 65
3467 $1.50 "Battle of Texel, 1673" 60 65
3468 $1.50 "Battle of Scheveningen, 1653" . . . 60 65
3469 $1.50 "Battle against Barbary Pirates, 1600s" 60 65
3470 $1.50 "Capture of Royal Charles, 1667" 60 65
3471 $1.50 "The Glorious First of June, 1794" 60 65
3472 $1.50 "The Moonlight Battle, 1780" 60 65
3473 $1.50 "Great Ships of the Jacobean Navy, 1623" . . 60 65
3474 $1.50 "Battle of the Gulf of Genoa, 1795" 60 65
3475 $1.50 "Battle of the Nile, 1798" 60 65
3476 $1.50 "Battle of St. Lucia, 1778" 60 65
3477 $2 "Battle of Trafalgar, 1805" (vert) 80 85
3478 $3 "Henry VIII embarking at Dover, 1520" (vert) . . 1·20 1·30
MS3479 Two sheets, each 135 × 67 mm. (a) $6 "H.M.S. *Repulse* (battle cruiser), 1924". (b) $6 "Battle of Navarino, 1827". Set of 2 sheets . . . . 4·75 5·00

The date on No. 3466 is incorrect. The *Royal Prince* was sunk by the Dutch in 1666.

171 Lady Elizabeth Bowes-Lyon as a Young Child

2001. 101st Birthday of Queen Elizabeth, the Queen Mother.

3480 **171** $2 black and yellow . . 80 85
3481 – $2 multicoloured 80 85
3482 – $2 black and yellow . . 80 85
3483 – $2 multicoloured 80 85
MS3484 151 × 155 mm. $6 multicoloured . . . . 2·40 2·50

DESIGNS: No. 3481, Queen Mother in Rhodesia, 1957; 3482, Queen Elizabeth with Princess Elizabeth and Princess Anne, 1950; 3483, Queen Mother in blue hat, 1988. (37 × 50 mm); No. **MS**3484, Queen Mother inspecting Black Watch.

172 John F. Kennedy on *P.T. 109*

2001. John F. Kennedy (American President) Commemoration. Multicoloured.

3485 $1.50 Type **172** 60 65
3486 $1.50 John Kennedy in chair 60 65
3487 $1.50 Facing left 60 65
3488 $1.50 Facing forward, smiling 60 65
3489 $1.50 Wearing spotted tie 60 65
3490 $1.50 Wearing striped tie . . 60 65
MS3491 120 × 82 mm. $6 John Kennedy with Nikita Khrushchev (First Secretary of U.S.S.R.) (horiz) . . . . 2·40 2·50

173 Jacqueline Kennedy Onassis

175 Princess Diana in Evening Dress

174 General George Patton and Tank

2001. Jacqueline Kennedy Onassis (widow of American president) Commemoration. Multicoloured.

3492 $1.50 Type **173** 60 65
3493 $1.50 Wearing red coat 60 65
3494 $1.50 In green dress 60 65
3495 $1.50 Wearing evening cloak 60 65
3496 $1.50 In matching pink hat and coat 60 65
3497 $1.50 Jacqueline Kennedy Onassis and hot air balloon 60 65
MS3498 Two sheets. (a) 68 × 83 mm. $6 Portrait with face value at top right. (b) 83 × 68 mm. $6 Portrait with face value at top left 4·75 5·00

2001. American Military Leaders. Multicoloured.

3499 75c. Type **174** 30 35
3500 75c. General Joseph Stilwell with President and Mrs. Chiang Kai-shek 30 35
3501 75c. Admiral Thomas Kinkaid and marine landing 30 35
3502 75c. General Jonathan Wainwright and Filipino troops 30 35
3503 75c. Lt.-General James Doolittle and aircraft carrier 30 35
3504 75c. General Matthew Ridgway and cheering crowd 30 35
3505 75c. General Maxwell Taylor and B-17s 30 35
3506 75c. Admiral Richmond Turner and island landing 30 35
3507 75c. General Curtis LeMay and heavy bombers 30 35
3508 75c. General Hoyt Vandenberg and fighter aircraft 30 35
3509 75c. General Carl Spaatz and explosion of atomic bomb 30 35
3510 75c. Admiral Raymond Spruance and burning Japanese battleship 30 35
3511 75c. General Omar Bradley and D-Day landings 30 35
3512 75c. General George Marshall and Marine Corps memorial 30 35
3513 75c. General Douglas MacArthur and return to the Philippines 30 35
3514 75c. Admiral William Halsey and carrier landing 30 35
3515 75c. General Dwight Eisenhower and reviewing troops 30 35
3516 75c. Admiral Chester Nimitz and beach landing 30 35
3517 75c. Admiral William Leahy and aircraft carriers 30 35
3518 75c. General Henry Arnold and heavy bomber 30 35
3519 75c. Admiral Ernest King and battleships 30 35
3520 75c. General George Washington and seated with his wife 30 35
3521 75c. General John Pershing and parade 30 35
MS3522 Two sheets, each 150 × 139 mm. (a) $6 General Dwight Eisenhower (38 × 49 mm). (b) $6 General Douglas MacArthur (38 × 49 mm) 4·75 5·00

2001. 40th Birth Anniv of Diana, Princess of Wales. Multicoloured.

3523 $1.50 Type **175** 60 65
3524 $1.50 Wearing ski suit 60 65
3525 $1.50 In pale blue hat 60 65

176 *Nudaurelia cytheria* (moth)

2001. Moths. Multicoloured.

3526 75c. Type **176** 30 35
3527 90c. *Janomima westwoodi* 35 40
3528 $1.50 *Actias selene* 60 65
3529 $1.50 *Amphicallia bellatrix* 60 65
3530 $1.50 *Citheronia regalis* 60 65
3531 $1.50 *Arctica caja* 60 65
3532 $1.50 *Leto venus* 60 65
3533 $1.50 *Alcides zodiaca* 60 65
3534 $1.50 *Graellsia isabellae* 60 65
3535 $1.50 *Dysphania cuprina* 60 65
3536 $1.50 *Automeris io* 60 65
3537 $1.50 *Agarista agricola* 60 65
3538 $1.50 *Callioratis millari* 60 65
3539 $1.50 *Othreis fullonia* 60 65
3540 $2 *Lasiocampa quercus* 80 85
3541 $3 *Chrysiridia riphearia* 1·20 1·30
MS3542 Two sheets, each 77 × 106 mm. (a) $6 *Divana diva* (vert). (b) $6 *Argema mimosae* (vert) 4·75 5·00

No. 3539 is inscribed "Otthreis" in error.

177 Queen Elizabeth in Spotted Dress

178 Horse on Background of Chinese Characters

2002. Golden Jubilee. Multicoloured.

3543 $2 Type **177** 80 85
3544 $2 Queen Elizabeth wearing pink hat 80 85
3545 $2 Queen Elizabeth in evening dress 80 85
3546 $2 Queen Elizabeth wearing sunglasses 80 85
MS3547 76 × 109 mm. $6 Princess Elizabeth with family 2·40 2·50

2002. Chinese New Year ("Year of the Horse"). Showing different horses.

3548 **178** 75c. multicoloured 30 35
3549 – $1.25 multicoloured 50 55
3550 – $2 multicoloured 80 85
MS3551 70 × 102 mm. **178** $6 black, light orange and orange 2·40 2·50

179 US Flag on Twin Towers

180 Amerigo Vespucci

2002. "United We Stand". Support for Victims of 11 September 2001 Attacks.

3552 **179** 80c. multicoloured 30 35

2002. 550th Birth Anniv of Amerigo Vespucci (explorer).

3553 **180** $1 multicoloured 40 45
3554 – $2 multicoloured 80 85
3555 – $3 multicoloured 1·20 1·40
MS3556 75 × 58 mm. $6 multicoloured 2·40 2·50

DESIGNS: $2 to $6 Various portraits.

181 F1 86, 1986

2002. Ferrari Racing Cars. Sheet 147 × 165 mm containing T **181** and similar horiz designs. Multicoloured.

MS3557 $1.50 Type **181**; $1.50 F1 89, 1989; $1.50 F 92 A, 1992; $1.50 F1 93, 1993; $1.50 412 T1, 1994; $1.50 F310, 1996 2·40 2·50

2002. International Year of Mountains. Two sheets containing horiz designs as T **512** of Grenada. Multicoloured.

MS3558 143 × 93 mm. $2 Kilimanjaro, Tanzania; $2 Mount Kenya; $2 Mount Kea, Hawaii; $2 Mount Fuji, Japan 3·25 3·50
MS3559 115 × 65 mm. $6 Ko'olau Mountains, Hawaii 2·40 2·50

182 Waterfall

2002. International Year of Ecotourism. Two sheets containing T **182** and similar horiz designs. Multicoloured.

MS3561 80 × 98 mm. $6 Blue-hooded euphonias 2·40 2·50
MS3560 137 × 105 mm. $1.50 Type **182**; $1.50 Ringed kingfisher; $1.50 Butterfly; $1.50 Rock beauty (fish); $1.50 Cactus; $1.50 Orchid 4·25 4·50

183 Olympic Rings and Skier (airborne)

184 *Bombus auricomus* (bumble bee)

2002. Winter Olympic Games, Salt Lake City.Multicoloured.

3562 $3 Type **183** 1·20 1·40
3563 $3 Olympic rings and skier (different) 1·20 1·40
MS3564 82 × 113 mm. Nos. 3562/3 2·40 2·75

2002. World Scout Jamboree, Thailand. Two sheets each containing multicoloured designs as T **515** of Grenada.

MS3565 107 × 90 mm. $2 Scout badge and campfire; $2 Scout hiking; $2 Boy scout feeding calf; $2 Girl saluting 3·25 3·50
MS3566 98 × 70 mm. $2 Scout at seashore (vert) 80 85

2002. Chiune Sugihara (Japanese Consul-general in Lithuania who rescued Jews, 1939–40) Commemoration. Two sheets each 60 × 90 mm containing vert designs as T **511** of Grenada.

MS3567 (a) $6 Sugihara and map showing route from Lithuania to Japan. (b) $6 Sugihara and wife Set of 2 sheets 4·75 5·00

2002. Flora and Fauna. Miniature sheets containing T **184** and similar multicoloured designs.

MS3568 135 × 170 mm. $1 Type **184**; $1 *Anax junius* (dragonfly); $1 *Dynastes tityus* (Hercules beetle); $1 *Coccinella novemrotata* (ladybug); $1 *Callicore maimuna* (figure-of-eight butterfly); $1 *Tenodera aridifolia sinensis* (praying mantis) 2·40 2·50
MS3569 135 × 170 mm. $1 Sperm whale; $1 Bottlenose whale; $1 Sei Whale; $1 Killer whale; $1 Humpback whale ("Humback Whale"); $1 Pygmy sperm whale 2·40 2·50
MS3570 135 × 170 mm. $2 *Anartia jatrophae*; $2 *Phoebis philea*; $2 *Cepheuptychia cephus*; $2 *Prepona meander*; $2 *Mesene phareus*; $2 *Morpho peleides* 4·75 5·00
MS3571 135 × 170 mm. $2 *Coprinus comatus*; $2 *Leucocoprinus rachodes*; $2 *Collybia iocephala*; $2 *Lepiota acutesquamosa*; $2 *Morchella crassipes*; $2 *Mycena galericulata* 4·75 5·00
MS3572 Four sheets, each 100 × 70 mm. (a) $6 *Anax junius* (dragonfly) (horiz). (b) $6 Blue whale (horiz). (c) $6 *Cepheuptychia cephus* (butterfly) (horiz). (d) $6 *Amanita phalloides* (mushroom) (horiz) Set of 4 sheets 9·75 10·00

No. **MS**3568 shows insects, **MS**3569 shows whales, **MS**3570 shows butterflies and **MS**3571 fungi.

2002. 25th Death Anniv of Elvis Presley. As T **518a** of Grenada. Multicoloured (No. 3573) or black and brown (No. **MS**3574).

3573 $1 Elvis Presley with guitar 40 45
MS3574 150 × 215 mm. $1 × 9 containing nine different portraits of Elvis Presley 3·50 3·75

2002. "Amphilex '02" International Stamp Exhibition, Amsterdam. As T **518b** of Grenada. (a) Dutch Nobel Prize Winners. Sheet 150 × 100 mm.

MS3575 $1.50 Paul J. Crutzen (Chemistry, 1995) (black and green); $1.50 Nobel medal (black and brown); $1.50 Martinus Veltman (Physics, 1999) (black and mauve); $1.50 Hendrik Lorentz (Physics, 1902) (black and blue); $1.50 Christiaan Eijkman (Medicine, 1929) (black and green); $1.50 Gerard 't Hooft (Physics, 1999) (black and brown) 4·25 4·50

(b) Dutch Lighthouses. Sheet 128 × 148 mm. Multicoloured.

MS3576 $1.50 Ameland; $1.50 Vlieland; $1.50 Julianadorp; $1.50 Noordwijk; $1.50 Hoek van Holland; $1.50 Goeree 2·40 2·50

(c) Dutch Women's Traditional Costumes. Sheet 120 × 140 mm containing multicoloured designs, each 36 × 50 mm.

MS3577 $3 Marken, Noord-Holland; $3 Staphorst, Overijsel; $3 Walchheren, Zeeland 4·25 4·50

185 Teddy Bear holding "HAPPY BIRTHDAY" in Heart

2002. Centenary of the Teddy Bear (1st issue). T **185** and similar vert designs. Multicoloured.

MS3578 140 × 142 mm. 50c. Type **185**; $1 With waistcoat, briefcase and bowler hat; $2 Wearing raincoat, sunglasses and hat; $5 Wearing boxer shorts with heart pattern 3·50 3·75
MS3579 85 × 115 mm. 15c. Teddy Bear wearing Guardsmans plumed helmet; $2 Panda teddy bear wearing black hat; $3 Wearing beret and ruff; $4 White teddy bear wearing grey top hat 4·50 4·75

No. **MS**3578 is heart-shaped.

See also Nos. 3611/12.

2002. World Cup Football Championship, Japan and Korea. Miniature sheets containing vert designs as T **524** of Grenada. Multicoloured.

MS3580 165 × 82 mm. $1.50 Oliver Neuville (Germany) and Eddie Pope (USA); $1.50 Claudio Reyna (USA) and Miroslav Klose (Germany); $1.50 Christian Ziege (Germany) and Frankie Hejduk (USA); $1.50 Nadal (Spain) and Jung Hwan Ahn (South Korea); $1.50 Luis Enrique (Spain) and Chong Gug Song (South Korea); $1.50 Park Ji Sung (South Korea) and Mendieta Gaizka (Spain) 2·40 2·50
MS3581 165 × 82 mm. $1.50 Danny Mills (England) and Ronaldo (Brazil); $1.50 Roque Junior (Brazil) and Emil Heskey (England); $1.50 Sol Campbell (England) and Rivaldo (Brazil); $1.50 Lamine Diatta (Senegal) and Hakan Sukur (Turkey); $1.50 Umit Davala (Turkey) and Khalilou Fadiga (Senegal); $1.50 El Hadji Diouf (Senegal) and Tugay Kerimoglu (Turkey) 2·40 2·50
MS3582 Four sheets, each 82 × 82 mm. (a) $3 Oliver Kahn (Germany); $3 Brad Friedel (Germany). (b) $3 Chun Soo Lee (South Korea); $3 Juan Carlos Valeron (Spain). (c) $3 David Beckham (England) and Roberto Carlos (Brazil); $3 Ronaldinho (Brazil) and Nicky Butt (England). (d) $3 Alpay Ozalan (Turkey); $3 Khalilou Fadiga (Senegal) Set of 4 sheets 9·75 10·00

2002. Christmas. Religious Paintings. As T **523a** of Grenada. Multicoloured.

3583 15c. "The Redeemer and the Four Apostles" (Carpaccio) 10 10
3584 25c. "The Miracle of the Relic of the Cross" (Carpaccio) (vert) 10 15
3585 50c. "The Presentation in the Temple" (Carpaccio) 20 25

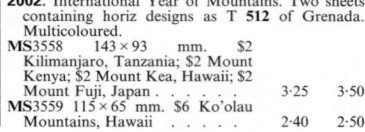

3586 $2 "The Visitation" (Carpaccio) 80 85
3587 $3 "The Birth of the Virgin" (Carpaccio) . . . . 1·20 1·40
MS3588 62 × 90 mm. $6 "Madonna and Child and Two Angels" (detail) (Cimabue) (vert) . . . 2·40 2·50

186 "Year of Ram" (Ren Yi)

2003. Chinese New Year ("Year of the Ram").
MS3589 179 × 108 mm. 186 $1.25 × 4 multicoloured . . . . 2·00 2·25

2003. *Columbia* Space Shuttle Commemoration. Sheet 183 × 146 mm, containing vert designs as T **533** of Grenada showing crew members. Multicoloured.
MS3590 $1 David Brown; $1 Commander Rick Husband; $1 Laurel Clark; $1 Kalpana Chawla; $1 Michael Anderson; $1 William McCool; $1 Ilan Ramon . . . 2·75 3·00

2003. Japanese Art. Paintings by Toyohara Kunichika showing Famous Actors. As T **535** of Grenada. Multicoloured
3591 50c. "Ichikawa Danjuro IX as the Beggar Akushichibyoe Kagekiyo" 20 25
3592 75c. "Ichikawa Danjuro IX as the Female Demon Ewanari" 30 35
3593 $1.25 "Sawamura Tossho II as Sutewakamaru" . . . 50 55
3594 $3 "Band0 Hikosaburo V as Nikki Damjo" . . . . . 1·20 1·40
MS3595 175 × 137 mm. $2 "Nakamura Shikan IV as Keyamura Rokusuke"; $2 "Bando Hikosaburo V as Ichimisai no Musume Osono"; $2 "Ichikawa Sadanji I as Wada no Shimobe Busuke"; $2 "Ichikawa Sadanji I as Kiyomizu no Yoshitaka" . . 3·25 3·50
MS3596 122 × 82 mm. $6 "Onoe Kikugoro V as Torii Tsuneemon returning to Mikawa" (horiz) 2·40 2·50

2003. 450th Death Anniv of Lucas Cranach the Elder (artist). As T **536** of Grenada. Multicoloured.
3597 25c. "The St. Mary Altarpiece" (detail) (vert) 10 15
3598 $1 "The St. Mary Altarpiece" (different detail) (vert) 40 45
3599 $1.25 "Altar Piece of the Princes" (detail) (vert) . . 50 55
3600 $3 Frederick the Wise with St. Bartholomew (detail of altarpiece) (vert) . . . . 1·20 1·40
MS3601 150 × 160 mm. $2 "Judith at the Table of Holofernes" (detail); $2 "St. Catherine Altarpiece" (detail); $2 "Judith killing Holofernes" (detail); $2 "The Martyrdom of St. Catherine" (detail) . . . . 3·25 3·50
MS3602 102 × 123 mm. $6 "Cardinal Albrecht of Brandenbourg as St. Jerome in the Wilderness" (vert) . . . . 2·40 2·50

2003. 85th Death Anniv of Gustav Klimt (artist). As T **537** of Grenada. Multicoloured.
3603 15c. "Le Chapeau de Plumes Noires" 10 10
3604 25c. "Le Schloss Kammer am Attersee" 10 15
3605 50c. "Malcesine sur le Lac de Garde" 20 25
3606 75c. "Ferme en Haute-Autriche" 30 35
3607 $1.25 "Portrait d'une Dame" 50 60
3608 $4 "La Frise Beethoven" (detail) . . . . 1·60 1·75
MS3609 126 × 178 mm. $2 "Portrait de la Baronne Elisabeth Bachofen-Echt"; $2 "Portrait d'une Dame"; $2 "Portrait d'Emilie Floge"; $2 "Portrait d'Adele Bloch-Bauer" 3·25 3·50
MS3610 103 × 81 mm. $6 "Le Baiser" (detail). Imperf . . . . 2·40 2·50

2003. Centenary of the Teddy Bear (2nd issue). Embroidered Fabric Teddy Bears. As T **538** of Grenada. Self-adhesive. Imperf.
3611 $15 ochre, silver and red . . 4·50 4·75
MS3612 126 × 157 mm. No. 3611 × 4 18·00 19·00

2003. Centenary of Tour de France Cycle Race. As T **540** of Grenada showing past winners. Multicoloured.
MS3613 160 × 100 mm. $2 Ferdinand Kubler (1950); $2 Hugo Koblet (1951); $2 Fausto Coppi (1952); $2 Louison Bobet (1953) 3·25 3·50
MS3614 160 × 100 mm. $2 Louison Bobet (1954); $2 Louison Bobet (1955); $2 Roger Walkowiak (1956); $2 Jacques Anquetil (1957) 3·25 3·50
MS3615 160 × 100 mm. $2 Gastone Nencini (1960); $2 Jacques Anquetil (1961); $2 Jacques Anquetil (1962); $2 Jacques Anquetil (1963) . . . . 3·25 3·50
MS3616 Three sheets, each 100 × 70 mm. (a) $6 Louison Bobet (1953--1955). (b) $6 Jacques Anquetil (1957). (c) $6 Eddy Merckx (1969) Set of 3 sheets 7·25 7·50

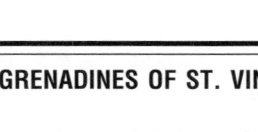

187 John Kennedy, Choate Graduate, 1935

2003. 40th Death Anniv of President John F. Kennedy.
MS3617 144 × 131 mm. $2 Type **187** (agate, black and); $2 John Kennedy, 1946 (multicoloured); $2 With Jacqueline Kennedy on tennis court (multicoloured); $2 With young John F. Kennedy Jnr (multicoloured) . . . . 3·25 3·50
MS3618 144 × 131 mm. $2 With Jacqueline Kennedy (black, brown and grey); $2 Announcing Cuban blockade, 1962 (agate and mauve); $2 Sitting in chair, White House, 1962 (brown and black); $2 Jackie Kennedy with children at funeral, 1963 (black, mauve and purple) 3·25 3·50

188 Charles Lindbergh

2003. 75th Anniv of First Solo Trans-atlantic Flight. Multicoloured (No. **MS**3620).
MS3619 129 × 144 mm. $2 Type **188** (blue, grey and red); $2 Lindbergh and Ryan NYP Special *Spirit of St. Louis* (purple, blue and red); $2 Lindbergh and *Spirit of St. Louis* (black and red); $2 Lindbergh (purple, blue and red) . . . . 3·25 3·50
MS3620 129 × 144 mm. $2 Lindbergh (looking forward); $2 Lindbergh (looking left); $2 Lindbergh on arrival in Paris, 1927; $2 Lindbergh and *Spirit of St. Louis* . . . . 3·25 3·50

189 La Sagesse

2003. International Year of Freshwater. Multicoloured.
MS3621 150 × 88 mm. $2 Type **189**; $2 Annadale Falls; $2 Grand Etang . . . . 2·40 2·50
MS3622 100 × 70 mm. $6 St. George 2·40 2·50

OFFICIAL STAMPS

1982. Optd **P.R.G.** (a) Nos. 400/12 and 414.
O 1 5c. Yellow-tailed snapper . . 10 20
O 2 6c. Mutton snapper 10 20
O 3 10c. Cocoa damselfish . . . 10 20
O 4 12c. Royal gramma 10 20
O 5 15c. Cherub angelfish . . . 10 20
O 6 20c. Black-barred soldierfish 10 20
O 7 25c. Mottled grouper 10 20
O 8 30c. Long-snouted butterflyfish 15 20
O 9 40c. Puddingwife 15 25
O10 50c. Midnight parrotfish . . 20 30
O11 90c. Redspotted hawkfish . . 40 55
O12 $1 Hogfish 40 60
O13 $3 Beau Gregory . . . . . 1·25 2·50
O14 $10 Barred hamlet . . . . . 4·25 6·50

(b) Nos. 444/6 and 448/9.
O15 30c. Prince Charles and Lady Diana Spencer . . . 2·00 2·00
O16 40c. Prince Charles and Lady Diana Spencer . . . 1·60 1·60
O17 40c. Type **50** . . . . 2·00 2·75
O18 $2 Type **50** . . . . 2·50 3·50
O19 $4 Prince Charles as parachutist . . . . 6·50 8·50

(c) Nos. 473/6.
O20 **54** 20c. multicoloured 10 20
O21 – 40c. multicoloured 15 25
O22 – $1 multicoloured 35 70
O23 – $2 multicoloured . . . . 70 1·60

GRENADINES OF ST. VINCENT

Pt. 1

Part of a group of Islands south of St. Vincent that include Bequia, Mustique, Canouan and Union.

100 cents = 1 dollar.

1973. Royal Wedding. As T **101a** of Gibraltar. Multicoloured. Background colours given.
1 25c. green 10 10
2 $1 brown 15 15

1974. Nos. 286/300 of St. Vincent optd **GRENADINES OF.**
3 1c. Green-backed heron ("Green Heron") 10 10
4 2c. Lesser Antillean bullfinches ("Bullfinch") 15 15
25 3c. St. Vincent amazon ("St. Vincent Parrot") . . . 25 30
6 4c. Rufous-throated solitaire ("Soufriere Bird") (vert) . . 10 10
7 5c. Red-necked pigeon ("Ramier") (vert) 10 10
8 6c. Bananaquits 10 10
9 8c. Purple-throated carib ("Humming Bird") 10 10
10 10c. Mangrove cuckoo (vert) 10 10
11 12c. Common black hawk ("Black Hawk") (vert) . . . 20 15
12 20c. Bare-eyed thrush 20 20
13 25c. Lesser Antillean tanager ("Prince") 20 20
14 50c. Blue hooded euphonia . . 40 40
15 $1 Barn owl (vert) 80 75
16 $2.50 Yellow-bellied elaenia ("Crested Elaenia") (vert) 80 1·00
17 $5 Ruddy quail dove . . . . 1·00 1·75

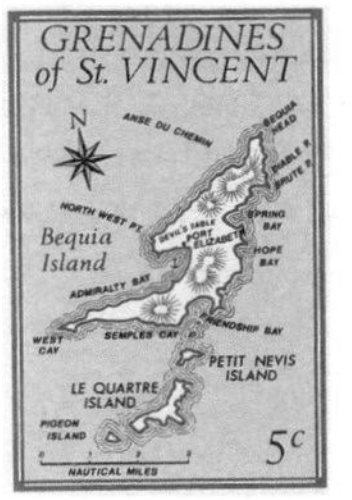

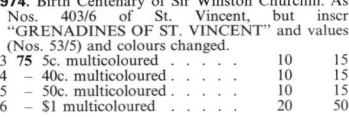

2 Map of Bequia

1974. Maps (1st series).
18 **2** 5c. black, green & deep green 10 10
19 – 15c. multicoloured 10 10
20 – 20c. multicoloured 10 10
21 – 30c. black, pink and red . . 10 10
22 – 40c. black, violet and purple 10 10
23 – $1 black, ultramarine and blue 20 20
MAPS: 15c. Prune Island; 20c. Mayreau Island and Tobago Cays; 30c. Mustique Island; 40c. Union Island; $1 Canouan Island.
See also Nos. 85/8.

3a U.P.U. Emblem

1974. Centenary of U.P.U. Multicoloured.
26 2c. Type **3a** 10 10
27 15c. Globe within posthorn . . 10 10
28 40c. Map of St. Vincent and hand-cancelling 10 10
29 $1 Map of the World 25 15

4 Boat-building

1974. Bequia Island (1st series). Multicoloured.
34 5c. Type **4** 10 15
31 30c. Careening at Port Elizabeth 10 15
32 35c. Admiralty Bay 10 15
33 $1 Fishing-boat race 15 25
See also Nos. 185/88.

5 Music Volute

1974. Shells and Molluscs. Multicoloured.
35A 1c. American thorny oyster 10 10
36A 2c. Zigzag scallop 10 10
37A 3c. Reticulated cowrie-helmet 10 10
38A 4c. Type **5** 10 10
39A 5c. Amber pen shell 10 10
40A 6c. Angular triton 10 10
41A 8c. Flame helmet 10 10
42A 10c. Caribbean olive . . . 10 10
43A 12c. American or common sundial 10 10
44A 15c. Glory of the Atlantic cone 25 20
45B 20c. Flame auger 30 20
46A 25c. King venus 50 20
47A 35c. Long-spined star shell 35 25
48A 45c. Speckled tellin 35 30
49A 50c. Rooster-tail conch . . 40 25
50B $1 Green star shell 60 60
51A $2.50 Antillean or incomparable cone . . . 60 75
52A $5 Rough file clam 75 80
52cA $10 Measled cowrie . . . . 3·50 1·00
Nos. 38/42, 45, 47 and 49/50 come with and without an imprint below the design.

1974. Birth Centenary of Sir Winston Churchill. As Nos. 403/6 of St. Vincent, but inscr "GRENADINES OF ST. VINCENT" and values (Nos. 53/5) and colours changed.
53 **75** 5c. multicoloured 10 15
54 – 40c. multicoloured 10 15
55 – 50c. multicoloured 10 15
56 – $1 multicoloured 20 50

6 Cotton House, Mustique

1975. Mustique Island. Multicoloured.
57 5c. Type **6** 10 10
58 35c. "Blue Waters", Endeavour Bay 10 10
59 45c. Endeavour Bay 10 10
60 $1 "Les Jolies Eaux", Gelliceaux Bay 25 20

7 "Danaus plexippus"

1975. Butterflies. Multicoloured.
61 3c. Type **7** 20 10
62 5c. "Agraulis vanillae" 25 10
63 35c. "Battus polydamas" . . . 50 10
64 45c. "Evenus dindymus" and "Junonia evarete" 50 10
65 $1 "Anartia jatrophae" . . . 75 45

8 Resort Pavilion

1975. Petit St. Vincent. Multicoloured.
66 5c. Type **8** 10 20
67 35c. The Harbour 10 20
68 45c. The Jetty 15 20
69 $1 Sailing in coral lagoon . . 50 1·10

9 Ecumenical Church, Mustique

1975. Christmas. Multicoloured.
70 5c. Type **9** 10 10
71 25c. Catholic Church, Union Island 10 10
72 50c. Catholic Church, Bequia 10 10
73 $1 Anglican Church, Bequia 25 15

10 Sunset Scene

1976. Union Island (1st series). Multicoloured.
74 5c. Type **10** 10 25
75 35c. Customs and Post Office, Clifton 10 20
76 45c. Anglican Church, Ashton 10 20
77 $1 Mail schooner, Clifton Harbour 25 80
See also Nos. 242/5.

11 Staghorn Coral

1976. Corals. Multicoloured.
78 5c. Type **11** 10 10
79 35c. Elkhorn coral 20 10
80 45c. Pillar coral 20 10
81 $1 Brain coral 40 20

12 25c. Bicentennial Coin

1976. Bicentenary of American Revolution.
82 **12** 25c. silver, black and blue 10 10
83 – 50c. silver, black and red . . 20 10
84 – $1 silver, black and mauve 25 20
DESIGNS: 50c. Half-dollar coin; $1 One dollar coin.

1976. Maps (2nd series). As T **2**.
85 5c. black, deep green and green 15 15
86 10c. black, green and blue . . 15 10
87 35c. black, brown and red . . 30 20
88 45c. black, red and orange . . 30 25
Nos. 85/8 exist in 7 different designs to each value as follows: A, Bequia, B, Canouan, C, Mayreau, D, Mustique, E, Petit St. Vincent, F, Prune, G, Union. To indicate any particular design use the appropriate catalogue No. together with the suffix for the island concerned.

13 Station Hill School and Post Office

1977. Mayreau Island. Multicoloured.
89 5c. Type **13** 10 10
90 35c. Church at Old Wall . . . 10 10
91 45c. La Sourciere Anchorage 20 10
92 $1 Saline Bay 35 15

14 Coronation Crown Coin

1977. Silver Jubilee. Multicoloured.
93 25c. Type **14** 15 10
94 50c. Silver Wedding crown . . 20 10
95 $1 Silver Jubilee crown . . . 20 15

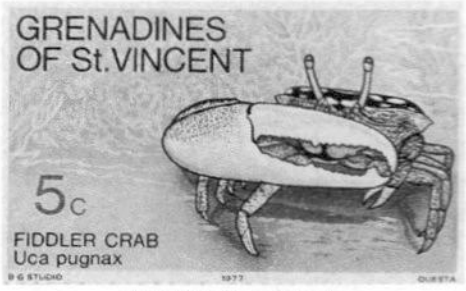

15 Fiddler Crab

1977. Crustaceans. Multicoloured.
96 5c. Type **15** 15 15
97 35c. Ghost crab 25 15
98 50c. Blue crab 30 20
99 $1.25 Spiny lobster 60 90

16 Snorkel Diving

1977. Prune Island. Multicoloured.
100 5c. Type **16** 15 15
101 35c. Palm Island Resort . . . 20 15
102 45c. Casuarina Beach 20 15
103 $1 Palm Island Beach Club 60 1·10

17 Mustique Island

1977. Royal Visit. Surch as in T **17**.
104 **17** 40c. turquoise and green 20 10
105 $2 ochre and brown . . . 45 25

18 The Clinic, Charlestown

1977. Canouan Island (1st series). Mult.
106 5c. Type **18** 10 15
107 35c. Town jetty, Charlestown 20 15
108 45c. Mail schooner arriving at Charlestown 20 15
109 $1 Grand Bay . . . . 40 1·00
See also Nos. 307/10.

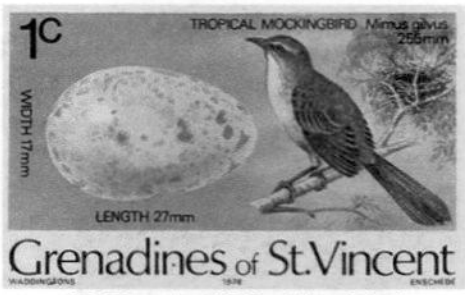

19 Tropical Mockingbird

1978. Birds and their Eggs. Multicoloured.
110 1c. Type **19** 10 60
111 2c. Mangrove cuckoo 15 60
112 3c. Osprey 20 60
113 4c. Smooth-billed ani 20 60
114 5c. House wren 20 40
115 6c. Bananaquit 20 40
116 8c. Carib grackle 20 45
117 10c. Yellow-bellied elaenia . . 20 45
118 12c. Collared plover . . . . 30 1·25
119 15c. Cattle egret 30 45
120 20c. Red-footed booby . . . 30 45
121 25c. Red-billed tropic bird . . 30 45
122 40c. Royal tern . . . . 45 1·00
123 50c. Grenada flycatcher ("Rusty-tailed Flycatcher") 45 1·00
124 80c. American purple gallinule ("Purple Gallinule") . . . . 70 1·00
125 $1 Broad-winged hawk . . . 75 1·00
126 $2 Scaly-breasted ground dove ("Common Ground Dove") . . . . 75 1·60
127 $3 Laughing gull . . . . . . 1·00 1·75
128 $5 Common noddy ("Brown Noddy") . . . . 1·25 1·75
129 $10 Grey kingbird . . . . . 2·00 2·25

19a Worcester Cathedral

1978. 25th Anniv of Coronation. British Cathedrals. Multicoloured.
130 5c. Type **19a** 10 10
131 40c. Coventry Cathedral . . 10 10
132 $1 Winchester Cathedral . . 15 20
133 $3 Chester Cathedral 25 45
MS134 130 × 102 mm. Nos. 130/3 45 80

20 Green Turtle

1978. Turtles. Multicoloured.
135 5c. Type **20** 10 10
136 40c. Hawksbill turtle 15 10
137 50c. Leatherback turtle . . . 15 10
138 $1.25 Loggerhead turtle . . . 40 40

21 Three Kings following Star   **22** Sailing Yachts

1978. Christmas. Scenes and Verses from the Carol "We Three Kings". Multicoloured.
139 5c. Type **21** 10 10
140 10c. King presenting gold . . 10 10
141 25c. King presenting frankincense 10 10
142 50c. King presenting myrrh 10 10
143 $2 Kings paying homage to infant Jesus 30 20
MS144 154 × 175 mm. Nos. 139/43 70 1·25

1979. National Regatta.
145 **22** 5c. multicoloured 10 10
146 – 40c. multicoloured 20 10
147 – 50c. multicoloured 25 10
148 – $2 multicoloured 75 60
DESIGNS: 40c. to $2, Various sailing yachts.

22a Green Iguana

1979. Wildlife. Multicoloured.
149 20c. Type **22a** 10 15
150 40c. Common opossum ("Manicou") 15 15
151 $2 Red-legged tortoise . . . 60 1·10

22b Sir Rowland Hill

1979. Death Centenary of Sir Rowland Hill. Multicoloured.
152 80c. Type **22b** 15 15
153 $1 Great Britain 1d. and 4d. stamps of 1858 with "A10" (Kingstown, St. Vincent) postmark 15 25
154 $2 St. Vincent ½d and 1d. stamps of 1894 with Bequia postmark 25 40
MS155 165 × 115 mm. Nos. 124/6 and 152/4 . . . . 1·40 2·50

22c Young Child

1979. International Year of the Child. Designs showing portraits of young children.
156 **22c** 6c. black, silver and blue 10 10
157 – 40c. black, silver & salmon 10 10
158 – $1 black, silver and buff 20 10
159 – $3 black, silver and lilac 45 30

22d National Flag and "Ixora salicifolia" (flower)

1979. Independence. Multicoloured.
160 5c. Type **22d** 10 10
161 40c. House of Assembly and "Ixora odorata" (flower) 10 10
162 $1 Prime Minister R. Milton Cato and "Ixora javanica" (flower) 20 20

23 False Killer Whale

1980. Whales and Dolphins. Multicoloured.
163 10c. Type **23** 45 30
164 50c. Spinner dolphin 45 35
165 90c. Bottle-nosed dolphin . . 50 80
166 $2 Short-finned pilot whale ("Blackfish") . . . . . . 1·25 2·25

23a Queen Elizabeth II

1980. "London 1980" International Stamp Exhibition. Multicoloured.
167 40c. Type **23a** 10 15
168 50c. St. Vincent 2c. stamp of 1965 . . . . 15 15
169 $3 First Grenadines stamps 40 1·25
MS170 165 × 115 mm. Nos. 122/3, 127 and 167/9 . . . . 2·00 2·50

23b Running   **24** Scene and Verse from the Carol "De Borning Day"

1980. Sport. Multicoloured.
171 25c. Type **23b** 10 10
172 50c. Sailing 10 10
173 $1 Long-jumping 20 20
174 $2 Swimming 30 30

1980. Hurricane Relief. Nos. 171/4 optd **HURRICANE RELIEF 50c**.
175 **22** 25c.+50c. multicoloured . . 10 30
176 – 50c.+50c. multicoloured . . 15 40
177 – $1+50c. multicoloured . . 20 50
178 – $2+50c. multicoloured . . 30 70

1980. Christmas. Multicoloured.
179 5c. Type **24** 10 10
180 50c. "Mary and de Baby lonely" 10 10
181 60c. "Mary and de Baby weary" 10 10

182 $1 "Mary and de Baby rest easy" 15 15
183 $2 "Star above shine in de sky" 25 25
MS184 159 × 178 mm. Nos. 179/83 50 1·40

25 Post Office, Port Elizabeth

1981. Bequia Island (2nd series). Mult.
185 50c. Type **25** 15 20
186 60c. Moonhole 15 20
187 $1.50 Fishing boats, Admiralty Bay 30 55
188 $2 "The Friendship Rose" (yacht) at jetty 50 70

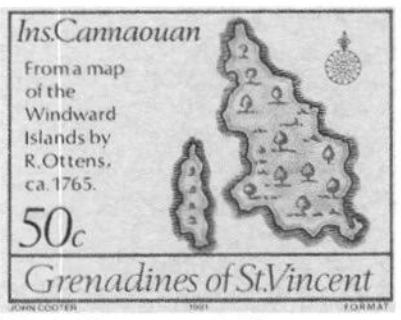

26 Ins. Cannaouan (from map of Windward Islands by R. Ottens, c. 1765)

1981. Details from Early Maps. Multicoloured.
189 50c. Type **26** 30 30
190 50c. Cannouan Is. (from chart by J. Parsons, 1861) 30 30
191 60c. Ins. Moustiques (from map of Windward Islands by R. Ottens, c. 1765) . . 30 35
192 60c. Mustique Is. (from chart by J. Parsons, 1861) . . . 30 35
193 $2 Ins. Bequia (from map of Windward Islands by R. Ottens, c.1765) 50 75
194 $2 Bequia Is. (from map surveyed in 1763 by T. Jefferys) 50 75

26a "Mary"

1981. Royal Wedding. Royal Yachts. Multicoloured.
195 50c. Type **26a** 10 15
196 50c. Prince Charles and Lady Diana Spencer 35 40
197 $3 "Alexandra" 20 30
198 $3 As No. 196 . . . . . . 60 90
199 $3.50 "Britannia" 25 35
200 $3.50 As No. 196 . . . . . 65 90
MS201 120 × 109 mm. $5 As No. 196 75 75

27 Bar Jack

1981. Game Fish. Multicoloured.
204 10c. Type **27** 15 10
205 50c. Tarpon 30 10
206 60c. Cobia 35 10
207 $2 Blue marlin . . . . 1·00 70

28 H.M.S. "Experiment" (frigate)

1982. Ships. Multicoloured.
208 1c. Type **28** 10 20
209 3c. "Lady Nelson" (cargo liner) 15 20
210 5c. "Daisy" (brig) 20 20
211 6c. Carib canoe 10 20
212 10c. "Hairoun Star" (freighter) 20 10
213 15c. "Jupiter" (liner) 40 10
214 20c. "Christina" (steam yacht) 40 10
215 25c. "Orinoco" (mail paddle-steamer) 40 15
216 30c. H.M.S. "Lively" (frigate) 40 15
217 50c. "Alabama" (Confederate warship) 50 30
218 60c. "Denmark" (freighter) 60 30
219 75c. "Santa Maria" . . . . 1·00 50
220 $1 "Baffin" (research vessel) 80 55
221 $2 "Queen Elizabeth 2" (liner) . . . . 1·00 1·25
222 $3 R.Y. "Britannia" . . . . 1·00 1·75
223 $5 "Geeststar" (freighter) . . 1·00 2·00
224 $10 "Grenadines Star" (ferry) 1·25 5·00

29 Prickly Pear Fruit

30 Anne Neville, Princess of Wales, 1470

1982. Prickly Pear Cactus. Multicoloured.
225 10c. Type **29** 15 15
226 50c. Prickly pear flower buds 35 35
227 $1 Flower of prickly pear cactus 60 60
228 $2 Prickly pear cactus . . . 1·25 1·25

1982. 21st Birthday of Princess of Wales. Multicoloured.
229 50c. Type **30** 10 15
230 60c. Coat of arms of Anne Neville 10 15
231 $6 Diana, Princess of Wales 60 80

31 Old and New Uniforms

1982. 75th Anniv of Boy Scout Movement. Multicoloured.
232 $1.50 Type **31** 50 75
233 $2.50 Lord Baden-Powell . . 60 1·00

1982. Birth of Prince William of Wales. Nos. 224/6 optd **ROYAL BABY** and Island name.
234 50c. Type **30** 10 15
235 60c. Coat of arms of Anne Neville 10 15
236 $6 Diana, Princess of Wales 60 80

Nos. 229/32 exist optd with 5 different island names as follows: A, Bequia, B, Canouan, C, Mayreau, D, Mustique, E, Union Island. To indicate any particular overprint use the appropriate catalogue No. together with the suffix for the island concerned.

33 Silhouette Figures of Mary and Joseph

1982. Christmas. Silhouette of figures. Multicoloured.
237 10c. Type **33** 10 10
238 $1.50 Animals in stable . . . 45 45
239 $2.50 Mary and Joseph with baby Jesus 60 60
MS240 168 × 99 mm. Nos. 237/9 1·00 2·00

1983. No. 123 surch **45c**.
241 45c. on 50c. Grenada flycatcher 45 30

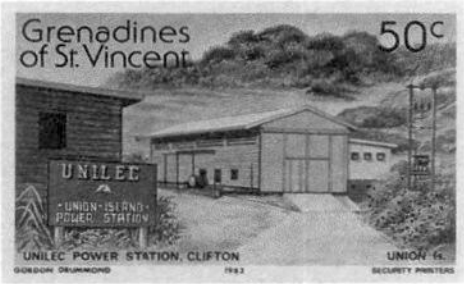

35 Power Station, Clifton

1983. Union Island (2nd issue). Multicoloured.
242 50c. Type **35** 25 15
243 60c. Sunrise, Clifton harbour 25 15
244 $1.50 Junior Secondary School, Ashton 60 40
245 $2 Frigate Rock and Conch Shell Beach 85 55

36 British Man-of-war

37 Montgolfier Balloon, 1783

1983. Bicentenary of Treaty of Versailles. Mult.
246 45c. Type **36** 35 15
247 60c. American man-of-war 35 15
248 $1.50 Soldiers carrying U.S flags 75 45
249 $2 British troops in battle . . 80 55

1983. Bicentenary of Manned Flight. Mult.
250 45c. Type **37** 15 15
251 60c. Ayres Turbo Thrush Commander (horiz) 15 15
252 $1.50 Lebaudy-Juillot airship No. 1 "La Jaune" (horiz) 40 45
253 $2 Space shuttle "Columbia" (horiz) 40 55
MS254 110 × 145 mm. Nos. 250/3 1·00 1·50

38 Coat of Arms of Henry VIII

39 Quarter Dollar and Half Dollar, 1797

1983. Leaders of the World. British Monarchs. Multicoloured.
255 60c. Type **38** 10 25
256 60c. Henry VIII 10 25
257 60c. Coat of Arms of James I 10 25
258 60c. James I 10 25
259 75c. Henry VIII at Hampton Court 10 25
260 75c. Hampton Court 10 25
261 75c. James I at Edinburgh Castle 10 25
262 75c. Edinburgh Castle . . . 10 25
263 $2.50 The "Mary Rose" . . 25 35
264 $2.50 Henry VIII and Portsmouth harbour . . . 25 35
265 $2.50 Gunpowder Plot . . . 25 35
266 $2.50 James I and Gunpowder Plot 25 35

1983. Old Coinage. Multicoloured.
267 20c. Type **39** 10 10
268 45c. Nine Bitts, 1811–14 . . 15 15
269 75c. Twelve Bitts and Six Bitts, 1811–14 . . . . . 25 25
270 $3 Sixty-six Shillings, 1798 80 80

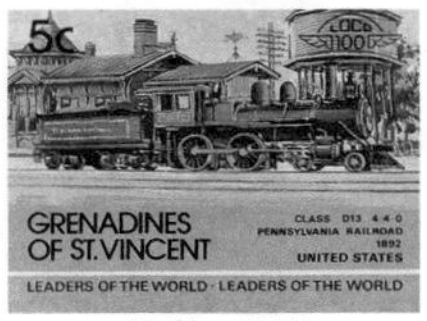

40 Class D13

1984. Leaders of the World. Railway Locomotives (1st series). The first design in each pair shows technical drawings and the second the locomotive at work.
271 5c. multicoloured 10 10
272 5c. multicoloured 10 10
273 10c. multicoloured 10 10
274 10c. multicoloured 10 10
275 15c. multicoloured 10 15
276 15c. multicoloured 10 15
277 35c. multicoloured 10 20
278 35c. multicoloured 10 20
279 45c. multicoloured 10 20
280 45c. multicoloured 10 20
281 60c. multicoloured 15 20
282 60c. multicoloured 15 20
283 $1 multicoloured 15 25
284 $1 multicoloured 15 25
285 $2.50 multicoloured 25 35
286 $2.50 multicoloured 25 35

DESIGNS: Nos. 271/2, Class D13, U.S.A., 1892 (Type **40**); 273/4, High Speed Train 125, Great Britain (1980); 275/6, Class T9, Great Britain (1899); 277/8, "Claud Hamilton", Great Britain (1900); 279/80, Class J, U.S.A. (1941); 281/2, Class D16, U.S.A. (1895); 283/4, "Lode Star", Great Britain (1907); 285/6, "Blue Peter", Great Britain (1948).

See also Nos. 321/26, 351/8, 390/7, 412/9, 443/58, 504/19 and 520/35.

41 Spotted Eagle Ray

1984. Reef Fishes. Multicoloured.
287 45c. Type **41** 25 20
288 60c. Queen triggerfish 25 35
289 $1.50 White spotted filefish 40 1·25
290 $2 Schoolmaster . . . . . . 40 1·50

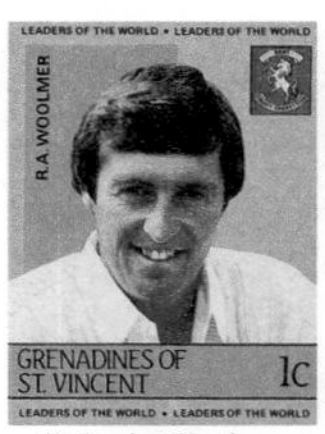

42 R. A. Woolmer

44 Lady of the Night

43 Junior Secondary School

1984. Leaders of the World. Cricketers (1st series). The first design in each pair shows a portrait and the second the cricketer in action.
291 1c. multicoloured 10 10
292 1c. multicoloured 10 10
293 3c. multicoloured 10 10
294 3c. multicoloured 10 10
295 5c. multicoloured 10 10
296 5c. multicoloured 10 10
297 30c. multicoloured 30 30
298 30c. multicoloured 30 30
299 60c. multicoloured 40 40
300 60c. multicoloured 40 40
301 $1 multicoloured 40 40
302 $1 multicoloured 40 40
303 $2 multicoloured 45 70
304 $2 multicoloured 45 70
305 $3 multicoloured 55 80
306 $3 multicoloured 55 80

DESIGNS: Nos. 291/2, R. A. Woolmer (Type **42**); K. S. Ranjitsinhji; 295/6, W. R. Hammond; 297/8, D. L. Underwood; 299/300, W. G. Grace; 301/2, E. A. E. Baptiste; 303/4, A. P. E. Knott; 305/6, L. E. G. Ames.

See also Nos. 331/8 and 364/9.

1984. Canouan Island (2nd series). Multicoloured.
307 35c. Type **43** 20 20
308 45c. Police Station 50 25
309 $1 Post Office 50 50
310 $3 Anglican Church . . . . 1·00 1·75

1984. Leaders of the World. Railway Locomotives (2nd issue). As T **40**. The first design in each pair shows technical drawings and the second the locomotive at work.
311 1c. multicoloured 10 10
312 1c. multicoloured 10 10
313 5c. multicoloured 10 10
314 5c. multicoloured 10 10
315 20c. multicoloured 15 15
316 20c. multicoloured 15 15
317 35c. multicoloured 15 15
318 35c. multicoloured 15 15
319 60c. multicoloured 25 25
320 60c. multicoloured 25 25
321 $1 multicoloured 25 30
322 $1 multicoloured 25 30
323 $1.50 multicoloured 30 40
324 $1.50 multicoloured 30 40
325 $3 multicoloured 35 55
326 $3 multicoloured 35 55

DESIGNS: Nos. 311/12, Class C62, Japan (1948); 313/14, Class V, Great Britain (1903); 315/16, Richard Trevithick's "Catch-Me-Who-Can", Great Britain (1808); 317/18, Class E10, Japan (1948); 319/20, "J. B. Earle", Great Britain (1904); 321/2, No. 762 "Lyn", Great Britain (1898); 323/4, "Talyllyn", Great Britain (1865); 325/6, "Cardean", Great Britain (1906).

1984. Night-blooming Flowers. Mult.
327 35c. Type **44** 30 30
328 45c. Four o'clock 35 35
329 75c. Mother-in-law's tongue 45 60
330 $3 Queen of the night . . . . 1·10 2·75

1984. Leaders of the World. Cricketers (2nd series). As T **42**. The first in each pair listed shows a head portrait and the second the cricketer in action.
331 5c. multicoloured 10 10
332 5c. multicoloured 10 10
333 30c. multicoloured 25 20
334 30c. multicoloured 25 20
335 $1 multicoloured 30 40
336 $1 multicoloured 30 40
337 $2.50 multicoloured 45 80
338 $2.50 multicoloured 45 80

DESIGNS: Nos. 331/2, S. F. Barnes; 333/4, R. Peel; 335/6, H. Larwood; 337/8, Sir John Hobbs.

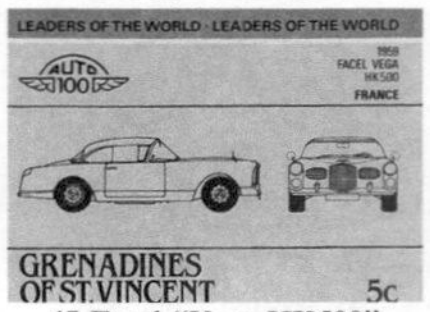
45 Facel "Vega HK500"

1984. Leaders of the World. Automobiles (1st series). The first design in each pair shows technical drawings and the second paintings.

339	5c. black, blue and green	10	10
340	5c. multicoloured	10	10
341	25c. black, lilac and pink	10	10
342	25c. multicoloured	10	10
343	50c. black, blue and orange	15	15
344	50c. multicoloured	15	15
345	$3 black, stone and brown	30	45
346	$3 multicoloured	30	45

DESIGNS: Nos. 339/40, Facel "Vega HK500" (Type **45**); 341/2, BMW "328"; 343/4, Frazer-Nash "TT Replica 1.5L"; 345/6, Buick "Roadmaster Riviera".

See also Nos. 378/85 and 431/42.

46 Three Wise Men and Star

1984. Christmas. Multicoloured.

347	20c. Type **46**	10	10
348	45c. Journeying to Bethlehem	15	25
349	$3 Presenting gifts	70	1·40
MS350	177 × 107 mm. Nos. 347/9	1·00	2·00

1985. Leaders of the World. Railway Locomotives (3rd series). As T **40**. The first in each pair shows technical drawings and the second the locomotive at work.

351	1c. multicoloured	10	10
352	1c. multicoloured	10	10
353	15c. multicoloured	10	10
354	15c. multicoloured	10	10
355	75c. multicoloured	20	25
356	75c. multicoloured	20	25
357	$3 multicoloured	50	70
358	$3 multicoloured	50	70
MS359	142 × 122 mm. Nos. 355/8	1·75	6·50

DESIGNS: Nos. 351/2, P.L.M. "Grosse C", France (1898); 353/4, Class C12, Japan (1932); 355/6, Class D50, Japan (1923); 357/8, "Fire Fly", Great Britain (1840).

47 Caribbean King Crab

1985. Shell Fish. Multicoloured.

360	25c. Type **47**	20	15
361	60c. Queen or pink conch	30	35
362	$1 White sea urchin	35	60
363	$3 West Indian top shell or wilk	75	2·00

1985. Leaders of the World. Cricketers (3rd series). As T **42** (55, 60c.) the first in each pair showing a head portrait and the second the cricketer in action, or horiz designs showing teams ($2).

364	55c. multicoloured	25	35
365	55c. multicoloured	25	35
366	60c. multicoloured	25	40
367	60c. multicoloured	25	40
368	$2 multicoloured	40	85
369	$2 multicoloured	40	85

DESIGNS—VERT (As T **42**): Nos. 364/5 M. D. Moxon; 366/7, L. Potter. HORIZ (59 × 42 mm): No. 368, Kent team; 369, Yorkshire team.

48 "Cypripedium calceolus"

1985. Leaders of the World. Flowers. Multicoloured.

370	5c. Type **48**	10	10
371	5c. "Gentiana asclepiadea"	10	10
372	55c. "Clianthus formosus"	15	20
373	55c. "Clemisia coriacea"	15	20
374	60c. "Erythronium americanum"	15	20
375	60c. "Laelia anceps"	15	20
376	$2 "Leucadendron discolor"	35	50
377	$2 "Meconopsis horridula"	35	50

1985. Leaders of the World. Automobiles (2nd series). As T **45**. The first in each pair shows technical drawings and the second paintings.

378	5c. black, yellow and blue	10	10
379	5c. multicoloured	10	10
380	60c. black, yellow and orange	15	15
381	60c. multicoloured	15	15
382	$1 black, green and blue	15	20
383	$1 multicoloured	15	20
384	$1.50 black, blue and green	15	25
385	$1.50 multicoloured	15	25

DESIGNS: Nos. 378/9, Winton (1903); 380/1, Invicta 4½ litre (1932); 382/3, Daimler "SP250 Dart" (1959); 384/5, Brabham "Repco BT19" (1966).

49 Windsurfing

1985. Tourism. Watersports. Multicoloured.

386	35c. Type **49**	15	15
387	45c. Water-skiing	15	15
388	75c. Scuba-diving	15	25
389	$3 Deep-sea game fishing	30	1·40

1985. Leaders of the World. Railway Locomotives (4th series). As T **40**. The first design in each pair shows technical drawings and the second the locomotive at work.

390	10c. mutlicoloured	10	10
391	10c. multicoloured	10	10
392	40c. multicoloured	20	20
393	40c. multicoloured	20	20
394	50c. multicoloured	20	20
395	50c. multicoloured	20	20
396	$2.50 multicoloured	70	80
397	$2.50 multicoloured	70	80

DESIGNS: Nos. 390/1, Class 581 electric train, Japan (1968); 392/3, 231-132BT, Algeria (1936); 394/5, "Slieve Gullion", Ireland (1913); 396/7, Class "Beattie" well tank, Great Britain (1874).

50 Passion Fruits and Blossom

1985. Fruits and Blossoms. Multicoloured.

398	30c. Type **50**	15	20
399	75c. Guava	25	40
400	$1 Sapodilla	35	55
401	$2 Mango	50	1·10
MS402	145 × 120 mm. Nos. 398/401	2·00	2·25

51 Queen Elizabeth, the Queen Mother

1985. Leaders of the World. Life and Times of Queen Elizabeth, the Queen Mother. Various vertical portraits.

403	**51**	40c. multicoloured	10	20
404	–	40c. multicoloured	10	20
405	–	75c. multicoloured	15	20
406	–	75c. multicoloured	15	20
407	–	$1.10 multicoloured	15	20
408	–	$1.10 multicoloured	15	20
409	–	$1.75 multicoloured	15	30
410	–	$1.75 multicoloured	15	30
MS411		85 × 114 mm. $2 multicoloured; $2 multicoloured	50	1·50

Each value, issued in pairs, shows a floral pattern across the bottom of the portraits which stops short of the left-hand edge on the first stamp and of the right-hand edge on the second.

1985. Leaders of the World. Railway Locomotives (5th series). As T **40**. The first design in each pair shows technical drawings and the second the locomotive at work.

412	35c. multicoloured	15	20
413	35c. multicoloured	15	20
414	70c. multicoloured	20	30
415	70c. multicoloured	20	30
416	$1.20 multicoloured	30	40
417	$1.20 multicoloured	30	40
418	$2 multicoloured	40	65
419	$2 multicoloured	40	65

DESIGNS: Nos. 412/13, "Coronation", Great Britain (1937); 414/15, Class E18, Germany (1935); 416/17, Hayes type, U.S.A. (1854); 418/19, Class 2120, Japan (1890).

1985. Royal Visit. Nos. 199/200, 222, 287, 398 and 407/8 optd **CARIBBEAN ROYAL VISIT 1985** or surch also.

420	**50**	30c. multicoloured	80	1·50
421	**41**	45c. multicoloured	1·00	1·75
422	–	$1.10 multicoloured (No. 407)	1·75	4·00
423	–	$1.10 multicoloured (No. 408)	1·75	4·00
424	–	$1.50 on $3.50 mult (No. 199)	2·00	2·25
425	–	$1.50 on $3.50 mult (No. 200)	20·00	23·00
426	–	$3 multicoloured (No. 222)	2·75	3·75

52 Donkey Man

1985. Traditional Dances. Multicoloured.

427	45c. Type **52**	10	30
428	75c. Cake dance (vert)	15	40
429	$1 Bois-Bois man (vert)	15	55
430	$2 Maypole dance	25	1·10

1986. Leaders of the World. Automobiles (3rd series). As T **45**. The first in each pair shows technical drawings and the second paintings.

431	15c. black, lilac and mauve	10	10
432	15c. multicoloured	10	10
433	45c. black, yellow and brown	10	20
434	45c. multicoloured	10	20
435	60c. black, green and blue	10	25
436	60c. multicoloured	10	25
437	$1 black, brown and green	15	25
438	$1 multicoloured	15	25
439	$1.75 black, yellow and orange	15	35
440	$1.75 multicoloured	15	35
441	$3 multicoloured	25	45
442	$3 multicoloured	25	45

DESIGNS: Nos. 431/2, Mercedes-Benz 4.5 litre (1914); 433/4, Rolls Royce "Silver Wraith" (1954); 435/6, Lamborghini "Countach" (1974); 437/8, Marmon "V-16" (1932); 439/40, Lotus-Ford "49 B" (1968); 441/2, Delage 1.5 litre (1927).

1986. Leaders of the World. Railway Locomotives (6th series). As T **40**. The first in each pair shows technical drawings and the second the locomotive at work.

443	15c. multicoloured	15	10
444	15c. multicoloured	15	10
445	45c. multicoloured	20	20
446	45c. multicoloured	20	20
447	60c. multicoloured	20	30
448	60c. multicoloured	20	30
449	75c. multicoloured	20	35
450	75c. multicoloured	20	35
451	$1 multicoloured	25	40
452	$1 multicoloured	25	40
453	$1.50 multicoloured	25	50
454	$1.50 multicoloured	25	50
455	$2 multicoloured	30	65
456	$2 multicoloured	30	65
457	$3 multicoloured	30	80
458	$3 multicoloured	30	80

DESIGNS: Nos. 443/4, Class T15, Germany (1897); 445/6, Class 13, Great Britain (1900); 447/8, "Halesworth", Great Britain (1879); 449/50, Class "Problem", Great Britain (1859); 451/2, Class "Western" diesel, Great Britain (1961); 453/4, Drummond's "Bug", Great Britain (1899); 455/6, Class "Clan", Great Britain (1951); 457/8, Class 1800, Japan (1884).

52a Queen Elizabeth II

1986. 60th Birthday of Queen Elizabeth II. Mult.

459	5c. Type **52a**	15	15
460	$1 At Princess Anne's christening, 1950	30	40
461	$4 Princess Elizabeth	60	1·25
462	$6 In Canberra, 1982 (vert)	75	1·50
MS463	85 × 115 mm. $8 Queen Elizabeth II (different)	1·50	4·50

53 Handmade Dolls

1986. Handicrafts. Multicoloured.

464	10c. Type **53**	10	10
465	60c. Basketwork	20	35
466	$1 Scrimshaw work	30	50
467	$3 Model sailing dinghy	80	2·25

54 Uruguayan Team

1986. World Cup Football Championship, Mexico. Multicoloured.

468	1c. Type **54**	10	10
469	10c. Polish team	10	10
470	45c. Bulgarian player (28 × 42 mm)	25	30
471	75c. Iraqi player (28 × 42 mm)	35	40
472	$1.50 South Korean player (28 × 42 mm)	60	90
473	$2 Northern Irish player (28 × 42 mm)	70	1·10
474	$4 Portuguese team	1·00	1·50
475	$5 Canadian team	1·00	1·50
MS476	Two sheets, 85 × 114 mm. (a) $1 As No. 474. (b) $3 Type **54**. Set of 2 sheets	1·50	2·75

55 "Marasmius pallescens"

1986. Fungi. Multicoloured.

477	45c. Type **55**	2·25	75
478	60c. "Leucocoprinus fragilissimus"	2·50	1·10
479	75c. "Hygrocybe occidentalis"	2·75	1·60
480	$3 "Xerocomus hypoxanthus"	8·00	7·00

55a Miss Sarah Ferguson and Princess Diana applauding

1986. Royal Wedding (1st issue). Multicoloured.

481	60c. Type **55a**	20	30
482	60c. Prince Andrew at shooting match	20	30
483	$2 Prince Andrew and Miss Sarah Ferguson (horiz)	60	90
484	$2 Prince Charles with Prince Andrew, Princess Anne and Princess Margaret on balcony (horiz)	60	90
MS485	115 × 85 mm. $8 Duke and Duchess of York in carriage after wedding (horiz)	2·75	4·50

1986. Royal Wedding (2nd issue). Nos. 481/4 optd **Congratulations to T.R.H. The Duke & Duchess of York**.

486	60c. Miss Sarah Ferguson and Princess Diana applauding	30	65
487	60c. Prince Andrew at shooting match	30	65
488	$2 Prince Andrew and Miss Sarah Ferguson (horiz)	1·00	1·25
489	$2 Prince Charles, Prince Andrew, Princess Anne and Princess Margaret on balcony (horiz)	1·00	1·25

56 "Brachymesia furcata"

1986. Dragonflies. Multicoloured.
490 45c. Type **56** 25 20
491 60c. "Lepthemis vesiculosa" 30 40
492 75c. "Perithemis domitta" 30 45
493 $2.50 "Tramea abdominalis (vert) 45 1·40

1986. Centenary of Statue of Liberty. Vert views of Statue as T **323a** of Grenada in seperate miniature sheets. Multicoloured.
MS494 Nine sheets, each 85 × 115 mm. $1.50; $1.75; $2; $2.50; $3; $3.50; $5; $6; $8. Set of 9 sheets 3·00 12·00

57 American Kestrel ("Sparrow Hawk") **58** Santa playing Steel Band Drums

1986. Birds of Prey. Multicoloured.
495 10c. Type **57** 75 45
496 45c. Common black hawk ("Black Hawk") 1·90 50
497 60c. Peregrine falcon ("Duck Hawk") 2·25 1·25
498 $4 Osprey ("Fish Hawk") 5·00 6·50

1986. Christmas. Multicoloured.
499 45c. Type **58** 30 30
500 60c. Santa windsurfing 35 35
501 $1.25 Santa skiing 60 85
502 $2 Santa limbo dancing 1·10 1·60
MS503 166 × 128 mm. Nos. 499/502 7·00 8·00

1987. Railway Locomotives (7th series). As T **40**. The first in each pair shows technical drawings and the second the locomotive at work.
504 10c. multicoloured 15 10
505 10c. multicoloured 15 10
506 40c. multicoloured 25 25
507 40c. multicoloured 25 25
508 50c. multicoloured 30 30
509 50c. multicoloured 30 30
510 60c. multicoloured 30 30
511 60c. multicoloured 30 30
512 75c. multicoloured 30 40
513 75c. multicoloured 30 40
514 $1 multicoloured 30 50
515 $1 multicoloured 30 50
516 $1.25 multicoloured 30 60
517 $1.25 multicoloured 30 60
518 $1.50 multicoloured 40 75
519 $1.50 multicoloured 40 75
DESIGNS: Nos. 504/5, Class 1001, No. 1275, Great Britain (1874); 506/7, Class 4P Garratt, Great Britain (1927); 508/9, "Papyrus", Great Britain (1929); 510/11, Class VI, Great Britain (1930); 512/13, Class 40 diesel, No. D200, Great Britain (1958); 514/15, Class 42 "Warship" diesel, Great Britain (1958); 516/17, Class P-69, U.S.A. (1902); 518/19, Class 60-3 Shay, No. 15, U.S.A. (1913).

1987. Railway Locomotives (8th series). As T **40**. The first in each pair shows technical drawings and the second the locomotive at work.
520 10c. multicoloured 15 15
521 10c. multicoloured 15 15
522 40c. multicoloured 25 30
523 40c. multicoloured 25 30
524 50c. multicoloured 30 35
525 50c. multicoloured 30 35
526 60c. multicoloured 30 40
527 60c. multicoloured 30 40
528 75c. multicoloured 30 45
529 75c. multicoloured 30 45
530 $1 multicoloured 30 45
531 $1 multicoloured 30 45
532 $1.50 multicoloured 40 55
533 $1.50 multicoloured 40 55
534 $2 multicoloured 45 70
535 $2 multicoloured 45 70
DESIGNS: Nos. 520/1, Class 142, East Germany (1977); 522/3, Class 120, West Germany (1979); 524/5, Class X, Australia (1954); 526/7, Class 59, Great Britain (1986); 528/9, New York Elevated Railroad "Spuyten Duyvel", U.S.A. (1875); 530/1, Camden & Amboy Railroad "Stevens" and rebuilt "John Bull", U.S.A. (1832); 532/3, Class HI-d, No. 2850, Canada (1938); 534/5, "Pioneer Zephyr" 3-car diesel set, U.S.A. (1934).

59 Queen Elizabeth with Prince Andrew

1987. Royal Ruby Wedding and 150th Anniv of Queen Victoria's Accession.
536 **59** 15c. multicoloured 20 15
537 – 45c. brown, black and yellow 25 20
538 – $1.50 multicoloured 30 55
539 – $3 multicoloured 45 1·00
540 – $4 multicoloured 50 1·25
MS541 85 × 115 mm. $6 multicoloured 2·00 3·25
DESIGNS: 45c. Queen Victoria and Prince Albert, c. 1855; $1.50, Queen and Prince Philip after Trooping the Colour, 1977; $3 Queen and Duke of Edinburgh, 1953; $4 Queen in her study, c. 1980; Princess Elizabeth, 1947.

60 Banded Coral Shrimp

1987. Marine Life. Multicoloured.
542 45c. Type **60** 55 35
543 50c. Arrow crab and flamingo tongue 60 50
544 65c. Cardinal fish 70 90
545 $5 Moray eel 2·00 4·00
MS546 85 × 115 mm. $5 Porcupinefish ("Puffer Fish") 2·50 5·00

61 "Australia IV"

1988. Ocean Racing Yachts. Multicoloured.
547 50c. Type **61** 30 35
548 65c. "Crusader II" 35 50
549 75c. "New Zealand II" 40 60
550 $2 "Italia" 60 1·25
551 $4 "White Crusader" 70 2·00
552 $5 "Stars and Stripes" 70 2·25
MS553 100 × 140 mm. $1 "Champosa V" 1·25 2·00

62 Seine-fishing Boats racing

1988. Bequia Regatta. Multicoloured.
554 5c. Type **62** 10 15
555 50c. "Friendship Rose" (cruising yacht) 15 30
556 75c. Fishing boats racing 20 45
557 $3.50 Yachts racing 75 2·25
MS558 115 × 85 mm. $8 Port Elizabeth, Bequia (60 × 40 mm) 3·25 6·00

63 Britten Norman Islander making Night Approach

1988. Mustique Airways. Multicoloured.
559 15c. Type **63** 10 15
560 65c. Beech Baron aircraft in flight 15 35
561 75c. Britten Norman Islander over forest 15 35
562 $5 Beech Baron on airstrip 1·00 2·25
MS563 115 × 85 mm. $10 Baleine Falls (36 × 56 mm) 2·50 5·50

64 "Sv. Pyotr" in Arctic (Bering) **65** Asif Iqbal Razvi

1988. Explorers. Multicoloured.
564 15c. Type **64** 35 20
565 75c. Bering's ships in pack ice 40 30
566 $1 Livingstone's steam launch "Ma-Robert" on Zambesi 40 40
567 $2 Meeting of Livingstone and H. M. Stanley at Ujiji 50 75
568 $3 Speke and Burton at Tabori 50 1·00
569 $3.50 Speke and Burton in canoe on Lake Victoria 50 1·25
570 $4 Sighting the New World, 1492 60 1·40
571 $4.50 Columbus trading with Indians 60 1·50
MS572 Two sheets, each 115 × 85 mm. (a) $5 Sextant and coastal scene. (b) $5 "Santa Maria" at anchor. Set of 2 sheets 2·50 5·50

1988. Cricketers of 1988 International Season. Multicoloured.
573 20c. Type **65** 40 30
574 45c. R. J. Hadlee 60 50
575 75c. M. D. Crowe 80 80
576 $1.25 C. H. Lloyd 90 1·25
577 $1.50 A. R. Boarder 1·00 1·50
578 $2 M. D. Marshall 1·25 2·00
579 $2.50 G. A. Hick 1·25 2·25
580 $3.50 C. G. Greenidge (horiz) 1·25 2·75
MS581 115 × 85 mm. $3 As $2 3·75 7·00

66 Pam Shriver

1988. International Tennis Players. Mult.
582 15c. Type **66** 20 20
583 50c. Kevin Curran (vert) 20 30
584 75c. Wendy Turnbull (vert) 25 35
585 $1 Evonne Cawley (vert) 35 50
586 $1.50 Ilie Nastase 40 65
587 $2 Billie Jean King (vert) 45 75
588 $3 Bjorn Borg (vert) 55 1·25
589 $3.50 Virginia Wade with Wimbledon trophy (vert) 60 1·50
MS590 115 × 85 mm. $2.25, Stefan Edberg with Wimbledon cup; $2.25, Steffi Graf with Wimbledon trophy 1·50 3·50
No. 584 is inscribed "WENDY TURNBALL" in error.

67 Mickey and Minnie Mouse visiting Fatehpur Sikri

1989. "India-89" International Stamp Exhibition. Designs showing Walt Disney cartoon characters in India. Multicoloured.
591 1c. Type **67** 10 10
592 2c. Mickey and Minnie Mouse aboard "Palace on Wheels" train 10 10
593 3c. Mickey and Minnie Mouse passing Old Fort, Delhi 10 10
594 5c. Mickey and Minnie Mouse on camel, Pinjore Gardens, Haryana 10 10
595 10c. Mickey and Minnie Mouse at Taj Mahal, Agra 15 10
596 25c. Mickey and Minnie Mouse in Chandni Chowk, Old Delhi 25 10
597 $4 Goofy on elephant with Mickey and Minnie Mouse at Agra Fort, Jaipur 3·25 3·50
598 $5 Goofy, Mickey and Minnie Mouse at Gandhi Memorial Cape Comorin 3·25 3·50
MS599 Two sheets, each 127 × 102 mm. (a) $6 Mickey and Minnie Mouse in vegetable cart, Jaipur. (b) $6 Mickey and Minnie Mouse leaving carriage, Qutab Minar, New Delhi (vert). Set of 2 sheets 8·50 10·00

1989. Japanese Art. As T **177a** of Gambia but horiz. Multicoloured.
600 5c. "The View at Yotsuya" (Hokusai) 20 20
601 30c. "Landscape at Ochanomizu" (Hokuju) 50 50
602 45c. "Itabashi" (Eisen) 60 60
603 65c. "Early Summer Rain" (Kunisada) 75 75
604 75c. "High Noon at Kasumigaseki" (Kuniyoshi) 80 80
605 $1 "The Yoshiwara Embankment by Moonlight" (Kuniyoshi) 1·00 1·00
606 $4 "The Bridge of Boats at Sano" (Hokusai) 2·75 3·00
607 $5 "Lingering Snow on Mount Hira" (Kunitora) 2·75 3·00
MS608 Two sheets, each 103 × 76 mm. (a) $6 "Colossus of Rhodes" (Kunitora). (b) $6 "Shinobazu Pond" (Kokan). Set of 2 sheets 7·00 8·00

68 Player with Ball and Mt. Vesuvius **71** "Marpesia petreus"

70 Command Module "Columbia"

1989. World Cup Football Championship, Italy (1st issue). Designs showing players and Italian landmarks. Multicoloured.
609 $1.50 Type **68** 1·40 1·40
610 $1.50 Fallen player, opponent kicking ball and Coliseum 1·40 1·40
611 $1.50 Player blocking ball and Venice 1·40 1·40
612 $1.50 Player tackling and Forum, Rome 1·40 1·40
613 $1.50 Two players competing for ball and Leaning Tower, Pisa 1·40 1·40
614 $1.50 Goalkeeper and Florence 1·40 1·40
615 $1.50 Two players competing for ball and St. Peter's, Vatican 1·40 1·40
616 $1.50 Player kicking ball and Pantheon 1·40 1·40
Nos 609/16 were printed together, se-tenant, forming a composite foreground design.
See also Nos. 680/3.

1989. 500th Anniv (1992) of Discovery of America by Columbus (1st issue). Pre-Columbian Arawak Society. As T **97a** of Grenadines of Grenada. Multicoloured.
617 25c. Arawak smoking tobacco 45 30
618 75c. Arawak rolling cigar 75 65
619 $1 Applying body paint 90 80
620 $1.50 Making fire 1·25 1·50
621 $1.50 Cassava production 1·25 1·50
622 $1.50 Woman baking bread 1·25 1·50
623 $1.50 Using stone implement 1·25 1·50
624 $4 Arawak priest 2·50 3·00
MS625 Two sheets, each 70 × 84 mm. (a) $6 Arawak chief. (b) $6 Men returning from fishing expedition. Set of 2 sheets 12·00 13·00
Nos. 620/3 were printed together, se-tenant, forming a composite design.
See also Nos. 818/23 and 864/5.

1989. 20th Anniv of First Manned Landing on Moon. Multicoloured.
626 5c. Type **70** 40 40
627 40c. Astronaut Neil Armstrong saluting U.S. flag 1·25 85
628 55c. "Columbia" above lunar surface 1·50 1·00
629 65c. Lunar module "Eagle" leaving moon 1·50 1·25
630 70c. "Eagle" on Moon 1·50 1·25
631 $1 "Columbia" re-entering Earth's atmosphere 1·60 1·60

632 $3 "Apollo 11" emblem . . . 3·00 3·25
633 $5 Armstrong and Aldrin on Moon . . . 3·25 3·75
MS634 Two sheets, each 110×82 mm. (a) $6 Launch of "Apollo 11" (vert). (b) $6 "Apollo 11" splashdown. Set of 2 sheets . . . 11·00 12·00

1989. Butterflies. Multicoloured.
635 5c. Type **71** . . . 50 50
636 30c. "Papilio androgeus" . . 1·25 60
637 45c. "Strymon maesites" . . 1·50 65
638 65c. "Junonia coenia" . . . 1·75 1·40
639 75c. "Eurema gratiosa" . . . 2·00 1·50
640 $1 "Hypolimnas misippus" . . 2·00 1·75
641 $4 "Urbanus proteus" . . . 4·25 4·50
642 $5 "Junonia evarete" . . . 4·25 4·50
MS643 Two sheets. (a) 76×104 mm. $6 "Phoebis agarithe". (b) 104×76 mm. $6 "Dryas julia". Set of 2 sheets . . . 15·00 13·00

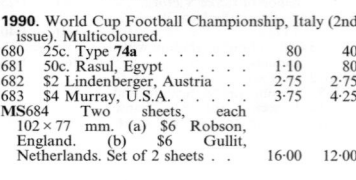

72 "Solanum urens"

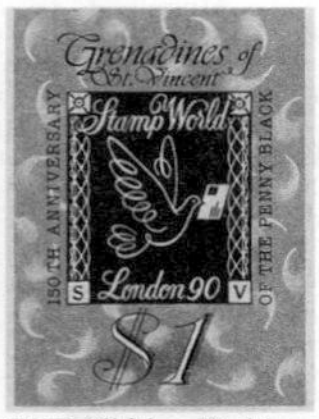

74 Exhibition Emblem

1989. Flowers from St. Vincent Botanical Gardens. Multicoloured.
644 80c. Type **72** . . . 1·50 1·50
645 $1.25 "Passiflora andersonii" 2·00 2·00
646 $1.65 "Miconia andersonii" 2·25 2·25
647 $1.85 "Pitcairnia sulphurea" 2·50 2·50

1989. Christmas. As T **183** of Gambia. Mult.
648 5c. Goofy and Mickey Mouse in Rolls Royce "Silver Ghost", 1907 . . . 20 15
649 10c. Daisy Duck driving first Stanley Steamer, 1897 . . 20 15
650 15c. Horace Horsecollar and Clarabelle Cow in Darracq "Genevieve", 1904 . . . 25 20
651 45c. Donald Duck driving Detroit electric coupe, 1914 55 40
652 55c. Mickey and Minnie Mouse in first Ford, 1896 55 40
653 $2 Mickey Mouse driving Reo "Runabout", 1904 . . 2·00 2·00
654 $3 Goofy driving Winton mail truck, 1899 . . . 2·75 2·75
655 $5 Mickey and Minnie Mouse in Duryea car, 1893 3·50 4·00
MS656 Two sheets, each 127×102 mm. (a) $6 Mickey and Minnie Mouse in Pope-Hartford, 1912. (b) $6 Mickey and Minnie Mouse in Buick "Model 10", 1908. Set of 2 sheets . . . 10·00 12·00

1990. 50th Anniv of Second World War. As T **354c** of Grenada. Multicoloured.
657 10c. Destroyer in action, First Battle of Narvik, 1940 . . 35 25
658 15c. Allied tank at Anzio, 1944 . . . 45 35
659 20c. U.S. carrier under attack, Battle of Midway, 1942 . . . 50 40
660 45c. North American B-25 Mitchell bombers over Gustav Line, 1944 . . . 80 70
661 55c. Map showing Allied zones of Berlin, 1945 . . . 85 75
662 65c. German U-boat pursuing convoy, Battle of the Atlantic, 1943 . . . 90 80
663 90c. Allied tank, North Africa, 1943 . . . 1·25 1·00
664 $3 U.S. forces landing on Guam, 1944 . . . 2·75 2·75
665 $5 Crossing the Rhine, 1945 3·75 3·75
666 $6 Japanese battleships under attack, Lete Gulf, 1944 . 4·25 4·25
MS667 100×70 mm. $6 Avro Type 683 Lancaster Mk III on "Dambusters" raid, 1943 . . . 5·00 6·00

1990. "Stamp World London 90" International Stamp Exhibition (1st issue). Mickey's Shakespeare Company. As T **193** of Gambia showing Walt Disney cartoon characters. Multicoloured.
668 20c. Goofy as Mark Anthony ("Julius Caesar") . . . 30 20
669 30c. Clarabelle Cow as the Nurse ("Romeo and Juliet") . . . 35 25
670 45c. Pete as Falstaff ("Henry IV") . . . 50 40
671 50c. Minnie Mouse as Portia ("The Merchant of Venice") . . . 55 40
672 $1 Donald Duck as Hamlet ("Hamlet") . . . 1·00 85
673 $2 Daisy Duck as Ophelia ("Hamlet") . . . 1·75 2·00
674 $4 Donald and Daisy Duck as Benedick and Beatrice ("Much Ado About Nothing") . . . 3·00 3·25
675 $5 Minnie Mouse and Donald Duck as Katherine and Petruchio ("The Taming of the Shrew") . . 3·00 3·25
MS676 Two sheets, each 127×101 mm. (a) $6 Clarabelle as Titania ("A Midsummer Night's Dream") (vert). (b) $6 Mickey Mouse as Romeo ("Romeo and Juliet") (vert). Set of 2 sheets 11·00 12·00

1990. "Stamp World London 90" International Stamp Exhibition (2nd issue). 150th Anniv of the Penny Black.
677 **74** $1 black, pink and mauve 1·50 1·25
678 – $5 black, lilac and blue . . 3·75 4·25
MS679 130×100 mm. $6 black and pale blue . . . 5·00 6·00
DESIGNS: $5 Negative image of Penny Black; $6 Penny Black.

74a McCleish, Scotland

1990. World Cup Football Championship, Italy (2nd issue). Multicoloured.
680 25c. Type **74a** . . . 80 40
681 50c. Rasul, Egypt . . . 1·10 80
682 $2 Lindenberger, Austria . . 2·75 2·75
683 $4 Murray, U.S.A. . . . 3·75 4·25
MS684 Two sheets, each 102×77 mm. (a) $6 Robson, England. (b) $6 Gullit, Netherlands. Set of 2 sheets . . 16·00 12·00

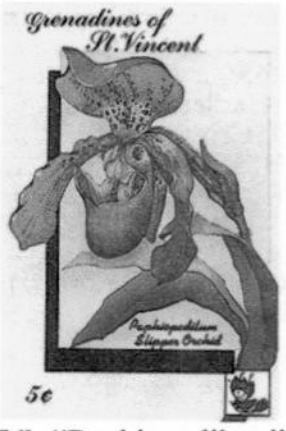

74b "Paphiopedilum"

1990. "EXPO 90" International Garden and Greenery Exposition, Osaka. Orchids. Mult.
685 5c. Type **74b** . . . 80 50
686 25c. "Dendrobium phalaenopsis" and "Cymbidium hybrid" . . . 1·75 90
687 30c. "Miltonia candida hybrid" . . . 1·75 90
688 50c. "Epidendrum ibaguense" and "Cymbidium" Elliot Rogers . . . 2·25 1·25
689 $1 "Rossioglossum grande" 2·75 1·75
690 $2 "Phalaenopsis" Elisa Chang Lou and "Masdevallia coccinea" . . 3·25 2·50
691 $4 "Cypripedium acaule" and "Cypripedium calceolus" 3·75 4·00
692 $5 "Orchis spectabilis" . . 3·75 4·00
MS693 Two sheets, each 108×78 mm. (a) $6 "Dendrobium anosmum". (b) $6 "Epidendrum ibaguense" and "Phalaenopsis". Set of 2 sheets . . . 13·00 13·00

75 Scaly-breasted Ground Dove ("Common Ground Dove")

1990. Birds of the Caribbean. Multicoloured.
694 5c. Type **75** . . . 20 20
695 25c. Purple martin . . . 40 40
696 45c. Painted bunting . . . 70 70
697 55c. Blue-hooded euphonia . 80 80
698 75c. Blue-grey tanager . . 1·00 1·00
699 $1 Red-eyed vireo . . . 1·25 1·25
700 $2 Palm chat . . . 2·00 2·00
701 $3 Northern jacana ("North American Jacana") . . . 2·50 2·50
702 $4 Green-throated carib . . 2·75 2·75
703 $5 St. Vincent amazon ("St. Vincent Parrot") . . 3·00 3·00
MS704 Two sheets, each 117×87 mm. (a) $3 Magnificent frigate bird; $3 Bananaquit. (b) $6 Red-legged honeycreeper. Set of 2 sheets . . . 9·50 10·00

1991. 90th Birthday of Queen Elizabeth the Queen Mother. As T **194** of Gambia.
705 $2 multicoloured . . . 1·90 1·25
706 $2 multicoloured . . . 1·90 1·25
707 $2 multicoloured . . . 1·90 1·25
708 $2 multicoloured . . . 1·90 1·25
709 $2 multicoloured . . . 1·90 1·25
710 $2 multicoloured . . . 1·90 1·25
711 $2 multicoloured . . . 1·90 1·25
712 $2 multicoloured . . . 1·90 1·25
713 $2 multicoloured . . . 1·90 1·25
714 $2 multicoloured . . . 1·90 1·25
715 $2 multicoloured . . . 1·90 1·25
716 $2 multicoloured . . . 1·90 1·25
717 $2 multicoloured . . . 1·90 1·25
718 $2 multicoloured . . . 1·90 1·25
719 $2 multicoloured . . . 1·90 1·25
720 $2 multicoloured . . . 1·90 1·25
721 $2 multicoloured . . . 1·90 1·25
722 $2 multicoloured . . . 1·90 1·25
723 $2 multicoloured . . . 1·90 1·25
724 $2 multicoloured . . . 1·90 1·25
725 $2 multicoloured . . . 1·90 1·25
726 $2 multicoloured . . . 1·90 1·25
727 $2 multicoloured . . . 1·90 1·25
728 $2 multicoloured . . . 1·90 1·25
729 $2 multicoloured . . . 1·90 1·25
730 $2 multicoloured . . . 1·90 1·25
731 $2 multicoloured . . . 1·90 1·25
MS732 Nine sheets containing details of designs indicated. (a) 120×115 mm. $5 As No. 705. (b) 115×120 mm. $5 As No. 710. (c) 115×120 mm. $5 As No. 712. (d) 115×120 mm. $5 As No. 715. (e) 120×115 mm. $5 As No. 719. (f) 120×115 mm. $5 As No. 720. (g) 120×115 mm. $5 As No. 724. (h) 120×115 mm. $5 As No. 726. (i) 120×115 mm. $5 As No. 730. Set of 9 sheets . . . 30·00 27·00
DESIGNS: No. 705, Lady Elizabeth Bowes-Lyon with sister; 706, Young Lady Elizabeth in long dress; 707, Young Lady Elizabeth wearing a hat; 708, Lady Elizabeth leaning on wall; 709, Lady Elizabeth on pony; 710, Studio portrait; 711, Lady Elizabeth in evening dress; 712, Duchess of York in fur-lined cloak; 713, Duchess of York holding rose; 714, Coronation, 1937; 715, King and Queen with Princess Elizabeth at Royal Lodge, Windsor; 716, Queen Elizabeth in blue hat; 717, King George VI and Queen Elizabeth; 718, Queen Elizabeth with Princess Elizabeth; 719, Queen Elizabeth watching sporting fixture; 720, Queen Elizabeth in white evening dress; 721, Princess Anne's christening, 1950; 722, Queen Mother with yellow bouquet; 723, Queen Mother and policewoman; 724, Queen Mother at ceremonial function; 725, Queen Mother in pink coat; 726, Queen Mother in academic robes; 727, Queen Mother in carriage with Princess Margaret; 728, Queen Mother in blue coat and hat; 729, Queen Mother with bouquet; 730, Queen Mother outside Clarence House on her birthday; 731, Queen Mother in turquoise coat and hat.

1991. Death Centenary (1990) of Vincent van Gogh (artist). As T **200b** of Gambia. Mult.
733 5c. "View of Arles with Irises" . . . 40 30
734 10c. "Saintes-Maries" (vert) 40 30
735 15c. "Old Woman of Arles" (vert) . . . 50 30
736 20c. "Orchard in Blossom, bordered by Cypresses" . . 55 30
737 25c. "Three White Cottages in Saintes-Maries" . . . 55 30
738 35c. "Boats at Saintes-Maries" . . . 70 40
739 40c. "Interior of a Restaurant in Arles" . . . 75 45
740 45c. "Peasant Women" (vert) 80 50
741 55c. "Self-portrait" (vert) . . 90 60
742 60c. "Pork Butcher's Shop from a Window" (vert) . . 1·00 70
743 75c. "The Night Cafe in Arles" . . . 1·10 80
744 $1 "2nd Lieut. Millet of the Zouaves" . . . 1·40 95
745 $2 "The Cafe Terrace, Place du Forum, Arles at Night" (vert) . . . 2·25 2·25
746 $3 "The Zouave" (vert) . . . 2·75 3·00
747 $4 "The Two Lovers" (detail) (vert) . . . 3·50 3·75
748 $5 "Still Life" . . . 3·75 4·00
MS749 Four sheets, each 112×76 mm. (a) $5 "Street in Saintes-Maries" (horiz). (b) $5 "Lane near Arles" (horiz). (c) $6 "Harvest at La Crau, with Montmajour in the Background" (horiz). (d) $6 "The Sower". Imperf. Set of 4 sheets . . . 21·00 19·00

1991. 65th Birthday of Queen Elizabeth II. As T **198a** of Gambia. Multicoloured.
750 15c. Inspecting the Yeomen of the Guard . . . 30 20
751 40c. Queen Elizabeth II with the Queen Mother at the Derby, 1988 . . . 55 30
752 $2 The Queen and Prince Philip leaving Euston, 1986 2·00 2·00
753 $4 The Queen at the Commonwealth Institute, 1987 . . . 2·75 3·00
MS754 68×90 mm. $5 Queen Elizabeth and Prince Philip with Prince Andrew in naval uniform . . . 4·75 4·75

1991. 10th Wedding Anniv of Prince and Princess of Wales. As T **198b** of Gambia. Multicoloured.
755 10c. Prince and Princess at polo match, 1987 . . . 1·00 30
756 50c. Separate family portraits 1·75 55
757 $1 Prince William and Prince Henry at Kensington Palace, 1991 . . . 1·75 1·00
758 $5 Portraits of Prince Charles and Princess Diana . . . 4·75 4·00
MS759 68×90 mm. $5 Separate portraits of Prince and Princess and sons . . . 8·00 5·00

76 Class 150 Steam Locomotive and Map

1991. "Phila Nippon '91" International Stamp Exhibition, Toyko. Japanese Railway Locomotives. Each in black, red and green.
760 10c. Type **76** . . . 80 50
761 25c. Class 7100 locomotive, "Benkei", 1880 . . . 1·10 80
762 35c. Class 8620 steam locomotive, 1914 . . . 1·40 90
763 50c. Class C53 steamlined steam locomotive, 1928 . . 1·90 1·25
764 $1 Class DD51 diesel-hydraulic locomotive, 1962 2·50 1·90
765 $2 Class KTR001 electric railcar Tango Explorer (inscr "RF 22327") . . . 3·00 3·00
766 $4 Class EF55 electric locomotive, 1936 . . . 3·50 4·25
767 $5 Class EF58 electric locomotive, 1946 . . . 3·50 4·25
MS768 Four sheets, each 114×73 mm showing frontal views. (a) $6 Class 9600 steam locomotive (1913) (vert). (b) $6 Class C57 steam locomotive (1937) (vert). (c) $6 Class C62 steam locomotive (1948) (vert). (d) $6 Class 4100 tank locomotive (1912) (vert). Set of 4 sheets . . . 19·00 19·00

77 President Gorbachev and Brandenburg Gate

1991. Anniversaries and Events. Multicoloured.
769 45c. Type **77** . . . 40 40
770 60c. General de Gaulle in Djibouti, 1959 . . . 1·25 55
771 65c. "DIE MAUER MUSS WEG!" slogan . . . 65 65
772 80c. East German border guard escaping to West . . 80 80
773 $1 "Abduction from the Seraglio" . . . 3·75 1·75
774 $1.50 Lilienthal and glider . . 2·00 1·75
775 $1.75 Trans-Siberian identity plate . . . 3·00 2·75
776 $1.75 Trans-Siberian steam locomotive (vert) . . . 3·00 2·75
777 $2 Czechoslovakia 1918 20h. stamp and scout delivering mail . . . 3·00 3·00
778 $2 Zurich couple maypole dancing . . . 3·00 3·00
779 $2 Man and woman in Vaud traditional costumes . . 3·00 3·00
780 $2 Georg Laves (architect) and Hoftheater . . . 3·00 3·00
781 $3 Dresden, 1749 . . . 6·00 4·50
782 $4 Scouts and cog train on Snowdon (vert) . . . 4·50 5·00
MS783 Eleven sheets. (a) 100×71 mm. $5 Arms of Berlin. (b) 100×71 mm. $5 Berlin police badge. (c) 77×112 mm. $5 De Gaulle in civilian dress. (d) 69×101 mm. $5 General Charles de Gaulle (vert). (e) 75×101 mm. $5 Portrait of Mozart (vert). (f) 75×101 mm. $5 Bust of Mozart (vert). (g) 115×85 mm. $5 Trans-Siberian Class P36 No. 0250 steam locomotive leaving Moscow at night (43×56 mm). (h) 118×89 mm. $5 Jamboree emblem (buff background) (vert). (i) 118×89 mm. $5 Jamboree emblem (bluish violet background) (vert). (j) 101×72 mm. $5 Arms of Appenzell and Thurgau. (k) 101×72 mm. $5 Old Hanover Set of 11 sheets . . . 35·00 38·00
Anniversaries and Events:—Nos. 769, 771/2, **MS**783a/b, Bicentenary of Brandenburg Gate; 770, **MS**783c/d, Birth centenary of Charles de Gaulle (French statesman); 773, 781, **MS**783e/f, Death bicentenary of Mozart; 774, Centenary of Otto Lilienthal's gliding experiments; 775/6, **MS**783g, Centenary of Trans-Siberian Railway; 777, 782, **MS**783h/i. 50th death anniv of Lord Baden-Powell and World Scout Jamboree, Korea; 778/9, **MS**783j, 700th anniv of Swiss Confederation; 780, **MS**783k, 750th anniv of Hanover.

78 Japanese Aircraft and Submarines leaving Truk

1991. 50th Anniv of Japanese Attack on Pearl Harbor. Multicoloured.

784 $1 Type **78** . . . . 1·90 1·60
785 $1 "Akagi" (Japanese aircraft carrier) . . . . 1·90 1·60
786 $1 Nakajima B5N2 "Kate" bombers . . . . 1·90 1·60
787 $1 Nakajima B5N2 "Kate" bombers attacking Battleship Row . . . . . 1·90 1·60
788 $1 Burning aircraft, Ford Island airfield . . . . . . 1·90 1·60
789 $1 Doris Miller winning Navy Cross . . . . 1·90 1·60
790 $1 U.S.S. "West Virginia" and "Tennessee" (battleships) ablaze . . . . 1·90 1·60
791 $1 U.S.S. "Arizona" (battleship) sinking . . . . 1·90 1·60
792 $1 U.S.S. "New Orleans" (cruiser) . . . . 1·90 1·60
793 $1 President Roosevelt declaring war . . . . . . 1·90 1·60

78a Pluto pulling Mickey Mouse in Sledge, 1974

1991. Christmas. Walt Disney Company Christmas Cards. Multicoloured.

794 10c. Type **78a** 60 30
795 55c. Mickey, Pluto and Donald Duck watching toy band, 1961 . . . . 1·25 70
796 65c. "The Same Old Wish", 1942 . . . . 1·40 85
797 75c. Mickey, Peter Pan, Donald and Nephews with Merlin the magician, 1963 1·50 95
798 $1.50 Mickey and Donald with leprechauns, 1958 . . 2·50 2·50
799 $2 Mickey and friends with book "Old Yeller", 1957 2·75 2·75
800 $4 Mickey controlling Pinocchio, 1953 . . . . . 4·00 4·25
801 $5 Cinderella and Prince dancing, 1987 . . . . . . 4·00 4·25
MS802 Two sheets, each 128 × 102 mm. (a) $6 Santa Claus and American bomber, 1942. (b) $6 Snow White, 1957. Set of 2 sheets . . . . 13·00 14·00

1992. 40th Anniv of Queen Elizabeth II's Accession. As T **202a** of Gambia. Multicoloured.

803 15c. View across bay 75 20
804 45c. Schooner at anchor, Mayreau . . . . 1·25 25
805 $2 Hotel on hillside . . . . 1·75 1·75
806 $4 Tourist craft at anchor . . 3·75 3·75
MS807 Two sheets, each 74 × 97 mm. (a) $6 Beach and palms. (b) $6 Aerial view of hotel by beach. Set of 2 sheets . . . 9·50 10·00

78b Big Pete as Hernando Cortes in Mexico

1992. International Stamp Exhibitions. Walt Disney cartoon characters. Multicoloured. (a) "Grenada '92", Spain. Spanish Explorers.

808 15c. Type **78b** 30 15
809 40c. Mickey Mouse as Hernando de Soto at Mississippi River 50 30
810 $2 Goofy as Vasco Nunez de Balboa sights Pacific . . . 1·75 1·75
811 $4 Donald Duck as Francisco Coronado on Rio Grande 2·75 3·00
MS812 127 × 102 mm. $6 Mickey as Ponce de Leon . . . . 4·25 4·75

(b) "World Columbian Stamp Expo '92", Chicago. Local Personalities.

813 10c. Mickey Mouse and Pluto outside Walt Disney's birthplace 30 20
814 50c. Donald Duck and nephews in George Pullman's railway sleeping car . . . . 1·50 55
815 $1 Daisy Duck as Jane Addams (social reformer) and Hull House . . . . . 1·60 85
816 $5 Mickey as Carl Sandburg (novelist, poet and historian) . . . . 3·75 4·00
MS817 127 × 102 mm. $6 Daisy as Mrs O'Leary with her cow (source of Chicago fire of 1871) . . . 4·25 4·75

79 King Ferdinand and Queen Isabella of Spain

1992. 500th Anniv of Discovery of America by Columbus (2nd issue). Multicoloured.

818 10c. Type **79** 25 25
819 45c. "Santa Maria" and "Nina" in Acul Bay, Haiti 50 50
820 55c. "Santa Maria" (vert) . . 55 55
821 $1 Ships of Columbus (vert) 1·40 1·40
822 $4 Wreck of "Santa Maria" 2·50 2·50
823 $5 "Pinta" and "Nina" . . . 2·75 2·75
MS824 Two sheets, each 114 × 85 mm. (a) $6 Columbus landing on San Salvador. (b) $6 "Santa Maria" in storm. Set of 2 sheets . . . . 7·00 8·00

79a "Paulogramma sp."

1992. "Genova '92" International Thematic Stamp Exhibition (1st issue). Butterflies. Multicoloured.

825 15c. Type **79a** 75 65
826 20c. "Heliconius cydno" . . 80 70
827 30c. "Eutresis hypereia" . . . 85 75
828 45c. "Eurytides columbus" (vert) . . . . 1·40 1·25
829 55c. "Papilio ascolius" . . . 1·40 1·25
830 75c. "Anaea pasibula" . . . 1·40 1·25
831 80c. "Heliconius doris" . . . 1·40 1·25
832 $1 "Perisama pitheas" . . . 1·40 1·25
833 $2 "Batesia hypochlora" . . . 2·00 2·00
834 $3 "Heliconius erato" . . . 2·50 2·50
835 $4 "Elzunia cassandrina" . . 2·75 2·75
836 $5 "Sais ivcidice" . . . . . 2·75 2·75
MS837 Three sheets, each 109 × 79 mm. (a) $6 "Oleria tigilla" (horiz). (b) $6 "Dismorphia orise" (horiz). (c) $6 "Podotricha telesiphe" (horiz). Set of 3 sheets . . . . 11·00 12·00
See also Nos. 851/62.

79b "Entoloma bakeri"

1992. Fungi. Multicoloured.

838 10c. Type **79b** 50 50
839 15c. "Hydropus paraensis" 55 55
840 20c. "Leucopaxillus gracillimus" 60 60
841 45c. "Hygrotrama dennisianum" 80 80
842 50c. "Leucoagaricus hortensis" 80 80
843 65c. "Pyrrhoglossum pyrrhum" . . . . 1·00 1·00
844 75c. "Amanita craeoderma" 1·00 1·00
845 $1 "Lentinus bertieri" . . . 1·25 1·25
846 $2 "Dennisiomyces griseus" 2·00 2·00
847 $3 "Xerulina asprata" . . . 2·50 2·50
848 $4 "Hygrocybe acutoconica" 3·00 3·00
849 $5 "Lepiota spiculata" . . . 3·00 3·00
MS850 Three sheets, each 101 × 68 mm. (a) $6 "Pluteus crysophlebius". (b) $6 "Amanita lilloi". (c) $6 "Lepiota volvatua". Set of 3 sheets . . . . 12·00 13·00

1992. "Genova '92" International Thematic Stamp Exhibition (2nd issue). Hummingbirds. As T **370a** of Grenada. Multicoloured.

851 5c. Antillean crested hummingbird (female) (horiz) 40 30
852 10c. Blue-tailed emerald (female) 40 30
853 35c. Antillean mango (male) (horiz) 55 45
854 45c. Antillean mango (female) (horiz) 55 45
855 55c. Green-throated carib (horiz) 65 55
856 65c. Green violetear (male) 80 70
857 75c. Blue-tailed emerald (male) (horiz) 90 80
858 $1 Purple-throated carib . . 1·25 1·00
859 $2 Copper-rumped hummingbird (horiz) . . . 2·25 2·00
860 $3 Rufous-breasted hermit . . 3·25 2·75
861 $4 Antillean crested hummingbird (male) . . . 4·00 3·50
862 $5 Green-breasted mango (male) . . . . 4·25 3·75
MS863 Three sheets, each 105 × 74 mm. (a) $6 Blue-tailed emerald. (b) $6 Antillean mango. (c) $6 Antillean crested hummingbird. Set of 3 sheets 13·00 14·00

1992. 500th Anniv of Discovery of America by Columbus (3rd issue). Organization of East Caribbean States. As T **372a** of Grenada. Multicoloured.

864 $1 Columbus meeting Amerindians 75 75
865 $2 Ships approaching island 2·75 2·50

1992. Olympic Games, Albertville and Barcelona. As T **372** of Grenada. Multicoloured.

866 10c. Men's volleyball 70 40
867 15c. Men's gymnastics (horiz) 85 50
868 25c. Men's cross-country skiing . . . . 1·00 60
869 30c. Men's 110 m hurdles (horiz) . . . . 1·00 60
870 45c. Men's 120 m ski-jumping (horiz) . . . . 1·10 70
871 55c. Women's 4 × 100 m relay 1·25 80
872 75c. Men's triple jump . . . 1·60 1·00
873 80c. Men's mogul skiing . . 1·60 1·00
874 $1 Men's 110 m butterfly swimming (horiz) . . . . 1·60 1·25
875 $2 "Tornado" Class yachting (horiz) . . . . 2·25 1·75
876 $3 Men's decathlon (horiz) 2·50 2·75
877 $5 Show jumping (horiz) . . 3·75 3·75
MS878 Three sheets, each 101 × 70 mm. (a) $6 Ice hockey (horiz). (b) $6 Men's single luge (horiz). (c) $6 Football. Set of 3 sheets . . . . 14·00 14·00

1992. Christmas. Religious Paintings. As T **207b** of Gambia. Multicoloured.

879 10c. "Our Lady with St. Roch and St. Anthony of Padua" (Giorgione) . . 60 30
880 40c. "Anthony of Padua" (Master of the Embroidered Leaf) 80 55
881 45c. "Madonna and Child" (detail) (Orazio Gentileschi) 90 60
882 50c. "Madonna and Child with St. Anne (detail) (Da Vinci) 95 65
883 55c. "The Holy Family" (Crespi) . . . . 1·00 70
884 65c. "Madonna and Child" (Del Sarto) . . . . 1·10 80
885 75c. "Madonna and Child with Sts. Lawrence and Julian" (Gentile da Fabriano) . . . . 1·25 90
886 $1 "Virgin and Child" (detail) (School of Parma) 1·50 1·10
887 $2 "Madonna with the Iris" (detail) (style of Durer) . . 2·50 2·25
888 $3 "Virgin and Child with St. Jerome and St. Dominic" (Lippi) . . . 3·00 3·00
889 $4 "Rapolano Madonna" (Ambrogio Lorenzetti) . . 3·50 3·75
890 $5 "The Virgin and Child with Angels in a Garden with a Rose Hedge" (Stefano da Verona) . . . 3·50 3·75
MS891 Three sheets, each 73 × 98 mm. (a) $6 "Madonna and Child with Grapes" (detail) (Cranach the Elder). (b) $6 "Virgin and Child with St. John the Baptist" (detail) (Botticelli). (c) $6 "Madonna and Child with St. Anne" (different detail) (Da Vinci). Set of 3 sheets . . . . 15·00 15·00

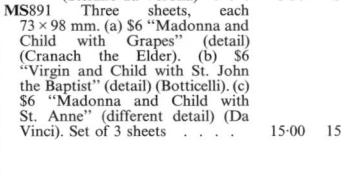

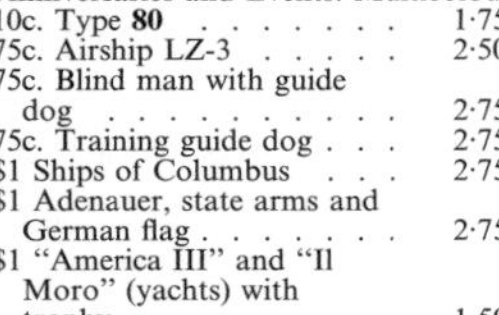

80 "Nina" in Baracoa Harbour

1992. Anniversaries and Events. Multicoloured.

892 10c. Type **80** . . . . 1·75 75
893 75c. Airship LZ-3 . . . . . 2·50 1·75
894 75c. Blind man with guide dog . . . . 2·75 1·75
895 75c. Training guide dog . . . 2·75 1·75
896 $1 Ships of Columbus . . . 2·75 1·75
897 $1 Adenauer, state arms and German flag . . . . 2·75 1·75
898 $1 "America III" and "Il Moro" (yachts) with trophy . . . . 1·50 1·50
899 $1 Hands breaking bread and emblem (vert) . . . . . 1·50 1·50
900 $2 "Voyager 2" and planet 3·25 2·50
901 $3 Adenauer and children watching Berlin Airlift . . 2·75 3·00
902 $4 Airship LZ-37 in flames 3·25 3·75
903 $4 Adenauer and ruins in Cologne . . . . 3·00 3·75
904 $4 Mozart with his wife Constanze (vert) . . . . . 6·00 4·50
905 $5 Adenauer and modern office blocks . . . . 3·00 4·50
MS906 Seven sheets. (a) 100 × 70 mm. $6 Columbus sighting land. (b) 100 × 70 mm. $6 Count von Zeppelin facing left. (c) 110 × 70 mm. $6 Count von Zeppelin facing right. (d) 100 × 70 mm. $6 Konrad Adenauer (vert). (e) 100 × 70 mm. $6 Konrad Adenauer. (f) 100 × 70 mm. $6 "Mars Observer" spacecraft. (g) 100 × 70 mm. $6 Costume for "Don Giovanni" by Cassandre. Set of 7 sheets . . 35·00 38·00

ANNIVERSARIES AND EVENTS: Nos. 892, 896, **MS**906a, 500th anniv of discovery of America by Columbus; Nos. 893, 902, **MS**906b/c, 75th death anniv of Count Ferdinand von Zeppelin (airship pioneer); Nos. 894/5, 75th anniv of International Association of Lions Clubs; Nos. 897, 901, 903, 905, **MS**906d/e, 25th death anniv of Konrad Adenauer (German statesman); No. 898, Americas Cup yachting championship; No. 899, International Conference on Nutrition, Rome; No. 900, **MS**906f, International Space Year; No. 904, **MS**906g, Death bicentenary of Mozart.

81 Olivia and Flaversham

1992. Walt Disney Cartoon Films.

907/50 60c. × 44 multicoloured. . . Set of 44 . . . . 23·00 24·00
MS951 Ten sheets, each 127 × 103 mm. $6 × 10 multicoloured. Set of 10 sheets 35·00 38·00

Nos. 907/50 were printed as five se-tenant sheetlets, each of nine different designs except that for "Darkwing Duck" which contains eight vertical designs (Nos. 943/50). The other four sheetlets depict scenes from "The Great Mouse Detective", "Oliver and Company", "The Legend of Sleepy Hollow" and "Ducktales the Movie".

No. **MS**951 contains two sheets for each film. On one sheet in the pairs for "The Legend of Sleepy Hollow", "Ducktales the Movie" and "Darkwing Duck" the stamp design is vertical.

1992. 15th Death Anniv of Elvis Presley (singer). As T **260** of Dominica. Mult.

952 $1 Elvis Presley . . . . . . 2·75 2·25
953 $1 Elvis with guitar . . . . 2·75 2·25
954 $1 Elvis with microphone . . 2·75 2·25

82 Prince Mickey searching for Bride

1992. "Tales of Uncle Scrooge" (fairy stories). Walt Disney cartoon characters.

955/1008 60c. × 54 multicoloured. Set of 54 . . . . 25·00 26·00
MS1009 Twelve sheets, each 128 × 102 mm or 102 × 128 mm. $6 × 12 multicoloured. Set of 12 sheets . . . . 45·00 48·00

Nos. 955/1008 (issued as six sheetlets each of nine different designs) depict scenes from "The Princess and the Pea", "Little Red Riding Hood", "Goldilocks and the Three Bears", "The Pied Piper of Hamelin", "Hop O'-My-Thumb" and "Puss in Boots".

No. **MS**1009 contains two sheets for each story, all being horizontal with the exception of the second sheet for "Puss in Boots". Of the stamp designs in these miniature sheets the two for "Little Red Riding Hood" and one of each for "Goldilocks and the Three Bears", "The Pied Piper of Hamelin" and "Puss in Boots" are vertical.

83 Oleander

1994. Medicinal Plants. Multicoloured.

1010 5c. Type **83** 55 50
1011 10c. Beach morning glory 60 30
1012 30c. Calabash 85 30
1013 45c. Portia tree 95 30
1014 55c. Cashew . . . . 1·00 40
1015 75c. Prickly pear . . . . . 1·40 70

1016	$1 Shell ginger	1·60	80
1017	$1.50 Avocado pear	2·25	2·00
1018	$2 Mango	2·50	2·50
1019	$3 Blood flower	3·00	3·25
1020	$4 Sugar apple	3·25	4·00
1021	$5 Barbados lily	3·25	4·00

OFFICIAL STAMPS

1982. Nos. 195/200 optd **OFFICIAL**.

O1	50c. "Mary"	10	15
O2	50c. Prince Charles and Lady Diana Spencer	30	35
O3	$3 "Alexandra"	20	20
O4	$3 Prince Charles and Lady Diana Spencer	65	70
O5	$3.50 "Britannia"	20	20
O6	$3.50 Prince Charles and Lady Diana Spencer	65	70

APPENDIX

The following stamps have either been issued in excess of postal needs, or have not been made available to the public in reasonable quantities at face value.

BEQUIA

1984.

Leaders of the World. Railway Locomotives (1st series). Two designs for each value, the first showing technical drawings and the second the locomotive at work. 1, 5, 10, 25, 35, 45c., $1.50, $2, each × 2.

Grenadines of St. Vincent 1982 Ships definitives (Nos. 208/24) optd **BEQUIA**. 1, 3, 5, 6, 10, 15, 20, 25, 30, 50, 60, 75c., $1, $2, $3, $5, $10.

Leaders of the World. Automobiles (1st series). Two designs for each value, the first showing technical drawings and the second the car in action. 5, 40c., $1, $1.50, each × 2.

Leaders of the World. Olympic Games, Los Angeles. 1, 10, 60c., $3, each × 2.

Leaders of the World. Railway Locomotives (2nd series). Two designs for each value, the first showing technical drawings and the second the locomotive at work. 1, 5, 10, 35, 75c., $1, $2.50, $3, each × 2.

Leaders of the World. Automobiles (2nd series). Two designs for each value, the first showing technical drawings and the second the car in action. 5, 10, 20, 25, 75c., $1, $2.50, $3, each × 2.

1985.

Leaders of the World. Railway Locomotives (3rd series). Two designs for each value, the first showing technical drawings and the second the locomotive at work. 25, 55, 60c., $2, each × 2.

Leaders of the World. Dogs. 25, 35, 55c., $2, each × 2.

Leaders of the World. Warships of the Second World War. Two designs for each value, the first showing technical drawings and the second the ship at sea. 15, 50c., $1, $1.50, each × 2.

Leaders of the World. Flowers. 10, 20, 70c., $2.50, each × 2.

Leaders of the World. Automobiles (3rd series). Two designs for each value, the first showing technical drawings and the second the car in action. 5, 25, 50c., $1, $1.25, $2, each × 2.

Leaders of the World. Railway Locomotives (4th series). Two designs for each value, the first showing technical drawings and the second the locomotive at work. 25, 55, 60, 75c., $1, $2.50, each × 2.

Leaders of the World. Life and Times of Queen Elizabeth the Queen Mother. Two designs for each value showing different portraits. 20, 65c., $1.35, $1.80, each × 2.

Leaders of the World. Automobiles (4th series). Two designs for each value, the first showing technical drawings and the second the car in action. 20, 45c., $1.50, $2, each × 2.

1986.

Leaders of the World. Automobiles (5th series). Two designs for each value, the first showing technical drawings and the second the car in action. 25, 50, 65, 75c., $1, $3, each × 2.

60th Birthday of Queen Elizabeth II. 5, 75c., $2, $8.

World Cup Football Championship, Mexico. 1, 2, 5, 10, 45, 60, 75c., $1.50, $1.50, $2, $3.50, $6.

Royal Wedding (1st issue). 60c., $2, each × 2.

Railway Engineers and Locomotives. $1, $2.50, $3, $4.

Royal Wedding (2nd issue). Previous issue optd "**Congratulations T.R.H. The Duke & Duchess of York**". 60c., $2, each × 2.

Automobiles (6th series). Two designs for each value, the first showing technical drawings and the second the car in action. 20, 60, 75, 90c., $1, $3, each × 2.

1987.

Automobiles (7th series). Two designs for each value, the first showing technical drawings and the second the car in action. 5, 20, 35, 60, 75, 80c., $1.25, $1.75, each × 2.

Royal Ruby Wedding. 15, 75c., $1, $2.50, $5.

Railway Locomotives (5th series). Two designs for each value, the first showing technical drawings and the second the locomotive at work. 15, 25, 40, 50, 60, 75c., $1, $2, each × 2.

1988.

Explorers. 15, 50c., $1.75, $2, $2.50, $3, $3.50, $4.

International Lawn Tennis Players. 15, 45, 80c., $1.25, $1.75, $2, $2.50, $3.

1989.

"Philexfrance '89" International Stamp Exhibition, Paris. Walt Disney Cartoon Characters. 1, 2, 3, 4, 5, 10c., $5, $6.

1991.

Centenary of Otto Lilienthal's Gliding Experiments. $5.

50th Anniv of Japanese Attack on Pearl Harbor. 50c., $1.

Death Anniv of Mozart. 10, 75c., $4.

50th Death Anniv of Lord Baden-Powell and World Jamboree, Korea. 50c., $1, $2, $3.

1997.

Diana, Princess of Wales Commemoration. $1.

2000.

Faces of the Millennium: Queen Elizabeth the Queen Mother. Collage of miniature flower photographs. $1 × 8.

2001.

Endangered Species. Turtles. $1.40 × 4.

2002.

Ferrari Racing Cars. $1.10 × 8.

Chinese New Year ("Year of the Horse"). $1.40 × 4.

Golden Jubilee. 80c. × 4.

25th Death Anniv of Elvis Presley (1st issue). $1 (in sheetlet of 9).

Shirley Temple in Captain January. $1.40 × 6, $2 × 4.

Queen Elizabeth the Queen Mother Commemoration. $2 × 2.

"United We Stand". Support for Victims of 11 September 2001 Terrorist Attacks. $2 (in sheetlet of 4).

2003.

Centenary of the Teddy Bear. $2 × 8.

Chinese New Year ("Year of the Ram"). $1 × 6.

5th Death Anniv of Diana, Princess of Wales. $2 × 8.

50th Anniv of General Motors Chevrolet Corvette. $2 × 4.

40th Death Anniv of President John F. Kennedy. $2 × 4.

25th Death Anniv of Elvis Presley (2nd issue). 90c. × 2 (in sheetlet of 9).

Birds of the Caribbean. 90c., $1, $1.40, $2.

CANOUAN

1997.

Diana, Princess of Wales Commemoration. $1.

2000.

100th Birthday of Queen Elizabeth the Queen Mother. $1.40 (in sheetlet of 6).

2003.

40th Death Anniv of President John F. Kennedy. $2 × 4.

"United We Stand". Support for Victims of 11 September 2001 Terrorist Attacks. $2 (in sheetlet of 4).

25th Death Anniv of Elvis Presley. 90c. (in sheetlet of 9).

Butterflies of the Caribbean. 90c., $1, $1.40, $2.

MUSTIQUE

1997.

Diana, Princess of Wales Commemoration. $1.

2000.

Faces of the Millennium: Queen Elizabeth the Queen Mother. Collage of miniature flower photographs. $1 × 8.

2003.

21st Birthday of Prince William of Wales. $3 × 3.

50th Anniv of Coronation. $3 × 3.

Centenary of Circus Clowns. $2 × 4.

50th Anniv of General Motors Chevrolet Corvette. $2 × 4.

Centenary of General Motors Cadillac. $2 × 4.

40th Death Anniv of President John F. Kennedy. $2 × 4.

"United We Stand". Support for Victims of 11 September 2001 Terrorist Attacks. $2 (in sheetlet of 4).

25th Death Anniv of Elvis Presley. 90c. (in sheetlet of 9).

PALM ISLAND

2003.

Centenary of the Circus Clown. $2 × 4.

"United We Stand". Support for Victims of 11 September 2001 Terrorist Attacks. $2 (in sheetlet of 4).

25th Death Anniv of Elvis Presley. 90c. (in sheetlet of 9).

TOBAGO CAYS

2003.

21st Birthday of Prince William of Wales. $3 × 3.

50th Anniv of Coronation. $3 × 3.

50th Anniv of General Motors Chevrolet Corvette. $2 × 4.

Centenary of General Motors Cadillac. $2 × 4.

40th Death Anniv of President John F. Kennedy. $2 × 4.

"United We Stand". Support for Victims of 11 September 2001 Terrorist Attacks. $2 (in sheetlet of 4).

UNION ISLAND

1984.

Leaders of the World. British Monarchs. Two designs for each value forming a composite picture. 1, 5, 10, 20, 60c., $3, each × 2.

Leaders of the World. Railway Locomotives (1st series). Two designs for each value, the first showing technical drawings and the second the locomotive at work. 5, 60c., $1, $2.

Grenadines of St. Vincent 1982 Ships definitives (Nos. 208/24) optd **UNION ISLAND**. 1, 3, 5, 6, 10, 15, 20, 25, 30, 50, 60, 75c., $1, $2, $3, $5, $10.

Leaders of the World. Cricketers. Two designs for each value, the first showing a portrait and the second the cricketer in action. 1, 10, 15, 55, 60, 75c., $1.50, $3, each × 2.

Leaders of the World. Railway Locomotives (2nd series). Two designs for each value, the first showing technical drawings and the second the locomotive at work. 5, 10, 20, 25, 75c., $1, $2.50, $3, each × 2.

1985.

Leaders of the World. Automobiles (1st series). Two designs for each value, the first showing technical drawings and the second the car in action. 1, 50, 75c., $2.50, each × 2.

Leaders of the World. Birth Bicentenary of John J. Audubon (ornithologist). Birds. 15, 50c., $1, $1.50, each × 2.

Leaders of the World. Railway Locomotives (3rd series). Two designs for each value, the first showing technical drawings and the second the locomotive at work. 5, 50, 60c., $2, each × 2.

Leaders of the World. Butterflies. 15, 25, 75c., $2, each × 2.

Leaders of the World. Automobiles (2nd series). Two designs for each value, the first showing technical drawings and the second the car in action. 5, 60c., $1, $1.50, each × 2.

Leaders of the World. Automobiles (3rd series). Two designs for each value, the first showing technical drawings and the second the car in action. 10, 55, 60, 75, 90c., $1, $1.50, $2, each × 2.

Leaders of the World. Life and Times of Queen Elizabeth the Queen Mother. Two designs for each value showing different portraits. 55, 70c., $1.05, $1.70, each × 2.

1986.

Leaders of the World. Railway Locomotives (4th series). Two designs for each value, the first showing technical drawings and the second the locomotive at work. 15, 30, 45, 60, 75c., $1.50, $2.50, $3, each × 2.

60th Birthday of Queen Elizabeth II. 10, 60c., $2, $8.

World Cup Football Championship, Mexico. 1, 10, 30, 75c., $1, $2.50, $3, $6.

Royal Wedding (1st issue). 60c., $2, each × 2.

Automobiles (4th series). Two designs for each value, the first showing technical drawings and the second the car in action. 10, 60, 75c., $1, $1.50, $3, each × 2.

Royal Wedding (2nd issue). Previous issue optd as Bequia. 60c., $2, each × 2.

Railway Locomotives (5th series). Two designs for each value, the first showing technical drawings and the second the locomotive at work. 15, 45, 60, 75c., $1, $1.50, $2, $3, each × 2.

1987.

Railway Locomotives (6th series). Two designs for each value, the first showing technical drawings and the second the locomotive at work. 15, 25, 40, 50, 60, 75c., $1, $2, each × 2.

Royal Ruby Wedding. 15, 45c., $1.50, $3, $4.

Railway Locomotives (7th series). Two designs for each value, the first showing technical drawings and the second the locomotive at work. 15, 20, 30, 45, 50, 75c., $1, $1.50, each × 2.

1989.

"Philexfrance 89" International Stamp Exhibition, Paris. Walt Disney Cartoon Characters. 1, 2, 3, 4, 5, 10c., $5, $6.

1997.

Diana, Princess of Wales Commemoration. $1.

2000.

Faces of the Millennium: Queen Elizabeth the Queen Mother. Collage of miniature flower photographs. $1x8.

2002.

Chinese New Year ("Year of the Horse"). $1.40 × 4.

Endangered Species. Shortfin Mako Shark. $1 × 4.

"United We Stand". Support for Victims of 11 September 2001 Terrorist Attacks. $2 (in sheetlet of 4).

Queen Elizabeth the Queen Mother Commemoration. $2 × 3.

Ferrari Cars. $1.10 × 8.

2003.

Centenary of the Teddy Bear. $2 × 8.

Chinese New Year ("Year of the Ram"). $1 × 6.

25th Death Anniv of Diana, Princess of Wales. $1.40 × 6, $2 × 4.

40th Death Anniv of President John F. Kennedy. $2 × 4.

25th Death Anniv of Elvis Presley. 90c. × 9.

2004.

Chinese New Year ("Year of the Monkey"). "Monkey and Cat" painting by Yi Yuan-Chi. $1.40 (in sheetlet of 4).

GRIQUALAND WEST Pt. 1

A British colony, later annexed to the Cape of Good Hope and now part of South Africa, whose stamps it uses.

12 pence = 1 shilling;
20 shillings = 1 pound.

1874. Stamp of Cape of Good Hope ("Hope" seated) with pen-and-ink surch.

1	4	1d. on 4d. blue	£1000	£1700

1877. Stamps of Cape of Good Hope ("Hope" seated) optd **G. W.**

2	6	1d. red	£475	80·00
3		4d. blue	£375	70·00

1877. Stamps of Cape of Good Hope ("Hope" seated) optd **G.**

14	6	½d. grey	7·00	8·50
16		1d. red	8·00	5·50
6a	4	4d. blue	£160	27·00
26	6	4d. blue	23·00	3·75
27	4	6d. violet	£110	6·50
28		1s. green	90·00	4·00
29	6	5s. orange	£325	7·50

GUADELOUPE Pt. 6

An overseas department of France, formerly a Fr. colony in the W. Indies, consisting of a group of islands between Antigua and Dominica. Now uses the stamps of France.

100 centimes = 1 franc.

1894. French Colonies, "Peace and Commerce" type, surch **G. P. E.** and new value in frame.

6	H	20 on 30c. brown	50·00	42·00
7		25 on 35c. black on orange	50·00	48·00

1889. French Colonies, "Commerce" type, surch **GUADELOUPE** and value in figures and words in plain frame.

8	J	3c. on 20c. red on green	1·50	3·50
9		15c. on 20c. red on green	16·00	9·25
10		25c. on 20c. red on green	15·00	9·00

1889. French Colonies, "Commerce" type, surch **GUADELOUPE** and value in figures and words in ornamental frame.

11	J	5c. on 1c. black on blue	4·75	6·75
12		10c. on 40c. red on yellow	22·00	29·00
13		15c. on 20c. red on green	21·00	12·00
14		25c. on 30c. brown on drab	28·00	26·00

1890. French Colonies, "Commerce" type, surch **5 C. GPE.**

15	J	5c. on 10c. black on lilac	6·75	5·00
16		5c. on 1f. olive on green	7·25	6·25

1891. French Colonies, "Ceres" and "Commerce" types, optd **GUADELOUPE**.

21	J	1c. black on blue	50	40
22		2c. brown on buff	1·25	55
23		4c. brown on grey	4·00	5·00
24		5c. green on light green	5·25	4·25
25		10c. black on lilac	14·00	10·50
26		15c. blue on light blue	12·50	1·75
27		20c. red on green	35·00	32·00
28		25c. black on pink	27·00	2·50
19	F	30c. brown	£225	£225
29	J	30c. brown on drab	40·00	28·00
30		35c. black on orange	75·00	65·00
31		40c. red on yellow	50·00	42·00
32		75c. red on pink	£110	£120

20	F	80c. red	£600	£750
33	J	1f. green	70·00	75·00

1892. "Tablet" key-type inscr "GUADELOUPE ET DEPENDANCES" in red (1, 5, 15, 25, 50 (No. 52), 75c., 1f.) or blue (others).

34	D	1c. black on blue	95	45
35		2c. brown on buff	95	70
37		4c. brown on grey	1·25	3·00
38		5c. green on light green	2·00	85
39		10c. black on lilac	11·50	3·75
49		10c. red	4·75	1·25
40		15c. blue	13·00	50
50		15c. grey	9·00	40
41		20c. red on green	5·00	4·75
42		25c. black on pink	5·75	1·00
51		25c. blue	70·00	75·00
43		30c. brown on drab	27·00	18·00
44		40c. red on yellow	29·00	13·00
45		50c. red on pink	28·00	19·00
52		50c. brown on blue	22·00	30·00
46		75c. brown on yellow	29·00	30·00
47		1f. green	28·00	30·00

1903. "Tablet" key-type surch **G & D** (5, 15c., 1f.) or **G et D** (10, 40c.) and new value.

53b	D	5 on 30c. brown on buff	3·75	5·75
54		10 on 40c. red on yellow	6·00	9·50
55		15 on 50c. red	9·25	11·00
56		40 on 1f. green	8·25	13·00
57d		1f. on 75c. brown on yellow	35·00	40·00

1904. Nos. 56/7 further optd **1903** in frame.

59c	D	40 on 1f. green	35·00	42·00
60		1f. on 75c. brown on yellow	70·00	55·00

49 Mt. Houllemont, Basse-Terre

50 La Soufriere

51 Pointe-a-Pitre, Grande Terre

1905.

61	**49**	1c. black on blue	10	10
62		2c. brown on yellow	15	15
63		4c. brown on grey	40	15
64		5c. green	2·50	15
83		5c. blue	15	15
65		10c. red	2·25	15
84		10c. green	1·50	1·90
85		10c. red on blue	20	30
66		15c. lilac	1·00	15
67	**50**	20c. red on green	15	15
86		20c. green	15	1·75
68		25c. blue	1·25	15
87		25c. green	1·00	15
69		30c. black	3·50	3·00
88		30c. red	60	2·50
89		30c. olive on lilac	1·75	1·00
70		35c. black on yellow	90	70
71		40c. red on yellow	1·60	1·50
72		45c. brown on lilac	2·25	2·75
90		45c. red	90	2·75
73		50c. green on yellow	5·00	3·25
91		50c. blue	55	1·90
92		50c. mauve	65	25
93		65c. blue	1·90	3·00
74		75c. red on blue	1·10	2·75
75	**51**	1f. black on green	1·90	2·75
94		1f. blue	1·25	2·75
76		2f. red on orange	1·10	2·25
77		5f. blue on orange	7·75	10·00

1912. Nos. 37 and 43/4 surch in figures.

78	D	05 on 4c. brown on grey	65	2·50
79		05 on 30c. brown on drab	80	2·75
80		10 on 40c. red on yellow	1·25	3·50

1915. Surch **5c** and red cross.

81	**49**	10c.+5c. red	3·00	4·50
82		15c.+5c. lilac	1·10	4·75

1924. Surch in figures and bars.

95	**51**	25c. on 5f. blue on orange	55	3·00
96		65 on 1f. green	90	3·00
97		85 on 1f. green	1·75	3·25
98	**50**	90c. on 75c. red	60	3·25
99	**51**	1f.05 on 2f. red	20	3·00
100		1f.25 on 1f. blue	15	2·50
101		1f.50 on 1f. blue	30	2·00
102		3f. on 5f. brown	1·50	3·00
103		10f. on 5f. red on yellow	4·00	14·50
104		20f. on 5f. mauve on red	11·00	16·00

53 Sugar Refinery

54 Saints Harbour

55 Pointe-a-Pitre Harbour

1928.

105	**53**	1c. mauve and yellow	10	2·25
106		2c. red and black	10	90
107		3c. mauve and yellow	10	2·25
108		4c. brown and green	25	1·90
109		5c. green and red	15	1·40
110		10c. blue and brown	15	20
111		15c. black and red	15	30
112		20c. brown and mauve	15	1·00
113	**54**	25c. olive and blue	15	15
114		30c. green and deep green	15	15
115		35c. green	60	2·75
116		40c. mauve and yellow	15	25
117		45c. grey and purple	45	3·00
118		45c. deep green and green	55	3·25
119		50c. red and green	20	20
120		55c. red and blue	1·25	2·50
121		60c. red and blue	40	3·00
122		65c. red and black	65	60
123		70c. red and black	15	3·25
124		75c. green and red	25	1·25
125		80c. brown and red	75	2·25
126		90c. red	90	3·75
127		90c. blue and red	55	3·25
128	**55**	1f. blue and red	3·75	1·50
129		1f. orange and red	2·50	2·75
130		1f. brown and blue	60	2·75
131		1f.05 red and blue	2·50	3·50
132		1f.10 green and orange	3·50	4·75
133		1f.25 brown and blue	1·25	3·00
134		1f.25 orange and red	2·25	3·25
135		1f.40 mauve and blue	2·00	3·25
136		1f.50 light blue and blue	20	30
137		1f.60 orange and mauve	2·25	3·25
138		1f.75 brown and mauve	4·25	1·75
139		1f.75 blue	6·50	7·25
140		2f. brown and green	35	60
141		2f.25 blue	45	3·25
142		2f.50 green and orange	65	3·25
143		3f. black and brown	30	1·90
144		5f. red and blue	65	1·25
145		10f. brown and mauve	85	3·00
146		20f. red and green	50	4·00

1931. "Colonial Exhibition" key-types inscr "GUADELOUPE".

147	E	40c. black and green	3·50	4·50
148	F	50c. black and mauve	2·50	3·75
149	G	90c. black and red	5·75	7·75
150	H	1f.50 black and blue	4·50	5·00

57 Richelieu founding W. India Co., 1635

58 Victor Hughes and Corsairs, 1793

1935. West Indies Tercentenary.

151	**57**	40c. brown	11·00	11·50
152		50c. red	10·50	10·00
153		1f.50 blue	11·00	11·50
154	**58**	1f.75 mauve	10·50	7·50
155		5f. brown	7·50	10·00
156		10f. green	11·50	10·50

58a Sailing Ships

1937. International Exhibition, Paris.

157	–	20c. violet	40	3·25
158	**58a**	30c. green	50	3·25
159	–	40c. red	55	3·75
160	–	50c. brown	1·00	3·00
161	–	90c. red	80	3·75
162	–	1f.50 blue	1·25	3·25
MS162a		120 × 100 mm. 3f. blue (as T **58a**). Imperf	10·00	16·00

DESIGNS—VERT: 20c. Allegory of Commerce; 50c. Allegory of Agriculture. HORIZ: 40c. Berber Negress and Annamite; 90c. France with torch of Civilization; 1f.50, Diane de Poitiers.

58b Pierre and Marie Curie

1938. International Anti-cancer Fund.

163	**58b**	1f.75+50c. blue	3·75	16·00

58c

1939. New York World's Fair.

164	**58c**	1f.25 red	1·90	3·00
165		2f.25 blue	2·00	3·00

58d Storming the Bastille

1939. 150th Anniv of French Revolution.

166	**58d**	45c.+25c. green and black	7·50	11·50
167		70c.+30c. brown & black	9·00	12·50
168		90c.+35c. orange & black	9·00	12·50
169		1f.25+1f. red and black	8·50	12·50
170		2f.25+2f. blue and black	8·50	12·50

1944. Surch **Un franc** (No. 177) or in figures (others).

(a) On Nos. 164/5.

178		40c. on 1f.25 red	2·25	2·75
179		40c. on 2f.25 blue	2·75	3·50

(b) On Issue of 1928.

172	**54**	40c. on 35c. green	45	3·00
173		50c. on 25c. olive and blue	15	40
174		50c. on 65c. red and black	55	2·50
175		1f. on 90c. red	1·75	3·75
176		1f. on 90c. blue and red	1·40	2·75
177		1f. on 65c. red and black	40	2·25

(c) On No. 99.

171	**51**	4f. on 1f.05 on 2f. red	3·50	4·00

58e

58f Felix Eboue

1944. Mutual Aid and Red Cross Funds.

180	**58e**	5f.+20f. blue	80	3·50

1945.

181	**58f**	2f. black	10	20
182		25f. green	85	3·00

63

1945.

183	**63**	10c. blue and orange	25	2·75
184		30c. green and orange	35	2·75
185		40c. blue and red	75	3·00
186		50c. orange and green	35	95
187		60c. grey and blue	40	2·75
188		70c. grey and green	1·25	3·00
189		80c. green and yellow	90	3·00
190		1f. purple and green	50	1·10
191		1f.20 mauve and green	1·10	2·75
192		1f.50 brown and red	90	1·40
193		2f. red and blue	1·00	1·25
194		2f.40 red and green	1·75	3·50
195		3f. brown and blue	55	50
196		4f. blue and orange	85	1·60
197		4f.50 orange and green	90	1·50
198		5f. violet and green	90	1·75
199		10f. green and mauve	75	40
200		15f. grey and orange	1·00	1·00
201		20f. grey and orange	1·25	60

63a Fairey FC-1

1945. Air.

202	**63a**	50f. green	1·60	2·75
203		100f. red	1·40	1·90

63b "Victory"

1946. Air. Victory.

204	**63b**	8f. brown	60	2·25

63c Chad

1946. Air. From Chad to the Rhine.

205	**63c**	5f. olive	75	3·50
206	–	10f. blue	60	3·75
207	–	15f. purple	75	1·75
208	–	20f. red	1·50	3·75
209	–	25f. black	60	1·75
210	–	50f. brown	60	1·40

DESIGNS: 10f. Koufra; 15f. Mareth; 20f. Normandy; 25f. Paris; 50f. Strasbourg.

64 Woman and Port Basse-Terre

65 Cutting Sugar Cane

66 Guadeloupe Woman

67 Sud Ouest Bretagne over Guadeloupe Woman and Fishing Boats

1947.

211	**64**	10c. lake (postage)	15	2·25
212		30c. brown	15	2·50
213		50c. green	15	2·25
214	**65**	60c. brown	15	2·50
215		1f. red	25	2·25
216		1f.50 blue	30	2·50
217	–	2f. green	35	3·25
218	–	2f.50 red	65	3·00
219	–	3f. blue	85	2·75
220	–	4f. violet	1·25	3·25
221	–	5f. green	1·00	3·25
222	–	6f. red	1·75	1·10
223	–	10f. blue	2·25	2·75
224	–	15f. purple	1·25	2·50
225	–	20f. red	2·50	2·25
226	**66**	25f. green	2·75	4·50
227		40f. orange	2·25	4·50
228	–	50f. purple (air)	6·75	8·50
229	–	100f. blue	7·00	9·50
230	**67**	200f. red	11·00	12·50

DESIGNS—As Type **66**: 2f. to 3f. Women carrying pineapples; 4f. to 6f. Woman in kerchief facing left; 10f. to 20f. Picking coffee. As Type **67**: 50f. Latecoere 631 flying boat over village; 100f. Short Hythe flying boat landing in bay.

POSTAGE DUE STAMPS

D 1

D 3

1876.

D1	D 1	15c. black on blue	35·00	28·00
D2		25c. black on white	£700	£500
D3		30c. black on white	75·00	50·00
D4		40c. black on blue	†	£21000
D5		40c. black on white	£850	£700

1884. Imperf.

D 8	D 3	5c. black on white	11·50	22·00
D 9		10c. black on blue	55·00	32·00
D10		15c. black on lilac	90·00	50·00
D11		20c. black on red	£120	90·00
D12		30c. black on yellow	£120	£100
D13		35c. black on grey	40·00	32·00
D14		50c. black on green	15·00	14·50

1903. Postage Due stamps of French Colonies surch **G & D 30** in frame.

D59b	U	30 on 60c. brown on buff	£190	£190
D61c		30 on 1f. red on yellow	£275	£275

D 48 Gustavia Bay, Island of St. Bartholomew

D 56 Allee Dumanoir, Capesterre

D 68 Palms and Houses

1905.

D63	D 48	5c. blue	15	25
D64		10c. brown	15	35
D65		15c. green	20	2·75
D66		20c. brown on yellow	20	1·10
D67		30c. red	15	2·25
D68		50c. black	50	4·75
D69		60c. orange	35	3·25
D70		1f. lilac	1·00	5·00

1926. Surch in figures and words and **a percevoir**.

D105	D 48	2f. on 1f. grey	50	3·75
D106		3f. on 1f. blue	75	4·25

1928.

D147	D 56	2c. mauve and brown	15	2·25
D148		4c. brown and blue	15	2·00
D149		5c. brown and green	15	1·10
D150		10c. yellow and mauve	15	1·25
D151		15c. olive and red	15	2·00
D152		20c. olive and orange	15	2·50
D153		25c. green and red	25	2·50
D154		30c. yellow and blue	25	1·25
D155		50c. red and brown	30	2·75
D156		60c. black and blue	50	3·00
D157		1f. red and green	90	2·75
D158		2f. red and brown	75	3·50
D159		3f. blue and mauve	85	3·25

1947.

D231	D 68	10c. black	15	2·50
D232		30c. green	15	2·50
D233		50c. blue	15	2·25
D234		1f. green	20	2·75
D235		2f. blue	35	2·75
D236		3f. brown	85	3·25
D237		4f. purple	75	3·50
D238		5f. violet	80	3·75
D239		10f. red	75	4·25
D240		20f. purple	1·40	4·50

GUAM — Pt. 22

An island in the Pacific Ocean belonging to the United States. Now uses U.S. stamps.

100 cents = 1 dollar.

1899. Stamps of United States optd **GUAM**.

1	1c. green (No. 283)	16·00	20·00
2	2c. red (No. 270)	14·00	20·00
4	3c. violet (No. 271)	£100	£140
5	4c. brown (No. 285)	£110	£140
6	5c. blue (No. 286)	23·00	35·00
7	6c. purple (No. 287a)	£100	£150
8	8c. brown (No. 275)	95·00	£140
9	10c. brown (No. 289)	35·00	45·00
11	15c. green (No. 290)	£120	£130
12	50c. orange (No. 278)	£225	£275
13	$1 black (No. 279)	£275	£300

SPECIAL DELIVERY STAMP

1899. Special Delivery stamp of United States optd **GUAM**.

E15	E 46	10c. blue (No. E283)	£120	£150

GUANACASTE — Pt. 15

A province of Costa Rica whose stamps it now uses.

100 centavos = 1 peso.

Stamps of Costa Rica optd.

1885. Stamps of 1883 optd **Guanacaste** or **GUANACASTE**.

G 1	8	1c. green	2·00	2·00
G36		2c. red	2·00	2·00
G 3		5c. violet	8·00	3·00
G 4		10c. orange	8·00	8·00
G 5		40c. blue	15·00	15·00

1887. Stamps of 1887 optd **Guanacaste**.

G37	14	5c. violet	10·00	4·00
G39		10c. orange	2·00	2·00

1887. Fiscal stamps optd **Guanacaste** or **GUANACASTE**.

G44	1c. red	£150	£150
G41	2c. blue	25·00	25·00

1889. Stamps of 1889 optd **GUANACASTE**.

G62	17	1c. brown	75	75
G63		2c. blue	75	75
G64		5c. orange	75	75
G65		10c. lake	75	75
G56		20c. green	80	70
G57		50c. red	2·00	2·00
G59		1p. blue	4·00	4·00
G60		2p. violet	6·00	6·00
G61		5p. olive	20·00	20·00

GUATEMALA — Pt. 15

A republic of Central America; independent since 1847.

1871. 100 centavos = 8 reales = 1 peso.
1927. 100 centavos de quetzal = 1 quetzal.

1 Arms

2

3 Liberty

1871.

1	1	1c. bistre	50	6·50
2		5c. brown	3·00	5·00
3		10c. blue	3·50	5·75
4		20c. red	2·75	5·00

1873.

5	2	4r. mauve	£200	5·00
6		1p. yellow	£100	70·00

1875. Various frames

7	3	¼r. black	90	2·25
8		½r. green	90	2·00
9		1r. blue	90	2·00
10		2r. red	90	2·00

4 Native Indian

5 Resplendent Quetzal

1878.

11	4	½r. green	50	2·00
12		2r. red	85	2·75
13		4r. mauve	85	3·00
14		1p. yellow	1·40	6·00

1879.

15	5	¼r. green and brown	7·00	9·00
16		1r. green and black	11·00	14·00

For similar stamps, but inscr differently, see Nos. 21/25.

1881. Surch.

17	5	1c. on ¼r. green and brown	11·50	16·00
18	4	5c. on ½r. green	3·50	5·00
19	5	10c. on 1r. green and black	17·00	23·00
20	4	20c. on 2r. red	24·00	27·00

1881. As T **5** inscr "UNION POSTAL UNIVERSAL—GUATEMALA". Centres in green.

21	5	1c. black	3·50	2·00
22		2c. brown	3·50	2·00
23		5c. red	6·50	2·50
24		10c. lilac	3·25	2·00
25		20c. yellow	3·25	2·40

7 President J. Rufino Barrios

(8)

1886. Railway stamp variously surch as T **8**.

26	7	25c. on 1p. red	85	70
27		50c. on 1p. red	85	70
28		75c. on 1p. red	85	70
29		100c. on 1p. red	1·40	1·40
30		150c. on 1p. red	1·40	1·25

9 Arms of Guatemala

16 Steamship, arms, portrait of Pres. J. M. Reyna Barrios and locomotive in centre. Arms of El Salvador, Honduras, Nicaragua and Costa Rica in corners

1886.

43a	9	1c. blue	2·75	30
44		2c. brown	3·75	35
46		5c. violet	4·50	25
47		6c. mauve	5·75	40
48		10c. red	4·75	25
49		20c. green	11·00	75
50		25c. orange	35·00	2·75
37		50c. olive	28·00	7·50
38		75c. red	20·00	6·00
39		100c. brown	28·00	14·00
40		150c. blue	35·00	24·00
41		200c. yellow	30·00	18·00

See also Nos. 101/9.

1886. Surch **PROVISIONAL. 1886. 1 UN CENTAVO.**

42h	9	1c. on 2c. brown	4·25	10·00

1894. Surch **1894**, bar and value.

55	9	1c. on 2c. brown	1·75	1·60
51		2c. on 100c. brown	9·50	7·50
57		6c. on 150c. blue	15·00	8·75
53		10c. on 75c. red	13·00	9·50
54		10c. on 200c. yellow	9·50	5·75

1895. Surch **1895 1 CENTAVO** and bar.

59	9	1c. on 5c. violet	90	60

1897. Central American Exhibition.

62	16	1c. black on grey	60	45
63		2c. black on green	60	45
64		6c. black on orange	60	45
65		10c. black on blue	60	45
66		12c. black on red	95	80
67		18c. black on white	8·50	7·00
68		20c. black on red	1·40	1·00
69		25c. black on brown	1·40	1·00
70		50c. black on brown	1·40	1·00
71		75c. black on blue	70·00	60·00
72		100c. black on green	1·40	1·00
73		150c. black on pink	£120	£100
74		200c. black on mauve	1·40	1·00
75		500c. black on green	1·40	1·00

1897. Surch **UN CENTAVO 1898**.

76	16	1c. on 12c. black on red	1·10	1·10

1898. Surch **1898**, bar and value.

77	9	1c. on 5c. violet	2·75	15
78		1c. on 25c. orange	6·25	4·00
79		1c. on 50c. olive	5·50	3·25
80		1c. on 75c. red	5·50	3·25
81		6c. on 5c. violet	6·25	1·00
82		6c. on 10c. red	24·00	17·00
83		6c. on 20c. green	10·00	6·50
84		6c. on 100c. brown	10·00	6·50
85		6c. on 150c. blue	10·00	6·50
86		6c. on 200c. yellow	10·00	6·50
87		10c. on 20c. green	10·00	6·50

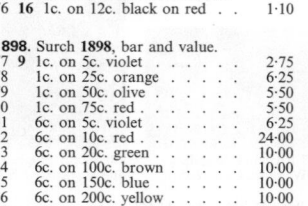

20

22

1898. Fiscal stamps as T **20** optd **CORREOS NACIONALES** or surch **2 CENTAVOS** also.

88	20	1c. blue	1·50	1·50
89		2c. on 1c. blue	2·50	2·50

1898. Fiscal stamps dated "1898" as T **22** surch **CORREOS NACIONALES** and value.

90	22	1c. on 10c. blue	50	50
91		2c. on 1c. red	2·40	1·75
92		2c. on 5c. violet	85	70
93		2c. on 10c. blue	4·50	4·75
94		2c. on 25c. red	5·00	5·50
95		2c. on 50c. blue	5·50	6·00
96		6c. on 1p. violet	2·75	3·00
97		6c. on 5p. blue	5·00	5·00
98		6c. on 10p. green	5·00	5·00

1899. Surch **Un 1 Centavo 1899**.

99	9	1c. on 5c. violet	80	50

1900. Surch **1900 1 CENTAVO**.

100	9	1c. on 10c. red	85	70

1900.

101	9	1c. green	1·00	30
102		2c. red	1·00	30
103		5c. blue	3·75	1·00
104		6c. green	1·10	30
105		10c. brown	3·75	40
106		20c. mauve	11·00	11·00
107		20c. brown	17·00	24·00
108		25c. yellow	11·00	11·00
109		25c. green	17·00	24·00

1901. Surch **1901** and value.

110	9	1c. on 20c. green	1·25	85
111		1c. on 25c. orange	1·25	85
112		2c. on 20c. green	3·50	2·25

1902. Fiscal stamp surch **CORREOS NACIONALES 1902** and value in figures and words.

113	20	1c. on 1c. blue	2·40	1·50
114		2c. on 1c. blue	2·40	1·25

1902. Fiscal stamp, dated "1898", surch **CORREOS 1902 Seis 6 Cts.**

115	22	6c. on 25c. red	40	1·75

30 Arms

31 J. Rufino Barrios Statue

35 Statesmen discussing Independence (after painting by E. Bravo)

47 President Manuel Estrada Cabrera

1902. Inscr "U.P.U. 1902".

116	30	1c. purple and green	15	15
117	31	2c. black and red	15	15
118a	–	5c. black and blue	20	15
119	–	6c. green and yellow	20	15
120	–	10c. blue and orange	15	15
121	35	12½c. black and blue	15	15
122	–	20c. black and red	45	20
141	–	25c. black and blue	55	20
123a	–	50c. blue and brown	30	15
124	–	75c. black and lilac	35	20
125	–	1p. black and brown	45	20
126	–	2p. black and orange	55	35
142	47	5p. black and red	70	70

DESIGNS—HORIZ: 5c. La Reforma Palace; 6c. Temple of Minerva; 10c. Lake Amatitlan; 20c. Cathedral; 25c. G.P.O.; 50c. Columbus Theatre; 75c. Artillery Barracks; 1p. Columbus Monument; 2p. Indian Institute.

1903. Surch **1903 25 CENTAVOS**.

127	9	25c. on 1c. green	2·00	65
128		25c. on 2c. red	2·60	65
129		25c. on 6c. green	4·00	2·40
130		25c. on 10c. brown	17·00	5·25
131		25c. on 75c. red	22·00	13·00
132		25c. on 150c. blue	22·00	13·00
133		25c. on 200c. yellow	25·00	15·00

1908. Surch **1908** and value in figures and words.

134	–	1c. on 10c. blue and orange (No. 120)	35	35
135	35	2c. on 12½c. black and blue	35	35
136	–	6c. on 20c. black and red (No. 122)	30	30

1909. Surch **1909** and value in figures and words.

137	2c. on 75c. blk & lil (No. 124)	55	55
138	6c. on 50c. bl & brn (No. 123)	30	30
139	12½c. on 2p. black and orange (No. 126)	45	45

45 M. Garcia Granados

1910. Granados Centenary.
140 **45** 6c. black and bistre 55 35

1911. Surch **1911 Un Centavo.**
143 **45** 1c. on 6c. black and bistre 13·00 5·00

1911. Surch **Correos de Guatemala 1911** and value.
144 2c. on 5c. (No. 118a) 1·00 50
145 6c. on 10c. (No. 120) 85 85

1912. Surch **1912** and value.
146 1c. on 20c. (No. 122) 35 35
147 2c. on 50c. (No. 123a) 35 35
148 5c. on 75c. (No. 124) 90 90

1913. Surch **1913** and value.
149 1c. on 50c. (No. 123a) 30 30
150 6c. on 1p. (No. 125) 45 45
151 12½c. on 2p. (No. 126) 45 45

1916. Surch with value only.
156 **30** 2c. on 1c. purple and green 30 30
152 6c. on 1c. purple and green 30 30
153 12½c. on 1c. purple & green 30 30
154 **31** 25c. on 2c. black and red 20 20

59 Pres. Manuel Estrada Cabrera **60**

1917. Re-election of President Cabrera.
155 **59** 25c. brown and blue 35 20

1918.
157 **60** 1p.50 blue 80 30

61 Arms **64** Technical School

1919. Buildings and Obligatory Tax G.P.O. Rebuilding Fund (No. 158).
158 **61** 12½c. red (obligatory tax) 20 15
159 – 30c. black and red (postage) 4·00 75
160 – 60c. black and olive 90 45
161 **64** 90c. black and brown 70 70
169 – 1p.50 orange and blue 50 30
162 – 3p. black and green 1·75 45
170 – 5p. green and sepia 1·25 40
171 – 15p. red and black 45·00 17·00
DESIGNS—Dated 1918: 30c. Radio station; 60c. Maternity hospital; 3p. Arms. Dated 1921: 1p.50, Monolith at Quirigua; 5p. Garcia Granados Monument; 15p. La Penitenciaria railway bridge, Guatemala City.

1920. Nos. 159/60 surch **1920 2 centavos.**
163 2c. on 30c. black and red 65 65
164 2c. on 60c. black and olive 25 25

1920. No. 126 surch **25 Centavos** and bars.
165 25c. on 2p. black and orange 35 30

68

1920. Telegraph stamp as T **68** optd **CORREOS.**
166 **68** 25c. green 25 15

1921. Surch **1921** and value in words.
167 12½c. on 20c. black and red (No. 122) 35 20
168 50c. on 75c. black and lilac (No. 124) 45 35

1921. Optd **1921 CORREOS.**
173 **63** 25c. green 35 20

1921. Surch **1921 CORREOS DOCE Y MEDIO.**
172 **68** 12½c. on 25c. green 30 20

1922. Surch **1922** and value in words.
174 – 12½c. on 20c. (No. 122) 30 30
175 – 12½c. on 60c. (No. 160) 70 70
176 **64** 12½c. on 90c. (No. 161) 70 70
179 – 12½c. on 3p. (No. 162) 30 25
180 – 12½c. on 5p. (No. 170) 70 65
181 – 12½c. on 15p. (No. 171) 1·60 1·10
185 – 25c. on 30c. (No. 159) 1·40 1·40
186 – 25c. on 60c. (No. 160) 1·40 1·40
187 – 25c. on 75c. (No. 124) 45 45
188 **64** 25c. on 90c. (No. 161) 1·40 1·40
189 – 25c. on 1p. (No. 125) 35 35
190 – 25c. on 1p.50 (No. 169) 35 35
191 – 25c. on 2p. (No. 126) 55 55
192 – 25c. on 3p. (No. 162) 45 45
193 – 25c. on 5p. (No. 170) 1·10 1·10
184 – 25c. on 15p. (No. 171) 2·00 2·00

80 Independence Centenary Palace **81** National Palace, Antigua

1922.
195 **80** 12½c. green 20 15
196 **81** 25c. brown 20 15

82 Columbus Theatre **83** Resplendent Quetzal **84** Garcia Granados Monument

1923.
197 **82** 50c. red 45 30
198 **83** 1p. green 80 30
199 **84** 5p. orange 1·40 55

1924. Surch **1924** and value.
200 – 1p. on 1p.50 (No. 169) 35 30
201 **84** 1p.25 on 5p. orange 55 45

87 Pres. J. R. Barrios **88** Dr. L. Montufar

1924.
202 – 6c. olive (as No. 119) 20 15
203 **81** 25c. brown 20 15
204 – 50c. red (as No. 123a) 20 15
205 – 1p. brown (as No. 125) 20 15
206 **87** 1p.25 blue 50 15
207 – 2p. orange (as No. 126) 35 25
208 **88** 2p.50 purple 55 30
209 – 3p. green (as No. 162) 2·40 55
210 – 15p. black (as No. 171) 5·50 3·50
These all have imprint "PERKINS BACON & CO. LD. LONDRES" at foot.

1925. No. 201 further surch with two bars.
211 **84** 1p. on 5p. orange 55 45

89 Aurora Park **90** General Post Office

91 National Observatory **92** Proposed new G.P.O.

1926. Dated "1926".
212 – 6c. bistre (as No. 119) 15 15
213 **89** 12½c. green 15 15
214 **81** 25c. brown 15 15
215 **90** 50c. red 20 15
216 – 1p. brown (as No. 125) 20 20
217 **87** 1p.50 blue 20 20
218 **91** 2p. orange 85 70
219 **88** 2p.50 purple 1·75 70
220 – 3p. green (as No. 162) 55 30
221 – 5p. lilac (as No. 170) 70 45
222 – 15p. black (as No. 171) 7·25 3·50
These all have imprint "WATERLOW & SONS LIMITED, LONDRES" at foot.

1927. Obligatory Tax. G.P.O. Rebuilding Fund.
223 **92** 1c. olive 15 15

1928. Surch **1928** and value.
224 **91** ½c. de q. on 2p. orange 70 55
225 – ½c. de q. on 5p. lilac (No. 221) 35 30
226 **88** 1c. de q. on 2p.50 purple (No. 219) 35 30

95 Pres. J. R. Barrios **96** Dr. L. Montufar

97 Garcia Granados **98** General Orellana

99 City Arms, Guatemala

1929.
227 **91** ½c. green 70 15
228 **81** 1c. sepia 20 15
229 **95** 2c. blue 20 15
230 **96** 3c. lilac 20 15
231 **97** 4c. yellow 20 20
232 **98** 5c. red 30 15
233 – 10c. brown (as No. 119) 45 15
234 – 15c. blue (as No. 125) 55 15
235 **31** 25c. brown 90 20
236 **89** 30c. green 1·10 35
237 – 50c. red (as No. 120) 1·75 45
238 **99** 1q. black 3·00 55
These all have imprint "T. DE LA RUE & CO. LD. LONDRES" at foot.

1929. Air. Nos. 210 and 222 surch **SERVICIO POSTAL AEREO ANO DE 1928** and new value.
239 3c. on 15p. black (222) 2·25 2·25
240 5c. on 15p. black (222) 1·00 1·00
240a 5c. on 15p. black (210) 4·50 4·50
241 15c. on 15p. black (222) 2·75 2·75
242 20c. on 15p. black (222) 4·50 4·50

1929. Air. Surch **SERVICIO POSTAL AEREO ANO DE 1929 Q0.03.**
243 **88** 3c. on 2p.50 purple (No. 208) 1·00 1·00

1929. Opening of Guatemala–El Salvador Railway. No. 220 surch **FERROCARRIL ORIENTAL 1929** and new value.
244 3c. on 3p. green 3·00 3·00
245 5c. on 3p. green 3·00 3·00

1930. Opening of Los Altos Railway. No. 222 surch **FERROCARRIL DE LOS ALTOS Inaugurado en 1929** and value in words.
246 1c. on 15p. black 1·75 2·25
247 2c. on 15p. black 1·75 2·25
248 3c. on 15p. black 1·75 2·25
249 5c. on 15p. black 1·75 2·25
250 15c. on 15p. black 1·75 2·25

104 Bridge and Permanent Way

1930. Opening of Los Altos Railway.
251 – 2c. black and purple 2·00 1·25
252 **104** 3c. black and red 4·25 3·25
253 – 5c. blue and orange 4·25 3·25
DESIGNS: 2c. Quetzaltenango Dam; 5c. Quetzaltenango railway station.

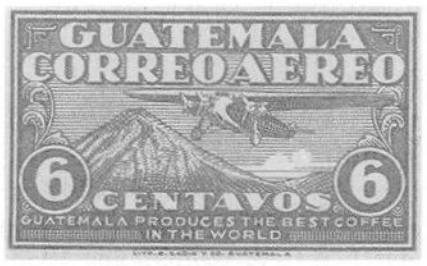

105 Fokker Super Trimotor over Mt. Agua

1930. Air.
254 **105** 6c. red 75 55

1930. Air. Surch **SERVICIO AEREO INTERIOR 1930** and value in words.
255 1c. on 3p. green (No. 220) 20 20
256 2c. on 3p. green 50 90
257 3c. on 3p. green 50 90
258 4c. on 3p. green 70 70
259 10c. on 15p. black (No. 222) 5·50 3·75

1931. Air. Optd **EXTERIOR - 1931.**
260 **105** 6c. red 70 70

1931. Air. Optd **AEREO EXTERIOR 1931.**
261 **97** 4c. yellow 35 30

1931. Air. Optd **AEREO INTERNACIONAL 1931.**
262 – 15c. blue (No. 234) 1·00 35
263 **89** 30c. green (No. 236) 1·75 60

1931. Air. Optd **Primer Vuelo Posta BARRIOS-MIAMI 1931.**
264 **95** 2c. blue 1·75 2·00
265 **96** 3c. lilac 1·75 2·00
266 – 15c. blue (No. 234) 1·75 2·00

1932. Air. Surch **SERVICIO AEREO INTERIOR 1932** and value.
267 **87** 2c. on 1p.50 blue (217) 75 60
268 – 3c. on 3p. green (220) 70 20
270 – 10c. on 15p. black (222) 19·00 12·50
271 – 15c. on 15p. black (222) 24·00 19·00

114 Monolith of Quirigua

1932.
272 **114** 3c. red 50 15
See also Nos. 416a/b.

1933. Air. Optd **AEREO INTERIOR 1933.**
273 **97** 4c. yellow 35 20

116 Flag of the Race, Columbus and Tecum Uman

1933. 441st Anniv of Departure of Columbus from Palos.
274 **116** ½c. green 35 70
275 1c. brown 70 85
276 2c. blue 70 85
277 3c. mauve 70 50
278 5c. red 70 70

1934. Air. (a) Optd **AERO EXTERIOR 1934.**
280 **98** 5c. red 1·75 15
281 – 15c. blue (No. 234) 1·75 35

(b) Optd **AEREO INTERIOR 1934.**
279 **95** 2c. blue 55 20

117 Barrios' Birthplace

118 Barrios and "Agamemnon" (freighter)

1935. Birth Centenary of J. R. Barrios.
282 **117** ½c. pink & green (postage) 35 40
283 – 1c. blue and orange 35 40
284 – 2c. black and orange 35 45
285 – 3c. blue and red 3·50 2·00
286 – 4c. red and blue 3·50 9·00
287 – 5c. brown and green 2·75 3·50
288 – 10c. red and green 4·00 4·50
289 – 15c. brown and green 3·50 4·00
290 – 25c. black and red 3·50 4·00
291 **118** 10c. blue and brown (air) 4·75 4·00
292 – 15c. brown and grey 1·40 1·50
293 – 30c. violet and red 1·40 1·00
DESIGNS—POSTAGE—HORIZ: 1c. San Lorenzo; 2c. Barrios and Official Decree; 3c. Arms and locomotive; 5c. Telegraph office and Barrios; 10c. Polytechnic School; 15c. Police H.Q.; 25c. Pres. Ubico, arms and Barrios. VERT: 4c. G.P.O. AIR—HORIZ: Barrios and (15c.) tomb, (30c.) statue.

120 Lake Atitlan

121 Resplendent Quetzal

122 Arms and Map of Guatemala

1935.

293a	–	½c. blue and green	15	15
294	120	1c. red and brown	20	15
295	121	3c. green and orange	1·25	30
296		3c. green and red	1·25	30
297	–	4c. red and blue	45	20
297a	122	5c. brown and blue	55	20

DESIGNS—As Type **120**: ½c. Govt. Printing Works; 4c. National Assembly.

123 Lake Amatitlan

1935. Air. (a) Inscr "INTERIOR" (37 × 17 mm).

298	123	2c. brown	15	15
299	–	3c. blue	40	20
300	–	4c. black	35	10
300a	–	4c. blue	30	10
301	–	6c. green	35	15
301a		6c. violet	2·75	10
302	–	10c. red	35	35
303	–	15c. orange	45	55
303a	–	15c. green	45	65
304	–	30c. olive	4·00	5·25
304a	–	30c. brown	50	35
305	–	50c. purple	12·00	11·50
305a	–	50c. blue	2·75	2·00
306	–	1q. orange	12·00	15·00
306a		1q. red	3·00	2·00

DESIGNS: 3c. Puerto Barrios; 4c. San Felipe; 6c., 1q. Different view of Lake Amatitlan; 10c. Livingston; 15c. San Jose; 30c. Atitlan; 50c. La Aurora Airport.

(b) Inscr "EXTERIOR" (34 × 15 mm) (except Nos. 319/20 which are 46 × 20 mm).

307		1c. brown	10	10
308		2c. red	20	20
309		3c. mauve	35	35
309a		4c. yellow	1·25	1·00
309b		4c. red	70	50
310		5c. blue	1·75	40
310a		5c. orange	1·50	25
311		10c. brown	35	25
311a		10c. green	35	25
312		15c. red	35	10
312a		15c. orange	30	10
313		20c. blue	1·60	2·00
313a		20c. red	35	25
314		25c. black	2·00	2·40
314a		25c. green	65	35
315		30c. green	9·50	6·00
315a		30c. red	3·75	30
316		50c. red	22·00	24·00
316a		50c. violet	17·00	10·00
317		1q. blue	15·00	21·00
318		1q. green	5·00	6·00
319		2q.50 olive and red	3·50	2·00
320		5q. blue and orange	4·75	2·75

DESIGNS: 1c. Guatemala City; 2c., 15c. (No. 312) Views of Central Park; 3c. Cerrito del Carmen; 4c. Estuary of R. Dulce; 5c. Plaza J. R. Barrios; 10c. National Liberators' Monument; 15c. (No. 312a) R. Dulce; 20c. Quezaltenango; 25c. Antigua; 30c. Puerto Barrios; 50c. San Jose; 1q. Aurora Airport; 2q.50, Islet; 5q. Rocks on Atlantic Coast.

1936. Obligatory Tax. 65th Anniv of Liberal Revolution. Optd **1871 30 DE JUNIO 1936**.

321	92	1c. green	35	35

1936. Obligatory Tax. 115th Anniv of Independence. Optd **1821 15 de SEPTIEMBRE 1936**.

322	92	1c. green	45	25

1936. Obligatory Tax. National Fair. Optd **FERIA NACIONAL 1936**.

323	92	1c. olive	55	55

1937. Philatelic Exhibition Fund. Optd **EXPOSICION FILATELICA 1937** or surch **+1** also.

325	120	1c.+1c. red and brown	90	70
326	121	3c.+1c. green and orange	90	70
327		3c.+1c. green and red	90	70
329	–	4c.+1c. (No. 300a)	75	75
328	122	5c.+1c. brown and blue	90	70
330	–	6c.+1c. (No. 301a)	75	75
331	–	10c.+1c. (No. 311a)	75	75
332	–	15c.+1c. (No. 312a)	75	75
324	92	1c. olive	40	40

128 Resplendent Quetzal

129 General Ubico on horseback

130 Quezaltenango

1937. Second Term of Pres. Ubico. (a) Postage.

333	128	½c. red and blue	80	50
334	–	1c. brown and grey	45	45
335	–	2c. red and violet	45	45
336	–	3c. blue and purple	35	35
337	–	4c. olive and yellow	1·40	1·25
338	–	5c. purple and red	1·40	1·25
339	–	10c. black and purple	2·00	2·40
340	–	15c. red and blue	1·60	2·40
341	–	25c. violet and orange	2·00	2·50
342	–	50c. orange and green	3·00	3·75
343	129	1q. purple and brown	15·00	17·00
344	–	1q.50 brown and olive	15·00	17·00

DESIGNS: As Type **128**—VERT: 1c. Tower of the Reformer; 5c. National Congress entrance; 10c. Customs House. HORIZ: 2c. Union Park, Quezaltenango; 3c. G.P.O; 4c. Government Building, Retalhuleu; 15c. Aurora Airport; 25c. National Fair; 50c. Presidential Guards' Barracks. As Type **129**: 1q.50, Gen. Ubico.

(b) Air. As T **130**, inscr "INTERIOR" and optd with aeroplane.

345	130	2c. black and red	20	15
346	–	3c. black and blue	70	85
347	–	4c. black and yellow	20	15
348	–	6c. black and green	50	35
349	–	10c. black and purple	1·40	1·50
350	–	15c. black and orange	1·00	70
351	–	30c. black and olive	2·50	2·00
352	–	50c. black and blue	3·50	3·00
353	–	75c. black and violet	7·00	7·50
354	–	1q. black and red	7·50	8·00

DESIGNS: 3c. Lake Atitlan; 4c. Progressive colony on Lake Amatitlan; 6c. Carmen Hill; 10c. Relief map; 15c. National University; 30c. Plaza Espana; 50c. Aurora Police Station; 75c. Aurora Amphitheatre; 1q. Aurora Airport.

(c) Air. As T **130** inscr "EXTERIOR" and optd with aeroplane.

355	–	1c. blue and orange	15	15
356	–	2c. violet and red	25	20
357	–	3c. brown and purple	70	70
358	–	5c. red and green	2·75	2·00
359	–	10c. green and red	85	70
360	–	15c. olive and pink	55	35
361	–	20c. black and blue	1·75	1·10
362	–	25c. red and grey	1·75	1·75
363	–	30c. violet and green	85	85
364	–	50c. blue and purple	30·00	30·00
365	–	1q. purple and olive	7·00	8·00
366	–	1q.50 brown and red	7·00	8·00

DESIGNS: 1c. Seventh Avenue; 2c. Liberators' Monument; 3c. National Printing Offices; 5c. National Museum; 10c. Central Park; 15c. Escuintla Park; 20c. Mobile Police; 25c. Slaughter-house, Escuintla; 30c. Campo de Marte Stadium; 50c. Plaza Barrios; 1q. Polytechnic; 1q.50, Aurora Airport.

1938. 150th Anniv of U.S. Constitution. Optd **1787-1789 CL ANIVERSARIO DE LA CONSTITUCION EE. UU. 1937-1939.**

367	92	1c. olive	25	20

1938. Obligatory Tax. No. 223 optd **1938**.

368a	92	1c. olive	25	15

134

1938. 1st Central American Philatelic Exhibition. (a) Air. As T **134** inscr "PRIMERA EXPOSICION FILATELICA CENTRO AMERICANA".

369	134	1c. brown and orange	25	25
370	–	2c. brown and red	25	25
371	–	3c. brown, buff and green	40	40
372	–	4c. brown and purple	55	55
373	–	5c. brown and grey	35	40
374	–	10c. brown and blue	70	1·00

DESIGNS: 2c. to 10c. Various portraits as Type **134**.

(b) Postage. No. 223 optd **Primera Exposicion Filatelica Centroamericana 1938**.

375	92	1c. olive	25	15

137 La Merced Church

1939. Optd with flying quetzal. (a) Inland Air Mail. As T **137** inscr "CORREO AEREO INTERIOR".

376	137	1c. brown and olive	15	15
377	–	2c. green and red	20	20
378	–	3c. olive and blue	20	25
379	–	4c. green and pink	20	15
380	–	5c. blue and purple	25	25
381	–	6c. grey and orange	35	30
382	–	10c. grey and brown	75	35
383	–	15c. black and purple	1·00	25
384	–	30c. red and blue	1·10	40
385	–	50c. violet and orange	1·50	60
386	–	1q. blue and green	2·40	2·00

DESIGNS: 2c. Christ's Church Ruins, Antigua; 3c. Aurora Airport; 4c. Campo de Marte Stadium; 5c. Cavalry Barracks; 6c. Palace of Justice; 10c. Customs House, San Jose; 15c. Post Office, Retalhuleu; 30c. Municipal Theatre, Quezaltenango; 50c. Customs House, Retalhuleu; 1q. Departmental Palace, Retalhuleu.

(b) Foreign Air Mail. As T **137** inscr "AEREO EXTERIOR" (10c. and 25c.) or "AEREO INTERNACIONAL".

387	–	1c. brown and sepia	15	15
388	–	2c. black and green	25	30
389	–	3c. green and blue	20	20
390	–	4c. green and brown	20	20
391	–	5c. red and green	40	15
392	–	10c. slate and red	1·60	15
393	–	15c. red and blue	2·40	15
394	–	20c. yellow and green	75	30
395	–	25c. olive and purple	3·75	25
396	–	30c. grey and red	1·00	20
397	–	50c. orange and red	1·50	25
398	–	1q. green and orange	2·75	40

DESIGNS: 1c. Mayan Altar, Aurora Park; 2c. Ministry of Health; 3c. Lake Amatitlan; 4c. Lake Atitlan; 5c. Bridge over Tamazulapa; 10c. National Liberators' Monument; 15c. Palace of the Captains General; 20c. Carmen Hill; 25c. Barrios Square; 30c. Mayan Altar, Archaeological Museum; 50c. Carlos III Fountain; 1q. Antigua.

1939. Obligatory Tax. No. 223 optd **1939**.

399	92	1c. olive	25	15

140 National Flower (White Nun)

142 Arms and Map of Guatemala

1939.

400	–	½c. brown and green	20	20
401	140	2c. black and blue	1·00	35
402	–	3c. green and brown	1·60	65
403	–	3c. green and red	1·60	65
404	142	5c. red and blue	1·25	1·25

DESIGNS: ½c. Mayan calendar; 3c. Resplendent quetzal.

1939. No. 229 surch **UN CENTAVO**.

405	95	1c. on 2c. blue	30	20

1940. Obligatory Tax. No. 223 optd **1940**.

406	92	1c. olive	25	15

1940. 50th Anniv of Pan-American Union. (a) Optd **Conmemorativo Union Panamericana 1890-1940**.

407	92	1c. olive	25	15

(b) Air. Optd **UNION PANAMERICANA 1890-1940 CORREO AEREO.**

408	–	15c. blue (No. 234)	35	20

1940. Surch with new values.

409	31	1c. on 25c. brown	25	15
410	–	5c. on 50c. red (No. 237)	35	30

1941. Obligatory Tax. Optd **1941**.

411	92	1c. olive	25	15

1941. Obligatory Tax. Surch **CONSTRUCCION** (twice) and **UN CENTAVO**.

412	95	1c. on 2c. blue	25	15

1941. Air. 2nd Pan-American Health Day. Optd **DICIEMBRE 2 1941 SEGUNDO DIA PAN-AMERICANO DE LA SALUD.**

414	–	2c. black and green (No. 388)	55	30

1941. Surch ½ **MEDIO CENTAVO** ½.

415	31	½c. on 25c. brown	20	20

1942. Obligatory Tax. Surch **CONSTRUCCION 1942 UN CENTAVO.**

416	95	1c. on 2c. blue	25	15

1942. As T **114**, but tablet dated "1942".

416a		3c. green	35	20
416b		3c. blue	35	20

153 Archway between wings of new G.P.O.

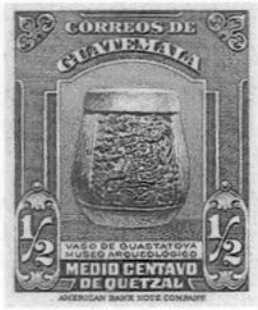

154 Guastatoya Vase

1942. Obligatory Tax.

417a	153	1c. brown	25	15

1942.

418	154	½c. brown	20	15
419	–	1c. red	25	15

DESIGN—HORIZ: 1c. Old people's home.

156 Ruins of Zakuleu

157 National Printing Works

158 National Police H.Q.

159 San Carlos Borromeo University, Antigua

1943.

420	156	½c. brown (postage)	15	10
421	157	2c. red	20	15
422	158	10c. mauve (air)	50	15
423	159	15c. brown	55	15

160 Don Pedro de Alvarado

161 Archway between wings of new G.P.O.

1943. Air. 400th Anniv of Founding of Antigua.

424	160	15c. blue	55	15

1943. Obligatory Tax.

425	161	1c. orange	25	15

162 Rafael Maria Landivar

1943. 150th Death Anniv of R. M. Landivar (poet).

426	162	5c. blue	35	20

163 National Palace

1944. Inauguration of National Palace.

427	163	3c. green (postage)	20	15
444		5c. red (air)	35	15
445		10c. lilac	35	15
446		15c. blue	35	30

1945. Optd **25 de junio de 1944 PALACIO NACIONAL** and bar.

428	163	3c. blue	35	15

1945. Air. Optd **PALACIO NACIONAL** and bar.

429	163	5c. red	30	20

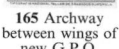

165 Archway between wings of new G.P.O.

166 Allegory of the Revolution

1945. Obligatory Tax.

430	165	1c. orange	25	15
479		1c. blue	25	15

1945. Revolution of 20 October 1944.

431	166	3c. blue (postage)	15	15
432		5c. red (air)	45	30
433		6c. green	45	30
434		10c. violet	45	30
435		15c. blue	45	30

1945. Air. Book Fair. No. 389 surch **1945 FERIA DEL LIBRO 2½ CENTAVOS**.

436		2½c. on 3c. green and blue	1·40	1·40

168 Jose Milla y Vidaurre (author)

169 Archbishop Pavo Enriquez de Rivera

170 Torch

1945.

437	168	1c. green (postage)	15	15
438	169	2c. violet	15	15
439		5c. red (air)	35	20
678		5c. olive	20	10
679		5c. blue	20	10
680		5c. green	20	10
681		5c. orange	20	10
682		5c. violet	20	10
683		5c. grey	20	10
440	168	7½c. purple	50	90
441		7½c. blue	30	30

For stamps as Type **169** but dated "1660 1951" see Nos. 523/27.

1945. 1st Anniv of Revolution of 20 October 1944.

442	170	3c. blue (postage)	20	15
443		5c. mauve (air)	45	30

171 Jose Batres y Montufar (military leader and writer)

174 Rowland Hill

1945.

447	171	½c. brown (postage)	25	20
448		3c. blue	30	20
449		3c. green	35	30
450	–	10c. green (air)	50	25

DESIGN—HORIZ: 10c. Montufar.

1946. Centenary of First Postage Stamps.

451	–	1c. olive & violet (postage)	30	25
452	174	5c. brown and grey (air)	25	20
453	–	15c. blue, green and red	35	35

DESIGNS: 1c. U.P.U. Monument, Berne; 15c. Hemispheres and quetzal.

175 Signing the Declaration of Independence

176 Franklin D. Roosevelt

1946. Air. 125th Anniv of Independence.

454	175	5c. red	15	10
455		6c. brown	20	15
456		10c. violet	25	20
457		20c. blue	50	45

1947. Air. 2nd Anniv of Revolution of 20 October 1944. As T **170** but inscr "1944 1946" instead of "1944 1945" and "II" for "I".

458		1c. green	20	15
459		2c. red	20	15
460		3c. violet	20	15
461		5c. blue	25	15

1947. Air.

462	176	5c. red	20	15
463		6c. blue	25	15
464		10c. blue	55	20
465		30c. black	1·75	1·40
466		50c. violet	1·75	1·75
467		1q. green	2·75	2·75

177 "Labour"

180 Football Match

1948. Labour Day and 1st Anniv of Adoption of Labour Code.

468	177	1c. green	20	15
469		2c. purple	20	15
470		3c. blue	20	15
471		5c. red	20	15

1948. Optd **1948**.

472	142	5c. red and blue	20	15

1948. Air. Optd **1948 AEREO**.

473	142	5c. red and blue	25	20

1948. Air. 4th Central American and Caribbean Football Championship Games.

474	180	3c. black and red	40	20
475		5c. black and green	50	30
476		10c. black and mauve	60	70
477		30c. black and blue	2·00	2·40
478		50c. black and yellow	2·75	2·75

181 Fray Bartolome de Las Casas and Indian

182 Seal of University of Guatemala

1949. Fray Bartolome de Las Casas ("Apostle of the Indians").

480	181	½c. red	20	15
661		½c. blue	15	10
481		1c. brown	20	15
662		1c. violet	15	10
663		2c. green	15	10
664		3c. red	15	10
484		4c. blue	30	20
665a		4c. brown	10	10

1949. Air. Latin-American Universities' Congress.

485	182	3c. blue and red	35	35
486		10c. blue and green	75	55
487		50c. blue and yellow	1·90	2·10

183 Gathering Coffee

184 Tecum Uman Monument

1950. Tourist Propaganda. (a) Postage.

488	183	½c. olive, blue and pink	30	15
489	–	½c. blue and brown	20	15
490	–	1c. olive, brown and yellow	30	15
491	–	1c. green and orange	20	15
492	–	2c. blue, green and red	30	15
493	–	2c. brown and red	20	15
494	–	3c. brown, blue and violet	30	15
495	–	6c. violet, orange & green	55	15

DESIGNS—As Type **183**: ½c. (No. 489), 3c. Cutting sugar canes; 1c. (No. 490), 2c. (No. 493), Agricultural colony; 1c. (No. 491), 2c. (No. 492), Banana trees; 6c. International Bridge.

(b) Air. Multicoloured centres.

496	–	3c. red	55	15
497	184	5c. lake	55	15
498	–	8c. black	30	20
499	–	13c. brown	60	35
500	–	35c. violet	1·50	1·75

DESIGNS—As Type **184**—HORIZ: 3c. Lake Atitlan; 8c. San Cristobal Church; 35c. Momostenango Cliffs. VERT: 13c. Weaver.

185 Footballers

186 Ministry of Health Badge

187 Nursing School

1950. Air. 6th Central American and Caribbean Games. Inscr "VI JUEGOS DEPORTIVOS 1950".

501	185	1c. black and violet	35	15
502	–	3c. black and red	40	15
503	–	4c. black and brown	50	20
504	–	8c. black and purple	60	20
505	–	35c. black and blue	1·40	1·90
506	–	65c. green	3·00	3·00

DESIGNS—HORIZ: 4c. Pole vaulting; 35c. Diving; 65c. Stadium. VERT: 3c. Runners; 8c. Tennis.

1950. Social Assistance and Public Health Fund.

507	186	1c. blue and red (postage)	20	15
508	–	3c. red and green (Nurse)	35	20
509	–	5c. brown and blue (Map)	55	35
511	–	5c. red, green & violet (air)	25	20
512	187	10c. green and brown	40	35
513	–	50c. purple, green and red	1·40	1·60
514	–	1q. olive, green and yellow	1·60	1·75

DESIGNS—As Type **187**: 5c. Nurse; 50c., 1q. Zacapa and Roosevelt Hospitals.

1951. No. E479 without surcharge for use as ordinary postage.

517	E 181	4c. black and green	35	30

188 School

1951. Aerial views of schools as T **188**.

519	188	½c. brown and violet	20	15
520	–	1c. green and lake	20	15
521	188	2c. brown and blue	20	20
522	–	4c. purple and black	30	20

1952. As No. 438 but dated "1660 1951" below portrait.

523	169	½c. violet	15	10
524		1c. red	15	10
525		2c. green	15	10
526		4c. orange	20	15
527		4c. blue	15	10

189 Ceremonial Axehead

190 Flag and Constitution

1953. Air.

528	189	3c. drab and blue	20	20
529		5c. brown and slate	20	20
530		10c. slate and violet	45	35

1953. Air. Presidential Succession, 1951.

531	190	1c. multicoloured	30	20
532		2c. multicoloured	35	30
533		4c. multicoloured	45	35

191 R. Alvarez Ovalle (music), J. J. Palma (words)

1953. National Anthem.

534	191	½c. grey and violet	35	20
535		1c. brown and grey	45	20
536		2c. olive and brown	45	25
537		3c. olive and blue	45	25

192 "Work and Play"

193 Horse Racing

1953. Air. National Fair. Inscr "FERIA NACIONAL".

538	–	1c. red and blue	20	15
539	–	4c. green and orange	90	25
540	192	5c. brown and green	55	30
541	193	15c. lilac and brown	85	75
542	–	20c. blue and red	75	70
543	–	30c. blue and sepia	85	1·00
544	–	50c. black and violet	1·00	1·00
545	–	65c. green and blue	1·75	1·90
546	–	1q. green and red	25·00	15·00

DESIGNS—VERT: 1c. National dance; 4c. National flower (white nun); 30c. Picture and corn cob; 1q. Resplendent quetzal. HORIZ: 20c. Ruins of Zakuleu; 50c. Champion bull; 65c. Cycle-racing.

194 Indian Warrior

196 Flags of Guatemala and ODECA

1954. Air. National Revolutionary Army Commemoration.

547	194	1c. red	35	35
548		2c. blue	35	35
549		4c. green	35	35
550		5c. turquoise	55	45
551		6c. orange	55	45
552		10c. violet	70	55
553		20c. sepia	1·90	2·00

1954. As T **5** but inscr "UNION POSTAL UNIVERSAL GUATEMALA" around oval.

554		1c. blue	90	35
1222		1c. green	25	10
555		2c. violet	45	25
556		2c. brown	60	25
1222a		2c. blue	25	10
557		3c. red	60	25
558		3c. blue	60	25
1225		3c. brown	25	10
1226		3c. green	25	10
1227		3c. orange	25	10
559		4c. orange	1·00	25
560		4c. violet	90	25
1228		4c. brown	25	10
561		5c. brown	1·50	35
562		5c. red	1·50	35
563		5c. green	1·00	35
564		5c. grey	1·75	35
1228a		5c. mauve	25	10
565		6c. green	1·50	55
1229		6c. blue	25	10

1954. Air. 3rd Anniv of Organization of Central American States.

566	196	1c. multicoloured	20	15
567		2c. multicoloured	20	15
568		4c. multicoloured	30	20

197 Goalkeeper

198 Red Cross and Globe

1955. Golden Jubilee of Football in Guatemala. Inscr "1902–1952".

569	–	4c. violet (Camposeco)	70	45
570	–	4c. red (Camposeco)	70	45
571	–	4c. green (Camposeco)	70	45
572	–	10c. green (Matheu)	2·00	55
573	197	15c. blue	2·00	1·50

1956. Red Cross. Inscr "CONMEMORATIVAS CRUZ ROJA".

574	198	1c. red & brown (postage)	20	20
575	–	3c. red and green	20	20
576	–	4c. red and black	25	20
577	–	5c.+15c. red and blue	60	90
578	–	15c.+50c. red and lilac	1·40	1·75
579	198	25c.+50c. red and blue	1·40	1·75
580	–	35c.+1q. grn & red (air)	3·50	3·75
581	–	50c.+1q. red and blue	3·50	3·75
582	–	1q.+1q. red and green	3·50	3·75

DESIGNS: 3c., 15c. Telephone and red cross; 4c., 5c. Nurse, patient and red cross; 35c. Red Cross ambulance; 50c. Nurse and hospital; 1q. Red Cross nurse.

199 Road Map of Guatemala
200 Maya Warrior

1956. Revolution of 1954–55. Inscr "LIBERACION 1954-55".

583 – ½c. violet (postage) . . . 15 10
584 **199** 1c. green 15 10
585 – 3c. sepia 15 10
586 **200** 2c. multicoloured (air) . . 20 15
587 – 4c. black and red 20 15
588 – 5c. brown and blue . . . 30 30
589 – 6c. blue and sepia 20 20
590 – 20c. brown, blue and violet . . . . 1·00 1·00
591 – 30c. olive and blue . . . 1·75 1·00
592 – 65c. green and brown . . 1·50 1·75
593 – 1q. multicoloured . . . . 2·25 2·40
594 – 5q. brown, blue and green 9·00 9·50

DESIGNS: ½c. Liberation dagger symbol; 3c. Oil production; 4c. Family; 5c. Sword smashing Communist emblems; 6c. Hands holding map and cogwheel; 20c. Martyrs' Monument; 30c. Champerico Port; 65c. Telecommunications symbols; 1q. Flags of ODECA countries; 5q. Pres. Armas.

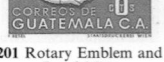

201 Rotary Emblem and Road Map
203 Esquipulas Cathedral and "Black Christ"

1956. Air. 50th Anniv of Rotary International.

595 **201** 4c. bistre and blue 35 30
596 6c. bistre and green . . . 35 30
597 35c. bistre and violet . . 1·00 1·40

1957. Air. Red Cross Fund. Nos. 577/9 optd **AEREO-1957** and ornaments.

598 – 5c.+15c. red and blue . . 4·00 4·50
599 – 15c.+50c. red and lilac . . 4·00 4·50
600 **198** 25c.+50c. red and blue . . 4·00 4·50

1957. Esquipulas Highway Fund. Inscr "PRO-CARRETERA ESQUIPULAS JUNIO 1957".

601 **203** 1½c.+½c. violet and brown (postage) 70 45
602 – 10c.+1q. brown and green (air) . . . . 4·00 4·50
603 – 15c.+1q. green and sepia 4·00 4·50
604 – 20c.+1q. slate and brown 4·00 4·50
605 – 25c.+1q. red and lilac . . 4·00 4·50

DESIGNS—HORIZ: 10c. Esquipulas Cathedral. VERT: 15c. Cathedral and "Black Christ"; 20c. Map of Guatemala and "Black Christ"; 25c. Bishop of Esquipulas.

204 Red Cross, Map and Resplendent Quetzal

1958. Air. Red Cross.

606 **204** 1c. multicoloured 55 30
607 – 2c. red, brown and blue . 35 15
608 – 3c. brown, red and blue . 35 15
609 – 4c. red, green and brown . 35 15

DESIGNS—VERT: 2c. J. R. Angulo, Mother and Child. HORIZ: 3c. P. de Bethancourt and Invalid; 4c. R. Ayau and Red Cross.

1959. Birth Centenary of R. A. Ovalle (composer of National Anthem). Optd **1858 1958 CENTENARIO**.

610 **191** ½c. grey and violet 30 30

1959. Air. Pres. Castillo Armas Commem. As No. 594 but inscr "LIBERACION 3 DE JULIO DE 1954", etc. Centre in blue and yellow. Frame colours given.

615 1c. black 15 15
616 2c. red 15 15
617 4c. brown 15 15
618 6c. green 20 15
619 10c. violet 35 25
620 20c. green . . . . 1·00 65
621 35c. grey . . . . 1·75 95

1959. Air. United Nations. Optd **HOMENAJE A LAS NACIONES UNIDAS**.

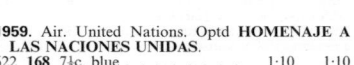

622 **168** 7½c. blue . . . . 1·10 1·10

207 Caravel of 1532 and freighter "Quetzaltenango"

1959. Air. Central American Merchant Marine Commemoration.

623 **207** 6c. blue and red 80 15

1959. Air. Guatemala's Claim to Belize (British Honduras). As No. 509 optd **BELICE ES NUESTRO** and **AEREO**.

624 5c. brown and blue 35 20

1959. Air. Centenary of First Export of Coffee. No. 589 optd **1859 CENTENARIO PRIMERA EXPORTACION DE CAFE 1959**.

625 6c. blue and sepia 55 20

210 Pres. and Senora Morales

1959. Air. Visit of President of Honduras.

626 **210** 6c. brown 20 15

211 Red Cross Shield

1960. Red Cross Commemoration. Cross in red.

627 **211** 1c.+1c. blue and brown (postage) 30 20
628 – 3c.+3c. blue and lilac . . 30 20
629 **211** 4c.+4c. blue and black . . 30 25
630 – 5c.+5c. blue, pink and red (air) . . . . 1·40 1·50
631 – 6c.+6c. green and red . . 1·40 1·50
632 – 10c.+10c. pink, blue and deep blue . . . . 1·40 1·50
633 – 15c.+15c. red, blue and brown . . . . 1·40 1·50
634 – 20c.+20c. green, pink and purple . . . . 1·40 1·50
635 – 25c.+25c. pink, blue and grey . . . . 1·40 1·50
636 – 30c.+30c. multicoloured 1·40 1·50

DESIGNS—3c., 5c. Wounded soldier at Solferino; 6c., 20c. Houses and debris afloat on flood waters; 10c., 25c. Earth, Moon and planets; 15c., 30c. Red Cross H.Q., Guatemala City.

1960. Air. World Refugee Year. Nos. 606/9 optd **ANO MUNDIAL DE REFUGIADOS** or surch also.

637 1c. multicoloured . . . . . . 2·10 1·75
638 2c. red, brown and blue . . . 90 70
639 3c. brown, red and blue . . . 90 70
640 4c. red, green and brown . . 90 70
641 6c. on 1c. multicoloured . . . 5·00 2·50
642 7c. on 2c. red, brown and blue . . . . 1·50 1·25
643 10c. on 3c. brown, red & blue 2·50 2·75
644 20c. on 4c. red, green & brown . . . . 2·75 2·75

1960. Air. Founding of City of Melchor de Mencos. No. 589 optd **Fundacion de la cuidad Melchor de Mencos 30-IV-1960**.

645 6c. blue and sepia . . . . . 1·10 1·10

213 Abraham Lincoln

1960. Air. 150th Birth Anniv of Abraham Lincoln.

646 **213** 5c. blue 30 20
647 30c. violet . . . . 70 1·00
648 50c. slate . . . . 3·50 4·00

214 UNESCO Headquarters, Paris

1960. Air. Inauguration of UNESCO. Headquarters Building, Paris (1958).

649 **214** 5c. violet and mauve . . . 15 15
650 6c. sepia and blue 20 15
651 8c. red and green 35 20
652 20c. blue and brown . . . 85 90

1961. Air. Red Cross. Nos. 606/9 optd **MAYO DE 1960**.

653 1c. multicoloured . . . . . . 1·25 75
654 2c. red, brown and blue . . . 45 40
655 3c. brown, red and blue . . . 45 40
656 4c. red, green and brown . . 45 40

216 Romulus, Remus and Wolf
217 Independence Ceremony

1961. Plaza Italia Inauguration.

657 **216** 3c. blue 15 15

1962. Air. 140th Anniv of Independence.

658 **217** 4c. sepia 15 15
659 5c. blue 20 15
660 15c. violet 70 35

1962. Air. Malaria Eradication. Optd **1962 EL MUNDO UNIDO CONTRA LA MALARIA**.

666 **214** 6c. sepia and blue 55 85

219 Dr. Jose Luna

1962. Air. Guatemalan Doctors.

667 **219** 1c. violet and olive . . . 35 15
668 – 4c. green and yellow . . . 35 15
669 – 5c. brown and blue . . . 35 15
670 – 6c. black and salmon . . 35 15
671 – 10c. brown and green . . 55 20
672 – 20c. blue and mauve . . . 70 45

DOCTORS: 4c. R. Robles; 5c. N. Esparragoza; 6c. J. Ortega; 10c. D. Gonzalez; 20c. J. Flores.

1962. Air. Pres. Ydigoras's Tour of Central America. No. 589 optd **PRESIDENTE YDIGORAS FUENTES RECORRE POR TIERRA CENTRO AMERICA 14 A 20 DIC. 1962**.

673 6c. blue and sepia 60 55

1963. Air. New ODECA Charter Commemoration. Optd **CONMEMORACION FIRMA NUEVA CARTA ODECA.—1962**.

674 **214** 6c. sepia and blue 30 15
675 8c. red and green 35 15

222 Girl with Basket of Fruit on head
224 Arms

1963. Air. National Fair, 1960.

676 **222** 1c. multicoloured 15 10

1963. Air. Presidential Meeting. No. 589 with 11-line opt starting **REUNION PRESIDENTES: KENNEDY**.

677 6c. blue and sepia . . . . . 2·40 1·60

1963.

684 **224** 10c. red 35 15
685 10c. black 30 15
686 10c. brown 30 15
687 20c. violet 55 20
688 20c. blue 55 20

225 Harvester (after "The Reaper", Mathieson)
226 Ceiba (national tree)

1963. Air. Freedom from Hunger.

689 **225** 5c. turquoise 20 15
690 10c. blue 35 20

1963. Air.

691 **226** 4c. green and sepia . . . 15 15

227 Pedro Bethancourt tending sick man
228 Patzun Palace

1964. Campaign for Canonization of Pedro Bethancourt.

692 **227** 2½c. brown (postage) . . 15 10
693 2½c. blue (air) 10 10
694 3c. orange 10 10
695 4c. violet 15 10
696 5c. green 20 10

1964. Air. Guatemalan Palaces.

697 **228** 1c. brown and red 15 10
698 – 3c. green and mauve . . . 20 10
699 – 4c. lake and blue 20 15
700 – 5c. blue and brown . . . 25 15
701 – 6c. blue and green 25 15

PALACES: 3c. Coban; 4c. Retalhuleu; 5c. San Marcos; 6c. Los Capitanes Generales.

229 Municipal Building

1964. Air. New Buildings. (a) As T **229**.

702 **229** 3c. brown and blue . . . 15 15
703 – 4c. blue and brown . . . 20 15

DESIGN: 4c. Social Security Building.

(b) Designs as Nos. 702/3 but different style frame and inscr, and new designs.

704 – 3c. green (As No. 703) . . 20 10
705 – 4c. slate 20 10
706 **229** 7c. blue 25 15
707 – 7c. bistre 25 15

DESIGNS: 4c. University Rectory; 7c. (No. 707), Engineering Faculty.

1964. Air. Olympic Games, Tokyo. Optd with Olympic rings and **OLIMPIADAS TOKIO-1964**.

708 **204** 1c. . . . . 1·50 2·00
709 – 2c. (No. 607) 75 75
710 – 3c. (No. 608) 75 75
711 – 4c. (No. 609) 75 75

1964. Air. New York World's Fair. Optd **FERIA MUNDIAL DE NEW YORK**.

712 **204** 1c. . . . . 1·40 1·10
713 – 2c. (No. 607) 50 50
714 – 3c. (No. 608) 50 50
715 – 4c. (No. 609) 50 50

1964. Air. Surch **HABILITADA 1964** and value.

716 **204** 7c. on 1c. 75 45
717 – 9c. on 2c. (No. 607) . . . 40 35
718 – 13c. on 3c. (No. 608) . . 45 45
719 – 21c. on 4c. (No. 609) . . 75 75

1964. Air. 8th Cycle Race. Optd **VIII VUELTA CICLISTICA**.

720 **204** 1c. . . . . 1·40 1·40
721 – 2c. (No. 607) 70 70
722 – 3c. (No. 608) 70 70
723 – 4c. (No. 609) . . . . . . 70 1·00

234 Pres. Kennedy

1964. Air. Pres. Kennedy Commemoration.

724	**234**	1c. violet	70	55
725		2c. green	70	55
726		3c. brown	70	55
727		7c. blue	70	55
728		50c. green	4·00	4·25

235 Centenary Emblem

237 Bishop F. Marroquin

1964. Air. Red Cross Centenary. Emblem in silver and red.

730	**235**	7c. blue	55	35
731		9c. orange	55	35
732		13c. violet	85	35
733		21c. green	50	70
734		35c. brown	1·00	1·00
735		1q. bistre	1·60	2·00

1964. 15th Anniv (1963) of International Society of Guatemala Collectors. No. 559 optd **HOMENAJE A LA "I.S.G.C." 1948–1963**.

736		4c. orange	50	30

1985. Air. 400th Death Anniv of Bishop Marroquin.

737	**237**	4c. brown and purple	15	10
738		7c. sepia and grey	25	15
739		9c. black and blue	30	15

1965. Air. Optd **AYUDENOS MAYO 1965**. Emblem in silver and red.

740	**235**	7c. blue	35	30
741		9c. orange	45	35
742		13c. violet	55	45
743		21c. green	70	60
744		35c. brown	70	95

239 Scout Badge

240 Flags

1966. Air. 5th Regional Scout Training Conference, Guatemala City. Multicoloured.

745		5c. Type **239**	35	15
746		9c. Scouts by campfire	45	25
747		10c. Scout carrying torch and flag	55	35
748		15c. Scout saluting	70	55
749		20c. Lord Baden-Powell	90	90

1966. Air. "Centro America". 145th Anniv of Central American Independence.

750	**240**	6c. multicoloured	25	15

241 Nefertari's Temple, Abu Simbel

242 Arms

1966. Air. Nubian Monuments Preservation.

751	**241**	21c. violet and bistre	55	35

1966. Air.

752	**242**	5c. orange	20	10
753		5c. green	20	10
754		5c. grey	20	10
755		5c. violet	20	10
756		5c. blue	20	10
757		5c. deep blue	20	10
758		5c. violet	20	10
759		5c. green	15	10
760		5c. lake	15	10
761		5c. green on yellow	15	10

243 Mgr. M. Rossell y Arellano

244 Mario M. Montenegro (revolutionary)

1966. Air. Monseigneur Rossell Commem.

765	**243**	1c. violet	20	15
766		2c. green	25	10
767		3c. sepia	25	15
768		7c. blue	35	25
769		50c. slate	95	1·10

1966. Air. Montenegro Commemoration.

770	**244**	2c. red	15	10
771		3c. orange	20	15
772		4c. red	25	15
773		5c. grey	35	15
774		5c. blue	35	15
775		5c. green	35	15
776		5c. black	35	15

245 Morning Glory

1967. Air. Flowers. Multicoloured.

777		4c. Type **245**	25	15
778		8c. "Bird of Paradise" (horiz)	25	15
779		10c. "White Nun" orchid (national flower) (horiz)	35	25
780		20c. "Nymphs of Amatitlan"	60	35

246 Institute Emblem

1967. Air. 8th General Assembly of Pan-American Geographical and Historical Institute (1965).

781	**246**	4c. purple, black & brown	20	15
782		5c. blue, black and bistre	35	15
783		7c. blue, black and yellow	55	15

247 Map of Guatemala and British Honduras

1967. Guatemala's Claim to British Honduras.

784	**247**	4c. blue, red and green	15	10
785		5c. blue, red and yellow	20	10
786		6c. blue, grey and orange	20	15

1967. Air. Guatemalan Victory in "Norceca" Football Games. No. 704 optd **GUATEMALA CAMPEON III Norceca Foot-Ball** and football motif.

787		3c. green	35	30

1967. Air. American Heads of State Meeting, Punta del Este. No. 705 optd **REUNION JEFES DE ESTADO AMERICANO, PUNTA DEL ESTE** etc.

788		4c. slate	70	55

250 "Peace and Progress"

1967. Air. International Co-operation.

789	**250**	7c. multicoloured	35	15
790		21c. multicoloured	55	35

251 Yurrita Church

1967. Air. Religion in Guatemala.

791	**251**	1c. brown, green and blue	20	10
792	–	2c. brown, pur & salmon	25	10
793	–	3c. indigo, red and blue	25	10
794	–	4c. green, purple & salmon	25	10
795	–	5c. brown, purple & green	25	10
796	–	7c. black, blue and mauve	35	15
797	–	10c. blue, violet and yellow	55	20

DESIGNS—HORIZ: 2c. Santo Domingo Church; 3c. San Francisco Church; 7c. Mercy Church, Antigua; 10c. Metropolitan Cathedral. VERT: 4c. Antonio Jose de Irisarri; 5c. Church of the Recollection.

252 Lincoln

1967. Air. Death Centenary (1965) of Abraham Lincoln.

798	**252**	7c. red and blue	35	20
799		9c. black and green	45	25
800		11c. black and brown	45	25
801		15c. red and blue	45	35
802		30c. green and purple	1·00	1·10

1967. Air. 8th Central American Scout Camporee. Nos. 745/9 optd **VIII Camporee Scout Centroamericano Diciembre 1-8/1967**.

803		5c. Type **239**	35	35
804		9c. Scouts by campfire	55	55
805		10c. Scout carrying torch and flag	70	70
806		15c. Scout saluting	70	70
807		20c. Lord Baden-Powell	90	90

1967. Air. Award of Nobel Prize for Literature to Miguel Angel Asturias (1st issue). Nos. 694/5 optd **"Premio Nobel de Literatura - 10 diciembre 1967 - Miguel Angel Asturias"**.

808	**227**	3c. orange	35	30
809	–	4c. violet	35	30

See also No. 838.

255 UNESCO Emblem and Children

1967. Air. 20th Anniv (1966) of UNESCO

810	**255**	4c. green	15	10
811		5c. blue	20	15
812		7c. grey	25	15
813		21c. purple	60	60

256 Institute Emblem

1967. Air. 25th Anniv of Inter-American Institute of Agricultural Sciences.

814	**256**	9c. black and green	45	45
815		25c. red and brown	95	95
816		1q. ultramarine and blue	2·40	2·40

1968. Air. 3rd Meeting of Central American Presidents. Optd **III REUNION DE PRESIDENTES Nov. 15-18, 1967**.

817	**204**	1c. (No. 606)	1·90	1·50
819	–	2c. (No. 607)	70	70
821	–	3c. (No. 608)	70	70
823	**235**	7c. (No. 730)	70	70
824		9c. (No. 731)	70	90
825		13c. (No. 732)	95	90
826		21c. (No. 733)	1·40	70
827		35c. (No. 734)	1·10	1·10

258 "Madonna of the Choir"

260 Miguel Angel Asturias

1968. Air. 400th Anniv of "Madonna of the Choir".

828a	**258**	4c. blue	10	10
829		7c. slate	35	15
830		9c. green	55	15
830a		9c. lilac	25	10
831		10c. red	70	15
832		10c. grey	45	15
832a		10c. blue	25	10
833		1q. purple	2·40	2·00
834		1q. yellow	2·40	2·00

1968. Air. 11th Cycle Race. Nos. 784/6 optd **AEREO XI VUELTA CICLISTICA 1967**.

835	**247**	4c. blue, red and green	55	55
836		5c. blue, red and yellow	55	55
837		6c. blue, grey and orange	45	45

1968. Air. Award of Nobel Prize for Literature to Miguel Angel Asturias.

838	**260**	20c. blue	70	35

1968. Air. Campaign for Conservation of the Forests. No. 789 optd **AYUDA A CONSERVAR LOS BOSQUES.–1968.**

839	**250**	7c. multicoloured	35	15

1968. Air. Human Rights Year. No. 626 optd **1968.– ANO INTERNACIONAL DERECHOS HUMANOS.–ONU.**

840	**210**	6c. brown	55	30

1968. Air. Nahakin Scientific Expedition. No. 589 optd **Expedicion Cientifica** etc.

841		6c. blue and sepia	30	20

264 "Visit Guatemala"

265 Mayan Ball Game Ring and Resplendent Quetzal

1968. Air. Tourism.

842	**264**	10c. red and green	60	25
843		20c. red and black	85	50
844		50c. blue and red	1·25	1·25

1968. Olympic Games, Mexico. Quetzal in green and red.

845	**265**	1c. black	55	20
850		1c. slate	55	20
846		5c. yellow	70	35
851		5c. pink	40	35
852		5c. brown	40	35
853		5c. blue	40	35
847		8c. orange	85	50
848		15c. blue	1·60	70
849		30c. violet	2·75	2·25

1968. Air. 20th Anniv of Federation of Central American Universities. No. 705 optd **CONFEDERACION DE UNIVERSIDADES CENTROAMERICANAS 1948 1968**.

854		4c. slate	30	15

267 Presidents Gustavo Diaz Ordaz and Julio Cesar Mendez Montenegro

1968. Air. Exchange Visits of Mexican and Guatemalan Presidents.

855	**267**	5c. multicoloured	15	15
856		10c. blue and ochre	35	20
857		25c. blue and ochre	55	50

268 I.T.U. Emblem and Symbols

269 Young Girl and Poinsettia

1968. Air. Centenary (1965) of I.T.U.

858	268	7c. blue	20	15
859		15c. black and green	35	15
859a		15c. brown and orange	55	15
860		21c. purple	55	35
861		35c. red and green	70	35
862		75c. green and red	1·40	1·40
863		3q. brown and red	4·50	4·50

1969. Help for Abandoned Children.

864	269	2½c. ochre, red and green	20	10
865		2½c. orange, red and green	20	10
866		5c. black, red and green	30	10
867		21c. violet, red and green	65	55

1969. Air. Nos. 845/9 optd **AEREO** and motifs. Quetzal in green and red.

868	265	1c. black	95	40
869		5c. yellow	1·25	60
870		8c. orange	1·00	1·10
871		15c. blue	1·25	1·25
872		30c. violet	1·75	1·25

271 Dante

273 "Apollo 11" and Moon Landing

272 Map of Central and South America

1969. Air. 700th Birth Anniv (1965) of Dante.

873	271	7c. blue and plum	20	10
874		10c. blue	25	10
875		20c. green	35	15
876		21c. slate and brown	70	25
877		35c. violet and green	1·00	55

1969. Air. 20th Anniv of Latin-American Universities Union.

878	272	2c. mauve and black	15	10
879	–	9c. black and grey	25	15

DESIGN: (26 × 27 mm) 9c. University seal.

1969. Air. 1st Man on the Moon.

881	273	50c. black and purple	1·40	1·40
882		1q. black and blue	2·40	2·50

1970. 50th Anniv of Int Labour Organization. Nos. 847/8 optd **Cincuentenario O.I.T.** and ornaments.

884	265	8c. orange, green and red	50	20
886		15c. blue, green and red	75	30

275 Lake Atitlan

1970. Air. Conservation of Atitlan Grebes. Multicoloured.

888	4c. Type **275**	15	15
889	9c. Family of Atitlan Grebes	3·50	55
890	20c. Young grebe in nest (vert)	5·00	1·40

276 Dr. V. M. Calderon

1970. Air. 1st Death Anniv of Dr. Victor M. Calderon (medical scientist).

892	276	1c. black and blue	15	10
893		2c. black and green	15	10
894		9c. black and yellow	30	15

277 Hand holding Bible

280 Maya Indians and C.A.R.E. Package

279 Arms and Newspaper

1970. Air. 400th Anniv of Spanish Bible.

895	277	5c. multicoloured	15	10

1971. Air. Surch **VALE Q0.50**.

896	268	50c. on 3q. brown and red	1·25	1·25

1971. Air. Stamp Centenary (1st issue) and Centenary of Newspaper "Gaceta de Guatemala".

897	279	2c. blue and red	10	10
899b		5c. brown and red	10	10
899		25c. blue and red	55	35
899c		50c. mauve and brown	90	35

See also Nos. 988/9d.

1971. 25th Anniv of C.A.R.E. (Co-operative for American Relief Everywhere). Mult.

900	1c. Type **280** (black inscr) (postage)	15	10
901	1c. Type **280** (brown inscr)	15	10
902	1c. Type **280** (violet inscr)	15	10
903	2c. Maya porter and C.A.R.E. parcel (air)	15	15
904	5c. Two Maya warriors and parcel	20	20
905	10c. C.A.R.E. parcel within Maya border	35	20

SIZES: 2c. (36 × 30 mm); 50c. (46 × 27 mm); 10c. (28 × 31 mm).

282 J. Rufino Barrios, M. Garcia Granados and Emblems

1971. Air. Centenary of Liberal Reforms.

909	282	2c. multicoloured	60	15
910		10c. multicoloured	1·60	30
911		50c. multicoloured	4·75	3·75
912		1q. multicoloured	9·50	7·50

283 J. A. Chavarry Arrue (stamp engraver) and Leon Bilak (philatelist)

1971. Air. "Homage to Philately".

913	283	1c. black and green	10	10
914		2c. black and brown	15	10
915		5c. black and orange	15	15

1971. Air. "INTERFER 71" Int Fair, Guatemala. Optd **FERIA INTERNACIONAL "INTERFER-71" 30 Oct. al 21 Nov.**

916	207	6c. blue and red	20	15

285 Flag and Map

286 Maya Statue and UNICEF Emblem

1971. Air. 150th Anniv of Central American Independence.

917	285	1c. blue, black and lilac	10	10
918		3c. blue, brown and pink	10	10
919		5c. blue, brown & orange	15	10
920		9c. blue, black and green	25	15

1971. Air. 25th Anniv of UNICEF.

921	286	1c. green	10	10
921a		2c. purple	15	10
922		50c. purple	1·10	1·10
923		1q. blue	2·00	2·00

287 Boeing "Peashooter" and North American P-51 Mustang

1972. Air. 50th Anniv of Guatemala Air Force.

924	287	5c. blue and brown	20	10
925	–	10c. blue	50	20

DESIGN—56 × 32 mm: 10c. Bleriot XI airplane.

289 Ruins of Capuchin Monastery

1972. Air. Tourism. Ruins of Antigua.

927	289	1c. blue and light blue	20	10
928	A	1c. blue and light blue	20	10
929	B	1c. blue and light blue	20	10
930	C	1c. blue and light blue	20	10
931	D	1c. blue and light blue	20	10
932	E	1c. blue and light blue	20	10
933	289	2c. black and brown	15	10
934	A	2c. black and brown	15	10
935	B	2c. black and brown	15	10
936	C	2c. black and brown	15	10
937	D	2c. black and brown	15	10
938	E	2c. black and brown	15	10
939	289	2½c. black, mauve & silver	35	10
940	A	2½c. black, mauve & silver	35	10
941	B	2½c. black, mauve & silver	35	10
942	C	2½c. black, mauve & silver	35	10
943	D	2½c. black, mauve & silver	35	10
944	E	2½c. black, mauve & silver	35	10
945	289	5c. black, blue and orange	70	15
946	A	5c. black, blue and orange	70	15
947	B	5c. black, blue and orange	70	15
948	C	5c. black, blue and orange	70	15
949	D	5c. black, blue and orange	70	15
950	E	5c. black, blue and orange	70	15
951	289	20c. black and yellow	55	35
952	A	20c. black and yellow	55	35
953	B	20c. black and yellow	55	35
954	C	20c. black and yellow	55	35
955	D	20c. black and yellow	55	35
956	E	20c. black and yellow	55	35
957	289	1q. lt blue, red and blue	2·40	1·75
958	A	1q. lt blue, red and blue	2·40	1·75
959	B	1q. lt blue, red and blue	2·40	1·75
960	C	1q. lt blue, red and blue	2·40	1·75
961	D	1q. lt blue, red and blue	2·40	1·75
962	E	1q. lt blue, red and blue	2·40	1·75

DESIGNS: A, "La Recoleccion" archways; B, Cathedral ruins; C, Santa Clara courtyard; D, San Francisco gateway; E, Fountain, Central Park.

See also Nos. 1230/41.

290 Pres. Carlos Arana Osorio

1973. National Census.

963	290	2c. black and blue	10	10
964	–	3c. brown, pink & orange	15	10
965	290	5c. purple, mauve & black	20	10
966	–	8c. green, black & emerald	35	10

DESIGNS—VERT: 3c. Pres. Osorio seated; 8c. Pres. Osorio standing.

291 Francisco Ximenez

1973. International Book Year (1972).

967	291	2c. black and green	10	10
968		3c. brown and orange	10	10
969a		3c. black and yellow	10	10
969		6c. black and blue	20	10

292 Simon Bolivar and Map

293 Eleanor Roosevelt

1973. Air. Simon Bolivar, "The Liberator".

970	292	3c. black and red	10	10
971		3c. blue and orange	10	10
972		5c. black and yellow	15	10
973		5c. black and green	15	10

1973. Air. 90th Birth Anniv (1974) of Eleanor Roosevelt (sociologist).

974	293	7c. blue	15	10

294 Star Emblem

1973. Air. Centenary of Polytechnic School.

975	294	5c. yellow, brown & blue	10	10

See also Nos. 1000/1.

1973. Air. Nos. 927/32 optd **"II Feria Internacional" INTERFER/73 31 Octubre-Noviembre 18 1973 GUATEMALA.**

976	289	1c. blue and light blue	20	10
977	A	1c. blue and light blue	20	10
978	B	1c. blue and light blue	20	10
979	C	1c. blue and light blue	20	10
980	D	1c. blue and light blue	20	10
981	E	1c. blue and light blue	20	10

296 1c. Stamp of 1871

1973. Air. Stamp Centenary (1971). (2nd issue).

988	296	1c. brown	15	10
988a		6c. orange	15	10
988b		6c. green	15	10
988c		6c. blue	15	10
988d		6c. grey	15	10
989		1q. red	1·75	1·75

297 School Building

1973. Air. Centenary of Instituto Varones, Chiquimula.
990 **297** 3c. multicoloured 10 10
991 5c. red and black 15 10

1974. No. 863 surch **Desvalorizadas a Q0.50** and leaves.
992 **268** 50c. on 3q. brown and red 85 70

1974. Air. Centenary of Universal Postal Union. Nos. 927/32 optd **UPU HOMENAJE CENTENARIO 1874 1974** and U.P.U. emblem.
993 **289** 1c. blue and light blue . . 25 20
994 A 1c. blue and light blue . . 25 20
995 B 1c. blue and light blue . . 25 20
996 C 1c. blue and light blue . . 25 20
997 D 1c. blue and light blue . . 25 20
998 E 1c. blue and light blue . . 25 20

300 Barrios and Granados

1974. Air. Centenary (1973) of Polytechnic School (2nd issue).
1000 **300** 6c. red, grey and blue . . 15 10
1001 – 25c. multicoloured . . . 45 20
DESIGN—VERT: 25c. School building.

1974. Air. Protection of the Resplendent Quetzal (Guatemala's national bird). No. 800 surch with bars, **VALE 10c. Proteccion del Ave Nacional el Quetzal** and bird.
1002 **252** 10c. on 11c. black & brn 75 25

302 Costume of San Martin Sacatepequez

1974. Air. Guatemalan Costumes. Mult.
1003 2c. Solola costume 10 10
1004 2½c. Type **302** 10 10
1005 9c. Coban costume 20 10
1006 20c. Chichicastenango costume 35 15

303 Mayan Girl and Resplendent Quetzals

1975. Air. International Women's Year.
1007 **303** 8c. multicoloured 40 15
1008 20c. multicoloured . . . 1·00 50

304 Rotary Emblem

1975. Air. 50th Anniv of Guatemala City Rotary Club.
1009 **304** 10c. multicoloured . . . 15 10
1010 15c. multicoloured . . . 30 15

305 I.W.Y. Emblem and Orchid

1975. Air. International Women's Year (2nd series).
1011 **305** 1c. multicoloured 10 10
1012 8c. multicoloured 15 10
1013 26c. multicoloured . . . 45 20

306 Ruined Village

1976. Air. Earthquake of 4 February 1976. Multicoloured.
1014 1c. Type **306** 10 10
1015 3c. Food queue 10 10
1016 5c. Jaguar Temple, Tikal . . 15 10
1017 10c. Broken bridge 20 10
1018 15c. Open-air casualty station 35 15
1019 20c. Harvesting sugarcane . . 35 15
1020 25c. Ruined house 55 20
1021 30c. Reconstruction, Tecpan . 70 20
1022 50c. Ruined church, Cerrodel Carmen 90 35
1023 75c. Clearing debris . . . . 1·40 55
1024 1q. Military aid . . . . . . 1·75 70
1025 2q. Lake Atitlan . . . . . 3·50 1·40
Text in panels expresses gratitude for foreign aid.

307 Eagle and Resplendent Quetzal Emblems

1976. Air. Bicentenary of American Revolution. Multicoloured.
1029 1c. Type **307** 30 15
1030 2c. Boston Tea Party . . . 10 10
1031 3c. Thomas Jefferson (after G. Stuart) (vert) 10 10
1032 4c. Eagle and resplendent quetzal emblems (vert) . . 30 15
1033 5c. "Death of Gen. Warren at Bunker Hill" (detail, Trumbull) 10 10
1034 10c. "Washington reviewing his Ragged Army" (detail, Trego) 20 10
1035 15c. "Washington rallying the Troops at Monmouth" (detail, Leutze) 20 15
1036 20c. Eagle and resplendent quetzal emblems (diff) . . 50 25
1037 25c. "Meeting of Generals at Yorktown after the Surrender" (detail, Peale) 55 20
1038 30c. "Washington crossing the Delaware" (detail, Leutze) 70 20
1039 35c. Eagle and resplendent quetzal emblems (diff) . . 90 50
1040 40c. "Declaration of Independence" (detail, Trumbull) 60 30
1041 45c. "Patrick Henry before Virginia House of Burgesses" (detail, Rothermel) (vert) 90 35
1042 50c. "Congress voting Independence" (detail, Savage) . . . . 1·00 35
1043 1q. George Washington (after G. Stuart) (vert) . . 1·75 1·50
1044 2q. Abraham Lincoln (after D. D. Eisenhower) (vert) 2·75 2·75
1045 3q. Benjamin Franklin (after C. W. Peale) (vert) . . . 4·00 4·00
1046 5q. John F. Kennedy (35 × 55 mm) . . . . . . 7·00 2·50

308 Quetzal Coin

1976. Air. 50th Anniv of Quetzal Currency.
1051 **308** 8c. black, orange and blue 20 10
1052 20c. black, mauve & blue 45 20

309 "The Engineers" (sculpture)

1976. Air. Centenary of Engineering School, Guatemala City.
1053 **309** 9c. blue 20 10
1054 10c. green 20 10

310 Sculpture of Christ (Pedro de Mendoza)

1977. Holy Week. Multicoloured.
1055 6c. Type **310** (postage) . . . 10 10
1056 8c. Sculpture of Christ (Lanuza Brothers) 15 10
1057 3c. Statue of Christ (air) . . 10 10
1058 4c. Statue of Christ (vert) 10 10
1059 7c. Statue of Christ (vert) 20 10
1060 9c. Statue of Christ (vert) 25 10
1061 20c. Statue of Christ and Virgin (vert) 55 15
1062 26c. Statue of Christ . . . 70 55

311 Deed to Site of Guatemala City

312 Arms of Quetzaltenango

1977. Air. Bicentenary of Nueva Guatemala de la Asuncion (Guatemala City). Multicoloured.
1064 6c. Type **311** 10 10
1065 7c. City Hall and Bank of Guatemala (horiz) 10 10
1066 8c. Site of first legislative assembly (horiz) 10 10
1067 9c. Archbishop's arms (horiz) 10 10
1068 22c. Arms of Guatemala City 30 15

1977. Air. 150th Anniv of Founding of Quetzaltenango.
1071 **312** 7c. black and silver . . . 15 10
1072 – 30c. orange and blue . . 55 20
DESIGN: 30c. City Hall and torch.

313 "Interfer 77" Emblem

315 "The Holy Family"

314 Mayan Bas-relief

1977. 4th International Fair, Guatemala City.
1073 **313** 7c. multicoloured 10 10

1977. Air. 14th Congress of Latin Notaries.
1074 **314** 10c. black and red . . . 20 10

1977. Air. Christmas. Multicoloured.
1075 1c. Type **315** 10 10
1076 2c. Boy and girl with animals, and Jesus in crib 10 10
1077 4c. Boy and girl with Mary and Jesus 15 10

316 Man from Almolongo

317 Virgin of Sorrows, Antigua

1978. Air. Guatemalan Costumes. Mult.
1078 1c. Type **316** 10 10
1079 2c. Woman from Nebaj . . 10 10
1080 5c. Couple from San Juan Cotzal 15 10
1081 6c. Couple from Todos Santos 20 10
1082 20c. Couple from Regidores 70 15
1083 30c. Woman from San Cristobal 70 20

1978. Air. Holy Week. Multicoloured.
1085 2c. Type **317** 10 10
1086 4c. Virgin of Mercy, Antigua 15 10
1087 5c. Virgin of Anguish, Yurrita 15 10
1088 6c. Virgin of the Rosary, Santo Domingo 15 10
1089 8c. Virgin of Sorrows, Santo Domingo 20 10
1090 9c. Virgin of the Rosary, Quetzaltenango 20 15
1091 10c. Virgin of the Immaculate Conception, Church of St. Francis . . 25 15
1092 20c. Virgin of the Immaculate Conception, Cathedral Church 55 20

318 Footballer

319 Gymnastics

1978. Air. World Cup Football Championship, Argentina.
1094 **318** 10c. multicoloured . . . 20 15

1978. Air. 13th Central American and Caribbean Games, Medellin, Colombia.
1095 **319** 6c. mauve, blue and black 10 10
1096 – 6c. brt blue, blue & black 15 10
1097 – 6c. blue, brt blue & black 15 10
1098 – 6c. blue, mauve and black 15 10
1099 – 8c. mauve, blue and black 15 10
DESIGNS: No. 1096, Volleyball; 1097, Target Shooting; 1098, Weightlifing; 1099, Running.

320 "Cattleya pachecoi"

321 University Seal

1978. Air. Orchids. Multicoloured.
1100 1c. Type **320** 10 10
1101 1c. "Sobralia xantholeuca" 10 10
1102 1c. "Cypripedium irapeanum" 10 10
1103 1c. "Oncidium splendidum" 10 10
1104 3c. "Cattleya bowringiana" 10 10
1105 3c. "Encyclia cordigera" . . 10 10
1106 3c. "Epidendrum imatophyllum" 10 10
1107 3c. "Barkeria skinneri" . . 10 10
1108 8c. "Spiranthes speciosa" . . 20 10
1109 20c. "Lycaste skinneri" . . 55 15

1978. Air. 300th Anniv of San Carlos University of Guatemala. Multicoloured.
1110 6c. Type **321** 15 10
1111 7c. Students from different faculties (26 × 46 mm) . . 15 10
1112 12c. 17th-century student . . 20 10
1113 14c. Student and molecular model 30 10

322 Brown and White Children

323 Planting Seedling

1978. Air. Guatemalan Children's Year (1977). Multicoloured.

1114	6c. Type **322**	15	10
1115	7c. Child skipping	15	10
1116	12c. "Helping Hand"	20	10
1117	14c. Hands protecting Indian girl	30	10

1979. Air. Forestry. Multicoloured.

1118	6c. Type **323**	10	10
1119	8c. Burnt forest	15	10
1120	9c. Woodland scene	15	10
1121	10c. Sawmill	15	10
1122	26c. Forest conservation	35	15

324 Ocellated Turkey

325 Clay Jar

1979. Air. Wildlife Conservation. Mult.

1124	1c. Type **324**	70	30
1125	3c. White-tailed deer (horiz)	25	10
1126	5c. King vulture	2·10	30
1127	7c. Great horned owl	4·25	95
1128	9c. Ocelot	55	10

1979. Air. Archaeological Treasures from Tikal. Multicoloured.

1130	2c. Type **325**	10	10
1131	3c. Ceramic head of Mayan woman	10	10
1132	4c. Earring	10	10
1133	5c. Vase	10	10
1134	6c. Ceramic figure	10	10
1135	7c. Carved bone	10	10
1136	8c. Striped vase	15	10
1137	10c. Tripod vase with lid	15	10

326 Presidential Guard Headquarters

327 National Coat of Arms

1979. 30th Anniv of Presidential Guard. Multicoloured.

1138	10c. Type **326** (postage)	15	10
1139	8c. Presidential Guard insignia (air)	15	10

1979. Air. Municipal Arms. Multicoloured.

1140	8c. Type **327**	15	10
1141	8c. Alta Verapaz	15	10
1142	8c. Baja Verapaz	15	10
1143	8c. Chimal Tenango	15	10
1144	8c. Chiquimula	15	10
1145	8c. Escuintla	15	10
1146	8c. Flores (Peten)	15	10
1147	8c. Guatemala	15	10
1148	8c. Huehuetenango	15	10
1149	8c. Izabal	2·50	75
1150	8c. Jalapa	15	10
1151	8c. Jutiapa	15	10
1152	8c. Mazatenango	15	10
1153	8c. El Progreso	15	10
1154	8c. Quezaltenango	15	10
1155	8c. Quiche	15	10
1156	8c. Retalhuleu	15	10
1157	8c. Sacatepequez	15	10
1158	8c. San Marcos	15	10
1159	8c. Santa Rosa	15	10
1160	8c. Solola	15	10
1161	8c. Totonicapan	15	10
1162	8c. Zacapa	15	10

328 Rotary Emblem and Girl with Flowers

329 The Creation of the World

1980. 75th Anniv of Rotary International. Multicoloured.

1164	4c. Type **328**	10	10
1165	6c. Diamond, emblem and resplendent quetzal	40	20
1166	10c. Paul P. Harris (founder), emblem and resplendent quetzal	60	60

1981. Air. "Popol Vuh". Designs showing medallic illustrations of Guatemalan history and legends from the Sacred Book of the Ancient Quiches of Guatemala. (a) The Creation.

1167	**329** 1c. black and mauve	10	10
1168	– 2c. black and green	10	10
1169	– 4c. black and blue	10	10
1170	– 8c. black and yellow	15	10
1171	– 10c. black and pink	15	10
1172	– 22c. black and brown	30	10

(b) The Adventures of Hun Ahpu and Xbalanque.

1173	– 1c. black and mauve	10	10
1174	– 4c. black and violet	10	10
1175	– 6c. black and brown	10	10
1176	– 8c. black and green	15	10
1177	– 10c. black and yellow	15	10
1178	– 26c. black and green	35	10

(c) The Founding of the Quiche Race.

1179	– 2c. black and mauve	10	10
1180	– 4c. black and blue	10	10
1181	– 6c. black and pink	10	10
1182	– 8c. black and yellow	15	10
1183	– 10c. black and green	15	10
1184	– 30c. black and green	45	15

(d) The Territorial Expansion of the Quiches.

1185	– 3c. black and blue	10	10
1186	– 4c. black and violet	10	10
1187	– 6c. black and pink	10	10
1188	– 8c. black and grey	15	10
1189	– 10c. black and green	15	10
1190	– 50c. black and mauve	70	20

DESIGNS: No. 1168, Populating the earth; 1169, Birth of the stick-men; 1170, Destruction of the stick-men; 1171, Creation of the men of corn; 1172, "Thanks to the creator"; 1173, Origin of the twin semi-gods; 1174, Punishment of the Princess Xquic; 1175, Odyssey of Hun Ahpu and Xbalanque; 1176, The test in Xibalba; 1177, Multiplication of the prodigies; 1178, The deification of Hun Ahpu and Xbalanque; 1179, Balam Quitze, father of Caviquib; 1180, Caha Paluma, wife of Balam Quitze; 1181, Balam Acab, father of Nihaibab; 1182, Chomiia, wife of Balam Acab; 1183, Mahucutah, father of Ahau Quiche; 1184, Tzununiha, wife of Mahucutah; 1185, Cotuha, Quiche monarch; 1186, The invincible Cotuha and Iztayul; 1187, Cucumatz, the prodigious king; 1188, Warrior with captive; 1189, "None can conquer or kill the king"; 1190, "This was the greatness of the Quiches".

330 Early and Modern Telephones (cent)

1981. Air. Anniversaries.

1191	– 3c. red and black	10	10
1192	– 5c. blue and black	10	10
1193	**330** 6c. multicoloured	10	10
1194	– 7c. multicoloured	10	10
1195	– 12c. multicoloured	15	10
1196	– 25c. multicoloured	35	10

DESIGNS—26 × 46 mm: 3c. Thomas Edison (centenary of gramophone). 29 × 39 mm: 7c. Charles Lindbergh (50th anniv of solo Atlantic flight); 12c. Jose Cecilio del Valle (patriot, birth bicentenary), 25c. Jesues Castillo (composer, birth centenary). 46 × 26 mm: 5c. Spool of film (50th anniv of sound film).

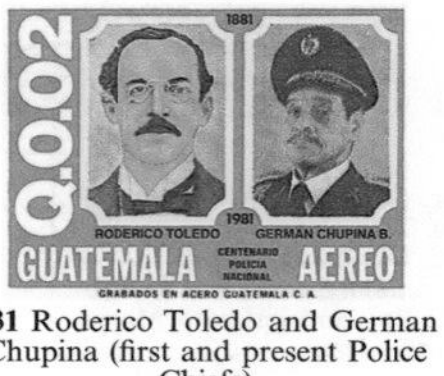

331 Roderico Toledo and German Chupina (first and present Police Chiefs)

1981. Air. Centenary of National Police. Multicoloured.

1197	2c. Type **331**	10	10
1198	4c. Police Headquarters	10	10

332 Mayan Sun Calendar

1981. Air. 7th Latin American Aviculture Congress.

1199	**332** 1c. green, yellow & black	10	10

333 Bernardo O'Higgins (Chile)

1982. Air. Liberators of the Americas.

1200	**333** 2c. multicoloured	10	10
1201	– 3c. multicoloured	10	10
1202	– 4c. multicoloured	10	10
1203	– 10c. grey and black	15	10

DESIGNS—(31 × 45 mm): 4c. Jose de San Martin (Argentine); 10c. Miguel Garcia Granados (Guatemala). (26 × 35 mm): 3c. Jose Artigas (Uruguay).

334 General Barrios and Bank

1982. Air. Centenary of Banco de Occidente.

1204	**334** 1c. multicoloured	10	10
1205	– 2c. black, red and blue	10	10
1206	– 3c. multicoloured	10	10
1207	– 4c. multicoloured	10	10

DESIGNS—HORIZ: 2c. Bank building. VERT: 3c. Centenary emblem; 4c. Centenary medals.

335 Old and New Bank Buildings, Guatemala City

1982. Air. 50th Anniv of National Mortgage Bank.

1208	**335** 1c. multicoloured	10	10
1209	– 2c. black, yellow & green	10	10
1210	– 5c. multicoloured	10	10
1211	– 10c. black, yellow & grn	15	10

DESIGNS—HORIZ: 2c. Bank emblem; 10c. Bank and Anniversary emblems. VERT: 5c. Bronze anniversary medallion.

336 Brother Pedro

337 I.T.U. and W.H.O. Emblems with Ribbons forming Caduceus

1983. Air. Blessed Brother Pedro. Mult.

1212	1c. Type **336**	10	10
1213	20c. Apparition of Virgin Mary	30	10

1983. Air. World Communications and Health Day.

1214	**337** 10c. yellow, red and black	15	10

338 Hands holding Bible

340 F.A.O. Emblem and Starving Children

339 Train crossing Las Vacas Bridge

1983. Air. Centenary (1982) of Evangelical Church in Guatemala. Multicoloured.

1215	3c. Type **338**	10	10
1216	5c. Central Evangelical Church	10	10

1983. Air. Centenary (1980) of Guatemalan Railways. Multicoloured.

1217	10c. Type **339**	75	65
1218	25c. General Barrios and trains at station	2·00	1·50
1219	30c. Train crossing Lake Amatitlan Dam	2·25	1·75

1983. Air. World Food Day (1981). Mult.

1220	8c. Maize and Globe	10	10
1221	1q. Type **340**	95	70

1984. Air. As Nos. 927/32 and 945/50 but colours changed. Values inscribed in black.

1230	**289** 1c. black and green	10	10
1231	A 1c. black and green	10	10
1232	B 1c. black and green	10	10
1233	C 1c. black and green	10	10
1234	D 1c. black and green	10	10
1235	E 1c. black and green	10	10
1236	**289** 5c. black and orange	10	10
1237	A 5c. black and orange	10	10
1238	B 5c. black and orange	10	10
1239	C 5c. black and orange	10	10
1240	D 5c. black and orange	10	10
1241	E 5c. black and orange	10	10

341 Pope John Paul II

1984. Air. Papal Visit. Multicoloured.

1242	4c. Type **341**	10	10
1243	8c. Woman kneeling before Pope	15	10

342 Rafael Landivar

1984. Air. 250th Birth Anniv of Rafael Landivar (poet). Multicoloured.

1244	2c. Type **342**	10	10
1245	4c. Landivar's tomb, Antigua Guatemala (horiz)	10	10

343 Casariego y Acevedo

344 Bank's Emblem

1984. Air. 1st Death Anniv of Cardinal Mario Casariego y Acevedo, Archbishop of Guatemala.

1246	**343** 10c. multicoloured	15	10

1984. Air. 20th Anniv of Central American Bank for Economic Integration.

1247	**344** 30c. multicoloured	50	15

345 Planting Coffee, 1870

1984. Air. Coffee.
1248 **345** 1c. black and brown . . 10 10
1249 – 2c. black and flesh . . . 10 10
1250 – 3c. black and stone . . . 10 10
1251 – 4c. black and buff . . . 30 10
1252 – 5c. multicoloured 10 10
1253 – 10c. multicoloured . . . 15 10
1254 – 12c. multicoloured . . . 15 10
1255 – 25c. multicoloured . . . 1·40 30
1256 – 25c. black and brown . . 35 10
1257 – 30c. multicoloured . . . 40 10
DESIGNS: As T **345**: 2c. Harvesting coffee, 1870; 3c. Drying coffee beans, 1870; 4c. Exporting coffee, 1870; 5c. Grafting seedlings; 10c. Instant coffee; 12c. Harvesting and processing coffee; 25c. (1255) Exporting coffee (different). (81 × 108 mm): 25c. (1256) Women picking coffee. (100 × 81 mm): 30c. Globe and coffee beans.

346 "Beaver" Cub and Tikal Pyramid

1985. Air. 75th Anniv of Boy Scout Movement. Multicoloured.
1258 5c. Type **346** 10 10
1259 6c. "Wolf" cub and Captains Palace, Old Guatemala 10 10
1260 8c. Scout, xylophone player and countryside 15 10
1261 10c. Rover scout and dancers 15 10
1262 20c. Lord Baden-Powell (founder) and Carlos Cipriani (founder of Guatemalan scouts) . . . 30 10

347 Family **348** Emblem

1985. Air. Inter-American Family Year.
1263 **347** 10c. multicoloured . . . 15 10

1985. Air. 25th Anniv of Central American Air Navigation Services Association.
1264 **348** 10c. multicoloured . . . 15 10

349 Morse Key, Samuel Morse, J. Rufino Barrios and Telegraph Aerial

1985. Air. National Telegraph Service.
1265 **349** 4c. black and brown . . 10 10

350 Olympic Rings and Maya Pelota Player

1986. Air. 90th Anniv of First Modern Olympic Games and Foundation of International Olympic Committee. Multicoloured.
1266 8c. Type **350** 15 10
1267 10c. Rings and Baron Pierre de Coubertin 15 10

351 Rescue Team with Person in Cradle

1986. Air. Volunteer Firemen (1st series).
1268 **351** 6c. multicoloured 10 10
See also Nos. 1271/2.

352 Temple of Minerva, Quetzaltenango

1986. Air. Centenary (1984) of Independence Fair, Quetzaltenango. Multicoloured.
1269 8c. Type **352** 15 10
1270 10c. City arms in courtyard of Quetzaltenango Municipal Palace 15 10

353 Fire behind Fireman carrying Child **354** Arms

1986. Air. Volunteer Firemen (2nd series). Multicoloured.
1271 8c. Type **353** 15 10
1272 10c. Searching rubble after explosion (33 × 24 mm) 15 10

1986. Air. 25th Anniv (1976) of Association of Telegraphists and Radio-Telegraph Operators.
1273 **354** 6c. multicoloured 25 15

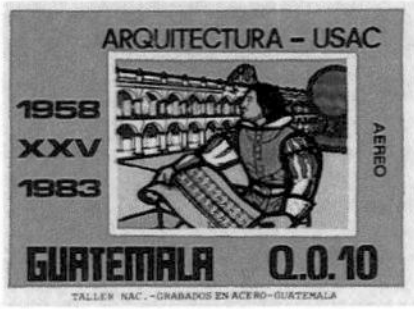

355 Architect with Plans looking at Building

1987. Air. 25th Anniv of San Carlos University Architecture Faculty.
1274 **355** 10c. multicoloured . . . 15 10

356 Emblem and Boeing 727

1987. Air. 40th Anniv of I.C.A.O. Mult.
1275 8c. Type **356** 15 10
1276 10c. Boeing 727 airplane on runway (vert) 15 10

357 Aerial View of Site

1987. Air. Chixoy Hydro-electric Plant.
1277 **357** 2c. multicoloured 10 10

358 Dr. Cayetano Francos y Monroy, Archbishop of Guatemala (founder)

1987. Air. Bicentenary (1981) of St. Joseph Children's College. Multicoloured.
1278 8c. Type **358** 10 10
1279 10c. College emblem 15 10

359 Column beside Man studying Book

1987. Air. Regional Book Promotion Centre for Latin America and Caribbean.
1280 **359** 12c. multicoloured . . . 15 10

360 Girls in Traditional Costumes

1987. Coban Folklore Festival. Mult.
1281 50c. Girl weaving 55 15
1282 1q. Type **360** . . . . 1·25 30

361 Cesar Branas

1987. Air. Writers (1st series).
1283 **361** 6c. orange and black . . 10 10
1284 – 8c. red and black 10 10
1285 – 9c. purple and black . . 15 10
DESIGNS: 8c. Rafael Arevalo Martinez; 9c. Jose Milla y Vidaurre.
See also Nos. 1297/8 and 1307/11.

362 Footballer

1987. Air. Pan-American Games National Football Selection.
1286 **362** 10c. blue and black . . . 15 10

363 Miguel Angel Asturias Cultural Centre **364** Stylized Dove

1987.
1287 **363** 1c. blue 10 10
1287a 2c. brown 10 10
1288 3c. blue 10 10
1289 4c. mauve 10 10
1290 5c. orange 10 10
1291 6c. green 10 10
1292 7c. red 10 10
1293 8c. mauve 10 10
1294 9c. black 10 10
1295 10c. green 15 10

1988. Air. Writers (2nd series). As T **361**.
1297 4c. red and black 10 10
1298 5c. brown and black 10 10
DESIGNS: 4c. Enrique A. Hidalgo; 5c. Enrique Gomez Carrillo.

1988. Air. "Esquipulas II—A Firm Step towards Peace".
1299 **364** 10c. green 15 10
1300 – 40c. red 45 10
1301 – 60c. blue 65 20
DESIGNS—HORIZ: 40c. Three stylized doves. VERT: 60c. Stylized dove.

366 St. John and Boys

1989. Death Centenary of St. John Bosco (founder of Salesian Brothers).
1303 **366** 40c. black and gold . . . 55 15

367 Birds

1989. Air. Bicentenary of French Revolution.
1304 **367** 1q. red, blue and black 90 35

368 Madrid Codex (detail)

1990. Air. America. Pre-Columbian Culture. Multicoloured.
1305 10c. Type **368** 10 10
1306 20c. Tikal Pyramid 10 10

1990. Air. Writers (3rd series). As T **361**.
1307 1c. mauve and black 10 10
1308 2c. orange and black . . . 10 10
1309 3c. blue and black 10 10
1310 7c. black and green 10 10
1311 10c. black and yellow . . . 10 10
DESIGNS: 1c. Flavio Herrera; 2c. Rosendo Santa Cruz; 3c. Werner Ovalle Lopez; 7c. Clemente Marroquin Rojas; 10c. Miguel Angel Asturias.

369 Games Emblem

1990. 6th Central American and Caribbean University Games. Multicoloured.
1312 15c. Type **369** 10 10
1313 20c. Mascot holding flame (vert) 10 10
1314 25c. Mascot playing volleyball 10 10
1315 30c. Mascot playing football 10 10
1316 45c. Mascot performing judo movement 10 10
1317 1q. Mascot playing baseball 25 10
1318 2q. Mascot playing basketball 45 10
1319 3q. Mascot hurdling 70 20

370 Family, Cereal and Emblem

1990. Air. 40th Anniv of Central America and Panama Nutrition Institute.
1320 **370** 20c. multicoloured . . . 10 10

371 Palais de l'Athenee, Geneva (venue of founding meeting)

1990. Air. 125th Anniv (1988) of International Red Cross.
1321 **371** 50c. multicoloured . . . 15 10

372 Arms

1991. Air. Centenary of National Defence Staff.
1322 **372** 20c. multicoloured . . . 10 10

373 Atitlan Lake

1991. America. Natural World. Multicoloured.
1323 10c. Pacaya Volcano in eruption 10 10
1324 60c. Type **373** 15 10

374 Martin and Vicente Pinzon

1992. Air. America. 500th Anniv of Discovery of America by Columbus. Each black and green.
1325 40c. Type **374** 35 15
1326 60c. Christopher Columbus and "Santa Maria" (vert) 40 15

375 Crops

1992. Air. 50th Anniv of International Institute for Agricultural Co-operation.
1327 **375** 10c. multicoloured . . . 10 10

376 Emblem

377 "Encyclia cochleata"

1992. International Anti-AIDS Campaign.
1328 **376** 1q. multicoloured . . . 25 10

1994. Air. Orchids (1st series). Multicoloured.
1329 50c. Type **377** 10 10
1330 1q. "Encyclia vitellina" . . 20 10
1331 2q. "Odontoglossum uroskinneri" 45 10
See also Nos. 1355/6.

378 Family around Tree

1994. 50th Anniv of 20 October Revolution. Multicoloured.
1332 40c. Type **378** 10 10
1333 60c. Dove on hand (horiz) 15 10
1334 1q. Man holding book and rifle 20 10
1335 2q. Representations of social developments since 1944 45 10
1336 3q. Three youths supporting torch ("Revolution, Liberty, Justice and Peace") 65 15

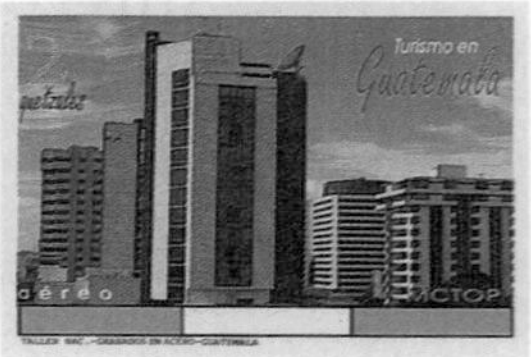

379 City Buildings

1995. Air. Tourism. Multicoloured.
1337 20c. White water rafting . . 10 10
1338 40c. Windsurfing 10 10
1339 60c. Pleasure boat on Lake Atitlan 15 10
1340 80c. Tourist launch "Crucero" 15 10
1341 1q. Erupting volcano . . . 20 10
1342 2q. Type **379** 45 10
1343 3q. Parrots on perch (vert) 65 15
1344 4q. Mayan ruins (vert) . . . 90 20
1345 5q. Ceremony (vert) . . . . 1·10 25

380 Greeting Crowd

1996. Air. Papal Visit. Pope John Paul II. Multicoloured.
1350 10c. Type **380** 10 10
1351 1q. Holding child 20 10
1352 1q.75 Holding crucifix and wearing mitre 35 10
1353 1q.90 Wearing cross and red cloak 40 10
1354 2q.90 Wearing red hat . . . 60 15

1996. Air. Orchids (2nd series). As T **377**. Mult.
1355 20c. "Phragmipedium caudatum" 10 10
1356 1q.50 "Odontoglossum laeve" 30 10

381 Carlos Merida

1996. Air. Personalities.
1357 **381** 40c. lt blue, blue & black 10 10
1358 – 50c. brown, blue & black 10 10
1359 – 60c. brown, blue & black 10 10
DESIGNS: 50c. Jose Eulalio Samayoa; 60c. Manuel Montufar y Coronado.

382 University Hall

1997. Buildings. Multicoloured.
1360 50c. Type **382** 10 10
1361 1q. Brewery 20 10

383 Breastfeeding

1997. Air. Breastfeeding Campaign.
1362 **383** 1q. multicoloured . . . 20 10

384 Parent and Child (Marion Contreras Castanaza)

1997. 50th Anniv (1996) of UNICEF "Children and Peace". Multicoloured.
1363 10c. Type **384** 10 10
1364 20c. Child riding birds (Marvin Sac Coyoy) (horiz) 10 10

385 Child writing (Education)

1997. Air. Public Finance Projects. Mult.
1365 20c. Type **385** 10 10
1366 60c. Child receiving medication (health) . . . 10 10
1367 80c. Road (infrastructure) 15 10
1368 1q. Family (security) 20 10

386 Jorge Rybar (pioneer) and Machinery

1998. Air. 50th Anniv of Guatemala Plastics Industry.
1369 **386** 10c. multicoloured . . . 10 10

387 1875 Postcard and Emblem

1999. Air. 50th Anniv (1998) of El Quetzal (International Society of Guatemala Stamp Collectors).
1370 **387** 1q. multicoloured . . . 20 10

388 Francisco Marroquin (first bishop of Guatemala)

2001. Birth Anniversaries (1999). Multicoloured.
1371 3q. Type **388** (500th anniv) 50 30
1372 4q. Jacinto Rodriguez Diaz (aviation pioneer) (centenary) 65 40
1373 8q.75, Miguel Angel Asturias (Nobel Prize winner for Literature) (centenary) . . . . 1·25 75
1374 10q. Cesar Branas (writer and historian) (centenary) 1·60 1·00

389 Church Architecture, Antigua and Hermano Pedro

2002. Air. 3rd Visit of Pope John Paul II (50c., 2, 5, 8q.75). 12th Anniv Canonisation of Hermano Pedro (monk and humanitarian) (20, 25c., 1q.). Multicoloured.
1375 20c. Type **389** 10 10
1376 25c. Hermano Pedro holding bell rope 10 10
1376 50c. Hermano Pedro and Pope John Paul II (horiz) 10 10
1378 1q. Nativity, his alms bell and Hermano Pedro (head) 15 10
1379 2q. Pope John Paul II and Archbishop Rudolfo Toruno (horiz) 30 20
1380 5q. Fountain, part of door lintel and Pope John Paul II (horiz) 75 45
1381 8q. 75 Pope John Paul II, clock tower and Government Palace (horiz) . . . . 1·25 75
MS1382 153 × 128 mm As Nos. 1375/81 . . . . 2·60 2·60

390 Guatemalan Flag, Globe, Envelopes, Quetzal Bird and Flags

2002. Air. 125th Anniv of Universal Postal Union (1999). Multicoloured.
1383 20c. Type **390** 10 10
1384 2q. UPU emblem 30 20
1385 3q. Globe with map of Americas encircled by bird 40 25
1386 5q. Globe with hands holding envelopes and flags 70 40

391 Mt. Everest

2002. Air. 1st Anniv of Jaime Vinals' Ascent of Everest.
1387 **391** 3q. multicoloured . . . 20 10

392 Children

2002. Air. Centenary of Pan-American Health Organization.
1388 **392** 4q. multicoloured . . . 60 35

EXPRESS LETTER STAMPS.

1940. No. 231 optd **EXPRESO**.
E411 **97** 4c. yellow 85 35

E **181** Motorcyclist

1948. Surch.
E479 E **181** 10c. on 4c. blk & grn . . . 1·00 60

OFFICIAL STAMPS

O **41** O **100**

1902.
O127 O **41** 1c. green . . . . . . 2·50 1·25
O128 2c. red . . . . . . 2·50 1·25
O129 5c. blue . . . . . . 3·00 1·00
O130 10c. purple . . . . . 3·50 1·00
O131 25c. orange . . . . . 3·50 1·00

1929.
O239 O **100** 1c. blue 30 30
O240 2c. sepia 30 30
O241 3c. green 30 30
O242 4c. purple 35 35
O243 5c. lake 35 35
O244 10c. brown 40 40
O245 25c. blue 85 70

1939. Air. Nos. 369/74 optd **OFICIAL OFICIAL.**
O400 **134** 1c. brown and orange 50 75
O401 – 2c. brown and red . . . 50 75
O402 – 3c. brown, buff & green 50 75
O403 – 4c. brown and purple 50 75
O404 – 5c. brown and grey . . 50 75
O405 – 10c. brown and blue . . 50 75

GUERNSEY Pt. 1

An island in the English Channel off N.W. coast of France. Occupied by German Forces from June 1940 to May 1945. "Regional" issues were introduced from 1958 (see after GREAT BRITAIN). The island's postal service was organised as a separate postal administration in 1969.

(a) War Occupation Issues.

1

1941.
1 **1** ½d. green . . . . 3·00 1·50
2 1d. red . . . . 2·00 90
3 2½d. blue . . . . 3·25 4·00

(b) Independent Postal Administration.

4 Castle Cornet and Edward the Confessor

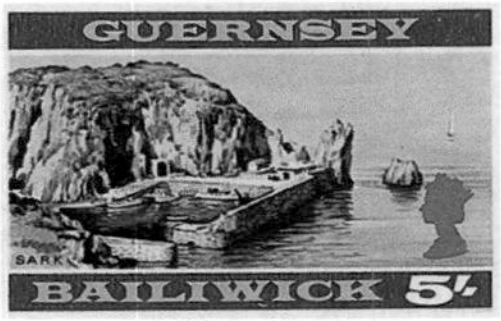

5 View of Sark

1969.
13 **4** ½d. mauve and black . . . 10 10
14 – 1d. blue and black* . . . 10 10
14b – 1d. blue and black* 30 30
15 – 1½d. brown and black . . . 10 10
16 – 2d. multicoloured 10 10
17 – 3d. multicoloured 15 15
18 – 4d. multicoloured 20 25
19 – 5d. multicoloured 20 20
20 – 6d. multicoloured 20 30
21 – 9d. multicoloured 30 30
22 – 1s. multicoloured 30 30
23 – 1s.6d. green and black* . . 25 30
23b – 1s.6d. green and black* . . 2·00 1·75
24 – 1s.9d. multicoloured 80 80
25 – 2s.6d. violet and black . . . 3·25 2·75
26 **5** 5s. multicoloured . . . . . 2·50 2·25
27 – 10s. multicoloured . . . . . 18·00 18·00
28a – £1 multicoloured . . . . . 2·25 2·25

DESIGNS—As Type **4**: 1d. Map and William I; 1½d. Martello tower and Henry II; 2d. Arms of Sark and King John; 3d. Arms of Alderney and Edward III; 4d. Guernsey lily and Henry V; 5d. Arms of Guernsey and Elizabeth I; 6d. Arms of Alderney and Charles II; 9d. Arms of Sark and George III; 1s. Arms of Guernsey and Queen Victoria; 1s.6d., As 1d.; 1s.9d. Guernsey lily and Elizabeth I; 2s.6d. Martello tower and King John. As Type **5**: 10s. View of Alderney; 20s. View of Guernsey.

*On Nos. 14 and 23 the degree of latitude is inscr (incorrectly) as 40° 30' N. On Nos. 14b and 23b it has been corrected to 49° 30'.

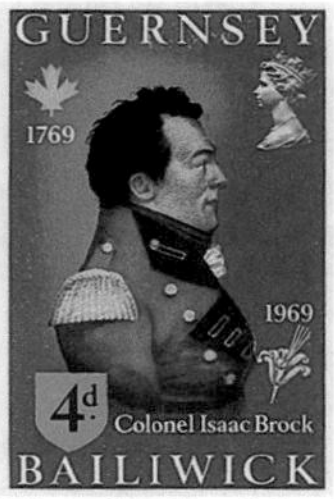

19 Isaac Brock as Colonel

1969. Birth Bicent of Sir Isaac Brock. Mult.
29 4d. Type **19** 20 20
30 5d. Sir Isaac Brock as Major-General 20 20
31 1s.9d. Isaac Brock as Ensign 90 75
32 2s.6d. Arms and flags (horiz) 90 75

23 H.M.S. "L103" (landing craft) entering St. Peter's Harbour

1970. 25th Anniv of Liberation.
33 **23** 4d. blue 20 20
34 – 5d. brown, lake and grey . . 30 20
35 – 1s.6d. brown and buff . . . 1·10 90

DESIGNS—HORIZ: 5d. H.M.S. "Bulldog" and H.M.S. "Beagle" (destroyers) entering St. Peter Port. VERT: 1s.6d. Brigadier Snow reading Proclamation.

26 Guernsey "Toms" **32** St. Peter's Church, Sark

1970. Agriculture and Horticulture. Mult.
36 4d. Type **26** 55 20
37 5d. Guernsey cow 70 20
38 9d. Guernsey bull . . . . . 3·00 1·30
39 1s.6d. Freesias . . . . . . 3·00 2·40

1970. Christmas. Churches (1st series). Mult.
40 4d. St. Anne's Church, Alderney (horiz) 20 10
41 5d. St. Peter's Church (horiz) 20 10
42 9d. Type **32** . . . . 1·00 75
43 1s.6d. St. Tugual Chapel, Herm . . . . 1·00 1·00
See also Nos. 63/6.

34 Martello Tower and King John

1971. Decimal Currency. Nos. 13, etc, but with new colours and decimal values as T **34**.
44 ½p. mauve and black (as No. 13) 10 15
45 1p. blue and black (as No. 14b) 10 10
46 1½p. brown & black (as No. 15) 15 15
47 2p. multicoloured (as No. 18) 15 15
48 2½p. multicoloured (as No. 19) 15 10
49 3p. multicoloured (as No. 17) 20 20
50 3½p. multicoloured (as No. 24) 20 20
51 4p. multicoloured (as No. 16) 20 20
52 5p. green and black (as No. 14b) 20 20
53 6p. multicoloured (as No. 20) 20 20
54 7½p. multicoloured (as No. 22) 30 35
55 9p. multicoloured (as No. 21) 65 65
56a 10p. violet & black (as No. 25) . . . . 1·25 1·25
57 20p. multicoloured (as No. 26) 70 70
58 50p. multicoloured (as No. 27) . . . . 1·25 1·25

35 Hong Kong 2c. of 1862

1971. Thomas De La Rue Commemoration.
59 **35** 2p. purple 35 15
60 – 2½p. red 35 15
61 – 4p. green . . . . 1·10 1·00
62 – 7½p. blue . . . . 1·60 1·50

DESIGNS (Each showing portraits of Queen Elizabeth and Thomas De La Rue): 2½p. Great Britain 4d. of 1855–7; 4p. Italy 5c. of 1862; 7½p. Confederate States 5c. of 1862.

1971. Christmas. Churches (2nd series). As T **32**. Multicoloured.
63 2p. Ebenezer Church, St. Peter Port (horiz) 10 10
64 2½p. Church of St. Pierre du Bois (horiz) 10 10
65 5p. St. Joseph's Church, St. Peter Port . . . . 1·00 1·00
66 7½p. Church of St. Philippe de Torteval . . . . 1·00 1·00

37 "Earl of Chesterfield" (1794)

1972. Mail Packet Ships (1st series). Mult.
67 2p. Type **37** 15 10
68 2½p. "Dasher" (1827) 15 10
69 7½p. "Ibex" (1891) 30 35
70 9p. "Alberta" (1900) 40 50
See also Nos. 80/3.

1972. World Conference of Guernsey Breeders, Guernsey. As No. 38 but size 48 × 29 mm, and additional inscription with face value changed.
71 5p. multicoloured 30 30

39 Bermuda Buttercup

1972. Wild Flowers. Multicoloured.
72 2p. Type **39** 10 10
73 2½p. Heath spotted orchid (vert) 10 10
74 7½p. Kaffir fig 45 40
75 9p. Scarlet pimpernel (vert) . . 50 50

40 Angels adoring Christ **42** "The Good Shepherd"

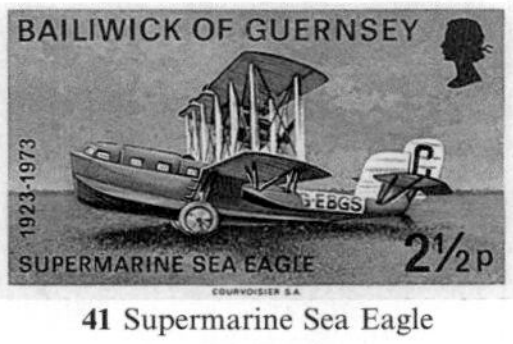

41 Supermarine Sea Eagle

1972. Royal Silver Wedding and Christmas. Stained-glass Windows from Guernsey Churches. Multicoloured.
76 2p. Type **40** 10 10
77 2½p. The Epiphany 15 10
78 7½p. The Virgin Mary 30 25
79 9p. Christ 35 35
See also Nos. 89/92.

1973. Mail Packet Boats (2nd series). As T **37**. Multicoloured.
80 2½p. "St. Julien" (1925) . . . 10 10
81 3p. "Isle of Guernsey" (1930) 20 20
82 7½p. "St. Patrick" (1947) . . . 40 40
83 9p. "Sarnia" (1961) 45 45

1973. 50th Anniv of Air Service. Mult.
84 2½p. Type **41** 10 10
85 3p. Westland Wessex trimotor 10 10
86 5p. De Havilland Dragon Rapide 25 25
87 7½p. Douglas DC-3 . . . . . 30 30
88 9p. Vickers Viscount 800 "Anne Marie" 40 40

1973. Christmas. Stained-glass Windows from Guernsey Churches. Multicoloured.
89 2½p. Type **42** 10 10
90 3p. Christ at the well of Samaria 10 10
91 7½p. St. Dominic 30 30
92 20p. Mary and the Child Jesus 40 40

43 Princess Anne and Capt. Mark Phillips

1973. Royal Wedding.
93 **43** 25p. multicoloured 45 45

44 "John Lockett", 1875

1974. 150th Anniv of Royal National Lifeboat Institution. Multicoloured.
94 2½p. Type **44** 10 10
95 3p. "Arthur Lionel", 1912 . . 10 10
96 8p. "Euphrosyne Kendal", 1954 . . . . 20 20
97 10p. "Arun", 1972 . . . . . 20 25

45 Private, East Regt, 1815 **46** Driver, Field Battery, Royal Guernsey Artillery, 1848

1974. Guernsey Militia. Multicoloured. (a) As T **45**.
98 ½p. Type **45** 10 10
99 1p. Officer, 2nd North Regt, 1825 . . . . 10 10
100 1½p. Gunner, Guernsey Artillery, 1787 . . . . . 10 10
101 2p. Gunner, Guernsey Artillery, 1815 . . . . . 10 10
102 2½p. Corporal, Royal Guernsey Artillery, 1868 10 10
103 3p. Field Officer, Royal Guernsey Artillery, 1895 10 10
104 3½p. Sergeant, 3rd Regt, 1867 . . . . 10 10
105 4p. Officer, East Regt, 1822 10 10
105a 5p. Field Officer, Royal Guernsey Artillery, (1895) 15 15
106 5½p. Colour-Sergeant of Grenadiers, East Regt, 1833 . . . . 10 10
107 6p. Officer, North Regt, 1834 . . . . 10 10
107a 7p. Officer, East Regt, 1822 25 25
108 8p. Field Officer, Rifle Company, 1868 . . . . . 15 10
109 9p. Private, 4th West Regt, 1785 . . . . 15 10
110 10p. Field Officer, 4th West Regt, 1824 . . . . . . 15 10

(b) As T **46**.
111 20p. Type **46** 30 40
112 50p. Officer, Field Battery, Royal Guernsey Artillery, 1868 . . . . 90 1·00
113 £1 Cavalry Trooper, Light Dragoons, 1814 (horiz) . . 1·90 1·75

47 Badge of Guernsey and U.P.U. Emblem

1974. Centenary of U.P.U. Multicoloured.
114 2½p. Type **47** 10 10
115 3p. Map of Guernsey 10 10
116 8p. U.P.U. Building, Berne, and Guernsey flag 20 20
117 10p. "Salle des Etats" 20 20

48 "Cradle Rock"

1974. Renoir Paintings. Multicoloured.
118 3p. Type **48** 10 10
119 5½p. "Moulin Huet Bay" 10 10
120 8p. "Au Bord de la Mer" (vert) 25 25
121 10p. Self-portrait (vert) 25 25

49 Guernsey Spleenwort

50 Victor Hugo House

1975. Guernsey Ferns. Multicoloured.
122 3½p. Type **49** 10 10
123 4p. Sand quillwort 10 10
124 8p. Guernsey quillwort 25 25
125 10p. Least adder's tongue 25 25

1975. Victor Hugo's Exile in Guernsey. Mult.
126 3½p. Type **50** 10 10
127 4p. Candie Gardens (vert) 10 10
128 8p. United Europe Oak, Hauteville (vert) 25 25
129 10p. Tapestry Room, Hauteville 25 25
MS130 114 × 143 mm. Nos. 126/9 65 90

51 Globe and Seal of Bailiwick

1975. Christmas. Multicoloured.
131 4p. Type **51** 10 10
132 6p. Guernsey flag 10 10
133 10p. Guernsey flag and Alderney shield (horiz) 25 25
134 12p. Guernsey flag and Sark shield (horiz) 25 25

52 Les Hanois

1976. Bailiwick Lighthouses. Multicoloured.
135 4p. Type **52** 10 10
136 6p. Les Casquets 10 10
137 11p. Quesnard 20 20
138 13p. Point Robert 25 25

53 Milk Can

1976. Europa.
139 **53** 10p. brown and green 20 20
140 – 25p. grey and blue 40 35
DESIGN: 25p. Christening cup.

54 Pine Forest, Guernsey

1976. Bailiwick Views. Multicoloured.
141 5p. Type **54** 10 10
142 7p. Herm and Jethou 10 10
143 11p. Grand Greve Bay, Sark (vert) 25 25
144 13p. Trois Vaux Bay, Alderney (vert) 25 25

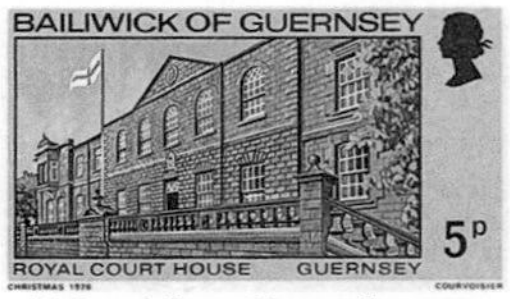

55 Royal Court House, Guernsey

1976. Christmas. Buildings. Multicoloured.
145 5p. Type **55** 10 10
146 7p. Elizabeth College, Guernsey 10 10
147 11p. La Seigneurie, Sark 25 25
148 13p. Island Hall, Alderney 25 25

56 Queen Elizabeth II

58 Statue-menhir, Castel

57 Woodland, Talbot's Valley

1977. Silver Jubilee. Multicoloured.
149 7p. Type **56** 20 15
150 35p. Queen Elizabeth (half-length portrait) 55 40

1977. Europa. Multicoloured.
151 7p. Type **57** 15 15
152 25p. Pastureland, Talbot's Valley 45 45

1977. Prehistoric Monuments. Multicoloured.
153 5p. Type **58** 10 10
154 7p. Megalithic tomb, St. Saviour (horiz) 10 10
155 11p. Cist, Tourgis (horiz) 25 25
156 13p. Statue-menhir, St. Martin 25 25

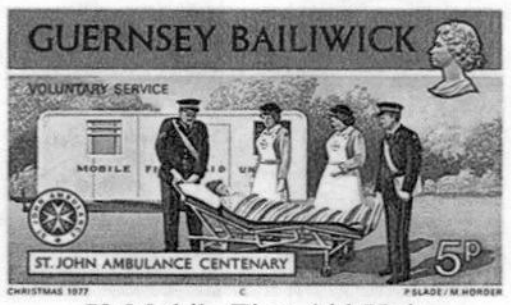

59 Mobile First Aid Unit

1977. Christmas and St. John Ambulance Centenary. Multicoloured.
157 5p. Type **59** 10 10
158 7p. Mobile radar unit 10 10
159 11p. Marine ambulance "Flying Christine II" (vert) 25 25
160 13p. Cliff rescue (vert) 25 25

60 View from Clifton, c. 1830

1978. Old Guernsey Prints (1st series).
161 **60** 5p. black and green 10 10
162 – 7p. black and stone 10 10
163 – 11p. black and pink 25 25
164 – 13p. black and blue 25 25
DESIGNS: 7p. Market Square, St. Peter Port, c. 1838; 11p. Petit-Bo Bay, c. 1839; 13p. The Quay, St. Peter Port, c. 1830.
See also Nos. 249/52.

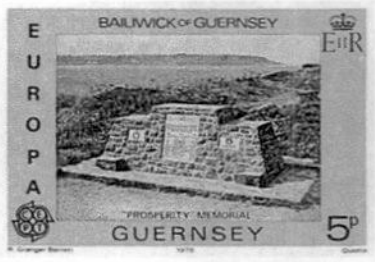

61 "Prosperity" Memorial

62 Queen Elizabeth II

1978. Europa. Multicoloured.
165 5p. Type **61** 10 10
166 7p. Victoria Monument (vert) 25 25

1978. 25th Anniversary of Coronation.
167 **62** 20p. black, grey and blue 30 45

1978. Royal Visit. As T **62**, but inscr "VISIT OF H.M THE QUEEN AND H.R.H THE DUKE OF EDINBURGH JUNE 28–29, 1978 TO THE BAILIWICK OF GUERNSEY".
168 7p. black, grey and green 20 20

63 Northern Gannet

1978. Birds. Multicoloured.
169 5p. Type **63** 10 10
170 7p. Firecrest 15 15
171 11p. Dartford warbler 20 20
172 13p. Spotted redshank 25 20

64 Solanum

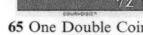

1978. Christmas. Multicoloured.
173 5p. Type **64** 10 10
174 7p. Christmas rose 10 10
175 11p. Holly (vert) 20 20
176 13p. Mistletoe (vert) 25 25

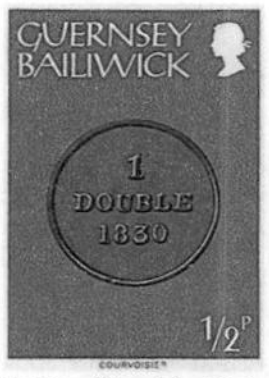

65 One Double Coin, 1830

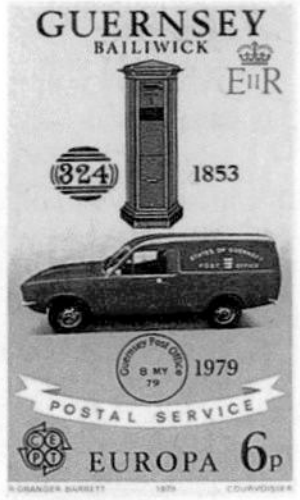

67 Pillar-box and Postmark, 1853, and Mail Van and Postmark, 1979

1979. Coins.
177 **65** ½p. multicoloured 10 10
178 – 1p. multicoloured 10 10
179 – 2p. multicoloured 10 10
180 – 4p. multicoloured 10 10
181 – 5p. black, silver and brown 10 10
182 – 6p. black, silver and red 15 10
183 – 7p. black, silver and green 15 15
184 – 8p. black, silver and brown 15 15
185 – 9p. multicoloured 15 15
186 – 10p. multicoloured (green background) 30 25
187 – 10p. multicoloured (orange background) 20 15
188 – 11p. multicoloured 20 15
189 – 11½p. multicoloured 20 15
190 – 12p. multicoloured 20 15
191 – 13p. multicoloured 25 20
192 – 14p. black, silver and blue 25 20
193 – 15p. black, silver and brown 25 25
194 – 20p. black, silver and brown 30 30
195 – 50p. black, silver and red 85 60
196 – £1 black, silver and green 1·75 1·10
197 – £2 black, silver and blue 3·75 2·00
198 – £5 multicoloured 7·50 6·50

DESIGNS—VERT (As Type **65**): 1p. Two doubles, 1899; 2p. Four doubles, 1902; 4p. Eight doubles, 1959; 5p. Three pence, 1956; 6p. Five new pence, 1968; 7p. Fifty new pence, 1969; 8p. Ten new pence, 1970; 9p. Half new penny, 1971; 10p. (both) One new penny, 1971; 11p. Two new pence, 1971; 11½p. Half penny, 1979; 12p. One penny, 1977; 13p. Two pence, 1977; 14p. Five pence, 1977; 15p. Ten pence, 1977; 20p. Twenty-five pence, 1972. (26 × 45 mm): 50p. William I commemorative 10s., 1966; £5 Seal of the Bailiwick. HORIZ (45 × 26 mm): £1 Silver Jubilee crown, 1977; £2 Royal Silver Wedding crown, 1972.

1979. Europa. Communications. Multicoloured.
201 6p. Type **67** 10 10
202 8p. Telephone, 1897 and telex machine, 1979 20 20

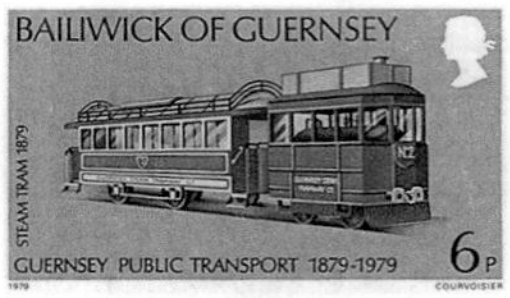

68 Steam Tram, 1879

1979. History of Public Transport. Multicoloured.
203 6p. Type **68** 10 10
204 8p. Electric tram, 1896 15 10
205 11p. Motor bus, 1911 20 15
206 13p. Motor bus, 1979 20 25

69 Bureau and Postal Headquarters

1979. 10th Anniv of Guernsey Postal Administration. Multicoloured.
207 6p. Type **69** 10 10
208 8p. "Mails and telegrams" 15 10
209 13p. "Parcels" 20 15
210 15p. "Philately" 25 25
MS211 120 × 80 mm. Nos. 207/10 80 80

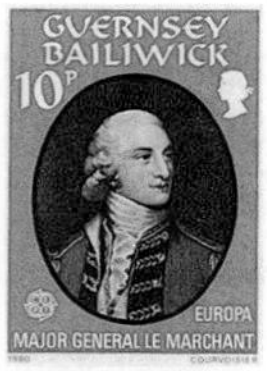

70 Major-General Le Marchant

1980. Europa. Personalities. Multicoloured.
212 10p. Type **70** 15 15
213 13½p. Admiral Lord de Saumarez 30 25

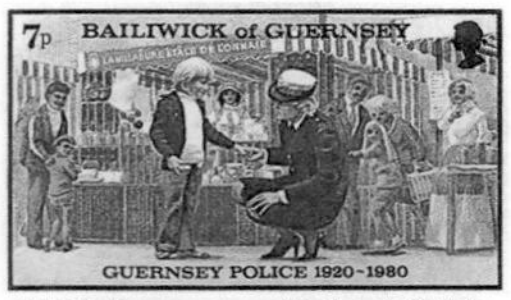

71 Policewoman with Lost Child

1980. 60th Anniv of Guernsey Police Force. Mult.
214 7p. Type **71** 15 15
215 15p. Motorcycle escort 25 25
216 17½p. Dog-handler 30 25

72 Golden Guernsey Goat

1980. Golden Guernsey Goats. Multicoloured.
217 7p. Type **72** 10 10
218 10p. Head of goat 20 15
219 15p. Goat 25 20
220 17½p. Goat and kids 40 35

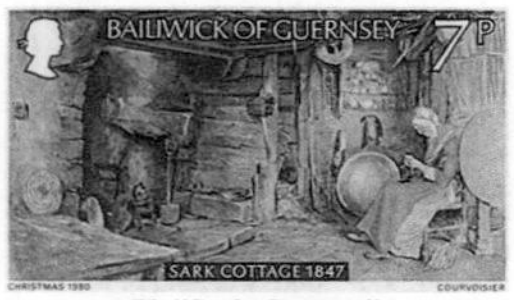

73 "Sark Cottage"

1980. Peter Le Lievre Paintings. Multicoloured.
221 7p. Type **73** 15 10
222 10p. "Moulin Huet" 20 15

223 13½p. "Boats at Sea" 25 20
224 15p. "Cow Lane" (vert) . . . 25 25
225 17½p. "Peter Le Lievre" (vert) 40 35

74 "Polyommatus icarus"

1981. Butterflies. Multicoloured.
226 8p. Type **74** 15 15
227 12p. "Vanessa atalanta" . . . 20 20
228 22p. "Aglais urticae" 35 35
229 25p. "Lasiommata megera" 40 40

75 Sailors paying respect to "Le Petit Bonhomme Andriou" (rock resembling head of a man)

76 Prince Charles

1981. Europa. Folklore.
230 **75** 12p. gold, brown & lt brn 25 15
231 – 18p. gold, blue and light blue 30 30
DESIGN: 18p. Fairies and Guernsey lily.

1981. Royal Wedding. Multicoloured.
232 8p. Type **76** 15 10
233 8p. Prince Charles and Lady Diana Spencer 15 10
234 8p. Lady Diana 15 10
235 12p. Type **76** 25 25
236 12p. As No. 233 . . . . . 25 30
237 12p. As No. 234 . . . . . . 25 30
238 25p. Royal Family (49 × 32 mm) 65 60
MS239 104 × 127 mm. Nos. 232/8 3·00 2·75

77 Sark Launch

1981. Inter-island Transport. Multicoloured.
240 8p. Type **77** 15 15
241 12p. Britten Norman "short nose" Trislander airplane 25 20
242 18p. Hydrofoil 30 30
243 22p. Herm catamaran 45 45
244 25p. "Sea Trent" (coaster) . . 55 55

78 Rifle Shooting

1981. Int Year for Disabled Persons. Mult.
245 8p. Type **78** 15 10
246 12p. Riding 25 20
247 22p. Swimming 45 35
248 25p. Circuit construction . . . 55 40

1982. Old Guernsey Prints (2nd series). Prints from Sketches by T. Compton. As T **60**.
249 8p. black and blue 15 15
250 12p. black and green 25 20
251 22p. black and brown 40 40
252 25p. black and lilac 50 50
DESIGNS: 8p Jethou; 12p. Fermain Bay; 22p. The Terres; 25p. St. Peter Port.

79 Sir Edgar MacCulloch (founder-president) and Guille-Alles Library, St. Peter Port

1982. Cent of La Societe Guernesiaise. Mult.
253 8p. Type **79** 15 15
254 13p. French invasion fleet crossing English Channel, 1066 ("history") 25 15
255 20p. H.M.S "Crescent", 1793 ("history") 40 25
256 24p. Dragonfly ("entomology") 50 40
257 26p. Common snipe caught for ringing ("ornithology") 55 50
258 29p. Samian bowl, 160–200 A.D. ("archaeology"). . . 60 55
The 13p. and 20p. designs also include the Europa C.E.P.T. emblem.

80 "Sea Scouts"

82 Flute Player and Boats

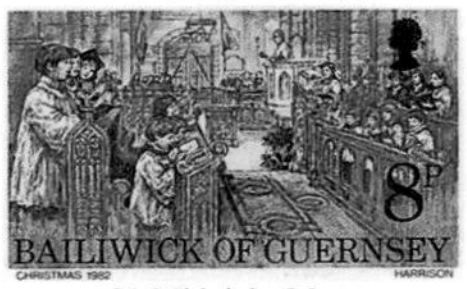

81 Midnight Mass

1982. 75th Anniv of Boy Scout Movement. Mult.
259 8p. Type **80** 15 25
260 13p. "Scouts" 30 25
261 26p. "Cub Scouts" 55 50
262 29p. "Air Scouts" . . . . . 65 1·10

1982. Christmas. Multicoloured.
263 8p. Type **81** 15 15
264 13p. Exchanging gifts 25 15
265 24p. Christmas meal 50 45
266 26p. Exchanging cards . . . 55 50
267 29p. Queen's Christmas message 65 55

1982. Centenary of Boys' Brigade. Multicoloured.
268 8p. Type **82** 15 10
269 13p. Cymbal player and tug o' war 25 20
270 24p. Trumpet player and bible class 40 40
271 26p. Drummer and cadets marching 55 50
272 29p. Boys' Brigade band . . 65 55

83 Building Albert Pier Extension, 1850s

1983. Europa. Development of St. Peter Port Harbour. Multicoloured.
273 13p. Type **83** 20 15
274 13p. St. Peter Port harbour, 1983 . . . . 20 15
275 20p. St. Peter Port, 1680 . . 30 30
276 20p. Artist's impression of future development scheme 30 30

84 "View at Guernsey" (Renoir)

1983. Cent of Renoir's Visit to Guernsey. Mult.
277 9p. Type **84** 20 15
278 13p. "Children on the Seashore" (25 × 39 mm) . . 25 25
279 26p. "Marine, Guernesey" . . 55 50
280 28p. "La Bale du Moulin Huet a travers les Arbres" 85 80
281 31p. "Brouillard a Guernesey" . . . . 1·00 90

85 Launching "Star of the West", 1869, and Capt. J. Lenfestey

1983. Guernsey Shipping (1st series). Mult.
282 9p. Type **85** 20 20
283 13p. Leaving St. Peter Port 25 15
284 26p. Off Rio Grande Bar . . 50 50
285 28p. Off St. Lucia 80 75
286 31p. Map of 1879–80 voyage 85 80
See also Nos. 415/19.

86 Dame of Sark as Young Woman

1984. Birth Centenary of Sibyl Hathaway, Dame of Sark. Multicoloured.
287 9p. Type **86** 20 20
288 13p. German occupation, 1940–45 . . . . 30 15
289 26p. Royal visit, 1957 . . . . 70 55
290 28p. Chief Pleas 75 70
291 31p. The Dame of Sark rose 80 75

87 C.E.P.T. 25th Anniversary Logo

1984. Europa.
292 **87** 13p. light blue, blue & black 25 15
293 20½p. green, dp green & blk 55 50

88 The Royal Court and St. George's Flag

89 St. Apolline Chapel

1984. Links with the Commonwealth. Mult.
294 9p. Type **88** 20 15
295 31p. Castle Cornet and Union flag 85 85

1984. Views. Multicoloured.
296 1p. Little Chapel 10 10
297 2p. Fort Grey (horiz) . . . 10 10
298 3p. Type **89** 10 10
299 4p. Petit Port (horiz) . . . 10 10
300 5p. Little Russel (horiz) . . 15 10
301 6p. The Harbour, Herm (horiz) 15 15
302 7p. Saints (horiz) 15 15
303 8p. St. Saviour 20 15
304 9p. New Jetty (inscr "Cambridge Berth") (horiz) 20 10
305 10p. Belvoir, Herm (horiz) 25 15
306 11p. La Seigneurie, Sark (horiz) 25 15
306b 12p. Petit Bot 35 15
307 13p. St. Saviours reservoir (horiz) 25 25
308 14p. St. Peter Port 25 20
309 15p. Havelet 30 30
309c 16p. Hostel of St. John (horiz) 30 20
309d 18p. Le Variouf 30 20
310 20p. La Coupee, Sark (horiz) 45 25
310b 21p. King's Mills (horiz) . . 45 30
310c 26p. Town Church 70 50
311 30p. Grandes Rocques (horiz) 65 60
312 40p. Torteval Church . . . 70 70
313 50p. Bordeaux (horiz) . . . 80 75
314 £1 Albecq (horiz) . . . . . 1·90 1·40
315 £2 L' Ancresse (horiz) . . . 3·75 2·75
See also Nos. 398/9a.

90 "A Partridge in a Pear Tree"

91 Sir John Doyle and Coat of Arms

1984. Christmas. "The Twelve Days of Christmas". Multicoloured.
316 5p. Type **90** 15 15
317 5p. "Two turtle doves" . . . 15 15
318 5p. "Three French hens" . . 15 15
319 5p. "Four colly birds" . . . 15 15
320 5p. "Five gold rings" 15 15
321 5p. "Six geese a-laying" . . . 15 15
322 5p. "Seven swans a-swimming" 15 15
323 5p. "Eight maids a-milking" 15 15
324 5p. "Nine drummers drumming" 15 15
325 5p. "Ten pipers piping" . . . 15 15
326 5p. "Eleven ladies dancing" 15 15
327 5p. "Twelve lords a-leaping" 15 15

1984. 150th Death Anniv of Lt.-General Sir John Doyle. Multicoloured.
328 13p. Type **91** 30 25
329 29p. Battle of Germantown, 1777 (horiz) 65 60
330 31p. Reclamation of Braye du Valle, 1806 (horiz) . . . 75 70
331 34p. Mail for Alderney, 1812 (horiz) 90 85

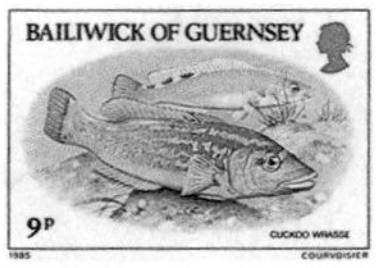

92 Cuckoo Wrasse

1985. Fishes. Multicoloured.
332 9p. Type **92** 30 25
333 13p. Red gurnard 40 25
334 29p. Red mullet . . . . . . 1·00 90
335 31p. Mackerel . . . . 1·00 90
336 34p. Oceanic sunfish . . . . 1·10 90

93 Dove

1985. 40th Anniv of Peace in Europe.
337 **93** 22p. multicoloured 60 50

94 I.Y.Y. Emblem and Young People of Different Races

1985. International Youth Year. Multicoloured.
338 9p. Type **94** 25 15
339 31p. Girl Guides cooking over campfire 75 70

95 Stave of Music enclosing Flags

1985. Europa. European Music Year. Multicoloured.
340 14p. Type **95** 30 25
341 22p. Stave of music and musical instruments . . . 60 55

96 Guide Leader, Girl Guide and Brownie

97 Santa Claus

1985. 75th Anniv of Girl Guide Movement.
342 **96** 34p. multicoloured . . . . 1·00 90

1985. Christmas. Gift-bearers. Multicoloured.
343 5p. Type **97** 25 15
344 5p. Lussibruden (Sweden) . . 25 15
345 5p. King Balthazar 25 15
346 5p. Saint Nicholas (Netherlands) 25 15
347 5p. La Befana (Italy) 25 15
348 5p. Julenisse (Denmark) . . . 25 15
349 5p. Christkind (Germany) . . 25 15
350 5p. King Wenceslas (Czechoslovakia) 25 15
351 5p. Shepherd of Les Baux (France) 25 15
352 5p. King Caspar 25 15
353 5p. Baboushka (Russia) . . . 25 15
354 5p. King Melchior 25 15

98 "Vraicing"

1985. Paintings by Paul Jacob Naftel. Multicoloured.
355 9p. Type **98** 20 20
356 14p. "Castle Cornet" 25 25
357 22p. "Rocquaine Bay" . . . 65 65
358 31p. "Little Russel" . . . . 1·00 1·00
359 34p. "Seaweedgatherers" . . 1·25 1·25

99 Squadron off Nargue Island, 1809

100 Profile of Queen Elizabeth II (after R. Maklouf)

1986. 150th Death Anniv of Admiral Lord De Saumarez. Multicoloured.
360 9p. Type **99** 30 25
361 14p. Battle of the Nile, 1798 40 30
362 29p. Battle of St. Vincent, 1797 . . . . 75 70
363 31p. H.M.S "Crescent" off Cherbourg, 1793 . . . . . 1·00 95
364 34p. Battle of the Saints, 1782 . . . . 1·00 1·00

1986. 60th Birthday of Queen Elizabeth II.
365 **100** 60p. multicoloured . . . 1·50 1·25

101 Northern Gannet and Nylon Net ("Operation Gannet")

102 Prince Andrew and Miss Sarah Ferguson

1986. Europa. Nature and Environmental Protection. Multicoloured.
366 10p. Type **101** 30 30
367 14p. Loose-flowered orchid 40 40
368 22p. Guernsey elm 70 70

1986. Royal Wedding. Multicoloured.
369 14p. Type **102** 60 50
370 34p. Prince Andrew and Miss Sarah Ferguson (different) (47 × 30 mm) . . . . . . 1·00 90

103 Bowls

105 "While Shepherds Watched their Flocks by Night"

104 Guernsey Museum and Art Gallery, Candie Gardens

1986. Sport in Guernsey. Multicoloured.
371 10p. Type **103** 25 20
372 14p. Cricket 35 20
373 22p. Squash 50 45
374 29p. Hockey 90 80
375 31p. Swimming (horiz) . . . 90 80
376 34p. Shooting (horiz) . . . . 1·00 90

1986. Cent of Guernsey Museums. Mult.
377 14p. Type **104** 30 15
378 29p. Fort Grey Maritime Museum 85 80
379 31p. Castle Cornet 85 80
380 34p. National Trust of Guernsey Folk Museum . . 1·00 90

1986. Christmas. Carols. Multicoloured.
381 6p. Type **105** 20 20
382 6p. "In The Bleak Midwinter" 20 20
383 6p. "O Little Town of Bethlehem" 20 20
384 6p. "The Holly and the Ivy" 20 20
385 6p. "O Little Christmas Tree" 20 20
386 6p. "Away in a Manger" . . 20 20
387 6p. "Good King Wenceslas" 20 20
388 6p. "We Three Kings of Orient Are" 20 20
389 6p. "Hark the Herald Angels Sing" 20 20
390 6p. "I Saw Three Ships" . . 20 20
391 6p. "Little Donkey" 20 20
392 6p. "Jingle Bells" 20 20

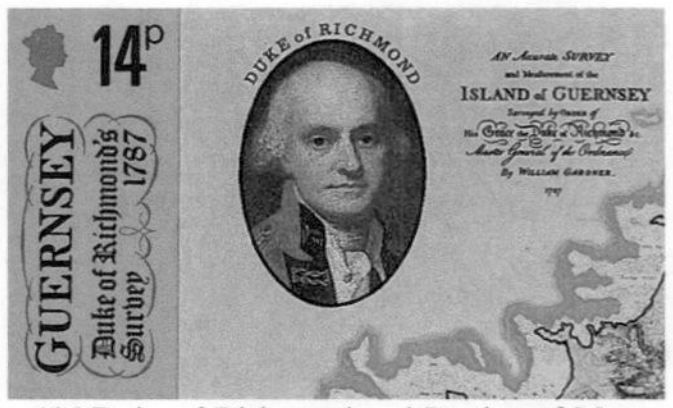

106 Duke of Richmond and Portion of Map

1987. Bicentenary of Duke of Richmond's Survey of Guernsey. Sheet 134 × 103 mm containing T **106** and similar horiz designs showing sections of map. Multicoloured.
MS393 14p. Type **106**; 29p. North-east; 31p. South-west; 34p. South-east . . . . 2·50 2·75
The stamps within No. **MS**393 show a composite design of the Duke of Richmond's map of Guernsey.

107 Post Office Headquarters

108 Sir Edmund Andros and La Plaiderie, Guernsey

1987. Europa. Modern Architecture. Mult.
394 15p. Type **107** 25 20
395 15p. Architect's elevation of Post Office Headquarters 25 20
396 22p. Guernsey Grammar School 30 35
397 22p. Architect's elevation of Grammar School 30 35

1987. Designs as Nos. 306, 306b, 309 and 309c but smaller.
398 11p. La Seigneurie, Sark (22 × 18 mm) 50 50
398a 12p. Petit Bot (18 × 22 mm) 40 40
399 15p. Havelet (18 × 22 mm) 60 60
399a 16p. Hostel of St. John (22 × 18 mm) 50 50

1987. 350th Birth Anniv of Sir Edmund Andros (colonial administrator). Multicoloured.
400 15p. Type **108** 30 15
401 29p. Governor's Palace, Virginia 80 60
402 31p. Governor Andros in Boston 85 75
403 34p. Map of New Amsterdam (New York), 1661 . . . . 1·10 1·00

109 The Jester's Warning to Young William

110 John Wesley preaching on the Quay, Alderney

1987. 900th Death Anniv of William the Conqueror. Multicoloured.
404 11p. Type **109** 20 15
405 15p. Hastings battlefield . . . 30 25
406 15p. Norman soldier with pennant 30 25
407 22p. William the Conqueror 60 60
408 22p. Queen Matilda and Abbaye aux Dames, Caen 60 60
409 34p. William's coronation regalia and Halley's Comet 1·00 1·10

1987. Bicentenary of John Wesley's Visit to Guernsey. Multicoloured.
410 7p. Type **110** 20 15
411 15p. Wesley preaching at Mon Plaisir, St. Peter Port 25 25
412 29p. Preaching at Assembly Rooms 80 75
413 31p. Wesley and La Ville Baudu (early Methodist meeting place) 90 85
414 34p. Wesley and first Methodist Chapel, St. Peter Port 90 85

111 "Golden Spur" off St. Sampson Harbour

1988. Guernsey Shipping (2nd series). "Golden Spur". Multicoloured.
415 11p. Type **111** 25 25
416 15p. "Golden Spur" entering Hong Kong harbour . . . 35 35
417 29p. Anchored off Macao . . 90 85
418 31p. In China Tea Race . . . 90 85
419 34p. "Golden Spur" and map showing voyage of 1872–74 95 95

112 Rowing Boat and Bedford "Rascal" Mail Van

1988. Europa. Transport and Communications. Multicoloured.
420 16p. Type **112** 35 35
421 16p. Rowing boat and Vickers Viscount mail plane 35 35
422 22p. Postman on bicycle and horse-drawn carriages, Sark 70 70
423 22p. Postmen on bicycles and carriage 70 70
Nos. 420/1 and 422/3 were each printed together, se-tenant, the two stamps of each value forming a composite design.

113 Frederick Corbin Lukis and Lukis House, St. Peter Port

1988. Birth Bicentenary of Frederick Corbin Lukis (archaeologist). Multicoloured.
424 12p. Type **113** 25 25
425 16p. Natural history books and reconstructed pot . . . 30 25
426 29p. Lukis directing excavation of Le Creux es Faies and prehistoric beaker 90 85
427 31p. Lukis House Observatory and garden . . 90 85
428 34p. Prehistoric artifacts . . 90 90

114 "Cougar", "Rocky" and "Annabella" (powerboats) and Westland Wessex Rescue Helicopter off Jethou

1988. World Offshore Powerboat Championships. Multicoloured.
429 16p. Type **114** 35 25
430 30p. "Poul Pilot" (powerboat) in Gouliot Passage 85 85
431 32p. Start of race at St. Peter Port (vert) . . . . 1·00 90
432 35p. Admiralty chart showing course (vert) . . . . 1·10 1·00

115 Joshua Gosselin and Herbarium

116 Coutances Cathedral, France

1988. Bicentenary of Joshua Gosselin's "Flora Sarniensis". Multicoloured.
433 12p. Type **115** 25 25
434 16p. Hares-tail grass 40 35
435 16p. Dried hares-tail grass . . 40 35
436 23p. Variegated catchfly . . . 55 50
437 23p. Dried variegated catchfly 55 50
438 35p. Rock sea lavender . . . 1·00 1·00

1988. Christmas. Ecclesiastical Links. Mult.
439 8p. Type **116** 20 20
440 8p. Interior of Notre Dame du Rosaire Church, Guernsey 20 20
441 8p. Stained glass, St. Sampson's Church, Guernsey 20 20
442 8p. Dol-de-Bretagne Cathedral, France 20 20
443 8p. Bishop's throne, Town Church, Guernsey . . . 20 20
444 8p. Winchester Cathedral . . 20 20
445 8p. St. John's Cathedral, Portsmouth 20 20
446 8p. High altar, St. Joseph's Church, Guernsey . . . 20 20
447 8p. Mont Saint-Michel, France 20 20
448 8p. Chancel, Vale Church, Guernsey 20 20
449 8p. Lychgate, Forest Church, Guernsey 20 20
450 8p. Marmoutier Abbey, France 20 20

117 Le Cat (Tip Cat)

118 Outline Map of Guernsey

1989. Europa. Children's Toys and Games. Multicoloured.
451 12p. Type **117** 25 20
452 16p. Girl with Cobo Alice doll 40 40
453 23p. Le Colimachaon (hopscotch) 80 85

1989. Coil Stamp. No value expressed.
454 **118** (–) blue 60 60
455 (–) green 65 70
No. 454 is inscribed "MINIMUM BAILIWICK POSTAGE PAID" and No. 455 "MINIMUM FIRST CLASS POSTAGE TO UK PAID". They were initally sold at 14p. and 18p. but this was changed in line with postage rate rises.

119 Guernsey Airways De Havilland Dragon Express and Mail Van

1989. 50th Anniv of Guernsey Airport (Nos. 456, 458 and 460) and 201 Squadron's Affiliation with Guernsey (Nos. 457, 459 and 461). Mult.
456 12p. Type **119** 35 30
457 12p. Supermarine Southampton II flying boat at mooring 35 30
458 18p. B.E.A. De Havilland Rapide 50 50
459 18p. Short S.25 Sunderland Mk V flying boat taking off 50 50
460 35p. Air U.K. British Aerospace BAe 146 . . . . 1·00 90
461 35p. Avro Shackleton M.R.3 1·00 1·00

120 "Queen Elizabeth II" (June Mendoza)

122 Two-toed Sloth

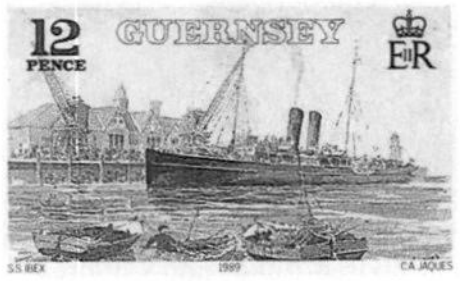

121 "Ibex" at G.W.R. Terminal, St. Peter Port

1989. Royal Visit.
462 **120** 30p. multicoloured . . . 75 80

1989. Centenary of Great Western Railway Steamer Service to Channel Islands. Multicoloured.
463 12p. Type **121** 20 20
464 18p. "Great Western" (paddle-steamer) in Little Russel 45 45
465 29p. "St. Julien" passing Casquets Light 70 75
466 34p. "Roebuck" off Portland 90 95
467 37p. "Antelope" and boat train on Weymouth Quay 1·10 1·10
MS468 115 × 117 mm. Nos. 463/7 3·00 3·25

1989. 10th Anniv of Guernsey Zoological Trust. Animals of the Rainforest. Multicoloured.
469 18p. Type **122** 70 70
470 29p. Capuchin monkey . . . 70 70
471 32p. White-lipped tamarin . . 70 70
472 34p. Common squirrel-monkey 70 70
473 37p. Common gibbon 70 70

123 Star

125 Penny Black and Mail Steamer off St. Peter Port, 1840

124 Sark Post Office, c. 1890

1989. Christmas. Christmas Tree Decorations. Multicoloured.
474 10p. Type **123** 25 20
475 10p. Fairy 25 20
476 10p. Candles 25 20
477 10p. Bird 25 20
478 10p. Present 25 20
479 10p. Carol-singer 25 20
480 10p. Christmas cracker . . . 25 20
481 10p. Bauble 25 20
482 10p. Christmas stocking . . . 25 20
483 10p. Bell 25 20
484 10p. Fawn 25 20
485 10p. Church 25 20

1990. Europa. Post Office Buildings.
486 **124** 20p. deep brown, sepia and light brown 45 45
487 – 20p. multicoloured . . . 45 45
488 – 24p. deep brown, sepia and light brown 60 65
489 – 24p. multicoloured . . . 60 65
DESIGNS: No. 487, Sark Post Office, 1990; 488, Arcade Post Office counter, St. Peter Port, c. 1840; 489, Arcade Post Office counter, St. Peter Port, 1990.

1990. 150th Anniv of the Penny Black. Mult.
490 14p. Type **125** 35 35
491 20p. Penny Red, 1841 and pillar box of 1853 . . . . 45 45
492 32p. Bisected 2d., 1940 and German Army band . . . 80 80
493 34p. Regional 3d., 1958 and Guernsey emblems . . . . 1·00 1·00
494 37p. Independent postal administration 1½d., 1969 and queue outside Main Post Office . . . . 1·00 1·00
MS495 151 × 116 mm. Nos. 490/4 3·00 3·50
No. **MS**495 also commemorates "Stamp World London '90" International Stamp Exhibition.

126 Lt. Philip Saumarez writing Log Book

1990. 250th Anniv of Anson's Circumnavigation. Multicoloured.
496 14p. Type **126** 30 30
497 20p. Anson's squadron leaving Portsmouth, 1740 40 40
498 29p. Ships at St. Catherine's Island, Brazil 80 80
499 34p. H.M.S. "Tryal" (sloop) dismasted, Cape Horn, 1741 . . . . 90 90
500 37p. Crew of H.M.S. "Centurion" on Juan Fernandez 95 90

127 Grey Seal and Pup

1990. Marine Life. Multicoloured.
501 20p. Type **127** 45 45
502 26p. Bottle-nosed dolphin . . 95 95
503 31p. Basking shark . . . . . 1·00 1·00
504 37p. Common porpoise . . . 1·25 1·25

128 Blue Tit and Great Tit

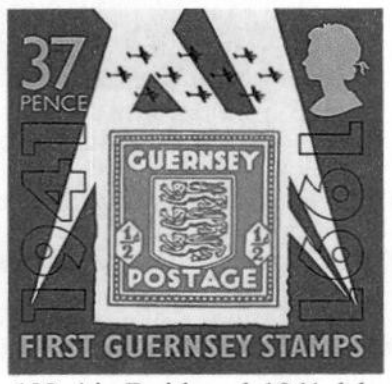

129 Air Raid and 1941 ½d. Stamp

1990. Christmas. Winter Birds. Multicoloured.
505 10p. Type **128** 35 30
506 10p. Snow bunting 35 30
507 10p. Common kestrel ("Kestrel") 35 30
508 10p. Common starling ("Starling") 35 30
509 10p. Western greenfinch ("Greenfinch") 35 30
510 10p. European robin ("Robin") 35 30
511 10p. Winter wren 35 30
512 10p. Barn owl 35 30
513 10p. Mistle thrush 35 30
514 10p. Grey heron ("Heron") . . 35 30
515 10p. Chaffinch 35 30
516 10p. River kingfisher ("Kingfisher") 35 30

1991. 50th Anniv of First Guernsey Stamps. Multicoloured.
517 37p. Type **129** . . . . 1·00 1·10
518 53p. 1941 1d. stamp . . . . 1·30 1·50
519 57p. 1944 2½d. stamp . . . . 1·30 1·50

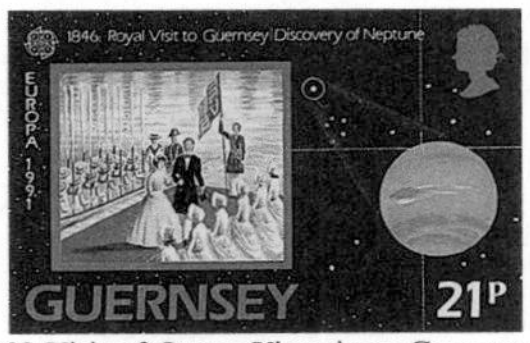

130 Visit of Queen Victoria to Guernsey, and Discovery of Neptune, 1846

1991. Europa. Europe in Space. Multicoloured.
520 21p. Type **130** 55 50
521 21p. Visit of Queen Elizabeth II and Prince Philip to Sark, and "Sputnik" (first artificial satellite), 1957 . . . . . . 55 50
522 26p. Maiden voyage of "Sarnia" (ferry) and "Vostok I" (first manned space flight), 1961 . . . 65 60
523 26p. Cancelling Guernsey stamps, and first manned landing on Moon, 1969 . . 65 60

131 Children in Guernsey Sailing Trust "GP14" Dinghy

132 Pair of Oystercatchers

1991. Centenary of Guernsey Yacht Club. Mult.
524 15p. Type **131** 45 15
525 21p. Guernsey Regatta . . . 70 25
526 26p. Lombard Channel Islands' Challenge race . . 80 80
527 31p. Rolex Swan Regatta . . 90 1·10
528 37p. Old Gaffers' Association gaff-rigged yacht . . . . . 1·00 1·40
MS529 163 × 75 mm. As Nos. 524/8, but "GUERNSEY" and face values in yellow . . . . 4·00 4·00

1991. Nature Conservation. L'Eree Shingle Bank Reserve. Multicoloured.
530 15p. Type **132** 40 45
531 15p. Three ruddy turnstones 40 45
532 15p. Dunlins and ruddy turnstones 40 45
533 15p. Curlew and ruddy turnstones 40 45
534 15p. Ringed plover with chicks 40 45
535 21p. Gull, sea campion and sea radish 50 45
536 21p. Yellow horned poppy 50 45
537 21p. Pair of common stonechats, hare's foot clover and fennel 50 45
538 21p. Hares's foot clover, fennel and slender oat . . 50 45
539 21p. Sea kale on shore . . . 50 45
Nos. 530/4 and 535/9 were each printed together, se-tenant, with the backgrounds forming composite designs.

133 "Rudolph the Red-nosed Reindeer" (Melanie Sharpe)

134 Queen Elizabeth II in 1952

1991. Christmas. Children's Paintings. Mult.
540 12p. Type **133** 30 30
541 12p. "Christmas Pudding" (James Quinn) 30 30
542 12p. "Snowman" (Lisa Guille) 30 30
543 12p. "Snowman in Top Hat" (Jessica Ede-Golightly) . . 30 30
544 12p. "Robins and Christmas Tree" (Sharon Le Page) . . 30 30
545 12p. "Shepherds and Angels" (Anna Coquelin) 30 30
546 12p. "Nativity" (Claudine Lihou) 30 30
547 12p. "Three Wise Men" (Jonathan Le Noury) . . . 30 30
548 12p. "Star of Bethlehem and Angels" (Marcia Mahy) . . 30 30
549 12p. "Christmas Tree" (Laurel Garfield) 30 30
550 12p. "Santa Claus" (Rebecca Driscoll) 30 30
551 12p. "Snowman and Star" (Ian Lowe) 30 30

1992. 40th Anniv of Accession. Multicoloured.
552 23p. Type **134** 50 50
553 28p. Queen Elizabeth in 1977 65 65
554 33p. Queen Elizabeth in 1986 90 90
555 39p. Queen Elizabeth in 1991 1·10 1·10

135 Christopher Columbus

1992. 500th Anniv of Discovery of America by Columbus. Multicoloured.
556 23p. Type **135** 65 60
557 23p. Examples of Columbus's signature 65 60
558 28p. "Santa Maria" . . . . 1·25 1·25
559 28p. Map of first voyage . . 1·25 1·25
MS560 157 × 77 mm. Nos. 556/9 4·50 5·00

136 Guernsey Calves

1992. 150th Anniv of Royal Guernsey Agricultural and Horticultural Society. Sheet, 93 × 71 mm.
MS561 **136** 75p. multicoloured 2·10 2·00

137 Stock

138 Building the Ship

1992. Horticultural Exports. Multicoloured.
562 1p. "Stephanotis floribunda" 10 10
563 2p. Potted hydrangea . . . 10 10
564 3p. Type **137** 10 10
565 4p. Anemones 15 15
566 5p. Gladiolus 15 15
567 6p. "Asparagus plumosus" and "Gypsophila paniculata" 15 15
568 7p. Guernsey lily 20 20
569 8p. Enchantment lily . . . 20 20
570 9p. Clematis "Freckles" . . 20 25
571 10p. Alstroemeria 25 25
572 16p. Standard carnation (horiz) 50 35
572b 18p. Standard rose 55 45
573 20p. Spray rose 60 50
574 23p. Mixed freesia (horiz) 60 55
575 24p. Standard rose (horiz) 70 60
576 25p. Iris "Ideal" (horiz) . . 70 60
576b 26p. Freesia "Pink Glow" 70 60
577 28p. Lisianthus (horiz) . . . 80 65
578 30p. Spray chrysanthemum (horiz) 80 70
579 40p. Spray carnation . . . 1·00 75
580 50p. Single freesia (horiz) 1·20 90
581 £1 Floral arrangement (35 × 26½ mm) . . . . . 2·00 1·50
582 £2 Chelsea Flower Show exhibit (35 × 26½ mm) . . 4·00 3·00
582a £3 "Floral Fantasia" (exhibit) (35 × 28 mm) . . 6·00 5·00

1992. "Operation Asterix" (excavation of Roman ship). Multicoloured.
583 16p. Type **138** 45 35
584 23p. Loading the cargo . . . 60 45
585 28p. Ship at sea 80 70
586 33p. Ship under attack . . . 95 90
587 39p. Crew swimming ashore 1·10 1·00

139 Tram No. 10 decorated for Battle of Flowers

1992. Guernsey Trams. Multicoloured.
588 16p. Type **139** 45 30
589 23p. Tram No 10 passing Hougue a la Perre 60 35
590 28p. Tram No. 1 at St. Sampsons 75 80
591 33p. First steam tram at St. Peter Port, 1879 . . . . 80 1·00
592 39p. Last electric tram, 1934 1·00 1·10

140 Man in Party Hat

141 Rupert Bear, Bingo and Dog

1992. Christmas. Seasonal Fayre. Multicoloured.
593 13p. Type **140** 30 30
594 13p. Girl and Christmas tree 30 30
595 13p. Woman and balloons . . 35 30
596 13p. Mince pies and champagne 30 30
597 13p. Roast turkey 30 30
598 13p. Christmas pudding . . . 30 30
599 13p. Christmas cake 30 30
600 13p. Fancy cakes 30 30
601 13p. Cheese 30 30
602 13p. Nuts 30 30
603 13p. Ham 30 30
604 13p. Chocolate log 30 30

Nos. 593/604 were printed together, se-tenant, forming a composite design.

1993. Rupert Bear and Friends (cartoon characters created by Mary and Herbert Tourtel).
605 **141** 24p. multicoloured . . . 50 50
MS606 116 × 97 mm. 16p. Airplane and castle; 16p. Professor's servant and Autumn Elf; 16p. Algy Pug; 16p. Baby Badger on sledge; 24p. Bill Badger, Willie Mouse, Reggie Rabbit and Podgy playing in snow; 24p. Type **141**; 24p. The Balloonist avoiding Gregory on toboggan; 24p. Tiger Lily and Edward Trunk . . . . 4·50 4·00
The 24p. values in No. **MS**606 are as Type **141**; the 16p. designs are smaller, each 25½ × 26 mm.

142 Tapestry by Kelly Fletcher

1993. Europa. Contemporary Art. Multicoloured.
607 24p. Type **142** 70 70
608 24p. "Le Marchi a Paissaon" (etching and aquatint, Sally Reed) (48 × 33½ mm) . . . 70 70
609 28p. "Red Abstract" (painting, Molly Harris) . . 80 80
610 28p. "Dress Shop, King's Road" (painting, Damon Bell) (48 × 33½ mm) 80 80

143 Arrest of Guernsey Parliamentarians, Fermain Bay

1993. 350th Anniv of Siege of Castle Cornet. Multicoloured.
611 16p. Type **143** 35 35
612 24p. Parliamentary ships attacking Castle Cornet . . 60 60
613 28p. Parliamentary captives escaping 75 75
614 33p. Castle cannon firing at St. Peter Port 85 85
615 39p. Surrender of Castle Cornet, 19 December 1651 90 90
MS616 203 × 75 mm. Nos. 611/15 3·25 4·00

144 Playing Cards

145 "The Twelve Pearls"

1993. Birth Bicentenary of Thomas de la Rue (printer).
617 **144** 16p. multicoloured . . . 40 45
618 – 24p. multicoloured . . . 65 65
619 – 28p. multicoloured . . . 80 80
620 – 33p. red 95 95
621 – 39p. green . . . . 1·10 1·10
DESIGNS: 24p. Fountain pens; 28p. Envelope-folding machine; 33p. Great Britain 1855 4d. stamp; 39p. Thomas de la Rue and Mauritius £1 banknote.

1993. Christmas. Stained Glass Windows by Mary-Eily de Putron from the Chapel of Christ the Healer. Multicoloured.
622 13p. Type **145** 30 30
623 13p. "Healing rays" 30 30
624 13p. "Hand of God over the Holy City" 30 30
625 13p. "Wing and Seabirds" (facing left) 30 30
626 13p. "Christ the Healer" . . 30 30
627 13p. "Wing and Seabirds" (facing right) 30 30
628 13p. "The Young Jesus in the Temple" 30 30
629 13p. "The Raising of Jairus' Daughter" 30 30
630 13p. "Suffer little Children to come unto Me" 30 30
631 13p. "Pilgrim's Progress" . . 30 30
632 13p. "The Light of the World" 30 30
633 13p. "Raphael, the Archangel of Healing, with Tobias" 30 30

146 Les Fouaillages (ancient burial ground)

1994. Europa. Archaeological Discoveries. Multicoloured.
634 24p. Type **146** 55 55
635 24p. Mounted Celtic warrior 55 55
636 30p. Jars, arrow heads and stone axe from Les Fouaillages 80 75
637 30p. Sword, spear head and torque from King's Road burial 80 75

147 Canadian Supermarine Spitfires Mk V over Normandy Beaches

1994. 50th Anniv of D-Day. Sheet 93 × 71 mm.
MS638 **147** £2 multicoloured . . 4·00 4·25

148 Peugeot "Type 3", 1894

1994. Cent of First Car in Guernsey. Mult.
639 16p. Type **148** 40 40
640 24p. Mercedes "Simplex", 1903 . . . . 60 45
641 35p. Humber tourer, 1906 . . 90 1·00
642 41p. Bentley sports tourer, 1936 . . . . 1·00 1·00
643 60p. MG TC Midget, 1948 1·50 1·40

1994. "Philakorea '94" International Stamp Exhibition, Seoul. Sheet 110 × 90 mm containing No. 581.
MS644 £1 multicoloured . . . . 2·20 3·00

149 "Trident" (Herm ferry)

1994. 25th Anniv of Guernsey Postal Administration. Multicoloured.
645 16p. Type **149** 35 30
646 24p. Handley Page Super Dart Herald of Channel Express 55 50
647 35p. Britten Norman Trislander of Aurigny Air Services 75 75
648 41p. "Bon Marin de Serk" (Sark ferry) 85 85
649 60p. Map of Bailiwick . . . 1·40 1·25
MS650 150 × 100 mm. Nos. 645/9 4·00 4·25

150 Dolls' House

151 Seafood "Face"

1994. Christmas. Bygone Toys. Multicoloured.
651 13p. Type **150** 40 20
652 13p. Doll 40 20
653 13p. Teddy in bassinette . . 40 20
654 13p. Sweets in pillar box and playing cards 40 20
655 13p. Spinning top 40 20
656 13p. Building blocks 40 20
657 24p. Rocking horse 75 60
658 24p. Teddy bear 75 60
659 24p. Tricycle 75 60
660 24p. Wooden duck 75 60
661 24p. Hornby toy locomotive 75 60
662 24p. Ludo game 75 60

Nos. 651/6 and 657/62 respectively were printed together, se-tenant, forming composite designs.

1995. Greetings Stamps. "The Welcoming Face of Guernsey". Multicoloured.
663 24p. Type **151** 60 55
664 24p. Buckets and spade "face" 60 55
665 24p. Flowers "face" 60 55
666 24p. Fruit and vegetables "face" 60 55
667 24p. Sea shells and seaweed "face" 60 55
668 24p. Anchor and life belts "face" 60 55
669 24p. Glasses, cork and cutlery "face" 60 55
670 24p. Butterflies and caterpillars "face" 60 55
MS671 137 × 109 mm. Nos. 663/70 4·25 4·25

152 Winston Churchill and Wireless

1995. 50th Anniv of Liberation. Multicoloured.
672 16p. Type **152** 45 30
673 24p. Union Jack and Royal Navy ships off St. Peter Port 60 50
674 35p. Royal Arms and military band 90 90
675 41p. "Vega" (Red Cross supply ship) 90 90
676 60p. Rejoicing crowd . . . . 1·50 1·25
MS677 189 × 75 mm. Nos. 672/6 4·25 4·50

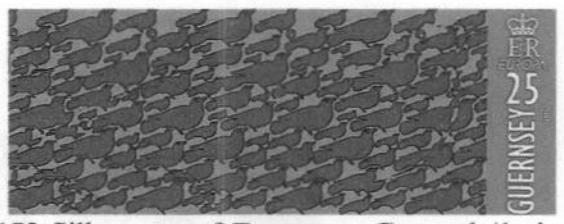

153 Silhouette of Doves on Ground (½-size illustration)

1995. Europa. Peace and Freedom. Multicoloured.
678 25p. Type **153** 50 65
679 30p. Silhouette of doves in flight 65 85
The designs of Nos. 678/9 each provide a stereogram or hidden three-dimensional image of a single dove.

154 Prince Charles, Castle Cornet and Bailiwick Arms

1995. Royal Visit.
680 **154** £1.50 multicoloured . . . 3·00 3·25

1995. "Singapore '95" International Stamp Exhibition. Sheet 110 × 90 mm. containing No. 581.
MS681 £1 multicoloured . . . . 2·75 2·75

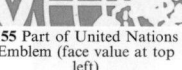

155 Part of United Nations Emblem (face value at top left)

156 "Christmas Trees for Sale in Bern" (Cornelia Huisboum-Weibel)

1995. 50th Anniv of United Nations. Designs showing different segments of the United Nations Emblem. Each blue and gold.
682 50p. Type **155** . . . . 1·10 1·10
683 50p. Face value at top right 1·10 1·10
684 50p. Face value at bottom left . . . . 1·10 1·10
685 50p. Face value at bottom right . . . . 1·10 1·10

1995. Christmas. 50th Anniv of UNICEF Multicoloured.
686 13p. Type **156** (face value at left) 40 35
687 13p. "Christmas Trees for Sale in Bern" (face value at right) 40 35
688 13p.+1p. "Evening Snowfall" (Katerina Mertikas) (face value at left) 40 45
689 13p.+1p. "Evening Snowfall" (face value at right) 40 45
690 24p. "It came upon a Midnight Clear" (Georgia Guback) (face value at left) 70 70
691 24p. "It came upon a Midnight Clear" (Georgia Guback) (face value at right) 70 70
692 24p.+2p. "Children of the World" (face value at left) 70 70
693 24p.+2p. "Children of the World" (face value at right) 70 70
Nos. 686/7, 688/9, 690/1 and 692/3 were printed together, se-tenant, each pair forming a composite design.

157 Princess Anne (President, Save the Children Fund) and Children

1996. Europa. Famous Women. Multicoloured.
694 25p. Type **157** 55 50
695 30p. Queen Elizabeth II and people of the Commonwealth 70 75

158 England v. U.S.S.R., 1968 (value at right)

1996. European Football Championship. Multicoloured.
696 16p. Type **158** 55 55
697 16p. England v. U.S.S.R., 1968 (value at left) 55 55
698 24p. Italy v. Belgium, 1972 (value at right) 75 75
699 24p. Italy v. Belgium, 1972 (value at left) 75 75
700 35p. Ireland v. Netherlands, 1988 (value at right) . . . 80 80
701 35p. Ireland v. Netherlands, 1988 (value at left) 80 80
702 41p. Denmark v. Germany, 1992 final (value at right) 95 95
703 41p. Denmark v. Germany, 1992 final (value at left) . . 95 95

159 Maj-Gen. Brock meeting Tecumseh (Indian chief)

1996. "CAPEX '96" International Stamp Exhibition, Toronto. Sheet 110 × 90 mm. containing T **159** and similar horiz design.
MS704 24p. Type **159**; £1 Major-General Sir Isaac Brock on horseback, 1812 . . . . 2·50 2·75

160 Ancient Greek Runner

162 The Annunciation

161 Humphrey Bogart as Philip Marlowe

1996. Centenary of Modern Olympic Games. Ancient Greek Athletes. Each black, yellow and orange.
705 16p. Type **160** 50 40
706 24p. Throwing the javelin . . 95 90
707 41p. Throwing the discus . . 1·10 1·25
708 55p. Wrestling (53 × 31 mm) 1·40 1·50
709 60p. Jumping . . . . 1·60 1·75
MS710 192 × 75 mm. Nos. 705/9 5·25 5·25

No. 708 also includes the "OLYMPHILEX '96" International Stamp Exhibition, Atlanta, logo.

1996. Centenary of Cinema. Screen Detectives. Multicoloured.

711	16p. Type **161**	40	40
712	24p. Peter Sellers as Inspector Clouseau	60	60
713	35p. Basil Rathbone as Sherlock Holmes	85	85
714	41p. Margaret Rutherford as Miss Marple	90	90
715	60p. Warner Oland as Charlie Chan	1·40	1·40

1996. Christmas. Multicoloured.

716	13p. Type **162**	30	25
717	13p. Journey to Bethlehem	30	25
718	13p. Arrival at the inn	30	25
719	13p. Angel and shepherds	30	25
720	13p. Mary, Joseph and Jesus in stable	30	25
721	13p. Shepherds worshipping Jesus	30	25
722	13p. Three Kings following star	30	25
723	13p. Three Kings with gifts	30	25
724	13p. The Presentation in the Temple	30	25
725	13p. Mary and Jesus	30	25
726	13p. Joseph warned by angel	30	25
727	13p. The Flight into Egypt	30	25
728	24p. Mary cradling Jesus (horiz)	60	40
729	25p. The Nativity (horiz)	60	60

163 Holly Blue

1997. Endangered Species. Butterflies and Moths. Multicoloured.

730	18p. Type **163**	55	50
731	25p. Hummingbird hawk-moth	65	60
732	26p. Emperor moth	85	85
733	37p. Brimstone	1·10	1·10
MS734	92 × 68 mm. £1 Painted Lady	2·50	2·50

No. **MS**734 includes the "HONG KONG '97" International Stamp Exhibition logo on the sheet margin.

164 Gilliatt fighting Octopus

1997. Europa. Tales and Legends. Scenes from "Les Travailleurs de la Mer" by Victor Hugo. Multicoloured.

735	26p. Type **164**	55	60
736	31p. Gilliatt grieving on rock	75	65

165 Shell Beach, Herm

168 Teddy Bear making Cake

167 Transistor Radio, Microphone and Radio Logos

1997. Guernsey Scenes (1st series). Multicoloured. Self-adhesive.

737	18p. Type **165**	60	30
738	25p. La Seigneurie, Sark (vert)	70	60
739	26p. Castle Cornet, Guernsey	80	75

166 19th-century Shipyard, St. Peter Port

1997. "Pacific '97" World Philatelic Exhibition, San Francisco. Sheet 110 × 90 mm. containing T **166** and similar horiz design.

MS740	30p. green and gold; £1 multicoloured ("Costa Rica Packet" (barque))	3·00	3·00

See also Nos. 770/3.

1997. Methods of Communication. Multicoloured.

741	18p. Type **167**	40	40
742	25p. Television, video camera and satellite dish	60	60
743	26p. Fax machine, telephones and mobile phone	60	60
744	37p. Printing press, newspaper and type	85	85
745	43p. Stamp, coding machine and postbox	1·00	1·00
746	63p. CD, computer and disk	1·50	1·50

1997. Christmas. Teddy Bears. Multicoloured.

747	15p. Type **168**	45	45
748	25p. Teddy bears decorating Christmas tree	70	70
749	26p. Two teddy bears in armchair	70	70
750	37p. Teddy bear as Father Christmas	1·00	1·00
751	43p. Teddy bears unwrapping presents	1·10	1·10
752	63p. Teddy bears eating Christmas dinner	1·60	1·60
MS753	123 × 107 mm. Nos. 747/52	4·50	4·50

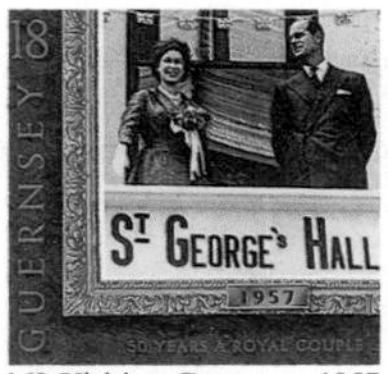

169 Visiting Guernsey, 1957

1997. Golden Wedding of Queen Elizabeth and Prince Philip. Multicoloured.

754	18p. Type **169**	40	40
755	25p. Coronation Day, 1953	60	60
756	26p. Royal Family, 1957	60	60
757	37p. On royal yacht, 1972	90	90
758	43p. Queen Elizabeth and Prince Philip at Trooping the Colour, 1987	1·00	1·00
759	63p. Queen Elizabeth and Prince Philip, 1997	1·40	1·40

No. 755 is inscribed "1947" in error.

170 Tapestry of 11th-century Guernsey (St. Martin)

171 Fort Grey

1998. The Millennium Tapestries Project. Each showing a different century contributed by individual parishes. Multicoloured.

760	25p. Type **170**	60	60
761	25p. 12th-century (St. Saviour)	60	60
762	25p. 13th-century (Vale)	60	60
763	25p. 14th-century (St. Sampson)	60	60
764	25p. 15th-century (Torteval)	60	60
765	25p. 16th-century (Castel)	60	60
766	25p. 17th-century (St. Andrew)	60	60
767	25p. 18th-century (Forest)	60	60
768	25p. 19th-century (St. Pierre du Bois)	60	60
769	25p. 20th-century (St. Peter Port)	60	60

1998. Guernsey Scenes (2nd series). Multicoloured. Self-adhesive.

770	(20p.) Type **171**	45	55
771	(20p.) Grand Havre	45	55
772	(25p.) Little Chapel	55	65
773	(25p.) Guernsey cow	55	65

Nos. 770/1 are inscribed "Bailiwick Minimum Postage Paid" and were intially sold at 20p. Nos. 772/3 are inscribed "UK Minimum Postage Paid" and were initially sold at 25p.

172 Fairey IIIC, Balloon, Sopwith Camel and Avro 504

1998. 80th Anniv of the Royal Air Force. Multicoloured.

774	20p. Type **172**	50	50
775	25p. Fairey Swordfish, Tiger Moth, Supermarine Walrus and Gloster Gladiator	60	60
776	30p. Hawker Hurricane, Supermarine Spitfire, Vickers Wellington, Short Sunderland (flying boat), Westland Lysander and Bristol Blenheim	70	70
777	37p. De Havilland Mosquito, Avro Lancaster, Auster III, Gloster Meteor and Horsa glider	85	85
778	43p. Canberra, Hawker Sea Fury, Bristol Sycamore, Hawker Hunter, Handley Page Victor and BAe Lightning	95	95
779	63p. Pavania Tornado GRI, BAe Hawk, BAe Sea Harrier, Westland Lynx (helicopter) and Hawker Siddeley Nimrod	1·40	1·40

173 Jules Rimet (first President of F.I.F.A)

1998. 150th Anniv of the Cambridge Rules for Football. Sheet 110 × 90 mm containing T **173** and similar horiz design.

MS780	30p. Type **173**; £1.75, Bobby Moore and Queen Elizabeth II, 1966	3·50	4·00

174 Girls in Traditional Costume watching Sheep Display, West Show

1998. Europa. Festivals. Multicoloured.

781	20p. Type **174**	45	45
782	25p. Marching band and "Battle of Flowers" exhibit, North Show	55	55
783	30p. Prince Charles, monument and tank, Liberation Day	65	65
784	37p. Goat, dahlias and show-jumping, South Show	85	85

The 25p. and 30p. incorporate the "EUROPA" emblem.

175 Outward Motorboat

176 Royal Yacht "Britannia"

1998. Maritime Heritage. Multicoloured.

785	1p. Type **175**	10	10
786	2p. St. John Ambulance inshore rescue dinghy	10	10
787	3p. Pilot boat, St. Peter Port	10	10
788	4p. "Flying Christine III" (St. John Ambulance launch)	10	10
789	5p. Crab fishing boat	10	10
790	6p. Herm Island ferry	10	10
791	7p. "Sarnia" (St. Peter Port Harbour Authority launch)	15	20
792	8p. "Leopardess" (States' fisheries protection launch)	15	20
793	9p. Trawler	20	25
794	10p. Powerboat (27 × 27 mm)	20	25
795	20p. Dart 18 racing catamaran (27 × 27 mm)	40	45
796	30p. 30ft Bermuda-rigged sloop (27 × 27 mm)	60	65
797	40p. Motor cruiser (27 × 27 mm)	80	85
798	50p. Ocean-going sailing yacht (27 × 27 mm)	1·00	1·10
799	75p. Motor yacht "Beaucette Marina" (27 × 27 mm)	1·50	1·30
800	£1 "Queen Elizabeth 2" (liner) (35 × 26 mm)	2·00	1·80
801	£3 "Oriana" (liner) (35 × 26 mm)	6·00	5·50
802	£5 Type **176**	13·00	10·00

177 Modern Tree, Teletubby and Playstation

1998. 150th Anniv of the Introduction of the Christmas Tree. Multicoloured.

810	17p. Type **177**	40	40
811	25p. 1960s tinsel tree, toy bus and doll	60	60
812	30p. 1930s gold foil tree, panda and toy tank	70	70
813	37p. 1920s tree, model of "Bluebird" and doll	90	90
814	43p. 1900 tree, teddy bear and toy train	90	90
815	63p. 1850s tree, wooden doll and spinning top	1·50	1·50
MS816	160 × 94 mm. Nos. 810/15	5·00	7·00

178 Elizabeth Bowes Lyon, 1907

180 Burnet Rose and Local Carriage Label

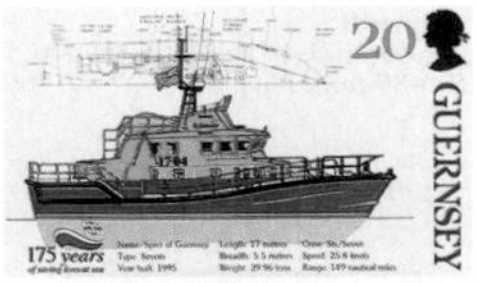

179 "Spirit of Guernsey", 1995

1999. Life and Times of Queen Elizabeth the Queen Mother. Multicoloured.

817	25p. Type **178**	70	65
818	25p. On wedding day, 1923	70	65
819	25p. Holding Princess Elizabeth, 1926	70	65
820	25p. At Coronation, 1937	70	65
821	25p. Visiting bombed areas of London, 1940 (wearing green hat)	70	65
822	25p. Fishing near Auckland, New Zealand, 1966	70	65
823	25p. At Guernsey function, 1963 (wearing tiara)	70	65
824	25p. Receiving flowers on her birthday, 1992	70	65
825	25p. Presenting trophy, Sandown Park races, 1989	70	65
826	25p. Opening Royal Norfolk Regimental Museum, Norwich, 1990 (wearing blue hat)	70	65

1999. 175th Anniv of Royal National Lifeboat Institution. Multicoloured.

827	20p. Type **179**	50	50
828	25p. "Sir William Arnold", 1973	60	60
829	30p. "Euphrosyne Kendal", 1954	70	70
830	38p. "Queen Victoria", 1929	90	90
831	44p. "Arthur Lionel", 1912	1·10	1·10
832	64p. "Vincent Kirk Ella", 1888	1·50	1·50

1999. Europa. Parks and Gardens. Herm Island. Designs each showing a different local carriage label. Multicoloured.

833	20p. Type **180**	50	45
834	25p. Atlantic puffin	60	55
835	30p. Small heath butterfly	70	65
836	38p. Shells on Shell Beach	90	80

181 Prince Edward and Miss Sophie Rhys-Jones

1999. Royal Wedding. Sheet 93 × 70 mm.

MS837	**181** £1 Multicoloured	2·50	2·25

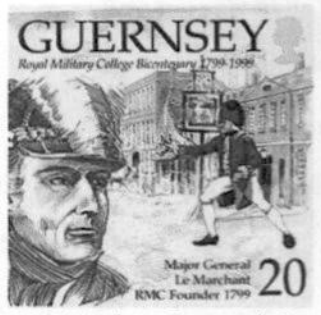

182 Major-General Le Marchant (founder) and Cadet at Sword Drill

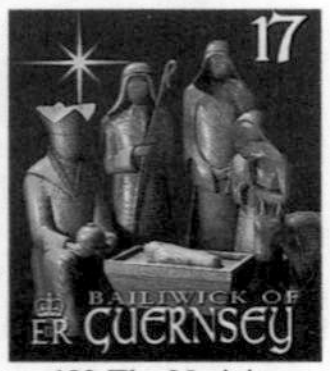

183 The Nativity

1999. Bicentenary of The Royal Military Academy, Sandhurst. Multicoloured.

838	20p. Type **182**	50	45
839	25p. The Duke of York (official sponsor) and cadet on horseback	60	55
840	30p. Field-Marshal Earl Haig and cadets on parade	75	70
841	38p. Field-Marshal Viscount Montgomery and bridging exercise	90	85
842	44p. David Niven (actor) and rifle practice	1·10	1·00
843	64p. Sir Winston Churchill and tank	1·50	1·50

1999. Christmas. Wood Carvings by Denis Brehaut from Notre Dame Church. Multicoloured.

844	17p. Type **183**	45	40
845	25p. Virgin Mary and Child	60	55
846	30p. Holy Family	75	70
847	38p. Cattle around manger	90	85
848	44p. Adoration of the Shepherds	1·10	1·00
849	64p. Adoration of the Magi	1·50	1·50
MS850	159 × 86 mm. Nos. 844/9	5·50	5·50

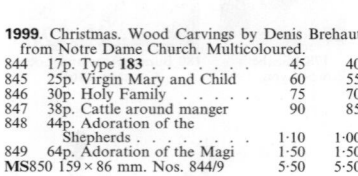

184 "Space Bus" (Fallon Ephgrave)

2000. New Millennium. "Stampin' the Future" (children's stamp design competition). Multicoloured.

851	20p. Type **184**	60	45
852	25p. "Children holding hands" (Abigail Downing)	60	55
853	30p. "No Captivity" (Laura Martin)	70	65
854	38p. "Post Office of the Future" (Sarah Haddow)	90	80
855	44p. "Solar-powered car" (Sophie Medland)	1·00	95
856	64p. "Woman flying" (Danielle McIver)	1·40	1·40

185 Bristol Blenheim

2000. 60th Anniv of Battle of Britain. R.A.F. Aircraft. Multicoloured.

857	21p. Type **185**	50	50
858	26p. Hawker Hurricane	60	55
859	36p. Boulton Paul Defiant II	90	85
860	40p. Gloster Gladiator	95	95
861	45p. Bristol Beaufighter IF	1·10	1·10
862	65p. Supermarine Spitfire IIc	1·50	1·50

186 Guernsey Flag on Kite and "2000"

187 *Iris stylosa*

2000. Europa. Multicoloured.

863	21p. Type **186**	50	45
864	26p. Stylized sails bearing national flowers	60	55
865	36p. "Building Europe"	1·00	90
866	65p. Rainbow and three doves	1·60	1·60

2000. "A Botanist's Sketchbook". Restoration of Candie Gardens, St. Peter Port. Multicoloured.

867	26p. Type **187**	55	55
868	26p. *Watsonia*	55	55
869	26p. *Richardia maculata*	55	55
870	26p. *Narcissus bulbocodium*	55	55
871	26p. *Triteleia laxa*	55	55
872	26p. *Tigridia pavonia*	55	55
873	26p. *Agapanthus umbellatus*	55	55
874	26p. *Sparaxis*	55	55
875	26p. *Pancratium maritimum*	55	55
876	26p. *Nerine sarniensis*	55	55

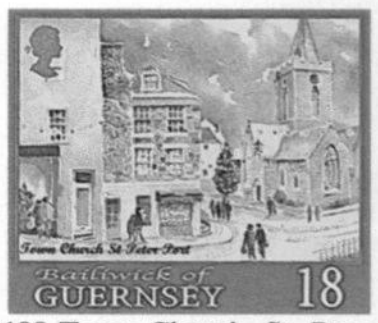

188 Town Church, St. Peter Port

189 Queen Victoria and Diamond Jubilee Statue

2000. Christmas. Snow Scenes. Multicoloured.

877	18p. Type **188**	40	40
878	26p. Children leaving St. Sampson's Church	60	55
879	36p. Flying kite by Vale Church	90	85
880	40p. Carol singing outside St. Pierre du Bois Church	95	95
881	45p. Building snowman near St. Martin's Church	1·10	1·10
882	65p. Street scene including St. John's Church, St. Peter Port	1·50	1·50
MS883	160 × 86 mm. Nos. 877/82	5·50	6·00

2001. Death Centenary of Queen Victoria. Each incorporating a different portrait of Queen Victoria. Multicoloured.

884	21p. Type **189**	50	50
885	26p. Letter of thanks to Guernsey, 1846	60	55
886	36p. Statues of Queen Victoria and Prince Albert	90	85
887	40p. Stone commemorating 1846 visit	95	95
888	45p. Statue of Prince Albert	1·10	1·10
889	65p. Victoria Tower, 1848	1·50	1·50
MS890	165 × 80 mm. Nos. 884/9	6·00	7·00

No. **MS**890 includes the logo of the "Hong Kong 2001" Stamp Exhibition on the sheet margin.

190 River kingfisher ("Kingfisher")

2001. Europa. Water Birds. Multicoloured.

891	21p. Type **190**	60	40
892	26p. Garganey	70	75
893	36p. Little egret	90	1·00
894	65p. Little ringed plover	1·70	1·90

191 Cavalier King Charles Spaniel

192 La Corbiere Sunset

2001. Centenary of Guernsey Dog Club. Mult.

895	22p. Type **191**	55	50
896	27p. Miniature schnauzer	65	60
897	36p. German shepherd dog	90	85
898	40p. Cocker spaniel	95	95
899	45p. West highland white terrier	1·10	1·10
900	65p. Dachshund	1·50	1·50

2001. Island Scenes. Multicoloured. Self-adhesive.

901	(22p.) Type **192**	45	50
902	(22p.) Rue des Hougues	45	50
903	(22p.) St. Saviour's Reservoir	45	50
904	(22p.) Shell Beach, Herm	45	50
905	(22p.) Telegraph Bay, Alderney	45	50
906	(27p.) Alderney Railway	55	60
907	(27p.) Vazon Bay	55	60
908	(27p.) La Coupee, Sark	55	60
909	(27p.) Les Hanois Lighthouse	55	60
910	(27p.) Albecq Beach	55	60

Nos. 901/5 were intended for postage within the Bailiwick and are inscribed "GY". They were each initially sold at 22p. Nos. 906/10 were intended for postage to Great Britain and are inscribed "UK". They were each initially sold at 27p.

193 Droplet of Water on Leaf ("Vision")

2001. Incorporation of Guernsey Post Ltd. Multicoloured. (a) Square designs as T **193**.

921	22p. Type **193**	45	50
922	27p. Hummingbird ("Understanding")	55	60
923	36p. Butterfly's wing ("Individuality")	70	75
924	40p. Sea shell ("Strength")	80	85
925	45p. Honeycomb ("Community")	90	95
926	65p. Dandelion ("Maturity")	1·25	1·40

(b) Design as No. 28a (1969 £1), but redrawn.

927	£1 View of Guernsey from the sea	5·00	5·50

No. 927 differs from the original 1969 stamp by showing the Queen's portrait without a tiara and by showing "GUERNSEY BALIWICK" in white instead of grey.

194 "Tree of Joy", St. Peter Port

196 Juggling

195 Victor Hugo and St. Peter Port

2001. Christmas. Festive Lights. Multicoloured.

928	19p. Type **194**	40	45
929	27p. Cross, Les Cotils Christian Centre	55	60
930	36p. Les Ruettes Cottage, St. Saviour's	75	80
931	40p. Farmhouse, Le Preel, Castel	1·00	1·10
932	45p. Sark Post Office	1·10	1·20
933	65p. High Street, St. Peter Port	1·50	1·60
MS934	150 × 100 mm. Nos. 928/33	6·00	6·50

2002. Birth Bicentenary of Victor Hugo (French author). *Les Miserables* (novel). Multicoloured.

935	22p. Type **195**	45	50
936	27p. Cosette	55	60
937	36p. Valjean	75	80
938	40p. Inspector Javert	90	95
939	45p. Cosette and Marius	1·10	1·10
940	65p. Novel and score for *Les Miserables* (musical by Alain Boublil and Claude-Michel Schonberg)	1·50	1·60
MS941	150 × 100 mm. Nos. 935/40	5·25	6·00

The 27p. value reproduces the main image from promotional material for Cameron Mackintosh's musical production.

2002. Europa. The Circus. Multicoloured.

942	22p Type **196**	45	50
943	27p. Clowns	55	60
944	36p. Trapeze artists	70	75
945	40p. Knife thrower	80	90
946	45p. Acrobat	90	95
947	65p. High-wire cyclist	1·25	1·40

197 Queen Elizabeth and Crowd

198 Original Pillar Box, Union Street

2002. Golden Jubilee. Multicoloured.

948	22p. Type **197**	45	50
949	27p. Queen Elizabeth at St. Peter Port	55	60
950	36p. Queen Elizabeth and Prince Philip at St. Anne's School, Alderney	70	75
951	40p. Queen Elizabeth and La Seigneurie, Sark	80	85
952	45p. At Millennium Stone, L'Ancresse	90	95
953	65p. In evening dress and floodlit Castle Cornet	1·25	1·40

2002. 150th Anniv of First Pillar Box. Sheet, 55 × 90 mm.

MS954	**198** £1.75 multicoloured	4·00	4·50

199 Family and Ferry, La Maseline

2002. Holidays on Sark. Multicoloured.

955	27p. Type **199**	55	60
956	27p. Passenger tractors	55	60
957	27p. Campsite	55	60
958	27p. Cyclists at La Coupee	55	60
959	27p. Swimming in Venus Pool	55	60
960	27p. La Seigneurie gardens	55	60
961	27p. Posting cards	55	60
962	27p. Carriage ride	55	60
963	27p. Tea at a café	55	60
964	27p. On the beach at Creux Harbour	55	60

200 Elizabeth College and Cadet Corps Parade, 1934

2002. 60th Anniv of Herbert Le Patourel's Victoria Cross. Multicoloured.

965	22p. Type **200**	45	50
966	27p. Captain Le Patourel in action, Tunisia 1942, and V.C	55	60
967	36p. Captain Le Patourel and nurse, 1943	70	75
968	40p. Award ceremony, Cairo, 1943	80	85
969	45p. Major Le Patourel welcomed home to Guernsey, 1948	1·25	1·40

201 Queen Elizabeth the Queen Mother and Bouquet (½-size illustration)

2002. Queen Elizabeth the Queen Mother Commemoration. Sheet 140 × 98 mm.

MS971	**201** £2 multicoloured	4·00	4·25

202 Mary and Jesus

2002. Christmas. Multicoloured.

972	22p. Type **202**	45	50
973	27p. Mary, Joseph and Jesus in the stable	55	60
974	36p. Angel appearing to shepherds	70	75
975	40p. Shepherds with Mary and Jesus	80	85
976	45p. Three Wise Men	90	95
977	65p. Stable with star overhead	1·25	1·50
MS978	131 × 101 mm. Nos. 972/7	4·00	4·50

203 Lancaster Bomber and Crew

2003. Memories of the Second World War. 60th Anniv of Operation Tunnel (£1.50) and Dambusters Raid (others) (1st issue). Multicoloured.

979	22p. Type **203**	45	50
980	27p. Flight of Lancaster bombers crossing English coast	55	60
981	36p. Lancaster bombers in enemy searchlights	70	75
982	40p. Dropping bouncing bombs	80	85
983	£1.50 H.M.S. *Charybdis* (cruiser) and H.M.S. *Limbourne* (destroyer) (40 × 30 mm)	3·00	3·25

See also Nos. 1027/31.

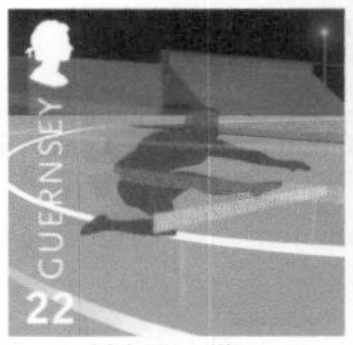

204 Hurdling

205 St. Peter Port Harbour ("Naturally Guernsey", 2003)

2003. Island Games, Guernsey. Multicoloured.

984	22p. Type **204**	45	50
985	27p. Cycling	55	60
986	36p. Gymnastics	75	80
987	40p. Sailing	80	85
988	45p. Golf	90	95
989	65p. Running	1·25	1·40
MS990	140 × 75 mm. Nos. 984/9	4·75	5·00

2003. Europa. Poster Art. Multicoloured.

991	22p. Type **205**	45	50
992	27p. Motor-cruiser off Guernsey ("The islands of Guernsey", 1995)	55	60
993	36p. "Children on the Seashore" (Renoir) ("Holiday Guernsey", 1988)	75	80
994	40p. St. Peter Port Harbour ("Bailiwick of Guernsey", 1978)	80	85
995	45p. St. Peter Port and cliffs ("Guernsey - The Charming Channel Island", 1968)	90	95
996	65p. Secluded bay ("Guernsey", 1956)	1·25	1·40

206 H.M.S. *Guernsey*

2003. Decommissioning of H.M.S. *Guernsey* (fishery protection patrol vessel). Sheet 117 × 84 mm.

MS997	**206** £1.50 multicoloured	3·00	3·25

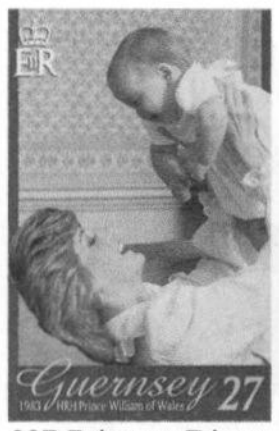

207 Princess Diana and Baby Prince William

208 Letters of Alphabet

2003. 21st Birthday of Prince William of Wales. Multicoloured.

998	27p. Type **207**	55	60
999	27p. Prince William, aged 3, with Prince Charles and Prince Harry at Kensington Palace	55	60
1000	27p. Aged 4, in Parachute Regiment uniform	55	60
1001	27p. Aged 7, with Prince Harry on his first day at Wetherby School	55	60
1002	27p. Aged 8, with Prince Charles at Guards Polo	55	60
1003	27p. Aged 9, on ski slopes with Princess Diana	55	60
1004	27p. On first day at Eton, 1995	55	60
1005	27p. With Prince Charles and Prince Harry at Balmoral, 1997	55	60
1006	27p. Wearing hard hat during Community project in Chile, 2000	55	60
1007	27p. Playing polo, 2002	55	60

2003.

1008	**208** £5 orange, blue and silver	10·00	10·50

The alphabet letters are printed in thermochromic ink which fades from pale orange to white when exposed to heat.

209 Sleeping Boy and Christmas Tree

2003. Christmas. Scenes from Poem "Twas the Night before Christmas" by Clement Clarke Moore. Multicoloured.

1009	10p. Type **209**	20	25
1010	27p. Boy opening shutter to see Santa's sleigh	55	60
1011	36p. Santa on roof with reindeer	70	75
1012	40p. Santa with presents	80	85
1013	45p. Santa leaving presents under Christmas tree	90	95
1014	65p. Santa in sleigh	1·25	1·50
MS1015	130 × 104 mm. Nos. 1009/14	4·50	4·75

210 Golden Snub-nosed Monkey

2004. Endangered Species (1st series). Golden Snub-nosed Monkey. Sheet 120 × 85 mm.

MS1016	210 £2 multicoloured	4·00	4·25

211 Clematis "Rosemoor"

2004. Raymond Evison's Guernsey Clematis. Multicoloured. Self-adhesive.

1017	(22p.) Type **211**	45	50
1018	(22p.) "Arctic Queen"	45	50
1019	(22p.) "Harlow Carr"	45	50
1020	(22p.) "Guernsey Cream"	45	50
1021	(22p.) "Josephine"	45	50
1022	(27p.) "Blue Moon"	55	60
1023	(27p.) "Wisley"	55	60
1024	(27p.) "Liberation"	55	60
1025	(27p.) "Royal Velvet"	55	60
1026	(27p.) "Hyde Hall"	55	60

Nos. 1017/21 were intended for postage within the Bailiwick and are inscribed "GY". They were each initially sold at 22p. Nos. 1022/6 were intended for postage to Great Britain and are inscribed "UK". They were each initially sold at 27p.

2004. Memories of the Second World War (2nd issue). 60th Anniv of D-Day Landings. As T **203**. Multicoloured.

1027	26p. Supermarine Spitfire	50	55
1028	32p. Landing craft and ship	65	70
1029	36p. Troops going ashore at Gold Beach	75	80
1030	40p. Troops in water	80	85
1031	£1.50 *Vega* (Red Cross supply ship) (40 × 29 mm)	3·00	3·25

212 Sandcastle, Rider, Bucket and Spade, Deckchair and Canoeist

2004. Europa. Holidays. Multicoloured.

1032	26p. Type **212**	50	55
1033	32p. Pathway sign, walking trails, bench and Guernsey landscapes	65	70
1034	36p. Lighthouse and yachts in marina, St. Peter Port	75	80
1035	40p. Glasses of red wine and meals on table	80	80
1036	45p. Statue-menhir at Castel and Loop Holed Tower, Le Gran'mere statue-menhir, Little Chapel and Victor Hugo statue	90	95
1037	65p. Guernsey Lily, wildflowers and robin	1·30	1·40

POSTAGE DUE STAMPS

D 1 Castle Cornet

1969. Face values in black.

D1	**D 1** 1d. plum	2·00	1·25
D2	2d. green	2·00	1·25
D3	3d. red	3·00	4·00
D4	4d. blue	4·00	5·00
D5	5d. ochre	4·50	4·00
D6	6d. turquoise	5·00	4·50
D7	1s. brown	10·00	8·00

1971. Decimal Currency. Face values in black.

D 8	**D 1** $\frac{1}{2}$p. plum	10	10
D 9	1p. green	10	10
D10	2p. red	10	10
D11	3p. blue	10	10
D12	4p. ochre	10	10
D13	5p. blue	10	10
D14	6p. violet	10	10
D15	8p. orange	20	25
D16	10p. brown	20	15
D17	15p. grey	30	40

D 2 St. Peter Port

1977. Face values in black.

D18	**D 2** $\frac{1}{2}$p. brown	10	10
D19	1p. purple	10	10
D20	2p. orange	10	10
D21	3p. red	10	10
D22	4p. blue	10	10
D23	5p. green	10	10
D24	6p. green	10	10
D25	8p. brown	10	10
D26	10p. blue	10	10
D27	14p. green	15	15
D28	15p. violet	15	15
D29	16p. red	20	20

D 3 Milking Cow

1982. Guernsey Scenes, c. 1990.

D30	**D 3** 1p. blue and green	10	10
D31	– 2p. brown, lt brown & blue	10	10
D32	– 3p. green and lilac	10	10
D33	– 4p. green and orange	10	10
D34	– 5p. blue and green	10	10
D35	– 16p. blue and light blue	30	35
D36	– 18p. blue and green	35	40
D37	– 20p. green and blue	40	45
D38	– 25p. blue and pink	50	55
D39	– 30p. green and yellow	60	65
D40	– 50p. brown and blue	1·00	1·10
D41	– £1 lt brown and brown	2·00	2·10

DESIGNS: 2p. Vale Mill; 3p. Sark cottage; 4p. Quayside, St. Peter Port; 5p. Well, Water Lane, Moulin Huet; 16p. Seaweed gathering; 18p. Upper Walk, White Rock; 20p. Cobo Bay; 25p. Saint's Bay; 30p. La Coupee, Sark; 50p. Old Harbour, St. Peter Port; £1 Greenhouses, Doyle Road, St. Peter Port.

ALDERNEY

The following issues are provided by the Guernsey Post Office for use on Alderney. They are also valid for postal purposes throughout the rest of the Bailiwick of Guernsey.

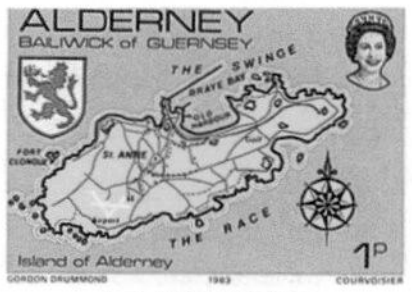

A 1 Island Map

1983. Island Scenes. Multicoloured.

A 1	1p. Type **A 1**	10	10
A 2	4p. Hanging Rock	10	10
A 3	9p. States' Building, St. Anne	15	15
A 4	10p. St. Anne's Church	20	15
A 5	11p. Yachts in Braye Bay	20	20
A 6	12p. Victoria St., St. Anne	25	20
A 7	13p. Map of Channel	25	20
A 8	14p. Fort Clonque	30	20
A 9	15p. Corblets Bay and Fort	35	20
A10	16p. Old Tower, St. Anne	35	25
A11	17p. Golf course and Essex Castle	40	30
A12	18p. Old Harbour	40	30
A12a	20p. Quesnard Lighthouse	1·00	90
A12b	21p. Braye Harbour	1·00	90
A12c	23p. Island Hall	95	85
A12d	24p. "J.T. Daly" (steam locomotive)	1·75	1·75
A12e	28p. "Louis Marchesi of the Round Table" (lifeboat)	2·25	2·25

Nos. A12a/e are larger, 38 × 27 mm.

A 2 Oystercatcher

1984. Birds. Multicoloured.

A13	9p. Type **A 2**	1·10	60
A14	13p. Ruddy turnstone ("Turnstone")	1·10	75
A15	26p. Ringed plover	2·50	2·75
A16	28p. Dunlin	2·50	2·75
A17	31p. Curlew	2·50	1·70

A **3** Westland Wessex HU Mk 5 Helicopter of the Queen's Flight

1985. 50th Anniv of Alderney Airport. Mult.
A18 9p. Type A **3** . . . . 1·40 70
A19 13p. Britten Norman "long nose" Trislander . . . . . 1·75 1·00
A20 29p. De Havilland Heron 1B 3·00 2·50
A21 31p. De Havilland Dragon Rapide "Sir Henry Lawrence" . . . . 3·50 2·75
A22 34p. Saro Windhover flying boat "City of Portsmouth" 3·50 2·75

A **4** Royal Engineers, 1890 A **5** Fort Grosnez

1985. Regiments of the Alderney Garrison. Multicoloured.
A23 9p. Type A **4** 25 20
A24 14p. Duke of Albany's Own Highlanders, 1856 . . . . 80 40
A25 29p. Royal Artillery, 1855 80 70
A26 31p. South Hampshire Regiment, 1810 . . . . . 1·10 1·10
A27 34p. Royal Irish Regiment, 1782 . . . . 1·40 1·40

1986. Alderney Forts. Multicoloured.
A28 10p. Type A **5** 80 20
A29 14p. Fort Tourgis 90 80
A30 31p. Fort Clonque . . . . . 2·50 3·00
A31 34p. Fort Albert . . . . . . 2·50 3·00

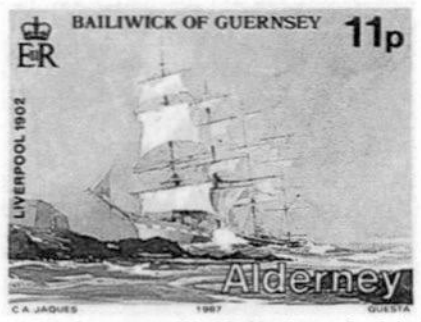

A **6** "Liverpool" (full-rigged ship), 1902

1987. Alderney Shipwrecks. Multicoloured.
A32 11p. Type A **6** . . . . . . 1·60 50
A33 15p. "Petit Raymond" (schooner), 1906 . . . . . 1·75 60
A34 29p. "Maina" (yacht), 1910 3·75 3·50
A35 31p. "Burton" (steamer), 1911 . . . . 4·00 3·50
A36 34p. "Point Law" (oil tanker), 1975 . . . . . . 4·00 4·25

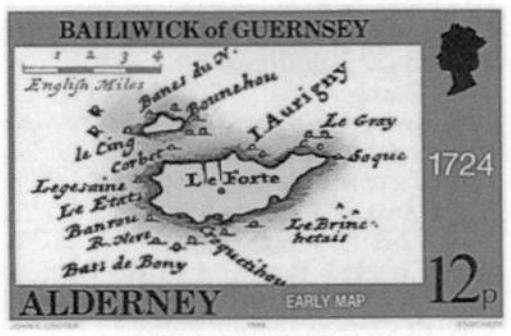

A **7** Moll's Map of 1724

1989. 250th Anniv of Bastide's Survey of Alderney.
A37 A **7** 12p. multicoloured . . . 25 25
A38 – 18p. black, blue & brown 45 30
A39 – 27p. black, blue and green . . . . 95 1·10
A40 – 32p. black, blue and red 1·10 1·10
A41 – 35p. multicoloured . . . 1·50 1·40
DESIGNS: 18p. Bastide's survey of 1739; 27p. Goodwin's map of 1831; 32p. General Staff map of 1943; 35p. Ordnance Survey map, 1988.

A **8** H.M.S. "Alderney" (bomb ketch), 1738

1990. Royal Navy Ships named after Alderney.
A42 A **8** 14p. black and bistre . . 25 20
A43 – 20p. black and brown . . 45 35
A44 – 29p. black and brown . . 1·00 1·00
A45 – 34p. black and blue . . . 1·10 1·50
A46 – 37p. black and blue . . . 1·40 1·50
DESIGNS: 20p. H.M.S. "Alderney" (sixth rate), 1742; 29p. H.M.S. "Alderney" (sloop), 1755; 34p. H.M.S. "Alderney" (submarine), 1945; 37p. H.M.S. "Alderney" (patrol vessel), 1979.

A **9** Wreck of H.M.S. "Victory", 1744

1991. Automation of The Casquets Lighthouse. Multicoloured.
A47 21p. Type A **9** 80 50
A48 26p. Lighthouse keeper's daughter rowing back to the Casquets . . . . . . 1·90 1·70
A49 31p. MBB-Bolkow Bo 105D helicopter leaving pad on St. Thomas Tower . . . . 2·00 2·25
A50 37p. Northern wheater and yellow wagtail over lighthouse . . . . 2·75 3·25
A51 50p. Trinity House vessel "Patricia" and arms . . . 3·75 3·50

A **10** Two French Warships on Fire A **11** Spiny Lobster

1992. 300th Anniv of the Battle of La Hogue. Multicoloured.
A52 23p. Type A **10** . . . . . . 1·10 1·00
A53 28p. Crews leaving burning ships . . . . 2·40 2·50
A54 33p. French warship sinking 3·00 3·00
A55 50p. "The Battle of La Hogue" (47 × 32 mm) . . 3·50 3·50
Nos. A52/4 show details of the painting on the 50p. value.

1993. Endangered Species. Marine Life. Mult.
A56 24p. Type A **11** . . . . . . 1·25 1·40
A57 28p. Plumose anemone . . . 1·25 1·40
A58 33p. Starfish . . . . 1·25 1·40
A59 39p. Sea urchin . . . . . . 1·25 1·40
Nos. A56/9 were printed together, se-tenant, the backgrounds forming a composite design.

A **12** Blue-tailed Damselfly, Dark Hair Water Crowfoot and Branched Bur-reed

1994. Flora and Fauna. Multicoloured.
A60 1p. Type A **12** 10 10
A61 2p. White-toothed shrew and flax-leaved St. John's wort 10 10
A62 3p. Fulmar and kaffir fig 10 10
A63 4p. Clouded yellow (butterfly) and red clover 10 10
A64 5p. Bumble bee, prostrate broom and giant broom-rape 10 10
A65 6p. Dartford warbler and lesser dodder 15 20
A66 7p. Peacock (butterfly) and stemless thistle 15 20
A67 8p. Mole and bluebell . . . 15 20
A68 9p. Great green grasshopper and common gorse 20 25
A69 10p. Six-spot burnet (moth) and viper's bugloss . . . 20 25
A70 16p. Common blue (butterfly) and pyramidal orchid 55 40
A70b 18p. Small tortoiseshell (butterfly) and buddleia 35 40
A71 20p. Common rabbit and creeping buttercup . . . 40 45
A72 24p. Greater black-backed gull and sand crocus . . 50 55
A72b 25p. Rock pipit and sea stock 50 55
A72c 26p. Sand digger wasp and sea bindweed (horiz) . . 50 55
A73 30p. Atlantic puffin and English stonecrop 60 65
A74 40p. Emperor (moth) and bramble 80 85
A75 50p. Pale-spined hedgehog and pink oxalis . . . . . 1·00 1·25
A76 £1 Common tern and Bermuda grass (horiz) . . 2·00 2·25
A77 £2 Northern gannet and "Fucus vesiculosus" (seaweed) (horiz) . . . . 4·00 4·50

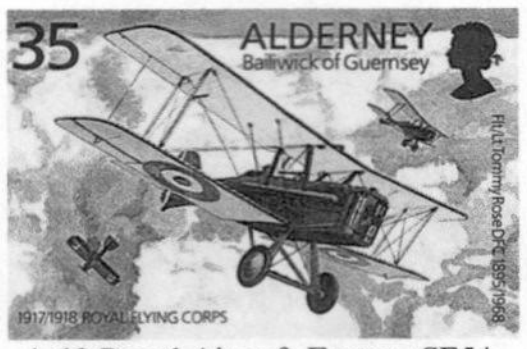

A **13** Royal Aircraft Factory SE5A

1995. Birth Cent of Tommy Rose (aviator). Mult.
A78 35p. Type A **13** 95 95
A79 35p. Miles Master II and other Miles aircraft . . . 95 95
A80 35p. Miles Aerovan and Miles Monitor 95 95
A81 41p. Miles Falcon Six winning King's Cup air race, 1935 . . . . 1·10 1·10
A82 41p. Miles Hawk Speed Six winning Manx Air Derby, 1947 . . . . 1·10 1·10
A83 41p. Miles Falcon Six breaking U.K.–Cape record, 1936 . . . . . . 1·10 1·10

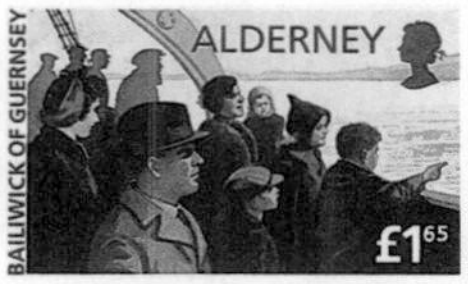

A **14** Returning Islanders

1995. 50th Anniv of Return of Islanders to Alderney. Sheet 93 × 70 mm.
MSA84 A **14** £1.65, multicoloured 4·00 4·00

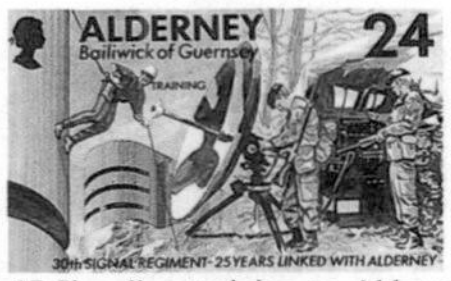

A **15** Signallers training on Alderney

1996. 25th Anniv of Adoption of 30th Signal Regiment by Alderney. Multicoloured.
A85 24p. Type A **15** . . . . . . 1·10 1·10
A86 41p. Communications station, Falkland Islands 1·10 1·10
A87 60p. Dish aerial and Land Rover, Gulf War . . . . 1·10 1·10
A88 75p. Service with United Nations . . . . 1·10 1·10
Nos. A85/8 were printed together, se-tenant, forming a composite design.

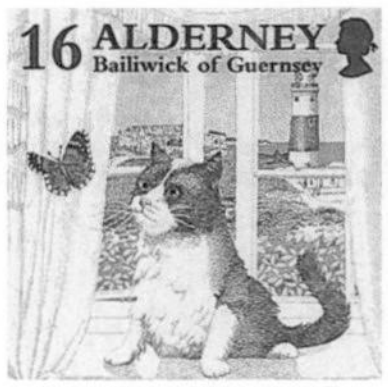

A **16** Cat with Butterfly A **17** Harold Larwood

1996. Cats. Multicoloured.
A89 16p. Type A **16** 45 35
A90 24p. Blue and white on table 65 40
A91 25p. Tabby kitten grooming blue and white persian kitten 65 65
A92 35p. Red persian under table 95 90
A93 41p. White cat with tortoiseshell and white in toy cart . . . . 1·10 1·00
A94 60p. Siamese playing with wool . . . . 1·75 1·40
MSA95 144 × 97 mm. Nos. A89/94 5·50 6·00

1997. 150th Anniv of Cricket on Alderney. Multicoloured.
A 96 18p. Type A **17** 50 30
A 97 25p. John Arlott 65 35
A 98 37p. Pelham J. Warner . . 1·00 1·25
A 99 43p. W. G. Grace . . . . 1·25 1·50
A100 63p. John Wisden . . . . 1·60 1·75
MSA101 190 × 75 mm. Nos. A96/100 and label . . . . . . 7·00 7·50

A **18** Railway under Construction A **19** Modern Superlite Helmet and Wreck of "Point Law" (oil tanker)

1997. Garrison Island (1st series). 150th Anniv of Harbour. Multicoloured.
A102 18p. Type A **18** 45 45
A103 18p. "Ariadne" (paddle steamer) at anchor . . . 45 45
A104 25p. Quarrying stone . . . 65 65
A105 25p. Quarry railway 65 65
A106 26p. Queen Victoria and Prince Albert on Alderney 70 70
A107 26p. Royal Yacht "Victoria and Albert" and guard of honour 70 70
A108 31p. Railway workers greet Queen Victoria 80 80
A109 31p. Royal party in railway wagons 80 80
See also Nos. A116/23, A132/9, A154/61 and A176/83.

1998. 21st Anniv of Alderney Diving Club. Multicoloured.
A110 20p. Type A **19** 60 40
A111 30p. Cousteau-Gagnan demand valve and wreck of "Stella" (steamer) . . 85 85
A112 37p. Heinke closed helmet and "Liverpool" (full-rigged ship) . . . . . . 1·00 1·10
A113 43p. Siebe closed helmet . . 1·30 1·30
A114 63p. Deane open helmet . . 1·90 1·90
MSA115 190 × 75 mm. Nos. A110/14 and label . . . . . . 5·00 5·00

1998. Garrison Island (2nd series). As Type A **18**. Multicoloured.
A116 20p. Alderney Post Office 50 50
A117 20p. Traders in Victoria Street 50 50
A118 25p. Court House 60 60
A119 25p. Police Station and fire engine 60 60
A120 30p. St. Anne's Church . . 70 70
A121 30p. Wedding party at Albert Gate 70 70
A122 37p. "Courier" (ferry) at Braye Bay 85 85
A123 37p. Fishermen at quay . . 85 85

A **20** Stained Glass Window commemorating Mary Rogers (Chief Stewardess)

1999. Centenary of the Wreck of "Stella" (mail steamer). Sheet 110 × 90 mm containing Type A **20** and similar horiz design.
MSA124 25p. Type A **20**; £1.75, "Stella" leaving Southampton 4·75 6·00

A **21** Solar Eclipse at 10.15 am A **22** Peregrine Falcon attacking Ruddy Turnstone

1999. Total Eclipse of the Sun (11 August). Designs showing stages of the eclipse. Multicoloured.
A125 20p. Type A **21** 50 50
A126 25p. At 10.51 am 60 60
A127 30p. At 11.14 am 70 70
A128 38p. At 11.16 am 90 90
A129 44p. At 11.17 am . . . . . 1·00 1·40
A130 64p. At 11.36 am . . . . . 1·50 1·90
MSA131 191 × 80 mm. Nos. A125/30 and label . . . . . . 4·75 5·50
No. **MS**A131 also includes the "PHILEX FRANCE '99", Paris, and the "iBRA '99", Nuremberg, emblems on the sheet margin.

1999. Garrison Island (3rd series). Forts. As Type A **18**. Multicoloured.
A132 20p. Field gun and crew, Fort Grosnez, c. 1855 . . 45 45
A133 20p. Parade of 9th Bn, Royal Garrison Artillery 45 45

A134 25p. The Arsenal, Fort Albert, c. 1862 . . . . . 55 55
A135 25p. Royal Engineers loading wagons 55 55
A136 30p. 2nd Bn, Royal Scots on parade 65 65
A137 30p. Garrison at work, Fort Tourgis, c. 1865 . . . . 65 65
A138 38p. Gun emplacement, Fort Houmet Herbe, c. 1870 . . . . . 80 80
A139 38p. Royal Alderney Artillery Militia loading cannon 80 80

Nos. A132/3, A134/5, A136/7 and A138/9 respectively were printed together, se-tenant, forming composite designs.

2000. Endangered Species. Peregrine Falcon. Multicoloured.
A140 21p. Type A **22** 50 45
A141 26p. Two falcons and prey 55 55
A142 34p. Falcon guarding eggs 70 75
A143 38p. Falcon feeding young 75 80
A144 44p. Falcon and prey . . . 1·00 1·00
A145 64p. Two young falcons . . 1·40 1·50

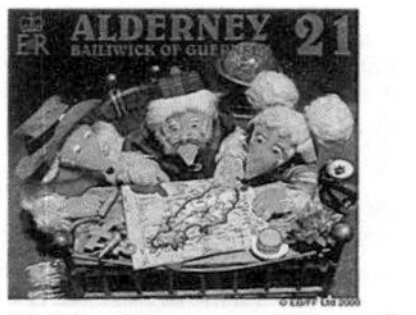

A **23** Wombles around Map of Alderney

2000. "A Wombling Holiday" (characters from children's television programme). Multicoloured.
A146 21p. Type A **23** 45 45
A147 26p. Alderney and Shansi on beach 55 55
A148 36p. Wellington by lighthouse 75 75
A149 40p. Madame Cholet and Bungo having picnic . . 90 85
A150 45p. Tomsk playing golf . . 1·10 95
A151 65p. Orinoco at airport . . 1·50 1·40
MSA152 160 × 86 mm. Nos. A146/51 . . . . 4·70 5·00

A **24** Queen Elizabeth the Queen Mother on Alderney, 1984

2000. Queen Elizabeth the Queen Mother's 100th Birthday. Sheet 93 × 70 mm.
MSA153 A **24** £1.50 multicoloured 3·75 3·75

2000. Garrison Island (4th series). Events. As Type A **18**. Multicoloured.
A154 21p. Regimental boxing tournament 45 45
A155 21p. Sports Day, Alderney Gala Week, 1924 . . . . 45 45
A156 26p. Regimental orchestra playing at Ball 55 55
A157 26p. Garrison Ball in Fort Albert Mess, 1873 . . . 55 55
A158 36p. Royal Engineers' colour party, 1859 . . . 75 75
A159 36p. Royal Artillery on parade, Queen's 40th Birthday, 1859 . . . . . 75 75
A160 40p. Royal Artillery guard of honour 90 85
A161 40p. Arrival of Maj.-Gen. Marcus Slade, 1863 . . . 90 85

Nos. A154/5, A156/7, A158/9 and A160/1 were each printed together, se-tenant, forming a composite design.

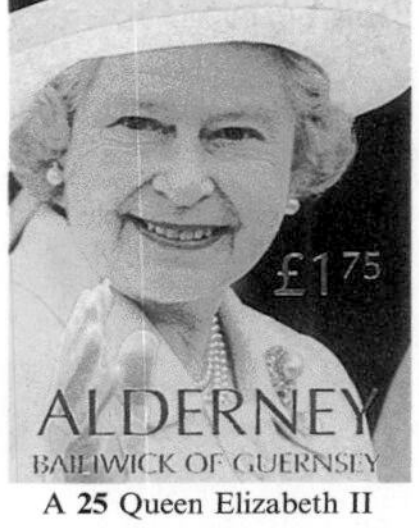

A **25** Queen Elizabeth II

2001. 75th Birthday of Queen Elizabeth II. Sheet 70 × 70 mm.
MSA162 A **25** £1.75 multicoloured 3·50 3·75

A **26** Nurse with Clipboard and Patient in X-Ray

2001. Community Services (1st series). Healthcare. Multicoloured.
A163 22p. Type A **26** 45 50
A164 27p. Nurse with tray and Mignot Memorial Hospital 55 60
A165 36p. Doctor and Princess Anne visiting hospital, 1972 . . . . 70 75
A166 40p. Nurse from 1960s and maternity unit 80 85
A167 45p. Nurse from 1957 and Queen Elizabeth II laying hospital foundation stone 90 95
A168 65p. Nurse of 1926 with baby and opening of original hospital . . . . 1·25 1·40

See also Nos. A197/202 and A217/22.

A **27** "Feathery" Golf Ball, 1901

2001. 30th Anniv of Alderney Golf Club. Multicoloured.
A169 22p. Type A **27** 45 50
A170 27p. Golfing fashions of the 1920s 55 60
A171 36p. Alderney Golf Course in 1970s 75 80
A172 40p. Modern putter 80 85
A173 45p. Modern golf gloves and shoes 90 95
A174 65p. Modern "lofted wood" 1·25 1·40
MSA175 190 × 75 mm. Nos. A169/74 . . . . 4·50 5·50

No. **MS**A175 includes the "Philanippon '01" logo on the sheet margin.

A **28** Construction of New Breakwater, 1853

2001. Garrison Island (5th series). The Royal Navy. Multicoloured.
A176 22p. Type A **28** 45 50
A177 22p. Official party inspecting harbour, 1853 45 50
A178 27p. H.M.S. *Emerald*, (steam frigate), 1860 . . 55 60
A179 27p. Disembarking troops from H.M.S. *Emerald*, 1860 . . . . 55 60
A180 36p. Moored torpedo boats, 1890 . . . . 70 75
A181 36p. Quick-firing gun on railway wagon, 1890 . . 70 75
A182 40p. H.M.S. *Majestic* (battleship) at anchor, 1901 . . . . 80 85
A183 40p. Torpedo boats outside harbour, 1901 . . . . . 80 85

Nos. A176/7, A178/9, A180/1 and A182/3 were each printed together, se-tenant, each pair forming a composite design.

A **29** Queen Elizabeth and Prince Philip arriving at London Airport, Feb 1952

A **30** Northern Hobby

2002. Golden Jubilee. Sheet 159 × 98 mm.
MSA184 A **29** £2 purple and gold 4·00 4·25

2002. Migrating Birds (1st series). Raptors. Multicoloured.
A185 22p. Type A **30** 45 50
A186 27p. Black kite 55 60
A187 36p. Merlin 70 75
A188 40p. Honey buzzard . . . 80 85
A189 45p. Osprey 90 95
A190 65p. Marsh harrier . . . . 1·25 1·40
MSA191 170 × 80 mm. Nos. A185/90 . . . . 4·50 5·00

See also Nos. A210/**MS**A216.

A **31** Coal Fire Beacon, 1725

A **32** St. Edward's Crown

2002. 50th Anniv of Electrification of Les Casquets Lighthouse. Multicoloured.
A192 22p. Type A **31** 45 50
A193 27p. Oil lantern, 1779 . . . 55 60
A194 36p. Argand lamp, 1790 . . 70 75
A195 45p. Revolving light, 1818 90 95
A196 65p. Electric light, 1952 . . 1·25 1·40

No. A196 is inscribed "Elictrification" in error.

2002. Community Services (2nd series). Emergency Medical Aid. As Type A **26**. Multicoloured.
A197 22p. Ambulance technician, and ambulance station 45 50
A198 27p. Ambulance technician using radio, and ambulance 55 60
A199 36p. Doctor, and loading patient onto aircraft . . . 70 75
A200 40p. Pilot, and Trislander over Alderney 80 85
A201 45p. Emergency operator, and patient on stretcher 90 95
A202 65p. Lifeboatman, and *Roy Barker One* (lifeboat) . . 1·25 1·40

2003. 50th Anniv of Coronation. Sheet 128 × 90 mm.
MSA203 A **32** £2 multicoloured

A **33** Wright Brothers' Flyer I, 1903

2003. Centenary of Powered Flight. Multicoloured.
A204 22p. Type A **33** 45 50
A205 27p. Alcock and Brown's Vickers FB-27 Vimy, 1919 . . . . 55 60
A206 36p. Douglas DC-3, 1936 75 80
A207 40p. De Havilland DH106 Comet 1, 1946 . . . . . 80 85
A208 45p. British Aerospace/ Aerospatiale Concorde, 1969 . . . . 90 95
A209 65p. Projected Airbus Industrie A380 . . . . . 3·50 3·75

2003. Migrating Birds (2nd series). Seabirds. Type A **30**. Multicoloured.
A210 22p. Arctic tern 45 50
A211 27p. Great skua 55 60
A212 36p. Sandwich tern 70 75
A213 40p. Sooty shearwater . . . 80 85
A214 45p. Arctic skua 90 95
A215 65p. Manx shearwater . . . 1·25 1·40
MSA216 80 × 170 mm. Nos. A210/15 . . . . 4·50 5·00

2003. Community Services (3rd series). Alderney Police. Ss Type A **26**. Multicoloured.
A217 22p. Policeman with clipboard and constables on beat 45 50
A218 27p. Policeman and Land Rover 55 60
A219 36p. Forensic team 75 80
A220 40p. Police constable and policeman with child cyclist 80 85
A221 45p. Policeman directing traffic and police at scene of accident 90 95
A222 65p. Policewoman and policeman with customs officer . . . . 1·25 1·40

A **34** *Hypholoma fasciculare*

A **35** Boys playing Football, Tourgis Close

2004. Fungi. Multicoloured.
A223 22p. Type A **34** 45 50
A224 27p. *Aleuria aurantia* . . . 55 60
A225 36p. *Coprinus micaceus* . . 75 80
A226 40p. *Langermannia gigantean* 80 85
A227 45p. *Macrolepiota procera* 90 95
A228 65p. *Xylaria hypoxylon* . . 1·25 1·50

2004. Centenary of FIFA (Federation Internationale de Football Association). Multicoloured.
A229 26p. Type A **35** 50 55
A230 32p. Three children playing football, Braye Beach . . 65 70
A231 36p. Two boys playing football in playground . . 75 80
A232 40p. Teenagers playing football, Arch Bay . . . 80 85
A233 45p. Football match . . . 90 95
A234 65p. Father and two children playing football, Arch Bay . . . . 1·30 1·40

GUINEA Pt. 13

The former French Colony on the W. coast of Africa which became fully independent in 1958.

1959. 100 centimes = 1 franc.
1973. 100 caury = 1 syli.
1986. 100 centimes = 1 franc.

1959. Stamps of Fr. West Africa optd **REPUBLIQUE DE GUINEE** or surch also.
188 – 10f. mult (No. 118) . . . . 2·00 2·50
189 **20** 45f. on 20f. pur, grn & ol 2·00 2·50

10 Pres. Sekou Toure

1959. Proclamation of Independence.
190 **10** 5f. red 20 10
191 10f. blue 30 20
192 20f. orange 50 35
193 65f. green . . . . 1·60 1·00
194 100f. violet . . . . 2·50 1·90

12 Tamara Lighthouse and Fishing Boats

13 Flying Doves

1959.
201 **12** 1f. red (postage) 10 10
202 2f. green 10 10
203 3f. brown 10 10
204 – 5f. blue 15 15
205 – 10f. purple 15 10
206 – 15f. brown 85 25
207 – 20f. purple 60 30
208 – 25f. brown . . . . 1·50 30
209 **13** 40f. blue (air) 35 25
210 50f. green 55 40
211 100f. lake . . . . 1·25 65
212 200f. red . . . . 2·25 1·25
213 500f. red . . . . 6·00 3·25

DESIGNS—VERT: 5f. Palms and dhow; 20f. Pres. Sekou Toure. HORIZ: 10f. Pirogue being launched; 15f. African Elephant (front view); 25f. African Elephant (side view).

14 Mangoes

16 "Raising the Flag"

15 Lockheed Super Constellation Airliner

1959. Fruits in natural colours. Frame colours given.
214 – 10f. red (Bananas) 15 15
215 – 15f. green (Grapefruit) . . 25 15
216 – 20f. brown (Lemons) . . . 45 20
217 **14** 25f. blue 55 30
218 – 50f. violet (Pineapple) . . . 1·00 35

1959. Air.
219 **15** 100f. blue, brown & mauve 1·75 95
220 200f. mauve, brown & grn 5·00 1·25
221 – 500f. multicoloured . . . . 8·00 2·50
DESIGN: 500f. Lockheed Super Constellation airliner on ground.

1959. 1st Anniv of Independence.
222 **16** 50f. multicoloured 55 25
223 100f. multicoloured . . . . 1·25 65

18 Africans acclaiming U.N. Headquarters Building

1959. U.N.O.
230 **18** 1f. blue & orange (postage) 15 10
231 2f. purple and green . . . 15 10
232 3f. brown and red 15 10
233 5f. brown and turquoise . . 15 10
234 50f. green, blue & brn (air) 65 50
235 100f. green, red and blue 90 70
Nos. 234/5 are larger (45 × 26 mm).

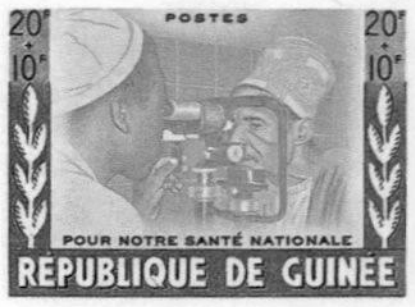

19 Eye-testing

20 "Uprooted Tree"

1960. National Health. Inscr "POUR NOTRE SANTE NATIONALE".
236 **19** 20f.+10f. red and blue . . 75 70
237 – 30f.+20f. violet & orange 75 70
238 – 40f.+20f. blue and red . . 1·10 95
239 – 50f.+50f. brown and green 2·00 1·60
240 – 100f.+100f. green & pur . . 2·75 2·10
DESIGNS—HORIZ: 30f. Laboratory assistant; 40f. Spraying trees. VERT: (28½ × 40 mm): 50f. Research with microscope; 100f. Operating theatre.

1960. World Refugee Year.
241 **20** 25f. multicoloured 50 35
242 50f. multicoloured 70 45

21 U.P.U. Monument, Berne

23 Flag and Map

1960. 1st Anniv of Admission to U.P.U. Background differs for each value.
243 **21** 10f. black and brown . . . 15 10
244 15f. lilac and mauve . . . 25 15
245 20f. indigo and blue . . . 40 15
246 – 25f. myrtle and green . . . 55 15
247 – 50f. sepia and orange . . . 65 25
DESIGN: 25f., 50f. As Type **10** but vert.

1960. Olympic Games. Optd **Jeux Olympiques Rome 1960** and Olympic rings.
248 **16** 50f. multicoloured (postage) . . . . 5·00 5·00
249 100f. multicoloured . . . . 7·50 7·50
250 **15** 100f. blue, grn & mve(air) 6·50 4·50
251 200f. mauve, brown & grn 13·00 6·50
252 – 500f. multi (No. 221) . . . 32·00 32·00

1960. 2nd Anniv of Independence.
253 **23** 25f. multicoloured 30 25
254 30f. multicoloured 40 35

1960. 15th Anniv of U.N.O. Optd **XVEME ANNIVERSAIRE DES NATIONS UNIES**. (a) Nos. 214/18. Fruits in natural colours.
255 – 10f. red 20 20
256 – 15f. green 30 25
257 – 20f. brown 35 30
258 **14** 25f. blue 45 35
259 – 50f. violet 75 60

(b) Nos. 230/35.
260 **18** 1f. blue & orange (postage) 10 10
261 2f. purple and green . . . 10 10
262 3f. brown and red 10 10
263 5f. brown and turquoise . . 10 10
264 50f. green, blue & brn (air) 65 70
265 100f. green, red and blue 90 70

1961. Surch **1961** and value.
266 **20** 25f.+10f. multicoloured . . 4·75 4·75
267 50f.+20f. multicoloured . . 4·75 4·75

27 Bohar Reedbuck

1961. Centres in brown, green and blue. Inscriptions and value tablets in colours given.
268 **27** 5f. turquoise 15 10
269 10f. green 15 10
270 25f. violet 40 15
271 40f. orange 55 20
272 50f. red . . . . 1·25 25
273 75f. blue . . . . 1·75 45

28 Guinea Flag and Exhibition Hall, Conakry

1961. First Three-Year Plan. Flag in red, yellow and green.
274 **28** 5f. blue and red 15 15
275 10f. brown and red 15 15
276 25f. green and red 25 25

29 Helmeted Guineafowl

1961. Guineafowl in purple and blue.
277 **29** 5f. mauve and blue 40 20
278 10f. red and blue 45 20
279 25f. red and blue 45 35
280 40f. brown and blue . . . 80 40
281 50f. bistre and blue . . . 90 60
282 75f. olive and blue . . . . 2·25 75

1961. Protection of Animals. Surch **POUR LA PROTECTION DE NOS ANIMAUX +5 FRS.**
283 **27** 5f.+5f. turquoise 15 15
284 10f.+5f. green 25 15
285 25f.+5f. violet 55 30
286 40f.+5f. orange 70 40
287 50f.+5f. red 95 55
288 75f.+5f. blue . . . . . . 1·50 70

31 Patrice Lumumba

1962. 1st Death Anniv of Lumumba (Congo leader).
289 **31** 10f. multicoloured 30 25
290 25f. multicoloured 40 25
291 50f. multicoloured 60 30

1962. Malaria Eradication (1st issue). Nos. 236/40 optd with Malaria Eradication emblem and **ERADICATION DE LA MALARIA**.
292 **19** 20f.+10f. red and blue . . 35 35
293 – 30f.+20f. violet and orange 50 50
294 – 40f.+20f. blue and red . . 60 60
295 – 50f.+50f. brown & green 1·25 1·25
296 – 100f.+100f. green & pur . . 2·50 2·50

33 King Mohammed V and Map

34a Posthorn on North Africa

34 Mosquito and Emblem

1962. 1st Anniv of Casablanca Conference.
297 **33** 25f. multicoloured 95 25
298 75f. multicoloured . . . . 1·90 45

1962. Air. Malaria Eradication (2nd issue).
299 **34** 25f. black and orange . . . 40 20
300 50f. black and red 50 35
301 100f. black and green . . . 1·00 60

1962. African Postal Union Commemoration.
303 **34a** 25f. green, brown & orge 65 15
304 100f. orange and brown 1·60 40

1962. Guinea-fowl stamps surch **POUR LA PROTECTION DE NOS OISEAUX +5 FRS.**
305 **29** 5f.+5f. 60 35
306 10f.+5f. 60 45
307 25f.+5f. 80 55
308 40f.+5f. 95 70
309 50f.+5f. . . . . 2·10 90
310 75f.+5f. . . . . 3·75 1·90

36 Bote-player

37 Hippopotamus

1962. Native Musicians.
311 **36** 30c. red, grn & bl (postage) 15 10
312 A 50c. green, brown & salmon 15 10
313 B 1f. purple and green . . . 15 10
314 C 1f.50 turquoise, red & yell 15 10
315 D 2f. green, red and mauve 15 10
316 C 3f. violet, green & turquoise 15 10
317 B 10f. blue, brown and orange 25 10
318 D 20f. red, sepia and olive . . 30 20
319 **36** 25f. violet, sepia and olive 45 25
320 A 40f. mauve, green and blue 45 35
321 **36** 50f. blue, red and rose . . 60 40
322 A 75f. blue, brown and ochre 2·50 55
323 D 100f. blue, red & pink (air) 1·10 50
324 200f. red and blue . . . . 2·50 75
325 E 500f. blue, violet and brown . . . . 6·50 2·50
DESIGNS—(Musicians playing). HORIZ: A, Bolon; C, Koni; D, Kora; E, Balafon. VERT: B, Flute.

1962. Wild Game.
326 **37** 10f. sepia, green and orange 30 10
327 – 25f. brown, sepia and green 60 20
328 – 30f. sepia, yellow and olive 70 20
329 **37** 50f. sepia, green and blue 1·00 35
330 – 75f. brown, purple and lilac . . . . 1·50 60
331 – 100f. sepia, yellow & turq 2·00 80
DESIGNS: 25f., 75f. Lion; 30f., 100f. Leopard.

38 Boy at Blackboard

43 Crowned Crane

39 Alfa Yaya

1962. Campaign Against Illiteracy.
332 **38** 5f. sepia, yellow and red 10 10
333 – 10f. sepia, orange and purple 10 10
334 **38** 15f. sepia, green and red 20 10
335 – 20f. sepia, turquoise & pur 30 20
DESIGN: 10f., 20f. Teacher at blackboard.

1962. African Heroes and Martyrs.
336 **39** 25f. sepia, turquoise & gold 30 15
337 – 30f. sepia, ochre and gold 40 20
338 – 50f. sepia, purple and gold 55 25
339 – 75f. sepia, green and gold 1·10 40
340 – 100f. sepia, red and gold 1·40 60
PORTRAITS: 30f. King Behanzin; 50f. King Ba Bemba of Sikasso; 75f. Almamy Samory; 100f. Chief Tierno Aliou of the Goumba.

1962. Algerian Refugees Fund. Surch **Aide aux Refugies Algeriens** and premium.
341 **33** 25f.+15f. multicoloured . . 65 65
342 75f.+25f. multicoloured . . 1·25 1·25

1962. Air. "The Conquest of Space". Optd with capsule and **La Conquete De L'Espace**.
343 **13** 40f. blue 50 25
344 50f. green 60 30
345 100f. lake . . . . 1·00 50
348 200f. red . . . . 1·75 95

1962. Birds. Multicoloured.
349 30c. Type **43** (postage) . . . 70 15
350 50c. Grey parrot (horiz) . . . 70 15
351 1f. Abyssinian ground hornbill (horiz) 80 15
352 1f.50 White spoonbill (horiz) 80 30
353 2f. Bateleur (horiz) 80 30
354 3f. Type **43** . . . . 1·00 30
355 10f. As 50c. (horiz) . . . . . 1·00 30
356 20f. As 1f. (horiz) . . . . . 1·25 60
357 25f. As 1f.50 (horiz) . . . . 1·60 60
358 40f. As 2f. (horiz) . . . . . 1·60 60
359 50f. Type **43** . . . . 1·75 85
360 75f. As 50c. (horiz) . . . . . 4·00 90
361 100f. As 1f. (horiz) (air) . . . 4·50 1·10
362 200f. As 1f.50 (horiz) . . . . 7·50 2·50
363 500f. As 2f. (horiz) . . . . . 16·00 5·50

44 Handball

1963. Sports.
364 **44** 30c. purple, red and green (postage) 10 10
365 A 50c. violet, lilac and blue 10 10
366 B 1f. sepia, orange and green 10 10
367 C 1f.50 blue, orange & purple 10 10
368 D 2f. blue, turquoise & purple 10 10
369 **44** 3f. purple, olive and blue 10 10
370 A 4f. violet, mauve and blue 10 10
371 B 5f. sepia, green and purple 15 10
372 C 10f. blue and bright purple 20 10
373 D 20f. blue, orange and red 30 15
374 **44** 25f. purple, green and black 40 15
375 A 30f. violet, black and blue 45 25
376 B 100f. sepia, lake & grn (air) 1·10 40
377 C 200f. blue, brown & purple 2·25 90
378 D 500f. blue, brown & purple 5·00 2·25
DESIGNS: A, Boxing; B, Running; C, Cycling; D, Canoeing.

45 Campaign Emblem

1963. Freedom from Hunger.
379 **45** 5f. yellow and red 10 10
380 10f. yellow and green 10 10
381 15f. yellow and brown 15 10
382 25f. yellow and olive 25 15

46 "Amauris niavius"

1963. Butterflies. Multicoloured.
383 10c. Type **46** (postage) 10 10
384 30c. "Papilio demodocus" 10 10
385 40c. As 30c. 10 10
386 50c. "Graphum policenes" 10 10
387 1f. "Papilio nireus" 15 10
388 1f.50 Type **46** 20 10
389 2f. "Papilio menestheus" 20 10
390 3f. As 30c. 20 10
391 10f. As 50c. 35 10
392 20f. As 1f. 60 15
393 25f. Type **46** 1·00 20
394 40f. As 2f. 1·40 30
395 50f. As 30c. 1·90 35
396 75f. As 1f. 2·75 60
397 100f. Type **46** (air) 1·75 35
398 200f. As 50c. 4·00 80
399 500f. As 2f. 8·00 2·50

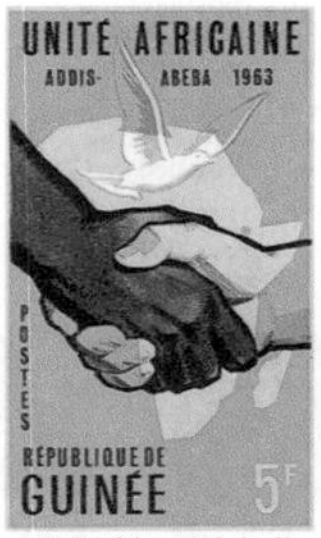

47 "African Unity"

1963. Conf of African Heads of State, Addis Ababa.
400 **47** 5f. sepia, blk & turq on grn 10 10
401 10f. sepia, black and yellow on yellow 10 10
402 15f. sepia, black & ol on ol 15 10
403 25f. sepia, black and brown on cinnamon 25 15

48 Capsule encircling Globe

1963. Centenary of Red Cross.
404 **48** 5f. red and green (postage) 10 10
405 10f. red and blue 15 10
406 15f. red and yellow 20 15
407 25f. red and black (air) 45 20

1963. Air. 1st Pan-American Conakry–New York Direct Air Service. Optd **PREMIER SERVICE DIRECT CONAKRY–NEW YORK PAN AMERICAN 30 JUILLET 1963**.
409 **15** 10f. blue, green and mauve 1·90 75
410 200f. mauve, brown & green 3·25 1·25

1963. Olympic Games Preparatory Commission, Conakry. Nos. 364/6 surch **COMMISSION PREPARATOIRE AUX JEUX OLYMPIQUES A CONAKRY**, rings and new value.
411 40f. on 30c. purple, red and green 1·00 80
412 50f. on 50c. violet, lilac and blue 1·40 1·10
413 75f. on 1f. sepia, orange & grn 2·40 1·90

51 Jewel Cichlid

1964. Guinea Fishes. Multicoloured.
414 30c. Type **51** (postage) 10 10
415 40c. Golden pheasant panchax 10 10
416 50c. Blue gularis 10 10
417 1f. Banded jewelfish and jewel cichlid 10 10
418 1f.50 Yellow gularis 10 10
419 2f. Six-banded lyretail 25 10
420 5f. Type **51** 25 10
421 30f. As 40c. 65 20
422 40f. As 50c. 1·25 35
423 75f. As 1f. 2·25 55
424 100f. As 1f.50 (air) 2·25 55
425 300f. As 2f. 7·00 1·75

52 President Kennedy

53 Pipeline under Construction

1964. Pres. Kennedy Memorial Issue. Flag in red and blue.
426 **52** 5f. violet & black (postage) 10 10
427 25f. violet and green 25 20
428 50f. violet and brown 60 30
429 100f. black and violet (air) 1·00 85

1964. Inaug of Piped Water Supply, Conakry.
430 **53** 5f. red 10 10
431 – 10f. violet 10 10
432 – 20f. brown 15 10
433 – 30f. blue 30 15
434 – 50f. green 55 30
DESIGNS—HORIZ: 10f. Reservoir; 20f. Joining pipes; 30f. Transporting pipes; 50f. Laying pipes.

54 Ice hockey

1964. Winter Olympic Games, Innsbruck. Rings, frame and tablet in gold.
435 **54** 10f. olive & green (postage) 15 10
436 – 25f. slate and violet 40 20
437 – 50f. black and blue 75 40
438 – 100f. black & brn (air) 1·10 55
DESIGNS: 25f. Ski-jumping; 50f. Skiing; 100f. Figure-skating.

1964. Air. Olympic Games, Tokyo (1st issue). Nos. 376/8 optd **JEUX OLYMPIQUES TOKYO 1964** and Olympic rings.
439 100f. sepia, lake and green 1·50 1·00
440 200f. blue, brown and purple 2·25 1·50
441 500f. blue, brown and purple 5·00 3·50

56 Eleanor Roosevelt with Children

1964. 15th Anniv of Declaration of Human Rights.
442 **56** 5f. green (postage) 10 10
443 10f. orange 10 10
444 15f. blue 15 10
445 25f. red 30 15
446 50f. violet (air) 70 30

57 Striped Hyena

1964. Animals.
447 **57** 5f. sepia and yellow 20 10
448 30f. sepia and blue 40 20
449 – 40f. black and mauve 55 25
450 – 75f. sepia and green 1·50 30
451 – 100f. sepia and ochre 2·00 50
452 – 300f. deep violet and orange 4·00 1·75
ANIMALS: 40f., 300f. African buffalo; 75f., 100f. African elephant.

58 Guinea Pavilion

1964. New York World's Fair.
453 **58** 30f. green and lilac 25 15
454 40f. green and purple 40 15
455 50f. green and brown 50 15
456 75f. blue and red 75 25
See also Nos. 484/87.

60 Nefertari, Isis and Hathor

1964. Nubian Monuments Preservation. Mult.
458 10f. Type **60** (postage) 20 15
459 25f. Pharaoh in battle 25 15
460 50f. The Nile—partly submerged sphinxes 45 20
461 100f. Rameses II, entrance hall of Great Temple, Abu Simbel 1·10 45
462 200f. Lower part of Colossi, Abu Simbel 2·00 80
463 300f. Nefertari (air) 3·75 1·60

61 Athlete with Torch

62 Doudou (Boke) Mask

1965. Olympic Games, Tokyo (2nd issue). Multicoloured.
464 5f. Weightlifter and children (postage) 15 10
465 10f. Type **61** 15 10
466 25f. Pole vaulting 25 20
467 40f. Running 30 20
468 50f. Judo 50 30
469 75f. Japanese hostess 1·00 45
470 100f. Air hostess and Convair Coronado airliner (horiz) (air) 1·50 55

1965. Native Masks and Dancers. Mult.
472 20c. Type **62** (postage) 10 10
473 40c. Niamou (Nzerekore) mask 10 10
474 60c. "Yoki" (Boke) statuette 10 10
475 80c. Guekedou dancer 10 10
476 1f. Niamou (Nzerekore) mask 10 10
477 2f. Macenta dancer 15 10
478 15f. Niamou (Nzerekore) mask 25 15
479 20f. Tom-tom beater (forest region) 45 15
480 60f. Macenta "Bird-man" dancer 95 45
481 80f. Bassari (Koundara) dancer 1·10 55
482 100f. Karana sword dancer 1·60 70
483 300f. Niamou (Nzerekore) mask (air) 4·50 1·50

1965. New York World's Fair. As Nos. 453/6 but additionally inscr "1965".
484 **58** 30f. orange and green 20 15
485 40f. green and red 30 15
486 50f. violet and blue 45 25
487 75f. violet and brown 65 35

63 Metal-work

1965. Native Handicrafts. Multicoloured.
489 15f. Type **63** (postage) 15 10
490 20f. Pottery 20 15
491 60f. Dyeing 60 35
492 80f. Basket-making 85 45
493 100f. Ebony-work (air) 1·25 45
494 300f. Ivory-work 4·50 1·25

64 I.T.U. Emblem and Symbols

1965. I.T.U. Centenary.
495 **64** 25f. multicoloured (postage) 30 15
496 50f. multicoloured 60 25
497 100f. multicoloured (air) 1·10 40
498 200f. multicoloured 2·00 65

67 U.N. Headquarters and I.C.Y. Emblem

1965. I.C.Y.
501 **67** 25f. red and green (postage) 25 15
502 45f. red and violet 35 20
503 75f. red and brown 70 30
504 100f. orange and blue (air) 1·25 45

68 Polytechnic Institute, Conakry

1965. 7th Anniv of Independence. Mult.
505 25f. Type **68** (postage) 15 15
506 30f. Camayenne Hotel 20 15
507 40f. Gbessia Airport 60 30
508 75f. "28 Septembre" Stadium 55 35
509 200f. Polytechnic Institute, North facade (air) 1·40 1·00
510 500f. Ditto, West facade 4·25 2·50
Nos. 509/10 are larger, 53 × 23 mm.

69 Moon, Globe and Satellite

70 Sabre Dance, Karana

1965. "To the Moon". Multicoloured.
511 5f. Type **69** (postage) 15 10
512 10f. Trajectory of "Ranger 7" 20 10
513 25f. "Relay" satellite 30 20
514 45f. "Vostok 1, 2" and Globe 55 25
515 100f. "Ranger 7" approaching Moon (vert) (25 × 36 mm) (air) 85 40
516 200f. Launching of "Ranger 7" (vert) (25 × 36 mm) 2·00 75
Nos. 512/14 are larger, 36 × 25½ mm.

1966. Guinean Dances. Multicoloured.
519 10c. Type **70** (postage) 10 10
520 30c. Young girls' dance, Lower Guinea 10 10
521 50c. Tiekere musicians, "Eyora" (bamboo) dance, Bandjinguene (horiz) (36 × 29 mm) 10 10
522 5f. Doundouba dance, Kouroussa 10 10
523 40f. Bird-man's dance, Macenta 85 30
524 100f. Kouyate Kandia, national singer (horiz) (36 × 29 mm) (air) 1·25 45
See also Nos. 561/6.

1966. Stamp Cent Exn, Cairo. Nos. 460 and 463 optd **CENTENAIRE DU TIMBRE CAIRE 1966**.
525 50f. multicoloured (postage) 55 40
526 300f. multicoloured (air) 2·25 1·50

1966. Pan Arab Games, Cairo (1965). Nos. 464/5, 467/9 optd **JEUX PANARABES CAIRE 1965** and pyramid motif.
527 – 5f. multicoloured (postage) 20 15
528 **61** 10f. multicoloured 20 15
529 – 40f. multicoloured 55 35

530 – 50f. multicoloured 70 45
531 – 75f. multicoloured 1·25 75
532 – 100f. multicoloured (air) 1·25 40

73 Vonkou Rocks, Telimele — **74** UNESCO Emblem

1966. Landscapes (1st series). Multicoloured.
534 20f. Type **73** (postage) 15 10
535 25f. Artificial lake, Coyah 20 10
536 40f. Waterfalls, Kate 35 15
537 50f. Bridge, Forecariah 45 20
538 75f. Liana bridge 70 35
539 100f. Lighthouse and bay, Boulbinet (air) 1·50 45
See also Nos. 603/608.

1966. 20th Anniv of UNESCO (a) Postage.
540 **74** 25f. multicoloured 40 20

(b) Air. Nos. 509/10 optd **vingt ans 1946 1966** and UNESCO Emblem.
541 200f. multicoloured 2·00 1·25
542 500f. multicoloured 4·50 2·75

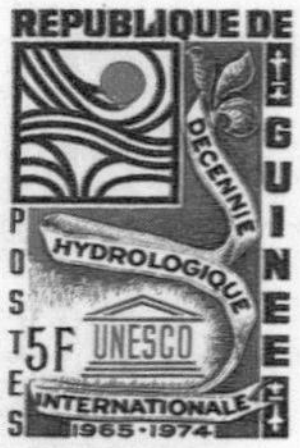

76 — **78** Decade and UNESCO Symbols

1966. Guinean Flora and Female Headdresses. Similar designs.
543 **76** 10c. multicoloured (postage) 10 10
544 – 20c. multicoloured 10 10
545 – 30c. multicoloured 10 10
546 – 40c. multicoloured 10 10
547 – 3f. multicoloured 10 10
548 – 4f. multicoloured 10 10
549 – 10f. multicoloured 15 10
550 – 25f. multicoloured 55 10
551 – 30f. multicoloured 70 15
552 – 50f. multicoloured 1·10 30
553 **76** 80f. multicoloured 1·40 40
554 – 200f. multicoloured (air) 2·75 75
555 – 300f. multicoloured 4·50 1·50
Nos. 551/555 are 29 × 42 mm.

1966. Int Hydrological Decade.
558 **78** 5f. red and blue 10 10
559 25f. red and green 20 10
560 100f. red and purple 1·00 50

1966. Guinean National Ballet. Designs show various dances as T **70**.
561 60c. multicoloured 10 10
562 1f. multicoloured 10 10
563 1f.50 multicoloured 15 10
564 25f. multicoloured 35 20
565 50f. multicoloured 85 30
566 75f. multicoloured 1·40 50
SIZES—VERT: (26 × 36 mm): 60c., 1f., 1f.50, 50f. HORIZ: (36 × 29 mm): 25f., 75f.

79 "Village"

1966. 20th Anniv of UNICEF Multicoloured designs showing children's drawings.
567 2f. "Elephant" 10 10
568 3f. "Doll" 10 10
569 10f. "Girl" 10 10
570 20f. Type **79** 15 10
571 25f. "Footballer" 35 15
572 40f. "Still Life" 55 20
573 50f. "Bird in Tree" 70 25

80 Dispensing Medicine

1967. Inauguration of W.H.O. Headquarters, Geneva. Multicoloured.
574 30f. Type **80** 25 10
575 50f. Doctor examining child 35 20
576 75f. Nurse weighing baby 60 30
577 80f. W.H.O. Building and flag 75 45

81 Niamou Mask

1967. Guinean Masks. Multicoloured.
578 10c. Banda-di (Kanfarade Boke region) 10 10
579 30c. Niamou (N'zerekore region) (different) 10 10
580 50c. Type **81** 10 10
581 60c. Yinadjinkele (Kankan region) 10 10
582 1f. As 10c. 10 10
583 1f.50 As 30c. 10 10
584 5f. Type **81** 15 10
585 25f. As 60c. 20 10
586 30f. As 10c. 30 10
587 50f. As 30c. 55 20
588 75f. As Type **81** 1·10 35
589 100f. As 60c. 1·50 50

82 Research Institute

1967. Pastoria Research Institute. Mult.
590 20c. Type **82** (postage) 10 10
591 30c. "Python regius" (snake) 10 10
592 50c. Extracting snake's venom 10 10
593 1f. "Python sebae" 10 10
594 2f. Attendants handling viper 10 10
595 5f. Gabon viper 10 10
596 20f. "Dendroaspis viridis" 35 10
597 30f. As 5f. 65 10
598 50f. As 1f. 1·10 20
599 75f. As 50c. 1·60 30
600 200f. As 20c. (air) 2·25 80
601 300f. As 2f. 4·00 1·50
Nos. 596/601 are 56 × 26 mm.

1967. Landscapes (2nd series). As T **73**. Mult.
603 5f. Loos Islands (postage) 10 10
604 30f. Tinkisso waterfalls 20 10
605 70f. The "Elephant's Trunk", Kakoulima 45 10
606 80f. Seashore, Ratoma 70 20
607 100f. House of explorer Olivier de Sanderval (air) 1·10 35
608 200f. Aerial view of Conakry 1·60 75

83 People's Palace, Conakry

1967. 20th Anniv of Guinean Democratic Party and Inaug of People's Palace. Multicoloured.
609 5f. Type **83** (postage) 10 10
610 30f. African elephant's head 50 50
611 55f. Type **83** 40 25
612 200f. As 30f. (air) 1·75 1·00

1967. 50th Anniv of Lions Int Landscape series optd **AMITE DES PEUPLES GRACE AU TOURISME 1917 – 1967** and Lions Emblem.
613 5f. (No. 603) (postage) 15 10
614 30f. (No. 604) 30 20
615 40f. (No. 536) 35 20
616 50f. (No. 537) 45 25
617 70f. (No. 605) 60 35
618 75f. (No. 538) 85 45
619 80f. (No. 606) 1·00 45
620 100f. (No. 539) (air) 1·10 60
621 100f. (No. 607) 1·10 60
622 200f. (No. 608) 2·00 1·10

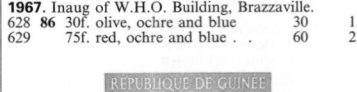

85 Section of Mural — **86** W.H.O. Building, Brazzaville

1967. Air. "World of Tomorrow". Jose Vanetti's Mural, Conference Building, U.N. Headquarters.
623 – 30f. multicoloured 20 15
624 – 50f. multicoloured 30 20
625 **85** 100f. multicoloured 80 40
626 – 200f. multicoloured 1·60 60
DESIGNS: 50f. to 200f. Various sections of mural.

1967. Inaug of W.H.O. Building, Brazzaville.
628 **86** 30f. olive, ochre and blue 30 15
629 75f. red, ochre and blue 60 25

87 Human Rights Emblem

1968. Human Rights Year.
630 **87** 30f. red, green and ochre 25 15
631 40f. red, blue and violet 30 15

88 Coyah, Oubreka Region

1968. Regional Costumes and Habitations. Multicoloured.
632 20c. Type **88** (postage) 10 10
633 30c. Kankan Region 10 10
634 40c. Kankan, Upper Guinea 10 10
635 50c. Forest region 10 10
636 60c. Foulamory, Gaoual Region 10 10
637 5f. Cognagui, Koundara Region 10 10
638 15f. As 50c. 15 10
639 20f. As 20c. 30 15
640 30f. As 30c. 45 20
641 40f. Fouta-Djallon, Middle Guinea 70 25
642 100f. Labe, Middle Guinea 1·50 40
643 300f. Bassari, Koundara Region (air) 3·25 1·00
The 60c. to 300f. are larger (60 × 39 mm).

89 "The Village Story-teller"

1968. Paintings of African Legends (1st series). Multicoloured.
644 25f. Type **89** (postage) 15 10
645 30f. "The Moon and the Stars" 15 10
646 75f. "Leuk the Hare sells his Sister" (vert) 60 35
647 80f. "The Hunter and the Female Antelope" 1·00 35
648 100f. "Old Faya's Inheritance" (vert) (air) 1·00 30
649 200f. "Soumangourou Kante killed by Djegue" 2·00 45

1968. Paintings of African Legends (2nd series). As T **89**. Multicoloured.
651 15f. "Little Demons of Mount Nimba" (postage) 10 10
652 30f. "Lan, the Baby Buffalo" (vert) 20 10
653 40f. "The Nianablas and the Crocodiles" 30 20
654 50f. "Leuk the Hare and the Drum" (vert) 50 20
655 70f. "Malissadio—the Young Girl and the Hippopotamus" (air) 75 20
656 300f. "Little Goune, Son of the Lion" (vert) 3·25 1·10

90 Olive Baboon

1968. African Fauna. Multicoloured.
658 5f. Type **90** (postage) 15 10
659 10f. Leopards 20 10
660 15f. Hippopotami 30 15
661 20f. Crocodile 55 20
662 30f. Warthog 70 20
663 50f. Kob 85 25
664 75f. African buffalo 1·60 45
665 100f. Lions (air) 1·75 40
666 200f. African elephant 4·00 1·00
Nos. 665/6 are 50 × 35 mm.

91 Robert F. Kennedy

1968. "Martyrs of Liberty". Multicoloured.
668 30f. Type **91** (postage) 20 10
669 75f. Martin Luther King 50 20
670 100f. John F. Kennedy 65 35
671 50f. Type **91** (air) 45 15
672 100f. Martin Luther King 80 25
673 200f. John F. Kennedy 1·75 60

92 Running

1969. Olympic Games, Mexico (1968). Multicoloured.
674 5f. Type **92** (postage) 10 10
675 10f. Boxing 10 10
676 15f. Throwing the javelin 15 10
677 25f. Football 25 10
678 30f. Hurdling 30 10
679 50f. Throwing the hammer 50 25
680 75f. Cycling 70 25
681 100f. Gymnastics (air) 70 30
682 200f. Exercising on rings 1·25 50
683 300f. Pole-vaulting 2·50 95
The 25, 100, 200 and 300f. are larger, 57 × 30 mm. Each design also shows one of three different sculptured figures.

1969. Moon Flight of "Apollo 8". Nos. 514/16 optd **APOLLO 8 DEC. 1968** and earth and moon motifs or surch also.
684 30f. on 45f. mult (postage) 35 35
685 45f. multicoloured 35 35
686 25f. on 200f. mult (air) 35 15
687 100f. multicoloured 1·10 65
688 200f. multicoloured 2·00 1·00

95 "Tarzan"

1969. "Tarzan" (famous Guinea Chimpanzee). Multicoloured.
689 25f. Type **95** 25 15
690 30f. "Tarzan" in front of Pastoria Institute 30 20
691 75f. "Tarzan" and family 65 25
692 100f. "Tarzan" squatting on branch 1·25 40

96 Pioneers lighting Fire

1969. Guinean Pioneer Youth Organization. Multicoloured.

693	5f. Type **96**	10	10
694	25f. Pioneer and village	20	10
695	30f. Pioneers squad	25	10
696	40f. Playing basketball	35	20
697	45f. Two pioneers	40	20
698	50f. Pioneers emblem	50	25

97 "Apollo" Launch

1969. 1st Man on the Moon. Multicoloured.

700	25f. Type **97**	15	10
701	30f. View of Earth	20	10
702	50f. Modules descent to the Moon	35	10
703	60f. Astronauts on Moon	45	20
704	75f. Landing module on Moon	50	25
705	100f. Take-off from Moon	1·00	40
706	200f. "Splashdown"	2·00	1·00

No. 705 is 35 × 71 mm.

The above stamps were issued with English and French inscriptions.

98 Pylon and Heavy Industry

1969. 50th Anniv of I.L.O. Multicoloured.

707	25f. Type **98**	20	10
708	30f. Broadcasting studio	20	10
709	75f. Harvesting	50	20
710	200f. Making pottery	1·40	65

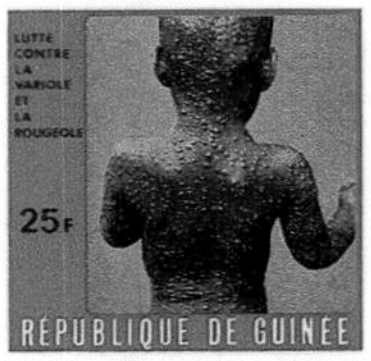

99 Child suffering from Smallpox

1970. Campaign Against Measles and Smallpox. Multicoloured.

711	25f. Type **99**	15	10
712	30f. Mother and child with measles	20	15
713	40f. Inoculating girl	30	15
714	50f. Inoculating boy	50	25
715	60f. Inoculating family	60	25
716	200f. Dr. Edward Jenner	2·25	1·00

100 O.E.R.S. Countries on Map of Africa

1970. Meeting of Senegal River Riparian States Organization (Organisation des Etats Riverains du Fleuve Senegal).

717	**100**	30f. multicoloured	20	15
718		200f. multicoloured	1·50	95

NOTE: The Riparian States are Guinea, Mali, Mauritania and Senegal.

101 Dish Aerial and Open book

1970. World Telecommunications Day.

719	**101**	5f. black and blue	15	15
720		10f. black and red	15	15
721		50f. black and yellow	45	15
722		200f. black and lilac	2·00	95

102 Lenin

1970. Birth Centenary of Lenin. Multicoloured.

723	5f. Type **102**	10	10
724	20f. "Lenin in the Smolny" (Serov)	20	10
725	30f. "Lenin addressing Workers" (Serov)	25	15
726	40f. "Lenin speaking to Servicemen" (Vasiliev)	40	15
727	100f. "Lenin with Crowd" (Vasilev)	1·00	35
728	200f. Type **102**	1·75	1·00

103 Congo Tetra

1971. Fishes. Multicoloured.

729	5f. Type **103**	15	10
730	10f. Red-spotted gularis	20	10
731	15f. Red-chinned panchax	20	10
732	20f. Six-barred distichodus	35	15
733	25f. Jewel cichlid	40	25
734	30f. Rainbow krib	65	25
735	40f. Two-striped lyretail	75	25
736	45f. Banded jewelfish	1·10	35
737	50f. Red-tailed notho	1·25	50
738	75f. Freshwater butterflyfish	2·25	55
739	100f. Golden trevally	2·75	65
740	200f. African mouth-brooder	5·50	1·75

104 Violet-crested Turaco

1971. Wild Birds. Multicoloured.

741	5f. Type **104** (postage)	75	50
742	20f. Golden oriole	1·00	60
743	30f. Blue headed coucal	1·10	75
744	40f. Great grey shrike	1·25	90
745	75f. Vulturine guineafowl	2·75	1·10
746	100f. Southern ground hornbill	4·50	1·50
747	50f. Type **104** (air)	1·50	1·00
748	100f. As 20f.	2·00	1·25
749	200f. As 75f.	7·25	1·75

105 UNICEF Emblem on Map of Africa

1971. 25th Anniv of UNICEF

750	**105**	25f. multicoloured	15	10
751		30f. multicoloured	20	10
752		50f. multicoloured	35	15
753		60f. multicoloured	50	20
754		100f. multicoloured	80	35

106 John and Robert Kennedy and Martin Luther King

1972. Air. Martyrs for Peace. Embossed on silver or gold foil.

755	**106**	300f. silver	3·25	
756		1500f. gold, cream and green	16·00	

107 Jules Verne and Moon Rocket

1972. Air. Moon Exploration. Embossed on silver or gold foil.

757	**107**	300f. silver	3·25	
758		1200f. gold	13·00	

108 Pres. Richard Nixon

1972. Air. Pres. Nixon's Visit to Peking. Embossed on gold or silver foil.

759	**108**	90f. silver	75	
760	–	90f. silver	75	
761	–	90f. silver	75	
762	–	90f. silver	75	
763	**108**	290f. gold	2·50	
764	–	290f. gold	2·50	
765	–	290f. gold	2·50	
766	–	290f. gold	2·50	
767	–	1200f. gold and red	13·00	

DESIGNS—VERT: Nos. 760, 764, Chinese table-tennis player; 761, 765, American table-tennis player; 762, 766, Mao Tse-tung. HORIZ: (45 × 35 mm): No. 767, Pres. Nixon and Mao Tse-tung.

109 "Flying Flatfish"

1972. Imaginary Space Creatures. Mult.

768	5f. Type **109**	10	10
769	20f. "Radioactive crab"	20	10
770	30f. "Space octopus"	25	10
771	40f. "Rocket-powered serpent"	45	10
772	100f. "Winged eel"	1·10	40
773	200f. "Flying dragon"	2·00	70

110 African Child

1972. Racial Equality Year. Multicoloured.

774	15f. Type **110** (postage)	10	10
775	20f. Asiatic child	15	10
776	30f. Indian youth	20	10
777	50f. European girl	45	20
778	100f. Heads of four races	85	35
779	100f. As No. 778 (air)	90	40

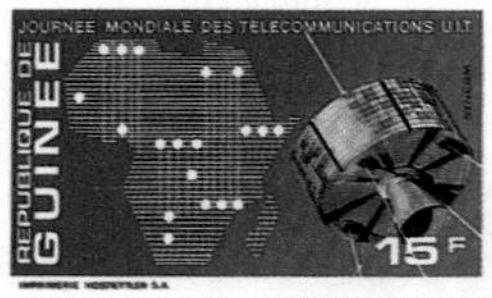

111 "Syncom" and African Map

1972. World Telecommunications Day. Mult.

780	15f. Type **111** (postage)	15	10
781	30f. "Relay"	25	10
782	75f. "Early Bird"	60	30
783	80f. "Telstar"	1·00	40
784	100f. As 30f. (air)	1·00	35
785	200f. As 75f.	1·90	65

112 APU Emblem and Dove with Letter

1972. 10th Anniv of African Postal Union.

786	**112**	15f. mult (postage)	10	10
787		30f. multicoloured	20	10
788		75f. multicoloured	50	25
789		80f. multicoloured	65	40
790	–	100f. multicoloured (air)	85	40
791	–	200f. multicoloured	1·75	75

DESIGNS: 100f. to 200f. APU emblem and airmail envelope.

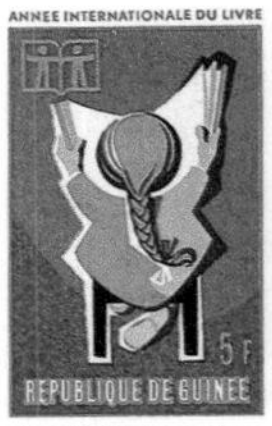

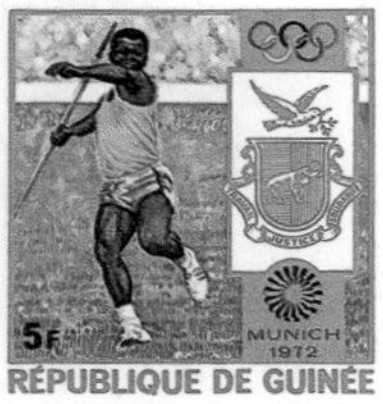

113 Child reading Book

114 Throwing the Javelin

1972. International Book Year. Multicoloured.

792	5f. Type **113**	10	10
793	15f. Book with sails	15	10
794	40f. Girl with book and plant	30	15
795	50f. "Key of Knowledge" and open book	50	20
796	75f. "Man" reading book and globe	75	40
797	200f. Open book and laurel sprigs	1·75	70

1972. Olympic Games, Munich. Mult.

798	5f. Type **114** (postage)	10	10
799	10f. Pole-vaulting	10	10
800	25f. Hurdling	25	10
801	30f. Throwing the hammer	35	10
802	40f. Boxing	50	15
803	50f. Gymnastics (horse)	65	25
804	75f. Running	90	35
805	100f. Gymnastics (rings) (air)	1·50	45
806	200f. Cycling	2·75	85

1972. U.N. Environmental Conservation Conf, Stockholm. Nos. 750/4 optd **UNE SEULE TERRE** and emblem.

808	**105**	25f. multicoloured	20	10
809		30f. multicoloured	20	10
810		50f. multicoloured	45	15
811		60f. multicoloured	70	25
812		100f. multicoloured	1·00	50

116 Dimitrov addressing "Reichstag Fire" Court

1972. 90th Birth Anniv of George Dimitrov (Bulgarian statesman).

813	**116** 5f. blue, gold and green	10	10
814	– 25f. blue, gold and green	15	10
815	– 40f. blue, gold and green	30	20
816	– 100f. blue, gold and green	80	35

DESIGNS: 25f. In Moabit Prison, Berlin, 1933; 40f. Writing memoirs; 100f. G. Dimitrov.

117 Emperor Haile Selassie

118 "Syntomeida epilais"

1972. Emperor Haile Selassie of Ethiopia's 80th Birthday. Multicoloured.

817	40f. Type **117**	35	20
818	200f. Emperor Haile Selassie in military uniform	1·60	80

1973. Guinean Insects. Multicoloured.

819	5f. Type **118**	10	10
820	15f. "Hippodamia californica"	25	10
821	30f. "Tettigonia viridissima"	50	15
822	40f. "Apis mellifica"	60	25
823	50f. "Photinus pyralis"	85	30
824	200f. "Ancyluris formosissima"	3·50	1·25

119 Dr. Kwame Nkrumah

1973. 10th Anniv of Organization of African Unity.

825	**119** 1s.50 black, gold & green	15	10
826	– 2s.50 black, gold & green	25	10
827	– 5s. black, gold and green	50	25
828	– 10s. violet and gold	1·00	45

DESIGNS: Nos. 826/8, different portraits of Dr. Kwame Nkrumah similar to Type **119**.

120 Institute of Applied Biology, Kindia

1973. 25th Anniv of W.H.O. Multicoloured.

829	1s. Type **120**	10	10
830	2s.50 Preparing vaccine from an egg	25	10
831	3s. Filling ampoules with vaccine	30	20
832	4s. Sterilization of vaccine	40	20
833	5s. Packing vaccines	60	25
834	10s. Preparation of vaccine base	1·25	40
835	20s. Inoculating patient	2·50	75

Nos. 833/35 are 48 × 31 mm.

121 Volcanic Landscape

1973. 500th Birth Anniv of Copernicus. Mult.

836	50c. Type **121**	10	10
837	2s. Sun over desert	20	10
838	4s. Earth and Moon	35	10
839	5s. Lunar landscape	60	15
840	10s. Jupiter	1·25	35
841	20s. Saturn	2·25	70

122 Loading Bauxite at Quayside

1974. Air. Bauxite Industry, Bok. Mult.

843	4s. Type **122**	50	15
844	6s. Bauxite train	2·50	40
845	10s. Bauxite mining	2·75	50

123 "Clappertonia ficifolia"

125 Pioneers testing Rope-bridge

124 Drummers and Pigeon

1974. Flowers of Guinea. Multicoloured.

846	50c. Type **123** (postage)	10	10
847	1s. "Rothmannia longiflora"	10	10
848	2s. "Oncoba spinosa"	20	10
849	3s. "Venidium fastuosum"	30	15
850	4s. "Bombax costatum"	50	15
851	5s. "Clerodendrum splendens"	75	20
852	7s.50 "Combretuni grandiflorum"	1·25	25
853	10s. "Mussaendra erythrophylla"	1·50	40
854	12s. "Argemone mexicana"	1·75	60
855	20s. "Thunbergia alata" (air)	2·50	80
856	25s. "Diascia barberae"	3·50	80
857	50s. "Kigelia africana"	7·00	1·90

SIZES—VERT: Nos. 847/9, As Type **123**; 850/3, 36 × 47 mm. DIAMOND: Nos. 854/7, 61 × 61 mm.
No. 855 is wrongly inscr "Thunbegia alata".

1974. Centenary of U.P.U. Multicoloured.

858	5s. Type **124**	40	20
859	6s. Runner and pigeon	55	25
860	7s.50 Monorail train, lorry and pigeon	1·40	35
861	10s. Boeing 707, "United States" (liner) and pigeon	1·50	60

1974. National Pioneers (Scouting) Movement. Multicoloured.

863	50c. Type **125**	15	10
864	2s. "On safari"	25	10
865	4s. Using field-telephone	35	15
866	5s. Cooking on camp-fire	60	15
867	7s.50 Saluting	85	35
868	10s. Playing basketball	1·75	55

127 Chimpanzee

1975. Wild Animals. Multicoloured.

871	1s. Type **127**	10	10
872	2s. Impala	20	10
873	3s. Warthog	35	10
874	4s. Waterbuck	40	20
875	5s. Leopard	60	20
876	6s. Greater kudu	60	25
877	6s.50 Common zebra	75	35
878	7s.50 African buffalo	75	35
879	8s. Hippopotamus	1·25	35
880	10s. Lion	1·50	40
881	12s. Black rhinoceros	1·90	45
882	15s. African elephant	2·75	80

128 Lion and Lioness beside Pipeline

1975. 10th Anniv of African Development Bank.

884	5s. Type **128**	70	20
885	7s. African elephants beside pipeline	1·00	30
886	10s. Lions beside pipeline (horiz)	1·25	35
887	20s. African elephant and calf beside pipeline (horiz)	2·25	80

129 Women playing Saxophones

1976. Int Women's Year (1975). Mult.

888	5s. Type **129**	40	20
889	7s. Women playing guitars	60	30
890	9s. Woman railway shunter	3·75	50
891	15s. Woman doctor	1·75	65
892	20s. Genetics emblems	2·25	90

130 Gymnastics

1976. Olympic Games, Montreal. Mult.

894	3s. Type **130**	25	10
895	4s. Long jump	35	15
896	5s. Throwing the hammer	40	20
897	6s. Throwing the discus	45	25
898	6s.50 Hurdling	50	25
899	7s. Throwing the javelin	50	30
900	8s. Running	60	30
901	8s.50 Cycling	95	35
902	10s. High-jumping	1·10	35
903	15s. Putting the shot	1·60	60
904	20s. Pole vaulting	2·25	65
905	25s. Football	2·75	90

131 Bell and Early Telephone

1976. Telephone Centenary. Multicoloured.

907	5s. Type **131**	50	20
908	7s. Bell and wall telephone	75	25
909	12s. Bell and satellite "Syncom"	1·40	50
910	15s. Bell and satellite "Telstar"	1·75	60

132 "Collybia fusipes"

1977. Mushrooms. Multicoloured.

912	5s. Type **132** (postage)	1·50	20
913	7s. "Lycoperdon perlatum"	2·25	25
914	9s. "Boletus edulis"	3·00	35
915	9s.50 "Lactarius deliciosus"	3·00	45
916	11s.50 "Agaricus campestris"	4·75	80
917	10s. "Morchella esculenta" (air)	3·50	40
918	12s. "Lepiota procera"	4·50	60
919	15s. "Cantharellus cibarius"	6·50	1·10

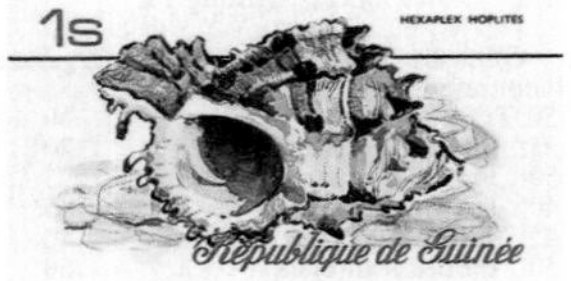

133 Duplex Murex

1977. Sea Shells. Multicoloured.

921	1s. Type **133**	10	10
922	2s. Wavy-leaved turrid	25	10
923	4s. Queen marginella	60	15
924	5s. "Tympanotonos radula"	90	20
925	7s. Striped marginella	1·00	25
926	8s. Doris harp	1·40	30
927	10s. Obtuse demoulia	1·75	45
928	20s. Pitted frog shell	3·25	80
929	25s. Adanson's marginella	4·00	1·00

Nos. 927/9 are 50 × 34 mm.

134 President Sekou Toure

1977. 30th Anniv of Guinean Democratic Party (PDG). Multicoloured.

930	5s. Type **134**	35	25
931	10s. Labourers and oxen	95	45
932	20s. Soldier driving tractor	2·10	95
933	25s. Pres. Toure addressing U.N. General Assembly	2·50	1·25
934	30s. Pres. Toure (vert)	3·00	1·50
935	40s. As 30s.	3·75	1·60

135 "Varanus niloticus"

1977. Reptiles. Multicoloured.

937	3s. Type **135** (postage)	35	10
938	4s. "Hyperolius quinquevittatus"	40	15
939	5s. "Uromastix"	50	15
940	6s. "Scincus scincus"	75	15
941	6s.50 "Agama agama"	95	20
942	7s. "Naja melanoleuca"	1·10	20
943	8s.50 "Python regius"	1·40	25
944	20s. "Bufo mauritanicus"	3·00	60
945	10s. "Chamaeleo diepis" (air)	2·00	30
946	15s. "Crocodylus niloticus"	2·75	50
947	25s. "Testudo elegans"	4·25	75

136 Eland (male)

1977. Endangered Animals. Multicoloured.

948	1s. Type **136** (postage)	15	10
949	1s. Eland (female)	15	10
950	1s. Eland (young)	15	10
951	2s. Chimpanzee (young)	20	10
952	2s. Chimpanzee	20	10
953	2s. Chimpanzee sitting	20	10
954	2s.50 African elephant	30	10
955	2s.50 African elephant	30	10
956	2s.50 African elephant	30	10
957	3s. Lion	50	10
958	3s. Lioness	50	10
959	3s. Lion Cub	50	10
960	4s. Indian palm squirrel	60	15
961	4s. Indian palm squirrel	60	15
962	4s. Indian palm squirrel	60	15
963	5s. Hippopotamus	80	20
964	5s. Hippopotamus	80	20
965	5s. Hippopotamus	80	20
966	5s. Type **136** (air)	60	20
967	5s. As No. 949	60	20
968	5s. As No. 950	60	20
969	8s. As No. 954	1·50	25
970	8s. As No. 955	1·50	25
971	8s. As No. 956	1·50	25
972	9s. As No. 963	1·50	25
973	9s. As No. 964	1·50	25
974	9s. As No. 965	1·50	25
975	10s. As No. 951	1·75	30

976	10s. As No. 952	1·75	30
977	10s. As No. 953	1·75	30
978	12s. As No. 960	1·75	40
979	12s. As No. 961	1·75	40
980	12s. As No. 962	1·75	40
981	13s. As No. 957	2·00	50
982	13s. As No. 958	2·00	50
983	13s. As No. 959	2·00	50

Issued se-tenant in strips of three within the sheet, each strip showing different views of the same animal.

137 Lenin taking Parade in Red Square, Moscow

1976. 60th Anniv of Russian Revolution. Multicoloured.

984	2s.50 Lenin's first speech in Moscow (postage)	25	10
985	5s. Lenin addressing revolutionary crowd	45	15
986	7s.50 Lenin with militiamen	85	20
987	8s. Type **137**	1·10	20
988	10s. Russian ballet (air)	2·00	30
989	30s. Pushkin Monument	3·75	75

138 Pres. Giscard d'Estaing at Microphones

1979. Visit of President Giscard d'Estaing of France.

990 **138**	3s. brown and light brown (postage)	30	10
991 –	5s. brown, green and deep green	55	15
992 –	6s.50 brown, mauve and deep mauve	80	20
993 –	7s. brown, light blue and blue	85	20
994 –	8s.50 brown, rose & red	1·25	30
995 –	10s. brown, light violet and violet	1·60	40
996 –	20s. brown, green and deep green	3·50	65
997 –	25s. multicoloured (air)	4·00	1·25

DESIGNS—HORIZ: 5s. President Giscard d'Estaing and Sekou Toure in conference; 6s.50, Presidents signing agreement; 7s. Presidents at official meeting; 8s.50, Presidents with their wives; 10s. Presidents in conference; 20s. Toasting the agreement. VERT: 25s. President Giscard d'Estaing.

139 "20,000 Leagues Under the Sea"

1979. 150th Birth Anniv (1978) of Jules Verne. Multicoloured.

998	1s. Type **139** (postage)	10	10
999	3s. "The Children of Captain Grant"	30	10
1000	5s. "The Mysterious Island"	60	15
1001	7s. "A Captain of Fifteen Years"	1·25	35
1002	10s. "The Amazing Adventure of Barsac"	1·75	50
1003	20s. "Five Weeks in a Balloon" (air)	2·25	40
1004	25s. "Robur the Conqueror"	3·00	60

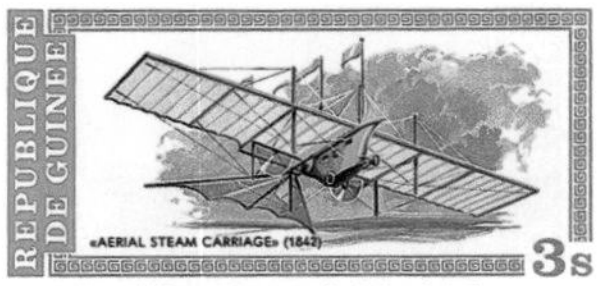

140 William Henson's "Aerial Steam Carriage", 1842

1979. Aviation History. Multicoloured.

1005	3s. Type **140**	30	10
1006	5s. Wright Type A (inscr "Flyer I"), 1903	55	15
1007	6s.50 Caudron C-46O, 1934	75	20
1008	7s. Charles Lindbergh's "Spirit of St. Louis", 1927	95	20
1009	8s.50 Bristol Beaufighter, 1940	1·25	20
1010	10s. Bleriot XI, 1909	1·50	25
1011	20s. Boeing 727-100, 1963	2·75	55
1012	20s. Concorde	3·50	70

141 Hafla Football Team

1979. Hafla Football Club's Victories. Mult.

1013	1s. Type **141**	10	10
1014	2s. Team members with cup (vert)	20	20
1015	5s. President Toure presenting medals	60	15
1016	7s. President Toure presenting cup (vert)	85	20
1017	8s. Ahmed Sekou Toure Cup (vert)	95	25
1018	10s. Team captains shaking hands (vert)	1·25	30
1019	20s. The winning goal	2·40	75

142 Children dancing round Tree

1980. International Year of the Child. Mult.

1020	2s. Type **142**	15	10
1021	4s. "Heureuse Enfance"	40	15
1022	5s. Steam train (horiz)	1·60	15
1023	7s. Village (horiz)	85	20
1024	10s. Boy climbing tree (horiz)	1·25	25
1025	25s. Children of different races (horiz)	3·00	70

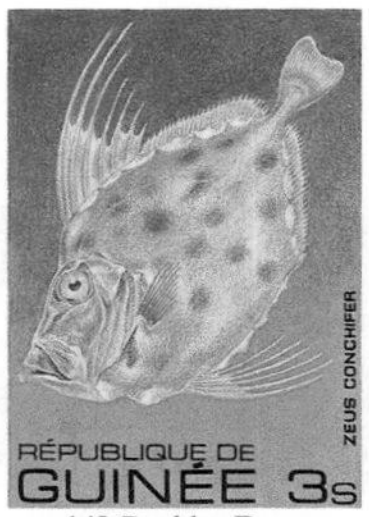

143 Buckler Dory

1980. Fishes, Multicoloured.

1026	1s. Robust butterflyfish (horiz)	10	10
1027	2s. Blue-pointed porgy (horiz)	20	15
1028	3s. Type **143**	35	15
1029	4s. African hind (horiz)	45	25
1030	5s. Spotted seahorse	55	25
1031	6s. Marine hatchetfish (horiz)	90	30
1032	7s. Half-banded snake-eel (horiz)	1·40	30
1033	8s. Flying gurnard	1·60	40
1034	9s. West African squirrel-fish (horiz)	1·75	40
1035	10s. Guinean fingerfish	1·90	40
1036	12s. African sergeant major (horiz)	2·25	75
1037	15s. West African trigger-fish (horiz)	3·00	1·00

144 Rocket on Launch Pad

1980. 10th Anniv of 1st Moon Landing. Mult.

1038	1s. Type **144**	10	10
1039	2s. Earth from the Moon	20	10
1040	4s. Armstrong descending from lunar module	35	15
1041	5s. Armstrong on the Moon	50	15
1042	7s. Astronaut collecting samples	75	20
1043	8s. Parachute descent	95	25
1044	12s. Winching capsule aboard recovery vessel	1·60	35
1045	20s. Astronauts	3·00	70

145 Dome of the Rock

1981. Palestinian Solidarity.

1046 **145**	8s. multicoloured	1·40	55
1047	11s. multicoloured	1·90	70

146 Map of Member States and Agricultural Produce

1982. 5th Anniv of Economic Community of West African States. Multicoloured.

1048	6s. Type **146**	85	30
1049	7s. Transport	4·50	75
1050	9s. Heavy industry	1·40	45

147 Ataturk as Soldier

1982. Birth Centenary of Kemal Ataturk (Turkish statesman). Multicoloured.

1051	7s. Type **147** (postage)	95	40
1052	10s. Ataturk as statesman	1·25	50
1053	25s. Equestrian statue (horiz)	3·50	85
1054	25s. As No. 1053 (air)	4·00	85

148 Football

1982. Olympic Games, Moscow. Multicoloured.

1055	1s. Type **148** (postage)	10	10
1056	2s. Basketball	20	15
1057	3s. Diving	25	15
1058	4s. Gymnastics	30	15
1059	5s. Boxing	55	20
1060	6s. High jumping	75	25
1061	7s. Running	95	35
1062	8s. Long jumping	1·10	40
1063	9s. Fencing (air)	1·10	20
1064	10s. Football (vert)	1·25	30
1065	11s. Basketball (vert)	1·40	45
1066	20s. Diving (vert)	3·00	55
1067	25s. Boxing (vert)	3·50	65

149 Balaidos Stadium, Vigo

1982. World Cup Football Championship, Spain. Football Stadia. Mult.

1068	6s. Type **149** (postage)	90	15
1069	8s. El Molinon, Gijon	1·10	25
1070	9s. San Mames, Bilbao	1·60	30
1071	10s. Sanchez Pizjuan, Seville	1·75	35
1072	10s. Luis Casanova, Valencia (air)	1·75	35
1073	20s. Nou Camp, Barcelona	3·50	45
1074	25s. Santiago Bernabeu, Madrid	4·50	65

150 Wrestling

151 Marquis d'Arlandes, Pilatre de Rozier and Montgolfier Balloon, 1783

1983. Olympic Games, Los Angeles (1st issue). Multicoloured.

1075	5s. Type **150** (postage)	40	15
1076	7s. Weightlifting	50	25
1077	10s. Gymnastics	95	35
1078	15s. Discus	1·60	60
1079	20s. Kayak (air)	1·60	50
1080	25s. Equestrian	2·25	80

See also Nos. 843/9.

1983. Bicentenary of Manned Flight. Mult.

1082	5s. Type **151** (postage)	55	15
1083	7s. Jean-Francois Pilatre de Rozier and Montgolfier balloon "Marie Antoinette", 1784	65	25
1084	10s. Henri Dupuy de Lome and airship, 1872 (horiz)	95	35
1085	15s. Major A. Parseval and "Airship No. 1", 1906 (horiz)	1·60	60
1086	20s. Count Zeppelin and airship "Bodensee", 1919 (horiz) (air)	1·60	50
1087	25s. Balloon "Double Eagle II" and crew, 1978	2·25	80

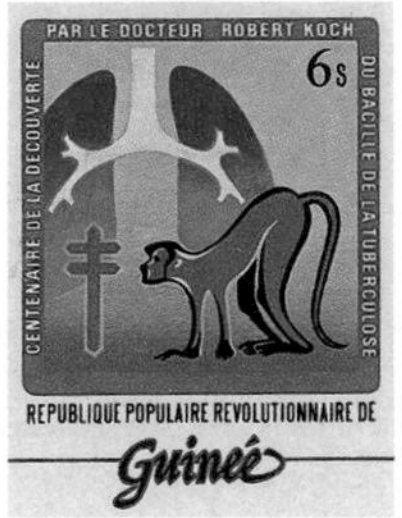

152 Lungs and Monkey

1983. Centenary of Discovery of Tubercle Bacillus. Multicoloured.

1089	6s. Type **152**	75	20
1090	10s. Cow	1·25	30
1091	11s. Robert Koch and microscope	1·50	35
1092	12s. Koch using microscope	1·75	50
1093	15s. Laboratory	2·25	55
1094	20s. Scientist with test tube and monkey	3·00	70
1095	25s. Doctor examining young boy	3·50	95

153 Disabled and Emblem

1983. International Year of Disabled Persons.

1096 **153**	10s. multicoloured	1·25	55
1097	20s. multicoloured	2·50	1·00

154 Mosque, Conakry

1983. 25th Anniv of Independence.
1098 **154** 1s. multicoloured 10 10
1099 2s. multicoloured 20 10
1100 5s. multicoloured 40 15
1101 10s. multicoloured . . . 90 40

155 Citizens with Scrolls

1983. 10th Anniv of Mano River Union. Multicoloured.
1103 2s. Type **155** 20 10
1104 7s. Union emblem 50 25
1105 8s. Map and presidents of Guinea, Sierra Leone and Liberia 60 25
1106 10s. Signing the Declaration of Union 85 35

156 Biathlon

1983. Winter Olympic Games, Sarajevo. Multicoloured.
1108 5s. Type **156** (postage) . . . 50 15
1109 7s. Luge 60 25
1110 10s. Slalom . . . . 1·25 40
1111 15s. Speed skating . . . . . 1·60 60
1112 20s. Ski jump (air) . . . . 1·90 55
1113 25s. Ice dancing . . . . . . 2·50 80

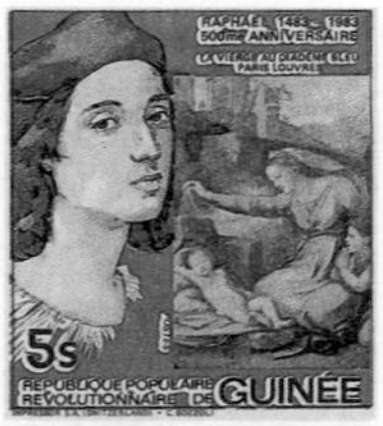

157 Raphael and "Virgin with the Blue Diadem"

1984. Anniversaries (1983). Multicoloured.
1115 5s. Type **157** 40 20
1116 7s. Rubens and "Holy Family" 60 25
1117 10s. Rembrandt and "Portrait of Saskia" . . . 95 40
1118 15s. Goethe and scene from "The Young Werther" . . . 1·40 60
1119 20s. Lord Baden-Powell and scout camp . . . . 1·75 55
1120 25s. P. P. Harris and speaker at Rotary meeting 2·50 80

158 Abraham Lincoln

1984. Personalities. Multicoloured.
1122 5s. Type **158** (postage) . . . 40 20
1123 7s. Jean-Henri Dunant (founder of Red Cross) 65 25
1124 10s. Gottlieb Daimler (automobile designer) . . 1·25 40
1125 15s. Louis Bleriot (pilot) . . 1·75 55
1126 20s. Paul P. Harris (founder of Rotary Club) (air) . . 1·75 65
1127 25s. Auguste Piccard (ocean explorer) . . . . 2·50 85

159 "The Mystic Marriage of Sts. Catherine and Sebastian" (detail, Correggio)

1984. Paintings. Multicoloured.
1129 5s. Type **159** (postage) . . . 40 20
1130 7s. "The Holy Family" (A. Durer) 60 25
1131 10s. "The Veiled Lady" (Raphael) . . . . 1·00 40
1132 15s. "Portrait of a Young Man" (A. Durer) . . . . 1·25 55
1133 20s. "Portrait of Soutine" (A. Modigliani) (air) . . . 1·75 65
1134 25s. "The Esterhazy Madonna" (Raphael) . . 2·50 85

160 Congo River Steamer and Canoe

1984. Transport. Multicoloured.
1136 5s. Type **160** (postage) . . . 60 20
1137 7s. Airship "Graf Zeppelin" 70 25
1138 10s. Daimler car, 1886 . . . 1·50 40
1139 15s. Beyer-Garratt steam locomotive . . . . 2·40 1·25
1140 20s. Latecoere seaplane "Comte de la Vaulx" (air) 1·75 55
1141 25s. Savoia Marchetti S-73 airplane . . . . 2·50 80

161 W. Hoppe and D. Schauerhammer (bobsleigh)

1984. Winter Olympic Gold Medal Winners. Multicoloured.
1143 5s. Type **161** (postage) . . . 40 20
1144 7s. T. L. Wassberg (cross-country skiing) 60 25
1145 10s. G. Boucher (speed skating) . . . . 1·00 40
1146 15s. K. Witt (ladies figure skating) . . . . 1·50 65
1147 20s. W. D. Johnson (downhill skiing) (air) . . 2·00 85
1148 25s. U.S.S.R. (ice hockey) 2·75 90

162 T. Ruiz and C. Costie (Synchronized Swimming Duet)

1985. Olympic Games Gold Medal Winners. Multicoloured.
1150 5s. Type **162** (postage) . . . 40 20
1151 7s. R. Klimke, H. Krug and U. Sauer, West Germany (team dressage) 85 25
1152 10s. McKee and Buchan, U.S.A. (sailing, "Flying Dutchman" class) 95 40
1153 15s. Mark Todd (equestrian three-day event) . . . . . 1·25 65
1154 20s. Daley Thompson (decathlon) (air) . . . . 2·00 75
1155 25s. M. Smith, C. Homfeld, L. Burr and J. Fargis, U.S.A. (equestrian team jumping) . . . . 2·25 85

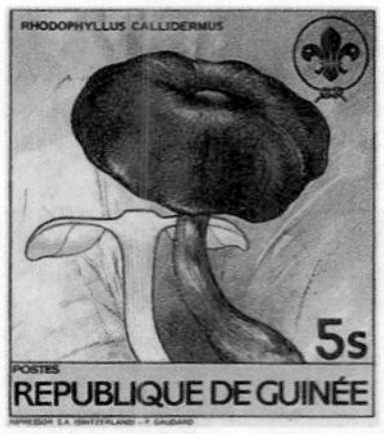

163 "Rhodophyllus callidermus"

1985. Fungi. Multicoloured.
1157 5s. Type **163** (postage) . . . 80 35
1158 7s. "Agaricus niger" . . . . 1·00 45
1159 10s. "Thermitomyces globulus" . . . . 1·90 70
1160 15s. "Amanita robusta" . . 2·50 1·10
1161 20s. "Lepiota subradicans" (air) . . . . 3·50 1·00
1162 25s. "Cantharellus rhodophylus" . . . . . . 3·75 1·10

164 Hermann Oberth and 2-Stage Conical Motor Rocket

1985. Space Achievements. Multicoloured.
1164 7s. Type **164** (postage) . . . 50 25
1165 10s. "Lunik 1" 95 40
1166 15s. "Lunik 2" on Moon, 1959 . . . . 1·25 55
1167 20s. "Lunik 3" photographing hidden face of Moon . . . . . . 1·90 75
1168 30s. Armstrong, Aldrin and Collins (first manned landing on Moon) (air) 2·50 75
1169 35s. Sally Ride (first American woman in space) . . . . 3·25 80

165 Maimonides in Jewish Quarter (850th birth anniv)

1985. Anniversaries and Events. Multicoloured.
1171 7s. Type **165** (postage) . . . 80 35
1172 10s. Christopher Columbus departing from Palos, 1492 . . . . 1·75 50
1173 15s. Frederic Bartholdi and Statue of Liberty (centenary) . . . . 1·50 55
1174 20s. Queen Mother with Duke of York and Princess Elizabeth (85th birthday) . . . . 1·75 75
1175 30s. Ulf Merbold and space shuttle "Columbia" (air) 2·50 75
1176 35s. Prince Charles and Lady Diana Spencer (Royal Wedding) . . . . 3·00 85

166 Black-billed Cuckoo

1995. Birth Bicentenary of John J. Audubon (ornithologist). Multicoloured.
1178 7s. Type **166** (postage) . . . 65 25
1179 10s. Carolina parakeet . . . 1·00 50
1180 15s. American darter (vert) 1·50 85
1181 20s. Red-shouldered hawk 3·25 1·10
1182 30s. Eastern screech owl (air) . . . . 4·00 1·25
1183 35s. Brown thrasher (vert) 5·00 1·75

167 Blue-point Siamese

1985. Cats and Dogs. Multicoloured.
1185 7s. Type **167** (postage) . . . 60 25
1186 10s. Cocker spaniel . . . . 1·25 40
1187 15s. Poodles . . . . 1·50 55
1188 20s. Persian blue cat . . . . 2·00 70
1189 25s. European tortoiseshell cat . . . . 2·40 85
1190 30s. German shepherd dog (air) . . . . 2·75 85
1191 35s. Abyssinian cats . . . . 3·25 95
1192 40s. Boxer dog . . . . . . 3·75 1·25

168 Bebeto and Footballers

1985. World Cup Football Championship, Mexico (1986) (1st issue). Multicoloured.
1194 7s. Type **168** (postage) . . . 60 25
1195 10s. Rinat Dassaev . . . . 1·25 40
1196 15s. Phil Neal . . . . . . 1·50 55
1197 20s. Jean Tigana . . . . . 2·40 70
1198 30s. Fernando Chalana (air) 3·00 75
1199 35s. Michel Platini . . . . 3·50 85
See also Nos. 1268/71.

1985. Air. Nos. 1126 and 1119/20 optd.
1201 20s. **80e ANNIVERSAIRE 1905 1985** (1126) . . . 1·60 90
1202 20s. **Rassemblement Jambville-1985** (1119) . . 1·60 90
1203 25s. **80e ANNIVERSAIRE 1905 1985** (1120) . . . . 2·25 1·25

1985. Nos. 1157/62 surch.
1205 1s. on 5s. Type **163** (postage) 20 10
1206 2s. on 7s. "Agaricus niger" 50 10
1207 8s. on 10s. "Thermitomyces globulus" . . . . 1·50 40
1208 30s. on 15s. "Amanita robusta" . . . . 4·50 1·25
1209 35s. on 20s. "Lepiota subradicans" (air) . . . . 4·75 1·40
1210 40s. on 25s. "Cantharellus rhodophyllus" . . . . . 5·25 1·90

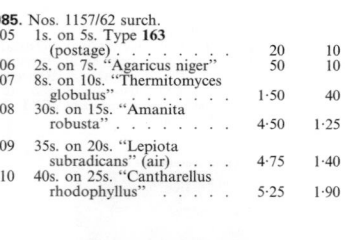

171 Class 8 F Locomotive

1985. Trains (1st series). Multicoloured.
1212 7s. Type **171** (postage) . . . 1·10 40
1213 15s. Class III electric locomotive, Germany . . 3·00 1·00
1214 25s. Pacific steam locomotive No. 270 . . . 5·00 1·50
1215 35s. German electric commuter train Series 420 (air) . . . . 6·50 2·40
Nos. 1213 and 1215 commemorate 150th anniv of German railways.
See also Nos. 1252/5.

172 Columbus and "Pinta"

1985. 480th Death Anniv of Christopher Columbus (explorer) (1st issue). Multicoloured.
1217 10s. Type **172** (postage) . . 1·75 70
1218 20s. "Santa Maria" . . . . 3·00 1·10
1219 30s. "Nina" (air) . . . . . 3·50 1·25
1220 40s. "Santa Maria" and crow's nest . . . . 4·50 1·75
See also Nos. 1257/60.

173 Chopin, aged Eight, playing Piano

1986. International Youth Year. Multicoloured.

1222	10s. Type **173** (postage)	1·10	45
1223	20s. Sandro Botticelli and "Birth of Venus"	1·75	65
1224	35s. Gioachino Antonio Rossini, aged 15, conducting orchestra	3·50	90
1225	25s. Pablo Picasso and "Paul as Harlequin" (air)	2·25	85

174 Bayeux Tapestry

1986. Appearance of Halley's Comet. Multicoloured.

1227	5f. Type **174** (postage)	10	10
1228	30f. Comet as seen by the Arabs	20	10
1229	40f. Comet as seen by Montezuma II	30	15
1230	50f. Edmond Halley and trajectory diagram	40	15
1231	300f. Halley and Sir Isaac Newton (air)	2·25	55
1232	500f. Comet, Earth, sun, "Giotto", Soviet and N.A.S.A. space probes	4·00	1·10

175 "Challenger" Space Shuttle Memorial Roll

1986. Air. "Challenger" Astronauts Commem. Multicoloured.

1234	100f. Type **175**	70	30
1235	170f. Shuttle diagram and Christa McAuliffe holding model	1·25	55

1986. Various stamps surch. (a) Nos. 1212/15 (Trains).

1237	2f. on 7s. multicoloured	50	10
1238	25f. on 15s. multicoloured	70	15
1239	50f. on 25s. multicoloured	1·25	25
1240	90f. on 35s. multicoloured	2·60	50

(b) Nos. 1217/20 (Columbus).

1242	5f. on 10s. multicoloured	30	15
1243	35f. on 20s. multicoloured	45	15
1244	70f. on 30s. multicoloured	75	30
1245	200f. on 40s. multicoloured	1·75	80

(c) Nos. 1222/5 (International Youth Year).

1247	5f. on 10s. mult (postage)	15	10
1248	35f. on 20s. multicoloured	25	15
1249	90f. on 35s. multicoloured	60	25
1250	50f. on 25s. mult (air)	30	15

177 Dietrich Autorail Diesel Railcar

1986. Trains (2nd series). Multicoloured.

1252	20f. Type **177** (postage)	25	10
1253	100f. Class T.13 steam locomotive No. 7906, Prussia	1·25	25
1254	300f. German steam locomotive No. 01220	3·50	80
1255	400f. Autorail ABH-3 type 5020 diesel train (air)	4·75	95

Nos. 1253/4 commemorate 150th anniv of German Railways.

178 Building Fort Navidad and Map of First Voyage, 1492–93

1986. 480th Death Anniv of Christopher Columbus (explorer) (2nd issue). Multicoloured.

1257	40f. Type **178** (postage)	30	15
1258	70f. Disembarking at Hispaniola and map of second voyage, 1493–96	55	20
1259	200f. Columbus on deck with natives and map of third voyage, 1498–1500	1·50	50
1260	500f. Columbus and crew with natives and map of fourth voyage, 1502–04 (air)	3·50	1·40

179 Prince and Princess of Wales and Prince William

1986. Celebrities. Multicoloured.

1262	30f. Type **179** (postage)	20	10
1263	40f. Alain Prost (1985 Formula I world champion)	25	10
1264	100f. Duke and Duchess of York	60	20
1265	300f. Elvis Presley (entertainer)	2·75	75
1266	500f. Michael Jackson (entertainer) (air)	3·50	1·00

180 Pfaff, Trophy and Satellite

1986. World Cup Football Championship, Mexico (2nd issue). Multicoloured.

1268	100f. Type **180** (postage)	75	20
1269	300f. Michel Platini	2·25	60
1270	400f. Matthaus	3·00	80
1271	500f. Diego Maradona (air)	3·75	1·00

181 Judo

1987. Olympic Games, Seoul (1988). Mult.

1273	20f. Type **181** (postage)	15	10
1274	30f. High jumping	20	10
1275	40f. Handball	25	10
1276	100f. Gymnastics	60	20
1277	300f. Javelin throwing (air)	1·75	55
1278	500f. Showjumping	3·00	80

182 Rifle shooting

1987. Winter Olympic Games, Calgary (1988) (1st issue). Multicoloured.

1280	50f. on 40f. Type **182** (postage)	30	10
1281	100f. Cross-country skiing	65	20
1282	400f. Ski jumping (air)	2·75	75
1283	500f. Two-man bobsleigh	3·25	85

183 Skiing

1987. Winter Olympic Games, Calgary (1988) (2nd issue). Multicoloured.

1285	25f. Type **183** (postage)	20	10
1286	50f. Ice hockey	40	15
1287	100f. Men's figure skating	70	20
1288	150f. Slalom	1·25	35
1289	300f. Speed skating (air)	2·00	70
1290	500f. Four-man bobsleigh	3·25	1·10

184 S. K. Doe, Gen. Lansana Conte, Gen. J. Momoh and National Flags

1987. 10th Anniv of River Mano Reconciliation.

1292	**184** 40f. multicoloured	25	15
1293	50f. multicoloured	30	15
1294	75f. multicoloured	50	25
1295	100f. multicoloured	70	35
1296	150f. multicoloured	90	45

185 Dimetrodon

1987. Prehistoric Animals. Multicoloured.

1297	50f. Type **185** (postage)	45	15
1298	100f. Iguanodon	80	25
1299	200f. Tylosaurus	1·50	55
1300	300f. Cave bear	2·50	75
1301	400f. Sabre-tooth tiger (air)	3·25	85
1302	500f. Stegosaurus	4·25	1·10

186 Statue and Portrait of Marquis de Lafayette (revolutionary)

1987. Celebrities. Multicoloured.

1304	50f. Type **186** (230th birth anniv) (postage)	35	15
1305	100f. Ettore Bugatti (motor manufacturer) (40th death anniv) and "White Elephant"	70	25
1306	200f. Gary Kasparov (world chess champion) and game diagram of Kasparov v. Karpov, 1986	2·00	65
1307	300f. Flag and George Washington (first U.S. President) (bicentenary of American constitution)	2·00	75
1308	400f. Boris Becker (tennis player) (air)	3·50	85
1309	500f. Winston Churchill (statesman)	4·00	1·10

188 Tennis Player and Emblem

1987. Olympic Games, Seoul (1988). Tennis.

1311	**188** 50f. mult (postage)	40	10
1312	– 100f. multicoloured	70	25
1313	– 150f. multicoloured	1·10	35
1314	– 200f. multicoloured	1·50	55
1315	– 300f. multicoloured (air)	2·00	75
1316	– 500f. multicoloured	3·50	1·10

DESIGNS: 100f. to 500f. Various tennis players.

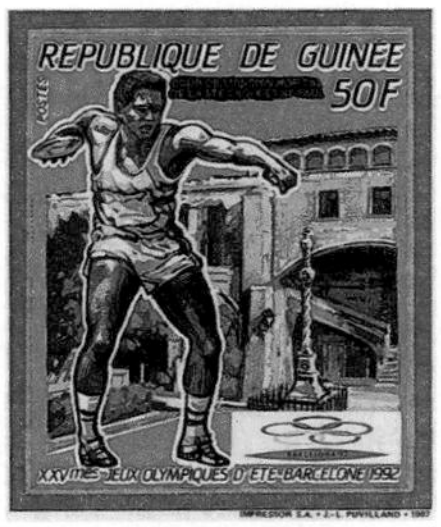

189 Discus thrower and Courtyard of Hospital of the Holy Cross and St. Paul

1987. Olympic Games, Barcelona (1992). Multicoloured.

1318	50f. Type **189** (postage)	30	10
1319	100f. Statue of Pablo Casals (cellist) and pole vaulter	60	25
1320	150f. Long jumper and Labyrinth of Horta	90	35
1321	170f. Lizard in Guell Park and javelin thrower	1·00	40
1322	400f. Gymnast and Church of Mercy (air)	2·50	75
1323	500f. Tennis player and Picasso Museum	3·00	95

190 African Wild Dogs

1987. Endangered Wildlife. Multicoloured.

1325	50f. Type **190** (postage)	35	10
1326	70f. African wild dog	55	20
1327	100f. African wild dogs stalking prey	75	25
1328	170f. African wild dog chasing prey	1·25	40
1329	400f. South African crowned cranes (air)	4·00	1·00
1330	500f. Giant eland	3·50	1·40

191 "Galaxy"–"Grasp"

1988. Space Exploration. Multicoloured.

1332	50f. Type **191** (postage)	30	10
1333	150f. "Energia"–"Mir" link-up	1·00	25
1334	200f. NASA space station	1·40	40
1335	300f. "Ariane-5" rocket depositing satellite payload	2·00	70
1336	400f. Mars "Rover" space vehicle (air)	2·75	85
1337	450f. Venus "Vega" space probe	3·00	95

192 Red-headed Bluebill

193 Queen Elizabeth II and Prince Philip

1988. Scouts, Birds and Butterflies. Designs showing scouts studying featured animals. Multicoloured.

1339	50f. Type **192** (postage)	50	10
1340	100f. "Medon nymphalidae" (butterfly)	65	25
1341	150f. Red bishop	1·25	40
1342	300f. Beautiful sunbird	2·40	70
1343	400f. "Sophia nymphalidae" (butterfly) (air)	3·00	1·00
1344	450f. "Rumia nymphalidae" (butterfly)	3·00	1·10

1988. Celebrities. Multicoloured.

1346	200f. Type **193** (40th wedding anniv (1987)) (postage)	1·25	40
1347	250f. Fritz von Opel (car designer) and "Rak 2 Opel", 1928	1·75	55
1348	300f. Wolfgang Amadeus Mozart (composer)	2·25	55
1349	400f. Steffi Graf (tennis player)	3·00	70
1350	450f. Edwin "Buzz" Aldrin (astronaut) (air)	3·25	80
1351	500f. Paul Harris (founder of Rotary International)	3·50	95

194 Vreni Schneider (Women's Slalom and Giant Slalom)

195 Scientist using Microscope

1988. Calgary Winter Olympic Games Gold Medal Winners. Multicoloured.

1353	50f. Type **194** (postage)	30	10
1354	150f. Matti Nykaenen (Ski jumping)	1·10	25
1355	250f. Marina Kiehl (Women's downhill)	1·75	40
1356	400f. Frank Piccard (Men's super giant slalom)	2·50	75
1357	100f. Frank-Peter Roetsch (Biathlon) (air)	70	25
1358	450f. Katarina Witt (Women's figure skating)	2·75	95

1988. World Health Day. Multicoloured.

1360	50f. Type **195**	20	10
1361	150f. Nurse vaccinating boy	55	15
1362	500f. Dental check	1·90	50

196 Baron Pierre de Coubertin (founder of modern Olympics)

1988. International Olympic Committee.

1363	**196**	50f. multicoloured	20	10
1364		100f. multicoloured	40	10
1365		150f. multicoloured	55	15
1366		500f. multicoloured	1·90	50

197 Hands exchanging Letter

198 Earth Communications Station

1988. 25th Anniv of Pan-African Postal Union.

1367	**197**	50f. multicoloured	20	10
1368		75f. multicoloured	30	10
1369		100f. multicoloured	40	10
1370		150f. multicoloured	55	15

1988. Inauguration of MT 20 International Transmission Centre.

1371	**198**	50f. multicoloured	20	10
1372		100f. multicoloured	40	10
1373		150f. multicoloured	55	15

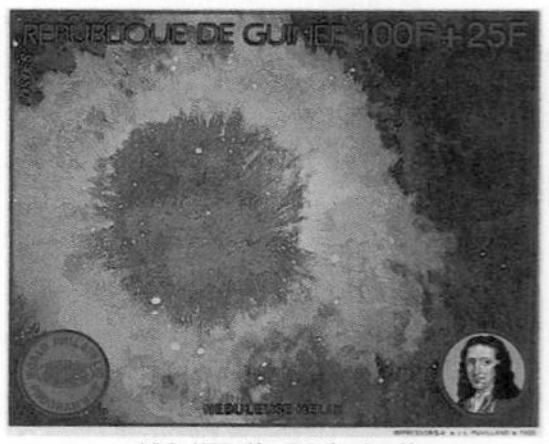

199 "Helix Nebular"

1989. Appearance of Halley's Comet. Nebulae. Multicoloured.

1374	100f.+25f. Type **199** (postage)	50	15
1375	150f.+25f. Orion	70	20
1376	200f.+25f. "The Eagle"	90	25
1377	250f.+25f. "Triffid"	1·10	30
1378	300f.+25f. Eta-Carinae (air)	1·25	30
1379	500f.+25f. NGC 2264	2·00	50

200 Diving

1989. Olympic Games, Barcelona (1992) (1st issue). Multicoloured.

1381	50f. Type **200** (postage)	20	10
1382	100f. Running (vert)	40	10
1383	150f. Shooting	60	15
1384	250f. Tennis (vert)	1·00	25
1385	400f. Football (air)	1·60	40
1386	500f. Equestrian (dressage) (vert)	2·00	50

201 Oath of the Tennis Court and Jean Sylvain Bailly (President of National Assembly)

1989. "Philexfrance 89" Stamp Exhibition and Bicentenary of French Revolution. Mult.

1388	250f. Type **201** (postage)	1·00	25
1389	300f. King addressing the Three Estates and Comte de Mirabeau	1·25	30
1390	400f. 18th July 1790 celebrations and Marquis de La Fayette	1·60	40
1391	450f. The King's arrest at Varennes and Jerome Petion (first President of the Convention) (air)	1·75	45

202 Girl carrying Plants

1989. 10th Anniv (1987) of International Fund for Agricultural Development. Campaign for Self-sufficiency. Multicoloured.

1393	25f. Type **202**	10	10
1394	50f. Men irrigating crops	20	10
1395	75f. Family with cattle	30	10
1396	100f. Fishermen	70	20
1397	150f. Harvesting crops	60	15
1398	300f. Pumping water	1·25	30

203 Buildings, Vehicles and Envelopes on Map

1989. 15th Anniv of Mano River Union. Mult.

1399	150f. Type **203**	60	15
1400	300f. Map and Presidents of member countries	1·25	30

204 Emblem, Banknotes and Produce

1989. 25th Anniv of African Development Bank.

1401	**204**	300f. multicoloured	1·25	30

205 Skiing and Super-Tignes

1990. Winter Olympic Games, Albertville (1992). Multicoloured.

1402	150f. Type **205** (postage)	55	15
1403	250f. Cross-country skiing and Le Lavachet	90	25
1404	400f. Bobsleighing and Val-Claret	1·40	35
1405	500f. Speed skating and Meribel (air)	1·75	45

206 Presidents Bush and Gorbachev (1989 Summit, Malta)

1990. Multicoloured.

1407	200f. Type **206** (postage)	70	20
1408	250f. De Gaulle's appeal to resist, June 1940	90	25
1409	300f. Pope Jean-Paul II, President Gorbachev and dove (1989 meeting)	1·10	30
1410	400f. Concorde and TGV Atlantique express train, France	3·25	1·00
1411	450f. Robin Yount (cent of Baseball) (air)	1·60	40
1412	500f. "Galileo" space probe	1·75	45

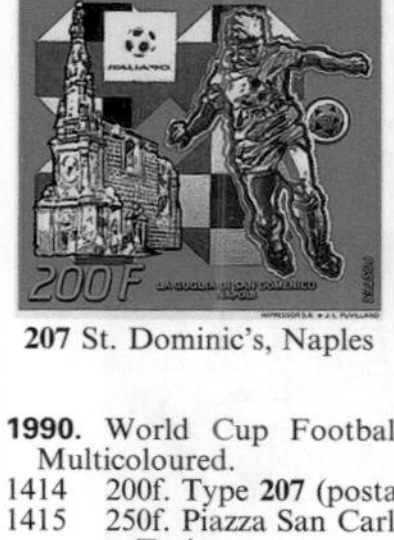

207 St. Dominic's, Naples

208 View of Exhibition

1990. World Cup Football Championship, Italy. Multicoloured.

1414	200f. Type **207** (postage)	70	20
1415	250f. Piazza San Carlo, Turin	90	25
1416	300f. San Cataldo church	1·10	30
1417	450f. St. Francis's Church, Udine (air)	1·60	40

1991. "Telecom 91" International Telecommunications Exhibition. Multicoloured.

1419	150f. Type **208**	55	10
1420	300f. Emblem (horiz)	1·10	30

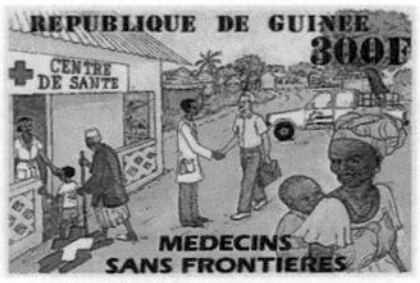

209 Health Centre

1991. Medecins sans Frontieres.

1421	**209**	300f. multicoloured	1·10	30

210 "Madonna della Tenda"

1991. Christmas (1990). Paintings by Raphael. Multicoloured.

1422	50f. Type **210** (postage)	20	10
1423	100f. Small Cowper Madonna	40	10
1424	150f. Tempi Madonna	55	15
1425	250f. Niccolini Madonna	95	25
1426	300f. Orleans Madonna (air)	1·10	30
1427	500f. Solly Madonna	1·90	50

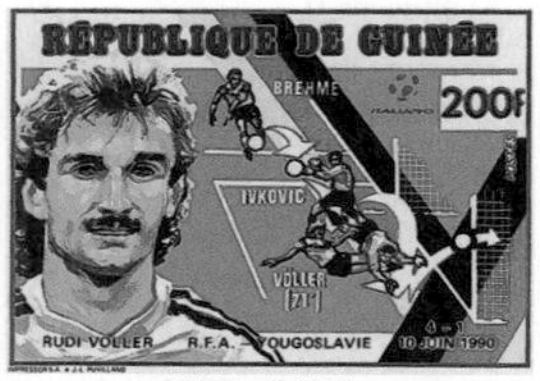

211 Rudi Voller

1991. West Germany, 1990 World Cup Football Champion. West German Players and Goals Scored. Multicoloured.

1429	200f. Type **211** (postage)	75	20
1430	250f. Uwe Bein	95	25
1431	300f. Pierre Littbarski	1·10	30
1432	400f. Jurgen Klinsmann	1·50	35
1433	450f. Lothar Matthaus (air)	1·75	45
1434	500f. Andreas Brehme	1·90	50

212 Fairey Swordfish sinking "Bismarck" (German battleship) and Admirals Raeder and Tovey

1991. Battles of Second World War. Mult.

1436	100f. Type **212** (postage)	55	10
1437	150f. Aichi D3A "Val" bombers sinking U.S.S. "Yorktown" (aircraft carrier) and Admirals Yamamoto and Nimitz (Battle of Midway)	70	15
1438	200f. American torpedo boat and Admirals Kondo and Halsey (Guadalcanal)	85	20
1439	250f. "Crusader III" tanks, Hawker Hurricane Mk II aircraft, Rommel and Montgomery (El Alamein)	95	25
1440	300f. "Tiger II" tanks and Generals Guderian and Patton (Ardennes) (air)	1·10	30
1441	450f. Grumman TBF Avenger aircraft sinking "Yamato" (Japanese battleship) and Admiral Kogo and General MacArthur	2·00	45

1991. Various stamps surch.

1443	100f. on 170f. mult (No. 1321) (postage)	15	10
1444	100f. on 170f. mult (No. 1328)	15	10
1445	100f. on 250f. mult (No. 1388)	15	10
1446	100f. on 400f. mult (No. 1270)	15	10
1447	100f. on 400f. mult (No. 1349)	15	10
1448	100f. on 400f. mult (No. 1356)	15	10
1449	100f. on 400f. mult (No. 1404)	15	10
1450	100f. on 400f. mult (No. 1410)	2·25	1·00

1451 100f. on 500f. mult (No. 1362) 15 10
1452 100f. on 500f. mult (No. 1366) 15 10
1453 100f. on 400f. mult (No. 1301) (air) 15 10
1454 100f. on 400f. mult (No. 1308) 15 10
1455 100f. on 400f. mult (No. 1322) 15 10
1456 100f. on 400f. mult (No. 1329) . . . . 1·50 40
1457 100f. on 400f. mult (No. 1343) 15 10
1458 100f. on 400f. mult (No. 1385) 15 10
1459 300f. on 450f. mult (No. 1350) 50 15
1460 300f. on 450f. mult (No. 1411) 50 15

214 Nat King Cole Trio

1991. Music and Films. Multicoloured.
1461 100f. Type **214** (postage) . . 15 10
1462 150f. Yul Brynner and scene from "The Magnificent Seven" 25 10
1463 250f. Judy Garland and scene from "The Wizard of Oz" 40 10
1464 300f. Steve McQueen and scene from "Papillon" . . 50 15
1465 500f. Gary Cooper and scene from "Sergeant York" (air) 80 20
1466 600f. Bing Crosby and scene from "High Society" . . 1·00 25

215 Dancer

216 Doves, Map and Pope John Paul II

1991. African Tourism Year. Multicoloured.
1468 100f. Type **215** 15 10
1469 150f. Baskets (horiz) 25 10
1470 250f. Drum (horiz) 40 10
1471 300f. Flautist 50 15

1991. Papal Visit. Litho.
1472 **216** 150f. multicoloured . . . 25 10

217 "ERS-1" Observation Satellite and Earth

1991. Anniversaries and Events. Mult.
1473 100f. Type **217** (postage) . . 15 10
1474 150f. "Sunflowers" (Vincent van Gogh, 1888) 25 10
1475 200f. Napoleon I (170th death anniv) 35 15
1476 250f. Henri Dunant (founder of Red Cross) and Red Cross volunteers 40 10
1477 300f. Bicentenary of Brandenburg Gate and second anniversary of fall of Berlin Wall 50 15
1478 400f. Pope John Paul II's tour of Africa, 1989 . . . 65 15
1479 450f. Garry Kasparov and Anatoli Karpov (World Chess Championship, 1990) (air) 75 20
1480 500f. Boy feeding dove and Rotary International and Lions International emblems 80 20

218 Care-a-Lot and Care Bears around Globe

1991. Ecology. Care Bear cartoon characters. Multicoloured.
1481 50f. Type **218** 10 10
1482 100f. Care Bears around sink ("Save Water!") . . 15 10
1483 200f. Care Bears in tree ("Recycle!") 35 15
1484 300f. Traffic jam and Care Bear ("Control Noise") 50 15
1485 400f. Elephant and Care Bear ("Protect Our Wild Life") (horiz) 65 15

219 Player, Trophy and Little Five Points **220** Emblem

1992. World Cup Football Championship, U.S.A. (1994) (1st issue). Multicoloured.
1487 100f. Type **219** (postage) . . 15 10
1488 300f. Germany player and Fulton Stadium, Atlanta 40 10
1489 400f. Player and Inman Park 50 15
1490 500f. Player and Museum of Fine Art (air) 65 15
See also Nos. 1565/8.

1992. 75th Anniv of Lions International.
1492 **220** 150f. multicoloured . . . 25 10
1493 400f. multicoloured . . . 65 15

221 Emblem

1992. International Nutrition Conference, Rome.
1494 **221** 150f. mult (postage) . . 25 10
1495 400f. multicoloured . . . 65 15
1496 500f. multicoloured (air) 80 20

222 Scene from "The Devil and Catherine" and Antonin Dvorak (composer)

1992. Anniversaries and Events. Multicoloured.
1497 200f. Type **222** (150th birth (1991)) (postage) 25 10
1498 300f. Antonio Vivaldi (composer) (250th death (1991)) and as choirmaster to the Hospital of the Pieta, Venice 40 10
1499 350f. Meeting of airship "Graf Zeppelin" and Santos-Dumont's flying boat and Count Ferdinand von Zeppelin (airship pioneer) 45 10
1500 400f. Projected locomotive emerging from Channel Tunnel (construction) . . 2·75 75
1501 450f. Konrad Adenauer (German statesman) and Brandenburg Gate, Berlin (bicentenary of Gate) (air) 60 15
1502 500f. Emperor Hirohito of Japan (third death anniv) 65 15

223 Charlie Chaplin (actor) and Scene from "Modern Times"

1992. Anniversaries and Events. Multicoloured.
1504 50f. Type **223** (15th death anniv) (postage) 10 10
1505 100f. Pavilion and Christopher Columbus ("Expo '92" World's Fair, Seville) 30 10
1506 150f. St. Peter's Square, Rome 20 10
1507 200f. Marlene Dietrich (actress, death) in scene from "Shanghai Express" 25 10
1508 250f. Michael Schumacher and Formula 1 racing car 35 10
1509 300f. Rocket launch and John Glenn (30th anniv of Glenn's three-orbit flight in "Mercury" space capsule) 40 10
1510 400f. Bill Koch (skipper) and "America 3" (yacht) (winner of Americas Cup) (air) 50 15
1511 450f. Victory of Washington Redskins in 26th American Superbowl baseball championships 60 15
1512 500f. Recovery of "Intelsat VI" satellite by "Endeavour" space shuttle 65 15

1993. 50th Death Anniv (1991) of Robert Baden-Powell (founder of Scouting Movement). Nos. 1339/44 optd **50eme ANNIVERSAIRE DE LA MORT DE BADEN POWEL**.
1515 **192** 50f. mult (postage) . . . 70 10
1516 – 100f. multicoloured . . . 15 10
1517 – 150f. multicoloured . . . 1·10 40
1518 – 300f. multicoloured . . . 2·25 65
1519 – 400f. multicoloured (air) 50 15
1520 – 450f. multicoloured . . . 60 15

1993. Bicentenary of Year One of First Republic of France. Nos. 1388/91 optd **BICENTENAIRE DE L'AN I DE LA REPUBLIQUE FRANCAISE**.
1522 **201** 250f. mult (postage) . . 35 10
1523 – 300f. multicoloured . . . 40 10
1524 – 400f. multicoloured . . . 50 15
1525 – 450f. multicoloured (air) 60 15

1993. Winter Olympic Games, Albertville, Gold Medal Winners. Nos. 1402/5 variously optd.
1527 150f. **SLALOM GEANT Alberto Tomba, Italie** (postage) 20 10
1528 250f. **SKI NORDIQUE Vegard Ulvang, Norvege** 35 15
1529 400f. **BOB A DEUX G. Weder/D. Acklin, Suisse** 50 15
1530 500f. **PATINAGE DE VITESSE Olaf Zinke 1000m., Allemagne** (air) 65 15

1993. World Cup Football Championship, Italy, Results. Nos. 1414/17 optd **1. ALLEMAGNE 2. ARGENTINE 3. ITALIE**.
1532 **207** 200f. mult (postage) . . 25 10
1533 – 250f. multicoloured . . . 35 15
1534 – 300f. multicoloured . . . 40 15
1535 – 450f. multicoloured (air) 60 15

1993. Air. Bobby Fischer–Boris Spassky Chess Match (1537) and 75th Anniv of Lions International (1538). Nos. 1479/80 optd.
1537 450f. **RENCONTRE FISCHER - SPASSKY 3 SEPT au 5 NOV 1992 AU MONTENEGRO** . . 60 15
1538 500f. **75eme ANNIVERSAIRE LIONS** 65 15

230 West Germany Footballer and Little White House

1993. Olympic Games, Atlanta (1996) (1st issue). Multicoloured.
1539 150f. Type **230** (postage) . . 20 10
1540 250f. Cyclist and Georgia World Congress Center 35 10
1541 400f. Basketball player and underground station . . . 50 15
1542 500f. Baseball player and steam train, New Georgia Railroad (air) . . . . . . 4·50 75
See also Nos. 1623/7.

231 Ice Hockey and "Whale Hunt" (sculpture) **232** "Luna 3" and Dark Side of Moon

1993. Winter Olympic Games, Lillehammer, Norway (1994). Multicoloured.
1544 150f. Type **231** (postage) . . 20 10
1545 250f. Two-man bobsleigh and Edvard Grieg's house 35 10
1546 400f. Biathlon and Fredrikstad Park (air) . . 50 15
1547 450f. Ski jumping and Eidsvoll Manor 60 15

1993. 25th Anniv (1994) of First Manned Moon Landing. Multicoloured.
1549 150f. Type **232** 20 10
1550 150f. "Ranger 7" 10 10
1551 150f. "Luna 9" 20 10
1552 150f. "Surveyor 1" (first lunar probe) 20 10
1553 150f. Lunar "Orbiter 1" and moon 20 10
1554 150f. Launch of "Saturn 5" (rocket) carrying "Apollo 11" 20 10
1555 150f. "Apollo 11" command module in lunar orbit . . 20 10
1556 150f. Astronaut climbing from "Apollo 11" 20 10
1557 150f. "Apollo 12" astronaut recovering "Surveyor 1" camera 20 10
1558 150f. Explosion of "Apollo 13" 20 10
1559 150f. "Luna 16" probe (first collection of lunar samples by automatic probe) 20 10
1560 150f. Lunokhod of "Luna 17" (first lunar vehicle) . . 20 10
1561 150f. Alan Shepard playing golf on moon 20 10
1562 150f. First lunar jeep from "Apollo 15" mission . . . 20 10
1563 150f. First lunar telescope from "Apollo 16" mission 20 10
1564 150f. Astronaut from "Apollo 17" (last "Apollo" mission) 20 10

233 San Francisco

1993. World Cup Football Championship, U.S.A. (1994) (2nd issue). Multicoloured.
1565 100f. Type **233** (postage) . . 15 10
1566 300f. Washington D.C. . . . 40 10
1567 400f. Renaissance Center, Detroit 50 15
1568 500f. Dallas (air) 65 15

234 Euparkeria

1993. Prehistoric Animals. Multicoloured.
1570 50f. Type **234** 10 10
1571 50f. Plateosaurus 10 10
1572 50f. Anchisaurus 10 10
1573 50f. Ornithosuchus 10 10

1574	100f. Megalosaurus	15	10
1575	100f. Scelidosaurus	15	10
1576	100f. Camptosaurus	15	10
1577	100f. Ceratosaurus	15	10
1578	250f. Ouranosaurus	35	10
1579	250f. Dicraeosaurus	35	10
1580	250f. Tarbosaurus	35	10
1581	250f. Gorgosaurus	35	10
1582	250f. Polacanthus	35	10
1583	250f. Deinonychus	35	10
1584	250f. Corythosaurus	35	10
1585	250f. Spinosaurus	35	10

235 Prince Johann I of Liechtenstein **236** Johann Kepler and "Pluto" Space Probe

1994. Multicoloured. (a) Battle of Austerlitz, 1805.

1587	150f. Type **235**	20	10
1588	150f. Marshal Joachim Murat	20	10
1589	600f. Napoleon (59 × 47 mm)	80	20

Nos. 1587/9 were issued together, se-tenant, forming a composite design of a battle scene.

(b) Battle of the Moskva, 1912.

1590	150f. Marshal Michel Ney	20	10
1591	150f. Prince Pyotr Ivanovich Bagration	20	10
1592	600f. Napoleon on horseback (59 × 47 mm)	80	20

Nos. 1590/2 were issued together, se-tenant, forming a composite design of a battle scene.

(c) Normandy Landings, 1944.

1593	150f. Field-Marshal Erwin Rommel (wrongly inscr "Romel")	20	10
1594	150f. Gen. George Patton	20	10
1595	600f. Gen. Dwight David Eisenhower (59 × 47 mm)	80	20

Nos. 1593/5 were issued together, se-tenant, forming a composite design of a battle scene.

(d) Battle of the Ardennes, 1944.

1596	150f. Lt.-Gen. William H. Simpson	20	10
1597	150f. Gen. Heinz Guderian	20	10
1598	600f. Tank battle scene (59 × 47 mm)	80	20

Nos. 1596/8 were issued together, se-tenant, forming a composite design of a battle scene.

1994. Astronomers. Multicoloured.

1599	300f. Type **236**	40	10
1600	300f. Sir Isaac Newton and "Voyager" space probe	40	10
1601	500f. Nicolas Copernicus and "Galileo" space probe (59 × 47 mm)	65	15

Nos. 1599/1601 were issued together, se-tenant, forming a composite design.

1994. Winter Olympic Games, Lillehammer. Gold Medal Winners. Nos. 1544/7 variously optd.

1602	150f. **MEDAILLE D'OR SUEDE** (postage)	20	10
1603	250f. **G. WEDER D. ACKLIN SUISSE**	35	10
1604	400f. **F.B. LUNDBERG NORVEGE** (air)	50	15
1605	450f. **J. WEISSFLOG ALLEMAGNE**	60	15

1994. World Cup Football Championship, U.S.A., Winners. Nos. 1565/8 optd **1. BRESIL 2. ITALIE 3. SUEDE.**

1607	**233** 100f. mult (postage)	15	10
1608	– 300f. multicoloured	40	10
1609	– 400f. multicoloured	50	15
1610	– 500f. multicoloured (air)	65	15

239 Banea Dam

1995. Garafiri Water Management. Mult.

1612	100f. Type **239**	10	10
1613	150f. Donkea	20	10
1614	200f. Tinkisso overflow (vert)	25	10
1615	250f. Waterfalls	30	10
1616	500f. Water works, Kinkon	60	15

240 Red and White Persian

1995. Cats. Multicoloured.

1617	150f. Type **240** (inscr "Tortoiseshell")	20	10
1618	250f. Tabby and white	30	10
1619	500f. Black smoke persian ("Smoke long-haired")	60	15
1620	500f. Red tabby	60	15
1621	500f. Tortoiseshell and white persian ("longhair")	60	15

241 Throwing the Javelin **242** Eurasian Goldfinch

1995. Olympic Games, Atlanta (1996) (2nd issue). Multicoloured.

1623	150f. Type **241**	20	10
1624	250f. Boxing	30	10
1625	500f. Football	60	15
1626	500f. Basketball	60	15
1627	500f. Weightlifting	60	15

1995. Birds. Multicoloured.

1629	150f. Type **242**	20	10
1630	250f. Nightingale ("Luscinia megarhynchos")	30	10
1631	500f. Island canary ("Serinus canaria")	60	15
1632	500f. Chaffinch ("Fringilla coelebs")	60	15
1633	500f. Western greenfinch ("Carduelis chloris")	60	15

243 Mona Monkey

1995. Mammals. Multicoloured.

1635	150f. Type **243**	20	10
1636	250f. Savanna monkey	35	10
1637	500f. Demidoff's galago ("Galagoides demidovi")	65	15
1638	500f. Hare ("Lepus crawshayi") (horiz)	65	15
1639	500f. Giant ground pangolin ("Manis gigantea") (horiz)	65	15

244 Pup-150 (Great Britain)

1995. Aircraft. Multicoloured.

1641	100f. Type **244**	15	10
1642	150f. Gardan GY-80 "Horizon" (France)	20	10
1643	250f. Piper J-3 Cub (U.S.A.)	35	10
1644	500f. Piper PA-28 Cherokee Arrow (U.S.A.)	65	15
1645	500f. Pilatus PC-6 Porter (Switzerland)	65	15
1646	500f. Valmet L-90TP Redigo (Finland)	65	15

245 Yoked Oxen

1995. 50th Anniv of F.A.O. Multicoloured.

1648	200f. Type **245**	25	10
1649	750f. Nutrition lesson	1·00	25

246 Jacobean Lily **247** Players

1995. Flowers. Multicoloured.

1650	100f. Type **246**	15	10
1651	150f. "Rudbeckia purpurea"	20	10
1652	250f. Himalayan blue poppy	35	10
1653	500f. Iris "Starshine"	65	15
1654	500f. Rose "Gail Borden"	65	15
1655	500f. Sweet pea ("Lathyrus odoratus")	65	15

1995. World Cup Football Championship, France (1998) (1st issue). Multicoloured.

1657	150f. Type **247**	20	10
1658	250f. Player challenging player No. 2	35	10
1659	500f. Players in blue and white shirt and red shirt in tackle	65	15
1660	500f. Players Nos. 3 and 10 running after ball	65	15
1661	500f. Player No. 2 high-kicking ball	65	15

See also Nos. 1719/24.

248 Arab Horse **249** "Leccinum nigrescens"

1995. Arab Horses. Multicoloured.

1663	100f. Type **248**	15	10
1664	150f. Dark brown horse with white star	20	10
1665	250f. Chestnut	35	10
1666	500f. Grey	65	15
1667	500f. Bay	65	15
1668	500f. Bay with harness and rein (horiz)	65	15

1995. Fungi. Multicoloured.

1670	150f. Type **249**	20	10
1671	250f. "Boletus rhodoxanthus"	35	10
1672	500f. "Cantharellus lutescens"	65	15
1673	500f. Brown roll-rim ("Paxillus involutus")	65	15
1674	500f. "Xerocomus rubellus"	65	15

250 Enterprise, 1832

1995. Veteran Omnibuses. Multicoloured.

1676	250f. Type **250**	35	10
1677	300f. Daimler, 1898	40	10
1678	400f. V.H. Bussing, 1904	50	15
1679	450f. M.A.N. autobus, 1906	60	15
1680	500f. M.A.N. autocar, 1934	65	15

251 Locomotive "Tom Thumb", 1829, U.S.A.

1996. Rail Transport. Multicoloured.

1681	200f. Type **251**	25	10
1682	250f. Locomotive "Genf", 1858, Switzerland (68 × 27 mm)	30	10
1683	300f. Canterbury Frozen Meat Company Dubs locomotive, 1873, New Zealand	35	10
1684	400f. Bagnall fireless steam accumulator locomotive No. 2, Great Britain	50	15
1685	450f. Werner von Siemen's first electric locomotive, 1879, and passenger carriage (68 × 27 mm)	60	15
1686	500f. North London Tramways Company tram, 1885–89, Great Britain	65	15

252 Rock Formation **253** Red Siskin

1996. Multicoloured.

1688	200f. Type **252**	25	10
1689	750f. Child	95	25
1690	1000f. Women carrying faggots	1·25	30

1996. Birds. Multicoloured.

1691	200f. Type **253**	25	10
1692	250f. Red-cheeked cordon-bleu	30	10
1693	300f. Chestnut-breasted minnikin	35	10
1694	400f. Paradise sparrow	50	10
1695	450f. Gouldian finch	55	15
1696	500f. Red bishop	60	15

254 Bull Terrier **256** Chestnut

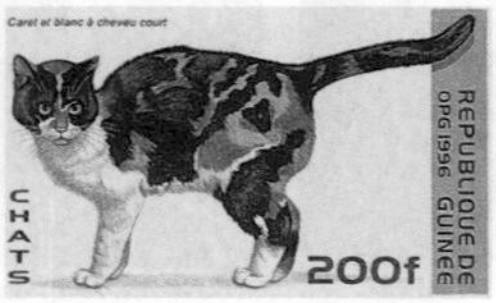

255 Tortoiseshell and White Shorthair

1996. Dogs. Multicoloured.

1698	200f. Type **254**	25	10
1699	250f. Elkhound	30	10
1700	300f. Akita	35	10
1701	400f. Collie	50	10
1702	450f. Rottweiler	55	15
1703	500f. Boxer	60	15

1996. Cats. Multicoloured.

1705	200f. Type **255**	25	10
1706	250f. Bicolour shorthair	30	10
1707	300f. Tortoiseshell and white Japanese bobtail	35	10
1708	400f. Chocolate point Himalayan	50	10
1709	450f. Red longhair	55	15
1710	500f. Blue Persian	60	15

1996. Fungi. Multicoloured.

1712	200f. Type **256**	25	10
1713	250f. Granular	30	10
1714	300f. Destroying angel	35	10
1715	400f. Milky blue	50	10
1716	450f. Violet cortinarius	55	15
1717	500f. Rough-stemmed	60	15

257 Players **258** "Paphiopedilum millmoore"

1997. World Cup Football Championship, France (1998) (2nd issue). Multicoloured.

1719	200f. Type **257**	25	10
1720	250f. Player No. 5	30	10
1721	300f. Three players	35	10
1722	400f. Player dribbling ball past opposition (horiz)	45	10

1723	450f. Player No. 12 with opposing player on ground (horiz)	50	15
1724	500f. Ball passing lunging goalkeeper (horiz)	55	15

1997. Orchids. Multicoloured.

1726	200f. Type **258**	25	10
1727	250f. "Paphiopedilum ernest read"	30	10
1728	300f. "Paphiopedilum harrisianum"	35	10
1729	400f. "Paphiopedilum gaudianum"	45	10
1730	450f. "Paphiopedilum papa rohl"	50	15
1731	500f. "Paphiopedilum sea cliff"	55	15

259 Giraffe

1997. Mammals. Multicoloured.

1733	200f. Type **259**	25	10
1734	250f. White rhinoceros (vert)	30	10
1735	300f. Warthog	35	10
1736	400f. Cheetah	45	10
1737	450f. African elephant (vert)	50	15
1738	500f. Pygmy hippopotamus	55	10

260 H.M.S. "Captain" (turret ship, Great Britain, 1870)

1997. 19th-Century Warships. Multicoloured.

1740	200f. Type **260**	30	15
1741	250f. "Kaiser Wilhelm" (ironclad, Germany, 1869)	35	15
1742	300f. H.M.S. "Temeraire" (turret ship, Great Britain, 1871)	40	15
1743	400f. "Mouillage" (turret ship, Italy, 1866)	50	15
1744	450f. H.M.S. "Inflexible" (battleship, Great Britain, 1881)	55	20
1745	500f. "Magenta" (ironclad, France, 1862)	60	20

261 "Siganus trispilos"

1997. Fishes. Multicoloured.

1747	200f. Type **261**	25	10
1748	250f. Dusky parrotfish	30	10
1749	300f. Harlequin tuskfish	35	10
1750	400f. Masked unicornfish	45	10
1751	450f. "Hypoplectrus gemma"	50	15
1752	500f. Red-tailed surgeon-fish	55	15

262 Officer, Von Witerfeldt's Regiment

264 14th-century Thai Knight, Rook and King

263 Baldwin Steam Locomotive

1997. Prussian Infantry Uniforms. Mult.

1754	200f. Type **262**	25	10
1755	250f. Non-commissioned officer, Von Kanitz's Regiment	30	10
1756	300f. Private, Prince Franz von Anhalt-Dessau's Regiment	35	10
1757	400f. Private, Von Kalnein's Regiment	45	10
1758	450f. Grenadier, Duke Ferdinand of Brunswick's Regiment	50	15
1759	500f. Grenadier musician, Rekow's Guards Battalion	55	15

1997. Steam Locomotives. Multicoloured.

1761	200f. Type **263**	25	10
1762	250f. Steam locomotive No. 1	30	10
1763	300f. Vulcan steam locomotive	35	10
1764	400f. Commonwealth Edison Company Baldwin steam locomotive No. 2	50	15
1765	450f. TCID Railroad steam locomotive No. 108	60	15
1766	500f. Pittsburgh-Hanover Coal Company steam locomotive No. 3	65	15

1997. Chess Pieces. Multicoloured.

1768	200f. Type **264**	25	10
1769	250f. Chinese pawn, king and knight, 1930	30	10
1770	300f. Portuguese ivory "seahorse" pawn, queen and king, 1920	35	10
1771	400f. German pewter "military" knight, king and pawn	45	10
1772	450f. Russian amber queen, king, bishop and knight from reign of Catherine II	50	15
1773	500f. Max Ernst's designs for queen, king, bishop and knight	55	15

265 Siberian Husky

1997. Dogs. Multicoloured.

1775	200f. Type **265**	25	10
1776	250f. Teckel	30	10
1777	300f. Boston terrier	35	10
1778	400f. Basset hound	45	10
1779	450f. Dalmatian	50	15
1780	500f. Rottweiler	55	15

POSTAGE DUE STAMPS

D 11

D 17

1959.

D195	D **11**	1f. green	15	15
D196		2f. red	15	15
D197		3f. brown	30	20
D198		5f. blue	90	45
D199		10f. orange	1·60	70
D200		20f. mauve	3·25	1·60

1959.

D224	D **17**	1f. red	10	15
D225		2f. orange	15	15
D226		3f. lake	15	15
D227		5f. green	40	30
D228		10f. sepia	1·00	90
D229		20f. blue	1·90	1·60

APPENDIX

The following stamps have either been issued in excess of postal needs or have not been available to the public in reasonable quantities at face value. Such stamps may later be given full listing if there is evidence of regular postal use.

1982.

World Cup Winners. Nos. 1068/74 optd.

1983.

Olympic Games, Los Angeles. 100s.

Bicentenary of Manned Flight. 100s.

Winter Olympic Games, Sarajevo. 100s.

1984.

Winter Olympic Gold Medal Winners. 100s.

1985.

Space Achievements. 200s.

Anniversaries and Events. 85th Birthday of Queen Elizabeth the Queen Mother. 100s.

1986.

Appearance of Halley's Comet. 1500f.

1987.

Winter Olympic Games, Seoul. 1500f.

1989. Embossed on gold foil.

Scout and Butterfly. Air 1500f.

Bicentenary of French Revolution. Air 1500f.

1990. Embossed on gold foil.

World Cup Football Championship, Italy. Air 1500f.

Winter Olympic Games, Albertville (1992). Air 1500f.

De Gaulle and Free French Forces. Air 1500f.

1992. Embossed on gold foil.

Olympic Games, Barcelona. Air 1500f.

World Cup Football Championship, U.S.A. (1994) (1st issue). Air 1500f. (vert design).

Elvis Presley. Air 1500f.

Pope John Paul II's African Tour. Air 1500f.

1993. Embossed on gold foil.

Bicentenary of Year One of First Republic of France. Air. Optd on 1989 French Revolution issue. 1500f.

Olympic Games, Atlanta. Air 1500f.

Winter Olympic Games, Lillehammer, Norway. Air 1500f.

World Cup Football Championship, U.S.A. (1994) (2nd issue). Air 1500f. (square design).

1995. Embossed on gold foil.

Normandy Landing, 1944. Air. Optd on 1990 De Gaulle Appendix. 1500f.

GUINEA–BISSAU Pt. 13

Following an armed rebellion against Colonial rule, the independence of former Portuguese Guinea was recognised on 10 September 1974.

1974. 100 centavos = 1 escudo.
1976. 100 centavos = 1 peso.

77 Amilcar Cabral, Map and Flag

1974. 1st Anniv of Proclamation of Republic. Country name inscr in white.

426	77	1p. multicoloured	50	40
427		2.5p. multicoloured	75	65
428		5p. multicoloured	15·00	8·50
429		10p. multicoloured	2·50	2·00

1975. No. 425 of Portuguese Guinea optd **REP. DA BISSAU**.

430	2e. multicoloured	60	60

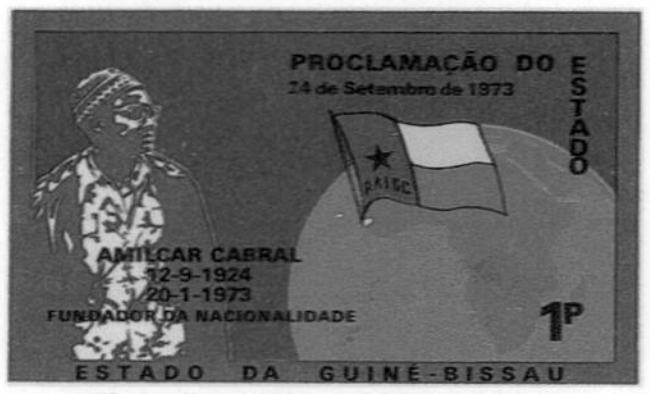

79 Amilcar Cabral, Map and Flag

1975. 2nd Anniv of Proclamation of Republic (1st issue). Country name inscr in black.

431	79	1p. multicoloured	45	30
432		2.5p. multicoloured	60	45
433		5p. multicoloured	2·50	1·40
434		10p. multicoloured	2·50	2·25

See also Nos. 439/440.

80 Amilcar Cabral, Arms and Flag

1975. 51st Birth Anniv of Amilcar Cabral (founder of P.A.I.G.C.).

435	80	1e. multicoloured	20	10
436		10e. multicoloured	80	40

81 Family, Arms and Flag

1975. 19th Anniv of P.A.I.G.C. (Partido Africano da Independencia da Guine e do Cabo Verde).

437	81	2e. multicoloured	50	20
438		10e. multicoloured	2·00	75

82 Pres. Luis Cabral, Arms and Flag

1975. 2nd Anniv of Proclamation of Republic (2nd issue).

439	82	3e. multicoloured	40	20
440		5e. multicoloured	85	30

83 General Henry Knox (after Stuart) and Cannons of Ticonderoga (after Lovell)

1976. Bicentenary of American Independence (1st issue). Multicoloured.

441	5e. Type **83** (postage)	25	15
442	10e. General Putnam and Battle of Bunker Hill	55	30
443	15e. Washington and Crossing of the Delaware	80	35
444	20e. General Kosciuszko and Battle of Saratoga	1·25	50
445	30e. General von Steuben and Valley Forge (air)	1·75	90
446	40e. Lafayette and Monmouth Court House	2·00	1·00

See also Nos. 503/6.

84 Masked Dancer

1976. Dancers. Multicoloured

448	2p. Type **84** (postage)	30	10
449	3p. Dancer and drummer	35	15
450	5p. Dancers on stilts	60	20
451	10p. Dancers with spears and bows (air)	65	40
452	15p. Masked dancer	1·00	50
453	20p. "Devil" dancer	1·50	65

1976. Cent of Universal Postal Union (1st issue). Nos. 1448/53 optd **CENTENARIO DA U.P.U. 1874. MEMBRO DA U.P.U. 1974** and emblem.

455	84	2p. multicoloured (post)	10	10
456	–	3p. multicoloured	20	10
457	–	5p. multicoloured	25	15
458	–	10p. multicoloured (air)	50	25
459	–	15p. multicoloured	65	40
460	–	20p. multicoloured	90	50

See also Nos. 518/23.

1976. Nos. 435/40 surch in new currency.

462	1p. on 1e. multicoloured	10	10
463	2p. on 2e. multicoloured	10	10
464	3p. on 3e. multicoloured	15	10
465	5p. on 5e. multicoloured	25	15
466	10p. on 10e. multicoloured	50	30
467	10p. on 10e. multicoloured	50	30

87 Amilcar Cabral and Funeral

1976. 3rd Anniv of Amilcar Cabral's Assassination.

468	87	3p. multicoloured	15	10
469		5p. multicoloured	20	15
470		6p. multicoloured	25	20
471		10p. multicoloured	40	25

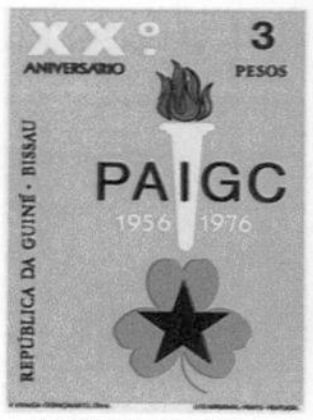

88 Party Emblem

89 Launch of "Soyuz" Spacecraft

1976. 20th Anniv of P.A.I.G.C.

472	88	3p. multicoloured	15	15
473		15p. multicoloured	65	50
474		50p. multicoloured	1·60	1·25

1976. Air. "Apollo–Soyuz" Space Link. Mult.

475	5p. Type **89**	25	15
476	10p. Launch of "Apollo" spacecraft	45	30
477	15p. Leonov, Stafford and meeting in Space	80	45
478	20p. Eclipse of the Sun	1·25	55
479	30p. Infra-red photograph of Earth	1·75	85
480	40p. Return of Spacecraft to Earth	2·25	95

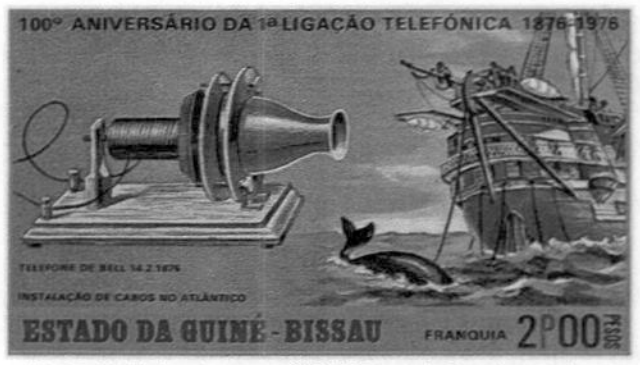

90 Bell Telephone of 1876 and Laying First Atlantic Cable

1976. Telephone Centenary. Multicoloured.

482	2p. Type **90** (postage)	15	10
483	3p. French telephone of 1890 and first telephone box, 1893	20	10
484	5p. German automatic telephone of 1908 and automatic telephone, 1898	25	15
485	10p. English telephone of 1910 and trans-horizon link, 1963 (air)	55	25
486	15p. French telephone of 1924 and communications satellite	85	45
487	20p. Modern telephone and "Molnya" satellite	1·25	50

91 Women's Figure Skating

1976. Winter Olympic Games, Innsbruck. Mult.

489	1p. Type **91** (postage)	15	10
490	3p. Ice-hockey	30	10
491	5p. Bobsleighing	30	15
492	10p. Pairs figure-skating (air)	55	30
493	20p. Cross-country skiing	1·25	45
494	30p. Speed skating	1·75	85

92 Footballers and Montreal Skyline

1976. Olympic Games, Montreal. Mult.

496	1p. Type **92**	10	10
497	3p. Pole vaulting	15	10
498	5p. Hurdling	25	15
499	10p. Discus throwing	45	25
500	20p. Running	90	50
501	30p. Wrestling	1·40	75

93 "Viking" orbiting Mars

1976. Bicentenary of American Revolution (2nd issue). Multicoloured. (a) Postage. Horiz designs as T **83**.

503	3p.50 Crispus Attuck and Boston Massacre	30	10
504	5p. Martin Luther King and Capitol	40	20

(b) Air. Success of "Viking" Mission. Vert.

505	25p. Type **93**	1·25	65
506	35p. Lander scooping samples from surface of Mars	1·75	90

94 Amilcar Cabral

1977. 4th Death Anniv of Amilcar Cabral. Multicoloured.

507	50c. Type **94** (postage)	15	10
508	3p.50 Luis Cabral addressing U.N. Assembly	35	10
509	15p. Type **94** (air)	55	30
510	30p. As No. 508	1·25	50

95 Henri Dunant (Peace, 1901)

1977. 75th Anniv of 1st Nobel Prizes. Mult.

511	3p.50 Type **95** (postage)	30	10
512	5p. Albert Einstein (Physics, 1921)	35	20
513	6p. Irene and Jean-Frederic Joliot-Curie (Chemistry, 1935)	75	20
514	30p. Alexander Fleming (Medicine, 1945)	1·75	90
515	35p. Ernest Hemingway (Literature, 1954) (air)	2·00	90
516	40p. J. Tinbergen (Economic Sciences, 1969)	2·25	1·00

96 Postal Runner and "Telstar" Satellite

1977. Centenary (1974) of Universal Postal Union (2nd issue). Multicoloured.

518	3p.50 Type **96** (postage)	25	15
519	5p. A.E.G. J-II biplane, and satellites circling globe	35	15
520	6p. Mail van and satellite control room	55	15
521	30p. Stage-coach and astronaut cancelling letters on Moon	1·75	50
522	35p. French locomotive (1844) and "Intelsat 4" satellite (air)	6·50	2·75
523	40p. Aircraft and "Apollo"–"Soyuz" link	2·50	90

97 Coronation Coach

1977. Silver Jubilee of Queen Elizabeth II. Multicoloured.

525	3p.50 Type **97** (postage)	20	10
526	5p. Coronation ceremony	25	15
527	10p. Yeoman of the Guard and Crown Jewels	45	25
528	20p. Trumpeter sounding fanfare	90	45
529	25p. Royal Horse Guard (air)	1·25	50
530	30p. Royal Family on balcony	1·50	70

98 Congress Emblem

99 "Massacre of the Innocents" (detail)

1977. 3rd P.A.I.G.C. Congress, Bissau.
532 **98** 3p.50 multicoloured . . . 25 15

1977. 400th Birth Anniv of Peter Paul Rubens (artist). Multicoloured.

533	3p.50 Type **99** (postage) . . .	20	10
534	5p. "Rape of the Daughters of Leukippos"	25	15
535	6p. "Lamentation of Christ" (horiz)	35	15
536	30p. "Francisco IV Gonzaga, Prince of Mantua"	1·60	50
537	35p. "The Four Continents" (detail) (horiz) (air)	1·75	50
538	40p. "Marquise Brigida Spinola Doria"	2·25	60

100 Santos-Dumont's Airship "Ballon No. 6"

1978. Airships. Multicoloured.

540	3p.50 Type **100** (postage) . .	25	15
541	5p. Beardmore airship R-34 crossing Atlantic	35	15
542	10p. "Norge" over North Pole	55	20
543	20p. "Graf Zeppelin" over Abu Simbel	1·40	50
544	25p. "Hindenburg" over New York (air)	1·75	70
545	30p. "Graf Zeppelin", Concorde airliner and space shuttle	2·25	75

101 Footballers, Cup and Poster (Uruguay, 1930)

1978. World Cup Football Championship, Argentina. Multicoloured.

547	3p.50 Type **101** (postage) . .	20	10
548	5p. "Coupe du Monde, 1938"	25	15
549	10p. Brazil, 1950	55	25
550	20p. Chile, 1962	1·10	45
551	25p. Mexico, 1970 (air) . . .	1·40	50
552	30p. "FIFA World Cup 1974" (Germany)	1·60	65

DESIGNS: showing match scenes and posters from previous championships.

102 Black Antelope

1978. Endangered Animals. Multicoloured.

554	3p.50 Type **102** (postage) . .	30	10
555	5p. Fennec	75	30
556	6p. Secretary bird	1·00	50
557	30p. Hippopotamuses	2·00	65
558	35p. Cheetahs (air)	2·25	65
559	40p. Gorillas	2·50	75

103 Microwave-antenna

104 Child

1978. Telecommunications Day.
561 **103** 3p.50 multicoloured . . . 20 15
562 10p. multicoloured . . . 55 30

1978. Children's Day.

563	**104**	50c. blue and green . . .	10	10
564	–	3p. bright red and red . .	15	10
565	–	5p. light brown and brown	25	15
566	–	30p. brown and red . . .	1·40	1·00

DESIGNS: 3p. Amilcar Cabral and child; 5p. Children; 30p. Two children playing.

105 Reading the Proclamation

1978. 25th Anniv of Coronation of Queen Elizabeth II. Multicoloured.

567	3p. Type **105** (postage) . . .	20	10
568	5p. Queen and Prince Philip in Coronation Coach . . .	25	15
569	10p. Queen and Prince Philip	45	25
570	20p. Mounted drummer . . .	90	45
571	25p. Imperial State Crown and St. Edward's Crown (air)	1·25	50
572	30p. Queen holding orb and sceptre	1·25	65
573	100p. Queen, stained glass window and Imperial State Crown (55 × 38 mm) . . .	4·50	1·50

106 Wright Brothers and Wright Flyer I

1978. History of Aviation. Multicoloured.

575	3p.50 Type **106** (postage) . .	20	10
576	10p. Alberto Santos-Dumont	45	20
577	15p. Louis Bleriot	75	35
578	20p. Charles Lindbergh (air)	90	40
579	25p. Moon landing	1·25	50
580	30p. Space shuttle	1·50	65

1978. World Cup Football Championship Results. Nos. 547/52 optd **10 ARGENTINA 20 HOLANDA 30 BRAZIL**.

582	3p.50 multicoloured (postage)	20	10
583	5p. multicoloured	25	15
584	10p. multicoloured	45	25
585	20p. multicoloured	1·10	55
586	25p. multicoloured (air) . . .	1·25	55
587	30p. multicoloured	1·50	70

108 "Virgin and Child", 1497

1978. 450th Death Anniv of Albrecht Durer (artist). Multicoloured.

589	3p.50 Type **108** (postage) . .	20	10
590	5p. "Virgin and Child", 1507	25	15
591	6p. "Virgin and Child", 1512	30	15
592	30p. "Virgin", 1518	1·40	70
593	35p. "Virgin and Child with St. Anne", 1519 (air) . . .	1·75	50
594	40p. "Virgin of the Pear", 1526	2·00	75

109 Rowland Hill and Wurttemberg 70k. Stamp, 1873

1978. Death Centenary of Rowland Hill.

596	3p.50 Type **109** (postage) . .	15	10
597	5p. Belgian 10c. stamp, 1849	25	15
598	6p. Monaco 5f. stamp, 1885	30	20
599	30p. Spanish 10r. stamp, 1851	1·50	70
600	35p. Swiss 5r. stamp, 1851 (air)	1·75	50
601	40p. Naples ½t. stamp, 1860	2·00	75

DESIGNS: 5p. to 40p. show Rowland Hill and stamp.

110 Nurse immunising Child

1979. International Year of the Child (1st issue). Multicoloured.

603	3p.50 Type **110** (postage) . .	20	10
604	10p. Children drinking . . .	55	25
605	15p. Children with book . .	1·00	35
606	20p. Space shuttle (air) . . .	1·00	40
607	25p. "Skylab" space station	1·40	50
608	30p. Children playing chess	2·00	75

See also Nos. 616/19.

111 Family

1979. National Census.

610	**111**	50c. brown, blue and pink	10	10
611		2p. brown, blue & lt blue	15	10
612		4p. brown, blue and yellow	25	15

112 Wave Pattern and Human Figures

113 Monument

1979. World Telecommunications Day. Mult.
613 50c. Type **112** 10 10
614 4p. Wave pattern and human figures (different) 20 15

1979. 20th Anniv of Pindjiuouiti Massacre.
615 **113** 4p.50 multicoloured . . . 30 15

114 Classroom Scene

1980. International Year of the Child (2nd issue). Multicoloured.

616	6p. Type **114** (postage) . . .	30	25
617	10p. Jules Verne and child reading novel (vert)	45	30
618	25p. Locomotive "Northumbrian" (1831), Japanese "Hikari" express train and child with toy steam locomotive (vert) . .	9·00	1·25
619	35p. Man and child with bows and arrows (vert) . .	1·60	75

115 Amilcar Cabral, Workers and Children reading Books

1980. Literacy Campaign. Multicoloured.

621	3p.50 Type **115** (postage) . .	20	10
622	5p. Luis Cabral displaying school textbooks	30	15
623	15p. Type **115** (air)	80	50
624	25p. As No. 622	1·40	75

116 Globe and Cogwheel

1980. Technical Co-operation among Developing Countries.
625 **116** 3p.50 multicoloured . . . 20 10
626 6p. multicoloured 30 20
627 10p. multicoloured . . . 45 30

117 Wood Carvings

118 Ernst Udet

1980. Handicrafts. Multicoloured.

628	3p. Type **117**	20	10
629	6p. Weaving (horiz)	30	20
630	20p. Bust and statuette (horiz)	1·00	50

1980. History of Aviation. Air Aces of 1st World War. Multicoloured.

631	3p.50 Type **118** (postage) . .	25	15
632	5p. Charles Nungesser . . .	35	25
633	6p. Manfred von Richthofen	55	25
634	30p. Francesco Baracca . . .	1·75	70
635	35p. Willy Coppens de Houthulst (air)	2·10	75
636	40p. Charles Guynemer . . .	2·50	90

119 Speed Skating

1980. Winter Olympic Games, Lake Placid. Multicoloured.

638	3p. Type **119** (postage) . . .	20	10
639	5p. Downhill	30	20
640	6p. Luge	40	25
641	30p. Cross country skiing . .	1·75	70
642	35p. Downhill skiing (air) . .	2·00	75
643	40p. Figure skating	2·40	90

120 Putting the Shot

1980. Olympic Games, Moscow. Multicoloured.

645	3p.50 Type **120** (postage)	20	15
646	5p. Gymnastics (ring exercise)	25	20
647	6p. Long jump	35	25
648	30p. Fencing	1·50	70
649	35p. Gymnastics (backward somersault) (air)	1·75	75
650	40p. Running	2·00	90

121 Congress Meeting

1980. 16th Anniv of Cassaca Congress.

652	**121** 3p.50 multicoloured	15	10
653	6p.50 multicoloured	30	20
654	10p. multicoloured	40	30

122 Satellites

1981. Space Achievements. Multicoloured.

655	3p.50 Type **122** (postage)	20	10
656	5p. Satellite	25	15
657	6p. Rocket	30	15
658	30p. Space Shuttle "Columbia"	1·75	95
659	35p. "Viking I" (air)	1·75	75
660	40p. U.S.–Soviet space link	2·00	90

123 Platini (France) and Football Scene

1981. World Cup Football Championship, Spain. Multicoloured.

662	3p.50 Type **123** (postage)	30	10
663	5p. Bettega (Italy)	35	15
664	6p. Rensenbrink (Netherlands)	45	15
665	30p. Rivelino (Brazil)	1·90	80
666	35p. Rummenigge (West Germany) (air)	1·90	80
667	40p. Kempes (Argentina)	2·00	90

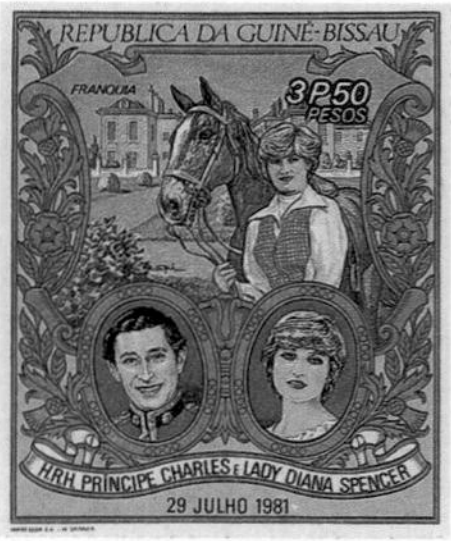

124 Lady Diana Spencer with Horse

1981. Wedding of Prince of Wales. Multicoloured.

669	3p.50 Type **124** (postage)	20	15
670	5p. Investiture of Prince of Wales	25	15
671	6p. Lady Diana Spencer with Children	30	15
672	30p. St. Paul's Cathedral	1·25	95
673	35p. Althorp House (air)	1·40	1·00
674	40p. Arms of Prince of Wales	1·50	1·25

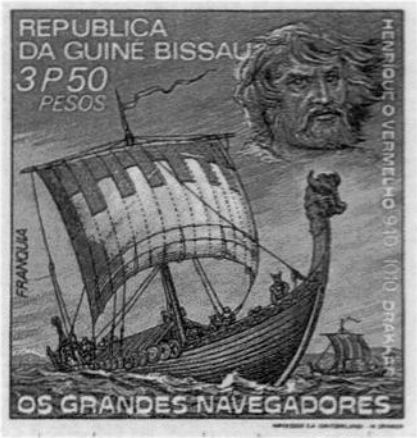

125 Eric the Red and Viking Ship

1981. Navigators. Multicoloured.

676	3p.50 Type **125** (postage)	25	15
677	5p. Vasco da Gama and "Sao Gabriel"	30	15
678	6p. Magellan and "Vitoria"	35	20
679	30p. Cartier and "Emerillon"	2·00	1·00
680	35p. Drake and "Golden Hind" (air)	2·50	1·25
681	40p. Cook and H.M.S. "Endeavour"	2·75	1·60

126 "Girl with Bare Feet"

1981. Birth Centenary of Pablo Picasso. Multicoloured.

683	3p.50 Type **126** (postage)	20	15
684	5p. "Acrobat on Ball"	25	15
685	6p. "Pierrot"	30	15
686	30p. "Girl in front of a Mirror"	1·50	95
687	35p. "The First Steps" (air)	2·00	1·00
688	40p. "Woman in Turkish Dress"	2·25	1·25

127 "Retable of St. Zeno" (Mantegna)

1981. Christmas. Multicoloured.

690	3p.50 Type **127** (postage)	20	15
691	5p. "Virgin with Child" (Bellini)	25	15
692	6p. "Virgin and Child with Cherubs" (Mantegna)	30	15
693	25p. "Madonna Campori" (Correggio)	1·50	1·00
694	30p. "Virgin and Child" (Memling) (air)	2·00	1·10
695	35p. "Virgin and Child" (Bellini)	2·25	1·25

128 Archery

1982. 75th Anniv of Boy Scout Movement. Multicoloured.

697	3p.50 Type **128** (postage)	15	10
698	5p. First aid	20	15
699	6p. Bugler	25	15
700	30p. Cub scouts	1·60	80
701	35p. Girl scout in canoe (air)	2·25	90
702	40p. Scouts with model aircraft	2·40	1·25

129 Keegan

1982. World Cup Football Championship, Spain. Multicoloured.

704	3p.50 Type **129** (postage)	20	10
705	5p. Rossi	20	15
706	6p. Zico	25	15
707	30p. Arconada	1·60	80
708	35p. Kempes (air)	2·25	1·00
709	40p. Kaltz	2·50	1·10

130 Lady Diana Spencer

1982. 21st Birthday of Princess of Wales. Multicoloured.

711	3p.50 Type **130** (postage)	15	10
712	5p. Playing croquet	25	15
713	6p. Lady Diana with pony	30	15
714	30p. Fishing	1·75	80
715	35p. Engagement picture (air)	1·90	90
716	40p. Honeymoon picture	2·00	1·10

1982. Birth of Prince William of Wales. Nos. 711/16 optd **21 DE JULHO 1982. GUILHERMO ARTHUR FILIPE LUIS PRINCIPE DE GALES.**

718	3p.50 multicoloured (postage)	20	10
719	5p. multicoloured	25	15
720	6p. multicoloured	30	15
721	30p. multicoloured	1·60	95
722	35p. multicoloured (air)	1·90	1·10
723	40p. multicoloured	2·00	1·25

132 National Colours

1982. Visit of President Eanes of Portugal. Multicoloured.

725	4p.50 Type **132**	10	10
726	20p. Doves on national colours	20	10

133 Montgolfier Balloon

1983. Bicentenary of Manned Flight. Mult.

727	50c. Type **133**	10	10
728	2p.50 Charles's hydrogen balloon	15	10
729	3p.50 Charles Green's balloon "Royal Vauxhall"	20	10
730	5p. Gaston Tissandier's balloon "Zenith"	30	10
731	10p. Salomon Andree's balloon "Ornen" over Arctic	60	20
732	20p. Stratosphere balloon "Explorer II"	1·25	40
733	30p. Modern hot-air balloons	2·00	60

134 Hamadryas Baboon

136 Satellite

1983. African Primates. Multicoloured.

735	1p. Type **134**	10	10
736	1p.50 Gorilla	20	10
737	3p.50 Gelada	30	10
738	5p. Mandrill	40	15
739	8p. Chimpanzee	80	20
740	20p. Eastern black-and-white colobus	1·50	50
741	30p. Diana monkey	2·40	85

1983. Cosmonautics Day. Multicoloured.

743	1p. Type **136**	10	10
744	1p.50 Satellite (different)	15	10
745	3p.50 Rocket carrying space shuttle	20	10
746	5p. Satellite (different)	30	15
747	8p. Satellite (different)	60	20
748	20p. Satellite (different)	1·25	45
749	30p. "Soyuz" docking with "Salyut"	2·00	70

137 Woodcut from Caxton's "Game and Playe of Chesse", Arabian Pawn and Rook

1983. Chess. Multicoloured.

751	1p. Type **137**	15	10
752	1p.50 12th-century European king and knight	15	10
753	3p.50 Mid 18th-century German rook, queen and king	25	10
754	5p. Late 12th/early 13th-century Danish bishop and knight	40	10
755	10p. 18th-century French king and queen	80	25
756	20p. 18th-century Venetian king, knight and queen	1·75	55
757	40p. 19th-century faience knight, queen and rook	3·00	1·10

138 "Vision of Ezekiel"

1983. 500th Birth Anniv of Raphael (artist). Multicoloured.

759	1p. Type **138**	10	10
760	1p.50 "Tempi Madonna"	10	10
761	3p.50 "Della Tenda Madonna"	20	10
762	5p. "Orleans Madonna"	25	10
763	8p. "La Belle Jardiniere"	45	20
764	15p. "Small Cowper Madonna"	90	35
765	30p. "St. George and the Dragon"	2·00	60

139 Swimming

1983. Olympic Games, Los Angeles (1932 and 1984) (1st issue). Multicoloured.

767	1p. Type **139**	10	10
768	1p.50 Hurdling	15	10

769 3p.50 Fencing 20 10
770 5p. Weightlifting 30 10
771 10p. Marathon 60 15
772 20p. Show jumping . . . . . 1·10 35
773 40p. Cycling . . . . 2·40 65
See also Nos. 843/9.

141 Rowland Hill and Penny Black

1983. World Communications Year. Mult.
776 50c. Type **141** 10 10
777 2p.50 Samuel Morse and morse machine 15 10
778 3p.50 Heinrich Rudolf Hertz and electromagnetic wave diagrams 20 10
779 5p. Lord Kelvin and "Agamemnon" (cable ship) 50 10
780 10p. Alexander Graham Bell and telephones 60 15
781 20p. Guglielmo Marconi and wireless apparatus . . . . 1·40 40
782 30p. Vladimir Kosma Zworykin and television . . 1·60 55

142 JAAC Emblem

1983. First JAAC Congress. Multicoloured.
784 4p. Crowd and emblem . . . 25 15
785 5p. Type **142** 30 15

143 Speed Skating

145 U.D.E.M.U. Emblem

144 Hoeing Vegetable Patch

1983. Winter Olympic Games, Sarajevo (1st issue). Multicoloured.
786 1p. Type **143** 10 10
787 1p.50 Ski jumping 15 10
788 3p. Cross-country skiing . . 20 10
789 5p. Bobsleigh 25 10
790 10p. Ice hockey 70 25
791 15p. Ice skating . . . . . . 1·10 30
792 20p. Luge . . . . 1·25 35
See also Nos. 816/22.

1983. World Food Day.
794 **144** 1p.50 multicoloured . . . 10 10
795 2p. multicoloured 15 10
796 4p. multicoloured 30 15

1983. Democratic Union of Women. Multicoloured.
798 4p.50 Type **145** 30 15
799 7p.50 Flag and woman . . . 50 20
800 9p. Woman sewing 70 30
801 12p. Women working on plantation . . . . 1·00 45

146 "Canna coccinea"

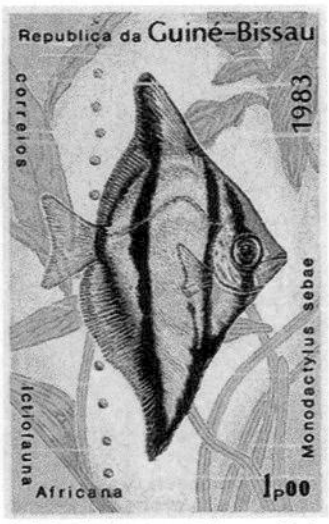

147 Guinean Fingerfish

1983. Flowers. Multicoloured.
802 1p. Type **146** 15 10
803 1p.50 "Bouganville litoralis" 20 10
804 3p.50 "Euphorbia milii" . . 25 10
805 5p. "Delonix regia" 30 10
806 8p. "Bauhinia variegata" . . 50 15
807 10p. "Spathodea campanulata" 70 20
808 30p. "Hibiscus rosa-sinensis" 2·00 60

1983. Fishes. Multicoloured.
809 1p. Type **147** 20 15
810 1p.50 Clown loach 25 15
811 3p.50 Spotted climbing-perch 35 20
812 5p. Berthold's panchax . . . 50 20
813 8p. Red-barred lyretail . . . 75 30
814 10p. Two-striped lyretail . . 1·10 40
815 30p. Lyre-tailed panchax . . 3·50 1·40

148 Ski Jumping

1984. Winter Olympic Games, Sarajevo (2nd issue). Multicoloured.
816 50c. Type **148** 10 10
817 2p.50 Speed skating 15 10
818 3p.50 Ice hockey 30 10
819 5p. Cross-country skiing . . 35 10
820 6p. Downhill skiing 60 15
821 20p. Ice skating . . . . . . 1·25 40
822 30p. Two-man bobsleigh . . 2·00 60

149 Duesenberg, 1928

1984. 150th Birth Anniv of Gottlieb Daimler (automobile designer). Multicoloured.
824 5p. Type **149** 15 10
825 8p. MG "Midget", 1932 . . 25 10
826 15p. Mercedes, 1928 . . . . 50 20
827 20p. Bentley, 1928 . . . . . 60 30
828 24p. Alfa Romeo, 1929 . . . 85 30
829 30p. Datsun, 1932 . . . . . 1·25 35
830 35p. Lincoln, 1932 . . . . . 1·75 40

150 Sud Aviation Caravelle

1984. 40th Anniv of I.C.A.O. Multicoloured.
832 8p. Type **150** 25 10
833 22p. Douglas DC-6B 80 30
834 80p. Ilyushin Il-76 . . . . . 2·25 90

151 "Dona Tadea Arias de Enriquez" (Goya)

153 Fabric Headdress

152 Football

1984. "Espana 84" International Stamp Exhibition, Madrid. Multicoloured.
835 3p. "Virgin and Child" (Morales) 15 10
836 6p. Type **151** 20 10
837 10p. "Saint Cassilda" (Zurbaran) 30 10
838 12p. "Saints Andrew and Francis" (El Greco) . . . 35 15
839 15p. "Infanta Isabel Clara Eugenia" (Coello) 55 15
840 35p. "Queen Maria of Austria" (Velazquez) . . . 1·40 45
841 40p. "The Trinity" (El Greco) . . . . 1·75 55

1984. Olympic Games, Los Angeles (2nd issue). Multicoloured.
843 6p. Type **152** 15 10
844 8p. Show jumping 25 10
845 15p. Sailing 50 15
846 20p. Hockey 70 20
847 22p. Handball 75 20
848 30p. Canoeing . . . . 1·10 35
849 40p. Boxing . . . . 1·75 60

1984. "Lubrapex 84" Portuguese–Brazilian Stamp Exhibition, Lisbon. Multicoloured.
851 7p.50 Type **153** 25 15
852 7p.50 Headdress 25 15
853 7p.50 Carved bird headdress 25 15
854 7p.50 Wooden mask 25 15
855 7p.50 Carving of horse . . . 25 15
856 7p.50 Statuette 25 15

154 Tiger

1984. Wild Cats. Multicoloured.
857 3p. Type **154** 15 10
858 6p. Lions 25 10
859 10p. Clouded leopard 35 15
860 12p. Cheetahs 45 20
861 15p. Lynx 60 25
862 35p. Leopard . . . . 1·40 55
863 40p. Snow leopard . . . . . 1·75 65

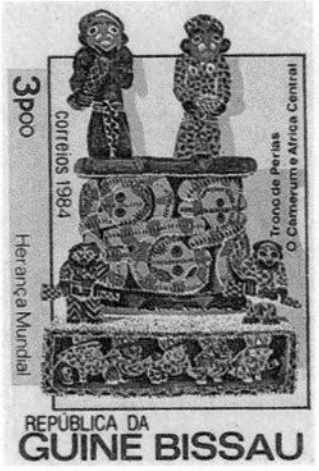

155 Pearl Throne, Cameroun

156 Amilcar Cabral making Speech

1984. World Heritage. Multicoloured.
864 3p. Type **155** 10 10
865 6p. Antelope (carving), West Sudan 20 10
866 10p. Setial, East Africa . . . 30 15
867 12p. Mask, West African coast 40 20
868 15p. Leopard (statuette), Guinea coast 60 25
869 35p. Carved statuette of woman, Zaire . . . . . . 1·25 50
870 40p. Funeral figures, South-east Africa and Madagascar . . . . 1·25 55

1984. 60th Birth Anniv of Amilcar Cabral. Multicoloured.
871 5p. Type **156** 15 10
872 12p. Amilcar Cabral in combat dress 35 15
873 20p. Amilcar Cabral memorial 60 25
874 50p. Amilcar Cabral mausoleum . . . . 1·50 60

157 Mechanic working on Engine

1984. 11th Anniv of Independence. Mult.
875 3p. Type **157** 10 10
876 6p. Children in school . . . 20 10
877 10p. Laying bricks 30 10
878 12p. Doctor tending child (vert) 35 20
879 15p. Sewing (vert) 40 20
880 35p. Telephonist and switchboard . . . . 1·25 50
881 40p. P.A.I.G.C. headquarters 1·25 55

158 Grey Whales

1984. Whales. Multicoloured.
882 5p. Type **158** 25 10
883 8p. Blue whales 30 15
884 15p. Bottle-nosed dolphins 60 25
885 20p. Sperm whale 70 25
886 24p. Killer whale 85 35
887 30p. Bowhead whale . . . . 1·50 40
888 35p. Sei whale . . . . 1·75 45

159 "Hypolimnas dexithea"

1984. Butterflies and Moths. Multicoloured.
889 3p. Type **159** 15 15
890 6p. "Papilio arcturus" . . . 20 15
891 10p. "Morpho menelaus terrestris" 35 15
892 12p. "Apaturina erminea" . . 45 20
893 15p. "Prepona praeneste" . . 70 25
894 35p. "Ornithoptera paradisea" . . . . 1·60 55
895 40p. "Morpho hecuba obidona" . . . . 1·60 60

160 Carl Lewis (400 m relay)

1984. Olympic Gold Medallists, Los Angeles. Multicoloured.
896 6p. Type **160** 15 10
897 8p. Koji Gushiken (men's gymnastics) 15 10
898 15p. Dr. Reiner Klimke (individual dressage) . . . 45 20
899 20p. Tracie Ruiz (synchronized swimming) 55 20
900 22p. May Lou Retton (women's gymnastics) . . . 65 25
901 30p. Michael Gross (100 m freestyle and 100 m butterfly) 90 35
902 40p. Edwin Moses (400 m hurdles) . . . . . 1·25 50

161 White Mountain Central Railway locomotive, 1926, U.S.A.

1984. Locomotives. Multicoloured.
904 5p. Type **161** 20 15
905 8p. Talyllyn Mountain Railway locomotive No. 86, 1886, Great Britain 25 15
906 15p. Wuppetal Overhead Railway, 1901, Germany 50 20
907 20p. Peruvian mountain rack railway locomotive 60 25
908 24p. Steam locomotive, Achensee rack railway, Austria 80 30
909 30p. Vitznau–Rigi rack railway locomotive, Switzerland . . . . 1·10 40
910 35p. Vitznau–Rigi rack railway locomotive No. 7, Switzerland . . . . 1·60 60

162 Harley Davidson Motor Cycle

1985. Centenary of Motor Cycle. Mult.

912 5p. Type **162** 20 15
913 8p. Kawasaki 25 15
914 15p. Honda 45 20
915 20p. Yamaha 70 30
916 25p. Suzuki . . . . 1·00 35
917 30p. BMW . . . . 1·40 45
918 35p. Moto Guzzi . . . . . . 1·50 50

163 Brown Pelican **164** "Clitocybe gibba"

1985. Air. Birth Bicentenary of John J. Audubon (ornithologist). Multicoloured.

920 5p. Type **163** 45 20
921 10p. American white pelican 75 30
922 20p. Great blue heron . . . 1·40 45
923 40p. Greater flamingo . . . 3·00 1·00

1985. Fungi. Multicoloured.

924 7p. Type **164** 35 15
925 9p. "Morchella elata" 50 20
926 12p. "Lepista nuda" 75 25
927 20p. "Lactarius deliciosus" . . 90 30
928 30p. "Russula virescens" . . 1·25 35
929 35p. "Chroogomphus rutilus" 1·75 50

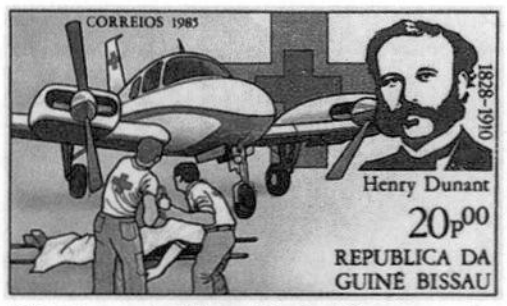

165 Dunant, Piper Twin Commanche and Volunteers attending Patient

1985. 75th Death Anniv of Henri Dunant (Red Cross founder). Multicoloured.

930 20p. Type **165** 40 15
931 25p. Doctor and volunteer putting patient in ambulance 50 15
932 40p. Helicopter team attending wounded soldier 75 35
933 80p. Volunteers in boat rescuing man from water 1·40 55

166 Long-haired White Cat **167** Vincenzo Bellini, 1820 Harp and 16th-century Descant Viol

1985. Cats. Multicoloured.

934 7p. Type **166** 20 15
935 10p. Siamese cat 25 15
936 12p. Grey cat 30 15
937 15p. Tortoiseshell cat 40 15
938 20p. Ginger cat 55 20
939 40p. Tabby cat . . . . . . 1·00 35
940 45p. Short-haired white cat 1·40 35

1985. International Music Year. Composers. Multicoloured.

942 4p. Type **167** (150th death anniv of Bellini) 15 15
943 5p. Robert Schumann (175th birth anniv) and pyramid piano, 1829 . . . . 15 15
944 7p. Frederic Chopin (175th birth anniv) and piano, 1817 . . . . 15 15
945 12p. Luigi Cherubini (225th birth anniv), 1720 baryton and 18th-century quinton 20 15
946 20p. Giovanni Battista Pergolesi (275th birth anniv) and harpsichord, 1734 . . . . 45 15
947 30p. Georg Friedrich Handel (300th birth anniv), 1825 valve trumpet and 18th-century timpani . . . 65 20
948 50p. Heinrich Schutz (400th birth anniv), 17th-century bass viol and 1680 oboe . . 1·00 45

168 "Santa Maria" **169** U.N. Emblem, Rainbow and Peace Doves

1985. Sailing Ships. Multicoloured.

950 8p. Type **168** 30 15
951 15p. 16th-century Dutch carrack 40 15
952 20p. "Mayflower" 50 15
953 30p. "St. Louis" (French galleon) 75 20
954 35p. "Royal Sovereign" (galleon), 1660 . . . . . . 85 20
955 45p. "Soleil Royal" (17th-century French warship) 1·25 35
956 80p. 18th-century British naval brig . . . . 1·90 60

1985. 40th Anniv of U.N.O.

957 **169** 10p. multicoloured . . . 25 15
958 – 20p. blue and brown . . . 50 35
DESIGN: 20p. U.N. emblem in "40".

170 "Madonna of the Rose Garden" (detail)

1985. "Italia '85" International Stamp Exhibition, Rome. Paintings by Botticelli. Multicoloured.

959 7p. Type **170** 15 10
960 10p. "Venus and Mars" (detail) 15 10
961 12p. "St. Augustine in his Study" (detail) 20 15
962 15p. "Spring" (detail) 25 15
963 20p. "Virgin and Child" (detail) 35 15
964 40p. "Virgin and Child with St. John" (detail) . . . . 1·00 30
965 45p. "Birth of Venus" (detail) 1·10 35

171 Youths dancing

1985. International Youth Year. Mult.

967 7p. Type **171** 10 10
968 13p. Windsurfing 20 15
969 15p. Roller skating 20 15
970 25p. Hang-gliding 35 15
971 40p. Surfing 55 25
972 50p. Skateboarding 75 40
973 80p. Free-falling from airplane . . . . 1·50 60

172 Alfa Touring Car

1986. Anniversaries and Events. Mult.

975 15p. Tail of comet . . . . . 1·25 50
976 15p. Head of comet . . . . 1·25 50
977 15p. Type **172** . . . . 1·25 50
978 15p. Frankfurt am Main railway station, 1914 . . . 2·25 75
979 15p. Top of trophy . . . . . 2·50 1·00
980 15p. Base of trophy . . . . 2·50 1·00
981 15p. Olympic rings . . . . . 3·00 1·00
982 15p. View of Barcelona . . . 3·00 1·00
983 15p. Part of space station . . 1·25 50
984 15p. Deflectors . . . . 1·25 50
985 15p. Space station and Shuttle . . . . 1·25 50
986 15p. Part of space station and Earth . . . . 1·25 50
987 15p. Boris Becker's head and arm . . . . 1·50 75
988 15p. Becker's body . . . . . 1·50 75
989 15p. Lendl's head and arms 1·50 75
990 15p. Lendl's body and legs 1·50 75

ANNIVERSARIES: Nos. 975/6, Appearance of Halley's Comet; 977, Centenary of motor car; 978, 150th anniv of German railways; 979/80, World Cup Football Championship, Mexico; 981, Olympic Games, Seoul (1988); 982, "500th anniv of discovery of America by Columbus" Exhibition and Olympic Games, Barcelona (1992); 983/6, 25 years of manned space flights; 987/8, Wimbledon Men's Singles champion, 1986; 989/90, Ivan Lendl, winner of U.S. Masters Tournament, 1986.

Nos. 975/90 were printed together in se-tenant sheetlets of 16 stamps, stamps for the same event forming a composite design.

173 "Santa Maria"

1987. 500th Anniv (1992) of Discovery of America by Columbus. Multicoloured.

992 50p. Type **173** . . . . . . 2·25 80
993 50p. View of Seville . . . . 2·25 80
994 50p. Pedro Alvares Cabral disembarking at Bahia . . 2·00 60
995 50p. View of Seville (different) . . . . 2·25 80

1987. Nos. 352/5, 359 and 362/3 of Portuguese Guinea surch **DA BISSAU** and new value.

997 100p. on 20c. Type **51** . . . 35 15
998 200p. on 35c. African rock python 70 25
999 300p. on 70c. Boomslang . . 1·10 35
1000 400p. on 80c. West African mamba . . . . 1·25 40
1001 500p. on 3e.50 Brown house snake . . . . 1·50 50
1002 1000p. on 15e. Striped beauty snake . . . . . . 3·00 1·00
1003 2000p. on 20e. African egg-eating snake (horiz) . . . 6·00 3·00

1987. No. 430 surch **2500,00**.

1004 **76** 2500p. on 2e. mult . . . 7·00 3·25

176 Ice Dancing

1988. Winter Olympic Games, Calgary. Mult.

1005 5p. Type **176** 10 10
1006 10p. Luge 10 10
1007 50p. Skiing 30 15
1008 200p. Downhill skiing . . . 75 30
1009 300p. Ski-bobbing . . . . . 1·25 40
1010 500p. Ski jumping (vert) . . 2·00 55
1011 800p. Speed skating (vert) . 3·00 1·10

177 Yachting **178** Football

1988. Olympic Games, Seoul. Multicoloured.

1013 5p. Type **177** 10 10
1014 10p. Equestrian events (horiz) 10 10
1015 50p. High jumping (horiz) 15 10
1016 200p. Rifle shooting (horiz) 70 30
1017 300p. Triple jumping . . . 1·10 40
1018 500p. Tennis . . . . 2·00 50
1019 800p. Archery . . . . . . 2·75 1·00

1988. "Essen 88" Stamp Fair and European Football Championship, Germany.

1021 **178** 5p. multicoloured . . . 10 10
1022 – 10p. multicoloured . . . 10 10
1023 – 50p. multicoloured . . 15 10
1024 – 200p. multicoloured . . 70 30
1025 – 300p. multicoloured . . 1·10 40
1026 – 500p. multicoloured . . 2·00 50
1027 – 800p. multicoloured . . 2·75 1·10

DESIGNS: 10 to 800p. Various footballing scenes.

179 Lioness

1988. Animals. Multicoloured.

1029 5p. Type **179** 10 10
1030 10p. Ferruginous pygmy owl 10 10
1031 50p. Hoopoe (horiz) 25 10
1032 200p. Common zebra (horiz) 30 10
1033 300p. African elephant . . . 50 20
1034 500p. Vulturine guineafowl 3·00 1·25
1035 800p. Black rhinoceros . . . 1·25 50

180 Machel

1988. 2nd Death Anniv of Pres. Samora Machel of Mozambique. Multicoloured.

1036 10p. Type **180** 10 10
1037 50p. With arm raised . . . 10 10
1038 200p. With soldier 30 10
1039 300p. Wearing suit 50 20

181 Henry Dunant (founder)

1988. 125th Anniv of Int Red Cross. Mult.

1040 10p. Type **181** 10 10
1041 50p. Dr. T. Maunoir . . . 10 10
1042 200p. Dr. Louis Appia . . . 30 10
1043 800p. Gustave Moynier . . 1·25 50

182 Basset Hound

1988. Dogs. Multicoloured.

1044 5p. Type **182** 10 10
1045 10p. Grand bleu de Gascogne 10 10
1046 50p. Italian spinone 10 10
1047 200p. Yorkshire terrier . . . 30 10
1048 300p. Munsterlander 50 20
1049 500p. Pointer 80 30
1050 800p. German shorthaired pointer . . . . 1·25 50

183 Egyptian Ship, 3300 B.C.

1988. Sailing Ships. Multicoloured.

1052 5p. Type **183** 10 10
1053 10p. Ship of Sahu Re, 2500 B.C. (wrongly inscr "2700 B.C.") 10 10
1054 50p. Ship of Hatshepshut, 1500 B.C 10 10
1055 200p. Ship of Rameses III, 1200 B.C 35 10

1056 300p. Greek trireme, 480 B.C. 60 25
1057 500p. Etruscan bireme, 600 B.C. . . . . 1·00 40
1058 800p. 12th-century Venetian galley . . . . 1·50 65

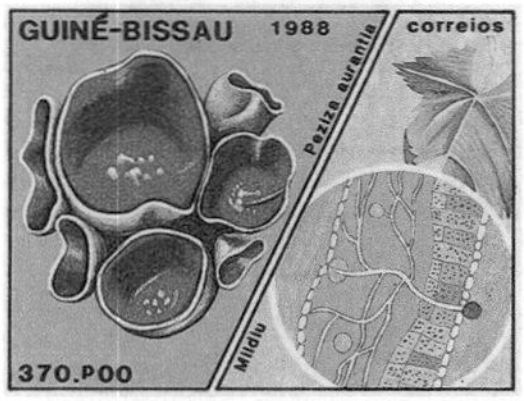

184 "Peziza aurantia"

1988. Fungi. Multicoloured.
1059 370p. Type **184** 75 30
1060 470p. Morel . . . . 1·00 35
1061 600p. Caesar's mushroom 1·25 45
1062 780p. Fly agaric . . . . . 1·60 55
1063 800p. Deadly amanite . . . 1·60 55
1064 900p. Cultivated mushroom 1·90 70
1065 945p. Pixie stool . . . . . 2·10 75

185 Francois-Andre Philidor and Rook
186 Trumpeter, Flag Bearer and Drummer

1988. "Finlandia 88" International Stamp Exhibition, Helsinki. Chess. Multicoloured.
1066 5p. Type **185** 10 10
1067 10p. Howard Staunton and chessmen 10 10
1068 50p. Adolf Anderssen and queen 10 10
1069 200p. Paul Morphy and pawn 30 10
1070 300p. Wilhelm Steinitz and knight 50 20
1071 500p. Emanuel Lasker and bishop 80 30
1072 800p. Jose Capablanca and king . . . . 1·25 50

1988. Abel Djassi Pioneers Organisation. Multicoloured.
1074 10p. Type **186** 10 10
1075 50p. Girls saluting 10 10
1076 200p. Drawing on floor (horiz) 30 10
1077 300p. Playing ball (horiz) . . 50 20

187 Monument
188 Woman with Long Hair

1988. 400th Anniv of Cacheu. Multicoloured.
1078 10p. Type **187** 10 10
1079 50p. Fort (horiz) 10 10
1080 200p. Early building (horiz) 35 10
1081 300p. Church (horiz) . . . 50 20

1989. Traditional Hairstyles.
1082 **188** 50p. multicoloured . . . 10 10
1083 – 100p. multicoloured . . 15 10
1084 – 200p. multicoloured . . 30 10
1085 – 350p. multicoloured . . 60 25
1086 – 500p. multicoloured . . 80 30
1087 – 800p. multicoloured . . 1·25 50
1088 – 1000p. multicoloured . . 1·60 65
DESIGNS: 100p. to 1000p. Different hairstyles.

189 Bombalon

1989. Traditional Musical Instruments. Mult.
1089 50p. Type **189** 10 10
1090 100p. Flute 15 10
1091 200p. Tambor 35 15
1092 350p. Dondon 65 25
1093 500p. Balafon 90 35
1094 800p. Kora . . . . 1·50 60
1095 1000p. Nhanhero . . . . . 1·75 70

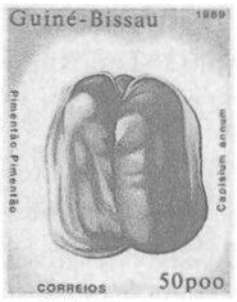

190 Seychelles Blue Pigeon
191 Pimento

1989. Birds. Multicoloured.
1096 50p. Type **190** 15 15
1097 100p. Laughing dove . . . 20 15
1098 200p. Namaqua dove . . . 50 30
1099 350p. Purple-breasted ground dove 80 50
1100 500p. African collared dove 1·25 70
1101 800p. Pheasant pigeon . . . 2·10 1·25
1102 1000p. Emerald dove . . . 2·75 1·40

1989. Plants.
1104 **191** 50p. blue 10 10
1105 – 100p. violet 15 10
1106 – 200p. green 35 15
1107 – 350p. red 65 25
1108 – 500p. brown 90 35
1109 – 800p. brown . . . . . . 1·50 60
1110 – 1000p. green . . . . . 1·75 70
DESIGNS: 100p. Solanum; 200p. "Curcumis peco"; 350p. Tomato; 500p. "Solanum itiopium"; 800p. "Hibiscus esculentus"; 1000p. Baguiche.

192 Madrid Rapid Transit Train No. M-2004, Spain

1989. Trains. Multicoloured.
1111 50p. Type **192** 15 10
1112 100p. Class TEM-2 diesel locomotive, Russia . . . 20 10
1113 200p. Diesel locomotive, Brazil 50 15
1114 350p. Diesel railcar, Spain 95 25
1115 500p. Type 55E electric locomotive, Czechoslovakia . . . . . 1·40 35
1116 800p. Class Tu-7E diesel shunting locomotive, Russia . . . . 2·25 60
1117 1000p. Electric multiple unit, Spain (68 × 27 mm) . . . 2·60 70

193 Hurdling

1989. Olympic Games, Barcelona (1992) (1st issue). Multicoloured.
1119 50p. Type **193** 10 10
1120 100p. Boxing 20 10
1121 200p. High jumping 35 15
1122 350p. Sprinters in starting blocks 60 25
1123 500p. Runner leaving starting block 90 35
1124 800p. Gymnastics . . . . . 1·50 60
1125 1000p. Pole vaulting . . . . 1·75 70
See also Nos. 1245/8.

194 "Limelight"
196 Teotihuacan Pot

195 "La Marseillaise" (relief by Rude from Arc de Triomphe)

1989. Lilies. Multicoloured.
1127 50p. Type **194** 10 10
1128 100p. "Lilium candidum" 20 10
1129 200p. "Lilium pardalinum" 35 15
1130 350p. "Lilium auratum" . . 65 25
1131 500p. "Lilium canadense" 90 35
1132 800p. "Enchantment" . . . 1·50 60
1133 1000p. "Black Dragon" . . 1·75 70

1989. "Philex France 89" International Stamp Exhibition, Paris. Multicoloured.
1135 50p. Type **195** 10 10
1136 100p. Champ de Mars . . . 20 10
1137 200p. Storming of the Bastille 35 15
1138 350p. Fete (27 × 44 mm) . . 65 25
1139 500p. Dancing round Tree of Liberty 90 35
1140 800p. Rouget de Lisle singing "The Marseillaise" 1·50 60
1141 1000p. Storming of the Bastille (different) . . . . 1·75 70

1989. "Brasiliana 89" International Stamp Exhibition, Rio de Janeiro. Multicoloured.
1143 50p. Type **196** 10 10
1144 100p. Mochica jar 20 10
1145 200p. Jaina statuette 35 15
1146 350p. Nayarit anthrozoomorphic jug . . 65 25
1147 500p. Inca vase 90 35
1148 800p. Hopewell statuette of mother and child . . . . 1·50 60
1149 1000p. Taina mask . . . . 1·75 70

197 Players Tackling

1989. World Cup Football Championship, Italy (1990). Multicoloured.
1151 50p. Type **197** 10 10
1152 100p. Players and ball . . . 20 10
1153 200p. Players and ball (different) 35 15
1154 350p. "Scissors" kick . . . 65 25
1155 500p. Goalkeeper 90 35
1156 800p. Foul . . . . 1·50 60
1157 1000p. Player scoring goal 1·75 70

198 Trachodon

1989. Prehistoric Animals. Multicoloured.
1159 50p. Type **198** 10 10
1160 100p. Edaphosaurus (68 × 22 mm) 20 10
1161 200p. Mesosaurus 35 15
1162 350p. "Elephas primigenius" 65 25
1163 500p. Tyrannosaurus (horiz) 90 35
1164 800p. Stegosaurus (horiz) . . 1·50 60
1165 1000p. "Cervus megaceros" 1·75 70
No. 1162 is inscribed "Elephius primigenius" in error.

199 Speed Skating

1989. Winter Olympic Games, Albertville (1992). Multicoloured.
1166 50p. Type **199** 10 10
1167 100p. Figure skating 20 10
1168 200p. Ski jumping 35 15
1169 350p. Skiing 65 25
1170 500p. Skiing (different) . . . 90 35
1171 800p. Bobsleighing . . . . 1·50 60
1172 1000p. Ice hockey . . . . . 1·75 70

200 African Buffalo
201 "Adoration of Baby Jesus" (Fra Filippo Lippi)

1989. Animals
1174 **200** 50p. brown and red . . 10 10
1175 – 100p. ultramarine & blue 20 10
1176 – 200p. green & light green 35 15
1177 – 350p. purple and lilac . . 65 25
1178 – 500p. chestnut and brown 90 35
1179 – 800p. violet & deep violet . . . . 1·50 60
1180 – 1000p. deep red and red 1·75 70
1181 – 1500p. red and yellow 2·75 1·10
DESIGNS: 100p. Steppe zebra; 200p. Black rhinoceros; 350p. Okapi; 500p. Rhesus macacque; 800p. Hippopotamus; 1000p. Cheetah; 1500p. Lion.

1989. Christmas. Multicoloured.
1182 50p. Type **201** 10 10
1183 100p. "Adoration of the Kings" (Pieter Brueghel) 20 10
1184 200p. "Adoration of the Kings" (Jan Mostaert) . . 35 15
1185 350p. "Nativity" (Albert Durer) 65 25
1186 500p. "Adoration of the Kings" (Peter Paul Rubens) 90 35
1187 800p. "Adoration of the Kings" (Roger van der Weyden) . . . . 1·50 60
1188 1000p. "Adoration of the Kings" (Francesco Francia) (horiz) . . . . . 1·75 70

202 Pope John-Paul II and Map
204 Cockerel and Hen

1990. Papal Visit. Multicoloured.
1189 500p. Type **202** 80 20
1190 1000p. Pope and couple . . 1·60 40

1990. "Lubrapex 90" Brazilian–Portuguese Stamp Exhibition, Brasilia. Coop Fowls. Multicoloured.
1193 500p. Type **204** 85 35
1194 800p. Common turkey . . . 1·25 50
1195 1000p. Duck and ducklings 1·60 65

205 Radar Rainfall Map

1990. World Meteorology Day. Multicoloured.
1197 1000p. Type **205** . . . . . 1·60 65
1198 3000p. Campbell-Stokes heliograph . . . . 5·00 2·00

206 Crying Man and Baby in Womb
207 Cotton Plant

1990. 40th Anniv of U.N. Development Programme.
1199 **206** 1000p. multicoloured . . 1·60 65

1991. Traditional Cotton Weaving. Mult.
1200 400p. Type **207** 60 25
1201 500p. Weaver 75 30
1202 600p. Traditional cloth pattern 95 40

208 Mickey Mouse

1991. Carnival Masks. Multicoloured.
1204 200p. Type **208** 30 10
1205 300p. Hippopotamus . . . 45 20
1206 600p. Buffalo 75 30
1207 1200p. Buffalo (different) . . 95 40

209 Royal Threadfin

1991. Fishes. Multicoloured.
1208 300p. Type **209** 45 20
1209 400p. Guinean fingerfish . . 95 55
1210 500p. Goree spadefish . . . 1·60 85
1211 600p. Long-finned pompano 2·00 90

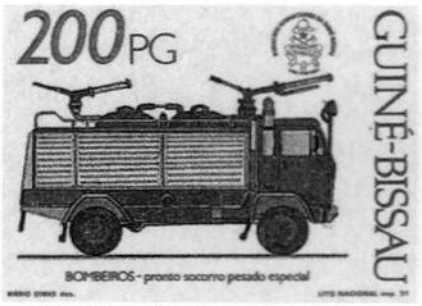

210 Fire Engine with Water Cannons **211** Lizard Buzzard

1991. Fire and First Aid Service. Mult.
1212 200p. Type **210** 30 10
1213 500p. Fire engine with ladders 75 30
1214 800p. Emergency vehicle with ladders . . . . . . 1·25 50
1215 1500p. Ambulance . . . . 2·25 90

1991. Birds. Multicoloured.
1216 100p. Type **211** 25 15
1217 250p. Crowned crane . . . 75 15
1218 350p. Abyssinian ground hornbill . . . . 1·10 35
1219 500p. Saddle-bill stork . . . 1·50 40

212 "Best Wishes" **213** Fula

1991. Greetings Stamps. Multicoloured.
1221 250p. Type **212** 40 10
1222 400p. Couple embracing ("With love") 65 25
1223 800p. Horn-blower and map of Africa ("Congratulations") . . . 1·25 50
1224 1000p. Doves ("Season's greetings") . . . . 1·50 60

1992. Traditional Costume. Multicoloured.
1225 400p. Type **213** 10 10
1226 600p. Balanta 15 10
1227 1000p. Fula (different) . . . 25 10
1228 1500p. Manjaco 40 15

214 "Landolfia owariensis" **215** Cigarette and Fruit "Hearts"

1992. Fruits. Multicoloured.
1229 500p. Type **214** 15 10
1230 1500p. "Dialium guineensis" 40 15
1231 2000p. "Adansonia digitata" 50 20
1232 3000p. "Parkia biglobosa" 75 30

1992. World Health Day. "Health in Rhythm with the Heart". Multicoloured.
1233 1500p. Type **215** 40 15
1234 4000p. "Heart" running over food . . . . 1·00 40

216 "Cassia alata"

1992. "Lubrapex 92" Brazilian–Portuguese Stamp Exhibition, Lisbon. Plants. Multicoloured.
1235 100p. Type **216** 10 10
1236 400p. "Perlebia purpurea" 10 10
1237 1000p. "Caesalpinia pulcherrima" 25 15
1238 1500p. "Adenanthera pavonina" 40 15
Nos. 1235/8 were issued together, se-tenant, forming a composite design.

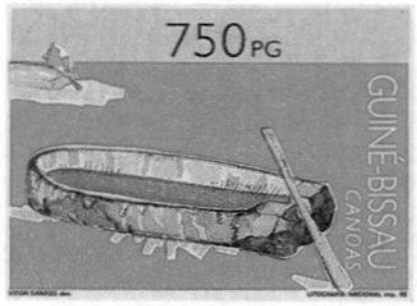

217 Canoe

1992. Canoes. Multicoloured.
1240 750p. Type **217** 35 10
1241 800p. Pirogue 35 10
1242 1000p. Pirogue (different) 45 10
1243 1300p. Skiff 60 20

218 Volleyball

1992. Olympic Games, Barcelona (2nd issue). Multicoloured.
1245 600p. Basketball 15 10
1246 1000p. Type **218** 25 10
1247 1500p. Handball 40 15
1248 2000p. Football 50 20

219 "Afzelia africana" **221** Colobus

1992. Forest Preservation. Multicoloured.
1249 1000p. Type **219** 25 10
1250 1500p. African mahogany 40 15
1251 2000p. Iroko 50 20
1252 3000p. Ambila 75 30

1992. The Red Colobus. Multicoloured.
1254 2000p. Type **221** 50 20
1255 2000p. Colobus sitting in tree fork 50 20
1256 2000p. Mother and young 50 20
1257 2000p. Two colobus on tree branch 50 20

222 Puff Adder

1993. Reptiles. Multicoloured.
1258 1500p. Type **222** 40 15
1259 3000p. African dwarf crocodile 80 30
1260 4000p. Nile monitor . . . 1·10 45
1261 5000p. Rainbow lizard . . . 1·40 55

224 Waterside Village

1993. Tourism. Multicoloured.
1264 1000p. Type **224** 25 10
1265 2000p. Masked villagers on shore and crops 55 20
1266 4000p. Villages on offshore islands . . . . 1·10 45
1267 5000p. Crops on island . . 1·40 55
Nos. 1264/7 were issued together, se-tenant, forming a composite design.

225 Bracelet

1994. Jewellery. Multicoloured.
1268 1500p. Type **225** 40 15
1269 3000p. Tribal mask pendant 80 30
1270 4000p. Circles pendant . . . 1·10 45
1271 5000p. Filigree pendant . . 1·40 55

226 "Erythrina senegalensis"

1994. Medicinal Plants. Multicoloured.
1273 2000p. Type **226** 20 10
1274 3000p. "Cassia occidentalis" 30 10
1275 4000p. "Gardenia ternifolia" 45 20
1276 6000p. "Cochlospermum tinctorium" 65 25

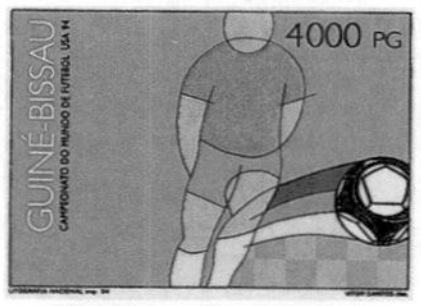

227 Player kicking Ball

1994. World Cup Football Championship, U.S.A. Multicoloured.
1277 4000p. Type **227** 40 15
1278 5000p. Goalkeeper making save 55 20
1279 5500p. Heading the ball . . 60 25
1280 6500p. Dribbling the ball . . 70 30

228 Common Egg-eater (Dasypeltis scabra)

1994. "Philakorea 1994" International and "Singpex '94" Stamp Exhibitions. Snakes. Multicoloured.
1281 5000p. Type **228** 45 20
1282 5000p. Green snake ("Philothamnus sp.") . . 45 20
1283 5000p. Black-lipped cobra ("Naja melanoleuca") . . 45 20
1284 5000p. African python ("Python sebae") 45 20

229 Collecting Fruits **231** Hands and Emblem

230 Women fishing

1995. Palm Oil. Multicoloured.
1286 3000p. Type **229** 20 10
1287 6500p. Crushing fruit . . . 45 20
1288 7500p. Palm oil production 55 20
1289 8000p. Animals and pot of palm oil 80 35

1995. 50th Anniv of United Nations Food and Agriculture Organization. Multicoloured.
1290 3000p. Type **230** 20 10
1291 6500p. Farmer on tractor 45 10
1292 7500p. Basket of fruit . . . 55 15
1293 8000p. Women and children queuing 60 15

1995. 50th Anniv of United Nations. Multicoloured.
1295 4000p. Type **231** 30 10
1296 5500p. United Nations emblem 40 10
1297 7500p. Guinea-Bissau flag and emblem 55 15
1298 8000p. Hands holding dove and emblem 60 15

GUYANA Pt. 1

Formerly British Guiana. Attained independence on 26 May 1966, and changed its name to Guyana.

100 cents = 1 dollar

CANCELLED REMAINDERS. In 1969 remainders of some issues were put on the market cancelled-to-order in such a way as to be indistinguishable from genuine postally used copies for all practical purposes. Our quotations, which are indicated by an asterisk, are the same for cancelled-to-order or postally used copies.

1966. Nos. 331 etc of British Guiana optd **GUYANA INDEPENDENCE 1966**.
399 **55** 1c. black 10 10
421 – 2c. green 10 10
422 – 3c. green and brown . . . 30 10
400 – 4c. violet 10 10
388 – 5c. red and black 40 10
424 – 6c. green 10 10
401 – 8c. blue 10 10
391 – 12c. black and brown . . . 10 10
435 – 24c. black and orange . . 5·00 10
393 – 36c. red and black 30 30
405 – 48c. blue and red 30 50
395 – 72c. red and green 50 50
396 – $1 multicoloured . . . . . 3·75 35
397 – $2 mauve . . . . 1·50 75
398 – $5 blue and black . . . . 1·00 2·00

74 Flag and Map

1966. Independence. Multicoloured.
408 5c. Type **74** 20 10
409 15c. Type **74** 25 10
410 25c. Arms of Guyana 25 10
411 $1 Arms of Guyana . . . . 85 1·25

76 Bank Building

1966. Opening of Bank of Guyana.
412 **76** 5c. multicoloured 10 10
413 25c. multicoloured 10 10

77 British Guiana One Cent Stamp of 1856

1967. World's Rarest Stamp Commemoration.

414	**77**	5c. multicoloured	10	10*
415		25c. multicoloured	10	10*

78 Chateau Margot

1967. 1st Anniv of Independence. Multicoloured.

416		6c. Type **78**	10	10*
417		15c. Independence Arch	10	10*
418		25c. Fort Island (horiz)	10	10*
419		$1 National Assembly (horiz)	20	15

83 "Millie" (Blue and Yellow Macaw)

84 Wicket-keeping

1967. Christmas.

441	**83**	5c. yellow, blue, black grn	10	10*
443		5c. yellow, blue, black red	10	10*
442		25c. yellow, blue, blk vio	15	10*
444		25c. yellow, blue, blk grn	15	10*

1968. M.C.C.'s West Indies Tour. Multicoloured.

445		5c. Type **84**	10	10*
446		6c. Batting	10	10*
447		25c. Bowling	30	10*

87 Pike Cichlid

102 "Christ of St. John of the Cross" (Salvador Dali)

1968. Multicoloured.

448		1c. Type **87**	10	10
449		2c. Red paranha ("Pirai")	10	10
450		3c. Peacock cichlid ("Lukunani")	10	10
451		5c. Armoured catfish ("Hassar")	10	10
489		6c. Black acara ("Patua")	10	80
490		10c. Spix's guan (vert)	30	60
491		15c. Harpy eagle (vert)	30	10
455		20c. Hoatzin (vert)	60	10
493		25c. Guianan cock of the rock (vert)	30	10
494		40c. Great kiskadee (vert)	60	1·00
495		50c. Brazilian agouti ("Accouri")	35	15
459		60c. White-lipped peccary	80	10
460		$1 Paca ("Labba")	80	10
461		$2 Nine-banded armadillo	1·00	2·00
462		$5 Ocelot	1·00	3·00

1968. Easter.

463	**102**	5c. multicoloured	10	10*
464		25c. multicoloured	20	10*

103 "Efficiency Year"

1968. "Savings Bonds and Efficiency". Multicoloured.

465		6c. Type **103**	10	10*
466		25c. Type **103**	10	10*
467		30c. "Savings Bonds"	10	10*
468		40c. "Savings Bonds"	10	10*

105 Open Book, Star and Crescent

1968. 1400th Anniv of Holy Quran.

469	**105**	6c. black, gold and flesh	10	10*
470		25c. black, gold and lilac	10	10*
471		30c. black, gold and green	10	10*
472		40c. black, gold and blue	10	10*

107 Broadcasting Greetings

1968. Christmas.

473	**107**	6c. brown, black and green	10	10*
474		25c. brown, violet green	10	10*
475	–	30c. green and turquoise	10	10*
476	–	40c. red and turquoise	10	10*

DESIGNS: 30c. and 40c. Map showing radio link, Guyana–Trinidad.

109 Festival Ceremony

1969. Hindu Festival of Phagwah. Multicoloured.

477		6c. Type **109**	10	10
478		25c. Ladies spraying scent	10	10
479		30c. Type **109**	10	10
480		40c. As No. 478	10	10

111 "Sacrament of the Last Supper" (Dali)

1969. Easter.

481	**111**	6c. multicoloured	10	10
482		25c. multicoloured	10	10
483		30c. multicoloured	10	10
484		40c. multicoloured	10	10

112 Map showing "CARIFTA" Countries

114 Building "Independence" (first aluminium ship)

1969. 1st Anniv of "CARIFTA".

500	**112**	6c. red, blue and turquoise	15	15
501	–	25c. lemon, brown and red	15	15

DESIGN—HORIZ: 25c. "Strength in Unity".

1969. 50th Anniv of I.L.O.

502	**114**	30c. blue, black and silver	40	25
503	–	40c. multicoloured	50	25

DESIGN—HORIZ: 40c. Bauxite processing plant.

116 Scouts raising Flag

1969. 3rd Caribbean Scout Jamboree and Diamond Jubilee of Scouting in Guyana. Multicoloured.

504		6c. Type **116**	10	10
505		8c. Camp-fire cooking	10	10
506		25c. Type **116**	10	10
507		30c. As 8c.	10	10
508		50c. Type **116**	15	15

118 Gandhi and Spinning-wheel

1969. Birth Centenary of Mahatma Gandhi.

509	**118**	6c. black, brown and olive	20	50
510		15c. black, brown and lilac	25	50

119 "Mother Sally" Dance Troupe

121 Forbes Burnham and Map

1969. Christmas. Unissued stamps optd as in T **119**. Multicoloured.

511		5c. Type **119**	10	10
512		6c. City Hall, Georgetown	10	10
513		25c. Type **119**	10	10
514		60c. As 6c.	20	25

1970. Republic Day.

515	**121**	5c. sepia, ochre and blue	10	10
516	–	6c. multicoloured	10	10
517	–	15c. multicoloured	15	10
518	–	25c. multicoloured	20	15

DESIGNS—VERT: 6c. Rural self-help. HORIZ: 15c. University of Guyana; 25c. Guyana House.

125 "The Descent from the Cross"

128 "Mother and Child" (Philip Moore)

127 "Peace" and U.N. Emblem

1970. Easter. Paintings by Rubens. Multicoloured.

519		5c. Type **125**	10	10
520		6c. "Christ on the Cross"	10	10
521		15c. Type **125**	20	15
522		25c. As 6c.	20	15

1970. 25th Anniv of United Nations. Mult.

523		5c. Type **127**	10	10
524		6c. U.N. emblem, gold-panning and drilling	10	10
525		15c. Type **127**	10	10
526		25c. As 6c.	10	15

1970. Christmas.

527	**128**	5c. multicoloured	10	10
528		6c. multicoloured	10	10
529		15c. multicoloured	15	15
530		25c. multicoloured	15	15

129 National Co-operative Bank

1971. Republic Day.

531	**129**	6c. multicoloured	10	10
532		15c. multicoloured	15	15
533		25c. multicoloured	15	15

130 Racial Equality Symbol

131 Young Volunteer felling Tree (from painting by J. Criswick)

1971. Racial Equality Year.

534	**130**	5c. multicoloured	10	10
535		6c. multicoloured	10	10
536		15c. multicoloured	15	15
537		25c. multicoloured	15	15

1971. 1st Anniv of Self-help Road Project.

538	**131**	5c. multicoloured	10	10
539		20c. multicoloured	20	10
540		25c. multicoloured	20	10
541		50c. multicoloured	30	1·75

132 Yellow Allamanda

134 Obverse and Reverse of Guyana $1 Coin

133 Child praying at Bedside

1971. Flowering Plants. Multicoloured.

542		1c. Pitcher Plant of Mt. Roraima	10	10
543		2c. Type **132**	10	10
544		3c. Hanging heliconia	10	10
545		5c. Annatto tree	10	10
546		6c. Cannon-ball tree	10	10
547		10c. Cattleya	3·25	10
548a		15c. Christmas orchid	65	10
549		20c. "Paphinia cristata"	3·00	20
550		25c. Marabunta	5·00	7·00
550ab		25c. Marabunta	45	10
551		40c. Tiger beard	3·50	10
552		50c. "Guzmania lingulata"	40	85
553		60c. Soldier's cap	30	65
554		$1 "Chelonanthus uliginoides"	30	55
555		$2 "Norantea guianensis"	35	55
556		$5 "Odontadenia grandiflora"	55	55

No. 550 shows the flowers facing upwards and has the value in the centre. No. 550ab has the flowers facing downwards with the value to the right.

1971. Christmas. Multicoloured.

557		5c. Type **133**	10	10
558		20c. Type **133**	10	10
559		25c. Carnival masquerader (vert)	10	10
560		50c. As 25c.	20	60

1972. Republic Day.

561	**134**	5c. silver, black and red	10	10
562	–	20c. silver, black and red	15	10
563	**134**	25c. silver, black and blue	15	15
564	–	50c. silver, black and green	25	45

DESIGN: 20c., 50c. Reverse and obverse of Guyana $1 coin.

135 Hands and Irrigation Canal

136 Map and Emblem

1972. Youman Nabi (Mohammed's Birthday).

565	**135**	5c. multicoloured	10	10
566		25c. multicoloured	10	10

567	30c. multicoloured	10	10
568	60c. multicoloured	20	20

1972. Conference of Foreign Ministers of Non-aligned Countries.

569 **136**	8c. multicoloured	10	10
570	25c. multicoloured	10	10
571	40c. multicoloured	15	15
572	50c. multicoloured	20	20

137 Hand reaching for Sun

138 Joseph, Mary and the Infant Jesus

1972. 1st Caribbean Festival of Arts.

573 **137**	8c. multicoloured	10	10
574	25c. multicoloured	10	10
575	40c. multicoloured	15	20
576	50c. multicoloured	20	25

1972. Christmas.

577 **138**	8c. multicoloured	10	10
578	25c. multicoloured	10	10
579	40c. multicoloured	15	25
580	50c. multicoloured	15	25

139 Umana Yana (Meeting-house)

141 Stylised Blood Cell

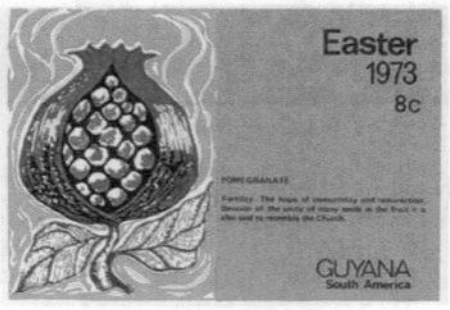

140 Pomegranate

1973. Republic Day. Multicoloured.

581	8c. Type **139**	10	10
582	25c. Bethel Chapel	10	10
583	40c. As 25c.	20	20
584	50c. Type **139**	25	20

1973. Easter. Multicoloured.

585	8c. Type **140**	10	10
586	25c. Cross and map (34 × 17 mm)	10	10
587	40c. As 25c.	10	10
588	50c. Type **140**	15	15

1973. 25th Anniv of Guyana Red Cross.

589 **141**	8c. red and black	10	10
590	25c. red and purple . . .	25	15
591	40c. red and blue	35	50
592	50c. red and green	50	1·00

142 Steel-Band Players

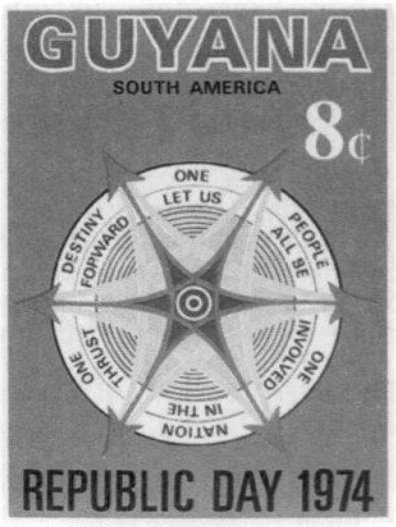

143 Symbol of Progress

1973. Christmas. Multicoloured.

593	8c. Type **142**	10	10
594	25c. Type **142**	20	10
595	40c. "Virgin and Child" stained-glass window (34 × 47mm)	40	75
596	50c. As 40c.	40	75

1974. Republic Day. Multicoloured.

597	8c. Type **143**	10	10
598	25c. Wai-Wai Indian	10	10
599	40c. Type **143**	15	30
600	50c. As 25c.	15	40

1974. No. 546 surch **8c**.

601	8c. on 6c. multicoloured . . .	10	10

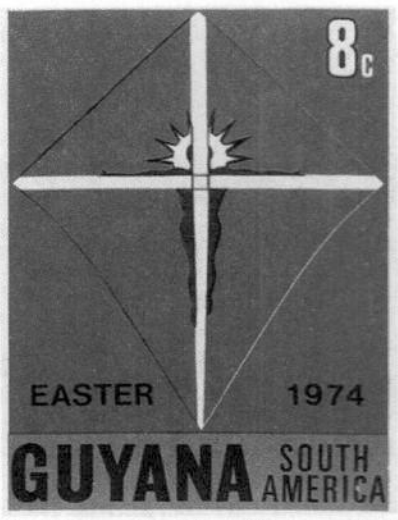

145 Kite with Crucifixion Motif

1974. Easter.

602 **145**	8c. multicoloured	10	10
603 –	25c. black and green . . .	10	10
604 –	40c. black and mauve . .	10	15
605 **145**	50c. multicoloured	15	25

DESIGN: Nos. 603/4, "Crucifixion" in pre-Columbian style.

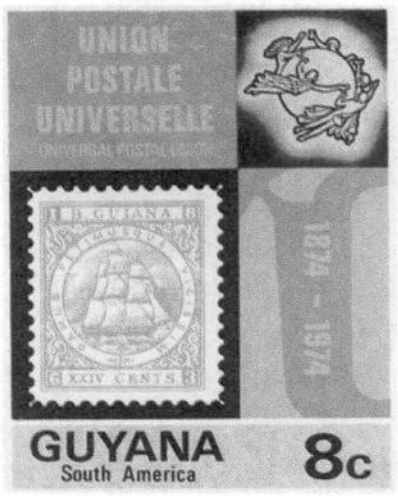

146 British Guiana 24c. Stamp of 1874

148 Buck Toyeau

147 Guides with Banner

1974. Centenary of Universal Postal Union.

606 **146**	8c. multicoloured	25	10
607 –	25c. lt green, green black	35	10
608 **146**	40c. multicoloured	35	20
609 –	50c. green, brown black	45	45

DESIGN—VERT (42 × 25 mm): 25, 50c. U.P.U. emblem and Guyana postman.

1974. Golden Jubilee of Girl Guides. Mult.

610	8c. Type **147**	20	10
611	25c. Guides in camp	30	15
612	40c. As 25c.	45	40
613	50c. Type **147**	45	45

1974. Christmas. Multicoloured.

615	8c. Type **148**	10	10
616	35c. Five-fingers and awaras	10	10
617	50c. Pawpaw and tangerine	15	10
618	$1 Pineapple and sapodilla	30	60
MS619	127 × 94 mm. Nos. 615/18	70	2·50

1975. No. 544 surch **8c**.

620	8c. on 3c. multicoloured . . .	10	10

149 Golden Arrow of Courage

150 Old Sluice Gate

1975. Republic Day. Guyana Orders and Decorations. Multicoloured.

621	10c. Type **149**	10	10
622	35c. Cacique's Crown of Honour	10	15
623	50c. Cacique's Crown of Valour	15	20
624	$1 Order of Excellence . . .	35	60

1975. Silver Jubilee of International Commission on Irrigation and Drainage. Multicoloured.

625	10c. Type **150**	10	10
626	35c. Modern sluice gate (horiz)	10	15
627	50c. Type **150**	15	30
628	$1 As 35c.	35	60
MS629	162 × 121 mm. Nos. 625/8	75	2·75

151 I.W.Y. Emblem and Rock Drawing

1975. International Women's Year. Designs showing different rock drawings.

630 **151**	10c. green and yellow . .	10	10
631 –	35c. violet and blue . . .	15	10
632 –	50c. blue and orange . .	20	15
633 –	$1 brown and blue . . .	30	45
MS634	178 × 89 mm. Nos. 630/3	75	3·00

152 Freedom Monument

153 G.N.S. Emblem

1975. Namibia Day. Multicoloured.

635	10c. Type **152**	10	10
636	35c. Unveiling of Monument	15	10
637	50c. Type **152**	25	10
638	$1 As 35c.	35	35

1975. 1st Anniv of National Service.

639 **153**	10c. yellow, green & violet	10	10
640 –	35c. orange, green & violet	10	10
641 –	50c. blue, green and brown	15	15
642 –	$1 mauve, green & lt green	40	40
MS643	196 × 133 mm. Nos. 639/42	75	2·00

Nos. 640/2 are as Type **153** but have different symbols within the circle.

154 Court Building, 1875, and Forester's Badge

1975. Centenary of Guyanese Ancient Order of Foresters. Multicoloured.

644	10c. Type **154**	10	10
645	35c. Rock drawing of hunter and quarry	10	10
646	50c. Crossed axes and bugle-horn	15	10
647	$1 Bow and arrow	40	40
MS648	129 × 97 mm. Nos. 644/7	75	2·25

1976. No. 553 surch **35c**.

649	35c. on 60c. Soldier's cap . .	20	15

156 Shoulder Flash

157 Triumphal Arch

1976. 50th Anniv of St. John Ambulance in Guyana.

650 **156**	8c. silver, black and mauve	10	10
651 –	15c. silver, black & orange	10	10
652 –	35c. silver, black and green	20	20
653 –	40c. silver, black and blue	25	25

Nos. 651/3 are as Type **156** but show different shoulder flashes.

1976. 10th Anniv of Independence. Multicoloured.

654	8c. Type **157**	10	10
655	15c. Stylised Victoria Regia lily	10	10
656	35c. "Onward to Socialism"	15	15
657	40c. Worker pointing the way	15	15
MS658	120 × 100 mm. Nos. 654/7	50	1·50

1976. West Indies Victory in World Cricket Cup. As T **223a** of Grenada.

659	15c. Map of the Caribbean	90	1·50
660	15c. Prudential Cup	90	1·50

158 Flame in Archway

159 Festival Emblem and "Musical Instrument"

1976. Deepavali Festival. Multicoloured.

661	8c. Type **158**	10	10
662	15c. Flame in hand	10	10
663	35c. Flame in bowl	15	20
664	40c. Goddess Latchmi . . .	15	25
MS665	94 × 109 mm. Nos. 661/4	50	1·50

1977. Second World Black and African Festival of Arts and Culture, Nigeria.

666 **159**	10c. red, black and gold	10	10
667	25c. violet, black and gold	15	10
668	50c. blue, black and gold	20	25
669	$1 green, black and gold	35	75
MS670	90 × 157 mm. Nos. 666/9	75	3·00

160 1c. and 5c. Coins

1977. New Coinage.

671 **160**	8c. multicoloured	20	10
672 –	15c. brown, grey and black	25	10
673 –	35c. green, grey and black	45	30
674 –	40c. red, grey and black	50	35
675 –	$1 multicoloured	80	1·25
676 –	$2 multicoloured	1·25	2·75

DESIGNS: 15c.10 and 25c. coins; 35c., 50c. and $1 coins; 40c. $5 and $10 coins; $1 $50 and $100 coins; $2 Reverse of $1 coin.

161 Hand Pump, c. 1850

1977. National Fire Prevention Week. Mult.

677	8c. Type **161**	1·00	10
678	15c. Steam engine, c. 1860 .	1·40	10
679	35c. Fire engine, c. 1930 . .	1·60	60
680	40c. Fire engine, 1977	1·60	85

162 Cuffy Monument

1977. Cuffy Monument (commemorating 1763 Slave Revolt). Multicoloured.

681	8c. Type **162**	10	10
682	15c. Cuffy Monument (different view)	10	10
683	35c. Type **162**	15	20
684	40c. As 15c.	15	30

163 American Manatee

1978. Wildlife Conservation. Multicoloured.

685	8c. Type **163**	65	10
686	15c. Giant sea turtle	85	20
687	35c. Harpy eagle (vert) . . .	3·25	1·50
688	40c. Iguana (vert)	3·25	1·50

164 L.F.S. Burnham (Prime Minister) and Parliament Buildings, Georgetown

1978. 25th Anniv of Prime Minister's Entry into Parliament.
689 **164** 8c. black, violet and grey . . 10 10
690 – 15c. black, blue and grey . . 10 10
691 – 35c. black, red and grey . . 15 20
692 – 40c. black, orange and grey 15 20
MS693 176 × 118 mm. Nos. 689/92 . . 55 1·00
DESIGNS: 15c. Burnham, graduate and children ("Free Education"); 35c. Burnham and industrial works (Nationalization of Bauxite Industry); 40c. Burnham and village scene ("The Co-operative Village").

165 Dr. George Giglioli (scientist and physician) **166** "Prepona pheridamas"

1978. Nat Science Research Council. Mult.
694 10c. Type **165** 15 10
695 30c. Institute of Applied Science and Technology . . 20 15
696 50c. Emblem of National Science Research Council . . 25 25
697 60c. Emblem of Commonwealth Science Council (commemorating the 10th meeting) (horiz) . . 25 25

1978. Butterflies. Multicoloured.
698 5c. Type **166** . . . . 1·50 10
699 10c. "Archonias bellona" . . 1·50 10
700 15c. "Eryphanis polyxena" . . 1·50 10
701 20c. "Helicopis cupido" . . 1·50 10
702 25c. "Nessaea batesii" . . . 1·50 10
702a 30c. "Nymphidium mantus" . . 1·25 2·25
703 35c. "Anaea galanthis" . . 1·50 10
704 40c. "Morpho rhetenor" (male) . . . . 1·50 10
705 50c. "Hamadryas amphinome" . . . . . . 1·50 20
705a 60c. "Papilio androgeus" . . 1·25 1·00
706 $1 "Agrias claudina" (vert) (25 × 39 mm) . . . . . . 3·75 20
707 $2 "Morpho rhetenor" (female) (vert) (25 × 39 mm) . . . . . . 5·50 35
708 $5 "Morpho deidamia" (vert) (25 × 39 mm) . . . 6·50 90
708a $10 "Elbella patrobas" . . . 4·50 4·25

168 Amerindian Stone-chip Grater in Preparation **169** Dish Aerial by Night

1978. National/International Heritage Year. Multicoloured.
709 10c. Type **168** 10 10
710 30c. Cassiri and decorated Amerindian jars 15 10
711 50c. Fort, Kyk-over-al . . . 20 15
712 60c. Fort Island 20 20

1979. Satellite Earth Station. Multicoloured.
713 10c. Type **169** 10 10
714 30c. Dish aerial by day . . . 20 15
715 50c. Satellite with solar veins . . 30 15
716 $3 Cylinder satellite . . . . 1·00 90

170 Sir Rowland Hill and British Guiana 1850 12c. "Cottonreel" Stamp

1979. Death Cent of Sir Rowland Hill. Mult.
717 10c. Type **170** 15 10
718 30c. British Guiana 1856 1c. black on magenta stamp (vert) 20 15
719 50c. British Guiana 1898 1c. Mount Roraima stamp . . 30 15
720 $3 Printing press used for early British Guiana stamps (vert) 45 80

171 "Me and my Sister" **172** "An 8 Hour Day"

1979. International Year of the Child. Children's Paintings. Multicoloured.
721 10c. Type **171** 10 10
722 30c. "Fun with the Fowls" (horiz) 15 15
723 50c. "Two Boys catching Ducks" (horiz) 15 20
724 $3 "Mango Season" (horiz) . . 45 1·25

1979. 60th Anniv of Guyana Labour Union. Multicoloured.
725 10c. Type **172** 10 10
726 30c. "Abolition of Night Baking" (horiz) 10 10
727 50c. "Introduction of the Workmen's Compensation Ordinance" 15 15
728 $3 H. N. Critchlow (founder) . . 55 90

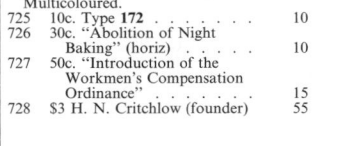

173 Guyana Flag

1980. 10th Anniv of Republic.
729 **173** 10c. multicoloured 10 10
730 – 35c. black and orange . . 30 10
731 – 60c. multicoloured 50 20
732 – $3 multicoloured 80 90
DESIGNS: 35c. Demerara River Bridge; 60c. Kaieteur Falls; $3 "Makanaima, the Great Ancestral Spirit of the Amerindians".

174 Common Snook

1980. "London 1980" International Stamp Exhibition. Fishes. Multicoloured.
733 35c. Type **174** 20 20
734 35c. Trahira ("Haimara") . . 20 20
735 35c. Electric eel 20 20
736 35c. Golden rivulus 20 20
737 35c. Golden pencilfish . . . 20 20
738 35c. Four-eyed fish 20 20
739 35c. Red piranha ("Pirai") . . 20 20
740 35c. Smoking hassar 20 20
741 35c. Manta 20 20
742 35c. Festival cichlid ("Flying patwa") 20 20
743 35c. Arapaima 20 20
744 35c. Peacock cichlid ("Lukanani") 20 20

175 Children's Convalescent Home (Community Service)

1980. 75th Anniv of Rotary International. Multicoloured.
745 10c. Type **175** 10 10
746 30c. Georgetown Rotary Club and Rotary International emblems . . 10 10
747 50c. District 404 emblem (vert) 20 20
748 $3 Rotary anniversary emblem (vert) 80 80

176 "C" encircling Globe, Caduceus Emblem and Sea

1980. 25th Anniv of Commonwealth Caribbean Medical Research Council. Multicoloured.
749 10c. Type **176** 10 10
750 60c. Researcher with microscope, Caduceus emblem, stethoscope and beach scene 40 20
751 $3 Caduceus emblem, "C" encircling researcher and island silhouettes . . . . . 1·10 1·00

177 "Virola surinamensis"

1980. Christmas. Trees and Foliage. Multicoloured.
752 10c. Type **177** 10 10
753 30c. "Hymenaea courbaril" . . 20 10
754 50c. "Mora excelsa" 30 15
755 $3 "Peltogyne venosa" . . . 80 1·10

178 Brazilian Tree Porcupine **181** Map of Guyana

1981. Wildlife. Multicoloured.
756 30c. Type **178** 30 40
757 30c. Red howler 30 40
758 30c. Common squirrel-monkey 30 40
759 30c. Two-toed sloth 30 40
760 30c. Brazilian tapir 30 40
761 30c. Collared peccary . . . 30 40
762a 30c. Six-banded armadillo . . 30 40
763 30c. Tamandua 30 40
764 30c. Giant anteater 30 40
765 30c. Murine opossum . . . 30 40
766 30c. Brown four-eyed opossum 30 40
767 30c. Brazilian agouti 30 40

1981. Liberation of Southern Africa Conference. No. 635 surch **1981 CONFERENCE $1.05**.
768 $1.05 on 10c. Type **152** . . . 40 30

1981. Royal Wedding (1st issue). Nos. 554 and 556 surch **ROYAL WEDDING 1981** and value.
769c $3.60 on $5 "Odontadenia grandiflora" 60 65
770 $7.20 in $1 "Chelonanthus uliginoides" 60 60
See also Nos. 841/3 and 930/6.

1981. Fiscal stamps surch for postal use.
771 **181** 10c. on 3c. black, blue and red 30 10
940 15c. on 2c. black, blue and grey 50 15
941 20c. on 2c. black, blue and grey . . . . . . 4·00 30
1029 25c. on 2c. black, blue and grey 50 10
772 30c. on 2c. black, blue and grey 45 15
989 40c. on 2c. black, blue and grey . . . . . . 1·00 15
945 45c. on 2c. black, blue and grey . . . . . . 1·75 45
773 50c. on 2c. black, blue and grey 40 15
774 60c. on 2c. black, blue and grey 45 15
948 75c. on 2c. black, blue and grey . . . . . . 6·00 25
775 75c. on 3c. black, blue and red 45 20
949 80c. on 2c. black, blue and grey . . . . . . 6·00 20
950 85c. on 2c. black, blue and grey 75 25
951 100c. on 3c. black, blue and red . . . . 1·00 35
952 110c. on 3c. black, blue and red 80 30
953 120c. on 3c. black, blue and red . . . . 8·00 35
954 125c. on 3c. black, blue and red . . . . 2·25 35
955 130c. on 3c. black, blue and red . . . . 1·00 35
956 150c. on 3c. black, blue and red . . . . 8·50 40
957 160c. on 3c. black, blue and red . . . . 2·00 40
958 170c. on 3c. black, blue and red . . . . 1·40 45
959 175c. on 3c. black, blue and red . . . . 6·00 45
960 180c. on 3c. black, blue and red . . . . 2·00 60
961 200c. on 3c. black, blue and red . . . . 2·25 45
962 210c. on 3c. black, blue and red . . . . 7·00 50
963 220c. on 3c. black, blue and red . . . . 8·50 50
964 235c. on 3c. black, blue and red . . . . 8·00 50
965 240c. on 3c. black, blue and red . . . . 9·00 50
966 250c. on 3c. black, blue and red . . . . 2·25 50
967 300c. on 3c. black, blue and red . . . . 12·00 55
968 330c. on 3c. black, blue and red . . . . 2·75 65
969 375c. on 3c. black, blue and red . . . . 8·00 75
970 400c. on 3c. black, blue and red . . . . 10·00 75
971 440c. on 3c. black, blue and red . . . . 4·00 75
972 500c. on 3c. black, blue and red . . . . 3·50 1·10
973 550c. on 3c. black, blue and red . . . . 4·00 1·25
974 625c. on 3c. black, blue and red . . . . 2·75 1·75
975 1500c. on 2c. black, blue and grey . . . . . . 11·00 3·00
976 2000c. on 2c. black, blue and grey . . . . . . 11·00 3·75

1981. No. 544 surch **7.20**.
775c 720c. on 3c. multicoloured . . 80·00 15·00

1981. Various stamps optd **1981**.
791 – 15c. mult (No. 491) . . . 13·00 10
864 – 15c. mult (No. 548a) . . 4·00 10
810 – 15c. mult (No. 659) . . . 6·00 20
811 – 15c. mult (No. 660) . . . 4·50 20
776 **105** 25c. black, gold and lilac . . 10 10
777 30c. black, gold and green 15 10
778 – 35c. mult (No. 645) . . . 15 10
792 – 40c. mult (No. 457) . . . 10·00 40
811c – 40c. mult (No. F5) . . . – £200
812 – 50c. mult (No. 623) . . . 60 20
813 **150** 50c. multicoloured . . . 1·00 20
814 – 50c. blue and orange (No. 632) . . . . . . 23·00 2·25
815 – 50c. mult (No. 646) . . . 2·75 20
816 **159** 50c. blue, black and gold . . 13·00 2·00
817 – 50c. mult (No. F6) . . . 4·00 20
818 – 60c. mult (No. 731) . . . 60 20
819 – 60c. mult (No. 750) . . . 60 20
865 – $1 mult (No. 554) . . . 40 20
820 – $1 mult (No. 624) . . . 6·00 55
821 **159** $1 green, black and gold . . 5·00 30
866 – $2 mult (No. 555) . . . 90 35
823 – $3 mult (No. 732) . . . 2·00 65
824 – $5 mult (No. 556) . . . 3·25 1·25

1981. Nos. 545 and 556 surch.
780 75c. on 5c. Annatto tree . . 50 50
781 210c. on $5 "Odontadenia grandiflora" . . . . . . 80 1·00
781b 220c. on 5c. Annatto tree . . 95·00 8·50

1981. Nos. D8/11 surch **ESSEQUIBO IS OURS**.
782A **D 2** 10c. on 2c. black . . . 15 10
783A 15c. on 12c. red 15 15
784A 20c. on 1c. green 15 20
785B 45c. on 2c. black . . . 30 15
786A 55c. on 4c. blue 20 20
787B 60c. on 4c. blue 30 10
788A 65c. on 2c. black . . . 30 15
789B 70c. on 4c. blue 30 30
790A 80c. on 4c. blue 30 20

1981. Nos. 545, 554, 556, 716, 843, F7 and F9 surch.
794 50c. on 5c. Annatto tree (postage) 30 20
795 120c. on $1 "Chelonanthus uliginoides" 75 40
796 140c. on $1 "Chelonanthus uliginoides" 70 40
797 150c. on $2 "Norantea guianensis" (F9) 75 40
800 220c. on $3 Cylinder satellite . . 1·75 45
801 250c. on $5 "Odontadenia grandiflora" . . . . 1·25 45
802 280c. on $5 "Odontadenia grandiflora" . . . . 1·50 50
798 360c. on $2 "Norantea guianensis" (F9) . . . . . 3·00 60
803 375c. on $5 "Odontadenia grandiflora" . . . . 1·75 55
799 720c. on 60c. Soldier's Cap (F7) . . . . 3·00 1·00
804 $1.10 on $2 "Norantea guianensis" (843) (air) . . 1·00 1·00
No. 804 has the Royal Wedding opt cancelled by three bars.

1981. No. 448 surch.
805 **87** 15c. on 1c. mult (postage) . . 70 20
806 100c. on 1c. mult (air) . . 70 40
807 110c. on 1c. multicoloured . . 70 40

1981. No. 700 optd **ESSEQUIBO IS OURS**.
808 15c. "Eryphanis polyxena" . . 5·00 10

1981. Various stamps surch.
825 **116** 55c. on 6c. multicoloured . . 3·00 80
826 **111** 70c. on 6c. multicoloured . . 1·00 20
827 100c. on 6c. mult . . . . 1·25 20
828 – 100c. on 8c. multicoloured (No. 505) . . . . . . 3·00 20

829 **152** 100c. on $1.05 on 10c. mult (No. 768) . . . . 32·00 4·00
830 **116** 110c. on 6c. mult . . . . 2·00 30
831 **149** 110c. on 10c. mult . . . 2·50 30
832 **151** 110c. on 10c. green and yellow . . . . . . 6·00 45
834 – 125c. on $2 multicoloured (No. 555) . . . . . . 13·00 80
835 **116** 180c. on 6c. mult . . . . 2·25 45
840 – 240c. on $3 multicoloured (No. 728) . . . . . . 8·00 75
836 **116** 400c. on 6c. mult . . . . 3·50 80
837a 440c. on 6c. mult . . . . 1·00 55
838 – 550c. on $10 multicoloured (No. O21) . . . . 8·00 1·00
839 – 625c. on 40c. mult (No. F5) . . . . 14·00 1·75

1981. Royal Wedding (2nd issue). Nos. 544 and 555/6 surch **Royal Wedding 1981** (No. 843 **Air Mail** also) and value.
841 60c. on 3c. Hanging heliconia (postage) 30 35
842 75c. on $5 "Odontadenia grandiflora" 30 35
843 $1.10 on $2 "Norantea guianensis" (air) 30 35

1981. World Cup Football Championship, Spain (1982) (1st issue). No. 781a optd **Espana 82**.
844 220c. on 5c. Annatto tree . . 2·00 40
See also Nos. 937/9 and 1218.

1981. 150th Birth Anniv of Heinrich von Stephan (founder of U.P.U.) No. 720 surch **1831-1981 Von Stephan 330**.
845 330c. on $3 Printing press used for early British Guiana stamps . . . . . . 1·10 55

1981. No. 489 surch with large figure over smaller figure.
847 12c. on 12c. on 6c. Black acara ("Patua") 20 25
848 15c. on 10c. on 6c. Black acara ("Patua") 15 10
849 15c. on 30c. on 6c. Black acara ("Patua") 15 10
850 15c. on 50c. on 6c. Black acara ("Patua") 15 10
851 15c. on 60c. on 6c. Black acara ("Patua") 15 10
Nos. 847/51 are further surcharges on previously unissued stamps.

214 Coromantyn Free Negro Armed Ranger, c. 1772, and Cuffy Monument

1981. 16th Anniv of Guyana Defence Force. Multicoloured.
853 15c. on 10c. Type **214** . . . 25 10
854 50c. Private, 27th Foot Regiment, c. 1825 . . . . 35 30
855 $1 on 30c. Private, Col. Fourgeoud's Marines, c. 1775 . . . . . 40 45
856 $1.10 on $3 W.O. and N.C.O., Guyana Defence Force, 1966 . . . . 40 70
The 15c., $1 and $1.10 values are surcharged on previously unissued stamps.

215 Louis Braille

1981. International Year for Disabled Persons. Famous Disabled People. Multicoloured.
857 15c. on 10c. Type **215** . . . 25 10
858 50c. Helen Keller and Rajkumari Singh 40 40
859 $1 on 60c. Beethoven and Sonny Thomas 40 50
860 $1.10 on $3 Renoir 35 55
The 15c., $1 and $1.10 values are surcharged on previously unissued stamps.

1981. No. 489 surch (Nos. 862/3 optd **AIR** also).
861 12c. on 6c. Black acara ("Patua") (postage) . . . 15 10
862b 50c. on 6c. Black acara ("Patua") (air) 20 15
863 $1 on 6c. Black acara ("Patua") 50 30

1981. Nos. 601, 620, 644, O13, 717, 720, 728, 749, 751 and 755 surch (Nos. 868/9 twice).
867 110c. on 10c. Type **154** . . 3·00 30
868 110c. on 110c. on 8c. on 3c. Hanging heliconia . . . . 3·00 40
869 110c. on 110c. on 8c. on 6c. Cannon-ball tree . . . . 3·00 40
869b 110c. on 10c. on 25c. Marabunta . . . . 2·25 40
870 110c. on 10c. Type **170** . . 2·00 30
871 110c. on 10c. Type **176** . . 8·00 50
872 110c. on $3 Printing press used for early British Guiana stamps . . . . . 1·75 30
873 110c. on $3 H. N. Critchlow 6·50 45
874 110c. on $3 Caduceus emblem, "C" encircling researcher and island silhouettes . . . . 1·50 30
875 110c. on $3 "Peltogyne venosa" . . . . 4·00 50

1981. No. 698 surch **Nov 81 50c.**
876 50c. on 5c. Type **166** . . . . 8·50 20

222 Yellow Allamanda ("Allamanda cathartica")

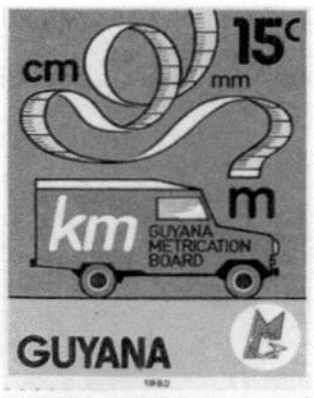

225 Tape Measure and Guyana Metrication Board Van

1981. Flowers.
877 **222** 15c. on 2c. lilac, blue and green 15 15
878 – 15c. on 8c. lilac, blue and mauve 15 15
DESIGN: 15c. on 8c. Mazaruni pride ("Sipanea prolensis").
Nos. 877/8 are surcharged on previously unissued stamps.

1981. Air. Human Rights Day. No. 748 surch **Human Rights Day 1981 110 AIR.**
879 110c. on $3 Rotary anniversary emblem . . . 1·00 60

1981. 35th Anniv of UNICEF No. 724 surch **UNICEF 1946 - 1981 125.**
880 125c. on $2 "Mango Season" 1·25 40

1981. "Cancun 81" International Conference. No. 698 surch **Cancun 81 50c.**
880c 50c. on 5c. Type **166** . . . . 4·00 55

1982. Metrication. Multicoloured.
881 15c. Type **225** 40 40
882 15c. "Metric man" 40 40
883 15c. "Postal service goes metric" 40 40
884 15c. Weighing child on metric scales 40 40
885 15c. Canje Bridge 40 40
886 15c. Tap filling litre bucket 40 40

1982. Various stamps optd **1982**.
887 – 20c. multicoloured (No. 549) . . . . . . 1·00 20
888 **105** 25c. black, gold and lilac 60 15
889 – 25c. mult (No. 550ab) . . 1·25 20
See also Nos. 914/17, 919/21, 923/4, 977, 992/8, 1001, 1004, 1006/8, 1015, 1017, 1059, 1117 and OP3/4.

1982. No. 506 optd **POSTAGE** and Nos. 546 and 601 surch.
890 20c. on 6c. Cannon-ball tree 20 10
892 25c. Type **116** . . . . 1·00 10
893 125c. on 8c. on 6c. Cannon-ball tree 20 20

230 Guyana Soldier and Flag

1982. Savings Campaign.
894 **230** $1 multicoloured 30 20
No. 894 is a fiscal stamp optd for postal use. See also Nos. 913 and 990.

1982. 125th Birth Anniv of Lord Baden-Powell and 75th Anniv of Boy Scout Movement. Nos. 543, 545 and 601 surch as given in brackets.
895 15c. on 2c. Type **132** **(BADEN POWELL 1857–1982)** 30 45
896 15c. on 2c. Type **132 (Scout Movement 1907–1982)** . . 30 40
897 15c. on 2c. Type **132 (1907–1982)** . . . . 2·00 2·25
898 15c. on 2c. Type **132 (1857–1982)** . . . . 2·00 2·25
899 15c. on 2c. Type **132 (1982)** 10 10
900 110c. on 5c. Annatto tree **(BADEN POWELL 1857–1982)** 60 20
901 110c. on 5c. Annatto tree **(Scout Movement 1907–1982)** 60 20
902 110c. on 5c. Annatto tree **(1907–1982)** . . . . 2·50 2·50
903 110c. on 5c. Annatto tree **(1857–1982)** . . . . 2·50 2·50
904 110c. on 5c. Annatto tree **(1982)** 60 20
905 125c. on 8c. on 6c. Cannon-ball tree **(BADEN POWELL 1857–1982)** . . 60 20
906 125c. on 8c. on 6c. Cannon-ball tree **(Scout Movement 1907–1982)** 60 20
907 125c. on 8c. on 6c. Cannon-ball tree **(1907–1982)** . . . 2·50 2·50
908 125c. on 8c. on 6c. Cannon-ball tree **(1857–1982)** . . . 2·50 2·50
909 125c. on 8c. on 6c. Cannon-ball tree **(1982)** 60 20

1982. 250th Birth Anniv of George Washington. Nos. 718 and 720 surch **Geo Washington 1732 . . . 1982** and value and No. 708 optd **GEORGE WASHINGTON 1732–1982.**
910 100c. on $3 Printing press used for early British Guiana stamps 45 30
911 400c. on 30c. British Guiana 1856 1c. black on purple 1·60 1·25
912 $5 "Morpho deidamia" . . . 9·00 5·50

1982. Savings Campaign. As T **230**. Mult.
913 110c. on $5 Guyana male and female soldiers with flag 50 20
No. 913 is a fiscal stamp surch for postal use. See also No. 990.

1982. Easter. Optd **1982** or surch also.
914 **111** 25c. multicoloured 20 15
915 30c. multicoloured 20 15
916 45c. on 6c. multicoloured 20 25
917 75c. on 40c. multicoloured 35 25

1982. No. 703 surch **20.**
918 20c. on 35c. "Anaea galanthis" . . . . 5·00 10

1982. No. F5 optd **1982 180.**
919 180c. on 40c. Tiger beard . . 3·50 40

1982. Nos. 555/6 optd **1982.**
920 $2 "Norantea guianensis" . . 80 30
921 $5 "Odontadenia grandiflora" 1·00 70

1982. No. 542 surch **220.**
922 220c. on 1c. Pitcher Plant of Mt. Roraima . . . . . . 1·00 40

1982. Nos. 472 and 684 optd **1982.**
923 **105** 40c. black, gold and blue 35 15
924 – 40c. multicoloured 50 25

1982. Nos. 469, 751 and 842/3 surch.
925 **105** 80c. on 6c. black, gold and flesh 30 20
926 85c. on 6c. black, gold and flesh 50 20
927 – 160c. on $1.10 on $2 mult (No. 843) 40 30
928 – 210c. on $3 mult (No. 751) . . . . . . 5·00 40
929 – 235c. on 75c. on 85 mult (No. 842) . . . . . . 2·50 60

1982. Royal Wedding (3rd issue). Nos. 841/3 surch.
930 85c. on 60c. on 3c. Hanging heliconia . . . . 4·00 50
931 130c. on 60c. on 3c. Hanging heliconia . . . . 2·50 45
932 160c. on. $1.10 on $2 "Norantea guianensis" . . 3·00 1·00
933 170c. on $1.10 on $2 "Norantea guianensis" . . 6·50 4·50
934 210c. on 75c. on $5 "Odontadenia grandiflora" 2·25 40
935 235c. on 75c. on $5 "Odontadenia grandiflora" 3·50 1·40
936 330c. on $1.10 on $2 "Norantea guianensis" . . 1·50 40

1982. World Cup Football Championship, Spain (2nd issue). Nos. 544, 546 and 554 optd **ESPANA 1982** or surch also.
937 $1 "Chelonanthus uliginoides" 75 40
938 110c. on 3c. Hanging heliconia 75 25
939 250c. on 6c. Cannon-ball tree 1·00 60
See also No. 1218.

1982. No. 548a optd 1982.
977 15c. Christmas orchid . . . . 7·50 10

1982. No. O26 optd **POSTAGE.**
978 110c. on 6c. Type **116** . . . 2·75 35

1982. Air. 21st Birthday of Princess of Wales. Nos. 542, 545 and 555 surch **AIR Princess of Wales 1961–1982.**
979 110c. on 5c. Annatto tree . . 1·50 30
980 220c. on 1c. Pitcher Plant of Mt. Roraima . . . . . . 1·75 80
981 330c. on $2 "Norantea guianensis" . . . . 1·75 1·25

1982. Birth of Prince William of Wales. Surch **H.R.H Prince William 21st June 1982.** (a) On stamps of British Guiana with additional opt **GUYANA.**
982 50c. on 2c. green (No. 332) 75 30
983 $1.10 on 3c. green and brown (No. 333) . . . . 1·75 50

(b) On stamps of Guyana previously optd **GUYANA INDEPENDENCE 1966.**
984 50c. on 2c. green (No. 421) 14·00 3·50
985 $1.10 on 3c. green and brown (No. 422) . . . . 24·00 3·50
986 $1.25 on 6c. green (No. 424) 60 60
987 $2.20 on 24c. black and orange (No. 435) . . . . . 1·50 1·50

1982. Savings Campaign. As No. 913 but showing inverted comma before "OURS" in opt.
990 110c. on $5 Guyana male and female soldiers with flag . . . . 5·50 75

1982. Italy's Victory in World Cup Football Championship. No. F7 surch **ESPANA 1982 ITALY $2.35.**
991 $2.35 on 180c. on 60c. Soldier's cap . . . . 3·75 55

1982. Wildlife Protection. Nos. 687 and 733/8 optd **1982.**
992 35c. Harpy eagle . . . . . . 2·00 40
993 35c. Type **174** . . . . 2·00 40
994 35c. Trahira ("Haimara") . . 2·00 40
995 35c. Electric eel . . . . . . 2·00 40
996 35c. Golden rivulus . . . . . 2·00 40
997 35c. Golden pencilfish . . . 2·00 40
998 35c. Four-eyed fish . . . . . 2·00 40

1982. Central America and Caribbean Games, Havana. Nos. 542/3 surch **C.A. & CARIB GAMES 1982**.
999 50c. on 2c. Type **132** . . . 1·00 25
1000 60c. on 1c. Pitcher plant of Mt. Roraima . . . . . . 1·25 15

1982. No. 730 optd **1982**.
1001 35c. black and orange . . . 50 20

1982. Nos. 841 and 979 further surch.
1002 130c. on 60c. on 3c. Hanging heliconia 40 30
1003 170c. on 110c. on 5c. Annatto tree 70 45

1982. No. 841 surch **1982 440**.
1004 440c. on 60c. on 3c. Hanging heliconia 75 45

1982. Commonwealth Games, Brisbane, Australia. No. 546 surch **Commonwealth GAMES AUSTRALIA 1982 1.25**.
1005 $1.25 on 6c. Cannon-ball tree . . . . 1·00 30

1982. Nos. 552, 641 and 719 optd **1982**.
1006 50c. multicoloured (No. 552) 1·50 25
1007 50c. blue, green and brown (No. 641) . . . . 1·00 25
1008 50c. multicoloured (No. 719) 60 25

1982. Various Official stamps additionally optd **POSTAGE**.
1009 15c. Christmas Orchid (No. O 23) . . . . 12·00 30
1010 50c. "Guzmania lingulata" (No. O14) 90 15
1011 100c. on $3 Cylinder satellite (No. O19) . . . . 1·00 35

1982. International Food Day. No. 617 optd **INT. FOOD DAY 1982**.
1012 50c. Pawpaw and tangerine 8·50 65

1982. International Year of the Elderly. No. 747 optd **INT. YEAR OF THE ELDERLY**.
1013 50c. District 404 emblem . . 7·00 50

1982. Centenary of Robert Koch's Discovery of Tubercle Bacillus. No. 750 optd **Dr. R. KOCH CENTENARY TBC BACILLUS DISCOVERY**.
1014 60c. Researcher with microscope, Caduceus emblem, stethoscope and beach scene . . . . . . 2·00 30

1982. International Decade for Women. No. 633 optd **1982**.
1015 $1 brown and blue . . . . 2·00 60

1982. Birth Centenary of F. D. Roosevelt (American statesman). No. 706 optd **F. D. ROOSEVELT 1882-1982**.
1016 $1 "Agrias claudina" . . . 4·25 50

1982. 1st Anniv of G.A.C. Inaugural Flight Georgetown to Boa Vista, Brazil. No. 842 optd **1982 GAC Inaug. Flight Georgetown–Boa Vista, Brasil 200**.
1017 200c. on 75c. on $5 "Odontadenia grandiflora" . . . . . . 6·00 1·40

1982. CARICOM Heads of Government Conference, Kingston, Jamaica. Nos. 881/6 surch **50 CARICOM Heads of Gov't Conference July 1982**.
1018 50c. on 15c. Type **225** . . . 1·25 30
1019 50c. on 15c. "Metric man" 1·25 30
1020 50c. on 15c. "Postal service goes metric" . . . . . . 1·25 30
1021 50c. on 15c. Weighing child on metric scales . . . . . 1·25 30
1022 50c. on 15c. Canje Bridge 1·25 30
1023 50c. on 15c. Tap filling litre bucket . . . . 1·25 30

1982. Christmas. Nos. 895/9 optd **CHRISTMAS 1982**.
1024 15c. on 2c. Type **132** (surch **BADEN POWELL 1857–1982**) 25 15
1025 15c. on 2c. Type **132** (surch **Scout Movement 1907–1982**) 25 15
1026 15c. on 2c. Type **132** (surch **1907–1982**) 85 75
1027 15c. on 2c. Type **132** (surch **1857–1982**) 85 75
1028 15c. on 2c. Type **132** (surch **1982**) . . . . 10·00 11·00

1982. Nos. 543 and 546 surch in figures (no "c" after face value).
1034 15c. on 2c. Type **132** . . . 15 10
1035 20c. on 6c. Cannon-ball tree 15 10
See also No. 1086.

1982. No. 489 surch.
1032 50c. on 6c. Black acara ("Patua") 20 15
1033 100c. on 6c. Black acara ("Patua") 40 30

1983. Optd **1983**.
1036 – 15c. mult (No. 655) . . . 3·50 1·50
1037 – 15c. brown, grey and black (No. 672) . . . 1·50 10
1038 – 15c. mult (No. 682) . . . 40 10
1039 **214** 15c. on 10c. mult 35 10
1040 **215** 15c. on 10c. mult 15 10
1041 – 50c. mult (No. 646) . . . 4·00 25
1042 – 50c. mult (No. 696) . . . 4·00 25
1043 – 50c. mult (No. 719) . . . 1·50 25
See also Nos. 1060/1, 1069/70, 1072/9c, 1096, 1101 and 1110/16.

1983. No. O17 optd **POSTAGE**.
1044 15c. Harpy Eagle . . . . . 13·00 10

1983. National Heritage. Nos. 710/12 and 778 surch.
1045 90c. on 30c. Cassiri and decorated Amerindian jars 85 50
1046 90c. on 35c. Rock drawing of hunter and quarry . . 35 20
1047 90c. on 50c. Fort Kyk-over-al 85 50
1048 90c. on 60c. Fort Island . . 1·25 20

258 Guyana Flag (inscr. "60TH BIRTHDAY ANNIVERSARY")

262

1983. 60th Birthday of President Burnham and 30 Years in Parliament. Multicoloured.
1049 25c. Type **258** 15 20
1050 25c. As T **258** but position of flag reversed and inscr "30th ANNIVERSARY IN PARLIAMENT" . . 15 20
1051 $1.30 Youth display (41 × 25 mm) 40 65
1052 $6 Presidential standard (43½ × 25 mm) . . . . . 70 2·75

1983. Surch in words.
1053 **170** 50c. on 10c. mult (No. 717) . . . . . 2·75 30
1054 – 50c. on 400c. on 30c. mult (No. 911) . . . 3·25 30
1055 **152** $1 on 10c. mult (No. 635) . . . . . 7·50 45
1056 $1 on $1.05 on 10c. mult (No. 768) . . . 6·50 45
1056a – $1 on $1.10 on $2 mult (No. 843) . . . . . 1·00 2·50
1057 – $1 on 220c. on 5c. mult (No. 844) . . . . . 7·50 75
1058 – $1 on 330c. on $2 mult (as No. 981) . . . . 2·50 45
1059 – $1 on $12 on $1.10 on $2 multicoloured (No. P3) . . . . . . 1·75 2·00
See also Nos. 1080/4.

1983. No. 859 optd **1983**.
1060 $1 on 60c. Beethoven and Sonny Thomas . . . . . 6·00 45

1983. Conference of Foreign Ministers of Non-aligned Countries, New Delhi. No. 569 surch **FIFTY CENTS** and No. 570 optd **1983**.
1061 **136** 25c. multicoloured . . . 75 25
1062 50c. on 8c. multicoloured 1·00 25

1983. No. 771 further surch **20**.
1064 **181** 20c. on 10c. on 3c. black, blue and red . . 55 10

1983. Commonwealth Day. Nos. 424 and 435 surch **Commonwealth Day 14 March 1983**, emblem and value.
1065 **60** 25c. on 6c. green . . . . 1·00 20
1066 $1.20 on 6c. green 50 50
1067 **63** $1.30 on 24c. black and orange . . . . 3·00 55
1068 $2.40 on 24c. black and orange . . . . 3·50 1·50

1983. Easter. Nos. 482/3 optd **1983**.
1069 **111** 25c. multicoloured . . . 15 10
1070 30c. multicoloured . . . 30 15

1983. 25th Anniv of International Maritime Organization. British Guiana fiscal stamp optd.
1071 **262** $4.80 blue and green . . 2·00 4·00

1983. Optd **1983**.
1072 **152** 50c. mult (No. 637) . . 1·50 25
1073 **159** 50c. blue, black and yellow (No. 668) . . 1·50 25
1073a – 50c. mult (No. 723) . . 26·00 2·00
1074 – 50c. mult (No. 854) . . 60 25
1075 – 50c. mult (No. 858) . . 4·25 25
1076 – $1 mult (No. 628) . . . 4·00 45
1077 – $1 mult (No. 638) . . . 4·75 45
1078 – $1 mult (No. 675) . . . 4·00 45
1079 – $1 on 30c. mult (No. 855) . . . . . 1·25 45
1079a – $3 mult (No. 720) . . . 22·00 1·25
1079b – $3 mult (No. 724) . . . 32·00 2·25
1079c – $3 mult (No. 748) . . . 80·00 8·50

1983. Surch **FIFTY CENTS**.
1080 **148** 50c. on 8c. mult (No. 615) . . . . . . 1·75 25
1081 **162** 50c. on 8c. mult (No. 681) . . . . . . 6·00 25
1082 **171** 50c. on 10c. mult (No. 721) . . . . . . 3·00 25
1083 – 50c. on 10c. on 25c. mult (No. O13) . . . . . . 6·00 25
1084 – 50c. on 330c. on $3 mult (No. 845) . . . . . . 4·00 25

1983. Surch in figures with **c** after new face value.
1098 **105** 15c. on 6c. black, gold and pink (No. 469) . . 10 10
1100 – 20c. on 6c. multicoloured (No. 546) 15 10
1087 **111** 50c. on 6c. multicoloured (No. 481) 40 30
1099 – 50c. on 6c. multicoloured (No. 489) 30 30

1983. No. 489 surch **$1**.
1088 $1 on 6c. Black acara ("Patua") . . . . 1·75 30

1983. No. 639 surch **110**.
1089 **153** 110c. on 10c. yellow, green and violet . . . 1·75 50

1983. Nos. 551 and 556 surch.
1090 250c. on 40c. Tiger beard 7·50 55
1091 400c. on $5 "Odontadenia grandiflora" . . . . . . 5·50 70

1983. World Telecommunications and Health Day. Nos. 842 and 980 further surch.
1092 25c. on 220c. on 1c. Pitcher plant of Mt. Roraima (surch **ITU 1983 25**) . . 40 40
1093 25c. on 220c. on 1c. Pitcher plant of Mt. Roraima (surch **WHO 1983 25**) 40 40
1094 25c. on 220c. on 1c. Pitcher plant of Mt. Roraima (surch **17 MAY '83 ITU/ WHO 25**) 40 40
1095 $4.50 on 75c. on $5 "Odontadenia grandiflora" (surch **ITU/ WHO 17 MAY 1983**) . . 13·00 1·50
1095a 235c. on 75c. on $5 (No. 929) . . . . 1·50 1·00

1983. 30th Anniv of President's Entry into Parliament. Nos. 690 and 692 surch in words, No. 1096 additionally optd **1983**.
1096 $1 on 15c. black, blue and grey . . . . 6·00 50
1097 $1 on 40c. black, orange and grey . . . . 10·00 50

1983. No. 611 optd **1983**.
1101 25c. Guides in camp . . . . 48·00 4·00

1983. 15th World Scout Jamboree, Alberta. Nos. 835/6 and O25 optd **CANADA 1983**, Nos. 1103 and 1105 additionally surch.
1103 – $1.30 on 100c. on 8c. multicoloured . . . . 2·00 1·00
1104 **116** 180c. on 6c. mult . . . . 2·00 1·50
1105 $3.90 on 400c. on 6c. multicoloured . . . . 3·00 3·50

1983. Nos. 659/60 surch.
1106 60c. on 15c. Map of the Caribbean . . . . 11·00 40
1107 $1.50 on 15c. Prudential Cup . . . . 13·00 1·50

1983. As Nos. 1049/50, but without commemorative inscr above flag.
1108 25c. As Type **258** 15 15
1109 25c. As No. 1050 . . . . . 15 15

1983. Optd **1983**.
1110 **105** 30c. black, gold and green (No. 471) . . . 75 20
1111 – 30c. multicoloured (No. 695) . . . . . . 9·50 30
1112 – 30c. multicoloured (No. 718) . . . . . . 4·50 20
1113 – 30c. multicoloured (No. 722) . . . . . . 8·00 20
1114 – 30c. multicoloured (No. 746) . . . . . . 14·00 20
1115 – 60c. multicoloured (No. 697) . . . . . . 9·00 20
1116 – 60c. multicoloured (No. 731) . . . . . . 5·50 20

1983. No. 553 optd **1982**.
1117 60c. Soldier's cap . . . . . 4·00 35

1983. Surch.
1118 **157** 120c. on 8c. mult (No. 654) . . . . . . 2·25 40
1119 – 120c. on 10c. red, black and gold (No. 666) . . 2·25 40
1120 – 120c. on 35c. mult (No. 622) . . . . . . 2·25 40
1121 – 120c. on 35c. orange, green and violet (No. 640) . . . . . . 2·25 40

1983. Nos. 716 and 729 surch.
1122 120c. on 10c. Type **173** . . 2·00 40
1123 120c. on 375c. on $3 Cylinder satellite . . . . 1·75 40

No. 1123 also carries an otherwise unissued surcharge in red reading **INTERNATIONAL SCIENCE YEAR 1982 375**. As issued much of this is obliterated by two heavy bars.

1983. British Guiana No. D1a and Guyana No. D8 surch **120 GUYANA**.
1124 D **1** 120c. on 1c. green . . . 1·50 45
1125 D **2** 120c. on 1c. olive . . . 1·50 45

1983. CARICOM Day. No. 823 additionally surch **CARICOM DAY 1983 60**.
1126 60c. on $3 "Makanaima the Great Ancestral Spirit of the Amerindians" . . . . 1·00 35

271 "Kurupukari"

1983. Riverboats.
1127 **271** 30c. black and red . . . 20 20
1128 – 60c. black and violet . . 20 35
1129 – 120c. black and yellow 25 60
1130 – 130c. black 25 65
1131 – 150c. black and green . . 25 80
DESIGNS: 60c. "Makouria"; 120c. "Powis"; 130c. "Pomeroon"; 150c. "Lukanani".

1983. Unissued Royal Wedding surch similar to No. 843 additionally surch.
1132 $2.30 on $1.10 on $2 "Norantea guianensis" . . 60 40
1133 $3.20 on $1.10 on $2 "Norantea guianensis" . . 60 40

1983. Bicentenary of Manned Flight and 20th Anniv of Guyana Airways. Nos. 701/2a optd as indicated in brackets.
1134 20c. multicoloured (**BW**) . . 80 35
1135 20c. multicoloured (**LM**) . . 80 35
1136 20c. multicoloured (**GY 1963 1983**) 80 35
1137 20c. multicoloured (**JW**) . . 80 35
1138 20c. multicoloured (**CU**) . . 80 35
1139 20c. multicoloured (**Mont Golfier 1783-1983**) . . . 80 35
1140 25c. multicoloured (**BGI**) . . 1·50 60
1141 25c. multicoloured (**GEO**) 35 10
1142 25c. multicoloured (**MIA**) 1·50 60
1143 25c. multicoloured (**BVB**) 1·50 60
1144 25c. multicoloured (**PBM**) 1·50 60
1145 25c. multicoloured (**Mont Golfier 1783-1983**) . . . 40 15
1146 25c. multicoloured (**POS**) 1·50 60
1147 25c. multicoloured (**JFK**) . . 1·50 60
1148 30c. multicoloured (**AHL**) 80 30
1149 30c. multicoloured (**BCG**) 80 30
1150 30c. multicoloured (**BMJ**) 80 30
1151 30c. multicoloured (**EKE**) 80 30
1152 30c. multicoloured (**GEO**) 80 30
1153 30c. multicoloured (**GFO**) 80 30
1154 30c. multicoloured (**IBM**) 80 30
1155 30c. multicoloured (**Mont Golfier 1783-1983**) 35 15
1156 30c. multicoloured (**KAI**) . . 80 30
1157 30c. multicoloured (**KAR**) 80 30
1158 30c. multicoloured (**KPG**) 80 30
1159 30c. multicoloured (**KRG**) 80 30
1160 30c. multicoloured (**KTO**) 80 30
1161 30c. multicoloured (**LTM**) 80 30
1162 30c. multicoloured (**MHA**) 80 30
1163 30c. multicoloured (**MWJ**) 80 30
1164 30c. multicoloured (**MYM**) 80 30
1165 30c. multicoloured (**NAI**) . . 80 30
1166 30c. multicoloured (**ORJ**) 80 30
1167 30c. multicoloured (**USI**) . . 80 30
1168 30c. multicoloured (**VEG**) 80 30

1983. No. 649 further surch **240**.
1169 240c. on 35c. on 60c. Soldier's cap . . . . . . 2·50 1·00

1983. F.A.O. Fisheries Project. Nos. 448 and 450 surch **FAO 1983** and value.
1170 30c. on 1c. Type **87** 25 15
1171 $2.60 on 3c. Peacock cichlid ("Lukunani") . . . . . . 2·00 2·75

277 G.B. 1857 1d. with Georgetown "AO3" Postmark

1983. 125th Anniv of Use of Great Britain Stamps in Guyana. (a) Inscriptions in black.
1172 **277** 25c. brown and black . . 15 10
1173 – 30c. red and black . . . 15 15
1174 – 60c. violet and black . . 25 30
1175 – 120c. green and black . . 50 55

(b) Inscriptions in blue.
1176 **277** 25c. brown and black . . 15 10
1177 – 25c. red and black . . . 15 10
1178 – 25c. violet and black . . 15 10
1179 – 25c. green and black . . 15 10
1180 **277** 30c. brown and black . . 15 15
1181 – 30c. red and black . . . 15 15
1182 – 30c. violet and black . . 15 15

1183 – 30c. green and black . . 15 15
1184 **277** 45c. brown and black . . 30 25
1185 – 45c. red and black . . 30 25
1186 – 45c. violet and black . . 30 25
1187 – 45c. green and black . . 30 25
1188 **277** 120c. brown and black 30 55
1189 – 130c. red and black . . . 30 60
1190 – 150c. violet and black . . 30 70
1191 – 200c. green and black . . 30 95

DESIGNS: Nos. 1173, 1177, 1181, 1185, 1189, G.B. 1857 4d. red; Nos. 1174, 1178, 1182, 1186, 1190, G.B. 1856 6d. lilac; Nos. 1175, 1179, 1183, 1187, 1191, G.B. 1856 1s. green.

Each design incorporates the "AO3" postmark except Nos. 1189/91 which show mythical post-marks of the Crowned-circle type inscribed "DEMERARA", "BERBICE" or "ESSEQUIBO".

1983. International Communications Year. No. 716 surch **INT. COMMUNICATIONS YEAR 50**.
1192 50c. on 375c. on $3 Cylinder satellite . . . . 4·50 30

No. 1192 also carries an otherwise unissued "375" surcharge. As issued much of this surcharge is obliterated by two groups of six horizontal lines.

1983. St. John Ambulance Commemoration. Nos. 650 and 653 surch.
1193 **156** 75c. on 8c. silver, black and mauve . . . . . 4·50 50
1194 – $1.20 on 40c. silver, black and blue . . . . 6·50 75

1983. International Food Day. No. 616 surch **$1.20 Int. Food Day 1983**.
1195 $1.20 on 35c. Five-fingers and awaras . . . . 1·00 50

1983. 65th Anniv of I.L.O. and 25th Death Anniv of H. N. Critchlow (founder of Guyana Labour Union). No. 840 further optd **1918-1983 I.L.O.**
1196 240c. on $3 H. N. Critchlow 1·50 1·50

1983. Deepavali Festival. Nos. 661 and 663/4 surch.
1197 25c. on 8c. Type **158** . . . 20 10
1198 $1.50 on 35c. Flame in bowl 1·25 60
1199 $1.50 on 40c. Goddess Latchmi 80 60

1983. No. 732 optd **1982** and No. 798 further optd **1983**.
1200 $3 "Makanaima the Great Ancestral Spirit of the Amerindians" . . . . . . 1·00 70
1201 360c. on $2 "Norantea guianensis" . . . . 1·10 80

1983. Wildlife Protection. Nos. 686 and 688 surch and No. 852 optd **1983**.
1202 30c. Six-banded armadillo 75 15
1203 60c. on 15c. Giant sea turtle 1·25 30
1204 $1.20 on 40c. Iguana . . . 1·75 50

1983. Human Rights Day. No. 1079c optd **Human Rights Day**.
1205 $3 Rotary anniversary emblem . . . . 2·00 1·25

1983. Olympic Games, Los Angeles (1984) (1st issue). Nos. 733/44 surch **LOS ANGELES 1984 125**, Nos. 1206/17 further surch **55**.
1206 55c. on 125c. on 35c. Type **174** 25 25
1207 55c. on 125c. on 35c. Trahira ("Haimara") . . 25 25
1208 55c. on 125c. on 35c. Electric eel 25 25
1209 55c. on 125c. on 35c. Golden rivulus 25 25
1210 55c. on 125c. on 35c. Golden pencilfish . . . 25 25
1211 55c. on 125c. on 35c. Four-eyed fish 25 25
1212 55c. on 125c. on 35c. Red piranha ("Pirai") 25 25
1213 55c. on 125c. on 35c. Smoking hassar 25 25
1214 55c. on 125c. on 35c. Manta 25 25
1215 55c. on 125c. on 35c. Festive cichlid ("Flying patwa") 25 25
1216 55c. on 125c. on 35c. Arapaima 25 25
1217 55c. on 125c. on 35c. Peacock cichlid ("Lukanani") 25 25
1217a 125c. on 35c. Type **174** . . 7·50
1217b 125c. on 35c. Trahira ("Haimara") . . . . . 7·50
1217c 125c. on 35c. Electric eel 7·50
1217d 125c. on 35c. Golden rivulus . . . . 7·50
1217e 125c. on 35c. Golden pencilfish . . . . 7·50
1217f 125c. on 35c. Four-eyed fish . . . . 7·50
1217g 125c. on 35c. Red piranha ("Pirai") . . . . . . 7·50
1217h 125c. on 35c. Smoking hassar . . . . . . 7·50
1217i 125c. on 35c. Manta . . . 7·50
1217j 125c. on 35c. Festive cichlid ("Flying patwa") 7·50
1217k 125c. on 35c. Arapaima . . 7·50
1217l 125c. on 35c. Peacock cichlid ("Lukanani") . . 7·50

See also Nos. 1308/17 and 1420.

1983. No. F7 with unissued **ESPANA 1982** surch further optd **1983**.
1218 180c. on 60c. Soldier's cap 3·25 65

1983. Commonwealth Heads of Government Meeting, New Delhi. No. 542 surch **COMMONWEALTH HEADS OF GOV'T MEETING–INDIA 1983 150**.
1219 150c. on 1c. Pitcher plant of Mt. Roraima . . . . . . 3·25 60

1983. Christmas. No. 861 further surch **CHRISTMAS 1983 20c**.
1220 20c. on 12c. on 6c. Black acara ("Patua") . . . . . 2·25 10

1984. Nos. 838 and F9 optd **POSTAGE**.
1221 $2 "Norantea guianensis" 3·50 70
1221b 550c. on $10 "Elbella patrobas" . . . . 19·00 8·50

1984. Flowers. Unissued stamps as T **222** surch.
1222 17c. on 2c. lilac, blue and green . . . . 3·25 2·00
1223 17c. on 8c. lilac, blue and mauve . . . . 3·25 2·00

1984. Republic Day. No. 703 and 705a variously optd or surch.
1224 25c. on 35c. mult (surch **ALL OUR HERITAGE 25**) 50 20
1225 25c. on 35c. mult (surch **1984 25**) 75 30
1226 25c. on 35c. mult (surch **REPUBLIC DAY 25**) . . 75 30
1227 25c. on 35c. mult (surch **25**) 75 30
1228 25c. on 35c. mult (surch **BERBICE 25**) . . . . . 3·25 3·25
1229 25c. on 35c. mult (surch **DEMERARA 25**) . . . . 3·25 3·25
1230 25c. on 35c. mult (surch **ESSEQUIBO 25**) . . . . 3·25 3·25
1232 60c. mult (optd **ALL OUR HERITAGE**) . . . . . 1·75 75
1233 60c. mult (optd **REPUBLIC DAY**) . . . . 1·75 75
1234 60c. mult (optd **1984**) . . . 1·75 75

1984. Guyana Olympic Committee Appeal. Nos. 841/3 surch **OLYMPIC GAMES 84 25c POSTAGE (+2.25 SURTAX)** and rings, the whole surch inverted.
1235 25c.+$2.25 on 60c. on 3c. Hanging heliconia . . . . 2·75 6·00
1236 25c.+$2.25 on 75c. on $5 "Odontadenia grandiflora" . . . . 2·75 6·00
1237 25c.+$2.25 on $1.10 on $2 "Norantea guianensis" . . 2·75 6·00

1984. Nature Protection. Various stamps optd **Protecting our Heritage**, some additionally surch.
1238 20c. on 15c. mult (No. 491) 14·00 10
1239 20c. on 15c. mult (No. 791) 14·00 10
1240a 20c. on 15c. mult (No. 1044) . . . . . . 24·00 1·25
1241 25c. mult (No. 550ab) . . 21·00 10
1242 30c. on 15c. mult (No. 548a) . . . . . . 20·00 30
1243 40c. multicoloured (No. 457) . . . . 15·00 20
1244 50c. multicoloured (No. 552) . . . . 2·75 25
1245 50c. multicoloured (No. F6) . . . . 2·75 25
1246 60c. multicoloured (No. 459) . . . . 9·50 30
1247 90c. on 40c. mult (No. 551) 16·00 50
1248 180c. on 40c. mult (No. 919) . . . . 16·00 90
1249 $2 multicoloured (No. 461) 50·00 1·50
1250 225c. on 10c. mult (No. 490) . . . . 23·00 1·00
1251 260c. on $1 mult (No. 460) 11·00 1·00
1252 320c. on 40c. mult (No. 551) . . . . 12·00 2·25
1253 350c. on 40c. mult (No. 551) . . . . 20·00 2·75
1254 380c. on 50c. mult (No. 495) . . . . 10·00 2·75
1255 450c. on $5 mult (No. 462) 7·00 2·75

1984. Easter. Nos. 483 and 916/17 optd **1984** and No. 481 surch **130**.
1256 **111** 30c. multicoloured . . . 20 20
1257 45c. on 6c. multicoloured 25 25
1258 75c. on 40c. multicoloured 35 35
1259 130c. on 6c. multicoloured 65 60

1984. Nos. 937/9 and 991 surch.
1260 75c. on $1 "Chelonanthus uliginoides" . . . . . . 9·50 35
1261 75c. on 110c. on 3c. Hanging heliconia . . . . 9·50 35
1262 225c. on 250c. on 6c. Cannon-ball tree . . . . 3·00 1·25
1263 230c. on $2.35 on 180c. on 60c. Soldier's cap . . . . 3·00 1·00

1984. Nos. 899/901, 904/6 and 909 surch.
1264 20c. on 15c. on 2c. Type **132** (No. 899) . . . . . . 1·50 30
1265 75c. on 110c. on 5c. Annatto tree (No. 904) . . 9·00 70
1266 90c. on 110c. on 5c. Annatto tree (No. 900) . . 5·50 85
1267 90c. on 110c. on 5c. Annatto tree (No. 901) . . 7·00 85
1268 120c. on 125c. on 8c. on 6c. Cannon-ball tree (No. 905) . . . . 7·00 1·00
1269 120c. on 125c. on 8c. on 6c. Cannon-ball tree (No. 906) . . . . 7·00 1·00
1270 120c. on 125c. on 8c. on 6c. Cannon-ball tree (No. 909) . . . . 2·75 1·00

1984. World Telecommunications and Health Day. Nos. 802 and 980 surch.
1271 25c. on 220c. on 1c. Pitcher plant of Mt. Roraima (surch **ITU DAY 1984 25**) 40 40
1272 25c. on 220c. on 1c. Pitcher plant of Mt. Roraima (surch **WHO DAY 1984 25**) 40 40
1273 25c. on 220c. on 1c. Pitcher plant of Mt. Roraima (surch **ITU/WHO DAY 1984 25**) 40 40
1274 $4.50 on 280c. on $5 "Odontadenia grandiflora" (surch **ITU/ WHO DAY 1984 $4.50**) 2·50 2·00

1984. No. 1005 surch **120**.
1275 120c. on $1.25 on 6c. Cannon-ball tree . . . . 7·00 55

1984. World Forestry Conference. No. 755 optd **1984** and Nos. 752/4 and 875 surch.
1276 55c. on 30c. "Hymenaea courbaril" . . . . 2·75 30
1277 75c. on 110c. on $3 "Peltogyne venosa" . . . 40 35
1278 160c. on 50c. "Mora excelsa" 75 70
1279 260c. on 10c. Type **177** . . 1·25 1·25
1280 $3 "Peltogyne venosa" . . . 1·40 1·40

1984. No. 625 surch.
1281 55c. on 110c. on 10c. Type **150** . . . . 1·00 30
1282 90c. on 110c. on 10c. Type **150** . . . . 1·25 45

Nos. 1281/2 also carry an otherwise unissued 110c. surch.

1984. U.P.U. Congress, Hamburg. Nos. 1188/91 optd **UPU Congress 1984 Hamburg**.
1283 120c. brown and black . . . 50 60
1284 130c. red and black . . . 55 70
1285 150c. violet and black . . . 60 75
1286 200c. green and black . . . 80 90

1984. Nos. 982/3 and 986/7 surch.
1287 45c. on 50c. on 2c. green . . 60 25
1288 60c. on $1.10 on 3c. olive and brown . . . . 2·75 40
1289 120c. on $1.25 on 6c. green 75 55
1290 200c. on $2.20 on 24c. black and orange . . . . 7·00 1·10

1984. Nos. 979/80 and 1003 surch and No. 981 optd **1984**.
1291 75c. on 110c. on 5c. Annatto tree 60 35
1292 120c. on 170c. on 110c. on 5c. Annatto tree 80 55
1293 200c. on 220c. on 1c. Pitcher plant of Mt. Roraima . . 18·00 1·25
1294 330c. on $2 "Norantea guianensis" . . . . 1·75 1·75

1984. CARICOM Day. No. 1200 additionally surch **CARICOM DAY 1984 60**.
1295 60c. on $3 "Makanaima the Great Ancestral Spirit of the Amerindians" 40 30

1984. No. 544 surch **150**.
1296 150c. on 3c. Hanging heliconia . . . . 1·25 65

1984. CARICOM Heads of Government Conference. No. 544 surch **60 CARICOM HEADS OF GOV'T CONFERENCE JULY 1984**.
1297 60c. on 3c. Hanging heliconia 40 30

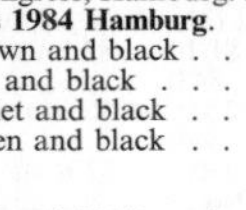

301 Children and Thatched School

1984. Cent of Guyana Teachers' Association. Mult.
1298 25c. Type **301** 10 15
1299 25c. Torch and graduates 10 15
1300 25c. Torch and target emblem 10 15
1301 25c. Teachers of 1884 and 1984 in front of school . . 10 15

1984. 60th Anniv of International Chess Federation. No. 1048 optd or surch also.
1302 25c. on 90c. on 60c. Fort Island (surch **INT. CHESS FED. 1924–1984 25**) . . . . 2·00 50
1303 25c. on 90c. on 60c. Fort Island (surch **1984 25**) . . 3·00 90
1304 75c. on 90c. on 60c. Fort Island (surch **INT. CHESS FED. 1924–1984 75**) . . . . 2·00 75
1305 75c. on 90c. on 60c. Fort Island (surch **1984 75**) . . 3·00 1·25
1306 90c. on 60c. Fort Island (optd **INT. CHESS FED. 1924–1984**) . . . . 2·00 80
1307 90c. on 60c. Fort Island (optd **1984**) . . . . 3·00 1·50

1984. Olympic Games, Los Angeles (2nd issue). No. 1051 surch.
1308 25c. on $1.30 mult (surch **TRACK AND FIELD 25**) 20 25
1309 25c. on $1.30 mult (surch **BOXING 25**) 20 30
1310 25c. on $1.30 mult (surch **OLYMPIC GAMES 1984 LOS ANGELES 25**) . . . 20 30
1311 25c. on $1.30 mult (surch **CYCLING 25**) . . . . . 2·25 50
1312 25c. on $1.30 mult (surch **OLYMPIC GAMES 1984 25**) . . . . 4·00 1·25
1313 $1.20 on $1.30 mult (surch **TRACK AND FIELD $1.20**) . . . . 1·00 1·10
1314 $1.20 on $1.30 mult (surch **BOXING $1.20**) . . . . 1·00 1·10
1315 $1.20 on $1.30 mult (surch **OLYMPIC GAMES 1984 LOS ANGELES $1.20**) 1·00 1·25
1316 $1.20 on $1.30 mult (surch **CYCLING $1.20**) . . . . 4·00 1·75
1317 $1.20 on $1.30 mult (surch **OLYMPIC GAMES 1984 $1.20**) . . . . 4·25 4·00

1984. 60th Anniv of Girl Guide Movement in Guyana. Nos. 900/9 surch **25 GIRL GUIDES 1924-1984**.
1318 25c. on 110c. on 5c. Annatto tree (No. 900) . . 25 20
1319 25c. on 110c. on 5c. Annatto tree (No. 901) . . 25 20
1320 25c. on 110c. on 5c. Annatto tree (No. 902) . . 80 60
1321 25c. on 110c. on 5c. Annatto tree (No. 903) . . 80 60
1322 25c. on 110c. on 5c. Annatto tree (No. 904) . . 9·00 9·50
1323 25c. on 125c. on 8c. on 6c. Cannon-ball tree (No. 905) 25 20
1324 25c. on 125c. on 8c. on 6c. Cannon-ball tree (No. 906) 25 20
1325 25c. on 125c. on 8c. on 6c. Cannon-ball tree (No. 907) 80 60
1326 25c. on 125c. on 8c. on 6c. Cannon-ball tree (No. 908) 80 60
1327 25c. on 125c. on 8c. on 6c. Cannon-ball tree (No. 909) . . . . 9·00 9·50

1984. Various stamps surch.
1328 20c. on 15c. on 2c. Type **132** (No. 1034) . . 30 10
1341 25c. on 10c. Cattleya (No. 547) . . . . 45·00 2·00
1343 25c. on 15c. Christmas orchid (No. 548a) . . . £120 5·00
1342 25c. on 15c. Christmas orchid (No. 864) . . . 19·00 15
1346 25c. on 15c. Christmas orchid (No. 977) . . . . 15·00 10
1347 25c. on 15c. Christmas orchid (No. 1009) . . . 15·00 10
1348 25c. on 15c. Christmas orchid (No. O23) . . . . 15·00 10
1342a 25c. on 35c. on 60c. Soldier's cap (No. 649) 95·00 4·75
1331 60c. on 110c. on 8c. on 3c. Hanging heliconia (As No. 868 but with only one **110**) . . . . . . 29·00 4·75
1332 120c. on 125c. on 8c. on 6c. Cannon-ball tree (No. 893) . . . . 5·00 50
1333 120c. on 125c. on $2 "Norantea guianensis" (No. 834) . . . . . . 60·00 7·00
1334 120c. on 125c. on $2 "Norantea guianensis" (No. O20) . . . . 3·50 50
1335 120c. on 140c. on $1 "Chelonanthus uliginoides" (No. 796) 5·50 50
1349 130c. on 110c. on $2 "Norantea guianensis" (No. 804) . . . . 85·00 4·75
1350 130c. on 110c. on $2 "Norantea guianensis" (No. O22) . . . . 1·25 1·25
1336 200c. on 220c. on 1c. Pitcher plant of Mt. Roraima (No. 922) . . . 16·00 75
1337 320c. on $1.10 on $2 "Norantea guianensis" (No. 804) . . . . 1·50 75
1338 350c. on 375c. on $5 "Odontadenia grandiflora" (No. 803) 3·75 80
1339 390c. on 400c. on $5 "Odontadenia grandiflora" (No. 1091) 4·50 90

1340 450c. on $5 "Odontadenia grandiflora" (No. O16) 7·50 2·75
1351a 600c. on $7.20 on $1 "Chelonanthus uliginoides" (No. 770) 50 60

1984. Various stamps optd **1984**.
1352 20c. "Paphinia cristata" (No. 549) 25·00 10
1358 25c. Marabunta (No. 550) 85·00 4·50
1359 25c. Marabunta (No. F4) 5·50 50
1359a 25c. Marabunta (No. F4a) 2·00 30
1354 50c. on 8c. Type **136** (No. 1062) 10·00 25
1355 60c. on 1c. Pitcher plant of Mt. Roraima (No. 1000) 2·00 25
1356 $2 "Norantea guianensis" (No. O33) 1·25 60
1360 $3.60 on $5 "Odontadenia grandiflora" (No. 769) 85 1·10

1984. No. 899 optd with fleur-de-lis.
1358a 25c. Marabunta 85·00 4·50

1984. 40th Anniv of I.C.A.O. Nos. 981, 1017 and 1148/68 optd **ICAO** or as indicated.
1361 30c. multicoloured (No. 1148) 1·00 80
1362 30c. multicoloured (No. 1149) 1·00 80
1363 30c. multicoloured (No. 1150) 1·00 80
1364 30c. multicoloured (No. 1151) 1·00 80
1365 30c. multicoloured (No. 1152) 1·00 80
1366 30c. multicoloured (No. 1153) 1·00 80
1367 30c. multicoloured (No. 1154) (optd **IMB/ ICAO**) 1·00 80
1368 30c. multicoloured (No. 1155) (optd **KCV/ ICAO**) 1·00 80
1369 30c. multicoloured (No. 1156) (optd **KAI/ ICAO**) 1·00 80
1370 30c. multicoloured (No. 1157) 1·00 80
1371 30c. multicoloured (No. 1158) 1·00 80
1372 30c. multicoloured (No. 1155) (optd **1984**) 1·00 80
1373 30c. multicoloured (No. 1155) (optd **KPM/ ICA**) 1·00 80
1374 30c. multicoloured (No. 1159) 1·00 80
1375 30c. multicoloured (No. 1160) 1·00 80
1376 30c. multicoloured (No. 1161) 1·00 80
1377 30c. multicoloured (No. 1155) (optd **PMT/ ICAO**) 1·00 80
1378 30c. multicoloured (No. 1162) 1·00 80
1379 30c. multicoloured (No. 1163) 1·00 80
1380 30c. multicoloured (No. 1164) 1·00 80
1381 30c. multicoloured (No. 1165) 1·00 80
1382 30c. multicoloured (No. 1166) 1·00 80
1383 30c. multicoloured (No. 1167) 1·00 80
1384 30c. multicoloured (No. 1168) 1·00 80
1385 200c. on 330c. on $2 multicoloured (No. 981) 75 85
1386 200c. on 75c. on $5 multicoloured (No. 1017) 3·00 2·00
No. 1385 also carries an otherwise unissued surch **G.A.C. Inaug. Flight Georgetown–Toronto 200**.

1984. Wildlife Protection. Nos. 756/67 optd **1984**.
1387 30c. Type **178** 30 25
1388 30c. Red howler 30 25
1389 30c. Common squirrel-monkey 30 25
1390 30c. Two-toed sloth 30 25
1391 30c. Brazilian tapir 30 25
1392 30c. Collared peccary 30 25
1393 30c. Six-banded armadillo 30 25
1394 30c. Tamandua ("Ant Eater") 30 25
1395 30c. Giant anteater 30 25
1396 30c. Murine opossum 30 25
1397 30c. Brown four-eyed opossum 30 25
1398 30c. Brazilian agouti 30 25

1984. Nos. D10/11 surch **120 GUYANA**.
1399 D **2** 120c. on 4c. blue 1·50 45
1402 120c. on 12c. red 1·50 45

1984. 175th Birth Anniv of Louis Braille (inventor of alphabet for the blind). No. 1040 surch **$1.50**.
1403 $1.50 on 15c. on 10c. Type **215** 6·50 55

1984. International Food Day. No. 1012 surch **1**.
1404 150c. on 50c. Pawpaw and tangerine 2·00 55

The surcharge places a "1" alongside the original face value and obliterates the "1982" date on the previous overprint.

1984. Birth Centenary of H. N. Critchlow (founder of Guyana Labour Union). No. 873 surch **240** and No. 1196, both optd 1984.
1405 240c. on 110c. on $3 H. N. Critchlow (No. 873) 1·00 65
1406 240c. on $3 H. N. Critchlow (No. 1196) 6·50 70

1984. Nos. 910/12 and 1184/7 surch.
1407 **277** 25c. on 45c. brown and black 15 15
1408 – 25c. on 45c. red and black (No. 1185) 15 15
1409 – 25c. on 45c. violet and black (No. 1186) 15 15
1410 – 25c. on 45c. green and black (No. 1187) 15 15
1411 – 120c. on 100c. on $3 mult (No. 910) 9·50 45
1412 – 120c. on 400c. on 30c. mult (No. 911) 90 45
1413 – 320c. on $5 multicoloured (No. 912) 17·00 1·75

1984. Deepavali Festival. Nos. 544/5 surch **MAHA SABHA 1934-1984** and new value.
1414 25c. on 5c. Annatto tree 50 10
1415 $1.50 on 3c. Hanging heliconia 2·75 1·00

1984. A.S.D.A. Philatelic Exhibition, New York. Nos. 1188/91 optd **Philatelic Exhibition New York 1984**.
1416 **277** 120c. brown and black 40 45
1417 – 130c. red and black 45 50
1418 – 150c. violet and black 50 55
1419 – 200c. green and black 70 75

1984. Olympic Games, Los Angeles (3nd issue). Design as No. 1051, but with Olympic rings and inscr "OLYMPIC GAMES 1984 LOS ANGELES".
1420 $1.20 Youth display (41 × 25 mm) 1·50 45

1984. Nos. 847, 861, 1099 and 1088 surch.
1421 20c. on 12c. on 12c. on 6c. multicoloured (No. 847) 60 10
1422 20c. on 12c. on 6c. mult (No. 861) 75·00 5·50
1423 25c. on 50c. on 6c. mult (No. 1099) 30 10
1424 60c. on $1 on 6c. mult (No. 1088) 45 25

318 Pair of Swallow-tailed Kites on Tree

1984. Christmas. Swallow-tailed Kites. Mult.
1425 60c. Type **318** 3·00 1·75
1426 60c. Swallow-tailed kite on branch 3·00 1·75
1427 60c. Kite in flight with wings raised 3·00 1·75
1428 60c. Kite in flight with wings lowered 3·00 1·75
1429 60c. Kite gliding 3·00 1·75
Nos. 1425/9 were printed together, se-tenant, with the backgrounds forming a composite design. Each stamp is inscribed "CHRISTMAS 1982".

319 St. George's Cathedral, Georgetown

1985. Georgetown Buildings. Each black and stone.
1430 25c. Type **319** 10 10
1431 60c. Demerara Mutual Life Assurance Building 15 25
1432 120c. As No. 1431 25 45
1433 120c. Town Hall 25 45
1434 120c. Victoria Law Courts 25 45
1435 200c. As No. 1433 25 75
1436 300c. As No. 1434 30 1·10
Nos. 1432/4 were printed together, se-tenant, forming a composite design.

1985. International Youth Year. No. 1420 optd **International Youth Year 1985**.
1437 $1.20 Youth display 2·50 45
Examples of No. 1420 used for this overprint all show the second line of the original inscription as "LOS ANGELLES".

1985. Republic Day. Nos. 1049/50 and 1052 optd or surch **Republic Day 1970-1985**.
1438 25c. Type **238** 40 40
1439 25c. Flag (inscr "30th ANNIVERSARY IN PARLIAMENT") 40 40
1440 120c. on $6 Presidential standard 1·00 1·00
1441 130c. on $6 Presidential standard 1·10 1·10

322 Young Ocelot on Branch

1985. Wildlife Protection. Multicoloured.
1442A 25c. Type **322** (green background) 1·75 10
1443A 60c. Young ocelot (different) (brown background) 30 25
1444B 120c. As No. 1443 15 20
1445B 120c. Type **322** 15 20
1446B 120c. Young ocelot (different) (brown background) 15 20
1447A 130c. As No. 1446 45 60
1448A 320c. Scarlet macaw (28 × 46 mm) 3·25 1·50
1449A 330c. Young ocelot reaching for branch (28 × 46 mm) 90 1·50

1985. Revenue stamp as T **181**, and Nos. 912, 940, 1016 and No. O24 surch.
1450 30c. on 50c. mult (No. O24) 50 10
1451 55c. on 2c. black, blue and grey 65 20
1452 55c. on 15c. on 2c. black, blue and grey (940) 65 20
1453 90c. on $1 mult (No. 1016) 6·00 30
1454 225c. on $5 mult (No. 912) 15·00 1·40
1455 230c. on $5 mult (No. 912) 15·00 1·60
1456 260c. on $5 mult (No. 912) 15·00 1·75

1985. International Youth Year Save the Children Fund Campaign. Nos. 880, 1073a, 1079b and 1082 optd **International Youth Year 1985** or surch also.
1457 50c. "Two Boys catching Ducks" (No. 1073a) 2·25 20
1458 50c. on 10c. Type **171** (No. 1082) 7·00 20
1459 120c. on 125c. on $3 "Mango Season" (No. 880) 2·25 45
1460 $3 "Mango Season" (No. 1079b) 2·25 1·10

1985. 125th Anniv of British Guiana Post Office (1st issue). No. 699 surch **25** and names of post offices and postal agencies open in 1860.
1461 25c. on 10c. mult (**Airy Hall**) 1·25 1·25
1462 25c. on 10c. multicoloured (**Belfield Arab Coast**) 1·25 1·25
1463 25c. on 10c. multicoloured (**Belfield E. C. Dem.**) 1·25 1·25
1464 25c. on 10c. mult (**Belladrum**) 1·25 1·25
1465 25c. on 10c. multicoloured (**Beterver-wagting**) 1·25 1·25
1466 25c. on 10c. multicoloured (**Blairmont Ferry**) 1·25 1·25
1467 25c. on 10c. mult (**Boeraserie**) 1·25 1·25
1468 25c. on 10c. mult (**Brahm**) 1·25 1·25
1469 25c. on 10c. mult (**Bushlot**) 1·25 1·25
1470 25c. on 10c. mult (**De Kinderen**) 1·25 1·25
1471 25c. on 10c. multicoloured (**Fort Wellington**) 1·25 1·25
1472 25c. on 10c. mult (**Georgetown**) 1·25 1·25
1473 25c. on 10c. mult (**Hague**) 1·25 1·25
1474 25c. on 10c. mult (**Leguan**) 1·25 1·25
1475 25c. on 10c. mult (**Mahaica**) 1·25 1·25
1476 25c. on 10c. mult (**Mahaicony**) 1·25 1·25
1477 25c. on 10c. multicoloured (**New Amsterdam**) 1·25 1·25
1478 25c. on 10c. mult (**Plaisance**) 1·25 1·25
1479 25c. on 10c. multicoloured (**No. 6 Police Station**) 1·25 1·25
1480 25c. on 10c. mult (**Queenstown**) 1·25 1·25
1481 25c. on 10c. multicoloured (**Vergenoegen**) 1·25 1·25
1482 25c. on 10c. mult (**Vigilance**) 1·25 1·25
1483 25c. on 10c. multicoloured (**Vreed-en-Hoop**) 1·25 1·25
1484 25c. on 10c. mult (**Wakenaam**) 1·25 1·25
1485 25c. on 10c. multicoloured (**Windsor Castle**) 1·25 1·25
See also Nos. 1694/1717, 2140/64 and 2278/2301.

1985. I.T.U./W.H.O. Day. Nos. 1148/68 optd **1985** or with single capital letter.
1486 30c. multicoloured (1148) 1·25 1·25
1487 30c. multicoloured (1149) 1·25 1·25
1488 30c. multicoloured (1150) 1·25 1·25
1489 30c. multicoloured (1151) 1·25 1·25
1490 30c. multicoloured (1152) 1·25 1·25
1491 30c. multicoloured (1153) 1·25 1·25
1492 30c. multicoloured (1154) (**I**) 1·25 1·25
1493 30c. multicoloured (1155) (**T**) 1·25 1·25
1494 30c. multicoloured (1156) (**U**) 1·25 1·25
1495 30c. multicoloured (1157) 1·25 1·25
1496 30c. multicoloured (1158) 1·25 1·25
1497 30c. multicoloured (1155) (**W**) 1·25 1·25
1498 30c. multicoloured (1155) (**H**) 1·25 1·25
1499 30c. multicoloured (1155) (**O**) 1·25 1·25
1500 30c. multicoloured (1159) 1·25 1·25
1501 30c. multicoloured (1160) 1·25 1·25
1502 30c. multicoloured (1161) (**D**) 1·25 1·25
1503 30c. multicoloured (1155) (**A**) 1·25 1·25
1504 30c. multicoloured (1162) (**Y**) 1·25 1·25
1505 30c. multicoloured (1163) 1·25 1·25
1506 30c. multicoloured (1164) 1·25 1·25
1507 30c. multicoloured (1165) 1·25 1·25
1508 30c. multicoloured (1166) 1·25 1·25
1509 30c. multicoloured (1167) 1·25 1·25
1510 30c. multicoloured (1168) 1·25 1·25

1985. No. 861 surch **20**.
1511 20c. on 12c. on 6c. Patua 5·50 10

1985. 10th Anniv of Caribbean Agricultural Research Development Institute. No. 544 surch **60 CARDI 1975-1985**.
1512 60c. on 3c. Hanging heliconia 3·75 35

1985. No. 839 surch **600**.
1513 600c. on 625c. on 40c. Tiger beard 38·00 3·75

1985. 80th Anniv of Rotary International. Nos. 707 and 879 surch **ROTARY INTERNATIONAL 1905-1985**.
1514 120c. on 110c. on $3 Rotary anniversary emblem 18·00 75
1515 300c. on $2 "Morpho rhetenor" 12·00 3·50

1985. CARICOM Day. No. 1200 surch **CARICOM DAY 1985 60**.
1516 60c. on $3 "Makanaima the Great Ancestral Spirit of the Amerindians" 3·00 40

1985. 135th Anniv of First British Guiana Stamps. No. 870 surch **135th Anniversary Cotton Reel 1850-1985 120**.
1517 120c. on 110c. on 10c. Type **170** 1·50 70

"REICHENBACHIA" ISSUES. Due to the proliferation of these designs the catalogue uses the book plate numbers as description for each design. The following index gives the species on each plate.

Series 1
Plate No. 1 (Series 1) "Odontoglossum crispum"
Plate No. 2 (Series 1) "Cattleya percivaliana"
Plate No. 3 (Series 1) "Cypripedium sanderianum"
Plate No. 4 (Series 1) "Odontoglossum rossi"
Plate No. 5 (Series 1) "Cattleya dowiana aurea"
Plate No. 6 (Series 1) "Coelogyne cristata maxima"
Plate No. 7 (Series 1) "Odontoglossum insleayi splendens"
Plate No. 8 (Series 1) "Laelia euspatha"
Plate No. 9 (Series 1) "Dendrobium wardianum"
Plate No. 10 (Series 1) "Laelia autumnalis xanthotropis"
Plate No. 11 (Series 1) "Phalaenopsis grandiflora aurea"
Plate No. 12 (Series 1) "Cattleya lawrenceana"
Plate No. 13 (Series 1) "Masdevallia shuttleworthii" and "M. xanthocorys"
Plate No. 14 (Series 1) "Aeranthus sesquipedalis"
Plate No. 15 (Series 1) "Cattleya mendelii Duke of Marlborough"
Plate No. 16 (Series 1) "Zygopetalum intermedium"
Plate No. 17 (Series 1) "Phaius humblotii"
Plate No. 18 (Series 1) "Chysis bractescens"
Plate No. 19 (Series 1) "Masdevallia backhousiana"
Plate No. 20 (Series 1) "Cattleya citrina"
Plate No. 21 (Series 1) "Oncidium jonesianum" and "Oncidium jonesianum phaeanthum"
Plate No. 22 (Series 1) "Saccolabium giganteum"
Plate No. 23 (Series 1) "Cypripedium io"
Plate No. 24 (Series 1) "Odontoglossum blandum"
Plate No. 25 (Series 1) "Maxillaria sanderiana"
Plate No. 26 (Series 1) "Odontoglossum Edward II"
Plate No. 27 (Series 1) "Vanda teres"
Plate No. 28 (Series 1) "Odontoglossum hallii xanthoglossum"
Plate No. 29 (Series 1) "Odontoglossum crispum hrubyanum"
Plate No. 30 (Series 1) "Oncidium concolor"
Plate No. 31 (Series 1) "Trichopilia suavis alba"
Plate No. 32 (Series 1) "Cattleya superba splendens"
Plate No. 33 (Series 1) "Odontoglossum luteo-purpureum"
Plate No. 34 (Series 1) "Cypripedium niveum"
Plate No. 35 (Series 1) "Stanhopea shuttleworthii"
Plate No. 36 (Series 1) "Laelia anceps percivaliana"
Plate No. 37 (Series 1) "Odontoglossum hebraicum"
Plate No. 38 (Series 1) "Cypripedium oenanthum superbum"
Plate No. 39 (Series 1) "Dendrobium superbiens"
Plate No. 40 (Series 1) "Laelia harpophylla"
Plate No. 41 (Series 1) "Lycaste skinneri" and "alba"
Plate No. 42 (Series 1) "Phalaenopsis stuartiana"
Plate No. 43 (Series 1) "Cattleya trianaei ernesti"
Plate No. 44 (Series 1) "Sobralia xantholeuca"
Plate No. 45 (Series 1) "Odontoglossum crispum kinlesideanum"
Plate No. 46 (Series 1) "Cattleya trianaei schroederiana"
Plate No. 47 (Series 1) "Epidendrum vitellinum"
Plate No. 48 (Series 1) "Laelia anceps stella" and "barkeriana"
Plate No. 49 (Series 1) "Odontoglossum harryanum"
Plate No. 50 (Series 1) "Dendrobium leechianum"
Plate No. 51 (Series 1) "Phalaenopsis speciosa"
Plate No. 52 (Series 1) "Laelia elegans schilleriana"
Plate No. 53 (Series 1) "Zygopetalum wendlandi"
Plate No. 54 (Series 1) "Cypripedium selligerum majus"
Plate No. 55 (Series 1) "Angraecum articulatum"
Plate No. 56 (Series 1) "Laelia anceps sanderiana"

Plate No. 57 (Series 1) "Vanda coerulea"
Plate No. 58 (Series 1) "Dendrobium nobile sanderianum"
Plate No. 59 (Series 1) "Laelia gouldiana"
Plate No. 60 (Series 1) "Odontoglossum grande"
Plate No. 61 (Series 1) "Cypripedium rothschildianum"
Plate No. 62 (Series 1) "Vanda sanderiana"
Plate No. 63 (Series 1) "Dendrobium aureum"
Plate No. 64 (Series 1) "Oncidium macranthum"
Plate No. 65 (Series 1) "Cypripedium tautzianum"
Plate No. 66 (Series 1) "Cymbidium mastersi"
Plate No. 67 (Series 1) "Angraecum caudatum"
Plate No. 68 (Series 1) "Laelia albida"
Plate No. 69 (Series 1) "Odontoglossum roezlii"
Plate No. 70 (Series 1) "Oncidium ampliatum majus"
Plate No. 71 (Series 1) "Renanthera lowii"
Plate No. 72 (Series 1) "Cattleya warscewiczii"
Plate No. 73 (Series 1) "Oncidium lanceanum"
Plate No. 74 (Series 1) "Vanda hookeriana"
Plate No. 75 (Series 1) "Cattleya labiata gaskelliana"
Plate No. 76 (Series 1) "Epidendrum prismatocarpum"
Plate No. 77 (Series 1) "Cattleya guttata leopoldi"
Plate No. 78 (Series 1) "Oncidium splendidum"
Plate No. 79 (Series 1) "Odontoglossum hebraicum aspersum"
Plate No. 80 (Series 1) "Cattleya dowiana var chrysotoxa"
Plate No. 81 (Series 1) "Cattleya trianae alba"
Plate No. 82 (Series 1) "Odontoglossum humeanum"
Plate No. 83 (Series 1) "Cypripedium argus"
Plate No. 84 (Series 1) "Odontoglossum luteo-purpureum prionopetalum"
Plate No. 85 (Series 1) "Cattleya rochellensis"
Plate No. 86 (Series 1) "Odontoglossum triumphans"
Plate No. 87 (Series 1) "Phalaenopsis casta"
Plate No. 88 (Series 1) "Oncidium tigrinum"
Plate No. 89 (Series 1) "Cypripedium lemoinierianum"
Plate No. 90 (Series 1) "Catasetum bungerothii"
Plate No. 91 (Series 1) "Cattleya ballantiniana"
Plate No. 92 (Series 1) "Dendrobium brymerianum"
Plate No. 93 (Series 1) "Cattleya eldorado crocata"
Plate No. 94 (Series 1) "Odontoglossum sanderianum"
Plate No. 95 (Series 1) "Cattleya labiata warneri"
Plate No. 96 (Series 1) "Odontoglossum schroderianum"

Series 2

Plate No. 1 (Series 2) "Cypripedium morganiae burfordiense"
Plate No. 2 (Series 2) "Cattleya bowringiana"
Plate No. 3 (Series 2) "Dendrobium formosum"
Plate No. 4 (Series 2) "Phaius tuberculosus"
Plate No. 5 (Series 2) "Odontoglossum crispum mundyanum"
Plate No. 6 (Series 2) "Laelia praestans"
Plate No. 7 (Series 2) "Dendrobium phalaenopsis var statterianum"
Plate No. 8 (Series 2) "Cypripedium boxalli atratum"
Plate No. 9 (Series 2) "Odontoglossum wattianum"
Plate No. 10 (Series 2) "Cypripedium lathamianum inversum"
Plate No. 11 (Series 2) "Paphinia rugosa" and "Zygopetalum xanthinum"
Plate No. 12 (Series 2) "Dendrobium melanodiscus"
Plate No. 13 (Series 2) "Laelia anceps schroderiana"
Plate No. 14 (Series 2) "Phaius hybridus cooksonii"
Plate No. 15 (Series 2) "Disa grandiflora"
Plate No. 16 (Series 2) "Selenipedium hybridum grande"
Plate No. 17 (Series 2) "Cattleya schroederae alba"
Plate No. 18 (Series 2) "Lycaste skinnerii armeniaca"
Plate No. 19 (Series 2) "Odontoglossum excellens"
Plate No. 20 (Series 2) "Laelio-cattleya elegans var blenheimensis"
Plate No. 21 (Series 2) "Odontoglossum coradinei"
Plate No. 22 (Series 2) "Odontoglossum wilckeanum var rothschildianum"
Plate No. 23 (Series 2) "Cypripedium lawrenceanum hyeanum"
Plate No. 24 (Series 2) "Cattleya intermedia punctatissima"
Plate No. 25 (Series 2) "Laelia purpurata"
Plate No. 26 (Series 2) "Masdevallia harryana splendens"
Plate No. 27 (Series 2) "Selenipedium hybridum nitidissimum"
Plate No. 28 (Series 2) "Cattleya mendelii var measuresiana"
Plate No. 29 (Series 20 "Odontoglossum vexillarium" ("miltonia vexillaria")
Plate No. 30 (Series 2) "Saccolabium coeleste"
Plate No. 31 (Series 2) "Cypripedium hybridum youngianum"
Plate No. 32 (Series 2) "Miltonia (hybrida) bleuana"
Plate No. 33 (Series 2) "Laelia grandis"
Plate No. 34 (Series 2) "Cattleya labiata var lueddemanniana"
Plate No. 35 (Series 2) "Odontoglossum coronarium"
Plate No. 36 (Series 2) "Cattleya granulosa var schofieldiana"
Plate No. 37 (Series 2) "Odontoglossum (hybridum) leroyanum"
Plate No. 38 (Series 2) "Cypripedium (hybridum) laucheanum" and "eyermanianum"
Plate No. 39 (Series 2) "Cychnoches chlorochilon"
Plate No. 40 (Series 2) "Cattleya O'Brieniana"
Plate No. 41 (Series 2) "Odontoglossum ramosissimum"
Plate No. 42 (Series 2) "Dendrobium phalaenopsis var"
Plate No. 43 (Series 2) "Cypripedium (hybridum) pollettianum" and "maynardii"
Plate No. 44 (Series 2) "Odontoglossum naevium"
Plate No. 45 (Series 2) "Cypripedium (hybridum) castleanum"
Plate No. 47 (Series 2) "Cattleya amethystoglossa"
Plate No. 48 (Series 2) "Cattleya (hybrida) arnoldiana"
Plate No. 49 (Series 2) "Cattleya labiata"
Plate No. 50 (Series 2) "Dendrobium (hybridum) venus" and "cassiope"
Plate No. 51 (Series 2) "Selenipedium (hybridum) weidlichianum"
Plate No. 52 (Series 2) "Cattleya mossiae var reineckiana"
Plate No. 53 (Series 2) "Cymbidium lowianum"
Plate No. 54 (Series 2) "Oncidium loxense"
Plate No. 56 (Series 2) "Coelogyne sanderae"
Plate No. 58 (Series 2) "Coelogyne pandurata"
Plate No. 59 (Series 2) "Schomburgkia sanderiana"
Plate No. 60 (Series 2) "Oncidium superbiens"
Plate No. 61 (Series 2) "Dendrobium johnsoniae"
Plate No. 62 (Series 2) "Laelia hybrida behrensiana"
Plate No. 63 (Series 2) Hybrid "Calanthes Victoria Regina", "Bella" and "Burfordiense"
Plate No. 64 (Series 2) "Cattleya mendelii Quorndon House var"
Plate No. 65 (Series 2) "Arachnanthe clarkei"
Plate No. 66 (Series 2) "Zygopetalum burtii"
Plate No. 67 (Series 2) "Cattleya (hybrida) parthenia"
Plate No. 68 (Series 2) "Phalaenopsis sanderiana" and "intermedia portei"
Plate No. 69 (Series 2) "Phaius blumei var assamicus"
Plate No. 70 (Series 2) "Angraecum humblotii"
Plate No. 71 (Series 2) "Odontoglossum pescatorei"
Plate No. 72 (Series 2) "Cattleya rex"
Plate No. 73 (Series 2) "Zygopetalum crinitum"
Plate No. 74 (Series 2) "Cattleya lueddemanniana alba"
Plate No. 75 (Series 2) "Cymbidium (hybridum) winnianum"
Plate No. 76 (Series 2) Hybrid "Masdevallias courtauldiana", "geleniana" and "measuresiana"
Plate No. 77 (Series 2) "Cypripedium (hybridum) calypso"
Plate No. 78 (Series 2) "Masdevallia chimaera var mooreana"
Plate No. 79 (Series 2) "Miltonia phalaenopsis"
Plate No. 80 (Series 2) "Lissochilus giganteus"
Plate No. 82 (Series 2) "Thunia brymeriana"
Plate No. 83 (Series 2) "Miltonia moreliana"
Plate No. 84 (Series 2) "Oncidium kramerianum"
Plate No. 85 (Series 2) "Cattleya Victoria Regina"
Plate No. 86 (Series 2) "Zygopetalum klabochorum"
Plate No. 87 (Series 2) "Laelia autumnalis alba"
Plate No. 88 (Series 2) "Spathoglottis kimballiana"
Plate No. 89 (Series 2) "Laelio-cattleya" ("The Hon. Mrs. Astor")
Plate No. 90 (Series 2) "Phaius hybridus amabilis" and "marthiae"
Plate No. 91 (Series 2) "Zygopetalum rostratum"
Plate No. 92 (Series 2) "Coelogyne swaniana"
Plate No. 93 (Series 2) "Laelio-cattleya (hybrida) phoebe"
Plate No. 94 (Series 2) "Epidendrum atro-purpureum var randianum"
Plate No. 95 (Series 2) "Dendrobium imperatrix"
Plate No. 96 (Series 2) "Vanda parishii var marriottiana"

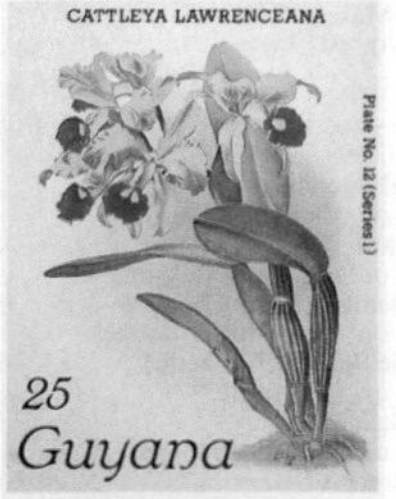

331 "Cattleya lawrenceana" (Plate No. 12 (Series 1))

1985. Centenary of Publication of Sanders' "Reichenbachia" (1st issue). Orchids. Mult.

1518	25c. Type **331**	50	30
1519	60c. Plate No. 2 (Series 1)	60	35
1520	60c. Plate No. 7 (Series 1)	60	35
1521	60c. Plate No. 10 (Series 1)	60	35
1522	60c. Plate No. 19 (Series 1)	60	35
1523	60c. Plate No. 31 (Series 1)	60	35
1524	120c. Plate No. 27 (Series 1)	75	55
1525	130c. Plate No. 3 (Series 1)	75	55
1759	130c. Plate No. 6 (Series 1)	75	20
1760	130c. Plate No. 13 (Series 1)	75	20
1528	130c. Plate No. 18 (Series 1)	4·00	55
1761	130c. Plate No. 20 (Series 1)	75	20
1762	130c. Plate No. 25 (Series 1)	75	20
1531	130c. Plate No. 29 (Series 1)	2·75	55
1532	130c. Plate No. 30 (Series 1)	2·75	55
1533	200c. Plate No. 4 (Series 1)	2·75	85

See also Nos. 1551/66, 1571/1806, 1597, 1620/1863, 1663/73, 1679/83, 1731/8, 1747/54, 1809/19, 1822, 1868/9, 1872/81, 1884/7, 1907, 1912/15, 1916/24, 1925/9, 2066/73, 2171/8, 2180/2, 2190/3, 2216/18, 2219/20, 2225/7, 2235/42, **MS**2275, 2314/18, 2322/5, 2328, **MS**2332, 2314/18, 2322/5, 2329, 2468/71, 2498/2511 and 2605/8.

332 Arms of Guyana

337 Leaders of the 1763 Rebellion

1985.

1535b	**332** 25c. multicoloured	15	20

For Type **332** within frame, see No. 2183.

1985. 85th Birthday of Queen Elizabeth the Queen Mother (1st issue). Nos. 1528 and 1531/2 optd **QUEEN MOTHER 1900-1985.**

1536	130c. Plate No. 18 (Series 1)	80	80
1537	130c. Plate No. 29 (Series 1)	80	80
1538	130c. Plate No. 30 (Series 1)	80	80
MS1539	100 × 126 mm. 200c. × 4 Plate 4 (Series 1)	6·50	5·50

The four stamps in No. **MS**1539 are overprinted **LADY BOWES-LYON 1900-1923, DUCHESS OF YORK 1923-1937, QUEEN ELIZABETH 1937-1952** or **QUEEN MOTHER 1952-1985.**
See also No. **MS**1570.

1985. International Youth Year. Nos. 900/4 surch **25 International Youth Year 1985.**

1540	25c. on 110c. on 5c. multicoloured (900)	15	15
1541	25c. on 110c. on 5c. multicoloured (901)	15	15
1542	25c. on 110c. on 5c. multicoloured (902)	60	60
1543	25c. on 110c. on 5c. multicoloured (903)	60	60
1544	25c. on 100c. on 5c. multicoloured (904)	8·50	8·50

1985. 75th Anniv of Girl Guide Movement. No. 612 surch **225 1910-1985.**

1545	225c. on 350c. on 225c. on 40c. Guides in camp	38·00	2·75

No. 1545 also carries two otherwise unissued surcharges at top right.

1985. Birth Bicentenary of John J. Audubon (ornithologist). No. 992 surch **J. J. Audubon 1785-1985 240.**

1546	240c. on 35c. Harpy eagle	30·00	3·25

1985. 150th Anniv (1984) of Abolition of Slavery (1st issue).

1547	**337** 25c. black and grey	25	10
1548	– 60c. black and mauve	20	25
1549	– 130c. black and blue	25	50
1550	– 150c. black and lilac	60	55

DESIGNS: 60c. Damon and Parliament Buildings, Georgetown; 130c. Quamina and Demerara, 1823; 150c. "Den Arendt" (slave ship), 1627.
For these designs in changed colours see Nos. 2552/5.

1985. Centenary of Publication of Sanders' "Reichenbachia" (2nd issue). As T **331** showing orchids. Multicoloured.

1551	25c. Plate No. 52 (Series 1)	1·75	25
1763	55c. Plate No. 9 (Series 1)	55	10
1764	55c. Plate No. 22 (Series 1)	55	10
1765	55c. Plate No. 49 (Series 1)	55	10
1766	55c. Plate No. 64 (Series 1)	55	10
1556	60c. Plate No. 44 (Series 1)	70	35
1557	60c. Plate No. 47 (Series 1)	70	35
1558	120c. Plate No. 36 (Series 1)	2·00	55
1559	130c. Plate No. 16 (Series 1)	2·00	55
1560	130c. Plate No. 38 (Series 1)	2·00	55
1561	150c. Plate No. 32 (Series 1)	2·00	55
1562	150c. Plate No. 34 (Series 1)	2·00	55
1563	150c. Plate No. 35 (Series 1)	2·00	55
1564	150c. Plate No. 41 (Series 1)	2·00	55
1565	150c. Plate No. 48 (Series 1)	2·00	55
1566	150c. Plate No. 62 (Series 1)	2·00	55

1985. Signing of Guyana–Libya Friendship Treaty. No. 621 surch **Guyana/Libya Friendship 1985 150.**

1567	**149** 150c. on 10c. mult	9·00	2·75

1985. Namibia Day. No. 636 surch **150.**

1568	150c. on 35c. Unveiling of monument	2·75	55

1985. World Cup Football Championship, Mexico (1986) (1st issue). No. F2 surch **Mexico 1986 275.**

1569	275c. on 3c. Hanging heliconia	12·00	2·50

See also No. 1727.

1985. 85th Birthday of Queen Elizabeth the Queen Mother (2nd issue). Sheet 120 × 129 mm containing No. 1529 × 4 optd as No. **MS**1539, each stamp surch **200.**

MS1570	200c. on 130c. × 4 Plate No. 20 (Series 1)	18·00	7·00

1985. Centenary of Publication of Sanders' "Reichenbachia" (3rd issue). As T **331** showing orchids. Multicoloured.

1571	25c. Plate No. 8 (Series 1)	2·00	20
1572	25c. Plate No. 23 (Series 1)	2·00	20
1573	25c. Plate No. 51 (Series 1)	2·00	20
1574	25c. Plate No. 61 (Series 1)	2·00	20
1575	25c. Plate No. 63 (Series 1)	2·00	20
1576	25c. Plate No. 70 (Series 1)	2·00	20
1577	25c. Plate No. 72 (Series 1)	2·00	20
1578	120c. Plate No. 1 (Series 1) (horiz)	2·00	55
1579	120c. Plate No. 11 (Series 1) (horiz)	2·00	55
1580	120c. Plate No. 28 (Series 1) (horiz)	2·00	55
1767	150c. Plate No. 40 (Series 1) (horiz)	50	20
1768	150c. Plate No. 42 (Series 1) (horiz)	50	20
1769	150c. Plate No. 45 (Series 1) (horiz)	50	20
1584	200c. Plate No. 14 (Series 1)	2·25	80
1585	200c. Plate No. 21 (Series 1) (horiz)	2·25	80
1770	200c. Plate No. 43 (Series 1) (horiz)	55	30

1985. 30th Anniv of Commonwealth Caribbean Medical Research Council. Nos. 819, 871, 874, 928 and 1014 optd **1955–1985** or surch also.

1587	– 60c. mult (No. 819)	20	25
1588	– 60c. mult (No. 1014)	20	25
1589	**176** 120c. on 110c. on 10c. multicoloured (No. 871)	40	45
1590	– 120c. on 110c. on $3 mult (No. 874)	40	45
1592	– 120c. on 210c. on $3 mult (No. 928)	40	45

1985. 20th Anniv of Guyana Defence Force. No. 856 surch **1965-1985.**

1593	25c. on $1.10 on $3 W.O. and N.C.O; Guyana Defence Force, 1966	1·00	10
1594	225c. on $1.10 on $3 W.O. and N.C.O; Guyana Defence Force, 1966	2·50	1·25

1985. Fire Prevention. Nos. 678 and 680 optd **1985** and surch.

1595	25c. on 40c. Fire engine, 1977	12·00	20
1596	320c. on 15c. Steam engine, circa 1860	23·00	5·00

1985. Centenary of Publication of Sanders' "Reichenbachia" (4th issue). As T **331**. Mult.

1597	60c. Plate No. 55 (Series 1)	1·50	30

1985. Columbus Day. Unissued value as T **331** surch **350 CRISTOBAL COLON 1492-1992.** Mult.

1598	350c. on 120c. Plate No. 65 (Series 1)	6·50	3·25

1985. 20th Death Anniv of Sir Winston Churchill. No. 707 optd **SIR WINSTON CHURCHILL 1965-1985.**

1599	$2 "Morpho rhetenor" (female)	14·00	3·00

1985. 35th Anniv of International Commission of Irrigation and Drainage. No. 625 with unissued surcharge further surch **1950-1985.**

1600	**150** 25c. on 110c. on 10c. multicoloured	30	10
1601	200c. on 110c. on 10c. multicoloured	1·25	85

1985. 40th Anniv of U.N.O. Nos. 714/16, 800 and O19 optd **United Nations 1945-1985.**

1602	30c. multicoloured (No. 714)	1·75	10
1603	50c. multicoloured (No. 715)	1·75	20
1604	100c. on $3 mult (No. O19)	1·50	40
1605	225c. on 220c. on $3 mult (No. 800)	15·00	75
1606	$3 multicoloured (No. 716)	3·50	2·00

1985. Nos. 551/3, O14/15, O18, O21, OP1/2 and F7 optd **POSTAGE.**

1607	30c. on $2 "Norantea guianensis" (No. O18)	40	10
1608	40c. Tiger beard (No. 551)	42·00	80
1609	50c. "Guzmania lingulata" (No. 552)	40	20
1610	50c. "Guzmania lingulata" (No. O14)	40	20
1611	60c. Soldier's cap (No. 553)	3·25	25
1612	60c. Soldier's cap (No. O15)	3·00	25
1613	60c. Soldier's cap (No. F7)	1·75	25
1614	$10 "Elbella patrobas" (No. O21)	27·00	8·00
1615	$15 on $1 "Chelonanthus uliginoides" (No. OP1)	8·00	9·50
1616	$20 on $1 "Chelonanthus uliginoides" (No. OP2)	9·00	11·00

1985. Deepavali Festival. Nos. 542/3 surch **Deepavali 1985.**

1617	25c. on 2c. Type **132**	75	10
1618	150c. on 1c. Pitcher plant of Mt. Roraima	3·00	1·25

1985. Christmas. Sheet 120 × 129 mm containing No. 1764 × 4 optd **Christmas 1985.**

MS1619	55c. × 4 Plate No. 22 (Series 1), each with a different overprint (Type **350**, **Happy New Year**, **Merry Christmas** or **Happy Holidays**)	7·00	4·00

1985. Centenary of Publication of Sanders' "Reichenbachia" (5th issue). As T **331** showing orchids. Multicoloured.

1620	25c. Plate No. 59 (Series 1)	1·00	20
1771	30c. Plate No. 53 (Series 1)	30	10
1622	60c. Plate No. 57 (Series 1) (horiz)	1·25	35
1623	60c. Plate No. 73 (Series 1) (horiz)	1·25	35
1624	60c. Plate No. 75 (Series 1) (horiz)	1·25	35
1772	75c. Plate No. 55 (Series 1)	35	15
1773	100c. Plate No. 65 (Series 1)	35	15
1627	120c. Plate No. 37 (Series 1)	2·00	55
1628	120c. Plate No. 46 (Series 1)	2·00	55
1629	120c. Plate No. 56 (Series 1)	2·00	55
1630	120c. Plate No. 58 (Series 1)	2·00	55
1631	120c. Plate No. 67 (Series 1)	2·00	55
1632	130c. Plate No. 66 (Series 1)	2·00	65
1633	150c. Plate No. 26 (Series 1)	2·25	75
1634	200c. Plate No. 33 (Series 1) (horiz)	2·50	85
1774	225c. Plate No. 24 (Series 1)	50	35

The 30, 75, 100 and 225c. values have "GUYANA" in blue.

351 Clive Lloyd (cricketer)

1985. Clive Lloyd's Testimonial Year. Multicoloured.
1636 25c. Type **351** 40 60
1637 25c. Clive Lloyd, bat and wicket 40 60
1638 25c. Cricket equipment . . . 40 60
1639 60c. As No. 1638 (25 × 33 mm) 40 40
1640 $1.30 As No. 1637 (25 × 33 mm) 40 85
1641 $2.25 Type **351** (25 × 33 mm) . . . . . . 40 1·25
1642 $3.50 Clive Lloyd with the Prudential Cup (36 × 56 mm) . . . . . . 45 1·75

1985. Wildlife Protection. Nos. 756/67 optd **1985**.
1643 30c. Type **178** 75 75
1644 30c. Red howler 75 75
1645 30c. Common squirrel-monkey 75 75
1646 30c. Two-toed sloth 75 75
1647 30c. Brazilian tapir 75 75
1648 30c. Collared peccary . . . 75 75
1649 30c. Six-banded armadillo 75 75
1650 30c. Tamandua 75 75
1651 30c. Giant anteater 75 75
1652 30c. Murine opossum . . . 75 75
1653 30c. Brown four-eyed opossum 75 75
1654 30c. Brazilian agouti 75 75

1985. No. 847 surch **20**.
1655 20c. on 12c. on 12c. on 6c. Black acara ("Patua") . . 5·00 15

1986. Centenary of the Appearance of "Reichenbachia" Volume 1. Nos. 1768 and 1770 optd **REICHENBACHIA 1886-1986**.
1657 150c. Plate No. 42 (Series 1) 4·00 70
1658 200c. Plate No. 43 (Series 1) 4·00 85

1986. Republic Day. Nos. 1108/9 and 1052 optd **Republic Day 1986** or surch also.
1659 25c. As Type **258** 10 10
1660 25c. As No. 1050 . . . . . 10 10
1661 120c. on $6 Presidential standard 40 50
1662 225c. on $6 Presidential standard 70 90

1986. Centenary of Publication of Sanders' "Reichenbachia" (6th issue). As T **331**. Mult.
1663 40c. Plate No. 77 (Series 1) 75 20
1664 45c. Plate No. 54 (Series 1) 75 25
1665 50c. Plate No. 92 (Series 1) 75 25
1666 60c. Plate No. 95 (Series 1) 80 30
1667 75c. Plate No. 5 (Series 1) 85 35
1668 90c. Plate No. 84 (Series 1) 95 40
1669 150c. Plate No. 78 (Series 1) 1·25 60
1670 200c. Plate No. 79 (Series 1) 1·60 80
1671 300c. Plate No. 83 (Series 1) 2·25 1·40
1672 320c. Plate No. 50 (Series 1) 2·25 1·60
1673 360c. Plate No. 85 (Series 1) 2·50 1·75

1986. Easter. No. 481 optd **1986** and surch also.
1674 **111** 25c. on 6c. multicoloured 25 10
1675 50c. on 6c. multicoloured 40 20
1676 100c. on 6c. mult 60 40
1677 200c. on 6c. mult . . . . 1·00 70

1986. 60th Anniv of St. John's Ambulance in Guyana. No. 652 surch **1926 1986 150**.
1678 150c. on 35c. silver, black and green . . . . . . 3·00 55

1986. Centenary of Publication of Sanders' "Reichenbachia" (7th issue). As T **331**. Mult.
1679 25c. Plate No. 71 (Series 1) (horiz) . . . . 1·50 20
1680 120c. Plate No. 69 (Series 1) (horiz) . . . . 2·25 55
1681 150c. Plate No. 87 (Series 1) (horiz) . . . . 2·50 65
1682 225c. Plate No. 60 (Series 1) 2·50 90
1683 350c. Plate No. 94 (Series 1) (horiz) . . . . 2·75 1·75

1986. 60th Birthday of Queen Elizabeth II. No. 1759/60 optd **1926 1986 QUEEN ELIZABETH**.
1684 130c. Plate No. 13 (Series 1) 3·50 1·25
MS1685 100 × 126 mm. 130c. on 130c., 200c. on 130c., 260c. on 130c., 330c. on 130c., Plate No. 6 (Series 1) . . . . 7·50 7·50
The original face values on No. **MS**1685 are obliterated by a floral pattern.

1986. Wildlife Protection. Nos. 685, 739/44 and 993/8 surch **Protect the** and value.
1686 60c. on 35c. Type **174** . . 35 35
1687 60c. on 35c. Trahira ("Haimara") 35 35
1688 60c. on 35c. Electric eel . . 35 35
1689 60c. on 35c. Golden rivulus 35 35
1690 60c. on 35c. Golden pencilfish 35 35
1691 60c. on 35c. Four-eyed fish 35 35
1691a 60c. on 35c. Red piranha ("Pirai") . . . . 9·50 2·75
1691b 60c. on 35c. Smoking hassar . . . . 9·50 2·75
1691c 60c. on 35c. Manta . . . . 9·50 2·75
1691d 60c. on 35c. Festive cichlid ("Flying patwa") . . . . 9·50 2·75
1691e 60c. on 35c. Arapaima . . 9·50 2·75
1691f 60c. on 35c. Peacock cichlid ("Lukanani") . . 9·50 2·75
1692 $6 on 8c. Type **163** . . . . 3·00 2·75

1986. No. 799 surch **600**.
1693 600c. on 720c. on 60c. Soldier's cap . . . . . . 17·00 2·00

1986. 125th Anniv of British Guiana Post Office (2nd issue). No. 702a surch **25** and names of postal agencies opened between 1860 and 1880.
1694 25c. on 30c. mult (surch **Abary**) . . . . 1·00 1·00
1695 25c. on 30c. multicoloured (surch **Anna Regina**) . . . 1·00 1·00
1696 25c. on 30c. multicoloured (surch **Aurora**) . . . . . 1·00 1·00
1697 25c. on 30c. multicoloured (surch **Bartica Grove**) . . 1·00 1·00
1698 25c. on 30c. multicoloured (surch **Bel Air**) . . . . . 1·00 1·00
1699 25c. on 30c. multicoloured (surch **Belle Plaine**) . . . 1·00 1·00
1700 25c. on 30c. multicoloured (surch **Clonbrook**) . . . . 1·00 1·00
1701 25c. on 30c. multicoloured (surch **T.P.O. Dem. Railway**) . . . . 1·00 1·00
1702 25c. on 30c. multicoloured (surch **Enmore**) . . . . . 1·00 1·00
1703 25c. on 30c. multicoloured (surch **Fredericksburg**) . . 1·00 1·00
1704 25c. on 30c. multicoloured (surch **Good Success**) . . 1·00 1·00
1705 25c. on 30c. mult (surch **1986**) . . . . 1·00 1·00
1706 25c. on 30c. multicoloured (surch **Mariabba**) . . . . 1·00 1·00
1707 25c. on 30c. multicoloured (surch **Massaruni**) . . . . 1·00 1·00
1708 25c. on 30c. mult (surch **Nigg**) . . . . 1·00 1·00
1709 25c. on 30c. multicoloured (surch **No. 50**) . . . . . 1·00 1·00
1710 25c. on 30c. multicoloured (surch **No. 63 Benab**) . . 1·00 1·00
1711 25c. on 30c. multicoloured (surch **Philadelphia**) . . . 1·00 1·00
1712 25c. on 30c. multicoloured (surch **Sisters**) . . . . . 1·00 1·00
1713 25c. on 30c. multicoloured (surch **Skeldon**) . . . . . 1·00 1·00
1714 25c. on 30c. multicoloured (surch **Suddie**) . . . . . 1·00 1·00
1715 25c. on 30c. multicoloured (surch **Taymouth Manor**) 1·00 1·00
1716 25c. on 30c. mult (surch **Wales**) . . . . 1·00 1·00
1717 25c. on 30c. mult (surch **Whim**) . . . . 1·00 1·00

1986. 20th Anniv of Independence. (a) No. 332 of British Guiana surch **GUYANA INDEPENDENCE 1966-1986**, Nos. 424 and 435 of Guyana surch **1986** and No. 656 surch **25**.
1718 25c. on 2c. green (No. 332) 15 10
1719 25c. on 35c. mult (No. 656) 15 10
1720 60c. on 2c. green (No. 332) 25 10
1721 120c. on 6c. green (No. 424) 40 20
1722 130c. on 24c. black and orange (No. 435) . . . . 6·50 45

(b) Nos. 1188/91 surch **INDEPENDENCE 1966-1986**.
1723 **277** 25c. on 120c. brown, black and blue (No. 1188) 25 20
1724 – 25c. on 130c. red, black and blue (No. 1189) 25 20
1725 – 25c. on 150c. violet and blue (No. 1190) . . . 25 20
1726 – 225c. on 200c. green, black and blue (No. 1191) 65 60

1986. World Cup Football Championship, Mexico (2nd issue). No. 544 surch **MEXICO 1986 225**.
1727 225c. on 3c. Hanging heliconia . . . . 16·00 2·50

1986. CARICOM Day. No. 705a optd **CARICOM DAY 1986**.
1728 60c. "Papilio androgeus" . . 10·00 60

1986. CARICOM Heads of Government Conference, Georgetown. Nos. 544 and 601 surch **CARICOM HEADS OF GOV'T CONFERENCE JULY 1986** and value.
1729 25c. on 8c. on 6c. Cannon-ball tree . . . . 2·50 20
1730 60c. on 3c. Hanging heliconia . . . . 3·00 40

1986. Centenary of Publication of Sanders' "Reichenbachia" (8th issue). As T **331**. Mult.
1731 30c. Plate No. 86 (Series 1) 1·25 15
1732 55c. Plate No. 17 (Series 1) 50 20
1733 60c. Plate No. 93 (Series 1) 50 20
1734 100c. Plate No. 68 (Series 1) 2·00 20
1735 130c. Plate No. 91 (Series 1) 2·25 30
1736 250c. Plate No. 74 (Series 1) 75 75
1737 260c. Plate No. 39 (Series 1) 75 75
1738 375c. Plate No. 90 (Series 1) 3·75 1·25

1986. International Peace Year. Nos. 542 and 546 surch **INT. YEAR OF PEACE** and value.
1739 25c. on 1c. Pitcher plant of Mt. Roraima 60 40
1740 60c. on 6c. Cannon-ball tree 1·25 1·25
1741 120c. on 6c. Cannon-ball tree . . . . 1·25 1·25
1742 130c. on 6c. Cannon-ball tree . . . . 1·25 1·25
1743 150c. on 6c. Cannon-ball tree . . . . 1·25 1·25

363 Halley's Comet and British Guiana 1907 2c. Stamp

1986. Appearance of Halley's Comet.
1744 **363** 320c. red, black and lilac 40 65
1745 – 320c. multicoloured . . . 40 65
MS1746 76 × 50 mm. Nos. 1744/5. Imperf . . . . 1·50 1·25
DESIGN: No. 1745, Guyana 1985 320c. scarlet macaw stamp.

1986. Centenary of Publication of Sanders' "Reichenbachia" (9th issue). As T **331**. Mult.
1747 40c. Plate No. 96 (Series 1) 2·00 15
1748 45c. Plate No. 81 (Series 1) 30 15
1749 90c. Plate No. 89 (Series 1) 50 20
1750 100c. Plate No. 88 (Series 1) 3·50 20
1751 150c. Plate No. 76 (Series 1) 3·50 35
1752 180c. Plate No. 15 (Series 1) 50 40
1753 320c. Plate No. 82 (Series 1) 60 90
1754 330c. Plate No. 80 (Series 1) 3·50 1·25

1986. No. 489 surch **20**.
1755 20c. on 6c. Patua . . . . . 7·00 15

1986. 50th Anniv of Guyana United Sadr Islamic Association. Nos. 469/70 optd **GUSIA 1936-1986**, No. 1757 surch also.
1756 **105** 25c. black, gold and lilac 3·50 25
1757 $1.50 on 6c. black, gold and flesh . . . . . . 7·00 2·25

1986. Regional Pharmacy Conference. No. 545 surch **REGIONAL PHARMACY CONFERENCE 1986 130**.
1758 130c. on 5c. Annatto tree 8·00 65

1986. Centenary of Publication of Sanders' "Reichenbachia" (10th issue). As T **331**. Mult.
1809 30c. Plate No. 30 (Series 2) 1·25 15
1810 45c. Plate No. 21 (Series 2) (horiz) 50 15
1811 75c. Plate No. 8 (Series 2) 50 15
1812 80c. Plate No. 42 (Series 2) (horiz) 50 15
1813 90c. Plate No. 4 (Series 2) 55 25
1814 130c. Plate No. 38 (Series 2) 3·00 35
1815 160c. Plate No. 5 (Series 2) (horiz) . . . . 3·00 40
1816 200c. Plate No. 9 (Series 2) 75 50
1817 320c. Plate No. 12 (Series 2) 1·75 90
1818 350c. Plate No. 29 (Series 2) (horiz) . . . . 2·00 90
1819 360c. Plate No. 34 (Series 2) 5·50 90

1986. 20th Anniv of Independence (2nd issue). As T **332** but additionally inscr "1966–1986" at foot.
1820 25c. multicoloured . . . . . 1·50 25

1986. Centenary of Publication of Sanders' "Reichenbachia" (11th issue). Design as No. 1735, but with different face value. Mult.
1822 40c. Plate No. 91 (Series 1) 1·00 15

1986. Nos. 1361/84 surch **120**.
1823 120c. on 30c. mult (No. 1361) . . . . 2·00 1·50
1824 120c. on 30c. mult (No. 1362) . . . . 2·00 1·50
1825 120c. on 30c. mult (No. 1363) . . . . 2·00 1·50
1826 120c. on 30c. mult (No. 1364) . . . . 2·00 1·50
1827 120c. on 30c. mult (No. 1365) . . . . 2·00 1·50
1828 120c. on 30c. mult (No. 1366) . . . . 2·00 1·50
1829 120c. on 30c. mult (No. 1367) . . . . 2·00 1·50
1830 120c. on 30c. mult (No. 1368) . . . . 2·00 1·50
1831 120c. on 30c. mult (No. 1369) . . . . 2·00 1·50
1832 120c. on 30c. mult (No. 1370) . . . . 2·00 1·50
1833 120c. on 30c. mult (No. 1371) . . . . 2·00 1·50
1834 120c. on 30c. mult (No. 1372) . . . . 2·00 1·50
1835 120c. on 30c. mult (No. 1373) . . . . 2·00 1·50
1836 120c. on 30c. mult (No. 1374) . . . . 2·00 1·50
1837 120c. on 30c. mult (No. 1375) . . . . 2·00 1·50
1838 120c. on 30c. mult (No. 1376) . . . . 2·00 1·50
1839 120c. on 30c. mult (No. 1377) . . . . 2·00 1·50
1840 120c. on 30c. mult (No. 1378) . . . . 2·00 1·50
1841 120c. on 30c. mult (No. 1379) . . . . 2·00 1·50
1842 120c. on 30c. mult (No. 1380) . . . . 2·00 1·50
1843 120c. on 30c. mult (No. 1381) . . . . 2·00 1·50
1844 120c. on 30c. mult (No. 1382) . . . . 2·00 1·50
1845 120c. on 30c. mult (No. 1383) . . . . 2·00 1·50
1846 120c. on 30c. mult (No. 1384) . . . . 2·00 1·50

1986. 12th World Orchid Conference, Tokyo (1st issue). Unissued design as No. 1731, but with different face value, surch **12th World Orchid Conference TOKYO JAPAN MARCH 1987 650**.
1847 650c. on 40c. Plate No. 86 (Series 1) . . . . 15·00 4·75
No. 1847 is inscribed "ONTOGLOSSUM TRIUMPHANS" in error.
See also No. 2138.

1986. Columbus Day. Unissued design as No. 1774, but with different face value, surch **1492-1992 CHRISTOPHER COLUMBUS 320**.
1864 320c. on 150c. Plate No. 24 (Series 1) . . . . 5·50 2·00

1986. International Food Day. Nos. 1170/1 further surch **1986** and value.
1866 50c. on 30c. on 1c. Type **87** 3·25 15
1867 225c. on $2.60 on 3c. Peacock cichlid ("Lukunani") . . . . . . 9·50 2·00

1986. Centenary of Publication of Sanders' "Reichenbachia" (12th issue). As T **331**, one as No. 1731 with different face value. Mult.
1868 40c. Plate No. 86 (Series 1) 75 15
1869 90c. Plate No. 10 (Series 2) 1·00 30

1986. Air. 40th Annivs of UNICEF and UNESCO No. 706 surch.
1870 120c. on $1 "Agrias claudina" (surch **UNICEF 1946-1986 AIR 120**) . . . 6·50 6·50
1871 120c. on $1 "Agrias claudina" (surch **UNESCO 1946-1986 AIR 120**) . . . . 6·50 6·50

1986. Centenary of Publication of Sanders' "Reichenbachia" (13th issue). As T **331**. Mult.
1872 45c. Plate No. 17 (Series 2) 40 15
1873 50c. Plate No. 33 (Series 2) 40 15
1874 60c. Plate No. 27 (Series 2) 60 15
1875 75c. Plate No. 56 (Series 2) 70 25
1876 85c. Plate No. 45 (Series 2) 6·50 40
1877 90c. Plate No. 13 (Series 2) 90 30
1878 200c. Plate No. 44 (Series 2) 1·25 55
1879 300c. Plate No. 50 (Series 2) 1·75 75
1880 320c. Plate No. 10 (Series 2) 1·75 90
1881 390c. Plate No. 6 (Series 2) 1·75 1·25

1986. Deepavali Festival. Nos. 543 and 601 surch **Deepavali 1986** and value.
1882 25c. on 2c. Type **132** . . . 2·00 10
1883 200c. on 8c. on 6c. Cannon-ball tree . . . . 7·00 1·75

1986. Centenary of Publication of Sanders' "Reichenbachia" (14th issue). As T **331**, two as Nos. 1732 and 1734 with different face values. Multicoloured.
1884 40c. Plate No. 68 (Series 1) 1·25 15
1885 80c. Plate No. 17 (Series 1) 2·00 25
1886 200c. Plate No. 2 (Series 2) 1·40 60
1887 225c. Plate No. 24 (Series 2) 1·40 70

1986. Christmas. No. 489 surch **CHRISTMAS 1986 20**.
1888 20c. on 6c. Black acara ("Patua") . . . . 3·25 10
MS1889 215 × 75 mm. 120c. on 60c. × 5 Nos. 1425/9 . . . . . 7·00 7·00

1986. Wildlife Protection. Nos. 756/67 optd **1986**.
1894 30c. Type **178** . . . . . . 1·60 1·60
1895 30c. Red howler . . . . . 1·60 1·60
1896 30c. Common squirrel-monkey . . . . 1·60 1·60
1897 30c. Two-toed sloth . . . . 1·60 1·60
1898 30c. Brazilian tapir . . . . 1·60 1·60
1899 30c. Collared peccary . . . 1·60 1·60
1900 30c. Six-banded armadillo 1·60 1·60
1901 30c. Tamandua . . . . . . 1·60 1·60
1902 30c. Giant anteater . . . . 1·60 1·60
1903 30c. Murine opossum . . . 1·60 1·60
1904 30c. Brown four-eyed opossum . . . . 1·60 1·60
1905 30c. Brazilian agouti . . . . 1·60 1·60

1986. No. 1642 surch **$15**.
1906 $15 on $3.50 Clive Lloyd with Prudential Cup . . . 38·00 19·00

1986. Centenary of Publication of Sanders' "Reichenbachia" (15th issue). Design as No. 1877, but with different face value. Mult.
1907 50c. Plate No. 13 (Series 2) 65 15

375 Memorial

1986. President Burnham Commemoration. Multicoloured.
1908 25c. Type **375** 10 10
1909 120c. Map of Guyana and flags 20 20

1910 130c. Parliament Buildings and mace 20 20
1911 $6 L. F. Burnham and Georgetown mayoral chain (vert) 60 1·25

1986. Centenary of Publication of Sanders' "Reichenbachia" (16th issue). As Nos. 1765/6, 1874 and 1887 but with different face values. Multicoloured.
1912 50c. Plate No. 49 (Series 1) 75 20
1913 50c. Plate No. 64 (Series 1) 75 20
1914 85c. Plate No. 24 (Series 2) 75 40
1915 90c. Plate No. 27 (Series 2) 4·50 70

1986. Centenary of Publication of Sanders' "Reichenbachia" (17th issue). As T **331**. Mult.
1916 25c. Plate No. 20 (Series 2) 20 20
1917 40c. Plate No. 7 (Series 2) 45 15
1918 85c. Plate No. 15 (Series 2) 3·00 30
1919 90c. Plate No. 3 (Series 2) 60 20
1920 120c. Plate No. 14 (Series 2) 60 30
1921 130c. Plate No. 32 (Series 2) 60 30
1922 150c. Plate No. 22 (Series 2) 70 45
1923 320c. Plate No. 18 (Series 2) 90 75
1924 330c. Plate No. 28 (Series 2) 90 90

1987. Centenary of Publication of Sanders' "Reichenbachia" (18th issue). As Nos. 1772, 1876, 1886, 1918 and 1923 but with different face values. Multicoloured.
1925 35c. Plate No. 45 (Series 2) 40 15
1926 50c. Plate No. 15 (Series 2) 40 20
1927 50c. Plate No. 55 (Series 1) 40 20
1928 85c. Plate No. 18 (Series 2) 5·50 45
1929 90c. Plate No. 2 (Series 2) 50 30

1987. 10th Anniv of Guyana Post Office Corporation (1st issue). Unissued designs as Nos. 1771 and 1774, but with different face values, surch or optd **G P O C 1977 1987**.
1930 $2.25 Plate No. 53 (Series 1) 3·25 50
1931 $10 on 150c. Plate No. 24 (Series 1) 8·75 9·00
See also Nos. 2074/80.

1987. Various "Reichenbachia" issues surch.
2375 120c. on 40c. Plate No. 91 (Series 1) (No. 1822) 60 40
2380 120c. on 40c. Plate No. 90 (Series 1) 60 40
2387 120c. on 50c. Plate No. 9 (Series 1) 60 40
1994 120c. on 50c. Plate No. 49 (Series 1) (No. 1912) 50 40
1995 120c. on 50c. Plate No. 64 (Series 1) (No. 1913) 50 40
2388 120c. on 50c. Plate No. 22 (Series 1) 60 40
2389 120c. on 50c. Plate No. 3 (Series 2) 60 40
2390 120c. on 50c. Plate No. 6 (Series 2) 60 40
2391 120c. on 50c. Plate No. 20 (Series 2) 60 40
2392 120c. on 50c. Plate No. 32 (Series 2) 60 40
2019 120c. on 50c. Plate No. 24 (Series 1) 50 40
2020 120c. on 50c. Plate No. 53 (Series 1) 50 40
2021 120c. on 50c. Plate No. 65 (Series 1) 50 40
1980 120c. on 55c. Plate No. 9 (Series 1) (No. 1763) 50 40
2003 120c. on 55c. Plate No. 49 (Series 1) (No. 1765) 50 40
1981 120c. on 55c. Plate No. 64 (Series 1) (No. 1766) 50 30
2006 120c. on 55c. Plate No. 22 (Series 1) (No. 1764) 50 40
2009 120c. on 55c. Plate No. 15 (Series 1) 50 40
2010 120c. on 55c. Plate No. 81 (Series 1) 50 40
2011 120c. on 55c. Plate No. 82 (Series 1) 50 40
2012 120c. on 55c. Plate No. 89 (Series 1) 50 40
2394 120c. on 60c. Plate No. 2 (Series 1) (No. 1519) 60 30
2027 120c. on 60c. Plate No. 10 (Series 1) (No. 1521) 50 40
2028 120c. on 60c. Plate No. 19 (Series 1) (No. 1522) 50 40
2029 120c. on 60c. Plate No. 31 (Series 1) (No. 1523) 50 40
2030 120c. on 60c. Plate No. 5 (Series 1) 50 40
2403 120c. on 60c. Plate No. 50 (Series 1) 60 40
2404 120c. on 60c. Plate No. 54 (Series 1) 60 40
2405 120c. on 60c. Plate No. 69 (Series 1) 60 40
2034 120c. on 60c. Plate No. 71 (Series 1) 50 40
2406 120c. on 60c. Plate No. 79 (Series 1) 60 40
2036 120c. on 60c. Plate No. 87 (Series 1) 50 40
2407 120c. on 60c. Plate No. 94 (Series 1) 60 40
2038 120c. on 75c. Plate No. 60 (Series 1) 50 40
2039 120c. on 75c. Plate No. 83 (Series 1) 50 40
2040 120c. on 75c. Plate No. 92 (Series 1) 50 40
2041 120c. on 75c. Plate No. 95 (Series 1) 50 40
1933 200c. on 25c. Plate No. 8 (Series 1) (No. 1571) 60 50
1934 200c. on 25c. Plate No. 51 (Series 1) (No. 1573) 60 50
1949 200c. on 25c. Plate No. 52 (Series 1) (No. 1551) 60 50
1951 200c. on 25c. Plate No. 72 (Series 1) (No. 1577) 60 50
1952 200c. on 25c. Plate No. 71 (Series 1) (No. 1679) 60 50
1953 200c. on 30c. Plate No. 86 (Series 1) (No. 1731) 60 50
1954 200c. on 30c. Plate No. 53 (Series 1) (No. 1771) 60 50
1932 200c. on 40c. Plate No. 90 (Series 1) 60 50
1937 200c. on 40c. Plate No. 68 (Series 1) (No. 1884) 60 50
1955 200c. on 40c. Plate No. 77 (Series 1) (No. 1663) 60 50
1956 200c. on 40c. Plate No. 86 (Series 1) (No. 1868) 60 50
1957 200c. on 45c. Plate No. 81 (Series 1) (No. 1748) 60 50
1958 200c. on 45c. Plate No. 77 (Series 1) 60 50
1959 200c. on 45c. Plate No. 78 (Series 1) 60 50
1960 200c. on 45c. Plate No. 85 (Series 1) 60 50
2044 200c. on 45c. Plate No. 84 (Series 1) 50 40
1939 200c. on 50c. Plate No. 92 (Series 1) (No. 1665) 60 50
1940 200c. on 50c. Plate No. 22 (Series 1) 60 50
1961 200c. on 50c. Plate No. 24 (Series 1) 60 50
1962 200c. on 50c. Plate No. 53 (Series 1) 60 50
1963 200c. on 50c. Plate No. 65 (Series 1) 60 50
2046 200c. on 50c. Plate No. 55 (Series 1) (No. 1927) 90 50
1941 200c. on 55c. Plate No. 22 (Series 1) (No. 1764) 60 50
1964 200c. on 55c. Plate No. 49 (Series 1) (No. 1765) 60 50
1965 200c. on 55c. Plate No. 17 (Series 1) (No. 1732) 60 50
2050 200c. on 55c. Plate No. 15 (Series 1) 2·50 50
2051 200c. on 55c. Plate No. 81 (Series 1) 2·50 50
2052 200c. on 55c. Plate No. 82 (Series 1) 7·00 50
2053 200c. on 55c. Plate No. 89 (Series 1) 2·50 50
1942 200c. on 60c. Plate No. 5 (Series 1) 60 50
1967 200c. on 60c. Plate No. 7 (Series 1) (No. 1520) 60 50
1968 200c. on 60c. Plate No. 10 (Series 1) (No. 1521) 60 50
1969 200c. on 60c. Plate No. 19 (Series 1) (No. 1522) 60 50
1970 200c. on 60c. Plate No. 31 (Series 1) (No. 1523) 60 50
1971 200c. on 60c. Plate No. 44 (Series 1) (No. 1556) 60 50
1972 200c. on 60c. Plate No. 47 (Series 1) (No. 1557) 60 50
1973 200c. on 60c. Plate No. 57 (Series 1) (No. 1622) 60 50
1974 200c. on 60c. Plate No. 73 (Series 1) (No. 1623) 60 50
1975 200c. on 60c. Plate No. 75 (Series 1) (No. 1624) 60 50
1976 200c. on 60c. Plate No. 71 (Series 1) 60 50
1977 200c. on 60c. Plate No. 87 (Series 1) 60 50
1943 200c. on 75c. Plate No. 5 (Series 1) (No. 1667) 60 50
1944 200c. on 75c. Plate No. 60 (Series 1) 60 50
1945 200c. on 75c. Plate No. 92 (Series 1) 60 50
1946 200c. on 85c. Plate No. 18 (Series 2) (No. 1928) 60 50
1947 200c. on 375c. Plate No. 90 (Series 1) (No. 1738) 60 50
1987 225c. on 40c. Plate No. 91 (Series 1) (No. 1822) 70 60
1988 225c. on 40c. Plate No. 90 (Series 1) 70 60
2055 225c. on 40c. Plate No. 86 (Series 1) (No. 1868) 1·75 60
2056 225c. on 40c. Plate No. 68 (Series 1) (No. 1884) 90 60
1988a 225c. on 50c. Plate No. 92 (Series 1) (No. 1665) 12·00 3·25
1989 225c. on 50c. Plate No. 22 (Series 1) 70 60
1990 225c. on 60c. Plate No. 55 (Series 1) (No. 1597) 70 60
1990a 225c. on 60c. Plate No. 95 (Series 1) (No. 1666) 12·00 3·25
1991 225c. on 60c. Plate No. 93 (Series 1) (No. 1733) 70 60
2058 225c. on 65c. Plate No. 76 (Series 1) 90 60
2059 225c. on 65c. Plate No. 80 (Series 1) 90 60
2060 225c. on 65c. Plate No. 88 (Series 1) 90 60
2061 225c. on 65c. Plate No. 96 (Series 1) 90 60
1992 225c. on 80c. Plate No. 93 (Series 1) 70 60
1978 225c. on 90c. Plate No. 89 (Series 1) (No. 1749) 65 55
1993 225c. on 150c. Plate No. 42 (Series 1) (No. 1657) 70 60
2062 600c. on 80c. Plate No. 17 (Series 1) (No. 1885) 1·50 1·75
2063 600c. on 80c. Plate No. 39 (Series 1) 1·50 1·75
2064 600c. on 80c. Plate No. 74 (Series 1) 1·50 1·75
2065 600c. on 80c. Plate No. 93 (Series 1) 1·50 1·75

1987. Nos. 1518 and 1572 surch **TWO DOLLARS**.
1935 $2 on 25c. Plate No. 12 (Series 1) (No. 1518) 1·00 60
1936 $2 on 25c. Plate No. 23 (Series 1) (No. 1572) 1·00 60

1987. Various "Reichenbachia" issues surch **1987**.
1983 $10 on 25c. Plate No. 53 (Series 1) 2·50 2·75
1984 $12 on 80c. Plate No. 74 (Series 1) 2·75 3·00
1985 $15 on 80c. Plate No. 39 (Series 1) 3·25 3·75
1986 $25 on 25c. Plate No. 53 (Series 1) 5·50 6·00

1987. Centenary of Publication of Sanders' "Reichenbachia" (19th issue). Multicoloured.
2066 180c. Plate 41 (Series 2) 75 40
2067 230c. Plate 25 (Series 2) 80 50
2068 300c. Plate 85 (Series 2) 5·00 90
2069 330c. Plate 82 (Series 2) 5·50 1·00
2070 425c. Plate 87 (Series 2) 5·50 1·10
2071 440c. Plate 88 (Series 2) 5·50 1·10
2072 590c. Plate 52 (Series 2) 1·50 1·50
2073 650c. Plate 65 (Series 2) 1·75 1·75

1987. 10th Anniv of Guyana Post Office Corporation (2nd issue). Nos. 543, 545, 548a and 601 surch **Post Office Corp. 1977-1987**.
2074 25c. on 2c. Type **132** 15 10
2075 25c. on 5c. Annatto tree 15 10
2076 25c. on 8c. on 6c. Cannon-ball tree 15 10
2077 25c. on 15c. Christmas orchid 3·75 10
2078 60c. on 15c. Christmas orchid 7·00 15
2079 $1.20 on 2c. Type **132** 75 75
2080 $1.30 on 15c. Christmas orchid 8·00 2·25

1987. No. 1535b surch **1987 200**.
2081 **332** 200c. on 25c. mult 3·00 1·50

1987. Various "Reichenbachia" issues optd **1987**.
2112 120c. Plate No. 1 (Series 1) (No. 1578) 2·50 70
2113 120c. Plate No. 11 (Series 1) (No. 1579) 2·00 70
2114 120c. Plate No. 28 (Series 1) (No. 1580) 2·50 70
2115 120c. Plate No. 37 (Series 1) (No. 1627) 1·40 70
2116 120c. Plate No. 46 (Series 1) (No. 1628) 6·00 70
2117 120c. Plate No. 56 (Series 1) (No. 1629) 2·00 70
2118 120c. Plate No. 58 (Series 1) (No. 1630) 2·00 70
2132 120c. Plate No. 67 (Series 1) (No. 1631) 50 40
2084 130c. Plate No. 3 (Series 1) (No. 1525) 50 40
2093 130c. Plate No. 6 (Series 1) (No. 1759) 50 40
2094 130c. Plate No. 20 (Series 1) (No. 1761) 50 40
2087 130c. Plate No. 18 (Series 1) (No. 1536) 50 40
2088 130c. Plate No. 29 (Series 1) (No. 1537) 50 40
2089 130c. Plate No. 30 (Series 1) (No. 1538) 50 40
2090 130c. Plate No. 16 (Series 1) (No. 1559) 50 40
2091 130c. Plate No. 66 (Series 1) (No. 1632) 50 40
2092 130c. Plate No. 13 (Series 1) (No. 1684) 50 40
2109 130c. Plate No. 91 (Series 1) (No. 1735) 50 40
2111 130c. Plate No. 25 (Series 1) (No. 1762) 50 40
2123 150c. Plate No. 40 (Series 1) (No. 1767) 1·75 70
2124 150c. Plate No. 45 (Series 1) (No. 1769) 1·40 70
2125 150c. Plate No. 42 (Series 1) (No. 1657) 4·00 70
2137 150c. Plate No. 26 (Series 1) (No. 1633) 50 50
2095 200c. Plate No. 4 (Series 1) (No. 1533) 60 50
2096 200c. Plate No. 14 (Series 1) (No. 1584) 60 50
2097 200c. Plate No. 21 (Series 1) (No. 1585) 60 50
2098 200c. Plate No. 33 (Series 1) (No. 1634) 60 50
2099 200c. Plate No. 43 (Series 1) (No. 1658) 60 50
2100 200c. Plate No. 79 (Series 1) (No. 1670) 60 50
2101 200c. Plate No. 9 (Series 2) (No. 1816) 60 50
2102 200c. Plate No. 2 (Series 2) (No. 1886) 60 50
2103 250c. Plate No. 74 (Series 1) (No. 1736) 70 60
2104 260c. Plate No. 39 (Series 1) (No. 1737) 70 60

1987. 12th World Orchid Conference, Tokyo (2nd issue). Nos. 1763 surch **12th World Orchid Conference 650**.
2138 650c. on 55c. Plate No. 9 (Series 1) 8·00 4·50

1987. 125th Anniv of British Guiana Post Office (3rd issue). No. 699 surch **25** and names of postal agencies opened by 1885.
2140 25c. on 10c. multicoloured (surch **AGRICOLA**) 1·50 1·10
2141 25c. on 10c. multicoloured (surch **BAGOTVILLE**) 1·50 1·10
2142 25c. on 10c. multicoloured (surch **BOURDA**) 1·50 1·10
2143 25c. on 10c. multicoloured (surch **BUXTON**) 1·50 1·10
2144 25c. on 10c. multicoloured (surch **CABACABURI**) 1·50 1·10
2145 25c. on 10c. mult (surch **CARMICHAEL STREET**) 1·50 1·10
2146 25c. on 10c. mult (surch **COTTON TREE**) 1·50 1·10
2147 25c. on 10c. multicoloured (surch **DUNOON**) 1·50 1·10
2148 25c. on 10c. multicoloured (surch **FELLOWSHIP**) 1·50 1·10
2149 25c. on 10c. multicoloured (surch **GROVE**) 1·50 1·10
2150 25c. on 10c. multicoloured (surch **HACKNEY**) 1·50 1·10
2151 25c. on 10c. multicoloured (surch **LEONORA**) 1·50 1·10
2152 25c. on 10c. mult (surch **1987**) 1·50 1·10
2153 25c. on 10c. multicoloured (surch **MALLALI**) 1·50 1·10
2154 25c. on 10c. multicoloured (surch **PROVIDENCE**) 1·50 1·10
2155 25c. on 10c. multicoloured (surch **RELIANCE**) 1·50 1·10
2156 25c. on 10c. multicoloured (surch **SPARTA**) 1·50 1·10
2157 25c. on 10c. multicoloured (surch **STEWARTVILLE**) 1·50 1·10
2158 25c. on 10c. multicoloured (surch **TARLOGY**) 1·50 1·10
2159 25c. on 10c. mult (surch **T.P.O. BERBICE RIV.**) 1·50 1·10
2160 25c. on 10c. multicoloured (surch **T.P.O. DEM. RIV.**) 1·50 1·10
2161 25c. on 10c. multicoloured (surch **T.P.O. ESSEO. RIV.**) 1·50 1·10
2162 25c. on 10c. mult (surch **T.P.O. MASSARUNI RIV.**) 1·50 1·10
2163 25c. on 10c. multicoloured (surch **TUSCHEN (De VRIENDEN)**) 1·50 1·10
2164 25c. on 10c. multicoloured (surch **ZORG**) 1·50 1·10

1987. 50th Anniv of First Georgetown to Port-of-Spain Flight by P.A.A. No. 708a optd **28 MARCH 1927 PAA GEO-POS**.
2165 $10 "Elbella patrobas" 20·00 9·50

1987. No. 704 surch **25**.
2166 25c. on 40c. "Morpho rhetenor" (male) 11·00 30

1987. Easter. Nos. 481/2 and 484 optd **1987** or surch also.
2167 **111** 25c. multicoloured 50 10
2168 120c. on 6c. mult 75 20
2169 320c. on 6c. mult 1·25 70
2170 500c. on 40c. mult 1·75 1·25

1987. Centenary of Publication of Sanders' "Reichenbachia" (20th issue). As T **331**. Mult.
2171 240c. Plate No. 47 (Series 2) 80 45
2172 260c. Plate No. 39 (Series 2) 90 55
2173 275c. Plate No. 58 (Series 2) (horiz) 90 55
2174 390c. Plate No. 37 (Series 2) (horiz) 1·10 70
2175 450c. Plate No. 19 (Series 2) (horiz) 1·50 90
2176 460c. Plate No. 54 (Series 2) (horiz) 1·50 90
2177 500c. Plate No. 51 (Series 2) 1·75 1·10
2178 560c. Plate No. 1 (Series 2) 2·00 1·50

1987. No. 706 optd **1987**.
2179 **167** $1 multicoloured 11·00 65

1987. Centenary of Publication of Sanders' "Reichenbachia" (21st issue). As T **331**. Mult.
2180 500c. Plate No. 86 (Series 2) 1·50 1·10
2181 520c. Plate No. 89 (Series 2) 1·50 1·25
2182 $20 Plate No. 83 (Series 2) 4·50 7·00

1987. As T **332** but within frame.
2183 25c. multicoloured 90 50
2184 25c. multicoloured 90 50

No. 2183 has a bird with a short tail (as in Type **332**) in the lower part of the arms; No. 2184 has a bird with crest and long tail.

1987. "Capex '87" International Stamp Exhibition, Toronto. Nos. 1744/5 optd **CAPEX '87**.
2185 **363** 320c. red, black and lilac 1·75 2·00
2186 – 320c. multicoloured . . . 1·75 2·00

1987. Commonwealth Heads of Government Meeting, Vancouver. Nos. 1066/8 further optd **1987**.
2187 $1.20 on 6c. green 75 20
2188 $1.30 on 24c. black orange 7·50 30
2189 $2.40 on 24c. black orange 9·00 2·50

1987. Centenary of Publication of Sanders' "Reichenbachia" (22nd issue). As T **331**. Mult.
2190 400c. Plate No. 80 (Series 2) 1·25 80
2191 480c. Plate No. 77 (Series 2) 1·50 1·00
2192 600c. Plate No. 94 (Series 2) 1·50 1·50
2193 $25 Plate No. 72 (Series 2) 4·50 8·00

396 Steam Locomotive No. 4 "Alexandra"

1987. Guyana Railways.
2194 **396** $1.20 green 25 30
2195 – $1.20 green 25 30
2196 – $1.20 green 25 30
2197 – $1.20 green 25 30
2198 **396** $1.20 purple 25 30
2199 – $1.20 purple 25 30
2200 – $1.20 purple 25 30
2201 – $1.20 purple 25 30
2202 **396** $3.20 blue 80 90
2203 – $3.20 blue 80 90
2204 – $3.20 blue 80 90
2205 – $3.20 blue 80 90
2206 – $3.20 blue 80 90
2207 – $3.30 black 80 90
2208 **396** $3.30 black 80 90
2209 – $3.30 black 80 90
2210 – $3.30 black 80 90
2211 – $3.30 black 80 90
2212 – $10 multicoloured . . . 60 1·50
2213 – $12 multicoloured . . . 60 1·75
DESIGNS—As T **396**: Nos. 2195, 2199, 2203, 2207, Front view of diesel locomotive; Nos. 2196, 2200, 2204, 2210, Steam locomotive with searchlight; Nos. 2197, 2201, 2205, 2209, Side view of diesel locomotive No. 21. (82 × 55 mm): No. 2206, Molasses warehouses and early locomotive; No. 2211, Diesel locomotive and passenger train. (88 × 39 mm): No. 2212, Cattle train and Parika–Rosignol Railway route map; No. 2213, Molasses train and Parika–Rosignol Railway route map.

1987. 50th Anniv of First Flights from Georgetown to Massaruni and Mabaruma. No. 706 optd.
2214 $1 multicoloured (optd **FAIREY NICHOLL 8 AUG 1927 GEO-MAZ**) 9·00 9·00
2215 $1 multicoloured (optd **FAIREY NICHOLL 15 AUG 1927 GEO-MAB**) 9·00 9·00

1987. Centenary of Publication of Sanders' "Reichenbachia" (23rd issue). As T **331**. Mult.
2216 200c. Plate No. 43 (Series 2) 5·00 1·25
2217 200c. Plate No. 48 (Series 2) 5·00 1·25
2218 200c. Plate No. 92 (Series 2) 5·00 1·25

1987. Centenary of Publication of Sanders' "Reichenbachia" (24th issue). No. 2219 surch 600. Multicoloured.
2219 600c. on 900c. Plate No. 74 (Series 2) . . . . 4·50 4·75
2220 900c. Plate No. 74 (Series 2) 4·50 4·75

1987. Columbus Day.
2221 225c. on 350 c on 120c. Plate No. 65 (Series 1) (No. 1598 further surch **225**) . . . . 1·25 50
2222 950c. on 900c. Plate No. 74 (Series 2) (No. 2220 surch **950 CRISTOVAO COLOMBO 1492 – 1992**) 2·25 2·75
2223 950c. on 900c. Plate No. 74 (Series 2) (No. 2220 surch **950 CHRISTOPHE COLOMB 1492 – 1992**) 2·25 2·75
MS2224 76 × 50 mm. $20 on 320c. × 2 Nos. 1744/5 . . . . . 7·00 8·00

1987. Centenary of Publication of Sanders' "Reichenbachia" (25th issue). As T **331**. Mult.
2225 325c. Plate No. 68 (Series 2) (horiz) . . . . 1·50 1·10
2226 420c. Plate No. 95 (Series 2) (horiz) . . . . 1·75 1·75
2227 575c. Plate No. 60 (Series 2) 9·00 4·50

1987. Deepavali Festival. Nos. 544/5 surch **DEEPAVALI 1987** and new value.
2228 25c. on 3c. Hanging heliconia . . . . 1·75 10
2229 $3 on 5c. Annatto tree . . . 6·00 2·50

1987. Christmas. No. 489 surch **CHRISTMAS 1987 20**, and previously unissued miniature sheet containing Nos. 1425/9 and No. **MS**1619 surch.
2230 20c. on 6c. Black acara ("Patua") . . . . 3·25 10
MS2231 215 × 75mm. 120c. on 60c. × 5 Nos. 1425/9 . . . . . 8·00 4·00
MS2232 120 × 129mm. 225c. on 55c. × 4 Plate No. 22 (Series 1), each with a different overprint (**Christmas 1985 ,Happy New Year, Merry Christmas** or **Happy Holidays**) . . . . 1·60 1·75

1987. Royal Ruby Wedding. Nos. 1684/5 optd **1987** (130c.) or surch **120**.
2233 130c. Plate No. 13 (Series 1) 4·50 1·25
MS2234 600c. on 130c. on 130c., 600c. on 200c. on 130c., 600c. on 260c. on 130c., 600c. on 330c. on 130c., Plate No. 6 (Series 1) . . 9·00 10·00

1987. Centenary of Publication of Sanders' "Reichenbachia" (26th issue). As T **331**. Mult.
2235 255c. Plate No. 61 (Series 2) 3·50 1·25
2236 290c. Plate No. 53 (Series 2) 3·50 1·50
2237 375c. Plate No. 96 (Series 2) 2·00 1·60
2238 680c. Plate No. 64 (Series 2) 8·50 2·75
2239 720c. Plate No. 49 (Series 2) 9·50 4·50
2240 750c. Plate No. 66 (Series 2) 3·00 4·50
2241 800c. Plate No. 79 (Series 2) 3·00 4·75
2242 850c. Plate No. 76 (Series 2) 3·00 4·75

1987. Air. No. 1620 surch **AIR 75**.
2243 75c. on 25c. Plate No. 59 (Series 1) . . . . 8·50 1·00

1987. Wildlife Protection. Nos. 756/67 optd **1987**, Nos. 1432/4 surch **Protect our Heritage '87 320** and Nos. 1631/3, 1752/3 and 1847 optd **PROTECT OUR HERITAGE '87**.
2244 30c. Type **178** 30 25
2245 30c. Red howler 30 25
2246 30c. Common squirrel-monkey 30 25
2247 30c. Two-toed sloth 30 25
2248 30c. Brazilian tapir 30 25
2249 30c. Collared peccary . . . 30 25
2250 30c. Six-banded armadillo 30 25
2251 30c. Tamandua 30 25
2252 30c. Giant anteater 30 25
2253 30c. Murine opossum . . . 30 25
2254 30c. Brown four-eyed opossum 30 25
2255 30c. Brazilian agouti 30 25
2256 120c. Plate No. 67 (Series 1) 80 30
2257 130c. Plate No. 66 (Series 1) 80 30
2258 150c. Plate No. 26 (Series 1) 85 35
2259 180c. Plate No. 15 (Series 1) 90 40
2260 320c. Plate No. 82 (Series 1) 1·25 60
2261 320c. on 120c. Demerara Mutual Life Assurance Building . . . . 1·25 1·50
2262 320c. on 120c. Town Hall 1·25 1·50
2263 320c. on 120c. Victoria Law Courts . . . . 1·25 1·50
2264 650c. on 40c. Plate No. 86 (Series 1) . . . . 2·75 3·50

1987. Air. Various "Reichenbachia" issues optd **AIR**.
2265 60c. Plate No. 55 (Series 1) (No. 1597) . . . . 6·50 6·50
2463 75c. Plate No. 55 (Series 1) (No. 1772) 90 55
2464 75c. Plate No. 5 (Series 1) (No. 1667) 90 55
2466 75c. Plate No. 83 (Series 1) 90 55
2467 75c. Plate No. 95 (Series 1) 90 55

1988. World Scout Jamboree, Australia. No. 837a optd **AUSTRALIA 1987 JAMBOREE 1988** and Nos. 830, 837a and 1104 surch **$10 AUSTRALIA 1987 JAMBOREE 1988**.
2266 **116** 440c. on 6c. mult (No. 837a) . . . . . 7·50 60
2267 $10 on 110c. on 6c. mult (No. 830) . . . 75 90
2268 $10 on 180c. on 6c. mult (No. 1104) . . . 75 90
2269a $10 on 440c. on 6c. mult (No. 837a) . . . 75 90

1988. 10th Anniv of International Fund for Agricultural Development. Nos. 448 and 450 surch **IFAD For a World Without Hunger**.
2270 25c. on 1c. Type **87** . . . . 1·75 10
2271 $5 on 3c. Lukunani . . . . 6·50 4·00

1988. Republic Day. Nos. 545, 548a and 555 surch **Republic Day 1988**.
2272 25c. on 5c. Annatto tree . . 10 10
2273 120c. on 15c. Christmas orchid . . . . 7·50 70
2274 $10 on $2 "Noranthea guianensis" . . . . 2·75 3·50

1988. Centenary of Publication of Sanders' "Reichenbachia" (27th issue). Four sheets, each 102 × 127 mm, containing vert designs as T **331**. Multicoloured.
MS2275 (a) 320c. Plate No. 46 (Series 2); 330c. Plate No. 55 (Series 2); 350c. Plate No. 57 (Series 2); 500c. Plate No. 81 (Series 2). (b) 320c. Plate No. 55 (Series 2); 330c. Plate No. 46 (Series 2); 350c. Plate No. 81 (Series 2); 500c. Plate No. 57 (Series 2). (c) 320c. Plate No. 57 (Series 2); 330c. Plate No. 81 (Series 2); 350c. Plate No. 46 (Series 2); 500c. Plate No. 55 (Series 2). (d) 320c. Plate No. 81 (Series 2); 330c. Plate No. 57 (Series 2); 350c. Plate No. 55 (Series 2); 500c. Plate No. 46 (Series 2). Set of 4 sheets . . . 17·00 13·00

1988. Centenary of Publication of Sanders' "Reichenbachia" (28th series). As T **331**. Multicoloured.
2276 $10 Plate No. 40 (Series 2) 1·50 2·25
2277 $12 Plate No. 91 (Series 2) 1·50 2·25

1988. 125th Anniv of British Guiana Post Office (4th issue). No. 702a surch **25** and names of postal agencies opened between 1886 and 1900.
2278 25c. on 30c. multicoloured (surch **Albouystown**) . . . 1·25 1·00
2279 25c. on 30c. multicoloured (surch **Anns Grove**) . . . 1·25 1·00
2280 25c. on 30c. multicoloured (surch **Amacura**) . . . . 1·25 1·00
2281 25c. on 30c. multicoloured (surch **Arakaka**) . . . . . 1·25 1·00
2282 25c. on 30c. multicoloured (surch **Baramanni**) . . . . 1·25 1·00
2283 25c. on 30c. multicoloured (surch **Cuyuni**) . . . . . 1·25 1·00
2284 25c. on 30c. multicoloured (surch **Hope Placer**) . . . 1·25 1·00
2285 25c. on 30c. multicoloured (surch **H M P S**) . . . . 1·25 1·00
2286 25c. on 30c. mult (surch **Kitty**) . . . . 1·25 1·00
2287 25c. on 30c. multicoloured (surch **M'M'Zorg**) . . . . 1·25 1·00
2288 25c. on 30c. multicoloured (surch **Maccaseema**) . . . 1·25 1·00
2289 25c. on 30c. mult (surch **1988**) . . . . 1·25 1·00
2290 25c. on 30c. multicoloured (surch **Morawhanna**) . . . 1·25 1·00
2291 25c. on 30c. multicoloured (surch **Naamryck**) . . . . 1·25 1·00
2292 25c. on 30c. mult (surch **Purini**) . . . . 1·25 1·00
2293 25c. on 30c. multicoloured (surch **Potaro Landing**) . . 1·25 1·00
2294 25c. on 30c. multicoloured (surch **Rockstone**) . . . . 1·25 1·00
2295 25c. on 30c. multicoloured (surch **Rosignol**) . . . . . 1·25 1·00
2296 25c. on 30c. multicoloured (surch **Stanleytown**) . . . 1·25 1·00
2297 25c. on 30c. multicoloured (surch **Santa Rosa**) . . . 1·25 1·00
2298 25c. on 30c. multicoloured (surch **Tumatumari**) . . . 1·25 1·00
2299 25c. on 30c. multicoloured (surch **Weldaad**) . . . . . 1·25 1·00
2300 25c. on 30c. multicoloured (surch **Wismar**) . . . . . 1·25 1·00
2301 25c. on 30c. mult (surch **TPO Berbice Railway**) . . 1·25 1·00

1988. Olympic Games, Seoul (1st issue). Nos. 1206/17 further surch **120 Olympic Games 1988**.
2302 120c. on 55c. on 125c. on 35c. Type **174** . . . . . 1·50 1·50
2303 120c. on 55c. on 125c. on 35c. Trahira ("Haimara") 1·50 1·50
2304 120c. on 55c. on 125c. on 35c. Electric eel . . . . . 1·50 1·50
2305 120c. on 55c. on 125c. on 35c. Golden rivulus . . . 1·50 1·50
2306 120c. on 55c. on 125c. on 35c. Golden pencilfish . . 1·50 1·50
2307 120c. on 55c. on 125c. on 35c. Four-eyed fish . . . 1·50 1·50
2308 120c. on 55c. on 125c. on 35c. Red piranha ("Pirai") 1·50 1·50
2309 120c. on 55c. on 125c. on 35c. Smoking hassar . . . 1·50 1·50
2310 120c. on 55c. on 125c. on 35c. Manta . . . . 1·50 1·50
2311 120c. on 55c. on 125c. on 35c. Festive cichlid ("Flying patwa") . . . . . 1·50 1·50
2312 120c. on 55c. on 125c. on 35c. Arapaima . . . . . 1·50 1·50
2313 120c. on 55c. on 125c. on 35c. Peacock cichlid ("Lukanani") . . . . . . 1·50 1·50
See also Nos. 2476/95.

1988. Centenary of Publication of Sanders' "Reichenbachia" (29th issue). As T **331**. Mult.
2314 320c. Plate No. 62 (Series 2) 2·00 50
2315 475c. Plate No. 73 (Series 2) 2·50 1·00
2316 525c. Plate No. 36 (Series 2) 3·00 1·25
2317 530c. Plate No. 69 (Series 2) 1·00 1·25
2318 $15 Plate No. 67 (Series 2) 2·50 4·50

1988. CARICOM Day. Nos. 545/6 and 555 surch **Caricom Day 1988** and new value.
2319 25c. on 5c. Annatto tree . . 25 10
2320 $1.20 on 6c. Cannon-ball tree 60 10
2321 $10 on $2 "Norantea guianensis" . . . . 3·50 4·25

1988. Centenary of Publication of Sanders' "Reichenbachia" (30th issue). As T **331**. Mult.
2322 700c. Plate No. 62 (Series 2) 1·00 1·50
2323 775c. Plate No. 59 (Series 2) 1·25 1·75
2324 875c. Plate No. 31 (Series 2) 8·00 2·25
2325 950c. Plate No. 78 (Series 2) 1·75 2·50

1988. 40th Anniv of World Health Day. No. 705a optd.
2326 60c. "Papilio androgeus" (optd **WHO 1948-1988**) 14·00 15·00
2327 60c. "Papilio androgeus" (optd **1988**) 35 10

1988. Centenary of Publication of Sanders' "Reichenbachia" (31st issue). As T **331**. Mult.
2328 350c. Plate No. 74 (Series 2) 2·00 1·00

1988. Centenary of Publication of Sanders' "Reichenbachia" (32nd issue). As T **331**, but additionally inscr "1985–1988". Multicoloured.
2329 130c. Plate No. 73 (Series 2) 1·50 25
2330 200c. Plate No. 96 (Series 2) 50 30
2331 260c. Plate No. 16 (Series 2) 3·00 90
MS2332 Four sheets, each 102 × 127 mm. (a) 120c. Plate No. 81 (Series 2); 120c. Plate No. 57 (Series 2); 120c. Plate No. 55 (Series 2); 120c. Plate No. 46 (Series 2). (b) 150c. Plate No. 57 (Series 2); 150c. Plate No. 81 (Series 2); 150c. Plate No. 46 (Series 2); 150c. Plate No. 55 (Series 2). (c) 225c. Plate No. 46 (Series 2); 225c. Plate No. 55 (Series 2); 225c. Plate No. 57 (Series 2); 225c. Plate No. 81 (Series 2). (d) 305c. Plate No. 55 (Series 2); 305c. Plate No. 46 (Series 2); 305c. Plate No. 81 (Series 2); 305c. Plate No. 57 (Series 2). Set of 4 sheets 7·50 5·00

1988. Conservation of Resources. (a) Nos. 1444/6 optd.
2333 120c. Young Ocelot (No. 1444) (optd **CONSERVE TREES**) . . 80 70
2334 120c. Young Ocelot (No. 1444) (optd **CONSERVE ELECTRICITY**) 80 70
2335 120c. Young Ocelot (No. 1444) (optd **CONSERVE WATER**) 80 70
2336 120c. Type **322** (optd **CONSERVE ELECTRICITY**) 80 70
2337 120c. Type **322** (optd **CONSERVE WATER**) 80 70
2338 120c. Type **322** (optd **CONSERVE TREES**) . . 80 70
2339 120c. Young Ocelot (No. 1446) (optd **CONSERVE WATER**) 80 70
2340 120c. Young Ocelot (No. 1446) (optd **CONSERVE TREES**) . . 80 70
2341 120c. Young Ocelot (No. 1446) (optd **CONSERVE ELECTRICITY**) 80 70

(b) Nos. 1634, 1670, 1683 and 1774 optd **CONSERVE WATER**.
2342 200c. Plate No. 33 (Series 1) 80 70
2343 200c. Plate No. 79 (Series 1) 80 70
2344 225c. Plate No. 24 (Series 1) 80 70
2345 350c. Plate No. 94 (Series 1) 80 70

1988. Road Safety Campaign. Nos. 2194/2201 optd.
2346 **396** $1.20 green (optd **BEWARE OF ANIMALS**) . . . . . 1·10 1·10
2347 – $1.20 green (No. 2195) (optd **BEWARE OF CHILDREN**) . . . . 1·10 1·10
2348 – $1.20 green (No. 2196) (optd **DRIVE SAFELY**) . . . . . . 1·10 1·10
2349 – $1.20 green (No. 2197) (optd **DO NOT DRINK AND DRIVE**) 1·10 1·10
2350 **396** $1.20 purple (optd **BEWARE OF ANIMALS**) . . . . . 1·10 1·10
2351 – $1.20 purple (No. 2199) (optd **BEWARE OF CHILDREN**) . . . . 1·10 1·10

2352 – $1.20 purple (No. 2200) (optd **DRIVE SAFELY**) . . . . . . 1·10 1·10
2353 – $1.20 purple (No. 2201) (optd **DO NOT DRINK AND DRIVE**) 1·10 1·10

1988. No. 706 optd **1988** or surch **120**.
2354 $1 "Agrias claudina" . . . 5·00 90
2355 120c. on $1 "Agrias claudina" . . . . 5·00 90

1988. Various "Reichenbachia" issues surch.
2356 120c. on 25c. Plate No. 61 (Series 1) (No. 1574) . . . 1·00 70
2357 120c. on 25c. Plate No. 63 (Series 1) (No. 1575) . . . 1·00 70
2358 120c. on 25c. Plate No. 70 (Series 1) (No. 1576) . . . 1·00 70
2359 120c. on 25c. Plate No. 59 (Series 1) (No. 1620) . . . 1·00 70
2360 120c. on 25c. Plate No. 71 (Series 1) (No. 1679) . . . 1·00 70
2429 120c. on 25c. Plate No. 72 (Series 1) (No. 1577) . . . 1·00 70
2361 120c. on 30c. Plate No. 53 (Series 1) (No. 1771) . . . 1·00 70
2362 120c. on 30c. Plate No. 86 (Series 1) (No. 1731) . . . 1·00 70
2363 120c. on 30c. Plate No. 30 (Series 2) (No. 1809) . . . 1·00 70
2365 120c. on 30c. Plate No. 7 (Series 2) . . . . 1·00 70
2366 120c. on 30c. Plate No. 14 (Series 2) . . . . 1·00 70
2368 120c. on 30c. Plate No. 22 (Series 2) . . . . 1·00 70
2369 120c. on 30c. Plate No. 28 (Series 2) . . . . 1·00 70
2371 120c. on 35c. Plate No. 45 (Series 2) (No. 1925) . . . 1·00 70
2372 120c. on 40c. Plate No. 77 (Series 1) (No. 1663) . . . 1·00 70
2374 120c. on 40c. Plate No. 96 (Series 1) (No. 1747) . . . 1·00 70
2377 120c. on 40c. Plate No. 86 (Series 1) (No. 1868) . . . 1·00 70
2378 120c. on 40c. Plate No. 68 (Series 1) (No. 1884) . . . 1·00 70
2381 120c. on 45c. Plate No. 54 (Series 1) (No. 1664) . . . 1·00 70
2382 120c. on 45c. Plate No. 81 (Series 1) (No. 1748) . . . 1·00 70
2383 120c. on 45c. Plate No. 21 (Series 2) (No. 1810) . . . 1·00 70
2384 120c. on 50c. Plate No. 92 (Series 1) (No. 1665) . . . 1·00 70
2385 120c. on 50c. Plate No. 13 (Series 2) (No. 1907) . . . 1·00 70
2386 120c. on 50c. Plate No. 15 (Series 2) (No. 1926) . . . 1·00 70
2393 120c. on 55c. Plate No. 17 (Series 1) (No. 1732) . . . 1·00 70
2395 120c. on 60c. Plate No. 57 (Series 1) (No. 1622) . . . 1·00 70
2397 120c. on 60c. Plate No. 73 (Series 1) (No. 1623) . . . 1·00 70
2398 120c. on 60c. Plate No. 75 (Series 1) (No. 1624) . . . 1·00 70
2400 120c. on 60c. Plate No. 95 (Series 1) (No. 1666) . . . 1·00 70
2401 120c. on 60c. Plate No. 93 (Series 1) (No. 1733) . . . 1·00 70
2402 120c. on 60c. Plate No. 27 (Series 2) (No. 1874) . . . 1·00 70
2408 120c. on 70c. Plate No. 8 (Series 2) . . . . 1·00 70
2409 120c. on 70c. Plate No. 9 (Series 2) . . . . 1·00 70
2411 120c. on 70c. Plate No. 12 (Series 2) . . . . 1·00 70
2413 120c. on 70c. Plate No. 17 (Series 2) . . . . 1·00 70
2414 120c. on 80c. Plate No. 39 (Series 1) . . . . 1·00 70
2415 120c. on 80c. Plate No. 74 (Series 1) . . . . 1·00 70
2416 120c. on 80c. Plate No. 93 (Series 1) . . . . 1·00 70
2417 120c. on 85c. Plate No. 45 (Series 2) (No. 1876) . . . 1·00 70
2418 120c. on 85c. Plate No. 24 (Series 2) (No. 1914) . . . 1·00 70
2419 120c. on 85c. Plate No. 15 (Series 2) (No. 1918) . . . 1·00 70
2420 120c. on 85c. Plate No. 18 (Series 2) (No. 1928) . . . 1·00 70
2421 120c. on 90c. Plate No. 84 (Series 1) (No. 1668) . . . 1·00 70
2422 120c. on 90c. Plate No. 89 (Series 1) (No. 1749) . . . 1·00 70
2423 120c. on 90c. Plate No. 10 (Series 2) (No. 1869) . . . 1·00 70
2424 120c. on 90c. Plate No. 13 (Series 2) (No. 1877) . . . 1·00 70
2425 120c. on 90c. Plate No. 27 (Series 2) (No. 1915) . . . 1·00 70
2426 120c. on 90c. Plate No. 2 (Series 2) (No. 1929) . . . 1·00 70
2427 200c. on 80c. Plate No. 42 (Series 2) (No. 1812) . . . 1·00 70
2428 200c. on 90c. Plate No. 4 (Series 2) (No. 1813) . . . 1·00 70
2430 240c. on 140c. Plate No. 30 (Series 2) . . . . 1·00 70
2431 240c. on 140c. Plate No. 34 (Series 2) . . . . 1·00 70
2432 240c. on 425c. Plate No. 87 (Series 2) (No. 2070) . . . 1·00 70
2433 260c. on 375c. Plate No. 90 (Series 1) (No. 1378) . . . 1·00 70

1988. Conservation of Resources. Various "Reichenbachia" issues optd **CONSERVE OUR RESOURCES**.
2434 100c. Plate No. 65 (Series 1) (No. 1773) 90 60
2435 100c. Plate No. 68 (Series 1) (No. 1734) 90 60
2436 100c. Plate No. 88 (Series 1) (No. 1750) 90 60
2438 120c. Plate No. 27 (Series 1) (No. 1524) 90 60
2439 120c. Plate No. 36 (Series 1) (No. 1558) 90 60
2440 120c. Plate No. 37 (Series 1) (No. 1627) 90 60
2441 120c. Plate No. 56 (Series 1) (No. 1629) 90 60
2442 120c. Plate No. 58 (Series 1) (No. 1630) 90 60
2443 120c. Plate No. 67 (Series 1) (No. 1631) 90 60
2444 120c. Plate No. 69 (Series 1) (No. 1680) 90 60
2445 130c. Plate No. 38 (Series 1) (No. 1560) 90 60
2446 130c. Plate No. 66 (Series 1) (No. 1632) 90 60
2447 130c. Plate No. 91 (Series 1) (No. 1735) 90 60
2448 130c. Plate No. 13 (Series 1) (No. 1760) 90 60
2249 130c. Plate No. 20 (Series 1) (No. 1761) 90 60
2450 150c. Plate No. 26 (Series 1) (No. 1633) 90 60
2451 150c. Plate No. 78 (Series 1) (No. 1669) 90 60
2452 150c. Plate No. 87 (Series 1) (No. 1681) 90 60
2453 150c. Plate No. 76 (Series 1) (No. 1751) 90 60
2454 250c. Plate No. 74 (Series 1) (No. 1736) 90 60

1988. 125th Anniv of International Red Cross. Nos. 2202/5 and 2207/10 optd with cross.
2455 **396** $3.20 blue . . . . 1·50 1·50
2456 – $3.20 blue (No. 2203) . . 1·50 1·50
2457 – $3.20 blue (No. 2204) . . 1·50 1·50
2458 – $3.20 blue (No. 2205) . . 1·50 1·50
2459 – $3.30 black (No. 2207) 1·50 1·50
2460 **396** $3.30 black . . . . . . 1·50 1·50
2461 – $3.30 black (No. 2209) 1·50 1·50
2462 – $3.30 black (No. 2210) 1·50 1·50

1988. Centenary of Publication of Sanders' "Reichenbachia" (33rd issue). As T **331**. Mult.
2468 270c. Plate No. 90 (Series 2) 3·50 70
2469 360c. Plate No. 84 (Series 2) 75 1·00
2470 550c. Plate No. 70 (Series 2) (horiz) . . . . 1·75 2·00
2471 670c. Plate No. 71 (Series 2) (horiz) . . . . 2·00 2·50

1988. 60th Anniv of Cricket in Guyana. Nos. 1584, 1670, 1681 and 1815 optd **1928 – 1988 CRICKET JUBILEE** or surch also.
2472 200c. Plate No. 14 (Series 1) 18·00 20·00
2473 200c. Plate No. 79 (Series 1) 1·00 40
2474 800c. on 150c. Plate No. 87 (Series 1) . . . . 7·50 9·50
2475 800c. on 160c. Plate No. 5 (Series 2) . . . . 3·25 3·25

1988. Olympic Games, Seoul. (a) Nos. 1628, 1634, 1671, 1681, 1683, 1814, 1818/19, 1880 and 2069 optd **OLYMPIC GAMES 1988** or surch also.
2476 120c. Plate No. 46 (Series 1) 40 40
2477 130c. Plate No. 38 (Series 2) 40 40
2478 150c. Plate No. 87 (Series 1) 40 40
2479 200c. Plate No. 33 (Series 1) 40 40
2480 300c. Plate No. 83 (Series 1) 40 40
2481 300c. on 360c. Plate No. 34 (Series 2) 60 60
2482 320c. Plate No. 10 (Series 2) 60 60
2483 330c. Plate No. 82 (Series 2) 60 60
2484 350c. Plate No. 94 (Series 1) 60 60
2485 350c. Plate No. 29 (Series 2) 60 60

(b) Design as No. 1420 but incorrectly inscr "LOS ANGELLES" optd or surch **OLYMPICS 1988** (A) or **KOREA 1988** (B).
2486 $1.20 multicoloured (A) . . 40 40
2487 $1.20 multicoloured (B) . . 40 40
2488 130c. on $1.20 mult (A) . . 40 40
2489 130c. on $1.20 mult (B) . . 40 40
2490 150c. on $1.20 mult (A) . . 40 40
2491 150c. on $1.20 mult (B) . . 40 40
2492 200c. on $1.20 mult (A) . . 50 50
2493 200c. on $1.20 mult (B) . . 50 50
2594 350c. on $1.20 mult (A) . . 60 60
2495 350c. on $1.20 mult (B) . . 60 60

1988. Columbus Day. Nos. 1672/3 optd or surch **V CENTENARY OF THE LANDING OF CHRISTOPHER COLUMBUS IN THE AMERICAS**.
2496 320c. Plate No. 50 (Series 1) 2·50 60
2497 $15 on 360c. Plate No. 85 (Series 1) . . . . 4·50 6·00

1988. Centenary of Publication of Sanders' "Reichenbachia" (34th issue). As T **331**. Mult.
2498 100c. Plate No. 44 (Series 2) 60 55
2499 130c. Plate No. 42 (Series 2) (horiz) 60 55
2500 140c. Plate No. 4 (Series 2) 75 65
2501 160c. Plate No. 50 (Series 2) 75 65
2502 175c. Plate No. 51 (Series 2) 90 75
2503 200c. Plate No. 11 (Series 2) 3·50 1·10
2504 200c. Plate No. 23 (Series 2) 3·50 1·10
2505 200c. Plate No. 26 (Series 2) 3·50 1·10
2506 200c. Plate No. 75 (Series 2) 3·50 1·10
2507 200c. Plate No. 93 (Series 2) 3·50 1·10
2508 250c. Plate No. 79 (Series 2) 1·00 1·00
2509 280c. Plate No. 62 (Series 2) 1·25 1·25
2510 285c. Plate No. 63 (Series 2) 5·00 1·75
2511 380c. Plate No. 35 (Series 2) 5·50 2·00

1988. Christmas (1st issue). Various "Reichenbachia" issues optd or surch. (a) Optd or surch **SEASON'S GREETINGS**.
2519 120c. on 100c. Plate No. 6 (Series 1) 70 70
2520 120c. on 100c. Plate No. 13 (Series 1) 70 70
2521 120c. on 100c. Plate No. 20 (Series 1) 70 70
2522 120c. on 100c. Plate No. 25 (Series 1) 70 70
2523 120c. on 100c. Plate No. 40 (Series 1) (horiz) 25 25
2524 120c. on 100c. Plate No. 42 (Series 1) (horiz) 25 25
2525 120c. on 100c. Plate No. 43 (Series 1) (horiz) 25 25
2526 120c. on 100c. Plate No. 45 (Series 1) (horiz) 25 25
2512 150c. Plate No. 32 (Series 1) (No. 1561) 70 70
2513 150c. Plate No. 62 (Series 1) (No. 1566) 70 70
2514 225c. Plate No. 60 (Series 1) (No. 1682) 70 70
2532 240c. on 180c. Plate No. 15 (Series 1) (No. 1752) . . . 70 70
2515 260c. Plate No. 39 (Series 1) (No. 1737) 70 70
2516 320c. Plate No. 82 (Series 1) (No. 1753) 70 70
2517 330c. Plate No. 80 (Series 1) (No. 1754) 70 70
2518 360c. Plate No. 85 (Series 1) (No. 1673) 70 70

(b) Optd **SEASON'S GREETINGS 1988**.
2527 225c. Plate No. 24 (Series 1) (No. 1774) . . . . 1·25 1·25
2528 225c. Plate No. 60 (Series 1) (No. 1682) . . . . 1·25 1·25
2530 225c. on 350c. on 120c. Plate No. 65 (Series 1) (No. 2221) . . . . 1·25 1·25
MS2531 120 × 129 mm. 225c. on 55c. × 4 Plate No. 22 (Series 1) each with a different overprint (**Christmas 1987**, **Happy New Year**, **Merry Christmas** or **Happy Holidays**) (No. **MS**2232) . . . 3·75 3·75

1988. Christmas (2nd issue). Nos. 489, 1188/91 and 1449 surch or optd **CHRISTMAS 1988**.
2533 – 20c. on 6c. mult (No. 489) 25 10
2534 **277** 120c. brown, black bl . . 35 50
2535 – 120c. on 130c. red, black and blue (No. 1189) 35 50
2536 – 120c. on 150c. violet, black and blue (No. 1190) 35 50
2537 – 120c. on 200c. green, black and blue (No. 1191) 35 50
2538 – 500c. on 330c. mult (No. 1449) . . . . . 2·25 3·00

1988. AIDS Information Campaign. Nos. 707/8a optd or surch with various slogans.
2539 120c. on $5 "Morpho deidamia" (A) . . . . . 3·00 3·00
2540 120c. on $5 "Morpho deidamia" (B) . . . . . 3·00 3·00
2541 120c. on $5 "Morpho deidamia" (C) . . . . . 3·00 3·00
2542 120c. on $5 "Morpho deidamia" (D) . . . . . 3·00 3·00
2543 120c. on $5 "Morpho deidamia" (E) . . . . . 3·00 3·00
2544 120c. on $10 "Elbella patrobas" (A) . . . . . 3·00 3·00
2545 120c. on $10 "Elbella patrobas" (B) . . . . . . 3·00 3·00
2546 120c. on $10 "Elbella patrobas" (C) . . . . . . 3·00 3·00
2547 120c. on $10 "Elbella patrobas" (D) . . . . . 3·00 3·00
2548 120c. on $10 "Elbella patrobas" (E) . . . . . . 3·00 3·00
2549 $2 "Morpho rhetenor" (female) (E) . . . . . . 9·50 2·75
2550 $5 "Morpho deidamia" (E) 11·00 7·00
2551 $10 "Elbella patrobas" (E) 13·00 11·00
OVERPRINTS: (A) **Be compassionate towards AIDS victims.**; (B) **Get information on AIDS. it may save your life.**; (C) **Get the facts. Education helps to prevent AIDS.**; (D) **Say no to Drugs and limit the spread of AIDS.**; (E) **Protect yourself from AIDS. Better safe than sorry.**

1988. 150th Anniv of Abolition of Slavery (1984) (2nd issue). Designs as Nos. 1547/50, but colours changed.
2552 **337** 25c. black and brown . . 15 10
2553 – 60c. black and lilac . . 20 15
2254 – 130c. black and green . . 25 50
2555 – 150c. black and blue . . 30 75

1989. Olympic Medal Winners, Seoul. Nos. 1672, 1923 and 2178 surch **SALUTING WINNERS OLYMPIC GAMES 1988**.
2556 550c. on 560c. Plate No. 1 (Series 2) . . . . 1·50 1·25
2557 900c. on 320c. Plate No. 18 (Series 2) . . . . 2·00 2·50
2558 1050c. on 320c. Plate No. 50 (Series 1) . . . . 2·50 3·25

1989. Republic Day. Nos. 2194/2201 and 2212 optd **REPUBLIC DAY 1989**.
2559 **396** $1.20 green 60 70
2560 – $1.20 green (No. 2195) 60 70
2561 – $1.20 green (No. 2196) 60 70
2562 – $1.20 green (No. 2197) 60 70
2563 **396** $1.20 purple 60 70
2564 – $1.20 purple (No. 2199) 60 70
2565 – $1.20 purple (No. 2200) 60 70
2566 – $1.20 purple (No. 2201) 60 70
2567 – $10 multicoloured . . . 3·50 4·50

1989. Nos. 2202/5 and 2207/10 surch **$5.00**.
2568 **396** $5 on $3.20 blue . . . . 2·00 2·25
2569 – $5 on $3.20 blue (No. 2203) . . . . . 2·00 2·25
2570 – $5 on $3.20 blue (No. 2204) . . . . . 2·00 2·25
2571 – $5 on $3.20 blue (No. 2205) . . . . . 2·00 2·25
2572 – $5 on $3.30 black (No. 2207) . . . . . 2·00 2·25
2573 **396** $5 on $3.30 black . . . 2·00 2·25
2574 – $5 on $3.30 black (No. 2209) . . . . . 2·00 2·25
2575 – $5 on $3.30 black (No. 2210) . . . . . 2·00 2·25

1989. Various "Reichenbachia" issues surch.
2576 120c. on 140c. Plate No. 25 (Series 2) . . . . 2·00 2·00
2577 120c. on 140c. Plate No. 52 (Series 2) . . . . 2·00 2·00
2578 120c. on 140c. Plate No. 65 (Series 2) . . . . 2·00 2·00
2580 120c. on 140c. Plate No. 38 (Series 2) . . . . 2·00 2·00
2581 120c. on 140c. Plate No. 41 (Series 2) . . . . 2·00 2·00
2579 120c. on 175c. Plate No. 54 (Series 2) . . . . 2·00 2·00
2582 170c. on 175c. Plate No. 58 (Series 2) . . . . 2·25 2·25
2583 250c. on 280c. Plate No. 66 (Series 2) . . . . 2·50 2·50
2584 250c. on 280c. Plate No. 67 (Series 2) . . . . 2·50 2·50
2585 300c. on 290c. Plate No. 53 (Series 2) (No. 2236) . . . 2·50 2·50

1989. Nos. 1744/5 and 2185/6 surch **TEN DOLLARS $10.00** (Nos. 2586, 2588) or **TEN DOLLARS** (Nos. 2587, 2589).
2586 **363** $10 on 320c. red, black and lilac (No. 1744) 3·25 3·75
2587 – $10 on 320c. mult (No. 1745) . . . . . 3·25 3·75
2588 **363** $10 on 320c. red, black and lilac (No. 2185) 3·25 3·75
2589 – $10 on 320c. mult (No. 2186) . . . . . 3·25 3·75

1989. Nos. O54/7, O59/63 and O65/9 optd **POSTAGE** or surch also.
2591 125c. on 130c. Plate No. 92 (Series 2) . . . . 1·75 1·75
2592 125c. on 140c. Plate No. 36 (Series 2) . . . . 1·75 1·75
2593 150c. Plate No. 43 (Series 2) 1·75 1·75
2594 150c. on 175c. Plate No. 31 (Series 2) . . . . 1·75 1·75
2595 250c. Plate No. 59 (Series 2) 2·00 2·00
2596 250c. on 225c. Plate No. 26 (Series 2) . . . . 2·00 2·00
2597 250c. on 230c. Plate No. 68 (Series 2) . . . . 2·00 2·00
2598 250c. on 275c. Plate No. 69 (Series 2) . . . . 2·00 2·00
2599 300c. on 275c. Plate No. 90 (Series 2) . . . . 2·00 2·00
2750 350c. Plate No. 95 (Series 2) 2·00 2·00
2601 350c. on 330c. Plate No. 23 (Series 2) . . . . 2·00 2·00
2602 600c. Plate No. 70 (Series 2) 2·25 2·50
2603 $12 Plate No. 71 (Series 2) 3·00 4·00
2604 $15 Plate No. 84 (Series 2) 3·25 4·25

1989. Centenary of Publication of Sanders' "Reichenbachia" (35th issue). As T **331**. Mult.
2605 200c. Plate No. 49 (Series 2) 2·75 2·75
2606 200c. Plate No. 53 (Series 2) 2·75 2·75
2607 200c. Plate No. 60 (Series 2) 2·75 2·75
2608 200c. Plate No. 64 (Series 2) 2·75 2·75

1989. No. 1442 surch **250**.
2609 **322** 250c. on 25c. mult . . . 5·50 70

1989. 40th Anniv of Guyana Red Cross. No. 1872 surch **RED CROSS 1948 1988** and new value.
2610 375c. on 45c. Plate No. 17 (Series 2) . . . . 2·25 2·00
2611 425c. on 45c. Plate No. 17 (Series 2) . . . . 2·25 2·00

1989. World Health Day. Nos. 1875 and 2239 surch with new value and inscr as indicated.
2612 250c. on 75c. Plate No. 56 (Series 2) surch **HEALTH FOR ALL** . . . . 1·50 1·50
2613 250c. on 75c. Plate No. 56 (Series 2) surch **ALL FOR HEALTH** . . . . 1·50 1·50

2614 675c. on 720c. Plate No. 49 (Series 2) surch **ALL FOR HEALTH** . . . . 2·25 3·25
2615 675c. on 720c. Plate No. 49 (Series 2) surch **HEALTH FOR ALL** . . . . 2·25 3·25

1989. Scouting Anniversaries. Nos. 1873, 1879, 2322, 2509 and unissued value as No. 1873 optd or surch also.
2616 250c. on 50c. Plate No. 33 (Series 2) (surch **BOY SCOUTS 1909 1989**) . . 1·25 1·25
2617 250c. on 50c. Plate No. 33 (Series 2) (surch **GIRL GUIDES 1924 1989**) . . . 1·25 1·25
2618 250c. on 100c. Plate No. 33 (Series 2) (surch **BOY SCOUTS 1909 1989**) . . 1·25 1·25
2619 250c. on 100c. Plate No. 33 (Series 2) (surch **GIRL GUIDES 1924 1989**) . . . 1·25 1·25
2620 300c. Plate No. 50 (Series 2) (optd **BOY SCOUTS 1909 1989**) . . . . 1·25 1·25
2621 300c. Plate No. 50 (Series 2) (optd **GIRL GUIDES 1924 1989**) . . . . 1·25 1·25
2622 $25 on 280c. Plate No. 62 (Series 2) (surch **LADY BADEN POWELL 1889 – 1989**) . . . . 5·50 7·00
2623 $25 on 700c. Plate No. 62 (Series 2) (surch **LADY BADEN POWELL 1889 – 1989**) . . . . 5·50 7·00

The events commemorated are the 80th anniv of Boy Scout Movement in Guyana, 65th anniv of Girl Guide Movement in Guyana and birth centenary of Lady Baden-Powell.

1989. 150 Years of Photography. No. 1881 surch **PHOTOGRAPHY 1839 – 1989** and new value.
2624 550c. on 390c. Plate No. 6 (Series 2) . . . . 3·25 3·50
2625 650c. on 390c. Plate No. 6 (Series 2) . . . . 3·25 3·50

1989. 70th Anniv of International Labour Organization. No. 1875 surch **I.L.O. 1919-1989 300.**
2627 300c. on 75c. Plate No. 56 (Series 2) . . . . 7·00 1·90

1989. Various stamps surch.
2628 80c. on 6c. Patua (No. 489) 40 20
2629 $1 on 2c. Type **132** 40 20
2630 $2.05 on 3c. Hanging heliconia (No. 544) . . . 40 25
2641 $2.55 on 5c. Annatto tree (No. 545) 40 25
2642 $3.25 on 6c. Cannon-ball tree (No. 546) 40 25
2633 $5 on 6c. Type **111** 40 30
2634 $6.40 on 10c. "Archonias bellona" (No. 699) . . . 5·50 75
2648 $6.40 on $3.30 black (No. 2207) . . . . . . 4·50 3·50
2649 $6.40 on $3.30 black (No. 2208) . . . . . . 4·50 3·50
2650 $6.40 on $3.30 black (No. 2209) . . . . . . 4·50 3·50
2651 $6.40 on $3.30 black (No. 2210) . . . . . . 4·50 3·50
2646 640c. on 675c. on 720c. Plate No. 49 (Series 2) (No. 2614) . . . . . . 1·75 2·00
2647 640c. on 675c. on 720c. Plate No. 49 (Series 2) (No. 2615) . . . . . . 1·75 2·00
2637a $7.65 on 35c. "Anaea galanthus" (No. 703) . . 5·50 1·00
2638 $7.65 on 40c. "Morpho retenor" (male) (No. 704) . . . . 6·50 1·00
2652 $7.65 on $3.20 blue (No. 2202) . . . . . . 4·50 3·50
2653 $7.65 on $3.20 blue (No. 2203) . . . . . . 4·50 3·50
2654 $7.65 on $3.20 blue (No. 2204) . . . . . . 4·50 3·50
2655 $7.65 on $3.20 blue (No. 2205) . . . . . . 4·50 3·50
2635 $8.90 on 60c. "Papilio androgeus" (No. 705a) 7·50 1·25
2643 $50 on $2 "Morpho rhetenor" (female) (No. 707) . . . . 18·00 9·00
2644 $100 on $2 "Morpho rhetenor" (female) (No. 707) . . . . 26·00 19·00

1989. CARICOM Day. No. 1878 surch **CARICOM DAY 125.**
2656 125c. on 200c. Plate No. 44 (Series 2) . . . . 4·00 90

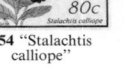

454 "Stalachtis calliope"

455 Kathryn Sullivan (first U.S. woman to walk in space)

1989. Butterflies (1st series). Multicoloured.
2657 80c. Type **454** 60 10
2658 $2.25 "Morpho rhetenor" 70 15
2659 $5 "Agrias claudia" 80 15
2660 $6.40 "Marpesia marcella" 85 20
2661 $7.65 "Papilio zagreus" . . 90 30
2662 $8.90 "Chorinea faunus" . . 1·00 30
2663 $25 "Euptychia cephus" . . 2·75 2·75
2664 $100 "Nessaea regina" . . . 7·00 9·00
See also Nos. 2789/2861 and **EMS**18/19.

1989. 25 Years of Women in Space. Mult.
2665 $6.40 Type **455** 70 20
2666 $12.80 Svetlana Savitskaya (first Soviet woman to walk in space) . . . . . 1·10 45
2667 $15.30 Judy Resnik and Christa McAuliffe and "Challenger" logo . . . . 1·10 45
2668 $100 Sally Ride (first U.S. woman astronaut) . . . . 7·50 8·50

1989. Centenary of Ahmadiyya (Moslem organization). Nos. 543/5 surch **AHMADIYYA CENTENARY 1899-1989.**
2669 80c. on 2c. Type **132** . . . 3·50 50
2670 $6.40 on 3c. Hanging heliconia . . . . 11·00 4·75
2671 $8.90 on 5c. Annatto tree 12·00 6·50

457 Head of Harpy Eagle

458 Channel-billed Toucan

1990. Endangered Species. Harpy Eagle. Multicoloured.
2672 $2.25 Type **457** 75 25
2673 $5 Harpy eagle with monkey prey . . . . 1·00 30
2674 $8.90 Eagle on branch (facing right) . . . . . . 1·50 50
2675 $30 Eagle on branch (facing left) . . . . 3·25 3·50

1990. Birds of Guyana. Multicoloured.
2676 $15 Type **458** . . . . 1·50 70
2677 $25 Blue and yellow macaw 1·75 50
2678 $50 Wattled jacana (horiz) 3·25 2·50
2679 $60 Hoatzin . . . . 3·50 2·75
MS2680 Two sheets, each 110 × 80 mm. (a) $100 Great kiskadee. (b) $100 Amazon kingfisher Set of 2 sheets . . . 11·00 11·00

1990. 85th Anniv of Rotary International. Optd **Rotary International 1905-1990** and emblem. (a) On Nos. 2657/64.
2681 80c. Type **454** . . . . . . 1·50 30
2682 $2.25 "Morpho rhetenor" 1·75 50
2683 $5 "Agrias claudia" . . . . 2·25 50
2684 $6.40 "Marpesia marcella" 2·25 55
2685 $7.65 "Papilio zagreus" . . 2·25 55
2686 $8.90 "Chorinea faunus" . . 2·50 65
2687 $25 "Euptychia cephus" . . 5·00 5·50
2688 $100 "Nessaea regina" . . . 12·00 14·00

(b) On Nos. 2665/8.
2689 $6.40 Type **455** . . . . . . 1·25 40
2690 $12.80 Svetlana Savitskaya (first Soviet woman to walk in space) . . . . . 1·75 1·00
2691 $15.30 Judy Resnik and Christa McAuliffe with "Challenger" logo . . . . 1·75 1·10
2692 $100 Sally Ride (first U.S. woman astronaut) . . . . 9·00 11·00

460 Indian Post Runner, 1837

1990. 150th Anniv of the Penny Black and 500th Anniv of Thurn and Taxis Postal Service. Multicoloured.
2693/2746 $15.30 × 27, $17.80 × 9, $20 × 18 . . . . Set of 54 . . . . 32·00 35·00
MS2747 Three sheets, each 116 × 86 mm. (a) $150 Post boy. (b) $150 Thurn and Taxis (Northern District) 3sgr. of 1852. (c) $150 Thurn and Taxis (Southern District) 6k. of 1852 Set of 3 sheets . . . . 13·00 14·00
Nos. 2693/2746 depict various forms of mail transport.

1990. 9th Conference of Rotary District 405, Georgetown. Nos. 1759, 1762/3 and 1765/6 surch **ROTARY DISTRICT 405 9th CONFERENCE MAY 1990 GEORGETOWN** and new value.
2748 80c. on 55c. Plate No. 9 (Series 1) . . . .
2749 80c. on 55c. Plate No. 49 (Series 1) . . . .
2750 80c. on 55c. Plate No. 64 (Series 1) . . . .
2751 $6.40 on 130c. Plate No. 6 (Series 1) . . . .
2752 $6.40 on 130c. Plate No. 25 (Series 1) . . . .
2753 $7.65 on 130c. Plate No. 25 (Series 1) . . . .

1990. 90th Birthday of Queen Elizabeth the Queen Mother. Nos. 2657/64 surch **90th Birthday H.M. The Queen Mother.**
2754 80c. Type **454** . . . . . . 1·25 40
2755 $2.25 "Morpho rhetenor" 1·50 50
2756 $5 "Agrias claudia" . . . . 2·00 60
2757 $6.40 "Marpesia marcella" 2·25 60
2758 $7.65 "Papilio zagreus" . . 2·50 75
2759 $8.90 "Chorinea faunus" . . 2·50 90
2760 $25 "Euptychia cephus" . . 5·00 5·00
2761 $100 "Nessaea regina" . . . 12·00 14·00
See also Nos. **EMS**31/3.

463 Collared Trogon

464 "Melinaea idae"

1990. Birds. Multicoloured.
2762 80c. Marbled wood quail ("Guiana Partridge") (horiz) 30 10
2763 $2.55 Type **463** 40 15
2764 $3.25 Chestnut-tipped toucanet ("Derby Aracari") 40 15
2765 $5 Black-necked aracari . . 50 20
2766 $5.10 Green aracari 50 30
2767 $5.80 Ivory-billed aracari . . 50 30
2768 $6.40 Guiana toucanet . . . 50 30
2769 $6.50 Channel-billed toucan ("Sulphur-breasted Toucan") 50 30
2770 $7.55 Red-billed toucan . . 65 30
2771 $7.65 Toco toucan 65 30
2772 $8.25 Tawny-tufted toucanet ("Natterers Toucanet") 65 30
2773 $8.90 Eared trogon ("Welcome Trogon") . . 65 30
2774 $9.75 Elegant trogon ("Doubtful Trogon") . . 65 30
2775 $11.40 Collared trogon ("Banded Aracari") . . . 75 40
2776 $12.65 Golden-headed quetzal ("Golden-headed Train Bearer") 75 40
2777 $12.80 Rufous-breasted hermit 75 40
2778 $13.90 Band tail barbthroat 75 40
2779 $15.30 White-tipped sickle-bill 80 50
2780 $17.80 Black jacobin 90 60
2781 $19.20 Fiery topaz 90 60
2782 $22.95 Tufted coquette . . . 1·00 70
2783 $26.70 Ecuadorian pied-tail 1·00 70
2784 $30 Resplendent quetzal ("Quetzal") . . . . 1·00 70
2785 $50 Green-crowned brilliant 1·75 1·25
2786 $100 Emerald-chinned hummingbird . . . . . . 2·75 2·75
2787 $190 Lazuline sabre-wing . . 4·50 5·00
2788 $225 Beryline hummingbird 4·50 5·50

1990. Butterfiles (2nd series). Multicoloured.
2789/2860 80c., $2.55, $5, $6.40, $7.65, $8.90, $10 × 64, $50 and $100 . . . . Set of 72 . . . . 24·00 25·00
MS2861 Four sheets, each 102 × 71 mm. (a) $150 "Heliconius aoede". (b) $150 "Phyciodes clio" (horiz). (c) $190 "Thecla hemon". (d) $190 "Nymphidium caricae" Set of 4 sheets . . . . 18·00 20·00
DESIGNS—VERT: $2.55, "Rhetus dysonii"; $5 "Actinote anteas"; $6.40, "Heliconius tales"; $7.65, "Thecla telemus"; $8.90, "Theope eudocia"; $10 (2795), "Heleconius vetustus"; 2796, "Mesosemia eumene"; 2797, "Parides phosphorus"; 2798, "Polystichtis emylius"; 2799, "Xanthocleis aedesia"; 2800, "Doxocopa agathina"; 2801, "Adelpha plesaure"; 2802, "Heliconius wallacei"; 2803, "Notheme eumeus"; 2804, "Melinaea mediatrix"; 2805, "Theritas coronata"; 2806, "Dismorphia orise"; 2807, "Phyciodes ianthe"; 2808, "Morpho aega"; 2809, "Zaretis isidora"; 2810, "Pierella lena"; 2811, "Heliconius silvana"; 2812, "Eunica alcmena"; 2813, "Mechanitis polymnia"; 2814, "Mesosemia ephyne"; 2815, "Thecla erema"; 2816, "Callizona acesta"; 2817, "Stalachtis phaedusa"; 2818, "Battus belus"; 2819, "Nymula phliasus"; 2820, "Parides childrenae"; 2821, "Stalachtis euterpe"; 2822, "Dysmathia portia"; 2823, "Tithorea hermias"; 2824, "Prepona pheridamas"; 2825, "Dismorphia fortunata"; 2826, "Hamadryas amphinome"; $50 "Heliconius vicini"; $100 "Amarynthis meneria". HORIZ: $10 (2827), "Thecla falerina"; 2828, "Pheles heliconides"; 2829, "Echenias leucocyana"; 2830, "Heliconius xanthocles"; 2831, "Mesopthalma idotea"; 2832, "Parides aeneas"; 2833, "Heliconius numata"; 2834, "Thecla critola"; 2835, "Themone pais"; 2836, "Nymula agle"; 2837, "Adelpha cocala"; 2838, "Anaea eribotes"; 2839, "Prepona demophon"; 2840, "Selenophanes cassiope"; 2841, "Consul hippona"; 2842, "Antirrhaea avernus"; 2843, "Thecla telemus"; 2844, "Thyridia confusa"; 2845, "Heliconius burneyi"; 2846, "Parides lysander"; 2847, "Eunica orphise"; 2848, "Adelpha melona"; 2849, "Morpho menelaus"; 2850, "Nymula phylleus"; 2851, "Stalachtis phlegia"; 2852, "Theope barea"; 2853, "Morpho perseus"; 2854, "Lycorea ceres"; 2855, "Archonias bellona"; 2856; "Caeronis chorinaeus"; 2857, "Vila azeca"; 2858, "Nessaea batesii".
Nos. 2795/2810, 2811/26, 2827/42 and 2843/58 respectively were printed together, se-tenant, forming composite designs.

465 "Vanillia inodora"

466 Ivory-billed Woodpecker

1990. Flowers. Multicoloured.
2862/2965 $7.65, $8.90, $10 × 32, $12.80 × 65, $15.30, $17.80, $20, $25 and $100 . . . . Set of 104 . . . . . . 24·00 24·00
MS2966 Five sheets. (a) 65 × 95 mm. $150 "Delonix regia" (horiz). (b) 86 × 65 mm. $150 "Hexisea bidentata" (horiz). (c) 70 × 105 mm. $150 "Galeandra devonianal" (horiz). (d) 68 × 110 mm. $150 "Lecythis ollaria". (e) 74 × 104 mm. $190 "Ionopsis utricularioides" Set of 5 sheets . . . . 16·00 17·00
DESIGNS—VERT: $8.90, "Epidendrum ibaguense"; $10 (2864), "Dichea muricata"; 2865, "Octomeria erosilabia"; 2866, "Spiranthes orchioides"; 2867, "Brassavola nodosa"; 2868, "Epidendrum rigidum"; 2869, "Brassia caudata"; 2870, "Pleurothallis diffusa"; 2871, "Aspasia variegata"; 2872, "Stenia pallida"; 2873, "Cyrtopodium punctatum"; 2874, "Cattleya deckeri"; 2875, "Cryptarrhena lunata"; 2876, "Cattleya violacea"; 2877, "Caularthron bicornutum"; 2878, "Oncidium carthagenense"; 2879, "Galeandra devoniana"; 2880, "Bifrenaria aurantiaca"; 2881, "Epidendrum ciliare"; 2882, "Dichaea picta"; 2883, "Scaphyglottis violacea"; 2884, "Cattleya percivaliana"; 2885, Map and national flag; 2886, "Epidendrum difforme"; 2887, "Eulophia maculata"; 2888, "Spiranthes tenuis"; 2889, "Peristoria guttata"; 2890, "Pleurothallis pruinosa"; 2891, "Cleistes rosea"; 2892, "Maxillaria variabilis"; 2893, "Brassavola cucullata"; 2894,"Epidendrum moyobambae"; 2895, "Oncidium orthostate"; $12.80, "Maxillaria parkeri"; $12.80 (2897), "Brassavola martiana"; 2898, "Paphinia cristata"; 2899, "Aganisia pulchella"; 2900, "Oncidium lanceanum"; 2901, "Lockhartia imbricata"; 2902, "Caularthron bilamellatum"; 2903, "Oncidium nanum"; 2904, "Pleurothallis ovalifolia"; 2905, "Galeandra dives"; 2906, "Cycnoches loddigesii"; 2907, "Ada aurantiaca"; 2908, "Catasetum barbatum"; 2909, "Palmorchis pubescens"; 2910, "Epidendrum anceps"; 2911, "Huntleya meleagris"; 2912, "Sobralia sessilis"; $15.30, "Epidendrum nocturnum"; $17.80, "Catasetum discolor"; $20 "Scuticaria hadwenii"; $25 "Epidendrum fragrans"; $100 "Epistephium parviflorum". HORIZ: $12.80 (2913), "Cochlospermum vitifolium"; 2914, "Eugenia malaccensis"; 2915, "Plumiera rubra"; 2916, "Erythrina glauca"; 2917, "Spathodea campanulata"; 2918, "Jacaranda filicifolia"; 2919, "Samanea saman"; 2920, "Cassia fistula"; 2921, "Abutilon integerrimum"; 2922, "Lagerstroemia speciosa"; 2923, "Tabebuia serratifolia"; 2924, "Guaiacum officinale"; 2925, "Solanum macranthum"; 2926, "Peltophorum roxburghii"; 2927, "Bauhinia variegata"; 2928, "Plumiera alba"; 2929, "Maxillaria camaridii"; 2930, "Vanilla pompona"; 2931, "Stanhopea grandiflora"; 2932, "Oncidium pusillum"; 2933, "Polycycnis vittata"; 2934, "Cattleya lawrenceana"; 2935, "Menadenium labiosum"; 2936, "Rodriguezia secunda"; 2937, "Mormodes buccinator"; 2938, "Otostylis brachystalix"; 2939, "Maxillaria discolor"; 2940, "Liparis elata"; 2941, "Gongora maculata"; 2942, "Koellensteinia graminea"; 2943, "Rudolfiella aurantiaca"; 2944, "Scuticaria steelei"; 2945, "Gloriosa rothschildiana"; 2946, "Pseudocalymma alliaceum"; 2947, "Callichlamys latifolia"; 2948, "Distictis riversii"; 2949, "Maurandya barclaiana"; 2950, "Beaumontia fragrans"; 2951, "Phaseolus caracalla"; 2952, "Mandevilla splendens"; 2953, "Solandra longiflora"; 2954, "Passiflora coccinea"; 2955, "Allamanda cathartica"; 2956, "Bauhinia galpini"; 2957, "Verbena maritima"; 2958, "Mandevilla sauveolens"; 2959, "Phryganocydia corymbosa"; 2960, "Jasminum sambac".
Nos. 2864/79, 2880/95, 2897/2912, 2913/28, 2929/44 and 2945/60 respectively were printed together, se-tenant, forming composite designs.

1990. Fauna. Multicoloured.
2967/86 $12.80 × 20 (vert designs showing endangered birds) . .
2987/3006 $12.80 × 20 (vert designs showing tropical birds) . . .
3007/26 $12.80 × 20 (vert designs showing prehistoric animals)
3027/46 $12.80 × 20 (horiz designs showing endangered wildlife)
Set of 80 . . . . . . 32·00 32·00

DESIGNS—VERT: No. 2968, Cauca guan; 2969, Sun conure; 2970, Resplendent quetzal ("Quetzal"); 2971, Long-wattled umbrellabird; 2972, Banded cotinga; 2973, Blue-throated conure ("Blue-chested Parakeet"); 2974, West Mexican chachalaca ("Rufous-bellied Chachalaca"); 2975, Yellow-faced amazon; 2976, Toucan barbet; 2977, Red siskin; 2978, Guianan cock-of-the-rock ("Cock-of-the-Rock"); 2979, Hyacinth macaw; 2980, Yellow cardinal; 2981, Bare-necked umbrellabird; 2982, Saffron toucanet; 2983, Red-billed curassow; 2984, Spectacled parrotlet; 2985, Lovely cotinga; 2986, Black-bellied gnateater ("Black-breasted Gnateater"); 2987, Swallow-tailed kite; 2988, Hoatzin; 2989, Ruby-topaz hummingbird; 2990, American black vulture; 2991, Rufous-tailed jacamar; 2992, Scarlet macaw; 2993, Rose-breasted thrush tanager; 2994, Toco toucan; 2995, Bearded bellbird; 2996, Blue-crowned motmot; 2997, Green oropendola; 2998, Pompadour cotinga; 2999, Vermilion flycatcher; 3000, Blue and yellow macaw; 3001, White-barred piculet; 3002, Great razor-billed curassow; 3003, Ruddy quail dove; 3004, Paradise tanager; 3005, American darter ("Anhinga"); 3006, Greater flamingo; 3007, Palaelodus; 3008, Archaeotrogon; 3009, Teratornis mirabilis ("Vulture"); 3010, Bradypus tridactylus; 3011, Natalus stramineus bat; 3012, Cebidae; 3013, Cuvieronius; 3014, Phororhacos; 3015, Smilodectes; 3016, Megatherium; 3017, Titanotylopus; 3018, Teleoceras; 3019, Macrauchenia; 3020, Mylodon; 3021, Smilodon; 3022, Glyptodon; 3023, Protohydrocherus; 3024, Archaeohyrax; 3025, Pyrotherium; 3026, Platypittamys. HORIZ: $12.80 (3027), Harpy eagle and hyacinth macaw; 3028, Andean condor; 3029, Amazonian umbrellabird; 3030, Spider monkeys; 3031, Hyacinth macaws; 3032, Red siskin; 3033, Toucan barbet; 3034, Three-toed sloth; 3035, Guanacos; 3036, Spectacled bear; 3037, White-lipped peccary; 3038, Maned wolf; 3039, Jaguar; 3040, Spectacled cayman; 3041, Giant armadillo; 3042, Giant anteater; 3043, South American river otter; 3044, Yapok; 3045, Central American river turtle; 3046, Cauca guan.

Nos. 2967/86, 2987/3006, 3007/26 and 3027/46 respectively were printed together, se-tenant, forming composite designs.

No. 2982 is inscribed "Toucanette" and No. 2995 "Belllbird", both in error.

See also **EMS**34/5.

467 National Flag

1991. 25th Anniv of Independence. Sheet 100 × 70 mm. Litho. Imperf.
MS3047 **467** $225 multicoloured 5·50 6·00

468 Ramon Folist (Cuba) (fencing, 1990)

1991. Winter Olympic Games, Albertville (1st issue), and Olympic Games, Barcelona. Previous Gold Medal Winners. Multicoloured.
3048/3119 $15.30 × 9, $17.80 × 9, $20 × 18, $25 × 18 and $30 × 18 . . . .
Set of 72 . . . . 32·00 35·00
MS3120 Three sheets, each 98 × 70 mm. (a) $150 Johannes Kolehmainen (Finland) (10,000 metres, 1912) (vert). (b) $150 Paavo Nurmi (Finland) (5000 metres, 1924) (vert). (c) $190 Nedo Nadi (Italy) (fencing, 1920) (vert)
Set of 3 sheets . . . . 11·00 12·00

DESIGNS: $15.30 (3049), Lucien Gaudin (France) (fencing, 1924); 3050, Ole Lilloe-Olsen (Norway) (shooting, 1924); 3051, Morris Fisher (U.S.A.) (rifle shooting, 1924); 3052, Ray Ewry (U.S.A.) (long jump, 1900); 3053, Hubert van Innes (Belgium) (archery, 1900); 3054, Alvin Kraenzlein (U.S.A.) (hurdles, 1900); 3055, Johnny Weissmuller (U.S.A.) (swimming, 1924); 3056, Hans Winkler (West Germany) (show jumping, 1956); $17.80 (3057), Viktor Chukarin (Russia) (gymnastics, 1952); 3058, Agnes Keleti (Hungary) (gymnastics, 1952); 3059, Barbel Wochel (East Germany) (200 metres, 1980); 3060, Eric Heiden (U.S.A.) (speed skating, 1980); 3061, Alvodar Gerevich (Hungary) (fencing, 1932); 3062, Giuseppe Delfino (Italy) (fencing, 1952); 3063, Alexander Tikhonov (Russia) (skiing, 1980); 3064, Pahud de Mortanges (Netherlands) (equestrian, 1932); 3065, Patricia McCormick (U.S.A.) (diving, 1952); $20 (3066), Olga Korbut (Russia) (gymnastics, 1972); 3067, Lyudmila Turischeva (Russia) (gymnastics, 1972); 3068, Lasse Viren (Finland) (10,000 metres, 1972); 3069, George Miez (Switzerland) (gymnastics, 1936); 3070, Roland Matthes (East Germany) (swimming, 1972); 3071, Pal Kovaks (Hungary) (fencing, 1936); 3072, Jesse Owens (U.S.A.) (200 metres, 1936); 3073, Mark Spitz (U.S.A.) (swimming, 1972); 3074, Eduardo Mangiarotti (Italy) (fencing, 1936); 3075, Nelli Kim (Russia) (gymnastics, 1976); 3076, Viktor Krovopuskov (Russia) (fencing, 1976); 3077, Viktor Sidiak (Russia) (fencing, 1976); 3078, Nikolai Andrianov (Russia) (gymnastics, 1976); 3079, Nadia Comaneci (Rumania) (gymnastics, 1976); 3080, Mitsuo Tsukahara (Japan) (gymnastics, 1976); 3081, Yelena Novikova-Belova (Russia) (fencing, 1976); 3082, John Naber (U.S.A.) (swimming, 1976); 3083, Kornella Ender (Rumania) (swimming, 1976); $25 (3084), Lydia Skoblikova (Russia) (speed skating, 1964); 3085, Ivar Ballangrud (Norway) (speed skating, 1936); 3086, Clas Thunberg (Finland) (speed skating, 1928); 3087, Anton Heida (U.S.A.) (gymnastics, 1904); 3088, Akinori Nakayama (Japan) (gymnastics, 1968); 3089, Sixten Jernberg (Sweden) (skiing, 1964); 3090, Yevgeniy Grischin (Russia) (speed skating, 1956); 3091, Paul Radmilovic (East Germany) (waterpolo, 1920); 3092, Charles Daniels (U.S.A.) (swimming, 1904); 3093, Sawao Kato (Japan) (gymnastics, 1968); 3094, Rudolf Karpati (Hungary) (fencing, 1948); 3095, Jeno Fuchs (Hungary) (fencing, 1908); 3096, Emil Zatopek (Czechoslovakia) (10,000 metres, 1948); 3097, Fanny Blankers-Koen (Netherlands) (hurdles, 1948); 3098, Melvin Sheppard (U.S.A.) (4 x 400 metres relay, 1908); 3099, Gert Fredriksson (Sweden) (kayak, 1948); 3100, Paul Elvstrom (Denmark) (sailing, 1948); 3101, Harrison Dillard (U.S.A.) (100 metres, 1948); $30 (3102), Al Oerter (U.S.A.) (discus, 1956); 3103, Polina Atsakhova (Russia) (gymnastics, 1956); 3104, Takashi Ono (Japan) (gymnastics, 1956); 3105, Valentin Muratov (Russia) (gymnastics, 1956); 3106, Henri St. Cyr (Sweden) (equestrian, 1956); 3107, Iain Murray Rose (Australia) (swimming, 1956); 3108, Larisa Latynina (Russia) (gymnastics, 1956); 3109, Carlo Pavesi (Italy) (fencing, 1956); 3110, Dawn Fraser (Australia) (swimming, 1956); 3111, Betty Cuthbert (Australia) (400 metres, 1964); 3112, Vera Caslavska (Czechoslovakia) (gymnastics, 1964); 3113, Galin Kulakova (Russia) (skiing, 1972); 3114, Yukio Endo (Japan) (gymnastics, 1972); 3115, Vladimir Morozov (Russia) (kayak, 1972); 3116, Boris Shaklin (Russia) (gymnastics, 1964); 3117, Don Schollander (U.S.A.) (swimming, 1964); 3118, Gyozo Kulscar (Hungary) (fencing, 1964); 3119, Christian D'Oriloa (France) (fencing, 1956).

Nos. 3048/56, 3057/65, 3066/74, 3075/83, 3084/92, 3093/3101, 3102/10 and 3111/19 respectively were printed together, se-tenant, forming composite designs.

Sheetlets containing Nos. 3057/65, 3084/92 and 3111/19 were subsequently re-issued with Nos. 3063, 3086 and 3113 overprinted "ALBERTVILLE '92".

See also Nos. 3186/94 and 3246/54.

1991. 85th Anniv of Rotary International (1990). (a) Nos. 2789/94 and 2859/60 optd or surch **Paul Percy Harris Founder 1868-1947** and emblem (A) or with Rotary emblem and **1905-1990** (B).
3121 80c. Type **464** (B) 10 10
3122 $2.55 "Rhetus dysonii" (A) 10 10
3123 $5 "Actinote anteas" (A) . . 10 10
3124 $6.40 "Heliconius tales" (A) 10 10
3125 $7.65 "Thecla telemus" (A) 10 10
3126 $100 on $8.90 "Theope eudocia" (A) . . . . . . 1·50 1·60
3127 $190 on $50 "Heliconius vicini" (B) . . . . . . 2·50 3·00
3128 $225 on $100 "Amarynthis meneria" (B) . . . . . 2·75 3·25

(b) Nos. 2795/2810 optd or surch as Nos. 3121/8 or with emblems and inscriptions of other international organizations.
3129 $10 "Heliconius vetustus" (B) 15 15
3130 $10 "Mesosemia eumene" (optd Boy Scout emblem and **1907–1992**) 15 15
3131 $10 "Parides phosphorus" (optd Lions Club emblem and **1917–1992**) 15 15
3132 $10 "Polystichtis emylius" (A) 15 15
3133 $10 "Xanthocleis aedesia" (optd **125 Years Red Cross** and cross) 15 15
3134 $10 "Doxocopa agathina" (optd with part Rotary emblem) 15 15
3135 $10 "Adelpha plesaure" (optd with part Rotary emblem) 15 15
3136 $10 "Heliconius wallacei" (optd **125 Years Red Cross** and cross) 15 15
3137 $10 "Notheme eumeus" (optd Lions Club emblem and **1917–1992**) 15 15
3138 $10 "Melinaea mediatrix" (optd with part Rotary emblem) 15 15
3139 $10 "Theritas coronata" (optd with part Rotary emblem) 15 15
3140 $10 "Dismorphia orise" (optd Boy Scout emblem and **1907–1992**) 15 15
3141 $50 on $10 "Phyciodes ianthe" (A) 70 70
3142 $75 on $10 "Morpho aega" (surch Boy Scout emblem and **1907–1992**) . . . . . 1·25 1·40
3143 $100 on $10 "Zaretis isidora" (surch Lions Club emblem and **1917–1992**) . . . . 1·50 1·60
3144 $190 on $10 "Pierella lena" (B) . . . . 2·50 3·00
MS3145 Two sheets, each 102 × 71 mm. (a) $400 on $150 "Heliconius aoede". (b) $500 on $150 "Phyciodes clio" Set of 2 sheets . . . . 9·00 9·25

Nos. **MS**3145a/b only show the new face values on the stamps and have international organization emblems overprinted on the sheet margins.

1991. 65th Birthday of Queen Elizabeth II and 70th Birthday of Prince Philip. As T **198a** of Gambia. Multicoloured.
3146 $12.80 Queen and Prince Philip in evening dress . . 25 20
3147 $15.30 Queen Elizabeth II 25 20
3148 $100 Queen and Prince Philip . . . . 1·25 1·40
3149 $130 Prince Philip . . . . . 1·50 1·60
3150 $150 Prince Philip in R.A.F. uniform . . . . 1·75 1·90
3151 $200 The Queen with Queen Elizabeth the Queen Mother . . . . 2·50 2·75
MS3152 68 × 90 mm. $225 Queen Elizabeth II . . . . 3·00 3·25

1991. 10th Wedding Anniv of Prince and Princess of Wales. As T **198b** of Gambia. Multicoloured.
3153 $8.90 Prince and Princess of Wales 30 20
3154 $50 Separate portraits of Princess and sons . . . . 1·00 80
3155 $75 Prince Charles with Prince William . . . . . 1·25 1·50
3156 $190 Princess Diana with Prince Henry . . . . . . 2·75 3·50
MS3157 68 × 90 mm. $225 Separate portraits of Prince Charles, Prince William and Princess Diana with Prince Henry . . . . 3·25 3·50

1991. 75th Anniv of Lions International (1992). (a) Nos. 2789/94 and 2859/60 optd or surch **Melvin Jones Founder 1880-1961** (A) or with Lions Club emblem and **Lions International 1917–1992** (B).
3158 80c. Type **464** (B) 15 10
3159 $2.55 "Rhetus dysonii" (B) 20 15
3160 $5 "Actinote anteas" (A) . . 30 20
3161 $6.40 "Heliconius tales" (A) 30 25
3162 $7.65 "Thecla telemus" (A) 30 25
3163 $100 on $8.90 "Theope eudocia" (A) . . . . . . 1·50 1·50
3164 $190 on $50 "Heliconius vicini" (B) . . . . 2·50 2·75
3165 $225 on $100 "Amarynthis meneria" (B) . . . . . 2·50 2·75

(b) Nos. 2843/58 optd or surch as Nos. 3158/65 or with emblems and inscriptions of other international organizations.
3166 $10 "Thecla telemus" (optd Lions Club emblem and **1917–1992**) 15 15
3167 $10 "Thyridia confusa" (optd Rotary emblem and **1905–1990**) 15 15
3168 $10 "Heliconius burneyi" (optd Boy Scout emblem and **1907–1992**) 15 15
3169 $10 "Parides lysander" (A) 15 15
3170 $10 "Eunica orphise" (optd **125 Years Red Cross** and cross) 15 15
3171 $10 "Adelpha melona" (optd with part Lions Club emblem) 15 15
3172 $10 "Morpho menelaus" (optd with part Lions Club emblem) 15 15
3173 $10 "Nymula phylleus" (optd **125 Years Red Cross** and cross) 15 15
3174 $10 "Stalachtis phlegia" (optd Rotary emblem and **1905–1990**) 15 15
3175 $10 "Theope barea" (optd with part Lions Club emblem) 15 15
3176 $10 "Morpho perseus" (optd with part Lions Club emblem) 15 15
3177 $10 "Lycorea ceres" (optd Boy Scout emblem and **1907–1992**) 15 15
3178 $50 on $10 "Archonias bellona" (A) 70 70
3179 $75 on $10 "Caerois chorinaeus" (surch Boy Scout emblem and **1907–1992**) . . . . 1·25 1·40
3180 $100 on $10 "Vila azeca" (surch Rotary emblem and **1905–1990**) . . . . . 1·50 1·60
3181 $190 on $10 "Nessaea batesii" (surch Lions Club emblem and **1917–1992**) 2·50 3·00
MS3182 Two sheets, each 102 × 71 mm. (a) $400 on $190 "Nymphidium caricae". (b) $500 on $190 "Thecla hemon" Set of 2 sheets . . . . 10·00 11·00

Nos. **MS**3182a/b only show new face values on the stamps and have international organization emblems overprinted on the sheet margins.

1991. "Phila Nippon '91" International Stamp Exhibition, Tokyo. Sheetlets containing Nos. 2880/95 and 2897/2912, now sold as miniature sheets, and **MS**2966d with some stamps surch **$50** and inscriptions and exhibition logo on the sheet margins, all in red.
MS3183 135 × 203 mm. $10 × 12; $25 on $10; $50 on $10; $75 on $10; $130 on $10 . . . . 8·00 8·50
MS3184 135 × 203 mm. $12.80 × 12; $25 on $12.80; $50 on $12.80; $75 on $12.80; $100 on $12.80 . . . 8·00 8·50
MS3185 68 × 110 mm. $250 on $150 "Lecythis ollaria" . . . . . . 3·75 4·00

1991. Winter Olympic Games, Albertville (1992) (2nd issue). Nos. 2738/46 optd or surch **ALBERTVILLE 92** or **XVIth Olympic Winter Games in Albertville** (No. 3190).
3186/94 $20 x 6, $70 on $20, $100 on $20, $190 on $20 . .
Set of 9 . . . . 16·00 17·00

1991. John F. Kennedy and Sir Winston Churchill Commemorations. Nos. **MS**2966c and **MS**2966e surch **$600** in black or red.
MS3195 70 × 105 mm. $600 on $150 "Galeandra devoniana" (horiz)
MS3196 74 × 104 mm. $600 on $190 "Ionopsis utricularioides" . . .

No. **MS**3195 is additionally overprinted with "IN MEMORIAM John F. Kennedy 1917–1963", "First Man on Moon July 20, 1969" and "Apollo 11" emblem, and No. **MS**3196 "IN MEMORIAM Sir Winston S. Churchill 1874–1965" and "50th Anniversary World War II" on sheet margins.

474 "Akagi" (Japanese aircraft carrier)

1991. 50th Anniv of Japanese Attack on Pearl Harbor. Each blue, red and black.
3197 $50 Type **474** 85 85
3198 $50 Beached Japanese midget submarine 85 85
3199 $50 Mitsubishi A6M Zero-Sen fighter 85 85
3200 $50 U.S.S. "Arizona" (battleship) under attack 85 85
3201 $50 Aichi D3A1 "Val" dive bomber 85 85
3202 $50 U.S.S. "California" (battleship) sinking . . . 85 85
3203 $50 Curtiss P-40 fighters taking off 85 85
3204 $50 U.S.S. "Cassin" and U.S.S. "Downes" damaged in dry dock . . 85 85
3205 $50 Boeing B-17 Flying Fortress crash landing at Bellows Field 85 85
3206 $50 U.S.S. "Nevada" (battleship) on fire 85 85

475 Brandenburg Gate and Location Plan

1991. Anniversaries and Events. Multicoloured.
3207 $10 Type **475** 20 20
3208 $25 President Bush, President Lech Walesa of Poland and Brandenburg Gate 50 50
3209 $25 Scout handshake . . . 50 50
3210 $30 Scouts hiking at Philmont Scout Ranch . . 60 60
3211 $40 Jamboree and Scout Movement emblems . . . 70 70
3212 $60 General de Gaulle at Venice, 1944 . . . . . . 90 90
3213 $75 De Gaulle with Khrushchev, 1960 . . . . 1·25 1·25
3214 $75 Mozart and Castle of Laxenburg . . . . 1·25 1·25
3215 $75 Caroline Herschel (astronomer) and Old Town Hall, Hanover . . 1·25 1·25
3216 $75 Map of Switzerland and woman in Valais costume 1·25 1·25
3217 $80 De Gaulle at Algiers, 1958 . . . . 1·40 1·40
3218 $80 Mozart and death of Leopold II . . . . 1·40 1·40
3219 $80 Otto Lilienthal and "Flugzeug Nr. 3" . . . . 1·40 1·40
3220 $100 Chancellor Kohl, Foreign Minister Genscher and Brandenburg Gate . . . 1·50 1·50
3221 $100 Lord Baden-Powell (vert) . . . . 1·50 1·50
3222 $100 De Gaulle with Pope Paul VI, 1967 . . . . . . 1·50 1·50
3223 $100 Mozart and birthplace, Salzburg . . . . 1·50 1·50
3224 $100 Class P36 steam locomotive . . . . 1·50 1·50
MS3225 Six sheets. (a) 67 × 99 mm. $150 General De Gaulle (vert). (b) 75 × 104 mm. $190 General De Gaulle (different) (vert). (c) 101 × 71 mm. $190 Ceremonial helmet and statues from Brandenburg Gate. (d) 114 × 83 mm. $190 Rocket-flown commemorative cover, 1960. (e) 73 × 104 mm. $190 Mozart cameo (vert). (f) 103 × 74 mm. $190 Arms of Berne and Solothurn Set of 6 sheets . . . . 15·00 16·00

ANNIVERSARIES AND EVENTS—Nos. 3207/8, 3220, **MS**3225c, Bicentenary of Brandenburg Gate, Berlin; 3209/11, 3221, **MS**3225d, 17th World Scout Jamboree, Korea; 3212/13, 3217, 3222, **MS**3225a/b, Birth centenary (1990) of Charles de Gaulle (French statesman); 3214, 3218, 3223, **MS**3225e, Death bicentenary of Mozart; 3215, 750th anniv of Hanover; 3216, **MS**3225f, 700th anniv of Swiss Confederation; 3219, Centenary of Otto Lilienthal's first gliding experiments; 3224, Centenary of Trans-Siberian Railway.

No. 3222 is inscribed "Pope John VI" in error.

476 Disney Characters Carol Singing, 1989

1991. Christmas. Walt Disney Christmas Cards. Multicoloured.
3226 80c. Type **476** 10 10
3227 $2.55 Disney characters and carol singers in tram, 1962 15 15
3228 $5 Donald Duck and Pluto with parcel, 1971 . . . . 20 20
3229 $6.40 "SEASON'S GREETINGS" and Mickey Mouse with candle, 1948 . . . . . . 30 20
3230 $7.65 Mickey Mouse as Father Christmas, 1947 30 20
3231 $8.90 Shadow of Pinocchio with candle, 1939 . . . . 30 20
3232 $50 Three Little Pigs dancing on wolf rug, 1933 1·25 1·25
3233 $50 Conductor and Donald Duck, 1940 (vert) . . . . 1·25 1·25
3234 $50 Elephant and ostrich carol singing, 1940 (vert) 1·25 1·25
3235 $50 Hippo, centaurs, Pinocchio and Goofy, 1940 (vert) . . . . 1·25 1·25
3236 $50 Snow White, Dopey, Mickey and Minnie, 1940 (vert) . . . . 1·25 1·25
3237 $50 Dino, Pluto and Walt Disney, 1940 (vert) . . . 1·25 1·25
3238 $50 Mickey Mouse in sleigh, 1974 (vert) . . . . 1·25 1·25
3239 $50 Three Little Pigs, Winnie the Pooh, Bambi and Thumper, 1974 (vert) 1·25 1·25
3240 $50 Baloo, King Louis, Lady and the Tramp, 1974 (vert) . . . . 1·25 1·25
3241 $50 Alice, Robin Hood, the Cheshire Cat and Goofy, 1974 (vert) . . . . 1·25 1·25
3242 $50 Dumbo, Pinocchio, Peter Pan, Tinkerbelle, Seven Dwarfs and Donald Duck, 1974 (vert) . . . . 1·25 1·25
3243 $50 Pluto pulling sleigh, 1974 (vert) . . . . 1·25 1·25
3244 $200 Mickey and mice carol singing, 1949 . . . . . . 4·00 5·00
MS3245 Eight sheets. (a) 127 × 101 mm. $260 Mickey, Minnie, Clarabelle and Pluto in mail coach, 1932 (vert). (b) 127 × 101 mm. $260 Mickey's House, 1935 (vert). (c) 101 × 127 mm. $260 Jose Carioca, Rooster and Donald Duck on flying carpet, 1944 (vert). (d) 101 × 127 mm. $260 Casey at the Bat and dancers, 1945. (e) 127 × 101 mm. $260 Mickey, Donald and Goofy on musical score, 1946. (f) 127 × 101 mm. $260 Picture of Winnie the Pooh, 1969. (g) 127 × 101 mm. $260 Father Christmas in chimney, 1969 (vert). (h) 101 × 127 mm. $260 Letters of film titles forming Mickey Mouse, 1978 (vert) Set of 8 sheets . . . . 30·00 30·00

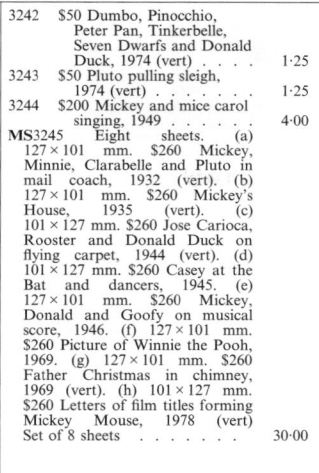

477 Gus Gander playing Ice Hockey

1991. Winter Olympic Games, Albertville (1992) (3rd issue). Walt Disney Cartoon Characters. Multicoloured.
3246 $6.40 Type **477** 35 10
3247 $7.65 Mickey and Minnie Mouse in bobsleigh . . . 40 10
3248 $8.90 Donald's Nephews on luge and skis 45 10
3249 $12.80 Goofy freestyle skiing 60 20
3250 $50 Goofy ski jumping . . 1·75 1·25
3251 $100 Donald and Daisy Duck speed skating . . . 2·50 2·00
3252 $130 Pluto cross-country skiing . . . . 2·75 2·75
3253 $190 Mickey and Minnie Mouse ice dancing . . . . 3·50 4·50
MS3254 Two sheets, each 125 × 100 mm. (a) $225 Donald's nephew curling. (b) $225 Donald Duck slalom skiing Set of 2 sheets 8·00 8·50

478 Columbus landing on Trinidad

479 Tom Mix in "The Great K & A Train Robbery", 1926

1992. 500th Anniv of Discovery of America by Columbus. Multicoloured.
3255 $6.40 Type **478** 55 40
3256 $7.65 Columbus the map-maker 65 45
3257 $8.90 Fleet blown off course 65 45
3258 $12.80 Map of third voyage and Columbus in chains 65 55
3259 $15.30 Sighting land 65 55
3260 $50 "Nina" and "Pinta" . . 1·75 1·00
3261 $75 "Santa Maria" . . . . 2·00 1·25
3262 $100 Columbus trading with Amerindians . . . . . . 2·25 1·75
3263 $125 Crew and sea monster 2·75 2·75
3264 $130 Columbus landing on San Salvador and map of first voyage . . . . 2·75 2·75
3265 $140 Priest and Amerindians 2·75 2·75
3266 $150 Columbus before King Ferdinand and Queen Isabella of Spain . . . . 2·75 2·75
MS3267 Three sheets, each 126 × 91 mm. (a) $280 "Nina" (vert). (b) $280 Columbus (vert). (c) $280 Early map of Caribbean Set of 3 sheets . . . . 13·00 15·00

1992. Classic Movie Posters. Multicoloured.
3268 $8.90 Type **479** 50 40
3269 $12.80 Richard Dix and Irene Dunne in "Cimarron", 1931 . . . . 60 50
3270 $15.30 Fatty Arbuckle in "Buzzin' Around", 1934 60 50
3271 $25 Tom Tyler in "The Adventures of Captain Marvel", 1941 . . . . . 80 70
3272 $30 Boris Karloff in "The Mummy", 1932 . . . . . 1·25 85
3273 $50 Rudolph Valentino in "A Sainted Devil", 1924 1·40 1·10
3274 $75 Seven posters for "A Tale of Two Cities", 1935 1·75 1·40
3275 $100 Chester Conklin in "A Tugboat Romeo", 1916 2·50 1·90
3276 $130 Douglas Fairbanks in "The Thief of Bagdad", 1924 . . . . 2·75 2·25
3277 $150 Laurel and Hardy in "Bacon Grabbers", 1929 3·25 3·00
3278 $190 Marx Brothers in "A Night at the Opera", 1935 4·00 4·25
3279 $200 Orson Welles in "Citizen Kane", 1941 . . 4·00 4·25
MS3280 Four sheets. (a) 70 × 99 mm. $225 Babe Ruth in "Babe Comes Home", 1927. (b) 70 × 99 mm. $225 Mae West in "She Done Him Wrong", 1933. (c) 70 × 99 mm. $225 Charlie Chaplin in "The Circus", 1928. (d) 99 × 70 mm. $225 Poster for never-made film "Zeppelin", 1933. Imperf Set of 4 sheets . . . . 15·00 17·00

1992. Easter. Paintings by Durer. As T **204a** of Gambia. Multicoloured.
3281 $6.40 "The Martyrdom of Ten Thousand" (detail) 25 10
3282 $7.65 "Adoration of the Trinity" (detail of Virgin Mary) 25 10
3283 $12.80 "The Martyrdom of Ten Thousand" (execution detail) 40 20
3284 $15.30 "Adoration of the Trinity" (different detail) 45 25
3285 $50 "The Martyrdom of Ten Thousand" (detail of bishop) . . . . 1·00 75
3286 $100 "Adoration of the Trinity" (different detail) 1·50 1·50
3287 $130 "The Martyrdom of Ten Thousand" (different detail) . . . . 1·75 2·00
3288 $190 "Adoration of the Trinity" (different detail) 3·25 4·00
MS3289 Two sheets, each 71 × 101 mm. (a) $225 "The Martyrdom of Ten Thousand". (b) $225 "Adoration of the Trinity" (detail of Christ on cross) Set of 2 sheets . . . . 8·00 8·50

1992. Baha'i Holy Year. Surch **BAHA'I HOLY YEAR 1992** and value.
3290 $6.40 on 60c. Plate No. 10 (Series 1) (No. 1521) . . .
3291 $7.65 on 60c. Plate No. 31 (Series 1) (No. 1523) . . .
3292 $8.90 on 60c. Plate No. 19 (Series 1) (No. 1522) . . .
3293 $50 on 60c. Plate No. 2 (Series 1) (No. 1519) . . .

481 Queen Elizabeth II and Duke of Edinburgh

1992. 40th Anniv of Queen Elizabeth II's Accession. Multicoloured.
3294 $8.90 Type **481** 55 25
3295 $12.80 Queen at Trooping the Colour 65 30
3296 $100 Queen at Coronation 3·25 2·50
3297 $130 Queen in Garter robes 3·75 3·25
MS3298 Two sheets, each 119 × 79 mm. (a) $225 Queen in Coronation robes. (b) $225 Queen in blue dress Set of 2 sheets . . 8·00 8·50

482 Holy Cross Church, Annai Rupununi

1992. 150th Anniv of Diocese of Guyana. Multicoloured.
3299 $6.40 Type **482** 15 10
3300 $50 St. Peter's Church . . . 80 65
3301 $100 Interior of St. George's Cathedral (vert) . . . . . 1·50 1·60
3302 $190 Map of Guyana (vert) 2·75 3·75
MS3303 104 × 70 mm. $225 Religious symbols . . . . . . 3·75 4·00

483 Burmese

1992. Cats. Multicoloured.
3304 $5 Type **483** 20 10
3305 $6.40 Turkish van 20 10
3306 $12.80 American shorthair 30 20
3307 $15.30 Sphynx 30 20
3308 $50 Egyptian mau . . . . . 1·00 1·00
3309 $50 Russian blue . . . . . 1·00 1·00
3310 $50 Havana brown . . . . 1·00 1·00
3311 $50 Himalayan . . . . . . 1·00 1·00
3312 $50 Manx . . . . 1·00 1·00
3313 $50 Cornish rex . . . . . . 1·00 1·00
3314 $50 Black Persian . . . . . 1·00 1·00
3315 $50 Scottish fold . . . . . 1·00 1·00
3316 $50 Siamese . . . . 1·00 1·00
3317 $100 Japanese bobtail . . . 1·50 1·25
3318 $130 Abyssinian . . . . . 1·75 1·75
3319 $225 Oriental shorthair . . 2·75 3·25
MS3320 Four sheets, each 99 × 69 mm. (a) $250 Chartreuse (vert). (b) $250 Turkish angora (vert). (c) $250 Maine coon (vert). (d) $250 Chinchilla (vert) Set of 4 sheets . . . . 14·00 15·00

484 Red Howler

1992. Animals of Guyana. Multicoloured.
3321 $8.90 Type **484** 20 10
3322 $12.80 Ring-tailed coati . . 25 20
3323 $15.30 Jaguar 30 20
3324 $25 Two-toed sloth 50 30
3325 $50 Giant armadillo . . . . 1·00 80
3326 $75 Giant anteater . . . . 1·50 1·75
3327 $100 Capybara . . . . . . 1·75 1·90
3328 $130 Ocelot . . . . 2·00 2·25
MS3329 Two sheets, each 70 × 100 mm. (a) $225 Woolly opossum (vert). (b) $225 Night monkey (vert) Set of 2 sheets 8·00 9·00

No. **MS**3329a is inscribed "WOLLY OPOSSUM" in error.

485 Oligocene Mammoth

1992. Elephants. Multicoloured.
3330 $50 Type **485** . . . . 1·50 1·25
3331 $50 Mid-Miocene stegodon 1·50 1·25
3332 $50 Pliocene mammoth . . 1·50 1·25
3333 $50 Carthaginian elephant crossing Alps, 219 B.C. 1·50 1·25
3334 $50 Ceremonial elephant of Maharaja of Mysore, India . . . . 1·50 1·25
3335 $50 Elephant pulling teak trunks, Burma . . . . . 1·50 1·25
3336 $50 Tiger-hunting by elephant, India . . . . . 1·50 1·25
3337 $50 Elephant towing raft on River Kwai, Thailand . . 1·50 1·25
MS3338 110 × 80 mm. $225 African elephant . . . . 5·00 5·00

486 Palomino

1992. Horses. Multicoloured.
3339 $190 Type **486** . . . . . . 3·00 3·00
3340 $190 Appaloosa . . . . . . 3·00 3·00
3341 $190 Clydesdale . . . . . . 3·00 3·00
3342 $190 Arab . . . . 3·00 3·00
3343 $190 Morgan . . . . 3·00 3·00
3344 $190 Friesian . . . . 3·00 3·00

3345 $190 Pinto . . . . 3·00 3·00
3346 $190 Thoroughbred . . . . 3·00 3·00
MS3347 109 × 80 mm. $190 Lipizzaner (47 × 29 mm) . . . 4·00 4·25
No. 3340 is inscribed "APALOOSA" in error.

1992. International Conference on Nutrition, Rome. Surch **INT. CONFERENCE ON NUTRITION 1992** and value.
3348 $6.40 on 150c. Plate No. 45 (Series 1) (No. 1769) . . .
3349 $7.65 on 150c. Plate No. 42 (Series 1) (No. 1768) . . .
3350 $8.90 on 150c. Plate No. 40 (Series 1) (No. 1767) . . .
3351 $10 on 200c. Plate No. 43 (Series 1) (No. 1658) . . .
3352 $50 on 200c. Plate No. 43 (Series 1) (No. 1658) . . .

488 Marklin Swiss "Crocodile" Locomotive, 1933

1992. "Genova '92" International Thematic Stamp Exhibition. Toy Trains from German Manufacturers. Multicoloured.
3353/61 $45 × 9 Made by Marklin: Type **488**; French tramcar, 1902; British "Flatiron" tank engine, 1913; German switching engine, 1970; Third class carriage, 1909; American style locomotive, 1904; Zurich tramcar, 1928; Central London Railway locomotive in Paris-Orleans livery, 1904; British GWR "Great Bear" locomotive, 1909 . .
3362/70 $45 × 9 Made by Marklin: LMS "Precursor" tank engine, 1923; American "Congressional Limited" passenger carriage, 1908; Swiss Type "Ae 3/6" locomotive, 1934; German Class 80, 1975; British Southern Railways third class carriage, 1926; LNWR Bowen-Cooke tank engine, 1913; London Underground "Two Penny Tube", 1901; French Paris-Orsay steeplecab, 1920; Passenger locomotive, 1895 . . . .
3371/9 $45 × 9 Made by Marklin: American style locomotive, 1907; German passenger carriage, 1908; British Great Eastern Railway locomotive, 1908; London Underground steeplecab, 1904; Santa Fe Railroad diesel locomotive, 1962; British GNR locomotive, 1903; Caledonian Railway "Cardean", 1906; British LNWR passenger carriage, 1903; Swiss St. Gotthard Railway locomotive, 1920 . .
3380/8 $45 × 9 Made by Marklin: British LB SCR tank engine No. 22, 1920; Central London Railway steeplecab locomotive, 1904; German "Borsig" streamlined, 1935; French Paris-Lyon-Mediterranee first class carriage, 1929; American style locomotive No. 1021, 1904; French Paris-Orsay long-nose steeplecab, 1920; British LNER "Cock o' the North", 1936; Prussian State Railways Class P8, 1975; German diesel railcar set, 1937 . . .
3389/97 $45 × 9 Marklin North British Railway "Atlantic", 1913; Bing British LNWR "Precursor", 1916; Marklin British GWR "King George V", 1937; Marklin "Kaiser Train" passenger carriage, 1901; Bing side tank locomotive No. 88, 1904; Marklin steeplecab, 1912; Marklin "Adler", 1935; Bing British GWR "County of Northampton", 1909; Bing British Midland Railway "Black Prince", 1908 . . . .
3398/3406 $45 × 9 Made by Bing: Midland Railway "Deeley Type" No. 483, 1909; British Midland Railway No. 2631, 1903; German Pacific, 1927; British GWR third class coach, 1926; British LSWR "M7" No. 109, 1909; Side tank engine "Pilot", 1901; British LNWR Webb "Cauliflower", 1912; Side tank locomotive No. 112, 1910; British GNR "Stirling Single", 1904 . . . . . .
3407/15 $45 × 9 Carette tin "Penny Bazaar" train, 1904; Winteringham locomotive, 1917; Carette British Northeastern Railway Smith Compound, 1905; Carette S.E. C.R. steam railcar, 1908; Carette British Great Northern Railway Stirling Single No. 776, 1903; Carette British Midland Railways locomotive No. 1132M, 1911; Carette London Metropolitan Railway Co. "Westinghouse" locomotive No. 5, 1908; Carette Clestory carriage, 1907; Carette steam railcar No. 1, 1906
3416/24 $45 × 9 Made by Bing: Engine and tender, 1895; British Midland Railway "Single" No. 650, 1913; No. 524/510 reversible locomotive, 1916; "Kaiser Train" passenger carriage, 1902; British rural station, 1915; British LSWR M7 tank locomotive, 1909; "Windcutter", 1912; British Great Central Railway "Sir Sam Fay", 1914; Scottish Caledonian Railway "Dunalastair" locomotive, 1910) . .
3353/3424 Set of 72 . . . . 45·00 48·00
MS3425 Eight sheets, each 116 × 83 mm. (a) $350 Bing contractor's locomotive No. 18, 1904 (51 × 39 mm). (b) $350 Marklin rack railway steeplecab locomotive, 1908 (51 × 39 mm). (c) $350 Bing British GWR "County of Northampton" locomotive, 1909 (51 × 39 mm).(d) $350 Marklin French Paris–Lyon–Mediterranean Pacific locomotive, 1912 (51 × 39 mm). (e) $350 Bing Pabst Blue Ribbon beer refrigerator wagon, 1925 (51 × 39 mm). (f) $350 Marklin French "Mountain Etat" locomotive, 1933 (51 × 39 mm). (g) $350 Marklin German National Railroad Class 0-1 Pacific locomotive, 1937 (51 × 39 mm). (h) $350 Marklin American "Commodore Vanderbilt" locomotive, 1937 (51 × 39 mm) Set of 8 sheets . . . . 30·00 32·00

1992. Postage Stamp Mega Event, New York. Sheet 100 × 70 mm, containing multicoloured design as T **207a** of Gambia, but vert.
MS3426 $325 Statue of Liberty 6·00 7·00

489 Aquarius

1992. Signs of the Zodiac. Multicoloured.
3427 $30 Type **489** 85 85
3428 $30 Pisces 85 85
3429 $30 Aries 85 85
3430 $30 Taurus 85 85
3431 $30 Gemini 85 85
3432 $30 Cancer 85 85
3433 $30 Leo 85 85
3434 $30 Virgo 85 85
3435 $30 Libra 85 85
3436 $30 Scorpio 85 85
3437 $30 Sagittarius 85 85
3438 $30 Capricorn 85 85

490 City Walls and Two Birds

1992. Bible Stories (1st series). David and Goliath. Multicoloured.
3439 $25 Type **490** 50 50
3440 $25 City walls and one bird at right 50 50
3441 $25 Sun over city gateway 50 50
3442 $25 City walls and one bird at left 50 50
3443 $25 City walls and no birds 50 50
3444 $25 Philistine army and edge of shield 50 50
3445 $25 Goliath's head and torso 50 50
3446 $25 Goliath's arm and spear 50 50
3447 $25 Philistine army and spearhead 50 50
3448 $25 Philistine infantry . . . 50 50
3449 $25 Philistine cavalry and infantry 50 50
3450 $25 Goliath's shield 50 50
3451 $25 Goliath's waist and thigh 50 50
3452 $25 David with sling 50 50
3453 $25 Israelite soldier with spear 50 50
3454 $25 Two Israelite soldiers with spears and shields . . 50 50
3455 $25 Goliath's right leg . . . 50 50
3456 $25 Goliath's left leg (face value at foot) 50 50
3457 $25 David's legs and Israelite standard 50 50
3458 $25 Three Israelite soldiers 50 50
3459 $25 Israelite soldier and parts of two shields . . . 50 50
3460 $25 Israelite soldier with sword 50 50
3461 $25 Back of Israelite soldier 50 50
3462 $25 Israelite soldier leaning on rock 50 50
3463 $25 Israelite soldier looking left 50 50
Nos. 3439/63 were printed together, se-tenant, forming a composite design.
See also Nos. 4020/4116.

491 Count Von Zeppelin and Airship over Lake Constance, 1909

1992. Anniversaries and Events. Multicoloured.
3464 $12.80 Type **491** 50 35
3465 $50 "Voyager I" and Jupiter 1·50 1·00
3466 $50 Adenauer with Pres. Kennedy, 1961 . . . . . 1·00 1·00
3467 $100 Aeromedical airlift . . 2·00 2·00
3468 $100 Boutu ("Amazon Dolphin") . . . . 2·00 2·00
3469 $130 Baby gorilla . . . . . 2·50 2·50
3470 $130 Mobile eye screening unit and doctor with child 2·50 2·50
3471 $130 "Stars and Stripes" (winning yacht, 1987) . . 2·50 2·50
3472 $130 Lift-off of "Voyager I", 1977 . . . . 2·50 2·50
3473 $190 Adenauer with President De Gaulle of France, 1962 . . . . . . 3·25 3·25
3474 $225 Von Zeppelin and airship preparing for take-off, 1905 . . . . 3·50 3·50
MS3475 Four sheets. (a) 76 × 105 mm. $225 Ferdinand von Zeppelin (vert). (b) 116 × 80 mm. $225 Earth from Space (vert). (c) 84 × 111 mm. $225 Konrad Adenauer (vert). (d) 87 × 111 mm. $225 "Hyperohus marmoratus" (tree frog) (vert) Set of 4 sheets 15·00 16·00

ANNIVERSARIES and EVENTS: Nos. 3464, 3474, **MS**3475a, 75th death anniv of Count Ferdinand von Zeppelin; 3465, 3472, **MS**3475b, International Space Year; 3466, 3473, **MS**3475c, 75th death anniv of Konrad Adenauer (German statesman); 3467, United Nations World Health Organization projects; 3468/9, **MS**3475d, Earth Summit '92, Rio; 3470, 75th anniv of International Association of Lions Clubs; 3471, Americas Cup Yachting Championship.

492 Hyacinth Macaw

1993. South American Parrots. Multicoloured.
3476 80c. Type **492** 30 15
3477 $6.40 Scarlet macaw (preening) 50 25
3478 $7.65 Buffon's macaw ("Green Macaw") (vert) 50 25
3479 $15.30 Orange-chinned parakeet ("Tovi Parakeet") 70 50
3480 $50 Blue and yellow macaw 1·00 80
3481 $100 Military macaw (vert) 1·50 1·25
3482 $130 Green-winged macaw ("Red and Green Macaw") (vert) . . . . . 1·75 1·75
3483 $190 Chestnut-fronted macaw ("Severa Macaw") 2·50 3·00
MS3484 Two sheets, each 108 × 74 mm. (a) $225 Scarlet macaw. (b) $225 Monk parakeet (vert) Set of 2 sheets . . . . . 7·00 7·50

493 Crimson Topaz

1993. Birds of Guyana. Multicoloured.
3485 $50 Type **493** 75 75
3486 $50 Bearded bellbird 75 75
3487 $50 Amazonian umbrellabird 75 75
3488 $50 Paradise jacamar . . . 75 75
3489 $50 Paradise tanager 75 75
3490 $50 White-tailed trogon . . 75 75
3491 $50 Scarlet macaw 75 75
3492 $50 Hawk-headed parrot ("Red-fan Parrot") . . . 75 75
3493 $50 Red-billed toucan . . . 75 75
3494 $50 White-faced antcatcher ("White-plumed Antbird") 75 75
3495 $50 Crimson-hooded manakin 75 75
3496 $50 Guianan cock of the rock 75 75
MS3497 70 × 100 mm. $325 Tufted coquette (horiz) . . . . 5·00 5·50
Nos. 3485/96 were printed together, se-tenant, with the backgrounds forming a composite design.

494 Manatee surfacing **495** Tamandua

1993. Endangered Species. American Manatee ("Caribbean Manatee"). Multicoloured.
3498 $6.40 Type **494** 60 30
3499 $7.60 Cow and calf feeding 60 30
3500 $8.90 Manatee underwater 60 30
3501 $50 Two manatees . . . . 2·25 2·25

1993. Animals of Guyana. Multicoloured.
3502 $50 Type **495** 75 75
3503 $50 Pale-throated sloth ("Three-toed Sloth") . . . 75 75
3504 $50 Red howler 75 75
3505 $50 Four-eyed opossum . . 75 75
3506 $50 Black spider monkey . . 75 75
3507 $50 Giant otter 75 75
3508 $50 Red brocket 75 75
3509 $50 Brazilian tree porcupine 75 75
3510 $50 Tayra 75 75
3511 $50 Brazilian tapir 75 75
3512 $50 Ocelot 75 75
3513 $50 Giant armadillo 75 75
MS3514 100 × 70 mm. $325 Paca 4·50 5·00
Nos. 3502/13 were printed together, se-tenant, the backgrounds forming a composite design.
No. 3505 is inscribed "Four-eyed Opossium" in error.

496 Pteranodon

1993. Prehistoric Animals. Multicoloured.
3515/26 $30 × 12 (Type **496**; Cearadactylus; Eudimorphodon; Pterodactylus; Stauirkosaurus; Euoplocephalus; Tuojiangosaurus; Oviraptor; Protoceratops; Panaoplosaurus; Psittacosaurus; Corythosaurus) . . . .
3527/38 $30 × 12 (Sordes; Quetzalcoatlus; Archaeopteryx in flight; Rhamphorynchus; Spinosaurus; Anchisaurus; Stegosaurus; Leaellynosaurs; Minmi; Heterdontosaurus; Esothosaurus; Deninonychus) . . . .
3539/50 $30 × 12 (Archaeopteryx on branch; Pteranodon (different); Quetzalcoatlus (three); Protoavis; Dicraeosaurus; Moschops; Lystrosaurus; Dimetrondon; Staurikosaurus; Cacops; Diarthrognathus; Estemmenosuchus) . .
3515/50 Set of 36 . . . . 17·00 19·00
Nos. 3515/26, 3527/38 and 3539/50 respectively were printed together, se-tenant, with the backgrounds forming composite designs.

1993. 40th Anniv of Coronation. As T **215a** of Gambia. Multicoloured.
3551 $25 Queen Elizabeth II in Coronation robes (photograph by Cecil Beaton) 85 85
3552 $50 Royal gems . . . . . . 1·25 1·25
3553 $75 Queen Elizabeth and Prince Philip . . . . . . 1·40 1·40
3554 $130 Queen opening Parliament . . . . 1·75 2·00
MS3555 69 × 100 mm. $325 "Queen in Coronation Robes" (Sir James Gunn) (28½ × 42½ mm) . . . . 5·00 5·50

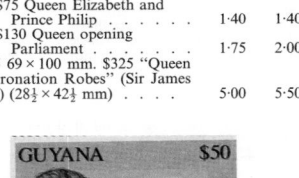

497 Gabriel Marquez (author)

1993. Famous People of the Twentieth Century. Multicoloured. (a) Arts and Literature.
3556 $50 Type **497** 75 75
3557 $50 Pablo Picasso (artist) . . 75 75
3558 $50 Cecil De Mille (film director) 75 75
3559 $50 Martha Graham (dancer) 75 75
3560 $50 Peace dove (inscr "20th Century Arts and Literature") 75 75
3561 $50 Charlie Chaplin (actor) 75 75
3562 $50 Paul Robeson (actor) 75 75
3563 $50 Rudolph Dunbar (musician) 75 75
3564 $50 Louis Armstrong (musician) 75 75
MS3565 100 × 70 mm. $250 Elvis Presley (singer) (vert) . . . . . 3·50 3·50

(b) Science and Medicine.
3566 $50 Louis Leakey (archaeologist and anthropologist) 75 75
3567 $50 Jonas Salk (discoverer of polio vaccine) 75 75
3568 $50 Hideyo Noguchi (bacteriologist) 75 75
3569 $50 Karl Landsteiner (pathologist) 75 75
3570 $50 As No. 3550, but inscr "20th Century Science and Medicine" 75 75
3571 $50 Sigmund Freud (founder of psychoanalysis) 75 75
3572 $50 Louis Pasteur (chemist) 75 75
3573 $50 Madame Curie (physicist) 75 75
3574 $50 Jean Baptiste Perrin (physicist) 75 75
MS3575 100 × 70 mm. $250 Einstein's Theory of Relativity equation (vert) . . . . 3·50 3·50

(c) Sports Personalities.
3576 $50 O. J. Simpson (American football) . . . 75 75
3577 $50 Rohan Kanhai (cricket) 75 75
3578 $50 Gabriela Sabatini (tennis) 75 75
3579 $50 Severiano Ballesteros (golf) 75 75
3580 $50 As No. 3550, but inscr "20th Century Sports" . . 75 75
3581 $50 Franz Beckenbauer (football) 75 75
3582 $50 Pele (football) 75 75
3583 $50 Wilt Chamberlain (basketball) 75 75
3584 $50 Nadia Comaneci (gymnastics) 75 75
MS3585 100 × 70 mm. $250 Jackie Robinson (baseball) (vert) . . 3·50 3·50

(d) Peace and Humanity.
3586 $100 Mahatma Gandhi (India) . . . . 1·10 1·10
3587 $100 Dalai Lama (Tibet) . . 1·10 1·10
3588 $100 Michael Manley (Jamaica) . . . . 1·10 1·10
3589 $100 Perez de Cuellar (U.N. Secretary-General) . . . . 1·10 1·10
3590 $100 Peace dove and globe 1·10 1·10
3591 $100 Mother Teresa (India) 1·10 1·10
3592 $100 Martin Luther King (U.S.A.) . . . . 1·10 1·10
3593 $100 Pres. Nelson Mandela (South Africa) . . . . . 1·10 1·10
3594 $100 Raoul Wallenberg (Sweden) . . . . 1·10 1·10
MS3595 100 × 70 mm. $250 Nobel Peace Prize scroll (vert) . . . . 3·50 3·50

(e) Politics.
3596 $100 Nehru (India) . . . . 1·10 1·10
3597 $100 Dr. Eric Williams (Trinidad and Tobago) . . 1·10 1·10
3598 $100 Pres. John F. Kennedy (U.S.A.) . . . . 1·10 1·10
3599 $100 Pres. Hugh Desmond Hoyte (Guyana) . . . . 1·10 1·10
3600 $100 Peace dove and map of the Americas . . . . . . 1·10 1·10
3601 $100 Friedrich Ebert (Germany) . . . . 1·10 1·10
3602 $100 Pres F. D. Roosevelt (U.S.A.) . . . . 1·10 1·10
3603 $100 Mikhail Gorbachev (Russia) . . . . 1·10 1·10
3604 $100 Sir Winston Churchill (Great Britain) . . . . . 1·10 1·10
MS3605 100 × 70 mm. $250 Flags of United Nations and member countries (vert) . . . . 3·50 3·50

(f) Transportation and Technology.
3606 $100 Douglas DC-3 cargo plane . . . . 1·25 1·25
3607 $100 Space Shuttle . . . . 1·25 1·25
3608 $100 Concorde . . . . . . 1·25 1·25
3609 $100 Count Ferdinand von Zeppelin and "Graf Zeppelin" . . . . 1·25 1·25
3610 $100 Peace dove and rocket trails . . . . 1·25 1·25
3611 $100 Marconi and aerial tower . . . . 1·25 1·25
3612 $100 Adrian Thompson (mountaineer) and Mt. Roraima . . . . 1·25 1·25
3613 $100 "Hikari" express train, Japan . . . . 1·25 1·25
3614 $100 Johann von Neumann and computer . . . . . . 1·25 1·25
MS3615 100 × 70 mm. $250 Lunar module "Eagle" on Moon . . 4·00 4·00
Nos. 3556/64, 3566/74, 3576/84, 3586/94, 3596/3604 and 3606/14 respectively were printed together, se-tenant, with composite background designs on Nos. 3586/94, 3596/3604 and 3606/14.
No. 3562 is inscribed "Paul Roebeson" in error.

498 "Bather, Paris" (Picasso)

1993. Anniversaries and Events. Multicoloured (except No. **MS**3628c).
3616 $15.30 Type **498** 15 20
3617 $25 Willy Brandt with Prime Minister of Israel Golda Meir, 1969 (horiz) 40 40
3618 $50 "Pantaloons" (left half) (Tadeusz Brzozowski) . . 50 55
3619 $50 Georg Hackl (men's single luge, 1992) 70 70
3620 $50 Astrolabe 70 70
3621 $75 Miedzyrecz Castle . . . 75 80
3622 $100 "Two Nudes" (Picasso) 1·00 1·10
3623 $130 "Pantaloons" (right half) (Tadeusz Brzozowski) . . . . . . 1·25 1·40
3624 $130 Karen Magnussen (women's figure skating, 1972) . . . . 1·50 1·50
3625 $190 "Nude seated on a Rock" (Picasso) . . . . . 1·90 2·25
3626 $190 Willy Brandt at Georgsmarienhutten Steel Mill, 1969 (horiz) . . . . 2·25 2·50
3627 $190 Dish aerial . . . . . 2·25 2·50
MS3628 Five sheets. (a) 104 × 75 mm. $300 Copernicus. (b) 75 × 104 mm. $325 "The Rescue" (detail) (Picasso). (c) 104 × 75 mm. $325 Willy Brandt giving interview, 1969 (brown and black). (d) 99 × 70 mm. $325 "Children in the Garden" (Wladyslaw Podkowinski) (horiz). (e) 75 × 104 mm. $325 German four-man bobsleigh team, 1992 Set of 5 sheets . . . . 20·00 22·00
ANNIVERSARIES and EVENTS: Nos. 3616, 3622, 3625, **MS**3628b, 20th death anniv of Picasso (artist); 3617, 3626, **MS**3628c, 80th birth anniv (1992) of Willy Brandt (German politician); 3618, 3621, 3623, **MS**3628d, "Polska '93" International Stamp Exhibition, Poznan; 3619, 3624, **MS**3628e, Winter Olympic Games '94, Lillehammer; 3620, 3627, **MS**3628a, 450th death anniv of Copernicus (astronomer).
Nos. 3618 and 3623 were printed together, se-tenant, forming a composite design showing the complete painting.

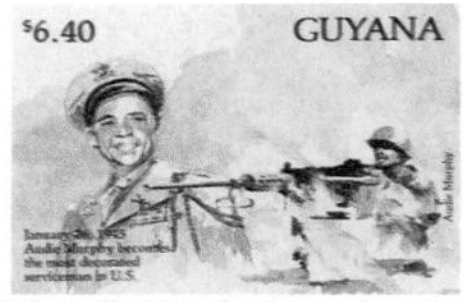

499 Audie Murphy (most decorated U.S. serviceman)

1993. 50th Anniv of Second World War (1st issue). Multicoloured.
3629 $6.40 Type **499** 70 20
3630 $7.65 Allied troops in Normandy (8 June 1944) 70 25
3631 $8.90 American howitzer crew, Battle of Montecassino (18 May 1944) 75 30
3632 $12.80 American aircraft attacking "Yamato" (Japanese battleship), Battle of East China Sea (7 April 1945) 80 50
3633 $15.30 St. Basil's Cathedral, Moscow (Foreign Ministers' Conference, 19 October 1943) 80 50
3634 $50 American troops crossing Rhine at Remagen (7 March 1945) 1·50 75
3635 $100 Boeing B-29 Superfortresses raiding Japan from China (15 June 1944) . . . . . 2·25 1·75
3636 $130 General Patton and map of Sicily (17 August 1943) . . . . 2·50 2·25
3637 $190 Destruction of "Tirpitz" (German battleship) (12 November 1944) . . . . 3·25 3·25
3638 $200 American forces in Brittany (1 August 1944) 3·25 3·25
3639 $225 American half-track (ceasefire in Italy, 2 May 1945) . . . . 3·50 3·75
MS3640 100 × 69 mm. $325 Meeting of American and Russian troops on the Elbe (25 April 1945) . . 5·00 6·00
No. 3631 is inscribed "Monte Casino" in error. See also Nos. 3641/60 and 3942/61.

500 R.A.A.F. Bristol Type 156 Beaufighter, Battle of the Bismarck Sea (2-4 March 1943)

501 Stuart Pearce (England)

1993. 50th Anniv of Second World War (2nd issue). Multicoloured.
3641 $50 Type **500** 80 80
3642 $50 Lockheed P-38 Lightning attacking Admiral Yamamoto's plane, Bougainville (7 April 1943) 80 80
3643 $50 Consolidated B-24 Liberator bombers, Tarawa (17-19 September 1943) 80 80
3644 $50 North American B-25 Mitchell bomber, Rabaul (12 October 1943) 80 80
3645 $50 U.S. Navy aircraft attacking Makin (19 November 1943) . . . 80 80
3646 $50 U.S.A.A.F. bombers on first daylight raid over Germany (27 January 1943) 80 80
3647 $50 R.A.F. De Havilland D.H.98 Mosquito bombers on first daylight raid over Berlin (30 January 1943) 80 80
3648 $50 Allied aircraft over Hamburg (24-30 July 1943) 80 80
3649 $50 Consolidated B-24 Liberators bombing Ploesti oil refineries, Rumania (1 August 1943) 80 80
3650 $50 German nightfighter attacking Allied bombers over Berlin (18 November 1943) 80 80
3651 $50 Japanese aircraft carriers during Operation 1 (7 April 1943) 80 80
3652 $50 Lt. John F. Kennedy's motor torpedo boat U.S.S. "PT109" in Blackett Strait (1 August 1943) 80 80
3653 $50 U.S.S. "Enterprise" (aircraft carrier) 80 80
3654 $50 American battleships bombarding Rabaul (12 October 1943) 80 80
3655 $50 American landing craft at Cape Gloucester (26 December 1943) . . . 80 80
3656 $50 Commissioning of U.S.S. "Bogue" (first anti-submarine escort carrier) (February 1943) 80 80
3657 $50 Grumman FM-2 Wildcat fighters from U.S.S. "Bogue" sinking "U-118" 80 80
3658 $50 U-boat launching torpedo during peak of Battle of the Atlantic (March 1943) 80 80
3659 $50 Surrender of Italian fleet at Malta (10 September 1943) 80 80
3660 $50 H.M.S. "Duke of York" (battleship) sinking "Scharnhorst" (26 December 1943) . . . 80 80

1993. World Cup Football Championship, U.S.A. (1994) (1st issue). Multicoloured.
3661 $5 Type **501** 15 10
3662 $6.40 Ronald Koeman (Netherlands) 15 10
3663 $7.65 Gianluca Vialli (Italy) 20 10
3664 $12.80 McStay (Scotland) and Alemao (Brazil) . . . 30 20
3665 $15.30 Ceulemans (Belgium) and Butcher (England) . . 30 20
3666 $50 Dragan Stojkovic (Yugoslavia) 75 65
3667 $100 Ruud Gullit (Netherlands) . . . . . . 1·25 1·25
3668 $130 Miloslav Kadlec (Czechoslovakia) . . . . 1·40 1·50
3669 $150 Ramos (Uruguay) and Berthold (Germany) . . . 1·75 2·00
3670 $190 Baggio (Italy) and Wright (England) . . . . 2·25 2·50
3671 $200 Yarentchuck (Russia) and Renquin (Belgium) 2·40 2·75
3672 $225 Timofte (Rumania) and Aleinikov (Russia) . . 2·50 3·00
MS3673 Two sheets. (a) 101 × 73 mm. $325 Salvatore Schillaci (Italy) and Jose Pintos (Uruguay) (horiz). (b) 73 × 101 mm. $325 Rene Higuita (Colombia) Set of 2 sheets . . 8·00 8·50
See also Nos. 4142/58.

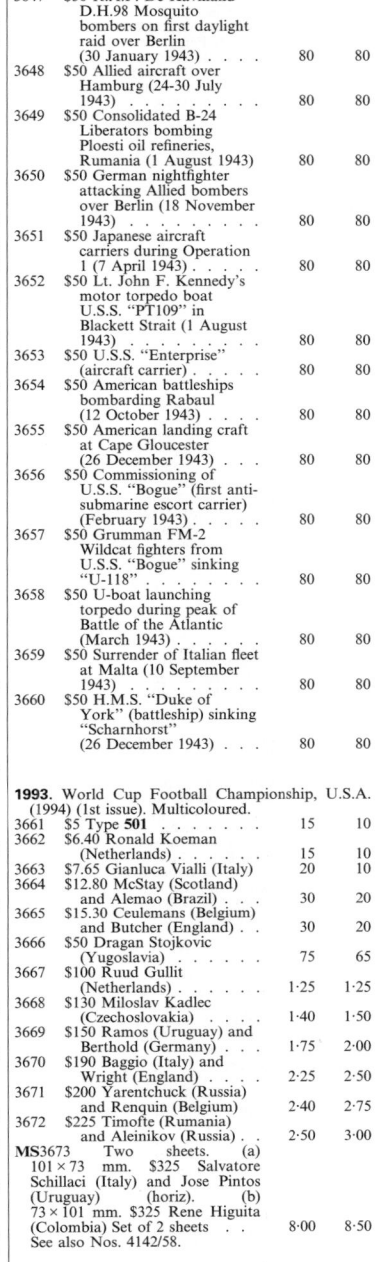

502 Sir Shridath Ramphal

503 "Donald's Better Self", 1938

1993. 1st Recipients of Order of the Caribbean Community. Multicoloured.
3674 $7.65 Type **502** 60 50
3675 $7.65 William Demas 60 50
3676 $7.65 Derek Walcott . . . . 1·00 65

1993. Christmas. Paintings by Rubens and Durer. As T **211b** of Gambia. Each black, yellow and red (Nos. 3678, 3680/1, 3684) or multicoloured (others).
3677 $6.40 "The Holy Family under the Apple Tree" (detail) (Rubens) 15 10
3678 $7.65 "The Virgin in Glory" (detail) (Durer) 15 10
3679 $12.80 "The Holy Family under the Apple Tree" (different detail) (Rubens) 20 15
3680 $15.30 "The Virgin in Glory" (different detail) (Durer) 20 20
3681 $50 "The Virgin in Glory" (different detail) (Durer) 70 55

3682 $130 "The Holy Family under the Apple Tree" (different detail) (Rubens) 1·50 1·60
3683 $190 "The Holy Family under the Apple Tree" (different detail) (Rubens) 2·25 2·50
3684 $250 "The Virgin in Glory" (different detail) (Durer) 2·75 3·25
MS3685 Two sheets. (a) 126 × 101 mm. $325 "The Holy Family under the Apple Tree" (Rubens). (b) 101 × 126 mm. $325 "The Virgin in Glory" (woodcut by Durer from "The Life of the Virgin") Set of 2 sheets . . . . 6·50 7·75

1993. Bicentenary of the Louvre, Paris. As T **209b** of Gambia. Multicoloured.
3686 $50 "Mona Lisa" (Leonardo da Vinci)
3687/94 $50 × 8 "Self-portrait with Spectacles" (Chardin), "Infanta Maria Theresa" (Velazquez); "Spring" (Arcimboldo); "The Virgin of Sorrows" (Bouts); "The Student" (Fragonard); "Francois I" (Clouet); "Le Condottiere" (Antonello da Messina); "La Bohemienne" (Hals)
3695/3702 $50 × 8 "The Village Bride" (left detail) (Greuze); "The Village Bride" (centre detail); "The Village Bride" (right detail); "Self-portrait" (Melendez); "The Knight, the Girl and the Mountain" (Baldung-Grien); "The Young Beggar" (Murillo); "The Pilgrims of Emmaus" (left detail) (Le Nain); "The Pilgrims of Emmaus" (right detail) . . . . . .
3703/10 $50 × 8 "Woman with a Flea" (detail) (Crespi); "The Woman with Dropsy" (detail) (Dou); "Portrait of a Couple" (Ittenbach); "Cleopatra" (Moreau); "Riches" (Vouet); "Old Man and Young Boy" (Ghirlandaio); "Louis XIV" (Rigaud); "The Drinker" (Pieter de Hooch) . . . . . .
3711/18 $50 × 8 "Woman with a Flea" (Crespi); "Self-portrait at Easel" (Rembrandt); "Algerian Women" (detail) (Delacroix); "Head of a Young Man" (Raphael); "Venus and The Graces" (detail) (Botticelli); "Still Life with Chessboard" (detail) (Lubin Baugin); "Lady Macbeth" (Fussli); "The Smoke-filled Room" (detail) (Chardin) . . . . .
3719/26 $50 × 8 "The Virgin with the Rabbit" (Titian); "The Virgin with the Rabbit" (detail of head) (Titian); "The Beautiful Gardener" (detail) (Raphael); "The Lace-maker" (Vermeer); "Jeanne d'Aragon" (detail) (Raphael); "The Astronomer" (Vermeer); "The Rialto Bridge" (detail) (Canaletto); "Sigismond Malatesta" (Piero della Francesca) . .
3686/3726 Set of 41 . . . . 26·00 28·00
MS3727 Six sheets, each 95 × 70 mm. (a) $325 "Mona Lisa" and details (Leonardo da Vinci) (84 × 56 mm). (b) $325 "The Coronation of Napoleon I" (David) (84 × 56 mm). (c) $325 "Farmyard" (Jan Brueghel the Younger) (84 × 56 mm). (d) $325 "The Marriage Feast at Cana" (Veronese) (84 × 56 mm). (e) $325 "The Fortune-teller" (Caravaggio) (84 × 56 mm). (f) $325 "The Rialto Bridge" (Canaletto) (84 × 56 mm) Set of 6 sheets . . . . 23·00 25·00

1993. Donald Duck Film Posters. Multicoloured.
3728/35 $60 × 8 Type **503**; "Donald's Golf Game", 1938; "Sea Scouts", 1939; "Donald's Penguin", 1939; "A Good Time for a Dime", 1941; "Truant Officer Donald"; "Orphan's Benefit", 1941; "Chef Donald", 1941 . . . .
3736/43 $60 × 8 "The Village Smithy"; "Donald's Snow Fight"; "Donald's Garden"; "Donald's Gold Mine"; "The Vanishing Private"; "Sky Trooper"; "Bellboy Donald"; "The New Spirit", all 1942 . . . .
3744/51 $60 × 8 "Saludos Amigos", 1943; "The Eyes Have It", 1945; "Donald's Crime", 1945; "Straight Shooters", 1947; "Donald's Dilemma", 1947; "Bootle Beetle", 1947; "Daddy Duck", 1948; "Soup's On", 1948 . . . .
3752/9 $80 × 8 "Donald's Happy Birthday", 1949; "Sea Salts", 1949; "Honey Harvester", 1949; "All in a Nutshell", 1949; "The Greener Yard", 1949; "Slide, Donald, Slide", 1949; "Lion Around", 1950; "Trailer Horn", 1950
3760/7 $80 × 8 "Bee at the Beach", 1950; "Out on a Limb", 1950; "Corn Chips", 1951; "Test Pilot Donald", 1951; "Lucky Number", 1951; "Out of Scale", 1951; "Bee on Guard", 1951; "Let's Stick Together", 1952 . . .
3768/75 $80 × 8 "Trick or Treat", 1952; "Don's Fountain of Youth", 1953; "Rugged Bear", 1953; "Canvas Back Duck", 1953; "Dragon Around", 1954; "Grin and Bear It", 1954; "The Flying Squirrel", 1954; "Up a Tree", 1955 . . . .
3776/81 $80 × 8 Scenes from "Pirate Gold": In the crow's nest; Aracuan Bird carrying treasure chest; Donald with treasure map; Donald at souvenir stall; Aracuan Bird with Donald; Donald on jetty (all horiz) . . . .
3728/81 Set of 56 . . . . 45·00 50·00
MS3782 Five sheets, each 129 × 103 mm. (a) $500 Book cover of "The Wise Little Hen", 1934 (horiz). (b) $500 Sketch for "Timber", 1941. (c) $500 Fan-card for "The Three Caballeros", 1945 (horiz). (d) $500 Fan-card for "Melody Time", 1948. Imperf. (e) $500 Donald Duck Set of 5 sheets 26·00 28·00

504 Aladdin

505 President Dr. Cheddi Jagan

1993. "Aladdin" (film). Disney Cartoon Characters. Multicoloured.
3783/90 $7.65 × 8 Type **504**; Abu the monkey; Jasmine; Rajah the tiger; Jafar; Iago the parrot; The Sultan; The Genie . . . . .
3791/9 $50 × 9 Jafar and magic scarab; Tiger Head entrance, Cave of Wonders; Jafar; Aladdin and Abu at breakfast; Aladdin rescuing Jasmine; Aladdin, Jasmine and Abu; Rajah comforts Jasmine; Jafar disguised as an old man; Aladdin and Abu in treasure chamber (all horiz)
3800/8 $65 × 9 Aladdin with lamp and magic carpet; The Genie measuring Aladdin; Abu turned into an elephant; Aladdin in disguise at palace; Aladdin and Jasmine on magic carpet; Aladdin in disguise, Jasmine and Sultan; Aladdin fighting Jafar; Aladdin and Jasmine; The Genie with suitcase and golf clubs (all horiz) . . .
3783/3808 Set of 26 . . . . 15·00 16·00
MS3809 Four sheets, each 127 × 102 mm. (a) $325 Aladdin, The Genie, Abu and magic carpet in Cave of Wonders (horiz). (b) $325 Aladdin in disguise on elephant. (c) $325 Aladdin and Jasmine on magic carpet (horiz). (d) $325 The Genie, The Sultan, Jasmine, Aladdin and Abu (horiz) Set of 4 sheets . . . . 18·00 19·00

1993. 1st Anniv of Election of President Jagan.
3810 **505** $6.40 multicoloured . . 40 30
MS3811 97 × 69 mm. $325 "REBIRTH OF DEMOCRACY" emblem . . . . 3·50 4·00

1994. "Hong Kong '94" International Stamp Exhibition (1st issue). As T **222a** of Gambia. Multicoloured.
3812 $50 Hong Kong 1984 Royal Hong Kong Jockey Club $1.30 stamp and Happy Valley Racecourse 80 90
3813 $50 Guyana 1992 Movie Posters $190 stamp and Happy Valley Racecourse 80 90
Nos. 3812/13 were printed together, se-tenant, with the centre part of each pair forming a composite design.

1994. "Hong Kong '94" International Stamp Exhibition (2nd issue). Ch'ing Dynasty Snuff Boxes (Nos. 3814/19) or Porcelain (Nos. 3820/5). As T **222b** of Gambia. Multicoloured.
3814 $20 Painted enamel in shape of bamboo 35 40
3815 $20 Painted enamel showing woman 35 40
3816 $20 Amber with lions playing ball 35 40
3817 $20 Agate in shape of two gourds 35 40
3818 $20 Glass overlay with dog design 35 40
3819 $20 Glass with foliage design 35 40
3820 $20 Covered jar with dragon design 35 40
3821 $20 Rotating brush-holder 35 40
3822 $20 Covered jar with horses design 35 40
3823 $20 Amphora vase with bats and peaches 35 40
3824 $20 Tea caddy with Fo dogs 35 40
3825 $20 Vase with camellias and peaches design 35 40

1994. Centenary of the Sign for the Mahdi. Nos. 1622/4 and 1634 surch **CENTENARY Sign For The MAHDI 1894-1994** and new value.
3826 $6 on 60c. Plate No. 73 (Series 1) (horiz) . . . .
3827 $20 on 200c. Plate No. 33 (Series 1) (horiz) . . . .
3828 $30 on 60c. Plate No. 57 (Series 1) (horiz) . . . .
3829 $35 on 60c. Plate No. 75 (Series 1) (horiz) . . . .
The surcharges on Nos. 3826 and 3828 show the third line as "MADHI".

1994. Hummel Figurines. As T **501a** of Ghana. Multicoloured.
3830 $20 Girl holding inscribed heart 25 25
3831 $25 Boy with heart under arm 30 30
3832 $35 Baker 40 40
3833 $50 Girl with pot of flowers 60 55
3834 $60 Girl with trumpet, pot plant and bird 70 65
3835 $130 Four girls . . . . . . 1·50 1·50
3836 $190 Boy and two girls with dog . . . . 2·25 2·50
3837 $250 Boy with cake and dog 2·75 3·50
MS3838 Two sheets, each 92 × 124 mm. (a) $6 As No. 3835; $25 No. 3831; $30 As No. 3830; $190 No. 3836. (b) $20 As No. 3832; $35 As No. 3837; $60 No. 3834; $130 As No. 3833 Set of 2 sheets . . . . 5·00 5·25

1994. 75th Anniv of I.L.O. Nos. 1760 and 1629/30 surch **I L O 75th Anniversary 1919-1994** and new value.
3839 $6 on 130c. Plate No. 13 (Series 1) . . . .
3840 $30 on 120c. Plate No. 58 (Series 1) . . . .
3841 $35 on 120c. Plate No. 56 (Series 1) . . . .

1994. Centenary (1992) of Sierra Club (environmental protection society). Endangered Species. As T **224a** of Gambia. Multicoloured.
3842 $70 Red Kangaroo with young 90 90
3843 $70 Head of American alligator 90 90
3844 $70 Head of bald eagle . . 90 90
3845 $70 Giant panda eating bamboo 90 90
3846 $70 Head of red kangaroo 90 90
3847 $70 Alaskan brown bear sitting 90 90
3848 $70 Bald eagle 90 90
3849 $70 Head of giant panda . . 90 90
3850 $70 Red kangaroo (horiz) 90 90
3851 $70 Whooping crane facing left (horiz) 90 90
3852 $70 Male whooping crane in courtship display (horiz) 90 90
3853 $70 Whooping crane looking right (horiz) . . . 90 90
3854 $70 Alaskan brown bear and cub (horiz) 90 90
3855 $70 Alaskan brown bear fishing (horiz) 90 90
3856 $70 Bald eagle on branch (horiz) 90 90
3857 $70 Giant panda (horiz) . . 90 90
3858 $70 American alligator (logo at left) (horiz) 90 90
3859 $70 American alligator (logo at right) (horiz) 90 90
3860 $70 Italian Alps at sunrise (horiz) 90 90
3861 $70 Italian Alps and meadow (horiz) 90 90
3862 $70 Mono Lake at sunset (horiz) 90 90
3863 $70 Rock pinnacles, Mono Lake (horiz) 90 90
3864 $70 Sea lion 90 90
3865 $70 Head of sea lion . . . 90 90
3866 $70 Sea lions on rocks . . . 90 90
3867 $70 Rock pinnacles, Mono Lake 90 90
3868 $70 Sierra Club Centennial emblem (black, brown and green) 90 90
3869 $70 Lake, Italian Alps . . . 90 90
3870 $70 Summit of Matterhorn 90 90
3871 $70 Matterhorn and village 90 90
3872 $70 Clouds over Matterhorn 90 90

1994. Royal Visit. Nos. 3551/4 optd **ROYAL VISIT FEB 19-22, 1994**.
3873 $25 Queen Elizabeth II in Coronation robes (photograph by Cecil Beaton) . . . . 1·25 1·40
3874 $50 Royal gems . . . . . . 1·75 1·90
3875 $75 Queen Elizabeth and Prince Philip . . . . . . 2·00 2·25
3876 $130 Queen opening Parliament . . . . 2·25 2·50
MS3877 69 × 100 mm. $325 "Queen in Coronation Robes" (Sir James Gunn) (28½ × 42½ mm) . . . . 6·50 7·00

509 "Cestrum parqui"

1994. Flowers. Multicoloured.
3878 $6.40 Type **509** 10 10
3879 $7.65 "Brunfelsia calycina" 10 10
3880 $12.80 "Datura rosei" . . . 10 15
3881 $15.30 "Ruellia macrantha" 15 20
3882 $50 "Portlandia albiflora" . 50 55
3883 $50 "Clusia grandiflora" . . 50 55
3884 $50 "Begonia haageana" . . 50 55
3885 $50 "Fuchsia simplicicaulis" 50 55
3886 $50 "Guaiacum officinale" 50 55
3887 $50 "Pithecoctenium cynanchoides" 50 55
3888 $50 "Sphaeralcea umbellata" 50 55
3889 $50 "Erythrina poeppigiana" 50 55
3890 $50 "Steriphoma paradoxa" 50 55
3891 $50 "Allemanda violacea" 50 55
3892 $50 "Centropogon cornutus" 50 55
3893 $50 "Passiflora quadrangularis" 50 55
3894 $50 "Victoria amazonica" . 50 55
3895 $50 "Cobaea scandens" . . 50 55
3896 $50 "Pyrostegia venusta" . 50 55
3897 $50 "Petrea kohautiana" . . 50 55
3898 $50 "Hippobroma longiflora" 50 55
3899 $50 "Cleome hassleriana" 50 55
3900 $50 "Verbena peruviana" 50 55
3901 $50 "Tropaeolum peregrinum" 50 55

3902 $50 "Plumeria rubra" . . . 50 55
3903 $50 "Selenicereus grandiflorus" 50 55
3904 $50 "Mandevilla splendens" 50 55
3905 $50 "Pereskia aculeata" . . 50 55
3906 $50 "Ipomoea learii" . . . 50 55
3907 $130 "Pachystachys coccinea" . . . . 1·25 1·40
3908 $190 "Beloperone guttata" 1·90 2·25
3909 $250 "Ferdinandusa speciosa" . . . . . . 2·50 3·00
MS3910 Two sheets, each 99 × 70 mm. (a) $325 "Lophospermum erubescens". (b) $325 "Columnea fendleri" Set of 2 sheets . . . . 6·50 7·50

Nos. 3883/94 and 3895/3906 respectively were printed together, se-tenant, forming composite background designs.

1994. 25th Anniv of First Moon Landing (1st issue). As T **227a** of Gambia. Multicoloured.

3911 $60 Walter Dornberger and launch of first A-4 rocket 90 90
3912 $60 Rudolph Nebel and "Surveyor 1" 90 90
3913 $60 Robert H. Goddard and "Apollo 7" 90 90
3914 $60 Kurt Debus and view of Earth from Moon ("Apollo 8") 90 90
3915 $60 James T. Webb and "Apollo 9" 90 90
3916 $60 George E. Mueller and "Apollo 10" lunar module 90 90
3917 $60 Wernher von Braun and launch of "Apollo 11" . . 90 90
3918 $60 Rocco A. Petrone and "Apollo 11" astronaut on Moon 90 90
3919 $60 Eberhard Rees and "Apollo 12" astronaut on Moon 90 90
3920 $60 Charles A. Berry and damaged "Apollo 13" . . 90 90
3921 $60 Thomas O. Paine and "Apollo 14" before splashdown 90 90
3922 $60 A. F. Staats and "Apollo 15" on Moon . . 90 90
3923 $60 Robert R. Gilruth and "Apollo 16" astronaut on Moon 90 90
3924 $60 Ernst Stuhlinger and "Apollo 17" crew on Moon 90 90
3925 $60 Christopher C. Kraft and X-30 National Aero-Space Plane 90 90
3926 $60 Rudolf Opitz and Messerschmitt Me 163B Komet (rocket engine), 1943 . . . . 90 90
3927 $60 Clyde W. Tombaugh and "face" on Mars . . . 90 90
3928 $60 Hermann Oberth and scene from "The Girl in the Moon" 90 90
MS3929 125 × 112 mm. $325 Frank J. Everest Jr and "Apollo 11" anniversary logo . . . . 4·50 5·00

See also Nos. 4169/87.

1994. Centenary of International Olympic Committee. Medal Winners. As T **227b** of Gambia. Multicoloured.

3930 $20 Nancy Kerrigan (U.S.A.) (1994 figure skating silver) 30 30
3931 $35 Sawao Kato (Japan) (1976 gymnastics gold) . . 50 50
3932 $130 Florence Griffith Joyner (U.S.A.) (1988 100 and 200 metres gold) . . 1·75 2·00
MS3933 110 × 80 mm. $325 Mark Wasmeier (Germany) (1994 super giant slalom and giant slalom gold) . . . . 4·00 4·50

1994. Centenary of First English Cricket Tour to the West Indies (1995). As T **397a** of Grenada. Multicoloured.

3934 $20 Clive Lloyd (Guyana and West Indies) (vert) . . 55 30
3935 $35 Carl Hooper (Guyana and West Indies) and Wisden Trophy 65 50
3936 $60 Graham Hick (England) and Wisden Trophy . . . 1·10 1·25
MS3937 79 × 100 mm. $200 English team of 1895 (black and brown) 2·75 3·00

1994. 50th Anniv of D-Day. Aircraft. As T **227c** of Gambia. Multicoloured.

3938 $6 Supermarine Spitfire Mk XI fighter on photo reconnaissance 30 15
3939 $35 North American B-25 Mitchell bomber 75 50
3940 $190 Republic P-47 Thunderbolt fighters . . . 2·75 3·50
MS3941 109 × 79 mm. $325 Avro Type 683 Lancaster bomber of 419 Squadron . . . . 4·25 4·75

1994. 50th Anniv of Second World War (3rd issue). As T **500**. Multicoloured.

3942 $60 Paratroops drop, D-Day 90 80
3943 $60 Glider assault, D-Day 90 80
3944 $60 U.S.S. "Arkansas" (battleship) bombarding Omaha Beach, D-Day . . 90 80
3945 $60 U.S. fighters attacking train 90 80
3946 $60 Allied landing craft approaching beaches . . . 90 80
3947 $60 Troops in beach obstacles 90 80
3948 $60 Commandos leaving landing craft 90 80
3949 $60 U.S. flail tank destroying mines 90 80
3950 $60 U.S. tank breaking through sea wall 90 80
3951 $60 Tanks and infantry advancing 90 80
3952 $60 Landings at Anzio (22 January 1944) 90 80
3953 $60 R.A.F. attacking Amiens Prison (18 February 1944) . . . 90 80
3954 $60 Soviet Army tank in Sevastopol (9 May 1944) 90 80
3955 $60 British bren-gun carriers at the Gustav Line (19 May 1944) 90 80
3956 $60 D-Day landings (6 June 1944) 90 80
3957 $60 "V-1" over London (13 June 1944) 90 80
3958 $60 Allies entering Paris (19 August 1944) 90 80
3959 $60 German "V-2" rocket ready for launch (8 September 1944) . . . 90 80
3960 $60 Sinking of "Tirpitz" (German battleship) (12 November 1944) . . . 90 80
3961 $60 U.S. tanks at Bastogne (29 December 1944) . . . 90 80

1994. "Philakorea '94" International Stamp Exhibition, Seoul (1st issue). As T **227d** of Gambia. Multicoloured.

3962 $6 Socialist ideals statue, Pyongyang (vert) 10 10
3963 $25 Statue of Admiral Yi Sun-sin (vert) 30 30
3964 $60 Fruits and mountain peaks 70 75
3965 $60 Manchurian crane, bamboo and peaks . . . 70 75
3966 $60 Rising sun and two cranes on pine 70 75
3967 $60 Five cranes on pine and peak 70 75
3968 $60 Three cranes in flight 70 75
3969 $60 Sea, rocky shore and fungi 70 75
3970 $60 Sea, rocky shore and fruit 70 75
3971 $60 Hind at seashore and fruit 70 75
3972 $60 Stag in pine forest . . . 70 75
3973 $60 Deer and fungi by waterfall 70 75
3974 $60 Tops of pines and mountain peaks 70 75
3975 $60 Manchurian crane in flight 70 75
3976 $60 Three cranes on pine tree 70 75
3977 $60 Crane on pine tree . . . 70 75
3978 $60 Top of fruit tree 70 75
3979 $60 Stag and two hinds on mountainside 70 75
3980 $60 Deer and fungi 70 75
3981 $60 Stag by waterfall and hind drinking 70 75
3982 $60 Pine tree, fruit and fungi 70 75
3983 $60 Fungi on mountainside 70 75
3984 $120 Sokkat'ap Pagoda, Pulguksa . . . . 1·40 1·60
3985 $130 Village Guardian (statue), Chejudo Island 1·40 1·60
MS3986 Two sheets. (a) 104 × 73 mm. $325 Europeans at the Korean Court (early lithograph). (b) 73 × 104 mm. $325 Pagoda by Ch'urae-am Rock Set of 2 sheets . . . . 6·50 6·75

Nos. 3964/73 and 3974/83, all 23 × 49 mm, were printed together, se-tenant, in sheetlets of 10, each sheetlet forming a composite design showing panels from a screen painting of longevity symbols from the late Chosun dynasty.

See also Nos. 4117/41.

510 Miki Maya

1994. 80th Anniv of Takarazuka Revue of Japan. Multicoloured.

3987 $20 Type **510** 55 60
3988 $20 Fubuki Takane 55 60
3989 $20 Seika Kuze 55 60
3990 $20 Saki Asaji 55 60
3991 $60 Mira Anju (34 × 47 mm) 75 80
3992 $60 Yuki Amami (34 × 47 mm) 75 80
3993 $60 Maki Ichiro (34 × 47 mm) 75 80
3994 $60 Yu Shion (34 × 47 mm) 75 80

511 "Heliconius melpomene"

1994. Butterflies. Multicoloured.

3995 $6 Type **511** 20 20
3996 $20 "Helicopis cupido" . . 45 45
3997 $25 "Agrias claudina" . . . 50 50
3998 $30 "Parides coelus" 60 60
3999 $50 "Heliconius hecale" . . 75 75
4000 $50 "Anaea marthesia" . . 75 75
4001 $50 "Brassolis astyra" . . . 75 75
4002 $50 "Heliconius melpomene" 75 75
4003 $50 "Haetera piera" 75 75
4004 $50 "Morpho diana" . . . 75 75
4005 $50 "Parides coelus" 75 75
4006 $50 "Catagramma pitheas" 75 75
4007 $50 "Nessaea obrinus" . . . 75 75
4008 $50 "Automeris janus" . . . 75 75
4009 $50 "Papilio torquatus" . . 75 75
4010 $50 "Eunica sophonisba" . . 75 75
4011 $50 "Ceratinia nise" 75 75
4012 $50 "Panacea procilla" . . . 75 75
4013 $50 "Pyrrhogyra neaerea" 75 75
4014 $50 "Morpho deidamia" . . 75 75
4015 $50 "Dismorphia orise" . . 75 75
4016 $60 "Morpho diana" . . . 85 85
4017 $190 "Dismorphia orise" . . 2·50 3·00
4018 $250 "Morpho deidamia" 3·00 3·50
MS4019 Four sheets. (a) 104 × 76 mm. $325 "Anaea eribotes". (b) 104 × 76 mm. $325 "Eunica sophonisba". (c) 110 × 80 mm. $325 "Hamadryas velutina" (39 × 30 mm). (d) 110 × 80 mm. $325 Agrias claudina (39 × 30 mm) Set of 4 sheets . . . . 14·00 16·00

512 Jacob

513 Peregrine Falcon

1994. Bible Stories (2nd series). Multicoloured.

(a) Joseph.

4020/43 $20 × 24 arranged as blocks of 4 depicting Jacob giving Joseph a coat of many colours (Type **512** at top left); Joseph thrown into a pit; Joseph sold as a slave; Joseph accused by Potiphar's wife; Joseph interprets Pharoah's dreams; Joseph reunited with his brothers . . . . .

(b) The Parting of the Red Sea.

4044/67 $20 × 24 Palm trees on shore; Pyramids; Palm trees on shore and black cloud; Three palm trees; Blue and white dove; Red and white bird; Egyptian army engulfed by sea; Yellow and white dove; Red and green fishes; Egyptian chariot with wall of water at left; Chariots between walls of water; Dolphins; Two doves; Israelites and water to left; Israelites and water to right; Turquoise and purple fishes; Israelites with tree at left; Iraelites with goats; Moses; Israelites with tree at right; Israelites with woman on horse; Israelites with old man and woman carrying pack; Israelites with woman carrying young child; Israelites with cart . . . .

(c) Ruth.

4068/91 $20 × 24 arranged as blocks of 6 depicting Ruth and Naomi; Ruth gleaning in cornfield; Boaz establishing kinsman's rights; Naomi with Ruth, Boaz and Obed . . .

(d) Daniel in the Lions' Den.

4092/4116 $20 × 25 Palm fronds and hibiscus flower; Magnificent frigate bird and palm fronds; Magnificent frigate birds and tops of stone pillars; Magnificent frigate bird, pillars and sail at bottom right; Hibiscus, sails of ship and top of pillar; Yellow arum lilies and palm trees; Heads of adult and immature magnificent frigate birds and palm trees; Palm trees, butterfly and stone pillars; Two butterflies and stone pillars; Stone pillar and sailing ship; Great egret (standing); Purple irises and palm trees; Daniel; Angel; Donkey foal; Orchids; Lioness and two cubs; Daniel's legs and lions; Lion; Three crowns; Goat and kid; Kid; Cub and head of lion; Lioness; Great egret in flight . . . . . .

4020/4116 Set of 97 . . . . 24·00 26·00

Nos. 4020/43, 4044/67, 4068/91 and 4092/4116 respectively were printed together, se-tenant, forming composite designs.

1994. "Philakorea '94" International Stamp Exhibition, Seoul (2nd issue). Birds of the World. Multicoloured.

4117 $35 Type **513** 55 55
4118 $35 Great spotted woodpecker 55 55
4119 $35 White-throated kingfisher 55 55
4120 $35 Andean cock of the rock ("Peruvian Cock of the Rock") 55 55
4121 $35 Yellow-headed amazon 55 55
4122 $35 Victoria crowned pigeon 55 55
4123 $35 Little owl 55 55
4124 $35 Common pheasant ("Ring-necked Pheasant") 55 55
4125 $35 Eurasian goldfinch ("Goldfinch") 55 55
4126 $35 Jay 55 55
4127 $35 Keel-billed toucan ("Sulphur-breasted Toucan") 55 55
4128 $35 Blue and white flycatcher ("Japanese Blue Flycatcher") 55 55
4129 $35 Northern goshawk . . . 55 55
4130 $35 Northern lapwing ("Lapwing") 55 55
4131 $35 Long-wattled umbrellabird ("Ornate Umbrellabird") 55 55
4132 $35 Slaty-headed parakeet 55 55
4133 $35 Regent bowerbird . . . 55 55
4134 $35 Egyptian goose 55 55
4135 $35 White-winged crossbill 55 55
4136 $35 Bohemian waxwing ("Waxwing") 55 55
4137 $35 Ruff 55 55
4138 $35 Hoopoe 55 55
4139 $35 Superb starling 55 55
4140 $35 Great jacamar 55 55
MS4141 Two sheets, each 70 × 100 mm. (a) $325 American bald eagle. (b) $325 Gould's violetear Set of 2 sheets . . . . 11·00 11·00

514 Paulo Futre (Portugal)

1994. World Cup Football Championship, U.S.A. (2nd issue). Multicoloured.
4142 $6 Type **514** 10 10
4143 $35 Lyndon Hooper (Canada) 35 40
4144 $60 Enzo Francescoli (Uruguay) 60 65
4145 $60 Paolo Maldini (Italy) 60 65
4146 $60 Guyana player 60 65
4147 $60 Bwalya Kalusha (Zambia) 60 65
4148 $60 Diego Maradona (Argentina) 60 65
4149 $60 Andreas Brehme (Germany) 60 65
4150 $60 Eric Wynalda (U.S.A.) (pursuing ball) 60 65
4151 $60 John Doyle (U.S.A.) 60 65
4152 $60 Eric Wynalda (U.S.A.) (kicking ball) 60 65
4153 $60 Thomas Dooley (U.S.A.) 60 65
4154 $60 Ernie Stewart (U.S.A.) 60 65
4155 $60 Marcelo Balboa (U.S.A.) 60 65
4156 $60 Bora Milutinovic (U.S.A. coach) 60 65
4157 $190 Freddy Rincon (Colombia) 1·90 2·00
MS4158 Two sheets. (a) 105 × 75 mm. $325 "94" symbol and player. (b) 75 × 105 mm. $325 Oiler Watson (U.S.A.) Set of 2 sheets 6·50 6·75

Nos. 4145/50 and 4151/6 respectively were printed together, se-tenant, forming composite background designs.

515 Anja Fichtel (individual foil, 1988)

1994. Olympic Games, Atlanta (1996) (1st issue). Previous German Gold Medal Winners. Mult.
4159 $6 Type **515** 15 10
4160 $25 Annegret Richter (100 m, 1976) (vert) 35 30
4161 $30 Heike Henkel (high jump, 1992) (vert) 40 35
4162 $35 Armin Hary (100 m, 1960) (vert) 40 40
4163 $50 Heide Rosendahl (long jump, 1972) (vert) 60 65
4164 $60 Josef Neckermann (dressage, 1968) (vert) 70 75
4165 $130 Heike Drechsler (long jump, 1988) (vert) 1·40 1·50
4166 $190 Ulrike Mayfarth (high jump, 1984) (vert) 2·25 2·50
4167 $250 Michael Gross (200 m freestyle and 100 m butterfly, 1984) 2·75 3·25
MS4168 Three sheets. (a) 105 × 75 mm. $135 Markus Wasmeier (skiing, 1994) (vert); $190 Katja Seizinger (skiing, 1994) (vert). (b) 105 × 75 mm. $325 Franziska van Almsick (swimming, 1992) (vert). (c) 75 × 105 mm. $325 Steffi Graf (tennis, 1988, 1992) (vert) Set of 3 sheets 8·50 9·00

See also Nos. 4492/4508 and 4739/88.

516 Dog Laika and Rocket, 1957

1994. 25th Anniv of First Moon Landing (2nd issue). Multicoloured.
4169 $60 Type **516** 80 80
4170 $60 Yuri Gagarin (first man in space), 1961 80 80
4171 $60 John Glenn (first American to orbit Earth), 1962 80 80
4172 $60 Edward White walking in space, 1965 80 80
4173 $60 Neil Armstrong, walking on Moon and "Apollo 11" logo 80 80
4174 $60 "Luna 16" leaving Moon, 1970 80 80
4175 $60 Lunar Module 1 on Moon, 1970 80 80
4176 $60 Skylab 1, 1973 80 80
4177 $60 Astronauts and Apollo–Soyuz link-up, 1975 80 80
4178 $60 "Mars 3" 80 80
4179 $60 "Mariner 10" 80 80
4180 $60 "Voyager" 80 80
4181 $60 "Pioneer" 80 80
4182 $60 "Giotto" 80 80
4183 $60 "Magellan" 80 80
4184 $60 "Galileo" 80 80
4185 $60 "Ulysses" 80 80
4186 $60 "Cassini" 80 80
MS4187 Two sheets, each 142 × 104 mm. (a) $325 "Apollo 11" astronauts. (b) $325 "Galileo" Set of 2 sheets 8·50 9·00

Nos. 4178/86 were printed together, se-tenant, with the backgrounds forming a composite design of Space.

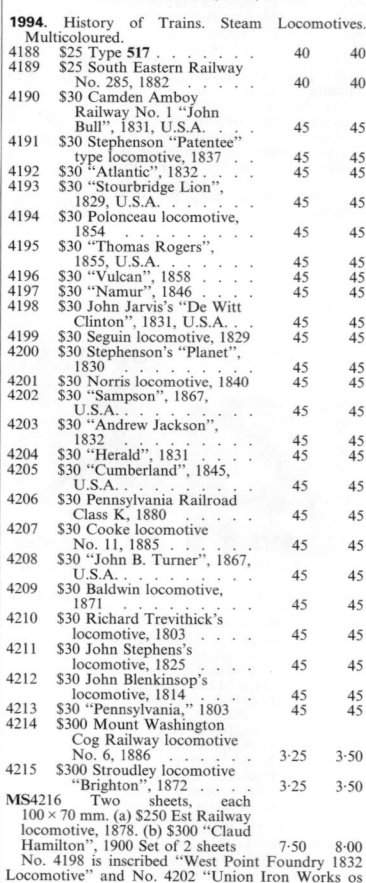

517 South Caroline Railroad "Best Friend of Charleston", 1830, U.S.A.

1994. History of Trains. Steam Locomotives. Multicoloured.
4188 $25 Type **517** 40 40
4189 $25 South Eastern Railway No. 285, 1882 40 40
4190 $30 Camden Amboy Railway No. 1 "John Bull", 1831, U.S.A. 45 45
4191 $30 Stephenson "Patentee" type locomotive, 1837 45 45
4192 $30 "Atlantic", 1832 45 45
4193 $30 "Stourbridge Lion", 1829, U.S.A. 45 45
4194 $30 Polonceau locomotive, 1854 45 45
4195 $30 "Thomas Rogers", 1855, U.S.A. 45 45
4196 $30 "Vulcan", 1858 45 45
4197 $30 "Namur", 1846 45 45
4198 $30 John Jarvis's "De Witt Clinton", 1831, U.S.A. 45 45
4199 $30 Seguin locomotive, 1829 45 45
4200 $30 Stephenson's "Planet", 1830 45 45
4201 $30 Norris locomotive, 1840 45 45
4202 $30 "Sampson", 1867, U.S.A. 45 45
4203 $30 "Andrew Jackson", 1832 45 45
4204 $30 "Herald", 1831 45 45
4205 $30 "Cumberland", 1845, U.S.A. 45 45
4206 $30 Pennsylvania Railroad Class K, 1880 45 45
4207 $30 Cooke locomotive No. 11, 1885 45 45
4208 $30 "John B. Turner", 1867, U.S.A. 45 45
4209 $30 Baldwin locomotive, 1871 45 45
4210 $30 Richard Trevithick's locomotive, 1803 45 45
4211 $30 John Stephens's locomotive, 1825 45 45
4212 $30 John Blenkinsop's locomotive, 1814 45 45
4213 $30 "Pennsylvania," 1803 45 45
4214 $300 Mount Washington Cog Railway locomotive No. 6, 1886 3·25 3·50
4215 $300 Stroudley locomotive "Brighton", 1872 3·25 3·50
MS4216 Two sheets, each 100 × 70 mm. (a) $250 Est Railway locomotive, 1878. (b) $300 "Claud Hamilton", 1900 Set of 2 sheets 7·50 8·00

No. 4198 is inscribed "West Point Foundry 1832 Locomotive" and No. 4202 "Union Iron Works os San Francisco", both error.

1994. Christmas. Religious Paintings. As T **231a** of Gambia. Multicoloured.
4217 $6 "Joseph with the Christ Child" (Guido Reni) 15 10
4218 $20 "Adoration of the Christ Child" (Girolamo Romanino) 30 25
4219 $25 "Adoration of the Christ Child with St. Barbara and St. Martin" (Raffaello Botticini) 35 30
4220 $30 "Holy Family" (Pompeo Batoni) 40 35
4221 $35 "Flight into Egypt" (Bartolommeo Carducci) 45 40
4222 $60 "Holy Family and the Baptist" (Andrea del Sarto) 80 70
4223 $120 "Sacred Conversation" (Cesare de Sesto) 2·00 2·25
4224 $190 "Madonna and Child with Saints Joseph and John the Baptist" (Pontormo) 2·75 3·50
MS4225 Two sheets. (a) 112 × 93 mm. $325 "Presentation of Christ in the Temple" (Fra Bartolommeo). (b) 85 × 95 mm. $325 "Holy Family and St. Elizabeth and St. John the Baptist" (Francisco Primaticcio) Set of 2 sheets 7·50 8·00

518 Riker and Dr. Crusher

1994. "Star Trek Generations" (film). Designs showing "Enterprise" crew in 19th-century naval uniforms (Nos. 4226/34) or in 23rd-century (Nos. 4235/43). Multicoloured.
4226 $100 Type **518** 1·75 1·50
4227 $100 Geordi, Dr. Crusher with Lt. Worf in chains 1·75 1·50
4228 $100 Captain Picard 1·75 1·50
4229 $100 Data and Geordi 1·75 1·50
4230 $100 "U.S.S. Enterprise" (sailing ship) 1·75 1·50
4231 $100 Captain Picard and Riker on quarterdeck 1·75 1·50
4232 $100 Data 1·75 1·50
4233 $100 Lt. Worf 1·75 1·50
4234 $100 Dr. Crusher 1·75 1·50
4235 $100 Captain Picard 1·75 1·50
4236 $100 Riker 1·75 1·50
4237 $100 Captain Kirk 1·75 1·50
4238 $100 Soron with phaser 1·75 1·50
4239 $100 Captains Kirk and Picard on horseback 1·75 1·50
4240 $100 Klingon women 1·75 1·50
4241 $100 Captains Kirk and Picard 1·75 1·50
4242 $100 Troi 1·75 1·50
4243 $100 Captain Picard and Data 1·75 1·50
4244 $100 "BOLDLY GO" film poster 1·75 1·50
MS4245 86 × 103 mm. $500 U.S.S. "Enterprise" from film poster (horiz) 5·50 6·00

519 Cross and Map of Guyana

1994. Centenary of Sisters of Mercy in Guyana.
4246 **519** $60 multicoloured 1·00 80

1994. 1st Recipients of Order of the Caribbean Community. As T **393a** of Grenada. Mult.
4247 $60 Sir Shridath Ramphal 65 75
4248 $60 William Demas 65 75
4249 $60 Derek Walcott 1·60 75

520 Garfield Sobers congratulating Brian Lara

1995. Brian Lara's Achievements in Cricket. Multicoloured.
4250 $20 Type **520** 35 25
4251 $30 Brian Lara setting world record for highest Test Match score (vert) 45 35
4252 $375 Lara and Chanderpaul 4·25 4·75
MS4253 70 × 100 mm. $300 Brian Lara (vert) 3·25 3·50

521 Babe Ruth

1995. Birth Centenary of Babe Ruth (baseball player). Each brown and black.
4254 $65 Type **521** 70 80
4255 $65 Preparing to bat (full-length photo) 70 80
4256 $65 Head and shoulders portrait (cap with limp brim) 70 80
4257 $65 In retirement (bare-headed) 70 80
4258 $65 Running (in plain shirt) 70 80
4259 $65 Head and shoulders portrait (cap with emblem and stiff brim) 70 80
4260 $65 Wearing "NEW YORK" shirt 70 80
4261 $65 Preparing to hit (in "NEW YORK" shirt) 70 80
4262 $65 Wearing "YANKEES" shirt 70 80
4263 $65 At base with bat on shoulder (in striped shirt) 70 80
4264 $65 Watching the ball (in striped shirt) 70 80
4265 $65 In cap and coat at Old Timer's Day, Yankee Stadium, 1948 70 80
MS4266 89 × 118 mm. $500 Babe Ruth (horiz) 5·00 5·25

522 Mickey Mouse as Family Doctor

1995. Disney Characters at Work. Multicoloured.
4267/75 $30 × 9 Type **522**; Goofy and optometrist; Daisy Duck as nurse; Scrooge McDuck as psychiatrist; Daisy Duck as physiotherapist; Horace Horsecollar and dentist; Goofy and radiologist; Goofy as pharmacist; Big Pete as chiropractor
4276/84 $30 × 9 Mickey Mouse as vet; Donald Duck training seals; Ludwig von Duck as animal psychiatrist; Goofy as ornithologist; Daisy Duck grooming Old English sheepdog; Minnie Mouse as herpetologist; Mickey Mouse as pet shop keeper with Pluto; J. Audubon Woodlore as park ranger; Donald Duck as aquarist
4285/93 $30 × 9 Mickey Mouse as animator with Pluto; Goofy the tailor with Mickey Mouse; Pete the glassblower with Morty; Minnie Mouse painting Clarabelle; Daisy Duck sculpting Donald; Donald Duck as potter; Chip and Dale the watchmakers; Donald Duck the locksmith; Grandma Duck making quilt

4294/4301 $35 × 8 Mickey Mouse as policeman; Donald Duck as fireman; Uncle Scrooge as ambulance driver; Grandma Duck as crossing patrol; Daisy Duck as museum attendant and Donald as visitor; Goofy as census taker and family of rabbits; Horace Horsecollar and Big Pete as street maintenance workers; Donald Duck as sanitation worker at recycling bin (all vert) . . . .
4302/9 $35 × 8 Mickey Mouse with Pluto driving lorry; Mickey Mouse as carpenter sawing; Goofy riding road drill; Minnie Mouse with electric drill; Donald Duck driving forklift; Minnie Mouse and Goofy as construction contractors; Mickey Mouse with Pluto as carpenter making table; Pluto driving bulldozer (all vert)
4310/17 $35 × 8 Mickey Mouse as plumber; Mickey Mouse the paperboy; Huey, Dewey and Louie moving furniture; Big Pete as handyman; Donald Duck and nephews house painting; Goofy as washing machine repairman; Minnie Mouse as babysitter; Daisy Duck as carer (all vert) . . . .
4267/4317 Set of 51 . . . . 21·00 23·00
MS4318 Six sheets. (a) 132 × 107 mm. $200 Goofy as surgeon. (b) 107 × 129 mm. $200 Goofy the zookeeper. (c) 132 × 107 mm. $200 Ferdie riding Pluto for photographer (vert). (d) 107 × 129 mm. $200 Horace Horsecollar campaigning for mayor. (e) 132 × 107 mm. $200 Minnie Mouse as carpenter and puppies. (f) 107 × 129 mm. $200 Minnie Mouse as maid Set of 6 sheets . . . . 25·00 25·00

No. 4271 is inscribed "PHYSICAL THEREPIST" in error.

1995. Centenary of Salvation Army. Nos. 1519 and 1521/3 surch **SALVATION ARMY 1895 – 1995** and new value.
4319 $6 on 60c. Plate No. 10 (Series 1) . . . .
4320 $20 on 60c. Plate No. 19 (Series 1) . . . .
4321 $30 on 60c. Plate No. 2 (Series 1) . . . .
4322 $35 on 60c. Plate No. 31 (Series 1) . . . .

524 Pig

525 Northern Goshawk ("Goshawk")

1995. Chinese New Year ("Year of the Pig"). Symbolic pigs. Multicoloured.
4323 $20 Type **524** 60 55
4324 $30 Pig facing left 65 60
4325 $50 Pig facing front (face value bottom right) . . . 80 80
4326 $100 Pig facing front (face value bottom left) . . . . 1·25 1·40
MS4327 67 × 89 mm. $50 × 4 As Nos. 4323/6 . . . . 3·25 3·25
MS4328 104 × 76 mm. $150 Pig's head . . . . 2·00 2·25

1995. Birds. Multicoloured.
4329 $5 Type **525** 10 10
4330 $6 Northern lapwing ("Lapwing") 10 10
4331 $8 Long-wattled umbrellabird ("Ornate Umbrellabird") 10 10
4332 $15 Slaty-headed parakeet 10 15
4333 $19 Regent bowerbird . . . 10 15
4334 $20 Egyptian goose 10 15
4335 $25 White-winged crossbill 15 20
4336 $30 Bohemian waxwing ("Waxwing") 20 25
4337 $35 Ruff 20 25
4338 $60 Hoopoe 35 40
4339 $100 Superb starling 60 65
4340 $500 Great jacamar . . . . 3·00 3·25

526 Norwegian Forest Cat

1995. "Singapore '95" International Stamp Exhibition. Multicoloured.
4341/52 $35 × 12 Cats (Type **526**; Scottish fold; Red Burmese; British blue-hair; Abyssinian; Siamese; Exotic shorthair; Turkish van cat; Black Persian; Black-tipped burmilla; Singapura; Calico shorthair) . . . . . .
4353/64 $35 × 12 Dogs (Gordon setter; Long-haired chihuahua; Dalmatian; Afghan hound; Old English bulldog; Miniature schnauzer; Clumber spaniel; Pekingese; St. Bernard; English cocker spaniel; Alaskan malamute; Rottweiler) . . . . . .
4365/76 $35 × 12 Horses (chestnut thoroughbred colt; liver chestnut quarter horse; black Friesian; chestnut Belgian; Appaloosa; Lippizaner; chestnut hunter; British shire; Palomino; pinto ("Seal Brown Point"); Arab; Afghanistan kabardin)
4341/76 Set of 36 . . . . 15·00 17·00
MS4377 Three sheets, each 87 × 71 mm. (a) $300 Maine coon. (b) $300 Golden retriever. (c) $300 American anglo-arab Set of 3 sheets . . . . 9·00 9·50

No. 4355 is inscribed "Dalmation", No. 4367 "Freisian" and No. 4370 "Lipizzanas", all in error.

527 Captain John Smith leaving for New World, 1607

1995. "Pocahontas". Characters and scenes from Disney cartoon film. Multicoloured. (a) Vert designs showing characters.
4378/85 $50 × 8 Pocahontas and Meeko; John Smith; Chief Powhatan; Kocoum; Ratcliffe; Wiggins; Nakoma; Thomas . . . . . .

(b) Horiz designs showing film scenes.
4386/94 $8 × 9 Type **527**; Ratcliffe; Chief Powhatan greeted by his people; Pocahontas standing on cliff; Pocahontas, Nakoma and Meeko in canoe; Powhatan asking Pocahontas to marry Kocoum; Pocahontas receiving her mother's necklace; Pocahontas seeking guidance from Grandmother Willow; Pocahontas watching arrival of "Susan Constant" . .
4395/4403 $30 × 9 Ratcliffe claiming land for English Crown; Kekata having vision; Meeting of John Smith and Pocahontas; Namantack watching settlers; Powhatan and wounded Namantack; Pocahontas showing John Smith the colours of the wind; Nakoma finds Pocahontas with John Smith; Pocahontas offering John "Indian gold" (corn); Pocahontas, John Smith and Grandmother Willow
4404/12 $35 × 9 Kocoum telling Pocahontas about the war council; Nakoma telling Kocoum to find Pocahontas; John Smith and Kocoum wrestling over knife; Powhatan sentencing John to death; Pocahontas and Grandmother Willow; Pocahontas saving John Smith; Ratcliffe under arrest; Powhatan draping his cloak over wounded John Smith; Pocahontas and John Smith saying goodbye . . . . . .
4378/4412 Set of 35 . . . . . . 30·00 32·00
MS4413 Four sheets. (a) 98 × 120 mm. $300 Meeko. (b) 132 × 107 mm. $325 Pocahontas hiding. (c) 132 × 107 mm. $325 Powhatan and Pocahontas. (d) 132 × 107 mm. $325 Pocahontas kneeling (vert) Set of 4 sheets 26·00 27·00

1995. 95th Birthday of Queen Elizabeth the Queen Mother. As T **239a** of Gambia.
4414 $100 brown, light brown and black . . . . . . 1·50 1·50
4415 $100 multicoloured . . . . 1·50 1·50
4416 $100 multicoloured . . . . 1·50 1·50
4417 $100 multicoloured . . . 1·50 1·50
MS4418 – 121 × 126 mm. $325 multicoloured . . . . 3·50 3·75

DESIGNS: No. 4414, Queen Elizabeth the Queen Mother (pastel drawing); 4415, Wearing purple hat; 4416, Wearing turquoise hat; 4417, At desk (oil painting); **MS**4418, Wearing blue dress and mink stole.

528 Paul Harris (founder) and Rotary Emblem

1995. 90th Anniv of Rotary International. Multicoloured.
4419 **528** $200 multicoloured . . . 2·00 2·50
MS4420 104 × 74 mm. $300 Rotary emblems . . . . 3·00 3·50

529 Girl carrying Sack on Head

1995. 50th Anniv of F.A.O. Multicoloured.
4421 $35 Type **529** 50 65
4422 $60 Man and woman carrying sacks of food aid 80 95
4423 $200 Woman holding sack 2·00 2·40
MS4424 104 × 74 mm. $300 Bowl of food and F.A.O. emblem . . . 3·00 3·50

Nos. 4421/3 were printed together, se-tenant, forming a composite design.

530 Scouts around Campfire

1995. 18th World Scout Jamboree, Netherlands. Multicoloured.
4425 $20 Type **530** 30 25
4426 $25 Scout on beach 35 30
4427 $30 Scouts hiking 40 35
4428 $35 Scout snorkelling . . . 45 40
4429 $60 Scout saluting and flag of Guyana 70 65
4430 $200 Scout fishing from boat . . . . 2·00 2·50
MS4431 Two sheets, each 100 × 70 mm. (a) $300 Scout putting up tent. (b) Scout canoeing Set of 2 sheets . . . . 6·00 6·25

1995. 50th Anniv of End of World War II in Europe. As T **237a** of Gambia. Multicoloured.
4432 $60 American tank during Battle of the Bulge . . . 85 90
4433 $60 Allied tanks crossing Siegfried Line 85 90
4434 $60 Liberated concentration camp prisoners 85 90
4435 $60 Allied plane dropping food to Dutch 85 90
4436 $60 U.S. infantry patrol, North Italy 85 90
4437 $60 "Daily Mail" headline announcing Hitler's death 85 90
4438 $60 Soviet tanks entering Berlin 85 90
4439 $60 Surrender of "U858" in U.S. waters 85 90
MS4440 105 × 74 mm. $300 Soviet troops raising flag on Brandenburg Gate (56 × 42 mm) 3·00 3·25

No. 4433 is incorrectly inscribed "SIGFRIED LINE".

1995. 50th Anniv of End of Second World War in the Pacific. As T **239b** of Gambia. Multicoloured.
4441 $60 P61 Black Widow . . . 85 90
4442 $60 PT boat 85 90
4443 $60 Martin B-26 Marauder bomber 85 90
4444 $60 U.S.S. "San Juan" (cruiser) 85 90
4445 $60 "Gato" class submarine 85 90
4446 $60 Destroyer 85 90
MS4447 107 × 77 mm. $300 Cruiser and aircraft carrier . . . . . . 3·00 3·25

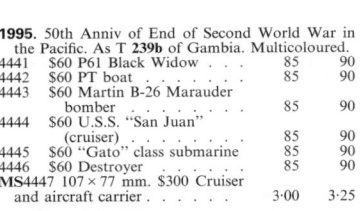

531 Thanksgiving (U.S.A.)

1995. Holidays of the World. Multicoloured.
4448 $60 Type **531** 85 90
4449 $60 Christmas (Germany) 85 90
4450 $60 Hanukkah (Israel) . . . 85 90
4451 $60 Easter (Spain) 85 90
4452 $60 Carnivale (Brazil) . . . 85 90
4453 $60 Bastille Day (France) 85 90
4454 $60 Independence Day (India) 85 90
4455 $60 St. Patrick's Day (Ireland) 85 90
MS4456 105 × 76 mm. $300 Chinese New Year (China) . . . . . . 3·00 3·25

532 Map of the Americas and U.N. Soldier

1995. 50th Anniv of United Nations. Multicoloured.
4457 $35 Type **532** 45 50
4458 $60 Map of Africa and Western Asia 75 75
4459 $200 Map of Eastern Asia and Australasia with refugees . . . . 2·25 2·75

MS4460 74 × 104 mm. $300 Secretary-General Boutros Boutros Ghali . . . . 3·00 3·50

Nos. 4457/9 were printed together, se-tenant, forming a composite design.

533 Four-eyed Butterflyfish

1995. Marine Life. Multicoloured.

4461 $30 Type **533** 70 75
4462 $30 Lemon shark 70 75
4463 $35 Blue-headed wrasse . . 70 75
4464 $35 Green turtle 70 75
4465 $60 Three-spotted damselfish 70 75
4466 $60 Sawfish 70 75
4467 $60 Sei whales 70 75
4468 $60 Great barracuda 70 75
4469 $60 Mutton snapper 70 75
4470 $60 Hawksbill turtle 70 75
4471 $60 Spanish hogfish 70 75
4472 $60 Queen angelfish 70 75
4473 $60 Porkfish 70 75
4474 $60 Trumpetfish 70 75
4475 $60 Lesser electric ray . . . 70 75
4476 $60 Tiger shark 70 75
4477 $60 Needlefish 70 75
4478 $60 Horse-eyed jack 70 75
4479 $60 Princess parrotfish . . . 70 75
4480 $60 Yellow-tailed snapper 70 75
4481 $60 Spotted snake eel . . . 70 75
4482 $60 Buffalo trunkfish . . . 70 75
4483 $60 Cherubfish angelfish . . 70 75
4484 $60 French angelfish 70 75
4485 $80 Cocoa damselfish (vert) 90 1·00
4486 $80 Sergeant major (vert) 90 1·00
4487 $80 Beaugregory (vert) . . . 90 1·00
4488 $80 Yellow-tailed damselfish (vert) . . . . 90 1·00
4489 $200 Fin-spot wrasse . . . 2·25 2·40
4490 $200 Stingray . . . . 2·25 2·40
MS4491 Two sheets, each 100 × 70 mm. (a) $300 Great white shark. (b) $300 Leatherback turtle Set of 2 sheets . . . . 11·00 11·00

Nos. 4461, 4463, 4465 and 4489; Nos. 4462, 4464, 4466 and 4490; Nos. 4467/75; Nos. 4476/84 and Nos. 4485/8 respectively were printed together, se-tenant, the backgrounds forming composite designs.

534 Pole Vaulting

535 Sand Martin

1995. Olympic Games, Atlanta (1996) (2nd issue). Multicoloured.

4492 $60 Type **534** 90 85
4493 $60 Long jumping 90 85
4494 $60 Woman with relay baton 90 85
4495 $60 Wrestling 90 85
4496 $60 Discus (side view) . . . 90 85
4497 $60 Basketball 90 85
4498 $60 Boxing 90 85
4499 $60 Weightlifting 90 85
4500 $60 Shot put 90 85
4501 $60 Man in relay race . . . 90 85
4502 $60 Female gymnast on beam 90 85
4503 $60 Cycling 90 85
4504 $60 Synchronized swimming 90 85
4505 $60 Hurdling 90 85
4506 $60 Male gymnast on pommel horse 90 85
4507 $60 Discus (front view) . . 90 85
MS4508 Two sheets. (a) 105 × 75 mm. $300 Athletes at start of race. (b) 75 × 105 mm. $300 Long jumping Set of 2 sheets 6·00 6·25

Nos. 4492/9 and 4500/7 respectively were printed together, se-tenant, the backgrounds forming composite designs.

1995. Wildlife. Multicoloured.

4509 $20 Type **535** 70 70
4510 $35 House martin 70 70
4511 $60 Northern hobby ("Hobby") 75 75
4512 $60 Olive colobus 90 90
4513 $60 Violet-backed starling 90 90
4514 $60 Diana monkey 90 90
4515 $60 African palm civet . . . 90 90
4516 $60 Giraffe and zebras . . . 90 90
4517 $60 African linsang 90 90
4518 $60 Royal antelope 90 90
4519 $60 Duikers 90 90
4520 $60 Palm squirrel 90 90
4521 $200 Long-tailed skua . . . 90 90
MS4522 Two sheets, each 110 × 80 mm. (a) $300 Brush pig and giant forest hog. (b) $300 Chimpanzee Set of 2 sheets . . 6·00 6·50

Nos. 4509/11 and 4521; and 4512/20 respectively were printed together, se-tenant, forming composite background designs.

536 Queenstown Jama Masjid

1995. Centenary of Queenstown Jama Masjid (mosque), Georgetown.

4523 **536** $60 multicoloured . . . 75 60

537 Woman Soldier with Sub-machine Gun

1995. 30th Anniv of Guyana Defence Force. Multicoloured.

4524 $6 Type **537** 15 10
4525 $60 Soldier with rifle . . . 85 70

538 Bank Logo and Headquarters

1995. 25th Anniv of Caribbean Development Bank.

4526 **538** $60 multicoloured . . . 70 60

1995. Christmas. Religious Paintings. As T **245a** of Gambia. Multicoloured.

4527 $25 "Angel of the Annunciation" (Carracci) 50 30
4528 $30 "Virgin of the Annunciation" (Carracci) 55 35
4529 $35 "Assumption of the Madonna" (Carracci) . . 60 40
4530 $60 "Baptism of Christ" (Carracci) 90 70
4531 $100 "Madonna and Child with Saints" (detail) (Carracci) . . . . 1·60 1·75
4532 $300 "Birth of the Virgin" (Carracci) . . . . 3·75 5·00
MS4533 Two sheets, each 101 × 127 mm. (a) $325 "Madonna and Child enthroned with Ten Saints" (Rosso Fiorentino). (b) $325 "Mystic Marriage of St. Catherine" (Carracci) Set of 2 sheets . . . . 7·00 8·00

539 John Lennon

540 Albrecht Kossel (1910 Medicine)

1995. 15th Death Anniv of John Lennon (musician).

4534 **539** $35 multicoloured . . . 1·00 80

1995. Centenary of Nobel Trust Fund. Multicoloured.

4535/43 $35 × 9 Type **540**; Arthur H. Compton (1927 Physics); N. M. Butler (1931 Peace); Charles Laveran (1907 Medicine); George R. Minot (1934 Medicine); Henry H. Dale (1936 Medicine); Jacques Monod (1965 Medicine); Alfred Hershey (1969 Medicine); Par Lagerkvist (1951 Literature) . . . . . .

4544/52 $35 × 9 Norman F. Ramsey (1989 Physics); Chen Ning Yang (1957 Physics); Earl W. Sutherland Jr. (1971 Medicine); Paul Karrer (1937 Chemistry); Harmut Michel (1988 Chemistry); Richard Kuhn (1938 Chemistry); P. A. M. Dirac (1933 Physics); Victor Grignard (1912 Chemistry); Richard Willstatter (1915 Chemistry) . . . . . .

4553/61 $35 × 9 Adolf von Baeyer (1905 Chemistry); Hideki Yukawa (1949 Physics); George W. Beadle (1958 Medicine); Edwin M. McMillan (1951 Chemistry); Samuel C. C. Ting (1976 Physics); Saint-John Perse (1960 Literature); John F. Enders (1954 Medicine); Felix Bloch (1952 Physics); P. B. Medawar (1960 Medicine) . . . . . .

4562/70 $35 × 9 Nikolai Basov (1964 Physics); Klas Arnoldson (1908 Peace); Rene Sully-Prudhomme (1901 Literature); Robert W. Wilson (1978 Physics); Hugo Theorell (1955 Medicine); Nelly Sachs (1966 Literature); Hans von Euler-Chelpin (1929 Chemistry); Mairead Corrigan (1976 Peace); Willis E. Lamb Jr. (1955 Physics) . . . .

4571/9 $35 × 9 Francis Crick (1962 Medicine); Manne Siegbahn (1924 Physics); Eisaku Sato (1974 Peace); Robert Koch (1905 Medicine); Edgar D. Adrian (1932 Medicine); Erwin Neher (1991 Medicine); Henry Taube (1983 Chemistry); Norman Angell (1933 Peace); Robert Robinson (1947 Chemistry) . . . . . .

4580/8 $35 × 9 Henri Becquerel (1903 Physics); Igor Tamm (1958 Physics); Georges Kohler (1984 Medicine); Gerhard Domagk (1939 Medicine); Yasunari Kawabata (1968 Literature); Maurice Allais (1988 Economic Sciences); Aristide Briand (1926 Peace); Pavel Cherenkov (1958 Physics); Feodor Lynen (1964 Medicine) . . . .

4535/88 Set of 54 . . . . 38·00 40·00
MS4589 Six sheets, each 106 × 76 mm. (a) $300 Lech Walesa (1983 Peace). (b) $300 Heinrich Böll (1972 Literature). (c) $300 Henry A. Kissinger (1973 Peace). (d) $300 Kenichi Fukui (1981 Chemistry). (e) $300 Yasunari Kawabata (1968 Literature). (f) $300 Le Duc Tho (1973 Peace) Set of 6 sheets . . 20·00 21·00

Nos. 4535/43, 4544/52, 4553/61, 4562/70, 4571/9 and 4580/8 respectively were printed together, se-tenant, with the backgrounds forming composite designs.

541 David Copperfield

1995. David Copperfield (magician). Multicoloured.

4590 $60 Type **541** 70 75
4591 $60 David Copperfield in cloak and top hat 70 75
4592 $60 With flaming torch . . 70 75
4593 $60 David Copperfield in close up 70 75
4594 $60 Head of Statue of Liberty 70 75
4595 $60 David Copperfield climbing rope 70 75
4596 $60 With handcuffs 70 75
4597 $60 With woman dancer . . 70 75
4598 $60 David Copperfield wearing white shirt . . . 70 75
MS4599 76 × 106 mm. $300 David Copperfield with rose . . . . 3·00 3·50

Nos. 4590/8 were printed together, se-tenant, forming a composite background design.

542 Marilyn Monroe

1995. 70th Birth Anniv of Marilyn Monroe (entertainer). Multicoloured.

4600 $60 Type **542** 65 65
4601 $60 Marilyn Monroe with circular earrings 65 65
4602 $60 Marilyn Monroe (red top right corner) 65 65
4603 $60 Marilyn Monroe (signature at bottom right) 65 65
4604 $60 With hair over left eye 65 65
4605 $60 With pink satin at left 65 65
4606 $60 With arm raised 65 65
4607 $60 With pink satin at bottom right 65 65
4608 $60 With square earring . . 65 65
MS4609 76 × 105 mm. $300 Marilyn Monroe in pink satin dress (horiz) 3·00 3·25

Nos. 4600/8 were printed together, se-tenant, with the background forming a composite design.

543 Rat

1995. Chinese New Year ("Year of the Rat").

4610 **543** $20 multicoloured . . . 25 20
4611 – $30 multicoloured (face value bottom left) . . 35 30
4612 – $50 multicoloured (face value top right) . . . 65 50
4613 – $100 multicoloured (face value top left) . . . . 1·10 1·25
MS4614 68 × 92 mm. $50 × 4 As Nos. 4610/13 . . . . 2·00 2·25
MS4615 106 × 76 mm. $150 multicoloured . . . . 1·75 2·00

DESIGNS: $30 to $150 Symbolic rats.

544 City Children

1996. 50th Anniv of U.N.I.C.E.F. Sheet 110 × 87 mm, containing T **544** and similar horiz designs. Multicoloured.

MS4616 $1100 Type **544**; $1100 Youth worker and children (face value at top right); $1100 City children (face value at bottom right; $1100 Youth worker and children (face value at bottom right) . . . . 40·00

1996. Paintings by Rubens. As T **421** of Grenada. Multicoloured.

4617 $6 "The Garden of Love" (detail) 15 10
4618 $10 "Two Sleeping Children" 20 10
4619 $20 "All Saints Day" . . . 35 20
4620 $25 "Sacrifice of Abraham" 35 25
4621 $30 "The Last Supper" . . 40 30
4622 $35 "The Birth of Henry of Navarre" 45 30
4623 $40 Study of standing female saint 50 35
4624 $50 "The Garden of Love" (different detail) 60 45
4625 $60 "The Garden of Love" (different detail) 70 50
4626 $200 "The Martyrdom of St. Livinus" . . . . . . 2·00 2·25
4627 $200 "St. Francis of Paola" 2·00 2·25
4628 $300 "The Union of Maria de Medici and Henry IV" 3·00 3·75
MS4629 Three sheets. (a) 70 × 100 mm. $325 "The Three Crosses" (56 × 84 mm). (b) 100 × 70 mm. $325 "Decius Mus addressing the Legions" (84 × 56 mm). (c) 100 × 70 mm. $325 "Triumph of Henry IV" (84 × 56 mm). P 14 Set of 3 sheets 11·00 12·00

545 Apatosaurus

1996. Prehistoric Animals. Multicoloured.

4630/41 $35 × 12 Type **545**; Archaeopteryx; Dimorphodon; Deinonychus; Coelophysis; Tyrannosaurus; Triceratops; Anatosaurus; Saltasaurus; Allosaurus; Oviraptor; Stegosaurus
4642/53 $35 × 12 Ornithomimus; Pteranodon; Rhamphorynchus; Ornitholestes; Brachiosaurus; Parasaurolophus; Ceratosaurus; Camarasaurus; Euoplocephalus; Scutellosaurus; Compsognathus; Stegoceras . . . . . .
4654/65 $35 × 12 Eudimorphodon; Criorhynchus; Elasmosaurus; Rhomaleosaurus; Ceresiosaurus; Mesosaurus; Grendelius; Nothosaurus; Mixosaurus; Placodus; Coelacanth; Mosasaurus . . . . .
4666/77 $35 × 12 Tarbosaurus; Hadrosaurus; Polacanthus; Psittacosaurus; Ornitholestes; Yangchuanosaurus; Scelidosaurus; Kentrosaurus; Coelophysis; Lesothosaurus; Plateosaurus; Staurikosaurus (all vert)
4630/77 Set of 48 . . . . 21·00 22·00
MS4678 Two sheets, each 101 × 58 mm. (a) $60 Saurolophus; $60 Muttaburrasaurus; $60 Dicraeosaurus. (b) $60 Heterodontosaurus; $60 Compsognathus; $60 Ornithomimosaure (all vert) Set of 2 sheets . . . . 4·50 5·50
MS4679 Five sheets. (a) 106 × 76 mm. $300 Struthiomimus. (b) 76 × 106 mm. $300 Tyrannosaurus rex (vert). (c) 76 × 106 mm. $300 Apatosaurus and Allosaurus. (d) 106 × 76 mm. $300 Quetzalcoatlus. (e) 106 × 76 mm. $300 Lagosuchus Set of 5 sheets . . . . 19·00 21·00

Nos. 4630/41, 4642/53, 4654/65 and 4666/77 respectively were printed together, se-tenant, with the backgrounds forming composite designs.

1996. "CHINA 96" International Stamp Exhibition, Beijing. T **546** and similar vert designs. Multicoloured.

MS4680 130 × 95 mm. $60 Summer Palace, Beijing (39 × 51 mm) 1·25 1·40
MS4681 Two sheets, each 146 × 116 mm. (a) $60 Type **546**; $60 Panda holding bamboo stem; $60 Eating bamboo stalk; $60 On all fours. (b) $60 Panda lying on tree branch (logo at left); $60 Lying on branch (logo at right; $60 Exploring hollow in tree (logo at left); $60 Sitting on trunk (logo at right) Set of 2 sheets . . . . 7·00 7·00

The stamps in No. **MS**4681 form composite designs showing rocks and stream (a) or dead tree (b).

546a Deng Xiaoping writing Inscription

1996. Deng Xiaoping (Chinese leader) Commemoration. Multicoloured.

4681c $30 Type **546a** 35 40
4681d $30 Deng Xiaoping addressing meeting (value in red) 35 40
4681e $30 Signing first day cover for army officer (value in yellow) 35 40
4681f $30 Waving 35 40
4681g $30 As No. 4681d (value in yellow) 35 40
4681h $30 As No. 4681e (value in red) 35 40
MS4681i 73 × 101 mm. $300 Deng Xiaoping applauding (vert) . . 3·25 3·50

547 "Morchella esculenta" and "Doryphorella princeps" (leaf beetle)

549 Hulda Gates

1996. Fungi of Guyana. Multicoloured.

4682 $20 Type **547** 45 30
4683 $25 Green-spored mushroom 45 30
4684 $30 Common mushroom and leaf beetle 50 30
4685 $35 Pine cone mushroom and "Danaus plexippus" caterpillar 50 30
4686 $60 "Armillaria mellea" . . 70 70
4687 $60 "Gomphus floccosus" 70 70
4688 $60 "Pholiota astragalina" 70 70
4689 $60 "Helvellaa crispa" . . . 70 70
4690 $60 "Hygrophorus miniatus" 70 70
4691 $60 "Omphalotus olearius" 70 70
4692 $60 "Hygrocybe acutoconica" 70 70
4693 $60 "Mycena viscosa" . . . 70 70
4694 $60 Cockle-shell lentinus . . 70 70
4695 $60 "Volvariella surrecta" 70 70
4696 $60 "Lepiota josserandii" 70 70
4697 $60 "Boletellus betula" . . 70 70
4698 $60 "Amanita muscaria" . . 70 70
4699 $60 "Russula claroflava" and "Semiotus angulatus" (click beetle) 70 70
4700 $60 "Dictyophora duplicata" and "Musca domestica" (house fly) . . 70 70
4701 $60 "Stropharia" and "Editha magnifica" (butterfly hunter) 70 70
4702 $60 "Leotia viscosa" . . . 70 70
4703 $60 "Calostoma cinnabarina" 70 70
4704 $60 Stalkless paxillus . . . 70 70
4705 $60 "Amanita spissa" . . . 70 70
MS4706 Two sheets, each 114 × 84 mm. (a) $300 "Mycena leaiana" and Yellow grosbeak (bird). (b) $300 "Tubifera ferryginosa", "Clavulina amethystina" and "Ramaria formosa" (horiz) Set of 2 sheets 7·50 8·00

Nos. 4686 and 4692 are inscribed "Armillauella mellea" and "Hygzocybe acutoconica", both in error.

1996. 70th Birthday of Queen Elizabeth II. As T **255a** of Gambia. Multicoloured.

4707 $100 Queen Elizabeth II . . 1·40 1·50
4708 $100 Queen wearing green and blue jacket and hat 1·40 1·50
4709 $100 Queen at State Opening of Parliament . . 1·40 1·50
MS4710 103 × 125 mm. $325 Queen in Garter robes . . . . 4·25 4·50

1996. Commonwealth Pharmacy Week. Unissued values in designs of Nos. 1810 and 1873 surch **COMMONWEALTH PHARMACY WEEK JUNE 16th 22nd 1996**.

4711 $6 on 130c. Plate No. 21 (Series 2) . . . .
4712 $60 on 100c. Plate No. 33 (Series 2) . . . .

1996. Centenary of Radio. Entertainers. As T **259a** of Gambia. Multicoloured.

4713 $20 Frank Sinatra 50 30
4714 $35 Gene Autry 50 30
4715 $60 Groucho Marx 60 50
4716 $200 Red Skelton . . . . . 2·00 2·25
MS4717 104 × 74 mm. $300 Burl Ives . . . . 3·50 4·00

1996. 3000th Anniv of Jerusalem. Multicoloured.

4718 $30 Type **549** 80 40
4719 $35 Church of St. Mary Magdalene 80 40
4720 $200 Absalom's Tomb, Kidron Valley . . . . . 2·50 3·00
MS4721 105 × 76 mm. $300 Children's Holocaust Memorial, Yad Vashem . . . . 4·00 4·25

550 Long-billed Starthroat

1996. Birds of the World. Multicoloured.

4722 $60 Type **550** 70 70
4723 $60 Velvet-purple coronet 70 70
4724 $60 Racquet-tailed coquette 70 70
4725 $60 Violet-tailed sylph . . . 70 70
4726 $60 Broad-tailed hummingbird 70 70
4727 $60 Blue-tufted starthroat 70 70
4728 $60 White-necked jacobin 70 70
4729 $60 Ruby-throated hummingbird 70 70
4730 $60 Blue and yellow macaw 70 70
4731 $60 Andean condor 70 70
4732 $60 Guiana crested eagle ("Crested Eagle") 70 70
4733 $60 White-tailed trogon . . 70 70
4734 $60 Toco toucan 70 70
4735 $60 Great horned owl . . . 70 70
4736 $60 Andean cock-of-the-rock 70 70
4737 $60 Great curassow 70 70
MS4738 Two sheets, each 101 × 70 mm. (a) $300 Sparkling violetear ("Gould's Sparkling Violet-ear"). (b) $300 Ornate hawk eagle (horiz) Set of 2 sheets . . 7·50 8·00

Nos. 4722/9 and 4730/7 respectively were printed together, se-tenant, the backgrounds forming composite designs.

551 Pancratium (ancient Olympic event)

1996. Olympic Games, Atlanta (3rd issue). Multicoloured.

4739 $20 Type **551** 40 30
4740 $30 Olympic Stadium, Melbourne, 1956 . . . 40 30
4741/9 $50 × 9 Volleyball; Basketball; Tennis; Table tennis; Baseball; Handball; Hockey; Water polo; Football
4750/8 $50 × 9 Cycling; Hurdling; High jumping; Diving; Weight- lifting; Canoeing; Wrestling; Gymnastics; Running (all vert) . . . .
4759/67 $50 × 9 Florence Griffith-Joyner (track and field) (U.S.A.); Ines Geissler (swimming) (Germany); Nadia Comaneci (gymnastics) (Rumania); Tatiana Gutsu (gymnastics) (Unified team); Ogla Korbut (gymnastics) (Russia); Barbara Krause (swimming) (Germany); Olga Bryzgina (track and field) (Russia); Fanny Blankers-Koen (track and field) (Holland); Irena Szewinska (track and field) (Poland) (all vert) . . . .
4768/76 $50 × 9 Gerd Wessig (Germany); Jim Thorpe (U.S.A.); Norman Read (New Zealand); Lasse Viren (Finland); Milt Campbell (U.S.A.); Abebe Bikila (Ethiopia); Jesse Owens (U.S.A.); Viktor Saneev (Russia); Waldemer Cierpinski (Germany) (all track and field) (all vert) . . . .
4777/85 $50 × 9 Ditmar Schmidt (handball) (Germany); Pam Shriver (tennis doubles) (U.S.A.); Zina Garrison (tennis doubles) (U.S.A); Hyun Jung-Hua (table tennis doubles) (Korea); Steffi Graf (tennis) (Germany); Michael Jordan (basketball) (U.S.A.); Karch Kiraly (volleyball) (U.S.A.); "Magic" Johnson (basketball) (U.S.A.); Ingolf Weigert (handball) (Germany) (all vert) . . . .
4786 $60 Leonid Spirin winning 20 kilometre walk, 1956 (vert) . . . 60 60
4787 $200 Lars Hall, Gold medal winner, Modern Pentathalon, 1952 and 1956 (Sweden) (vert) . . 1·75 2·00
4739/87 Set of 49 . . . . 25·00 27·00
MS4788 Two sheets. (a) 104 × 74 mm. $300 Carl Lewis, Gold medal winner, track and field, 1984, 1988 and 1992 (U.S.A.). (b) 74 × 104 mm. $300 U.S.A. defeating Korea at baseball, 1988 Set of 2 sheets 6·50 7·50

Nos. 4741/9, 4750/8, 4759/67, 4768/76 and 4777/85 (the last three showing Gold medal winners) respectively were printed together, se-tenant, forming composite background designs.

No. **MS**4788a is inscribed "1985" in error.

552 Mickey's Bait Shop

1996. Mickey Mouse and Friends Outdoors. Multicoloured.

4789 $60 Type **552** . . . . 1·00 1·00
4790 $60 Mickey and Pluto as lumberjacks . . . . . . 1·00 1·00
4791 $60 Mickey fishing . . . . 1·00 1·00
4792 $80 Donald Duck in BMX bike championships (vert) 1·25 1·25
4793 $80 Goofy as ice hockey superstar (vert) . . . . . 1·25 1·25
4794 $80 Donald Duck at Malibu Surf City (vert) . . . . . 1·25 1·25
4795 $100 Mickey as naval captain (vert) . . . . . . 1·40 1·40
4796 $100 Captain Mickey's Seamanship School (vert) 1·40 1·40
4797 $100 Mickey as sailor with ship's wheel and full-rigged sailing ship (vert) 1·40 1·40
MS4798 Five sheets. (a) 124 × 101 mm. $250 Mickey as Pinkerton detective (vert). (b) 104 × 126 mm. $250 Mickey as U.S. Marshal (vert). (c) 125 × 104 mm. $250 Mickey as train conductor and Transcontinental Railroad locomotive. (d) 101 × 124 mm. $300 Donald Duck as mountaineer. (e) 104 × 124 mm. $325 Mickey as trapper (vert) Set of 5 sheets . . . . 21·00 22·00

553 Two Gun Mickey

1996. Disney Antique Toys. Multicoloured.

4799 $6 Type **553** 50 50
4800 $6 Wood-jointed Mickey figure 50 50
4801 $6 Donald jack-in-the-box 50 50
4802 $6 Rocking Minnie 50 50
4803 $6 Fireman Donald Duck 50 50
4804 $6 Long-billed Donald Duck 50 50
4805 $6 Painted-wood Mickey figure 50 50
4806 $6 Wind-up Jiminy Cricket 50 50
MS4807 Two sheets, each 131 × 105 mm. (a) $300 Mickey doll. (b) $300 Carousel Set of 2 sheets . . . . 10·00 10·00

554 Elvis Presley

1996. 60th Birth Anniv (1995) of Elvis Presley. Multicoloured, background colours given.

4808 **554** $100 red . . . . 1·40 1·25
4809 – $100 mauve . . . . . . 1·40 1·25
4810 – $100 brown . . . . . . 1·40 1·25
4811 – $100 blue . . . . 1·40 1·25
4812 – $100 purple . . . . . . 1·40 1·25
4813 – $100 blue . . . . 1·40 1·25

DESIGNS: Nos. 4809/13, Various portraits.

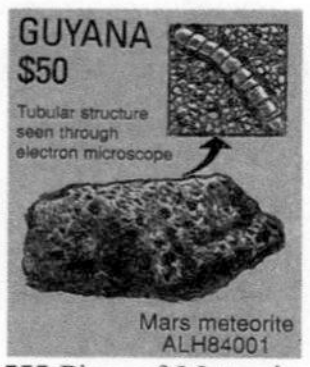

555 Piece of Meteorite showing Fossil

1996. Mars Meteorite. Sheet 104 × 76 mm.

MS4814 **555** $50 multicoloured 2·00 1·75

556 Birman

1996. Cats of the World. Multicoloured.

4815 $60 Type **556** 70 70
4816 $60 American curl 70 70
4817 $60 Turkish angora 70 70
4818 $60 European shorthair (Italy) 70 70
4819 $60 Persian (Great Britain) 70 70
4820 $60 Scottish fold 70 70
4821 $60 Sphynx (Canada) . . . 70 70
4822 $60 Malayan (Thailand) . . 70 70
4823 $60 Cornish rex (Great Britain) 70 70
4824 $60 Norwegian forest (vert) 70 70
4825 $60 Russian shorthair (vert) 70 70
4826 $60 European shorthair (Italy) (vert) 70 70
4827 $60 Birman (vert) 70 70
4828 $60 Ragdoll (U.S.A.) (vert) 70 70
4829 $60 Egyptian mau (vert) . . 70 70
4830 $60 Persian (Great Britain) (vert) 70 70
4831 $60 Turkish angora (vert) 70 70
4832 $60 Siamese (vert) 70 70
MS4833 Two sheets, each 107 × 72 mm. (a) $300 Himalayan (U.S.A.). (b) $300 Maine coon (U.S.A.) (vert) Set of 2 sheets 6·50 7·50

Nos. 4815/23 and 4824/32 respectively were printed together, se-tenant, with the backgrounds forming composite designs.

557 Hyed Snapper

1996. Marine Life. Multicoloured.

4834 $6 Type **557** 15 15
4835 $6 Angelfish 15 15
4836 $20 Boxfish 30 20
4837 $25 Golden damselfish . . . 30 25
4838 $30 Goblin shark and coelacanth 35 35
4839 $30 "Jason" (American remote-controlled submersible) 35 35
4840 $30 Deep-water invertebrates 35 35
4841 $30 Submarine NR-1 . . . 35 35
4842 $30 Giant squid 35 35
4843 $30 Sperm whale 35 35
4844 $30 Volcanic vents and "Alvin" (submersible) . . 35 35
4845 $30 Air-recycling pressure suits and shipwreck . . . 35 35
4846 $30 "Shinkai" 6500 (submersible) 35 35
4847 $30 Giant tube worms . . . 35 35
4848 $30 Anglerfish 35 35
4849 $30 Six-gill shark 35 35
4850 $30 Autonomous underwater vehicle ABE 35 35
4851 $30 Octopus and viperfish 35 35
4852 $30 Swallower and hatchetfish 35 35
4853 $35 Clown triggerfish . . . 35 30
4854 $60 Red gorgonians 65 65
4855 $60 Soft coral and butterflyfish 65 65
4856 $60 Soft coral and slender snapper 65 65
4857 $60 Common clownfish, anemone and mushroom coral 65 65
4858 $60 Anemone and horse-eyed jack 65 65
4859 $60 Splendid coral trout . . 65 65
4860 $60 Anemones 65 65
4861 $60 Brain coral 65 65
4862 $60 Cup coral 65 65
4863 $200 Harlequin tuskfish . . 2·25 2·50
MS4864 Two sheets, each 98 × 68 mm. (a) $300 Caribbean flower coral. (b) $300 Sea anemone Set of 2 sheets . . . . 6·50 7·50

Nos. 4838/52 and 4854/62 respectively were printed together, se-tenant, with the backgrounds forming composite designs.

No. 4853 is inscribed "CLOWN TUGGERFISH" in error.

558 Snow White and Reindeer

1996. Christmas. Disney's "Snow White and the Seven Dwarfs". Multicoloured.

4865 $6 Type **558** 30 10
4866 $20 Doc with presents . . . 80 25
4867 $25 Dopey and Sneezy . . . 80 30
4868 $30 Sleepy, Happy and Bashful 80 35
4869 $35 Dopey and Santa Claus 80 40
4870 $60 Dopey with socks at fireplace . . . . 1·50 1·00
4871 $100 Dopey and Grumpy 2·50 2·50
4872 $200 Dopey dressed as Santa Claus . . . . . . 3·75 4·50
MS4873 Two sheets, each 122 × 102 mm. (a) $300 Snow White, Doc and squirrel. (b) $300 Dopey and Christmas tree Set of 2 sheets . . . . 12·00 12·00

559 Hotel Tower

1996. 50th Anniv of Hotel Tower, Georgetown.

4874 **559** $30 multicoloured . . . 70 40

561 Ox

1997. Chinese New Year. "Year of the Ox".

4882 **561** $20 multicoloured . . . 35 25
4883 – $30 multicoloured . . . 50 40
4884 – $35 multicoloured . . . 55 50
4885 – $50 multicoloured . . . 75 80
MS4886 101 × 72 mm. $150 multicoloured . . . . 2·00 2·25
MS4887 68 × 90 mm. $50 As No. 4882 (value bottom right); $50 As No. 4883 (value bottom left); $50 As No. 4884 (value top right); $50 As No. 4885 (value top left) 2·00 2·25

DESIGNS: Nos. 4883/7 depict symbolic oxen.

562 Mickey with Traditional Box of Sweets

1997. Mickey Mouse and Friends celebrate Chinese New Year. Multicoloured.

4888 $6 Type **562** 40 25
4889 $20 Mickey and Minnie at home with friends 50 35
4890 $25 Mickey and Minnie hanging fortune lantern 50 35
4891 $30 Minnie and Daisy with paper silhouette 55 55
4892 $30 Mickey and friends receiving traditional red money 55 55
4893 $30 Mickey in lion dance . . 55 55
4894 $30 Mickey preparing Chinese calligraphy wall hangings 55 55
4895 $30 Mickey with symbols of surplus 55 55
4896 $30 Donald Duck playing with fireworks 55 55
4897 $30 Donald, Mickey and Minnie on ox 55 55
4898 $35 Donald Duck and friends at New Year flower market 55 55
4899 $60 Mickey and Minnie as "harmonious man and woman" 90 90
MS4900 Two sheets, each 133 × 109 mm. (a) $150 Mickey Mouse marching (vert). (b) $200 Mickey and ox Set of 2 sheets 6·00 6·00

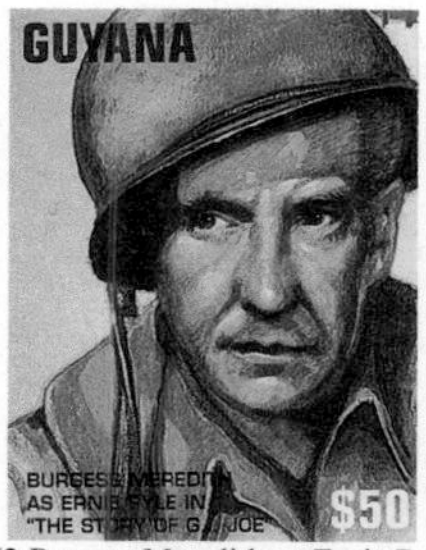

563 Burgess Meredith as Ernie Pyle in "The Story of G.I. Joe"

1997. Centenary of Cinema. Second World War Films. Multicoloured.

4901 $50 Type **563** 70 70
4902 $50 M. E. Clifton-James as General Montgomery in "I was Monty's Double" 70 70
4903 $50 Audie Murphy as himself in "To Hell and Back" 70 70
4904 $50 Gary Cooper as Dr. Wassell in "The Story of Dr. Wassell" 70 70
4905 $50 James Mason as Erwin Rommel in "The Desert Fox" 70 70
4906 $50 Manart Kippen as Stalin in "Mission to Moscow" 70 70
4907 $50 Robert Taylor as Col. Paul Tibbets in "Above and Beyond" 70 70
4908 $50 James Cagney as Admiral Bill Halsey in "The Gallant Hours" . . 70 70
4909 $50 John Garfield as Al Schmid in "Pride of the Marines" 70 70
MS4910 105 × 75 mm. $300 George C. Scott as Gen. George S. Patton in "Patton" (horiz) . . . . . 5·00 5·50

564 "Washington in Battle"

1997. Bicentenary of George Washington's Retirement from U.S. Presidency. Multicoloured.

4911 $60 Type **564** 60 60
4912 $60 "Washington taking Presidential Oath" 60 60
4913 $60 "Washington seated in Armchair" (engraving after Chappel) 60 60
4914 $60 "Col. Washington of the Virginia Militia" (Charles W. Peale) . . . 60 60
4915 $60 "George Washington" (Rembrandt Peale) . . . 60 60
4916 $60 "Washington addressing Constitutional Convention" (Junius B. Stearns) 60 60
4917 $60 "Washington on his way to Continental Congress" 60 60
4918 $60 "Washington on a White Charger" (John Faed) 60 60
4919 $60 "Washington surveying" (engraving by G. R. Hall) 60 60
4920 $60 "Washington praying at Valley Forge" (bas-relief) 60 60
4921 $60 "Death of Gen. Mercer at Battle of Princeton" (John Trumbull) 60 60
4922 $60 "Washington taking Command at Cambridge" 60 60
4923 $60 "Washington before Battle of Trenton" (John Trumbull) 60 60
4924 $60 "Washington and his Family at Mount Vernon" (Alonzo Chappel) 60 60
4925 $60 "Washington's Inauguration" (Chappel) 60 60
4926 $60 "Washington" (Adolph Ulrich Wertmuller) . . . 60 60
4927 $60 "Washington accepts Commission as Commander- in-Chief" (Currier & Ives lithograph) 60 60
4928 $60 "Washington" (mezzotint by Sartain) . . 60 60
4929 $60 "Mount Vernon" 60 60
4930 $60 "Washington with Farm Workers" (print by Junius B. Stearns) 60 60
4931 $60 "Wedding of Nellie Custis" (Ogden) 60 60
4932 $60 "Washington crossing the Delaware" (Leutze) 60 60
4933 $60 "Washington and Gen. Braddock" 60 60
4934 $60 "Washington's Birthplace" (Currier & Ives lithograph) 60 60
4935 $300 "George Washington" (Gilbert Stuart) (66 × 91 mm) . . . . . . 2·50 3·00
4936 $300 "Washington at Yorktown" (James Peale) (66 × 91 mm) . . . . . . 2·50 3·00

565 Pres. Kennedy and "Eternal Flame"

1997. 80th Birth Anniv of Pres. John F. Kennedy.

4937 **565** $50 violet 75 75

No. 4937 is in the same design as the U.S.A. Memorial Issue of 1964.

1997. 50th Anniv of U.N.E.S.C.O. Multicoloured. As T **273a** of Gambia.

4938 $20 Hall at Horyu-ji, Japan 20 20
4939 $25 Coastline, Scandola Nature Reserve, France 25 25
4940 $30 Great Wall turret, China 30 30
4941 $35 Bedroom in the Residenz, Wurzburg, Germany 35 30
4942 $60 Monastery of Batalha, Portugal 60 60
4943 $60 Cathedral of Aquisgran, Aachen, Germany (vert) 60 60
4944 $60 Trier Cathedral, Germany (vert) 60 60
4945 $60 Column of Augusta Treveror, Trier (vert) . . 60 60
4946 $60 The Residenz and garden, Wurzburg (vert) 60 60
4947 $60 Interior of church, Wurzburg (vert) 60 60
4948 $60 The Residenz and lake, Wurzburg (vert) 60 60
4949 $60 Riverside houses, Inselstadt, Bamberg, Germany (vert) 60 60

4950 $60 Cathedral interior, Speyer, Germany (vert) 60 60
4951 $60 Monastery of Thessaloniki, Greece (vert) 60 60
4952 $60 Church tower, Monastery of Mystras, Greece (vert) 60 60
4953 $60 Interior of Church of Santa Sofia, Thessaloniki (vert) 60 60
4954 $60 Monastery and ruins, Mystras (vert) 60 60
4955 $60 Aerial view of Monastery at Mystras (vert) 60 60
4956 $60 City wall, Thessaloniki (vert) 60 60
4957 $60 Wall painting, Mystras Monastery (vert) 60 60
4958 $60 Paintings in Museum of Byzantine Art, Thessaloniki (vert) 60 60
4959 $60 Monastery of Poblet, Catalonia, Spain (vert) 60 60
4960 $60 Salamanca, Spain (vert) 60 60
4961 $60 Toledo, Spain (vert) 60 60
4962 $60 Florence Cathedral, Italy (vert) 60 60
4963 $60 Leaning Tower of Pisa, Italy (vert) 60 60
4964 $60 Courtyard and tower, Convent of Cristo in Tomas, Portugal (vert) 60 60
4965 $60 Main door, Convent of Cristo in Tomas (vert) 60 60
4966 $60 Cloisters, Convent of Cristo in Tomas (vert) 60 60
4967 $80 Tower, Horyu-ji, Japan 70 70
4968 $80 Temple with verandah, Kyoto, Japan 70 70
4969 $80 Temple and pillar, Kyoto 70 70
4970 $80 Temples and lake, Horyu-Ji 70 70
4971 $80 Three-storey temple, Horyu-Ji 70 70
4972 $80 University of Virginia, U.S.A. 70 70
4973 $80 Yosemite National Park, U.S.A. 70 70
4974 $80 Yellowstone National Park, U.S.A. 70 70
4975 $80 Olympic National Park, U.S.A. 70 70
4976 $80 Everglades, U.S.A. 70 70
4977 $80 Street, Cuzco, Peru 70 70
4978 $80 Potosi, Bolivia 70 70
4979 $80 Fortress of San Lorenzo, Panama 70 70
4980 $80 Sangay National Park, Ecuador 70 70
4981 $80 Los Glaciares National Park, Argentina 70 70
4982 $200 City walls, Dubrovnik, Croatia 1·75 2·00
MS4983 Four sheets, each 126×101 mm. (a) $300 Golden Buddha, Mount Taishan, China. (b) $300 Monastery garden, Batalha, Portugal. (c) $300 Virgin and Child (statue), Bamberg Cathedral, Germany. (d) $300 Monastery, Mount Athos, Greece Set of 4 sheets 11·00 12·00

566 "Morchella hortensis"

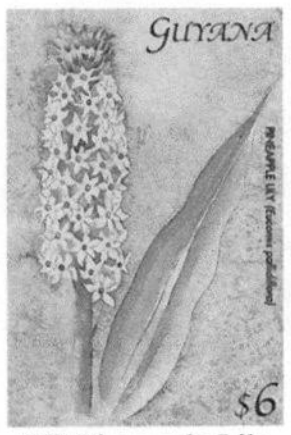

567 Pineapple Lily

1997. Fungi of the World. Multicoloured.
4984 $6 Type **566** 20 15
4985 $20 "Boletus chrysenteron" 25 20
4986 $25 "Hygrophorus agathosmus" 30 25
4987 $30 "Cortinarius violaceus" 35 30
4988 $35 "Acanthocystis geogenius" 40 30
4989 $60 "Mycena polygramma" 65 50
4990 $80 "Coprinus picaceus" 75 75
4991 $80 "Stropharia umbonatescens" 75 75
4992 $80 "Paxillus involutus" 75 75
4993 $80 "Amanita inaurata" 75 75
4994 $80 "Lepiota rhacodes" 75 75
4995 $80 "Russula amoena" 75 75
4996 $80 "Volvaria volvacea" 75 75
4997 $80 "Psalliota augusta" 75 75
4998 $80 "Tricholoma aurantium" 75 75
4999 $80 "Pholiota spectabilis" 75 75
5000 $80 "Cortinarius armillatus" 75 75
5001 $80 "Agrocybe dura" 75 75
5002 $200 "Hebeloma radicosum" 1·75 2·00
5003 $300 "Coprinus comatus" 2·75 3·00
MS5004 Two sheets, each 76×105 mm. (a) $300 "Pholiota mutabilis". (b) $300 "Amanita muscaria" Set of 2 sheets 6·50 7·00

1997. Flowers. Multicoloured.
5005 $6 Type **567** 15 15
5006 $6 Blue columbine 15 15
5007 $20 Petunia 20 20
5008 $25 Lily of the Nile 25 25
5009 $30 Bird of paradise 30 30
5010 $35 African daisy 35 30
5011 $60 Cape daisy 60 60
5012 $60 Monarch slipperwort 60 60
5013 $60 Passion flower 60 60
5014 $60 Butterfly iris 60 60
5015 $60 Red-hot poker 60 60
5016 $60 Water lily "Dir G. T. Moore" 60 60
5017 $60 Painted tongue "Superbissima" 60 60
5018 $60 Canariensis orchid 60 60
5019 $60 Annual chrysanthemum 60 60
5020 $80 Tulips 70 70
5021 $80 Liatris 70 70
5022 $80 Roses 70 70
5023 $80 Gerber daisies 70 70
5024 $80 Sunflowers 70 70
5025 $80 Chrysanthemums 70 70
5026 $80 Gazania 70 70
5027 $80 Cape water lily 70 70
5028 $200 Insigne lady's slipper 1·75 2·25
MS5029 105×75 mm. $300 Petunias 3·00 3·50

568 Deng Xiaoping inspecting Rural Sichuan, 1980

1997. Deng Xiaoping (Chinese leader) Commem.
5030 **568** $100 multicoloured 1·00 1·00
MS5031 100×70 mm. $150 Deng Xiaoping on visit to foundry 1·50 1·60

1997. 10th Anniv of Chernobyl Nuclear Disaster. As T **276a** of Gambia. Multicoloured.
5032 $200 As Type **276a** of Gambia 1·75 2·00
5033 $200 As Type **276a** of Gambia, but inscribed "CHABAD'S CHILDREN OF CHERNOBYL" at foot 1·75 2·00

1997. 50th Death Anniv of Paul Harris (founder of Rotary International). As T **276b** of Gambia. Mult.
5034 $200 Paul Harris and volunteers with children ("Health, hunger and humanity") 1·75 2·00
MS5035 77×107 mm. $300 Group of boys ("Mutual respect among all faiths, races and cultures") 2·50 3·00

1997. Golden Wedding of Queen Elizabeth II and Prince Philip. As T **276c** of Gambia. Multicoloured (except Nos. 5038/9).
5036 $60 Queen Elizabeth II wearing tiara 90 90
5037 $60 Royal coat of arms 90 90
5038 $60 Wedding photograph, 1947 (black) 90 90
5039 $60 Engagement photograph (black) 90 90
5040 $60 Broadlands, Romsey (honeymoon residence) 90 90
5041 $60 Duke of Edinburgh 90 90
MS5042 99×70 mm. $300 Queen and Duke of Edinburgh 4·00 4·25

1997. "Pacific '97" International Stamp Exhibition, San Francisco. Death Centenary of Heinrich von Stephan (founder of U.P.U.). As T **276d** of Gambia.
5043 $100 sepia 1·00 1·25
5044 $100 brown 1·00 1·25
5045 $100 green 1·00 1·25
MS5046 82×118 mm. $300 black and blue 2·75 3·00
DESIGNS: No. 5043, Roman post cart from frieze; 5044, Von Stephan and Mercury; 5045, Cable car, Boston, 1907; **MS**5046, Von Stephan and ancient Egyptian messenger.

1997. 175th Anniv of Brothers Grimm's Third Collection of Fairy Tales. Hansel and Gretel. As T **277a** of Gambia. Multicoloured.
5047 $100 Hansel and Gretel lost in forest 1·40 1·40
5048 $100 Gingerbread house 1·40 1·40
5049 $100 Witch 1·40 1·40
MS5050 124×96 mm. $500 Gretel pushing witch into oven (horiz) 6·00 6·50

1997. 300th Anniv of Mother Goose Nursery Rhymes. Multicoloured design as T **276a** of Gambia. Sheet 75×101 mm.
MS5051 $300 "Cock-a-doodle-doo" (vert) 3·75 4·00

1997. Birth Bicentenary of Hiroshige (Japanese painter). "One Hundred Famous Views of Edo". As T **541a** of Ghana. Multicoloured.
5052 $80 "Oumayagashi" 1·00 1·00
5053 $80 "Ryogoku Ekoin and Moto-Yanagibashi Bridge" 1·00 1·00
5054 $80 "Point of Success and Oumayagashi, Asakusa River" 1·00 1·00
5055 $80 "Fireworks at Ryogoku" 1·00 1·00
5056 $80 "Dyers' Quarter, Kanda" 1·00 1·00
5057 $80 "Cotton-goods Lane, Odenma-cho" 1·00 1·00
MS5058 Two sheets, each 102×127 mm. (a) $300 "Suruga-cho". (b) $300 "Yatsukoji, inside Sujikai Gate" Set of 2 sheets 7·00 8·00

569 Tortoise

1997. "Hong Kong '97" International Stamp Exhibition. Return of Hong Kong to China. Mult.
5059 $80 Type **569** 80 80
5060 $80 Dragon 80 80
5061 $80 Unicorn 80 80
5062 $80 Phoenix 80 80
5063 $80 Barn swallow ("Swallow") and willow (vert) 80 80
5064 $80 River kingfisher ("Kingfisher") and chrysanthemum (vert) 80 80
5065 $80 Common crane ("Crane") and pine (vert) 80 80
5066 $80 Common peafowl ("Peacock") and peony (vert) 80 80
5067 $80 "Bird of Paradise" kite with two tail feathers (vert) 80 80
5068 $80 Large "eyed" kite with blue tail ribbons (vert) 80 80
5069 $80 "Phoenix" kite with "flaming" tail (vert) 80 80
5070 $80 "Insect" kite with red tail ribbons (vert) 80 80
5071 $200 Chinese landscape (face value at top left) (50×75 mm) 2·00 2·25
5072 $200 Chinese landscape (face value at bottom right) (50×75 mm) 2·00 2·25
MS5073 159×110 mm. $500 Junk in Hong Kong harbour (50×75 mm) 5·00 5·50

570 Markus Wasmeier (skier)

571 Chihuahua

1997. Winter Olympic Games, Nagano, Japan (1998). Multicoloured.
5074 $30 Type **570** 35 35
5075 $30 Jens Weissflog (ski-jumper) 35 35
5076 $30 Erhard Keller 35 35
5077 $30 Rosi Mittermaier (skier) 35 35
5078 $30 Gunda Niemann (speed skater) 35 35
5079 $30 Peter Angerer (skier) 35 35
5080 $30 Gorg Thoma (ski-jumper) 35 35
5081 $35 Katja Seizinger (skier) 35 35
5082 $60 Gorg Hackl (luge) 70 70
5083 $60 Gunda Niemann (Germany) (3000 and 5000 m speed skating gold medals, 1992) 70 70
5084 $60 Tony Nash and Robin Dixon (Great Britain) (bobsleigh gold medal, 1964) 70 70
5085 $60 Switzerland (4 man bobsleigh gold medal, 1988) 70 70
5086 $60 Piet Kleine (Holland) (speed skating gold medal, 1976) 70 70
5087 $60 Oksana Baiul (Ukraine) (figure skating gold medal, 1994) 70 70
5088 $60 Cathy Turner (U.S.A.) (500 m speed skating gold medal, 1994) 70 70
5089 $60 Brian Boitano (U.S.A.) (figure skating gold medal, 1988) 70 70
5090 $60 Nancy Kerrigan (U.S.A.) (figure skating silver medal, 1994) 70 70
5091 $200 Katarina Witt (skater) 2·00 2·25
MS5092 Three sheets. (a) 106×81 mm. $300 Jean-Claude Killy (France) (slalom skiing gold medal), 1968. (b) 106×81 mm. $300 Chen Lu (China) (figure skating gold medal, 1992). (c) 76×106 mm. $300 Swiss 4-man bobsleigh team Set of 3 sheets 9·50 10·00
No. 5081 is inscribed "KATIA", No. 5087 "BAIUI", No. 5091 "KATHARINA" and No. **MS**5092c "GERMANY", all in error.

1997. Cats and Dogs. Multicoloured.
5093 $20 Type **571** 45 25
5094 $25 Norfolk terrier 45 25
5095 $30 Norwegian forest cat 45 30
5096 $35 Oriental spotted tabby 45 30
5097 $60 Welsh terrier 70 70
5098 $60 Abyssinian (horiz) 70 70
5099 $60 Chocolate colorpoint shorthair (horiz) 70 70
5100 $60 Silver tabby (horiz) 70 70
5101 $60 Persian (horiz) 70 70
5102 $60 Maine coon cat and kitten (horiz) 70 70
5103 $60 Brown-shaded Burmese (horiz) 70 70
5104 $60 Persian kitten (horiz) 70 70
5105 $60 Siamese (horiz) 70 70
5106 $60 British shorthair (horiz) 70 70
5107 $60 Shar-pei 70 70
5108 $60 Chihuahua 70 70
5109 $60 Chow chow 70 70
5110 $60 Sealyham terrier 70 70
5111 $60 Collie 70 70
5112 $60 German shorthair pointer 70 70
5113 $60 Bulldog 70 70
5114 $60 German shepherd dog 70 70
5115 $60 Old English sheepdog 70 70
5116 $200 Asian smoke (cat) 2·00 2·25
MS5117 Two sheets, each 105×76 mm. (a) $300 Manx cat. (b) $300 Tibetan spaniel Set of 2 sheets 8·00 8·00

572 Verdin

1997. Birds of the World. Multicoloured.
5118 $25 Type **572** 50 30
5119 $30 Wood thrush (vert) 50 30
5120 $60 Rufous-sided towhee 75 50
5121 $80 Groove-billed ani 90 90
5122 $80 Green honeycreeper 90 90
5123 $80 Emerald toucanet 90 90
5124 $80 Wire-tailed manakin 90 90
5125 $80 Hoatzin 90 90
5126 $80 Rufescent tiger heron ("Tiger Heron") 90 90
5127 $80 Magenta-throated woodstar 90 90
5128 $80 Anna's hummingbird 90 90
5129 $80 Long-tailed hermit 90 90
5130 $80 White-tipped sicklebill 90 90
5131 $80 Red-footed plumeleteer 90 90
5132 $80 Fiery-throated hummingbird 90 90
5133 $200 Pygmy nuthatch (vert) 2·00 2·25
MS5134 Two sheets, each 70×100 mm. (a) $300 Pinnated bittern. (b) $300 Keel-billed toucan Set of 2 sheets 8·00 8·00

573 Pres. Cheddi Jagan in 1947 and 1997 with National Assembly Building

1997. 50th Anniv of Pres. Cheddi Jagan's Election to Parliament.
5135 **573** $6 multicoloured 15 15
5136 $30 multicoloured 50 50

574 Princess Diana

575 Presidents Clinton (U.S.A.) and Cheddi Jagan (Guyana)

1997. Diana, Princess of Wales Commemoration. Multicoloured.
5137 $80 Type **574** 90 90
5138 $80 Princess Diana in black V-neck dress 90 90
5139 $80 In red dress with diamante pattern on front 90 90
5140 $80 In white evening dress with narrow shoulder straps 90 90
5141 $80 In white evening dress with one shoulder bare 90 90
5142 $80 In lavender dress 90 90
MS5143 Two sheets, each 107×108 mm. (a) $300 In red sleeveless dress (33×51 mm). (b) $300 In white blouse (33×51 mm) Set of 2 sheets 7·00 7·50

1997. President Clinton's Caribbean Visit. Mult.
5144 $6 Type **575** 15 10
5145 $30 As Type **575**, but different portrait of Pres. Jagan 45 35

5146 $30 Presidents Clinton and Jagan, flags and sunrise over sea (horiz) 45 35
5147 $100 Presidents Clinton and Jagan, flags and sunrise over beach (horiz) . . . . 1·50 1·75

576 President Jiang Zemin, Flags, and New York Skyline by Day

1997. Visit of President Jiang Zemin of China to New York. Two sheets, each 125×84 mm, containing T **576** and similar horiz design. Multicoloured.
MS5148 Two sheets. (a) $200 Type **576**. (b) $300 President Jiang Zemin, flags, and New York at night Set of 2 sheets . . . . . 5·50 6·00

1997. Christmas. Paintings. As T **284a** of Gambia. Multicoloured.
5149 $25 Cupid from "The Triumph of Galatea" (Raphael) 30 10
5150 $30 Different Cupid from "The Triumph of Galatea" (Raphael) . . . 30 10
5151 $35 Cupid from "Primavera" (Botticelli) 35 15
5152 $60 "Angel Musicians" (Agostino di Duccio) . . 65 30
5153 $100 Cupid from illustration No. 1212, *Life Magazine* 28/1/06 . . . . 1·25 1·40
5154 $200 Angels from "Madonna and Saints" (Rosso Fiorentino) . . . 2·00 2·75
MS5155 Two sheets. (a) 95×105 mm. $300 "The Gardens of Love" (Rubens). (b) 105×95 mm. $300 "Cherubs" (Philippe de Champaigne) Set of 2 sheets . . . . 7·50 8·00

577 Abraham Lincoln

579 Tiger sitting (face value at bottom right)

578 Fogarty's Department Store, Georgetown

1997. 75th Anniversaries, 1997–2001. Multicoloured.
5156 $60 Type **577** (Dedication of Lincoln Memorial, Washington, 1922) . . . 75 75
5157 $60 Mask of Tutankhamun (discovery of tomb, 1922) 75 75
5158 $60 Alexander Graham Bell and early telephone, 1922 (75th death anniv) 75 75
5159 $60 John L. Baird and first television, 1923 . . . . . 75 75
5160 $60 President Warren G. Harding, 1923 (75th death anniv) 75 75
5161 $60 Presidency of Calvin Coolidge, 1923 . . . . . 75 75
5162 $60 Skier (first Winter Olympics, Chamonix, France, 1924) 75 75
5163 $60 Sun Yat-sen (Chinese leader), 1925 (75th death anniv) 75 75
5164 $60 Charles Darwin (ban on teaching of evolution, Tennessee, U.S.A., 1925) 75 75
5165 $60 Robert Goddard (first liquid fuel rocket, 1926) 75 75
5166 $60 Richard E. Byrd (first flight over North Pole, 1926) 75 75
5167 $60 Liberty Bell (Sesquicentennial Exposition, Philadelphia, 1926) 75 75

1997. Buildings in Guyana. Multicoloured.
5168 $6 Type **578** 15 15
5169 $30 St. Rose's High School (150th anniv) 50 50

1998. Chinese New Year ("Year of the Tiger"). Multicoloured.
5170 $50 Type **579** 30 35
5171 $50 Tiger sitting (face value bottom left) 30 35
5172 $50 Tiger standing (face value top right) 30 35
5173 $50 Tiger standing (face value top left) 30 35
MS5174 102×72 mm. $150 Tiger with Chinese characters in background 90 95

580 Kentrosaurus

1998. Prehistoric Animals. Multicoloured.
5175 $25 Type **580** 20 25
5176 $30 Lesothosaurus 20 25
5177 $35 Stegoceras 25 30
5178 $55 Ceresiosaurus 40 45
5179 $55 Nothosaurus 40 45
5180 $55 Rhomaleosaurus . . . 40 45
5181 $55 Grendelius 40 45
5182 $55 Mixosaurus 40 45
5183 $55 Mesosaurus 40 45
5184 $55 Placodus 40 45
5185 $55 Stethacanthus 40 45
5186 $55 Coelacanth 40 45
5187 $55 Quetzalcoatlus 40 45
5188 $55 Pteranodon 40 45
5189 $55 Peteinosaurus 40 45
5190 $55 Criorhychus 40 45
5191 $55 Pterodaustro 40 45
5192 $55 Eudimorphodon 40 45
5193 $55 Archeopteryx 40 45
5194 $55 Dimorphodon 40 45
5195 $55 Sharovipteryx 40 45
5196 $60 Lagosuchus 40 45
5197 $100 Herrerasaurus 70 75
5198 $200 Iguanodon . . . . . 1·40 1·50
MS5199 Two sheets, each 106×76 mm. (a) $300 Yangchuanosaurus (vert). (b) $300 Styracosaurus (vert) Set of 2 sheets 4·25 4·50
Nos. 5178/86 and 5187/95 were each printed together, se-tenant, with the backgrounds forming composite designs.

581 Bryan Berard

1998. Ice Hockey Players. Multicoloured.
5200 $35 Type **581** 20 25
5201 $35 Ray Bourque 20 25
5202 $35 Martin Brodeur 20 25
5203 $35 Pavel Bure 20 25
5204 $35 Chris Chelios 20 25
5205 $35 Sergei Fedorov 20 25
5206 $35 Peter Forsberg 20 25
5207 $35 Wayne Gretzky 20 25
5208 $35 Dominik Hasek 20 25
5209 $35 Brett Hull 20 25
5210 $35 Jarome Iginla 20 25
5211 $35 Jaromir Jagr 20 25
5212 $35 Paul Kariya 20 25
5213 $35 Saku Koivu 20 25
5214 $35 John LeClair 20 25
5215 $35 Brian Leetch 20 25
5216 $35 Eric Lindros 20 25
5217 $35 Patrick Marleau . . . 20 25
5218 $35 Mark Messier 20 25
5219 $35 Mike Modano 20 25
5220 $35 Chris Osgood 20 25
5221 $35 Zigmund Palffy . . . 20 25
5222 $35 Felix Potvin 20 25
5223 $35 Jeremy Roenick 20 25
5224 $35 Patrick Roy 20 25
5225 $35 Joe Sakic 20 25
5226 $35 Sergei Samsonov . . . 20 25
5227 $35 Teemu Selanne 20 25
5228 $35 Brendan Shanahan . . 20 25
5229 $35 Ryan Smyth 20 25
5230 $35 Jocelyn Thibault . . . 20 25
5231 $35 Joe Thornton 20 25
5232 $35 Keith Tkachuk 20 25
5233 $35 John Vanbiesbrouck . . 20 25
5234 $35 Steve Yzerman 20 25
5235 $35 Dainius Zubrus 20 25

582 Argentine Team

1998. World Cup Football Championship, France. Showing competing teams and trophy. Multicoloured.
5236 $30 Type **582** 20 25
5237 $30 Austria 20 25
5238 $30 Belgium 20 25
5239 $30 Brazil 20 25
5240 $30 Bulgaria 20 25
5241 $30 Cameroon 20 25
5242 $30 Chile 20 25
5243 $30 Colombia 20 25
5244 $30 Croatia 20 25
5245 $30 Denmark 20 25
5246 $30 England 20 25
5247 $30 France 20 25
5248 $30 Germany 20 25
5249 $30 Holland 20 25
5250 $30 Iran 20 25
5251 $30 Italy 20 25
5252 $30 Jamaica 20 25
5253 $30 Japan 20 25
5254 $30 Mexico 20 25
5255 $30 Morocco 20 25
5256 $30 Nigeria 20 25
5257 $30 Norway 20 25
5258 $30 Paraguay 20 25
5259 $30 Rumania 20 25
5260 $30 Saudi Arabia 20 25
5261 $30 Scotland 20 25
5262 $30 South Africa 20 25
5263 $30 South Korea 20 25
5264 $30 Spain 20 25
5265 $30 Tunisia 20 25
5266 $30 U.S.A. 20 25
5267 $30 Yugoslavia 20 25
MS5268 Two sheets, each 110×85 mm. (a) $300 Okada, Japan (vert). (b) $300 Nakata, Japan (vert) Set of 2 sheets . . 3·50 3·75

583 Dutch Fluyt

1998. Sailing Ships. Multicoloured.
5269 $80 Type **583** 50 55
5270 $80 *Alastor* (barque) . . . 50 55
5271 $80 *Falcon* (medieval ship) 50 55
5272 $80 *Red Rover* (barque) . . 50 55
5273 $80 *British Anglesey* (full-rigged ship) 50 55
5274 $80 *Archibald Russell* (barque) 50 55
5275 $80 14th century double-ended Scandinavian ship 50 55
5276 $80 Portuguese caravel . . . 50 55
5277 $80 *Nina* (Columbus) . . . 50 55
5278 $80 *Fannie* (schooner) . . . 50 55
5279 $80 *Vitoria* (Magellan) . . . 50 55
5280 $80 Arab sambook 50 55
MS5281 Two sheets. (a) 76×106 mm. $300 *Half Moon* (Hudson). (b) 106×76 mm. $300 Osberg ship Set of 2 sheets . . 3·50 3·75
No. 5274 is inscribed "ARCHIBALD RUSSEL" in error.

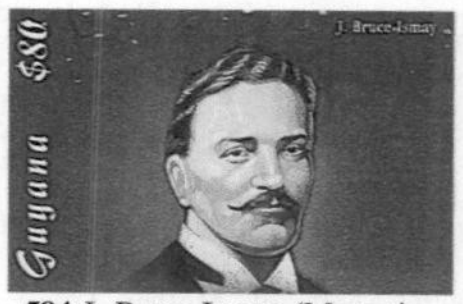

584 J. Bruce Ismay (Managing Director of White Star Line)

1998. 85th Anniv of Sinking of the Titanic (liner). Multicoloured.
5282 $80 Type **584** 50 55
5283 $80 Jack Phillips (wireless operator) 50 55
5284 $80 Margaret Brown (passenger) 50 55
5285 $80 Capt. Edward J. Smith 50 55
5286 $80 Frederick Fleet (crew member) 50 55
5287 $80 Thomas Andrews (Managing Director of Harland & Wolff) 50 55
MS5288 100×70 mm. $300 *Titanic* sinking . . . . 1·80 1·90

1998. 25th Anniv of Caribbean Community. As T **454a** of Grenada. Multicoloured.
5289 $20 Flags of Grenada and CARICOM 10 15

585 Queen Elizabeth the Queen Mother

1998. 98th Birthday of Queen Elizabeth the Queen Mother.
5290 **585** $90 multicoloured . . . 55 60

1998. France's Victory in World Cup Football Championship. Nos. 5239, 5244/5, 5247, 5251, 5258, 5260 and 5262 optd **FRANCE WINNERS**. Multicoloured.
5291 $30 Brazil 20 25
5292 $30 Croatia 20 25
5293 $30 Denmark 20 25
5294 $30 France 20 25
5295 $30 Italy 20 25
5296 $30 Paraguay 20 25
5297 $30 Saudi Arabia 20 25
5298 $30 South Africa 20 25

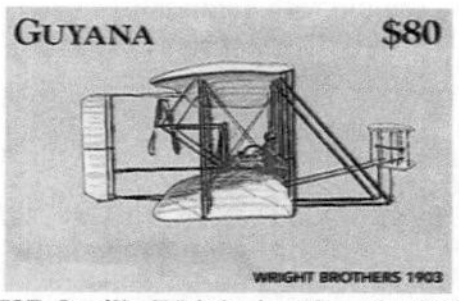

587 Orville Wright in *Flyer I*, 1903

1998. Aircraft. Multicoloured.
5299 $80 Type **587** 50 55
5300 $80 Bleriot, 1911 . . . . . 50 55
5301 $80 Curtiss Jenny, 1919 . . 50 55
5302 $80 Zeppelin LZ-10 *Schwaben*, 1911 . . . . . 50 55
5303 $80 W-8B, 1923 . . . . . . 50 55
5304 $80 DH66, 1926 . . . . . 50 55
5305 $80 A7K Corsair II 50 55
5306 $80 A6E Intruder 50 55
5307 $80 U2 spy plane 50 55
5308 $80 Blackhawk helicopter 50 55
5309 $80 F-16 . . . . 50 55
5310 $80 Phantom II 50 55
MS5311 Two sheets, each 70×100 mm. (a) $300 A-10 Warthog. (b) $300 HH-65A Dolphin helicopter Set of 2 sheets 3·50 3·75
Nos. 5299/304 and 5305/10 were each printed together, se-tenant, with the backgrounds forming composite designs.

588 Panda climbing Tree

589 Mountain Gorilla

1998. Giant Pandas. Multicoloured.
5312 $80 Type **588** 50 55
5313 $80 Panda sitting on tree trunk 50 55
5314 $80 Panda climbing bamboo 50 55
5315 $80 Panda chewing bamboo 50 55
5316 $80 Panda snapping bamboo stalk 50 55
5317 $80 Panda eating foliage . . 50 55
MS5318 100×70 mm. $300 Panda with leaves . . . . 1·80 1·90
Nos. 5312/17 were printed together, se-tenant, with the backgrounds forming a composite design.

1998. Mountain Gorillas. Multicoloured.
5319 $80 Type **589** 50 55
5320 $80 Gorilla climbing tree . . 50 55
5321 $80 Gorilla eating foliage 50 55
5322 $80 Female gorilla sitting on ground 50 55
5323 $80 Baby gorilla eating twig 50 55
5324 $80 Male gorilla in forest 50 55
MS5325 100×70 mm. $300 Young gorilla eating leaf . . . . . . 1·80 1·90
Nos. 5319/24 were printed together, se-tenant, with the backgrounds forming a composite design.

590 Christian Lautenschlager in Grand Prix Mercedes, 1914

1998. History of Grand Prix Motor Racing. Mult.
5326 $80 Type **590** 50 55
5327 $80 P. Etancelin in Bugatti Type 35B, 1930 . . . . . 50 55
5328 $80 Louis Chiron in Alfa Romeo P3, 1934 . . . . 50 55
5329 $80 Richard Seaman in Mercedes-Benz W154, 1938 . . . . 50 55
5330 $80 Tazio Nuvolari in Auto Union D Type, 1938 . . . 50 55
5331 $80 Juan Fangio in Alfa Romeo 158, 1951 . . . . 50 55
5332 $80 Stirling Moss in Mercedes-Benz W196, 1955 . . . . 50 55
5333 $80 Phil Hill in Ferrari Dino 246, 1960 . . . . 50 55
5334 $80 Jack Brabham in Brabham-Repco BT19, 1966 . . . . 50 55
5335 $80 John Miles in Lotus Ford 72, 1970 . . . . . . 50 55
5336 $80 Alain Prost in Renault RE40, 1983 . . . . . . 50 55
5337 $80 David Coulthard in McLaren Mercedes MP4/13, 1998 . . . . . . 50 55
MS5338 Two sheets, each 100 × 70 mm. (a) $300 Ferenc Szisz in Grand Prix Renault, 1906 (56 × 42 mm). (b) $300 Stirling Moss in Maserati 250F, 1956 (56 × 42 mm) Set of 2 sheets . . 3·50 3·75

591 Comic Book Title (½-size illustration)

1998. 50th Anniv of Disney's Uncle Scrooge Character. Designs showing text and illustrations from comic book *Christmas on Bear Mountain* (drawn by C. Barks). Mult.
5339 $35 Type **591** 60 60
5340 $35 Uncle Scrooge sitting in armchair 60 60
5341 $35 Uncle Scrooge looking out window 60 60
5342 $35 James the butler holding telephone 60 60
5343 $35 Uncle Scrooge at foot of staircase 60 60
5344 $35 Donald Duck with open fridge 60 60
5345 $35 Uncle Scrooge entering attic 60 60
5346 $35 Uncle Scrooge in limousine 60 60
5347 $35 Huey, Dewey and Louie at window 60 60
5348 $35 Car in snow 60 60
5349 $35 Ducks in bed 60 60
5350 $35 Donald in chair with nephews 60 60
5351 $35 Donald refusing nephews 60 60
5352 $35 Ducks and rabbit . . . 60 60
5353 $35 Ducks with Christmas tree 60 60
5354 $35 Baby bear climbing down Christmas tree . . . 60 60
5355 $35 Ducks in panic 60 60
5356 $35 Baby bear running . . . 60 60
5357 $35 Ducks searching 60 60
5358 $35 Nephews and tree . . . 60 60
5359 $35 Huey, Dewey and Louie tripping on roller skate 60 60
5360 $35 Frightened nephew . . 60 60
5361 $35 Baby bear on roller skate 60 60
5362 $35 Donald hiding in light fitting 60 60
5363 $35 Baby bear with chocolate 60 60
5364 $35 Louie climbing Christmas tree 60 60
5365 $35 Baby bear evading Louie 60 60
5366 $35 Nephews searching bedroom 60 60
5367 $35 Donald peering down from light fitting 60 60
5368 $35 Mother bear chasing Donald 60 60
5369 $35 Donald jumping through window 60 60
5370 $35 Bears after eating . . . 60 60
5371 $35 Ducks looking through window 60 60
5372 $35 Donald and sleeping mother bear 60 60
5373 $35 Uncle Scrooge outside cabin 60 60
5374 $35 Uncle Scrooge in bear suit behind sofa 60 60
5375 $35 Uncle Scrooge in bear suit surprised 60 60
5376 $35 Uncle Scrooge with James 60 60
5377 $35 Ducks on Christmas Day 60 60
5378 $35 Donald fainting 60 60
MS5379 220 × 175 mm. $300 Carl Barks (37 × 50 mm); $300 Uncle Scrooge pursued by bear (50 × 37 mm) . . . . 6·50 6·50

Only issued in stamp booklets in which each pane contains two pairs separated by a horizontal gutter margin showing further parts of the comic strip. Each stamp shows two drawings of which the first in each instance is described for the listing.

1998. 50th Anniv of Organization of American States. As T **454b** of Grenada.
5380 $40 yellow, violet and black 25 30

1998. 25th Death Anniv of Pablo Picasso (painter). As T **291a** of Gambia. Multicoloured.
5381 $25 "Sleeping Peasants" . . 15 20
5382 $60 "Large Nude in Red Armchair" (vert) 35 40
5383 $200 "Female Head" (vert) 1·20 1·30
MS5384 102 × 126 mm. $300 "Man and Woman" (vert) . . . . . 1·80 1·90

592 James E. West (first Scout executive) and Early Eagle Scouts

1998. 19th World Scout Jamboree, Chile. Mult.
5385 $160 Type **592** . . . . . . 95 1·00
5386 $160 Pres. John F. Kennedy greeting Explorers, 1961 95 1·00
5387 $160 Walter Schirra (astronaut) receiving Special Merit badge, 1962 95 1·00

593 Mahatma Gandhi as Lawyer in South Africa, 1906

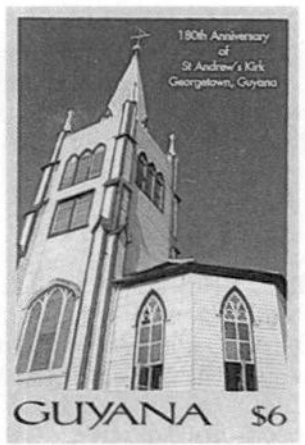

594 St. Andrew's Kirk, Georgetown

1998. 50th Death Anniv of Mahatma Gandhi. Mult.
5388 $100 Type **593** 60 65
5389 $100 Gandhi on Bengal walk, 1946 (56 × 42 mm) 60 65
5390 $100 Gandhi with Jawaharlal Nehru and Sardar Patel, 1948 (56 × 42 mm) 60 65
5391 $100 Gandhi during fast, 1947 . . . . 60 65
MS5392 70 × 66 mm. $300 Gandhi and Jawaharlal Nehru (horiz) 1·80 1·90

1998. 80th Anniv of Royal Air Force. As T **292a** of Gambia. Multicoloured.
5393 $100 Avro Lancaster B2 . . 60 65
5394 $100 PBY-5A Catalina amphibian 60 65
5395 $100 Hawk T1As of Red Arrows 60 65
5396 $100 Avro Lancaster and De Havilland D.H. 98 Mosquito 60 65
5397 $100 BAe Hawk T1A . . . 60 65
5398 $100 C-130 Hercules 60 65
5399 $100 Panavia Tornado GR1 60 65
5400 $100 BAe Hawk 200 in desert camouflage 60 65
5401 $150 BAe Nimrod R1P . . 90 95
5402 $150 Panavia Tornado F3 ADV 90 95
5403 $150 CH-47 Chinook helicopter 90 95
5404 $150 Panavia Tornado GR1A in front of hangar 90 95
MS5405 Set of six sheets, each 91 × 68 mm. (a) $200 Eagle and Bristol F2B fighter. (b) $200 Spitfire and EF2000 Eurofighter. (c) $300 Tiger Moth and EF2000 Eurofighter. (d) $300 Eurofighter. (e) $300 Bristol F2B fighter and two Montagu's harrier (birds). (f) $300 Bristol F2B fighter and Golden eagle Set of 6 sheets . . 9·50 9·75

1998. 1st Death Anniv of Diana, Princess of Wales. As T **293a** of Gambia.
5406 $60 multicoloured 35 40

1998. Birth Bicentenary of Eugene Delacroix (painter). As T **293** of Gambia. Multicoloured.
5407 $60 "Corner of the Studio" (vert) 35 40
5408 $60 "Count Mornay's Apartment" (vert) 35 40
5409 $60 "Hamlet and the Two Gravediggers" (vert) . . . 35 40
5410 $60 "George Sand" (vert) 35 40
5411 $60 "The Fiancee of Abydos" (vert) 35 40
5412 $60 "The Champs-Elysses" (vert) 35 40
5413 $60 "Lioness" (vert) 35 40
5414 $60 "Alfred Bruyas" (vert) 35 40
5415 $60 "The Sultan of Morocco" (vert) 35 40
5416 $60 "Indian with Kukri" (vert) 35 40
5417 $60 "Man in Turkish Dress" (vert) 35 40
5418 $60 "Studies of Jewish Women" (vert) 35 40
5419 $60 "Arab Horseman giving Signal" (vert) 35 40
5420 $60 "Arab Horsemen charging" (vert) 35 40
5421 $60 "A Seated Moor" (vert) 35 40
5422 $60 "Jewish Woman in Traditional Dress" (vert) 35 40
MS5423 Two sheets, each 100 × 90 mm. (a) $300 "Death of Sardanpole". (b) $300 "Jewish Wedding, Morocco" Set of 2 sheets . . . . 3·50 3·75

1999. 180th Anniv of St. Andrew's Kirk, Georgetown. Multicoloured.
5424 $6 Type **594** 10 10
5425 $30 Front of church 20 25
5426 $60 Front and side of church 35 40

595 Rabbit

1999. Chinese New Year ("Year of the Rabbit"). Multicoloured.
5427 $50 Type **595** 30 35
5428 $50 Rabbit (face value at bottom left) 30 35
5429 $50 Rabbit (face value at top right) 30 35
5430 $50 Rabbit (face value at top left) 30 35
MS5431 112 × 70 mm. $150 Rabbit on background of Chinese characters 90 95

596 Pongo driving Steam Locomotive

1999. Disney Trains. Cartoon characters. Multicoloured.
5432 $100 Type **596** . . . . . . 1·00 1·00
5433 $100 Puppies watching television . . . . 1·00 1·00
5434 $100 Perdita, Roger and Anita . . . . 1·00 1·00
5435 $100 Nanny with puppies 1·00 1·00
5436 $100 Horace, Jasper and Cruella De Vil . . . . . 1·00 1·00
5437 $100 Rhino pulling Little John and Friar Tuck . . 1·00 1·00
5438 $100 Maid Marian, Robin Hood and Lady Kluck . . 1·00 1·00
5439 $100 Sir Hiss and Prince John . . . . 1·00 1·00
5440 $100 Allan-a-Dale on elephant . . . . 1·00 1·00
5441 $100 Rabbit family and Toby Turtle . . . . . . 1·00 1·00
5442 $100 Doc driving train . . . 1·00 1·00
5443 $100 Grumpy, Happy, Sleepy and Bashful singing . . . . 1·00 1·00
5444 $100 Snow White and Prince with diamonds . . 1·00 1·00
5445 $100 Old Witch, animals from forest and Sneezy 1·00 1·00
5446 $100 Dopey and racoon on trolley . . . . 1·00 1·300
5447 $100 Triton driving locomotive . . . . 1·00 1·00
5448 $100 Flounder with pearls 1·00 1·00
5449 $100 Ariel, The Little Mermaid . . . . 1·00 1·00
5450 $100 Sebastian and friends in band . . . . 1·00 1·00
5451 $100 Ursula . . . . 1·00 1·00
MS5452 Five sheets. (a) 127 × 112 mm. $300 Horace, Jasper and Cruella De Vil (*101 Dalmatians*). (b) 127 × 112 mm $300 Robin Hood and Little John (*Robin Hood*). (c) 230 × 180 mm. $200 Doc driving train and $200 Dopey and racoon on trolley (vert) (*Snow White*). (d) 110 × 27 mm. $300 Ariel kissing statue (*The Little Mermaid*). (e) 127 × 110 mm. $300 Ariel holding starfish (*The Little Mermaid*) Set of 5 sheets 13·00 13·00

Nos. 5432/6 (characters from *101 Dalmatians*), Nos. 5437/41 (*Robin Hood*), Nos. 5442/6 (*Snow White*) and Nos. 5447/51 (*The Little Mermaid*) were each printed together, se-tenant, forming composite designs.

597 Huey skateboarding

1999. 70th Birthday of Mickey Mouse. Multicoloured.
5453 $80 Type **597** 80 80
5454 $80 Mickey Mouse skateboarding 80 80
5455 $80 Dewey skateboarding (purple cap) 80 80
5456 $80 Louie skateboarding (red cap) 80 80
5457 $80 Goofy skateboarding (lilac boots) 80 80
5458 $80 Donald Duck skateboarding (with cap) 80 80
5459 $80 Minnie Mouse rollerblading 80 80
5460 $80 Goofy rollerblading . . 80 80
5461 $80 Daisy Duck rollerblading (red boots) 80 80
5462 $80 Baby Duck rollerblading (yellow wheels) 80 80
5463 $80 Donald Duck rollerblading 80 80
5464 $80 Mickey Mouse rollerblading (red helmet) 80 80
5465 $80 Baby Duck rollerblading (mauve wheels) 80 80
5466 $80 Daisy Duck rollerblading (mauve boots) 80 80
5467 $80 Mickey Mouse rollerblading (mauve helmet) 80 80
5468 $80 Goofy skateboarding (red boots) 80 80
5469 $80 Dewey rollerblading . . 80 80
5470 $80 Donald Duck skateboarding (without cap) 80 80
MS5471 Three sheets. (a) 112 × 127 mm. $300 Dewey skateboarding. (b) 127 × 112 mm. $300 Daisy Duck. (c) 127 × 112 mm. $300 Goofy (horiz) Set of 3 sheets . . . . 8·50 8·50

598 *Pelargonium domesticum*

1999. Flowers of the World. Multicoloured.
5472 $60 Type **598** 35 40
5473 $60 *Oncidium macranthum* and butterfly 35 40
5474 $60 *Bepi orchidglades* . . . 35 40
5475 $60 *Helianthus maximiliani* (two flowers) 35 40
5476 $60 *Cattleya walkeriana* . . 35 40
5477 $60 *Cattleya frasquita* . . . 35 40
5478 $60 *Helianthus maximiliani* (single bloom) 35 40
5479 $60 *Paphiopedilum insigne sanderae* and *lilium longifolium* 35 40
5480 $60 *Lilium longifolium* . . . 35 40
5481 $60 *Dendrobium nobile* . . . 35 40
5482 $60 *Phalaenopsis schilleriana* 35 40
5483 $60 *Cymbidium alexette* . . 35 40
5484 $60 *Rhododendron nudiflorum* and hummingbird 35 40
5485 $60 *Phragmipedium besseae* and *laelia cinnabarina* . . 35 40
5486 $60 *Masdevallia veitchiana, laelia cinnabarina* and hummingbird 35 40
5487 $60 *Calochortus nuttallii* . . 35 40
5488 $60 *Brassolaelio cattleya* "Puregold" 35 40
5489 $60 *Laelia cinnabarina* . . . 35 40
5490 $90 *Leptotes bicolor* and *masdevallia ignea* 55 60
5491 $90 *Sophrolaelio cattleya* and *anguloa clowesii* . . . 55 60
5492 $90 *Laelia pumila* 55 60
5493 $90 *Masdevallia ignea* 55 60
5494 $90 *Dendrobium phalaenopsis* 55 60
5495 $90 *Anguloa clowesii* 55 60
MS5496 Two sheets, each 106 × 75 mm. (a) $300 *Iris pseudacorus*. (b) $300 *Ascocentrum miniatum* (vert) Set of 2 sheets 3·50 3·75

Nos. 5472/80, 5481/9 and 5490/5 were each printed together, se-tenant, with the backgrounds forming composite designs.

No. **MS**5496b is inscribed "Asocentrum" in error.

599 *Philaethria dido*

1999. Caribbean Butterflies. Multicoloured.

5497	$80 Type **599**	50	55
5498	$80 *Papilio troilus*	50	55
5499	$80 *Eueides isabella*	50	55
5500	$80 *Colobura dirce*	50	55
5501	$80 *Agraulis vanillae*	50	55
5502	$80 *Callicore maimuna*	50	55
5503	$80 *Thecla coronata*	50	55
5504	$80 *Battus polydamus*	50	55
5505	$80 *Morpho peleides*	50	55
5506	$80 *Doxocopa cherubina*	50	55
5507	$80 *Metamorpha stelenes*	50	55
5508	$80 *Catonephele numili*	50	55
MS5509	Two sheets. (a) 76 × 107 mm. $300 *Papilio cresphontes* (vert). (b) 107 × 76 mm. $300 *Battus philenor* (vert) Set of 2 sheets	3·50	3·75

Nos. 5504 and 5509b are both inscribed "Baltus" in error.

600 Actor from *The Dream* **601** *Boletus aereus*

1999. Akira Kurosawa (Japanese film director) Commemoration. Multicoloured (except No. 5519).

5510	$80 Type **601**	50	55
5511	$80 Actor from *Red Beard*	50	55
5512	$80 Scene from *Rashomon*	50	55
5513	$80 Scene from *Seven Samurai*	50	55
5514	$80 Actor from *Kagemusha*	50	55
5515	$80 Scene from *Yojimbo*	50	55
5516	$130 Akira Kurosawa wearing blue cap (horiz)	80	85
5517	$130 Resting head on right hand (horiz)	80	85
5518	$130 Wearing black jumper (horiz)	80	85
5519	$130 Looking through camera (horiz) (brown and black)	80	85
MS5520	98 × 68 mm. $300 Actor from *Dreams*	1·80	1·90

1999. Fungi. Multicoloured.

5521	$25 *Coprinus atramentarius* (28 × 33 mm)	15	20
5522	$35 *Hebeloma crustuliniforme* (28 × 33 mm)	20	25
5523	$60 Type **601**	35	40
5524	$60 *Coprinus comatus*	35	40
5525	$60 *Inocybe godeyi*	35	40
5526	$60 *Morchella crassipes*	35	40
5527	$60 *Lepiota acutesquamosa*	35	40
5528	$60 *Amanita phalloides*	35	40
5529	$60 *Boletus spadiceus*	35	40
5530	$60 *Cortinarius collinitus*	35	40
5531	$60 *Lepiota procera*	35	40
5532	$60 *Russula ochroleuca*	35	40
5533	$60 *Hygrophorus hypotheius*	35	40
5534	$60 *Amanita rubescens*	35	40
5535	$60 *Boletus satanas*	35	40
5536	$60 *Amanita echinocephala*	35	40
5537	$60 *Amanita muscaria*	35	40
5538	$60 *Boletus badius*	35	40
5539	$60 *Hebeloma radicosum*	35	40
5540	$60 *Mycena polygramma*	35	40
5541	$100 *Russula nigricans* (28 × 33 mm)	60	65
5542	$200 *Tricholoma aurantium* (28 × 33 mm)	1·20	1·30
MS5543	Two sheets. (a) 70 × 98 mm. $300 *Pluteus cervinus*. (b) 98 × 70 mm. $300 *Lepiota acutesquamosa* Set of 2 sheets	3·50	3·75

No. **MS**5543b is inscribed "Acutesquamoso" in error.

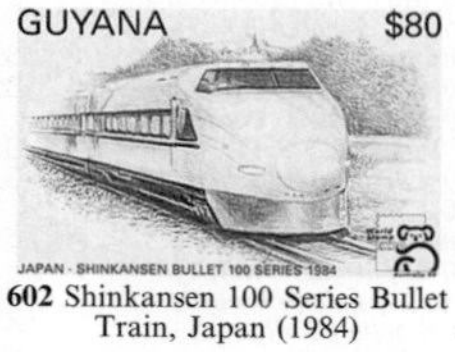

602 Shinkansen 100 Series Bullet Train, Japan (1984)

1999. "Australia '99" International Stamp Exhibition, Melbourne. Trains. Multicoloured (except Nos. 5550/5, each brown, yellow and black, and **MS**5568b/d).

5544	$80 Type **602**	50	55
5545	$80 Ukrainian ZMGR diesel locomotive, Russia (1983)	50	55
5546	$80 Rhatische Bahn electric locomotive No. 706, Germany	50	55
5547	$80 Eurostar T.G.V. train, France (1986)	50	55
5548	$80 Atlantique T.G.V. train, France (1989)	50	55
5549	$80 Class 86-6 diesel locomotive No. 86604, Great Britain	50	55
5550	$80 Joseph Clark steam locomotive, U.S.A. (1868)	50	55
5551	$80 Diamond Stack Bethel steam locomotive, U.S.A. (1863)	50	55
5552	$80 New York Central steam locomotive No. 999, U.S.A. (1890)	50	55
5553	$80 Boston and Maine steam locomotive *Ballardville*, U.S.A. (1876)	50	55
5554	$80 Portland Rochester Railroad steam locomotive, U.S.A. (1863)	50	55
5555	$80 Baltimore and Ohio Railroad steam locomotive, U.S.A. (1881)	50	55
5556	$80 Burlington Northern GP 39-2 diesel locomotive, U.S.A. (1974)	50	55
5557	$80 CSX GP40-2 diesel locomotive, U.S.A. (1967)	50	55
5558	$80 Erie Lackawana Railroad GP 9 diesel locomotive, U.S.A. (1956)	50	55
5559	$80 Amtrak P 42 Genesis No. 82 train, U.S.A. (1993)	50	55
5560	$80 Erie Railroad S-2 diesel locomotive, U.S.A. (1948)	50	55
5561	$80 Pennsylvania Railroad S-1 diesel locomotive, U.S.A. (1947)	50	55
5562	$80 Northern and Western steam locomotive No. 610, U.S.A. (1933)	50	55
5563	$80 Pennsylvania Railroad M1B Mountain steam locomotive, U.S.A. (1930)	50	55
5564	$80 Reading Railroad FP7A diesel locomotive, U.S.A. (1951)	50	55
5565	$80 New York Central steam locomotive No. 765, U.S.A. (1940)	50	55
5566	$80 Union Pacific steam locomotive No. 3985, U.S.A. (1963)	50	55
5567	$80 GP 15-15-1 diesel locomotive, U.S.A. (1956)	50	55
MS5568	Four sheets. (a) 70 × 98 mm. $300 George Nagelmackers (founder of International Sleeping Car Co.) (vert). (b) 70 × 98 mm. $300 R. F. Trevithick (engineer, Japanese National Railways) (vert) (violet and black). (c) 70 × 98 mm. $300 Alfred de Glehn (locomotive designer) (vert) (brown and black). (d) 98 × 70 mm. $300 George Stephen (president of Canadian Pacific) (vert) (brown and black) Set of 4 sheets	7·25	7·50

1999. Royal Wedding. As T **298** of Gambia. Multicoloured.

5569	$150 Sophie Rhys-Jones in multicoloured dress	90	95
5570	$150 Prince Edward with Sophie Rhys-Jones inspecting guard of honour	90	95
5571	$150 Sophie Rhys-Jones wearing grey jacket	90	95
5572	$150 Prince Edward wearing striped shirt	90	95
5573	$150 Prince Edward and Sohpie Rhys-Jones at the races	90	95
5574	$150 Sophie Rhys-Jones holding blue folder	90	95
5575	$150 Prince Edward wearing blue shirt	90	95
5576	$150 Sophie Rhys-Jones wearing black outfit	90	95
MS5577	Two sheets, each 83 × 66 mm. (a) $300 Prince Edward and Sophie Rhys-Jones in front of blossom (horiz). (b) $300 Prince Edward and Sophie Rhys-Jones in front of building (horiz) Set of 2 sheets	3·50	3·75

1999. John Glenn's Return to Space. As T **136** of Grenadines of Grenada. Multicoloured.

5578	$100 John Glenn (American astronaut) in spacesuit, 1962	60	65
5579	$100 Relaxing after landing, 1962	60	65
5580	$100 As Senator for Ohio, 1974	60	65
5581	$100 In spacesuit and helmet for Space Shuttle flight, 1998	60	65
5582	$100 In spacesuit without helmet, 1998	60	65

No. 5582 is dated "1992" in error.

1999. "iBRA '99" International Stamp Exhibition, Nuremberg. As T **299a** of Gambia. Multicoloured.

5583	$60 Class E10 electric locomotive, Germany, 1952 (vert)	35	40
5584	$200 Early steam locomotive, Der Adler, Germany, 1835	1·20	1·30

No. 5584 is inscribed "CLASS 01 STEAM EXPRESS TRAIN, GERMANY, 1926" in error.

1999. 150th Death Anniv of Katsushika Hokusai (Japanese artist). As T **299b** of Gambia. Multicoloured.

5585	$80 "Travellers climbing a Mountain Path"	50	55
5586	$80 "Washing Clothes in a River"	50	55
5587	$80 "The Blind" (old man smiling)	50	55
5588	$80 "The Blind" (man with beard)	50	55
5589	$80 "Convolvulus and Tree-frog"	50	55
5590	$80 "Fishermen hauling a Net"	50	55
5591	$80 "Hibiscus and Sparrow"	50	55
5592	$80 "Hydrangea and Swallow"	50	55
5593	$80 "The Blind" (man yawning)	50	55
5594	$80 "The Blind" (old man frowning)	50	55
5595	$80 "Irises"	50	55
5596	$80 "Lilies"	50	55
MS5597	Two sheets, each 101 × 72 mm. (a) $300 "Flowering Cherries at Mount Yoshino" (vert). (b) $300 "View of Stone Causeway" (vert) Set of 2 sheets	3·50	3·75

1999. 10th Anniv of U.N. Rights of the Child Convention. As T **299c** of Gambia. Multicoloured.

5598	$150 Two girls	90	95
5599	$150 Two boys	90	95
5600	$150 One boy	90	95
MS5601	$300 Prince Talal, U.N.I.C.E.F. special envoy, 1980	1·80	1·90

Nos. 5598/600 were printed together, se-tenant, with the backgrounds forming a composite design.

1999. "PhilexFrance '99" International Stamp Exhibition, Paris. Railway Locomotives. Two sheets, each 106 × 82 mm, containing horiz designs as T **299d** of Gambia. Multicoloured.

MS5602	(a) $300 Class 7000 high-speed locomotive, 1949–55. (b) $300 Class 241-P steam locomotive, 1947–49 Set of 2 sheets	3·50	3·75

1999. 250th Birth Anniv of Johann von Goethe (German writer). As T **299e** of Gambia.

5603	$150 green, black and blue	90	95
5604	$150 blue, violet and black	90	95
5605	$150 blue, brown and black	90	95
MS5606	78 × 109 mm. $300 brown, chocolate and black	1·80	1·90

DESIGNS—HORIZ: No. 5603, Lynceus singing from the watchtower; 5604, Von Goethe and Von Schiller; 5605, The Fallen Icarus. VERT: **MS**5606, Mephistopheles as a salamander.

603 Kurt Masur (German conductor and musician) **604** Pope John Paul II praying

1999. Year of the Older Person. Multicoloured (except No. **MS**5625).

5607	$50 Type **603**	30	35
5608	$50 Rupert Murdoch (newspaper publisher)	30	35
5609	$50 Margaret Thatcher (former British Prime Minister)	30	35
5610	$50 Pope John Paul II	30	35
5611	$50 Mikhail Gorbachev (Russian leader)	30	35
5612	$50 Ted Turner (American politician)	30	35
5613	$50 Sophia Loren (Italian actress)	30	35
5614	$50 Nelson Mandela (South African leader)	30	35
5615	$50 John Glenn (American astronaut)	30	35
5616	$50 Luciano Pavarotti (Italian opera singer)	30	35
5617	$50 Queen Elizabeth, the Queen Mother	30	35
5618	$50 Jimmy Carter (former American President)	30	35
5619	$100 Ronald Reagan (former American president) in football shirt	60	65
5620	$100 Ronald Reagan wearing black shirt	60	65
5621	$100 Ronald Reagan in military uniform	60	65
5622	$100 Ronald Reagan wearing stetson	60	65
5623	$100 Ronald Reagan feeding chimp with bottle	60	65
5624	$100 Ronald Reagan in evening dress	60	65
MS5625	111 × 111 mm. $300 Ronald Reagan in star (black)	1·80	1·90

1999. Pope John Paul II. Multicoloured.

5626	$80 Type **604**	50	55
5627	$80 Pope John Paul II (face value at top right)	50	55
5628	$80 Pope John Paul II smiling (face value at bottom left)	50	55
5629	$80 With crucifix	50	55
5630	$80 Pope John Paul II wearing black cloak	50	55
5631	$80 Pope John Paul II (face value at bottom right)	50	55

1999. 30th Anniv of First Manned Landing on Moon. As T **298c** of Gambia but horiz. Multicoloured.

5632	$80 Konstantin Tsiolkovsky and first Russian artificial satellite, 1959 (vert)	50	55
5633	$80 Launch of "Apollo 11" (vert)	50	55
5634	$80 Astronaut descending onto Moon (vert)	50	55
5635	$80 Collecting samples of lunar rock (vert)	50	55
5636	$80 "Apollo 11" lunar module, *Eagle* (vert)	50	55
5637	$80 Splashdown of command module *Columbia* (vert)	50	55
5638	$80 "Apollo 11" after launch	50	55
5639	$80 "Apollo 11" modules after separation from rocket	50	55
5640	$80 Astronaut leaving *Eagle* for moon walk	50	55
5641	$80 Seismic experiments equipment	50	55
5642	$80 *Eagle* leaving Moon	50	55
5643	$80 *Eagle* after splashdown	50	55
MS5644	Two sheets, each 106 × 83 mm. (a) $300 Astronaut saluting American flag on Moon. (b) $300 Astronaut Michael Collins Set of 2 sheets	3·50	3·75

605 *Breitling Orbiter 3* (balloon) **606** Sidney Sheldon

1999. 1st Non-stop Round-the-World Balloon Flight by *Breitling Orbiter 3*. Multicoloured.

5645	$150 Type **605**	90	95
5646	$150 Flight logo	90	95
5647	$150 Bertrand Piccard (balloonist)	90	95
5648	$150 Brian Jones (balloonist)	90	95
MS5649	100 × 70 mm. $300 *Breitling Orbiter 3*	1·80	1·90

1999. Great Authors of the 20th Century. Sidney Sheldon.

5650	**606** $80 multicoloured	50	55

607 Scarlet Macaw ("Marron Macaw")

1999. South American Lories and Parrots. Multicoloured.

5651	$60 Type **607**	35	40
5652	$60 Thick-billed parrot	35	40
5653	$60 Golden-crowned conure	35	40
5654	$60 Yellow-collared macaw	35	40
5655	$60 Double yellow-headed amazon	35	40
5656	$60 Mountain parakeet ("Golden-fronted Parakeet")	35	40
5657	$60 Maroon-bellied conure	35	40
5658	$60 Nanday conure	35	40
5659	$60 Hyacinth macaw	35	40
5660	$60 Blue and yellow macaw ("Blue and Gold Macaw")	35	40
5661	$60 Blue-fronted amazon	35	40
5662	$60 Amazon parrot	35	40
5663	$60 Sun conure	35	40
5664	$60 Orange-chinned parakeet ("Tivi Parakeet")	35	40

5665 $60 Golden conure ("Bavaria's Conure") 35 40
5666 $60 Fairy lorikeet 35 40
MS5667 Two sheets, each 110 × 85 mm. (a) $300 Jendaya conure (horiz). (b) $300 Grey-cheeked parakeet Set of 2 sheets 3·50 3·75

Nos. 5651/8 and 5659/66 were each printed together, se-tenant, with the backgrounds forming composite designs.

Nos. 5653, 5657 and 5658 are inscribed "CANURE", "BILLED" and "NANDAYA", all in error.

608 Queen Elizabeth the Queen Mother during Second World War

1999. Queen Elizabeth the Queen Mother's 99th Birthday. Multicoloured.

5668 $60 Type **608** 35 40
5669 $60 Wedding of Duke and Duchess of York, 1923 35 40
5670 $60 Lady Elizabeth Bowes-Lyon as a child 35 40
5671 $60 At Coronation, 1937 35 40
5672 $60 Queen Mother, 1971 35 40
5673 $60 Queen Mother wearing red hat, 1991 35 40
5674 $60 Lady Elizabeth Bowes-Lyon, 1914 35 40
5675 $60 Queen Mother, 1988 35 40
5676 $60 At Royal Agricultural Show during 1950s 35 40
5677 $60 Queen Mother, 1960 35 40
MS5678 50 × 76 mm. $1000 Queen Mother holding bouquet (43 × 69 mm). Imperf 6·00 6·25

1999. "Queen Elizabeth the Queen Mother's Century". As T **305a** of Gambia.

5679 $130 multicoloured 80 85
5680 $130 black and gold 80 85
5681 $130 black and gold 80 85
5682 $130 multicoloured 80 85
MS5683 154 × 158 mm. $400 multicoloured 2·40 2·50

DESIGNS: No. 5679, Duchess of York with Princess Elizabeth, 1928; 5680, Lady Elizabeth Bowes-Lyon, 1914; 5681, Queen Elizabeth with Princess Elizabeth, 1940; 5682, Queen Elizabeth the Queen Mother in Venice, 1984. (37 × 50 mm)—**MS**5683, Queen Mother in Canada, 1988.

609 Mei Lanfang

1999. "China '99" International Stamp Exhibition, Beijing. 40th Death Anniv of Mei Lanfang (Chinese opera singer). Sheet 118 × 78mm.

MS5684 $400 multicoloured 2·40 2·50

610 Wang Guangning **612** Dragon

611 Inter-American Development Bank Logo

1999. Chinese Football League Players. Multicoloured.

5685 $50 Type **610** 30 35
5686 $50 Gao Feng ("H" emblem) 30 35
5687 $50 Jian Hong (goalkeeper) (bull emblem) 30 35
5688 $50 Gao Zhongxun (Yanbian football club) 30 35
5689 $50 Yao Xia (SCQXFC) 30 35
5690 $50 Zhang Yuning ("E" emblem) 30 35
5691 $50 Zhang Weihua (Matsunichi) 30 35
5692 $50 Dragon logo 30 35
5693 $60 Cai Sheng (winged comma logo) 35 40
5694 $60 Li Weifeng ("A" emblem) 35 40
5695 $60 Xie Zhaoyang (Beijing Guoan) 35 40
5696 $60 Li Xiaopeng (LNTS) 35 40
5697 $60 Hao Haidong (Dalian Wanda) 35 40
5698 $60 Zhang Xiaorui (TEDA) 35 40
5699 $60 Qi Hong (Shenhu) 35 40
5700 $60 Dragon logo 35 40

1999. John F. Kennedy Jr. Commemoration. As T **307** of Gambia. Multicoloured.

5701 $80 John Junior as a child with mother 50 55
5702 $80 John Junior under father's desk 50 55
5703 $80 John and Jacqueline Kennedy as a young couple 50 55
5704 $80 Jacqueline Kennedy 50 55
5705 $80 John Junior with sister, Caroline 50 55
5706 $80 President John Kennedy 50 55
5707 $160 John Junior at father's funeral 95 1·00
5708 $160 John Junior as an adult with mother, Jacqueline 95 1·00
5709 $160 John Junior in front of U.S. flag 95 1·00

1999. Birth Centenary of Enzo Ferrari, 1998 (car manufacturer). As T **564a** of Ghana. Multicoloured.

5710 $30 312 T2 racing car 20 25
5711 $35 553 F.1 racing car 20 25
5712 $60 D 50 racing car 35 40
5713 $100 212 Export sports car 1·00 1·00
5714 $100 410 Superamerica saloon 1·00 1·00
5715 $100 125 S sports car 1·00 1·00
5716 $200 246 F.1 racing car 1·20 1·30
5717 $300 126/C2 racing car 1·80 1·90
5718 $400 312/B2 racing car 2·40 2·50
MS5719 104 × 70 mm. $300 512 S sports cars (93 × 35 mm) 1·80 1·90

1999. 40th Anniv of Inter-American Development Bank.

5720 **611** $30 multicoloured 20 25

1999. New Millennium (1st issue). People and Events of Eleventh Century (1050–1100). As T **310b** of Gambia. Multicoloured.

5721 $35 Indians with pots (Anasazi trading centre, 1050) 20 25
5722 $35 Catalan "Black Virgin" statue (carved, 1050) 20 25
5723 $35 Horse archer (Seljuk conquest of Armenia, 1064) 20 25
5724 $35 Halley's Comet (appearance, 1066) 20 25
5725 $35 Norman cavalry (Battle of Hastings, 1066) 20 25
5726 $35 William I of England (crowned, 1066) 20 25
5727 $35 Samurai warriors (power of Fujiwara clan checked, 1068) 20 25
5728 $35 Henry IV, Holy Roman Emperor (excommunicated, 1076) 20 25
5729 $35 Timbuktu (founded, 1087) 20 25
5730 $35 Students (foundation of Bologna University, 1088) 20 25
5731 $35 Gondola, Venice (introduction, 1094) 20 25
5732 $35 El Cid (Spanish warrior) (capture of Valencia, 1094) 20 25
5733 $35 Mounted knights (First Crusade, 1095) 20 25
5734 $35 Saracen infantry (capture of Jerusalem, 1099) 20 25
5735 $35 Statue of Guanyin (Chinese deity) (carved, 1100) 20 25
5736 $35 Couple and quote from the Rubiayat of Omar Khayyam (written, 1100) (55 × 36 mm) 20 25
5737 $35 Decorating jar (introduction of Syrian style storage jars, 1100) 20 25

1999. New Millennium (2nd issue). People and Events of Twentieth Century (1910–1919). As T **471a** of Grenada. Multicoloured.

5738 $35 Poster for Grafton Gallery's Post Impressionist Exhibition, 1910 20 25
5739 $35 Trial scene and oil rig (Standard Oil case, 1911) 20 25
5740 $35 Harriet Quimby (first American woman pilot, 1911) 20 25
5741 $35 U.S. Senate (declaration of war, 1917) 20 25
5742 $35 Sinking of *Titanic*, 1912 20 25
5743 $35 Emperor Pu Yi (formation of Chinese Republic, 1913) 20 25
5744 $35 Statue over entrance (opening of Grand Central Station, New York, 1913) 20 25
5745 $35 Archduke Francis Ferdinand of Austria and cavalry (assassinated, 1914) 20 25
5746 $35 Map and lock gates (opening of Panama Canal, 1914) 20 25
5747 $35 Lawrence of Arabia (Arab revolt, 1916) 20 25
5748 $35 Burning buildings, Dublin (Easter Rising, 1916) 20 25
5749 $35 Lenin and revolutionaries (Russian Revolution, 1917) 20 25
5750 $35 Tsar Nicholas II and family (murdered, 1917) 20 25
5751 $35 Treaty of Versailles, 1918 20 25
5752 $35 Three patients and poster (influenza epidemic, 1919) 20 25
5753 $35 Leo Tolstoy and Mark Twain (deaths, 1910) (55 × 36 mm) 20 25
5754 $35 Walter Gropius and Bauhaus (opened 1919) 20 25

Dates on Nos. 5750 and 5751 are transposed. No. 5754 is inscribed "Bahaus" in error.

1999. Faces of the Millennium. Diana, Princess of Wales. As T **307a** of Gambia. Multicoloured.

5755 $80 Top of head (face value at left) 50 55
5756 $80 Top of head (face value at right) 50 55
5757 $80 Ear (face value at left) 50 55
5758 $80 Eye and temple (face value at right) 50 55
5759 $80 Cheek (face value at left) 50 55
5760 $80 Cheek (face value at right) 50 55
5761 $80 Blue background (face value at left) 50 55
5762 $80 Chin (face value at right) 50 55

Nos. 5755/62 were printed together, se-tenant, in sheetlets of 8 with the stamps arranged in two vertical columns separated by a gutter also containing miniature flower photographs. When viewed as a whole the sheetlet forms a portrait of Diana, Princess of Wales.

2000. Chinese New Year ("Year of the Dragon"). Multicoloured.

5763 $100 Type **612** (face value bottom right) 60 65
5764 $100 Dragon (face value bottom left) 60 65
5765 $100 Dragon (face value top right) 60 65
5766 $100 Dragon (face value top left) 60 65
MS5767 102 × 70 mm. $300 Dragon on background of Chinese characters 1·80 1·90

613 Cugnot's Steam-powered Fardier (1769)

2000. Cars. Multicoloured.

5768 $100 Type **613** 60 65
5769 $100 Marcus's motor carriage (1875) 60 65
5770 $100 Benz Velo (1894) 60 65
5771 $100 Bordino's steam carriage (1854) 60 65
5772 $100 Benz Motorwagen (1886) 60 65
5773 $100 Black Model T Ford (1908) 60 65
5774 $100 Duesenberg Model A phaeton (1926) 60 65
5775 $100 Mercedes-Benz Model K (1927) 60 65
5776 $100 Rolls-Royce Phantom I (1928) 60 65
5777 $100 Auburn 851 Speedster (1935) 60 65
5778 $100 Mercedes-Benz 540K Cabriolet B (1936) 60 65
5779 $100 Volkswagen Beetle (1949) 60 65
5780 $100 Ford Thunderbird (1957) 60 65
5781 $100 Jaguar XK150 (1957) 60 65
5782 $100 Chevrolet Corvette Stingray (1968) 60 65
5783 $100 BMW 2002 Turbo (1973) 60 65
5784 $100 Porsche 911 Turbo (1975) 60 65
5785 $100 Volkswagen Beetle (1999) 60 65
5786 $100 Daimler (1886) 60 65
5787 $100 Opel Luzman (1898) 60 65
5788 $100 Benz Landaulet Coupe (1899) 60 65
5789 $100 Peugeot Vis-a-vis (1892) 60 65
5790 $100 Benz Patent Motor Car (1886) 60 65
5791 $100 Benz Velo (1894) 60 65
5792 $100 Ford (1896) 60 65
5793 $100 De Dion-Bouton Populare (1903) 60 65
5794 $100 Adler (1900) 60 65
5795 $100 Vauxhall (1904) 60 65
5796 $100 Rolls Royce Silver Ghost (1908) 60 65
5797 $100 Model T Ford (1908) (different) 60 65
MS5798 Five sheets. (a) 105 × 80 mm. $400 Mercedes Benz 60/70 (1904) (50 × 38 mm). (b) 105 × 80 mm. $400 Mercedes Benz Type 320 Cabriolet (1939) (50 × 38 mm). (c) 105 × 80 mm. $400 Mercedes Benz 300 SL Gullwing (1954) (50 × 38 mm). (d) 81 × 63 mm. $400 Runabout (1910) (50 × 38 mm). (e) 81 × 63 mm. $400 Turner Miesse (1904) (50 × 38 mm) Set of 5 sheets 12·00 12·50

No. 5791 is inscribed "VELD" in error.

614 Top of Head

2000. Faces of the Millennium. George Washington. Designs showing a collage of miniature bank note photographs. Multicoloured.

5799 $80 Type **614** 50 55
5800 $80 Top of head (face value at right) 50 55
5801 $80 Ear (face value at left) 50 55
5802 $80 Cheek (face value at right) 50 55
5803 $80 Right shoulder (face value at left) 50 55
5804 $80 Left shoulder (face value at right) 50 55
5805 $80 Right upper arm (face value at left) 50 55
5806 $80 Left upper arm (face value at right) 50 55

Nos. 5799/806 were printed together, se-tenant, in sheetlets of 8 with the stamps arranged in two vertical columns separated by a gutter also containing miniature photographs. When viewed as a whole the sheetlet forms a portrait of George Washington.

615 Hogfish (*Lachnolaimus maximus*)

2000. Tropical Marine Life. Multicoloured.

5807 $30 Type **615** 20 25
5808 $35 Flamingo-tongue cowrie (*Cyphoma gibbosum*) 20 25
5809 $60 Permit (*Trachinotus falcatus*) 35 40
5810 $80 Lionfish (*Pterois volitans*) (vert) 50 55
5811 $80 Bottle-nosed dolphin (*Tursiops truncatus*) (vert) 50 55
5812 $80 Jellyfish (*Diplulmaris antarctica*) (vert) 50 55
5813 $80 Grey angelfish (*Pomacanthus arcuatus*) (vert) 50 55
5814 $80 Spotted eagle ray (*Aetobatus narinari*) (vert) 50 55
5815 $80 Grey reef shark (*Carcharhinus amblyrhynchos*) (vert) 50 55
5816 $80 Sea bass (*Sacura margaritacea*) (vert) 50 55
5817 $80 Giant octopus (*Octopus dolfeini*) (vert) 50 55
5818 $80 Great barracuda (*Sphyraena barracuda*) 50 55
5819 $80 Gulper eel (*Saccopharynx sp*) 50 55
5820 $80 Sea slug (*Chromodoris amoena*) 50 55
5821 $80 Blue marlin (*Makaira nigricans*) 50 55
5822 $80 Killer whale (*Orcinus orcai*) 50 55
5823 $80 Reid's seahorse (*Hippocampus reidi*) 50 55
5824 $80 Green sea turtle (*Chelonia mydas*) 50 55
5825 $80 Sailfin blenny (*Emblemaria pandionis*) 50 55
5826 $80 Indigo hamlet (*Hypoplectrus indigo*) 50 55
5827 $80 Scallop (*Chlamys hastata*) 50 55
5828 $80 Flag rockfish (*Sebastes rubrivinctus*) 50 55
5829 $80 Lookdown (*Selene vomer*) 50 55

5830 $80 Orange marginella (*Marginella carnea*) . . . 50 55
5831 $80 Harbour seal (*Phocus vitulina*) 50 55
5832 $80 Dolphin fish (*Coryphaena hippurus*) . . 50 55
5833 $80 Coney (*Epinephelus fulvus*) 50 55
5834 $100 Spot-finned hogfish (*Bodianus pulchellus*) . . . 60 65
5835 $200 Porkfish (*Anisotremus virginicus*) . . . . 1·20 1·30
5836 $300 Orange-throated darter (*Etheostoma spectabile*) . . 1·80 1·90
MS5837 Three sheets. (a) 85 × 110 mm. $400 Snakestar (*Asteroschema tenue*) (vert). (b) 85 × 110 mm. $400 Penpoint gunnel (*Apodichthys flavidus*) (vert). (c) 110 × 85 mm. $400 Spotted cleaner shrimp (*Periclimenes pedersoni* (57 × 42 mm) Set of 3 sheets . . 7·25 7·50

Nos. 5810/17, 5818/25 and 5826/33 were each printed together, se-tenant, with the backgrounds forming composite designs.

2000. 18th Birthday of Prince William. As T **312b** of Gambia. Multicoloured.

5838 $100 Prince William with Prince Harry 60 65
5839 $100 As a young boy, holding present 60 65
5840 $100 Prince William wearing suit and white shirt . . . 60 65
5841 $100 Wearing suit and blue shirt 60 65
MS5842 100 × 80 mm. $400 Dressed for skiing (37 × 50 mm) . . . . 2·40 2·50

2000. "EXPO 2000" World Stamp Exhibition, Anaheim, USA. Space Satellites. As T **582a** of Ghana. Multicoloured.

5843 $100 "Apollo 11" 60 65
5844 $100 "Pioneer" and Saturn 60 65
5845 $100 Nasa/Esa "Soho" Satellite 60 65
5846 $100 Nasa "Mars Orbiter" and Mars 60 65
5847 $100 Space Shuttle and International Space Station 60 65
5848 $100 "Giotto" and Halley's Comet 60 65
5849 $100 "Amsat IIIC" (vert) 60 65
5850 $100 "Sret" (vert) 60 65
5851 $100 "Inspector" (vert) . . 60 65
5852 $100 "Stardust" (vert) . . . 60 65
5853 $100 "Temisat" (vert) . . . 60 65
5854 $100 "Arsene" (vert) 60 65
5855 $100 "Cesar" with Argentine and Spanish flags 60 65
5856 $100 "Sirio 2" with Italian flag 60 65
5857 $100 "Taos S 80" with French flag 60 65
5858 $100 "Viking" with Swedish flag 60 65
5859 $100 "SCD 1" with Brazilian flag 60 65
5860 $100 "Offeq 1" with Israeli flag 60 65
MS5861 Two sheets. (a) 106 × 76 mm. $400 "Solar Max". (b) 76 × 106 mm. $400 Clementine French Satellite "Ariane V 124" (vert) . . . . 5·50 5·75

No. 5845 is inscribed "Satellit" in error.

2000. 25th Anniv of "Apollo-Soyuz" Joint Project. As T **582a** of Ghana. Multicoloured.

5862 $200 Thomas Stafford and Vance Brand ("Apollo 18" astronauts) 1·20 1·40
5863 $200 "Apollo 18" command module . . . . 1·20 1·40
5864 $200 Thomas Stafford and Valeri Kubasov (Russian cosmonaut) . . . . 1·20 1·20
MS5865 88 × 71 mm. $400 Donald Slayton and Thomas Stafford ("Apollo 18" astronauts) (horiz) 2·40 2·50

2000. 50th Anniv of Berlin Film Festival. As T **582c** of Ghana. Multicoloured.

5866 $100 "Das Boot ist Voll", 1981 . . . . 60 65
5867 $100 "David", 1979 . . . . 60 65
5868 $100 "Hong Gaoliang", 1988 . . . . 60 65
5869 $100 "Die Ehe der Maria Braun", 1979 . . . . . 60 65
5870 $100 "The Whisperers", 1967 . . . . 60 65
5871 $100 "Le Vieil Homme et L'Enfant", 1967 . . . . . 60 65
MS5872 97 × 103 mm. $400 "Love Streams", 1984 . . . . 2·40 2·50

No. 5871 omits "L'ENFANT" from the film title.

2000. 175th Anniv of Stockton and Darlington Line (first public railway). As T **582c** of Ghana. Multicoloured.

5873 $200 Timothy Hackworth 1·20 1·40
5874 $200 Hackworth's "Sans Pareil" engine . . . . . 1·20 1·40
5875 $200 Bramhope Tunnel, Otley . . . . 1·20 1·40

Nos. 5874 and 5875 are inscribed "Sansareil" and "Branhope", both in error.

616 Johann Sebastian Bach

617 Rohan Kanhai

2000. 250th Death Anniv of Johann Sebastian Bach (German composer). Sheet 88 × 76 mm.
MS5876 **616** $400 multicoloured 2·40 2·50

2000. Election of Albert Einstein (mathematical physicist) as Time Magazine "Man of the Century". Sheet 117 × 91 mm, containing vert design as T **312d** of Gambia. Multicoloured.
MS5877 $400 Albert Einstein . . 2·40 2·50

2000. Centenary of First Zeppelin Flight. As T **582c** of Ghana. Multicoloured.

5878 $200 Count von Zeppelin and LZ-1 airship, 1900 . . 1·20 1·40
5879 $200 Von Zeppelin and LZ-2, 1906 . . . . 1·20 1·40
5880 $200 Von Zeppelin and LZ-9, 1911 . . . . 1·20 1·40
MS5881 84 × 114 mm. $400 LZ-127 Zeppelin, 1928 (50 × 38 mm) 2·40 2·50

2000. Olympic Games, Sydney. As T **582f** of Ghana. Multicoloured.

5882 $160 Henry Robert Pearce (single sculls rower), Los Angeles (1932) . . . . . 95 1·00
5883 $160 Volleyball . . . . . . 95 1·00
5884 $160 Olympic Park, Canada (1976) and Canadian flag 95 1·00
5885 $160 Ancient Greek athletes 95 1·00

2000. West Indies Cricket Tour and 100th Test Match at Lord's. Multicoloured.

5886 $100 Type **617** 60 65
5887 $300 Clive Lloyd . . . . . 1·80 1·90
MS5888 121 × 104 mm. $400 Lord's Cricket Ground, London (horiz) 2·40 2·50

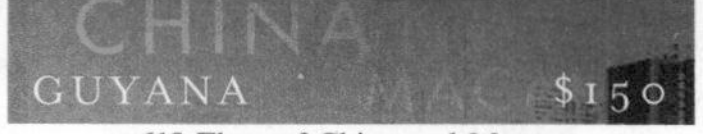

618 Flags of China and Macau

2000. Return of Macau to Chinese Sovereignty. Sheet 144 × 119 mm, containing T **618** and similar horiz design. Multicoloured.
MS5889 $150 Type **618**; $150 Downtown Macau . . . . . . 1·80 1·90

2000. Betty Boop (cartoon character). As T **308** of Gambia. Multicoloured.

5890 $80 Betty Boop wearing striped shirt 50 55
5891 $80 With shopping bags . . 50 55
5892 $80 Kneeling on cushion . . 50 55
5893 $80 As belly dancer 50 55
5894 $80 Putting on shoe 50 55
5895 $80 Wearing cowboy boots 50 55
5896 $80 Betty Boop dancing . . 50 55
5897 $80 In flowered trousers . . 50 55
5898 $80 In black dress 50 55
MS5899 Twenty-two sheets. (a) 137 × 87 mm. $400 In blue dress and fur stole; (b) 137 × 87 mm. $400 In polka dot dress; (c) 120 × 95 mm. $400 Standing in shell; (d) 111 × 127 mm. $400 In red dress by the sea; (e) 121 × 95 mm. $400 Wearing brown coat and red scarf; (f) 120 × 95 mm. $400 With tennis racket; (g) 121 × 101 mm. $400 Winking; (h) 120 × 96 mm. $400 Wearing black feather boa and brown hat; (i) 95 × 133 mm. $400 With sad expression (horiz). (j) 91 × 143 mm. $400 Wearing ruff; (k) 90 × 140 mm. $400 Wearing orange t-shirt and baseball hat (horiz). (l) 90 × 140 mm. $400 Wearing red vest top; (m) 140 × 90 mm. $400 Wearing pink baseball hat; (n) 90 × 140 mm. $400 Wearing red dress and orange sash; (o) 89 × 139 mm. $400 Holding present; (p) 89 × 139 mm. $400 Wearing party hat (horiz). (q) 89 × 139 mm. $400 Wearing sailor's hat; (r) 89 × 139 mm. $400 In red bikini; (s) 89 × 139mm. $400 With sunglasses on head; (t) 89 × 139 mm. $400 In mauve vest top and blue dungarees (horiz). (u) 89 × 139 mm. $400 In mauve vest top; (v) 89 × 139 mm. $400 With mauve flower in hair Set of 22 sheets . . . . 50·00 55·00

2000. Scenes from *I Love Lucy* (American T.V. comedy series). As T **309** of Gambia, but vert. Multicoloured.

5900 $60 Lucy reading a thriller 35 40
5901 $60 Lucy and Ricky talking 35 40
5902 $60 Ricky whispering to Lucy 35 40
5903 $60 Lucy looking out of window 35 40
5904 $60 Lucy behind Ethel . . . 35 40
5905 $60 Ricky holding red scarf over Lucy 35 40
5906 $60 Ethel and Lucy with frying pan 35 40
5907 $60 Ricky with frying pan 35 40
5908 $60 Lucy and Ethel sitting on sofa next to coffee table 35 40
MS5909 Ten sheets. (a) 120 × 95 mm. $400 Lucy in pink dressing gown. (b) 120 × 95 mm. $400 Lucy with dustbin lid. (c) 100 × 134 mm. $400 Lucy wearing glasses. (d) 138 × 100 mm. $400 Lucy wearing blue hat and green coat. (e) 93 × 137 mm. $400 Lucy dancing the rumba. (f) 137 × 100 mm. $400 Lucy wearing green hat. (g) 100 × 134 mm. $400 Lucy with knives. (h) 137 × 100 mm. $400 Lucy wearing black hat. (i) 93 × 137 mm. $400 Lucy in checked shirt. (j) 137 × 100 mm. $400 Lucy wearing leis Set of 10 sheets . . . . . 24·00 25·00

2000. Scenes from *The Three Stooges* (American T.V. comedy series). As T **310** of Gambia. Multicoloured.

5910 $80 Larry, Moe and Curly (The Three Stooges) with man in green jacket . . . 50 55
5911 $80 Larry and Moe with skeleton 50 55
5912 $80 Shemp with hair standing on end 50 55
5913 $80 Larry, Moe and Curly with fingers in mouths . . 50 55
5914 $80 Larry, Moe and Curly reading a book 50 55
5915 $80 Larry, Moe and Curly holding man in bowler hat 50 55
5916 $80 Shemp pointing a gun at Larry and Moe 50 55
5917 $80 Moe and Shemp holding Larry (being kicked in stomach by man in blue) 50 55
5918 $80 Moe and Shemp looking at man in window 50 55
5919 $80 Moe pointing syphon bottle at Larry, with Shemp behind 50 55
5920 $80 Larry, Moe and Shemp as cave men (Moe with rock on head) 50 55
5921 $80 Moe with cow 50 55
5922 $80 Shemp with bucket on head 50 55
5923 $80 Moe, Shemp and Larry as cavemen (three wise monkeys) 50 55
5924 $80 Moe, Shemp and Larry as cavemen (Shemp holding large rock) . . . 50 55
5925 $80 Larry, Moe and Shemp wearing pith helmets . . . 50 55
5926 $80 Moe, Shemp and Larry in front of painting 50 55
5927 $80 Moe, Larry and Shemp with false beards 50 55
MS5928 Four sheets (a) 92 × 122 mm. $400 Shemp wearing tam-o'-shanter (vert). (b)122 × 92 mm. $400 Larry with skeleton. (c) 131 × 103 mm. $400 Larry with lady in blue dress (vert). (d) 131 × 103 mm. $400 Moe being pulled by collar Set of 4 sheets . . . . 9·50 9·75

619 Outline Drawing of Dove on Head

2000. 3rd Annual Caribbean Media Conference, Georgetown.
5929 **619** $100 multicoloured . . . 60 65

2000. "Euro 2000" Football Championship. As T **316** of Gambia. Multicoloured.

5930 $80 Turkish team 50 55
5931 $80 Slovenian team 50 55
5932 $80 Yugoslavian team . . . 50 55
5933 $80 Swedish team 50 55
5934 $80 Belgian team 50 55
5935 $80 Spanish team 50 55
5936 $80 French team 50 55
5937 $80 English team 50 55
5938 $80 Danish team 50 55
5939 $80 German team 50 55
5940 $80 Italian team 50 55
5941 $80 Dutch team 50 55
5942 $80 Portuguese team 50 55
5943 $80 Romanian team 50 55
5944 $80 Czech team 50 55
5945 $80 Norwegian team 50 55
MS5946 Two sheets, each 102 × 80 mm. (a) $400 Stefan Kuntz, 1966 (vert). (b) $400 Jurgen Klinsmann holding trophy, 1996 (vert) Set of 2 sheets . . . . . 4·75 5·00

620 Lee Hyo-Ri

2000. Fine Killing Liberty (FIN.K.L), Korean Girl Group. Multicoloured (except No. 5954).

5947 $80 Type **620** 50 55
5948 $80 Ok Ju-Hyun (head tilted to left) 50 55
5949 $80 Lee Jin (looking sideways) 50 55
5950 $80 Lee Jin (facing forwards) 50 55
5951 $80 FIN.K.L 50 55
5952 $80 Sung Yu-Ri (head tilted to left) 50 55
5953 $80 Lee Hyo-Ri (no hat) . . 50 55
5954 $80 Sung Yu-Ri (facing forwards) (purple, black and blue) 50 55
5955 $80 Ok Ju-Hyun smiling . . 50 55

621 *Amanita calyptroderma*

2000. "The Stamp Show 2000" International Stamp Exhibition, London. Fungi. Multicoloured.

5956 $100 Type **621** 60 65
5957 $100 *Polyporus brumalis* . . 60 65
5958 $100 *Hygrophorus pudorinus* 60 65
5959 $100 *Aeryginosa stropharia geophila* 60 65
5960 $100 *Amanita muscaria* . . . 60 65
5961 $100 *Armillaria mellea* . . . 60 65
5962 $100 *Hygrophoracaea* 60 65
5963 $100 *Russula xerampelina* 60 65
5964 $100 *Hygrophorus coccineus* 60 65
5965 $100 *Psilocybe stuntzii* . . . 60 65
5966 $100 *Rhodotus palmatus* . . 60 65
5967 $100 *Lactarius indigo* . . . 60 65
5968 $100 *Gomphus floccosus* . . 60 65
5969 $100 *Amanita caesarea* . . . 60 65
5970 $100 *Leotia viscose* 60 65
5971 $100 *Entoloma salmoneum* 60 65

5972 $100 *Cheimonophyllum candidissimus* 60 65
5973 $100 *Cortinarius multiformis* 60 65
MS5974 Three sheets. (a) 99 × 69 mm. $400 *Marasmius rotula*. (b) 69 × 99 mm. $400 *Volvariella pusilla* (vert). (c) 99 × 69 mm. $400 *Trametes versicolour* Set of 3 sheets . . . 7·25 7·50

Nos. 5956/61, 5962/7 and 5968/73 were each printed together, se-tenant, with the backgrounds forming composite designs.

Nos. 5956/8, 5961/2, 5964/5, 5967, 5969, 5972, **MS**5974a and **MS**5974c are inscribed "calyptzoderma", "crumalis", "pydorinus", "Armillariella", "Hygrophotaceae", "cocineus", "psilcybe stuntaii", "lactaius", "Aminita", "candidissimis", "zotula" and "Tzametes", all in error.

622 *Bougainvillea spectabilis*

2000. Flowers. Multicoloured.
5975 $35 Type **622** 20 25
5976 $60 *Euphorbia milii* 35 40
5977 $100 *Cordia sebestena* (vert) 60 65
5978 $100 *Heliconia wagneriana* (vert) 60 65
5979 $100 *Dendrobium phalaenopsis* (vert) 60 65
5980 $100 *Passiflora caerulea* (vert) 60 65
5981 $100 *Oncidium nubigenum* (vert) 60 65
5982 $100 *Hibiscus rosa-sinensis* (vert) 60 65
5983 $100 *Lantana camara* . . . 60 65
5984 $100 *Jatropha integerrima* 60 65
5985 $100 *Plumeria alba* 60 65
5986 $100 *Strelitzia reginae* . . . 60 65
5987 $100 *Clerodendrum splendens* 60 65
5988 $100 *Thunbergia grandiflora* 60 65
5989 $200 *Catharanthus roseus* . . 1·20 1·40
5990 $300 *Ipomoea carnea* . . . 1·80 1·90
MS5991 Two sheets (a) 83 × 103 mm. $400 *Cattleya granulose* (vert). (b) 103 × 83 mm. $400 *Guzmania lingulata* Set of 2 sheets . . . . 4·75 5·00

Nos. 5983/8 were printed together, se-tenant, the backgrounds forming a composite design.

623 *Russelia equisetiformis*

2000. Flowers of Central America. Multicoloured.
5992 $35 Type **623** 20 25
5993 $60 *Sprekelia formosissima* 35 40
5994 $100 *Bignonia capreolata* . . 60 65
5995 $100 *Calceolaria herbeo-hybrida* 60 65
5996 $100 *Canna generalis* . . . 60 65
5997 $100 *Bauhinia grandiflora* . . 60 65
5998 $100 *Amaranthus caudatus* 60 65
5999 $100 *Abutilon megapotamicum* 60 65
6000 $100 *Ipomoea tricolor* ("Morning Glory") . . . 60 65
6001 $100 *Lantana camara* . . . 60 65
6002 $100 *Cantua buxifolia* . . . 60 65
6003 $100 *Fuschia* 60 65
6004 $100 *Eichhornia crassipes* . . 60 65
6005 $100 *Cosmos sulphureus* . . 60 65
6006 $200 *Passiflora quadrangularis* . . . . . 1·20 1·40
6007 $300 *Mirabilis jalapa* . . . 1·80 1·90
MS6008 Two sheets, each 100 × 70 mm. (a) $400 *Oeceoclades maculate*. (b) $400 *Passiflora van-volxemii* ("Tasconia") . . . . 4·75 5·50

No. 6004 is inscribed "Eichornia", in error.

2000. Victims of Munich Olympics Massacre (1972) Commemoration. As T **328** of Gambia showing Israeli athletes and officials. Multicoloured.
6009 $40 Yaakov Springer (weightlifting referee) . . 25 30
6010 $40 Andrei Schpitzer (fencing referee) 25 30
6011 $40 Amitsur Shapira (athletics coach) 25 30
6012 $40 David Berger (weightlifter) 25 30
6013 $40 Ze'ev Friedman (weightlifter) 25 30
6014 $40 Joseph Gottfreund (wrestling referee) 25 30
6015 $40 Moshe Weinberg (wrestling referee) 25 30
6016 $40 Kahat Shor (shooting coach) 25 30
6017 $40 Mark Slavin (wrestler) 25 30
6018 $40 Eliezer Halffin (wrestler) 25 30
6019 $40 Joseph Romano (weightlifter) 25 30
6020 $40 Munich Olympics stadium 25 30
MS6021 127 × 101 mm. $400 Israeli athlete with Olympic torch (vert) 2·40 2·50

2000. Queen Elizabeth the Queen Mother's 100th Birthday. As T **318** of Gambia. Multicoloured.
6022 $100 Queen Elizabeth the Queen Mother 60 65

624 Heads of Two Angels

2000. Christmas and Holy Year. Multicoloured.
6023 $60 Type **624** 35 40
6024 $90 Two angels 55 60
6025 $120 Heads of two angels (different) 70 70
6026 $180 As $90 . . . . 1·10 1·20
6027 $180 Type **624** . . . . . . 1·10 1·20
6028 $180 As $120 . . . . 1·10 1·20
6029 $180 Two angels with drapery . . . . 1·10 1·20
6030 $400 As No. 6029 . . . . . 2·40 2·50
MS6031 121 × 110 mm. $400 Holy Child (horiz) . . . . 2·40 2·50

625 Snake

2001. Chinese New Year ("Year of the Snake"). Multicoloured.
6032 $80 Type **625** 50 55
6033 $80 Snake (face value at top right) 50 55
6034 $80 Snake (face value at bottom right) 50 55
6035 $80 Snake (face value at bottom left) 50 55
MS6036 85 × 65 mm. $250 Snake (vert) . . . . 1·50 1·60

626 Prime Minister's Residence, Georgetown

2001. Tourist Attractions. Multicoloured.
6037 $90 Type **626** 55 60
6038 $90 Kaieteur Falls (vert) . . 55 60

2001. Faces of the Millennium. Queen Elizabeth the Queen Mother's 100th Birthday. As T **307a** of Gambia showing collage of miniature flower photographs. Multicoloured.
6039 $80 Top left side of head . . 50 55
6040 $80 Top right side of head 50 55
6041 $80 Eye and temple 50 55
6042 $80 Temple 50 55
6043 $80 Right cheek 50 55
6044 $80 Left cheek 50 55
6045 $80 Chin 50 55
6046 $80 Neck 50 55

Nos. 6039/46 were printed together, se-tenant, in sheetlets of 8 with the stamps arranged in two vertical columns separated by a gutter also containing miniature photographs. When viewed as a whole, the sheetlet forms a portrait of the Queen Mother.

2001. Faces of the Millennium: 80th Birthday of Pope John Paul II. As T **307a** of Gambia showing collage of miniature religious photographs. Multicoloured.
6047 $100 Back of head 60 65
6048 $100 Front of forehead . . 60 65
6049 $100 Ear 60 65
6050 $100 Eye 60 65
6051 $100 Neck 60 65
6052 $100 Cheek 60 65
6053 $100 Shoulder of robe . . . 60 65
6054 $100 Hands 60 65

Nos. 6047/54 were printed together, se-tenant, in sheetlets of 8 with the stamps arranged in two vertical columns separated by a gutter also containing miniature photographs. When viewed as a whole, the sheetlet forms a portrait of the Pope.

627 Chow Yun-Fat

2001. Chow Yun-Fat (Hong Kong actor). Multicoloured.
6055 $60 Type **627** 35 40
6056 $60 Wearing maroon coat 35 40
6057 $60 Wearing dark suit and grey shirt 35 40
6058 $60 In cream jacket, black shirt and white T-shirt . . 35 40
6059 $60 Wearing dark suit, white shirt and grey tie 35 40
6060 $60 In dark overcoat . . . 35 40

2001. Characters from Pokemon (children's cartoon series). As T **332a** of Gambia. Multicoloured.
6061 $100 "Staryu No. 120" . . 60 65
6062 $100 "Seaking No. 119" . . 60 65
6063 $100 "Tentacool No. 72" 60 65
6064 $100 "Magikarp No. 129" 60 65
6065 $100 "Seadra No. 117" . . 60 65
6066 $100 "Goldeen No. 118" . . 60 65
MS6067 74 × 114 mm. $400 "Horsea No. 116" (vert) . . . . 2·40 2·50

628 Boxer Dog

2001. "Hong Kong 2001" Stamp Exhibition. Cats and Dogs. Multicoloured.
6068 $35 Type **628** 20 25
6069 $60 Cinnamon ocicat . . . 35 40
6070 $60 Devon Rex 35 40
6071 $60 Egyptian Mau 35 40
6072 $60 Turkish angora 35 40
6073 $60 Sphynx 35 40
6074 $60 Persian 35 40
6075 $60 American wirehair . . . 35 40
6076 $60 Exotic shorthair . . . 35 40
6077 $60 American curl 35 40
6078 $80 Airedale terrier . . . 50 55
6079 $80 Greyhound 50 55
6080 $80 Afghan hound 50 55
6081 $80 Samoyed 50 55
6082 $80 Field spaniel 50 55
6083 $80 Scottish terrier 50 55
6084 $80 Brittany spaniel (brown and white) 50 55
6085 $80 Boston terrier 50 55
6086 $100 Smooth dachshund . . 60 65
6087 $300 White Manx . . . . . 1·80 1·90
MS6088 Two sheets, each 100 × 80 mm. (a) $400 Birman (cat). (b) $400 Dalmatian Set of 2 sheets . . . . 4·75 5·00

Nos. 6070/7 (cats) and 6078/85 (dogs) were each printed together, se-tenant, with the backgrounds forming composite designs. No. 6081 is inscribed "Samoyeo" in error. Nos. 6070/85 and **MS**6088 all show the "Hong Kong 2001" logo on the sheet margins.

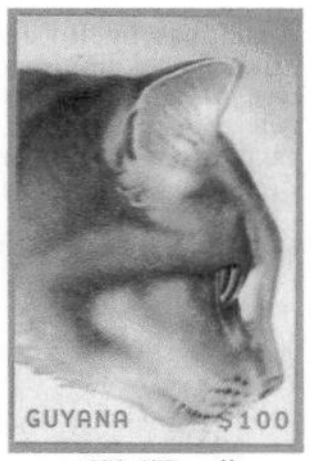

629 "Tom"

2001. Cats and Dogs of the Cinema. Multicoloured.
6089 $100 Type **629** 60 65
6090 $100 "Puff" (Siamese) . . . 60 65
6091 $100 "Jag" (silver tabby) . . 60 65
6092 $100 "Fritz" (Burmese, with paw curled) 60 65
6093 $100 "Smokey" (Burmese) 60 65
6094 $100 "Thor" (white cat) . . 60 65
6095 $100 "Pup" (small black and tan dog) 60 65
6096 $100 "Yogi" (white dog in snow) 60 65
6097 $100 "Hooch" (mastiff) . . 60 65
6098 $100 "Huxley Blu" (collie) 60 65
6099 $100 "Snowflake" (small white dog) 60 65
6100 $100 "Red" (Irish setter) . . 60 65
MS6101 Two sheets, each 67 × 86 mm. (a) $400 "Spike" (kitten). (b) $400 "Baron of Fillmore" (German shepherd dog) Set of 2 sheets . . . . 4·75 5·00

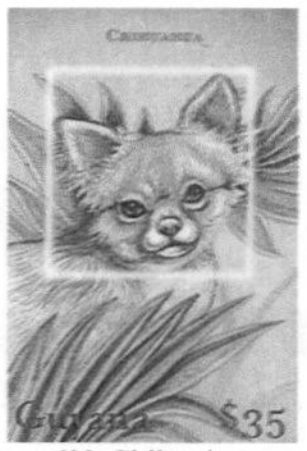

630 Chihuahua

2001. Dogs and Cats in the Caribbean. Multicoloured.
6102 $35 Type **630** 20 25
6103 $60 Persian tabby 35 40
6104 $80 Rottweiler 50 55
6105 $80 German shepherd . . . 50 55
6106 $80 Burmese mountain dog 50 55
6107 $80 Shar Pei 50 55
6108 $80 Dachshund 50 55
6109 $80 Jack Russell 50 55
6110 $80 Boston terrier 50 55
6111 $80 Corgi 50 55
6112 $80 American shorthair . . 50 55
6113 $80 Somali 50 55
6114 $80 Balinese 50 55
6115 $80 Egyptian Mau 50 55
6116 $80 Scottish fold 50 55
6117 $80 Sphynx 50 55
6118 $80 Korat 50 55
6119 $100 Colourpoint shorthair 60 65
6120 $200 Cocker spaniel . . . . 1·20 1·40
MS6121 Two sheets, each 76 × 86 mm. (a) $400 Beagle. (b) $400 Abyssinian (cat) Set of 2 sheets . . . . 4·75 5·00

Nos. 6104/11 (dogs) and 6112/18 (cats) were each printed together, se-tenant, with the backgrounds forming composite designs that extend onto the sheetlet margins.

631 George Washington

2001. George Washington (American president) Commemoration.
6122 **631** $300 multicoloured . . . 1·80 1·90

632 Hello Kitty in Alice in Wonderland

2001. Hello Kitty (cartoon character). Twelve sheets, each 100 × 145 mm, containg vert designs as T **632** of Hello Kitty in European (No. **MS**6120a/f) or Japanese (No. **MS**6120g/l) fairy tales. Multicoloured.
MS6123 (a) $400 Type **632**. (b) $400 Cinderella. (c) $400 Heidi. (d) $400 The Wizard of Oz. (e) $400 Peter Pan. (f) $400 Little Red Riding Hood. (g) $400 Three in a Boat. (h) $400 Bamboo Princess. (i) $400 The Fisherman. (j) $400 Up a Tree. (k) $400 On a Bear. (l) $400 In the Snow Set of 12 sheets 29·00 30·00

633 American Securities and Exchange Commission Office (founded 1934)

2001. People and Events of Early 20th Century. Multicoloured.

6124 $60 Type **633** 35 40
6125 $60 Herbert Hoover (American President, elected 1928) 35 40
6126 $60 Al Jolson in *The Jazz Singer* (first talking film, 1927) 35 40
6127 $60 J. Edgar Hoover (Director of F.B.I., appointed 1924) 35 40
6128 $60 Alexander Fleming (discovered penicillin, 1928) 35 40
6129 $60 Radio and microphone (Federal Communications Commission set up, 1927) 35 40
6130 $60 Charles Lindbergh (first solo transatlantic flight, 1927) 35 40
6131 $60 Albert Einstein (awarded Nobel physics prize, 1921) 35 40
6132 $60 Paul von Hindenburg (German leader, died 1934, succeeded by Hitler) 35 40
6133 $60 American flag and certificate (American Social Security Act, 1935) 35 40
6134 $60 Amelia Earhart (first solo flight from Hawaii to California) 35 40
6135 $60 Marcus Garvey (founder of Universal Negro Improvement Association, prison sentence commuted and deported, 1927) 35 40

634 Ronald Reagan

2001. 90th Birthday of Ronald Reagan (American President). Multicoloured (except Nos. 6136/8).

6136 $60 Type **634** (lilac and black) 35 40
6137 $60 With chimp in *Bedtime for Bonzo* (lilac and black) 35 40
6138 $60 Wearing cowboy hat (grey and black) 35 40
6139 $60 In dark suit and black tie 35 40
6140 $60 With Nancy Reagan . . 35 40
6141 $60 Pointing 35 40
6142 $60 Getting into car and waving 35 40
6143 $60 Signing reduction of nuclear arms treaty with Mikhail Gorbachev, 1987 35 40
6144 $60 Helping demolish Berlin Wall, 1989 . . . . 35 40
6145 $60 With President Clinton 35 40

635 "Girl at a Hot Spring Resort" (Hashiguchi Goyo)

2001. "Philanippon '01" International Stamp Exhibition, Tokyo. Japanese Paintings. Multicoloured.

6146 $25 Type **635** 15 20
6147 $25 "Hanaogi with Maidservant" (Eishosai Choki) 15 20
6148 $30 "Morokoshi of the Echizenya" (Rekisentei Eiri) 20 15
6149 $30 "Courtesan receiving a Letter of Invitation" (Suzuki Harunobu) . . . 20 15
6150 $35 "Mother and Daughter on an Outing" (Katsushika Hokusai) . . 20 25
6151 $35 "Two Girls on Way to (or from) the Bathhouse" (S. Harunobu) 20 25
6152 $60 "Matron in Love" (Kitagawa Utamaro) . . . 35 40
6153 $60 "Girl and Frog" (S. Harunobu) 35 40
6154 $80 "Insects, reptiles and amphibians at a Pond" (38 × 72 mm) 50 55
6155 $80 "Rose Mallow and Fowl" (38 × 72 mm) . . . 50 55
6156 $80 "Rooster, Sunflower and Morning Glories" (38 × 72 mm) 50 55
6157 $80 "Group of Roosters" (38 × 72 mm) 50 55
6158 $80 "Black Rooster and Nandina" (38 × 72 mm) 50 55
6159 $80 "Birds and Autumn Maples" (38 × 72 mm) . . 50 55
6160 $80 "Wagtail and Roses" (38 × 72 mm) 50 55
6161 $80 "Cockatoos in a Pine" (38 × 72 mm) 50 55
6162 $100 "Three Beauties of High Fame" (K. Utamaro) 60 65
6163 $100 "The Courtesan Midorigi" (Chokosai Eisho) 60 65
6164 $100 Bridge (38 × 72 mm) 60 65
6165 $100 Causeway and summer house (38 × 72 mm) . . . 60 65
6166 $100 Island in lake with single tree (38 × 72 mm) 60 65
6167 $100 Rocky islet and waterfalls tumbling into lake (38 × 72 mm) 60 65
6168 $100 Shugakuin Imperial Villa with Japanese letters (38 × 72 mm) 60 65
6169 $100 Trees with Japanese letters (38 × 72 mm) . . . 60 65
6170 $120 "Girls After the Bath" (K. Utamaro) (38 × 72 mm) 70 75
6171 $120 "Summer Evening on Riverbank at Hama-Cho" (Torii Kiyonaga) (38 × 72 mm) 70 75
6172 $120 "A Beauty in the Wind" (Kaigetsudo Ando) (38 × 72 mm) 70 75
6173 $120 "Sisters (Shimainozu)" (Tsuji Kako) (38 × 72 mm) 70 75
6174 $120 "Kasamori Osen" (S. Harunobu) (38 × 72 mm) 70 75
6175 $160 "Ichikawa Ebizo" behind Screen (30 × 38 mm) . . . . . . 95 1·00
6176 $160 "Ichikawa Ebizo" in red jacket (30 × 38 mm) 95 1·00
6177 $160 "Ichikawa Ebizo" with musicians (30 × 38 mm) 95 1·00
6178 $160 "Ichikawa Ebizo" being dressed as warrior (30 × 38 mm) . . . . . . 95 1·00
6179 $200 "Girl breaking off Branch of Flowering Tree" (S. Harunobu) . . 1·20 1·40
6180 $200 "Maiko" (Tsuchida Bakusen) . . . . 1·20 1·40
MS6181 Five sheets. (a) 120 × 80 mm. $400 "Wintry Sky" (Higashibara Hosen). (b) 120 × 80 mm. $400 "Woman holding a Flower" (Kajiwara Hisako). (c) 120 × 80 mm. $400 "Palace of Immortals in an Autumn Valley" (Okochi Yako). (d) 80 × 120 mm. $400 Fish and Octopus from the "Colourful Realm of living Beings" (I. Jakuchu). (e) 80 × 120 mm. $400 "Portrait of Takami Senseki" (Watanabe Kazan). All imperf set of 5 sheets . . . . 12·00 12·50

Nos. 6154/61 (paintings by Ito Jakuchu), 6164/9 ("Procession to the Shugakuin Imperial Villa" by Kakimoto Sesshin), 6170/4 (Japanese Women) and 6175/8 ("Ichikawa Ebizo" (actor) by Toshusai Sharaku) were each printed together, se-tenant, in sheetlets of 4, 5, 6 or 8 with enlarged inscribed margins.

Nos. 6164/9 and 6175/8 each form a composite design.

636 Queen Victoria, 1850

2001. Death Centenary of Queen Victoria. Multicoloured.

6182 $200 Type **636** . . . . . 1·20 1·40
6183 $200 Queen Victoria, 1843 1·20 1·40
6184 $200 Queen Victoria wearing crown, 1859 . . . 1·20 1·40
6185 $200 Queen Victoria in feathered hat, 1897 . . . 1·20 1·40
6186 $200 Princess Victoria, 1829 1·20 1·40
6187 $200 Queen Victoria with hair in bun, 1837 . . . . 1·20 1·40
6188 $200 In uniform for troop review, 1840 . . . . . . 1·20 1·40
6189 $200 Wearing crown and white veil, 1897 . . . . . 1·20 1·40
MS6190 Two sheets, each 88 × 120 mm. (a) $400 Queen Victoria. (b) $400 Queen Victoria in old age Set of 2 sheets . . . 4·75 5·00

2001. 75th Death Anniv of Claude-Oscar Monet (artist). As T **339** of Gambia. Multicoloured.

6191 $150 "Village Street near Honfleur" 90 95
6192 $150 "Road to Chailly" . . 90 95
6193 $150 "Train in the Countryside" 90 95
6194 $150 "Quai du Louvre" . . 90 95
MS6195 136 × 111 mm. $400 "Flowering Garden" (vert) . . 2·40 2·50

2001. 75th Birthday of Queen Elizabeth II. As T **340** of Gambia. Multicoloured.

6196 $150 Queen Elizabeth wearing pink hat 90 95
6197 $150 Wearing red coat and hat 90 95
6198 $150 Wearing white turban style hat 90 95
6199 $150 Wearing tiara 90 95
MS6200 80 × 110 mm. $400 Queen Elizabeth wearing yellow dress and pearls (38 × 50 mm) . . . 2·40 2·50

2001. Death Centenary of Giuseppe Verdi (Italian composer). Vert designs as T **342** of Gambia. Multicoloured.

6201 $160 Verdi (face value at bottom left) . . . . . . 95 1·00
6202 $160 Rigoletto and score . . 95 1·00
6203 $160 Ernani and opera score 95 1·00
6204 $160 Verdi (face value at bottom right) . . . . . . 95 1·00
MS6205 77 × 117 mm. $400 Verdi 2·40 2·50

Nos. 6201/4 were printed together, se-tenant, with the backgrounds forming a composite design.

2001. Death Centenary of Henri de Toulouse-Lautrec (artist). As T **343** of Gambia. Multicoloured.

6206 $160 "Maurice Joyant in the Baie de Somme" (horiz) 95 1·00
6207 $160 "Monsieur Boileau" (horiz) . . . . 95 1·00
6208 $160 "Monsieur, Madame and the Dog" (horiz) . . 95 1·00
MS6209 66 × 85 mm. $400 "Monsieur" . . . . 2·40 2·50

637 Top Right of Head

2001. Faces of the Millennium. John F. Kennedy. Showing collage of miniature photographs from Kennedy's years as President. Multicoloured.

6210 $80 Type **637** 50 55
6211 $80 Top left of head 50 55
6212 $80 Top of right cheek . . . 50 55
6213 $80 Top of left cheek . . . 50 55
6214 $80 Bottom of right cheek 50 55
6215 $80 Bottom of left cheek . . 50 55
6216 $80 Bottom right of chin . . 50 55
6217 $80 Bottom left of chin . . 50 55

Nos. 6210/17 were printed together, se-tenant, in sheetlets of 8 with the stamps arranged in two vertical columns separated by a gutter also containing miniature photographs. When viewed as a whole, the sheetlet forms a portrait of JFK.

EXPRESS LETTER STAMPS

1986. Various stamps surch **EXPRESS** and new values.

E1 $12 on 350c. on 120c. multicoloured (No. 1598) 7·00 7·00
E2 $15 on 40c. multicoloured (No. 1868) . . . . 9·00 9·00
E3 $20 on $6.40 multicoloured 7·00 7·00
E4 $25 on 25c. multicoloured (as No. 1771, but value changed) . . . . 13·00 13·00

No. E3 was previously a miniature sheet for Halley's Comet containing two 320c. stamps. As surch the original values on both designs have been cancelled and replaced by a single $20 face value.

1987. No. E3 additionally optd with small Maltese cross above surch.

E5 $20 on $6.40 multicoloured 7·00 7·00

1987. Centenary of Publication of Sanders' "Reichenbachia". As T **331** additionally inscr "EXPRESS". Multicoloured.

E6 $15 Plate No. 11 (Series 2) . . 5·00 5·00
E7 $20 Plate No. 93 (Series 2) . . 3·50 4·00
E8 $25 Plate No. 63 (Series 2) . . 4·75 6·00
E9 $45 Plate No. 35 (Series 2) . . 7·50 9·50

1987. Nos. 1744/5 imperf between surch **EXPRESS FORTY DOLLARS** and star.

E10 $40 on $6.40 multicoloured 12·00 12·00

1987. No. E2 additionally optd **1987**.

E11 $15 on 40c. multicoloured . . 11·00 5·50

1988. Nos. 2206 and 2211 surch **SPECIAL DELIVERY** and new value.

E12 $40 on $3.20 blue . . . . . 10·00 11·00
E13 $45 on $3.30 black . . . . . 10·00 11·00

1989. Imperf between pairs of Nos. 1744/5 and 2185/6 surch **EXPRESS FORTY DOLLARS** (without stars).

E14 $40 on $6.40 multicoloured (Nos. 1744/5) . . . . . . 6·00 6·50
E15 $40 on $6.40 multicoloured (Nos. 2185/6) . . . . . . 6·00 6·50

1989. Nos. 2206 and 2211 surch **SPECIAL DELIVERY** and new value.

E16 $190 on $3.30 black . . . . 17·00 19·00
E17 $225 on $3.20 blue . . . . . 18·00 20·00

1989. Butterflies. Two sheets, each 97 × 67 mm, containing vert designs as T **454** optd **EXPRESS**. Multicoloured.

EMS18 $130 "Phareas coeleste" 5·00 5·00
EMS19 $190 "Papilio torquatus" 6·00 6·00

1989. Women in Space. Sheet 92 × 67 mm, containing vert design as T **455** optd **EXPRESS**. Multicoloured.

EMS20 $190 Valentina Tereshkova (first woman cosmonaut) . . 4·25 4·50

1989. "World Stamp Expo '89" International Stamp Exhibition, Washington. Nos. **EMS**18/19 optd with logo.

EMS21 $130 "Phareas coeleste" 4·00 4·00
EMS22 $190 "Papilio torquatus" 4·50 4·50

Nos. EMS21/22 show additional overprints on sheet margins.

1990. 85th Anniv of Rotary International. Nos. EMS18/20 optd **ROTARY INTERNATIONAL 1905–1990** and emblem on sheet margins only.

EMS23 $130 "Phareas coeleste" 3·75 3·75
EMS24 $190 "Papilio torquatus" 5·50 5·50
EMS25 $190 Valentina Tereshkova (first woman cosmonaut) . . 4·00 5·50

1990. "Stamp World London '90" International Stamp Exhibition. Nos. **EMS**18/20 optd **Stamp World London '90** and emblem on sheet margins only.

EMS26 $130 "Phareas coeleste" (R.) . . . . 3·75 3·75
a. Opt in black . . . . .
EMS27 $190 "Papilio torquatus" 5·50 5·50
EMS28 $190 Valentina Tereshkova (first woman cosmonaut) . . 4·00 5·50

1990. "Belgica '90" International Stamp Exhibition, Brussels. Nos. **EMS**18 and **EMS**20 additionally optd **BELGICA PHILATELIC EXPOSITION 1990** and emblem in black on sheet margins only.

EMS29 $130 "Phareas coeleste" 4·00 4·00
EMS30 $190 Valentina Tereshkova (first woman cosmonaut) . . 4·50 5·00

1990. 90th Birthday of Queen Elizabeth the Queen Mother. Nos. **EMS**18/20 optd **90TH BIRTHDAY H.M. THE QUEEN MOTHER** on sheet margins only.

EMS31 $130 "Phareas coeleste" 3·50 3·50
EMS32 $190 "Papilio torquatus" 4·00 4·00
EMS33 $190 Valentina Tereshkova (first woman cosmonaut) . . 4·00 4·00

1990. Fauna. Two sheets, each 110 × 80 mm, containing vert designs as T **466**, but larger (40 × 55 mm) inscr EXPRESS. Multicoloured.

EMS34 $130 Harpy Eagle . . . . 3·50 3·50
EMS35 $150 Ocelot . . . . . . 3·50 3·50

OFFICIAL STAMPS

1981. Nos. 556, F4a and F6/7 optd **OPS** or surch also.

O13 10c. on 25c. Marabunta . . 3·50 2·25
O14 50c. "Guzmania lingulata" 1·00 30
O15 60c. Soldier's cap . . . . . 1·00 20
O16 $5 "Odontadenia grandiflora" . . . . . . 1·75 1·75

1981. Nos. 491, 708a, 716, 804, 834 and F9 optd **OPS** or surch also.

O17 15c. Harpy eagle (postage) 9·50 65
O18 30c. on $2 "Norantea guianensis" (F9) 45 30
O19 100c. on $3 Cylinder satellite 2·00 40
O20 125c. on $2 "Norantea guianensis" . . . . 1·00 60
O21 $10 "Elbella patrobas" . . . 9·50 10·00

O22 $1.10 on $2 "Norantea guianensis" (804) (air) . . 75 2·00

1981. Nos. 548a, 719, 828 and 830 optd **OPS** or surch also.
O23 15c. Christmas orchid . . . 8·50 1·50
O24 50c. British Guiana 1898 1c. stamp . . . . 1·25 35
O25 100c. on 8c. Camp-fire cooking . . . . 1·25 50
O26 110c. on 6c. Type **116** . . . 2·00 1·25

1982. Various stamps optd **OPS**.
O27 – 20c. multicoloured (No. 701) . . . . . . 5·50 60
O28 **136** 40c. multicoloured . . . 75 15
O29 – 40c. red, grey and black (No. 674) . . . . . . 1·00 15
O30 – $2 multicoloured (No. 676) . . . . . . 7·00 75

1982. Nos. 911 and 980 optd or surch **OPS**.
O31 250c. on 400c. on 30c. multicoloured (postage) . . 80 60
O32 220c. on 1c. multicoloured (air) . . . . 1·00 60

1982. No. F9 optd **OPS**.
O33 $2 "Norantea guianensis" . . 8·00 2·00

1982. Air. No. 979 optd **OPS**.
O34 110c. on 5c. Annatto tree . . 1·25 40

1984. No. 912 surch **OPS**.
O35 150c. on $5 multicoloured 6·00 2·75
O36 200c. on $5 multicoloured 6·50 3·00
O37 225c. on $5 multicoloured 6·50 3·25
O38 230c. on $5 multicoloured 6·50 3·25
O39 260c. on $5 multicoloured 6·50 3·50
O40 320c. on $5 multicoloured 8·00 4·00
O41 350c. on $5 multicoloured 8·50 4·50
O42 600c. on $5 multicoloured 10·00 6·50

1984. Nos. O32 and O34 surch and No. 981 optd **OPS**.
O43 25c. on 110c. on 5c. Annatto tree . . . . 1·50 40
O44 30c. on 110c. on 5c. Annatto tree . . . . 1·50 45
O45 45c. on 220c. on 1c. Pitcher plant of Mt. Roraima . . 1·60 55
O46 55c. on 110c. on 5c. Annatto tree . . . . 1·75 60
O47 60c. on 220c. on 1c. Pitcher plant of Mt. Roraima . . 1·75 60
O48 75c. on 220c. on 1c. Pitcher plant of Mt. Roraima . . 2·00 70
O49 90c. on 220c. on 1c. Pitcher plant of Mt. Roraima . . 2·00 80
O50 120c. on 220c. on 1c. Pitcher plant of Mt. Roraima . . 2·25 1·25
O51 130c. on 220c. on 1c. Pitcher plant of Mt. Roraima . . 2·25 1·25
O52 330c. on $2 "Norantea guianensis" . . . . 4·00 4·00

1987. Centenary of Publication of Sanders' "Reichenbachia". As T **331** additionally inscr "OFFICIAL". Multicoloured.
O53 120c. Plate No. 48 (Series 2) 1·75 45
O54 130c. Plate No. 92 (Series 2) 1·75 45
O55 140c. Plate No. 36 (Series 2) 75 35
O56 150c. Plate No. 43 (Series 2) 1·75 50
O57 175c. Plate No. 31 (Series 2) 80 40
O58 200c. Plate No. 61 (Series 2) 1·75 60
O59 225c. Plate No. 26 (Series 2) 1·75 60
O60 230c. Plate No. 68 (Series 2) (horiz) 50 50
O61 250c. Plate No. 59 (Series 2) 50 60
O62 260c. Plate No. 69 (Series 2) 50 60
O63 275c. Plate No. 90 (Series 2) 1·75 75
O64 320c. Plate No. 75 (Series 2) 1·75 80
O65 330c. Plate No. 23 (Series 2) 3·00 1·00
O66 350c. Plate No. 95 (Series 2) (horiz) 50 80
O67 600c. Plate No. 70 (Series 2) (horiz) . . . . 75 1·60
O68 $12 Plate No. 71 (Series 2) (horiz) . . . . 1·40 2·50
O69 $15 Plate No. 84 (Series 2) 1·50 2·75

OFFICIAL PARCEL POST STAMPS

1981. Nos. P1/2 optd **OPS**.
OP1 $15 on $1 "Chelonanthus uliginoides" . . . . 10·00 2·25
OP2 $20 on $1 "Chelonanthus uliginoides" . . . . 10·00 2·75

1983. No. 843 surch **OPS Parcel Post $12.00** and additionally optd **1982**.
OP3 $12 on $1.10 on $2 "Norantea guianensis" . . 70·00 17·00

1983. No. OP3 with additional **OPS** opt.
OP4 $12 on $1.10 on $2 "Norantea guianensis" . . 22·00 4·00

1983. No. P4 optd **OPS**.
OP5 $12 on $1.10 on $2 "Norantea guianensis" . . 7·50 4·00

PARCEL POST STAMPS

1981. No. 554 surch **PARCEL POST** and new value.
P1 $15 on $1 "Chelonanthus uliginoides" . . . . 10·00 3·00
P2 $20 on $1 "Chelonanthus uliginoides" . . . . 10·00 6·00

1983. No. 843 surch **PARCEL POST $12.00**.
P3 $12 on $1.10 on $2 "Norantea guianensis" . . . . 2·25 2·50

1983. Unissued Royal Wedding surch, similar to No. 843, further surch **Parcel Post $12.00**.
P4 $12 on $1.10 on $2 "Norantea guianensis" . . . . 1·00 1·75

1985. No. 673 surch **TWENTY FIVE DOLLARS PARCEL POST 25.00**.
P5 $25 on 35c. green, grey and black . . . . 24·00 19·00

POSTAGE DUE STAMPS

D 2

1987.
D 8 **D 2** 1c. green . . . . 25 3·50
D 9 2c. black . . . . 25 3·50
D10 4c. blue . . . . 25 3·50
D11 12c. red . . . . 25 3·50

POSTAL FISCAL STAMPS

1975. Nos. 543/5 and 550ab/6 optd **REVENUE ONLY**.
F 1 2c. Type **132** 50 40
F 2 3c. Hanging heliconia . . . 50 40
F 3 5c. Annatto tree 75 30
F 4 25c. Marabunta . . . . . . 3·25 30
F 4a 25c. Marabunta (No. 550) 15·00 13·00
F 5 40c. Tiger beard . . . . . 5·50 30
F 6 50c. "Guzmania lingulata" 70 40
F 7 60c. Soldier's cap 75 50
F 8 $1 "Chelonanthus uliginoides" . . . . . . 75 1·25
F 9 $2 "Norantea guianensis" 1·00 2·75
F10 $5 "Odontadenis grandiflora" . . . . . . 1·75 9·00

Although intended for fiscal use Nos. F1/F10 were allowed by the postal authorities as an "act of grace" to do duty as postage stamps until 30 June 1976.

GWALIOR Pt. 1

A "convention" state of Central India.

12 pies = 1 anna; 16 annas = 1 rupee.

1885. Queen Victoria stamps of India optd **GWALIOR** at foot and native opt at top.
1 **23** ½a. turquoise . . . . £110 23·00
2 – 1a. purple . . . . 75·00 27·00
6 – 1a.6p. brown . . . . 70·00
3 – 2a. blue . . . . 65·00 13·00
8 – 4a. green (No. 69) . . . . 75·00
9 – 6a. brown (No. 80) . . . . 75·00
10 – 8a. mauve . . . . 70·00
11 – 1r. grey (No. 101) . . . . 70·00

Stamps of India overprinted **GWALIOR** above native overprint unless otherwise stated.

1885. Queen Victoria.
16c **23** ½a. turquoise 35 10
17 – 9p. red . . . . 30·00 50·00
18 – 1a. purple . . . . 1·00 20
20c – 1a.6p. brown . . . . . . 1·40 50
21c – 2a. blue . . . . 1·25 10
23 – 2a.6p. green . . . . 6·00 17·00
25c – 3a. orange . . . . 2·00 15
14 – 4a. green (No. 69) . . . . 21·00 12·00
27c – 4a. green (No. 96) . . . . 3·00 70
29 – 6a. brown (No. 80) . . . . 2·00 7·00
30c – 8a. mauve . . . . 3·75 85
32c – 12a. purple on red . . . . 3·25 65
33c – 1r. grey (No. 101) . . . . 2·75 1·50
34 **37** 1r. green and red . . . . 3·75 3·25
35 **38** 2r. red and orange . . . . 5·50 3·00
36 3r. brown and green . . . . 7·50 3·50
37 5r. blue and violet . . . . 14·00 6·50

1899. Queen Victoria.
38 **40** 3p. red 30 20
39 3p. grey . . . . 6·50 60·00
40 **23** ½a. green . . . . 50 1·10
41 – 1a. red . . . . 1·00 35
42 – 2a. lilac . . . . 1·40 4·25
43 – 2½a. blue . . . . 1·10 5·00

1903. King Edward VII.
46A **41** 3p. grey 70 20
48A – ½a. green (No. 122) . . . 20 10
49A – 1a. red (No. 123) 20 10
50A – 2a. lilac . . . . 1·25 70
52B – 2a.6p. blue . . . . 1·25 7·50
53A – 3a. orange . . . . 1·50 35
54A – 4a. olive . . . . 1·50 40
56B – 6a. bistre . . . . 4·50 1·25
57A – 8a. mauve . . . . 3·25 1·40
59B – 12a. purple on red . . . . 3·75 3·25
60A – 1r. green and red . . . . 2·50 1·75
61B **52** 2r. red and orange . . . . 9·00 11·00
62B 3r. brown and green . . . 26·00 45·00
63B 5r. blue and violet . . . . 19·00 27·00

1907. King Edward VII inscr "INDIA POSTAGE AND REVENUE".
65 ½a. green (No. 149) 50 20
66 1a. red (No. 150) . . . . . . 1·50 20

1912. King George V.
67 **55** 3p. grey 10 10
68 **58** ½a. green 20 10
102 **79** ½a. green 50 20
88 **80** 9p. green . . . . 1·75 20
69 **57** 1a. red 25 10
80 1a. brown 70 10
103 **81** 1a. brown 20 10
90 **82** 1a.3p. mauve 50 15
81 **58** 1½a. brown (No. 165) . . . 1·50 50
82 1½a. red 20 20
70 **59** 2a. purple 60 10
91 **70** 2a. lilac 75 30
104 **59** 2a. red . . . . 1·75 2·50
83 **61** 2½a. blue . . . . 1·75 1·75
84 2½a. orange 35 50
71 **62** 3a. orange 60 25
92 3a. blue . . . . 1·00 40
72 **63** 4a. olive 60 60
93 **71** 4a. green . . . . 1·25 1·00
73a **64** 6a. bistre . . . . 1·00 1·00
74 **65** 8a. mauve . . . . 1·10 70
75 **66** 12a. red . . . . 1·25 2·75
76 **67** 1r. brown and green . . . 6·50 70
77 2r. red and brown . . . . 4·50 4·50
78 5r. blue and violet . . . . 20·00 6·50

1922. No. 192 (King George V) optd **GWALIOR** only.
79 **57** 9p. on 1a. red 10 50

1928. King George V. Optd in larger type (19 mm long).
96 **67** 1r. brown and green . . 2·00 3·00
97w 2r. red and orange . . . 7·00 4·00
98 5r. blue and violet . . . 17·00 24·00
99 10r. green and red . . . 50·00 38·00
100 15r. blue and olive . . . 80·00 60·00
101 25r. orange and blue . . £170 £140

1938. King George VI.
105 **91** 3p. slate . . . . 6·50 10
106 ½a. brown . . . . 7·00 10
107 9p. green . . . . 40·00 3·25
108 1a. red . . . . 6·50 15
109 3a. green (No. 253) . . . 17·00 3·75
110 4a. brown (No. 255) . . . 42·00 2·50
111 6a. green (No. 256) . . . 3·00 8·00
112 **93** 1r. slate and brown . . . 8·00 1·50
113 2r. purple and brown . . . 40·00 9·00
114 5r. green and blue . . . 30·00 32·00
115 10r. purple and red . . . 30·00 40·00
116 15r. brown and green . . . 90·00 £160
117 25r. slate and purple . . . 80·00 £120

1942. King George VI.
118 **100a** 3p. slate 45 10
119 ½a. mauve 45 10
120 9p. green 45 10
121 1a. red 40 10
122 **101** 1½a. violet . . . . . . 6·00 20
123 2a. red 65 20
124 3a. violet . . . . 13·00 1·00
125 **102** 4a. brown . . . . 1·75 20
126 6a. green . . . . 14·00 23·00
127 8a. violet . . . . 2·75 2·75
128 12a. purple . . . . 4·50 20·00

OFFICIAL STAMPS

Stamps of India overprinted with native inscription at top and bottom, unless otherwise stated.

1895. Queen Victoria.
O 1 **23** ½a. turquoise 30 10
O 3 – 1a. purple . . . . 1·00 10
O 5 – 2a. blue . . . . 1·40 40
O 7 – 4a. green (No. 96) . . . . 1·75 1·00
O 9 – 8a. mauve . . . . 2·00 1·40
O10 **37** 1r. green and red . . . . 5·50 3·00

1901. Queen Victoria.
O23 **40** 3p. red 50 30
O24 3p. grey . . . . 1·50 2·25
O26 **23** ½a. green 50 10
O27 – 1a. red . . . . 4·25 10
O28 – 2a. lilac . . . . 85 1·50

1903. King Edward VII.
O29 **41** 3p. grey 60 10
O41 – ½a. green (No. 122) . . . 2·50 15
O32 – 1a. red (No. 123) 70 10
O33a – 2a. lilac . . . . 1·50 30
O44 – 4a. olive . . . . 3·00 1·00
O36 – 8a. mauve . . . . 4·50 70
O38 – 1r. green and red . . . . 2·75 1·75

1907. King Edward VII inscr "POSTAGE & REVENUE".
O49 – ½a. green (No. 149) . . . . 1·25 15
O48 – 1a. red (No. 150) . . . . . 5·00 15

1913. King George V.
O51 **55** 3p. grey 20 10
O62 **56** ½a. green 10 15
O73 **79** ½a. green 15 15
O63 **80** 9p. green 10 15
O53a **57** 1a. red 30 10
O64 1a. brown 10 10
O74 **81** 1a. brown 15 15
O65 **82** 1a.3p. mauve 50 15
O55 **59** 2a. purple 70 50
O66 **70** 2a. lilac 20 15
O75 **59** 2a. red 20 40
O77 **63** 4a. olive 60 75
O67 **71** 4a. green 60 30
O68 **65** 8a. mauve . . . . 50 1·00
O58 **67** 1r. brown and green . . 24·00 2·00

1922. No. O97 (King George V Official) optd **GWALIOR** only.
O59 **57** 9p. on 1a. red 10 30

1927. King George V. Optd in large type (21 mm long).
O69 **67** 1r. brown and green . . . 1·00 1·75
O70 2r. red and orange . . . . 11·00 12·00
O71 5r. blue and violet . . . . 16·00 £150
O72 10r. green and red £120 £350

1938. King George VI.
O78 **91** ½a. brown . . . . 6·50 30
O79 1a. red . . . . 1·10 20
O91 **93** 1r. slate and brown . . . 10·00 16·00
O92 2r. purple and brown . . 18·00 75·00
O93 5r. green and blue . . . . 30·00 £450
O94 10r. purple and red . . . 80·00 £900

1940. King George VI. Optd at bottom only.
O80 **O 20** 3p. slate 50 10
O81 ½a. brown . . . . . . 3·25 25
O82 ½a. purple 50 10
O83 9p. green 70 60
O84 1a. red . . . . 2·25 10
O85 1a.3p. brown . . . . . 38·00 1·75
O86 1a.6p. violet . . . . . 1·00 30
O87 2a. orange . . . . . . 1·00 30
O88 4a. brown . . . . . . 1·25 2·25
O89 8a. violet . . . . . . 3·50 7·50

1942. No. O65 surch **1A 1A** and bar.
O90 **82** 1a. on 1¼a. mauve . . . . 23·00 2·75

HAITI Pt. 15

The W. portion of the island of Hispaniola in the West Indies. A republic, independent from 1804.

100 centimes = 1 gourde or piastre.

1 Liberty

2 Pres. Salomon

1881. Imperf.
1 **1** 1c. red . . . . 5·00 3·00
2 2c. purple . . . . 6·50 3·25
3 3c. bistre . . . . 11·00 4·00
4 5c. green . . . . 18·00 7·00
5 7c. blue . . . . 12·50 2·50
6 20c. brown . . . . 45·00 16·00

1882. Perf.
7 **1** 1c. red . . . . 3·25 1·00
9 2c. purple . . . . 5·00 1·50
12 3c. bistre . . . . 6·50 2·25
15 5c. green . . . . 3·75 75
17 7c. blue . . . . 5·00 1·25
20 20c. brown . . . . 4·50 1·00

1887.
24 **2** 1c. lake 30 30
25 2c. mauve 55 50
26 3c. blue 50 40
27 5c. green . . . . 2·10 40

1890. Surch **DEUX 2 CENT**.
28 **2** 2c. on 3c. blue 40 35

4 Tree with Leaves upright

5 Tree with Leaves drooping

6

1891. Tree with leaves upright.
29 **4** 1c. mauve 40 15
30 2c. blue 60 20
31 3c. lilac 60 40
31a 3c. grey 80 50
32 5c. orange . . . . 2·25 40
33 7c. red . . . . 4·75 1·75

1892. Surch **DEUX 2 CENT**.
34 **4** 2c. on 3c. lilac 85 70
34a 2c. on 3c. grey 85 70

1893. Tree with leaves drooping.
35a **5** 1c. purple 15 10
41 1c. blue 20 20
36 2c. blue 20 10
42 2c. red 40 25
37 3c. lilac 60 40
43 3c. brown 20 15
38 5c. orange . . . . 2·25 20
44 5c. green 20 15
39 7c. red 40 35
45 7c. grey 30 20

40 20c. brown 80 60
46 20c. orange 40 40

1898. Surch **DEUX 2 CENT.**
47 **5** 2c. on 20c. brown 85 25
48 2c. on 20c. orange 35 25

1898.
49a **6** 2c. red 20 15
50a 5c. green 20 15

8 Pres. Simon Sam

9

1898.
51 **8** 1c. blue 10 10
67 **9** 1c. green 10 10
52 **8** 2c. orange 15 15
68 **9** 2c. red 15 15
53 **8** 3c. green 15 15
54 **9** 4c. red 15 15
55 **8** 5c. brown 15 15
69 **9** 5c. blue 10 10
56 **8** 7c. grey 15 15
57 **9** 8c. red 20 15
58 10c. orange 15 15
59 15c. olive 35 25
60 **8** 20c. black 30 25
61 50c. lake 35 25
62 1g. mauve . . . . 1·40 1·25

1902. Optd **MAI Gt Pre 1902** in frame.
70 **8** 1c. blue 45 45
71 **9** 1c. green 35 15
72 **8** 2c. orange 45 45
73 **9** 2c. red 35 15
74 **8** 3c. green 35 35
75 **9** 4c. red 45 45
76 **8** 5c. brown 90 90
77 **9** 5c. blue 35 35
78 **8** 7c. grey 45 45
79 **9** 8c. red 45 45
80 10c. orange 45 45
81 15c. olive . . . . 2·10 1·50
82 **8** 20c. black . . . . 3·25 1·75
83 50c. lake . . . . 7·50 3·75
84 1g. mauve . . . . 9·50 7·75

12 Arms

13 J.-J. Dessalines

1904. Cent of Independence. Optd **1804 POSTE PAYE 1904** in frame. T **12** and portraits as T **13**.
89 **12** 1c. green 25 25
90 – 2c. black and red 30 30
91 – 5c. black and blue 30 30
92 **13** 7c. black and red 30 30
93 – 10c. black and yellow . . . 30 30
94 – 20c. black and grey 30 30
95 – 50c. black and olive 30 30
DESIGNS: 2, 5c. Toussaint l'Ouverture; 20, 50c. Petion.

1904. Nos. 89/95 but without opt.
96 1c. green 20 15
97 2c. black and red 20 15
98 5c. black and blue 20 15
99 7c. black and red 20 15
100 10c. black and yellow 20 15
101 20c. black and grey 20 15
102 50c. black and olive 20 15

15 Pres. Nord Alexis

1904. External Mail. Optd **1804 POSTE PAYE 1904** in frame.
103 **15** 1c. green 45 35
104 2c. red 45 35
105 5c. blue 45 35
106 10c. brown 45 35
107 20c. orange 45 35
108 50c. plum 45 35

1904. Nos. 103/108, but without opt.
109 **15** 1c. green 10 10
110 2c. red 10 10
111 5c. blue 10 10
112 10c. brown 10 10
113 20c. orange 10 10
114 50c. plum 10 10

1906. Optd **SERVICE EXTERIEUR PROVISOIRE EN PIASTRES FORTES** in oval.
117 **8** 1c. blue 55 45
118 **9** 1c. green 55 55
119 **8** 2c. orange . . . . 1·10 1·10
120 **9** 2c. red 90 90
121 **8** 3c. green 90 90
122 **9** 4c. red . . . . 3·75 3·00
123 **8** 5c. brown . . . . 3·75 3·00
124 **9** 5c. blue 45 45
125 **8** 7c. grey . . . . 3·00 3·00
126 **9** 8c. red 45 45
127 10c. orange 85 55
128 15c. olive . . . . 1·10 60
129 **8** 20c. black . . . . 3·75 3·00
130 50c. lake . . . . 3·75 1·75
131 1g. mauve . . . . 6·25 4·75

19 Pres. Nord Alexis

20 Arms

1906.
132 **19** 1c. de g. blue 20 10
133 **20** 2c. de g. orange 35 15
134 2c. de g. yellow 55 15
135 **19** 3c. de g. grey 30 10
136 **20** 7c. de g. green 55 35

21 Iron Market, Port-au-Prince

24 Pres. A. T. Simon

1906. Currency changed from "gourdes" to "piastres".
137 **20** 1c. de p. green 20 15
138 **19** 2c. de p. red 35 20
139 **21** 3c. de p. sepia . . . . . . 1·75 40
140 3c. de p. orange . . . . . 4·25 4·50
141 – 4c. de p. red 55 30
167 – 4c. de p. olive . . . . . . 5·50 4·25
142 **19** 5c. de p. blue . . . . . . 1·10 20
143 – 7c. de p. grey 85 45
168 – 7c. de p. red . . . . 12·50 8·25
144 – 8c. de p. red . . . . 4·00 1·25
169 – 8c. de p. olive . . . . . . 17·00 11·00
145 – 10c. de p. orange 55 20
170 – 10c. de p. brown . . . . . 7·25 7·50
146 – 15c. de p. olive . . . . . 1·10 45
171 – 15c. de p. yellow . . . . . 3·25 1·75
147 **19** 20c. de p. blue . . . . . . 1·10 45
148 **20** 50c. de p. red . . . . . . 1·75 1·25
172 50c. de p. yellow . . . . . 3·75 2·50
149 – 1pi. red . . . . 3·25 2·10
173 – 1pi. red . . . . 3·75 3·00
DESIGNS—As Type **21**: 4c. Palace of Sans Souci-Milot; 7c. Independence Palace, Gonaives; 8c. Entrance to Catholic College, Port-au-Prince; 10c. Catholic Monastery and Church, Port-au-Prince; 15c. Government Offices, Port-au-Prince; 1pi. President's Palace, Port-au-Prince.

1906. Surch with value in double-lined frame Without opt.
154 **15** 1c. on 5c. blue 30 20
155 1c. on 10c. brown 25 10
156 1c. on 20c. orange 20 15
157 2c. on 10c. brown 25 20
158 2c. on 20c. orange 20 20
159 2c. on 50c. plum 35 20

1910.
160 **24** 1c. de g. black and red . . 15 15
161 2c. de p. black and red . . 55 35
162 5c. de p. black and blue . . 7·75 55
163 20c. de p. black and green 6·25 4·75

25 Pres. C. Leconte

38

1912. Various frames.
164 **25** 1c. de g. lake 20 20
165 2c. de g. orange 25 20
166 5c. de p. blue 55 20

1914. Optd **GL O.Z. 7 FEV. 1914** in frame. A. On 1898 issue.
174 **9** 8c. red . . . . 7·75 6·25

B. On 1904 issue, without opt.
175 **15** 1c. green (No. 109) . . . . 22·00 19·00
176 2c. red . . . . 22·00 19·00
177 5c. blue 45 15
178 10c. brown 45 15
179 20c. orange 45 35
180 50c. plum . . . . 1·75 55

C. On pictorial stamps of 1906.
181 **20** 2c. de g. yellow 35 15
182 **19** 3c. de g. grey 35 20

D. On pictorial stamps of 1906.
183 **20** 1c. de p. green (No. 137) 35 25
184 **19** 2c. de p. red (No. 138) . . 55 25
185 **21** 3c. de p. sepia (No. 139) 4·25 75
186 3c. de p. orange (No. 140) 3·25 3·25
187 – 4c. de p. red (No. 141) . . 45 60
198 – 4c. de p. olive (No. 167) 75 40
188 – 7c. de p. grey (No. 143) . . 1·75 1·75
200 – 7c. de p. red (No. 168) . . 1·75 1·75
189 – 8c. de p. red (No. 144) . . 5·25 2·50
201 – 8c. de p. olive (No. 169) 6·50 6·50
190 – 10c. de p. orange (No. 145) 55 55
202 – 10c. de p. brown (No. 170) 85 55
191 – 15c. de p. olive (No. 146) 1·75 1·75
203 – 15c. de p. yellow (No. 171) 75 45
192 **19** 20c. de p. blue (No. 147) 2·25 55
194 **20** 50c. de p. red (No. 148) . . 3·75 3·75
204 50c. de p. yellow (No. 172) 3·75 3·75
195 – 1pi. red (No. 149) . . . . 3·75 3·75
205 – 1pi. red (No. 173) . . . . 3·75 3·75

E. On stamp of 1910.
193 **24** 20c. de p. black and green 2·40 2·40

F. On stamps of 1912.
196 **25** 1c. de g. lake 25 20
197 2c. de g. orange 45 30
199 5c. de p. blue 70 20

1914. Stamps of 1904, without the opt, surch **GL O.Z 7 FEV 1914 7 CENT** in diamond frame.
213 **15** 7c. on 20c. orange (No. 113) 45 20
214 7c. on 50c. plum (No. 114) 35 20

1914. Pictorial stamps of 1906 (Nos. 148/73), surch **GL OZ 1 CENT DE PIASTRE 7 FEV. 1914** in frame.
215 **20** 1c. de p. on 50c. red . . . 30 20
216 1c. de p. on 50c. yellow . . 45 35
217 – 1c. de p. on 1p. red . . . 45 35
218 – 1c. de p. on 1p. red . . . 55 45

1915.
219 – 2c. de g. black and yellow 45
220 **38** 5c. de g. black and green 45
221 – 7c. de g. black and red . . 45
PORTRAIT: 2, 7c. O. Zamor.

1915. As T **24**, inscr "EMISSION 1914".
222 1c. de p. black and green . . 85
223 3c. de p. black and olive . . 15
224 5c. de p. black and blue . . . 25
225 7c. de p. black and orange 60
226 10c. de p. black and brown 20
227 15c. de p. black and olive . . 25
228 20c. de p. black and brown 55
DESIGNS: 1c., 5c., 10c., 15c. O. Zamor; 3c., 20c. Arms; 7c. T. Auguste.

1915. Surch with figure in frame.
229 1 on 5c. blue (No. 111) . . . 85 85
230 1 on 7c. grey (No. 143) . . . 10 10
231 1 on 10c. brown (No. 112) 15 15
232 1 on 20c. orange (No. 107) 45 35
233 1 on 20c. orange (No. 113) 55 70
234 1 on 50c. plum (No. 108) . . 1·10 55
235 1 on 50c. plum (No. 114) . . 15 10
236 2 on 1pi. red (No. 172) . . . 20 15

1917. Surch **GOURDE** and value in frame. A. On provisional stamps of 1906.
237 **8** 1c. on 50c. lake (No. 130) 16·00 11·00
238 1c. on 1g. mauve (No. 131) 19·00 14·00

B. On pictorial stamps of 1906
239 – 1c. on 4c. de p. red (No. 141) 15 15
240 – 1c. on 4c. de p. olive (No. 167) 30 30
241 – 1c. on 7c. de p. red (No. 168) 45 45
242 – 1c. on 10c. de p. orange (No. 145) 10 10
243 – 1c. on 15c. de p. yellow (No. 171) 45 30
244 **19** 1c. on 20c. de p. blue (No. 147) 20 15
246 **24** 1c. on 20c. de p. black and green (No. 163) . . . . 2·50 2·50
247 **20** 1c. on 50c. de p. red (No. 148) 20 15
249 – 1c. on 50c. de p. yellow (No. 172) 85 85
250 – 1c. on 1p. red (No. 173) 85 85
251 **21** 2c. on 3c. de p. sepia (No. 139) . . . . 2·75 1·50
252 2c. on 3c. de p. orange (No. 140) . . . . 3·50 1·50
253 – 2c. on 8c. de p. red (No. 144) . . . . 2·25 75
255 – 2c. on 8c. de p. olive (No. 169) . . . . 3·25 2·50
256 – 2c. de p. on 10c. brown (No. 170) 35 45
257 – 2c. on 15c. de p. olive (No. 146) 20 10
258 – 2c. on 15c. de p. yellow (No. 171) 45 45
259 **19** 2c. on 20c. de p. blue (No. 147) 25 15
260 – 5c. on 10c. de p. brown (No. 170) 45 45
261 – 5c. on 15c. de p. yellow (No. 171) . . . . 3·25 3·25

1919. For inland use. Provisionals of 1914. (a) Surch with new value without frame.
262 – 1c. on 15c. de p. olive (No. 191) 20 20
263 **19** 1c. on 20c. de p. blue (No. 192) 20 20
264 **24** 1c. on 20c. de p. black and green (No. 193) 35 35
265 – 1c. on 1p. red (No. 195) 20 15
267 – 1c. on 1p. red (No. 205) 35 35

(b) Surch with new value in frame.
268 – 2c. on 4c. de p. red (No. 187) 35 35
269 – 2c. on 8c. de p. red (No. 189) . . . . 2·75 1·50
270 – 2c. on 8c. de p. olive (No. 201) . . . . 3·75 1·75
271 **24** 2c. on 20c. de p. black and green 30 15
272 **20** 2c. on 50c. de p. red (No. 194) 15 10
274 2c. on 50c. de p. yellow (No. 204) 15 35
275 – 2c. on 1p. red (No. 195) 1·75 1·75
276 – 2c. on 1p. red (No. 205) 90 90
277 **21** 3c. on 3c. de p. sepia (No. 185) . . . . 3·00 1·25
278 – 3c. on 7c. de p. red (No. 200) 35 20
279 **21** 5c. on 3c. de p. sepia (No. 185) . . . . 4·50 1·75
280 5c. on 3c. de p. orange (No. 186) . . . . 6·00 7·00
281 – 5c. on 4c. de p. red (No. 187) 45 45
282 – 5c. on 4c. de p. olive (No. 198) 25 25
283 – 5c. on 7c. de p. grey (No. 188) 30 30
284 – 5c. on 7c. de p. red (No. 200) 35 35
285 **15** 5c. on 7c. on 20c. orange (No. 213) 35 35
286 5c. on 7c. on 50c. plum (No. 214) . . . . 2·40 2·40
287 **19** 5c. on 10c. de p. orange (No. 190) 25 25
289 – 5c. on 10c. de p. orange (No. 190) 45 45
288 – 5c. on 15c. de p. yellow (No. 203) 35 35
No. 289 has the word "PIASTRE" in the surcharge.

1919. Postage Due stamps surch **POSTES** and new value in frame.
290 **D 23** 5c. de g. on 10c. de p. purple (No. D211) . . 35 35
291 5c. de g. on 50c. de p. olive (No. D153) . . . 9·25 7·75
292 5c. de g. on 50c. de p. olive (No. D212) . . . 45 45

48 "Agriculture"

1920.
294 **48** 3c. de g. orange . . . . . 2·50 3·50
295 5c. de g. green . . . . . . 5·00 25
296 – 10c. de g. red 55 30
297 – 15c. de g. violet 45 15
298 – 25c. de g. blue 55 15
DESIGN: 10c., 15c., 25c. "Commerce".

50 Pres. L. J. Borno

51 Christophe's Citadel

54 Coffee

1924.
299 **50** 5c. green 20 10
300 **51** 10c. red 35 10
301 – 20c. blue 40 15
304 **54** 35c. green . . . . 1·75 25
302 **50** 50c. black and orange . . 40 20
303 – 1g. olive . . . . 1·10 25
DESIGNS—VERT: 20c. Map of W. Indies. HORIZ: 1g. National Palace.

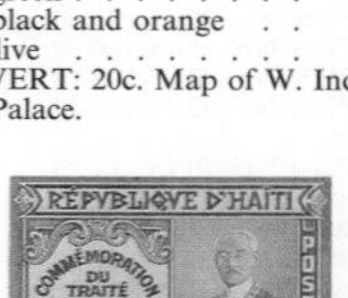
55 Pres. Borno

1929. Frontier Agreement between Haiti and Dominican Republic.
305 **55** 10c. red 30 20

56 Fokker Super Trimotor over Port-au-Prince

1929. Air.
306 **56** 25c. green 35 30
307 50c. violet 55 20
308 75c. red . . . . 1·10 90
309 1g. blue . . . . 1·50 1·10

57 Salomon and S. Vincent

1931. 50th Anniv of U.P.U. Membership.

310	57	5c. green	85	45
311	–	10c. red (S. Vincent)	85	45

1933. Air. "Columbia" New York–Haiti Flight. Surch **COLUMBIA VOL-DIRECT N.-Y.–P.AU-P. BOYD-LYON 60 CTS.**

311a		60c. on 20c. blue (No. 301)	42·00	42·00

59 Pres. S. Vincent

60 Prince's Aqueduct

1933. T **59** and designs as T **60**.

312	59	3c. orange	10	10
313		3c. green	15	10
316	60	5c. green	15	10
317		5c. olive	45	10
318	–	10c. red	35	10
320	–	10c. brown	35	10
321	–	25c. blue	40	20
322	–	50c. brown	1·75	20
323	–	1g. green	1·75	20
324	–	2g.50 olive	2·75	35

DESIGNS: 10c. Fort National; 25c. Palace of Sans Souci; 50c. Christophe's Chapel, Milot; 1g. King's Gallery, Citadel; 2g.50, Vallieres Battery.

62 Fokker Super Trimotor over Christophe's Citadel

1933. Air.

325	62	50c. orange	3·25	40
326		50c. olive	3·00	40
327		50c. red	1·75	1·10
328		50c. black	1·40	40
329		60c. brown	40	10
330		1g. blue	1·10	35

63 Alexandre Dumas and his Father and Son

1935. Visit of French Delegation to West Indies.

331	63	10c. brown & red (postage)	40	30
332		25c. brown and blue	1·10	35
333		60c. brown and violet (air)	3·00	1·75

64 Arms of Haiti, and George Washington

1938. Air. 150th Anniv of U.S. Constitution.

334	64	60c. blue	25	25

1939. Surch **25c** between bars.

335	54	25c. on 35c. green	45	30

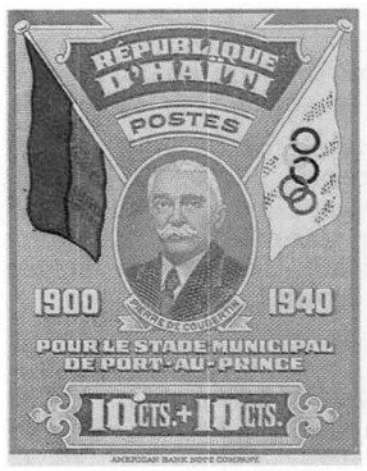

66 Pierre de Coubertin

67

1939. Port-au-Prince Athletic Stadium Fund.

336	66	10c.+10c. red (postage)	18·00	18·00
337		60c.+40c. violet (air)	12·00	12·00
338		1g.25+60c. black	12·00	12·00

1941. 3rd Caribbean Conference.

339	67	10c. red (postage)	65	35
340		25c. blue	40	25
341		60c. olive (air)	2·25	40
342		1g.25 violet	2·10	25

68 Our Lady of Perpetual Succour

1942. Our Lady of Perpetual Succour (National Patroness).

343	68	3c. purple (postage)	35	30
344		5c. green	35	30
345		10c. red	35	30
346		15c. orange	40	30
347		20c. brown	40	30
348		25c. blue	1·10	30
349		50c. red	1·60	65
350		2g.50 brown	5·50	1·45
351		5g. violet	11·50	2·75

The 5g. is larger (32½ × 47 mm).

352	68	10c. olive (air)	35	15
353		25c. blue	35	35
354		50c. green	45	30
355		60c. red	90	25
356		1g.25 black	1·90	25

69 Admiral Killick and Flagship "Crete-a-Pierrot"

1943. 41st Death Anniv of Admiral Killick.

358	69	3c. orange (postage)	15	50
359		5c. green	55	25
360		10c. red	55	15
361		25c. blue	70	25
362		50c. olive	1·40	35
363		5g. brown	5·50	3·75
364		60c. violet (air)	95	35
365		1g.25 black	3·75	1·90

1944. Surch (a) Postage.

366	59	0.02 on 3c. green	15	15
367		0.05 on 3c. green	20	20
368	68	0.10 on 15c. orange	35	30
369	69	0.10 on 25c. blue	35	30
370	–	0.10 on 1g. olive (No. 303)	35	15
371	–	0.20 on 2g.50 olive (No. 324)	35	30

(b) Air.

372	62	0.10 on 60c. brown	55	30

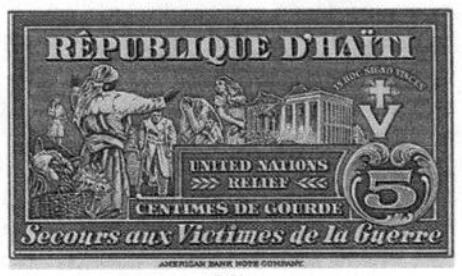

71

1944. Obligatory Tax. United Nations Relief Fund.

373	71	5c. blue	90	35
374		5c. black	90	35
375		5c. olive	90	35
376		5c. violet	90	35
377		5c. brown	90	35
378		5c. green	90	35
379		5c. red	90	35

72 Nurse and Wounded Soldier

73 Franklin D. Roosevelt

1945. Red Cross stamps. Cross in red.

381	72	3c. black (postage)	10	10
382		5c. green	15	10
383		10c. orange	20	10
384		20c. brown	15	10
385		25c. blue	30	10
386		35c. orange	30	20
387		50c. red	35	25
388		1g. olive	40	30
389		2½g. violet	1·75	25
390		20c. orange (air)	15	10
391		25c. blue	15	10
392		50c. brown	20	10
393		60c. purple	25	10
394		1g. yellow	90	15
395		1g.25c. red	70	30
396		1g.35c. green	70	30
397		5g. black	4·50	1·75

1946. Air.

398	73	20c. black	15	15
399		60c. black	20	10

74 Capois-la-Mort

75 J.-J. Dessalines

1946.

400	74	3c. orange (postage)	10	10
401		5c. green	10	10
402		10c. red	10	10
403		20c. black	10	10
404		25c. blue	10	10
405		35c. orange	20	15
406		50c. brown	25	20
407		1g. olive	35	10
408		2g.50 grey	90	35
409		20c. red (air)	10	10
410		25c. green	10	10
411		50c. orange	15	10
412		60c. purple	20	10
413		1g. slate	35	10
414		1g.25 violet	40	35
415		1g.35 black	45	30
416		5g. red	1·40	90

1947. 141st Death Anniv of Emperor Jean-Jacques Dessalines, founder of National Independence.

417	75	3c. orange (postage)	10	10
418		5c. green	10	10
419		5c. violet	45	10
420		10c. red	10	10
421		25c. blue	20	10
422		20c. brown (air)	20	10

1947. Surch.

423	74	10c. on 35c. orge (postage)	20	10
424		5c. on 1g.35 black (air)	55	20
425		30c. on 50c. orange	45	30
426		30c. on 1g.35 black	45	40

77 Sanatorium and Mosquito

1949. Air. Anti-T.B. and Malaria Fund. Cross in red.

427	77	20c.+20c. sepia	6·25	4·50
428		30c.+30c. green	6·25	4·50
429		45c.+45c. brown	6·25	4·50
430		80c.+80c. violet	6·25	4·50
431		1g.25+1g.25 red	6·25	4·50
432		1g.75+1g.75 blue	6·25	4·50

78 Washington, Dessalines and Bolivar

1949. Obligatory Tax. Bicent of Port-au-Prince.

434	78	5c. red	20	15
435		5c. brown	20	15
436		5c. orange	20	15
437		5c. grey	20	15
438		5c. violet	20	15
439		5c. blue	20	15
440		5c. green	20	15
441		5c. black	20	15

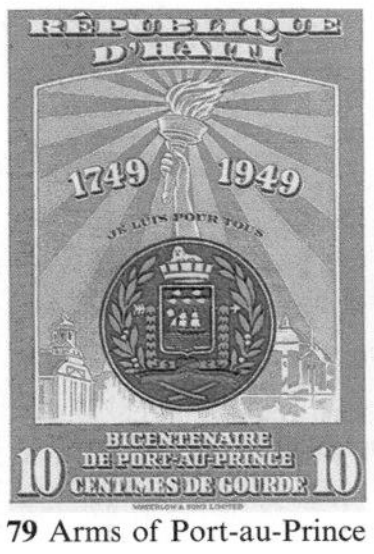

79 Arms of Port-au-Prince

83 Cocoa

80 Columbus and "Santa Maria"

1950. Bicentenary of Port-au-Prince Exhibition. (a) Postage. Multicoloured arms.

442	79	10c. red	15	10

(b) Air.

443	80	30c. blue and grey	3·25	70
444	–	1g. black (Pres. D. Estime)	45	30

1950. 75th Anniv of U.P.U. Optd **U P U 1874 1949** or surch also.

445	78	3 on 5c. grey (postage)	10	10
446		5c. green	25	20
447		10 on 5c. red	25	20
448		20 on 5c. blue	35	35
449	74	30 on 25c. green (air)	30	30
450		1g. slate	35	30
451		1.50 on 1g.35 black	60	40

1951. National Products.

456	83	5c. green (postage)	25	10
457	–	30c. orange (Bananas) (air)	30	20
458	–	80c. pink and green (Coffee)	85	35
459	–	5g. grey (Sisal)	3·00	2·50

84 Isabella the Catholic

85 Pres. Magloire and Nursery, La Saline

1951. Air. 5th Birth Cent of Isabella the Catholic.

460	84	15c. brown	25	15
461		30c. blue	45	45

1953. Projects realized by Pres. Magloire. Designs with medallion of president.

462	85	5c. green (postage)	10	10
463	–	10c. red	15	10
464	–	20c. blue (air)	15	10
465	–	30c. brown	30	15
466	–	1.50g. black	45	45
467	–	2.50g. violet	90	65

DESIGNS—HORIZ: 10c. Road-making; 20c. Anchorage, Cap-Haitien; 30c. Workers' estate, St. Martin; 1.50g. Old Cathedral restoration; 2.50g. School canteen.

1953. 150th Death Anniv of Toussaint l'Ouverture. No. 405 surch **7 AVRIL 1803 - 1953 50.**

469	74	50c. on 35c. orange	35	20

1953. Air. 150th Anniv of National Flag. Surch **18 MAI 1803 - 1953 50.**

470	74	50c. on 60c. purple	35	15
471		50c. on 1g.35 black	35	15

87 J.-J. Dessalines and Pres. Magloire

88 Toussaint l'Ouverture

89 Marie-Jeanne and Lamartiniere on La Crete-a-Pierrot

1954. 150th Anniv of Independence. (a) As T **87/8**.

472	87	3c. black and blue (postage)	10	10
473	88	5c. black and green	20	10
474	–	5c. black and green	15	10
475	–	5c. black and green	20	10
476	–	5c. black and green	15	10
477	87	10c. black and red	15	10
478	–	15c. black and lilac	20	10
479	88	50c. black and green (air)	35	20
480	–	50c. black and green	35	20
481	–	50c. black and red	35	20
482	–	50c. black and brown	35	20
483	–	50c. black and blue	35	20
484	–	1g. black and grey	45	25
485	–	1g.50 black and mauve	90	60
486	87	7g.50 black and orange	3·00	3·00

PORTRAITS—As Type **88**. Nos. 474, 482, Lamartiniere; Nos. 475, 482, Boisrond-Tonnerre; Nos. 476, 483, 485, A. Petion; No. 478, Capois-La-Mort; No. 480, J. J. Dessalines; No. 481, H. Christophe.

For stamps as No. 480 without dates see Nos. 533/4.

(b) As T **89**.

487	**89**	25c. orange (postage)	20	10
488	–	25c. slate	20	10
489	**89**	50c. red (air)	25	10
490		50c. black	25	10
491	–	50c. pink	25	15
492	–	50c. blue	25	15

DESIGN—HORIZ: Nos. 488, 491, 492, Battle of Vertieres; Nos. 489/92 are larger (31½ × 26 mm).

90 Mme. Magloire

91 Tomb and Arms of King Henri Christophe

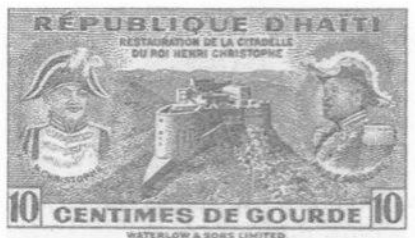

92 Christophe, Citadel and Pres. Magloire

1954.

493	**90**	10c. orange (postage)	15	10
494		10c. blue	15	10
495		20c. red (air)	10	10
496		50c. brown	20	20
497		1g. green	45	35
498		1g.50 red	45	40
499		2g.50 green	65	60
500		5g. blue	1·90	1·40

1954. Restoration of Christophe's Citadel. (a) T **91**. Flag in black and red.

501	**91**	10c. red (postage)	15	10
502		50c. orange (air)	35	15
503		1g. blue	40	30
504		1g.50 green	60	50
505		2g.50 grey	1·10	65
506		5g. red	1·75	1·25

(b) T **92**.

507	**92**	10c. red (postage)	15	10
508		50c. black and orange (air)	35	15
509		1g. black and blue	40	30
510		1g.50 black and green	60	50
511		2g.50 black and grey	1·10	65
512		5g. black and red	1·75	1·25

93 Columbus's Drawing of Fort de la Nativite

1954. Air.

513	**93**	50c. red	35	30
514		50c. slate	35	30

94 Sikorsky S-55 Helicopter over Ruins

95 Sikorsky S-55 Helicopter

1955. Obligatory Tax. Cyclone "Hazel" Relief Fund (1st issue).

515	**94**	10c. blue	10	10
516		10c. green	10	10
517		10c. orange	10	10
518		10c. black	15	10
519		20c. red	10	10
520		20c. green	15	10

1955. Obligatory Tax. Cyclone "Hazel" Relief Fund (2nd issue).

521	**95**	10c. black & grey (postage)	10	10
522		20c. deep blue and blue	15	10
523		10c. red and brown (air)	15	10
524		20c. red and pink	15	10

96 J.-J. Dessalines

97 Pres. Magloire and Monument

1955. Dessalines Commemoration.

525	**96**	3c. black & brown (postage)	10	10
526		5c. black and lilac	10	10
527		10c. black and red	10	10
528		10c. black and pink	10	10
529		25c. black and blue	20	10
530		25c. black and light blue	20	10
531		20c. black and green (air)	10	10
532		20c. black and orange	10	10

1955. Air. As No. 480 but without dates and colours changed.

533		50c. black and blue	30	10
534		50c. black and grey	30	15

1955. 21st Anniv of Haitian Army.

535	**97**	10c. blue & black (postage)	30	25
536		10c. red and black	30	25
537		1g.50 green and black (air)	35	20
538		1g.50 blue and black	45	20

98 Mallard

99 Douglas DC-4, Liner and Map

1955.

539	–	10c. blue (postage)	4·00	55
540	**98**	25c. green and turquoise	5·00	80
541	**99**	50c. black and grey (air)	1·00	20
542	–	50c. red and grey	30	15
543	**99**	75c. green and turquoise	1·25	45
544	–	1g. olive and blue	55	30
545	–	2g.50 orange	20·00	4·00
546	**98**	5g. red and buff	32·00	6·50

DESIGNS—VERT: 10c., 2g.50, Greater flamingo. HORIZ: 50c. (No. 542), 1g. Car on coast road.

100 Immanuel Kant

1956. 10th Anniv of 1st Int Philosophical Congress.

547	**100**	10c. blue (postage)	15	10
548		50c. brown (air)	25	15
549		75c. green	35	20
550		1g.50 mauve	85	45

101 Zim Basin and Waterfall

1957.

552	**101**	10c. orange & bl (postage)	15	10
553		50c. green & turq (air)	20	15
554		1g.50 green and blue	35	30
555		2g.50 blue and light blue	60	45
556		5g. violet and blue	1·40	1·10

102 J.-J. Dessalines and Monument

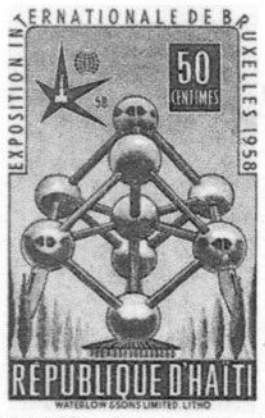

103 The "Atomium"

1958. Birth Bicentenary of J. J. Dessalines.

557	**102**	5c. green & black (postage)	10	10
558		10c. red and black	10	10
559		25c. blue and black	20	10
560		20c. grey and black (air)	10	10
561		50c. orange and black	25	15

1958. Brussels International Exhibition.

562	**103**	50c. brown (postage)	30	15
563	–	75c. green	30	20
564	**103**	1g. violet	35	25
565	–	1g.50 orange	30	25
566	**103**	2g.50 red (air)	60	35
567	–	5g. blue	85	60

DESIGN—HORIZ: 75c., 1g.50, 5g. Exhibition view.

104 Sylvio Cator making Long Jump

106 Head of U.S. Satellite

1958. Sylvio Cator (athlete) Commem.

569	**104**	5c. green (postage)	10	10
570		10c. brown	10	10
571		20c. purple and mauve	15	10
572	–	50c. black (air)	20	10
573	–	50c. green	20	10
574	–	1g. brown	35	15
575	–	5g. black and grey	1·40	70

DESIGN—HORIZ: Nos. 572/75, Sylvio Cator making long jump (head-on view).

1958. Red Cross. Nos. 564/66 surch with red cross and **+50 CENTIMES**.

576	**103**	1g.+50c. violet (postage)	2·50	2·50
577	–	1g.50+50c. orange	2·50	2·50
578	**103**	2g.50+50c. red (air)	2·75	2·75

1958. I.G.Y. Inscr as in T **106**.

579	**106**	10c. lake & turq (postage)	15	10
580	–	20c. black and orange	2·00	90
581	–	50c. red and green	35	25
582	–	1g. black and blue	80	20
583	**106**	50c. lake and blue (air)	20	20
584	–	1g.50 brown and red	4·50	1·60
585	–	2g. red and blue	1·10	35

DESIGNS: 20c., 1g.50, King penguins on icefloe; 50c., 2g. Giant radio telescope; 1g. Ocean-bed exploration.

107 Duvalier

108 Map of Haiti

1958. 1st Anniv of Installation of President Francois Duvalier. Commemorative inscr in blue.

587	**107**	10c. blk & pink (postage)	10	10
588		50c. black and green	35	15
589		1g. black and red	55	30
590		5g. black and salmon	1·60	1·10
591	–	50c. black and red (air)	60	20
592	–	2g.50 black and orange	80	55
593	–	5g. black and mauve	1·10	90
594	–	7g.50 black and green	1·60	1·25

DESIGN: Nos. 591/94 as Type **107** but horiz.

1958. As T **107** but without commem. inscr. (a) Postage. Vert portrait.

596		5c. black and blue	10	10
597		10c. black and pink	10	10
598		20c. black and yellow	10	10
599		50c. black and green	20	15
600		1g. black and red	30	20
601		1g.50 black and pink	45	35
602		2g.50 black and lavender	70	60
603		5g. black and salmon	1·10	85

(b) Air. Horiz portrait.

604		50c. black and red	25	15
605		1g. black and violet	30	25
606		1g.50 black and brown	50	35
607		2g. black and pink	60	35
608		2g.50 black and orange	60	35
609		5g. black and mauve	1·10	85
610		7g.50 black and green	1·90	1·10

1958. United Nations.

611	**108**	10c. red (postage)	10	10
612		25c. green	15	10
613	–	50c. red and blue (air)	20	10
614	**108**	75c. blue	30	15
615		1g. brown	45	20

DESIGN: 50c. Flags of Haiti and U.N.

1959. 10th Anniv of Declaration of Human Rights. Nos. 611/15 optd **10TH ANNIVERSARY OF THE UNIVERSAL DECLARATION OF HUMAN RIGHTS**. (a) Postage. (i) English.

617	**108**	10c. red	10	10
618		25c. green	25	15

(ii) French.

617	**108**	10c. red	10	10
618		25c. green	25	15

(iii) Portuguese.

617	**108**	10c. red	10	10
618		25c. green	25	15

(iv) Spanish.

617	**108**	10c. red	10	10
618		25c. green	25	15

(b) Air. (i) English.

619	–	20c. red and blue	30	30
620	**108**	75c. blue	40	40
621		1g. brown	90	90

(ii) French.

619	–	20c. red and blue	30	30
620	**108**	75c. blue	40	40
621		1g. brown	90	90

(iii) Portuguese.

619	–	20c. red and blue	30	30
620	**108**	75c. blue	40	40
621		1g. brown	90	90

(iv) Spanish.

619	–	20c. red and blue	30	30
620	**108**	75c. blue	40	40
621		1g. brown	90	90

Overprinted alternately in different languages through the sheet of 25.

110 Pope Pius XII with Children

1959. Pope Pius XII Commemoration. Inscr "PIE XII PAPE DE LA PAIX".

622	**110**	10c. olive & blue (postage)	10	10
623	–	50c. brown and green	25	15
624	–	2g. sepia and lake	40	35
625	**110**	50c. violet and green (air)	20	10
626	–	1g.50 brown and olive	35	15
627	–	2g.50 blue and purple	60	30

DESIGNS: 50c. (No. 623), 1g.50, Pope at prayer; 2g., 2g.50, Pope giving blessing.

1959. Red Cross. (a) United Nations stamps surch with red cross and **+25 CENTIMES**.

628	**108**	10c.+25c. (postage)	25	20
629		25c.+25c.	35	30
630	–	50c.+25c. (air)	35	35
631	**108**	75c.+25c.	45	35
632		1g.+25c.	65	70

(b) Pope Pius XII stamps surch with red cross and **+50 CENTIMES.**

633	**110**	10c.+50c. (postage)	45	20
634	–	50c.+50c.	45	30
635	–	2g.+50c.	65	90
636	**110**	50c.+50c. (air)	60	60
637	–	1g.50+50c.	60	60
638	–	2g.50+50c.	65	65

111 Abraham Lincoln when a young man

1959. 150th Birth Anniv of Abraham Lincoln.

639	**111**	50c. purple & bl (postage)	30	15
640	–	1g. brown and green (air)	30	20
641	–	2g. myrtle and green	35	20
642	–	2g.50 blue and buff	40	35

PORTRAITS of Lincoln (bearded): 1g. Looking right; 2g., 2g.50, Looking left. The designs include various buildings associated with Lincoln.

1959. World Refugee Year (1st issue). Nos. 639/42 surch **Nations Unies ANNEE DES REFUGIES 1959-1960 + 20 Centimes**.

644	**111**	50c.+20c. purple and blue (postage)	45	45
645	–	1g.+20c. brown and green (air)	60	60
646	–	2g.+20c. myrtle and green	60	60
647	–	2g.50+20c. blue & buff	70	70

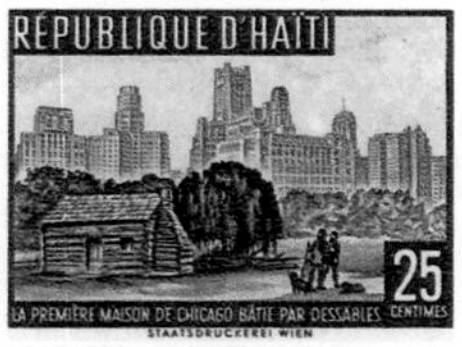

113 Chicago's First House and Modern Skyline

1959. 3rd Pan-American Games, Chicago.
649 **113** 25c. sepia & blue (postage) 30 15
650 – 50c. multicoloured 30 20
651 – 75c. sepia and blue . . . 45 25
652 – 50c. brown & turq (air) 35 20
653 **113** 1g. turquoise and purple 60 35
654 – 1g.50 multicoloured . . . 65 45
DESIGNS—HORIZ: 50c., 1g.50, Discus-thrower and Haitian flag. VERT: 50c. (air), 75c. J. B. Paul Dessables (founder of Chicago) and map.

114

1959. Obligatory Tax. Literacy Fund. (a) Postage. (i) Size 40 × 23 mm.
655 **114** 5c. green 10 10
656 10c. black 10 10
657 10c. red 10 10

(ii) Size 29 × 17 mm.
658 **114** 5c. green 10 10
659 5c. red 10 10
660 10c. blue 10 10

(b) Air. Size 29 × 17 mm.
661 **114** 5c. yellow 10 10
662 10c. blue 10 10
663 10c. orange 10 10

1959. Sports Fund. Nos. 649/54 surch **POUR LE SPORT + 0.75 CENTIMES.**
664 25c.+75c. sepia and blue (postage) 45 45
665 50c.+75c. multicoloured . . . 60 45
666 75c.+75c. sepia and blue . . 60 45
667 50c.+75c. brown & turq (air) 60 45
668 1g.+75c. turquoise and purple 60 45
669 1g.50+75c. multicoloured . . 60 60

1960. UNICEF Commem. Nos. 600 and 607/8 surch **Hommage a l'UNICEF +G.0,50.**
670 1g.+50c. blk & red (postage) 60 60
671 2g.+50c. black and pink (air) 65 65
672 2g.50+50c. black and orange 1·10 1·10

1960. Winter Olympic Games. Nos. 650 and 652/4 optd with Olympic rings and **VIIIEME JEUX OLYMPIQUES D'HIVER CALIFORNIE USA 1960.**
673 50c. multicoloured (postage) 1·10 90
674 50c. brown and turquoise (air) 70 70
675 1g. turquoise and purple . . 1·10 1·10
676 1g.50 multicoloured . . . . 1·25 1·25

118 "Uprooted Tree"

1960. World Refugee Year (2nd issue).
677 **118** 10c. grn & orge (postage) 10 10
678 50c. purple and violet . . 20 15
679 50c. brown and blue (air) 20 15
680 1g. red and green 45 30

1960. Surch in figures.
682 **96** 5c. on 3c. black and brown 10 10
683 10c. on 3c. black and brown 15 10

1960. 28th Anniv of Haitian Red Cross. 1945 Red Cross stamps optd "**28eme ANNIVERSAIRE**" or surch also.
684 **72** 1g. on 2½g. violet (postage) 45 35
685 2½g. violet 85 65
686 20c. on 1g.35 green (air) 20 10
687 50c. on 60c. purple 25 15
688 50c. on 1g.35 green 25 20
689 50c. on 2½g. violet 25 20
690 60c. purple 30 20
691 1g. on 1g.35 green 35 35
692 1g.35 green 60 55
693 2g. on 1g.35 green 95 85
No. 689 is also optd **Avion.**

121 "Sugar Queen, 1960" and Beach

1960. Election of Miss Claudinette Fouchard ("Miss Haiti") as World "Sugar Queen, 1960".
694 – 10c. violet & brn (postage) 15 10
695 – 20c. black and brown . . 20 10
696 **121** 50c. brown and blue . . . 45 10
697 – 1g. brown and green . . . 45 20
698 – 50c. brown and mauve (air) 35 15
699 **121** 2g.50 brown and blue . . 55 35
DESIGNS: Sugar Queen and—10c., 1g. Plantation (different views); 20c., 50c. Harvesting.

1960. Education Campaign. Surch **ALPHABETISATION** and premium.
700 **118** 10c.+20c. green and orange (postage) . . . 25 15
701 10c.+30c. green & orge 30 25
702 50c.+20c. purple & vio . . 30 35
703 50c.+30c. purple & vio . . 40 35
704 50c.+20c. black and blue (air) 25 15
705 50c.+30c. black and blue 35 25
706 1g.+20c. red and green . . 60 45
707 1g.+30c. red and green . . 60 45

123 Olympic Torch, Victory Parade at Athens, 1896, and Melbourne Stadium

1960. Olympic Games, Rome.
708 **123** 10c. blk & orge (postage) 10 10
709 – 20c. blue and red 10 10
710 – 50c. green and brown . . 20 10
711 – 1g. blue and black 45 15
712 – 50c. purple and bistre (air) 15 15
713 – 1g.50 mauve and green . . 35 25
714 – 2g.50 slate, purple & blk 60 35
DESIGNS: 20c. and 1g.50, "The Discus-thrower" and Rome Stadium; 50c. (No. 710), Pierre de Coubertin (founder) and Athletes Parade, Melbourne; 50c. (No. 712), As Type **123** but P. de Coubertin inset; 1g. Athens Stadium, 1896; 2g.50, Victory Parade, Athens, 1896, and Athletes' Parade, Melbourne.

1960. Nos. 710/3 surch **+25 CENTIMES.**
716 50c.+25c. grn & brn (postage) 35 25
717 1g.+25c. blue and black . . . 45 30
718 50c.+25c. purple & bis (air) 25 20
719 1g.50+25c. mauve and green 30 25

125 Occide Jeanty

1960. Birth Cent of Occide Jeanty (composer).
720 **125** 10c. pur & orge (postage) 15 10
721 – 20c. purple and blue . . . 30 10
722 **125** 50c. sepia and green . . . 40 20
723 50c. blue and yellow (air) 20 10
724 – 1g.50 slate and mauve . . 45 25
DESIGN: 20c., 1g.50, Jeanty and Capitol, Port-au-Prince.

126 U.N., New York

1960. 15th Anniv of U.N.O.
731 **126** 1g. black & grn (postage) 35 20
732 50c. black and red (air) 20 10
733 1g.50 black and blue . . . 45 25

127 Sud Aviation Caravelle

1960. Air. Aviation Week.
735 **127** 20c. blue and red 10 10
736 – 50c. brown and green . . 30 20
737 – 50c. blue and green . . . 30 20
738 – 50c. black and green . . . 30 20
739 **127** 1g. green and red 45 25
740 – 1g.50 pink and blue . . . 50 35
DESIGNS: 50c. (3) Boeing 707 airliner and Wright Flyer I; 1g.50, Boeing 707 and 60c. "Columbia" stamp of 1933.

1961. U.N.I.C.E.F. Child Welfare Fund. Surch **UNICEF +25 centimes.**
748 **126** 1g.+25c. black and green (postage) 45 30
749 50c.+25c. black and red (air) 30 25
750 1g.50+25c. black & bl . . 55 35

129 Alexandre Dumas (father and son)

1961. Alexandre Dumas Commemoration.
751 – 5c. brown & blue (postage) 10 10
752 – 10c. black, purple and red 10 10
753 **129** 50c. blue and red 30 20
754 – 50c. black and blue (air) 30 15
755 – 1g. red and black 35 20
756 – 1g.50 black and green . . 55 35
DESIGNS—HORIZ: 5c. Dumas' House; 50c. (No. 754), A. Dumas and "The Three Musketeers". VERT: 10c. A. Dumas and horseman in "Twenty Years After"; 1g. A. Dumas (son) and "The Lady of the Camellias" (Marguerite Gauthier); 1g.50, A. Dumas, and "The Count of Monte Cristo".

130 Pirates

1961. Tourist Publicity.
761 – 5c. yellow & blue (postage) 10 10
762 **130** 10c. yellow and mauve . . 10 10
763 – 15c. orange and green . . 10 10
764 – 20c. orange and brown . . 40 10
765 – 50c. yellow and blue . . . 80 20
766 – 20c. yellow and blue (air) 40 10
767 – 50c. orange and violet . . 80 20
768 – 1g. yellow and green . . . 35 25
DESIGNS: Nos. 761, 768, Map of Tortuga; No. 763, Two pirates on beach; Nos. 764, 766, Pirate ships attacking galleon; Nos. 765, 767, Pirate in rigging.

1961. Re-election of Pres. Duvalier. Optd **Dr. F. Duvalier President 22 Mai 1961.**
769 **102** 5c. green & blk (postage) 10 10
770 10c. red and black 10 10
771 25c. blue and black . . . 20 15
772 **74** 2g.50 grey 65 45
773 **102** 20c. grey and black (air) 10 10
774 50c. orange and black . . 20 15
775 **99** 75c. green and turquoise 35 30

1961. Air. 18th World Scout Conference, Lisbon. Nos. 735 and 739/40 surch **18e CONFERENCE INTERNATIONALE DU SCOUTISME MONDIAL. LISBONNE SEPTEMBRE 1961 +0,25** and Scout emblem.
776 20c.+25c. blue and red . . . 30 20
777 1g.+25c. green and red . . . 45 35
778 1g.50+25c. pink and blue . . 55 55

1961. U.N. and Haitian Malaria Eradication Campaign. Surch **OMS SNEM +20 CENTIMES.**
780 **126** 1g.+20c. black and green (postage) 45 35
781 **126** 50c.+20c. black and red (air) 85 85
782 1g.50+20c. black & bl . . 1·10 1·10

1961. Duvalier-Ville Reconstruction Fund Nos. 598, 600, 602, 604/5 and 608/10 surch with U.N.I.C.E.F. emblem, **Duvalier-Ville** and premium.
783 20c.+25c. black and yellow (postage) 30 25
787 1g.+50c. black and red . . . 60 45
788 2g.50+50c. black and blue . . 65 50
784 50c.+25c. black and red (air) 25 25
785 1g.+50c. black and violet . . 25 25
789 2g.50+50c. black and orange 40 30
786 5g.+50c. black and mauve . . 85 60
790 7g.50+50c. black and green 90 85

1962. Colonel Glenn's Space Flight. Nos. 761, 768 optd **EXPLORATION SPATIALE JOHN GLENN** and outline of capsule or surch also.
795 50c. on 5c. yell & bl (postage) 45 30
796 1g.50 on 5c. yellow and blue 90 65
797 1g. yellow and green (air) . . 30 30
798 2g. on 1g. yellow and green 85 70

136 Campaign Emblem

1962. Malaria Eradication.
799 **136** 5c. blue and red (postage) 10 10
800 – 10c. green and brown . . 10 10
801 **136** 50c. red and blue 30 15
802 – 20c. red and violet (air) 10 10
803 **136** 50c. red and green 20 15
804 – 1g. blue and orange . . . 35 25
DESIGN: 10c., 20c., 1g. As Type **136** but with long side of triangle at top.

1962. World Refugee Year (3rd issue). As T **118** but additionally inscr "1962" and colours changed.
806 **118** 10c. orange & bl (postage) 10 10
807 50c. green and mauve . . 25 20
808 50c. brown and blue (air) 15 15
809 1g. black and buff 25 25

137 Scout Badge

1962. 22nd Anniv of Haitian Boy Scout Movement.
811 **137** 3c. orange, black and violet (postage) 10 10
812 – 5c. brown, olive and black 10 10
813 – 10c. brown, black & green 10 10
814 **137** 25c. black, lake and olive 15 10
815 – 50c. green, violet and red 30 15
816 – 20c. slate, green and purple (air) 10 10
817 **137** 50c. brown, green and red 25 15
818 – 1g.50 turq, sepia & brn 45 35
DESIGNS—VERT: 5c., 20c., 50, c. (post) Scout and camp. HORIZ: 10c., 1g.50, Lord and Lady Baden-Powell.

1962. Surch with premium. (a) Nos. 799/804.
820 **136** 5c.+25c. (postage) 20 15
821 – 10c.+25c. 25 20
822 **136** 50c.+25c. 30 20
823 – 20c.+25c. (air) 20 20
824 **136** 50c.+25c. 25 25
825 – 1g.+25c. 35 30

(b) Nos. 806/9.
827 **118** 10c.+20c. (postage) . . . 15 15
828 50c.+20c. 25 15
829 50c.+20c. (air) 25 15
830 1g.+20c. 35 30

1962. Air. Port-au-Prince Airport Construction Fund. Optd **AEROPORT INTERNATIONAL 1962**, with No. 832 additionally optd **Poste Aerienne.**
831 – 20c. No. 816 . . . . . . 15 10
832 – 50c. No. 815 . . . . . . 25 15
833 **137** 50c. No. 817 . . . . . . 25 15
834 – 1g.50 No. 818 . . . . . 45 35

140 Tower, World's Fair

1962. "Century 21" Exn (World's Fair), Seattle.
835 140 10c. purple & bl (postage) 10 10
836 20c. blue and red 10 10
837 50c. green and yellow 35 10
838 1g. red and green 55 20
839 50c. black and lilac (air) 25 10
840 1g. red and grey 45 15
841 1g.50 purple and orange 55 20

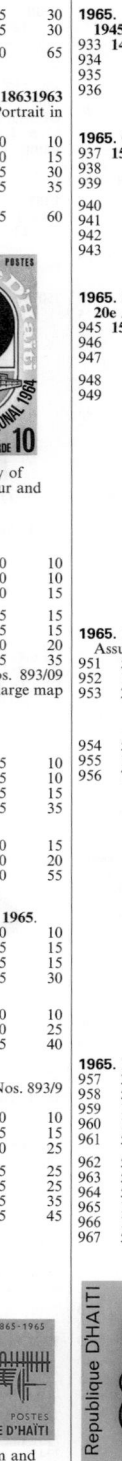

141 Town plan and 1904 10c. stamp

1963. Duvalier-ville Commemoration.
843 141 5c. black, yellow and violet (postage) 10 10
844 10c. black, yellow and red 10 10
845 25c. black, yellow and grey 20 15
846 – 50c. brown & orange (air) 20 15
847 – 1g. brown and blue 35 30
848 – 1g.50 brown and green 55 45
DESIGN: Nos. 846/8 Houses and 1881 2c. stamp.

1963. "Peaceful Uses of Outer Space". Nos. 837/38 and 841/2 optd **UTILISATIONS PACIFIQUES DE L'ESPACE** and space capsule.
853 140 50c. green and yellow (postage) 20 15
854 1g. red and green 45 30
855 1g. red and grey (air) 45 35
856 1g.50 purple and orange 65 65

1963. Literacy Campaign. Surch **ALPHABETISATION + 0,10**.
857 141 25c.+10c. (postage) 15 10
858 – 50c.+10c. (No. 846) (air) 25 15
859 – 1g.50+10c. (No. 848) 35 35

143 Harvesting

145 Dessalines Statue

144 Dag Hammarskjold and U.N. Emblem

146 "Alphabetisation"

1963. Freedom from Hunger.
860 143 10c. orange and black (postage) 10 10
861 20c. turquoise and black 10 10
862 50c. mauve and black (air) 15 10
863 1g. green and black 30 20

1963. Air. Dag Hammarskjold Commemoration. Portrait in blue.
864 144 20c. brown and bistre 10 10
865 50c. red and blue 20 20
866 1g. blue and mauve 30 30
867 1g.50 green and grey 55 45
Nos. 864/67 were printed in sheets of 25 (5 × 5) with a map of Sweden in the background covering most stamps in the second and third vertical rows.

1963. Dessalines Commemoration.
869 145 5c. red & brown (postage) 10 10
870 10c. blue, green and ochre 10 10
871 50c. green and brown (air) 20 10
872 50c. purple, violet and blue 20 10

1963. Obligatory Tax. Education Fund.
873 146 10c. red (postage) 10 10
874 10c. blue 10 10
875 10c. olive 10 10
876 10c. brown (air) 10 10
877 10c. violet 10 10
878 10c. violet 10 10
See also Nos. 974/78, 1157/63 and 1260/1.

1964. Mothers' Festival. Optd **FETE DES MERES 1964** or surch also.
879 145 10c. blue, green and ochre (postage) 10 10
880 50c. green and brown (air) 25 15
881 50c. purple, violet and blue 25 15
882 1g.50 on 80c. pink and green (No. 458) 35 25

1964. Winter Olympic Games, Innsbruck. Surch **JEUX OLYMPIQUES D'HIVER INNSBRUCK 1964 0.50+0.10**, Olympic rings and Games emblem.
883 137 50c.+10c. on 3c. (postage) 45 30
884 50c.+10c. on 5c. (No. 812) 45 30
885 – 50c.+10c. on 10c. (No. 813) 45 30
886 137 50c.+10c. on 25c. 45 30
887 101 50c.+10c. on 2g.50 (air) 70 65

1964. Air. Red Cross Cent (1963). Optd **18631963** and Centenary Emblem, on surch also. Portrait in blue.
888 144 20c. brown and bistre 30 10
889 50c. red and blue 30 15
890 1g. blue and mauve 45 30
891 1g.50 green and grey 55 35
892 2g.50+1g.25 on 1g.50 green and grey 85 60

150 Weightlifting

151 Our Lady of Perpetual Succour and Airport

1964. Olympic Games, Tokyo (1st issue).
893 150 10c. sepia & blue (postage) 10 10
894 25c. sepia and salmon 10 10
895 – 50c. sepia and mauve 20 15
896 150 50c. sepia and purple (air) 15 15
897 – 50c. sepia and green 15 15
898 – 75c. sepia and yellow 20 20
899 – 1g.50 sepia and grey 35 35
DESIGN: Nos. 895, 897/99, Hurdling; Nos. 893/09 were printed in sheets of 50 (10 × 5) with a large map of Japan in the background.

1964. International Airport.
901 151 10c. blk & ochre (postage) 15 10
902 25c. black and turquoise 25 10
903 50c. black and green 35 15
904 1g. black and red 55 35
905 50c. black and orange (air) 30 15
906 1g.50 black and mauve 40 20
907 2g.50 black and violet 1·10 55

1965. International Airport Opening. Optd **1965**.
908 151 10c. blk & ochre (postage) 10 10
909 25c. black and turquoise 25 15
910 50c. black and green 35 15
911 1g. black and red 55 30
912 50c. black and orange (air) 30 10
913 1g.50 black and mauve 50 25
914 2g.50 black and violet 75 40

1965. Olympic Games. Tokyo (2nd issue). Nos. 893/9 surch **+5 c**.
915 150 10c.+5c. (postage) 10 10
916 – 25c.+5c. 15 15
917 – 50c.+5c. 30 25
918 150 50c.+5c. (air) 25 25
919 – 50c.+5c. 25 25
920 – 75c.+5c. 35 35
921 – 1g.50+5c. 45 45

154 Unisphere

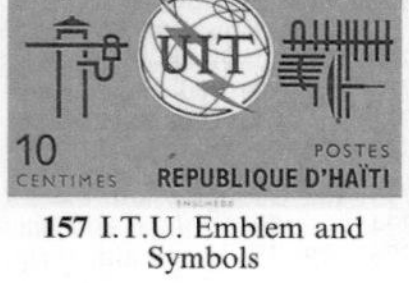

157 I.T.U. Emblem and Symbols

155 "Likala" (freighter) in Port

1965. New York World's Fair.
923 154 10c. mult (postage) 10 10
924 – 20c. purple and yellow 15 10
925 154 50c. multicoloured 30 20
926 – 50c. blue and yellow (air) 25 10
927 – 1g.50 black and yellow 45 30
928 154 5g. multicoloured 1·60 1·40
DESIGN: 20c., 50c. (No. 926), 1g.50, "Reaching for the Stars" (statue).

1965. Haitian Merchant Marine Commemoration.
929 155 10c. mult (postage) 50 15
930 50c. multicoloured 80 20
931 50c. multicoloured (air) 70 15
932 1g.50 multicoloured 1·40 55

1965. Air 20th Anniv of U.N. Optd **O.N.U. 1945-1965.** Portrait in blue.
933 144 20c. brown and bistre 10 10
934 50c. red and blue 15 10
935 1g. blue and mauve 25 20
936 1g.50 green and grey 20 30

1965. Centenary of I.T.U.
937 157 10c. mult (postage) 10 10
938 25c. multicoloured 15 10
939 50c. multicoloured 20 15
940 50c. multicoloured (air) 15 10
941 1g. multicoloured 30 25
942 1g.50 multicoloured 45 35
943 2g. multicoloured 65 50

1965. 25th Anniv of U.N.E.S.C.O. Nos. 937/41 optd **20e Anniversaire UNESCO**.
945 157 10c. mult (postage) 20 20
946 25c. multicoloured 55 55
947 50c. multicoloured 75 75
948 50c. multicoloured (air) 90 35
949 1g. multicoloured 1·75 70

158 Cathedral Facade

1965. Bicentenary of Cathedral of Our Lady of the Assumption, Port-au-Prince. Mult.
951 5c. Type **158** (postage) 10 10
952 10c. High Altar (vert) 10 10
953 25c. "Our Lady of the Assumption" (painting) (vert) 10 10
954 50c. Type **158** (air) 20 10
955 1g. High Altar (vert) 30 20
956 7g.50 as 25c. but larger, 38 × 51 mm 1·75 1·25

159 "Passiflora quadrangularis"

1965. Haitian Flowers. Multicoloured.
957 3c. Type **159** (postage) 10 10
958 5c. "Sambucus canadensis" 10 10
959 10c. "Hibiscus esculentus" 10 10
960 15c. As 5c. 10 10
961 50c. Type **159** 30 15
962 50c. Type **159** (air) 15 10
963 50c. As 5c. 15 10
964 50c. As 10c. 15 10
965 1g.50 As 5c. 45 35
966 1g.50 As 10c. 45 35
967 5g. Type **159** 1·10 75

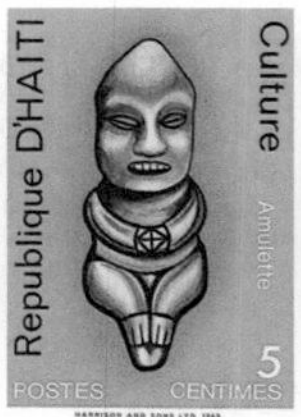

160 Amulet

162 Astronauts and "Gemini" Capsules

1966. "Culture". Multicoloured.
968 5c. Type **160** (postage) 10 10
969 10c. Carved stool and Veve decoration (horiz) 10 10
970 50c. Type **160** 20 15
971 50c. Carved stool and Veve decoration (horiz) (air) 20 15
972 1g.50 Type **160** 55 45
973 2g.50 Modern abstract painting (52 × 37 mm) 60 50

1966. Obligatory Tax. Education Fund. As T **146** but larger (17 × 25½ mm).
974 146 10c. green (postage) 10 10
975 10c. violet 10 10
977 10c. orange (air) 10 10
978 10c. blue 10 10

1966. State Visit of Emperor Haile Selassie of Ethiopia. Nos. 969 and 971/3 optd **Hommage Haile Selassie 1er 24-25 Avril 1966**.
979 – 10c. mult (postage) 15 15
980 – 50c. multicoloured (air) 20 15
981 160 1g.50 multicoloured 55 45
982 – 2g.50 multicoloured 60 50

1966. Space Rendezvous. Astronauts and capsules in brown.
983 162 5c. indigo & blue (postage) 10 10
984 10c. violet and blue 10 10
985 25c. green and blue 15 10
986 50c. red and blue 25 15
987 – 50c. indigo and blue (air) 20 15
988 – 1g. green and blue 35 30
989 – 1g.50 red and blue 55 45
DESIGN: Nos. 987/9, Astronauts and "Gemini" capsules (different arrangement).

163 Football and Pres. Duvalier

1966. Caribbean Football Championships. Portrait in black. (i) Inscr "CHAMPIONNAT DE FOOTBALL DES CARAIBES".
990 163 5c. green & flesh (postage) 10 10
991 – 10c. green and blue 10 10
992 163 15c. green and apple 10 10
993 – 50c. green and lilac 25 15
994 163 50c. purple and sage (air) 15 15
995 – 1g.50 purple and pink 55 45

(ii) As Nos. 990/5 but additionally inscr "COUPE DR. FRANCOIS DUVALIER 22 JUIN".
996 163 5c. grn & flesh (postage) 10 10
997 – 10c. green and blue 10 10
998 163 15c. green and apple 10 10
999 – 50c. green and lilac 25 15
1000 163 50c. purple and sage (air) 15 15
1001 – 1g.50 purple and pink 55 45
DESIGN: 10c., 50c. (No. 991, 993), 1g.50, Footballer and Pres. Duvalier.

164 Audio-visual Aids

1966. National Education.
1002 – 5c. purple, green and pink (postage) 10 10
1003 – 10c. sepia, lake & brown 10 10
1004 164 25c. violet, blue and green 10 10
1005 – 50c. pur, grn & yell (air) 15 15
1006 – 1g. sepia, brown & orge 30 30
1007 164 1g.50 blue, turq & grn 45 45
DESIGNS—VERT: 5c., 50c. Young Haitians walking towards ABC "sun"; 10c., 1g. Scouting—hat, knot and saluting hand.

165 Dr. Albert Schweitzer and Maps of Alsace and Gabon

1967. Schweitzer Commem. Multicoloured.
1008 5c. Type **165** (postage) 10 10
1009 10c. Dr. Schweitzer and organ pipes 10 10
1010 20c. Dr. Schweitzer and Hospital Deschapelles, Haiti 15 10
1011 50c. As 20c. (air) 20 15
1012 1g. As 20c. 35 30
1013 1g.50 Type **165** 50 45
1014 2g. As 10c. 65 55

166 J.-J. Dessalines and Melon

1967. Dessalines Commem. With Portrait of Dessalines. Multicoloured.
1015 5c. Type **166** (postage) 10 10
1016 10c. Chou (cabbage) 10 10
1017 20c. Mandarine (orange) 10 10
1018 50c. Mirliton (gourd) 15 15
1019 50c. Type **166** (air) 15 10

1020 1g. As 20c. 30 20
1021 1g.50 As 20c. 45 35

1967. World Scout Jamboree, Idaho. Nos. 957/8, 960/1, 963 and 965 surch **12e Jamboree Mondial 1967** or with additional premium only.
1022 10c.+10c. on 5c. (postage) 10 10
1023 15c.+10c. 10 10
1024 50c. on 3c. 20 15
1025 50c.+10c. 20 20
1026 50c.+10c. (air) 20 20
1027 1g.50+50c. 60 50

1967. World Fair, Montreal. Nos. 968/70 and 972 optd **EXPO CANADA 1967** and emblem, also surch with new values (1g. and 2g.).
1028 **160** 5c. mult (postage) 10 10
1029 – 10c. multicoloured 10 10
1030 **160** 50c. multicoloured 15 15
1031 1g. on 5c. multicoloured 35 30
1032 1g.50 multicoloured (air) 55 45
1033 2g. on 1g.50 mult 70 55

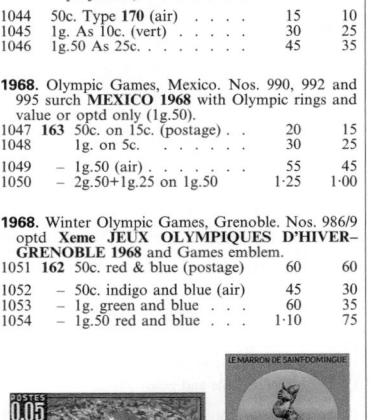

169 Head of Duvalier and Guineafowl Emblem

1967. 10th Anniv of Duvalierists Revolution.
1034 **169** 5c. gold and red (postage) 10 10
1035 10c. gold and blue 10 10
1036 25c. gold and brown 15 10
1037 50c. gold and purple 25 15
1038 1g. gold and green (air) 45 30
1039 1g.50 gold and violet 70 45
1040 2g. gold and red 90 55

170 "Literacy"

1967. National Education. Multicoloured.
1041 5c. Type **170** (postage) 10 10
1042 10c. "Scouting" (Scout badge) (vert) 10 10
1043 25c. "Visual Aids" (slide projection) 15 10
1044 50c. Type **170** (air) 15 10
1045 1g. As 10c. (vert) 30 25
1046 1g.50 As 25c. 45 35

1968. Olympic Games, Mexico. Nos. 990, 992 and 995 surch **MEXICO 1968** with Olympic rings and value or optd only (1g.50).
1047 **163** 50c. on 15c. (postage) 20 15
1048 1g. on 5c. 30 25
1049 – 1g.50 (air) 55 45
1050 – 2g.50+1g.25 on 1g.50 1·25 1·00

1968. Winter Olympic Games, Grenoble. Nos. 986/9 optd **Xeme JEUX OLYMPIQUES D'HIVER–GRENOBLE 1968** and Games emblem.
1051 **162** 50c. red & blue (postage) 60 60
1052 – 50c. indigo and blue (air) 45 30
1053 – 1g. green and blue 60 35
1054 – 1g.50 red and blue 1·10 75

173 Bois Caiman Ceremony

174 "The Unknown Slave"

1968. Slaves' Revolt Commem.
1055 **173** 5c. mult (postage) 10 10
1056 10c. multicoloured 10 10
1057 25c. multicoloured 10 10
1058 50c. multicoloured 20 15
1059 50c. multicoloured (air) 15 10
1060 50c. multicoloured 15 10
1061 1g. multicoloured 30 30
1062 1g. multicoloured 30 25
1063 1g.50 multicoloured 45 45
1064 2g. multicoloured 45 55
1065 5g. multicoloured 85 60
Nos. 1060 and 1062/4 are in a larger size—49½ × 36 mm.

1968. Inaug of Slavery Freedom Monument.
1066 **174** 5c. black & blue (postage) 10 10
1067 10c. black and brown 10 10
1068 20c. black and violet 15 10
1069 25c. black and blue 15 10
1070 50c. black and green 30 15
1071 50c. black and ochre (air) 20 15
1072 1g. black and red 35 25
1073 1g.50 black and orange 55 35

1968. Air. Nos. 1044/6 surch **CULTURE + 0.10**.
1074 **170** 50c.+10c. mult 20 20
1075 – 1g.+10c. multicoloured 30 30
1076 – 1g.50+10c. mult 45 45

176 Various Arms and Palm

1968. Consecration of Haitian Bishopric.
1077 **176** 5c. mult (postage) 10 10
1078 – 10c. multicoloured 10 10
1079 – 25c. multicoloured 20 10
1080 **176** 50c. multicoloured (air) 15 10
1081 – 1g. multicoloured 30 25
1082 – 1g.50 multicoloured 45 35
1083 – 2g.50 multicoloured 70 65
DESIGNS—HORIZ: (50 × 30 mm): 10c., 1g., 2g.50, Virgin Mary; 25c., 1g.50, Cathedral, Port-au-Prince.

177 Boeing 727-100 over Control Tower

1968. Inauguration of Duvalier Airport, Port-au-Prince. Portrait in black.
1084 **177** 5c. brown & bl (postage) 10 10
1085 10c. brown and blue 10 10
1086 25c. brown and lilac 10 10
1087 – 50c. purple & violet (air) 20 15
1088 – 1g.50 purple and blue 55 35
1089 – 2g.50 purple & turquoise 70 45
DESIGN: 50c., 1g.50, 2g.50, Boeing 727-100 over airport entrance.

178 President Duvalier, Emblems and Map

1968. Air. 4th Anniv of Francois Duvalier's "Life Presidency". Die-stamped in gold.
1090 **178** 30g. gold, black and red 16·00

179 Slave breaking Chains

1968. "Revolt of the Slaves" (1791).
1091 **179** 5c. mauve, purple and blue (postage) 10 10
1092 10c. mauve, pur & orge 10 10
1093 25c. mauve, pur & ochre 10 10
1094 50c. mauve, pur & lil (air) 15 10
1095 1g. mauve, purple & grn 35 25
1096 1g.50 mauve, pur & bl 50 35
1097 2g. mauve, purple & turq 60 45

180 "Learning the Alphabet"

1968. "National Education". Multicoloured.
1098 5c. Type **180** (postage) 10 10
1099 10c. Children watching TV screen ("Education by Audio-visual Methods") 10 10
1100 50c. Hands with ball ("Education Through Sport") 15 10
1101 50c. As No. 1099 (air) 15 10
1102 1g. As No. 1100 30 25
1103 1g.50 As No. 1099 55 35

181 Boesman and Balloon

182 Airmail Cachet of 1925

1968. Air. Boesman's Balloon Flight.
1104 **181** 70c. brown and green 40 30
1105 1g.75 brown and blue 1·00 70

1968. Air. Galiffet's Balloon Flight of 1784. Each black and purple on mauve.
1106 70c. Airplane and "AVION" ("2 May 1925") 35 35
1107 70c. Type **182** 35 35
1108 70c. "AVION" and airplane ("28 March 1927") 35 35
1109 70c. "HAITI POSTE AVION" and airplane ("12 July 1927") 35 35
1110 70c. Airplane and "AVION" within ring ("13 Sept 1927") 35 35
1111 70c. "LINDBERGH" and airplane ("6th February 1928") 35 35
Nos. 1106/11 were issued together se-tenant within a small sheet containing two blocks of six (3 × 2) with an overall background design representing Galiffet's balloon.

183 Churchill as Elder Brother of Trinity House

1968. Churchill Commemoration. Mult.
1112 3c. Type **183** (postage) 10 10
1113 5c. Churchill painting 10 10
1114 10c. As Knight of the Garter 10 10
1115 15c. 79th birthday portrait and troops 10 10
1116 20c. Churchill and Farman M.F.7 floatplane 10 10
1117 25c. Karsh portrait and taking leave of the Queen 10 10
1118 50c. Giving "V" sign and Houses of Parliament 15 10
1119 50c. As No. 1116 (air) 15 10
1120 75c. As No. 1115 25 15
1121 1g. As No. 1117 30 25
1122 1g.50 As No. 1118 45 35

1969. Nos. 1070/2 surch.
1124 **174** 70c. on 50c. (postage) 45 20
1125 70c. on 50c. (air) 35 25
1126 1g.75 on 1g. 85 55

185 Blue-hooded Euphonia

1969. Birds. Multicoloured.
1127 5c. Type **185** (postage) 1·10 30
1128 10c. Hispaniolan trogon 1·10 30
1129 20c. Palm chat 1·25 30
1130 25c. Stripe-headed tanager 1·60 40
1131 50c. Type **185** 2·25 45
1132 50c. As 10c. (air) 2·00 60
1133 1g. Black-cowled oriole 2·25 1·10
1134 1g.50 As 25c. 2·75 1·50
1135 2g. Hispaniolan woodpecker 3·25 2·00

186 "Theato, Paris-1900"

1969. Winners of Olympic Marathon showing commemorative inscr and stamp of "host" country. Multicoloured.
1136 5c. "Louis, Athens-1896" (postage) 10 10
1137 10c. Type **186** 15 15
1138 15c. "Hicks, St. Louis-1904" 15 15
1139 20c. "Hayes, London-1908" 25 25
1140 20c. "McArthur, Stockholm-1912" 25 25
1141 25c. "Kolehmainen, Antwerp-1920" 40 40
1142 25c. "Steenroos, Paris-1924" 40 40
1143 25c. "El Quafi, Amsterdam-1928" 40 40
1144 30c. "Zabala, Los Angeles-1932" (air) 45 45
1145 50c. "Son, Berlin-1936" 70 70
1146 60c. "Cabrera, London-1948" 90 90
1147 75c. "Zatopek, Helsinki-1952" 1·25 1·25
1148 75c. "Mimoun, Melbourn-1956" 1·25 1·25
1149 90c. "Bikila, Rome-1960" 1·50 1·50
1150 1g. "Bikila, Tokyo-1964" 1·75 1·75
1151 1g.25 "Wolde, Mexico-1968" 2·50 2·50
Nos. 1136, 1139, 1142 and 1149 are larger, size 66 × 36 mm.

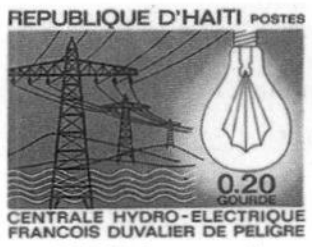

187 Pylons and Electric Light Bulb

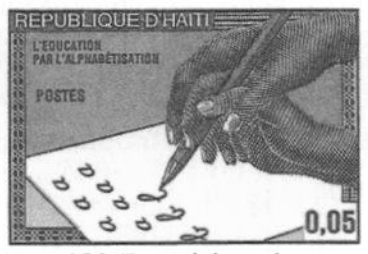

189 Practising the Alphabet

1969. Construction of Duvalier Hydro-electric Scheme.
1153 **187** 20c. violet & bl (postage) 10 10
1154 20c. blue and violet (air) 10 10
1155 25c. green and red 10 10
1156 25c. red and green 15 10

1969. Obligatory Tax. Education Fund. As Nos. 974/8.
1157 **146** 10c. brown (postage) 10 10
1158 10c. blue 10 10
1159 10c. purple (air) 10 10
1160 10c. red 10 10
1161 10c. yellow 10 10
1162 10c. green 10 10
1163 10c. maroon 10 10

1969. 50th Anniv of League of Red Cross Societies. Various stamps surch **50 eme. Anniversaire de la Ligue des Societes de la Croix Rouge**.
1164 10c.+10c. (No. 1099) (postage) 10 10
1165 50c.+20c. (No. 1100) 20 20
1166 50c.+20c. (No. 1101) (air) 30 20
1167 1g.50+25c. (No. 1103) 70 50

1969. "National Education". Multicoloured.
1168 5c. Type **189** (postage) 10 10
1169 10c. Children at play (vert) 10 10
1170 50c. Audio-visual education (vert) 15 10
1171 50c. As No. 1170 (vert) (air) 15 10
1172 1g. Type **189** 35 20
1173 1g.50 As No. 1169 (vert) 55 35

190 I.L.O. Emblem

1969. 50th Anniv of I.L.O.
1174 **190** 5c. green & blk (postage) 10 10
1175 10c. brown and black 10 10
1176 20c. blue and black 10 10
1177 25c. red and black (air) 15 10
1178 70c. orange and black 25 15
1179 1g.75 violet and black 40 45

191 "Papilio zonaria"

1969. Haitian Butterflies. Multicoloured.
1180 10c. Type **191** (postage) . . 15 10
1181 20c. "Zerene cesonia" . . . 30 10
1182 25c. "Papilio machaonides" 35 10
1183 50c. "Danaus eresimus" (air) 45 10
1184 1g.50 "Anaea marthesia" . . 1·40 60
1185 2g. "Prepona antimache" . . 1·75 85

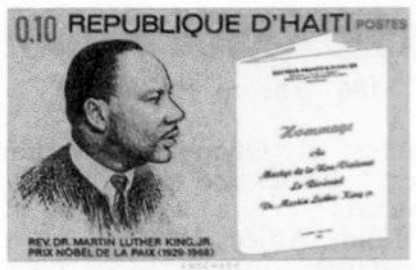

192 Dr. Martin Luther King

1970. Dr. Martin Luther King (American Civil Rights leader) Commemoration.
1186 **192** 10c. brown, red and ochre (postage) . . . 10 10
1187 20c. black, red & bl . . 10 10
1188 25c. black, red and pink 10 10
1189 50c. black, red and green (air) 20 10
1190 1g. black, red and orange 35 25
1191 1g.50 black, red and blue 55 35

193 "Laeliopsis dominguensis" **194** U.P.U. Monument Berne, and Map of Haiti

1970. Haitian Orchids. Multicoloured.
1192 10c. Type **193** (postage) . . 10 10
1193 20c. "Oncidium haitiense" 15 10
1194 25c. "Oncidium calochilum" 25 15
1195 50c. "Tetramicra elegans" (air) 15 10
1196 1g.50 "Epidendrum truncatum" 45 35
1197 2g. "Oncidium desertorum" 65 50

1970. 16th U.P.U. Congress, Tokyo.
1198 **194** 10c. brown, black and green (postage) . . . 10 10
1199 – 25c. yellow, black and red 15 10
1200 – 50c. green, black and blue 35 25
1201 – 50c. brn, blk & vio (air) 15 10
1202 – 1g.50 yellow, blk & red 55 35
1203 **194** 2g. brown, black & green 70 50
DESIGNS—VERT: 25c., 1g.50, Stylized "propeller". HORIZ: 50c. (both), Doves and globe.

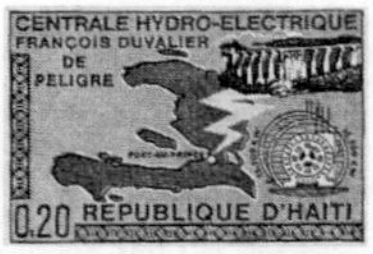

195 Map, Dam and Generator

1970. Construction of Duvalier Central Hydro-electric Power Station. Multicoloured.
1205 20c. Type **195** 15 10
1206 25c. Map, dam and pylon 20 10

1970. 25th Anniv of United Nations. Nos. 1200/203 optd **XXVe ANNIVERSAIRE O.N.U.** and emblem.
1207 – 50c. green, black and blue (postage) 20 15
1208 – 50c. brown, blk & bl (air) 20 10
1209 – 1g.50 yellow, blk & red 55 35
1210 **194** 2g. brown, black & green 70 50

197 Power Station and Pylon **198** Fort Nativity, 1492

1970. Obligatory Tax. Duvalier Hydro-electric Project.
1212 **197** 20c. brown & lil (postage) 15 10
1213 20c. grey and brown (air) 15 10
1214 20c. violet and blue . . . 15 10
See also No. 1268.

1970. Christmas.
1215 **198** 3c. brn & yell (postage) 10 10
1216 5c. black and green . . . 20 15
1217 – 1g.50 mult (sepia panel) (air) 55 35
1218 – 1g.50 mult (blue panel) 55 35
1219 – 2g. multicoloured . . . 60 50
DESIGN—SQUARE (33 × 33 mm): Nos. 1217/19, "Haitian Nativity" (Toussaint Auguste).

199 "The Oriental" (Rembrandt) **200** Football

1971. Paintings. Multicoloured.
1220 5c. Type **199** (postage) . . . 10 10
1221 10c. "The Ascension" (C. Bazile) 10 10
1222 20c. "Irises in a vase" (Van Gogh) 15 10
1223 50c. "The Baptism of Christ" (C. Bazile) . . . 30 15
1224 50c. "The Nativity" (R. Benoit) (air) 20 15
1225 1g. "Head of a Negro" (Rubens) 35 30
1226 1g.50 As 10c. 55 45

1971. World Cup Football Championship, Mexico (1970).
1228 **200** 5c. black and orange . . 10 10
1229 50c. black and brown . . 25 15
1230 – 50c. black, yellow & pink 25 15
1231 – 1g. black, yellow and lilac 40 25
1232 **200** 1g.50 black and drab . . 55 45
1233 – 5g. black, yellow and grey . . . . 1·10 1·00
DESIGNS: Nos. 1230/31, 1233, Jules Rimet Cup.

1971. Inauguration of Duvalier Central Power Station. Surch **INAUGURATION 22-7-71** and premium.
1235 **195** 20c.+50c. mult 30 25
1236 – 25c.+1g.50 mult (No. 1206) 70 55

202 Balloon and Airmail Stamp of 1929

1971. Air. 40th Anniv of Airmail Service (1969).
1237 **202** 20c. black, red and blue 25 10
1238 50c. black, red and blue 45 20
1239 – 1g. black and orange . . 1·00 50
1240 – 1g.50 black and mauve 1·60 60
DESIGN: 1g., 1g.50, Concorde and 1929 air stamp.

1971. Obligatory Tax. Education Fund. Nos. 1205/6 surch **ALPHABETISATION** and value.
1242 **195** 20c.+10c. mult 15 10
1243 – 25c.+10c. mult 15 10

1972. Air. "INTERPEX" International Stamp Exhibition, New York Nos. 1237/40 optd **INTERPEX 72** and emblem.
1244 **202** 20c. black, red and blue 15 10
1245 50c. black, red and blue 55 20
1246 – 1g. black and orange . . 95 50
1247 – 1g.50 black and mauve 1·40 75

205 J.-J. Dessalines and Emblem **208** "Sun" and "EXPO" Emblem

1972. Jean-Jacques Dessalines ("founder of Haiti") Commemoration (1st issue).
1248 **205** 5c. black & grn (postage) 10 10
1249 10c. black and blue . . . 10 10
1250 25c. black and orange 10 10
1251 50c. black and green (air) 20 10
1252 2g.50 black and lilac . . 55 20
See also Nos. 1304/10, 1343/52, 1357/60, 1413/17 and 1451/2.

1972. Air. 5th "Haipex" Congress. Nos. 1237/40 optd **HAIPEX 5eme. CONGRES** and emblem.
1253 **202** 20c. black, red and blue 15 10
1254 – 50c. black, red and blue 55 20
1255 – 1g. black and orange . . 95 45
1256 – 1g.50 black and mauve 1·40 65

1972. Air. "Belgica 72" Stamp Exhibition, Brussels. Nos. 1238/40 optd **BELGICA 72** and emblem.
1257 50c. black, red and blue . . 55 20
1258 1g. black and orange . . . 90 55
1259 1g.50 black and mauve . . . 1·60 65

1972. Obligatory Tax. As Nos. 974/8.
1260 **146** 5c. red 10 10
1261 5c. blue 10 10

1972. "EXPO 70" World Fair, Osaka, Japan (1970).
1262 **208** 10c. mult (postage) . . . 10 10
1263 – 25c. multicoloured . . . 10 10
1264 – 50c. multicoloured (air) 15 10
1265 – 1g. multicoloured . . . 35 25
1266 – 1g.50 multicoloured . . 45 30
1267 – 2g.50 multicoloured . . 90 55
DESIGNS—HORIZ: Nos. 1264/7, Sun Tower and emblem.

1972. Obligatory Tax. Duvalier Hydro-electric Project. As Nos. 1212/14.
1268 **197** 20c. brown and blue . . 10 10

209 Basket Vendors **210** Headquarters and Map

1973. 20th Anniv of Caribbean Travel Assn. Multicoloured.
1269 50c. Type **209** 20 10
1270 80c. Postal bus service . . . 30 20
1271 1g.50 Type **209** 55 30
1272 2g.50 As 80c. 75 55

1973. Air. Education Fund. As Nos. 977/8 but larger size 17 × 25 mm.
1273 **146** 10c. brown and blue . . 10 10
1274 10c. brown and green . . 10 10
1275 10c. brown and orange 10 10

1973. Air. 70th Anniv of Pan-American Health Organization. Multicoloured.
1276 **210** 50c. multicoloured . . . 15 10
1277 80c. multicoloured . . . 25 20
1278 1g.50 multicoloured . . 45 30
1279 2g. multicoloured . . . 55 45

211 Miniature Melo

1973. Marine Life. Multicoloured.
1280 5c. Type **211** (postage) . . . 15 10
1281 10c. "Nemaster rubiginosa" 10 10
1282 25c. "Cyerce cristallina" . . 30 10
1283 50c. "Desmophyllum riisei" 15 10
1284 50c. "Platypodia spectabilis" (air) 15 10
1285 85c. "Goniaster tessellatus" 25 20
1286 1g.50 "Stephanocyathus diadema" 45 30
1287 2g. "Phyllangia americana" 55 35

211a Royal Gramma

1973. Fishes. Multicoloured.
1288 10c. Type **211a** (postage) . . 20 10
1289 50c. Blue tang 35 15
1290 50c. Black-capped basslet (air) 35 15
1291 85c. Rock beauty 55 30
1292 1g.50 Peppermint basslet . 1·00 55
1293 5g. Creole wrasse . . . . . 2·00 1·00

212 Haitian Flag

1973. Air.
1294 **212** 80c. black and red . . . 25 20
1295 – 80c. black and red . . . 25 20
1296 – 1g.85 black and red . . 55 30
1297 – 1g.85 black and red . . 55 30
DESIGNS—As Type **212**: No. 1295, Flag and arms (framed). (47 × 29 mm): No. 1296, Flag and arms; No. 1297, Flag and Pres. Jean-Claude Duvalier.

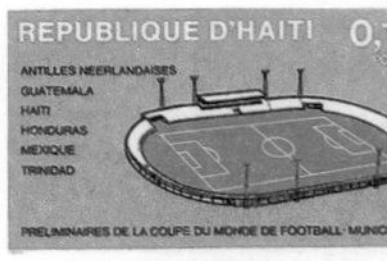

213 Football Stadium **214** J.-J. Dessalines

1973. World Cup Football Championship. Preliminary Games between Caribbean Countries.
1298 **213** 10c. green, black and brown (postage) . . . 10 10
1299 – 20c. mauve, black & brn 10 10
1300 **213** 50c. green, blk & red (air) 15 10
1301 80c. green, black & blue 25 20
1302 – 1g.75 green, black & brn 50 35
1303 – 10g. green, black & brn 1·75 1·25
DESIGNS: 20c., 1g.75, 10g. World Cup stamp of 1971.

1974. Jean-Jacques Dessalines Commemoration (2nd issue).
1304 **214** 10c. green & bl (postage) 10 10
1305 20c. black and red . . . 10 10
1306 25c. violet and brown . . 10 10
1307 50c. blue and brown (air) 15 10
1308 80c. brown and grey . . 20 20
1309 1g. purple and green . . 30 20
1310 1g.75 green and mauve 50 35

215 Symbol of Solar System **216** Pres. Jean-Claude Duvalier

1974. 500th Birth Anniv (1973) of Nicolas Copernicus (astronomer). Multicoloured.
1311 10c. Type **215** (postage) . . 10 10
1312 25c. Copernicus 10 10
1313 50c. Type **215** (air) 15 10
1314 50c. As 25c. 15 10
1315 80c. Type **215** 25 20
1316 1g. As 25c. 30 20
1317 1g.75 Type **215** 50 35

1974.
1319 **216** 10c. grn & gold (postage) 10 10
1320 20c. purple and gold . . 10 10
1321 50c. blue and gold . . . 15 10
1322 50c. purple and gold (air) 15 15
1323 80c. red and gold . . . 25 20
1324 1g. purple and gold . . 30 20
1325 1g.50 blue and gold . . 45 30
1326 1g.75 violet and gold . . 55 35
1327 5g. grey and gold . . . 85 60

1975. Air. Nos. 1296/7 surch.
1328 80c. on 1g.85 black and red 25 20
1329 80c. on 1g.85 black and red 25 20

1975. Air. Centenary of U.P.U. Nos. 1296/7 optd **1874 UPU 1974 100 ANS.**
1330 1g.85 black and red 55 30
1331 1g.85 black and red 55 30

219 Haiti 60c. Stamp of 1937

1976. Bicentenary of American Revolution.
1332 **219** 10c. mult (postage) . . . 10 10
1333 – 50c. multicoloured (air) 15 10
1334 – 80c. multicoloured . . 25 15
1335 – 1g.50 multicoloured . . 45 30
1336 – 7g.50 multicoloured . . 1·75 1·25

DESIGN: 50c. to 7g.50, text with names of Haitians at Siege of Savannah.

1976. Surch.
1337 **205** 80c. on 25c. black and pink (postage) 35 20
1338 – 80c. on 10c. mult (No. 1288) 35 20
1339 **214** 80c. on 25c. violet & brn 35 20
1340 **215** 80c. on 10c. mult 35 20
1341 – 80c. on 85c. mult (No. 1285) (air) 25 20
1342 – 80c. on 85c. mult (No. 1291) 25 20

1977. Jean-Jacques Dessalines Commem (3rd issue).
1343 **205** 20c. black and brown (postage) 10 10
1344 50c. black and mauve 15 10
1345 75c. black and yellow (air) 20 20
1346 1g. black and blue 30 15
1347 1g.25 black and olive 35 30
1348 1g.50 black and grey 45 30
1349 1g.75 black and red 50 35
1350 2g. black and yellow 55 45
1351 5g. black and blue 85 60
1352 10g. black and brown 1·75 1·25

1977. Air. Lindbergh's Transatlantic Flight Nos. 1313/14 and 1316/17 optd or surch **C. LINDBERGH. N.Y.-PARIS 1927-1977**.
1353 1g. Copernicus 30 20
1354 1g.25 on 50c. Type **215** 35 30
1355 1g.25 on 50c. Copernicus 35 30
1356 1g.25 on 1g.75 Type **215** 35 30

1977. Jean-Jacques Dessalines Commem (4th issue).
1357 **205** 10c. black and mauve (postage) 10 10
1358 50c. black and brown 15 10
1359 80c. black and green (air) 25 15
1360 1g. black and brown 30 20

1977. Air. Various stamps surch **G. O.80.**
1361 – 80c. on 1g.50 mult (No. 1266) 20 20
1366 – 80c. on 1g.50 mult (No. 1335) 20 20
1364 **215** 80c. on 1g.75 mult 20 20
1365 **216** 80c. on 1g.75 violet and gold 20 20
1363 – 80c. on 1g.85 black and red (No. 1296) 20 20
1362 – 80c. on 2g.50 mult (No. 1267) 20 20

1978. Surch **1.00**.
1367 **205** 1g. on 20c. black & brn 30 20
1368 1g. on 1g.75 black and red 30 20
1369 1g.25 on 75c. black and yellow 35 25
1370 1g.25 on 1g.50 black and green 35 25
Nos. 1368/70 have the inscription "AVION" obliterated by the surcharge.

224 J.-C. Duvalier Telecommunications Stations

1978. Telephone Centenary (1976). Mult.
1372 10c. Type **224** (postage) 10 10
1373 20c. Video telephone 10 10
1374 50c. Alexander Graham Bell (vert) 15 10
1375 1g. Satellite over Earth (air) 30 15
1376 1g.25 Type **224** 35 25
1377 2g. Wall telephone, 1890 (vert) 55 45

225 Flag-raising Ceremony

1978. Olympic Games, Montreal (1976). Multicoloured.
1378 5c. Type **225** (postage) 10 10
1379 25c. Cycling 10 10
1380 50c. High jump 15 10
1381 1g.25 Horse jumping (air) 35 25
1382 2g.50 Basketball 70 55
1383 5g. Yachting 1·40 1·10

226 Mother feeding Baby

227 Mother feeding Child

1979. 50th Anniv of Inter-American Child Institute. Multicoloured.
1384 25c. Type **226** (postage) 10 10
1385 1g.25 Type **226** (air) 35 25
1386 2g. Nurse vaccinating child 55 45

1979. 30th Anniv of Co-operative for American Relief Everywhere (CARE). Multicoloured.
1387 25c. Type **227** (postage) 10 10
1388 50c. Type **227** 15 15
1389 1g. Spinning cotton (air) 30 20
1390 1g.25 As No. 1389 35 25
1391 2g. As No. 1389 55 45

228 Human Rights Emblem

229 Anteor Firmin and Book

1979. 30th Anniv of Declaration of Human Rights.
1392 **228** 25c. mult (postage) 10 10
1393 1g. multicoloured (air) 30 20
1394 1g.25 multicoloured 35 25
1395 2g. multicoloured 55 45

1979. International Anti-Apartheid Year.
1396 **229** 50c. pink and brown (postage) 15 15
1397 1g. green and brown (air) 30 20
1398 1g.25 blue and brown 35 25
1399 2g. olive and brown 55 45

230 Children playing

1979. International Year of the Child.
1400 **230** 10c. mult (postage) 10 10
1401 25c. multicoloured 10 10
1402 50c. multicoloured 15 10
1403 1g. multicoloured (air) 30 20
1404 1g.25 multicoloured 35 25
1405 2g.50 multicoloured 45 55
1406 5g. multicoloured 85 60

1980. Air. Wedding of President Duvalier. Nos. 1322 and 1325/6 optd **27 5 80 JOUR FASTE**.
1407 **216** 50c. purple and gold 15 10
1408 1g.50 blue and gold 45 30
1409 1g.75 violet and gold 50 40

1980. Nos. 1252, 1357 and 1359 surch **TIMBRE POSTE** with value changed.
1410 **205** 1g. on 2g.50 black & lil 30 20
1411 1g.25 on 10c. blk & mve 35 35
1412 1g.25 on 80c. blk & grn 35 55

1980. Jean-Jacques Dessalines Commemoration (5th issue).
1413 **205** 25c. black and orange (postage) 10 10
1414 1g. black and grey (air) 30 20
1415 1g.25 black and pink 35 25
1416 2g. black and green 55 45
1417 5g. black and blue 85 60

233 Henri Christophe Citadel

1980. World Tourism Conference, Manila. Multicoloured.
1418 5c. Type **233** (postage) 10 10
1419 25c. Sans-Souci Palace 10 10
1420 50c. Vallieres market 15 10
1421 1g. Type **233** (air) 30 20
1422 1g.25 As No. 1419 35 25
1423 1g.50 Carnival dancers 45 30
1424 2g. Women with flowers 55 45
1425 2g.50 As No. 1424 70 50

234 Players and Flag of Uruguay (1930)

1980. 50th Anniv of First World Cup Football Championship. Multicoloured.
1426 10c. Type **234** (postage) 10 10
1427 20c. Italy (1934) 10 10
1428 25c. Italy (1938) 10 10
1429 50c. Uruguay (air) 15 10
1430 75c. West Germany (1954) 20 20
1431 1g. Brazil (1958) 30 20
1432 1g.25 Brazil (1962) 35 25
1433 1g.50 England (1966) 45 30
1434 1g.75 Brazil (1970) 50 40
1435 2g. West Germany (1974) 55 45
1436 5g. Argentina (1978) 85 60

235 "Woman with Birds and Flowers" (Hector Hyppolite)

237 President Duvalier, Dish Aerial and Freighter at Quayside

1981. Paintings. Multicoloured.
1437 5c. Type **235** (postage) 10 10
1438 10c. "Going to Church" (Gregoire Etienne) 10 10
1439 20c. "Street Market" (Petion Savain) 10 10
1440 25c. "Market Sellers" (Michele Manual) 10 10
1441 50c. Type **235** (air) 15 10
1442 1g.25 As No. 1438 35 25
1443 2g. As No. 1439 55 45
1444 5g. As No. 1440 85 60

1981. Various stamps surch **1.25**.
1445 **233** 1g.25 on 5c. mult (postage) 35 30
1446 **235** 1g.25 on 5c. mult 35 30
1447 – 1g.25 on 10c. mult (No. 1438) 35 30
1448 – 1g.25 on 20c. mult (No. 1427) 35 30
1449 – 1g.25 on 1g.50 mult (No. 1423) (air) 35 30
1450 **205** 2g. on 5g. black and blue (No. 1417) 55 45
The surcharge on No. 1446 is inverted.

1982. Jean-Jacques Dessalines ("founder of Haiti") Commemoration (6th issue).
1451 **205** 1g.25 black and brown 35 30
1452 2g. black and violet 55 45

1982. 10th Anniv of Duvalier Reforms ("Jean-Claudisme").
1453 **237** 25c. green and black 15 10
1454 50c. green and black 25 10
1455 1g. purple and black 50 20
1456 1g.25 blue and black 55 30
1457 2g. orange and black 75 45
1458 5g. orange and black 2·25 1·10

1982. Nos. 1453 and 1455/7 optd **1957- 1982 25 ANS DE REVOLUTION**.
1459 **237** 25c. green and black 10 10
1460 1g. purple and black 35 30
1461 1g.25 blue and black 45 40
1462 2g. orange and black 65 60

239 Scouts planting Trees

1983. 75th Anniv of Boy Scout Movement. Multicoloured.
1463 5c. Type **239** (postage) 10 10
1464 10c. Lord Baden-Powell (vert) 10 10
1465 25c. Scout teaching villagers to read 25 10
1466 50c. As No. 1464 15 10
1467 75c. As No. 1465 (air) 65 20
1468 1g. Type **239** 30 20
1469 1g.25 As No. 1465 90 30
1470 2g. As No. 1464 55 45

240 Our Lady of Perpetual Succour

1983. Centenary of Miracle of Our Lady of Perpetual Succour.
1471 **240** 10c. mult (postage) 10 10
1472 20c. multicoloured 10 10
1473 25c. multicoloured 10 10
1474 50c. multicoloured 15 10
1475 **240** 75c. multicoloured (air) 20 20
1476 1g. multicoloured 30 20
1477 1g.25 multicoloured 35 30
1478 1g.50 multicoloured 45 30
1479 1g.75 multicoloured 50 45
1480 – 2g. multicoloured 55 45
1481 – 5g. multicoloured 85 60
Nos. 1480/1 differ slightly in design of the frame.

241 Arms of Haiti and U.P.U. Monument, Berne

1983. Centenary (1981) of U.P.U. Membership.
1483 **241** 5c. brown, red and black (postage) 10 10
1484 – 10c. brown, black & blue 10 10
1485 – 25c. green, black and red 10 10
1486 – 50c. green, red and black 15 10
1487 – 75c. lilac, black and blue (air) 20 20
1488 – 1g. blue, red and black 30 20
1489 – 1g.25 blue, black and red 35 30
1490 – 2g. blue, black and red 55 45
DESIGNS: 50c., 1g. Type **241**; 10, 75c. L. F. Salomon and J. C. Duvalier; 25c., 1g.25, 2g. First Haitian stamp and U.P.U. Monument, Berne.

242 Argentine and Belgian Footballers

1983. World Cup Football Championship, Spain.
1491 **242** 5c. black & bl (postage) 10 10
1492 – 10c. black and brown 10 10
1493 – 20c. black and green 10 10
1494 – 25c. black and green 10 10
1495 – 50c. black and yellow 15 10
1496 – 1g. multicoloured (air) 30 20
1497 – 1g.25 multicoloured 35 30
1498 – 1g.50 multicoloured 45 30
1499 – 2g. multicoloured 55 45
1500 – 2g.50 multicoloured 65 55
DESIGNS—VERT: 10c. Northern Ireland and Yugoslavia; 20c. England and France; 25c. Spain and Northern Ireland; 50c. Italian player with Cup. HORIZ: 1g. Brazil and Scotland; 1g.25, Northern Ireland and France; 1g.50, Poland and Cameroun; 2g. Italy and West Germany; 2g.50, Argentine and Brazil.

243 1c. Stamp of 1881

1984. Stamp Centenary (1981).
1501 **243** 5c. mult (postage) 10 10
1502 – 10c. multicoloured 10 10
1503 – 25c. multicoloured 10 10
1504 – 50c. multicoloured 20 15
1505 – 75c. yellow, brown and silver (air) 25 20
1506 – 1g. blue, red and gold 35 30
1507 – 1g.25 multicoloured 45 40
1508 – 2g. gold, brown and green 70 60
DESIGNS: 10c. 1881 2c. stamp; 25c., 1881 3c. stamp; 50c. 1881 7c. stamp; 75c., 1g. Pres. Salomon; 1g.25, 2g. Pres. Duvalier.

244 Modern Communications Equipment

1984. World Communications Year.
1509 **244** 25c. blue and purple . . 10 10
1510 50c. blue and olive . . . 20 15
1511 – 1g. orange, brown & grn 35 30
1512 – 1g.25 orange, brown & bl 45 40
1513 – 2g. blue, orange and black 70 60
1514 – 2g.50 blue, bistre & blk 1·00 80
DESIGNS—VERT: 1g., 1g.25, Pres. Petion's drum; 2g., 2g.50, W.C.Y. emblem as satellite over globe.

245 Javelin-thrower, Runner and Polevaulter

1984. Olympic Games, Los Angeles.
1515 **245** 5c. black, green and red 10 10
1516 10c. black, olive and red 10 10
1517 – 25c. black, green and red 10 10
1518 – 50c. black, ochre and red 20 15
1519 – 1g. black, blue and red 35 30
1520 – 1g.25 black, blue & orge 45 40
1521 – 2g. black, violet and red 70 60
DESIGNS—HORIZ: 25c., 50c. Hurdler. VERT: 1g. to 2g.50, Long jumper.

246 Head of "The Unknown Indian", Toussaint Square, Louverture

1984. 500th Anniv of Arrival of Europeans in America (1st issue).
1523 **246** 5c. mult (postage) . . . 10 10
1524 10c. multicoloured . . . 10 10
1525 25c. multicoloured . . . 10 10
1526 50c. multicoloured . . . 15 10
1527 – 1g. multicoloured (air) 25 20
1528 – 1g.25 multicoloured . . 35 30
1529 – 2g. multicoloured . . . 55 50
DESIGN: 1 to 2g. "The Unknown Indian".
See also Nos. 1539/44.

247 Simon Bolivar and Alexandre Petion

1985. Birth Bicentenary of Simon Bolivar. Mult.
1531 5c. Type **247** (postage) . . . 10 10
1532 25c. Bolivar and Alexandre Petion (different) 10 10
1533 50c. Bolivar and flags of members of Grand Colombian Confederation 15 10
1534 1g. Type **247** (air) 25 20
1535 1g.25 As No. 1532 . . . . 30 25
1536 2g. Type **247** 50 45
1537 7g.50 As No. 1532 . . . . 1·60 1·25

248 Chief Henri

250 Planting Saplings

1986. 500th Anniv of Arrival of Europeans in America (2nd issue).
1539 **248** 10c. mult (postage) . . . 10 10
1540 25c. multicoloured . . . 10 10
1541 50c. multicoloured . . . 15 10
1542 – 1g. multicoloured (air) 25 15
1543 – 1g.25 multicoloured . . 30 20
1544 – 2g. multicoloured . . . 35 25
DESIGN: 1 to 2g. Chief Henri hunting.

1986. Various stamps surch.
1546 **241** 25c. on 5c. brown, red and black (postage) . . 10 10
1547 **242** 25c. on 5c. black & blue 10 10
1548 **243** 25c. on 5c. multicoloured 10 10
1549 – 25c. on 75c. mult (1430) (air) 10 10
1550 – 25c. on 75c. mult (1467) 10 10
1551 – 25c. on 1g.50 mult (1122) 10 10

1986. International Youth Year (1985). Mult.
1552 10c. Type **250** (postage) . . 10 10
1553 25c. I.Y.Y. emblem 10 10
1554 50c. Boy and girl scouts and flag 15 10
1555 1g. Type **250** (air) 25 15
1556 1g.25 As No. 1553 . . . . 30 20
1557 2g. As No. 1554 . . . . . 50 40

251 Dove above Peace Year Emblem on Globe

1987. International Peace Year (1986) and 40th Anniv of United Nations Educational, Scientific and Cultural Organization.
1559 **251** 10c. mult (postage) . . . 10 10
1560 25c. multicoloured . . . 10 10
1561 50c. multicoloured . . . 15 10
1562 1g. multicoloured (air) 25 15
1563 1g.25 multicoloured . . 30 25
1564 2g.50 multicoloured . . 60 50

252 Peralte and Flag

1989. Charlemagne Peralte Commemoration.
1566 **252** 25c. mult (postage) . . . 10 10
1567 50c. multicoloured . . . 15 10
1568 1g. multicoloured (air) 25 15
1569 2g. multicoloured . . . 50 40
1570 3g. multicoloured . . . 80 70

253 Slaves and Tree forming Fist

1991. Bicentenary of Uprising of Slaves. Mult.
1572 25c. Type **253** (postage) . . 10 10
1573 50c. Type **253** 10 10
1574 1g. Gathering of slaves around fire (air) 10 10
1575 2g. As No. 1574 . . . . . 25 20
1576 3g. As No. 1574 . . . . . 35 30

254 Amerindian watching Europeans landing

1993. America. 500th Anniv (1992) of Discovery of America by Columbus. Multicoloured.
1578 25c. Type **254** (postage) . . 20 10
1579 50c. Type **254** 20 10
1580 1g. Columbus's fleet at anchor and rowing boats on shore (vert) (air) . . . 20 10
1581 2g. As No. 1580 . . . . . 30 15
1582 3g. As No. 1580 . . . . . 50 30

255 Map of Haiti and Emblem

1995. 25th General Assembly of Organization of American States. Multicoloured.
1584 50c. Type **255** 10 10
1585 75c. Type **255** 10 10
1586 1g. Map of Americas and emblems (vert) 10 10
1587 2g. As No. 1586 . . . . . 15 10
1588 3g. As No. 1586 . . . . . 25 20
1589 5g. As No. 1586 . . . . . 40 35

256 Dove holding Flags in Beak

1995. 50th Anniv of U.N.O. Multicoloured.
1591 50c. Type **256** (postage) . . 10 10
1592 75c. Type **256** 10 10
1593 1g. Dove with olive branch flying over flags (air) . . . 10 10
1594 2g. As No. 1593 . . . . . 15 10
1595 3g. As No. 1593 . . . . . 25 20
1596 5g. As No. 1593 . . . . . 40 35

1996. Various stamps surch **XXIIIES JEUX OLYMPIQUES LOS ANGELES 1984**.
1598 2g. on 1g.25 black, blue and orange (1520) (postage) 15 10
1599 1g. on 1g.25 mult (1556) (air) 10 10
1600 3g. on 1g.25 mult (1535) . . 20 15
1601 3g. on 1g.25 mult (1477) . . 20 15

259 Players

1996. Olympic Games, Atlanta. Multicoloured. (a) Centenary of Volleyball.
1605 50c. Type **259** 10 10
1606 75c. Umpire and players . . 10 10
1607 1g. Players holding Olympic Flame 10 10
1608 2g. Players jumping for ball 15 10

(b) 1984 Medal Winners.
1609 3g. 400 m hurdles (U.S.A.) 20 15
1610 10g. Decathlon (gold, Great Britain) 70 60
Nos. 1605/6 were issued together, se-tenant, forming a composite design of a match scene and Nos. 1607/8 a composite design of a map.

260 "Virgin and Child" (Jacopo Bellini)

1996. Christmas. Multicoloured.
1612 2g. Type **260** 15 10
1613 3g. "Adoration of the Shepherds" (Bernardo Strozzi) 20 15
1614 6g. "Virgin and Child" (Giovanni Bellini) 45 35
1615 10g. "Virgin and Child" (Francesco Mazzola) . . . 70 60
1616 25g. "Adoration of the Magi" (Gentile da Fabriano) . . . . 1·75 1·40

50-me ANNIVERSAIRE DE L'UNICEF
261 Children in Street

1997. 50th Anniv (1996) of U.N.I.C.E.F.
1618 **261** 4g. multicoloured . . . 30 25
1619 5g. multicoloured . . . 35 30
1620 6g. multicoloured . . . 45 35
1621 10g. multicoloured . . . 70 60
1622 20g. multicoloured . . . 1·40 1·25

262 Sleeping Beauty

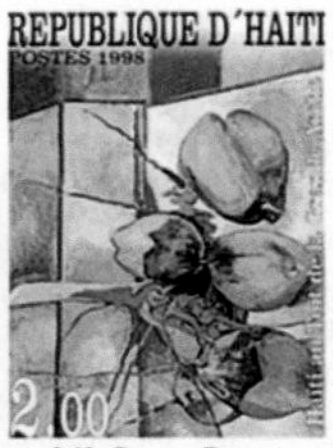

263 Cocoa Beans

1998. 175th Anniv (1997) of 3rd Collection of Fairy Tales by Brothers Grimm. Multicoloured.
1623 2g. Type **262** 15 10
1624 3g. Snow White 20 15
1625 4g. Sleeping Beauty and Prince 30 25
1626 6g. Man in bed (Water of Life) 45 35
1627 10g. Cinderella 70 60
1628 20g. Serving patient with the Water of Life . . . . . . 1·40 1·25

1998. Grande Arche Roof Competition, Paris. "Haiti: Women and Creation". Multicoloured.
1630 2g. Type **263** 20 15
1631 3g. Swords and flags 30 25
1632 5g. Boy with model churches 45 35
1633 6g. Woman with artist's palette and brush 55 45

OFFICIAL STAMPS

1960. Nos. 736/40 optd **OFFICIEL**.
O742 – 50c. brown and green † 25
O743 – 50c. blue and green . . † 25
O744 – 50c. black and green . . † 25
O745 **127** 1g. green and red . . . † 35
O746 – 1g.50 pink and blue . . † 55
The above were only issued precancelled.

O 135 Dessalines' Statue

1962. Air. (a) Size 20½ × 37½ mm.
O791 **O 135** 50c. sepia and blue 20 15
O792 1g. red and blue . . . 35 30
O793 1g.50 blue and bistre 55 45

(b) Size 30½ × 40 mm.
O794 **O 135** 5g. green and red . . 1·10 1·00

PARCEL POST STAMPS

1960. Optd **COLIS POSTAUX**.
P725 **102** 5c. green & blk (postage) 10 10
P726 10c. red and black . . . 10 10
P727 25c. blue and black . . 15 15
P728 **74** 2g.50 grey . . . . . . 1·10 1·10
P729 **102** 50c. orange & black (air) 25 20
P730 **101** 5g. violet and blue . . . 2·10 1·75

P 130 Arms

1961.
P757 **P 130** 50c. violet and bistre (postage) 35 15
P758 1g. blue and red . . . 55 30
P759 2g.50 lake & grn (air) 90 70
P760 5g. green and orange 1·50 1·10

POSTAGE DUE STAMPS

D 10

D 23

1898.
D63 **D 10** 2c. blue 20 25
D64 5c. brown 35 40

D65		10c. orange	50	50
D66		50c. grey	1·00	1·00

1902. Optd **MAI Gt Pre 1902** in frame.

D85	D 10	2c. blue	45	50
D86		5c. brown	45	50
D87		10c. orange	50	50
D88		50c. grey	3·75	2·10

1906.

D150	D 23	2c. red	45	35
D151		5c. blue	1·50	1·50
D152		10c. purple	1·50	1·50
D153		50c. olive	6·75	3·75

1914. Optd **GL O. Z. 7 FEV. 1914** in frame.

D206	D 10	5c. brown	45	35
D207		10c. orange	40	40
D208		50c. grey	3·25	2·25

1914. Optd **GL O. Z 7 FEV. 1914** in frame.

D209	D 23	2c. red	55	35
D210		5c. blue	90	55
D211		10c. purple	2·60	2·25
D212		50c. olive	4·75	3·00

D 83

1951.

D452	D 83	10c. red	10	10
D453		20c. brown	15	15
D454		40c. green	20	20
D455		50c. yellow	30	30

SPECIAL DELIVERY STAMP

S 86 G.P.O.

1953.

E468	S 86	25c. red	30	30

APPENDIX

The following stamps have either been issued in excess of postal needs or have not been available to the public in reasonable quantities at face value. Such stamps may later be given full listing if there is evidence of regular postal use.

1968.

Medal Winners, Winter Olympic Games, Grenoble. Postage 5, 10, 20, 25, 50c., 1g.50; Air 2g.

1969.

Moon Landing of "Apollo 11". Optd on 1969 Birds issue. Nos. 1132/5. Air 50c., 1g.50, 2g.

Space Flights of "Apollo 7" and "Apollo 8". Postage 10, 15, 20, 25c.; Air 70c., 1g.25, 1g.50.

1970.

Moon Mission of "Apollo 12". Postage 5, 10, 15, 20, 25, 30, 40, 50c.; Air 25, 30, 40, 50, 75c., 1g., 1g., 1g.25, 1g.50.

1971.

Safe Return of "Apollo 13". Optd on 1970 "Apollo 12" issue. Postage 5, 10, 15, 20, 25, 30, 40, 50c.; Air 25, 30, 40, 50, 75c., 1g., 1g.25, 1g.50.

1972.

Gold Medal Winners Olympic Games, Munich. Air 50, 75c., 1g.50, 2g.50, 5g.

1973.

American and Russian Space Exploration. Postage 5, 10, 20, 25, 50c., 2g.50, 5g.; Air 50, 75c., 1g.50, 2g.50, 5g.

Moon Mission of "Apollo 17". Optd on 1973 Space Exploration issue. 50c., 2g.50, 5g.

HAMBURG — Pt. 7

A port in north-west Germany, formerly a Free City. In 1867 it joined the North German Confederation.

16 schillinge = 1 mark.

1

3

4

1859. Imperf.

1	1	½s. black	85·00	£600
2		1s. brown	85·00	70·00
3		2s. red	85·00	95·00
4		3s. blue	85·00	£120
6		4s. green	£110	£1100
7		7s. orange	80·00	40·00
10		9s. yellow	£180	£1800

1864. Imperf.

11	3	1¼s. lilac	£130	70·00
15		1¼s. grey	85·00	70·00
17		1¼s. blue	£425	£900
18	4	2½s. green	£130	£130

1864. Perf.

19	1	½s. black	5·25	9·00
20		1s. brown	10·50	14·50
21	3	1¼s. mauve	70·00	9·00
25	1	2s. red	13·00	18·00
27	4	2½s. green	£110	25·00
30	1	3s. blue	30·00	30·00
33		4s. green	8·50	18·00
34		7s. orange	£140	£120
37		7s. mauve	9·00	14·50
38		9s. yellow	22·00	£1800

5

1866. Roul.

44	5	1¼s. mauve	32·00	32·00
45		1¼s. pink	7·25	£120

1867. Perf.

46	1	2½s. green	11·00	75·00

HANOVER — Pt. 7

In north-east Germany. An independent kingdom until 1866, when it was annexed by Prussia.

1850. 12 pfennige = 1 gutegroschen.
24 gutengroschen = 1 thaler.
1858. 10 (new) pfennige = 1 (new) groschen.
30 (new) groschen = 1 thaler.

2

4

1850. On coloured paper. Imperf.

1	2	1ggr. black on blue	£2750	43·00
2		1ggr. black on green	70·00	7·25
3		1/30th. black on orange	£110	42·00
4		1/30th. black on red	£100	41·00
5		1/15th. black on blue	£170	70·00
6		1/10th. black on orange	£200	55·00

1853. Imperf.

18	4	3pf. pink	70·00	80·00

1855. With coloured network. Imperf.

12	4	3pf. pink and black	£425	£300
14	2	1ggr. black and green	70·00	7·25
15		1/30th. black and pink	£140	29·00
16		1/15th. black and blue	£120	70·00
10		1/10th. black and orange	£200	£150

5 King George V

6

1859. Imperf.

23	5	1gr. pink	3·00	2·20
25a		2gr. blue	18·00	29·00
28		3gr. yellow	£130	60·00
29		3gr. brown	25·00	46·00
31		10gr. green	£250	£750

1860. Imperf.

32a	6	½gr. black	£170	£180

1863. Imperf.

34	4	3pf. green	£350	£900

1864. Roul.

35a	4	3pf. green	27·00	60·00
36a	6	½gr. black	£250	£250
37a	5	1gr. pink	7·25	2·50
38		2gr. blue	£110	50·00
39a		3gr. brown	60·00	70·00

HATAY — Pt. 16

Hatay was returned to Turkey in June 1939.

1939. 100 santims = 40 paras = 1 kurus.

1939. Stamps of Turkey surch **HATAY DEVLETI** and value.

32	112	10s. on 20pa. orange	35	20
33		25s. on 1k. green	35	20
34		50s. on 2k. violet	45	25
35		75s. on 2½k. green	40	20
36		1k. on 4k. grey	1·70	1·10
37		1k. on 5k. red	55	35
38		1½k. on 3k. brown	60	35
39		2½k. on 4k. grey	80	45
40		5k. on 8k. blue	2·20	1·10
41		12½k. on 20k. green	3·25	1·70
42		20k. on 25k. blue	4·25	2·40

9 Map of Hatay

10 Flag of Hatay

1939.

48	9	10pa. orange and blue	25	10
49		30pa. violet and blue	25	15
50		1½k. olive and blue	45	25
51	–	2½k. green	45	25
52	–	3k. blue	50	30
53	–	5k. red	60	35
54	10	6k. red and blue	65	35
55		7½k. red and green	80	50
56		12k. red and violet	1·10	70
57		12½k. red and blue	1·20	70
58	–	17½k. red	2·30	1·20
59	–	25k. olive	2·75	1·40
60	–	50k. blue	6·25	3·00

DESIGNS—HORIZ: 2½, 3, 5k. Lions of Antioch; 17½, 25, 50k. Parliament House, Antioch.

1939. Commemorating Turkish Annexation. Optd **T. C. ilhak tarihi 30-6-1939**.

65	9	10pa. orange and blue	35	20
66		30pa. violet and blue	45	25
67		1½k. olive and blue	45	25
68	–	2½k. green (No. 51)	60	35
69	–	3k. blue (No. 52)	65	35
70	–	5k. red (No. 53)	70	40
71	10	6k. red and blue	70	40
72		7½k. red and green	90	55
73		12k. red and violet	1·10	60
74		12½k. red and blue	1·10	70
75	–	17½k. red (No. 58)	2·10	1·10
76	–	25k. olive (No. 59)	4·00	2·20
77	–	50k. blue (No. 60)	8·00	4·75

POSTAGE DUE STAMPS

1939. Postage Due stamps of Turkey optd **HATAY DEVLETI** or surch also.

D43	D 121	1k. on 2k. blue	80	45
D44		3k. violet	1·70	95
D45		4k. on 5k. green	1·70	95
D46		5k. on 12k. red	2·00	1·30
D47		12k. red	29·00	18·00

D 11 Castle at Antioch

1939.

D61	D 11	1k. red	90	55
D62		3k. brown	80	55
D63		4k. green	1·50	55
D64		5k. grey	2·10	75

1939. Nos. D61/4 optd **T. C. ilhak tarihi 30-6-1939**.

D73	D 11	1k. red	1·40	70
D74		3k. brown	1·70	85
D75		4k. green	2·40	1·30
D76		5k. grey	2·50	1·40

HAWAII — Pt. 22

A group of islands in the central Pacific, an independent kingdom till 1893 when a provisional government was set up. Annexed in 1898 by the United States. Now a State of the U.S.A.

100 cents = 1 dollar.

1

3 Kamehameha III

1851. Inscr "Hawaiian Postage". Imperf.

1	1	2c. blue	£450000	£225000
2		5c. blue	£28000	£16000
3		13c. blue	£14000	£11000

On Nos. 1/2 the value is expressed in words.

1852. Inscr "H.L. & US. Postage". Imperf.

4	1	13c. blue	£35000	£17000

1853. Imperf.

18	3	5c. blue	16·00	
19		13c. red	£160	

5

6 Kamehameha IV

1859. Inter-island post.

9	5	1c. blue	£4750	£3500
12		1c. black	£275	£625
10		2c. blue	£3750	£2250
14d		2c. black	£425	£350

1862. Imperf.

22	6	2c. red	30·00	£100

7 Princess Victoria Kamamalu

12

1864. Perf.

27	7	1c. mauve	7·00	5·75
41	–	2c. red	11·50	7·00
42	–	5c. blue	11·50	2·50
30	–	6c. green	19·00	6·50
31	–	18c. red	65·00	27·00

DESIGNS: 2c. Kamehameha IV; 5c., 6c. Portraits of Kamehameha V; 18c. H.E. Mataio Kekuanaoa.

1865. Inter-island post.

32	12	1c. blue	£190	
33		2c. blue	£190	
34		5c. blue on blue	£600	£425
35	–	5c. blue on blue	£500	£350

DESIGN: No. 35, As Type **12** but inscr "HAWAIIAN POSTAGE" on left side of frame.

16 Princess Likelike

22 Princess (later Queen) Liliuokalani

1875.

38	16	1c. blue	4·50	7·75
39		1c. green	2·10	1·40
36	–	2c. brown	5·75	2·25
40b	–	2c. red	3·00	75
44	–	10c. black	27·00	15·00
45	–	10c. red	25·00	9·75
46	–	10c. brown	23·00	7·75
37	–	12c. black	42·00	21·00
47	–	12c. lilac	55·00	25·00
48	–	15c. brown	42·00	19·00
49	–	25c. purple	95·00	42·00
50	–	50c. red	£120	60·00
51	–	$1 red	£170	£100

DESIGNS: 2c. King Kalakaua; 10c. Same in uniform; 12c. Prince Leleiohoku; 15c. Queen Kapiolani; 25c. Statue of Kamehameha I; 50c. King Lunalilo; $1, Queen Emma Kaleleonalani.

1890.

53	22	2c. violet	3·50	1·10

1893. Stamps of 1864, 1875 and 1889, optd **Provisional GOVT. 1893**.

54	7	1c. mauve	5·50	9·50
55	16	1c. blue	4·50	9·50

56		1c. green	1·25	2·25
57	–	2c. brown	7·50	15·00
58	22	2c. violet	1·25	95
67	–	2c. red (No. 41)	50·00	55·00
68	–	2c. red (No. 40b)	1·00	1·75
60	–	5c. blue	4·50	2·00
61	–	6c. green	11·50	20·00
62	–	10c. black	7·00	11·00
70	–	10c. red	11·50	23·00
71	–	10c. brown	5·75	9·75
64	–	12c. black	7·00	13·50
65	–	12c. lilac	£120	£160
73	–	15c. brown	15·00	23·00
74	–	18c. red	19·00	27·00
66	–	25c. purple	19·00	30·00
75	–	50c. red	45·00	70·00
76	–	$1 red	85·00	£130

24 Arms

26 Statue of King Kamehameha I

1894.

77	24	1c. orange	1·75	1·00
89		1c. green	1·25	90
78	–	2c. brown	1·75	40
90a	–	2c. pink	1·10	60
79	26	5c. red	3·50	1·25
91		5c. blue	4·00	2·25
80	–	10c. green	4·50	3·25
81	–	12c. blue	9·50	10·00
82	–	25c. blue	9·50	10·00

DESIGNS—HORIZ: 2c. Honolulu; 12c. "Arawa" (steamer). VERT: 10c. Star and palms; 25c. President S. B. Dole.

OFFICIAL STAMPS

O 30 Secretary L. A. Thurston

1896.

O83	O 30	2c. green	28·00	13·00
O84		5c. brown	28·00	13·00
O85		6c. blue	32·00	13·00
O86		10c. red	28·00	13·00
O87		12c. orange	40·00	13·00
O88		25c. violet	45·00	13·00

HELIGOLAND — Pt. 1

An island off the N. coast of Germany, ceded to that country by Great Britain in 1890.

1867. 16 schillings = 1 mark.
1875. 100 pfennig = 1 mark.

Many of the Heligoland stamps found in old collections and the majority of those offered at a small fraction of catalogue prices today, are reprints which have very little value.

1

1867. Perf (½, 1, 2 and 6 sch. also roul).

5	1	¼sch. green and red	26·00	£1500
6b		½sch. green and red	95·00	£150
7		¾sch. red and green	29·00	£1100
8a		1sch. red and green	£120	£180
9		1½sch. green and red	65·00	£250
3		2sch. red and green	11·00	55·00
4		6sch. green and red	13·00	£250

2

3

4

5

1875.

10	2	1pf. (¼d.) green and red	11·00	£500
11		2pf. (½d.) red and green	11·00	£600
12a	3	3pf. (⅝d.) green, red yellow	£160	£850
13	2	5pf. (¾d.) green and red	11·00	19·00
14a		10pf. (1½d.) red and green	11·00	20·00
15b	3	20pf. (2½d.) green, red and yellow	14·00	29·00
16	2	25pf. (3d.) green and red	13·00	28·00
17		50pf. (6d.) red and green	20·00	35·00
18	4	1m. (1s.) green, red and black	£140	£200
19	5	5m. (5s.) green, red and black	£150	£950

HOI-HAO (HOIHOW) — Pt. 17

An Indo-Chinese post office in China, closed in 1922.

1901. 100 centimes = 1 franc.
1918. 100 cents = 1 piastre.

HOI HAO
州瓊
(1)

1902. Stamps of Indo-China "Tablet" key-type, optd with T **1**. Chinese characters read "HOI-HAO" and are the same on every value.

1	D	1c. black on blue	1·60	2·75
2		2c. brown on yellow	3·25	3·75
3		4c. red on grey	2·50	3·25
4		5c. green	2·50	3·50
5		10c. black on lilac	5·25	6·50
6		15c. blue	£1300	£550
7		15c. grey	2·25	2·00
8		20c. red on green	21·00	23·00
9		25c. black on red	9·00	6·00
10		30c. brown	40·00	42·00
11		40c. red on yellow	32·00	35·00
12		50c. red on rose	35·00	48·00
13		75c. brown on orange	£200	£180
14		1f. olive	£650	£550
15		5f. mauve on lilac	£550	£450

1903. Stamps of Indo-China, "Tablet" key-type, surch as T **1**. Chinese characters indicate the value and differ for each denomination.

16	D	1c. black on blue	1·60	2·25
17		2c. brown on yellow	2·50	2·25
18		4c. red on grey	2·00	3·75
19		5c. green	2·00	3·75
20		10c. red	2·25	2·50
21		15c. grey	2·00	3·75
22		20c. red on green	3·50	8·25
23		25c. blue	2·00	3·50
24		25c. black on red	4·25	4·25
25		30c. brown	3·50	4·25
26		40c. red on yellow	45·00	50·00
27		50c. red on rose	30·00	50·00
28		50c. brown on blue	£100	£110
29		75c. brown on orange	45·00	50·00
30		1f. olive	60·00	60·00
31		5f. mauve on lilac	£170	£170

1906. Stamps of Indo-China surch **HOI-HAO** and with value in Chinese.

32	8	1c. olive	2·50	3·25
33		2c. red on yellow	2·25	3·00
34		4c. mauve on blue	2·75	3·75
35		5c. green	4·25	4·75
36		10c. red	3·50	4·75
37		15c. brown on blue	4·50	4·75
38		20c. red on green	5·75	7·00
39		25c. blue	7·50	9·50
40		30c. brown on cream	9·00	9·50
41		35c. black on yellow	10·50	15·00
42		40c. black on grey	11·50	17·00
43		50c. brown	16·00	18·00
44	D	75c. brown on orange	38·00	42·00
45	8	1f. green	30·00	38·00
46		2f. brown on yellow	38·00	42·00
47	D	5f. mauve on lilac	£100	£120
48	8	10f. red on green	£130	£130

1908. Native types of Indo-China surch **HOIHAO** (1 to 50c.) or **HOI-HAO** (others) and with value in Chinese.

49	10	1c. black and olive	55	75
50		2c. black and brown	60	1·25
51		4c. black and blue	1·25	1·75
52		5c. black and green	1·50	2·50
53		10c. black and red	1·75	3·50
54		15c. black and violet	5·00	6·25
55	11	20c. black and violet	4·75	7·75
56		25c. black and blue	5·25	5·75
57		30c. black and brown	5·75	7·75
58		35c. black and green	6·25	7·75
59		40c. black and brown	6·00	7·25
60		50c. black and red	7·50	10·50
61	12	75c. black and orange	8·50	11·50
62		1f. black and red	19·00	24·00
63		2f. black and green	38·00	42·00
64		5f. black and blue	70·00	80·00
65		10f. black and violet	£100	£110

1919. Stamps as last surch in addition with value in figures and words.

66	10	⅖c. on 1c. black and olive	1·25	3·00
67		⅘c. on 2c. black and brown	70	2·50
68		1⅗c. on 4c. black and blue	1·75	3·00
69		2c. on 5c. black and green	1·90	2·50
70		4c. on 10c. black and red	3·00	3·25
71		6c. on 15c. black and violet	1·60	2·25
72	11	8c. on 20c. black and violet	3·25	4·00
73		10c. on 25c. black and blue	5·50	6·50
74		12c. on 30c. black & brown	2·75	3·50
75		14c. on 35c. black and green	2·25	3·50
76		16c. on 40c. black & brown	2·75	3·75
77		20c. on 50c. black and red	3·25	3·75
78	12	30c. on 75c. black & orange	3·75	4·50
79	–	40c. on 1f. black and red	10·00	11·00
80	–	80c. on 2f. black and green	22·00	24·00
81	–	2p. on 5f. black and blue	60·00	70·00
82	–	4p. on 10f. black and violet	£150	£170

HONDURAS — Pt. 15

A republic of C. America, independent since 1838.

1866. 8 reales = 1 peso.
1878. 100 centavos = 1 peso.
1933. 100 centavos = 1 lempira.

1 Seal of Honduras

5 Pres. F. Morazan

6

1866. Imperf.

1	1	2r. black on green	60	
2		2r. black on red	60	

1878. Perf.

31	5	1c. violet	40	60
32		2c. brown	40	70
33		½r. black	40	70
34		1r. green	1·25	1·25
35		2r. blue	1·75	1·75
36		4r. red	2·75	2·00
37		1p. orange	3·00	3·00

1890.

45	6	1c. green	25	30
46		2c. red	25	30
47		5c. blue	25	30
48		10c. orange	25	30
49		20c. bistre	25	30
50		25c. red	25	35
51		30c. violet	25	70
52		40c. blue	25	60
53		50c. brown	25	60
54		75c. green	25	1·50
55		1p. lake	25	1·75

8 President Bogran

10

1891.

56	8	1c. blue	15	20
57		2c. brown	15	20
58		5c. green	15	20
59		10c. red	15	20
60		20c. lake	15	25
61		25c. red	20	30
62		30c. grey	20	60
63		40c. green	15	60
64		50c. sepia	15	60
65		75c. violet	15	90
66		1p. brown	15	1·25
67	–	2p. black and brown	60	3·50
68	–	5p. black and violet	60	4·00
69	–	10p. black and green	60	4·00

DESIGN (LARGER): 2, 5, 10p. Pres. Bogran facing left.

1892. 400th Anniv of Discovery of America.

70	10	1c. grey	20	25
71		2c. blue	20	25
72		5c. green	20	25
73		10c. green	20	30
74		20c. red	20	30
75		25c. brown	20	50
76		30c. blue	20	50
77		40c. orange	20	80
78		50c. brown	20	65
79		75c. lake	20	1·00
80		1p. violet	20	1·25

11 Gen. Cabanas

12

1893.

81	11	1c. green	20	30
82		2c. red	20	30
83		5c. blue	20	30
84		10c. brown	20	30
85		20c. brown	20	40
86		25c. blue	20	50
87		30c. orange	20	70
88		40c. black	20	90
89		50c. sepia	20	1·00
90		75c. violet	20	1·40
91		1p. brown	20	1·60

1895.

92	12	1c. red	20	20
93		2c. blue	20	20
94		5c. grey	20	30
95		10c. lake	20	30
96		20c. lilac	20	60
97		30c. lilac	20	90
98		50c. brown	20	1·25
99		1p. green	20	1·60

13 President Arias

14 Steam Train

1896.

100	13	1c. blue	30	30
101		2c. brown	30	30
102		5c. purple	90	30
103		10c. red	30	30
104		20c. green	75	40
105		30c. blue	50	60
106		50c. lake	70	1·00
107		1p. sepia	1·25	1·75

1898.

108	14	1c. brown	20	10
109		2c. red	30	15
110		5c. blue	30	15
111		6c. purple	40	20
112		10c. blue	40	35
113		20c. bistre	1·00	95
114		50c. orange	2·10	3·50
115		1p. green	2·50	4·00

16 General Santos Guardiola

17 President Medina

1903.

118	16	1c. green	25	20
119		2c. red	25	25
120		5c. blue	25	25
121		6c. lilac	30	25
122		10c. brown	30	30
123		20c. blue	35	35
124		50c. red	70	70
125		1p. orange	70	70

1907. Perf or imperf.

127	17	1c. green	25	25
136		1c. black	10·00	7·50
128a		2c. red	30	25
129		5c. blue	35	30
130		6c. violet	35	30
131		10c. sepia	35	35
132		20c. blue	60	55
133		50c. red	70	70
134		1p. orange	90	65

1910. Surch in figures.

137	17	1 on 20c. blue	4·00	3·50
138		5 on 20c. blue	4·00	3·50
139		10 on 20c. blue	4·00	3·50

20

23

1911.

140	20	1c. violet	15	15
141		2c. green	15	15
142		5c. red	15	15
143		6c. blue	30	30
144		10c. blue	35	35
145		20c. yellow	45	45
146		50c. brown	1·10	1·10
147		1p. olive	1·60	1·25

1911. Optd **XC Aniversario de la Independencia**.

157	20	2c. green	8·00	7·50

1912. Election of President Manuel Bonilla.

158	23	1c. red	9·25	9·25

1913. 90th Anniv of Independence. Surch **2 CENTAVOS**.

159	20	2c. on 1c. violet	65	50

1913. Surch in figures and words.

161	20	2c. on 1c. violet	4·50	4·00
162		2c. on 10c. blue	1·10	90
163		2c. on 20c. yellow	3·00	3·00
164		5c. on 1c. violet	1·10	50
165		5c. on 10c. blue	1·40	90
166		6c. on 1c. violet	1·40	90

26 Gen. T. Sierra

27 Gen. M. Bonilla

1913.

167 **26** 1c. brown 20 15
168 2c. red 25 20
169 **27** 5c. blue 30 20
170 5c. blue 30 20
171 6c. violet 40 30
172 6c. mauve 45 35
173 **26** 10c. blue 50 50
174 10c. brown . . . . 1·10 50
175 20c. brown 70 55
176 **27** 50c. red . . . . 1·40 1·25
177 1p. green . . . . 1·60 1·25

1914. Surch.
178 **26** 1c. on 2c. red 50 50
179 5c. on 2c. red 90 90
180 **27** 5c. on 6c. violet . . . . . 1·60 1·60
181 **26** 5c. on 10c. brown . . . . 1·75 1·25
182 10c. on 2c. red . . . . . . 1·60 1·60
184 **27** 10c. on 6c. violet . . . . . 1·60 1·60
185 10c. on 50c. red . . . . . 4·00 3·00

32 Railway Bridge over River Ulua at Pimienta

34 Pres. Francisco Bertrand

1915. Dated "1915".
186 **32** 1c. brown . . . . 2·50 35
187 2c. red . . . . 2·75 35
188 – 5c. blue 25 10
189 – 6c. violet 25 20
190 **32** 10c. blue . . . . 6·75 50
191 20c. brown . . . . 9·00 4·50
192 – 50c. red 70 70
193 – 1p. green . . . . 1·40 1·25
DESIGN: 5c., 6c., 50c., 1p. Bonilla Theatre.

1916.
194 **34** 1c. orange . . . . 1·75 1·90

1918. No. O206 optd **CORRIENTE** and bar.
195 5c. blue . . . . 1·75 1·40

36 Statue of Francisco Morazan

36a

1919. Dated "1919" at top.
196 **36** 1c. brown 10 10
197 2c. red 20 10
198 5c. red 20 10
199 6c. mauve 25 10
200 10c. blue 25 20
201 15c. blue 55 25
202 15c. violet 45 25
203 20c. brown 50 25
204 50c. brown . . . . 1·10 70
205 1p. green . . . . 2·75 1·50

1920. Assumption of Power by Gen. R. L. Gutierrez.
206 **36a** 2c. red . . . . 1·90 1·75
207 2c. gold (51 × 40 mm) . . 5·75 5·25
208 2c. silver (51 × 40 mm) . . 5·75 5·25
209 2c. red (51 × 40 mm) . . . 5·25 4·75

1921. As T **36**, but dated "1920" at top.
210 **36** 6c. purple . . . . 3·00 1·75

1922. Surch **VALE SEIS CTS**.
211 **36** 6c. on 2c. red 30 25

1923. Surch **HABILITADO VALE** and value in words and figures.
212 **36** $0.10 on 1c. brown . . . . 1·10 75
213 $0.50 on 2c. red . . . . . 1·10 1·10
214 1p. on 5c. red . . . . . . 2·00 2·00

39 Dionisio de Herrera

40 M. Paz Baraona

1923.
215 **39** 1c. olive 20 10
216 2c. red 20 10
217 6c. purple 20 10
218 10c. blue 30 15
219 20c. brown 60 25
220 50c. red . . . . 1·25 55
221 1p. green . . . . 2·25 70

1925. Inaug of President Baraona. Imperf or perf.
222 **40** 1c. blue . . . . 1·75 1·75
224 1c. red . . . . 4·50 4·50
225 1c. brown . . . . 7·25 7·25

1925. Air. Nos. 186/93 optd **AERO CORREO** or surch also.
227 5c. blue . . . . 65·00 65·00
229 10c. blue £225 £225
231 20c. brown £160 £160
235 25c. on 1c. brown £110 £110
236 25c. on 5c. blue £200 £200
236c 25c. on 10c. blue £50000
237 25c. on 20c. brown £225 £225
233 50c. red £300 £300
234 1p. green £900 £900

1926. Optd **Acuerdo Mayo 3 de 1926 HABILITADO**.
238 **36** 6c. mauve 95 70

1926. Optd **HABILITADO 1926**.
242 **32** 2c. red . . . . 3·75 3·25
243 **36** 2c. red 20 20

1926. Optd **1926**.
239 – 6c. violet (No. 189) . . . . 1·75 1·75
240 **36** 6c. violet . . . . 2·10 2·10

1926. Surch **Vale 6 Cts. 1926** and bar.
243d **36** 6c. on 10c. blue 35 20

1927. Surch **vale 6 cts. 1927** and bar.
244 **36** 6c. on 15c. violet 70 70
245 **32** 6c. on 20c. brown . . . . 3·75 3·25
246 **36** 6c. on 20c. brown 65 55

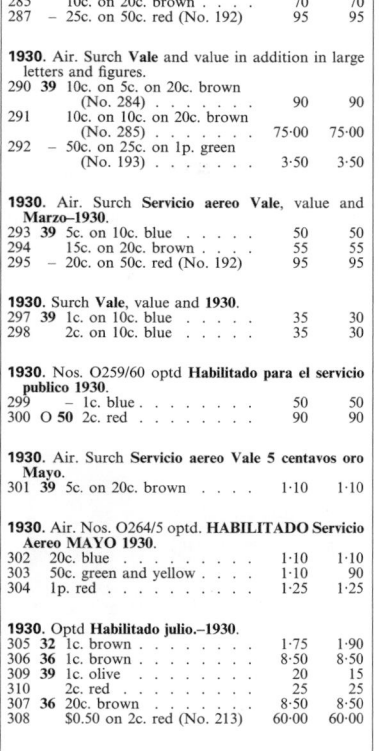

47 Copan Ruins

1927. Various designs as T **47**.
247 – 1c. blue (Road) 20 15
248 **47** 2c. red 20 10
249 – 5c. purple (Pine tree) . . . 20 10
250 – 5c. blue (Pine tree) . . . . 2·75 1·60
251 – 6c. black (Palace) 60 55
252 – 6c. blue (Palace) 25 15
253 – 10c. blue (P. Leiva) 45 20
254 – 15c. blue (Pres. Soto) . . . 60 25
255 – 20c. blue (Lempira) 75 35
256 – 30c. brown (Map) . . . . 1·25 70
257 – 50c. green (Pres. Lindo) . . 1·60 90
258 – 1p. red (Columbus) . . . . 3·25 1·40

50 President Colindres and Vice-President Chavez

1929. Installation of President Colindres.
259 **50** 1c. lake . . . . 2·40 2·40
260 – 2c. green . . . . 2·40 2·40
DESIGN—VERT: 2c. Pres. Colindres.

1929. Air. (a) Surch **Servicio aereo Vale**, value and **1929**.
262 **39** 5c. on 20c. brown . . . . 1·40 1·40
263 10c. on 50c. red . . . . . 1·90 1·60
264 15c. on 1p. green . . . . . 3·25 3·25
261 25c. on 50c. red . . . . . 3·75 3·75
(b) Surch **Servicio Aereo Internacional 1929** and value.
265 **39** 5c. on 10c. blue 50 50
266 20c. on 50c. red 95 95

1929. Herrera Monument type, dated "1924–1928". Surch **Vale 1 cts. XI 1929**.
267 1c. on 6c. mauve 70 70

1929. Nos. 247/58 optd **1929a1930**.
268 – 1c. blue 15 10
269 **47** 2c. red 20 20
270 – 5c. purple 30 20
271 – 5c. blue 70 55
272 – 6c. black . . . . 1·75 1·40
273 – 6c. blue 30 15
274 – 10c. blue 30 15
275 – 15c. blue 30 15
276 – 20c. blue 30 20
277 – 30c. brown 55 45
278 – 50c. green 70 70
279 – 1p. red . . . . 1·90 1·90

1930. Air. No. O264 optd **HABILITADO Servicio Aereo Internacional 1930**.
281 – 50c. green and yellow . . . 1·40 1·40

1930. Air. Surch **Servicio Aereo Internacional Vale**, value and **1930**.
282 **39** 5c. on 10c. blue 55 55
284 5c. on 20c. brown £100 £100
285 10c. on 20c. brown 70 70
287 – 25c. on 50c. red (No. 192) 95 95

1930. Air. Surch **Vale** and value in addition in large letters and figures.
290 **39** 10c. on 5c. on 20c. brown (No. 284) 90 90
291 10c. on 10c. on 20c. brown (No. 285) . . . . 75·00 75·00
292 – 50c. on 25c. on 1p. green (No. 193) . . . . . . 3·50 3·50

1930. Air. Surch **Servicio aereo Vale**, value and **Marzo–1930**.
293 **39** 5c. on 10c. blue 50 50
294 15c. on 20c. brown 55 55
295 – 20c. on 50c. red (No. 192) 95 95

1930. Surch **Vale**, value and **1930**.
297 **39** 1c. on 10c. blue 35 30
298 2c. on 10c. blue 35 30

1930. Nos. O259/60 optd **Habilitado para el servicio publico 1930**.
299 – 1c. blue 50 50
300 O **50** 2c. red 90 90

1930. Air. Surch **Servicio aereo Vale 5 centavos oro Mayo**.
301 **39** 5c. on 20c. brown . . . . 1·10 1·10

1930. Air. Nos. O264/5 optd. **HABILITADO Servicio Aereo MAYO 1930**.
302 20c. blue . . . . 1·10 1·10
303 50c. green and yellow . . . . 1·10 90
304 1p. red . . . . 1·25 1·25

1930. Optd **Habilitado julio.–1930**.
305 **32** 1c. brown . . . . 1·75 1·90
306 **36** 1c. brown . . . . 8·50 8·50
309 **39** 1c. olive 20 15
310 2c. red 25 25
307 **36** 20c. brown . . . . 8·50 8·50
308 $0.50 on 2c. red (No. 213) 60·00 60·00

66 Title Page, First Issue Government Gazette

1930. Newspaper Centenary.
311 **66** 2c. blue 45 45
312 2c. orange 45 45
313 2c. red 45 45

67 National Palace, Tegucigalpa

1930. Air.
314 **67** 5c. yellow 55 30
315 10c. red 75 55
316 15c. green . . . . 1·10 70
317 20c. violet . . . . 1·40 70
318 1p. brown . . . . 3·50 2·75

68 Pres. Baraona

69 Amapala

1931.
319 **68** 1c. sepia 15 10
320 – 2c. red 15 10
321 – 5c. violet 55 10
322 – 6c. green 25 10
323 **69** 10c. brown 35 15
324 – 15c. blue 35 15
325 – 20c. black 55 20
326 – 50c. olive . . . . 1·40 60
327 – 1p. slate . . . . 2·40 1·10
DESIGNS—As Type **68**: 2c. Pres. Bonilla; 15c. Copan Ruins; 20c. Columbus. As Type **69**: 5c. Lake Yojoa; 6c. Tegucigalpa Palace; 50c. Discovery of America; 1p. Loarq Bridge at Loarq.

1931. Nos. 319/27 and 314/18 optd **T.S.de.C.**
328 **68** 1c. sepia (postage) 20 15
329 – 2c. red 25 15
330 – 5c. violet 50 25
331 – 6c. green 25 15
332 **69** 10c. brown 35 30
333 – 15c. blue 35 25
334 – 20c. black 45 25
335 – 50c. olive . . . . 2·75 2·50
336 – 1p. slate . . . . 3·50 3·25
337 **67** 5c. yellow (air) . . . . . 1·10 1·10
338 10c. red . . . . 2·50 2·50
339 15c. green . . . . 3·50 3·50
339a 20c. violet . . . . 4·25 4·25
339b 1p. brown . . . . 9·25 9·25

1931. Air. Surch **Servicio aereo interior Vale 15 cts Octubre 1931**.
340 **39** 15c. on 20c. . . . . 3·50 3·50
344a **32** 15c. on 20c. (No. O209) 22·00 22·00
342 **36** 15c. on 20c. (No. O218) 4·25 4·25
344c **39** 15c. on 20c. (No. O226) 1·00 1·00
343 – 15c. on 50c. (No. O210) 4·25 4·25
346 **36** 15c. on 50c. (No. O219) 3·25 3·25
341 – 15c. on 1p. (No. O265) 4·25 4·25
Nos. 342/3 come with or without the original OFICIAL overprint obliterated.

1932. Air. Surch **S.–Aereo VI. 15 cts. XI 1931.**
347 **39** 15c. on 20c. brown . . . 3·00 3·00
348 **36** 15c. on 50c. (No. O219) . . 3·00 3·00
349 – 15c. on 50c. (No. O264) . . 3·00 3·00
350 – 15c. on 1p. (No. O265) . . 2·40 2·40

1932. Air. Nos. O328/36 optd **Servicio Aereo Exterior. Habilitado X. 1931.**
350c O **70** 1c. blue 35 35
350d 2c. purple 90 90
350e 5c. olive . . . . 1·10 1·10
350f 6c. red . . . . 1·10 1·10
350g 10c. green . . . . . . 1·25 1·25
350h 15c. brown . . . . . . 1·75 1·75
350i 20c. brown . . . . . . 1·75 1·75
350j 50c. violet . . . . . . 1·40 1·40
350k 1p. orange . . . . . . 1·75 1·75

1932. Nos. O223/25 surch **Aereo interior VALE 15 Cts. 1932**.
351 **39** 15c. on 2c. red 45 45
352 15c. on 6c. purple 45 45
353 15c. on 10c. blue 45 45

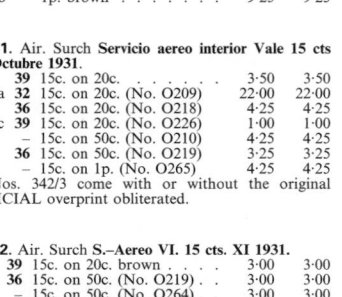

78 Pres. Carias and Vice-Pres. Williams

1933. Inauguration of Pres. Carias.
355 **78** 2c. red 30 25
356 6c. green 35 25
357 10c. blue 45 30
358 15c. orange 55 35

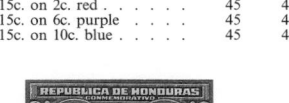

79 Flag of the Race

1933. 441st Anniv of Departure of Columbus from Palos.
359 **79** 2c. blue 35 30
360 6c. yellow 45 35
361 10c. yellow 55 45
362 15c. violet 70 60
363 50c. red . . . . 3·00 2·40
364 1l. green . . . . 4·75 4·75

80 Pres. T. Carias

1935. Inscr as in T **80**.
365 – 1c. green 20 15
366 **80** 2c. red 20 20
367 – 5c. blue 25 25
368 – 6c. brown 35 35
DESIGNS: 1c. Masonic Temple, Tegucigalpa; 5c. National Flag; 6c. Pres. T. E. Palma.

82 Tegucigalpa

1935. Air. Inscr as in T **82**.
369 – 8c. blue 10 10
370 **82** 10c. grey 20 10
371 – 15c. olive 30 15
372 – 20c. green . . . . 3·75 60
373 – 40c. brown 55 20
374 – 50c. yellow . . . . 16·00 4·25
375 – 1l. green . . . . 1·75 1·40
DESIGNS: 8c. G.P.O. and Congress Building; 15c. Map of Honduras; 20c. Presidential Palace and Mayol Railway Bridge; 40c. Different view of Tegucigalpa; 50c. Great horned owl; 1l. National Arms.

84 President Carias and Carias Bridge

1937. Re-election of President Carias.
376 **84** 6c. red and olive . . . . . 2·00 1·00
377 21c. green and violet . . . 3·00 1·25
378 46c. orange and brown . . 5·25 1·60
379 55c. blue and black . . . . 7·00 3·25

85 Book of the Constitution and Flags of U.S. and Honduras

1937. Air. 150th Anniv of U.S. Constitution.
380 **85** 46c. multicoloured . . . . 1·40 1·25

86 Comayagua Cathedral

1937. Air. 400th Anniv of Comayagua.
381 **86** 2c. red 20 10
382 – 8c. blue 25 15
383 – 15c. black 45 35
384 – 50c. brown . . . . 1·75 1·10
DESIGNS: 8c. Founding of Comayagua; 15c. Portraits of Caceres and Carias; 50c. Lintel of Royal Palace.

90 Arms of Honduras

91 Copan Ruins

1939. Dated "1939 1942".
385 **90** 1c. yellow (postage) . . . 10 10
386 – 2c. red 10 10
387 – 3c. red 15 10
388 – 5c. orange 20 15
389 – 8c. blue 25 20
DESIGNS: 2c. Central District Palace; 3c. Map of Honduras; 5c. Choluteca Bridge; 8c. National flag.

390 **91** 10c. brown (air) 15 10
391 – 15c. blue 20 10
392 – 21c. slate 35 10
393 – 30c. green 45 10
394 – 40c. violet 70 15
395 – 46c. brown 70 45
396 – 55c. green 90 60
397 – 66c. black . . . . 1·40 80
398 – 1l. olive . . . . 2·10 55
399 – 2l. red . . . . 3·00 1·75
DESIGNS: 15c. Pres. Carias; 21c. Mayan Temple; 30c. J. C. del Valle; 40c. The Presidency; 46c. Statue of Lempira; 55c. Suyapa Church; 66c. J. T. Reyes; 1l. Choluteca Hospital; 2l. R. Rosa.

1940. Air. Dedication of Columbus Memorial Lighthouse. Official stamps optd **Correo Aereo Habilitado para Servicio Publico Pro-Faro-Colon-1940**.
400 O **92** 2c. blue and green . . . 20 15
401 5c. blue and orange . . 25 25
402 8c. blue and brown . . . 25 25
403 15c. blue and red . . . 35 35
404 46c. blue and olive . . . 70 70
405 50c. blue and violet . . 70 70
406 1l. blue and brown . . . 3·00 2·00
407 2l. blue and red . . . . 5·75 4·50

97 Francisco Morazan

98 Red Cross

1941. Obligatory Tax. Death Centenary of Gen. Morazan.
408 **97** 1c. brown 15 10

1941. Obligatory Tax. Red Cross.
409 **98** 1c. blue and red 15 10

1941. Air. Official stamps optd **Habilitada para el Servicio Publico 1941**.
410 O **92** 5c. blue and orange . . 2·50 25
411 8c. blue and brown . . . 4·00 25

1941. Air. Official stamps surch **Rehabilitada para el Servicio Publico 1941 Vale** and value in words.
412 O **92** 3c. on 2c. blue and green 30 20
413 8c. on 2c. blue and green 35 30
414 8c. on 15c. blue and red 35 25
415 8c. on 46c. blue & olive 55 45
416 8c. on 50c. blue & violet 70 55
417 8c. on 1l. blue & brown 1·10 70
418 8c. on 2l. blue and red 1·40 1·10

1942. Air. Surch **Correo Aereo** and value.
419 8c. on 15c. blue (No. 391) . . 60 20
420 16c. on 46c. brown (No. 395) 60 20

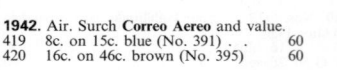

102 Morazan's Birthplace

103 Tomb

1942. Air. Death Centenary of Gen. Morazan.
421 – 2c. orange 10 10
422 – 5c. blue 10 10
423 **102** 8c. purple 15 10
424 **103** 14c. black 30 30
425 – 16c. olive 20 20
426 – 21c. blue 90 70
427 – 1l. blue . . . . 2·75 1·75
428 – 2l. brown . . . . 7·25 5·75
DESIGNS—HORIZ: 2c. Commemoration plate; 5c. Battle of La Trinidad; 16c. Morazan's monument (as in Type **36**); 21c. Church where Morazan was baptised; 1l. Arms of C. American Federation. VERT: 2l. Morazan.

105 Coat of Arms

106 Western Hemisphere

1943. Air.
429 **105** 1c. green 10 10
430 – 2c. blue 10 10
431 – 5c. green 20 10
432 – 6c. green 20 10
433 – 8c. purple 25 10
434 – 10c. brown 25 10
435 – 15c. red 25 10
436 – 16c. red 30 10
437 – 21c. blue 40 10
438 – 30c. brown 45 10
439 – 40c. red 45 10
440 – 55c. black 70 55
441 – 1l. green . . . . 1·25 1·10
442 **106** 2l. lake . . . . 3·50 3·00
443 – 5l. orange . . . . 8·75 8·75
DESIGNS—HORIZ: 2c. National flag; 5c. Cattle; 8c. Rosario; 15c. Tobacco plant; 21c. Orchid; 30c. Oranges; 40c. Wheat; 5l. Map of Honduras. VERT: 6c. Banana Tree; 10c. Pine tree; 16c. Sugar cane; 55c. Coconut palms; 1l. Maize.

114 Agricultural College

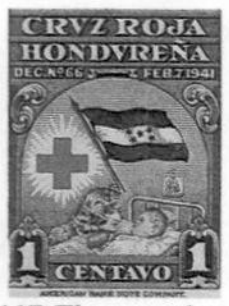
117 Flag, mother and child

1944. Air. Inauguration of Pan-American Agricultural College.
444 **114** 21c. green 30 20

1944. Optd **HABILITADO 1944-45**.
445 **90** 1c. yellow 30 30
446 – 2c. red (No. 386) 45 45

1945. Air. Surch **Correo Aereo HABILITADO Acd. No 798-1945** and value.
447 – 1c. on 50c. (No. 384) . . . 10 10
448 **86** 2c. on 2c. red 15 10
449 – 8c. on 15c. (No. 383) . . . 20 20
450 **91** 10c. on 10c. brown . . . 35 30
451 – 15c. on 15c. (No. 391) . . 20 20
452 – 30c. on 21c. (No. 392) . . 3·00 3·00
453 – 40c. on 40c. (No. 394) . . 1·75 1·40
454 – 1l. on 46c. (No. 395) . . . 1·75 1·40
455 – 2l. on 66c. (No. 397) . . . 3·00 3·00

1945. Obligatory Tax. Red Cross.
456 **117** 1c. brown and red . . . 15 10
456a – 1c. red and brown . . . 15 10
DESIGN: No. 456a, Red Cross.

118 Arms of Honduras

1946. Air. Coats of Arms.
457 **118** 1c. red 10 10
458 – 2c. orange 10 10
459 – 5c. violet 20 10
461 – 15c. purple 35 20
462 – 21c. blue 35 30
463 – 1l. green . . . . 1·40 90
464 – 2l. grey . . . . 2·10 1·60
ARMS: 2c. Von Gracias and Trujillo; 5c. Comayagua and S. J. de Olancho; 15c. Honduras Province and S. J. de Puerto Caballos; 21c. Comayagua and Tencoa; 1l. Jerez de la Frontera de Choluteca and San Pedro de Zula; 2l. San Miguel de Heredia de Tegucigalpa.

119 Broken Column and F. D. Roosevelt

1946. Air. Allied Victory over Japan and Death of Pres. Roosevelt. (a) Inscr "F.D.R."
460 **119** 8c. brown 70 55

(b) Inscr "FRANKLIN D. ROOSEVELT".
465 **119** 8c. brown 45 30

120 Honduras and Copan Antiquities

1947. Air. 1st International Conference of Caribbean Archaeologists. Various frames.
466 **120** 16c. green 35 15
467 22c. yellow 25 15
468 40c. orange 55 35
469 1l. blue 90 90
470 2l. mauve . . . . 3·00 3·00
471 5l. brown . . . . 7·25 6·50

121 Flag and Arms of Honduras

122 Galvez, Carias and Lozano

123 National Stadium

124 President Galvez

1949. Air. Inauguration of President Juan Manuel Galvez. Inscr "CONMEMORATIVA DE LA SUCESION PRESIDENCIAL", etc.
472 **121** 1c. blue 10 10
473 **124** 2c. red 10 10
474 – 5c. blue 10 10
475 – 9c. brown 10 10
476 – 15c. brown 20 10
477 **122** 21c. black 35 10
478 **123** 30c. olive 45 15
479 – 40c. grey 70 20
480 – 1l. brown . . . . 1·10 35
481 – 2l. violet . . . . 2·00 1·75
482 – 5l. red . . . . 5·75 5·25
DESIGNS—HORIZ: 40c. Toncontin Customs House; 5l. Galvez and Lozano. VERT: 5c., 15c. Lozano (different frames); 9c. Galvez; 1l. Palace of Tegucigalpa; 2l. Carias.

1951. Air. 75th Anniv of **U.P.U. Optd U.P.U. 75 Aniversario 1874-1949**.
483 **120** 16c. green 55 55
484 – 22c. yellow 70 70
485 – 40c. orange 70 70
486 – 1l. blue . . . . 2·40 2·40
487 – 2l. mauve . . . . 3·50 3·50
488 – 5l. brown . . . . 26·00 26·00

1951. Air. Founding of Central Bank. Nos. 472/81 optd **Conmemorativa Fundacion Banco Central Administracion Galvez–Lozano Julio 1o. de 1950**.
489 1c. blue 10 10
490 2c. red 10 10
491 5c. blue 10 10
492 9c. brown 15 10
493 15c. brown 15 10
494 21c. black 25 25
495 30c. olive 45 35
496 40c. grey 70 65
497 1l. brown . . . . 1·75 1·25
498 2l. violet . . . . 4·50 3·25

127 Discovery of America

128 Isabella the Catholic

1952. Air. 500th Anniv of Birth of Isabella the Catholic.
499 **127** 1c. slate and orange . . . 10 10
500 – 2c. brown and blue . . . 10 10
501 – 8c. sepia and green . . . 20 10
502 **128** 16c. black and blue . . . 30 20
503 – 30c. green and violet . . . 55 55
504 – 1l. black and red . . . . 1·40 1·10
505 **127** 2l. violet and brown . . . 2·75 2·75
506 **128** 5l. olive and purple . . . 7·00 7·00
DESIGNS—HORIZ: 2c.1l. King Ferdinand and Queen Isabella receive Columbus; 8c. Surrender of Granada; 30c. Queen Isabella pledging her jewels.

1953. Air. Surch **HABILITADO 1953** and value.
507 **122** 5c. on 21c. black 10 10
508 8c. on 21c. black 20 10
509 16c. on 21c. black 35 20

1953. Air. Nos. O507/509 and O512/14 surch **HABILITADO 1953** and value or optd only.
510 **127** 10c. on 1c. olive & purple 10 10
511 12c. on 1c. olive & purple 10 10
512 – 15c. on 2c. violet & brn 15 15
513 – 20c. on 2c. violet & brn 25 25
514 – 24c. on 2c. violet & brn 25 25
515 – 25c. on 2c. violet & brn 25 25
516 – 30c. on 8c. black and red 25 25
517 – 35c. on 8c. black and red 30 30
518 – 50c. on 8c. black and red 45 45
519 – 60c. on 8c. black and red 55 55
520 – 1l. sepia and green . . . 1·40 1·25
521 **127** 2l. brown and blue . . . 3·50 2·75
522 **128** 5l. slate and orange . . . 9·00 9·00

130 U.N. Emblem

1953. Air. United Nations. Inscr as in T **130**.
523 – 1c. blue and black 10 10
524 **130** 2c. blue and black 15 10
525 – 3c. violet and black . . . 20 15
526 – 5c. green and black . . . 15 15
527 – 15c. brown and black . . 35 30
528 – 30c. brown and black . . 90 75
529 – 1l. red and black . . . . 6·00 5·25
530 – 2l. orange and black . . . 7·25 6·00
531 – 5l. green and black . . . 18·00 16·00
DESIGNS: 1c. U.N. and Honduras flags; 3c. U.N. Building, New York; 5c. Arms of U.S.A; 15c. Pres. J. M. Galvez; 30c. Indian girl (U.N.I.C.E.F.); 1l. Refugee mother and child (U.N.R.R.A.); 2l. Torch and open book (U.N.E.S.C.O.); 5l. Cornucopia (F.A.O.).

1955. Air. 50th Anniv of Rotary International. Nos. O532/38 optd with rotary emblem, **1905 1955**, clasped hands and laurel sprigs or surch also.
532 1c. blue and black 15 15
533 2c. green and black 15 15
534 3c. orange and black 20 20
535 5c. red and black 25 25
536 8c. on 1c. blue and black . . 15 15
537 10c. on 2c. green and black 20 20
538 12c. on 3c. orange and black 25 25
539 15c. sepia and black 35 35
540 30c. purple and black . . . . 1·10 1·10
541 1l. olive and black . . . . 18·00 18·00

1956. Air. 10th Anniv of U.N.O. Nos. O523/5 and 527/31 optd **ONU X ANIVERSARIO 1945-1955**.
542 1c. blue and black 20 20
543 2c. green and black 20 20
544 3c. orange and black 25 25
545 5c. red and black 30 30
546 15c. brown and black . . . 35 35
547 30c. brown and black . . . 55 55

548 1l. red and black . . . . . . 3·50 3·00
549 2l. orange and black . . . . 5·25 4·00
550 5l. green and black . . . . . 13·00 11·00

133 J. Lozano Diaz

134 Southern Highway

1956. Air.
551 – 1c. blue and black 10 10
552 **133** 2c. blue and black 10 10
553 **134** 3c. sepia and black . . . 10 10
554 – 4c. purple and black . . . 10 10
555 – 5c. red and black 10 10
556 – 8c. multicoloured 10 10
557 – 10c. green and black . . . 15 10
558 – 12c. green and black . . . 15 10
559 – 15c. black and red 20 10
560 – 20c. blue and black . . . 20 15
561 **133** 24c. purple and black . . 25 20
562 – 25c. green and black . . . 30 25
563 – 30c. red and black 30 25
564 – 40c. brown and black . . 35 30
565 – 50c. turquoise and black . . 45 35
566 – 60c. orange and black . . 55 45
567 – 1l. purple and black . . . 1·40 1·10
568 – 2l. red and black . . . . 2·75 1·75
569 – 5l. lake and black . . . . 5·25 3·50
DESIGNS—HORIZ: 1c. Suyapa Basilica; 8c. Landscape and cornucopia; 10c. National Stadium; 12c. United States School; 15c. Projected Central Bank of Honduras; 20c. Legislative Building; 25c. Projected Development Bank; 30c. Toncontin Airport; 40c. J. R. Molina Bridge; 60c. Treasury Building; 1l. Blood Bank. VERT: 4c. Dona de Estrada Palma; 5c. Dona de Morazan; 50c. Peace Memorial; 2l. Electrical Communications Building; 5l. Presidential Palace.

135 Revolutionary Flag

136 Flags of Honduras and the U.S.A. and Book

1957. Air. Revolution of October 21, 1956. Frames in black.
570 **135** 1c. blue and yellow . . . 10 10
571 – 2c. purple, green & orange 10 10
572 **135** 5c. blue and pink 15 10
573 – 8c. violet, olive and orange 20 10
574 – 10c. brown and violet . . 20 15
575 **135** 12c. blue and turquoise 25 20
576 – 15c. brown and green . . 30 25
577 – 30c. grey and pink . . . 45 25
578 – 1l. brown and blue . . . 1·40 1·25
579 – 2l. grey and green . . . . 2·75 1·75
DESIGNS: 2c., 8c. Obelisk and mountains; 10c., 15c., 1l. Indian with bow and arrow; 30c., 2l. Arms of 1821.

NOTE. In July 1958 after stocks of current issues had been looted, eighteen different facsimile signatures validated the remaining stamps for use.

1958. Air. Bi-national Centre Commem. (Institute of American Culture). Flags in national colours.
580 **136** 1c. blue 10 10
581 2c. red 10 10
582 5c. green 10 10
583 10c. brown 20 20
584 20c. orange 35 20
585 30c. red 35 30
586 50c. grey 45 35
587 1l. yellow . . . . 1·10 95
588 2l. olive . . . . 3·00 1·90
589 5l. blue . . . . 4·50 4·50

137 Abraham Lincoln

138 Henri Dunant

1959. Air. 150th Birth Anniv of Abraham Lincoln. Flags in blue and red.
590 **137** 1c. green 15 15
591 – 2c. blue 15 15
592 – 3c. violet 20 20
593 – 5c. red 20 20
594 – 10c. slate 25 20
595 – 12c. sepia 25 20
596 **137** 15c. orange 35 20
597 – 25c. purple 55 30
598 – 50c. blue 70 55
599 – 1l. brown . . . . 1·40 1·25
600 – 2l. olive . . . . 1·90 1·40
601 – 5l. yellow . . . . 4·00 3·25
DESIGNS—HORIZ: 2c., 25c. Lincoln's birthplace; 3c., 50c. Gettysburg Address; 5c., 1l. Lincoln at conference to free slaves; 10c., 2l. Assassination of Lincoln; 12c., 5l. Lincoln Memorial, Washington.

1959. Obligatory Tax. Red Cross.
602 **138** 1c. red and blue 15 10
647 1c. red and green 20 10
648 1c. red and brown 20 10
Nos. 647/8 have no frame around portrait and values are at left.

139 Constitution of 21 December 1957

1959. Air. 2nd Anniv of New Constitution. Inscr "21 DE DICIEMBRE DE 1957".
603 **139** 1c. red, blue and brown 10 10
604 – 2c. brown 10 10
605 – 3c. blue 10 10
606 – 5c. orange 20 10
607 **139** 10c. red, blue and green 25 10
608 – 12c. red 35 20
609 – 25c. violet 70 25
610 – 50c. grey-blue . . . . . 1·10 35
DESIGNS—HORIZ: 2, 12c. Inaug of Pres. R. V. Morales. VERT: 3, 25c. Pres. R. V. Morales; 5, 50c. Flaming torch.

140 King Alfonso XIII of Spain and Map

1961. Air. Settlement of Boundary Dispute with Nicaragua.
611 **140** 1c. blue 10 10
612 – 2c. pink 10 10
613 – 5c. green 10 10
614 – 10c. brown 15 10
615 – 20c. red 30 20
616 – 50c. brown 70 55
617 – 1l. slate . . . . 1·10 90
DESIGNS: 2c. 1906 award (document); 5c. Arbitration commission, 1907; 10c. International Court of Justice, The Hague; 20c. 1960 award (document); 50c. Pres. Morales Foreign Minister Puerto and map; 1l. Presidents Davila and Morales.

1964. Air. Freedom from Hunger. Flags in National colours. Optd **FAO Luncha Contra el Hambre**.
621 **136** 1c. blue 20 20
622 2c. red 20 20
623 5c. green 25 25
624 30c. red . . . . 1·10 70
625 2l. olive . . . . 5·25 4·00

1964. Air. Olympic Games, Tokyo. Optd with Olympic Rings and **1964**.
626 – 1c. blue & black (No. 523) 15 15
627 **130** 2c. blue and black 25 25
628 – 3c. violet & blk (No. 525) 30 30
629 – 15c. brn & blk (No. 527) 55 55
See also No. O646.

144 Ancient Stadium

1964. Air. "Homage to Sport" and Olympic Games, Tokyo.
630 **144** 1c. black and green . . . 10 10
631 – 2c. black and mauve . . . 10 10
632 – 5c. black and blue . . . 15 15
633 – 8c. black and grey-green 25 25
634 **144** 10c. black and bistre . . . 35 30
635 – 12c. black and yellow . . 55 35
636 – 1l. black and buff . . . 1·40 90
637 – 2l. black and olive . . . 3·00 1·75
638 **144** 3l. black and red . . . . 4·50 2·75
DESIGNS: 2c., 12c. Boundary stones; 5c., 1l. Mayan ball player; 8c., 2l. Olympic Stadium, Tokyo.

1964. Air. Surch.
639 – 4c. on 5c. (No. 593) . . . 15 10
618 **137** 6c. on 15c. 20 10
619 – 8c. on 25c. (No. 597) . . 20 10
640 – 10c. on 15c. (No. 476) . . 15 10
620 – 10c. on 50c. (No. 598) . . 30 20
641 – 12c. on 16c. (No. 425) . . 15 10
642 – 12c. on 21c. (No. 426) . . 25 10
643 **120** 12c. on 22c. 25 10
644 30c. on 1l. 45 25
645 – 40c. on 1l. (No. 480) . . . 65 30
646 **120** 40c. on 2l. 65 30
See also Nos. 716/18 and O647/18.

1965. Air. Presidential Investiture of General Lopez. Optd **Toma de Posesion General Oswaldo Lopez A. Junio 6, 1965**. Flags in blue and red.
649 **137** 1c. green 10 10
650 – 2c. green 10 10
651 – 3c. violet (No. 592) . . . 10 10
652 – 5c. red (No. 593) 10 10
653 **137** 15c. orange 20 15
654 – 25c. purple (No. 597) . . 30 20
655 – 50c. red 50 35
656 – 2l. olive (No. 600) . . . . 1·75 1·40
657 – 5l. yellow (No. 601) . . . 5·25 3·50

147 Ambulance and Clinic

1965. Air. Order of Malta Campaign Against Leprosy.
658 **147** 1c. blue 25 25
659 – 5c. green 35 35
660 – 12c. black 55 55
661 – 1l. brown . . . . 1·75 1·75
DESIGNS: 5c. Hospital; 12c. Patients receiving treatment; 1l. Map of Honduras.

148 Father Subirana

151 2r. Stamp of 1866

1965. Air. Death Cent of Father Manuel de Jesus Subirana. Centres in black and gold; inscr in black.
662 – 1c. violet 10 10
663 – 2c. flesh 10 10
664 **148** 8c. pink 10 10
665 – 10c. purple 10 10
666 – 12c. brown 20 15
667 – 20c. green 35 30
668 – 1l. sage . . . . 1·75 70
669 – 2l. blue . . . . 3·00 1·75
DESIGNS: 1c. Abraham, Jicaque Indian; 2c. Allegory of Catechism; 10c. Msgr. Juan de Jesus Zepeda; 12c. Pope Pius IX; 20c. Subirana's Tomb, Yoro; 1l. Hermitage; 2l. Jicaque Indian woman and child.

1965. Air. Churchill Commemoration. Nos. 499/500 and 470 optd **IN MEMORIAM Sir Winston Churchill 1874-1965**.
671 **127** 1c. black and orange . . 35 35
672 – 2c. brown and blue . . . 70 70
673 – 2l. mauve . . . . 5·75 5·00
See also No. O674.

1966. Air. Pope Paul's Visit to U.N. Organisation. Nos. 662/68 optd **CONMEMORATIVA Visita S. S. Pablo VI a la ONU. 4-X-1965**.
675 – 1c. violet 15 10
676 – 2c. flesh 15 10
677 **148** 8c. pink 25 15
678 – 10c. purple 25 15
679 – 12c. brown 30 15
680 – 20c. green 35 20
681 – 1l. sage . . . . 2·40 90

1966. Air. Stamp Centenary. Inscriptions in black (1c., 2c.) or in gold (others).
682 **151** 1c. black, green and gold 10 10
683 – 2c. blue, black and orange 10 10
684 – 3c. purple and red 10 10
685 – 4c. indigo and blue . . . 10 10
686 – 5c. purple and mauve . . 5·00 2·00
687 – 6c. violet and lilac 10 10
688 – 7c. slate and turquoise . . 10 10
689 – 8c. indigo and blue . . . 15 15
690 – 9c. blue and cobalt . . . 15 15
691 – 10c. black and olive . . . 15 15
692 – 12c. yellow, black & green 15 15
693 – 15c. purple and mauve . . 25 25
694 – 20c. black and orange . . 30 30
695 – 30c. blue and yellow . . . 35 35
696 – 40c. multicoloured 55 55
697 – 1l. green and emerald . . 1·25 1·10
698 – 2l. black and grey . . . . 2·25 1·75
DESIGNS—VERT: 2c. Honduras; 5c. air stamp of 1925; 3c. T. Estrada Palma, 1st Director of Posts; 8c. Sir Rowland Hill; 10c. Pres. Arellano; 12c. Postal emblem; 15c. H. von Stephan; 30c. Honduras flag; 40c. Honduras arms; 1l. U.P.U. Monument, Berne; 2l. J. M. Medina (statesman). HORIZ: 4c. Post Office, Tegucigalpa; 5c. Steam locomotive No. 59; 6c. 19th-century mule transport; 7c. 19th-century sorting office; 9c. Mail van; 20c. Curtiss C-46 Commando mail plane.
See also No. E700.

1966. Air. World Cup Football Championship, Final Match between England and West Germany. Optd **CAMPEONATO DE FOOTBALL Copa Mundial 1966 Inglaterra-Alemania Wembley, Julio 30**.
701 – 2c. vio & brn (No. O508) 20 20
702 **128** 16c. black and blue . . . 35 35
703 **127** 2l. violet and brown . . . 7·25 5·75

1967. Air. 20th Anniv of U.N.O. Nos. 662/4 and 666/9 optd **CONMEMORATIVA del XX Aniversario ONU 1966**.
704 – 1c. violet 20 20
705 – 2c. flesh 25 25
706 **148** 8c. pink 35 35
707 – 12c. brown 55 45
708 – 20c. green 70 60
709 – 1l. sage . . . . 1·75 1·40
710 – 2l. blue . . . . 3·00 2·75

1967. Birth Bicentenary of Simeon Canas y Villacorta (slave liberator). Nos. 551, 553, 559, 552 and 568. Optd **Simeon Canas y Villacorta Libertador de los esclavos en Centro America 1767-1967**.
711 1c. blue and black 15 15
712 3c. sepia and black 25 25
713 15c. black and red 35 35
714 25c. green and black 70 55
715 2l. red and black . . . . . . 2·00 1·75

1967. Air. Nos. E570 and 480/1 surch.
716 E **135** 10c. on 20c. grey, black and red 20 10
717 – 10c. on 1l. brown . . . 20 10
718 – 10c. on 2l. violet . . . 20 10

156 J. C. del Valle (Honduras)

1967. Air. Founding of Central-American Journalists' Federation.
719 **156** 11c. black, blue and gold 10 10
720 – 12c. black, yellow and blue 10 10
721 – 14c. black, green and silver 15 10
722 – 20c. black, green & mauve 20 15
723 – 30c. black, yellow and lilac 25 25
724 – 40c. gold, blue and violet 70 70
725 – 50c. green, red and olive 70 70
DESIGNS: 12c. Ruben Dario (Nicaragua); 14c. J. B. Montufar (Guatemala); 20c. F. Gavidia (El Salvador); 30c. J. M. Fernandez (Costa Rica); 40c. Federation emblem; 50c. Central American map.

157 Olympic Rings and Flags of Mexico and Honduras

1968. Air. Olympic Games, Mexico. Mult.
726 1c. Type **157** 15 15
727 2c. Type **157** 25 25
728 5c. Italian flag and boxing . . 30 30
729 10c. French flag and skiing 35 35
730 12c. West German flag and show-jumping 55 55
731 50c. British flag and athletics 1·75 1·75
732 1l. U.S. flag and running . . 5·75 5·75

158 J. F. Kennedy and Rocket Launch

1968. Air. International Telecommunications Union Centenary. Multicoloured.
734 1c. Type **158** 15 15
735 2c. Dish aerial and telephone 20 20
736 3c. Dish aerial and television 20 20
737 5c. Dish aerial, globe and I.T.U. emblem as satellite 35 35
738 8c. "Early Bird" satellite . . 50 50
739 10c. Type **158** 55 55
740 20c. Type **158** 75 75

1969. Air. Robert F. Kennedy Commemoration. Nos. 734 and 739/40 optd **In-Memoriam Robert F. Kennedy 1925-1968**.
741 1c. multicoloured 40 40
742 10c. multicoloured 40 40
743 20c. multicoloured 40 40

1969. Air. Gold Medal Winners, Olympic Games. Nos. 735/8 optd **Medallas de Oro Mexico 1968**.
744 2c. multicoloured 25 25
745 3c. multicoloured 25 25
746 5c. multicoloured 40 40
747 8c. multicoloured 75 75

161 Patient and Nurse

1969. Obligatory Tax. Red Cross.
748 **161** 1c. red and blue 15 10

162 Rocket Launch

1969. Air. First Man on the Moon. Mult.
749 5c. Type **162** 10 10
750 10c. Moon 10 10
751 12c. Lunar landing module leaving space-ship (horiz) 15 10
752 20c. Astronaut on Moon (horiz) 15 15
753 24c. Lunar landing module taking off from Moon . . 20 15
754 30c. Capsule re-entering Earth's atmosphere (horiz) 30 20

1970. No. E700 optd with **"HABILITADO"** for use as ordinary postage stamp.
755 20c. brown, orange and gold 35 25

1970. Air. Various stamps surch in figures.
756 **151** 4c.+1c. (No. 682) . . . 10 10
757 – 4c.+3c. (No. 525) . . . 10 10
758 – 5c.+1c. (No. 662) . . . 10 10
759 – 5c.+7c. (No. 688) . . . 10 10
760 – 8c.+2c. (No. 663) . . . 20 20
761 – 10c.+2c. (No. 500) . . 25 25
762 **133** 10c.+2c. (No. 552) . . 25 25
763 – 10c.+3c. (No. 525) . . 25 25
764 **134** 10c.+3c. (No. 553) . . 25 25
765 – 10c.+3c. (No. 684) . . 25 25
766 – 10c.+9c. (No. 690) . . 10 10
767 **156** 10c.+11c. (No. 719) . . 10 10
768 – 12c.+14c. (No. 721) . . 15 15
769 E **135** 12c.+20c. (No. E570) . . 15 15
770 – 12c.+1l. (No. 480) . . . 15 15
771 – 15c.+12c. (No. 783) . . 35 35
772 – 30c.+12c. (No. 783) . . 70 70
773 – 40c.+24c. (No. 753) . . 90 90
774 – 40c.+50c. (No. 731) . . 90 90

1970. Air. Safe Return of "Apollo 13". Nos. 749/54 optd **Admiracion al Rescate del Apolo XIII, James A. Lovell, Fred W. Haise Jr., John L. Swigert Jr.**
775 5c. multicoloured 10 10
776 10c. multicoloured 15 15
777 12c. multicoloured 20 20
778 20c. multicoloured 30 30
779 24c. multicoloured 35 35
780 30c. multicoloured 45 45

165 J. A. Sanhueza (firefighter)

166 Hotel Honduras Maya

1970. Air. Campaign Against Forest Fires. Multicoloured.
781 5c. Type **165** 10 10
782 8c. R. Ordonez Rodriguez (firefighter) 15 10
783 12c. Fire Brigade emblems (horiz) 15 15
784 20c. Flag, map and emblems 30 25
785 1l. Emblems, and flags of Honduras, U.N. and U.S.A. 70 65

1970. Air. Opening of Hotel Honduras Maya, Tegucigalpa.
787 **166** 12c. black and blue . . . 25 25

1972. Air. 50th Anniv of Honduras Masonic Grand Lodge. Nos. 749 and 751/3. optd **Aniversario Gran Logia de Honduras 1922-1972** or surch also.
791 5c. multicoloured 25 30
792 12c. multicoloured 55 45
793 1l. on 20c. multicoloured . . 1·10 70
794 2l. on 24c. multicoloured . . 1·75 1·40

168 Soldiers' Bay, Guanaja

1972. Air. 150th Anniv of Independence (1970). Multicoloured.
795 4c. Type **168** 10 10
796 5c. Bugler sounding "Last Post" (vert) 10 10
797 6c. Lake Yojoa 10 10
798 7c. "The Banana Carrier" (R. Aguilar) (vert) 10 10
799 8c. Soldiers marching and fly-past 15 10
800 9c. "Brassavola digbyana" (national flower) (vert) . . 15 10
801 10c. As 9c. 20 10
802 12c. Machine-gunner 20 10
803 15c. Tela beach at sunset . . 25 10
804 20c. Stretcher-bearers 25 10
805 30c. "San Antonio de Oriente" (A. Velasquez) . . 35 25
806 40c. Ruins of Copan 55 30
807 50c. "Woman from Huacal" (P. Zelaya Sierra) 55 35
808 1l. Trujillo Bay . . . . . . 1·75 90
809 2l. As 9c. . . . . 1·75 1·40

169 Sister Maria Rosa and Child

1972. Air. "S.O.S." Children's Villages in Honduras. Each brown, green and gold.
812 10c. Type **169** 20 10
813 15c. "S.O.S. Villages" emblem (horiz) 25 10
814 30c. Father J. T. Reyes (educationalist) 45 15
815 40c. First Central American "S.O.S." village (horiz) . . 45 20
816 1l. "Future Citizen" (boy) . . 1·40 70

170 Map of Honduras

1973. Air. 25th Annivs of National Cartographic Service (10c.) and Joint Cartographic Work (12c.).
817 **170** 10c. multicoloured 35 25
818 – 12c. multicoloured 45 25
DESIGN: 12c. Similar to Type **170** but with two badges and inscr "25 Anos de Labor Cartografica Conjunta".

171 Illustration from "Habitante de la Osa"

1973. Air. 25th Anniv of U.N.E.S.C.O. and Juan Ramon Molina (poet) Commem. Multicoloured.
819 8c. Type **171** 20 10
820 20c. Juan Ramon Molina . . 70 30
821 1l. Illustration from "Tierras Mares y Cielos" . . . . . 1·40 70
822 2l. U.N.E.S.C.O. emblem . . 2·40 1·60

1973. Air. Census and World Population Year. Various stamps optd **Censos de Poblacion y Vivienda, marzo 1974. 1974 Ano Mundial de Poblacion.**
824 **169** 10c. brown, green and gold 10 10
828 **170** 10c. multicoloured 10 10
829 – 12c. mult (No. 818) . . . 30 15
825 – 15c. brown, green and gold (No. 813) 35 20
826 – 30c. brown, green and gold (No. 814) 10 10
827 – 40c. brown, green and gold (No. 815) 10 10

1974. Air. Various stamps surch.
830 – 2c. on 1c. blue and black (No. 551) 10 10
831 **137** 2c. on 1c. green 10 10
832 – 3c. on 1c. blue and black (No. 551) 10 10
833 **137** 3c. on 1c. green 10 10
834 – 16c. on 1c. bl & blk (551) 15 15
835 **135** 16c. on 1c. bl, yell & blk 15 15
836 **137** 16c. on 1c. green 15 15
837 – 16c. on 1c. mult (O602) 15 15
838 – 16c. on 1c. violet (662) . . 15 15
839 **170** 18c. on 10c. mult 20 15
840 – 18c. on 12c. mult (818) . . 20 15
841 **171** 18c. on 8c. mult 20 15
842 **169** 18c. on 10c. mult 20 15
843 – 50c. on 30c. mult (814) . . 55 45
844 **137** 1l. on 2l. mauve . . . . 1·40 1·00
845 – 1l. on 2l. violet (No. 481) 1·40 1·00
846 – 1l. on 50c. blue (610) . . 1·40 1·00
847 – 1l. on 30c. mult (814) . . 90 70

1974. Air. Honduras' Children's Villages. 25th Anniv. Nos. 786/9 optd **1949-1974 SOS Kinderdorfer Internacional Honduras-Austria**.
851 **169** 10c. multicoloured 15 10
852 – 15c. multicoloured 20 15
853 – 30c. multicoloured 25 15
854 – 40c. multicoloured 35 25

175 Flags of West Germany and Austria

1975. Air. Centenary (1974) of U.P.U. Mult.
855 1c. Type **175** 10 10
856 2c. Belgium and Denmark . . 10 10
857 3c. Spain and France 10 10
858 4c. Hungary and Russia . . . 10 10
859 5c. Great Britain and Italy 10 10
860 10c. Norway and Sweden . . 20 10
861 12c. Honduras 25 15
862 15c. United States and Switzerland 35 20
863 20c. Greece and Portugal . . 35 20
864 30c. Rumania and Yugoslavia 55 25
865 1l. Egypt and Netherlands . . 1·75 1·50
866 2l. Luxembourg and Turkey 3·00 3·00

176 Jalteva Youth Centre

1976. Air. International Women's Year (1975). Multicoloured.
868 8c. Humuya Youth Centre 10 10
869 16c. Type **176** 20 10
870 18c. Sra Arellano and I.W.Y. emblem 20 15
871 30c. El Carmen Youth Centre, San Pedro Sula . . 35 20
872 55c. Flag of National Social Welfare Organization (vert) 55 35
873 1l. Sports and recreation grounds, La Isla . . . . . 1·10 65
874 2l. Women's Social Centre . . 1·75 1·75

177 "CARE" Package

1976. Air. 20th Anniv of "CARE" (Co-operative for American Relief Everywhere) in Honduras.
875 **177** 1c. blue and black 10 10
876 – 5c. mauve and black . . . 10 10
877 **177** 16c. red and black 20 10
878 – 18c. green and black . . . 25 10
879 **177** 30c. blue and black . . . 35 20
880 – 50c. green and black . . . 55 30
881 **177** 55c. brown and black . . 55 30
882 – 70c. purple and black . . 70 45
883 **177** 1l. blue and black . . . . 1·10 65
884 – 2l. orange and black . . . 1·75 1·75
DESIGN—HORIZ: 5c., 18c., 50c., 70c., 2l. "CARE" on globe.
Each of the above stamps has a different inscription detailing "CARE's" various fields of activities in Honduras.

178 White-tailed Deer in Burnt Forest

179 Boston Tea Party and "Liberty" Flag

1976. Air. Forest Protection. Multicoloured.
885 10c. Type **178** 15 10
886 16c. COHDEFOR emblem 15 10
887 18c. Forest stream (horiz) . . 15 15
888 30c. Live and burning trees 35 20
889 50c. Type **178** 80 30
890 70c. Protection emblem . . . 70 45
891 1l. Forest of young trees (horiz) . . . . 1·10 65
892 2l. As 30c. . . . . 1·75 1·75
COHDEFOR = Corporacion Hondurena de Desarollo Forestal.

1976. Air. Bicentenary of American Revolution. Multicoloured.
894 1c. Type **179** 10 10
895 2c. Hoisting the "Liberty and Union" flag 10 10
896 3c. Battle of Bunker Hill and Pine Tree flag 10 10
897 4c. Loading stores aboard "Washington" and "An Appeal to Heaven" flag . . 10 10
898 5c. First naval ensign and navy warship 30 15
899 6c. Presidential Palace, Tegucigalpa, and Honduras flag 10 10
900 18c. Capitol, Washington and U.S. flag 35 30
901 55c. Washington at Valley Forge and Grand Union flag 70 40
902 2l. Battle scene and Bennington flag . . . . . 1·75 1·50
903 3l. Betsy Ross flag . . . . . 3·00 3·00

180 Queen Sophia of Spain

181 Mayan Stelae

1977. Air. Visit of King and Queen of Spain. Multicoloured.
905 16c. Type **180** 15 10
906 18c. King Juan Carlos . . . 15 10
907 30c. Queen Sophia and King Juan Carlos 25 20
908 2l. Arms of Honduras and Spain (horiz) . . . . . . 1·40 1·40

1978. Air. "Honduras 78". Stamp Exhibition. Multicoloured.
909 15c. Type **181** 20 10
910 18c. Giant head 25 15
911 30c. Kneeling figure 35 20
912 55c. Sun God 70 60

182 Del Valle's Birthplace

1978. Air. Birth Bicentenary of Jose Cecelio del Valle. Multicoloured.
914 8c. Type **182** 10 10
915 14c. La Merced Church, Choluteca 15 10
916 15c. Baptismal font (vert) . . 15 10
917 20c. Reading Independence Act 25 15
918 25c. Portrait, documents and map of Central America 30 15
919 40c. Portrait (vert) 45 35
920 1l. Monument, Choluteca (vert) . . . . 1·10 90
921 3l. Bust (vert) . . . . 3·00 3·00

183 Rural Heath Centre

1978. Air. 75th Anniv (1977) of Panamerican Health Organization. Multicoloured.

922 5c. Type **183** 10 10
923 6c. Child at water tap 10 10
924 10c. Los Laureles Dam, Tegucigalpa 10 10
925 20c. Rural aqueduct 25 10
926 40c. Teaching hospital, Tegucigalpa 55 30
927 2l. Parents and child . . . . 1·75 1·75
928 3l. Vaccination of child . . . 3·00 3·00
929 5l. Panamerican Health Organization Building, Washington . . . . 4·50 4·50

184 Luis Landa and "Botanica"

1978. Air. Birth Centenary of Professor Luis Landa (botanist). Multicoloured.

930 14c. Type **184** 20 15
931 16c. Map of Honduras . . . 20 15
932 18c. Medals received by Landa 20 15
933 30c. Birthplace, San Ignacio 20 15
934 2l. "Brassavola" (national flower) . . . . 2·00 1·75
935 3l. Women's normal school 3·00 3·00

1978. Air. Argentina's Victory in World Cup Football Championship. Nos. 909/12 optd with **Argentina Campeon Holanda sub-Campeon XI Campeonato Mundial de Football** and emblem.

936 **181** 15c. multicoloured 10 10
937 – 18c. multicoloured 15 15
938 – 30c. multicoloured 30 20
939 – 55c. multicoloured 55 30

186 Central University

1978. Air. 400th Anniv of Founding of Tegucigalpa.

941 **186** 6c. brown and black . . . 10 10
942 – 6c. multicoloured 10 10
943 – 8c. brown and black . . . 10 10
944 – 8c. multicoloured 10 10
945 – 10c. brown and black . . 10 10
946 – 10c. multicoloured 10 10
947 – 16c. brown and black . . 20 10
948 – 16c. multicoloured 20 10
949 – 20c. brown and black . . 20 15
950 – 20c. multicoloured 20 15
951 – 40c. brown and black . . 45 25
952 – 40c. multicoloured 45 25
953 – 50c. brown and black . . 55 35
954 – 50c. multicoloured 55 35
955 – 5l. brown and black . . . 4·50 4·50
956 – 5l. multicoloured . . . . 4·50 4·50

DESIGNS—HORIZ: No. 942, University City; No. 943, Manuel Bonilla Theatre; No. 944, Present Manuel Bonilla Theatre; No. 947, National Palace; No. 948, Presidential House; No. 949, General San Felipe Hospital; No. 950, Teaching Hospital; No. 951, Parish Church and Convent of San Francisco; No. 952, Metropolitan Cathedral; No. 953, Old view of Tegucigalpa; No. 954, Modern view of Tegucigalpa. VERT: No. 945, Court House; No. 946, North Boulevard highway intersection; No. 955, Arms of San Miguel de Tegucigalpa; No. 956, President Marco Aurelio Soto.

187 Footballers jumping for Ball

1978. Air. 7th Youth Football Championship of Central American Football League. Multicoloured.

958 15c. Type **187** 20 10
959 30c. Goalkeeper (horiz) . . . 35 15
960 55c. Tackling 55 30
961 1l. Goalkeeper and players (horiz) . . . . 1·10 90
962 2l. Players at goalmouth (horiz) . . . . 1·75 1·75

188 National Postal Emblem

1979. Air. Centenary of Honduras's U.P.U. Membership (1st issue). Multicoloured.

963 2c. Type **188** 10 10
964 15c. U.P.U. emblem 15 10
965 25c. Roman Rosa (vert) . . . 20 15
966 50c. Marco Aurelio Soto (vert) 35 30

See also Nos. 975/6.

189 Rotary Emblem and "50"

1979. Air. 50th Anniv of Tegucigalpa Rotary Club.

967 **189** 3c. orange, turquoise & bis 10 10
968 5c. green, emerald & bistre 10 10
969 50c. ochre, mauve & bistre 35 30
970 2l. blue, violet and bistre 1·40 1·00

190 Map of Caratasca Lagoon

1979. Air. 50th Anniv of Pan-American Institute of History and Geography. Multicoloured.

971 5c. Type **190** 10 10
972 10c. Aerial view of Fort San Fernando de Omoa 10 10
973 24c. Institute anniversary emblem (vert) 20 15
974 5l. Map of Santanilla Islands 3·00 3·00

191 Model of New General Post Office Building

1980. Air. Centenary (1979) of U.P.U. Membership (2nd issue).

975 **191** 24c. multicoloured 20 15
976 – 3l. brown, yellow & black 1·75 1·75

DESIGN: 3l. 19th century Post Office.

192 "Landscape" (Roman E. Cooper)

1980. Air. International Year of the Child (1979). Multicoloured.

977 1c. "Workers in a Field (J. E. Mejia) (horiz) 10 10
978 5c. Type **192** 10 10
979 15c. "Sitting boy" (D. M. Zavala) 20 10
980 20c. I.Y.C. emblem 35 15
981 30c. "Beach scene" (M. A. Hernandez) (horiz) 45 20

193 Hill and "Maltese Cross" Cancellations

1980. Air. Death Centenary (1979) of Sir Rowland Hill. Multicoloured.

983 1c. Type **193** 10 10
984 2c. Great Britain "Penny Black" 10 10
985 5c. 1866 Honduras 2r. green 15 10
986 10c. 1866 Honduras 2r. rose 20 15
987 15c. Honduras postal emblem 35 15
988 20c. Flags of Honduras and United Kingdom 75 40

Nos. 987/8 are 46 × 34 mm.

194 Visitacion Padilla (founder of Honduras section)

1981. Air. 50th Anniv of Inter-American Women's Commission. Multicoloured.

990 2c. Type **194** 10 10
991 10c. Maria Trinidad del Cid (founder of Honduras section) 15 10
992 40c. Intubucana Indian mother and child 50 30
993 1l. Emblem (horiz) 65 65

195 "O'Higgins during the Liberation of Chile" (Cosmo San Martin)

1981. Air. Bernardo O'Higgins Commemoration. Multicoloured.

994 16c. Type **195** 15 10
995 20c. Don Ambrosio O'Higgins (father) (vert) . . 20 15
996 30c. "Bernardo O'Higgins" (Jose Gil de Castro) (vert) 35 20
997 1l. "Bernardo O'Higgins laying-down Office" (M. Antonio Caro) 70 70

196 National Sports Emblem

1981. Air. World Cup Football Championship Preliminary Round. Multicoloured.

998 20c. Type **196** 15 15
999 50c. Footballer and map of Honduras 30 30
1000 70c. Flags of Honduras, CONCACAF and FIFA 40 40
1001 1l. National stadium 60 60

197 Curtiss Condor II Biplane

1983. Air. 50th Anniv of Honduras Air Force. Multicoloured.

1003 3c. Type **197** 10 10
1004 15c. North America Texan 35 15
1005 25c. Chance Vought F4U-5 Corsair 40 25
1006 65c. Douglas C-47 Skytrain 85 65
1007 1l. Cessna Dragonfly . . . 90 65
1008 2l. Dassault Super Mystere SMB-11 . . . . 1·90 1·25

198 U.P.U. Monument, Berne

1983. Air. Election to U.P.U. Executive Council (1979). Multicoloured.

1010 16c. Type **198** 20 15
1011 18c. 18th U.P.U. Congress emblem 25 15
1012 30c. Honduras's postal emblem 20 20
1013 55c. View of Rio de Janeiro 45 45
1014 2l. "Stamp" showing pigeon on globe (vert) . . . . . 1·25 1·25

199 I.Y.D.P. Emblem

1983. Air. International Year of Disabled Persons.

1016 **199** 25c. multicoloured . . . 40 25

200 National Library, Tegucigalpa

1983. Air. Centenary (1980) of National Library and Archives. Multicoloured.

1017 9c. Type **200** 10 10
1018 1l. Books 60 60

1983. Air. Papal Visit. Nos. 951/2 optd **CONMEMORATIVA DE LA VISITA DE SS. JUAN PABLO II 8 de marzo de 1983.**

1019 40c. brown and black . . . 35 35
1020 40c. multicoloured 35 35

202 Agricultural Produce

203 Hands reaching for Open Book

1983. Air. World Food Day (1981).

1021 **202** 65c. multicoloured . . . 40 40

1983. Air. Literacy Campaign (1980). Mult.

1022 40c. Type **203** 25 20
1023 1l.50 Family with books . . 90 90

204 Motorway Bridge over River Comayagua

1983. 20th Anniv of Inter-American Development Bank. Multicoloured.

1024 1l. Type **204** 60 55
1025 2l. Luis Borgran Technical Institute . . . . 1·25 1·00

205 Arms

206 Hand, Dove and Map on Globe

1984. Air. 2nd Anniv of Return of Constitutional Government. Multicoloured.

1026 20c. Type **205** 40 20
1027 20c. President Roberto Suazo Cordova 40 20

1984. "Internationalization of Peace".

1028 **206** 78c. black, blue and green 75 45
1029 85c. black, orange & grn 80 50
1030 95c. black, orange & grn 90 55
1031 1l.50 black, red & green 1·25 75
1032 2l. black, lt grn & green 1·50 1·00
1033 5l. black, purple & green 3·25 2·40

207 Front Page of "La Gaceta"

1984. Air. 150th Anniv of "La Gaceta".
1034 **207** 10c. brown, black & grn . . . 10 10
1035 20c. brown, black & sepia 20 15

1986. Various stamps surch.
1036 **184** 60c. on 14c. mult (postage) 40 25
1037 **177** 5c. on 1c. blue and black (air) 10 10
1038 – 10c. on 8c. mult (No. 868) 10 10
1039 **176** 20c. on 16c. mult 15 10
1040 – 50c. on 14c. mult (No. 915) 35 15
1041 – 85c. on 6c. mult (No. 942) 50 30
1042 **186** 85c. on 6c. brown & blk 50 30
1043 – 95c. on 6c. brown & blk 70 40
1044 – 95c. on 6c. mult (No. 942) 70 40
1045 **177** 1l. on 1c. blue and black 70 40

1986. Air. "Exfilhon '86" Stamp Exhibition and World Cup Winners. Nos. 951/2 optd.
1046 40c. **"EXFILHON '86"/ ARGENTINA CAMPEON/ MEXICO'86** (951) 25 15
1047 40c. **"EXFILHON '86"/ ALEMANIA FEDERAL Sub Campeon/ MEXICO'86** (952) . . . 25 15
1048 40c. **"EXFILHON '86"/ "FRANCIA TERCER LUGAR"/ MEXICO'86** (952) 25 15
1049 40c. **"EXFILHON '86"/ "BELGICA–CUARTO LUGAR"/ MEXICO'86** (951) 25 15

210 Phulapanzak

211 Pres. Jose Azcona and Flag

1986. Air. Tourism. Multicoloured.
1050 20c. Type **210** 15 10
1051 78c. Aerial view of Bahia Island beach and jetty (horiz) 45 25
1052 85c. Yacht off Bahia Islands (horiz) . . . . 1·50 60
1053 95c. Yojoa lake 60 35
1054 1l. Woman painting pottery 60 35

1987. Air. 1st Anniv of Democratic Government.
1056 **211** 20c. multicoloured . . . 15 10
1057 85c. multicoloured . . . 50 30

212 Edward Warner Award Medal

213 "Eupatorium cyrillinelsonii"

1987. 25th Anniv (1985) of Central American Air Navigation Services Association. Mult.
1058 2c. Type **212** 10 10
1059 5c. Flags of member countries (horiz) 10 10
1060 60c. Transmission mast, arrows and airplane (horiz) 50 20
1061 75c. Emblem 45 25
1062 1l. Members' flags and emblem (horiz) 60 35

1987. Air. Flowering Plants. Multicoloured.
1064 10c. Type **213** 10 10
1065 20c. "Salvia ernestivargasii" 15 10
1066 95c. "Robinsonella erasmi-sosae" 60 35

214 Turquoise-browed Motmot

216 Emblem

215 Family and House on Emblem

1987. Air. Birds. Multicoloured.
1067 50c. Type **214** . . . . . . 2·40 35
1068 60c. Keel-billed toucan . . . 3·00 40
1069 85c. Yellow-headed amazon 4·50 60

1987. 30th Anniv of Housing Institute.
1070 **215** 5c. multicoloured 10 10
1071 – 95c. black, brown & blue 60 35
DESIGN: 95c. Emblem.

1987. Air. 30th Anniv of Honduras National Autonomous University.
1072 **216** 1l. red, black and yellow 60 35

217 Emblem

218 Emblem of President

1987. Air. 50th Anniv of Honduras Red Cross.
1073 **217** 20c. red and blue 15 10

1988. Air. 17th Lions International Latin-American and Caribbean Forum, Honduras.
1074 **218** 95c. blue and yellow . . 60 35

219 1913 Headquarters Building, La Ceiba

1988. Air. 75th Anniv of Banco Atlantida.
1075 10c. Type **219** 10 10
1076 85c. Present headquarters building, Tegucigalpa . . 50 30

1988. Nos. 941/4 surch.
1078 5c. on 6c. brown and black 10 10
1079 5c. on 6c. multicoloured . . 10 10
1080 20c. on 8c. brown and black 10 10
1081 20c. on 8c. multicoloured . . 10 10

221 Postal Messenger

222 Athletes

1988. Air. "Exfilhon 88" Stamp Exhibition, Honduras.
1082 **221** 85c. brown 50 30
1083 – 2l. brown and red . . . 1·10 60
DESIGN: 2l. Handstamp on cover.

1988. Air. Olympic Games, Seoul.
1085 **222** 85c. black, yellow & mve 50 30
1086 – 1l. yellow, black & orge 60 35
DESIGN: 1l. Ball games equipment.

223 Three-legged Tub

228 Monkey swinging through Trees

1988. Air. 500th Anniv (1992) of Discovery of America by Christopher Columbus. Mult.
1088 10c. Type **223** 10 10
1089 25c. Bowl (horiz) 15 10
1090 30c. Dish with legs shaped as animal heads (horiz) 20 15
1091 50c. Jug 35 20

1989. Air. Various stamps surch.
1093 – 10c. on 16c. brown and black (No. 947) . . . 10 10
1094 – 10c. on 16c. mult (No. 948) 10 10
1095 – 15c. on 6c. mult (No. 923) 10 10
1096 **195** 20c. on 16c. mult 10 10
1097 **176** 50c. on 16c. mult 10 10
1098 – 95c. on 18c. mult (No. 910) 20 15
1099 – 1l. on 16c. mult (No. 836) 20 15

1990. Air. 4th Central American Games. Nos. 887 and 878 surch **IV Juegos Olimpicos Centroamericanos** and value.
1101 75c. on 18c. multicoloured 15 10
1102 85c. on 18c. green and black 20 15

1990. Air. Nos. 915 and 870 surch **L. 0.20**.
1103 20c. on 14c. multicoloured 10 10
1104 20c. on 18c. multicoloured 10 10

1990. Air. 50th Anniv (1989) of I.H.C.I. Nos. 930 and 915 surch **"50 Aniversario IHCI" 1939–1989** and new value.
1105 **184** 20c. on 14c. mult 10 10
1106 – 1l. on 14c. multicoloured 20 15

1990. Air. The Black-handed Spider Monkey. Multicoloured.
1107 10c. Type **228** 10 10
1108 10c. Mother and baby . . . 10 10
1109 20c. Monkey swinging through trees (different) 10 10
1110 20c. Mother and baby (different) 10 10

1990. Air. World Cup Football Championship, Italy. No. 960 surch **ITALIA '90 L.1.00**.
1111 1l. on 55c. multicoloured . . 20 15

230 Institute Building

1990. Air Centenary of Luis Bogran Technical Institute, Tegucigalpa.
1113 **230** 20c. red, black and green 10 10
1114 – 85c. multicoloured . . . 20 15
DESIGN: 85c. Cogwheel, globe and Institute emblem.

231 Emblem

232 "Santa Maria", Shoreline, Fish and Fruit

1990. Air. 45th Anniv of F.A.O.
1116 **231** 95c. multicoloured . . . 20 15

1990. America. The Natural World. Mult.
1117 20c. Type **232** 30 10
1118 1l. Maize, fish, fruit and palm (horiz) 20 15

233 Congress Emblem

1990. Air. 30th Anniv and 17th Congress of Inter-American Construction Industry Federation.
1119 **233** 20c. black and green . . 10 10
1120 – 1l. black and blue . . . 20 15
DESIGN—HORIZ: 1l. Jose Cecilio del Valle Palace, Tegucigalpa (Ministry of Foreign Relations).

234 Virgin and Child with Apostles

1990. Air. Christmas. Multicoloured.
1121 20c. Type **234** 10 10
1122 95c. Virgin and Child (vert) 20 15

235 St. John Bosco (founder) (after Mario Caffaro Roke)

1990. Air. 80th Anniv of Salesian Brothers in Honduras. Multicoloured.
1124 75c. Type **235** 15 10
1125 1l. Bosco and National Youth Sanctuary, Tegucigalpa 20 15

236 Pres. Callejas

1991. Air. 1st Anniv of Presidency of Rafael Leonardo Callejas. Multicoloured.
1126 30c. Type **236** 10 10
1127 2l. Pres. Callejas wearing sash 45 25

237 "Strymon melinus"

1991. Air. Butterflies. Multicoloured.
1128 85c. Type **237** 15 10
1129 90c. "Diorina sp." 20 15
1130 1l.50 "Hyalophora cecropia" 30 20

238 "Rhyncholaelia glauca"

1991. Air. Orchids. Multicoloured.
1132 30c. Type **238** 10 10
1133 50c. "Oncidium splendidum" (vert) . . . 10 10
1134 95c. "Laelia anceps (vert) 20 10
1135 1l.50 "Cattleya skinneri" . . 30 20

239 International Latin Lawyers Union Emblem and Flags

1991. Air. 6th Caribbean and North and Central American Lawyers' Day.
1136 **239** 50c. multicoloured . . . 10 10

241 Emblem, Flags and Carving

1991. Air. 25th Anniv of Italian–Latin American Institute.
1138 **241** 1l. multicoloured 20 10

242 Meeting of Old and New Worlds

1991. Air. "Espamer '91" Spain–Latin America Stamp Exhibition, Buenos Aires.
1139 **242** 2l. multicoloured 45 30

243 Valle

1991. Air. Birth Centenary of Rafael Heliodoro Valle.
1141 **243** 2l. black and red 45 30

244 Show Jumping

1991. Air. 11th Pan-American Games, Havana. Multicoloured.
1142 30c. Type **244** 10 10
1143 85c. Judo 20 10
1144 95c. Swimming 20 10

245 St Manuel de Colohete's Church, Gracias, Lempira

1991. Air. Churches. Multicoloured.
1146 30c. Type **245** 10 10
1147 95c. Church of Mercy, Gracias, Lempira 20 10
1148 1l. Comayagua Cathedral 20 10

246 Stone Carving and Cobs of Corn

1991. Air. America. Pre-Columbian Civilizations. Multicoloured.
1149 25c. Type **246** 10 10
1150 40c. Stone carving, dried corn and map 10 10
1151 1l.50 Stone carving and map of Honduras 30 20

247 Means of Control **248** Poinsettias in Basket

1991. Air. 4th International Congress on Pest Control. Multicoloured.
1152 30c. Type **247** 10 10
1153 75c. Hoeing crop (scientific co-operation) 15 10
1154 1l. Co-operation of scientists and producers 20 10

1991. Christmas. Multicoloured.
1156 1l. Type **248** 20 10
1157 2l. Poinsettia in chicken-shaped pot 45 30

249 "Taking Possession of the New Continent" (Enrique Escher)

1992. Air. 75th Anniv of Savings Bank of Honduras. Multicoloured.
1158 85c. Type **249** 25 15
1159 1l. "First Celebration of Mass in the Americas" (Maury Flores) 45 15

250 Presidents Callejas and Cossiga of Italy

1992. Air. 2nd Year in Office of President Rafael Leonardo Callejas. Multicoloured.
1161 20c. Type **250** 10 10
1162 2l. Callejas with Pope . . . 40 25

251 View From Crow's Nest **252** Skiing

1992. Air. America 1991. 500th Anniv of Discovery of America. Multicoloured.
1163 90c. Type **251** 15 10
1164 1l. Fleet 30 10
1165 2l. Ship approaching island 50 25

1992. Winter Olympic Games, Albertville. Mult.
1166 50c. Type **252** 10 10
1167 3l. Jenny Palacios de Stillo (cross-country skier) . . . 60 40

253 Athletics **254** "Seller" (Manuel Rodriguez)

1992. Olympic Games, Barcelona. Mult.
1168 20c. Type **253** 10 10
1169 50c. Tennis 10 10
1170 85c. Football 15 10

1992. Mother's Day. Paintings. Multicoloured.
1171 20c. Type **254** 10 10
1172 50c. "Grandmother and Baby" (Manuel Rodriguez) 10 10
1173 5l. "Sellers" (Maury Flores) 95 60

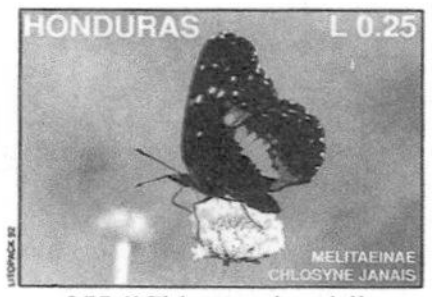

255 "Chlosyne janais"

1992. Butterflies. Multicoloured.
1174 25c. Type **255** 10 10
1175 85c. "Agrilus vanillae" . . . 15 10
1176 3l. "Morpho granadensis" 60 40

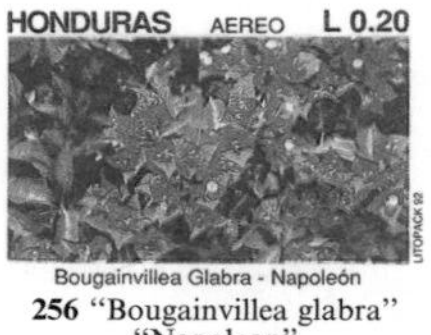

256 "Bougainvillea glabra" "Napoleon"

1992. Air. Flowers. Multicoloured.
1178 20c. Type **256** 10 10
1179 30c. "Canna indica" 10 10
1180 75c. "Epiphyllum sp." . . . 15 10
1181 95c. "Sobralia macrantha" 20 10

257 Dam **258** Crops

1992. Air. General Francisco Morazan Hydroelectric Project. Multicoloured.
1182 85c. Type **257** 15 10
1183 4l. Inner view of dam (horiz) 75 45

1992. Air. 50th Anniv of Inter-American Institute for Agricultural Co-operation.
1184 **258** 95c. multicoloured (white background) 20 10
1185 95c. multicoloured (black background) 20 10

259 "Huancasco" (Arturo Lopez Rodezno) **260** Morazan on Horseback (after Francisco Cisneros)

1992. Air. Children's Day. Multicoloured.
1186 25c. Type **259** 10 10
1187 95c. "Bougainvillea" (Enrique Escher) 20 10
1188 2l. "Melissa" (Cesar Ordonez) 40 25

1992. Air. Birth Bicentenary of General Francisco Morazan. Multicoloured.
1189 5c. Type **260** 10 10
1190 10c. Statue of Morazan, Ampala 10 10
1191 50c. Morazan's watch and sword (horiz) 10 10
1192 95c. Josefa Lastiri de Morazan (wife) 20 10

261 Globe as Pot filled with Food

1992. Air. Int Nutrition Conference, Rome.
1194 **261** 1l.05 multicoloured . . . 20 10

262 Cinnamon Hummingbird

1992. Air. "Exfilhon '92" National Stamp Exhibition, Tegucigalpa. Multicoloured.
1195 1l.50 Type **262** . . . . . . 2·25 20
1196 2l.45 Scarlet macaw . . . . 3·25 30

263 Bee-keeping

1992. Air. 50th Anniv of Pan-American School of Agriculture. Multicoloured.
1198 20c. Type **263** 10 10
1199 85c. Tending goats 15 10
1200 1l. Ploughing with oxen . . 20 10
1201 2l. Hoeing (vert) 40 25

264 Fruit, Locomotive, Clock and Bridge

1992. Air. Centenary of El Progreso (City).
1202 **264** 1l.55 multicoloured . . . 2·75 90

265 Amerindian Village **266** Columbus's Fleet and Landing Craft

1992. Air. America. 500th Anniv of Discovery of America by Columbus. Multicoloured.
1203 35c. Type **265** 10 10
1204 5l. Columbus's landing party meeting Amerindians . . 1·25 60

1992. Air. 500th Anniv of Discovery of America by Columbus. Details of "The First Mass" by Roque Zelaya. Multicoloured.
1205 95c. Type **266** 20 10
1206 1l. Mass (horiz) 20 10
1207 2l. View of village (horiz) . . 40 25

267 Road and Bridge

1992. Air. 1st Central America–Panama Highway Maintenance Congress, San Pedro Sula. Multicoloured.
1208 20c. Type **267** 10 10
1209 85c. Bulldozer 15 10

268 The Greasy Pole

1992. Air. Christmas. Multicoloured.
1210 20c. Type **268** 10 10
1211 85c. Crib, San Antonio de Flores (horiz) 15 10

269 Globes, Children and Emblem

1992. Air. 90th Anniv of Pan-American Health Organization.
1212 **269** 3l.95 multicoloured . . . 75 45

1992. Air. Nos. 894 and 899/900 surch.
1213 **179** 20c. on 1c. multicoloured 10 10
1214 – 20c. on 6c. multicoloured 10 10
1215 – 85c. on 18c. mult 15 10

271 Pres. Callejas at Ceremony **272** Mother and Child

1993. Air. 3rd Year of Rafael L. Callejas's Presidential Term and International Court of Justice's Decision on Border with El Salvador. Multicoloured.
1216 90c. Type **271** 15 10
1217 1l.05 Map (horiz) 20 10

1993. Air. Mother's Day. Multicoloured.
1218 50c. Type **272** 10 10
1219 95c. Mother and child (different) 20 10

273 American Manatee

1993. Air. Endangered Mammals. Mult.
1220 85c. Type **273** 15 10
1221 2l.45 Puma 50 30
1222 10l. Jaguar (vert) . . . . . 1·90 1·25

274 Scarlet Macaws **276** 30r. "Bull's Eye" Stamp

1993. Air. National Symbols. Multicoloured.
1223 25c. Type **274** 10 10
1224 95c. White-tailed deer . . . 15 10

1993. Air. Various stamps surch.
1225 – 20c. on 3c. mult (No. 896) 10 10
1226 **189** 20c. on 3c. orange, blue and bistre 10 10
1227 **197** 20c. on 3c. multicoloured 10 10
1228 – 20c. on 8c. mult (No. 868) 10 10
1229 **182** 20c. on 8c. multicoloured 10 10
1230 **176** 50c. on 16c. mult 10 10
1231 **177** 50c. on 16c. red and black 10 10
1232 – 50c. on 16c. mult (No. 886) 10 10
1233 **180** 50c. on 16c. mult 10 10
1234 – 50c. on 16c. mult (No. 931) 10 10
1235 **195** 50c. on 16c. mult 10 10
1236 – 50c. on 18c. mult (No. 870) 10 10
1237 – 50c. on 18c. mult (No. 910) 10 10
1238 – 50c. on 18c. mauve and black (No. 1011) . . . 10 10
1239 – 85c. on 18c. green and black (No. 878) . . . 10 10
1240 – 85c. on 18c. mult (No. 906) 10 10
1241 – 85c. on 18c. mult (No. 932) 10 10
1242 – 85c. on 18c. mult (No. 937) 10 10
1243 – 85c. on 24c. mult (No. 973) 10 10
1244 **191** 85c. on 24c. mult 10 10

1993. Air. 150th Anniv of 1st Brazilian Stamps. Multicoloured.
1245 20c. Type **276** 10 10
1246 50c. 60r. "Bull's eye" stamp 10 10
1247 95c. 90r. "Bull's eye" stamp 15 10

277 Atlantida

1993. Air. Departments. Multicoloured.
1248 20c. Type **277** 10 10
1249 20c. Colon 10 10
1250 20c. Cortes 10 10
1251 20c. Choluteca 10 10
1252 20c. El Paraiso 10 10
1253 20c. Francisco Morazan . . 10 10
1254 50c. Comayagua (vert) . . . 10 10
1255 50c. Copan (vert) 10 10
1256 50c. Intibuca (vert) 10 10
1257 50c. Bahia Islands (vert) . . 10 10
1258 50c. Lempira (vert) 10 10
1259 50c. Ocotepeque (vert) . . . 10 10
1260 1l.50 La Paz 20 10
1261 1l.50 Olancho 20 10
1262 1l.50 Santa Barbara 20 10
1263 1l.50 Valle 20 10
1264 1l.50 Yoro 20 10
1265 1l.50 Gracias a Dios 20 10

278 Muscovy Duck

1993. Air. America. Endangered Birds. Mult.
1266 20c. Ornate hawk eagle (vert) 95 45
1267 80c. Type **278** 95 45
1268 2l. Harpy eagle . . . . . . 2·25 50

279 Painting by Julia Padilla

1993. Air. 40th Anniv of United Nations Development Programme.
1269 **279** 95c. multicoloured . . . 15 10

280 Church **281** Ramon Rosa

1993. Air. Christmas. Paintings by Aida Lara de Pedemonte. Multicoloured.
1270 20c. Type **280** 10 10
1271 85c. Flower vendor 10 10

1993. Air. Personalities. Multicoloured.
1272 25c. Type **281** 10 10
1273 65c. Jesus Aguilar Paz . . . 10 10
1274 85c. Augusto Coello 10 10

282 Grey Angelfish

1993. Air. Fishes. Multicoloured.
1275 20c. Type **282** 15 10
1276 85c. Queen angelfish 20 10
1277 3l. Banded butterflyfish . . 65 45

283 Norma Callejas planting Tree **284** Family with Rushes (Aida Lara de Pedemonte)

1994. Air. 4th Year of Rafael L. Callejas's Presidential Term. Multicoloured.
1278 95c. Type **283** 15 10
1279 1l. Pres. Callejas and Government House (horiz) 15 10

1994. International Year of the Family.
1280 **284** 1l. multicoloured 15 10

285 Dove and Maps on Globe **286** "Madonna and Child"

1994. Air. International Peace and Development in Central America Conference, Tegucigalpa.
1281 **285** 1l. multicoloured 15 10

1994. Air. Christmas. Paintings by Gelasio Gimenez. Multicoloured.
1282 95c. Type **286** 10 10
1283 1l. "Holy Family" 15 10

287 "Family Scene" (Delmer Mejia) **288** Pres. Reina

1995. Air. 50th Anniv of U.N.O. Mult.
1284 1l. "The Sowing: Ecological Family" (Elisa Dulcey) . . 15 10
1285 2l. Type **287** 25 15
1286 3l. Anniversary emblem . . 40 25

1995. Air. 1st Anniv of Presidency of Carlos Roberto Reina. Multicoloured.
1287 80c. Type **288** 10 10
1288 95c. Pres. Reina with arms raised (horiz) 10 10
1289 1l. Pres. Reina at summit conference (horiz) 15 10

289 Postman loading Mail Van

1995. Air. America. Postal Transport. Paintings by Ramiro Rodriguez Zelaya. Multicoloured.
1290 1l.50 Type **289** 20 10
1291 2l. Postman on motor cycle 25 15

290 "Boletellus russelli"

1995. Air. Fungi. Multicoloured.
1292 1l. "Marasmius cohaerens" (horiz) 45 15
1293 1l. Blue leg ("Lepista nuda") (horiz) 45 15
1294 1l. "Polyporus pargamenus" (horiz) 45 15
1295 1l. "Fomes sp." (horiz) . . 45 15
1296 1l. "Paneolus sphinctrinus" (horiz) 45 15
1297 1l. "Hygrophorus aurantiaca" (horiz) . . . 45 15
1298 1l.50 The blusher ("Amanita rubescens") 65 20
1299 1l.50 "Boletus frostii" . . . 65 20
1300 1l.50 "Fomes annosus" . . 65 20
1301 1l.50 "Psathyrella sp." . . . 65 20
1302 1l.50 Type **290** 65 20
1303 1l.50 "Marasmius spegazzinii" 65 20
1304 2l. "Amanita sp." 80 25
1305 2l. Golden tops ("Psilocybe cubensis") 80 25
1306 2l. Royal boletus ("Boletus regius") 80 25
1307 2l. Black trumpet ("Craterellus cornucopioides") 80 25
1308 2l. "Auricularia delicata" . . 80 25
1309 2l. "Clavariadelphus pistilaris" 80 25
1310 2l.50 "Scleroderma aurantium" (horiz) . . . 95 35
1311 2l.50 "Amanita praegraveolens" (horiz) 95 35
1312 2l.50 Chanterelle ("Cantharellus cibarius") (horiz) 95 35
1313 2l.50 "Geastrum triplex" (horiz) 95 35
1314 2l.50 "Russula emetica" (horiz) 95 35
1315 2l.50 "Boletus pinicola" (horiz) 95 35
1316 3l. "Fomes versicolor" (horiz) . . . . 1·25 40
1317 3l. "Cantharellus purpurascens" (horiz) . . 1·25 40
1318 3l. "Lyophyllum decastes" (horiz) . . . . 1·25 40
1319 3l. Oyster fungus ("Pleurotus ostreatus") (horiz) . . . . 1·25 40
1320 3l. "Boletus ananas" (horiz) 1·25 40
1321 3l. Caesar's mushroom ("Amanita caesarea") (horiz) . . . . 1·25 40

291 "Food for All"

1995. Air. 50th Anniv of F.A.O.
1322 **291** 3l. multicoloured 25 15

292 Family and Farm over Globe

1995. Air. 50th Anniv of CARE (Co-operative for Assistance and Remittances Overseas). Multicoloured.
1323 1l.40 Type **292** 15 10
1324 5l.40 Crop farming 55 35
1325 5l.40 Keel-billed toucan, orchid, planting tree and animals at waterfall . . . 55 35

294 People around Japanese Character

1995. 20th Anniv of Japanese Overseas Co-operation Voluntary Workers in Honduras. Multicoloured.
1327 1l.40 Type **294** (postage) . . 15 10
1328 4l.30 Amerindian-style figures on pages of leaflet (horiz) (air) 40 25
1329 5l.40 Volunteer and people in traditional costumes (horiz) 55 35

295 Scorpion Mud Turtle

1995. Air. America. Environmental Protection. Multicoloured.
1330 1l.40 Type **295** 15 10
1331 4l.54 "Alpinia purpurata" (flower) (vert) 45 30
1332 10l. Common caracara ("Caracara") (vert) . . . 1·00 65

296 "Agalychnis sp."

1995. Air. Reptiles and Amphibians. Mult.
1333 5l.40 Type **296** 55 35
1334 5l.40 Iguana 55 35

297 Bell

1995. Air. Christmas. Multicoloured.
1335 1l.40 Type **297** 15 10
1336 5l.40 Crib figures (horiz) . . 55 35
1337 6l.90 Deer (carving) 70 45

298 "SICA" over Map

1996. Air. 3rd Anniv of Central American Integration System. Multicoloured.
1338 1l.40 Type **298** (signing of Protocol, 1991) 15 10
1339 4l.30 Emblem 40 25
1340 5l.40 Presidents of Central American countries at 17th Summit 55 35

299 Allegorical Design

1996. Air. United Nations Decade against Drug Abuse and Drug Trafficking. Multicoloured.
1341 1l.40 Type **299** 15 10
1342 5l.40 Woman's head with butterfly as hat (vert) . . 55 35
1343 10l. Guitar and bar of music 1·00 65

300 Traditional Headdress

1996. Air. Bicentenary of Arrival of Garifunas Tribe in Honduras. Multicoloured.
1344 1l.40 Type **300** 15 10
1345 5l.40 Tribesmen dancing to music (horiz) 55 35
1346 10l. Drums (horiz) . . . . 1·00 60

301 Steam Locomotive "San Jose"

1996. Air. "Exfilhon 96" National Stamp Exn, Tegucigalpa. Railway Locomotives. Mult.
1347 5l.40 Type **301** 95 55
1348 5l.40 Diesel railcar No. 203 95 55

302 Football

1996. Air. 6th Central American Games, San Pedro Sula (1997). Multicoloured.
1350 4l.30 Type **302** 40 25
1351 4l.54 Volleyball and games emblem 45 30
1352 5l.40 Games mascot (vert) 55 35

303 Honduran and International Badges

1996. Air. 75th Anniv of Honduran Scouts' Association. Multicoloured.
1353 2l.15 Type **303** 20 10
1354 5l.40 Anniversary emblem (vert) 50 30
1355 6l.90 Scout feeding deer (vert) 65 40

304 Poinsettia and Candles

1996. Air. Christmas. Multicoloured.
1356 1l.40 Type **304** 15 10
1357 3l. Poinsettia 25 15
1358 5l.40 As Type **304** but vert 50 30

305 Opatoro Man

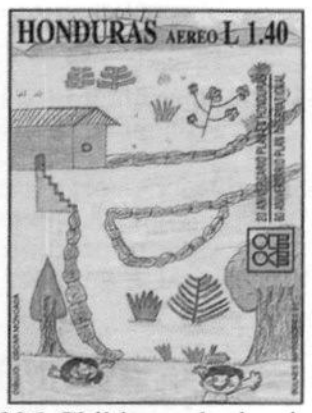

306 Children playing in River (Oscar Moncada)

1997. Air. America (1996). Traditional Costumes. Multicoloured.
1359 4l.55 Type **305** 40 25
1360 5l.40 Jocomico woman . . . 50 30
1361 10l. Intibuca couple 90 60

1997. Air. 20th Anniv of Honduran Plan and 60th Anniv of International Plan. Multicoloured.
1362 1l.40 Type **306** 15 10
1363 5l.40 Girl beside river (Nataly Alexandra Reyes) (horiz) 50 30
1364 9l.70 Street (Walter Enrique Martinez) (horiz) 90 60

307 Red-tailed Hawk

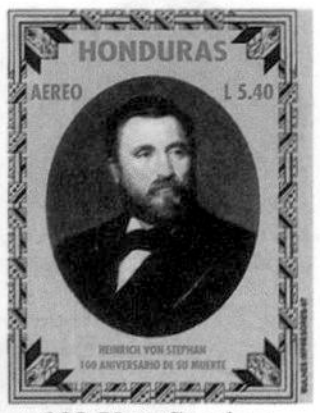

308 Von Stephan

1997. Birds. Multicoloured.
1365 1l.40 Type **307** (postage) . . 15 10
1366 1l.50 Keel-billed toucan . . 15 10
1367 2l. Red-billed whistling duck 20 10
1368 2l.15 Collared forest falcon 20 10
1369 3l. Common caracara . . . 25 15
1370 5l.40 King vulture (air) . . 50 30

1997. Air. Death Centenary of Dr. Heinrich von Stephan (founder of U.P.U.).
1372 **308** 5l.40 multicoloured . . . 50 30

309 Children and Adults in Room (Yorvin Ramon Toro)

1997. Air. World Population Day. Mult.
1373 1l.40 Type **309** 15 10
1374 6l.90 Family group and house (Marvin Lamberth Harry) 65 40

310 "Rothschildia forbesi"

1997. Air. Butterflies and Moths. Mult.
1375 1l. Type **310** 10 10
1376 1l.40 "Parides photinus" . . 15 10
1377 2l.15 Emperor 20 10
1378 3l. Jamaican kite swallowtail 25 15
1379 4l.30 "Parides iphidamas" 40 25
1380 5l.40 Monarch 50 30

311 St. Theresa

312 Observatory

1997. Air. Death Centenary of St. Theresa of Lisieux. Multicoloured.
1382 1l.40 Type **311** 10 10
1383 5l.40 St. Theresa (different) 45 30

1997. Air. 150th Anniv of National University and 40th Anniv of Free University. Multicoloured.
1384 1l.40 Type **312** 10 10
1385 5l.40 Statue of Fr. Jose Trinidad Reyes (founder) 45 30
1386 10l. Woman with book guiding boy 90 60

313 Diana, Princess of Wales

314 Children around Statue (Nelson Leonel Rodriguez)

1997. Air. Diana, Princess of Wales Commemoration. Multicoloured.
1387 1l.40 Type **313** 10 10
1388 5l.40 Visiting minefield (horiz) 45 30

1997. Air. 37th Anniv of Alcoholics Anonymous (rehabilitation organization).
1390 **314** 5l.40 multicoloured . . . 45 30

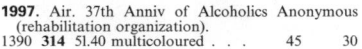

315 "Christ of Picacho" (statue)

316 Basketball

1997. Air. Christmas. Multicoloured.
1391 1l.40 Type **315** 10 10
1392 5l.50 "Virgin of Suyapa" . . 50 30

1997. Air. 6th Central American Games, San Pedro Sula. Multicoloured.
1393 1l.40 Type **316** 10 10
1394 1l.40 Baseball (batting) . . . 10 10
1395 1l.40 Football 10 10
1396 1l.40 Squash 10 10
1397 1l.40 Volleyball 10 10
1398 1l.40 Handball 10 10
1399 1l.40 Bowls 10 10
1400 1l.40 Table tennis 10 10
1401 1l.40 Rings on map of Honduras 10 10
1402 1l.40 Baseball (bowling) . . 10 10
1403 1l.50 Taekwondo (kicking) 15 10
1404 1l.50 Karate (one hand raised) 15 10
1405 1l.50 Judo (bowing) 15 10
1406 1l.50 Wrestling 15 10
1407 1l.50 Weightlifting 15 10
1408 1l.50 Boxing 15 10
1409 1l.50 Body-building 15 10
1410 1l.50 Fencing 15 10
1411 1l.50 Games emblem 15 10
1412 1l.50 Shooting 15 10
1413 2l.15 Cycling (on bicycle) . . 20 10
1414 2l.15 Road cycle racing (running beside bicycle) 20 10
1415 2l.15 Swimming 20 10
1416 2l.15 Water polo 20 10
1417 2l.15 Hurdling 20 10
1418 2l.15 Gymnastics (ring exercise) 20 10
1419 2l.15 Horse riding 20 10
1420 2l.15 Tennis 20 10
1421 2l.15 Pedrito Pichete (Games mascot) 20 10
1422 2l.15 Chess 20 10

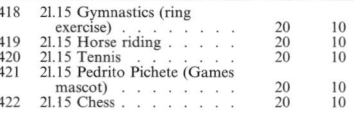

317 "Cichlasoma dovii"

1997. Air. Fishes. Multicoloured.
1423 1l.40 Type **317** 10 10
1424 2l. "Cichlasoma spilurum" (facing left) 20 10
1425 3l. "Cichlasoma spilurum" (facing right) 25 15
1426 5l.40 "Astyanay fasciatus" 45 30

318 Queen Triggerfish

320 Sculpted Skull from Temple 16

319 Postman on Motor Cycle

1998. Air. 50th Anniv of Bancahsa. Marine Life of Bahia Coral Reef. Multicoloured.
1427 2l.50 Type **318** 20 10
1428 2l.50 White grunt ("Haemulon plumieri") 20 10
1429 2l.50 French angelfish ("Pomacanthus paru") . . 20 10
1430 2l.50 Wrasse (juvenile) ("Halichoeres garnoti") 20 10
1431 2l.50 Grey angelfish (complete fish) ("Pomacanthus arcuatus") 20 10
1432 2l.50 Queen angelfish ("Holacanthus ciliaris") 20 10
1433 2l.50 Diver and "Pseud opterogorgia" (coral) . . 20 10
1434 2l.50 Diver's oxygen tank and "Pseud opterogorgia" 20 10
1435 2l.50 Six fingers of pillar coral ("Dendrogyra cylindrus") (inscr in Latin) 20 10
1436 2l.50 Squirrelfish facing right ("Holocentrus adscensionis") 20 10
1437 2l.50 Three fingers of pillar coral ("Dendrogyra cylindrus") (inscr in Latin) 20 10
1438 2l.50 "Stegastes fuscus" (fish) 20 10
1439 2l.50 "Gorgonia mariae" (coral) 20 10
1440 2l.50 Three fingers of pillar coral (inscr in English) . . 20 10
1441 2l.50 Head of grey angelfish ("Pomacanthus arcuatus") 20 10
1442 2l.50 Squirrelfish facing left ("Holocentrus adscensionis") 20 10
1443 2l.50 "Eusmilia fastigiata" (coral) 20 10
1444 2l.50 Midnight parrotfish ("Scarus coelestinus") . . 20 10
1445 2l.50 One finger of pillar coral (inscr in English) . . 20 10
1446 2l.50 Hogfish ("Lachnolaimus maximus") 20 10

Nos. 1427/46 were issued together, se-tenant, forming a composite design.

1998. Air. America (1997). Postal Service. Multicoloured.
1447 5l.40 Type **319** 45 30
1448 5l.40 Post Office 45 30

1998. Air. Maya Culture. Multicoloured.
1449 1l. Type **320** 10 10
1450 1l.40 Stone carving 10 10
1451 2l.15 Steles H and F 20 10
1452 5l.40 Carved water vessel . . 45 30

321 Players and Trophy

1998. Air. World Cup Football Championship, France. Multicoloured.

1454	5l.40 Type **321**	45	30
1455	10l. Players in tackle and trophy (vert)	90	60

322 Green Iguana

1998. Air. Reptiles. Multicoloured.

1457	1l.40 Type **322**	10	10
1458	2l. Eyelash viper	20	10
1459	3l. Green lizards	25	15
1460	5l.40 Coral snake	45	30

323 Robin giving Gift to Girl

1998. Air. Christmas. Multicoloured.

1462	3l. Type **323**	25	15
1463	5l.40 Child Jesus in crib (horiz)	45	30
1464	10l. Child leading donkey	85	55

324 Flores and his Wife greeting Pope

1999. Air. 1st Anniv of Inauguration of President Carlos Roberto Flores.

1465	5l.40 Type **324**	45	30
1466	10l. President and Mary Flores (vert)	85	55

325 Floods, Central Zone

1999. Air. Hurricane Mitch Victims' Fund. Mult.

1467	5l.40 Type **325**	45	30
1468	5l.40 Man carrying boy on back through flood and black-tailed trogon	45	30
1469	5l.40 Prince Felipe of Spain and Mary Flores (President's wife)	45	30
1470	5l.40 Child crying and orchid	45	30
1471	5l.40 People clearing timber in Comayaguela and orchid	45	30
1472	5l.40 People wading through flood in North Zone and spectacled owl	45	30
1473	5l.40 Destruction of La Hoya quarter, Tegucigalpa, and orchid	45	30
1474	5l.40 Soldier helping woman and child in North Zone and lance-tailed manakin	45	30
1475	5l.40 Collapsed houses in rural zone and orchids	45	30
1476	5l.40 Collapsed bridge and damaged motor cars ("Red Vial") and red-capped manakin	45	30
1477	5l.40 Damaged houses, motor cars and uprooted trees ("Red Vial") and orchids	45	30
1478	5l.40 Mexican soldiers with dogs and airplane	45	30
1479	5l.40 Two children swimming in North Zone and sinaloa martin	45	30
1480	5l.40 Mary and President Flores with Hillary Clinton (wfe of U.S. President)	45	30
1481	5l.40 Crowd before collapsed building in South Zone and rufous motmot	45	30
1482	5l.40 President Flores and George Bush (U.S. President, 1988–92)	45	30
1483	5l.40 Three men digging out rubble and tufted jay	45	30
1484	5l.40 Helicopter on beach and orchid	45	30
1485	5l.40 Car submerged under flood water in North Zone and bare-necked umbrellabird	45	30
1486	5l.40 Tipper Gore (U.S. Vice-president's wife) and Mary Flores in flooded building	45	30
1487	5l.40 Flooded banana plantation and orchid	45	30
1488	5l.40 Tegucigalpa submerged under flood water and red-breasted blackbird and green bird	45	30
1489	5l.40 Traffic jam behind rocks from landslide ("Red Vial")	45	30
1490	5l.40 Comayaguela and ridgway's cotinga	45	30
1491	5l.40 Destruction of Comayaguela street and orchid	45	30
1492	5l.40 People carrying plank in Eastern Zone and scarlet macaw	45	30
1493	5l.40 Mexican truck being filled with debris and orchid	45	30
1494	5l.40 Bulldozer clearing street and white-tipped sicklebill	45	30
1495	5l.40 President Flores and President Chirac of France	45	30
1496	5l.40 Comayaguela commercial zone flooded and tooth-billed hummingbird	45	30
1497	5l.40 People looking at flood water in Tegucigalpa and lineated woodpecker	45	30
1498	5l.40 Stranded BMW motor car in Comayaguela street and hoffmann's conure	45	30

326 Pilar Salinas

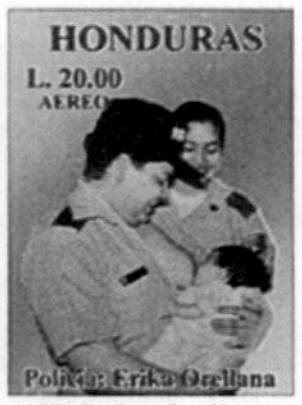

327 Enka Orellana breast-feeding Baby

1999. Air. America (1998). Famous Women. Mult.

1499	2l.60 Type **326**	20	10
1500	7l.30 Clementina Suarerz (poet)	65	40
1501	10l.65 Mary Flores (President's wife)	90	60

1999. Air. Mothers' Day. Multicoloured.

1502	20l. Type **327**	1·75	1·10
1503	30l. *Paphiopedilum urbanianum* (horiz)	2·75	1·75
1504	50l. *Miltoniopsis vexillaria* (horiz)	4·50	3·00

1999. No. 748 surch.

1505	2l.60 on 1c. blue and red	25	15
1506	7l.85 on 1c. blue and red	75	50
1507	10l.65 on 1c. blue and red	1·00	65
1508	11l.55 on 1c. blue and red	1·10	65
1509	12l.45 on 1c. blue and red	1·10	65
1510	13l.85 on 1c. blue and red	1·25	80

329 Orange-fronted Conure

330 Salvador Moncada (scientist) and Pipette

1999. Air. 30th Anniv of Sogerin Bank. Birds. Mult.

1511	3l. Type **329**	30	10
1512	3l. White-fronted amazon (*Amazona albifrons*)	30	10
1513	3l. Yellow-naped amazon (*Amazona auropalliata*)	30	10
1514	3l. Red-lored amazon (*Amazona autumnalis*)	30	10
1515	3l. Sun-bittern (*Eurypga helias*)	30	10
1516	3l. Great curassow (*Crax rubra*)	30	10
1517	3l. Orange-chinned parakeet (*Brotogeris jugularis*)	30	10
1518	3l. White-capped parrot (*Pionus senilis*)	30	10
1519	3l. Brown-throated conure (*Aratinga rubritorques*)	30	10
1520	3l. Great tinamou (*Tinamus major*)	30	10
1521	5l. King vulture (*Sarcorhamphus papa*)	45	30
1522	5l. White hawk (*Leucopternis albicollis*)	45	30
1523	5l. Harpy eagle (*Harpia harpyja*)	45	30
1524	5l. Spectacled owl (*Pulsatrix perspicillata*)	45	30
1525	5l. Ornate hawk eagle (*Spizaetus ornatus*)	45	30
1526	5l. Resplendent quetzal (*Pharomachrus mocinno*)	45	30
1527	5l. Emerald toucanet (*Aulacorhynchus prasinus*)	45	30
1528	5l. Honduras emerald (*Amazilia luciae*)	45	30
1529	5l. Scarlet macaw (*Ara macao*)	45	30
1530	5l. Yucatan woodpecker (*Centuras pygmaeus*)	45	30
1531	10l. Jabiru (*Jabiru mycteria*) (wrongly inscr "Jaberu")	90	60
1532	10l. Hook-billed kite (*Chondrohierax uncinatus*)	90	60
1533	10l. Resplendent quetzal (*Pharomachrus mocinno*) (different)	90	60
1534	10l. Keel-billed toucan (*Ramphastos sulfuratus*)	90	60

Nos. 1511/30 were issued together, se-tenant, forming a composite design.

1999. Air. New Millennium. Multicoloured.

1535	2l. Type **330**	20	10
1536	8l.65 Albert Einstein (scientist, formulator of Theory of Relativity, 1905)	80	50
1537	10l. Wilhelm Rontgen (scientist, discoverer of X-rays, 1895)	95	60
1538	14l.95 George Stephenson (engineer) (inventor of steam locomotive, 1829) and *Rocket* (horiz)	1·40	90

331 Headquarters

1999. Air. 40th Anniv of Inter-American Development Bank.

1539	**331**	18l.30 multicoloured	1·60	1·10

332 Josemaria Escriva de Balaguer (founder)

334 St. Peter

333 Statue and View of Cedros, Francisco Morazan Province

1999. Air. 70th Anniv (1998) of Founding of Opus Dei (religious organization).

1540	**332**	2l.60 multicoloured	25	15
1541		16l.40 multicoloured	1·50	1·00

1999. Air. 175th Anniv of National Congress. Mult.

1542	4l.30 Type **333**	40	25
1543	10l. Rafael Pineda Ponce (Congress President) and building	90	60

2000. Holy Year 2000. Multicoloured.

1544	4l. Open gateway into garden	35	20
1545	4l.30 Type **334**	40	25
1546	4l.30 As Type **334**, but with country name and face value in yellow	40	25
1547	6l.90 Jesus (statue) and Jerusalem (horiz)	65	40
1548	7l.30 Pope John Paul II addressing crowd (horiz)	70	45
1549	10l. Pope John Paul II	95	60
1550	14l. Pope John Paul II and Pres. Carlos Roberto Flores	1·25	80
1551	14l. As No. 1550 but with country name at right	1·25	80

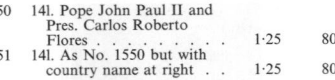

335 Pres. Flores and Reunion Consultative Group, Stockholm, Sweden

2000. 2nd Anniv of Inauguration of President Carlos Roberto Flores. Multicoloured.

1552	10l. Type **335**	95	60
1553	10l.65 Flores and General Mario Hung Pacheco	1·00	65

336 Left Half of Marimba

2000. Air. Musical Instruments. Multicoloured.

1554	1l.40 Type **336**	15	10
1555	1l.40 Right half of Marimba	15	10
1556	1l.40 Ayotl	15	10
1557	2l.60 Maracas	25	15
1558	2l.60 Guiro	25	15
1559	2l.60 Chinchin	25	15
1560	2l.60 Raspador	25	15
1561	2l.60 Quijada de Caballo	25	15
1562	3l. Fish-shaped whistle	25	15
1563	3l. Aztec drum	25	15
1564	3l. Whistle ("Pito Zoomorfo de un tono")	25	15
1565	3l. Whistle ("Pito Zoomorfo de dos tonos")	25	15
1566	3l. Tun	25	15
1567	4l. Tecomate	35	20
1568	4l. Deerskin drum	35	20
1569	4l. Guacalitos	35	20
1570	4l. Women standing to left of marimba	35	20
1571	4l. Men standing to right of marimba	35	20
1572	10l. Maya drum	90	55
1573	10l. Teponaxtle	90	55

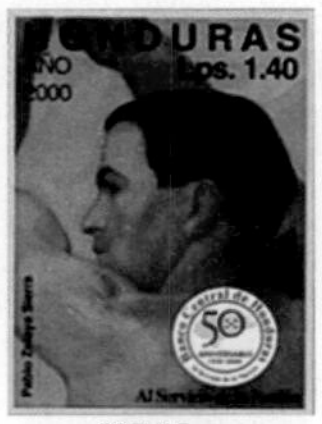

337 Man

2000. 50th Anniv of Central Honduras Bank. Paintings by Pablo Zelaya Sierra. Multicoloured.

1575	1l.40 Type **337**	15	10
1576	1l.40 Dog barking	15	10
1577	1l.40 View of town on hillside	15	10
1578	1l.40 Back of woman's head	15	10
1579	1l.40 Woman holding bowl	15	10
1580	2l. Building surrounded by trees	20	10
1581	2l. Old woman wearing black gown	20	10
1582	2l. Two women talking	20	10
1583	2l. Woman wrapped in white sheet	20	10
1584	2l. View of walled town	20	10
1585	2l.60 Birds and animals	25	15
1586	2l.60 Trees	25	15
1587	2l.60 Nun beside harp	25	15
1588	2l.60 Archers	25	15
1589	2l.60 Moon over sea	25	15
1590	2l.60 Sculpture of woman's head	25	15
1591	2l.60 Gardener in grounds of large house	25	15
1592	2l.60 Sculpture of man's head and open fan	25	15
1593	10l. Lemons on white table cloth	90	50
1594	10l. Pile of books	90	50

338 1925 25c. on 10c. Airmail Stamp

2000. Air. 75th Anniv of Honduras Airmail Stamps. Multicoloured.
1595 7l.30 Type **338** 65 35
1596 10l. Thomas Canfield Pounds (founder of Central American Airline) (vert) 90 50
1597 10l.65 General Rafael Lopez Gutierrez (President of Honduras, 1920–24) (vert) 95 55

339 Flower and Rifle

2000. Air. America (1999). A New Millennium without Arms. Multicoloured.
1599 10l. Type **339** 90 50
1600 10l.65 White dove and soldier 95 55
1601 14l. Steam train and bomb (horiz) . . . . 1·25 75

340 Ivan Guerrero and Mario Chirinos (football)

2000. Air. Olympic Games, Sydney. Multicoloured.
1602 2l.60 Type **340** 25 15
1603 10l.65 Ramon Valle (swimming) (vert) 95 55
1604 12l.45 Gina Coello (running) (vert) . . . . 1·10 65

342 Children and White-crowned Parrot

2000. Air. International Year of Volunteers. Multicoloured.
1607 2l.60 Type **342** 25 15
1608 10l.65 Boy and flower . . . 95 55

343 Mary and Jesus

2000. Air. Christmas. Multicoloured.
1609 1l.60 Type **343** 15 10
1610 7l.30 Nativity (vert) 65 35
1611 14l. Pavement art . . . . . 1·25 75

344 Yellow-naped Amazon (*Amazona auroalliata*)

346 Cardinal Rodriguez as a Child with his Father

2001. Air. America. AIDS Awareness Campaign. Monogamy. Multicoloured.
1612 2l.60 Type **344** 25 15
1613 4l.30 Common ground dove (*Columbina passerine*) (horiz) 35 20
1614 10l.65 Scarlet macaw (*Ara macao*) 95 55
1615 20l. Harpy eagle (*Aguila harpia*) . . . . 1·80 1·00

2001. Air. Various stamps surch.
1616 2l. on 16c. brown and black (No. 947) 20 10
1617 2l. on 16c. multicoloured (No. 948) 20 10
1618 2l.60 on 3c. orange, blue and brown (No. 967) . . 25 15
1619 2l.60 on 3c. multicoloured (No. 1003) 25 15
1620 2l.60 on 8c. multicoloured (No. 914) 25 15
1621 2l.60 on 16c. multicoloured (No. 931) 25 15
1622 3l. on 16c. multicoloured (No. 886) 35 15
1623 4l. on 9c. multicoloured (No. 1017) 35 20
1624 4l.30 on 6c. multicoloured (No. 899) 35 20
1625 7l.30 on 6c. brown and black (No. 941) 65 35
1626 7l.30 on 6c. multicoloured (No. 942) 65 35
1627 10l. on 16c. orange-red and black (No. 877) 90 50
1628 10l.65 on 16c. multicoloured (No. 994) 90 50
1629 14l. on 16c. multicoloured (No. 905) . . . . 1·25 75

2001. Air. Cardinal Oscar Andreas Rodriguez. Multicoloured.
1630 2l.60 Type **346** 25 15
1631 2l.60 Seated, wearing white vestments 25 15
1632 2l.60 Seated, at Seminary, 1964 . . . . 25 15
1633 2l.60 Consecration as Archbishop 25 15
1634 2l.60 At home, 1960 . . . . 25 15
1635 2l.60 Kneeling before Pope John Paul II and other clergy, Vatican, 2001 . . 25 15
1636 2l.60 Celebrating Mass, 1970 25 15
1637 2l.60 Woman wearing dark glasses, Cardinal Rodriguez and crowd, Vatican 25 15
1638 2l.60 Pope John Paul II and Cardinal Rodriguez wearing sash, 1993 . . . 25 15
1639 2l.60 Leaving airplane as Cardinal, 2001 . . . . . 25 15
1640 10l.65 Woman, Cardinal Rodriguez and Pope John Paul II, 1993 (47 × 40 mm) 95 55
1641 10l.65 Audience with Pope John Paul II, 2001 (47 × 40 mm) 95 55
1642 10l.65 Receiving cardinal ring from Pope John Paul II (47 × 40 mm) 95 55
1643 10l.65 Addressing crowd, 2001 (47 × 40 mm) 95 55
1644 10l.65 Kneeling before Pope John Paul II, Rome, 1993 (47 × 40 mm) 95 55
1645 10l.65 Pope John Paul II and Cardinal Rodriguez, 2000 (47 × 40 mm) 95 55
1646 15l. As No. 1645 enlarged to show crowd (164 × 132 mm) . . . . . 1·50 80

347 Stylized Mother and child

348 Jug

2001. Air. 50th Anniv of United Nations High Commissioner for Refugees. Multicoloured.
1647 2l.60 Type **347** 25 15
1648 10l.65 Refugees (horiz) . . . 95 55

2001. Air. 50th Anniv of Banco Occidente. Mayan Ceramics. Multicoloured.
1649 2l. Type **348** 20 10
1650 2l. Man-shaped jar 20 10
1651 2l. Seated figure with raised arms 20 10
1652 2l. Three-legged cylindrical vase 20 10
1653 2l. Textured censer with crouching animal on lid 20 10
1654 3l. Seated figure (scribe) . . 25 15
1655 3l. Cylindrical decorated jar 25 15
1656 3l. Three conjoined pots . . 25 15
1657 3l. Head 25 15
1658 3l. Man-shaped jar, arms forming handles 25 15
1659 5l. Decorated pot with handles and legs 40 25
1660 5l. Curved pot with lip and handles 40 25
1661 5l. Censer with large animal on lid 40 25
1662 5l. Seated figure with hands on knees 40 25
1663 5l. Man-shaped jar showing teeth 40 25
1664 6l.90 Pot with handles and narrow base 65 40
1665 6l.90 Seated figure with hands on knees (different) 65 40
1667 6l.90 Jar in shape of seated figure holding pole . . . 65 40
1668 6l.90 Tall cylindrical vase . . 65 40
1669 6l.90 Textured pot with animal-shaped handles . . 65 40

349 Juan Ramon Molina Bridge

2001. Air. Honduras–Japan Diplomatic Relations. Sheet 153 × 127 mm containing T **349** and similar horiz designs showing views of bridge. Multicoloured.
MS1670 2l.60 Type **349**; 10l.65, Side view; 13l.65 From beneath . . 1·20 1·20

EXPRESS LETTER STAMPS

1953. No. O507 surch **ENTREGA INMEDIATA 1953 L O.20**.
E523 **127** 20c. on 1c. olive & pur 1·60 1·60

E **135** Lockheed Constellation

1956. Air. Optd **ENTREGA INMEDIATA** as in Type E **135**.
E570 E **135** 20c. grey and black 60 50

1966. Stamp Cent. Design similar to T **144**.
E700 20c. brown, gold & lt brown 45 45
DESIGN—HORIZ: 20c. Motor cyclist.

1972. As T **168**, but inscr "ENTREGA INMEDIATA". Multicoloured.
E811 20c. Chance Vought F4U-5 Corsair fighter aircraft . . 45 25

1975. No. E811 surch.
E848 60c. on 20c. multicoloured 75 55

1976. As T **178**.
E893 60c. Deer in forest 70 40

OFFICIAL STAMPS
Various stamps overprinted **OFICIAL**.

1890. Stamps of 1890.
O56 **6** 1c. yellow 15
O57 2c. yellow 15
O58 5c. yellow 15
O59 10c. yellow 15
O60 20c. yellow 15
O61 25c. yellow 15
O62 30c. yellow 15
O63 40c. yellow 15
O64 50c. yellow 15
O65 75c. yellow 15
O66 1p. yellow 15

1891. Stamps of 1891.
O70 **8** 1c. yellow 15
O71 2c. yellow 15
O72 5c. yellow 15
O73 10c. yellow 15
O74 20c. yellow 15
O75 25c. yellow 15
O76 30c. yellow 15
O77 40c. yellow 15
O78 50c. yellow 15
O79 75c. yellow 15
O80 1p. yellow 15

1898. Stamps of 1898.
O116 **14** 5c. blue 70
O117 10c. blue 70
O118 20c. bistre 75
O119 50c. orange . . . . . . 1·50
O120 1p. green . . . . 3·00

1911. Stamps of 1911.
O148 **20** 1c. violet 90 35
O149 2c. green 55 55
O150 5c. red 90 90
O151 6c. blue . . . . 1·60 1·25
O152 10c. blue 90 70
O153 20c. yellow 90 90
O154 50c. brown . . . . . . 3·25 2·50
O155 1p. olive . . . . 7·00 5·75

1914. No. O150 and O148 surch.
O186 **20** 1c. on 5c. red . . . . . 1·10 90
O187 2c. on 5c. red . . . . . 1·25 90
O188 10c. on 1c. violet . . . . 2·25 2·25
O189 10c. on 5c. red . . . . . 8·75 8·75
O190 20c. on 1c. violet . . . . 1·60 1·60

1914. No. O190 and O146 surch **OFICIAL** and value.
O191 **20** 10c. on 20c. on 1c. violet 3·50 3·50
O193 20c. on 50c. brown . . . 3·25 3·25

1915. Stamps of 1913.
O194 **26** 1c. brown 25 25
O195 2c. red 25 25
O197 **27** 5c. blue 25 25
O198 6c. violet 85 85
O199 **26** 10c. brown 70 70
O200 20c. brown . . . . . . 1·75 1·75
O202 **27** 50c. red . . . . 3·50 3·50

1915. No. 168 surch **OFICIAL $0.01**.
O203 **26** 1c. on 2c. red . . . . . 1·75 1·75

1915. Stamps of 1915.
O204 **32** 1c. brown . . . . 2·00 2·25
O205 2c. red . . . . 2·00 2·25
O206 – 5c. blue 20 20
O207 – 6c. violet 30 30
O208 **32** 10c. blue . . . . 8·00 8·00
O209 20c. brown . . . . . . 4·50 6·00
O210 – 50c. red . . . . 1·25 1·25
O211 – 1p. green . . . . 2·25 2·25

1921. Stamps of 1919.
O212 **36** 1c. brown . . . . 1·60 1·60
O213 2c. red . . . . 3·75 3·75
O214 5c. red . . . . 3·75 3·75
O215 6c. mauve 35 35
O216 10c. blue 45 45
O217 15c. blue 50 50
O218 20c. brown 70 70
O219 50c. brown . . . . . . 1·10 1·10
O220 1p. green . . . . 1·60 1·60

1925. Stamps of 1923.
O222 **39** 1c. olive 10 10
O223 2c. red 15 15
O224 **39** 6c. purple 25 25
O225 10c. blue 35 35
O226 20c. brown 45 45
O227 50c. red 95 95
O228 1p. green . . . . 1·40 1·40

O **50** J. R. Molina

1929.
O259 – 1c. blue 15 15
O260 O **50** 2c. red 20 20
O261 – 5c. violet 30 30
O262 – 10c. green 35 35
O263 – 20c. blue 45 45
O264 – 50c. green and yellow 90 90
O265 – 1p. brown . . . . . . 1·60 1·60
DESIGNS: J. C. Valle; 5c. Coffee tree; 10c. J. T. Reyes; 20c. Tegucigalpa Cathedral; 50c. Lake Yojoa; 1p. Wireless station.

1930. Air. Nos. O224/8 surch **Servicio aereo Vale 5 centavos VI-1930** or optd **Servicio aereo Habilitado VI-1930**.
O319 **39** 5c. on 6c. purple . . . . 1·10 1·10
O320 6c. purple . . . . 50·00 50·00
O321 10c. blue . . . . 1·00 1·00
O322 20c. brown . . . . . . 1·00 1·00
O323 50c. red . . . . 1·50 1·50
O324 1p. green . . . . 1·00 1·00

O **70** Tegucigalpa

1931.
O328 O **70** 1c. blue 20 20
O329 2c. purple 75 75
O330 5c. olive 90 90
O331 6c. red 90 90
O332 10c. green . . . . . . 1·00 1·00
O333 15c. brown . . . . . . 1·75 1·75
O334 20c. brown . . . . . . 1·75 1·75
O335 50c. violet . . . . . . 1·25 1·25
O336 1p. orange . . . . . . 1·75 1·75

1933. Air. Various stamps surch **Aereo Oficial Vale 1933** and new value.
O354 **66** 20c. on 2c. blue . . . . 3·50 3·50
O355 20c. on 2c. orange . . . 3·50 3·50
O356 20c. on 2c. red . . . . 3·50 3·50
O357 40c. on 2c. orange . . . 2·10 2·10
O358 40c. on 2c. red . . . . 4·25 4·25
O360 – 40c. on 5c. purple (249) 4·25 4·25
O361 – 40c. on 5c. blue (250) . . 7·00 7·00
O362 – 40c. on 5c. purple (270) 4·25 4·25
O363 – 40c. on 5c. blue (271) . . 9·50 9·50
O370 – 40c. on 5c. violet (O261) 95 95
O372 **39** 60c. on 6c. purple (O224) 70 70
O365 – 70c. on 5c. blue (188) . . 3·00 3·00
O374 – 70c. on 5c. blue (O206) 5·50 5·50
O366 **39** 70c. on 10c. blue . . . . 3·50 3·50
O375 **32** 70c. on 10c. blue (O208) 28·00 28·00
O377 **36** 70c. on 10c. blue (O216) 4·75 4·75
O378 **39** 70c. on 10c. blue (O225) 3·50 3·50
O380 **36** 70c. on 15c. blue (O217) 90·00 90·00
O381 90c. on 10c. blue (O216) 5·50 5·50
O382 90c. on 15c. blue (O217) 4·00 4·00
O383 **39** 1l. on 2c. red . . . . . 1·40 1·40
O367 **36** 1l. on 20c. brown . . . . 3·50 3·50
O384 1l. on 20c. brown (O218) 2·50 2·50
O385 **39** 1l. on 20c. brown (O226) 4·00 4·00
O368 1l. on 50c. red . . . . . 14·00 14·00
O386 **36** 1l. on 50c. brown (O219) 1·90 1·90
O387 **39** 1l. on 50c. red (O227) . . 4·25 4·25
O369 **36** 1.20l. on 1p. green . . . 1·10 1·10

O388 – 1.20l. on 1p. grn (O211) 9·50 9·50
O389 39 1.20l. on 1p. grn (O288) 1·60 1·60

1935. Stamps of 1931 optd **HABILITADO 1935–1938** between thick lines.
O390 O 70 1c. blue 20 20
O391 2c. purple 20 20
O392 5c. olive 25 25
O393 6c. red 35 35
O394 10c. green 40 40
O395 15c. brown 45 45
O396 20c. brown 55 55
O397 50c. violet 1·25 1·25

O 92 Coat of Arms and National Flag

1939. Air.
O400 O 92 2c. blue and green 10 10
O401 5c. blue and orange 10 10
O402 8c. blue and brown 15 15
O403 15c. blue and red 35 30
O404 46c. blue and olive 45 45
O405 50c. blue and violet 60 45
O406 1l. blue and brown 1·75 1·75
O407 2l. blue and red 3·00 3·00

1952. Air. 500th Birth Anniv of Isabella the Catholic. As Nos. 499/506 but colours changed, optd **OFICIAL**.
O507 127 1c. olive and purple 10 10
O508 – 2c. violet and brown 10 10
O509 – 8c. black and red 15 15
O510 128 16c. green and violet 25 25
O511 – 30c. black and blue 30 30
O512 – 1l. sepia and green 1·50 1·25
O513 127 2l. brown and blue 3·00 3·00
O514 128 5l. slate and orange 7·00 7·00

1953. Air. United Nations. As Nos. 523/31 but colours changed (except 1c.), optd **OFICIAL**.
O532 – 1c. blue and black 10 10
O533 130 2c. green and black 10 10
O534 – 3c. orange and black 20 20
O535 – 5c. red and black 20 20
O536 – 15c. sepia and black 30 30
O537 – 30c. purple and black 55 55
O538 – 1l. olive and black 4·00 2·75
O539 – 2l. purple and black 5·00 3·25
O540 – 5l. blue and black 11·50 11·00

1956. Air. As Nos. 551/69 but colours changed, optd **OFICIAL**.
O570 1c. lake and black 10 10
O571 2c. red and black 10 10
O572 3c. purple and black 10 10
O573 4c. orange and black 10 10
O574 5c. turquoise and black 10 10
O575 8c. multicoloured 15 15
O576 10c. brown and black 15 15
O577 12c. red and black 15 15
O578 15c. black and red 15 15
O579 20c. olive and black 15 15
O580 24c. blue and black 20 20
O581 25c. purple and black 25 25
O582 30c. green and black 25 25
O583 40c. orange and black 35 35
O584 50c. red and black 35 35
O585 60c. purple and black 45 45
O586 1l. sepia and black 1·75 1·40
O587 2l. blue and black 3·00 2·40
O588 5f. blue and black 5·75 5·25

1957. Air. Revolution of 21 October 1956. Nos. 570/9 optd **OFICIAL**. Frames in black.
O589 1c. blue and yellow 10 10
O590 2c. purple, green and orange 10 10
O591 5c. blue and pink 10 10
O592 8c. violet, olive and orange 10 10
O593 10c. brown and violet 15 15
O594 12c. blue and turquoise 15 15
O595 15c. brown and green 20 15
O596 30c. grey and pink 35 35
O597 1l. brown and blue 1·75 1·40
O598 2l. grey and green 3·00 2·40

1959. Air. Abraham Lincoln. 150th Birth Anniv No. 590/601 but colours changed and optd **OFICIAL**. Flags in blue and red.
O602 1c. yellow 10 10
O603 2c. olive 10 10
O604 3c. brown 10 10
O605 5c. blue 10 10
O606 10c. purple 15 15
O607 12c. orange 15 15
O608 15c. sepia 20 20
O609 25c. slate 30 30
O610 50c. red 45 45
O611 1l. violet 1·10 1·10
O612 2l. blue 1·75 1·75
O613 5l. green 5·25 5·25

1964. Air. Pres. Kennedy Memorial Issue. Optd **IN MEMORIAM JOHN F. KENNEDY 22 NOVIEMBRE 1963**.
O626 1c. yellow (No. O602) 15 15
O627 2c. olive (No. O603) 20 20
O628 3c. brown (No. O604) 25 25
O629 5c. blue (No. O605) 30 30
O630 15c. sepia (No. O608) 1·40 1·10
O631 50c. red (No. O610) 5·75 4·75

1964. Air. Nos. O611/14 surch.
O647 10c. on 50c. red 15 10
O648 12c. on 15c. sepia 25 10
O649 12c. on 25c. slate 25 10
O621 20c. on 25c. slate 45 35

1964. Air. Olympic Games, Tokyo. Optd with Olympic Rings and **1964**.
O632 2l. purple & black (No. O539) 5·75 4·75

1965. Air. Nos. 630/38 optd **OFICIAL**.
O650 144 1c. black and green 10 10
O651 – 2c. black and mauve 10 10
O652 – 5c. black and blue 15 15
O653 – 8c. black and green 15 15
O654 144 10c. black and bistre 25 25
O655 – 12c. black and yellow 30 30
O656 – 1l. black and buff 3·00 2·75
O657 – 2l. black and olive 6·50 5·75
O658 144 3l. black and red 7·50 7·00

1965. Air. Churchill Commem. Optd **IN MEMORIAM Sir Winston Churchill 1874-1965**.
O674 128 16c. green and violet 70 70

1971. Air. Various official stamps surch in figures.
O788 134 10c. on 3c. (O572) 25 10
O789 – 10c. on 2c. (O603) 25 10
O790 – 10c. on 3c. (O604) 25 10

1974. Air. Nos. O570 and O602 surch.
O849 2c. on 1c. lake and black 10 10
O850 2c. on 1c. yellow 10 10

HONG KONG Pt. 1, Pt. 17

Former British colony at the mouth of the Canton R., consisting of the island of Hong Kong and peninsula of Kowloon. Under Japanese Occupation from 25 December 1941, until liberated by British forces on 16 September 1945.

Hong Kong became a Special Administrative Region of the People's Republic of China on 1 July 1997.

100 cents = 1 Hong Kong dollar.

1

1862.
8a 1 2c. brown £120 7·00
34 4c. grey 12·00 1·25
10 6c. lilac £400 12·00
11b 8c. yellow £400 11·00
12a 12c. blue 28·00 5·50
22 16c. yellow £1800 65·00
4 18c. lilac £600 50·00
14 24c. green £500 8·50
15a 30c. red £700 15·00
16 30c. mauve £225 5·50
17a 48c. red £1000 26·00
18 96c. olive £38000 £650
19 96c. grey £1300 55·00

1877. Surch in figures and words, thus **5 cents.**
23 1 5c. on 8c. yellow £950 £100
24 5c. on 18c. lilac £900 60·00
25 10c. on 12c. blue £950 55·00
26 10c. on 16c. yellow £4250 £150
27 10c. on 24c. green £1300 85·00
20 16c. on 18c. lilac £2250 £150
21 28c. on 30c. mauve £1200 50·00

1880.
33 1 2c. red 35·00 1·50
56 2c. green 27·00 85
57 4c. red 19·00 85
35 5c. blue 27·00 85
58 5c. yellow 22·00 6·50
30 10c. mauve £550 14·00
37a 10c. green £130 1·25
38 10c. purple on red 23·00 1·25
59 10c. blue 50·00 1·75
39a 30c. green 80·00 20·00
61 30c. brown 40·00 22·00
31 48c. brown £1200 90·00

1885. Surch in figures and words, thus **20 CENTS.**
54 1 10c. on 30c. green £550 £1000
40 20c. on 30c. red £100 5·50
45a 20c. on 30c. green £110 £140
41 50c. on 48c. brown £375 30·00
46 50c. on 48c. purple £250 £275
42 $1 on 96c. olive £700 65·00
47 $1 on 96c. purple on red £750 £350
53a $1 on 96c. black £2750 £3750

1891. Surch in figures and words, thus **7 cents.**
43 1 7c. on 10c. green 70·00 8·00
44 14c. on 30c. mauve £160 60·00

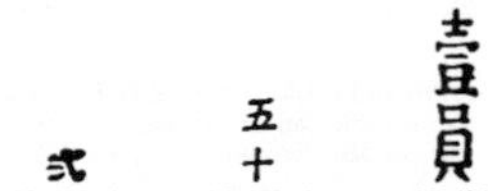

13 (20c.) 14 (50c.) 15 ($1)

1891. T 1 surch with figures and words and with Chinese surch also.
55 – 10c. on 30c. green 48·00 70·00
48a 13 20c. on 30c. green 32·00 7·00
49 14 50c. on 48c. purple 75·00 5·50
50 15 $1 on 96c. purple on red £425 22·00
52a $1 on 96c. black £150 27·00

The Chinese surch on No. 55 is larger than Type **13**.

1891. 50th Anniv of Colony. Optd **1841 Hong Kong JUBILEE 1891**.
51 1 2c. red £450 £110

20

24

1903.
62 20 1c. purple and brown 2·00 50
91 1c. brown 4·25 1·00
77 2c. green 7·00 1·25
78a 4c. purple on red 9·00 75
93 4c. red 8·00 40
79a 5c. green and orange 15·00 5·00
94 6c. brown and purple 23·00 4·50
66 8c. grey and violet 10·00 1·25
81 10c. purple and blue on blue 18·00 1·25
95 10c. blue 24·00 40
68 12c. green & purple on yell 8·50 4·25
83a 20c. grey and brown 30·00 2·25
96 20c. purple and green 45·00 42·00
84 30c. green and black 38·00 21·00
97 30c. purple and yellow 50·00 25·00
85 50c. green and purple 65·00 9·00
98 50c. black on green 40·00 15·00
86 $1 purple and olive £110 24·00
87a $2 grey and red £200 95·00
99 $2 red and black £275 £275
88 $3 grey and blue £225 £190
89 $5 purple and green £400 £350
76 $10 grey and orange on blue £1000 £425

1912.
117 24 1c. brown 1·00 40
118 2c. green 2·50 50
118c 2c. grey 18·00 7·50
119 3c. grey 6·00 1·00
120a 4c. red 3·00 30
121 5c. violet 8·50 30
103 6c. orange 4·25 1·00
104 8c. grey 23·00 5·00
123 8c. orange 4·00 1·50
124 10c. blue 4·25 30
106 12c. purple on yellow 5·50 7·00
125 20c. purple and olive 4·75 30
126 25c. purple 4·50 70
127 30c. purple and orange 10·00 1·50
128 50c. black on green 13·00 30
129 $1 purple and blue on blue 32·00 50
130 $2 red and black £110 6·00
131 $3 green and purple £170 60·00
132 $5 green and red on green £475 70·00
116 $10 purple and black on red £600 85·00

1935. Silver Jubilee. As T **10a** of Gambia.
133 3c. blue and black 4·00 3·50
134 5c. green and blue 8·50 3·50
135 10c. brown and blue 20·00 1·75
136 20c. grey and purple 38·00 8·00

1937. Coronation. As T **10b** of Gambia.
137 4c. green 4·50 4·00
138 15c. red 10·00 3·25
139 25c. blue 13·00 2·75

29 King George VI

30 Street Scene

1938.
140 29 1c. brown 1·75 2·00
141 2c. grey 2·00 30
142 4c. orange 4·50 1·25
143 5c. green 1·25 20
144 8c. brown 1·75 2·50
145b 10c. violet 6·00 70
146 15c. red 2·00 30
147 20c. black 1·25 30
148 20c. red 7·00 40
149 25c. blue 29·00 1·75
150 25c. olive 4·75 1·75
151a 30c. olive 24·00 8·50
152 30c. blue 7·00 20
153c 50c. lilac 9·00 20
154 80c. red 5·00 95
155 $1 purple and blue 8·00 3·00
156 $1 orange and green 18·00 30
157 $2 orange and green 70·00 17·00
158 $2 violet and red 30·00 3·25
159 $5 purple and red 60·00 50·00
160 $5 green and violet 80·00 7·50
161 $10 green and violet £500 90·00
162 $10 violet and blue £140 29·00

1941. Centenary of British Occupation. Dated "1841 1941".
163 30 2c. orange and brown 5·00 2·00
164 – 4c. purple and mauve 5·00 3·00
165 – 5c. black and green 3·00 50
166 – 15c. black and red 6·00 1·75
167 – 25c. brown and blue 13·00 5·00
168 – $1 blue and orange 48·00 7·50

DESIGNS—HORIZ: 4c. "Empress of Japan" (liner) and junk; 5c. University; 15c. Harbour; $1 "Falcon" (clipper) and Short S.23 Empire "C" Class flying boat. VERT: 25c. Hong Kong Bank.

For Japanese issues see "Japanese Occupation of Hong Kong".

36

1946. Victory.
169 36 30c. blue and red 2·75 1·75
170 $1 brown and red 3·50 75

1948. Silver Wedding. As T **11b/c** of Gambia.
171 10c. violet 3·00 1·00
172 $10 red £275 85·00

1949. U.P.U. As T **11d/g** of Gambia.
173 10c. violet 4·50 1·00
174 20c. red 17·00 3·00
175 30c. blue 15·00 2·75
176 80c. mauve 35·00 9·50

1953. Coronation. As T **11h** of Gambia.
177 10c. black and purple 6·00 30

1954. As T **29** but portrait of Queen Elizabeth, facing left.
178 5c. orange 1·75 20
179 10c. lilac 2·50 10
180a 15c. green 4·50 45
181 20c. brown 6·00 30
182a 25c. red 4·00 1·50
183 30c. grey 5·00 20
184 40c. blue 6·00 40
185 50c. purple 6·50 20
186 65c. grey 19·00 9·50
187 $1 orange and green 7·50 20
188 $1.30 blue and red 23·00 1·50
189 $2 violet and red 12·00 60
190 $5 green and purple 75·00 2·00
191 $10 violet and blue 60·00 9·00

38 University Arms

1961. Golden Jubilee of Hong Kong University.
192 38 $1 multicoloured 7·00 2·00

39 Statue of Queen Victoria

40 Queen Elizabeth II (after Annigoni)

1962. Stamp Centenary.
193 39 10c. black and mauve 60 10
194 20c. black and blue 1·75 2·00
195 50c. black and bistre 4·00 40

1962.
196 40 5c. orange 75 60
223 10c. violet 70 50
198 15c. green 3·25 1·75
199 20c. brown 2·50 1·25
200 25c. red 3·00 3·00
201 30c. blue 2·50 10
202 40c. turquoise 2·75 70
203 50c. red 1·75 30
230 65c. blue 6·50 7·00
231 $1 sepia 18·00 1·75
206 – $1.30 multicoloured 5·00 20
207 – $2 multicoloured 7·00 65
208 – $5 multicoloured 17·00 1·25
209 – $10 multicoloured 32·00 2·50
210 – $20 multicoloured £140 24·00

Nos. 206/10 are as T **40** but larger 26 × 40½ mm.

1963. Freedom from Hunger. As T **20a** of Gambia.
211 $1.30 green 45·00 8·00

1963. Cent of Red Cross. As T **20b** of Gambia.
212 10c. red and black 5·00 30
213 $1.30 red and blue 27·00 8·00

1965. Centenary of I.T.U. As T **44** of Gibraltar.
214 10c. purple and yellow 4·00 25
215 $1.30 olive and green 25·00 5·50

1965. I.C.Y. As T **45** of Gibraltar.
216 10c. purple and turquoise 3·00 25
217 $1.30 green and lavender 20·00 5·50

1966. Churchill Commem. As T **46** of Gibraltar.
218 10c. blue 3·00 15
219 50c. green 3·50 30

220		$1.30 brown	17·00	3·00
221		$2 violet	30·00	10·00

1966. Inauguration of W.H.O. Headquarters, Geneva. As T **54** of Gibraltar.

237		10c. black, green and blue	3·00	30
238		50c. black, purple and ochre	10·00	1·75

1966. 20th Anniv of U.N.E.S.C.O. As T **56a/c** of Gibraltar.

239		10c. multicoloured	3·50	20
240		50c. yellow, violet and olive	13·00	90
241		$2 black, purple and orange	55·00	20·00

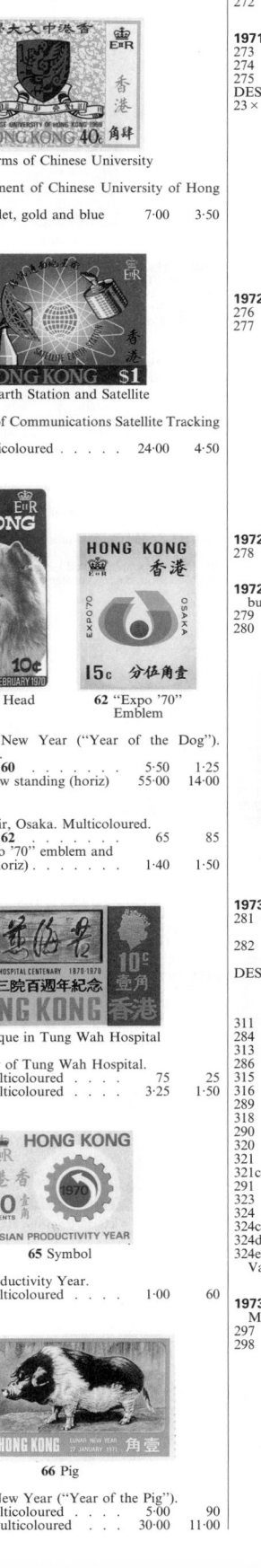

42 Rams' Heads on Chinese Lanterns

1967. Chinese New Year ("Year of the Ram").

242	**42**	10c. red, olive and yellow	4·00	50
243	–	$1.30 green, red and yellow	32·00	11·00

DESIGN: $1.30, Three rams.

44 Cable Route Map

1967. Completion of Malaysia–Hong Kong Link of SEACOM Telephone Cable.

244	**44**	$1.30 blue and red	17·00	4·50

45 Rhesus Macaques in Tree

1968. Chinese New Year ("Year of the Monkey").

245	**45**	10c. gold, black and red	4·50	50
246	–	$1.30 gold, black and red	30·00	10·00

DESIGN: $1.30, Family of rhesus macaques.

47 "Iberia" (liner) at Ocean Terminal

1968. Sea Craft.

247	**47**	10c. multicoloured	2·00	15
248	–	20c. blue, black and brown	3·25	1·00
249	–	40c. orange, black & mauve	11·00	10·00
250	–	50c. red, black and green	7·50	75
251	–	$1 yellow, black and red	16·00	5·50
252	–	$1.30 blue, black and pink	45·00	4·25

DESIGNS: 20c. Pleasure launch; 40c. Car ferry; 50c. Passenger ferry; $1 Sampan; $1.30, Junk.

53 "Bauhinia blakeana"

1968. Multicoloured.

253		65c. Type **53**	9·00	50
254		$1 Arms of Hong Kong	9·00	40

55 "Aladdin's Lamp" and Human Rights Emblem

1968. Human Rights Year.

255	**55**	10c. orange, black and green	1·50	75
256		50c. yellow, black & purple	4·50	2·25

56 Cockerel

1969. Chinese New Year ("Year of the Cock"). Multicoloured.

257		10c. Type **56**	5·00	1·00
258		$1.30 Cockerel (vert)	55·00	14·00

58 Arms of Chinese University

1969. Establishment of Chinese University of Hong Kong.

259	**58**	40c. violet, gold and blue	7·00	3·50

59 Earth Station and Satellite

1969. Opening of Communications Satellite Tracking Station.

260	**59**	$1 multicoloured	24·00	4·50

60 Chow's Head

62 "Expo '70" Emblem

1970. Chinese New Year ("Year of the Dog"). Multicoloured.

261		10c. Type **60**	5·50	1·25
262		$1.30 Chow standing (horiz)	55·00	14·00

1970. World Fair, Osaka. Multicoloured.

263		15c. Type **62**	65	85
264		25c. "Expo '70" emblem and junks (horiz)	1·40	1·50

64 Plaque in Tung Wah Hospital

1970. Centenary of Tung Wah Hospital.

265	**64**	10c. multicoloured	75	25
266		50c. multicoloured	3·25	1·50

65 Symbol

1970. Asian Productivity Year.

267	**65**	10c. multicoloured	1·00	60

66 Pig

1971. Chinese New Year ("Year of the Pig").

268	**66**	10c. multicoloured	5·00	90
269		$1.30 multicoloured	30·00	11·00

67 "60" and Scout Badge

68 Festival Emblem

1971. Diamond Jubilee of Scouting in Hong Kong.

270	**67**	10c. black, red and yellow	75	10
271		50c. black, green and blue	3·75	1·00
272		$2 black, mauve and violet	22·00	12·00

1971. Hong Kong Festival.

273	**68**	10c. orange and purple	1·25	20
274	–	50c. multicoloured	2·75	1·00
275	–	$1 multicoloured	8·50	7·00

DESIGNS—39 × 23 mm: 50c. Coloured streamers. 23 × 39 mm: $1 "Orchid".

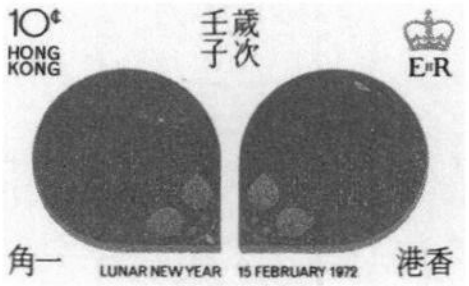

69 Stylized Rats

1972. Chinese New Year. ("Year of the Rat").

276	**69**	10c. red, black and gold	3·50	50
277		$1.30 red, black and gold	32·00	11·00

70 Tunnel Entrance

1972. Opening of Cross-Harbour Tunnel.

278	**70**	$1 multicoloured	5·00	2·25

1972. Royal Silver Wedding. As T **98** of Gibraltar, but with Phoenix and Dragon in background.

279		10c. multicoloured	30	15
280		50c. multicoloured	1·10	1·40

72 Ox

73 Queen Elizabeth II

1973. Chinese New Year ("Year of the Ox").

281	**72**	10c. orange, brown & black	2·50	50
282	–	$1.30 yellow, orange & black	7·00	7·00

DESIGN—HORIZ: $1.30, Ox.

1973.

311	**73**	10c. orange	55	30
284		15c. green	7·00	8·00
313		20c. violet	50	10
286		25c. brown	11·00	8·50
315		30c. blue	70	70
316		40c. blue	1·25	2·50
289		50c. red	1·50	60
318		60c. lavender	1·75	2·50
290		65c. brown	14·00	11·00
320		70c. yellow	1·75	75
321		80c. red	2·25	3·25
321c		90c. brown	5·00	2·25
291		$1 green	2·25	80
323	–	$1.30 yellow and violet	2·50	30
324	–	$2 green and brown	3·00	1·25
324c	–	$5 pink and blue	4·75	1·75
324d	–	$10 pink and green	8·00	6·00
324e	–	$20 pink and black	13·00	12·00

Values of $1.30 and above are size 27 × 32 mm.

1973. Royal Wedding. As T **101a** of Gibraltar. Multicoloured. Background colours given.

297		50c. brown	50	15
298		$2 mauve	2·25	2·00

75 Festival Symbols forming Chinese Character

1973. Hong Kong Festival.

299	**75**	10c. red and green	40	10
300	–	50c. mauve and orange	2·00	95
301	–	$1 green and mauve	4·75	4·75

DESIGNS—Festival symbols arranged to form a Chinese character: 10c. "Hong"; 50c. "Kong"; $1 "Festival".

76 Tiger

1974. Chinese New Year ("Year of the Tiger").

302	**76**	10c. multicoloured	3·50	50
303	–	$1.30 multicoloured	11·00	12·00

DESIGN—VERT: $1.30, similar to Type **76**.

77 Chinese Mask

1974. Arts Festival.

304	**77**	10c. multicoloured	75	10
305	–	$1 multicoloured	6·00	4·25
306	–	$2 multicoloured	9·00	8·50
MS307		159 × 94 mm. Nos. 304/6	50·00	40·00

DESIGNS: $1, $2, Chinese masks similar to T **77**.

78 Pigeons with Letters

1974. Centenary of U.P.U.

308	**78**	10c. blue, green and black	40	10
309	–	50c. mauve, orange & black	1·00	40
310	–	$2 multicoloured	5·25	4·25

DESIGNS: 50c. Globe within letters; $2 Hands holding letters.

79 Stylized Hare

1975. Chinese New Year ("Year of the Hare").

327	**79**	10c. silver and red	1·00	60
328	–	$1.30 gold and green	8·00	8·00

DESIGN: $1.30, Pair of hares.

80 Queen Elizabeth II, the Duke of Edinburgh and Hong Kong Arms

1975. Royal Visit.

329	**80**	$1.30 multicoloured	2·75	2·00
330		$2 multicoloured	3·75	4·25

81 Mid-Autumn Festival

82 Melodious Laughing Thrush ("The Hwamei")

1975. Hong Kong Festivals of 1975. Mult.

331		50c. Type **81**	2·00	50
332		$1 Dragon-boat Festival	8·00	2·50

333	$2 Tin Hau Festival	28·00	9·50
MS334	102 × 83 mm. Nos. 331/3	90·00	45·00

1975. Birds. Multicoloured.

335	50c. Type **82**	2·50	50
336	$1.30 Chinese bulbul	8·50	5·00
337	$2 Black-capped kingfisher	16·00	12·00

83 Dragon

1976. Chinese New Year ("Year of the Dragon").

338 **83**	20c. mauve, purple and gold	75	10
339 –	$1.30 green, red and gold	6·50	3·25

DESIGN: $1.30, As Type **83** but dragon reversed.

84 "60" and Girl Guides Badge

1976. Diamond Jubilee of Girl Guides. Multicoloured.

354	20c. Type **84**	50	10
355	$1.30 Badge, stylized diamond and "60"	5·50	4·00

85 "Postal Services" in Chinese Characters

1976. Opening of New G.P.O.

356 **85**	20c. green, grey and black	75	10
357 –	$1.30 orange, grey and black	3·75	2·00
358 –	$2 yellow, grey and black	6·50	4·50

DESIGNS: $1.30, Old G.P.O; $2 New G.P.O.

86 Tree Snake on Branch

1977. Chinese New Year ("Year of the Snake"). Multicoloured.

359	20c. Type **86**	50	15
360	$1.30 Snake facing left	4·25	4·75

87 Presentation of the Orb

1977. Silver Jubilee. Multicoloured.

361	20c. Type **87**	40	10
362	$1.30 The Queen's visit, 1975	1·25	1·25
363	$2 The Orb (vert)	1·50	1·50

88 Tram Cars

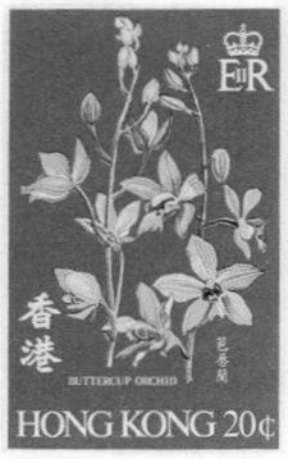

89 Buttercup Orchid

1977. Tourism. Multicoloured.

364	20c. Type **88**	55	10
365	60c. Star ferryboat	1·50	2·25
366	$1.30 The Peak Railway	2·75	2·25
367	$2 Junk and sampan	3·50	3·75

1977. Orchids. Multicoloured.

368	20c. Type **89**	1·25	20
369	$1.30 Lady's slipper orchid	4·00	2·25
370	$2 Susan orchid	6·00	4·75

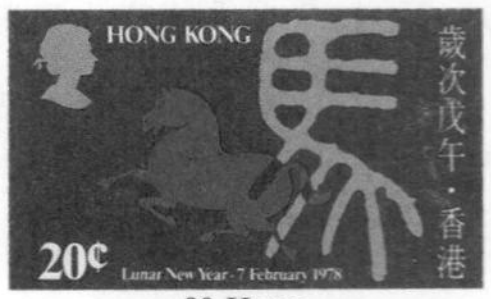

90 Horse

1978. Chinese New Year ("Year of the Horse").

371 **90**	20c. mauve, olive and bistre	50	10
372	$1.30 orange, brn & lt brn	3·75	4·50

91 Queen Elizabeth II

1978. 25th Anniv of Coronation.

373 **91**	20c. mauve and blue	40	10
374	$1.30 blue and mauve	1·50	2·25

92 Girl and Boy holding Hands

1978. Centenary of Po Leung Kuk (children's charity). Multicoloured.

375	20c. Type **92**	30	15
376	$1.30 Ring of children	1·25	2·50

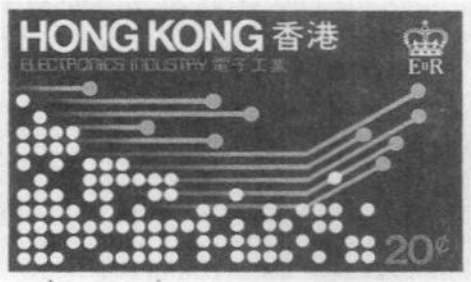

93 Electronics Industry

1979. Hong Kong Industries.

377 **93**	20c. yellow, olive & orange	30	10
378 –	$1.30 multicoloured	80	1·75
379 –	$2 multicoloured	85	2·25

DESIGNS: $1.30, Toy industry; $2 Garment industry.

94 "Precis orithya"

96 Tsui Shing Lau Pagoda

95 Diagrammatic View of Railway Station

1979. Butterflies. Multicoloured.

380	20c. Type **94**	80	10
381	$1 "Graphium sarpedon"	1·50	80
382	$1.30 "Heliophorus epicles"	1·75	1·60
383	$2 "Danaus genutia"	2·00	4·25

1979. Mass Transit Railway. Multicoloured.

384	20c. Type **95**	70	10
385	$1.30 Diagrammatic view of car	1·75	80
386	$2 Plan showing route of railway	1·75	2·25

1980. Rural Architecture.

387 **96**	20c. black, mauve & yellow	40	20
388 –	$1.30 multicoloured	80	1·25
389 –	$2 multicoloured	1·10	2·50

DESIGNS—HORIZ: $1.30, Village house, Sai O; $2 Ching Chung Koon Temple.

97 Queen Elizabeth the Queen Mother

1980. 80th Birthday of The Queen Mother.

390 **97**	$1.30 multicoloured	1·00	1·25

98 Botanical Gardens

1980. Parks. Multicoloured.

391	20c. Type **98**	40	15
392	$1 Ocean Park	60	60
393	$1.30 Kowloon Park	70	95
394	$2 Country parks	1·40	3·25

99 Red-spotted Grouper

1981. Fishes. Multicoloured.

395	20c. Type **99**	30	15
396	$1 Golden thread-finned bream	60	45
397	$1.30 Scar-breasted tuskfish	65	70
398	$2 Blue-barred orange parrotfish	90	2·75

100 Wedding Bouquet from Hong Kong

101 Suburban Development

1981. Royal Wedding. Multicoloured.

399	20c. Type **100**	30	10
400	$1.30 Prince Charles in Hong Kong	55	40
401	$5 Prince Charles and Lady Diana Spencer	1·75	3·00

1981. Public Housing.

402 **101**	20c. multicoloured	25	10
403 –	$1 multicoloured	65	50
404 –	$1.30 multicoloured	75	80
405 –	$2 multicoloured	90	2·00
MS406	148 × 105 mm. Nos. 402/5	4·25	6·00

DESIGNS: $1 to $2, Various suburban developments.

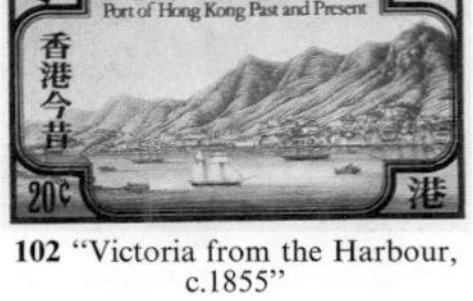

102 "Victoria from the Harbour, c.1855"

1982. Hong Kong Port, Past and Present. Multicoloured.

407	20c. Type **102**	50	15
408	$1 "West Point, Hong Kong, 1847"	1·25	80
409	$1.30 Fleet of junks	1·40	85
410	$2 Liner "Queen Elizabeth 2" at Hong Kong	2·50	3·00

103 Large Indian Civet

1982. Wild Animals.

411 **103**	20c. black, pink and brown	40	15
412 –	$1 multicoloured	75	60
413 –	$1.30 black, green & orange	80	70
414 –	$5 black, brown and yellow	2·00	3·75

DESIGNS: $1 Chinese pangolin; $1.30, Chinese porcupine; $5 Indian muntjac.

104 Queen Elizabeth II

107 Dancing

106 Table Tennis

1982.

415 **104**	10c. light red, red & yellow	80	60
416	20c. blue, violet & lavender	1·00	1·00
417	30c. lt violet, violet & pink	1·50	30
418	40c. red and blue	1·50	30
475	50c. chestnut, brn & grn	1·00	40
476	60c. purple and grey	1·50	1·10
477	70c. green, myrtle & yellow	3·50	40
478	80c. bistre, brown & green	3·75	2·00
479	90c. dp green, grn & turq	4·25	50
480	$1 dp orange, orange & red	1·75	40
481	$1.30 blue and mauve	2·50	45
482	$1.70 dp blue, blue & grn	4·00	1·50
483	$2 blue and pink	3·75	1·50
484 –	$5 red, purple and yellow	9·00	3·50
485 –	$10 brown and light brown	9·00	4·50
486 –	$20 red and blue	10·00	7·50
487 –	$50 red and grey	32·00	27·00

Nos. 484/7 are as Type **104** but larger, 26 × 30 mm.

1982. Sport for the Disabled. Multicoloured.

431	30c. Type **106**	50	10
432	$1 Racing	75	80
433	$1.30 Basketball	2·75	1·50
434	$5 Archery	6·00	6·50

1983. Performing Arts.

435 **107**	30c. light blue and blue	50	10
436 –	$1.30 red and purple	1·50	1·25
437 –	$5 green and deep green	4·00	5·50

DESIGNS: $1.30, "Theatre"; $5 "Music".

108 Aerial View of Hong Kong

1983. Commonwealth Day. Multicoloured.

438	30c. Type **108**	70	10
439	$1 "Liverpool Bay" (container ship)	1·75	1·25
440	$1.30 Hong Kong flag	1·75	1·25
441	$5 Queen Elizabeth II and Hong Kong	3·50	6·50

109 Victoria Harbour

1983. Hong Kong by Night. Multicoloured.

442	30c. Type **109**	1·25	15
443	$1 Space Museum, Tsim Sha Tsui Cultural Centre	3·75	1·50
444	$1.30 Fireworks display	4·75	2·00
445	$5 "Jumbo", floating restaurant	15·00	10·00

110 Old and new Observatory Buildings

1983. Centenary of Hong Kong Observatory.

446	**110**	40c. orange, brown & black	75	10
447	–	$1 mauve, dp mauve & blk	2·00	1·75
448	–	$1.30 blue, dp blue & black	2·75	1·75
449	–	$5 yellow, green and black	8·00	9·50

DESIGNS: $1 Wind measuring equipment; $1.30, Thermometer; $5 Ancient and modern seismometers.

111 De Havilland D.H.86 Dragon Express "Dorado" (Hong Kong–Penang Service, 1936)

1984. Aviation in Hong Kong. Multicoloured.

450	40c. Type **111**	1·00	15
451	$1 Sikorsky S-42B flying boat (San Francisco–Hong Kong Service, 1937)	2·25	1·75
452	$1.30 Cathay-Pacific Boeing 747 jet leaving Kai Tak Airport	3·25	1·75
453	$5 Baldwin brothers' balloon, 1891 (vert)	9·00	12·00

112 Map by Capt. E. Belcher, 1836

1984. Maps of Hong Kong.

454	40c. Type **112**	1·00	20
455	$1 Bartholomew map of 1929	1·75	1·25
456	$1.30 Early map of Hong Kong waters	8·00	1·75
457	$5 Chinese-style map of 1819	11·00	11·00

113 Cockerel

1984. Chinese Lanterns. Multicoloured.

458	40c. Type **113**	1·00	15
459	$1 Dog	2·00	1·40
460	$1.30 Butterfly	3·00	1·75
461	$5 Fish	9·50	12·00

114 Jockey on Horse and Nurse with Baby ("Health Care")

1984. Centenary of Royal Hong Kong Jockey Club. Designs showing aspects of Club's charity work. Multicoloured.

462	40c. Type **114**	1·25	20
463	$1 Disabled man playing handball ("Support for Disabled")	2·00	1·75
464	$1.30 Ballerina ("The Arts")	3·00	2·00
465	$5 Humboldt penguins ("Ocean Park")	9·00	11·00
MS466	178 × 98 mm. Nos. 462/5	25·00	27·00

115 Hung Sing Temple

1985. Historic Buildings. Multicoloured.

467	40c. Type **115**	60	20
468	$1 St. John's Cathedral	1·25	1·60
469	$1.30 The Old Supreme Court Building	1·50	1·75
470	$5 Wan Chai Post Office	7·00	10·00

116 Prow of Dragon Boat

1985. 10th International Dragon Boat Festival. Designs showing different parts of dragon boat. Multicoloured.

488	40c. Type **116**	50	15
489	$1 Drummer and rowers	1·75	1·25
490	$1.30 Rowers	3·00	1·60
491	$5 Stern of boat	9·25	11·00
MS492	190 × 100 mm. Nos. 488/91	22·00	23·00

117 The Queen Mother with Prince Charles and Prince William, 1984

1985. Life and Times of Queen Elizabeth the Queen Mother. Multicoloured.

493	40c. At Glamis Castle, aged 7	60	10
494	$1 Type **117**	1·75	1·25
495	$1.30 The Queen Mother, 1970 (from photo by Cecil Beaton)	2·00	1·40
496	$5 With Prince Henry at his christening (from photo by Lord Snowdon)	3·25	5·00

118 Melastoma

1985. Native Flowers. Multicoloured.

497	40c. Type **118**	1·50	20
498	50c. Chinese lily	1·75	40
499	60c. Grantham's camellia	2·00	1·25
500	$1.30 Narcissus	3·25	1·25
501	$1.70 Bauhinia	3·75	1·50
502	$5 Chinese New Year flower	7·00	12·00

119 Hong Kong Academy for Performing Arts

1985. New Buildings. Multicoloured.

503	50c. Type **119**	80	15
504	$1.30 Exchange Square (vert)	1·75	1·50
505	$1.70 Hong Kong Bank Headquarters (vert)	2·00	1·75
506	$5 Hong Kong Coliseum	5·50	12·00

120 Halley's Comet in the Solar System

1986. Appearance of Halley's Comet. Mult.

507	50c. Type **120**	1·25	20
508	$1.30 Edmond Halley and Comet	2·00	1·40
509	$1.70 Comet over Hong Kong	2·75	1·50
510	$5 Comet passing the Earth	11·00	11·00
MS511	135 × 80 mm. Nos. 507/10	22·00	25·00

120a At Wedding of Miss Celia Bowes-Lyon, 1931

1986. 60th Birthday of Queen Elizabeth II. Multicoloured.

512	50c. Type **120a**	50	10
513	$1 Queen in Garter procession, Windsor Castle, 1977	85	60
514	$1.30 In Hong Kong, 1975	1·10	70
515	$1.70 At Royal Lodge, Windsor, 1980 (from photo by Norman Parkinson)	1·25	75
516	$5 At Crown Agents Head Office, London, 1983	4·00	6·50

121 Mass Transit Train, Boeing 747 Airliner and Map of World

1986. "Expo '86" World Fair, Vancouver. Multicoloured.

517	50c. Type **121**	80	30
518	$1.30 Hong Kong Bank Headquarters and map of world	1·50	1·00
519	$1.70 Container ship and map of world	2·25	1·40
520	$5 Dish aerial and map of world	6·50	8·00

122 Hand-liner Sampan

1986. Fishing Vessels. Designs showing fishing boat and outline of fish. Multicoloured.

521	50c. Type **122**	80	15
522	$1.30 Stern trawler	1·50	1·10
523	$1.70 Long liner junk	2·25	1·40
524	$5 Junk trawler	7·00	9·50

123 "The Second Puan Khequa" (attr Spoilum)

1986. 19th-century Hong Kong Portraits. Multicoloured.

525	50c. Type **123**	40	15
526	$1.30 "Chinese Lady" (19th-century copy)	1·40	1·25
527	$1.70 "Lamqua" (self-portrait)	1·50	1·40
528	$5 "Wife of Wo Hing Qua" (attr G. Chinnery)	4·00	6·50

124 Rabbit

1987. Chinese New Year ("Year of the Rabbit"). Designs showing stylized rabbits.

529	**124**	50c. multicoloured	75	15
530	–	$1.30 multicoloured	1·75	1·40
531	–	$1.70 multicoloured	2·00	1·40
532	–	$5 multicoloured	7·00	7·00
MS533		133 × 84 mm. Nos. 529/32	38·00	26·00

Nos. 530/1 have the "0" omitted from their face values.

125 "Village Square, Hong Kong Island, 1838" (Auguste Borget)

1987. 19th-century Hong Kong Scenes. Mult.

534	50c. Type **125**	70	15
535	$1.30 "Boat Dwellers, Kowloon Bay, 1838 (Auguste Borget)	2·00	1·25
536	$1.70 "Flagstaff House, 1846" (Murdoch Bruce)	2·50	1·40
537	$5 "Wellington Street, late 19th-century" (C. Andrasi)	7·50	11·00

126 Queen Elizabeth II and Central Victoria

127 Hong Kong Flag

1987.

538B	**126**	10c. multicoloured	75	60
539A		40c. multicoloured	1·50	2·00
602		50c. multicoloured	1·50	40
603		60c. multicoloured	1·25	30
604		70c. multicoloured	1·75	1·25
605		80c. multicoloured	1·75	1·25
606		90c. multicoloured	1·25	1·00
607		$1 multicoloured	1·50	40
607a		$1.20 multicoloured	3·50	3·50
608		$1.30 multicoloured	2·00	60
609		$1.40 multicoloured	2·00	70
547A		$1.70 multicoloured	3·00	80
610		$1.80 multicoloured	1·50	60
611		$2 multicoloured	1·50	50
611a		$2.30 multicoloured	3·50	3·50
612	–	$5 multicoloured	4·50	1·75
613	–	$10 multicoloured	6·50	6·00
614	–	$20 multicoloured	11·00	11·00
615	–	$50 multicoloured	19·00	20·00

DESIGNS—25 × 31 mm: Queen Elizabeth II and $5 Kowloon; $10 Victoria Harbour; $20 Legislative Council Building; $50 Government House.

With the exception of Nos. 607a and 611a which are dated, all the above exist with or without a date in the design.

1987.

554a	**127**	10c. multicoloured	50	1·00
554b	–	50c. brown, red and black	1·25	1·75
554c	–	80c. mauve, green & blk	1·00	2·75
554d	–	90c. blue, brown & black	1·00	1·75
554e	–	$1.30 green, blue & black	1·75	2·50
554f	–	$2.30 brown, violet & blk	2·00	3·25

DESIGN: 50c. to $2.30, Map of Hong Kong.

128 Alice Ho Miu Ling Nethersole Hospital, 1887

1987. Hong Kong Medical Centenaries. Mult.

555	50c. Type **128**	1·00	20
556	$1.30 Matron and nurses, Nethersole Hospital, 1891	2·25	1·40
557	$1.70 Scanning equipment, Faculty of Medicine	2·75	1·40
558	$5 Nurse and patient, Faculty of Medicine	8·50	8·00

129 Casual Dress with Fringed Hem, 220–589

1987. Historical Chinese Costumes. Multicoloured.

559	50c. Type **129**	55	10
560	$1.30 Two-piece dress and wrap, 581–960	1·40	1·25
561	$1.70 Formal dress, Song Dynasty, 960–1279	1·75	1·50
562	$5 Manchu empress costume, 1644–1911	5·75	7·50

130 Dragon

1988. Chinese New Year ("Year of the Dragon"). Designs showing dragons.

563	**130**	50c. multicoloured	75	15
564	–	$1.30 multicoloured	1·50	1·25
565	–	$1.70 multicoloured	1·75	1·40
566	–	$5 multicoloured	3·25	5·50
MS567		134 × 88 mm. Nos. 563/6	13·00	15·00

131 White-throated Kingfisher ("White-breasted Kingfisher")

132 Chinese Banyan

1988. Hong Kong Birds. Multicoloured.
568 50c. Type **131** . . . . 1·00 30
569 $1.30 Fukien niltava . . . . 2·00 1·60
570 $1.70 Black kite . . . . . . 2·50 1·75
571 $5 Lesser pied kingfisher . . 4·00 7·00

1988. Trees of Hong Kong. Multicoloured.
572 50c. Type **132** 35 10
573 $1.30 Hong Kong orchid tree 70 65
574 $1.70 Cotton tree 90 85
575 $5 Schima . . . . 2·50 5·50
MS576 135 × 85 mm. Nos. 572/5 12·00 9·50

133 Lower Terminal, Peak Tramway

134 Hong Kong Catholic Cathedral

1988. Centenary of The Peak Tramway. Mult.
577 50c. Type **133** 35 10
578 $1.30 Tram on incline . . . 70 1·00
579 $1.70 Peak Tower Upper Terminal . . . . 90 1·25
580 $5 Tram . . . . 2·50 5·00
MS581 160 × 90 mm. Nos. 577/80 9·00 9·50

1988. Centenary of Hong Kong Catholic Cathedral.
582 **134** 60c. multicoloured . . . . 1·25 1·50

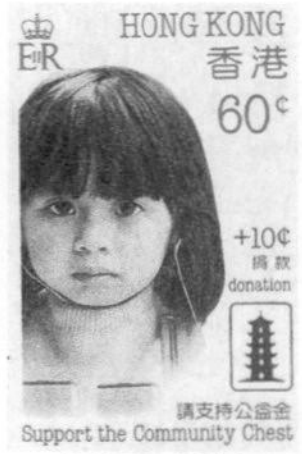

135 Deaf Girl

137 Girl and Doll

136 Snake

1988. Community Chest Charity.
583 **135** 60c.+10c. black, red & bl 60 1·25
584 – $1.40+20c. black, red and green . . . . 80 1·40
585 – $1.80+30c. black, red and orange . . . . 1·25 1·75
586 – $5+$1 black, red & brn 3·25 6·00
DESIGNS: $1.40, Elderly woman; $1.80, Blind boy using braille typewriter; $5 Mother and baby.

1989. Chinese New Year ("Year of the Snake"). Multicoloured.
587 60c. Type **136** 45 15
588 $1.40 Snake and fish . . . 1·75 70
589 $1.80 Snake on branch . . . 1·90 85
590 $5 Coiled snake . . . . . . 6·25 7·25
MS591 135 × 85 mm. Nos. 587/90 14·00 9·50

1989. Cheung Chau Bun Festival. Multicoloured.
592 60c. Type **137** 55 15
593 $1.40 Girl in festival costume 1·25 80
594 $1.80 Paper effigy of god Taai Si Wong . . . . 1·40 90
595 $5 Floral gateway . . . . . 3·50 6·00

138 "Twins" (wood carving, Cheung Yee)

139 Lunar New Year Festivities

1989. Modern Art. Multicoloured.
596 60c. Type **138** 50 15
597 $1.40 "Figures" (acrylic on paper, Chan Luis) . . . . 1·25 80
598 $1.80 "Lotus" (copper sculpture, Van Lau) . . . 1·40 90
599 $5 "Zen Painting" (ink and colour on paper, Lui Shou-kwan) . . . . 3·00 4·75

1989. Hong Kong People. Multicoloured.
616 60c. Type **139** 75 10
617 $1.40 Shadow boxing and horse racing . . . . 2·00 80
618 $1.80 Foreign-exchange dealer and traditional builder . . . . 2·00 90
619 $5 Multi-racial society . . . 4·50 7·00

140 University of Science and Technology

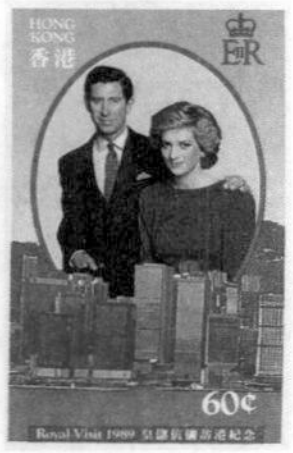

141 Prince and Princess of Wales and Hong Kong Skyline

1989. Building for the Future.
620 **140** 60c. black, yellow & brn 45 15
621 – 70c. blk, pale pink & pink 50 40
622 – $1.30 black, lt green & grn . . . . 1·00 1·00
623 – $1.40 black, lt blue & blue 1·00 70
624 – $1.80 black, turquoise & bl . . . . 1·25 1·00
625 – $5 brown, orange and red 6·00 6·50
DESIGNS: 70c. Cultural Centre; $1.30, Eastern Harbour motorway interchange; $1.40, New Bank of China Building; $1.80, Convention and Exhibition Centre; $5 Mass Transit electric train.

1989. Royal Visit. Multicoloured.
626 60c. Type **141** . . . . 1·25 30
627 $1.40 Princess of Wales . . . 2·25 1·10
628 $1.80 Prince of Wales . . . . 1·60 1·10
629 $5 Prince and Princess of Wales in evening dress . . 6·50 7·50
MS630 128 × 75 mm. No. 629 . . 14·00 9·00

143 Horse

1990. Chinese New Year ("Year of the Horse").
631 **143** 60c. multicoloured 85 20
632 – $1.40 multicoloured . . . 1·75 1·25
633 – $1.80 multicoloured . . . 1·90 1·25
634 – $5 multicoloured . . . . 6·00 7·50
MS635 135 × 85 mm. Nos. 631/4 13·00 13·00
DESIGNS: $1.40 to $5, Different horse designs.

144 Chinese Lobster Dish

145 Air Pollution and Clean Air

1990. International Cuisine. Designs showing various dishes. Multicoloured.
636 60c. Type **144** 60 15
637 70c. Indian 60 40
638 $1.30 Chinese vegetables . . 1·00 1·00
639 $1.40 Thai . . . . 1·00 65
640 $1.80 Japanese . . . . 1·25 90
641 $5 French . . . . 4·25 7·50

1990. U.N. World Environment Day. Mult.
642 60c. Type **145** 40 15
643 $1.40 Noise pollution and music 85 80
644 $1.80 Polluted and clean water . . . . 1·00 80
645 $5 Litter on ground and in bin . . . . 2·75 4·00

1990. "New Zealand 1990" International Stamp Exhibition, Auckland. Sheet 130 × 75 mm, containing No. 613.
MS646 $10 multicoloured . . . . 95·00 95·00

146 Street Lamp and Des Voeux Road, 1890

1990. Centenary of Electricity Supply.
647 **146** 60c. black, bistre & brown 50 15
648 – $1.40 multicoloured . . . 1·10 1·00
649 – $1.80 black, bistre and blue . . . . 1·25 1·00
650 – $5 multicoloured . . . . 2·50 5·50
MS651 155 × 85 mm. Nos. 648 and 650 . . . . 6·50 9·00
DESIGNS: $1.40, Street Lamp and "Jumbo" (floating restaurant), 1940; $1.80, Street lamp and pylon, 1960; $5 Street lamp and Hong Kong from harbour, 1980.

147 Christmas Tree and Skyscrapers

1990. Christmas. Multicoloured.
652 50c. Type **147** 25 10
653 60c. Dove with holly 25 15
654 $1.40 Firework display . . . 80 40
655 $1.80 Father Christmas hat on skyscraper . . . . . . 1·00 50
656 $2 Children with Father Christmas . . . . 1·40 1·40
657 $5 Candy stick with bow and Hong Kong skyline . . . . 3·00 5·00

148 Ram

1991. Chinese New Year ("Year of the Ram").
658 **148** 60c. multicoloured 25 15
659 – $1.40 multicoloured . . . 65 60
660 – $1.80 multicoloured . . . 80 70
661 – $5 multicoloured . . . . 2·75 4·75
MS662 135 × 85 mm. Nos. 658/61 6·50 8·50
DESIGNS: $1.40 to $5, Different ram designs.

149 Letter "A", Clock, Teddy Bear and Building Bricks (Kindergarten)

150 Rickshaw

1991. Education. Multicoloured.
663 80c. Type **149** 50 20
664 $1.80 Globe, laboratory flask and mathematical symbols (Primary and Secondary) 1·25 80
665 $2.30 Machinery (Vocational) 1·40 1·40
666 $5 Mortar board, computer and books (Tertiary) . . . 3·50 6·00

1991. 100 Years of Public Transport. Mult.
667 80c. Type **150** 30 15
668 90c. Double-decker bus . . . 70 75
669 $1.70 Harbour ferry . . . . 1·10 1·25
670 $1.80 Double-deck tram . . . 1·40 80
671 $2.30 Mass Transit electric train . . . . 2·00 2·25
672 $5 Jetfoil . . . . 3·50 6·50

151 Victorian Pillar Box and Cover of 1888

152 Bronze Buddha, Lantau Island

1991. 150th Anniv of Hong Kong Post Office. Multicoloured.
673 80c. Type **151** 40 15
674 $1.70 Edwardian pillar box and cover . . . . 90 1·00
675 $1.80 King George V pillar box and cover of 1935 . . 1·00 75
676 $2.30 King George VI pillar box and cover of 1938 . . 1·40 2·00
677 $5 Queen Elizabeth II pillar box and cover of 1989 . . 3·75 7·00
MS678 130 × 75 mm. $10 As No. 677 13·00 17·00
See also Nos. **MS**745 and **MS**899.

1991. Landmarks.
679 **152** 80c. red and black 50 15
680 – $1.70 green and black . . 1·00 1·25
681 – $1.80 violet and black . . 1·75 80
682 – $2.30 blue and black . . . 1·25 2·00
683 – $5 orange and black . . . 3·50 7·00
DESIGNS: $1.70, Peak Pavilion; $1.80, Clocktower of Kowloon–Canton Railway Station; $2.30, Catholic Cathedral; $5 Wong Tai Sin Temple.

1991. "Phila Nippon '91" International Stamp Exhibition, Tokyo. Sheet 130 × 75 mm, containing No. 613.
MS684 $10 multicoloured . . . . 42·00 38·00

1991. Olympic Games, Barcelona (1992) (1st issue). Sheet 130 × 75 mm, containing No. 613.
MS685 $10 multicoloured . . . . 18·00 18·00
See also Nos. 696/700 and **MS**722.

153 Monkey

1992. Chinese New Year ("Year of the Monkey").
686 **153** 80c. multicoloured 40 15
687 – $1.80 multicoloured . . . 80 70
688 – $2.30 multicoloured . . . 1·25 1·75
689 – $5 multicoloured . . . 2·75 6·50
MS690 135 × 85 mm. Nos. 686/9 11·00 14·00
DESIGNS: $1.80 to $5, Different monkey designs.

1992. 40th Anniv of Queen Elizabeth II's Accession. As T **179a** of Gibraltar. Multicoloured.
691 80c. Royal barge in Hong Kong harbour 30 15
692 $1.70 Queen watching dancing display 60 70
693 $1.80 Fireworks display . . . 60 35
694 $2.30 Three portraits of Queen Elizabeth . . . . . 90 1·00
695 $5 Queen Elizabeth II . . . 2·00 3·25

154 Running

1992. Olympic Games, Barcelona. Multicoloured.
696 80c. Type **154** 40 20
697 $1.80 Swimming and javelin 80 1·00
698 $2.30 Cycling . . . . 1·60 1·75
699 $5 High jump . . . . 2·25 4·75
MS700 130 × 75 mm. As Nos. 696/9* 6·50 9·00
*The stamps from No. **MS**700 show the inscriptions in different colours, instead of the black on Nos. 696/9. The designs of the $1.80 and $5 values from the miniature sheet have also been rearranged so that "HONG KONG" and the Royal Cypher occur at the right of the inscription.

1992. "World Columbian Stamp Expo '92" Exhibition, Chicago. Sheet 130 × 75 mm, containing No. 613, but colours changed.
MS701 $10 multicoloured . . . . 4·25 7·50

155 Queen Elizabeth II

157 Principal Male Character

156 Stamps and Perforation Gauge

1992.

702	155	10c. mauve, blk & cerise	30	50
702bp		20c. black, indigo & bl	1·00	1·75
703		50c. red, black and yellow	30	30
704		60c. blue, black and light blue	2·00	50
705		70c. mauve, black and lilac	2·00	65
706		80c. mauve, black and pink	30	20
707		90c. green, blk & grey	30	20
708		$1 brown, black and yellow	35	20
708b		$1.10 red, black & orge	1·00	1·00
709		$1.20 violet, blk & lilac	35	25
757c		$1.30 blue, black and orange	50	80
709c		$1.40 green, black and yellow	1·25	70
709d		$1.50 brown, black and blue	1·25	1·75
709e		$1.60 green, black and lilac	1·25	1·50
710		$1.70 ultram, blk & bl	80	1·00
711		$1.80 mauve, black and grey	1·25	55
711a		$1.90 green, black and stone	80	1·25
764		$2 blue, black and green	60	75
712b		$2.10 red, black & green	1·75	1·75
713		$2.30 brown, black and pink	2·50	75
759		$2.40 blue, blk & grey	1·00	1·50
713b		$2.50 green, black and yellow	1·00	1·25
713c		$2.60 choc, blk & brn	1·25	2·25
713d		$3.10 brown, black and blue	1·25	80
759e		$5 green, black & lt grn	1·25	2·50
715	–	$10 brown, black and cinnamon	3·25	2·75
716	–	$20 red, black & orange	4·25	4·50
717	–	$50 dp grey, blk & grey	8·50	11·00

Nos. 715/17 are as Type **155**, but larger, 26 × 30 mm.

1992. Stamp Collecting. Multicoloured.

718	80c. Type **156**	30	25
719	$1.80 Handstamp of 1841, 1891 Jubilee overprint and tweezers	60	75
720	$2.30 Stamps of 1946 and 1949 under magnifying glass	85	1·25
721	$5 2c. of 1862 and watermark detector	2·00	4·00

1992. Olympic Games, Barcelona (3rd issue). As No. **MS**700, but additionally inscribed "To Commemorate the Opening of the 1992 Summer Olympic Games 25 July 1992", in English and Chinese, at foot of sheet.

MS722 130 × 75 mm. As Nos. 696/9 3·50 5·50

1992. "Kuala Lumpur '92" International Stamp Exhibition. Sheet 130 × 75 mm, containing design as No. 715, but colours changed.

MS723 $10 blue, black and light blue 4·25 7·00

1992. Chinese Opera. Multicoloured.

724	80c. Type **157**	1·00	25
725	$1.80 Martial character	1·70	1·60
726	$2.30 Principal female character	2·00	2·25
727	$5 Comic character	4·00	7·00

158 Hearts

1992. Greetings Stamps. Multicoloured.

728	80c. Type **158**	30	20
729	$1.80 Stars	55	60
730	$2.30 Presents	75	1·00
731	$5 Balloons	1·60	3·00

159 Cockerel

1993. Chinese New Year ("Year of the Cock").

732	**159**	80c. multicoloured	30	20
733	–	$1.80 multicoloured	70	80
734	–	$2.30 multicoloured	95	1·25
735	–	$5 multicoloured	2·25	4·25

MS736 133 × 84 mm. Nos. 732/5 5·25 7·50

DESIGNS: $1.80 to $5, Different cock designs.

160 Pipa

161 Central Waterfront, Hong Kong in 1954

1993. Chinese String Musical Instruments. Multicoloured.

737	80c. Type **160**	40	20
738	$1.80 Erhu	70	80
739	$2.30 Ruan	95	1·25
740	$5 Gehu	2·00	3·75

1993. 40th Anniv of Coronation. Multicoloured.

741	80c. Type **161**	40	20
742	$1.80 Hong Kong in 1963	70	75
743	$2.30 Hong Kong in 1975	90	1·25
744	$5 Hong Kong in 1992	2·25	4·00

1993. 150th anniv of Hong Kong Post Office (2nd issue). Sheet 130 × 75 mm, containing No. 715.

MS745 $10 brown, black and cinnamon 5·00 7·00

1993. "Hong Kong '94" International Stamp Exhibition. Sheet 115 × 78 mm, containing design as No. 715, but colours changed.

MS746 $10 purple, black, yellow and blue 4·50 5·00

162 University of Science and Technology Building and Student

1993. Hong Kong's Contribution to Science and Technology. Multicoloured.

747	80c. Type **162**	25	20
748	$1.80 Science Museum building and energy machine exhibit	40	40
749	$2.30 Governor's Award and circuit board	60	90
750	$5 Dish aerials and world map	1·25	3·50

1993. "Bangkok '93" International Stamp Exhibition. Sheet 131 × 75 mm, containing design as No. 715, but colours changed.

MS751 $10 emerald, deep green and blue-green 2·75 4·00

163 Red Calico Egg-fish

1993. Goldfish. Multicoloured.

752	$1 Type **163**	40	20
753	$1.90 Red cap oranda	70	50
754	$2.40 Red and white fringetail	90	1·25
755	$5 Black and gold dragon-eye	2·25	4·00

MS756 130 × 75 mm. Nos. 752/5 7·00 9·00

164 Dog

1994. Chinese New Year ("Year of the Dog").

766	**164**	$1 multicoloured	30	20
767	–	$1.90 multicoloured	50	55
768	–	$2.40 multicoloured	70	1·00
769	–	$5 multicoloured	1·75	3·50

MS770 133 × 84 mm. Nos. 766/9 10·00 10·00

DESIGNS: $1.90 to $5, Different dog designs.

1994. "Hong Kong '94" International Stamp Exhibition. Sheet 130 × 75 mm, containing No. 759e.

MS771 **155** $5 green, black and light green 2·75 6·00

165 Modern Police Constables on Traffic Duty

1994. 150th Anniv of Royal Hong Kong Police Force. Multicoloured.

772	$1 Type **165**	30	20
773	$1.20 Marine policeman with binoculars	40	50
774	$1.90 Police uniforms of 1950	55	50
775	$2 Tactical firearms unit officer with sub-machine gun	75	1·00
776	$2.40 Early 20th-century police uniforms	90	1·25
777	$5 Sikh and Chinese constables of 1900	2·75	4·25

166 Dragon Boat Festival

1994. Traditional Chinese Festivals. Multicoloured.

778	$1 Type **166**	35	20
779	$1.90 Lunar New Year	60	70
780	$2.40 Seven Sisters Festival	85	1·25
781	$5 Mid-Autumn Festival	1·75	3·75

1994. Conference of Commonwealth Postal Administrations, Hong Kong. Sheet 134 × 83 mm, containing No. 715.

MS782 $10 brown, black and cinnamon 5·00 7·50

167 Swimming

1994. 15th Commonwealth Games, Victoria, Canada. Multicoloured.

783	$1 Type **167**	25	20
784	$1.90 Bowls	40	55
785	$2.40 Gymnastics	50	1·00
786	$5 Weightlifting	90	3·25

168 Dr. James Legge and Students

1994. Dr. James Legge (Chinese scholar) Commemoration.

787 **168** $1 multicoloured 55 60

169 Alcyonium Coral

1994. Corals. Multicoloured.

788	$1 Type **169**	35	20
789	$1.90 Zoanthus	45	60
790	$2.40 Tubastrea	55	1·00
791	$5 Platygyra	1·00	3·00

MS792 130 × 75 mm. Nos. 788/91 4·50 6·50

170 Pig

1995. Chinese New Year ("Year of the Pig").

793	**170**	$1 multicoloured	30	30
794	–	$1.90 multicoloured	50	80
795	–	$2.40 multicoloured	60	1·10
796	–	$5 multicoloured	1·00	3·00

MS797 130 × 84 mm. Nos. 793/6 4·25 6·00

DESIGNS: $1.90 to $5, Different pig designs.

171 Hong Kong Rugby Sevens

1995. International Sporting Events in Hong Kong. Multicoloured.

798	$1 Type **171**	45	20
799	$1.90 The China Sea Yacht Race	60	80
800	$2.40 International Dragon Boat Races	85	1·10
801	$5 Hong Kong International Horse Races	1·75	3·50

172 Tsui Shing Lau Pagoda

1995. Hong Kong Traditional Rural Buildings. Multicoloured.

802	$1 Type **172**	30	25
803	$1.90 Sam Tung Uk village	45	65
804	$2.40 Lo Wai village	60	1·00
805	$5 Man Shek Tong house	1·10	3·00

173 Regimental Badge

1995. Disbandment of the Royal Hong Kong Regiment. Multicoloured.

806	$1.20 Type **173**	40	25
807	$2.10 Regimental guidon (horiz)	50	65
808	$2.60 Colour of Hong Kong Volunteer Defence Corps, 1928 (horiz)	60	1·00
809	$5 Cap badge of Royal Hong Kong Defence Force, 1951	1·00	2·75

1995. "Singapore '95" International Stamp Exhibition. Sheet 130 × 75 mm, containing design as No. 715, but colours changed.

MS810 $10 mauve, green, yellow and lilac 4·00 6·50

1995. 50th Anniv of End of Second World War. Sheet 130 × 75 mm, containing No. 715.

MS811 $10 brown, black and cinnamon 4·50 6·50

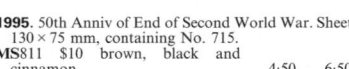

174 Bruce Lee

1995. Hong Kong Film Stars. Multicoloured.

812	$1.20 Type **174**	2·00	55
813	$2.10 Leung Sing-por	2·25	1·40
814	$2.60 Yam Kim-fai	3·00	1·75
815	$5 Lin Dai	3·50	4·50

175 Rat

1996. Chinese New Year ("Year of the Rat").
816 **175** $1.20 multicoloured . . . 25 30
817 – $2.10 multicoloured . . . 45 55
818 – $2.60 multicoloured . . . 50 65
819 – $5 multicoloured . . . . 1·25 1·75
MS820 133 × 83 mm. Nos. 816/19 3·00 3·50
DESIGNS: $2.10 to $5, Rats (different).

1996. Visit "HONG KONG '97" Stamp Exhibition (1st issue). Sheet 130 × 80 mm, containing design as No. 715, but colours changed.
MS821 $10 orange, black and green 5·00 7·50
See also Nos. **MS**827, **MS**841 and **MS**872/3.

176 Rhythmic Gymnastics

1996. Olympic Games, Atlanta. Multicoloured with Royal cypher and face values in black and Olympic rings multicoloured.
822 $1.20 Type **176** 25 25
823 $2.10 Diving 45 65
824 $2.60 Athletics 55 75
825 $5 Basketball . . . . 1·75 3·25
MS826 130 × 75 mm. As Nos. 822/5, but Royal Cypher and Olympic Rings in gold and face values in black (medal in bottom sheet margin) . . . . 3·00 3·50
See also Nos. 832/5.

1996. Visit "HONG KONG '97" Stamp Exhibition (2nd issue). Sheet 130 × 80 mm, containing design as No. 715, but colours changed.
MS827 $10 green, deep green and violet . . . . 3·00 3·00

177 Painted Pottery Basin, c. 4500–3700 B.C.

1996. Archaeological Discoveries. Multicoloured.
828 $1.20 Type **177** 35 25
829 $2.10 Stone "yue" (ceremonial axe), c. 2900–2200 B.C. 40 65
830 $2.60 Stone "ge" (halberd), c. 2200–1500 B.C. . . . . 45 1·00
831 $5 Pottery tripod, c. 25–220 A.D. . . . . 1·00 2·50

1996. Opening of Centennial Olympic Games, Atlanta. Designs as Nos. 822/5, but with Royal Cypher and Olympic Rings in gold and face values in colours quoted.
832 $1.20 Type **176** (mauve) . . . 35 25
833 $2.10 As No. 823 (blue) . . . 40 60
834 $2.60 As No. 824 (green) . . . 45 90
835 $5 As No. 825 (red) . . . . 1·00 2·75
MS836 130 × 75 mm. As No. **MS**826, but with medal in top margin . . . . 2·75 4·50
The stamps in Nos. **MS**826 and **MS**836 are similar. The miniature sheets differ in the marginal inscriptions and illustrations. No. **MS**826 is inscribed "1996 OLYMPIC GAMES" and has a Gold Medal in the bottom margin. No. **MS**836 is inscribed "TO COMMEMORATE THE OPENING OF THE CENTENNIAL OLYMPIC GAMES 19 JULY 1996" and has the medal in the top margin.

178 Pat Sin Leng Mountain

1996. Mountains. Multicoloured.
837 $1.30 Type **178** 45 35
838 $2.50 Ma On Shan (40 × 35 mm) . . . . 65 1·00
839 $3.10 Lion Rock (35 × 40 mm) . . . . 85 1·40
840 $5 Lantau Peak (25 × 46½ mm) . . . . . . 1·10 2·25

1996. Visit "HONG KONG '97" Stamp Exhibition (3rd issue). Sheet 130 × 80 mm, containing design as No. 715, but colours changed.
MS841 $10 green, black and red 2·50 3·50

1996. Hong Kong Team's Achievements at Atlanta Olympic Games. Sheet 130 × 75 mm, containing No. 715.
MS842 $10 brown, black and cinnamon . . . . 2·50 3·25

179 Main Building, University of Hong Kong, 1912

1996. Urban Heritage. Multicoloured.
843 $1.30 Type **179** 30 70
844 $2.50 Western Market, 1906 50 85
845 $3.10 Old Pathological Institute, 1905 . . . . . . 55 1·00
846 $5 Flagstaff House, 1846 . . 70 2·25

1996. Serving the Community. Sheet 130 × 75 mm, containing design as No. 619, but smaller, 25 × 35 mm. Multicoloured.
MS847 $5 Multi-racial society . . 1·00 1·25

180 Part of Hong Kong Skyline

1997.
848 **180** 10c. purple and pink . . . 15 30
849 – 20c. brown and red . . . 30 30
850 – 50c. green and orange . . 20 40
851 – $1 blue and yellow . . . 30 20
852 – $1.20 green and yellow . . 30 40
853 – $1.30 violet and green . . 30 25
854 – $1.40 purple and green . . 30 40
855 – $1.60 purple and green . . 30 50
856 – $2 green and blue 40 50
857 – $2.10 turquoise and blue 40 60
858 – $2.50 violet and mauve 50 1·00
859 – $3.10 purple and mauve 60 70
860 – $5 mauve and orange . . 1·25 1·00
861 – $10 multicoloured (28 × 32 mm) . . . . . 2·00 2·50
862 – $20 multicoloured (28 × 32 mm) . . . . . 3·50 5·00
863 – $50 multicoloured (28 × 32 mm) . . . . . 8·00 11·00
MS864 273 × 53 mm. Nos. 848/60 6·00 7·50
MS865 95 × 72 mm. Nos. 861/3 16·00 19·00
DESIGNS: 20c. to $50, Different sections of Hong Kong skyline.
See also Nos. **MS**872/3 and **MS**892.

1997. Visit "HONG KONG '97" Stamp Exhibition (4th issue). Sheet 130 × 80 mm, containing No. 861, with marginal illustration in violet.
MS872 $10 multicoloured . . . . 1·75 3·50

1997. Visit "HONG KONG '97" Stamp Exhibition (5th issue). Sheet 130 × 80 mm, containing No. 861, with marginal illustration in brown.
MS873 $10 multicoloured . . . . 1·75 3·50

181 Ox

1997. Chinese New Year ("Year of the Ox").
874 **181** $1.30 multicoloured . . . 25 25
875 $2.50 multicoloured . . . 40 55
876 $3.10 multicoloured . . . 55 90
877 $5 multicoloured . . . . 85 2·00
MS878 133 × 84 mm. Nos. 874/7 2·00 3·50

182 Yellow-breasted Bunting

1997. Migratory Birds. Multicoloured.
884 $1.30 Type **182** 30 35
885 $2.50 Great knot 40 55
886 $3.10 Falcated teal 55 90
887 $5 Black-faced spoonbill . . 85 2·00

183 Hong Kong Stadium

1997. Modern Landmarks. Multicoloured.
888 $1.30 Type **183** 25 25
889 $2.50 Peak Tower 50 55
890 $3.10 Hong Kong Convention and Exhibition Centre . . . . 75 1·10
891 $5 Lantau bridge . . . . . . 1·10 2·50
MS892 130 × 76 mm. No. 891 . . 1·25 1·75

1997. Paralympic Games, Atlanta (1996). Sheet 130 × 75 mm, containing No. 861.
MS898 $10 multicoloured . . . . 1·75 2·75

1997. History of the Hong Kong Post Office. Sheet 130 × 75 mm, containing design as No. 677, but redrawn smaller, 22 × 38 mm.
MS899 $5 multicoloured . . . . 1·00 1·75

184 House of Sam Tung Uk

186 Clam

185 Graphs and Hong Kong Bank (Finance and Banking)

1997. Establishment of Hong Kong as Special Administrative Region of People's Republic of China. Multicoloured.
900 $1.30 Type **184** 30 15
901 $1.60 Hong Kong Bank and vehicles 30 15
902 $2.50 Buildings and Hong Kong Convention and Exhibition Centre 45 30
903 $2.60 Container Terminal . . 45 30
904 $3.10 Junks and dolphins . . 60 30
905 $5 Bauhinia flower and clouds 85 30

1997. World Bank Group and International Monetary Fund Annual Meetings. Multicoloured.
907 $1.30 Type **185** 30 15
908 $2.50 Share prices (Investment) and Stock Exchange 45 30
909 $3.10 Map on printed circuit and dish aerial (Trade and Telecommunications) . . . 60 45
910 $5 Satellite image and road junctions (Infrastructure and Transport) 70 45

1997. Sea Shells. Multicoloured.
911 $1.30 Type **186** 30 15
912 $2.50 Cowrie 45 30
913 $3.10 Cone 55 45
914 $5 Murex 70 45

187 Tiger

1998. Chinese New Year ("Year of the Tiger").
915 **187** $1.30 multicoloured . . . 30 15
916 $2.50 multicoloured . . . 45 30
917 $3.10 multicoloured . . . 60 45
918 $5 multicoloured 70 45

188 "Star", 1900s

1998. Centenary of Star Ferry. Multicoloured.
920 $1.30 Type **188** 30 15
921 $2.50 "Star", 1910s–20s . . . 45 30
922 $3.10 "Star", 1920s–1950s . . 45 30
923 $5 "Star", 1950s onwards . . 85 30

189 Observation Lounge

1998. Inauguration of Hong Kong International Airport, Chek Lap Kok. Multicoloured.
924 $1.30 Type **189** 30 15
925 $1.60 Couple boarding train 30 15
926 $2.50 Train and suspension bridge 45 30
927 $2.60 Concourse and mail vans at Airmail Centre . . 45 30
928 $3.10 Aircraft in bays 60 30
929 $5 Airplane taking off . . . 85 30

191 Grasshopper and Cub Scouts and Knot

192 Graphic Design

1998. 85th Anniv of Hong Kong Scout Association. Multicoloured.
932 $1.30 Type **191** 30 15
933 $2.50 Two scouts, knot, watchtower and tents . . . 45 30
934 $3.10 Two venture scouts, knot, sailing dinghies and helicopter 45 30
935 $5 Rover scout and adult leader, knot and buildings 85 30

1998. Hong Kong Design. Multicoloured.
936 $1.30 Type **192** 30 15
937 $2.50 Product design 45 30
938 $3.10 Interior design 45 45
939 $5 Fashion design 85 45

193 Dragonfly Kite

194 Rabbit ("Kung Hei Fat Choi")

1998. Kites. Multicoloured.
940 $1.30 Type **193** 30 15
941 $2.50 Dragon kite 45 30
942 $3.10 Butterfly kite 45 45
943 $5 Goldfish kite 85 45

1999. Chinese New Year ("Year of the Rabbit"). Multicoloured.
945 $1.30 Type **194** 30 15
946 $2.50 Rabbit and scroll ("Good Health") 45 30
947 $3.10 Rabbit and tangerine ("Good Luck") 60 45
948 $5 Rabbit and sweet tray ("May all your wishes come true") 85 45
The gold panels of the designs can be scratched off to reveal a greeting in Chinese characters as given in brackets. Prices for Nos. 945/8 are for examples with the gold panels intact.

196 Calligraphy

1999. International Year of the Elderly. Mult.
950 $1.30 Type **196** 30 15
951 $2.50 Holding bird cage . . . 45 30
952 $3.10 Playing chess 60 60
953 $5 Holding walking stick (voluntary services) 85 70

198 Bus

1999. Public Transport. Multicoloured.
956 $1.30 Type **198** 30 15
957 $2.40 Minibus 45 30
958 $2.50 Tram 60 45
959 $2.60 Taxi 70 45
960 $3.10 "Airport Express" train 85 60

199 Hong Kong Harbour

1999. Hong Kong–Singapore Joint Issue. Mult.
961 $1.20 Type **199** 30 15
962 $1.30 Singapore skyline . . . 30 15
963 $2.50 Giant Buddha, Lantau Island, Hong Kong 45 30
964 $2.60 Merlion statue, Sentosa Island, Singapore 45 30
965 $3.10 Street scene, Hong Kong 60 45
966 $5 Bugis Junction, Singapore 85 45

200 Flags of Hong Kong and People's Republic, and Hong Kong

1999. 50th Anniv of People's Republic of China. Multicoloured.
969 $1.30 Type **200** 45 15
970 $2.50 "Bauhinia blakeana" and Hong Kong harbour 60 45
971 $3.10 Chinese dragon dance 70 45
972 $5 Firework display over Hong Kong . . . . 1·10 70

201 Museum of Tea Ware

202 Dolphins

1999. Hong Kong Landmarks and Tourist Attractions. Multicoloured. (a) Size 24 × 29 mm (10c. to $5) or 26 × 31 mm (others).
973 10c. Type **201** 10 10
974 20c. St. John's Cathedral . . 10 10
975 50c. Legislative Council building 10 10
976 $1 Tai Fu Tai 30 10
977 $1.20 Wong Tai Sin Temple 30 10
978 $1.30 Victoria Harbour . . 30 10
979 $1.40 Hong Kong Railway Museum 30 10
980 $1.60 Tsim Sha Tsui clocktower 30 10
980a $1.80 Hong Kong Stadium 45 10
980b $1.90 Western Market . . 45 10
981 $2 Happy Valley racecourse 45 10
982 $2.10 Kowloon–Canton Railway 45 10
982a $2.40 Repulse Bay 45 10
983 $2.50 Chi Lin Nunnery, Kowloon 45 10
983b $3 The Peak Tower 60 10
984 $3.10 Giant Buddha, Po Lin Monastery, Lantau Island 70 10
985 $5 Pagoda, Aw Boon Haw Gardens 85 10
986 $10 Tsing Ma bridge . . . 1·70 30
986a $13 Hong Kong Cultural Centre . . . . 2·20 60
987 $20 Hong Kong Convention and Exhibition Centre . . 3·50 1·40
988 $50 Hong Kong International Airport . . 8·50 3·50

(b) Size 20 × 24 mm.
991 10c. As Type **201** 10 10
992 50c. As No. 975 . . . . . 10 10
993 $1.30 As No. 978 . . . . . 30 25
993a $1.40 As No. 979 . . . . . 30 10
994 $1.60 As No. 980 . . . . . 30 30
994a $1.80 As No. 980a 45 10
994b $2.40 As No. 982a 45 10
994c $3 As No. 984 . . . . . . 60 10

1999. Endangered Species. Indo-Pacific Humpbacked Dolphin ("Chinese White Dolphin").
995 **202** $1.30 multicoloured . . . 30 10
996 – $2.50 multicoloured . . . 45 30
997 – $3.10 multicoloured . . . 45 45
998 – $5 multicoloured 85 60
DESIGNS: $2.50 to $5 Various designs showing dolphins as Type **202**.

204 Victoria Harbour

206 Dragon

205 Scales on Globe (Au Chung-yip)

2000. New Millennium.
1001 **204** $50 multicoloured . . . 12·50 12·50
No. 1001 is embossed with 22 carat gold.

2000. New Millennium. Winning Entries in Children's Millennium Stamp Design Competition. Mult.
1002 $1.30 Type **205** 30 10
1003 $2.50 Globe, space shuttle, houses and children watering (Cheung Hang) 45 30
1004 $3.10 Planets (Valerie Teh) 60 45
1005 $5 Planets, spacecraft and satellite (Tsui Ming-yin) 85 45

2000. Chinese New Year ("Year of the Dragon").
1006 **206** $1.30 multicoloured . . 30 30
1007 – $2.50 multicoloured . . 45 45
1008 – $3.10 multicoloured . . 60 45
1009 – $5 multicoloured . . . . 1·00 60
DESIGNS: $2.50 to $5 Various dragons.

207 Hong Kong Heritage Museum, Sha Tin

2000. Museums and Libraries. Multicoloured.
1013 $1.30 Type **207** 30 10
1014 $2.50 Central Library, Causeway Bay 45 30
1015 $3.10 Museum of Coastal Defence, Shau Kei Wan 60 45
1016 $5 Museum of History, Tsim Sha Tsui East . . . 85 60

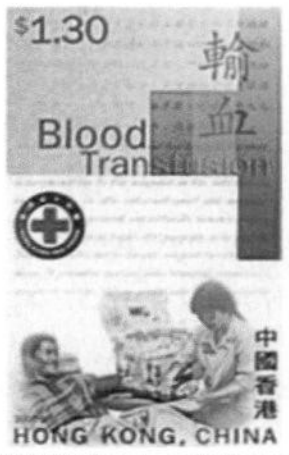

208 Patient and Nurse (Blood Transfusion)

209 Lantern Fly

2000. 50th Anniv of Hong Kong Red Cross. Multicoloured.
1018 $1.30 Type **208** 30 10
1019 $2.50 Doctor and child (Special Education and Care for the Disabled) . . 45 30
1020 $3.10 Man distributing blankets (Disaster relief) 60 45
1021 $5 Volunteer and young man (Youth and Voluntary services) . . . 85 45

2000. Insects. Multicoloured.
1023 $1.30 Type **209** 30 10
1024 $2.50 Yellow-spotted emerald 45 30
1025 $3.10 Hong Kong birdwing (butterfly) 60 45
1026 $5 Red-cap tortoise beetle 1·00 60

211 Cycling and Tennis

2000. Olympic Games, Sydney. Multicoloured.
1029 $1.30 Type **211** 30 10
1030 $2.50 Table tennis and running 45 30
1031 $3.10 Wrestling and rowing 60 45
1032 $5 Diving and wind surfing 85 45

212 View of Street (Establishment of Chamber, 1900)

2000. Centenary of General Chamber of Commerce. Multicoloured.
1033 $1.30 Type **212** 30 10
1034 $2.50 Old and new headquarters (relocation, 1922) 45 30
1035 $3.10 Victims of Pak Tin village fire receiving aid 60 45
1036 $5 Man using abacus and hand using mouse 85 60

215 Snake

216 Leaves and Pebbles ("Happy Memories")

2001. Chinese New Year ("Year of the Snake").
1040 **215** $1.30 multicoloured . . 30 10
1041 – $2.50 multicoloured . . 45 30
1042 – $3.10 multicoloured . . 60 45
1043 – $5 multicoloured 85 45
DESIGNS: $2.50 to $5 Showing various snakes.

2001. Greetings Stamps. Multicoloured.
1045 $1.30 Type **216** 30 10
1046 $1.60 Swans ("Happy Valentine's Day") 30 30
1047 $2.50 Chicks ("Happy Birthday") 60 30
1048 $2.60 Cherry blossom ("Happy New Year") . . 60 30
1049 $3.10 Bamboo ("A Successful Year") 70 30
1050 $5 Poinsettia ("Merry Christmas") . . . . . . 1·10 45

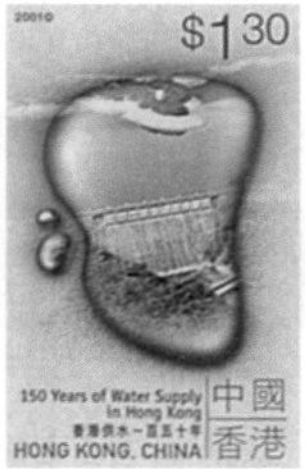

219 Tai Tam Tuk Reservoir

2001. 150th Anniv of Hong Kong's Public Water Supply. Multicoloured.
1053 $1.30 Type **219** 30 10
1054 $2.50 Plover Cove Reservoir 45 30
1055 $3.10 Guangdong to Hong Kong water pipeline . . . 60 45
1056 $5 Water monitoring equipment and chemical symbols 85 45

220 Ng Cho-fan and Pak Yin

2001. Hong Kong Film Stars. Multicoloured.
1057 $1.30 Type **220** 30 10
1058 $2.50 Sun Ma Si-tsang and Tang Bik-wan 45 30
1059 $3.10 Cheung Wood-yau and Wong Man-lei . . . 60 45
1060 $5 Mak Bing-wing and Fung Wong-nui 85 45

221 Dragon Boat and Sydney Opera House

2001. Dragon Boat Racing. Multicoloured.
1062 $5 Type **221** . . . . 1·00 45
1063 $5 Dragon boat racing and Hong Kong Convention and Exhibition Centre . . 1·00 45

222 Emblem

2001. Choice of Beijing as 2008 Olympic Host City.
1065 **222** $1.30 multicoloured . . 45 30

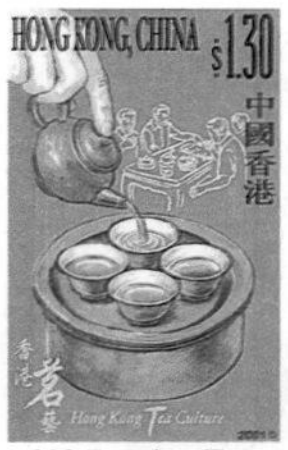

223 Pouring Tea (Gongfu tea)

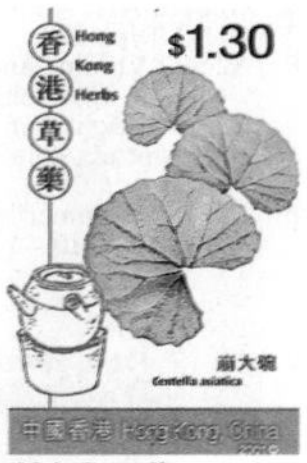

224 *Centella asiatica*

2001. Tea Culture. Multicoloured.
1067 $1.30 Type **223** 30 10
1068 $2.50 Hong Kong style tea 45 30
1069 $3.10 Pouring water (Yum Cha and Dim Sum) . . . 60 45
1070 $5 Pouring hot water in to tea pot 85 45

2001. Medicinal Herbs. Multicoloured.
1071 $1.30 Type **224** 30 10
1072 $2.50 *Lobelia chinensis* . . . 45 30
1073 $3.10 *Gardenia jasminoides* 60 45
1074 $5 *Scutellaria indica* 85 45

225 Child dressed as Bear

226 Horse

2001. Children's Stamps. Self-adhesive gum.
1075 $1.30 Type **225** 30 30
1076 $2.50 Child dressed as duck 60 30
1077 $3.10 Child dressed as pot plant 70 45
1078 $5 Child dressed as bee . . 1·10 45
MS1079 130 × 92 mm. Nos. 1075/8 2·75 1·70
The stamps had portions of the design left white for users to colour as they wished. Such embellishments did not affect the postal validity of the stamps.

2002. Chinese New Year ("Year of the Horse").
1080 **226** $1.30 multicoloured . . 30 10
1081 – $2.50 multicoloured . . 45 30
1082 – $3.10 multicoloured . . 60 45
1083 – $5 multicoloured 85 45
MS1084 Two sheets, each 135 × 85 mm. (a) Nos. 1080/3. (b) No. 1083. Imperf . . . . . . 3·25 2·20
DESIGNS: Nos. 1081/3, showing horses.

2002. Serving the Community Festival 2002. Sheet 75 × 130 mm, containing design as No. 985.
MS1085 $5 multicoloured . . . . 1·10 70

227 Snake

2002. Chinese New Year ("Year of the Snake"). Sheet 135 × 90 mm.
MS1086 $50 Type **227**; $50 Horse ("Year of the Horse") . . . . 18·00 14·00
No. **MS**1086 has the snake and the horse embossed in gold and silver foil.

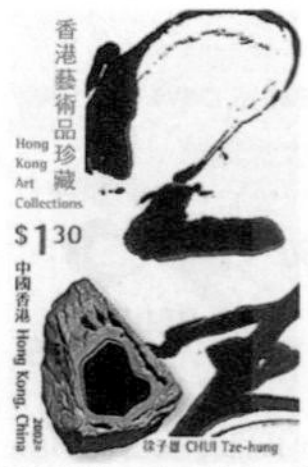

228 "Lines in Motion" (detail, Chui Tze-hung)

2002. Modern Art. Multicoloured.
1087 $1.30 Type **228** 30 10
1088 $2.50 "Volume and Time" (detail, Hon Chi-fun) . . 45 30
1089 $3.10 "Bright Sun" (sculpture, detail, Aries Lee) 60 45
1090 $5 "Midsummer" (detail, Irene Chou) 85 45

229 Face and Periodic Table (Education)

2002. Information Technology. Multicoloured.
1091 $1.40 Type **229** 25 10
1092 $2.40 Face, world map and internet symbols (communications) 40 25
1093 $3 Face, film and musical notes (entertainment) . . 55 40
1094 $5 Face, buildings and city (commerce) 80 40

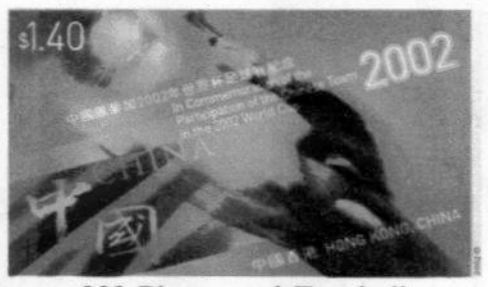

230 Player and Football

2002. World Cup Football Championship. Japan and South Korea. Multicoloured.
1095 $1.40 Type **230** 25 10
1096 $1.40 Players tackling and crowd 25 10

231 North Atlantic Pink Tree Coral, Pacific Orange Cup Coral and North Pacific Horn Coral

2002. Corals. Multicoloured.
1097 $1.40 Type **231** 25 10
1098 $2.40 North Atlantic giant orange tree coral and black coral 40 25
1099 $3 *Dendronepthea gigantea* and *Dendronepthea* . . . 55 40
1100 $5 *Tubastrea* and *Echinogorgia* and island 80 40
MS1101 161 × 85 mm. Nos. 1097/1100 . . . . 2·00 1·40
Stamps in similar designs were issued by Canada.

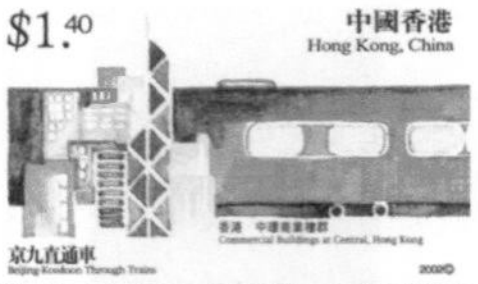

232 Hong Kong Buildings and Train

2002. 5th Anniv of Bejing--Kowloon Through Train Service. Multicoloured.
1102 $1.40 Type **232** 25 10
1103 $2.40 Wuhan--Changjiang Bridge and train 40 25
1104 $3 Pagodas, Shaolin Monastery, Zhengzhou and train 55 40
1105 $5 Temple of Heaven, Bejing and front of train 95 40
Nos. 1102/5 were issued together, forming a composite design of a train.

233 Chinese White Dolphins and Coral

2002. 5th Anniv of Hong Kong's Status as Special Administrative Region of People's Republic of China. Multicoloured.
1106 $1.40 Type **233** 25 10
1107 $2.40 School children and bauhinia flowers 40 25
1108 $3 Birds in flight over Hong Kong airport 50 40
1109 $5 Flags of China and Hong Kong, buildings and fireworks 80 50
MS1110 135 × 85 mm. Nos. 1106/9 2·10 1·40

2002. "PHILAKOREA 2002" World Stamp Exhibition, Seoul, South Korea. Sheet 131 × 75 mm, containing design as No. 986.
MS1111 $10 multicoloured . . . 2·00 1·40

2002. "AMPHILEX 2002" World Stamp Exhibition, Amsterdam. Sheet 130 × 75 mm, containing design as No. 986.
MS1112 $10 multicoloured . . . 2·00 1·40

2002. Hukou Waterfall Shanxi, People's Republic of China. Sheet 140 × 90 mm, containing design as No. 986.
MS1113 $10 multicoloured . . . 2·00 1·40

234 Ping Chau

2002. Geology of Hong Kong. Multicoloured.
1114 $1.40 Type **234** 25 10
1115 $2.40 Port Island 40 25
1116 $3 Po Pin Chau 80 40
1117 $5 Lamma Island . . . . . 1·80 1·00
MS1118 136 × 81 mm. Nos. 1114/17 2·10 1·40

235 Radar Signal and Luopan (fengshui compass)

2002. Cultural Diversity. Multicoloured.
1119 10c. Type **235** 10 10
1120 20c. Calculator and abacus 10 10
1121 50c. Incense coils and stained-glass window . . 10 10
1122 $1 Chair and Luohan (bed) 25 10
1123 $1.40 Dim Sum (dumplings) and loaves of bread . . . 25 10
1124 $1.80 Cutlery and chopsticks 25 10
1125 $1.90 Canned drinks and tea caddies 25 10
1126 $2 European and oriental wedding cakes 40 10
1127 $2.40 Erhu (stringed instrument) and violin . . 55 10
1128 $2.50 Oriental letterbox and internet symbol 55 10
1129 $3 Yachts and Dragon boat 55 10
1130 $5 Traditional tiled roof and modern office block . . . 95 15
1131 $10 Ballet dancers and Chinese opera character 1·70 15
1132 $13 Chess pieces and Xiangqi pieces (Chinese chess) . . . . 2·10 30
1133 $20 Christmas lights and mid-autumn festival lantern . . . . 3·50 45
1134 $50 Sculptures "Oval with points" (Henry Moore) and "Tai Chi series: Single Whip" (Ju Ming) 15·00 2·75
MS1135 Two sheets (a) 210 × 150 mm. Nos. 1119/30 (b) 122 × 101 mm. Nos. 1131/4 . . 20·00 15·00

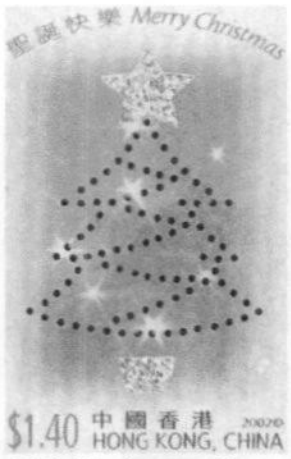

236 Christmas Tree

2002. Christmas. Multicoloured.
1146 $1.40 Type **236** 25 10
1147 $2.40 Bauble 40 25
1148 $3 Snowman 55 40
1149 $5 Bell 80 40

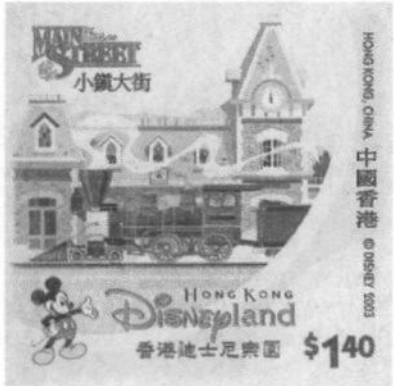

237 Train and Station (Main Street)

2003. Disneyland Hong Kong. Multicoloured.
1150 $1.40 Type **237** 25 10
1151 $2.40 Castle (Fantasyland) 40 25
1152 $3 Tree house (Adventureland) 55 40
1153 $5 Pylons (Tomorrowland) 80 40
MS1154 135 × 85 mm. Nos. 1150/3 2·10 1·40
Nos. 1150/**MS**1154 each have an embossed figure of Mickey Mouse in the lower left corner.

238 Argali Ram

2003. Chinese New Year ("Year of the Ram"). Multicoloured.
1155 $1.40 Type **238** 25 10
1156 $2.40 Sheep 49 25
1157 $3 Tahr ram 55 40
1158 $5 Gazella ram 80 40
MS1159 Two sheets, each 135 × 85 mm. (a) Nos. 1155/8; (b) $5 No. 1158 Set of 2 sheets . . 4·00 2·40

(b) Flocked paper. P 13. Litho Cartor.
1160 $10 As No. 1008 ("Year of the Dragon") . . . . . . 2·00 1·40
1161 $10 As No. 1042 ("Year of the Snake") . . . . . . 2·00 1·40
1162 $10 As No. 1081 ("Year of the Horse") . . . . . . 2·00 1·40
1163 $10 As No. 1158 ("Year of the Ram") . . . . . . 2·00 1·40

(c) Size 38 × 51 mm. Ordinary paper.
MS1164 135 × 90 mm. $50 As No. 1162 ("Year of the Horse") (37 × 50 mm); $50 As No. 1157 (37 × 50 mm) . . . .
No. **MS**1164 has the horse and ram embossed with gold and silver foil.

239 Letter Writing

2003. Traditional Trades and Crafts. Multicoloured.
1165 $1.40 Type **239** 25 10
1166 $1.80 Bird cage maker (vert) 25 10
1167 $2.40 Qipao tailoring (women's clothes) 40 10
1168 $2.50 Hairdressing (vert) . . 55 10
1169 $3 Making dough figures (vert) 55 10
1170 $5 Olive seller 95 15
MS1171 219 × 123 mm. Nos. 1165/70 2·75 65

240 Hong Kong Skyline

2003. Hong Kong 2004 International Stamp Exhibition (1st issue). Sheet 135 × 85 mm.
MS1172 **240** $10 multicoloured 2·00 1·40
See also No. **MS**1190.

241 The Master-of-Nets Garden, Suzhou

2003. Mainland Landscapes. Sheet 140 × 90 mm.
MS1173 **241** $10 multicoloured 2·00 1·40

242 Fukien Tea (semi-cascade)

2003. Miniature Landscapes. Multicoloured.
1174 $1.40 Type **242** 25 10
1175 $2.40 Hedge Sagereti (informal upright) 55 10
1176 $3 Fire-thorn (cascade) (vert) 55 15
1177 $5 Chinese Hackberry (root on rock) (vert) 80 40

243 Ear-spot Angelfish

2003. Aquarium Fish. Multicoloured.
1178 $1.40 Type **243** 25 10
1179 $2.40 Copper-banded butterflyfish 55 10
1180 $3 Dwarf gourami 55 15
1181 $5 Red discus 80 40

244 Bottles and Man holding Firework ("Celebrations")

2003. Greetings Stamps. With service indicator. Multicoloured.
1182 ($1.40) Type **244** ("Local Mail Postage") 25 10
1183 ($1.40) Man and heart-shaped tree ("Care and Love") 25 10
1184 ($3) No. 1182 ("Air Mail Postage") 55 15
1185 ($3) No. 1183 . . . . 55 15
No. 1182/3 were for use on letters up to 30 grams within Hong Kong and 1184/5 were for use on airmail letters up to 20 grams to addresses outside Hong Kong.

245 Pied Avocet

2003. Water Birds. Multicoloured.
1186 $1.40 Type **245** 25 10
1187 $2.40 Horned grebe 55 10
1188 $3 Great crested grebe . . . 55 15
1189 $5 Black-throated diver . . 80 40
Stamps of the same design were issued by Sweden.

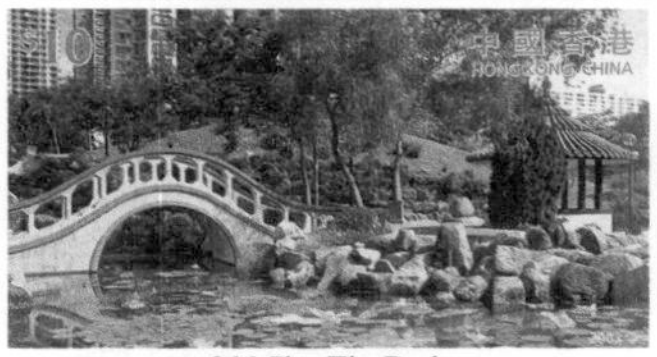

246 Sha Tin Park

2003. Hong Kong 2004 International Stamp Exhibition (2nd issue). Sheet 135×85 mm.

MS1190	246	$10 multicoloured	2·00	1·40

247 Astronaut and Satellite

2003. First Chinese Manned Space Flight. Multicoloured.

1191	$1.40 Type **247**	25	10
1192	$1.40 Shenzhou-5 space craft	25	10

248 Drum — **249** Potola Palace, Lhasa

2003. Traditional Instruments. Multicoloured.

1193	$1.40 Type **248**	25	10
1194	$2.40 Clappers	55	10
1195	$3 Cymbals	55	10
1196	$5 Gongs	80	40
MS1197	130×75 mm. $13 Bell (35×45 mm)		

2003. UNESCO World Heritage Sites in China. Multicoloured.

1198	$1.40 Type **249**	25	10
1199	$1.80 Imperial Palace, Beijing (47×39 mm)	25	10
1200	$2.40 First Qin Emperor's Mausoleum, Shaanxi Province (47×39 mm)	55	10
1201	$2.50 Mount Huangshan, Anhui Province (39×47 mm)	55	10
1202	$3 Old Town, Lijang (39×47 mm)	55	10
1203	$5 Jiuzhaigou valley, Sichuan Province (77×30 mm)	80	40

250 Building Development and People on Walkways

2003. Development of Public Housing. Multicoloured.

1204	$1.40 Type **250**	25	10
1205	$2.40 L-shaped development and women through window	55	10
1206	$3 High-rise development and man reading with children	55	10
1207	$5 High-rise development and family walking in park	80	40

POSTAGE DUE STAMPS

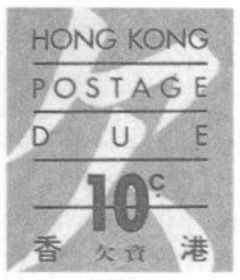

D **1** Post-office Scales — D **2**

1923.

D 1ab	D 1	1c. brown	30	1·00
D 2a		2c. green	11·00	5·00
D 6a		2c. grey	1·10	10·00
D 3a		4c. red	27·00	7·00
D 7a		4c. orange	2·50	10·00
D18		5c. red (21×18 mm)	2·50	5·50
D 4		6c. yellow	27·00	13·00
D 8		6c. red	9·50	5·50
D 9		8c. brown	5·50	32·00
D 5		10c. blue	24·00	8·50
D15		10c. violet	3·50	4·25
D16		20c. black	6·00	4·25
D22		50c. blue	4·50	10·00

1976. As Type D **1** but smaller design 21×17 mm with redrawn value.

D25a	D 1	10c. violet	80	2·00
D26a		20c. grey	1·50	2·25
D27a		50c. blue	1·50	2·75
D28a		$1 yellow	1·40	4·00

1987.

D31	D 2	10c. green	10	40
D32		20c. brown	10	40
D33		50c. violet	10	20
D34		$1 orange	15	20
D35		$5 blue	80	1·60
D36		$10 red	1·60	3·00

JAPANESE OCCUPATION OF HONG KONG

100 sen = 1 yen.

(1) (2)

1945. Stamps of Japan surch as T **1** (No. J1) or T **2**.

J1	126	1.50yen on 1s. brown	30·00	27·00
J2	84	3yen on 2s. red	12·00	21·00
J3		5yen on 5s. red (No. 396)	£900	£150

HORTA — Pt. 9

A district of the Azores for which separate issues were used from 1892 to 1905.

1865. 1000 reis = 1 milreis.

1892. As T **4** of Funchal, but inscr "HORTA".

4	5r. yellow	2·25	1·60
5	10r. mauve	2·25	2·00
6	15r. brown	2·25	2·10
7	20r. lilac	2·50	2·50
2	25r. green	4·00	1·00
8	50r. blue	6·25	3·00
22	75r. red	7·00	4·50
10	80r. green	9·25	8·75
23	100r. brown on yellow	40·00	19·00
24	150r. red on rose	45·00	40·00
25	200r. blue on blue	45·00	40·00
26	300r. blue on brown	45·00	40·00

1897. "King Carlos" key-type inscr "HORTA". Name and value in red (Nos. 46 and 41) or black (others).

28	S	2½r. grey	45	30
29		5r. orange	45	30
30		10r. green	45	30
31		15r. brown	6·25	4·75
42		15r. green	1·25	1·00
32		20r. lilac	1·25	1·00
33		25r. green	2·10	90
43		25r. red	1·25	60
34		50r. blue	2·40	80
45		65r. blue	90	65
35		75r. red	2·25	1·00
46		75r. brown on yellow	9·50	8·25
36		80r. mauve	1·25	85
37		100r. blue on blue	2·40	85
47		115r. red on pink	1·60	1·25
48		130r. brown on yellow	1·60	1·25
38		150r. brown on yellow	1·60	1·10
49		180r. black on pink	1·60	1·25
39		200r. purple on pink	4·50	3·75
40		300r. blue on pink	8·00	6·00
41		500r. black on blue	10·00	9·50

HUNGARY — Pt. 2

A country in central Europe. A Kingdom ruled by the Emperor of Austria until 1918. A Republic was then proclaimed, and later a Soviet style constitution was adopted. In 1919 parts of the country were occupied by France, Serbia and Rumania, including Budapest. Following the withdrawal of the Rumanians a National Republic was instituted, and in 1920 Hungary was declared a Monarchy with Admiral Nicholas Horthy as Regent. In 1946 Hungary became a Republic again.

1858. 100 krajczar = 1 forint.
1900. 100 filler (heller) = 1 korona (krone).
1926. 100 filler = 1 pengo.
1946. 100 filler = 1 forint.

1 — 2

1871.

8	1	2k. yellow	60·00	12·00
9		3k. green	£110	40·00
10		5k. red	75·00	2·25
11		10k. blue	£325	21·00
12		15k. brown	£325	29·00
13		25k. lilac	£225	85·00

1874.

26	2	2k. mauve	1·40	30
28		3k. green	1·10	30
29		5k. red	6·00	30
31		10k. blue	4·25	45
32a		20k. grey	5·50	45

1888. Numerals in black on the krajczar values, in red on the forint values.

39a	2	1k. black	60	25
40		2k. mauve and light mauve	80	20
41		3k. green and light green	90	20
42		5k. red and pink	1·10	30
43		8k. orange and yellow	1·25	20
44		10k. blue	4·50	20
45		12k. brown and green	10·00	50
46		15k. red and blue	6·00	40
47		20k. grey	7·50	75
48		24k. purple and red	20·00	70
62		30k. olive and brown	4·75	2·50
63		50k. red and orange	14·50	22·00
51		1fo. grey and silver	£150	1·50
38i		3fo. brown and gold	12·00	4·50

7 "Turul" (mythical bird of the Magyars) — **8** King Francis Joseph wearing Hungarian Crown — **12**

1900. Figures of value in black.

99	7	1f. grey	15	10
100		2f. yellow	10	10
118		3f. orange	10	10
67		4f. mauve	45	15
102		5f. green	10	10
69a		6f. purple	70	30
103		6f. drab	20	10
120		6f. green	10	10
121		10f. red	10	10
105		12f. lilac	20	10
122		12f. lilac on yellow	15	10
123		16f. green	15	15
124		20f. brown	20	10
125		25f. blue	20	10
126		30f. brown	20	10
127		35f. purple	20	10
111		50f. red	75	10
128		50f. red on blue	20	10
112		60f. green	2·50	10
130		60f. green on pink	90	10
131		70f. brown and green	30	10
132		80f. violet	30	10
133	8	1k. red	2·00	10
134		2k. blue	4·50	10
81		3k. blue	38·00	2·75
135		5k. red	4·75	2·00

1913. Flood Charity stamps. As T **7/8**, but with label as T **12**.

136	12	1f.+2f. grey	70	70
137		2f.+2f. yellow	40	45
138		3f.+2f. orange	40	45
139		5f.+2f. green	35	35
140		6f.+2f. drab	65	70
141		10f.+2f. red	25	20
142		12f.+2f. lilac on yellow	1·10	1·00
143		16f.+2f. green	75	85
144		20f.+2f. brown	2·40	1·60
145		25f.+2f. blue	75	65
146		30f.+2f. brown	1·10	50
147		35f.+2f. purple	1·00	50
148		50f.+2f. lake on blue	5·25	2·40
149		60f.+2f. green on red	6·25	1·25
150	8	1k.+2f. red	25·00	9·75
151		2k.+2f. blue	55·00	40·00
152		5k.+2f. red	19·00	18·00

1914. War Charity. Nos. 136/52 (with labels) surch **Hadi segely Ozvegyeknek es arvaknak ket (2) filler**.

153	12	1f.+2f. grey	60	45
154		2f.+2f. yellow	60	40
155		3f.+2f. orange	60	50
156		5f.+2f. green	35	20
157		6f.+2f. drab	65	45
158		10f.+2f. red	35	20
159		12f.+2f. lilac on yellow	65	40
160		16f.+2f. green	65	35
161		20f.+2f. brown	65	45
162		25f.+2f. blue	1·00	50
163		30f.+2f. brown	1·40	50
164		35f.+2f. purple	3·50	1·25
165		50f.+2f. lake on blue	2·00	65
166		60f.+2f. green on red	5·50	1·25
167	8	1k.+2f. red (No. 150)	60·00	32·00
168		2k.+2f. blue (No. 151)	21·00	21·00
169		5k.+2f. red (No. 152)	22·00	17·00

1915. War Charity. Stamps of 1900 (without labels) surch as last round the stamp.

170	7	1f.+2f. grey	10	10
171		2f.+2f. yellow	10	10
172		3f.+2f. orange	10	10
173		5f.+2f. green	10	10
174		6f.+2f. drab	10	10
175		10f.+2f. red	10	10
176		12f.+2f. lilac on yellow	10	10
177		16f.+2f. green	30	30
178		20f.+2f. brown	30	35
179		25f.+2f. blue	10	10
180		30f.+2f. brown	10	10
181		35f.+2f. purple	10	10
182		50f.+2f. lake on blue	35	30
183		60f.+2f. green on red	70	70
185	8	1k.+2f. red (No. 133)	1·60	1·10
186		2k.+2f. blue (No. 134)	2·50	2·10
187		5k.+2f. red (No. 135)	7·25	10·00

18 Harvesters — **19** Parliament Buildings, Budapest

1916. As T **18** but with white figures in top corners.

243	18	10f. red	45	25
244		15f. purple	25	25

1916. Inscr "MAGYAR KIR. POSTA".

245	18	2f. brown	10	10
246		3f. red	10	10
247		4f. slate	10	10
248		5f. green	10	10
249		6f. blue	10	10
250		10f. red	50	10
251		15f. violet	10	10
252		20f. brown	10	10
253		25f. blue	10	10
254		35f. brown	10	10
255		40f. olive	10	10
256	19	50f. purple	10	10
257		75f. blue	10	10
258		80f. green	25	10
259		1k. lake	10	10
260		2k. brown	20	10
261		3k. grey and violet	65	10
262		5k. brown	60	15
263		10k. mauve and brown	90	50

In Type **19** the colours of the centres differ slightly from those of the frames.

For later issues in Types **18** and **19**, see Nos. 372/86 and 404/11.

20 In Trenches — **22** "Turul" at bay — **23** Queen Zita

1916. War Charity.

264	20	10f.+2f. red	20	20
265	–	15f.+2f. violet	20	20
266	22	40f.+2f. lake	25	30

DESIGN: 15f. Hand to hand combat.

1916. Coronation.

267	23	10f. mauve	40	50
268	–	15f. red (Emperor Charles IV)	40	50

1917. War Charity Exhibition. Nos. 243/4 surch **Jozsef foherczeg vezerezredes hadi kiallitasa 1 korona** (= "Prince Joseph. Chief Colonel General War Exhibition").

269	18	10f.+1k. red	50	50
270		15f.+1k. violet	50	50

1918. Air. Surch **REPULO POSTA** and value.

271	19	1k.50 on 75f. blue	15·00	19·00
272		4k.50 on 2k. brown	13·50	17·00

27 Charles IV — **28** Zita

1918.

273	27	10f. red	10	10
274		15f. violet	10	10
275		20f. brown	10	10
276		25f. blue	10	10
277	28	40f. olive	10	10
278		50f. purple	10	10

1918. Optd **KOZTARSASAG**. (a) War Charity Stamps (Nos. 264/6).

279	20	10+2f. red	10	10
280	–	15+2f. violet	10	10
281	22	40+2f. red	10	10

(b) Harvesters and Parliament.

282	18	2f. brown	10	10
283		3f. red	10	10
284		4f. grey	10	10
285		5f. green	10	10
286		6f. blue	10	10
287		10f. red	10	10
288		20f. brown	10	10
289		40f. green	10	10
290	19	1k. red	10	10
291		2k. brown	10	10
292		3k. grey and violet	40	50
293		5k. brown	1·25	1·40
294		10k. mauve and brown	2·25	1·75

(c) Charles and Zita.

295	27	10f. pink	10	10
296		15f. purple	10	10
297		20f. brown	10	10
298		25f. blue	10	10
299	28	40f. green	20	25
300		50f. purple	20	25

1919. As T **18/19**, but inscr "MAGYAR POSTA".

301	18	2f. brown	10	10
302		4f. grey	10	10
303		5f. green	10	10
304		6f. blue	10	10
305		10f. red	10	10
306		15f. violet	10	10
307		20f. brown	10	10
308		20f. green	10	10
309		25f. blue	10	10
310		40f. green	10	10
311		40f. red	10	10
312		45f. orange	10	10
313	19	50f. purple	10	10
314		60f. blue and brown	10	10
315		95f. blue	10	10
316		1k. red	10	10
317		1k. blue and indigo	10	10
318		1k.20 green	10	10
319		1k.40 green	10	10
320		2k. brown	10	10
321		3k. grey and violet	10	10
322		5k. brown	10	10
323		10k. mauve and brown	50	35

32 Karl Marx

1919.

324	32	20f. red and brown	20	20
325	–	45f. green and orange	20	20
326	–	60f. brown and grey	2·75	3·50
327	–	75f. brown and red	3·00	3·50
328	–	80f. brown and olive	3·00	3·50

PORTRAITS: 45f. S. Petofi; 60f. Ignacs Martinovics; 75f. G. Dozsa; 80f. F. Engels.

1919. Nos. 301 etc optd **MAGYAR TANACSKOZTARSASAG.** (second word hyphenated on 2 to 45f.) (= "Hungarian Soviet Republic").

329	18	2f. brown	25	35
330		3f. purple	25	35
331		4f. grey	25	35
332		5f. green	25	35
333		6f. blue	25	35
334		10f. red	25	35
335		15f. violet	25	35
336		20f. brown	25	35
337		25f. blue	25	35
338		40f. green	25	35
339		45f. orange	25	35
340	19	50f. purple	20	35
341		95f. blue	20	35
342		1k. red	20	35
343		1k.20 green	20	75
344		1k.40 green	40	35
345		2k. brown	65	1·10
346		3k. grey and violet	65	70
347		5k. brown	70	1·25
348		10k. mauve and brown	1·00	1·60

1919. Entry of National Army into Budapest. Nos. 303 etc optd **A nemzeti hadsereg bevonulasa. 1919. XI/16.**

348a	18	5f. green	90	1·00
348b		10f. red	90	1·00
348c		15f. violet	90	1·00
348d		20f. brown	90	1·00
348e		25f. blue	90	1·00

(36)

(37)

1920. Nos. 329/48 optd with T **36** (2 to 45f.) or **37** (others).

349	18	2f. brown	40	40
350		3f. purple	10	10
351		4f. grey	60	80
352		5f. green	10	10
353		6f. blue	10	10
354		10f. red	10	10
355		15f. violet	10	10
356		20f. brown	10	10
357		25f. blue	10	10
358		40f. green	95	1·10
359		45f. orange	95	1·10
360	19	50f. purple	95	1·10
361		95f. blue	95	1·10
362		1k. red	95	1·10
363		1k.20 green	1·50	2·00
364		1k.40 green	1·50	2·00
365		2k. brown	1·90	2·10
366		3k. grey and violet	1·90	2·10
367		5k. brown	40	50
368		10k. mauve and brown	3·00	5·00

38 Returning P.O.W.

42 Madonna and Child

1920. Returned Prisoners-of-War Fund.

369	38	40f.+1k. lake	75	75
370	–	60f.+2k. brown	75	75
371	–	1k.+5k. blue	75	75

DESIGNS—HORIZ: 60f. Prison Camp. VERT: 1k. Family Reunion.

1920. Re-issue of T **18** inscr "MAGYAR KIR. POSTA".

372	18	5f. brown	10	10
373		10f. purple	10	10
374		40f. red	10	10
375		50f. green	10	10
376		50f. blue	10	10
377		60f. black	10	10
378		1k. green	10	10
379		1½k. purple	10	10
380		2k. blue	10	10
381		2½k. green	10	10
382		3k. brown	10	10
383		4k. red	10	10
384		4½k. violet	10	10
385		5k. brown	10	10
386		6k. blue	10	10
387		10k. brown	10	10
388		15k. black	10	10
389		20k. red	10	10
390		25k. orange	10	10
391		40k. green	10	10
392		50k. blue	10	10
393		100k. purple	10	10
394		150k. green	15	10
395		200k. green	15	10
442		300k. red	15	10
397		350k. violet	20	10
443		400k. blue	10	10
444		500k. black	10	10
445		600k. bistre	10	10
446		800k. yellow	10	20

1920. Air. No. 263 surch **LEGI POSTA** and value.

401	19	3k. on 10k. mauve & brn	1·10	2·40
402		8k. on 10k. mauve & brn	1·10	2·40
403		12k. on 10k. mauve & brn	1·10	2·40

1920. Re-issue of T **19** inscr "MAGYAR KIR. POSTA".

404	19	2k.50 blue	10	10
405		3k.50 grey	10	10
406		10k. brown	10	10
407		15k. grey	10	10
408		20k. red	10	10
409		25k. orange	10	10
410		30k. lake	15	10
411		40k. green	15	10
412		50k. blue	15	10
413		100k. brown	15	10
414		400k. green	25	10
415		500k. violet	25	10
416		1000k. red	25	10
448		2000k. red	45	45

1921.

418	42	50k. blue and brown	30	10
419		100k. brown and bistre	60	20
420		200k. ultramarine and blue	60	20
421		500k. mauve and purple	60	20
422		1000k. purple and mauve	60	20
423		2000k. mauve and green	50	20
424		2500k. brown and bistre	35	20
425		3000k. mauve and red	35	20
426		5000k. light green and green	75	20
427		10000k. blue and violet	75	20

44 Statue of Petofi in National Dress

45 John, the hero, on flying dragon

47 Death of Petofi

1923. Birth Centenary of Petofi (poet).

428	44	10k. (+ 10k.) blue	70	80
429	45	15k. (+ 15k.) blue	1·75	2·25
430	–	25k. (+ 25k.) brown	70	80
431	47	40k. (+ 40k.) red	2·75	3·50
432	–	50k. (+ 50k.) purple	2·75	3·50

DESIGNS—VERT (As Type **45**): 25k. Petofi; 50k. Petofi addressing the people.

49 Icarus over Budapest

50

1924. Air.

433	49	100k. pink and brown	1·10	2·00
434		500k. light green and green	1·10	2·00
435		1000k. brown and bistre	1·10	2·00
436		2000k. blue and deep blue	1·10	2·00
436a		5000k. mauve and purple	2·40	2·40
436b		10000k. purple and red	2·40	2·40

1924. Tuberculosis Relief Fund.

437	50	300k. (+ 300k.) blue	3·50	5·25
438	–	500k. (+ 500k.) brown	3·75	5·25
439	–	1000k. (+ 1000k.) green	3·75	5·25

DESIGNS: 500k. Mother and child; 1000k. Bowman.

53 M. Jokai

55

1925. Birth Cent of Maurus Jokai (novelist).

449	53	1000k. brown and green	4·00	5·00
450		2000k. brown	3·00	1·00
451		2500k. brown and blue	4·00	5·00

1925. Sports Association Fund.

452	–	100k.(+100k.) brn & grn	2·60	2·60
453	–	200k.(+200k.) grn & brn	2·60	3·25
454	–	300k.(+300k.) blue	4·25	3·50
455	–	400k.(+400k.) green & bl	4·25	5·00
456	–	500k.(+500k.) purple	5·25	7·00
457	–	1000k.(+1000k.) red	6·75	7·50
458	55	2000k.(+2000k.) purple	8·75	8·50
459	–	2500k.(+2500k.) sepia	10·50	9·50

DESIGNS—HORIZ: 100k. Athletes; 500k. Fencing. VERT: 200k. Skiing; 300k. Skating; 400k. Diving; 1000k. Scouts; 2500k. Hurdles.

56 Crown of St. Stephen

57 Matthias Church and Fisher's Bastion

60 Madonna and Child

58 Royal Palace, Budapest

59

1926. T **59** is without boat.

460	56	1f. black	45	10
461		2f. blue	45	10
462		3f. orange	45	10
463		4f. mauve	45	10
464		6f. green	45	10
465		8f. mauve	90	10
466	57	10f. blue	90	10
467		16f. violet	90	10
468		20f. red	90	10
469		25f. brown	90	10
470	59	30f. green	2·75	10
471	58	32f. violet	3·00	15
472		40f. blue and deep blue	5·25	15
473	59	46f. blue	3·75	10
474		50f. black	4·00	10
475		70f. red	5·50	10
476	60	1p. violet	25·00	50
477		2p. red	25·00	70
478		5p. blue	25·00	3·25

See also Nos. 502/6.

61 The fabulous "Turul"

62 Mercury astride a "Turul"

1927. Air.

478a	61	4f. orange	85	65
479		12f. green	85	70
480		16f. brown	85	55
481		20f. red	85	55
482		32f. purple	2·50	1·90
483		40f. blue	2·25	1·00
484	62	50f. red	2·25	1·25
485		72f. olive	2·50	1·40
486		80f. violet	2·50	1·10
487		1p. green	2·50	1·25
488		2p. red	5·00	5·50
489		5p. blue	25·00	32·00

66 Royal Palace, Budapest

67 St. Stephen

1928. T **66** has the boat in a different place and a redrawn frame.

502	66	30f. green	2·40	10
503		32f. purple	2·75	30
504		40f. blue	2·75	10
505		46f. green	2·75	10
506		50f. brown	1·75	10

1928. 890th Death Anniv of St. Stephen of Hungary.

507	67	8f. green	85	45
508		16f. red	1·10	45
509		32f. blue	3·00	2·50

1929. Colours changed.

510	67	8f. red	45	40
511		16f. violet	50	1·25
512		32f. bistre	2·10	1·00

68 Admiral Horthy

69 St. Emeric

1930. 10th Anniv of Regency.

513	68	8f. green	1·40	25
514		16f. violet	1·40	30
515		20f. red	4·50	2·50
516		32f. brown	4·00	5·25
517		40f. blue	6·50	1·50

1930. 900th Death Anniv of St. Emeric.

518	69	8f.+2f. green	60	80
519	–	16f.+4f. purple	85	1·00
520	–	20f.+4f. red	2·75	2·40
521	–	32f.+8f. blue	3·25	3·25

DESIGNS—VERT: 16f. St. Stephen and Queen Gisela; 20f. St. Ladislas. HORIZ: 32f. Sts. Gellert and Emeric.

1931. Surch.

526	56	2 on 3f. orange	70	25
527		6 on 8f. mauve	70	15
528	57	10 on 16f. violet	70	15
525		20 on 25f. brown	1·40	1·10

1931. Air. Optd **Zeppelin 1931**.

529	62	1p. orange	35·00	60·00
530		2p. purple	35·00	60·00

73 St. Elizabeth

75 Madonna and Child

77

1932. 700th Death Anniv of St. Elizabeth of Hungary.

531	73	10f. blue	45	30
532		20f. red	45	30
533	–	32f. purple	1·60	1·60
534	–	40f. blue	1·00	85

DESIGN—18 × 28 mm: 32, 40f. St. Elizabeth giving cloak to the poor.

1932.

535	75	1p. green	13·00	50
536		2p. red	13·00	80

537 5p. blue . . . . 55·00 4·50
538 10p. brown . . . . 75·00 30·00

1932. No. 527 further surch **2**.
540 **56** 2 on 6 on 8f. mauve . . . 85 35

1932. Famous Hungarians.
541 – 1f. grey 30 10
542 – 2f. orange 30 10
543 – 4f. blue 30 10
543a **77** 5f. brown 30 10
544 – 6f. green 30 10
545 – 10f. green 30 10
546 – 16f. violet 30 10
547 – 20f. red 50 10
547a – 25f. green 60 25
548 – 30f. brown 50 25
549 – 32f. purple 70 25
550 – 40f. blue 70 25
551 – 50f. green 95 40
552 – 70f. red . . . . 1·40 35
DESIGNS: 1f. I. Madach, poet, 1823–64; 2f. J Arany, poet, 1817–82; 4f. I. Semmelweis, physician, 1818–65; 5f. F. Kolcsey, poet, 1790–1838; 6f. L. Eotvos, physicist, 1848–1919; 10f. I. Szechenyi, statesman, 1791–1860; 16f. F. Deak, statesman, 1803–76; 20f. F. Liszt, composer, 1811–86; 25f. M. Vorosmarty, poet, 1800–55; 30f. L. Kossuth, statesman, 1802–94; 32f. I. Tisza, statesman, 1861–1918; 40f. M. Munkacsy, painter, 1844–1900; 50f. S. Korosi Csoma, explorer, 1784–1842; 70f. F. Bolyai, mathematician, 1775–1856.

1933. Surch **10**.
553 **59** 10 on 70f. red 90 30

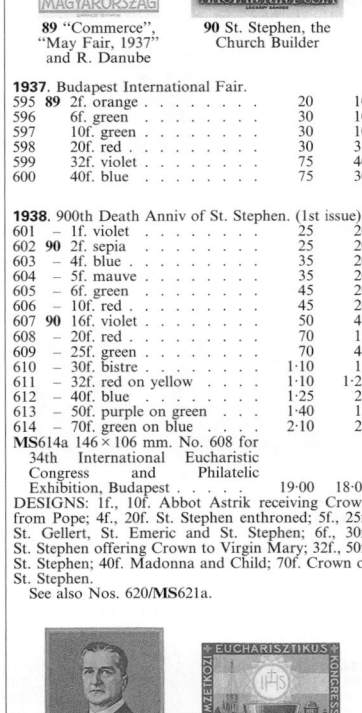

79 "Justice for Hungary" over Danube

80 Gift Plane from Mussolini

1933. Air.
554 **79** 10f. green . . . . 1·25 45
555 16f. violet . . . . 1·25 45
556 **80** 20f. red . . . . 3·00 85
557 40f. blue . . . . 3·25 85
558 – 48f. black . . . . 13·00 2·50
559 – 72f. brown . . . . 22·00 2·75
560 – 1p. green . . . . 21·00 2·75
561 – 2p. red . . . . 30·00 13·50
562 – 5p. grey . . . . 60·00 £120
DESIGNS—VERT: As Type **80**: 48, 72f. "Spirit of Flight" on wing of Lockheed Model 8A Sirius; 1, 2, 5p. Mercury and propeller.

83 "The Stag of Hungary"

1933. International Scout Jamboree, Godollo.
563 **83** 10f. green . . . . 1·10 45
564 16f. red . . . . 1·75 2·40
565 20f. red . . . . 1·50 75
566 32f. yellow . . . . 4·50 3·50
567 40f. blue . . . . 5·25 2·75

1934. 2nd Hungarian Philatelic Exhibition, Budapest, and Jubilee of First Hungarian Philatelic Society (L.E.H.E.). Sheet 64 × 76 mm containing No. 547 in changed colour.
MS568 20f. red . . . . 75·00 90·00

84 Ferenc Rakoczi II

85 Cardinal Peter Pazmany

1935. Death Bicentenary of Prince Rakoczi.
569 **84** 10f. green . . . . 1·00 30
570 16f. violet . . . . 3·25 3·25
571 20f. red . . . . 1·00 45
572 32f. red . . . . 7·25 4·50
573 40f. blue . . . . 5·50 4·75

1935. Tercentenary of Budapest University.
574 **85** 6f. green . . . . 1·00 1·25
575 – 10f. green 45 30
576 **85** 16f. violet . . . . 1·90 1·60
577 20f. mauve 45 40
578 – 32f. red . . . . 2·25 2·25
579 – 40f. blue . . . . 1·90 2·25
DESIGN—HORIZ (35 × 25 mm): 10f., 32f., 40f. Pazmany signing deed.

87 Fokker F.VIIb/3m

1936. Air.
580 **87** 10f. green 30 25
581 20f. red 30 25
582 36f. brown 45 25
583 – 40f. blue 45 25
584 – 52f. orange 60 75
585 – 60f. violet . . . . 16·00 2·00
586 – 80f. green . . . . 2·10 55
587 – 1p. green . . . . 2·10 45
588 – 2p. lake . . . . 5·00 1·60
589 – 5p. blue . . . . 18·00 18·00
DESIGNS: 40f. to 80f. Fokker F.VIIb/3m over Parliament Buildings; 1p. to 5p. Fokker F.VIIb/3m (different).

88 Ancient Buda

1936. 250th Anniv of Recapture of Buda from Turks.
590 **88** 10f. green 55 35
591 – 16f. mauve . . . . 2·25 2·25
592 – 20f. red 55 35
593 – 32f. brown . . . . 2·25 2·25
594 **88** 40f. blue . . . . 2·25 2·25
DESIGNS: 16f. Angel of Peace over Buda; 20f. Arms of Buda; 32f. Colour bearer and bugler.

89 "Commerce", "May Fair, 1937" and R. Danube

90 St. Stephen, the Church Builder

1937. Budapest International Fair.
595 **89** 2f. orange 20 10
596 6f. green 30 10
597 10f. green 30 10
598 20f. red 30 35
599 32f. violet 75 40
600 40f. blue 75 30

1938. 900th Death Anniv of St. Stephen. (1st issue).
601 – 1f. violet 25 20
602 **90** 2f. sepia 25 20
603 – 4f. blue 35 20
604 – 5f. mauve 35 20
605 – 6f. green 45 20
606 – 10f. red 45 20
607 **90** 16f. violet 50 45
608 – 20f. red 70 15
609 – 25f. green 70 45
610 – 30f. bistre . . . . 1·10 15
611 – 32f. red on yellow . . . . 1·10 1·25
612 – 40f. blue . . . . 1·25 20
613 – 50f. purple on green . . . 1·40 15
614 – 70f. green on blue . . . . 2·10 25
MS614a 146 × 106 mm. No. 608 for 34th International Eucharistic Congress and Philatelic Exhibition, Budapest . . . . . 19·00 18·00
DESIGNS: 1f., 10f. Abbot Astrik receiving Crown from Pope; 4f., 20f. St. Stephen enthroned; 5f., 25f. St. Gellert, St. Emeric and St. Stephen; 6f., 30f. St. Stephen offering Crown to Virgin Mary; 32f., 50f. St. Stephen; 40f. Madonna and Child; 70f. Crown of St. Stephen.
See also Nos. 620/**MS**621a.

92 Admiral Horthy

93 Eucharistic Symbols

1938.
615 **92** 1p. green 75 10
616 2p. sepia . . . . 1·25 10
617 5p. blue . . . . 1·90 1·25

1938. 34th International Eucharistic Congress.
618 – 16f.+16f. blue . . . . . . 3·00 4·00
619 **93** 20f.+20f. red . . . . . . 3·00 4·00
MS619a 130 × 149 mm 6f.+6f. green; 10f.+10f. red; 16f.+16f. blue; 20f.+20f. red; 32f.+32f. purple; 40f.+40f. blue; 50f.+50f. mauve 35·00 40·00
DESIGNS: 6f. St. Stephen; 10f.St. Emeric; 16f. (619), St Ladislas; 16f. St. Laszio; 20f. Offering crown to Virgin Mary; 32f. St. Elizabeth; 40f. Bishop Maurice and Pecs Cathedral; 50f. St. Margaret.

94 St. Stephen the Victorious

1938. 900th Death Anniv of St. Stephen (2nd issue).
620 **94** 10f.+10f. purple . . . . . 2·00 3·25
621 – 20f.+20f. red . . . . . . 2·00 3·25
MS621a 153 × 113 mm. 6f.+6f. green; 10f.+10f. red; 16f.+16f. brown; 20f.+20f. red; 32f.+32f. blue; 40f.+40f. blue; 50f.+50f. purple . . . . 25·00 35·00
DESIGNS: St. Stephen the missionary; 16f. On throne; 20f. Offering crown to Virgin Mary; 32f. Receiving bishops and monks; 40f. Queen Gisela, St. Stephen and St. Emeric; 50f. On bier.

95 Debrecen College

100 Statue representing Northern Provinces

1938. 400th Anniv of Debrecen College.
622 **95** 6f. green 25 10
623 – 10f. brown 20 10
624 – 16f. red 25 20
625 – 20f. red 20 10
626 – 32f. green 45 40
627 – 40f. blue 45 30
DESIGNS—HORIZ: 10, 20f. 18th and 19th-cent views of College. VERT: 16f. 18th-century students as firemen; 32f. Prof. Marothi; 40f. Dr. Hatvani.

1938. Acquisition of Czech Territory. As Nos. 608 and 614 optd **HAZATERES 1938**.
628 20f. red . . . . 1·25 1·25
629 70f. brown on blue . . . . . 1·25 1·25

1939. "Hungary for Hungarians" Patriotic Fund.
630 **100** 6f.+3f. green 35 50
631 – 10f.+5f. green 35 40
632 – 20f.+10f. red 35 40
633 – 30f.+15f. green 60 70
634 – 40f.+20f. blue . . . . . 60 1·10
DESIGNS: 10f. Fort at Munkacs; 20f. Admiral Horthy leading troops into Komarom; 30f. Cathedral of St. Elizabeth of Hungary, Kassa; 40f. Girls offering flowers to soldiers.

101 Crown of St. Stephen

102 Esztergom Basilica

1939.
635 **101** 1f. purple 10 10
636 2f. green 10 10
690 3f. brown 10 10
637 4f. brown 10 10
638 5f. violet 10 10
639 6f. green 10 10
693 8f. green 10 10
640 10f. brown 10 10
695 12f. red 10 10
641 16f. violet 10 10
642 – 20f. red 10 10
697 – 24f. red 10 10
643 – 25f. blue 10 10
699 – 30f. mauve 10 10
645 – 32f. brown 15 10
700 **102** 40f. green 15 10
701 – 50f. green 15 10
702 – 70f. red 30 10
698 – 80f. brown 35 20
DESIGNS—As T **101**: 20, 24f. St. Stephen; 25, 80f. Madonna and Child. As T **102**: 30f. Buda Cathedral; 32f. Debrecen Reformed Church; 50f. Budapest Evangelical Church; 70f. Kassa Cathedral.
For further issues in these designs, see Nos. 751/5.

103 Guides' Salute

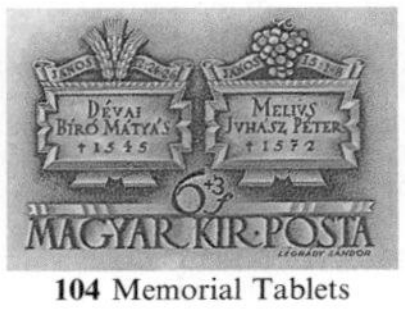

104 Memorial Tablets

1939. Girl Guides' Rally, Godollo. Inscr "I. PAX-TING".
649 **103** 2f. orange 15 30
650 – 6f. green 25 30
651 – 10f. brown 25 30
652 – 20f. pink 70 50
DESIGNS: 6f. Lily symbol and Hungarian arms; 10f. Guide and girl in national costume; 20f. Dove of peace.

1939. National Protestant Day and Int Protestant Cultural Fund.
653 **104** 6f.+3f. green 65 70
654 – 10f.+5f. purple 65 70
655 – 20f.+10f. red 65 70
656 – 32f.+16f. brown . . . . . 80 1·25
657 – 40f.+20f. blue . . . . . 80 1·50
MS657a 77 × 112 mm. No. 656 32f. brown. Perf or imperf . . . . 30·00 30·00
DESIGNS—HORIZ: 10f., 20f. G. Karoli and A. Molnar di Szenci (translators of the Bible and the Psalms). VERT: 32f. Prince Gabriel Bethlen; 40f. Zsuzsanna Lorantffy.

106 Boy Scout with Kite

107 Regent and Szeged Cathedral

1940. Admiral Horthy Aviation Fund.
658 **106** 6f.+6f. green 15 30
659 – 10f.+10f. brown 60 50
660 – 20f.+20f. red . . . . . . 90 1·10
DESIGNS: 10f. "Spirit of Flight"; 20f. St. Elizabeth carrying Crown and Cross of St. Stephen.

1940. 20th Anniv of Regency.
661 **107** 6f. green 15 20
662 – 10f. brown and olive . . . 15 25
663 – 20f. red 30 30
DESIGNS: 10f. Admiral Horthy (dated "1920 1940"); 20f. Kassa Cathedral and Angelic bellringer (dated "1939").

108 Stemming the Flood

1940. Flood Relief Fund.
664 **108** 10f.+2f. purple 30 30
665 20f.+4f. orange 30 30
666 20f.+50f. brown 65 80
MS666a 77 × 112 mm. T **108**. 20f.+1p. green . . . . 5·00 4·50

109 Hunyadi Family Arms

110 Hunyadi Castle

1940. 500th Birth Anniv of King Matthias Hunyadi and Cultural Institutes Fund.
667 **109** 6f.+3f. green 25 45
668 **110** 10f.+5f. brown 25 45
669 – 16f.+8f. olive 35 60
670 – 20f.+10f. red 40 65
671 – 32f.+16f. grey 40 70
MS671a 89 × 113 mm. 20f.+1p. green (as No. 670) . . . . . . 5·00 3·75
DESIGNS—VERT: 16f. Bust of King Matthias (dated "1440–1490"); 32f. Corvin Codex (dated "1473"). HORIZ: 20f. Equestrian Statue of King Matthias.

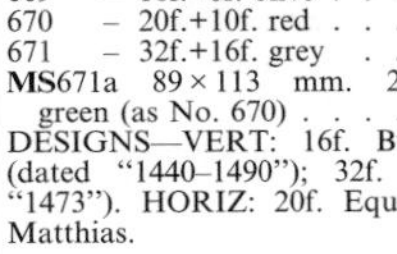

111 Crown of St. Stephen

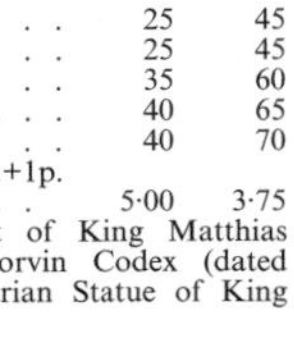

112 Madonna and Martyr

1940. Recovery from Rumania of North-Eastern Transylvania.
672 **111** 10f. green and yellow . . 20 10

1940. Transylvanian Relief Fund. Various designs dated "1940".
673 – 10f.+50f. green 50 70
674 **112** 20f.+50f. red 50 60
675 – 32f.+50f. brown . . . . . 65 1·00
DESIGNS: 10f. Prince Csaba and soldier; 32f. Mother offering child to Fatherland.

113 Spirit of Music

1940. Artists' Relief Fund. Inscr "MAGYAR MUVESZETERT".
676 **113** 6f.+6f. green . . . . . . 90 1·10
677 – 10f.+10f. brown . . . . . 90 1·10
678 – 16f.+16f. violet . . . . . 90 1·10
679 – 20f.+20f. red . . . . . . 90 1·10
MS679a 123 × 84 mm. 6f.+6f. brown; 10f.+10f. red; 16f.+16f. green; 20f.+20f. lilac . . . . . 4·25 6·00
DESIGNS—VERT: 10f. Sculpture; 16f. Painting. HORIZ: 20f. Poetry (Pegasus).

114 Pilot

1941. Air. Horthy Aviation Fund. Various allegorical designs inscribed "HORTHY MIKLOS NEMZETI REPULO ALAP".
680 **114** 6f.+6f. olive 35 55
681 – 10f.+10f. brown 65 55
682 – 20f.+20f. red 65 55
683 – 32f.+32f. blue 65 55
DESIGNS: 10f. Youth releasing model glider; 20f. Glider; 32f. Madonna.

1941. Acquisition of Yugoslav Territory. Overprinted **DEL-UISSZATER** ("The South Comes Home").
684 **101** 10f. brown 10 10
685 – 20f. red (No. 642) 10 10

116 Admiral Horthy

1941.
686 **116** 1p. green and yellow . . . 15 15
687 2p. brown and yellow . . 15 20
688 5p. purple and yellow . . 25 45

118 Szechenyi

119 Giant opening Straits of Kazan

1941. 150th Birth Anniv of Count Szechenyi.
703 **118** 10f. olive 10 10
704 – 16f. brown 10 10
705 **119** 20f. red 10 10
706 – 32f. orange 30 30
707 – 40f. blue 60 30
DESIGNS: 16f. Count Szechenyi and Academy of Science; 32f. Budapest Chain Bridge; 40f. Mercury, Locomotive and "Szent Istvan" (river steamer).

120 Infantry in Action

121 Pilot and Airplane

1941. Soldiers' Gifts Fund. Inscr "HONVEDEINK KARACSONYARA 1941". (a) 1st issue.
708 **120** 8f.+12f. green 30 40
709 – 12f.+18f. brown 30 40
710 – 20f.+30f. blue 30 40
711 – 40f.+60f. brown 30 40
DESIGNS: 12f. Artillery; 20f. Tanks; 40f. Cavalryman and cyclist.

(b) 2nd Issue (for Christmas gifts).
712 – 20f.+40f. red . . . . 1·00 2·00
DESIGN: Soldier in helmet; cross and sword.

1942. Air. Horthy Aviation Fund. Inscr "HORTHY MIKLOS NEMZETI REPULO ALAP".
713 **121** 8f.+8f. green 30 45
714 – 12f.+12f. blue 85 60
715 – 20f.+20f. brown 85 60
716 – 30f.+30f. red 45 45
DESIGNS—VERT: 30f. Airmen and Turul. HORIZ: 12f. Aircraft and horsemen; 20f. Airplane and archer.

122 Blood Transfusion

123 Vice-regent Stephen Horthy

1942. Red Cross Fund. Cross in red.
717 **122** 3f.+18f. green . . . . . 70 1·10
718 – 8f.+32f. brown . . . . . 70 1·10
719 – 12f.+50f. purple . . . . 70 1·10
720 – 20f.+1p. blue . . . . . . 70 1·10
DESIGNS: 8f. First aid; 12f. Wireless and carrier-pigeon service; 20f. Bereaved parents and orphans.

1942. Air. Mourning for Stephen Horthy and Horthy Aviation Fund.
721 – 20f. black 25 20
722 **123** 30f.+20f. violet 35 25
No. 721 is squarer in shape than No. 722 and is dated "1904–1942".

124 Stephen Horthy's Widow

125 King Ladislas

1942. Red Cross Fund. Cross and Crown in red.
723 **124** 6f.+1p. blue . . . . . . 1·50 2·25
724 – 8f.+1p. green . . . . . . 1·50 2·25
725 – 20f.+1p. brown . . . . . 1·50 2·25
DESIGNS—HORIZ: 8f. Nurse and wounded soldier. VERT: 20f. Stephen Horthy's mother.

1942. Cultural Funds.
726 **125** 6f.+6f. brown 25 55
727 – 8f.+8f. green 25 55
728 – 12f.+12f. brown 25 55
729 – 20f.+20f. green 25 55
730 – 24f.+24f. brown 25 55
731 – 30f.+30f. red 25 55
DESIGNS—Statuettes: 8f. Ladislas on horseback; 20f. Bela IV with architect; 30f. Lajos the Great enthroned. King's heads; 12f. Bela IV; 24f. Lajos the Great.

126 Prince Arpad

127 St. Stephen's Crown

1943.
732 **126** 1f. grey 10 10
733 – 2f. orange 10 10
734 – 3f. blue 10 10
735 – 4f. brown 10 10
736 – 5f. red 10 10
737 – 6f. blue 10 10
738 – 8f. green 10 10
739 – 10f. brown 10 10
740 – 12f. green 10 10
741 – 18f. black 10 10
742 **127** 20f. brown 10 10
743 – 24f. purple 10 10
744 **127** 30f. red 10 10
745 – 30f. red 10 10
746 **127** 50f. blue 10 10
747 80f. brown 10 10
748 1p. green 10 10
749 2p. brown 10 25
750 5p. purple 10 10
DESIGNS: 2f. King Ladislas; 3f. Miklos Toldi; 4f. Janos Hunyadi; 5f. Pal Kinizsi; 6f. Miklos Zrinyi; 8f. Ferenc Rakoczi II; 10f. Andre Hadik; 12f. Artur Gorgey; 18f. and 24f. Madonna; 30f. (No. 745), St. Margaret.

1943. As T **102** (designs and colours changed).
751 – 30f. red 10 10
752 – 40f. grey 10 10
753 **102** 50f. blue 10 10
754 – 70f. green 10 10
755 – 80f. brown 10 10
DESIGNS: 30f. Kassa Cathedral; 40f. Debrecen Reformed Church; 70f. Budapest Evangelical Church; 80f. Buda Cathedral.

128 Mounted Archer

129 Model Glider

1943. Wounded Soldiers' Relief Fund. Inscr as in T **128**.
756 **128** 1f.+1f. grey 10 10
757 – 3f.+1f. lilac 30 30
758 – 4f.+1f. brown 20 15
759 – 8f.+2f. green 20 15
760 – 12f.+2f. brown 20 15
761 – 20f.+2f. brown 20 15
762 – 40f.+4f. grey 20 15
763 – 50f.+6f. brown 20 15
764 – 70f.+8f. blue 20 15
DESIGNS—VERT: 3f., 4f. Magyar soldier with battle-axe and buckler; 8f. Warrior with shield and sword; 20f. Musketeer; 50f. Artilleryman; 70f. Magyar Arms. HORIZ: 12f. Lancer; 40f. Hussar.

1943. Air. Horthy Aviation Fund. Inscr "HORTHY MIKLOS NEMZETI REPULO ALAP".
765 **129** 8f.+8f. green 70 40
766 – 12f.+12f. blue 70 40
767 – 20f.+20f. brown . . . . . 1·25 65
768 – 30f.+30f. red 70 65
DESIGNS: 12f. Gliders in flight; 20f. White-tailed sea eagle and aircraft; 30f. Cant Z.1007 bis Alcione bomber and gliders.

130 Shepherds and Angels

1943. Christmas.
769 **130** 4f. green 10 20
770 – 20f. blue 10 20
771 – 30f. red 10 20
DESIGNS: 20f. Nativity; 30f. Adoration of the Wise Men.

131 Nurse and Soldier

1944. Red Cross Fund. Cross and Crown in red.
772 **131** 20f.+20f. brown 30 25
773 – 30f.+30f. brown 30 25
774 – 50f.+50f. purple 30 25
775 – 70f.+70f. blue 30 25
DESIGNS: 30f. Soldier, nurse, mother and child; 50f. Nurse shielding a lamp over the Fallen; 70f. Soldier with crutches, nurse and sapling.

132 Drummer and Flags

133 St. Elizabeth

1944. 50th Death Anniv of Kossuth (statesman).
776 – 4f. brown 10 10
777 **132** 20f. green 10 10
778 – 30f. red 10 10
779 – 50f. blue 10 10
DESIGNS—VERT: 4f. Kossuth and family group; 50f. Portrait. HORIZ: 30f. Kossuth speaking before an assembly.

1944. Famous Women.
780 **133** 20f. bistre 10 10
781 – 24f. purple 10 20
782 – 30f. red 10 10
783 – 50f. blue 10 10
784 – 70f. red 10 20
785 – 80f. brown 10 20
PORTRAITS: 24f. St. Margaret; 30f. Elizabeth Szilagyi; 50f. Dorothy Kanizsai; 70f. Zsuzsanna Lorantffy; 80f. Ilona Zrinyi.

1945. Stamps as Nos. 732/48, surch **FELSZABADULAS** (= Liberation) **1945 apr 4** and value. On yellow or blue surface-tinted paper (same price).
786 10f. on 1f. grey . . . . . . 75 1·10
787 20f. on 3f. blue . . . . . . 75 1·10
788 30f. on 4f. brown . . . . . 75 1·10
789 40f. on 6f. blue . . . . . . 75 1·10
790 50f. on 8f. green . . . . . 75 1·10
791 1p. on 10f. brown . . . . . 75 1·10
792 150f. on 12f. green . . . . 75 1·10
793 2p. on 18f. black . . . . . 75 1·10
794 3p. on 20f. brown . . . . . 75 1·10
795 5p. on 24f. purple . . . . . 75 1·10
796 6p. on 50f. blue . . . . . 75 1·10
797 10p. on 80f. brown . . . . 75 1·10
798 20p. on 1p. green . . . . . 75 1·10

135 Bajcsy-Zsilinszky

1945. Bajcsy-Zsilinszky (patriot).
799 **135** 1p.+1p. purple 45 60

1945. Provisionals. 1st issue. Surch **1945** and value. (a) On stamps of 1943, Nos. 732/50, surface-tinted paper.
800 10f. on 4f. brown on blue . . 10 10
801 10f. on 10f. brown on blue 15 25
802 10f. on 12f. green on yellow 10 10
803 20f. on 1f. grey on yellow . . 10 10
804 20f. on 18f. black on yellow 10 10
805 28f. on 5f. red on blue . . . 10 10
806 30f. on 30f. red on blue (No. 745) 10 10
807 30f. on 30f. red on blue (No. 744) 10 10
808 40f. on 24f. purple on yellow 10 10
809 42f. on 20f. brown on yellow 10 10
810 50f. on 50f. blue on yellow 10 10
811 60f. on 8f. green on yellow 10 10
812 1p. on 80f. brown on blue . . 10 10
813 1p. on 1p. green on yellow 10 10
814 150f. on 6f. blue on yellow 35 75
815 2p. on 2p. brown on blue . . 10 10
816 3p. on 3f. blue on yellow . . 15 25
817 5p. on 5p. purple on yellow 10 10
818 10p. on 2f. orange on blue 2·75 4·75

(b) On Famous Women Series of 1944 (Nos. 780/5), surface-tinted paper.
819 20f. on 20f. bistre on blue . . 10 10
820 30f. on 30f. red on blue . . . 10 10
821 40f. on 24f. purple on yellow 10 10
822 50f. on 50f. blue on yellow 10 10
823 80f. on 80f. brown on yellow 10 10
824 1p. on 70f. red on blue . . . 10 10

1945. Provisionals. 2nd issue. Surch **1945** and value. (a) On stamps of 1943, Nos. 732/48, surface-tinted paper.
825 40f. on 10f. brown on blue 10 10
826 1p. on 20f. brown on yellow 10 10
827 1.60p. on 12f. green on yellow 10 10
828 2p. on 4f. brown on blue . . 10 10
829 4p. on 30f. red on blue (No. 744) 10 10
830 5p. on 8f. green on yellow . . 10 10
831 6p. on 50f. blue on yellow . . 10 10
832 7p. on 1p. green on yellow 10 10
833 9p. on 1f. grey on yellow . . 10 10
834 10p. on 80f. brown on blue 10 10

(b) On Famous Women Series of 1944. (Nos. 780/3), surface-tinted paper.
835 80f. on 24f. purple on yellow 10 10
836 3p. on 50f. blue on yellow . . 10 10
837 8p. on 20f. bistre on blue . . 10 10
838 20p. on 30f. red on blue . . 10 10

1945. National High School Fund. Nos. 776/9, with coloured surfaces, surch **BEKE A NEPFOISKOLAKERT**, new value and premium.
839 **132** 3p.+9p. on 20f. green on yellow 15 30
840 – 4p.+12p. on 4f. brown on blue 15 30
841 – 8p.+24p. on 50f. blue on yellow 15 30
842 – 10p.+30p. on 30f. red on blue 15 30

138 Mining

1945. Int Trade Union Conference, Paris.
843 **138** 40f. grey . . . . 2·75 3·75
844 – 1p.60 brown . . . . . . 2·75 3·75
845 – 2p. green . . . . 2·75 3·75
846 – 3p. purple . . . . 2·75 3·75
847 – 5p. red . . . . 2·75 3·75
848 – 8p. brown . . . . 2·75 3·75
849 – 10p. red . . . . 2·75 3·75
850 – 20p. blue . . . . 2·75 3·75
DESIGNS: Trade Symbols—1p.60, Hammer and anvil (ironworking); 2p. Winged wheel (railway workers); 3p. Trowel and bricks (building); 5p. Plough (agriculture); 8p. Carrier pigeon (communications); 10p. Compasses (engineering); 20p. Winged pen and book (clerks).

139 I. Sallai and S. Furst

1945. National Relief Fund.
851 **139** 2p.+2p. brown . . . . . 75 1·25
852 – 3p.+3p. red . . . . . . 75 1·25
853 – 4p.+4p. violet . . . . . 75 1·25
854 – 6p.+6p. green . . . . . 75 1·25
855 – 10p.+10p. red . . . . . 75 1·25
856 – 15p.+15p. olive . . . . . 75 1·25
857 – 20p.+20p. brown . . . . 75 1·25
858 – 40p.+40p. blue . . . . . 75 1·25

PORTRAITS: 3p. L. Kabok and I. Monus; 4p. F. Rozsa and Z. Schonherz; 6p. A. Koltoi and P. Knurr; 10p. G. Sarkozi and I. Nagy; 15p. V. Tartsay and J. Nagy; 20p. J. Kiss and E. Bajcsy-Zsilinszky; 40p. E. Sagvari and O. Hoffmann.

1945. Provisionals. 3rd issue. Nos. 738, 740/1 and 745 (coloured surfaces) surch **1945** and new value.

859 40p. on 8f. green on yellow 10 10
860 60p. on 18f. black on yellow 10 10
861 100p. on 12f. green on yellow 10 10
862 300p. on 30f. red on blue . . 10 10

140 Reconstruction

1945.

863 **140** 12p. olive 30 45
864 20p. green 10 10
865 24p. brown 30 35
866 30p. black 10 10
867 40p. green 10 10
868 60p. red 10 10
869 100p. orange 10 10
870 120p. blue 10 10
871 140p. red 30 30
872 200p. brown 10 10
873 240p. blue 10 10
874 300p. red 10 10
875 500p. green 10 10
876 1000p. purple 10 10
877 3000p. red 10 10

Owing to the collapse of the pengo, the following stamps were overprinted to show the postage rate for which they were valid, and they were sold at the appropriate rate for the day. **Any** or **Nyomtatv** = Sample Post or Printed Matter. **Hlp** or **Helyi lev. lap** = Local Postcard. **Hl** or **Helyi level** = Local Letter. **Tlp** or **Tavolsagi lev.-lap** = Inland Postcard. **Tl** or **Tavolsagi level** = Inland Letter. **Ajl** or **Ajanlas** = Registered Letter. **Cs.** or **Csomag** = Parcel.

1946. Optd as above. (a) First Issue.

878 **126** "Any. 1" on 1f. grey . . 10 10
879 – "Hlp. 1" on 8p. on 20f. bistre on blue (No. 837) 10 10
880 – "Hl. 1" on 50f. blue (No. 783) 10 10
881 – "Tlp. 1" on 4f. brown (No. 735) 10 10
882 – "Tl. 1" on 10f. brown (No. 739) 10 10
883 **133** "Ajl. 1" on 20f. bistre 10 10
883b **127** "Cs. 5-1" on 30f. red (No. 744) . . . . . . 12·00 12·00
884 – "Cs. 5-1" on 70f. red (No. 784) 10 10
885 – "Cs. 10-1" on 70f. red (No. 784) 10 10
885a **127** "Cs. 10-1" on 80f. brown (No. 747) . . . 11·00 13·50

(b) Second Issue.

886 **126** "Any. 2" on 1f. grey . . 10 10
887 – "Hlp. 2" on 8p. on 20f. bistre on blue (No. 837) 10 10
888 – "Hl. 2" on 40f. on 10f. brown on blue (No. 825) 10 10
889 – "Tlp. 2" on 4f. brown (No. 735) 10 10
890 – "Tl. 2" on 10f. on 4f. brown on blue (No. 800) 10 10
891 – "Ajl. 2" on 12f. green (No. 740) 10 10
892 – "Cs. 5-2" on 24f. purple (No. 743) 10 10
893 – "Cs. 10-2" on 80f. brown (No. 785) 10 10

(c) Third Issue.

894 – "Nyomtatv. 20gr." on 60f. on 8f. green on yellow (No. 811) 10 10
895 – "Helyi lev.-lap" on 2f. bistre on blue (as No. 780) . . . 10 10
896 – "Helyi level" on 10f. brown on blue (as No. 739) . . . 10 10
897 – "Tavolsagi lev.-lap" on 4f. brown (No. 735) 10 10
898 – "Tavolsagi level" on 18f. black (No. 741) 10 10
899 – "Ajanlas" on 24f. purple (No. 781) 10 10
900 – "Csomag 5 kg" on 2p. on 4f. brown on blue (No. 828) 10 10
901 – "Csomag 10kg." on 30f. red on blue (as No. 782) . . . 10 10

Abbreviations used in the following issues:
ez(er) p. = thousand pengos.
m(illio) p. = million pengos.
m.p. (milpengo) = million pengos.
md.p. (milliard. p) = thousand million pengos.
b.p. (billio. p) = million million pengos.
ez. ap (ezer adopengo) = thousand "tax" pengos.
m. ap. (millio adopengo) = million "tax" pengos.

143

144

1946. Foundation of Republic.

902 **143** 3ez. p. brown 10 10
903 15ez. p. blue 10 10

1946.

904 **144** 4ez. p. brown 10 10
905 10ez. p. red 10 10
906 15ez. p. blue 10 10
907 20ez. p. brown 10 10
908 30ez. p. purple 10 10
909 50ez. p. grey 10 10
910 80ez. p. blue 10 10
911 100ez. p. red 10 10
912 160ez. p. green 10 10
913 200ez. p. green 10 10
914 500ez. p. red 10 10
915 640ez. p. olive 10 10
916 800ez. p. violet 10 10

145

146

1946. 75th Anniv of First Hungarian Stamps.

917 **145** 500+500ez. p. green . . . 1·10 1·40
918 1+1m. p. brown . . . . 1·10 1·40
919 1.5+1.5m. p. red . . . . 1·10 1·40
920 2+2m. p. blue . . . . . 1·10 1·40

1946.

921 **146** 1m.p. red 10 20
922 2m.p. blue 10 20
923 3m.p. brown 10 20
924 4m.p. grey 10 20
925 5m.p. violet 10 20
926 10m.p. green 10 20
927 20m.p. red 10 20
928 50m.p. green 10 20

147 Posthorn and Arms

148 Posthorn

149 Dove and Letter

1946.

929 **147** 100m.p. red 10 20
930 200m.p. red 10 20
931 500m.p. red 10 20
932 1000m.p. red 10 20
933 2000m.p. red 10 20
934 3000m.p. red 10 20
935 5000m.p. red 10 20
936 10,000m.p. red 10 20
937 20,000m.p. red 10 20
938 30,000m.p. red 10 20
939 50,000m.p. red 10 20

1946.

940 **148** 100md.p. green and red 10 25
941 200md.p. green and red 10 25
942 500md.p. green and red 10 25

1946.

943 **149** 1b.p. black and red . . . 10 30
944 2b.p. black and red . . . 10 30
945 5b.p. black and red . . . 10 30
946 10b.p. black and red . . . 10 30
947 20b.p. black and red . . . 10 30
948 50b.p. black and red . . . 10 30
949 100b.p. black and red . . 10 30
950 200b.p. black and red . . 10 30
951 500b.p. black and red . . 10 30
952 1000b.p. black and red . . 10 30
953 10,000b.p. black and red 10 40
954 50,000b.p. black and red 15 50
955 100,000b.p. black and red 15 50
956 500,000b.p. black and red 15 50

150 Locomotive "Heves", 1846

151 Posthorn

1946. Centenary of Hungarian Railways.

957 **150** 10000ap. brown . . . . . 5·50 4·50
958 – 20000ap. blue . . . . . 5·50 4·50
959 – 30000ap. green . . . . . 5·50 4·50
960 – 40000ap. red . . . . . . 5·50 4·50

DESIGNS: 20000ap. Class 424 steam locomotive; 30000ap. Class V44 electric locomotive; 40000ap. "Arpad" diesel railcar, 1935.

1946.

961 **151** 5ez. ap. green and black 10 25
962 10ez. ap. green and black 10 25
963 20ez. ap. green and black 10 25
964 50ez. ap. green and black 10 25
965 80ez. ap. green and black 10 25
966 100ez. ap. green and black 10 25
967 200ez. ap. green and black 10 25
968 500ez. ap. green and black 10 30
969 1m. ap. red and black . . 10 50
970 5m. ap. red and black . . 10 50

152 Industry

153 Agriculture

1946. Currency Reform.

971 **152** 8fi. brown 10 10
972 10fi. brown 10 10
973 12fi. brown 10 10
974 20fi. brown 10 10
975 30fi. brown 10 10
976 40fi. brown 10 10
977 60fi. brown 10 10
978 **153** 1fo. green 45 10
979 1fo. 40 green 45 10
980 2fo. green 75 10
981 3fo. green . . . . 3·00 10
982 5fo. green 75 10
983 10fo. green . . . . . . 1·50 45

154 Ceres

155 Liberty Bridge

1946. Agricultural Fair.

984 **154** 30fi.+60fi. green . . . . . 4·25 4·00
985 60fi.+1fo. 20 red . . . . 4·25 4·00
986 1fo.+2fo. blue . . . . . 4·25 4·00

1947. Air. Views.

987 – 10fi. red 20 10
988 – 20fi. grey 20 10
989 **155** 50fi. brown 50 10
990 – 70fi. green 50 10
991 – 1fo. blue . . . . 2·25 10
992 – 1fo. 40 brown . . . . . 2·50 10
993 – 3fo. green . . . . 3·50 30
994 – 5fo. lilac . . . . 2·50 1·25

DESIGNS: 10fi. Loyalty Tower, Sopron; 20fi. Esztergom Cathedral; 70fi. Palace Hotel, Lillafured; 1fo. Vajdahunyad Castle, Budapest; 1fo. 40, Visegrad Fortress; 3fo. "Falcone" (racing yacht) on Lake Balaton; 5fo. Parliament Buildings and Kossuth Bridge.

156 Gyorgy Dozsa

157 Doctor examining X-Ray

1947. Liberty issue.

995 **156** 8fi. red 15 10
996 – 10fi. blue 15 10
997 – 12fi. brown 15 10
998 – 20fi. green 35 10
999 – 30fi. brown 35 10
1000 – 40fi. purple 50 10
1001 – 60fi. red 50 10
1002 – 1fo. blue 60 10
1003 – 2fo. violet 95 30
1004 – 4fo. green . . . . 1·90 35

PORTRAITS: 10fi. A. Budai Nagy; 12fi. T. Esze; 20fi. I. Martinovics; 30fi. J. Batsanyi; 40fi. L. Kossuth; 60fi. M. Tancsics; 1fo. S. Petofi; 2fo. E. Ady; 4fo. A. Jozsef.

1947. Welfare Organizations. Inscr "SIESS! ADJ! SEGITS!" (trans. "Come! Give! Help!").

1005 – 8fi.+50fi. blue . . . . . 3·75 3·50
1006 **157** 12fi.+50fi. brown . . . . 3·75 3·50
1007 – 20fi.+50fi. green . . . . 3·75 3·50
1008 – 60fi.+50fi. red 30 90

DESIGNS: 8fi. Doctor testing syringe; 20fi. Nurse and child; 60fi. Released prisoner-of-war.

158 Emblem of Peace

159 Liberty Statue

1947. Peace Treaty.

1009 **158** 60fi. red 30 20

1947. 30th Anniv of Soviet Union and Hungarian–Soviet Cultural Society Fund.

1010 – 40fi.+40fi. brn & grn . . 2·25 3·75
1011 **159** 60fi.+60fi. grey and red 45 2·25
1012 – 1fo.+1fo. black & blue 2·25 3·75

PORTRAITS: 40fi. Lenin; 1fo. Stalin.

161 Savings Bank

162 16th-century Mail Coach

1947. Savings Day. Inscr "TAKAREKOS JELENBOLDOG JOVO".

1013 – 40fi. red (beehive) . . . 25 10
1014 **161** 60fi. red 25 10

1947. Stamp Day.

1015 **162** 30fi. (+ 50fi.) brown . . 6·75 7·50

165 Arms of Hungary

167 Johann Gutenberg

1948. Centenary of Insurrection.

1016 – 8fi. red 20 10
1017 – 10fi. blue 20 10
1018 – 12fi. brown 20 10
1019 – 20fi. green 65 10
1020 – 30fi. brown 30 10
1021 – 40fi. purple 30 10
1022 – 60fi. red 75 10
1023 **165** 1fo. blue 75 10
1024 2fo. brown . . . . . . 1·00 20
1025 3fo. green . . . . 1·25 35
1026 4fo. red . . . . 3·50 45

DESIGNS—HORIZ: 8fi., 40fi. Hungarian independence flag; 10fi. Printing press; 12fi. Latticed window; 20fi. Shako, trumpet and sword; 30fi., 60fi. Slogan.

1948. Air. Explorers and Inventors.

1027 **167** 1fi. red 10 10
1028 – 2fi. mauve 25 30
1029 – 4fi. blue 25 30
1030 – 5fi. brown 25 30
1031 – 6fi. green 25 40
1032 – 8fi. purple 25 30
1033 – 10fi. brown 45 50
1034 – 12fi. green 90 35
1035 – 30fi. red . . . . 1·25 65
1036 – 40fi. violet . . . . . . 80 1·10

PORTRAITS: 2fi. Christopher Columbus; 4fi. Robert Fulton; 5fi. George Stephenson; 6fi. David Schwarz and Count Ferdinand von Zeppelin; 8fi. Thomas Edison; 10fi. Louis Bleriot; 12fi. Roald Amundsen; 30fi. Kalman Kando; 40fi. Alexander Popov.

168 Chain Bridge, Budapest

1948. Air. Re-opening of Budapest Chain Bridge. Sheets 74 × 65 mm.

MS1036a 2fo.+18fo. Red . . . . 75·00 90·00
MS1036b **168** 3fo.+18fo. blue . . 75·00 90·00

DESIGN: 20fo. Shows a more distant view of the bridge.

169 Lorand Eotvos

1948. Birth Centenary of L. Eotvos (physicist).

1037 **169** 60fi. red 75 30

170 William Shakespeare

1948. Air. Writers.
1038 **170** 1fi. blue 20 15
1039 – 2fi. red 30 15
1040 – 4fi. green 30 15
1041 – 5fi. mauve 40 30
1042 – 6fi. blue 40 30
1043 – 8fi. brown 40 30
1044 – 10fi. red 40 40
1045 – 12fi. violet 45 45
1046 – 30fi. brown 90 70
1047 – 40fi. brown . . . . . . 1·10 1·25
PORTRAITS: 2fi. Voltaire; 4fi. Goethe; 5fi. Byron; 6fi. Victor Hugo; 8fi. Edgar Allan Poe; 10fi. Petofi; 12fi. Mark Twain; 30fi. Tolstoy; 40fi. Gorki.

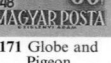

171 Globe and Pigeon

172 Symbolizing Industry, Agriculture and Culture

1948. 5th National Philatelic Exhibition.
1048 **171** 30fi. blue . . . . 3·25 3·75
Sold at 1fo.30 (incl 1fo. entrance fee).

1948. 17th Trades' Union Congress.
1049 **172** 30fi. red 25 10

173 Agricultural Worker

174 Reproduction of T **32**

1949. International Women's Day.
1050 **173** 60fi.+60fi. mauve . . . . 1·10 1·10

1949. 30th Anniv of Bolshevist Regime.
1051 **174** 40fi. brown and red . . 35 15
1052 – 60fi. olive and red . . . 35 15
DESIGN: 60fi. Reproduction of No. 325.

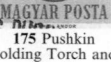

175 Pushkin holding Torch and Scroll

176 Symbolising Workers of Five Continents

1949. 150th Birth Anniv of A. S. Pushkin (poet).
1053 **175** 1fo.+1fo. red . . . . . 5·00 5·25
MS1053a 52 × 62 mm. 1fo.+1fo. Red 15·00 15·00
DESIGN—HORIZ: No. **MS**1053a, Puhkin writing.

1949. 2nd World Federation of Trade Unions Congress, Milan. Flag in red.
1054 **176** 30fi. brown . . . . . . 2·00 2·10
1055 40fi. purple . . . . . . 2·00 2·10
1056 60fi. red . . . . 2·00 2·10
1057 1fo. blue . . . . 2·00 2·10

177 Sandor Petofi

178 Heads and Globe

1949. Death Centenary of Petofi (poet).
1058 **177** 40fi. purple 45 20
1096 40fi. brown 50 20
1059 60fi. red 20 10
1060 1fo. blue 20 15
1098 1fo. green 35 20

1949. World Youth Festival, Budapest.
1061 **178** 20fi. brown 65 70
1062 – 30fi. green 65 70
1063 – 40fi. bistre . . . . . . 75 1·00
1064 – 60fi. red . . . . 75 1·00
1065 – 1fo. blue . . . . 1·60 1·60
MS1065a 100 × 130 mm.
Nos. 1061/5, but colours changed 20·00 20·00
DESIGNS: 30fi. Three clenched fists; 40fi. Man breaking chains; 60fi. Young people and banner; 1fo. Workers and tractor.

179 Hungarian Coat-of-Arms

1949. Ratification of Constitution. Arms in blue, brown, red and green.
1066 **179** 20fi. green 65 50
1067 60fi. red 65 30
1068 1fo. blue 70 30

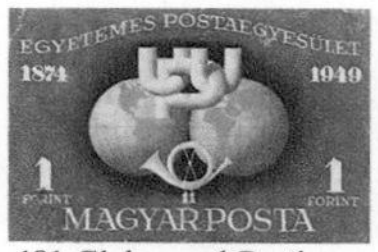

181 Globes and Posthorn

1949. 75th Anniv of U.P.U.
1069 **181** 60fi. red (postage) . . . 30 35
1070 1fo. blue 45 35
1071 – 2fo. brown (air) 80 65
MS1072 128 × 98 mm. 3fo. (× 4) brown and red £300 £300
DESIGN: 2, 3fo. Lisunov Li-2 airplane replaces posthorn.

182 Chain Bridge

1949. Centenary of Budapest Chain Bridge.
1073 **182** 40fi. green (postage) . . 50 35
1074 60fi. brown 50 35
1075 1fo. blue 50 35
1076 1fo.60 red (air) 80 75
1077 2fo. olive 80 50
MS1077a 136 × 100 mm. 50 fo. Lilac £225 £225
DESIGN—VERT: 50fo. Drawing board, plans, etc.

183 Postman and Forms of Transport

184 Joseph Stalin

1949. Air. Stamp Day.
1078 **183** 50fi. grey . . . . 3·75 3·75

1949. Stalin's 70th Birthday.
1079 **184** 60fi. red 50 25
1080 1fo. blue 50 30
1081 2fo. brown . . . . . . 1·00 50

185 Miners

1950. Five Year Plan.
1082 **185** 8fi. grey 75 10
1083 – 10fi. purple 45 10
1084 – 12fi. red 45 10
1085 – 20fi. green 45 10
1086 – 30fi. purple 50 10
1087 – 40fi. brown 90 10
1088 – 60fi. red 90 10
1089 – 1fo. violet and yellow . . 1·10 10
1090 – 1fo.70 green and yellow . 1·90 30
1091 – 2fo. red and orange . . 2·10 35
1092 – 3fo. blue and buff . . . 2·40 40
1093 – 4fo. green and orange . . 2·50 45
1094 – 5fo. purple and yellow . 4·25 1·00
1095 – 10fo. brown and yellow 5·25 2·50
DESIGNS: 10fi. Iron foundry; 12fi. Power station; 20fi. Textiles; 30fi. Factory workers' entertainment; 40fi. Mechanical farming; 60fi. Village co-operative office; 1fo. Class 303 steam locomotive on bridge; 1fo.70, Family at health resort; 2fo. Soldier and tank; 3fo. Freighter and Lisunov Li-2 airplane; 4fo. Cattle; 5fo. Draughtsman and factory; 10fo. Sportsman, woman and football match.

186 Philatelic Museum

1950. 20th Anniv of P.O. Philatelic Museum.
1099 **186** 60fi. brown and black (postage) . . . . . . 4·50 5·75
1100 – 2fo. red and yellow (air) 6·75 6·50
DESIGN—HORIZ: 2fo. Globe, coach, Douglas DC-4 airliner and stamps.

188 Family Greeting Soviet Troops

1950. 5th Anniv of Liberation.
1101 **188** 40fi. black 90 60
1102 60fi. lake 60 35
1103 1fo. blue 60 30
1104 2fo. brown 90 35

189 Chess Match

1950. 1st International Candidates Chess Tournament, Budapest. Designs incorporate rook and chessboard.
1105 **189** 60fi. mauve (postage) . . 1·75 45
1106 – 1fo. blue . . . . 3·25 1·10
1107 – 1fo.60 brown (air) . . . 4·50 1·90
DESIGNS: 1fo. Trade Union Building; 1fo.60, Map.

190 Workers and Star

1950. May Day. Inscr as in T **190**.
1108 **190** 40fi. brown . . . . . . 1·90 60
1109 – 60fi. red 90 20
1110 **190** 1fo. blue . . . . 1·10 45
DESIGN: 60fi. Two workers.

191 Workers and Flag

1950. World Federation of Trade Unions Congress, Budapest.
1111 – 40fi. green (postage) . . 1·10 55
1112 **191** 60fi. red 75 25
1113 – 1fo. brown (air) . . . . 1·10 40
DESIGNS: 40fi. Statue, dove and globes; 1fo. Globes, Chain Bridge and Parliament Buildings.

192 Baby and Nursery

1950. Children's Day.
1114 **192** 20fi. brown and grey 90 1·00
1115 – 30fi. mauve and brown 40 30
1116 – 40fi. green and blue . . 40 30
1117 – 60fi. red and brown . . £1500 £1500
1117a – 60fi. red and brown . . 40 30
1118 – 1fo.70 blue and green 1·25 75
DESIGNS: 30fi. Baby boy and holiday scene; 40fi. Schoolgirl and classroom; 60fi. Pioneer boy and camp; 1fo.70, Pioneer boy and girl and model glider class.
No. 1117 is inscr "UTANPOTLASUNK A JOVO HARCAIHOZ" and No. 1117a is inscr "SZABAD HAZABAN BOLDOG IFJUSAG".

193 Workers and Globe

1950. 1st Congress of Young Workers, Budapest.
1119 **193** 20fi. green 75 45
1120 – 30fi. orange 30 10
1121 – 40fi. brown 30 10
1122 – 60fi. mauve 35 30
1123 – 1fo.70 green . . . . . . 1·00 45
DESIGNS—HORIZ: 30fi. Foundry worker and cauldron. VERT: 40fi. Man, woman and banner; 60fi. Workers, banner and Liberty Statue; 1fo.70, Three workers and banner.

194 Peonies

195 Miner

1950. Flowers.
1124 **194** 30fi. purple and green . . 60 25
1125 – 40fi. green, yellow & mve 60 35
1126 – 60fi. brown, yellow & grn . . . . 1·40 40
1127 – 1fo. violet, red and green 2·25 1·10
1128 – 1fo.70 violet, grn & lilac 5·25 65
DESIGNS: 40fi. Pasque flowers; 60fi. Yellow pheasant's-eye; 1fo. Geranium; 1fo.70, Campanulas.

1950. 2nd National Inventions Exhibition.
1129 **195** 40fi. brown . . . . . . 1·00 45
1130 – 60fi. red 90 30
1131 – 1fo. blue . . . . 1·25 75
DESIGNS: 60fi. Turner; 1fo. Building factory.

196 Liberty Statue

1950. Air.
1132 **196** 20fi. red 10 10
1133 – 30fi. violet 10 10
1134 – 70fi. purple 20 10
1135 – 1fo. brown 20 10
1136 – 1fo.60 blue 70 10
1137 – 2fo. red 45 10
1138 – 3fo. black . . . . . . 2·10 30
1139 – 5fo. blue . . . . 1·10 45
1140 – 10fo. brown . . . . . . 3·50 75
1140a – 20fo. green . . . . . . 14·50 4·00
DESIGNS—VERT: 30fi. Crane and buildings; 70fi. Diosgyor steelworks; 1fo. "Stalinyec" tractor; 1fo.60, "Szeged" (freighter); 2fo. Combine harvester; 3fo. Class 303 steam locomotive; 5fo. Matyas Rakosi steel-mill; 10, 20fo. Lisunov Li-2 airplane at Budaors airport.
For No. 1139 but on silver paper see No. 1437.

198 Worker signing Peace Petition

1950. Peace Propaganda.
1141 **198** 40fi. brown and blue . . 4·00 2·50
1142 – 60fi. green and orange 1·10 2·25
1143 – 1fo. brown and green . . 4·00 9·00
DESIGNS—VERT: 60fi. Girl holding dove. HORIZ: 1fo. Soldier, mother and children.

199 Swimmers

1950.
1144 **199** 10fi. blue and light blue (postage) 10 10
1145 – 20fi. brown and orange 10 10
1146 – 1fo. green and olive . . 50 45
1147 – 1fo.70 red and vermilion 1·00 75
1148 – 2fo. violet and brown . . 1·50 1·00
1149 – 30fi. mauve & violet (air) 35 10
1150 – 40fi. blue and green . . 35 10

1151 – 60fi. orange, brown & grn . . . . 1·10 10
1152 – 70fi. brown and grey . . 85 45
1153 – 3fo. chestnut and brown 2·25 1·10
DESIGNS—POSTAGE: 20fi. Vaulting; 1fo. Mountaineering; 1fo.70, Basketball; 2fo. Motor cycling. AIR: 30fi. Volleyball; 40fi. Throwing the javelin; 60fi. Emblem of "Ready for work and action" movement; 70fi. Football; 3fo. Gliding.

200 Jozef Bem and Battle of Piski

201 Workers and Soldier

1950. Death Centenary of Gen. Bem.
1154 **200** 40fi. brown 75 25
1155 60fi. red 75 30
1156 1fo. blue . . . . 1·50 55
MS1156a 98 × 78 mm. **200** 2fo. (+2fo.) purple. Imperf . . . . 35·00 35·00

1951. 2nd Hungarian Communist Party Congress.
1157 **201** 10fi. green 30 10
1158 – 30fi. brown 45 25
1159 – 60fi. red 50 35
1160 – 1fo. blue . . . . 1·10 40
DESIGNS—HORIZ: 30fi. Workers, soldier and banner; 60fi. Portrait and four workers with flags. VERT: 1fo. Procession with banner.

202 Flags

203 Mare and Foal

1951. Hungarian–Soviet Amity. Inscr "MAGYAR SZOVJET BARATSAG HONAPJA 1951".
1161 **202** 60fi. red 35 10
1162 – 1fo. violet 45 30
DESIGN: 1fo. Hungarian and Russian workers.

1951. Livestock Expansion Plan.
1163 **203** 10fi. brown and ochre (postage) 25 10
1164 – 30fi. brown and red . . 45 30
1165 – 40fi. brown and green . . 50 45
1166 – 60fi. brown and orange 65 45
1167 **203** 20fi. brown & green (air) 35 30
1168 – 70fi. ochre and brown 65 60
1169 – 1fo. brown and blue . . 1·60 1·25
1170 – 1fo.60 chestnut & brown 3·25 2·25
DESIGNS: 30, 70fi. Sow and litter; 40fi., 1fo. Ewe and lamb; 60fi., 1fo.60, Cow and calf.

204 Worker

1951. May Day. Inscr "1951 MAJUS".
1171 **204** 40fi. brown 65 45
1172 – 60fi. red 50 10
1173 – 1fo. blue 50 30
DESIGNS—VERT: 60fi. People with banners. HORIZ: 1fo. Labour Day rally.

205 Leo Frankel

206 Street-fighting

1951. 80th Anniv of Paris Commune.
1174 **205** 60fi. brown 50 25
1175 **206** 1fo. blue and red 75 25

207 Children's Heads

208 Ganz Wagon Works

1951. Int Children's Day. Inscr "NEMZETKOZI GYERMEKNAP 1951".
1176 **207** 30fi. brown 30 20
1177 – 40fi. green 45 20
1178 – 50fi. brown 45 20
1179 – 60fi. mauve 45 30
1180 – 1fo.70 blue . . . . . . 1·10 20
DESIGNS: 40fi. Flying model airplane; 50fi. Diesel train on Budapest Pioneer Railway; 60fi. Chemistry experiment; 1fo.70, Blowing bugle.

1951. Rebuilding Plan (1st series).
1180a – 8fi. green 35 10
1180b – 10fi. violet 45 10
1180c – 12fi. red 60 10
1181 **208** 20fi. green 60 10
1182 – 30fi. orange 70 10
1183 – 40fi. brown 70 10
1183a – 50fi. blue 35 10
1184 – 60fi. red 90 10
1184a – 70fi. brown 45 10
1184b – 80fi. purple . . . . . . 1·40 10
1185 – 1fo. blue . . . . 1·50 10
1185a – 1fo.20 red . . . . . . 1·90 10
1185b – 1fo.70 blue . . . . . . 1·40 10
1185c – 2fo. green . . . . . . 1·40 10
1186 – 3fo. purple . . . . . . 2·25 10
1186a – 4fo. olive . . . . . . 2·25 15
1186b – 5fo. black . . . . . . 3·75 15
BUILDINGS: 8fi. Stalin School; 10fi. Szekesfehervar railway station; 12fi. Ujpest medical dispensary; 30fi. Flats; 40fi. Central Railway Station, Budapest; 50fi. Inota power station; 60fi. Matyas Rakosi Cultural Institute; 70fi. Hajdunanas grain elevator; 80fi. Tiszalok dam; 1fo. Kilian Road School; 1fo.20, Mining Apprentices Institute, Ajkacsingervolgy; 1fo.70, Iron and Steel Apprentices Institute, Csepel; 2fo. Cultural Centre, Hungarian Optical Works; 3fo. Building Workers' Union Headquarters; 4fo. Miners' Union Headquarters; 5fo. Flats.
See also Nos. 1296/1304.

209 Gorky

210 Engineers and Tractors

1951. 15th Death Anniv of Maksim Gorky (Russian writer).
1187 **209** 60fi. red 20 20
1188 1fo. blue 30 25
1189 2fo. purple 65 55

1951. 1st Anniv of Five Year Plan.
1190 **210** 20fi. sepia (postage) . . . 20 20
1191 – 30fi. blue 30 25
1192 – 40fi. red 25 20
1193 – 60fi. brown 25 20
1194 – 70fi. brown (air) 40 20
1195 – 1fo. green 40 30
1196 – 2fo. purple . . . . . . 1·60 65
DESIGNS: 30fi. Doctor X-raying patient; 40fi. Workman instructing apprentices; 60fi. Girl driving tractor; 70fi. Electrical engineers constructing pylon; 1fo. Young people and recreation home; 2fo. Lisunov Li-2 airplane over Stalin (later Arpad) Bridge.

211 1871 Stamp without portrait and Hungarian Arms

212 Soldiers Parading

1951. 80th Anniv of 1st Hungarian Postage Stamp.
1197 **211** 60fi. green 45 30
1198 1fo.+1fo. red . . . . . 9·75 8·00
1199 2fo.+2fo. blue . . . . . 12·50 11·00
MS1199a Air. Three sheets each 78 × 97 mm. Nos. 1197/9 Set of 3 sheets £150 £170

1951. Army Day.
1200 **212** 1fo. brown (postage) . . 80 25
1201 – 60fi. blue (air) 50 25
DESIGN—VERT: 60fi. Tanks and Liberty Statue.

213 Lily of the Valley

214 Revolutionaries and Flags

1951. Flowers.
1202 – 30fi. violet, blue and green 40 10
1203 **213** 40fi. myrtle and green . . 85 50
1204 – 60fi. red, pink and green 55 20
1205 – 1fo. blue, red and green 1·25 35
1206 – 1fo.70 brown, yell & grn 2·75 1·40
FLOWERS: 30fi. Cornflowers; 60fi. Tulips; 1fo. Poppies; 1fo.70, Cowslips.

1951. 34th Anniv of Russian Revolution.
1207 **214** 40fi. green 65 30
1208 – 60fi. blue 65 25
1209 – 1fo. red 65 30
DESIGNS: 60fi. Lenin addressing revolutionaries; 1fo. Lenin and Stalin.

215 Parade before Stalin Statue

1951. Stalin's 72nd Birthday.
1210 **215** 60fi. red 90 40
1211 1fo. blue . . . . 1·00 45

216 Bolshoi State Theatre, Moscow

1952. Views of Moscow.
1212 **216** 60fi. lake and green . . . 65 15
1213 – 1fo. brown and red . . . 65 25
1214 – 1fo.60 olive and lake . . 55 50
DESIGNS: 1fo. Lenin Mausoleum; 1fo.60, Kremlin.

217 Rakosi and Peasants

218 Rakosi

1952. 60th Birth Anniv of Rakosi.
1215 **217** 60fi. purple 65 25
1216 **218** 1fo. brown 65 25
1217 – 2fo. blue . . . . 1·25 45
DESIGN: 2fo. Rakosi and foundry workers.

219 L. Kossuth

1952. Heroes of 1848 Revolution.
1218 **219** 20fi. green 10 10
1219 – 30fi. purple (Petofi) . . . 15 10
1220 – 50fi. black (Bem) 45 20
1221 – 60fi. lake (Tancsics) . . 45 10
1222 – 1fo. blue (Damjanich) . . 45 20
1223 – 1fo.50 brown (Nagy) . . 60 60

220 Pied Avocet

1952. Air. Birds.
1224 **220** 20fi. black and green . . 10 10
1225 – 30fi. black and green . . 25 10
1226 – 40fi. black, yellow & brn 30 10
1227 – 50fi. black and orange 30 10
1228 – 60fi. black and red . . . 30 10
1229 – 70fi. black, orange & red 45 25
1230 – 80fi. black, yellow & grn 60 30
1231 – 1fo. black, red and blue 85 40
1232 – 1fo.40 multicoloured . . 1·00 45
1233 – 1fo.60 black, grn & brn 1·25 60
1234 – 2fo.50 black and purple 2·50 1·00
DESIGNS: 30fi. White stork; 40fi. Golden oriole; 50fi. Kentish plover; 60fi. Black-winged stilt; 70fi. Lesser grey strike; 80fi. Great bustard; 1fo. Western red-footed falcon; 1fo.40, European bee eater; 1fo.60, Glossy ibis; 2fo.50, Great egret.

1952. Budapest Philatelic Exn. No. 1050 with bars obliterating inscription and premium.
1235 **173** 60fi. mauve . . . . . . 35·00 40·00

222 Drummer and Flags

1952. May Day. Inscr "1952 MAJUS I".
1236 **222** 40fi. red and green . . . 90 50
1237 – 60fi. red and brown . . 60 25
1238 – 1fo. red and brown . . . 90 25
DESIGNS: 60fi. Workers; 1fo. Workman and globe.

223 Running

1952. 15th Olympic Games, Helsinki.
1239 **223** 30fi. brown (postage) . . 35 10
1240 – 40fi. green 35 10
1241 – 60fi. red 50 10
1242 – 1fo. blue 80 45
1243 – 1fo.70 orange (air) . . . 1·25 80
1244 – 2fo. brown . . . . . . 1·25 1·10
DESIGNS: 40fi. Swimming; 60fi. Fencing; 1fo. Gymnastics; 1fo.70, Throwing the hammer; 2fo. Stadium.

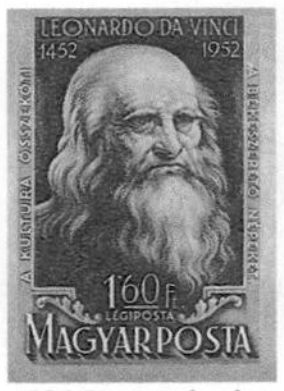

224 Leonardo da Vinci

225 Train and Railwayman

1952. Air. 500th Birth Anniv of Leonardo da Vinci and 150th Birth Anniv of Victor Hugo.
1245 **224** 1fo.60 blue 75 45
1246 – 2fo. purple (Victor Hugo) 75 75

1952. Railway Day. Inscr "1952 VIII 10".
1247 **225** 60fi. brown 70 25
1248 – 1fo. green . . . . 1·25 30
DESIGN: 1fo. Railway tracks.

226 Mechanical Coal-cutter

227 L. Kossuth

1952. Miners' Day. Inscr as in T **226**.
1249 **226** 60fi. brown 70 25
1250 – 1fo. green . . . . 1·00 30
DESIGN: 1fo. Miners operating machinery.

1952. 150th Birth Anniv of Kossuth (statesman).
1251 **227** 40fi. olive on pink . . . 35 25
1252 – 60fi. black on blue . . . 30 25
1253 **227** 1fo. lilac on yellow . . . 45 35
DESIGN: 60fi. Statue of Kossuth.

228 Gy Dozsa

229 Boy, Girl and Stamp Exhibition

1952. Army Day. Inscr as T **228**.
1254 20fi. lilac (J. Hunyadi) . . . 30 10
1255 30fi. green (T **228**) 30 10
1256 40fi. blue (M. Zrinyi) . . . 30 10
1257 60fi. purple (I. Zrinyi) . . . 35 25

1258 1fo. turquoise (B. Vak) . . 60 25
1259 1fo.50 brown (A. Stromfeld) 90 45

1952. Air. Stamp Day. Inscr "XXV. BELYEGNAP 1952".
1260 – 1fo.+1fo. blue . . . . . 5·50 6·00
1261 **229** 2fo.+2fo. red . . . . . 5·50 6·00
DESIGN: 1fo. Children examining stamps.

230 Lenin and Revolutionary Council

1952. 35th Anniv of Russian Revolution.
1262 **230** 40fi. olive and purple . . 1·25 40
1263 – 60fi. olive and black . . 60 10
1264 – 1fo. olive and red . . . 1·25 20
DESIGNS: 60fi. Stalin and Cossacks; 1fo. Marx, Engels, Lenin, Stalin and Spassky Tower.

231 Harvester

1952. 3rd Hungarian Peace Congress. Inscr as in T **231**.
1265 **231** 60fi. red on yellow . . 45 10
1266 – 1fo. brown on green . . 45 30
DESIGN—HORIZ: 1fo. Workers' discussion group.

232 Tunnel Construction

1953. Budapest Underground Railway. Inscr "BUDAPESTI FOLDALATTI GYORSVASUT".
1267 **232** 60fi. green 90 25
1268 – 1fo. lake 90 40
DESIGN—HORIZ: 1fo. Underground map and station.

233 Russian Flag and Tank **234** Eurasian Red Squirrel

1953. 10th Anniv of Battle of Stalingrad.
1269 **233** 40fi. red 80 25
1270 – 60fi. brown . . . . . 1·10 35
DESIGN: 60fi. Soldier, map and flags.

1953. Air. Forest Animals.
1271 **234** 20fi. brown and olive . . 30 10
1272 – 30fi. sepia and brown . . 30 10
1273 – 40fi. sepia and green . . 35 10
1274 – 50fi. sepia and brown . . 45 30
1275 – 60fi. brown and turquoise 60 30
1276 – 70fi. brown and olive . . 60 30
1277 – 80fi. brown and green . . 90 45
1278 – 1fo. brown and green . . 1·25 55
1279 – 1fo.50 black and bistre 1·90 1·00
1280 – 2fo. sepia and brown . . 3·00 1·00
DESIGNS—HORIZ: 30fi. West European hedgehog; 40fi. Brown hare; 60fi. European otter; 70fi. Red fox; 1fo. Roe deer; 1fo.50, Wild boar. VERT: 50fi. Beech marten; 80fi. Fallow deer; 2fo. Red deer.

235 Stalin **236** Rest Home, Galyateto

1953. Death of Stalin.
1281 **235** 60fi. black 30 20
MS1281a 51 × 72 mm. 2fo. purple (T **235**) . . . . 18·00 23·00

1953. Workers' Rest Homes.
1282 **236** 30fi. brown (postage) . . 20 10
1283 – 40fi. blue 30 10
1284 – 50fi. ochre 30 10
1285 – 60fi. green 30 10
1286 – 70fi. red 30 25
1287 – 1fo. turquoise (air) . . . 45 30
1288 – 1fo.50 purple 60 45
DESIGNS: 40fi. Terrace, Mecsek; 50fi. Parad Spa; 60fi. Sports field, Kekes; 70fi. Balaton-fured Spa; 1fo. Children paddling at Balaton; 1fo.50, Lillafured Rest Home.

237 Young People and Banners **238** Karl Marx

1953. May Day.
1289 **237** 60fi. brown & red on yell 60 20

1953. 70th Death Anniv of Karl Marx.
1290 **238** 1fo. black on pink . . . 60 20
See also No. 2354.

239 Peasants and Flag

1953. 250th Anniv of Rakoczi Rebellion.
1291 **239** 20fi. orange & grn on grn 60 30
1292 – 30fi. orange and purple 75 50
1293 – 40fi. orange & blue on pk 80 70
1294 – 60fi. orange & grn on yell . . . . 90 1·10
1295 – 1fo. red & brown on yell 1·40 1·25
DESIGNS: 30fi. Drummer and insurgents; 40fi. Battle scene; 60fi. Cavalryman attacking soldier; 1fo. Ferenc Rakoczi II.

1953. Rebuilding Plan (2nd series). As T **208**.
1296 8fi. green 25 10
1297 10fi. lilac 25 10
1298 12fi. red 30 10
1299a 20fi. green . . . . 1·25 10
1300 30fi. orange 30 10
1301 40fi. brown 30 10
1302 50fi. blue 35 10
1303a 60fi. red . . . . 3·50 10
1304 70fi. brown 40 10
BUILDINGS: 8fi. Day nursery, Ozd; 10fi. Nursing school, Szombathely; 12fi. Workers houses, Komlo; 20fi. Department store, Ujpest; 30fi. Factory, Maly; 40fi. General Hospital, Fovaros; 50fi. Gymnasium, Sztalinvaros; 60fi. Post Office, Csepel; 70fi. Blast-furnace, Diosgyor.

240 Cycling

1953. Opening of People's Stadium. Budapest. Inscr "1953 NEPSTADION".
1313 **240** 20fi. brown and orange (postage) 10 10
1314 – 30fi. brown and green . . 10 10
1315 – 40fi. brown and blue . . 10 10
1316 – 50fi. brown and olive . . 10 10
1317 – 60fi. brown and yellow 10 10
1318 – 80fi. brown & turq (air) 10 10
1319 – 1fo. brown and purple 10 20
1320 – 2fo. brown and green . . 1·60 55
1321 – 3fo. brown and red . . 2·10 55
1322 – 5fo. turquoise and brown 3·00 2·00
DESIGNS: 30fi. Swimming; 40fi. Gymnastics; 50fi. Throwing the discus; 60fi. Wrestling; 80fi. Water polo; 1fo. Boxing; 2fo. Football; 3fo. Running; 5fo. Stadium.

241 Kazar **242** Postwoman Delivering Letters

1953. Provincial Costumes.
1323 **241** 20fi. green 75 20
1324 – 30fi. brown . . . . . . 1·00 40
1325 – 40fi. blue . . . . . . 1·25 15
1326 – 60fi. red . . . . 1·50 1·50
1327 – 1fo. turquoise . . . . . 2·25 90
1328 – 1fo.70 green . . . . . . 3·50 1·60
1329 – 2fo. red . . . . 5·75 2·00
1330 – 2fo.50 purple . . . . . 8·50 5·50
PROVINCES: 30fi. Ersekcsanad; 40fi. Kalocsa; 60fi. Sioagard; 1fo. Sarkoz; 1fo.70, Boldog; 2fo. Orhalom; 2fo.50, Hosszuheteny.

1953. Stamp Day.
1331 **242** 1fo.+1fo. turquoise . . . 3·00 3·00
1332 2fo.+2fo. lilac . . . . . 3·00 3·00

1953. Air. Hungarian Football Team's Victory at Wembley. No. 1320 optd **LONDON-WEMBLEY 1953. XI 25. 6:3.**
1333 2fo. brown and green . . . 17·00 18·00

244 Bihari **245** Lenin

1953. Air. Hungarian Composers.
1334 **244** 30fi. grey and brown . . 20 10
1335 – 40fi. orange and brown (Erkel) 30 10
1336 – 60fi. green & brn (Liszt) 30 10
1337 – 70fi. red and brown (Mosonyi) 35 20
1338 – 80fi. blue and brown (Goldmark) 45 25
1339 – 1fo. bistre and brown (Bartok) 60 35
1340 – 2fo. lilac and brown (Kodaly) . . . . . . 1·10 50

1954. 30th Death Anniv of Lenin.
1341 **245** 40fi. green . . . . 1·25 1·10
1342 – 60fi. brown 80 30
1343 – 1fo. lake . . . . 1·25 90
DESIGNS: 60fi. Lenin addressing meeting; 1fo. Profile portrait of Lenin.

246 Turnip Beetle **247** Mother and Baby

1954. Air. Insects.
1344 **246** 30fi. brown and orange 30 30
1345 – 40fi. brown and green . . 35 30
1346 – 50fi. black and red . . . 45 45
1347 – 60fi. brown, yell & lilac 50 45
1348 – 80fi. claret, purple & grn 65 60
1349 – 1fo. black and brown . . 85 60
1350 – 1fo.20 brown and green 90 75
1351 – 1fo.50 dp brown & brn 1·25 90
1352 – 2fo. brown and chestnut 1·75 1·25
1353 – 3fo. brown and green . . 2·25 1·50
INSECTS—HORIZ: 40fi. Crawling cockchafer; 50fi. Longhorn beetle; 60fi. Hornet; 1fo.20, European field cricket; 1fo.50, European rhinoceros beetle; 2fo. Stag beetle. VERT: 80fi. Apple beetle; 1fo. Corn beetle; 3fo. Great silver water beetle.

1954. Child Welfare.
1354 – 30fi. blue (postage) . . . 20 10
1355 **247** 40fi. bistre 30 10
1356 – 60fi. lilac 45 20
1357 – 1fo. green (air) 65 20
1358 – 1fo.50 red 95 20
1359 – 2fo. turquoise . . . . . 1·25 55
DESIGNS: 30fi. Woman having blood-test; 60fi. Doctor examining child; 1fo. Children in creche; 1fo.50, Doctor, mother and child; 2fo. Children in nursery school.

248 Worker and Flag **249** Maypole

1954. 35th Anniv of Proclamation of Hungarian Soviet Republic.
1360 – 40fi. blue and red . . . 3·50 1·40
1361 **248** 60fi. brown and red . . 6·50 1·75
1362 – 1fo. black and red . . . 9·50 2·25
DESIGNS—HORIZ: 40fi. Worker reading book; 1fo. Soldier with rifle.

1954. May Day. Inscr "1954-MAJUS I".
1363 **249** 40fi. olive 20 10
1364 – 60fi. red 30 10
DESIGN: 60fi. Worker and flag.

250 Agricultural Worker

1954. 3rd Hungarian Communist Party Congress, Budapest.
1365 **250** 60fi. red on yellow . . . 20 20

251 Boy building Model Glider

1954. Air.
1366 **251** 40fi. grey and brown . . 20 10
1367 – 50fi. brown and grey . . 30 10
1368 – 60fi. grey and brown . . 20 20
1369 – 80fi. brown and violet 30 20
1370 – 1fo. grey and brown . . 30 20
1371 – 1fo.20 brown and green 45 30
1372 – 1fo.50 grey and purple 1·25 45
1373 – 2fo. brown and blue . . 1·60 65
DESIGNS—As Type **251**: 60fi. Gliders; 1fo. Parachutists; 1fo.50, Lisunov Li-2 airplane. 43 × 43 mm; 50fi. Boy flying model airplane; 80fi. Libis KB-6T Matajur aircraft and hangar; 1fo.20, Letov C-4 biplane; 2fo. Mikoyan Gurevich MiG-15 jet fighters.

252 Hungarian National Museum **253** Paprika

1954. 5th Anniv of Constitution.
1374 **252** 40fi. blue 90 50
1375 – 60fi. brown 60 35
1376 – 1fo. brown . . . . . . 1·10 50
DESIGNS: 60fi. Hungarian Coat of Arms; 1fo. Dome of Parliament Buildings, Budapest.

1954. Fruits. Multicoloured.
1377 40fi. Type **253** 40 10
1378 50fi. Tomatoes 40 10
1379 60fi. Grapes 40 10
1380 80fi. Apricots 45 40
1381 1fo. Apples 75 55
1382 1fo.20 Plums . . . . . . 1·10 55
1383 1fo.50 Cherries . . . . . . 2·10 75
1384 2fo. Peaches . . . . 2·40 1·25

254 M. Jokai

255 C. J. Apacai

1954. 50th Death Anniv of Jokai (novelist).

1385	**254**	60fi. green	60	20
1386		1fo. purple	90	50

1954. Hungarian Scientists.

1387	**255**	8fi. black on yellow	10	10
1388	–	10fi. lake on pink	10	10
1389	–	12fi. black on blue	10	10
1390	–	20fi. brown on yellow	10	10
1391	–	30fi. blue on pink	10	10
1392	–	40fi. green on yellow	20	10
1393	–	50fi. brown on green	20	10
1394	–	60fi. blue on pink	30	10
1395	–	1fo. olive	35	10
1396	–	1fo.70 red on yellow	60	10
1397	–	2fo. turquoise	1·00	10

PORTRAITS: 10fi. S. Korosi Csoma; 12fi. A. Jedlik; 20fi. I. Semmelweis; 30fi. J. Irinyi; 40fi. F. Koranyi; 50fi. A. Vambery; 60fi. K. Than; 1fo. O. Herman; 1fo.70, T. Puskas; 2fo. E. Hogyes.

256 Speed Skaters

1955. Air. Winter Sports.

1398	–	40fi. brown, blue & black	60	20
1399	–	50fi. red, green and brown	60	20
1400	–	60fi. red, blue and brown	75	30
1401	–	80fi. green, brown & blk	90	30
1402	–	1fo. red, blue and brown	1·25	30
1403	**256**	1fo.20 red, green & blk	1·25	1·60
1404	–	1fo.50 red, green & brn	2·00	2·10
1405	–	2fo. red, green and brown	2·10	1·10

DESIGNS—VERT: 40fi. Boys on toboggan; 60fi. Ice-yacht; 1fo. Ski jumper; 1fo.50, Skier turning. HORIZ: 50fi. Cross-country skier; 80fi. Ice-hockey players; 2fo. Figure skaters.

257 Blast Furnace

1955. 10th Anniv of Liberation.

1406	–	40fi. brown and red	40	30
1407	**257**	60fi. red and green	70	50
1408	–	1fo. green and brown	70	80
1409	–	2fo. brown and green	90	1·00

DESIGNS—VERT: 40fi. Reading room; 2fo. Liberty statue. HORIZ: 1fo. Combine harvester.

258 "1st May"

1955. May Day.

1410	**258**	1fo. red	30	20

259 State Printing Works

1955. Cent of Hungarian State Printing Office.

1411	**259**	60fi. brown and green	20	20
MS1411a		97 × 77 mm. Air. T **259** 5fo. red and green	18·00	24·00

260 Young Workers and Flag

1955. 2nd Congress of Young Workers' Federation.

1412	**260**	1fo. brown	40	20

261 Postilion

262 Radio Mechanic

1955. Opening of P.O. Museum.

1413	**261**	1fo. purple	30	20

1955. Workers.

1414	–	8fi. brown	10	10
1415	–	10fi. turquoise	10	10
1416	–	12fi. orange	10	10
1417	**262**	20fi. olive	10	10
1418	–	30fi. red	10	10
1419	–	40fi. brown	70	10
1420	–	50fi. blue	15	10
1421	–	60fi. red	15	10
1422	–	70fi. olive	15	10
1423	–	80fi. purple	20	10
1424	–	1fo. blue	20	10
1425	–	1fo.20 bistre	30	10
1426	–	1fo.40 green	45	10
1427	–	1fo.70 lilac	45	10
1428	–	2fo. lake	55	10
1429	–	2fo.60 red	70	10
1430	–	3fo. green	1·00	10
1431	–	4fo. blue	2·10	10
1432	–	5fo. brown	1·50	10
1433	–	10fo. violet	3·00	40

DESIGNS: 8fi. Market gardener; 10fi. Fisherman; 12fi. Bricklayer; 30fi. Potter; 40fi. Railway guard; 50fi. Shop assistant; 60fi. Post Office worker; 70fi. Herdsman; 80fi. Mill-girl; 1fo. Boat-builder; 1fo.20, Carpenter; 1fo.40, Tram conductor; 1fo.70, Swineherd; 2fo. Welder; 2fo.60, Tractor-driver; 3fo. Horse and groom; 4fo. Bus driver; 5fo. Telegraph lineman; 10fo. Miner.

263 M. Csokonai Vitez

1955. Hungarian Poets.

1434	**263**	60fi. black	60	25
1435	–	1fo. blue	55	20
1436	–	2fo. red	60	45

PORTRAITS: 1fo. M. Vorosmarty; 2fo. A. Jozsef.

1955. Air. Light Metal Industries Int Congress, Budapest. As No. 1139.

1437		5fo. blue on silver	13·50	13·50

264 Bela Bartok

1955. 10th Death Anniv of Bartok (composer).

1438	**264**	60fi. brown (postage)	60	20
1439		1fo. green (air)	1·50	1·25
1440		1fo. brown	3·00	1·75

265 "Hargita" Diesel Multiple Unit

1955. Transport.

1441	**265**	40fi. brown and green	30	10
1442	–	60fi. bistre and green	20	10
1443	–	80fi. brown and green	30	20
1444	–	1fo. green and brown	35	20
1445	–	1fo.20 black and brown	1·25	50
1446	–	1fo.50 brown and black	60	40
1447	–	2fo. brown and green	1·50	65

DESIGNS: 60fi. Motor coach; 80fi. Motor cyclist; 1fo. Lorry; 1fo.20, Class 303 steam locomotive; 1fo.50, Tipper; 2fo. "Beke" (freighter).

266 Puli Sheepdog

1956. Hungarian Dogs.

1448	**266**	40fi. black, red and yellow	10	10
1449	–	50fi. black, buff and blue	10	10
1450	–	60fi. black, red and green	20	15
1451	–	80fi. black, orge & grey	20	30
1452	–	1fo. black, orange & turq	20	30
1453	–	1fo.20 black, brn & orge	35	35
1454	–	1fo.50 black, buff & bl	95	50
1455	–	2fo. black, brown & mve	1·50	85

DESIGNS—RECTANGULAR (36 × 26 mm): 50fi. Puli and cattle; 1fo.50, Kuvasz sheepdog and cottage. (27 × 35 mm): 80fi. Hungarian retriever. (27 × 38 mm): 1fo. Hungarian retriever carrying mallard. As Type **266**: 60fi. Pumi; 1fo.20, Kuvasz sheepdog; 2fo. Komondor sheepdog.

268 Pioneers' Badge

269 Hunyadi on Horseback

1956. 10th Anniv of Pioneers Movement.

1456	**268**	1fo. red	20	10
1457		1fo. grey	20	10

1956. 500th Death Anniv of Janos Hunyadi.

1458	**269**	1fo. brown on yellow	40	40

270 Miner

271 Horse-jumping

1956. Miners' Day.

1459	**270**	1fo. blue	40	10

1956. Olympic Games. Inscr "1956". Centres in brown.

1460	–	20fi. blue (Canoeing)	10	20
1461	**271**	30fi. olive	10	20
1462	–	40fi. brown (Fencing)	25	20
1463	–	60fi. turquoise (Hurdling)	25	20
1464	–	1fo. red (Football)	30	20
1465	–	1fo.50 violet (Weightlifting)	45	35
1466	–	2fo. green (Gymnastics)	1·00	45
1467	–	3fo. mauve (Basketball)	2·00	1·00

272 Chopin

1956. Hungarian–Polish Philatelic Exn, Budapest.

1468	–	1fo. blue (Liszt)	3·00	2·25
1469	**272**	1fo. mauve	3·00	2·25

1957. Hungarian Red Cross Fund. Nos. 1417 etc., surch with shield, cross and premium.

1470	**262**	20fi.+20fi. olive	20	20
1471	–	30fi.+30fi. red	30	30
1472	–	40fi.+40fi. brown	45	30
1473	–	60fi.+60fi. red	30	40
1474	–	1fo.+1fo. blue	50	60
1475	–	2fo.+2fo. lake	1·10	1·00

274 Dr. L. Zamenhof

1957. Air. 70th Anniv of Esperanto.

1476	–	60fi. brown	45	20
1477	**274**	1fo. green	50	25

DESIGN—HORIZ: 60fi. Esperanto Star.

275 Letters, Letter-box and Globe

276 Janos Arany

1957. Air. Hungarian Red Cross Fund. Cross in red.

1478	**275**	60fi.+30fi. brown	45	25
1479	–	1fo.+50fi. lilac	60	25
1480	–	2fo.+1fo. red	1·25	30
1481	–	3fo.+1fo.50 blue	1·60	65
1482	–	5fo.+2fo.50 grey	2·75	1·50
1483	–	10fo.+5fo. green	4·50	2·25

DESIGNS: 1fo. Postal coach; 2fo. Top of telegraph pole; 3fo. Radio aerial mast; 5fo. Desk telephone; 10fo. (46 × 31 mm) Posthorn.

1957. 75th Death Anniv of Janos Arany (poet).

1484	**276**	2fo. blue	35	20

277 Arms

1957. Inauguration of National Emblem.

1485	**277**	60fi. red	35	15
1486		1fo. green	35	20

278 Congress Emblem

1957. 4th W.F.T.U. Congress, Leipzig.

1487	**278**	1fo. red	30	20

279 Courier

1957. Air. Stamp Day.

1488	**279**	1fo.(+4fo.) brown and bistre on cream	75	75
1489	–	1fo.(+4fo.) brown and bistre on cream	75	75

DESIGN: No. 1489, Tupolev Tu-104A airplane over Budapest.

280 Dove of Peace and Flags

1957. 40th Anniv of Russian Revolution. Flags multicoloured.

1490	**280**	60fi. black and grey	30	10
1491	–	1fo. black and drab	35	10

DESIGN: 1fo. Lenin.

281 Komarom Tumbler Pigeons

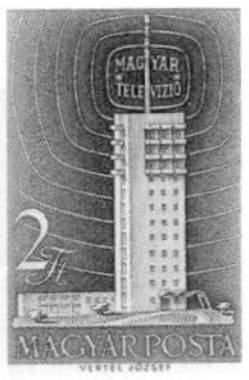
282 Television Building

1957. Int Pigeon-fanciers' Exn, Budapest.

1492	**281**	30fi. brown, yellow and green (postage)	10	10
1493	–	40fi. black and brown	10	10
1494	–	60fi. grey and blue	20	10
1495	–	1fo. brown and grey	45	10
1496	–	2fo. grey and mauve	75	35
1497	–	3fo. grn, grey & red (air)	90	35

DESIGNS: 40fi. Two short-beaked Budapest pigeons; 60fi. Giant domestic pigeon; 1fo. Three Szeged pigeons; 2fo. Two Hungarian fantail pigeons; 3fo. Two carrier pigeons.

IMPERFORATE STAMPS. Most modern Hungarian stamps issued up to the end of 1991 also exist imperforate.

1958. Inaug of Hungarian Television Service.
1498 **282** 2fo. purple 75 35
MS1498a 49 × 70 mm. **282** 2fo. (+23fo.) green . . . . 22·00 27·00

283 Mother and Child

1958. Savings Campaign.
1499 **283** 20fi. deep green and green 20 10
1500 – 30fi. purple and green . . 20 10
1501 – 40fi. brown and bistre 30 10
1502 – 60fi. myrtle and red . . 45 10
1503 – 1fo. brown and green . . 45 10
1504 – 2fo. green and orange . . 1·10 70
DESIGNS: 30fi. Old man feeding pigeons; 40fi. Schoolboys with savings stamps; 60fi. "The Cricket and the Ant."; 1fo. Bees on honeycomb; 2fo. Hands holding banknotes.

284 Hungarian Pavilion

1958. Air. Brussels International Exhibition. Inscr "BRUXELLES 1958".
1505 **284** 20fi. brown and red . . 30 15
1506 – 40fi. sepia and blue . . . 35 15
1507 – 60fi. sepia and red . . . 35 15
1508 – 1fo. brown and ochre . . 35 15
1509 – 1fo.40 multicoloured . . 65 15
1510 – 2fo. sepia and brown . . 65 15
1511 – 3fo. sepia and green . . 1·00 25
1512 – 5fo. multicoloured . . . 1·40 75
MS1512a 72 × 98 mm. 10fo. mauve 22·00 22·00
DESIGNS—HORIZ: 40fi. Map of Hungary and exhibits; 60fi. Parliament Buildings, Budapest; 1fo. Chain Bridge, Budapest; 1fo.40, Arms of Belgium and Hungary and Exhibition emblem; 5fo. Exhibition emblem. VERT: 2fo. "Mannekin Pis" statue, Brussels; 3fo. Town Hall, Brussels; 10fo. Girl in national costume as T **241**.

285 Arms of Hungary

286 Youth with Book

1958. 1st Anniv of Amended Constitution. Arms multicoloured.
1513 **285** 60fi. red 10 10
1514 1fo. green 20 10
1515 2fo. drab 35 20

1958. 5th Youth Festival, Keszthely.
1516 **286** 1fo. brown 45 45

287 Town Hall, Prague and Posthorn

1958. Organization of Socialist Countries' Postal Administrations Conference, Prague.
1517 **287** 60fi. green (postage) . . 30 25
1518 – 1fo. lake (air) 30 25
DESIGN: 1fo. Prague Castle, telegraph pole and wires.

288 "Linum dolomiticum"

1958. Flowers.
1519 **288** 20fi. yellow and purple 30 10
1520 – 30fi. brown and blue . . 20 10
1521 – 40fi. brown, buff & sepia 35 10
1522 – 60fi. mauve and green 50 10
1523 – 1fo. green and red . . . 75 10
1524 – 2fo. yellow and green . . 1·40 10
1525 – 2fo.50 pink and blue . . 1·60 45
1526 – 3fo. pink, lt green & grn 2·10 75
FLOWERS—TRIANGULAR: 30fi. "Kitaibelia vitifolia"; 2fo.50, "Dianthus collinus"; 3fo. "Rosa sancti andreae". VERT: (20½ × 31 mm): 40fi. "Doronicum hungaricum"; 60fi. "Colchicum arenarium"; 1fo. "Helleborus purpuracens"; 2fo. "Hemerocallis lilio-asphodelus".
For miniature sheet containing stamps as T **288**, see No. **MS**1533a.

289 Table-tennis Bat and Ball

1958. European Table-tennis and Swimming Championships, and World Wrestling Championships, Budapest.
1527 **289** 20fi. red on pink 10 10
1528 – 30fi. olive on green . . . 10 10
1529 – 40fi. purple on yellow . . 30 10
1530 – 60fi. brown on blue . . . 35 10
1531 – 1fo. blue on blue 60 20
1532 – 2fo.50 red on yellow . . 1·10 45
1533 – 3fo. blue on turquoise 1·60 75
DESIGNS—VERT: 30fi. Table-tennis player; 40fi. Wrestlers; 1fo. Water-polo player; 2fo.50, High-diver. HORIZ: 60fi. Wrestlers; 3fo. Swimmer.

1958. International Philatelic Federation Congress, Brussels.
MS1533a 111 × 111 mm. Nos. 1519/20 and 1525/6 in new colours . . . . 28·00 28·00

290

291 Airliner over Millennium Monument Budapest

1958. Air. (a) Int Correspondence Week.
1534 **290** 60fi. bistre and purple 20 10
1535 – 1fo. bistre and blue . . . 45 30
(b) National Stamp Exhibition, Budapest.
1536 – 1fo.(+2fo.) bistre and red 45 65
1537 **290** 1fo.(+2fo.) bistre and green 45 65
DESIGNS: No. 1535, Posthorn, envelope and transport; No. 1536, Stamp and magnifier.

1958. Air. 40th Anniv of 1st Hungarian Air Mail Stamp.
1538 **291** 3fo. purple, red and drab 90 30
1539 – 5fo. blue, red and drab 1·10 45
DESIGN: 5fo. Airliner over Sopron Tower.
For similar stamps but without commemorative inscription see Nos. 1542/51.

292 Red Flag

1958. 40th Anniv of Hungarian Communist Party and Founding of the "Red Journal".
1540 **292** 1fo. red and brown . . . 30 10
1541 – 2fo. red and blue 30 20
DESIGN: 2fo. Hand holding up the newspaper "Voros Ujsag" (Red Journal).

1958. Air. As T **291** but with "LEGIPOSTA" at top in place of commem inscription. On cream paper.
1542 – 20fi. green and red . . . 10 10
1543 – 30fi. violet and red . . 10 10
1544 – 70fi. purple and red . . 10 10
1545 – 1fo. blue and red 20 10
1546 – 1fo.60 purple and red . . 35 10
1547 – 2fo. green and red . . . 60 10
1548 – 3fo. brn & red 60 20
1549 **291** 5fo. green and red . . . 1·00 25
1550 – 10fo. blue and red . . . 60 60
1551 – 20fo. sepia and red . . . 5·50 85
DESIGNS: Airliner over: 20fi. Town Hall, Szeged; 30fi. Sarospatak Castle; 70fi. Town Hall, Gyor; 1fo. Opera House, Budapest; 1fo.60, Old City of Veszprem; 2fo. Chain Bridge, Budapest; 3fo. Sopron Tower; 10fo. Danube Embankment, Budapest; 20fo. Budapest Cathedral.

293 Rocket approaching the Moon

1959. I.G.Y. Achievements.
1552 – 10fi. brown and red . . 10 10
1553 – 20fi. black and blue . . 55 10
1554 – 30fi. buff and green . . . 60 10
1555 – 40fi. light blue and blue 1·50 25
1556 **293** 60fi. green and blue . . 75 30
1557 – 1fo. brown and red . . . 1·25 45
1558 – 5fo. brown & deep brown . . . . . . 1·90 55
DESIGNS—(31½ × 21 mm): 10fi. Eotvos torsion balance (gravimetry); 20fi. Ship using echo-sounder (oceanography); 30fi. "Northern Lights" and polar scene. (35½ × 26½ mm): 40fi. Russian polar camp and Antarctic route map; 1fo. Observatory and the sun; 5fo. Russian "Sputnik" and American "Vanguard" (artificial satellites).
See also No. 1605.

294 Revolutionary

296 Nagy Model of Locomotive "Deru", 1847

295 Rose

1959. 40th Anniv of Proclamation of Hungarian Soviet Republic.
1559 **294** 20fi. red and purple . . 10 10
1560 60fi. red and blue . . . 10 10
1561 1fo. red and brown . . . 20 20

1959. May Day.
1562 **295** 60fi. red, green and lilac 75 10
1563 1fo. red, green and brown . . . . 1·00 20

1959. Transport Museum issue.
1564 **296** 20fi. mult (postage) . . . 35 10
1565 – 30fi. green, black and buff 35 10
1566 – 40fi. multicoloured . . . 45 10
1567 – 60fi. multicoloured . . . 40 10
1568 – 1fo. multicoloured . . . 45 25
1569 – 2fo. multicoloured . . . 75 25
1570 – 2fo.50 multicoloured (blue background) . . 90 35
1571 – 3fo. multicoloured (air) 1·90 1·40
DESIGNS—HORIZ: 30fi. Ganz diesel railcar; 60fi. Csonka motor car; 1fo. Ikarusz rear-engine motor coach; 2fo. First Lake Balaton steamer "Kisfaludy"; 2fo.50, Stagecoach; 3fo. Aladar Zselyi's monoplane. VERT: 40fi. Early railway semaphore signal.
See also No. 1572.

1959. Int Philatelic Federation Congress, Hamburg. As No. 1570 but colours changed.
1572 2fo.50 multicoloured (yellow background) . . . . . . 1·25 1·40

297 Posthorn

1959. Organization of Socialist Countries' Postal Administration Conference, Berlin.
1573 **297** 1fo. red 50 55

298 Great Cormorant

1959. Water Birds. Inscr "1959".
1574 **298** 10fi. black and green . . 20 10
1575 – 20fi. green and blue . . 30 10
1576 – 30fi. violet, myrtle & orge 35 85
1577 – 40fi. grey and green . . 50 25
1578 – 60fi. brown and purple 60 25
1579 – 1fo. black and turquoise 60 50
1580 – 2fo. black and red . . . 1·10 50
1581 – 3fo. brown and bistre . . 1·90 1·00
DESIGNS: 20fi. Little egret; 30fi. Purple heron; 40fi. Great egret; 60fi. White spoonbill; 1fo. Grey heron; 2fo. Squacco heron; 3fo. Glossy ibis.

299 10th-century Man-at-Arms

300 Bathers at Lake Balaton

1959. 24th World Fencing Championships, Budapest. Inscr as in T **299**.
1582 **299** 10fi. black and blue . . 10 10
1583 – 20fi. black and lemon . . 10 10
1584 – 30fi. black and violet . . 20 10
1585 – 40fi. black and red . . . 20 10
1586 – 60fi. black and purple . . 20 10
1587 – 1fo. black and turquoise 45 10
1588 – 1fo.40 black and orange 75 10
1589 – 3fo. black and green . . 1·90 30
DESIGNS (Evolution of Hungarian swordsmanship): 20fi. 15th-century man-at-arms; 30fi. 18th-century soldier; 40fi. 19th-century soldier; 60fi. 19th-century cavalryman. Fencer: at the assault (1fo.); on guard (1fo.40); saluting (3fo.).

1959. Lake Balaton Summer Courses.
1590 – 30fi. bl on yell (postage) 20 10
1591 – 40fi. red on green . . . 10 10
1592 **300** 60fi. brown on pink . . 20 10
1593 – 1fo.20 violet on pink . . 50 10
1594 – 2fo. red on yellow . . . 75 30
1595 – 20fi. green (air) 10 10
1596 – 70fi. blue 20 10
1597 – 1fo. red and blue 30 10
1598 – 1fo.70 brown on yellow 75 40
DESIGNS—VERT: 20fi. Tihany (view); 30fi. "Kek Madar" (yacht); 70fi. "Tihany" (waterbus); 1fo. Waterlily and view of Heviz; 1fo.20, Anglers; 1fo.70, "Saturnus" (yacht) and statue of fisherman (Balaton pier); 2fo. Holiday-makers and "Beloiannis" (lake steamer). HORIZ: 40fi. Vintner with grapes.

301

302 Shepherd with Letter

1959. 150th Death Anniv of Haydn (composer).
1599 **301** 40fi. yellow and purple 30 10
1600 – 60fi. buff and slate . . . 45 25
1601 – 1fo. orange and red . . 85 20
MS1601a 94 × 76 mm. 3fo. purple; 3fo. green (each 27 × 35 mm) 12·50 10·50
DESIGNS—HORIZ: 60fi. Fertod Chateau. VERT: 1fo. Hayden; 3fo (purple) "J h" and music score; 3fo. Green "F SCH" and prose quotation.
No. **MS**1601a also commemorates Schiller's birth bicentenary.

1959. Birth Bicentenary of Schiller (poet). As T **301** but inscr "F. SCHILLER" etc.
1602 40fi. yellow and olive . . . 35 10
1603 60fi. pink and blue 35 10
1604 1fo. yellow and purple . . 75 10
DESIGNS—VERT: 40fi. Stylized initials "F" and "Sch" and Schiller's birthplace; 1fo. Schiller. HORIZ: 60fi. Pegasus.
See also No. **MS**1601a.

1959. Landing of Russian Rocket on the Moon. As T **293** with addition of Russian Flag and "22 h 02' 34" on Moon in red.
1605 **293** 60fi. green and blue . . 35 10

1959. Stamp Day and National Stamp Exn.
1606 **302** 2fo. purple . . . . . . 1·25 1·25

303 "Taking Delivery"

1959. International Correspondence Week.
1607 **303** 60fi. multicoloured . . . 35 10

304 Lenin and Szamuely

1959. Russian Stamp Exhibition, Budapest.
1608 **304** 20fi. brown and red . . 20 10
1609 – 40fi. lake & brown on bl 20 10
1610 – 60fi. buff and blue . . . 20 10
1611 – 1fo. multicoloured . . . 35 20
DESIGNS: 40fi. Pushkin; 60fi. Mayakovsky; 1fo. Arms with hands clasping flag.

305 Swallowtail

306

1959. Butterflies and Moths. Butterflies in natural colours, background colours given.
1612 **305** 20fi. black and green (postage) 40 10
1613 – 30fi. black and blue . . 40 10
1614 – 40fi. black and brown . . 50 20
1615 – 60fi. black and bistre . . 75 20
1616 – 1fo. black and green (air) 1·10 40
1617 – 2fo. black and lilac . . . 2·25 90
1618 – 3fo. black and green . . 3·25 1·50
DESIGNS—HORIZ: 30fi. Hebe tiger moth; 40fi. Adonis blue; 2fo. Death's-head hawk moth. VERT: 60fi. Purple emperor; 1fo. Scarce copper; 3fo. Red emperor.

1959. 7th Socialist Workers' Party Congress. Flag in red and green.
1619 **306** 60fi. brown 20 10
1620 – 1fo. red 20 10
DESIGN: 1fo. Flag inscr "MSZMP VII. KONGRESSZUSA".

307 "Fairy Tales"

308 Sumeg Castle

1959. Fairy Tales (1st series). Centres and inscr in black.
1621 **307** 20fi. multicoloured . . . 20 10
1622 – 30fi. pink 20 10
1623 – 40fi. turquoise 30 10
1624 – 60fi. blue 50 10
1625 – 1fo. yellow 70 20
1626 – 2fo. green 90 30
1627 – 2fo.50 salmon . . . . . 1·25 35
1628 – 3fo. red . . . . 1·25 60
FAIRY TALE SCENES: 30fi. "The Sleeping Beauty"; 40fi. "Mat the Goose"; 60fi. "The Cricket and the Ant"; 1fo. "Mashenka and the Bears"; 2fo. "The Babes in the Wood"; 2fo.50, "The Pied Piper of Hamelin"; 3fo. "Little Red Riding Hood".
See also Nos. 1702/9 and 2133/41.

1960. Hungarian Castles. On white paper.
1629 **308** 8fi. purple 10 10
1630 – 10fi. brown 10 10
1631 – 12fi. blue 10 10
1632 – 20fi. green 10 10
1633 – 30fi. brown 10 10
1634 – 40fi. turquoise 10 10
1635 – 50fi. brown 10 10
1636 – 60fi. red 30 10
1637 – 70fi. green 30 10
1638 – 80fi. purple 10 10
1639 – 1fo. blue 30 10
1640 – 1fo.20 purple 45 10
1641 – 1fo.40 blue 45 10
1642 – 1fo.70 lilac ("SOMLO") 45 10
1642a – 1fo.70 lilac ("SOMLYO") . . . 55 10
1643 – 2fo. bistre 55 10
1644 – 2fo.60 blue 60 10
1645 – 3fo. brown 60 10
1646 – 4fo. violet 70 10
1647 – 5fo. green 90 30
1648 – 10fo. red . . . . 1·25 40
CASTLES—As Type **308**: 10fi. Kisvarda; 12fi. Szigliget; 20fi. Tata; 30fi. Diosgyor; 40fi. Simon Tornya; 50fi. Fuzer; 60fi. Sarospatak; 70fi. Nagyvazsony; 80fi. Egervar. 28½ × 21½ mm: 1fo. Vitany; 1fo.20, Sirok; 1fo.40, Siklos; 1fo.70, Somlyo; 2fo. Boldogko; 2fo.60, Holloko; 4fo. Eger. 21½ × 28½ mm: 3fo. Csesznek; 5fo. Koszeg; 10fo. Sarvar.
See also Nos. 1694/700.

309 Halas Lace

310 Cross-country Skiing

1960. Halas Lace (1st series). Designs showing lace as T **309**. Inscriptions and values in orange.
1649 **304** 20fi. sepia 20 20
1650 – 30fi. violet 20 20
1651 – 40fi. turquoise 40 20
1652 – 60fi. brown 45 25
1653 – 1fo. green 75 25
1654 – 1fo.50 green 95 35
1655 – 2fo. blue . . . . 1·50 40
1656 – 3fo. red . . . . 2·75 65
Nos. 1650/1, 1654/5 are larger 38 × 44 mm.
See also Nos. 1971/8.

1960. Winter Olympic Games.
1657 **310** 30fi. bistre and blue . . 10 20
1658 – 40fi. bistre and green . . 20 20
1659 – 60fi. bistre and red . . . 30 20
1660 – 80fi. bistre and violet . . 40 20
1661 – 1fo. bistre and turquoise 70 25
1662 – 1fo.20 bistre and lake . . 75 45
1663 – 2fo.+1fo. mult . . . . . 1·75 60
DESIGNS: 40fi. Ice hockey; 60fi. Ski jumping; 80fi. Speed skating; 1fo. Skiing; 1fo.20, Figure skating; 2fo. Games emblem.

311 Kato Haman

312 Yellow Pheasant's-eye and Quill

1960. Celebrities and Anniversaries. Portrait as T **311**.
1664 60fi. purple (T **311**) 20 10
1665 60fi. brown (Clara Zetkin) 20 10
1666 60fi. violet (Garibaldi) . . . 20 10
1667 60fi. green (I. Turr) 20 10
1668 60fi. red (I. Tukory) 20 10
1669 60fi. deep blue and blue (O. Herman) 20 10
1670 60fi. brown (Beethoven) . . 20 10
1671 60fi. red (F. Mora) 20 10
1672 60fi. black and grey (B. I. Toth) 30 10
1673 60fi. purple and mauve (D. Banki) 20 10
1674 60fi. deep green and green (A. G. Pattantyus) . . . 20 10
1675 60fi. blue and cobalt (I. P. Semmelweis) 20 10
1676 60fi. brown (Joliot-Curie) . . 20 10
1677 60fi. red (F. Erkel) 20 10
1678 60fi. blue and light blue (J. Bolyai) 20 10
1679 60fi. red (V. I. Lenin) . . . 20 10
COMMEMORATIVE EVENTS: Nos. 1664/5, Int Women's Day: 1666, Centenary of Sicilian Expedition; 1669, 125th Birth Anniv; 1670, Martonvasar Beethoven Concerts: 1671, Szeged Festival: 1672, Miners' Day: 1677, 150th Birth Anniv; 1678, Birth Centenary; 1679, 90th Birth Anniv.

1960. Stamp Exhibition Budapest.
1680 **312** 2fo.(+4fo.) yellow, green and brown . . . . . 90 1·00

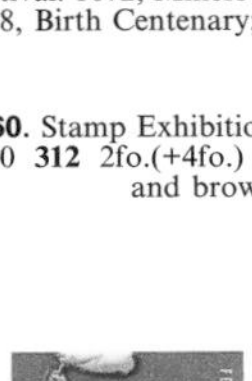
313 Soldier

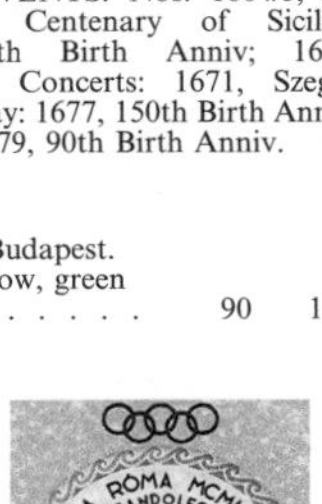
314 Rowing

1960. 15th Anniv of Liberation.
1681 **313** 40fi. brown and red . . 35 30
1682 – 60fi. red, green and brown 35 30
DESIGN—HORIZ: 60fi. Student with flag (inscr "1945 FELSZABADULASUNK... 1960").

1960. Summer Olympic Games. Centres and inscr in black (3fo. multicoloured). Circular frames in bistre. Background colours given.
1683 10fi. blue (T **314**) 10 10
1684 20fi. brown (Boxing) 10 10
1685 30fi. lilac (Archery) 10 10
1686 40fi. ochre (Discus) 10 10
1687 50fi. red (Ball game) 10 10
1688 60fi. green (Javelin) 10 10
1689 1fo. purple (Horse-riding) 35 10
1690 1fo.40 blue (Wrestling) . . . 40 10
1691 1fo.70 brown (Swordplay) 45 20
1692 2fo.+1fo. red (Romulus, Remus and Wolf) 65 40
1693 3fo. grey (Olympic Rings and Arms of Hungary) . . 1·75 70
MS1693a 67 × 95 mm. 10fo. multicoloured . . . . 15·00 17·00

1960. International Philatelic Federation Congress, Warsaw. Sheet 161 × 122 mm containing four of No. 1656, each in different colours, side by side with commemorative labels.
MS1693b 3fo. (× 4) . . . . . . 7·50 8·25

1960. Hungarian Castles. As Nos. 1629, 1632/3, 1636/7 and 1641/2 but printed on coloured paper.
1694 8fi. purple on blue 10 10
1695 20fi. bronze on green . . . 20 10
1696 30fi. brown on yellow . . . 20 10
1697 60fi. red on pink 30 10
1698 70fi. green on blue 35 10
1699 1fo.40 blue on blue 60 10
1700 1fo.70 lilac on blue ("SOMLO") . . . . . . 1·40 10

315 Girl in Mezokovesd Provincial Costume

316 "The Turnip"

1960. Stamp Day.
1701 **315** 2fo.(+4fo.) mult . . . . 1·10 1·25

1960. Fairy Tales (2nd series). Multicoloured.
1702 20fi. Type **316** 10 10
1703 30fi. "Snow White and the Seven Dwarfs" 10 10
1704 40fi. "The Miller, Son and Donkey" 10 10
1705 60fi. "Puss in Boots" . . . 20 10
1706 80fi. "The Fox and the Raven" 30 10
1707 1fo. "The Maple-wood Pipe" 60 20
1708 1fo.70 "The Stork and the Fox" 75 35
1709 2fo. "Momotaro" (Japanese tale) . . . . 1·25 1·00

317 F. Rozsa

318 Eastern Grey Kangaroo with Young

1961. Celebrities and Anniversaries. Portraits as T **317**.
1710 1fo. brown (T **317**) 10 10
1711 1fo. turquoise (G. Kilian) 10 10
1712 1fo. red (J. Rippi-Ronai) . . 10 10
1713 1fo. olive (S. Latinka) . . . 10 10
1714 1fo. green (M. Zalka) . . . 10 10
1715 1fo. lake (J. Katona) . . . 10 10
COMMEMORATIVE EVENTS: No. 1710, Press Day; No. 1711, Gyorgy Kilian Sports Movement; No. 1712, Birth Cent; No. 1713, 75th Birth Anniv; No. 1714, 65th Birth Anniv.

1961. Budapest Zoo Animals. Inscr "ZOO 1961".
1716 **318** 20fi. black and orange 20 10
1717 – 30fi. sepia and green . . 20 10
1718 – 40fi. brown and chestnut 30 10
1719 – 60fi. grey and mauve . . 50 10
1720 – 80fi. yellow and black . . 65 10
1721 – 1fo. brown and green . . 65 10
1722 – 1fo.40 sepia and turquoise . . . . . . 1·00 10
1723 – 2fo. black and red . . . 1·75 60
1724 – 2fo.60 brown and violet 1·75 80
1725 – 3fo. multicoloured . . . 1·90 1·25
DESIGNS—HORIZ: 30fi. American bison; 60fi. Indian elephant and calf; 80fi. Tiger and cubs; 1fo.40, Polar bear; 2fo. Common zebra and foal; 2fo.60, European bison cow with calf. VERT: 40fi. Brown bear; 1fo. Ibex; 3fo. Main entrance, Budapest Zoo.

319 Child chasing Butterfly

320 Launching of Rocket "Vostok"

1961. Health. Inscr "1961". Cross in red.
1726 **319** 30fi. black, purple & brn 10 10
1727 – 40fi. sepia, blue & turq 25 10
1728 – 60fi. yellow, grey & violet 30 10
1729 – 1fo. multicoloured . . . 30 10
1730 – 1fo.70 yellow, blue & grn 45 10
1731 – 4fo. green and grey . . . 1·40 10
DESIGNS—As Type **319**: 40fi. Patient on operating table. LARGER (29½ × 35 mm): 60fi. Ambulance and stretcher; 1fo. Traffic lights and scooter; 1fo.70, Syringe and jars; 4fo. Emblem of Health Department.

1961. World's First Manned Space Flight. Inscr "1961.IV.12".
1732 **320** 1fo. brown and blue . . 75 65
1733 – 2fo. brown and blue . . 3·00 2·75
DESIGN: 2fo. Gagarin and "Vostok" in flight.

321 Roses

322 "Venus" Rocket

1961. May Day.
1734 **321** 1fo. red and green . . . 30 10
1735 – 2fo. red and green . . . 35 20
DESIGN: 2fo. As Type **321** but roses and inscr reversed.

1961. Launching of Soviet "Venus" Rocket. Inscr "VENUSZ RAKETA 1961 11.12".
1736 **322** 40fi. black, bistre and blue 50 40
1737 – 60fi. black, bistre and blue . . . . 50 1·10
1738 – 80fi. black and blue . . 70 1·10
1739 – 2fo. bistre and violet-blue . . . . 1·60 1·90
DESIGNS: 60fi. Separation of rocket capsule in flight; 80fi. Capsule and orbit diagram; 2fo. Allegory of flying woman and crescent moon.

323 Conference Emblem, Letter and Transport

1961. Organization of Socialist Countries' Postal Administrations Conference.
1740 **323** 40fi. black and orange 20 10
1741 – 60fi. black and mauve 20 10
1742 – 1fo. black and blue . . . 20 25
DESIGNS: 60fi. Television aerial; 1fo. Radar receiving equipment.

324 Hungarian Flag

325 George Stephenson

1961. International Stamp Exhibition, Budapest. (a) 1st issue. Background in silver.
1743 **324** 1fo. red, green and black 20 30
1744 – 1fo.70 multicoloured . . 20 45
1745 – 2fo.60 multicoloured . . 1·10 90
1746 – 3fo. multicoloured . . . 1·90 1·40

(b) 2nd issue. Background in gold. Inscriptions at left altered on 1fo. and 3fo.
1747 **324** 1fo. red, green and black 20 35
1748 – 1fo.70 multicoloured . . 20 45
1749 – 2fo.60 multicoloured . . 90 85
1750 – 3fo. multicoloured . . . 2·00 1·10
DESIGNS: 1fo.70, Late spider orchids; 2fo.60, Small tortoiseshell; 3fo. Eurasian goldfinch.
See also Nos. 1765/8.

1961. Communications Ministers' Conference, Budapest. Inscr "KOZLEKEDESUGYI", etc.
1751 **325** 60fi. olive 20 10
1752 – 1fo. bistre, black and blue 30 10
1753 – 2fo. brown 30 20
DESIGNS: 1fo. Communications emblems; 2fo. J. Landler (Minister of Communications).

326 Football and Club Badge

1961. 50th Anniv of VASAS Sports Club. Badge in gold, red and blue.

1754	326	40fi. orange, black and gold	10	10
1755	–	60fi. green, black and gold	10	10
1756	–	1fo. bistre, black and gold	10	20
1757	–	2fo.+1fo. blue, blk & gold	75	55

DESIGNS: 60fi. Wrestling; 1fo. Vaulting; 2fo. Sailing.

327 Three Racehorses

1961. Racehorses.

1758	327	30fi. multicoloured	10	10
1759	–	40fi. multicoloured	20	10
1760	–	60fi. multicoloured	30	20
1761	–	1fo. black, green and orange	35	20
1762	–	1fo.70 sepia, black and green	75	35
1763	–	2fo. black, blue and brown	90	35
1764	–	3fo. multicoloured	1·60	45

DESIGNS: 40fi. Three hurdlers; 60fi. Trotting race (two horses); 1fo. Trotting race (three horses); 1fo.70, Two racehorses and two foals; 2fo. Hungarian trotter "Baka"; 3fo. 19th century champion mare, "Kincsem".

328 Budapest

1961. Stamp Day and International Stamp Exhibition, Budapest (3rd issue). Designs as T **328**.

1765	328	2fo.+1fo. bl, brn & ol	80	1·00
1766	–	2fo.+1fo. bl, brn & ol	80	1·00
1767	–	2fo.+1fo. bl, brn & ol	80	1·00
1768	–	2fo.+1fo. bl, brn & ol	80	1·00

Nos. 1765/8 are printed together in sheets of 40 (4 × 10) with one vertical row of each design. Horizontal strips of four form a composite panorama of Budapest.

329 Music, Keyboard and Silhouette

1961. 150th Birth and 75th Death Anniv of Liszt (composer).

1769	329	60fi. black and gold	30	10
1770	–	1fo. black	45	25
1771	–	2fo. green and blue	1·00	50
MS1771a		71 × 98 mm. 10fo. multicoloured	11·00	9·50

DESIGNS—VERT: 1fo. Statue; 10fo. Head profile over piano keys. HORIZ: 2fo. Music Academy.

330 Lenin

1961. 22nd Soviet Communist Party Congress, Moscow.

1772	330	1fo. brown	20	10

331 Monk's Hood

332 Nightingale

1961. Medicinal Plants. Multicoloured.

1773	20fi. Type **331**	10	10
1774	30fi. Centaury	10	10
1775	40fi. Blue iris	20	10
1776	60fi. Thorn-apple	20	10
1777	1fo. Purple hollyhock	45	10
1778	1fo.70 Hop	60	10
1779	2fo. Poppy	1·25	20
1780	3fo. Mullein	1·25	50

1961. Birds of Woods and Fields. Multicoloured. Inscr "1961".

1781	30fi. Type **332**	10	10
1782	40fi. Great tit	10	10
1783	60fi. Chaffinch (horiz)	20	10
1784	1fo. Jay	30	10
1785	1fo.20 Golden oriole (horiz)	45	10
1786	1fo.50 Blackbird (horiz)	70	20
1787	2fo. Yellowhammer	85	25
1788	3fo. Northern lapwing (horiz)	1·50	40

333 M. Karolyi

334 Railway Signals

333a Globe and Gagarin, Titov and Glenn (½-size illustration)

1962. Celebrities and Anniversaries. Inscr "1962".

1789	333	1fo. sepia	10	10
1790	–	1fo. brown (F. Berkes)	10	10
1791	–	1fo. blue (J. Pech)	10	10
1792	–	1fo. violet (A. Chazar)	10	10
1793	–	1fo. blue (Dr. F. Hutyra)	10	10
1794	–	1fo. red (G. Egressy)	10	10

ANNIVERSARIES: Nos. 1789/90, 5th Co-operative Movement Congress; 1791, 75th anniv of Hydrographic Institute; 1792, 50th anniv of Sports Club for the Deaf; 1793, 175th anniv of Hungarian Veterinary Service; 1794, 125th anniv of National Theatre.

1962. World Space Flights of Gagarin, Titov and Glenn. Sheet 109 × 70 mm.

MS1794a	333a	10fo. multicoloured	7·50	10·50

1962. 14th Int Railwaymen's Esperanto Congress.

1795	334	1fo. green	25	10

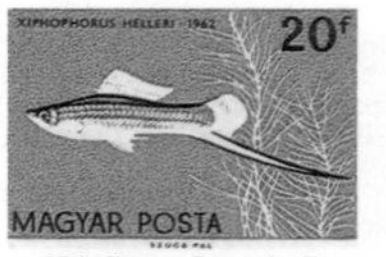

335 Green Swordtail

1962. Ornamental Fishes. Inscr "1962". Mult.

1796	20fi. Type **335**	10	10
1797	30fi. Paradise fish	10	10
1798	40fi. Fan-tailed guppy	10	10
1799	60fi. Siamese fighting fish	20	10
1800	80fi. Tiger barb	20	10
1801	1fo. Freshwater angelfish	35	10
1802	1fo.20 Sunfish	35	10
1803	1fo.50 Lyretail panchax	60	10
1804	2fo. Neon tetra	75	25
1805	3fo. Blue discus	90	55

336 Flags of Argentina and Bulgaria

1962. World Football Championships, 1962. Inscr "CHILE 1962". Flags in national colours: ball, flagpole, value, etc., in bistre.

1806	–	30fi. mauve	10	10
1807	–	40fi. green	25	10
1808	–	60fi. lilac	30	10
1809	–	1fo. blue	35	20
1810	336	1fo.70 orange	65	20
1811	–	2fo. turquoise	75	30
1812	–	3fo. red	1·10	40
1813	–	4fo.+1fo. green	1·50	80
MS1813a		72 × 92 mm. 10fo. multicoloured	6·75	6·75

FLAGS: 30fi. Colombia and Uruguay; 40fi. U.S.S.R. and Yugoslavia; 60fi. Switzerland and Chile; 1fo. German Federal Republic and Italy; 2fo. Hungary and Great Britain; 3fo. Brazil and Mexico; 4fo. Spain and Czechoslovakia. The two flags on each stamp represent the football teams playing against each other in the first round. VERT: (28½ × 39 mm)—10fo. Goal keeper and map.

337 Gutenberg

338 Campaign Emblem

1962. Centenary of Hungarian Printing Union.

1814	337	1fo. blue	20	10
1815	–	1fo. brown	20	10

PORTRAIT: No. 1815, Miklos Kis (first Hungarian printer).

1962. Malaria Eradication.

1816	338	2fo.50 bistre and black	75	45
MS1816a		111 × 76 mm. 2fo.50 (× 4) green and black	9·00	9·75

339 "Beating Swords into Ploughshares"

340 Festival Emblem

1962. World Peace Congress, Moscow.

1817	339	1fo. brown	10	10

1962. World Youth Festival, Helsinki.

1818	340	3fo. multicoloured	45	20

341 Icarus

342 Hybrid Tea

1962. Air. Development of Flight.

1819	341	30fi. bistre and blue	10	10
1820	–	40fi. blue and green	10	10
1821	–	60fi. red and blue	25	10
1822	–	80fi. silver, blue & turq	30	10
1823	–	1fo. silver, blue & purple	35	10
1824	–	1fo.40 orange and blue	35	25
1825	–	2fo. brown and turquoise	55	20
1826	–	3fo. blue, silver and violet	60	30
1827	–	4fo. silver, black & green	85	40

DESIGNS: 40fi. Modern glider and Lilienthal monoplane glider; 60fi. Zlin Trener 6 and Rakos's monoplane; 80fi. Airship "Graf Zeppelin" and Montgolfier balloon; 1fo. Ilyushin Il-18B and Wright Flyer I; 1fo.40, Nord 3202 sports airplane and Peter Nesterov's Nieuport biplane; 2fo. Mil Mi-6 helicopter and Asboth's helicopter; 3fo. Myasichev Mya-4 airliner and Zhukovsky's wind tunnel; 4fo. Space rocket and Tsiolkovsky's rocket.

1962. Rose Culture. Roses in natural colours. Background colours given.

1828	–	20fi. brown	20	10
1829	342	40fi. myrtle	30	10
1830	–	60fi. violet	35	10
1831	–	80fi. red	45	10
1832	–	1fo. myrtle	60	20
1833	–	1fo.20 orange	75	35
1834	–	2fo. turquoise	1·75	45

ROSES: 20fi. Floribunda; 60fi. to 2fo. Various hybrid teas.

343 Globe, "Vostok 3" and "Vostok 4" (⅔-size illustration)

1962. Air. 1st "Team" Manned Space Flight.

1835	343	1fo. brown and blue	50	45
1836	–	2fo. brown and blue	50	45

DESIGN: 2fo. Cosmonauts Nikolaev and Popovich.

344 Weightlifting

345 Austrian 2kr. stamp of 1850

1962. European Weightlifting Championships, Budapest.

1837	344	1fo. brown	25	20

1962. 35th Stamp Day.

1838	345	2fo.+1fo. brown & yell	50	75
1839	–	2fo.+1fo. brown & pk	50	75
1840	–	2fo.+1fo. brown & bl	50	75
1841	–	2fo.+1fo. brown & grn	80	85
MS1841a		91 × 110 mm. Nos. 1838/41 in block of four	4·50	5·25

DESIGNS: Hungarian stamps of: No. 1839, 1919 (75fi. Dozsa); No. 1840, 1955 (1fo. 50 Skiing); No. 1841, 1959 (3fo. "Vanessa atalanta").

346 Primitive and Modern Oilwells

1962. 25th Anniv of Hungarian Oil Industry.

1842	346	1fo. green	10	10

347 Gagarin

1962. Air. Astronautical Congress, Paris.

1843	347	40fi. ochre and purple	20	10
1844	–	60fi. ochre and green	20	10
1845	–	1fo. ochre and turquoise	35	10
1846	–	1fo.40 ochre and brown	60	20
1847	–	1fo.70 ochre and blue	75	20
1848	–	2fo.60 ochre and violet	1·00	35
1849	–	3fo. ochre and brown	1·40	50

ASTRONAUTS: 60fi. Titov; 1fo. Glenn; 1fo.40, Scott Carpenter; 1fo.70, Nikolaev; 2fo.60, Popovich; 3fo. Schirra.

348 Cup and Football

349 Osprey

1962. "Budapest Vasas" Football Team's Victory in Central European Cup Competition.

1850	348	2fo.+1fo. mult	45	50

1962. Air. Birds of Prey. Multicoloured.

1851	30fi. Eagle owl	30	10
1852	40fi. Type **349**	30	10
1853	60fi. Marsh harrier	35	20
1854	80fi. Booted eagle	50	30
1855	1fo. African fish eagle	60	40
1856	2fo. Lammergeier	95	55
1857	3fo. Golden eagle	1·25	65
1858	4fo. Common kestrel	1·60	80

350 Racing Motor Cyclist

1962. Motor Cycle and Car Sports. Mult.

1859	20fi. Type **350**	10	10
1860	30fi. Sidecar racing	10	10

1861 40fi. "Scrambling" (hill climb) 10 10
1862 60fi. Dirt-track racing . . . 20 10
1863 1fo. Wearing "garland" . . 35 10
1864 1fo.20 Speed trials 45 20
1865 1fo.70 Sidecar trials 65 20
1866 2fo. "Go-kart" racing . . . 85 20
1867 3fo. Car racing . . . . . . 1·10 70

351 Ice Skater

1963. European Figure Skating and Ice Dancing Championships, Budapest.
1868 **351** 20fi. green, brown & lilac 10 10
1869 – 40fi. black, brn & salmon 10 10
1870 – 60fi. multicoloured . . . 30 20
1871 – 1fo. multicoloured . . . 45 20
1872 – 1fo.40 multicoloured . . 65 20
1873 – 2fo. red, brown and green 95 30
1874 – 3fo. multicoloured . . . 1·90 50
MS1874a 66 × 94 mm. 10fo. multicoloured . . . . 6·50 5·00
DESIGNS—VERT: 40fi., 2fo. Skater leaping; 60fi., 1fo. Pairs dancing; 1fo.40, Skater turning; 10fo. (29 × 38 mm), Figure skater and flags. HORIZ: 3fo. Pair dancing.

352 J. Batsanyi

1963. Celebrities and Anniversaries.
1875 40fi. lake (Type **352**) 10 10
1876 40fi. green (F. Entz) 10 10
1877 40fi. blue (I. Markovits) . . 10 10
1878 40fi. olive (L. Weiner) . . . 45 10
1879 60fi. purple (Dr. F. Koranyi) 45 10
1880 60fi. bronze (G. Gardonyi) 10 10
1881 60fi. brown (P. de Coubertin) 20 10
1882 60fi. violet (J. Eotvos) . . . 10 10
ANNIVERSARIES: No. 1875, Revolutionary, birth bicent; No. 1876. Horticulture College founder, Horticulture cent; No. 1877, Inventor, Hungarian Shorthand, cent; No. 1878, Composer, Budapest Music Competitions; No. 1879, Tuberculosis researcher, 50th death anniv; No. 1880, Novelist, birth cent; No. 1881, Olympic Games reviver, birth cent; No. 1882, Author, 150th birth anniv.

353 Bulgarian 21. Rocket Stamp of 1959

1963. Organization of Socialist Countries Postal Administrations Conference, Budapest.
1883 – 20fi. red, yellow and green 10 10
1884 **353** 30fi. red, brown & purple 10 10
1885 – 40fi. purple and blue . . 10 10
1886 – 50fi. violet and blue . . 10 10
1887 – 60fi. multicoloured . . . 10 10
1888 – 80fi. turquoise, black & bl 10 10
1889 – 1fo. multicoloured . . . 20 10
1890 – 1fo.20 yellow, violet & bl 45 10
1891 – 1fo.40 blue, red & brown 30 10
1892 – 1fo.70 brn, grn & lt brn 45 10
1893 – 2fo. orange, blue & pur 45 10
1894 – 2fo.60 violet, red & grn 65 65
DESIGNS: Various "space" stamps—HORIZ: 20fi. Albania 11.50 (1962); 40fi. Czechoslovakia 80h. (1962); 50fi. China 8f. (1958); 60fi. N. Korea 10ch. (1961); 80fi. Poland 40g. (1959); 1fo. Hungary 60fi. (1961); 1fo.40, East Germany 25pf. (1961); 1fo.70, Rumania 11.20 (1957); 2fo.60, N. Vietnam 6x. (1961). VERT: 1fo.20, Mongolia 30m. (1959); 2fo. Russia 6k. (1961).

354 Fair Emblem

1963. International Fair, Budapest.
1895 **354** 1fo. violet 30 10

355 Erkel (composer)

1963. Students' Erkel Memorial Festival, Gyula.
1896 **355** 60fi. brown 45 10

356 Roses

1963. 5th National Rose Show, Budapest.
1897 **356** 2fo. red, green and brown 60 10

357 Helicon Monument

1963. 10th Youth Festival, Keszthely.
1898 **357** 40fi. blue 10 10

358 Chain Bridge and "Snow White" (Danube steamer)

1963. Transport and Communications.
1899 **358** 10fi. blue 10 10
1900 – 20fi. green 10 10
1901 – 30fi. blue 10 10
1902 – 40fi. orange 10 10
1902b – 40fi. grey 30 20
1903 – 50fi. brown 30 30
1904 – 60fi. red 30 10
1905 – 70fi. olive 30 10
1906 – 80fi. brown 20 10
1906a – 1fo. brown 10 10
1907 – 1fo. purple 20 10
1908 – 1fo.20 brown . . . . 2·40 75
1909 – 1fo.20 violet 20 10
1910 – 1fo.40 green 35 10
1911 – 1fo.70 brown 85 10
1912 – 2fo. turquoise 45 10
1913 – 2fo.50 purple 75 10
1914 – 2fo.60 olive . . . . 1·25 10
1915 – 3fo. blue 45 10
1916 – 4fo. blue 75 10
1917 – 5fo. brown . . . . . . 1·25 10
1918 – 6fo. ochre . . . . . . 1·25 10
1919 – 8fo. mauve . . . . . . 1·75 20
1920 – 10fo. green . . . . . . 1·75 1·00
DESIGNS—As Type **358**: HORIZ: 20fi. Tramcar; 30fi. Open-deck bus; 40fi. (No. 1902), Articulated bus; 40fi. (No. 1902b), Budapest 100 Post Office; 50fi. Railway truck with gas cylinders; 60fi. Trolley bus; 70fi. Railway T.P.O. coach; 80fi. Motor cyclist. VERT: 1fo. (No. 1906a), Hotel Budapest. $28\frac{1}{2} \times 21$ mm: 1fo. (No. 1907) Articulated trolley bus; 1fo.40, Postal coach; 1fo.70, Diesel-electric multiple unit train; 2fo. T.V. broadcast coach; 2fo.50, Tourist coach; 2fo.60, Signalbox and train; 3fo. Parcels conveyor; 5fo. Railway fork-lift truck; 6fo. Telex operator; 8fo. Telephonist and map; 10fo. Postwoman. $21 \times 28\frac{1}{2}$ mm: 1fo.20, (No. 1908), Mail plane and trolley on tarmac; 1fo.20, (No. 1909), Control tower, Miskole; 4fo. Pylon, Pecs.
See also Nos. 2767/70.

359 Holidaymaker and "Beloiannis" (lake steamer)

1963. Cent of Siofok Resort, Lake Balaton.
1921 – 20fi. black, green and red 55 10
1922 **359** 40fi. multicoloured . . . 55 20
1923 – 60fi. orange, brown & bl 90 25
DESIGNS—TRIANGULAR: 20fi. "Tihany" (water bus); 60fi. Yacht.

359a Spaceship over Globe

1963. Air. Space Flights of "Vostok 5" and "Vostok 6". Sheet 64 × 94 mm.
MS1923a **359a** 10fo. light blue, blue and gold . . . . 6·50 8·50

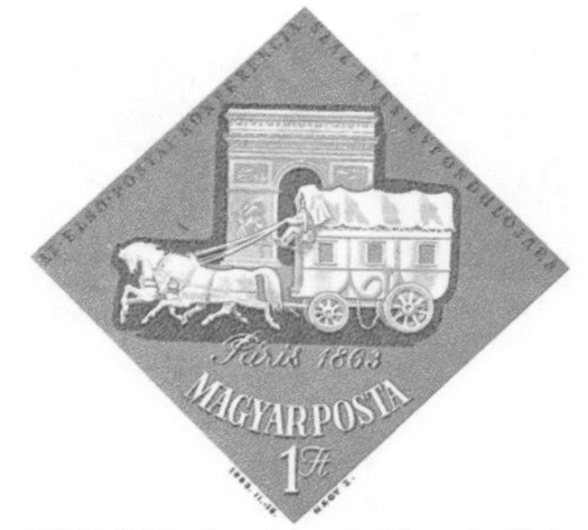

360 Mail Coach and Arc de Triomphe, Paris

1963. Centenary of Paris Postal Conference.
1924 **360** 1fo. red 30 10

361 Performance in front of Szeged Cathedral

1963. Summer Drama Festival, Szeged.
1925 **361** 40fi. blue 10 10

362 Child with towel

364 Karancssag

363 Pylon and Map

1963. Red Cross Cent. Inscr "1863–1963". Mult.
1926 30fi. Type **362** 10 10
1927 40fi. Girl with medicine bottle and tablets 10 10
1928 60fi. Girls of three races . . 20 10
1929 1fo. Girl and "heart" . . . 20 10
1930 1fo.40 Boys of three races 30 10
1931 2fo. Child being medically examined 35 20
1932 3fo. Hands tending plants 95 30

1963. Village Electrification.
1933 **363** 1fo. black and grey . . . 30 10

1963. Provincial Costumes.
1934 **364** 20fi. lake 20 10
1935 – 30fi. green (Kapuvar) . . 20 10
1936 – 40fi. brown (Debrecen) 20 10
1937 – 60fi. blue (Hortobagy) 30 20
1938 – 1fo. red (Csokoly) . . . 45 20
1939 – 1fo.70 violet (Dunantul) 50 20
1940 – 2fo. turquoise (Bujak) . . 60 30
1941 – 2fo.50 red (Alfold) . . . 75 35
1942 – 3fo. blue (Mezokovesd) 1·90 70

365 Hyacinth

367 Calendar

366 Skiing (slalom)

1963. Stamp Day. Flowers. Multicoloured.
1943 2fo.+1fo. Type **365** 60 65
1944 2fo.+1fo. Narcissus 60 65
1945 2fo.+1fo. Chrysanthemum 60 65
1946 2fo.+1fo. Tiger lily 60 65
MS1946a 76 × 91 mm. Nos. 1943/6 but smaller (20 × 27 mm) in block of four . . . . 3·75 4·00

1963. Winter Olympic Games, Innsbruck, 1964. "MAGYAR" and emblems red and black; centres brown: background colours given.
1947 **366** 40fi. green 10 10
1948 – 60fi. violet 10 10
1949 – 70fi. blue 10 10
1950 – 80fi. green 10 10
1951 – 1fo. orange 20 10
1952 – 2fo. blue 35 10
1953 – 2fo.60 purple 90 50
1954 – 4fo.+1fo. blue . . . . 1·00 55
DESIGNS: 60fi. Skiing (biathlon); 70fi. Ski jumping; 80fi. Rifle-shooting on skis; 1fo. Figure skating (pairs); 2fo. Ice hockey; 2fo.60, Speed skating; 4fo. Bobsleighing.

1963. New Year Issue. Hungarian Postal and Philatelic Museum Fund. Multicoloured.
1955 20fi. Type **367** 10 10
1956 30fi. Young chimney-sweep with glass of wine 10 10
1957 40fi. Four-leafed clover . . 10 10

1958	60fi. Piglet in top-hat	10	10
1959	1fo. Young pierrot	20	10
1960	2fo. Chinese lanterns and mask	30	10
1961	2fo.50+1fo.20 Holly, mistletoe, clover and horseshoe	45	20
1962	3fo.+1fo.50 Piglets with balloon	90	30

SIZES: As Type **367**—HORIZ: 20fi., 1fo., 3fo. VERT: 40fi. LARGER (28 × 38 mm.): 30fi., 60fi., 2fo., 2fo.50.

368 Moon Rocket

1964. Space Research. Multicoloured.

1963	30fi. Type **368**	10	10
1964	40fi. Venus rocket	20	10
1965	60fi. "Vostok 1" (horiz)	20	10
1966	1fo. U.S. spaceship	30	10
1967	1fo.70 Soviet team space flights	45	10
1968	2fo. "Telstar" (horiz)	50	20
1969	2fo.60 Mars rocket	75	30
1970	3fo. "Space Research" (rockets and tracking equipment) (horiz)	85	1·00

368a Skier racing

1964. Winter Olympic Games, Innsbruck, 1964. Sheet 65 × 60 mm.

MS1970a	**368a** 10fo. multicoloured	4·50	6·00

369 Swans

1964. Halas Lace (2nd series). Lace patterns die-stamped in white on black; inscriptions black.

1971	**369** 20fi. green	30	10
1972	– 30fi. yellow	45	10
1973	– 40fi. red	60	10
1974	– 60fi. olive	75	10
1975	– 1fo. orange	90	10
1976	– 1fo.40 blue	1·10	20
1977	– 2fo. turquoise	1·25	25
1978	– 2fo.60 violet	1·60	45

LACE PATTERNS—VERT: (38½ × 45 mm.): 30fi. Peacocks; 40fi. Pigeons; 60fi. Peacock; 1fo. Deer; 1fo.40, Fisherman; 2fo. Pigeons. As Type **369**: 2fo.60, Butterfly.

370 Armour and Swords

371 Basketball

372 Dozsa and Kossuth

373 Fair and Emblem

374 "Breasting the Tape"

1964. Anniversaries and Events of 1964. Designs as T **370/4**, some showing portraits. (a) As T **370**.

1979	60fi. purple (I. Madach)	10	10
1980	60fi. olive (E. Szabo)	10	10
1981	60fi. olive (A. Fay)	10	10
1982	1fo. red (Skittles)	1·00	60
1983	2fo. brown (T **370**)	35	10

ANNIV OR EVENT: No. 1979, (author, death cent.); No. 1980, (founder of Municipal Libraries, 60th anniv); No. 1981, (death cent.); No. 1982, (1st European Skittles Championships, Budapest); No. 1983, (50th anniv of Hungarian Fencing Assn.).

(b) As T **371**.

1984	60fi. turquoise (Stalactites and stalagmites)	20	10
1985	60fi. blue (Bauxite excavator)	10	10
1990	60fi. red (K. Marx)	10	10
1986	1fo. green (Forest and waterfall)	30	10
1987	2fo. brown (Galileo)	50	10
1988	2fo. lake (Shakespeare)	45	10
1989	2fo. blue (T **371**)	1·10	30

ANNIV OR EVENT—VERT: No. 1984, (Aggteleki Cave); No. 1985, (30th anniv or Hungarian Aluminium Production); No. 1986, (National Forestry Federation Congress); No. 1987, (400th birth anniv); No. 1988 (400th birth anniv); No. 1989, (European Women's Basketball Championships). HORIZ: No. 1990, (cent of "First International").

(c) As T **372**.

1991	1fo. blue (T **372**)	30	10
1992	3fo.+1fo.50, black, grey and orange (Sports Museum, Budapest)	75	25

ANNIV OR EVENT: No. 1991, (60th Anniv of City of Cegled); No. 1992, (Lawn Tennis Historical Exn, Budapest).

(d) T **373**.

1993	1fo. green (Budapest Int Fair)	30	10

(e) As T **374**.

1994	60fi. slate ("Alba Regia" statue)	10	10
1995	1fo. brown (M. Ybl)	30	10
1996	2fo. brown (T **374**)	35	10
1997	2fo. dull pur (Michelangelo)	45	10

ANNIV OR EVENT: No. 1994, (Szekesfehervar Days); No. 1995, (architect, 150th birth anniv); No. 1996, (50th anniv of Hungarian–Swedish Athletic Meeting); No. 1997, (400th death anniv).

375 Eleanor Roosevelt

377 Peaches ("Magyar Kajszi")

376 Fencing

1964. Eleanor Roosevelt Commemoration.

1998	**375** 2fo. ochre, deep brown and brown	30	20
MS1998a	112 × 76 mm. 4 × 2 fo. (each 39 × 20 mm) in different colours, showing portrait	2·25	2·50

1964. Olympic Games, Tokyo. Multicoloured.

1999	30fi. Type **376**	10	10
2000	40fi. Gymnastics	10	10
2001	60fi. Football	10	10
2002	80fi. Horse-jumping	10	10
2003	1fo. Running	20	10
2004	1fo.40 Weightlifting	30	10
2005	1fo.70 Gymnastics (trapeze)	30	10
2006	2fo. Throwing the hammer, and javelin	35	10
2007	2fo. 50 Boxing	75	10
2008	3fo.+1fo. Water-polo	75	45

1964. National Peaches and Apricots Exn, Budapest. Designs of peaches or apricots. Multicoloured.

2009	40fi. "J.H. Hale"	10	10
2010	60fi. Type **377**	10	10
2011	1fo. "Mandula Kajszi"	30	10
2012	1fo.50 "Borsi Rozsa"	35	10
2013	1fo.70 "Alexander"	60	10
2014	2fo. "Champion"	75	20
2015	2fo.60 "Elberta"	95	30
2016	3fo. "Mayflower"	1·40	50

378 Lilac

1964. Stamp Day. Multicoloured.

2017	2fo.+1fo. Type **378**	50	60
2018	2fo.+1fo. Mallard	1·60	1·40
2019	2fo.+1fo. Gymnast	50	60
2020	2fo.+1fo. Rocket and globe	50	60
MS2020a	85 × 100 mm. Nos. 2017/20 but smaller (20 × 27½ mm) in block of four	3·25	2·75

378a Mt. Fuji and Stadium

1964. Air. Summer Olympic Games, Tokyo. Sheet 56 × 83 mm.

MS2020b	**378a** 10fo. multicoloured	4·50	6·00

379 Pedestrian Road Crossing

1964. Road Safety. Multicoloured.

2021	20fi. Type **379**	20	10
2022	60fi. Child with ball running into road	35	10
2023	1fo. Woman and child waiting to cross road	60	25

379a Venus, Rocket and Globe

1964. Three-manned Space Flight. Sheet 87 × 74 mm.

MS2023a	**379a** 10fo. multicoloured	4·50	6·00

380 Arpad Bridge, Budapest

1964. Opening of Reconstructed Elizabeth Bridge, Budapest.

2024	**380** 20fi. grey, green and blue (postage)	10	10
2025	– 30fi. green, blue & brown	10	10
2026	– 60fi. brown, grn & dp brn	30	10
2027	– 1fo. brown, bl & dp brn	45	10
2028	– 1fo.50 grey, blue & brn	65	10
2029	– 2fo. grey, green & brown	85	25
2030	– 2fo.50 grey, blue & brn	1·75	85

(b) Air.

MS2030a	95 × 49 mm. 10fo. green	5·00	5·25

BUDAPEST BRIDGES: 30fi. Margaret; 60fi. Chain; 1fo. Elizabeth; 1fo.50, Liberty; 2fo. Petofi; 2fo.50, South; 10fo. Elizabeth (different).

381 Common Pheasant

1964. "Hunting". Multicoloured.

2034	20fi. Type **381**	30	10
2035	30fi. Wild boar	10	10
2036	40fi. Grey partridges	45	10
2037	60fi. Brown hare	20	10
2038	80fi. Fallow deer	30	10
2039	1fo. Mouflon	45	10
2040	1fo.70 Red deer	75	10
2041	2fo. Great bustard	1·90	30
2042	2fo.50 Roe deer	90	40
2043	3fo. Emblem of Hunters' Federation	75	60

382 Horse-riding and Medals

1965. Olympic Games, Tokyo—Hungarian Winners' Medals. Medals: Gold and brown (G); Silver and black (S); Bronze and brown (B).

2044	20fi. brown and olive (G)	10	10
2045	30fi. brown and violet (S)	10	10
2046	50fi. brown and olive (G)	10	10
2047	60fi. brown and light blue (G)	10	10
2048	70fi. brown, slate & stone (B)	20	10
2049	80fi. brown and green (G)	35	10
2050	1fo. brown, violet & mauve (S)	30	10
2051	1fo.20 brown and blue (S)	35	20
2052	1fo.40 brown and grey (S)	60	20
2053	1fo.50 brown and bistre (G)	65	20
2054	1fo.70 brown and red (S)	90	30
2055	3fo. brown and turquoise (G)	1·25	80

DESIGNS: 20fi. Type **382**; 30fi. Gymnastics; 50fi. Rifle-shooting; 60fi. Water-polo; 70fi. Putting the shot; 80fi. Football; 1fo. Weightlifting; 1fo.20, Canoeing; 1fo.40, Throwing the hammer; 1fo.50, Wrestling; 1fo.70, Throwing the javelin; 3fo. Fencing.

383 Mil Mi-4 Helicopter and Polar Station

384 Asters

1965. International Quiet Sun Year.

2056	**383** 20fi. orange, black & blue	10	10
2057	– 30fi. green, black & grey	10	10
2058	– 60fi. yellow, black & mve	10	10
2059	– 80fi. yellow, black & grn	20	10
2060	– 1fo.50 multicoloured	20	10
2061	– 1fo.70 black, mauve & bl	30	10
2062	– 2fo. red, black and blue	95	20
2063	– 2fo.50 yellow, blk & brn	50	20
2064	– 3fo. black, blue & yellow	95	50
MS2065	62 × 85 mm. 10fo. black, orange and blue	4·50	5·00

DESIGNS: 30fi. Rocket and radar aerials; 60fi. Rocket and diagram; 80fi. Radio telescope; 1fo.50, Compass needle on Globe; 1fo.70, Weather balloon; 2fo. Northern Lights and Adelie Penguins; 2fo.50, Space satellite; 3fo. I.Q.S.Y. emblem and world map; 10fo. Sun flares, snow crystals and rain.

1965. 20th Anniv of Liberation. Multicoloured.

2066	20fi. Type **384**	10	10
2067	30fi. Peonies	10	10
2068	50fi. Carnations	10	10
2069	60fi. Roses	10	10
2070	1fo.40 Lilies	30	10
2071	1fo.70 Godetia	35	10
2072	2fo. Gladiolus	45	10
2073	2fo.50 Parrot tulips	50	20
2074	3fo. Mixed bouquet	1·10	50

385 Leonov in Space

386 "Red Head" (after Leonardo da Vinci)

1965. Air. "Voskhod 2" Space Flight.
2075 **385** 1fo. grey and violet . . . 30 10
2076 – 2fo. brown and purple 90 50
DESIGN: 2fo. Belyaev and Leonov.

1965. Int Renaissance Conference, Budapest.
2077 **386** 60fi. brown and ochre 20 10

387 Nikolaev, Tereshkova and View of Budapest

1965. Visit of Astronauts Nikolaev and Tereshkova.
2078 **387** 1fo. brown and blue . . 30 10

388 I.T.U. Emblem and Symbols

1965. Centenary of I.T.U.
2079 **388** 60fi. blue 10 10

389 Reproduction of Austria Type 109

1965. International Philatelic Exhibition, Vienna ("WIPA 1965"). Sheet 102 × 75 mm containing two of T **389** and two labels showing commemorative covers.
MS2080 **389** 2fo. (× 2) blue and grey 3·75 4·75

390 French 13th-cent Tennis **391** Marx and Lenin

1965. "History of Tennis".
2081 **390** 30fi.+10fi. lake on buff 10 10
2082 – 40fi.+10fi. blk on lilac 10 10
2083 – 60fi.+10fi. green on bis 20 10
2084 – 70fi.+30fi. pur on turq 30 10
2085 – 80fi.+40fi. blue on lav . . 35 10
2086 – 1fo.+50fi. green on yell 60 10
2087 – 1fo.50+50fi. brown on green 60 30
2088 – 1fo.70+50fi. blk on bl . . 65 45
2089 – 2fo.+1fo. red on green 75 60
DESIGNS: 40fi. Hungarian 16th-cent game; 60fi. French 18th-cent "long court"; 70fi. 16th-cent "tennys courte"; 80fi. 16th-cent court at Fontainebleau; 1fo. 17th-cent game; 1fo.50, W. C. Wingfield and Wimbledon Cup, 1877; 1fo.70, Davis Cup, 1900. 2fo. Bela Kehrling in play.

1965. Organization of Socialist Countries' Postal Administrations Congress, Peking.
2090 **391** 60fi. multicoloured . . . 10 10

392 I.C.Y. Emblem and Pulleys **393** Equestrian Act

1965. International Co-operation Year.
2091 **392** 2fo. red 30 10
MS2092 75 × 98 mm T **392** but smaller (21 × 29 mm) in blokc of four, each in a different colour 3·00 3·00

1965. "Circus 1965". Multicoloured.
2093 20fi. Type **393** 10 10
2094 30fi. Musical clown 10 10
2095 40fi. Performing elephant . . 20 10
2096 50fi. Performing seal 20 10
2097 60fi. Lions 40 10
2098 1fo. Wild cat leaping through burning hoops 35 25
2099 1fo.50 Black panthers . . . 60 25
2100 2fo.50 Acrobat with hoops 75 25
2101 3fo. Performing panther and dogs . . . . 1·00 35
2102 4fo. Bear on bicycle . . . . 1·60 90

394 Rescue Boat

1965. Danube Flood Relief.
2103 **394** 1fo.+50fi. brown & bl . . 1·00 1·00
MS2104 113 × 79 mm. 10fo.+5 fo. brown (Another rescue boat as T **394**) . . . . 3·00 3·50

395 Dr. I. Semmelweis

1965. Death Cent of Ignac Semmelweis (physician).
2105 **395** 60fi. brown 10 10

396 Running

1965. University Games, Budapest. Multicoloured (except **MS**2115).
2106 20fi. Type **396** 10 10
2107 30fi. Start of swimming race 10 10
2108 50fi. Diving 10 10
2109 60fi. Gymnastics 20 10
2110 80fi. Tennis 20 10
2111 1fo.70 Fencing 30 10
2112 2fo. Volleyball 40 10
2113 2fo.50 Basketball 60 10
2114 4fo. Water-polo 80 45
MS2115 195 × 75 mm. Horiz design (38 × 28 mm) showing stadium. 10fo. chestnut, ochre and grey 4·25 4·50

397 Congress Emblem

1965. 6th W.F.T.U. Congress, Warsaw.
2116 **397** 60fi. blue 10 10

398 "Phyllocactus hybridum"

1965. Succulents and Orchids. Multicoloured.
2117 20fi. Type **398** 10 10
2118 30fi. "Cattleya warszewiczii" 10 10
2119 60fi. "Rebutia calliantha" 20 10
2120 70fi. "Paphiopedilum hybridum" 30 10
2121 80fi. "Opuntia rhodantha" 30 10
2122 1fo. "Laelia elegans" . . . 50 10
2123 1fo.50 "Zygocactus truncatus" 45 10
2124 2fo. "Strelitzia reginae" . . 60 10
2125 2fo.50 "Lithops weberi" . . 65 30
2126 3fo. "Victoria amazonica" 1·40 45

399 Reproduction of No. 1127

1965. Stamp Day. Designs show reproductions of Hungarian stamps. Multicoloured.
2127 2fo.+1fo. Type **399** . . . . 50 1·10
2128 2fo.+1fo. No. 1280 . . . . 1·60 1·10
2129 2fo.+1fo. No. 1873 . . . . 50 1·10
2130 2fo.+1fo. No. 1733 . . . . 50 1·10
MS2131 100 × 85 mm. Nos. 2127/30 but smaller . . . . 3·00 4·00

400 F.I.R. Emblem

1965. 5th International Federation of Resistance Fighters Congress, Budapest.
2132 **400** 2fo. blue 10 10

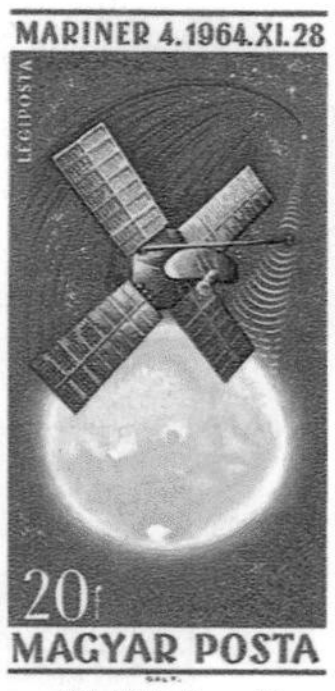

401 The Magic Horse **402** "Mariner 4"

1965. Fairy Tales (3rd series). Scenes from "The Arabian Nights Entertainments". Multicoloured.
2133 20fi. Type **401** 10 10
2134 30fi. Sultan Schahriah and Scheherazade 10 10
2135 50fi. Sinbad's 5th Voyage (ship) 10 10
2136 60fi. Aladdin and Genie of the Lamp 20 10
2137 80fi. Haroun al Rashid . . . 40 10
2138 1fo. The Magic Carpet . . . 45 10
2139 1fo.70 The Fisherman and the Genie 60 10
2140 2fo. Ali Baba 75 10
2141 3fo. Sinbad's 2nd Voyage (roc—legendary bird) . . 1·40 45

1965. Air. Space Research.
2142 **402** 20fi. black, yellow & blue 20 10
2143 – 30fi. violet, yellow & brn 20 10
2144 – 40fi. brown, mauve & bl 30 10
2145 – 60fi. multicoloured . . 45 10
2146 – 1fo. multicoloured . . . 70 20
2147 – 2fo.50 black, grey & pur 95 30
2148 – 3fo. black, green & brn 1·10 50
MS2149 105 × 85 mm. 10fo. multicoloured . . . . 4·00 4·00
DESIGNS—VERT: 30fi. "San Marco" (Italian satellite); 40fi. "Molnyija 1" (Polish satellite); 60fi. Moon rocket; 1fo. "Shapir" rocket; 2fo.50, "Szonda 3" satellite; 3fo. "Syncom 3" satellite. HORIZ: 10fo. Satellites orbiting Globe.

403 Scarlet Tiger Moth

1966. Butterflies and Moths. Multicoloured.
2150 20fi. Type **403** 10 10
2151 60fi. Orange tip 20 10
2152 70fi. Meleager's blue 35 10
2153 80fi. Scarce swallowtail . . . 45 10
2154 1fo. Common burnet . . . 45 10
2155 1fo.50 Southern festoon . . 60 25
2156 2fo. Camberwell beauty . . 60 25
2157 2fo.50 Nettle-tree butterfly 75 25
2158 3fo. Clouded yellow 95 55

404 Bela Kun

1966. Anniversaries of 1966.
2159 60fi. black and red (T **404**) 10 10
2160 60fi. black and blue (T. Esze) 35 10
2161 1fo. violet (Shastri) 15 10
2162 2fo. brown and ochre (I. Szechenyi) 35 10
2163 2fo. sepia and bistre (M. Zrinyi) 30 10
2164 2fo. sepia and green (S. Koranyi) 35 10
EVENTS: No. 2159, 80th Birth anniv (workers' leader); 2160, (after statue by M. Nemeth) 300th Birth anniv (war hero); 2161, Death commem (Indian Prime Minister); 2162, 175th Birth anniv (statesman); 2163, 400th Death anniv (military commander); 2164, Birth cent (scientist).

405 "Luna 9" in Space **406** Crocus

1966. Moon Landing of "Luna 9".
2165 **405** 2fo. black, yellow & violet 45 10
2166 – 3fo. black, yellow & blue 70 45
DESIGN—HORIZ: 3fo. "Luna 9" on Moon.

1966. Flower Protection. Multicoloured.
2167 20fi. Type **406** 40 10
2168 30fi. European cyclamen . . 50 10
2169 60fi. Ligularia 75 20
2170 1fo.40 Orange lily . . . . . 1·10 20
2171 1fo.50 Fritillary . . . . . . 1·40 20
2172 3fo. "Dracocephalum ruyschiana" . . . . . . 3·25 70

407 Order of Labour (bronze) **409** Barn Swallows

408 Early Transport and Budapest Railway Station, 1846

1966. Hungarian Medals and Orders. Mult.
2173 20fi. Type **407** 10 10
2174 30fi. Order of Labour (silver) 10 10
2175 50fi. Banner Order of Republic, 3rd class (21½ × 28½ mm) 10 10
2176 60fi. Order of Labour (gold) 10 10
2177 70fi. Banner Order of Republic, 2nd class (25 × 30½ mm) 10 10

2178 1fo. Red Banner Order of Labour 20 10
2179 1fo.20 Banner Order of Republic, 1st class (28½ × 38 mm) 25 20
2180 2fo. Order of Merit of Republic 60 20
2181 2fo.50 Hero of Socialist Labour 80 30

1966. Re-opening of Transport Museum, Budapest.
2182 **408** 1fo. brown, green & yell 40 15
2183 – 2fo. blue, brown & green 70 35
DESIGN: 2fo. Modern transport and South Station, Budapest.

1966. Protection of Birds. Multicoloured.
2184 20fi. Type **409** 40 10
2185 30fi. Long-tailed tits 45 10
2186 60fi. Red crossbill 60 10
2187 1fo.40 Middle-spotted woodpecker . . . . . . 1·25 35
2188 1fo.50 Hoopoe . . . . . . 1·25 55
2189 3fo. Forest and emblem of National Forestry Association . . . . 1·25 75

410 W.H.O. Building

1966. Inaug of W.H.O. Headquarters, Geneva.
2190 **410** 2fo. black and blue . . . 35 10

411 Football

1966. World Cup Football Championships (1st issue). Sheet 76 × 108 mm.
MS2191 **411** 10fo. multicoloured 3·75 5·75
See also Nos. 2194/2202.

412 Nuclear Research Institute

1966. 10th Anniv of United Nuclear Research Institute, Dubna (U.S.S.R.).
2192 **412** 60fi. black and green . . 35 10

413 Buda Fortress, after Schedel's "Chronicle" (1493)

1966. 20th Anniv of U.N.E.S.C.O. and 72nd Executive Board Session, Budapest.
2193 **413** 2fo. violet and blue . . . 35 20

414 Jules Rimet, Football and Cup

1966. World Cup Football Championship (2nd issue). Multicoloured.
2194 20fi. Type **414** 10 10
2195 30fi. Montevideo, 1930 . . . 10 10
2196 60fi. Rome, 1934 . . . . . 15 10
2197 1fo. Paris, 1938 . . . . . . 30 10
2198 1fo.40 Rio de Janeiro, 1950 35 10
2199 1fo.70 Berne, 1954 . . . . 50 10
2200 2fo. Stockholm, 1958 . . . 70 30
2201 2fo.50 Santiago de Chile, 1962 . . . . 1·00 45
2202 3fo.+1fo. World Cup emblem on Union Jack, and map of England . . . 1·25 1·25

415 Girl Pioneer and Emblem

1966. 20th Anniv of Hungarian Pioneers Movement.
2203 **415** 60fi. red and violet . . . 30 10

416 Fire Engine

1966. Centenary of Voluntary Fire Brigades.
2204 **416** 2fo. black and orange . . 60 25

417 Red Fox

1966. Hunting Trophies. Multicoloured.
2205 20fi. Type **417** 10 10
2206 60fi. Wild boar 15 10
2207 70fi. Wild cat 25 10
2208 80fi. Roe deer 25 10
2209 1fo.50 Red deer 55 10
2210 2fo.50 Fallow deer . . . . 1·25 25
2211 3fo. Mouflon . . . . 1·40 70

418 Throwing the Discus

1966. 8th European Athletic Championships, Budapest. Multicoloured.
2212 20fi. Type **418** 10 10
2213 30fi. High-jumping 10 10
2214 40fi. Throwing the javelin 20 10
2215 50fi. Throwing the hammer 25 10
2216 60fi. Long-jumping 35 25
2217 1fo. Putting the shot 60 25
2218 2fo. Pole-vaulting 95 70
2219 3fo. Running . . . . 1·25 1·60
MS2220 105 × 75 mm. 10fo. Hurdling . . . . 4·50 6·00

419 Archery

420 Helsinki

1966. Stamp Day. Multicoloured.
2221 2fo.+50fi. Types **419** 75 80
2222 2fo.+50fi. Grapes 75 80
2223 2fo.+50fi. Poppies 75 80
2224 2fo.+50fi. Space dogs . . . 75 80
MS2225 98 × 84 mm. Nos. 2221/4 3·00 4·25

1966. Air.
2226 **420** 20fi. red 10 10
2227 – 50fi. brown 10 10
2228 – 1fo. blue 15 10
2229 – 1fo.10 black 20 10
2230 – 1fo.20 orange 20 10
2231 – 1fo.50 green 30 10
2232 – 2fo. blue 35 10
2233 – 2fo.50 red 40 10
2234 – 3fo. green 55 15
2235 – 4fo. brown . . . . . . 1·60 1·25
2236 – 5fo. violet 70 20
2237 – 10fo. blue . . . . . . 1·90 40
2238 – 20fo. green . . . . . 3·00 60
DESIGNS—Ilyushin Il-18 over: 50fi. Athens; 1fo. Beirut; 1fo.10, Frankfurt; 1fo.20, Cairo; 1fo.50, Copenhagen; 2fo. London; 2fo.50, Moscow; 3fo. Paris; 4fo. Prague; 5fo. Rome; 10fo. Damascus; 20fo. Budapest.
For 2fo.60 in similar design see No. 2369.

421 "Girl in the Woods" (after Barabas)

1966. Paintings in Hungarian National Gallery (1st series). Multicoloured.
2239 60fi. Type **421** 30 15
2240 1fo. "Mrs. Istvan Bitto" (Barabas) 35 25
2241 1fo.50 "Laszlo Hunyadi Farewell" (Benczur) . . . 65 25
2242 1fo.70 "Woman Reading" (Benczur) (horiz) 70 25
2243 2fo. "The Faggot-carrier" (Munkacsy) 75 25
2244 2fo.50 "The Yawning Apprentice" (Munkacsy) 1·00 40
2245 3fo. "Woman in Lilac" (Szinyei) . . . . 1·50 80
MS2246 97 × 79 mm. 10fo. "Picnic in May" (Szinyei) . . . . . . 9·00 9·75
See also Nos. 2282/8, 2318/**MS**2325, 2357/**MS**2364, 2411/**MS**2418, 2449/**MS**2456 and 2525/**MS**2532.

422 "Vostok 3" and "Vostok 4" (Nikolaev and Popovich)

1966. Twin Space Flights. Multicoloured.
2247 20fi. Type **422** 10 10
2248 60fi. Borman and Lovell, Schirra and Stafford . . . 20 10
2249 80fi. Bykovsky and Tereshkova 20 10
2250 1fo. Stafford and Cernan . . 30 10
2251 1fo.50 Belyaev and Leonov (Leonov in space) 50 20
2252 2fo. McDivitt and White (White in space) 60 20
2253 2fo.50 Komarov, Feoktistov and Yegorov . . . . . . 1·10 30
2254 3fo. Conrad and Gordon . . 1·40 70

423 Kitaibel and "Kitaibelia vitifolia"

424 Militiaman

1967. 150th Death Anniv of Pal Kitaibel (botanist). Carpathian Flowers. Multicoloured.
2255 20fi. Type **423** 10 10
2256 60fi. "Dentaria glandulosa" 20 10
2257 1fo. "Edraianthus tenuifolius" 30 10
2258 1fo.50 "Althaea pallida" . . 50 10
2259 2fo. "Centaurea mollis" . . 65 15
2260 2fo.50 "Sternbergia colchiciflora" . . . . . . 1·25 25
2261 3fo. "Iris hungarica" . . . 1·40 75

1967. 10th Anniv of Workers' Militia.
2262 **424** 2fo. blue 30 10

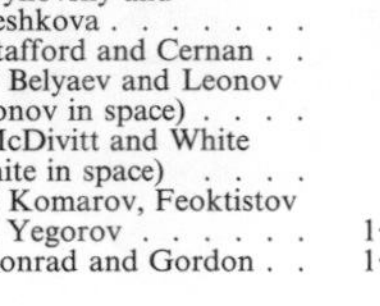

425 Faustus Verancsics' Parachute Descent, 1617

1967. Air. "Aerofila 67". Airmail Stamp Exhibition, Budapest. (a) 1st issue.
2263 2fo.+1fo. sepia and yellow 85 85
2264 2fo.+1fo. sepia and blue . . 85 85
2265 2fo.+1fo. sepia and green 85 85
2266 2fo.+1fo. sepia and pink . . 85 85
MS2267 116 × 90 mm. Nos. 2263/6 3·75 4·00

(b) 2nd issue.
2268 2fo.+1fo. blue and green . . 85 85
2269 2fo.+1fo. blue and orange 85 85
2270 2fo.+1fo. blue and yellow 85 85
2271 2fo.+1fo. blue and pink . . 85 85
MS2272 116 × 90 mm. Nos. 2268/71 3·75 4·00

DESIGNS: No. 2263, Type **425**; No. 2264, David Schwartz's aluminium airship, 1897; No. 2265, Erno Horvath's monoplane, 1911; No. 2266, PKZ-2 helicopter, 1918; No. 2268, Parachutist; No. 2269, Mil Mi-1 helicopter; No. 2270, Tupolev Tu-154 airliner; No. 2271, "Luna 12".

426 I.T.Y. Emblem and Transport

1967. International Tourist Year.
2273 **426** 1fo. black and blue . . . 30 10

427 "Milton", after Orial Petrics

1967. "Amphilex" Stamp Exhibition, Amsterdam. Sheet 81 × 91 mm.
MS2274 **427** 10fo. multicoloured 3·75 5·50

428 "Ferenc Deak" (paddle-steamer), Schonbuchel Castle and Austrian Flag (⅔-size illustration)

1967. 25th Session of Danube Commission. Vessels of Mahart Shipping Company.
2275 **428** 30fi. multicoloured . . . 90 15
2276 – 60fi. multicoloured . . . 1·40 30
2277 – 1fo. multicoloured . . . 2·25 35
2278 – 1fo.50 multicoloured . . 3·75 55
2279 – 1fo.70 multicoloured . . 4·75 85
2280 – 2fo. multicoloured . . . 5·00 1·70
2281 – 2fo.50 multicoloured . . 5·50 2·50
DESIGNS (Vessels, backgrounds and flags): 60fi. River-bus "Revfulop" Bratislava Castle, Czechoslovakia; 1fo. Diesel passenger boat "Hunyadi", Buda Castle, Hungary; 1fo.50, Diesel tug "Szekszard", Golubac Castle, Yugoslavia; 1fo.70, Tug "Miscolc", Vidin Castle, Bulgaria; 2fo. Motor-freighter "Tihany", Galati shipyard. Rumania; 2fo.50, Hydrofoil "Siraly I", port of Izmail, U.S.S.R.

429 "Szidonia Deak" (A. Gyorgyi)

1967. Paintings in National Gallery, Budapest (2nd series). Multicoloured.
2282 60fi. "Liszt" (M. Munkacsy) 25 25
2283 1fo. "Self-portrait" (S. Lanyi) 40 25
2284 1fo.50 "Portrait of a Lady" (J. Borsos) 50 25
2285 1fo.70 "The Lovers" (after P. Szinyei Merse) (horiz) 75 25
2286 2fo. Type **429** 80 25
2287 2fo.50 "National Guardsman" (J. Borsos) 90 25
2288 3fo. "Louis XV and Madame Dubarry" (G. Benczur) . . . . . . 1·10 50

430 Poodle

1967. Dogs. Multicoloured.

2289	30fi. Type **430**	15	10
2290	60fi. Collie (23½ × 35 mm)	25	10
2291	1fo. Pointer	35	10
2292	1fo.40 Fox terriers (23½ × 35 mm)	50	10
2293	2fo. Pumi	70	20
2294	3fo. Alsatian (23½ × 35 mm)	85	60
2295	4fo. Puli	1·40	1·00

431 Sterlet

1967. 14th International Anglers' Federation Congress, and World Angling Championships, Dunaujvaros. Multicoloured.

2296	20fi. Type **431**	10	10
2297	60fi. Zander	20	10
2298	1fo. Common carp	25	10
2299	1fo.70 Wels	65	10
2300	2fo. Northern pike	70	10
2301	2fo.50 Asp	85	55
2302	3fo.+1fo. Anglers' and C.I.P.S. (Federation) emblem	1·25	1·00

432 "Prince Igor" (Borodin)

1967. Popular Operas. Designs showing scenes from various operas. Multicoloured.

2303	20fi. Type **432**	20	10
2304	30fi. "Der Freischutz" (Weber)	20	10
2305	40fi. "The Magic Flute" (Mozart)	35	10
2306	60fi. "Bluebeard's Castle" (Bartok)	50	10
2307	80fi. "Carmen" (Bizet) (vert)	65	20
2308	1fo. "Don Carlos" (Verdi) (vert)	85	20
2309	1fo.70 "Tannhauser" (Wagner) (vert)	1·00	45
2310	3fo. "Laszlo Hunyadi" (Erkel) (vert)	1·40	1·75

433 "Teaching" (14th-cent class)

1967. 600th Anniv of Higher Education in Hungary.

2311	**433**	2fo. green and gold	35	10

434 Faculty Building

1967. 300th Anniv of Political Law and Science Faculty, Lorand Eotvos University, Budapest.

2312	**434**	2fo. green	35	10

435 "Lenin as Teacher"

1967. 50th Anniv of October Revolution. Multicoloured.

2313	60fi. Type **435**	20	10
2314	1fo. "Lenin"	20	10
2315	3fo. "Lenin aboard the Aurora"	55	25

436 "Venus 4"

1967. Landing of "Venus 4" on planet Venus.

2316	**436**	5fo. multicoloured	90	80

437 19th-centenary Mail Coach

1967. Centenary of Hungarian Postal Administration. Sheet 85 × 95 mm.

MS2317	**437**	10fo. multicoloured	3·00	3·75

437a "Brother and Sister" (A. Fenyes)

1967. Paintings in National Gallery, Budapest (3rd series). Multicoloured.

2318	60fi. Type **437a**	20	10
2319	1fo. "Boys Wrestling on Beach" (O. Glatz)	30	10
2320	1fo.50 "October" (K. Ferenczy)	50	10
2321	1fo.70 "Women by the River" (I. Szonyi) (horiz)	55	20
2322	2fo. "Godfather's Breakfast" (I. Csok)	55	20
2323	2fo.50 "The Eviction Order" (G. Derkovits)	60	25
2324	3fo. "Self-Portrait" (T. Csontvary)	70	40
MS2325	78 × 100 mm. 10fo. "The Apple Pickers" (B. Uitz) (larger 37½ × 60 mm)	2·25	3·00

"Women by the River" (1fo.70) is in a private collection in Budapest.

See also Nos. 2357/**MS**2364 and 2411/**MS**2418.

438 Rifle-shooting on Skis

1967. Winter Olympic Games, Grenoble. Multicoloured.

2326	30fi. Type **438**	10	10
2327	60fi. Figure skating (pairs)	20	10
2328	1fo. Bobsleighing	20	10
2329	1fo.40 Downhill skiing	30	10
2330	1fo.70 Figure skating	40	10
2331	2fo. Speed skating	55	15
2332	3fo. Ski jumping	65	45
2333	4fo.+1fo. Ice stadium, Grenoble	1·10	80
MS2334	116 × 99 mm. 10fo. Ice hockey goal keeper (61 × 61 mm)	3·50	3·25

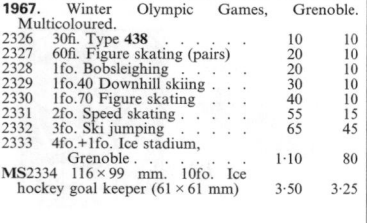

439 Kalman Kando, Class V43 Electric Locomotive and Map

1968. Kando Commemoration.

2335	**439**	2fo. blue	35	10

440 Cat

1968. Cats. Multicoloured.

2336	20fi. Type **440**	25	10
2337	60fi. Cream angora	30	10
2338	1fo. Smoky angora	40	20
2339	1fo.20 Domestic kitten	50	20
2340	1fo.50 White angora	70	20
2341	2fo. Striped angora	80	20
2342	2fo.50 Siamese	1·10	40
2343	5fo. Blue angora	1·60	1·00

441 Zoltan Kodaly (composer)

442 City Hall, Arms, Grapes and Apricot

1968. Kodaly Commemoration.

2344	**441**	5fo. multicoloured	1·10	65

1968. 600th Anniv of Kecskemet.

2345	**442**	2fo. brown	35	10

443 White Stork

444 Karl Marx

1968. International Council for Bird Preservation Congress, Budapest. Protected Birds. Mult.

2346	20fi. Type **443**	20	10
2347	50fi. Golden orioles	30	10
2348	60fi. Imperial eagle	35	15
2349	1fo. Western red-footed falcons	40	15
2350	1fo.20 Eurasian scops owl	55	20
2351	1fo.50 Great bustard	70	30
2352	2fo. European bee eaters	1·40	35
2353	2fo.50 Greylag goose	1·75	85

1968. 150th Birth Anniv of Karl Marx.

2354	**444**	1fo. purple	15	10

See also No. 1290.

445 Icarus falling in space

446 Student

1968. In Memoriam. Astronauts White, Gagarin and Komarov. Sheet 95 × 77 mm.

MS2355	**445**	10fo. multicoloured	3·00	3·75

1968. 150th Anniv of Mosonmagyarovar Agricultural College.

2356	**446**	2fo. green	35	10

1968. Paintings in National Gallery, Budapest (4th series). As T **437a**. Multicoloured.

2357	40fi. "Girl with a Pitcher" (Goya)	10	10
2358	60fi. "Head of an Apostle" (El Greco)	20	10
2359	1fo. "Boy with Apples" (Nunez) (horiz)	25	10
2360	1fo.50 "The Repentant Magdalen" (El Greco)	35	25
2361	2fo.50 "The Breakfast" (Velasquez) (horiz)	70	25
2362	4fo. "St. Elizabeth" (detail from "The Holy Family"; El Greco)	80	35
2363	5fo. "The Knife-grinder" (Goya)	1·00	70
MS2364	88 × 95 mm. 10fo. "Portrait of a Girl" (Palma Vecchio)	3·00	3·75

447 Lake Steamer, Flags and Badacsony Hills

448 Ilyushin Il-18 over St. Stephen's Cathedral, Vienna

1968. Lake Balaton Resorts. Multicoloured.

2365	20fi. Type **447**	15	10
2365a	40fi. Type **447**	15	10
2366	60fi. Tihany peninsula, tower and feather	15	10
2367	1fo. Yachts and buoy, Balatonalmadi	15	10
2368	2fo. Szigliget bay, vineyard, wine and fish	35	15

1968. Air. 50th Anniv of Budapest–Vienna Airmail Service.

2369	**448**	2fo.60 violet	60	15

449 Class 424 Steam Locomotive No. 176

451 M. Tompa

450 Grazing Stud

1968. Centenary of Hungarian State Railways.

2370	**449**	2fo. multicoloured	1·10	30

1968. Horse-breeding on the Hortobagy "puszta" (Hungarian steppe). Multicoloured.

2371	30fi. Type **450**	15	10
2372	40fi. Horses in storm	15	10
2373	60fi. Grooms horse-racing	20	10
2374	80fi. Horse-drawn sleigh	30	10
2375	1fo. Four-in-hand	40	10
2376	1fo.40 Seven-in-hand	55	10
2377	2fo. Driving five horses	60	10

2378 2fo.50 Groom preparing evening meal 65 35
2379 4fo. Five-in-hand . . . . . 1·10 75

1968. Death Centenary of Mihaly Tompa (poet).
2380 **451** 60fi. violet 10 10

452 Festival Emblem, Bulgarian and Hungarian Couples in National Costume

1968. 9th World Youth Festival, Sofia.
2381 **452** 60fi. multicoloured . . . 20 10

453 Breasting the Tape

454 Swimming

1968. Air. Olympic Games, Mexico. Mult.
MS2382 81 × 101 mm **453** 10fo. multicoloured (postage) . . . . 3·00 3·75

2383 20fi. Type **454**(air) 10 10
2384 60fi. Football 10 10
2385 80fi. Wrestling 10 10
2386 1fo. Canoeing 10 10
2387 1fo.40 Gymnastics 30 10
2388 2fo.+1fo. Horse-jumping . . 60 40
2389 3fo. Fencing 85 30
2390 4fo. Throwing the Javelin 1·25 55

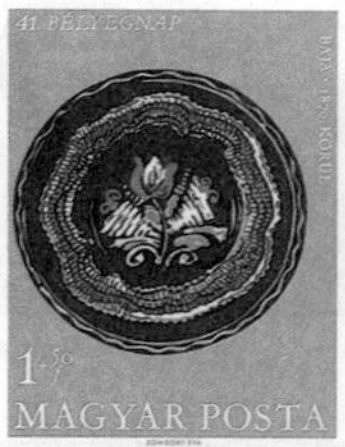

455 Baja Plate, 1870 **456** Society Emblem

1968. Stamp Day. Hungarian Ceramics. Mult.
2391 1fo.+50fi. Type **455** 55 65
2392 1fo.+50fi. West Hungarian jug, 1618 . . . . 55 65
2393 1fo.+50fi. Tiszafured flagon, 1847 . . . . 55 65
2394 1fo.+50fi. Mezocsat flask, 1848 . . . . 55 65
MS2395 74 × 96 mm. 2fo.+50fi. North Hungarian jug, 1672; 2fo.+50fi. Mezocsat plate, 1843; 2fo.+50fi. Moragy plate, 1860; 2fo.+50fi. Debrecen pitcher, 1793 3·00 3·75
The designs from the miniature sheet are smaller, measuring 25 × 35 mm.

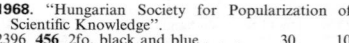

1968. "Hungarian Society for Popularization of Scientific Knowledge".
2396 **456** 2fo. black and blue . . . 30 10

457 Rocket Hesperus **459** "Workers of the World Unite" (Bertalan Por's 1918 poster)

458 Two Girls waving Flags

1968. Garden Flowers. Multicoloured.
2397 20fi. Type **457** 15 10
2398 60fi. Pansy 30 10
2399 80fi. Zinnias 45 10
2400 1fo. Morning Glory 65 25
2401 1fo.40 Petunia 85 25
2402 1fo.50 Purslane 90 25
2403 2fo. Michaelmas daisies . . 1·10 35
2404 2fo.50 Dahlia . . . . 1·25 90

1968. Children's Stamp Designs for 50th Anniv of Hungarian Communist Party. Multicoloured.
2405 40fi. Type **458** 35 10
2406 60fi. Children with flags and banner 45 10
2407 1fo. Pioneer bugler in camp 55 15

1968. 50th Anniv of Hungarian Communist Party.
2408 **459** 1fo. black, red and gold 15 10
2409 – 2fo. multicoloured . . . 15 10
DESIGN—HORIZ: 2fo. "Martyrs" (statue by Zoltan Kiss).

460 Human Rights Emblem **461** Endre Ady

1968. Human Rights Year.
2410 **460** 1fo. brown 30 10

1968. Paintings in National Gallery, Budapest (5th series). Italian Masters. As T **437a**. Mult.
2411 40fi. "Esterhazy Madonna" (Raphael) 10 10
2412 60fi. "The Annunciation" (Strozzi) 10 10
2413 1fo. "Portrait of a Young Man" (Raphael) 15 10
2414 1fo.50 "The Three Graces" (Naldini) 30 10
2415 2fo.50 "Portrait of a Man" (Sebastian del Piombo) . . 55 35
2416 4fo. "The Doge Marcantonio Trevisani" (Titian) 85 55
2417 5fo. "Venus, Cupid and Jealousy" (Bronzino) . . 1·25 90
MS2418 116 × 73 mm. 10fo. "Bathsheba bathing" (Ricci). Imperf . . . . 3·00 4·00

1969. 50th Death Anniv of Endre Ady (poet).
2419 **461** 1fo. black, purple & gold 20 10

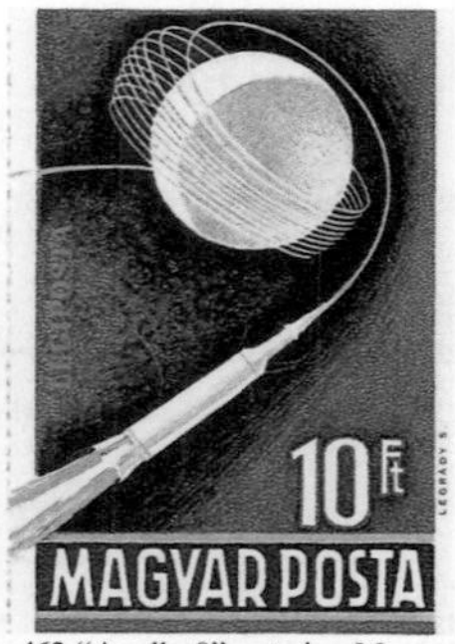

462 Press Emblem **463** "Apollo 8" entering Moon Orbit

1969. Centenary of Athenaeum Press.
2420 **462** 2fo. multicoloured . . . 30 10

1969. Air. Moon Flight of "Apollo 8". Sheet 111 × 81 mm.
MS2421 **463** 10fo. multicoloured 3·00 3·75

464 Throwing the Javelin

1969. Olympic Gold Medal Winners. Mult.
2422 40fi. Type **464** 10 10
2423 60fi. Canoeing 10 10
2424 1fo. Football 15 10
2425 1fo.20 Throwing the Hammer 15 10
2426 2fo. Fencing 30 10
2427 3fo. Wrestling 55 10
2428 4fo. Kayak-canoeing 80 20
2429 5fo. Horse-jumping . . . . 1·10 70
MS2430 111 × 84 mm. 10fo. Ancient Greek Athlete and Olympic Flame 3·75 4·50

465 Poster by O. Danko

1969. 50th Anniv of Proclamation of Hungarian Soviet Republic.
2431 **465** 40fi. black, red and gold 10 10
2432 – 60fi. black, red and gold 10 10
2433 – 1fo. black, red and gold 10 10
2434 – 2fo. multicoloured . . . 10 10
2435 – 3fo. multicoloured . . . 25 20
MS2436 97 × 71 mm. 10fo. black, red and grey . . . . 2·25 2·50
DESIGNS: 60fi. "Lenin" by unknown artist; 1fo. "Young Man Breaking Chains" (R. Steiner); 2fo. "Worker" (I. Foldes and G. Vegh); 3fo. "Soldier" (unknown artist). HORIZ—(52 × 40 mm): 10fo. "Workers with Banner" (R. Bereny).

466 Space Link-up of "Soyuz 4" and "Soyuz 5"

1969. Air. Space Flights of "Soyuz 4" and "Soyuz 5". Multicoloured.
2437 2fo. Type **466** 40 40
2438 2fo. Link-up and astronauts "walking" in Space . . . 40 40

467 Jersey Tiger Moth

1969. Butterflies and Moths. Multicoloured.
2439 40fi. Type **467** 25 10
2440 60fi. Eyed hawk moth . . . 25 10
2441 80fi. Painted lady 25 10
2442 1fo. Foxy charaxes 30 10
2443 1fo.20 Lesser fiery copper 40 10
2444 2fo. Large blue 75 20
2445 3fo. Dark crimson underwing . . . . 1·10 50
2446 4fo. Peacock . . . . 1·25 85

468 I.L.O. Emblem

1969. 50th Anniv of Int Labour Organisation.
2447 **468** 1fo. brown and red . . . 20 10

469 Chain Bridge, Budapest

1969. "Budapest 71" Stamp Exhibition.
2448 **469** 5fo.+2fo. multicoloured 1·10 1·40

470 "Black Pigs" (Gauguin)

1969. Paintings in National Gallery, Budapest (6th series). French Masters. Multicoloured.
2449 40fi. Type **470** 10 10
2450 60fi. "The Ladies" (Toulouse-Lautrec) (horiz) 10 10
2451 1fo. "Venus on Clouds" (Vouet) 15 10
2452 2fo. "Lady with Fan" (Manet) (horiz) 35 10
2453 3fo. "Petra Camara" (Chasseriau) 80 15
2454 4fo. "The Cowherd" (Troyon) (horiz) . . . . 1·10 20
2455 5fo. "The Wrestlers" (Courbet) . . . . 1·50 55
MS2456 75 × 97 mm. 10fo. "Pomona" (Fouche) . . . . . 3·00 3·75

471 Vac **472** "PAX"

1969. Danube Towns. Multicoloured.
2457 40fi. Type **471** 10 10
2458 1fo. Szentendre 20 10
2459 1fo.20 Visegrad 25 10
2460 3fo. Esztergom 50 10

1969. 20th Anniv of Int Peace Movement.
2461 **472** 1fo. gold, dp blue & blue 20 10

473 Astronauts on Moon ($\frac{1}{2}$-size illustration)

1969. Air. First Man on the Moon (1st issue). Sheet 133 × 89 mm.
MS2462 **473** 10fo. multicoloured 4·50 5·50
See also Nos. 2487/94.

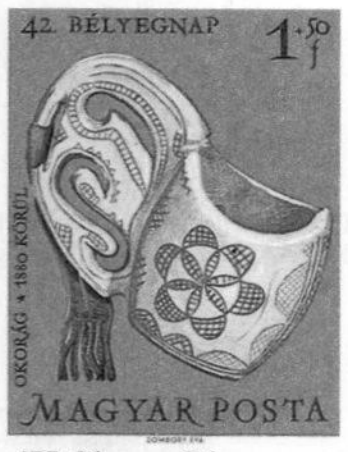

474 Zelkova Leaf (fossil) **475** Okorag Stirrupcup, 1880

1969. Centenary of Hungarian Geological Institute. Minerals and Fossils. Multicoloured.
2463 40fi. Type **474** 15 10
2464 60fi. Greenockite calcite sphalerite crystals 20 10
2465 1fo. Hungarian herring (fossilized fish) 25 10
2466 1fo.20 Quartz crystals . . . 25 10
2467 2fo. "Reineckia crassicostata" (ammonite) 35 10
2468 3fo. Copper ore 55 20

2469 4fo. "Placochelys placodonta" (fossilized turtle) . . . . 1·25 60
2470 5fo. Cuprite crystals . . . . 1·60 95

1969. Stamp Day. Hungarian Folk Art. Wood-carvings. Multicoloured.
2471 1fo.+50fi. Type **475** 55 65
2472 1fo.+50fi. Felsotizavidek jar, 1898 . . . . 55 65
2473 1fo.+50fi. Somogyharsagy pot, 1935 . . . . 55 65
2474 1fo.+50fi. Alfold smoking-pipe, 1740 . . . . 55 65
MS2475 75 × 96 mm. 2fo.+50fi. × 4 (a) Csorna panel, 1879; (b) Okany mug, 1914; (c) Sellye casket, 1899; (d) Lengyeltoti box, 1880 . . . 2·25 2·50
The designs in **MS**2475 are smaller, each 31 × 40 mm.

476 "The Scientist at his Table" (Rembrandt)

1969. Int "History of Art" Congress, Budapest.
2476 **476** 1fo. sepia 30 10

477 Horse-jumping

1969. World Pentathlon Championships, Budapest. Multicoloured.
2477 40fi. Type **477** 25 10
2478 60fi. Fencing 30 10
2479 1fo. Pistol-shooting 50 25
2480 2fo. Swimming 70 25
2481 3fo. Running 90 25
2482 5fo. All five sports . . . . 1·25 95

478 Postcard and Letterbox

1969. Centenary of 1st Hungarian Postcard.
2483 **478** 60fi. ochre and red . . . 10 10

479 Mahatma Gandhi

481 "Janos Nagy" (self-portrait)

480 Hemispheres

1969. Birth Centenary of Mahatma Gandhi.
2484 **479** 5fo. multicoloured . . . 1·25 65

1969. World Trade Unions Federations Congress, Budapest.
2485 **480** 2fo. blue and brown . . 25 10

1969. 50th Death Anniv of Janos Nagy (painter).
2486 **481** 5fo. multicoloured . . . 90 30

482 "Flight to the Moon" (after Jules Verne)

1969. Air. 1st Man on the Moon (2nd issue). Multicoloured.
2487 40fi. Type **482** 10 10
2488 60fi. Tsiolkovsky's "space station" 10 10
2489 1fo. "Luna 1" 20 10
2490 1fo.50 "Ranger 7" 35 10
2491 2fo. "Luna 9" 50 10
2492 2fo.50 "Apollo 8" 55 15
2493 3fo. "Soyuz 4" and "5" . . 70 15
2494 4fo. "Apollo 10" . . . . . 1·10 40

483 "St John the Evangelist" (Van Dyck)

1969. Dutch Paintings in Hungarian Museums. Multicoloured.
2495 40fi. Type **483** 10 10
2496 60fi. "Peasants" (P. de Molyn) 10 10
2497 1fo. "Boy lighting Pipe" (H. Terbruggen) 25 10
2498 2fo. "The Musicians" (detail, Jan Steen) 45 10
2499 3fo. "Woman reading Letter" (P. de Hooch) . . 75 15
2500 4fo. "The Fiddler" (Dirk Hals) 90 30
2501 5fo. "J. Asselyn" (Frans Hals) . . . . 1·25 55
MS2502 73 × 97 mm. 10fo. "Mucius Scaevola before Porsenna" (Rubens and Van Dyck) . . . 3·00 3·25

484 Kiskunfelegyhaza Pigeon

1969. International Pigeon Exn, Budapest.
2503 **484** 1fo. multicoloured . . . 30 10

485 Daimler (1886)

1970. Air. Old Motor Cars. Multicoloured.
2504 40fi. Type **485** 20 10
2505 60fi. Peugeot (1894) 25 10
2506 1fo. Benz (1901) 30 10
2507 1fo.50 Cudell (1902) 40 25
2508 2fo. Rolls-Royce (1908) . . 60 25
2509 2fo.50 Ford "T" (1908) . . 80 25
2510 3fo. Vermorel (1912) . . . . 1·10 50
2511 4fo. Csonka (1912) . . . . 1·40 1·25

486 View of Budapest

487 "Soyuz 6, 7, 8"

1970. "Budapest 71" Stamp Exhibition and Centenary of Hungarian Stamps (1st series). Multicoloured. Background colours given.
2512 **486** 2fo.+1fo. brown 50 55
2513 – 2fo.+1fo. lilac 50 55
2514 – 2fo.+1fo. blue 50 55
DESIGNS: Nos. 2513/4 show different views of Budapest, in style as Type **486**.
See also Nos. 2572/**MS**2576 and 2604/**MS**2608.

1970. Air. Space Exploration. Multicoloured.
2515 3fo.(× 4) Type **487** . . . . 2·25 2·25
2516 3fo.(× 4) Astronauts on Moon ("Apollo 12") . . . 2·25 2·25
Nos. 2515/6 were only available each in small sheets of four, and are priced thus.

489 Budapest Panorama, 1945 (-size illustration)

1970. 25th Anniv of Liberation. Sheet 159 × 83 mm containing T **489** and similar horiz design. Multicoloured.
MS2518 5fo. × 2 (a) Type **489**; (b) Budapest panorama, 1970 . . 3·00 3·75

488 Underground Train at Station

1970. Opening of Budapest Underground Railway.
2517 **488** 1fo. blue, turquoise & blk 35 10

490 Cloud Formation, Satellite and Globe

491 Lenin

1970. Cent of Hungarian Meteorological Service.
2519 **490** 1fo. multicoloured . . . 30 10

1970. Birth Centenary of Lenin. Mult.
2520 1fo. Lenin Statue, Budapest 10 10
2521 2fo. Type **491** 10 10

492 Lehar and Music

1970. Birth Cent of Franz Lehar (composer).
2522 **492** 2fo. multicoloured . . . 50 25

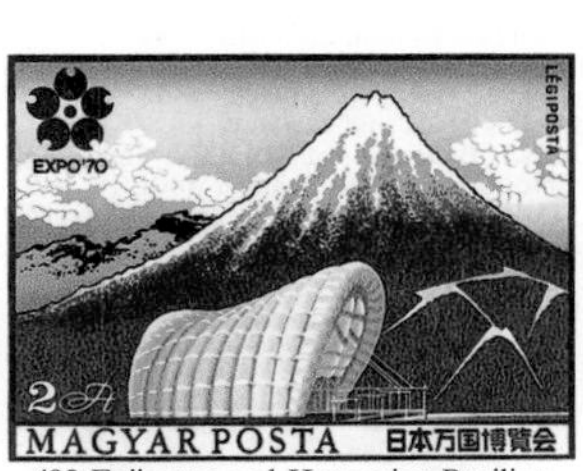

493 Fujiyama and Hungarian Pavilion

1970. Air. Expo 70. Multicoloured.
2523 2fo. Type **493** 55 55
2524 3fo. Tower of the Sun and Peace Bell 55 55

494 "Samson and Delilah" (M. Rocca)

1970. Paintings in National Gallery, Budapest (7th series). Multicoloured.
2525 40fi. Type **494** 10 10
2526 60fi. "Joseph's Dream" (G. B. Langetti) 15 10
2527 1fo. "Clio" (P. Mignard) . . 20 10
2528 1fo.50 "Venus and Satyr" (S. Ricci) (horiz.) 25 10
2529 2fo.50 "Andromeda" (F. Furini) 55 15
2530 4fo. "Venus, Adonis and Cupid" (L. Giordano) . . 90 35
2531 5fo. "Allegory" (woman) (C. Giaquinto) . . . . . 1·10 70
MS2532 100 × 85 mm. 10fo. "Diane and Callisto" (Janssens) (horiz) 3·00 3·25
The design of **MS**2532 is larger, 64 × 46 mm.

495 "Apollo 13" over Moon

1970. Air. Space Flight of "Apollo 13". Sheet 112 × 90 mm containing T **495** and three other similar horiz designs. Multicoloured.
MS2533 2fo.50 × 4 (a) Type **495**; (b) In flight; (c) Descent; (d) In sea 2·50 2·75

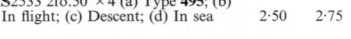

496 Beethoven (from statue at Martonvasar)

497 Foundryman

1970. Birth Bicentenary of Beethoven.
2534 **496** 1fo. green, lilac & yellow 90 25

1970. Bicent of Diosgyor Foundry, Miskolc.
2535 **497** 1fo. multicoloured . . . 25 10

498 St. Stephen

500 Illuminated Initial

499 Rowing Four

1970. 1,000th Birth Anniv of St. Stephen (King Stephen I of Hungary).
2536 **498** 3fo. multicoloured . . . 60 25

1970. 17th European Women's Rowing Championships, Lake Tata.
2537 **499** 1fo. multicoloured . . . 35 10

1970. Stamp Day. Paintings and Illuminated Initials from Codices of King Matthias.
2538 1fo.+50fi. Type **500** 55 65
2539 1fo.+50fi. "N" and flowers 55 65

2540 1fo.+50fi. "O" and ornamentation 55 65
2541 1fo.+50fi. "King Matthias" 55 65
MS2542 66 × 86 mm. 2fo.+50fi. × 4 (a) "Bishop Ransanus with King Matthias and Queen Beatrix"; (b) "Q" and "Old Humanist"; (c) "C" and "Appianus of Alexandria"; (d) "A" and "King David on Throne" . . . . 3·25 4·00

501 "Soyuz 9" on Transporter

1970. Air. "Soyuz 9" Space Mission. Sheet 108 × 87 mm containing T **501** and three similar horiz designs. Multicoloured.
MS2543 2fo.50 × 4 (a) Type **501**; (b) Launch; (c) In flight; (d) Cosmonauts . . . . 2·50 2·75

502 "Bread" (sculpture by I. Szabo) and F.A.O. Emblem

1970. 7th F.A.O. European Regional Conference, Budapest.
2544 **502** 1fo. multicoloured . . . 20 10

503 Boxing

1970. 75th Anniv of Hungarian Olympic Committee. Multicoloured.
2545 40fi. Type **503** 10 10
2546 60fi. Canoeing 10 10
2547 1fo. Fencing 10 10
2548 1fo.50 Water-polo 20 10
2549 2fo. Gymnastics 45 10
2550 2fo.50 Throwing the Hammer 50 20
2551 3fo. Wrestling 55 30
2552 5fo. Swimming 90 70

504 Family and "Flame of Knowledge"

1970. 5th Education Congress, Budapest.
2553 **504** 1fo. blue, green & orange 20 10

505 Chalice of Benedek Suky, c. 1400

1970. Goldsmiths' Craft. Treasures from Budapest National Museum and Esztergom Treasury. Multicoloured.
2554 40fi. Type **505** 10 10
2555 60fi. Altar-cruet, c. 1500 . . 10 10
2556 1fo. "Nadasdy" goblet, 16th-century 20 10
2557 1fo.50 Coconut goblet with gold case, c. 1600 . . . . 25 10
2558 2fo. Silver tankard of M. Toldalaghy, c. 1623 40 10
2559 2fo.50 Communion-cup of G.I. Rakoczi, c. 1670 . . 60 15
2560 3fo. Tankard, c. 1690 . . . 80 25
2561 4fo. "Bell-flower" cup, c. 1710 . . . . . . 1·25 75

506 "The Virgin and Child" ("Giampietrino", G. Pedrini)

1970. Paintings. Religious Art from Christian Museum, Esztergom. Multicoloured.
2562 40fi. Type **506** 10 10
2563 60fi. "Love" (G. Lazzarini) 10 10
2564 1fo. "Legend of St. Catherine of Alexandria" ("Master of Bat") 15 10
2565 1fo.50 "Adoration of the Shepherds" (F. Fontebasso) (horiz.) 30 10
2566 2fo.50 "Adoration of the Magi" ("Master of Aranyosmarot") 65 20
2567 4fo. "Temptation of St. Anthony the Hermit" (J. de Cock) . . . . . . 1·00 30
2568 5fo. "St. Sebastian" (Palmezzano) . . . . . . 1·10 70
MS2569 72 × 84 mm. 10fo. "The Maid and the Unicorn" (unknown Lombard painter) . . . . . . 3·25 4·00

507 Mauthausen Camp Memorial (A. Makrisz)

1970. 25th Anniv of Liberation of Concentration Camps.
2570 **507** 1fo. brown and blue . . 30 10

508 "Luna 16" in Flight

1971. Air. "Luna 16" Space Mission. Sheet 108 × 87 mm containing T **508** and three other similar horiz designs. Multicoloured.
MS2571 2fo.50 × 4 (a) Type **508**; (b) Parachute landing; (c) On Moon's surface; (d) Nosecone . . . . 2·50 2·75

509 Budapest, 1470

1971. "Budapest 71" Stamp Exhibition and Centenary of Hungarian Stamps (2nd series). "Budapest Through the Ages".
2572 **509** 2fo.+1fo. black & yell 50 65
2573 – 2fo.+1fo. black & mve 50 65
2574 – 2fo.+1fo. black & grn . . 50 65
2575 – 2fo.+1fo. black & orge 50 65
MS2576 110 × 75 mm. 2fo.+1fo. × 4 (a) black and orange; (b) black and pale green; (c) black and violet; (d) black and mauve . . 2·25 2·50
DESIGNS: Budapest in: No. 2573, 1600; No. 2574, 1638; No. 2575, 1770. Smaller (40 × 18 mm)—No. **MS**2575, Budapest in (a) 1777, (b) 1850, (c) 1895, (d) 1970.

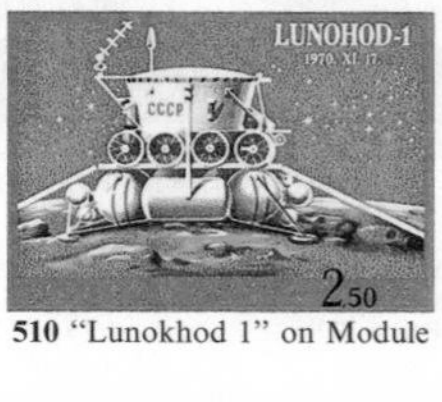

510 "Lunokhod 1" on Module

1971. Air. Moon Mission of "Luna 17" and "Lunokhod 2". Sheet 108 × 87 mm containing T **510** and three other similar horiz designs. Multicoloured.
MS2577 2fo.50 × 4 (a) Type **510**; (b) "Luna 17" leaving Earth; (c) "Luna 17" nearing Moon; (d) "Lunokhod 1" on Moon's surface 2·50 2·75

511 "The Marseillaise" (sculpture by Rude)

512 Bela Bartok

1971. Centenary of Paris Commune.
2578 **511** 3fo. brown and green . . 50 20

1971. 90th Birth Anniv of Bela Bartok (composer).
2579 **512** 1fo. black, grey and red 90 10

513 Gyor in 1594

1971. 700th Anniv of Gyor.
2580 **513** 2fo. multicoloured . . . 35 10

514 Astronauts on Moon

1971. Air. "Apollo 14" Moon Mission. Sheet 120 × 70 mm.
MS2581 **514** 10fo. multicoloured 3·00 3·75

1971. Birth Centenary of Andras L. Achim (peasant leader). Portrait in similar style to T **512**.
2582 1fo. black, grey and green 20 10

516 Hunting European Bison

1971. World Hunting Exhibition, Budapest. Multicoloured.
2583 40fi. Type **516**(postage) . . 15 10
2584 60fi. Hunting wild boar . . 15 10
2585 80fi. Deer-stalking 30 20
2586 1fo. Falconry 95 25
2587 1fo.20 Stag-hunting 60 30
2588 2fo. Great bustards with young . . . . 1·60 55
2589 3fo. Netting fish . . . . . 1·00 65
2590 4fo. Angling . . . . 1·40 80

MS2591 145 × 100mm. 10fo. Herd of roe deer (air) . . . . 2·25 2·50
The design of the 10fo. is larger, 72 × 46 mm.

517 "Portrait of a Man" (Durer)

1971. 500th Birth Anniv of Albrecht Durer (artist). Sheet 80 × 100 mm.
MS2592 **517** 10fo. multicoloured 2·25 2·50

518 Emblem on Flower

1971. 25th Anniv of Hungarian Young Pioneers.
2593 **518** 1fo. multicoloured . . . 45 10

519 F.I.R. Emblem

1971. 20th Anniv of International Federation of Resistance Fighters.
2594 **519** 1fo. multicoloured . . . 45 10

520 "Walking in the Garden" (Toyokuni School)

1971. Japanese Colour Prints from Ferenc Hopp Collection, Budapest. Multicoloured.
2595 40fi. Type **520** 10 10
2596 60fi. "Geisha in boat" (Yeishi) 15 10
2597 1fo. "Woman with scroll-painting" (Yeishi) 25 10
2598 1fo.50 "Oirans" (Kiyonaga) 40 10
2599 2fo. "Awabi Fishers" (Utamaro) 50 25
2600 2fo.50 "Scated Oiran" (Harunobu) 60 25
2601 3fo. "Peasant Girl carrying Faggots" (Hokusai) . . . 95 30
2602 4fo. "Women and Girls Walking" (Yeishi) . . . . 1·10 90

521 Locomotive "Bets" and Route Map (1846)

1971. 125th Anniv of Hungarian Railways.
2603 **521** 1fo. multicoloured . . . 50 10

522 Hungarian Newspaper Stamp of 1871

1971. "Budapest 71" Stamp Exhibition and Centenary of Hungarian Stamps (3rd series). Mult.
2604 2fo.+1fo. Type **522** 35 45
2605 2fo.+1fo. 45f. "Petofi" stamp of 1919 . . . . . 35 45
2606 2fo.+1fo. 40k. "Harvesters" stamp of 1920 . . . . 35 45
2607 2fo.+1fo. 16f.+16f. "Art" stamp of 1940 . . . . . 35 45
MS2608 115 × 99 mm. 2fo.+1fo. × 4 (a) 60f.+60f. "Liberty" stamp of 1947; (b) 2fo. "Costume" stamp of 1953; (c) 2fo. Air stamp of 1958; (d) 1fo. "Space" stamp of 1965 3·00 3·25

523 Griffin with Inking Balls

1971. Cent of State Printing Office, Budapest.
2609 **523** 1fo. multicoloured . . . 35 40

524 O.I.J. Emblem and Page of "Magyar Sajto"

1971. 25th Anniv of Int Organisation of Journalists.
2610 **524** 1fo. gold and blue . . . 20 10

525 Volkov, Dobrovolsky and Patsaev (½-size illustration)

1971. Air. "Soyuz 11" Cosmonauts Memorial Issue. Sheet 133 × 90 mm.
MS2611 **525** 10fo. multicoloured 3·00 4·00

526 J. Winterl (founder) and "Waldsteinia geoides"

1971. Bicentenary of Botanical Gardens, Budapest. Multicoloured.
2612 40fi. Type **526** 10 10
2613 60fi. "Bromeliaceae" 15 10
2614 80fi. "Titanopsis calcarea" . . 20 10
2615 1fo. "Vinca herbacea" . . . 25 10
2616 1fo.20 "Gymnocalycium mihanovichii" 25 10
2617 2fo. "Nymphaea gigantea" 45 10
2618 3fo. "Iris arenaria" 75 30
2619 5fo. "Paeonia banatica" . . 1·25 75

527 Horse-racing

1971. Equestrian Sport. Multicoloured.
2620 40fi. Type **527** 15 10
2621 60fi. Trotting 20 10
2622 80fi. Cross-country riding 20 10
2623 1fo. Show-jumping 25 10
2624 1fo.20 Start of race 30 10
2625 2fo. Polo 55 10
2626 3fo. Steeplechasing 85 25
2627 5fo. Dressage . . . . 1·40 75

528 "Execution of Koppany"

529 Racial Equality Year Emblem

1971. Miniatures from the "Illuminated Chronicle" of King Lajos I of Hungary. Multicoloured.
2628 40fi. Type **528** 15 10
2629 60fi. "The Pursuit of King Peter" 15 10
2630 1fo. "Bazarad's Victory over King Karoly I" 20 10
2631 1fo.50 "The Strife between King Salamon and Prince Geza" 35 10
2632 2fo.50 "The Founding of Obuda Monastery by King Stephen and Queen Gisela" 55 15
2633 4fo. "Reconciliation of King Kalman and his brother, Almos" 75 25
2634 5fo. "King Ladislas I supervising the construction of Nagyvarad Church" . . . 1·10 50
MS2635 84 × 87 mm. 10fo. "The Funeral of Prince Emeric and the Binding of Vazul" . . . . . . 3·00 3·00
The design of the 10fo. is larger, 51 × 60 mm.

1971. Racial Equality Year.
2636 **529** 1fo. multicoloured . . . 20 10

530 Ice Hockey

1971. Winter Olympic Games, Sapporo, Japan (1972). Multicoloured.
2637 40fi. Type **530** 10 10
2638 60fi. Downhill skiing . . . 20 10
2639 80fi. Figure skating (female) 20 10
2640 1fo. Ski jumping 25 10
2641 1fo.20 Cross-country skiing 35 10
2642 2fo. Figure skating (male) 50 10
2643 3fo. Bobsleighing 60 25
2644 4fo. Rifle-shooting (Biathlon) . . . . 1·00 60
MS2645 133 × 89 mm. 10fo. Buddha 3·25 4·00
The design of the 10fo. is larger, 89 × 51 mm.

531 Astronauts aboard Moon Rover (-size illustration)

1972. Air. Moon Flight of "Apollo 15". Sheet 120 × 76 mm.
MS2646 **531** 10fo. multicoloured 3·00 3·25

532 Class 303, 1950

1972. Railway Steam Locomotives. Mult.
2647 40fi. Type **532** 25 10
2648 60fi. Class P6, 1902, Prussia 25 10
2649 80fi. Class 380, 1894, Italy 35 15
2650 1fo. Class P36, 1950, Russia 55 15
2651 1fo.20 Heisler locomotive, Japan 60 30
2652 2fo. Scottish Caledonian tank locomotive, 1837 . . 80 35
2653 4fo. Class 166, 1882, Austria 1·10 70
2654 5fo. Locomotive "Continent", 1854 . . . . 1·40 90

533 "J. Pannonius" (A. Mantegna)

535 Doorway of Csempeszkopacs Church

534 "Mariner 9"

1972. 500th Death Anniv of Janus Pannonius (poet).
2655 **533** 1fo. multicoloured . . . 15 10

1972. Exploration of Mars. Multicoloured.
2656 2fo. Type **534** 45 45
2657 2fo. "Mars 2 and 3" 45 45

1972. Protection of Monuments.
2658 **535** 3fo. green 75 15

536 Hungarian Greyhound

1972. Dogs. Multicoloured.
2659 40fi. Type **536** 15 10
2660 60fi. Afghan hound (head) 20 10
2661 80fi. Irish wolfhound . . . 20 10
2662 1fo.20 Borzoi (head) 25 10
2663 2fo. Greyhound 50 20
2664 4fo. Whippet (head) . . . . 1·10 35
2665 6fo. Afghan hound . . . . 1·60 85

537 J. Imre, E. Grosz and L. Blaskovics

1972. 1st. European Oculists' Congress, Budapest. Famous Oculists.
2666 **537** 1fo. brown and red . . . 75 10
2667 – 2fo. brown and blue . . 1·10 30
DESIGN: 2fo. A. Gullstrand, V. P. Filatov and J. Gonin.

538 Footballers and Flag of Hungary

1972. Air. European Football Championships. Footballers and Flags of participating countries. Multicoloured.
2668 40fi. Type **538** 10 10
2669 60fi. Rumania 15 10
2670 80fi. West Germany 20 10
2671 1fo. England 30 15
2672 1fo.20 Yugoslavia 40 15
2673 2fo. Russia 55 20
2674 4fo. Italy 85 75
2675 5fo. Belgium . . . . 1·10 1·10

539 "V. Miskolcz" postmark, 1818–43

1972. Stamp Day.
2676 **539** 2fo.+1fo. black & blue 55 70
2677 – 2fo.+1fo. black & yell 55 70
2678 – 2fo.+1fo. black & grn . 55 70
2679 – 2fo.+1fo. mult 55 70
MS2680 105 × 90 mm. 2fo.+1fo. × 4 (a) Wax impression of signet ring, 1953; (b) Letter of Rakoczi era, 1705; (c) Courier letter of 1708; (d) V. Tokai postmark, 1752 . . . 3·25 3·45
DESIGNS: No. 2677, "Szegedin" postmark, 1827–48; 2678, "Esztergom" postmark, 1848–51; 2679, "Budapest 71" stamp cent, cancellation, 1971.

540 Girl reading Book

541 Roses

1972. International Book Year.
2681 **540** 1fo. multicoloured . . . 20 10

1972. National Rose Exhibition.
2682 **541** 1fo. multicoloured . . . 35 10

542 Globe and Olympic Rings (-size illustration)

1972. Air. Olympic Games, Munich (1st issue). Sheet 117 × 68 mm.
MS2683 **542** 10fo. multicoloured 675 850
See also Nos. 2687/**MS**2695.

543 G. Dimitrov

544 "St. Martin and the Beggar"

1972. 90th Birth Anniv of Georgi Dimitrov (Bulgarian leader).
2684 **543** 3fo. multicoloured . . . 30 15

1972. "Belgica '72" Stamp Exhibition, Brussles. Sheet 69 × 94 mm.
MS2685 **544** 10fo. multicoloured 3·00 3·75

545 Gy. Dozsa

1972. 500th Birth Anniv of Gyorgy Dozsa (revolutionary).
2686 **545** 1fo. multicoloured . . . 20 10

546 Football

1972. Olympic Games, Munich (2nd issue). Multicoloured.
2687 40fi. Type **546**(postage) . . 10 10
2688 60fi. Water-polo 10 10
2689 80fi. Javelin-throwing . . . 15 10
2690 1fo. Kayak-canoeing 20 10
2691 1fo.20 Boxing 30 10
2692 2fo. Gymnastics 50 10

2693 3fo.+1fo. Wrestling 75 35
2694 5fo. Fencing . . . . 1·10 60

MS2695 115 × 90 mm. 10fo. Show-jumping (air) . . . . 3·75 4·00
The design on the 10fo. is larger, 43 × 43 mm.

547 Prince Geza indicating Site of Szekesfehervar

1972. Millenary of Szekesfehervar and 750th Anniv of "Aranybulla" (legislative document). Multicoloured.
2696 40fi. Type **547** 10 10
2697 60fi. King Stephen and shield 10 10
2698 80fi. Soldiers and cavalry . . 15 10
2699 1fo.20 King Stephen drawing up legislation . . 35 10
2700 2fo. Mason sculpting column 45 10
2701 4fo. Merchant displaying wares to King Stephen . . 80 20
2702 6fo. Views of Szekesfehervar and Palace . . . . 1·10 40
MS2703 136 × 90 mm. 10fo. King Andrew II at presentation of "Aranybulla" to the court . . 3·00 3·00
The design on the 10fo. is larger, 95 × 47 mm.

548 Parliament Building, Budapest

1972. Constitution Day. Multicoloured.
2704 5fo. Type **548** 50 10
2705 6fo. Parliament in session 70 20

549 Eger and "Bulls Blood"

1972. World Wines Competition, Budapest Multicoloured.
2706 1fo. Type **549** 35 10
2707 2fo. Tokay and "Tokay Aszu" 65 20

550 Ear of Wheat and Emblems on Open Book

1972. 175th Anniv of Georgikon Agricultural Academy, Keszthely.
2708 **550** 1fo. multicoloured . . . 15 10

551 "Rothschild" Vase

553 Commemorative Emblem

552 Class M62 Diesel Train and U.I.C. Emblem

1972. Herendi Porcelain. Multicoloured.
2709 40fi. Type **551** 15 10
2710 60fi. "Poisson" bonboniere 15 10
2711 80fi. "Victoria" vase 20 10
2712 1fo. "Miramare" dish . . . 20 10
2713 1fo.20 "Godollo" pot . . . 25 10
2714 2fo. "Empire" tea-set . . . 35 10
2715 4fo. "Apponyi" dish 75 30
2716 5fo. "Baroque" vase . . . . 1·25 65
The 60fi., 1fo.20, and 4fo. are size 34 × 36 mm.

1972. 50th Anniv of Int Railway Union.
2717 **552** 1fo. red 50 10

1972. 25th Anniv of National Economy Plan.
2718 **553** 1fo. yellow, sepia & brn 20 10

554 River Steamer and Old Obuda

1972. Centenary of Unification of Buda, Obuda and Pest as Budapest.
2719 **554** 1fo. purple and blue . . 30 10
2720 – 1fo. blue and purple . . 30 10
2721 – 2fo. green and brown . . 30 10
2722 – 2fo. brown and green . . 30 10
2723 – 3fo. brown and green . . 40 10
2724 – 3fo. green and brown . . 40 10
DESIGNS: No. 2720, River hydrofoil and modern Obuda; 2721, Buda, 1872; 2722, Budapest, 1972; 2723, Pest, 1872; 2724, Parliament Buildings, Budapest.

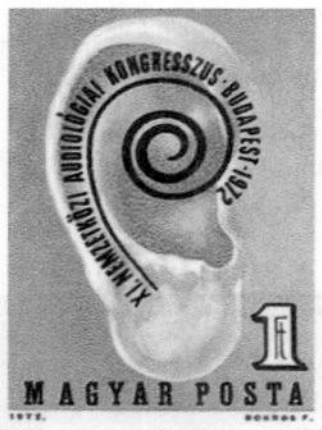

555 Congress Emblem within Ear

1972. Int Audiological Congress, Budapest.
2725 **555** 1fo. multicoloured . . . 30 10

556 "Apollo 16"

1972. Air. Moon Flight of "Apollo 16". Sheet 120 × 75 mm.
MS2726 **556** 10fo. multicoloured 3·00 3·00

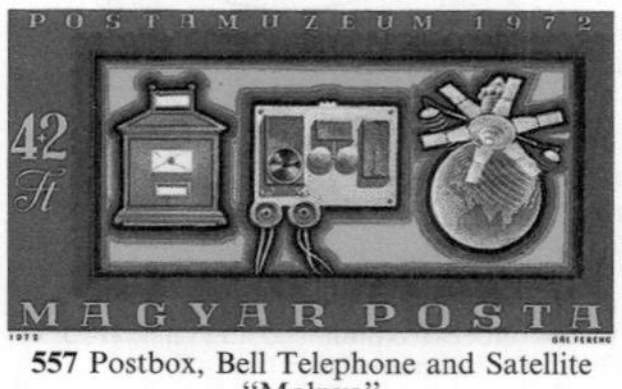

557 Postbox, Bell Telephone and Satellite "Molnya"

1972. Reopening of Postal and Philatelic Museums, Budapest. Multicoloured.
2727 4fo.+2fo. Type **557** 75 80
2728 4fo.+2fo. Globe, posthorn and stamps 75 80

558 Miklos Radnoti (poet)

1972. Radnoti Commemoration.
2729 **558** 1fo. multicoloured . . . 10 10

559 F. Martos **560** "The Muses" (J. Rippl-Ronai)

1972. 75th Birth Anniv of Flora Martos (patriot).
2730 **559** 1fo. multicoloured . . . 10 10

1972. Stained Glass Windows. Multicoloured.
2731 40fi. Type **560** 15 10
2732 60fi. "16th-century Scribe" (F. Sebestenyl) 15 10
2733 1fo. "Exodus to Egypt" (K. Lotz and B. Szekely) 20 10
2734 1fo.50 "Prince Arpad's Messenger" (J. Percz) . . 35 10
2735 2fo.50 "The Nativity" (L. Sztehlo) 55 10
2736 4fo. "Prince Arpad and Leaders" (K. Kernstock) 95 20
2737 5fo. "King Matthias reprimands the Rich Aristocrats" (J. Haranghy) . . . . . . 1·40 55

561 "Textiles"

1972. Opening of Textiles Technical Museum, Budapest.
2738 **561** 1fo. multicoloured . . . 30 10

562 Main Square, Szarvas **563** S. Petofi

1972. Views.
2739 **562** 40fi. brown and orange 10 10
2739a – 40fi. black and green 10 10
2740 – 1fo. blue and light blue 10 10
2741 – 1fo. brown and yellow 10 10
2742 – 3fo. green and blue . . 50 10
2743 – 4fo. red and orange . . 50 10
2743a – 4fo. brown and pink . . 60 10
2744 – 5fo. blue and cobalt . . 45 10
2745 – 6fo. brown and red . . 1·00 10
2746 – 7fo. violet and lilac . . 85 10
2747 – 8fo. deep green & green 1·10 10
2748 – 10fo. brown and yellow 1·40 10
2749 – 20fo. multicoloured . . 3·25 15
2750 – 50fo. multicoloured . . 5·75 70
DESIGNS: 21 × 18 mm: 40fi. (No. 2739a) Rotunda (public health centre), Vasvar; 1fo. (No. 2740) Salgotarjan; 1fo. (No. 2741) Nyirbator. 28 × 22 mm: 3fo. Tokay; 4fo. (No. 2743) Esztergom; 4fo. (No. 2743a) Szentendre; 5fo. Szolnok; 6fo. Dunaujvaros; 7fo. Kaposvar; 8fo. Vac; 10fo. Kiskunfelegyhaza; 20fo. Veszprem; 50ra. Pecs.

1972. 150th Birth Anniv of Sandor Petofi (poet and patriot).
2762 – 1fo. red 10 10
2763 **563** 2fo. lilac 20 10
2764 – 3fo. green 40 20
DESIGNS: 1fo. Petofi making speech in Cafe Pilvax; 3fo. Petofi on horseback during War of Independence, 1848–49.

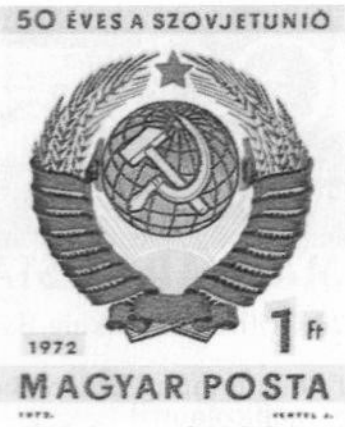

564 Arms of U.S.S.R.

1972. 50th Anniv of U.S.S.R.
2765 **564** 1fo. multicoloured . . . 10 10

565 Code Map and Crow Symbol

1973. Introduction of Postal Codes.
2766 **565** 1fo. black and red . . . 15 10

1973. As Nos. 1912, 1915/16 and 1918 but smaller.
2767 2fo. blue (22 × 19 mm) . . . 35 20
2768 3fo. blue (22 × 19 mm) . . . 55 30
2769 4fo. green (19 × 22 mm) . . 70 45
2770 6fo. ochre (22 × 19 mm) . . 1·40 75

566 Astronaut on Moon

1973. Air. Moon Flight of "Apollo 17". Sheet 69 × 110 mm.
MS2771 **566** 10fo. multicoloured 3·50 4·00

567 I. Madach **568** Carnival Mask

1973. 150th Birth Anniv of Imre Madach (writer).
2772 **567** 1fo. multicoloured . . . 20 10

1973. Busho-Walking Ceremony, Mohacs. Carnival Masks.
2773 **568** 40fi. multicoloured . . . 10 10
2774 – 60fi. multicoloured . . . 10 10
2775 – 80fi. multicoloured . . . 15 10
2776 – 1fo.20 multicoloured . . 30 10
2777 – 2fo. multicoloured . . . 45 15
2778 – 4fo. multicoloured . . . 75 20
2779 – 6fo. multicoloured . . . 1·40 55

569 Copernicus

1973. 500th Birth Anniv of Copernicus.
2780 **569** 3fo. blue 90 45

570 "Venus 8" (-size illustration)

1973. Air. Space Flight of "Venus 8". Sheet 110 × 93 mm.

MS2781	**570** 10fo. multicoloured	3·00	3·25

571 Show-jumping (Pentathlon) and Gold Medal

1973. Hungarian Medal Winners, Olympic Games, Munich. Multicoloured.

2782	40fi. Type **571**	15	10
2783	60fi. Weightlifting (Gold)	15	10
2784	1fo. Canoeing (Silver)	30	10
2785	1fo.20 Swimming (Silver)	50	10
2786	1fo.80 Boxing (Gold)	40	10
2787	4fo. Wrestling (Gold)	80	20
2788	6fo. Fencing (Gold)	1·25	75

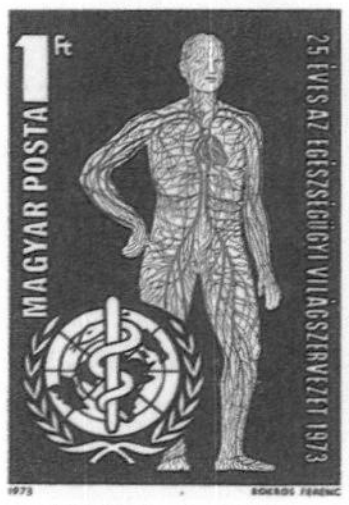

572 Biological Man **573** Winter Wrens

1973. 25th Anniv of W.H.O.

2790	**572** 1fo. brown and green	20	10

1973. Air. Hungarian Birds. Multicoloured.

2791	40fi. Type **573**(postage)	25	10
2792	60fi. Rock thrush	30	10
2793	80fi. European robins	35	10
2794	1fo. Firecrests	40	15
2795	1fo.20 Linnets	55	15
2796	2fo. Blue tits	60	25
2797	4fo. Bluethroat	1·00	40
2798	5fo. Grey wagtails	1·40	45

MS2799	132 × 88 mm. 10fo. Girl igniting Olympic Flame (air)	4·50	60

The design of the 10fo. is larger, 83 × 46 mm.

574 Soldier and Weapons

1973. Military Stamp Collectors' Exn, Budapest.

2799	**574** 3fo. multicoloured	45	25

575 "Budapest 61" 1fo. Stamp

1973. "IBRA 73" Stamp Exn, Munich, and "POLSKA '73", Poznan. Reproductions of Hungary Exhibition stamps. Multicoloured.

2800	40fi. Type **575**(postage)	10	10
2801	60fi. "Budapest 61" 1fo.70 stamp	10	10
2802	80fi. "Budapest 61" 2fo.60 stamp	15	10
2803	1fo. "Budapest 61" 3fo. stamp	30	10
2804	1fo.20 "Budapest 71" 2fo. stamp	20	10
2805	2fo. "Budapest 71" 2fo. stamp	30	10
2806	4fo. "Budapest 71" 2fo. stamp	1·00	45
2807	5fo. "Budapest 71" 2fo. stamp	1·00	55

MS2808	130 × 81 mm. 10fo. Bavaria's first stamp, Town Hall and Olympic complex, Munich (air)	3·25	3·00

The design of the 10fo. is larger, 83 × 46 mm.

576 Setting Type and Preparing Ink **578** "Europa" Poster

577 "Storm over Hortobagy Puszta"

1973. 500th Anniv of Book-printing in Hungary.

2809	**576** 1fo. black and gold	10	10
2810	– 3fo. black and gold	50	15

DESIGN: 3fo. Printer operating press.

1973. Paintings by Csontvary Kosztka. Mult.

2811	40fi. Type **577**	10	10
2812	60fi. "Mary's Well, Nazareth"	15	10
2813	1fo. "Carriage drive by Moonlight" (vert)	25	10
2814	1fo.50 "Pilgrimage to the Lebanese Cedars" (vert)	30	10
2815	2fo.50 "The Lone Cedar"	40	10
2816	4fo. "Waterfall at Jajce"	90	20
2817	5fo. "Ruins of Greek Theatre at Taormina"	1·10	60
MS2818	114 × 75 mm. 10fo. "Riding at the Seaside"	3·00	3·25

The design of the 10fo. is larger, 91 × 43 mm.

1973. European Security and Co-operation Conference, Helsinki.

2819	**578** 2fo.50 brown and black	2·75	2·75

579 "Rosa gallica" **580** "Let's be friends...!"

1973. Wild Flowers. Multicoloured.

2820	40fi. Type **579**	15	10
2821	60fi. "Cyclamen europaeum"	20	10
2822	80fi. "Pulmonaria mollissima"	25	10
2823	1fo.20 "Bellis perennis"	30	10
2824	2fo. "Adonis vernalis"	45	10
2825	4fo. "Viola cyanea"	75	15
2826	6fo. "Papaver rhoeas"	1·00	50

1973. Road Safety.

2827	**580** 40fi. green and red	10	10
2828	– 60fi. violet and orange	15	10
2829	– 1fo. blue and red	25	10

DESIGNS: 60fi. "Not even a glass!" (hand reaching for tumbler); 1fo. "Cyclist – use a lamp" (car running down cyclist).

581 Silver "Eagle" Disc

1973. Jewelled Treasures, National Museum. Multicoloured.

2830	2fo.+50fi. Type **581**	55	75
2831	2fo.+50fi. Serpent's head ring	55	75
2832	2fo.+50fi. "Loving couple" buckle	55	75
2833	2fo.+50fi. Silver "floral" buckle	55	75
MS2834	75 × 101 mm. 2fo.+50fi. × 4 (a) Opaline pendant; (b) Jewelled buckle; (c) Floral pin; (d) Rosette pendant	375	325

The designs in **MS**2834 are each 25 × 36 mm.

582 "Skylab" photographing Earth

1973. Air. "Skylab" Space-station. Sheet 114 × 75 mm.

MS2835	**582** 10fo. multicoloured	2·75	4·00

583 "The Three Kings" (Master of the High Altar, Szmrecsany)

1973. Esztergom Millennium. "Old Master" Paintings in the Christian Museum. Mult.

2836	40fi. Type **583**	10	10
2837	60fi. "Angels making Music" (Master "B.E.")	10	10
2838	1fo. "The Adoration of the Magi" (anon.)	15	10
2839	1fo.50 "The Annunciation" (Szmrecsany Master)	30	10
2840	2fo.50 "Angels making Music" (different Master "B.E.")	45	10
2841	4fo. "The Visitation of Mary and Elizabeth" (Szmrecsany Master)	70	25
2842	5fo. "The Legend of St. Catharine of Alexandria" (Master Bati)	1·00	40
MS2843	73 × 101 mm. 10fo. "The Birth of Jesus" (Szmrecsany Master)	3·00	3·00

584 Csokonai's Statue, Debrecen

1973. Birth Bicentenary of M. Csokonai Vitez (poet).

2844	**584** 2fo. multicoloured	45	10

585 J. Marti **586** B. Pesti

1973. 120th Birth Anniv of Jose Marti (Cuban patriot).

2845	**585** 1fo. brown, red and blue	10	10

1973. 30th Death Anniv of Barnabas Pesti (patriot).

2846	**586** 1fo. lt brown, brown & bl	10	10

588 Kayak-canoeing

1973. World Aquatic Sports Championships, Belgrade and Tampere. Multicoloured.

2855	40fi. Type **588**	15	10
2856	60fi. Water polo	15	10
2857	80fi. Men's solo kayak	20	10
2858	1fo.20 Swimming	25	10
2859	2fo. Men's kayak fours	40	10
2860	4fo. Men's solo canoe	65	20
2861	6fo. Men's double canoe	1·10	65

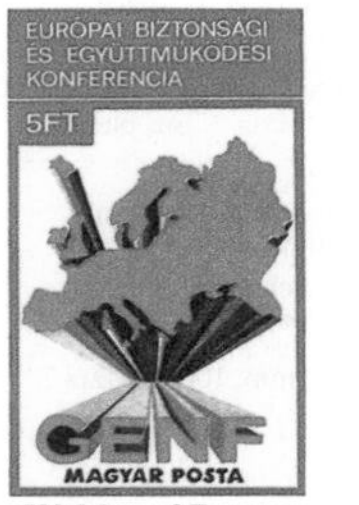

589 Map of Europe

1974. European Security and Co-operation Conference, Geneva. Sheet 143 × 71 mm containing two stamps as T **589** together with a double-size label depicting Geneva.

MS2862	**589** 50fo. × 2 gold, blue and green	7·50	8·25

590 Lenin

1974. 50th Death Anniv of Lenin

2863	**590** 2fo. brown, blue and gold	30	10

591 J. Boczor, I. Bekes and T. Elek

1974. Hungarian Heroes of the French Resistance.

2864	**591** 3fo. multicoloured	50	10

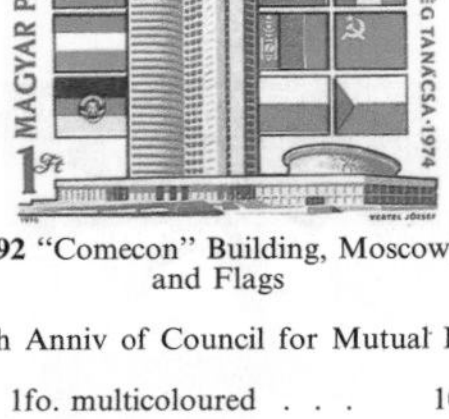

592 "Comecon" Building, Moscow, and Flags

1974. 25th Anniv of Council for Mutual Economic Aid.

2865	**592** 1fo. multicoloured	10	10

593 Savings Bank Emblem, Note and Coins **595** Pres. Salvador Allende

594 "Mariner 4" on course for Mars

1974. 25th Anniv of National Savings Bank.
2866 **593** 1fo. multicoloured . . . 10 10

1974. Mars Research Projects. Multicoloured.
2867 40fi. Type **594** (postage) . . 10 10
2868 60fi. "Mars 2" approaching Mars 15 10
2869 80fi. "Mariner 4" space probe 20 10
2870 1fo. Mt. Palomar telescope and Mars photo 35 10
2871 1fo.20 "Mars 3" on planet's surface 45 10
2872 5fo. "Mariner 9" approaching Mars and satellites . . . . 1·25 20
2873 6fo. G. Schiaparelli and Martian "canals" map (air) . . . . 1·50 75
MS2874 96 × 91 mm. 10fo. "Mars 7" in Space . . . . 3·00 3·25

1974. Pres. Allende of Chile Commemoration.
2875 **595** 1fo. multicoloured . . . 20 10

596 "Mona Lisa" (Leonardo da Vinci)

1974. Exhibition of "Mona Lisa" in Japan.
2876 **596** 4fo. multicoloured . . . 6·00 5·25

597 2k. Stamp of 1874 and Mallow

1974. Centenary of Hungarian "Envelope Design" Stamps. Sheet 103 × 87 mm containing T **597** and similar horiz design. Multicoloured.
MS2877 2fo.50 × 5 (a) Type **597**; (b) 3k. stamp and aster; (c) 5k. stamp and daisy; (d) 10k. stamp and columbine . . . . 3·00 3·35

598 Dove with Letter

1974. Centenary of U.P.U. Multicoloured.
2878 40fi. Type **598** 10 10
2879 60fi. Mail coach 10 10
2880 80fi. Early mail van and postbox 15 10
2881 1fo.20 Balloon post 20 10
2882 2fo. Diesel mail train . . . 65 10
2883 4fo. Post-bus 80 15
2884 6fo. Tupolev Tu-154 mail plane . . . . 1·40 35
MS2885 132 × 106 mm. 2fo.50 × 4 (a) As 60fi.; (b) As 80fi. but design reversed; (c) As 6fo.; (d) "Apollo 15" . . . . 3·00 3·75
The designs in **MS**2885 are smaller, 45 × 30 mm. and are redrawn so that only part of the U.P.U. Monument falls on each stamp.

599 Swiss 2½r. "Basle Dove" Stamp of 1845

1974. "Internaba 1974" Stamp Exn, Basle.
2886 **599** 3fo. multicoloured . . . 1·25 95

600 13th-century miniature from King Alfonso X's "Book of Chess, Dice and Tablings" and Pawn

1974. 50th Anniv of International Chess Federation and 21st Chess Olympiad, Nice.
2887 **600** 40fi. black, green and blue 25 10
2888 – 60fi. black, brown & lilac 40 10
2889 – 80fi. black, yellow & grn 60 10
2890 – 1fo.20 black, yellow and lilac 70 15
2891 – 2fo. black, stone and blue . . . . 1·00 15
2892 – 4fo. black, yellow & pink 1·40 60
2893 – 6fo. black, brown & grn 1·50 80
DESIGNS: 60fi. 15th-century woodcut from "The Game and Playe of Chesse" by William Caxton and knight; 80fi. 15th-century illustration from Italian chess book and bishop; 1fo.20, "The Chess Players" (17th-century engraving by Jacob van der Heyden) and rook; 2fo. Kempelen's chess playing machine (1769) and king; 4fo. Geza Maroczy (Hungarian master) and queen; 6fo. View of Nice and tournament emblem.

601 Passenger Train, 1874

1974. Centenary of the Budapest Rack Railway. Sheet 132 × 96 mm. containing T **601** and similar horiz designs. Multicoloured.
MS2894 2fo.50 Type **601**; 2fo.50 Goods train, 1874; 2fo.50 Passenger train, 1929; 2fo.50 Passenger train, 1973 . . . . . 3·25 4·00

602 Congress Emblem

1974. 4th International Economists' Congress, Budapest.
2895 **602** 2fo. black, blue and silver 30 10

603 "Woman Bathing" (K Lotz)

1974. Nudes. Paintings. Multicoloured.
2896 40fi. Type **603** 15 10
2897 60fi. "Awakening" (K. Brocky) 15 10
2898 1fo. "Venus and Cupid" (K. Brocky) (horiz) . . . 25 10
2899 1fo.50 "After Bathing" (K. Lotz) 45 10
2900 2fo.50 "Honi soit qui mal y pense" (reclining nude) (I. Csok) (horiz) 65 15
2901 4fo. "After Bathing" (B. Szkely) 90 25
2902 5fo. "Devotion" (E. Korb) 1·10 70
MS2903 75 × 102 mm. 10fo. "Lark" (P.M. Szinyei) (50 × 71 mm) . . 3·00 3·75

604 "Mimi" (Czobel)

605 "Intersputnik" Satellite Tracking Radar

1974. 91st Birth Anniv of Bela Czobel (painter).
2904 **604** 1fo. multicoloured . . . 45 10

1974. 25th Anniv of Technical and Scientific Co-operation between Hungary and Soviet Union.
2905 **605** 1fo. violet and blue . . . 15 10
2906 – 3fo. mauve and green . . 35 10
DESIGN—HORIZ: 3fo. Power installations.

606 Neruda

607 Swedish 3s. Stamp, 1855, and "Swedish Lion"

1974. Pablo Neruda (Chilean poet) Commem.
2907 **606** 1fo. brown, deep brown and blue 10 10

1974. "Stockholmia 74" International Stamp Exhibition.
2908 **607** 3fo. green, blue and gold 75 1·00

608 Tanks and Infantry

1974. Military Day.
2909 **608** 1fo. black, red and gold (postage) 20 10
2910 – 2fo. blk, grn & gold (air) 35 10
2911 – 3fo. black, blue and gold 55 15
DESIGNS—VERT: 2fo. Guided missile and radar. HORIZ: 3fo. Parachutist, helicopter and jet fighter.

609 J. A. Segner and Moon

1974. 270th Birth Anniv of Janos Segner (scientist).
2912 **609** 3fo. multicoloured . . . 50 15

610 Hansa Brandenburg C-1 Biplane, 1918

1974. Air. "Aerofila 1974" International Airmail Exhibition, Budapest. Multicoloured.
2913 2fo.+1fo. Type **610** . . . . 1·00 1·00
2914 2fo.+1fo. Airship "Graf Zeppelin" . . . . 1·00 1·00
2915 2fo.+1fo. Hot air balloon 1·00 1·00
2916 2fo.+1fo. Mil Mi-1 helicopter . . . . 1·00 1·00
MS2917 107 × 92 mm. 2fo.+1fo. Hungarian 1k.50 stamp, 1918; 2fo. + 1fo. Hungarian 500k. stamp, 1924; 2fo.+1fo. Hungarian 3fo. stamp, 1970; 2fo. + 1fo. Hungarian 3fo. stamp, 1970; 2fo.+1fo. Hungarian 10fo. stamp, 1972 . . . . 3·75 4·25

611 Purple Tiger Moth

1974. Butterflies and Moths. Multicoloured.
2918 40fi. Type **611** 25 10
2919 60fi. Marbled white 35 10
2920 80fi. Apollo 40 15
2921 1fo. Spurge hawk moth . . 50 15
2922 1fo.20 Clifden's nonpareil 60 30
2923 5fo. Purple emperor . . . . 1·50 45
2924 6fo. Purple-edged copper . . 1·90 90

612 Istvan Pataki

613 Mother and Child

1974. Hungarian Antifascist Martyrs. Mult.
2925 1fo. Type **612** 10 10
2926 1fo. Robert Kreutz 10 10

1974. "Mothers".
2927 **613** 1fo. black, yellow & blue 10 10

614 Puppy

616 F. Bolyai

615 Lambarene Hospital

1974. Young Animals. (1st series). Mult.
2928 40fi. Type **614** 10 10
2929 60fi. Kittens (horiz) 15 10
2930 80fi. Rabbit 20 10
2931 1fo.20 Foal (horiz) 30 10
2932 2fo. Lamb 55 10
2933 4fo. Calf (horiz) 85 20
2934 6fo. Piglet . . . . 1·40 75
See also Nos. 3014/20.

1975. Birth Centenary of Dr. Albert Schweitzer (Nobel Peace Prize Winner). Multicoloured.
2935 40fi. Type **615** 10 10
2936 60fi. Casualty being treated 15 10
2937 80fi. Casualty being transported by canoe . . 20 10
2938 1fo.20 Charitable goods arriving by freighter . . . 30 10
2939 2fo. View of Lambarene, doves, globe and Red Cross emblem 50 10

2940 4fo. Schweitzer's Nobel Peace Prize medal and inscription 80 15
2941 6fo. Schweitzer and organ-pipes . . . . 1·10 35

1975. Birth Bicentenary of Farkas Bolyai (mathematician).
2942 **616** 1fo. grey and red 20 10

617 Carrier-pigeon

1975. Air. Pigeon-racing Olympics, Budapest.
2943 **617** 3fo. multicoloured . . . 1·00 75

618 Karolyi

1975. Birth Centenary of Count Mihaly Karolyi (politician).
2944 **618** 1fo. brown and blue . . 10 10

619 Woman's Head

1975. International Woman's Year.
2945 **619** 1fo. black and blue . . . 10 10

620 "Railway Rebuilding" (⅔-size illustration)

1975. 30th Anniv of Liberation. Mult.
2946 40fi. Type **620** 25 10
2947 60fi. Hammer and sickle representing agriculture 10 10
2948 2fo. Blacksmith's hammer representing Communist party action 10 10
2949 4fo. Power hammer as "3" representing the "Three Year Heavy Industry Plan" . . . . 1·10 20
2950 5fo. Blocks of Flats representing "developed socialist society" 45 15

621 1915 "Arrow"

1975. 75th Anniv of Hungarian Automobile Club. Vintage Motor Cars. Multicoloured.
2951 40fi. Type **621** 20 10
2952 60fi. 1911 "Swift" 20 10
2953 80fi. 1908 Ford "T" 25 10
2954 1fo. 1901 Mercedes 30 15
2955 1fo.20 1912 Panhard Levassor 40 15
2956 5fo. 1906 Csonka . . . . . 1·25 30
2957 6fo. Hungarian Automobile Club and international motoring organizations' emblems . . . . 2·00 65

622 "Creation of Adam" (from ceiling of Sistine Chapel) (½-size illustration)

1975. 500th Birth Anniv of Michelangelo. Sheet 126 × 90 mm.
MS2958 **622** 10fo. multicoloured 3·75 4·50

623 Academy Building

1975. 150th Anniv of National Academy of Sciences. Multicoloured.
2959 1fo. Type **623** 20 20
2960 2fo. Dates "1825" and "1975" 30 20
2961 3fo. Count Istvan Szechenyi (statesman) . . . . 1·00 40

624 Olympic Stadium, Moscow

1975. "Socphilex V" International Stamp Exhibition, Moscow.
2962 **624** 5fo. multicoloured . . . 90 1·25

625 French 1f. Stamp, 1964

1975. "Arphila 75" International Stamp Exhibition, Paris.
2963 **625** 5fo. multicoloured . . . 90 1·25

626 Electric Railway Locomotive and Transformer

1975. 75th Anniv of Hungarian Electro-technical Association.
2964 **626** 1fo. multicoloured . . . 60 10

627 "Sputnik 2"

1975. Air. "Apollo–Soyuz" Space Link. Mult.
2965 40fi. Type **627** 10 10
2966 60fi. "Mercury Atlas 5" . . 10 10
2967 80fi. "Lunokhod 1" (moon vehicle) 15 10
2968 1fo.20 "Apollo 15" (moon vehicle) 25 10
2969 2fo. Launch of "Soyuz" from Baikonur 45 10
2970 4fo. Launch of "Apollo" . . 90 15
2971 6fo. "Apollo–Soyuz" link-up 1·40 45
MS2972 129 × 100 mm. 10fo. "Apollo" and "Soyuz" in linking manoeuvre (65 × 42 mm) . . . 3·00 3·00

628 Sword, Epee, Rapier, and Globe

1975. World Fencing Championships, Budapest.
2973 **628** 1fo. multicoloured . . . 20 10

629 Whale Pavilion

1975. International Exposition, Okinawa (1st issue). Sheet 116 × 95 mm.
MS2974 **629** 10fo. multicoloured 2·75 2·50
See also Nos. 2986/92.

630 Map of Europe and Cogwheel (½-size illustration)

1975. Air. European Security and Co-operation Conference, Helsinki. Sheet 157 × 82 mm.
MS2975 **630** 10fo. multicoloured 7·50 7·50

631 A. Zimmermann

1975. Birth Centenary of Dr. Agoston Zimmermann (veterinary surgeon).
2976 **631** 1fo. dp brown, brn & bl 15 10

632 Branches of Tree symbolizing 14 Languages

634 Anjou Wall Fountain

633

1975. Int Finno-Ugrian Congress, Budapest.
2977 **632** 1fo. multicoloured . . . 10 10

1975. Air. Hungarian Stamps since 1945. Sheet 150 × 95 mm. Multicoloured.
MS2978 Hungarian 1fo. Stamp, 1964, 2fo. Stamp, 1961 and 2fo.50 Stamp, 1973 . . . . 3·00 3·75

1975. Stamp Day. Preservation of Monuments. Monuments in Visegrad Palace. Multicoloured.
2979 2fo.+1fo. Type **634** . . . . 1·50 1·75
2980 2fo.+1fo. Anjou well house 1·50 1·75
2981 2fo.+1fo. Hunyadi wall fountain . . . . 1·50 1·75
2982 2fo.+1fo. Hercules fountain 1·50 1·75
MS2983 128 × 100 mm. 2fo.+1fo. Detail of Hunyadi wall fountain (26 x 37 mm); 2fo.+1fo. Madonna of Visegrad (52 × 37 mm); 2fo.+1fo. Detail of Hercules fountain (26 × 37 mm); 2fo.+1fo. View of Visegrad in 1480 (105 × 37 mm) . . . . 9·00 10·00

635 Hungarian Arms and Map

636 Ocean Pollution

1975. 25th Anniv of Hungarian Council System. Multicoloured.
2984 1fo. Type **635** 15 10
2985 1fo. Voters participating in council election 15 10

1975. International Exposition, Okinawa. Environmental Protection (2nd issue). Multicoloured.
2986 40fi. Type **636** 10 10
2987 60fi. Strangled rose (water pollution) 15 10
2988 80fi. Clown anemonefish struggling for uncontaminated water (river pollution) 20 10
2989 1fo. Dead carnation (soil pollution) 30 10
2990 1fo.20 Falling bird (air pollution) 40 10
2991 5fo. Infected lung (smoke pollution) . . . . 1·00 15
2992 6fo. Healthy and skeletal hands (life and death) . . 1·25 30

637 Mariska Gardos (writer) (1885–1973)

1975. Birth Annivs of Celebrities. Each black and red.
2993 1fo. Type **637** 15 10
2994 1fo. Imre Tarr (soldier) (1900–1937) 15 10
2995 1fo. Imre Meso (Communist martyr) (1905–1956) . . . 15 10

638 Treble Clef, Organ and Orchestra

1975. Centenary of Ferenc Liszt Music Academy, Budapest.
2996 **638** 1fo. multicoloured . . . 30 10

639 18th-century Icon of Szigetcsep

1975. Hungarian Icons depicting the Virgin and Child. Multicoloured.
2997 40fi. Type **639** 10 10
2998 60fi. 18th-century Icon of Graboc 20 10
2999 1fo. 18th-century Icon of Esztergom 20 10
3000 1fo.50 18th-century Icon of Vatoped 40 10

3001 2fo.50 17th-century Icon of Tottos 60 10
3002 4fo. 17th-century Icon of Gyor 75 20
3003 5fo. 18th-century Icon of Kazan . . . . 1·25 70

640 Mother and Child, Flags and Radar Equipment (⅔-size illustration)

1975. 20th Anniv of Warsaw Treaty.
3004 **640** 1fo. multicoloured . . . 10 10

641 Ice Hockey

1975. Winter Olympic Games, Innsbruck. Multicoloured.
3005 40fi. Type **641** 25 10
3006 60fi. Slalom skiing 25 10
3007 80fi. Slalom skiing (different) 25 10
3008 1fo.20 Ski jumping 35 10
3009 2fo. Speed skating 40 10
3010 4fo. Cross-country skiing . . 80 15
3011 6fo. Bobsleighing . . . . . 1·00 50
MS3012 130 × 80 mm. 10fo. Pairs figure skating (65 × 42 mm) . . 3·00 3·25

642 Banknotes of 1925 and 1975

1976. 50th Anniv of State Banknote Printing Office, Budapest.
3013 **642** 1fo. multicoloured . . . 35 10

1976. Young Animals (2nd series). As T **614**. Multicoloured.
3014 40fi. Wild boars (horiz) . . 10 10
3015 60fi. Eurasian red squirrels 15 10
3016 80fi. Lynx (horiz) 20 10
3017 1fo.20 Wolf cubs 35 10
3018 2fo. Red fox cubs (horiz) . . 50 10
3019 4fo. Brown bear cubs . . . 80 15
3020 6fo. Lion cubs (horiz) . . . 1·25 45

643 Alexander Graham Bell, Telecommunications Satellite and Dish Aerial

1976. Telephone Centenary.
3021 **643** 3fo. multicoloured . . . 60 65

644 "Horses in Storm" (K. Lotz)

1976. Air. Tourist Publicity. Paintings. Sheet 95 × 135 mm containing T **644** and similar square design. Multicoloured.
MS3022 5fo. Type **644**; 5fo. "Morning at Tihany" (J. Halapy) 3·00 3·25

645 "Clash between Rakoczi's Kuruts and Hapsburg Soldiers"

1976. 300th Birth Anniv of Prince Ferenc Rakoczi II (soldier). Paintings. Multicoloured.
3023 40fi. Type **645** 10 10
3024 60fi. "Meeting of Rakoczi and Tamas Esze" 15 10
3025 1fo. "The Parliament of Onod" (Mor Than) . . . 30 10
3026 2fo. "Kuruts' Encampment" 75 15
3027 3fo. "Ilona Zrinyi" (Rakoczi's mother) (vert) 1·25 30
3028 4fo. "Kuruts Officers" (vert) 1·60 35
3029 5fo. "Prince Rakoczi II" (A. Manyoki) (vert) . . . 2·25 90

646 Metric System Act, 1876

647 Knight

1976. Centenary of Introduction of Metric System into Hungary. Multicoloured.
3030 1fo. Type **646** 15 10
3031 2fo. Istvan Krusper (scientist) and vacuum balance 25 20
3032 3fo. Interferometer, space rocket and emblem . . . 55 25

1976. Stamp Day. Gothic Statues from Buda Castle.
3033 2fo.50+1fo. Type **647** . . . 80 75
3034 2fo.50+1fo. Armour bearer 80 75
3035 2fo.50+1fo. Apostle 80 75
3036 2fo.50+1fo. Bishop 80 75
MS3037 107 × 100 mm. 2fo.50+1fo. Man wearing brimmed hat; 2fo.50+1fo. Woman in wimple; 2fo.50+1fo. Man wearing cloth hat; 2fo.50+1fo. Man in fur cap 2·50 2·50
The designs in **MS** are horiz, 35 × 28 mm, and show statue heads only.

648 U.S. 6c. Stamp, 1968

1976. "Interphil '76" Int Stamp Exn, Philadelphia.
3038 **648** 5fo. multicoloured . . . 1·25 1·25

649 "Children Playing" (E. Gebora) within "30"

1976. 30th Anniv of Hungarian Pioneers Movement.
3039 **649** 1fo. multicoloured . . . 20 10

650 Truck, Tractor and Safety Headgear with Emblem

1976. Industrial Safety.
3040 **650** 1fo. multicoloured . . . 20 10

651 "Intelstar IV" Telecommunications Satellite

1976. Olympic Games, Montreal. Mult.
3041 40fi. Type **651**(postage) . . 10 10
3042 60fi. Horse-jumping 10 10
3043 1fo. Swimming 15 10
3044 2fo. Canoeing 35 10
3045 3fo. Fencing 60 10
3046 4fo. Javelin-throwing . . . 70 25
3047 5fo. Gymnastics 85 35

MS3048 135 × 85 mm. 20fo. black, grey and red (air) . . . . . 4·50 6·00
DESIGN: 44 × 57 mm. 20fo. Olympic Stadium, Montreal.

652 Danish 1851 4 R.B.S. Stamp and "Little Mermaid" Statue

1976. "Hafnia '76" International Stamp Exhibition, Copenhagen.
3049 **652** 3fo. multicoloured . . . 75 75

653 "Flora" (Titian)

1976. 400th Death Anniv of Titian (painter).
3050 **653** 4fo. multicoloured . . . 60 25

654 "Discovery of King Lajos II's Body" (B. Szekely)

1976. 450th Anniv of Battle of Mohacs. Sheet 82 × 81 mm.
MS3051 **654** 20fo. multicoloured 3·00 3·25

655 Pal Gyulai (1826–1909)

656 "Hussar" (Zs. Kisfaludy-Strobl)

1976. Writers' Anniversaries.
3052 **655** 2fo. black and red . . . 30 10
3053 – 2fo. black, yellow & gold 30 10
DESIGN: No. 3053, Daniel Berzsenyi (1776–1836).

1976. 150th Anniv of Herend China Factory.
3054 **656** 4fo. multicoloured . . . 75 15

657 Tuscany 1q. Stamp, 1851 and Arms of Milan

1976. "Italia '76" International Stamp Exhibition, Milan.
3055 **657** 5fo. multicoloured . . . 2·25 3·00

658 Russian Dancer, Flags and Building

1976. 2nd Anniv of House of Soviet Culture and Science, Budapest.
3056 **658** 1fo. multicoloured . . . 15 10

659 Ignac Bogar

1976. Hungarian Labour Movement Celebrities.
3057 **659** 1fo. brown and red . . . 10 10
3058 – 1fo. brown and red . . . 10 10
3059 – 1fo. brown and red . . . 10 10
PORTRAITS: No. 3058, Rudolf Golub; No. 3059, Jozsef Madzsar.

660 Dr. F. Koranyi and Dispensary

1976. 75th Anniv of Koranyi T.B. Dispensary.
3060 **660** 2fo. multicoloured . . . 35 10

661 Launch of "Viking" Mission

1976. Air. Space Probes to Mars and Venus. Multicoloured.
3061 40fi. Type **661** 10 10
3062 60fi. "Viking" in flight . . . 15 10
3063 1fo. "Viking" on Mars . . . 20 10
3064 2fo. Launch of "Venera" . . 30 10
3065 3fo. "Venera 9" in flight . . 55 10
3066 4fo. "Venera 10" descending to Venus 80 20
3067 5fo. "Venera" on Venus . . 90 45
MS3068 97 × 81 mm. 20fo. "Viking 1" landing on Mars (42 × 65 mm) 3·00 3·50

662 Locomotive No. 4, 1875

1976. Cent of Gyor-Sopron Railway. Mult.

3069	40fi. Type **662**	20	10
3070	60fi. Locomotive No. 17, 1885	25	10
3071	1fo. Rail-bus. 1925	30	10
3072	2fo. Steam locomotive, 1920	55	10
3073	3fo. Diesel railcar, 1926	75	10
3074	4fo. Diesel railcar, 1934	1·25	20
3075	5fo. Diesel railcar, 1971	2·00	55

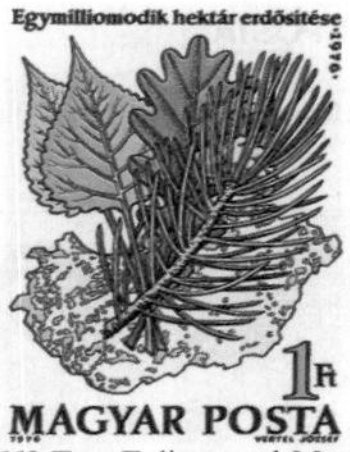

663 Tree Foliage and Map

1976. "Afforestation of 1,000,000th Hectare".

3076	**663** 1fo. multicoloured	20	10

664 Weightlifting and Wrestling (silver medals)

1976. Olympic Games, Montreal. Hungarian Medal-winners. Multicoloured.

3077	40fi. Type **664**	10	10
3078	60fi. Men's solo kayak and Women's pairs kayak (silver medals)	20	10
3079	1fo. Men's gymnastics (horse) (gold medal)	25	10
3080	4fo. Women's rapier (gold medal)	1·25	15
3081	6fo. Men's javelin (gold medal)	1·50	45
MS3082	80 × 95 mm. 20fo. Water-polo (Gold medal)	3·00	3·25

665 White Spoonbill

1977. Birds of Hortabagy National Park. Multicoloured.

3083	40fi. Type **665**	25	10
3084	60fi. White stork	30	10
3085	1fo. Purple heron	35	15
3086	2fo. Great bustard	45	20
3087	3fo. Common crane	70	30
3088	4fo. Pied wagtail	1·25	50
3089	5fo. Garganey	1·60	65

666 Imre Abonyi (champion driver) and Carriage, 1976

1977. Historic Horse-drawn Vehicles. Mult.

3090	40fi. Type **666**	20	10
3091	60fi. Omnibus, 1870	25	10
3092	1fo. Hackney-carriage, 1890	30	10
3093	2fo. 19th-century mail coach	40	10
3094	3fo. 18th-century covered wagon	70	20
3095	4fo. Coach, 1568	90	45
3096	5fo. Saint Elizabeth's carriage, 1430	1·10	1·00

667 Common Peafowl

1977. Peafowl and Pheasants. Multicoloured.

3097	40fi. Type **667**	20	10
3098	60fi. Green peafowl	25	10
3099	1fo. Congo peafowl	25	10
3100	3fo. Great Argus pheasant	75	15
3101	4fo. Himalayan monal pheasant	1·10	25
3102	6fo. Burmese peacock-pheasant	1·10	95

668 Front Page of "Nepszava" and Printing Works

1977. Centenary of Newspaper "Nepszava".

3103	**668** 1fo. black, red and gold	20	10

669 Flower painting (Mihaly Munkacsy)

1977. Flower Paintings by Hungarian Artists. Multicoloured.

3104	40fi. Type **669**	10	10
3105	60fi. Jakab Bogdany	10	10
3106	1fo. Istvan Csok (horiz)	15	10
3107	2fo. Janos Halapy	30	10
3108	3fo. Jozsef Rippl-Ronai (horiz)	65	15
3109	4fo. Janos Tornyai	85	30
3110	5fo. Jozsef Koszta	1·00	65

670 Isaac Newton and Lens

1977. 250th Death Anniv of Isaac Newton (mathematician).

3111	**670** 3fo. black, brown and red	65	65

671 Children Running

673 Janos Vajda

672 "Acrofila 74" 2fo.+1fo. Stamp

1977. Youth Sports.

3112	**671** 3fo.+1fo. 50 mult	75	70

1977. Stamp Exhibitions.

3113	**672** 3fo. multicoloured	1·10	1·25

1977. 150th Birth Anniv of Janos Vajda (poet).

3114	**673** 1fo. stone, black & green	35	10

674 Netherlands 5c. Stamp, 1852

1977. "Amphilex 77" International Stamp Exhibition, Amsterdam.

3115	**674** 3fo. multicoloured	90	1·00

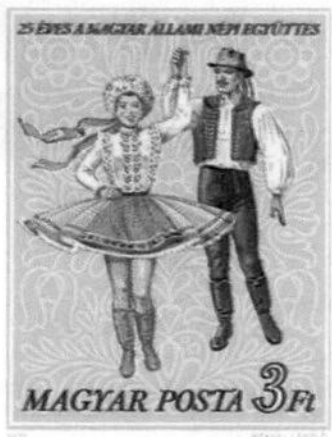

675 "Wedding at Nagyrede" Dance

1977. 25th Anniv of State Folk Ensemble.

3116	**675** 3fo. multicoloured	90	15

676 "Bathsheba at the Fountain"

1977. 400th Birth Anniv of Peter Paul Rubens. Sheet 70 × 94 mm.

MS3117	**676** 20fo. multicoloured	7·50	8·25

677 View of Sopron (from medieval engraving), Arms and Fidelity Tower

1977. 700th Anniv of Sopron.

3118	**677** 1fo. multicoloured	1·10	1·25

678 Kincsem (champion racehorse)

1977. 150th Anniv of Horse Racing in Hungary.

3119	**678** 1fo. multicoloured	1·25	1·25

679 East German 10pf. Stamp, 1957

1977. "Sozphilex 77" Stamp Exhibition, East Berlin.

3120	**679** 3fo. multicoloured	1·00	1·00

680 Scythian Iron Bell (6th century B.C.)

681 "Sputnik 1"

1977. Stamp Day and 175th Anniv of Hungarian National Museum. Art Treasures.

3121	**680** 2fo. brown and blue	75	75
3122	– 2fo. brown and violet	75	75
3123	– 2fo. brown & deep brown	75	75
3124	– 2fo. gold and mauve	75	75
MS3125	73 × 83 mm. 10fo. multicoloured	3·00	3·25

DESIGNS: No. 3122, Bronze candlestick, 12-13th century; 3123, Copper aquamanile, 13th century; 3124, Cast gold Christ (from crucifix), 11th century. 32 × 47 mm—10fo. Plate from crown of Constantinus Monomakhosz, 11th century.

1977. Space Research. Multicoloured.

3126	40fi. Type **681**(postage)	10	10
3127	60fi. "Skylab"	15	10
3128	1fo. "Soyuz–Salyut 5" space station	20	10
3129	3fo. "Luna 24"	60	10
3130	4fo. "Mars 3"	1·25	20
3131	6fo. "Viking"	1·50	50
MS3132	98 × 78 mm. 20fo. Viking Lander on Mars (air)	3·25	3·50

682 Map, Dove and "Europa"

1977. Air. European Security Conference, Belgrade. Sheet 125 × 75 mm.

MS3133	**682** 20fo. multicoloured	6·00	5·25

683 Tupolev Tu-154

1977. Air.

3134	**683** 60fl. black and orange	15	10
3135	– 1fo.20 black and lilac	20	10
3136	– 2fo. black and orange	30	10
3137	– 2fo.40 black & turquoise	35	10
3138	– 4fo. black and blue	45	10
3139	– 5fo. black and mauve	65	10
3140	– 10fo. black and blue	1·90	30
3141	– 20fo. black and green	2·75	75

DESIGNS—As T **683**: 1fo.20, Douglas DC-8-62; 2fo. Ilyushin Il-62M; 2fo.40, Airbus Industrie A300B4; 4fo. Boeing 747; 5fo. Tupolev Tu-144; 10fo. Concorde. 38 × 28 mm: 20fo. Ilyushin Il-86.

684 Montgolfier Brothers and Balloon

1977. Air. Airships. Multicoloured.

3142	40fi. Type **684**	10	10
3143	60fi. David Schwarz and his aluminium airship	20	10
3144	1fo. Alberto Santos-Dumont and airship "Ballon No. 5" over Paris	30	10
3145	2fo. K. E. Tsiolkovsky and airship "Lebedi" over Kremlin	45	10
3146	3fo. Roald Amundsen and airship "Norge" over North Pole	70	20
3147	4fo. Hugo Eckener and airship "Graf Zeppelin" over Mount Fuji	1·00	30
3148	5fo. Ferdinand Zeppelin and "Graf Zeppelin" over Chicago World Exhibition	1·50	50
MS3149	98 × 78 mm. 20fo. Airship LZ-127 "Graf Zeppelin" over Budapest (58 × 36 mm)	4·00	4·00

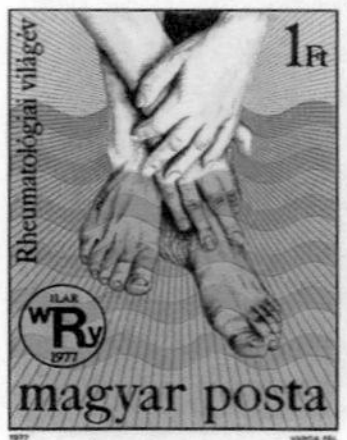

685 Feet Immersed in Water

686 Ervin Szabo

1977. World Rheumatism Year.
3150 **685** 1fo. multicoloured . . . 35 10

1977. Anniversaries.
3151 – 1fo. black and red . . . 10 10
3152 **686** 1fo. grey, black and red 10 10
DESIGNS: No 3151, Jamos Szanto Kovacs (agrarian socialist movement leader, 125th birth anniv); 3152, Type **686** (director of Municipal Libraries, journalist and labour movement leader, birth centenary).

687 Monument to Hungarian Participants, Omsk

1977. 60th Anniv of Russian Revolution.
3153 **687** 1fo. black and red . . . 10 10

688 Endre Ady

689 Lesser Panda

1977. Birth Centenary of Endre Ady (poet).
3154 **688** 1fo. blue 30 30

1977. Bears. Multicoloured.
3155 40fi. Type **689** 15 10
3156 60fi. Giant panda 20 10
3157 1fo. Asiatic black bear . . . 35 10
3158 4fo. Polar bear . . . . . . 1·50 15
3159 6fo. Brown bear . . . . . 2·10 45

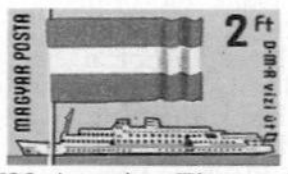

690 Austrian Flag and Passenger Ship

1977. 30th Anniv of Re-establishment of Danube Commission. Sheet 130 × 93 mm containing T **690** and similar horiz designs.
MS3160 2fo. × 11 multicoloured 13·50 13·00
DESIGNS—Flags and ships of : Austria, Bulgaria, Czechoslovakia, France, Netherlands, Yugoslavia, Hungary, West Germany, Rumania, Switzerland, Soviet Union.

691 Border-country Lancer, 17th-cent

1978. Hussars. Multicoloured.
3161 40fi. Type **691** 15 10
3162 60fi. Kuruts horseman, 1710 20 10
3163 1fo. Baranya hussar, 1762 30 10
3164 2fo. Palatine Hussars officer, 1809 . . . . 45 10
3165 4fo. Alexander Hussar, 1848 85 20
3166 6fo. Trumpeter, 5th Honved Regiment, 1900 . . . . . 1·25 55

692 Moon Station

1978. Air. Science Fiction in Space Research. Multicoloured.
3167 40fi. Type **692** 10 10
3168 60fi. Moon settlement . . . 15 10
3169 1fo. Phobos 25 10
3170 2fo. Exploring an asteroid 45 10
3171 3fo. Spacecraft in gravitational field of Mars 65 10
3172 4fo. One of Saturn's rings 95 15
3173 5fo. "Jupiter 3" . . . . . . 1·25 45

693 School of Arts and Crafts

1978. Bicent of School of Art and Crafts.
3174 **693** 1fo. multicoloured . . . 10 10

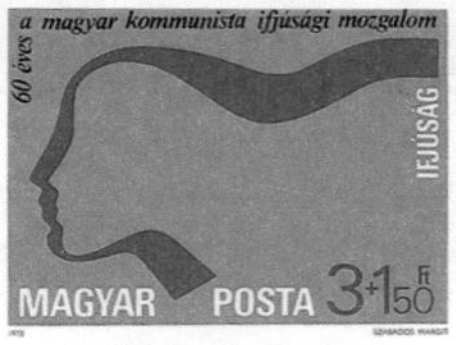

694 Profile Heads

1978. Youth Stamp Exhibition, Hatvan.
3175 **694** 3fo.+1fo.50 silver, red and black . . . . . . 1·50 1·50

695 "Generations" (Gyula Derkovits)

1978. "Socphilex 78" Stamp Exhibition, Szombathely.
3176 **695** 3fo.+1fo.50 mult 75 90

696 Louis Bleriot

1978. Air. Famous Aviators and their Airplanes. Multicoloured.
3177 40fi. Type **696** 15 10
3178 60fi. John Alcock and Arthur Whitten Brown . . 20 10
3179 1fo. Albert C. Read 25 10
3180 2fo. Hermann Kohl, Gunther Hunefeld and James Fitzmaurice 55 10
3181 3fo. Amy Johnson and Jim Mollison 75 15
3182 4fo. Georgy Endresz and Sandor Magyar 95 20
3183 5fo. Wolfgang von Gronau 1·00 70
MS3184 96 × 79 mm. 20fo. Wright Brothers and "Flyer" (74 × 25 mm) . . . . 3·75 4·00

697 Glass Vase and Glass-blowing Tube

1978. Centenary of Ajka Glass Works.
3185 **697** 1fo. multicoloured . . . 15 10

698 West Germany and Poland

1978. World Cup Football Championship, Argentina, Multicoloured.
3186 2fo. Type **698** 55 20
3187 2fo. Hungary and Argentina 55 20
3188 2fo. France and Italy . . . 55 20
3189 2fo. Tunisia and Mexico . . 55 20
3190 2fo. Sweden and Brazil . . 55 20
3191 2fo. Spain and Austria . . . 55 20
3192 2fo. Peru and Scotland . . . 55 20
3193 2fo. Iran and Netherlands 55 20
MS3194 98 × 76 mm. 20fo. World Cup emblem and goal mouth (37 × 27 mm) . . . . 3·75 4·00

699 Canadian 3d. Stamp, 1851

1978. "Capex 78" International Stamp Exhibition, Toronto.
3195 **699** 3fo. multicoloured . . . 1·50 90

700 Diesel MK 45 Locomotive

702 Festival Emblem

701 Leif Eriksson

1978. 30th Anniv of Budapest Pioneer Railway.
3196 **700** 1fo. multicoloured . . . 25 10

1978. Explorers. Two sheets each 130 × 100 mm containing horiz designs as T **701**.
MS3197 Two sheets (a) 2fo. × 4 yellow and black (T **701**); orange and black (Christopher Columbus); orange and black (Vasco da Gama); pink and black (Ferdinand Magellan). (b) 2fo. × 4 yellow and black (Sir Francis Drake); apple green and black (Henry Hudson); green and black (James Cook); light blue and black (Robert Peary) 2 sheets . . . . 6·75 7·25

1978. 11th World Youth and Students' Festival, Havana. Multicoloured.
3198 1fo. Type **702** 10 10
3199 1fo. Map of Cuba and emblem 10 10

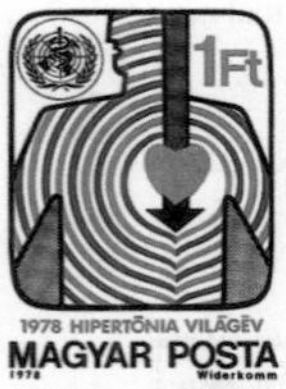

703 Human Torso and Heart

705 Dove and Fist holding Olive Branch

704 Jules Verne and illustration from "A Journey to the Moon"

1978. World Hypertension Year.
3200 **703** 1fo. red, black and blue 10 10

1978. Air. 150th Birth Anniv of Jules Verne (novelist). Sheet 97 × 78 mm.
MS3201 **704** 20fo. black and yellow 3·75 4·00

1978. 20th Anniv of Communist Party Review "Peace and Socialism".
3202 **705** 1fo. red and black . . . 10 10

706 Vladimir Remek cancelling Letters, "Salyut 6" and "Soyuz 28"

1978. Air. "Praga 1978" International Stamp Exhibition, Prague.
3203 **706** 3fo. multicoloured . . . 75 85

707 Toshiba Automatic Letter Sorting Equipment

1978. Automation of Letter Sorting.
3204 **707** 1fo. multicoloured . . . 30 30

708 Putto offering Grapes

1978. Stamp Day. Mosaics. Multicoloured.
3205 2fo. Type **708** . . . . 1·50 1·60
3206 2fo. Tiger . . . . 1·50 1·60
3207 2fo. Bird . . . . 1·50 1·60
3208 2fo. Dolphin . . . . 1·50 1·60
MS3209 88 × 61 mm. 10fo. Hercules aiming arrow at Centaur Nessus fleeing with Nymph Deianeira (51 × 32 mm) . . . . 6·25 6·75

709 Methods of Communication

1978. Organization of Socialist Countries' Postal Administrations Conference, Tbilisi.
3210 **709** 1fo. multicoloured . . . 35 10

710 Imre Thokoly

1978. 300th Anniv of Thokoly's Revolt.
3211 **710** 1fo. black and yellow . . 35 10

711 Hungarian Regalia

1978. Return of Hungarian Regalia. Sheet 76 × 96 mm.
MS3212 **711** 20fo. multicoloured 6·75 6·25

712 "The Red Coach" (novel)

1978. Birth Cent of Gyula Krudy (novelist).
3213 **712** 3fo. red and black . . . 50 10

713 St. Ladislas (bust, Gyor Cathedral)

1978. 900th Anniv of Accession of St. Ladislas.
3214 **713** 1fo. multicoloured . . . 30 10

714 Buildings and Arms of Koszeg

1978. 650th Anniv of Koszeg.
3215 **714** 1fo. multicoloured . . . 35 10

715 Samu Czaban and Gizella Berzeviczy

1978. Birth Centenaries of Samu Czaban and Gizella Berzeviczy (teachers).
3216 **715** 1fo. multicoloured . . . 30 25

716 Communist Party Emblem

1978. 60th Anniv of Hungarian Communist Party.
3217 **716** 1fo. red, grey and black 10 10

717 "Girl cutting Bread"

1978. Ceramics by Margit Kovacs. Mult.
3218 1fo. Type **717** 30 10
3219 2fo. "Girl with Pitcher" . . 45 25
3220 3fo. "Boy Potter" 80 30

718 "Self-portrait in Fur Coat"

1978. 450th Death Anniv of Albrecht Durer (artist). Multicoloured.
3221 40fi. "Madonna with Child" 10 10
3222 60fi. "Adoration of the Magi" (horiz) 10 10
3223 1fo. Type **718** 20 10
3224 2fo. "St. George" 40 10
3225 3fo. "Nativity" (horiz) . . . 65 10
3226 4fo. "St. Eustace" 80 20
3227 5fo. "The Four Apostles" 1·00 60
MS3228 78 × 99 mm. 20fo. sepia and stone ("Dancing Peasant Couple") (36 × 59 mm) . . . . 3·25 4·00

719 Human Rights Emblem

720 Child with Dog

1979. 30th Anniv of Declaration of Human Rights.
3229 **719** 1fo. blue and light blue 75 1·00

1979. International Year of the Child (1st issue). Multicoloured.
3230 1fo. Type **720** 65 50
3231 1fo. Family group 65 50
3232 1fo. Children of different races . . . . 2·40 3·00
See also Nos. 3287/93.

721 "Soldiers of the Red Army, Forward!" (poster by Bela Uitz)

1979. 60th Anniv of First Hungarian Soviet Republic.
3233 **721** 1fo. black, red and grey 10 10

722 "Girl Reading" (Ferenc Kovacs)

1979. Youth Stamp Exhibition, Bekescsaba.
3234 **722** 3fo.+1fo.50 grey, blue and black 65 75

723 Chessmen and Cup

1979. 23rd Chess Olympiad, Buenos Aires (1978).
3235 **723** 3fo. multicoloured . . . 1·10 90

724 Alexander Nevski Cathedral, Sofia, and First Bulgarian Stamp

1979. "Philaserdica 79" International Stamp Exhibition, Sofia.
3236 **724** 3fo. multicoloured . . . 75 80

725 Stephenson's "Rocket", 1829

1979. International Transport Exhibition, Hamburg. Depicting development of the railway. Mult.
3237 40fi. Type **725** 20 10
3238 60fi. Siemens's electric locomotive, 1879 . . . . 20 10
3239 1fo. Locomotive "Pioneer", 1851 (wrongly dated "1936") 30 10
3240 2fo. Hungarian Class MAV I.e pulling "Orient Express", 1883 . . . . . 40 15
3241 3fo. "Trans-Siberian Express", 1898 . . . . . 55 30
3242 4fo. Japanese "Hikari" express train, 1964 . . . 80 40
3243 5fo. German "Transrapid 05" Maglev train, 1979 90 85
MS3244 78 × 95 mm. 20fo. European railway map (51 × 36 mm) . . . . 9·75 6·50

726 Soyuz Gas Pipeline and Compressor Station

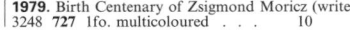

727 Zsigmond Moricz (after J. Rippl-Ronai)

1979. 30th Anniv of Council of Mutual Economic Aid. Multicoloured.
3245 1fo. Type **726** 15 10
3246 2fo. Pylon and dam, Lenin hydro-electric power station, Dnepropetrovsk 35 10
3247 3fo. Council building, Moscow 35 10

1979. Birth Centenary of Zsigmond Moricz (writer).
3248 **727** 1fo. multicoloured . . . 10 10

728 City Hall, Helsinki (1952 Games)

1979. Olympic Games, Moscow (1980) (1st issue). Multicoloured.
3249 40fi. Type **728** 10 10
3250 60fi. Colosseum, Rome (1960) 10 10
3251 1fo. Asakusa Temple, Tokyo (1964) 35 10
3252 2fo. Cathedral, Mexico City (1968) 55 10
3253 3fo. Frauenkirche, Munich (1972) 70 15
3254 4fo. Modern quarter, Montreal (1976) . . . . . 1·10 15
3255 5fo. Lomonosov University, Moscow, and Misha the bear (mascot) (1980) . . . 1·25 60
See also Nos. 3323/29.

729 "Child with Horse and Greyhounds" (Janos Vaszary)

1979. Animal Paintings. Multicoloured.
3256 40fi. Type **729** 20 10
3257 60fi. "Coach and Five" (Karoly Lotz) 25 10
3258 1fo. "Lads on Horseback" (Celesztin Pallya) 30 10
3259 2fo. "Farewell" (Karoly Lotz) 40 20
3260 3fo. "Horse Market" (Celeztin Pallya) 55 20
3261 4fo. "Wandering" (Bela Ivanyi-Grunwald) 65 40
3262 5fo. "Ready for Hunting" (Karoly Sterio) . . . . . 1·00 90

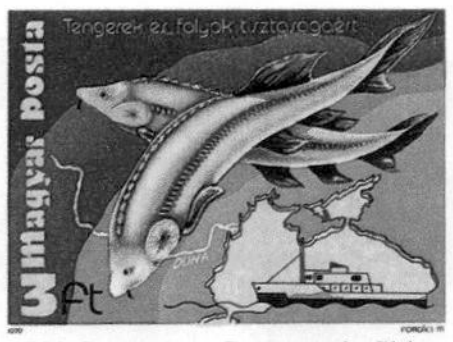

730 Sturgeon, Cousteau's Ship "Calypso" and Black Sea

1979. Sea and River Purity.
3263 **730** 3fo. multicoloured . . . 65 10

731 Globe and Five Pentathlon Sports

1979. Pentathlon World Championship, Budapest.
3264 **731** 2fo. multicoloured . . . 60 10

732 Stephen I Denarius (reverse)

1979. 9th International Numismatic Congress, Berne. Designs showing old Hungarian coins. Multicoloured.
3265 1fo. Type **732** 30 10
3266 2fo. Bela III copper coin (obverse) 45 20

3267 3fo. Louis the Great groat (reverse) 55 30
3268 4fo. Matthias I gold forint (obverse) 70 75
3269 5fo. Wladislaw II gulden (reverse) . . . . 1·00 1·25

733 Design for Proposed Hungarian Stamp of 1848

734 Light Passenger Locomotive

1979. Stamp Day. Sheet 70 × 56 mm.
MS3270 **733** 10fo. multicoloured 3·75 3·75

1979. Centenary of Gyor—Sopron–Ebenfurt Railway. Sheet 98 × 79 mm containing T **734** and similar horiz designs. Multicoloured.
MS3271 5fo. Type **734**; 5fo. Class 424 steam locomotive; 5fo. Class 520 locomotive; 5fo. Diesel locomotive Type M41 . . . . 4·50 4·25

735 Flags and Globe filled with Coins

1979. World Savings Day
3272 **735** 1fo. multicoloured . . . 20 10

736 "Vega-Chess" (Victor Vasarely)

737 European Otter

1979. Modern Art.
3273 **736** 1fo. multicoloured . . . 10 10

1979. Protected Animals. Multicoloured.
3274 40fi. Type **737** 20 10
3275 60fi. Wild cat 20 10
3276 1fo. Pine marten 40 10
3277 2fo. Eurasian badger . . . 55 10
3278 4fo. Steppe polecat . . . . 1·25 20
3279 6fo. Beech marten . . . . . 1·75 70

738 Ski Jumping

1979. Air. Winter Olympic Games, Lake Placid (1980). Multicoloured.
3280 40fi. Type **738** 30 10
3281 60fi. Figure skating 35 10
3282 1fo. Slalom 55 15
3283 2fo. Ice hockey 75 20
3284 4fo. Bobsleigh . . . . . . 1·25 20
3285 6fo. Cross-country skiing . . 1·60 55
MS3286 97 × 73 mm. 20fo. Ice dancing (square, 49 × 49 mm) 5·25 5·00

739 "Tom Thumb"

1979. International Year of the Child (2nd issue). Designs depicting children's stories. Mult.
3287 40fi. Type **739** 15 10
3288 60fi. "The Ugly Duckling" (Andersen) 30 10
3289 1fo. "The Fisher and the Goldfish" 40 10
3290 2fo. "Cinderella" 70 10
3291 3fo. "Gulliver's Travels" (Swift) 90 10
3292 4fo. "The Little Pig and the Wolves" 95 20
3293 5fo. "Gallant John" . . . . 1·25 50
MS3294 78 × 98 mm. 20fo. "Fairy Ilona" . . . . 3·75 4·00

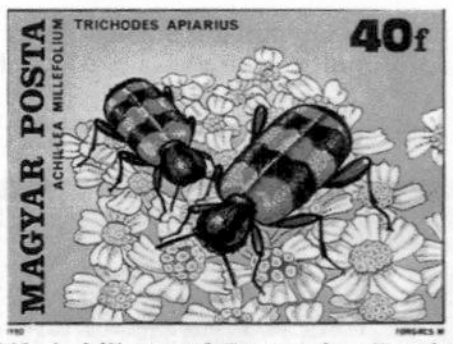

740 Achillea and Bee-eating Beetles

1980. Pollination. Multicoloured.
3295 40fl. Type **740** 15 10
3296 60fl. Gaillardia and bee . . 15 10
3297 1fo. Rudbeckia and red admiral 20 10
3298 2fo. Dog rose and rose chafer 40 10
3299 4fo. "Petroselinum hortense" and striped bug 80 20
3300 6fo. Achillea and longhorn beetle . . . . 1·25 55

741 Hanging Gardens of Babylon

1980. Seven Wonders of the Ancient World. Mult.
3301 40fi. Type **741** 15 10
3302 60fi. Temple of Artemis, Ephesus 15 10
3303 1fo. Statue of Zeus, Olympia 20 10
3304 2fo. Mausoleum of Halicarnassus 40 10
3305 3fo. Colossus of Rhodes . . 55 15
3306 4fo. Pharos, Alexandria . . 70 20
3307 5fo. Pyramids of Egypt . . 1·75 60

742 Gabor Bethlen (copperplate)

1980. 400th Birth Anniv of Gabor Bethlen (Prince of Transylvania).
3308 **742** 1fo. multicoloured . . . 10 10

743 Tihany Abbey

1980. 925th Anniv of Foundation of Tihany Abbey.
3309 **743** 1fo. multicoloured . . . 10 10

744 Easter Sepulchre

1980. Easter Sepulchre of Garamszentbenedek. Designs showing details of sepulchre. Mult.
3310 1fo. Type **744** 15 10
3311 2fo. Three Marys 35 10
3312 3fo. Apostle Jacob 45 20
3313 4fo. Apostle Thaddeus . . . 60 35
3314 5fo. Apostle Andrew 80 70

745 Bunch of Wild Flowers

1980. 35th Anniv of Liberation.
3315 **745** 1fo. multicoloured . . . 20 10

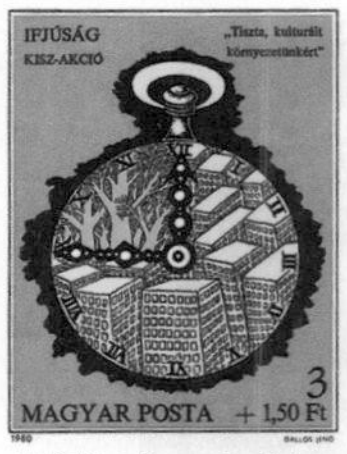

746 Watch symbolising Environmental Protection

747 Attila Jozsef

1980. Youth Stamp Exhibition, Dunaujvaros.
3316 **746** 3fo.+1fo.50 mult 60 65

1980. 75th Birth Anniv of Attila Jozsef (poet).
3317 **747** 1fo. green and red . . . 10 10

748 "Madonna and Child" Stamp of 1921 with Inverted Centre

1980. 50th Anniv of Hungarian Stamp Museum.
3318 **748** 1fo. multicoloured . . . 1·10 1·25

749 Great Britain 2d. Blue and Life Guard

1980. "London 1980" International Stamp Exhibition.
3319 **749** 3fo. multicoloured . . . 75 75

750 Soviet and Hungarian Cosmonauts

751 Margit Kaffka

1980. Air. Soviet–Hungarian Space Flight.
3320 **750** 5fo. multicoloured . . . 1·50 30

1980. Birth Centenary of Margit Kaffka (writer).
3321 **751** 1fo. yellow, black & vio 20 10

752 Norwegian 1951 Olympic Stamp and Statue "Mother and Child" (Gustav Vigeland)

1980. "Norwex 80" International Stamp Exhibition, Oslo.
3322 **752** 3fo. multicoloured . . . 75 75

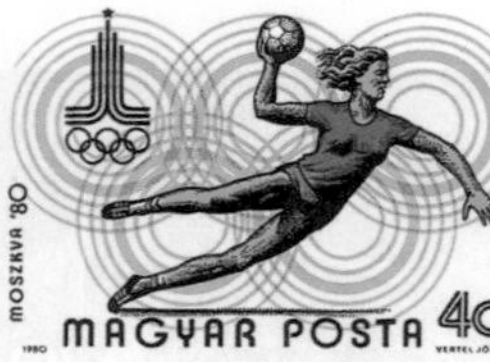

753 Handball

1980. Air. Olympic Games, Moscow (2nd issue). Multicoloured.
3323 40fi. Type **753** 10 10
3324 60fi. Double kayak 10 10
3325 1fo. Running 20 10
3326 2fo. Gymnastics 40 10
3327 3fo. Show-jumping (modern pentathlon) 65 10
3328 4fo. Wrestling 80 15
3329 5fo. Water polo . . . . . 1·10 55
MS3330 71 × 87 mm. 20fo. Runners with Olympic flame . . . . . 3·75 3·25

754 Endre Hogyes (physician) and Congress Emblem

756 Zoltan Schonherz

755 B. Farkos, V. Kubasov and Space Station

1980. 28th International Congress of Physiological Sciences, Budapest.
3331 **754** 1fo. multicoloured . . . 10 10

1980. Air. Soviet–Hungarian Space Flight (2nd issue). Sheet 72 × 93 mm.
MS3332 **755** 20fo. multicoloured 4·50 5·75

1980. 75th Birth Anniv of Zoltan Schonherz (Workers' Movement member).
3333 **756** 1fo. multicoloured . . . 10 10

757 Decanter

759 Bertalan Por (self-portrait)

758 Greek Athletes and Olympic Gold Medal

1980. Stamp Day. Glassware. Multicoloured.
3334 1fo. Type **757** 20 20
3335 2fo. Wine glass, Budapest 40 20
3336 3fo. Drinking glass, Zay-Ugrocz 60 50
MS3337 68 × 79 mm. 10fo. Drinking glass, Pecs (25 × 35 mm) . . . 2·40 2·40

1980. Air. Olympic Champions. Sheet 84 × 65 mm.
MS3338 **758** 20fo. multicoloured 3·25 3·25

1980. Birth Centenary of Bertalan Por (artist).
3339 **759** 1fo. multicoloured . . . 10 10

760 Greylag Goose

1980. Protected Birds. Multicoloured.
3340 40fi. Type **760** 20 10
3341 60fi. Black-crowned night herons 25 10
3342 1fo. Common shovelers . . 30 15
3343 2fo. White-winged black tern 65 25
3344 4fo. Great crested grebes . . 1·40 65
3345 6fo. Black-winged stilts . . 2·00 1·10
MS3346 75 × 95 mm. 20fo. Great egrets (40 × 63 mm) . . . . . 4·75 4·25

761 Peace Dove and Map of Europe

1980. European Security and Co-operation Conference, Madrid. Sheet 99 × 78 mm.
MS3347 **761** 20fo. multicoloured 3·25 3·00

762 Johannes Kepler

1980. 350th Death Anniv of Johannes Kepler (astronomer).
3348 **762** 1fo. multicoloured . . . 30 10

763 Karoly Kisfaludy

1980. 150th Death Anniv of Karoly Kisfaludy (dramatist and poet).
3349 **763** 1fo. multicoloured . . . 20 10

764 U.N. Building, New York

1980. 25th Anniv of United Nations Membership. Multicoloured.
3350 40fi. Type **764** 15 10
3351 60fi. U.N. building, Geneva 10 10
3352 1fo. International Centre, Vienna 20 10
3353 2fo. U.N. and Hungarian flags 40 10
3354 4fo. U.N. emblem and Hungarian arms 80 15
3355 6fo. World map . . . . . . 1·75 80

765 Ferenc Erdei

766 Bela Szanto

1980. 70th Birth Anniv of Ferenc Erdei (agricultural economist and politician).
3356 **765** 1fo. multicoloured . . . 10 10

1981. Birth Centenary of Bela Szanto (founder member of Hungarian Communist Party).
3357 **766** 1fo. multicoloured . . . 10 10

767 Lajos Batthyany (after Miklos Barabas)

1981. 175th Birth Anniv of Lajos Batthyany (politician).
3358 **767** 1fo. multicoloured . . . 10 10

768 Cheetah

769 "Graf Zeppelin" over Tokyo

1981. Air. Birth Centenary of Kalman Kittenberger (explorer and zoologist). Multicoloured.
3359 40fi. Type **768** 20 10
3360 60fi. Lion 20 10
3361 1fo. Leopard 30 10
3362 2fo. Black rhinoceros . . . 55 10
3363 3fo. Greater kudu 60 25
3364 4fo. African elephant . . . 1·00 25
3365 5fo. Kittenberger and Hungarian National Museum . . . . 2·25 95

1981. Air. "Luraba" International Exhibition of Aero- and Astro-philately, Lucerne. "Graf Zeppelin" Flights. Multicoloured.
3366 1fo. Type **769** (first round-the-world flight, 1929) . . 15 10
3367 2fo. Franz Josef Land and icebreaker "Malygin" (Polar flight, 1931) . . . 45 10
3368 3fo. Nine-arch Bridge, Hortobagy (Hungary flight, 1931) 45 10
3369 4fo. Hostentor, Lubeck (Baltic flight, 1931) . . . 60 10
3370 5fo. Tower Bridge (England flight, 1931) 70 25
3371 6fo. Federal Palace, Chicago (World Exhibition flight, 1933) 75 25
3372 7fo. Lucerne (1st Swiss flight, 1929) 85 80

770 Bela Bartok (after Ferenczy Beni)

1981. Birth Centenary of Bela Bartok (composer). Sheet 100 × 80 mm containing T **770** and similar vert design. Multicoloured.
MS3373 10fo. Type **770**; 10fo. Illustration for "Cantata Profana" 4·50 4·50

771 Flag of House of Arpad (11th century)

1981. Historical Hungarian Flags. Mult.
3374 40fi. Type **771** 20 10
3375 60fi. Hunyadi Family flag (15th century) 30 10
3376 1fo. Flag of Gabor Bethlen (1600) 50 10
3377 2fo. Flag of Ferenc Rakoczi II (1706) 70 10
3378 4fo. "Honved" (1848–49) . . 1·00 20
3379 6fo. Troop Flag (1919) . . . 1·40 55

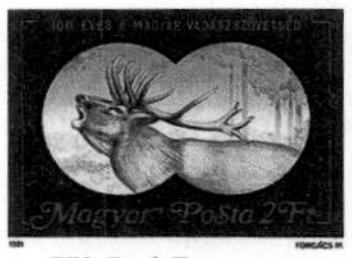

772 Red Deer seen through Binoculars

773 First Hungarian Telephone Exchange

1981. Cent of Association of Hungarian Huntsmen.
3380 **772** 2fo. multicoloured . . . 35 10

1981. Centenary of First Hungarian Telephone Exchange, Budapest.
3381 **773** 2fo. multicoloured . . . 60 10

774 Henri Dunant (founder) and Map of Europe

1981. 3rd European Conference of Red Cross and Red Crescent Societies, Budapest. Sheet 98 × 78 mm.
MS3382 **774** 20fo. multicoloured 4·50 4·00

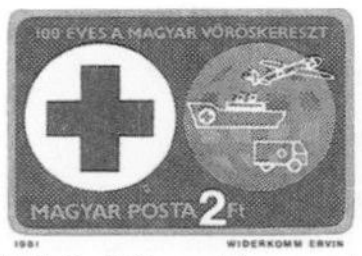

775 Red Cross, Transport and Globe

776 Airship LZ-127 "Graf Zeppelin"

1981. Cent of Hungarian Red Cross.
3383 **775** 2fo. orange and red . . 30 10

1981. "WIPA 1981" International Stamp Exhibition, Vienna. Sheet 80 × 60 mm containing T **776** and similar horiz designs depicting "WIPA 1933" souvenir labels.
MS3384 5fo. green and black (Type **776**); 5fo. purple and black (Rocket); 5fo. brown and black (Dispatch rider); 5fo. blue and black (Sailing ship) . . . . . 4·50 4·00

777 I.Y.D.P. Emblem and Person pushing Wheelchair

1981. International Year of Disabled Persons.
3385 **777** 2fo.+1fo. green & yell 75 70

778 Young People and Factory

779 Stephenson and "Locomotion"

1981. 10th Young Communist League Congress, Budapest.
3386 **778** 4fo.+2fo. mult . . . . . 90 1·00

1981. Birth Bicentenary of George Stephenson (railway pioneer).
3387 **779** 2fo. yellow, grey & brown 75 25

780 Bela Vago

1981. Birth Centenary of Bela Vago (founder member of Hungarian Communist Party).
3388 **780** 2fo. green and brown . . 35 10

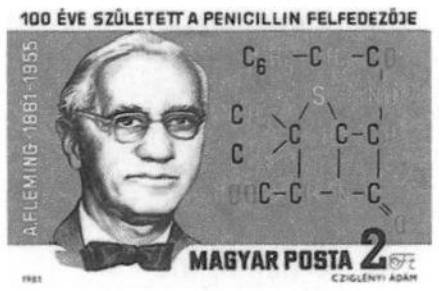

781 Alexander Fleming

1981. Birth Centenary of Alexander Fleming (discoverer of penicillin).
3389 **781** 2fo. multicoloured . . . 55 20

782 Bridal Chest from Szentgal

1981. Stamp Day. Bridal Chests. Mult.
3390 1fo. Type **782** 20 10
3391 2fo. Chest from Hodmezovasarhely . . . 50 30
MS3392 76 × 55 mm. 10fo. Chest from Bacs (43 × 23 mm) . . . 3·75 3·75

783 Calvinist College

784 Hands holding F.A.O. Emblem

1981. 450th Anniv of Calvinist College, Papa.
3393 **783** 2fo. multicoloured . . . 35 10

1981. World Food Day.
3394 **784** 2fo. multicoloured . . . 75 10

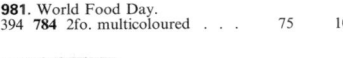

785 German Costume

786 "Franz I" (1830) and "Ferene Deak" on 30fi. Stamp

1981. National Costumes of Hungarian Ethnic Minorities. Multicoloured.
3395 1fo. Slovakian costume . . 1·40 1·40
3396 2fo. Type **785** . . . . 1·40 1·40
3397 3fo. Croatian costume . . . 1·40 1·40
3398 4fo. Rumanian costume . . 1·40 1·40

1981. 125th Anniv of Danube Commission. Paddle-steamers and Danube Commission stamps issued in 1967. Multicoloured.
3399 1fo. Type **786** 40 15
3400 1fo. "Arpad" (1834) and "Revfulop" on 60fi. stamp 40 15
3401 2fo. "Szechenyi" (1853) and "Hunyadi" on 1fo. stamp 55 25

3402 2fo. "Grof Szechenyi Istvan" (1896) and "Szekszard" on 1fo.50 stamp 55 25
3403 4fo. "Zsofia" (1914) and "Miscolc" on 1fo.70 stamp 90 45
3404 6fo. "Felszabadulas" (1917) and "Tihany" on 2fo. stamp . . . . 1·60 95
3405 8fo. "Rakoczi" (1964) and "Siraly I" on 2fo.50 stamp . . . . 2·10 1·50
MS3406 96×77 mm. 20fo. Hydrofoil "Solyom" and 1fo. stamp (49×39 mm) . . . . . 5·50 4·75

787 "Mother Breast-feeding" (pottery, Margit Kovacs)

788 "Pen Pals" (Rockwell)

1981. Christmas. Multicoloured.
3407 1fo. Type **787** 15 20
3408 2fo. "Madonna of Csurgo" (bronze Amerigo Tot) . . 60 20

1981. Illustrations by Norman Rockwell and Anna Lesznai. Multicoloured.
3409 1fo. Type **788** 15 15
3410 2fo. "Courting under the Clock at Midnight" (Rockwell) 30 15
3411 2fo. "Maiden Voyage" (Rockwell) 30 15
3412 4fo. "Threading the Needle" (Rockwell) 65 55
3413 4fo. "At the End of the Village" (detail) (Lesznai) 65 55
3414 5fo. "Dance" (detail) (Lesznai) 95 80
3415 6fo. "Sunday" (detail) (Lesznai) . . . . 1·25 1·25

789 "La Tolette"

1981. Birth Centenary of Pablo Picasso (artist). Sheet 61×86 mm.
MS3416 **789** 20fo. multicoloured . . . . 4·25 4·25

790 Militiaman at Shooting Practice

791 Congress Emblem and Havana

1982. 25th Anniv of Workers' Militia. Mult.
3417 1fo. Type **790** 15 15
3418 4fo. Three generations of militiamen 60 15

1982. 10th World Trade Unions Federation Congress, Havana.
3419 **791** 2fo. multicoloured . . . 30 10

792 Gyula Alpari

793 Dr. Robert Koch

1982. Birth Centenary of Gyula Alpari (journalist).
3420 **792** 2fo. yellow, purple & brn 30 10

1982. Cent of Discovery of Tubercle Bacillus.
3421 **793** 2fo. multicoloured . . . 40 10

794 Tennis Racket and Ball

796 Table Tennis Player and Map of Europe

795 Hungary v. Egypt, 1934

1982. Youth Stamp. European Junior Tennis Cup.
3422 **794** 4fo.+2fo. mult . . . . . 1·10 1·10

1982. World Cup Football Championship, Spain. Multicoloured.
3423 1fo. Type **795** 20 10
3424 1fo. Italy v. Hungary, 1938 20 10
3425 2fo. West Germany v. Hungary, 1954 . . . . . 40 10
3426 2fo. Hungary v. Mexico, 1958 . . . . 40 10
3427 4fo. Hungary v. England, 1962 . . . . 85 10
3428 6fo. Hungary v. Brazil, 1966 1·25 15
3429 8fo. Argentina v. Hungary, 1978 . . . . 1·60 65
MS3430 100×68 mm. 10fo. Barcelona stadium; 10fo. Madrid stadium . . . . 4·50 4·25

1982. European Table Tennis Championship, Budapest.
3431 **796** 2fo. multicoloured . . . 50 10

797 "Pascali"

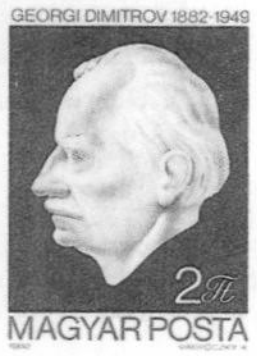

798 Georgi Dimitrov

1982. Roses. Multicoloured.
3432 1fo. Type **797** 25 15
3433 1fo. "Michele Meilland" . . 25 15
3434 2fo. "Diorama" 40 15
3435 2fo. "Wendy Cussons" . . . 40 15
3436 3fo. "Blue Moon" 70 20
3437 3fo. "Invitation" 70 20
3438 4fo. "Tropicana" . . . . . 1·10 50
MS3439 70×92 mm. 10fo. Bunch of roses (35×57 mm) . . . . . . 3·50 3·75

1982. Birth Centenary of Georgi Dimitrov (Bulgarian statesman).
3440 **798** 2fo. grey, green & brown 30 35

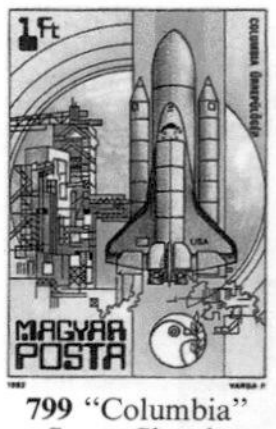

799 "Columbia" Space Shuttle

800 Watermark

1982. Space Research. Multicoloured.
3441 1fo. Type **799** 20 10
3442 1fo. Neil Armstrong (first man on Moon) 20 10
3443 2fo. A. Leonov (first space-walker) 35 10
3444 2fo. Yuri Gagarin (first man in space) 35 10
3445 4fo. Laika (first dog in space) 75 20
3446 4fo. "Sputnik I" (first artificial satellite) 75 20
3447 6fo. K. E. Tsiolkovsky (Russian scientist) . . . . 1·25 50

1982. Bicentenary of Diosgyor Paper-mill.
3448 **800** 2fo. multicoloured . . . 30 10

801 Rubik Cube

1982. World Rubik Cube Championship, Budapest.
3449 **801** 2fo. multicoloured . . . 30 10

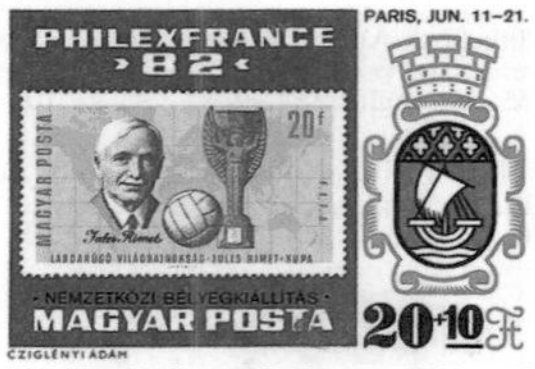

802 World Cup 20fi. Stamp, 1966, and Paris Arms

1982. "Philexfrance 82" International Stamp Exhibition, Paris. Sheet 98×72 mm.
MS3450 **802** 20fo.+10fo. mult . . 3·75 3·75

803 Col. Mihaly Kovats (after S. Finta)

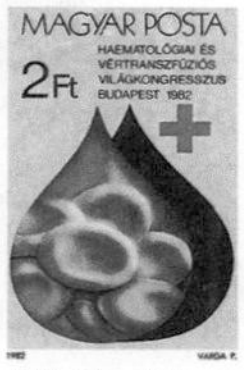

804 Blood Drop

1982. 250th Birth Anniv of George Washington. Sheet 90×72 mm containing T **803** and similar vert design. Multicoloured.
MS3451 5fo. Type **803**; 5fo. Washington on horseback (after F. Kemmelmeyer) . . . . . . 3·25 3·25

1982. World Haematology Congress, Budapest.
3452 **804** 2fo. multicoloured . . . 30 10

805 Zirc Abbey and Seal of King Bela III

806 Fishermen's Bastion, Budapest

1982. 800th Anniv of Zirc Abbey.
3453 **805** 2fo. multicoloured . . . 30 10

1982. Stamp Day. Multicoloured.
3454 4fo.+2fo. Type **806** . . . . 95 1·00
3455 4fo.+2fo. Cupola of Parliament, Budapest . . 95 1·00

807 Budapest (½-size illustration)

1982. 10th Anniv of European Security and Co-operation Conference, Brussels. Sheet 100×84 mm.
MS3456 **807** 20fo.+10fo. mult . . 4·50 4·00

808 Kner Emblem

1982. Cent of Kner Printing Office, Gyoma.
3457 **808** 2fo. yellow, black and red 30 10

809 Agricultural Symbols on Map of Hungary

1982. "Agrofila '82" Stamp Exhibition, Godollo.
3458 **809** 5fo. multicoloured . . . 1·00 1·00

810 Horse-drawn Bus and Underground Train

1982. 150th Anniv of Public Transport in Budapest.
3459 **810** 2fo. multicoloured . . . 45 10

811 Budapest Polytechnic University

812 Gyorgy Boloni

1982. Bicentenary of University Engineering Education.
3460 **811** 2fo. brown, stone & blue 30 10

1982. Birth Centenary of Gyorgy Boloni (journalist).
3461 **812** 2fo. yellow, brown and deep brown 30 10

813 Lenin

1982. 65th Anniv of Russian Revolution.
3462 **813** 5fo. multicoloured . . . 80 10

814 Vuk and Bird

1982. Vuk the Fox Cub (cartoon character). Multicoloured.
3463 1fo. Type **814** 20 10
3464 1fo. Two dogs 20 10
3465 2fo. Vuk and cock 40 10
3466 2fo. Vuk and owl 40 10
3467 4fo. Vuk and geese 80 10
3468 6fo. Vuk and frog . . . . . 1·25 60
3469 8fo. Vuk, old fox and butterflies . . . . 1·60 1·00

815 St. Stephen (sculpture, Imre Varga)

816 Dog and Cat crossing road

1982. Works of Art in Hungarian Chapel, Vatican. Multicoloured.

3470 2fo. Type **815** 50 55
3471 2fo. "Pope Silvester II making donation to St. Stephen" (37 × 18 mm) 50 55
3472 2fo. "St. John of Capistrano ringing Angelus to commemorate Hungarian victory over Turks" (37 × 18 mm) 50 55
3473 2fo. "Pope Paul VI showing Cardinal Lekai site of Hungarian Chapel" (37 × 18 mm) 50 55
3474 2fo. "Pope John Paul II consecrating chapel" (37 × 18 mm) 50 55
3475 2fo. "Madonna" (sculpture, Imre Varga) 50 55

Nos. 3471/5 were printed together, se-tenant, forming a composite design of a relief by Amerigo Tot.

1982. New Year.
3476 **816** 2fo. multicoloured . . . 40 10

817 Zoltan Kodaly

1982. Birth Centenary of Zoltan Kodaly (composer). Sheet 66 × 95 mm.
MS3477 **817** 20fo. brown and stone 3·50 3·00

818 Goethe (after Heinrich Kolbe)

1982. 150th Death Anniv of Johann Wolfgang Goethe (writer). Sheet 93 × 74 mm.
MS3478 **818** 20fo. multicoloured 3·50 3·50

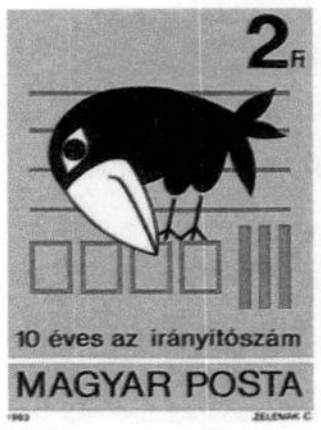

819 Raven and Envelope Address Marks
821 Student at School Door

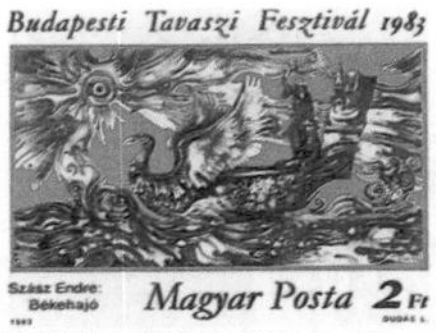

820 "Ship of Peace" (Endre Szasz)

1983. 10th Anniv of Postal Codes.
3479 **819** 2fo. black, grey and red 30 10

1983. Budapest Spring Festival.
3480 **820** 2fo. grey, gold and black 30 10

1983. Youth Stamp Exhibition, Baja.
3481 **821** 4fo.+2fo. mult . . . . . 90 1·00

822 Gyula Juhasz
823 Menner's Balloon, 1811

1983. Birth Cent of Gyula Juhasz (writer).
3482 **822** 2fo. dp brown, brn & blk 30 10

1983. Air. Bicent of Manned Flight. Mult.
3483 1fo. Type **823** (1st manned flight in Hungary) 15 10
3484 1fo. Captive observation balloon at Budapest Exhibition, 1896 . . . . 15 10
3485 2fo. Pursuit race, 1904 . . . 40 15
3486 2fo. Hot-air balloon "Pannonia", 1977 . . . . 40 15
3487 4fo. Hot-air balloon "Malev", 1981 . . . . . 70 35
3488 4fo. Hungarian National Defence Union balloon, 1982 . . . . 70 35
3489 5fo. Non-rigid airship over Mecsek television tower, 1981 . . . . 95 50
MS3490 88 × 74 mm. 20fo. Hot-air balloons (39 × 49 mm) . . . . 3·00 3·00

824 Szentgotthard Monastery and Seal

1983. 800th Anniv of Szentgotthard.
3491 **824** 2fo. multicoloured . . . 30 10

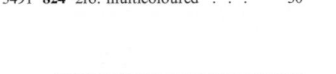

825 Watermill, Tapolca

1983. "Tembal 83" Thematic Stamps Exhibition, Basel.
3492 **825** 5fo. multicoloured . . . 90 95

826 Parliament Buildings, Budapest

1983. 5th Inter-Parliamentary Union Conference, Budapest. Sheet 95 × 77 mm.
MS3493 **826** 20fo. multicoloured 4·25 3·50

827 Jeno Hamburger

1983. Birth Centenary of Jeno Hamburger (doctor and revolutionary).
3494 **827** 2fo. brown, blue and red 30 10

828 "Giovanna d'Aragona"

1983. 500th Birth Anniv of Raphael (artist). Mult.
3495 1fo. Type **828** 15 10
3496 1fo. "Lady with Unicorn" 15 10
3497 2fo. "Madonna of the Chair" 30 10
3498 2fo. "Madonna of the Grand Duke" 30 10
3499 4fo. "La Muta" 55 10
3500 6fo. "Lady with a Veil" . . 95 45
3501 8fo. "La Fornaria" . . . . 1·10 70
MS3502 66 × 89 mm. 20fo. "Esterhazy Madonna" (24 × 37 mm) . . . . 3·75 3·75

829 Vagi and Newspapers
830 Bolivar and Map of Americas

1983. Birth Centenary of Istvan Vagi (secretary of Socialist Workers' Party).
3503 **829** 2fo. multicoloured . . . 30 10

1983. Birth Bicent of Simon Bolivar.
3504 **830** 2fo. multicoloured . . . 30 10

831 Globe and Congress Emblem
833 Lesser Spotted Eagle

832 Martin Luther

1983. 68th Universal Esperanto Congress, Budapest.
3505 **831** 2fo. multicoloured . . . 30 10

1983. 500th Anniv of Martin Luther (religious reformer). Sheet 80 × 65 mm.
MS3506 **832** 20fo. multicoloured 3·50 3·50

1983. Birds of Prey. Multicoloured.
3507 1fo. Type **833** 25 15
3508 1fo. Imperial eagle 25 15
3509 2fo. White-tailed sea eagle 50 20
3510 2fo. Western red-footed falcon 50 20
3511 4fo. Saker falcon 80 45
3512 6fo. Rough-legged buzzard 1·50 65
3513 8fo. Common buzzard . . . 1·75 1·00

834 Bee collecting Pollen
835 Old National Theatre (after R. Alt)

1983. 29th Apimondia (Bee Keeping) Congress, Budapest.
3514 **834** 1fo. multicoloured . . . 25 10

1983. Stamp Day. Engravings of Budapest Buildings.
3515 **835** 4fo.+2fo. yellow, brown and black . . . . . . 1·10 1·10
3516 – 4fo.+2fo. yellow, brown and black . . . . . . 1·10 1·10
MS3517 80 × 63 mm. 20fo.+10fo. yellow and brown . . . . . . 3·75 3·75

DESIGNS—As T **835**: No. 3516, Municipal concert hall, Pest (after H. Luders). 27 × 44 mm—**MS**3517, Holy Trinity Square, Buda (after Rudolf Alt).

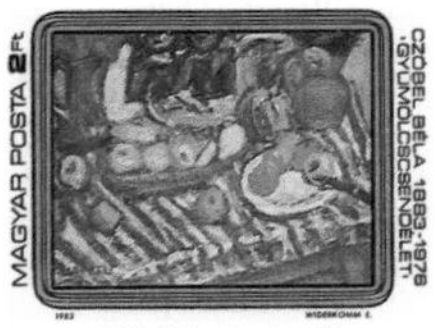

836 "Fruit-piece"

1983. Birth Centenary of Bela Czobel (artist).
3518 **836** 2fo. multicoloured . . . 30 10

837 "Molnya" Satellite and Kekes TV Tower
838 Flags encircling Globe

1983. World Communications Year. Mult.
3519 1fo. Type **837** 15 10
3520 1fo. Dish aerials and rockets 15 10
3521 2fo. Manual telephone exchange and modern "TMM-81" telephone . . 35 10
3522 3fo. Computer terminal . . 50 10
3523 5fo. Automatic letter-storing equipment 85 25
3524 8fo. Teletext and newspaper mastheads . . . . . . 1·50 55
MS3525 70 × 90 mm. 20fo. "Molnya" satellite (29 × 44 mm) 3·00 3·25

1983. 34th International Astronautical Federation Congress, Budapest.
3526 **838** 2fo. multicoloured . . . 30 10

839 Kremlin, Moscow

1983. "Sozphilex '83" Stamp Exhibition, Moscow.
3527 **839** 2fo. multicoloured . . . 45 45

840 Congress Palace, Madrid

1983. European Security and Co-operation Conference, Madrid. Sheet 98 × 78 mm.
MS3528 **840** 20fo. multicoloured 3·75 4·00

841 Babits (after Jozsef Rippl-Ronai)
842 "Madonna with Rose"

1983. Birth Cent of Mihaly Babits (writer).
3529 **841** 2fo. multicoloured . . . 30 10

1983. Christmas. Multicoloured.
3530 1fo. Type **842** 15 10
3531 2fo. Altar painting, Csik-menasag 30 10

843 Zanka

844 Ice Dancing

1983. Hungarian Resorts. Multicoloured.
3532 1fo. Type **843** 40 10
3533 2fo. Hajduszoboszlo 40 10
3534 5fo. Heviz 55 15

1983. Winter Olympic Games, Sarajevo.
3535 **844** 1fo. multicoloured . . . 25 10
3536 – 1fo. multicoloured . . . 25 10
3537 – 2fo. multicoloured (man lifting girl) 45 10
3538 – 2fo. multicoloured . . . 45 10
3539 – 4fo. multicoloured (man with both arms bent) 75 15
3540 – 4fo. multicoloured (man with one arm outstretched) 75 15
3541 – 6fo. multicoloured . . . 1·00 50
MS3542 70 × 70 mm. 20fo. multicoloured (49 × 39 mm) . . 3·50 3·25
DESIGNS: Nos. 3536/42, Different ice dancing designs.

845 "Virgin with Six Saints" (Tiepolo)

1984. Paintings Stolen from Museum of Fine Arts, Budapest. Sheet 130 × 98 mm containing T **845** and similar multicoloured designs.
MS3543 2fo. Type **845**; 2fo. "Esterhazy Madonna" (Raphael); 2fo. "Portrait of Giorgione" (imitator of Giorgione); 2fo. "Portrait of a Woman" (Tintoretto); 2fo. "Pietro Bempo" (Raphael); 2fo. "Portrait of a Man" (Tintoretto); 8fo. "Rest on the Flight into Egypt" (Tiepolo) (47 × 32 mm) . . . . 3·50 3·50

846 Csoma (statue) and Sepulchre, Darjeeling

847 "Energy" and Sun

1984. Birth Bicentenary of Sandor Korosi Csoma (traveller and philologist).
3544 **846** 2fo. multicoloured . . . 30 10

1984. Save Energy Campaign.
3545 **847** 1fo, red and black . . . 10 10

848 Parent and Child

849 40fi. Goya Stamp, 1968

1984. Youth Stamp.
3546 **848** 4fo.+2fo. mult 90 95

1984. International Stamp Exhibitions. Sheet 125 × 104 mm containing T **849** and similar vert designs. Multicoloured.
MS3547 4fo. Type **849** ("Espana 84", Madrid); 4fo. 20fi. kangaroo stamp, 1961 ("Ausipex 84", Melbourne); 4fo. 1fo. Schiller stamp, 1959 ("Philatelia '84", Stuttgart) . . . . 2·50 2·75

850 Hair Ornaments from Rakamaz

1984. Archaeological Finds.
3548 **850** 1fo. stone and brown . . 20 10
3549 – 1fo. stone and brown . . 20 10
3550 – 2fo. stone and brown . . 30 10
3551 – 2fo. stone and brown . . 30 10
3552 – 4fo. stone and brown . . 50 10
3553 – 6fo. stone and brown . . 80 15
3554 – 8fo. stone and brown . . 1·25 40
DESIGNS: No. 3549, Purse plates from Szolnok-Strazsahalom and Galgocz; 3550, Hair ornaments from Sarospatak; 3551, St. Stephen's sword (Prague) and Attila's sword (Aachen); 3552, Bowl from Ketpo; 3553, Stick handles from Hajdudorog and Szabadattyan; 3554, Saddle-bow from Izsak and bit and stirrups from Muszka.

851 Cracow and Emblem

852 "Epiphile dilecta"

1984. 25th Session of Permanent Committee of Posts and Telecommunications, Cracow, Poland.
3555 **851** 2fo. multicoloured . . . 30 10

1984. Butterflies. Multicoloured.
3556 1fo. Type **852** 35 10
3557 1fo. "Agrias sara" 35 10
3558 2fo. Blue morpho ("Morpho cypris") 60 20
3559 2fo. "Ancyluris formosissima" 60 20
3560 4fo. African monarch . . . 80 25
3561 6fo. "Catagramma cynosura" . . . . 1·25 60
3562 8fo. Paradise birdwing . . . 1·60 70
No. 3557 is inscribed "Agra sara".

853 "Archer"

854 Hevesi

1984. Birth Centenary of Zsigmond Kisfaludy Strobl (sculptor).
3563 **853** 2fo. brown and yellow . . 35 10

1984. Birth Centenary of Akos Hevesi (activist in working-class movement).
3564 **854** 2fo. multicoloured . . . 35 10

855 Doves around Map of Hungary

856 World Map and Airplane

1984. Peace Festival, Pusztavacs.
3565 **855** 2fo. multicoloured . . . 35 10

1984. World Aerobatics Championship, Bekescsaba.
3566 **856** 2fo. multicoloured . . . 35 10

857 Four-in-hand

858 Conference Emblem

1984. World Team-driving Championships, Szilvasvarad.
3567 **857** 2fo. multicoloured . . . 35 10

1984. 14th Organization of Socialist Countries' Postal Administrations Conference, Budapest.
3568 **858** 2fo. multicoloured . . . 35 10

859 Four-handled Vase

1984. Stamp Day. Multicoloured.
3569 1fo. Type **859** 25 10
3570 2fo. Platter with flower decoration 40 10
MS3571 80 × 63 mm. 10fo. Cover with 1874 3k. stamp (44 × 27 mm) 3·00 3·00

860 "Music crowned by Fame" (fresco, Mor Than)

1984. Reopening of Budapest Opera House. Multicoloured.
3572 1fo. Type **860** 25 10
3573 2fo. Central staircase . . . 45 15
3574 5fo. Auditorium 85 45
MS3575 80 × 65 mm. 20fo. Facade and floor plan (49 × 39 mm) . . 3·75 3·25

861 Atrium Hyatt Hotel

1984. Budapest Hotels along the Danube. Multicoloured.
3576 1fo. Type **861** 20 10
3577 2fo. Duna Intercontinental 40 15
3578 4fo. Forum 60 20
3579 4fo. Thermal Hotel, Margaret Island 60 20
3580 5fo. Hilton 75 25
3581 8fo. Gellert . . . . 1·25 35
MS3582 78 × 55 mm. 20fo. Hilton (different) (36 × 25 mm) . . . . 3·00 3·25

862 Cep ("Boletus edulis")

863 Kato Haman (Labour Movement leader)

1984. Edible Mushrooms. Multicoloured.
3583 1fo. Type **862** 40 15
3584 1fo. Scotch bonnet ("Marasmius orcades") 40 15
3585 2fo. Common morel ("Morchella esculenta") 60 15
3586 2fo. Field mushroom ("Agaricus campester") 60 15
3587 3fo. Chanterelle ("Cantharellus cibarius") 75 20
3588 3fo. Parasol mushroom ("Macrolepiota procera") 75 20
3589 4fo. Boot-lace fungus . . . 95 50

1984. Birth Centenaries.
3590 **863** 2fo. brown, gold and black 35 10
3591 – 2fo. brown, gold and black 35 10
DESIGN: No. 3591, Bela Balazs (writer).

864 "Virgin and Child" (small altar, Trencseny)

865 Torah Crown (Buda)

1984. Christmas
3592 **864** 1fo. multicoloured . . . 20 10

1984. Reopening of Jewish Museum, Budapest, Multicoloured.
3593 1fo. Type **865** 25 10
3594 1fo. Chalice (Moscow) . . . 25 10
3595 2fo. Torah shield (Vienna) 40 10
3596 2fo. Elias chalice (Warsaw) 40 10
3597 4fo. Esrog holder (Augsburg) 65 10
3598 6fo. Candle holder (Warsaw) 85 25
3599 8fo. Urn (Pest) . . . . . . 1·10 55

866 Barn Owl

867 Long Jumping and Emblem

1984. Owls. Multicoloured.
3600 1fo. Type **866** 40 15
3601 1fo. Little owl 40 15
3602 2fo. Tawny owl 70 15
3603 2fo. Long-eared owl 70 15
3604 4fo. Snowy owl . . . . . . 1·10 35
3605 6fo. Ural owl . . . . 1·50 60
3606 8fo. Eagle owl . . . . . . 1·75 75

1985. 90th Anniv of Hungarian Olympic Committee. Sheet 86 × 70 mm.
MS3607 **867** 20fo. multicoloured 4·25 4·00

868 Novi Sad Bridge, Yugoslavia

1985. Danube Bridges. Multicoloured.
3608 1fo. Type **868** 20 10
3609 1fo. Baja, Hungary 20 10
3610 2fo. Arpad bridge, Budapest 40 15
3611 2fo. Bratislava, Czechoslovakia 40 15
3612 4fo. Reichsbrucke bridge, Vienna 65 25
3613 6fo. Linz, Austria 85 40
3614 8fo. Regensburg, West Germany . . . . 1·10 55
MS3615 65 × 80 mm. 20fo. Elizabeth and Chain Bridges, Budapest (49 × 39 mm) . . . . 3·50 3·50

869 Laszlo Rudas

870 Woman and Flowers

1985. Birth Centenary of Laszlo Rudas (philosopher and socialist).
3616 **869** 2fo. brown, gold & black 35 10

1985. International Women's Day.
3617 **870** 2fo. multicoloured . . . 35 10

871 1925 200k. Skiing Stamp

873 "Little Red Riding Hood"

872 Liberty Bridge, Liberation Statue and Fireworks

1985. "Olymphilex '85" International Olympic Stamps Exhibition, Lausanne.
3618 **871** 4fo. green, gold and blue . . . 60 25
3619 – 5fo. blue, brown and gold 75 25
DESIGN: 5fo. 1925 300k. Skating stamp.

1985. 40th Anniv of Liberation. Sheet 70 × 95 mm.
MS3620 **872** 20fo. multicoloured . . . 3·50 3·25

1985. Birth Centenary of Jacob Grimm (folklorist).
3621 **873** 4fo.+2fo. mult . . . . . 1·25 1·10

874 Gyorgy Lukacs

875 Title Page

1985. Birth Centenary of Gyorgy Lukacs (philosopher).
3622 **874** 2fo. multicoloured . . . 35 10

1985. 300th Anniv of Totfalusi Bible.
3623 **875** 2fo. black and gold . . . 35 10

876 Peter Pazmany (founder)

877 Boxing

1985. 350th Anniv of Lorand Eotvos University.
3624 **876** 2fo. grey and red 35 40

1985. 26th European Boxing Championships, Budapest.
3625 **877** 2fo. multicoloured . . . 35 10

878 Women Footballers

1985. International Youth Year. Mult.
3626 1fo. Type **878** 20 10
3627 2fo. Windsurfing 35 10
3628 2fo. Women exercising . . . 35 10
3629 4fo. Karate 55 10
3630 4fo. Go-karting 55 10
3631 5fo. Hang gliding 80 40
3632 6fo. Skate-boarding 75 50

879 Monorail Train

1985. "Expo '85" World's Fair, Tsukuba. Mult.
3633 2fo. Type **879** 55 10
3634 4fo. Fuyo Theatre 60 25

880 Common Flicker

1985. Birth Bicentenary of John J. Audubon (ornithologist). Multicoloured.
3635 2fo. Type **880** (postage) . . 45 15
3636 2fo. Bohemian waxwing . . 45 15
3637 2fo. Pileated woodpecker . . 45 15
3638 4fo. Northern oriole 85 30
3639 4fo. Common flicker (air) 85 30
3640 6fo. Common cardinal . . . 1·40 50

881 Nonius XXXVI

1985. Bicentenary of Horsebreeding at Mezohegyes. Multicoloured.
3641 1fo. Type **881** 30 10
3642 2fo. Furioso XXIII 45 10
3643 4fo. Gidran I 85 15
3644 4fo. Ramses III 85 15
3645 6fo. Krozus I . . . . 1·25 40

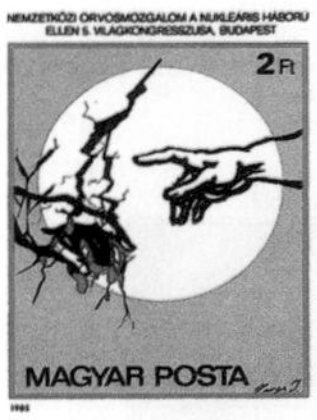

882 Hand pointing to Cracked Earth (Imre Varga)

883 Handel, Kettledrum and Horn

1985. 5th Congress of International Association of Physicians against Nuclear War, Budapest.
3646 **882** 2fo. multicoloured . . . 35 10

1985. Music Year. Multicoloured.
3647 1fo. Type **883** (300th birth anniv) 30 10
3648 2fo. Bach and Thomas Church organ, Leipzig (300th birth anniv) . . . 55 10
3649 4fo. Luigi Cherubini, harp, bass violin and baryton (225th anniv) 85 10
3650 4fo. Chopin and piano (175th birth anniv) . . . 85 10
3651 5fo. Mahler, viola, double horn and kettledrum (125th birth anniv) . . . 1·25 35
3652 6fo. Ferenc Erkel, viola and bass tuba (175th birth anniv) . . . . 1·40 60

884 Red Square and Emblem

1985. 12th World Youth and Students' Festival, Moscow. Sheet 89 × 69 mm.
MS3653 **884** 20fo. multicoloured . . . 3·00 3·00

885 Finlandia Palace

1985. 10th Anniv of Helsinki Agreement. Sheet 92 × 75 mm.
MS3654 **885** 20fo. multicoloured . . . 4·25 3·50

886 Key with Globe as Head

887 Flags on Computer Keyboards

1985. World Tourism Day.
3655 **886** 2fo. multicoloured . . . 35 10

1985. "COMNET '85" Computer Networks Conference, Budapest.
3656 **887** 4fo. multicoloured . . . 35 10

888 Budapest

1985. European Security and Co-operation Conference, Budapest.
MS3657 **888** 20fo. multicoloured . . . 5·25 4·50

889 Water Holder

890 Italian 1960 5l. Stamp

1985. Stamp Day. Haban Ceramics. Mult.
3658 1fo. Type **889** 15 15
3659 2fo. Tankard with cover . . 40 50
MS3660 80 × 60 mm. 10fo. Hexagonal medicine holder . . 2·75 3·00

1985. "Italia '85" International Stamp Exhibition, Rome.
3661 **890** 5fo. multicoloured . . . 1·00 1·00

891 Dove and U.N. Emblem

892 Red Lily

1985. 40th Anniv of United Nations Organization.
3662 **891** 4fo. turquoise, bl & dp bl 45 10

1985. Lily Family. Multicoloured.
3663 1fo. Type **892** 25 10
3664 2fo. Turk's-cap lily 35 10
3665 2fo. Dog's tooth violet . . . 35 10
3666 4fo. Tiger lily 60 10
3667 4fo. Snake's-head fritillary 60 10
3668 5fo. Day lily 80 35
3669 6fo. "Bulbocodium vernum" 1·00 50

893 Carol Singers

1985. Christmas.
3670 **893** 2fo. multicoloured . . . 35 10

894 Istvan Ries

895 Three Houses under One Roof

1985. Birth Centenary of Istvan Ries (Minister of Justice).
3671 **894** 2fo. multicoloured . . . 35 10

1985. S.O.S. Childrens' Village.
3672 **895** 4fo.+2fo. multicoloured 1·25 1·25

896 Fantic "Sprinter", 1984

1985. Centenary of Motor Cycle.
3673 **896** 1fo. black, orange & blue 25 10
3674 – 2fo. black, yellow & blue 40 10
3675 – 2fo. black, green and grey 40 10
3676 – 4fo. multicoloured . . . 60 10
3677 – 4fo. black, green and grey 60 10
3678 – 5fo. multicoloured . . . 85 25
3679 – 6fo. multicoloured . . . 1·10 55
DESIGNS: No. 3674, Harley-Davidson "Duo-Glide", 1960; 3675, Suzuki "Katana GSX", 1983; 3676, BMW "R47", 1927; 3677, Rudge-Whitworth, 1935; 3678, NSU, 1910; 3679, Daimler, 1885.

897 "Ice" Satellite and Dinosaurs

898 Bela Kun

1986. Air. Appearance of Halley's Comet. Multicoloured.
3680 2fo. Type **897** 45 10
3681 2fo. "Vega" satellite and detail of Bayeux Tapestry showing comet 45 10
3682 2fo. "Suisei" satellite and German engraving of 1507 . . . . 45 10
3683 4fo. "Giotto" satellite and "The Magi" (tapestry after Giotto) 75 10
3684 4fo. "Astron" satellite and Virgo, Leo, Corvus, Crater and Hydra constellations 75 10
3685 6fo. Space shuttle and Edmond Halley (wrongly inscr "Edmund") . . . . 1·25 50

1986. Birth Centenary of Bela Kun (Communist Party leader).
3686 **898** 4fo. multicoloured . . . 35 10

899 "Challenger" (space shuttle)

1986. Challenger Astronauts Commemoration. Sheet 92 × 79 mm.
MS3687 **899** 20fo. multicoloured 4·50 4·50

900 Guide Dog

901 Running for Ball

1986. The Blind.
3688 **900** 4fo. multicoloured . . . 35 10

1986. World Cup Football Championship, Mexico. Multicoloured.
3689 2fo. Type **901** 40 10
3690 2fo. Heading ball 40 10
3691 4fo. Tackling 85 10
3692 4fo. Goalkeeper diving for ball 85 10
3693 4fo. Goalkeeper catching ball 85 10
3694 6fo. Tackling (different) . . 1·25 55
MS3695 80 × 60 mm. 20fo. Team celebrating (40 × 30 mm) . . . 4·25 3·75

902 Cable Railway

903 Rose "Yankee Doodle"

1986. Re-opening of Buda Castle Cable Railway.
3696 **902** 2fo. brown, yell & orge 35 10

1986. "Ameripex '86" International Stamp Exhibition, Chicago. Sheet 80 × 100 mm containing T **903** and similar vert designs. Multicoloured.
MS3697 5fo. Type **903**; 5fo. Rose "America"; 10fo. Statue of George Washington, Budapest and exhibition emblem (25 × 70 mm) 3·50 3·00

904 Japanese and Hungarian Dolls

1986. Hungarian Days in Tokyo.
3698 **904** 4fo. multicoloured . . . 45 10

905 Fay

906 Flag and "40"

1986. Birth Bicentenary of Andras Fay (writer, politician and founder of First Hungarian Savings Bank Union).
3699 **905** 4fo. brown & pale brown 60 50

1986. Youth Stamp. 40th Anniv of Young Pioneers Movement.
3700 **906** 4fo.+2fo. multicoloured 1·00 1·00

907 Ferrari Racing Cars, 1961 and 1985

1986. Centenary of Motor Car. Multicoloured.
3701 2fo. Type **907** 40 10
3702 2fo. Alfa Romeo racing cars, 1932 and 1984 . . . . 40 10
3703 2fo. Volkswagen "Beetle", 1936, and Porsche "959", 1986 . . . . 40 10
3704 4fo. Renault "14 CV", 1902, and "5 GT Turbo", 1985 85 15
3705 4fo. Fiat "3 1/2", 1899, and "Ritmo", 1985 . . . . . 85 15
3706 6fo. Daimler, 1886, and Mercedes-Benz "230 SE", 1986 . . . . 1·25 50

908 "Wasa" (Swedish ship of the line), 1628

1986. "Stockholmia '86" Int Stamp Exhibition.
3707 **908** 2fo. multicoloured . . . 75 85

909 Moritz Kaposi (cancer specialist)

1986. 14th International Cancer Congress, Budapest.
3708 **909** 4fo. multicoloured . . . 50 10

910 "Recapture of Buda Castle" (Gyula Benczur) (½-size Illustration)

1986. 300th Anniv of Recapture of Buda from Turks.
3709 **910** 4fo. multicoloured . . . 45 10

911 "Tranquillity"

1986. Stamp Day. Multicoloured.
3710 2fo. Type **911** 30 35
3711 2fo. "Confidence" 30 35
MS3712 80 × 60 mm. 10fo. "Hope" (28 × 49 mm) . . . . 3·00 3·00

912 Fragment of 15th-cent Carpet from Anatolia

1986. 5th International Oriental Carpets and Tapestry Conference, Vienna and Budapest.
3713 **912** 4fo. multicoloured . . . 45 10

913 Model of New Theatre

1986. National Theatre, Budapest. Sheet 63 × 85 mm.
MS3714 **913** 20fo.+10fo. brown, stone and light brown . . . . 3·75 3·75

914 Piano and Liszt

915 Dove

1986. 175th Birth Anniv of Franz Liszt (pianist and composer).
3715 **914** 4fo. deep green and green 50 10

1986. International Peace Year.
3716 **915** 4fo. multicoloured . . . 70 70

916 Hofburg Palace, Vienna, and Map

1986. European Security and Co-operation Conference Review Meeting, Vienna. Sheet 65 × 80 mm.
MS3717 **916** 20fo. multicoloured 4·25 4·00

917 Pogany

918 Munnich

1986. Birth Centenary of Jozsef Pogany (writer and journalist).
3718 **917** 4fo. multicoloured . . . 45 10

1986. Birth Centenary of Ferenc Munnich (former Prime Minister).
3719 **918** 4fo. multicoloured . . . 45 10

919 Heads

1986. 12th General Assembly of World Federation of Democratic Youth, Budapest.
3720 **919** 4fo. multicoloured . . . 45 10

920 Apricots ("Kajszi" C.235)

1986. Fruits. Multicoloured.
3721 2fo. Type **920** 40 10
3722 2fo. Cherries ("Good bearer of Erd") 40 10
3723 4fo. Apples ("Jonathan" M.14) 80 10
3724 4fo. Raspberries ("Nagymaros") 80 10
3725 4fo. Peaches ("Piroska") . . 80 10
3726 6fo. Grapes ("Zalagyongye") . . . . 1·00 40

921 Forgach Castle, Szecseny

922 Wild Cat

1986. Castles. Inscr "MAGYAR POSTA".
3727 **921** 2fo. bistre and yellow . . 30 10
3728 – 3fo. green and light green 30 10
3729 – 4fo. blue and light blue 45 10
3730 – 5fo. red and pink . . . 55 10
3731 – 6fo. brown and orange 65 10
3732 – 8fo. red and orange . . 75 10
3733 – 10fo. brown and ochre 80 10
3734 – 20fo. green and yellow 1·50 10
3735 – 30fo. light green and green . . . . 1·90 30
3736 – 40fo. blue and light blue 2·25 35
3737 – 50fo. deep red and red 2·75 45
3738 – 70fo. deep grey and grey 3·25 60
3739 – 100fo. violet and lilac . . 6·00 95
DESIGNS: 3fo. Savoya Castle, Rackeve; 4fo. Batthyany Castle, Kormend; 5fo. Szechenyi Castle, Nagycenk; 6fo. Rudnyanszky Castle, Nagyteteny; 8fo. Szapary Castle, Buk; 10fo. Festetics Castle, Keszthely; 20fo. Brunswick Castle, Martonvasar; 30fo. De La Motte Castle, Noszvaj; 40fo. L'Huillier-Coburg Castle, Edeleny; 50fo. Teleki-Degenfeld Castle, Szirak; 70fo. Magochy Castle, Pacin; 100fo. Esterhazy Castle, Fertod.
See also Nos. 3888 and 4045/9.

1986. Protected Animals. Multicoloured.
3740 2fo. Type **922** 40 10
3741 2fo. European otter 40 10
3742 2fo. Stoat 40 10
3743 4fo. Eurasian red squirrel 85 15
3744 4fo. East European hedgehog 85 15
3745 6fo. European pond turtle 1·25 45

923 St. Stephen I (coronation cloak, 1030)

924 Death Cap ("Amanita phalloides")

1986. Kings (1st series).
3746 **923** 2fo. brown, blue and red 40 10
3747 – 2fo. brown, grey and red 40 10
3748 – 4fo. brown, green and red 75 10
3749 – 4fo. brown, grey and red 75 10
3750 – 6fo. brown, blue and red 1·25 35
DESIGNS: No. 3747, Geza I (enamel portrait on Hungarian crown, 1070); 3748, St. Ladislas I (Gyor Cathedral, 1400); 3749, Bela III (Kalocsa Cathedral statue, 1200); 3750, Bela IV (Jak church statue, 1230).
See also Nos. 3835/7.

1986. Fungi. Multicoloured.
3751 2fo. Type **924** 45 20
3752 2fo. Fly agaric ("Amanita muscaria") 45 20
3753 2fo. Red-staining inocybe ("Inocybe patouillardi") 45 20
3754 4fo. Olive-wood pleurotus ("Omphalotus olearius") 95 45
3755 4fo. Panther cap ("Amanita pantherina") 95 45
3756 6fo. Beefsteak morel . . . . 1·40 75

925 Banded Gourami

926 "Sitting Woman"

1987. Fishes. Multicoloured.
3757 2fo. Type **925** 35 10
3758 2fo. Thread-finned rainbowfish ("Iriathorina werneri") 35 10
3759 2fo. Zebra mbuna ("Pseudotropheus zebra") 35 10
3760 4fo. Ramirez dwarf cichlid ("Papiliochromis ramirezi") 70 15
3761 4fo. Multicoloured lyretail ("Aphyosemion multicolor") 70 15
3762 6fo. Bleeding-heart tetra ("Hyphessobrycon erythrostigma") . . . . . 1·00 40

1987. Birth Centenary of Bela Uitz (painter).
3763 **926** 4fo. multicoloured . . . 45 10

927 Abstract

928 Flag, Books, Torch and Dove

1987. Birth Centenary of Lajos Kassak (writer and painter).
3764 **927** 4fo. black and red . . . 45 10

1987. 30th Anniv of Young Communist League.
3765 **928** 4fo.+2fo. mult . . . . . 90 1·00

929 Hippocrates (medical oath)

930 Food Jar, Hodmezovasarhely

1987. Pioneers of Medicine (1st series).
3766 **929** 2fo. brown and blue . . 35 10
3767 – 4fo. green and black . . 70 10
3768 – 4fo. blue and black . . . 70 10
3769 – 4fo. brown and black . . 70 10
3770 – 6fo. brown and black . . 1·00 40
DESIGNS: No. 3767, Avicenna ("Kanun" book of medical rules); 3768, Ambroise Pare (improved treatment of wounds); 3769, William Harvey (circulation of blood); 3770, Ignac Semmelweis (aseptic treatment of wounds).
See also Nos. 3939/43.

1987. Neolithic and Copper Age Art. Multicoloured.
3771 **930** 2fo. brown and green . . 50 10
3772 – 4fo. brown and flesh . . 80 10
3773 – 4fo. brown and pink . . 80 10
3774 – 5fo. brown and green . . 1·10 40
DESIGNS: No. 3772, Altar, Szeged; 3773, Statue with sickle, Szegvar-Tuzkoves; 3774, Vase with face, Center.

931 King Matthias's Cross

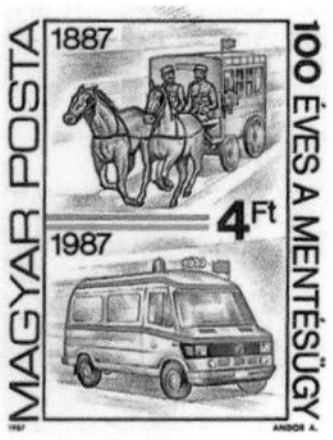

932 Old and Modern Ambulances

1987. Re-opening of Esztergom Cathedral Treasury. Sheet 64 × 80 mm.
MS3775 **931** 20fo. multicoloured 3·50 3·25

1987. Cent of Hungarian First Aid Association.
3776 **932** 4fo. multicoloured . . . 45 10

933 Toronto ("Capex '87")

1987. International Stamp Exhibitions. Mult.
3777 5fo. Type **933** . . . . 90 1·10
3778 5fo. "Olymphilex 87" building, Rome . . . . . 90 1·10
3779 5fo. "Hafnia 87" building, Copenhagen . . . . . . 90 1·10

934 Jozsef Marek

1987. Bicentenary of University of Veterinary Sciences, Budapest.
3780 **934** 4fo. silver, blue and black 45 10

935 Teleki, Route Map and Porters

1987. Cent of Samuel Teleki's African Expedition.
3781 **935** 4fo. multicoloured . . . 45 10

936 Printing Shop (17th-century wood-print, Abraham von Werdt)

937 James Cook and H.M.S. "Resolution"

1987. 125th Anniv of Hungarian Printing, Paper and Press Workers' Union.
3782 **936** 4fo. brown and stone . . 45 10

1987. Antarctic Exploration. Multicoloured.
3783 2fo. Type **937** 40 15
3784 2fo. Fabian von Bellingshausen and seals 40 15
3785 2fo. Ernest Shackleton and emperor penguins 40 15
3786 4fo. Roald Amundsen and huskies 70 25
3787 4fo. Robert F. Scott and "Terra Nova" 70 25
3788 6fo. Richard Byrd and Ford Trimotor "Floyd Bennett" 1·10 45
MS3789 86 × 70 mm. 20fo. Mirnyi Research Station (32 × 42 mm) 6·00 5·75

938 Old and New Railway Emblems and Institute

939 Flowers and Dolphin

1987. Cent of Railway Officers' Training Institute.
3790 **938** 4fo. black and blue . . . 45 10

1987. Stamp Day. Carvings from Buda Castle.
3791 **939** 2fo. indigo, blue & azure 30 30
3792 – 4fo. olive, green & turq 60 70
MS3793 68 × 88 mm. 10fo. agate, grey and lilac . . . . 2·50 2·40
DESIGNS: 4fo. King Matthias's arms; 10fo. Capital of Column.

940 Jesse Altar

941 "Orchis purpurea"

1987. Gyongyospata Church.
3794 **940** 4fo. multicoloured . . . 90 1·00

1987. Orchids. Multicoloured.
3795 2fo. Type **941** 40 10
3796 2fo. "Cypripedium calceolus" 40 10
3797 4fo. "Ophrys scolopax" . . 70 10
3798 4fo. "Himantoglossum hircinum" 70 10
3799 5fo. "Cephalanthera rubra" 95 20
3800 6fo. "Epipactis atrorubens" 1·10 40
MS3801 40 × 60 mm. 20fo. Orchids (24 × 33 mm) . . . . 3·50 3·25

942 Speed Skating

945 "The White Crane" (Japanese folk tale)

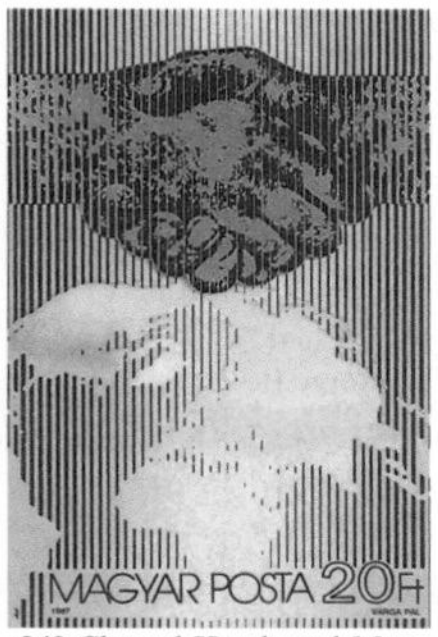

943 Clasped Hands and Map

1987. Winter Olympic Games, Calgary. Mult.
3802 2fo. Type **942** 30 10
3803 2fo. Cross-country skiing . . 30 10
3804 4fo. Biathlon 60 10
3805 4fo. Ice hockey 60 10
3806 4fo. Four-man bobsleigh . . 60 10
3807 6fo. Ski jumping 95 30
MS3808 50 × 60 mm. 20fo. Slalom (24 × 41 mm) . . . . 3·50 3·50

1987. U.S.–Soviet Strategic Arms Reduction Talks, Washington. Sheet 78 × 82 mm.
MS3809 **943** 20fo. multicoloured 3·75 3·75

1987. Fairy Tales. Multicoloured.
3816 2fo. Type **945** 35 10
3817 2fo. "The Fox and the Raven" (Aesop) 35 10
3818 4fo. "The Hare and The Tortoise" (Aesop) 75 20
3819 4fo. "The Ugly Duckling" (Hans Christian Andersen) 75 20
3820 6fo. "The Brave Little Lead Soldier" (Hans Christian Andersen) . . . . 1·10 45

946 Zeppelin and Airship LZ-2

1988. 150th Birth Anniv of Ferdinand von Zeppelin (airship pioneer).
3821 **946** 2fo. black and blue . . . 40 15
3822 – 4fo. deep brown & brown 70 25
3823 – 4fo. purple and lilac . . 70 25
3824 – 8fo. olive and green . . 1·25 45
DESIGNS: No. 3822, LZ-4; 3823, "Schwaben"; 3824, "Graf Zeppelin".

947 Skater

949 Monus

948 Woman's Head

1988. World Figure Skating Championships, Budapest. Skaters from 19th-century to date. Multicoloured.
3825 2fo. Type **947** 30 10
3826 2fo. Man wearing hat . . . 30 10
3827 4fo. Woman 60 10
3828 4fo. Man in hat and coat 60 10
3829 5fo. Woman in modern skating dress 70 10
3830 6fo. Pair 90 30
MS3831 89 × 72 mm. 20fo. Pair (different) (32 × 47 mm) . . . . 3·50 3·50

1988. Stamp Day. "Socfilex" International Stamp Exhibition, Kecskemet. Sheet 72 × 54 mm.
MS3832 **948** 20fo.+10fo. mult . . 4·25 4·00

1988. Birth Centenary of Illes Monus (newspaper editor).
3833 **949** 4fo. blue, red and black 45 10

950 18th-cent Postmaster's Uniform

1988. Stamp Exhibitions.
MS3834 **950** 4fo. black and stone 1·10 1·00

1988. Kings (2nd series). As T **923**.
3835 2fo. brown, green and red 30 10
3836 4fo. brown, blue and red . . 60 10
3837 6fo. brown, violet and red 95 30
DESIGNS: 2fo. Karoly I (Charles Robert) (detail of decorated initial from "Illuminated Chronicle", 1358); 4fo. Lajos the Great (relief, St. Simeon's reliquary, Zara, 1380); 6fo. Zsigmond (Sigismund of Luxembourg) (after great seal, 1433).

951 Rowing

952 Computer Drawing of Head

1988. Olympic Games, Seoul. Multicoloured.
3838 2fo. Type **951** 35 15
3839 4fo. Hurdling 60 15
3840 4fo. Fencing 60 15
3841 6fo. Boxing 95 55
MS3842 70 × 80 mm. 20fo. Tennis (31 × 40 mm) . . . . 4·50 4·25

1988. 6th Anniv of "Dilemma" (first computer-animated film).
3843 **952** 4fo. multicoloured . . . 50 10

953 Card and Emblem

1988. Eurocheque Congress, Budapest.
3844 **953** 4fo. multicoloured . . . 45 10

954 "Santa Maria", 1492

955 Damaged Head

1988. Ships. Multicoloured.
3845 2fo. Type **954** 45 30
3846 2fo. "Mayflower", 1620 . . 45 30
3847 2fo. "Sovereign of the Seas", 1637 . . . . . . 45 30
3848 4fo. "Jylland" (steam warship), 1860 . . . . . 95 40
3849 6fo. "St. Jupat" (yacht), 1985 . . . . 1·50 55

1988. Anti-drugs Campaign.
3850 **955** 4fo. multicoloured . . . 45 10

956 Green-winged Teal ("Anas crecca")

957 Steam Train

1988. Wild Ducks. Multicoloured.
3851 2fo. Type **956** 55 25
3852 2fo. Common goldeneye ("Bucephula clangula") 55 25

3853 4fo. European wigeon (“Anas penelope”) . . . 1·00 30
3854 4fo. Red-crested pochard (“Netta rufina”) . . . . . 1·00 30
3855 6fo. Gadwell . . . . 1·25 55
MS3856 90 × 73 mm. 20fo. Mallard (“Anas platyrhynchos”) . . . 5·00 4·50

1988. Exhibits in Toy Museum, Kecskemet. Multicoloured.
3857 2fo. Type **957** 45 15
3858 2fo. See-saw 30 10
3859 4fo.+2fo. Pecking chicks . . 80 30
3860 5fo. Johnny Hussar 70 30

958 Facade

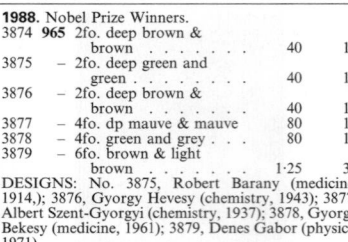

959 Congress Emblem

1988. 450th Anniv of Debrecen Calvinist College.
3861 **958** 4fo. multicoloured . . . 40 10

1988. 58th American Society of Travel Agents Congress, Budapest.
3862 **959** 4fo. multicoloured . . . 40 10

960 Lloyd C.II Biplane

961 Post Official's Collar and Badge

1988. Air. Hungarian Biplanes.
3863 **960** 1fo. green 10 10
3864 – 2fo. purple 25 10
3865 – 4fo. bistre 40 15
3866 – 10fo. blue 95 55
3867 – 12fo. red . . . . 1·25 55
DESIGNS: 2fo. Hansa Brandenburg C-I; 4fo. UFAG C-I; 10fo. Gerle 13 scout plane; 12fo. WM 13 trainer.

1988. Centenary of Post Office Training School.
3868 **961** 4fo. red, blue and brown 45 10

962 Baross and Postal Savings Bank, Budapest

1988. Stamp Day. 140th Birth Anniv of Gabor Baross (politician). Multicoloured.
3869 2fo. Type **962** 45 35
3870 4fo. Baross with telephone and telegraph equipment 1·40 75
MS3871 80 × 70 mm. 10fo. Baross and East Railway Station, Budapest . . . . 2·75 3·00

963 Lengyel

964 Christmas Tree

1988. Birth Centenary of Gyula Lengyel (labour movement activist).
3872 **963** 4fo. multicoloured . . . 50 10

1988. Christmas.
3873 **964** 2fo. multicoloured . . . 35 10

965 Richard Adolf Zsigmondy (chemistry, 1925)

966 Szakasits

1988. Nobel Prize Winners.
3874 **965** 2fo. deep brown & brown 40 10
3875 – 2fo. deep green and green 40 10
3876 – 2fo. deep brown & brown 40 10
3877 – 4fo. dp mauve & mauve 80 10
3878 – 4fo. green and grey . . . 80 10
3879 – 6fo. brown & light brown . . . . . . 1·25 30
DESIGNS: No. 3875, Robert Barany (medicine, 1914,); 3876, Gyorgy Hevesy (chemistry, 1943); 3877, Albert Szent-Gyorgyi (chemistry, 1937); 3878, Gyorgy Bekesy (medicine, 1961); 3879, Denes Gabor (physics, 1971).

1988. Birth Centenary of Arpad Szakasits (President, 1948–50).
3880 **966** 4fo. multicoloured . . . 50 10

967 Stadium and Emblem

968 Silver Teapot from Pest, 1846

1988. Hungarian Medals at Seoul Olympic Games. Sheet 70 × 90 mm.
MS3881 **967** 20fo. multicoloured 3·75 4·25

1988. Metal Work.
3882 **968** 2fo. blue and brown . . 35 10
3883 – 2fo. deep brown & brown 35 10
3884 – 4fo. lilac and brown . . 70 30
3885 – 5fo. green and brown . . 90 30
DESIGNS: No. 3883, 18th-century silver pot, Buda; 3884, Silver sugar basin from Pest, 1822; 3885, Pierced cast iron plate from Resicabanya, 1850.

969 Emblem

970 Wallisch

1989. Foundation of Post and Savings Bank Company.
3886 **969** 5fo. blue, silver and black 45 10

1989. Birth Centenary of Kalman Wallisch (workers' movement activist).
3887 **970** 3fo. blue and red 40 10

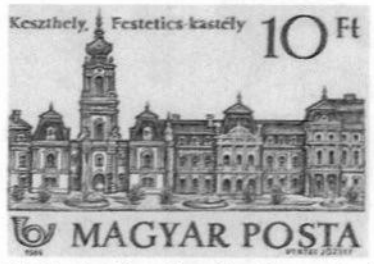

971 Festetics Castle, Keszthely

1989.
3888 **971** 10fo. brown and bistre 50 10

972 Athletes

973 Houses of Parliament and Big Ben London

1989. 2nd International Indoor Athletics Championships, Budapest.
3889 **972** 3fo. multicoloured . . . 40 10

1989. Centenary of Interparliamentary Union. Sheet 78 × 90 mm containing T **973** and similar vert design. Multicoloured.
MS3890 10fo. Type **973**; 10fo. Parliament Building, Budapest 3·50 3·00

974 Gyetvai

975 “Sky-high Tree” (detail, carpet)

1989. Birth Centenary of Janos Gyetvai (journalist).
3891 **974** 3fo. green and red . . . 40 10

1989. 27th National Youth Stamp Exn, Veszprem.
3892 **975** 5fo.+2fo. mult . . . . . 1·00 90

976 O Bajan

1989. Bicentenary of Babolina Stud Farm. Mult.
3893 3fo. Type **976** 45 45
3894 3fo. Stud officer 45 45
3895 3fo. Gazal II 45 45

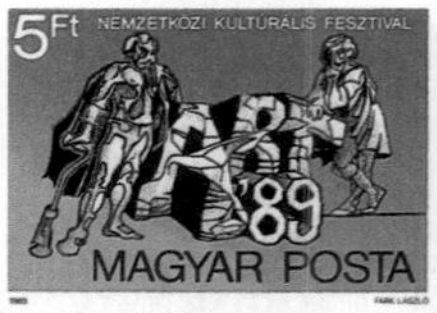

977 Disabled People and “ART ’89”

978 Arrangement of Narcissi, Crocuses and Violets

1989. “Art ’89” International Festival of Disabled People and their Artist Friends.
3896 **977** 5fo. multicoloured . . . 45 10

1989. Flower Arrangements. Multicoloured.
3897 2fo. Type **978** 30 10
3898 3fo. Irises, tulips and lilies (horiz) 45 10
3899 3fo. Roses and chrysanthemums 45 10
3900 5fo. Dahlias and lilies (horiz) 75 30
3901 10fo. Roses, Chinese lanterns and holly . . . . 1·40 45

979 Birds

1989. Bicentenary of French Revolution.
3902 **979** 5fo. black, red and blue 45 10
MS3903 80 × 70 mm. **979** 20fo. black, red and blue (49 × 28 mm) 4·50 5·00

980 Model of Veszto Church

981 Photographer with Camera

1989. Veszto Church Excavation.
3904 **980** 3fo. multicoloured . . . 40 10

1989. 150th Anniv of Photography.
3905 **981** 5fo. lt brown, blk & brn 45 10

982 Turistvandi Water-mill

1989. Mills. Multicoloured.
3906 2fo. Type **982** 25 10
3907 3fo. Szarvas horse-driven mill 40 10
3908 5fo. Kiskunhalas windmill 65 15
3909 10fo. Shipmill, River Drava 1·25 25

983 Footprint and U.S. Flag

1989. 20th Anniv of First Manned Landing on Moon. Sheet 80 × 70 mm.
MS3910 **983** 20fo. multicoloured 3·50 2·75

984 Messenger Glider

1989. “Old Timer” Rally, Budakeszi Airport, and 60th Anniv of Gliding in Hungary. Multicoloured.
3911 3fo. Type **984** 45 15
3912 5fo. Pal glider 75 30

985 Sand Lizard

1989. Endangered Reptiles. Multicoloured.
3913 2fo. Type **985** 25 10
3914 3fo. Green lizard 40 10
3915 5fo. Grass snake (“Natrix natrix”) 60 10
3916 5fo. Orsinis's viper (“Vipera rakosiensis”) 60 10
3917 10fo. European pond terrapin . . . . 1·25 30

986 Competitors

1989. 31st World Modern Pentathlon Championships, Budapest.
3918 **986** 5fo. multicoloured . . . 45 10

1989. Nos. 3851 and 3853 surch.
3919 3fo. on 2fo. multicoloured 35 30
3920 5fo. on 4fo. multicoloured 55 45

988 Baradla Cave, Aggtelek

989 Carriage

1989. 10th World Speleology Congress, Budapest. Multicoloured.
3921 3fo. Type **988** 30 10
3922 5fo. Szemlohegy cave, Budapest 55 10

3923 10fo. Anna Cave, Lillafured 1·25 30
3924 12fo. Tapolca cave lake, Miskolctapolca 1·40 30

1989. World Two-in-Hand Carriage Driving Championship, Balatonfenyves.
3925 **989** 5fo. multicoloured 70 10

990 Zsuzsa Kossuth (War of Independence nurse)

991 Memorial Statue, Arad

1989. Stamp Day. 125th Anniv of Red Cross Movement.
3926 **990** 5fo. black, blue and red 45 45
3927 – 10fo. multicoloured 95 95
MS3928 82 × 65 mm. 20fo.+10fo. mult 4·25 4·50
DESIGNS: 10fo. Florence Nightingale (nursing pioneer) and decoration. 27 × 44 mm—20fo. "Battle of Solferini" (Carlo Bossoli).

1989. 140th Death Anniv of "Martyrs of Arad". Sheet 110 × 75 mm.
MS3929 **991** 20fo.+10fo. mult 4·25 4·50
The surcharge was for the erection of a new statue.

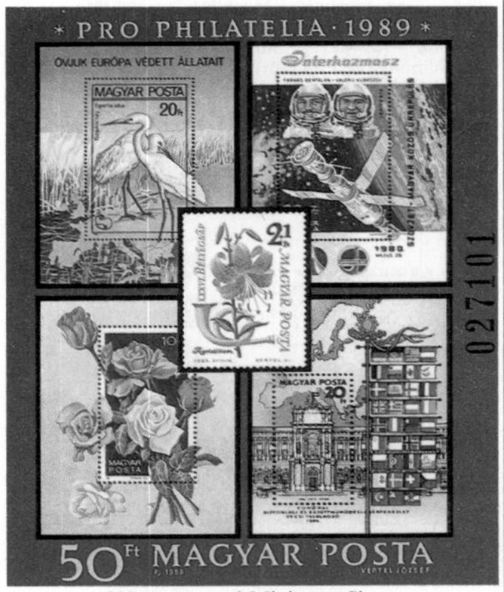

992 Stamp and Miniature Sheets

1989. Pro Philatelia. Sheet 72 × 92 mm.
MS3930 **992** 50fo. multicoloured 7·25 7·75

993 Flowers and Broken Barbed Wire

1989. Dismantling of Electrified Fence on Western Border.
3931 **993** 5fo. multicoloured 45 10

994 "Conquest of Hungary" (Mor Than)

1989. 1100th Anniv of Arpad as Prince of the Magyars.
3932 **994** 5fo. multicoloured 70 10

995 Flight into Egypt

996 Nehru

1989. Christmas.
3933 **995** 3fo. multicoloured 50 10

1989. Birth Centenary of Jawaharlal Nehru (Indian statesman).
3934 **996** 3fo. brown and stone 50 10

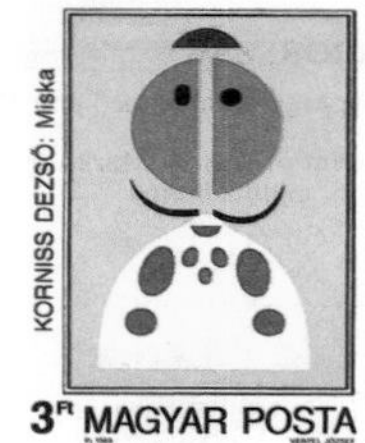

997 "Miska" (Dezso Korniss)

1990. Modern Hungarian Paintings. Mult.
3935 3fo. Type **997** 40 10
3936 5fo. "Sunrise" (Lajos Kassak) 60 10
3937 10fo. "Grotesque Burial" (Endre Balint) 1·25 30
3938 12fo. "Remembered Toys" (Tihamer Gyarmathy) 1·50 45

1989. Pioneers of Medicine (2nd series). As T **929**.
3939 3fo. green 40 10
3940 3fo. brown 40 10
3941 4fo. black 55 10
3942 6fo. grey 75 30
3943 10fo. purple 1·25 30
DESIGNS: No. 3939, Claudius Galenus (anatomist and physiologist); 3940, Paracelsus (pharmacy); 3941, Andreas Vesalius (dissection); 3942, Rudolf Virchow (pathology of cells); 3943, Ivan Petrovich Pavlov (blood circulation, digestion and nervous system).

998 Hands holding Coin

1990. 150th Anniv of Savings Banks in Hungary.
3944 **998** 5fo. multicoloured 45 10

999 Sewing Machine

1000 Wall Telephone and Jozsefvaros Telephone Exchange

1990. 125th Anniv of Singer Sewing Machine.
3945 **999** 5fo. brown and cinnamon 45 10

1990. Posts and Telecommunications. Mult.
3946 3fo. Type **1000** 25 10
3947 5fo. Pillar box and Head Post Office, Budapest 40 10

1001 Northern Bullfinch ("Pyrrhula pyrrhula")

1002 "Protea compacta"

1990. Birds. Multicoloured.
3960 3fo. Type **1001** 50 20
3961 3fo. River kingfisher ("Alcedo atthis") 50 20
3962 3fo. Syrian woodpecker ("Dendrocopos syriacus") 50 20
3963 5fo. Hoopoe ("Upupa epops") 95 30
3964 5fo. European bee eater ("Merops apiaster") 95 30
3965 10fo. European roller 1·75 60

1990. African Flowers. Multicoloured.
3966 3fo. Type **1002** 40 10
3967 3fo. "Leucadendron spissifolium" 40 10
3968 3fo. "Leucadendron tinctum pubibracteolatum" 40 10
3969 5fo. "Protea barbigera" 75 10
3970 5fo. "Protea lepidocarpodendron neriifolia" 75 10
3971 10fo. "Protea cynaroides" 1·50 30
MS3972 64 × 82 mm. 20fo. Mixed bouquet (25 × 36 mm) 4·50 4·50

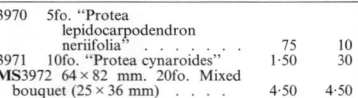

1003 Sarospatak Teachers' Training School

1990. 28th National Youth Stamp Exhibition, Sarospatak.
3973 **1003** 8fo.+4fo. mult 1·50 1·25

1004 Janos Hunyadi (regent)

1005 Penny Black

1990. The Hunyadis. Multicoloured.
3974 5fo. Type **1004** 50 10
3975 5fo. King Matthias I Corvinus 50 10

1990. "Stamp World London 90" International Stamp Exhibition. 150th Anniv of the Penny Black. Sheet 88 × 60 mm.
MS3976 **1005** 20fo. multicoloured 4·25 4·00

1006 Gaspar Karoli (statue)

1007 Footballers

1990. 400th Anniv of Publication of Karoli Bible (first Hungarian translation).
3977 **1006** 8fo. cream, green & red 1·00 10

1990. World Cup Football Championship, Italy.
3978 **1007** 3fo. multicoloured 35 10
3979 – 5fo. multicoloured (ball on ground) 60 10
3980 – 5fo. multicoloured (ball in air) 60 10
3981 – 8fo. multicoloured (dribbling) 95 10
3982 – 8fo. mult (heading ball into goal) 95 10
3983 – 10fo. multicoloured 1·25 30
MS3984 95 × 70 mm. 20fo. mult 3·50 3·75
DESIGNS: Nos. 3979/84, Various footballing scenes.

1008 Hand writing with Quill Pen

1990. 300th Birth Anniv of Kelemen Mikes (writer).
3985 **1008** 8fo. black and gold 90 10

1009 "Weaver" (Noemi Ferenczy)

1010 Kazinczy

1990. Birth Centenaries of Noemi and Beni Ferenczy (artists).
3986 **1009** 3fo. multicoloured 45 10
3987 – 5fo. black and brown 75 10
DESIGN: 5fo. Bronze figure (Beni Ferenczy).

1990. 159th Death Anniv of Ferenc Kazinczy (writer and language reformer).
3988 **1010** 8fo. multicoloured 60 10

1011 Kolcsey (after Anton Einsle)

1013 Cabernet Franc Grapes, Hajos

1012 "St. Stephen" (carving in Parliament Hall) and Arms

1990. Birth Bicentenary of Ferenc Kolcsey (composer of national anthem).
3989 **1011** 8fo. multicoloured 60 10

1990. New State Arms.
3990 **1012** 8fo. multicoloured 60 10
MS3991 70 × 90 mm. 20fo. Arms (33 × 49 mm) 5·25 5·25

1990. Wine Grapes and Regions (1st series). Multicoloured.
3992 3fo. Type **1013** 30 10
3993 5fo. Cabernet Sauvignon, Villany 45 10
3994 8fo. Riesling, Badacsony 75 10
3995 8fo. Kadarka, Szekszard 75 10
3996 8fo. Leanyka, Eger 75 10
3997 10fo. Furmint, Tokaj-Hegyalja 1·00 10
See also Nos. 4363/5, 4436/7, 4521/2, 4596/7 and 4686/7.

1014 "Feast"

1990. Stamp Day. Paintings by Ender Szasz. Multicoloured.
3998 8fo. Type **1014** 70 75
3999 12fo. "Message" 1·10 1·10
MS4000 70 × 90 mm. 20fo.+10fo. "Yesterday" (39 × 44 mm) 4·25 4·00

1015 Tarbosaurus

1990. Prehistoric Animals. Multicoloured.
4001 3fo. Type **1015** 35 10
4002 5fo. Brontosaurus 55 10
4003 5fo. Dimorphodon 55 10
4004 5fo. Stegosaurus 55 10
4005 8fo. Platybelodon 90 10
4006 10fo. Mammoth 1·25 30

1016 Dinosaurs reading

1990. International Literacy Year.
4007 **1016** 10fo. multicoloured . . 90 10

1017 Bird holding Letter

1990. 60th Anniv of Stamp Museum, Budapest.
4008 **1017** 5fo. red and green . . . 50 10

1018 "Great Courier" (detail, Albrecht Durer)

1990. Pro Philatelia. 500th Anniv of Regular European Postal Services. Sheet 90 × 71 mm.
MS4009 **1018** 50fo. black, red and yellow . . . . 7·25 6·00

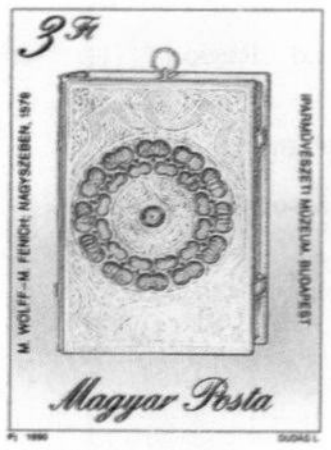

1019 Book-shaped Travelling Clock, by M. Fenich and M. Wolff, 1576
1020 "Madonna and Child" (Sandro Botticelli)

1990. Clocks. Multicoloured.
4010 3fo. Type **1019** 40 10
4011 5fo. Clock by Hans Schmidt, 1643 . . . . . 65 10
4012 5fo. Rococo style clock by J. M. Welz, 1790 . . . . 65 10
4013 10fo. Clock by Johann Hillrich, 1814 . . . . . . 1·40 45

1990. Christmas.
4014 **1020** 5fo. multicoloured . . . 45 10

1021 Lorand Eotvos (inventor) and Torsion Pendulum
1022 "Mandevilla splendens"

1991. Centenary of Torsion Pendulum.
4015 **1021** 12fo. multicoloured . . 90 10

1991. Flowers of the Americas. Mult.
4016 5fo. Type **1022** 25 10
4017 7fo. "Lobelia cardinalis" . . 35 10
4018 7fo. Cup and saucer flower 35 10
4019 12fo. "Steriphoma paradoxa" 60 10
4020 15fo. Shrimp plant 75 30
MS4021 58 × 80 mm. 20fo. Mixed bouquet (27 × 43 mm) . . . . 3·00 2·50

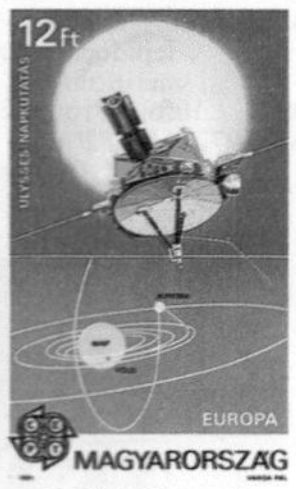

1023 Post Office, Budapest
1024 "Ulysses" Jupiter Probe

1991. Hungarian Full Membership of Council of Europe and Entry into C.E.P.T. (European Posts and Telecommunications Conference). Mult.
4022 5fo. Type **1023** . . . . . . 2·10 1·60
4023 7fo. Post Office, Pecs . . . 3·25 2·50

1991. Europa. Europe in Space. Multicoloured.
4024 12fo. Type **1024** 75 90
4025 30fo. "Cassini" and "Huygens" (wrongly inscr "Hughes") Saturn probes 1·75 2·10

1025 "Peter and the Wolf" (tapestry, Gabriella Hajnal)

1991. Youth Stamp.
4026 **1025** 12fo.+6fo. mult 90 90

1026 Gorilla

1991. 125th Anniv of Budapest Zoological and Botanic Gardens. Multicoloured.
4027 7fo. Type **1026** 30 30
4028 12fo. Polar bear 65 40
4029 12fo. Rhinoceros 65 40
4030 12fo. Keel-billed toucan . . 65 40
4031 20fo. Orchid and glasshouse 85 90

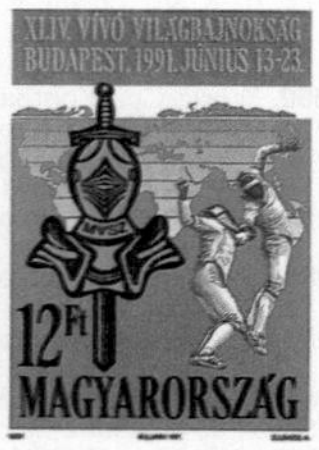

1027 Teleki
1028 Map, Emblem and Fencers

1991. 50th Death Anniv of Count Pal Teleki (Prime Minister, 1920–21 and 1939–41).
4032 **1027** 12fo. brn, cinn & blk . 75 75

1991. 44th World Fencing Championships, Budapest.
4033 **1028** 12fo. multicoloured . . 75 75

1029 Mariapocs

1991. Visit of Pope John Paul II (1st issue). Shrines to Virgin Mary. Multicoloured.
4034 7fo. Type **1029** 35 30
4035 12fo. Mariagyud 55 60
4036 12fo. Celldomolk 55 60
4037 12fo. Mariaremete 55 60
4038 20fo. Esztergom 95 90

1030 "Appeggi Landscape" and Marko

1991. Birth Bicent of Karoly Marko (painter).
4039 **1030** 12fo. multicoloured . . 75 75

1031 Lilienthal and Monoplane Gliders, 1891

1991. Centenary of First Heavier-than-Air Manned Flight by Otto Lilienthal.
4040 **1031** 7fo. black, ochre & brn 40 30
4041 – 12fo. black, drab & bis 70 55
4042 – 20fo. dp blue, azure & bl . . . . 1·10 85
4043 – 30fo. black, lilac & vio 1·60 1·40
DESIGNS: 12fo. Wright brothers' Flyer 1, 1903; 20fo. Santos-Dumont's "14 bis", 1906; 30fo. Aladar Zselyi's monoplane, 1910.

1032 Players
1034 Map of Europe and Congress Emblem

1033 Pope John Paul II

1991. Centenary of Basketball.
4044 **1032** 12fo. multicoloured . . 75 70

1991. Castles. Inscr "MAGYARORSZAG". As T **921**.
4045 7fo. brown and sepia . . . 30 20
4047 12fo. ultramarine and blue 50 45
4049 15fo. brown and green . . . 50 45
DESIGNS—32 × 25 mm; 7fo. Esterhazy Castle, Papa; 12fo. Dory Castle, Mihaly, 35 × 26 mm; 15fo. Festetics Castle, Keszthely.

1991. Papal Visit (2nd issue). Sheet 60 × 80 mm.
MS4055 **1033** 50fo. black and blue 4·50 4·50

1991. 3rd International Hungarian Philological Society Congress, Szeged.
4056 **1034** 12fo. multicoloured . . 75 50

1035 Szechenyi
1036 Mozart as Child

1991. Birth Bicentenary of Count Istvan Szechenyi (social reformer).
4057 **1035** 12fo. red 75 50

1991. Stamp Day. Death Bicentenary of Wolfgang Amadeus Mozart (composer). Multicoloured.
4058 12fo. Type **1036** 55 50
4059 20fo. Mozart as youth . . . 95 70
MS4060 80 × 61 mm. 30fo.+15fo. Mozart as man (24 × 36 mm) 4·50 4·50

1037 "Telecom 91"

1991. "Telecom 91" International Telecommunications Exhibition, Geneva.
4061 **1037** 12fo. multicoloured . . 75 60

1991. 35th Anniv of 1956 Uprising, No. 4047 optd **A FORRADALOM EMLEKERE 1956 1991.**
4062 12fo. ultramarine and blue 75 60

1039 Sebastian Cabot
1040 Arms of Order

1991. 500th Anniv (1992) of Discovery of America by Columbus. Multicoloured.
4063 7fo. Type **1039** 45 30
4064 12fo. Amerigo Vespucci . . 65 60
4065 12fo. Hernan Cortes 65 60
4066 15fo. Ferdinand Magellan 90 75
4067 20f. Francisco Pizarro . . . 1·10 90
MS4068 85 × 71 mm. 30fo. Columbus (21 × 33 mm) . . . 2·00 2·50

1991. Postal Convention with Sovereign Military Order of Malta.
4069 **1040** 12fo. multicoloured . . 75 60

1041 "Virgin of Mariapocs"
1042 Flower

1991. Christmas. Multicoloured.
4070 7fo. Type **1041** 55 45
4071 12fo. "Virgin of Mariaremete" 70 65

1991. Human Rights.
4072 **1042** 12fo. multicoloured . . 75 70

1043 Biathlon
1044 1871 25k. Stamp

1991. Winter Olympic Games, Albertville (1992). Multicoloured.
4073 7fo. Type **1043** 35 30
4074 12fo. Slalom 55 45
4075 15fo. Four-man bobsleigh 70 60
4076 20fo. Ski jumping 95 75
4077 30fo. Ice hockey . . . . . 1·40 1·25
MS4078 73 × 54 mm. 30fo. Ice skating (pairs) (26 × 36 mm) . . 2·75 2·75

1991. Pro Philatelia. Sheet 90 × 71 mm.
MS4079 **1044** 50fo. violet . . . . 3·25 3·50

1045 Arms
1046 Holloko

1992. 350th Anniv of Piarist Order in Hungary.
4080 **1045** 10fo. gold, blue and ultramarine 35 35

1992. U.N.E.S.C.O. World Heritage Site.
4081 **1046** 15fo. multicoloured . . 90 90

1047 Swimming

1992. Olympic Games, Barcelona. Mult.
4082 7fo. Type **1047** 80 60
4083 9fo. Cycling 95 90
4084 10fo. Gymnastics 95 90
4085 15fo. Running . . . . . . 1·50 1·50

1048 "Indian's Head" Map

1049 Comenius

1992. "Expo '92" World's Fair, Seville. Fantasy Maps. Multicoloured.
4086 10fo. Type **1048** 60 60
4087 10fo. Islands, sea monsters and "Santa Maria" forming face 60 60
4088 15fo. "Conquistador's head" map . . . . 1·00 60
4089 15fo. Navigation instruments and map forming face . . . . . . 1·00 60

1992. 400th Birth Anniv of Jan Komensky (Comenius) (educationist).
4090 **1049** 15fo. multicoloured . . 75 75

1050 Mindszenty

1992. Birth Centenary of Cardinal Jozsef Mindszenty, Archbishop of Esztergom.
4091 **1050** 15fo. brn, cream & red 75 75

1051 Statue of Mayan Man

1052 "Self-portrait" (Renata Toth)

1992. Europa. 500th Anniv of Discovery of America by Columbus. Multicoloured.
4092 15fo. Type **1051** 70 75
4093 40fo. Statue of Mayan woman . . . . 1·90 2·25

1992. Youth Stamps. Children's Drawings. Multicoloured.
4094 9fo.+4fo. Type **1052** 50 50
4095 10fo.+4fo. "The Sun Shines for Me" (Sandor Pusoma) (horiz) 50 50
4096 15fo.+4fo. "I will be a Beauty King" (Endre Knipf) 75 75

1053 Gymnasts and Emblem

1992. European Gymnastics Championships, Budapest.
4097 **1053** 15fo. multicoloured . . 75 60

1054 St. Margaret (after J. S. Scott)

1055 Saker Falcon

1992. 750th Birth Anniv of St. Margaret.
4098 **1054** 15fo. turq, lt bl & bl . . 75 60

1992. Birds of Prey. Multicoloured.
4099 9fo. Type **1055** 35 30
4100 10fo. Booted eagle 35 45
4101 15fo. Short-toed eagle . . . 55 60
4102 40fo. Red kite . . . . . . 1·40 1·00

1056 Wallenberg

1057 Millennium Monument, Budapest

1992. 80th Birth Anniv of Raoul Wallenberg (Swedish diplomat).
4103 **1056** 15fo. grey, red and green 50 60

1992. 3rd World Federation of Hungarians Congress, Budapest.
4104 **1057** 15fo. multicoloured . . 50 60

1058 Theodore von Karman (space pioneer, birth centenary (1991))

1992. Anniversaries.
4105 **1058** 15fo. grey, black and deep grey 55 45
4106 – 40fo. grey, black & brn 1·40 1·40
DESIGN: 40fo. Neumann Janos (mathematician, 35th death anniv).

1059 Current Hungarian Post Emblem

1061 Entwined Cables

1060 Church of the Holy Family, Barcelona, and Medals

1992. Stamp Day. "Eurofilex '92" International Postal History Exhibition, Budapest.
4107 **1059** 10fo.+5fo. multicoloured 75 75
4108 15fo.+5fo. multicoloured . . . . 1·00 1·00
MS4109 91 × 66 mm. 50fo.+20fo. brown, cinnamon and black . . 3·00 3·00
DESIGNS—VERT Hungarian Royal Post emblem, 1867. 39 × 29 mm—50fo. "Postal Riders" (etching, Ferenc Helbing).
See also No. 4111.

1992. Hungarian Olympic Games (Barcelona) Medal Winners. Sheet 61 × 80 mm.
MS4110 **1060** 50fo.+20fo. mult 3·00 3·00

1992. As No. 4108 but without premium and commemorative inscription.
4111 **1059** 15fo. multicoloured . . 55 60

1992. "Europa Telecom '92" Telecommunications Exhibition, Budapest.
4112 **1061** 15fo. multicoloured . . 55 45

1062 Istvan Bathory (King Stefan I of Poland)

1063 Pieces on Board

1992. Princes of Transylvania. Multicoloured.
4113 10fo. Type **1062** 35 30
4114 15fo. Istvan Bocskai 45 45
4115 40fo. Gabor Bethlen . . . . 1·25 1·25

1992. 10th European Chess Team Championship, Debrecen.
4116 **1063** 15fo. multicoloured . . 75 75

1064 "Clianthus formosus"

1065 Postal Rider of Prince Ferenc Rakoczi II, 1703–11

1992. Australian Flowers. Multicoloured.
4117 9fo. Type **1064** 35 30
4118 10fo. "Leschenaultia biloba" 35 45
4119 15fo. "Anigosanthos manglesii" 55 60
4120 40fo. "Comesperma ericinum" . . . . . . 1·40 1·25
MS4121 64 × 83 mm. 50fo. Mixed flowers (31 × 41 mm) . . . . . 3·00 2·75

1992. Post Office Uniforms. Multicoloured.
4122 10fo. Type **1065** 40 30
4123 15fo. Postmen, 1874 . . . . 55 30

1066 "Holy Family" (iron relief, 1850)

1067 "Arachnis flos-aeris"

1992. Christmas.
4124 **1066** 15fo. black and blue . . 45 45

1993. Asian Flowers. Multicoloured.
4125 10fo. Type **1067** 35 30
4126 10fo. "Dendrobium densiflorium" 35 30
4127 15fo. "Lilium speciosum" 50 60
4128 15fo. "Meconopsis aculeata" 50 60
MS4129 64 × 83 mm. 50fo. Mixed bouquet (31 × 41 mm) . . . . 3·00 4·50

1068 Shield Decoration of Deer

1993. Scythian Remains in Hungary. Mult.
4130 10fo. Type **1068** 45 30
4131 17fo. Gilt-silver embossed deer 75 75

1069 Single Sculls

1993. Centenary of Rowing Association.
4132 **1069** 17fo. multicoloured . . 75 75

1070 Queen Beatrix and King Matthias I Corvinus (detail of Missal) (½-size illustration)

1993. King Matthias I Corvinus's "Missale Romanum".
4133 **1070** 15fo. multicoloured . . 75 75
MS4134 106 × 156 mm. 40fo. Illustration from missal (59 × 39 mm) . . . . 1·75 2·50

1071 Animals in Wood

1072 Competitors and Globe

1993. Youth Stamps. Tapestries by Erzsebet Szekeres. Multicoloured.
4135 10fo.+5fo. Type **1071** . . . 70 60
4136 17fo.+8fo. Animals in tree hiding from dragons . . . 1·25 1·00

1993. World Motocross Championships, Cserenfa.
4137 **1072** 17fo. multicoloured . . 45 45

1073 Diagram of Solar System and Copernicus

1993. "Polska'93" International Stamp Exn.
4138 **1073** 17fo. multicoloured . . 45 75

1074 Paks Catholic Church

1075 Cauliflower Clavaria

1993. Europa. Contemporary Art. Architecture by Imre Makovecz. Multicoloured.
4139 17fo. Type **1074** 55 45
4140 45fo. Hungarian pavilion at "Expo '92" World's Fair, Seville . . . . 1·00 1·00

1993. Fungi. Multicoloured.
4141 10fo. Type **1075** 25 30
4142 17fo. Death trumpet 55 45
4143 45fo. Caesar's mushroom . . 1·10 1·00

1076 "St. Christopher" (Albrecht Durer)

1993. European Year of the Aged.
4144 **1076** 17fo. black, cream and silver 45 45

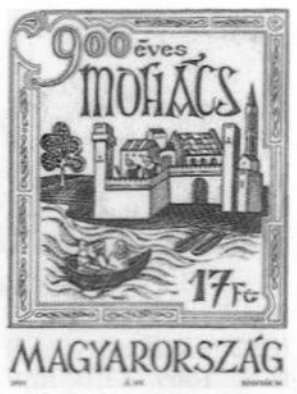

1077 Class 326 and 424 Steam Locomotives **1078** Rowing Boat approaching Town

1993. 125th Anniv of Hungarian Railways.
4145 **1077** 17fo. blue and cobalt 45 45

1993. 900th Anniv of Mohacs.
4146 **1078** 17fo. brown, cinnamon and red 45 45

1079 Poplar Admiral **1080** Kalman Latabar

1993. Butterflies. Multicoloured.
4147 10fo. Type **1079** 25 30
4148 17fo. "Aricia artaxerxes" . . 50 45
4149 30fo. "Plebejides pylaon" . . 70 75

1993. Great Humourists. Multicoloured.
4150 17fo. Type **1080** 55 30
4151 30fo. Charlie Chaplin . . . 75 75

1081 Ribbon Dove over North-western Europe

1993. 20th Anniv of European Security and Co-operation Conference, Helsinki. Sheet 82 × 62 mm.
MS4152 **1081** 50fo. multicoloured 1·75 2·25

1082 Solar Panel absorbing Sun's Rays **1083** Laszlo Nemeth

1993. International Solar Energy Society Congress, Budapest.
4153 **1082** 17fo. multicoloured . . 45 45

1993. Writers. Each blue and azure.
4154 17fo. Type **1083** 45 45
4155 17fo. Dezso Szabo 45 45
4156 17fo. Antal Szerb 45 45

1084 Zoltan Nagy and 1953 20fi. Stamp

1993. Stamp Day. Designers. Multicoloured.
4157 10fo.+5fo. Type **1084** . . . 45 45
4158 17fo.+5fo. Sandor Legrady and 1938 50f. stamp . . . 70 75
MS4159 56 × 75 mm. 50fo.+20fo. Ferenc Helbing and 1932 10p. stamp (35 × 26 mm) . . . . . 2·25 1·90

1085 Arms

1993. 175th Anniv of Faculty of Agronomics, Pannon Agricultural University, Magyarovar.
4160 **1085** 17fo. multicoloured . . 45 45

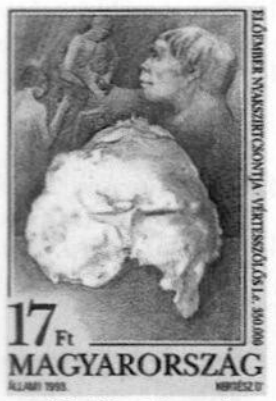

1086 "Szent Istvan", 1892 **1087** Prehistoric Man and Skull (Vertesszolos)

1993. Hungarian Ships. Multicoloured.
4161 10fo. Type **1086** 25 30
4162 30fo. "Szent Istvan" (battleship), 1915 . . . . 80 75

1993. Palaeolithic Remains in Hungary. Mult.
4163 17fo. Type **1087** 60 30
4164 30fo. Men round fire and stone tool (Szeleta Cave, Lillafured) 90 75

1088 Route-map of Central Europe

1993. Roman Roads. Sheet 80 × 65 mm.
MS4165 **1088** 50fo. multicoloured 1·75 1·75

1089 "Madonna and Child" (altarpiece by F. A. Hillebrant, Szekestehervar Cathedral) **1091** Antall

1090 Szechenyi Chain Bridge (½-size illustration)

1993. Christmas.
4166 **1089** 10fo. multicoloured . . 30 30

1993. "Expo '96" World's Fair, Budapest (1st issue).
4167 **1090** 17fo. dp green & green 55 45
4168 – 30fo. purple and claret 75 75
4169 – 45fo. dp brown & brown . . . . 1·10 1·25
DESIGNS—HORIZ: 30fo. Opera House. VERT: 45fo. Matthias Church.
See also Nos. 4236/8 and 4268/9.

1993. Jozsef Antall (Prime Minister since 1990) Commemoration.
4170 **1091** 19fo. multicoloured . . 50 40
MS4171 70 × 50 mm. No. 4170 90 1·25

1092 Skiing

1994. Winter Olympic Games, Lillehammer, Norway. Multicoloured.
4172 12fo. Type **1092** 35 30
4173 19fo. Ice hockey 70 30

1093 Douglas DC-3

1994. 50th Anniv of I.C.A.O.
4174 **1093** 56fo. multicoloured . . 1·50 1·00

1094 "Golgotha" (detail, Mihaly Munkacsy) **1095** Mihaly Munkacsy (self-portrait)

1994. Easter.
4175 **1094** 12fo. multicoloured . . 35 30

1994. Artists' 150th Birth Anniversaries. Multicoloured.
4176 12fo. Gyula Benczur (self-portrait) 40 30
4177 19fo. Type **1095** 65 45

1096 Kossuth **1097** Hen with Chicks

1994. Death Centenary of Lajos Kossuth (Governor of 1849 Republic).
4178 **1096** 19fo. multicoloured . . 50 45

1994. The Great Bustard. Multicoloured.
4179 10fo. Type **1097** 30 30
4180 10fo. Bustards taking off . . 30 30
4181 10fo. Cock in mating display 30 30
4182 10fo. Hen with chicks (different) 30 30

1098 Bem **1099** Discovery of Franz Josef Land (120th anniv)

1994. Birth Bicent of Jozsef Bem (revolutionary).
4183 **1098** 19fo. multicoloured . . 60 45

1994. Europa. Discoveries. Multicoloured.
4184 19fo. Type **1099** 60 60
4185 50fo. Mark Aurel Stein and Buddha (expeditions in Asia) . . . . 1·50 1·40

1100 "The Little Prince" **1101** Balint Balassi (poet, 400th death)

1994. Youth Stamp. 50th Anniv of Disappearance of Antoine de Saint-Exupery (writer and pilot).
4186 **1100** 19fo.+5fo. mult 75 75

1994. Writers' Anniversaries.
4187 **1101** 19ft. pink and brown 60 45
4188 – 19ft. stone and grey . . 60 45
DESIGN: No. 4188, Miklos Josika (novelist, birth bicentenary).

1102 Horsemen **1104** Elvis Presley and Players

1103 Athens Stadium, 1896

1994. 1100th Anniv (1996) of Magyar Conquest (1st issue). Multicoloured.
4189 19ft. Type **1102** 60 45
4190 19ft. Arpad and standard bearers (58 × 39 mm) . . 60 45
4191 19ft. Mounted archer . . . 60 45
Nos. 4189/91 were issued together, se-tenant, forming a composite design of a detail of the painting "in the round" commissioned to celebrate the millenary of the Conquest.
See also Nos. 4240/2 and 4275/7.

1994. Centenary of International Olympic Committee. Multicoloured.
4192 12ft. Olympic medals of 1896 and 1992 . . . . . 35 30
4193 19ft. Type **1103** 55 45
4194 19ft. Ancient Greek athletes, Olympic flag and flame 55 45
4195 35ft. Pierre de Coubertin (founder) . . . . 1·10 75

1994. World Cup Football Championship, U.S.A. American Entertainers. Multicoloured.
4196 19ft. Type **1104** 60 45
4197 19ft. Marilyn Monroe and players 60 45
4198 35ft. John Wayne and players . . . . 1·10 75

1105 Family

1994. International Year of the Family.
4199 **1105** 19fo. multicoloured . . 55 30

1106 Summer Snowflake

1994. European Flowers. Multicoloured.
4200 12fo. Type **1106** 35 30
4201 19fo. Common rock-rose . . 50 45
4202 35fo. "Eryngium alpinum" 95 75
4203 50fo. Pennycress . . . . . 1·40 90
MS4204 64 × 83 mm. 100fo. Mixed bouquet (31 × 40 mm) . . . . 3·00 3·00

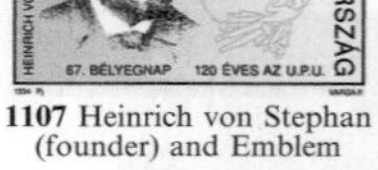

1107 Heinrich von Stephan (founder) and Emblem **1108** Csik Megye

1994. 120th Anniv of Universal Postal Union.
4205 **1107** 19fo. grey, brown & blk 50 30
4206 – 35fo. blue, brown & blk 1·00 75
MS4207 98 × 71 mm. 50fo.+25fo. brown, black and blue (Heinrich von Stephan) (vert); 50fo.+25 fo. brown, black and violet (Gervay Mihaly) (vert) . . . . 4·50 2·40

DESIGN: 35fo. Gervay Mihaly (first Director General of Posts) and U.P.U. emblem.

1994. Traditional Patterns.
4208 – 1fo. violet and black 10 10
4209 – 2fo. multicoloured 10 10
4210 – 3fo. multicoloured 10 10
4210a – 5fo. multicoloured 10 10
4211 – 9fo. multicoloured 15 10
4212 **1108** 11fo. multicoloured 25 10
4213 – 12fo. multicoloured 25 10
4214 – 13fo. multicoloured 30 10
4215 – 14fo. multicoloured 35 30
4216 – 16fo. multicoloured 45 10
4217 – 17fo. black, grey & red 35 10
4218 – 19fo. multicoloured 50 10
4219 – 22fo. multicoloured 50 30
4220 – 24fo. multicoloured 45 30
4220a – 24fo. multicoloured 35 30
4220b – 27fo. multicoloured 35 30
4221 – 32fo. multicoloured 60 10
4222 – 35fo. multicoloured 70 30
4223 – 38fo. multicoloured 75 60
4224 – 40fo. multicoloured 75 30
4225 – 50fo. multicoloured 1·10 30
4225a – 65fo. black, red and grey 55 45
4226 – 75fo. multicoloured 1·10 45
4226a – 79fo. multicoloured 65 60
4227 – 80fo. multicoloured 1·25 45
4228 – 90fo. multicoloured 75 75
4229 – 100fo. multicoloured 80 75
4229a – 200fo. multicoloured 2·00 1·25
4230 – 300fo. multicoloured 3·50 1·50
4231 – 500fo. multicoloured 5·50 2·25

DESIGNS: 1fo. Torocko; 2fo. Buzsak; 3fo. Vas megye (flowers); 5fo. Rabakoz; 9, 24fo. (4220) Felfold; 12, 27fo. Vas megye (birds); 13, 32fo. Debrecen; 14, 80fo. Sarkoz; 16fo. Csiki-Medence; 17, 35, 65fo. Dunantul; 19, 24fo. (4220a) Kalocsa; 22, 90fo. Heves megye; 300fo. Kalocsa (different); 38, 75fo. Oroshaza; 40fo. Kalotaszeg; 50fo. Szentgal; 79fo. Moldvai csango; 100fo. Szecseny videke; 200fo. Mezokovesd; 500fo. Szolnok megye.

1109 Budapest

1994. Conference of Security and Co-operation in Europe Summit, Budapest. Sheet 92 × 70 mm.
MS4232 **1109** 100fo. multicoloured 3·00 2·25

1110 Hebrew Tombstone

1111 "Nativity"

1994. Holocaust Victims' Commemoration.
4233 **1110** 19fo. multicoloured 45 30

1994. Christmas. Paintings by Pal Molnar. Multicoloured.
4234 12fo. Type **1111** 30 30
4235 35fo. "Flight into Egypt" (31 × 29 mm) 70 60

1112 National Museum

1994. "Expo '96" World's Fair, Budapest (2nd issue). Budapest landmarks.
4236 **1112** 19fo. green 45 30
4237 – 19fo. brown 45 30
4238 – 19fo. violet 45 30

DESIGNS: No. 4237, University of Technical Sciences; 4238, Vajdahunyad Castle.

1113 "Ferencz Jozsef I" (paddle-steamer) and "Baross" (container ship)

1995. Cent of Hungarian Shipping Company.
4239 **1113** 22fo. multicoloured 60 45

1995. 1100th Anniv (1996) of Magyar Conquest (2nd issue). As T **1102**. Multicoloured.
4240 22fo. Ox cart 65 45
4241 22fo. Arpad's consort in ox cart (59 × 39 mm) 65 45
4242 22fo. Men and pack ox 65 45

Nos. 4240/2 were issued together, se-tenant, forming a composite design of a detail of the painting "in the round" commissioned to celebrate the millenary of the Conquest.

1114 Lamb of God

1116 Weather Map and Barometer

1115 Paddle-steamer

1995. Easter.
4243 **1114** 14fo. purple and black 40 30

1995. 150th Anniv of Steamer Service on River Tisza (14fo.) and Birth Bicentenary of Pal Vasarhelyi (engineer) (60fo.). Multicoloured.
4244 14fo. Type **1115** 45 30
4245 60fo. Vasarhelyi (after Miklos Barabas) and survey ship 1·90 90

1995. Anniversaries. Multicoloured.
4246 22fo. Type **1116** (125th anniv of Hungarian Meteorological Service) 60 45
4247 22fo. Emblem (50th anniv of F.A.O.) (25 × 41 mm) 60 45
4248 22fo.+10fo. John the Hero (150th anniv of poem by Petofi) (37 × 45mm) 85 60

No. 4248 is the 1995 Youth Stamp.

1117 White Stork and Frog

1118 Allied Flags forming Dove over Map of Europe

1995. European Nature Conservation Year. Multicoloured.
4249 14fo. Type **1117** 40 30
4250 14fo. Red squirrel 40 30
4251 14fo. Blue tit 40 30
4252 14fo. Butterfly and hedgehog 40 30

Nos. 4249/52 were issued together, se-tenant, forming a composite design.

1995. Europa. Peace and Freedom.
4253 **1118** 22fo. multicoloured 60 45

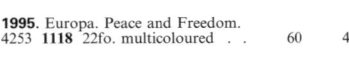

1119 Gymnastics and Ferenc Kemeny (founder)

1995. Centenary of Hungarian Olympic Committee. Multicoloured.
4254 22fo. Type **1119** 60 30
4255 60fo. Throwing the javelin 1·50 60
4256 100fo. Fencing 2·75 1·10

1120 Exhibition Emblem

1995. "Olympiafila '95" International Olympic and Sports Stamps Exhibition, Budapest.
4257 **1120** 22fo.+11fo. mult (rings in yellow) 90 60
4258 22fo.+11fo. mult (rings in purple) 90 60

1121 Saint Ladislas (detail of fresco, Szekelyderzs Castle Chapel)

1122 Almasy

1995. 900th Death Anniv of St. Ladislas, King of Hungary.
4259 **1121** 22fo. multicoloured 60 45

1995. Birth Centenary of Laszlo Almasy (explorer).
4260 **1122** 22fo. multicoloured 60 45

1123 Museum of Applied Arts, Budapest, and Lechner

1995. 150th Birth Anniv of Odon Lechner (architect).
4261 **1123** 22fo. multicoloured 60 40

1124 "K XVIII 1923" (Laszlo Moholy-Nagy)

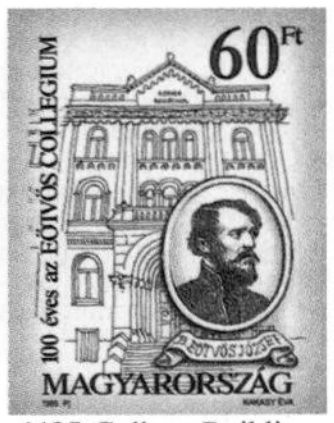

1125 College Building and Jozsef Eotvos (founder)

1995. Artists' Birth Centenaries. Multicoloured.
4262 22fo. Type **1124** 55 35
4263 22fo. "The Fiddler" (Aurel Bernath) 55 35

1995. Centenary of Eotvos College.
4264 **1125** 60fo. multicoloured 1·40 90

1126 Postal Carriage and Map of Postal Routes

1995. Stamp Day. Multicoloured.
4265 22fo. Type **1126** 50 45
4266 40fo. Airplane and route map 1·00 60
MS4267 80 × 61 mm. 100fo.+30fo. Children looking at stamp album (29 × 44 mm) 3·00 2·40

1995. "Expo '96" World's Fair, Budapest (3rd issue). As T **1112** showing Budapest landmarks.
4268 22fo. grey 55 40
4269 22fo. purple 55 40

DESIGNS: No. 4268, West Railway Station; 4269, Music Hall.

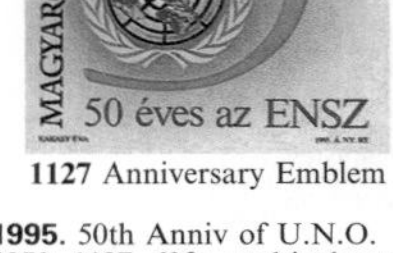

1127 Anniversary Emblem

1128 Sparklers

1995. 50th Anniv of U.N.O.
4270 **1127** 60fo. multicoloured 1·40 75

1995. Christmas. Multicoloured.
4271 14fo. Type **1128** 30 30
4272 60fo. Three wise men in stable 1·25 75

1129 St Elizabeth bathing Leper

1995. Saint Elizabeth of Hungary.
4273 **1129** 22fo. multicoloured 60 30

1130 Nobel Medals

1995. Centenary of Nobel Trust Fund.
4274 **1130** 100fo. multicoloured 2·25 1·25

1996. 1100th Anniv of Magyar Conquest (3rd issue). As T **1102**. Multicoloured.
4275 24fo. Rejoicing crowd 50 30
4276 24fo. Shaman presenting sacrificial white horse (59 × 39 mm) 50 30
4277 24fo. Bards 50 30

Nos. 4275/7 were issued together, se-tenant, forming a composite design.

1131 Leather Purse

1133 Headquarters

1132 Monastery (after Xaver Zsoldos)

1996. 9th-century Relics from Kares Cemeteries. Multicoloured.
4278 24fo. Type **1131** 60 45
4279 24fo. Gold and silver sabre hilt 60 45

1996. Millenary of Pannonhalma Monastery (1st issue). Sheet 100 × 80 mm.
MS4280 **1132** 100fo. violet 2·25 2·75

See also Nos. 4290/1 and 4305/6.

1996. Centenary of Journalists' Association.
4281 **1133** 50fo. multicoloured 1·10 60

1134 Emblem

1135 Swimming

1996. Promotion of Hungarian Production.
4282 **1134** 24fo. black, red & green 55 30

1996. Centenary of Modern Olympic Games and Olympic Games, Atlanta. Multicoloured.
4283 24fo. Type **1135** 50 30
4284 50fo. Tennis (Csilla Orosz) 1·10 60
4285 75fo. Canoeing 1·60 90

1996. 1100th Anniv of Magyar Conquest (4th issue). Sheet 150 × 190 mm containing previous designs. Multicoloured.
MS4286 19fo. × 3 Nos. 4189/91; 22fo. × 3 Nos. 4240/2; 24fo. × 3 Nos. 4275/7 4·50 2·10

1136 First Carriage

1996. Centenary of Budapest Underground Railway.
4287 **1136** 24fo. multicoloured . . 55 30

1137 Queen Gizella (wife of St. Stephen)

1996. Europa. Famous Women. Hungarian Queens. Multicoloured.
4288 24fo. Type **1137** 50 30
4289 75fo. Queen Elisabeth (wife of Francis Joseph I) . . . 1·60 1·25

1138 Triumphal Arch (entrance to Cathedral)
1139 Bird and "DRUG"

1996. Millenary of Pannonhalma Monastery (2nd issue).
4290 **1138** 17fo. brown 40 30
4291 – 24fo. blue 55 30
DESIGN: 24fo. Monks gathered in cloisters.

1996. International Day against Drug Abuse.
4292 **1139** 24fo. multicoloured . . 55 30

1140 Denes Mihaly (television pioneer)

1996. Inventors. Multicoloured.
4293 24fo. Type **1140** 50 30
4294 50fo. Laszlo Biro and ballpoint pen . . . . . . 1·00 60
4295 75fo. Zoltan Bay and Moon radar . . . . 1·50 90

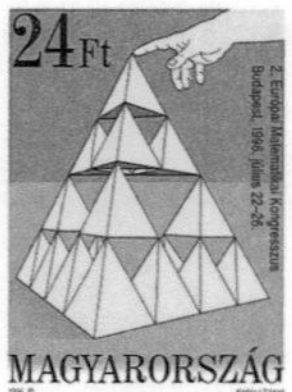

1141 Laszlo Vitez (puppet)
1143 Pyramid

1142 "Heves", 1846

1996. Youth Stamp. Puppet Festival, Budapest.
4296 **1141** 24fo.+10fo. mult . . . 75 60

1996. 150th Anniv of Hungarian Railways. Steam Locomotives. Multicoloured.
4297 17fo. Class 303 . . . . . . 30 30
4298 24fo. Class 325 . . . . . . 45 45
4299 24fo. Type **1142** 45 45
On No. 4299 the nameplate is inscribed "PEST".

1996. 2nd European Mathematics Congress, Budapest.
4300 **1143** 24fo. multicoloured . . 45 30

1144 Hungarian Long-horned Wood Beetle ("Ropalopus ungaricus")

1996. "NATUREXPO '96" International Nature Conservation Exhibition, Budapest. Mult.
4301 13fo. Type **1144** 30 30
4302 13fo. Lynx ("Lynx lynx") 30 30
4303 13fo. Siberian iris ("Iris sibirica") 30 30
4304 13fo. Great egret ("Egretta alba") 30 30

1996. Millenary of Pannonhalma Monastery (3rd issue).. As T **1138**.
4305 17fo. brown 35 30
4306 24fo. green 50 30
DESIGNS: 17fo. Refectory; 24fo. Main library.

1145 Homage to Prince Arpad (from "Vienna Picture Chronicle")
1146 1871 10k. Engraved Stamp

1996. Stamp Day. "Budapest '96" International Stamp Exhibition, Budapest. Mult.
4307 17fo. Type **1145** 35 30
4308 24fo. Prince Arpad on horseback and soldiers (from "Vienna Picture Chronicle") 65 30
MS4309 92 × 72 mm. 150fo.+50fo. 1944 1f. Prince Arpad stamp, first page of Deeds of Hungarians and detail of "Compact sealed with Blood" (mural by Bertalan Szekely, Kecskemet Town Hall) 2·50 3·75

1996. World Convention of Hungarian Stamps and Postal History.
4310 **1146** 24fo. multicoloured . . 55 30

1147 Map and Paddle-steamer "Kisfaludy"

1996. 150th Anniv of Steamer Service on Lake Balaton.
4311 **1147** 17fo. multicoloured . . 55 30

1148 Mastheads and Demonstration

1996. 40th Anniv of 23 October Uprising. Multicoloured.
4312 13fo. Type **1148** 25 30
4313 16fo. Newspaper, burning flag and motor vehicle . . 30 30
4314 17fo. Men with rifles and newspaper 30 30
4315 24fo. Newspaper and Imre Nagy (Prime Minister, Oct–Nov 1956) 35 30
MS4316 76 × 75 mm. 40fo. Imre Nagy and government members (44 × 29 mm) 55 60

1149 Atlanta and Medals

1996. Hungarian Medal Winners at Olympic Games. Sheet 85 × 55 mm.
MS4317 **1149** 150fo. multicoloured 3·00 2·00

1150 "Madonna and Child with Two Angels" (Matteo di Giovanni)

1996. Christmas. Multicoloured.
4318 17fo. Type **1150** 35 30
4319 24fo. "Adoration of the Wise Men" (Salzburg Master) 50 30

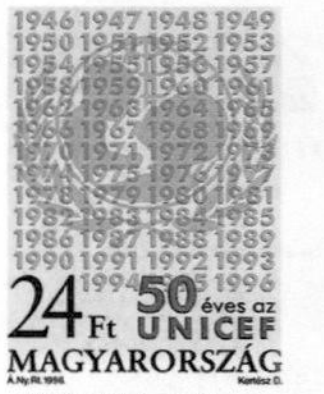

1151 List of Years
1152 Bust, Book, Quill and Shield

1996. 50th Anniv of U.N.I.C.E.F.
4320 **1151** 24fo. multicoloured . . 45 30

1996. Birth Bicentenary of Miklos Wesselenyi (writer).
4321 **1152** 24fo. multicoloured . . 45 30

1153 Kalman Mikszath and Characters

1997. Writers' Birth Anniversaries. Mult.
4322 27fo. Type **1153** (150th anniv) 60 45
4323 27fo. Aron Tamasi (cent) . . 60 45

1154 Baranya

1997. Arms. Multicoloured. (a) As T **1154**.
4324 27fo. Type **1154** 30 45
4325 27fo. Bacs-Kiskun 30 45
4326 27fo. Bekes 30 45
4327 27fo. Borsod-Abauj-Zemplen 30 45
4328 27fo. Fejer 30 45
4329 27fo. Gyor-Moson-Sopron 30 45
4330 27fo. Heves 30 45
4331 27fo. Jasz-Nagykun-Szolnok 30 45
4332 27fo. Komarom-Esztergom 30 45
4333 27fo. Nograd 30 45
4334 27fo. Pest 30 45
4335 27fo. Somogy 30 45
4336 27fo. Tolna 30 45
4337 27fo. Vas 30 45
4338 27fo. Veszprem 30 45
4339 27fo. Zala 30 45

(b) Size 50 × 32 mm.
4340 27fo. Hajku-Bihar 30 45
4341 27fo. Budapest 30 45
4342 27fo. Csongrad 30 45
4343 27fo. Szabolcs-Szatmar-Bereg 30 45
MS4344 Four sheets, each 78 × 125 mm. (a) Nos. 4324/33 and 4340 plus label; (b) Nos. 4328/33; (c) Nos. 4334/9; (d) Nos. 4341/3 Set of 4 sheets . . . . 10·50 10·50

1155 Badge, Camp and Sailing

1997. 90th Anniv of Scout Movement.
4345 **1155** 20fo. multicoloured . . 35 30

1156 Book, Knight and Arany

1997. 150th Anniv of Composition of "Miklos Toldi" by Janos Arany (winning entry in poetry competition).
4346 **1156** 27fo.+10fo. mult . . . 70 60

1157 St. Adalbert
1158 Emblem and City

1997. Death Millenary of St. Adalbert (Bishop of Prague).
4347 **1157** 80fo. lilac . . . . . . 1·50 1·25

1997. World Customs' Union Conference, Budapest.
4348 **1158** 90fo. multicoloured . . 1·50 80

1159 Gemsboks

1997. African Animals. Multicoloured.
4349 16fo. Type **1159** 25 30
4350 20fo. Common zebras . . . 30 30
4351 20fo. Black rhinoceroses . . 30 30
4352 27fo. Lions 40 45
MS4353 91 × 64 mm. 90fo. African elephants . . . . 1·50 2·25

1160 "The Enchanted Hart"

1997. Europa. Tales and Legends. Mult.
4354 27fo. Type **1160** 55 45
4355 90fo. King St. Stephen overseeing burial of Prince Geza (death millenary) . . 1·90 1·25

1161 Schraetzer ("Gymnocephalus schraetzer")

1997. Fishes. Multicoloured.
4356 20fo. Type **1161** 40 30
4357 20fo. Bullhead "Cottus gobio" 40 30
4358 20fo. Schneider "Alburnoides bipunctatus" 40 30
4359 20fo. Spiny loach ("Cobitis taenia") 40 30
Nos. 4356/9 were issued together, se-tenant, forming a composite design.

1162 St. Jadwiga (after Peter Prokop)
1163 Janos Selye

1997. Canonization of Queen Jadwiga of Poland.
4360 **1162** 90fo. multicoloured . . 1·50 1·25

1997. Int Congress on Stress, Budapest.
4361 **1163** 90fo. multicoloured . . 1·50 60

1997. No. 4220 surch **60 f.**
4362 60fo. on 24fo. multicoloured 1·00 60

1997. Wine Grapes and Regions (2nd series). As T **1013**. Multicoloured.
4363 27fo. Harslevelu, Gyongyos 50 45
4364 27fo. Nemes Kadarka, Kiskoros 50 45
4365 27fo. Teltfurtu Ezerjo, Mor 50 45

1165 Flower surrounded by Flood Waters

1997. Flood Relief Funds.
4366 **1165** 27fo.+100fo. mult . . . 2·40 1·50

1166 Postman and Csonka Tricycle, 1900

1997. Stamp Day. Multicoloured.
4367 27fo.+5fo. Type **1166** . . . 40 45
4368 55fo.+5fo. Registered letter receiving-machine, 1906 (vert) 65 75
MS4369 82 × 68 mm. 90fo.+30fo. Csonka post van, 1905 . . . . 1·40 2·10

1167 Nativity

1997. Christmas. Multicoloured.
4370 20fo. Type **1167** 40 30
4371 27fo. Adoration of the Wise Men 50 60

1168 Weightlifter **1169** Skiing

1997. 68th World Weightlifting Championships, Thailand.
4372 **1168** 90fo. multicoloured . . 1·50 60

1998. Winter Olympic Games, Nagano, Japan. Multicoloured.
4373 30fo. Type **1169** 60 45
4374 100fo. Snowboarding . . . 2·00 1·25

1170 Szechenyi with Camera

1998. Birth Centenary of Zsigmond Szechenyi (travel writer).
4375 **1170** 60fo. multicoloured . . 90 75

1171 Leaf and Lyrics

1998. 175th Anniv of National Hymn by Ferenc Kolcsey.
4376 **1171** 75fo. multicoloured . . 1·50 90

1172 Balint Postas holding Envelope **1173** Hearts and Post Box

1998. Introduction of Balint Postas (post mascot). Multicoloured.
4377 23fo. Type **1172** 35 30
4378 24fo. Balint Postas bowing 40 30
4379 30fo. Balint Postas with arms outstretched 50 45
4380 65fo. Balint Postas flying . . 1·10 75

1998. St. Valentine's Day.
4381 **1173** 24fo. multicoloured . . 45 30

1174 Szilard **1175** Sandor Petofi (poet)

1998. Birth Cent of Leo Szilard (scientist).
4382 **1174** 50fo. multicoloured . . 90 60

1998. 150th Anniv of March Revolution, 1848. Multicoloured.
4383 23fo. Type **1175** 25 30
4384 24fo. Mihaly Tancsics (politician and workers' newspaper editor) and inkwell 30 30
4385 30fo. Lajos Kossuth (Governor of 1849 Republic) and coin . . . 40 45
MS4386 78 × 65 mm. 150fo.+50fo. Leaders of the Revolution (44 × 29 mm) . . . . 2·40 3·00

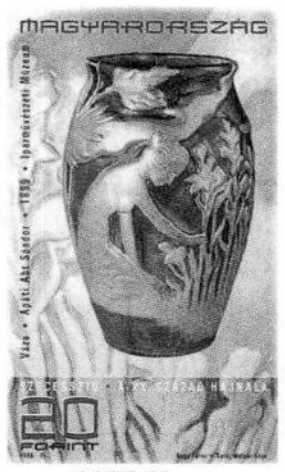

1176 "The Resurrection of Christ" (El Greco) **1177** Vase

1998. Easter.
4387 – 24fo. red and black . . 30 30
4388 **1176** 30fo. multicoloured . . 40 45
DESIGN: 27 × 39 mm—24fo. Dots forming outline of egg.

1998. Ceramics. Multicoloured.
4389 20fo. Type **1177** 25 30
4390 24fo. Bowl decorated with butterflies (horiz) 30 30
4391 30fo. Spiral vase 35 45
4392 95fo. Bowl with lid (horiz) 1·10 1·25

1178 Postman

1998. Stamp Day. 250th Anniv of Inauguration of Postal Service by Empress Maria Theresa. Multicoloured.
4393 24fo.+10fo. Type **1178** . . . 40 45
4394 30fo.+10fo. Mounted courier 50 75
MS4395 80 × 61 mm. 150fo. Horse-drawn post coach . . . . . . 1·90 2·40

1179 American Bison

1998. American Animals. Multicoloured.
4396 23fo. Type **1179** 25 30
4397 24fo. Brown bear 30 30
4398 24fo. Mississippi alligator 30 30
4399 30fo. Ocelot 35 45
MS4400 90 × 60 mm. 150fo. Marvellous spatule-tail . . . . 1·75 2·40

1180 Jendrassik **1181** Hurdling

1998. Birth Centenary of Gyorgy Jendrassik (engineer).
4401 **1180** 100fo. blue . . . . . . 1·75 1·25

1998. European Light Athletics Championships, Budapest. Multicoloured.
4402 24fo. Type **1181** 25 30
4403 65fo. High jumping 70 90
4404 80fo. Throwing the hammer 90 1·10

1182 Canoe

1998. World White-water Canoeing Championships, Szeged.
4405 **1182** 30fo. multicoloured . . 50 45

1183 Players

1998. World Cup Football Championship, France. Multicoloured.
4406 30fo. Type **1183** 35 35
4407 110fo. Players with ball on ground . . . . 1·40 1·40
Nos. 4406/7 were issued together, se-tenant, forming a composite design.

1184 Baross (after Miklos Barabos) **1185** Signalman and Pioneers in Railway Carriage

1998. 150th Birth Anniv of Gabor Baross (politician).
4408 **1184** 60fo. multicoloured . . 1·10 75

1998. 50th Anniv of Budapest Pioneer Railway.
4409 **1185** 24fo. multicoloured . . 45 30

1186 Congress Emblem **1187** Carved Poles

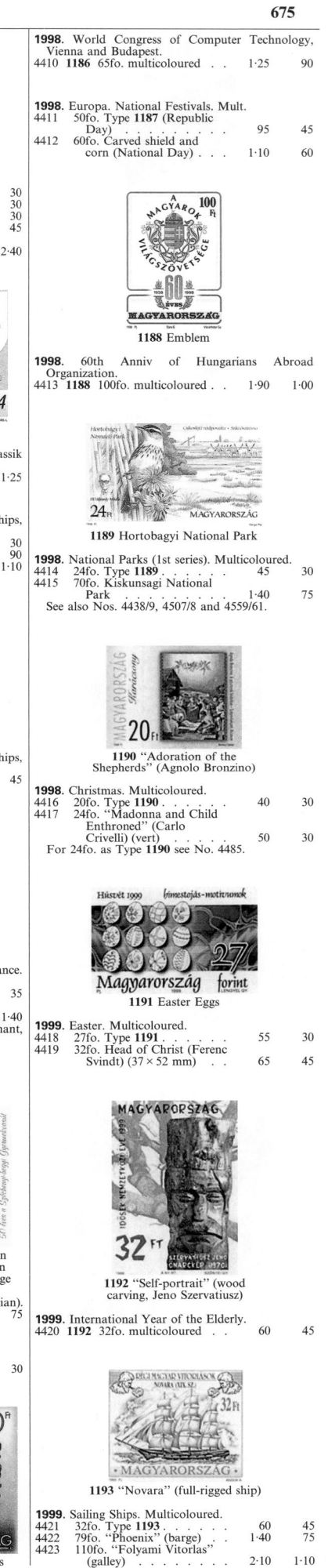

1998. World Congress of Computer Technology, Vienna and Budapest.
4410 **1186** 65fo. multicoloured . . 1·25 90

1998. Europa. National Festivals. Mult.
4411 50fo. Type **1187** (Republic Day) 95 45
4412 60fo. Carved shield and corn (National Day) . . . 1·10 60

1188 Emblem

1998. 60th Anniv of Hungarians Abroad Organization.
4413 **1188** 100fo. multicoloured . . 1·90 1·00

1189 Hortobagyi National Park

1998. National Parks (1st series). Multicoloured.
4414 24fo. Type **1189** 45 30
4415 70fo. Kiskunsagi National Park . . . . 1·40 75
See also Nos. 4438/9, 4507/8 and 4559/61.

1190 "Adoration of the Shepherds" (Agnolo Bronzino)

1998. Christmas. Multicoloured.
4416 20fo. Type **1190** 40 30
4417 24fo. "Madonna and Child Enthroned" (Carlo Crivelli) (vert) 50 30
For 24fo. as Type **1190** see No. 4485.

1191 Easter Eggs

1999. Easter. Multicoloured.
4418 27fo. Type **1191** 55 30
4419 32fo. Head of Christ (Ferenc Svindt) (37 × 52 mm) . . 65 45

1192 "Self-portrait" (wood carving, Jeno Szervatiusz)

1999. International Year of the Elderly.
4420 **1192** 32fo. multicoloured . . 60 45

1193 "Novara" (full-rigged ship)

1999. Sailing Ships. Multicoloured.
4421 32fo. Type **1193** 60 45
4422 79fo. "Phoenix" (barge) . . 1·40 75
4423 110fo. "Folyami Vitorlas" (galley) . . . . 2·10 1·10

1194 Path of Eclipse

1999. Total Solar Eclipse (11 Aug). Sheet 105 × 76 mm.
MS4424 **1194** 1999fo. multicoloured 30·00 16·00

1195 Artur Gorgey (commander of Upper Danube)

1999. 150th Anniv of 1848–49 Uprising. Multicoloured.
4425 24fo. Type **1195** 30 30
4426 27fo. Lajos Batthyany (politician) 35 30
4427 32fo. General Jozef Bem . . 40 30
MS4428 78 × 65 mm. 100fo. "The Battle of Tapioticske" (detail, Mor Than) (44 × 27 mm) . . . . . 1·25 90

1196 Scene from "Bobo and the Hare" (animated film)

1999. Youth Stamp.
4429 **1196** 52fo.+25fo. mult . . . 1·50 75

1197 Cathedrals within Map and Emblem

1199 Papai

1198 The Five Sports

1999. 50th Anniv of North Atlantic Treaty Organization.
4430 **1197** 110fo. multicoloured . . 1·90 1·25

1999. 5th World Pentathlon Championship, Budapest. Sheet 86 × 70 mm.
MS4431 **1198** 100fo. multicoloured 1·90 90

1999. 350th Birth Anniv of Ferenc Pariz Papai (scientist, physician and lexicographer).
4432 **1199** 50fo. green and orange 75 45

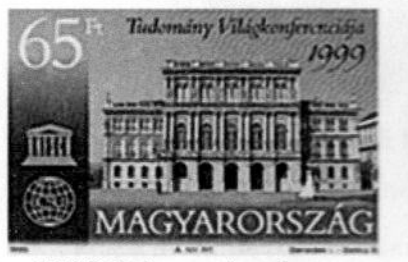
1200 Science Academy, Budapest

1201 Anniversary Badge on Scroll

1999. World Science Congress, Budapest.
4433 **1200** 65fo. multicoloured . . 1·00 60

1999. Centenary of Ferencvaros Sports Club.
4434 **1201** 100fo. multicoloured . . 1·50 90

1202 Council Flag

1999. 50th Anniv of Council of Europe.
4435 **1202** 50fo. multicoloured . . 75 60

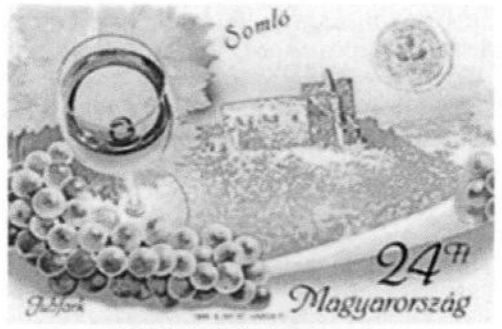
1203 Juhfark, Somlo

1999. Wine Grapes and Regions (3rd series). Multicoloured.
4436 24fo. Type **1203** 30 40
4437 27fo. Kekfrankos, Sopron 30 45

1999. Europa. Parks and Gardens. National Parks (2nd series). As T **1189**. Multicoloured.
4438 27fo. Aggtelek National Park 40 30
4439 32fo. Bukk National Park 50 45

1204 Bengali Tiger

1999. Asian Animals. Multicoloured.
4440 27fo. Type **1204** 40 30
4441 32fo. Giant panda 50 45
4442 52fo. Black leopard 80 60
4443 79fo. Orang-utan . . . . . 1·10 75
MS4444 78 × 75 mm. 100fo. Mandarin (49 × 29 mm) . . . 1·50 1·25

1205 Title Page of Decree

1999. Stamp Day. 250th Anniv of Decree by Empress Maria Theresa establishing Regular Mail Coach Service. Multicoloured.
4445 32fo.+15fo. Type **1205** . . . 60 60
4446 52fo.+20fo. Passengers boarding coach and woman with letters . . . 95 75
MS4447 75 × 60 mm. 150fo. Horses and mail coach (31 × 41 mm) 2·00 1·50

1206 Common Poppy

1207 Cukor

1999. Greetings Stamps. Flowers. Multicoloured.
4448 27fo. Type **1206** 35 30
4449 32fo. Trumpet gentian . . . 1·40 30

1999. Birth Centenary of George Cukor (film director).
4450 **1207** 50fo. multicoloured . . 65 45

1208 U.P.U. Emblem

1210 High-backed Chair, Szepesseg (17th century)

1209 Woodcut by Samuel Mikoviny (from "Notitia Hungarie" by Matyas Bel)

1999. 125th Anniv of Universal Postal Union. "China '99" International Stamp Exhibition, Peking.
4451 **1208** 32fo. multicoloured . . 1·25 1·50

1999. International Book Fair, Frankfurt.
4452 **1209** 40fo. multicoloured . . 50 45

1999. Antique Furniture.
4453 – 1fo. green and yellow 10 10
4454 – 2fo. green and black 10 10
4455 – 3fo. red and black . . 10 10
4456 – 4fo. brown 10 10
4457 – 5fo. deep blue and blue 10 10
4458 – 6fo. brown and sepia 10 10
4459 – 7fo. brown and pink 10 10
4460 – 8fo. black and grey . . 10 10
4461 **1210** 10fo. bistre and black 10 10
4464 – 20fo. green and black 10 10
4467 – 26fo. green and black 10 10
4468 – 29fo. green and black 15 10
4469 – 30fo. mauve and black 15 10
4470 – 31fo. dp mauve and mve 15 10
4470a – 32fo. pink and red . . 15 10
4470b – 33fo. pink and red . . 15 10
4470c – 35fo. pink and red . . 15 10
4471 – 40fo. brown & lt brown 20 10
4472 – 50fo. blue and black 25 10
4474 – 60fo. olive and green 30 10
4475 – 65fo. ochre and brown 30 10
4476 – 70fo. brown and black 35 15
4478 – 80fo. grey and black 40 20
4480 – 90fo. lilac and purple 45 20
4481 – 100fo. brown and black 50 25
4482 – 134fo. ochre and brown 70 10
4483 – 200fo. blue and green 1·00 50
DESIGNS—VERT: 1fo. Wooden stool, 1910; 2fo. Heves County wooden chair, 1838; 3fo. 19th-century gilded chair; 4fo. Armchair by Geza Marota; 5fo. Chair by Odon Farago; 6fo. Wooden chair by Marton Kovacs; 7fo. Ornate chair, 1853; 8fo. 19th-century chair; 9fo. 18th-century wooden armchair; 20fo. Armchair by Karoly Lingel, 1915; 26, 31fo. Neo-Gothic chair, 1850; 29fo. Magyargee wooden chair, 1879; 30fo. Armchair by Karoly Nagy, 1935; 32, 33fo. Ornate backed chair, 1890; 35fo. 18th-century carver; 40fo. Ornate chair, 1896; 50fo. Prince Pal Esterhazy's armchair (16th-century); 60fo. Chair, 1840; 65fo. Cane-bottomed ornate armchair, 1920; 70fo. Chair with umbrella-shaped back, 1820; 80fo. High backed chair; 90fo. Upholstered armchair by Lajos Kozma. HORIZ: 100fo. Couch by Lajos Kozma, 1920; 134fo. Double-seated chair, 1900; 200fo. Ornate couch, 1810.

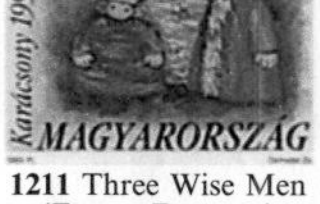
1211 Three Wise Men (Zsuzsa Demeter)

1212 Wigner

1999. Christmas. Multicoloured
4485 24fo. Type **1190** 30 30
4486 27fo. Type **1211** 35 30
4487 32fo. "Madonna and Child" (stained glass window, Miksa Roth) (vert) . . . 45 30

1999. 97th Birth Anniv of Jeno Wigner (physicist).
4488 **1212** 32fo. blue 45 30

1213 Paddle-steamer passing under Bridge

1214 Coronation Sceptre

1999. 150th Anniv of Chain Bridge, Budapest. Sheet 87 × 57 mm.
MS4489 **1213** 150fo. blue, red and green . . . . 1·90 1·50

2000. New Millenium.
4490 **1214** 28fo. bistre and purple 35 30
4491 30fo. bistre and purple 40 45
4492 – 34fo. multicoloured . . 45 45
4493 – 36fo. multicoloured . . 45 45
4494 – 40fo. multicoloured . . 50 60
DESIGN:—34, 36, 40fo. Millennium flag.

1215 Miklos Kis Misztotfalusi (printer, 350th anniv)

1216 Fekete and Animal Characters

2000. Birth Anniversaries.
4495 **1215** 30fo. grn, stone & brn 35 45
4496 – 40fo. blue, stone & brn 45 60
4497 – 50fo. red, stone & brn 50 60
4498 – 80fo. brown and stone 75 1·10
DESIGNS—40fo. Anyos Jedlik (physicist, bicentenary); 50fo. Jeno Kvassay (engineer, 150th anniv); 80fo. Jeno Barcsay (artist, centenary).

2000. Youth Stamp. Birth Centenary of Istvan Fekete (writer).
4499 **1216** 60fo.+30fo. mult . . . 1·25 1·10

1217 Hungarian Cultural Foundation and Exhibition Emblem

2000. "Hunphilex 2000" Stamp Exn, Budapest.
4500 **1217** 200fo.+100fo. mult . . 3·25 3·75

1218 Mihaly Vorosmarty (poet, bicentenary)

1220 Airport Building and Lisunov Li-2 Airplane

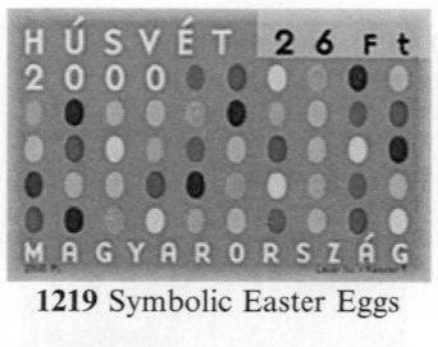

1219 Symbolic Easter Eggs

2000. Birth Anniversaries.
4501 **1218** 50fo. green and black 60 45
4502 – 50fo. brown and black 60 45
4503 – 50fo. green and black 60 45
4504 – 50fo. brown and black 60 45
4505 – 50fo. green and black 60 45

DESIGNS: No. 4502, Mari Jaszai (actress, 150th anniv); 4503, Sandor Marai (writer, centenary); 4504, Lujza Blaha (actress, 150th anniv); 4505, Lorinc Szabo (poet and translator, centenary).

2000. Easter. Multicoloured.
4506 26fo. Type **1219** 30 30
4507 28fo. Decorated egg (29 × 31 mm) 35 30

2000. National Parks (3rd series). As T **1189**. Mult.
4508 29fo. Ferto-Hansag National Park 35 30
4509 34fo. Duna-Drava National Park 40 45

2000. 50th Anniv of Ferihegy International Airport.
4510 **1220** 136fo. multicoloured . . 1·50 1·25

1221 Banded Wren

1222 Jigsaw Puzzle

2000. Australian Animals. Multicoloured.
4511 26fo. Type **1221** 20 30
4512 28fo. Opossum 25 30
4513 83fo. Koala 65 75
4514 90fo. Red kangaroo 75 90
MS4515 107 × 70 mm. 110fo. Duck-billed platypus . . . . 1·25 1·25

2000. Europa. Multicoloured.
4516 34fo. Type **1222** 90 45
4517 54fo. "Building Europe" . . 1·40 60

1223 Boat on Corinthian Canal, and Istvan Turr (engineer)

2000. "EXPO 2000" World's Fair, Hanover, Germany.
4518 **1223** 80fo. multicoloured . . 90 75

1224 Bisected and Complete 6k. Austrian Empire Stamps

2000. "WIPA 2000" International Stamp Exhibition, Vienna. 150th Anniv of Hungarian Stamps.
4519 **1224** 110fo. multicoloured . . 1·25 1·10

1225 Queen Gizella I

2000. Stamp Day. Showing decorative figures from Coronation Gown. Multicoloured.
4520 26fo. Type **1225** 30 30
4521 28fo. King Istvan I 35 30

1226 Balatonfured-Csopak

2000. Wine Grapes and Regions (4th series). Mult.
4522 29fo. Type **1226** 25 30
4523 34fo. Aszar-Neszmely . . . 30 30

1227 Evangelical Church, Budapest

1229 Boeing 767-200

1228 Globe

2000. Churches. Multicoloured.
4524 30fo. Type **1227** 40 30
4525 30fo. St. Anthony's Friars' Church, Eger 40 30
4526 30fo. Reformed Church, Takos 40 30
4527 30fo. Abbey Church, Jak . . 40 30

2000. Millennium. Sheet 120 × 70 mm.
MS4528 **1228** 2000fo. multicoloured 18·00 18·00

2000. 90th Anniv of Hungarian Aviation.
4529 **1229** 120fo. multicoloured . . 1·50 1·10

1230 King Laszlo, 1077–95

2000. New Millennium (1st series). Multicoloured.
4530 50fo. Type **1230** 25 10
4531 50fo. Issue of Golden Bull (charter of rights for freemen) by King Andrew II, 1222 . . . . 25 10
4532 50fo. St. Elizabeth and the Mongol invasion, 1241 . . 25 10
4533 50fo. Reign of King Sigismund, 1395–1437 . . 25 10
4534 50fo. Janos Hunyadi (regent) and Janos Kapisztran 25 10
4535 50fo. Reign of King Matthias, 1458–90 . . . . 25 10
4536 50fo. The Crucifixion, Miklos Zrinyi (military commander) and Siege of Szigetvas, 1566 . . . . . 25 10
4537 50fo. Horseman, battle scenes and the recapture of Buda Castle and Gyor 25 10
4538 50fo. People outside Church, Transylvania 25 10
4539 50fo. Peter Pazmany (founder) and University, Budapest, 1635 . . . . . 25 10

Nos. 4530/4 and 4535/9 were issued together, se-tenant, forming a composite design.

See also Nos. 4585/**MS**4595.

1231 Detail of Coronation Gown

2000. "HUNPHILEX 2000" International Stamp Exhibition, Budapest. Multicoloured.
MS4540 93 × 72 mm. 200fo.+100fo. Type **1231** . . . . 1·75 1·75

1232 Dohany Utca Synagogue, Budapest

1233 Mary and Jesus leaving Bethlehem

2000. Hungary–Israel Joint Issue.
4541 **1232** 120fo. multicoloured . . 1·50 1·00

2000. Christmas. Multicoloured.
4542 26fo. Type **1233** 30 30
4543 28fo. Church (27 × 28 mm) 35 30
4544 29fo. Christmas tree (27 × 28 mm) 40 30
4545 34fo. Nativity scene on watch face (32 × 36 mm) 45 30

1234 Emblem and Writing Desk

2000. 50th Anniv of Convention on Human Rights.
4546 **1234** 50fo. multicoloured . . 60 45

1235 Rifle Shooting

2000. Olympic Games, Sydney. Multicoloured.
4547 30fo. Type **1235** 35 30
4548 40fo. Weightlifting 45 45
4549 80fo. Gymnastics 95 75
MS4550 85 × 63 mm. 120fo. Two-man kayak . . . . 1·40 1·40

1236 Eger Castle and Extract from Poem

1238 Man blowing Trumpet

1237 Profiles

2001. Youth Stamp. Centenary of *Eclipse of the Crescent Moon* (poem by Geza Gardonyi).
4551 **1236** 60fo.+30fo. mult . . . 40 40

2001. European Year of Languages.
4552 **1237** 100fo. multicoloured . . 50 25

2001. Greetings Stamps. Multicoloured.
4553 36fo. Type **1238** 20 10
4554 36fo. Couple dancing . . . 20 10
4555 36fo. Baby in cradle 20 10
4556 36fo. Clown 20 10
4557 36fo. Woman and child . . 20 10

1239 Ice-skater

2001.
4558 **1239** 140fo. multicoloured . . 70 35

1240 Easter Eggs and Rabbit

1242 Emblem and Vegetation

1241 Mk 48 Diesel Locomotive, Lillafured State Forest Railway

2001. Easter.
4559 **1240** 28fo. multicoloured . . 15 10

2001. National Parks (4th series). As T **1189**. Multicoloured.
4560 28fo. Upper Balaton National Park 15 10
4561 36fo. Koros-Maros National Park 20 10
4562 70fo. Duna-Ipoly National Park 35 15

2001. Light Railways. Multicoloured.
4563 31fo. Type **1241** 15 10
4564 36fo. 490 series steam locomotive, Keeskemet Light Railway 20 10
4565 100fo. 394 series steam locomotive, Szechenyi Railway Museum 50 25
4566 150fo. C50 diesel locomotive, Csomoder State Forest Railway . . 70 35

2001. Anniversaries. Multicoloured.
4567 70fo. Type **1242** (50th anniversaries of International Plant Protection Convention and European and Mediterranean Plant Protection Organization) 35 15
4568 80fo. Globe, people and emblem (50th anniv of United Nations High Commissioner for Refugees) 40 20

1243 Door Inlay, St. Adalbert Basilica

2001. Millenary of Archdiocese of Esztergom.
4569 **1243** 124fo. multicoloured . . 60 30

1244 Ringed Seal (*Phoca hispida*)

2001. Animals. Multicoloured.
4570 28fo. Type **1244** 15 10
4571 36fo. Wolf (*Canis lupus*) . . 20 10
4572 70fo. Herman's tortoise (*Testudo hermanni*) . . . 35 15
4573 90fo. River kingfisher (*Alcedo atthis*) 45 20
MS4574 90 × 66 mm. 200fo. Red deer males (*Cervus elaphus*) . . 1·75 1·75

1245 Chest containing Water

1246 1871 1k. Newspaper Stamp

2001. Europa. Water Resources. Multicoloured.
4575 36fo. Type **1245** 20 10
4576 90fo. Open globe filled with water 45 20

2001. Stamp Day. 130th Anniv of Hungarian Stamps. Multicoloured.
4577 36fo. Type **1246** 20 10
4578 90fo. 1871 3k. stamp . . . 45 20
MS4579 60 × 75 mm. 200fo.+40fo. "Pigeon Post" (Miklos Barabas) (39 × 49 mm) . . . . 2·10 2·10

1247 Players

2001. European Water Polo Championship, Budapest.
4580 **1247** 150fo. multicoloured . . 70 35

1248 Scout's Hats

2001. 4th European Conference of Former Scouts and Guides, Budapest.
4581 **1248** 150fo. multicoloured . . 70 30

1249 Drawing (Aladar Korosfoi-Kriesch)

2001. Art Anniversaries.
4582 **1249** 100fo. blue, mauve and lilac 50 25
4583 – 150fo. black and blue (49 × 21 mm) 70 35
DESIGNS—VERT: 100fo. Type **1249** (centenary of Godollo Artists' Colony). HORIZ: 150fo. Emblems representing different branches of the arts (centenary of FESZEK Club).

1250 Athletics Race

2001. World Youth Athletics Championship, Debrecen.
4584 **1250** 140fo. multicoloured . . 65 35

1251 Ferenc Rakovic and Ilona Zrinyi

2001. New Millennium (2nd series). Multicoloured.
4585 50fo. Type **1251** 20 10
4586 50fo. Terezia Maria and royal horse guard 20 10
4587 50fo. Istvan Szechenyi and Chain Bridge 20 10
4588 50fo. Newspaper headline and man on horseback . . 20 10
4589 50fo. Janos Arany, "The Solitary Cedar" (detail, Tivadar Csontvary Kosztka) and Parliament buildings 20 10
4590 50fo. First World War soldiers and map 20 10
4591 50fo. Mihaly Babits 20 10
4592 50fo. Chain Bridge and Bishop Vilmos Apor . . . 20 10
4593 50fo. Tanks and soldiers (Revolution, 1956) and Zoltan Kodaly (composer) 20 10
4594 50fo. Young children and Millennium flag 20 10
MS4595 105 × 75 mm. 2001fo. Crown (39 × 31 mm) . . . . . 10·00 5·00

1252 Pannonhalma-Sokoroalja

2001. Wine Grapes and Regions (5th series). Multicoloured.
4596 60fo. Type **1252** 25 10
4597 70fo. Balatonboglar 30 15

1253 Common Peacock (30 m mosaic)

2001. Guinness Record Attempt by Hungarian Post Office to Create World's Largest Mosaic from Used Postage Stamps.
4598 **1253** 10fo. multicoloured . . 10 10

1254 Bridge

2001. Reconstruction of Maria Valeria Bridge, Estergom–Parkany.
4599 **1254** 36fo. multicoloured . . 15 10

1255 Angel and Decorations

1256 1871 2k. Stamp and Emblem

2001. Christmas.
4600 **1255** 36fo. multicoloured . . 15 10

2001. 150th Anniv of Hungarian Stamp Printing.
4601 **1256** 150fo. multicoloured . . 75 30

1257 Ice Hockey Player

2002. Winter Olympic Games, Salt Lake City, U.S.A.
4602 **1257** 160fo. multicoloured . . 70 35

1258 Soldiers fighting (Defence of Eger Castle)

2002. Youth Stamp. 450th Anniv of War with Ottoman Empire. Sheet 120 × 68 mm containing T **1258** and similar multicoloured designs.
MS4603 50fo. Type **1258**; 50fo. Istvan Losonczy and Turkish soldiers, Timisoara; 100fo. + 50fo. Soldiers and pages (Battle of Dregely Castle) (39 × 29 mm) 1·10 55

1259 Ordinary "Penny-farthing" Bicycle

1260 Easter Eggs

2002. History of the Bicycle. Multicoloured.
4604 40fo. Type **1259** 20 10
4605 40fo. Tricycle, 1900s 20 10
4606 40fo. Karoly Iszer (chairman of Budapest Sport Club) 20 10
4607 40fo. Four-man cycle . . . 20 10

2002. Easter.
4608 **1260** 30fo. multicoloured . . 30 10

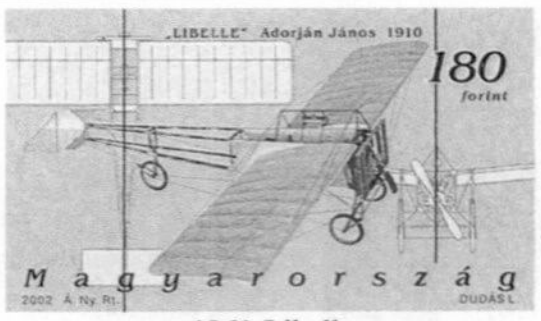
1261 Libelle

2002. Aviation. Multicoloured.
4609 180fo. Type **1261** 80 40
4610 190fo. Hungarian Lloyd Aircraft and Engine Factory biplane 85 40

1262 Lajos Kossuth

2002. Birth Anniversaries. Multicoloured.
4611 33fo. Type **1262** (statesman, bicentenary) 15 10
4612 134fo. Janos Bolyai (mathematician, bicentenary) 60 30
4613 150fo. Gyula Illyes (poet and writer, centenary) . . 65 30

1263 Stage Set for *The Tragedy of Man* (Imre Madach)

2002. Inauguration of New National Theatre, Budapest. Sheet 85 × 60 mm.
MS4614 **1263** 500fo. multicoloured 2·25 1·10

1264 Parliament Building

2002. Centenary of Inauguration of Parliament Building. Sheet 97 × 67 mm.
MS4615 **1264** 500fo. multicoloured 2·25 1·10

1265 "S.O.S."

2002. Environmental Protection.
4616 **1265** 158fo. multicoloured . . 75 35

1266 Book of Psalms of King David

2002. Bicentenaries of Hungarian National Museum and National Szechenyi Library. Exhibits from the institutions. Multicoloured.
MS4617 150fo. Type **1266**; 150fo. Illumination from the second volume of King Matthias's Book of Rites; 150fo. Civil Guard of Pest Standard, 1848; 150fo. Holy water basin, 1903 . . . . . . 3·50 3·50

1267 Deer

2002. Centenary of Halas Lace. Multicoloured.
4618 100fo. Type **1267** 55 30
4619 110fo. Swan 60 30
4620 140fo. Couple 80 40

1268 Wild Cat (*Felis sylvestris*)

2002. Fauna. Multicoloured.
4621 30fo. Type **1268** 20 10
4622 38fo. Crimean bull lizard (*Podarcis taurica*) 20 10
4623 110fo. Jay (*Garrulus glandarius*) 60 30
4624 160fo. Alpine longhorn beetle (*Rosalia alpina*) . . 90 45
MS4625 90 × 65 mm. 500fo. Sterlet (*Acipenser ruthenus*) . . . . . 3·00 3·00

1269 Elephant

2002. Europa. Circus.
4626 **1269** 62fo. multicoloured . . 35 20

1270 Players

1271 Dog and Kennel (Etesd meg)

2002. World Cup Football Championship, Japan and South Korea.
4627 **1270** 160fo. multicoloured . . 90 45

2002. Greetings Stamps. Designs as Nos. 4448/9 but with change of face value.
4628 30fo. Common poppy . . . 20 10
4629 38fo. Trumpet gentian . . . 20 10

2002. Greetings Stamps. Self-adhesive. Multicoloured.
4630 38fo. Type **1271** 20 10
4631 38fo. Washing line (Megszulettem!) 20 10
4632 38fo. Present outside house (Sok boldogsagot!) . . . 20 10
4633 38fo. Sofa and plant (Ontozdmeg...!) 20 10
4634 38fo. Man in room (Ennyire szeretlek!) 20 10
Nos. 4630/4 were issued together, se-tenant, forming a composite design.

1272 "Stone-pelter" (Karoly Ferenczy)

2002. Art. Multicoloured.
4635 62fo. Type **1272** 35 20
4636 188fo. "Ballerina" (statue, Ferenc Medgyessy) (vert) 1·10 55

1273 Buda Castle

2002. U.N.E.S.C.O. World Heritage Sites. Multicoloured.
4637 100fo. Type **1273** 55 30
4638 150fo. Holloko, Nograd . . 85 45
4639 180fo. Aggtelek-Carst Caves (horiz) . . . . 1·00 50

1274 Facade and Statue

2002. Millenary of Kalocsa Archdiocese.
4640 **1274** 150fo. multicoloured . . 85 45

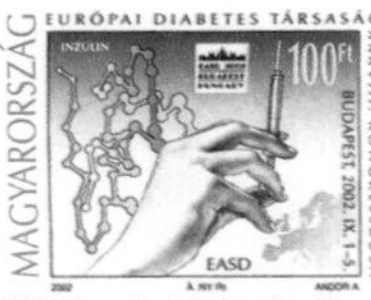

1275 Insulin Molecule, Hand holding Syringe and Map of Europe

2002. Medical Events in 2002. Multicoloured.
4641 100fo. Type **1275** (38th European Diabetes Association Congress) . . 55 30
4642 150fo. Arms, arrows and map of Europe (16th European Society of Elbow and Shoulder Surgeons Congress) . . . 95 45

1276 "Pound Cake Madonna"

2002. 75th Anniv of Stamp Day. Birth Centenary of Margit Kováacs (ceramicist). Multicoloured.
4643 33fo. Type **1276** 20 10
4644 38fo. "Family Photograph Album" 20 10
MS4645 86 × 72 mm. 400fo.+200fo. "St. George, The Dragon Slayer" (25 × 36 mm) . . . . 3·50 3·50

1277 "Adoration of the Magi"

2002. Christmas. Paintings by Erzsebet Udvardi. Multicoloured.
4646 30fo. Type **1277** 20 10
4647 38fo. "Bethelem" 20 10

1278 Gymnast

1279 Rakoczi Mansion, Tekirdag

2002. World Gymnastics Championships, Debrecen.
4648 **1278** 160fo. multicoloured . . 90 45

2002. Cultural Heritage. Multicoloured.
4649 40fo. Type **1279** 20 10
4650 110fo. Pasha Gazi Kasim Mosque, Pecs 60 30
Stamps in similar designs were issued by Turkey.

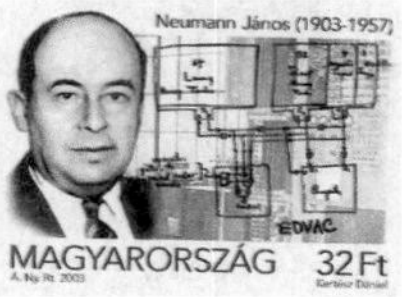

1280 John von Neuman

2003. Birth Anniversaries. Multicoloured.
4651 32fo. Type **1280** (computing pioneer) (centenary) . . . 15 10
4652 40fo. Rezso Soo (botanist) (centenary) 20 10
4653 60fo. Karoly Zipernowsky (electrical engineer) (150th) 30 15

1281 Frankenthal Coffee Set

1283 Crucifixion

1282 Retreating Soldiers

2003. Herend Porcelain. Sheet 138 × 71 mm containing T **1281** and similar vert designs. Multicoloured.
MS4654 150fo. Type **1281**; 150fo. Blue coffee pot, cup and saucer; 150fo. Tall vase; 150fo. Siang Noir shell bowl and jug . . . . . . 2·50 2·50

2003. 60th Anniv of Second Royal Hungarian Army's Defeat at the River Don.
4655 **1282** 40fo. multicoloured . . 20 10

2003. Easter.
4656 **1283** 32fo. multicoloured . . 15 10

1284 Title Page

2003. Sport (1st issue). Centenary of "Nemzeti Sport" (sports magazine).
4657 **1284** 150fo. multicoloured . . 80 40
See also Nos. 4670 and 4673.

1285 Church

1286 BMX Cyclist

2003. Greetings Stamps. Multicoloured. Self-adhesive.
4658 40fo. Type **1285** 20 10
4559 40fo. Two flowers 20 10
4660 40fo. Flower 20 10
4661 40fo. Decorated eggs . . . 20 10
4662 40fo. Candles in window and Christmas tree . . . 20 10

2003. Youth Stamps. Extreme Sports. Multicoloured.
4663 100fo. Type **1286** 50 25
4664 100fo. Snowboarding . . . 50 25
4665 100fo. Parachuting 50 25
4666 100fo. White water canoeing 50 25

1287 Rogner Hotel, Heviz

2003. Tourism. Spa Hotels. Multicoloured.
4667 110fo. Type **1287** 60 30
4668 120fo. Helia Hotel, Budapest 65 30

1288 Gerle 13 Aircraft, 1933

2003. Hungarian Aviation. Multicoloured.
4669 142fo. Type **1288** 75 35
4670 160fo. L-2 Roma, 1925 . . 85 40

1289 *Columbia*

2003. Space Shuttle *Columbia* Memorial. Sheet 92 × 72 mm.
MS4671 **1289** 500fo. multicoloured 2·75 2·75

1290 Championship Emblem

2003. Sport (2nd issue). World Division I Ice Hockey Championship, Budapest.
4672 **1290** 110fo. multicoloured . . 60 30

1291 Stadium

2003. Sport (3rd issue). Budapest Sports Arena.
4673 **1291** 120fo. multicoloured . . 65 30

1292 Hand holding Quill Pen

2003. Signing of Treaty of Accession to the European Union. Sheet 106 × 70 mm.
MS4674 **1292** 500fo. multicoloured 2·75 2·75

1293 Police Motorcyclist

2003. Police Service.
4675 **1293** 65fo. multicoloured . . 35 15

1294 Statue of Seated Woman (Danubius fountain)

1295 Kuruc Sabre, Sword and Mace

2003. Stamp Day. Multicoloured.
4676 35fo. Type **1294** 20 10
4677 40fo. Statue of seated woman (Danubius fountain) (different) . . . 20 10
MS4678 81 × 60 mm. 400fo.+100fo. "Calvin Square" (Jozsef Molnar) 2·75 2·75

2003. 300th Anniv of Rakoczi's War of Independence. Sheet 121 × 61 mm containing T **1295** and similar vert designs. Multicoloured.
MS4679 120fo. Type **1295**; 120fo. Coins; 120fo. Old National flag, pipes and drums; 120fo. Pistols and powder horn . . . . . . 2·50 2·50

1296 Steppe Polecat (*Mustela eversmanni*)

2003. Fauna. Multicoloured.
4680 30fo. Type **1296** 15 10
4681 38fo. Short-toed lark (*Calandrella brachydactyla*) 20 10
4682 110fo. European tree frog (*Hyla arborea*) 60 30
4683 160fo. European weatherfish (*Misgurnus fossilis*) . . . 85 40
MS4684 90 × 65 mm. 500 fo. Ladybird spider (*Eresus cinnaberinus*) (inscr "cinnabarinus") . . . . 2·75 2·75

1297 "Only Posters" (Istvaán Orosz)

2003. Europa. Poster Art.
4685 **1297** 65fo. red, yellow and black 35 15

1298 Bukkaljai

2003. Wine Grapes and Regions (6th series). Multicoloured.
4686 60fo. Type **1298** 35 15
4687 130fo. Balaton-felvideki . . 70 35

1299 King Ladislaus and Unknown Queen

2003. King Ladislaus' Robe (11th-century). Sheet 108 × 70 mm.
MS4688 **1299** 300fo. multicoloured 1·60 1·60

1300 Bishop Gerard and Angel (sculpture, Imre Varga)

1301 Crowds and Anniversary Emblem

2003. Art. Multicoloured.

4689		32fo. Type **1300**	15	10
4690		60fo. "Roman Bridge at Mostar" (Tivadar Csontvary Kosztka) (horiz)	35	15

2003. 50th Anniv of People's Stadium. 50th Anniv of Hungarian Football Team's Victory over England. Sheet 103 × 68 mm containing T **1301** and similar horiz design. Multicoloured.

MS4691		250fo. Type **1301**; 250fo. Goal and players	2·75	2·75

1302 European Union Emblem as Clock Face

2003. Hungary's Accession to European Union (2nd issue). Multicoloured.

4692		115fo. Type **1302**	60	30
4693		130fo. As No. 4692 but with clock hands moved forward	70	35

1303 Fruit and Vegetables

2003. Nutrition.

4694	**1303**	120fo. multicoloured	65	30

1304 Feet and Cycle Wheel

2003. European Car-free Day.

4695	**1304**	150fo. multicoloured	80	40

1305 *Dactylorhiza fuchsia sooana*

2003. Birth Centenary of Rezso Soo (botanist).

4696	**1305**	44fo. multicoloured	25	10

1306 The Illuminated Chronicle

2003. Ancient Books. Multicoloured.

4697		44fo. Type **1306**	25	10
4698		44fo. The Book of Zhou Rites	25	10

Stamps of a similar design were issued by Republic of China.

EXPRESS LETTER STAMPS

E 36

1916. Inscr "MAGYAR KIR. POSTA".

E245	E **36**	2f. olive and red	20	20

1916. Optd **KOZTARSASAG**.

E301	E **36**	2f. olive and red	20	30

1919. Inscr "MAGYAR POSTA".

E349	E **36**	2f. olive and red	15	15

IMPERIAL JOURNAL STAMPS

J 1

J 2

1868. Imperf.

J52	J **1**	1k. blue	60	30
J 3	J **2**	1k. blue	£13000	£8000
J53		2k. brown	2·50	3·00

No. J3 has the arms at the foot as in Type J **2** but the corner designs differ.

NEWSPAPER STAMPS

N 2 St. Stephen's Crown and Posthorn

N 4

N 9

1871. Posthorn turned to left. Imperf.

N8	N **2**	1k. red on white	60·00	25·00

1872. As Type N **2** but with posthorn turned to right. Imperf.

N14		1k. red	8·50	1·25

1874. Imperf.

N64	N **4**	1k. orange	60	30

1900. Imperf.

N136	N **9**	(2f.) orange	10	10
N401		(10f.) blue	10	10
N402		(20f.) purple	10	10

OFFICIAL STAMPS

O 44

1921.

O428	O **44**	10f. black and purple	20	15
O429		20f. black and brown	20	15
O430		60f. black and grey	20	15
O431		100f. black and red	20	15
O432		250f. black and blue	20	15
O433		350f. black and blue	20	15
O434		500f. black and brown	20	15
O435		1000f. black and brown	20	15

1922. Nos. O429/33 surch (No. O439 optd **KORONA** only).

O436	O **44**	15k. on 20f. black and brown	10	10
O437		25k. on 60f. black and grey	10	10
O438		150k. on 100f. black and pink	15	10
O439		(350)k. on 350f. black and blue	40	20
O440		2000k. on 250f. black and blue	40	45

1922.

O441	O **44**	5k. brown	10	10
O442		10k. brown	10	10
O443		15k. grey	10	10
O444		25k. orange	10	10
O445		50k. red and brown	10	10
O446		100k. red and bistre	10	10
O447		150k. red and green	10	10
O448		300k. red	10	10
O449		350k. red and violet	10	10
O450a		500k. red and orange	15	10
O451		600k. red and bistre	20	20
O452		1000k. red and blue	25	20
O453		3000k. red and violet	70	60
O454		5000k. red and blue	90	70

PARCEL POST STAMPS

1954. No. 979 surch.

P1398	**153**	1fo.70 on 1fo.40 green	1·10	45
P1399		2fo. on 1fo.40 green	1·50	45
P1400		3fo. on 1fo.40 green	1·10	1·10

POSTAGE DUE STAMPS

D 9

1903. Inscr "MAGYAR KIR. POSTA". Figures in centre in black.

D170	D **9**	1f. green	20	10
D171		2f. green	20	10
D172		5f. green	20	10
D173		6f. green	40	30
D174		10f. green	50	30
D175		12f. green	25	10
D176		20f. green	20	10
D177		50f. green	25	10
D 91		100f. green	75	1·00

1915. Surch **20**.

D188	D **9**	20 on 100f. black & grn	45	90

1915. As Type D **9**, but figures in red.

D190	D **9**	1f. green	10	10
D191		2f. green	10	10
D192		5f. green	35	10
D193		6f. green	10	10
D194		10f. green	10	10
D195		12f. green	10	10
D196		15f. green	10	10
D197		20f. green	10	10
D198		30f. green	10	10
D349		40f. green	15	15
D350		50f. green	15	15
D351		120f. green	15	15
D352		200f. green	15	15
D430		2k. green	40	90
D431		5k. green	20	20
D432		50k. green	20	20

1919. Overprinted **KOZTARSASAG**.

D325	D **9**	2f. red and green	10	10
D326		3f. red and green	10	10
D327		10f. red and green	10	10
D328		20f. red and green	10	10
D329		40f. red and green	10	10
D324		50f. black and green	1·25	1·25
D330		50f. red and green	10	10

1919. As Type D **9** but inscr "MAGYAR POSTA" and optd with T **37** and **MAGYAR TANACS KOZTARSASAG**. Figures in black.

D369	D **9**	2f. green	50	50
D370		3f. green	50	50
D371		10f. green	3·00	5·25
D372		20f. green	50	50
D373		40f. green	50	50
D374		50f. green	50	50

1919. As Type D **9**, but inscr "MAGYAR POSTA". Figures in Black.

D375	D **9**	2f. green	10	10
D376		3f. green	10	10
D377		20f. green	10	15
D378		40f. green	10	15
D379		50f. green	10	15

1921. Surch **PORTO** and value. Inscr "MAGYAR KIR POSTA".

D428	**18**	100f. on 15f. purple	10	10
D429		500f. on 15f. purple	10	10
D433		2½k. on 10f. purple	15	15
D434		3k. on 15f. purple	15	15
D437		6k. on 1½k. purple	10	10
D435		9k. on 40f. green	15	15
D438		10k. on 2½k. green	10	10
D436		12k. on 60f. green	15	15
D439		15k. on 1½k. purple	10	10
D440		20k. on 2½k. green	10	10
D441		25k. on 1½k. purple	10	10
D442		30k. on 1½k. purple	10	10
D443		40k. on 2½k. green	10	10
D444		50k. on 1½k. purple	10	10
D445		100k. on 4½k. purple	10	10
D446		200k. on 4½k. purple	10	10
D447		300k. on 4½k. purple	10	10
D448		500k. on 2k. blue	10	10
D449		500k. on 3k. brown	10	10
D450		1000k. on 2k. blue	10	10
D451		1000k. on 3k. brown	10	10
D452		2000k. on 2k. blue	40	10
D453		2000k. on 3k. brown	90	30
D454		5000k. on 5k. brown	80	60

D 61

D 84

D 115

1926.

D479	D **61**	1f. red	15	10
D480		2f. red	15	10
D481		3f. red	65	60
D482		4f. red	10	10
D483		5f. red	1·40	90
D509		8f. red	20	10
D510		10f. red	10	10
D486		16f. red	20	10
D512		20f. red	25	10
D487		32f. red	35	35
D513		40f. red	45	10
D489		50f. red	55	25
D490		80f. red	1·10	70

1927. Nos. 434/36b surch **PORTO** and value.

D491	**49**	1f. on 500k. light green and green	20	10
D492		2f. on 1000k. brown and bistre	20	10
D493		3f. on 2000k. blue and deep blue	25	15
D494		5f. on 5000k. mauve and purple	65	90
D495		10f. on 10000k. purple and red	55	60

1931. Surch.

D529	D **61**	4f. on 5 red	20	25
D534		10f. on 16f. red	70	1·10
D531		10f. on 80f. red	35	25
D532		12f. on 50f. red	60	75
D533		20f. on 32f. red	60	70

1934.

D569	D **84**	2f. blue	10	10
D570		4f. blue	10	10
D571		6f. blue	10	10
D572		8f. blue	10	10
D573		10f. blue	10	10
D574		12f. blue	10	10
D575		16f. blue	10	10
D576		20f. blue	10	10
D577		40f. blue	25	10
D578		80f. blue	45	25

1941.

D684	D **115**	2f. brown	10	10
D685		3f. brown	10	10
D686		4f. brown	10	10
D687		6f. brown	10	10
D688		8f. brown	10	10
D689		10f. brown	10	10
D690		12f. brown	10	10
D691		16f. brown	10	10
D692		18f. brown	10	10
D693		20f. brown	10	10
D694		24f. brown	10	10
D695		30f. brown	10	10
D696		36f. brown	10	10
D697		40f. brown	10	10
D698		50f. brown	10	10
D699		60f. brown	10	10

1945. Surch **1945** and value. Blue surface-tinted paper.

D825	D **115**	10f. on 2f. brown	10	10
D826		10f. on 3f. brown	10	10
D827		20f. on 4f. brown	10	10
D828		20f. on 6f. brown	3·00	6·00
D829		20f. on 8f. brown	10	10
D830		40f. on 12f. brown	10	10
D831		40f. on 16f. brown	10	10
D832		40f. on 18f. brown	10	10
D833		60f. on 24f. brown	10	10
D834		80f. on 30f. brown	10	10
D835		90f. on 36f. brown	10	10
D836		1p. on 10f. brown	10	10
D837		1p. on 40f. brown	10	10
D838		2p. on 20f. brown	10	10
D839		2p. on 50f. brown	10	10
D840		2p. on 60f. brown	10	10
D841		10p. on 3f. brown	10	10
D842		12p. on 8f. brown	10	10
D843		20p. on 24f. brown	10	10

D 154 Numeral

D 201

D 215

1946.

D984	D **154**	4f. red and brown	10	10
D985		10f. red and brown	10	10
D986		20f. red and brown	40	40
D987		30f. red and brown	10	10
D988		40f. red and brown	10	10
D989		50f. red and brown	75	15
D990		60f. red and brown	60	10
D991		1fo.20 red and brown	90	10
D992		2fo. red and brown	1·90	25

1950.

D1114	D **154**	4fi. purple	10	10
D1115		10fi. purple	10	10
D1116		20fi. purple	10	10
D1117		30fi. purple	10	10
D1118		40fi. purple	45	10
D1119		50fi. purple	75	10
D1120		60fi. purple	60	10
D1121		1fo.20 purple	85	10
D1122		2fo. purple	1·90	15

1951. Fiscal stamps surch with Arms. **MAGYAR POSTA PORTO** and value.

D1157	D **201**	8fi. brown	20	20
D1158		10fi. brown	20	20
D1159		12fi. brown	35	35

1951.

D1210	D **215**	4fi. brown	10	10
D1211		6fi. brown	10	10
D1212		8fi. brown	10	10
D1213		10fi. brown	10	10
D1214		14fi. brown	10	10
D1215		20fi. brown	10	10
D1216		30fi. brown	10	10
D1217		40fi. brown	10	10
D1218		50fi. brown	25	10
D1219		60fi. brown	30	10

D1220		1fo.20 brown	40	10
D1221		2fo. brown	60	35

D 240

D 282

1953. 50th Anniv of 1st Hungarian Postage Due Stamps.

D1305	**D 240**	4fl. black and green	10	10
D1306		6fi. black and green	10	10
D1307		8fi. black and green	10	10
D1308		10fi. black and green	10	10
D1309		12fi. black and green	10	10
D1310		14fi. black and green	10	10
D1311		16fi. black and green	10	10
D1312		20fi. black and green	10	10
D1313		24fi. black and green	10	10
D1314		30fi. black and green	10	10
D1315		36fi. black and green	10	10
D1316		40fi. black and green	10	10
D1317		50fi. black and green	10	10
D1318		60fi. black and green	10	10
D1319		70fi. black and green	10	10
D1320		80fi. black and green	10	10
D1321		1fo.20 black & green	25	10
D1322		2fo. black and green	30	10

1958. Forint values are larger (31 × 22 mm).

D1498	**D 282**	4fi. black and red	10	10
D1499		6fi. black and red	10	10
D1500		8fi. black and red	10	10
D1501		10fi. black and red	10	10
D1502		12fi. black and red	10	10
D1503		14fi. black and red	10	10
D1504		16fi. black and red	10	10
D1505		20fi. black and red	10	10
D1506		24fi. black and red	10	10
D1507		30fi. black and red	10	10
D1508		36fi. black and red	10	10
D1509		40fi. black and red	10	10
D1510		50fi. black and red	10	10
D1511		60fi. black and red	10	10
D1512		70fi. black and red	20	10
D1513		80fi. black and red	20	10
D1514	–	1fo. brown	20	10
D1515	–	1fo.20 brown	30	10
D1516	–	2fo. brown	50	10
D1517	–	4fo. brown	90	10

D **587** Money-order Cancelling Machine

D **944** Foot Messenger

1973. Postal Operations.

D2847	**D 587**	20fi. brown and red	10	10
D2848	–	40fi. blue and red	10	10
D2849	–	80fi. violet and red	15	10
D2850	–	1fo. green and red	15	10
D2851	–	1fo.20 green and red	20	10
D2852	–	2fo. violet and red	70	10
D2853	–	3fo. blue and red	40	10
D2854	–	4fo. brown and red	45	10
D2855	–	8fo. purple and red	90	10
D2856	–	10fo. green and red	1·25	10

DESIGNS—As Type D **587**: 40fi. Parcel scales, self-service post office; 80fi. Automatic parcels-registration machine; 1fo. Data-recording machine; 28 × 22 mm: 1fo. 20, Ilyushin Il-18 mail plane and van; 2fo. Diesel mail train; 3fo. Postman on motor cycle; 4fo. Postman at mailboxes; 8fo. Toshiba automatic sorting machine; 10f. Postman on motor cycle (different).

1987. Postal History. Multicoloured.

D3810		1fo. Type D **944**	10	10
D3811		4fo. Post rider	25	10
D3812		6fo. Horse-drawn mail coach	40	10
D3813		8fo. Railway mail carriage	55	10
D3814		10fo. Mail van	70	10
D3815		20fo. Mail plane	1·50	20

SAVINGS BANK STAMP

B 17

1916.

B199	**B 17**	10f. purple	10	10

SZEGED

The following issues were made by the Hungarian National Government led by Admiral Horthy, which was set up in Szeged in 1919, then under French occupation, and which later replaced the Communist regime established by Bela Kun.

100 filler = 1 korona.

1919. Stamps of Hungary optd **MAGYAR NEMZETI KORMANY Szeged, 1919.** or surch.

(a) War Charity stamps of 1916.

1	**20**	10f. (+2f.) red	25	25
2	–	15f. (+2f.) violet	45	45
3	**22**	40f. (+2f.) lake	2·10	2·10

(b) Harvesters and Parliament Types.

4	**18**	2f. brown	30	30
5		3f. red	30	30
6		5f. green	30	30
7		6f. blue	6·50	6·50
8		15f. violet	30	30
9		20f. brown (No. 307)	16·00	16·00
10		25f. blue (No. 309)	30	30
11	**19**	50f. purple	3·25	3·25
12		75f. blue	30	30
13		80f. green	3·25	3·25
14		1k. lake	30	30
15		2k. brown	30	30
16		3k. grey and violet	35	35
17		5k. brown	20·00	20·00
18		10k. lilac and brown	20·00	20·00

(c) Nos. 5 and 14 further surch.

19	**18**	45 on 3f. red	35	35
20	**19**	10 on 1k. lake	2·00	2·00

(d) Karl and Zita stamps.

21	**27**	10f. red	30	30
22		20f. brown	30	30
23		25f. blue	10·00	10·00
24	**28**	40f. olive	1·00	1·00

The following (Nos. 25/39) are also optd **KOZTARSASAG**. (e) War Charity stamp.

25	**22**	40f. (+2f.) lake	3·25	3·25

(f) Harvesters and Parliament Types.

26	**18**	3f. red	6·50	6·50
27		4f. slate	45	45
28		5f. green	4·00	4·00
29		6f. blue	2·00	2·00
30		10f. red	4·00	4·00
31		20f. brown	20·00	20·00
32		20 (f) on 2f. bistre	25	25
33		40f. olive	25	25
34	**19**	3k. grey and violet	16·00	16·00

(g) Karl and Zita stamps.

35	**27**	10f. red	5·00	5·00
36		15f. violet	65	65
37		20f. brown	18·00	18·00
38		25f. blue	4·75	4·75
39	**28**	50f. purple	25	25

EXPRESS LETTER STAMPS

1919. No. E245 optd as above.

E41	**E 18**	2f. olive and red	2·00	2·00

NEWSPAPER STAMP

1919. No. N136 optd **MAGYAR NEMZETI KORMANY Szeged, 1919.**

N40	**N 9**	(2f.) orange	25	25

POSTAGE DUE STAMPS

Nos. D191, etc. (a) Optd as above.

D42	**D 9**	2f. red and green	65	65
D43		6f. red and green	1·40	1·40
D44		10f. red and green	90	90
D45		12f. red and green	90	90
D46		20f. red and green	65	65
D47		30f. red and green	90	90

(b) No. E41 surch **PORTO** and new value.

D48	**E 18**	50f. on 2f. olive and red	65	65
D49		100f. on 2f. olive & red	1·40	1·40

HYDERABAD Pt. 1

A state in India. Now uses Indian stamps.

12 pies = 1 anna; 16 annas = 1 rupee.

1

1869.

1	**1**	1a. green	15·00	6·50

2

3

1870.

2	**2**	½a. brown	4·00	4·00
3		2a. green	45·00	40·00

1871.

13	**3**	½a. brown	1·75	10
13d		½a. red	1·75	10
14		1a. purple	5·00	5·00
14b		1a. brown	90	15
14c		1a. black	1·50	10
15		2a. green	2·75	15
16b		3a. brown	1·40	85
17b		4a. grey	3·75	2·00
17c		4a. green	3·75	1·25
18		8a. brown	1·75	2·75
19		12a. blue	3·00	5·50
19a		12a. green	3·25	3·50

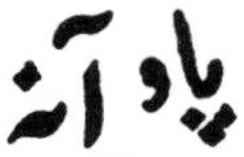
(4)

1898. Surch with T **4**.

20	**3**	¼a. on ½a. brown	50	85

5

6

1900.

21	**5**	¼a. blue	4·75	3·25

1905.

22	**6**	¼a. blue	1·25	45
32 d		¼a. grey	50	10
33		¼a. purple	75	10
23 b		½a. red	2·50	25
34		½a. green	60	10
26		1a. red	1·75	10
27cb		2a. lilac	1·25	10
28 b		3a. orange	1·10	60
29 c		4a. green	1·00	30
30 c		8a. purple	1·10	50
31 c		12a. green	4·00	2·25

8 Symbol

9

1915.

35	**8**	½a. green	70	10
58		½a. red	1·75	1·75
36		1a. red	1·25	10
37	**9**	1r. yellow	9·00	11·00

(10)

1930. Surch as T **10**.

38	**6**	4p. on ¼a. grey	65·00	18·00
39		4p. on ¼a. purple	25	10
40	**8**	8p. on ½a. green	25	10

12 Symbols

13 The Char Minar

1931.

60	**12**	2p. brown	1·00	2·00
41		4p. black	30	10
59		6p. red	7·00	6·00
42		8p. green	50	10
43	**13**	1a. brown	50	10
44	–	2a. violet	2·50	10
45	–	4a. blue	1·40	60
46	–	8a. orange	4·75	3·25
47	–	12a. red	4·75	10·00
48	–	1r. yellow	4·75	3·25

DESIGNS—HORIZ (32½ × 21 mm): 2a. High Court of Justice; 4a. Osman Sagar Reservoir; 12a. Bidar College. VERT: 8a. Entrance to Ajanta Caves; 1r. Victory Tower, Daulatabad.

In No. 59 "POSTAGE" is at foot.

15 Unani General Hospital

1937. Inscr "H.E.H. THE NIZAM'S SILVER JUBILEE".

49	**15**	4p. slate and violet	60	1·25
50	–	8p. slate and brown	90	1·25
51	–	1a. slate and yellow	1·00	1·00
52	–	2a. slate and green	1·25	4·00

DESIGNS: 8p. Osmania General Hospital; 1a. Osmania University; 2a. Osmania Jubilee Hall.

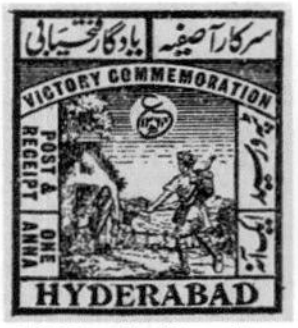
16 Family Reunion

17 Town Hall

1945. Victory Commemoration.

53	**16**	1a. blue	10	10

1947. Reformed Legislature.

54	**17**	1a. black	1·25	1·50

18 Power House, Hyderabad

1947. Inscr as in T **18**.

55	**18**	1a.4p. green	1·00	1·75
56	–	3a. blue	1·50	3·00
57	–	6a. brown	3·50	13·00

DESIGNS—HORIZ: 3a. Kaktyai Arch, Warangal Fort; 6a. Golkunda Fort.

OFFICIAL STAMPS

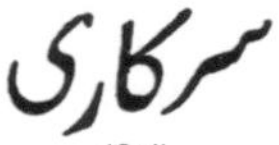
(O 1)

1873. Optd with Type O **1**.

O2a	**2**	½a. brown	—	£450
O1	**1**	1a. green	70·00	20·00
O3a	**2**	2a. olive	—	£150

1873. Optd with Type O **1**.

O9a	**3**	½a. brown	7·50	2·75
O11		1a. brown	85·00	60·00
O12a		1a. drab	1·75	1·75
O19		1a. black	70·00	20
O13a		2a. green	3·50	4·50
O20d		3a. brown	4·00	1·50
O15a		4a. grey	14·00	14·00
O20e		4a. green	£320	4·00
O16b		8a. brown	38·00	30·00
O17a		12a. blue	42·00	65·00
O20g		12a. green	—	70·00

1909. Optd as Type O **1**, or similar smaller opt.

O37e	**6**	¼a. grey	1·00	35
O38		¼a. lilac	2·25	10
O21a		½a. red	£110	15
O39d		½a. green	2·00	10
O40	**8**	½a. green	2·00	10
O54		½a. red	9·00	6·00
O31	**6**	1a. red	1·00	15
O41e	**8**	1a. red	1·25	10
O32b	**6**	2a. lilac	1·25	40
O33b		3a. orange	11·00	2·25
O34d		4a. green	2·50	15
O35		8a. purple	4·00	20
O36		12a. green	15·00	1·00

1930. Official stamps surch as T **10**.

O42	**6**	4p. on ¼a. grey	£275	17·00
O43		4p. on ¼a. lilac	1·00	10
O45		8p. on ½a. green	35·00	45·00
O44	**8**	8p. on ½a. green	75	10

1934. Optd as Type O **1** but smaller.

O55	**12**	2p. brown	7·00	8·50
O46		4p. black	1·50	10
O56		6p. red	10·00	20·00
O47		8p. green	70	10
O48	**13**	1a. brown	1·00	10
O49	–	2a. violet (No. 44)	5·00	10
O50	–	4a. blue (No. 45)	2·00	20
O51	–	8a. orange (No. 46)	9·50	50
O52	–	12a. red (No. 47)	7·00	1·50
O53	–	1r. yellow (No. 48)	16·00	2·00

ICELAND Pt. 11

An island lying S.E. of Greenland. An independent state formerly under the Danish sovereign, now a republic.

1873. 96 skilling = 1 riksdaler.
1876. 100 aurar (singular: eyrir) = 1 krona.

1

þrír

(6)

1873.

1	1	2s. blue	£600	£1300
5		3s. grey	£225	£950
2		4s. red	£110	£550
3		8s. brown	£225	£800
7		16s. yellow	75·00	£425

1876.

42	1	3a. yellow	3·25	11·50
27		4a. grey and red	16·00	11·00
13		5a. blue	£350	£700
28		5a. green	2·75	1·80
29a		6a. grey	16·00	9·50
30		10a. red	9·00	1·70
31		16a. brown	65·00	55·00
18a		20a. mauve	32·00	£300
32a		20a. blue	36·00	18·00
33		25a. blue and brown	19·00	15·00
19		40a. green	85·00	£100
23b		40a. mauve	26·00	25·00
24		50a. red and blue	65·00	50·00
25		100a. purple and brown	55·00	60·00

1897. Surch as T **6** with figure **3** under word.

38	1	3 on 5a. green	£400	£325

1897. Surch as T **6**.

40	1	3 on 5a. green	£400	£325

10 King Christian IX

12 Kings Christian IX and Frederik VIII

13 Jon Sigurdsson

1902.

43	10	3a. orange	6·50	1·60
44		4a. red and grey	4·00	80
45		5a. green	20·00	50
46		6a. brown	18·00	4·25
47		10a. red	5·00	45
48		16a. brown	4·75	4·50
49		20a. blue	1·80	1·70
50		25a. green and brown	2·75	3·00
51		40a. mauve	3·75	2·75
52		50a. black and grey	5·50	14·50
53		1k. brown and blue	6·00	7·25
54		2k. blue and brown	23·00	44·00
55		5k. grey and brown	£150	£130

1902. Optd **I GILDI '02–'03**.

67	1	3a. yellow	85	1·50
68		4a. grey and red	29·00	34·00
69		5a. green	65	3·50
71		6a. grey	75	4·00
73		10a. red	90	4·75
74		16a. brown	23·00	26·00
75		20a. blue	60	5·75
77		25a. blue and brown	70	8·00
79		40a. mauve	60	26·00
80		50a. red and blue	2·75	55·00
65		100a. purple and brown	45·00	45·00

1907.

81	12	1e. red and green	1·50	55
82		3a. brown	3·50	70
83		4a. red and grey	1·50	80
84		5a. green	65·00	65
85		6a. grey	35·00	1·90
114		10a. red	2·50	1·30
87		15a. green and red	5·25	70
88		16a. brown	7·50	18·00
89		20a. blue	8·00	2·20
90		25a. green and brown	6·25	5·75
91		40a. red	5·75	7·75
92		50a. red and grey	7·00	6·50
93		1k. brown and blue	19·00	36·00
94		2k. green and brown	26·00	44·00
95		5k. blue and brown	£170	£225

1911. Birth Centenary of Jon Sigurdsson (historian and Althing member).

96	13	1e. green	2·00	80
97		3a. brown	3·25	6·25
98		4a. blue	1·10	95
99		6a. grey	8·75	12·00
100		15a. violet	9·25	1·00
101		25a. orange	20·00	22·00

1912. As T **13**, but portrait of King Frederik VIII and "JON SIGURDSSON" omitted.

102		5a. green	25·00	6·00
103		10a. red	20·00	6·50
104		20a. blue	35·00	8·50
105		50a. red	6·50	18·00
106		1k. yellow	26·00	36·00
107		2k. red	15·00	33·00
108		5k. brown	£120	£140

15 King Christian X

22 Landing Mails at Vik

1920.

116	15	1e. red and green	55	55
117		3a. brown	3·50	6·50
184		4a. red and grey	1·60	1·20
119		5a. green	2·00	1·10
185		6a. grey	2·10	2·50
186		7a. green	50	1·00
121		8a. brown	6·00	1·20
122		10a. red	2·40	4·75
133		10a. green	3·50	75
187		10a. brown	£100	50
123		15a. violet	31·00	65
124		20a. blue	2·50	7·50
134		20a. brown	65·00	70
125		25a. green and brown	15·00	90
135		25a. red	14·00	22·00
189		30a. green and red	28·00	3·00
127		40a. red	48·00	1·90
136		40a. blue	60·00	7·25
128		50a. red and grey	£170	5·75
191		1k. brown and blue	40·00	3·25
130		2k. green and brown	£250	17·00
131		5k. blue and brown	60·00	8·25
193		10k. black and green	£300	£140

1921. Various types surch.

137	10	5a. on 16a. brown	3·00	17·00
138	12	5a. on 16a. brown	1·60	4·25
139	15	10a. on 5a. green	8·50	2·50
140	10	20a. on 25a. green & brn	5·00	4·00
141	12	20a. on 25a. green & brn	4·50	4·25
142	10	20a. on 40a. mauve	7·50	12·00
143	12	20a. on 40a. red	7·75	10·50
144	10	30a. on 50a. grey	35·00	14·50
145		50a. on 5k. grey & brown	46·00	28·00
146	15	1k. on 40a. blue	£120	30·00
147	13	2k. on 25a. orange	£100	80·00
148	–	10k. on 50a. red (No. 105)	£250	£275
149	–	10k. on 1k. yell (No. 106)	£275	£400
150	10	10k. on 2k. black & brn	50·00	17·00
150a	12	10k. on 5k. black & brn	£325	£425

1925.

151	22	7a. green	38·00	3·75
152	–	10a. brown and blue	42·00	45
153	–	20a. red	41·00	45
154	–	35a. blue	65·00	4·00
155	22	50a. brown and green	60·00	85

DESIGNS: 10a., 35a. Reykjavik and Esjaberg (mountain); 20a. National Museum, Reykjavik.

1928. Air. Optd with airplane.

156	15	10a. red	90	7·25
157	12	50a. purple and grey	41·00	85·00

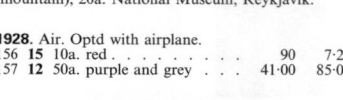

24 Discovery of Iceland

25 Gyrfalcon

1930. Parliament Millenary Celebration.

158	–	3a. violet and lilac (postage)	1·90	4·50
159	24	5a. blue and grey	2·00	4·50
160	–	7a. green and dp green	2·00	4·75
161	–	10a. purple and mauve	6·50	7·50
162	–	15a. dp blue & blue	1·80	4·75
163	–	20a. red and pink	31·00	42·00
164	–	25a. brown and lt brown	5·75	7·25
165	–	30a. green and grey	4·75	6·50
166	–	35a. blue & ultramarine	6·00	8·00
167	–	40a. red, blue and grey	4·75	6·00
168	–	50a. dp brown and brown	60·00	70·00
169	–	1k. green and grey	48·00	65·00
170	–	2k. blue and green	65·00	80·00
171	–	5k. orange and yellow	35·00	60·00
172	–	10k. lake and red	34·00	60·00
173	25	10a. blue & dp blue (air)	17·00	30·00

DESIGNS—HORIZ: 3a. Parliament House, Reykjavik; 7a. Encampment at Thingvellir; 10a. Arrival of Ingolf Arnarsson; 15a. Naming the Island; 20a. Chieftains riding to the "Althing" (Parliament); 25a. Discovery of Arnarsson's pillar; 30a. View of Thingvellir; 35a. Queen Aud; 40a. National flag; 50a. Proclamation at Thingvellir; 1k. Map of Iceland; 2k. Winter-bound farmstead; 5k. Woman spinning; 10k. Viking sacrifice to Thor.

26 Snaefellsjokull

1930. Air. Parliamentary Millenary Celebration.

174	26	15a. blue and brown	23·00	30·00
175	–	20a. blue and brown	22·00	28·00
176	–	35a. brown and green	46·00	50·00
177	–	50a. blue and green	46·00	50·00
178	–	1k. red and green	46·00	50·00

DESIGNS: 20a. Old Icelandic fishing boat; 35a. Icelandic pony; 50a. The Gullfoss Falls; 1k. Statue of Arnarsson, Reykjavik.

1931. Air. Optd **Zeppelin 1931**.

179	15	30a. green and red	28·00	85·00
180		1k. brown and blue	8·75	85·00
181		2k. green and brown	50·00	85·00

29 Gullfoss Falls

30 Shipwreck and Breeches-buoy

1931.

195	29	5a. grey	10·50	40
196		20a. red	9·00	20
197		35a. blue	16·00	5·50
198		60a. mauve	9·75	60
199		65a. brown	1·60	60
200		75a. blue	80·00	20·00

1933. Philanthropic Associations.

201	30	10a.+10a. brown	1·20	3·25
202	–	20a.+20a. red	1·20	3·25
203	30	35a.+25a. blue	1·20	3·25
204	–	50a.+25a. green	1·20	3·25

DESIGNS: 20a. Children gathering flowers; 50a. Aged fisherman and rowing boat.

1933. Air. Balbo Transatlantic Mass Formation Flight. Optd **Hopflug Itala 1933**.

205	15	1k. brown and blue	£180	£325
206		5k. blue and brown	£425	£1100
207		10k. black and green	£1100	£2200

32 Avro 504K Biplane over Thingvellir

1934. Air.

208	32	10a. blue	2·00	1·40
209		20a. green	3·75	4·25
210a	–	25a. violet	17·00	12·00
211	–	50a. purple	3·25	3·75
212	–	1k. brown	18·00	18·00
213	–	2k. red	8·00	7·50

DESIGNS: 25a., 50a. Monoplane and Aurora Borealis; 1k., 2k. Monoplane over map of Iceland.

33 Dynjandi Falls

35 Matthias Jochumsson

36 King Christian X

1935.

214	33	10a. blue	23·00	20
215	–	1k. green	36·00	20

DESIGN—HORIZ: 1k. Mt. Hekla.

1935. Birth Centenary of M. Jochumsson (poet).

216	35	3a. green	60	2·10
217		5a. grey	15·00	70
218		7a. green	24·00	1·10
219		35a. blue	50	80

1937. Silver Jubilee of King Christian X.

220	36	10a. green	1·30	11·50
221		30a. brown	1·30	4·75
222		40a. red	1·30	4·75

MS223 128½ × 112 mm. **36** 15a. violet; 25a. red; 50a. blue (sold at 2k.) 38·00 £200

37 The Great Geyser

37b Leif Eiriksson's Statue, Reykjavik

1938.

226	37	15a. purple	3·75	5·50
227		20a. red	21·00	25
228		35a. blue	60	45
229	–	40a. brown	10·00	15·00
230	–	45a. blue	70	40
231	–	50a. green	20·00	50
232a	–	60a. blue	3·00	5·00
233	–	1k. blue	2·75	25

The frames of the 40a. to 1k. differ from Type **37**.

1938. Leif Eiriksson's Day. Sheet 140 × 100 mm.
MS233b 30a. red (T **37b**), 40a. violet; 60a. green (sold at 2k.) 3·25 21·00
DESIGNS: 40a. Figure from statue; 60a. Part of globe showing Iceland and Vinland (larger).

38 Reykjavik University

1938. 20th Anniv of Independence.

234	38	25a. green	4·50	9·25
235		30a. brown	4·50	8·25
236		40a. purple	4·50	8·25

1939. Surch **5**.

237	35	5 on 35a. blue	45	70

40 Trylon and Perisphere

1939. New York World's Fair.

238	40	20a. red	3·25	4·25
239	–	35a. blue	3·25	6·00
240	–	45a. green	4·00	6·75
241	–	2k. black	45·00	£110

DESIGNS: 35a. Viking longship and route to America; 45a., 2k. Statue of Thorfinn Karlsefni, Reykjavik.

41 Atlantic Cod

42 Icelandic Flag

1939.

242a	41	1e. blue	45	2·75
243a	–	3a. violet	35	55
244a	41	5a. brown	45	30
245	–	7a. green	3·75	5·25
246	42	10a. red and blue	2·00	65
247a	–	10a. green	43·00	35
248	–	10a. black	25	15
249	–	12a. green	35	50
250a	41	25a. red	30·00	30
251		25a. brown	35	30
252	–	35a. red	40	25
253	41	50a. green	55	20

DESIGN: 3, 7, 10a. (Nos. 247a/8), 12, 35a. Atlantic herring.

43 Statue of Thorfinn Karlsefni

46 Statue of Snorri Sturluson (O. Vigeland)

1939.

254	43	2k. grey	2·50	25
255		5k. brown	20·00	30
256		10k. brown	9·00	1·30

1940. New York World's Fair. Optd **1940**.

257	40	20a. red	9·50	16·00
258	–	35a. blue (No. 239)	10·00	16·00
259	–	45a. green (No. 240)	9·50	16·00
260	–	2k. black (No. 241)	85·00	£225

1941. Surch **25**.

261	35	25a. on 3a. olive	50	75

1941. 700th Death Anniv of Snorri Sturluson (historian).

262	46	25a. red	75	1·30
263		50a. blue	1·80	3·50
264		1k. olive	1·80	3·25

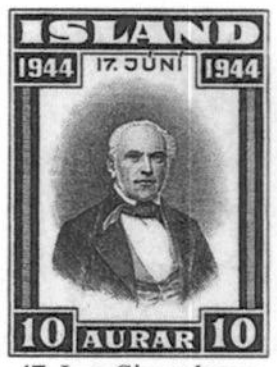

47 Jon Sigurdsson (historian and Althing member)

48 Grumman G-21 Goose Amphibian over Thingvellir

1944. Proclamation of Republic.
265 **47** 10a. grey . . . 35 60
266 25a. brown . . . 35 60
267 50a. green . . . 35 60
268 1k. black . . . 60 60
269 5k. brown . . . 3·00 9·50
270 10k. brown . . . 43·00 65·00

1947. Air.
271 **48** 15a. orange . . . 65 85
272 – 30a. black . . . 65 1·00
273 – 75a. red . . . 50 75
274 – 1k. blue . . . 50 75
275 – 1k.80 blue . . . 11·00 10·50
276 – 2k. brown . . . 1·30 1·50
277 – 2k.50 green . . . 22·00 75
278 – 3k. green . . . 1·20 1·50
279 – 3k.30 blue . . . 9·25 £425
DESIGNS—HORIZ: 30a. Consolidated PBY-5 Catalina flying boat over Isafjordur; 75a. Douglas DC-3 over Eyjafjord; 1k.80, Douglas DC-3 over Snaefellsjokull; 2k.50, Consolidated PBY-5 Catalina over Eiriksjokull; 3k. Douglas DC-4 over Reykjavik; 3k.30, Douglas DC-4 over Oraefajokull. VERT: 1k. Grumman G-21 Goose over Sethisfjordur, Strandatindur; 2k. Consolidated PBY-5 Catalina over Hvalfjordur, Thyrill.

For stamps as Type **48** but without airplane, see Nos. 346/8.

50 Mt. Hekla in Eruption

53 Hospital and Child

1948. Inscr "HEKLA 1947".
280 **50** 12a. purple . . . 20 15
281 – 25a. green . . . 1·40 15
282 – 35a. red . . . 45 15
283 **50** 50a. brown . . . 1·80 15
284 – 60a. blue . . . 5·50 2·50
285 – 1k. brown . . . 13·50 15
286 – 10k. violet . . . 43·00 90
DESIGNS—VERT: 35a., 60a. Mt. Hekla in Eruption (different view). HORIZ: 25a., 1k., 10k. Mt. Hekla.

1949. Red Cross Fund.
287 **53** 10a.+10a. green . . . 35 55
288 – 35a.+15a. red . . . 35 65
289 – 50a.+25a. brown . . . 40 65
290 – 60a.+25a. blue . . . 50 70
291 – 75a.+25a. blue . . . 1·10 95
DESIGNS: 35a. Nurse and patient; 50a. Nurse arranging patient's bed; 60a. Aged couple; 75a. Freighter and ship's lifeboat.

54 Pony Pack-train

1949. 75th Anniv of U.P.U.
292 **54** 25a. green . . . 25 45
293 – 35a. red . . . 25 50
294 – 60a. blue . . . 25 90
295 – 2k. orange . . . 1·00 95
DESIGNS: 35a. Reykjavik; 60a. Map of Iceland; 2k. Almannagja Gorge.

55 "Ingolfur Arnarson" (trawler)

56 Bishop Jon Arason

1950.
296 – 5a. brown . . . 15 15
297 **55** 10a. grey . . . 30 30
298 – 20a. brown . . . 30 25
299 **55** 25a. red . . . 30 20
300 – 60a. green . . . 10·00 14·50
301 – 75a. orange . . . 45 25
302 – 90a. red . . . 45 30
303 – 1k. brown . . . 4·00 25
304 **55** 1k.25 purple . . . 16·00 25
305 1k.50 blue . . . 12·00 30
306 – 2k. violet . . . 14·50 30
307 – 5k. green . . . 25·00 55
308 – 25k. black . . . £120 13·00
DESIGNS—As T **55**: 5, 90a., 2k. Vestmannaeyjar harbour; 20, 75a., 1k. Tractor; 60a., 5k. Flock of sheep; 25k. Parliament Building, Reykjavik (29½ × 23½ mm).

1950. 400th Death Anniv of Bishop Arason.
309 **56** 1k.80 red . . . 2·30 2·50
310 3k.30 green . . . 1·30 2·40

57 Postman, 1776

58 President Bjornsson

1951. 175th Anniv of Icelandic Postal Service.
311 **57** 2k. blue . . . 1·90 1·70
312 – 3k. purple . . . 1·90 2·40
DESIGN: 3k. as 2k. but Saab 90 Scandia aeroplane replaces man.

1952. Death of S. Bjornsson (first President of Iceland).
313 **58** 1k.25 blue . . . 2·00 20
314 2k.20 green . . . 50 3·00
315 5k. blue . . . 6·25 1·00
316 10k. brown . . . 30·00 21·00

1953. Netherlands Flood Relief Fund. Surch **Hollandshjalp 1953 + 25**.
317 – 75a.+25a. orange (No. 301) 65 2·40
318 **55** 1k.25+25a. purple . . . 1·40 3·50

60 "Reykjabok" (Saga of Burnt Njal)

62 Hannes Hafstein

1953.
319 **60** 10a. black . . . 15 15
320 – 70a. green . . . 20 20
321 – 1k. red . . . 35 15
322 – 1k.75 blue . . . 23·00 1·10
323 – 10k. brown . . . 11·00 70
DESIGNS: 70a. Hand writing on manuscript; 1k. "Stjorn" (15th century manuscript); 1k.75, Books and candle; 10k. Page from "Skardsbok" (14th century law manuscript).

1954. No. 282 surch **5 AURAR** and bars.
324 5a. on 35a. red . . . 20 15

1954. 50th Anniv of Appointment of Hannes Hafstein as First Native Minister of Iceland. Portraits of Hafstein.
325 **62** 1k.25 blue . . . 2·20 35
326 – 2k.45 green . . . 19·00 27·00
327 – 5k. red . . . 13·50 3·25

63 Icelandic Wrestling

64 St. Thorlacas

1955. Icelandic National Sports.
328 **63** 75a. brown . . . 20 25
329 – 1k.25 blue (Diving) . . . 30 25
330 **63** 1k.50 red . . . 60 25
331 – 1k.75 blue (Diving) . . . 30 25

1956. 9th Centenary of Consecration of First Icelandic Bishop and Skalholt Rebuilding Fund. Inscr as in T **64**.
332 **64** 75a.+25a. red . . . 15 30
333 – 1k.25+75a. brown . . . 15 35
334 – 1k.75+1k.25 black . . . 90 1·10
DESIGNS—HORIZ: 1k.25, Skalholt Cathedral, 1772. VERT: 1k.75, J. P. Vidalin, Bishop of Skalholt, 1698–1720.

65 Skogafoss

67 Map of Iceland

1956. Power Plants and Waterfalls.
335 **65** 15a. blue . . . 15 20
336 – 50a. green . . . 15 20
337 – 60a. brown . . . 2·20 2·75
338 – 1k.50 violet . . . 22·00 60
339 – 2k. brown . . . 1·70 35
340 – 2k.45 black . . . 5·50 5·50
341 – 3k. blue . . . 3·00 55
342 – 5k. green . . . 8·00 1·20
DESIGNS—HORIZ: 50a. Ellidaarvirkjun; 60a. Godafoss; 1k.50, Sogsvirkjun; 2k. Dettifoss; 2k.45, Andakilsarvirkjun; 3k. Laxarvirkjun. VERT: 5k. Gullfoss.

1956. 50th Anniv of Icelandic Telegraph System.
343 **67** 2k.30 blue . . . 30 65

67a Whooper Swans

1956. Northern Countries' Day.
344 **67a** 1k.50 red . . . 70 80
345 1k.75 blue . . . 8·50 8·75

1957. Designs as T **48** but airplane omitted.
346 2k. green . . . 2·50 20
347 3k. blue . . . 2·50 20
348 10k. brown . . . 5·25 45
DESIGNS—HORIZ: 2k. Snaefellsjokull; 3k. Eiriksjokull; 10k. Oraefajokull.

68 Presidential Residence, Bessastadir

69 Norwegian Spruce

1957.
349 **68** 25k. black . . . 13·50 3·25

1957. Reafforestation Campaign.
350 **69** 35a. green . . . 20 20
351 – 70a. green . . . 20 20
DESIGN: 70a. Icelandic birch and saplings.

70 Jonas Hallgrimsson

71 River Beauty

72 Icelandic Pony

1957. 150th Birth Anniv of Hallgrimsson (poet).
352 **70** 5k. black and green . . . 1·10 40

1958. Flowers. Multicoloured.
353 1k. Type **71** . . . 20 20
354 2k.50 Wild pansy . . . 30 45

1958.
355 **72** 10a. black . . . 40 15
356 1k. red . . . 50 25
357 2k.25 brown . . . 40 25

73 Icelandic Flag

74 Old Government House

1958. 40th Anniv of Icelandic Flag.
358 **73** 3k.50 red and blue . . . 1·10 50
359 50k. red and blue . . . 5·00 4·50
No. 359 is 23½ × 26½ mm.

1958.
360 **74** 1k.50 blue . . . 20 25
361 2k. green . . . 40 40
362 3k. red . . . 20 25
363 4k. brown . . . 40 40

75 Jon Thorkelsson with Children

76 Vickers Viscount 700 and 1919 Avro 504K Biplane

1959. Death Bicentenary of Jon Thorkelsson (Johannes Thorkillius, Rector of Skalholt).
364 **75** 2k. green . . . 45 50
365 3k. purple . . . 45 50

1959. Air. 40th Anniv of Iceland Civil Aviation.
366 **76** 3k.50 blue . . . 65 55
367 – 4k.05 green . . . 50 80
DESIGN: 4k.05, Douglas DC-4 and Avro 504K aircraft.

77 Atlantic Salmon

78 "The Outcast" (after Jonsson)

1959.
368 **77** 25a. blue . . . 20 25
369 – 90a. black and brown . . . 30 30
370 – 2k. black . . . 45 10
371 **77** 5k. green . . . 4·00 75
372 – 25k. violet and yellow . . . 10·00 10·00
DESIGNS—VERT: 90a., 2k. Eiders; 25k. Gyr falcon.

1960. World Refugee Year.
373 **78** 2k.50 brown . . . 15 20
374 4k.50 blue . . . 90 90

78a Conference Emblem

1960. Europa.
375 **78a** 3k. green . . . 90 40
376 5k.50 blue . . . 65 1·30

79 Dandelions

80 Sigurdsson

1960. Wild Flowers.
377 – 50a. violet, green and myrtle (Campanulas) . . . 15 15
378 – 1k.20 violet, green and brown (Geraniums) . . . 15 25
379 **79** 2k.50 yellow, green & brn 20 20
380 – 3k.50 yellow, green and blue (Buttercup) . . . 65 15
See also Nos. 412/15 and 446/7.

1961. 150th Birth Anniv of Jon Sigurdsson (historian and Althing member).
381 **80** 50a. red . . . 15 20
382 3k. blue . . . 1·20 1·00
383 5k. purple . . . 55 55

81 Reykjavik Harbour

1961. 175th Anniv of Reykjavik.
384 **81** 2k.50 blue and green . . . 55 25
385 4k.50 blue and violet . . . 70 30

82 Doves

1961. Europa.
386 **82** 5k.50 multicoloured . . . 40 60
387 6k. multicoloured . . . 40 60

83 B. Sveinsson

84 Productivity Institute

1961. 50th Anniv of Iceland University.
388 **83** 1k. brown . . . 15 20
389 – 1k.40 blue . . . 15 20

390 – 10k. green 90 80
MS391 99 × 50 mm. Nos. 388/90. Imperf . . . . 45 1·00
DESIGNS—VERT: 1k.40, B. M. Olsen (first Vice-chancellor). HORIZ: 10k. University building.

1962. Icelandic Buildings.
392 **84** 2k.50 blue 25 20
393 – 4k. green 35 25
394 – 6k. brown 50 20
DESIGNS: 4k. Fishing Research Institute; 6k. Agricultural Society's Headquarters.

85 Europa "Tree"

1962. Europa.
395 **85** 5k.50 brown, green & yell 25 20
396 6k.50 brown, green & yell 50 60

86 Cable Map

1962. Opening of North Atlantic Submarine Telephone Communications.
397 **86** 5k. green, red and lavender 95 45
398 7k. green, red and blue . . 40 25

87 S. Gudmundsson (scholar and curator) **88** Herring Catch

1963. Centenary of National Museum.
399 **87** 4k. brown and bistre . . . 50 25
400 – 5k.50 brown and olive . . 45 25
DESIGN: 5k.50, Detail from carving on church door, Valthjofsstad.

1963. Freedom from Hunger.
401 **88** 5k. multicoloured 75 20
402 7k.50 multicoloured . . . 25 25

89 View of Akureyri

1963.
403 **89** 3k. green 20 25

90 "Co-operation"

1963. Europa.
404 **90** 6k. yellow, ochre and brown 40 40
405 7k. yellow, green and blue 40 40

91 Ambulance

1963. Red Cross Centenary.
406 **91** 3k.+50a. multicoloured . . 25 70
407 3k.50+50a. mult 25 50

92 "Gullfoss" (cargo liner) **93** Scout Emblem

1964. 50th Anniv of Iceland Steamship Co.
408 **92** 10k. black, purple and blue 1·50 1·10

1964. Icelandic Boy Scouts Commemoration.
409 **93** 3k.50 multicoloured . . . 40 15
410 4k.50 multicoloured . . . 40 30

94 Arms of Iceland **95** Europa "Flower"

1964. 20th Anniv of Icelandic Republic.
411 **94** 25k. multicoloured . . . . 1·50 1·30

1964. Wild Flowers. As T **79**. Multicoloured.
412 50a. Mountain avens 15 15
413 1k. Glacier buttercup 10 10
414 1k.50 Bogbean 25 20
415 2k. White clover 30 15

1964. Europa.
416 **95** 4k.50 turquoise, cream and brown 50 30
417 9k. sepia, cream and blue 70 50

96 Running **97** Rock Ptarmigan (summer plumage)

1964. Olympic Games, Tokyo.
418 **96** 10k. black and green . . . 70 60

1965. Charity stamps.
419 **97** 3k.50+50a. mult . . . . . 70 1·20
420 – 4k.50+50a. mult . . . . . 75 1·20
DESIGN: 4k.50, Rock ptarmigan in winter plumage.

98 "Sound Waves" **99** Eruption, November 1963

1965. Centenary of I.T.U.
421 **98** 4k.50 green 75 65
422 7k.50 blue 25 20

1965. Birth of Surtsey Island. Multicoloured.
423 1k.50 Type **99** 50 50
424 2k. Surtsey in April 1964 (horiz) 50 50
425 3k.50 Surtsey in September 1964 (horiz) 75 55

100 Europa "Sprig"

1965. Europa.
426 **100** 5k. green, brown and ochre 95 95
427 8k. green, brown & turq 90 64

101 E. Benediktsson

1965. 25th Death Anniv of Einar Benediktsson (poet).
428 **101** 10k. brown, black and blue . . . . 2·25 3·00

102 Girl in National Costume **103** White-tailed Sea Eagle

1965.
429 **102** 100k. multicoloured . . . 4·75 5·00

1966. Multicoloured.
430 20k. Great northern diver . . 3·00 3·25
431 50k. Type **103** . . . . . . 6·50 7·00

104 Londrangar **105** Europa "Ship"

1966. Landscapes (1st series). Multicoloured.
432 2k.50 Type **104** 20 30
433 4k. Myvatn 40 30
434 5k. Bulandstindur 50 30
435 6k.50 Dyrholaey 60 30
See also Nos. 465/8.

1966. Europa.
436 **105** 7k. turquoise blue and red 1·30 1·30
437 8k. brown, cream and red 1·30 1·30

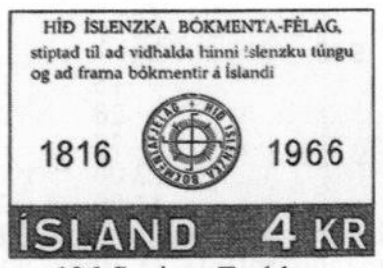

106 Society Emblem **107** Cogwheels

1966. 150th Anniv of Icelandic Literary Society.
438 **106** 4k. blue 30 20
439 10k. red 65 60

1967. Europa.
440 **107** 7k. blue, brown and yellow . . . . 1·40 1·10
441 8k. blue, grey and green 1·40 1·00

108 Old and New Maps of Iceland

1967. World Fair, Montreal.
442 **108** 10k. multicoloured . . . 30 40

109 Trade Symbols

1967. 50th Anniv of Icelandic Chamber of Commerce.
443 **109** 5k. multicoloured 25 25

110 Nest and Eggs of Ringed Plover

1967. Charity stamps.
444 **110** 4k.+50a. multicoloured 65 1·30
445 – 5k.+50a. multicoloured 65 1·30
DESIGN: 5k. Nest and eggs of rock ptarmigan.

1968. Wild Flowers. As T **79**. Multicoloured.
446 50a. Saxifrage 20 15
447 2k.50 Orchid 20 20

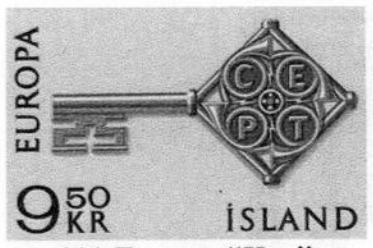

111 Europa "Key"

1968. Europa.
448 **111** 9k.50 mauve, black & yell 1·30 90
449 10k. yellow, sepia & green 1·30 95

112 Right-hand Traffic

1968. Adoption of Changed Rule of the Road.
450 **112** 4k. brown and yellow . . 15 20
451 5k. brown 15 20

113 "Fridriksson and Boy" (statue by S. Olafsson) **114** Library Interior

1968. Birth Cent of Pastor Fridrik Fridriksson (founder of Icelandic Y.M.C.A. and Y.W.C.A.).
452 **113** 10k. black and blue . . . 35 30

1968. 150th Anniv of National Library.
453 **114** 5k. brown and buff . . . 10 15
454 20k. ultramarine and blue 95 90

115 Jon Magnusson (former Prime Minister) **116** Viking Ships

1968. 50th Anniv of Independence.
455 **115** 4k. lake 25 20
456 50k. sepia . . . . 4·00 3·75

1969. 50th Anniv of Northern Countries' Union.
457 **116** 6k.50 red 45 45
458 10k. blue 45 45

117 Colonnade

1969. Europa.
459 **117** 13k. multicoloured . . . 2·50 2·10
460 14k.50 multicoloured . . 75 65

118 Republican Emblem (after S. Jonsson) **119** Boeing 727 Airliner

1969. 25th Anniv of Republic.
461 **118** 25k. multicoloured . . . 95 65
462 100k. multicoloured . . . 4·75 5·75

1969. 50th Anniv of Icelandic Aviation.
463 **119** 9k.50 ultramarine & blue 45 50
464 – 12k. ultramarine and blue 45 50
DESIGN: 12k. Canadair CL-44-D4 (inscr "Rolls-Royce 400").

120 Snaefellsjokull

1970. Landscapes (2nd series). Multicoloured.
465 1k. Type **120** 15 20
466 4k. Laxfoss and Baula . . . 15 20
467 5k. Hattver (vert) 15 20
468 20k. Fjardagil (vert) . . . . 1·20 45

121 First Court Session

122 Part of "Skardsbok" (14th-cent law manuscript)

1970. 50th Anniv of Icelandic Supreme Court.
469 **121** 6k.50 multicoloured . . . 20 20

1970. Icelandic Manuscripts. Multicoloured.
470 5k. Type **122** 15 20
471 15k. Part of preface to "Flateyjarbok" 50 60
472 30k. Illuminated initial from "Flateyjarbok" . . . . . 1·00 1·00

123 "Flaming Sun"

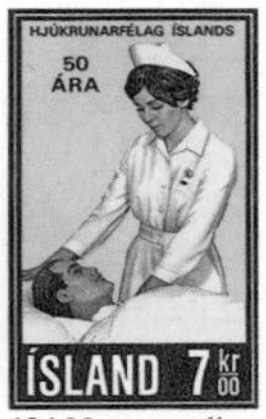

124 Nurse tending Patient

1970. Europa.
473 **123** 9k. yellow and brown . . 2·50 1·70
474 25k. brown and green . . 2·50 1·80

1970. 50th Anniv of Icelandic Nurses Assn.
475 **124** 7k. ultramarine and blue 25 25

125 G. Thomsen

126 "The Halt" (T. B. Thorlaksson)

1970. 150th Birth Anniv of Grimur Thomsen (poet).
476 **125** 10k. indigo and blue . . . 30 30

1970. International Arts Festival, Reykjavik.
477 **126** 50k. multicoloured . . . 1·20 1·10

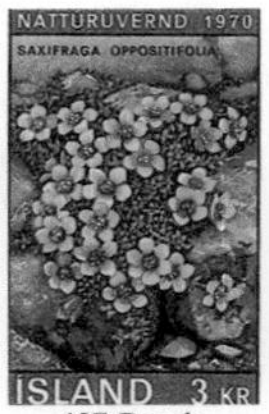

127 Purple Saxifrage

128 U.N. Emblem and Map

1970. Nature Conservation Year. Mult.
478 3k. Type **127** 25 25
479 15k. Lakagigar (view) 85 80

1970. 25th Anniv of United Nations.
480 **128** 12k. multicoloured . . . 30 45

129 "Flight" (A. Jonsson)

1971. "Help for Refugees".
481 **129** 10k. multicoloured . . . 40 45

130 Europa Chain

1971. Europa.
482 **130** 7k. yellow, red and black 2·00 1·30
483 15k. yellow, blue and black . . . . 1·90 1·10

131 Postgiro Emblem

132 Society Emblem

1971. Inauguration of Postal Giro Service.
484 **131** 5k. blue and light blue . . 15 25
485 7k. green and light green 15 25

1971. Centenary of Icelandic Patriotic Society.
486 **132** 30k. lilac and blue . . . . 1·00 70
487 – 100k. black and grey . . 5·50 5·50
DESIGN: 100k. T. Gunnarsson (president and editor).

133 Freezing Plant and Haddock ("Melanogrammus aeglefinus")

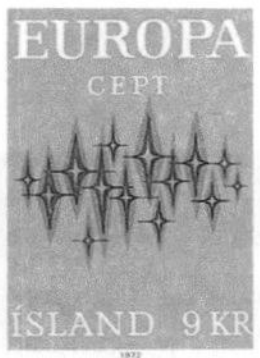

135 "Communications"

134 Mt. Herdubreid

1971. Icelandic Fishing Industry. Mult.
488 5k. Type **133** 15 20
489 7k. Landing catch and Atlantic cod ("Gadus morhua") 15 20
490 20k. Canning shrimps and "Pandalus borealis" . . . 70 65

1972.
491 **134** 250k. multicoloured . . . 45 25

1972. Europa.
492 **135** 9k. multicoloured . . . . 1·30 70
493 13k. multicoloured . . . 1·30 1·50

136 "Municipalities"

1972. Centenary of Icelandic Municipal Laws.
494 **136** 16k. multicoloured . . . 20 20

137 World Map on Chessboard

1972. World Chess Championship, Reykjavik.
495 **137** 15k. multicoloured . . . 25 25

138 Tomatoes

1972. Hot-house Plant Cultivation. Mult.
496 8k. Type **138** 15 20
497 12k. Steam source and valve 15 20
498 40k. Rose cultivation . . . . 1·00 85

139 Contour Map and Continental Shelf

1972. Iceland's Offshore Claims.
499 **139** 9k. multicoloured 20 20

140 Arctic Tern feeding Young

141 Europa "Posthorn"

1972. Charity Stamps.
500 **140** 7k.+1k. multicoloured . . 45 55
501 9k.+1k. multicoloured . . 50 60

1973. Europa.
502 **141** 13k. multicoloured . . . 2·50 2·10
503 25k. multicoloured . . . 35 35

142 Postman and 2s. stamp of 1873

144 Pres. Asgeirsson

143 "The Nordic House", Reykjavik

1973. Stamp Centenary. Multicoloured.
504 10k. Type **142** 45 30
505 15k. Pony train 15 20
506 20k. "Esja" (mail steamer) 15 20
507 40k. Mail van 15 20
508 80k. Beech Model 18 mail plane . . . . 1·70 90

1973. Nordic Countries' Postal Co-operation.
509 **143** 9k. multicoloured 45 15
510 10k. multicoloured . . . 1·30 1·20

1973. 5th Death Anniv of Asgeir Asgeirsson (politician).
511 **144** 13k. red 30 25
512 15k. blue 30 20

145 Exhibition Emblem

146 "The Elements"

1973. "Islandia 73" Stamp Exhibition. Mult.
513 17k. Type **145** 35 30
514 20k. Exhibition emblem (different) 35 25

1973. Centenary of I.M.O.
515 **146** 50k. multicoloured . . . 45 40

147 "Ingolfur and High-Seat Pillar" (tapestry, J. Briem)

148 "Horseman" (17th-century wood-carving)

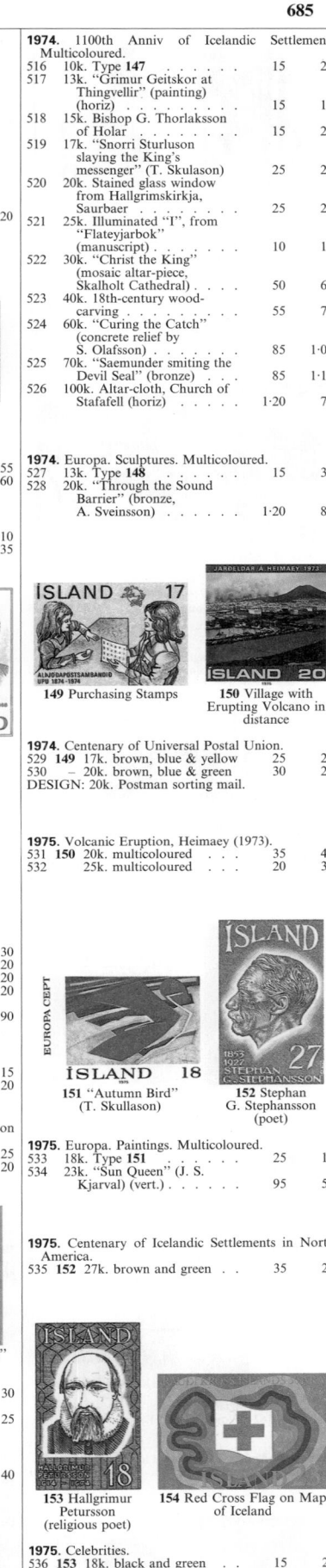

1974. 1100th Anniv of Icelandic Settlement. Multicoloured.
516 10k. Type **147** 15 20
517 13k. "Grimur Geitskor at Thingvellir" (painting) (horiz) 15 15
518 15k. Bishop G. Thorlaksson of Holar 15 20
519 17k. "Snorri Sturluson slaying the King's messenger" (T. Skulason) 25 20
520 20k. Stained glass window from Hallgrimskirkja, Saurbaer 25 20
521 25k. Illuminated "I", from "Flateyjarbok" (manuscript) 10 15
522 30k. "Christ the King" (mosaic altar-piece, Skalholt Cathedral) 50 60
523 40k. 18th-century wood-carving 55 70
524 60k. "Curing the Catch" (concrete relief by S. Olafsson) . . . . 85 1·00
525 70k. "Saemunder smiting the Devil Seal" (bronze) . . . 85 1·10
526 100k. Altar-cloth, Church of Stafafell (horiz) . . . . . 1·20 75

1974. Europa. Sculptures. Multicoloured.
527 13k. Type **148** 15 30
528 20k. "Through the Sound Barrier" (bronze, A. Sveinsson) . . . . . . 1·20 80

149 Purchasing Stamps

150 Village with Erupting Volcano in distance

1974. Centenary of Universal Postal Union.
529 **149** 17k. brown, blue & yellow 25 20
530 – 20k. brown, blue & green 30 25
DESIGN: 20k. Postman sorting mail.

1975. Volcanic Eruption, Heimaey (1973).
531 **150** 20k. multicoloured . . . 35 40
532 25k. multicoloured . . . 20 30

151 "Autumn Bird" (T. Skullason)

152 Stephan G. Stephansson (poet)

1975. Europa. Paintings. Multicoloured.
533 18k. Type **151** 25 15
534 23k. "Sun Queen" (J. S. Kjarval) (vert.) 95 55

1975. Centenary of Icelandic Settlements in North America.
535 **152** 27k. brown and green . . 35 25

153 Hallgrimur Petursson (religious poet)

154 Red Cross Flag on Map of Iceland

1975. Celebrities.
536 **153** 18k. black and green . . 15 20
537 – 23k. blue 15 20
538 – 30k. red 15 25
539 – 50k. blue 35 25
PORTRAITS: 23k. Arni Magnusson (historian); 30k. Jon Eiriksson (statesman); 50k. Einar Jonsson (painter and sculptor).

1975. 50th Anniv of Icelandic Red Cross.
540 **154** 23k. multicoloured . . . 25 25

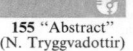

155 "Abstract" (N. Tryggvadottir)

156 "Bertel Thorvaldsen" (self-statue)

1975. International Women's Year.
541 **155** 100k. multicoloured . . . 80 50

1975. Centenary of Thorvaldsen Society (Charity organization).
542 **156** 27k. multicoloured . . . 45 35

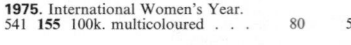

157 "Forestry"

158 "Landscape" (Asgrimur Jonsson)

1975. Reafforestation.
543 **157** 35k. multicoloured . . . 45 25

1976. Birth Cent of Asgrimur Jonsson (painter).
544 **158** 150k. multicoloured . . . 95 1·10

159 Wooden Bowl

1976. Europa. Old Wooden Crafts. Mult.
545 35k. Type **159** 90 90
546 45k. Spinning-wheel (vert) . . 90 85

160 Title page of Postal Services Order

161 Iceland 5a. Stamp with Reykjavik Postmark, 1876

1976. Bicent of Icelandic Postal Services.
547 **160** 35k. brown 35 30
548 – 45k. blue 30 30
DESIGN: 45k. Signature appended to Postal Services Order.

1976. Cent of Icelandic Aurar Currency Stamps.
549 **161** 30k. multicoloured . . . 20 35

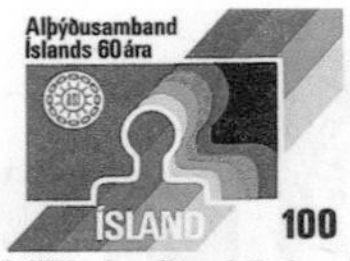

162 "Workers" and Federation Emblem

1976. 60th Anniv of Icelandic Labour Federation.
550 **162** 100k. multicoloured . . . 70 50

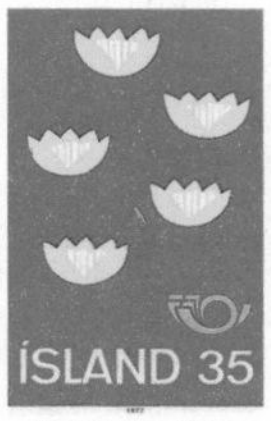

163 Water-lilies

164 Ofaerufoss, Eldgja

1977. Nordic Countries' Co-operation in Nature Conservation and Environment Protection.
551 **163** 35k. multicoloured . . . 60 40
552 45k. multicoloured . . . 65 40

1977. Europa. Multicoloured.
553 45k. Type **164** . . . . . . 1·90 70
554 85k. Kirkufell from Grundarfjord 55 40

165 Harlequin Duck

166 Co-operative Emblem

1977. European Wetlands Campaign.
555 **165** 40k. multicoloured . . . 25 25

1977. 75th Anniv of Federation of Icelandic Co-operative Societies.
556 **166** 60k. blue and light blue 60 40

167 Thermal Spring and Rheumatic Treatment

1977. World Rheumatism Year.
557 **167** 90k. multicoloured . . . 50 40

168 Cairn and Glacier

169 Thorvaldur Thoroddsen (geologist)

1977. 50th Anniv of Icelandic Touring Club.
558 **168** 45k. blue 35 50

1978. Famous Icelanders.
559 **169** 50k. green and brown . . 15 20
560 – 60k. brown and green . . 50 60
DESIGN: 60k. Briet Bjarnhedinsdottir (suffragette).

170 Videy Mansion

1978. Europa. Multicoloured.
561 80k. Type **170** 65 55
562 120k. Husavik Church (vert.) 85 45

171 Dr. A. Johannesson, Junkers W.34 "Island 1" and Junkers F-13 "Island 2"

1978. 50th Anniv of Domestic Flights.
563 **171** 60k. black and blue . . . 30 30
564 – 100k. multicoloured . . . 45 25
DESIGN: 100k. Fokker F.27 Friendship TF-F1K.

172 Skeidara Bridge

1978. Skeidara Bridge.
565 **172** 70k. multicoloured . . . 15 15

173 "Lava Scene near Mt. Hekla" (J. Stefansson)

1978.
566 **173** 1000k. multicoloured . . 3·00 2·75

174 Wreck of "Sargon" and Breeches-buoy

1978. 50th Anniv of National Life-Saving Association of Iceland.
567 **174** 60k. black 15 20

175 "Reykjanesviti" Lighthouse

176 Halldor Hermannsson

1978. Centenary of Lighthouses in Iceland.
568 **175** 90k. multicoloured . . . 35 35

1978. Birth Centenary of Halldor Hermannsson (scholar and librarian).
569 **176** 150k. blue 35 35

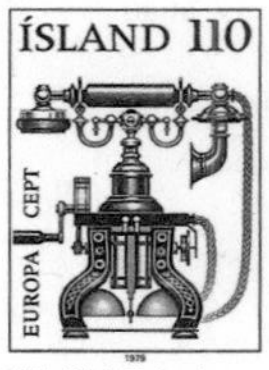

177 Old Telephone

178 Bjarni Thorsteinsson (clergyman and composer)

1979. Europa. Multicoloured.
570 110k. Type **177** 95 35
571 190k. Posthorn and mailbag 1·00 80

1979. Famous Icelanders.
572 – 80k. purple 15 20
573 **178** 100k. black 15 20
574 – 120k. red 15 20
575 – 130k. brown 30 40
576 – 170k. red 50 45
DESIGNS: 80k. Ingibjorg H. Bjarnason (headmistress and first female member of Althing); 120k. Petur Gudjohnsen (organist); 130k. Sveinbjorn Sveinbjornson (composer); 170k. Torfhildur Holm (poetess and novelist).

179 Children with Flowers

180 Icelandic Arms to 1904 and 1904–19

1979. International Year of the Child.
577 **179** 140k. multicoloured . . . 45 40

1979. 75th Anniv of Ministry of Iceland.
578 **180** 500k. multicoloured . . . 1·10 75

181 Sigurdsson and I. Einarsdottir

1979. Death Centenaries of Jon Sigurdsson (historian and Althing member) and of his wife, Ingibjorg Einarsdottir.
579 **181** 150k. black 25 35

182 Part of Kringla Leaf (MS of "Heimskringla")

183 Icelandic Dog

1979. 800th Birth Anniv of Snorri Sturluson (saga writer).
580 **182** 200k. multicoloured . . . 30 40

1980. Fauna.
581 **183** 10k. black 15 15
582 – 90k. brown 15 20
583 – 160k. purple 50 20
584 – 170k. black 40 60
585 – 190k. brown 30 40
DESIGNS: 90k. Arctic fox; 160k. Greater redfish; 170k. Atlantic puffins; 190k. Common seal.

184 Jon Sveinsson alias Nonni (writer)

185 Rowan Berries

1980. Europa.
586 **184** 140k. pink and black . . 50 35
587 – 250k. pink and black . . 80 60
DESIGN: 250k. Gunnar Gunnarsson (writer).

1980. Year of the Tree.
588 **185** 120k. multicoloured . . . 15 40

186 Sports Complex, Reykjavik

187 Embroidered Cushion

1980. Olympic Games, Moscow.
589 **186** 300k. turquoise 50 50

1980. Nordic Countries' Postal Co-operation. Multicoloured.
590 150k. Carved and painted cabinet door 60 45
591 180k. Type **187** 80 55

188 University Hospital

189 Loudspeaker

1980. 50th Anniv of University Hospital.
592 **188** 200k. multicoloured . . . 40 30

1980. 50th Anniv of State Broadcasting Service.
593 **189** 400k. multicoloured . . . 70 35

(New currency. 100 (old) Kronur = 1 (new) Krona).

190 Magnus Stephensen (Chief Justice and publisher)

191 Loftur the Sorcerer

1981. Famous Icelanders.
594 **190** 170a. blue 30 20
595 – 190a. green 30 25

DESIGN: 190a. Finnur Magnusson (writer and Keeper of Privy Archives).

1981. Europa. Illustrations of Icelandic legends. Multicoloured.
596 180a. Type **191** . . . . . . 1·10 65
597 220a. Witch wading the deeps off Iceland . . . . 1·10 75

192 Winter Wren

193 Human Jigsaw

1981. Birds.
598 **192** 50a. brown 10 15
599 – 100a. blue 10 15
600 – 200a. black 45 30
DESIGNS: 100a. Golden plover; 200a. Common raven.

1981. International Year for Disabled Persons.
601 **193** 200a. multicoloured . . . 20 25

194 Skyggnir Dish Aerial

195 "Hauling the Line" (Gunnlaugur Scheving)

1981. 75th Anniv of Icelandic Telephone Service.
602 **194** 500a. multicoloured . . . 45 45

1981.
603 **195** 5000a. multicoloured . . 3·00 3·25

196 Medieval Driftwood crucifix from Alftamyri

197 Leaf-bread (star pattern)

1981. Millenary of Missionary Work in Iceland.
604 **196** 200a. lilac 20 20

1981. Christmas. Multicoloured.
605 200a. Type **197** 60 50
606 250a. Leaf-bread (tree pattern) 60 45

198 Common Northern Whelk

199 Casting Dais Post into Sea (first Iceland settlement, 874)

1982. Shells.
607 **198** 20a. red 10 15
608 – 600a. brown 70 25
DESIGN: 600a. Iceland scallop.

1982. Europa. Multicoloured.
609 350a. Type **199** . . . . . . 1·80 65
610 450a. Discovery of Vinland (America), 1000 . . . . . 1·80 80

200 Sheep

201 Co-operative Trading House, Husavik

1982. Domestic Animals.
611 **200** 300a. brown 85 45
612 – 400a. red 35 25
613 – 500a. grey 35 25
DESIGNS: 400a. Cow; 500a. Cat.

1982. Centenary of Thingeyjar Co-operative Society.
614 **201** 1000a. black and brown 55 35

202 Horseman

1982. Iceland Ponies and Horsemanship.
615 **202** 700a. multicoloured . . . 40 30

203 Holar

1982. Cent of Holar Agricultural College.
616 **203** 1500a. multicoloured . . 70 60

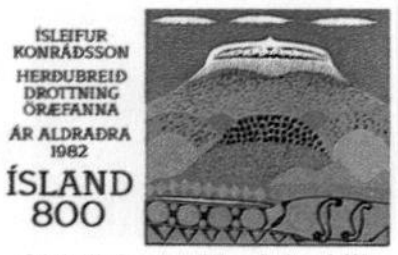

204 "Mount Herdubreid" (Isleifur Konradsson)

205 T. Sveinsdottir

1982. Year of the Aged.
617 **204** 800a. multicoloured . . . 45 35

1982. Famous Icelanders. Thorbjorg Sveinsdottir (midwife and founder of Icelandic Women's Association).
618 **205** 900a. brown 35 35

206 Reynistadur Monastery Seal

1982. "Nordia 84" Stamp Exhibition, Reykjavik (1st issue). Sheet 82 × 80 mm containing T **206** and similar vert design.
MS619 400a. brown and black; 800a. brown and black (sold at 18k.) 4·00 4·25
DESIGN:—800a. Thingeyrar Monastery seal.
See also Nos. **MS**636 and **MS**645.

207 Doves and Opening of "The Night was such a Splendid One"

1982. Christmas. Multicoloured.
620 300a. Type **207** 45 35
621 350a. Bells and close of "The Night was such a Splendid One" (composed by Sigvaldi Kaldalons from poem by E. Sigurdsson) . . 55 55

208 Marsh Marigold

209 Mount Sulur

1983. Flowers. Multicoloured.
622 7k.50 Type **208** 35 20
623 8k. Alpine catchfly 50 25
624 10k. Marsh cinquefoil . . . 1·00 25
625 20k. Water forgetmenot . . . 2·10 1·10

1983. Nordic Countries' Postal Co-operation. "Visit the North". Multicoloured.
626 4k.50 Type **209** 75 65
627 5k. Urridafossar Falls . . . 75 65

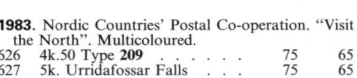

210 Thermal Area and Heat-exchange Plant

211 Stern Trawler

1983. Europa. Multicoloured.
628 5k. Type **210** . . . . 3·50 90
629 5k.50 Thermal area heating houses . . . . 11·00 1·30

1983. Fishing Industry.
630 **211** 11k. blue 65 65
631 – 13k. blue 90 50
DESIGN: 13k. Line fishing.

212 "Laki Craters" (Finnur Jonsson)

1983. Bicentenary of Skafta Eruption.
632 **212** 15k. multicoloured . . . 55 45

213 Skiing

1983. Outdoor Sports. Multicoloured.
633 12k. Type **213** 90 45
634 14k. Jogging 90 45

214 Aircraft and W.C.Y. Emblem

1983. World Communications Year.
635 **214** 30k. multicoloured . . . 1·40 1·00

215 Seal of Bishop Magnus Eyjolfsson

1983. "Nordia 84" Stamp Exhibition, Reykjavik (2nd issue). Sheet 82 × 80 mm containing T **215** and similar vert design.
MS636 8k. blue and black; 12k. green and black (sold at 30k.) 5·75 5·75
DESIGN: 12k. seal of Bishop Ogmundur Palsson.

216 Virgin Mary and Child

217 Pres. Eldjarn

1983. Christmas. Multicoloured.
637 600a. Type **216** 65 45
638 650a. Visitation of the Angel 65 45

1983. 1st Death Anniv (September) of Kristjan Eldjarn (President, 1968–80).
639 **217** 6k.50 red 75 65
640 7k. blue 40 25

218 Burnet Rose

219 Bridge

1984. Flowers. Multicoloured.
641 6k. Type **218** 70 40
642 25k. Silverweed 80 35
See also Nos. 648/9, 657/60 and 717/18.

1984. Europa. 25th Anniv of European Post and Telecommunications Conference.
643 **219** 6k.50 deep blue and blue 1·50 55
644 7k.50 dp purple & purple 60 45

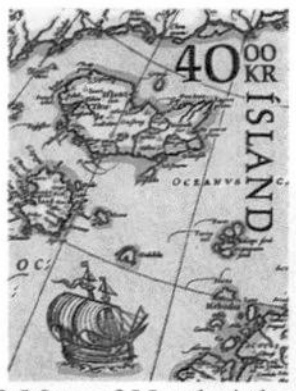

220 Map of North Atlantic by Abraham Ortelius, 1570

1984. "Nordia 84" Stamp Exhibition, Reykjavik (3rd issue). Sheet 114 × 76 mm.
MS645 **220** 40k. multicoloured (sold at 60k.) . . . . 9·00 9·00

221 Icelandic Flags

222 I.O.G.T. Lodge, Akureyri

1984. 40th Anniv of Republic.
646 **221** 50k. multicoloured . . . 3·75 2·10

1984. Centenary of International Order of Good Templars in Iceland.
647 **222** 10k. green 65 40

1984. Flowers. As T **218**. Multicoloured.
648 6k.50 Wild azalea 55 40
649 7k.50 Alpine bearberry . . . 55 45

223 Basalt symbolising Industries

224 Bjorn Bjarnarson (founder) (after J. P. Wildenradt)

1984. 50th Anniv of Confederation of Icelandic Employers.
650 **223** 30k. multicoloured . . . 1·40 95

1984. Centenary of National Gallery.
651 **224** 12k. black, brown and green 70 45
652 – 40k. black, green and red 1·80 1·20
DESIGN: 40k. New gallery building.

225 Virgin and Child

226 Text from Bible

1984. Christmas.
653 **225** 600a. blue, lt blue & gold 50 25
654 – 650a. red and gold . . . 60 25
DESIGN: 650a. Angel with Christmas rose.

1984. 400th Anniv of Gudbrand's Bible.
655 **226** 6k.50 red 50 30
656 – 7k.50 purple 40 60
DESIGN: 7k.50, Illustration from Bible.

1985. Flowers. As T **218**. Multicoloured.
657 8k. Stone bramble 40 25
658 9k. Rock speedwell 55 30

659 16k. Sea pea . . . . 1·70 65
660 17k. Alpine whitlow-grass . . 80 50

227 Lady playing Langspil

228 Swedish Whitebeam

1985. Europa. Music Year. Multicoloured.
661 6k.50 Type **227** . . . . 1·20 40
662 7k.50 Man playing Icelandic violin . . . . 1·10 1·10

1985. Centenary of Iceland Horticultural Society.
663 **228** 20k. multicoloured . . . 80 55

229 Girl and I.Y.Y. Emblem

230 Common Squid

1985. International Youth Year.
664 **229** 25k. multicoloured . . . 80 65

1985. Marine Life.
665 **230** 7k. purple 30 20
666 – 8k. brown 30 20
667 – 9k. red 50 50
DESIGNS: 8k. Common spider crab; 9k. Sea anemone.

231 Rev. Hannes Stephensen (politician)

1985. Famous Icelanders.
668 **231** 13k. red 45 35
669 – 30k. violet 65 60
DESIGN: 30k. Jon Gudmundsson (editor and politician).

232 "Flight Yearning"

233 Snow Scene

1985. Birth Centenary of Johannes Sveinsson Kjarval (artist).
670 **232** 100k. multicoloured . . . 4·00 3·50

1985. Christmas. Multicoloured.
671 8k. Type **233** 45 25
672 9k. Snow scene (different) . . 70 50

234 Pied Wagtail

1986. Birds. Multicoloured.
673 6k. Type **234** 40 20
674 10k. Pintail . . . . 1·20 50
675 12k. Merlin 95 50
676 15k. Razorbill 90 50
See also Nos. 697/700, 720/1, 726/7, 741/2 and 763/4.

235 Skaftafell National Park

1986. Europa. Multicoloured.
677 10k. Type **235** . . . . . . 5·00 1·20
678 12k. Jokulsargljufur National Park . . . . 2·40 75

236 Stykkisholmur

1986. Nordic Countries' Postal Co-operation. Twinned Towns. Multicoloured.
679 10k. Type **236** 75 65
680 12k. Seydisfjordur 75 40

237 Head Office, Reykjavik

1986. Centenary of National Bank. Mult.
681 **237** 13k. green 55 50
682 – 250k. brown . . . . . . 10·00 5·75
DESIGN: 250k. Reverse of first National Bank 5k. note.

238 First Official Seal

239 Early Telephone Equipment

1986. Bicentenary of Reykjavik.
683 **238** 10k. red 50 30
684 – 12k. brown 60 30
685 – 13k. green 50 45
686 – 40k. blue . . . . 1·80 85
DESIGNS: 12k. "Reykjavik pond, 1856" (illustration from "Journey in the Northern Seas" by Charles Edmond); 13k. Women washing clothes in natural hot water brook, Laugardalur; 40k. City Theatre.

1986. 80th Anniv of Icelandic Telephone and Telegraph Service. Multicoloured.
687 10k. Type **239** 40 20
688 20k. Modern digital telephone system 95 65

240 Hvita River Crossing, 1836 (after Auguste Mayer)

241 "Christmas at Peace"

1986. Stamp Day. Sheet 95 × 67 mm.
MS689 **240** 20k. black (sold at 30k.) 2·75 4·00

1986. Christmas. Multicoloured.
690 10k. Type **241** 60 30
691 12k. "Christmas Night" . . . 45 45

242 "Svanur" (ketch) anchored off Olafsvik

1987. 300th Anniv of Olafsvik Trading Station.
692 **242** 50k. purple . . . . 2·20 1·20

243 Terminal and Boeing 727 Tail

1987. Opening of Leif Eiriksson Terminal, Keflavik Airport.
693 **243** 100k. multicoloured . . . 3·75 1·60

244 Christ carrying Cross

245 Rask

1987. Europa. Stained Glass Windows by Leifur Breidfoerd, Fossvogur Cemetery Chapel. Multicoloured.
694 12k. Type **244** 85 60
695 15k. Soldiers and peace dove 85 50

1987. Birth Bicentenary of Rasmus Kristjan Rask (philologist).
696 **245** 20k. black 80 60

1987. Birds. As T **234**. Multicoloured.
697 13k. Short-eared owl 60 35
698 40k. Redwing . . . . 1·80 1·10
699 70k. Oystercatcher . . . . . 3·00 1·80
700 90k. Mallard . . . . 4·25 2·10

246 Girl Brushing Teeth

247 Vulture

1987. Dental Protection.
701 **246** 12k. multicoloured . . . 55 40

1987. National Guardian Spirits. Each red.
702 13k. Type **247** 60 70
703 13k. Dragon 60 70
704 13k. Bull 60 70
705 13k. Giant 60 70
See also Nos. 713/16, 732 and 743/50.

248 Djupivogur Trading Station, 1836 (after Auguste Mayer)

1987. Stamp Day. Sheet 95 × 67 mm.
MS706 **248** 30k. black (sold at 45k.) 3·25 3·75

249 Christmas Tree

250 Steinn Steinarr (poet)

1987. Christmas. Multicoloured.
707 13k. Type **249** 65 35
708 17k. "Christmas Light" . . . 65 55

1988. Famous Icelanders. Multicoloured.
709 16k. Type **250** 65 30
710 21k. David Stefansson (writer) 65 55

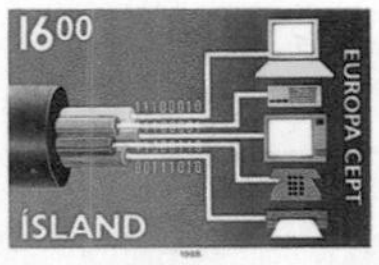

251 Transmission of Messages by Modern Data System

1988. Europa. Communications. Multicoloured.
711 16k. Type **251** 70 40
712 21k. Phone pad and globe within envelope (transmission of letters by facsimile machine) . . . . 1·60 1·50

1988. National Guardian Spirit. As Nos. 702/5 but values and colour changed.
713 16k. black (Type **247**) . . . 75 75
714 16k. black (Dragon) 75 75
715 16k. black (Bull) 75 75
716 16k. black (Giant) 75 75

1988. Flowers. As T **218**. Multicoloured.
717 10k. Tufted vetch 55 25
718 50k. Wild thyme . . . . . . 2·20 75

252 Handball

254 Mother and Baby

253 "Nupsstadur Farm, Fljotshverfi, 1836" (after Auguste Mayer)

1988. Olympic Games, Seoul.
719 **252** 18k. multicoloured . . . 70 45

1988. Birds. As T **234**. Multicoloured.
720 5k. Black-tailed godwit . . . 15 20
721 30k. Long-tailed duck . . . 1·40 65

1988. Stamp Day. Sheet 95 × 67 mm.
MS722 **253** 40k. black (sold at 60k.) 3·75 4·25

1988. 40th Anniv of W.H.O. "Health for All in 2000".
723 **254** 19k. multicoloured . . . 80 35

255 Fisherman with Haul of Fish

1988. Christmas. Multicoloured.
724 19k. Type **255** 65 45
725 24k. Trawler and buoy . . . 1·20 1·70

1989. Birds. As T **234**. Multicoloured.
726 19k. Red-necked phalarope . . 75 45
727 100k. Snow buntings . . . . 4·25 2·30

256 Peysufot (dress costume)

257 Children at Seaside

1989. Nordic Countries' Postal Co-operation. Traditional Costumes. Multicoloured.
728 21k. Type **256** 85 35
729 26k. Upphlutur (everyday wear) 85 50

1989. Europa. Childrens' Toys and Games. Multicoloured.
730 21k. Type **257** . . . . . . 2·20 55
731 26k. Girl with hoop and boy with hobby-horse . . . . 2·20 70

1989. National Guardian Spirits. As No. 703 but colour and value changed.
732 500k. brown (Dragon) . . . 16·00 7·00

258 Mount Skeggi, Arnarfjord

1989. Landscapes. Multicoloured.
733 35k. Type **258** . . . . . . 1·40 50
734 45k. Namaskard thermal spring . . . . 1·60 80
See also Nos. 757/8 and 765/6.

259 College

1989. Cent of Hvanneyri Agricultural College.
735 **259** 50k. multicoloured . . . 1·50 90

260 Seaman throwing Barrels at Whales

1989. Stamp Day. "Nordia 91" Stamp Exhibition, Reykjavik (1st issue). Sheet 114 × 74 mm containing T **260** and similar vert designs, showing details of the 1539 Carta Marina by Olaus Magnus.
MS736 30k. Type **260**; 30k. Ship harpooning whale; 30k. Sea serpent encircling ship (sold at 130k.) . . . . 5·00 6·75
See also Nos. **MS**760 and **MS**771.

261 Stefan Stefansson (co-founder) and Flowers

262 "Virgin and Child"

1989. Centenary of Icelandic Natural History Society. Multicoloured.
737 21k. Type **261** 65 40
738 26k. Bjarni Saemundsson (first Chairman) and Atlantic cod 90 50

1989. Christmas. Multicoloured.
739 21k. Type **262** 65 40
740 26k. "Three Wise Men" . . . 1·00 60

1990. Birds. As T **234**. Multicoloured.
741 21k. European wigeons . . . 70 45
742 80k. Pink-footed goose and goslings . . . . 2·10 1·10

1990. National Guardian Spirits. As Nos. 702/5 but value and colours changed.
743 5k. green (Type **247**) 15 25
744 5k. green (Dragon) 15 25
745 5k. green (Bull) 15 25
746 5k. green (Giant) 15 25
747 21k. blue (Type **247**) 60 70
748 21k. blue (Dragon) 60 70
749 21k. blue (Bull) 60 70
750 21k. blue (Giant) 60 70

263 Gudrun Larusdottir (writer and politician) (after Halldor Petursson)

264 Posthouse Street, Reykjavik, Post Office and Old Scales

1990. 110th Birth Anniversaries. Mult.
751 21k. Type **263** 75 45
752 21k. Ragnhildur Petursdottir (women's educationist) (after Asgrimur Jonsson) 75 45

1990. Europa. Post Office Buildings. Mult.
753 21k. Type **264** . . . . . . 1·00 70
754 40k. Thoenglabakki 4, Reykjavik, Post Office and modern scales . . . . . . 2·20 1·00

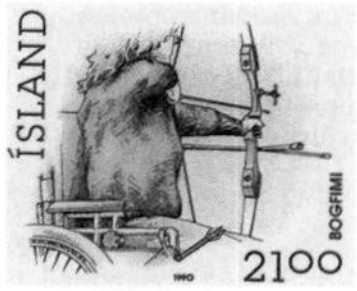

265 Archery

1990. Sport. Multicoloured.
755 21k. Type **265** 70 45
756 21k. Football 65 40

1990. Landscapes. As T **258**. Multicoloured.
757 25k. Hvitserkur, Hunafjord 70 45
758 200k. Lomagnupur . . . . . 5·75 3·00

266 Bird, Stars and Map

1990. European Tourism Year.
759 **266** 30k. multicoloured . . . 90 45

267 Denmark

1990. Stamp Day. "Nordia 91" Stamp Exhibition, Reykjavik (2nd issue). Sheet 114 × 74 mm containing T **267** and similar vert designs, showing details of the 1539 Carta Marina by Olaus Magnus.
MS760 40k. Type **267**; 40k. Sweden; 40k. Gotland and sailing ship (sold at 170k.) . . . . 7·00 7·50

268 Children around Christmas Tree

1990. Christmas. Multicoloured.
761 25k. Type **268** . . . . . . 1·20 55
762 30k. Carol singers . . . . . 1·10 65

1991. Birds. As T **234**. Multicoloured.
763 25k. Slavonian grebes . . . . 1·00 35
764 100k. Northern gannets . . . 3·50 1·60

1991. Landscapes. As T **258**. Multicoloured.
765 10k. Mt. Vestrahorn 60 20
766 300k. Kverkfjoll range . . . 9·50 5·00

269 Meteorological Information

1991. Europa. Europe in Space. Mult.
767 26k. Type **269** . . . . . . 2·10 60
768 47k. Telecommunications satellite . . . . 2·10 1·10

270 Jokulsarlon

1991. Nordic Countries' Postal Co-operation. Tourism. Multicoloured.
769 26k. Type **270** . . . . . . 1·20 60
770 31k. Strokkur hot spring . . 1·30 75

271 Western Iceland

1991. "Nordia 91" Stamp Exhibition (3rd issue). Sheet 114 × 74 mm containing T **271** and similar vert designs, showing details of the 1539 Carta Marina by Olaus Magnus.
MS771 50k. Type **271**; 50k. Arms and central part of Iceland; 50k. Eastern Iceland, ice floes and compass rose (sold at 215k.) 7·75 8·50

272 Golf

273 Pall Isolfsson (composer) (after Hans Muller)

1991. Sports. Multicoloured.
772 26k. Type **272** 85 45
773 26k. Glima (wrestling) . . . 85 45

1991. Famous Icelanders. Multicoloured.
774 60k. Ragnar Jonsson (founder of Reykjavik College of Music) (after Joannes Kjarval) (horiz) . . 1·80 1·00
775 70k. Type **273** . . . . . . 2·20 1·40

274 College Building and Student using Sextant

1991. Cent of College of Navigation, Reykjavik.
776 **274** 50k. multicoloured . . . 1·60 90

275 "Soloven" (mail brigantine)

276 "Light of Christmas"

1991. Stamp Day. Ships. Multicoloured.
777 30k. Type **275** . . . . . . 2·20 1·40
778 30k. "Arcturus" (cargo liner) 2·20 1·40
779 30k. "Gullfoss I" (cargo liner) . . . . 2·20 1·40
780 30k. "Esja II" (cargo liner) 2·20 1·40

1991. Christmas. Multicoloured.
781 30k. Type **276** . . . . . . 1·00 50
782 35k. Star . . . . 1·20 75

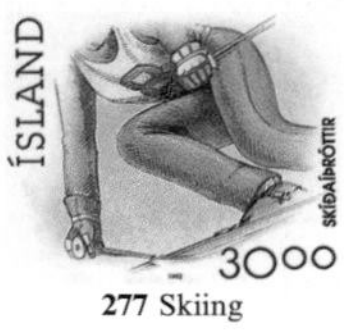

277 Skiing

1992. Sport. Multicoloured.
783 30k. Type **277** . . . . . . 1·10 55
784 30k. Volleyball . . . . 1·10 55

278 Map and "Santa Maria"

1992. Europa. 500th Anniv of Discovery of America by Columbus. Multicoloured.
785 55k. Map and Viking ship (Leif Eriksson) . . . . . . 1·80 1·30
786 55k. Type **278** . . . . . . 1·80 1·30
MS787 85 × 67 mm. Nos. 785/6 3·00 3·50

279 Agricultural and Industrial Symbols

1992. 75th Anniv of Iceland Chamber of Commerce (30k.) and 50th Anniv of Icelandic Freezing Plants Corporation (35k.). Multicoloured.
788 30k. Type **279** 90 60
789 35k. Trawler and Atlantic cod . . . . 1·40 75

280 River Fnjoska Bridge, Skogar

282 Face and Candle reflected in Window

281 Ford "TT", 1920–26

1992. Bridges. Multicoloured.
790 5k. Type **280** 15 20
791 250k. River Olfusa bridge, Selfoss . . . . 8·25 5·50
See also Nos. 804/5.

1992. Postal Vehicles. Multicoloured.
792 30k. Type **281** . . . . . . 1·70 1·30
793 30k. Citroen snowmobile, 1929 . . . . 1·70 1·30
794 30k. Mail/passenger transport car "RE 231", 1933 . . . 1·70 1·30
795 30k. Ford bus, 1946 . . . . 1·70 1·30

1992. Christmas. Multicoloured.
796 30k. Type **282** . . . . . . 1·20 60
797 35k. Full moon . . . . . . 1·40 70

283 Gyr Falcon with Chicks

284 Handball

1992. Endangered Species. The Gyr Falcon. Multicoloured.
798 5k. Type **283** 30 20
799 10k. Beating wings . . . . . 1·20 40
800 20k. Eating . . . . 1·80 80
801 35k. On ground . . . . . . 3·25 1·30

1993. Sport. Multicoloured.
802 30k. Type **284** 85 45
803 30k. Running 85 45

1993. Bridges. As T **280**. Multicoloured.
804 90k. River Hvita bridge, Ferjukot . . . . 3·00 1·60
805 150k. River Jokulsa a Fjollum bridge, Grimsstadir . . . . 5·25 3·00

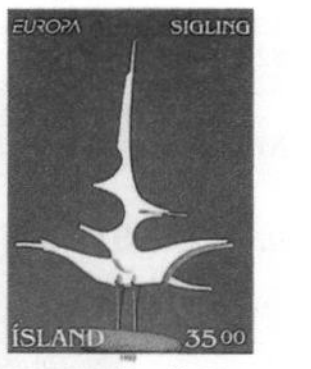

285 The Blue Lagoon, Svartsengi

286 "Sailing" (Jon Gunnar Arnason)

1993. Nordic Countries' Postal Co-operation. Tourism. Multicoloured.
806 30k. Type **285** 95 60
807 35k. Perlan (The Pearl), Reykjavik . . . . 1·20 85

1993. Europa. Contemporary Art. Mult.
808 35k. Type **286** . . . . . . 1·40 1·10
809 55k. "Hatching of the Jet" (Magnus Tomasson) . . . 2·10 1·70

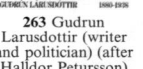

287 1933 1k. Balbo Flight Stamp

1993. 60th Anniv of Balbo Transatlantic Mass Formation Flight. Sheet 110 × 76 mm containing T **287** and similar vert designs. Multicoloured.

MS810 10k. Type **287**; 50k. 1933 5k. Balbo flight stamp; 100k. 1933 10k. Balbo flight stamp (sold at 200k.) . . . . 5·75 6·00

288 Junkers "F-13" Seaplane "Sulan" D-483

1993. 65th Anniv of 1st Icelandic Postal Flight. Multicoloured.

811	30k. Type **288**	1·80	90
812	30k. Waco YKS-7 seaplane TF-0RH	1·80	1·00
813	30k. Grumman G-21 Goose amphibian TF-VK	1·80	1·00
814	30k. Consolidated PBY-5 Catalina flying boat "Old Peter" TF-TSP	1·80	1·00

289 Three Wise Men adoring Child

290 Swimming

1993. Christmas. Multicoloured.

815	30k. Type **289**	95	60
816	35k. Madonna and Child . .	1·10	85

1994. Sport. Multicoloured.

817	30k. Type **290**	1·00	45
818	30k. Weightlifting	1·00	45

291 Finger Puppets

1994. International Year of the Family.

819 **291**	40k. multicoloured . . .	1·10	65

292 St. Brendan visiting Iceland

1994. Europa. St. Brendan's Voyages. Multicoloured.

820	35k. Type **292**	1·30	80
821	55k. St. Brendan discovering Faroe Islands	1·90	1·30
MS822	81 × 76 mm. Nos. 820/1	2·75	2·50

293 Conductor and Instruments

1994. 50th Anniv of Independence. Art and Culture. Multicoloured.

823	30k. Type **293** (44th anniv of Icelandic Symphony Orchestra)	90	45
824	30k. Pottery (55th anniv of College of Arts and Crafts)	90	45
825	30k. Cameraman and actors (16th anniv of National Film Fund)	90	45
826	30k. Ballerina and modern dancers (21st anniv of Icelandic Dance Company)	90	45
827	30k. Theatre masks (44th anniv of Icelandic National Theatre)	90	45

294 Gisli Sveinsson (President of United Althing, 1944)

1994. 50th Anniv of New Constitution.

828 **294**	30k. multicoloured . . .	95	65

295 Sveinn Bjornsson (1944–52)

1994. 50th Anniv of Republic. Presidents. Sheet 118 × 71 mm containing T **295** and similar vert designs. Multicoloured.

MS829 50k. Type **295**; 50k. Asgeir Asgeirsson (1952–68); 50k. Kristjan Eldjarn (1968–80); 50k. Vigdis Finnbogadottir (1980 onwards) . . . . 5·50 5·50

296 Children looking at Stamp Album

1994. Stamp Day. Stamp Collecting. Sheet 120 × 50 mm containing T **296** and similar square designs. Multicoloured.

MS830 30k. Type **296**; 35k. Magnifying glass over stamps; 100k. Girl and elderly man studying globe (sold at 200k.) 6·00 6·25

297 Woman and Stars

1994. Christmas. Multicoloured.

831	30k. Type **297**	1·00	60
832	35k. Man and stars	1·20	85

298 Emblem and Airplane

1994. 50th Anniv of I.C.A.O.

833 **298**	100k. multicoloured . . .	3·25	1·60

299 Flag and Salvation Army Members

300 Geyser

1995. Anniversaries. Multicoloured.

834	35k. Type **299** (centenary of Salvation Army in Iceland)	1·10	70
835	90k. Map of fjord (centenary of Seydisfjordur)	2·75	1·40

1995. 14th World Men's Handball Championship. Multicoloured.

836	35k. Type **300**	1·30	1·70
837	35k. Stadium	1·30	1·70
838	35k. Volcano	1·30	1·70
839	35k. Entrance to fjord . . .	1·30	1·70

301 Laufas

302 "Spell-broken" (sculpture, Einar Jonsson)

1995. Nordic Countries' Postal Co-operation. Tourism. Multicoloured.

840	30k. Type **301**	95	55
841	35k. Fjallsjokull Glacier . . .	1·10	65

1995. Europa. Peace and Freedom.

842 **302**	35k. multicoloured . . .	1·20	1·00
843	55k. multicoloured . . .	1·60	1·40

303 "Laura" (mail ship)

1995. Mail Ships. Multicoloured.

844	30k. Type **303**	1·10	1·00
845	30k. "Dronning Alexandrine"	1·10	1·00
846	30k. "Laxfoss"	1·10	1·00
847	30k. "Godafoss III"	1·10	1·00

304 Redpoll ("Acanthis flammea")

1995. European Nature Conservation Year. Birds. Multicoloured.

848	25k. Type **304**	75	45
849	250k. Common snipe ("Gallinago gallinago") . .	7·50	5·25

305 Boeing 757

1995. 40th Anniv of Iceland–Luxembourg Air Link.

850 **305**	35k. multicoloured . . .	1·10	75

306 Hraunfossar Waterfalls (left detail)

1995. "Nordia 96" Stamp Exhibition, Reykjavik (1st issue). Sheet 105 × 65 mm containing T **306** and similar horiz design. Multicoloured.

MS851 10k. Type **306**; 150k. Waterfalls (right detail) (sold at 200k.) . . . . 5·75 6·00

The stamps form a composite design.

See also No. **MS**871.

307 Snowman and Snowwoman

308 Anniversary Emblem

1995. Christmas. Multicoloured.

852	30k. Type **307**	90	60
853	35k. Coloured fir trees . . .	1·40	65

1995. 50th Anniv of U.N.O.

854 **308**	100k. multicoloured . . .	3·25	1·80

309 Common Cormorant ("Phalacrocorax carbo")

1996. Birds. Multicoloured.

855	20k. Type **309**	55	40
856	40k. Barrow's goldeneye ("Bucephala islandica") . .	1·30	80

310 "Seamen in a Boat" (Gunnlaugur Scheving)

1996. Paintings. Multicoloured.

857	100k. Type **310**	2·75	1·80
858	200k. "At the Washing Springs" (Kristin Jonsdottir)	6·25	3·50

311 Halldora Bjarnadottir (founder of women's societies)

1996. Europa. Famous Women. Mult.

859	35k. Type **311**	1·20	80
860	55k. Olafia Johannsdottir (women's rights campaigner and temperance worker) . . .	2·10	1·40

312 1931 Buick

1996. Post Buses. Multicoloured.

861	35k. Type **312**	1·10	75
862	35k. 1933 Studebaker	1·10	75
863	35k. 1937 Ford	1·10	75
864	35k. 1946 Reo	1·10	75

313 Running

1996. Olympic Games, Atlanta. Mult.

865	5k. Type **313**	15	15
866	25k. Javelin	75	60
867	45k. Long jumping	1·40	1·00
868	65k. Shot put	2·20	1·60

314 Hospital Ward

1996. Centenary of Order of the Sisters of St. Joseph in Iceland.
869 **314** 65k. black, stone & purple . . . 2·00 1·80

315 School

1996. 150th Anniv of Reykjavik School.
870 **315** 150k. multicoloured . . . 4·25 3·25

316 Godafoss Waterfalls (central detail)

1996. "Nordia 96" Stamp Exhibition, Reykjavik (2nd issue). Sheet 105 × 65 mm containing T **316** and similar square designs. Multicoloured.
MS871 45k. Type **316**; 65k. Waterfalls (right detail); 90k. Waterfalls (left detail) (sold at 300k.) . . . . 7·50 5·50
The stamps form a composite design.

317 Reykjavik Cathedral

318 "Virgin Mary holding Child Jesus" (ivory figurine)

1996. Bicentenary of Reykjavik Cathedral.
872 **317** 45k. multicoloured . . . 1·40 1·00

1996. Christmas. Exhibits from National Museum of Iceland. Multicoloured.
873 35k. Type **318** . . . . . . 1·20 65
874 45k. Pax depicting Nativity 1·80 95

319 Red-breasted Merganser ("Mergus serrator")

1997. Ducks. Multicoloured.
875 10k. Type **319** 35 40
876 500k. Green-winged teal ("Anas crecca") . . . . . 13·50 12·50

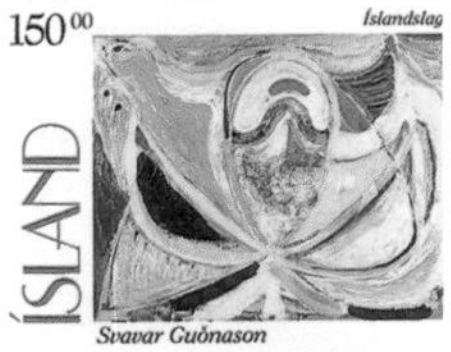
320 "Song of Iceland" (Svavar Gudnason)

1997. Paintings. Multicoloured.
877 150k. Type **320** . . . . . . 5·25 3·75
878 200k. "The Harbour" (Thorvaldur Skulason) . . 6·00 4·25

321 De Havilland D.H.89A Dragon Rapide

1997. Mail Planes. Multicoloured.
879 35k. Type **321** 95 80
880 35k. Stinson S.R. 8B Reliant seaplane 95 80
881 35k. Douglas DC-3 Dakota 95 80
882 35k. De Havilland D.H.C.6 Twin Otter 95 80

322 Hurdling

1997. 7th European Small States' Games. Multicoloured.
883 35k. Type **322** . . . . . . 1·10 1·10
884 45k. Sailing . . . . 1·50 1·00

323 "The Deacon of Myrka"

1997. Europa. Tales and Legends. Paintings by Asgrimur Jonsson. Multicoloured.
885 45k. Type **323** . . . . . . 1·50 1·10
886 65k. "Surtla at Blalandseyjar" . . . . . . 2·20 1·60

324 Printer's Colour Control and Pieces of Type

1997. Centenary of Formation of Icelandic Printers' Association (now part of Union of Icelandic Graphic Workers).
887 **324** 90k. multicoloured . . . 2·75 2·20

325 Stefania Gudmundsdattir and Idno Theatre

326 Western Islands Eight-oared Fishing Boat

1997. Centenary of Reykjavik Theatre.
888 **325** 100k. multicoloured . . . 3·25 2·10
The actress is shown in the role of the Fairy in "New Year's Night" by Indridi Einarsson.

1997. Stamp Day. Icelandic Boats. Sheet 110 × 76 mm containing T **326** and similar square designs. Each black, brown and chestnut.
MS889 35k. Type **326**; 65k. Engey six-oared sailing boat, 1912; 100k. Egil (Breidafjordur boat), 1904 (sold at 250k.) . . . . 5·50 6·00

327 Wise Men

1997. Christmas. Multicoloured.
890 35k. Type **327** . . . . . . 1·20 75
891 45k. Nativity . . . . 1·50 1·00

328 Mounted Mail Carrier

1997. Rural Post.
892 **328** 50k. multicoloured . . . 1·50 1·00

329 Downhill Skiing

1998. Winter Olympic Games, Nagano, Japan. Multicoloured.
893 35k. Type **329** . . . . . . 1·10 70
894 45k. Cross-country skiing . . 1·50 1·00

330 Sailing Dinghies

1998. Nordic Countries' Postal Co-operation. Sailing. Multicoloured.
895 35k. Type **330** . . . . . . 1·20 75
896 45k. Yachts . . . . 1·60 1·10

331 Lumpsucker ("Cyclopterus lumpus")

1998. Fishes (1st series). Multicoloured.
897 5k. Type **331** 20 20
898 10k. Atlantic cod ("Gadus morhua") 20 25
899 60k. Skate ("Raja batis") . . 1·70 1·70
900 300k. Atlantic wolffish ("Anarhichas lupus") . . . 8·00 8·75
MS901 100 × 68 mm. Nos. 897/900 5·50 4·75
See also Nos. 913/14, 972/3 and 983/4.

332 Children waving Flags

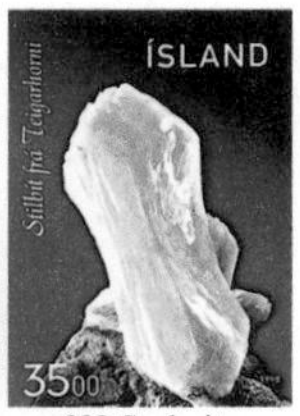
333 Scolecite

1998. Europa. National Festivals. National Day. Multicoloured.
902 45k. Type **332** . . . . . . 1·40 1·30
903 65k. Statue of President Jon Sigurdsson and flags . . . 2·20 1·50

1998. Minerals (1st series). Multicoloured.
904 35k. Type **333** 90 70
905 45k. Stilbite . . . . 1·50 1·10
See also Nos. 933/4.

334 Hospital

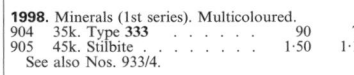

335 Anniversary Emblem

1998. Centenary of Founding of Leprosy Hospital, Laugarnes.
906 **334** 70k. multicoloured . . . 2·10 1·80

1998. 125th Anniv of First Iceland Stamps.
907 **335** 35k. multicoloured . . . 1·20 90

336 Peat-cutter

337 Cat and Houses (Thelma Ingolfsdottir)

1998. Stamp Day. Agricultural Tools. Sheet 110 × 76 mm containing T **336** and similar square designs.
MS908 35k. green, black and grey; 65k. ochre, black and grey; 100k. blue, black and grey (sold at 250k.) . . . . 5·00 5·75
DESIGNS: 65k. Mower; 100k. Grinder.

1998. Christmas. Multicoloured.
909 35k. Type **337** . . . . . . 1·20 95
910 45k. Two angels (Telma Thrastardottir) . . . . . . 1·50 1·20

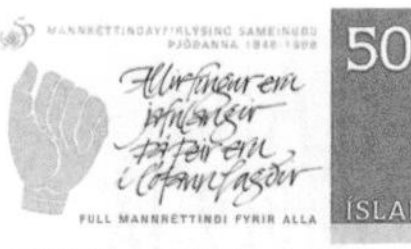
338 Writing and Hand forming Fist

1998. 50th Anniv of Universal Declaration of Human Rights.
911 **338** 50k. black, green and red 1·60 1·30

339 Leifs

1999. Birth Centenary of Jon Leifs (composer).
912 **339** 35k. multicoloured . . . 1·10 90

1999. Fishes (2nd series). As T **331**. Multicoloured.
913 35k. Plaice ("Pleuronectes platessa") . . . . 1·00 90
914 55k. Atlantic herring ("Clupea harengus") . . . 1·70 1·10

340 Killer Whale ("Orcinus orca")

1999. Marine Mammals (1st series). Multicoloured.
915 35k. Type **340** . . . . . . 1·10 95
916 45k. Sperm whale ("Physeter macrocephalus") . . . . . 1·40 1·10
917 65k. Blue whale ("Balaenoptera musculus") 2·20 1·70
918 85k. Common porpoise ("Phocoena phocoena") . . 2·75 2·20
MS919 100 × 80 mm. Nos. 915/19 3·75 4·25
See also Nos. 966/9 and 1000/3.

341 Arnold Jung's Steam Locomotive "Minor", 1892

1999. Transport. Multicoloured.
920 25k. Type **341** . . . . . . 1·20 90
921 50k. Type **341** . . . . . . 2·40 1·70
922 75k. "Sigurfari" (fishing cutter) . . . . 3·75 3·00

342 Dates and Doves

1999. 50th Anniv of Council of Europe.
923 **342** 35k. multicoloured . . . 1·10 90

343 Larch Boletes ("Suillus grevillei")

1999. Fungi (1st series). Multicoloured.
924 35k. Type **343** . . . . . . 1·10 1·00
925 75k. Field mushrooms ("Agaricus campestris") . . 2·10 2·00
See also Nos. 954/5.

344 Skutustadagigar, Lake Myvatn

1999. Europa. Parks and Gardens. Multicoloured.
926 50k. Type **344** . . . . . . 1·60 1·40
927 75k. Arnarstapi Point . . . . 2·10 2·10

345 Wheat ("Land Graedsla")

1999. Nature Conservation. Multicoloured.
928 35k. Type **345** . . . . . . 1·10 90
929 35k. Rainbow and tree within sun ("Loft") . . . . 1·10 95
930 35k. Nest with eggs ("Vot Lendis") . . . . 1·10 95
931 35k. Tree stump ("Skog Raekt") . . . . 1·10 95
932 35k. Fish and birds ("Stlendur") . . . . 1·10 95

1999. Minerals (2nd series). As T **333**. Mult.
933 40k. Calcite . . . . 1·00 95
934 50k. Heulandite . . . . . . 1·60 1·40

346 "Facescape" (Erro)

1999. Reykjavik, European Cultural City. Mult.
935 35k. Type **346** . . . . . . 1·00 95
936 50k. Cultural symbols . . . 1·60 1·40

347 "Danish Sailing Ship off Drangey" (Carl Baagoe)

1999. Stamp Day. Sheet 110 × 65 mm.
MS937 **347** 200k. brown and black (sold at 250k.) . . . . 4·00 4·25

348 Man cleaning Globe (Jona Greta Gudmundsdottir)

1999. "Stampin' the Future". Winning Entries in Children's International Painting Competition.
938 **348** 35k. multicoloured . . . 1·20 85

349 Goblin (Stiff-legs)

351 Chanterelle (*Cantharellus cibarius*)

350 Embroidered Altar Frontal, Holar Cathedral

1999. Christmas. Yule Goblins. Multicoloured.
939 35k. Type **349** . . . . . . 1·10 1·00
940 35k. Leaping over rock (Gully-gawk) . . . . . . 1·10 1·00
941 35k. With arm raised (Stubby) . . . . 1·10 1·00
942 35k. Licking spoon (Spoon-licker) . . . . 1·10 1·00
943 35k. With hand in cooking pot (Pot-scraper) . . . . . 1·10 1·00
944 35k. With finger in mouth (Bowl-licker) . . . . . . 1·10 1·00
945 35k. Opening door (Door-slammer) . . . . 1·10 1·00
946 35k. Drinking from ladle (Skyr-gobbler) . . . . . . 1·10 1·00
947 35k. Carrying sausages (Sausage-swiper) . . . . . 1·10 1·00
948 35k. Looking through window (Window-peeper) 1·10 1·00
949 50k. With nose raised (Door-sniffer) . . . . 1·40 1·40
950 50k. With leg of meat (Meat-hook) . . . . 1·40 1·40
951 50k. With candles (Candle-beggar) . . . . 1·40 1·40

2000. Millenary of Christianity in Iceland. Mult.
952 40k. Type **350** 45 55
MS953 70 × 46 mm. 40k. Family singing hymns (29 × 39 mm) . . 45 55

2000. Fungi (2nd series). Multicoloured.
954 40k. Type **351** . . . . . . 1·20 1·20
955 50k. Shaggy ink cap (*Coprinus comatus*) . . . . 1·60 1·40

352 Statue of Thorfinn Karlsefni (early settler) and Globe

2000. Millenary of Discovery of the Americas by Leif Eriksson. Multicoloured.
956 40k. Type **352** . . . . . . 1·20 1·30
957 50k. Viking longship under sail . . . . 1·50 1·50
958 75k. Longship on shore . . . 2·40 2·20
959 90k. Leif Eriksson and globe 3·00 2·40
MS960 96 × 76 mm. Nos. 956/9 3·25 3·00

353 Quill and Profile

2000. New Millennium. Multicoloured.
961 40k. Type **353** . . . . . . 1·20 1·20
962 50k. Family tree, man and computer chip . . . . . 1·60 1·40

354 Steam Roller

2000. Transport. Multicoloured.
963 50k. Type **354** . . . . . . 1·30 1·40
964 75k. Fire engine . . . . . . 2·30 2·40

355 "Building Europe"

356 Pansy (*Violea x wittrockiana*)

2000. Europa.
965 **355** 50k. multicoloured . . . 1·70 1·50

2000. Marine Mammals (2nd series). As T **340**. Mult.
966 5k. Bottlenose whale (*Hyperoodon ampullatus*) 20 25
967 40k. Atlantic white-sided dolphin (*Lagenorhynchus actus*) . . . . 1·20 1·20
968 50k. Humpback whale (*Megaptera novaeangliae*) 1·40 1·40
969 75k. Minke whale (*Balaenoptera acutorostrata*) 2·20 2·30

2000. Summer Flowers (1st series). Multicoloured.
970 40k. Type **356** . . . . . . 1·30 1·10
971 50k. Petunia (*Petunia x hybrida*) . . . . 1·60 1·40
See also Nos. 986/7.

2000. Fishes (3rd series). As T **331**. Multicoloured.
972 10k. Haddock (*Melanogrammus aeglefinus*) 30 30
973 250k. Capelin (*Mallotus villosus*) . . . . 6·00 6·75

357 Dark Marbled Carpet (*Chioroclysta citrata*)

2000. Butterflies. Multicoloured.
974 40k. Type **357** . . . . . . 1·10 1·00
975 50k. Antler (*Cerapteryx graminis*) . . . . 1·30 1·30

358 "Icelandic settlers on the Shore of Lake Winnipeg" (Arni Sigurdsson)

2000. Stamp Day. Sheet 88 × 73 mm.
MS976 **358** 200k. multicoloured (sold at 250k.) . . . . 4·00 4·00

359 Viking Settler's House

2000. Early Dwellings. Multicoloured.
977 45k. Type **359** . . . . . . 1·10 1·10
978 75k. Viking turf houses, Stong Thjorsardal . . . . 2·20 2·00

360 Leppaludi

2000. Christmas. Ogres. Multicoloured.
979 40k. Type **360** . . . . . . 1·10 1·00
980 50k. Gryla . . . . 1·20 1·20
MS981 105 × 75 mm. As Nos. 979/80, but 21 × 36 mm) 1·50 1·25

361 Super Puma Helicopter, Fokker 27 Airplane and *Tyr* (ship)

363 Marigold (*Calendula officinalis*)

362 Man's Face, Tents and Emblem

2001. 75th Anniv of Coast Guard Service in Iceland.
982 **361** 20k. multicoloured . . . 30 60

2001. Fishes. As T **331**. Multicoloured.
983 55k. Greenland halibut (*Reinhardtius hippogolossides*) . . . . . 85 1·00
984 80k. Saithe (*Pollachius virens*) 1·30 1·60

2001. 50th Anniv of United Nations Commissioner for Refugees.
985 **362** 50k. black and brown . . 80 95

2001. Summer Flowers. Multicoloured.
986 55k. Type **363** . . . . . . 85 1·00
987 65k. Livingstone daisy (*Dorotheanthus bellidformis*) 1·00 1·30

364 Dog

2001. Icelandic Sheepdogs. Multicoloured.
988 40k. Type **364** 75 85
989 80k. Black and white dog . . 1·60 1·10

365 TF-OGN

2001. Airplanes. Multicoloured.
990 55k. Type **365** . . . . 1·10 1·00
991 80k. Klemm KL-25E . . . . 2·40 1·10

366 Woman's Head and Waterfall

2001. Europa. Water Resources. Multicoloured.
992 55k. Type **366** . . . . 1·10 90
993 80k. Cupped hands and wave 1·60 1·10

367 Walking

2001. Horses. Multicoloured.
994 40k. Type **367** 70 75
995 50k. Running walk 75 90
996 55k. Trotting 85 95
997 60k. Pacing . . . . 1·00 90
998 80k. Cantering . . . . 1·40 1·10

2001. Domestic Letter Rate. No. 915 optd **Bref 50g**.
999 (53k.) multicoloured . . . . 1·00 80

2001. Marine Mammals (3rd series). As T **340**. Multicoloured.
1000 5k. Large-beaked dolphin (*Lagenorhynchus albirostris*) 15 20
1001 40k. Fin whale (*Balaenoptera physalus*) 70 75
1002 80k. Sei whale (*Balaenoptera borealis*) . . . . 1·40 1·50
1003 100k. Long-finned pilot whale (*Globicephala melas*) 1·70 1·90

369 Grimsey

2001. Islands (1st series). Multicoloured.
1004 40k. Type **369** 70 60
1005 55k. Papey 85 80
See also Nos. 1031/2 and 1061/2.

370 Esja Mountain

2001. Stamp Day. Sheet 105 × 48 mm.
MS1006 **370** 250k. multicoloured 4·25 3·25

371 Brautarholt Church, Kjalarnes

2001. Christmas. Multicoloured.
1007 (42k.) Type **371** 70 55
1008 55k Viomyri Church, Skagafjorour 85 75

372 Northern Wheatear (*Oenanthe oenanthe*)

2001. Birds (1st series). Multicoloured.
1009 42k. Type **372** 65 60
1010 250k. Ringed plover (*Charadrius hiaticula*) . . 4·25 3·25
See also Nos. 1036/7 and 1055/6.

373 Brown Birch Bolete (*Leccinum scabrum*)

2002. Fungi. Multicoloured. (a) Inscr "Bref 20g".
1011 (42k.) Type **373** 70 60
(b) With face value.
1012 85k. Hedgehog fungus (*Hydnum repandum*) . . . 1·40 1·20
No. 1011 was for use on domestic mail up to 20 grammes.

374 Stanley and 2 h.p. Mollerup Engine

2002. Centenary of First Motorboat in Iceland.
1013 **374** 60k. multicoloured . . . 1·00 85

375 Mount Snaefell

2002. International Year of the Mountain. Inscr "Bref 20g".
1014 **375** (42k.) multicoloured . . 70 60
No. 1014 was for use on domestic mail up to 20 grammes.

376 Laxness

2002. Birth Centenary of Halldor Laxness (writer and Nobel Prize winner).
1015 **376** 100k. multicoloured . . 1·70 1·40
MS1016 75 × 45 mm. No. 1015 1·70 1·70

377 "Waterfall" (sculpture, Ruri) and Emblem

2002. Nordic Countries' Postal Co-operation. Modern Art. Multicoloured. (a) Inscr "Bref 20g".
1017 (42k.) Type **377** (50th anniv of Nordic Council) . . . 70 60
(b) With face value.
1018 60k. "Tension" (sculpture, Hafsteinn Austmann) and emblem . . . . 1·00 85
No. 1017 was for use on domestic mail up to 20 grammes.

378 Grotta

379 House and Sesselja Sigmundsdottir

2002. Lighthouses. Multicoloured.
1019 60k. Type **378** . . . . . . 1·00 85
1020 85k. Kogur . . . . 1·40 1·20

2002. Birth Centenary of Sesselja H. Sigmundsdottir (mental health pioneer and environmentalist).
1021 **379** 45k. multicoloured . . . 75 65

380 Trapeze Artists and Clown

2002. Europa. Circus. Multicoloured.
1022 60k. Type **380** . . . . . . 1·00 85
1023 85k. Marionette's head and lion leaping through flaming hoop . . . . . . 1·40 1·20

381 Lobelia (*Lobelia erinus*)

2002. Summer Flowers. Multicoloured.
1024 10k. Type **381** 15 15
1025 200k. Cornflower (*Centaurea cyanus*) . . . . 3·50 2·75

382 Arctic Charr (*Salvelinus alpinus*)

2002. Fish from Lake Thingvallavatn. Multicoloured. (a) Inscr "Bref 20g".
1026 (45k.) Type **382** 75 65
(b) Inscr "Bréf 50g".
1027 (55k.) Brown trout (*Salmo trutta*) (vert) 90 80
(c) With face value.
1028 60k. Arctic charr (*Salvelinus alpinus*) . . . . 1·00 85
1029 90k. Arctic charr (*Salvelinus alpinus*) . . . . 1·50 1·30
1030 200k. Arctic charr (*Salvelinus alpinus*) . . . 3·50 2·75
No. 1026 was for use on domestic mail up to 20 grammes.
No. 1027 was for use on domestic mail up to 50 grammes.

2002. Islands (2nd series). As T **369**. Multicoloured.
1031 45k. Vigur 75 65
1032 55k. Flatey 90 80

383 South Street, Reykjavik, and Mount Keilir (volcano)

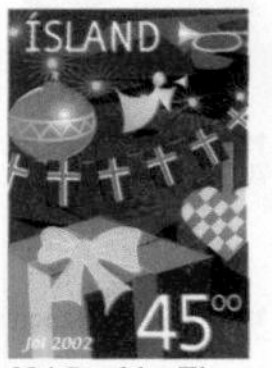

384 Bauble, Flags and Gift

2002. Stamp Day. Sheet 85 × 55 mm.
MS1033 **383** 250k. multicoloured 4·25 4·25

2002. Christmas. Multicoloured.
1034 45k. Type **384** 75 65
1035 60k. Gifts . . . . 1·00 85

385 Common Redshank (*Tringa totanus*)

2002. Birds (2nd series). Multicoloured.
1036 50k. Type **385** 85 70
1037 85k. Grey phalarope (*Phalaropus fulicarius*) . . 1·40 1·20

386 Modern Policemen

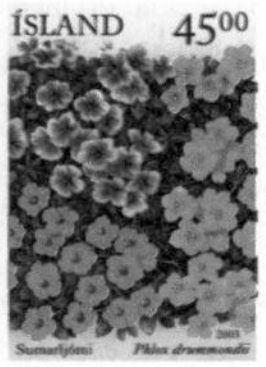

387 Annual Phlox (*Phlox drummondii*)

2003. Bicentenary of Icelandic Police Force. Multicoloured.
1038 45k. Type **386** 75 65
1039 55k. 1803 policeman 90 75

2002. Summer Flowers. Multicoloured.
1040 45k. Type **387** 75 60
1041 60k. Treasure flower (*Gazania x hybrida*) . . . 95 80

388 Bull and Audhumla (mythological cow)

2003. Icelandic Cattle. Multicoloured.
1042 45k. Type **388** 75 65
1043 85k. Red-mottled cow . . . 1·40 1·20

389 Map, Crow and Sailing Ship

2003. Nordia 2003 International Stamp Exhibition, Rekjavik. Sheet 86 × 76 mm.
MS1044 **389** 250k. multicoloured 4·00 3·50

390 *Saefari*

2003. Ferries. Multicoloured.
1045 45k. Type **390** 70 60
1046 45k. *Saevar* 70 60
1047 60k. *Herjolfur* 95 80
1048 60k. *Baldur* 95 80

391 Church

392 Hen and Cockerel

2003. Centenary of Free Church, Reykjavik.
1049 **391** 200k. multicoloured . . 3·00 2·50

2003. Icelandic Poultry.
1050 **392** 45k. multicoloured . . . 70 60

393 Posters

2003. Europa. Poster Art. Multicoloured.
1051 60k. Type **393** 95 80
1052 60k. Posters (different) . . . 95 80

394 Friendship (Orn Agustsson)

2003. Winning Entry in Children's Stamp Design Competition.
1053 **394** 45k. multicoloured . . . 70 60

395 District Officer and Family

2003. 300th Anniv of First Census.
1054 **395** 60k. multicoloured . . . 95 80

2003. Birds (3rd series). As T **385**. Multicoloured.
1055 70k. Meadow pipit (*Anthus pratensis*) . . . . 1·10 85
1056 250k. Whimbrel (*Numenius phaeopus*) . . . . 4·00 3·50

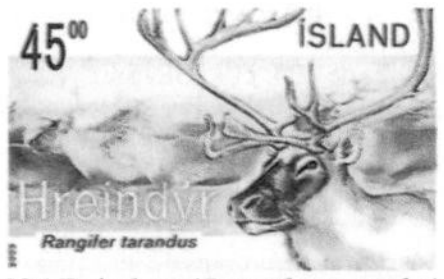

396 Reindeer (*Rangifer tarandus*)

2003.
1057 **396** 45k. multicoloured . . . 70 60

397 Barrack converted to House

2003. Stamp Day. Sheet 120 × 58 mm.
MS1058 **397** 250k. multicoloured 4·00 3·50

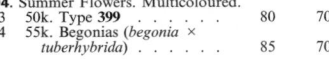

398 Girl hanging Baubles on Tree

399 Marigolds (*Tagetes patula*)

2003. Christmas. Multicoloured.
1059 45k. Type **398** 70 60
1060 60k. Boy lighting candles . . 95 80

2003. Islands (3rd series). As T **369**.
1061 85k. Heimaey . . . . 1·30 1·10
1062 200k. Hrísey . . . . 3·00 1·70

2004. Summer Flowers. Multicoloured.
1063 50k. Type **399** 80 70
1064 55k. Begonias (*begonia × tuberhybrida*) 85 70

400 Hannes Hafstein (first minister)

2004. Centenary of Icelandic Home Rule. Multicoloured.
1065 150k. Type **400** . . . . . . 2·40 2·00
MS1066 79 × 50 mm. No. 1065 2·40 2·00

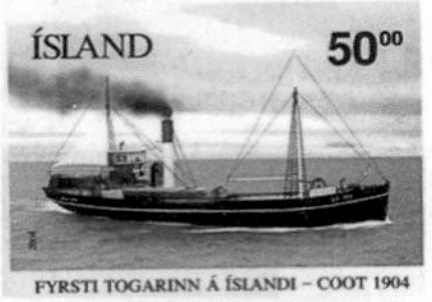

401 *Coot* (trawler)

2004.
1067 **401** 50k. blue and black . . 80 70

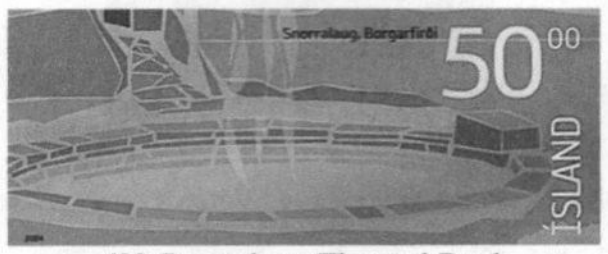

402 Snorralaug Thermal Pool

2004. Geo-thermal Energy. Multicoloured.
1068 50k. Type **402** 80 70
1069 55k. Vent, dome and steam (30 × 48 mm) 85 70
1070 60k. Pipeline 95 80
1071 90k. Turbine . . . . . . 1·40 1·20
1072 250k. Map of Iceland, mid Atlantic ridge and clouds (30 × 48 mm) . . . . . . 4·00 3·30

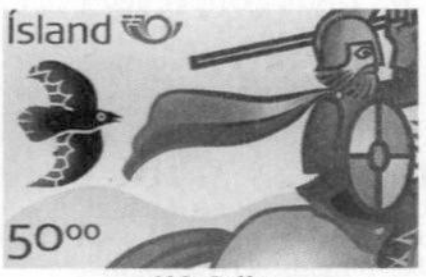

403 Odin

2004. Norse Mythology. Sheet 105 × 70 mm containing T **403** and similar horiz design. Multicoloured.
MS1073 50k. Type **403**; 60k. Sleipnir (Odin's horse) . . . . 1·90 1·90
Stamps of a similar theme were issued by Aland Islands, Denmark, Faroe Islands, Finland, Greenland, Norway and Sweden.

404 Ford Fairlane Victoria, 1956

2004. Cars. Multicoloured.
1074 60k. Type **404** 95 80
1075 60k. Pobeta, 1954 . . . . . 95 80
1076 85k. Chevrolet Bel Air, 1955 1·30 1·10
1077 85k. Volkswagen, 1952 . . . 1·30 1·10

OFFICIAL STAMPS

1873. As T **1** but inscr "PJON. FRIM." at foot.
O 8 4s. green . . . . 46·00 £225
O10 8s. mauve £300 £425

O 4

1876.
O36 O 4 3a. yellow . . . . . . 9·25 15·00
O37 4a. grey . . . . . . 19·00 22·00
O21b 5a. brown . . . . . . 5·75 9·25
O22a 10a. blue . . . . . . 48·00 6·75
O23a 16a. red . . . . . . 14·00 26·00
O24a 20a. green . . . . . . 10·00 13·00
O25 50a. mauve . . . . . . 46·00 50·00

1902. As T **10**, but inscr "PJONUSTA".
O81 3a. sepia and yellow . . . . 3·00 1·40
O82 4a. sepia and green . . . . 3·50 1·20
O83 5a. sepia and brown . . . . 3·00 1·60
O84 10a. sepia and blue . . . . 3·25 2·25
O85 16a. sepia and red . . . . 2·10 6·75
O86 20a. sepia and green . . . 12·50 4·25
O87 50a. sepia and mauve . . . 5·75 9·00

1902. Optd **I GILDI '02–'03.**
O94 O 4 3a. yellow . . . . . . 75 1·50
O95 4a. grey . . . . . . 75 1·30
O96 5a. brown . . . . . . 75 4·00
O97 10a. blue . . . . . . 75 1·75
O91 16a. red . . . . . . 10·00 34·00
O98 20a. green . . . . . . 80 12·00
O93 50a. mauve . . . . . . 3·50 33·00

1907. As T **12**, but inscr "PJONUSTU".
O 99 3a. sepia and yellow . . . 6·25 4·00
O100 4a. sepia and green . . . 2·40 4·50
O101 5a. sepia and brown . . . 6·75 2·50
O102 10a. sepia and blue . . . 2·00 2·10
O103 15a. sepia and blue . . . . 3·25 10·50
O104 16a. sepia and red . . . . 3·00 15·00
O105 20a. sepia and green . . . 7·50 3·75
O106 50a. sepia and mauve . . . 5·00 7·25

1920. As T **15**, but inscr "PJONUSTU".
O132 3a. black and yellow . . . 1·90 1·70
O133 4a. black and green . . . 80 1·70
O134 5a. black and orange . . . 60 65
O135 10a. black and blue . . . . 3·75 45
O136 15a. black and blue 45 45
O137 20a. black and green . . . 28·00 2·30
O138 50a. black and violet . . . 31·00 90
O139 1k. black and red . . . . 31·00 1·30
O140 2k. black and blue . . . 4·00 10·00
O141 5k. black and brown . . . 26·00 29·00

1922. Optd **Pjonusta**.
O153 **15** 20a. on 10a. red . . . . 15·00 1·20
O151a **13** 2k. red (No. 107) . . . 35·00 38·00
O152 5k. brown (No. 108) . . £180 £130

1930. Parliamentary Commemoratives of 1930 optd **Pjonustumerki**.
O174 **24** 3a. violet and lilac (postage) . . . . . 7·75 21·00
O175 – 5a. blue and grey . . . . 7·75 21·00
O176 – 7a. green and dp green . . 7·75 21·00
O177 – 10a. purple and mauve . . 7·75 21·00
O178 – 15a. dp blue & blue . . . 7·75 21·00
O179 – 20a. red and pink . . . . 7·75 21·00
O180 – 25a. brown & lt brown . . 7·75 21·00
O181 – 30a. green and grey . . . 7·75 21·00
O182 – 35a. blue & ultramarine . . 7·75 21·00
O183 – 40a. red, blue and grey . . 7·75 21·00
O184 – 50a. dp brown & brown . . £110 £140
O185 – 1k. green and grey . . . £110 £140
O186 – 2k. blue and green . . . £100 £160
O187 – 5k. orange and yellow . . £100 £130
O188 – 10k. lake and red £100 £130
O189 **25** 10a. blue & dp blue (air) 18·00 65·00

1936. Optd **Pjonusta**.
O220 **15** 7a. green . . . . 2·00 18·00
O221 10a. red . . . . 3·75 2·00
O222 **12** 50a. red and grey . . . . 18·00 16·00

IDAR Pt. 1

A state in Western India. Now uses Indian stamps.

12 pies = 1 anna; 16 annas = 1 rupee.

1 Maharaja Singh Himat

2 Maharaja Singh Himat

1939.
1c **1** ½a. green . . . . 13·00 18·00

1944.
3b **2** ½a. green . . . . 2·75 60·00
4 1a. violet . . . . 3·00 50·00
5 2a. blue . . . . 3·25 85·00
6 4a. red . . . . 3·50 90·00

IFNI Pt. 9

Spanish enclave on the Atlantic coast of Northern Morocco ceded in 1860.
By an agreement, made effective on 30 June 1969, Ifni was surrendered by Spain to Morocco.
100 centimos = 1 peseta.

1941. Stamps of Spain optd **TERRITORIO DE IFNI.**
1 **181** 1c. green (imperf) . . . . 6·00 5·25
2 **182** 2c. brown . . . . 6·00 5·25
3 **183** 5c. brown 85 55
4 10c. red . . . . 3·25 1·90
5 15c. green 75 55
6 **196** 20c. violet 75 55
7 25c. red 75 55
8 30c. blue 75 55
9 40c. slate . . . . 1·20 50
10 50c. slate . . . . 6·75 1·70
11 70c. blue . . . . 6·75 4·75
12 1PTA. black . . . . 6·75 4·75
13 2PTAS. brown . . . . 80·00 28·00
14 4PTAS. red £250 £140
15 10PTS. brown £800 £375

3 El Santuario

4 Nomad Family

1943.
16 A 1c. mauve & brown (postage) 15 15
17 B 2c. blue and green 15 15
18 C 5c. blue and purple 15 15
19 A 15c. green and deep green 15 15
20 B 20c. brown and violet . . . 15 15
21 A 40c. violet and purple . . . 20 20
22 B 45c. red and brown 25 25
35 **4** 50c. black and brown . . . 7·50 65
23 C 75c. blue and indigo . . . 25 25
24 A 1p. brown and red . . . . 1·50 1·50
25 B 3p. green and blue . . . . 1·80 1·80
26 C 10p. black and brown . . . 19·00 19·00
27 **3** 5c. brown and purple (air) 20 20
28 D 25c. brown and green . . . 20 20
29 **3** 50c. blue and indigo . . . 25 25
30 D 1p. blue and violet 25 25
31 **3** 1p.40 blue and green . . . 25 25
32 D 2p. brown and purple . . . 1·10 1·10
33 **3** 5p. violet and brown . . . 1·50 1·50
34 D 6p. green and blue . . . . 21·00 21·00
DESIGNS: A, Nomadic shepherds; B, Arab rifleman; C, La Alcazaba; D, Airplane over oasis.

1947. Air. Autogyro type of Spain optd **IFNI**.
36 **195** 5c. yellow . . . . 2·50 60
37 10c. green . . . . 2·50 60

1948. Stamps of Spain optd **Territorio de Ifni**.
45 **182** 2c. brown (postage) . . . 15 15
46 **183** 5c. brown 15 15
47 10c. red 15 15
48 15c. green 15 15
39 **229** 15c. green . . . . 3·00 55
49 **196** 25c. purple 15 15
50 30c. blue 15 15
51 **232** 40c. brown 15 15
52 45c. red 25 25
53 **196** 50c. grey 25 15
54 **232** 75c. blue 40 15
55 **201** 90c. green 40 25
41 **196** 1PTA. black 30 15
56 **201** 1p.35 violet . . . . 4·25 2·75
57 **196** 2PTAS. brown . . . . 3·00 1·90
58 4PTAS. pink . . . . 11·00 5·25
59 10PTAS. brown . . . . . 27·00 16·00
60 **195** 25c. red (air) 45 15
61 50c. brown 55 15
62 1p. blue 55 15
63 2p. green . . . . 3·00 60
64 4p. blue . . . . 8·50 3·25
65 10p. violet . . . . 11·50 6·75

1949. Stamp Day and 75th Anniv of U.P.U. Spanish stamps optd **Territorio de Ifni.**
42 **240** 50c. brown (postage) . . . 2·00 85
43 75c. blue . . . . 2·00 85
44 4p. olive (air) . . . . . . 2·40 85

8 General Franco

9 Lope Sancho de Valenzuela

1950. Child Welfare.
66 **8** 50c.+10c. sepia 35 25
67 1p.+25c. blue . . . . 14·00 5·50
68 6p.50+1p.65 green . . . . . 4·75 2·50

1950. Air. Colonial Stamp Day.
69 **9** 5p. green . . . . 1·90 60

10 Woman and Dove

11 General Franco

1951. Air. 500th Birth Anniv of Isabella the Catholic.
70 **10** 5p. red . . . . 21·00 6·25

1951. Gen. Franco's Visit to Ifni.
71 **11** 50c. orange 30 15
72 1p. brown . . . . 3·75 90
73 5p. green . . . . 30·00 8·75

12 Fennec Fox

13 Mother and Child

1951. Colonial Stamp Day.
74 **12** 5c.+5c. brown 15 15
75 10c.+5c. orange 15 15
76 60c.+15c. olive 30 15

1952. Child Welfare.
77 **13** 5c.+5c. brown 15 15
78 50c.+10c. black 15 15
79 2p.+30c. blue . . . . 1·10 40

14 Ferdinand the Catholic

15 Shag

1952. Air. 500th Birth Anniv of Ferdinand the Catholic.
80 **14** 5p. brown . . . . 27·00 5·75

1952. Colonial Stamp Day.
81 **15** 5c.+5c. brown 20 15
82 10c.+5c. red 20 15
83 60c.+15c. green 35 20

16

17 Addra Gazelle and Douglas DC-4 Airliner

1952. 400th Death Anniv of Leo Africanus (geographer).
84 **16** 5c. orange 15 15
85 35c. green 15 15
86 60c. brown 20 15

1953. Air.
87 **17** 60c. green 15 15
88 1p.20 lake 20 15
89 1p.60 brown 25 15
90 2p. blue . . . . 1·70 20
91 4p. myrtle 95 20
92 10p. purple . . . . 5·25 1·20

18 Musician

1953. Child Welfare. Inscr "PRO INFANCIA 1953".
93 **18** 5c.+5c. lake 15 15
94 – 10c.+5c. purple 15 15
95 **18** 15c. olive 15 15
96 – 60c. brown 20 15
DESIGN: 10c., 60c. Two native musicians.

19 Fish and Jellyfish

1953. Colonial Stamp Day. Inscr "DIA DEL SELLO COLONIAL 1953".
97 **19** 5c.+5c. blue 15 15
98 – 10c.+5c. mauve 15 15
99 **19** 15c. green 15 15
100 – 60c. brown 35 15
DESIGN: 10, 60c. Dusky grouper and seaweed.

20 Mediterranean Gull

21 Asclepiad

1954.

101	**20**	5c. orange	15	15
102	**21**	10c. green	15	15
103	–	25c. red	15	15
104	**20**	35c. green	15	15
105	**21**	40c. purple	15	15
106	–	60c. brown	15	15
107	**20**	1p. brown	8·00	55
108	**21**	1p.25 red	15	15
109	–	2p. blue	15	15
110	**21**	4p.50 green	20	40
111	–	5p. black	34·00	10·50

DESIGN—VERT: 25, 60c., 2, 5p. Cactus.

22 Woman and Child

23 Lobster

1954. Child Welfare. Inscr "PRO-INFANCIA 1954".

112	**22**	5c.+5c. orange	15	15
113	–	10c.+5c. mauve	15	15
114	**22**	15c. green	15	15
115	–	60c. brown	20	15

DESIGN: 10c., 60c. Woman and girl.

1954. Colonial Stamp Day. Inscr "DIA DEL SELLO COLONIAL 1954".

116	**23**	5c.+5c. brown	15	15
117	–	10c.+5c. violet	15	15
118	**23**	15c. green	15	15
119	–	60c. lake	20	15

DESIGN: 10, 60c. Smooth hammerhead.

24 Ploughman and "Justice"

1955. Native Welfare. Inscr "PRO-INDIGENAS 1955".

120	**24**	10c.+5c. purple	15	15
121	–	25c.+10c. lilac	15	15
122	**24**	50c. olive	20	15

DESIGN: 25c. Camel caravan and "Spain".

25 Eurasian Red Squirrel

1955. Colonial Stamp Day.

123	**25**	5c.+5c. brown	15	15
124	–	15c.+5c. bistre	15	15
125	**25**	70c. green	20	15

DESIGN: 15c. Eurasian red squirrel holding nut.

26 "Senecio antheuphorbium"

1956. Child Welfare. Inscr "PRO-INFANCIA 1956".

126	**26**	5c.+5c. green	15	15
127	–	15c.+5c. brown	15	15
128	**26**	20c. green	15	15
129	–	50c. sepia	20	15

DESIGN: 15c., 50c., "Limoniastrum ifniensis".

27 Arms of Sidi-Ifni and Drummer

28 Feral Rock Pigeons

1956. Colonial Stamp Day. Inscr "DIA DEL SELLO 1956".

130	–	5c.+5c. sepia	15	15
131	**27**	15c.+5c. brown	15	15
132	–	70c. green	20	15

DESIGNS—VERT: 5c. Arms of Spain and Bohar reedbucks. HORIZ: 70c. Arms of Sidi-Ifni, shepherd and sheep.

1957. Child Welfare Fund.

133	**28**	5c.+5c. green and brown	15	15
134	–	15c.+5c. brown & ochre	15	15
135	**28**	70c. brown and green	20	15

DESIGN: 15c. Stock pigeons in flight.

29 Golden Jackal

1957. Colonial Stamp Day. Inscr "DIA DEL SELLO 1957".

136	**29**	10c.+5c. brown & purple	15	15
137	–	15c.+5c. green and brown	15	15
138	**29**	20c. brown and green	20	15
139	–	70c. brown and green	20	15

DESIGN—VERT: 15c., 70c., Head of Golden jackal.

30 Barn Swallows and Arms of Valencia and Sidi-Ifni

1958. "Aid for Valencia".

140	**30**	10c.+5c. brown	15	15
141	–	15c.+10c. brown	15	15
142	–	50c.+10c. brown	20	15

31 Basketball

1958. Child Welfare Fund.

143	**31**	10c.+5c. brown	15	15
144	–	15c.+5c. brown	15	15
145	**31**	20c. green	15	15
146	–	70c. green	20	15

DESIGN: 15, 70c. Cycling.

32 Greater Spotted Dogfish

1958. Colonial Stamp Day.

147	**32**	10c.+5c. red	15	15
148	–	25c.+10c. purple	15	15
149	–	50c.+10c. brown	20	15

DESIGNS—VERT: 25c. Black-chinned guitar-fish. HORIZ: 50c. Fishing boats.

33 Ewe and Lamb

1959. Child Welfare Fund.

150	**33**	10c.+5c. brown	15	15
151	–	15c.+5c. brown	15	15
152	–	20c. turquoise	15	15
153	**33**	70c. green	20	15

DESIGNS—VERT: 15c. Native trader with mule; 20c. Mountain goat.

34 Footballer

35 Dromedaries

1959. Colonial Stamp Day. Inscr "DIA DEL SELLO 1959".

154	**34**	10c.+5c. brown	20	20
155	–	20c.+5c. myrtle	20	20
156	–	50c.+20c. olive	20	20

DESIGNS: 20c. Footballers; 50c. Javelin-thrower.

1960. Child Welfare.

157	**35**	10c.+5c. purple	20	20
158	–	15c.+5c. brown	20	20
159	–	35c. green	20	20
160	**35**	80c. green	20	20

DESIGNS: 15c. Wild boar; 35c. Red-legged partridges.

36 White Stork

1960. Birds.

161	**36**	25c. violet	20	20
162	–	50c. brown	20	20
163	–	75c. purple	20	20
164	**36**	1p. red	20	20
165	–	1p.50 turquoise	20	20
166	–	2p. purple	20	20
167	**36**	3p. blue	45	20
168	–	5p. brown	90	30
169	–	10p. green	3·00	90

BIRDS—HORIZ: 50c., 1p.50, 5p. Eurasian goldfinches. VERT: 75c., 2, 10p. Eurasian skylarks.

37 Church of Santa Cruze del Mar

38 High Jump

1960. Stamp Day. Inscr "DIA DEL SELLO 1960".

170	**37**	10c.+5c. brown	20	20
171	–	20c.+5c. green	20	20
172	**37**	30c.+10c. brown	20	20
173	–	50c.+50c. brown	20	20

DESIGN—HORIZ: 20c., 50c. School building.

1961. Child Welfare. Inscr "PRO-INFANCIA 1961".

174	**38**	10c.+5c. red	20	20
175	–	25c.+10c. violet	20	20
176	**38**	80c.+20c. turquoise	20	20

DESIGN—VERT: 25c. Football.

39

1961. 25th Anniv of General Franco as Head of State.

177	–	25c. grey	20	20
178	**39**	50c. brown	20	20
179	–	70c. green	20	20
180	**39**	1p. red	20	20

DESIGNS—VERT: 25c. Map. HORIZ: 70c. Government Building.

40 Camel and Motor Lorry

41 Admiral Jofre Tenorio

1961. Stamp Day. Inscr "DIA DEL SELLO 1961".

181	**40**	10c.+5c. lake	20	20
182	–	25c.+10c. plum	20	20
183	**40**	30c.+10c. brown	20	20
184	–	1p.+10c. orange	20	20

DESIGN: 25c., 1p. Freighter at wharf.

1962. Child Welfare. Inscr "PRO-INFANCIA 1962".

185	**41**	25c. violet	20	20
186	–	50c. turquoise	20	20
187	**41**	1p. brown	20	20

DESIGN: 50c. C. Fernandez-Duro (historian).

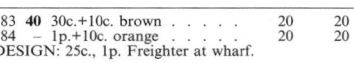

42 Desert Postman

43 "Golden Tower", Seville

1962. Stamp Day.

188	**42**	15c. blue	20	20
189	–	35c. mauve	20	20
190	**42**	1p. purple	20	20

DESIGN: 35c. Winged letter on hands.

1963. Seville Flood Relief.

191	**43**	50c. green	20	20
192	–	1p. brown	20	20

44 Moroccan Copper and Flower

1963. Child Welfare. Inscr "PRO-INFANCIA 1963".

193	–	25c. blue	20	20
194	**44**	50c. green	20	20
195	–	1p. red	20	20

DESIGN: 25c., 1p. Moroccan orange-tips.

45 Child and Flowers

1963. "For Barcelona".

196	**45**	50c. green	20	20
197		1p. brown	20	20

46 Beetle ("Steraspis speciosa")

47 Edmi Gazelle

1964. Stamp Day. Inscr "DIA DEL SELLO 1963".

198	**46**	25c. blue	20	20
199	–	50c. olive	20	20
200	**46**	1p. brown	20	20

DESIGN: 50c. Desert locust.

1964. Child Welfare.

201	**47**	25c. violet	20	20
202	–	50c. grey	20	20
203	**47**	1p. red	20	20

DESIGN: 50c. Head of roe deer.

48 Cyclists Racing

1964. Stamp Day.

204	**48**	50c. brown	20	20
205	–	1p. red	20	20
206	**48**	1p.50 green	20	20

DESIGN: 1p. Motor cycle racing.

49 Port Installation, Sidi Ifni

1965. 25th Anniv of End of Spanish Civil War.

207	–	50c. green	20	20
208	–	1p. red	20	20
209	**49**	1p.50 blue	20	20

DESIGNS—VERT: 50c. Ifnian; 1p. "Education" (children in class).

50 "Eugaster fernandezi"

1965. Child Welfare.

210	**50**	50c. purple	20	20
211	–	1p. red ("Halter halteratus")	20	20
212	**50**	1p.50 blue	20	20

51 Arms of Ifni

1965. Stamp Day.

213	–	50c. brown	20	20
214	**51**	1p. red	20	20
215	–	1p.50 blue	20	20

DESIGN—VERT: 50c., 1p.50, Golden Eagle.

52 De Havilland D.H.9C Biplanes

1966. Child Welfare.

216	–	1p. brown	20	20
217	–	1p.50 blue	20	20
218	**52**	2p.50 violet	1·10	1·10

DESIGN—VERT: 1p., 1p.50, Douglas DC-8 jetliner over Sidi Ifni.

53 Maid Alice Moth

54 Coconut Palm

1966. Stamp Day. Insects.

219	**53**	10c. green and red	20	20
220	–	40c. brown and deep brown	20	20
221	**53**	1p.50 violet and yellow	20	20
222	–	4p. blue and purple	20	20

DESIGN: 40c., 4p. African monarch (butterfly).

1967. Child Welfare.

223	**54**	10c. green and brown	20	20
224	–	40c. green and brown	20	20
225	**54**	1p.50 turquoise and sepia	20	20
226	–	4p. sepia and brown	20	20

DESIGN: 40c., 4p. Cactus.

55 Bulk Carrier and Floating Crane

1967. Inauguration of Port Ifni.

227	**55**	1p.50 brown and green	20	20

56 Skipper

1967. Stamp Day.

228	**56**	1p. green and blue	20	20
229	–	1p.50 purple and yellow	20	20
230	–	3p.50 red and blue	35	35

FISH—VERT: 1p.50, John Dory, HORIZ: 3p.50, Tub gurnard.

1968. Child Welfare. Signs of the Zodiac. As T **47** of Fernando Poo.

231		1p. mauve on yellow	20	20
232		1p.50 brown on pink	20	20
233		2p.50 violet on yellow	35	35

DESIGNS: 1p., Fishes (Pisces); 1p.50, Ram (Aries); 2p.50, Archer (Sagittarius).

57 Posting Letter

1968. Stamp Day.

234	**57**	1p. black and yellow	20	20
235	–	1p.50 black, plum and blue	20	20
236	–	2p.50 black, blue and green	20	20

DESIGNS: 1p.50, Dove with letter; 2p.50, Magnifying-glass and stamp.

EXPRESS LETTER STAMPS

1943. As T **4**, but view of La Alcazaba inscr "URGENTE".

E35		25c. red and green	1·20	1·20

1949. Express Letter stamp of Spain optd **Territorio de Ifni.**

E66	E **198**	25c. red	20	20

INDIA Pt. 1

A peninsula in the S. of Asia. Formerly consisted of British India and numerous Native States, some of which issued stamps of their own. Divided in 1947 into the Dominion of India and the Dominion of Pakistan. Now a republic within the British Commonwealth.

1852. 12 pies = 1 anna; 16 annas = 1 rupee.
1957. 100 naye paise = 1 rupee.
1964. 100 paisa = 1 rupee.

1

3

9

10

1852. "Scinde Dawk". Imperf.

S1	**1**	½a. white	£4500	£800
S2		½a. blue	£12000	£3500
S3		½a. red	£70000	£8000

1854. Imperf.

1	**3**	½a. red	£800	
2		½a. blue	55·00	15·00
14		1a. red	45·00	38·00
31	**10**	2a. green	85·00	24·00
23	**9**	4a. blue and red	£2500	£225

11

12

1855. Perf.

75	**11**	½a. blue	4·25	50
59		1a. brown	5·00	60
41		2a. pink	£450	28·00
63		2a. orange	21·00	2·00
46		4a. black	£200	4·75
64		4a. green	£325	21·00
73		8a. red	29·00	5·50

1860. Inscr "EAST INDIA POSTAGE". Various frames.

57	**12**	8p. mauve	11·00	9·50
77	–	9p. lilac	14·00	14·00
71	–	4a. green	20·00	2·25
81	–	6a. brown	5·50	1·50
72	–	6a.8p. grey	40·00	20·00
82	–	12a. brown	8·00	20·00
79	–	1r. grey	40·00	24·00

14

23

1866. Optd **POSTAGE.**

66	**14**	6a. purple	£600	£110

1882. Inscr "INDIA POSTAGE". Various frames.

84	**23**	½a. turquoise	3·75	10
86	–	9p. red	1·00	1·90
88	–	1a. purple	3·75	30
90	–	1a.6p. brown	1·00	1·25
91	–	2a. blue	3·75	30
94	–	3a. orange	8·00	1·00
96	–	4a. green	14·00	1·00
97	–	4a.6p. green	18·00	4·50
99	–	8a. mauve	22·00	2·00
100	–	12a. purple on red	7·00	3·25
101	–	1r. grey	15·00	5·00

1891. No. 97 surch **2½ As.**

102		2½a. on 4½a. green	3·00	60

40

37

38

1892. As 1882 and some new designs.

111	**40**	3p. red	40	10
112		3p. grey	75	1·00
113	**23**	½a. green	1·60	45
115	–	1a. red	1·75	20
116	–	2a. lilac	3·25	1·90
103	–	2a.6p. green	2·50	40
118	–	2a.6p. blue	3·25	4·00
106	**37**	1r. green and red	10·00	2·00
107	**38**	2r. red and brown	35·00	11·00
108		3r. brown and green	27·00	10·00
109		5r. blue and violet	38·00	25·00

1898. Surch ¼.

110	**23**	¼a. on ½a. turquoise	10	50

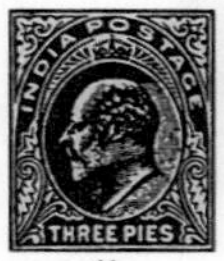

41

52

1902. As 1882 and 1892, but portrait of King Edward VII (inscribed "INDIA POSTAGE").

119	**41**	3p. grey	1·00	10
121	–	½a. green	1·50	20
123	–	1a. red	1·50	10
124	–	2a. violet	4·00	40
125	–	2a. mauve	3·25	10
126	–	2a.6p. blue	4·75	60
127	–	3a. orange	4·75	60
128	–	4a. green	3·00	60
132	–	6a. bistre	10·00	4·50
133	–	8a. purple	8·50	1·00
135	–	12a. purple on red	8·50	2·00
136	–	1r. green and red	6·50	70
139	**52**	2r. red and brown	38·00	4·00
140		3r. brown and green	25·00	19·00
142		5r. blue and violet	55·00	35·00
144		10r. green and red	£100	28·00
146		15r. blue and brown	£130	42·00
147		25r. orange and blue	£750	£800

1905. No. 121 surch ¼.

148		¼a. on ½a. green	55	10

1906. As Nos. 121 and 123, but inscr "INDIA POSTAGE REVENUE".

149		½a. green	3·00	10
150		1a. red	1·75	10

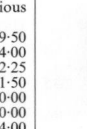

55

56

57

58

59

70

60

61

62

63

71

64

65

66

67

1911. *Two types of 1½a. brown. Type A as illustrated. Type B inscr "1½ As. ONE AND A HALF ANNAS".

201	**55**	3p. grey	30	10
202	**56**	½a. green	1·25	10
161	**57**	1a. red	2·25	15
203		1a. brown	50	10
163	**58**	1½a. brown (A)*	3·00	30
165		1½a. brown (B)*	3·25	4·00
204		1½a. red (B)*	2·00	10
166	**59**	2a. purple	3·25	40
169		2a. violet	5·50	50
206	**70**	2a. purple	1·40	10
170	**60**	2a.6p. blue	2·75	3·00
171	**61**	2a.6p. blue	2·75	20
207		2a.6p. orange	1·75	10
173	**62**	3a. orange	6·50	20
209		3a. blue	8·50	10
210	**63**	4a. olive	1·50	10
211	**71**	4a. green	6·00	10
177	**64**	6a. bistre	4·00	1·25
212	**65**	8a. mauve	4·00	10
213	**66**	12a. red	5·00	30
214	**67**	1r. brown and green	5·00	45
215		2r. red and orange	12·00	80
216		5r. blue and violet	24·00	1·25
217		10r. green and red	48·00	3·00
218w		15r. blue and olive	24·00	30·00
219		25r. orange and blue	95·00	35·00

See also Nos. 232, etc.

1921. Surch **NINE PIES** and bar.

192	**57**	9p. on 1a. red	85	30

1922. Surch ¼.

195	**56**	¼a. on ½a. green	50	35

72 De Havilland Hercules

1929. Air.

220w	**72**	2a. green	1·75	75
221		3a. blue	1·00	2·00
222		4a. olive	2·25	1·25
223		6a. bistre	2·25	1·00
224		8a. purple	2·75	1·00
225		12a. red	12·00	6·00

73 Purana Qila

1931. Inauguration of New Delhi.

226	**73**	¼a. green and orange	2·00	3·50
227	–	½a. violet and green	1·25	40
228	–	1a. mauve and brown	1·25	20
229	–	2a. green and blue	1·50	2·50
230	–	3a. brown and red	3·75	2·75
231	–	1r. violet and green	9·50	26·00

DESIGNS: ½a. War Memorial Arch; 1a. Council House; 2a. Viceroy's House; 3a. Secretariat; 1r. Dominion Columns and Secretariat.

79

80

81

82

83

84 Gateway of India, Bombay

1932.

232	**79**	½a. green	4·00	10
233	**80**	9p. green	1·75	10
234	**81**	1a. brown	4·50	10
235	**82**	1¼a. mauve	60	10
236	**70**	2a. red	9·50	4·00
236b	**59**	2a. red	3·75	50
237	**62**	3a. red	6·00	10
238	**83**	3½a. blue	4·00	20

1935. Silver Jubilee.

240	**84**	½a. black and green	85	20
241	–	9p. black and green	50	20
242w	–	1a. black and brown	60	10
243	–	1¼a. black and violet	50	10
244w	–	2½a. black and orange	1·75	1·00
245	–	3½a. black and blue	3·75	4·00
246	–	8a. black and purple	3·50	3·25

DESIGNS: 9p. Victoria Memorial, Calcutta; 1a. Rameswaram Temple, Madras; 1¼a. Jain Temple, Calcutta; 2½a. Taj Mahal, Agra; 3½a. Golden Temple, Amritsar; 8a. Pagoda in Mandalay.

91 King George VI

93 King George VI

92 Dak Runner

1937.

247	**91**	3p. slate	1·00	10
248		½a. brown	4·00	10
249		9p. green	8·00	20
250		1a. red	1·25	10
251	**92**	2a. red	4·75	30
252	–	2a.6p. violet	1·25	20
253	–	3a. green	6·00	30
254	–	3a.6p. blue	3·25	50
255	–	4a. brown	13·00	20
256	–	6a. blue	14·00	80
257	–	8a. violet	7·50	50
258	–	12a. red	18·00	1·10
259	**93**	1r. slate and brown	1·25	15
260		2r. purple and brown	4·25	30
261		5r. green and blue	22·00	50
262		10r. purple and red	17·00	80
263		15r. brown and green	70·00	60·00
264		25r. slate and purple	£100	18·00

DESIGNS—As Type **92**: 2a.6p. Dak bullock cart; 3a. Dak tonga; 3a.6p. Dak camel; 4a. Mail train; 6a. "Strathnaver" (liner); 8a. Mail lorry; 12a. Armstrong Whitworth Ensign 1 mail plane (small head).

100a King George VI

101 King George VI

102 King George VI

1940.

265	**100a**	3p. slate	30	10
266		½a. mauve	1·00	10
267		9p. green	1·00	10
268		1a. red	1·00	10
269	**101**	1a.3p. brown	1·00	10
269b		1½a. violet	1·25	10
270		2a. red	1·50	10
271		3a. violet	3·25	10
272		3½a. blue	1·00	50
273	**102**	4a. brown	1·00	10
274		6a. green	3·50	10
275		8a. violet	1·50	30
276		12a. purple	3·50	50
277	–	14a. purple	18·00	1·40

No. 277 is as No. 258, but with large head.

105 "Victory" and King George VI

1946. Victory Commemoration.

278	**105**	9p. green	50	1·00
279		1½a. purple	30	30
280		3½a. blue	85	70
281		12a. red	1·50	1·00

1946. Surch **3 PIES** and bars.

282	**101**	3p. on 1a.3p. brown	10	15

DOMINION OF INDIA

303 Douglas DC-4

1947. Independence. Inscr "15TH AUG 1947".

301	–	1½a. green	15	10
302	–	3½a. red, blue and green	1·00	2·00
303	**303**	12a. blue	1·50	2·50

DESIGNS—VERT: 1½a. Asokan capital. HORIZ: 3½a. Indian national flag.

1948. Air. Inauguration of India–U.K. Service. As T **303**, but showing Lockheed Constellation flying in opposite direction and inscr "AIR INDIA INTERNATIONAL FIRST FLIGHT 8TH JUNE 1948".

304		12a. black and blue	1·25	3·00

305 Mahatma Gandhi

1948. 1st Anniv of Independence.

305	**305**	1½a. brown	2·50	50
306		3½a. violet	4·25	2·50
307		12a. green	6·00	1·50
308	–	10r. brown and red	45·00	40·00

DESIGN—22½ × 37 mm: 10r. Profile portrait of Mahatma Gandhi.

307 Ajanta Panel

308 Konarak Horse

314 Bhuvanesvara

315 Gol Gumbad, Bijapur

319 Red Fort, Delhi

322 Satrunjaya Temple, Palitana

1949.

309	**307**	3p. violet	15	10
310	**308**	6p. brown	25	10
311	–	9p. green	40	10
312	–	1a. blue (A)	60	10
333	–	1a. blue (B)	3·50	10
313	–	2a. red	80	10
333b	–	2½a. lake	3·00	3·25
314	–	3a. salmon	1·50	10
315	–	3½a. blue	1·50	3·25
316	**314**	4a. lake	4·00	30
333c		4a. blue	6·00	10
317	**315**	6a. violet	1·50	75
318	–	8a. green	1·50	10
319	–	12a. blue	1·50	30
320	–	1r. violet and green	9·00	10
321	**319**	2r. red and violet	10·00	20
322	–	5r. green and brown	28·00	1·25
323	–	10r. brown and blue	48·00	7·00
324	**322**	15r. brown and red	16·00	19·00

1 anna: (A) Left arm of statue outstretched. (B) Reversed—right arm outstretched.

DESIGNS—As Type **307**: 9p. Trimurti; 1a. Bodhisattva; 2a. Nataraja. As Type **314**: 2½a., 3½a. Bodh Gaya Temple; 3a. Sanchi Stupa, East Gate. As Type **315**: 8a. Kandarya Mahadeva Temple; 12a. Golden Temple, Amritsar. As Type **319**—VERT: 1r. Victory Tower, Chittorgarh; 10r. Qutb Minar, Delhi. HORIZ: 5r. Taj Mahal, Agra.

323 Globe and Asokan Capital

1949. 75th Anniv of U.P.U.

325	**323**	9p. green	1·00	2·75
326		2a. red	1·00	2·50
327		3½a. blue	1·50	2·50
328		12a. red	2·00	2·50

REPUBLIC OF INDIA

324 Rejoicing Crowds

1950. Inauguration of Republic.

329	**324**	2a. red	1·25	50
330	–	3½a. blue	1·75	3·00
331	–	4a. violet	1·75	1·00
332	–	12a. purple	3·50	2·25

DESIGNS—VERT: 3½a. Quill, ink-well and verse. HORIZ: 4a. Ear of corn and plough; 12a. Spinning-wheel and cloth.

329 "Stegodon ganesa"

1951. Centenary of Geological Survey.

334	**329**	2a. black and red	2·00	1·00

330 Torch

331 Kabir

1951. 1st Asian Games, New Delhi.

335	**330**	2a. purple and orange	1·00	65
336		12a. brown and blue	4·00	1·75

1952. Indian Saints and Poets.

337	**331**	9p. green	30	40
338	–	1a. red (Tulsidas)	30	20
339	–	2a. orange (Meera)	1·50	25
340	–	4a. blue (Surdas)	1·50	60
341	–	4½a. mauve (Ghalib)	30	1·00
342	–	12a. brown (Tagore)	2·75	1·25

332 Locomotives of 1853 and 1953

1953. Centenary of Indian Railways.

343	**332**	2a. black	1·00	10

333 Mount Everest

1953. Conquest of Mount Everest.

344	**333**	2a. violet	1·25	10
345		14a. brown	3·00	25

334 Telegraph Poles of 1851 and 1951

1953. Centenary of Indian Telegraphs.

346	**334**	2a. green	30	10
347		12a. blue	2·50	40

335 Postal Transport, 1854

1954. Indian Stamp Centenary.

348	**335**	1a. purple	30	20
349	–	2a. mauve	30	10
350	–	4a. brown	2·75	1·50
351	–	14a. blue	1·50	40

DESIGNS: 2, 14a. "Airmail"; 4a. Postal transport, 1954.

338 U.N. Emblem and Lotus

1954. U.N. Day.

352	**338**	2a. turquoise	40	40

339 Forest Research Institute

1954. 4th World Forestry Congress, Dehra Dun.

353	**339**	2a. blue	20	10

340 Tractor

344 Woman Spinning

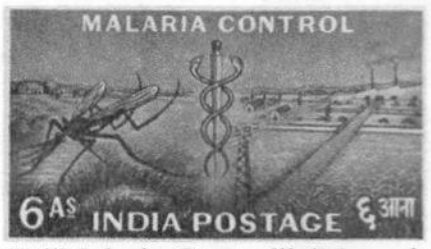

347 "Malaria Control" (Mosquito and Staff of Aesculapius)

1955. Five Year Plan.

354	**340**	3p. mauve	30	10
355	–	6p. violet	30	10
356	–	9p. brown	40	10
357	–	1a. green	45	10
358	**344**	2a. blue	30	10
359	–	3a. green	50	10
360	–	4a. red	50	10
361	**347**	6a. brown	1·50	10
362	–	8a. blue	6·00	10
363	–	10a. turquoise	3·75	2·75
364	–	12a. blue	2·50	10
365	–	14a. green	5·00	60
413	–	1r. myrtle	3·75	10
367	–	1r.2a. grey	2·25	3·50
368	–	1r.8a. purple	8·00	5·00
369	–	2r. mauve	4·25	10
415	–	5r. brown	9·00	40
371	–	10r. orange	14·00	4·75

DESIGNS—As Type **340**: 6p. Power loom; 9p. Bullock-driven well; 1a. Damodar Valley Dam; 4a. Bullocks; 8a. Chittaranjan Locomotive Works; 12a. Hindustan Aircraft Factory, Bangalore; 1r. Telephone engineer; 2r. Rare Earth Factory, Alwaye; 5r. Sindri Fertiliser Factory; 10r. Steel plant. As Type **344**: 3a. Naga woman hand-weaving. As Type **347**: 10a. Marine Drive, Bombay; 14a. Kashmir landscape; 1r.2a. Cape Comorin; 1r.8a. Mt. Kangchenjunga.

358 Bodhi Tree

1956. Buddha Jayanti.

372	**358**	2a. sepia	75	10
373	–	14a. red	4·00	3·75

DESIGN—HORIZ: 14a. Round parasol and Bodhi tree.

360 Lokmanya Bal Gangadhar Tilak

361 Map of India

1956. Birth Centenary of Tilak (journalist).

374	**360**	2a. brown	10	10

1957. Value in naye paise.

375	**361**	1n.p. green	10	10
376		2n.p. brown	10	10
377		3n.p. brown	10	10
402		5n.p. green	10	10
379		6n.p. grey	10	10
404		8n.p. turquoise	1·00	10
405		10n.p. myrtle	15	10
381		13n.p. red	30	10
407		15n.p. violet	60	10
408		20n.p. blue	30	10
409		25n.p. blue	30	10
410		50n.p. orange	30	10
411		75n.p. purple	40	10
412		90n.p. purple	5·50	10

362 The Rani of Jhansi

363 Shrine

1957. Centenary of Indian Mutiny.

386	**362**	15n.p. brown	40	10
387	**363**	90n.p. purple	1·50	1·25

364 Henri Dunant and Conference Emblem

1957. 19th Int Red Cross Conf, New Delhi.

388	**364**	15n.p. grey and red	10	10

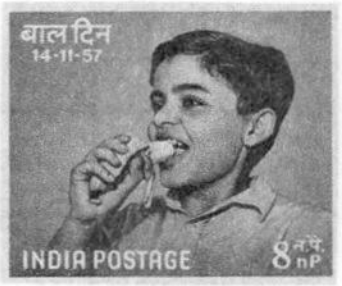

365 "Nutrition"

369 Calcutta University

1957. Children's Day.

389	**365**	8n.p. purple	10	15
390	–	15n.p. turquoise	10	10
391	–	90n.p. brown	25	15

DESIGNS—HORIZ: 15n.p. "Education". VERT: 90n.p. "Recreation".

1957. Centenary of Indian Universities.

392	–	10n.p. violet	15	60
393	**369**	10n.p. grey	15	60
394	–	10n.p. brown	30	60

DESIGNS—$21\frac{1}{2} \times 38$ mm: No. 392, Bombay University. As Type **369**: No. 394, Madras University.

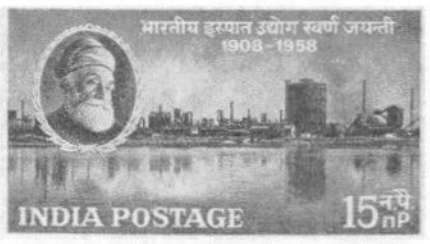

371 J. N. Tata (founder) and Steel Plant

1958. 50th Anniv of Steel Industry.

395	**371**	15n.p. red	10	10

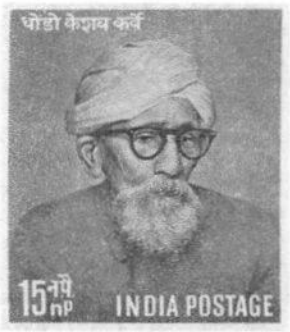

372 Dr. D. K. Karve

1958. Birth Centenary of Karve (educationist).

396	**372**	15n.p. brown	10	10

373 Westland Wapiti Biplane and Hawker Hunter

1958. Silver Jubilee of Indian Air Force.

397	**373**	15n.p. blue	1·00	10
398		90n.p. blue	1·25	2·00

375 Bipin Chandra Pal

1958. Birth Centenary of Pal (patriot).

418	**375**	15n.p. green	10	10

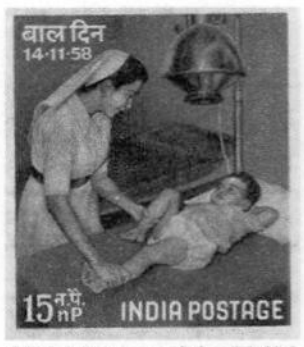

376 Nurse with Child Patient

377 Jagadish Chandra Bose

1958. Children's Day.

419	**376**	15n.p. violet	10	10

1958. Birth Centenary of Bose (botanist).

420	**377**	15n.p. turquoise	20	10

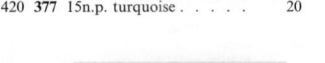

378 Exhibition Gate

1958. India 1958 Exhibition, New Delhi.

421	**378**	15n.p. purple	10	10

379 Sir Jamsetjee Jejeebhoy

381 Boys awaiting admission to Children's Home

380 "The Triumph of Labour" (after Chowdhury)

1959. Death Centenary of Sir Jamsetjee Jejeebhoy (philanthropist).

422	**379**	15n.p. brown	10	10

1959. 40th Anniv of I.L.O.

423	**380**	5n.p. green	10	10

1959. Children's Day.

424	**381**	15n.p. green	10	10

382 "Agriculture"

383 Thiruvalluvar (philosopher)

1959. 1st World Agriculture Fair, New Delhi.

425	**382**	15n.p. grey	30	10

1960. Thiruvalluvar Commemoration.

426	**383**	15n.p. purple	10	10

384 Yaksha pleading with the Cloud (from the "Meghaduta")

385 Shakuntala writing a letter to Dushyanta (from the "Shakuntala")

1960. Kalidasa (poet) Commemoration.

427	**384**	15n.p. grey	30	10
428	**385**	1r.3n.p. yellow and brown	1·60	1·75

386 S. Bharati (poet)

387 Dr. M. Visvesvaraya

1960. Subramania Bharati Commemoration.

429	**386**	15n.p. blue	10	10

1960. Birth Centenary of Dr. M. Visvesvaraya (engineer).

430	**387**	15n.p. brown and red	10	10

388 "Children's Health"

1960. Children's Day.

431	**388**	15n.p. green	10	10

389 Children greeting U.N. Emblem

1960. U.N.I.C.E.F. Day.

432	**389**	15n.p. brown and drab	10	10

390 Tyagaraja

391 "First Aerial Post" Cancellation

392 Air India Boeing 707 Airliner and Humber Sommer Biplane

1961. 114th Death Anniv of Tyagaraja (musician).

433	**390**	15n.p. blue	10	10

1961. 50th Anniv of 1st Official Airmail Flight, Allahabad–Naini.

434	**391**	5n.p. olive	1·10	30
435	**392**	15n.p. green and grey	1·10	30
436	–	1r. purple and grey	3·75	2·75

DESIGN—As Type **392**: 1r. H. Pecquet flying Humber Sommer plane, and "Aerial Post" cancellation.

394 Shivaji on Horseback

395 Motilal Nehru (politician)

1961. Chatrapati Shivaji (Maratha ruler) Commemoration.

437	**394**	15n.p. brown and green	80	40

1961. Birth Centenary of Pandit Motilal Nehru.

438	**395**	15n.p. brown and orange	30	10

396 Tagore (poet)

397 All India Radio Emblem and Transmitting Aerials

1961. Birth Centenary of Rabindranath Tagore.
439 **396** 15n.p. orange and turquoise 80 40

1961. Silver Jubilee of All India Radio.
440 **397** 15n.p. blue 10 10

398 Ray

399 Bhatkande

1961. Birth Centenary of Prafulla Chandra Ray (social reformer).
441 **398** 15n.p. grey 10 20

1961. Birth Centenary (1960) of V. N Bhatkande (composer).
442 **399** 15n.p. drab 10 10

400 Child at Lathe

401 Fair Emblem and Main Gate

1961. Children's Day.
443 **400** 15n.p. brown 10 20

1961. Indian Industries Fair, New Delhi.
444 **401** 15n.p. blue and red . . . 10 10

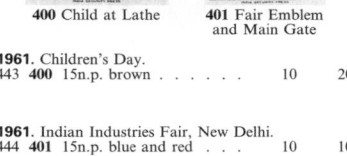

402 Indian Forest

403 Pitalkhora: Yaksha

1961. Centenary of Scientific Forestry.
445 **402** 15n.p. green and brown 40 30

1961. Cent of Indian Archaeological Survey.
446 **403** 15n.p. brown 20 10
447 – 90n.p. olive and brown 40 20
DESIGN—HORIZ: 90n.p. Kalibangan seal.

405 M. M. Malaviya

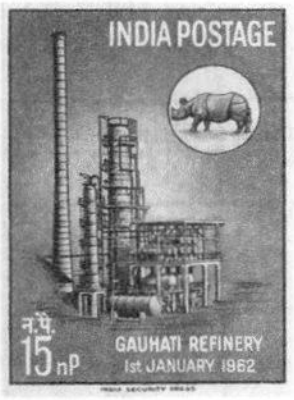

406 Gauhati Refinery

1961. Birth Centenary of Malaviya (educationist).
448 **405** 15n.p. slate 10 20

1962. Inauguration of Gauhati Oil Refinery.
449 **406** 15n.p. blue 40 20

407 Bhikaiji Cama

408 Village Panchayati and Parliament Building

1962. Birth Centenary of Bhikaiji Cama (patriot).
450 **407** 15n.p. purple 10 10

1962. Inauguration of Panchayati System of Local Government.
451 **408** 15n.p. mauve 10 10

409 D. Saraswati (religious reformer)

410 G. S. Vidhyarthi (journalist)

1962. Dayanard Saraswati Commem.
452 **409** 15n.p. brown 10 10

1962. Ganesh Shankar Vidhyarthi Commem.
453 **410** 15n.p. brown 10 10

411 Malaria Eradication Emblem

412 Dr. R. Prasad

1962. Malaria Eradication.
454 **411** 15n.p. yellow and lake . . 10 10

1962. Retirement of President Dr. Rajendra Prasad.
455 **412** 15n.p. purple 30 20

413 Calcutta High Court

1962. Centenary of Indian High Courts.
456 **413** 15n.p. green 50 20
457 – 15n.p. brown (Madras) 50 20
458 – 15n.p. slate (Bombay) . . 50 20

416 Ramabai Ranade

417 Indian Rhinoceros

1962. Birth Centenary of Ramabai Ranade (social reformer).
459 **416** 15n.p. orange 10 20

1962. Wild Life Week.
460 **417** 15n.p. brown and turquoise 40 15

418 "Passing the Flag to Youth"

1962. Children's Day.
461 **418** 15n.p. red and green . . . 15 20

419 Human Eye within Lotus Blossom

1962. 19th Int Ophthalmology Congress, New Delhi.
462 **419** 15n.p. brown 20 10

420 S. Ramanujan

1962. 75th Birth Anniv of Srinivasa Ramanujan (mathematician).
463 **420** 15n.p. brown 70 40

421 S. Vivekananda

423 Hands reaching for F.A.O. Emblem

1963. Birth Cent of Vivekananda (philosopher).
464 **421** 15n.p. brown and olive 40 20

1963. Surch.
465 **385** 1r. on 1r.3n.p. yellow and brown 30 10

1963. Freedom from Hunger.
466 **423** 15n.p. blue . . . . 1·25 30

424 Henri Dunant (founder) and Centenary Emblem

427 D. Naoroji (parliamentarian)

425 Artillery and Mil Mi-4 Helicopter

1963. Centenary of Red Cross.
467 **424** 15n.p. red and grey . . . 2·75 40

1963. Defence Campaign.
468 **425** 15n.p. green 55 10
469 – 1r. brown 70 65
DESIGN: 1r. Sentry and parachutists.

1963. Dadabhai Naoroji Commemoration.
470 **427** 15n.p. grey 10 10

428 Annie Besant (patriot and theosophist)

434 "School Meals"

1963. Annie Besant Commemoration.
471 **428** 15n.p. green 15 10
No. 471 is incorrectly dated "1837". Mrs. Besant was born in 1847.

1963. Wild Life Preservation. Animal designs as T **417**.
472 10n.p. black and orange . . . 75 1·50
473 15n.p. brown and green . . . 1·50 60
474 30n.p. slate and ochre . . . 3·75 1·50
475 50n.p. orange and green . . . 3·50 80
476 1r. brown and blue . . . . . 2·50 50

ANIMALS—As Type **417**: 10n.p. Gaur. 25½ × 35½ mm: 15n.p. Lesser panda; 30n.p. Indian elephant. 35½ × 25½ mm: 50n.p. Tiger; 1r. Lion.

1963. Children's Day.
477 **434** 15n.p. bistre 10 10

435 Eleanor Roosevelt at Spinning-wheel

1963. 15th Anniv of Declaration of Human Rights.
478 **435** 15n.p. purple 10 15

436 Dipalakshmi (bronze)

437 Gopabandhu Das (social reformer)

1964. 26th Int Orientalists Congress, New Delhi.
479 **436** 15n.p. blue 20 15

1964. Gopabandhu Das Commemoration.
480 **437** 15n.p. purple 10 10

438 Purandaradasa

439 S. C. Bose and I.N.A. Badge

1964. 400th Death Anniv of Purandaradasa (composer).
481 **438** 15n.p. brown 15 10

1964. 67th Birth Anniv of Subhas Chandra Bose (nationalist).
482 **439** 15n.p. olive 50 20
483 – 55n.p. black, orange & red 50 45
DESIGN: 35n.p. Bose and Indian National Army.

441 Sarojini Naidu

442 Kasturba Gandhi

1964. 85th Birth Anniv of Sarojini Naidu (poetess).
484 **441** 15n.p. green and purple 10 10

1964. 20th Death Anniv of Kasturba Gandhi.
485 **442** 15n.p. brown 10 10

443 Dr. W. M. Haffkine (immunologist)

444 Jawaharlal Nehru (statesman)

1964. Haffkine Commemoration.
486 **443** 15n.p. brown on buff . . 30 10

1964. Nehru Mourning Issue.
487 **444** 15p. slate 10 10

445 Sir Asutosh Mookerjee

1964. Birth Centenary of Sir Asutosh Mookerjee (education reformer).
488 **445** 15p. brown and olive . . 10 10

446 Sri Aurobindo

1964. 92nd Birth Anniv of Sri Aurobindo (religious teacher).
489 **446** 15p. purple 15 10

447 Raja R. Roy (social reformer)

1964. Raja Rammohun Roy Commemoration.
490 **447** 15n.p. brown 10 10

448 I.S.O. Emblem and Globe

1964. 6th Int Organization for Standardisation General Assembly, Bombay.
491 **448** 15p. red 15 20

449 Jawaharlal Nehru (from 1r. commemorative coin) **450** St. Thomas (after statue, Ortona Cathedral, Italy)

1964. Children's Day.
492 **449** 15p. slate 10 10

1964. St. Thomas Commemoration.
493 **450** 15p. purple 10 30
No. 493 was issued on the occasion of Pope Paul's visit to India.

451 Globe **452** J. Tata (industrialist)

1964. 22nd International Geological Congress.
494 **451** 15p. green 40 30

1965. Jamsetji Tata Commemoration.
495 **452** 15p. dull purple and orange 30 20

453 Lala Lajpat Rai

1965. Birth Centenary of Lala Lajpat Rai (social reformer).
496 **453** 15p. brown 20 10

454 Globe and Congress Emblem

1965. 20th International Chamber of Commerce Congress, New Delhi.
497 **454** 15p. green and red . . . 15 15

455 Freighter "Jalausha" and Visakhapatnam

1965. National Maritime Day.
498 **455** 15p. blue 30 30

456 Abraham Lincoln

1965. Death Centenary of Lincoln.
499 **456** 15p. brown and ochre . . 15 10

457 I.T.U. Emblem and Symbols

1965. Centenary of I.T.U.
500 **457** 15p. purple . . . . 1·00 30

458 "Everlasting Flame" **459** I.C.Y. Emblem

1965. 1st Death Anniv of Nehru.
501 **458** 15p. red and blue 15 10

1965. International Co-operation Year.
502 **459** 15p. green and brown . . 1·25 1·00

460 Climbers on Summit **466** Electric Locomotive

475 Dal Lake, Kashmir

1965. Indian Mount Everest Expedition.
503 **460** 15p. purple 20 10

1965.

504	–	2p. brown	10	50
505	–	3p. olive	30	2·75
505a	–	4p. brown	10	2·75
506	–	5p. red	10	10
507	–	6p. black	10	3·25
508	–	8p. brown	30	4·25
509	**466**	10p. blue	40	10
510	–	15p. green	2·75	10
511	–	20p. purple	6·00	10
512	–	30p. sepia	15	10
513	–	40p. purple	15	10
514	–	50p. green	20	10
515	–	60p. grey	35	10
516	–	70p. blue	60	10
517	–	1r. brown and plum	60	10
518	**475**	2r. blue and violet	2·00	10
519	–	5r. violet and brown	2·50	90
520	–	10r. black and green	17·00	80

DESIGNS—VERT (as Type **466**): 2p. Bidri vase; 3p. Brass lamp; 5p. "Family Planning"; 6p. Konarak elephant; 8p. Spotted deer ("Chital"); 30p. Indian dolls; 50p. Mangoes; 60p. Somnath Temple. (as Type **475**): 1r. Woman writing a letter (medieval sculpture). HORIZ (as Type **466**): 4p. Coffee berries; 15p. Plucking tea; 20p. Hindustan Aircraft Industries Ajeet jet fighter; 40p. Calcutta G.P.O.; 70p. Hampi Chariot (sculpture). (As Type **475**): 5r. Bhakra Dam, Punjab; 10r. Atomic reactor, Trombay.
See also Nos. 721/38c.

479 G. B. Pant (statesman) **480** V. Patel

1965. Govind Ballabh Pant Commemoration.
522 **479** 15p. brown and green . . 10 20

1965. 90th Birth Anniv of Vallabhbhai Patel (statesman).
523 **480** 15p. brown 10 30

481 C. Das **482** Vidyapati (poet)

1965. 95th Birth Anniv of Chittaranjan Das (lawyer and patriot).
524 **481** 15p. brown 10 10

1965. Vidyapati Commemoration.
525 **482** 15p. brown 10 10

483 Sikandra, Agra **484** Soldier, Hindustan Aircraft Industries Ajeet Jet Fighters and Cruiser "Mysore"

1966. Pacific Area Travel Assn Conf, New Delhi.
526 **483** 15p. slate 10 10

1966. Indian Armed Forces.
527 **484** 15p. violet . . . . 1·25 50

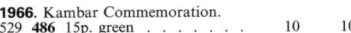

485 Lal Bahadur Shastri (statesman) **486** Kambar (poet)

1966. Shastri Mourning Issue.
528 **485** 15p. black 65 10

1966. Kambar Commemoration.
529 **486** 15p. green 10 10

487 B. R. Ambedkar **488** Kunwar Singh (patriot)

1966. 75th Birth Anniv of Dr. Bhim Rao Ambedkar (lawyer).
530 **487** 15p. purple 10 10

1966. Kunwar Singh Commemoration.
531 **488** 15p. brown 10 10

489 G. K. Gokhale

1966. Birth Centenary of Gopal Krishna Gokhale (patriot).
532 **489** 15p. purple and yellow . . 10 10

490 Acharya Dvivedi (poet) **491** Maharaja Ranjit Singh (warrior)

1966. Dvivedi Commemoration.
533 **490** 15p. drab 10 10

1966. Maharaja Ranjit Singh Commemoration.
534 **491** 15p. purple 60 20

492 Homi Bhabha (scientist) and Nuclear Reactor

1966. Dr. Homi Bhabha Commemoration.
535 **492** 15p. purple 15 30

493 A. K. Azad (scholar)

1966. Abul Kalam Azad Commemoration.
536 **493** 15p. blue 15 15

494 Swami Tirtha

1966. 60th Death Anniv of Swami Rama Tirtha (social reformer).
537 **494** 15p. blue 30 30

495 Infant and Dove Emblem

1966. Children's Day.
538 **495** 15p. purple 60 20

496 Allahabad High Court

1966. Centenary of Allahabad High Court.
539 **496** 15p. purple 40 30

497 Indian Family

1966. Family Planning.
540 **497** 15p. brown 15 15

498 Hockey Game

1966. India's Hockey Victory in 5th Asian Games.
541 **498** 15p. blue . . . . 1·25 60

499 "Jai Kisan"

500 Voter and Polling Booth

1967. 1st Death Anniv of Shastri.
542 **499** 15p. green 30 30

1967. Indian General Election.
543 **500** 15p. brown 15 15

501 Gurudwara Shrine, Patna

502 Taj Mahal, Agra

1967. 300th Birth Anniv (1966) of Guru Gobind Singh (Sikh religious leader).
544 **501** 15p. violet 50 15

1967. International Tourist Year.
545 **502** 15p. brown and orange 30 15

503 Nandalal Bose and "Garuda"

1967. 1st Death Anniv of Nandalal Bose (painter).
546 **503** 15p. brown 15 15

504 Survey Emblem and Activities

1967. Bicentenary of Survey of India.
547 **504** 15p. lilac 60 40

505 Basaveswara

1967. 800th Anniv of Basaveswara (reformer and statesman).
548 **505** 15p. red 15 15

506 Narsinha Mehta (poet)

507 Maharana Pratap

1967. Narsinha Mehta Commemoration.
549 **506** 15p. sepia 15 15

1967. Maharana Pratap (Rajput leader) Commem.
550 **507** 15p. brown 15 15

508 Narayana Guru

509 Pres. Radhakrishnan

1967. Narayana Guru (philosopher) Commem.
551 **508** 15p. brown 30 20

1967. 75th Birth Anniv of Sarvepalli Radhakrishnan (former President).
552 **509** 15p. red 50 15

510 Martyrs' Memorial, Patna

1967. 25th Anniv of "Quit India" Movement.
553 **510** 15p. lake 15 15

511 Route Map

512 Wrestling

1967. Centenary of Indo-European Telegraph Service.
554 **511** 15p. black and blue . . . 70 20

1967. World Wrestling Championships, New Delhi.
555 **512** 15p. purple and brown . . 50 20

513 Nehru leading Naga Tribesmen

514 Rashbehari Basu (nationalist)

1967. 4th Anniv of Nagaland as a State of India.
556 **513** 15p. blue 15 15

1967. Rashbehari Basu Commemoration.
557 **514** 15p. purple 15 20

515 Bugle, Badge and Scout Salute

1967. 60th Anniv of Scout Movement in India.
558 **515** 15p. brown . . . . 1·00 60

516 Men embracing Universe

517 Globe and Book of Tamil

1968. Human Rights Year.
559 **516** 15p. green 50 30

1968. Int Conf and Seminar of Tamil Studies, Madras.
560 **517** 15p. lilac 60 15

518 U.N. Emblem and Transport

1968. United Nations Conference on Trade and Development, New Delhi.
561 **518** 15p. blue 60 15

519 Quill and Bow Symbol

520 Maxim Gorky

1968. Centenary of "Amrita Bazar Patrika" (newspaper).
562 **519** 15p. sepia and yellow . . 15 15

1968. Birth Centenary of Maxim Gorky.
563 **520** 15p. plum 15 20

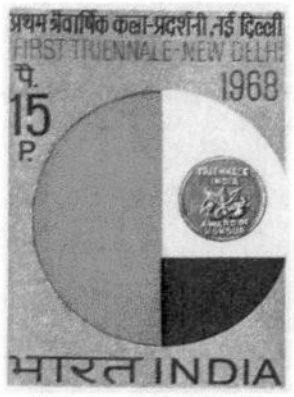
521 Emblem and Medal

522 Letter-box and "100,000"

1968. 1st Triennale Art Exhibition, New Delhi.
564 **521** 15p. orange, blue & lt blue 30 20

1968. Opening of 100,000th Indian Post Office.
565 **522** 20p. red, blue and black 40 15

523 Stalks of Wheat, Agricultural Institute and Production Graph

1968. Wheat Revolution.
566 **523** 20p. green and brown . . 30 15

524 "Self-portrait"

525 Lakshminath Bezbaruah

1968. 30th Death Anniv of Gaganendranath Tagore (painter).
567 **524** 20p. purple and ochre . . 50 15

1968. Birth Cent of Lakshminath Bezbaruah (writer).
568 **525** 20p. brown 30 15

526 Athlete's Legs and Olympic Rings

1968. Olympic Games, Mexico.
569 **526** 20p. brown and grey . . 15 15
570 1r. sepia and olive 50 15

527 Bhagat Singh and Followers

1968. 61st Birth Anniv of Bhagat Singh (patriot).
571 **527** 20p. brown 50 20

528 Azad Hind Flag, Swords and Chandra Bose (founder)

529 Sister Nivedita

1968. 25th Anniv of Azad Hind Government.
572 **528** 20p. blue 30 15

1968. Birth Cent of Sister Nivedita (social reformer).
573 **529** 20p. green 30 30

530 Marie Curie and Radium Treatment

1968. Birth Centenary of Marie Curie.
574 **530** 20p. lilac . . . . 1·40 60

531 Map of the World

532 Cochin Synagogue

1968. 21st Int Geographical Congress, New Delhi.
575 **531** 20p. blue 15 15

1968. 400th Anniv of Cochin Synagogue.
576 **532** 20p. blue and red . . . . 1·00 40

533 I.N.S. "Nilgiri"

1968. Navy Day.
577 **533** 20p. blue . . . . 1·75 40

534 Red-billed Blue Magpie

1968. Birds.
578 **534** 20p. multicoloured . . . 1·25 50
579 – 50p. red, black and green 1·25 1·50
580 – 1r. blue and brown . . . 2·50 1·00
581 – 2r. multicoloured . . . . 1·75 1·50
DESIGNS—HORIZ: 50p. Brown-fronted pied woodpecker; 2r. Yellow-backed sunbird. VERT: 1r. Slaty-headed scimitar babbler.

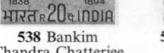

538 Bankim Chandra Chatterjee
539 Dr. Bhagavan Das

1969. 130th Birth Anniv of Chatterjee (writer).
582 **538** 20p. blue 15 20

1969. Birth Centenary of Das (philosopher).
583 **539** 20p. brown 15 15

540 Dr. Martin Luther King

1969. Martin Luther King Commemoration.
584 **540** 20p. brown 50 20

541 Mirza Ghalib and Letter Seal

1969. Death Centenary of Mirza Ghalib (poet).
585 **541** 20p. sepia, red and flesh 15 15

542 Osmania University

1969. 50th Anniv of Osmania University.
586 **542** 20p. green 15 20

543 Rafi Ahmed Kidwai and Lockheed Constellation Mail Plane

1969. 20th Anniv of "All-up" Airmail Scheme.
587 **543** 20p. blue . . . . 1·00 30

544 I.L.O. Badge and Emblem

1969. 50th Anniv of Int Labour Organization.
588 **544** 20p. brown 15 20

545 Memorial, and Hands dropping Flowers
546 K. Nageswara Rao Pantulu (journalist)

1969. 50th Anniv of Jallianwala Bagh Massacre, Amritsar.
589 **545** 20p. red 15 20

1969. Kasinadhuni Nageswara Rao Pantulu Commemoration.
590 **546** 20p. brown 15 20

547 Ardaseer Cursetjee Wadia, and Ships

1969. Ardaseer Cursetjee Wadia (ship-builder) Commemoration.
591 **547** 20p. turquoise 50 40

548 Serampore College
549 Dr. Zakir Husain

1969. 150th Anniv of Serampore College.
592 **548** 20p. plum 15 20

1969. President Dr. Zakir Husain Commemoration.
593 **549** 20p. sepia 15 20

550 Laxmanrao Kirloskar

1969. Birth Centenary of Laxmanrao Kirloskar (agriculturist).
594 **550** 20p. black 15 15

551 Gandhi and his Wife

1969. Birth Centenary of Mahatma Gandhi.
595 **551** 20p. brown 70 40
596 – 75p. flesh and drab . . . 1·25 90
597 – 1r. blue . . . . 1·25 65
598 – 5r. brown and orange . . 4·50 6·50
DESIGNS AND SIZES—VERT: 75p. Gandhi's head and shoulders (28 × 38 mm); 1r. Gandhi walking (woodcut) (20 × 38 mm). HORIZ: 5r. Gandhi with charkha (36 × 26 mm).

555 "Ajanta" (bulk carrier) and I.M.C.O. Emblem

1969. 10th Anniv of Inter-Governmental Maritime Consultative Organization.
599 **555** 20p. blue . . . . 1·75 40

556 Outline of Parliament Building and Globe

1969. 57th Inter-Parliamentary Conf, New Delhi.
600 **556** 20p. blue 15 20

557 Astronaut walking beside Space Module on Moon
558 Gurudwara Nankana Sahib (birthplace)

1969. 1st Man on the Moon.
601 **557** 20p. brown 50 30

1969. 500th Birth Anniv of Guru Nanak Dev (Sikh religious leader).
602 **558** 20p. violet 30 20

559 Tiger's Head and Hands holding Globe

1969. Int Union for the Conservation of Nature and Natural Resources Conf, New Delhi.
603 **559** 20p. brown and green . . 30 30

560 Sadhu Vaswani
561 Thakkar Bapa

1969. 90th Birth Anniv of Sadhu Vaswani (educationist).
604 **560** 20p. grey 15 15

1969. Birth Centenary of Thakkar Bapa (humanitarian).
605 **561** 20p. brown 15 20

562 Satellite, Television, Telephone and Globe

1970. 12th Plenary Assembly of Int Radio Consultative Committee.
606 **562** 20p. blue 40 20

563 C. N. Annadurai
564 M. N. Kishore and Printing Press

1970. 1st Death Anniv of Conjeevaram Natrajan Annadurai (statesman).
607 **563** 20p. purple and blue . . . 30 15

1970. 75th Death Anniv of Munshi Newal Kishore (publisher).
608 **564** 20p. lake 15 20

565 Nalanda College

1970. Centenary of Nalanda College.
609 **565** 20p. brown 60 50

566 Swami Shraddhanand (social reformer)

1970. Swami Shraddhanand Commemoration.
610 **566** 20p. brown 75 60

567 Lenin

1970. Birth Centenary of Lenin.
611 **567** 20p. brown and sepia . . 40 20

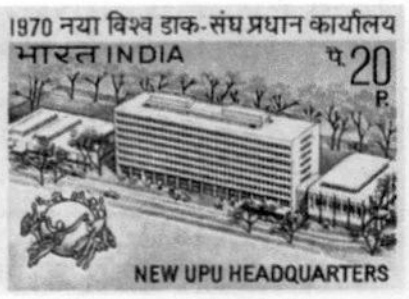

568 New U.P.U. H.Q. Building
569 Sher Shah Suri (15th century ruler)

1970. New U.P.U. Headquarters Building, Berne.
612 **568** 20p. green, grey and black 15 20

1970. Sher Shah Suri Commemoration.
613 **569** 20p. green 30 30

570 V. D. Savarkar (patriot) and Cellular Jail, Andaman Islands
571 "U N" and Globe

1970. Vinayak Damodar Savarkar Commem.
614 **570** 20p. brown 50 30

1970. 25th Anniv of United Nations.
615 **571** 20p. blue 40 20

572 Symbol and Workers

1970. Asian Productivity Year.
616 **572** 20p. violet 20 20

573 Dr. Montessori and I.E.Y. Emblem

1970. Birth Centenary of Dr. Maria Montessori (educationist).
617 **573** 20p. purple 30 30

574 J. N. Mukherjee (revolutionary) and Horse

1970. Jatindra Nath Mukherjee Commem.
618 **574** 20p. brown . . . . 1·50 30

575 V. S. Srinivasa Sastri **576** I. C. Vidyasagar

1970. Srinivasa Sastri (educationist) Commemoration.
619 **575** 20p. yellow and purple . . 30 30

1970. 150th Birth Anniv of Iswar Chandra Vidyasagar (educationist).
620 **576** 20p. brown and purple . . 40 30

577 Maharishi Valmiki

1970. Maharishi Valmiki (ancient author) Commem.
621 **577** 20p. purple 60 30

578 Calcutta Port

1970. Centenary of Calcutta Port Trust.
622 **578** 20p. blue . . . . 1·50 70

579 University Building

1970. 50th Anniv of Jamia Millia Islamia University.
623 **579** 20p. green 60 50

580 Jamnalal Bajaj **581** Nurse and Patient

1970. Jamnalal Bajaj (industrialist) Commemoration.
624 **580** 20p. grey 15 30

1970. 50th Anniv of Indian Red Cross.
625 **581** 20p. red and blue 60 40

582 Sant Namdeo **583** Beethoven

1970. 700th Birth Anniv of Sant Namdeo (mystic).
626 **582** 20p. orange 15 30

1970. Birth Bicentenary of Beethoven.
627 **583** 20p. orange and black . . 2·00 70

584 Children examining Stamps

1970. Indian National Philatelic Exhibition, New Delhi.
628 **584** 20p. orange and green . . 30 10
629 – 1r. brown and ochre . . . 2·50 1·00
DESIGN: 1r. Gandhi commemorative through magnifier.

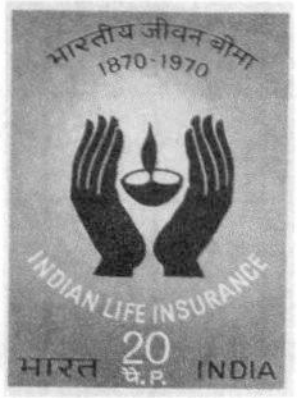

585 Girl Guide **586** Hands and Lamp (emblem)

1970. Diamond Jubilee of Girl Guide Movement in India.
630 **585** 20p. purple 60 30

1971. Centenary of Indian Life Insurance.
631 **586** 20p. brown and red . . . 20 30

587 Vidyapith Building

1971. 50th Anniv of Kashi Vidyapith University.
632 **587** 20p. brown 20 30

588 Sant Ravidas

1971. Sant Ravidas (15th-century mystic) Commemoration.
633 **588** 20p. red 65 30

589 C. F. Andrews **590** Acharya Narendra Deo (scholar)

1971. Birth Centenary of Charles Freer Andrews (missionary).
634 **589** 20p. brown 35 30

1971. 15th Death Anniv of Acharya Narendra Deo.
635 **590** 20p. green 15 30

591 Crowd and "100"

1971. Centenary of Decennial Census.
636 **591** 20p. brown and blue . . . 30 30

592 Sri Ramana Maharishi (mystic) **593** Raja Ravi Varma and "Damayanti and the Swan"

1971. 21st Death Anniv of Ramana Maharishi.
637 **592** 20p. orange and brown 20 30

1971. 65th Death Anniv of Ravi Varma (artist).
638 **593** 20p. green 60 50

594 Dadasaheb Phalke and Camera

1971. Birth Centenary of Dadasaheb Phalke (cinematographer).
639 **594** 20p. purple 70 40

595 "Abhisarika" (Tagore) **596** Swami Virjanand (Vedic scholar)

1971. Birth Centenary of Abanindranath Tagore (painter).
640 **595** 20p. grey, yellow & brown 40 30

1971. Swami Virjanand Commemoration.
641 **596** 20p. brown 30 40

597 Cyrus the Great and Procession

1971. 2500th Anniv of Charter of Cyrus the Great.
642 **597** 20p. brown 75 55

598 Globe and Money Box

1971. World Thrift Day.
643 **598** 20p. grey 20 30

599 Ajanta Caves Painting **600** "Women at Work" (Geeta Gupta)

1971. 25th Anniv of U.N.E.S.C.O.
644 **599** 20p. brown . . . . 1·50 70

1971. Children's Day.
645 **600** 20p. red 20 50

607 Refugees **608** C. V. Raman (scientist) and Light Graph

1971. Obligatory Tax. Refugee Relief. (a) Optd **REFUGEE RELIEF** in Hindi and English.
646 – 5p. red (No. 506) 60 10

(b) Optd **Refugee Relief**.
647 – 5p. red (No. 506) . . . . . 2·50 1·00

(c) Optd **REFUGEE RELIEF**.
649 – 5p. red (No. 506) . . . . . 3·25 1·50

(d) Optd **Refugee relief**.
650c – 5p. red (No. 506). . . . . 17·00 3·75

(e) Optd **Refugee Relief** in Hindi and English.
650d – 5p. red (No. 506) . . . .

(f) Type **607**.
651 **607** 5p. red 40 10

From 15 November 1971 until 31 March 1973 the Indian Government levied a 5p. surcharge on all mail, except postcards and newspapers, for the relief of refugees from the former East Pakistan.

1971. 1st Death Anniv of Chandrasekhara Venkata Raman.
652 **608** 20p. orange and brown 50 40

609 Visva Bharati Building and Rabindranath Tagore (founder)

1971. 50th Anniv of Visva Bharati University.
653 **609** 20p. sepia and brown . . 40 40

610 Cricketers

1971. Indian Cricket Victories.
654 **610** 20p. green, myrtle and sage . . . . 2·00 65

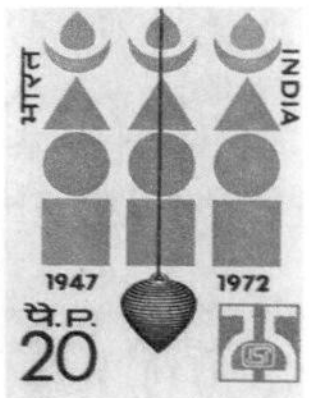

611 Map and Satellite **612** Elemental Symbols and Plumb-line

1972. 1st Anniv of Arvi Satellite Earth Station.
655 **611** 20p. purple 20 30

1972. 25th Anniv of Indian Standards Institution.
656 **612** 20p. grey and black . . . 15 50

613 Signal Box Panel

1972. 50th Anniv of Int Railways Union.
657 **613** 20p. multicoloured . . . 1·00 40

614 Hockey-player

1972. Olympic Games, Munich.
658 **614** 20p. violet . . . . 1·75 25
659 – 1r.45 green and lake . . . 2·50 2·00
DESIGN: 1r.45, Various sports.

615 Symbol of Sri Aurobindo **617** Inter-Services Crest

616 Celebrating Independence Day in front of Parliament

1972. Birth Centenary of Sri Aurobindo (religious teacher).
660 **615** 20p. yellow and blue . . . 20 30

1972. 25th Anniv of Independence. (1st issue).
661 **616** 20p. multicoloured . . . 65 30
See also Nos. 673/4.

1972. Defence Services Commemoration.
662 **617** 20p. multicoloured . . . 30 40

618 V. O. Chidambaran Pillai (trade union leader) and Ship

1972. Birth Cent of V. O. Chidambaran Pillai.
663 **618** 20p. blue and brown . . . 75 40

619 Bhai Vir Singh

620 T. Prakasam

1972. Birth Centenary of Bhai Vir Singh (poet).
664 **619** 20p. purple 60 40

1972. Birth Centenary of Tanguturi Prakasam (lawyer).
665 **620** 20p. brown 20 40

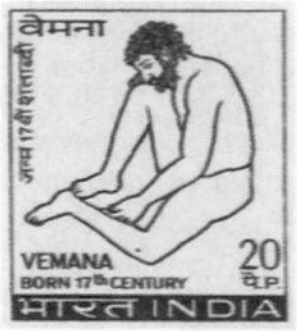

621 Vemana

622 Bertrand Russell

1972. 300th Birth Anniv of Vemana (poet).
666 **621** 20p. black 20 40

1972. Birth Centenary of Bertrand Russell (philosopher).
667 **622** 1r.45 black . . . . 3·25 2·75

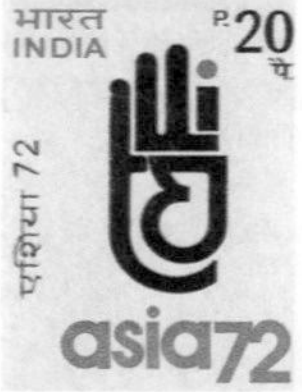

623 Symbol of "Asia '72"

1972. "Asia '72" (Third Asian International Trade Fair), New Delhi.
668 **623** 20p. black and orange . . 10 20
669 – 1r.45 orange and black . . 60 1·75
DESIGN: 1r.45, Hand of Buddha.

624 V. A. Sarabhai and Rocket

1972. 1st Death Anniv of Dr. Vikram A. Sarabhai (scientist).
670 **624** 20p. brown and green . . 20 40

625 Flag of U.S.S.R. and Kremlin Tower

1972. 50th Anniv of U.S.S.R.
671 **625** 20p. red and yellow . . . 20 60

626 Exhibition Symbol

627 "Democracy"

1973. "Indipex '73" Stamp Exhibition (1st issue).
672 **626** 1r.45 mauve, gold & black 45 1·25
See also No. 701/**MS**704.

1973. 25th Anniv of Independence (2nd issue). Multicoloured.
673 20p. Type **627** 15 15
674 1r.45 Hindustan Aircraft Industries Ajeet jet fighters over India Gate (38 × 20 mm) . . . . . . 1·40 1·60

628 Sri Ramakrishna Paramahamsa (religious leader)

629 Postal Corps Emblem

1973. Sri Ramakrishna Paramahamsa Commem.
675 **628** 20p. brown 40 60

1973. 1st Anniv of Army Postal Service Corps.
676 **629** 20p. blue and red 40 50

630 Flag and Map of Bangladesh

631 Kumaran Asan

1973. "Jai Bangla" (Inauguration of 1st Bangladesh Parliament).
677 **630** 20p. multicoloured . . . 15 40

1973. Birth Centenary of Kumaran Asan (writer and poet).
678 **631** 20p. brown 20 60

632 Flag and Flames

634 "Radha-Kishangarh" (Nihal Chand)

633 Dr. Bhim Rao Ambedkar (lawyer)

1973. Homage to Martyrs for Independence.
679 **632** 20p. multicoloured . . . 15 40

1973. Ambedkar Commemoration.
680 **633** 20p. green and purple . . 20 1·00

1973. Indian Miniature Paintings. Multicoloured.
681 20p. Type **634** 30 35
682 50p. "Dance Duet" (Aurangzeb's period) . . . 60 1·50
683 1r. "Lovers on a Camel" (Nasir-ud-din) . . . . . 80 1·75
684 2r. "Chained Elephant" (Zain-al-Abidin) . . . . . 1·10 2·50

635 Mount Everest

1973. 15th Anniv of Indian Mountaineering Foundation.
685 **635** 20p. blue 50 50

636 Tail of Boeing 747

1973. 25th Anniv of Air-India's International Services.
686 **636** 1r.45 blue and red . . . . 4·00 4·00

637 Cross, Church of St. Thomas' Mount, Madras

638 Michael Madhusudan Dutt (poet–Death Centenary)

1973. 19th Death Centenary of St. Thomas.
687 **637** 20p. grey and brown . . 20 60

1973. Centenaries.
688 **638** 20p. green and brown . . 1·00 65
689 – 30p. brown . . . . 1·25 2·50
690 – 50p. brown . . . . 1·50 2·50
691 – 1r. violet and red . . . . 1·50 1·50
DESIGNS—HORIZ: 30p. Vishnu Digambar Paluskar (musician, birth cent); 50p. Dr. G. A. Hansen (cent of discovery of leprosy bacillus); 1r. Nicolaus Copernicus (astronomer, 5th birth cent).

639 A. O. Hume

641 R. C. Dutt

640 Gandhi and Nehru

1973. Allan Octavian Hume (founder of Indian National Congress) Commemoration.
692 **639** 20p. grey 20 40

1973. Gandhi and Nehru Commemoration.
693 **640** 20p. multicoloured . . . 20 40

1973. Romesh Chandra Dutt (writer) Commem.
694 **641** 20p. brown 20 40

642 K. S. Ranjitsinhji

643 Vithalbhai Patel

1973. K. S. Ranjitsinhji (cricketer) Commemoration.
695 **642** 30p. green . . . . 3·50 3·50

1973. Vithalbhai Patel (lawyer) Commemoration.
696 **643** 50p. brown . . . . 30 1·00

644 Sowar of President's Bodyguard

645 Interpol Emblem

1973. Bicentenary of President's Bodyguard.
697 **644** 20p. multicoloured . . . 1·25 50

1973. 50th Anniv of Interpol.
698 **645** 20p. brown 30 40

646 Syed Ahmad Khan (social reformer)

1973. Syed Ahmad Khan Commemoration.
699 **646** 20p. brown . . . . 20 1·00

647 "Children at Play" (Bela Raval)

1973. Children's Day.
700 **647** 20p. multicoloured . . . 20 30

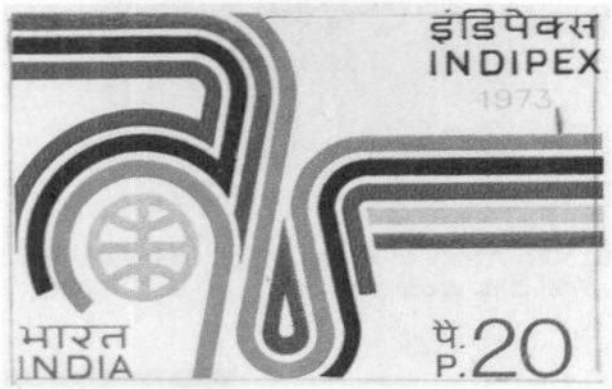

648 Indipex Emblem

1973. "Indipex '73" Philatelic Exhibition, New Delhi (2nd issue). Multicoloured.
701 20p. Type **648** 20 30
702 1r. Ceremonial elephant and 1½a. stamp of 1947 (vert) 1·00 1·50
703 2r. Common peafowl (vert) 1·25 3·00
MS704 127 × 127 mm. Nos. 672 and 701/3. Imperf . . . . 4·00 8·00

649 Emblem of National Cadet Corps

650 C. Rajagopalachari (statesman)

1973. 25th Anniv of National Cadet Corps.
705 **649** 20p. multicoloured . . . 20 30

1973. Chakravarti Rajagopalachari Commemoration.
706 **650** 20p. brown 20 50

651 "Sun" Mask

652 Chhatrapati

1974. Indian Masks. Multicoloured.
707 20p. Type **651** 15 15
708 50p. "Moon" mask 30 60

709 1r. "Narasimha" 55 80
710 2r. "Ravana" (horiz) . . . . 70 1·75
MS711 109 × 135 mm. Nos. 707/10 2·00 2·50

1974. 300th Anniv of Coronation of Chhatrapati Shri Shivaji Maharaj (patriot and ruler).
712 **652** 25p. multicoloured . . . 70 30

653 Maithili Sharan Gupta (poet)

654 Kandukuri Veeresalingam (social reformer)

1974. Indian Personalities (1st series).
713 **653** 25p. brown 15 50
714 – 25p. brown 15 50
715 – 25p. brown 15 50
PORTRAITS: No. 714, Jainarain Vyas (politician and journalist); No. 715, Utkal Gourab Madhusudan Das (social reformer).

1974. Indian Personalities (2nd series).
716 **654** 25p. brown 25 75
717 – 50p. purple . . . . 55 1·75
718 – 1r. brown . . . . 70 1·75
PORTRAITS: 50p. Tipu Sultan; 1r. Max Mueller (Sanskrit scholar).

655 Kamala Nehru

1974. Kamala Nehru Commemoration.
719 **655** 25p. multicoloured . . . 75 75

656 W.P.Y. Emblem

657 Spotted Deer

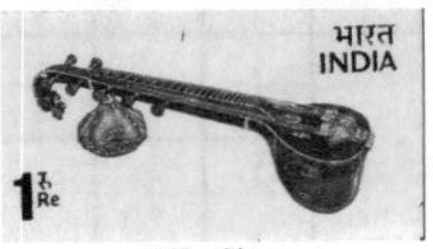

657a Sitar

1974. World Population Year.
720 **656** 25p. purple and brown . . 20 30

1974. (a) Values expressed with "p" or "Re".
721 – 15p. brown . . . . . . 3·25 1·00
722 **657** 25p. brown . . . . . . 1·00 2·00
723 **657a** 1r. brown and black . . 2·50 30

(b) Values expressed as numerals only.
724 – 2p. brown . . . . . . 1·25 3·00
725 – 5p. red 70 10
729 – 10p. blue 75 15
730 – 15p. brown . . . . . . 1·75 10
731 – 20p. green 15 10
732 – 25p. brown . . . . . . 7·50 2·75
732b – 30p. brown . . . . . . 4·25 55
733 – 50p. violet . . . . . . 6·50 20
734 – 60p. grey . . . . . . 2·75 1·00
735 **657a** 1r. brown and black . . 3·25 10
736 – 2r. violet and brown . . 14·00 40
737 – 5r. violet and brown . . 2·50 1·25
738d – 10r. grey and green . . 1·10 1·25
DESIGNS—VERT (as Type **657**): 2p. Bidri vase; 5p. "Family Planning"; 15p. Tiger; 25p. Gandhi; 30p. Indian dolls; 60p. Somnath Temple. HORIZ (as Type **657a**): 10p. Electric locomotive; 20p. Handicrafts toy; 50p. Great egret in flight. (As Type **657a**): 2r. Himalayas; 5r. Bhakra Dam, Punjab; 10r. Atomic reactor, Trombay.
For 30, 35, 50, 60p. and 1r. values as No. 732 see Nos. 968, 979, 1073, 1320 and 1436.

658 President V. Giri

660 Woman Flute-player (sculpture)

659 U.P.U. Emblem

1974. Retirement of President Giri.
739 **658** 25p. multicoloured . . . 15 30

1974. Centenary of U.P.U.
740 **659** 25p. violet, blue and black 30 10
741 – 1r. multicoloured 50 50
742 – 2r. multicoloured . . . . 75 2·00
MS743 – 108 × 108mm. Nos. 740/2 2·00 6·50
DESIGNS:—1r. Birds and nest, "Madhubani" style. VERT: 2r. Arrows around globe.

1974. Centenary of Mathura Museum.
744 **660** 25p. chestnut and brown 65 80
745 – 25p. chestnut and brown 65 80
DESIGN: No. 745, Vidyadhara with garland.

661 Nicholas Roerich (medallion by H. Dropsy)

1974. Birth Centenary of Professor Roerich (humanitarian).
746 **661** 1r. green and yellow . . . 65 55

662 Pavapuri Temple

1974. 2,500th Anniv of Bhagwan Mahavira's Attainment of Nirvana.
747 **662** 25p. black 60 20

663 "Cat" (Rajesh Bhatia)

1974. Children's Day.
748 **663** 25p. multicoloured . . . 1·00 50

664 "Indian Dancers" (Amita Shah)

1974. 25th Anniv of U.N.I.C.E.F. in India.
749 **664** 25p. multicoloured . . . 55 45

665 Territorial Army Badge

666 Krishna as Gopal Bal with Cows (Rajasthan painting on cloth)

1974. 25th Anniv of Indian Territorial Army.
750 **665** 25p. black, yellow & green 60 40

1974. 19th International Dairy Congress, New Delhi.
751 **666** 25p. purple and brown . . 40 40

667 Symbols and Child's Face

668 Marconi

1974. Help for Retarded Children.
752 **667** 25p. red and black . . . 60 60

1974. Birth Centenary of Guglielmo Marconi (radio pioneer).
753 **668** 2r. blue . . . . 2·25 1·25

669 St. Francis Xavier's Shrine, Goa

670 Saraswati (Deity of Language and Learning)

1974. St. Francis Xavier Celebration.
754 **669** 25p. multicoloured . . . 15 40

1975. World Hindi Convention, Nagpur.
755 **670** 25p. grey and red 40 40

671 Parliament House, New Delhi

1975. 25th Anniv of Republic.
756 **671** 25p. black, silver and blue 65 30

672 Table-tennis Bat

1975. World Table-tennis Championships, Calcutta.
757 **672** 25p. black, red and green 85 30

673 "Equality, Development and Peace"

1975. International Women's Year.
758 **673** 25p. multicoloured . . . 85 45

674 Stylized Cannon

676 Saraswati

675 Arya Samaj Emblem

1975. Bicent of Indian Army Ordnance Corps.
759 **674** 25p. multicoloured . . . 1·25 60

1975. Centenary of Arya Samaj Movement.
760 **675** 25p. red and brown . . . 40 40

1975. World Telugu Language Conf, Hyderabad.
761 **676** 25p. black and green . . 45 30

677 Satellite "Aryabhata"

1975. Launch of First Indian Satellite.
762 **677** 25p. lt blue, blue & purple 75 40

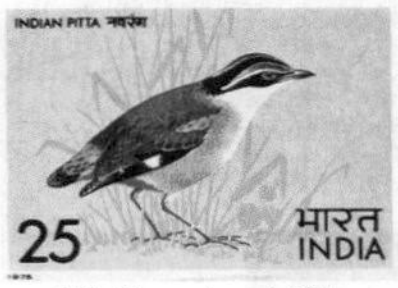

678 Blue-winged Pitta

1975. Indian Birds. Multicoloured.
763 25p. Type **678** 75 25
764 50p. Asian black-headed oriole . . . . 1·75 2·25
765 1r. Western tragopan (vert) 2·50 2·75
766 2r. Himalayan monal pheasant (vert) . . . . . 3·25 5·50

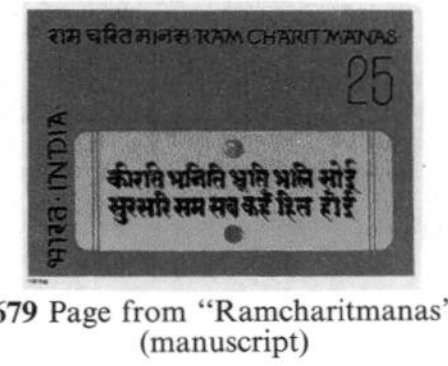

679 Page from "Ramcharitmanas" (manuscript)

1975. 4th Centenary of "Ramcharitmanas" (epic poem by Goswami Tulsidas).
767 **679** 25p. black, yellow and red 75 30

680 Young Women within Y.W.C.A. Badge

681 "The Creation"

1975. Centenary of Indian Y.W.C.A.
768 **680** 25p. multicoloured . . . 40 40

1975. 500th Birth Anniv of Michelangelo. "Creation" Frescoes from Sistine Chapel.
769 **681** 50p. multicoloured . . . 55 90
770 – 50p. multicoloured . . . 55 90
771 – 50p. multicoloured . . . 55 90
772 – 50p. multicoloured . . . 55 90
Nos. 770 and 772 are size 49 × 34 mm. The four stamps form a composite design.

682 Commission Emblem

683 Stylised Ground Antenna

1975. 25th Anniv of Int Commission on Irrigation and Drainage.
773 **682** 25p. multicoloured . . . 50 20

1975. Inauguration of Satellite Instructional Television Experiment.
774 **683** 25p. multicoloured . . . 50 20

684 St. Arunagirinathar

685 Commemorative Text

1975. 600th Birth Anniv of St. Arunagirinathar.
775 **684** 50p. purple and black . . 1·50 1·25

1975. Namibia Day.
776 **685** 25p. black and red . . . 50 50

686 Mir Anees (poet)

687 Memorial Temple to Ahilyabai Holkar (ruler)

1975. Indian Celebrities.
777 **686** 25p. green 30 75
778 **687** 25p. brown 30 75

688 Bharata Natyam

689 Ameer Khusrau

1975. Indian Dances. Multicoloured.
779 25p. Type **688** 65 20
780 50p. Orissi . . . . 1·00 2·00
781 75p. Kathak . . . . 1·25 2·25
782 1r. Kathakali . . . . 1·50 1·25
783 1r.50 Kuchipudi . . . . . . 2·25 3·75
784 2r. Manipuri . . . . 2·25 3·75

1975. 650th Death Anniv of Ameer Khusrau (poet).
785 **689** 50p. brown and bistre . . 1·25 2·00

690 V. K. Krishna Menon

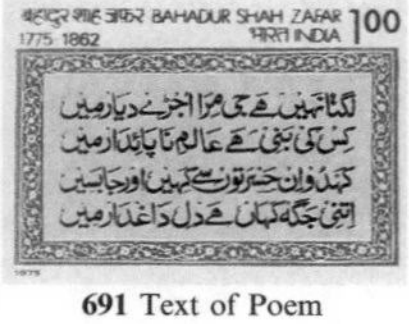

691 Text of Poem

1975. 1st Death Anniv of V. K. Krishna Menon (statesman).
786 **690** 25p. green . . . . 1·00 1·00

1975. Birth Bicentenary of Emperor Bahadur Shah Zafar.
787 **691** 1r. black, buff and brown 1·50 1·00

692 Sansadiya Soudha, New Delhi

1975. 21st Commonwealth Parliamentary Conference, New Delhi.
788 **692** 2r. green . . . . 2·00 2·75

693 V. Patel

694 N. C. Bardoloi

1975. Birth Centenary of Vallabhbhai Patel (statesman).
789 **693** 25p. green 15 50

1975. Birth Centenary of Nabin Chandra Bardoloi (politician).
790 **694** 25p. brown 30 50

695 "Cow" (Sanjay Nathubhai Patel)

1975. Children's Day.
791 **695** 25p. multicoloured . . . 70 70

696 Original Printing Works, Nasik Road

697 Gurdwara Sisganj (site of martyrdom)

1975. 50th Anniv of India Security Press.
792 **696** 25p. multicoloured . . . 40 40

1975. Tercentenary of the Martyrdom of Guru Tegh Bahadur (Sikh leader).
793 **697** 25p. multicoloured . . . 60 60

698 Theosophical Society Emblem

699 Weather Cock

1975. Centenary of Theosophical Society.
794 **698** 25p. multicoloured . . . 40 40

1975. Cent of Indian Meteorological Department.
795 **699** 25p. multicoloured . . . 60 60

700 Early Mail Cart

1975. "Inpex '75" Nat Philatelic Exn, Calcutta.
796 **700** 25p. black and brown . . 75 30
797 – 2r. brown, purple & black 2·50 3·50
DESIGN: 2r. Indian bishop mark, 1775.

701 L. N. Mishra

702 Tiger

1976. 1st Death Anniv of Lalit Narayan Mishra (politician).
798 **701** 25p. brown 40 40

1976. Birth Cent of Jim Corbett (naturalist).
799 **702** 25p. multicoloured . . . 1·00 70

703 Painted Storks

1976. Keoladeo Ghana Bird Sanctuary, Bharatpur.
800 **703** 25p. multicoloured . . . 1·00 70

704 Vijayanta Tank

1976. Bicent of 16th Light Cavalry Regiment.
801 **704** 25p. green and brown . . 1·75 40

705 Alexander Graham Bell

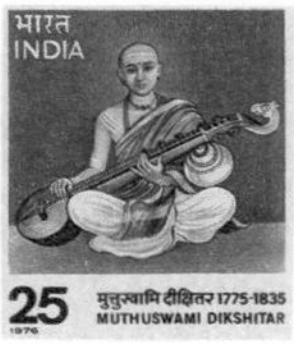

706 Muthuswami Dikshitar

1976. Alexander Graham Bell Commem.
802 **705** 25p. brown and black . . 1·00 50

1976. Birth Bicentenary of Muthuswami Dikshitar (composer).
803 **706** 25p. violet 70 50

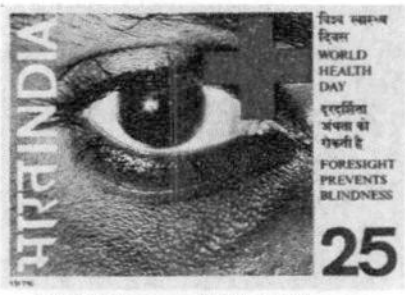

707 Eye and Red Cross

1976. World Health Day. Prevention of Blindness.
804 **707** 25p. brown and red . . . 1·00 60

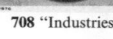

708 "Industries"

710 Nehru

709 Type WDM Diesel Locomotive, 1963

1976. Industrial Development.
805 **708** 25p. multicoloured . . . 30 30

1976. Locomotives. Multicoloured.
806 25p. Type **709** 55 10
807 50p. Rajputana Malwa Railway Class F/1 steam locomotive, 1895 . . . . . 1·50 55
808 1r. Southern Railway Class WP/1 steam locomotive, 1963 . . . . 2·75 1·25
809 2r. Great Peninsular Railway Class GIP steam locomotive, 1853 . . . . . 3·50 2·50

1976.
810b **710** 25p. violet . . . . . . 5·00 80
811 – 25p. brown . . . . . . 1·50 30
DESIGN: No. 811, Gandhi.
For these designs in a smaller format see Nos. 732, 968/9, 979/80, 1073/4 and 1320.

713 "Spirit of '76" (Willard)

714 K. Kamaraj (politician)

1976. Bicentenary of American Revolution.
812 **713** 2r.80 multicoloured . . . 1·25 1·25

1976. Kumaraswamy Kamaraj Commemoration.
813 **714** 25p. brown 15 15

715 "Shooting"

716 Subhadra Kumari Chauhan (poetess)

1976. Olympic Games, Montreal.
814 **715** 25p. violet and red . . . 30 10
815 – 1r. multicoloured . . . . 1·00 90
816 – 1r.50 mauve and black . . 2·00 3·00
817 – 2r.80 multicoloured . . . 1·75 4·25
DESIGNS: 1r. Shot-put; 1r.50, Hockey; 2r.80, Sprinting.

1976. S. K. Chauhan Commemoration.
818 **716** 25p. blue 15 50

717 Param Vir Chakra Medal

718 University Building, Bombay

1976. Param Vir Chakra Commemoration.
819 **717** 25p. multicoloured . . . 15 50

1976. 60th Anniv of Shreemati Nathibai Damodar Thackersey Women's University.
820 **718** 25p. violet 30 30

719 Bharatendu Harischandra (writer)

720 S. C. Chatterji

1976. Harischandra Commemoration.
821 **719** 25p. brown 15 30

1976. Birth Centenary of Sarat Chandra Chatterji (writer).
822 **720** 25p. black 15 30

721 Planned Family

722 Maharaja Agrasen and Coins

1976. Family Planning.
823 **721** 25p. multicoloured . . . 15 30

1976. Maharaja Agrasen Commemoration.
824 **722** 25p. brown 15 30

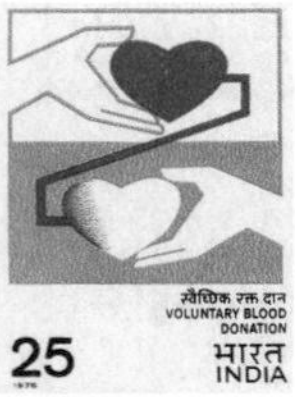

723 Swamp Deer
724 Hands holding Hearts

1976. Indian Wildlife. Multicoloured.

825	25p. Type **723**	55	40
826	50p. Lion	1·25	2·25
827	1r. Leopard (horiz)	1·75	2·25
828	2r. Caracal (horiz)	2·00	3·50

1976. Voluntary Blood Donation.
829 **724** 25p. yellow, red and black . . . 1·00 60

725 Suryakant Tripathi ("Nirala")
726 "Loyal Mongoose" (H. D. Bhatia)

1976. 80th Birth Anniv of "Nirala" (poet and novelist).
830 **725** 25p. violet 15 30

1976. Children's Day.
831 **726** 25p. multicoloured . . . 50 50

727 Hiralal Shastri (social reformer)
728 Dr. Hari Singh Gour (lawyer)

1976. Shastri Commemoration.
832 **727** 25p. brown 20 30

1976. Dr. Hari Singh Gour Commemoration.
833 **728** 25p. purple 20 30

729 Airbus Industrie A300B4

1976. Inauguration of Indian Airlines' Airbus Service.
834 **729** 2r. multicoloured . . . . 2·50 2·25

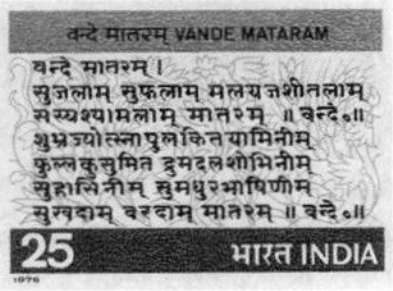

730 Hybrid Coconut Palm
731 First Stanza of "Vande Mataram"

1976. Diamond Jubilee of Coconut Research.
835 **730** 25p. multicoloured . . . 20 30

1976. Centenary of "Vande Mataram" (patriotic song by B. C. Chatterjee).
836 **731** 25p. multicoloured . . . 30 30

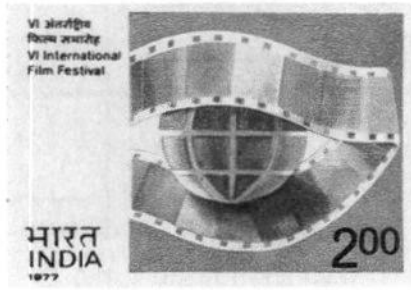

732 Globe and Film Strip

1977. 6th International Film Festival of India, New Delhi.
837 **732** 2r. multicoloured . . . . 1·10 2·00

733 Seismograph and Crack in Earth's Crust
734 Tarun Ram Phookun

1977. 6th World Conference on Earthquake Engineering, New Delhi.
838 **733** 2r. lilac . . . . 1·00 2·00

1977. Birth Cent of Tarun Ram Phookun (politician).
839 **734** 25p. grey 15 30

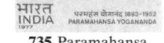

735 Paramahansa Yogananda
736 Asian Regional Red Cross Emblem

1977. Paramahansa Yogananda (religious leader) Commem.
840 **735** 25p. orange . . . . . . 1·00 80

1977. 1st Asian Regional Red Cross Conference, New Delhi.
841 **736** 2r. red, pink and blue . . 2·00 2·50

737 Fakhruddin Ali Ahmed
738 Emblem of Asian-Oceanic Postal Union

1977. Death of President Ahmed.
842 **737** 25p. multicoloured . . . 35 35

1977. 15th Anniv of Asian–Oceanic Postal Union.
843 **738** 2r. multicoloured . . . . 1·10 1·75

739 Narottam Morarjee and "Loyalty" (liner)
740 Makhanlal Chaturvedi (writer and poet)

1977. Birth Cent of Morarjee (ship owner).
844 **739** 25p. blue . . . . 1·00 1·00

1977. Chaturvedi Commemoration.
845 **740** 25p. brown 15 40

741 Mahaprabhu Vallabhacharya (philosopher)

1977. Vallabhacharya Commemoration.
846 **741** 1r. brown 30 40

742 Federation Emblem

1977. 50th Anniv of Federation of Indian Chambers of Commerce and Industry.
847 **742** 25p. purple, brown and yellow 15 40

744 "Environment Protection"

1977. World Environment Day.
848 **744** 2r. multicoloured . . . . 60 1·25

745 Rajya Sabha Chamber

1977. 25th Anniv of Rajya Sabha (Upper House of Parliament).
849 **745** 25p. multicoloured . . . 15 30

746 Lotus

1977. Indian Flowers. Multicoloured.

850	25p. Type **746**	25	15
851	50p. Rhododendron (vert)	45	1·25
852	1r. Kadamba (vert)	60	1·00
853	2r. Gloriosa lily	90	2·25

747 Berliner Gramophone

1977. Centenary of Sound Recording.
854 **747** 2r. brown and black . . . 1·00 2·00

748 Coomaraswamy and Siva
750 Dr. Samuel Hahnemann (founder of homeopathy)

749 Ganga Ram and Hospital

1977. Birth Centenary of Ananda Kentish Coomaraswamy (art historian).
855 **748** 25p. multicoloured . . . 40 40

1977. 50th Death Anniv of Sir Ganga Ram (social reformer).
856 **749** 25p. purple 30 30

1977. 32nd Int Homeopathic Congress, New Delhi.
857 **750** 2r. black and green . . . 3·50 2·75

751 Ram Manohar Lohia (politician)
752 Early Punjabi Postman

1977. Ram Manohar Lohia Commemoration.
858 **751** 25p. brown 40 30

1977. "Inpex '77" Philatelic Exn, Bangalore.
859 **752** 25p. multicoloured . . . 50 30
860 – 2r. grey and red . . . . . 2·00 2·75
DESIGN: 2r. "Lion and Palm" essay, 1853.

753 Scarlet "Scinde Dawks" of 1852

1977. "Asiana '77" Philatelic Exn, Bangalore.
861 **753** 1r. multicoloured . . . . 1·50 1·00
862 – 3r. blue, orange and black 3·00 3·75
DESIGN: 3r. Foreign mail arriving at Ballard Pier, Bombay, 1927.

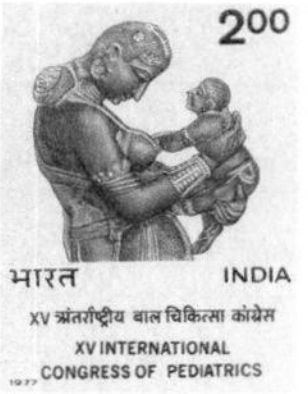

754 "Mother and Child" (Khajuraho sculpture)
756 Symbolic Sun

755 Statue of Kittur Rani Channamma, Belgaum

1977. 15th Int Congress of Pediatrics, New Delhi.
863 **754** 2r. blue and brown . . . 2·25 2·75

1977. Kittur Rani Channama (ruler) Commem.
864 **755** 25p. green . . . . 1·00 70

1977. Union Public Service Commission.
865 **756** 25p. multicoloured . . . 35 30

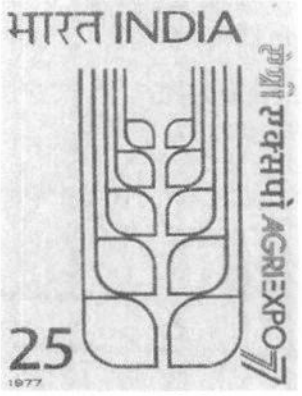

757 Ear of Corn
759 Jotirao Phooley (social reformer)

758 "Cats" (Nikur Dilipbhai Mody)

1977. "Agriexpo '77" Agricultural Exhibition, New Delhi.
866 **757** 25p. green 40 40

1977. Children's Day. Multicoloured.
867 25p. Type **758** 50 30
868 1r. "Friends" (Bhavsar Ashish Ramanlal) . . . . 2·25 3·00

1977. Indian Personalities.
869 **759** 25p. olive 30 75
870 – 25p. brown 30 75
DESIGN: No. 870, Senapti Bapat (patriot).

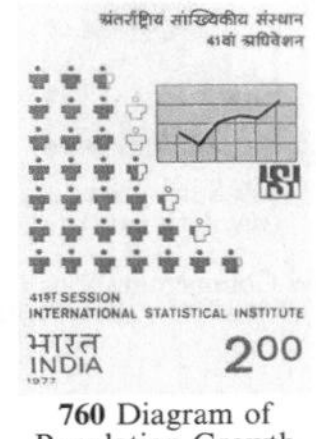

760 Diagram of Population Growth
761 Kamta Prasad Guru and Vyakarna (Hindi Grammar)

1977. 41st Session of International Statistical Institute, New Delhi.
871 **760** 2r. turquoise and red . . 60 1·00

1977. Kamta Prasad Guru (writer) Commem.
872 **761** 25p. brown 20 30

762 Kremlin Tower and Soviet Flag

763 Climber crossing a Crevice

1977. 60th Anniv of October Revolution.
873 **762** 1r. multicoloured 50 75

1978. Conquest of Kanchenjunga (1977). Multicoloured.
874 25p. Type **763** 10 10
875 1r. Indian flag near summit (horiz) 45 90

764 "Shikara" on Lake Dal, Kashmir

1978. 27th Pacific Area Travel Association Conference, New Delhi.
876 **764** 1r. multicoloured . . . . 2·00 1·50

765 Children in Library

1978. 3rd World Book Fair, New Delhi.
877 **765** 1r. brown and slate . . . 50 80

766 Mother-Pondicherry

767 Wheat and Globe

1978. Birth Centenary of Mother-Pondicherry (philosopher).
878 **766** 25p. brown and grey . . 20 30

1978. 5th International Wheat Genetics Symposium, New Delhi.
879 **767** 25p. yellow and turquoise 20 30

768 Nanalal Dalpatram Kavi (poet)

769 Surjya Sen (revolutionary)

1978. Nanalal Dalpatram Kavi Commemoration.
880 **768** 25p. brown 20 30

1978. Surjya Sen Commemoration.
881 **769** 25p. bistre and red . . . 20 30

770 "Two Vaishnavas" (Jamini Roy)

1978. Modern Indian Paintings. Multicoloured.
882 25p. Type **770** 20 30
883 50p. "The Mosque" (Sailoz Mookherjea) . . . . . . 40 1·25
884 1r. "Head" (Rabindranath Tagore) . . . . 70 1·50
885 2r. "Hill Women" (Amrita Sher Gil) . . . . 90 2·00

771 "Self-portrait" (Rubens)

772 Charlie Chaplin

1978. 400th Birth Anniv of Peter Paul Rubens.
886 **771** 2r. multicoloured . . . . 2·00 3·00

1978. Charlie Chaplin Commemoration.
887 **772** 25p. blue and gold . . . 1·25 70

773 Deendayal Upadhyaya (politician)

774 Syama Prasad Mookerjee

1978. Deendayal Upadhyaya Commemoration.
888 **773** 25p. brown and orange 20 40

1978. Syama Prasad Mookerjee (politician) Commemoration.
889 **774** 25p. brown 30 50

775 Airavat (mythological elephant), Jain Temple, Gujerat (Kachchh Museum)

776 Krishna and Arjuna in Battle Chariot

1978. Treasures from Indian Museums. Mult.
890 25p. Type **775** 30 30
891 50p. Kalpadruma (magical tree), Besnagar (Indian Museum) . . . . 40 1·25
892 1r. Obverse and reverse of Kushan gold coin (National Museum) . . . . 55 1·50
893 2r. Dagger and knife of Emperor Jehangir, Mughal (Salar Jung Museum) . . . 75 2·00

1978. Bhagawadgeeta (Divine Song of India) Commemoration.
894 **776** 25p. gold and red 20 30

777 Bethune College

1978. Centenary of Bethune College, Calcutta.
895 **777** 25p. brown and green . . 20 30

778 E. V. Ramasami

1978. E. V. Ramasami (social reformer) Commemoration.
896 **778** 25p. black 20 20

779 Uday Shankar

780 Leo Tolstoy

1978. Uday Shankar (dancer) Commem.
897 **779** 25p. brown 20 30

1978. 150th Birth Anniv of Leo Tolstoy (writer).
898 **780** 1r. multicoloured 30 30

781 Vallathol Narayana Menon

783 Machine Operator

782 "Two Friends" (Dinesh Sharma)

1978. Birth Centenary of Vallathol Narayana Menon (poet).
899 **781** 25p. purple and brown . . 15 40

1978. Children's Day.
900 **782** 25p. multicoloured . . . 20 40

1978. National Small Industries Fair, New Delhi.
901 **783** 25p. green 20 30

784 Sowars of Skinner's Horse

785 Mohammad Ali Jauhar

1978. 175th Anniv of Skinner's Horse (cavalry regiment).
902 **784** 25p. multicoloured . . . 1·00 70

1978. Birth Centenary of Mohammad Ali Jauhar (patriot).
903 **785** 25p. olive 20 30

786 Chakravarti Rajagopalachari

787 Wright Brothers and Flyer I

1978. Birth Centenary of Chakravarti Rajagopalachari (first post-independence Governor-General).
904 **786** 25p. brown 20 30

1978. 75th Anniv of Powered Flight.
905 **787** 1r. violet and yellow . . . 1·00 30

788 Ravenshaw College

1978. Centenary of Ravenshaw College, Cuttack.
906 **788** 25p. red and green . . . 20 30

789 Schubert

790 Uniforms of 1799, 1901 and 1979 with Badge

1978. 150th Death Anniv of Franz Schubert (composer).
907 **789** 1r. multicoloured . . . . 1·25 55

1979. 4th Reunion of Punjab Regiment.
908 **790** 25p. multicoloured . . . 1·25 70

791 Bhai Parmanand

792 Gandhi with Young Boy

1979. Bhai Parmanand (scholar) Commemoration.
909 **791** 25p. violet 20 30

1979. International Year of the Child.
910 **792** 25p. brown and red . . . 40 30
911 – 1r. brown and orange . . 60 1·50
DESIGN: 1r. India I.Y.C. emblem.

793 Albert Einstein

794 Rajarshi Shahu Chhatrapati

1979. Birth Centenary of Albert Einstein (physicist).
912 **793** 1r. blue 75 60

1979. Rajarshi Shahu Chhatrapati (ruler of Kolhapur State, and precursor of social reform in India) Commemoration.
913 **794** 25p. purple 20 30

795 Exhibition Logo

1979. "India '80" International Stamp Exhibition (1st issue).
914 **795** 30p. green and orange . . 20 30
See also Nos. 942/5 and 955/8.

796 Postcards under Magnifying Glass

797 Raja Mahendra Pratap

1979. Centenary of Indian Postcards.
915 **796** 50p. multicoloured . . . 20 40

1979. Raja Mahendra Pratap (patriot) Commemoration.
916 **797** 30p. green 20 40

798 Hilsa, Pomfret and Prawn

800 Jatindra Nath Das

1979.

920	–	2p. violet	10	30
921a	**798**	5p. blue	10	10
922a	–	10p. green	70	10
923	–	15p. green	20	10
924a	–	20p. red	70	10
925a	–	25p. brown	70	10
925bb	–	25p. green	75	10
926ab	–	30p. green	1·25	10
927	–	35p. purple	1·50	10
928c	–	50p. violet	1·00	10
929b	–	1r. brown	20	10
932a	–	2r. lilac	20	10
933c	–	2r.25 red and green . .	50	10
934	–	2r.80 red and green . .	2·00	1·00
934ca	–	3r.25 orange and green	25	30
935c	–	5r. red and green . . .	60	40
936b	–	10r. purple and green	30	45

DESIGNS—HORIZ: 2p. Adult education class; 10p. Irrigation canal; 25p. (925a) Chick hatching from egg; 25p. (925bb) Village, wheat and tractor; 30p. Harvesting maize; 50p. Woman dairy farmer, cows and milk bottles. (36 × 19 mm): 10r. Forest on hillside. VERT (17 × 20 mm): 15p. Farmer and agricultural symbols; 20p. Mother feeding child; 35p. "Family Welfare". (17 × 28 mm): 1r. Cotton plant; 2r. Weaving. (20 × 38 mm): 2r.25, Cashew; 2r.80, Apples; 3r.25, Oranges; 5r. Rubber tapping.

For 75p. in same design as No. 927 see No. 1214.

1979. 50th Death Anniv of Jatindra Nath Das (revolutionary).
941 **800** 30p. brown 20 40

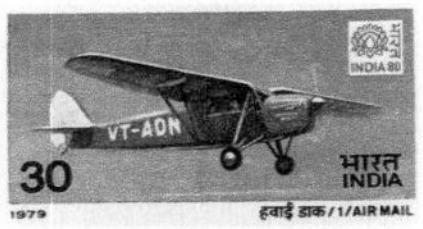

801 De Havilland Puss Moth

1979. "Air India 80" International Stamp Exhibition (2nd issue). Mail-carrying Aircraft. Multicoloured.

942	30p. Type **801**	50	25
943	50p. Indian Air Force Hindustan Aircraft Industries Chetak helicopter	70	45
944	1r. Indian Airlines Boeing 737 airliner	85	75
945	2r. Air India Boeing 747 airliner	1·10	95

802 Early and Modern Lightbulbs

1979. Centenary of Electric Lightbulb.
946 **802** 1r. purple 20 30

803 Gilgit Record

1979. International Archives Week.
947 **803** 30p. yellow and brown . . 20 60

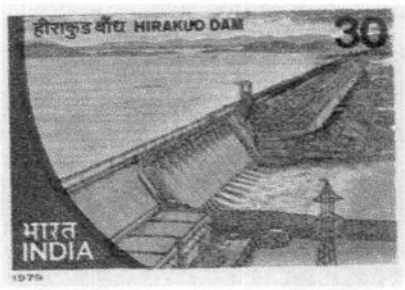

804 Hirakud Dam, Orissa

1979. 50th Anniv and 13th Congress of International Commission on Large Dams.
948 **804** 30p. brown and turquoise 20 30

805 Fair Emblem

806 Child learning to Read

1979. India International Trade Fair, New Delhi.
949 **805** 1r. black and red 20 30

1979. International Children's Book Fair, New Delhi.
950 **806** 30p. multicoloured . . . 20 30

807 Dove with Olive Branch and I.A.E.A. Emblem

1979. 23rd International Atomic Energy Agency Conference, New Delhi.
951 **807** 1r. multicoloured 20 45

808 Hindustan Aircraft Industries HAL-26 Pushpak Light Plane and Rohini-1 Glider

1979. Flying and Gliding.
952 **808** 30p. black, brown and blue . . . . 1·40 1·00

809 Gurdwara Baoli Sahib Temple, Goindwal, Amritsar District

810 Ring of People encircling U.N. Emblem and Cogwheel

1979. 500th Birth Anniv of Guru Amar Das (Sikh leader).
953 **809** 30p. multicoloured . . . 20 40

1980. 3rd United Nations Industrial Development Organization General Conference, New Delhi.
954 **810** 1r. multicoloured 20 30

811 Army Post Office and Postmarks

812 Energy Symbols

1980. "India '80" International Stamp Exhibition (3rd issue).

955	**811**	30p. green	40	30
956	–	50p. brown & deep brown	70	1·00
957	–	1r. red	80	1·00
958	–	2r. brown	80	2·00

DESIGNS: 50p. Money order transfer document, 1879; 1r. Copper prepayment ticket, 1774; 2r. Sir Rowland Hill and birthplace at Kidderminster.

1980. Institution of Engineers (India) Commem.
959 **812** 30p. gold and blue . . . 20 30

813 Uniforms of 1780 and 1980, Crest and Ribbon

814 Books

1980. Bicentenary of Madras Sappers.
960 **813** 30p. multicoloured . . . 1·00 60

1980. 4th World Book Fair, New Delhi.
961 **814** 30p. blue 30 30

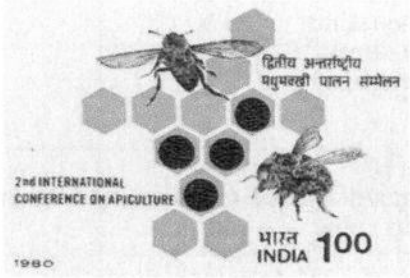

815 Bees and Honey-Comb

1980. 2nd International Conference on Agriculture.
962 **815** 1r. bistre and brown . . . 1·00 55

816 Welthy Fisher and Saksharta Nicketan (Literacy House), Lucknow

1980. Welthy Fisher (teacher) Commemoration.
963 **816** 30p. blue 30 30

817 Darul-Uloom, Deoband

818 Keshub Chunder Sen

1980. Darul-Uloom College Commemoration.
964 **817** 30p. green 20 30

1980. Keshub Chunder Sen (religious and social reformer) Commemoration.
965 **818** 30p. brown 30 30

819 Chhatrapati Shivaji Maharaj

820 Table Tennis

1980. 300th Death Anniv of Chhatrapati Shivaji Maharaj (warrior).
966 **819** 30p. multicoloured . . . 20 40

1980. 5th Asian Table Tennis Championships, Calcutta.
967 **820** 30p. purple 30 30

1980. As Nos. 732 and 810, but 17 × 20 mm in size.
968 30p. brown (Gandhi) . . . . 4·50 1·75
969 30p. violet (Nehru) . . . . 2·00 60

821 N. M. Joshi

822 Ulloor S. Parameswara Iyer

1980. Narayan Malhar Joshi (trade unionist) Commemoration.
970 **821** 30p. mauve 60 40

1980. Ulloor S. Parameswara Iyer (poet) Commemoration.
971 **822** 30p. purple 60 40

823 S. M. Zamin Ali

824 Helen Keller

1980. Syed Mohammed Zamin Ali (educationist and poet) Commemoration.
972 **823** 30p. green 20 40

1980. Birth Centenary of Helen Keller (campaigner for the handicapped).
973 **824** 30p. black and orange . . 1·00 40

825 High-jumping

826 Prem Chand

1980. Olympic Games, Moscow. Multicoloured.
974 1r. Type **825** 40 40
975 2r.80 Horse-riding . . . . . 1·75 3·25

1980. Birth Cent of Prem Chand (novelist).
976 **826** 30p. brown 20 50

827 Mother Teresa and Nobel Peace Prize Medallion

1980. Award of 1979 Nobel Peace Prize to Mother Teresa.
977 **827** 30p. violet . . . . 1·00 60

828 Lord Mountbatten

1980. Lord Mountbatten Commemoration.
978 **828** 2r.80 multicoloured . . . 2·50 2·75

1980. As Nos. 968/9, but new face value.
979 35p. brown . . . . 2·25 50
980 35p. violet 75 20
DESIGNS: No. 979, Gandhi; No. 980, Nehru.

829 Scottish Church College, Calcutta

830 Rajah Annamalai Chettiar

1980. 150th Anniv of Scottish Church College, Calcutta.
981 **829** 35p. lilac 20 30

1980. Rajah Annamalai Chettiar (banker and educationist) Commemoration.
982 **830** 35p. lilac 20 30

831 Gandhi marching to Dandi

832 Jayaprakash Narayan

1980. 50th Anniv of "Dandi March" (Gandhi's defiance of Salt Tax Law).
983 **831** 35p. black, blue and gold . . . 80 1·25
984 – 35p. black, mauve and gold . . . . 80 1·25
DESIGN: No. 984, Gandhi picking up handful of salt at Dandi.

1980. Jayaprakash Narayan (socialist) Commemoration.
985 **832** 35p. brown 50 60

833 Great Indian Bustard

1980. International Symposium on Bustards, Juipur.
986 **833** 2r.30 multicoloured . . . 1·00 2·00

834 Arabic Commemorative Inscription

1980. Moslem Year 1400 A.H. Commemoration.
987 **834** 35p. multicoloured . . . 15 30

835 "Girls Dancing" (Pampa Paul)

836 Dhyan Chand

1980. Children's Day.
988 **835** 35p. multicoloured . . . 1·00 40

1980. Dhyan Chand (hockey player). Commemoration.
989 **836** 35p. brown . . . . 1·25 85

837 Gold Mining

838 M. A. Ansari

1980. Cent of Kolar Gold Fields, Karnataka.
990 **837** 1r. multicoloured . . . . 1·60 30

1980. Mukhtayar Ahmad Ansari (medical practitioner and politician) Commemoration.
991 **838** 35p. green 40 40

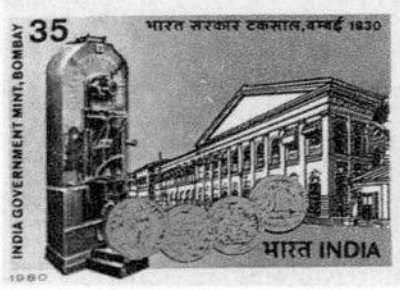

839 India Government Mint, Bombay

1980. 150th Anniv of India Government Mint, Bombay.
992 **839** 35p. black, blue and silver 20 30

840 Bride from Tamil Nadu

841 Mazharul Haque

1980. Brides in Traditional Costume. Multicoloured.
993 1r. Type **840** 40 75
994 1r. Rajasthan 40 75
995 1r. Kashmir 40 75
996 1r. Bengal 40 75

1981. Mazharul Haque (journalist) Commem.
997 **841** 35p. blue 20 40

842 St. Stephen's College

1981. Centenary of St. Stephen's College, Delhi.
998 **842** 35p. red 20 50

843 Gommateshwara

844 G. V. Mavalankar

1981. Millenium of Gommateshwara (statue at Shravanabelgola).
999 **843** 1r. multicoloured 20 30

1981. 25th Death Anniv of Ganesh Vasudeo Mavalankar (parliamentarian).
1000 **844** 35p. red 20 40

845 Flame of Martyrdom

1981. "Homage to Martyrs".
1001 **845** 35p. multicoloured . . . 20 30

846 Heinrich von Stephan and U.P.U. Emblem

1981. 150th Birth Anniv of Heinrich von Stephan (founder of U.P.U.).
1002 **846** 1r. brown 20 50

847 Disabled Child being helped by Able-bodied Child

1981. International Year for Disabled Persons.
1003 **847** 1r. black and blue . . . 20 30

848 Bhil

849 Stylized Trees

1981. Tribes of India. Muticoloured.
1004 1r. Type **848** 40 35
1005 1r. Dandami Maria 40 35
1006 1r. Toda 40 35
1007 1r. Khlamngam Naga . . . 40 35

1981. Forests Conservation.
1008 **849** 1r. multicoloured 20 30

850 Nilmoni Phukan

851 Sanjay Gandhi

1981. Nilmoni Phukan (poet) Commemoration.
1009 **850** 35p. brown 20 50

1981. 1st Death Anniv of Sanjay Gandhi (politician).
1010 **851** 35p. multicoloured . . . 40 65

852 Launch of "SLV 3" and Diagram of "Rohini"

853 Games Logo

1981. Launch of "SLV 3" Rocket with "Rohini" Satellite.
1011 **852** 1r. black, pink and blue 30 30

1981. Asian Games, New Delhi (1st issue). Multicoloured.
1012 1r. Type **853** . . . . 1·00 65
1013 1r. Games emblem and stylized hockey players . . 1·00 65
See also Nos. 1026, 1033, 1057, 1059 and 1061/6.

854 Flame of the Forest

855 W. F. D. Emblem and Wheat

1981. Flowering Trees. Multicoloured.
1014 35p. Type **854** 40 15
1015 50p. Crateva 75 75
1016 1r. Golden shower . . . . 1·00 50
1017 2r. Bauhinia . . . . 1·40 2·75

1981. World Food Day.
1018 **855** 1r. yellow and blue . . . 30 20

856 "Stichophthalma camadeva"

1981. Butterflies. Multicoloured.
1019 35p. Type **856** 90 20
1020 50p. "Cethosia biblis" . . . 1·75 1·75
1021 1r. "Cyrestis achates" (vert) 2·25 70
1022 2r. "Teinopalpus imperialis" (vert) . . . . 2·75 6·00

857 Bellary Raghava

1981. Bellary Raghava (actor) Commemoration.
1023 **857** 35p. green 70 30

858 Regimental Colour

859 "Toyseller" (Kumari Ruchita Sharma)

1981. 40th Anniv of Mahar Regiment.
1024 **858** 35p. multicoloured . . . 1·00 30

1981. Children's Day.
1025 **859** 35p. multicoloured . . . 75 30

860 Rajghat Stadium

861 Kashi Prasad Jayasawal and Yaudheya Coin

1981. Asian Games, New Delhi (2nd issue).
1026 **860** 1r. multicoloured . . . . 1·75 30

1981. Birth Centenary of Kashi Prasad Jayasawal (lawyer and historian).
1027 **861** 35p. blue 50 30

862 Indian and P.L.O. Flags, and People

1981. Palestinian Solidarity.
1028 **862** 1r. multicoloured . . . . 2·25 40

863 I.N.S. "Taragiri" (frigate)

1981. Indian Navy Day.
1029 **863** 35p. multicoloured . . . 2·25 1·25

864 Henry Heras and Indus Valley Seal

1981. Henry Heras (historian) Commemoration.
1030 **864** 35p. lilac 45 30

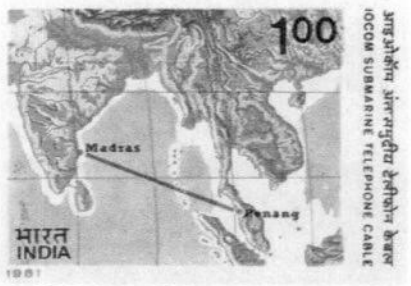

865 Map of South-East Asia showing Cable Route

1981. Inauguration of I.O.C.O.M. (Indian Ocean Commonwealth Cable) Submarine Telephone Cable.
1031 **865** 1r. multicoloured . . . . 2·25 35

866 Stylized Hockey-players and Championship Emblem

1981. World Cup Hockey Championship, Bombay.
1032 **866** 1r. multicoloured . . . . 1·25 30

867 Jawaharlal Nehru Stadium **868** Early and Modern Telephones

1981. Asian Games, New Delhi (3rd issue).
1033 **867** 1r. multicoloured 30 20

1982. Centenary of Telephone Services.
1034 **868** 2r. black, blue and grey 30 30

869 Map of World **870** Sir J. J. School of Art

1982. International Soil Science Congress, New Delhi.
1035 **869** 1r. multicoloured 30 20

1982. 125th Anniv of Sir J. J. School of Art, Bombay.
1036 **870** 35p. multicoloured . . . 20 20

871 "Three Musicians" **872** Deer (stone carving), 5th-century A.D.

1982. Birth Centenary (1981) of Picasso.
1037 **871** 2r.85 multicoloured . . . 1·40 50

1982. Festival of India. Ancient Sculpture. Multicoloured.
1038 2r. Type **872** 20 40
1039 3r.05 Kaliya Mardana (bronze statue), 9th-century A.D 35 60

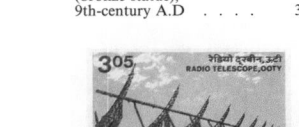

873 Radio Telescope, Ooty

1982. Festival of India. Science and Technology.
1040 **873** 3r.05 multicoloured . . . 35 40

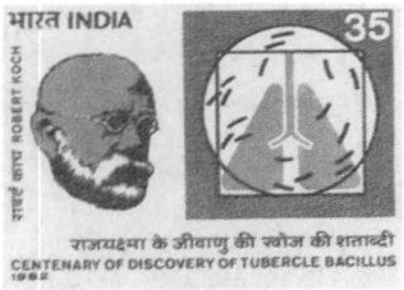

874 Robert Koch and Symbol of Disease

1982. Centenary of Robert Koch's Discovery of Tubercle Bacillus.
1041 **874** 35p. lilac . . . . 1·75 80

875 Durgabai Deshmukh

1982. 1st Death Anniv of Durgabai Deshmukh (social reformer).
1042 **875** 35p. blue 70 80

876 Blue Poppy **877** "Apple" Satellite

1982. Himalayan Flowers. Multicoloured.
1043 35p. Type **876** 70 30
1044 1r. Showy inula . . . . . . 1·75 30
1045 2r. Cobra lily . . . . 2·25 3·00
1046 2r.85 Brahma kamal . . . . 2·75 4·75

1982. 1st Anniv of "Apple" Satellite Launch.
1047 **877** 2r. multicoloured . . . . 50 1·00

878 Bidhan Chandra Roy

1982. Birth Centenary of Bidhan Chandra Roy (doctor and politician).
1048 **878** 50p. brown . . . . . . 1·00 1·50

879 "Sagar Samrat" Oil Rig

1982. 25th Anniv of Oil and Natural Gas Commission.
1049 **879** 1r. multicoloured . . . . 1·50 60

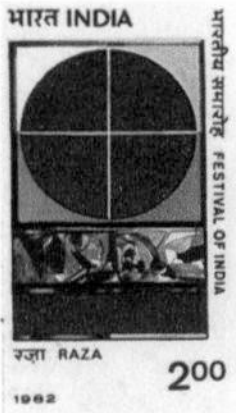

880 "Bindu" (S. H. Raza) **881** Red Deer Stag, Kashmir

1982. Festival of India. Contemporary Paintings. Multicoloured.
1050 2r. Type **880** 50 50
1051 3r.05 "Between the Spider and the Lamp" (M. F. Hussain) . . . . 75 1·25

1982. Wildlife Conservation.
1052 **881** 2r.85 multicoloured . . . 2·50 1·75

882 Westland Wapiti Biplane and Mikoyan Gurevich MiG-25 Aircraft

1982. 50th Anniv of Indian Air Force.
1053 **882** 1r. multicoloured . . . . 5·00 1·25

883 J. Tata with De Havilland Puss Moth

1982. 50th Anniv of Civil Aviation in India.
1054 **883** 3r.25 multicoloured . . . 4·50 1·75

884 Police Patrol

1982. Police Commemoration Day.
1055 **884** 50p. green 60 30

885 Coins and Economic Symbols

1982. Centenary of Post Office Savings Bank.
1056 **885** 50p. brown and light brown 20 20

886 Wrestling Bout

1982. Asian Games, New Delhi (4th issue).
1057 **886** 1r. multicoloured . . . . 1·00 30

887 Troposcatter Communication Link

1982. 1st Anniv of Troposcatter Communication Link between India and U.S.S.R.
1058 **887** 3r.05 multicoloured . . . 30 40

888 Arjuna shooting Arrow at Fish **889** "Mother and Child" (Deepak Sharma)

1982. Asian Games, New Delhi (5th issue).
1059 **888** 1r. multicoloured . . . . 1·75 30

1982. Children's Day.
1060 **889** 50p. multicoloured . . . 30 30

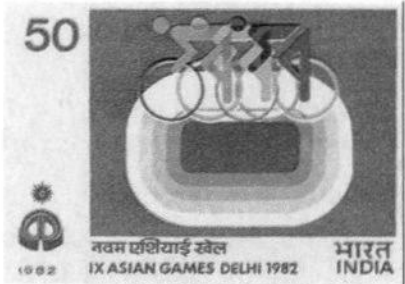

890 Stylized Cyclists

1982. Asian Games, New Delhi (6th issue). Multicoloured.
1061 50p. Type **890** 15 10
1062 2r. Javelin-throwing 25 30
1063 2r.85 Discus-throwing . . . 30 45
1064 3r.25 Football 40 55

891 "Enterprise" Dinghies Race

1982. Asian Games, New Delhi (7th issue). Multicoloured.
1065 2r. Type **891** . . . . 1·25 30
1066 2r.85 Rowing . . . . 1·75 70

892 Chetwode Building

1982. 50th Anniv of Indian Military Academy Dehradun.
1067 **892** 50p. multicoloured . . . 30 50

893 Purushottamdas Tandon

1982. Birth Cent of Purushottamdas Tandon (politician).
1068 **893** 50p. brown 30 80

894 Darjeeling Himalayan Railway

1982. Cent of Darjeeling Himalayan Railway.
1069 **894** 2r.85 multicoloured . . . 5·50 4·75

895 Vintage Rail Coach and Silhouette of Steam Locomotive

1982. "Inpex 82" Stamp Exhibition. Multicoloured.
1070 50p. Type **895** . . . . . . 1·00 1·00
1071 2r. 1854 ½ anna blue stamp and 1947 3½ anna Independence commem (33 × 44 mm) . . . . . . 2·50 3·00

896 Antarctic Camp

1983. 1st Indian Antarctic Expedition.
1072 **896** 1r. multicoloured . . . . 4·25 2·25

1983. As Nos. 968/9, but with new face value.
1073 50p. brown (Gandhi) . . . 4·00 2·25
1074a 50p. blue (Nehru) . . . . 2·50 70

897 Roosevelt with Stamp Collection

1983. Birth Centenary of Franklin D. Roosevelt (American statesman).
1075 **897** 3r.25 brown . . . . . . 55 1·25

898 "Siberian Cranes at Bharatpur" (Diane Pierce)

899 Jat Regiment Uniforms Past and Present

1983. International Crane Workshop, Bharatpur.
1076 **898** 2r.85 multicoloured . . . 3·00 3·00

1983. Presentation of Colours to Battalions of the Jat Regiment.
1077 **899** 50p. multicoloured . . . 2·00 1·75

900 Non-aligned Summit Logo

1983. 7th Non-aligned Summit Conference, New Delhi.
1078 **900** 1r. lt brown, brown & blk 20 30
1079 – 2r. multicoloured 30 95
DESIGN: 2r. Nehru.

901 Shore Temple, Mahabalipuram

1983. Commonwealth Day. Multicoloured.
1080 1r. Type **901** 15 30
1081 2r. Gomukh, Gangtotri Glacier . . . . 30 1·25

902 Acropolis and Olympic Emblems

1983. Int Olympic Committee Session, New Delhi.
1082 **902** 1r. multicoloured 30 50

903 "St. Francis and Brother Falcon" (statue by Giovanni Collina)

904 Karl Marx and "Das Kapital"

1983. 800th Birth Anniv of St. Francis of Assisi.
1083 **903** 1r. brown 65 30

1983. Death Centenary of Karl Marx.
1084 **904** 1r. brown 30 30

905 Darwin and Map of Voyage

1983. Death Centenary (1982) of Charles Darwin (naturalist).
1085 **905** 2r. multicoloured . . . . 3·25 3·25

906 Swamp Deer

907 Globe and Satellite

1983. 50th Anniv of Kanha National Park.
1086 **906** 1r. multicoloured . . . . 2·50 1·00

1983. World Communications Year.
1087 **907** 1r. multicoloured 40 40

908 Simon Bolivar

909 Meera Behn

1983. Birth Bicentenary of Simon Bolivar (South American statesman).
1088 **908** 2r. multicoloured . . . . 2·00 2·00

1983. India's Struggle for Freedom (1st series).
1089 50p. red and green . . . . 1·40 2·25
1090 50p. brown, green and red 1·40 2·25
1091 50p. multicoloured . . . . 1·40 2·00
1092 50p. brown, green and red 15 50
1093 50p. brown, green and orange 15 50
1094 50p. green, yellow and orange 15 50
DESIGNS—VERT: No. 1089, Type **909**; 1090, Mahadev Desai; 1092, Hemu Kalani (revolutionary); 1093, Acharya Vinoba Bhave (social reformer); 1094, Surendranath Banerjee (political reformer). HORIZ (43 × 31 mm): No. 1091, Quit India Resolution.
See also Nos. 1119/24, 1144/9, 1191/4, 1230/5, 1287/96 and 1345/9.

910 Ram Nath Chopra

1983. Ram Nath Chopra (pharmacologist) Commemoration.
1095 **910** 50p. red . . . . 50 1·25

911 Nanda Devi Mountain

1983. 25th Anniv of Indian Mountaineering Federation.
1096 **911** 2r. multicoloured . . . . 2·00 1·25

912 Great Indian Hornbill

913 View of Garden

1983. Centenary of Natural History Society, Bombay.
1097 **912** 1r. multicoloured . . . . 3·25 1·00

1983. Rock Garden, Chandigarh.
1098 **913** 1r. multicoloured . . . . 1·50 1·00

914 Golden Langur

1983. Indian Wildlife. Monkeys. Multicoloured.
1099 1r. Type **914** . . . . 2·00 50
1100 2r. Lion-tailed macaque . . 3·00 4·00

915 Ghats of Varanasi

1983. 5th General Assembly of World Tourism Organization.
1101 **915** 2r. multicoloured 60 60

916 Krishna Kanta Handique

918 Woman and Child (from "Festival" by Kashyap Premsawala)

1983. Krishna Kanta Handique (scholar).
1102 **916** 50p. blue 30 70

1983. Children's Day.
1103 **918** 50p. multicoloured . . . 30 50

920 "Udan Khatola", First Indian Hot Air Balloon

921 Tiger

1983. Bicentenary of Manned Flight.
1104 1r. Type **920** . . . . 1·00 20
1105 2r. Montgolfier balloon . . 1·40 1·25

1983. Ten Years of "Project Tiger".
1106 **921** 2r. multicoloured . . . . 3·50 3·75

922 Commonwealth Logo

923 "Pratiksha"

1983. Commonwealth Heads of Government Meeting, New Delhi. Multicoloured.
1107 1r. Type **922** 40 15
1108 2r. Goanese couple, early 19th century 85 50

1983. Birth Centenary of Nanda Lal Bose (artist).
1109 **923** 1r. multicoloured 30 30

925 Lancer in Ceremonial Uniform

926 Troopers in Ceremonial Uniform and Tank

1984. Bicentenary of 7th Light Cavalry.
1110 **925** 1r. multicoloured . . . . 3·25 1·40

1984. Presentation of Regimental Guidon to the Deccan Horse.
1111 **926** 1r. multicoloured . . . . 3·25 1·40

927 Society Building and Sir William Jones (founder)

1984. Bicentenary of Asiatic Society.
1112 **927** 1r. green and purple . . 30 50

928 Insurance Logo

1984. Centenary of Postal Life Insurance.
1113 **928** 1r. multicoloured 30 30

929 Hawker Siddeley Sea Harrier

1984. President's Review of the Fleet. Multicoloured.
1114 1r. Type **929** . . . . 1·50 2·00
1115 1r. "Vikrant" (aircraft carrier) . . . . 1·50 2·00
1116 1r. "Vela" (submarine) . . . 1·50 2·00
1117 1r. "Kashin" (destroyer) . . 1·50 2·00
Nos. 1114/17 were printed together, se-tenant, forming a composite design.

930 I.L.A. Logo and Hemispheres

1984. 12th International Leprosy Congress.
1118 **930** 1r. multicoloured 65 40

1984. India's Struggle for Freedom (2nd series). As T **909**.
1119 50p. green, lt green & orange 30 70
1120 50p. brown, green and orange 30 70
1121 50p. multicoloured . . . . 75 1·00
1122 50p. multicoloured . . . . 75 1·00
1123 50p. multicoloured . . . . 75 1·00
1124 50p. multicoloured . . . . 75 1·00
DESIGNS: No. 1119, Vasudeo Balvant Phadke (revolutionary); 1120, Baba Kanshi Ram (revolutionary); 1121, Tatya Tope; 1122, Nana Sahib; 1123, Begum Hazrat Mahal; 1124, Mangal Pandey.

932 "Salyut 7"

1984. Indo-Soviet Manned Space Flight.
1125 **932** 3r. multicoloured . . . . 80 1·00

935 G. D. Birla

1984. 90th Birth Anniv of G. D. Birla (industrialist).
1126 **935** 50p. brown . . . . . . 50 1·00

936 Basketball

937 Gwalior

1984. Olympic Games, Los Angeles. Multicoloured.

1127	50p. Type **936**	90	65
1128	1r. High jumping	75	30
1129	2r. Gymnastics (horiz)	1·00	1·50
1130	2r.50 Weightlifting (horiz)	1·25	2·50

1984. Forts. Multicoloured.

1131	50p. Type **937**	70	55
1132	1r. Vellore (vert)	95	30
1133	1r.50 Simhagad (vert)	1·75	2·75
1134	2r. Jodhpur	2·00	3·00

938 B. V. Paradkar and Newspaper

939 Dr. D. N. Wadia and Institute of Himalayan Geology, Dehradun

1984. B. V. Paradkar (journalist) Commemoration.
1135 **938** 50p. brown . . . . . . 50 1·00

1984. Birth Centenary (1983) of Dr. D. N. Wadia (geologist).
1136 **939** 1r. multicoloured . . . . 1·50 40

940 "Herdsman and Cattle in Forest" (H. Kassam)

942 Congress Emblem

941 Indira Gandhi

1984. Children's Day.
1137 **940** 50p. multicoloured . . . 75 1·00

1984. Prime Minister Indira Gandhi Commemoration (1st issue).
1138 **941** 50p. black, violet & orange . . . . 2·25 2·25
See also Nos. 1151, 1167 and 1170.

1984. 12th World Mining Congress, New Delhi.
1139 **942** 1r. black and yellow . . 1·50 30

943 Dr. Rajendra Prasad at Desk

944 Mrinalini (rose)

1984. Birth Centenary of Dr. Rajendra Prasad (former President).
1140 **943** 50p. multicoloured . . . 1·00 1·25

1984. Roses. Multicoloured.

1141	1r.50 Type **944**	2·25	2·25
1142	2r. Sugandha	2·50	2·50

945 "Fergusson College" (Gopal Deuskar)

1985. Centenary of Fergusson College, Pune.
1143 **945** 1r. multicoloured 70 55

1985. India's Struggle for Freedom (3rd series). As T **909**.

1144	50p. brown, green and orange	70	1·00
1145	50p. brown, green and orange	70	1·00
1146	50p. brown, green and orange	70	1·00
1147	50p. brown, green and orange	70	1·00
1148	50p. blue, green and orange	70	1·00
1149	50p. black, green and orange	70	1·00

DESIGNS—VERT: No. 1144, Narhar Vishnu Gadgil (politician); 1145, Jairamdas Doulatram (journalist); 1147, Kakasaheb Kalelkar (author); 1148, Master Tara Singh (politician); 1149, Ravishankar Maharaj (politician). HORIZ: No. 1146, Jatindra and Nellie Sengupta (politicians).

947 Gunner and Howitzer from Mountain Battery

1985. 50th Anniv of Regiment of Artillery.
1150 **947** 1r. multicoloured . . . . 4·25 1·50

948 Indira Gandhi making Speech

1985. Indira Gandhi Commemoration (2nd issue).
1151 **948** 2r. multicoloured . . . . 3·50 3·75

949 Minicoy Lighthouse

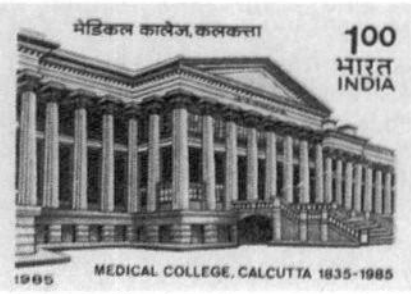

950 Medical College Hospital

1985. Centenary of Minicoy Lighthouse.
1152 **949** 1r. multicoloured . . . . 4·50 1·00

1985. 150th Anniv of Medical College, Calcutta.
1153 **950** 1r. yellow, brown & purple . . . . 3·00 70

951 Medical College, Madras

1985. 150th Anniv of Medical College, Madras.
1154 **951** 1r. light brown and brown . . . . 3·00 70

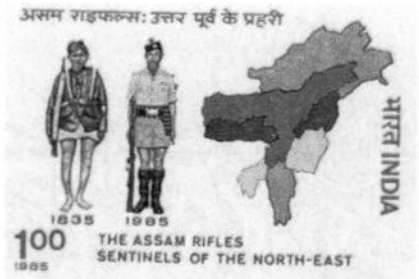

952 Riflemen of 1835 and 1985 and Map of North-East India

1985. 150th Anniv of Assam Rifles.
1155 **952** 1r. multicoloured . . . . 4·25 1·50

953 Potato Plant

1985. 50th Anniv of Potato Research in India.
1156 **953** 50p. deep brown and brown . . . . 1·50 1·60

954 Baba Jassa Singh Ahluwalia

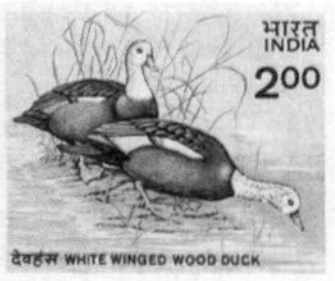

956 White-winged Wood Duck

955 St. Xavier's College

1985. Death Bicentenary (1983) of Baba Jassa Singh Ahluwalia (Sikh leader).
1157 **954** 50p. purple . . . . . . 1·50 1·60

1985. 125th Anniv of St. Xavier's College, Calcutta.
1158 **955** 1r. multicoloured . . . . 1·50 50

1985. Wildlife Conservation. White-winged Wood Duck.
1159 **956** 2r. multicoloured . . . . 6·50 5·50

957 "Mahara"

958 Yaudheya Copper Coin, c. 200 B.C.

1985. Bougainvillea. Multicoloured.

1160	50p. Type **957**	1·75	2·50
1161	1r. "H. B. Singh"	2·00	1·50

1985. Festival of India (1st issue).
1162 **958** 2r. multicoloured . . . . 2·75 2·25

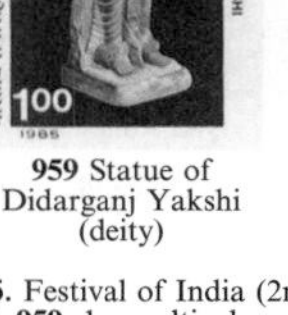

959 Statue of Didarganj Yakshi (deity)

962 Swami Haridas

1985. Festival of India (2nd issue).
1163 **959** 1r. multicoloured . . . . 1·50 40

1985. Swami Haridas (philosopher) Commemoration.
1164 **962** 1r. multicoloured . . . . 1·75 1·50

963 Stylized Mountain Road

1985. 25th Anniv of Border Roads Organization.
1165 **963** 2r. red, violet and black 2·00 3·00

964 Nehru addressing General Assembly

1985. 40th Anniv of United Nations Organization.
1166 **964** 2r. multicoloured . . . . 1·10 1·00

965 Indira Gandhi with Crowd

1985. Indira Gandhi Commemoration (3rd issue).
1167 **965** 2r. brown and black . . 2·50 3·00

966 Girl using Home Computer

1985. Children's Day.
1168 **966** 50p. multicoloured . . . 1·00 1·00

967 Halley's Comet

968 Indira Gandhi

1985. 19th General Assembly of International Astronomical Union, New Delhi.
1169 **967** 1r. multicoloured . . . . 2·00 1·50

1985. Indira Gandhi Commemoration (4th issue).
1170 **968** 3r. multicoloured . . . . 2·50 3·00

969 St. Stephen's Hospital

1985. Centenary of St. Stephen's Hospital, Delhi.
1171 **969** 1r. black and brown . . 1·00 40

971 Map showing Member States

1985. 1st Summit Meeting of South Asian Association for Regional Co-operation, Dhaka, Bangladesh. Multicoloured.

1172	1r. Type **971**	1·50	40
1173	3r. Flags of member nations (44 × 32 mm)	2·50	4·00

972 Shyama Shastri **975** Young Runners and Emblem

1985. Shyama Shastri (composer) Commemoration.
1174 **972** 1r. multicoloured . . . . 2·75 1·50

1985. International Youth Year.
1175 **975** 2r. multicoloured . . . . 2·75 1·50

976 Handel and Bach

1985. 300th Birth Annivs of George Frederick Handel and Johann Sebastian Bach (composers).
1176 **976** 5r. multicoloured . . . . 4·50 4·75

977 A. O. Hume (founder) and Early Congress Presidents

1985. Centenary of Indian National Congress. Designs showing miniature portraits of Congress Presidents.
1177 **977** 1r. black, orange, green and grey . . . . . . 2·00 2·50
1178 – 1r. black, orange and green . . . . 2·00 2·50
1179 – 1r. black, orange and green . . . . 2·00 2·50
1180 – 1r. black, orange, green and grey . . . . . . 2·00 2·50
Nos. 1178/80 each show sixteen miniature portraits. The individual stamps can be distinguished by the position of the face value and inscription which are at the top on Nos. 1177/8 and at the foot on Nos. 1179/80. No. 1180 shows a portrait of Prime Minister Rajiv Gandhi in a grey frame at bottom right.

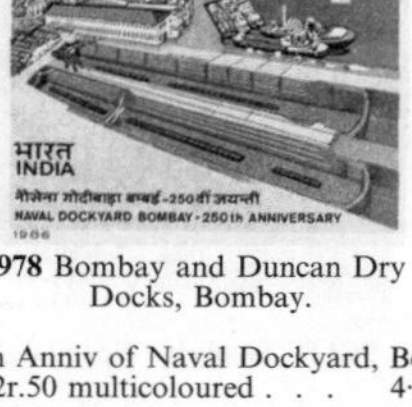

978 Bombay and Duncan Dry Docks, Bombay.

1986. 250th Anniv of Naval Dockyard, Bombay
1181 **978** 2r.50 multicoloured . . . 4·25 4·50

979 Hawa Mahal and Jaipur 1904 2a. Stamp

1986. "INPEX '86" Philatelic Exhibition, Jaipur. Multicoloured.
1182 50p. Type **979** . . . . . . 1·00 1·00
1183 2r. Mobile camel post office, Thar Desert . . . . . . 2·25 3·25

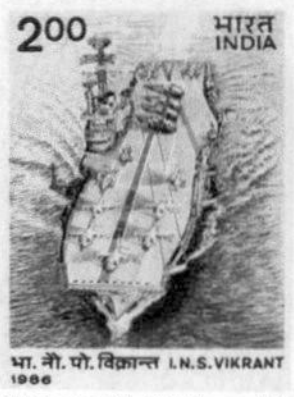

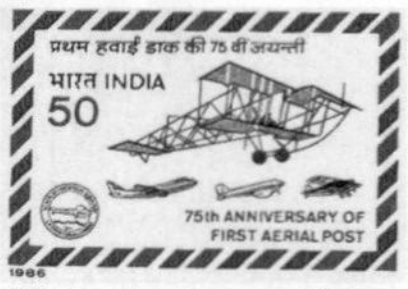

980 I.N.S. "Vikrant" (aircraft carrier) **981** Humber Sommer Biplane and Later Mail Planes

1986. Completion of 25 Years Service by I.N.S. "Vikrant".
1184 **980** 2r. multicoloured . . . . 6·50 6·00

1986. 75th Anniv of First Official Airmail Flight, Allahabad–Naini. Multicoloured.
1185 50p. Type **981** . . . . . . 2·25 2·00
1186 3r. Modern Air India Airbus Industries A300 mail plane and Humber Sommer biplane (37 × 24 mm) . . . . . . 4·75 7·00

982 Triennale Emblem **983** Chaitanya Mahaprabhu

1986. 6th Triennale Art Exhibition, New Delhi.
1187 **982** 1r. purple, yellow & black . . . . 1·50 1·00

1986. 500th Birth Anniv of Chaitanya Mahaprabhu (religious leader).
1188 **983** 2r. multicoloured . . . . 2·75 3·50

984 Main Building, Mayo College

1986. Mayo College (public school), Ajmer, Commemoration.
1189 **984** 1r. multicoloured . . . . 1·50 1·00

985 Two Footballers

1986. World Cup Football Championship, Mexico.
1190 **985** 5r. multicoloured . . . . 4·75 4·75

1986. India's Struggle for Freedom (4th series). As T **909**.
1191 50p. brown, green and red 1·40 2·00
1192 50p. brown, green and red 1·40 2·00
1193 50p. black, green and orange . . . . 1·40 2·00
1194 50p. brown, green and red 1·40 2·00
DESIGNS: No. 1191, Bhim Sen Sachar; 1192, Alluri Seeta Rama Raju; 1193, Sagarmal Gopa; 1194, Veer Surendra Sai.

987 Swami Sivananda **988** Volleyball

1986. Birth Centenary of Swami Sivananda (spiritual leader).
1195 **987** 2r. multicoloured . . . . 3·00 4·00

1986. Asian Games, Seoul, South Korea. Multicoloured.
1196 1r.50 Type **988** . . . . . . 2·50 2·75
1197 3r. Hurdling . . . . 3·00 4·00

989 Madras G.P.O.

1986. Bicentenary of Madras G.P.O.
1198 **989** 5r. black and red . . . . 4·50 5·00

990 Parachutist **991** Early and Modern Policemen

1986. 225th Anniv of 8th Battalion of Coast Sepoys (now 1st Battalion Parachute Regiment).
1199 **990** 3r. multicoloured . . . . 5·00 5·00

1986. 125th Anniv of Indian Police. Designs showing early and modern police.
1200 **991** 1r.50 multicoloured . . . 3·50 4·00
1201 – 2r. multicoloured . . . . 3·50 4·00
Nos. 1200/1 were printed together, se-tenant, forming a composite design.

992 Hand holding Flower and World Map

1986. International Peace Year.
1202 **992** 5r. multicoloured . . . . 3·75 1·75

993 "Girl Rock Climber" (Sujasha Dasgupta) **994** Windmill

1986. Children's Day.
1203 **993** 50p. multicoloured . . . 2·25 2·25

1986. Science and Technology.
1211 – 35p. red 10 10
1212 – 40p. red 10 10
1213 – 60p. green and red . . 10 10
1214a – 75p. red 10 10
1215 – 1r. black and red . . . 20 10
1217 – 5r. brown and orange 30 20
1218 – 20r. brown and blue . . 75 60
1219 **994** 50r. black, blue and mauve . . . . . . 2·25 2·00
DESIGNS—20 × 17 mm: 35p. Family planning. 37 × 20 mm: 60p. Indian family; 20r. Bio gas. 17 × 20 mm: 40p. Television set, dish aerial and transmitter; 75p. "Family" (as No. 927). 20 × 37 mm: 1r. Petrol pump nozzle (Oil conservation); 5r.Solar energy.

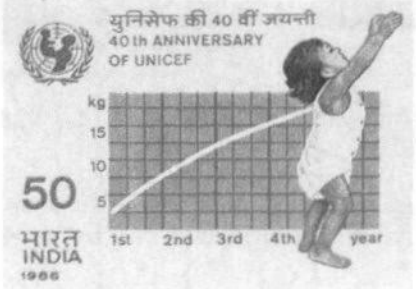

995 Growth Monitoring

1986. 40th Anniv of U.N.I.C.E.F. Multicoloured.
1221 50p. Type **995** . . . . . . 2·00 2·00
1222 5r. Immunization . . . . . 4·25 6·00

996 Tansen **997** Indian Elephant

1986. Tansen (musician and composer) Commem.
1223 **996** 1r. multicoloured . . . . 2·00 60

1986. 50th Anniv of Corbett National Park. Multicoloured.
1224 1r. Type **997** . . . . 3·50 1·00
1225 2r. Gharial . . . . 4·00 6·00

998 St. Martha's Hospital

1986. Centenary of St. Martha's Hospital, Bangalore.
1226 **998** 1r. blue, orange and black . . . . 2·25 1·60

999 Yacht "Trishna" and Route Map

1987. Indian Army Round the World Yacht Voyage, 1985–1987.
1227 **999** 6r.50 multicoloured . . . 4·50 4·00

1000 Map of Southern Africa and Logo **1001** Emblem

1987. Inauguration of AFRICA Fund.
1228 **1000** 6r.50 black . . . . . . 5·00 6·00

1987. 29th Congress of International Chamber of Commerce, New Delhi.
1229 **1001** 5r. violet, blue and red 3·50 2·25

1987. India's Struggle for Freedom (5th series). As T **909**.
1230 60p. brown, green and orange . . . . 2·50 30
1231 60p. violet, green and red 30 30
1232 60p. brown, green and red 30 30
1233 60p. blue, green and orange 30 30
1234 60p. brown, green and red 30 30
1235 60p. brown, green and red 30 30
1236 60p. red, green and orange 30 30
DESIGNS: No. 1230, Hakim Ajmal Khan; No. 1231, Lala Har Dayal; No. 1232, M. N Roy; No. 1233, Tripuraneni Ramaswamy Chowdary; No. 1234, Dr. Kailas Nath Katju; No. 1235, S. Satyamurti; No. 1236, Pandit Hriday Nath Kunzru.

1002 Blast Furnace and Railway Emblem **1003** Kalia Bhomora Bridge, Tezpur, Assam

1987. Cent of South Eastern Railway. Mult.
1237 1r. Type **1002** 40 15
1238 1r.50 Tank locomotive No. 691, 1887 (horiz) . . 45 35
1239 2r. Electric train on viaduct, 1987 . . . . 55 60
1240 4r. Steam locomotive, c. 1900 (horiz) 80 1·25

1987. Inauguration of Brahmaputra Bridge.
1241 **1003** 2r. multicoloured . . . 30 30

1004 Madras Christian College

1987. 150th Anniv of Madras Christian College.
1242 **1004** 1r.50 black and red . . 20 20

1005 Shree Shree Ma Anandamayee

1006 "Rabindranath Tagore" (self-portrait)

1987. Shree Shree Ma Anandamayee (Hindu spiritual leader) Commemoration.
1243 **1005** 1r. brown 65 20

1987. Rabindranath Tagore (poet) Commem.
1244 **1006** 2r. multicoloured . . . 40 30

1007 Garwhal Rifles Uniforms of 1887

1008 J. Krishnamurti

1987. Centenary of Garwhal Rifles Regiment.
1245 **1007** 1r. multicoloured . . . 60 20

1987. J. Krishnamurti (philosopher) Commem.
1246 **1008** 60p. brown . . . . . . 70 1·00

1009 Regimental Uniforms of 1887

1987. Centenary of 37th Dogra Regt (now 7th Battalion) (1 Dogra), Mechanised Infantry Regt.
1247 **1009** 1r. multicoloured . . . 50 20

1010 Hall of Nations, Pragati Maidan, New Delhi

1011 "Sadyah-Snata" Sculpture, Sanghol

1987. "India '89" International Stamp Exhibition, New Delhi (1st issue). Multicoloured.
1248 50p. Exhibition logo 10 15
1249 5r. Type **1010** 45 50
MS1250 156 × 58 mm. Nos. 1248/9 (sold at 8r.) . . . . 70 1·00
See also Nos. 1264/8, 1333/4, 1341/2 and 1358/61.

1987. Festival of India, U.S.S.R.
1251 **1011** 6r.50 multicoloured . . 1·00 75

1012 Flag and Stylized Birds with "40" in English and Hindi

1987. 40th Anniv of Independence.
1252 **1012** 60p. orange, green & bl 20 20

1013 Sant Harchand Singh Longowal

1014 Guru Ghasidas

1987. Sant Harchand Singh Longowal (Sikh leader) Commemoration.
1253 **1013** 1r. multicoloured . . . 75 20

1987. Guru Ghasidas (Hindu leader) Commemoration.
1254 **1014** 60p. red 20 20

1015 Thakur Anukul Chandra

1016 University of Allahabad

1987. Thakur Anukul Chandra (spiritual leader) Commemoration.
1255 **1015** 1r. multicoloured . . . 70 20

1987. Centenary of Allahabad University.
1256 **1016** 2r. multicoloured . . . 30 40

1017 Pankha Offering

1018 Chhatrasal on Horseback

1987. Phoolwalon Ki Sair Festival, Delhi.
1257 **1017** 2r. multicoloured . . . 30 40

1987. Chhatrasal (Bundela ruler) Commemoration.
1258 **1018** 60p. brown 30 20

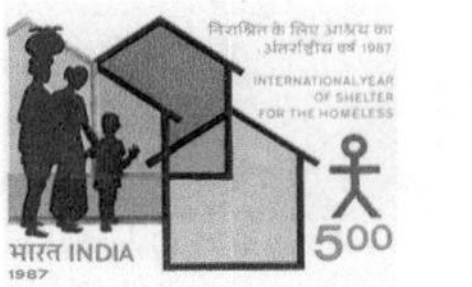

1019 Family and Stylized Houses

1987. International Year of Shelter for the Homeless.
1259 **1019** 5r. multicoloured . . . 50 60

1020 Map of Asia and Logo

1987. Asia Regional Conference of Rotary International.
1260 **1020** 60p. brown and green 15 15
1261 – 6r.50 multicoloured . . 60 80
DESIGN: 6r.50, Oral polio vaccination.

1021 Blind Boy, Braille Books and Computer

1987. Centenary of Service to Blind.
1262 **1021** 1r. multicoloured . . . 15 15
1263 – 2r. deep blue and blue 35 30
DESIGN: 2r. Eye donation.

1022 Iron Pillar, Delhi

1987. "India '89" International Stamp Exhibition, New Delhi (2nd issue). Delhi Landmarks. Mult.
1264 60p. Type **1022** 15 15
1265 1r.50 India Gate 20 20
1266 5r. Dewan-e-Khas, Red Fort 55 50
1267 6r.50 Old Fort 70 65
MS1268 100 × 86 mm. Nos. 1264/7 (sold at 15r.) . . . . 1·40 2·25

1023 Tyagmurti Goswami Ganeshdutt

1024 "My Home" (Siddharth Deshprabha)

1987. Tyagmurti Goswami Ganeshdutt (spiritual leader and social reformer) Commemoration.
1269 **1023** 60p. red 20 20

1987. Children's Day.
1270 **1024** 60p. multicoloured . . 30 20

1025 Chinar

1026 Logo (from sculpture "Worker and Woman Peasant" by V. Mukhina)

1987. Indian Trees. Multicoloured.
1271 **1025** 60p. multicoloured . . 15 15
1272 – 1r.50 multicoloured . . 20 20
1273 – 5r. black, green & brown 55 65
1274 – 6r.50 brown, red & green 80 80
DESIGNS—HORIZ: 1r.50, Pipal; 6r.50, Banyan. VERT: 5r. Sal.

1987. Festival of U.S.S.R., India.
1275 **1026** 5r. multicoloured . . . 50 50

1027 White Tiger

1028 Execution of Veer Narayan Singh

1987. Wildlife. Multicoloured.
1276 1r. Type **1027** 50 15
1277 5r. Snow leopard (horiz) . . 1·25 85

1987. Veer Narayan Singh (patriot) Commemoration.
1278 **1028** 60p. brown 20 20

1029 Rameshwari Nehru

1030 Father Kuriakose Elias Chavara

1987. Rameshwari Nehru (women's rights campaigner) Commemoration.
1279 **1029** 60p. brown 20 20

1987. Father Kuriakose Elias Chavara (founder of Carmelites of Mary Immaculate) Commemoration.
1280 **1030** 60p. brown 20 20

1031 Dr. Rajah Sir Muthiah Chettiar

1987. Dr. Rajah Sir Muthiah Chettiar (politician) Commemoration.
1281 **1031** 60p. grey 20 20

1032 Golden Temple, Amritsar

1033 Rukmini Devi and Dancer

1987. 400th Anniv of Golden Temple, Amritsar.
1282 **1032** 60p. multicoloured . . 40 20

1987. Rukmini Devi (Bharatanatyam dance pioneer) Commemoration.
1283 **1033** 60p. red 30 20

1034 Dr. Hiralal

1987. Dr. Hiralal (historian) Commemoration.
1284 **1034** 60p. blue 20 20

1035 Light Frequency Experiment and Bodhi Tree

1988. 75th Session of Indian Science Congress Association.
1285 **1035** 4r. multicoloured . . . 50 60

1036 Rural Patient

1037 U Tirot Singh

1988. 13th Asian Pacific Dental Congress.
1286 **1036** 4r. multicoloured . . . 50 50

1988. India's Struggle for Freedom (6th series). As T **909**.
1287 60p. black, green and orange 20 40
1288 60p. brown, green and orange 20 40
1289 60p. red, green and orange 20 40
1290 60p. purple, green and orange 20 40
1291 60p. purple, green and red 20 40
1292 60p. black, green and orange 20 40
1293 60p. lilac, green and red . . 20 40
1294 60p. deep green, green and red 20 30
1295 60p. brown, green and green 20 30
1296 60p. mauve, green and orange 20 30
DESIGNS: No. 1287, Mohan Lal Sukhadia; 1288, Dr. S. K. Sinha; 1289, Chandra Shekhar Azad; 1290, G. B. Pant; 1291, Dr. Anugrah Narain Singh; 1292, Kuladhor Chaliha; 1293, Shivprasad Gupta; 1294, Sarat Chandra Bose; 1295, Baba Kharak Singh; 1296, Sheikh Mohammad Abdullah.

1988. U Tirot Singh (Khasis leader) Commem.
1297 **1037** 60p. brown 20 20

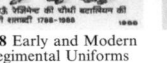

1038 Early and Modern Regimental Uniforms

1039 Balgandharva

1988. Bicentenary of 4th Battalion of the Kumaon Regiment.
1298 **1038** 1r. multicoloured . . . 30 20

1988. Birth Centenary of Balgandharva (actor).
1299 **1039** 60p. brown 20 20

1040 Soldiers and Infantry Combat Vehicle

1041 B. N. Rau

1988. Presentation of Colours to Mechanised Infantry Regiment.
1300 **1040** 1r. multicoloured . . . 35 20

1988. B. N. Rau (constitutional lawyer) Commemoration.
1301 **1041** 60p. black 20 20

1042 Mohindra Government College

1043 Dr. D. V. Gundappa

1988. Mohindra Government College, Patiala.
1302 **1042** 1r. mauve 20 20

1988. Dr. D. V. Gundappa (scholar) Commem.
1303 **1043** 60p. grey 20 20

1044 Rani Avantibai

1046 Maharshi Dadhichi

1045 "Malayala Manorama" Office, Kottayam

1988. Rani Avantibai of Ramgarh Commem.
1304 **1044** 60p. mauve 20 20

1988. Centenary of "Malayala Manorama" (newspaper).
1305 **1045** 1r. black and blue . . . 20 20

1988. Maharshi Dadhichi (Hindu saint) Commemoration.
1306 **1046** 60p. red 20 20

1047 Mohammad Iqbal

1988. 50th Death Anniv of Mohammad Iqbal (poet).
1307 **1047** 60p. gold and red . . . 20 20

1048 Samarth Ramdas

1049 Swati Tirunal Rama Varma

1988. Samarth Ramdas (Hindu spiritual leader) Commemoration.
1308 **1048** 60p. green 20 20

1988. 175th Birth Anniv of Swati Tirunal Rama Varma (composer).
1309 **1049** 60p. mauve 20 20

1050 Bhaurao Patil and Class

1988. Bhaurao Patil (educationist) Commem.
1310 **1050** 60p. brown 20 20

1051 "Rani Lakshmi Bai" (M. F. Husain)

1988. Martyrs from 1st War of Independence.
1311 **1051** 60p. multicoloured . . 20 20

1052 Broad Peak

1988. Himalayan Peaks.
1312 **1052** 1r.50 lilac, violet and blue 35 30
1313 – 4r. multicoloured . . . 70 60
1314 – 5r. multicoloured . . . 80 70
1315 – 6r.50 multicoloured . . 95 85
DESIGNS: 4r. K 2 (Godwin Austen); 5r. Kanchenjunga; 6r.50, Nanda Devi.

1053 Child with Grandparents

1988. "Love and Care for Elders".
1316 **1053** 60p. multicoloured . . 20 20

1054 Victoria Terminus, Bombay

1988. Centenary of Victoria Terminus Station, Bombay.
1317 **1054** 1r. multicoloured . . . 40 20

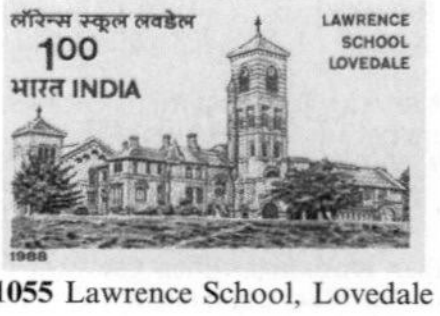

1055 Lawrence School, Lovedale

1988. 130th Anniv of Lawrence School, Lovedale.
1318 **1055** 1r. brown and green . . 30 20

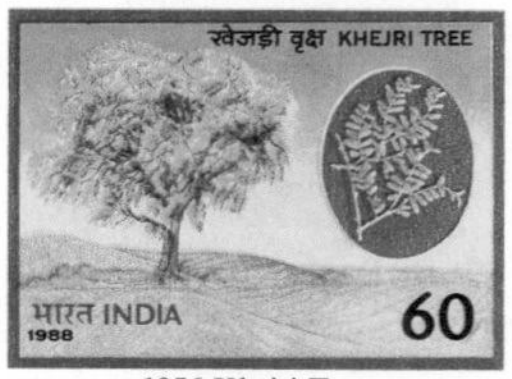

1056 Khejri Tree

1988. World Environment Day.
1319 **1056** 60p. multicoloured . . 20 15

1988. As No. 732, but new face value.
1320 60p. black (Gandhi) . . . . 1·50 20

1057 Rani Durgawati

1058 Acharya Shanti Dev

1988. Rani Durgawati (Gondwana ruler) Commemoration.
1322 **1057** 60p. red 20 20

1988. Acharya Shanti Dev (Buddhist scholar) Commemoration.
1323 **1058** 60p. brown 20 20

1059 Y. S. Parmar

1061 Durgadas Rathore

1060 Arm pointing at Proclamation in Marathi

1988. Dr. Yashwant Singh Parmar (former Chief Minister of Himachal Pradesh) Commemoration.
1324 **1059** 60p. violet 20 20

1988. 40th Anniv of Independence. Bal Gangadhar Tilak (patriot) Commemoration. Multicoloured.
1325 60p. Type **1060** 20 20
1326 60p. Battle scene 20 20
Nos. 1325/6 were printed together, se-tenant, forming a composite design showing a painting by M. F. Husain.

1988. 150th Birth Anniv of Durgadas Rathore (Regent of Marwar).
1327 **1061** 60p. brown 20 20

1062 Gopinath Kaviraj

1063 Lotus and Outline Map of India

1988. Gopinath Kaviraj (scholar) Commem.
1328 **1062** 60p. brown 20 20

1988. Hindi Day.
1329 **1063** 60p. red, green & brown 20 20

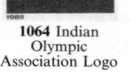

1064 Indian Olympic Association Logo

1065 Jerdon's Courser

1988. "Sports—1988" and Olympic Games, Seoul.
1330 **1064** 60p. purple 35 15
1331 – 5r. multicoloured . . . 2·50 75
DESIGN—HORIZ: 5r. Various sports.

1988. Wildlife Conservation. Jerdon's Courser.
1332 **1065** 1r. multicoloured . . . 2·50 45

1988. "India '89" International Stamp Exhibition, New Delhi (3rd issue). General Post Offices. As T **1022**. Multicoloured.
1333 4r. Bangalore G.P.O 50 50
1334 5r. Bombay G.P.O 50 50

1066 "Times of India" Front Page

1988. 150th Anniv of "The Times of India".
1335 **1066** 1r.50 black, gold & yell 20 20

1067 "Maulana Abul Kalam Azad" (K. Hebbar)

1988. Birth Centenary of Maulana Abul Kalam Azad (politician).
1336 **1067** 60p. multicoloured . . 20 20

1068 Nehru

1988. Birth Centenary (1989) of Jawaharlal Nehru (1st issue).
1337 **1068** 60p. black, orange and green 30 15
1338 – 1r. multicoloured . . . 35 15
DESIGN—VERT: 1r. "Jawaharlal Nehru" (Svetoslav Roerich).
See also No. 1393.

1069 Birsa Munda

1988. Birsa Munda (Munda leader) Commem.
1339 **1069** 60p. brown 20 20

1070 Bhakra Dam

1988. 25th Anniv of Dedication of Bhakra Dam.
1340 **1070** 60p. red 35 70

1071 Dead Letter Office Cancellations of 1886

1988. "India '89" International Stamp Exhibition, New Delhi (4th series). Postal Cancellations.
1341 **1071** 60p. brown, black & red 40 40
1342 – 6r.50 brown and black 1·40 1·40
DESIGN: 6r.50, Allahabad–Cawnpore travelling post office handstamp of 1864.

1072 K. M. Munshi

1988. Birth Centenary (1987) of K. M. Munshi (author and politician).
1343 **1072** 60p. green 20 20

1073 Mannathu Padmanabhan **1074** Lok Sabha Secretariat

1989. Mannathu Padmanabhan (social reformer) Commemoration.
1344 **1073** 60p. brown 20 20

1989. India's Struggle for Freedom (7th series). As T **909**.
1345 60p. black, green and orange 25 30
1346 60p. orange, green and lilac 25 50
1347 60p. black, green and orange 25 50
1348 60p. brown, green and orange 25 50
1349 60p. brown, green and orange 25 30
DESIGNS: No. 1345, Hare Krishna Mahtab; 1346, Balasaheb Gangadhar Kher; 1347, Raj Kumari Amrit Kaur; 1348, Saifuddin Kitchlew; 1349, Asaf Ali.

1989. 60th Anniv of Lok Sabha Secretariat (formerly Legislative Assembly Department).
1355 **1074** 60p. green 20 20

1075 Goddess Durga seated on Lion (5th-cent terracotta plaque) **1076** Baldev Ramji Mirdha

1989. 125th Anniv of Lucknow Museum.
1356 **1075** 60p. deep blue and blue 20 20

1989. Birth Centenary of Baldev Ramji Mirdha (nationalist).
1357 **1076** 60p. green 20 20

1077 Girl with Stamp Collection

1989. "India'89" International Stamp Exhibition, New Delhi (5th issue). Philately.
1358 **1077** 60p. yellow, red and blue 15 10
1359 – 1r.50 grey, yellow and black 20 15
1360 – 5r. red and blue 60 50
1361 – 6r.50 black, brown & bl 70 60
DESIGNS: 1r.50, Dawk gharry, c. 1842; 5r. Travancore 1888 2ch. conch shell stamp; 6r.50, Early Indian philatelic magazines.

1078 St. John Bosco and Boy **1079** Modern Tank and 19th-century Sowar

1989. St. John Bosco (founder of Salesian Brothers) Commemoration.
1362 **1078** 60p. red 20 20

1989. 3rd Cavalry Regiment.
1363 **1079** 60p. multicoloured . . 30 20

1080 Dargah Sharif, Ajmer

1989. Dargah Sharif (Sufi shrine), Ajmer.
1364 **1080** 1r. multicoloured . . . 20 20

1081 Task Force and Indian Naval Ensign

1989. President's Review of the Fleet.
1365 **1081** 6r.50 multicoloured . . 1·50 1·00

1082 Shaheed Laxman Nayak and Barbed Wire Fence

1989. Shaheed Laxman Nayak Commemoration.
1366 **1082** 60p. brown, grn & orge 20 20

1083 Rao Gopal Singh **1085** Bishnu Ram Medhi

1084 Sydenham College

1989. Rao Gopal Singh Commemoration.
1367 **1083** 60p. brown 20 20

1989. 75th Anniv (1988) of Sydenham College, Bombay.
1368 **1084** 60p. black 30 20

1989. Birth Centenary (1988) of Bishnu Ram Medhi (politician).
1369 **1085** 60p. green, dp grn & red 30 20

1086 Dr. N. S. Hardikar **1087** "Advaita" in Devanagari Script

1989. Birth Centenary of Dr. Narayana Subbarao Hardikar (nationalist).
1370 **1086** 60p. brown 20 20

1989. Sankaracharya (philosopher) Commem.
1371 **1087** 60p. multicoloured . . 20 20

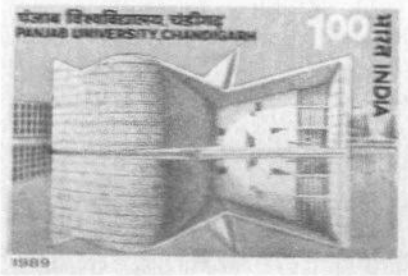

1088 Gandhi Bhavan, Punjab University

1989. Punjab University, Chandigarh.
1372 **1088** 1r. brown and blue . . 20 20

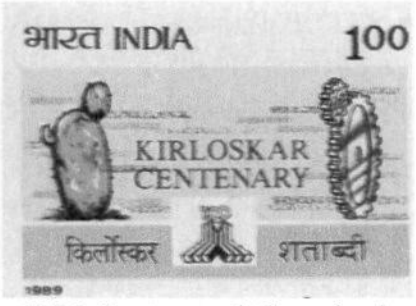

1089 Scene from Film "Raja Harischandra" **1090** Cactus and Cogwheels

1989. 75 Years of Indian Cinema.
1373 **1089** 60p. black and yellow 20 20

1989. Centenary of Kirloskar Brothers Ltd (engineering group).
1374 **1090** 1r. multicoloured . . . 20 20

1091 Early Class and Modern University Students

1989. Centenary of First D.A.V. College.
1375 **1091** 1r. multicoloured . . . 20 20

1092 Post Office, Dakshin Gangotri Base, Antarctica

1989. Opening of Post Office, Dakshin Gangotri Research Station, Antarctica.
1376 **1092** 1r. multicoloured . . . 1·00 20

1093 First Allahabad Bank Building

1989. 125th Anniv (1990) of Allahabad Bank.
1377 **1093** 60p. purple and blue . . 20 20

1094 Nehru inspecting Central Reserve Police, Neemuch, 1954

1989. 50th Anniv of Central Reserve Police Force (formerly Crown Representative's Police).
1378 **1094** 60p. brown . . . . . . 1·00 20

1095 Dairy Cow

1989. Centenary of Military Farms.
1379 **1095** 1r. multicoloured . . . 50 20

1096 Mustafa Kemal Ataturk

1989. 50th Death Anniv (1988) of Mustafa Kemal Ataturk (Turkish statesman).
1380 **1096** 5r. multicoloured . . . 1·25 60

1097 Dr. S. Radhakrishnan

1989. Birth Centenary (1988) of Dr. Sarvepalli Radhakrishnan (former President).
1381 **1097** 60p. black 20 20

1098 Football Match

1989. Cent of Mohun Bagan Athletic Club.
1382 **1098** 1r. multicoloured . . . 1·25 20

1099 Dr. P. Subbarayan **1100** Shyamji Krishna Varma

1989. Birth Centenary of Dr. P. Subbarayan (politician).
1383 **1099** 60p. brown 20 20

1989. Shyamji Krishna Varma (nationalist) Commemoration.
1384 **1100** 60p. brown, green & red 20 20

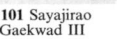

1101 Sayajirao Gaekwad III **1103** Namakkal Kavignar

1102 Symbolic Bird with Letter

1989. 50th Death Anniv of Maharaja Sayajirao Gaekwad III of Baroda.
1385 **1101** 60p. grey 20 20

1989. "Use Pincode" Campaign.
1386 **1102** 60p. multicoloured . . 65 20

1989. Namakkal Kavignar (writer) Commem.
1387 **1103** 60p. black 20 20

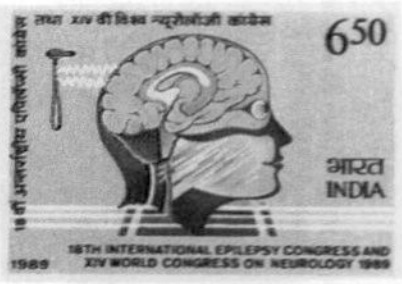

1104 Diagram of Human Brain

1989. 18th International Epilepsy Congress and 14th World Congress on Neurology, New Delhi.
1388 **1104** 6r.50 multicoloured . . 2·25 75

1105 Pandita Ramabai and Original Sharada Sadan Building

1989. Pandita Ramabai (women's education pioneer) Commemoration.
1389 **1105** 60p. brown 30 20

1106 Releasing Homing Pigeons

1989. Orissa Police Pigeon Post.
1390 **1106** 1r. red 50 20

1107 Acharya Narendra Deo **1108** Acharya Kripalani

1989. Birth Centenary of Acharya Narendra Deo (scholar).
1391 **1107** 60p. brown, grn & orge 20 20

1989. Acharya Kripalani (politician) Commemoration.
1392 **1108** 60p. black, green & red 20 20

1109 Nehru

1989. Birth Cent of Jawaharlal Nehru (2nd issue).
1393 **1109** 1r. brown, deep brown and buff 65 20

1110 Meeting Logo **1111** Sir Gurunath Bewoor

1989. 8th Asian Track and Field Meeting, New Delhi.
1394 **1110** 1r. black, orange & grn 30 20

1989. Sir Gurunath Bewoor (former Director-General, Posts and Telegraphs) Commemoration.
1395 **1111** 60p. brown 20 20

1112 Balkrishna Sharma Navin **1113** Abstract Painting of Houses

1989. Balkrishna Sharma Navin (politician and poet) Commemoration.
1396 **1112** 60p. black 20 20

1989. Cent of Bombay Art Society (1988).
1397 **1113** 1r. multicoloured . . . 20 20

1114 Lesser Florican **1115** Centenary Logo

1989. Wildlife Conservation. Lesser Florican.
1398 **1114** 2r. multicoloured . . . 1·50 55

1989. Centenary of Indian Oil Production.
1399 **1115** 60p. brown 30 20

1116 Dr. M. G. Ramachandran **1117** Volunteers working at Sukhna Lake, Chandigarh

1990. Dr. M. G. Ramachandran (former Chief Minister of Tamil Nadu) Commemoration.
1400 **1116** 60p. brown 40 20

1990. Save Sukhna Lake Campaign.
1401 **1117** 1r. multicoloured . . . 20 20

1118 Gallantry Medals

1990. Presentation of New Colours to Bombay Sappers.
1402 **1118** 60p. multicoloured . . 80 1·25

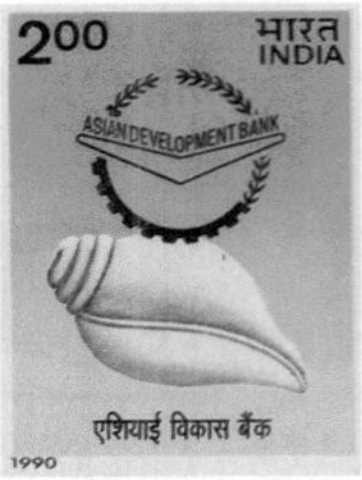

1119 Indian Chank Shell and Logo

1990. 23rd Annual General Meeting of Asian Development Bank, New Delhi.
1403 **1119** 2r. black, orange & yell 75 30

1120 Penny Black and Envelope

1990. 150th Anniv of the Penny Black.
1404 **1120** 6r. multicoloured . . . 1·25 40

1121 Ho Chi-Minh and Vietnamese House **1122** Chaudhary Charan Singh

1990. Birth Centenary of Ho Chi-Minh (Vietnamese leader).
1405 **1121** 2r. brown and green . . 30 30

1990. 3rd Death Anniv of Chaudhary Charan Singh (former Prime Minister).
1406 **1122** 1r. brown 20 20

1123 Armed Forces' Badge and Map of Sri Lanka **1124** Wheat

1990. Indian Peace-keeping Operations in Sri Lanka.
1407 **1123** 2r. multicoloured . . . 30 30

1990. 60th Anniv of Indian Council of Agricultural Research (1989).
1408 **1124** 2r. black, grn & dp grn 30 30

1125 Khudiram Bose **1127** K. Kelappan

1126 "Life in India" (Tanya Vorontsova)

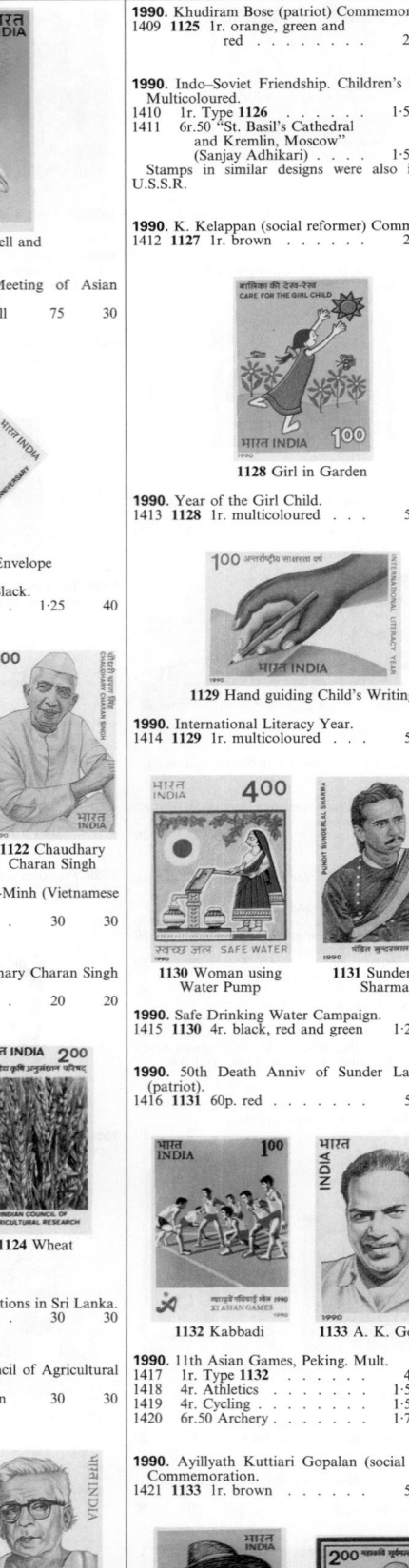

1990. Khudiram Bose (patriot) Commemoration.
1409 **1125** 1r. orange, green and red 20 20

1990. Indo–Soviet Friendship. Children's Paintings. Multicoloured.
1410 1r. Type **1126** . . . . . . 1·50 2·00
1411 6r.50 "St. Basil's Cathedral and Kremlin, Moscow" (Sanjay Adhikari) . . . . 1·50 2·00
Stamps in similar designs were also issued by U.S.S.R.

1990. K. Kelappan (social reformer) Commem.
1412 **1127** 1r. brown 20 20

1128 Girl in Garden

1990. Year of the Girl Child.
1413 **1128** 1r. multicoloured . . . 50 30

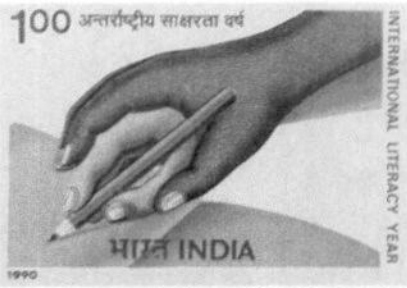

1129 Hand guiding Child's Writing

1990. International Literacy Year.
1414 **1129** 1r. multicoloured . . . 50 30

1130 Woman using Water Pump **1131** Sunder Lal Sharma

1990. Safe Drinking Water Campaign.
1415 **1130** 4r. black, red and green 1·25 1·75

1990. 50th Death Anniv of Sunder Lal Sharma (patriot).
1416 **1131** 60p. red 50 50

1132 Kabbadi **1133** A. K. Gopalan

1990. 11th Asian Games, Peking. Mult.
1417 1r. Type **1132** 40 20
1418 4r. Athletics . . . . 1·50 2·00
1419 4r. Cycling . . . . 1·50 2·00
1420 6r.50 Archery . . . . 1·75 2·50

1990. Ayillyath Kuttiari Gopalan (social reformer) Commemoration.
1421 **1133** 1r. brown 50 30

1134 Gurkha Soldier **1135** Suryamall Mishran

1990. 50th Anniv of 3rd and 5th Battalions, 5th Gurkha Rifles.
1422 **1134** 2r. black and brown . . 1·40 1·60

1990. 75th Birth Anniv of Suryamall Mishran (poet).
1423 **1135** 2r. brown and orange 50 65

1136 "Doll and Cat" (Subhash Kumar Nagarajan)

1990. Children's Day.
1424 **1136** 1r. multicoloured . . . 60 30

1137 Security Post and Border Guard on Camel

1138 Hearts and Flowers

1990. 25th Anniv of Border Security Force.
1425 **1137** 5r. blue, brown & black 1·50 1·75

1990. Greetings Stamps. Multicoloured.
1426 1r. Type **1138** 20 15
1427 4r. Ceremonial elephants (horiz) 50 65

1139 Bikaner

1990. Cities of India. Multicoloured.
1428 4r. Type **1139** 55 60
1429 5r. Hyderabad 65 75
1430 6r.50 Cuttack . . . . 90 1·25

1140 Bhakta Kanakadas and Udipi Temple

1141 Shaheed Minar Monument

1990. Bhakta Kanakadas (mystic and poet) Commemoration.
1431 **1140** 1r. red 55 30

1990. 300th Anniv of Calcutta.
1432 **1141** 1r. multicoloured . . . 30 20
1433 – 6r. black, brown and red . . . . 1·25 1·50
DESIGN—HORIZ (44 × 36 mm): 6r. 18th-century shipping on the Ganges.

1142 Dnyaneshwari (poet) and Manuscript

1143 Madan Mohan Malaviya (founder) and University

1990. 700th Anniv of Dnyaneshwari (spiritual epic).
1434 **1142** 2r. multicoloured . . . 30 50

1991. 75th Anniv of Banaras Hindu University.
1435 **1143** 1r. red 30 20

1991. As No. 732 but new face value.
1436 1r. brown (Gandhi) 20 10

1144 Road Users

1145 Exhibition Emblem

1991. International Traffic Safety Conference, New Delhi.
1437 **1144** 6r.50 black, blue and red . . . . 75 1·00

1991. 7th Triennale Art Exhibition, New Delhi.
1438 **1145** 6r.50 multicoloured . . 60 75

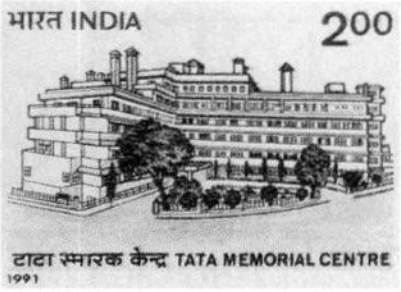

1146 Jagannath Sunkersett and Central Railways Headquarters

1147 Tata Memorial Centre

1991. 125th Death Anniv (1990) of Jagannath Sunkersett (educationist and railway pioneer).
1439 **1146** 2r. blue and red 50 60

1991. 50th Anniv of Tata Memorial Medical Centre.
1440 **1147** 2r. brown and stone . . 30 40

1148 River Dolphin

1991. Endangered Marine Mammals.
1441 **1148** 4r. brown, blue and green . . . . 1·50 1·50
1442 – 6r.50 multicoloured . . 2·00 2·00
DESIGN: 6r.50, Sea cow.

1149 Drugs

1150 Hand, Bomb Explosion and Dove

1991. International Conference on Drug Abuse, Calcutta.
1443 **1149** 5r. violet and red . . . 1·60 1·60

1991. World Peace.
1444 **1150** 6r.50 blk, lt brn & brn 75 1·00

1151 Remote Sensing Satellite "IA"

1991. Launch of Indian Remote Sensing Satellite "IA".
1445 **1151** 6r.50 brown and blue 60 1·00

1152 Babu Jagjivan Ram

1991. Babu Jagjivan Ram (politician) Commemoration.
1446 **1152** 1r. brown 20 20

1153 Dr. B. R. Ambedkar and Demonstration

1991. Birth Centenary of Dr. Bhimrao Ramji Ambedkar (social reformer).
1447 **1153** 1r. brown and blue . . 30 20

1154 Valar Dance

1991. Tribal Dances. Multicoloured.
1448 2r.50 Type **1154** 50 40
1449 4r. Kayang 70 80
1450 5r. Hozagiri . . . . 80 1·00
1451 6r.50 Velakali . . . . . . 1·00 1·60

1155 Ariyakudi Ramanuja Iyengar and Temples

1156 Karpoori Thakur

1991. Ariyakudi Ramanuja Iyengar (singer and composer) Commemoration.
1452 **1155** 2r. brown and green . . 50 65

1991. Jan Nayak Karpoori Thakur (politician and social reformer) Commemoration.
1453 **1156** 1r. brown 20 20

1157 Emperor Penguins

1991. 30th Anniv of Antarctic Treaty. Mult.
1454 5r. Type **1157** . . . . . . 1·75 2·00
1455 6r.50 Antarctic map and pair of Adelie penguins 1·75 2·00
Nos. 1454/5 were printed together, se-tenant, forming a composite design.

1158 Rashtrapati Bhavan Building, New Delhi

1991. 60th Anniv of New Delhi. Multicoloured.
1456 5r. Type **1158** . . . . . . 1·00 1·50
1457 6r.50 New Delhi monuments 1·00 1·50
Nos. 1456/7 were printed together, se-tenant, forming a composite design.

1159 Sri Ram Sharma Acharya

1991. Sri Ram Sharma Acharya (social reformer) Commemoration.
1458 **1159** 1r. green and red . . . 20 20

1160 "Shankar awarded Padma Vibhushan" (cartoon)

1991. Keshav Shankar Pillai (cartoonist) Commemoration.
1459 **1160** 4r. brown . . . . . . 1·00 1·50
1460 – 6r.50 lilac . . . . . . 1·40 2·00
DESIGN—VERT: 6r.50, "The Big Show".

1161 Sriprakash and Kashi Vidyapith University

1162 Gopinath Bardoloi

1991. 20th Death Anniv of Sriprakash (politician).
1461 **1161** 2r. brown & light brown 30 30

1991. Birth Centenary (1990) of Gopinath Bardoloi (Assamese politician).
1462 **1162** 1r. lilac 20 20

1163 Rajiv Gandhi

1991. Rajiv Gandhi (Congress Party leader) Commemoration.
1463 **1163** 1r. multicoloured . . . 65 50

1164 Muni Mishrimalji and Memorial

1991. Birth Centenary of Muni Mishrimalji (Jain religious leader).
1464 **1164** 1r. brown 30 20

1165 Mahadevi Verma (poetess) and "Varsha"

1991. Hindu Writers.
1465 **1165** 2r. black and blue . . . 15 25
1466 – 2r. black and blue . . . 15 25
DESIGN: No. 1466, Jayshankar Prasad (poet and dramatist) and scene from "Kamayani".

1166 Parliament House and C.P.A. Emblem

1991. 37th Commonwealth Parliamentary Association Conference, New Delhi.
1467 **1166** 6r.50 blue and brown 40 60

1167 Frog

1168 "Cymbidium aloifolium"

1991. Greetings Stamps.
1468 **1167** 1r. green and red . . . 20 45
1469 – 6r.50 red and green . . 35 55
DESIGN: 6r.50, Symbolic bird carrying flower.

1991. Orchids. Multicoloured.
1470 1r. Type **1168** 30 15
1471 2r.50 "Paphiopedilum venustum" 35 35
1472 3r. "Aerides crispum" . . . 40 50
1473 4r. "Cymbidium bicolour" 50 65
1474 5r. "Vanda spathulata" . . 55 70
1475 6r.50 "Cymbidium devonianum" . . . . . . 70 1·00

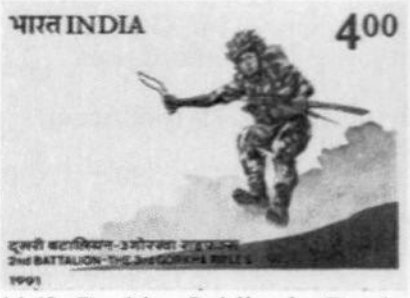

1169 Gurkha Soldier in Battle Dress

1170 Couple on Horse (embroidery)

1991. 90th Anniv of 2nd Battalion, Third Gurkha Rifles.
1476 **1169** 4r. multicoloured . . . 1·50 1·75

1991. 3rd Death Anniv of Kamaladevi Chattopadhyaya (founder of All India Handicrafts Board).
1477 **1170** 1r. lake, red and yellow 40 20
1478 – 6r.50 multicoloured . . 1·50 2·00
DESIGN: 6r.50, Traditional puppet.

1171 Chithira Tirunal and Temple Sculpture

1172 "Children in Traditional Costume" (Arpi Snehalbhai Shah)

1991. Chithira Tirunal Bala Rama Varma (former Maharaja of Travancore) Commemoration.
1479 **1171** 2r. violet 65 75

1991. Children's Day.
1480 **1172** 1r. multicoloured . . . 70 30

1173 Mounted Sowar and Tanks

1991. 70th Anniv (1992) of the 18th Cavalry Regiment.
1481 **1173** 6r.50 multicoloured . . 2·00 2·50

1174 Kites

1175 Sports on Bricks

1991. India Tourism Year.
1482 **1174** 6r.50 multicoloured . . 60 1·00

1991. International Conference on Youth Tourism, New Delhi.
1483 **1175** 6r.50 multicoloured . . 1·10 1·50

1176 "Mozart at Piano" (unfinished painting, J. Lange)

1177 Homeless Family

1991. Death Bicentenary of Mozart.
1484 **1176** 6r.50 multicoloured . . 1·50 2·00

1991. South Asian Association for Regional Co-operation Year of Shelter.
1485 **1177** 4r. brown and ochre . . 55 70

1178 People running on Heart

1991. "Run for Your Heart" Marathon, New Delhi.
1486 **1178** 1r. black, grey and red 20 20

1179 "Sidhartha with an Injured Bird" (Asit Kumar Haldar)

1991. Birth Centenary (1990) of Asit Kumar Haldar (artist).
1487 **1179** 2r. yellow, red and black 30 50

1180 Bhujangasana

1181 Y.M.C.A. Logo

1991. Yoga Exercises. Multicoloured.
1488 2r. Type **1180** 20 25
1489 5r. Dhanurasana 40 55
1490 6r.50 Ustrasana 50 70
1491 10r. Utthita trikonasana . . 85 1·25

1992. Centenary (1991) of National Council of Young Men's Christian Association.
1492 **1181** 1r. red and blue 20 20

1182 Madurai Temple Tower and Hooghly River Bridge

1183 Goat Seal from Harappa Culture, 2500 to 1500 B.C.

1992. 14th Congress of International Association for Bridge and Structural Engineering, New Delhi.
1493 **1182** 2r. brown, red and blue 75 90
1494 – 2r. brown, red and blue 75 90
DESIGN: No. 1494, Gate, Sanchi Stupa and Hall of Nations, New Delhi.

1992. 5th International Goat Conference, New Delhi.
1495 **1183** 6r. blue and brown . . 2·50 2·75

1184 Early 19th-century Letter with Mail Pouch and National Archives Building, New Delhi

1185 Krushna Chandra Gajapathi

1992. Centenary (1991) of National Archives.
1496 **1184** 6r. multicoloured . . . 50 75

1992. Krushna Chandra Gajapathi (former Chief Minister of Orissa) Commemoration.
1497 **1185** 1r. lilac 15 15

1186 Vijay Singh Pathik

1187 Hang-gliding

1992. Vijay Singh Pathik (writer) Commem.
1498 **1186** 1r. brown 15 15

1992. Adventure Sports. Multicoloured.
1499 2r. Type **1187** 25 20
1500 4r. Windsurfing 50 60
1501 5r. River rafting 60 75
1502 11r. Skiing . . . . 1·25 2·25

1188 Henry Gidney and Anglo-Indians

1992. 50th Death Anniv of Sir Henry Gidney (ophthalmologist).
1503 **1188** 1r. black and blue . . . 60 20

1189 Telecommunications Training Centre, Jabalpur

1190 Sardar Udham Singh

1992. 50th Anniv of Telecommunications Training Centre, Jabalpur.
1504 **1189** 1r. bistre 20 15

1992. Sardar Udham Singh (patriot) Commemoration.
1505 **1190** 1r. black and brown . . 20 15

1191 Men's Discus

1992. Olympic Games, Barcelona. Mult.
1506 1r. Type **1191** 30 10
1507 6r. Women's gymnastics . . 90 1·00
1508 8r. Men's hockey . . . . . 2·00 2·50
1509 11r. Boxing . . . . 2·00 2·75

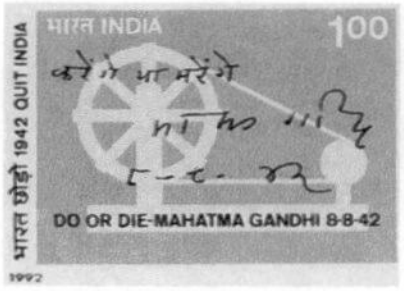

1192 Spinning Wheel Emblem

1992. 50th Anniv of "Quit India" Movement.
1510 **1192** 1r. black and pink . . . 1·50 30
1511 – 2r. black, brown & grey 2·25 2·50
DESIGN: 2r. Mahatma Gandhi and mantra.

1193 Treating Casualty

1992. 50th Anniv of 60th Parachute Field Ambulance.
1512 **1193** 1r. multicoloured . . . 1·25 40

1194 Dr. S. R. Ranganathan and Madras University

1992. Birth Centenary of Shiyali Ramamrita Ranganathan (librarian).
1513 **1194** 1r. blue . . . . 1·50 30

1195 "Dev Narayan"

1196 Hanuman Prasad Poddar

1992. Phad Scroll Paintings from Rajasthan.
1514 **1195** 5r. multicoloured . . . 60 1·00

1992. Hanuman Prasad Poddar (editor) Commemoration.
1515 **1196** 1r. green 15 15

1197 Mikoyan Guerevich MiG-29 Fighter and Ilyushin Il-76 Transport

1992. 60th Anniv of Indian Air Force. Mult.
1516 1r. Type **1197** . . . . . . 1·00 1·40
1517 10r. MiG-27 fighter and Westland Wapiti biplane 1·75 2·25

1198 Lighting Candle

1992. 150th Anniv of Sisters of Jesus and Mary's Arrival in India.
1518 **1198** 1r. blue and grey . . . 15 15

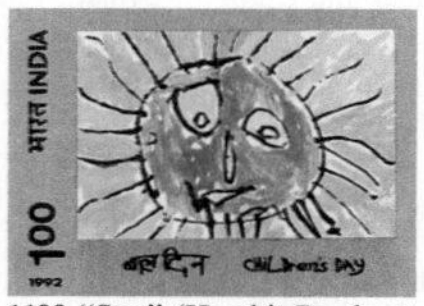

1199 "Sun" (Harshit Prashant Patel)

1992. Children's Day.
1519 **1199** 1r. multicoloured . . . 20 15

1200 Yogiji Maharaj

1992. Birth Centenary of Yogiji Maharaj (Hindu reformer).
1520 **1200** 1r. blue . . . . 1·50 30

1201 Army Service Corps Transport

1992. Army Service Corps Commemoration.
1521 **1201** 1r. multicoloured . . . 1·75 50

1202 Stephen Smith and Early Rocket Post Covers

1992. Birth Centenary (1991) of Stephen Smith (rocket mail pioneer).
1522 **1202** 11r. multicoloured . . . 1·00 1·50

1203 Electricity Pylons, Farmers and Crops

1992. 25th Anniv of Haryana State.
1523 **1203** 2r. red, dp green & green 15 15

1204 Madanlal Dhingra

1205 Osprey

1992. Madanlal Dhingra (revolutionary) Commemoration.
1524 **1204** 1r. brown, red and green 30 15

1992. Birds of Prey. Multicoloured.
1525 2r. Type **1205** 90 60
1526 6r. Peregrine falcon . . . . 1·25 1·10
1527 8r. Lammergeier . . . . . 1·40 1·75
1528 11r. Golden eagle . . . . . 1·60 2·00

1206 Pandit Ravishankar Shukla

1208 Fakirmohan Senapati

1207 William Carey

1992. Pandit Ravishankar Shukla (social reformer) Commemoration.
1529 **1206** 1r. purple 15 15

1993. Bicent of William Carey's Appointment as Baptist Missionary to India.
1530 **1207** 6r. multicoloured . . . 1·00 1·50

1993. Fakirmohan Senapati Commemoration.
1531 **1208** 1r. red 40 15

1209 Workers and C.S.I.R emblem

1993. 50th Anniv of Council of Scientific and Industrial Research.
1532 **1209** 1r. purple 40 15

1210 Parachute Drop and Field Gun

1993. 50th Anniv of 9th Parachute Field Artillery Regiment.
1533 **1210** 1r. multicoloured . . . 1·25 30

1211 Westland Wapiti Biplane

1993. 60th Anniv of No. 1 Squadron, Indian Air Force.
1534 **1211** 1r. multicoloured . . . 1·25 30

1212 Rahul Sankrityayan

1993. Birth Centenary of Rahul Sankrityayan (politician).
1535 **1212** 1r. black, cinnamon and brown 20 15

1213 Parliament Building and Emblem

1993. 89th Inter-Parliamentary Union Conference, New Delhi.
1536 **1213** 1r. black 20 15

1214 Neral Matheran Railway Tank Locomotive, 1905

1993. Mountain Locomotives. Multicoloured.
1537 1r. Type **1214** 60 20
1538 6r. Darjeeling and Himalayan Railway, Class B, 1889 . . . . 1·25 1·25
1539 8r. Nilgiri Hill Railway, 1914 . . . . 1·40 1·75
1540 11r. Kalka–Simla Railway, 1934 . . . . 1·90 2·50

1215 Students and College Building

1993. Centenary of Meerut College.
1541 **1215** 1r. black and brown . . 20 15

1216 Mahalanobis and Office Block

1993. Prasanta Chandra Mahalanobis Commemoration.
1542 **1216** 1r. brown 60 15

1217 Bombay Town Hall

1993. Centenary of Bombay Municipal Corporation.
1543 **1217** 2r. multicoloured . . . 20 30

1218 Abdul Ghaffar Khan and Mountainside

1993. Abdul Ghaffar Khan Commemoration.
1544 **1218** 1r. multicoloured . . . 15 15

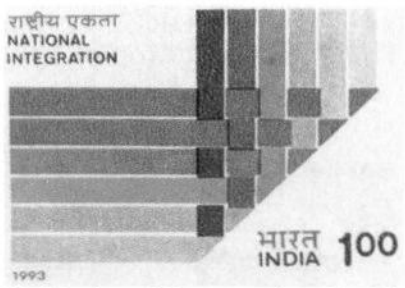

1219 National Integration Emblem

1993. National Integration Campaign.
1545 **1219** 1r. orange and green . . 15 15

1220 Dadabhai Naoroji and Houses of Parliament, London

1221 Swami Vivekananda and Art Institute, Chicago

1993. Centenary of Dadabhai Naoroji's Election to the House of Commons.
1546 **1220** 6r. multicoloured . . . 50 65

1993. Centenary of Swami Vivekananda's Chicago Address.
1547 **1221** 2r. orange and grey . . 50 50

1222 "Lagerstroemia speciosa"

1223 College Building and Emblem

1993. Flowering Trees.
1548 **1222** 1r. red, green and brown 20 15
1549 – 6r. multicoloured . . . 40 55
1550 – 8r. multicoloured . . . 55 80
1551 – 11r. multicoloured . . . 75 1·25
DESIGNS: 6r. "Cochlospermum religiosum"; 8r. "Erythrina variegata"; 11r. "Thespesia populnea".

1993. 50th Anniv of College of Military Engineering, Pune.
1552 **1223** 2r. multicoloured . . . 20 30

1224 Dr. Dwaram Venkataswamy Naidu playing Violin

1225 Children on Elephant

1993. Birth Centenary of Dwaram Venkataswamy Naidu (violinist).
1553 **1224** 1r. red 20 20

1993. Children's Day.
1554 **1225** 1r. multicoloured . . . 20 20

1226 People with Stress

1993. Heart Care Festival.
1555 **1226** 6r.50 multicoloured . . 60 80

1227 Dr. Kotnis performing Operation

1993. Dr. Dwarkanath Kotnis (surgeon) Commemoration.
1556 **1227** 1r. black 20 20

1228 Tea Symbol

1993. Indian Tea Production.
1557 **1228** 6r. green and red . . . 50 75

1229 Papal Seminary Arms and Building

1993. Centenary of Papal Seminary, Pune.
1558 **1229** 6r. multicoloured . . . 50 75

1230 Meghnad Saha and Eclipse of the Sun

1993. Meghnad Saha (astronomer) Commem.
1559 **1230** 1r. blue 30 20

1231 Speedpost Letter and Arrows circling Globe

1993. Inpex '93 National Stamp Exn, Calcutta. Multicoloured.
1560 1r. Type **1231** 20 15
1561 2r. "Custom-house Wharf, Calcutta" (Sir Charles D'Oyly) 55 60

1232 Dinanath Mangeshkar

1233 Nargis Dutt

1993. Dinanath Mangeshkar Commem.
1562 **1232** 1r. red 15 15

1993. Nargis Dutt Commemoration.
1563 **1233** 1r. red 15 15

1234 S. C. Bose inspecting Troops

1993. 50th Anniv of Indian National Army.
1564 **1234** 1r. green, dp grn & red 30 20

1235 Satyendra Nath Bose and Equation

1994. Birth Centenary of Satyendra Nath Bose (scientist).
1565 **1235** 1r. brown 50 15

1236 Dr. Sampurnanand

1994. Dr. Sampurnanand (politician) Commemoration.
1566 **1236** 1r. brown, green and red 15 10

1237 Scene from "Pather Panchali" (½-size illustration)

1994. Satyajit Ray (film director) Commemoration. Multicoloured.
1567 6r. Type **1237** . . . . . . 1·25 1·75
1568 11r. Satyajit Ray and Oscar (35 × 35 mm) . . . . . . 1·40 1·75

1238 Dr. Bhatnagar and University Building

1994. Dr. Shanti Swarup Bhatnagar (scientist) Commemoration.
1569 **1238** 1r. blue 15 10

1239 Prajapita Brahma and Memorial

1994. 25th Death Anniv of Prajapita Brahma (social reformer).
1570 **1239** 1r. lilac and blue . . . 15 10

1240 "Window" (K. Subramanyan)

1994. 8th Triennale Art Exhibition, New Delhi.
1571 **1240** 6r. orange, red and blue 50 60

1241 Agricultural Products and Tea Garden

1994. Centenary of United Planters' Association of Southern India.
1572 **1241** 2r. multicoloured . . . 20 20

1242 Indian Family

1242a Sanchi Stupa

1994.
1573 **1242** 75p. brown and red 10 10
1574 – 1r. mauve and green 10 10
1575 – 3r. purple 15 10
1576 **1242a** 5r. brown and green 25 20
DESIGNS (as T **1242**)—HORIZ: 1r. Family outside home. VERT: 3r. Baby and drop of polio vaccine.

1243 Rani Rashmoni on River Bank

1994. Birth Bicentenary of Rani Rashmoni.
1589 **1243** 1r. brown 15 10

1244 Indians releasing Peace Doves

1994. 75th Anniv of Jallianwala Bagh Massacre, Amritsar.
1590 **1244** 1r. black and red . . . 15 10

1245 Chandra Singh Garhwali

1994. 15th Death Anniv of Chandra Singh Garhwali (nationalist).
1591 **1245** 1r. green and orange . . 15 10

1246 Emblems and National Flag

1994. 75th Anniv of I.L.O.
1592 **1246** 6r. multicoloured . . . 50 65

1247 Silhouette of Drummer and Logo

1994. 50th Anniv of Indian People's Theatre Association.
1593 **1247** 2r. black, green and gold 15 15

1248 Statue of Sepoy

1249 Institute Building and Emblem

1994. Bicentenary of 4th Battalion, The Madras Regiment.
1594 **1248** 6r.50 multicoloured . . 55 75

1994. Bicentenary of Institute of Mental Health, Madras.
1595 **1249** 2r. red and blue 15 15

1250 Mahatma Gandhi and Indian Flag

1251 Symbols of Cancer

1994. 125th Birth Anniv of Mahatma Gandhi. Multicoloured.
1596 6r. Type **1250** . . . . . . 1·40 1·90
1597 11r. Aspects of Gandhi's life on flag (69 × 34 mm) . . . 1·60 3·25
Nos. 1596/7 were printed together, se-tenant, forming a composite design.

1994. 16th International Cancer Congress, New Delhi.
1598 **1251** 6r. multicoloured . . . 55 75

1252 Human Resources Emblem

1994. Human Resource Development World Conference, New Delhi.
1599 **1252** 6r. blue, red and azure 55 75

1253 "Me and My Pals" (Namarata Amit Shah)

1254 Family and Emblem

1994. Children's Day.
1600 **1253** 1r. multicoloured . . . 10 10

1994. International Year of the Family.
1601 **1254** 2r. multicoloured . . . 20 15

1255 "Taj Mahal" (illustration from Badsha Nama)

1994. Khuda Bakhsh Oriental Public Library, Patna, Commemoration.
1602 **1255** 6r. multicoloured . . . 4·00 1·00

1256 Grey Teal ("Andaman Teal")

1994. Endangered Water Birds. Multicoloured.
1603 1r. Type **1256** . . . . . . 7·00 2·00
1604 6r. Oriental white stork ("Eastern White Stork") 10·00 4·00
1605 8r. Black-necked crane . . . 10·00 4·50
1606 11r. Pink-headed duck . . . 11·00 6·00
It is reported that Nos. 1603/6 were withdrawn shortly after issue.

1257 J. R. D. Tata and Aspects of Industrial Symbols

1994. J. R. D. Tata (industrialist) Commemoration.
1607 **1257** 2r. multicoloured . . . 30 30

1258 School Building and Computer Class

1994. Centenary of Calcutta Blind School.
1608 **1258** 2r. red, brown and cinnamon 20 15

1259 Begum Akhtar

1261 Cavalryman, Infantryman and Dog Handler

1260 College Building

1994. 80th Birth Anniv of Begum Akhtar (singer).
1609 **1259** 2r. multicoloured . . . 4·75 4·50

1994. 125th Anniv of St. Xavier's College, Bombay.
1610 **1260** 2r. brown and blue . . 15 15

1994. 215th Anniv of Remount Veterinary Corps.
1611 **1261** 6r. multicoloured . . . 1·40 1·40

1262 College Building

1994. Bicentenary of College of Engineering, Guindy, Madras.
1612 **1262** 2r. red, brown and black 15 10

1263 Righthand Ornament of Bronze Stand

1265 Statue of King Rajaraja Chola

1264 "200" and Aspects of Postal Service (½-size illustration)

1994. Centenary of Baroda Museum.
1613 **1263** 6r. yellow and brown 2·50 1·50
1614 – 11r. yellow and brown 2·50 1·50
DESIGN: 11r. Bronze Rishabhanatha statue of Buddha on stand.

1994. Bicentenary of Bombay General Post Office.
1615 **1264** 6r. multicoloured . . . 5·00 1·75

1995. 8th International Conference-Seminar of Tamil Studies, Thanjavur.
1616 **1265** 2r. blue, ultramarine and black . . . . . 3·50 75

1266 Globe and Emblem **1267** Chhotu Ram

1995. 60th Anniv of National Science Academy.
1617 **1266** 6r. multicoloured . . . 50 80

1995. Chhotu Ram (social reformer) Commem.
1618 **1267** 1r. brown . . . . . . 1·00 25

1268 Film Reel and Globe

1995. Centenary of Cinema. Multicoloured.
1619 6r. Type **1268** . . . . . . 60 1·00
1620 11r. Film reel and early equipment . . . . 80 1·00

1269 Symbolic Hands and Children **1270** Prithviraj Kapoor and Mask

1995. South Asian Association for Regional Cooperation Youth Year.
1621 **1269** 2r. multicoloured . . . 20 20

1995. 50th Anniv of Prithvi Theatre.
1622 **1270** 2r. multicoloured . . . 3·75 75

1271 Field-Marshal Cariappa **1272** Textile Pattern

1995. Field-Marshal K. Cariappa Commemoration.
1623 **1271** 2r. multicoloured . . . 30 20

1995. "TEX-STYLES INDIA '95" Fair, Bombay.
1624 **1272** 2r. brown, buff and red 20 20

1273 Rafi Ahmed Kidwai **1274** K. L. Saigal, Film Reel and Gramophone

1995. Birth Centenary (1994) of Rafi Ahmed Kidwai (politician).
1625 **1273** 1r. brown 15 10

1995. 90th Birth Anniv of K. L. Saigal (singer).
1626 **1274** 5r. brown, grey and black . . . . 1·00 1·25

1275 R. S. Ruikar **1276** Radio Tower, Globe and Dish Aerial

1995. Birth Centenary of R. S. Ruikar (trade unionist).
1627 **1275** 1r. brown 15 10

1995. Centenary of Telecommunications.
1628 **1276** 5r. multicoloured . . . 1·00 1·25

1277 Leaves and Symbolic Houses

1995. Delhi Development Authority.
1629 **1277** 2r. multicoloured . . . 20 20

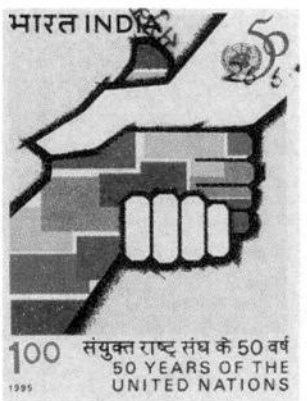

1278 Handshake **1279** Colonnade on Book Cover

1995. 50th Anniv of United Nations. Multicoloured.
1630 1r. Type **1278** 10 10
1631 6r. Work of U.N. Agencies 45 65

1995. Centenary of Bharti Bhawan Library, Allahabad.
1632 **1279** 6r. black, brown and red 55 75

1280 Globe showing South-east Asia

1995. 25th Anniv of Asian-Pacific Postal Training Centre, Bangkok.
1633 **1280** 10r. multicoloured . . . 1·00 1·25

1281 "75" and Taurus Formation Sign **1282** Louis Pasteur in Laboratory (from painting by Edelfelt)

1995. 75th Anniv of Area Army Headquarters, Delhi.
1634 **1281** 2r. multicoloured . . . 50 20

1995. Death Centenary of Louis Pasteur (chemist).
1635 **1282** 5r. black and stone . . 1·75 1·25

1283 La Martiniere College, Lucknow **1284** Gandhi in South Africa

1995. 150th Anniv of La Martiniere College, Lucknow.
1636 **1283** 2r. multicoloured . . . 20 20

1995. India-South Africa Co-operation. 125th Birth Anniv (1994) of Mahatma Gandhi.
1637 **1284** 1r. red 50 65
1638 – 2r. red 50 65
MS1639 68 × 80 mm. Nos. 1637/8 (sold at 8r.) . . . . 1·25 1·75
DESIGN: 2r. Gandhi wearing dhoti.

1285 Ears of Grain, "50" and Emblem on Globe **1286** P. M. Thevar

1995. 50th Anniv of F.A.O.
1640 **1285** 5r. multicoloured . . . 1·00 1·25

1995. Pasumpon Muthuramalingam Thevar (social reformer) Commemoration.
1641 **1286** 1r. red 15 10

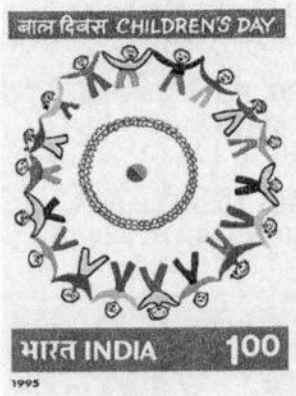

1287 W. C. Rontgen **1288** Children in Circle

1995. 150th Birth Anniv of W. C. Rontgen (discoverer of X-rays).
1642 **1287** 6r. multicoloured . . . 1·50 1·50

1995. Children's Day.
1643 **1288** 1r. multicoloured . . . 20 10

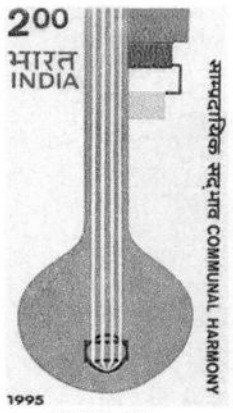

1289 Sitar **1290** Jat War Memorial, Bareilly

1995. Communal Harmony Campaign.
1644 **1289** 2r. multicoloured . . . 1·40 65

1995. Bicentenary of Jat Regiments.
1645 **1290** 5r. multicoloured . . . 1·50 1·25

1291 Men of Rajputana Rifles

1995. 175th Anniv of 5th (Napier's) Battalion, Rajputana Rifles.
1646 **1291** 5r. multicoloured . . . 1·75 1·25

1292 Sant Tukdoji Maharaj and Rural Meeting **1293** Dr. Yellapragada Subbarow

1995. Sant Tukdoji Maharaj Commemoration.
1647 **1292** 1r. brown 20 10
Although dated "1993", No. 1647 was not issued until the date quoted above.

1995. Dr. Yellapragada Subbarow (pharmaceutical scientist) Commemoration.
1648 **1293** 1r. brown 30 10

1294 Pres. Giani Zail Singh **1295** Dargah of Ala Hazrat Barelvi

1995. 1st Death Anniv of Pres. Giani Zail Singhn.
1649 **1294** 1r. multicoloured . . . 20 10

1995. 75th Death Anniv of Ala Hazrat Barelvi (Moslem scholar).
1650 **1295** 1r. multicoloured . . . 20 10

1296 Tata Institute Building

1996. 50th Anniv (1995) of Tata Institute of Fundamental Research.
1651 **1296** 2r. multicoloured . . . 30 20

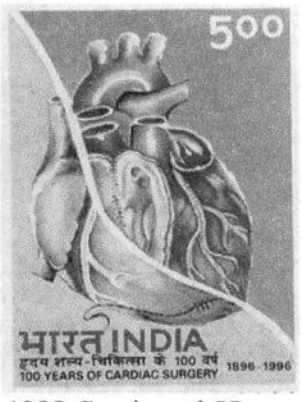

1297 Kasturba Gandhi **1298** Sectioned Heart

1996. 50th Anniv of the Kasturba Trust.
1652 **1297** 1r. grey, green and red 60 20

1996. 100 Years of Cardiac Surgery.
1653 **1298** 5r. multicoloured . . . 1·00 1·00

1299 C. K. Nayudu **1300** "Vasant" (Spring) (Ragini Basanti)

1996. Cricketers. Multicoloured.
1654 2r. Type **1299** 60 60
1655 2r. Vinoo Mankad 60 60
1656 2r. Deodhar 60 60
1657 2r. Vijay Merchant 60 60

1996. Miniature Paintings of the Seasons. Multicoloured.
1658 5r. Type **1300** . . . . . . 1·00 1·25
1659 5r. "Greeshma" (Summer) (Jyestha) . . . . 1·00 1·25
1660 5r. "Varsha" (Monsoon) (Rag Megh Malbar) . . . 1·00 1·25
1661 5r. "Hernant" (Winter) (Pausha) . . . . 1·00 1·25

1301 Kunjilal Dubey **1302** Morarji Desai

1996. Kunjilal Dubey Commemoration.
1662 **1301** 1r. brown & chocolate 20 10

1996. Birth Centenary of Morarji Desai (former Prime Minister) (1st issue).
1663 **1302** 1r. red 30 10
See also No. 1702.

1303 Blood Pheasant

1996. Himalayan Ecology. Multicoloured.
1664 5r. Type **1303** . . . . . . 1·00 1·25
1665 5r. Markhor (goat) . . . . . 1·00 1·25
1666 5r. "Meconopsis horridula" (Tsher Gnoin) (plant) . . 1·00 1·25
1667 5r. "Saussurea simpsoniana" (Sunflower) . . . . 1·00 1·25
MS1668 175 × 105 mm. Nos. 1664/7 (sold at 30r.) . . . . 2·50 3·25

1304 S.K.C.G. College Building

1996. Centenary of S.K.C.G. College, Gajapati.
1669 **1304** 1r. brown and cream 20 10

1305 Muhammad Ismail Sahib

1996. Birth Centenary of Muhammad Ismail Sahib (Moslem politician).
1670 **1305** 1r. purple 20 10

1306 Modern Stadium and Ancient Athens

1307 Sister Alphonsa

1996. Olympic Games, Atlanta. Multicoloured.
1671 5r. Type **1306** 35 50
1672 5r. Hand holding Olympic torch 35 50

1996. 50th Death Anniv of Sister Alphonsa.
1673 **1307** 1r. black and blue . . . 20 10

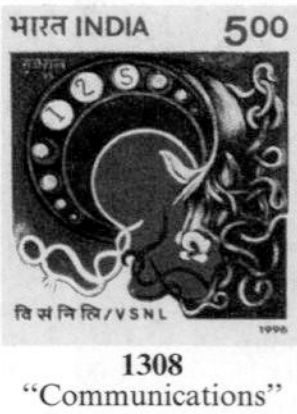

1308 "Communications"

1309 Sir Pherozeshah Mehta

1996. 125th Anniv of Videsh Sanchar Nigam Limited (telecommunications company).
1674 **1308** 5r. multicoloured . . . 1·00 1·00

1996. 150th Birth Anniv of Sir Pherozeshah Mehta (politician).
1675 **1309** 1r. blue 20 10

1310 Ahilyabai

1311 Chembai Vaidyanatha Bhagavathar

1996. Death Bicentenary (1995) of Ahilyabai (ruler of Holkar).
1676 **1310** 2r. brown and deep brown 30 20

1996. Birth Centenary of Chembai Vaidyanatha Bhagavathar (musician).
1677 **1311** 1r. brown and green . . 20 10

1312 Red Junglefowl Cockerel

1996. 20th World Poultry Congress, New Delhi.
1678 **1312** 5r. multicoloured . . . 1·75 1·50

1313 Rani Gaidinliu

1314 Nath Pai

1996. Rani Gaidinliu (Naga leader) Commemoration.
1679 **1313** 1r. blue 20 10

1996. 25th Death Anniv of Nath Pai (politician).
1680 **1314** 1r. blue 20 10

1315 Exhibition Logo

1317 Jananayak Debeswar Sarmah

1316 Historic Steam Locomotives

1996. INDEPEX '97 International Stamp Exhibition, New Delhi (1st issue).
1681 **1315** 2r. gold and purple . . 30 20
See also Nos. 1713/16, 1722/5, 1741/4 and 1758/61.

1996. 25th Anniv of National Rail Museum.
1682 **1316** 5r. multicoloured . . . 1·75 1·50

1996. Birth Centenary of Jananayak Debeswar Sarmah (politician).
1683 **1317** 2r. brown and deep brown 30 20

1318 Monument and Sikh Sentry

1996. 150th Anniv of Sikh Regiment.
1684 **1318** 5r. multicoloured . . . 1·00 1·00

1319 Dr. Salim Ali

1996. Birth Centenary of Salim Ali (ornithologist). Multicoloured.
1685 8r. Type **1319** . . . . . . 1·75 2·00
1686 11r. Painted storks at nest 1·75 2·00
Nos. 1685/6 were printed together, se-tenant, with the backgrounds forming a composite design.

1320 "Indian Village" (child's painting)

1996. Children's Day.
1687 **1320** 8r. multicoloured . . . 1·00 1·25

1321 Seeds in a Test-tube

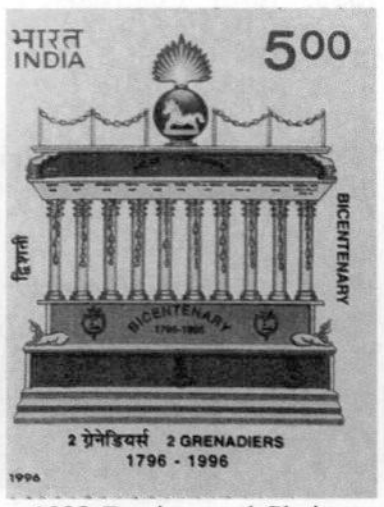

1322 Regimental Shrine

1996. 2nd International Crop Science Congress.
1688 **1321** 2r. multicoloured . . . 40 20

1996. Bicentenary of 2nd Battalion, Grenadiers.
1689 **1322** 5r. multicoloured . . . 1·00 1·00

1323 Woman writing

1324 Abai Konunbaev

1996. 10th Anniv of South Asian Association for Regional Co-operation (S.A.A.R.C.).
1690 **1323** 11r. multicoloured . . . 1·00 1·40

1996. 150th Birth Anniv (1995) of Abai Konunbaev (Kazakh poet).
1691 **1324** 5r. chestnut, brown and lilac . . . . 1·00 1·25

1325 Buglers in front of Memorial

1327 Victorian Doctors performing Operation

1326 Vivekananda Rock Memorial (½-size illustration)

1996. 25th Anniv of the Liberation of Bangladesh.
1692 **1325** 2r. multicoloured . . . 30 20

1996. 25th Anniv of Vivekananda Rock Memorial, Kanyakumari.
1693 **1326** 5r. multicoloured . . . 1·50 1·25

1996. 150th Anniv of Anaesthetics.
1694 **1327** 5r. multicoloured . . . 1·00 1·00

1328 Roorkee University Buildings

1997. 150th Anniv of Roorkee University.
1695 **1328** 8r. multicoloured . . . 80 1·25

1329 Dr. Vrindavanlal Verma

1997. Dr. Vrindavanlal Verma (writer) Commemoration.
1696 **1329** 2r. red 30 20

1330 Field Post Office

1331 Subhas Chandra Bose

1997. 25th Anniv of Army Postal Service Corps.
1697 **1330** 5r. multicoloured . . . 1·25 1·25

1997. Birth Centenary of Subhas Chandra Bose (nationalist).
1698 **1331** 1r. brown 30 10

1332 Jose Marti

1333 Conference Logo

1997. Jose Marti (Cuban writer) Commemoration.
1699 **1332** 11r. black and pink . . 80 1·25

1997. "Towards Partnership between Men and Women in Politics" Inter-Parliamentary Conference, New Delhi.
1700 **1333** 5r. multicoloured . . . 35 45

1334 St. Andrew's Church

1335 Morarji Desai

1997. St. Andrew's Church, Egmore, Madras Commemoration.
1701 **1334** 8r. multicoloured . . . 70 1·00

1997. Birth Centenary of Morarji Desai (former Prime Minister) (2nd issue).
1702 **1335** 1r. brown and deep brown 30 10

1336 Shyam Lal Gupt

1337 Saint Dnyaneshwar

1997. Birth Centenary (1996) of Shyam Lal Gupt (social reformer).
1703 **1336** 1r. cinnamon and brown 20 10

1997. 700th Death Anniv (1996) of Saint Dnyaneshwar.
1704 **1337** 5r. multicoloured . . . 60 60

1338 Parijati Tree

1997. Parijati Tree. Multicoloured.
1705 5r. Type **1338** 65 75
1706 6r. Parijati flower 65 75

1339 Monument, Rashtriya Military College

1997. 75th Anniv of Rashtriya Military College, Dehra Dun.
1707 **1339** 2r. multicoloured . . . 75 30

1340 Ram Manohar Lohia **1341** Society Centenary Emblem

1997. Ram Manohar Lohia Commemoration.
1708 **1340** 1r. multicoloured . . . 20 10

1997. Centenary of the Philatelic Society of India. Multicoloured.
1709 2r. Type **1341** 65 70
1710 2r. Cover of 1st "Philatelic Journal of India", 1897 65 70

1342 Gyandith Award Winners **1343** Madhu Limaye

1997. Gyandith Award Scheme.
1711 **1342** 2r. multicoloured . . . 30 20

1997. Madhu Limaye Commemoration.
1712 **1343** 2r. green 30 20

1344 Nalanda Monastic University

1997. "INDEPEX '97" International Stamp Exhibition, New Delhi (2nd issue). Buddhist Cultural Sites. Multicoloured.
1713 2r. Type **1344** 25 30
1714 6r. The Bodhi Tree, Bodhgaya 45 50
1715 10r. Stupa and Pillar, Vaishali 60 80
1716 11r. Stupa, Kushinagar . . 60 80

1345 Pandit Omkarnath Thakur **1346** Ram Sewak Yadav

1997. Birth Centenary of Pandit Omkarnath Thakur (musician).
1717 **1345** 2r. black and blue . . . 60 20

1997. Ram Sewak Yadav (politician) Commemoration.
1718 **1346** 2r. brown 30 20

1347 Sibnath Banerjee **1348** Rukmini Lakshmipathi

1997. Birth Centenary of Sibnath Banerjee (trade unionist).
1719 **1347** 2r. red and purple . . . 30 20

1997. Rukmini Lakshmipathi (social reformer) Commemoration.
1720 **1348** 2r. brown . . . . . . 1·00 40

1349 Sri Basaveswara **1350** Gopalpur-on-Sea Beach

1997. Sri Basaveswara (reformer and statesman) Commemoration.
1721 **1349** 2r. purple 30 20

1997. "INDEPEX '97" International Stamp Exhibition, New Delhi (3rd issue). Beaches. Multicoloured.
1722 2r. Type **1350** 25 15
1723 6r. Kovalam 65 55
1724 10r. Anjuna . . . . 80 1·00
1725 11r. Bogmalo . . . . 80 1·00

1351 Newspaper Masthead

1997. 50th Anniv of "Swatantra Bharat" (Hindi daily newspaper).
1726 **1351** 2r. multicoloured . . . 30 20

1352 Shah Nawaz Khan, P. K. Sahgal and G. S. Dhillon

1997. I.N.A. Trials Commemoration.
1727 **1352** 2r. multicoloured . . . 30 30

1353 Sir Ronald Ross (bacteriologist) **1354** Firaq Gorakhpuri

1997. Centenary of the Discovery of the Malaria Parasite by Sir Ronald Ross.
1728 **1353** 2r. grey . . . . 1·00 40

1997. Birth Centenary (1996) of Firaq Gorakhpuri (poet).
1729 **1354** 2r. brown 20 20

1355 Bhaktivedanta Swami

1997. Birth Centenary (1996) of Bhaktivedanta Swami (philosopher).
1730 **1355** 5r. brown . . . . . . 1·25 1·25

1356 Parachute Regiment Emblem

1997. Bicentenary of 2nd (Maratha) Battalion, Parachute Regiment.
1731 **1356** 2r. multicoloured . . . 50 30

1357 Fossil of "Birbalsahnia divyadarshanii" **1358** Swami Brahmanand

1997. 50th Anniv of Birbal Sahni Institute of Palaeobotany, Lucknow. Plant Fossils. Multicoloured.
1732 2r. Type **1357** 45 45
1733 2r. "Glossopteris" 45 45
1734 6r. "Pentoxylon" (reconstruction) . . . . . 90 1·00
1735 10r. "Williamsonia sewardiana" (model) . . . 1·40 1·50

1997. Swami Brahmanand (social reformer) Commemoration.
1736 **1358** 2r. grey and stone . . . 30 20

1359 "Sir William Jones" **1361** V. K. Krishna Menon

1360 Lawrence School Building and Crest

1997. 250th Birth Anniv (1996) of Sir William Jones (Sanskrit scholar).
1737 **1359** 4r. multicoloured . . . 35 40

1997. 150th Anniv of Lawrence School, Sanawar.
1738 **1360** 2r. multicoloured . . . 50 30

1997. Birth Centenary (1996) of V. K. Krishna Menon (politician).
1739 **1361** 2r. red 30 30

1362 Policemen and Globe

1997. 66th General Assembly Session of ICPO Interpol.
1740 **1362** 4r. multicoloured . . . 65 75

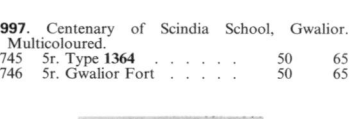

1363 Woman from Arunachal Pradesh **1364** Students in Meditation, Astachai

1997. "INDEPEX '97" International Stamp Exhibition, New Delhi (4th issue). Women's Costumes. Multicoloured.
1741 2r. Type **1363** 30 20
1742 6r. Gujarat costume 60 65
1743 10r. Ladakh costume . . . 80 90
1744 11r. Kerala costume 80 90

1997. Centenary of Scindia School, Gwalior. Multicoloured.
1745 5r. Type **1364** 50 65
1746 5r. Gwalior Fort 50 65

1365 "Ocimum sanctum"

1997. Medicinal Plants. Multicoloured.
1747 2r. Type **1365** 40 20
1748 5r. "Curcuma longa" . . . 60 60
1749 10r. "Rauvolfia serpentina" 85 95
1750 11r. "Aloe barbadensis" . . 85 95

1366 Sant Kavi Sunderdas **1367** K. Rama Rao

1997. 400th Birth Anniv (1996) of Sant Kavi Sunderdas (Hindu theologian).
1751 **1366** 2r. brown 60 30

1997. Birth Centenary of K. Rama Rao (parliamentarian and journalist).
1752 **1367** 2r. bistre and brown . . 75 30

1368 Jawaharlal Nehru and Child

1997. Children's Day.
1753 **1368** 2r. multicoloured . . . 35 30

1369 Animals on Globe **1370** Hazari Prasad Dwivedi

1997. World Convention on Reverence for All Life, Pune.
1754 **1369** 4r. multicoloured . . . 1·00 1·00

1997. 90th Birth Anniv of Hazari Prasad Dwivedi (scholar).
1755 **1370** 2r. grey 30 30

1372 Vallabhbhai Patel and Marchers

1997. 47th Death Anniv of Vallabhbhai Patel (politician).
1757 **1372** 2r. brown 35 30

1373 Head Post Office, Pune

1997. "INDEPEX '97" International Stamp Exhibition, New Delhi (5th issue). Post Office Heritage. Multicoloured.
1758 2r. Type **1373** 20 20
1759 6r. River mail barge 40 50
1760 10r. Jal Cooper (philatelist) and cancellations 70 85
1761 11r. "Hindoostan" (paddle-steamer) 70 85

1374 50th Anniversary Emblem

1997. 50th Anniv of Indian Armed Forces.
1762 **1374** 2r. multicoloured . . . 40 30

1375 Dr. Pattabhi Sitaramayya

1377 Ram Prasad Bismil and Ashfaqullah Khan

1376 Father Jerome d'Souza and Cathedral

1997. Dr. Pattabhi Sitaramayya (politician) Commemoration.
1763 **1375** 2r. brown 65 30

1997. Birth Centenary of Father Jerome d'Souza (academic).
1764 **1376** 2r. brown 30 30

1997. 70th Death Anniv of Ram Prasad Bismil and Ashfaqullah Khan (revolutionaries).
1765 **1377** 2r. brown 30 30

1378 Jail Buildings

1997. Cellular Jail, Port Blair.
1766 **1378** 2r. multicoloured . . . 30 30

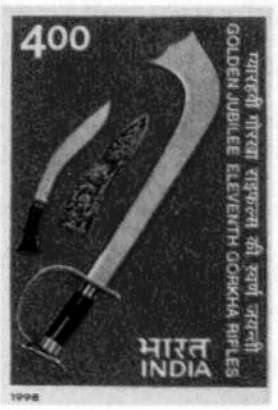

1379 Sword and Kukri

1998. 50th Anniv of 11th Gorkha Rifles.
1767 **1379** 4r. multicoloured . . . 1·50 1·00

1380 Nahar Singh

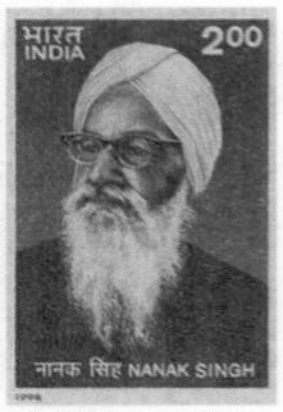

1381 Nanak Singh

1998. 140th Death Anniv of Nahar Singh (Sikh leader).
1768 **1380** 2r. purple 30 30

1998. Birth Centenary (1997) of Nanak Singh (writer).
1769 **1381** 2r. red 30 30

1382 Rotary International Emblem

1998. Meeting of Rotary International Council on Legislation, Delhi.
1770 **1382** 8r. yellow and blue . . 65 80

1383 Maharana Pratap

1384 V. S. Khandekar

1998. 400th Death Anniv of Maharana Pratap (Rajput leader).
1771 **1383** 2r. purple 30 30

1998. Birth Centenary of V. S. Khandekar (writer).
1772 **1384** 2r. red 30 30

1385 Elephant and Dancers

1998. India Tourism Day.
1773 **1385** 10r. multicoloured . . . 1·50 1·50

1386 Jagdish Chandra Jain

1998. Jagdish Chandra Jain (educationist) Commemoration.
1774 **1386** 2r. brown 30 30

1387 Gandhi as a Young Man and Peasants in Fields

1388 A. Vedaratnam

1998. 50th Death Anniv of Mahatma Gandhi. Multicoloured.
1775 2r. Type **1387** 40 45
1776 6r. Woman weaving and Gandhi distributing food 65 75
1777 10r. Gandhi collecting salt 85 90
1778 11r. Gandhi carrying flag . . 85 90

Nos. 1775/8 were printed together, se-tenant, with the backgrounds forming a composite design.

1998. Birth Centenary (1997) of A. Vedaratnam (social reformer).
1779 **1388** 2r. purple 30 30

1389 Anniversary Emblem

1391 Sir Syed Ahmad Khan

1390 Savitribai Phule

1998. 50th Anniv of Universal Declaration of Human Rights.
1780 **1389** 6r. multicoloured . . . 50 60

1998. Death Centenary (1997) of Savitribai Phule (educational reformer).
1781 **1390** 2r. brown 30 30

1998. Death Centenary of Sir Syed Ahmed Khan (social reformer).
1782 **1391** 2r. brown 55 30

1392 Barren Landscape and Living Forest

1998. 1st Assembly Meeting of Global Environment Facility, Delhi.
1783 **1392** 11r. multicoloured . . . 1·00 1·25

1393 Ramana Maharshi

1998. Ramana Maharshi (religious leader) Commemoration.
1784 **1393** 2r. lilac 30 30

1394 College Arms

1998. 50th Anniv of Defence Services Staff College, Wellington.
1785 **1394** 6r. red 80 80

1395 Diesel Train on Viaduct (⅔-size illustration)

1998. Completion of Konkan Railway.
1786 **1395** 8r. multicoloured . . . 1·00 1·25

1396 Narayan Ganesh Goray

1397 Dr. Zakir Husain

1998. Narayan Ganesh Goray (social reformer) Commemoration.
1787 **1396** 2r. brown 30 20

1998. Birth Centenary (1997) of Dr. Zakir Husain (former President of India).
1788 **1397** 2r. brown 30 20

1398 Mohammed Abdurahiman Shahib

1399 Lokanayak Omeo Kumar Das

1998. Mohammed Abdurahiman Shahib (nationalist) Commemoration.
1789 **1398** 2r. brown 30 20

1998. Lokanayak Omeo Kumar Das (writer) Commemoration.
1790 **1399** 2r. brown 30 20

1400 Vakkom Abdul Khader, Satyendra Chandra Bardhan and Fouja Singh

1998. Nationalist Martyrs Commemoration.
1791 **1400** 2r. brown and cinnamon 30 20

1401 Bishnu Dey, Tarashankar Bandopadhyay and Ashapurna Devi

1402 Big Ben, London

1998. Bangla Jnanpith Literary Award Winners Commemoration.
1792 **1401** 2r. brown 30 20

1998. 50th Anniv of First Air India International Flight.
1793 5r. Type **1402** 50 65
1794 6r. Lockheed Super Constellation airliner, globe and Gateway of India, Bombay (55 × 35 mm) 50 65

Nos. 1793/4 were printed together, se-tenant, forming a composite design.

1403 Dr. C. Vijiaraghavachariar

1405 Bhagawan Gopinathji

1404 Anniversary Logo and Savings Stream

1998. Dr. C. Vijiaraghavachariar (lawyer and social reformer) Commemoration.
1795 **1403** 2r. brown 60 30

1998. 50th Anniv of National Savings Organization. Multicoloured.
1796 5r. Type **1404** 35 40
1797 6r. Hand dropping coin into jar 35 40

Nos. 1796/7 were printed together, se-tenant, forming a composite design.

1998. Birth Centenary of Bhagawan Gopinathji (spiritual leader).
1798 **1405** 3r. brown 30 30

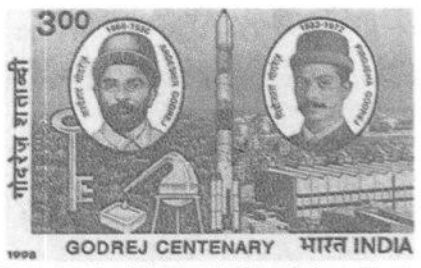
1406 Ardeshir and Pirojsha Godrej

1998. Centenary of Godrej (industrial conglomerate).
1799 **1406** 3r. green 30 30

1407 Aruna Asaf Ali

1998. Aruna Asaf Ali (nationalist) Commemoration.
1800 **1407** 3r. brown 30 30

1408 Iswar Chandra Vidyasagar (educationist) and College

1998. 125th Anniv of Vidyasagar College, Calcutta.
1801 **1408** 2r. black 20 15

1409 Shivpujan Sahai

1998. Shivpujan Sahai (writer) Commemoration.
1802 **1409** 2r. brown 20 15

1410 Red Fort, Delhi, and Spinning Wheel

1411 Gostha Behari Paul

1998. Homage to Martyrs for Independence. Multicoloured.
1803 3r. Type **1410** 30 30
1804 8r. Industrial and scientific development in modern India 70 90

1998. Gostha Paul (footballer) Commemoration.
1805 **1411** 3r. purple 30 20

1412 Youth Hostel and Logo

1998. 50th Anniv of Youth Hostels Association of India.
1806 **1412** 5r. multicoloured . . . 50 50

1413 Uniforms, Badge and Tank

1998. Bicentenary of 4th Battalion, Guards' Brigade (1 Rajput).
1807 **1413** 6r. multicoloured . . . 60 60

1414 Bhai Kanhaiyaji

1998. Bhai Kanhaiyaji (Sikh social reformer) Commemoration.
1808 **1414** 2r. red 20 15

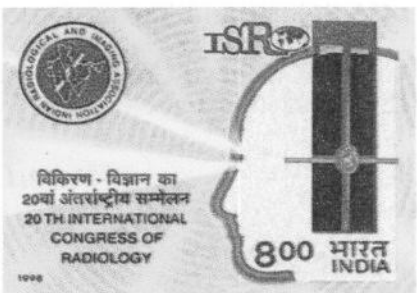
1415 Emblem and Diagram of Head

1998. 20th International Congress of Radiology.
1809 **1415** 8r. multicoloured . . . 1·00 1·10

1416 Dove of Peace and Boy reading Book

1417 Dr. Tristao Braganza Cunha

1998. 26th International Books for Young People Congress.
1810 **1416** 11r. multicoloured . . . 1·00 1·25

1998. Dr. Tristao Braganza Cunha (nationalist) Commemoration.
1811 **1417** 3r. brown 30 30

1418 Jananeta Hijam Irawat Singh

1419 Women Aviators and Bi-plane

1998. Jananeta Hijam Irawat Singh (social reformer) Commemoration.
1812 **1418** 3r. brown 30 30

1998. Indian Women's Participation in Aviation.
1813 **1419** 8r. blue . . . . 1·00 1·10

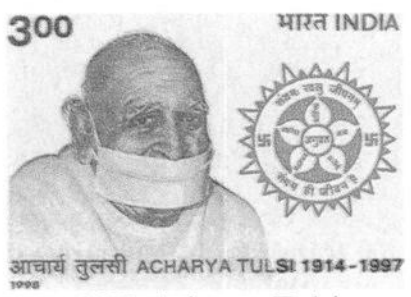
1420 Acharya Tulsi

1998. 1st Death Anniv of Acharya Tulsi (Jain religious leader).
1814 **1420** 3r. brown and orange . . 30 30

1421 Girl and Bird reading Book

1998. Children's Day.
1815 **1421** 3r. multicoloured . . . 30 30

1422 I.N.S. "Delhi" (destroyer)

1998. Navy Day.
1816 **1422** 3r. multicoloured . . . 50 40

1423 Mounted Trumpeter

1424 Sir David Sassoon and Library, Bombay

1998. 225th Anniv of President's Bodyguard.
1817 **1423** 3r. multicoloured . . . 65 40

1998. David Sassoon Library and Reading Room Commemoration.
1818 **1424** 3r. ultramarine and blue 30 30

1425 Regimental Arms and Soldier

1998. Bicentenary of 2nd Battalion, Rajput Regiment.
1819 **1425** 3r. multicoloured . . . 75 45

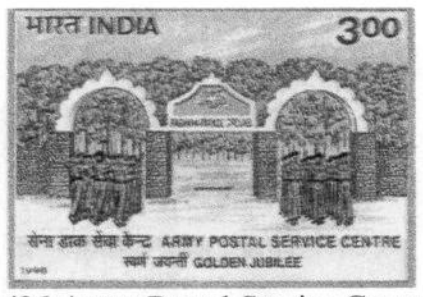
1426 Army Postal Service Centre, Kamptee

1998. 50th Anniv of Army Postal Service Training Centre.
1820 **1426** 3r. multicoloured . . . 65 40

1427 Connemara Public Library, Madras

1998. Centenary (1996) of Connemara Public Library.
1821 **1427** 3r. brown and ochre . . 30 30

1428 Neem Tree and Leaves

1429 Baba Raghav Das

1998. 50th Anniv of The Indian Pharmaceutical Congress Association.
1822 **1428** 3r. multicoloured . . . 65 40

1998. 40th Death Anniv of Baba Raghav Das (social reformer).
1823 **1429** 2r. violet 20 15

1430 Lt. Indra Lal Roy D.F.C.

1998. Birth Centenary of Indra Lal Roy (First World War pilot).
1824 **1430** 3r. multicoloured . . . 65 40

1431 Sant Gadge Baba

1998. Sant Gadge Baba (social reformer) Commemoration.
1825 **1431** 3r. lilac, blue and black 30 30

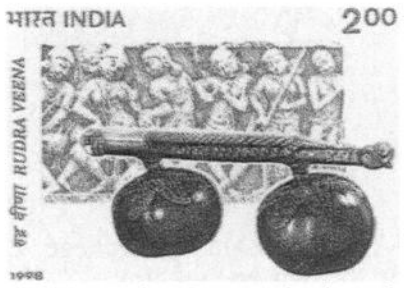
1432 Rudra Veena (stringed instrument)

1998. Musical Instruments. Multicoloured.
1826 2r. Type **1432** 30 15
1827 6r. Flute 55 45
1828 8r. Pakhawaj (wooden barrel drum) 70 80
1829 10r. Sarod (stringed instrument) 75 85

1433 "Chicoreus brunneus" (Murex shell)

1998. Shells. Multicoloured.
1830 3r. Type **1433** 50 50
1831 3r. "Cassis cornuta" (horned helmet) 50 50
1832 3r. "Cypraea staphylaea" (cowrie) 50 50
1833 11r. "Lambis lambis" (common spider conch) 1·40 1·60

1434 Stylized Police Officers

1999. 50th Anniv of Indian Police Service.
1834 **1434** 3r. multicoloured . . . 65 40

1435 Modern Weapon Systems

1999. 40th Anniv of Defence Research and Development Organization.
1835 **1435** 10r. multicoloured . . . 1·00 1·25

1436 Issue of "Orunodoi" (Assamese newspaper) for January, 1846

1999. 150th Anniv of Newspapers in Assam.
1836 **1436** 3r. black, yellow and orange 65 40

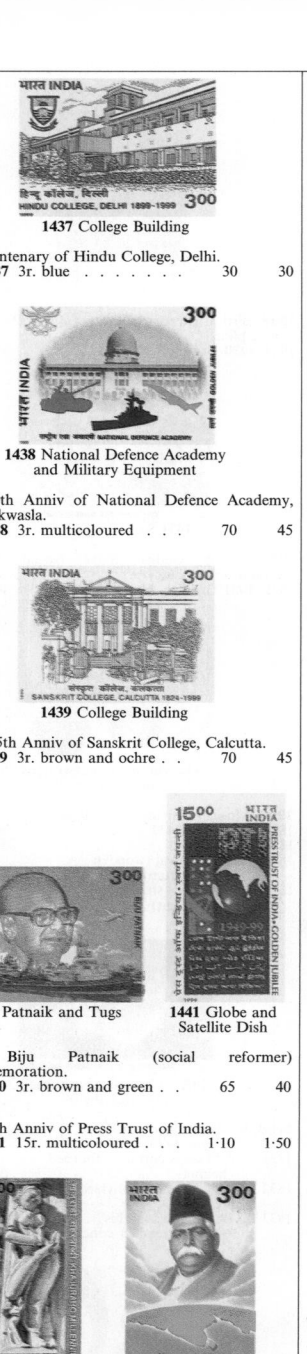

1437 College Building

1999. Centenary of Hindu College, Delhi.
1837 **1437** 3r. blue 30 30

1438 National Defence Academy and Military Equipment

1999. 50th Anniv of National Defence Academy, Khadakwasla.
1838 **1438** 3r. multicoloured . . . 70 45

1439 College Building

1999. 175th Anniv of Sanskrit College, Calcutta.
1839 **1439** 3r. brown and ochre . . 70 45

1440 Patnaik and Tugs

1441 Globe and Satellite Dish

1999. Biju Patnaik (social reformer) Commemoration.
1840 **1440** 3r. brown and green . . 65 40

1999. 50th Anniv of Press Trust of India.
1841 **1441** 15r. multicoloured . . . 1·10 1·50

1442 "Apsara removing a Thorn from her Foot" (temple statue)

1443 Dr. K. B. Hedgewar

1999. Millenary of the Khajuraho Temples.
1842 **1442** 15r. deep brown, light brown and black . . 1·10 1·50

1999. Dr. Keshavrao Hedgewar (founder of Rashtriya Swayamsevak Sangha) Commemoration.
1843 **1443** 3r. multicoloured . . . 30 30

1444 Terracotta Model Boat from Lothal, 2200 B.C., and Seal

1999. Maritime Heritage. Multicoloured.
1844 3r. Type **1444** 40 50
1845 3r. Ghurab (sailing ship) of Kanhoji Angre, 1700 . . 40 50

1445 Anandpur Sahib Temple

1999. 300th Anniv of the Khalsa Panth (Sikh Order).
1846 **1445** 3r. multicoloured . . . 75 45

1446 Bethune College

1999. 150th Anniv of Bethune Collegiate School, Calcutta.
1847 **1446** 3r. green 30 30

1447 Plane, Satellite and Rocket orbiting Globe

1999. Technology Day.
1848 **1447** 3r. multicoloured . . . 30 30

1448 Mumbai Port

1449 Handshake and Airliner

1999. 125th Anniv of Mumbai (Bombay) Port Trust.
1849 **1448** 3r. blue 30 30

1999. Mizoram Accord (peace agreement) Commemoration.
1850 **1449** 3r. multicoloured . . . 30 30

1450 Gulzarilal Nanda

1451 Jijabai and Chatrapati Shivaji

1999. Birth Centenary of Gulzarilal Nanda (former Prime Minster).
1851 **1450** 3r. multicoloured . . . 30 30

1999. Jijabai (mother of Chatrapati Shivaji (Maratha leader)) Commemoration.
1852 **1451** 3r. purple 30 30

1452 P. S. Kumaraswamy Raja

1999. P. S. Kumaraswamy Raja (politician) Commemoration.
1853 **1452** 3r. brown and blue . . 30 30

1453 Balai Chand Mukhopadhyay

1999. Birth Centenary of Balai Chand Mukhopadhyay ("Banaphool") (Bengali writer).
1854 **1453** 3r. blue 30 30

1454 River Sindhu, Ladakh

1999. Sindhu Darshan Festival.
1855 **1454** 3r. multicoloured . . . 30 30

1455 Soldier and Young Girl

1999. 50th Anniv of Geneva Conventions.
1856 **1455** 15r. black and red . . . 1·10 1·50

1456 Sardar Ajit Singh

1457 Kalki Krishnamurthy

1999. Heroes of Struggle for Freedom.
1857 **1456** 3r. brown and red . . . 30 30
1858 – 3r. brown and blue . . 30 30
1859 – 3r. blue and red 30 30
1860 – 3r. purple and drab . . 30 30
DESIGNS: No. 1858, Swami Ramanand Teerth; No. 1859, Vishwambhar Dayalu Tripathi; No. 1860, Swami Keshawanand.

1999. Birth Centenary of Kalki Krishnamurthy (Tamil writer).
1861 **1457** 3r. grey 25 25

1458 Ramdhari Sinha

1999. Ramdhari Sinha "Dinkar" (poet) Commemoration.
1862 **1458** 3r. brown and blue . . 25 25

1459 Jhaverchand Kalidas Meghani and Graves

1999. Jhaverchand Kalidas Meghani (writer) Commemoration.
1863 **1459** 3r. red and green . . . 25 25

1460 Rambrikish Benipuri and Statue of Horse

1999. Rambrikish Benipuri (writer and journalist) Commemoration.
1864 **1460** 3r. brown and light brown 25 25

1461 Kazi Nazrul Islam

1999. Birth Centenary of Kazi Nazrul Islam (Bengali poet).
1865 **1461** 3r. sepia and yellow . . 25 25

1462 Arati Gupta

1999. Arati Gupta (swimmer) Commemoration.
1866 **1462** 3r. multicoloured . . . 25 25

1463 Lionesses

1999. Endangered Species. Asiatic Lion. Mult.
1867 3r. Type **1463** 35 35
1868 3r. Lions and lionesses lying down 35 35
1869 3r. Lioness with cubs . . . 35 35
1870 15r. Two lions . . . . 1·10 1·50

1464 A. D. Shroff

1465 A. B. Walawalkar and Map

1999. A. D. Shroff (economist) Commemoration.
1871 **1464** 3r. green and brown . . 25 25

1999. A. B. Walawalkar (railway engineer) Commemoration.
1872 **1465** 3r. purple 30 25

1466 Chhaganlal K. Parekh and Medical Staff with Child

1999. Chhaganlal K. Parekh (social reformer) Commemoration.
1873 **1466** 3r. blue and brown . . 30 25

1467 Dr. T. M. A. Pai and Hospital

1999. 20th Death Anniv of Dr. T. M. A. Pai (educator).
1874 **1467** 3r. chocolate and stone 30 25

1468 Chhau Dance Masks

1999. 125th Anniv of Universal Postal Union. Traditional Arts and Crafts. Multicoloured.
1875 3r. Type **1468** 40 40
1876 3r. Elephant and horseman (Rathva wall painting) (vert) 40 40
1877 3r. Man ploughing (Muria ritual collar) 40 40
1878 15r. Angami ornament (vert) 1·10 1·50

1469 Veerapandia Kattabomman

1470 Ustad Allauddin Khan Saheb (sarod player)

1999. Death Bicentenary of Veerapandia Kattabomman (ruler of Panchalankuruchi).
1879 **1469** 3r. green 25 25

1999. Modern Masters of Indian Classical Music. Multicoloured.
1880 3r. Type **1470** 25 25
1881 3r. Musiri Subramania Iyer (singer) 25 25

1471 Brigadier Rajinder Singh
1472 Elephant and Rhinoceros

1999. Birth Centenary of Brigadier Rajinder Singh (First recipient of M.V.C. medal).
1882 **1471** 3r. purple 30 25

1999. Children's Day.
1883 **1472** 3r. multicoloured . . . 30 25

1473 Dam and Pumping Station

1999. Sri Sathya Sai Water Supply Project.
1884 **1473** 3r. multicoloured . . . 50 30

1474 Supreme Court, New Delhi

1999. 50th Anniv of Supreme Court of India.
1885 **1474** 3r. multicoloured . . . 25 25

1475 A. Vaidyanatha Iyer and Temple Tower

1999. March of Progress.
1886 **1475** 3r. red 30 30
1887 – 3r. brown and green . . 30 30
1888 – 3r. buff and black . . . 30 30
1889 – 3r. brown and green . . 30 30
DESIGNS: No. 1887, Dr. Punjabrao Deshmukh and symbols of agriculture; 1888, Indulal Kanaiyalal Yagnik and newspaper; 1889, Kakkan and machinery.

1476 Aspects of Thermal Power

1999. Centenary of Thermal Power.
1890 **1476** 3r. chocolate and brown 25 25

1477 "Hindustan Times" Front Pages from 1950 and 1999

1999. 75th Anniv of "Hindustan Times" Newspaper.
1891 **1477** 15r. multicoloured . . . 1·10 1·40

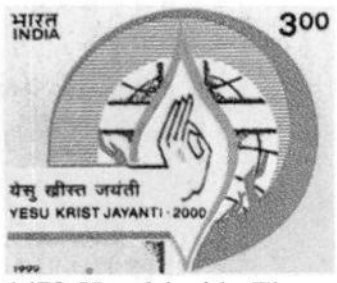

1478 Three Faces ("Small Family by Choice")
1479 Hand inside Flame in front of Cross

1999. 50th Anniv of Family Planning Association of India.
1892 **1478** 3r. multicoloured . . . 25 25

1999. 2000th Birth Anniv of Jesus Christ.
1893 **1479** 3r. multicoloured . . . 50 25

1480 Tabo Monastery and Mountains

1999. New Millennium. Unity in Diversity. Mult.
1894 5r. Type **1480** 50 60
1895 10r. Traditional scene . . . 60 80

1481 Agni II Rocket and Dove

2000. 41st Anniv of Defence Research and Development Organization.
1896 **1481** 3r. multicoloured . . . 30 25

1482 Sunrise

2000. New Millennium.
1897 **1482** 3r. multicoloured . . . 25 25

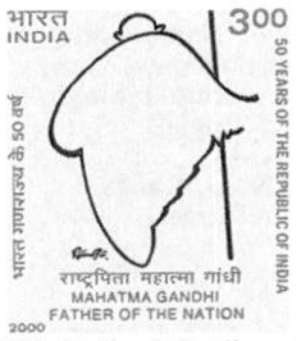

1483 Stylized Outline of Gandhi as Map of India

2000. 50th Anniv of Republic (1st issue).
1898 **1483** 3r. black and red . . . 20 20

1484 Karam Singh and Regimental Badge

2000. 50th Anniv of Republic (2nd issue). Gallantry Award Winners. Multicoloured.
1899 3r. Type **1484** 25 25
1900 3r. Abdul Hamid and armed jeep 25 25
1901 3r. Albert Ekka, hand grenades and knife . . . 25 25
1902 3r. N. J. S. Sekhon and jet fighter 25 25
1903 3r. M. N. Mulla and warship 25 25

1485 Batagur Terrapin

2000. "Millepex 2000" Stamp Exhibition, Bhubaneshwar. Endangered Species. Multicoloured.
1904 3r. Type **1485** 20 20
1905 3r. Olive Ridley turtle . . . 20 20

1486 Balwantrai Mehta
1487 Dr. Harekrushna Mahatab

2000. Balwantrai Mehta (former Chief Minister of Gujarot) Commemoration.
1906 **1486** 3r. multicoloured . . . 20 20

2000. Dr. Harekrushna Mahatab (former Chief Minister of Orissa) Commemoration.
1907 **1487** 3r. multicoloured . . . 20 20

1488 Arun Kumar Chanda
1490 Dr. Burgula Ramakrishna Rao

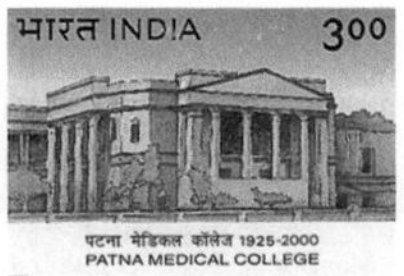

1489 Patna Medical College

2000. Arun Kumar Chanda (trade union leader) Commemoration.
1908 **1488** 3r. multicoloured . . . 20 20

2000. 75th Anniv of Patna Medical College.
1909 **1489** 3r. multicoloured . . . 20 15

2000. Birth Centenary (1999) of Dr. Burgula Ramakrishna Rao (Hyderabad Chief Minister).
1910 **1490** 3r. brown and yellow 20 15

1491 Potti Sriramulu

2000. Potti Sriramulu (Harijan activist) Commemoration.
1911 **1491** 3r. red 20 15

1492 Basawon Sinha
1493 Siroi Lily

2000. Basawon Sinha (politician) Commemoration.
1912 **1492** 3r. multicoloured . . . 20 15

2000. "Indepex Asiana 2000" International Stamp Exhibition, Calcutta (1st issue). Flora and Fauna of Manipur and Tripura. Multicoloured.
1913 3r. Type **1493** 35 35
1914 3r. Sangai deer 35 35
1915 3r. Wild guava 35 35
1916 15r. Slow loris . . . . . . 1·25 1·50
See also Nos. 1934/7 and 1966/71.

1494 Maharshi Dayananda Saraswati, Flame and Pages

2000. 125th Anniv of Arya Samaj (philosophical movement).
1918 **1494** 3r. multicoloured . . . 50 20

1495 Kankrej Breed

2000. Indigenous Breeds of Cattle. Multicoloured.
1919 3r. Type **1495** 40 40
1920 3r. Kangayam 40 40
1921 3r. Gir 40 40
1922 15r. Hallikar . . . . 1·25 1·50

1496 Blackbuck
1497 Leopard Cat

2000. Wildlife.
1923 **1496** 25p. brown 10 10
1924 – 50p. brown 10 10
1925 – 1r. blue 10 10
1925a – 2r. purple 10 10
1926 – 3r. violet 10 10
1927 – 4r. red 10 15
1928 **1497** 5r. brown and green 15 20
1929 – 10r. orange, brn & grn 25 30
1930 – 15r. red, brn & dp brn 40 45
1931 – 20r. yellow and green 50 55
1932 – 50r. red, brown & blue 1·30 1·40
DESIGNS—VERT (as Type **1496**): 50p. Nilgiri tahr; 1r. Saras crane ("Saras Crane"); 2r. Rose. As Type **1497**: 4r. Painted stork. (19 × 37 mm): 20r. Amaltaas (plant); 50r. Asiatic paradise flycatcher (bird) ("Paradise Flycatcher"). HORIZ (as Type **1497**): 3r. Smooth Indian otters. (37 × 19 mm): 10r. Tiger, Sundarban Reserve; 15r. Butterfly.

1498 Railway Locomotive at Dehradoon Station

2000. Centenary of Doon Valley Railway.
1933 **1498** 15r. multicoloured . . . 1·50 1·50

1499 Rose-coloured Starling ("Rosy Pastor")

2000. "Indepex Asiana 2000" International Stamp Exhibition, Calcutta (2nd issue). Migratory Birds. Multicoloured.
1934 3r. Type **1499** 50 50
1935 3r. Garganey ("Garganey Teal") 50 50
1936 3r. Forest wagtail 50 50
1937 3r. White stork 50 50
MS1938 157 × 114 mm. Nos. 1934/7 1·75 1·75

1500 N. T. Rama Rao

2000. Nandamuri Taraka Rama Rao (former Chief Minister of Andhra Pradesh) Commemoration.
1939 **1500** 3r. multicoloured . . . 20 10

1501 Swami Saraswati

1503 Vijaya Lakshmi Pandit (diplomat)

1502 Christian Medical College and Hospital, Vellore

2000. 50th Death Anniv of Swami Sahajanand Saraswati (rural reformer).
1940 **1501** 3r. mauve, brn & stone . . . 20 10

2000. Centenary of Christian Medical College and Hospital, Vellore.
1941 **1502** 3r. multicoloured . . . 20 10

2000. Social and Political Leaders. Each including the Indian flag. Multicoloured.
1942 3r. Type **1503** 30 30
1943 3r. Bahadur R. Srinivasan (social reformer) 30 30
1944 3r. Jaglal Choudhary (social reformer) 30 30
1945 3r. Radha Gobinda Baruah (social reformer) 30 30

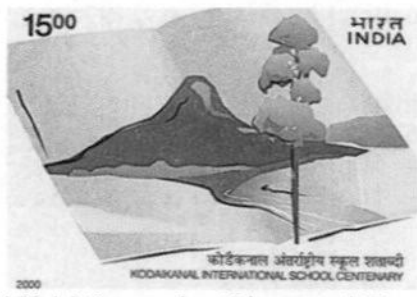
1504 Mountain, River and Tree inside Open Book

2000. Centenary of Kodaikanal International School.
1946 **1504** 15r. multicoloured . . . 1·00 1·25

1505 Discus

2000. Olympic Games, Sydney. Multicoloured.
1947 3r. Type **1505** 25 15
1948 6r. Tennis 40 35
1949 10r. Hockey 75 75
1950 15r. Weightlifting . . . . . 1·00 1·25

1506 "Oceansat-1"

2000. India's Space Programme. Multicoloured.
1951 3r. Type **1506** 40 40
1952 3r. "Insat 3B" in orbit . . . 40 40
1953 3r. Astronaut with flag, planets and spacecraft (vert) 40 40
1954 3r. Earth and spacecraft (vert) 40 40
Nos. 1953/4 were printed together, se-tenant, with the backgrounds forming a composite design.

1507 Krishna with Gopies (Anmana Devi)

2000. Madhubani-Mithila Paintings. Multicoloured.
1955 3r. Type **1507** 30 30
1956 3r. "Flower Girls" (Nirmala Devi) 30 30
1957 3r. "Ball and Sugriva" (Sanjula) (vert) 30 30
1958 5r. Geometrical pattern with sedan chair at foot (vert) 50 50
1959 10r. Geometrical pattern with elephant at foot (vert) 75 85

1508 Raj Kumar Shukla

1509 Dr. Shanker Dayal Sharma

2000. 125th Birth Anniv of Raj Kumar Shukla (social reformer).
1960 **1508** 3r. brown and buff . . 30 20

2000. 1st Death Anniv of Dr. Shanker Dayal Sharma (former President of India).
1961 **1509** 3r. multicoloured . . . 30 20

1510 Subhas Chandra Bose

1512 Maharaja Bijli Pasi

1511 "My Best Friend" (Phuhar Uppal)

2000.
1962 **1510** 1r. brown 10 10
1963 – 2r. black 10 10
1963a – 3r. blue 10 10
DESIGNS: 2r. Vallabhbhai Patel. 3r. Dr. B. R. Ambedkar.

2000. Children's Day.
1964 **1511** 3r. multicoloured . . . 40 25

2000. Maharaja Bijli Pasi of Bijnor Commemoration.
1965 **1512** 3r. multicoloured . . . 30 20

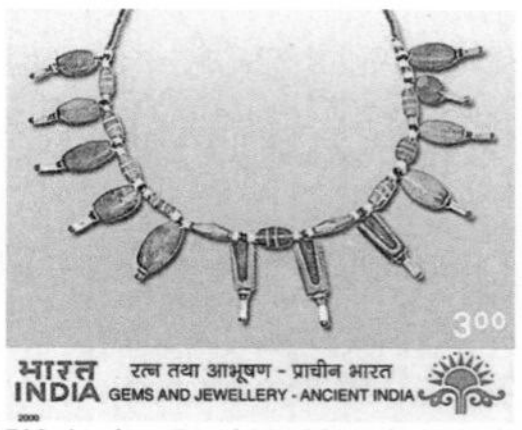
1513 Ancient Bead Necklace from Indus Valley

2000. "Indepex Asiana 2000" International Stamp Exhibition, Calcutta (3rd issue). Gems and Jewellery. Multicoloured.
1966 3r. Type **1513** 30 30
1967 3r. Gold necklace from Taxila 30 30
1968 3r. Turban ornament from Sarpech 30 30
1969 3r. Navaratna necklace . . 30 30
1970 3r. Bridal necklace from South India 30 30
1971 3r. Temple necklace from Rajasthan 30 30
MS1972 162 × 111 mm. Nos. 1966/7 and 1969/70 (sold at 15r.) . . . 1·60 1·75

1514 17th-century Marakkars Galley

2000. 400th Death Anniv of Admiral Kunjali IV Marakkars.
1973 **1514** 3r. multicoloured . . . 60 25

1515 Ustad Hafiz Ali Khan

2000. Ustad Hafiz Ali Khan (musician) Commemoration.
1974 **1515** 3r. multicoloured . . . 40 25

1516 Prithviraj Chauhan, King of Delhi

1518 Sane Guruji (writer)

1517 "St. Aloysius with Children" (painting)

2000. Historical Personalities. Multicoloured.
1975 3r. Type **1516** 35 35
1976 3r. Raja Bhamashah, Dewan of Mewar 35 35
1977 3r. Rajarshi Bhagyachandra, King of Manipur 35 35
1978 3r. General Zorawar Singh of Kashmir (horiz) . . . 35 35

2001. Centenary of Paintings in St. Aloysius College Chapel, Mangalore.
1979 **1517** 15r. multicoloured . . . 1·25 1·40

2001. Personalities. Multicoloured.
1980 3r. Type **1518** 35 35
1981 3r. E. M. S. Namboodiripad (Kerala politician) 35 35
1982 3r. Giani Gurmukh Singh Musafir (Punjab politician) 35 35
1983 3r. Prof. N. G. Ranga (social reformer) 35 35

1519 Sheel Bhadra Yajee

1520 Jubba Sahni

2001. Sheel Bhadra Yajee (patriot) Commemoration.
1984 **1519** 3r. multicoloured . . . 25 20

2001. Personalities. Multicoloured.
1985 3r. Type **1520** 25 25
1986 3r. Yogendra and Baikunth Shukla (patriot) 25 25

1521 Western Railway Building

2001. Western Railway Building, Churchgate, Mumbai.
1987 **1521** 15r. multicoloured . . . 1·00 1·10

1522 Census Emblem

2001. Census of India.
1988 **1522** 3r. multicoloured . . . 25 20

1523 *Tarangini* (cadet ship)

2001. International Fleet Review. Multicoloured.
1989 3r. Type **1523** 25 25
1990 3r. Maratha pal (sailing ship) 25 25
1991 3r. Maratha galbat (sailing ship) 25 25
1992 15r. Fleet Review logo . . . 1·00 1·10

1524 Rocks and Minerals

2001. 150th Anniv of Geological Survey of India.
1993 **1524** 3r. multicoloured . . . 25 20

1525 Soldier in Ceremonial Uniform and Himalaya Patrol

1526 Symbols of Jain Teaching

2001. Bicentenary of 4th Battalion, Maratha Light Infantry.
1994 **1525** 3r. multicoloured . . . 30 20

2001. 2600th Birth Anniv of Bhagwan Mahavira (Jain teacher).
1995 **1526** 3r. multicoloured . . . 30 20

1527 Yuri Gagarin and Rockets

2001. 40th Anniv of Man's First Space Flight.
1996 **1527** 15r. multicoloured . . . 1·00 1·10

1528 Frederic Chopin

2001. 190th Birth Anniv (2002) of Frederic Chopin (composer).
1997 **1528** 15r. multicoloured . . . 1·25 1·40

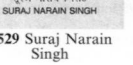

1529 Suraj Narain Singh

1530 B. P. Mandal

2001. Suraj Narain Singh (nationalist politician) Commemoration.
1998 **1529** 3r. multicoloured . . . 25 20

2001. B. P. Mandal (former Chief Minister of Bihar) Commemoration.
1999 **1530** 3r. multicoloured . . . 25 20

1531 Samanta Chandra Sekhar, Stars and Gola Yantra (instrument)

1532 "Sant Ravidas" (Phulan Runi)

2001. Samanta Chandra Sekhar (astronomer) Commemoration.
2000 **1531** 3r. black, vio & grn . . 25 20

2001. Sant Ravidas (philosopher-poet) Commem.
2001 **1532** 3r. multicoloured . . . 25 20

1533 Krishna Nath Sarmah

1535 Jhalkari Bai on Horseback

1534 Chandragupta Maurya

2001. Personalities. Multicoloured.
2002 4r. Type **1533** 40 40
2003 4r. C. Sankaran Nair (lawyer) 40 40
2004 4r. Syama Prasad Mookerjee (politician) 40 40
2005 4r. U Kiang Nongbah (guerilla leader) 40 40

2001. Emperor Chandragupta Maurya Commem.
2006 **1534** 4r. multicoloured . . . 30 30

2001. Jhalkari Bai (female warrior from Jhansi) Commemoration.
2007 **1535** 4r. multicoloured . . . 30 30

1536 *Fungia horrida* (coral)

2001. Corals. Multicoloured.
2008 4r. Type **1536** 20 20
2009 4r. *Acropora digitifera* . . . 20 20
2010 15r. *Montipora acquituberculata* 75 75
2011 45r. *Acropora formosa* . . . 1·75 2·25

1537 Dwarka Prasad Mishra

1538 Chaudhary Brahmparkash

2001. Birth Centenary of Dwarka Prasad Mishra (former Chief Minister of Madhya Pradesh).
2012 **1537** 4r. black and stone . . 25 20

2001. Chaudhary Brahmparkash (former Chief Minister of Delhi) Commemoration.
2013 **1538** 4r. black and blue . . . 25 20

1539 Revolution Monument, Shaheed Park, Ballia

1540 Jagdev Prasad

2001. 60th Anniv (2000) of August Revolution, Ballia.
2014 **1539** 4r. multicoloured . . . 25 20

2001. Jagdev Prasad (journalist and politician) Commemoration.
2015 **1540** 4r. multicoloured . . . 25 20

1541 Rani Avantibai

1542 Rao Tula Ram

2001. Rani Avantibai of Ramgarh Commemoration.
2016 **1541** 4r. multicoloured . . . 25 20

2001. Rao Tula Ram of Rewari (patriot) Commemoration.
2017 **1542** 4r. multicoloured . . . 25 20

1543 Chaudhary Devi Lal

1544 Satis Chandra Samanta

2001. Chaudhary Devi Lal (former Deputy Prime Minister) Commemoration.
2018 **1543** 4r. multicoloured . . . 25 20

2001. Satis Chandra Samanta (West Bengal politician) Commemoration.
2019 **1544** 4r. black and stone . . 25 20

1545 Sivaji Ganesan

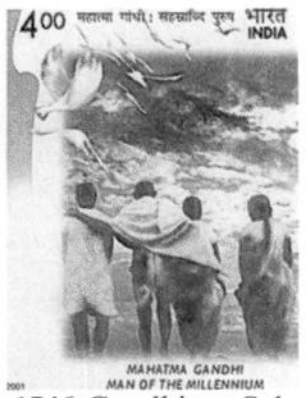
1546 Gandhi on Salt March

2001. Sivaji Ganesan (Tamil actor) Commemoration.
2020 **1545** 4r. multicoloured . . . 30 20

2001. "Mahatma Gandhi—Man of the Millennium". Multicoloured.
2021 4r. Type **1546** 30 30
2022 4r. Mahatma Gandhi . . . 30 30

1547 Bharathidsan (Tamil poet)

2001. Cultural Personalities. Each black, red and stone.
2023 4r. Type **1547** 25 25
2024 4r. Lachhu Maharaj (choreographer) 25 25
2025 4r. Master Mitrasen (writer) 25 25

1548 Jayaprakash Narayan

2001. Birth Centenary (2002) of Jayaprakash Narayan (socialist).
2026 **1548** 4r. multicoloured . . . 25 25

1549 Monkey in Tree and Crocodile

2001. Stories from "Panchatantra" (Indian fables). Multicoloured.
2027 4r. Type **1549** 20 25
2028 4r. Monkey on crocodile's back (29 × 39 mm) . . . 20 25
2029 4r. Lion and rabbit 20 25
2030 4r. Lion and rabbit at well (29 × 39 mm) 20 25
2031 4r. Snake attacking crows' eggs 20 25
2032 4r. Snake attacked by villagers (29 × 39 mm) . . 20 25
2033 4r. Geese and tortoise talking 20 25
2034 4r. Tortoise flying with geese (29 × 39 mm) 20 25

1550 Grocer selling Iodized Salt

1551 Thangal Kunju Musaliar

2001. Global Iodine Deficiency Disorders Day.
2035 **1550** 4r. multicoloured . . . 30 25

2001. Thangal Kunju Musaliar (industrialist and philanthropist) Commemoration.
2036 **1551** 4r. black and stone . . 30 25

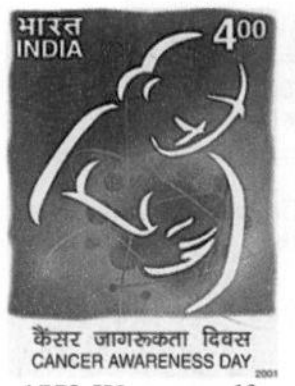
1552 Woman self-examining for Breast Cancer

1553 Maharajah Ranjit Singh

2001. Cancer Awareness Day.
2037 **1552** 4r. multicoloured . . . 30 25

2001. Bicentenary of Ranjit Singh's Coronation as Maharajah of the Punjab.
2038 **1553** 4r. multicoloured . . . 25 20

1554 Hands clasped around Globe

1556 Sobha Singh

1555 Dr. V. Shantaram and Film Scene

2001. Children's Day.
2039 **1554** 4r. multicoloured . . . 25 20

2001. Birth Centenary of Dr. V. Shantaram (film director).
2040 **1555** 4r. multicoloured . . . 25 20

2001. Birth Centenary of Sobha Singh (painter).
2041 **1556** 4r. multicoloured . . . 25 20

1557 Sun Temple, Konark

2001. Centenary of Conservation at Sun Temple, Konark. Multicoloured.
2042 4r. Type **1557** 25 20
2043 15r. Giant carved wheel, Sun Temple, Konark . . 1·00 1·25

1558 Handshake above Three Symbolic Figures

2001. International Year of Volunteers.
2044 **1558** 4r. multicoloured . . . 25 20

1559 Raj Kapoor and Film Characters

2001. Raj Kapoor (film actor and director) Commemoration.
2045 **1559** 4r. multicoloured . . . 50 25

1560 Digboi Refinery

2001. Centenary of Digboi Oil Refinery, Assam.
2046 **1561** 4r. multicoloured . . . 50 25

1561 Flowers, Fireworks and Christmas Tree

1562 Vijaya Raje Scindia

2001. Greetings. Multicoloured.
2047 3r. Type **1561** 30 20
2048 4r. Butterflies and flowers 40 35

2001. Vijaya Raje Scindia (politician and social reformer) Commemoration.
2049 **1562** 4r. multicoloured . . . 10 15

1563 Kedarnath Temple, Uttaranchal

2001. "Inpex-Empirepex 2001" National Stamp Exhibition. Temple Architecture.
2050 **1563** 4r. brown & lt brn . . 20 20
2051 – 4r. brown & lt brn . . 20 20
2052 – 4r. brown & lt brn . . 20 20
2053 – 15r. brown & lt brn . . 60 75
DESIGNS: No. 2051, Tryambakeshwar Temple, Maharashtra; 2052, Aundha Nagnath Temple, Maharashtra; 2053, Rameswaram Temple.

1564 Mine Winding Gear and Helmet in Hand

1565 Mount Everest and Climber

2002. Centenary of Directorate General of Mines Safety.
2054 **1564** 4r. multicoloured . . . 50 20

2002. Indian Army Expedition to Mt. Everest (2001).
2055 **1565** 4r. multicoloured . . . 50 20

1566 Gridhakuta Hills, Rajgir

2002. Bauddha Mahotsav Festival. Multicoloured.

2056	4r. Type **1566**	25	25
2057	4r. Dhamek Stupa, Sarnath	25	25
2058	8r. Mahaparinirvana Temple, Kushinagar . . .	50	50
2059	15r. Mahabodhi Temple, Bodhgaya	1·25	1·40

1567 Cartoon of Boy reading

2002. Year of Books.
2060 **1567** 4r. multicoloured . . . 50 20

1568 Swami Ramanand (mystic)

2002. Swami Ramanand (mystic) Commemoration.
2061 **1568** 4r. multicoloured . . . 50 20

1569 Tank and 19th-century Cannon

2002. Bicentenary of Indian Ordnance Factories.
2062 **1569** 4r. multicoloured . . . 50 20

1570 Sido and Kanhu Murmu

2002. Sido and Kanhu Murmu (Santal resistance fighters) Commemoration.
2063 **1570** 4r. multicoloured . . . 50 20

1571 First Railway Train, 1853

2002. 150th Anniv of Indian Railways.

2064	**1571** 15r. multicoloured . . .	1·00	1·10
MS2065	112 × 75 mm. No. 2064	1·00	1·25

1572 Kathakali Dancer (India)

2002. 50th Anniv of Diplomatic Relations between India and Japan. Multicoloured.

2066	15r. Type **1572**	95	1·00
2067	15r. Kabuki actor (Japan)	95	1·00
MS2068	100 × 70 mm. Nos. 2066/7	1·90	2·00

1573 Central Hall of Parliament, New Delhi

2002. 50th Anniv of Indian Parliament.
2069 **1573** 4r. gold 50 20

1574 Prabodhankar Thackeray

2002. Prabodhankar Thackeray (writer) Commemoration.
2070 **1574** 4r. black 50 20

1575 Cotton College, Guwahati

2002. Centenary of Cotton College (2001), Assam.
2071 **1575** 4r. purple and green . . 50 20

1576 P. L. Deshpande

2002. P. L. Deshpande (writer) Commemoration.
2072 **1576** 4r. multicoloured . . . 50 20

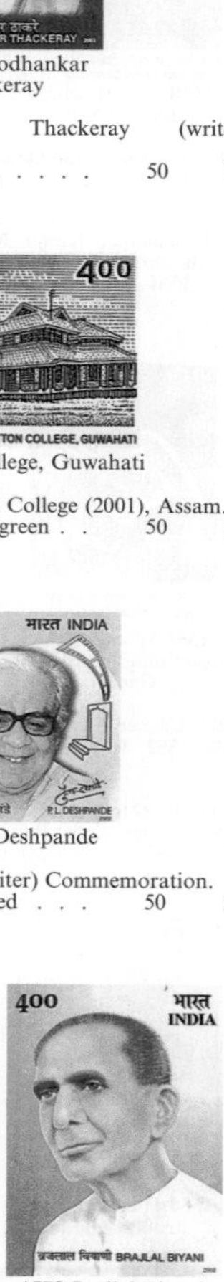

1577 Babu Gulabrai

1578 Brajlal Biyani

2002. Indian Literary Figures. Multicoloured.

2073	5r. Type **1577**	50	50
2074	5r. Pandit Vyas	50	50

2002. Brajlal Biyani (journalist and politician) Commemoration.
2075 **1578** 4r. multicoloured . . . 50 20

1579 Sree Thakur Satyananda

1580 Anna Bhau Sathe

2002. Sree Thakur Satyananda Commemoration.
2076 **1579** 5r. multicoloured . . . 55 35

2002. Anna Bhau Sathe (Marathi writer) Commemoration.
2077 **1580** 4r. black and grey . . . 50 20

1581 Anand Rishiji Maharaj

2002. 10th Death Anniv of Anand Rishiji Maharaj (Jain spiritual leader).
2078 **1581** 4r. multicoloured . . . 50 20

1582 Dr. Vithalrao Vikhe Patil

1583 Sant Tukaram

2002. Dr. Vithalrao Vikhe Patil (co-operative movement pioneer) Commemoration.
2079 **1582** 4r. multicoloured . . . 50 20

2002. Sant Tukaram (Marathi poet) Commemoration.
2080 **1583** 4r. multicoloured . . . 50 20

1584 Bhaurao Krishnarao Gaikwad

2002. Birth Centenary of Bhaurao Krishnarao Gaikwad (social reformer).
2081 **1584** 4r. multicoloured . . . 50 20

1585 Ayyan Kali

2002. Social Reformers. Multicoloured.

2082	5r. Type **1585**	40	50
2083	5r. Chandraprabha Saikiani	40	50
2084	5r. Gora	40	50

1586 Ananda Nilayam Vimanam, Tirumala

2002. 700th Anniv of Ananda Nilayam Vimanam Temple Tower, Tirumala.
2085 **1586** 15r. multicoloured . . . 1·00 1·10

1587 Kanika Bandopadhyay

2002. Kanika Bandopadhyay (singer) Commemoration.
2086 **1587** 5r. multicoloured . . . 55 35

1588 Arya Vaidya Sala, Kottakkal, and Vaidyaratnam Varier (founder)

2002. Centenary of Arya Vaidya Kottakkal Sala (Ayurvedic Medicine), Kottakkal.
2087 **1588** 5r. multicoloured . . . 70 70

1589 Bhagwan Baba

1590 Bihar Chamber of Commerce Logo

2002. Bhagwan Baba (mystic and philosopher) Commemoration.
2088 **1589** 5r. multicoloured . . . 70 70

2002. 75th Anniv (2001) of Bihar Chamber of Commerce.
2089 **1590** 4r. multicoloured . . . 60 40

1591 Asiatic Mangrove (*Rhizophora mucronata*)

2002. 8th Session of U.N. Conference on Climate Change, New Delhi. Mangroves. Multicoloured.

2090	5r. Type **1591**	30	30
2091	5r. Mangrove palm (*Nypa fruticans*)	30	30
2092	5r. Burma mangrove (*Bruguiera gymnorrhiza*)	30	30
2093	15r. Mangrove apple (*Sonneratia alba*)	1·10	1·25
MS2094	192 × 85 mm. Nos. 2090/3	1·75	1·90

1592 Swami Pranavananda

2002. Swami Pranavananda (social reformer) Commemoration.
2095 **159** 5r. multicoloured . . . . 1·00 1·00

1593 Vidhan Bhavan (State Assembly Building) and Samadhi (Buddhist Temple), Nagpur

2002. 300th Anniv of Nagpur.
2096 **1593** 5r. multicoloured . . . 70 70

1594 "Holi Festival" (Aakash Anand)

2002. Children's Day.
2097 **1594** 5r. multicoloured . . . 70 70

1595 Cane and Bamboo Ware

2002. Handicrafts. Multicoloured.
2098 5r. Type **1595** 40 45
2099 5r. Thewa ware (gold leaf work on coloured glass) 40 45
2100 5r. Patola fabric 40 45
2101 5r. Dhokra ornaments (metal casting) 40 45
MS2102 100 × 100 mm. Nos. 2098/101 . . . . 1·40 1·60

1596 Santidev Ghose

2002. Santidev Ghose (classical singer) Commemoration.
2103 **1596** 5r. multicoloured . . . 70 70

1597 Ajoy Kumar Mukherjee (leader) and Newspaper

2002. 60th Anniv of "National Government" of Tamluk (Tamralipta Jatiya Sarkar). Multicoloured.
2104 5r. Type **1597** 65 65
2105 5r. Matangini Hazra and demonstration 65 65

1598 Anglo Bengali Inter College, Allahabad

2002. Anglo-Bengali Inter College, Allahabad
2106 **1598** 5r. multicoloured . . . 15 20

1600 Dhirubhai H. Ambani

2002. Dhirubhai H. Ambani (industrialist) Commemoration.
2108 **1600** 5r. multicoloured . . . 15 20

1601 T. T. Krishnamachari

2002. T. T. Krishnamachari (Minister of Commerce and Industry, 1952–56, Finance Minister 1963–5) Commemoration.
2109 **1601** 5r. multicoloured . . . 15 20

1602 Golconda Fort

2002. Forts of Andrha Pradesh. Multicoloured.
2110 5r. Type **1602** 15 20
2111 5r. Palace, Chandragiri Fort 15 20

1603 Hindustan Aircraft Industries HT-2 Trainer, 1951

2003. Centenary of Powered Flight. Aero India 2003. Multicoloured.
2112 5r. Type **1603** 15 20
2113 5r. Hindustan Aircraft Industries Marut ground attack aircraft, 1961 . . . 15 20
2114 5r. Hindustan Aircraft Industries LCA light combat aircraft, 2001 . . 15 20
2115 15r. Hindustan Aircraft Industries Dhruv advanced light helicopter 40 45
MS2116 144 × 95 mm. Nos. 2112/15 85 1·00

1604 Ghantasala

2003. Ghantasala (singer and composer) Commemoration.
2117 **1604** 5r. brown and black . . 15 20

1605 S. L. Kirloskar and Cogwheels

2003. Birth Centenary of S. L. Kirloskar (industrialist).
2118 **1605** 5r. multicoloured . . . 15 20

1606 Kusumagraj

2003. Kusumagraj (Marathi poet) Commemoration.
2119 **1606** 5r. multicoloured . . . 15 20

1607 Sant Eknath **1608** Frank Anthony

2003. Sant Eknath (saint and poet) Commemoration.
2120 **1607** 5r. multicoloured . . . 15 20

2003. 10th Death Anniv of Frank Anthony (politician).
2121 **1608** 5r. multicoloured . . . 15 20

1609 Kakaji Maharaj **1610** *Commiphora wightii*

2003. Kakaji Maharaj (Swaminarayan spiritual leader and philosopher) Commemoration.
2122 **1609** 5r. multicoloured . . . 15 20

2003. Medicinal Plants of India. Multicoloured.
2123 5r. Type **1610** 15 20
2124 5r. *Bacopa monnieri* 15 20
2125 5r. *Emblica officinalis* . . . 15 20
2126 5r. *Withania somnifera* . . . 15 20
MS2127 130 × 80 mm. Nos. 2123/6 60 80

1611 Durga Das **1612** Kishore Kumar

2003. Durga Das (journalist and newspaper editor) Commemoration.
2128 **1611** 5r. multicoloured . . . 15 20

2003. "Golden Voices of Yesteryear". Multicoloured.
2129 5r. Type **1612** 15 20
2130 5r. Mukesh 15 20
2131 5r. Mohammed Rafi 15 20
2132 5r. Hemant Kumar 15 20
MS2133 89 × 105 mm. Nos. 2129/32 60 80

OFFICIAL STAMPS

1866. Optd **Service**.
O20 **11** ½a. blue . . . . 35·00 50
O 8 **12** 8p. mauve . . . . 20·00 50·00
O23 **11** 1a. brown . . . . 40·00 50
O27 2a. orange . . . . 5·00 2·25
O13 4a. green . . . . £190 75·00
O29 – 4a. green (No. 69) . . . . 3·00 1·50
O30 **11** 8a. red . . . . 3·25 1·50

1866. Fiscal stamp with head of Queen Victoria surch **SERVICE TWO ANNAS**.
O15 2a. purple £275 £225

1866. Fiscal stamps optd **SERVICE POSTAGE**.
O19 ½a. mauve on lilac . . . . . £400 85·00
O16 2a. purple £800 £400
O17 4a. purple £3250 £1100
O18 8a. purple £3750 £3750

1874. Optd **On H. M. S.** (Queen Victoria).
O31 **11** ½a. blue . . . . 11·00 20
O32 1a. brown . . . . 16·00 20
O33a 2a. orange . . . . 45·00 17·00
O34 – 4a. green (No. 69) . . . 16·00 3·00
O35 **11** 8a. red . . . . 7·50 5·00

1883. Queen Victoria stamps of 1882 and 1892 optd **On H. M. S.**
O37a **40** 3p. red 20 10
O39 **23** ½a. turquoise . . . . . . 1·50 10
O49 ½a. green . . . . 2·00 90
O41 – 1a. purple 75 10
O50 – 1a. red . . . . 3·00 10
O42 – 2a. blue . . . . 6·00 60
O51 – 2a. lilac . . . . 35·00 1·50
O44a – 4a. green . . . . 18·00 50
O46 – 8a. mauve . . . . 9·00 50
O48 **37** 1r. green and red . . . . 15·00 40

1902. King Edward VII stamps optd **On H. M. S.**
O54 **41** 3p. grey . . . . 2·50 75
O56 – ½a. green (No. 122) . . . 1·25 30
O57 – 1a. red (No. 123) . . . . 1·00 10
O59 – 2a. lilac . . . . 3·25 10
O60 – 4a. olive . . . . 12·00 30
O62 – 6a. bistre . . . . 1·50 15
O63 – 8a. mauve . . . . 6·00 1·00
O65 – 1r. green and red . . . . 4·00 80
O68 **52** 2r. red and orange . . . . 8·50 1·50
O69 5r. blue and violet . . . . 14·00 1·50
O70 10r. green and red . . . . 28·00 15·00
O71 15r. blue and olive . . . . 65·00 40·00
O72 25r. orange and blue . . . £140 60·00

1906. Nos. 149/50 optd **On H. M. S.**
O66 ½a. green . . . . 1·25 10
O67 1a. red . . . . 2·00 10

1912. King George V stamps optd **SERVICE**.
O109 **55** 3p. grey 15 10
O 76 **56** ½a. green 50 10
O 80 **57** 1a. red . . . . 1·00 10
O111 1a. brown 15 10
O 84 **59** 2a. mauve 75 30
O112 **70** 2a. lilac 30 10
O129 2a. red . . . . 1·00 2·50
O132 **63** 4a. olive . . . . 1·50 10
O113 **71** 4a. green 50 20
O 87 **64** 6a. bistre . . . . 1·50 2·50
O115 **65** 8a. mauve . . . . 1·25 10
O116 **66** 12a. red . . . . 70 2·50
O117 **67** 1r. brown and green . . . 3·25 1·00
O 92 2r. red and orange . . . 3·75 6·00
O 93 5r. blue and violet . . . 16·00 22·00
O 94 10r. green and red . . . 50·00 50·00
O 95 15r. blue and olive . . . 90·00 £100
O 96 25r. orange and blue . . . £200 £160

1921. No. O81 surch **NINE PIES**.
O97 **57** 9p. on 1a. red . . . . . . 1·25 75

1925. Nos. O70/2 surch in words.
O 99 **52** 1r. on 15r. blue and olive 4·25 4·00
O100 1r. on 25r. orange & blue 20·00 70·00
O101 2r. on 10r. green and red 3·75 4·25

1925. Nos. O94/6 surch in words.
O102 **67** 1r. on 15r. blue and olive 19·00 75·00
O103 1r. on 25r. orange & blue 5·00 11·00
O104 2r. on 10r. green and red £800

1926. No. O62 surch **ONE ANNA**.
O105 1a. on 6a. bistre 30 30

1926. Surch **SERVICE ONE ANNA** and two bars.
O106 **58** 1a. on 1¼a. brown (A) . . 20 10
O107 1a. on 1¼a. brown (B) . . 2·50 4·50
O108 **61** 1a. on 2a.6p. blue . . . 60 80

1932. Optd **SERVICE**.
O126 **79** ½a. green . . . . 1·00 10
O127 **80** 9p. green 30 15
O127b **81** 1a. brown . . . . . . 1·50 15
O128 **82** 1a.3p. mauve 30 10
O130a **59** 2a. red . . . . 1·25 10
O131 **61** 2a.6p. orange 50 10

1937. King George VI stamps optd **SERVICE**.
O135 **91** ½a. brown . . . . 17·00 70
O136 9p. green . . . . 19·00 80
O137 1a. red . . . . 3·50 10
O138 **93** 1r. slate and brown . . . 50 50
O139 2r. purple and brown . . 1·75 2·50
O140 5r. green and blue . . . 3·50 6·50
O141 10r. purple and red . . . 14·00 6·50

1939. King George V stamp surch **SERVICE 1A**.
O142 **82** 1a. on 1¼a. mauve . . . 12·00 20

O 20 King George VI **O 21** Asokan Capital

1939.
O143 **O 20** 3p. slate 50 10
O144 ½a. brown . . . . . 5·00 10
O144a ½a. purple 30 10
O145 9p. green 30 10
O146 1a. red 30 10
O146a 1a.3p. brown . . . . 3·25 70
O146b 1½a. violet 65 10
O147 2a. orange 60 10
O148 2½a. violet . . . . . 60 1·00
O149 4a. brown 60 10
O150 8a. violet 90 30

1948. 1st Anniv of Independence. Optd **SERVICE**.
O150a **305** 1½a. brown . . . . . 42·00 32·00
O150b 3½a. violet £750 £475
O150c 12a. green £2000 £1800
O150d – 10r. brown and red (No. 308) £12000

1950.
O151 **O 21** 3p. violet 15 10
O152 6p. brown 30 10
O153 9p. green . . . . . . 1·25 10
O154 1a. blue . . . . 1·25 10
O155 2a. red . . . . 1·75 10
O156 3a. red . . . . 4·00 2·25
O157 4a. purple . . . . . . 5·50 20
O158 4a. blue 50 10
O159 6a. violet . . . . . . 4·00 70
O160 8a. brown . . . . . . 2·00 10
O186 – 1r. violet 15 10
O187 – 2r. red 25 10
O188 – 5r. green 40 60
O189 – 10r. brown . . . . . 90 1·00
The rupee values are larger and with a different frame.

1957. Value in naye paise.
O175 **O 21** 1n.p. slate 10 10
O166 2n.p. violet 10 10
O167 3n.p. brown 10 10
O168 5n.p. green 10 10
O169 6n.p. turquoise 20 10
O180 10n.p. green 50 50
O170 13n.p. red 30 10
O182 15n.p. violet 10 10
O183 20n.p. red 70 10
O184 25n.p. blue 10 10
O185 50n.p. brown 70 10

O 23 **O 25** **O 26**

1967.

O200	O **23**	2p. violet	10	1·00
O201		3p. brown	40	1·25
O202		5p. green	10	10
O203		6p. blue	1·25	1·50
O204		10p. green	10	30
O205		15p. plum	10	30
O206		20p. red	10	30
O207		25p. red	11·00	3·75
O208		30p. blue	10	60
O209		50p. brown	10	60
O197		1r. purple	85	10

1971. Obligatory Tax. Refugee Relief. Optd **REFUGEE RELIEF** in English and Devanagari (No. O210) or in English only (No. O211).

O210	O **23**	5p. green	75	50
O211		5p. green	1·25	80
O213	O **25**	5p. green	20	20

See note below Nos. 646/51.

1976. Designs redrawn showing face-value in figures only and smaller Capital with Hindi motto beneath as Type O **26**.

O214	O **26**	2p. blue	20	1·25
O254		5p. green	10	10
O255		10p. green	10	10
O256		15p. purple	10	10
O257		20p. red	10	10
O258		25p. red	10	10
O259		30p. blue	10	10
O260		35p. violet	10	10
O268		40p. violet (17 × 19½ mm)	10	10
O269		50p. brown (17 × 19½ mm)	10	10
O263		60p. brown	10	10
O270		1r. purple (17 × 19½ mm)	10	10
O225b	–	2r. red	40	1·50
O226b	–	5r. green	60	2·25
O227	–	10r. red	1·25	3·50

The 2, 5 and 10r. values are larger.

O 27

O 28

1982. As 1977 and 1981 issue but with simulated perforations. Imperf.

O231	O **28**	5p. green	55	1·00
O232		10p. green	70	1·00
O233		15p. purple	70	1·00
O234		20p. red	75	1·00
O235		25p. red	1·50	2·00
O236		35p. violet	85	65
O237		50p. brown	1·50	1·50
O238		1r. brown	1·75	1·50
O239		2r. red	1·75	4·00
O240		5r. green	2·00	5·00
O241		10r. brown	2·50	7·00

1998. Redrawn with face value figures in bottom corners. Size 17 × 19½ mm.

O271	O **27**	2r. red	10	10
O272		5r. green	15	20
O273		10r. brown	30	35

(b) Size 16½ × 19 mm.

O273b	O **36**	50p. brown	10	10
O274	O **27**	1r. purple	10	10
O275		2r. red	10	10
O276		3r. orange	10	10
O278		5r. green	15	20
O279		10r. brown	25	30

INDIAN CUSTODIAN FORCES IN KOREA Pt. 1

Stamps used by the Indian Forces on custodian duties in Korea in 1953.

12 pies = 1 anna; 16 annas = 1 rupee.

भारतीय
संरक्षा कटक
कोरिया
(K 1)

1953. Stamps of India (archaeological series) optd with Type K **1**.

K 1	**307**	3p. violet	1·75	4·50
K 2	**308**	6p. brown	1·50	4·50
K 3	–	9p. green	1·75	4·50
K 4	–	1a. blue (B)	1·50	4·50
K 5	–	2a. red	1·50	4·50
K 6	–	2½a. lake	1·50	4·75
K 7	–	3a. salmon	1·50	4·75
K 8	**314**	4a. blue	1·75	4·75
K 9	**315**	6a. violet	8·50	9·00
K10	–	8a. green	1·75	9·00
K11	–	12a. blue	2·25	17·00
K12	–	1r. violet and green	3·00	17·00

INDIAN EXPEDITIONARY FORCES Pt. 1

Stamps used by Indian Forces during, and after, the War of 1914–18.

12 pies = 1 anna; 16 annas = 1 rupee.

1914. Stamps of India (King George V) optd **I. E. F.**

E 1	**55**	3p. grey	15	30
E 2	**56**	½a. green	50	30
E 3	**57**	1a. red	1·25	30
E 5	**59**	2a. lilac	1·25	30
E 6	**61**	2a.6p. blue	1·50	3·50
E 7	**62**	3a. orange	1·00	1·50
E 8	**63**	4a. olive	1·00	1·50
E 9	**65**	8a. mauve	1·25	2·50
E11	**66**	12a. red	2·25	6·00
E13	**67**	1r. brown and green	2·50	4·00

INDIAN FORCES IN INDO-CHINA Pt. 1

Stamps used by Indian Forces engaged in the International Commission in Indo-China.

1954. 12 pies = 1 anna; 16 annas = 1 rupee.
1957. 100 naye paise = 1 rupee.
1964. 100 paisa = 1 rupee.

अन्तर्राष्ट्रीय आयोग कम्बोज (N 1) — अन्तर्राष्ट्रीय आयोग लाओस (N 2) — अन्तर्राष्ट्रीय आयोग वियत नाम (N 3)

1954. Stamps of India (archaeological series) overprinted. (a) Optd with Type N **1** for use in Cambodia.

N1	**307**	3p. violet	1·25	9·00
N2	–	1a. blue (B)	90	75
N3	–	2a. red	90	80
N4	–	8a. green	1·50	3·00
N5	–	12a. blue	1·50	3·00

(b) Optd with Type N **2** for use in Laos.

N 6	**307**	3p. violet	1·25	9·00
N 7	–	1a. blue (B)	90	75
N 8	–	2a. red	90	80
N 9	–	8a. green	1·50	3·00
N10	–	12a. blue	1·50	3·00

(c) Optd with Type N **3** for use in Vietnam.

N11	**307**	3p. violet	1·25	9·00
N12	–	1a. blue (B)	90	75
N13	–	2a. red	90	80
N14	–	8a. green	1·50	3·00
N15	–	12a. blue	1·50	3·00

1957. Map type of India overprinted. (a) Optd with Type N **1** for use in Cambodia.

N16	**361**	2n.p. brown	75	30
N17		6n.p. grey	50	30
N18		13n.p. red	70	40
N19		50n.p. orange	2·25	1·25
N20		75n.p. purple	2·25	1·25

(b) Optd with Type N **2** for use in Laos.

N21	**361**	2n.p. brown	75	30
N39		3n.p. brown	10	20
N40		5n.p. green	10	15
N22		6n.p. grey	50	30
N23		13n.p. red	70	40
N24		50n.p. orange	2·25	1·25
N25		75n.p. purple	2·25	1·25

(c) Optd with Type N **3** for use in Vietnam.

N43	**361**	1n.p. turquoise	10	20
N26		2n.p. brown	75	30
N45		3n.p. brown	10	20
N46		5n.p. green	10	15
N27		6n.p. grey	50	30
N28		13n.p. red	70	40
N29		50n.p. orange	2·25	1·25
N30		75n.p. purple	2·25	1·25

1965. Children's Day stamp of India optd **ICC** for use in Laos and Vietnam.

N49	**469**	15p. slate	60	3·25

1968. Nos. 504/6, 509/10, 515 and 517/18, of India optd **ICC** in English and Devanagari, for use in Laos and Vietnam.

N50	–	2p. brown	10	2·75
N51	–	3p. olive	10	2·75
N52	–	5p. red	10	1·00
N53	–	10p. blue	1·75	2·00
N54	**467**	15p. green	60	2·00
N55	–	60p. grey	35	1·25
N56	–	1r. brown and plum	50	2·00
N57	–	2r. blue and violet	1·25	8·50

INDIAN U.N. FORCE IN CONGO Pt. 1

Stamps used by Indian Forces attached to the United Nations Force in Congo.

100 naye paise = 1 rupee.

1962. Map type of India optd **U.N. FORCE (INDIA) CONGO**.

U1	**361**	1n.p. turquoise	1·00	2·75
U2		2n.p. brown	1·00	1·00
U3		5n.p. green	1·00	70
U4		8n.p. turquoise	1·00	40
U5		13n.p. red	1·00	40
U6		50n.p. orange	1·00	70

INDIAN U.N. FORCE IN GAZA (PALESTINE) Pt. 1

Stamps used by Indian Forces attached to the United Nations Force in Gaza.

100 paise = 1 rupee.

1965. Children's Day stamp of India optd **UNEF**.

G1	**449**	15p. slate	1·75	6·50

INDO-CHINA Pt. 6

A French territory in south-east Asia. In 1949 it was split up into the three states of Vietnam, Cambodia and Laos.

1889. 100 centimes = 1 franc.
1918. 100 cents = 1 piastre.

1889. Stamp of French Colonies, "Commerce" type, surch. (a) **INDO-CHINE 1889 5 R-D**.

1	J	5 on 35c. black on orange	70·00	60·00

(b) **INDO-CHINE 89 5 R D**.

2	J	5 on 35c. black on orange	11·00	9·25

1892. "Tablet" key-type inscr "INDO-CHINE" in red (1, 5, 15, 25, 50 (No. 27), 75c., 1f.) or blue (others).

6	D	1c. black on blue	85	30
7		2c. brown on buff	1·75	1·75
8		4c. brown on grey	1·60	2·25
23		5c. green	3·00	80
10		10c. black on lilac	3·00	90
24		10c. red	4·00	35
11		15c. blue	32·00	30
25		15c. grey	8·00	35
12		20c. red on green	8·00	2·25
13		25c. black on pink	13·00	1·10
26		25c. blue	23·00	60
14		30c. brown on drab	19·00	6·00
15		40c. red on yellow	29·00	7·25
16		50c. red on pink	30·00	9·25
27		50c. brown on blue	15·00	2·75
17		75c. brown on orange	23·00	17·00
18		1f. green	42·00	19·00
19		5f. mauve on lilac	£100	85·00

1903. Surch.

28	D	5 on 15c. grey	45	1·25
29		15c. on 25c. blue	95	65

8 "Grasset" type

1904.

30	**8**	1c. green	20	15
31		2c. purple on yellow	30	15
32		4c. mauve on blue	30	15
33		5c. green	1·75	15
34		10c. pink	2·50	15
35		15c. brown on blue	2·50	20
36		20c. red on green	3·25	40
37		25c. blue	17·50	30
38		30c. brown on cream	6·75	2·00
39		35c. black on yellow	18·00	1·10
40		40c. black on grey	5·00	85
41		50c. brown	6·75	1·10
42		75c. red on orange	35·00	19·00
43		1f. green	21·00	3·50
44		2f. brown on yellow	45·00	27·00
45		5f. violet	£180	£140
46		10f. red on green	£160	£140

10 Annamite

11 Cambodian

12 Cambodian

1907.

51	**10**	1c. black and sepia	55	15
52		2c. black and brown	15	15
53		4c. black and blue	20	55
54		5c. black and green	2·75	20
55		10c. black and red	2·75	15
56		15c. black and violet	2·75	30
57	**11**	20c. black and violet	3·25	2·00
58		25c. black and blue	7·00	15
59		30c. black and brown	9·25	5·75
60		35c. black and green	3·25	20
61		40c. black and brown	4·00	2·50
62		45c. black and orange	12·00	5·25
63		50c. black and red	17·00	1·75
64	**12**	75c. black and orange	10·00	5·50
65	–	1f. black and red	48·00	9·50
66	–	2f. black and green	16·00	16·00
67	–	5f. black and blue	48·00	28·00
68	–	10f. black and violet	85·00	80·00

DESIGNS—As Type **12**: 1f. Annamites; 2f. Muong; 5f. Laotian; 10f. Cambodian.

1912. Surch in figures.

69	**8**	05 on 4c. mauve on blue	4·25	4·75
70		05 on 15c. brown on blue	50	20
71		05 on 30c. brown on cream	55	2·25
72		10 on 40c. black on grey	1·60	3·00
73		10 on 50c. brown	1·10	2·50
74		10 on 75c. red on orange	4·00	5·50

1914. Red Cross. Surch **5c** and cross.

76	**10**	5c.+5c. black and green	35	2·50
77		10c.+5c. black and red	45	30
78		15c.+5c. black and violet	1·25	3·00

1918. Nos. 75/6 and 78 further surch in figures and words.

79	**10**	4c. on 5c.+5c. blk & grn	3·25	5·50
80		6c. on 10c.+5c. black and red	2·75	5·00
81		8c. on 15c.+5c. blk & vio	10·00	17·00

1919. French stamps of "War Orphans" issue surch **INDOCHINE** and value in figures and words.

82	**23**	10c. on 15c.+10c. grey	2·50	3·50
83		16c. on 25c.+15c. blue	6·00	7·00
84	–	24c. on 35c.+25c. violet and grey	7·00	12·00
85	–	40c. on 50c.+50c. brown	14·00	23·00
86	**26**	80c. on 1f.+1f. red	23·00	35·00
87		4p. on 5f.+5f. blue & blk	£225	£225

1919. Surch in figures and words.

88	**10**	$\frac{2}{5}$c. on 1c. black and sepia	1·75	20
89		$\frac{4}{5}$c. on 2c. black and brown	1·60	35
90		$1\frac{3}{5}$c. on 4c. black and blue	3·50	25
91		2c. on 5c. black and green	2·50	20
92		4c. on 10c. black and red	1·25	15
93		6c. on 15c. black and violet	3·75	20
94	**11**	8c. on 20c. black and violet	4·00	90
95		10c. on 25c. black and blue	4·00	15
96		12c. on 30c. black & brown	6·00	1·00
97		14c. on 35c. black & green	3·25	55
98		16c. on 40c. black & brown	6·00	45
99		18c. on 45c. black & orange	7·50	2·50
100		20c. on 50c. black and red	10·50	1·10
101	**12**	30c. on 75c. black & orange	13·00	1·75
102	–	40c. on 1f. black and red	18·00	95
103	–	80c. on 2f. black and green	16·00	6·50
104	–	2p. on 5f. black and blue	85·00	70·00
105	–	4p. on 10f. black and violet	£120	£120

1922. As T **10** and **11** but value in cents or piastres.

115	**10**	$\frac{1}{10}$c. red and grey	15	90
116		$\frac{1}{5}$c. black and blue	15	15
117		$\frac{2}{5}$c. black and brown	20	1·00
118		$\frac{4}{5}$c. black and mauve	25	30
119		1c. black and brown	75	15
120		2c. black and green	30	15
121		3c. black and violet	40	20
122		4c. black and orange	90	15
123		5c. black and red	35	15
124	**11**	6c. black and red	50	20
125		7c. black and green	1·75	20
126		8c. black on lilac	1·40	65
127		9c. black and yellow	70	85
128		10c. black and blue	1·25	20
129		11c. black and violet	2·00	20
130		12c. black and brown	70	25
131		15c. black and orange	1·25	30
132		20c. black and blue	1·40	1·60
133		40c. black and red	2·25	2·00
134		1p. black and green	6·50	7·25
135		2p. black & purple on pink	10·50	11·00

22 Ploughman and Tower of Confucius

23 Bay of Along

24 Ruins of Angkor

1927.

136	**22**	$\frac{1}{10}$c. olive	15	2·75
137		$\frac{1}{5}$c. yellow	15	2·50
138		$\frac{2}{5}$c. blue	20	2·75
139		$\frac{4}{5}$c. brown	25	2·00
140		1c. orange	45	15
141		2c. green	60	20
142		3c. blue	1·40	20
143		4c. mauve	2·25	3·00
144		5c. violet	95	15
145	**23**	6c. red	1·50	20
146		7c. brown	1·25	1·25
147		8c. olive	1·75	2·75
148		9c. purple	2·25	2·75
149		10c. blue	2·25	40
150		11c. orange	1·75	2·75
151		12c. grey	1·75	2·50
152	**24**	15c. brown and red	10·00	9·00
153		20c. grey and violet	4·50	65
154	–	25c. mauve and brown	5·75	6·00
155	–	30c. olive and blue	3·50	4·00
156	–	40c. blue and red	5·25	4·25
157	–	50c. grey and green	6·25	3·00
158	–	1p. black, yellow and blue	12·00	12·00
159	–	2p. blue, orange and red	22·00	15·00

DESIGNS—As T **24**: 25, 30c. Wood-carver; 40, 50c. Temple, Thuat-Luong; 1, 2p. Founding of Saigon.

1931. "Colonial Exn" key-types inscr "INDOCHINE" and surch with new value.

160	F	4c. on 50c. mauve	3·00	3·50
161	G	6c. on 90c. red	3·25	4·25
162	H	10c. on 1f.50 blue	4·50	3·75

33 Junk

36 "Apsara", or dancing Nymph

1931.

163	**33**	$\frac{1}{10}$c. blue	15	2·00
164		$\frac{1}{5}$c. red	15	90
165		$\frac{2}{5}$c. orange	15	2·75
166		$\frac{1}{2}$c. brown	20	30
167		$\frac{4}{5}$c. violet	20	2·75
168		1c. brown	20	20
169		2c. green	35	20
170	–	3c. brown	20	20
171	–	3c. green	6·25	45
172	–	4c. blue	2·50	20
173	–	4c. green	1·40	2·50
174	–	4c. yellow	15	35
175	–	5c. purple	20	15
176	–	5c. green	45	2·50
177	–	6c. red	20	20
178	–	7c. black	20	20
179	–	8c. red	70	1·50
180	–	9c. black on yellow	20	85
181	–	10c. blue	1·10	20
182	–	10c. blue on pink	35	20
183	–	15c. brown	7·25	1·50
184	–	15c. blue	20	40
185	–	18c. blue	40	2·50
186	–	20c. red	20	15
187	–	21c. green	35	40
188	–	22c. green	50	1·50
189	–	25c. purple	3·00	1·25
190	–	25c. blue	85	1·50
191	–	30c. brown	75	20
192	**36**	50c. brown	90	15
193		60c. purple	50	20
194		70c. blue	85	1·10
195		1p. green	45	40
196		2p. red	55	50

DESIGNS—As Type **33**: 3c. to 9c. Ruins at Angkor; 10c. to 30c. Worker in rice field.

42 Farman F.190 Mail Plane

44 Emperor Bao Dai of Annam

1933. Air.

197	**42**	1c. brown	20	1·60
198		2c. green	15	1·25
199		5c. green	70	1·50
200		10c. brown	55	50
201		11c. red	1·60	2·25
202		15c. blue	2·25	1·60

203	16c. mauve	1·10	2·75
204	20c. green	2·50	1·25
205	30c. brown	65	30
206	36c. red	3·00	50
207	37c. green	80	30
208	39c. green	65	3·00
209	60c. purple	1·60	1·40
210	66c. green	2·00	1·75
211	67c. blue	75	2·75
212	69c. blue	65	3·00
213	1p. black	30	15
214	2p. orange	60	20
215	5p. violet	2·75	95
216	10p. red	4·75	2·75
217	20p. green	15·00	6·25
218	30p. brown	17·00	7·25

1936. Issue for Annam.

219 **44**	1c. brown	75	2·50
220	2c. green	1·00	2·75
221	4c. violet	1·25	45
222	5c. lake	1·60	3·00
223	10c. red	2·50	3·25
224	15c. blue	3·00	3·25
225	20c. red	2·75	3·50
226	30c. purple	2·50	3·25
227	50c. green	3·75	3·75
228	1p. mauve	6·00	6·25
229	2p. black	6·25	7·25

45 King Sisowath Monivong of Cambodia

46 Pres. Doumer

1936. Issue for Cambodia.

230 **45**	1c. brown	1·50	2·25
231	2c. green	1·60	2·25
232	4c. violet	1·60	2·25
233	5c. lake	2·25	3·00
234	10c. red	3·25	3·75
235	15c. blue	3·50	3·75
236	20c. red	2·75	3·50
237	30c. purple	3·00	3·50
238	50c. green	3·25	3·00
239	1p. mauve	3·75	3·00
240	2p. black	3·25	5·25

1937. Int Exn, Paris. As T **58a** of Guadeloupe.

241	2c. violet	65	3·00
242	3c. green	70	2·50
243	4c. red	30	1·00
244	6c. brown	50	45
245	9c. red	50	65
246	15c. blue	75	1·25
MS246a	120×100 mm. 30c. slate-lilac (as T **7**)	7·50	14·00

1938. Opening of Trans-Indo-China Railway.

247 **46**	5c. red (postage)	90	40
248	6c. brown	1·00	25
249	18c. blue	1·75	50
250	37c. orange (air)	25	25

1938. International Anti-cancer Fund. As T **58b** of Guadeloupe.

251	18c.+5c. blue	3·00	16·00

1939. New York World's Fair. As T **58c** of Guadeloupe.

252	13c. red	1·25	2·25
253	23c. blue	1·75	2·75

47 Mot Cot Pagoda, Hanoi

48 King Sihanouk of Cambodia

1939. San Francisco International Exhibition.

254 **47**	6c. sepia	1·50	1·50
255	9c. red	55	50
256	23c. blue	55	1·90
257	39c. purple	1·90	2·25

1939. 150th Anniv of French Revolution. As T **58d** of Guadeloupe.

258	6c.+2c. green & blk (postage)	7·25	14·00
259	7c.+3c. brown and black	7·25	14·00
260	9c.+4c. orange and black	9·50	14·00
261	13c.+10c. red and black	7·75	14·00
262	23c.+20c. blue and black	7·75	14·00
263	39c.+40c. black & orge (air)	18·00	35·00

1941. Coronation of King of Cambodia. No gum.

264 **48**	1c. orange	60	2·75
265	6c. violet	3·25	4·00
266	25c. blue	24·00	29·00

49 Processional Elephant

51 Hanoi University

1942. Fetes of Nam-Giao. No gum.

267 **49**	3c. brown	2·50	3·25
268	6c. red	3·00	3·00

1942. No. 189 surch **10 cents** and bars.

269	10c. on 25c. purple	2·00	2·50

1942. University Fund. No gum.

270 **51**	6c.+2c. red	50	3·00
271	15c.+5c. purple	55	2·50

Surch **10c +2 c**.

272 **51**	10c.+2c. on 6c.+2c. red	40	3·00

53 Marshal Petain

54 Shield and Sword

1942. No gum.

273 **53**	1c. brown	35	2·25
274	3c. brown	1·25	2·50
275	6c. red	25	1·40
276	10c. green	30	1·60
277	40c. blue	65	2·50
278	40c. grey	55	70

1942. National Relief Fund. No gum.

279 **54**	6c.+2c. red and blue	85	2·50
280	15c.+5c. black, red & bl.	45	40

Surch **10c +2 c**.

281 **54**	10c.+2c. on 6c.+2c. red and blue	40	2·75

55 Emperor Bao Dai of Annam

56 King Sihanouk of Cambodia

57 Empress Nam-Phaong of Annam

58 King Sisavang-Vong of Laos

1942. No gum.

282 **55**	½c. purple	30	3·25
283 **56**	1c. purple	35	2·50
284 **58**	1c. brown	40	2·25
285 **55**	6c. red	2·00	2·50
286 **56**	6c. red	45	1·90
287 **57**	6c. red	55	1·10
288 **58**	6c. red	35	2·25

59 Saigon Fair

60 Alexandre Yersin

1942. Saigon Fair. No gum.

289 **59**	6c. red	40	2·75

1943. No gum.

290 **60**	6c. red	65	3·00
291	15c. purple	35	2·25
292 –	15c. purple	35	1·90
293 –	20c. red	60	60
294 –	30c. brown	35	30
295 **60**	$1 green	40	30

DESIGNS—HORIZ: Nos. 292, 294, Alexandre de Rhodes; No. 293, Pigneau de Behaire, Bishop of Adran.

63 Do Huu-Vi

1943. Airmen. No gum.

296 **63**	6c.+2c. red	40	2·75
297 –	6c.+2c. red	45	2·50

Surch **10c +2 c**.

298 **63**	10c.+2c. on 6c.+2c. red	20	2·75
299 –	10c.+2c. on 6c.+2c. red	35	2·75

DESIGN—VERT: Nos. 297, 299, Roland Garros.

64 Doudart de Lagree

66 "Family, Homeland and Labour"

1943. Sailors. No gum.

300 **64**	1c. brown	15	40
301 A	1c. brown	45	2·00
302 B	1c. brown	35	2·50
303	5c. brown	25	1·60
304 C	6c. red	1·90	70
305 D	6c. red	75	2·50
306 E	6c. red	35	2·50
307 F	10c. green	25	2·25
308 **64**	15c. purple	35	2·50
309 F	20c. red	35	1·90
310 **64**	40c. blue	25	1·50
311 F	1p. green	40	2·75

DESIGNS—HORIZ: A, Francis Garnier; B, La Grandiere; C, Courbet; D, Rigault de Genouilly. VERT: E, Chasseloup Laubat; F, Charner.

1943. 3rd Anniv of National Revolution. No gum.

312 **66**	6c. red	40	95

67 De Lanessan

1944. Governors. No gum.

313 G	1c. brown	35	2·50
314 **67**	1c. brown	35	2·50
315 H	2c. mauve	25	2·25
316 J	4c. orange	20	60
317 H	4c. brown	25	50
318 K	5c. purple	40	2·25
319 J	10c. green	35	1·10
320 H	10c. green	25	2·00
321 K	10c. green	25	1·90
322 G	10c. green	45	95
323 **67**	15c. purple	60	1·25

DESIGNS—HORIZ: G, Van Vollenhoven; J, Auguste Pavie. VERT: H, Paul Doumer; K, Pierre Pasquier.

69 Athlete

1944. Juvenile Sports. No gum.

324 **69**	10c. purple and yellow	95	1·10
325	50c. red	90	3·25

70 Orleans Cathedral

1944. Martyr Cities. No gum.

326 **70**	15c.+60c. purple	60	3·25
327	40c.+1p.10 blue	70	3·50

1945. As T **149** of France surch **INDOCHINE** and values.

328	50c.+50c. on 2f. olive	50	3·00
329	1p.+1p. on 2f. brown	60	2·75
330	2p.+2p. on 2f. grey	1·00	3·00

1946. Air. Victory. As T **63b** of Guadeloupe.

331	80c. orange	30	1·10

1946. Air. From Chad to the Rhine. As T **63c** of Guadeloupe.

332	50c. green	2·00	3·25
333	1p. mauve	1·75	3·25
334	1p.50 red	1·50	3·25
335	2p. purple	1·90	3·25
336	2p.50 blue	1·90	3·50
337	5p. red	2·25	3·50

1946. Unissued stamps similar to T **24** with portrait of Marshal Petain optd with **R F** monogram.

338	10c. red	40	2·75
339	25c. blue	3·00	3·25

1949. Air. 75th Anniv of U.P.U. As T **39** of French Equatorial Africa.

340	3p. multicoloured	2·75	3·25

OFFICIAL STAMPS

1933. Stamps of 1931 (Nos. 168, etc.) optd **SERVICE**.

O197	1c. sepia	2·50	30
O198	2c. green	2·75	2·75
O199	3c. brown	2·50	2·75
O200	4c. blue	3·00	2·50
O201	5c. purple	2·75	25
O202	6c. red	1·50	2·75
O203	10c. blue	50	40
O204	15c. sepia	2·50	85
O205	20c. red	3·00	45
O206	21c. green	1·60	3·25
O207	25c. purple	1·25	3·50
O208	30c. brown	3·00	2·25
O209	50c. sepia	14·00	4·75
O210	60c. purple	1·25	3·00
O211	1p. green	42·00	12·00
O212	2p. red	10·00	13·00

1934. As T **11** but value in "CENTS" or "PIASTRES" and optd **SERVICE**.

O219	1c. brown	85	1·40
O220	2c. brown	1·00	1·75
O221	3c. green	2·25	2·25
O222	4c. red	3·50	75
O223	5c. orange	1·00	30
O224	6c. red	5·25	7·25
O225	10c. green	3·00	4·50
O226	15c. blue	2·50	3·00
O227	20c. green	3·25	2·50
O228	21c. violet	9·50	11·00
O229	25c. purple	10·00	8·75
O230	30c. violet	3·25	2·75
O231	50c. mauve	8·00	12·00
O232	60c. grey	13·00	13·00
O233	1p. blue	28·00	16·00
O234	2p. red	40·00	35·00

PARCEL POST STAMPS

1891. Stamp of French Colonies, "Commerce" type, optd **INDO-CHINE TIMBRE COLIS POSTAUX**.

P4 J	10c. black on lilac	15·00	4·25

1898. No. 10 optd **Colis Postaux**.

P20 D	10c. black on lilac	17·00	26·00

1899. Nos. 10 and 24 optd **TIMBRE COLIS POSTAUX**.

P21 D	10c. black on lilac	48·00	23·00
P22	10c. red	40·00	17·00

POSTAGE DUE STAMPS

1904. Postage Due stamps of French Colonies optd with value in figures.

D48 U	5 on 40c. black	30·00	11·00
D47	5 on 60c. brown on yellow	8·00	10·00
D49	10 on 60c. black	30·00	16·00
D50	30 on 60c. black	30·00	12·00

D **13** Annamite Dragon

D **28** Mot Cot Pagoda Hanoi

D **29** Annamite Dragon

1908.

D69 D **13**	2c. black	1·40	45
D70	4c. blue	40	80
D71	5c. green	1·40	25
D72	10c. red	3·00	20
D73	15c. violet	2·75	4·00
D74	20c. brown	1·75	90
D75	30c. olive	2·25	2·75
D76	40c. purple	7·00	8·00
D77	50c. blue	3·50	1·25
D78	60c. yellow	9·00	13·00
D79	1f. grey	19·00	23·00

D80 2f. brown 19·00 19·00
D81 5f. red 35·00 32·00

1919. Surch in figures and words.
D106 D 13 ⅘c. on 2c. black 1·90 2·75
D107 1⅗c. on 4c. blue 1·90 3·25
D108 2c. on 5c. green 3·25 1·25
D109 4c. on 10c. red 3·00 25
D110 6c. on 15c. violet 6·75 3·25
D111 8c. on 20c. brown 6·50 1·25
D112 12c. on 30c. green 8·25 2·00
D113 16c. on 40c. brown 6·00 1·90
D114 20c. on 50c. blue 13·00 7·50
D115 24c. on 60c. yellow 3·75 65
D116 40c. on 1f. grey 4·00 3·25
D117 80c. on 2f. brown 25·00 23·00
D118 2p. on 5f. red 48·00 28·00

1922. Type D 13, but values in cents or piastres.
D136 D 13 ⅖c. black 15 85
D137 ⅘c. black and red 15 2·00
D138 1c. black and yellow 40 50
D139 2c. black and green 1·40 65
D140 3c. black and violet 2·00 1·90
D141 4c. black and orange 1·60 2·00
D142 6c. black and olive 1·75 1·60
D143 8c. black on lilac 1·60 90
D144 10c. black and blue 1·60 1·25
D145 12c. blk & orge on grn 1·75 35
D146 20c. black & bl on yell 1·75 2·25
D147 40c. blk & red on grey 1·75 2·00
D148 1p. black & pur on pk 4·25 3·50

1927.
D160 D 28 ⅖c. orange and purple 15 2·25
D161 ⅘c. black and violet 15 2·25
D162 1c. grey and red 1·60 1·90
D163 2c. olive and green 1·25 40
D164 3c. blue and purple 1·00 2·75
D165 4c. brown and blue 1·40 40
D166 6c. red and scarlet 2·50 3·25
D167 8c. violet and brown 2·50 3·00
D168 D 29 10c. blue 1·60 2·50
D169 12c. brown 4·50 5·00
D170 20c. red 3·50 3·00
D171 40c. green 4·00 4·00
D172 1p. red 16·00 19·00

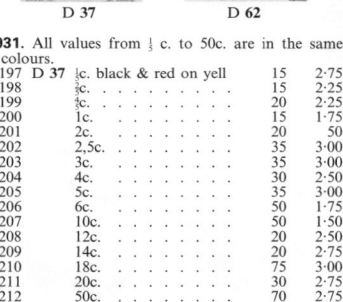

D 37

D 62

1931. All values from ⅕ c. to 50c. are in the same colours.
D197 D 37 ⅕c. black & red on yell 15 2·75
D198 ⅖c. 15 2·25
D199 ½c. 20 2·25
D200 1c. 15 1·75
D201 2c. 20 50
D202 2,5c. 35 3·00
D203 3c. 35 3·00
D204 4c. 30 2·50
D205 5c. 35 3·00
D206 6c. 50 1·75
D207 10c. 50 1·50
D208 12c. 50 2·50
D209 14c. 20 2·75
D210 18c. 75 3·00
D211 20c. 30 2·75
D212 50c. 70 2·75
D213 1p. blue and red on yell 2·00 3·50

1943.
D296 D 62 1c. red on yellow 45 3·00
D297 2c. red on yellow 1·00 3·00
D298 3c. red on yellow 80 3·00
D299 4c. red on yellow 40 3·00
D300 6c. red on yellow 90 3·00
D301 10c. red on yellow 1·10 2·75
D302 12c. blue on pink 40 3·00
D303 20c. blue on pink 40 2·75
D304 30c. blue on pink 1·75 3·00

INDO-CHINESE POST OFFICES IN CHINA Pt. 6, Pt. 17

General Issues.

100 centimes = 1 franc.

1902. Stamps of Indo-China, "Tablet" key-type, surch **CHINE** and value in Chinese.
15 D 1c. black on blue 1·40 1·60
2 2c. brown on buff 4·25 4·25
17 4c. brown on grey 2·50 3·75
18 5c. green 3·00 3·25
5 10c. red 3·25 4·25
6 15c. grey 6·50 6·25
20 20c. red on green 5·25 6·50
21 25c. black on pink 7·00 10·00
22 25c. blue 7·50 6·75
23 30c. brown on drab 4·00 5·75
24 40c. red on yellow 23·00 24·00
11 50c. red on pink 65·00 55·00
25 50c. brown on blue 9·50 10·50
26 75c. brown on orange 24·00 27·00
27 1f. green 30·00 38·00
28 5f. mauve on lilac 80·00 70·00

1904. Stamps of Indo-China surch **CHINE** and value in Chinese.
29 8 1c. olive 1·10 1·75
30 2c. red on yellow 1·00 1·75
31 4c. brown on grey £650 £525
32 5c. green 2·75 1·50
33 10c. red 2·00 2·25
34 15c. brown on blue 2·25 1·50
36 20c. red on green 9·50 13·00
37 25c. blue 4·25 4·25
38 40c. black on grey 3·75 3·75
39 1f. green £275 £200
40 2f. brown on yellow 25·00 25·00
41 10f. red on green £120 £120

INDONESIA Pt. 4, Pt. 21

An independent republic was proclaimed in Java and Sumatra on 17 August 1945 and lasted until the end of 1948. During this period the Dutch controlled the rest of the Netherlands Indies, renamed "Indonesia" in September 1948. On 27 December 1949 all Indonesia except New Guinea became independent as the United States of Indonesia which, during 1950, amalgamated with the original Indonesian Republic (Java and Sumatra), a single state being proclaimed on 15 August 1950 as the Indonesian Republic. This was within the Netherlands-Indonesian Union which was abolished on 10 August 1954.

100 cents (or sen) = 1 gulden (or rupiah).

A. DUTCH ADMINISTRATION

1948. Stamps of Netherlands Indies optd **INDONESIA** and bar or bars.
541 81 15c. orange 90 30
533 20c. blue 55 30
543 25c. green 30 30
535 40c. green 1·10 90
544 45c. mauve 35 30
545 50c. lake 1·10 30
536 80c. red 3·75 2·10
537a 1g. violet 1·25 30
538 – 2½g. orange (No. 479) 45·00 9·50
539 81 10g. green 90·00 30·00
540 25g. orange £125 55·00

86

87 Portal to Tjandi Poentadewa Temple

89 Globe and Arms of Berne

1949. New Currency.
548A 86 1s. grey 35 20
549A 2s. purple 55 20
550A 2½s. brown 35 20
551A 3s. red 55 20
552A 4s. green 55 55
553A 5s. blue 55 20
554A 7½s. green 55 20
555A 10s. mauve 35 20
556A 12½s. red 1·75 20
557A 87 15s. red 35 20
558A 20s. black 35 20
559A 25s. blue 35 20
560A – 30s. red 35 20
561A – 40s. green 55 20
562A – 45s. purple 55 3·50
563A – 50s. brown 55 20
564A – 60s. brown 75 1·75
565A – 80s. red 1·10 20
566A – 1r. violet 75 20
567A – 2r. green 4·50 20
568A – 3r. purple 90·00 20
569A – 5r. brown 65·00 35
570A – 10r. black 80·00 1·75
571A – 25r. brown 75 1·75
DESIGNS—As Type **87**: 30 to 45s. Sculpture from Temple at Bedjoening, Bali; 50 to 80s. Minangkabau house, Sumatra; 21 × 26 mm: 1 to 3r. Toradja house; 5 to 25r. Detail of Temple of Panahan.

1949. 75th Anniv of U.P.U.
572 89 15s. red 1·10 35
573 25s. blue 1·10 35

B. REPUBLIC, 1945–48
ISSUES FOR JAVA AND MADURA

1945. Stamps of Netherlands Indies optd **REPOEBLIK INDONESIA**.
J 1 46 1c. violet 1·10 1·70
J 2 2c. purple 4·50 5·50
J19 – 2c. red (No. 461) 1·10 2·30
J 4 – 2½c. red (No. 462) 1·40 2·30
J 5 – 3c. green (No. 463) 1·60 2·30
J 3 46 3½c. grey 50·00 55·00
J 6 71 4c. olive 1·60 2·30
J 7 5c. blue (No. 465) 65·00 75·00

1945. Stamps of Japanese Occupation of Netherlands Indies optd as above.
J 8 – 3½s. red (No. 2) £275 £375
J10 – 3½c. red (No. 5) 38·00 38·00
J 9 – 5s. green (No. 3) 14·00 9·50
J11 2 5s. green 45 75
J12 – 10c. blue (No. 7) 30 60
J13 – 20c. olive (No. 8) 55 85
J14 – 40c. purple (No. 9) 90 1·20
J15 4 60c. orange 1·20 1·40
J16 – 80s. brown (No. 11) 11·00 15·00

J 5 Bull

1945. Declaration of Independence. Inscr "17 AGOESTOES 1945". Perf or imperf.
J23 J 5 10s. (+ 10s.) brown 4·75 6·50
J24 – 20s. (+ 10s.) brown & red 5·75 6·50
DESIGN—VERT: 20s. Bull and Indonesian flag.

J 9 Boat in Storm

J 10 Wayang Puppet

1946.
J49 – 5s. blue 75 85
J50 – 20s. brown 85 1·10
J51 J 9 30s. red 70 2·75
DESIGNS: 5s. Road and mountains; 20s. Soldier on waterfront.

1946.
J52 J 10 50s. blue 14·00 11·00
J53 – 60s. red 4·25 £140
J54 – 80s. violet 52·00 £400
DESIGNS: 60s. Kris and flag; 80s. Temple.

J 13 Buffalo breaking Chains

J 14 Bandung, March, 1946

1946. Perf or imperf.
J55 J 13 3s. red 10 50
J56 J 14 5s. blue 45 65
J57 – 10s. black 7·50 10·00
J58 – 15s. purple 90 90
J59 – 30s. green 1·25 1·50
J60 – 40s. blue 1·00 1·00
J61a J 13 50s. black 1·10 1·00
J62 J 14 60s. lilac 1·50 2·00
J63 – 80s. red 1·25 8·75
J64 – 100s. red 1·00 1·00
J65 – 200s. lilac 1·10 1·90
J66 – 500s. red 5·00 7·50
J67 – 1000s. green 5·00 7·50
DESIGNS—HORIZ: 10, 15s. Soerabaya, November 1945; 30s. Anti-aircraft gunners; 100s. Ambarawa, November 1945; 200s. Wonokromo Dam, Soerabaya; 1000s. Cavalryman. VERT: 40s. Quay at Tandjong Priok; 80s. Airman; 500s. Mass meeting with flags, Djakarta.

1948. Postage Due Stamps of Netherlands Indies surch **SEGEL 25 sen PORTO**.
J68 D 7 25s. on 7½c. orange 14·00 28·00
J69 25s. on 15c. orange 9·50 24·00
Although surcharged for use as postage due stamps the above were employed for ordinary postal use.

J 16 "Labour and Transport"

J 18 Flag over Waves

1948. 3rd Anniv of Independence. Imperf.
J70 J 16 50s. blue 5·00 6·00
J71 100s. red 7·00 7·00

1949. Government's Return to Jogjakarta. Perf. or Imperf.
J77 J 18 100s. red 6·25 18·00
J78 150s. red 10·00 25·00

POSTAGE DUE STAMPS

1948. Nos. J67 and J70/1 optd **DENDA**, or surch also.
JD72 J 16 50s. blue – 20·00
JD73 – 100s. red – 20·00
JD74 – 1r. on 50s. blue (A) – 20·00
JD75 1r. on 50s. blue (B) – 20·00
JD76 – 1r. on 1000s. green – 20·00
A. Surcharged "RP 1"; B. Surcharged "1—RP".

ISSUES FOR SUMATRA

1946. Stamps of Netherlands Indies surch **Repoeblik Indonesia** and value.
S 1 – 15s. on 5c. blue (No. 465) 1·50 1·90
S 2 46 20s. on 3½c. grey 7·50 7·50
S 3 30s. on 1c. violet 7·50 7·50
S 4 40s. on 2c. purple 25 60
S 7 – 50s. on 17½c. orange (No. 431) 55·00 55·00
S 9 46 60s. on 2½c. bistre 7·50 5·25
S10 80s. on 3c. green 7·50 7·50
S11 – 1r. on 10c. red (No. 429) 6·00 6·00

S 9 Ploughing

S 10 Pres. Sukarno

S 12

1946. Freedom Fund.
S17 S 9 5s. (+25s.) green 75 2·30
S18 5s. (+25s.) blue 20 1·50
S19 – 15s. (+35s.) red 1·90 3·75
S20 – 15s. (+35s.) blue 20 1·50
S21 – 40s. (+60s.) orange 90 2·30
S22 – 40s. (+60s.) red 75 4·50
S23 – 40s. (+60s.) purple 7·50 24·00
S24 – 40s. (+60s.) brown 12·50 42·00
DESIGNS—VERT: 15s. Soldier and flag; 40s. Oil well and factories, Palembang.

1946.
S25 S 10 40s. (+60s.) red 75 5·75

1946. "FONDS KEMERDEKAAN" obliterated by one or two bars.
S27 S 9 5s. blue 45·00 £110
S28 – 40s. red (No. S22) 45·00 45·00

1946. As Type S 9 but without "FONDS KEMERDEKAAN". Perf or imperf.
S29 2s. red 1·00 15·00
S30 2s. brown 6·25 38·00
S31 3s. green 1·00 15·00
S32 3s. red 7·50 38·00
S33 3s. blue £180
S34 5s. blue 85 8·75
S35 15s. blue 60 4·00
S36 15s. green 4·00 38·00
S37 40s. brown 60 6·25
S38 40s. blue 20·00 60·00
DESIGNS: 2, 3, 5s. As Type **S 9**. 15s. Soldier and flag; 40s. Oil well and factories, Palembang.

1947. Fund for Palembang War Victims. Nos. S18, S20 and S23 optd **BPKPP** over triple circle.
S39 S 9 5s. blue 75·00 90·00
S40 – 15s. blue 75·00 90·00
S41 – 40s. brown 75·00 90·00

1947. Fiscal stamps of Japanese Occupation with blank panels optd in black with **prangko N.R.I.** and value as in Type S **12**.
S42 S 12 0f.50 orange 13·50 30·00
S43 1f. orange 11·50 23·00
S44 2f. orange 17·00 30·00
S45 2f.50 orange 12·00 15·00

1947. No. S25 surch with new value and bars.
S46 50s. on 40s. red 5·00 5·00
S47 1f. on 40s. red 6·75 6·75
S48 1f.50 on 40s. red 4·25 4·25
S49 2f.50 on 40s. red 75 2·30
S50 3f.50 on 40s. red 75 2·30
S51 5f. on 40s. red 75 2·30

1947. Surch with ornament and new value.
S63 1s. on 15s. (No. S35) 45 1·90
S64 5s. on 3s. (No. S33) 40 1·90
S65 10s. on 15s. red (as Nos. S35/6) 50 1·90
S52 30s. on 40s. (No. S28) 60 1·50
S66 50s. on 3s. (No. S32) 15·00 38·00
S53 50s. on 5s. (No. S34) 6·00 4·50
S59 50s. on 40s. (No. S28) 11·50 15·00
S54 1f. on 5s. (No. S34) 4·50 4·50
S60 1f. on 40s. (No. S28) 40 1·50
S55 1f.50 on 5s. (No. S34) 6·00 6·00
S61 1f.50 on 40s. (No. S28) 3·00 5·25
S62 2f.50 on 40s. (No. S28) 40 1·50
S56 1r. on 40s. (No. S37) 40 3·00
S57 2r. on 5s. (No. S34) 60 3·00

1947. No. S56 surch **50**.
S58 50(r.) on 1r. on 40s. 45·00 55·00

1947. Air. Surch **Pos Udara** with ornament and new value.
S67 10r. on 40s. (No. S22) 1·90 2·30
S68 20r. on 5s. (No. S34) 1·10 2·30

1947. Stamps of 1946 (Nos. S 29/37) surch.
S69 10s. on 15s. blue 11·50 11·50
S70 20s. on 15s. blue 11·50 11·50
S71 30s. on 15s. blue 11·50 6·00
S75 50s. on 5s. blue £600 £550
S76 50s. on 15s. blue £600 £600
S77 0f.50 on 15s. blue £550 £550
S78 1f. on 5s. blue £140 £140
S79 1f. on 15s. blue £275 £375
S72 1r. on 2s. red 47·00 47·00
S88 2r. on 3s. green 33·00 65·00
S80 2f.50 on 5s. blue £750 £650
S73 2f.50 on 15s. blue 14·00 14·00
S82 2f.50 on 40s. brown £550 £650
S85 2r.50 on 3s. green 19·00 28·00
S83 5f. on 15s. blue £750 £750
S74 5f. on 40s. brown £225 £170
S89 5r. on 15s. blue 7·00 11·50
S87 10r. on 3s. green 70·00 70·00
S91 20r. on 2s. red £225 £475
S92 50r. on 15s. blue £325 £475
S93 100r. on 15s. blue £110 £110
S94 150r. on 40s. red £140 £140
No. S94 is surcharged on No. S22 with a pen-stroke through "FONDS KEMERDEKAAN".

(S 23) "O.R.I." = "Oeang Repoeblik Indonesia" (Indonesian Republican Money)

1947. Change of Currency. Various stamps optd with Type S 23. (a) On stamps of Netherlands Indies.
S 99 1c. red (No. D226) 8·00 8·50
S 96 46 3c. green (No. 338) 4·75 6·00
S 97 71 4c. olive (No. 464) 7·25 8·00
S 98 – 5c. blue (No. 465) 3·50 5·50
S100 15c. red (No. D448) 6·00 7·25

(b) On stamps of Japanese Occupation of Netherlands Indies.
S101 – 1c. green (No. 15) 1·10 1·50
S102 – 2c. green (No. 16) 1·10 1·25
S103 – 3c. blue (No. 17) 1·10 1·25
S104 – 3½c. red (No. 18) 1·50 1·90
S105 – 4c. blue (No. 19) 2·50 3·75
S106 – 5c. orange (No. 20) 1·50 1·90
S107 – 10c. blue (No. 21) 6·00 6·75
S111 – 10c. red (No. 57) 85 1·10
S108 – 20c. brown (No. 22) 6·00 6·75
S112 – 25c. green (No. 62) 10·00 12·00
S109 6 30c. purple (No. 23) 1·10 1·10
S114 – 30c. brown (No. 63) 8·00 9·00
S110 – 50c. brown (No. 25) 2·20 2·20
S115 – 50c. red (No. 66) 10·50 13·00
S116 – 60c. blue (No. 67) 5·50 6·00
S117 – 80c. red (No. 68) 5·50 7·25
S118 – 1g. violet (No. 69) 11·00 12·50

(c) On stamps of Japan.
S119 – 1s. brown (No. 317) 1·00 1·50
S120 – 3s. green (No. 319) 1·00 1·50
S121 – 4s. green (No. 320) 5·00 5·50
S122 – 6s. orange (No. 322) 1·50 2·00
S123 – 25s. brn & choc (No. 329) 1·00 1·40
S124 – 30s. green (No. 330) 2·40 3·50
S125 – 50s. green & bis (No. 331) 1·00 1·50
S126 – 1y. brown and chocolate (No. 332) 2·40 3·50

(d) On stamps of Indonesia-Sumatra.
S149 – 1s. on 15s. bl (No. S63) 70 1·40
S136 – 2s. red (No. S29) 2·50 3·00
S137 – 3s. green (No. S31) 00 00
S138 – 3s. red (No. S32) 1·00 1·70
S132 S 9 5s. green (No. S17) 2·50 4·00
S133 – 5s. blue (No. S18) 90 1·30
S139 – 5s. blue (No. S34) 75 1·10
S150 – 10s. on 15s. red (No. S65) 2·40 3·75
S134 – 15s. blue (No. S20) 2·40 4·25
S140 – 15s. blue (No. S35) 75 1·10
S141 – 15s. green (No. S36) 3·75 5·50
S127 46 20s. on 3½c. grey (No. S2) 6·50 7·50
S128 – 30s. on 1c. violet (No. S3) 6·50 8·00
S146 – 30s. on 40s. red (No. S52) 80 1·30
S129 46 40s. on 2c. purple (No. S4) 3·00 5·00
S135 – 40s. red (No. S22) 2·75 3·50
S142 – 40s. brown (No. S37) 70 1·00
S151 – 50s. on 5s. blue (No. S53) 1·80 2·40
S143 – 1f.50 on 40s. red (No. S48) 6·50 30·00
S147 – 1f.50 on 40s. red (No. S61) 6·50 7·50
S152 – 1f.50 on 5s. blue (No. S55) 5·50 7·25
S153 – 2r. on 5s. blue (No. S57) 1·60 2·50
S144 – 2f.50 on 40s. red (No. S49) 6·25 7·50
S148 – 2f.50 on 40s. red (No. S62) 6·25 7·50
S145 – 3f.50 on 40s. red (No. S50) 6·25 7·50
S154 – 10r. on 40s. red (No. S67) 7·50 10·00

C. UNITED STATES OF INDONESIA

90 Indonesian Flag

1950. Inauguration of United States of Indonesia.
574 90 15s. red (20½ × 26 mm) 1·10 25
575 15s. red (18 × 23 mm) 6·50 1·10

1950. Stamps of 1949 optd **RIS**.
579 86 1s. grey 80 65
580 2s. purple 1·40 1·80
581 2½s. brown 80 65
582 3s. red 80 40
583 4s. green 80 65
584 5s. blue 80 65
585 7½s. green 80 65
586 10s. mauve 80 60
587 12½s. red 1·00 65
588 87 20s. black 24·00 28·00
589 25s. blue 80 60
590 – 30s. red 8·25 18·00
591 – 40s. green 80 40
592 – 45s. purple 1·60 1·00
593 – 50s. brown 1·40 85
594 – 60s. brown 7·00 10·50
595 – 80s. red 2·75 1·00
596 – 1r. violet 2·10 45
597 – 2r. green £350 90·00
598 – 3r. purple £120 55·00
599 – 5r. brown 49·00 16·00
600 – 10r. black 90·00 35·00
601 – 25r. brown 20·00 13·50

D. INDONESIAN REPUBLIC

94 Indonesian Arms

95 Maps and Torch

1950. 5th Anniv of Proclamation of Independence.
602 94 15s. red 2·00 25
603 25s. green 2·75 1·10
604 1r. sepia 9·75 1·70

1951. Asiatic Olympic Games, New Delhi.
605 95 5s.+3s. green 10 10
606 10s.+5s. blue 10 10
607 20s.+5s. red 10 10
608 30s.+10s. brown 25 15
609 35s.+10s. blue 2·75 2·10

96

97 General Post-Office, Bandung

98 "Spirit of Indonesia"

99 President Sukarno

1951.
610 96 1s. grey 40 75
611 2s. mauve 40 60
612 2½s. brown 5·00 15
613 5s. red 40 15
614 7½s. green 40 15
615 10s. blue 40 15
616 15s. violet 40 15
618 20s. red 40 15
619 25s. green 40 15
620 97 30s. red 10 10
621 35s. violet 65 10
622 40s. green 10 10
623 45s. purple 10 25
624 50s. brown 3·00 10
625 98 60s. brown 10 10
626 70s. grey 10 10
627 75s. blue 10 40
628 80s. purple 10 10
629 90s. green 10 10

1951.
630 99 1r. violet 25 10
631 1r.25 orange 1·60 10
632 1r.50 brown 25 10
633 2r. green 25 10
634 2r.50 brown 25 10
635 3r. blue 25 10
636 4r. green 25 10
637 5r. brown 25 10
638 6r. mauve 25 10
639 10r. grey 25 10
640 15r. stone 25 10
641 20r. purple 25 10
642 25r. red 65 10
643 40r. green 80 2·10
644 50r. violet 1·10 15

101 Sports Emblem

102 Doves

1951. National Sports Festival.
655 101 5a.+3s. green 35 40
656 10s.+5s. blue 35 40
657 20s.+5s. orange 35 40
658 30s.+10s. sepia 35 40
659 35s.+10s. blue 35 1·00

1951. U.N. Day.
660 102 7½s. green 2·75 80
661 10s. violet 80 40
662 20s. orange 2·00 80
663 30s. red 2·75 1·00
664 35s. blue 2·75 1·00
665 1r. sepia 21·00 3·25

1953. Natural Disasters Relief Fund. Surch **19 53 BENTJANA ALAM +10s.**
666 97 35s.+10s. violet 25 15

104 Melati Flowers

105 Merapi Volcano in Eruption

1953. Mothers' Day and 25th Anniv of Indonesian Women's Congress.
667 104 50s. green 20·00 55

1954. Natural Disasters Relief Fund.
668 105 15s.+10s. green 1·10 1·40
669 35s.+15s. violet 1·10 1·10
670 50s.+25s. red 1·10 1·10
671 75s.+25s. blue 1·10 1·10
672 1r.+25s. red 1·10 1·10
673 2r.+50s. brown 2·75 1·10
674a 3r.+1r. green 14·00 7·00
675a 5r.+2r.50 brown 16·00 9·75

106 Girls with Musical Instruments

107 Globe and Doves

1954. Child Welfare.
676 106 10s.+10s. purple 10 55
677 – 15s.+10s. green 10 65
678 – 35s.+15s. mauve 15 65
679 – 50s.+15s. purple 50 65
680 – 75s.+25s. blue 25 2·50
681 – 1r.+25s. red 35 4·50
DESIGNS: 15s. Menangkabau boy and girl performing Umbrella Dance; 35s. Girls playing "Tjongkak"; 50s. Boy on bamboo stilts; 75s. Ambonese boys playing flutes; 1r. Srimpi dancing girl.

1955. Asian–African Conference, Bandung.
682 107 15s. black 1·00 65
683 35s. brown 1·00 65
684 50s. red 3·00 65
685 75s. turquoise 1·60 65

108 Semaphore Signaller

109 Proclamation of Independence

1955. National Scout Jamboree.
686 – 15s.+10s. green 15 15
687 108 35s.+15s. blue 15 15
688 – 50s.+25s. red 15 15
689 – 75s.+25s. brown 15 15
690 – 1r.+50s. violet 15 15
DESIGNS: 15s. Indonesian scout badge; 50s. Scouts round campfire; 75s. Scout feeding baby sika deer; 1r. Scout saluting.

1955. 10th Anniv of Independence.
691 109 15s. green 80 65
692 35s. blue 80 65
693 50s. brown 5·25 40
694 75s. purple 1·10 55

110 Postmaster Sukarto

111 Electors

1955. 10th Anniv of Indonesian Post Office.
695 110 15s. brown 80 65
696 35s. red 80 65
697 50s. blue 6·00 1·50
698 75s. green 2·40 65

1955. 1st General Indonesian Elections.
699 111 15s. purple 40 35
700 35s. green 55 65
701 50s. red 2·00 80
702 75s. blue 75 35

112 Memorial Column, Wreath and Helmet

113 Weaving

1955. Heroes' Day.
703 112 25s. green 65 25
704 50s. blue 1·60 55
705 1r. red 12·00 25

1956. Blind Relief Fund.
706 113 15s.+10s. green 55 55
707 – 35s.+15s. brown 55 55
708 – 50s.+25s. red 1·20 1·10
709 – 75s.+50s. blue 55 55
DESIGNS—VERT: 35s. Basketwork; 50s. Map reading; 75s. Reading.

114 Torch and Book

115 Lesser Malay Chevrotain

1956. Asian and African Students' Conf, Bandung.
710 114 25s. blue 1·00 25
711 50s. red 5·00 1·00
712 1r. green 2·10 1·00

1956.
713 115 5s. blue 10 10
714 10s. brown 10 10
715 15s. purple 10 10
716 – 20s. green 10 10
717 – 25s. purple 10 10
718 – 30s. orange 10 10
719 – 35s. blue 10 10
720 – 40s. green 10 10
721 – 45s. purple 1·10 15
722 – 50s. bistre 10 10
723 – 60s. blue 15 10
724 – 70s. red 1·60 25
725 – 75s. sepia 15 10
726 – 80s. red 15 15
727 – 90s. green 15 15
DESIGNS: 20s. to 30s. Hairy-nosed otter; 35s. to 45s. Malayan pangolin; 50s. to 70s. Banteng; 75s. to 90s. Sumatran rhinoceros.

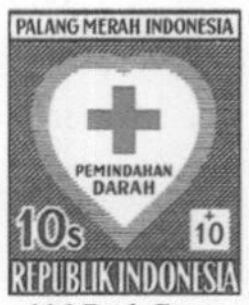

116 Red Cross

117

1956. Red Cross Fund.
728 116 10s.+10s. red and blue 10 10
729 15s.+10s. red & carmine 10 10
730 – 35s.+15s. red and brown 15 15
731 – 50s.+15s. red and green 25 15
732 – 75s.+25s. red & orange 35 25
733 – 1r.+25s. red and violet 50 40
DESIGNS: 35, 50s. Blood transfusion bottle; 75s., 1r. Hands and drop of blood.

1956. Bicentenary of Djokjakarta.
734 117 15s. green 1·60 50
735 35s. brown 1·60 50
736 50s. blue 3·00 80
737 75s. purple 3·00 80

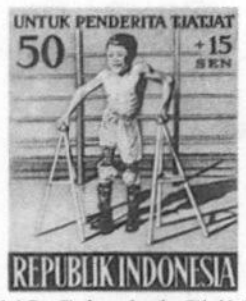

118 Crippled Child

119 Telegraph Key and Tape

1957. Cripples' Rehabilitation Fund. Inscr "UNTUK PENDERITA TJATJAT".
738 – 10s.+10s. blue 10 10
739 – 15s.+10s. brown 10 10
740 – 35s.+15s. red 10 10
741 118 50s.+15s. violet 25 25
742 – 75s.+25s. green 35 35
743 – 1r.+25s. red 50 50
DESIGNS: 10s. One-legged woman painting cloth; 15s. One-handed artist; 35s. One-handed machinist; 75s. Doctor tending cripple; 1r. Man writing with artificial arm.

1957. Centenary of Telegraphs in Indonesia.
744 119 10s. red 2·40 50
745 15s. blue 50 25
746 25s. black 40 15
747 50s. red 50 25
748 75s. green 50 15

120 Two men with Savings-box

1957. Co-operation Day. Inscr "HARI KOOPERASI".
749 **120** 10s. blue 55 40
750 – 15s. red 55 40
751 **120** 50s. green . . . . 1·00 65
752 – 1r. violet . . . . 1·40 15
DESIGN: 15s., 1r. "Co-operative Prosperity" (hands holding ear of rice and cotton).

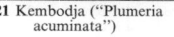

121 Kembodja ("Plumeria acuminata")

122 Convair CV 340 Airliner

1957. Various Charity Funds. Floral designs. Multicoloured.
753 10s.+10s. Type **121** . . . . 2·10 1·00
754 15s.+10s. Tjempakakuning (michelia) . . . . 1·50 1·00
755 35s.+15s. Matahari (sunflower) . . . . 1·00 80
756 50s.+15s. Melati (jasmine) . . 65 65
757 75s.+50s. Larat (orchid) . . . 65 65

1958. National Aviation Day. Inscr "HARI PENERBANGAN NASIONAL 9-4-1958".
758 **122** 10s. brown 15 10
759 – 15s. blue 15 15
760 – 35s. orange 35 25
761 **122** 50s. turquoise 65 40
762 – 75s. slate . . . . 1·10 55
DESIGNS: 15s. Hiller "Skeeter" helicopter; 35s. Nurtiano Sikumbang trainer; 75s. De Havilland Vampire jet fighter.

123 "Helping Hands"

124 Thomas Cup

1958. Indonesian Orphans Welfare Fund Inscr "ANAK PIATU".
763 **123** 10s.+10s. blue 15 15
764 – 15s.+10s. red 15 15
765 **123** 35s.+15s. green 15 15
766 – 50s.+25s. drab 15 15
767 **123** 75s.+50s. brown 15 15
768 – 1r.+50s. brown 15 15
DESIGN: 15s., 50s., 1r. Girl and boy orphans.

1958. Indonesian Victory in Thomas Cup World Badminton Championships, Singapore.
769 **124** 25s. red 15 15
770 50s. orange 15 15
771 1r. brown 25 15

125 Satellite encircling Globe

126 Racing Cyclist

1958. International Geophysical Year.
785 **125** 10s. pink, green and blue 90 55
786 15s. drab, violet and grey 25 15
787 35s. blue, sepia and pink 25 15
788 50s. brown, blue and drab 25 15
789 75s. lilac, black and yellow 25 15

1958. Tour of Java Cycle Race.
790 **126** 25s. blue 50 25
791 50s. red 80 25
792 1r. grey 50 25

127 "Human Rights"

128 Babirusa

1958. 10th Anniv of Declaration of Human Rights.
793 **127** 10s. sepia 15 15
794 – 15s. brown 15 15
795 – 35s. blue 25 15
796 – 50s. bistre 25 15
797 – 75s. green 25 15
DESIGNS: 15s. Hands grasping "Flame of Freedom"; 35s. Native holding candle; 50s. Family acclaiming "Flame of Freedom"; 75s. "Flame" superimposed on figure "10".

1959. Animal Protection Campaign.
798 **128** 10s. sepia and olive . . . 15 15
799 – 15s. sepia and brown . . 25 25
800 – 20s. sepia and green . . . 35 35
801 – 50s. sepia and brown . . 50 50
802 – 75s. sepia and red 50 50
803 – 1r. black and turquoise 55 55
ANIMALS: 15s. Anoa (buffalo); 20s. Orang-utan; 50s. Javan rhinoceros; 75s. Komodo lizard; 1r. Malayan tapir.

129 Indonesian Scout Badge

130

1959. 10th World Scout Jamboree, Manila. Inscr as in T **129**. Badges in red.
804 **129** 10s.+5s. bistre 15 15
805 – 15s.+10s. green 25 15
806 **129** 20s.+10s. violet 25 25
807 – 50s.+25s. olive 25 40
808 **129** 75s.+35s. brown 25 40
809 – 1r.+50s. slate 35 40
DESIGN: 15s., 50s., 1r. Scout badge within compass.

1959. Re-adoption of 1945 Constitution.
810 **130** 20s. red and blue 15 15
811 50s. black and red 15 15
812 75s. red and brown . . . 15 15
813 1r.50 black and green . . 25 15

131 Factory and Girder

132

1959. 11th Colombo Plan Conference, Djakarta.
814 **131** 15s. black and green . . . 15 10
815 – 20s. black and orange . . 15 10
816 **131** 50s. black and red 15 10
817 – 75s. black and blue . . . 15 10
818 – 1r.15 black and purple . . 15 10
DESIGNS: 20, 75s. Cogwheel and diesel train; 1r.15, Forms of transport and communications.

1960. Indonesian Youth Conference, Bandung. Inscr "1960".
819 **132** 15s.+5s. sepia and bistre 10 25
820 – 20s.+10s. sepia & green 15 25
821 **132** 50s.+25s. purple & blue 15 25
822 – 75s.+35s. green & bis . . 15 25
823 – 1r.15+50s. black & red . 35 25
DESIGNS: 20s., 75s. Test-tubes in frame; 1r.15, Youth wielding manifesto.

133 Refugee Camp

134 Tea plants

1960. World Refugee Year. Centres in black.
824 **133** 10s. purple 10 15
825 – 15s. ochre 10 15
826 – 20s. brown 10 15
827 **133** 50s. green 15 15
828 – 75s. blue 35 15
829 – 1r.15 red 35 90
DESIGNS: 15s., 75s. Outcast family; 20s., 1r.15, "Care of refugees" (refugee with protecting hands).

1960. Agricultural Products.
830 – 5s. grey 15 10
831 – 10s. brown 15 10
832 – 15s. purple 15 10
833 – 20s. bistre 15 10
834 **134** 25s. green 15 10
835 – 50s. blue 15 10
836 – 75s. red 15 10
837 – 1r.15 red 15 15
DESIGNS: 5s. Oil palm; 10s. Sugar cane; 15s. Coffee plant; 20s. Tobacco plant; 50s. Coconut palm; 75s. Rubber trees; 1r.15, Rice plants.

135 Mosquito

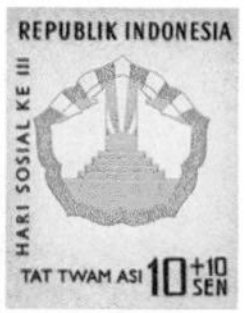

136 Socialist Emblem

1960. World Health Day.
838 **135** 25s. red 10 10
839 50s. brown 15 10
840 75s. green 15 10
841 3r. orange 40 15

1960. 3rd Socialist Day. Inscr as in T **136**.
842 **136** 10s.+10s. brown & blk . . 10 15
843 – 15s.+15s. purple & blk . . 10 15
844 – 20s.+20s. blue and black 15 15
845 – 50s.+25s. black & brn . . 15 25
846 – 75s.+25s. black & green 15 25
847 – 3r.+50s. black and red . . 15 40
DESIGNS: 15s. Emblem similar to Type **136** within plants; 20s. Lotus flower; 50s. Boy and girl; 75s. Ceremonial watering of plant; 3r. Mother with children.

137 Pres. Sukarno and Workers Hoeing

1961. National Development Plan.
848 **137** 75s. black 25 15

1961. Flood Relief Fund. Nos. 832/3 and 836 surch **BENTJANA ALAM 1961** and premium.
849 15s.+10s. purple 10 10
850 20s.+15s. brown 10 10
851 75s.+25s. red 10 10

139 Bull Race

1961. Tourist Publicity.
852 – 10s. purple 50 40
853 – 15s. grey 50 40
854 **139** 20s. orange 50 40
855 – 25s. red 50 40
856 – 50s. lake 50 40
857 – 75s. brown 50 40
858 – 1r. green 90 40
859 – 1r.50 bistre 90 40
860 – 2r. blue . . . . 1·30 40
861 – 3r. grey . . . . 1·30 40
DESIGNS: 10s. Ambonese boat; 15s. Tangkuban Perahu crater; 25s. Daja dancer; 50s. Toradja houses; 75s. Balinese temple; 1r. Lake Toba; 1r.50, Bali dancer; 2r. "Buffalo Hole" (gorge); 3r. Borobudur temple.

140 Stadium

1961. Thomas Cup World Badminton Championships.
863 **140** 75s. lilac and blue 10 10
864 1r. olive and green . . . 15 10
865 3r. salmon and blue . . . 25 15

141 "United Efforts"

1961. 16th Anniv of Independence.
866 **141** 75s. violet and blue . . . 10 10
867 1r.50 green and cream . . 10 10
868 3r. red and salmon . . . 35 15

142 Sultan Hasanuddin

1961. National Independence Heroes. Portraits in sepia; inscriptions in black.
869 – 20s. olive 10 35
870 **142** 25s. olive 15 35
871 – 30s. violet 15 35
872 – 40s. brown 15 35
873 – 50s. myrtle 15 35
874 – 60s. turquoise 15 35
875 – 75s. brown 90 35
876 – 1r. blue 90 35
877 – 1r.25 green 75 35
878 – 1r.50 green 90 35
879 – 2r. red 75 35
880 – 2r.50 red 90 35
881 – 3r. slate 75 35
882 – 4r. green 75 35
883 – 4r.50 purple 35 35
884 – 5r. red 80 35
885 – 6r. ochre 90 35
886 – 7r.50 blue . . . . 1·10 35
887 – 10r. green 75 35
888 – 15r. orange 75 35
PORTRAITS: 20s. Abdul Muis; 30s. Surjopranoto; 40s. Tengku Tjhik Di Tiro; 50s. Teuku Umar; 60s. K. H. Samanhudi; 75s. Capt. Pattimura; 1r. Raden Adjeng Kartini; 1r.25, K. H. Achmad Dahlan; 1r.50, Tuanku Imam Bondjol; 2r. Si Singamangaradja XII; 2r.50, Mohammed Husni Thamrin; 3r. Ki Hadjar Dewantoro; 4r. Gen. Sudirman; 4r.50, Dr. G. S. S. J. Ratulangie; 5r. Pangeran Diponegoro; 6r. Dr. Setyabudi; 7r.50, H. O. S. Tjokroaminoto; 10r. K. H. Agus Salim; 15r. Dr. Soetomo.

143 Census Emblems

1961. 1st Indonesian Census.
889 **143** 75s. purple 25 15

144 Nenas (pineapples)

145 Djataju

1961. Charity. Fruits.
890 **144** 20s.+10s. yellow, red and blue 50 40
891 – 75s.+25s. purple, green and slate 75 40
892 – 3r.+1r. red, yell & grn . . 1·20 1·20
FRUITS: 75s. Manggis; 3r. Rambutan.

1962. Ramayana Dancers.
893 **145** 30s. brown and ochre . . 35 40
894 – 40s. violet and purple . . 35 40
895 – 1r. purple and green . . . 50 40
896 – 1r.50 green and pink . . . 50 40
897 – 3r. blue and green . . . . 1·60 40
898 – 5r. brown and buff . . . 1·40 40
DANCERS: 40s. Hanoman; 1r. Dasamuka; 1r.50, Kidang Kentjana; 3r. Dewi Sinta; 5r. Rama.

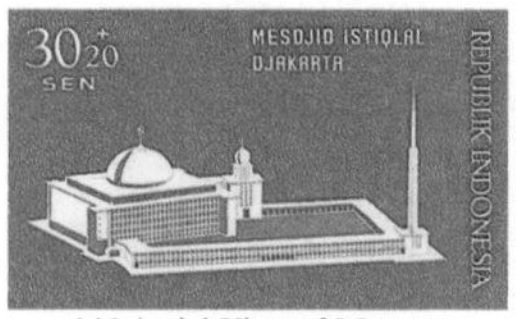

146 Aerial View of Mosque

1962. Construction of Istiqlal Mosque.
899 **146** 30s.+20s. blue & yellow 35 25
900 – 40s.+20s. red and yellow 35 25
901 **146** 1r.50+50s. brown & yell 35 25
902 – 3r.+1r. green and yellow 35 25
DESIGN: 40s., 3r. Ground-level view of Mosque.

147 Games Emblem

148 Campaign Emblem

1962. 4th Asian Games, Djakarta. Inscr as in T **147**.
903 – 10s. green and yellow . . 15 15
904 – 15s. brown and ochre . . 15 15
905 – 20s. lilac and green . . . 35 25
906 – 25s. red and green 35 25
907 – 30s. green and buff . . . 35 15
908 – 40s. ultramarine and blue 35 15
909 – 50s. brown and drab . . 35 35
910 – 60s. mauve and grey . . 35 35
911 – 70s. brown and red . . . 35 35
912 – 75s. brown and orange . . 35 15

913 – 1r. violet and blue 35 35
914 **147** 1r.25 blue and mauve . . 40 40
915 – 1r.50 red and mauve . . . 1·20 40
916 – 1r.75 red and pink . . . 80 40
917 **147** 2r. brown and green . . . 75 40
918 – 2r.50 blue and green . . . 80 40
919 **147** 3r. black and red 75 40
920 – 4r.50 green and red . . . 75 40
921 **147** 5r. green and bistre . . . 55 40
922 – 6r. red and brown 55 40
923 – 7r.50 brown and pink . . 55 25
924 – 10r. ultramarine and blue 1·10 55
925 – 15r. violet and light violet 1·20 1·10
926 – 20r. green and bistre . . 3·00 1·40
DESIGNS—VERT: 10s. Basketball; 20s. Weightlifting; 40s. Throwing the discus; 50s. Diving; 60s. Football; 70s. Press building; 75s. Boxing; 1r. Volleyball; 1r.50, Badminton; 1r.75, Wrestling; 2r.50, Shooting; 4r.50, Hockey; 6r. Water polo; 7r.50, Tennis; 10r. Table tennis; 15r. Cycling; 20r. "Welcome" monument. HORIZ: 15s. Main stadium; 25s. Hotel Indonesia; 30s. Road improvement.

1962. Malaria Eradication.
927 **148** 40s. blue and violet . . . 10 10
928 1r.50 orange and brown 10 10
929 3r. green and blue 10 10
930 6r. violet and black . . . 25 15
On the 1r.50 and 6r. the inscription is at top.

149 National Monument

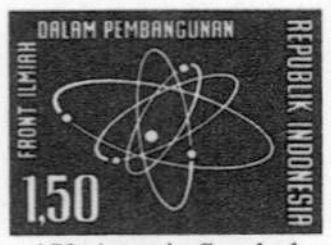

150 Atomic Symbol

1962. National Monument.
931 **149** 1r.+50c. brown & black 15 15
932 – 1r.50+50c. green & blue 15 15
933 **149** 3r.+1r. mauve and green 25 15
934 – 6r.+1r.50 blue and red . . 25 15
DESIGN: 1r.50, 6r. Aerial view of Monument.

1962. "Science for Development".
935 **150** 1r.50 blue and yellow . . 15 15
936 4r.50 red and yellow . . . 25 25
937 6r. green and yellow . . . 40 25

151 "Phalaenopis amabilis"

152 West Irian Monument, Djakarta

1962. Charity. Orchids. Multicoloured.
938 1r.+50s. "Vanda tricolor" (horiz) 30 15
939 1r.50+50s. Type **151** 35 15
940 3r.+1r. "Dendrobium phalaenopsis" 35 10
941 6r.+1r.50 "Paphiopedilum praestans" (horiz) 25 10

1963. Construction of West Irian Monument.
942 **152** 1r.+50c. green and red . . 25 10
943 1r.50+50c. sepia, black and mauve 15 10
944 3r.+1r. brown and blue 25 10
945 6r.+1r.50 bistre & grn . . 25 15

153 Conference Emblem

154 Rice Sheaves

1963. 12th Pacific Area Travel Association Conference, Djakarta.
946 **153** 1r. blue and green 15 15
947 – 1r.50 blue and olive . . . 15 15
948 **153** 3r. blue and brown . . . 40 15
949 – 6r. blue and orange . . . 40 15
DESIGNS: 1r.50, Prambanan Temple and Mt. Merapi; 6r. Balinese Meru in Pura Taman Ajun.

1963. Freedom from Hunger.
950 **154** 1r. yellow and blue . . . 10 10
951 – 1r.50 blue and green . . . 15 10
952 **154** 3r. yellow and red 15 10
953 – 6r. orange and black . . . 25 15

DESIGN—HORIZ: 1r.50, 6r. Tractor; Nos. 950/1 are inscr "CONTRE LA FAIM"; Nos. 952/3, "FREEDOM FROM HUNGER".

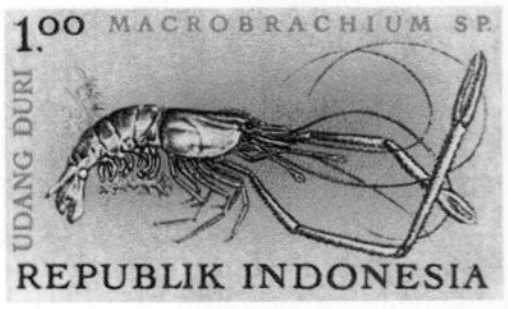

155 Lobster

1963. Marine Life. Multicoloured.
954 1r. Type **155** 35 15
955 1r.50 Kawakawa 35 15
956 3r. River snapper 80 35
957 6r. Chinese pomfret 80 50

156 Conference Emblem

1963. Asian-African Journalists' Conference.
958 **156** 1r. red and blue 15 10
959 – 1r.50 brown and lavender 15 10
960 – 3r. blue, black and olive 40 15
961 – 6r. salmon and black . . 55 25
DESIGNS—HORIZ: 1r.50, Pen, emblem and map. VERT: 3r. Pen. Globe and broken chain; 6r. Pen severing chain around Globe.

157 Indonesia, from Atjeh to Merauke

1963. Acquisition of West Irian (West New Guinea).
962 **157** 1r.50 orange, red & black 15 10
963 – 4r.50 blue, green & purple 15 15
964 – 6r. brown, yellow & green 80 50
DESIGNS: 4r.50, Parachutist; 6r. Greater bird of paradise.

158 Centenary Emblem

159 Volcano

1963. Centenary of Red Cross.
965 **158** 1r. green and red 25 15
966 – 1r.50 red and blue 25 15
967 **158** 3r. grey and red 25 15
968 – 6r. red and bistre 25 15
DESIGN: 1r.50, 6r. Red Cross (inscr in English).

1963. Bali Volcano Disaster Fund.
969 **159** 4r. (+2r.) red 15 10
970 6r. (+3r.) green 15 15

160 Bank of Indonesia, Djakarta

1963. National Banking Day.
971 **160** 1r.75 purple and blue . . 15 15
972 – 4r. green and yellow . . . 15 15
973 **160** 6r. brown and green . . . 15 10
974 – 12r. purple and orange . . 40 15
DESIGN—VERT: 4r., 12r. Daneswara, God of Prosperity.

161 Athletes with Banners

1963. Games of the New Emerging Forces, Djakarta.
975 **161** 1r.25 sepia and violet . . 10 10
976 – 1r.75 olive and buff . . 10 10
977 – 4r. sepia and green . . . 10 10
978 – 6r. sepia and brown . . . 25 15
979 – 10r. sepia and green . . . 25 15
980 – 12r. olive and red 35 15
981 – 25r. ultramarine and blue 50 35
982 – 50r. sepia and red 65 40
DESIGNS: 1r.75, "Pendet" dance; 4r. Conference Hall, Djakarta; 6r. Archery; 10r. Badminton; 12r. Throwing the javelin; 25r. Sailing; 50r. "Ganefo" torch.

162 "Papilio blumei"

163 Pres. Sukarno

1963. Social Day. Butterflies. Multicoloured.
983 1r.75+50s. Type **162** 40 15
984 4r.+1r. "Charaxes dehaani" 40 15
985 6r.+1r.50 Purple-spotted swallowtail 40 15
986 12r.+3r. "Troides amphrysus" 80 40

1964.
987 **163** 6r. blue and brown . . . 15 15
988 12r. purple and bistre . . 15 15
989 20r. orange and blue . . . 15 15
990 30r. blue and orange . . . 15 15
991 40r. brown and green . . 15 15
992 50r. green and red 15 15
993 75r. red and violet 15 15
994 100r. brown and grey . . 15 15
995 250r. grey and blue . . . 35 15
996 500r. gold and red . . . 50 35

164 Lorry and Trailer

165 Rameses II, Abu Simbel

1964.
997 – 1r. purple 15 15
998 **164** 1r.25 brown 15 15
999 – 1r.75 blue 15 15
1000 – 2r. red 15 15
1001 – 2r.50 blue 15 15
1002 – 4r. green 15 15
1003 – 5r. brown 15 15
1004 – 7r.50 green 15 15
1005 – 10r. orange 15 15
1006 – 15r. blue 15 15
1007 – 25r. blue 35 15
1008 – 35r. brown 35 15
DESIGNS—HORIZ: 1r. Ox-cart; 1r.75, "Hadju Agus Salim" (freighter); 2r. Lockheed Electra airliner; 4r. Cycle-postman; 5r. Douglas DC-3 airliner; 7r.50, Teletypist; 10r. Diesel train; 15r. "Sam Ratulangi" (freighter); 25r. Convair Coronado airliner; 35r. Telephone operator. VERT: 2r.50, Buginese sailing boat.

1964. Nubian Monuments Preservation. Monuments in brown.
1009 **165** 4r. drab 35 15
1010 – 6r. blue 35 15
1011 **165** 12r. pink 35 15
1012 – 18r. green 35 15
DESIGN: 6r., 18r., Trajan's Kiosk, Philae.

166 Various Stamps of Netherlands Indies and Indonesia

1964. Stamp Centenary.
1013 **166** 10r. multicoloured . . . 1·10 15

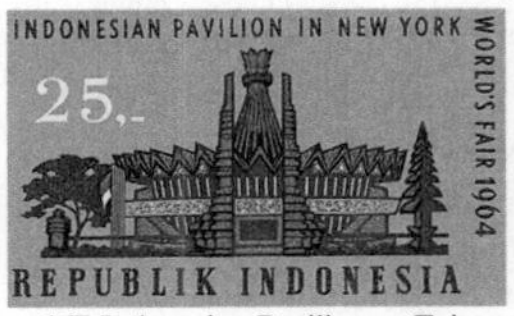

167 Indonesian Pavilion at Fair

1964. New York World's Fair.
1014 **167** 25r. red, blue and silver 55 40
1015 50r. red, turquoise & gold . . . . 1·40 40

168 Thomas Cup

170 Pied Fantail

169 "Sandjaja" and "Siliwanghi" (destroyers)

1964. Thomas Cup World Badminton Championships.
1016 **168** 25r. gold, red and green 25 25
1017 50r. gold, red and blue 25 25
1018 75r. gold, red and violet 80 80

1964. Indonesian Navy.
1019 **169** 20r. brown and yellow 40 10
1020 – 30r. black and red . . . 40 10
1021 – 40r. blue and green . . . 80 80
DESIGNS: 30r. "Nanggala" (submarine); 40r. "Matjan Tutul" (torpedo-boat).

1965. Social Day. Birds.
1022 **170** 4r.+1r. black, lilac and yellow 35 25
1023 – 6r.+1r.50 black, buff and green 35 25
1024 – 12r.+3r. black, blue and olive 55 35
1025 – 20r.+5r. yellow, red and purple 55 40
1026 – 30r.+7r.50 black, slate and mauve . . . . . 1·00 40
BIRDS: 6r. Zebra dove; 12r. Black drongo; 20r. Black-naped oriole; 30r. Java sparrow.

171 Map and Mosque

172 Scroll in Hand

1965. Afro-Asian Islamic Conf, Bandung.
1027 **171** 10r. blue and violet . . . 35 10
1028 – 15r. brown and orange 35 10
1029 **171** 25r. green and brown . . 50 15
1030 – 50r. purple and red . . . 50 50
DESIGN: 15r., 50r. Mosque and handclasp.

1965. 10th Anniv of First Afro-Asian Conference, Bandung.
1031 **172** 15r. red and silver . . . 25 10
1032 – 25r. gold, red & turquoise 25 10
1033 **172** 50r. blue and gold . . . 40 15
1034 – 75r. gold, red and lilac 65 65
DESIGN: 25r., 75r. Conference 10th-anniv emblem.

1965. Conf of "New Emerging Forces", Djakarta. T **163** additionally inscr "Conefo". Value, "Conefo" and frame in red; portrait colour given.
1035 1r.+1r. brown 15 10
1036 1r.25+1r.25 red 15 10
1037 1r.75+1r.75 purple 15 10
1038 2r.+2r. green 15 10
1039 2r.50+2r.50 brown 15 10
1040 4r.+3r.50 blue 15 10
1041 6r.+4r. green 15 10
1042 10r.+5r. brown 15 10
1043 12r.+5r.50 orange 15 10
1044 15r.+7r.50 turquoise 15 10
1045 20r.+10r. brown 15 10
1046 25r.+10r. violet 15 10
1047 40r.+15r. purple 15 10
1048 50r.+15r. violet 15 10
1049 100r.+25r. brown 25 15

174 Makara Mask and Rays

175 "Happy Family"

1965. Campaign against Cancer.
1050 **174** 20r.+10r. red and blue . . . 25 15
1051 30r.+15r. blue and red . . . 25 15

1965. The State's Five Principles and 20th Anniv of Republic.
1052 **175** 10r.+5r. yellow, black and brown 40 25
1053 – 20r.+10r. red, black and yellow 25 25
1054 – 25r.+10r. green, black and red 25 25
1055 – 40r.+15r. black, red and blue 50 25
1056 – 50r.+15r. yellow, black and mauve 50 25
DESIGNS: ("State's Principles"): 20r. "Humanitarianism" (globe and clasped hands); 25r. "Nationalism" (map and garland); 40r. "Democracy" (council meeting); 50r. "Belief in God" (churches and mosques).

177 Samudra Beach Hotel

1965. Tourist Hotels.
1060 **177** 10r.+5r. blue & turq . . 25 25
1061 – 25r.+10r. violet, black and green 35 35
1062 **177** 40r.+15r. brown, black and blue 40 35
1063 – 80r.+20r. pur & orge . . 65 35
DESIGN: 25r., 80r. Ambarrukmo Palace Hotel.

178 "Gloriosa superba"

180 Pres. Sukarno

1965. Flowers. Multicoloured, Inscr "1965" and with commas and dashes after figures of value.
1064 30r.+10r. Type **178** . . . . 1·00 1·00
1065 40r.+15r. "Hibiscus tiliaceus" . . . . 1·00 1·00
1066 80r.+20r. "Impatiens balsamina" . . . . 1·00 1·00
1067 100r.+25r. "Lagerstroemia Indica" . . . . 1·00 1·00
See also Nos. 1108/1116.

(Currency revalued. 100 (old) rupiahs = 1 (new) rupiah.)

1965. Revalued Currency. Optd **'65 Sen.** (a) On Nos. 989/94.
1068 **163** (20)s. on 20r. 15 10
1069 (30)s. on 30r. 15 15
1070 (40)s. on 40r. 15 15
1071 (50)s. on 50r. 15 15
1072 (75)s. on 75r. . . . . . 15 2·10
1073 (100)s. on 100r. 50 15
(b) On Nos. 1005/7.
1074 – (10)s. on 10r. 25 10
1075 – (15)s. on 15r. 25 10
1076 – (25)s. on 25r. 25 10

1966. Revalued Currency. Inscr "1967" (12r.) or "1966" (others). Values and frames turquoise (12r., 25r.) or chocolate (others); portrait and country name in colour given.
1077 **180** 1s. blue 15 10
1078 3s. olive 15 10
1079 5s. red 15 10
1080 8s. turquoise 15 10
1081 10s. blue 15 10
1082 15s. black 15 10
1083 20s. green 15 10
1084 25s. brown 15 10
1085 30s. blue 15 10
1086 40s. brown 15 10
1087 50s. violet 15 10
1088 80s. orange 15 10
1089 1r. green 15 10
1090 1r.25 brown 15 10
1091 1r.50 green 15 10
1092 2r. purple 25 10
1093 2r.50 slate 25 15
1094 5r. orange 35 35
1095 10r. olive 35 15
1096 12r. orange 35 15
1097 25r. violet 35 35

1966. Flowers. As T **178** but inscr "1966" and additionally inscr "sen" instead of commas and dashes. Multicoloured.
1108 10s.+5s. "Cassia alata" . . 1·00 1·00
1109 20s.+5s. "Barleria cristata" 1·00 1·00
1110 30s.+10s. "Ixora coccinea" 1·00 1·00
1111 40s.+10s. "Hibiscus rosa sinensis" . . . . 1·00 1·00

1966. National Disaster Fund. Floral designs as T **178** additionally inscr "BENTJANA ALAM NASIONAL 1966". Multicoloured.
1113 15a.+5s. "Gloriosa superba" 65 65
1114 25a.+5s. "Hibiscus tiliaceus" 65 65
1115 30s.+10s. "Impatiens balsamina" 65 65
1116 80s.+20s. "Lagerstroemia Indica" 65 65

181 Cleaning Ship's Rudder

182 Gen. A. Yani

1966. Maritime Day.
1117 **181** 20s. green and blue . . . 25 10
1118 – 40s. blue and pink . . . 25 10
1119 – 50s. brown and green . . 25 10
1120 – 1r. multicoloured 25 10
1121 – 1r.50 green and lilac . . 25 10
1122 – 2r. red and grey 25 15
1123 – 2r.50 red and mauve . . 25 20
1124 – 3r. black and green . . . 35 15
DESIGNS: 40s. Anyer Kidul lighthouse; 50s. Fisherman; 1r. Maritime emblem; 1r.50, Madurese sailing boat; 2r. Quayside; 2r.50 Pearl-diving; 3r. Liner in dry-dock.

1966. Victims of Attempted Communist Coup, 1965. Frames and date in blue.
1126 **182** 5r. brown 35 15
1127 A 5r. green 35 15
1128 B 5r. purple 35 15
1129 C 5r. olive 35 15
1130 D 5r. grey 35 15
1131 E 5r. violet 35 15
1132 F 5r. purple 35 15
1133 G 5r. green 35 15
1134 H 5r. purple 35 15
1135 I 5r. orange 35 15
PORTRAITS: A, Lt.-Gen. R. Soeprapto; B, Lt.-Gen. M. Harjono; C, Lt.-Gen. S. Parman; D, Maj.-Gen. D. Pandjaitan; E, Maj.-Gen. S. Siswomihardjo; F, Brig.-Gen. Katamso; G, Col. Soegijono; H, Capt. P. Tendean; I, Insp. K. S. Tubun.

183 Python

1966. Reptiles.
1136 **183** 2r.+25s. brown, green and flesh 15 15
1137 – 3r.+50s. grn, brn & lil 15 15
1138 – 4r.+75s. purple, buff and green 40 15
1139 – 6r.+1r. black, brn & bl 55 15
REPTILES: 3r. Chameleon; 4r. Crocodile; 6r. Green turtle.

184 Tjlempung

185 Pilot and Mikoyan Gurevich MiG-21 Fighter

1967. Musical Instruments.
1140 **184** 50s. red and black . . . 35 35
1141 – 1r. sepia and red 35 35
1142 – 1r.25 lake and blue . . . 35 35
1143 – 1r.50 green and violet . . 35 35
1144 – 2r. blue and ochre . . . 35 35
1145 – 2r.50 green and red . . . 35 35
1146 – 3r. green and purple . . 35 35
1147 – 4r. blue and orange . . . 55 35
1148 – 5r. red and blue 55 35
1149 – 6r. blue and mauve . . . 40 40
1150 – 8r. lake and green . . . 40 40
1151 – 10r. violet and red . . . 40 35
1152 – 12r. green and violet . . 65 55
1153 – 15r. violet and olive . . 50 35
1154 – 20r. black and sepia . . 50 35
1155 – 25r. black and green . . 60 35
INSTRUMENTS: 1r. Sasando; 1r.25, Foi doa; 1r.50, Kultjapi; 2r. Arababu; 2r.50, Genderang; 3r. Katjapi; 4r. Hape; 5r. Gangsa; 6r. Serunai; 8r. Rebab; 10r. Trompet; 12r. Totobuang; 15r. Tamburn; 20r. Kulintang; 25r. Keledi.

1967. Aviation Day. Multicoloured.
1156 2r.50 Type **185** 35 25
1157 4r. Convair Coronado airliner and control tower 35 20
1158 5r. Lockheed C-130 Hercules transport aircraft on tarmac 55 25

186 Thomas Cup and Silhouettes

187 Balinese Girl

1967. Thomas Cup World Badminton Championships. Multicoloured.
1159 5r. Type **186** 25 15
1160 12r. Thomas Cup on Globe 50 15

1967. International Tourist Year.
1161 **187** 12r. multicoloured . . . 1·10 90

188 Heroes Monument

191 Flood Victims

190 "Forest Fire"

1967. "Heroes of the Revolution". Monument.
1163 **188** 2r.50 brown and green 15 10
1164 – 5r. purple and drab . . 40 25
1165 – 7r.50 green and pink . . 40 25
DESIGNS—HORIZ: 5r. Monument and shrine. VERT: 7r.50, Shrine.

1967. Paintings by Raden Saleh.
1175 **190** 25r. red and green . . . 40 40
1176 – 50r. purple and red . . . 55 40
PAINTING: 50r. "A Fight to the Death".

1967. National Disaster Fund.
1178 **191** 1r.25+10s. blue & yell 35 35
1179 – 2r.50+25s. blue & yell 35 35
1180 – 4r.+40s. black & orge . . 35 35
1181 – 5r.+50s. black & orge . . 35 35
DESIGNS: 2r.50, Landslide; 4r. Burning house; 5r. Erupting volcano.

192 Human Rights Emblem

193 Academy Badge

1968. Human Rights Year.
1183 **192** 5r. red, green and blue 20 10
1184 12r. red, green and drab 20 10

1968. Indonesian Military Academy.
1185 **193** 10r. multicoloured . . . 50 25

194/6 "Sudhana and Manohara at Court of Druma" (relief on wall of Borobudur) (⅔-size illustration)

1968. "Save Borobudur Monument".
1186 **194** 2r.50+25s. deep green and green 35 35
1187 **195** 2r.50+25s. deep green and green 35 35
1188 **196** 2r.50+25s. deep green and green 35 35
1189 – 7r.50+75s. green and orange 65 35
DESIGN—VERT: 7r.50, Buddhist and statue of Buddha.

197 W.H.O. Emblem and "20"

1968. 20th Anniv of W.H.O.
1191 **197** 2r. purple and yellow . . 35 25
1192 – 20r. black and green . . 35 25
DESIGN: 20r. W.H.O. emblem.

198 Diesel Train (1967) and Steam Train (1867)

1968. Centenary (1967) of Indonesian Railways.
1193 **198** 20r. multicoloured . . . 75 25
1194 30r. multicoloured . . . 1·10 90

199 Scout with Pick

200 Butterfly Dancer

1968. "Wirakarya" Scout Camp.
1195 **199** 5r.+50s. brown & orge 25 15
1196 – 10r.+1r. grey & brown 55 35
1197 – 30r.+3r. brown & grn . . 90 55
DESIGNS—VERT: 10r. Bugler on hillside. HORIZ: (69 × 29 mm); 30r. Scouts in camp.

1968. Tourism.
1198 **200** 30r. multicoloured . . . 1·40 1·40

202 Observatory and Stars

1968. 40th Anniv of Bosscha Observatory.
1207 **202** 15r. blue, yellow & black 40 25
1208 – 30r. violet and orange 65 25
DESIGN—VERT: 30r. Observatory on Globe.

203/4 Yachting

1968. Olympic Games, Mexico.
1209 – 5r. green, brown & black 10 10
1210 **203** 7r.50 blue, yellow & red 25 15
1211 **204** 7r.50 blue, yellow & red 25 15
1212 – 12r. red, blue and yellow 25 10
1213 – 30r. brown, green & orge 50 25
DESIGNS:—28½ × 44½ mm: 5r. Weightlifting; 12r. Basketball. 44½ × 28½ mm: 30r. Dove and Olympic flame.

Nos. 1210/11 were issued together, se-tenant, forming the composite design illustrated.

205 "Eugenia aquea"

1968. Fruits. Multicoloured.
1215 7r.50 Type **205** 35 15
1216 15r. "Carica papaya" 50 25
1217 30r. "Durio zibethinus" (vert) 80 40

206 I.L.O. Emblem and part of Globe

207 R. Dewi Sartika

1969. 50th Anniv of I.L.O.
1219 **206** 5r. red and green 10 10
1220 – 7r.50 green and orange 15 10
1221 **206** 15r. red and violet 25 15
1222 – 25r. red and turquoise 50 25
DESIGN: 7r.50, 25r. I.L.O. emblem.

1969. National Independence Heroes.
1223 **207** 15r. green and violet 35 15
1224 – 15r. purple and green 35 15
1225 – 15r. blue and red 35 15
1226 – 15r. ochre and red 35 15
1227 – 15r. sepia and blue 35 15
1228 – 15r. lilac and blue 35 15
PORTRAITS: No. 1224, Tjut Nja Din; 1225, Tjut Nja Meuthia; 1226, Sutan Sjahrir; 1227, Dr. F. L. Tobing; 1228, General G. Subroto.

208 Woman with Flower

209 Red Cross "Mosaic"

1969. Women's Emancipation Campaign.
1229 **208** 20r.+2r. red, yellow and green 65 35

1969. 50th Anniv of League of Red Cross Societies.
1230 **209** 15r. red and green 40 15
1231 – 20r. red and yellow 40 35
DESIGN: 20r. Hands encircling Red Cross.

210 "Planned" Family and Factory

1969. South-East Asia and Oceania Family Planning Conference.
1232 **210** 10r. orange and green 35 15
1233 – 20r. mauve and green 50 25
DESIGN: 20r. "Planned" family and "National Prosperity".

211 Balinese Mask

1969. Tourism in Bali. Multicoloured.
1234 12r. Type **211** 35 25
1235 15r. Girl with offerings 65 35
1236 30r. Cremation rites 65 35

212 "Agriculture"

213 Dish Aerial

1969. Five-year Development Plan.
1238 – 5r. blue and green 25 10
1239 **212** 7r.50 yellow and purple 25 10
1240 – 10r. red and blue 25 10
1241 – 12r. red and blue 1·40 65
1242 – 15r. yellow and green 25 10
1243 – 20r. yellow and violet 25 10
1244 – 25r. red and black 25 15
1245 – 30r. black and red 50 15
1246 – 40r. orange and green 55 15
1247 – 50r. brown and orange 1·10 15
DESIGNS: 5r. Religious emblems ("Co-existence"); 10r. Modern family ("Social Welfare"); 12r. Crane and crate ("Overseas Trade"); 15r. Bobbins ("Clothing Industry"); 20r. Children in class ("Education"); 25r. Research worker ("Scientific Research"); 30r. Family and hypodermic syringe ("Health Care"); 40r. Tunas in net ("Fisheries"); 50r. Graph ("Statistics").

1969. Satellite Communications and Inauguration of Djatiluhur Earth Station. Multicoloured.
1248 15r. Type **213** 40 15
1249 30r. Communications satellite 55 50

214 Vickers Vimy Biplane over Borobudur Temple

1969. 50th Anniv of 1st England–Australia Flight by Ross and Keith Smith.
1253 **214** 75r. purple and red 55 50
1254 – 100r. green and yellow 55 55
DESIGNS: 100r. Vickers Vimy and map of Indonesia.

215 Noble Volute

1969. Sea Shells. Multicoloured.
1255 5r.+50c. Type **215** 55 55
1256 7r.50+50c. Common hairy triton 55 55
1257 10r.+1r. Common spider conch 80 80
1258 15r.+1r.50 Bramble murex 80 80

216 Indonesian Pavilion

217 Prisoner's Hands and Scales of Justice

1970. "Expo 70" World Fair, Osaka, Japan.
1259 **216** 5r. yellow, green & brn 55 25
1260 – 15r. red, blue and green 75 35
1261 **216** 30r. yellow, blue and red 1·40 55
DESIGN: 15r. Indonesian "Garuda" symbol.

1970. "Purification of Justice".
1262 **217** 10r. purple and red 55 35
1263 15r. purple and green 90 35

218 U.P.U. Monument, Berne

219 Timor Dancers

1970. Inauguration of New U.P.U. Headquarters Building, Berne.
1264 **218** 15r. red and green 65 35
1265 – 30r. blue and ochre 1·40 80
DESIGN: 30r. New Headquarters building.

1970. "Visit Indonesia Year". Traditional Dancers. Multicoloured.
1266 20r. Type **219** 1·10 50
1267 45r. Bali dancers 1·60 80

220 "Productivity" Symbol

221 Independence Monument

1970. Asian Productivity Year.
1269 **220** 5r. red, yellow and green 65 15
1270 30r. red, yellow and violet 1·40 65

1970. 25th Anniv of Independence.
1271 **221** 40r. violet, purple & blue 16·00 5·00

222 Emblems of Post and Giro, and of Telecommunications

223 U.N. Emblem and Doves

1970. 25th Anniv of Indonesian Post and Telecommunications Services.
1272 **222** 10r. brown, yellow & grn 5·00 25
1273 – 25r. black, yellow & pink 10·50 65
DESIGN: 25r. Telephone dial and P.T.T. worker.

1970. 25th Anniv of United Nations.
1274 **223** 40r. multicoloured 16·00 5·00

224 I.E.Y. Emblem on globe

225 "Chrysocoris javanus" (shieldbug)

1970. International Education Year.
1275 **224** 25r. brown, red & yellow 9·75 3·25
1276 – 50r. red, black and blue 20·00 5·00
DESIGNS: 50r. I.E.Y. emblem.

1970. Insects. Multicoloured.
1277 7r.50+50c. Type **225** 7·00 1·60
1278 15r.+1r.50 "Orthetrum testaceum" (darter) 12·00 8·25
1279 20r.+2r. "Xylocopa flavonigrescens" (carpenter bee) 24·00 5·75

226 Batik handicrafts

1971. "Visit ASEAN (South East Asian Nations Association) Year". Multicoloured.
1280 20r. Type **226** 3·00 1·40
1281 50r. Javanese girl playing angklung (musical instrument) (vert) 4·50 3·75
1282 75r. Wedding group, Minangkabau 11·50 5·25

227 Restoration of Fatahillah Park

1971. 444th Anniv of Djakarta. Multicoloured.
1284 15r. Type **227** 2·50 1·10
1285 65r. Performance at Lenong Theatre 4·50 4·00
1286 80r. Ismail Marzuki Cultural Centre 10·50 3·50

228 Sita and Rama

229 Pigeon with Letter, and Workers

1971. International Ramayana Festival.
1288 **228** 30r. multicoloured 2·75 80
1289 – 100r. black, blue and red 4·00 1·80
DESIGN: 100r. Rama.

1971. 5th Asian Regional Telecommunications Conf.
1290 **229** 50r. chocolate, brown and buff 2·10 1·00

230 U.P.U. Monument, Berne, and Hemispheres

1971. U.P.U. Day.
1291 **230** 40r. purple, black & blue 2·00 1·00

231 Schoolgirl

233 Microwave Tower

232 Clown Surgeonfish

1971. 25th Anniv of U.N.I.C.E.F. Mult.
1292 20r. Type **231** 2·75 55
1293 40r. Boy with rice-stalks 4·00 1·10

1971. Fishes (1st series). Multicoloured.
1294 15r. Type **232** 5·25 1·40
1295 30r. Moorish idol 10·50 3·75
1296 40r. Emperor angelfish 16·00 5·25
See also Nos. 1318/20, 1343/5, 1390/2 and 1423/5.

1972. 25th Anniv of E.C.A.F.E.
1297 **233** 40r. blue and turquoise 3·50 1·00
1298 – 75r. multicoloured 3·50 1·00
1299 – 100r. multicoloured 5·25 2·10
DESIGNS—VERT: 40r. E.C.A.F.E. emblem. HORIZ: 100r. Irrigation and highways.

234 Human Heart

235 Ancient and Modern Textile Production

1972. World Heart Month.
1300 **234** 50r. multicoloured 2·10 80

1972. 50th Anniv of Textile Technological Institute.
1301 **235** 35r. purple, yellow & orge 2·10 80

236 Children reading Books

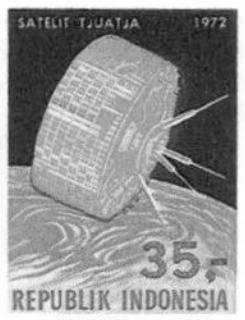

237 "Essa 8" Weather Satellite

1972. International Book Year.
1302 **236** 75r. multicoloured . . . 2·75 1·20

1972. Space Exploration.
1303 **237** 35r. brown, violet & blue 2·00 65
1304 – 50r. blue, black and pink 3·75 3·50
1305 – 60r. black, green & brn 6·50 1·10
DESIGNS: 50r. Astronaut on Moon; 60r. Indonesian "Kartika I" rocket.

238 Hotel Indonesia

1972. 10th Anniv of Hotel Indonesia.
1306 **238** 50r. green, pale grn & red . . . . 2·50 1·10

239 "Silat" (unarmed combat)

240 Family and Religious Buildings

1972. Olympic Games, Munich.
1307 **239** 20r. purple, cobalt & blue . . . . 1·40 15
1308 – 35r. violet, brown & mve 1·40 40
1309 – 50r. emer, dp grn & grn 2·75 75
1310 – 75r. rose, purple and pink . . . . 2·75 1·80
1311 – 100r. brown, blue & green . . . . 5·75 3·00
DESIGNS: 35r. Running; 50r. Diving; 75r. Badminton; 100r. Olympic stadium.

1972. Family Planning Campaign. Mult.
1312 30r. Type **240** . . . . . . 2·00 65
1313 75r. "Healthy family" . . . 3·75 2·40
1314 80r. "Family of workers" 6·00 3·00

241 Moluccas Dancer

242 Thomas Cup and Shuttlecock

1972. "Art and Culture" (1st series).
1315 **241** 30r. brown, pink & green 2·00 65
1316 – 60r. multicoloured . . . 5·00 2·75
1317 – 100r. bl, brn & cinnamon . . . . . . 7·00 2·75
DESIGNS—VERT: 60r. Couple and Toraja traditional house. HORIZ: 100r. West Irian traditional house.
See also 1336/8, 1373/5 and 1401/3.

1972. Fishes (2nd series). As T **232**. Mult.
1318 30r. Triangle butterflyfish 7·00 2·00
1319 50r. Royal angelfish . . . . 12·00 3·00
1320 100r. Clown triggerfish . . . 16·00 5·25

1972. Thomas Cup Badminton Championships, Djakarta.
1321 **242** 30r. blue and green . . . 80 25
1322 – 75r. red and green . . . 1·80 50
1323 – 80r. brown and red . . . 3·50 1·00
DESIGNS: 75r. Thomas Cup and Sports Centre; 80r. Thomas Cup and player.

243 Emblem, Anemometer and "Gatotkaca"

1973. I.M.O. and W.M.O. Weather Organization Centenary.
1324 **243** 80r. multicoloured . . . 2·00 80

244 "Health begins at Home"

245 Java Mask

1973. 25th Anniv of W.H.O.
1325 **244** 80r. blue, orange & green . . . . 1·60 80

1973. Tourism. Indonesian Folk Masks. Mult.
1326 30r. Type **245** . . . . . . 5·25 90
1327 60r. Kalimantan mask . . . 8·25 3·50
1328 100r. Bali mask . . . . . . 13·00 1·80

246 Savings Bank and Thrift Plant

247 Chess

1973. Two-Year National Savings Drive.
1329 **246** 25r. black, yellow & bis 90 50
1330 – 30r. green, gold & yellow 1·60 50
DESIGN—HORIZ: 30r. Hand and "City" savings bank.

1973. National Sports Week. Multicoloured.
1331 30r. Type **247** . . . . . . 1·60 1·10
1332 60r. Karate . . . . 2·75 1·10
1333 75r. Hurdling (horiz) . . . 5·00 90

248 International Policemen

1973. 50th Anniv of Interpol.
1334 **248** 30r. multicoloured . . . 90 35
1335 – 50r. yellow, purple & blk 1·60 65
DESIGN—VERT: 50r. Giant temple guard.

1973. "Art and Culture" (2nd series). Weaving and Fabrics. As T **241**. Multicoloured.
1336 60r. Parang Rusak pattern 2·50 2·00
1337 80r. Pagi Sore pattern . . . 5·00 2·10
1338 100r. Merak Ngigel pattern 9·00 3·75

249 "Food Cultivation"

1973. 10th Anniv of World Food Programme.
1339 **249** 30r. multicoloured . . . 2·10 65

250 "Religion"

252 Bengkulu Costume

251 Admiral Sudarso and Naval Battle of Arafuru

1973. Family Planning.
1340 **250** 20r. blue, light blue & red 80 40
1341 – 30r. black, yellow & brn 1·60 65
1342 – 60r. black, yellow & grn 3·25 55
DESIGNS: 30r. Teacher and class ("Population Education"); 60r. Family and house ("Health").

1973. Fishes (3rd series). As T **232**. Mult.
1343 40r. Powder-blue surgeonfish 1·60 1·10
1344 65r. Melon butterflyfish . . 6·50 2·00
1345 100r. Blue-ringed angelfish 8·25 3·25

1974. Naval Day.
1346 **251** 40r. multicoloured . . . 1·80 80

1974. Pacific Area Travel Association Conference, Djakarta. Provincial Costumes. Multicoloured.
1347 5r. Type **252** . . . . . . 16·00 1·10
1348 7r.50 Kalimantan, Timor . . 8·25 1·10
1349 10r. Kalimantan, Tengah . . 1·60 80
1350 15r. Jambi . . . . 1·60 80
1351 20r. Sulawesi, Tenggara . . 1·60 80
1352 25r. Nusatenggara, Timor 1·60 80
1353 27r.50 Maluku . . . . . . 1·60 1·60
1354 30r. Lampung . . . . . . 1·60 1·60
1355 35r. Sumatera, Barat . . . 1·60 80
1356 40r. Aceh . . . . 1·60 80
1357 45r. Nusatenggara, Barat . . 4·00 80
1358 50r. Riau . . . . 2·40 2·40
1359 55r. Kalimantan, Barat . . 3·25 80
1360 60r. Sulawesi, Utara . . . . 3·25 80
1361 65r. Sulawesi, Tengah . . . 3·25 80
1362 70r. Sumatera, Selatan . . . 3·50 80
1363 75r. Java, Barat . . . . . . 3·50 80
1364 80r. Sumatera, Utara . . . 3·50 80
1365 90r. Yogyakarta . . . . . 3·75 3·75
1366 95r. Kalimantan, Selatan . . 3·50 80
1367 100r. Java, Timor . . . . . 3·50 1·60
1368 120r. Irian, Jaya . . . . . 6·50 1·10
1369 130r. Java, Tengah . . . . 6·50 80
1370 135r. Sulawesi, Selatan . . . 7·25 80
1371 150r. Bali . . . . 7·25 80
1372 160r. Djakarta . . . . . . 7·25 1·60

1974. "Art and Culture" (3rd series). Shadow Plays. As T **241**. Multicoloured.
1373 40r. Baladewa . . . . . . 3·00 1·30
1374 80r. Kresna . . . . 5·25 2·50
1375 100r. Bima . . . . 6·50 2·50

254 Pres. Suharto

1974.
1376 **254** 40r. brown, green & blk 80 10
1377 50r. brown, blue & black 2·00 15
1378 65r. brown, mauve & blk 1·10 65
1379 75r. brown, yellow & blk 2·00 15
1380 100r. brown, yellow & blk . . . . 2·00 15
1381 150r. brown, green & blk 2·00 15
See also Nos. 1444/7.

255 "Improvement of Living Standards"

256 "Welfare"

1974. World Population Year.
1382 **255** 65r. multicoloured . . . 1·50 50

1974. Family Planning.
1383 **256** 25r. multicoloured . . . 1·00 40
1384 – 40r. blue, black and green . . . . 1·00 40
1385 – 65r. ochre, brown & yell 3·00 40
DESIGNS: 40r. Young couple ("Development"); 65r. Arrows ("Religion").

257 Bicycle Postmen

1974. Centenary of U.P.U.
1386 **257** 20r. brown, yellow & grn 2·50 50
1387 – 40r. brown, orange & bl 2·50 75
1388 – 65r. brown, yellow & blk 2·50 75
1389 – 100r. black, blue and red 2·50 2·00
DESIGNS: 40r. Mail-cart; 65r. Mounted postman; 100r. East Indies galley.

1974. Fishes (4th series). As T **232**. Mult.
1390 40r. Sail-finned tang . . . . 2·50 50
1391 80r. Blue-girdled angelfish 4·00 2·00
1392 100r. Mandarin fish . . . . 6·50 2·40

258 Drilling for Oil

1974. 17th Anniv of Pertamina Oil Complex. Multicoloured.
1393 40r. Type **258** 55 35
1394 75r. Oil refinery 55 35
1395 95r. Control centre (vert) . . 55 35
1396 100r. Road tanker (vert) . . 55 35
1397 120r. Fokker Fellowship airliner over storage tank farm (vert) 90 35
1398 130r. Pipelines and tanker (vert) 90 35
1399 150r. Petrochemical storage tanks 90 35
1400 200r. Offshore oil rig . . . 90 35

1975. "Art and Culture" (4th series). As T **241**.
1401 50r. silver, red and black . . 1·50 1·30
1402 75r. silver, green and black 2·40 1·30
1403 100r. yellow, blue and black 4·50 1·30
DESIGNS: 50r. Sumatran spittoon; 75r. Sumatran "sirh" dish; 100r. Kalimantan "sirh" dish.

260 "Donorship"

261 Measures and Globe

1975. Blood Donors' Campaign.
1404 **260** 40r. red, yellow and green . . . . 1·10 65

1975. Centenary of Metre Convention.
1405 **261** 65r. blue, red and yellow 2·00 65

262 Women in Public Service

1975. International Women's Year. Mult.
1406 40r. Type **262** . . . . . . 1·60 65
1407 100r. I.W.Y. emblem (21 × 29 mm) . . . . . . 2·10 65

263 "Dendrobium pakarena"

264 Stupas and Damaged Temple

1975. Tourism. Indonesian Orchids. Mult.
1408 40r. Type **263** . . . . . . 5·00 1·10
1409 70r. "Aeridachnis bogor" 5·00 2·10
1410 85r. "Vanda genta" . . . . 9·00 3·25

1975. U.N.E.S.C.O. "Save Borobudur Temple" Campaign. Multicoloured.
1411 25r. Type **264** . . . . . . 3·25 80
1412 40r. Buddhist shrines and broken wall . . . . . . 3·75 1·10
1413 65r. Stupas and damaged building (horiz) . . . . . 7·25 4·50
1414 100r. Buddha and stupas (horiz) . . . . 10·50 4·50

265 Battle of Banjarmasin

1975. 30th Anniv of Independence.
1415 **265** 25r. black and yellow . . 80 50
1416 – 40r. black and red . . . 1·10 50
1417 – 75r. black and red . . . 1·60 1·30
1418 – 100r. black and orange 1·60 1·00
DESIGNS: 40r. Battle of Batua; 75r. battle of Margarana; 100r. Battle of Palembang.

266 "Education"

267 Heroes' Monument, Surabaya

1975. Family Planning. Multicoloured.
1419 20r. Type **266** 65 15
1420 25r. "Religion" 1·00 25
1421 40r. "Prosperity" 1·60 50

1975. 30th Anniv of Independence War.
1422 **267** 100r. red and green 2·40 50

1975. Fishes (5th series). As T **232**. Mult.
1423 40r. Twin-spotted wrasse 1·60 50
1424 75r. Saddleback butterflyfish 5·00 1·50
1425 150r. Dusky batfish (vert) 6·50 3·00

269 Thomas Cup

1976. Indonesian Victory in World Badminton Championships. Multicoloured.
1428 20r. Type **269** 1·00 25
1429 40r. Uber cup 1·00 55
1430 100r. Thomas and Uber cups 2·10 55

270 Refugees and New Village

1976. World Human Settlements Day. Mult.
1431 30r. Type **270** 80 15
1432 50r. Old and restored villages 1·50 40
1433 100r. Derelict and rebuilt houses 1·60 40

271 Early and Modern Telephones

272 Human Eye

1976. Telephone Centenary.
1434 **271** 100r. brown, red & yell 1·30 50

1976. World Health Day. Multicoloured.
1435 20r. Type **272** 40 25
1436 40r. Blind man with stick 90 40

273 Main Stadium, Montreal

1976. Olympic Games, Montreal.
1437 **273** 100r. blue 1·30 55

274 Lake Tondano, Sulawesi

275 "Light Traffic" Station

1976. Tourism. Multicoloured.
1438 35r. Type **274** 80 40
1439 40r. Lake Kelimutu, Flores 80 40
1440 75r. Lake Maninjau, Sumatra 1·60 50

1976. Inauguration of Domestic Satellite System.
1441 **275** 20r. multicoloured 80 35
1442 – 50r. black and green 80 35
1443 – 100r. turquoise, bl & vio 1·40 65
DESIGNS: 50r. "Master control" station; 100r. "Palapa" satellite.

1976. As T **254** but with background of wavy lines.
1444 200r. brown, blue and green 8·25 15
1445 300r. brown, red and flesh 2·10 15
1446 400r. brown, green and yellow 4·00 35
1447 500r. brown, red and lilac 5·75 1·00

276 "Vanda Putri Serang"

1976. Orchids. Multicoloured.
1448 25r. "Arachnis flos-aeris" 2·40 1·00
1449 40r. Type **276** 2·40 1·00
1450 100r. "Coelogyne pandurata" 3·50 2·10

277 Stylized Tree

279 Open Book

278 Kelewang Dagger and Sheath (Timor)

1976. Reafforestation Week.
1452 **277** 20r. green, blue & brown 80 35

1976. Daggers and Sheaths.
1453 **278** 25r. green, black & brown 1·10 40
1454 – 40r. brown, yellow & orge 1·80 75
1455 – 100r. brown, yellow & grn 2·50 2·10
DESIGNS: 40r. Mandau dagger and sheath (Borneo); 100r. Rencong dagger and sheath (Aceh).

1976. Books for Children.
1457 **279** 20r. green, orange & blue 65 25
1458 – 40r. violet, red and yellow 1·30 40
DESIGN: 40r. Children reading book.

280 UNICEF Emblem

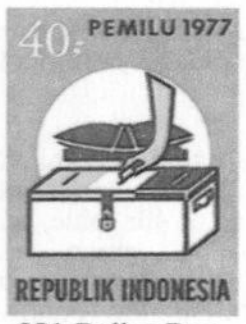

281 Ballot Box

1976. 30th Anniv of U.N.I.C.E.F.
1459 **280** 40r. blue, turquoise & vio 1·10 50

1977. Elections.
1460 **281** 40r. blue, yellow and grey 2·10 25
1461 – 75r. blue, yellow and pink 2·40 40
1462 – 100r. bistre, red and black 3·75 1·30
DESIGNS: 75r. Ballot box, factory and produce; 100r. Indonesian arrow.

282 Scout Emblems and Camp

283 Letter and A.O.P.U. Emblem

1977. 11th National Scout Jamboree. Mult.
1463 25r. Type **282** 60 35
1464 30r. Emblems, tent and trees 60 35
1465 40r. Emblems, tent and flags 1·40 75

1977. 15th Anniv of Asian–Oceanic Postal Union. Multicoloured.
1466 65r. Type **283** 80 35
1467 100r. Stylized carrier pigeon 1·40 50

284 Anniversary Emblem

285 Rose

1977. 450th Anniv of Jakarta.
1468 **284** 20r. blue and red 80 40
1469 – 40r. green and blue 80 40
1470 – 100r. blue and turquoise 1·60 80
DESIGNS: 40; 100r. Similar to Type **284** but with emblem and arms differently arranged.

1977. "Amphilex 77" International Stamp Exhibition, Amsterdam.
1472 **285** 100r. red, green and black 1·40 50
1473 – 100r. red, green and black 1·40 50
DESIGN: No. 1473, Envelope.

286 Sports Pictograms

287 Trophy

1977. 9th National Sports Week.
1475 **286** 40r. silver, green and red 2·50 1·60
1476 – 50r. silver, blue and red 3·50 1·60
1477 – 100r. gold, black and red 5·75 3·50
DESIGNS: 50; 100r. Similar to Type **286** but with different pictograms.

1977. 10th National Koran Reading Contest.
1478 **287** 40r. brown, green & yell 2·40 50
1479 – 100r. black, yellow & grn 3·00 90
DESIGN: 100r. Emblem.

288 Carrier Pigeon and Map

289 Government Officer, Djakarta Region

1977. 10th Anniv of Association of South East Asian Nations. Multicoloured.
1480 25r. Type **288** 50 15
1481 35r. Map of ASEAN members 2·10 65
1482 50r. Transport and flags of ASEAN members 2·10 80

1977. Economic and Cultural Co-operation with Pakistan.
1483 **289** 25r. brown, gold & green 65 25

290 "Taeniophyllum sp."

291 Child and Mosquito

1977. Orchids. Multicoloured.
1484 25r. Type **290** 2·40 80
1485 40r. "Phalaenopsis violacea" 2·40 1·60
1486 100r. "Dendrobium spectabile" 5·00 2·40

1977. National Health Campaign.
1488 **291** 40r. red, green and black 65 25

292 Proboscis Monkey

1977. Wildlife (1st series). Multicoloured.
1489 20r. Type **292** 80 40
1490 40r. Indian elephant 2·00 80
1491 100r. Tiger 5·25 1·60

293 Hands holding U.N. Emblem

294 Mother feeding Baby

1978. U.N. Conference on Technical Co-operation among Developing Countries.
1493 **293** 100r. blue and ultramarine 1·40 55

1978. Campaign for the Promotion of Breast Feeding.
1494 **294** 40r. green and blue 50 25
1495 – 75r. brown and red 90 40
DESIGN: 75r. Stylised mother and child.

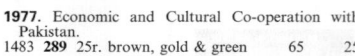

295 Dome of the Rock

1978. Palestine Welfare.
1496 **295** 100r. multicoloured 1·30 50

296 World Cup Emblem

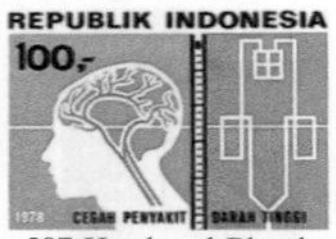

297 Head and Blood Circulation Diagram

1978. World Cup Football Championship, Argentina.
1497 **296** 40r. green, black and blue 65 25
1498 100r. mauve, black & bl 1·20 65

1978. World Health Day.
1499 **297** 100r. blue, black and red 1·20 50

298 Leather Puppets

1978. Puppets from Wayang Museum, Djakarta. Multicoloured.
1500 40r. Type **298** 2·40 65
1501 75r. Wooden puppets 2·50 1·30
1502 100r. Actors wearing masks 5·00 2·10

300 Congress Emblem

301 I.A.Y. Emblem

1978. 27th Congress of World Confederation of Organizations of the Teaching Profession, Djakarta.
1509 **300** 100r. grey . . . . 1·00 40

1978. International Anti-Apartheid Year.
1510 **301** 100r. blue and red . . . 1·10 40

302 Couple and Tree

303 Anniversary Emblem

1978. 8th World Forestry Congress, Djakarta.
1511 **302** 40r. blue and green . . . 25 15
1512 – 100r. dp green & lt green 1·00 50
DESIGN: 100r. People and trees.

1978. 50th Anniv of Youth Pledge.
1513 **303** 40r. brown and red . . . 65 25
1514 100r. brown, red and pink . . . . 1·00 40

1978. Wildlife (2nd series). As T **292**. Mult.
1515 40r. Long-nosed echidna . . 1·60 40
1516 75r. Sambar . . . . 2·40 80
1517 100r. Clouded leopard . . . 4·00 1·20

304 "Phalaenopsis sri rejeki"

307 Thomas Cup and Badminton Player

306 Douglas DC-3 over Volcano

1978. Orchids. Multicoloured.
1519 40r. Type **304** . . . . . . 1·20 40
1520 75r. "Dendrobium macrophillum" . . . . . 1·60 65
1521 100r. "Cymbidium fynlaysonianum" . . . . 3·25 90

1979. 30th Anniv of Garuda Indonesian Airways. Multicoloured.
1531 40r. Type **306** 80 35
1532 75r. Douglas DC-9-30 over village . . . . 1·00 35
1533 100r. Douglas DC-10 over temple . . . . 1·80 1·00

1979. Thomas Cup Badminton Championships, Djakarta.
1534 **307** 40r. pink and turquoise 50 50
1535 – 100r. brown and pink . . 1·00 80
1536 – 100r. brown and pink . . 1·00 80
DESIGNS: No. 1535, Player on left side of net hitting shuttlecock; 1536, Player on right side of net.
Nos. 1535/6 were issued together, se-tenant, forming a composite design.

308 "Paphiopedilum lowii"

309 Family and Houses

1979. Orchids. Multicoloured.
1537 60r. Type **308** . . . . . . 1·10 35
1538 100r. "Vanda limbata" . . . 1·60 50
1539 125r. "Phalaenopsis gigantea" . . . . 2·40 80

1979. 3rd Five Year Development Plan.
1541 **309** 35r. drab and green . . . 15 10
1542 – 60r. green and blue . . . 25 15
1543 – 100r. brown and blue . . 50 15
1544 – 125r. brown and green 65 25
1545 – 150r. yellow, orge & red 80 25
DESIGNS: 60r. Pylon, dam and fields; 100r. School and clinic; 125r. Loading produce at factory; 150r. Delivering mail.

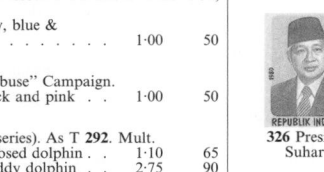

310/11 Mrs. R. A. Kartini

1979. Birth Centenary of Mrs. R. A. Kartini (pioneer of women's rights).
1546 **310** 100r. brown and green 80 40
1547 **311** 100r. green and brown 80 40

312 Bureau Emblem

313 Self Defence

1979. 50th Anniv of International Bureau of Education.
1549 **312** 150r. blue, lt blue & lilac 1·10 40

1979. 10th South East Asia Games, Djakarta.
1550 **313** 60r. yellow, black & grn 55 25
1551 – 125r. orange, grey & blue 90 40
1552 – 150r. yellow, black & red 1·30 65
DESIGNS: 125r. Games emblem; 150r. Main stadium, Senayan.

314 Co-operation Emblem

315 National I.Y.C. Emblem

1979. Co-operation Day.
1553 **314** 150r. multicoloured . . . 1·00 35

1979. International Year of the Child.
1554 **315** 60r. black and green . . 40 15
1555 – 150r. blue and black . . 1·00 40
DESIGN: 150r. International I.Y.C. emblem.

316 Exhibition Emblem

317 Drug Addict

1979. 3rd World Telecommunications Exhibition, Geneva
1556 **316** 150r. grey, blue & orange . . . . 1·00 50

1979. "End Drug Abuse" Campaign.
1557 **317** 150r. black and pink . . 1·00 50

1979. Wildlife (3rd series). As T **292**. Mult.
1558 60r. Bottle-nosed dolphin . . 1·10 65
1559 125r. Irrawaddy dolphin . . 2·75 90
1560 150r. Leatherback turtle . . 4·50 1·20

318 Pinisi Sailing Ship

1980. Djakarta–Amsterdam Spice Race.
1562 **318** 60r. blue 40 15
1563 – 125r. brown 65 40
1564 – 150r. purple . . . . . . 1·50 40
DESIGNS—HORIZ: 125r. Schooner made of cloves. VERT: 150r. Madurese sailing boat.

319 Riding the Rapids

1980. Adventure Sports. Multicoloured.
1566 60r. Type **319** 50 15
1567 125r. Mountaineering (vert) 90 50
1568 150r. Hang gliding . . . . 1·30 75

320 Cigarettes and Heart

321 Artificial Flowers in Vase

1980. Anti-smoking Campaign.
1570 **320** 150r. flesh, black and pink . . . . 1·00 40

1980. 2nd Flower Festival, Jakarta. Mult.
1571 125r. Type **321** . . . . . . 1·50 40
1572 150r. Artificial bouquet . . 1·80 65

322 Conference Building and Globe

323 Danau Poso Statue

1980. 25th Anniv of First Asian–African Conference, Bandung.
1573 **322** 150r. mauve and gold . . 1·00 40

1980. Prehistoric Monuments. Multicoloured.
1575 60r. Type **323** 65 25
1576 125r. Elephant stone, Pasemah Village, South Sumatra 80 50
1577 150r. Taman Bali sarcophagus . . . . . . 1·30 65

324 Discus Thrower

325 Draughtsman in Wheelchair

1980. Olympics for the Disabled, Arnhem.
1580 **324** 75r. brown and orange 90 35

1980. 30th Anniv of Disabled Veterans Corps.
1581 **325** 100r. yellow, blue & blk 90 35

326 President Suharto

327 People and Map of Indonesia

1980.
1581a **326** 10r. olive and green . . 1·60 10
1582 12r.50 green & lt green 35 10
1582a 25r. brown and orange 50 10
1583 50r. blue and green . . 35 35
1583a 55r. red and vermilion 50 10
1584 75r. brown and yellow 75 15
1585a 100r. blue, violet & mve 1·30 35
1586 200r. brown and orange 2·00 75
1586b 300r. violet, lilac & gold . . . . 2·00 25
1586c 400r. grey, pink and gold . . . . 2·00 25
Nos. 1585a and 1586 exist dated "1980" or "1981", and Nos. 1582a, 1583a and 1586b/c are dated "1983".
See also Nos. 1830/4.

1980. Population Census.
1587 **327** 75r. blue and pink . . . 40 15
1588 200r. blue and yellow . . 1·00 40

328 Ship laying Cable

329 Immigrants

1980. Inauguration of Singapore–Indonesia Submarine Cable.
1589 **328** 75r. green, dp grn & orge 55 15
1590 200r. blue, dp bl & orge 1·00 50

1980. Indonesian Immigration.
1591 **329** 12r.50 red and green . . 35 10

330 1946 50s. Stamp

331 Map of A.O.P.U. Members

1980. 35th Anniv of Independence.
1592 **330** 75r. cream, black & brn 50 35
1593 – 100r. cream, pur & gold 1·10 40
1594 – 200r. cream, pink and silver . . . . 1·50 65
DESIGNS—HORIZ: 100r. 1946 15s. stamp. VERT: 200r. 1946 15s. Freedom Fund stamp.

1980. 10th Anniv of Asian–Oceanic Postal Union Training School, Bangkok.
1595 **331** 200r. blue, lt blue & turq 1·30 25

332 O.P.E.C. Emblem on Globe

1980. 20th Anniv of Organization of Petroleum Exporting Countries.
1596 **332** 200r. turquoise, bl & red 1·30 35

333 Service Members with Linked Arms

1980. 35th Anniv of Armed Forces. Mult.
1597 75r. Indonesians hailing flag 75 25
1598 200r. Type **333** . . . . . . 1·10 40

334 Pesquet's Parrot

335 "Dendrobium insigne"

1980. Parrots. Multicoloured.
1599 75r. Type **334** . . . . . . 2·40 75
1600 100r. Chattering lory . . . 2·40 1·50
1601 200r. Rainbow lory . . . . 4·00 2·10

1980. Orchids. Multicoloured.
1603 75r. Type **335** . . . . . . 1·10 15
1604 100r. "Dendrobium discolor" . . . . 1·80 90
1605 200r. "Dendrobium lasianthera" . . . . . . 3·50 65

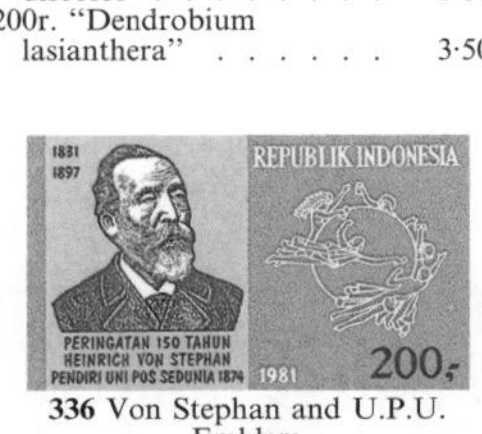

336 Von Stephan and U.P.U. Emblem

1981. 150th Birth Anniv of Heinrich von Stephan (U.P.U. founder).
1607 **336** 200r. blue and deep blue 1·30 65

337 Jamboree and Scouting Emblems

1981. 6th Asia–Pacific Scout Jamboree, Cibubur. Multicoloured.
1608 75r. Type **337** 40 35
1609 100r. Scout and Guide map-reading (vert) . . . . . . 1·10 35
1610 200r. Jamboree emblem and tents . . . . 1·30 75

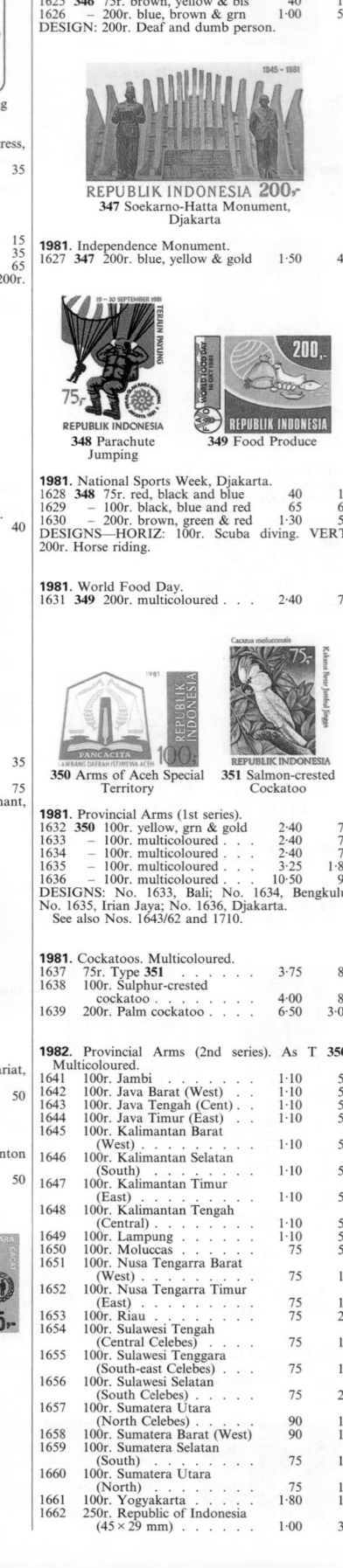

338 Ship (relief carving)

339 Child holding Blood Drop

1981. 5th Asian–Oceanic Postal Union Congress, Yogyakarta.
1612 **338** 200r. blue, black & lt bl 1·50 35

1981. Blood Donors.
1613 **339** 75r. blue, black and red 50 15
1614 – 100r. red and grey . . . 75 35
1615 – 200r. red, dp blue & blue 1·10 65
DESIGNS: 100r. Hands holding blood drop; 200r. Hands and blood drop.

340 Monuments

1981. International Family Planning Conference.
1616 **340** 200r. pale blue, brn & bl 1·00 40

341 "Song of Sritanjung"

1981. Traditional Balinese Paintings. Mult.
1617 100r. Type **341** . . . . . . 1·10 35
1618 200r. "Song of Sritanjung" (different) . . . . . . 1·60 75
Nos. 1617/18 were issued together, se-tenant, forming a composite design.

342 Secretariat Building and Emblem

343 Uber Cup

1981. Inauguration of A.S.E.A.N. Secretariat, Djakarta.
1620 **342** 200r. yellow, orge & pur 1·50 50

1981. International Ladies' Badminton Championships, Tokyo.
1621 **343** 200r. brown, yell & orge 2·40 50

344 "Tree of Life" (relief from Candi Mendut)

346 Blind Man

345 Students reading Koran, Mosque and Emblem

1981. World Environment Day.
1622 **344** 75r. bistre, grey and black 75 15
1623 – 200r. bistre, grey & black 1·20 35
DESIGN: 200r. "Yaksha Apacaka".

1981. 12th National Koran Reading Contest, Banda Aceh.
1624 **345** 200r. black, red & yellow 1·00 50

1981. International Year of Disabled Persons.
1625 **346** 75r. brown, yellow & bis 40 15
1626 – 200r. blue, brown & grn 1·00 50
DESIGN: 200r. Deaf and dumb person.

347 Soekarno-Hatta Monument, Djakarta

1981. Independence Monument.
1627 **347** 200r. blue, yellow & gold 1·50 40

348 Parachute Jumping

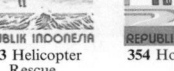

349 Food Produce

1981. National Sports Week, Djakarta.
1628 **348** 75r. red, black and blue 40 15
1629 – 100r. black, blue and red 65 65
1630 – 200r. brown, green & red 1·30 50
DESIGNS—HORIZ: 100r. Scuba diving. VERT: 200r. Horse riding.

1981. World Food Day.
1631 **349** 200r. multicoloured . . . 2·40 75

350 Arms of Aceh Special Territory

351 Salmon-crested Cockatoo

1981. Provincial Arms (1st series).
1632 **350** 100r. yellow, grn & gold 2·40 75
1633 – 100r. multicoloured . . . 2·40 75
1634 – 100r. multicoloured . . . 2·40 75
1635 – 100r. multicoloured . . . 3·25 1·80
1636 – 100r. multicoloured . . . 10·50 90
DESIGNS: No. 1633, Bali; No. 1634, Bengkulu; No. 1635, Irian Jaya; No. 1636, Djakarta.
See also Nos. 1643/62 and 1710.

1981. Cockatoos. Multicoloured.
1637 75r. Type **351** . . . . . . 3·75 80
1638 100r. Sulphur-crested cockatoo . . . . 4·00 80
1639 200r. Palm cockatoo . . . . 6·50 3·00

1982. Provincial Arms (2nd series). As T **350**. Multicoloured.
1641 100r. Jambi . . . . 1·10 50
1642 100r. Java Barat (West) . . 1·10 50
1643 100r. Java Tengah (Cent) . . 1·10 50
1644 100r. Java Timur (East) . . 1·10 50
1645 100r. Kalimantan Barat (West) . . . . 1·10 50
1646 100r. Kalimantan Selatan (South) . . . . 1·10 50
1647 100r. Kalimantan Timur (East) . . . . 1·10 50
1648 100r. Kalimantan Tengah (Central) . . . . 1·10 50
1649 100r. Lampung . . . . . . 1·10 50
1650 100r. Moluccas 75 50
1651 100r. Nusa Tengarra Barat (West) 75 15
1652 100r. Nusa Tengarra Timur (East) 75 15
1653 100r. Riau 75 25
1654 100r. Sulawesi Tengah (Central Celebes) 75 15
1655 100r. Sulawesi Tenggara (South-east Celebes) . . . 75 15
1656 100r. Sulawesi Selatan (South Celebes) 75 25
1657 100r. Sumatera Utara (North Celebes) 90 15
1658 100r. Sumatera Barat (West) 90 15
1659 100r. Sumatera Selatan (South) 75 15
1660 100r. Sumatera Utara (North) 75 15
1661 100r. Yogyakarta . . . . . 1·80 15
1662 250r. Republic of Indonesia (45 × 29 mm) . . . . . . 1·00 35

352 Hands enclosing Family

1982. 70th Anniv of Bumiputera Mutual Life Insurance Company.
1663 **352** 75r. yellow, plum & pur 40 15
1664 – 100r. yellow, lt grn & grn 80 35
1665 – 200r. multicoloured . . . 1·10 55
DESIGNS: 100r. Family in countryside; 200r. Hands supporting industrial activities.

353 Helicopter Rescue

354 Houses and Ballot Boxes

1982. 10th Anniv of Search and Rescue Institute.
1666 **353** 250r. multicoloured . . . 1·50 35

1982. General Election. Multicoloured.
1667 75r. Type **354** 40 15
1668 100r. Rural houses and ballot boxes 65 25
1669 200r. Houses and National arms . . . . 1·50 65

355 Human Figures, Satellite and Dove

357 Footballers

356 Thomas Cup

1982. 2nd U.N. Conference on Exploration and Peaceful Uses of Outer Space, Vienna.
1670 **355** 150r. blue, violet & black 75 40
1671 – 250r. green, light green and deep green . . . 1·30 65
DESIGN: 250r. Peace dove and text.

1982. Thomas Cup Badminton Championship, London.
1672 **356** 250r. multicoloured . . . 1·80 50

1982. World Cup Football Championship, Spain.
1674 **357** 250r. multicoloured . . . 1·80 50

358 Taman Siswa Emblem

1982. 60th Anniv of Taman Siswa (educational organization).
1676 **358** 250r. yellow, green & red 1·00 35

359 Flags forming "15"

1982. 15th Anniv of Association of South-East Asian Nations.
1677 **359** 150r. orange, red and blue . . . . 1·60 50

360 President Suharto

362 Rothschild's Mynah

1982.
1678 **360** 110r. red and orange . . 40 15
1679 250r. brown and orange 80 15
1680 275r. green and yellow 1·30 15
Nos. 1678 and 1680 are inscribed "1983".

1982. 3rd World National Parks Congress, Bali. Multicoloured.
1682 100r. Type **362** . . . . . . 3·25 40
1683 250r. King bird of paradise 5·00 1·20

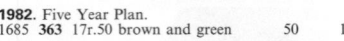

363 River Bridge

1982. Five Year Plan.
1685 **363** 17r.50 brown and green 50 10

364 Arfak Parotia

365 Scouts and Anniversary Emblem

1982. Birds of Paradise. Multicoloured.
1686 100r. Type **364** . . . . . . 2·00 40
1687 150r. Twelve-wired bird of paradise . . . . 3·25 80
1688 250r. Red bird of paradise 5·00 1·20

1983. 75th Anniv of Boy Scout Movement.
1690 **365** 250r. blue, green & violet 1·60 35

366 Temple Restoration and Relief

1983. Borobudur Temple.
1691 **366** 100r. green, blue & lt bl 1·60 50
1692 – 150r. lt green, grn & brn 1·60 50
1693 – 250r. black, dp brn & brn . . . . 5·25 2·75
DESIGNS—VERT: 150r. Temple and statue. HORIZ: 250r. Silhouette of temple and seated Buddha.

367 President Suharto

368 Gas Storage Tanks

1983.
1695 **367** 500r. brown . . . . . . 1·40 35

1983. 7th International Liquefied Natural Gas Conference, Djarkarta.
1696 **368** 275r. multicoloured . . . 1·40 35

369 Ships and Bird

370 Man and Woman reading Koran

1983. World Communications Year.
1697 **369** 75r. multicoloured . . . 25 15
1698 – 110r. multicoloured . . . 50 25
1699 – 175r. blue and red . . . 80 40
1700 – 275r. blue, dp blue & red 1·20 65
DESIGNS: 110r. Satellite and receiving station; 175r. Aircraft and dish aerial, 275r. Globe and letter.

1983. 13th National Koran Reading Competition.
1701 **370** 275r. yellow, green & blk 1·20 55

371 Eclipse and Map of Indonesia

1983. Total Solar Eclipse.
1702 **371** 110r. brn, dp brn & blk 65 25
1703 – 275r. blue, violet & purple . . . . . . 2·00 40
DESIGN: 275r. Map of Indonesia showing path of eclipse.

372 Satellite transmitting to Indonesia

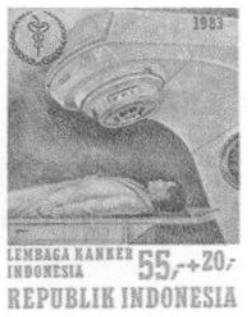

373 Patient receiving Radiation Treatment

1983. Launching of "Palapa B" Communications Satellite.
1705 **372** 275r. green, blue & silver 1·20 55

1983. Anti-cancer Campaign.
1706 **373** 55r.+20r. multicoloured 65 40
1707 75r.+25r. multicoloured 1·10 40

374 Agricultural Produce

1983. Agricultural Census.
1708 **374** 110r. grey, green & black 65 15
1709 – 275r. red, black and green . . . . 1·10 25
DESIGN: 275r. Farmer with produce.

1983. Provincial Arms (3rd series). As T **350**. Multicoloured.
1710 100r. Timor Timur . . . . 1·80 15

375 Traditional Weaving, Pakistan

1983. Indonesia–Pakistan Economic and Cultural Co-operation. Multicoloured.
1711 275r. Type **375** . . . . . . 1·60 75
1712 275r. Traditional weaving, Indonesia . . . . 1·60 75

376 Eruption of Krakatoa

1983. Centenary of Krakatoa Volcanic Eruption. Multicoloured.
1713 110r. Type **376** 50 25
1714 275r. Map showing position of Krakatoa . . . . . . 1·60 40

377 Casa-Nurtanio CN-235 Short-haul Passenger Aircraft

1983. Indonesian Aircraft.
1715 **377** 275r. multicoloured . . . 1·20 55

378 Tiger Barb

1983. Tropical Fishes. Multicoloured.
1717 110r. Type **378** . . . . . 2·00 65
1718 175r. Brilliant rasbora . . . . 2·00 65
1719 275r. Archerfish . . . . . . 6·00 2·00

379 Wilson's Bird of Paradise

1983. Birds of Paradise. Multicoloured.
1721 110r. Type **379** . . . . . . 1·60 40
1722 175r. Black sicklebill . . . . 2·40 50
1723 275r. Black-billed sicklebill 3·75 1·10
1724 500r. As No. 1723 . . . . . 5·75 3·00

380 Emblems of Peace and Co-operation

1983. Palestinian Solidarity.
1726 **380** 275r. blue, brown & silver . . . . 1·40 35

381 "Stop" Emblem

382 Agriculture

1984. Anti-poliomyelitis Campaign.
1732 **381** 110r. red, purple and blue 40 15
1733 – 275r. purple, orge & red 1·40 35
DESIGN: 275r. Emblem of Save the Children Fund.

1984. 4th Five Year Plan.
1734 **382** 55r. yellow and blue . . 15 10
1735 – 75r. green and brown . . 25 15
1736 – 110r. blue and orange . . 40 25
1737 – 275r. multicoloured . . . 1·10 65
DESIGNS: 75r. Casa-Nurtiano CN-235 airliner (aircraft industry); 110r. Shipbuilding; 275r. Telephone (telecommunications).

383 Manufacturing Plywood

1984. Forestry. Multicoloured.
1738 75r. Type **383** . . . . . . 1·10 15
1739 110r. Seedling . . . . . . 1·10 15
1740 175r. Measuring tree trunk 1·10 40
1741 275r. Transporting trees . . 1·10 55

384 Children playing with Toys

1984. Children's Day. Multicoloured.
1743 75r.+25r. Type **384** . . . . 1·10 15
1744 110r.+25r. Scout camp . . . 65 25
1745 175r.+25r. Children on farm 1·60 40
1746 275r.+25r. Scouts and guides in camp . . . . . 1·60 50

385 Flags of Member Nations

1984. Association of South-East Asian Nations Meeting, Djakarta.
1747 **385** 275r. multicoloured . . . 1·80 55

386 Pole Vaulting

387 Horse Dance

1984. Olympic Games, Los Angeles. Multicoloured.
1748 75r. Type **386** 50 15
1749 110r. Archery 50 15
1750 175r. Boxing 50 15
1751 250r. Shooting . . . . . . 1·60 50
1752 275r. Weightlifting . . . . 2·00 50
1753 325r. Swimming . . . . . 3·50 25

1984. Art and Culture. Multicoloured.
1754 75r. Type **387** 80 15
1755 110r. "Reog" mask . . . . 1·20 25
1756 275r. Lion dance . . . . . 1·20 65
1757 325r. "Barong" mask . . . 2·75 65

388 Thomas Cup (badminton)

1984. National Sports Day. Multicoloured.
1758 110r. Type **388** 80 25
1759 275r. Keep-fit exercise . . . 1·60 40

389 Map and Post Code Zones

390 Lauterbach's Bowerbird

1984. Introduction of New Post Code Zones.
1763 **389** 110r. blue, brown & orge 50 25
1764 275r. orange, blue & brn 1·10 65

1984. Birds. Multicoloured.
1765 75r. Type **390** . . . . . . 2·75 35
1766 110r. Flamed bowerbird . . 4·00 65
1767 275r. Arfak bird of paradise 5·25 2·40
1768 325r. Superb bird of paradise . . . . 5·25 1·60

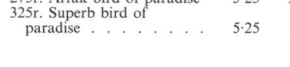

391 Flag and Fists

392 Boeing 747-200

1984. Youth Pledge.
1770 **391** 275r. black and red . . . 1·10 75

1984. 40th Anniv of I.C.A.O.
1771 **392** 275r. red, black and blue 1·20 75

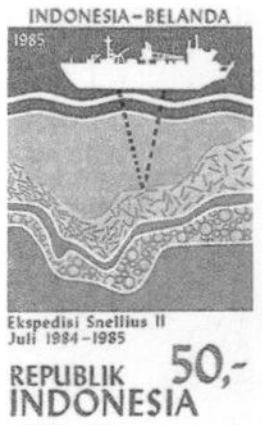

393 "Tyro" and Geological Structure of Seabed

394 Stylized Birds

1985. Indonesia–Belanda Expedition.
1772 **393** 50r. blue and brown . . 65 15
1773 – 100r. blue and purple . . 1·10 15
1774 – 275r. blue and green . . 1·20 35
DESIGNS: 100r. "Tyro" (oceanographic survey ship) and map; 275r. "Tyro" and coral reef.

1985. International Women's Day.
1775 **394** 100r. mauve and red . . 2·00 65
1776 – 275r. red and brown . . 3·00 3·00
DESIGN: 275r. Profile silhouettes.

395 Jet Airliner and workers

396 Pres. Suharto

1985. 4th Five Year Plan.
1777 **395** 75r. red and brown . . . 35 15
1778 – 140r. grey and brown . . 55 40
1779 – 350r. green and brown . . 1·50 1·00
DESIGNS: 140r. Children in classroom; 350r. Industrial equipment and buildings.

1985.
1780 **396** 140r. brown and red . . 65 15
1781 350r. mauve and red . . 1·50 15

397 Conference Building

1985. 30th Anniv of First Asian–African Conference, Bandung.
1786 **397** 350r. multicoloured . . . 1·60 50

398 Globe and Teenagers waving Palm Leaves

399 Profiles

1985. International Youth Year.
1787 **398** 75r. yellow, brown & grn 55 15
1788 – 140r. blue, green & mve 1·40 15
DESIGN: 140r. Flower on globe supported by teenagers.

1985. United Nations Women's Decade.
1789 **399** 55r. brown and green . . 50 25
1790 – 140r. blue, green & brn 80 25
DESIGN: 140r. Globe and decade emblems.

400 Housing and Hydro-electricity

401 Sky Diving

1985. 40th Anniv of Indonesian Republic.
1791 **400** 140r. green and red . . . 55 15
1792 – 350r. blue, mauve & yell 1·50 35
DESIGN: 350r. Tractor and industrial complex.

1985. National Sports Week, Djakarta. Multicoloured.
1793 55r. Type **401** 35 10
1794 100r. Unarmed combat . . . 80 15
1795 140r. High jumping 80 25
1796 350r. Sailboards (vert) . . . 1·30 50

402 O.P.E.C. Emblem and Globe

403 Tanker

1985. 25th Anniv of Organization of Petroleum Exporting Countries.
1797 **402** 40r. blue, mauve & orge 1·00 25

1985. Centenary of Indonesian Oil Industry. Multicoloured.
1798 140r. Type **403** 50 25
1799 250r. Refinery 90 40
1800 350r. Derrick and rigs . . . 1·30 80

404 Doves, "40" and U.N. Emblem

1985. 40th Anniv of U.N.O. Multicoloured.
1801 140r. Type **404** 50 15
1802 300r. Bombs and green leaves . . . . 1·10 40

405 Javan Rhinoceros

406 Emblem

1985. Wildlife.
1803 **405** 75r. brown, green & blue 1·00 25
1804 – 150r. brown, orge & grn 1·30 40
1805 – 300r. brown, blue and red . . . . 2·50 65
DESIGNS: 150r. Anoa; 300r. Komodo dragon.

1986. Economic Census. Each orange and violet.
1806 175r. Type **406** 65 25
1807 175r. Symbols of economy 65 25

407 Baby feeding, Powdered Milk, Syringe and Graph

408 Industry

1986. 40th Anniv of U.N.I.C.E.F.
1808 **407** 75r. multicoloured . . . 55 15
1809 – 140r. flesh, brown & pink 90 25
DESIGN: 140r. Vaccinating baby.

1986. 4th Five Year Plan.
1810 **408** 140r. multicoloured . . . 50 15
1811 – 500r. yellow, brown & bl 50 15
DESIGN: 500r. Agriculture.

409 Thomas Cup and Racket

410 Pinisi Sailing Ship

1986. Thomas (men's) and Uber (women's) Cup Badminton Championships, Djakarta.
1812 **409** 55r. black, yellow & blue 65 25
1813 – 150r. red, brown and gold . . . . 1·10 25
DESIGN: 150r. Thomas and Uber Cups and shuttlecock.

1986. "Expo 86" World's Fair, Vancouver.
1814 **410** 75r. black, red and yellow 50 15
1815 – 150r. multicoloured . . . 1·00 25
1816 – 300r. silver, red & purple 1·50 35
DESIGNS: 150r. Kentongan village drum and "Palapa" satellite; 300r. Indonesian pavilion emblem.

411 Guides on Parade

1986. National Jamboree. Multicoloured.
1817 100r. Type **411** 35 15
1818 140r. Guides cooking over fire . . . . 1·30 35
1819 210r. Scouts consulting map (vert) . . . . 1·60 55

412 "86"

1986. Indonesia Air Show.
1820 **412** 350r. multicoloured . . . 1·30 65

413 Tari Legong Kraton

1986. Traditional Dances. Multicoloured.
1821 140r. Type **413** . . . . . . 1·30 15
1822 350r. Tari Barong . . . . . 2·10 50
1823 500r. Tari Kecak . . . . . 3·00 55

414 Woman planting

1986. 19th International Society of Sugar Cane Technologists Congress, Djakarta. Multicoloured.
1824 150r. Type **414** 55 15
1825 300r. Cane and sugar spilled from sack . . . . 1·40 25

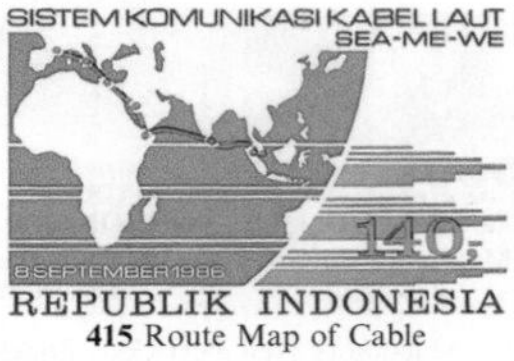
415 Route Map of Cable

1986. Opening of Sea-Me-We Communications Cable.
1826 **415** 140r. green, orange & vio 55 25
1827 – 350r. green, yellow & bl 1·40 55
DESIGN: 350r. Route map of cable (different).

416 Doves, Wheat and Globe

417 Party Emblems and Buildings

1986. International Peace Year. Each brown, green and black.
1828 350r. Type **416** . . . . . . 1·10 40
1829 500r. Dove with olive twig flying around globe . . . 1·50 15

1986.
1830 **326** 50r. deep brown & brown 15 10
1831 55r. red and pink . . . 35 10
1833 100r. ultramarine & blue 15 10
1834 300r. turq, grn & gold 1·00 10
1835 400r. green, turq & gold 1·30 15

1987. General Election.
1840 **417** 75r. blue, yellow & brn 50 10
1841 – 140r. green, orange & yell 50 15
1842 – 350r. blue, yellow & blk 1·30 35
DESIGNS: 140r. Party emblems and arms; 350r. Party emblems, map, wheat and ballot box.

418 Satellite and Globe

419 Boy carving Figures

1987. Launch of "Palapa B2" Satellite.
1843 **418** 350r. yellow, green & brn . . . . 1·00 40
1844 – 500r. multicoloured . . . 1·50 25
DESIGN—VERT: 500r. Rocket and satellite.

1987. 4th Five Year Plan.
1845 **419** 140r. brown, yellow & bl 25 15
1846 – 350.r. violet, grn & orge 65 35
DESIGN: 350r. Graph and cattle.

420 Crab and Scanner Unit

421 East Kalimantan Couple

1987. 10th Anniv of Indonesian Cancer Foundation.
1847 **420** 350r.+25r. yellow & bl 1·10 50

1987. Wedding Costumes (1st series). Mult.
1848 140r. Type **421** . . . . . . 1·60 35
1849 350r. Aceh couple . . . . . 9·75 4·50
1850 400r. East Timor couple . . 11·50 1·00
See also Nos. 1891/6, 1955/60, 1992/7 and 2010/15.

422 Weightlifting

423 Emblems

1987. 14th South-East Asia Games, Djakarta. Designs showing pictograms.
1851 **422** 140r. yellow, red and blue 40 15
1852 – 250r. blue, yellow and red 75 25
1853 – 350r. red, blue and brown . . . . 1·10 40
DESIGNS: 250r. Swimming; 350r. Running.

1987. 460th Anniv of Djakarta and 20th Anniv of Djakarta Fair.
1854 **423** 75r. blue, black & yellow 75 15
1855 – 100r. blue, black & yell 1·40 15
DESIGN—VERT: 100r. Emblems (different).

424 Children reading

425 Headquarters, Djakarta

1987. Children's Day and National Family Planning Co-ordination Board.
1856 **424** 100r. mauve and orange 40 15
1857 – 250r. yellow and blue . . 75 15
DESIGN—VERT: 250r. Globe, baby in cupped hands and dropper.

1987. 20th Anniv of Association of South-East Asian Nations.
1858 **425** 350r. multicoloured . . . 1·30 50

426 Emblem

427 Mount Bromo and Sand Craters

1987. 30th Anniv and 7th National Congress of Association of Specialists in Internal Diseases.
1859 **426** 300r. red and blue . . . 1·00 15

1987. Tourism. Multicoloured.
1860 140r. Type **427** 50 15
1861 350r. Bedugul Lake, Bali . . 1·60 55
1862 500r. Sea gardens, Bunaken Island . . . . 2·10 25

428 Woman with Broken Chains, Helmet and Pennant flying from Pen

429 Giant Gourami

1987. "Woman's Physical Revolution".
1863 **428** 75r. green, red and yellow 35 15
1864 – 100r. green, yellow & red 65 15
DESIGN: 100r. Women with rifles and barbed wire.

1987. Fishes.
1865 **429** 150r. mauve, yellow & bl 1·60 65
1866 – 200r. mauve, yellow & bl 1·60 35
1867 – 500r. black, yellow & bl 5·00 35
DESIGNS: 200r. Goldfish; 300r. Walking catfish.

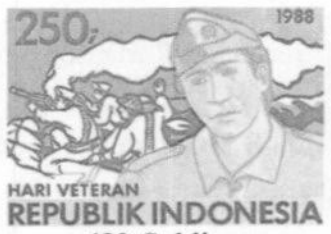
430 Soldiers

432 Carved Snake and Frog

431 Welder

1988. 31st Anniv of Veterans Legion.
1868 **430** 250r. green and orange 80 15

1988. National Safety and Occupational Health Day.
1869 **431** 350r. blue and green . . 1·10 50

1988. 8th Anniv of National Crafts Council.
1870 **432** 120r. blue and brown . . 65 10
1871 – 350r. blue and brown . . 1·00 50
1872 – 500r. brown and green 1·60 15
DESIGN: 350r. Cane rocking-chair; 500r. Bamboo goods.

433 Industrial Symbols

434 Indonesian Girls

1988. 4th Five Year Plan.
1873 **433** 140r. blue and green . . 25 15
1874 – 400r. purple and red . . 65 35
DESIGN: 400r. Fishing industry.

1988. "Expo 88" World's Fair, Brisbane. Multicoloured.
1875 200r. Type **434** 90 15
1876 300r. Indonesian girl 90 15
1877 350r. Indonesian girl and boy . . . . 1·50 65

435 Anniversary Emblem

436 "Dendrobium none betawi"

1988. 125th Anniv of Red Cross.
1879 **435** 350r. grey, black and red . . . 1·00 25

1988. Flowers. Multicoloured.
1880 400r. Type **436** . . . . . . 1·60 50
1881 500r. "Dendrobium abang betawi" . . . . 1·60 35

437 Running

438 Figures around Emblem

1988. Olympic Games, Seoul.
1882 **437** 75r. black, brown & gold 50 15
1883 – 100r. black, red and gold 1·10 15
1884 – 200r. black, mve & gold 1·10 50
1885 – 300r. black, green & gold 50 50
1886 – 400r. black, blue and gold 65 40
1887 – 500r. black, blue and gold . . . . 3·00 40
DESIGNS: 100r. Weightlifting; 200r. Archery; 300r. Table tennis; 400r. Swimming; 500r. Tennis.

1988. Centenary of International Women's Council.
1889 **438** 140r. black and blue . . 65 15

439 Family, Water and Ear of Wheat

440 President Suharto

1988. National Farmers' and Fishermen's Week.
1890 **439** 350r. stone and red . . . 1·10 50

1988. Wedding Costumes (2nd series). As T **421**. Multicoloured.
1891 55r. Sumatera Barat (West) 25 15
1892 75r. Jambi 15 10
1893 100r. Bengkulu 65 10
1894 120r. Lampung 90 10
1895 200r. Moluccas . . . . . . 1·60 15
1896 250r. Nusa Tenggara Timur (East) . . . . 2·10 1·10

1988.
1897 **440** 200r. blue, pink and red 35 15
1898 700r. mauve, lt grn & grn . . . . 1·10 15
1899 1000r. multicoloured . . 1·10 15

441 Emblem

442 Doves and Envelopes

1988. 13th Non-Aligned News Agencies Co-ordinating Committee Meeting, Djakarta.
1901 **441** 500r. blue and red . . . 1·20 35

1988. International Correspondence Week.
1902 **442** 140r. blue and red . . . 90 15

443 Means of Transport and Communications

1988. Asian–Pacific Transport and Communications Decade.
1904 **443** 350r. blue and black . . 1·10 50

444 Al Mashun Mosque, Medan

445 "Papilio gigon"

1988. Tourism. Multicoloured.
1905 250r. Type **444** 55 40
1906 300r. Pagaruyung Palace, Batusangkar 90 35
1907 500r. Keong Emas Theatre, Djakarta . . . . 2·10 35

1988. Butterflies. Multicoloured.
1909 400r. Type **445** . . . . . . 1·50 40
1910 500r. "Graphium androcles" 2·50 55

446 "Rafflesia sp."

447 "40" and Boeing 747

1989. Flowers. Multicoloured.
1916 200r. Type **446** 90 40
1917 1000r. "Amorphophallus titanum" . . . . 2·75 40

1989. 40th Anniv of Garuda Airline.
1919 **447** 350r. blue and green . . 2·00 55

448 Mother and Baby

449 Industrial Site

1989. Endangered Animals. The Orang-utan. Multicoloured.
1920 75r. Type **448** . . . . . . 3·75 1·60
1921 100r. Orang-utan in tree . . 3·75 75
1922 140r. Mother and baby in trees . . . . 3·75 75
1923 500r. Orang-utan . . . . . 11·50 6·50

1989. 5th Five Year Plan.
1925 **449** 55r. violet and green . . 10 10
1926 – 150r. blue and brown . . 25 15
1927 – 350r. green and orange 55 15
DESIGNS: 150r. Cement works; 350r. Gas plant.

450 Stamp and Map

451 Ki Hadjar Dewantara and Graduate

1989. 125th Anniv of First Netherlands Indies Stamp.
1928 **450** 1000r. green, purple & bl 2·00 15

1989. National Education Day.
1929 **451** 140r. red and purple . . 55 15
1930 – 300r. violet and green . . 1·00 35
DESIGN: 300r. Dewantara (founder of Taman Siswa School), pencil and books.

452 Emblem on Map

453 Flag and Cup

1989. 10th Anniv of Asia–Pacific Telecommunity.
1931 **452** 350r. purple and green 1·00 75

1989. Sudirman Cup.
1932 **453** 100r. brown and red . . 1·60 15

454 Students

455 Headquarters

1989. Children's Day.
1933 **454** 100r. brown and orange 50 10
1934 – 250r. blue and green . . 90 25
DESIGN: 250r. Youths exercising.

1989. 10th Anniv of Asia–Pacific Integrated Rural Development Centre.
1935 **455** 140r. brown and blue . . 75 15

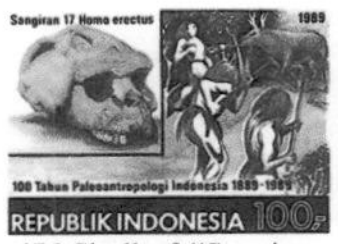
456 Skull of "Sangiran 17" and Hunters

457 Globe and People

1989. Centenary of Palaeoanthropology in Indonesia.
1936 **456** 100r. black and brown 65 10
1937 – 150r. green and red . . . 90 15
1938 – 200r. blue and brown . . 1·40 35
1939 – 250r. violet and brown 1·60 25
1940 – 300r. green and red . . . 2·00 40
1941 – 350r. blue and brown . . 2·40 25
DESIGNS—HORIZ: 150r. Skull of "Perning 1" and cavemen; 200r. Skull of "Sangiran 10" and hunter. VERT: 250r. Skull of "Wajak 1"; 300r. Skull of "Sambungmacan 1"; 350r. Skull of "Ngandong 7".

1989. Centenary of Interparliamentary Union.
1942 **457** 350r. green and blue . . 1·00 75

458 Kung Fu

1989. 12th National Games, Djakarta. Mult.
1943 75r. Type **458** 55 15
1944 100r. Tennis 55 15
1945 140r. Judo 55 15
1946 350r. Volleyball . . . . . . 1·60 75
1947 500r. Boxing . . . . 2·75 25
1948 1000r. Archery . . . . . . 3·50 65

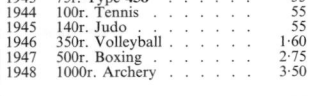

459 Taman Burung

460 Trophy

1989. Tourism. Multicoloured.
1949 120r. Type **459** 75 10
1950 350r. Prangko Museum . . 1·10 55
1951 500r. Istana Anak-Anak (vert) . . . . 2·00 35

1989. Film Industry.
1953 **460** 150r. ochre and brown 1·00 15

1989. Wedding Costumes (3rd series). As T **421**. Multicoloured.
1955 50r. Sumatera Utara (North) 35 10
1956 75r. Sumatera Selatan (South) 35 10
1957 100r. Djakarta 35 10
1958 140r. Sulawesi Utara (North Celebes) 75 15
1959 350r. Sulawesi Tengah (Central Celebes) . . . . 1·10 1·10
1960 500r. Sulawesi Selatan (South Celebes) . . . . . 1·60 55

461 Worker wearing Safety Belt and Flag

1990. Occupational Safety.
1962 **461** 200r. brown and green 80 15

462 Benteng Marlborough, Bengkulu

1990. Tourism. Multicoloured.
1963 200r. Type **462** . . . . . . 1·00 15
1964 400r. National Museum, Djakarta . . . . 1·50 35
1965 500r. Baiturrahman Mosque, Banda Aceh . . . . . . 1·50 50

463 "Mammilaria fragilis"

1990. Plants. Multicoloured.
1967 75r. Type **463** 40 10
1968 1000r. Bonsai of "Gmelina elliptica" . . . . 2·00 50

464 Tree-felling Equipment

1990. 5th Five Year Plan.
1970 **464** 200r. brown and blue . . 35 15
1971 – 1000r. black and blue . . 1·60 1·00
DESIGN: 1000r. Lighthouse and freighter.

465 Arrow pointing to Indonesia

466 Battle and Disabled Man using Soldering-iron

1990. Visit Indonesia Year (1991) (1st issue). Multicoloured.
1972 100r. Type **465** 35 10
1973 500r. Temple . . . . 1·30 35
See also Nos. 1998/2000.

1990. 40th Anniv of Disabled Veterans Corp.
1976 **466** 1000r. orange and green 1·60 1·00

467 Player and Goalkeeper

469 U.N. Population Award

1990. World Cup Football Championship, Italy. Multicoloured.
1977 75r. Type **467** 55 10
1978 150r. Player tackling 80 15
1979 400r. Players competing for high ball . . . . 1·80 40

1990. 20th Anniv of Family Planning Movement.
1981 **469** 60r. brown and red . . . 40 10

470 Figure with Pencil and Open Book

471 Children

1990. Population Census.
1982 **470** 90r. green and turquoise 55 10

1990. Children's Day.
1983 **471** 500r. purple and red . . 1·10 40

472 Soldier planting Flag

473 Buildings and Cultural Identities

1990. 45th Anniv of Independence. Mult.
1984 200r. Type **472** 65 15
1985 500r. Modern building and roads . . . . 1·10 50

1990. Indonesia–Pakistan Economic and Cultural Co-operation Organization. Multicoloured.
1987 75r. Type **473** 50 15
1988 400r. Dancer (vert) . . . . 1·10 40

474 Emblem

475 Anniversary Emblem

1990. 20th Anniv of Asian–Pacific Postal Training Centre.
1989 **474** 500r. blue & ultramarine 1·00 40

1990. 30th Anniv of Organization of Petroleum Exporting Countries.
1990 **475** 200r. black, grey & orge 80 15

476 Houses

477 Dancer and House

1990. Environmental Health.
1991 **476** 1000r. multicoloured . . 2·00 35

1990. Wedding Costumes (4th series). As T **421**. Multicoloured.
1992 75r. Java Barat (West) . . . 35 10
1993 100r. Java Tengah (Central) 40 10
1994 150r. Yogyakarta 40 10
1995 200r. Java Timur (East) . . 55 15
1996 400r. Bali 80 40
1997 500r. Nusa Tenggara Barat (West) 90 50

1991. Visit Indonesia Year (2nd issue). Dancers and Traditional Houses. Multicoloured.
1998 200r. Type **477** . . . . . . 1·00 15
1999 500r. House and dancer with saucers . . . . . . 1·40 55
2000 1000r. Dancer and house (different) . . . . 2·50 40

478 Emblem

479 Palace of Sultan Ternate, Moluccas

1991. 16th National Koran Reading Competition, Yogyakarta.
2002 **478** 200r. green and yellow 80 15

1991. Tourism. Multicoloured.
2003 500r. Type **479** . . . . . . 1·00 25
2004 1000r. Bari House, Palembang . . . . 1·60 35

480 Steel Mill

481 Damaged Lungs and Cigarette Smoke forming Skull

1991. 5th Five Year Plan.
2006 **480** 75r. red and blue 10 10
2007 – 200r. blue and black . . 25 15
DESIGN—HORIZ: 200r. Computer technology.

1991. Anti-smoking Campaign.
2008 **481** 90r. red and black . . . 55 10

482 Hands

483 Tents

1991. 24th Anniv of National Federation for the Welfare of the Mentally Handicapped.
2009 **482** 200r.+25r. black and red 80 25

1991. Wedding Costumes (5th series). As T **421**. Multicoloured.
2010 100r. Kalimantan Barat (West) 25 10
2011 200r. Kalimantan Tengah (Central) 80 15
2012 300r. Kalimantan Selatan (South) 50 15
2013 400r. Sulawesi Tenggara (South-east Celebes) . . . 55 25
2014 500r. Riau 80 35
2015 1000r. Irian Jaya . . . . . 1·00 55

1991. National Boy Scout Jamboree, Cibubur.
2016 **483** 200r. blue, black and red 1·10 15

484 Monument

485 Temples and Family

1991. 42nd Anniv of Return of Republican Government to Djokjakarta.
2017 **484** 200r. green and brown 80 15

1991. Farmers' Week.
2018 **485** 500r. yellow and blue . . 1·40 15

486 Cells

487 Weightlifters

1991. "chemindo '91" Chemistry Congress, Surabaya.
2019 **486** 400r. red and green . . . 1·00 15

1991. 5th Junior Men's and Fourth Women's Asian Weightlifting Championships, Manado.
2020 **487** 300r. red and black . . . 1·00 15

488 Parachutists

489 Red Cross and Hands

1991. World Parachuting Championships.
2021 **488** 500r. mauve and blue . . 1·00 15

1991. 46th Anniv of Indonesian Red Cross.
2022 **489** 200r. red and green . . . 80 15

490 Radio Mast

491 Script and Mosque

1991. 8th International Amateur Radio Union Region III Conference, Bandung.
2023 **490** 300r. blue and yellow . . 1·00 15

1991. Istiqlal Festival, Djakarta.
2024 **491** 200r. black and red . . . 1·00 15

492 Dancer and Inspectors

1991. International Convention on Quality Control Circles, Bali.
2025 **492** 500r. multicoloured . . . 1·20 50

493 Orang-utan

494 Model of Jakarta Post Office

1991. International Conference on Great Apes of the World. The Orang-utan. Multicoloured.
2026 200r. Type **493** . . . . . . 1·00 15
2027 500r. Orang-utan on forest path . . . . 1·20 25
2028 1000r. Orang-utan sitting on ground . . . . 2·50 55

1992. Automation of Postal Service. Mult.
2030 200r. Type **494** 40 15
2031 500r. Sorting machine . . . 80 35

495 "Phalaenopsis ambilis"

1992. Flowers. Multicoloured.
2032 200r. Type **495** 40 15
2033 500r. "Rafflesia arnoldii" . . 80 35
2034 1000r. "Jasminum sambac" 1·80 40

496 Buildings, Ballot Boxes and State Arms

1992. Parliamentary Elections. Mult.
2036 75r. Type **496** 15 10
2037 100r. Ballot boxes and globe 40 10
2038 500r. Ballot boxes and hands holding voting slips 1·00 25

497 Lembah Baliem, Irian Jaya

1992. Visit ASEAN Year. Multicoloured.
2039 300r. Type **497** 65 15
2040 500r. Tanah Lot, Bali . . . 1·00 35
2041 1000r. Lembah Anai, Sumatra Barat . . . . . 2·10 35

498 Road-building

499 Emblem and Crab

1992. 5th Five Year Plan.
2043 **498** 150r. purple and green 15 15
2044 – 300r. blue and mauve . . 55 15
DESIGN: 300r. Aircraft.

1992. 15th Anniv of Indonesian Cancer Foundation.
2045 **499** 200r.+25r. red & brown 40 15
2046 500r.+50r. red and blue 80 25

500 Weightlifting

501 White-crested Laughing Thrush

1992. Olympic Games, Barcelona. Mult.
2047 75r. Type **500** 25 10
2048 200r. Badminton 35 15
2049 300r. Sports pictograms . . 65 15
2050 500r. Tennis 80 40
2051 1000r. Archery . . . . . . 2·00 40

1992. Birds. Multicoloured.
2053 100r. Type **501** 25 10
2054 200r. Common golden-backed woodpecker . . . 50 15
2055 400r. Rhinoceros hornbill 1·00 50
2056 500r. Amboina king parrot 1·50 55

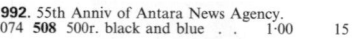

502 Busy Street (Tammy Filia)

1992. National Children's Day. Children's paintings. Multicoloured.
2058 75r. Type **502** 10 10
2059 100r. Children with balloons (Cynthia Widiyana Halim) 25 10
2060 200r. Native boats (Dandy Rahmad Adi Kurniawan) 55 15
2061 500r. Girl and bird (Intan Sari Dewi Saputro) . . . 1·40 80

503 Anniversary Emblem

504 Earth and "Palapa B-4" (satellite)

1992. 25th Anniv of Association of South-East Asian Nations. Multicoloured.
2062 200r. Type **503** 40 15
2063 500r. Map and flags of member nations . . . . . 1·20 40
2064 1000r. "25" and flags . . . 2·40 50

1992. Communications. Multicoloured.
2065 200r. Type **504** 40 15
2066 500r. "Palapa" satellite (16th anniv of launch) . . 80 40
2067 1000r. Old and modern telephones (modernization of telephone system) . . . 2·00 50

505 Emblem

506 Ngremo Dance, East Java

1992. 10th Non-Aligned Countries Summit, Djakarta. Multicoloured.
2068 200r. Type **505** 35 10
2069 500r. Members' flags and emblem 55 10

1992. Traditional Dances (1st series). Mult.
2070 200r. Type **506** 25 15
2071 500r. Gending Sriwijaya dance, South Sumatra . . 1·20 1·20
See also Nos. 2122/4, 2168/72, 2211/14, 2292/5, 2366/70 and 2476/80.

507 Anniversary Emblem

508 Antara Building, Djakarta

1992. 40th Anniv of International Planned Parenthood Federation.
2073 **507** 200r. blue and green . . 80 15

1992. 55th Anniv of Antara News Agency.
2074 **508** 500r. black and blue . . 1·00 15

509 Planting Saplings

1992. National Afforestation.
2075 **509** 500r. multicoloured . . . 1·00 25

1993. No. 1831 surch **50r.**
2076 **326** 50r. on 55r. red and pink 40 10

511 State Arms and Assembly Building

1993. 10th People's Consultative Assembly. Multicoloured.
2077 300r. Type **511** 40 15
2078 700r. Assembly hall . . . . 1·00 25

512 Soldiers and Buildings

1993. 5th Five Year Plan. Multicoloured.
2079 300r. Type **512** 35 35
2080 700r. Workers and arrow . . 75 75
2081 1000r. Runners . . . . . . 1·10 1·10

513 Swarm of "Ornithoptera goliath"

1993.
2082 **513** 1000r. multicoloured . . 1·60 25

514 Peristiwa Hotel, Yamato, and Adipura Kencana Medal

1993. 700th Anniv of Surabaya (300, 700r.) and "indo tourism 93" (1000r.). Multicoloured.
2083 300r. Type **514** 35 35
2084 700r. Modern city and World Habitat Award, 1992 . . . . 75 75
2085 1000r. Candi Bajang Ratu (temple) . . . . 1·10 1·10

1993. "indopex'93" Asian Stamp Exhibition, Surabaya. Nos. 2082/5 optd **indopex'93 surabaya**.
2086 **514** 300r. multicoloured . . . 35 15
2087 – 700r. multicoloured . . . 75 35
2088 **513** 1000r. mult (No. 2082) 2·00 80
2089 – 1000r. mult (No. 2085) 1·30 50

517 "Jasminum sambac" **518** Scouts making Road

1993. Environmental Protection. Mult.
2091 300r. Type **517** 35 15
2092 300r. Moth orchid ("Phalaenopsis amabilis") 35 15
2093 300r. "Rafflesia arnoldi" (flower) . . . . 1·30 40
2094 700r. Komodo dragon . . . 1·30 40
2095 700r. Asian bonytongue . . 1·30 40
2096 700r. Java hawk eagle . . . 1·30 40
Stamps of the same value were issued together, se-tenant, in strips of three stamps, each strip forming a composite design.

1993. 1st World Community Development Camp, Lebakharjo. Multicoloured.
2098 300r. Type **518** 35 15
2099 700r. Pres. Suharto greeting girl scout . . . . 1·00 15

519 President Suharto **520** "Papilio blumei"

1993.
2100 **519** 150r. multicoloured . . . 15 15
2101 300r. multicoloured . . . 35 15
2102 700r. multicoloured . . . 75 50
On No. 2102 part of the background is a draped flag.

1993. Int Butterfly Conference, Ujungpandang.
2103 **520** 700r. multicoloured . . . 1·00 15

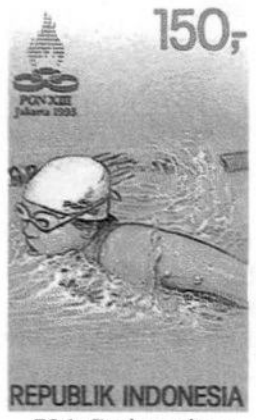

521 Swimming **522** Sigura-Gura Waterfall, North Sumatra

1993. "Pon XIII" Sports Week, Djakarta. Multicoloured.
2105 150r. Type **521** 15 15
2106 300r. Cycling 35 35
2107 700r. Mascot 75 75
2108 1000r. High jumping . . . . 1·10 1·10

1993. World Tourism Organization Meeting, Bali. Multicoloured.
2111 300r. Type **522** 35 35
2112 700r. Goa Petruk (cave), Central Java 75 75
2113 1000r. Danau Segara Anak (cove), West Nusa Tenggara (horiz) . . . . 1·10 1·10

523 General Soedirman **524** "Michelia champaca"

1993. Armed Forces. Each brown, black and red.
2115 300r. Type **523** 35 15
2116 300r. Lt.-Gen. Oerip Soemohardjo 35 15
Nos. 2115/16 were issued together, se-tenant, forming a composite design.

1993. Flora and Fauna. Multicoloured.
2117 300r. Type **524** 75 15
2118 300r. "Cananga adorata" 75 15
2119 300r. Orange-tailed shama ("Copsychus pyrrhopygus") 75 15
2120 300r. Southern grackle ("Gracula religiosa") . . 75 15

525 Plantation **526** South Sumatran Dancer

1993. Resettlement Programme.
2121 **525** 700r. multicoloured . . . 75 75

1993. Traditional Dances (2nd series). Mult.
2122 300r. Type **526** 55 15
2123 700r. West Kalimantan . . 1·00 15
2124 1000r. Irian Jaya . . . . . 1·30 25

527 Emblems **528** Working Women

1994. International Year of the Family.
2126 **527** 300r. multicoloured . . . 40 15

1994. 6th Five Year Plan. Multicoloured.
2127 100r. Type **528** 10 10
2128 700r. Graduate and school pupils 75 75
2129 2000r. Doctor, nurse and children . . . . 2·10 2·10

529 Netherlands Indies, Japanese Occupation and Indonesia Stamps

1994. 130th Anniv of 1st Netherlands Indies Stamps.
2130 **529** 700r. multicoloured . . . 80 40

530 Ladige's Rainbowfish

1994. Fishes. Multicoloured.
2131 300r. Type **530** 35 15
2132 700r. Boeseman's rainbow fish 90 35

531 Emblem **532** Figure, Globe, and Anniversary Emblem

1994. National Kidney Foundation.
2134 **531** 300r.+30r. mult 50 25

1994. 75th Anniv of International Red Cross Red Crescent Organization.
2135 **532** 300r. black, red and blue 40 15

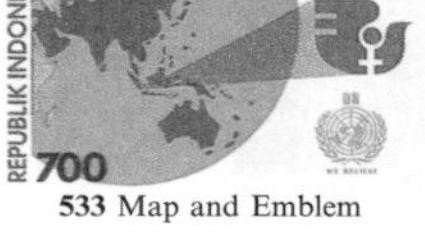

533 Map and Emblem **534** Player

1994. Asia–Pacific Ministerial Conference on Women, Djakarta.
2136 **533** 700r. multicoloured . . . 80 35

1994. World Cup Football Championship, U.S.A.
2137 **534** 150r. multicoloured . . . 15 10
2138 – 300r. multicoloured . . . 35 15
2139 – 700r. blue, red and black 75 40
2140 – 1000r. multicoloured . . 1·20 50
DESIGNS—VERT: 300r. Striker (mascot). HORIZ: 700r. Emblem; 1000r. Ball in net.

535 Player and Uber Cup (Women's) **536** Hand holding Scales

1994. Indonesian Victories in World Team Badminton Championships. Multicoloured.
2142 300r. Type **535** 40 15
2143 300r. Thomas Cup (Men's) 40 15
Nos. 2142/3 were issued together, se-tenant, forming a composite design.

1994. National Commission on Human Rights.
2145 **536** 700r. multicoloured . . . 80 15

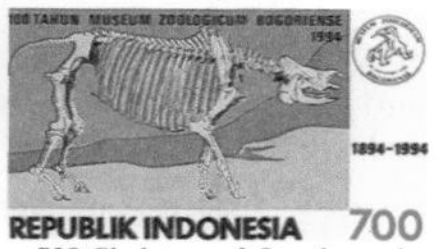

537 Vase with Bead Cover **538** Skeleton of Quadruped

1994. Indonesia–Pakistan Economic and Cultural Co-operation Organization. Multicoloured.
2147 300r. Type **537** 25 25
2148 700r. Blue and white vase 65 65

1994. Centenary of Bogoriense Zoological Museum. Multicoloured.
2149 700r. Type **538** 80 50
2150 1000r. Outline and skeleton of whale (80 × 22 mm) . . 1·10 55

539 Mascots

1994. 12th Asian Games, Hiroshima, Japan. Multicoloured.
2152 300r. Type **539** 25 25
2153 700r. Hurdling 65 65

540 Communications and Map **541** "Morus macroura"

1994. 25th Anniv of Bakosurtanal.
2154 **540** 700r. multicoloured . . . 80 35

1994. Flora and Fauna. Multicoloured.
2155 150r. Type **541** 40 15
2156 150r. "Oncosperma tiquillaria" 40 15
2157 150r. "Eucalyptus urophylla" 40 15
2158 150r. Moth orchid ("Phalaenopsis amabilis") 40 15
2159 150r. "Pometia pinnata" . . 40 15
2160 150r. Great argus pheasant ("Argusianus argus") . . 40 15
2161 150r. Blue-crowned hanging parrot ("Loriculus pusillus") 40 15
2162 150r. Timor helmeted friarbird ("Philemon buceroides") 40 15
2163 150r. Amboina king parrot ("Alisterus amboinensis") 40 15
2164 150r. Twelve-wired bird of paradise ("Seleucidis melanoleuca") 40 15
Nos. 2158 and 2161 are incorrectly inscribed, the correct Latin names are "*Dendrobium phalaenopsis*" and "*Loriculus galgulus*" respectively.

542 Venue

1994. Asia–Pacific Economic Co-operation Summit, Bogor.
2166 **542** 700r. multicoloured . . . 80 25

543 Airplane

1994. 50th Anniv of I.C.A.O.
2167 **543** 700r. multicoloured . . . 80 25

1994. Traditional Dances (3rd series). As T **506**. Multicoloured.
2168 150r. Mengaup, Jambi . . . 15 10
2169 300r. Topeng, West Java . . 25 15
2170 700r. Anging Mamiri, South Sulawesi 65 35
2171 1000r. Pisok, North Sulawesi 90 25
2172 2000r. Bidu, East Nusa Tenggara . . . . 1·80 1·00

544 Yogyakarta Palace

1995. 20th Anniv of World Tourism Organization. Multicoloured.
2174 300r. Type **544** 25 25
2175 700r. Floating market, Banjarmasin 65 65
2176 1000r. Pasola (equestrian tradition), Sumba 90 90

545 Children, President Suharto and First Lady

1995. "Dedication to the Nation".
2177 **545** 700r. multicoloured . . . 65 65

546 Letter from King of Klungkung, Bali

547 "Schizostachyum brachycladum"

1995. 6th Five Year Plan. National Letter Writing Campaign. Multicoloured.
2178 300r. Type **546** 25 25
2179 700r. Carrier pigeon (campaign mascot) and letters 65 65

1995. 4th International Bamboo Congress, Ubud, Bali. Multicoloured.
2180 300r. Type **547** 25 25
2181 700r. "Dendrocalamus asper" 65 65

548 N250 and National Flag

1995. Inaugural Flight of I.P.T.N. N250 Airliner.
2182 **548** 700r. multicoloured . . . 65 65

549 Anniversary Emblem

1995. 50th Anniv of Indonesian Republic. Multicoloured.
2183 300r. Type **549** 25 25
2184 700r. Boy with national flag 65 65

550 Kota Intan Drawbridge

1995. "Jakarta '95" Asian Stamp Exn. Mult.
2186 300r. Type **550** 25 25
2187 700r. Fatahillah Jakarta History Museum 65 65

551 "Dewarutji" (cadet barquentine), Pinisi Sailing Ship and Flag

1995. "Sail Indonesia '95" Tall Ships Race and Fleet Review.
2188 **551** 700r. multicoloured . . . 65 65

552 "Mother Love" (Patricia Saerang)

553 Mushaf Istiqlal (illuminated Islamic text)

1995. 10th Asia and Pacific Regional Conference of Rehabilitation International, Indonesia.
2190 **552** 700r.+100r. mult 75 75

1995. Istiqlal Festival.
2191 **553** 700r. multicoloured . . . 65 65

554 P.T.T. Monument

1995. 50th Anniv of Take-over of P.T.T. Headquarters by Republicans.
2192 **554** 700r. multicoloured . . . 65 65

555 Rice

556 Flags and Emblem

1995. 50th Anniv of F.A.O.
2193 **555** 700r. multicoloured . . . 65 65

1995. 50th Anniv of U.N.O. Multicoloured.
2194 300r. Type **556** 25 25
2195 700r. Emblem, Earth and rainbow 65 65

557 "Cyrtostachys renda"

1995. Flora and Fauna. Multicoloured.
2196 150r. Type **557** 15 10
2197 150r. Tiger ("Panthera tigris") 15 10
2198 150r. "Bouea macrophylla" 15 10
2199 150r. Javan rhinoceros ("Rhinoceros sondaicus") 15 10
2200 150r. "Santalum album" . . 15 10
2201 150r. Komodo dragon ("Varanus komodoensis") 15 10
2202 150r. "Diospyros celebica" 15 10
2203 150r. Maleo fowl ("Macrocephalon maleo") 15 10
2204 150r. "Nephelium ramboutan-ake" 15 10
2205 150r. Malay peacock-pheasant ("Polyplectron schleiermacheri") 15 10

558 Yogyakarta Palace

1995. Award of Aga Khan Prize for Architecture to Indonesia. Multicoloured.
2207 300r. Type **558** 25 25
2208 700r. Surakarta Palace . . . 65 65

559 Hill and Postal Carriers

560 Economic Sectors

1995. Birth Bicentenary of Sir Rowland Hill (instigator of postal stamps). Multicoloured.
2209 300r. Type **559** 25 25
2210 700r. Hill and Indonesian Postal Service emblem . . 65 65

1995. Traditional Dances (4th series). As T **506**. Multicoloured.
2211 150r. Nguri dance, West Nusa Tenggara 15 15
2212 300r. Muli Betanggai dance, Lampung 25 25
2213 700r. Mutiara dance, Moluccas 65 65
2214 1000r. Gantar dance, East Kalimantan 90 90

1996. Economic Census.
2216 **560** 300r. orange and blue . . 25 25
2217 – 700r. turquoise & orange 65 65
DESIGN—HORIZ: 700r. Graph of economic activity.

561 Satellite orbiting Earth

1996. Launch of "Palapa-C" Satellite. Mult.
2218 300r. Type **561** 25 25
2219 700r. Satellite orbiting Earth (triangular) 55 55

562 Mixed Flowers

563 Soemanang Soeriowinoto (Association head, 1946–47 and 1949–50)

1996. Greetings Stamps. "Happy Holiday". Inscr "Selamat Hari Raya". Multicoloured.
2220 150r. Type **562** 10 10
2221 300r. Mixed flowers (different) 25 25
2222 700r. Mixed flowers (different) 55 55

1996. 50th Anniv of Indonesian Journalists' Association. Multicoloured.
2223 300r. Type **563** 25 25
2224 700r. Djamaluddin Adinegoro (head of Indonesian Press Bureau Foundation and founder of Academy of Publicity and Publicity Faculty, Padjadjaran University) 55 55

564 Tank firing and Map

1996. 47th Anniv of Return of Republican Government to Djokjakarta. Multicoloured.
2225 700r.+100r. Type **564** . . . 65 65
2226 700r.+100r. Attack on Palace 65 65
Nos. 2225/6 were issued together, se-tenant, forming a composite design.

565 State House, Bandung

1996. "indonesia 96" International Youth Stamp Exhibition, Bandung. Multicoloured.
2227 300r. Type **565** 25 25
2228 700r. Painted parasols . . . 55 55

566 Indonesian Bear Cuscus

567 Roses

1996. Cuscuses. Multicoloured.
2230 300r. Australian spotted cuscus 25 25
2231 300r. Type **566** 25 25
Nos 2230/1 were issued together, se-tenant, forming a composite design.

1996. Greetings Stamps. "Congratulations and Best Wishes". Inscr "Selamat dan Sukses". Multicoloured.
2233 150r. Type **567** 10 10
2234 300r. Orchids 25 25
2235 700r. Chrysanthemums . . . 55 55

568 Students (Y. Edwin Purwanto)

1996. Compulsory Nine Year Education Programme. Winning Entries in Children's Stamp Design Competition. Multicoloured.
2236 150r. Type **568** 10 10
2237 300r. Children in playground (Andi Pradhana) 25 25
2238 700r. Teacher and pupils (Intan Sari Dewi) 55 55

569 Archery

1996. Olympic Games, Atlanta. Mult.
2239 300r. Type **569** 25 25
2240 700r. Weightlifting 55 55
2241 1000r. Badminton 90 90

571 Pres. Suharto and Procession

1996. National Youth Kirab. Multicoloured.
2244 300r. Type **571** 25 25
2245 700r. Pres. Suharto presenting national flag 55 55

572 Nusantara N-2130 Prototype over Soekarno-Hatta Airport

573 Scouts climbing over Rope Ladders

1996. Aviation and Maritime Year. Mult.
2246 300r. Type **572** 25 25
2247 700r. "Palindo Jaya" (inter-island ferry) 55 55

1996. National Scout Jamboree, Djakarta. Multicoloured.
2248 150r. Type **573** 10 10
2249 150r. Scouts on ladder and death slide 10 10
2250 150r. Scouts at base of rope ladders 10 10
2251 150r. Girl scouts constructing wooden apparatus 10 10
2252 150r. Scouts on unicycle and climbing frame 10 10
2253 150r. Girl scouts building frame on campsite 10 10
2254 150r. Soldering metal . . . 10 10
2255 150r. Girl at radio taking notes 10 10
Nos. 2248/55 were issued together, se-tenant, Nos. 2248/51 and 2252/5 forming composite designs.

574 Pinisi Prows and Wave

1996. 50th Anniv of Bank BNI. Multicoloured.
2256 300r. Type **574** 25 25
2257 700r. Pinisi sailing ship . . . 55 55

575 Mother and Child reading (Salt Iodization Programme)

1996. 50th Anniv of U.N.I.C.E.F. Each brown, green and mauve.
2258 300r. Type **575** 25 25
2259 700r. Giving oral vaccine to children (elimination of polio) 55 55
2260 1000r. Children (Children's Rights Convention) . . . 90 90

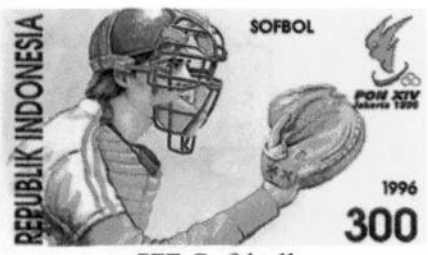

576 Ibu Tien Suharto **577** Softball

1996. Ibu Tien Suharto (First Lady) Commem.
2261 **576** 700r. multicoloured . . . 55 55

1996. National Sports Week. Multicoloured.
2263 300r. Type **577** 25 25
2264 700r. Hockey 55 55
2265 1000r. Basketball 90 90

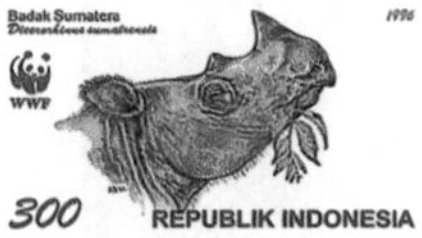

578 Head of Sumatran Rhinoceros

1996. The Sumatran Rhinoceros ("Dicerorhinus sumatrensis") and the Javan Rhinoceros ("Rhinoceros sondaicus"). Multicoloured.
2267 300r. Type **578** 40 25
2268 300r. Sumatran rhinoceros . . . 40 25
2269 300r. Javan rhinoceros . . . 40 25
2270 300r. Adult and baby Javan rhinoceros 40 25

579 Flower Arrangement **581** Sulawesi Hornbill

580 Coins and Banknotes

1996. Greetings Stamps. "Happy New Year". Inscr "Selamat Tahun Baru". Multicoloured.
2272 150r. Type **579** 10 10
2273 300r. Arrangement including red and yellow roses . . . 25 25
2274 700r. Arrangement including white rose and yellow chrysanthemums 55 55

1996. 50th Anniv of Financial Day.
2275 **580** 700r. multicoloured . . . 55 55

1996. National Flora and Fauna Day. Mult.
2276 300r. Type **581** 25 25
2277 300r. Irrawaddy dolphin ("Orcaella brevirostris") 25 25
2278 300r. Black-naped oriole ("Oriolus chinensis") . . 25 25
2279 300r. Sun bear ("Helarctos malayanus") 25 25
2280 300r. Rothschild's mynah ("Leucopsar rothschildi") 25 25
2281 300r. Lontar palms ("Borassus flabellifer") . . 25 25
2282 300r. Black orchid ("Coelogyne pandurata") 25 25
2283 300r. Michelia ("Michelia alba") 25 25
2284 300r. Giant aroid lily ("Amorphophallus titanum") 25 25
2285 300r. Majegau ("Dysoxylum densiflorum") 25 25

582 Somba Opu Fortress

1996. Eastern Region. Multicoloured.
2288 300r. Divers and sea-bed . . 25 25
2289 700r. Type **582** 55 55

583 School-children at Play **585** Children shaking Hands ("Happy Birthday")

584 Dish Aerial and Control Room

1996. National Movement of Foster Parents. Multicoloured.
2290 150r. Type **583** 15 15
2291 300r. Poor children and photograph of school-child (horiz) 25 25

1996. Traditional Dances (5th series). As T **506**. Multicoloured.
2292 150r. Baksa Kembang dance, South Kalimantan 10 10
2293 300r. Ngarojeng dance, Djakarta 25 25
2294 700r. Rampai dance, Aceh 55 55
2295 1000r. Boituka dance, East Timor 90 90

1997. Telecommunications Year. Mult.
2297 300r. Type **584** 25 25
2298 700r. Key pad, communications satellite orbiting Earth and woman using telephone 55 55

1997. Greetings Stamps.
2299 **585** 600r. multicoloured . . . 50 50
2300 – 600r. black, brn & mve 50 50
DESIGN: No. 2300, Heart and ribbons ("Best Wishes").

586 Transport, Ballot Boxes and National Flag

1997. General Election. Multicoloured.
2301 300r. Type **586** 25 25
2302 700r. State arms, map, ballot boxes and buildings 55 55
2303 1000r. State arms, ballot boxes, map and city skyline 90 90

587 Pres. Suharto and Wahyu Nusantaraaji

1997. Indonesia's 200,000,000th Citizen.
2305 **587** 700r. multicoloured . . . 55 55

588 Children with Stamp Collection **589** Wage Rudolf Soepratman

1997. 75th Anniv of Indonesian Philatelic Association. Multicoloured.
2306 300r. Type **588** 25 25
2307 700r. Magnifying glass on 1994 150r. Flora and Fauna stamp 55 55

1997. Cultural Anniversaries. Multicoloured.
2308 300r. Type **589** (composer of "Indonesia Raya" (national anthem), 60th death anniv (1998)) . . . 25 25
2309 700r. Usmar Ismail (film director, 25th death anniv (1996)) 55 55
2310 1000r. Self-portrait of Affandi (painter, 90th birth anniv) 90 90

590 Picture Jasper

1997. "Indonesia 2000" International Stamp Exn, Bandung (1st issue). Minerals. Multicoloured.
2312 300r. Type **590** 25 25
2313 700r. Chrysocolla 55 55
2314 1000r. Geode 90 90
See also Nos. 2403/5, 2529/3 and 2593/5.

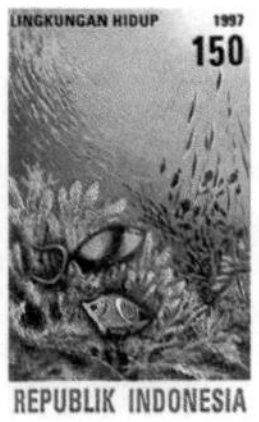

592 Crowd giving Thumbs Up to "No Smoking" Sign **593** Fishes and Coral Reef

1997. World "No Smoking" Day. Winning Entry in Students' Design Competition.
2317 **592** 1000r. multicoloured . . 90 90

1997. World Environment Day. Mult.
2318 150r. Type **593** 15 15
2319 300r. Rays and other fishes by brain and other corals 25 25
2320 700r. Two coralfishes amongst corals 55 55

594 Paksi Naga Liman Carriage (built by Pangeran Losari)

1997. 2nd Indonesian Royal Palace Festival, Cirebon. Multicoloured.
2322 300r. Type **594** 25 25
2323 700r. Singa Barong carriage (built by Ki Nataguna), 1549 . . . . 55 55

595 Venue's Main Gateway

1997. 18th National Koran Reading Contest, Jambi. Multicoloured.
2324 300r. Type **595** 25 25
2325 700r. Al Ikhsaniah Mosque, Olak Kemang, Jambi . . 55 55

596 Co-operatives Monument, Tasikmalaya **597** Pres. Suharto and Dr. Mohammad Hatta (first vice-president)

1997. 50th Anniv of Co-operatives Movement. Multicoloured.
2326 150r. Type **596** 10 10
2327 150r. Co-operatives Monument, Djakarta . . 10 10
2328 300r. Child's hand clasping adult's hand 25 25
2329 300r. Figure before globe . . 25 25
2330 700r. Type **597** 55 55

598 Hands on Globe

1997. 30th Anniv of Association of South-East Asian Nations. Multicoloured.
2331 300r. Type **598** 25 25
2332 700r. Ears of cereals forming "30th" and globe 55 55

599 Games Emblem and Mascot

1997. 19th South-East Asian Games, Djakarta. Multicoloured.
2333 300r. Type **599** 25 25
2334 300r. Torch carrier, flags and emblem 25 25
2335 700r. Running and throwing the discus 55 55
2336 700r. Hurdling and sprinting 55 55

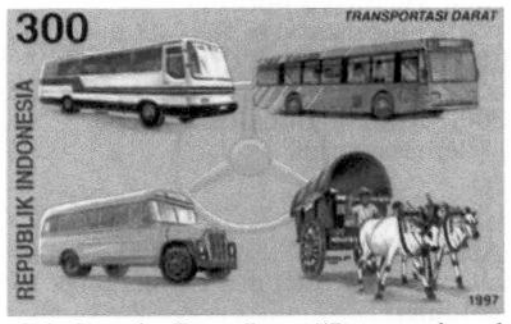

600 Coach, Bus, Java "International Harvester" Bus and Bullock Cart

1997. National Communications Day. Transport Development. Multicoloured.
2337 300r. Type **600** 25 25
2338 300r. Electric, express, diesel and steam railway locomotives 25 25
2339 700r. Container ship, passenger ship, cargo vessel and lette (Madurese sailing boat) 55 55
2340 700r. Seulawah and IPTN CN-235, CN-250 and N-2130 airliners 55 55

601 U.P.U. Monument and Mas Soeharto (first head of Indonesian P.T.T.)

1997. 50th Anniv of Indonesian Membership of U.P.U. Multicoloured.
2341 300r. Type **601** 25 25
2342 700r. Heinrich von Stephan (founder of U.P.U.) and monument 55 55

602 Assembly Emblem and Building

1997. People's Consultative Assembly General Session.
2343 **602** 700r. multicoloured . . . 55 55

603 Village Programme (Army)

1997. Armed Forces Day. Multicoloured.
2344 300r. Type **603** 25 25
2345 300r. Frigates and Jalesveva Jayamahe Monument, Surabaya (Navy) 25 25
2346 300r. "Blue Falcon" acrobatic team (Air Force) 25 25
2347 300r. Rapid Reaction Unit (Police Force) 25 25

605 Duku Fruit ("Lansium domesticum")

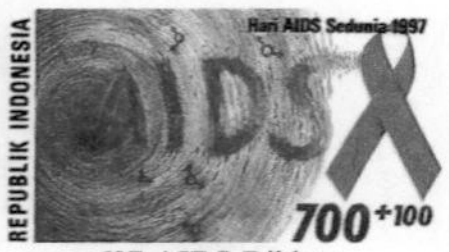

607 AIDS Ribbon

606 Oil Field

1997. National Flora and Fauna Day. Mult.
2349 300r. Type **605** 25 25
2350 300r. Salacca of Condet ("Salacca zalacca") . . . 25 25
2351 300r. Tengawang tungkul ("Shorea stenoptera") . . 25 25
2352 300r. Ebony ("Diospyros macrophylla") 25 25
2353 300r. Fibre orchid ("Diplocaulobium utile") 25 25
2354 300r. Belida fish ("Chitala lopis") 25 25
2355 300r. Brahminy kite ("Haliastur indus") . . . 25 25
2356 300r. Helmeted hornbill ("Rhinoplax vigil") . . . 25 25
2357 300r. Timor deer ("Cervus timorensis") 25 25
2358 300r. Anoa ("Bubalus depressicornis") 25 25

1997. Association of South-east Asian Nations Council on Petroleum Conference, Djakarta. Multicoloured.
2360 300r. Type **606** 25 25
2361 300r. Oil refinery 25 25
2362 300r. "Eka Putra" (oil tanker) 25 25
2363 300r. Petrol tankers 25 25

1997. World AIDS Day.
2364 **607** 700r.+100r. mult 50 50

608 Letter from Foster Son

1997. National Foster Parents Movement.
2365 **608** 700r. multicoloured . . . 50 50

1997. Traditional Dances (6th series). As T **506**. Multicoloured.
2366 150r. Mopuputi Cengke dance, Central Sulawesi 10 10
2367 300r. Mandan Talawang Nyai Balau dance, Central Kalimantan 25 25
2368 600r. Gambyong dance, Central Java 40 40
2369 700r. Cawan dance, North Sumatra 50 50
2370 1000r. Legong Keraton dance, Bali 65 65

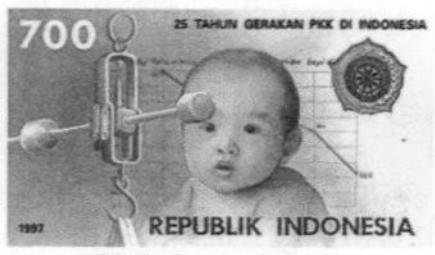

609 Baby and Scales

1997. 25th Anniv of Family Welfare Movement.
2372 **609** 700r. multicoloured . . . 50 50

610 Erau Festival, East Kalimantan

1998. Year of Art and Culture. Festivals. Multicoloured.
2373 300r. Type **610** 10 10
2374 700r. Tabot Festival, Bengkulu 25 25

611 Malin Kundang and his Mother

1998. Folk Tales (1st series). Multicoloured.(a) "Malin Kundung".
2375 300r. Type **611** 10 10
2376 300r. Malin returning home and rejecting mother . . . 10 10
2377 300r. Malin's mother praying to God to curse him 10 10
2378 300r. Malin's ship in storm 10 10
2379 300r. Malin turned to stone 10 10

(b) "Sangkuriang".
2380 300r. Dayang Sumbi weaving 10 10
2381 300r. Dayang Sumbi expelling her son Sanguriang after he killed their dog 10 10
2382 300r. Dayang Sumbi discovering her lover is her son 10 10
2383 300r. Dayang Sumbi creating fake dawn and Sanguriang hurling wooden boat 10 10
2384 300r. Tangkuban Parahu (upturned boat) Mountain 10 10

(c) "Roro Jonggrang".
2385 300r. Pengging people attacking Prambanan people 10 10
2386 300r. Bandung Bondowoso proposing to Roro Jonggrang 10 10
2387 300r. Bandung Bondowoso building temples 10 10
2388 300r. Women banging rice-mothers to prematurely announce dawn 10 10
2389 300r. Prambanan Temple and petrified Roro Jonggrang 10 10

(d) "Tengger".
2390 300r. Roro Anteng and Joko Seger marrying . . . 10 10
2391 300r. Roro and Joko praying to gods for a child 10 10
2392 300r. Volcano erupting . . . 10 10
2393 300r. Raden Kusuma (youngest son) sacrificing himself 10 10
2394 300r. Tengger people giving offerings to volcano . . . 10 10

Nos. 2375/94 were issued together, se-tenant, forming a composite design.
See also Nos. 2489/508, 2572/91, 2679/**MS**2699 and 2761/**MS**2781.

612 Djakarta Palace

1997. Presidential Palaces. Multicoloured.
2396 300r. Type **612** 10 10
2397 300r. Bogor Palace 10 10
2398 300r. Cipanas Palace . . . 10 10
2399 300r. Yogyakarta Palace . . 10 10
2400 300r. Tampak Siring Palace, Bali 10 10

613 Man and Pregnant Woman

1998. 50th Anniv of W.H.O. Multicoloured.
2401 300r. Type **613** 10 10
2402 700r. Mother and child (horiz) 10 10

1998. "Indonesia 2000" International Stamp Exhibition, Bandung (2nd issue). Minerals. As T **590**. Multicoloured.
2403 300r. Chrysopal 10 10
2404 700r. Tektite 15 15
2405 1000r. Amethyst 25 25

614 Boys playing Football

1998. World Cup Football Championship, France. Multicoloured.
2408 300r. Type **614** 10 10
2409 700r. Boys and goal-posts 15 15
2410 1000r. Boys challenging for ball 25 25

615 Tropical Rainforest

1998. Environmental Protection. Ecophila Stamp Day. Multicoloured.
2412 700r. Type **615** 15 15
2413 700r. Tropical rainforest (different) 15 15
Nos. 2412/13 were issued together, se-tenant, forming a composite design.

617 School-children and Drug Addict

1998. International Day Against Drug Abuse and Illicit Trafficking. Multicoloured.
2415 700r. Type **617** 15 15
2416 700r. Students campaigning against drugs 15 15

618 Besakih Temple (½-size illustration)

1998. Tourism. Multicoloured.
2417 700r. Type **618** 15 15
2418 700r. Taman Ayun Temple (31 × 23 mm) 15 15

620 Cattle Wagon and Truck

1998. Railway Rolling Stock. Multicoloured.
2421 300r. Type **620** 10 10
2422 300r. Truck and goods wagon 10 10
2423 300r. Green and yellow passenger carriages . . . 10 10
2424 300r. Passenger carriage and tender 10 10
2425 300r. Class B50 steam locomotive 10 10
2426 300r. Front half of Class D52 steam locomotive . . 10 10
2427 300r. Back half of Class D52 steam locomotive with tender 10 10
2428 300r. Passenger carriage with two doors 10 10
2429 300r. Observation car . . . 10 10
2430 300r. Goods wagon 10 10
Nos. 2421/30 were issued together, se-tenant, forming a composite design of a train.

621 Pres. Bacharuddin Habibie

1998.
2432 **621** 300r. multicoloured . . . 10 10
2433 700r. multicoloured . . . 15 15
2434 4500r. multicoloured . . 90 90
2435 5000r. multicoloured . . 1·00 1·00

622 Fencing

1998. 13th Asian Games, Bangkok, Thailand. Multicoloured.
2436 300r. Type **622** 10 10
2437 700r. Taekwondo 15 15
2438 4000r. Kung fu 80 80

623 "Baruna Jaya IV" (research ship)

1998. International Year of the Ocean.
2440 **623** 700r. multicoloured . . . 15 15

625 1974 20r. U.P.U. Stamp

1998. World Stamp Day. Multicoloured.
2442 700r. Type **625** 15 15
2443 700r. 1955 15s. Post Office Anniversary stamp . . . 15 15

626 Magpie Goose

1998. Waterfowl (1st series). Multicoloured.
2444 4000r. Type **626** . . . . . 1·00 1·00
2445 5000r. Spotted whistling duck . . . . 1·20 1·20
2446 10000r. Salvadori's duck . . 2·40 2·40
2447 15000r. Radjah shelduck . . 3·50 3·50
2448 20000r. White-winged wood duck . . . . 5·00 5·00
See also Nos. 2468/74 and 2628/9.

628 State Flag and Jayawijaya Peak

1998. "The Red and White Flag". Multicoloured.
2451 700r. Type **628** 15 15
2452 700r. State flag and Himalayan peak 15 15

629 State Flag

1998. Political Reforms. Multicoloured.

2453	700r. Type **629**	15	15
2454	700r. Dove and State flag	15	15
2455	1000r. Students in front of Parliament building (82 × 25 mm)	25	25

630 "Stelechocarpus burahol"

631 Monument at Blitar and Museum, Bogor

1998. Flora and Fauna. Multicoloured.

2456	500r. Type **630**	15	15
2457	500r. Tuberose ("Polianthes tuberosa")	15	15
2458	500r. Four o'clock ("Mirabilis jalapa")	15	15
2459	500r. "Mangifera casturi"	15	15
2460	500r. "Ficus minahassae"	15	15
2461	500r. Zebra dove ("Geopelia striata")	15	15
2462	500r. Red and green junglefowl hybrid ("Gallus varius x G. gallus")	15	15
2463	500r. Indian elephant ("Elephas maximus")	15	15
2464	500r. Proboscis monkey ("Nasalis larvatus")	15	15
2465	500r. Eastern tarsier ("Tarsius spectrum")	15	15

1998. 55th Anniv of Formation of Volunteer National Armed Forces (independence fighters).

2467	**631** 700r.+100r. mult	15	15

632 Australian White-eyed Duck

1998. Waterfowl (2nd series). Multicoloured.

2468	250r. Type **632**	10	10
2469	500r. Pacific black duck	10	10
2470	700r. Grey teal	15	15
2471	1000r. Cotton goose	25	25
2472	1500r. Green pygmy goose	35	35
2473	2500r. Indian whistling duck	50	50
2474	3500r. Wandering whistling duck	75	75

1998. Traditional Dances (7th series). As T **506**. Multicoloured.

2476	300r. Oreng oreng gae dance, Sulawesi Tenggara (South-east Celebes)	10	10
2477	500r. Persembahan dance, Bengkulu	10	10
2478	700r. Kipas (fan) dance, Riau	15	15
2479	1000r. Srimpi dance, Yogyakarta	25	25
2480	2000r. Pasambahan, Sumatera Barat (West)	40	40

633 Water Wheel and Power Lines

1999. Year of Creation and Engineering. Multicoloured.

2482	500r. Type **633**	10	10
2483	700r. Water pipe and pipe network in valley	15	15

634 Throwing the Shot

635 Emblem

1999. 7th Far East and South Pacific Games for Disabled Persons, Bangkok. Multicoloured.

2484	500r. Type **634**	10	10
2485	500r. Medal and wheelchair	10	10

1999. 50th Anniv of Garuda Indonesia (state airline). Multicoloured.

2486	500r. Type **635**	10	10
2487	700r. Jet engine	15	15
2488	2000r. Pilot, stewardess and airplane	40	40

1999. Folk Tales (2nd series). As T **611**. Multicoloured. (a) "Lake Toba".

2489	500r. Man and yellow fish	15	15
2490	500r. Man proposing to woman	15	15
2491	500r. Woman giving food for father to son Sam and Sam eating it	15	15
2492	500r. Wife turning back into a fish	15	15
2493	500r. Samosir Island and Lake Toba	15	15
	(b) "Banjarmasin".		
2494	500r. Rebels and contenders to throne	15	15
2495	500r. Local governors crown Prince Samudera	15	15
2496	500r. Tumenggung sends fleet to Samudera's capital, Bandar Masih	15	15
2497	500r. Samudera and Tumenggung meet on board ship	15	15
2498	500r. Ships in Banjarmasin Harbour	15	15
	(c) "Buleleng".		
2499	500r. I Gusti Gede Paseken leaving with guards for Den Bukit	15	15
2500	500r. Forest giant appearing to I Gusti Gede Paseken	15	15
2501	500r. I Gusti Gede Paseken lifting stranded ship	15	15
2502	500r. I Gusti Gede Paseken arriving before King of Den Bukit	15	15
2503	500r. Procession in kingdom of Buleleng	15	15
	(d) "Woiram".		
2504	500r. Woiram teaching archery to Woiwallytmang and with wife Donadebu	15	15
2505	500r. Mesan and Mecy looking for shrimps	15	15
2506	500r. Woiram cursing Demontin village	15	15
2507	500r. Woiwallytmang and Mecy clinging to tree trunk	15	15
2508	500r. Woiram's footprints in rock	15	15

Nos. 2489/2508 were issued together, se-tenant, forming a composite design.

638 "Ascosparassis heinricherii"

1999. Fungi. Multicoloured. (a) T **638** and similar diamond-shaped designs.

2512	500r. Type **638**	10	10
2513	500r. "Mutinus bambusinus"	10	10
2514	500r. "Mycena" sp.	10	10
2515	700r. "Gloephyllum imponens"	15	15
2516	700r. "Microporus xanthopus"	15	15
2517	700r. "Termitomyces eurrhizus"	15	15
2518	1000r. "Boedijnopeziza insititia"	25	25
2519	1000r. "Aseroe rubra"	25	25
2520	1000r. "Calostoma orirubra"	25	25
	(b) As Nos. 2512/14 but rectangular designs, size 31 × 23 mm.		
2521	500r. As No. 2513	15	15
2522	500r. As No. 2512	15	15
2523	500r. As No. 2514	15	15

639 Doctor and Patients outside Surgery

1999. Public Health Care Insurance.

2525	**639** 700r. multicoloured	15	15

641 Y2K "Bug"

1999. Millennium Bug (computer programming fault). Multicoloured.

2527	500r. Type **641**	15	15
2528	500r. Robot exploding	15	15

Nos. 2527/8 were issued together, se-tenant, forming a composite design.

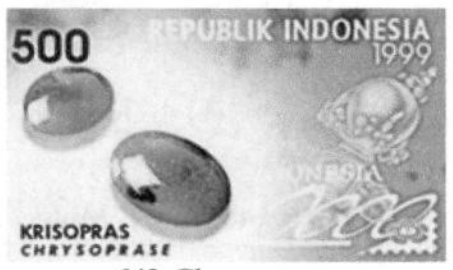

642 Chrysoprase

1999. "Indonesia 2000" International Stamp Exhibition, Bandung (3rd issue). Gemstones. Multicoloured.

2529	500r. Type **642**	15	15
2530	1000r. Smoky quartz	25	25
2531	2000r. Blue opal	55	55

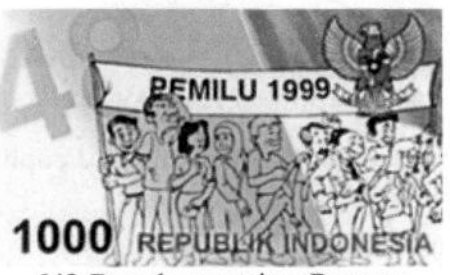

643 People carrying Banner

1999. General Election. Multicoloured.

2534	1000r. Type **643**	15	10
2535	1000r. Ballot box and map of Indonesia	15	10

Nos. 2534/5 were issued together, se-tenant, forming a composite design.

644 Girl in Blanket and People walking through Water

1999. Environmental Protection. Ecophila Stamp Day. Multicoloured.

2536	500r. Type **644**	15	15
2537	1000r. Boy swimming with duck, plant and berry	40	40
2538	2000r. Elderly woman drinking from jug	80	80

646 Nurses helping Children

1999. Red Cross.

2541	**646** 1000r. multicoloured	35	35

647 Frans Kaisiepo (Governor of Irian Jaya, 1964)

1999. National Heroes and Heroines.

2542	**647** 500r. brown & cinnamon	15	15
2543	– 500r. brown & cinnamon	15	15
2544	– 500r. brown & cinnamon	15	15
2545	– 500r. brown & cinnamon	15	15

DESIGNS: No. 2543, Maria Walanda Maramis (founder of "PIKAT" (women's education organization, 1917)); 2544, Dr. W. Z. Johannes (founder of Indonesian Christian Party, 1942); 2545, Martha Christina Tijahahu (revolutionary).

649 University Building, 1949

1999. 50th Anniv of Gadjah Mada University, Yogyakarkta. Multicoloured.

2547	500r. Type **649**	15	15
2548	1000r. University facade, 1999	40	40

650 Woman painting Parasol

1999. International Year of the Elderly Person.

2549	**650** 500r. multicoloured	15	15

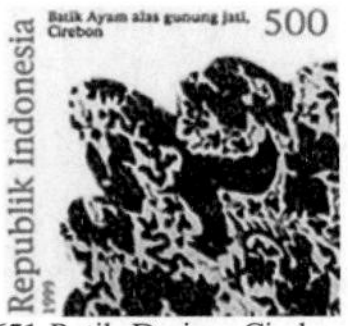

651 Batik Design, Cirebon

1999. Batik Designs. Different Batik designs. Mult.

2550	500r. Type **651**	15	15
2551	500r. Madura	15	15
2552	500r. Yogyakarta	15	15
2553	500r. Jambi	15	15

652 Pillar Box, Postman and Kantoon Post Office (½-size illustration)

1999. 125th Anniv of Universal Postal Union. Mult.

2554	500r. Type **652**	15	15
2555	500r. Modern postal building, motorcycle postman and pillar box	15	15
2556	1000r. Pillar box, left-hand side of Kantoon Post Office and postman on horseback (30 × 31 mm)	80	80
2557	1000r. Motorcycle postman, modern postal building and pillar box (30 × 31 mm)	80	80

653 Dog and Puppy

1999. Domestic Animals. Multicoloured.

2558	500r. Type **653**	15	15
2559	500r. Cockerel, hen and chick	15	15
2560	500r. Cat	15	15
2561	500r. Rabbits	15	15
2562	1000r. Feral rock pigeon (20 × 50 mm)	40	40
2563	1000r. Geese and gosling (20 × 50 mm)	40	40

Nos. 2558/9, 2560/1 and 2562/3 respectively were issued together, se-tenant, showing the composite design of a garden.

654 Globe, Diary and Clock Face

1999. New Millennium. Multicoloured.

2565	1000r. Type **654**	40	40
2566	1000r. "2000" and child's face	40	40

From 1 January 2000 stamps are inscribed "Indonesia".

655 Satellite and Fishes

2000. Year of Technology. Multicoloured.
2568 500r. Type **655** 15 15
2569 1000r. Greenhouse and plant 40 40

656 University Campus, Salemba

2000. 50th Anniv of University of Indonesia. Multicoloured.
2570 500r. Type **656** 15 15
2571 1000r. University building, Depok 40 40

2000. Folk Tales (3rd series). As T **611**. Multicoloured. (a) "*Tapak Tuan*".
2572 500r. Dragon finding baby on shore 25 25
2573 500r. Girl meeting other people 25 25
2574 500r. Dragon attacking boat and man 25 25
2575 500r. Man and dragon fighting 25 25
2576 500r. Dead dragon 25 25

(b) "*Batu Ballah*".
2577 500r. Mak Risah and children 25 25
2578 500r. Children playing . . . 25 25
2579 500r. Mak Risah saddened by her children 25 25
2580 500r. Mak Risah being swallowed by stone . . . 25 25
2581 500r. Mak Risah Rock . . . 25 25

(c) "*Sawerigading*".
2582 500r. Sariwegading proposing marriage to twin sister 25 25
2583 500r. We Tanriabeng refusing marriage 25 25
2584 500r. Sariwegdaing in stern of boat 25 25
2585 500r. Bow of boat and wedding 25 25
2586 500r. Bulupoloe Mountain 25 25

(d) "*7 Putri Kahyangan*".
2587 500r. Prince hiding wings and angel weeping 25 25
2588 500r. Prince and angel with their children and angel flying away from Earth 25 25
2589 500r. Prince flying on eagle's back to reclaim wife . . . 25 25
2590 500r. Angel refusing to return to Earth 25 25
2591 500r. Prince wearing magical crown 25 25
Nos. 2572/91 were issued together, se-tenant, forming a composite design.

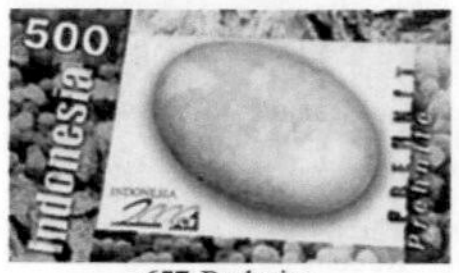

657 Prehnite

2000. "Indonesia 2000" International Stamp Exhibition, Bandung (4th issue). Gemstones. Multicoloured.
2593 500r. Type **657** 25 25
2594 1000r. Chalcedony 40 40
2595 2000r. Volcanic obsidian . . 75 75

658 I Brewok (Gun-Gun)

2000. Cartoon Characters. Each black and red.
2598 500r. Type **658** 25 25
2599 500r. "Pak Tuntung" (Basuki) 25 25
2600 500r. "Pak Bei" (Masdi Sunardi) 25 25
2601 500r. "Mang Ohle" (Didin D. Basuni) 25 25
2602 500r. "Panji Koming" (Dwi Koendoro) 25 25

659 Emblem and Weather Chart

2000. 50th Anniv of World Meteorological Organization.
2603 **659** 500r. multicoloured . . . 25 25

661 Cycling

2000. 15th National Sports Week. Multicoloured.
2605 500r. Type **661** 50 25
2606 1000r. Canoeing . . . . . 1·10 40
2607 2000r. High-jumping . . . . 2·10 55

663 Red-footed Booby's on Nest

2000. Environmental Protection. Ecophila Stamp Day. Multicoloured.
2609 500r. Type **663** 50 25
2610 1000r. Monkey . . . . . . 1·10 40
2611 2000r. Fishes . . . . 2·10 55

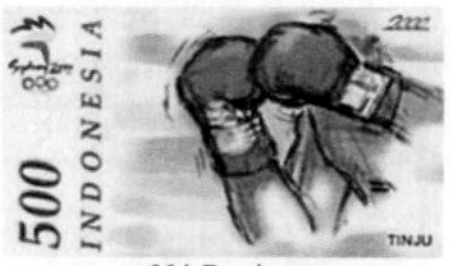

664 Boxing

2000. Olympic Games, Sydney. Multicoloured.
2613 500r. Type **664** 15 15
2614 500r. Judo 15 15
2615 1000r. Badminton 35 35
2616 1000r. Weightlifting 35 35
2617 2000r. Swimming 65 65
2618 2000r. Running 65 65

665 Komodo Dragon

2000. Endangered Species. The Komodo Dragon (*Varanus komodoensis*). Multicoloured.
2620 500r. Type **665** 40 40
2621 500r. Two dragons fighting 40 40
2622 500r. On branch 40 40
2623 500r. Two dragons walking 40 40

666 President Abdurrahman Wahid

2000. President and Vice-President. Multicoloured.
2625 1000r. Type **666** 40 40
2626 1000r. Vice-President Megawati Soekarnoputri 40 40

2000. Waterfowl (3rd series). As T **632**. Multicoloured.
2628 800r. Indian whistling duck (*Dendrocygna javanica*) . . 80 80
2629 900r. Australian white-eyed duck (*Aythya australis*) . . 1·00 1·00

668 Couple from D. I. Aceh

670 Hand holding 1989 500r. Endangered Species Stamp

669 Chairil Anwar (poet)

2000. Regional Costumes. Showing couples wearing traditional costumes from different regions. Multicoloured.
2630 900r. Type **668** 35 35
2631 900r. Jambi 35 35
2632 900r. Banten 35 35
2633 900r. D. I. Yogyakarta . . . 35 35
2634 900r. Kalimantan Tengah 35 35
2635 900r. Sulawesi Tenggara . . 35 35
2636 900r. Nusa Tenggara Timur 35 35
2637 900r. Sumatera Utara . . . 35 35
2638 900r. Bengkulu 35 35
2639 900r. D. K. I. Jakarta . . . 35 35
2640 900r. Jawa Timur 35 35
2641 900r. Kalimantan Timur . . 35 35
2642 900r. Sulawesi Selatan . . . 35 35
2643 900r. Maluku 35 35
2644 900r. Sumatera Barat . . . 35 35
2645 900r. Sumatera Selatan . . 35 35
2646 900r. Jawa Barat 35 35
2647 900r. Kalimantan Barat . . 35 35
2648 900r. Sulawesi Utara . . . 35 35
2649 900r. Bali 35 35
2650 900r. Maluku Utara 35 35
2651 900r. Riau 35 35
2652 900r. Lampung 35 35
2653 900r. Jawa Tengah 35 35
2654 900r. Kalimantan Selatan 35 35
2655 900r. Sulawesi Tengah . . . 35 35
2656 900r. Nusa Tenggara Barat 35 35
2657 900r. Irian Jaya 35 35

2000. Personalities. Multicoloured.
2658 900r. Type **669** 35 35
2659 900r. Ibu Sud (children's song writer) 35 35
2660 900r. Bing Slamet (entertainer) 35 35
2661 900r. S. Sudjojono (artist) 35 35
2662 900r. I. Ketut Maria (actor) 35 35

2000. Communications. Multicoloured.
2664 800r. Type **670** 25 25
2665 900r. Satellite, map, television and letter (horiz) 35 35
2666 1000r. Globe and computer monitor 40 40
2667 4000r. Airplane, globe and computer . . . . 1·50 1·50

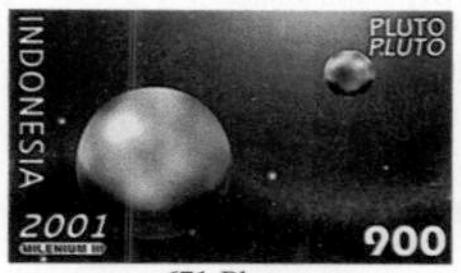

671 Pluto

2001. The Solar System. Multicoloured.
2668 900r. Type **671** 25 25
2669 900r. Neptune 25 25
2670 900r. Uranus 25 25
2671 900r. Saturn 25 25
2672 900r. Jupiter 25 25
2673 900r. Mars 25 25
2674 900r. Earth 25 25
2675 900r. Venus 25 25
2676 900r. Mercury 25 25
2677 900r. Sun 25 25
MS2678 120 × 71 mm. 5000r. Sun (different) . . . . 1·40 1·40

2001. Folk Tales (4th series). As T **611**. Multicoloured. (a) "Batang Tuaka".
2679 900r. Two snakes fighting and Tuaka with stone . . 25 25
2680 900r. Tuaka selling stone to merchant in Tumasik Port 25 25
2681 900r. Tuaka as a successful merchant with his wife . . 25 25
2682 900r. Mother cursing Tuaka and his wife 25 25
2683 900r. Tuaka and his wife become birds 25 25

(b) "Si Pitung".
2684 900r. Si Pitung and gang stealing money from Dutch sympathizers . . . 25 25
2685 900r. Si Pitung's gang leaving money for villagers 25 25
2686 900r. Dutch ruler fighting Si Pitung 25 25
2687 900r. Villagers mourning dead Si Pitung 25 25
2688 900r. Si Pitung Mosque . . 25 25

(c) "Terusan Nusa".
2689 900r. Tambing finding and eating dragon's egg . . . 25 25
2690 900r. Tambing turning into dragon 25 25
2691 900r. Dragon (Tambing) eating all the fish in the river 25 25
2692 900r. Tambing dying after eating his own tail 25 25
2693 900r. Empty river 25 25

(d) "Ile Mauraja".
2694 900r. Raja dreaming 25 25
2695 900r. Raja receiving cotton seeds from bearded man 25 25
2696 900r. Raja and wife 25 25
2697 900r. Snake on bed, burning village and snakes causing upheaval of village . . . 25 25
2698 900r. Mountain formed by village 25 25
MS2699 84 × 61 mm. 5000r. No. 2686 . . . . 1·40 1·40
Nos. 2679/98 were issued together, se-tenant, forming a composite design.

672 Arsa Wijaya, Bali

2001. Traditional Masks. Showing left (a) or right (b) sides of masks. Multicoloured.
2700 500r. Type **672** 15 15
2701 500r. Arsa Wijaya (b) . . . 15 15
2702 800r. Asmat, Irian Jaya (a) 25 25
2703 800r. Asmat (b) 25 25
2704 800r. Cirebon, Jawa Barat (a) 25 25
2705 800r. Cirebon (b) 25 25
2706 900r. Hudoq, Kalimantan Timur (a) 35 35
2707 900r. Hudoq (b) 35 35
2708 900r. Wayang Wong, Yogyakarta (a) 35 35
2709 900r. Wayang Wong (b) . . 35 35
MS2710 61 × 96 mm. 5000r. No. 2706 . . . . 1·60 1·60
Nos. 2700/1, 2702/3, 2704/5, 2706/7 and 2708/9 were issued together, se-tenant, each pair forming a composite design.

673 Beduk

2001. Traditional Instruments. Multicoloured.
2711 900r. Type **673** 15 15
2712 900r. Bende (bronze drum) 15 15
2713 900r. Kentongan (percussion) 15 15
2714 900r. Nafiri (horn) 15 15

674 Bouquet

2001. Greetings Stamps. Multicoloured.
2715 800r. Type **674** 15 15
2716 900r. Rose 25 25
2717 1000r. Bouquet of orange roses and leaves 35 35
2718 1500r. Large white flower and dark green leaf . . . 40 40
2719 2000r. Bouquet of yellow flowers with pink bow . . 55 55
2720 4000r. Amaryllis flower and ribbon . . . . 1·20 1·20
2721 5000r. Table decoration and candles . . . . 1·50 1·50
2722 10000r. White flower with yellow centre . . . . . . 3·00 3·00

675 Children and Fish (Surayadi)

2001. World Environment Day. Winning entries in Stamp Design Competition (Nos. 2723, 2725). Multicoloured.

2723	800r. Type **675**	25	25
2724	900r. Boys feeding deer	25	25
2725	1000r. Boy swimming with turtle (Lambok Hutabarat)	35	35
MS2726	82 × 50 mm. 3000r. As No. 2724	90	90

676 Youthful Sukarno wearing Turban

2001. Birth Centenary of Dr. Ahmed Sukarno (Bung Karno) (nationalist leader and first president). Multicoloured.

2727	500r. Type **676**	15	15
2728	800r. As young man wearing collar and tie	25	25
2729	900r. Wearing high-necked jacket	25	25
2730	1000r. Wearing uniform with lapel badges	35	35
MS2731	138 × 59 mm. 5000r. Giving speech	1·50	1·50

677 Policeman guiding Children across the Road

2001. Indonesian Police Force. Multicoloured.

2732	1000r. Type **677**	35	35
2733	1000r. Helicopter and women police officers giving directions	35	35

678 Scouts raising Flag

2001. National Scout Jamboree, Banyumas, Java. Multicoloured.

2734	1000r. Type **678**	35	35
2735	1000r. Erecting tent	35	35

Nos. 2734/5 were issued together, se-tenant, forming a composite design.

679 Kaki Siapa (blind man's buff)

2001. National Children's Day. Children's Games. Multicoloured.

2736	800r. Type **679**	15	15
2738	900r. Erang Bambu (stilt walking)	25	25
2739	1000r. Dakon (counting game)	25	25
2740	2000r. Kuda Pelepah Pisang (hobby horses)	40	40

680 Sunflower

2001. Philanippon '01 International Stamp Exhibition. Sheet 93 × 46 mm.

MS2741	**680** 10000r. multicoloured	3·25	3·25

681 Dr. R. Soeharso (founder) and Operating Theatre

2001. 50th Anniv of Dr. R. Soeharso Orthopaedic Hospital.

2742	**681** 1000r. multicoloured	15	15

682 Makasaar Post Office

2001. Post Office Architecture. Showing Post Office building. Multicoloured.

2743	800r. Type **682**	10	10
2744	900r. Bandung	15	15
2745	1000r. Balikpapan	15	15
2746	2000r. Padang	25	25

683 Perahu (boat)

2001. Traditional Transport. Multicoloured.

2747	1000r. Type **683**	15	15
2748	1000r. Becak Dayung (tricycle rickshaw)	15	15
2749	1000r. Andong (horse-drawn taxi)	15	15

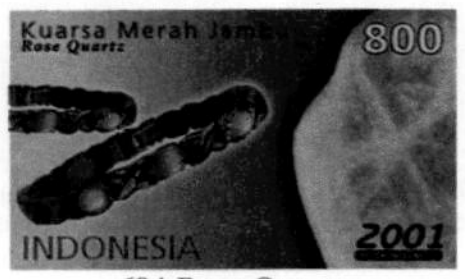

684 Rose Quartz

2001. Gemstones. Multicoloured.

2750	800r. Type **684**	10	10
2751	900r. Brecciated Jasper	15	15
2752	1000r. Malachite	15	15
MS2753	80 × 47 mm. 5000r. Diamond	1·60	1·60

685 Children encircling Globe

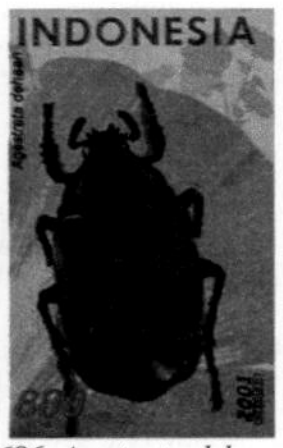

686 *Agestrata dehaan*

2001. United Nations Year of Dialogue among Civilizations.

2754	**685** 1000r. multicoloured	15	15

2001. Insects. Multicoloured.

2755	800r. Type **686**	10	10
2756	900r. *Mormolyce phyllodes*	15	15
2757	1000r. *Batocera rosenbergi*	15	15
2758	1000r. *Chrysochroa buqueti*	15	15
2759	2000r. *Chalcosoma Caucasus*	15	15
MS2760	61 × 90 mm. 5000r. No. 27590	2·10	2·10

2002. Folk Tales (5th series). As T **611**. Multicoloured. (a) Pulau Kembaro, Sumatera Selatan

2761	1000r. Two women	15	15
2762	1000r. Man and woman	15	15
2763	1000r. Boat sinking	15	15
2764	1000r. Man and woman standing in boat	15	15
2765	1000r. Serpent, boat and bridge	15	15
	(b) Nyi Roro Kidul, Jogjakarta		
2766	1000r. Prabu Siliwangi, Dewi Kaita and harem	15	15
2767	1000r. Dewi Kaita and mother changing	15	15
2768	1000r. Cast out of palace	15	15
2769	1000r. Dewi Kaita changing to Nyi Roro Kidul	15	15
2770	1000r. Sea	15	15
	(c) Aji Tatin, Kalimantan Timur		
2771	1000r. Palm tree, woman and man with arm outstretched	15	15
2772	1000r. Woman, bird and boat	15	15
2773	1000r. Woman with hand to head	15	15
2774	1000r. Boat breaking	15	15
2775	1000r. Sun and bird	15	15
	(d) Danau Tondano, Sulawesi Utara		
2776	1000r. Woman seated	15	15
2777	1000r. Man holding spear	15	15
2778	1000r. Man and woman dressed as man	15	15
2779	1000r. Three men under trees	15	15
2780	1000r. Tree and island	15	15
MS2781	108 × 61 mm. 5000r. No. 2765	75	75

Nos. 2761/5, 2766/70, 2771/5, 2776/80 respectively were issued together, se-tenant, forming a composite design.

687 Player with Shirt over Head

2002. World Cup Football Championships, Japan and South Korea. Multicoloured.

2782	1000r. Type **687**	15	15
2783	1500r. Players in front of goal	20	20
2784	2000r. Player	25	25
MS2785	52 × 80 mm. 5000r. No. 2784	75	75

688 Outline of Two Women

2002. 25th Anniv of Cancer Foundation.

2786	**688** 1000r. multicoloured	15	15

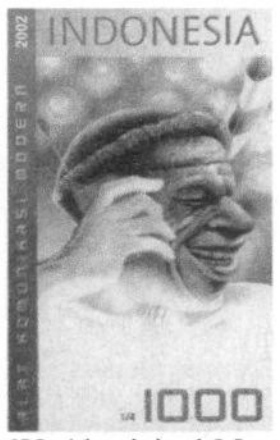

689 Aboriginal Man holding Cell Phone

2002. Communications. Multicoloured.

2787	1000r. Type **689**	15	15
2788	1000r. Woman holding hand set	15	15
2789	1000r. Computer, satellite and disc	15	15
2790	1000r. Satellite above globe	15	15

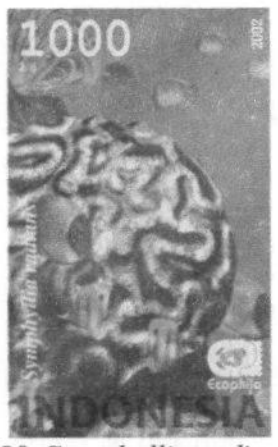

690 *Symphyllia radians*

2002. Marine Life. Ecophila. Multicoloured.

2791	1000r. Type **690**	15	15
2792	1000r. *Charonia tritonis*	15	15
2793	1500r. *Acanthaster planci*	20	20
2794	1500r. Polka dot grouper (*Cromileptes altivelis*)	20	20
2795	2000r. Blue tang (*Paracanthurus hepatus*)	25	25
2796	2000r. *Tridacna gigas*	25	25
MS2797	(a) 97 × 170 mm. Nos. 2791/5; (b) 60 × 91 mm. 5000r. No. 2793	1·70	1·70

691 Boy writing and Men dancing

2002. Nanggroe Aceh Province, Darussalam. Multicoloured.

2798	1500r. Type **691**	20	20
2799	3500r. Mosque	45	45

692 Family

2002. National Family Day.

2800	**692** 1000r. multicoloured	15	15

693 Solar Eclipse and Olympiad Emblem

2002. 33rd International Physics Olympiad, Bali. Multicoloured.

2801	1000r. Type **693**	15	15
2802	1000r. Colour spectrum and symbols	15	15

694 Bird-shaped Kite

2002. Layang-Layang. Kite Flying. Multicoloured.

2803	1000r. Type **694**	15	15
2804	1000r. Lion	15	15
2805	1000r. Rhomboid	15	15
2806	1000r. Winged kite	15	15
2807	1000r. Box and glider kites	15	15
MS2808	79 × 49 mm. 5000r. No. 2803	75	75

Nos. 2803/7 were issued together, se-tenant, forming a composite design.

695 Noni (*Morinda citrifolia*)

2002. Fruit. Multicoloured.

2809	300r. Type **695**	10	10
2810	500r. Mango (*Mangifera indica*)	10	10
2811	1500r. Star fruit (*Averrhoa carambola*)	20	20
2812	3000r. *Durio zibethinus*	40	40

696 Tari Pajaga Dancer, Salawesi Selatan

2002. Philakorea 2002 International Stamp Exhibition, Seoul. Sheet 48 × 80 mm.

MS2813	**696** 7000r. multicoloured	95	95

697 Mohammad Hatta

2002. Birth Centenary of Mohammad Hatta (first vice-president). Multicoloured.

2814	1000r. Type **697**	20	20
2815	1000r. Wearing high-necked jacket	20	20
2816	1500r. Wearing light jacket and dark tie	20	20
2817	1500r. Wearing light jacket and tie	20	20
MS2818	137 × 60 mm. 5000r. Wearing light suit and open neck shirt	75	75

EXPRESS LETTER STAMPS

E 189 "Garuda" Bird

1967. Inscr "1967".
E1166 **E 189** 10r. purple and blue . . . 55 15
E1167 15r. purple and orange . . . . . 1·00 40

1968. As Nos. E1166/7 but dated "1968".
E1202 **E 189** 10r. purple and blue 55 15
E1203 15r. purple & orange 80 25
E1204 20r. purple and yellow 80 25
E1205 30r. purple and green 1·20 50
E1206 40r. purple & lt pur 80 25

1969. As Nos. E1166/7 but dated "1969".
E1250 **E 189** 20r. purple and yellow 40 15
E1251 30r. purple and green 40 15
E1252 40r. purple & lt pur 55 15

POSTAGE DUE STAMPS

1950. Postage Due stamps of Netherlands Indies surch **BAJAR PORTO** and new value.
D576 2½s. on 50c. (No. D499) . . 1·00 65
D577 5s. on 100c. (No. D501) . . 2·75 1·00
D578 10s. on 75c. (No. D500) . . 5·75 1·40

D 100

D 268

D 333a

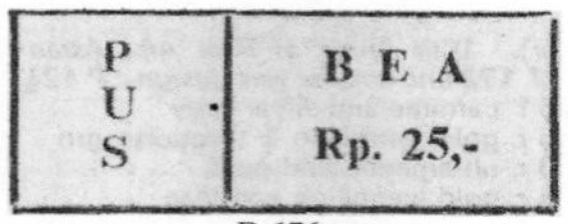

D 176

1951.
D645 **D 100** 2½s. orange 15 55
D646 5s. orange 15 10
D647 10s. orange 15 10
D648 15s. red 15 15
D773 15s. orange 25 55
D649 20s. blue 15 15
D774 20s. orange 25 55
D650 25s. olive 25 15
D775 25s. orange 25 55
D651 30s. brown 25 25
D776 30s. orange 25 50
D652 40s. green 25 25
D777 50s. orange . . . . . 1·50 55
D778 50s. green 10 10
D779 100s. orange 80 55
D780 100s. brown 10 10
D781 250s. blue 25 10
D782 500s. yellow 10 10
D783 750s. lilac 25 10
D784 1000s. salmon . . . 15 15
D654 1r. green . . . . . . 1·60 1·50

1965. Provisional issue for use on parcels.
D1057 **D 176** 25r. black on yellow 15

1966.
D1058 **D 100** 50r. red 10 10
D1059 100r. lake 15 15

1966. As Type **D 100**, but with coloured network background incorporating "1966".
D1098 5s. green and yellow . . . 25 25
D1099 10s. red and blue . . . 25 25
D1100 20s. blue and pink . . . 25 25
D1101 30s. sepia and red . . . 25 25
D1102 40s. violet and bistre . . . 25 25
D1103 50s. olive and mauve . . . 25 10
D1104 100s. lake and green . . . 25 10
D1105 200s. green and pink . . . 25 10
D1106 500s. yellow and blue . . 25 10
D1107 1000s. red and yellow . . 25 15

1967. As Nos. 1098/1107 but dated "1967".
D1168 50s. green and lilac . . . 15 15
D1169 100s. red and green . . . 15 15
D1170 200s. green and pink . . . 15 15
D1171 500s. brown and blue . . 50 35
D1172 1000s. mauve and yellow 50 35
D1173 15r. orange and grey . . . 1·00 50
D1174 25r. violet and grey . . . 1·60 1·00

1973. As Type **D 100** but inscr "BAYAR PORTO" and dated "1973".
D1320a 25r. violet and grey . . . 1·10 15

1974. As Type **D 100** but inscr "BAYAR PORTO" and dated "1974".
D1346 65r. green and yellow . . 1·80 40
D1347 125r. purple and pink . . 3·50 1·20

1975. As Type **D 100** but inscr "BAYAR PORTO" and dated "1975".
D1401 25r. violet and drab . . . 1·40 90

1976.
D1426 **D 268** 25r. violet and drab 50 50
D1427 65r. green and stone 1·00 1·00

1978. Various stamps surch **BAYAR PORTO** and value.
D1503 25r. on 1r. sepia and red (No. 1141) 40 40
D1504 50r. on 2r. blue and ochre (No. 1144) 40 40
D1505 100r. on 4r. blue and orange (No. 1147) . . . 80 80
D1506 200r. on 5r. red and blue (No. 1148) . . . . . . 1·60 1·60
D1507 300r. on 10r. violet and red (No. 1151) . . . . 2·30 2·30
D1508 400r. on 15r. violet and olive (No. 1153) . . . . 2·40 2·40

1978. Nos. 1145 and 1152 surch **BAYAR PORTO** and value.
D1523 40r. on 2r.50 green and red . . . . 1·10 1·10
D1524 40r. on 12r. green and violet . . . . 1·10 1·10
D1525 65r. on 2r.50 green and red . . . . 1·30 1·30
D1526 65r. on 12r. green and violet . . . . 2·30 2·30
D1527 125r. on 2r.50 green & red 75 75
D1528 125r. on 12r. green & violet . . . . 1·80 1·80
D1529 150r. on 2r.50 green & red 3·00 3·00
D1530 150r. on 12r. green & violet 75 75

1980. Dated "1980".
D1599 **D 268** 25r. mauve and drab 15 15
D1600 **D 333a** 50r. green and lilac 40 40
D1601 75r. purple and pink 65 65
D1062 **D 268** 125r. mauve & pink . . . . . . 1·00 75

1981. Dated "1981".
D1641 **D 333a** 25r. purple & stone 15 15
D1642 50r. green and lilac 35 35
D1643 75r. purple and pink 50 50
D1644 125r. purple & grn 1·00 1·00

1982. Dated "1982".
D1645 **D 333a** 125r. purple & pink 25 15

1983. Dated "1983".
D1728 **D 333a** 200r. lilac and blue 50 15
D1729 300r. green & yell 50 15
D1730 400r. green & buff 75 35
D1731 500r. brown & pink . . . . . . 1·00 50

1984. Dated "1984".
D1772 **D 333a** 25r. purple & stone 75 25
D1773 50r. green and lilac 75 35
D1774 500r. deep brown and brown . . . 7·75 1·00

1988. Dated "1988".
D1912 **D 333a** 1000r. pur & grey 75 55
D1913 2000r. red & mauve . . . . . . 1·50 1·10
D1914 3000r. red & yellow 2·50 1·60
D1915 5000r. green & blue 4·50 2·10

INDORE (HOLKAR STATE) Pt. 1

A state in C. India. Now uses Indian stamps.

12 pies = 1 anna; 16 annas = 1 rupee.

1 Maharaja Tukoji Rao Holkar II

2

1886.
2 **1** ½a. mauve . . . . 2·75 1·75

1889. No gum. Imperf.
4 **2** ½a. black on pink . . . . . . 3·00 3·75

3 Maharaja Shivaji Rao Holkar

5 Maharaja Tukoji Holkar III

1889.
5 **3** ¼a. orange . . . . 1·25 80
6a ½a. purple . . . . 1·75 15
7 1a. green . . . . 1·75 90
8 2a. red . . . . 4·75 1·50

1904.
9 **5** ¼a. orange 50 10
10 ½a. red . . . . 8·50 10
11 1a. green . . . . 1·75 10
12 2a. brown . . . . 11·00 75
13 3a. violet . . . . 18·00 7·00
14a 4a. blue . . . . 5·00 1·25
The ¼a. is inscr "HOLKAR".

पाव आना.

(6)

1905. No. 6a. surch as T **6**.
15 **3** ¼a. on ½a. purple . . . . . . 5·00 20·00

7 Maharaja Yeshwant Rao Holkar II

9 Maharaja Yeshwant Rao Holkar II

1928.
16 **7** ¼a. orange 40 20
17 ½a. purple . . . . 1·25 10
18 1a. green . . . . 2·25 10
19 1¼a. green . . . . 2·50 50
20 2a. brown . . . . 5·00 1·75
21 2a. green . . . . 13·00 1·40
22 3a. violet . . . . 1·50 9·00
23 3a. blue . . . . 17·00
24 3½a. violet . . . . 7·00 10·00
25 4a. blue . . . . 4·00 4·00
26 4a. yellow . . . . 27·00 1·60
27 8a. grey . . . . 5·50 4·50
28 8a. orange . . . . 21·00 20·00
29 12a. red . . . . 5·00 10·00
30 – 1r. black and blue . . . . . 8·00 14·00
31 – 2r. black and red . . . . . 42·00 45·00
32 – 5r. black and brown . . . . 75·00 80·00
The rupee values are larger, 23 × 28 mm.

1940. Surch diagonally in words.
33 – ¼a. on 5r. (No. 32) . . . . . 13·00 1·50
34 – ½a. on 2r. (No. 31) . . . . . 18·00 2·50
35 **7** 1a. on 1¼a. green (No. 19) . . 18·00 70

1940.
36 **9** ¼a. orange . . . . 2·00 10
37 ½a. red . . . . 2·50 10
38 1a. green . . . . 9·00 10
39 1¼a. green . . . . 14·00 1·25
40 2a. blue . . . . 11·00 1·00
41 4a. yellow . . . . 12·00 11·00
42 – 2r. black and red . . . . . . 11·00 £140
43 – 5r. black and orange . . . . 11·00 £180
The rupee values are larger, 23 × 28 mm.

OFFICIAL STAMPS

1904. Optd **SERVICE**.
S1 **5** ¼a. orange 30 80
S2 ½a. red 25 10
S3 1a. green 20 20
S4 2a. brown 30 30
S5 3a. violet . . . . 2·00 2·75
S6 4a. blue . . . . 4·00 1·50

INHAMBANE Pt. 9

A district of Mozambique, which used its own stamps from 1895 to 1920.

1895. 1000 reis = 1 milreis.
1913. 100 centavos = 1 escudo.

1895. 700th Birth Anniv of St. Anthony. Optd **CENTENARIO DE S. ANTONIO Inhambane MDCCCXCV**. (a) "Embossed" key-type inscr "PROVINCIA DE MOCAMBIQUE".
1 Q 5r. black . . . . 38·00 28·00
2 10r. green . . . . 38·00 28·00
3 20r. red . . . . 55·00 42·00
5 40r. brown . . . . 55·00 42·00
6 50r. blue . . . . 55·00 28·00
8 200r. violet . . . . 75·00 65·00
9 300r. orange . . . . 75·00 65·00

(b) "Figures" key type inscr "MOCAMBIQUE".
12 R 50r. blue . . . . 55·00 42·00
16 75r. red . . . . 90·00 70·00
13 80r. green . . . . 60·00 49·00
14 100r. brown on yellow . . . £200 £200
17 150r. red on rose . . . . . 90·00 70·00

1903. "King Carlos" key type inscr "INHAMBANE".
18 S 2½r. grey 40 40
19 5r. orange 40 40
20 10r. green 50 45
21 15r. green . . . . 1·30 90
22 20r. lilac . . . . 1·30 90
23 25r. red . . . . 1·30 90
24 50r. brown . . . . 3·00 1·30
25 65r. blue . . . . 14·00 8·00
26 75r. purple . . . . 2·40 1·70
27 100r. blue on blue . . . . . 2·40 1·70
28 115r. brown on pink . . . . 5·50 4·75
29 130r. brown on yellow . . . 5·50 4·75
30 200r. purple on pink . . . . 5·50 4·75
31 400r. blue on yellow . . . . 10·50 6·75
32 500r. black on blue . . . . . 15·00 10·00
33 700r. grey on yellow . . . . 24·00 16·00

1905. No. 25 surch **50 REIS** and bar.
34 S 50r. on 65r. blue . . . . . . 4·50 3·25

1911. 1903 issue optd **REPUBLICA**.
35 S 2½r. grey 30 30
36 5r. orange 30 30
37 10r. green 40 30
38 15r. green 40 30
39 20r. lilac 75 55
40 25r. red 75 55
41 50r. brown 40 30
42 75r. purple 55 40
43 100r. blue on blue 55 40
44 115r. brown on pink 75 55
45 130r. brown on yellow . . . 1·80 1·30
46 200r. purple on pink . . . . 1·10 70
47 400r. blue on yellow . . . . 1·80 1·30
48 500r. black on blue . . . . . 1·90 1·30
49 700r. black on yellow . . . . 2·50 1·90

1913. Surch **REPUBLICA INHAMBANE** and value on "Vasco da Gama" stamps. (a) Portuguese Colonies.
50 ¼c. on 2½r. green . . . . . . 1·10 70
51 ½c. on 5r. red . . . . 1·10 70
52 1c. on 10r. purple . . . . . . 1·10 70
53 2½c. on 25r. green . . . . . . 1·10 70
54 5c. on 50r. blue . . . . 1·30 70
55 7½c. on 75r. brown . . . . . . 2·00 1·40
56 10c. on 100r. brown . . . . . 2·00 1·40
57 15c. on 150r. bistre . . . . . 2·00 1·80

(b) Macao.
58 ¼c. on ½a. green . . . . 1·40 1·20
59 ½c. on 1a. red . . . . 1·40 1·20
60 1c. on 2a. purple . . . . 1·40 1·20
61 2½c. on 4a. green . . . . 1·40 1·20
62 5c. on 8a. blue . . . . 1·40 1·20
63 7½c. on 12a. brown . . . . . . 2·40 1·80
64 10c. on 16a. brown . . . . . . 2·00 90
65 15c. on 24a. bistre . . . . . . 2·00 90

(c) Timor.
66 ¼c. on ½a. green . . . . 1·40 1·20
67 ½c. on 1a. red . . . . 1·40 1·20
68 1c. on 2a. purple . . . . 1·40 1·20
69 2½c. on 4a. green . . . . 1·40 1·20
70 5c. on 8a. blue . . . . 1·40 1·20
71 7½c. on 12a. brown . . . . . . 2·40 1·80
72 10c. on 16a. brown . . . . . . 2·00 90
73 15c. on 24a. bistre . . . . . . 2·00 90

1914. No. 34 optd **REPUBLICA**.
74 S 50r. on 65r. blue . . . . . . 2·50 1·30

1914. "Ceres" key type inscr "INHAMBANE".
75 U ¼c. olive 70 45
76a ½c. black . . . . 2·10 1·60
77 1c. green 80 45
78 1½c. brown 80 45
79 2c. red 80 45
80 2½c. violet 35 30
81 5c. blue 50 45
82 7½c. brown 35 70
83 8c. grey . . . . 1·30 70
84 10c. red . . . . 1·30 90
85 15c. red . . . . 1·70 1·20
86 20c. green . . . . 1·80 1·20
87 30c. brown on green . . . . 2·10 1·30
88 40c. brown on red . . . . . 2·10 1·30
89 50c. orange on pink . . . . 4·50 2·30
90 1e. green on blue . . . . . 4·50 2·30

ININI Pt. 6

A territory in French Guiana, in the N.E. of S. America, separately administered from 1930 but reunited with Fr. Guiana in 1946.

100 centimes = 1 franc.

1931. Stamps of French Guiana optd **TERRITOIRE DE L'ININI** (Type **20**) or **Territoire de l'ININI** (others).

1	**20**	1c. green and lilac	30	3·00
2		2c. green and red	30	3·25
3		3c. green and violet	45	3·25
4		4c. mauve and brown	45	3·00
5		5c. orange and blue	35	3·25
6		10c. brown and mauve	20	2·75
7		15c. orange and brown	20	2·75
8		20c. green and blue	50	3·00
9		25c. brown and red	95	3·25
10	**21**	30c. green and deep green	3·00	4·00
11		30c. brown and green	55	3·25
12		35c. green and blue	2·50	3·50
13		40c. grey and brown	95	3·50
14		45c. green and olive	1·50	3·75
15		50c. grey and blue	65	3·50
16		55c. red and blue	2·75	5·00
17		60c. green and red	70	3·75
18		65c. green and red	2·75	4·50
19		70c. green and blue	1·60	3·75
20		75c. blue and black	3·50	4·50
21		80c. blue and black	2·25	3·75
22		90c. red and carmine	3·25	4·25
23		90c. brown and mauve	2·25	3·75
24		1f. brown and mauve	15·00	19·00
25		1f. red	2·75	3·75
26		1f. blue and black	65	3·75
27	**22**	1f.25 green and brown	1·25	4·00
28		1f.25 red	80	3·75
29		1f.40 mauve and brown	1·25	3·75
30		1f.50 light blue and blue	75	3·50
31		1f.60 green and brown	70	3·75
32		1f.75 brown and red	24·00	30·00
33		1f.75 blue and deep blue	1·10	4·00
34		2f. red and green	90	3·75
35		2f.25 blue	65	4·00
36		2f.50 brown and red	70	4·00
37		3f. mauve and red	2·50	3·75
38		5f. green and violet	1·40	3·75
39		10f. blue and green	1·10	3·75
40		20f. green and blue	1·50	4·25

1939. New York World's Fair. As T **58c** of Guadeloupe.

51	1f.25 red	5·25	7·50
52	2f.25 blue	5·25	7·50

1939. 150th Anniv of French Revolution. As T **58d** of Guadeloupe.

53	45c.+25c. green and black	13·00	19·00
54	70c.+30c. brown and black	12·50	19·00
55	90c.+35c. orange and black	12·50	19·00
56	1f.25+1f. red and black	12·50	19·00
57	2f.25+2f. blue and black	13·50	19·00

POSTAGE DUE STAMPS

1932. Postage Due Stamps of French Guiana optd **TERRITOIRE DE L'ININI**.

D41	**D 23**	5c. blue and deep blue	20	2·50
D42		10c. blue and brown	30	3·25
D43		20c. red and green	20	3·25
D44		30c. red and brown	20	3·25
D45		50c. brown and mauve	1·25	3·75
D46		60c. brown and red	1·60	3·75
D47	**D 24**	1f. brown and blue	1·75	3·75
D48		2f. green and red	2·00	5·00
D49		3f. grey and mauve	5·50	14·00

IONIAN ISLANDS Pt. 1

A group of islands off the W. coast of Greece, placed under the protection of Gt. Britain in 1815 and ceded to Greece in 1864.

12 pence = 1 shilling;
20 shillings = 1 pound.

1

1859. Imperf.

1	**1**	(½d.) orange	80·00	£500
2		(1d.) blue	20·00	£180
3		(2d.) red	15·00	£180

IRAN Pt. 16

A State of W. Asia.

1868. 20 shahis (or chahis) = 1 kran;
10 krans = 1 toman.
1932. 100 dinars = 1 rial.

NOTE.—The word "English" in the descriptive headings to various Persian issues is to be taken as referring to the lettering or figures and not to the language which is often French.

1   3 Nasred-Din   4 Nasred-Din

1868. Imperf or roul.

1	**1**	1(sh.) violet	70·00	
1c		1(sh.) grey	80·00	
15		1(sh.) black	10·00	15·00
2		2(sh.) green	50·00	
16		2(sh.) blue	80·00	40·00
35		2(sh.) black	£250	£3000
3		4(sh.) blue	70·00	
17		4(sh.) red	70·00	35·00
4		8(sh.) red	70·00	
8a		8(sh.) green	70·00	70·00
13		1(kr.) yellow	£1000	
18		1kr. red	£100	45·00
38		1kr. red on yellow	£1100	50·00
19		4kr. yellow	£300	45·00
36		4kr. blue	£120	70·00
40		5kr. violet	£225	£180
41		5kr. gold	£750	£200
39		1to. bronze on blue	£15000	£2500

1876. Perf.

20	**3**	1(sh.) black and mauve	4·00	2·00
24		2(sh.) black and green	5·00	1·50
25		5(sh.) black and pink	4·50	75
30		10(sh.) black and blue	6·00	3·00

1879. Perf.

45a	**4**	1(sh.) black and red	11·00	1·00
46a		2(sh.) black and yellow	14·00	1·10
47		5(sh.) black and green	13·00	60
48		10(sh.) black and mauve	£130	10·00
49		1(kr.) black and brown	40·00	90
50c		5(kr.) black and blue	18·00	50

5   6

1881.

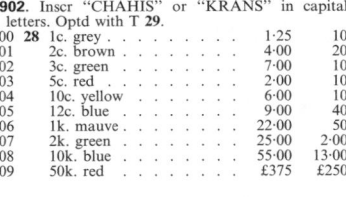

56	**5**	5c. mauve	5·00	2·00
57a		10c. red	4·50	1·50
61		25c. green	£100	1·00
62	**6**	50c. black, yellow and orange	75·00	6·00
69		50c. black	20·00	3·00
63		1f. black and blue	14·00	1·25
64		5f. black and red	14·00	1·00
65		10f. black, yellow and red (30½ × 36 mm)	15·00	2·75

1882. As T **5** and **6**.

66	–	5s. green	5·00	20
68	–	10s. black, yellow and orange	15·00	90

10   11   13

14   15   16

1885.

70	**10**	1c. green	5·00	60
71		2c. red	5·00	50
72		5c. blue	5·00	10
73	**11**	10c. brown	6·50	20
74		1k. grey	7·00	40
75		5k. purple	70·00	5·50

1885. Surch **OFFICIEL** and value in English and Persian.

81a	–	3 on 5s. green (No. 66)	18·00	5·50
76	–	6 on 5s. green (No. 66)	40·00	6·00
83	–	6 on 10s. (No. 68)	32·00	5·50
84	**6**	8 on 50c. black	60·00	9·00
78		12 on 50c. black	70·00	9·00
79	–	18 on 10s. (No. 68)	60·00	7·00
80	**6**	1t. on 5f. black and red	60·00	4·00

1889.

85	**13**	1c. pink	25	10
86		2c. blue	20	10
87		5c. mauve	20	10
88		7c. brown	1·00	30
89	**14**	10c. black	35	10
90		1k. orange	45	10
91		2k. red	3·00	90
92		5k. green	2·25	1·00

1891.

93	**15**	1c. black	20	10
94		2c. brown	30	10
95		5c. blue	15	10
96		7c. grey	65·00	2·00
97		10c. red	55	10
98		14c. orange	40	20
99	**16**	1k. green	7·00	15
100		2k. orange	£100	5·50
101		5k. orange	80	40

17   18   21 Muzaffered-Din

1894.

102	**17**	1c. mauve	30	10
103		2c. green	30	10
104		5c. blue	30	10
105		8c. brown	30	10
106	**18**	10c. yellow	50	15
107		16c. pink	2·50	60
108		1k. pink and yellow	2·00	15
109		2k. brown and blue	2·00	15
110		5k. violet and silver	2·25	30
111		10k. pink and gold	10·00	2·50
112		50k. green and gold	7·00	4·50

See also Nos. 116/24.

1897. Surch in English and Persian in frame.

113	**17**	5c. on 8c. brown	1·75	20
114	**18**	1k. on 5k. violet and silver	5·50	1·50
115		2k. on 5k. violet and silver	5·50	2·00

1898. Chahi values on white or green paper.

116	**17**	1c. grey	20	10
117		2c. brown	30	10
118		3c. purple	30	10
119		4c. red	30	10
120		5c. yellow	30	10
121		8c. orange	1·00	35
154		10c. blue	60	10
123		12c. red	90	10
124		16c. green	1·50	35
125	**21**	1k. blue	2·00	10
157		1k. red	1·75	20
126		2k. pink	2·00	10
158		2k. green	3·50	60
127		3k. yellow	2·00	20
159		3k. brown	5·00	1·00
128		4k. grey	2·00	50
160		4k. red	5·00	1·00
129		5k. green	2·00	50
161		5k. brown	7·50	1·00
130		10k. orange	3·50	75
162		10k. blue	17·00	3·50
131		50k. mauve	9·50	4·00
163		50k. brown	12·00	2·25

(21a)   (22)   (24)

1899. Optd with control mark of various scroll devices as T **21a**.

132	**17**	1c. grey	60	10
133		2c. brown	60	10
134		3c. purple	60	10
135		4c. red	60	10
136		5c. yellow	60	10
137		8c. orange	1·50	15
138		10c. blue	60	10
139		12c. red	1·25	10
140		16c. green	1·25	35
141	**21**	1k. blue	1·50	10
142		2k. pink	2·75	45
143		3k. yellow	8·50	1·50
144		4k. grey	8·50	1·50
145		5k. green	4·50	1·50
146		10k. orange	12·00	1·50
147		50k. mauve	10·00	4·00

1900. Optd with T **22** across two stamps.

164	**17**	1c. grey	20·00	2·00
165		2c. brown	20·00	2·00
166		3c. purple	28·00	3·00
167		4c. red	65·00	8·50
168		5c. yellow	7·50	1·00
169		10c. blue	£275	£110
170		12c. red	28·00	2·00

Prices quoted in this issue are for pairs.

1901. Surch in various ways in English and Persian.

176	**17**	5 on 8c. brown	2·00	25
179	**21**	12c. on 1k. red	10·00	4·00
180		5k. on 50k. brown	45·00	12·00

1902. Surch with T **24**.

177	**17**	5c. on 10c. blue	1·50	60
178	**21**	5c. on 1k. red	1·50	80

1902. Optd **PROVISOIRE 1319** in ornamental frame.

181	**17**	1c. grey	2·00	1·00
182		2c. brown	3·50	2·50
183		3c. purple	2·00	1·00
184		4c. red	2·00	1·00
185		5c. yellow	1·75	65
197		5 on 8c. brown (No. 176)	5·00	40
186		8c. orange	2·00	1·50
187		10c. blue	2·00	1·00
188		12c. red	3·50	1·00
198	**21**	12c. on 1k. (No. 179)	7·50	2·50
189	**17**	16c. green	7·00	3·00
190	**21**	1k. red	6·50	2·25
191		2k. green	–	10·00
192		3k. brown	–	25·00
193		4k. red	–	28·00
194		5k. brown	–	30·00
199		5k. on 50k. (No. 180)	25·00	9·00
195		10k. blue	–	30·00
196		50k. brown	–	32·00

28   (29)

1902. Inscr "CHAHIS" or "KRANS" in capital letters. Optd with T **29**.

200	**28**	1c. grey	1·25	10
201		2c. brown	4·00	20
202		3c. green	7·00	10
203		5c. red	2·00	10
204		10c. yellow	6·00	10
205		12c. blue	9·00	40
206		1k. mauve	22·00	50
207		2k. green	25·00	2·00
208		10k. blue	55·00	13·00
209		50k. red	£375	£250

1902. Surch **5 KRANS** in English and Persian.

210	**28**	5k. on 5k. yellow	60·00	7·00

1902. Optd **PROVISOIRE 1319** in ornamental frame.

211	**28**	1c. grey	20·00	10·00
212		2c. brown	20·00	10·00
213		3c. green	20·00	10·00
214		5c. red	20·00	10·00
215		12c. blue	20·00	10·00

34

1902. Inscr "Chahis" or "Krans" in lower case letters.

227	**34**	1c. grey	11·00	
228		2c. brown	20·00	
229		3c. green	11·00	
230		5c. red	11·00	10
231		10c. yellow	13·00	90
232		12c. blue	16·00	1·10
233		1k. mauve		
234		2k. green		
235		10k. blue		
236		50k. red	£425	

1902. Surch **5 KRANS** without T **29** opt.

237	**34**	5k. on 5k. yellow	30·00	

1903. Optd **PROVISOIRE 1903** and lion in frame, but without Arms opt (T **29**).

239	**28**	1c. grey	–	4·00
240		2c. brown	–	4·00
241		5c. red	–	4·00
242		10c. yellow	–	6·00
243		12c. blue	–	10·00
244		1k. mauve	–	11·00

38   39 Muzaffered-Din

1903.

246	**38**	1c. lilac	20	10
247		2c. grey	25	10
248		3c. green	30	10
249		5c. red	40	10
250		10c. brown	40	10

251		12c. blue	40	10
252	39	1k. purple	1·25	15
253		2k. blue	2·00	10
254		5k. brown	3·00	15
255		10k. red	7·50	30
256		20k. orange	12·00	60
257		30k. green	14·00	1·50
258		50k. green	55·00	14·00

See also Nos. 298/303.

1903. Surch in both English and Persian except those marked* which are surch in English only.

272	38	"1 CHAHI" on 3c. green	5·00	1·25
287		"1 CHAI" on 3c. green	3·50	40
288	39	1c. on 1k. purple	12·00	3·50
273	38	2c. on 3c. green	10·00	4·25
289	39	2c. on 5k. brown	17·00	6·00
277	38	3c. on 5c. red	2·50	10
278		6c. on 10c. brown	4·00	10
279	39	9c. on 1k. purple	5·00	15
274		12c. on 10k. red	16·00	3·75
275		2t. on 50k. green*	55·00	25·00
280		2t. on 50k. green	55·00	25·00
276		3t. on 50k. green*	55·00	25·00
281		3t. on 50k. green	55·00	25·00

50

52 Shah Muhammad Ali Mirza

1906. Optd **PROVISOIRE** and lion. Imperf. or perf.

292	50	1c. violet	50	10
293		2c. grey	60	10
294		3c. green	60	10
295		6c. red	1·00	10
296		10c. brown	11·00	50
297		13c. blue	6·00	35

1907.

298	38	1ch. violet on blue	15	10
299		2ch. grey on blue	15	10
300		3ch. green on blue	15	10
301		6ch. red on blue	15	10
302		9ch. yellow on blue	20	10
303		10ch. sepia on blue	20	10
305	52	13c. blue	50	10
306		26c. brown	50	10
307		1k. red	50	10
308		2k. green	50	10
309		3k. blue	60	10
311		4k. brown	1·75	30
312		5k. brown	1·25	15
313		10k. pink	2·00	15
314		20k. brown	4·75	25
315		30k. purple	5·00	40
316	–	50k. red and gold	20·00	17·00

The 50k. is larger with the head facing the other way.

(54)

56

1909. Nos. 298/315 optd as T **54**. Imperf.

320	38	1ch. on 1ch. violet on blue	30·00	20·00
321		1ch. on 2ch. grey on blue	30·00	20·00
322		1ch. on 3ch. green on blue	30·00	20·00
323		1ch. on 6ch. red on blue	30·00	20·00
324		1ch. on 9ch. yellow on blue	30·00	20·00
325		1ch. on 10ch. brown on bl	30·00	20·00
326	52	2ch. on 13ch. blue	32·00	22·00
327		2ch. on 26ch. brown	32·00	22·00
328		2ch. on 1kr. red	32·00	22·00
329		2ch. on 2kr. green	32·00	22·00
330		2ch. on 3kr. blue	32·00	22·00
331		2ch. on 4kr. yellow	32·00	22·00
333		2ch. on 5kr. brown	32·00	22·00
334		2ch. on 10kr. pink	32·00	22·00
335		2ch. on 20kr. black	35·00	24·00
336		2ch. on 30kr. purple	35·00	24·00

1909.

337	56	1c. purple and orange	35	10
338		2c. purple and violet	35	10
339		3c. purple and green	35	10
340		6c. purple and red	35	10
341		9c. purple and grey	40	10
342		10c. maroon and purple	70	10
343		13c. purple and blue	70	10
344		26c. purple and green	3·00	10
345		1k. brown, violet and silver	6·00	10
346		2k. brown, green and silver	6·00	10
347		3k. brown, grey and silver	7·00	15
348		4k. brown, blue and silver	12·00	40
349		5k. sepia, brown and gold	16·00	40
350		10k. brown, orange and gold	30·00	70
351		20k. brown, green and gold	30·00	1·40
352		30k. brown, red and gold	40·00	1·90

Stamps of this issue offered at very low prices are reprints.

For stamps as Type **56** but with curved inscriptions, see Nos. O836 etc.

57 Ahmed Mirza

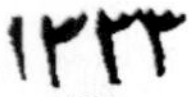

(65)

1911.

361	57	1c. orange and green	15	10
362		2c. brown and red	15	10
363		3c. green and grey	15	10
364		3c. green and brown	15	10
365		5c. red and brown	15	10
366		6c. red and grey	15	10
367		6c. red and green	15	10
368		9c. lilac and brown	15	10
369		10c. brown and red	15	10
370		12c. blue and green	15	10
371		13c. blue and violet	15	10
372		24c. green and purple	15	10
373		26c. green and blue	4·00	2·00
374		1k. red and blue	10	10
375		2k. purple and green	20	10
376		3k. black and lilac	25	10
377		4k. black and blue	4·00	2·00
378		5k. blue and red	20	10
379		10k. pink and brown	35	10
380		20k. buff and brown	55	10
381		30k. green and red	80	10

1911. Various stamps optd **Relais** in English and Persian.

382	56	2ch. purple and violet	13·00	3·00
383		3ch. purple and green	13·00	3·00
384		6ch. purple and red	13·00	3·00
385		13ch. purple and blue	13·00	3·00
386	57	2ch. brown and red	13·00	3·00
387		3ch. green and grey	13·00	3·00
388		6ch. red and grey	13·00	3·00
388a		13ch. blue and violet	13·00	3·00

1912. Optd **Officiel** in English and Persian.

389	57	1c. orange and green	40	10
390		2c. brown and red	40	10
391		3c. green and grey	40	10
392		6c. red and grey	1·75	10
393		9c. lilac and brown	85	15
394		10c. brown and red	85	15
395		13c. blue and violet	5·00	35
396		26c. green and blue	13·00	70
397		1k. red and blue	10·00	20
398		2k. purple and green	11·00	20
399		3k. black and lilac	15·00	20
400		5k. blue and red	17·00	20
401		10k. pink and brown	30·00	1·25
402		20k. buff and brown	30·00	2·00
403		30k. green and red	30·00	2·75

1914. Surch with new value and **1914** in English and Persian.

412	57	1c. on 13c. blue and violet	2·00	15
413		3c. on 26c. green and blue	2·00	15

1915. Surch with new value in frame and **1915** in English and Persian.

414	57	1c. on 5c. red and brown	1·75	10
415b		2c. on 5c. red and brown	1·75	10
416		6c. on 12c. blue and green	2·50	10

1915. Surch with new value in English and Persian.

417	56	5c. on 1k. (No. 345)	2·50	10
418		12c. on 13c. (No. 343)	3·25	10

1915. Optd with T **65** ("1333").

419	56	1c. purple and orange	40	10
420		2c. purple and violet	70	10
421		3c. purple and green	1·50	10
422		6c. purple and red	1·75	10
423		9c. purple and grey	3·50	10
424		10c. purple and mauve	7·00	20
425		1k. brown, violet and silver	7·50	15

66 The Imperial Crown

67 King Darius on his Throne

1915. Coronation of Shah Ahmed.

426	66	1c. blue and red	10	10
427		2c. red and blue	10	10
428		3c. green	10	10
429		5c. red	10	10
430		6c. red and green	10	10
431		9c. violet and brown	10	10
432		10c. brown and green	15	10
433		12c. blue	15	10
434		24c. sepia and brown	45	10
435	67	1k. black, brown and silver	45	10
436		2k. red, blue and silver	45	15
437		3k. brown, lilac and silver	45	15
438		5k. grey, brown and silver	45	15
439	–	1t. black, violet and gold	70	30
440	–	2t. brown, green and gold	70	30
441	–	3t. red, crimson and gold	1·00	30
442	–	5t. grey, blue and gold	1·00	30

DESIGNS: 1t. to 5t. Gateway of the Palace of Persepolis.

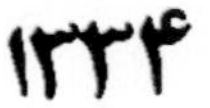

(69)

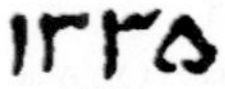

(73)

1915. Optd with T **69** ("1334").

477	56	1k. brown, violet and silver	5·50	40
478		10k. brown, orange and gold	20·00	75
479		20k. brown, green and gold	90·00	8·50
480		30k. brown, red and gold	35·00	2·75

1917. Surch with value in English only.

481	57	12c. on 1k. red and blue	£225	80·00
482		24c. on 1k. red and blue	£100	40·00

1917. Optd with T **73** ("1335") or surch also with new value in English and Persian.

483	56	1c. purple and orange	35·00	9·00
484		1c. on 2c. (No. 338)	4·00	10
485		1c. on 9c. (No. 341)	4·00	10
486		1c. on 10c. (No. 342)	4·00	10
490	57	1c. on 10c. brown and red	4·00	10
487	56	3c. on 9c. purple and grey	4·00	10
491	57	3c. on 10c. brown and red	4·00	35
488	56	3c. on 26c. (No. 344)	4·50	10
489		5c. on 13c. (No. 343)	4·25	10
492	57	5c. on 1k. red and blue	6·50	70
493		6c. on 10c. brown and red	4·25	80
494		6c. on 12c. blue and green	4·75	10

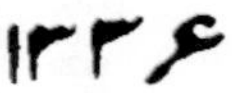

(78)

(82)

1918. Optd with T **78** ("1336").

507	56	2k. brown, green and silver	12·00	55

1918. Surch as T **78** and new value in English and Persian.

508	56	24c. on 4k. (No. 348)	13·00	50
509		10k. on 5k. (No. 349)	14·00	1·25

1918. Coronation issue of 1915 optd **Novembre 1918** (date also in Persian).

510	67	2k. red, blue and silver	2·00	1·50
511		3k. brown, lilac and silver	2·00	1·50
512		5k. grey, brown and silver	3·00	1·50
513	–	1t. black, violet and gold	3·00	1·50
514	–	2t. brown, green and gold	3·25	1·50
515	–	3t. red, crimson and gold	4·00	1·50
516	–	5t. grey, blue and gold	4·50	2·50

1918. Surch as T **82** and new value in English and Persian.

517	57	3c. on 12c. blue and green	5·00	10
518		6c. on 10c. brown and red	5·00	10
519		6c. on 1k. red and blue	5·00	10

1918. Optd with T **82** ("1337").

520	56	2k. brown, green and silver	28·00	1·50
521		3k. brown, grey and silver	12·00	70
522		4k. brown, blue and silver	65·00	2·75
523		5k. sepia, brown and gold	35·00	1·50
524		10k. brown, orange and gold	28·00	1·50
525		20k. brown, green and gold	£150	18·00
526		30k. brown, red and gold	48·00	3·25

84 Ahmed Mirza

92 Ahmed Mirza

1919. Type **84** surch **Provisoire 1919** and value in English and Persian.

527	84	1c. yellow	70	10
528		3c. green	1·00	10
529		5c. purple	2·00	10
530		6c. violet	4·00	10
531		12c. blue	6·00	15

1919. Surch **1919** and value in English and Persian.

532	13	2k. on 5c. mauve	1·60	70
533		3k. on 5c. mauve	1·60	70
534		4k. on 5c. mauve	1·60	70
535		5k. on 5c. mauve	1·60	70
536	15	10k. on 10c. red	1·60	70
537		20k. on 10c. red	2·25	1·10
538		30k. on 10c. red	2·25	1·10
539		50k. on 14c. orange	2·25	1·75

1921. Surch **6-CHAHIS** in English and Persian.

539a	57	6c. on 12c. blue and green	17·00	15

1921. Coup d'Etat of Reza Khan. Coronation issue of 1915 optd **21. FEV. 1921** in English and Persian.

540	66	3c. green	4·00	
541		5c. red	4·00	
542		6c. red and green	4·00	
543		10c. brown and green	4·00	
544		12c. blue	4·00	
545	67	1k. black, brown and silver	4·00	
546		2k. red, blue and silver	5·00	
547		5k. grey, brown and silver	6·00	
548	–	2t. brown, green and gold	6·00	
549	–	3t. red, crimson and gold	6·00	
550	–	5t. grey, blue and gold	6·00	

1922. Surch with value in English only.

551	57	10c. on 6c. brown & green	22·00	2·25
552		1k. on 12c. blue and green	22·00	3·50

1922. Surcharged with value in English only over **BENADERS**.

553	57	10c. on 6c. brown & green	15·00	2·25
554		1k. on 12c. blue and green	15·00	2·75

1922. Optd **CONTROLE 1922** in English and Persian.

555	57	1c. orange and green	35	10
556		2c. brown and red	35	10
557		3c. green and grey	35	10
558		3c. green and brown	40	10
559		3c. red and brown	20·00	3·50
560		6c. brown and green	35	10
561		9c. lilac and brown	70	10
562		10c. brown and red	70	10
563		12c. blue and green	1·10	10
564		24c. green and purple	3·50	10
565		1k. red and blue	9·00	10
566		2k. purple and green	13·00	10
567		3k. black and lilac	25·00	10
568		4k. blue and black	60·00	80
569		5k. blue and red	30·00	10
570		10k. red and brown	75·00	15
571		20k. yellow and brown	75·00	15
572		30k. green and red	85·00	15

1922. Surch in English and Persian.

573	57	3c. on 12c. (No. 563)	2·50	10
574		6c. on 24c. (No. 564)	3·25	10
575		10c. on 20k. (No. 571)	5·50	1·50
576		1k. on 30k. (No. 572)	14·00	3·00

1924.

577	92	1c. orange	20	10
578		2c. red	20	10
579		3c. brown	30	10
580		6c. sepia	30	10
581		9c. green	50	10
582		10c. violet	50	10
583		12c. red	50	10
584		1k. blue	1·00	10
585		2k. red and blue	2·00	10
586		3k. purple and violet	8·00	15
587		5k. sepia and red	12·00	30
588		10k. violet and sepia	25·00	1·25
589		20k. sepia and green	30·00	1·25
590		30k. black and orange	35·00	1·75

1924. Surch **p. re. 1924** and value in English and Persian.

591	84	1c. brown	15	10
592		2c. grey	15	10
593		3c. red	20	10
594		6c. orange	70	10

1925. Surch **p. re. 1925** and value in English and Persian.

595	84	2c. green	15	10
596		3c. red	20	10
597		6c. blue	35	10
598		9c. brown	1·50	10
599		10c. grey	3·25	15
600		1k. green	3·25	10
601		2k. mauve	15·00	20

94

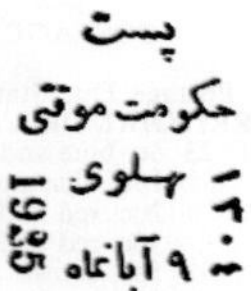

(95 "Provisional Pahlavi Government, 31 Oct 1925")

1925. Deposition of Shah Ahmed and Provisional Government of Riza Khan Pahlavi. Fiscal stamps as T **94** (various frames) optd with T **95**.

602	94	1c. red	1·50	70
603		2c. yellow	1·50	70
604		3c. green	1·50	70
605		5c. grey	7·00	1·10
606		10c. red	1·50	1·60
607		1k. blue	3·00	70

(96)

1926. Optd with T **96**.

608	92	1c. orange	30	10
609		2c. red	35	10
610		3c. brown	70	15
611		6c. sepia	20·00	18·00

1926. Optd **Regne de Pahlavi 1926** in English and Persian.

612	56	1c. purple and orange	20	10
613		2c. purple and violet	20	10
614		3c. purple and green	20	10
615		6c. purple and red	30	10
616		9c. purple and grey	65	10

617		10c. maroon and purple	65	10
618		13c. purple and blue	1·75	10
619		26c. purple and green	5·50	10
620		1k. brown, violet and silver	4·00	10
621		2k. brown, green and silver	4·50	10
622		3k. brown, grey and silver	4·50	15
623		4k. brown, blue and silver	55·00	30
624		5k. sepia, brown and gold	35·00	15
625		10k. brown, orange and gold	£200	15
626		20k. brown, green and gold	£225	30
627		30k. brown, red and gold	£225	1·10

98 Riza Shah Pahlavi

99 Riza Shah Pahlavi

1926.

628	98	1c. green	15	10
629		2c. blue	30	10
630		3c. green	55	10
631		6c. red	65	10
632		9c. red	7·50	10
633		10c. brown	13·00	10
634		12c. orange	17·00	10
635		15c. blue	20·00	10
636	99	1k. blue	32·00	65
637		2k. mauve	70·00	10·00

1927. Air. Optd with airplane and **POSTE AERIENNE** in English and Persian.

642	56	1c. purple and orange	30	20
643		2c. purple and violet	70	35
644		3c. purple and green	40	30
645		6c. purple and red	55	30
646		9c. purple and grey	55	30
647		10c. maroon and purple	70	35
648		13c. purple and blue	1·25	70
649		26c. purple and green	1·40	70
650		1k. brown, violet and silver	1·40	70
651		2k. brown, green and silver	3·00	1·50
652		3k. brown, grey and silver	4·50	1·75
653		4k. brown, blue and silver	10·00	4·75
654		5k. sepia, brown and gold	10·00	6·00
655		10k. brown, orange and gold	£400	£130
656		20k. brown, green and gold	£275	£130
657		30k. brown, red and gold	£275	£130

1928. Air. Fiscal stamps surch with Junkers F-13 airplane, **Poste aerien** and new value in French and Persian.

657a	94	3k. brown	55·00	16·00
657b		5k. brown	10·00	2·75
657c		1t. violet	10·00	4·00
657d		2t. green	16·00	7·00
657e		3t. green	23·00	8·00

102

104 Riza Shah Pahlavi

1929. Air. Fiscal stamps as T **102** (various frames) surch with Junkers F-13 airplane, **Poste aerienne** and value in French and Persian.

658	102	1c. green	10	10
659		2c. blue	20	10
660		3c. red	10	10
661		5c. brown	10	10
662		10c. green	15	10
663		1k. violet	35	10
664		2k. orange	70	20
665		3k. brown (22 × 30 mm)	50·00	8·00
666		5k. brown (22 × 33 mm)	6·00	3·00
667		10k. violet (21 × 31 mm)	15·00	5·50
668		20k. green (21 × 31 mm)	22·00	4·00
669		30k. green (21 × 31 mm)	27·00	8·00

1929.

670	104	1c. red and green	25	10
671		2c. blue and red	25	10
672		3c. green and red	25	10
673		6c. green and brown	25	10
674		9c. red and blue	50	10
675		10c. brown and green	85	10
676		12c. violet and black	1·10	10
677		15c. blue and yellow	2·00	10
678		24c. lake and olive	3·50	10
679		1k. black and blue	4·00	10
680		2k. violet and orange	8·00	10
681		3k. red and green	10·00	15
682		5k. green and brown	9·00	20
683		1t. red and blue	12·00	45
684		2t. black and red	25·00	2·00
685	–	3t. violet and gold	30·00	3·25

DESIGN: 3t. Shah enthroned (28½ × 39 mm).

106 Riza Shah Pahlavi and Elburz Mts

1930. Air.

686	106	1c. blue and yellow	10	10
687		2c. black and blue	15	10
688		3c. violet and olive	15	10
689		4c. blue and violet	15	10
690		5c. red and green	15	10
691		6c. green and red	15	10
692		8c. violet and grey	15	10
693		10c. red and blue	20	10
694		12c. orange and grey	25	10
695		15c. olive and brown	25	10
696		1k. red and blue	55	25
697		2k. blue and black	55	35
698		3k. green and brown	70	45
699		5k. black and red	1·75	55
700		1t. purple and orange	2·50	70
701		2t. brown and green	5·50	2·50
702		3t. green and purple	22·00	16·00

107

1931.

703	107	1c. blue and brown	20	10
704		2c. black and red	30	10
705		3c. brown and mauve	25	10
706		6c. violet and red	35	10
707		9c. red and blue	2·00	10
708		10c. grey and red	5·00	10
709		11c. red and blue	7·00	10
710		12c. mauve and blue	6·00	10
711		16c. red and black	5·50	10
712		27c. blue and black	12·00	10
713		1k. blue and red	12·00	10

108 Riza Shah Pahlavi

109

1933. New Currency.

714	108	5d. brown	15	10
715		10d. blue	15	10
716		15d. grey	30	10
717		30d. green	30	10
718		45d. blue	60	10
719		50d. mauve	60	10
720		60d. green	1·75	10
721		75d. brown	1·75	10
722		90d. red	1·75	10
723	109	1r. black and red	2·50	10
724		1r.20 red and black	7·00	15
725		1r.50 blue and yellow	12·00	15
726		2r. brown and blue	10·00	15
727		3r. green and mauve	25·00	35
728		5r. red and brown	32·00	7·00

110 "Justice"

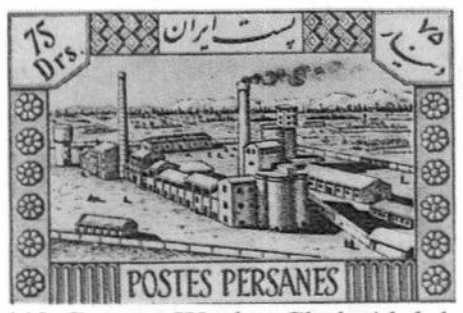
112 Cement Works, Chah-Abdul-Azim

1935. 10th Anniv of Riza Khan's Advent to Power.

729	110	5d. green and brown	20	10
730	–	10d. grey and orange	20	10
731	–	15d. blue and red	20	10
732	–	30d. green and black	55	10
733	–	45d. lake and olive	65	10
734	112	75d. brown and green	2·50	40
735	–	90d. red and blue	4·00	70
736	–	1r. violet and brown	14·00	3·75
737	–	1r.50 blue and purple	6·00	2·00

DESIGNS: 10d. Ruins of Persepolis (40 × 26 mm); 15d. "Education" (23 × 33 mm); 30d. De Havilland Tiger Moth biplanes over Teheran Aerodrome (38 × 25 mm); 45d. Sakhtessar Sanatorium, Mazanderan (40 × 27 mm); 90d. Gunboat "Palang" (38 × 24 mm); 1r. Railway bridge over R. Karun (42 × 29 mm); 1r.50, Post and Customs House, Teheran (42 × 27 mm).

1935. Optd **POSTES IRANIENNES**. (a) Stamps of 1929

738	104	1c. red and green	90·00	25·00
739		2c. blue and red	32·00	12·00
740		3c. green and red	16·00	8·50
741		6c. green and brown	20·00	12·00
742		9c. red and blue	9·00	6·50
743		1t. red and blue	9·00	85
744		2t. black and red	14·00	70
745	–	3t. violet and gold	10·00	3·00

(b) Stamps of 1931.

746	107	1c. blue and brown	90·00	28·00
747		2c. black and red	9·00	3·25
748		3c. brown and mauve	4·50	4·00
749		6c. violet and red	20·00	12·00
750		9c. red and blue	20·00	12·00
751		11c. red and blue	90	10
752		12c. mauve and blue	60·00	22·00
753		16c. red and black	1·60	10
754		27c. blue and black	1·60	10

(c) Stamps of 1933.

755	108	5c. brown	15	10
756		10d. blue	20	10
757		15d. grey	20	10
758		30d. green	1·10	10
759		45d. blue	1·10	30
760		50d. mauve	70	10
761		60d. green	70	10
762		75d. brown	2·50	10
763		90d. red	3·25	3·25
764	109	1r. black and red	10·00	14·00
765		1r.20 red and black	6·00	65
766		1r.50 blue and green	4·00	20
767		2r. brown and blue	6·00	20
768		3r. green and mauve	7·00	20
769		5r. red and brown	45·00	23·00

1935. Air. Air stamps of 1930 optd **Iran**.

770	106	1c. blue and yellow	20	10
771		2c. black and blue	20	10
772		3c. violet and olive	20	10
773		4c. blue and violet	20	10
774		5c. red and green	20	10
775		6c. green and red	20	10
776		8c. violet and grey	20	10
777		10c. red and blue	20	10
778		12c. orange and blue	20	10
779		15c. olive and brown	55	20
780		1k. red and blue	1·75	70
781		2k. blue and black	2·25	70
782		3k. green and brown	2·75	2·25
783		5k. black and red	1·50	70
784		1t. purple and orange	35·00	17·00
785		2t. brown and green	4·50	1·75
786		3t. green and purple	6·50	2·00

116

117 Riza Shah Pahlavi

117a

1935. Rial values are larger, 22 × 31 mm.

787	116	5d. violet	20	10
788		10d. purple	20	10
789		15d. blue	20	10
790		30d. green	35	10
791		45d. orange	75	10
792		50d. brown	1·50	10
793		60d. blue	6·50	10
794		75d. red	4·50	10
795		90d. red	4·50	10
796		1r. purple	7·50	10
797		1r.50 blue	13·00	35
798		2r. green	12·00	15
799		3r. brown	13·00	30
800		5r. grey	22·00	6·00

1936. Rial values are larger, 23 × 31 mm.

801	117	5d. violet	15	10
802		10d. mauve	15	10
803		15d. blue	30	10
804		30d. green	40	10
805		45d. red	55	10
806		50d. brown	80	10
807		60d. brown	55	10
808		75d. red	1·00	10
809		90d. red	1·60	10
810		1r. green	6·00	10
811		1r.50 blue	3·00	10
812		2r. blue	11·00	10
813		3r. purple	15·00	10
814		5r. green	20·00	45
815		10r. blue and brown	35·00	5·50

1938. 60th Birthday of Shah. Perf or imperf.

815a	117a	5d. blue	15	10
815b		10d. red	15	10
815c		30d. blue	15	10
815d		60d. brown	20	10
815e		90d. red	30	15
815f		1r. violet	1·00	
815g		1r.50 blue	35	15
815h		2r. red	1·00	
815i		5r. mauve	1·40	1·00
815j		10r. red	3·25	1·75

118 Riza Shah Pahlavi

119 Princess Fawzieh and Crown Prince

1938. Rial values are larger, 23 × 31 mm.

816	118	5d. violet	15	10
817		10d. mauve	15	10
818		15d. blue	15	10
819		30d. green	20	10
820		45d. red	30	10
821		50d. brown	30	10
822		60d. orange	30	10
823		75d. red	35	10
824		90d. red	70	10
825		1r. green	1·25	10
826		1r.50 blue	7·50	10
827		2r. blue	10·00	10
828		3r. purple	13·00	10
829		5r. green	20·00	25
830		10r. blue and brown	42·00	1·75

1939. Royal Wedding.

831	119	5d. brown	15	10
832		10d. violet	20	10
833		30d. green	70	20
834		90d. red	2·00	30
835		1r.50 blue	3·00	1·10

120 Railway Bridge over Karun River

123 Mohammed Riza Pahlavi

1942.

850	120	5d. violet	1·50	10
851		5d. orange	35	10
852	–	10d. mauve	2·75	20
853	–	10d. green	1·50	10
854	–	20d. violet	30	10
855	–	20d. mauve	30	10
856	–	25d. red	12·50	90
857	–	25d. violet	1·50	10
858	–	35d. green	25	10
859	–	50d. blue	50	10
860	–	50d. green	1·60	10
861	–	70d. brown	50	10
862	–	75d. purple	50	10
863	–	75d. red	7·75	10
864	–	1r. red	2·75	10
865	–	1r. purple	10·00	10
866	–	1r.50 red	1·60	10
867	120	2r. blue	4·00	10
868	–	2r. green	5·25	10
869	–	2r.50 blue	5·25	10
870	–	3r. green	80·00	10
871	–	3r. purple	10·50	10
872	–	5r. green	80·00	20
873	–	5r. blue	5·25	10
874	123	10r. black and orange	20·00	2·00
875		10r. black and brown	12·00	10
876		20r. violet and brown	£600	16·00
877		20r. black and orange	18·00	15
878		30r. green and black	£1400	9·75
879		30r. black and green	18·00	20
880		50r. red and blue	£200	12·00
881		50r. black and purple	32·00	25
882		100r. black and red	£250	28·00
883		200r. black and blue	£275	32·00

DESIGNS—HORIZ: 10d. Vereshk Railway Bridge, N. Iran; 20d. Granary, Ahwaz; 25d. Steam train on Karj Bridge; 50d. Ministry of Justice; 70d. School building. VERT: 35d. Museum; 75d. Side view of museum; 1 to 5r. Full-face portrait of Mohammed Riza Pahlavi.

124 Lion and Bull, Persepolis

1948. Fund to rebuild Avicenna's Tomb at Hamadan (1st issue).

899	124	50d.+25d. green	20	35
900	–	1r.+50d. red	40	50
901	–	2½r.+1¼r. blue	80	70
902	–	5r.+2½r. violet	1·75	1·50
903	–	10r.+5r. purple	3·00	2·00

DESIGNS—VERT: 1r. Persian Warrior, Persepolis. HORIZ: 2½r. Palace of Darius, Persepolis; 5r. Tomb of Cyrus, Pasargades; 10r. King Darius enthroned.

See also Nos. 909/13, 930/4, 939/43 and 1024/28.

126 National Flag

1949. Iran's War Effort.
904 **126** 25d. multicoloured . . . 50 15
905 – 50d. violet . . . . 3·50 70
906 – 1r.50 red . . . . 3·50 70
907 – 2r.50 blue . . . . 9·00 45
908 – 5r. green . . . . 9·00 1·00
DESIGNS: 50d. Bandar Shahpur (port); 1r.50, Lorries on winding road; 2r.50, Vereshk Railway Bridge; 5r. Mohammed Riza Pahlavi and map of Iran.

127 King Ardashir II   **128** King Ardashir I and Ahura Mazda

1949. Fund to rebuild Avicenna's Tomb (2nd issue).
909 **127** 50d.+25d. green 20 20
910 – 1r.+50d. red 30 20
911 – 2½r.+1¼r. blue 60 35
912 – 5r.+2½r. plum . . . . . 1·10 1·00
913 **128** 10r.+5r. green . . . . . 1·90 1·75
DESIGNS—VERT: 1r. King Narses. HORIZ: 2½r. King Shapur I and Emperor Valerian; 5r. Arch of Ctesiphon.

129 Mohammed Riza Pahlavi and Post and Customs House, Teheran

130 Old G.P.O., Teheran   **131** Mohammed Riza Pahlavi

1949.
914 – 5d. green and red 10 10
915 – 10d. brown and blue . . . 10 10
916 – 20d. blue and violet . . . 20 10
917 – 25d. blue and brown . . . 25 10
918 – 50d. blue and green . . . 30 10
919 – 75d. red and brown . . . 50 10
920 – 1r. green and violet . . . 60 10
921 – 1r.50 red and green . . . 1·50 10
922 **129** 2r. brown and red . . . . 2·25 10
923 – 2r.50 blue . . . . 2·25 10
924 – 3r. orange and blue . . . 4·50 10
925 – 5r. violet and red . . . 6·75 10
926 **130** 10r. green and red . . . . 14·50 15
927 20r. red and black . . . . £225 12·00
928 **131** 30r. blue and brown . . . 26·00 2·00
929 50r. blue and red . . . . 42·00 1·90
DESIGNS—HORIZ: All show buildings. In the dinar values, portrait is to right of stamp, and in rial values, to left; 5d. Ramsar Hotel, Darband, Caspian Sea; 10d. Zayende River Bridge; 20d. Bank Melli Iran building; 25d. Old Royal Palace, Isfahan; 50d. Chaharbagh School, Isfahan; 75d. Railway Square; 1r. Justice Ministry; 1r.50, Shah Mosque, Teheran; 2r.50, Parliament Building; 3r. The Great Gate, Isfahan; 5r. Isfahan.

132 Tomb of Ali Abarquh   **134** Allegory

1949. Fund to rebuild Avicenna's Tomb (3rd issue).
930 **132** 50d.+25d. green 20 20
931 – 1r.+50d. brown 25 20
932 – 2½r.+1¼r. blue 45 35
933 – 5r.+2½r. red 85 85
934 – 10r.+5r. olive . . . . . . 1·75 1·75
DESIGNS—VERT: 1r. Jami Mosque, Isfahan. HORIZ: 2½r. Tomb tower, Hamadan; 5r. Jami Mosque, Ardistan; 10r. Seljuk coin.

1950. 75th Anniv of U.P.U.
935 – 50d. lake . . . . 20·00 14·00
936 **134** 2r.50 blue . . . . 28·00 18·00
DESIGN—HORIZ: 50d. Hemispheres and doves.

135 Riza Shah Pahlavi and Mausoleum

1950. Interment of Riza Shah Pahlavi at Shah Abdul Azim.
937 **135** 50d. brown . . . . 6·50 2·50
938 2r. black . . . . 13·50 3·50

136 Tomb of Baba Afzal, Kashan

1950. Fund to Rebuild Avicenna's Tomb (4th issue).
939 **136** 50d.+25d. green 15 15
940 – 1r.+50d. blue 20 20
941 – 2½r.+1¼r. purple 35 30
942 – 5r.+2½r. red 85 75
943 – 10r.+5r. grey . . . . . . 1·90 1·50
DESIGNS—VERT: 1r. Gorgan vase; 2½r. Ghazan Tower, Bistam. HORIZ: 5r. Masjid-i Gawhar Shad Mosque, Meshed; 10r. Niche in wall of Mosque at Rezaieh.

139 Flag and Book

1950. 2nd Economic Conference of Islamic Countries.
944 **139** 1r.50+1r. multicoloured 12·00 3·25

140 Mohammed Riza Pahlavi in Military School Uniform

1950. Shah's 31st Birthday. Portraits of Shah at different ages, framed as T **140**.
945 **140** 25d. black and red . . . 2·00 20
946 – 50d. black and orange . . 2·00 30
947 – 75d. black and brown . . 12·00 1·40
948 – 1r. black and green . . . 8·00 1·60
949 – 2r.50 black and blue . . . 14·00 2·00
950 – 5r. black and red . . . . 20·00 2·50
PORTRAITS—Shah in uniform: 50d. Naval cadet; 75d. Boy Scout; 1r. Naval officer; 2r.50, Army officer-cadet; 5r. Army general.

142 Memorial

1950. 4th Anniv of Re-establishment of Control in Azerbaijan.
951 – 10d.+5d. brown . . . . . 7·00 1·25
952 **142** 50d.+25d. purple . . . . 7·50 1·40
953 – 1r.+50d. purple . . . . . 15·00 1·75
954 – 1r.50+75d. red and green 15·00 3·25
955 – 2r.50+1r.25 blue . . . . 16·00 5·00
956 – 3r.+1r.50 blue . . . . . 22·00 5·00
DESIGNS—VERT: 10d. Shah and map; 1r.50, Map and battle scene; 2r.50, Shah and flags. HORIZ: 1r. Troops marching; 3r. Cavalry parade.

143 Shah and Queen Soraya   **144** Farabi

1951. Royal Wedding. T **143** and similar portraits.
959 **143** 5d. purple . . . . 1·10 35
960 25d. orange . . . . . . 1·50 45
961 50d. green . . . . 3·25 55
962 – 1r. brown . . . . 3·75 90
963 – 1r.50 red . . . . 5·25 2·10
964 – 2r.50 blue . . . . 7·00 2·75
DESIGNS: 1r. to 2r.50, As T **143** but portraits centrally placed.

1951. Millenary of Death of Farabi (philosopher).
965 **144** 50d. red . . . . 3·00 60
966 2r.50 blue . . . . 11·00 1·75

145 Mohammed Riza Pahlavi   **146** Mohammed Riza Pahlavi

1951.
967 **145** 5d. red 10 10
968 10d. violet 10 10
969 20d. sepia 10 10
970 25d. blue 10 10
971 50d. green 40 10
972 50d. deep green . . . . . 5·25 10
973 75d. red 30 10
974 **146** 1r. green 50 10
975 1r. turquoise 50 10
976 1r.50 red 80 10
977 2r. brown . . . . 2·75 10
978 2r.50 blue . . . . 2·50 10
979 3r. orange . . . . 10·00 10
980 5r. green . . . . 10·00 10
981 10r. olive . . . . 26·00 80
982 20r. brown . . . . 13·50 30
983 30r. blue . . . . 7·75 40
984 50r. black . . . . 26·00 1·25

147 Coran Gate, Shiraz

1951. 600th Death Anniv of Saadi (Muslih-ad-Din) (poet).
985 **147** 25d.+25d. green . . . . . 1·50 45
986 – 50d.+50d. green . . . . . 1·50 55
987 – 1r.50+50d. blue . . . . . 7·00 1·25
DESIGNS—HORIZ: 50d. Tomb of Saadi. VERT: (as T **144**): 1r.50, Saadi.

150 Shah and Lockheed Super Constellation over Mosque

1952. Air.
988 – 50d. green 10 10
989 **150** 1r. red 15 10
990 2r. blue 20 10
991 3r. sepia 30 10
992 5r. lilac 45 10
993 10r. red 65 10
994 20r. violet . . . . 1·75 20
995 30r. olive . . . . 2·25 30
996 50r. brown . . . . 6·00 40
997 100r. sepia . . . . 65·00 3·50
998 200r. green . . . . 25·00 5·50
DESIGN: 50d. Shah and Lockheed Super Constellation airplane over Mt. Demavend.

151 Oil Well and Mosque

1953. Discovery of Oil at Qum. (a) Postage.
999 **151** 50d. bistre and green . . 1·00 10
1000 – 1r. bistre and mauve . . 1·00 10
1001 **151** 2r.50 bistre and blue . . 1·50 35
1002 – 5r. bistre and brown . . 2·10 80

(b) Air. With Lockheed Super Constellation airplane.
1003 **151** 3r. bistre and violet . . . 26·00 6·00
1004 – 5r. bistre and brown . . 35·00 8·00
1005 **151** 10r. bistre and green . . 45·00 12·00
1006 – 20r. bistre and purple . . 55·00 14·00
DESIGN: 1r., 5r. (2), 20r. As Type **151** but horiz.

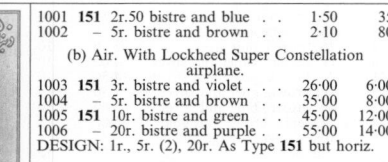

153 Power Station Boiler Plant

1953. 2nd Anniv of Nationalization of Oil Industry.
1007 **153** 50d. green . . . . 1·25 15
1008 – 1r. red . . . . 1·75 15
1009 – 2r.50 blue . . . . 7·00 40
1010 – 5r. orange . . . . 7·50 60
1011 – 10r. lilac . . . . 8·50 85
DESIGNS—HORIZ: 1r. Crude oil stabilizer; 5r. Pipe-lines; 10r. View of Abadan. VERT: 2r.50, Super fractionaters.

154 Family and U.N. Emblem   **155** Gymnast

1953. United Nations Day.
1012 **154** 1r. green and turquoise 50 20
1013 2r.50 blue and light blue 1·00 45

1953. Ancient Persian Sports.
1014 **155** 1r. green . . . . 1·40 85
1015 – 2r.50 blue . . . . 6·00 1·10
1016 – 3r. grey . . . . 18·00 1·40
1017 – 5r. ochre . . . . 12·00 3·25
1018 – 10r. violet . . . . 24·00 4·50
DESIGNS—HORIZ: 2r.50, Archer; 3r. Mountaineers. VERT: 5r. Polo-player (Persian Sports Club Badge); 10r. Lion-hunter.

156 Iranian Roach   **157** Machinery

1954. Nationalization of Fishing Industry.
1019 **156** 1r. multicoloured . . . . 2·00 55
1020 – 2r.50 multicoloured . . . 30·00 1·75
1021 – 3r. red . . . . 12·00 1·25
1022 **157** 5r. green . . . . 11·00 2·25
1023 – 10r. multicoloured . . . 20·00 5·50
DESIGNS—HORIZ: As Type **156**: 2r.50, Clupeid; 10r. Sturgeon. As Type **157**: 3r. Refrigeration machinery.

158 Hamadan   **159** Avicenna

1954. Fund to Rebuild Avicenna's Tomb (5th issue).
1024 **158** 50d.+25d. green 15 15
1025 **159** 1r.+½r. brown 20 20
1026 – 2½r.+1¼r. blue 45 30
1027 – 5r.+2½r. red 70 50
1028 – 10r.+5r. olive . . . . . 1·40 1·25
DESIGNS—VERT: As Type **159**: 2½r. Qabus tower, Gargan. HORIZ: As Type **158**: 5r. Old tomb of Avicenna; 10r. New tomb of Avicenna.

160 Shah in Military Uniform   **161** Hands breaking Chain

1954.
1029 **160** 5d. brown 10 10
1062 5d. violet 10 10
1030 10d. violet 10 10
1063 10d. red 10 10

1031 25d. red 10 10
1064 25d. brown 10 10
1032 50d. brown 10 10
1065 50d. red 10 10
1066 – 1r. green . . . . 1·25 10
1034 – 1r.50 red 75 10
1067 – 1r.50 brown . . . . . . 20·00 10
1035 – 2r. brown 75 10
1068 – 2r. green . . . . 1·90 10
1069 – 2r.50 blue 75 10
1037 – 3r. green . . . . 1·25 10
1070 – 3r. brown . . . . 5·25 10
1038 – 5r. green . . . . 2·50 10
1071 – 5r. purple . . . . 2·50 10
1039 – 10r. lilac . . . . 6·25 2·00
1072 – 10r. blue . . . . 4·25 10
1040 – 20r. blue . . . . 50·00 6·00
1073 – 20r. green . . . . 26·00 10
1041 – 30r. brown . . . . £110 20·00
1074 – 30r. orange . . . . . . £130 12·00
1042 – 50r. orange . . . . . . 38·00 2·00
1075 – 50r. brown . . . . £110 16·00
1043 – 100r. violet . . . . . . £475 38·00
1044 – 200r. yellow . . . . . . £110 12·00
DESIGN: 1r. to 200r. Shah in naval uniform.

1954. 1st Anniv of Return of Shah. Mult.
1045 2r. Type **161** . . . . 3·25 45
1046 3r. Hand holding torch and Iranian flag . . . . . . 5·00 70
1047 5r. Man clasping Iranian flag . . . . 9·00 1·25
SIZES: 3r. ($19\frac{1}{2} \times 27\frac{1}{2}$ mm); 5r. ($20\frac{1}{2} \times 28\frac{1}{2}$ mm).

162 Nurse and Child

163 Felling Trees

1954. U.N. Day.
1048 **162** 2r. orange and purple . . 1·75 50
1049 3r. orange and violet . . 1·90 1·00

1954. 4th World Forestry Congress. Inscr "4eme congres mondial forestier".
1050 **163** 1r. green and brown . . 16·00 3·50
1051 – 2r.50 blue and green . . 25·00 7·00
1052 – 5r. brown and lavender 50·00 15·00
1053 – 10r. lake and blue . . . 60·00 28·00
DESIGNS: 2r.50, Man carrying logs; 5r. Man operating circular saw; 10r. Ancient Persian galley.

164

165 Parliament Building

1955. National Costumes.
1054 **164** 1r. multicoloured . . . . 1·25 45
1055 – 2r. multicoloured . . . . 2·25 65
1056 – 2r.50 multicoloured . . . . 14·00 1·25
1057 – 3r. multicoloured . . . . 6·00 1·25
1058 – 5r. multicoloured . . . . 10·00 2·50
DESIGNS—2r. Male costume; 2r.50, 3r., 5r. Female costumes.

1955. 50th Anniv of Constitution.
1059 – 2r. green and purple . . 1·75 40
1060 – 3r. blue . . . . 3·50 60
1061 **165** 5r. orange and green . . 4·25 95
DESIGNS—HORIZ: 2r. Gateway of Parliament Building. VERT: 3r. Winged Statue.

167 U.N. Emblem and Hemispheres

168 Wrestlers

1955. United Nations Day.
1077 **167** 1r. orange and red . . . 65 30
1078 2r.50 light blue and blue 1·10 35

1955. International Success of Iranian Wrestlers.
1079 **168** 2r.50 multicoloured . . . 3·25 70

169 Hospital Buildings

1956. Opening of Nemazi Hospital, Shiraz. Multicoloured.
1080 – 50d. ($24 \times 33\frac{1}{2}$ mm) . . . 70 40
1081 **169** 1r. ($36 \times 24\frac{1}{2}$ mm) . . . 2·75 60
1082 – 2r.50 ($24 \times 33\frac{1}{2}$ mm) . . 3·50 1·25
1083 – 5r. (36×23 mm) . . . . 8·25 2·00
1084 – 10r. ($24 \times 33\frac{1}{2}$ mm) . . . 13·50 5·00
DESIGNS: 50d. Hospital garden; 2r.50, Spear thrower; 5r. Koran gate, Shiraz; 10r. Poet Hafiz and his tomb.

170

171 Tusi's Tomb, Maragheh

1956. 10th Anniv of National Olympic Committee.
1085 **170** 5r. lilac . . . . 15·00 5·50

1956. 700th Death Anniv of Nasir ed-Din Tusi, 1201–74 (astronomer and scientist).
1086 **171** 1r. orange . . . . 2·00 40
1087 – 2r.50 blue (Astrolabe) . . 4·00 60
1088 – 5r. lilac and sepia (Portrait) . . . . . . 6·50 1·00

172 Reveille

1956. National Scout Jamboree.
1089 **172** 2r.50 blue & ultramarine 7·00 3·50
1090 – 5r. mauve and lilac . . . 13·00 4·00
DESIGN: 5r. Shah in scout's uniform and badge.

173

174 U.N. Emblem and Young People

1956. World Health Organization.
1091 **173** 6r. mauve . . . . 1·60 70

1956. United Nations Day.
1092 **174** 1r. green 50 30
1093 – 2r.50 blue and green . . 1·25 50
DESIGN: 2r.50, U.N. emblem and scales of justice.

175 Telecommunications Centre, Teheran

1956. Centenary of Persian Telegraphs.
1094 **175** 2r.50 green and blue . . 2·00 90
1095 – 6r. mauve and pink . . . 6·00 1·40
DESIGN: 6r. Telegraph poles and mosque.

176 Shah and Pres. Mirza

1956. Visit of President of Pakistan.
1096 **176** 1r. multicoloured . . . . 1·00 20

177 Mohammed Riza Pahlavi

178 Mohammed Riza Pahlavi

1956.
1097 **177** 5d. red and rose 10 10
1098 10d. violet and blue . . 10 10
1099 25d. brown and sepia . . 10 10
1100 50d. olive and sepia . . 10 10
1101 1r. green and brown . . 10 10
1102 1r.50 brown and mauve 50 10
1103 2r. red and mauve . . . 50 10
1104 2r.50 blue & ultramarine 55 10
1105 3r. bistre and brown . . 1·25 10
1106 5r. red . . . . 1·50 10
1132 6r. blue and light blue 2·00 10
1133 10r. turquoise and green 2·50 10
1134 20r. olive and green . . 2·50 10
1135 30r. sepia and blue . . . 15·00 80
1136 50r. brown and sepia . . 26·00 80
1137 100r. red & bright purple £160 4·00
1138 200r. bistre and violet . . £100 32·00

1956.
1122 **178** 5d. plum and violet . . . 10 10
1123 10d. mauve and purple 10 10
1124 25d. orange and red . . 10 10
1125 50d. green and grey . . 10 10
1126 1r. turquoise and green 10 10
1127 1r.50 purple and mauve 50 10
1128 2r. turquoise and blue 55 10
1129 2r.50 turquoise and blue 55 10
1130 3r. red and rose . . . . 1·00 10
1131 5r. violet and blue . . . 95 10
1107 6r. mauve and lilac . . . 1·40 10
1108 10r. green and blue . . . 2·50 10
1109 20r. blue and green . . . 3·50 15
1110 30r. orange and red . . 26·00 8·00
1111 50r. sage and green . . . 13·00 2·00
1112 100r. red and purple . . £425 30·00
1113 200r. violet and purple £225 40·00

179 Lord Baden-Powell

180 Steam Express Train and Mosque

1957. Birth Centenary of Lord Baden-Powell (founder of Boy Scout movement).
1114 **179** 10r. brown and green . . 4·00 2·00

1957. Inauguration of Teheran–Meshed Railway. Multicoloured.
1115 2r.50 Track and signal . . . 5·00 85
1116 5r. Diesel train and map (horiz) . . . . 8·00 1·50
1117 10r. Type **180** . . . . . . 18·00 8·75

181 President Gronchi and Shah

1957. Visit of President of Italy.
1118 **181** 2r. grey, green and red 75 50
1119 – 6r. blue, green and red 2·00 75
DESIGN: 6r. Plaque and flags between ruins of Persepolis and Colosseum.

183 Queen Soraya and Ramsar Hotel

1957. 6th Medical Congress, Ramsar.
1120 **183** 2r. green and blue . . . 1·00 20

184 Shah and King Faisal II of Iraq

1957. Visit of King of Iraq.
1121 **184** 2r. blue, red and green 75 15

185 Globes within Laurel Sprays

1957. Int Cartographical Conf, Teheran.
1140 **185** 10r. multicoloured . . . 4·00 65

186 "Flight"

187 "The Weightlifter"

1957. Air. United Nations Day.
1141 **186** 10r. red and mauve . . . 1·10 60
1142 20r. purple and violet . . 1·60 1·00

1957. International Weightlifting Championships.
1143 **187** 10r. blue, green and red 1·50 35

188 Radio Mast and Buildings

189 Oil Derrick and "Bowl of Flames"

1958. 30th Anniv of Iranian Broadcasting Service.
1144 **188** 10r. sepia, buff and blue 1·75 65

1958. 50th Anniv of Iranian Oil Industry.
1145 **189** 2r. brown, yellow and grey . . . . 2·25 30
1146 10r. brown, yellow & blue . . . . 5·75 80

190 Exhibition Emblem

1958. Brussels International Exhibition.
1147 **190** 2r.50 red 45 10
1148 6r. red 80 20

191 Steam Train on Viaduct

1958. Inaug of Teheran–Tabriz Railway.
1149 **191** 6r. lilac . . . . 12·00 3·00
1150 – 8r. green . . . . 16·00 6·50
DESIGN: 8r. Steam express train and route map.

192 Mohammed Riza Pahlavi

193 U.N. Emblem and Map of Persia

1958.
1162 **192** 5d. violet 10 10
1163 5d. brown 10 10
1164 10d. red 10 10
1165 10d. green 10 10
1166 10d. turquoise 10 10
1167 25d. red 10 10
1168 25d. orange 20 10
1169 50d. blue 20 10
1170 50d. red 10 10
1171 1r. green 35 10
1172 1r. violet 35 10
1232 2r. brown . . . . 2·50 10
1176 3r. brown 50 10
1177 6r. blue 40 10
1179 8r. purple . . . . 1·40 10
1180 8r. brown 50 10
1181 10r. black 50 10
1182 14r. blue . . . . 3·00 10
1183 14r. green 50 10
1185 20r. green . . . . 2·00 10
1186 30r. red . . . . 2·50 20
1187 30r. brown 50 10
1188 50r. purple . . . . . . 26·00 25
1189 50r. blue . . . . 1·40 10
1190 100r. orange . . . . . . 2·50 75
1191 100r. green . . . . . . £100 2·00

1192 200r. green . . . . . . 26·00 1·40
1193 200r. mauve . . . . . . £225 2·40

1958. United Nations Day.
1194 **193** 6r. blue and light blue 75 60
1195 10r. violet and green . . 95 80

194 Clasped Hands

195 Rudagi playing Lyre

1958. 10th Anniv of Declaration of Human Rights.
1196 **194** 6r. brown and chocolate 35 20
1197 8r. olive and green . . . 90 35

1958. 1100th Birth Anniv of Rudagi (poet and musician).
1198 **195** 2r.50 blue . . . . 2·75 25
1199 – 5r. violet . . . . 5·75 45
1200 **195** 10r. sepia . . . . 10·00 90
DESIGN: 5r. Rudagi meditating.

196

1959. Red Cross Commemoration.
1201 **196** 1r. multicoloured 85 20
1202 6r. multicoloured . . . . 1·40 55

197 Wrestlers

198 Torch of Freedom

1959. World Wrestling Championships.
1203 **197** 6r. multicoloured . . . . 4·25 75

1959. United Nations Day.
1204 **198** 6r. red, brown and bistre 65 25

199 Shah and President Khan

1959. Visit of President of Pakistan.
1205 **199** 6r. multicoloured . . . . 2·50 45

200 I.L.O. Emblem

1959. 40th Anniv of I.L.O.
1206 **200** 1r. blue and light blue 50 20
1207 5r. brown and light brown 75 35

201 Pahlavi Foundation Bridge, Khorramshahr

1960. Opening of Pahlavi Foundation Bridge, Khorramshahr.
1208 **201** 1r. blue and brown . . . 75 10
1209 – 5r. green and blue . . . 1·00 30
DESIGN: 5r. Close-up view of bridge.

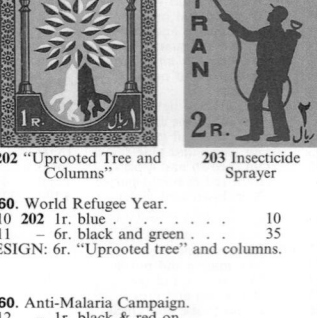

202 "Uprooted Tree and Columns"

203 Insecticide Sprayer

1960. World Refugee Year.
1210 **202** 1r. blue 10 10
1211 – 6r. black and green . . . 35 20
DESIGN: 6r. "Uprooted tree" and columns.

1960. Anti-Malaria Campaign.
1212 – 1r. black & red on yellow 30 15
1213 **203** 2r. blue, black & light bl 80 20
1214 – 3r. black and red on green . . . . 1·40 50
DESIGNS (30 × 37 mm): 1r., 3r. Different views of mosquito crossed out in red.

204 Polo Player

206 Scout Emblem within Flower

205 Shah and King Hussein

1960. "Olympic Games Week".
1215 **204** 1r. purple 50 20
1216 – 6r. violet and blue . . . 1·10 50
DESIGN: 6r. Archer.

1960. Visit of King of Jordan.
1217 **205** 6r. multicoloured . . . . 2·50 60

1960. 3rd National Scout Jamboree.
1218 **206** 1r. green 30 10
1219 – 6r. ochre, sepia and blue 60 20
DESIGN: 6r. Scout camp, Persepolis.

207 Shah and Queen Farah

1960. Royal Wedding.
1220 **207** 1r. green . . . . 1·00 40
1221 5r. blue . . . . 2·75 70

208 UN Emblem

210 Girl playing Pan-pipes

209 Shah and Queen Elizabeth II

1960. 15th Anniv of U.N.O.
1222 **208** 6r. sepia, blue and bistre 55 15

1961. Visit of Queen Elizabeth II.
1223 **209** 1r. brown 65 10
1224 6r. blue . . . . 1·10 20

1961. International Music Congress, Teheran.
1225 **210** 1r. stone and brown . . 50 10
1226 – 6r. slate 90 15
DESIGN—(24 × 39½ mm): 6r. Safiaddin Anmavi (musician).

211 Royal Family

1961. Birth of Crown Prince.
1227 **211** 1r. purple . . . . 1·00 50
1228 6r. blue . . . . 4·50 1·25

212 U.N. Emblem and Birds

213 Tree-planting

1961. United Nations Day.
1236 **212** 2r. red and blue 15 10
1237 6r. violet and blue . . . 45 20

1962. Afforestation Week.
1238 **213** 2r. blue, cream and green 25 10
1239 6r. green, blue & ultram 55 20

214 Worker

215 Family on Map

1962. Workers' Day.
1240 **214** 2r. multicoloured 15 10
1241 6r. multicoloured 45 30

1962. Social Insurance.
1242 **215** 2r. violet, black & yellow 15 10
1243 6r. blue, black & lt blue 45 30

216 Sugar Plantation

1962. Sugar Cane Production.
1244 **216** 2r. green, blue & ultram 25 15
1245 6r. blue, cream & ultram 65 30

217 Karaj Dam

1962. Inauguration of Karaj Dam.
1246 **217** 2r. green and brown . . 1·00 10
1247 6r. blue and ultramarine 1·40 20

218 Sefid Rud Dam

1962. Inauguration of Sefid Rud Dam.
1248 **218** 2r. buff, blue and myrtle 1·00 15
1249 – 6r. black, blue and brown . . . . 1·40 30
DESIGN: 6r. Distant view of dam.

219 U.N. Emblem

1962. 15th Anniv of U.N.E.S.C.O.
1250 **219** 2r. black, green and red 40 15
1251 6r. blue, green and red 85 30

220 Arrow piercing Mosquito

221 Mohammed Riza Pahlavi

222 Shah and Palace of Darius, Persepolis

1962. Malaria Eradication.
1252 **220** 2r. black and green . . . 15 10
1253 – 6r. blue and red 50 20
1254 – 10r. ultramarine and blue 90 25
DESIGNS—VERT (29½ × 34½ mm): 6r. Mosquito and insecticide-sprayer. HORIZ (As Type **220**):10r. Globe and campaign emblem.

1962.
1255 **221** 5d. green 10 10
1256 10d. brown 10 10
1257 25d. blue 10 10
1336 50d. turquoise 10 10
1337 1r. orange 15 10
1338 2r. violet 20 10
1339 5r. brown 65 10
1340 **222** 6r. blue . . . . 1·00 10
1341 8r. green 70 10
1342 10r. blue . . . . 1·00 10
1265a 11r. green 60 10
1266a 14r. violet . . . . . . 1·00 10
1345 20r. brown . . . . . . 1·10 20
1346 50r. red . . . . 1·25 45

223 Oil Pipelines

1962. 2nd Petroleum Symposium of Economic Commission for Asia and the Far East.
1269 **223** 6r. brown and blue . . . 40 15
1270 14r. brown and grey . . 85 35

224 Hippocrates and Avicenna

1962. W.H.O. Medical Congress, Teheran.
1271 **224** 2r. blue, brown and cream . . . . 1·00 15
1272 6r. blue, sage and green 1·50 30

225 New Houses

1962. United Nations Day.
1273 **225** 6r. blue and indigo . . . 45 15
1274 – 14r. green and blue . . . 95 20
DESIGN—HORIZ: 14r. Laying foundation stone.

226 "Bouquet for the Crown Prince"

1962. Crown Prince's Birthday.
1275 **226** 6r. blue . . . . 1·50 30
1276 14r. green . . . . 3·00 70

227 Persian Gulf Map **228** Hilton Hotel, Teheran

1962. Persian Gulf Seminar.
1277 **227** 6r. blue, pink & pale blue 40 15
1278 14r. blue, flesh and pink 85 30

1963. Opening of Royal Teheran Hilton Hotel.
1279 **228** 6r. blue . . . . 1·40 20
1280 14r. brown . . . . . . 2·25 45

229 Refugees

1963. Earthquake Relief Fund.
1281 **229** 14r.+6r. blue, brn & grn 90 60

230 Mohammed Riza Shah Dam

1963. Inaug of Mohammed Riza Shah Dam.
1282 **230** 6r. multicoloured . . . . 1·75 30
1283 14r. multicoloured . . . 3·75 65

231 Worker with Pickaxe **232** Bird and Globe

1963. Workers' Day.
1283a **231** 2r. black and yellow . . 45 10
1283b 6r. black and blue . . . 60 20

1963. Freedom from Hunger.
1284 **232** 2r. ultramarine, bl & bis 50 10
1285 – 6r. black, bistre and blue 90 20
1286 – 14r. bistre and green . . 2·00 45
DESIGNS: 6r. Globe and ears of wheat (stylized); 14r. Globe encircled by scroll, and campaign emblem.

233 Shah and Scroll

1963. Agrarian Reform Act.
1287 **233** 6r. green and blue . . . 90 20
1288 14r. green and yellow . . 2·00 55

234 Shah and King Frederick

1963. Visit of King of Denmark.
1289 **234** 6r. blue and indigo . . . 1·25 25
1290 14r. brown and sepia . . 3·00 50

235 Flags of Iran and India; Ibn Sina Mosque, Teheran, and Taj Mahal, India

1963. Visit of President Radhakrishnan of India.
1291 **235** 6r. multicoloured . . . . 1·60 25
1292 14r. multicoloured . . . 3·50 50

236 Shahnaz Dam **237** Centenary Emblem

1963. Inauguration of Shahnaz Dam.
1293 **236** 6r. ultramarine, bl & grn 1·50 25
1294 14r. green, blue and buff 2·25 50

1963. Red Cross Centenary.
1295 **237** 6r. multicoloured . . . . 1·75 30
1296 14r. grey, red and buff 3·75 60

238 Shah and Queen Juliana

1963. Visit of Queen of the Netherlands.
1304 **238** 6r. blue and ultramarine 2·50 30
1305 14r. green and black . . 3·25 60

240 Students in Class

1963. Formation of Literacy Teaching Corps.
1306 **240** 6r. multicoloured . . . . 1·50 15
1307 14r. multicoloured . . . 2·50 30

241 Pres. De Gaulle and View of Teheran

1963. Visit of President of France.
1308 **241** 6r. ultramarine and blue 1·75 30
1309 14r. brown and ochre . . 3·50 60

242 Plant, Route Map and Emblem

1963. Opening of Chemical Fertilizer Plant, Shiraz.
1310 **242** 6r. black, yellow and red 1·75 30
1311 – 14r. black, blue & yellow 3·50 60
DESIGN—HORIZ: 14r. Fertilizer plant and emblem.

243 Pres. Lubke and Shah Mosque, Isfahan

1963. Visit of President of German Federal Republic.
1312 **243** 6r. blue and violet . . . 1·75 30
1313 14r. brown and grey . . 3·50 55

244 U.N. Emblem

1963. United Nations Day.
1314 **244** 8r. multicoloured . . . . 1·25 20

245 Aircraft crossing U.N. Emblem **246** Crown Prince Riza

1963. Iranian Air Force in Congo.
1315 **245** 6r. multicoloured . . . . 1·25 20

1963. Children's Day.
1316 **246** 2r. brown 75 15
1317 6r. blue . . . . 1·00 25

247 Chairman Brezhnev

1963. Visit of Chairman of Soviet Presidium.
1318 **247** 5r. multicoloured . . . . 1·75 30
1319 11r. multicoloured . . . 2·75 50

248 Ataturk's Mausoleum

1963. 25th Death Anniv of Kemal Ataturk.
1320 **248** 4r. brown, grey and green . . . . 1·50 15
1321 – 5r. black, red and yellow 1·75 20
DESIGN: 5r. Kemal Ataturk.

249 Scales of Justice and Globe **250** Mother and Child

1963. 15th Anniv of Declaration of Human Rights.
1322 **249** 6r. black, blue and green 1·10 20
1323 14r. black, cream & brn 1·75 30

1963. Mothers Day.
1324 **250** 2r. multicoloured . . . . 1·00 15
1325 4r. multicoloured . . . . 2·00 20

251 Cogwheel and Map **252** Hand with Document (Profit-sharing)

1963. Industrial Development.
1326 **251** 8r. blue, cream & turq 1·75 30

1964. Six-Point Reform Law.
1327 **252** 2r. brown, violet and blue 40 10
1328 – 4r. brown and grey . . . 1·10 15
1329 – 6r. multicoloured . . . . 2·00 20
1330 – 8r. multicoloured . . . . 2·25 25
1331 – 10r. red, green & dp grn 2·50 30
1332 – 12r. brown and red . . . 3·25 35
DESIGNS: 4r. Factory and documents on scales (Sale of Shares to Workers); 6r. Worker on Globe (Education Corps); 8r. Tractor (Land reform); 10r. Trees (Nationalization of forests); 12r. Silhouettes within gateway (Votes for Women).

253 U.N. Emblem **254** Blossom

1964. 20th Economic Commission for Asia and the Far East Session, Teheran.
1347 **253** 14r. black and green . . 1·25 30

1964. New Year Greetings.
1348 **254** 50d. orange, sepia & grn 15 10
1349 1r. orange, black and blue 15 10

255 Weather Vane **256** "Tourism"

1964. World Meteorological Day.
1350 **255** 6r. violet and blue . . . 75 20

1964. 1st Anniv of Iranian Tourist Organization (INTO).
1351 **256** 6r. green, violet and black 90 20
1352 – 11r. orange, brown & blk . . . . 1·60 45
DESIGN: 11r. Winged beasts, column and INTO emblem.

257 Rudagi (blind poet)

1964. Opening of Blind Institute.
1353 **257** 6r. blue 90 20
1354 8r. brown . . . . 1·60 30

258 Sculptured Head

1964. "7000 Years of Persian Art" Exhibition.
1355 **258** 2r. blue and grey . . . . 1·50 10
1356 – 4r. ultramarine and blue 5·00 20
1357 – 6r. yellow and brown . . 3·00 30
1358 – 10r. green and yellow . . 5·00 50
DESIGNS—HORIZ: 4r. Sumerian war chariot on map. VERT: 6r. Golden cup with lion decorations; 10r. Sculptured head of man.

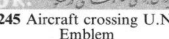

259 Shah and Emperor Haile Selassie

1964. Visit of Emperor of Ethiopia.
1359 **259** 6r. ultramarine and blue . . . 1·25 20

260 Congress Emblem

1964. 2nd Iranian Dental Assn Congress.
1360 **260** 2r. red, deep blue & blue 40 15
1361 – 4r. multicoloured . . . . 1·00 30
DESIGN: 4r. "2 IDA" in symbolic form.

261 Bark Beetle under Lens

1964. Inauguration of Plant Parasites and Diseases Research Institute.
1362 – 2r. brown, red and buff 1·00 15
1363 **261** 6r. indigo, brown & blue 1·75 30
DESIGN: 2r. Microscope, plants and research centre.

262 Plaque **263** Eleanor Roosevelt

1964. Mehregan Festival.
1364 **262** 8r. red and yellow . . . 1·25 15

1964. Eleanor Roosevelt Commemoration
1365 **263** 10r. blue and violet . . . 1·50 25

264 Clasped Hands and U.N. Emblem **265** Gymnast

1964. United Nations Day.
1366 **264** 6r. multicoloured 85 15
1367 – 14r. red, blue and orange 1·40 30
DESIGN: 14r. U.N. and "Bird" emblems.

1964. Olympic Games, Tokyo.
1368 **265** 4r. sepia, turquoise & brn 70 15
1369 – 6r. red and blue . . . . 1·00 25
DESIGN—Diamond (39 × 39 mm): 6r. Polo.

266 Crown Prince Riza

1964. Children's Day.
1370 **266** 1r. green and brown . . 50 10
1371 2r. red and blue . . . . 1·25 15
1372 6r. blue and red . . . . 2·25 30

267 Conference and U.N. Emblems

1964. Petro-Chemical Conf and Gas Seminar.
1373 **267** 6r. multicoloured 50 15
1374 8r. multicoloured . . . . 1·00 25

268 Shah and King Baudouin

1964. Visit of King of Belgium.
1375 **268** 6r. black, orange & yell 40 15
1376 8r. black, orange & green 85 15

269 Rhazes

1964. 1100th Birth Anniv of Rhazes (Zakariya Ar-Razi, alchemist).
1377 **269** 2r. multicoloured 60 15
1378 6r. multicoloured 90 20

270 Shah and King Olav

1965. Visit of King of Norway.
1379 **270** 2r. mauve and purple . . 50 15
1380 4r. green and olive . . . 90 20

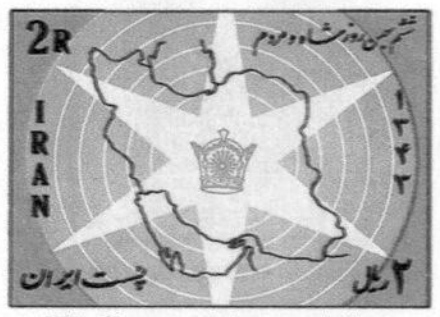

271 Crown, Map and Star

1965. Six-Point Reform Law.
1381 **271** 2r. orange, black and blue 30 15

272 Woman and U.N. Emblem

1965. 18th Session of United Nations Commission on Status of Women, Teheran.
1382 **272** 6r. black, blue & lt blue 45 10
1383 8r. blue, red and light red 80 15

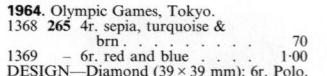

273 Festival Plant **274** Pres. Bourguiba and Minarets

1965. New Year Festival.
1384 **273** 50d. multicoloured . . . 10 10
1385 1r. multicoloured 20 10

1965. Visit of President of Tunisia.
1386 **274** 4r. multicoloured 75 15

275 Map of Oil Pipelines

1965. 14th Anniv of Nationalization of Oil Industry.
1387 6r. multicoloured 90 20
1388 **275** 14r. multicoloured . . . 1·75 40

276 I.T.U. Emblem and Symbols

1965. Centenary of I.T.U.
1389 **276** 14r. red and grey 90 30

277 I.C.Y. Emblem

1965. International Co-operation Year.
1390 **277** 10r. green and blue . . . 1·40 20

278 Boeing 727-100 and Airline Emblem

1965. Inauguration of Jet Services by Iranian National Airlines.
1391 **278** 14r. multicoloured . . . 1·00 35

279 "Co-operation" (Hands holding Book)

1965. 1st Anniv of Regional Development Co-operation Plan. Multicoloured.
1392 2r. Type **279** 20 10
1393 4r. Globe and flags of Turkey, Iran and Pakistan ($40\frac{1}{2} \times 24\frac{1}{2}$ mm) 30 15

280 Moot Emblem and Arabesque Pattern

1965. Middle East Rover (Scout) Moot.
1394 **280** 2r. multicoloured 40 15

281 Gateway of Parliament Building

1965. 60th Anniv of Iranian Constitution.
1397 **281** 2r. brown and mauve . . 30 10

282 Congress Emblem **283** Teacher and Class

1965. Iranian Dental Congress.
1398 **282** 6r. blue, mauve and silver 35 15

1965. World Eradication of Illiteracy Congress, Teheran. Multicoloured.
1399 2r. Type **283** 10 10
1400 5r. Globe showing alphabets (25 × 30 mm) 20 10
1401 6r. U.N.E.S.C.O. emblem and symbols (diamond, 36 × 36 mm) 30 15
1402 8r. Various scripts (35 × 23 mm) 30 15
1403 14r. Shah and multi-lingual inscriptions (41 × 52 mm) 1·10 30

284 Shah Riza Pahlavi

1965. 25th Anniv (actually 24th) of Shah's Accession.
1404 **284** 1r. red and grey 35 10
1405 2r. red and yellow . . . 70 10

285 Congress Emblem

1965. 14th Medical Congress.
1406 **285** 5r. ultramarine, bl & gold 40 10

286 President Jonas

1965. Visit of President of Austria.
1407 **286** 6r. blue and brown . . . 85 20

287 Plaque

1965. Mehregan Festival.
1408 **287** 4r. multicoloured 30 15
See also No. 1464.

289 U.N. Emblem and "Flowers" **290** Emblem and "Arches"

1965. United Nations Day.
1409 **289** 5r. multicoloured 30 15

1965. Iranian Industrial Exhibition, Teheran.
1410 **290** 3r. multicoloured 20 10

291 Crown Prince Riza **292** "Weightlifting"

1965. Children's Day.
1411 **291** 2r. chocolate, brn & gold 40 10

1965. World Weightlifting Championships, Teheran.
1412 **292** 10r. mauve, violet & blue 45 15

293 Open Book

1965. Book Week.
1416 **293** 8r. multicoloured 40 20

294 Shah and King Faisal

1965. Visit of King of Saudi Arabia.
1417 **294** 4r. brown and bistre . . 70 15

295 Scales of Justice

1965. Human Rights Day.
1418 **295** 14r. multicoloured . . . 45 20

296 Tractor (Land Reform)

1966. 3rd Anniv of Shah's White Revolution (Parliamentary Assent to Shah's Reform Plan).
1419 **296** 1r. brown and yellow . . 10 10
1420 – 2r. green and light green 15 10
1421 – 3r. brown and silver . . 15 10
1422 – 4r. violet and light violet 15 10
1423 – 5r. lake and red 15 10
1424 – 6r. brown and bistre . . 20 10
1425 – 7r. ultramarine and blue 30 15
1426 – 8r. ultramarine and blue 30 15
1427 – 9r. brown & light brown 35 20
DESIGNS: 2r. Trees (Nationalization of Forests); 3r. Cogwheel emblem (Sale of shares to workers); 4r. Cylinders (Profit-sharing); 5r. Parliament gateway (Votes for Women); 6r. Blackboard and pupils (Education Corps); 7r. Staff of Aesculapius (Medical Corps); 8r. Scales (Justice); 9r. Girders (Construction Corps).

297 Mohammed Riza Pahlavi **298** Shah and Ruins of Persepolis

1966.
1428 **297** 5d. green 10 10
1429 10d. brown 10 10
1430 25d. blue 10 10
1431 50d. turquoise 10 10
1432 1r. orange 10 10
1433 2r. violet 10 10
1434 4r. brown . . . . 3·00 10
1435 5r. sepia 15 10
1436 **298** 6r. blue 15 10
1437 8r. green 30 10
1438 10r. blue 20 10
1439 11r. green 70 10
1440 14r. violet . . . . 1·40 10
1441 20r. brown . . . . . . 10·00 10
1442 50r. red . . . . 3·50 10
1443 100r. blue . . . . 9·00 40
1444 200r. brown . . . . . . 7·00 75

299 Nurse taking Oath **300** Narcissus

1966. Nurses' Day.
1445 **299** 5r. blue and deep blue 25 15
1446 5r. mauve and red . . . 25 15

1966. New Year Festival.
1447 **300** 50d. multicoloured . . . 15 10
1448 1r. multicoloured 15 10
See also Nos. 1530/3.

301 Oil Rigs

1966. Inauguration of Six New Oil Companies in Persian Gulf.
1449 **301** 14r. black, purple & blue 70 20

302 Radar Aerial

1966. C.E.N.T.O. (Iran, Pakistan and Turkey) Telecommunications Organization.
1450 **302** 2r. green 15 10
1451 – 4r. orange and blue . . . 15 10
1452 – 6r. grey and purple . . . 25 10
1453 – 8r. indigo and blue . . . 35 10
1454 – 10r. brown and ochre . . 45 30
DESIGNS—VERT: 4r. Aerial and radio "waves"; 6r. "CENTO" and emblem; 8r. Emblem and "waves"; 10r. Bowl aerial and "waves".

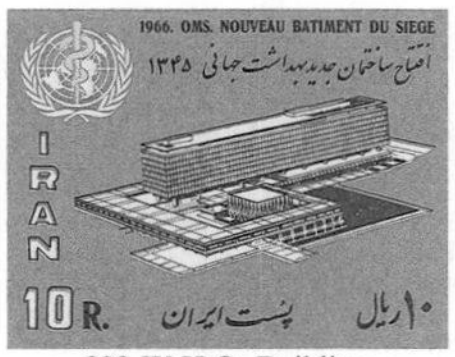

303 W.H.O. Building

1966. Inaug of W.H.O. Headquarters, Geneva.
1455 **303** 10r. black, blue & yellow 35 25

304 Globe Emblem and Motto

1966. Conference of International Women's Council, Teheran.
1456 **304** 6r. multicoloured 20 10
1457 8r. multicoloured 30 15

305 U.N.E.S.C.O. Emblem

1966. Air. 20th Anniv of U.N.E.S.C.O.
1458 **305** 14r. multicoloured . . . 75 30

306 Ruins of Persepolis, Map and Globe

1966. Int Iranology Congress, Teheran.
1459 **306** 14r. multicoloured . . . 50 15

307 Medical Emblem

1966. 15th Medical Congress, Teheran.
1460 **307** 4r. gold, blue & ultram 30 10

308 Parliament Gateway

1966. 55th Interparliamentary Union Conference, Teheran.
1461 **308** 6r. green, blue and red 25 10
1462 – 8r. green, blue and mauve 25 15
DESIGN: 8r. Senate Building.

309 President Sunay

1966. Visit of President of Turkey.
1463 **309** 6r. brown and violet . . 30 10

1966. Mehregan Festival. Plaque design similar to T **287** but vert (30 × 40 mm).
1464 6r. brown and bistre 25 10

310 Farmers

1966. Rural Courts of Justice.
1465 **310** 5r. brown and bistre . . 35 25

311 U.N. Emblem

1966. U.N. Day and 21st Anniv of U.N.O.
1466 **311** 6r. brown and black . . 20 10

312 Crown Prince **313** I.W.O. Emblem

1966. Children's Day.
1467 **312** 1r. blue 30 10
1468 2r. violet 30 10

1966. Iranian Women's Organization.
1469 **313** 5r. blue, black and gold 15 10

314 Strip of Film

1966. 1st Children's Film Festival, Teheran.
1470 **314** 4r. black, purple & violet 30 10

315 Counting on the Fingers **316** Cover of Book

1966. National Census.
1471 **315** 6r. brown and grey . . . 30 10

1966. Book Week.
1472 **316** 8r. brown, ochre and blue 20 15

317 Riza Shah Pahlavi

1966. Riza Shah Pahlavi Commemoration.
1473 **317** 1r. brown 60 10
1474 1r. blue 60 10
1475 – 2r. blue 60 10
1476 – 2r. green 60 10
Nos. 1475/6 show Riza Shah Pahlavi bare-headed.

318 E.R.O.P.A. Emblem and Map

1966. 4th General Assembly of Public Administrators Organization (E.R.O.P.A.).
1477 **318** 8r. brown and green . . 30 15

319 Shah with Farmers

1967. 5th Anniv of Land Reform Laws.
1485 **319** 6r. brown, yellow & bis 30 10

320 Torch and Stars

1967. 4th Anniv of Shah's White Revolution.
1486 **320** 2r. multicoloured 45 10
1487 – 6r. multicoloured 60 15
DESIGN: 6r. Shah acknowledging greetings.

321 Golden "Bull"

1967. Museum Week. Multicoloured.
1488 3r. Type **321** 20 10
1489 5r. Golden "leopard" . . . 25 15
1490 8r. Capital with rams' heads 60 25

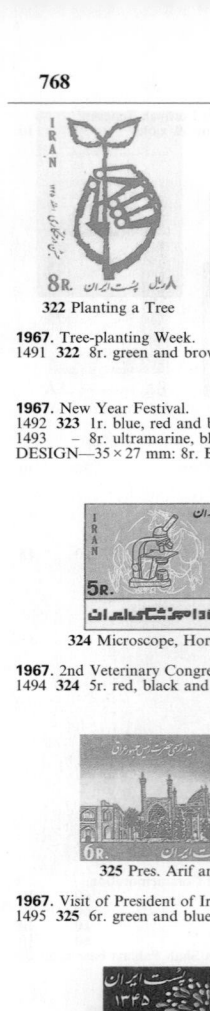

322 Planting a Tree

323 Goldfish

1967. Tree-planting Week.
1491 **322** 8r. green and brown . . 35 10

1967. New Year Festival.
1492 **323** 1r. blue, red and brown 10 10
1493 – 8r. ultramarine, bl & red 1·25 30
DESIGN—35 × 27 mm: 8r. Barn swallows.

324 Microscope, Horses and Emblem

1967. 2nd Veterinary Congress.
1494 **324** 5r. red, black and grey 20 10

325 Pres. Arif and Mosques

1967. Visit of President of Iraq.
1495 **325** 6r. green and blue . . . 30 10

326 U.N. Emblem and Fireworks

1967. U.N. Stamp Day.
1496 **326** 5r. multicoloured 30 10

327 Map showing Pipeline Routes

1967. Nationalization of Oil Industry.
1497 **327** 6r. multicoloured 60 15

328 Fencing

1967. Int Youth Fencing Championships, Teheran.
1498 **328** 5r. yellow and violet . . 30 10

329 Shah and King Bhumibol

1967. Visit of King of Thailand.
1499 **329** 6r. brown and light brown 40 20

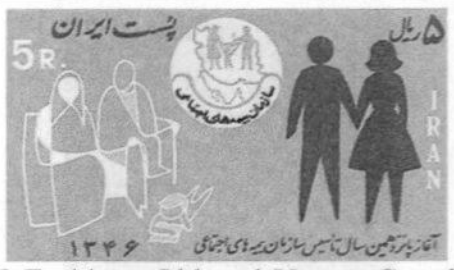

330 Emblem, Old and Young Couples

1967. 15th Anniv of Social Insurance Scheme.
1500 **330** 5r. blue and bistre . . . 20 10

331 Skiing

1967. Olympic Committee Meeting, Teheran.
1501 **331** 3r. brown and black . . 15 10
1502 – 6r. multicoloured 15 10
1503 – 8r. brown and blue . . . 25 15
DESIGNS: 6r. Olympic "shield"; 8r. Wrestling.

332 "LIONS" and Lions Head

1967. 50th Anniv of Lions International. Mult.
1504 3r. Type **332** 15 10
1505 7r. Lions emblem (36 × 42 mm) 40 15

333 President Stoica

1967. Visit of President of Rumania.
1506 **333** 6r. blue and orange . . . 25 10

334 I.T.Y. Emblem

1967. International Tourist Year.
1507 **334** 3r. blue and red 10 10

335 Iranian Pavilion

337 Globe and Schoolchildren

336 First Persian Stamp

1967. World Fair, Montreal.
1508 **335** 4r. red, gold and brown 10 10
1509 10r. brown, gold and red 20 10

1967. Stamp Centenary.
1510 **336** 6r. purple, blue & lt blue 20 10
1511 8r. purple, myrtle & green 25 10

1967. Campaign Against Illiteracy.
1512 **337** 3r. violet and blue . . . 15 10
1513 5r. brown and yellow . . 15 10

338 "Musician"

339 "Helping Hand"

1967. International Musical Education in Oriental Countries Conference, Teheran.
1514 **338** 14r. purple and brown 45 20

1967. 1st "S.O.S." Children's Village in Iran.
1515 **339** 8r. brown and yellow . . 1·60 60

340 Winged Ram

341 U.N. Emblem

1967. 1st Shiraz Arts Festival, Persepolis.
1516 **340** 8r. brown and bistre . . 35 10

1967. United Nations Day.
1517 **341** 6r. blue and bistre . . . 20 10

342 Shah Mohammed Riza Pahlavi and Empress Farah

343 Crown Prince Riza

1967. Coronation of Shah and Empress Farah.
1518 **342** 2r. brown, blue and silver 35 10
1519 10r. violet, blue and silver 70 25
1520 14r. multicoloured . . . 1·10 25

1967. Children's Day.
1521 **343** 2r. violet and silver . . . 15 10
1522 8r. brown and silver . . 40 15

344 Pres. G. Traikov

1967. Visit of President of Bulgaria.
1523 **344** 10r. brown and violet . . 20 10

345 Scout Emblem and Neckerchiefs

1967. Boy Scouts Co-operation Week.
1524 **345** 8r. brown and green . . 40 15

346 "Co-operation" (linked hands)

1967. Co-operation Year.
1525 **346** 6r. multicoloured 20 10

347 Shaikh Sabah

1968. Visit of Shaikh of Kuwait.
1526 **347** 10r. green and blue . . . 25 10

348 Shah and Text of Reform Plan

1968. 5th Anniv of Shah's White Revolution.
1527 **348** 2r. green, sepia and flesh 40 10
1528 8r. violet, green and blue 55 10
1529 14r. brown, blue & mve 80 20

1968. New Year Festival. As T **300**. Mult.
1530 1r. Almond blossom 10 10
1531 2r. Red tulips 10 10
1532 2r. Yellow tulips 15 10
1533 6r. Festival dancer 65 10

349 Oil Technician and Rig

350 W.H.O. Emblem

1968. National Oil Industry.
1534 **349** 14r. black, yellow & green 45 10

1968. 20th Anniv of W.H.O.
1535 **350** 14r. orange, blue & pur 40 10

351 Ancient Chariot (sculpture)

353 Human Rights Emblem

352 Shah and King Hassan

1968. 5th World Congress of Persian Archaeology and Art, Teheran.
1536 **351** 8r. multicoloured 25 10

1968. Visit of King of Morocco.
1537 **352** 6r. violet and flesh . . . 55 15

1968. Human Rights Conference, Teheran.
1538 **353** 8r. red and green 15 10
1539 – 14r. ultramarine and blue 20 15
DESIGN: 14r. As Type **353**, but rearranged, and inscr "INTERNATIONAL CONFERENCE ON HUMAN RIGHTS—TEHERAN 1968".

354 Footballer

355 Oil Refinery

1968. Asian Football Cup Finals, Teheran.
1540 **354** 8r. multicoloured 20 10
1541 10r. multicoloured . . . 40 15

1968. Inauguration of Teheran Oil Refinery.
1542 **355** 14r. multicoloured . . . 55 25

356 Empress Farah in Guides' Uniform
357 Mosquito Emblem

1968. Iranian Girl Guides "Great Camp".
1543 **356** 4r. blue and purple . . . 75 15
1544 6r. brown and red . . . 1·00 25

1968. 8th International Tropical Medicine and Malaria Congresses, Teheran.
1545 **357** 6r. purple and black . . 20 10
1546 14r. green and purple . . 45 15

358 Allegory of Literacy
359 "Horseman" and "Flower"

1968. World Illiteracy Eradication Campaign Day.
1547 **358** 6r. blue, brown and lilac 15 10
1548 14r. green, brown & yell 30 10

1968. 2nd Shiraz Arts Festival, Persepolis.
1549 **359** 14r. multicoloured . . . 45 15

360 Police Emblem on Map
361 Interpol Emblem

1968. Police Day.
1550 **360** 14r. multicoloured . . . 90 15

1968. 37th Interpol General Assembly.
1551 **361** 10r. purple, black & blue 50 15

362 U.N. Emblem and Dove

1968. United Nations Day.
1552 **362** 14r. ultramarine and blue 35 15

363 Empress Farah

1968. 1st Anniv of Coronation. Mult.
1553 6r. Type **363** . . . . 2·50 1·00
1554 8r. Shah Mohammed Riza Pahlavi . . . . 2·50 1·00
1555 10r. Family group . . . . . 2·50 1·00

364 Imperial Crown and Bulls' Heads Capital (festival emblem)
365 "Landscape"

1968. National Festival of Art and Culture, Teheran.
1556 **364** 14r. multicoloured . . . 45 15

1968. Children's Day. Children's Paintings. Multicoloured.
1557 2r. Type **365** 10 10
1558 3r. "Boat and House" (35 × 29 mm) 15 10
1559 5r. "Flowers" (35 × 29 mm) 20 10

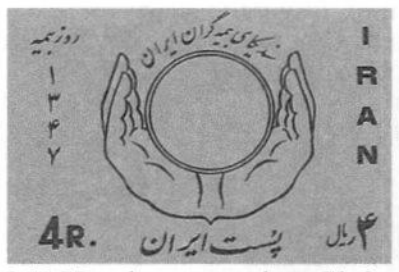
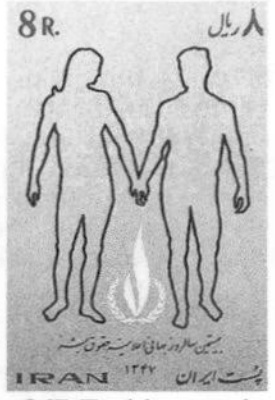

366 Hands supporting Globe
367 Emblem and Human Figures

1968. Insurance Day.
1560 **366** 4r. blue and grey 10 10
1561 – 5r. multicoloured 20 10
1562 – 8r. multicoloured 15 10
1563 – 10r. multicoloured . . . 75 20
DESIGNS: 5r. Factory aflame ("Fire risk"); 8r. Urban workers ("Life"); 10r. Insurance Institute emblem and transport ("Travel insurance").

1968. 20th Anniv of Declaration of Human Rights.
1564 **367** 8r. purple, ultram & bl 20 10

368 Justice, Construction Corps and Medical Corps

1969. 6th Anniv of Shah's White Revolution. Each green, brown and lilac.
1565 2r. Type **368** 30 10
1566 4r. Working conditions, civil engineering and irrigation 40 15
1567 6r. Land reform, nationalization of forests and sale of shares to workers 50 20
1568 8r. Profit-sharing, votes for women and education corps 80 20
Nos. 1565/8, each showing symbols of three of the reforms, were issued, se-tenant, forming a composite design of a rosette.

369 Shah Mohammed Riza Pahlavi

1969. 10,000th Day of Shah's Reign.
1569 **369** 6r. brown, red and blue 55 15

370 Eurasian Goldfinch

1969. New Year Festival. Multicoloured.
1570 1r. Type **370** 35 10
1571 2r. Common pheasant . . . 55 10
1572 8r. Roses 70 15

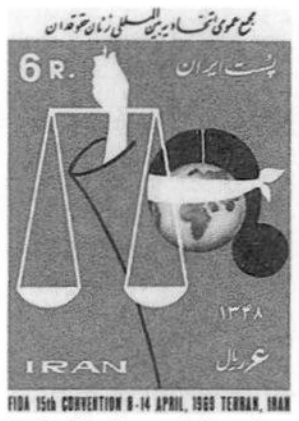

371 Scales of Justice and "Blindfold Globe"
372 Symbols of I.L.O.

1969. 15th FIDA (Female Jurists) Convention, Teheran.
1573 **371** 6r. black and blue . . . 30 10

1969. 50th Anniv of I.L.O.
1574 **372** 10r. violet and blue . . . 30 10

373 Wrestling "Throw"

1969. 3rd Aryamehr Cup International Wrestling Championships.
1575 **373** 10r. multicoloured . . . 40 10

374 "Flower and Birds"
375 Mask and Cord

1969. World Handicrafts Day.
1576 **374** 10r. multicoloured . . . 40 10

1969. "Philia 1969". Outdoor Course for Scout Patrol Leaders.
1577 **375** 6r. multicoloured 40 15

376 Mughal Miniature (Pakistan)

1969. 5th Anniv of Regional co-operation for Development. Miniatures. Multicoloured.
1578 25r. Type **376** . . . . . . 1·10 50
1579 25r. "Kneeling Figure" (Safavi, Iran) . . . . . . 1·10 50
1580 25r. "Suleiman the Magnificent and Court" (Ottoman, Turkey) . . . 1·10 50

377 Astronauts on Moon

1969. 1st Man on the Moon.
1581 **377** 24r. brown, blue and buff . . . . 2·50 85

378 "Education" (quotation from Shah's Declaration)

1969. Education Reform Conference.
1582 **378** 10r. red, green and buff 40 20

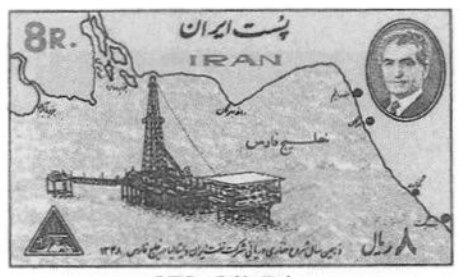

379 Oil Rig

1969. 10th Anniv of Iranian–Italian Marine Drilling Project.
1583 **379** 8r. multicoloured 70 15

380 Festival Emblem
381 Thumb-print and Cross

1969. 3rd Shiraz Arts Festival.
1584 **380** 6r. multicoloured 15 10
1585 8r. multicoloured 25 10

1969. International Anti-illiteracy Campaign.
1586 **381** 4r. multicoloured 20 10

382 Shah, Persepolis and U.P.U. Emblem (½-size illustration)

1969. 16th U.P.U. Congress, Tokyo.
1587 **382** 10r. multicoloured . . . 65 20
1588 14r. multicoloured . . . 1·60 30

383 Fair Emblem
384 "Justice"

1969. 2nd International Asian Trade Fair, Teheran. Multicoloured.
1589 8r. Type **383** 15 10
1590 14r. As T **383**, but inscr "ASIA 69" 20 10
1591 20r. Emblem and sections of globe (horiz) 50 20

1969. Rural Courts of Justice Day.
1592 **384** 8r. brown and green . . 30 10

385 U.N. Emblem
386 Festival Emblem

1969. 25th Anniv of United Nations Day.
1593 **385** 2r. blue and pale blue . . 15 10

1969. National Festival of Art and Culture, Teheran.
1594 **386** 2r. multicoloured 35 10

387 "In the Garden"

1969. Children's Week. Children's Drawings. Multicoloured.

1595		1r. Type **387**	15	10
1596		2r. "Three Children" (horiz)	20	10
1597		5r. "Mealtime" (horiz)	50	15

388 Global Emblem

1969. National Association of Parents and Teachers Congress, Teheran.

1598	**388**	8r. brown and blue	20	10

389 Earth Station

391 Mahatma Gandhi

(**390**)

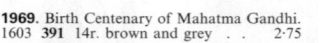

1969. Opening of 1st Iranian Satellite Communications Earth Station.

1599	**389**	6r. brown and ochre	20	10

1969. Air. 50th Anniv of 1st England–Australia Flight. No. 1281 surch as T **390**.

1600	**229**	4r. on 14r.+6r.	1·10	45
1601		10r. on 14r.+6r.	1·10	45
1602		14r. on 14r.+6r.	1·10	45

1969. Birth Centenary of Mahatma Gandhi.

1603	**391**	14r. brown and grey	2·75	70

392 Globe and Flags

1969. 50th Anniv of League of Red Cross Societies. Multicoloured.

1604		2r. Type **392**	30	10
1605		6r. Red Cross emblems on Globe	40	15

393 Shah and Reform Symbols

1970. 7th Anniv of Shah's White Revolution.

1606	**393**	1r. multicoloured	55	15
1607		2r. multicoloured	65	15

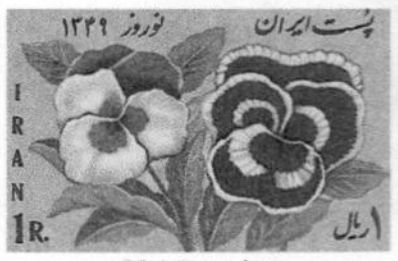
394 Pansies

396 "EXPO" Emblem

395 Nationalization Decree

1970. New Year Festival. Multicoloured.

1608		1r. Type **394**	15	10
1609		8r. New Year table (40 × 26 mm)	1·00	20

1970. 20th Anniv of Oil Industry Nationalization. Multicoloured.

1610		2r. Type **395**	50	15
1611		4r. Laying pipeline	70	15
1612		6r. Part of Kharg Island plant	75	15
1613		8r. Ocean terminal, Kharg Island (vert)	1·10	30
1614		10r. Refinery, Teheran	1·10	35

1970. "EXPO 70" World Fair, Osaka, Japan.

1615	**396**	4r. blue and mauve	15	10
1616		10r. violet and blue	35	15

397 Dish Aerial and Satellite

1970. Asian Plan Communications Committee Meeting, Teheran.

1617	**397**	14r. multicoloured	65	20

398 New U.P.U. H.Q.

1970. New U.P.U. Headquarters Building, Berne.

1618	**398**	2r. sepia, mauve & green	20	10
1619		4r. sepia, mauve and lilac	30	10

399 A.P.Y. Emblem

400 Stork carrying Baby

1970. Asian Productivity Year.

1620	**399**	8r. multicoloured	20	10

1970. 50th Anniv of Midwifery School.

1621	**400**	8r. blue and brown	30	15

401 Tomb of Cyrus the Great

1970. 2500th Anniv of Persian Empire (1st issue). Achaemenian Era.

1622	**401**	6r. violet, red and grey	50	15
1623	–	8r. green, black and pink	55	15
1624	–	10r. brown, red & yellow	80	30
1625	–	14r. brown, black & blue	1·40	70

DESIGNS—HORIZ: 10r. Religious ceremony (Median bas-relief); 14r. Achaemenian officers (bas-relief). VERT: 8r. Columns, Palace of Apadana.

See also Nos. 1629/32, 1633/6, 1640/2, 1658/61, 1664/7, 1674/7 and 1679/82.

402 Saiful Malook Lake (Pakistan)

1970. 6th Anniv of Regional Co-operation for Development. Multicoloured.

1626		2r. Type **402**	40	15
1627		2r. Seeyo-Se-Pol Bridge, Isfahan (Iran) (62 × 46 mm)	40	15
1628		2r. View from Fethiye (Turkey)	40	15

1970. 2500th Anniv of Persian Empire (2nd issue). Achaemenian Era. Designs as T **401**.

1629		2r. gold, deep green and green	50	15
1630		6r. gold, violet and green	50	20
1631		8r. gold, blue and orange	1·00	30
1632		14r. red, black and blue	1·40	75

DESIGNS—VERT: 2r. Eagle amulet; 6r. "Lion" goblet; 8r. Winged ibex statue. HORIZ: 14r. Tapestry.

1970. 2500th Anniv of Persian Empire (3rd issue). Coins of Sassanid and Parthian Eras. Designs as T **401**. Multicoloured, frames in gold.

1633		1r. Queen Buran dirham	50	15
1634		2r. Mithridates I dirham	55	15
1635		6r. Shapur I dirham	1·00	20
1636		8r. Ardeshir I dirham	1·40	55

405 Candle and Globe Emblem

1970. World Literacy Day.

1637	**405**	1r. multicoloured	10	10
1638		2r. multicoloured	15	10

406 Isfahan Tile

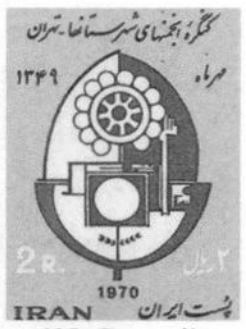
408 Councils Emblem

1970. International Architects' Congress, Isfahan.

1639	**406**	6r. multicoloured	20	15

1970. 2500th Anniv of Persian Empire (4th issue). Achaemenian and Sassanid Eras. Designs as T **401**.

1640		2r. multicoloured	50	15
1641		6r. brown, blue and lilac	1·00	20
1642		8r. green, red and lilac	1·25	30

DESIGNS—VERT: 2r. Sassanid arch and art. HORIZ: 6r. Archaemenian mounted courier; 8r. Seal of Darius I.

1970. 1st Congress of Provincial Councils.

1643	**408**	2r. violet and blue	10	10

409 Dove and U.N. Emblem

411 Festival Emblem

410 "1970" and I.A.T.A. Emblem

1970. United Nations Day.

1644	**409**	2r. ultramarine, pur & bl	10	10

1970. Air. 26th International Air Transport Association General Meeting, Teheran.

1645	**410**	14r. multicoloured	2·50	40

1970. National Festival of Art and Culture, Teheran.

1646	**411**	2r. multicoloured	15	10

412 "Goatherd and Goats"

1970. Children's Week. Children's Drawings. Multicoloured.

1647		50d. Type **412**	15	10
1648		1r. "Family picnic"	20	10
1649		2r. "Mosque"	40	10

413 Shah Mohammed Riza Pahlavi

1971. 8th Anniv of Shah's White Revolution.

1650	**413**	2r. multicoloured	20	20

414 Common Shelduck

1971. International Wetland and Waterfowl Conference, Ramsar. Multicoloured.

1651		1r. Type **414**	1·25	25
1652		2r. Ruddy shelduck	1·25	25
1653		8r. Greater flamingo (vert)	2·75	60

415 Riza Shah Pahlavi

1971. 50th Anniv of Rise of Pahlavi Dynasty.

1654	**415**	6r. multicoloured	1·40	30

416 Red Junglefowl

1971. New Year Festival. Birds. Multicoloured.

1655		1r. Type **416**	60	15
1656		2r. Barn swallow at nest	1·50	20
1657		6r. Hoopoe	4·00	60

417 Stone Bull's Head, Persepolis

1971. 2500th Anniv of Persian Empire (5th issue). Age of Cyrus the Great. Multicoloured.
1658 4r. Type **417** 90 15
1659 5r. Winged lion ornament 1·25 15
1660 6r. Persian Archer (bas-relief) . . . . 1·25 20
1661 8r. Imperial audience (bas-relief) . . . . 1·50 30

418 Prisoners' Rehabilitation

1971. Rehabilitation Week.
1662 **418** 6r. multicoloured . . . . 1·00 15
1663 8r. multicoloured . . . . 1·50 15

1971. 2500th Anniv of Persian Empire (6th issue). Art of Ancient Persia. As T **417**.
1664 1r. multicoloured 70 15
1665 2r. black and brown 70 15
1666 2r. brown, black and purple 70 15
1667 10r. black, blue and brown 90 30
DESIGNS—VERT: No. 1664, "Harpist" (mosaic); 1667, Bronze head of Parthian prince. HORIZ: No. 1665, "Shapur I hunting" (ornamental plate); 1666, "Investiture of Ardashir I" (bas-relief).

420 Badshahi Mosque, Lahore (Pakistan)

1971. 7th Anniv of Regional Co-operation for Development. Multicoloured.
1668 2r. Type **420** 30 15
1669 2r. Selimiye Mosque, Edirne, Turkey (vert) 30 15
1670 2r. Chaharbagh School, Isfahan (Iran) (vert) . . . 30 15

421 "Shiraz Arts"

1971. 5th Shiraz Arts Festival, Persepolis.
1671 **421** 2r. multicoloured 30 15

422 "Book-reading"

1971. World Literacy Day.
1672 **422** 2r. multicoloured 20 10

423 Kings Abdullah and Hussein II

1971. 50th Anniv of Hashemite Kingdom of Jordan.
1673 **423** 2r. multicoloured 20 10

424 National Steel Foundry

1971. 2500th Anniv of Persian Empire (7th issue). Modern Iran. Multicoloured.
1674 1r. Type **424** 30 15
1675 2r. Shahyad Aryamehr Memorial 65 15
1676 3r. Senate Building, Teheran 65 20
1677 11r. Shah Abbas the Great Dam . . . . 1·25 40

425 Ghatur Railway Bridge

1971. Inaug of Iran–Turkey Railway Link.
1678 **425** 2r. multicoloured . . . . 1·00 10

426 Shah Mohammed Riza Pahlavi

1971. 2500th Anniv of Persian Empire (8th issue). Pahlavi Era. Multicoloured.
1679 1r. Type **426** . . . . 1·40 50
1680 2r. Riza Shah Pahlavi . . . 1·50 50
1681 5r. Proclamation tablet of Cyrus the Great (horiz) 1·60 50
1682 10r. Pahlavi Crown . . . . 3·25 75

427 Racial Equality Year Emblem

428 Shah Mohammed Riza Pahlavi

1971. Racial Equality Year.
1683 **427** 2r. multicoloured 10 10

1971.
1684 **428** 5d. purple 10 10
1685 10d. red 10 10
1686 50d. green 10 10
1687 1r. green 10 10
1688 2r. brown 10 10
1689 6r. green 50 10
1690 8r. violet 90 10
1691 10r. purple 70 10
1692 11r. green . . . . . . 2·00 10
1693 14r. blue . . . . 7·50 10
1694 20r. mauve . . . . . . 5·50 15
1695 50r. ochre . . . . . . 3·25 50
Nos. 1689/95 are larger, 27 × 37 mm.
See also Nos. 1715/26b and 1846/50.

429 "Waiters at a Banquet"

1971. Children's Week. Children's Drawings. Multicoloured.
1696 2r. Type **429** 20 15
1697 2r. "Persepolis Ruins" (vert) 20 15
1698 2r. "Persian Archer" (vert) 20 15

430 U.N.E.S.C.O. Emblem

1971. 25th Anniv of U.N.E.S.C.O.
1699 **430** 6r. blue and purple . . . 30 15

431 Congress Emblem and Livestock

1971. 4th Iranian Veterinary Congress.
1700 **431** 2r. red, black and grey 30 10

432 I.L.O. Emblem and Globe

1971. 7th Asian International Labour Organization Regional Conference, Teheran.
1701 **432** 2r. orange, blue and black 20 10

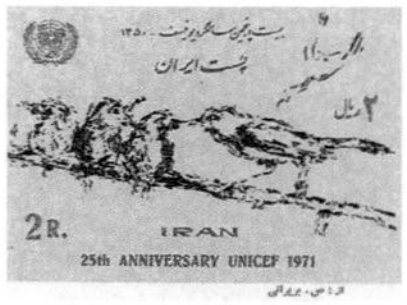

433 Bird feeding Young

1971. 25th Anniv of U.N.I.C.E.F.
1702 **433** 2r. multicoloured 20 10

434 Shah Mohammed Riza Pahlavi

1972. 9th Anniv of Shah's White Revolution.
1703 **434** 2r. multicoloured . . . . 1·00 15

435 Chukar Partridge

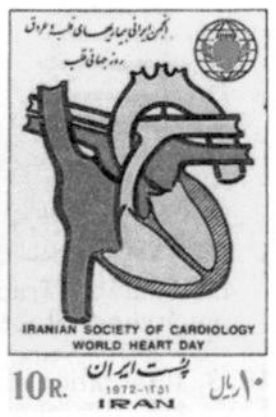

436 Human Heart

1972. New Year Festival. Birds. Multicoloured.
1705 1r. Type **435** 45 15
1706 1r. Pin-tailed sandgrouse . . 45 15
1707 2r. Swee waxbill and red-cheeked cordon-bleu . . . 2·40 20

1972. World Heart Day.
1708 **436** 10r. multicoloured . . . 80 20

437 Winged Ibex Symbol

438 Scarlet Roses

1972. International Film Festival, Teheran.
1709 **437** 6r. gold and blue 70 15
1710 – 8r. multicoloured . . . . 1·25 20
DESIGN: 8r. Symbolic spectrum.

1972. Roses. Multicoloured.
1711 1r. Type **438** 20 10
1712 2r. Yellow roses 50 10
1713 5r. Red rose 75 15

1972. As Nos. 1684/95, but with bistre frames and inscriptions.
1715 **428** 5d. purple 10 10
1716 10d. brown 10 10
1717 50d. green 10 10
1718 1r. green 10 10
1719 2r. brown 40 10
1720 6r. green 30 10
1721 8r. violet 35 15
1722 10r. purple 55 10
1723 11r. blue 70 15
1724 14r. blue . . . . 3·50 20
1725 20r. mauve . . . . . . 7·00 30
1726 50r. blue . . . . 2·50 65
1726a 110r. violet . . . . . . 3·50 75
1726b 200r. black . . . . . . 7·50 3·50
Nos. 1720/26b are larger, 27 × 37 mm.

439 "U.I.T." Emblem

1972. World Telecommunications Day.
1726c **439** 14r. multicoloured . . . 1·50 30

440 "Fisherman" (Cevat Dereli, Turkey)

442 Pens

441 Floral Patterns

1972. 8th Anniv of Regional Co-operation for Development. Paintings. Multicoloured.
1727 5r. Type **440** . . . . 1·00 25
1728 5r. "Iranian Woman" (Behzad, Iran) 90 25
1729 5r. "Will and Power" (A. R. Chughtai, Pakistan) . . . 90 25

1972. 6th Shiraz Arts Festival.
1730 **441** 6r. black, red and green 75 15
1731 8r. black and purple . . 1·00 20

1972. World Literacy Day.
1732 **442** 1r. multicoloured 15 10
1733 2r. multicoloured 20 10

443 "10" and Dental Emblem

444 A.B.U. Emblem within "9"

1972. 10th Annual Congress of Iranian Dental Association.
1734 **443** 1r. multicoloured 20 10
1735 2r. multicoloured 30 10

1972. 9th General Assembly of Asian Broadcasting Union, Teheran.
1736 **444** 6r. multicoloured 50 10
1737 8r. multicoloured 75 20

445 3ch. stamp of 1910 on Cover

447 Communications Emblem

446 Chess

1972. World Stamp Day.
1738 **445** 10r. multicoloured . . . 1·25 30

1972. Olympic Games, Munich. Iranian Sports. Multicoloured.
1739 1r. Type **446** . . . . 1·25 20
1740 2r. Hunting . . . . 1·25 20
1741 3r. Archery . . . . 1·50 20
1742 5r. Horse-racing . . . . . 1·50 20
1743 6r. Polo . . . . 1·50 20
1744 8r. Wrestling . . . . 1·60 25

1972. United Nations Day.
1746 **447** 10r. multicoloured . . . 1·10 25

448 "Children in Garden"

449 Festival Emblem

1972. Children's Week. Children's Drawings. Multicoloured.
1747 2r. Type **448** 35 10
1748 2r. "At the Theatre" 55 10
1749 6r. "Children at play" (horiz) . . . . 1·25 20

1972. National Festival of Art and Culture, Teheran.
1750 **449** 10r. multicoloured . . . 2·75 30

450 Family Planning Emblem

451 Scouting Emblem

1972. Family Planning Campaign.
1751 **450** 1r. multicoloured 15 10
1752 2r. multicoloured 20 10

1972. 20th Anniv of Scouting in Iran.
1753 **451** 2r. multicoloured 40 10

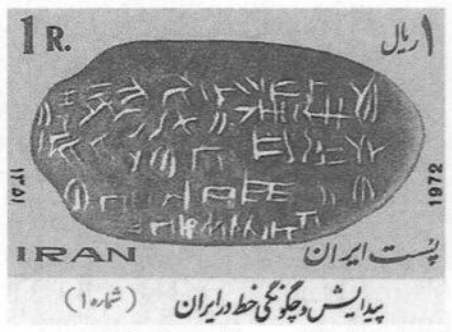

452 Cuneiform Seal

1973. "Origins of Writing" (1st issue). Impressions from ancient seals. Multicoloured. Background colours given.
1754 **452** 1r. blue 40 15
1755 – 1r. yellow 40 15
1756 – 1r. mauve 40 15
1757 – 2r. orange 45 15
1758 – 2r. green 45 15
1759 – 2r. buff 45 15
See also Nos. 1774/9 and 1822/7.

453 Open Books in Space

454 "Twelve Reforms"

1973. International Book Year. Multicoloured.
1760 2r. Type **453** 55 10
1761 6r. Illuminated manuscript 85 15

1973. 10th Anniv of Shah's White Revolution. Multicoloured.
1762 1r. Type **454** 15 10
1763 2r. Pyramid of 12 balls . . . 20 10
1764 6r. As Type **454** but size 71 × 92 mm. . . . . . . 1·00 45

455 Long-spined Seabream ("Sparus spinifer")

457 "Footballers"

456 W.H.O. Emblem

1973. New Year Festival. Fishes. Multicoloured.
1766 1r. Type **455** 55 10
1767 1r. Purple tang ("Acanthurus sp.") . . . 55 10
1768 2r. Two-banded seabream ("Anisotremus sp.") . . . 75 15
1769 2r. Sergeant major ("Abdufef") 75 15
1770 2r. Black-spotted snapper ("Lutyanus fulniflamma") 75 15

1973. 25th Anniv of W.H.O.
1771 **456** 10r. multicoloured . . . 80 20

1973. 15th Asian Youth Football Tournament, Teheran.
1772 **457** 14r. multicoloured . . . 1·00 25

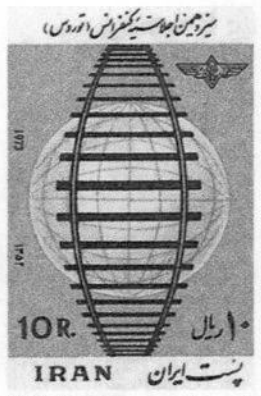

458 Railway Track encircling Globe

459 Ancient Aryan Script

1973. International Railway Conference, Teheran.
1773 **458** 10r. blue, black & mauve 1·25 20

1973. "Origins of Writing". Multicoloured.
1774 1r. Type **459** 25 15
1775 1r. Achaemenian priest and text 25 15
1776 1r. Kharochtani tablet . . . 25 15
1777 2r. Parthian medallion (Arsacid) 45 15
1778 2r. Parthian coin (Mianeh) 45 15
1779 2r. Gachtak inscribed medallion (Dabireh) . . . 45 15

460 Orchid

461 Carved Head, Tomb of Antiochus I (Turkey)

1973. Flowers. Multicoloured.
1780 1r. Type **460** 20 10
1781 2r. Hyacinth 30 10
1782 6r. Wild rose 90 30

1973. 9th Anniv of Regional Co-operation for Development. Multicoloured.
1783 2r. Type **461** 30 15
1784 2r. Statue, Lut excavations (Iran) 30 15
1785 2r. Street in Moenjodaro (Pakistan) 30 15

462 Shah and Oil Installations

463 Soldiers and "Sun"

1973. Full Independence for Iranian Oil Industry.
1786 **462** 5r. black and blue . . . 90 20

1973. 20th Anniv of Gen. Zahedi's Uprising.
1787 **463** 2r. multicoloured 20 10

464 Sportswomen and Globe

1973. 7th International Women's Congress on Physical Education and Sport, Teheran.
1788 **464** 2r. multicoloured (blue background) 20 10
1789 2r. multicoloured (green background) 20 10

465 Festival Poster

467 Wrestling

466 Shahyad Monument and Rainbow

1973. 7th Shiraz Arts Festival.
1790 **465** 1r. multicoloured 15 10
1791 5r. multicoloured 20 15

1973. Cent of World Meteorological Organization.
1792 **466** 5r. multicoloured 60 15

1973. World Wrestling Championships, Teheran.
1793 **467** 6r. multicoloured 55 10

468 Alphabetic "Sun"

469 Globe wearing Earphones

1973. World Literacy Day.
1794 **468** 2r. multicoloured 15 10

1973. Int Audio-visual Exhibition, Teheran.
1795 **469** 10r. multicoloured . . . 45 15

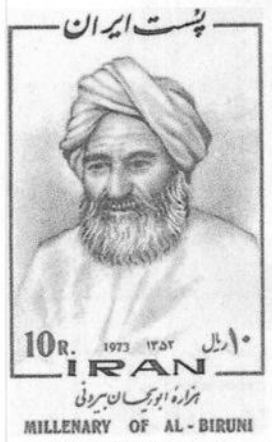

470 Al-Biruni

472 Crown Prince Cup

471 C.I.S.M. Badge and Emblem

1973. Birth Millenary of Abu al-Rayhan al-Biruni (mathematician and philosopher).
1796 **470** 10r. black and brown . . 80 20

1973. 25th Anniv of International Military Sports Council (C.I.S.M.)
1797 **471** 8r. multicoloured 30 15

1973. Crown Prince Cup Football Championship.
1798 **472** 2r. brown, black and lilac 15 10

473 Interpol Emblem

475 U.P.U. Emblem, Post-horn and Letter

474 Curves on Globe

1973. 50th Anniv of International Criminal Police Organization (Interpol).
1799 **473** 2r. multicoloured 30 10

1973. 25th Anniv of World Mental Health Federation.
1800 **474** 10r. multicoloured . . . 50 15

1973. World Post Day.
1801 **475** 6r. orange and blue . . . 30 10

476 Emblems within Honeycomb

477 Festival Emblem and "People"

1973. 5th Anniv of United Nations Volunteers.
1802 **476** 2r. multicoloured (brown background) 10 10
1803 2r. multicoloured (green background) 10 10

1973. National Festival of Art and Culture, Teheran.
1804 **477** 2r. multicoloured 20 10

478 Bosphorus Bridge

1973. 50th Anniv of Turkish Republic. Mult.
1805 2r. Type **478** 50 10
1806 8r. Meeting of Kemal Ataturk and Reza Shah Pahlavi 60 20

479 "House and Garden"

481 Cylinder of Cyrus and Red Cross Emblems

480 Ear of Grain and Cow

1973. Children's Week. Children's Drawings. Multicoloured.
1807 2r. Type **479** 25 15
1808 2r. "Collecting Fruit" . . . 25 15
1809 2r. "Caravan" (horiz) . . . 25 15

1973. 10th Anniv of World Food Programme.
1810 **480** 10r. multicoloured . . . 75 15

1973. 22nd Int Red Cross Conference, Teheran.
1811 **481** 6r. multicoloured 35 10

482 IATA Emblem

483 Emblem, Film and Flags

1973. Tourist Managers Congress, Teheran.
1812 **482** 10r. multicoloured . . . 35 15

1973. International Film Festival, Teheran.
1813 **483** 2r. multicoloured 20 10

484 Flame Emblem

485 Harp Emblem

1973. 25th Anniv of Declaration of Human Rights.
1814 **484** 8r. multicoloured 30 10

1973. "Art of Music" Festival.
1815 **485** 10r. red, green and black 40 15
1816 – 10r. ultram, bl & pur . . 40 15
DESIGN: No. 1816, Musical symbols.

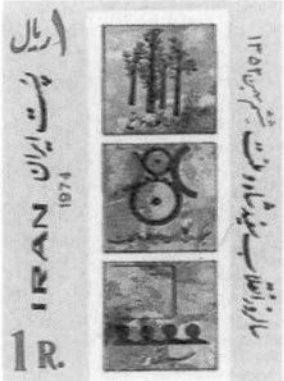
486 Reform Symbols

1974. 11th Anniv of Shah's White Revolution. Multicoloured.
1817 1r. Type **486** 20 15
1818 1r. Tractor, factory in cogwheel, women and parliament gate 20 15
1819 2r. Girders, hose and worker 20 15
1820 2r. Rod of Aesculapius, scales and road passing house 20 15

487 Pir Amooz Ketabaty Script

1974. "Origins of Writing" (3rd issue). Multicoloured.
1822 1r. Din Dabireh Avesta . . 40 15
1823 1r. Mo Eghely Ketabaty . . 40 15
1824 1r. Type **487** 40 15
1825 2r. Pir Amooz, Naskh style 40 15
1826 2r. Pir Amooz, decorative 40 15
1827 2r. Pir Amooz, decorative and architectural 40 15

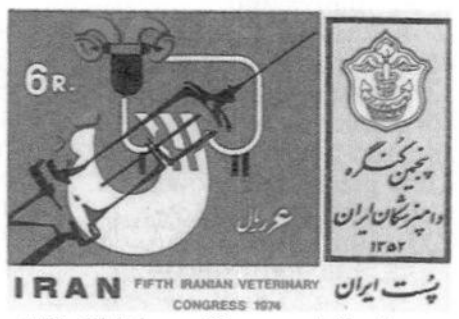
488 Chicken, Cow and Syringe

1974. 5th Iranian Veterinary Congress.
1828 **488** 6r. multicoloured 40 15

490 Scarce Swallowtail

491 Mevlana

1974. Nawrooz and Spring Festivals. Butterflies. Multicoloured, background colours given.
1841 **490** 1r. mauve 30 10
1842 – 1r. purple 30 10
1843 – 2r. green 65 10
1844 – 2r. brown 65 10
1845 – 2r. blue 65 10
DESIGNS: No. 1842, Swallowtail; 1843, Peacock; 1844, Painted lady; 1845, Cardinal.

1974. As Nos. 1684/95, but colours changed.
1846 **428** 50d. blue and orange . . 20 10
1847 1r. blue and green . . . 25 10
1848 2r. blue and red 40 10
1849 10r. blue and green . . . 4·50 10
1850 20r. blue and mauve . . 2·75 20
Nos. 1849/50 are larger, 27 × 37 mm.

1974. 700th Death Anniv of Jalal-udin Mevlana (poet).
1851 **491** 2r. multicoloured 20 10

492 Palace of Forty Columns, Isfahan

1974. 9th Near- and Middle-East Medical Congress, Isfahan.
1852 **492** 10r. multicoloured . . . 40 15

493 Asiatic Wild Ass

494 Gymnastics

1974. International Game and Wild Life Protection Congress, Teheran. Multicoloured.
1853 1r. Type **493** 20 15
1854 2r. Great bustard 40 10
1855 6r. Fawn and fallow deer . . 45 20
1856 8r. Caucasian black grouse 1·75 20

1974. 7th Asian Games, Teheran (1st series). Multicoloured.
1857 1r. Type **494** 15 10
1858 1r. Table tennis 20 10
1859 2r. Boxing 50 10
1860 2r. Hurdling 50 10
1861 6r. Weightlifting 70 15
1862 8r. Handball . . . . 1·25 15
See also Nos. 1874/9, 1890/3 and 1909.

495 Lion of St. Mark's

1974. U.N.E.S.C.O. "Save Venice" Campaign. Multicoloured.
1863 6r. Type **495** 30 10
1864 8r. Merchants at the Doge's court 65 15

496 Chain Link

497 Shah and Douglas DC-9-80 Super Eighty

1974. Farm Co-operatives' Day.
1865 **496** 2r. multicoloured 15 10

1974. Air.
1866 **497** 4r. black and orange . . 10 10
1867 10r. black and blue . . . 60 15
1868 12r. black and brown . . 70 20
1869 14r. black and green . . 1·00 20
1870 20r. black and mauve . . 1·25 30
1871 50r. black and blue . . . 5·50 80

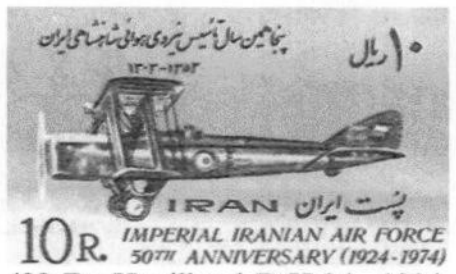
498 De Havilland D.H.9A, 1924

1974. 50th Anniv of Imperial Iranian Air Force. Multicoloured.
1872 10r. Type **498** . . . . . . 1·10 15
1873 10r. McDonnell Douglas F-4D Phantom II fighter of 1974 . . . . 1·10 15

499 Tennis (men's doubles)

500 Mazanderan Costume

1974. 7th Asian Games, Teheran (2nd series). Multicoloured.
1874 1r. Type **499** 15 10
1875 1r. Swimming 15 10
1876 2r. Wrestling 20 10
1877 2r. Hockey 20 10
1878 4r. Volleyball 60 15
1879 10r. Tennis (women's singles) . . . . 1·25 15

1974. Regional Costumes. Multicoloured.
1880 2r. Type **500** 70 20
1881 2r. Bakhtiari 70 20
1882 2r. Turkoman 70 20
1883 2r. Ghasgai 70 20
1884 2r. Kirmanshah (Kurdistan) 70 20
1885 2r. Sanandadj (Kurdistan) 70 20

501 Gold Cup

502 Iranian Carpet

1974. Iranian Football Championships.
1886 **501** 2r. yellow, brown & green 20 10

1974. 10th Anniv of Regional Co-operation for Development. Multicoloured.
1887 2r. Pakistani carpet (diamond) centre 35 15
1888 2r. Turkish carpet (striped) 35 15
1889 2r. Type **502** 35 15

503 Rifle-shooting

504 Persian King

1974. 7th Asian Games, Teheran (3rd series). Multicoloured.
1890 2r. Type **503** 30 15
1891 2r. Fencing 30 15
1892 2r. Football 30 15
1893 2r. Cycling 35 15

1974. 8th Shiraz Arts Festival, Persepolis.
1894 **504** 2r. multicoloured 15 10

506 Petrochemical Works, Khark

1974.
1896 **506** 5d. green and brown . . 10 10
1897 – 10d. orange and brown 25 10
1898 – 50d. green and brown . . 10 10
1899 – 1r. blue and brown . . . 15 10
1900 – 2r. purple and brown . . 20 10
1901 – 6r. brown and blue . . . 15 10
1902 – 8r. turquoise and blue 20 10
1903 – 10r. purple and blue . . 45 10
1904 – 14r. green and blue . . . 11·00 10
1905 – 20r. red and blue . . . 1·00 10
1906 – 50r. violet and blue . . . 1·75 20
DESIGNS—As T **506**: 10d. Railway bridge, Ghatur; 50d. Dam, Farahnaz; 1r. Oil Refinery; 2r. Radio telescope. 37 × 27 mm: 6r. Steelworks, Aryamehr; 8r. Tabriz University; 10r. Shah Abbas Kabir Dam; 14r. Teheran Opera House; 20r. Shahyad Square; 50r. Aryamehr Stadium.
See also Nos. 1939/49.

507 Family within Hands

509 Plan of Hasanlu

508 Aryamehr Stadium, Teheran

1974. State Education and Health Services. Multicoloured.
1907 2r. Type **507** 15 10
1908 2r. Children, pen and book within hands 15 10

1974. Seventh Asian Games, Teheran (4th series).
1909 **508** 6r. multicoloured 40 10

1974. 2nd International Architectural Congress, Shiraz.
1910 **509** 8r. multicoloured 30 10

510 Charioteer

1974. Centenary of U.P.U. Multicoloured.
1911 6r. Type **510** 30 10
1912 14r. U.P.U. emblem and letters 50 20

511 Road through Park

1974. Opening of Farahabad Park, Teheran. Multicoloured.
1913 1r. Type **511** 10 10
1914 2r. Recreation pavilion . . . 15 10

512 Festival Emblem

1974. National Festival of Art and Culture, Teheran.
1915 **512** 2r. multicoloured 15 10

513 Crown Prince in Aircraft

1974. Air. Crown Prince's Birthday.
1916 **513** 14r. multicoloured . . . 45 15

514 Destroyer "Palang"

1974. Navy Day.
1917 **514** 10r. multicoloured . . . 80 20

515 Scarecrow

516 Winged Bull Emblem

1974. Children's Week. Children's Drawings. Multicoloured.
1918 2r. Type **515** 15 10
1919 2r. Girl at spinning wheel (horiz) 15 10
1920 2r. New Year picnic (horiz) 15 10

1974. 3rd International Film Festival, Teheran.
1921 **516** 2r. multicoloured 15 10

517 W.P.Y. Emblem

1974. World Population Year.
1922 **517** 8r. multicoloured 30 10

518 Gold Butterfly Brooch

1974. 14th Wedding Anniv of Shah and Empress Farah. Multicoloured.
1923 6r. Type **518** 15 10
1924 8r. Gold diadem 20 10

519 Angel with Banner

1975. International Women's Year.
1925 **519** 2r. orange, blue and red 15 10

520 Emblems of Agriculture, Industry and the Arts

521 Tourism Year Emblem

1975. 12th Anniv of Shah's White Revolution.
1926 **520** 2r. multicoloured 15 10

1975. South Asia Tourism Year.
1927 **521** 6r. multicoloured 15 10

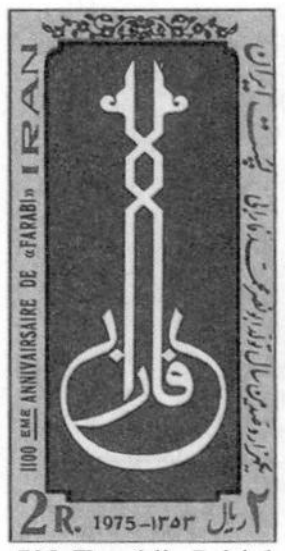
522 Farabi's Initial

523 Ornament

1975. 1100th Birth Anniv of Abu-Nasr al-Farabi (philosopher).
1928 **522** 2r. multicoloured 15 10

1975. New Year Festival. Multicoloured.
1929 1r. Type **523** 15 10
1930 1r. Blossoms and tree . . . 15 10
1931 1r. Arabesque and patterns 15 10

524 Nasser Khosrov

525 Persian Warriors

1975. Birth Millenary of Nasser Khosrov (poet).
1932 **524** 2r. black, red and bistre 15 10

1975. 70th Anniv of Rotary International. Multicoloured.
1933 2r. Type **525** 55 10
1934 10r. Charioteer (horiz) . . . 1·50 15

526 Biochemical Emblem

527 "Co-operative Peoples"

1975. 5th Biochemical Symposium.
1935 **526** 2r. multicoloured 15 10

1975. Co-operatives Day.
1936 **527** 2r. multicoloured 10 10

528 Ancient Signal-beacons

1975. World Telecommunications Day. Mult.
1937 6r. Type **528** 20 10
1938 8r. Telecommunications satellite 30 15

1975. As Nos. 1896/1906 but colours changed.
1939 **506** 5d. orange and turquoise 10 10
1940 – 10d. purple and turquoise 25 10
1941 – 50d. mauve and turquoise 10 10
1942 – 1r. blue and turquoise 20 10
1943 – 2r. brown and turquoise 20 10
1944 – 6r. violet and brown . . 50 10
1945 – 8r. red and brown . . . 70 10
1946 – 10r. green and brown . . 90 15
1947 – 14r. mauve and brown 6·00 25
1948 – 20r. turquoise and brown 1·75 30
1949 – 50r. blue and brown . . 1·75 70

529 "Iran Air" Boeing 747SP

1975. "Iran Air's" First Teheran–New York Flight.
1950 **529** 10r. multicoloured . . . 35 15

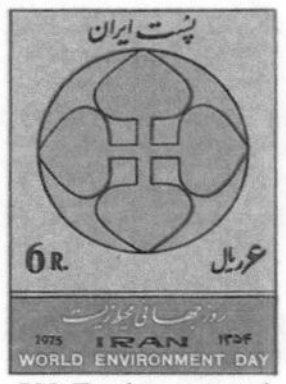

530 Environmental Emblem

532 Party Emblem

531 Dam and Reservoir

1975. World Environment Day.
1951 **530** 6r. multicoloured 20 10

1975. 25th Anniv of International Commission on Irrigation and Drainage.
1952 **531** 10r. multicoloured . . . 25 15

1975. Formation of Resurgence Party.
1953 **532** 2r. multicoloured 10 10

533 Saluting Hand

1975. 2nd National Girl Scout Camp, Teheran.
1954 **533** 2r. multicoloured 20 10

534 Festival Motif

1975. Festival of Tus (honouring poet Firdausi).
1955 **534** 2r. multicoloured 10 10

535 Iranian Tile

1975. 11th Anniv of Regional Co-operation for Development. Multicoloured.
1956 2r. Type **535** 15 10
1957 2r. Pakistani camel-skin vase (vert) 15 10
1958 2r. Turkish porcelain vase (vert) 15 10

536 Parliament Gateway

1975. 70th Anniv of Iranian Constitution.
1959 **536** 10r. multicoloured . . . 25 15

537 Stylized Column

538 Flags over Globe

1975. 9th Shiraz Arts Festival.
1960 **537** 8r. multicoloured 25 15

1975. International Literacy Symposium, Persepolis.
1961 **538** 2r. multicoloured 15 10

539 Stylized Globe

541 Festival Emblem

540 Envelope on World Map

1975. 3rd International Trade Fair, Teheran.
1962 **539** 2r. multicoloured 15 10

1975. World Post Day.
1963 **540** 14r. multicoloured . . . 45 15

1975. National Festival of Art and Culture, Teheran.
1964 **541** 2r. multicoloured 15 10

542 Face within Film

543 "Mother's Face"

1975. International Festival of Children's Films, Teheran.
1965 **542** 6r. multicoloured 15 10

1975. Children's Week. Multicoloured.
1966 2r. Type **543** 15 10
1967 2r. "Young Girl" 15 10
1968 2r. "Our House" (horiz) . . 15 10

544 "Sound Film"

545 Reform Symbols

1975. 4th International Film Festival, Teheran.
1969 **544** 8r. multicoloured 20 15

1976. 13th Anniv of Shah's White Revolution. Multicoloured.
1970 2r. Type **545** 10 10
1971 2r. Symbols representing "People" 10 10
1972 2r. Five reform symbols . . 10 10

546 Motor Cycle Patrol

547 Football Cup

1976. Highway Police Day. Multicoloured.
1973 2r. Type **546** 40 15
1974 6r. Bell Model 205 Iroquois police helicopter (horiz) 85 20

1976. 3rd International Football Cup.
1975 **547** 2r. multicoloured 15 10

548 Candlestick

549 Early and Modern Telephones

1976. New Year. Multicoloured.
1976 1r. Type **548** 15 10
1977 1r. Incense burner 15 10
1978 1r. Rosewater jug 15 10

1976. Telephone Centenary.
1979 **549** 10r. multicoloured . . . 25 15

550 Human Eye

1976. World Health Day.
1980 **550** 6r. multicoloured 30 10

551 Nurse holding Child

1976. 30th Anniv of Social Services Organization. Multicoloured.
1981 2r. Type **551** 15 10
1982 2r. Workshop apprentices 15 10
1983 2r. Handclasp (help the aged) (vert) 15 10

552 Linked Men on Map

553 Sound Waves and Headphones

1976. 10th Anniv of Iranian Co-operative Movement.
1984 **552** 2r. multicoloured 15 10

1976. World Telecommunications Day.
1985 **553** 14r. multicoloured . . . 30 15

554 "Patriotism"

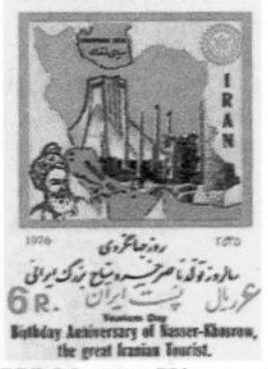
555 Nasser-Khosrow and Landmarks on Map

1976. National Resistance Organization.
1986 **554** 2r. multicoloured 15 10

1976. Tourism Day and Birth Anniv of Nasser-Khosrow "The Great Iranian Tourist".
1987 **555** 6r. multicoloured 15 10

556 Riza Shah Pahlavi

557 Olympic Flame and Emblem

1976. 12th Anniv of Regional Co-operation for Development. Multicoloured.
1988 2r. Type **556** 15 10
1989 6r. Mohammed Ali Jinnah (Pakistan) 25 15
1990 8r. Kemal Ataturk (Turkey) 35 15

1976. Olympic Games, Montreal.
1991 **557** 14r. multicoloured . . . 45 20

558 Riza Shah Pahlavi in Coronation Dress

1976. 50th Anniv of Pahlavi Dynasty. Mult.
1992 2r. Riza Shah Pahlavi and Mohammed Riza Pahlavi (horiz) 20 10
1993 6r. Type **558** 75 15
1994 14r. Mohammed Riza Pahlavi in Coronation dress . . . . 1·00 25

559 Festival Emblem

560 Conference Emblem

1976. 10th Shiraz Arts Festival.
1995 **559** 10r. multicoloured . . . 30 15

1976. 10th Asia–Pacific Scout Conference, Teheran.
1996 **560** 2r. multicoloured 15 10

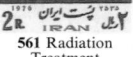

561 Radiation Treatment

562 Target and Presentation to Policewoman

1976. Campaign against Cancer.
1997 **561** 2r. multicoloured 20 10

1976. Police Day.
1998 **562** 2r. multicoloured 30 10

564 U.P.U. Emblem and Iranian Stamp on Envelope

1976. International Post Day.
2000 **564** 10r. multicoloured . . . 30 15

565 Crown Prince presenting Cup

566 Mohammed Riza Pahlavi, Riza Shah Pahlavi and Steam Train

1976. Society of Village Culture Houses.
2001 **565** 6r. multicoloured 20 10

1976. Railway Day.
2002 **566** 8r. multicoloured . . . . 1·25 50

567 Festival Emblem

568 Census Symbols

1976. National Festival of Art and Culture, Teheran.
2003 **567** 14r. multicoloured . . . 35 15

1976. National Census.
2004 **568** 2r. multicoloured 15 10

569 Flowers and Birds

570 Mohammed Ali Jinnah (Quaid-i-Azam)

1976. Children's Week. Multicoloured.
2005 2r. Type **569** 15 10
2006 2r. Flowers and bird 15 10
2007 2r. Flowers and butterfly . . 15 10

1976. Birth Centenary of Mohammed Ali Jinnah (first Governor-General of Pakistan).
2008 **570** 10r. multicoloured . . . 30 15

571 Tractor (Land reform)

572 Man in Guilan Costume

1977. 14th Anniv of Shah's White Revolution. Shah's head and frame in gold.
2009 **571** 5d. green and pink . . . 10 10
2010 – 10d. green and brown . . 10 10
2011 – 50d. blue and orange . . 10 10
2012 – 1r. blue and mauve . . . 10 10
2013 – 2r. green and orange . . 10 10
2014 – 3r. red and blue 10 10
2015 – 5r. lilac and green . . . 20 10
2016 – 6r. purple, brown & black 30 10
2017 – 8r. purple, blue and black 30 10
2018 – 10r. blue, green and black . . . . 1·40 10
2019 – 12r. brown, lilac & black 70 10
2020 – 14r. red, orange and black . . . . 1·00 10
2021 – 20r. orange, grey & black . . . . 2·00 10
2022 – 30r. green, blue and black . . . . 1·75 10
2023 – 50r. red, yellow and black . . . . 3·50 10
2024 – 100r. blue, mauve & blk 3·25 55
2025 – 200r. violet, green & blk 6·50 1·50

DESIGNS—21 × 28 mm: 10d. Trees (Nationalization of forests); 50d. Banknotes (Profit-sharing); 1r. Factory workers (Sale of shares to workers); 2r. Parliament gate (Votes for women); 3r. Teacher and pupils (Education corps); 5r. Doctor examining patient (Medical corps). 36 × 27 mm: 6r. Bulldozer (Civil engineering); 8r. Scales (Justice); 10r. Dam (Irrigation); 12r. Building site (Construction corps); 14r. Clock and receptionist (Working conditions); 20r. Screen and students (Adult literacy); 30r. Sound waves (Telecommunications); 50r. Students and pupils (Education); 100r. Baby in hands (Child care); 200r. Elderly couple (Care of the aged).

1977. New Year Festival. Multicoloured.
2026 1r. Type **572** 10 10
2027 2r. Women in Guilan costume 15 10

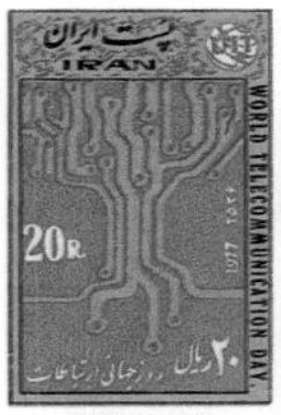
573 Circuit Diagram

574 Riza Shah Dam

1977. World Telecommunications Day.
2028 **573** 20r. multicoloured . . . 55 15

1977. Inauguration of Riza Shah Dam.
2029 **574** 5r. multicoloured 20 10

575 Olympic Rings

1977. Olympic Day.
2030 **575** 14r. multicoloured . . . 35 15

576 Turkish "Human Face" Vase

1977. 13th Anniv of Regional Co-operation for Development. Multicoloured.
2031 5r. Type **576** 20 10
2032 5r. Pakistani toy bullock cart 20 10
2033 5r. Iranian buff earthenware 20 10

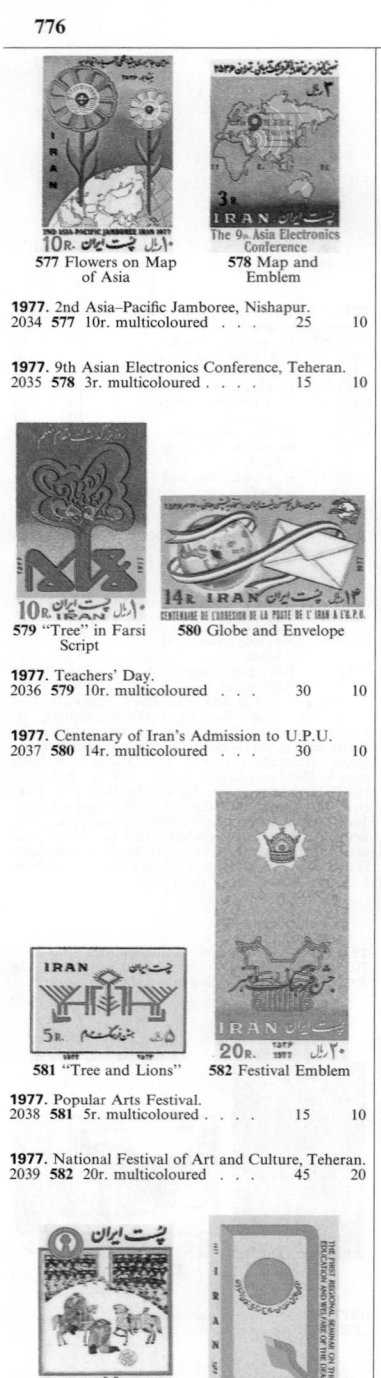

577 Flowers on Map of Asia

578 Map and Emblem

1977. 2nd Asia–Pacific Jamboree, Nishapur.
2034 **577** 10r. multicoloured . . . 25 10

1977. 9th Asian Electronics Conference, Teheran.
2035 **578** 3r. multicoloured 15 10

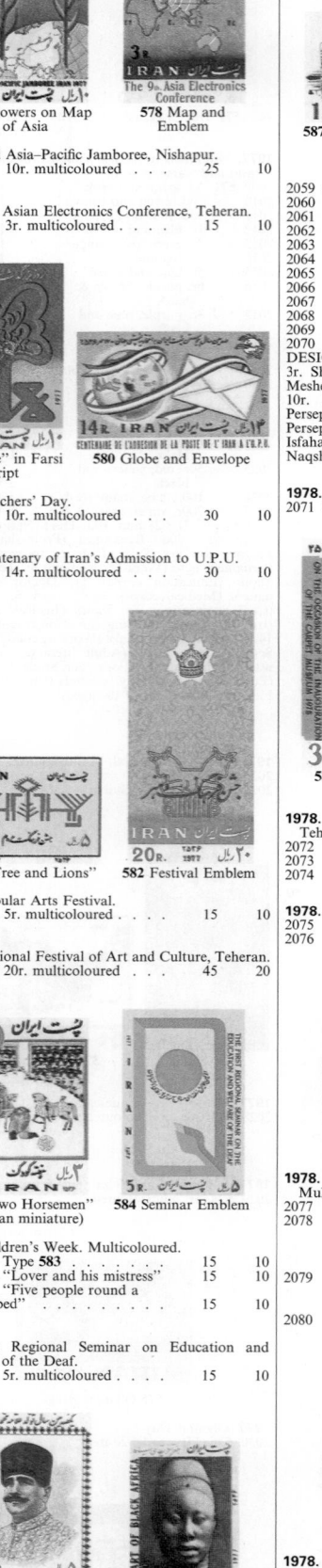

579 "Tree" in Farsi Script

580 Globe and Envelope

1977. Teachers' Day.
2036 **579** 10r. multicoloured . . . 30 10

1977. Centenary of Iran's Admission to U.P.U.
2037 **580** 14r. multicoloured . . . 30 10

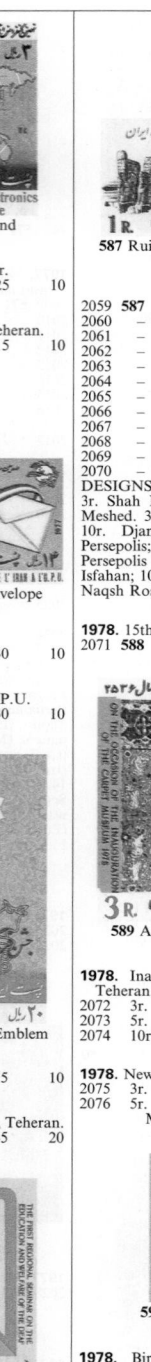

581 "Tree and Lions"

582 Festival Emblem

1977. Popular Arts Festival.
2038 **581** 5r. multicoloured 15 10

1977. National Festival of Art and Culture, Teheran.
2039 **582** 20r. multicoloured . . . 45 20

583 "Two Horsemen" (Persian miniature)

584 Seminar Emblem

1977. Children's Week. Multicoloured.
2040 3r. Type **583** 15 10
2041 3r. "Lover and his mistress" 15 10
2042 3r. "Five people round a bed" 15 10

1977. 1st Regional Seminar on Education and Welfare of the Deaf.
2043 **584** 5r. multicoloured 15 10

585 A. M. Iqbal

586 Bronze Head from Nigeria

1977. Birth Centenary of Allama Mohammad Iqbal (Pakistani poet).
2044 **585** 5r. multicoloured 15 10

1977. "Art of Black Africa" Exhibition, Teheran.
2045 **586** 20r. multicoloured . . . 1·60 30

587 Ruins at Persepolis

588 Mohammed Riza Pahlavi

1978.
2059 **587** 1r. brown and gold . . . 10 10
2060 – 2r. green and gold . . . 20 10
2061 – 3r. purple and gold . . . 30 10
2062 – 5r. green and gold . . . 40 10
2063 – 9r. brown and gold . . . 85 30
2064 – 10r. blue and gold . . . 3·50 35
2065 – 20r. red and gold . . . 1·00 30
2066 – 25r. blue and gold . . . 17·00 2·75
2067 – 30r. red and gold . . . 1·75 35
2068 – 50r. green and gold . . . 2·75 1·75
2069 – 100r. blue and gold . . . 9·00 4·25
2070 – 200r. violet and gold . . 12·00 9·00
DESIGNS: 30 × 23 mm: 2r. Khajou Bridge, Isfahan; 3r. Shah Mosque, Isfahan; 5r. Imam Riza Shrine, Meshed. 35 × 26 mm: 9r. Warrior frieze, Persepolis; 10r. Djameh Mosque, Isfahan; 20r. Bas-relief, Persepolis; 25r. Shaikh Lotfollah Mosque; 30r. Ruins, Persepolis (different); 50r. Ali Ghapou Palace, Isfahan; 100r. Stone relief, Tagh Bastan; 200r. Relief, Naqsh Rostam.

1978. 15th Anniv of Shah's White Revolution.
2071 **588** 20r. multicoloured . . . 1·75 30

589 Animals (carpet)

590 Costume of Mazandera Province

1978. Inauguration of Persian Carpets Museum, Teheran. Multicoloured.
2072 3r. Type **589** 15 10
2073 5r. Court scene 20 10
2074 10r. Floral pattern 30 15

1978. New Year Festival. Multicoloured.
2075 3r. Type **590** 15 10
2076 5r. Woman in costume of Mazandera Province . . . 25 10

591 Riza Shah Pahlavi and Crown Prince inspecting Girls' School

1978. Birth Centenary of Riza Shah Pahlavi. Multicoloured.
2077 3r. Type **591** 15 10
2078 5r. Riza Shah Pahlavi and Crown Prince at inauguration of Trans-Iranian Railway . . . . . 1·25 30
2079 10r. Riza Shah Pahlavi and Crown Prince at Palace of Persepolis 55 15
2080 14r. Shah handing Crown Prince officer's diploma 60 20

592 Satellite and Receiving Station

1978. 10th Anniv of Admission to International Telecommunications Union.
2081 **592** 20r. multicoloured . . . 65 20

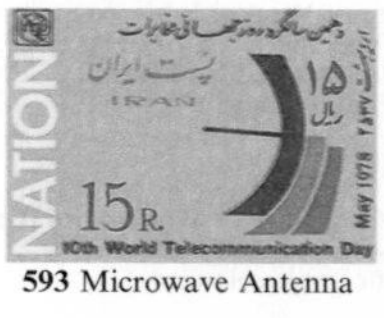

593 Microwave Antenna

1978. World Telecommunications Day.
2082 **593** 15r. multicoloured . . . 55 20

594 Welfare Legion Emblem

595 Pink Roses

1978. 10th Anniv of Universal Welfare Legion.
2083 **594** 10r. multicoloured . . . 20 10

1978. 14th Anniv of Regional Co-operation for Development. Roses. Multicoloured.
2084 5r. Type **595** 15 10
2085 10r. Salmon rose 35 10
2086 15r. Red roses 60 15

596 Rhazes and Pharmaceutical Equipment

1978. Pharmacists' Day.
2087 **596** 5r. multicoloured 20 10

597 Girl Guides and Aryamehr Arch

1978. 23rd World Girl Guides Conference, Teheran.
2088 **597** 5r. multicoloured 20 10

598 Riza Shah Pahlavi

1978. 50th Anniv of Bank Melli Iran. Mult.
2089 3r. Type **598** 40 15
2090 5r. Mohammed Riza Pahlavi 60 15

599 Young Girl and Bird

1978. Children's Week.
2091 **599** 3r. multicoloured 20 10

600 U.P.U. Emblem over Map of Iran

1978. World Post Day.
2092 **600** 14r. multicoloured . . . 50 10

601 Classroom and Communications Equipment

1978. 50th Anniv of Communications Faculty.
2093 **601** 10r. multicoloured . . . 60 10

602 Human Rights Emblem

603 Rose

1978. 30th Anniv of Human Rights Declaration.
2094 **602** 20r. multicoloured . . . 1·60 15

1979. New Year Festival. Multicoloured.
2095 2r. Type **603** 15 10
2096 3r. Man in Khurdistan costume 60 10
2097 5r. Woman in Khurdistan costume 90 15

604 Revolutionary Crowd

1979. Islamic Revolution. Multicoloured.
2098 3r. Type **604** 80 15
2099 5r. Hands holding flower, gun and torch 60 15
2100 10r. Protest march 70 30
2101 20r. Bloodied hands releasing dove (vert) . . . 1·60 30

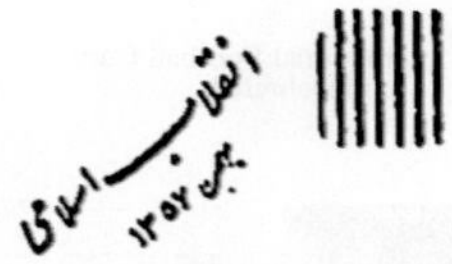

(605)

1979. Designs as T **587** optd with T **605**. (a) Nos. 1945/6.
2102 8r. red and brown . . . . . 1·00 15
2103 10r. green and brown . . . 24·00 85

(b) Nos. 2063/4, 2068/70 and unissued 15r. and 19r. stamps.
2104 9r. brown and gold . . . . 1·00 15
2105 10r. turquoise and gold . . . 30 15
2106 15r. mauve and gold 30 15
2107 19r. green and gold 65 15
2108 50r. green and gold . . . . 2·50 35
2109 100r. blue and gold . . . . 5·00 70
2110 200r. violet and gold . . . . 6·25 1·75
DESIGNS—HORIZ (36 × 26 mm): 15r. Rock carvings, Naqsh Rostam; 19r. Chehel Sotoon Palace, Isfahan.

606 Tulip formed from "Allah" and "Islamic Republic"

1979. Islamic Republic.
2111 **606** 5r. multicoloured 85 15

607 "Iranian Goldsmith" (Kamal el Molk)

1979. 15th Anniv of Regional Co-operation for Development. Paintings. Multicoloured.
2112 5r. Type **607** . . . . 1·50 15
2113 5r. "Turkish Harvest" (Namik Ismail) . . . . . 1·50 15
2114 5r. "Pakistan Village Scene" (Allah Baksh) . . . . 1·50 15

608 "Telecom 79"

1979. 3rd World Telecommunications Exhibition, Geneva.
2115 **608** 20r. gold, black and red 3·50 20

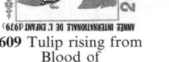

609 Tulip rising from Blood of Revolutionary

610 Persian Rug

1979. International Year of the Child. Children's Paintings. Multicoloured.
2116 2r. Type **609** 40 15
2117 3r. Children greeting the rising sun (vert) 50 15
2118 5r. Children with banners 1·00 15

1979.
2119 **610** 50d. brown and orange 10 10
2120 1r. blue and light blue 10 10
2121 2r. red and yellow . . . 10 10
2122 3r. blue and mauve . . . 10 10
2123 5r. olive and green . . . 15 10
2124 10r. black and pink . . . 25 10
2125 20r. brown and grey . . 35 10
2126 50r. violet and grey . . 85 10
2127 100r. black and green . . 4·00 70
2128 200r. blue and stone . . 3·00 1·50
Nos. 2126/8 are larger, 27 × 37 mm.

611 Globe in Envelope

612 Kashani and Astrolabe

1979. World Post Day.
2134 **611** 10r. multicoloured . . . 1·50 15

1979. 550th Death Anniv of Ghyath-al-din Jamshid Kashani (mathematician and astronomer).
2135 **612** 5r. black and brown . . 85 15

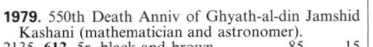

613 Kaaba, Mecca

1980. 1400th Anniv of Hegira (1st issue). Multicoloured.
2136 3r. Type **613** 10 10
2137 5r. Koran and globe (vert) 15 10
2138 10r. Pilgrim and Kaaba . . 30 10
See also Nos. 2148/51.

614 Flag and Revolutionaries

615 Dehkhoda

1980. 1st Anniv of Islamic Revolution. Mult.
2139 1r. Type **614** (28 × 40 mm) 10 10
2432 1r. As No. 2139 but 24 × 35 mm 10 10
2140 3r. Dagger and dripping blood (28 × 40 mm) . . . 10 10
2433 3r. As No. 2140 but 24 × 36 mm 15 15
2141 5r. Open window and rising sun (28 × 40 mm) 15 10
2435 5r. As No. 2141 but 24 × 36 mm 20 20

1980. Birth Centenary of Dehkhoda (compiler, Iranian encyclopedia).
2142 **615** 10r. multicoloured . . . 20 10

616 Female Costume of East Azerbaijan

617 M. Mossadegh

1980. New Year Festival. Multicoloured.
2143 3r. Type **616** 15 10
2144 5r. Male costume of East Azerbaijan 20 10

1980. Birth Centenary of Dr. Mohammed Mossadegh (statesman).
2145 **617** 20r. multicoloured . . . 45 20

618 Morteza Mottahari

619 Telephone

1980. 1st Death Anniv of Prof. Morteza Mottahari.
2146 **618** 10r. black and red . . . 20 10

1980. World Telecommunications Day.
2147 **619** 20r. black, green and red 40 15

620 Mosque Interior

1980. 1400th Anniv of Hegira (2nd issue). Multicoloured.
2148 50d. Type **620** 10 10
2149 1r. Crowd with banner . . . 10 10
2150 3r. Al-Biruni, Farabi and Avicenna 10 10
2151 5r. Mosque and Kaaba . . 15 10

621 Dr. Ali Shariati

622 Kaaba and Banner

1980. Dr. Ali Shariati (educator) Commemoration.
2152 **621** 5r. multicoloured 20 10

1980. Birth Anniv of Hazrat Mehdi (Shi'ite Imam).
2153 **622** 5r. green, red and black 20 10

623 Ayatollah Teleghani

624 O.P.E.C. Emblem and Globe

1980. Ayatollah Teleghani Commemoration.
2154 **623** 5r. multicoloured 35 10

1980. 20th Anniv of Organization of Petroleum Exporting Countries. Multicoloured.
2155 5r. Type **624** 20 10
2156 10r. Figures supporting O.P.E.C. emblem 35 10

625 Hands breaking Star of David around Dome of the Rock

626 Tulip and Feizieh Theological College

1980. "Let us Liberate Jerusalem".
2157 **625** 5r. multicoloured 20 10
2158 20r. multicoloured . . . 45 20

1981. 2nd Anniv of Islamic Revolution. Mult.
2159 3r. Type **626** (dated "1981" at right) 20 10
2434 3r. As No. 2159 but dated at left 15 15
2160 5r. Tulip (in red), drops of blood and "Martyr" in Persian script 25 10
2436 5r. As No. 2160 but orange tulip 20 20
2161 20r. Open tulip (in red) and crest of Republic 50 20
2441 20r. As No. 2161 but orange tulip 50 50

627 Male Costume of Lorestan

628 I.T.U. and W.H.O. Emblems with Ribbons forming Caduceus

1981. New Year Festival. Multicoloured.
2162 5r. Type **627** 20 10
2163 10r. Female costume, Lorestan 40 10

1981. World Telecommunications Day.
2164 **628** 5r. orange, black & green 20 10

630 Militia Training

631 Ayatollah Kashani

1981.
2165 **630** 50d. black and brown . . 10 10
2166 – 1r. purple and green . . 10 10
2167 – 2r. brown and blue . . . 10 10
2168 – 3r. black and green . . . 10 10
2169 – 5r. blue and brown . . . 15 10
2170 – 10r. ultramarine and blue 20 10
2171 – 20r. black and red . . . 50 20
2172 – 50r. black and mauve . . 80 30
2173 – 100r. black and brown 1·50 55
2174 – 200r. blue and black . . 3·50 75
DESIGNS—As Type **630**: 1r. Man and boy at school desk (Literacy campaign); 2r. Digging irrigation ditch. 37 × 27 mm: 3r. Massed prayers; 20r. Woman with rifle; 50r. Worker at lathe; 100r. Pilgrims around Kaaba. 27 × 37 mm: 5r. Revolutionary Guards emblem and crowd; 10r. Arabic tapestry; 200r. Niche in Mosque illuminated by sun.

1981. Birth Centenary of Ayatollah Kashani.
2175 **631** 15r. purple and green . . 35 15

632 Armed Forces

1981. Islamic Iranian Army.
2176 **632** 5r. multicoloured 20 10

633 Carrier Pigeon flying over Gun Barrels

1981. U.P.U. Day.
2177 **633** 20r. black and blue . . . 55 15

634 Inscription

1981. Millenary of "Nabj al-Blagah" (sacred book).
2178 **634** 25r. green, blue and black 50 15

635 Victims of Bomb at Islamic Party's Headquarters

1981. Iranian Bomb and War Victims, Commemoration.
2179 **635** 3r. black and red 15 10
2180 – 5r. brown & deep brown 20 10
2181 – 10r. multicoloured . . . 30 15
DESIGNS: 5r. President Rajai and Prime Minister Bahomar (bomb victims); 10r. Dr. Chamran (killed in Iran–Iraq War).

636 Ayatollah Tabatabaie

637 Hand writing on Board

1981. Death Centenary of Ayatollah Ghazi Tabatabaie.
2182 **636** 5r. brown, green and gold 15 10

1982. Literacy Campaign.
2183 **637** 5r. blue and gold 15 10

638 Text "God is Great" over Map of Iran

639 Banner around Globe

1982. 3rd Anniv of Islamic Revolution. Mult.
2184 5r. Type **638** 15 10
2185 10r. Dove forming tulip . . 25 15
2186 20r. "God is Great" over Globe 45 25

1982. Islamic Unity Week.
2187 **639** 25r. multicoloured . . . 50 15

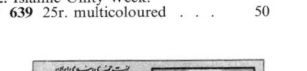

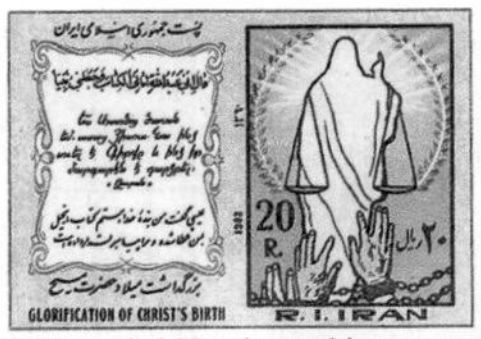

640 Manacled Hands reaching towards Christ

1982. Glorification of Christ's Birth.
2188 **640** 20r. multicoloured . . . 55 20

641 Male Costume of Khuzestan

642 National Flag

1982. New Year Festival. Multicoloured.
2189 3r. Type **641** 10 10
2190 5r. Female costume of Khuzestan 15 10

1982. 3rd Anniv of Islamic Republic.
2191 **642** 30r. black, red and green 50 20

643 Ayatollah Sadr

1982. 2nd Death Anniv of Ayatollah Sadr.
2192 **643** 50r. multicoloured . . . 60 30

644 Ayatollahs Madani and Dastghib

1982. Ayatollahs Sayed Assadollah Madani and Sayed Abdolhossein Dastghib Commemoration.
2193 **644** 50r. red, black and gold 60 30

645 Hand holding Cogwheels

646 Geometric Pattern

1982. Labour Day.
2194 **645** 100r. multicoloured . . . 1·40 50

1982. World Telecommunications Day.
2195 **646** 100r. multicoloured . . . 1·40 50

647 Symbolic Design

648 Rifles and Clenched Fist

1982. Mab'as Festival.
2196 **647** 32r. multicoloured . . . 60 20

1982. 19th Anniv of 1963 Islamic Rising.
2197 **648** 20r. black, red and silver 60 20

649 Lieutenant Islambuli

650 Ayatollah Beheshti

1982. Lieutenant Khaled Islambuli (assassin of Pres. Sadat of Egypt) Commemoration.
2198 **649** 2r. multicoloured 20 10

1982. 1st Death Anniv of Ayatollah Mohammed Hossein Beheshti.
2199 **650** 10r. multicoloured . . . 30 15

651 Soldiers, Tanks and Hand holding Banner

1982. Victims of War against Iraq Commemoration.
2200 **651** 5r. multicoloured 20 10

652 Dome of the Rock

1982. World Jerusalem Day.
2201 **652** 1r. multicoloured 20 10

653 Pilgrims around Kaaba

654 Globe and Letters

1982. Pilgrimage to Mecca.
2202 **653** 10r. multicoloured . . . 25 10

1982. World U.P.U. Day.
2203 **654** 30r. multicoloured . . . 65 20

655 Bloodied Hand releasing Dove

656 Casting Vote

1983. 4th Anniv of Islamic Revolution.
2204 **655** 30r. multicoloured (crowd in brown) . . 60 15
2445 30r. multicoloured (crowd in orange) . . 75 75

1983. 4th Anniv of Islamic Republic.
2205 **656** 10r. red, black and green 30 10

657 "Enlightenment"

658 Microwave Antenna and "83"

1983. Teachers' Day.
2206 **657** 5r. multicoloured 15 10

1983. World Communications Year.
2207 **658** 20r. blue, mauve & brown 55 10

659 Assembly

660 Doves and Crowd

1983. 1st Session of Islamic Consultative Assembly.
2208 **659** 5r. multicoloured 15 10

1983. 20th Anniv of 1963 Islamic Rising.
2209 **660** 10r. multicoloured . . . 25 10

661 Map of Persian Gulf and burning Oil Wells at Nowruz

1983. Ecology Week.
2210 **661** 5r. black, red and blue 30 10

662 Sadooghi

663 Hands holding Rifle over Dome of the Rock

1983. Ayatollah Mohammad Sadooghi Commem.
2211 **662** 20r. black and red . . . 55 10

1983. World Jerusalem Day.
2212 **663** 5r. yellow, brown & blue 20 10

664 Rajai and Bahomar

1983. Government Week (death anniv of Pres. Rajai and Prime Minister Dr. Bahomar).
2213 **664** 3r. orange and blue . . . 20 10

665 Cartridges and Text

666 Stamps and Map of Iran around Globe

1983. War Week.
2214 **665** 5r. green and red 20 10

1983. World U.P.U. Day.
2215 **666** 10r. multicoloured . . . 30 10

667 Esfahani

668 Mirza Kuchik Khan

1983. 4th Death Anniv of Ayatollah Ashrafi Esfahani.
2216 **667** 5r. multicoloured 15 10

1983. Religious and Political Personalities.
2217 – 1r. black and pink . . . 10 10
2218 **668** 2r. black and orange . . 10 10
2219 – 3r. black and blue . . . 10 10
2220 – 5r. black and red . . . 15 10
2221 – 10r. black and green . . 30 10
2222 – 20r. black and purple . . 55 20
2223 – 30r. black and brown . . 75 30
2224 – 50r. black and blue . . . 95 50
2225 – 100r. black and red . . . 2·00 65
2226 – 200r. black and green . . 4·00 1·25
DESIGNS: 1r. Sheikh Mohammed Khiabani; 3r. Seyd Modjtaba Navab Safavi; 5r. Seyd Jamal-ed-Din Assadabadi; 10r. Seyd Hassah Modaress; 20r. Sheikh Fazel Assad Nouri; 30r. Mirza Mohammed Hossein Naieni; 50r. Sheikh Mohammed Hossein Kashef; 100r. Seyd Hassan Shirazi; 200r. Mirza Reza Kermani.

669 Sword severing "Right of Veto" Hand

670 Storming the U.S. Embassy, Hostage and burning American Flag

1983. United Nations Day.
2228 **669** 32r. multicoloured . . . 60 30

1983. 4th Anniv of Storming of United States Embassy.
2229 **670** 28r. multicoloured . . . 40 10

671 Avicenna and Globe

1983. International Medical Seminar, Teheran.
2230 **671** 3r. purple and blue . . . 20 10

672 Young and Old Soldiers

1983. Preparation Day.
2231 **672** 20r. green, black and red 55 20

673 Fist with Gun and Dove

1983. Saddam's Crimes Conference.
2232 **673** 5r. black and mauve . . 20 10

674 Dr. Mohammad Mofatteh

675 Light shining on Globe

1983. 4th Death Anniv of Dr. Mohammed Mofatteh.
2233 **674** 10r. mauve, black & gold 30 10

1983. Mohammed's Birth Anniv.
2234 **675** 5r. blue, brown and green 20 10

676 Tulips and Flag

677 Nurse tending Wounded Soldier

1984. 5th Anniv of Islamic Revolution.
2235 **676** 10r. multicoloured . . . 30 10

1984. Nurses' Day.
2240 **677** 20r. multicoloured . . . 55 20

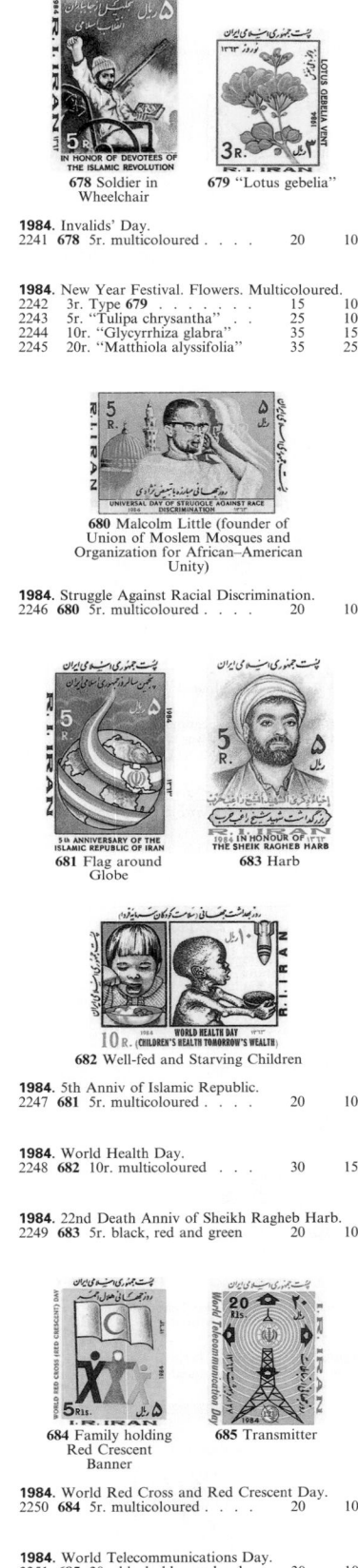

678 Soldier in Wheelchair

679 "Lotus gebelia"

1984. Invalids' Day.
2241 **678** 5r. multicoloured 20 10

1984. New Year Festival. Flowers. Multicoloured.
2242 3r. Type **679** 15 10
2243 5r. "Tulipa chrysantha" . . 25 10
2244 10r. "Glycyrrhiza glabra" 35 15
2245 20r. "Matthiola alyssifolia" 35 25

680 Malcolm Little (founder of Union of Moslem Mosques and Organization for African–American Unity)

1984. Struggle Against Racial Discrimination.
2246 **680** 5r. multicoloured 20 10

681 Flag around Globe

683 Harb

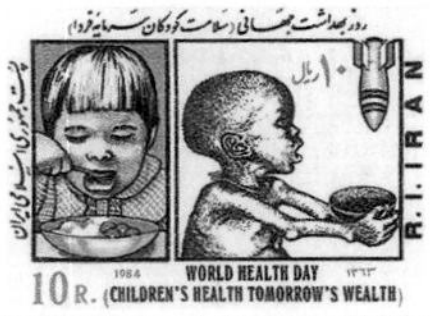

682 Well-fed and Starving Children

1984. 5th Anniv of Islamic Republic.
2247 **681** 5r. multicoloured 20 10

1984. World Health Day.
2248 **682** 10r. multicoloured . . . 30 15

1984. 22nd Death Anniv of Sheikh Ragheb Harb.
2249 **683** 5r. black, red and green 20 10

684 Family holding Red Crescent Banner

685 Transmitter

1984. World Red Cross and Red Crescent Day.
2250 **684** 5r. multicoloured 20 10

1984. World Telecommunications Day.
2251 **685** 20r. black, blue and red 30 10

686 Ghotb

688 Jerusalem, Map of Israel and Koran

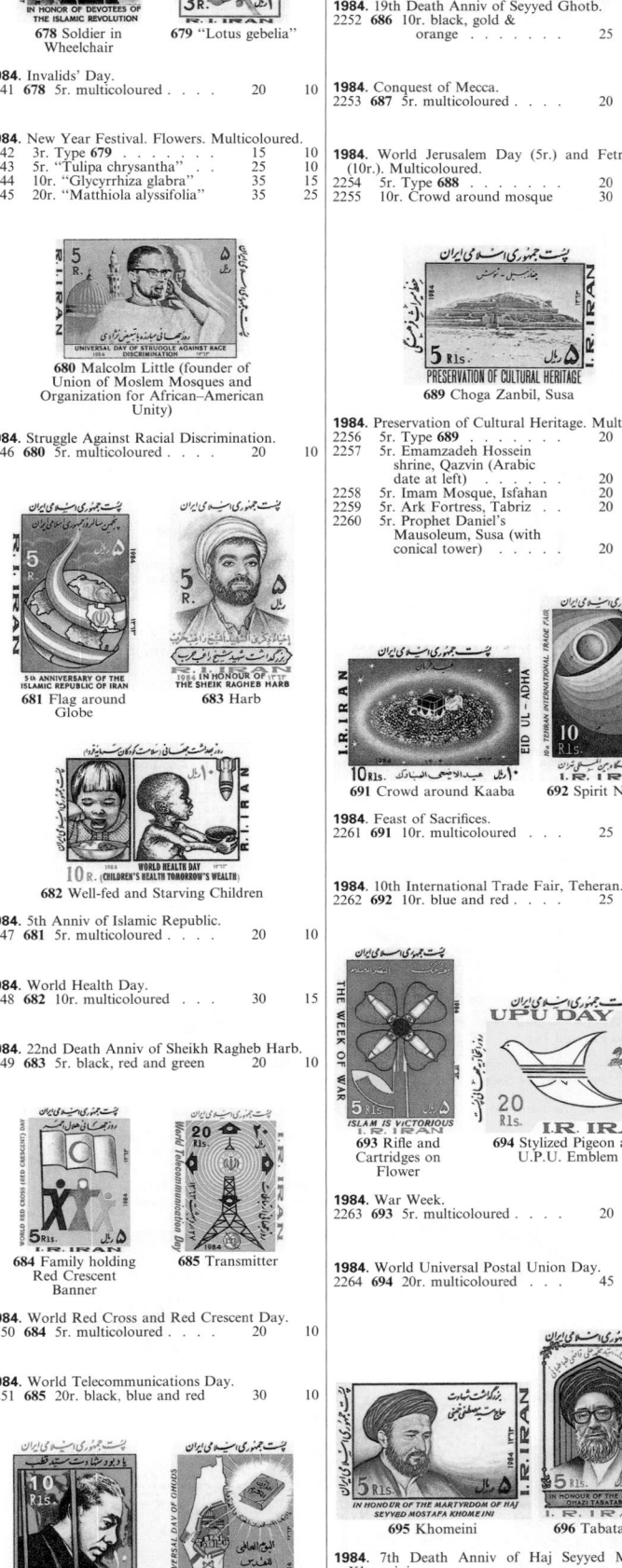

687 Kaaba and Destruction of Images

1984. 19th Death Anniv of Seyyed Ghotb.
2252 **686** 10r. black, gold & orange 25 15

1984. Conquest of Mecca.
2253 **687** 5r. multicoloured 20 10

1984. World Jerusalem Day (5r.) and Fetr Feast (10r.). Multicoloured.
2254 5r. Type **688** 20 10
2255 10r. Crowd around mosque 30 20

689 Choga Zanbil, Susa

1984. Preservation of Cultural Heritage. Mult.
2256 5r. Type **689** 20 10
2257 5r. Emamzadeh Hossein shrine, Qazvin (Arabic date at left) 20 10
2258 5r. Imam Mosque, Isfahan 20 10
2259 5r. Ark Fortress, Tabriz . . 20 10
2260 5r. Prophet Daniel's Mausoleum, Susa (with conical tower) 20 10

691 Crowd around Kaaba

692 Spirit Nebula

1984. Feast of Sacrifices.
2261 **691** 10r. multicoloured . . . 25 15

1984. 10th International Trade Fair, Teheran.
2262 **692** 10r. blue and red 25 15

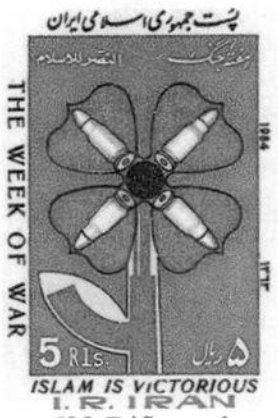

693 Rifle and Cartridges on Flower

694 Stylized Pigeon and U.P.U. Emblem

1984. War Week.
2263 **693** 5r. multicoloured 20 10

1984. World Universal Postal Union Day.
2264 **694** 20r. multicoloured . . . 45 30

695 Khomeini

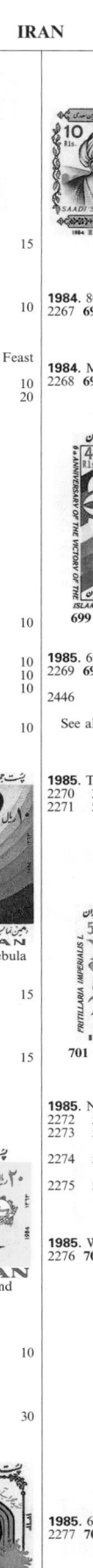

696 Tabatabaie

1984. 7th Death Anniv of Haj Seyyed Mostafa Khomeini.
2265 **695** 5r. multicoloured 20 10

1984. Ghazi Tabatabaie Commemoration.
2266 **696** 5r. black, gold and red 20 10

697 Saadi

698 Clasped Hands, Mosque and Koran

1984. 800th Birth Anniv of Saadi (poet) Congress.
2267 **697** 10r. multicoloured . . . 25 15

1984. Mohammed's Birth Anniv and Unity Week.
2268 **698** 5r. multicoloured 20 10

699 Doves as Petals

700 Sapling and Forest

1985. 6th Anniv of Islamic Revolution (1st issue).
2269 **699** 40r. multicoloured (tulip emblem in red) . . . 60 35
2446 40r. multicoloured (tulip emblem in mauve) . . 75 45
See also No. 2277.

1985. Tree Planting Day. Multicoloured.
2270 3r. Type **700** 15 10
2271 5r. Sapling growing near forest 20 10

701 Crown Imperial ("Fritillaria imperialis")

702 Procession of Women with Flags

1985. New Year Festival. Multicoloured.
2272 5r. Type **701** 20 10
2273 5r. Pilewort ("Ranunculus ficarioides") 20 10
2274 5r. Saffron crocus ("Crocus sativus") 20 10
2275 5r. "Primula heterochroma" 20 10

1985. Women's Day and Birth Anniv of Fatima.
2276 **702** 10r. multicoloured . . . 25 15

703 Tulip and Ballot Box

1985. 6th Anniv of Islamic Republic (2nd issue).
2277 **703** 20r. multicoloured . . . 50 30

704 Koran

1985. Mab'as Festival.
2278 **704** 10r. multicoloured . . . 25 15

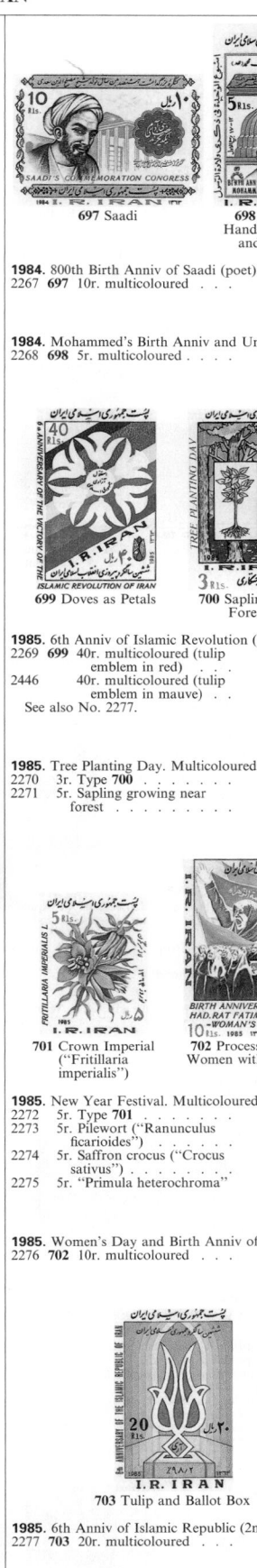

705 Globe, Chain, Banner, Kaaba and Scales

706 I.T.U. Emblem and Telephone Handsets

1985. World Day of the Oppressed.
2279 **705** 5r. multicoloured 20 10

1985. World Telecommunications Day.
2280 **706** 20r. multicoloured . . . 50 30

707 Soldier saluting and Bridge

1985. Liberation of Khorramshahr.
2281 **707** 5r. multicoloured 25 10

708 Fist, Rifles and Qum Theological College

1985. 22nd Anniv of 1963 Islamic Rising.
2282 **708** 10r. multicoloured . . . 25 15

709 Decorated Plates and Vases

1985. World Handicrafts Day.
2283 **709** 20r. multicoloured . . . 50 30

710 Map of Israel and Dome of the Rock

711 Arabic Script

1985. World Jerusalem Day.
2284 **710** 5r. multicoloured 20 10

1985. Fetr Feast.
2285 **711** 5r. blue, red and black 20 10

712 Organization Emblem

1985. 4th Anniv of Islamic Propagation Organization.
2286 **712** 5r. brown, green & black 20 10

713 Abdolhossein Amini and the Koran

714 Pilgrims around Holy Kaaba

1985. Ayatollah Sheikh Abdolhossein Amini (theologian) Commemoration.
2287 **713** 5r. multicoloured 20 10

1985. Pilgrimage to Mecca.
2288 **714** 10r. multicoloured . . . 30 15

715 Two Swords Pattern

716 Revolutionaries and Mosque

1985. Preservation of Cultural History. Ancient Ceramic Plates from Nishabur. Multicoloured.
2289 5r. Type **715** 20 10
2290 5r. Plate with border of Farsi script 20 10
2291 5r. Stylized bird pattern . . 20 10
2292 5r. Four leaves and knot pattern 20 10

1985. 50th Anniv of Rising in Goharshad Mosque, Meshed.
2293 **716** 10r. multicoloured . . . 30 15

717 Health Services

718 Red Tulips dripping Blood

1985. Government and People Week. Multicoloured.
2294 5r. Envelope, crane and mechanical digger 20 10
2295 5r. Factory, cogwheel and ear of wheat 20 10
2296 5r. Type **717** 20 10
2297 5r. Literacy campaign emblem on book 20 10

1985. 7th Anniv of "Bloody Friday" Riots.
2298 **718** 10r. multicoloured . . . 30 15

719 O.P.E.C. Emblem and "25"

720 Dead Iranian

1985. 25th Anniv of Organization of Petroleum Exporting Countries.
2299 **719** 5r. yellow and brown . . 20 10
2300 – 5r. blue and green . . . 20 10
DESIGN: No. 2300, O.P.E.C. emblem and world map.

1985. 5th Anniv of Iran–Iraq War. Multicoloured.
2301 5r. Type **720** 20 10
2302 5r. Dome of mosque and text "Ashura" 20 10
2303 5r. White doves with map of Iran under a hail of bombs 20 10
2304 5r. Oasis and exploding rifle 20 10

721 Symbolic Design

722 Envelopes and Posthorn

1985. Death Millenary of Ash-Sharif Ar-Radi (writer).
2305 **721** 20r. blue, gold & ultram 50 30

1985. World U.P.U. Day.
2306 **722** 20r. multicoloured . . . 50 30

723 Emblem

724 Seedling and Ear of Wheat in Hand

1985. World Standards Day.
2307 **723** 20r. multicoloured . . . 50 30

1985. Agricultural Training and Extension Year.
2308 **724** 5r. multicoloured 20 10

725 Seal of U.S. Embassy

726 Kaaba, Mosque and Clasped Hands

1985. 6th Anniv of Storming of United States Embassy.
2309 **725** 40r. multicoloured . . . 60 30

1985. Mohammed's Birth Anniv and Unity Week.
2310 **726** 10r. multicoloured . . . 30 15

727 Rose growing from Pen Nib and Tulip

728 Profiles and Symbols of Learning

1985. High Council of Cultural Revolution Anniv.
2311 **727** 5r. multicoloured 20 10

1985. International Youth Year. Mult.
2312 5r. Type **728** 20 10
2313 5r. Profiles and symbols of war 20 10
2314 5r. Profiles and symbols of industry and agriculture 20 10
2315 5r. Profiles and sports pictograms 20 10

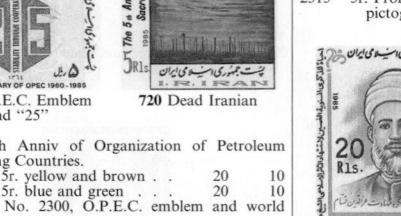

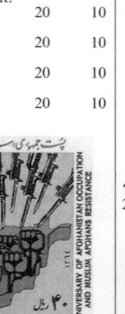

729 Ezzeddin Al-Qassam

730 Bayonets, Map and Clenched Fists

1985. 50th Death Anniv of Ezzeddin Al-Qassam.
2316 **729** 20r. brown, red and silver 50 30

1985. Afghan Resistance to Occupation.
2317 **730** 40r. multicoloured . . . 75 40

731 Mirza Taqi Khan Amir Kabir

732 Tulips and Crowd destroying Statue

1986. 135th Death Anniv of Mirza Taqi Khan Amir Kabir.
2318 **731** 5r. multicoloured 20 15

1986. 7th Anniv of Islamic Revolution.
2319 **732** 20r. multicoloured . . . 60 35

733 Sulayman Khater and Dome of the Rock

1986. 40th Death Anniv of Sulaymàn Khater.
2320 **733** 10r. black, blue and red 30 15

734 Woman, Child and Crowd

735 "Papaver orientale"

1986. Women's Day and Birth Anniv of Fatima.
2321 **734** 10r. multicoloured . . . 30 15

1986. New Year Festival. Flowers. Mult.
2322 5r. Type **735** 20 10
2323 5r. "Anemone coronaria" 20 10
2324 5r. "Papaver bracteatum" 20 10
2325 5r. "Anemone biflora" . . . 20 10

736 Fist and Text

737 Rose, Globe and Coloured Bands

1986. "2000th Day of Sacred Defence" (Iran–Iraq war).
2326 **736** 5r. green and red 20 15

1986. Struggle against Racial Discrimination.
2327 **737** 5r. multicoloured 20 15

738 Iranian Flag and Map

1986. 7th Anniv of Islamic Republic.
2328 **738** 10r. multicoloured . . . 30 15

739 Dome

740 Insignia

1986. Mab'as Festival.
2329 **739** 40r. multicoloured . . . 50 25

1986. Army Day.
2330 **740** 5r. multicoloured 25 15

741 Dead Soldier and Wrecked Helicopter

742 Text

1986. 6th Anniv of United States Landing at Tabas.
2331 **741** 40r. orange, green & blk 90 40

1986. World Day of the Oppressed. Birth Anniv of Imam Mahdi.
2332 **742** 10r. black, red and gold 30 20

743 Symbolic Design

744 Antennae and Radio Waves

1986. Teachers' Day.
2333 **743** 5r. multicoloured 20 15

1986. World Communications Day.
2334 **744** 20r. black, silver and blue 60 35

745 Soldier and Tanks

1986. International Children's Day.
2335 **745** 15r. multicoloured . . . 40 30
2336 – 15r. black, blue & mauve 40 30
DESIGN: No. 2336, Boy and text.

746 Qum Theological College and Sun Rays

747 Dome of the Rock, Map of Israel and Barbed Wire

1986. 23rd Anniv of 1963 Islamic Rising.
2337 **746** 10r. multicoloured . . . 30 15

1986. World Jerusalem Day.
2338 **747** 10r. multicoloured . . . 40 15

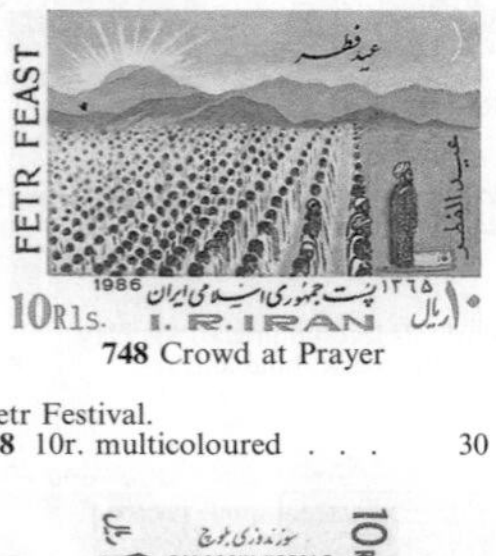

748 Crowd at Prayer

1986. Fetr Festival.
2339 **748** 10r. multicoloured . . . 30 15

749 Baluchi Needle Work

1986. World Handicrafts Day. Multicoloured.
2340 10r. Type **749** 30 20
2341 10r. Master craftswomen at work 30 20
2342 10r. Carpet 30 20
2343 10r. Engraved copper vase 30 20

750 Linked Hands around Map on Globe

751 Dr. Beheshti, Doves and Explosion

1986. Solidarity with South African People.
2344 **750** 10r. multicoloured . . . 30 15

1986. 5th Anniv of Bomb Explosion at Islamic Party Headquarters, Teheran.
2345 **751** 10r. multicoloured . . . 30 15

752 Ayatollah Mohammad Taqi Shirazi and Map

753 Shrine, Meshed

1986. Iraqi Muslim Rising.
2346 **752** 20r. multicoloured . . . 50 30

1986. Birth Anniv of Imam Riza.
2347 **753** 10r. multicoloured . . . 30 15

754 Crowd around Kaaba, Flag and Clenched Fists

755 Soltanieh Mosque

1986. Feast of Sacrifices.
2348 **754** 10r. multicoloured . . . 30 15

1986. Preservation of Cultural Heritage. Mult.
2349 5r. Type **755** 20 10
2350 5r. Mausoleum of Sohel Ben Ali, Astaneh 20 10
2351 5r. Bam fortress 20 10
2352 5r. Gateway of Blue Mosque, Tabriz 20 10

756 "Eid-ul-Ghadir" in Arabic

757 Graph, Roof and People

1986. Ghadir Festival.
2353 **756** 20r. light green, green and black 50 30

1986. Population and Housing Census.
2354 **757** 20r. multicoloured . . . 50 30

758 Missile Boat "Paykan" in Fist below Bombs

1986. 6th Anniv of Iran–Iraq War. Mult.
2355 **758** 10r. blue, black and red 55 15
2356 – 10r. red and black . . . 30 15
2357 – 10r. yellow, black and red 30 15
2358 – 10r. blue, black and red 30 15
2359 – 10r. green, black and red 30 15
DESIGNS: No. 2356, Khorramshar; 2357, Howeizah; 2358, Siege of Abadan; 2359, Susangard.

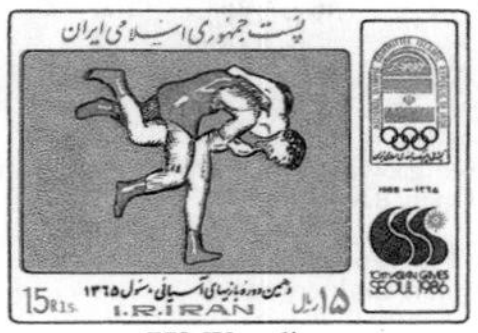
759 Wrestling

1986. 10th Asian Games, Seoul. Multicoloured.
2360 15r. Type **759** 35 20
2361 15r. Rifle shooting 35 20

760 Bird with Envelopes as Wings on Globe

1986. World Universal Postal Union Day.
2362 **760** 20r. multicoloured . . . 50 30

761 Emblem

762 Allameh Tabatabaie

1986. 40th Anniv of U.N.E.S.C.O.
2363 **761** 45r. blue, black and red 75 35

1986. 5th Death Anniv of Allameh Tabatabaie.
2364 **762** 10r. green, gold and black 20 15

763 Sun behind Dome and Minaret

764 Militiamen with Flags

1986. Mohammed's Birth Anniv and Unity Week.
2365 **763** 10r. multicoloured . . . 20 15

1986. "Mobilization of the Oppressed" Week.
2366 **764** 5r. multicoloured 20 15

765 Guerrilla Fighters

1986. Afghan Resistance to Occupation.
2367 **765** 40r. multicoloured . . . 65 30

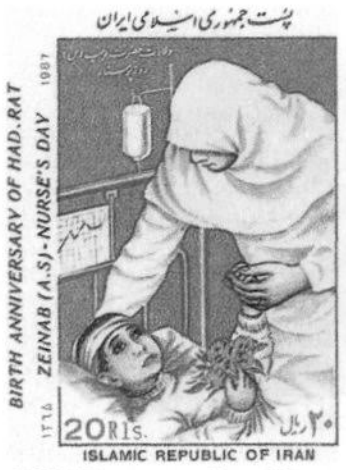
766 Nurse tending Boy

767 Emblem and Tulip on Globe

1987. Nurses' Day.
2368 **766** 20r. multicoloured . . . 50 30

1987. 5th Islamic Theology Conference, Teheran.
2369 **767** 20r. multicoloured . . . 50 30

768 Emblems of Revolution

1987. 8th Anniv of Islamic Revolution.
2370 **768** 20r. multicoloured (38 × 58 mm) 50 30
2444 20r. multicoloured (24 × 37 mm) 50 50

769 Emblem and Crowd

770 Woman and Soldiers

1987. 8th Anniv of Revolutionary Committees.
2371 **769** 10r. yellow, blue and red 30 15

1987. Women's Day and Birth Anniv of Fatima.
2372 **770** 10r. multicoloured . . . 30 15

771 Airbus Industrie A300 Aircraft and Banner around Globe

1987. 25th Anniv of Iranair.
2373 **771** 30r. multicoloured . . . 90 45

772 Ayatollah Naeini

773 Flag Irises

1987. 50th Death Anniv of Ayatollah Mirza Mohammad Hossein Naeini.
2374 **772** 10r. multicoloured . . . 30 15

1987. New Year Festival. Flowers. Mult.
2375 5r. Type **773** 20 10
2376 5r. Tulips 20 10
2377 5r. Dutch irises 20 10
2378 5r. Roses 20 10

774 Arabic Text and Arched Window

775 Flag as Star on Map

1987. Mab'as Festival.
2379 **774** 45r. lt green, grn & gold 70 35

1987. 8th Anniv of Islamic Republic.
2380 **775** 20r. multicoloured . . . 45 30

776 Soldiers with Flag

777 Emblems on Map and Dome of the Rock

1987. Revolutionary Guards' Day. Birth Anniv of Imam Hossein.
2381 **776** 5r. multicoloured 20 15

1987. Commemoration of Lebanese Hizbollah Dead.
2382 **777** 10r. red, green and grey 30 15

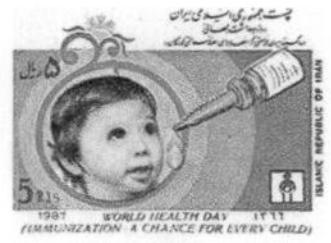
778 Child and Vaccination Dropper

779 Stars around Holy Kaaba

1987. World Health Day. Multicoloured.
2383 3r. Syringe and children . . 15 10
2384 5r. Type **778** 20 10

1987. World Day of the Oppressed. Birth Anniv of Imam Mahdi.
2385 **779** 20r. multicoloured . . . 50 30

780 Worker with Rifle and Koran, Factory and Cogwheel

781 Ayatollah Mottahari, Candle and Book

1987. International Labour Day.
2386 **780** 5r. multicoloured 20 15

1987. Teachers' Day.
2387 **781** 5r. red, yellow and blue 20 15

782 Map in Telephone Dial

783 12th-century Ceramic Lidded Pot, Rey

1987. World Telecommunications Day.
2388 **782** 20r. violet and blue . . . 50 30

1987. International Museums Day.
2389 **783** 20r. chestnut, brn & grey 50 30
2390 – 20r. brown, black & grn 50 30
DESIGN: No. 2390, Sassanian silver-gilt flower vase.

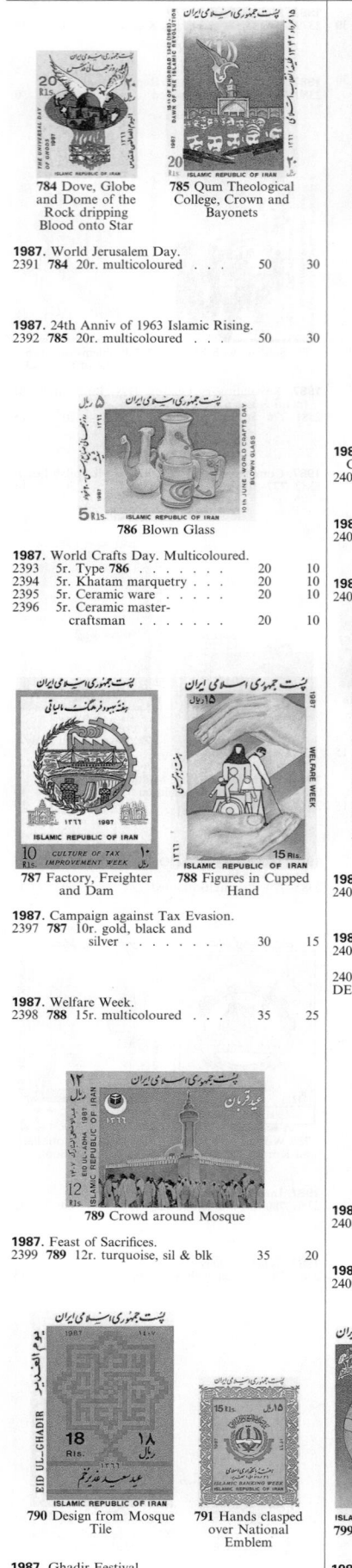

784 Dove, Globe and Dome of the Rock dripping Blood onto Star

785 Qum Theological College, Crown and Bayonets

1987. World Jerusalem Day.
2391 **784** 20r. multicoloured . . . 50 30

1987. 24th Anniv of 1963 Islamic Rising.
2392 **785** 20r. multicoloured . . . 50 30

786 Blown Glass

1987. World Crafts Day. Multicoloured.
2393 5r. Type **786** 20 10
2394 5r. Khatam marquetry . . . 20 10
2395 5r. Ceramic ware 20 10
2396 5r. Ceramic master-craftsman 20 10

787 Factory, Freighter and Dam

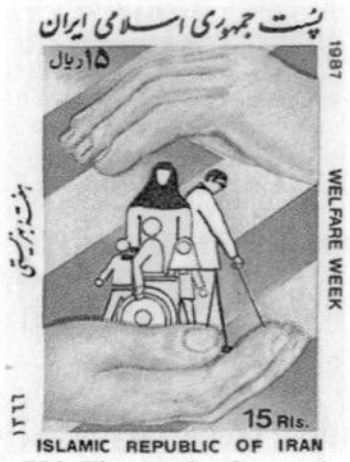

788 Figures in Cupped Hand

1987. Campaign against Tax Evasion.
2397 **787** 10r. gold, black and silver 30 15

1987. Welfare Week.
2398 **788** 15r. multicoloured . . . 35 25

789 Crowd around Mosque

1987. Feast of Sacrifices.
2399 **789** 12r. turquoise, sil & blk 35 20

790 Design from Mosque Tile

791 Hands clasped over National Emblem

1987. Ghadir Festival.
2400 **790** 18r. gold, green and black 45 30

1987. Islamic Banking Week.
2401 **791** 15r. brown, blue and gold 35 25

792 Typical Persian Calligraphy

794 Toothbrushes as Mouths

793 Blood running from Heart as Globe, Mosque and Kaaba

1987. 1st Iranian Calligraphers' Cultural and Artistic Congress.
2402 **792** 20r. multicoloured . . . 50 30

1987. Commemoration of Pilgrims killed at Mecca.
2403 **793** 8r. multicoloured 30 15

1987. 25th Anniv of Iranian Dentists Association.
2404 **794** 10r. multicoloured . . . 35 15

795 Dove with Globe as Eye

796 Rifleman and Armed Launch

1987. International Peace Day.
2405 **795** 20r. bronze and blue . . 50 30

1987. 7th Anniv of Iran–Iraq War.
2406 **796** 25r. green, blue and black 60 40
2407 – 25r. red, black and blue 60 40
DESIGN: No. 2407, Rifleman and soldiers.

797 Open Book on Crossed Pistols

798 People in Cupped Hands

1987. Police Day.
2408 **797** 10r. multicoloured . . . 50 20

1987. Int Social Security Co-operation Week.
2409 **798** 15r. black, blue and gold 35 25

799 Dove with Envelopes as Tail on Globe

800 American Flag, Great Seal and Capitol

1987. World Post Day. Multicoloured.
2410 15r. Type **799** 35 25
2411 15r. Dr. M. Ghandi (Postal Minister) commemoration 35 25

1987. 6th Anniv of Storming of United States Embassy.
2412 **800** 40r. multicoloured . . . 75 55

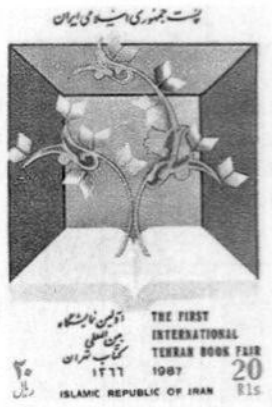

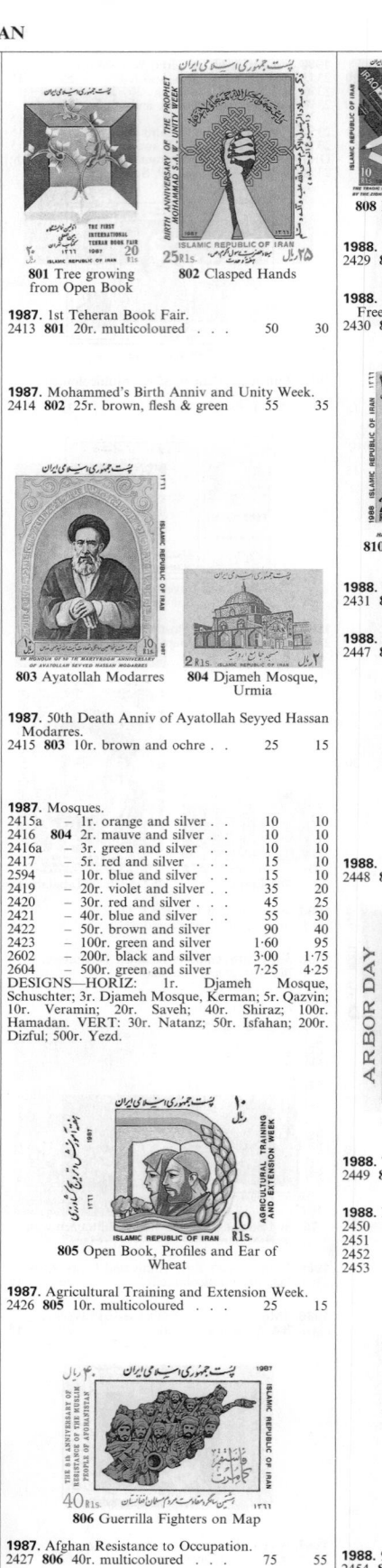

801 Tree growing from Open Book

802 Clasped Hands

1987. 1st Teheran Book Fair.
2413 **801** 20r. multicoloured . . . 50 30

1987. Mohammed's Birth Anniv and Unity Week.
2414 **802** 25r. brown, flesh & green 55 35

803 Ayatollah Modarres

804 Djameh Mosque, Urmia

1987. 50th Death Anniv of Ayatollah Seyyed Hassan Modarres.
2415 **803** 10r. brown and ochre . . 25 15

1987. Mosques.
2415a – 1r. orange and silver . . 10 10
2416 **804** 2r. mauve and silver . . 10 10
2416a – 3r. green and silver . . 10 10
2417 – 5r. red and silver . . . 15 10
2594 – 10r. blue and silver . . 15 10
2419 – 20r. violet and silver . . 35 20
2420 – 30r. red and silver . . . 45 25
2421 – 40r. blue and silver . . 55 30
2422 – 50r. brown and silver 90 40
2423 – 100r. green and silver 1·60 95
2602 – 200r. black and silver 3·00 1·75
2604 – 500r. green and silver 7·25 4·25
DESIGNS—HORIZ: 1r. Djameh Mosque, Schuschter; 3r. Djameh Mosque, Kerman; 5r. Qazvin; 10r. Veramin; 20r. Saveh; 40r. Shiraz; 100r. Hamadan. VERT: 30r. Natanz; 50r. Isfahan; 200r. Dizful; 500r. Yezd.

805 Open Book, Profiles and Ear of Wheat

1987. Agricultural Training and Extension Week.
2426 **805** 10r. multicoloured . . . 25 15

806 Guerrilla Fighters on Map

1987. Afghan Resistance to Occupation.
2427 **806** 40r. multicoloured . . . 75 55

807 Crowd with Banners

1988. 10th Anniv of Qum Uprising.
2428 **807** 20r. multicoloured . . . 50 30

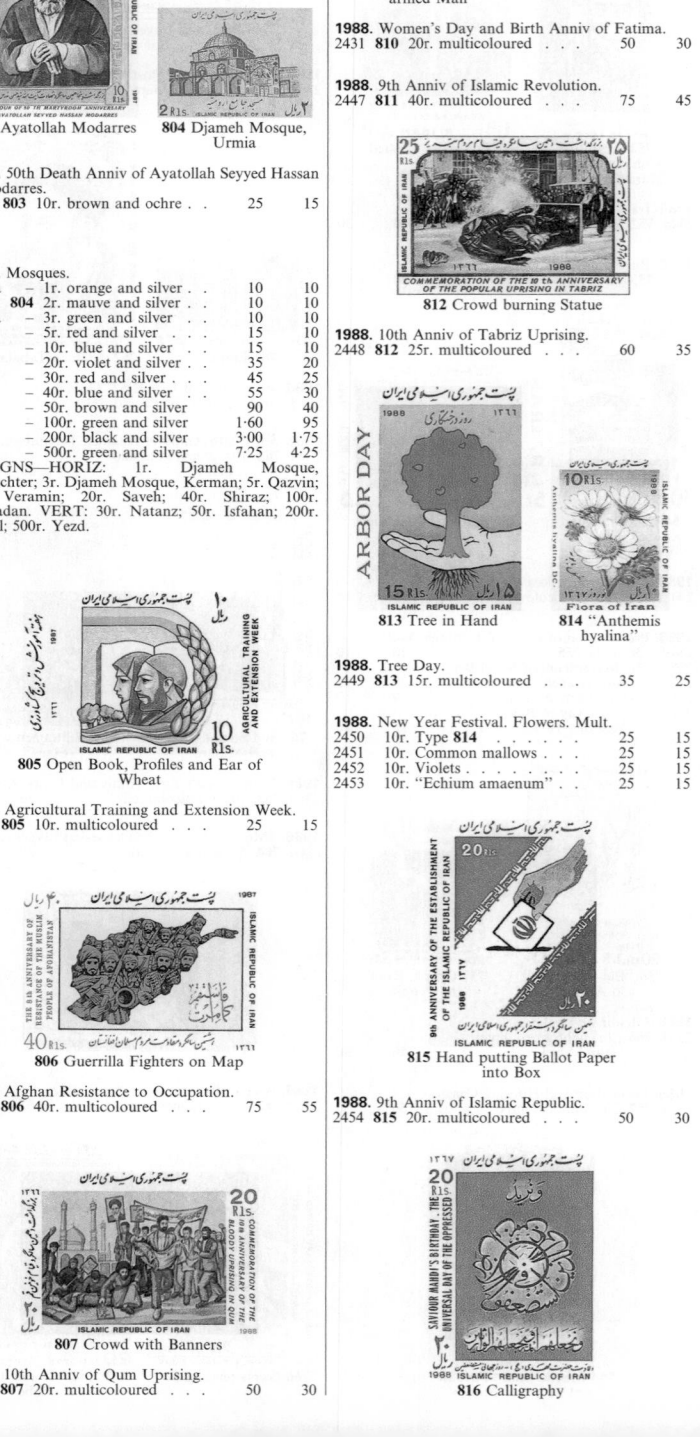

808 Bombs and Pencils

809 Takhti and Mountain

1988. Iranian Schools Victims' Commemoration.
2429 **808** 10r. multicoloured . . . 25 15

1988. Victory of Gholamreza Takhti in World Freestyle Wrestling Championships.
2430 **809** 15r. multicoloured . . . 35 25

810 Woman carrying armed Man

811 Text

1988. Women's Day and Birth Anniv of Fatima.
2431 **810** 20r. multicoloured . . . 50 30

1988. 9th Anniv of Islamic Revolution.
2447 **811** 40r. multicoloured . . . 75 45

812 Crowd burning Statue

1988. 10th Anniv of Tabriz Uprising.
2448 **812** 25r. multicoloured . . . 60 35

813 Tree in Hand

814 "Anthemis hyalina"

1988. Tree Day.
2449 **813** 15r. multicoloured . . . 35 25

1988. New Year Festival. Flowers. Mult.
2450 10r. Type **814** 25 15
2451 10r. Common mallows . . . 25 15
2452 10r. Violets 25 15
2453 10r. "Echium amaenum" . . 25 15

815 Hand putting Ballot Paper into Box

1988. 9th Anniv of Islamic Republic.
2454 **815** 20r. multicoloured . . . 50 30

816 Calligraphy

1988. World Day of the Oppressed. Birth Anniv of Imam Mahdi.
2455 **816** 20r. brown and blue . . 50 30

817 Shahid Mottahari Mosque and Theology School, Teheran

1988. Preservation of Cultural Heritage. Multicoloured.
2456 10r. Type **817** 25 15
2457 10r. Colonnade of Tarikhaneh Mosque, Damghan 25 15
2458 10r. Gateway of Sepahdari Mosque and Theology School, Arak (horiz) . . . 25 15
2459 10r. Agha Bozorg Mosque and Theology School, Kashan (courtyard with pool) (horiz) 25 15

818 Bomb, Gas Cloud and Victims

1988. Halabja Chemical Attack Victims' Commemoration.
2460 **818** 20r. multicoloured . . . 50 30

819 Map, Dome of the Rock and Palestinian

820 Satellite and Telephone Handset

1988. Palestinian "Intifida" Movement. Each brown, red and black.
2461 10r. Type **819** 30 15
2462 10r. Man with rounded beard 30 15
2463 10r. Man wearing crew-necked jumper 30 15
2464 10r. Man with long pointed beard 30 15
2465 10r. Crowd and hand holding stone 30 15

1988. World Telecommunications Day.
2466 **820** 20r. blue and green . . . 50 30

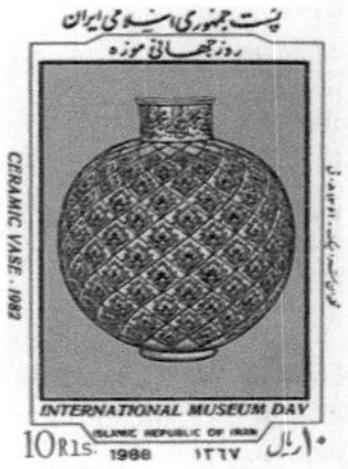

821 Ceramic Vase

822 Miners pushing Coal Truck

1988. International Museum Day. Multicoloured.
2467 10r. Type **821** 25 15
2468 10r. Iran Bastan Museum porch 25 15
2469 10r. 14th-century Tabriz silk rug 25 15
2470 10r. 7th-century B.C. gold ring, Arjan, Behbahan . . 25 15

1988. Mining Day.
2471 **822** 20r. multicoloured . . . 3·25 90

823 Children playing by River

824 Bleeding Dove and Broken Bayonets

1988. International Children's Day.
2472 **823** 10r. multicoloured . . . 30 15

1988. 25th Anniv of 1963 Islamic Rising.
2473 **824** 10r. multicoloured . . . 30 15

825 Glim Weaving

826 Child in Flower

1988. World Handicrafts Day. Multicoloured.
2474 10r. Type **825** 25 15
2475 10r. Miniature of horsemen 25 15
2476 10r. Glim weaver (horiz) . . 25 15
2477 10r. Straw basket (horiz) . . 25 15

1988. Child Health Campaign.
2478 **826** 20r. blue, green and black 35 20

827 Symbols of Industry and Agriculture

828 Balkhi

1988. Campaign Against Tax Evasion.
2479 **827** 20r. gold, blue and silver 35 20

1988. Allameh Balkhi (Afghan revolutionary writer) Commemoration.
2480 **828** 20r. black, red and silver 35 20

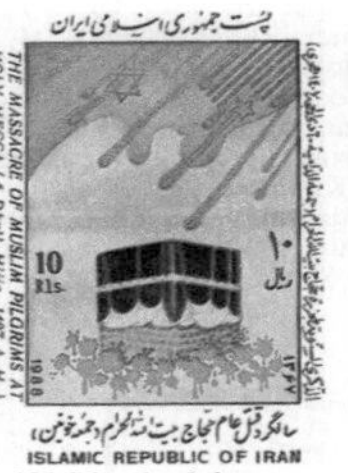

829 Blood raining on Holy Kaaba

830 Missile hitting Airplane

1988. 1st Anniv of Death of Mecca Pilgrims. Multicoloured.
2481 10r. Type **829** 20 15
2482 10r. Holy Kaaba and blood-stained robe 20 15

1988. Destruction of Iranair Passenger Airplane.
2483 **830** 45r. multicoloured . . . 1·00 45

831 Seyyed Ali Andarzgou

832 Central Bank, Teheran

1988. 10th Death Anniv of Seyyed Ali Andarzgou (revolutionary).
2484 **831** 20r. blue, black & brown 35 20

1988. Islamic Banking Week.
2485 **832** 20r. grey, brown and gold 35 20

833 Carrying away Victim

834 Weightlifting

1988. 10th Anniv of "Bloody Friday" Riots.
2486 **833** 25r. green, purple and red 45 25

1988. Olympic Games, Seoul. Multicoloured.
2487 10r. Type **834** 20 15
2488 10r. Men's gymnastics . . . 20 15
2489 10r. Judo 20 15
2490 10r. Football 20 15
2491 10r. Wrestling 20 15

835 Plant

836 Iranians and Rifle

1988. Agricultural Census.
2492 **835** 30r. yellow, black & grn 50 35

1988. 8th Anniv of Iran–Iraq War.
2493 **836** 20r. multicoloured . . . 35 20

837 Envelopes around Globe

1988. World Post Day.
2494 **837** 20r. green, black and blue 35 20

838 Child's Face and Profiles

1988. Parents' and Teachers' Co-operation Week.
2495 **838** 20r. multicoloured . . . 35 20

839 Clasped Hands and Emblem

1988. Mohammed's Birth Anniv and Unity Week.
2496 **839** 10r. multicoloured . . . 20 15

840 Fist and Shattered Eagle

841 Tree as Umbrella

1988. 7th Anniv of Storming of United States Embassy.
2497 **840** 45r. multicoloured . . . 75 45

1988. Insurance Day.
2498 **841** 10r. multicoloured . . . 20 15

842 Tomb of Hafiz

1988. International Hafiz (writer) Congress, Shiraz.
2499 **842** 20r. blue, gold and mauve 35 20

843 Agricultural Symbols on Open Book

1988. Agricultural Training and Extension Week.
2500 **843** 15r. multicoloured . . . 30 15

844 Parvin Etessami (writer)

1988. Iranian Celebrities of Science, Art and Literature. Multicoloured.
2501 10r. Type **844** 20 15
2502 10r. Qaem Maqam Farahani (writer) 20 15
2503 10r. Kamal al-Molk (artist) 20 15
2504 10r. Jalal al-Ahmad (writer) 20 15
2505 10r. Dr. Mohammad Mo'in (writer) 20 15

845 Map and Armed Afghan

1988. Afghan Resistance to Occupation.
2506 **845** 40r. multicoloured . . . 75 45

846 Satellite, Envelopes and Dish Aerial

847 Tulips and Script

1989. Asian and Pacific Transport and Communications Decade. Multicoloured.
2507 20r. Type **846** 45 30
2508 20r. Air transport 45 30

2509 20r. Road and rail transport 1·75 60
2510 20r. Shipping 65 30

1989. Air. 10th Anniv of Islamic Revolution.
2511 **847** 40r. mauve, gold & black 80 55
2512 50r. violet, gold and black 80 55

848 Sun illuminating Koran

1989. Mab'as Festival.
2513 **848** 20r. multicoloured . . . 35 25

849 Hands protecting Tree

1989. Tree Day.
2514 **849** 20r. multicoloured . . . 35 25

850 "Cephalanthera kurdica"

851 Wind Gauge and Wheat

1989. New Year Festival. Flowers. Mult.
2515 10r. Type **850** 20 15
2516 10r. "Dactylorhiza romana" 20 15
2517 10r. "Comperia comperiana" 20 15
2518 10r. "Orchis mascula" . . . 20 15

1989. World Meteorological Day. Mult.
2519 20r. Type **851** 40 25
2520 30r. Wind gauge, airplane and weather ship 80 35

852 State Arms

853 Refinery

1989. 10th Anniv of Islamic Republic.
2521 **852** 20r. multicoloured . . . 35 25

1989. Commissioning of First Phase of Abadan Oil Refinery.
2522 **853** 20r. multicoloured . . . 40 25

854 Mottahari

856 Satellite, Globe and Dish Aerial

855 Dome of the Rock and Barbed Wire

1989. Teachers' Day. 10th Death Anniv of Ayatollah Mottahari.
2523 **854** 20r. multicoloured . . . 35 25

1989. World Jerusalem Day.
2524 **855** 30r. multicoloured . . . 60 35

1989. World Telecommunications Day.
2525 **856** 20r. multicoloured . . . 40 25

857 Jar

858 Armed Men, Tent and Family with Sheep

1989. International Museums Day. 6th-century Gurgan Artefacts.
2526 **857** 20r. yellow, blue & black 40 25
2527 – 20r. blue, black & mauve 40 25
DESIGN: No. 2527, Flagon.

1989. Nomads' Day.
2528 **858** 20r. multicoloured . . . 35 20

859 Man engraving Vase

1989. World Crafts Day. Multicoloured.
2529 20r. Type **859** 35 25
2530 20r. Engraved copper vase 35 25
2531 20r. Engraved copper plate (vert) 35 25
2532 20r. Engraved copper wall-hanging (vert) 35 25

860 Khomeini and Crowd

861 Pasteur, Avicenna and Hand holding Quill

1989. Ayatollah Khomeini Commemoration.
2533 **860** 20r. orange, black and blue (postage) 40 20
2534 – 70r. blk, vio & gold (air) 1·10 70
DESIGN—HORIZ: 70r. Ayatollah Khomeini.

1989. "Philexfrance 89" International Stamp Exhibition, Paris. Each black, blue and brown, background colour given.
2535 **861** 30r. blue 50 35
2536 50r. brown 75 55

862 Map and Satellite

1989. 10th Anniv of Asia–Pacific Telecommunity.
2537 **862** 30r. orange, black & blue 50 30

863 Araghi

1989. 10th Death Anniv of Mehdi Araghi.
2538 **863** 20r. orange and purple 35 20

864 Shahryar and Monument

1989. Mohammed Hossein Shahryar (poet) Commemoration.
2539 **864** 20r. multicoloured . . . 35 20

865 U.N. Security Council Document

1989. 9th Anniv of Iran–Iraq War.
2540 **865** 20r. multicoloured . . . 35 20

866 Khomeini addressing Crowd

1989. Ayatollah Khomeini.
2541 – 1r. multicoloured 10 10
2542 – 2r. multicoloured 10 10
2543 **866** 3r. multicoloured 10 10
2544 – 5r. multicoloured 25 10
2545 – 10r. multicoloured . . . 60 10
2546 – 20r. multicoloured . . . 35 10
2547 – 30r. multicoloured . . . 50 30
2548 – 40r. multicoloured . . . 65 50
2549 – 50r. multicoloured . . . 80 50
2550 – 70r. multicoloured . . . 1·10 65
2551 – 100r. ultram, bl & grn 1·60 95
2552 – 200r. brown, yell & grn 3·00 1·50
2553 – 500r. multicoloured . . . 7·50 4·00
2554 – 1000r. multicoloured . . 15·00 8·25
DESIGNS: 1r. Rose and courtyard; 2r. Khomeini as young man; 5r. Khomeini going into exile; 10r. Khomeini's return from exile; 20r. Khomeini making speech; 30r. Boy kissing Khomeini; 40r. Ayatollahs; 50r. Khomeini; 70r. Meeting in house; 100r. Arabic inscription; 200r. Microphones and chair; 500r. Qum Mosque and roses; 1000r. Sun's rays.

867 Pigeon carrying Letter

1989. World Post Day.
2561 **867** 20r. multicoloured . . . 35 20

868 Multi-pointed Star in Window Arch

869 U.S. Emblem and Crowd in Dove

1989. Mohammed's Birth Anniv and Unity Week.
2562 **868** 10r. multicoloured . . . 15 10

1989. 8th Anniv of Storming of United States Embassy.
2563 **869** 40r. orange, black & blue 65 40

870 Iranian and Launch with Machine Gun

1989. 10th Anniv of People's Militia.
2564 **870** 10r. multicoloured . . . 30 15

871 Mehdi Elahi Ghomshei

1989. Iranian Celebrities of Science, Art and Literature.
2565 **871** 10r. red, black and gold 15 10
2566 – 10r. green, black and gold 15 10
2567 – 10r. yellow, black & gold 15 10
2568 – 10r. green, black and gold 15 10
2569 – 10r. mauve, black & gold 15 10
DESIGNS: No. 2566, Grand Ayatollah Seyyed Hossein Boroujerdi; 2567, Grand Ayatollah Sheikh Abdulkarim Haeri; 2568, Dr. Abdulazim Gharib; 2569, Seyyed Hossein Mirkhani.

872 Guiding Child's Hand

873 Book as Profiles forming Flower

1990. International Literacy Year.
2570 **872** 20r. multicoloured . . . 35 20

1990. Identity Cards.
2571 **873** 10r. multicoloured . . . 15 10

874 Drinking Vessel

1990. Cultural Heritage.
2572 **874** 20r. black and orange . . 35 20
2573 – 20r. black and green . . 35 20
DESIGN: No. 2563, Vase with stem.

875 Crowd

1990. 11th Anniv of Islamic Revolution.
2574 **875** 50r. multicoloured . . . 80 50

876 Emblem

877 Soldier in Wheelchair

1990. Int Koran Recitation Competition.
2575 **876** 10r. black, blue and green 15 10

1990. Invalids' Day.
2576 **877** 10r. multicoloured . . . 15 10

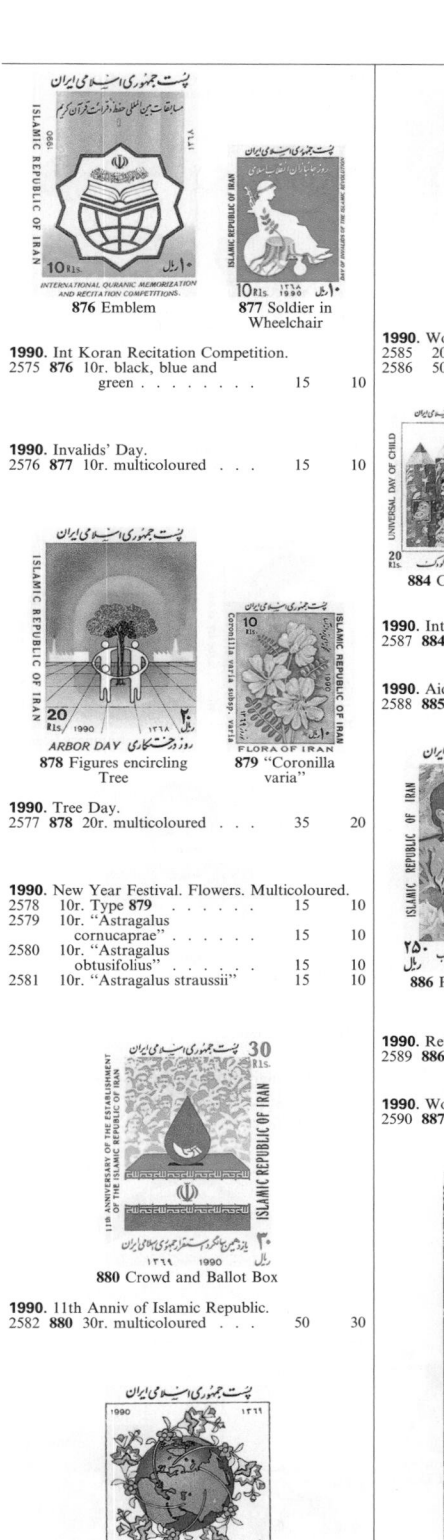

878 Figures encircling Tree

879 "Coronilla varia"

1990. Tree Day.
2577 **878** 20r. multicoloured . . . 35 20

1990. New Year Festival. Flowers. Multicoloured.
2578 10r. Type **879** 15 10
2579 10r. "Astragalus cornucaprae" 15 10
2580 10r. "Astragalus obtusifolius" 15 10
2581 10r. "Astragalus straussii" 15 10

880 Crowd and Ballot Box

1990. 11th Anniv of Islamic Republic.
2582 **880** 30r. multicoloured . . . 50 30

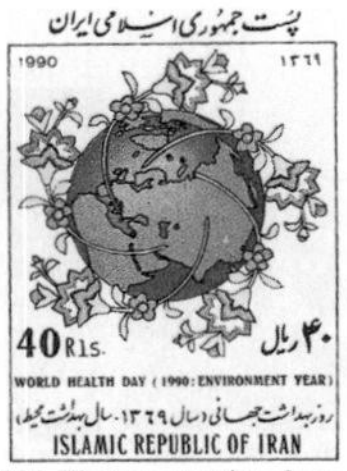

881 Flower growing from Globe

1990. World Health Day.
2583 **881** 40r. multicoloured . . . 65 40

882 Khomeini

1990. 1st Death Anniv of Ayatollah Khomeini.
2584 **882** 50r. multicoloured . . . 80 50

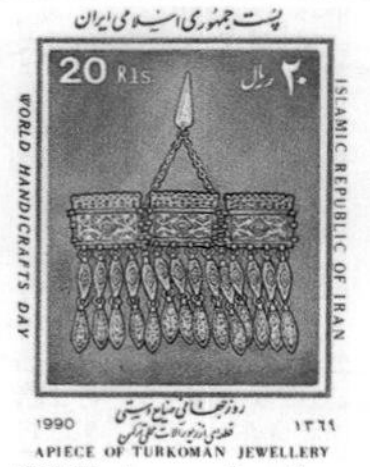

883 Turkoman Jewellery

1990. World Handicrafts Day. Multicoloured.
2585 20r. Type **883** 35 20
2586 50r. Gilded-steel bird . . . 80 50

884 Crayons

885 Seismograph on Map and Red Crescent Camp

1990. International Children's Day.
2587 **884** 20r. multicoloured . . . 35 20

1990. Aid for Earthquake Victims.
2588 **885** 100r. multicoloured . . . 1·60 95

886 P.O.W. and Roses

887 Ayatollah Khomeini and Dome of the Rock

1990. Returned Prisoners of War.
2589 **886** 250r. multicoloured . . . 3·75 2·00

1990. World Jerusalem Day.
2590 **887** 100r. multicoloured . . . 1·60 95

889 Flowers, Crowd and Khomeini

1991. 12th Anniv of Islamic Revolution.
2605 **889** 100r. multicoloured . . . 1·60 95

890 11th-century Gold Jug

1991. International Museum Day. Multicoloured.
2606 50r. Type **890** 80 50
2607 50r. 14th-century silver-inlaid brass basin 80 50

891 Flowers and Fists

892 Museum

1991. 11th Anniv of Iran–Iraq War.
2608 **891** 100r. multicoloured . . . 1·60 95

1991. Inauguration of Post Museum, Teheran.
2609 **892** 200r. brown and black 3·25 2·00

893 Headset on Globe

894 "Iris spuria"

1991. World Telecommunications Day (1990).
2610 **893** 50r. multicoloured . . . 80 50

1991. New Year Festival. Irises. Multicoloured.
2611 20r. Type **894** 35 20
2612 20r. "Iris lycotis" 35 20
2613 20r. "Iris demawendica" . . 35 20
2614 20r. "Iris meda" 35 20

895 Map, Dome of the Rock and Hosseini

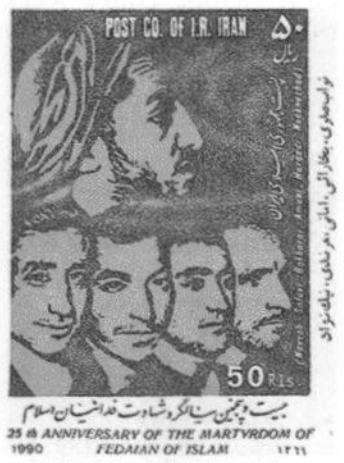

897 Revolutionaries

896 Light Beam on Mountains

1991. 10th Death Anniv of Saleh Hosseini.
2615 **895** 30r. red and black . . . 50 30

1991. Mab'as Festival.
2616 **896** 100r. multicoloured . . . 1·60 95

1991. 25th Death Anniv (1990) of Revolutionaries.
2617 **897** 50r. brown and orange 80 50

898 Arabic Script

1991. World Day of the Oppressed. Birth Anniv of Mahdi.
2618 **898** 50r. multicoloured . . . 80 50

899 Crowd, Flag and Ballot Box

1991. 12th Anniv of Islamic Republic.
2619 **899** 20r. multicoloured . . . 35 20

900 Map and Bayonets

901 Mother and Child

1991. World Jerusalem Day.
2620 **900** 100r. multicoloured . . . 1·60 95

1991. Women's Day and Birth Anniv of Fatima.
2621 **901** 50r. multicoloured . . . 80 50

902 Boroujerdi

903 Disasters

1991. 30th Death Anniv of Ayatollah Boroujerdi.
2622 **902** 200r. black and green . . 3·25 2·00

1991. International Decade for Natural Disaster Reduction.
2623 **903** 100r. multicoloured . . . 2·00 1·10

904 Book, Candle and Dr. Mottahari

1991. Teachers' Day.
2624 **904** 50r. yellow, orange & blk 80 50

905 Rays striking Globe

906 Mausoleum, Meshed

1991. World Telecommunications Day. "Telecommunications and Safety of Human Life".
2625 **905** 100r. multicoloured . . . 1·60 95

1991. Birth Anniv of Imam Riza. Multicoloured.
2626 10r. Type **906** 15 10
2627 30r. Tombstone 50 30

907 Khomeini

1991. 2nd Death Anniv of Ayatollah Khomeini.
2628 **907** 100r. multicoloured . . . 1·60 95

908 Karbala Shrine

1991. Iraqi Attack on Shi'ite Shrine, Karbala.
2629 **908** 70r. multicoloured . . . 1·10 65

909 Nisami

1991. 900th Birth Anniv of Nisami (writer) International Congress, Tabris.
2630 **909** 50r. multicoloured . . . 80 50

910 Archway

1991. 1330th Death Anniv of Ali ibn Ali Talib (Caliph).
2631 **910** 50r. multicoloured . . . 80 50

911 Hands reaching through Parched Earth to Blood Drop

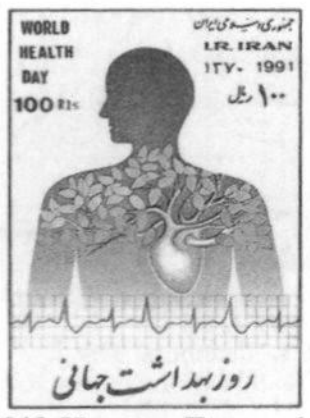
912 Heart as Tree and Cardiograph

1991. Blood Donation.
2632 **911** 50r. multicoloured . . . 80 50

1991. World Health Day.
2633 **912** 100r. multicoloured . . . 1·60 95

913 Nedjefi

1991. Marashi Nedjefi Commemoration.
2634 **913** 30r. multicoloured . . . 50 30

914 Doves flying from Cage

1991. 1st Anniv of Return of Prisoners of War.
2635 **914** 100r. multicoloured . . . 1·60 95

915 Engraved Brassware

1991. World Crafts Day. Multicoloured.
2636 40r. Type **915** 65 40
2637 40r. Gilded samovar 65 40

916 Ayatollah Lari

1991.
2638 **916** 30r. multicoloured . . . 50 30

917 Fist and Roses in Cartouche

918 Islamic Symbols

1991. 11th Anniv of Iran–Iraq War.
2639 **917** 20r. multicoloured . . . 35 20

1991. Islamic Unity Week.
2640 **918** 30r. multicoloured . . . 50 30

919 13th-century Kashan Ewer

920 Gharib

1991. International Museum Day. Multicoloured.
2641 20r. Type **919** 35 20
2642 40r. 13th-century Kashan ewer with bird's head lip 65 40

1991. Dr. Mohammed Gharib.
2643 **920** 100r. black and blue . . 1·60 95

921 Banners

922 Stamped Envelope

1991. Liberation of Khorramshahr.
2644 **921** 30r. multicoloured . . . 50 30

1991. World Post Day.
2645 **922** 70r. multicoloured . . . 1·10 65

923 Khaju-Ye Kermani

1991. International Congress on Khaju-Ye Kermani (writer).
2646 **923** 30r. multicoloured . . . 50 30

924 Globe and Seismograph

925 Cogwheel, Grain, Tree, Figures and Globe

1991. 1st International Seismology and Earthquake Engineering Conference.
2647 **924** 100r. multicoloured . . . 1·60 95

1991. World Food Day.
2648 **925** 80r. multicoloured . . . 1·25 75

926 Conference Emblem

927 Green Woodpecker and Flower Decoration

1991. Palestinian Peoples Conference.
2649 **926** 40r. gold and violet . . . 65 40

1991. 1st Asian Biennial Exhibition of Children's Book Illustrations.
2650 **927** 100r. multicoloured . . . 2·25 80

928 Script and Emblem

929 Festival Award

1991. Children's Book Fair, Teheran.
2651 **928** 20r. multicoloured . . . 35 20

1991. Roshd International Educational Film Festival.
2652 **929** 50r. multicoloured . . . 80 50

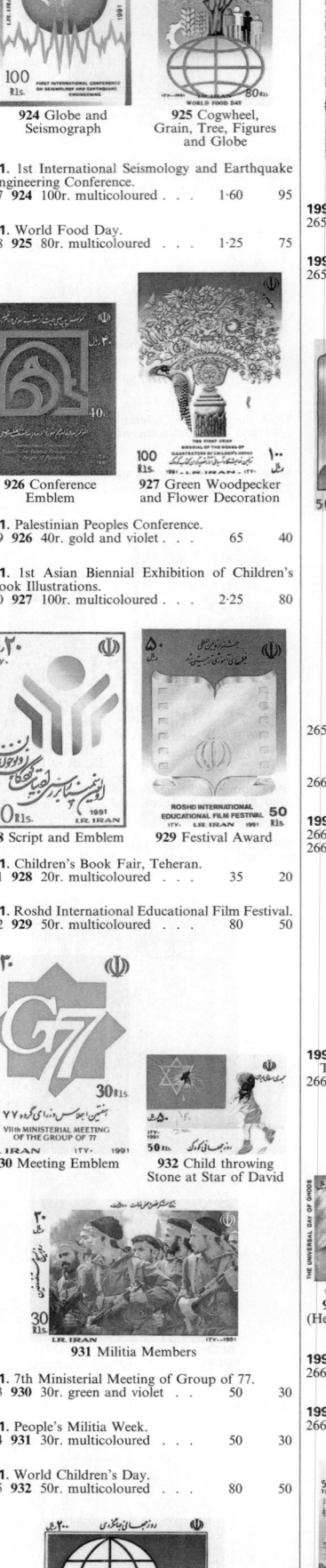

930 Meeting Emblem

932 Child throwing Stone at Star of David

931 Militia Members

1991. 7th Ministerial Meeting of Group of 77.
2653 **930** 30r. green and violet . . 50 30

1991. People's Militia Week.
2654 **931** 30r. multicoloured . . . 50 30

1991. World Children's Day.
2655 **932** 50r. multicoloured . . . 80 50

933 Globe and Doves

1991. World Tourism Day.
2656 **933** 200r. black, mauve & bl 3·00 1·60

934 Emblems

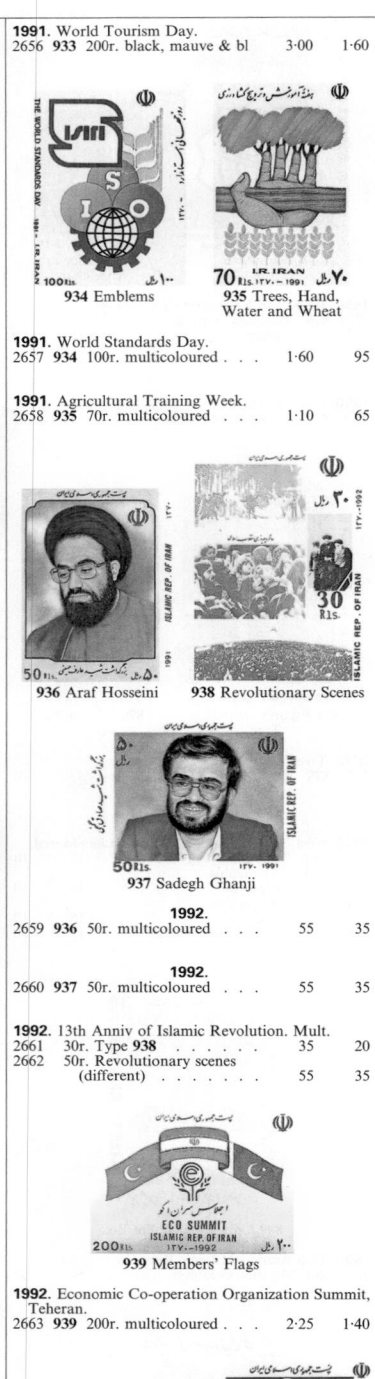

935 Trees, Hand, Water and Wheat

1991. World Standards Day.
2657 **934** 100r. multicoloured . . . 1·60 95

1991. Agricultural Training Week.
2658 **935** 70r. multicoloured . . . 1·10 65

936 Araf Hosseini

938 Revolutionary Scenes

937 Sadegh Ghanji

1992.
2659 **936** 50r. multicoloured . . . 55 35

1992.
2660 **937** 50r. multicoloured . . . 55 35

1992. 13th Anniv of Islamic Revolution. Mult.
2661 30r. Type **938** 35 20
2662 50r. Revolutionary scenes (different) 55 35

939 Members' Flags

1992. Economic Co-operation Organization Summit, Teheran.
2663 **939** 200r. multicoloured . . . 2·25 1·40

940 Seyd Abbas Musawi (Hezbollah Secretary-General) and Dome of the Rock

941 Planets, Satellite, Globe and Mobile Dish Aerial

1992. World Jerusalem Day.
2664 **940** 200r. multicoloured . . . 2·25 1·40

1992. World Meteorological Day.
2665 **941** 100r. multicoloured . . . 1·10 75

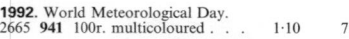

942 Badshahi Mosque, Lahore, Pakistan

943 Ayatollah Khomeini Voting

1992. South and West Asia Postal Union. Multicoloured.
2666 50r. Type **942** 60 35
2667 50r. Imam's Mosque, Isfahan 60 35
2668 50r. St. Sophia's, Istanbul, Turkey 60 35

1992. 13th Anniv of Islamic Republic.
2669 **943** 50r. multicoloured . . . 60 35

944 Embraer Bandeirante and Crates

1992. Establishment of Postal Air Service.
2670 **944** 60r. multicoloured . . . 80 45

945 Hands holding Trees **946** Tulips

1992. National Resources Week.
2671 **945** 100r. multicoloured . . . 1·10 75

1992. New Year Festival. Flowers. Multicoloured.
2672 20r. Type **946** 40 25
2673 20r. Rose 40 25
2674 40r. Orange blossom 50 30
2675 40r. Yellow jasmine 50 30

947 Members' Flags

1992. Economic Co-operation Organization.
2676 **947** 20r. multicoloured . . . 40 25

948 Morse Apparatus

1992. World Telecommunications Day. Mult.
2677 20r. Type **948** 40 25
2678 20r. Telegraph poles and wires 40 25
2679 20r. Old wall and candlestick telephones . . 40 25
2680 40r. Dish aerials 50 30
2681 40r. Satellite and Earth . . 50 30
Nos. 2677/81 were issued together, se-tenant, forming a composite design.

949 Sabzevari **950** Emblem

1992. Science, Art and Literature. Multicoloured.
2682 50r. Type **949** 60 35
2683 50r. Madjlessi (in turban) 60 35
2684 50r. Arabic script by Mir Emad 60 35
2685 50r. Samani (in fez) 60 35

1992. 21st Near East Regional Conference Session of F.A.O., Teheran.
2686 **950** 40r. green, blue and black 50 25

951 Globe, Equipment and Charts **952** Palm Trees

1992. International Surveying and Mapping Conf.
2687 **951** 40r. multicoloured . . . 50 25

1992. 2nd Anniv of Unification of Yemen.
2688 **952** 50r. multicoloured . . . 60 35

953 Dome of the Rock, Oasis and Child

1992. World Children's Day.
2689 **953** 50r. multicoloured . . . 50 30

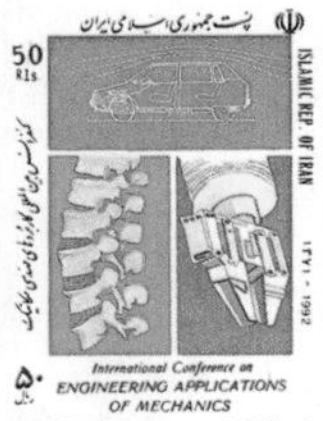

954 Khomeini **955** Diagram of Wind Tunnel Test, Section of Spine and Robot Hand

1992. 3rd Death Anniv of Ayatollah Khomeini.
2690 **954** 100r. multicoloured . . . 1·10 70

1992. International Engineering Applications of Mechanics Conference, Teheran.
2691 **955** 50r. multicoloured . . . 50 30

956 Building and Books

1992. Hajia Nosrat Baygom Amin Mo'in (lawyer) Commemoration.
2692 **956** 20r. multicoloured . . . 35 20

957 Emblem and Iranian Flag **958** ESCAP Emblem

1992. 6th Non-aligned News Agencies Pool Conference, Teheran.
2693 **957** 100r. multicoloured . . . 1·10 70

1992. Meeting of Economic and Social Commission for Asia and the Pacific Industry and Technology Ministers.
2694 **958** 100r. green, gold & black 1·10 70

959 Drugs in Hand **961** Khomeini winding Turban

960 Ceramic Bowl, Neyshabour City

1992. World Anti-drugs Day.
2695 **959** 100r. multicoloured . . . 1·00 60

1992. International Museum Day. Multicoloured.
2696 40r. Type **960** 45 25
2697 40r. Ceramic vessel, Shahroud City 45 25

1992. Prayers of Ayatollah Khomeini (1st series). Multicoloured.
2698 50r. Type **961** 50 30
2699 50r. Mosque and Khomeini 50 30
2700 50r. Khomeini 50 30
See also Nos. 2701/2 and 2703.

962 Arabic Script

1992. Prayers of Ayatollah Khomeini (2nd series).
2701 **962** 50r. turquoise and blue 50 30
2702 – 50r. yellow and green . . 50 30
DESIGN: No. 2702, Arabic script (different).

963 Kaaba **965** Arabic Script

964 Tanker

1992. Prayers of Ayatollah Khomeini (3rd series).
2703 **963** 50r. multicoloured . . . 50 30

1992. 25th Anniv of Iranian Shipping Lines.
2704 **964** 200r. multicoloured . . . 2·50 1·50

1992. Mohammed's Birth Anniv and Unity Week.
2705 **965** 40r. multicoloured . . . 40 25

966 Soldiers and Sun **968** Foundry and Steel Products

967 Patient and Doctor

1992. 12th Anniv of Iran–Iraq War. Multicoloured.
2706 20r. Type **966** 30 20
2707 40r. Soldier on riverbank (horiz) 40 20

1992. International History of Medicine in Islam and Iran Congress. Multicoloured.
2708 20r. Type **967** 30 20
2709 40r. Medical instruments . . 40 20

Nos. 2708/9 were issued together, se-tenant, forming a composite design.

1992. Steel Industry. Multicoloured.
2710 20r. Type **968** 30 20
2711 70r. Steel products and steel works 70 35
Nos. 2710/11 were issued together, se-tenant, forming a composite design.

969 Isfahan

1992. World Tourism Day. Multicoloured.
2712 20r. Type **969** 30 20
2713 20r. Mazandaran 30 20
2714 30r. Bushehr 45 25
2715 30r. Hormozgan 45 25

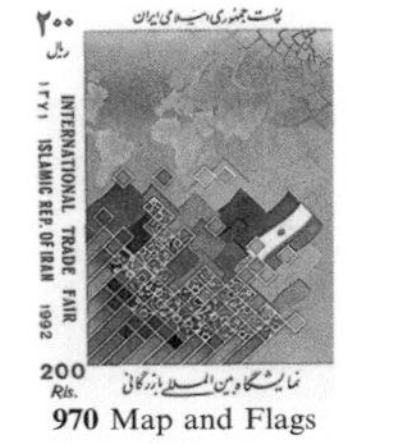

970 Map and Flags

1992. International Trade Fair.
2716 **970** 200r. multicoloured . . . 2·00 1·25

971 Early Post Office Service

1992. World Post Day.
2717 **971** 30r. brown and violet . . 50 30

972 Starving Child and Food Distribution

1992. World Food Day.
2718 **972** 100r. multicoloured . . . 3·50 1·25

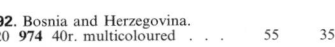

973 Child drawing **974** Flames and Child's Face

1992. International Children's and Youth Photographic Festival.
2719 **973** 40r. multicoloured . . . 65 35

1992. Bosnia and Herzegovina.
2720 **974** 40r. multicoloured . . . 55 35

975 Storming Embassy, Doves and Crow **976** Emblem

1992. Multicoloured.
2721 100r. Type **975** (11th anniv of storming of U.S. Embassy) . . . . 1·00 50
2722 100r. Soldiers, crows and doves (Students' Day) . . 1·00 50
2723 100r. Ayatollah Khomeini, crows and doves (13th anniv of Khomeini's return from exile) . . . . 1·00 50
Nos. 2721/3 were issued together, se-tenant, forming a composite design.

1992. 17th Annual Meeting of Islamic Development Bank Board of Governors.
2724 **976** 20r. multicoloured . . . 25 15

977 Flags and Dish Aerials on Maps

1992. Azerbaijan–Iran Telecommunications Co-operation.
2725 **977** 40r. multicoloured . . . 55 35

978 Star

1992. 10th Anniv of Islamic University.
2726 **978** 200r. green & deep green 2·00 1·25

979 Soldiers in Armed Motor Boat

1992. People's Militia Week.
2727 **979** 40r. multicoloured . . . 55 35

980 Shahryar

981 "Heaven and Hell"

1992. International Congress on Mohammed Hossein Shahryar (poet).
2728 **980** 80r. multicoloured . . . 75 40

1992. Women's Day and Birth Anniv of Fatima.
2729 **981** 70r. multicoloured . . . 65 35

982 Oil Derrick

1992. Oil Industry. Multicoloured.
2730 100r. Type **982** . . . . . . 1·00 50
2731 100r. Drilling . . . . 1·00 50

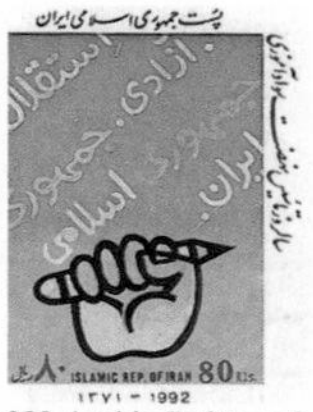
983 Arabic Script and Hand holding Pen

984 Ayatollah Mirza Abolhassan Sharani

1992. Literacy Campaign.
2732 **983** 80r. multicoloured . . . 75 40

1993. Celebrities. Multicoloured.
2733 20r. Type **984** 25 15
2734 20r. Prof. Mahmoud Hessabi and formula . . 25 15
2735 20r. Mohit Tabatabaie and books 25 15
2736 20r. Mehrdad Avesta and Arabic script 25 15

985 Narcissi

986 Wings and Koran

1993. Flowers. Multicoloured.
2737 20r. Type **985** 25 15
2738 30r. Blue and yellow irises 30 20
2738a 35r. Tulips 40 25
2739 40r. White irises 50 30
2740 50r. Jasmine 60 35
2741 60r. Viburnum berries . . 80 40
2742 70r. Pansies . . . . 1·10 60
2743 75r. Antirrhinums . . . . 1·10 60
2745 100r. Martagon lilies . . . 1·00 50
2746 120r. Petunias . . . . . . 1·60 75
2747 150r. Hyacinths . . . . . 1·25 70
2749 200r. Roses . . . . 2·00 1·25
2750 500r. Convolvulus . . . . 4·75 3·00
2751 1000r. Poppies . . . . . . 9·50 6·25

1993. Mab'as Festival.
2752 **986** 200r. multicoloured . . . 1·90 1·25

987 Rainbow and Emblem

988 Man in Wheelchair tying Girl's Ribbon

1993. Programming Day.
2753 **987** 100r. multicoloured . . . 90 50

1993. Invalids' Day. Multicoloured.
2754 20r. Type **988** 25 15
2755 40r. Medal winner in wheelchair 50 30
Nos. 2754/5 were issued together, se-tenant, forming a composite design.

989 Fatima Mosque, Qom

1993. Preservation of Cultural Heritage. Mult.
2756 40r. Type **989** 50 30
2757 40r. Interior of mosque . . 50 30

990 Hands reaching towards Sun

1993. World Day of the Oppressed. Birth Anniv of Mahdi.
2758 **990** 60r. multicoloured . . . 50 30

991 National Flag

1993. 14th Anniv of Islamic Revolution. Mult.
2759 20r. Type **991** 25 15
2760 20r. Flag and soldiers . . . 25 15
2761 20r. Guerrillas 25 15
2762 20r. Oil derricks, harvesters and crowd 25 15
2763 20r. Ayatollah Khomeini in motorcade and on arrival in Iran 25 15
Nos. 2759/63 were issued together, se-tenant, forming a composite design.

992 Volleyball

993 Ansari

1993. 1st Islamic Countries Women's Games. Multicoloured.
2764 40r. Type **992** 50 30
2765 40r. Basketball 50 30
2766 40r. Gold medal 50 30
2767 40r. Swimming 50 30
2768 40r. Running 50 30
Nos. 2764/8 were issued together, se-tenant, forming a compostite design.

1993. Congress on Sheikh Morteza Ansari.
2769 **993** 40r. multicoloured . . . 50 30

994 World Map as Tree Foliage and Rainbow

1993. Tree Day.
2770 **994** 70r. multicoloured . . . 90 55

995 Burning Tank and Man with Sling

996 Butterfly and Tulip

1993. World Jerusalem Day.
2771 **995** 20r. multicoloured . . . 25 15

1993. New Year Festival. Flowers and Butterflies. Multicoloured.
2772 20r. Type **996** 25 15
2773 20r. Butterfly and narcissus 25 15
2774 40r. Butterfly, tulips and rose 50 30
2775 40r. Butterfly and roses . . 50 30

997 Grass and Goldfish in Bowl

1993. Fetr Feast.
2776 **997** 100r. multicoloured . . . 2·25 1·25

998 Open Music Book

1993. 14th Anniv of Islamic Republic.
2777 **998** 40r. multicoloured . . . 40 25

999 Door and Landscape

1993. International Birth Millenary of Sheikh Mofeed Congress.
2778 **999** 80r. multicoloured . . . 80 50

1000 Emblem

1001 Globe

1993. 13th Asian and Pacific Labour Ministers' Conference, Teheran.
2779 **1000** 100r. multicoloured . . 1·00 60

1993. Int Congress for Advancement of Science and Technology in Islamic World.
2780 **1001** 50r. multicoloured . . . 50 30

1002 Mirror Box

1993. International Museum Day.
2781 **1002** 40r. multicoloured . . . 40 25

1003 Khomeini

1004 Girl on Swing

1993. 4th Death Anniv of Ayatollah Khomeini.
2782 **1003** 20r. multicoloured . . . 25 10

1993. World Children's Day.
2783 **1004** 50r. multicoloured . . . 50 30

1005 Knitted Socks

1006 Family at Window

1993. World Crafts Day.
2784 **1005** 70r. multicoloured . . . 70 45

1993. World Population Day.
2785 **1006** 30r. multicoloured . . . 30 20

1007 Football

1993. Student Games. Multicoloured.
2786 20r. Type **1007** 20 10
2787 40r. Judo and wrestling . . 40 25
2788 40r. Long jumping, weightlifting, badminton and basketball 40 25

1008 Butterfly and Film Frame

1993. International Children's and Youths' Film Festival, Isfahan.
2789 **1008** 60r. multicoloured . . . 60 30

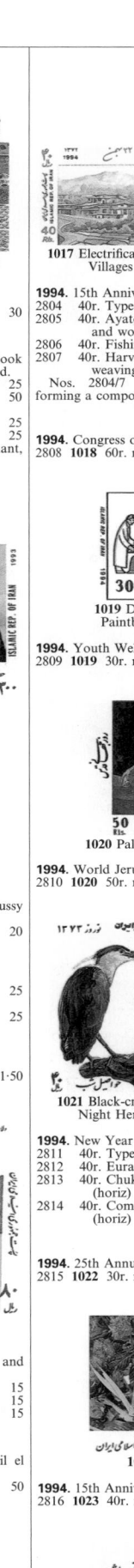

1009 Postal Messenger

1010 Stars and Birds

1993. World Post Day.
2790 **1009** 60r. multicoloured . . . 60 30

1993. 3rd International Biennial Children's Book Illustrations Exhibition, Teheran. Multicoloured.
2791 30r. Type **1010** 40 25
2792 30r. Moon and girl in boat 85 50
2793 30r. Cherub blowing trumpet 40 25
2794 30r. Trees and clouds . . . 40 25
Nos. 2791/4 were issued together, se-tenant, forming a composite design.

1011 Khaje Nassireddin Tussy

1013 Ayatollah Golpayegani

1012 Militia Member

1993. 719th Death Anniv of Khaje Nassireddin Tussy (scientist).
2795 **1011** 30r. multicoloured . . . 35 20

1993. People's Militia Week. Multicoloured.
2796 50r. Type **1012** 50 25
2797 50r. Woman tying headband for Militia member . . . 50 25

1993. Ayatollah Golpayegani Commem.
2798 **1013** 300r. multicoloured . . 3·00 1·50

1014 Hopscotch Grid drawn in Blood

1015 Flags

1993. Support for Moslems of Bosnia and Herzegovina. Multicoloured.
2799 40r. Type **1014** 45 15
2800 40r. Youth giving "V" sign 45 15
2801 40r. Woman and mosque . . 45 15

1994. Invalids' Day and Birthday of Abalfazil el Abbas.
2802 **1015** 80r. multicoloured . . . 80 50

1016 Trees and Ploughed Field in Book

1994. Agricultural Week.
2803 **1016** 60r. multicoloured . . . 65 40

1017 Electrification of Villages

1018 Dome of the Rock

1994. 15th Anniv of Islamic Revolution. Mult.
2804 40r. Type **1017** 65 40
2805 40r. Ayatollah Khomeini and workers with flag . . 65 40
2806 40r. Fishing and new roads 65 40
2807 40r. Harvesting wheat and weaving 65 40
Nos. 2804/7 were issued together, se-tenant, forming a composite design.

1994. Congress on Islamic Law.
2808 **1018** 60r. multicoloured . . . 70 40

1019 Doctor, Gymnast, Camera, Paintbrush, Book and Student

1994. Youth Welfare.
2809 **1019** 30r. multicoloured . . . 50 30

1020 Palestinian and Peaceful Scene

1994. World Jerusalem Day.
2810 **1020** 50r. multicoloured . . . 55 30

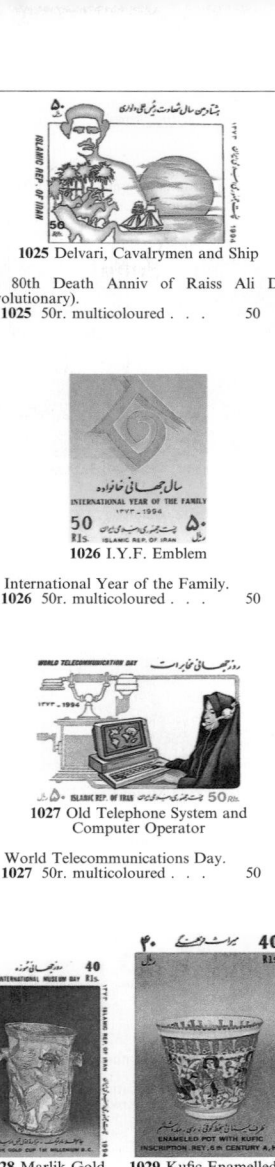

1021 Black-crowned Night Heron

1022 Ball and Rectangles

1994. New Year Festival. Birds. Multicoloured.
2811 40r. Type **1021** 75 40
2812 40r. Eurasian bittern 75 40
2813 40r. Chukar partridges (horiz) 75 40
2814 40r. Common pheasants (horiz) 75 40

1994. 25th Annual Mathematics Conference.
2815 **1022** 30r. multicoloured . . . 50 30

1023 Book and Roses

1994. 15th Anniv of Islamic Republic.
2816 **1023** 40r. multicoloured . . . 40 20

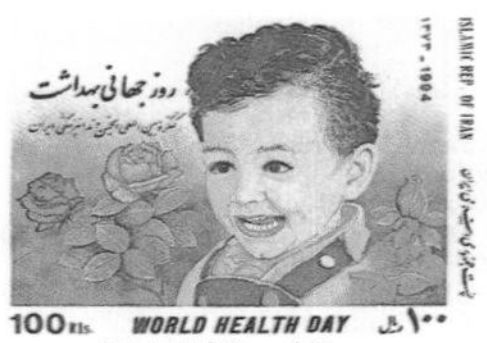

1024 Child and Roses

1994. World Health Day.
2817 **1024** 100r. multicoloured . . 1·00 40

1025 Delvari, Cavalrymen and Ship

1994. 80th Death Anniv of Raiss Ali Delvari (revolutionary).
2818 **1025** 50r. multicoloured . . . 50 20

1026 I.Y.F. Emblem

1994. International Year of the Family.
2819 **1026** 50r. multicoloured . . . 50 20

1027 Old Telephone System and Computer Operator

1994. World Telecommunications Day.
2820 **1027** 50r. multicoloured . . . 50 20

1028 Marlik Gold Cup

1029 Kufic Enamelled Pot

1994. International Museum Day.
2821 **1028** 40r. multicoloured . . . 50 20

1994. Cultural Preservation.
2822 **1029** 40r. multicoloured . . . 50 20

1030 Khomeini

1031 Motahhari

1994. 5th Death Anniv of Ayatollah Khomeini.
2823 **1030** 30r. multicoloured . . . 30 15

1994. 15th Death Anniv of Ayatollah Motahhari.
2824 **1031** 30r. multicoloured . . . 30 15

1032 Rose-water Sprinkler

1034 Mosaic and Rose

1033 Games Emblem

1994. World Crafts Day. Multicoloured.
2825 60r. Type **1032** 60 30
2826 60r. Silk weaving, Khorassan 60 30

1994. Islamic Countries' University Student Games.
2827 **1033** 60r. multicoloured . . . 55 30

1994. Mohammed's Birth Anniv and Unity Week.
2828 **1034** 30r. multicoloured . . . 30 15

1035 Cameraman

1994. 14th Anniv of Iran–Iraq War.
2829 **1035** 70r. multicoloured . . . 70 30

1036 Envelope

1994. World Post Day.
2830 **1036** 50r. multicoloured . . . 50 25

1037 Allegory of Woman

1038 Soldier

1994. Women's Day and Birth Anniv of Fatima.
2831 **1037** 70r. multicoloured . . . 70 30

1994. People's Militia Week.
2832 **1038** 30r. multicoloured . . . 35 15

1039 Book

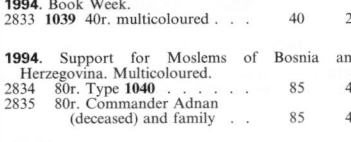

1040 Arms, Map and Town

1994. Book Week.
2833 **1039** 40r. multicoloured . . . 40 20

1994. Support for Moslems of Bosnia and Herzegovina. Multicoloured.
2834 80r. Type **1040** 85 40
2835 80r. Commander Adnan (deceased) and family . . 85 40

1041 Araki

1042 Arabic Script

1995. 2nd Death Anniv of Grand Ayatollah Mohammad Ali Araki (Shia leader).
2836 **1041** 100r. multicoloured . . 1·00 50

1995. World Day of the Oppressed. Birth Anniv of Mahdi.
2837 **1042** 50r. multicoloured . . . 50 25

1043 Flag, Dome and Man
1044 Crowd, National Flag and Ayatollah Khomeini

1995. Revolutionaries (1st series). Multicoloured.
2838 50r. Type **1043** 50 25
2839 50r. Man in patterned shirt 50 25
2840 50r. Man with full beard wearing grey shirt 50 25
2841 50r. Man in jacket and sweater looking to right 50 25
See also Nos. 2874/7, 2909/16, 2953/6, 3029/32 and 3034/7.

1995. 16th Anniv of Islamic Revolution.
2842 **1044** 100r. multicoloured . . 1·00 50

1045 Dome of the Rock
1046 Hand holding Tree

1995. World Jerusalem Day.
2843 **1045** 100r. multicoloured . . 1·00 50

1995. Tree Day.
2844 **1046** 50r. multicoloured . . . 50 25

1047 Hyacinths

1995. New Year Festival. Multicoloured.
2845 50r. Type **1047** 60 30
2846 50r. Pansies 60 30
2847 50r. Grass and bow 60 30
2848 50r. Tulips, bow and goldfish bowl 80 50

1048 Diesel Goods Train on Bridge

1995. Inauguration of Bafq–Bandar Abbas Railway.
2849 **1048** 100r. multicoloured . . 1·50 80

1049 Phoenix rising from Tulips
1050 Shapes

1995. 16th Anniv of Islamic Republic.
2850 **1049** 100r. multicoloured . . 1·00 50

1995. Press Festival.
2851 **1050** 100r. multicoloured . . 1·00 50

1051 Khomeini
1052 Arabic Script

1995. Ayatollah Ahmad Khomeini Commem.
2852 **1051** 50r. multicoloured . . . 50 25

1995. Invalids' Day.
2853 **1052** 80r. multicoloured . . . 80 40

1053 Yezd Mosque and Vaziri

1995. Ayatollah Ali Vaziri Commemoration.
2854 **1053** 100r. multicoloured . . 1·00 50

1054 Telecommunications

1995. World Telecommunications Day.
2855 **1054** 100r. multicoloured . . 1·00 50

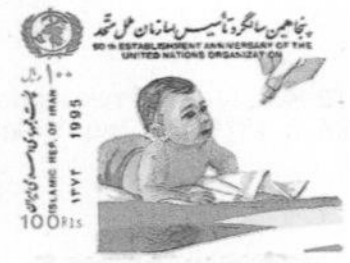

1055 Khomeini
1056 Immunizing Baby

1995. 6th Death Anniv of Ayatollah Khomeini.
2856 **1055** 100r. multicoloured . . 1·00 50

1995. 50th Anniv of U.N.O. Multicoloured.
2857 100r. Type **1056** . . . . . 1·00 50
2858 100r. Child laughing . . . . 1·00 50
2859 100r. Cereals and world map . . . . 1·00 50
2860 100r. Woman reading . . . 1·00 50

1057 Ashtiany
1059 Man with Gun and Book

1058 Dam Workers

1995. Iqbal Ashtiany (historian) Commem.
2861 **1057** 100r. multicoloured . . 1·00 50

1995. Government Week.
2862 **1058** 100r. multicoloured . . 1·00 50

1995. People's Militia Week.
2863 **1059** 100r. multicoloured . . 1·00 50

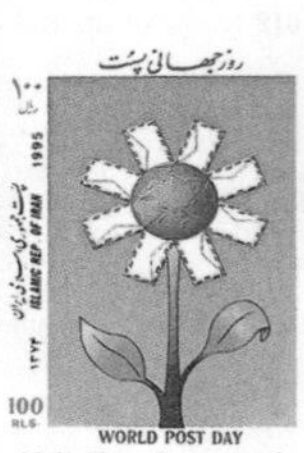

1060 Envelopes and Globe forming Flower
1061 Cypher

1995. World Post Day.
2864 **1060** 100r. multicoloured . . 1·00 50

1995. Prophet Mohammed Commemoration.
2865 **1061** 100r. multicoloured . . 1·00 50

1062 Tondgoyan
1063 Shaghaghi

1995. M. J. Tondgoyan (oil minister) Commem.
2866 **1062** 100r. multicoloured . . 1·00 50

1996. Fathi Shaghaghi (Islamic Jihad Secretary-General) Commemoration.
2867 **1063** 100r. multicoloured . . 1·00 50

1064 Crowd, Flowers and Ayatollah Khomeini
1065 Dome of the Rock

1996. 17th Anniv of Islamic Revolution.
2868 **1064** 100r. multicoloured . . 1·00 50

1996. World Jerusalem Day.
2869 **1065** 100r. multicoloured . . 1·00 50

1066 Common Cardinal

1996. New Year Festival. Birds. Multicoloured.
2870 100r. Type **1066** . . . . . 1·50 80
2871 100r. Budgerigar . . . . . 1·50 80
2872 100r. Golden oriole . . . . 1·50 80
2873 100r. European roller . . . 1·50 80

1996. Revolutionaries (2nd series). As T **1043**. Multicoloured.
2874 100r. Colonel-pilot Abbas Babaiy . . . . 1·00 50
2875 100r. Officer-pilot Ali Akbar Sharoudi . . . . 1·00 50
2876 100r. Commandant Mohammad Ebrahim Hemmat . . . . 1·00 50
2877 100r. Commandant Mohammad Boroudjerdi 1·00 50

1067 Ayatollah Khomeini, Ballot Box and Crowd
1068 Open Book, Flowers and Birds

1996. 17th Anniv of Islamic Republic.
2878 **1067** 200r. multicoloured . . 2·00 1·00

1996. International Book Fair, Teheran.
2879 **1068** 85r. multicoloured . . . 85 40

1069 Diesel Locomotive in Tunnel, Imam Riza's Shrine, Meshed, and Horses
1070 Camel Train and Prisoner tied to Stake

1996. Meshed–Sarakhs–Tajan International Railway.
2880 **1069** 200r. multicoloured . . 1·00 40

1996. Day of Prisoners of War and Missing in Action.
2881 **1070** 200r. multicoloured . . 2·00 1·00

1071 Khomeini

1996. 7th Death Anniv of Ayatollah Khomeini.
2882 **1071** 200r. multicoloured . . 2·00 1·00

1072 Carpet

1996. World Crafts Day.
2883 **1072** 200r. multicoloured . . 2·00 1·00

1073 Emblem

1996. 3rd Posts and Telecommunications Ministerial Conference, Teheran.
2884 **1073** 200r. multicoloured . . 2·00 1·00

1074 Zouqeblateyne Mosque

1996. Mohammed's Birth Anniv and Unity Week. Multicoloured.
2885 200r. Type **1074** . . . . . 2·00 1·00
2886 200r. Tomb of Imam Hossein (dome with flag flying to right) . . . . . 2·00 1·00
2887 200r. Prophet's Mosque (dome without flag) . . . 2·00 1·00
2888 200r. Tomb of Imam Riza (dome with flag flying to left) . . . . 2·00 1·00
2889 200r. Qaba Mosque (with four corner minarets) . . 2·00 1·00

1075 Teheran Underground

1996. Government Week. Multicoloured.
2890 200r. Type **1075** . . . . . 1·00 40
2891 200r. Ispahan iron works . . 1·00 40
2892 200r. Merchant fleet . . . . 1·00 40
2893 200r. Bandar-e-Imam oil refinery . . . . 1·00 40
2894 200r. Boumehen Earth Station . . . . 1·00 40

1076 Ardabily and Mosque Interior

1996. Allameh Moghaddas Ardabily Commem.
2895 **1076** 200r. multicoloured . . 2·00 1·00

1077 Artillery Position and Soldier praying

1996. 16th Anniv of Iran–Iraq War.
2896 **1077** 200r. multicoloured . . 2·00 1·00

1078 Cogs and Equipment

1996. World Standards Day.
2897 **1078** 200r. multicoloured . . 2·00 1·00

1079 Harvesting and Man working on "Globe" Rick

1996. World Food Summit, Rome.
2898 **1079** 200r. multicoloured . . 2·00 1·00

1080 Men, Houses and Women

1996. National Population and Housing Census.
2899 **1080** 200r. multicoloured . . 2·00 1·00

1081 Wrestlers

1996. 2nd World University Wrestling Championship, Teheran.
2900 **1081** 500r. multicoloured . . 4·75 2·40

1082 Ayatollah Khomeini embracing Youth

1083 Hands holding Tree

1997. 18th Anniv of Islamic Revolution. Mult.
2901 200r. Type **1082** . . . . . 2·25 1·00
2902 200r. Banner of Khomeini above crowd . . . . . . 2·25 1·00
2903 200r. Khomeini waving . . 2·25 1·00
2904 200r. Khomeini returning from exile in France . . . 2·25 1·00
2905 200r. Soldiers . . . . 2·25 1·00

1997. Tree Day.
2906 **1083** 200r. multicoloured . . 2·25 1·00

1084 Rainbow and National Flag

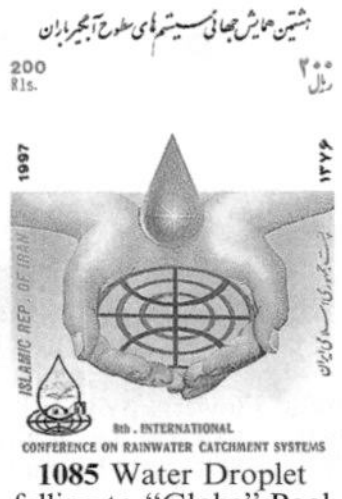
1085 Water Droplet falling to "Globe" Pool in Cupped Hands

1997. 18th Anniv of Islamic Republic.
2907 **1084** 200r. multicoloured . . 2·25 1·00

1997. 8th International Rainwater Catchment Systems Conference.
2908 **1085** 200r. multicoloured . . 2·25 1·00

1997. Revolutionaries (3rd series). As T **1043**. Multicoloured.
2909 100r. Alireza Mowahhed Danesh (blue flag, white turban) . . . . 1·25 50
2910 100r. Mohammad Reza Dastwareh (orange flag, white turban) . . . . . . 1·25 50
2911 100r. Abbas Karimi (blue flag, full-face without glasses) . . . . 1·25 50
2912 100r. Nasser Kazemi (orange flag, white vest with red trim) . . . . . 1·25 50
2913 100r. Youssef Kolahdouz (blue flag, three-quarter face) . . . . 1·25 50
2914 100r. Yadollah Kolhar (orange flag, full-face) . . 1·25 50
2915 100r. Fazlollah Mahallati (blue flag, full-face with glasses) . . . . 1·25 50
2916 100r. Abdollah Meyssami (orange flag, green vest and coat) . . . . 1·25 50

1086 Satellite, Letter, Globe and Computer

1087 Khomeini

1997. Post, Telecommunications and Productivity.
2917 **1086** 200r. multicoloured . . 2·25 1·00

1997. 8th Death Anniv of Ayatollah Khomeini.
2918 **1087** 200r. multicoloured . . 2·00 1·00

1088 Teheran Underground Railway Map and Tunnel

1089 Flora and Fauna

1997. National Achievements. Multicoloured.
2919 40r. Type **1088** 15 10
2920 50r. Cornfield and silo . . . 20 10
2921 65r. Medals from Student Scientific Olympiads . . . 25 10
2922 70r. Steelworks, Mobarakeh 30 15
2923 100r. Modern communications systems 40 20
2924 130r. Harbour and tanker 50 25
2925 150r. Oil refinery, Bandar Abbas 60 30
2926 200r. Martyr Radja-ee dam 75 35
2927 350r. Martyr Radja-ee power station . . . . . . 1·40 70
2928 400r. Foreign Ministry building . . . . 1·75 80
2929 500r. Child receiving oral vaccination . . . . 2·10 1·00
2930 650r. Koran Printing House and Koran . . . . 2·75 1·40
2931 1000r. Imam Khomeini International Airport, Teheran . . . . 4·25 2·10
2932 2000r. Tomb of Imam Khomeini, Teheran . . . 8·25 4·00

1997. 10th Anniv of Montreal Protocol (on reduction of use of chlorofluorocarbons).
2933 **1089** 200r. multicoloured . . 2·25 1·00

1090 Crowd with Flags and Banners

1091 Allama Mohammad Iqbal (Pakistani poet)

1997. 17th Anniv of Iran–Iraq War.
2934 **1090** 200r. multicoloured . . 2·25 1·00

1997. Iranian–Pakistani Culture. Multicoloured.
2935 200r. Type **1091** . . . . . 2·25 1·00
2936 200r. Jalal-ad-din Moulana Rumi (Persian mystic) . . 2·25 1·00

1092 Airplane, Letters and Computer

1997. World Post Day.
2937 **1092** 200r. multicoloured . . 2·25 1·00

1093 Frasheri and Etehemberg Mosque, Tirana

1997. 150th Birth Anniv (1996) of Naim Frasheri (Albanian writer).
2938 **1093** 200r. multicoloured . . 2·25 1·00

1094 Calligraphy

1095 Games Emblem

1997. 8th Islamic Summit, Teheran. Illustrated pages from the Koran. Each green, gold and red.
2939 300r. Type **1094** . . . . . 3·00 1·50
2940 300r. Page with rose at bottom left . . . . 3·00 1·50
2941 300r. Page with rose on right-hand side . . . . . 3·00 1·50
2942 300r. Page with rose at top left-hand corner . . . . . 3·00 1·50
2943 300r. Summit emblem . . . 3·00 1·50

1997. 2nd Islamic Countries Women's Games, Teheran.
2944 **1095** 200r. multicoloured . . 2·25 1·00

1096 Dome of the Rock

1998. World Jerusalem Day.
2945 **1096** 250r. multicoloured . . 10 10

1097 State Flags and Poppies

1998. 19th Anniv of Islamic Revolution. Mult.
2946 200r. Type **1097** 10 10
2947 200r. Harvesting grain . . . 10 10
2948 200r. Soldiers with flags . . 10 10
2949 200r. Crowd with banner of Khomeini 10 10
2950 200r. Ayatollah Khomeini 10 10
Nos. 2946/50 were issued together, se-tenant, forming a composite design.

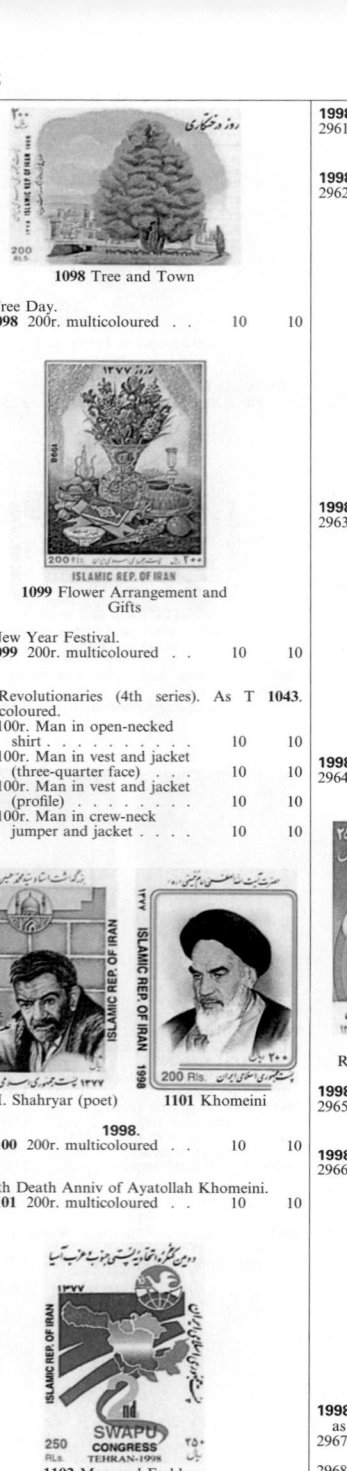

1098 Tree and Town

1998. Tree Day.
2951 **1098** 200r. multicoloured . . 10 10

1099 Flower Arrangement and Gifts

1998. New Year Festival.
2952 **1099** 200r. multicoloured . . 10 10

1998. Revolutionaries (4th series). As T **1043**. Multicoloured.
2953 100r. Man in open-necked shirt 10 10
2954 100r. Man in vest and jacket (three-quarter face) . . . 10 10
2955 100r. Man in vest and jacket (profile) 10 10
2956 100r. Man in crew-neck jumper and jacket 10 10

1100 M. Shahryar (poet)

1101 Khomeini

1998.
2957 **1100** 200r. multicoloured . . 10 10

1998. 9th Death Anniv of Ayatollah Khomeini.
2958 **1101** 200r. multicoloured . . 10 10

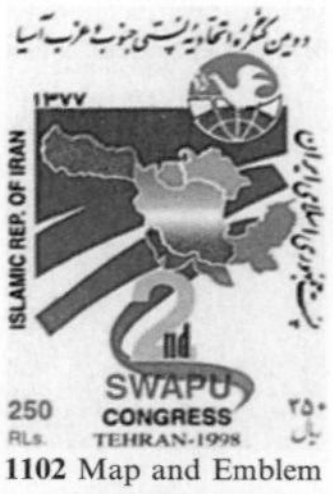
1102 Map and Emblem

1998. 2nd South and West Asia Postal Union Congress.
2959 **1102** 250r. multicoloured . . 10 10

1103 Player, Ball and Stadium

1998. World Cup Football Championship, France.
2960 **1103** 500r. multicoloured . . 20 10

1104 Globe and Headset

1105 Silver Vessel

1998. World Telecommunications Day.
2961 **1104** 200r. multicoloured . . 10 10

1998. World Handicrafts Day.
2962 **1105** 200r. multicoloured . . 10 10

1106 State Flag as Dove, Birds and Flowers

1998. 1st Anniv of Presidential Election.
2963 **1106** 200r. multicoloured . . 10 10

1107 Khomeini voting

1998. 19th Anniv of Islamic Republic.
2964 **1107** 250r. multicoloured . . 10 10

1108 Handshake, Rainbow and Doves

1109 Arabic Script

1998. Co-operation Day.
2965 **1108** 250r. multicoloured . . 10 10

1998. "1000th Friday of Public Prayer".
2966 **1109** 250r. blue, gold and black 10 10

(1110)

1998. Mosques. Nos. 2415a and 2416a surch as T **1110**.
2967 **1110** 200r. on 1r. orange and silver 10 10
2968 200r. on 3r. green and silver 10 10

1111 Globe and Shark's Fin

1998. International Year of the Ocean.
2969 **1111** 250r. multicoloured . . 10 10

1112 Arabic Script

1998. Sacred Defence Week.
2970 **1112** 250r. multicoloured . . 10 10

1113 Envelope and Clouds as World Map

1998. World Post Day.
2971 **1113** 200r. multicoloured . . 10 10

1114 Wrestlers

1998. World Wrestling Championship, Iran.
2972 **1114** 250r. multicoloured . . 10 10

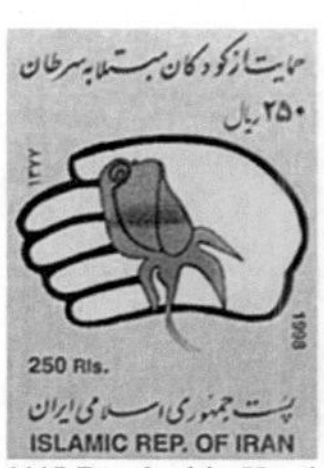
1115 Rosebud in Hand

1116 Navigation Instrument

1998. Children's Cancer Relief.
2973 **1115** 250r. multicoloured . . 10 10

1999. Museum Exhibit.
2974 **1116** 250r. multicoloured . . 10 10

1117 Khomeini

1999. 20th Anniv of Islamic Revolution.
2975 **1117** 250r. multicoloured . . 20 10

(1118) (1119)

1999. Flowers. Nos. 2738/a surch as T **1118**.
2976 200r. on 35r. multicoloured 15 10
2977 900r. on 30r. multicoloured 70 40

1999. International Book Fair, Teheran. No. 2879 surch as T **1119**.
2978 250r. on 85r. multicoloured 20 10

1120 Flag and Emblem

1999. 20th Anniv of Islamic Republic.
2979 **1120** 250r. multicoloured . . 20 10

1121 Emblem

1999. Ghadir Khom Religious Festival.
2980 **1121** 250r. multicoloured . . 20 10

1122 Harbour

1999. Ayatollah Khomeini Charity Fund. Mult.
2981 250r. Type **1122** 20 10
2982 250r. Houses 20 10

1123 Soldier, Tank, Ship and Aircraft

1999. Army Day.
2983 **1123** 250r. multicoloured . . 20 10

1124 Sadra al-Din Shirazi

1999. Sadra al-Din Shirazi (philosopher) Commem.
2984 **1124** 250r. multicoloured . . 20 10

1125 Khomeini

1999. 10th Death Anniv of Ayatollah Khomeini.
2985 **1125** 250r. multicoloured . . 20 10

1126 Parliament Building and Khomeini

1999. 20th Anniv of Iranian Parliament.
2986 **1126** 250r. multicoloured . . 20 10

1127 Emblem and Map

1999. Organization of Islamic Conference Interparliamentary Union Congress, Tehran.
2987 **1127** 250r. multicoloured . . 20 10

1128 Emblem and Dome

1999. Unity Week.
2988 **1128** 250r. multicoloured . . 20 10

1129 Tapestry

1130 River Kingfisher

1999. World Handicrafts Day.
2989 **1129** 250r. multicoloured . . 20 10

1999. Birds. Multicoloured.

2990	100r. Hoopoe	10	10
2991	150r. Type **1130**	15	10
2992	200r. Robin	15	10
2993	250r. Crested lark	20	10
2994	300r. Red-backed shrike	20	10
2995	350r. Roller	20	10
2996	400r. Blue tit	25	15
2997	500r. Bee eater	35	20
2998	1000r. Redwing	70	40
2999	2000r. Twite	1·30	60
2999a	3000r. Whitethroat	1·75	75
2999b	4500r. Collar dove	2·25	90

1131 Moon partially covering Sun

1999. Solar Eclipse. Multicoloured.

3000	250r. Type **1131**	20	10
3001	250r. Moon passing in front of Sun	20	10
3002	250r. Full solar eclipse . . .	20	10
3003	250r. Sun appearing from right-hand side of Moon	20	10
3004	250r. Sun appearing	20	10

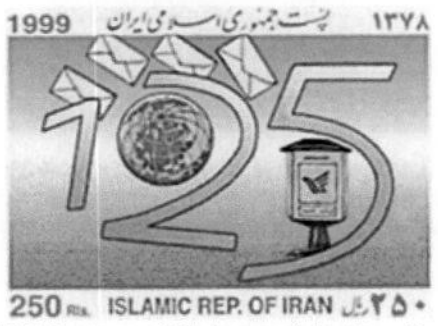
1132 Letters, Globe and Letter Box

1999. 125th Anniv of Universal Postal Union.
3005 **1132** 250r. multicoloured . . 20 10

1133 Chinese Girl

1999. International Children's Day. Showing children from different cultures. Multicoloured.

3006	150r. Type **1133**	15	10
3007	150r. Indian girl	15	10
3008	150r. Native American girl	15	10
3009	150r. Arabian boy	15	10
3010	150r. Iranian girl	15	10
3011	150r. Mexican boy	15	10
3012	150r. Eskimo boy	15	10
3013	150r. African girl	15	10
3014	150r. Russian boy	15	10
3015	150r. European girl	15	10

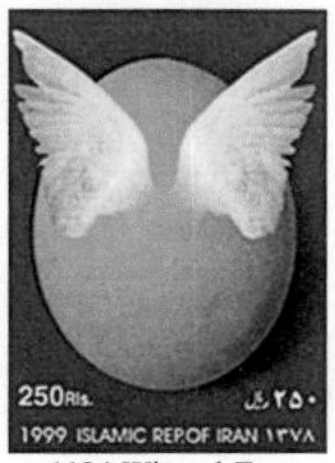
1134 Winged Egg

1999. International Children's Book Illustrations Exhibition. Multicoloured.

3016	250r. Type **1134**	20	10
3017	250r. Decorated egg	20	10
3018	250r. Egg decorated with white crescent	20	10
3019	250r. Egg decorated with flowers	20	10

1135 Ayatollah Mohammed Taghi

1999. Ayatollah Mohammed Taghi Commemoration.
3020 **1135** 250r. multicoloured . . 20 10

1136 Ayatollah Khomeni

2000. 21st Anniv of Islamic Revolution.
3021 **1136** 300r. multicoloured . . 20 10

2000. Flowers. Nos. 2741, 2743, 2746 surch **250 R.**

3022	250r. on 60r. multicoloured	20	10
3023	250r. on 75r. multicoloured	20	10
3024	250r. on 120r. multicoloured	20	10

1138 Bee Eaters

2000. New Year Festival.
3025 **1138** 300r. multicoloured . . 20 10

1139 Inscription

2000. National Archives Day.
3026 **1139** 300r. multicoloured . . 20 10

1140 Books, Cogs, Chimneys and Hand holding Torch

2000. 70th Anniv of Science and Technology University.
3027 **1140** 300r. multicoloured . . 20 10

1141 Mofatteh and Building

2000. Ayatollah Mofatteh Commemoration.
3028 **1141** 300r. multicoloured . . 20 10

1142 Khalil Motahar Nia

2000. Revolutionaries (5th series). Multicoloured.

3029	150r. Type **1142**	10	10
3030	150r. Haschem Etemadi (pink shirt)	10	10
3031	150r. Madjid Sepassi (green shirt)	10	10
3032	150r. Mahmud Sotoudeh (blue T-shirt and shirt) . .	10	10

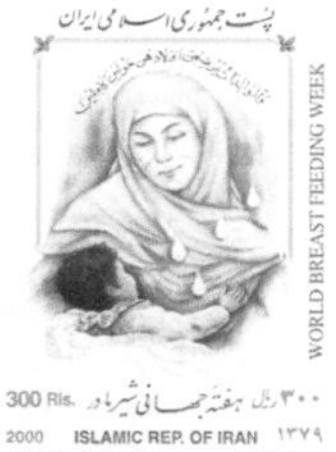
1143 Mother and Baby

2000. International Breast-feeding Week.
3033 **1143** 300r. multicoloured . . 20 10

1144 Hadj Reza Habubollahi

2000. Revolutionaries (6th series). Multicoloured.

3034	150r. Type **1144**	10	10
3035	150r. Hassan Agharebparast (shirt with epaulettes) . .	10	10
3036	150r. Mostafa Ravani Pou (white turban)	10	10
3037	150r. Mohsen Safavi (wearing glasses)	10	10

1145 Books and Educational Symbols

1147 Satellite and Dish

1146 Stylized Bird

2000. University Anniversary.
3038 **1145** 300r. multicoloured . . 20 10

2000. 8th Asian-Pacific Postal Union Congress, Tehran.
3039 **1146** 300r. blue, mauve and black 20 10

2000. International World Space Week. Multicoloured.

3040	500r. Type **1147**	35	20
3041	500r. Satellite and dish (different)	35	20

1148 Birds, Flowers and Calligraphy

2001. Eid-ul Ghadir.
3042 **1148** 500r. multicoloured . . 40 25

1149 Flowers, Calligraphy and Sun

2001. Year of Imam Ali.
3043 **1149** 500r. multicoloured . . 40 25

1150 Red-headed Bunting

2001. New Year Festival. Multicoloured.

3044	300r. Type **1150**	20	10
3045	300r. Hawfinch (vert) . . .	20	10

1151 Mosque and Mohamed Al Dorra and Father

2001. Intifada.
3046 **1151** 350r. multicoloured . . 25 15

1152 Chaffinch

2001. Belgica 2001 International Stamp Exhibition, Brussels. Multicoloured.

3047 350r. Type **1152** 25 15
3048 350r. Waxwing 25 15
3049 350r. Gate to Melli Bagh National Garden (vert) . . 25 15

1153 Mount Fuji, Japan

2001. Philanippon '01 International Stamp Exhibition, Tokyo. Multicoloured.

3050 250r. Type **1153** 20 10
3051 250r. Mount Damavand, Iran 20 10

1154 Flag, Globe and Iranian Buildings

2001. World Tourism Day.

3052 **1154** 500r. multicoloured . . 40 25

1155 Police Helicopters and Vehicles

2001. Police Week. Multicoloured.

3053 250r. Type **1155** 20 10
3054 250r. Flag, boats and Policeman 20 10

Nos. 3053/4 were issued together, se-tenant, forming a composite design.

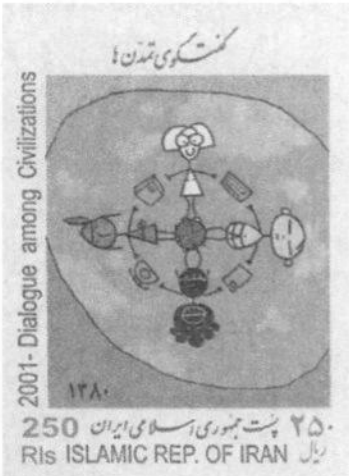

1156 Children encircling Globe

2001. United Nations Year of Dialogue among Civilizations. Multicoloured.

3055 250r. Type **1156** 20 10
3056 250r. European and Asian faces (horiz) 20 10

1157 Ball and Dove

2001. 3rd Islamic Women's Games, Tehran.

3057 **1157** 250r. multicoloured . . 20 10

1158 Koran and Flowers

2001. Koran.

3058 **1158** 500r. multicoloured . . 40 25

1159 P 232 *Tabarza*

2001. Navy Day. Multicoloured.

3059 500r. Type **1159** 40 25
3060 500r. Frigate 40 25
3061 500r. Helicopter and hovercraft 40 25
3062 500r. Submarine 40 25

1160 Bees on Honeycomb

2001. Bee-keeping.

3063 **1160** 500r. multicoloured . . 40 25

1161 Hands enclosing Face

2001. 50th Anniv of United Nations High Commissioner for Refugees.

3064 **1161** 500r. blue, black and mauve 40 25

1162 Vehicle, Roadways and Bridge

2001. Transportation Day. Multicoloured.

3065 350r. Type **1162** 25 15
3066 350r. Bridge, vehicles and buildings 25 15

Nos. 3065/6 were issued together, se-tenant, forming a composite design.

1163 Locomotive

2001. Tehran Subway. Multicoloured.

3067 500r. Type **1163** 40 25
3068 500r. Locomotive right view 40 25

1164 Samand Saloon Car

2002. 1st Iranian Manufactured Car. Multicoloured.

3069 500r. Type **1164** 40 25
3070 500r. Grey car (horiz) . . . 40 25

1165 Globe as Plant Pot containing Tree

2002. Tree Planting Day.

3071 **1165** 500r. multicoloured . . 40 25

1166 Squacco Heron (Ardeola ralloides)

2002. New Year Festival. Multicoloured.

3072 500r. Type **1166** 40 25
3073 500r. Hoopoe (*Upupa epops*) 40 25
3074 500r. Blue tit (*Parus caeruleus*) 40 25
3075 500r. Alexandrine parakeet (*Psittacula eupatria*) . . . 40 25

1167 Imam Hossein's Wounded Horse returning to Kerbala

2002. Death of Imam Hossein (grandson of Mohamed). Sheet 99 × 76 mm. Imperf.

MS3076 **1167** 400r. multicoloured 30 30

1168 Chestnut Tiger (*Danaus sita*)

2002. Butterflies. Multicoloured.

3077 400r. Type **1168** 30 20
3078 400r. Comma (*Polygonia c-album*) 30 20
3079 400r. Blue argus (*Precis orithya*) 30 20
3080 400r. Painted lady (*Vanessa cardui*) 30 20
3081 400r. *Papilio maacki* 30 20

1169 Caspian

2002. Horses. Multicoloured.

3082 400r. Type **1169** 30 20
3083 400r. Kurd 30 20
3084 400r. Turkoman 30 20
3085 400r. Arab 30 20

1170 *Hyoscyamus muticus*

2002. Philakorea 2002 International Stamp Exhibition, Seoul. Flowers. Multicoloured.

3086 400r. Type **1170** 30 20
3087 400r. *Fritillaria* ("Frittillaria") 30 20
3088 400r. *Calotropis procera* . . 30 20
3089 400r. *Ranuculus* 30 20

1171 Ayatollah Khomeini

2002. Birth Centenary of Ayatollah Khomeini.

3090 **1171** 400r. multicoloured . . 40 25

1172 Child and Dome of the Rock

2002. Jerusalem Day.

3091 **1172** 400r. multicoloured . . 30 20

1173 Iranian Decorated Pots

2002. Centenary of Brazil—Iran Diplomatic Relations. Multicoloured.

3092 400r. Type **1173** 30 20
3093 400r. Marajoara pots, Brazil 30 20

1174 Emblem

2002. 2nd Biennial Exhibition of Contemporary Islamic Painting.

3094 **1174** 400r. multicoloured . . 30 20

NEWSPAPER POSTAGE DUE STAMPS

1909. Optd **Imprimes** in English and Persian.

N319 **38** 2ch. grey on blue . . . . 13·00 2·00

OFFICIAL STAMPS

1902. Stamp of 1898 surch **Service** and value in English and Persian.

O224	**21**	5c. on 1k. red	4·00	50
O225		10c. on 1k. red	3·00	60
O226		12c. on 1k. red	4·25	1·40

1903. Stamps of 1903 optd **Service**.

O259	**38**	1c. lilac	15	10
O260		2c. grey	15	10
O261		3c. green	15	10
O262		5c. red	15	10
O263		10c. brown	15	10
O264		12c. blue	20	10
O265	**39**	1k. purple	40	10
O266		2k. blue	80	10
O267		5k. brown	6·00	20
O268		10k. red	6·00	50
O269		20k. orange	9·00	50
O270		30k. green	12·00	1·00
O271		50k. green	55·00	14·00

1905. Nos. 275/6 and 280/1 optd **Service**.

O283	**39**	2t. on 50k. green (275)	45·00	22·00
O285		2t. on 50k. green (280)	45·00	22·00
O284		3t. on 50k. green (276)	45·00	25·00
O286		3t. on 50k. green (281)	45·00	22·00

(O 57)

O 120

1911. Stamps of 1909 optd **Service** and with Type **O57**.

O353	**56**	1c. purple and orange	3·00	15
O354		2c. purple and violet	3·00	15
O355		3c. purple and green	3·00	20
O356		6c. purple and red	3·00	20
O357		9c. purple and grey	3·00	50
O358		10c. purple and mauve	6·00	60
O359		1k. brown, violet & silver	7·00	2·00
O360		2k. brown, green & silver	12·00	5·00

1915. Coronation stamps of 1915 optd **SERVICE** in English and Persian.

O460	**66**	1c. blue and red	10	10
O461		2c. red and blue	10	10
O462		3c. green	10	10
O463		5c. red	10	10
O464		6c. red and green	20	10
O465		9c. violet and brown	20	10
O466		10c. brown and green	20	10
O467		12c. blue	20	10
O468		24c. chocolate and brown	20	10
O469	**67**	1k. black, brown & silver	80	15
O470		2k. red, blue and silver	80	15
O471	–	3k. sepia, lilac and silver	80	20
O472	**67**	5k. grey, sepia and silver	85	20
O473	–	1t. black, violet and gold	85	35
O474	–	2t. brown, green and gold	90	35
O475	–	3t. red, crimson and gold	90	55
O476	–	5t. grey, blue and gold	1·25	60

1941.

O836	**O 120**	5d. violet	55	10
O837		10d. mauve	55	10
O838		25d. red	55	10
O839		50d. black	55	10
O840		75d. red	80	10
O841		1r. green	2·00	10
O842		1r.50 blue	2·25	10
O843		2r. blue	4·25	10
O844		3r. purple	8·50	10
O845		5r. green	12·00	20
O846		10r. blue and brown	35·00	40
O847		20r. mauve and blue	£130	1·50
O848		30r. green and violet	£250	2·75
O849		50r. brown and blue	£300	45·00

The rial values are larger (23 × 30 mm).

O 489 Red Lion and Sun Emblem

1974.

O1829	**O 489**	5d. violet and mauve	10	10
O1830		10d. mauve and blue	10	10
O1831		50d. orange & green	10	10
O1832		1r. blue and gold	10	10
O2046		1r. black and green	10	10
O1833		2r. green and orange	10	10
O2047		2r. brown and grey	10	10
O2048		3r. blue and orange	10	10
O2049		5r. green and pink	15	15
O1834		6r. green and yellow	35	10
O2050		6r. black and blue	15	15
O1835		8r. blue and yellow	35	15
O2051		8r. red and green	20	15
O1836		10r. blue and mauve	2·00	20
O2052		10r. turquoise & grn	35	20
O1837		11r. purple and blue	70	20
O2053		11r. blue and yellow	70	25
O1838		14r. red and blue	70	50
O2054		14r. green and grey	75	30
O2055		15r. blue and mauve	1·50	70
O1839		20r. blue and orange	70	55
O2056		20r. purple and yellow	1·75	30
O2057		30r. brown & orange	1·75	90
O1840		50r. brown and green	3·50	1·40
O2058		50r. black and gold	3·50	1·00

The 6r. to 50r. are larger, 23 × 37 mm.

PARCEL POST STAMPS

1915. Coronation stamps of 1915 optd **COLIS POSTAUX** in English and Persian.

P443	**66**	1c. blue and red	10	10
P444		2c. red and blue	10	10
P445		3c. green	10	10
P446		5c. red	10	10
P447		6c. red and green	20	10
P448		9c. violet and brown	20	10
P449		10c. brown and green	20	10
P450		12c. blue	20	10
P451		24c. chocolate and brown	20	10
P452	**67**	1k. black, brown & silver	70	15
P453		2k. red, blue and silver	70	15
P454		3k. sepia, lilac and silver	70	20
P455		5k. grey, sepia and silver	70	20
P456	–	1t. black, violet and gold	75	35
P457	–	2t. brown, green and gold	75	35
P458	–	3t. red, crimson and gold	80	55
P459	–	5t. grey, blue and gold	1·25	55

P 192

1958.

P1151	**P 192**	50d. drab	10	10
P1152		1r. red	10	10
P1153		2r. blue	20	10
P1154		3r. myrtle	15	10
P1478		5r. violet	15	10
P1479		10r. brown	30	15
P1480		20r. orange	50	35
P1481		30r. mauve	1·00	15
P1482		50r. lake	1·25	85
P1483		100r. yellow	2·75	1·00
P1484		200r. green	6·00	3·75

The word "IRAN" with a black frame is printed in reverse on the back of the above stamps and is intended to show through the stamps when attached to parcels.

POSTAL TAX STAMPS

T 142a Red Lion and Sun Emblem (8 lines to each ray)

1950. Hospitals Fund.

T1139	**T 142a**	50d. red and green	50	15
T1396		2r. red and lilac	80	15

1976. As T **142a** but with five lines to each ray.

T2007	**T 142a**	50d. red and green	1·25	20
T2008		2r. red and blue	1·75	20

IRAQ Pt. 1, Pt. 19

A country W. of Persia, formerly under Turkish dominion, then under British mandate after the 1914–18 War. An independent kingdom since 1932 until 14 July 1958, when the king was assassinated and a republic proclaimed.

1917. 16 annas = 1 rupee.
1931. 1000 fils = 1 dinar.

1918. Stamps of Turkey (Pictorial issue, Nos. 501/514) surch **IRAQ IN BRITISH OCCUPATION** and value in Indian currency.

1	¼a. on 5pa. purple	50	1·00
2	½a. on 10pa. green	70	20
3	1a. on 20pa. red	50	10
17	1½a. on 5pa. purple	1·50	1·00
5	2½a. on 1pi. blue	1·25	1·40
6	3a. on 1½pi. grey and red	1·25	25
7	4a. on 1¾pi. brown and grey	1·50	25
8	6a. on 2pi. black and green	1·60	1·25
9	8a. on 2½pi. green and orange	1·25	60
10	12a. on 5pi. lilac	1·75	4·00
11	1r. on 10pi. brown	2·25	1·40
12	2r. on 25pi. green	7·50	2·50
13	5r. on 50pi. red	20·00	21·00
14	10r. on 100pi. blue	50·00	17·00

2 Sunni Mosque, Muadhdham

3 Winged Cherub

4 Allegory of Date Palm

10 King Faisal I

1923.

41	**2**	½a. green	1·00	10
42	–	1a. brown	2·25	10
43	**3**	1½a. red	1·00	10
44	–	2a. buff	1·00	15
45	–	3a. blue	1·00	15
46	–	4a. violet	2·75	30
47	–	6a. blue	1·00	30
48	–	8a. bistre	3·00	30
49	**4**	1r. brown and green	5·00	1·50
50	**2**	2r. black	14·00	7·00
51		2r. bistre	40·00	3·25
52	–	5r. orange	27·00	13·00
53	–	10r. red	32·00	20·00

DESIGNS—30 × 24 mm: 1a. Gufas on the Tigris; 2a. Bull from Babylonian wall-sculpture; 6a., 10r. Shiah Mosque, Kadhimain. 34 × 24 mm: 3a. Arch of Ctesiphon. 24 × 30 mm: 4, 8a., 5r. Tribal Standard, Dulaim Camel Corps.

1927.

78	**10**	1r. brown	7·00	50

11 King Faisal I

12

1931.

80	**11**	½a. green	1·50	30
81		1a. brown	1·50	30
82		1½a. red	1·50	50
83		2a. orange	1·25	10
84		3a. blue	1·25	20
85		4a. purple	1·25	2·00
86		6a. blue	1·50	80
87		8a. green	1·50	2·50
88	**12**	1r. brown	3·50	2·00
89		2r. brown	5·50	4·75
90		5r. orange	19·00	12·00
91		10r. red	65·00	85·00
92	**10**	25r. violet	£500	£650

1932. Nos. 80/92 and 46 surch in "Fils" or "Dinar".

106	**11**	2f. on ½a. green	50	10
107		3f. on ½a. green	50	10
108		4f. on 1a. brown	2·25	25
109		5f. on 1a. brown	75	10
110		8f. on 1½a. red	50	50
111		10f. on 2a. orange	50	10
112		15f. on 3a. blue	1·50	1·00
113		20f. on 4a. purple	1·75	1·75
114	–	25f. on 4a. violet (No. 46)	2·75	4·00
115	**11**	30f. on 6a. blue	2·25	60
116		40f. on 8a. green	2·50	4·00
117	**12**	75f. on 1r. brown	2·00	4·00
118		100f. on 2r. brown	5·50	4·00
119		200f. on 5r. orange	14·00	24·00
120		½d. on 10r. red	55·00	90·00
121	**10**	1d. on 25r. violet	£100	£180

1932. As Types **10/12** but value in FILS or DINAR.

138	**11**	2f. blue	50	20
139		3f. green	50	10
140		4f. purple	50	10
141		5f. green	50	10
142		8f. red	1·50	10
143		10f. yellow	1·50	10
144		15f. blue	1·50	10
145		20f. orange	1·75	50
146		25f. mauve	1·75	50
147		30f. olive	2·25	15
148		40f. violet	1·50	80
149	**12**	50f. brown	1·50	20
150		75f. blue	3·00	2·75
151		100f. green	4·50	70
152		200f. red	13·00	3·25
153	**10**	½d. blue	40·00	35·00
154		1d. purple	80·00	80·00

16 King Ghazi

17

1934.

172	**16**	1f. violet	45	30
173		2f. blue	20	15
174		3f. green	20	15
175		4f. purple	25	15
176		5f. green	25	15
177		8f. red	35	15
178		10f. yellow	45	15
179		15f. blue	45	15
180		20f. orange	45	15
181		25f. mauve	85	20
182		30f. green	65	20
183		40f. violet	75	25
184	**17**	50f. brown	1·75	25
185		75f. blue	1·50	30
186		100f. green	1·90	45
187		200f. red	3·50	75
188	–	½d. blue	5·50	2·40
189	–	1d. red	38·00	12·00

DESIGN—23 × 27½ mm: ½, 1d. Portrait as in Types **16/17** but different frame.

19 Mausoleum of Sitt Zubaidah

21 Lion of Babylon

22 Spiral Tower of Samarra

1941.

208	**19**	1f. purple	10	10
209		2f. brown	10	10
210	–	3f. green	10	10
211	–	4f. violet	10	10
212	–	5f. red	20	10
213	**21**	8f. red	50	10
214		8f. yellow	10	10
215		10f. yellow	9·25	2·10
216		10f. red	50	10
217		15f. blue	85	20
218a		15f. black	85	30
219		20f. black	1·25	40
220		20f. blue	45	20
221	**22**	25f. purple	20	10
222		30f. orange	25	15
223b		40f. brown	85	40
224b	–	50f. blue	1·25	45
225a	–	75f. mauve	85	45
226	–	100f. olive	1·25	75
227	–	200f. orange	2·10	75
228	–	½d. blue	10·00	3·50
229a	–	1d. green	20·00	8·00

DESIGNS—HORIZ: 3f., 4f., 5f. King Faisal's Mausoleum (24 × 20 mm); ½d., 1d. Mosque of the Golden Dome, Samarra (24 × 21 mm). VERT: 50f., 75f. as Type **22**, but larger (21 × 24 mm); 100f., 200f. Oil Wells (20 × 22 mm).

26 King Faisal II

27

1942.

255	**26**	1f. brown and violet	35	35
256		2f. brown and blue	35	35
257		3f. brown and green	35	35
258		4f. sepia and brown	35	35
259		5f. brown and green	35	35
260		6f. brown and red	35	35
261		10f. brown and pink	35	35
262		12f. brown and green	35	35

1948.

271	**27**	1f. blue	30	10
272		2f. brown	15	10
273		3f. green	15	10
274		3f. red	3·50	90
275		4f. lilac	15	10
276		5f. red	15	10
277		5f. green	4·25	1·75
278		6f. mauve	1·00	10
279		8f. brown	2·50	45
280		10f. red	25	10
281		12f. green	20	10
282		14f. green	1·40	10
283		15f. black	4·25	85
284		16f. red	65	25
285		20f. blue	45	10
286		25f. purple	50	10
287		28f. blue	85	25
288		30f. orange	50	10
289		40f. brown	1·25	45
290		50f. blue	4·25	85
291		60f. blue	85	45
292		75f. mauve	85	45
293		100f. green	3·50	85
294		200f. orange	2·75	85
295		½d. blue	7·25	2·75
296		1d. green	24·00	10·00

The 50f. to 1d. are larger (22½ × 27½ mm).

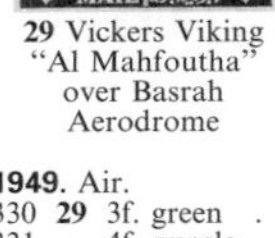
29 Vickers Viking "Al Mahfoutha" over Basrah Aerodrome

31 King Faisal I and Equestrian Statue

1949. Air.

330	**29**	3f. green	20	20
331	–	4f. purple	20	20
332	–	5f. brown	20	20
333	**29**	10f. red	2·50	85
334	–	20f. blue	85	45
335	–	35f. orange	75	45
336	–	50f. green	1·60	70
337	–	100f. violet	3·75	1·40

DESIGNS—As Type **29**: 4, 20f. "Al Mahfoutha" over Kut Barrage; 5, 35f. "Al Mahfoutha" over Faisal II Bridge. 31×22½ mm: 50, 100f. "Al Mahfoutha" over Dhiyala Railway Bridge.

1949. 75th Anniv of U.P.U.

339	–	20f. blue	1·75	1·25
340	**31**	40f. orange	2·50	1·25
341	–	50f. violet	5·50	4·50

DESIGNS: 20f. King Ghazi and mounted postman; 50f. King Faisal II, globe and wreath.

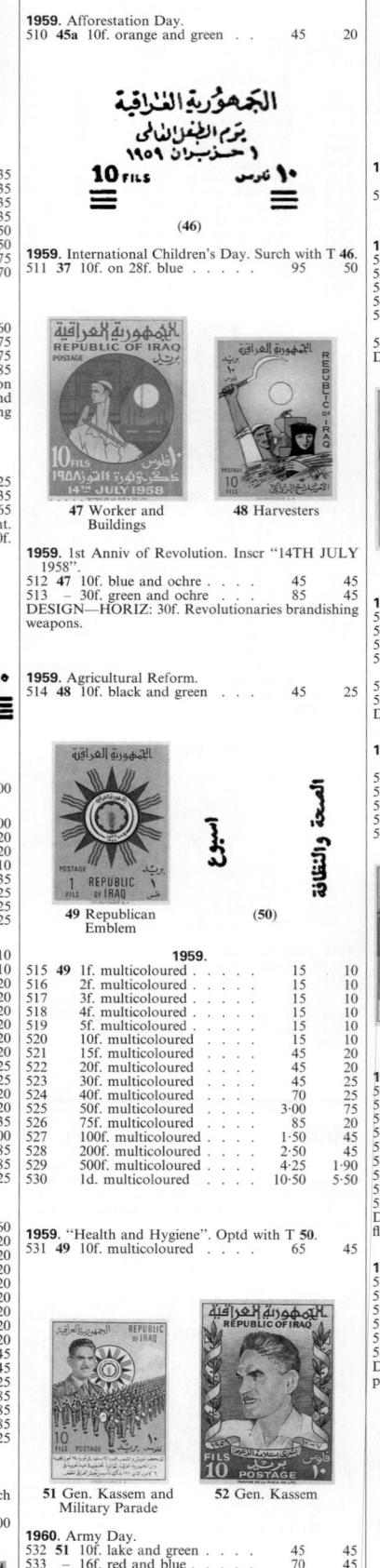

32 King Faisal II

33

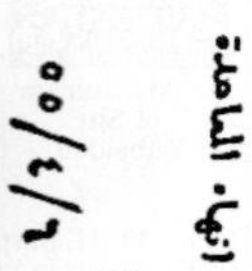
(35)

1953. Coronation of King Faisal II.

342	**32**	3f. red	85	85
343		14f. brown	1·75	85
344		28f. blue	4·75	1·25

1954.

346	**33**	1f. blue	35	15
347		2f. brown	15	10
348		3f. lake	15	10
349		4f. violet	15	10
350		5f. green	20	10
351		6f. mauve	20	10
352		8f. brown	20	10
353		10f. blue	20	10
354		15f. black	1·10	75
355		16f. red	1·75	1·50
356		20f. olive	85	20
357		25f. purple	85	10
358		30f. red	85	10
359		40f. brown	90	35
360		50f. blue	1·25	50
361		75f. mauve	2·10	60
362		100f. olive	3·75	60
363		200f. salmon	6·25	1·25

The 50f. to 200f. are larger (22×28 mm).

1955. Abrogation of Anglo-Iraqi Treaty. Optd with T **35**.

380	**33**	3f. lake	80	35
381		10f. blue	80	35
382	**27**	28f. blue	1·25	60

36 King Faisal II

1955. 6th Arab Engineers' Conference, Baghdad.

383	**36**	3f. red	65	30
384		10f. blue	1·40	55
385		28f. blue	2·10	1·25

37 King Faisal II and Globe

1956. 3rd Arab Postal Union Conference, Baghdad.

386	**37**	3f. red	85	45
387		10f. blue	90	45
388		28f. blue	1·25	85

38 King Faisal II and Power Loom

39 King Faisal II and Exhibition Emblem

1957. Development Week.

389	**38**	1f. blue and buff	30	20
390	–	3f. multicoloured	35	20
391	–	5f. multicoloured	30	25
392	–	10f. multicoloured	55	25
393	–	40f. multicoloured	1·25	85

DESIGNS: 3f. Irrigation dam; 5f. Residential road, Baghdad; 10f. Cement kiln; 40f. Tigris Bridge.

1957. Agricultural and Industrial Exn, Baghdad.

394	**39**	10f. brown and cream	60	50

(40)

1957. Silver Jubilee of Iraqi Red Crescent Society. No. 388 optd with T **40**.

395	**37**	28f. blue	3·00	1·25

41 King Faisal II

42 King Faisal II and Tanks

1957.

396	**41**	1f. blue	25	35
397		2f. brown	25	35
398		3f. red	25	35
399		4f. violet	25	35
400		5f. green	50	50
401		6f. red	50	50
402		8f. brown	1·00	75
403		10f. blue	75	70

1958. Army Day.

411	**42**	8f. grey and green	60	60
412	–	10f. black and brown	75	75
413	–	20f. brown and blue	75	75
414	–	30f. violet and red	1·25	85

DESIGNS—As T **42**: King Faisal II and: 10f. Platoon marching; 20f. Mobile artillery unit and De Havilland D.H.112 Venom jet fighters. 22½×27½ mm: 30f. King Faisal II (full-length portrait).

1958. Development Week. As T **38**, inscr "1958".

415		3f. green, drab and violet	25	25
416		5f. multicoloured	35	35
417		10f. multicoloured	1·10	65

DESIGNS—VERT: 3f. Sugar beet and refining plant. HORIZ: 5f. Building and pastoral scene; 10f. Irrigation dam.

(43 "Iraqi Republic") (44)

1958. Optd with T **43**. (a) On No. 189.

418		1d. purple	17·00	17·00

(b) On T **27**.

418a		1f. blue	21·00	7·00
419		12f. olive	35	20
420		14f. olive	35	20
421		16f. red	6·50	2·10
422		28f. blue	35	35
423		60f. blue	85	1·25
424		½d. blue	8·25	4·25
425		1d. green	21·00	8·25

(c) On T **33**.

426		1f. blue	15	10
427		2f. brown	15	10
428		4f. violet	20	20
429		5f. green	20	20
430		6f. mauve	20	20
431		8f. brown	25	20
432		10f. blue	25	20
433		15f. black	45	20
434		16f. red	1·40	25
435		20f. olive	1·90	1·25
436		25f. purple	25	20
437		30f. red	35	20
438		40f. brown	45	35
439		50f. blue	5·50	3·00
440		75f. mauve	1·75	85
441		100f. olive	4·25	85
442		200f. salmon	6·75	4·25

Nos. 439/42 are larger (22×28 mm).

(d) On T **41**.

443		1f. blue	1·75	60
444		2f. brown	20	20
445		3f. red	20	20
446		4f. violet	35	20
447		5f. green	45	20
448		6f. red	45	20
449		8f. brown	45	20
450		10f. blue	45	20
451		20f. green	45	20
452		25f. purple	75	45
453		30f. red	65	45
454		40f. brown	2·50	1·25
455		50f. purple	1·25	85
456		75f. green	1·25	85
457		100f. orange	1·50	85
458		200f. blue	7·00	1·25

Nos. 455/8 are larger (22½×27½ mm).

1958. Arab Lawyers Conf, Baghdad. Surch with T **44**.

506	**36**	10f. on 28f. blue	2·25	2·00

45 Republican Soldier and Flag

45a Orange Tree

1959. Army Day.

507	**45**	3f. blue	35	25
508		10f. olive	50	40
509		40f. violet	1·25	1·00

1959. Afforestation Day.

510	**45a**	10f. orange and green	45	20

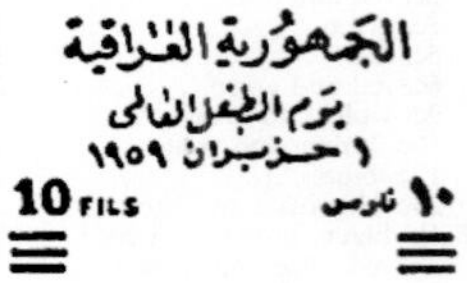
(46)

1959. International Children's Day. Surch with T **46**.

511	**37**	10f. on 28f. blue	95	50

47 Worker and Buildings

48 Harvesters

1959. 1st Anniv of Revolution. Inscr "14TH JULY 1958".

512	**47**	10f. blue and ochre	45	45
513	–	30f. green and ochre	85	45

DESIGN—HORIZ: 30f. Revolutionaries brandishing weapons.

1959. Agricultural Reform.

514	**48**	10f. black and green	45	25

49 Republican Emblem

(50)

1959.

515	**49**	1f. multicoloured	15	10
516		2f. multicoloured	15	10
517		3f. multicoloured	15	10
518		4f. multicoloured	15	10
519		5f. multicoloured	15	10
520		10f. multicoloured	15	10
521		15f. multicoloured	45	20
522		20f. multicoloured	45	20
523		30f. multicoloured	45	25
524		40f. multicoloured	70	25
525		50f. multicoloured	3·00	75
526		75f. multicoloured	85	20
527		100f. multicoloured	1·50	45
528		200f. multicoloured	2·50	45
529		500f. multicoloured	4·25	1·90
530		1d. multicoloured	10·50	5·50

1959. "Health and Hygiene". Optd with T **50**.

531	**49**	10f. multicoloured	65	45

51 Gen. Kassem and Military Parade

52 Gen. Kassem

1960. Army Day.

532	**51**	10f. lake and green	45	45
533	–	16f. red and blue	70	45
534	–	30f. olive, brown and buff	70	45
535	–	40f. violet and buff	1·10	65
536	–	60f. buff, chocolate & brn	1·40	85

DESIGNS—Gen. Kassem and: HORIZ: 16f. Infantry on manoeuvres; 60f. Partisans. VERT: 30f. Anti-aircraft gun-crew; 40f. Oilfield guards on parade.

1960. Gen. Kassem's Escape from Assassination.

537	**52**	10f. violet	45	25
538		30f. green	85	45

53 Al Rasafi (poet)

54 Gen. Kassem at Tomb of Unknown Soldier

1960. Al Rasafi Commemoration. Optd **1960** in English and Arabic.

539	**53**	10l. red	2·10	1·25

See also No 732.

1960. 2nd Anniv of Revolution.

540	–	6f. gold, olive and orange	45	45
541	**54**	10f. orange, green and blue	45	45
542		16f. orange, violet and blue	65	65
543	–	18f. gold, blue and orange	65	65
544	–	30f. gold, brown and orange	85	85
545	**54**	60f. orange, sepia and blue	1·75	1·25

DESIGN—VERT: 6f., 18f., 30f. Symbol of Republic.

55 Gen. Kassem, Flag and Troops

56 Gen. Kassem with Children

1961. Army Day.

546	**55**	3f. multicoloured	20	15
547		6f. multicoloured	20	15
548		10f. multicoloured	45	15
549	–	20f. black, yellow and green	45	40
550	–	30f. black, yellow & brown	45	40
551	–	40f. black, yellow and blue	85	55

DESIGN: 20, 30, 40f. Kassem and triumphal arch.

1961. World Children's Day. Main design brown; background colours given.

558	**56**	3f. yellow	55	40
559		6f. blue	75	40
560		10f. pink	1·00	40
561		30f. lemon	1·00	40
562		50f. green	1·75	40

57 Gen. Kassem saluting

58 Gen. Kassem and Army Emblem

1961. 3rd Anniv of Revolution.

563	–	1f. multicoloured	15	10
564	–	3f. multicoloured	15	10
565	**57**	5f. multicoloured	15	10
566	–	6f. multicoloured	15	10
567	–	10f. multicoloured	25	20
568	**57**	30f. multicoloured	45	35
569		40f. multicoloured	65	45
570	–	50f. multicoloured	1·25	90
571	–	100f. multicoloured	4·00	2·10

DESIGN: 1, 3, 6, 10, 50, 100f. Gen. Kassem and Iraqi flag.

1962. Army Day.

572	–	1f. multicoloured	15	10
573	–	3f. multicoloured	15	10
574	–	6f. multicoloured	20	10
575	**58**	10f. black, gold and lilac	40	20
576		30f. black, gold and orange	75	45
577		50f. black, gold and green	1·25	85

DESIGN—VERT: 1, 3, 6f. Gen. Kassem saluting and part of speech.

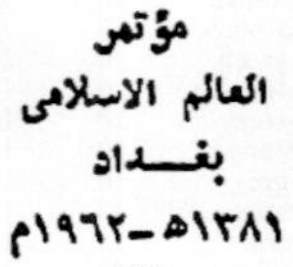
(59)

60 Gen. Kassem, Flag and Handclasp

1962. 5th Islamic Congress. Optd with T **59**.

578	**49**	3f. multicoloured	25	25
579		10f. multicoloured	25	25
580		30f. multicoloured	65	60

1962. 4th Anniv of Revolution. Flag in green and gold.

581	**60**	1f. orange and sepia	10	10
582		3f. green and sepia	10	10
583		6f. brown and black	10	10
584		10f. lilac and sepia	35	35

585		30f. red and sepia	50	40
586		50f. grey and sepia	1·00	70

61 Fanfare

62 Republican Emblem

1962. Millenary of Baghdad. Multicoloured.

603		3f. Type **61**	15	15
604		6f. Al Kindi (philosopher)	25	15
605		10f. Map of old "Round City" of Baghdad	45	20
606		40f. Gen. Kassem and flag	1·25	85

1962. Aerogramme Stamps.

607	**62**	14f. black and green	85	50
608		35f. black and red	1·25	75

Nos. 607/8 were originally issued only attached to aerogramme forms covering the old imprinted King Faisal II stamps, but later appeared in sheets.

63 Campaign Emblem

64 Gen. Kassem and Tanks

1962. Malaria Eradication.

609	**63**	3f. multicoloured	20	20
610		10f. multicoloured	50	20
611		40f. multicoloured	85	50

1963. Army Day.

612	**64**	3f. black and yellow	10	10
613		5f. sepia and purple	10	10
614		6f. black and green	10	10
615		10f. black and blue	25	20
616		10f. black and pink	25	20
617		20f. black and blue	50	35
618		40f. black and mauve	85	45
619		50f. sepia and blue	1·25	70

65 Gufas on the Tigris

66 Shepherd with Sheep

1963.

620	**65**	1f. green	20	10
621	–	2f. violet	25	15
622	**65**	3f. black	25	10
623	–	4f. black and yellow	30	15
624	–	5f. purple and green	40	15
625	–	10f. red	65	20
626	–	15f. brown and yellow	1·00	20
627	–	20f. violet	1·25	20
628	–	30f. orange	70	25
629	–	40f. green	1·40	15
630	–	50f. brown	5·25	45
631	–	75f. black and green	1·50	25
632	–	100f. purple	2·00	25
633	–	200f. brown	3·00	35
634	–	500f. blue	6·75	1·75
635	–	1d. purple	10·00	3·25

DESIGNS: 2f., 500f. Spiral tower of Samarra; 4f., 15f. Sumerian Harp; 5f., 75f. Republican emblem; 10f., 50f. Lion of Babylon; 20f., 40f. Koranic school of Abbasid period; 30f., 200f. Mosque and minarets; 100f., 1d. Winged bull of Kharsabad.

1963. Freedom from Hunger.

636	**66**	3f. black and green	35	15
637	–	10f. mauve and brown	45	25
638	–	20f. brown and blue	95	45

DESIGNS: 10f. Harvester; 20f. Trees.

67 Centenary Emblem

68 Helmet, Rifle and Flag

1963. Red Cross Centenary.

640	**67**	3f. violet and red	25	20
641		10f. blue and red	40	35
642	–	30f. blue and red	45	35

DESIGN—HORIZ: 30f. Hospital.

1964. Army Day.

643	**68**	3f. sepia, green and blue	20	15
644		10f. sepia, green and pink	45	25
645		30f. sepia, green and yellow	85	50

69 Revolutionaries and Flag

1964. 1st Anniv of 14th Ramadan Revolution. Flag in red, green and black.

646	**69**	10f. violet	45	25
647		30f. brown	85	45

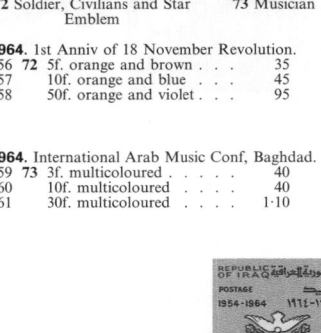

70 Shamash (Sun-God) and Hammurabi

71 Soldier raising Flag on Map of Iraq

1964. 15th Anniv of Declaration of Human Rights.

649	**70**	6f. olive and purple	45	35
650	–	10f. violet and orange	85	40
651	**70**	30f. green and blue	1·25	50

DESIGN: 10f. U.N. Emblem and Scales of Justice.

1964. 6th Anniv of Revolution.

652	–	3f. orange, grey and black	15	20
653	**71**	10f. red, black and green	25	20
654		20f. red, black and green	45	20
655	–	30f. orange, grey and black	85	50

DESIGN—HORIZ: 3f., 30f. Soldier "protecting" people and factories with outstretched arm.

72 Soldier, Civilians and Star Emblem

73 Musician

1964. 1st Anniv of 18 November Revolution.

656	**72**	5f. orange and brown	35	20
657		10f. orange and blue	45	20
658		50f. orange and violet	95	65

1964. International Arab Music Conf, Baghdad.

659	**73**	3f. multicoloured	40	25
660		10f. multicoloured	40	25
661		30f. multicoloured	1·10	55

74 Conference Emblem and Map

75 A.P.U. Emblem

1964. 9th Arab Engineer's Conf, Baghdad.

662	**74**	10f. green and mauve	50	35

1964. 10th Anniv of Arab Postal Union's Permanent Office.

663	**75**	3f. blue and red	20	20
664		10f. slate and purple	30	20
665		30f. blue and orange	85	45

76 Soldier, Civilians and Flag

77 Cogwheel and Factory

1965. Army Day.

666	**76**	5f. multicoloured	25	20
667		15f. multicoloured	30	20
668		30f. multicoloured	85	45

1965. 1st Arab Ministers of Labour Conf, Baghdad.

670	**77**	10f. multicoloured	45	25

78 Oil Tanker

79 Armed Soldier with Flag

1965. Inauguration of Deep Sea Terminal for Tankers.

671	**78**	10f. multicoloured	70	15

1965. 2nd Anniv of 14th Ramadan Revolution.

672	**79**	10f. multicoloured	45	25

80 Tree

81 Federation Emblem

1965. Tree Week.

673	**80**	6f. multicoloured	20	10
674		20f. multicoloured	65	35

1965. Arab Insurance Federation. Sun in gold.

675	**81**	3f. ultramarine and blue	25	20
676		10f. black and grey	25	20
677		30f. red and pink	80	45

82 Dagger of Deir Yassin, Palestine

1965. Deir Yassin Massacre.

678	**82**	10f. drab and black	35	25
679		20f. brown and blue	65	45

83 "Threat of Disease"

1965. World Health Day.

680	**83**	3f. multicoloured	35	20
681		10f. multicoloured	50	25
682		20f. multicoloured	1·10	65

84 I.T.U. Emblem and Symbols

1965. Centenary of I.T.U.

683	**84**	10f. multicoloured	45	20
684		20f. multicoloured	1·10	45

85 Flag and Map

86 Revolutionary and Flames

85a Lamp and Burning Library

1965. 1st Anniv of Iraq–U.A.R. Pact.

686	**85**	10f. multicoloured	35	20

1965. Reconstitution of Algiers University Library.

687	**85a**	5f. red, green and black	20	20
688		10f. green, red and black	30	20

1965. 45th Anniv of 1920 Rebellion.

689	**86**	5f. multicoloured	30	20
690		10f. multicoloured	30	20

87 Mosque

1965. Mohammed's Birthday.

691	**87**	10f. multicoloured	50	50

88 Factory and Ear of Wheat

90 Fair Emblem

89 I.C.Y. Emblem

1965. 7th Anniv of 14 July Revolution.

693	**88**	10f. multicoloured	35	35

1965. Air. International Co-operation Year.

694	**89**	5f. black and brown	50	50
695		10f. brown and green	75	60
696		30f. black and blue	2·10	75

1965. Baghdad Fair.

697	**90**	10f. multicoloured	25	20

91 Pres. Arif (photo by Studio Jean)

1965. 2nd Anniv of 18 November Revolution.

698	**91**	5f. blue and orange	20	20
699		10f. sepia and blue	45	25
700		50f. blue and mauve . . .	1·50	1·00

92 Census Graph

1965. National Census.

701	**92**	3f. black and purple . . .	25	20
702		5f. red and brown	25	20
703		15f. bistre and blue	85	45

93 Hawker Siddeley Trident 1E Airliner

1965. Air. Inauguration of Hawker Siddeley Trident 1E Aircraft by Iraqi Airways.

704	**93**	5f. multicoloured	40	30
705		10f. multicoloured	50	35
706		40f. multicoloured	1·50	85

94 Date Palms **95** Army Memorial

1965. 2nd F.A.O. Dates Conference, Baghdad.

707	**94**	3f. multicoloured	25	20
708		10f. multicoloured	55	20
709		15f. multicoloured	1·10	70

1966. 45th Anniv of Army Day.

710	**95**	2f. multicoloured	35	25
711		5f. multicoloured	35	25
712		40f. multicoloured	1·00	65

96 "Eagle" and Flag **96a** Arab League Emblem

1966. 3rd Anniv of 14th Ramadan Revolution.

713	**96**	5f. multicoloured	20	20
714		10f. multicoloured	25	20

1966. Arab Publicity Week.

715	**96a**	5f. green, brown & orange	25	25
716		15f. blue, purple and olive	40	25

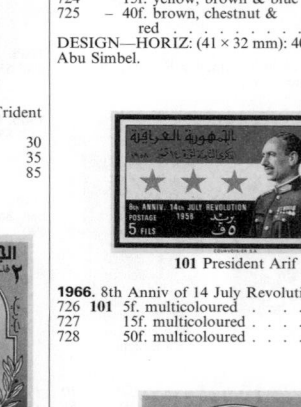

97 Footballers

1966. Arab Football Cup, Baghdad. Mult.

717		2f. Type **97**	25	25
718		5f. Goalkeeper with ball . . .	25	25
719		15f. Type **97**	85	45

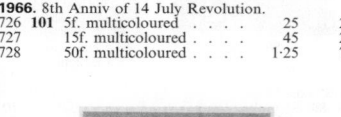

99 Excavator **100** Queen Nefertari

1966. Labour Day.

721	**99**	15f. multicoloured	25	15
722		25f. black, silver and red	35	20

1966. Nubian Monuments Preservation.

723	**100**	5f. yellow, black and olive	60	35
724		15f. yellow, brown & blue	85	35
725	–	40f. brown, chestnut & red	1·50	1·00

DESIGN—HORIZ: (41 × 32 mm): 40f. Rock temples, Abu Simbel.

101 President Arif

1966. 8th Anniv of 14 July Revolution.

726	**101**	5f. multicoloured	25	20
727		15f. multicoloured	45	20
728		50f. multicoloured	1·25	70

102

1966. Mohammed's Birthday.

729	**102**	5f. multicoloured	20	20
730		15f. multicoloured	25	20
731		30f. multicoloured	1·00	90

1966. As No. 539 but without opt.

732	**53**	10f. red	4·00	5·00

103 Iraqi Museum, Statue and Window **104** Revolutionaries

1966. Inauguration of Iraqi Museum, Baghdad. Multicoloured.

733		15f. Type **103**	40	40
734		50f. Gold headdress	1·10	65
735		80f. Sumerian head (vert) . .	1·90	1·10

1966. 3rd Anniv of 18 November Revolution.

736	**104**	15f. multicoloured	45	25
737		25f. multicoloured	85	45

105 "Magic Carpet"

1966. Air. Meeting of Arab International Tourist Union, Baghdad. Multicoloured.

738		2f. White stork emblem ($27\frac{1}{2}$ × 39 mm)	25	25
739		5f. Type **105**	20	20
740		15f. As 2f.	1·25	35
741		50f. Type **105**	1·75	70

106 U.N.E.S.C.O. Emblem

1966. 20th Anniv of U.N.E.S.C.O.

742	**106**	5f. brown, black and blue	20	10
743		15f. green, black and red	45	25

107 Soldier and Rocket-launchers

1967. Army Day.

744	**107**	15f. ochre, brown & yellow	35	20
745		20f. ochre, brown and lilac	50	25

108 Oil Refinery

1967. 6th Arab Petroleum Congress, Baghdad. Multicoloured.

747		5f. Congress emblem (vert)	20	20
748		15f. Type **108**	30	20
749		40f. Congress emblem (vert)	55	45
750		50f. Type **108**	1·25	75

109 "Spider's Web" Emblem **110** Worker holding Cogwheel

1967. Hajeer Year (1967).

751	**109**	5f. multicoloured	25	15
752		15f. multicoloured	30	20

1967. Labour Day.

753	**110**	10f. multicoloured	25	15
754		15f. multicoloured	30	15

111

1967. Mohammed's Birthday.

755	**111**	5f. multicoloured	25	20
756		15f. multicoloured	50	25

112 Flag and Hands with Clubs

1967. 47th Anniv of 1920 Rebellion.

757	**112**	5f. multicoloured	20	10
758		15f. multicoloured	30	15

113 Um Qasr Port **114** Costume

1967. 9th Anniv of 14 July Revolution and Inaug of Um Qasr Port. Multicoloured.

759		5f. Type **113**	40	20
760		10f. Freighter at quayside . .	45	20
761		15f. As 10f.	75	20
762		40f. Type **113**	2·25	1·10

1967. Iraqi Costumes.

765	**114**	2f. multicoloured (postage)	25	20
766	–	5f. multicoloured	25	15
767	–	10f. multicoloured	35	20
768	–	15f. multicoloured	75	45
769	–	20f. multicoloured	95	45
770	–	25f. multicoloured	1·00	50
771	–	30f. multicoloured	1·25	50
772	–	40f. multicoloured (air)	85	65
773	–	50f. multicoloured	1·50	85
774	–	80f. multicoloured	1·90	1·00

DESIGNS: 5f. to 80f. Different costumes.

115 Pres. Arif and Map

1967. 4th Anniv of 18 November Revolution. Multicoloured.

775		5f. President Arif	30	15
776		15f. Type **115**	45	20

116 Ziggurat of Ur

1967. International Tourist Year. Multicoloured.

777		2f. Type **116** (postage) . . .	25	15
778		5f. Statues of Nimroud . . .	25	15
779		10f. Babylon (arch)	30	15
780		15f. Minaret of Mosul (vert)	35	15
781		25f. Arch of Ctesiphon . . .	45	15
782		50f. Statue, Temple of Hatra (vert) (air)	1·75	25
783		80f. Spiral Minaret of Samarra (vert)	2·10	45
784		100f. Adam's Tree (vert) . .	1·75	60
785		200f. Aladdin ("Aladdin's Cave") (vert)	4·25	2·10
786		500f. Golden Mosque of Kadhimain	13·50	7·50

117 Guide Emblem and Saluting Hand

1967. Iraqi Scouts and Guides. Multicoloured.

787		2f. Type **117**	40	35
788		5f. Guides by camp-fire . . .	50	35
789		10f. Scout emblem and saluting hand	60	40
790		15f. Scouts setting up camp	1·00	45

118 Soldiers Drilling

1968. Army Day.

792	**118**	5f. brown, green and blue	30	20
793		15f. indigo, olive and blue	55	25

119 White-cheeked Bulbul

1968. Iraqi Birds. Multicoloured.

794	5f. Type **119**	70	25
795	10f. Hoopoe	90	25
796	15f. Jay	1·25	35
797	25f. Peregrine falcon	2·25	50
798	30f. White stork	2·75	50
799	40f. Black partridge	3·50	80
800	50f. Marbled teal	4·25	95

120 Battle Scene

1968. 5th Anniv of 14th Ramadan Revolution.

801	**120**	15f. orange, black and blue	50	30

121 Symbols of "Labour"

1968. Labour Day.

802	**121**	15f. multicoloured	30	20
803		25f. multicoloured	50	25

122 Football

1968. 23rd International Military Sports Council Football Championship. Multicoloured.

804	2f. Type **122**	30	20
805	5f. Goalkeeper in mid air	30	20
806	15f. Type **122**	55	20
807	25f. As 5f.	75	45

123 Soldier with Iraqi Flag

1968. 10th Anniv of 14 July Revolution.

809	**123**	15f. multicoloured	30	15

124 Anniversary and W.H.O. Emblems

1968. 20th Anniv of W.H.O.

810	–	5f. multicoloured	25	20
811	–	10f. multicoloured	25	20
812	**124**	15f. red, blue and black	30	25
813	–	25f. red, green and black	55	30

DESIGN—VERT: 5, 10f. Combined anniversary and W.H.O. emblems.

125 Human Rights Emblem

126 Mother and children

1968. Human Rights Year.

814	**125**	10f. red, yellow and blue	25	20
815		25f. red, yellow and green	30	20

1968. U.N.I.C.E.F. Commemoration.

817	**126**	15f. multicoloured	25	20
818		25f. multicoloured	40	30

127 Army Tanks

1969. Army Day.

820	**127**	25f. multicoloured	1·50	75

128 Agricultural Scene

1969. 6th Anniv of 14th Ramadan Revolution.

821	**128**	15f. multicoloured	45	25

129 Mosque and Worshippers

1969. Hajeer Year.

822	**129**	15f. multicoloured	45	25

130 Emblem of Iraqi Veterinary Medical Association

1969. 1st Arab Veterinary Union Conf, Baghdad.

823	**130**	10f. multicoloured	45	25
824		15f. multicoloured	60	35

131 Mahseer

1969. Multicoloured. (a) Postage. Fishes.

825	2f. Type **131**	50	35
826	3f. Sharpey's barbel	50	35
827	10f. Silver pomfret	60	35
828	100f. Pike barbel	2·50	1·25

(b) Air. Fauna.

829	2f. Striped hyena	20	15
830	3f. Leopard	20	15
831	5f. Mountain gazelle	20	15
832	10f. Head of Arab horse	75	50
833	200f. Arab horse	3·75	2·25

132 Kaaba, Mecca

1969. Mohammed's Birthday.

834	**132**	15f. multicoloured	45	20

133 I.L.O. Emblem

1969. 50th Anniv of I.L.O.

835	**133**	5f. yellow, blue and black	15	10
836		15f. yellow, green & black	20	10
837		50f. yellow, red and black	1·10	85

134 Weightlifting

135 Arms of Iraq and "Industry"

1969. Olympic Games, Mexico (1968). Mult.

839	3f. Type **134**	50	35
840	5f. High jumping	50	35
841	10f. As Type **134**	50	35
842	35f. As 5f.	1·00	70

1969. 11th Anniv of 14 July Revolution.

844	**135**	10f. multicoloured	20	20
845		15f. multicoloured	25	20

136 Rebuilding Roads

1969. Anniv of 17 July Revolution and Inaug of Baghdad International Airport. Mult.

846	10f. Type **136**	20	20
847	15f. Type **136**	35	25
848	20f. Airport building	70	45
849	200f. President Bakr (vert)	4·25	2·10

137 Ear of Wheat and Fair Emblem

139 Radio Beacon and Outline of Palestine

138 Floating Crane "Antara"

1969. 6th International Baghdad Fair.

850	**137**	10f. brown, gold and green	35	25
851		15f. red, gold and blue	50	30

1969. 50th Anniv of Port of Basra. Mult.

852	15f. Type **138**	30	15
853	20f. Harbour tender "Al-Walid"	40	15
854	30f. Pilot boat "Al-Rashid"	70	15
855	35f. Dredger "Hillah"	1·00	35
856	50f. Survey ship "Al-Fao"	1·75	65

1969. 10th Anniv of Iraqi News Agency.

857	**139**	15f. multicoloured	35	25
858		50f. multicoloured	75	45

140 Emblem, Book and Hands

1969. Campaign Against Illiteracy.

859	**140**	15f. multicoloured	25	15
860		20f. multicoloured	40	30

141 Ross and Keith Smith's Vickers Vimy Biplane

1969. Air. 50th Anniv of 1st England–Australia Flight.

861	**141**	15f. multicoloured	1·75	85
862		35f. multicoloured	2·50	1·75

142 Newspaper Headline

144 Iraqis supporting Wall

143 Soldier and Map

1969. Centenary of Iraqi Press.

864	**142**	15f. black, orange & yell	45	45

1970. Army Day.

865	**143**	15f. multicoloured	45	30
866		20f. multicoloured	65	55

1970. 7th Anniv of 14th Ramadan Revolution.

867	**144**	10f. multicoloured	20	20
868		15f. multicoloured	25	20

عيد نوروز
1970
(145)

مهرجان الربيع
الموصل
1970
(147)

146 Map of Arab Countries, and Slogans

1970. New Year ("Nawrooz"). Nos. 891/6 optd with T **145**.

869	2f. multicoloured	25	25
870	3f. multicoloured	25	25
871	5f. multicoloured	25	25
872	10f. multicoloured	50	25
873	15f. multicoloured	65	25
874	50f. multicoloured	1·75	1·10

1970. 23rd Anniv of Al-Baath Party. Mult.

875	15f. Type **146**	25	25
876	35f. Type **146**	45	45
877	50f. Iraqis acclaiming Party	1·25	55

1970. Mosul Spring Festival. Nos. 891/6 optd with T **147**.

879	2f. multicoloured	60	60
880	3f. multicoloured	60	60
881	5f. multicoloured	60	60
882	10f. multicoloured	60	60

883 15f. multicoloured 80 70
884 50f. multicoloured . . . . . 1·25 85

148 Iraqis celebrating Labour Day

1970. Labour Day.
885 **148** 10f. multicoloured 15 15
886 15f. multicoloured 15 15
887 35f. multicoloured . . . . 1·00 85

149 Kaaba, Mecca, Broken Statues and Koran

1970. Mohammed's Birthday.
888 **149** 15f. multicoloured 25 15
889 20f. multicoloured 30 25

150 Poppies

1970 ١٩٧٠
عيد الصحافة
(151)

1970. Spring Festival. Flowers. Multicoloured.
891 2f. Type **150** 40 25
892 3f. Narcissi 40 25
893 5f. Tulip 40 25
894 10f. Carnations 45 30
895 15f. Roses 85 45
896 50f. As 10f. . . . . 1·75 1·10

1970. Press Day. No. 864 optd with T **151**.
896a **142** 15f. black, orange & yell 45 45

152 Revolutionaries

1970. 50th Anniv of Revolution of 1920.
897 **152** 10f. black and green . . . 20 20
898 15f. black and gold . . . 30 20
899 – 35f. black and orange . . 70 35
DESIGN: 35f. Revolutionary and rising sun.

153 Bomb-burst and Broken Chain

1970. 12th Anniv of 14 July Revolution.
901 **153** 15f. multicoloured 25 15
902 20f. multicoloured 30 20

154 Hands and Map of Iraq

1970. 2nd Anniv of 17 July Revolution.
903 **154** 15f. multicoloured 25 15
904 25f. multicoloured 45 25

155 Pomegranates

1970. Fruits. Multicoloured.
905 3f. Type **155** 35 15
906 5f. Grapefruit 35 15
907 10f. Grapes 35 15
908 15f. Oranges 70 20
909 35f. Dates . . . . 1·75 1·50
The Latin inscriptions on Nos. 906/7 are transposed.

156 Kaaba, Mecca

1970. Hajeer Year.
910 **156** 15f. multicoloured 25 15
911 25f. multicoloured 45 25

الدورة السابعة
970 – ٩٧٠
(157)

1970. 7th Int Baghdad Fair. Optd with T **157**.
912 **137** 10f. brown, gold and green . . . . 2·10 1·25
913 15f. red, gold and blue . . 2·10 1·25

158 Arab League Flag and Map

1970. 25th Anniv of Arab League.
914 **158** 15f. purple, green and olive 20 15
915 35f. red, green and grey 45 40

159 Euphrates Bridge

1970. Air. National Development. Multicoloured.
916 10f. Type **159** . . . . . . 1·25 35
917 15f. Type **159** . . . . . . 2·00 50
918 1d. Pres. Bakr and banknotes (37 × 27 mm) . . . . . . 32·00 14·00

160 I.E.Y. Emblem

1970. International Education Year.
919 **160** 5f. multicoloured 20 15
920 15f. multicoloured 40 25

161 Baghdad Hospital and Society Emblem

1970. 50th Anniv of Iraq Medical Society.
922 **161** 15f. multicoloured 25 20
923 40f. multicoloured 85 50

162 Union Emblem

163 Sugar Beet

1970. Air. 10th Arab Telecommunications Union Conference, Baghdad.
924 **162** 15f. multicoloured 25 15
925 25f. multicoloured 45 35

1970. 12th Anniv of Mosul Sugar Refinery. Multicoloured.
926 5f. Type **163** 20 10
927 15f. Sugar refinery (horiz) . . 35 15
928 30f. Type **163** . . . . 1·25 60

164 O.P.E.C. Emblem

1970. 10th Anniv of Organization of Petroleum Exporting Countries (O.P.E.C.).
929 **164** 10f. blue, bistre and purple 45 25
930 40f. blue, bistre and green 1·50 1·00

165 Soldiers, Tank and Aircraft

1971. 50th Anniv of Army Day.
931 **165** 15f. black, mauve and gold 50 20
932 – 40f. multicoloured . . . . 1·50 85
DESIGN—42 × 35 mm: 40f. Soldiers and map of Middle East.

166 "Revolutionary Army"

1971. 8th Anniv of 14th Ramadan Revolution.
934 **166** 15f. multicoloured 30 20
935 40f. multicoloured 85 55

167 Pilgrims and Web

1971. Hajeer Year.
936 **167** 10f. multicoloured 15 10
937 15f. multicoloured 35 25

168 Pres. Bakr with Torch

1971. 1st Anniv of 11th March Manifesto.
938 **168** 15f. multicoloured 60 45
939 100f. multicoloured . . . 1·90 1·60

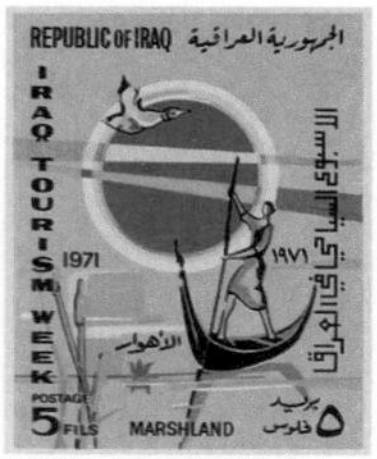
169 Boatman in Marshland

1971. Tourism Week. Multicoloured.
940 5f. Type **169** 20 10
941 10f. Stork over Baghdad . . 55 25
942 15f. Landscape ("Summer Resorts") 60 35
943 100f. "Return of Sinbad" . . 2·75 1·75

170 Blacksmith taming Serpent

1971. New Year ("Nawrooz").
944 **170** 15f. multicoloured 45 25
945 25f. multicoloured 55 35

1971. World Meteorological Day. Nos. 780 and 783 optd **W.M. DAY 1971** in English and Arabic.
946 15f. multicoloured (postage) 2·00 85
947 80f. multicoloured (air) . . . 4·25 3·25

172 Emblem and Workers

1971. 24th Anniv of Al-Baath Party. Mult.
948 15f. Type **172** 30 30
949 35f. Type **172** 50 50
950 250f. As Type **172** but central portion of design only (42 × 42 mm) . . . . . . 6·75 6·75
On No. 950 the circular centre is also perforated.

مهرجان الربيع
1971
(173)

174 Worker and Farm-girl

1971. Mosul Spring Festival. Nos. 765/6 and 770 optd with T **173**.
951 **114** 2f. multicoloured 40 25
952 – 5f. multicoloured 40 25
953 – 25f. multicoloured . . . . 1·25 75

1971. Labour Day.
954 **174** 15f. multicoloured 35 25
955 40f. multicoloured 60 50

175 Muslim at Prayer

1971. Mohammed's Birthday.
956 **175** 15f. multicoloured 35 25
957 100f. multicoloured . . . 1·40 1·10

176 Revolutionaries, and Hands with Broken Chains

1971. 13th Anniv of 14 July Revolution.
958 **176** 25f. multicoloured 45 20
959 50f. multicoloured . . . . 1·10 55

177 Rising Sun and "Prosperity"

1971. 3rd Anniv of 17 July Revolution.
960 **177** 25f. multicoloured 45 20
961 70f. multicoloured . . . . 1·60 85

182 Bank Emblem

1971. 30th Anniv of Rafidain Bank.
989 **182** 10f. multicoloured 45 30
990 15f. multicoloured 45 30
991 25f. multicoloured 45 30
992 65f. multicoloured . . . . 2·10 1·10
993 250f. multicoloured . . . 10·00 10·00
Nos. 992/3 are larger, 42 × 42 mm.

التعداد الزراعي العام

١٩٧١/١٠/١٥

(183)

1971. Agricultural Census. Nos. 905, 908/9 optd with T **183**.
994 3f. multicoloured . . . . . . 1·40 1·50
995 15f. multicoloured . . . . . . 1·40 1·50
996 35f. multicoloured . . . . . 1·40 1·50

184 Football

1971. 4th Pan-Arab Schoolboy Games, Baghdad. Multicoloured.
997 15f. Type **184** 35 25
998 25f. Throwing the discus and running 50 25
999 35f. Table tennis 85 50
1000 70f. Gymnastics . . . . . . 1·50 1·00
1001 95f. Volleyball and basketball . . . . 1·90 1·00

70 Fils ●●
يوم الطالب
٢٣ تشرين الثاني
٩٦١ – ٩٧١
٧ فلسا
●●

(185)

186 Society Emblem

1971. Students' Day. Nos. 892/3 surch and 895 optd as T **185**.
1003 15f. multicoloured . . . . . . 1·00 1·00
1004 25f. on 5f. multicoloured . . 1·50 1·50
1005 70f. on 3f. multicoloured . . 3·00 3·00

1971. Air. 20th Anniv of Iraqi Philatelic Society.
1006 **186** 25f. multicoloured . . . 1·10 75
1007 70f. multicoloured . . . 1·50 1·40

1971. 25th Anniv of U.N.I.C.E.F. Nos. 817/18 optd **25th Anniversary 971**.
1008 **126** 15f. multicoloured . . . 2·25 2·10
1009 25f. multicoloured . . . 2·25 2·10

188 Schoolchildren on Zebra Crossing

1971. 2nd Traffic Week.
1010 **188** 15f. multicoloured . . . 2·50 1·60
1011 25f. multicoloured . . . 2·50 1·60

189 A.P.U. Emblem

190 Racial Equality Year Symbol

1971. 25th Anniv of Founding of Arab Postal Union at Sofar Conference.
1012 **189** 25f. brown, yellow & grn 25 15
1013 70f. red, yellow and blue 1·10 70

1971. Racial Equality Year.
1014 **190** 25f. multicoloured . . . 20 20
1015 70f. multicoloured . . . 85 75

191 Soldiers with Flag and Torch

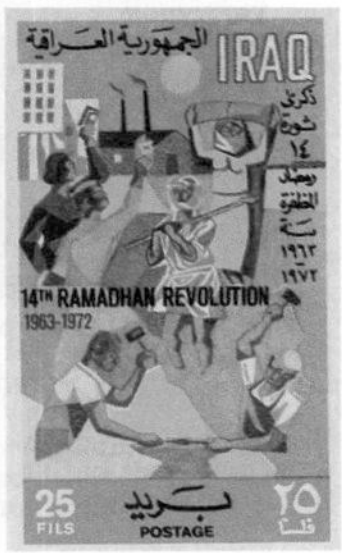

192 Workers

1972. Army Day.
1016 **191** 25f. multicoloured . . . 1·10 35
1017 70f. multicoloured . . . 2·00 1·40

1972. 9th Anniv of 14th Ramadan Revolution.
1018 **192** 25f. multicoloured . . . 1·40 45
1019 95f. multicoloured . . . 2·50 1·75

193 Mosque and Crescent

1972. Hajeer Year.
1020 **193** 25f. multicoloured . . . 25 20
1021 35f. multicoloured . . . 65 45

المؤتمر التاسع للاتحاد الوطني
لطلبة العراق
٢٥ شباط – ٢ آذار / ١٩٧٢

(194)

1972. Air. 9th Iraqi Students' Union Congress. Nos. 916/17 optd with T **194**.
1022 **159** 10f. multicoloured . . . 1·75 1·75
1023 15f. multicoloured . . . 1·75 1·75

195 Dove, Olive Branch and Manifesto

1972. 2nd Anniv of 11 March Manifesto.
1024 **195** 25f. blue, lt blue & black 55 20
1025 70f. purple, mauve & blk 2·00 1·10

196 Observatory and Weather Balloon on Isobar Map

197 Cogwheel Emblem

1972. World Meteorological Day.
1026 **196** 25f. multicoloured . . . 1·25 45
1027 35f. multicoloured . . . 2·25 1·25

1972. Iraqi Chamber of Commerce.
1028 **197** 25f. multicoloured . . . 35 20
1029 35f. multicoloured . . . 60 35

198 Oil Rig and Flame

1972. Inauguration of North Rumaila Oilfield.
1030 **198** 25f. multicoloured . . . 1·00 25
1031 35f. multicoloured . . . 1·10 85

199 Party Emblem

1972. 25th Anniv of Al Baath Party. Mult.
1032 10f. Type **199** 30 25
1033 25f. Emblem and inscription 50 35
1034 35f. Type **199** 65 45
1035 70f. As 25f. . . . . 1·90 1·60
SIZES—HORIZ: 25f., 70f. 51 × 27 mm.

200 Mountain Scene

1972. New Year ("Nawrooz").
1036 **200** 25f. mauve, yellow & blue 90 35
1037 70f. brown, yellow & blue . . . . 2·10 1·60

201 Congress "Quills" Emblem

204 Hand holding Spanner

202 Federation Emblem

1972. 3rd Arab Journalists Congress.
1038 **201** 25f. orange, black & grn 45 35
1039 35f. blue, black and green . . . . 1·25 1·10

1972. 4th Anniv of Iraqi Women's Federation.
1040 **202** 25f. multicoloured . . . 45 25
1041 35f. multicoloured . . . 1·25 1·10

1972. Labour Day.
1046 **204** 25f. multicoloured . . . 35 15
1047 35f. multicoloured . . . 65 20

205 Kaaba, Mecca

1972. Mohammed's Birthday.
1048 **205** 25f. black, gold and green 45 25
1049 35f. black, gold and violet . . . . 1·40 1·10

206 Shooting for Goal

1972. Air. 25th International Military Sports Council Football Championship, Baghdad. Multicoloured.
1050 10f. Type **206** 55 25
1051 20f. Players in goalmouth 80 35
1052 25f. Type **206** . . . . 1·10 45
1053 35f. As 20f. . . . . 1·60 65

207 Soldiers and Artillery

1972. 14th Anniv of 14 July Revolution.
1055 **207** 35f. multicoloured . . . 1·10 65
1056 70f. multicoloured . . . 2·40 1·60

208 "Spirit of Revolution"

1972. 4th Anniv of 17 July Revolution.
1057 **208** 25f. multicoloured . . . 90 50
1058 95f. multicoloured . . . 2·50 2·00

209 Scout Badge and Camp Scene

1972. 10th Jamboree and Conference of Arab Scouts, Mosul.
1059 **209** 20f. multicoloured . . . 1·50 1·00
1060 25f. multicoloured . . . 1·90 1·00

210 Guide Badge and Camp

1972. 4th Conference and Camp of Arab Guides, Mosul.
1061 **210** 10f. multicoloured . . . 90 60
1062 45f. multicoloured . . . 3·00 1·50

1972 ١٩٧٢

●● 70 Fils ٧٠ ●●

(211)

1972. 3rd Traffic Week. Nos. 1010/11 surch or optd as T **211**.
1063 **188** 25f. multicoloured . . . 3·00 2·10
1064 70f. on 15f. mult . . . . 4·75 4·25

مهرجان النخيل
وعيد التمور
١٩٧٢
70 Fils ٧٠

(212)

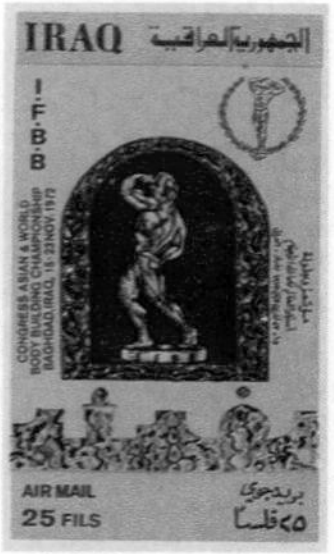

213 "Strong Man" Statuette

1972. Festival of Palm Trees and Feast of Dates. Nos. 707 and 709 surch as T **212**.
1065 **94** 25f. on 3f. multicoloured 2·10 1·25
1066 70f. on 15f. multicoloured 4·25 3·25

1972. Air. World Body-building Championships and Asian Congress, Baghdad. Multicoloured.
1067 25f. Type **213** . . . . 1·00 55
1068 70f. Ancient warriors and modern Strong Man . . . 2·10 1·50

214 Bank Building

1972. 25th Anniv of Central Bank of Iraq.
1069 **214** 25f. multicoloured . . . 95 35
1070 70f. multicoloured . . . 1·90 1·90

216 International Railway Union Emblem

1972. 50th Anniv of Int Railway Union.
1073 **216** 25f. multicoloured . . . 1·25 35
1074 45f. multicoloured . . . 3·00 1·90

1973. Various "Faisal" definitives with portrait obliterated with 3 bars. (a) 1954 issue.
1075 **33** 10f. blue . . . . 2·25 85
1076 15f. black . . . . 2·25 85
1077 25f. purple . . . . 2·25 85

(b) 1957 issue.
1078 **41** 10f. blue . . . . 2·25 85
1079 15f. black . . . . 2·25 85
1080 25f. purple . . . . 2·25 85

المؤتمر الدولي
للتاريخ/١٩٧٣

(219)

1973. International History Congress. Nos. 780, 783 and 786 optd with T **219**.
1094 15f. multicoloured (postage) 2·50 2·50
1095 80f. multicoloured (air) . . 4·25 4·25
1096 500f. multicoloured . . . . 38·00 38·00

220 Iraqi Oil Workers

1973. 1st Anniv of Nationalization of Iraqi Oil Industry.
1097 **220** 25f. multicoloured . . . 1·75 1·25
1098 70f. multicoloured . . . 3·75 2·10

221 Harp

225a Iraqis and Flags

1973.
1099 **221** 5f. black and orange . . 15 10
1100 10f. black and brown . . 15 10
1101 20f. black and mauve . . 20 10
1102 – 25f. black and blue . . . 35 15
1103 – 35f. black and green . . 40 20
1104 – 45f. black and blue . . . 40 25
1105 – 50f. yellow and green . . 65 25
1106 – 70f. yellow and violet . . 70 40
1107 – 95f. yellow and brown 1·25 65
DESIGNS: 25, 35, 45f. Minaret of Mosul; 50, 70, 95f. Statue of a Goddess.

1973. July Festivals.
1122 **225a** 25f. multicoloured . . . 70 25
1123 35f. multicoloured . . . 1·40 85

1973. International Journalists' Conference. Nos. 857/8 optd **I.O.J. SEPTEMBER 26-29. 1973**.
1124 **139** 15f. multicoloured . . . 2·10 2·10
1125 50f. multicoloured . . . 3·00 3·00

227 Interpol H.Q., Paris

1973. 50th Anniv of International Criminal Police Organization (Interpol).
1126 **227** 25f. multicoloured . . . 70 25
1127 70f. multicoloured . . . 3·50 2·25

228 Flags and Fair Emblems **229** W.M.O. Emblem

1973. 10th Baghdad International Fair.
1128 **228** 10f. multicoloured . . . 30 15
1129 20f. multicoloured . . . 70 30
1130 55f. multicoloured . . . 1·40 75

1973. Cent of World Meteorological Organization.
1148 **229** 25f. black, green & orge 45 15
1149 35f. black, green & mve 1·40 95

230 Arab Flags and Map

1973. 11th Session of Arab States' Civil Aviation Council, Baghdad.
1150 **230** 20f. multicoloured . . . 35 25
1151 35f. multicoloured . . . 1·10 75

المجلس التنفيذي
بغداد/١٩٧٣

(232)

233 Human Rights Emblem

1973. 6th Executive Council Meeting of Arab Postal Union, Baghdad. No. 665 optd with T **232**.
1153 **75** 30f. blue and orange . . . 3·25 2·10

1973. 25th Anniv of Declaration of Human Rights.
1154 **233** 25f. multicoloured . . . 35 15
1155 70f. multicoloured . . . 1·40 85

234 Shield and Military Activities

1974. 50th Anniv of Military College.
1156 **234** 25f. multicoloured . . . 35 25
1157 35f. multicoloured . . . 1·25 85

236 U.P.U. Emblem

1974. Centenary of Universal Postal Union.
1159 **236** 25f. multicoloured . . . 60 20
1160 35f. multicoloured . . . 65 35
1161 70f. multicoloured . . . 1·75 1·10

237 Allegory of Nationalization

1974. 2nd Anniv of Nationalization of Iraqi Oil Industry.
1162 **237** 10f. multicoloured . . . 25 15
1163 25f. multicoloured . . . 65 25
1164 70f. multicoloured . . . 1·75 1·75

238 Festival Theme **240** Cement Plant

239 National Front Emblem and Heads

1975. July Festivals.
1165 **238** 20f. multicoloured . . . 30 15
1166 35f. multicoloured . . . 85 45

1975. 1st Anniv of Progressive National Front.
1167 **239** 20f. multicoloured . . . 35 15
1168 50f. multicoloured . . . 1·40 85

1975. 25th Anniv of Iraqi Cement Industry.
1169 **240** 20f. multicoloured . . . 40 25
1170 25f. multicoloured . . . 40 30
1171 70f. multicoloured . . . 1·25 95

1975. Surch.
1172 **155** 10f. on 3f. multicoloured 2·50 1·10
1173 – 25f. on 3f. mult (No. 892) . . . . . . 3·75 1·25

242 W.P.Y. Emblem

1975. World Population Year (1974).
1174 **242** 25f. green and blue . . . 40 20
1175 35f. blue and mauve . . 70 30
1176 70f. violet and olive . . 1·75 1·10

243 Festival Emblems

1975. July Festivals.
1177 **243** 5f. multicoloured 20 15
1178 10f. multicoloured . . . 25 20
1179 35f. multicoloured . . . 1·10 65

244 Map and Emblems

1975. 10th Anniv of Arab Labour Organization.
1180 **244** 25f. multicoloured . . . 40 15
1181 35f. multicoloured . . . 65 55
1182 45f. multicoloured . . . 70 55

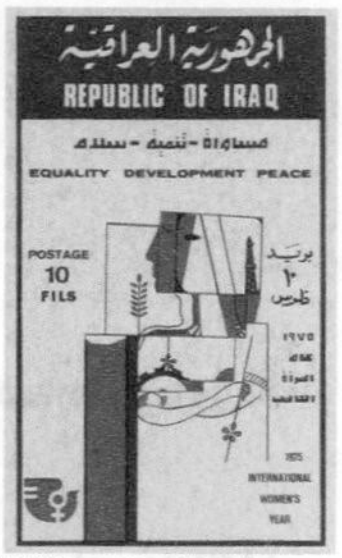

245 "Equality, Development, Peace"

1975. International Women's Year.
1183 **245** 10f. multicoloured . . . 35 15
1184 35f. multicoloured . . . 65 35
1185 70f. multicoloured . . . 2·00 1·75

246 Diyala Barrage

1975. 25th Anniv of International Commission on Irrigation and Drainage.
1187 **246** 3f. multicoloured 20 15
1188 25f. multicoloured . . . 45 25
1189 70f. multicoloured . . . 1·75 1·10

247 Company Seal

1975. 25th Anniv of National Insurance Company, Baghdad.
1190 **247** 20f. multicoloured . . . 35 15
1191 25f. multicoloured . . . 70 50

248 Court Musicians

1975. International Music Conference, Baghdad.
1193 **248** 25f. multicoloured . . . 55 25
1194 45f. multicoloured . . . 1·25 75

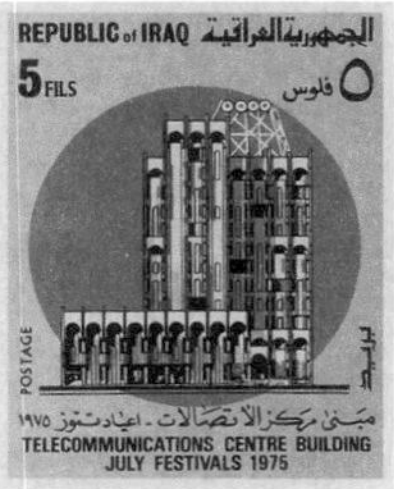

250 Telecommunications Centre

1975. Opening of Telecommunications Centre.
1203 **250** 5f. multicoloured 15 15
1204 10f. multicoloured . . . 20 15
1205 60f. multicoloured . . . 1·40 95

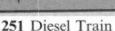

251 Diesel Train **252** Goddess (statue)

1975. 15th Taurus Railway Conference, Baghdad. Multicoloured.
1206 25f. Type **251** . . . . 2·75 2·25
1207 30f. Diesel locomotive . . . 3·75 3·00
1208 35f. Tank locomotive and train . . . . 5·50 4·25
1209 50f. Steam locomotive . . . 8·00 6·75

1976.
1210 **252** 5f. multicoloured 10 10
1211 10f. multicoloured . . . 10 10
1212 15f. multicoloured . . . 15 10
1213 – 20f. multicoloured . . . 20 10
1214 – 25f. multicoloured . . . 30 10
1215 – 30f. multicoloured . . . 40 10
1216 – 35f. multicoloured . . . 50 20
1217 – 50f. multicoloured . . . 70 20
1218 – 75f. multicoloured . . . 1·00 50
DESIGNS: 20, 25, 30f. Two females forming column; 35, 50, 75f. Head of bearded man.

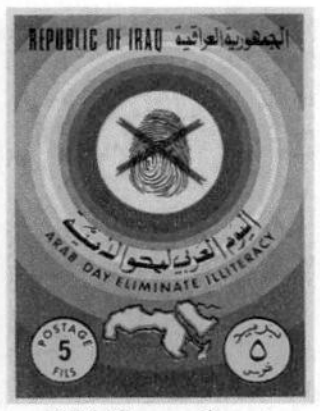

253 Soldier and Symbols of Industry and Agriculture **254** Crossed-out Thumbprint

1976. Arab Day.
1219 **253** 5f. multicoloured 20 15
1220 25f. multicoloured on silver 45 15
1221 50f. mult on gold . . . 1·25 50

1976. Arab Literacy Day.
1222 **254** 5f. multicoloured 15 10
1223 15f. multicoloured . . . 20 15
1224 35f. multicoloured . . . 1·25 45

255 Iraq Earth Station **256** Early and Modern Telephones

1976. 13th Anniv of Revolution of 14th Ramadan.
1225 **255** 10f. multicoloured . . . 25 10
1226 25f. multicoloured on silver 60 30
1227 75f. mult on gold . . . 2·10 1·40

1976. Telephone Centenary.
1228 **256** 35f. multicoloured . . . 55 25
1229 50f. multicoloured . . . 1·10 60
1230 75f. multicoloured . . . 1·60 1·10

257 Map and Emblem **258** Iraqi Family on Map

1976. 20th International Arab Trade Unions Conf.
1231 **257** 5f. mult (postage) . . . 25 20
1232 10f. multicoloured . . . 25 20
1233 75f. multicoloured (air) 2·10 1·10

1976. Police Day.
1234 **258** 5f. multicoloured 25 15
1235 15f. multicoloured . . . 35 15
1236 35f. multicoloured . . . 1·50 85

259 "Strategy" Pipeline **260** Human Eye

1976. 4th Anniv of Oil Nationalization.
1237 **259** 25f. multicoloured . . . 65 35
1238 75f. multicoloured . . . 2·10 1·25

1976. Air. World Health Day. "Foresight Prevents Blindness".
1240 **260** 25f. blue and black . . . 25 15
1241 35f. green and black . . 35 25
1242 50f. orange and brown 70 45

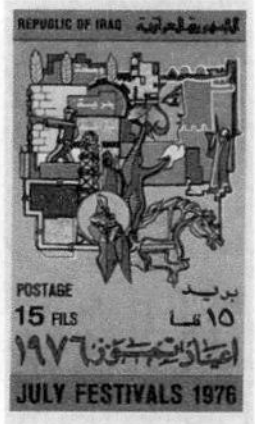

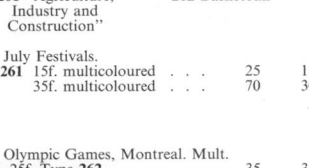

261 "Agriculture, Industry and Construction" **262** Basketball

1976. July Festivals.
1243 **261** 15f. multicoloured . . . 25 15
1244 35f. multicoloured . . . 70 30

1976. Olympic Games, Montreal. Mult.
1245 25f. Type **262** 35 35
1246 35f. Volleyball 50 40
1247 50f. Wrestling 75 50
1248 75f. Boxing . . . . 1·40 85

263 Bishop Capucci, Wounded Dove and Map of Palestine **264** River Kingfisher

1976. 2nd Anniv of Bishop Capucci's Arrest.
1250 **263** 25f. multicoloured . . . 40 20
1251 35f. multicoloured . . . 50 30
1252 75f. multicoloured . . . 1·60 1·10

1976. Birds. Multicoloured.
1253 5f. Type **264** . . . . 1·10 25
1254 10f. Turtle dove . . . . . . 1·25 40
1255 15f. Pin-tailed sandgrouse 1·50 45
1256 25f. Blue rock thrush . . . 2·50 55
1257 50f. Purple heron and grey heron . . . . 4·00 1·10
See also Nos. O1258/62.

265 Emblem within "15" **266** Children with Banner

1976. 15th Anniv of Iraqi Students' Union.
1263 **265** 30f. multicoloured . . . 35 10
1264 70f. multicoloured . . . 1·60 75

1976. 30th Anniv of U.N.E.S.C.O. "Children's Books". Multicoloured.
1265 10f. Type **266** 30 10
1266 25f. Children in garden . . 35 15
1267 75f. Children with Iraqi flag 1·90 1·40

267 Tanker "Rumaila" and Emblem

1976. 4th Anniv of First Iraqi Oil Tanker and 1st Anniv of Basrah Petroleum Co Nationalization. Multicoloured.
1268 10f. Type **267** 35 10
1269 15f. Type **267** 45 15
1270 25f. Oil jetty and installations 65 25
1271 50f. As 25f. . . . . 1·75 1·00

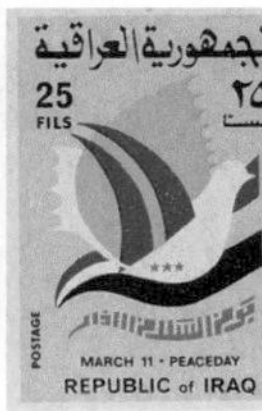

268 Islamic Design with Inscriptions **269** Dove Emblem

1977. Birthday of Prophet Mohammed.
1272 **268** 25f. multicoloured . . . 35 15
1273 35f. multicoloured . . . 70 65

1977. Peace Day.
1274 **269** 25f. multicoloured . . . 30 20
1275 30f. multicoloured . . . 45 30

270 Dahlia

1977. Flowers. Multicoloured.
1276 5f. Type **270** 20 10
1277 10f. "Lathyrus odoratus" . . 20 10
1278 35f. "Chrysanthemum coronarium" 65 25
1279 50f. "Verbena hybrida" . . 1·00 90

271 "V" Emblem with Doves

1977. 30th Anniv of Al-Baath Party. Mult.
1280 25f. Type **271** 35 15
1281 75f. Human figures as a flame . . . . 1·40 70

272 A.P.U. Emblem and Flags **273** 1st May Emblem

1977. 25th Anniv of Arab Postal Union.
1283 **272** 25f. multicoloured . . . 35 15
1284 35f. multicoloured . . . 55 40

1977. Labour Day.
1285 **273** 10f. multicoloured . . . 20 10
1286 30f. multicoloured . . . 45 15
1287 35f. multicoloured . . . 65 50

274 First Stage of Lift **275** Dome of the Rock

1977. 8th Asian Weightlifting Championships, Baghdad. Multicoloured.
1288 25f. Type **274** 60 45
1289 75f. Press-up stage of lift . . 1·60 1·00

1977. Palestinian Welfare.
1291 **275** 5f. multicoloured 70 15

276 Arabian Garden **277** Dove and Ear of Wheat

1977. Arab Tourism Year. Multicoloured.
1292 5f. Type **276** 15 10
1293 10f. Town view with minarets (horiz) 20 15
1294 30f. Country stream 50 25
1295 50f. Oasis (horiz) . . . . . 1·50 90

1977. July Festivals.
1296 **277** 25f. multicoloured . . . 45 20
1297 30f. multicoloured . . . 70 30

278 Map of Middle East and North Africa **279** Emblem

1977. U.N. Conference on Desertification.
1298 **278** 30f. multicoloured . . . 50 35
1299 70f. multicoloured . . . 1·40 70

1977. Census Day.
1300 **279** 20f. multicoloured . . . 20 15
1301 30f. multicoloured . . . 50 15
1302 70f. multicoloured . . . 90 60

280 Abstract Calligraphic Emblem **281** Kamal Jumblatt and Political Caricatures

1977. Al-Mutanabby Festival.
1303 **280** 25f. multicoloured . . . 20 15
1304 50f. multicoloured . . . 55 35

1977. Kamal Jumblatt (Lebanese socialist) Commemoration.
1305 **281** 20f. multicoloured . . . 20 15
1306 30f. multicoloured . . . 30 15
1307 70f. multicoloured . . . 75 50

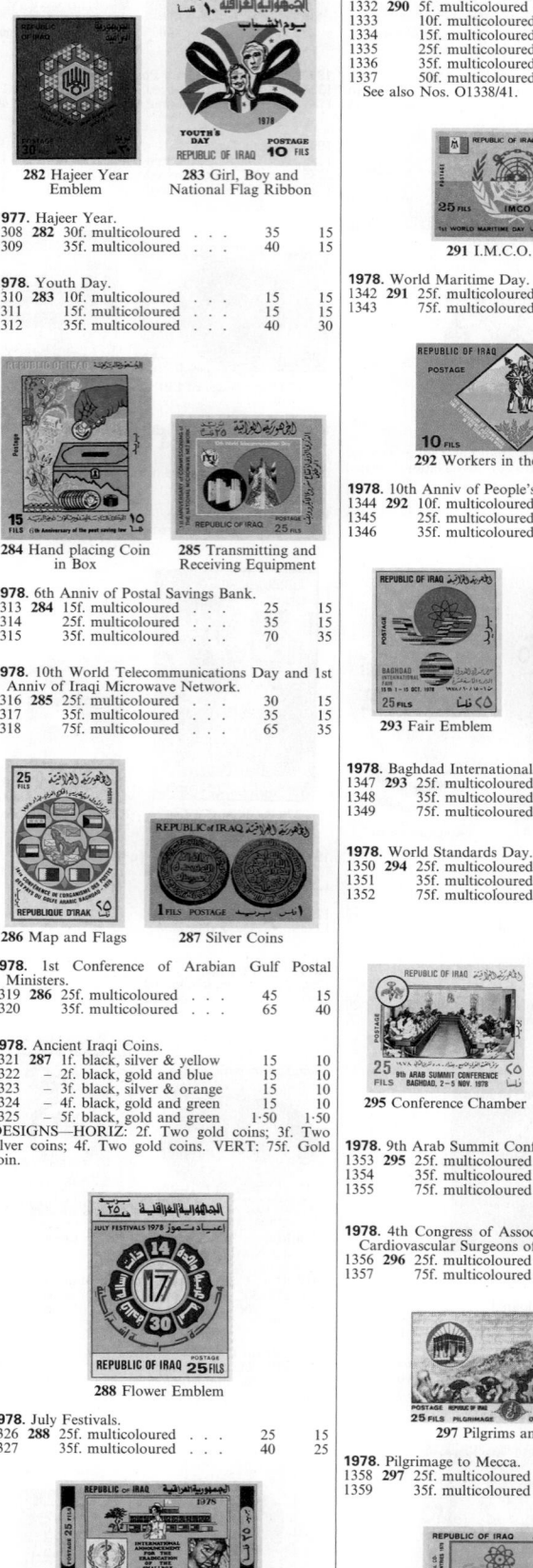

282 Hajeer Year Emblem

283 Girl, Boy and National Flag Ribbon

1977. Hajeer Year.
1308 **282** 30f. multicoloured . . . 35 15
1309 35f. multicoloured . . . 40 15

1978. Youth Day.
1310 **283** 10f. multicoloured . . . 15 15
1311 15f. multicoloured . . . 15 15
1312 35f. multicoloured . . . 40 30

284 Hand placing Coin in Box

285 Transmitting and Receiving Equipment

1978. 6th Anniv of Postal Savings Bank.
1313 **284** 15f. multicoloured . . . 25 15
1314 25f. multicoloured . . . 35 15
1315 35f. multicoloured . . . 70 35

1978. 10th World Telecommunications Day and 1st Anniv of Iraqi Microwave Network.
1316 **285** 25f. multicoloured . . . 30 15
1317 35f. multicoloured . . . 35 15
1318 75f. multicoloured . . . 65 35

286 Map and Flags

287 Silver Coins

1978. 1st Conference of Arabian Gulf Postal Ministers.
1319 **286** 25f. multicoloured . . . 45 15
1320 35f. multicoloured . . . 65 40

1978. Ancient Iraqi Coins.
1321 **287** 1f. black, silver & yellow 15 10
1322 – 2f. black, gold and blue 15 10
1323 – 3f. black, silver & orange 15 10
1324 – 4f. black, gold and green 15 10
1325 – 5f. black, gold and green 1·50 1·50
DESIGNS—HORIZ: 2f. Two gold coins; 3f. Two silver coins; 4f. Two gold coins. VERT: 75f. Gold coin.

288 Flower Emblem

1978. July Festivals.
1326 **288** 25f. multicoloured . . . 25 15
1327 35f. multicoloured . . . 40 25

289 Nurse, Hospital and Sick Child

1978. Global Eradication of Smallpox.
1329 **289** 25f. multicoloured . . . 25 15
1330 35f. multicoloured . . . 50 25
1331 75f. multicoloured . . . 1·40 75

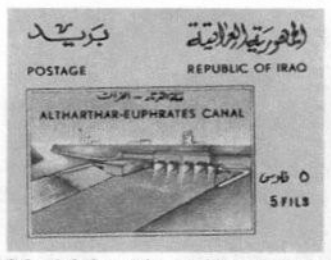

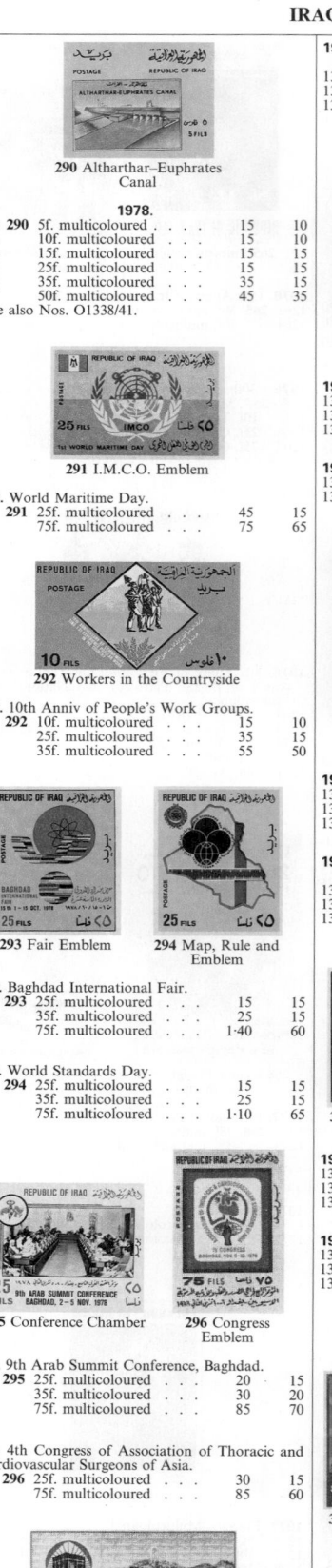

290 Altharthar–Euphrates Canal

1978.
1332 **290** 5f. multicoloured . . . 15 10
1333 10f. multicoloured . . . 15 10
1334 15f. multicoloured . . . 15 15
1335 25f. multicoloured . . . 15 15
1336 35f. multicoloured . . . 35 15
1337 50f. multicoloured . . . 45 35
See also Nos. O1338/41.

291 I.M.C.O. Emblem

1978. World Maritime Day.
1342 **291** 25f. multicoloured . . . 45 15
1343 75f. multicoloured . . . 75 65

292 Workers in the Countryside

1978. 10th Anniv of People's Work Groups.
1344 **292** 10f. multicoloured . . . 15 10
1345 25f. multicoloured . . . 35 15
1346 35f. multicoloured . . . 55 50

293 Fair Emblem

294 Map, Rule and Emblem

1978. Baghdad International Fair.
1347 **293** 25f. multicoloured . . . 15 15
1348 35f. multicoloured . . . 25 15
1349 75f. multicoloured . . . 1·40 60

1978. World Standards Day.
1350 **294** 25f. multicoloured . . . 15 15
1351 35f. multicoloured . . . 25 15
1352 75f. multicoloured . . . 1·10 65

295 Conference Chamber

296 Congress Emblem

1978. 9th Arab Summit Conference, Baghdad.
1353 **295** 25f. multicoloured . . . 20 15
1354 35f. multicoloured . . . 30 20
1355 75f. multicoloured . . . 85 70

1978. 4th Congress of Association of Thoracic and Cardiovascular Surgeons of Asia.
1356 **296** 25f. multicoloured . . . 30 15
1357 75f. multicoloured . . . 85 60

297 Pilgrims and Kaaba

1978. Pilgrimage to Mecca.
1358 **297** 25f. multicoloured . . . 30 15
1359 35f. multicoloured . . . 45 25

298 Map and Symbol

1978. U.N. Conference for Technical Co-operation among Developing Countries.
1360 **298** 25f. multicoloured . . . 25 15
1361 50f. multicoloured . . . 45 20
1362 75f. multicoloured . . . 75 50

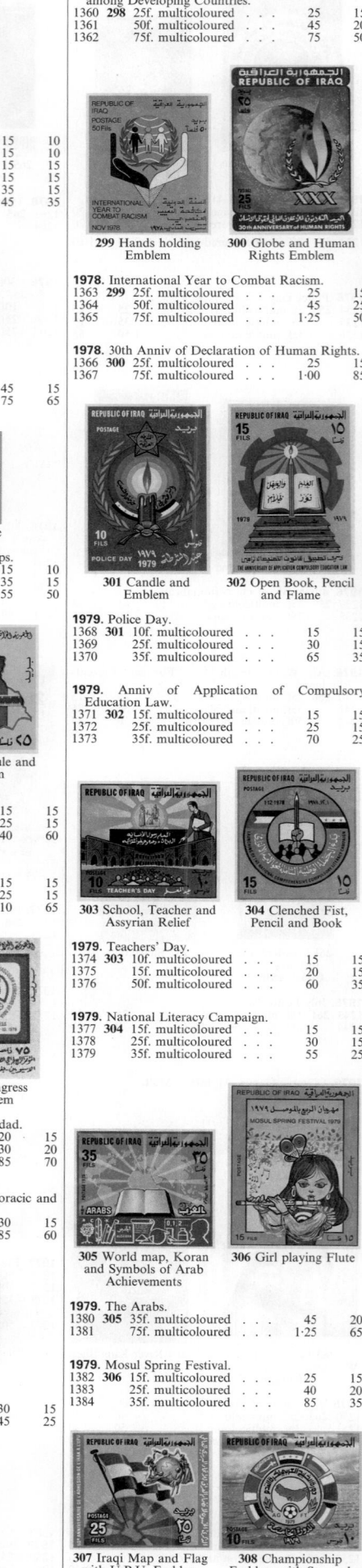

299 Hands holding Emblem

300 Globe and Human Rights Emblem

1978. International Year to Combat Racism.
1363 **299** 25f. multicoloured . . . 25 15
1364 50f. multicoloured . . . 45 25
1365 75f. multicoloured . . . 1·25 50

1978. 30th Anniv of Declaration of Human Rights.
1366 **300** 25f. multicoloured . . . 25 15
1367 75f. multicoloured . . . 1·00 85

301 Candle and Emblem

302 Open Book, Pencil and Flame

1979. Police Day.
1368 **301** 10f. multicoloured . . . 15 15
1369 25f. multicoloured . . . 30 15
1370 35f. multicoloured . . . 65 35

1979. Anniv of Application of Compulsory Education Law.
1371 **302** 15f. multicoloured . . . 15 15
1372 25f. multicoloured . . . 25 15
1373 35f. multicoloured . . . 70 25

303 School, Teacher and Assyrian Relief

304 Clenched Fist, Pencil and Book

1979. Teachers' Day.
1374 **303** 10f. multicoloured . . . 15 15
1375 15f. multicoloured . . . 20 15
1376 50f. multicoloured . . . 60 35

1979. National Literacy Campaign.
1377 **304** 15f. multicoloured . . . 15 15
1378 25f. multicoloured . . . 30 15
1379 35f. multicoloured . . . 55 25

305 World map, Koran and Symbols of Arab Achievements

306 Girl playing Flute

1979. The Arabs.
1380 **305** 35f. multicoloured . . . 45 20
1381 75f. multicoloured . . . 1·25 65

1979. Mosul Spring Festival.
1382 **306** 15f. multicoloured . . . 25 15
1383 25f. multicoloured . . . 40 20
1384 35f. multicoloured . . . 85 35

307 Iraqi Map and Flag with U.P.U. Emblem

308 Championship Emblem with Sea and Sky

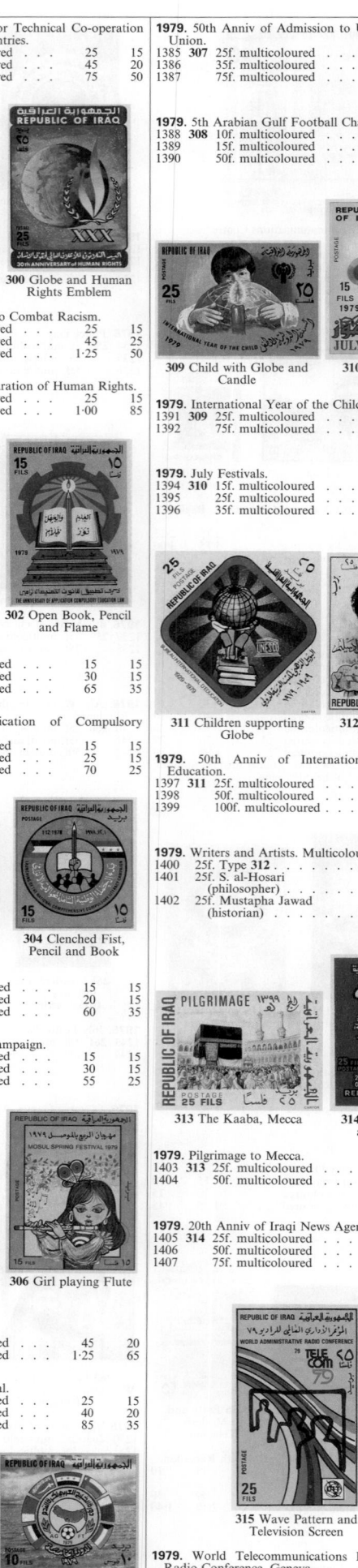

1979. 50th Anniv of Admission to Universal Postal Union.
1385 **307** 25f. multicoloured . . . 40 15
1386 35f. multicoloured . . . 55 25
1387 75f. multicoloured . . . 1·00 45

1979. 5th Arabian Gulf Football Championship.
1388 **308** 10f. multicoloured . . . 15 15
1389 15f. multicoloured . . . 25 15
1390 50f. multicoloured . . . 70 45

309 Child with Globe and Candle

310 Flower and Branch

1979. International Year of the Child.
1391 **309** 25f. multicoloured . . . 45 25
1392 75f. multicoloured . . . 1·10 75

1979. July Festivals.
1394 **310** 15f. multicoloured . . . 15 10
1395 25f. multicoloured . . . 25 25
1396 35f. multicoloured . . . 45 25

311 Children supporting Globe

312 Jawad Selim (sculptor)

1979. 50th Anniv of International Bureau of Education.
1397 **311** 25f. multicoloured . . . 45 25
1398 50f. multicoloured . . . 75 40
1399 100f. multicoloured . . . 1·10 85

1979. Writers and Artists. Multicoloured.
1400 25f. Type **312** 35 15
1401 25f. S. al-Hosari (philosopher) 35 15
1402 25f. Mustapha Jawad (historian) 35 15

313 The Kaaba, Mecca

314 Figure "20" and Globe

1979. Pilgrimage to Mecca.
1403 **313** 25f. multicoloured . . . 30 15
1404 50f. multicoloured . . . 55 25

1979. 20th Anniv of Iraqi News Agency.
1405 **314** 25f. multicoloured . . . 30 15
1406 50f. multicoloured . . . 65 20
1407 75f. multicoloured . . . 1·00 35

315 Wave Pattern and Television Screen

1979. World Telecommunications Exhibition and Radio Conference, Geneva.
1408 **315** 25f. multicoloured . . . 35 15
1409 50f. multicoloured . . . 50 30
1410 75f. multicoloured . . . 85 50

316 Clenched Fists and Refugee

1979. Palestinian Solidarity Day.
1411 **316** 25f. multicoloured . . . 45 15
1412 50f. multicoloured . . . 65 35
1413 75f. multicoloured . . . 1·10 65

317 Ahmed Hassan Al-Bakir
318 Boy with Violin

1979. Inaug of Pres. Saddam Hussain. Mult.
1414 25f. Type **317** 25 15
1415 35f. Pres. Hussain taking the oath 45 20
1416 75f. Type **317** 75 45
1417 100f. As No. 1415 . . . . . 1·10 85

1979. Activities of Vanguards (youth organization). Multicoloured.
1418 10f. Type **318** 10 10
1419 15f. Boys on building site 15 15
1420 25f. Boys on assault course and in personal combat 20 15
1421 35f. Vanguards emblem . . 45 20

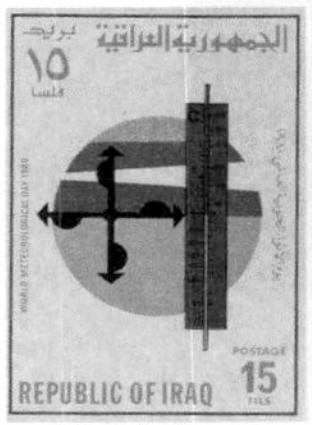

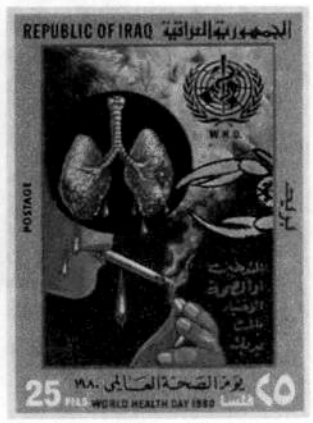

319 Wind-speed Indicator and Thermometer
320 Lighting Cigarette and Cancerous Lungs

1980. World Meteorological Day.
1422 **319** 15f. multicoloured . . . 15 15
1423 25f. multicoloured . . . 25 15
1424 35f. multicoloured . . . 45 25

1980. World Health Day. Anti-smoking Campaign.
1425 **320** 25f. multicoloured . . . 30 15
1426 35f. multicoloured . . . 45 15
1427 75f. multicoloured . . . 75 45

321 Festivals Emblem
322 Hurdling

1980. July Festivals.
1428 **321** 25f. multicoloured . . . 20 15
1429 35f. multicoloured . . . 25 15

1980. Olympic Games, Moscow. Multicoloured.
1431 15f. Type **322** 20 15
1432 20f. Weightlifting (vert) . . 30 15
1433 30f. Boxing 45 25
1434 35f. Football (vert) 50 35

323 "Rubus sanctus"

1980. Fruit. Multicoloured.
1436 5f. Type **323** 20 10
1437 15f. Peaches 35 15
1438 20f. Pears 50 15
1439 25f. Apples 60 15
1440 35f. Plums 80 30

324 Conference Emblem and Arabic Text
325 A.P.U. Emblem Posthorn and Map

1980. World Tourism Conference, Manila.
1441 **324** 25f. multicoloured . . . 25 15
1442 50f. multicoloured . . . 50 25
1443 100f. multicoloured . . . 95 65

1980. 11th Congress of Arab Postal Union, Baghdad.
1444 **325** 10f. multicoloured . . . 15 10
1445 30f. multicoloured . . . 25 15
1446 35f. multicoloured . . . 40 25

326 O.P.E.C. Emblem and Globe

1980. 20th Anniv of Organization of Petroleum Exporting Countries.
1447 **326** 30f. multicoloured . . . 50 20
1448 75f. multicoloured . . . 1·00 65

327 African Monarch

1980. Butterflies. Multicoloured.
1449 10f. Swallowtail 25 20
1450 15f. Type **327** 50 25
1451 20f. Red admiral 70 40
1452 30f. Clouded yellow . . . . 1·00 45

328 Mosque and Ka'aba

1980. 1400th Anniv of Hegira.
1453 **328** 15f. multicoloured . . . 20 15
1454 25f. multicoloured . . . 35 15
1455 35f. multicoloured . . . 45 20

329 Riflemen and Dome of the Rock on Map of Israel

1980. Palestinian Solidarity Day.
1456 **329** 25f. multicoloured . . . 30 15
1457 35f. multicoloured . . . 45 20
1458 75f. multicoloured . . . 1·00 50

330 Soldier and Rocket
331 "8" and Flags forming Torch

1981. 60th Anniv of Army Day.
1459 **330** 5f. multicoloured 15 10
1460 30f. multicoloured . . . 40 15
1461 75f. multicoloured . . . 90 50

1981. 18th Anniv of 14th Ramadan Revolution.
1462 **331** 15f. multicoloured . . . 15 10
1463 30f. multicoloured . . . 30 15
1464 35f. multicoloured . . . 40 20

332 Map of Arab States tied with Ribbon

1981. The Arabs.
1465 **332** 5f. multicoloured 10 10
1466 25f. multicoloured . . . 30 15
1467 35f. multicoloured . . . 45 20

333 Pres. Hussain and Modern Military Equipment
334 I.T.U. and W.H.O. Emblems and Ribbons forming Caduceus

1981. Saddam's Battle of Qadisiya.
1468 **333** 30f. multicoloured . . . 30 15
1469 35f. multicoloured . . . 40 15
1470 75f. multicoloured . . . 70 35

1981. World Telecommunications Day.
1472 **334** 25f. multicoloured . . . 35 20
1473 50f. multicoloured . . . 70 30
1474 75f. multicoloured . . . 1·10 60

335 Mil Mi-24 Helicopters attacking Ground Forces
336 Map and Flower enclosing Ballot Box

1981. 50th Anniv of Air Force. Mult.
1475 5f. Type **335** (postage) . . . 15 15
1476 10f. Antonov An-2 biplane trainer 25 15
1477 15f. "SAM-15" missile . . . 25 15
1478 120f. De Havilland Dragon Rapide biplane and Mikoyan Gurevich MiG-21 jet fighters (vert) (air) . . . . 2·50 1·50

1981. 1st Anniv of National Assembly Election.
1479 **336** 30f. multicoloured . . . 30 10
1480 35f. multicoloured . . . 45 15
1481 45f. multicoloured . . . 55 25

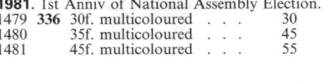

337 Festivals Emblem
338 Basket Weaver

1981. July Festivals.
1482 **337** 15f. multicoloured . . . 20 10
1483 25f. multicoloured . . . 30 15
1484 35f. multicoloured . . . 45 20

1981. Popular Industries. Multicoloured.
1485 5f. Type **338** 10 10
1486 30f. Copper worker 35 20
1487 35f. Potter 55 20
1488 50f. Weaver (horiz) 70 30

339 Saddam Hussain Gymnasium

1981. Modern Buildings. Multicoloured.
1489 45f. Type **339** 45 20
1490 50f. Palace of Conferences 45 20
1491 120f. As 50f. . . . . 1·25 95
1492 150f. Type **339** . . . . . . 1·75 1·10

340 Pilgrims

1981. Pilgrimage to Mecca.
1493 **340** 25f. multicoloured . . . 40 15
1494 45f. multicoloured . . . 65 25
1495 50f. multicoloured . . . 65 25

341 Harvesting

1981. World Food Day.
1496 **341** 30f. multicoloured . . . 30 15
1497 45f. multicoloured . . . 60 30
1498 75f. multicoloured . . . 90 55

343 Teacher with Deaf Child
344 Medal and Map

1981. International Year of Disabled Persons.
1501 **343** 30f. multicoloured . . . 30 15
1502 45f. multicoloured . . . 70 25
1503 75f. multicoloured . . . 95 60

1981. Martyr's Day.
1504 **344** 45f. multicoloured . . . 50 20
1505 50f. multicoloured . . . 50 20
1506 120f. multicoloured . . . 1·50 1·00
See also Nos. O1507/9.

345 "Ibn Khaldoon" (freighter)

1981. 5th Anniv of United Arab Shipping Company.
1507 **345** 50f. multicoloured . . . 75 35
1508 120f. multicoloured . . . 2·00 1·10

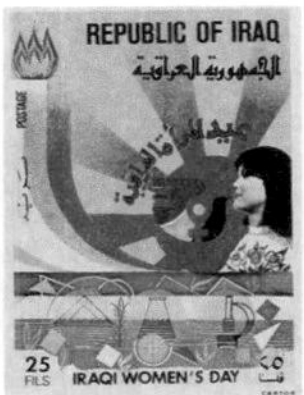

346 Woman and Symbols of Technology
347 President Hussain, "7" and "Flowers"

1982. Iraqi Women's Day.
1509 **346** 25f. multicoloured . . . 35 15
1510 45f. multicoloured . . . 60 30
1511 50f. multicoloured . . . 60 35

1982. 35th Anniv of Al-Baath Party. Mult.
1512 25f. Type **347** 35 15
1513 30f. Rainbow and "7 7 7" 35 15
1514 45f. Type **347** 55 35
1515 50f. As 30f. 55 35

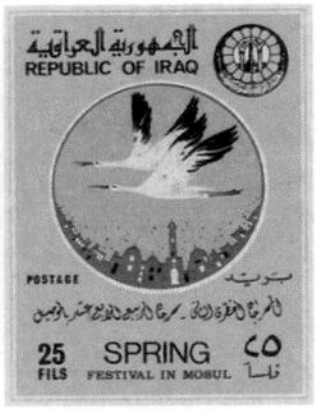

348 A.P.U. Emblem and Globe
349 White Storks

1982. 30th Anniv of Arab Postal Union.
1517 **348** 25f. multicoloured . . . 30 15
1518 45f. multicoloured . . . 50 25
1519 50f. multicoloured . . . 55 25

1982. Mosul Spring Festival. Multicoloured.
1520 25f. Type **349** . . . . 1·10 20
1521 30f. Doll 45 15
1522 45f. Type **349** . . . . 1·10 50
1523 50f. As 30f. 65 30

350 World Map, Factories and "1"

1982. Labour Day.
1524 **350** 25f. multicoloured . . . 30 10
1525 45f. multicoloured . . . 45 25
1526 50f. multicoloured . . . 50 30

351 Geometric Figure and I.T.U. Problem **352** Oil Gusher

1982. World Telecommunications Day.
1527 **351** 5f. multicoloured 10 10
1528 45f. multicoloured . . . 50 25
1529 100f. multicoloured . . . 1·10 70

1982. 10th Anniv of Oil Nationalization. Mult.
1530 5f. Type **352** 10 10
1531 25f. Type **352** 45 15
1532 45f. Bronze sculpture of bull and horse flanking couple holding model of oil rig 75 35
1533 50f. As 45f. 85 45

353 Nuclear Power Emblem and Lion **354** Footballers

1982. 1st Anniv of Attack on Iraqi Nuclear Reactor. Multicoloured.
1534 30f. Type **353** 45 15
1535 45f. Bomb aimed at egg . . 70 25
1536 50f. Type **353** 75 35
1537 120f. As No. 1535 . . . . . 1·50 95

1982. World Cup Football Championship, Spain. Multicoloured.
1538 5f. Type **354** 15 10
1539 45f. Three footballers . . . 50 30
1540 50f. Type **354** 50 30
1541 100f. As 45f. . . . . 1·10 75

355 President Hussain and Fireworks **356** Green Lizard

1982. July Festivals.
1543 **355** 25f. multicoloured . . . 25 15
1544 45f. multicoloured . . . 45 25
1545 50f. multicoloured . . . 45 30

1982. Reptiles. Multicoloured.
1546 25f. Type **356** . . . . 1·40 60
1547 30f. Asp . . . . 1·50 60
1548 45f. Two green lizards . . . 1·75 80
1549 50f. "Natrix tessellata" . . . 2·00 1·10

357 Pandit Nehru (India)

1982. 7th Non-Aligned Countries Conference, Baghdad. Multicoloured.
1550 50f. Type **357** 55 25
1551 50f. Josef Tito (Yugoslavia) 55 25
1552 50f. Abdul Nasser (Egypt) 55 25
1553 50f. Kwame Nkrumah (Ghana) 55 25
1554 100f. President Hussain (Iraq) . . . . 1·25 70

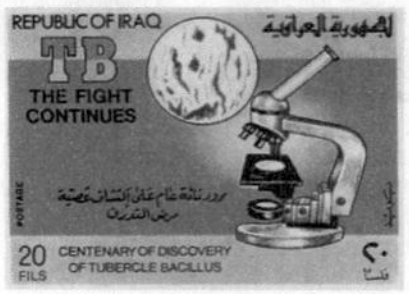
358 Microscope and Bacilli

1982. Cent of Discovery of Tubercule Bacillus.
1555 **358** 20f. multicoloured . . . 45 15
1556 50f. multicoloured . . . 80 25
1557 100f. multicoloured . . . 1·40 80

359 U.P.U. Building, Berne

1982. U.P.U. Day.
1561 **359** 5f. multicoloured 15 10
1562 45f. multicoloured . . . 45 25
1563 100f. multicoloured . . . 1·10 70

360 Drums

1982. Musical Instruments. Multicoloured.
1564 5f. Type **360** 15 10
1565 10f. Stringed board instrument 20 10
1566 35f. Bowed instruments . . 55 20
1567 100f. Mandolin . . . . . . 1·75 75

361 Mosque and Minaret, Mecca **362** Flowers

1982. Prophet Mohammed's Birthday. Mult.
1568 25f. Type **361** 25 15
1569 30f. Courtyard of mosque 25 15
1570 45f. Type **361** 40 25
1571 50f. As No. 1569 . . . . . 45 40

1982. Flowers. Multicoloured.
1572 10f. Type **362** 20 15
1573 20f. Flowers (different) . . . 30 15
1574 30f. Type **362** 35 20
1575 40f. As No. 1573 . . . . . 50 35
1576 50f. Type **362** 65 35
1577 100f. As No. 1573 . . . . . 1·10 60

1983. Nos. 1489/51 surch.
1578 60f. on 50f. Palace of Conferences 75 30
1579 70f. on 45f. Type **339** . . . 1·10 45
1580 160f. on 120f. Palace of Conferences . . . . . . 2·50 1·50

364 President Hussain

1983. July Festivals.
1583 **364** 30f. multicoloured . . . 30 15
1584 60f. multicoloured . . . 70 35
1585 70f. multicoloured . . . 75 35

365 Emblem and Interlocked Bands **366** Horseman and Map

1983. World Communications Year. Mult.
1586 5f. Type **365** 15 15
1587 25f. Hexagons of primary colours 25 15
1588 60f. Type **365** 75 45
1589 70f. As No. 1587 . . . . . 85 50

1983. Battle of Thiqar. Multicoloured.
1591 20f. Type **366** 25 15
1592 50f. Eagle swooping on pyre 65 30
1593 60f. Type **366** 70 35
1594 70f. As No. 1592 . . . . . 80 45

367 Fair Emblem and Silhouette of Baghdad **368** Pres. Hussain within Figure "9"

1983. Baghdad International Fair.
1595 **367** 60f. multicoloured . . . 65 30
1596 70f. multicoloured . . . 70 45
1597 160f. multicoloured . . . 1·50 1·10

1983. 9th Al-Baath Party Congress. Mult.
1598 30f. Type **368** 25 15
1599 60f. Eagle, torch, map and book 60 35
1600 70f. Type **368** 70 40
1601 100f. As No. 1599 . . . . . 1·00 55

369 Fishermen hauling Boat

1983. Paintings. Multicoloured.
1602 60f. Type **369** 65 45
1603 60f. Festive crowd 65 45
1604 60f. Hanging decorations . . 65 45
1605 70f. Crowd 75 55
1606 70f. Bazaar 75 55

370 Dove and Victim **371** Apartment Building

1983. Massacre of Palestinians in Sabra and Shatila Refugee Camps, Lebanon. Multicoloured.
1607 10f. Type **370** 20 10
1608 60f. Type **370** 70 35
1609 70f. Dove and clasped fist shedding blood and victims 75 45
1610 160f. As No. 1609 . . . . . 1·60 1·10

1983. Buildings.
1611 **371** 60f. lt green, black & grn 60 35
1612 – 70f. purple, black & grey 65 45
1613 – 160f. purple, blk & grey 1·50 85
1614 **371** 200f. green, black & olive . . . . 2·00 1·10
DESIGNS: 70, 160f. Apartment building (different).
See also Nos. O1615/16.

372 President Hussain

1983. 4th Anniv of President Hussain as Party and State Leader.
1617 **372** 60f. multicoloured . . . 65 35
1618 70f. multicoloured . . . 75 45
1619 250f. multicoloured . . . 2·50 1·50

373 Congress Emblem

1984. 25th International Military Medicine and Pharmacy Congress.
1620 **373** 60f. multicoloured . . . 65 35
1621 70f. multicoloured . . . 75 45
1622 200f. multicoloured . . . 2·25 1·10

374 President Hussain and Flowers

1984. Pres. Saddam Hussain's 47th Birthday. Multicoloured.
1623 60f. Type **374** 45 25
1624 70f. Pres. Hussain in army uniform 55 35
1625 160f. As No. 1623 . . . . . 1·60 1·25
1626 200f. Type **374** . . . . . . 1·90 1·25

375 Boxing

1984. Olympic Games, Los Angeles. Multicoloured.
1628 50f. Type **375** 50 40
1629 60f. Hurdling, weightlifting and wrestling 70 40
1630 70f. Type **375** 85 50
1631 100f. As No. 1629 . . . . . 1·10 65

376 Pres. Hussain and Horses' Heads **377** Flag as Ribbon and Two Domes

1984. Battle of Qadisiya. Multicoloured.
1633 50f. Type **376** 45 30
1634 60f. President Hussain and symbolic representation of battle 65 35
1635 70f. Type **376** 75 55
1636 100f. As No. 1634 . . . . . 1·10 60

1984. Martyr's Day. Multicoloured.
1638 50f. Type **377** 50 25
1639 60f. Woman holding rifle and medal 60 35
1640 70f. Type **377** 70 50
1641 100f. As No. 1639 . . . . . 1·00 65

378 Text

1985. 5th Anniv of President Hussain's Visit to Al-Mustansiriyah University.
1646 **378** 60f. red and blue 60 40
1647 70f. red and green . . . 70 45
1648 250f. red and black . . . 2·40 85

379 Pres. Hussain and Jet Fighters — **380** Pres. Hussain within Flower

1985. 54th Anniv of Iraqi Air Force. Mult.
1649 10f. Type **379** 25 10
1650 60f. Fighter airplanes trailing flag and "54" (horiz) . . . . 1·00 55
1651 70f. As No. 1650 . . . . . 1·10 60
1652 160f. Type **379** . . . . . . 2·75 1·40

1985. 48th Birthday of President Saddam Hussain. Multicoloured.
1654 30f. Type **380** 30 20
1655 60f. Pres. Hussain, candle and flowers 60 40
1656 70f. Type **380** 75 55
1657 100f. As No. 1655 . . . . . 1·10 75

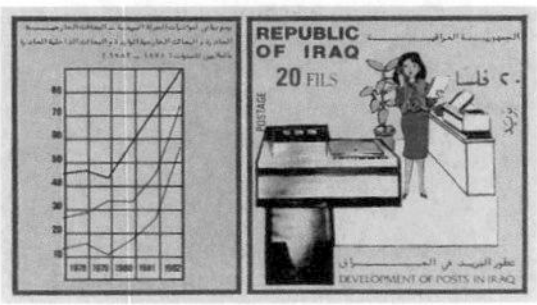

381 Graph and Modern Office

1985. Posts and Telecommunications Development. Multicoloured.
1659 20f. Type **381** 20 15
1660 50f. Dish aerial and graph 60 30
1661 60f. Type **381** 65 30
1662 70f. As No. 1660 . . . . . 75 45

382 Arms at Crossroads, and Building

1985. Saddam's Battle of Qadisiya. Multicoloured.
1663 10f. Type **382** 15 10
1664 20f. Pres. Hussain and emblem of Al-Baath Party 20 15
1665 60f. Type **382** 65 35
1666 70f. As No. 1664 . . . . . 70 55

383 Solar Energy Research Centre

1985.
1668 **383** 10f. multicoloured . . . 15 10
1669 50f. multicoloured . . . 60 30
1670 100f. multicoloured . . . 1·10 70

384 Disabled Children — **385** Hand holding Quill

1985. U.N.I.C.E.F. Child Survival Campaign. Multicoloured.
1671 10f. Type **384** 15 10
1672 15f. Toddler and baby . . . 25 15
1673 50f. Type **384** 60 30
1674 100f. As No. 1672 . . . . . 1·10 80

1985. Death Millenary of Al-Sharif Al-Radhi (poet).
1675 **385** 10f. multicoloured . . . 15 10
1676 50f. multicoloured . . . 45 30
1677 100f. multicoloured . . . 95 65

386 U.N. Emblem

1985. 40th Anniv of U.N.O.
1678 **386** 10f. multicoloured . . . 15 10
1679 40f. blue, black & yellow 45 25
1680 100f. multicoloured . . . 1·10 65

387 World Map

1985. Palestinian Solidarity Day.
1681 **387** 10f. multicoloured . . . 15 10
1682 50f. multicoloured . . . 55 30
1683 100f. multicoloured . . . 1·40 70

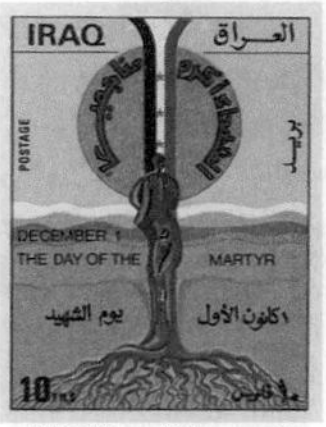

388 Flag, Man and Blood Vessels as Roots — **389** I.Y.Y. Emblem and Soldier with Flag

1985. Martyr's Day.
1684 **388** 10f. multicoloured . . . 15 10
1685 40f. multicoloured . . . 45 30
1686 100f. multicoloured . . . 95 60

1985. International Youth Year. Multicoloured.
1687 40f. Type **389** 35 20
1688 50f. Young couple, flag and I.Y.Y. emblem 50 25
1689 100f. Type **389** 90 60
1690 200f. As No. 1688 . . . . . 1·75 1·40

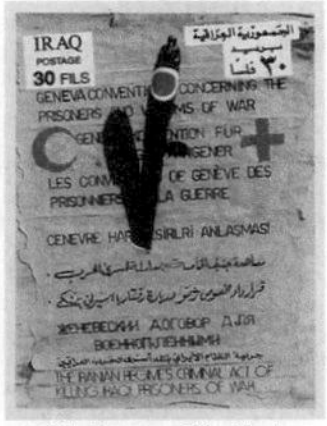

390 Pres. Hussain and Soldier in "6" — **391** Pen as Knife in Sheet of Text

1986. Army Day. Multicoloured.
1692 10f. Type **390** 15 15
1693 40f. Pres. Hussain, cogwheel, "6" and missiles (horiz) 45 20
1694 50f. Type **390** 55 30
1695 100f. As No. 1693 . . . . . 1·25 70

1986. Iraqi Prisoners of War Commemoration. Multicoloured.
1697 30f. Type **391** 30 20
1698 70f. Dove, cherub holding flag and three prisoners 75 45
1699 100f. Type **391** 95 60
1700 200f. As No. 1698 . . . . . 2·00 1·40

392 Pres. Hussain with Children — **393** Worker, Globe and Cogwheel

1986. 49th Birthday of President Saddam Hussain. Multicoloured.
1702 30f. Type **392** 30 15
1703 50f. Pres. Hussain and doves holding flag 60 20
1704 100f. Type **392** 90 65
1705 150f. As No. 1703 . . . . . 1·60 1·00

1986. Labour Day. Multicoloured.
1707 10f. Type **393** 10 10
1708 40f. Candle in cogwheel . . 35 15
1709 100f. Type **393** 90 65
1710 150f. As No. 1708 . . . . . 1·25 90

394 Pres. Hussain and "30 July 17"

1986. July Festivals and 7th Anniv of Pres. Hussain's State Leadership. Multicoloured.
1711 20f. Type **394** 15 10
1712 30f. Pres. Hussain and "17 1986" 25 15
1713 100f. Type **394** 90 60
1714 150f. As No. 1712 . . . . . 1·40 95

395 Pres. Hussain and Jet Fighter

1986. 55th Anniv of Iraqi Air Force. Multicoloured.
1716 30f. Type **395** 55 20
1717 50f. Pres. Hussain and jet fighters . . . . 1·10 30
1718 100f. Type **395** . . . . . . 2·10 1·25
1719 150f. As No. 1717 . . . . . 3·00 1·60

396 Refinery

1986. Oil Nationalization Day. Multicoloured.
1721 10f. Type **396** 15 10
1722 40f. Derrick and pipeline within flag (vert) 45 20
1723 100f. Type **396** . . . . . . 1·10 60
1724 150f. As No. 1722 . . . . . 1·60 1·10

397 Arab Warrior

1986. 1st Battle of Qadisiya. Multicoloured.
1725 20f. Type **397** 30 15
1726 60f. Pres. Hussain and battle scene 60 35
1727 70f. Type **397** 65 45
1728 100f. As No. 1726 . . . . . 95 60

398 Pres. Hussain, Battlefield and Cheering Soldiers — **399** Pres. Hussain

1986. Saadam's Battle of Qadisiya. Mult.
1729 30f. Type **398** 65 25
1730 40f. Pres. Hussain within flag "swords" and symbols of ancient and modern warfare (horiz) 90 35
1731 100f. Type **398** . . . . . . 1·50 1·00
1732 150f. As No. 1730 . . . . . 3·00 1·50

1986.
1734 **399** 30f. multicoloured . . . 50 15
1735 50f. multicoloured . . . 75 20
1736 100f. multicoloured . . . 1·40 40
1737 150f. multicoloured . . . 2·00 60
1738 250f. multicoloured . . . 3·50 1·10
1739 350f. multicoloured . . . 5·00 1·50

401 Women — **402** Flag and Treble Clef forming Dove

1986. Iraqi Women's Day. Multicoloured.
1744 30f. Type **401** 30 15
1745 50f. Woman and battle scenes (horiz) 70 25
1746 100f. Type **401** 95 60
1747 150f. As No. 1745 . . . . . 1·90 95

1986. International Peace Year. Multicoloured.
1748 50f. Type **402** 45 15
1749 100f. Globe, dove with flag and hand holding rifle and olive branch 95 55
1750 150f. Type **402** . . . . . . 1·40 90
1751 250f. As No. 1749 . . . . . 2·10 1·10

403 Freighter "Al Alwah" and Map — **404** Activities on Tree

1987. 10th Anniv of United Arab Shipping Company. Multicoloured.
1753 50f. Type **403** 45 20
1754 100f. Container ship "Khaled Ibn Al Waleed" 85 45
1755 150f. Type **403** . . . . . . 1·40 70
1756 250f. As No. 1754 . . . . . 1·75 1·10

1987. 40th Anniv of U.N.I.C.E.F. Mult.
1758 20f. Type **404** 15 15
1759 40f. Doves and "40" containing children and U.N.I.C.E.F. emblem (horiz) 25 20
1760 90f. Type **404** 65 40
1761 100f. As No. 1759 . . . . . 70 50

405 Pres. Hussain in "6" — **406** Torch, Cogwheel, Wheat and Map

1987. Army Day. Multicoloured.
1762 20f. Type **405** 15 10
1763 40f. Pres. Hussain and military scenes 25 15
1764 90f. Type **405** 50 25
1765 100f. As No. 1763 . . . . . 65 35

1987. 40th Anniv of Al-Baath Party. Mult.
1766 20f. Type **406** 15 10
1767 40f. Pres. Hussain, map and flag as "7" 20 15
1768 90f. Type **406** 50 25
1769 100f. As No. 1767 . . . . . 60 30

407 Pres. Hussain

1987. 50th Birthday of President Saddam Hussain. Multicoloured.
1770 20f. Type **407** 15 10
1771 40f. Anniversary dates, flowers and Pres. Hussain 20 15

1772 90f. Type **407** 50 30
1773 100f. As No. 1771 . . . . . 60 35

408 Pres. Hussain, Civilians, Soldiers and buried Soldier

1987. July Festivals and 8th Anniv of Pres. Hussain's State Leadership. Multicoloured.
1774 20f. Pres. Hussain and flag (horiz) 15 10
1775 40f. Type **408** 30 15
1776 90f. As No. 1174 . . . . . 55 35
1777 100f. Type **408** 70 45

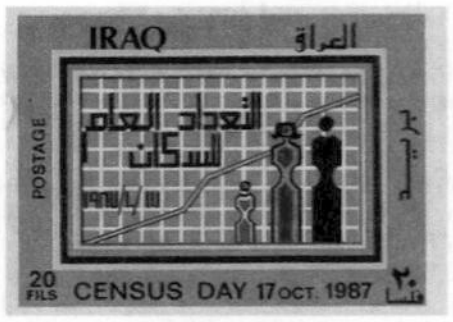

409 Symbolic Family on Graph

1987. Census. Multicoloured.
1778 20f. Type **409** 20 10
1779 30f. People on graph . . . 30 15
1780 50f. As No. 1779 . . . . . 40 20
1781 500f. Type **409** . . . . . 3·50 2·50

410 Pres. Hussain in "6" and Troops — **412** Flag as "V" and Lyre

411 "8" and Pres. Hussain

1988. Army Day. Multicoloured.
1782 20f. Type **410** 20 10
1783 30f. Soldier and medal (horiz) 20 15
1784 50f. Type **410** 35 20
1785 150f. As No. 1783 . . . . . 85 50

1988. 18th Anniv of People's Army (1786, 1788) and 25th Anniv of 8th February Revolution (others). Multicoloured.
1786 20f. Type **411** 20 10
1787 30f. Pres. Hussain and eagle on "8" (vert) 25 15
1788 50f. Type **411** 35 20
1789 150f. As No. 1787 . . . . . 1·00 60

1988. Art Day. Multicoloured.
1790 20f. Type **412** 20 10
1791 30f. Pres. Hussain, rifle as torch, clef and dove on film strip 25 15
1792 50f. Type **412** 35 25
1793 100f. As No. 1791 . . . . . 70 45

413 Rally and Ears of Wheat

1988. 41st Anniv of Al-Baath Party. Mult.
1795 20f. Type **413** 15 10
1796 30f. Flowers and "7 April 1947–1988" 15 15
1797 50f. Type **413** 35 25
1798 150f. As No. 1796 . . . . . 85 60

414 Emblem — **415** Pres. Hussain

1988. Regional Marine Environment Day. Multicoloured.
1799 20f. Type **414** 15 10
1800 40f. Fishes (horiz) 25 15
1801 90f. Type **414** 60 45
1802 100f. As No. 1800 . . . . . 80 50

1988. 51st Birthday of President Saddam Hussain. Multicoloured.
1803 20f. Type **415** 15 10
1804 30f. Pres. Hussain and hands holding flowers . . 20 15
1805 50f. Type **415** 35 20
1806 100f. As No. 1804 . . . . . 65 45

416 Emblem

1988. 40th Anniv of W.H.O. Multicoloured.
1808 20f. Type **416** 15 10
1809 40f. Red crescent protecting line of people (vert) . . . 20 15
1810 90f. Type **416** 65 45
1811 100f. As No. 1809 . . . . . 75 55

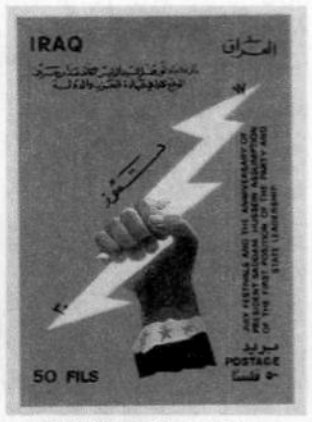

417 Bomb and Open Book showing School, Child and Wreath — **418** Hand holding Flash of Lightning

1988. Bilat Al-Shuhada School Bomb Victims. Multicoloured.
1812 20f. Type **417** 15 10
1813 40f. Explosion and girl (horiz) 25 15
1814 90f. Type **417** 60 45
1815 100f. As No. 1813 . . . . . 70 50

1988. July Festivals and 9th Anniv of President Hussain's State Leadership. Multicoloured.
1817 50f. Type **418** 35 25
1818 90f. Sun, map and Pres. Hussain 50 35
1819 100f. Type **418** 65 45
1820 150f. As No. 1818 . . . . . 1·00 70

419 Pres. Hussain and al-Sail al-Kabir Miqat

1988. President Hussain's Pilgrimage to Mecca.
1822 **419** 90f. multicoloured . . . 60 40
1823 100f. multicoloured . . . 70 50
1824 150f. multicoloured . . . 1·00 70

420 Mosul

1988. Tourism. Multicoloured.
1825 50f. Type **420** 60 40
1826 100f. Basrah 80 55
1827 150f. Baghdad (vert) . . . . 1·50 1·00

421 Pres. Hussain and Soldiers

1988. "Victorious Iraq".
1828 **421** 50f. multicoloured . . . 2·00 2·00
1829 100f. multicoloured . . . 4·25 4·25
1830 150f. multicoloured . . . 6·25 6·25

422 Emblem

1988. Navy Day. Multicoloured.
1831 50f. Type **422** 40 30
1832 90f. Missile boats 40 20
1833 100f. Type **422** 85 60
1834 150f. As No. 1832 . . . . . 70 30

423 Map and Hands holding Flag

1988. Liberation of Fao City.
1836 **423** 100f. multicoloured . . . 60 40
1837 150f. multicoloured . . . 1·25 90

424 Missile Launch from Winged Map — **425** Boxer and Hodori (mascot)

1988. Iraq Missile Research.
1839 **424** 100f. multicoloured . . . 60 40
1840 150f. multicoloured . . . 85 60

1988. Olympic Games, Seoul. Multicoloured.
1842 100f. Type **425** 85 60
1843 150f. Games emblem . . . 1·25 90

426 Dancers and Golden Cow — **427** Crescent and Camel Train

1988. 2nd Babylon International Festival.
1845 **426** 100f. multicoloured . . . 50 35
1846 150f. multicoloured . . . 80 55

1988. Mohammed's Birth Anniv.
1848 **427** 100f. multicoloured . . . 50 35
1849 150f. multicoloured . . . 75 55
1850 1d. multicoloured . . . 5·50 4·00

428 Hand holding Candle

انتصر العراق
١٩٨٨/٨/٨

(**429** "Victory")

1988. Martyr's Day.
1851 **428** 100f. multicoloured . . . 55 40
1852 150f. multicoloured . . . 80 55
1853 500f. multicoloured . . . 2·50 1·75

1988. Nos. 1738/9 optd with T **429**.
1854 **399** 250f. multicoloured . . . 1·40 1·00
1855 350f. multicoloured . . . 2·00 1·40

430 Family on Pedestrian Crossing

1989. Police Day.
1856 **430** 50f. multicoloured . . . 30 20
1857 100f. multicoloured . . . 55 40
1858 150f. multicoloured . . . 85 60

431 Children and Money

1989. Postal Savings Bank. (a) Size 32 × 32 mm.
1859 **431** 50f. multicoloured . . . 25 20

(b) Size 24 × 25 mm. With or without Arabic opt.
1860 – 100f. multicoloured 55 40
1861 – 150f. multicoloured 80 55

DESIGN: 100, 150f. Motif as Type **431** but with inscriptions differently arranged and inscr "REPUBLIC OF IRAQ".

432 Members' Flags and Leaders

1989. Formation of Arab Co-operation Council (Egypt, Iraq, Jordan and Yemen Arab Republic). Multicoloured.
1862 100f. Type **432** 55 40
1863 150f. Leaders in formal pose 80 55

433 Dates

1989. 1st Anniv of Liberation of Fao City.
1864 **433** 100f. multicoloured . . . 55 40
1865 150f. multicoloured . . . 80 55

434 Pres. Hussain

1989. 52nd Birthday of President Saddam Hussain.
1867 **434** 100f. multicoloured . . . 70 50
1868 150f. multicoloured . . . 1·10 75

435 Khairalla — **436** Hussain laying Mortar

1989. General Adnan Khairalla Commem.
1870 **435** 50f. multicoloured . . . 35 25
1871 100f. multicoloured . . . 70 50
1872 150f. multicoloured . . . 1·00 70

1989. Completion of Basrah Reconstruction Project.
1873 **436** 100f. multicoloured . . . 70 50
1874 150f. multicoloured . . . 1·00 70

437 Crane and Buildings

438 "Women"

1989. Start of Reconstruction of Fao City.
1875 **437** 100f. multicoloured . . . 70 50
1876 150f. multicoloured . . . 1·00 70

1989.
1877 **438** 100f. multicoloured . . . 70 50
1878 150f. multicoloured . . . 1·10 75
1879 1d. multicoloured . . . 5·75 4·00
1880 5d. multicoloured . . . 25·00 17·00

439 Pres. Hussain

440 Flag and Victory Signs

1989. July Festivals and 10th Anniv of President Hussain's State Leadership.
1881 **439** 50f. multicoloured . . . 30 20
1882 100f. multicoloured . . . 55 40
1883 150f. multicoloured . . . 90 65

1989. Victory Day.
1884 **440** 100f. multicoloured . . . 55 40
1885 150f. multicoloured . . . 90 65

441 Children, Heart and Bride

1989. Iraqi Family.
1887 **441** 50f. multicoloured . . . 30 20
1888 100f. multicoloured . . . 60 40
1889 150f. multicoloured . . . 95 65

442 Najaf

1989. Tourism. Multicoloured.
1890 100f. Type **442** 60 40
1891 100f. Arbil 60 40
1892 100f. Marsh Arab punt and Ziggurat of Ur 45 20

443 Map and Means of Transport

1989. 5th Session of Arab Ministers of Transport Council, Baghdad. Multicoloured.
1893 50f. Type **443** 60 20
1894 100f. Sun, means of transport and map . . . 90 30
1895 150f. Means of transport and members' flags (vert) 1·25 40

444 City and Pres. Hussain placing Final Stone

1989. Completion of Fao City Reconstruction.
1896 **444** 100f. multicoloured . . . 70 50
1897 150f. multicoloured . . . 1·00 70

445 Anniversary Emblem

1989. 30th Anniv of Iraqi News Agency.
1898 **445** 50f. multicoloured . . . 30 20
1899 100f. multicoloured . . . 60 40
1900 150f. multicoloured . . . 85 60

446 Emblem

447 Pansies

1989. 1st Anniv of Declaration of Palestinian State. Multicoloured.
1901 25f. Type **446** 15 10
1902 50f. Crowd of children . . . 30 20
1903 100f. Type **446** 60 40
1904 150f. As No. 1902 . . . . . 95 65

1989. Flowers. Multicoloured.
1905 25f. Type **447** 15 10
1906 50f. Antirrhinums 30 20
1907 100f. "Hibiscus trionum" . . 60 40
1908 150f. Mesembryanthemums 1·00 70

448 Map and Emblem

1989. Centenary of Interparliamentary Union.
1910 **448** 25f. multicoloured . . . 20 10
1911 100f. multicoloured . . . 60 40
1912 150f. multicoloured . . . 90 60

449 Sun, Flag, Doves and Mosque Domes

450 Dove, Red Crescent and Pres. Hussain

1989. Martyr's Day.
1913 **449** 50f. multicoloured . . . 25 20
1914 100f. multicoloured . . . 55 40
1915 150f. multicoloured . . . 80 55

1989. Iraqi Red Crescent Society.
1916 **450** 100f. multicoloured . . . 50 35
1917 150f. multicoloured . . . 75 55
1918 500f. multicoloured . . . 2·50 1·75

451 Members' Flags on Map

1990. 1st Anniv of Arab Co-operation Council.
1919 **451** 50f. multicoloured . . . 60 40
1920 100f. multicoloured . . . 1·00 70

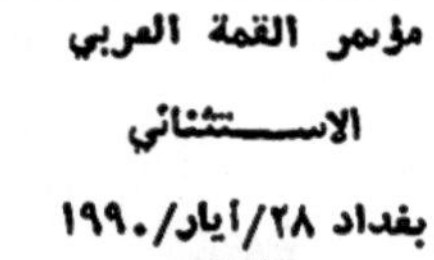
(**452**)

1990. Arab League Summit Conference, Baghdad. Nos. 1906 and 1908 optd with T **452**.
1922 50f. multicoloured 30 20
1923 150f. multicoloured 85 60

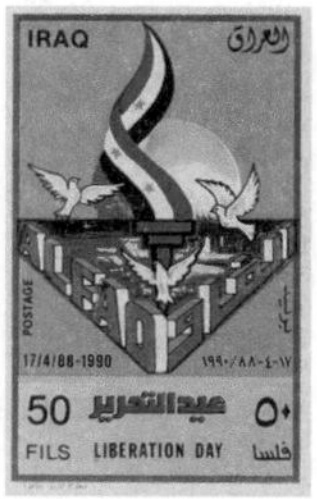
453 Doves and Flag as Flame

1990. 2nd Anniv of Liberation of Fao City.
1924 **453** 50f. multicoloured . . . 30 20
1925 100f. multicoloured . . . 60 40

OBLIGATORY TAX

28a King Faisal II

28b

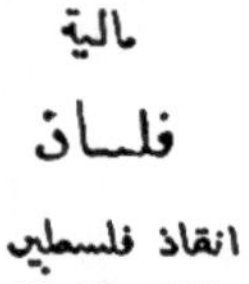
(**28c** "Tax 2 Fils Save Palestine")

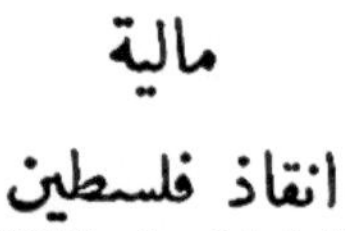
(**28d** "Tax Save Palestine")

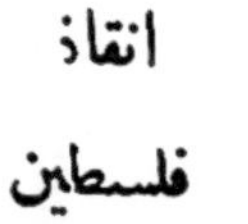
(**28e** "Save Palestine" (size varies))

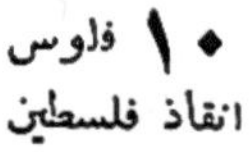
(**28g** "Tax 10 Fils Save Palestine" (size varies))

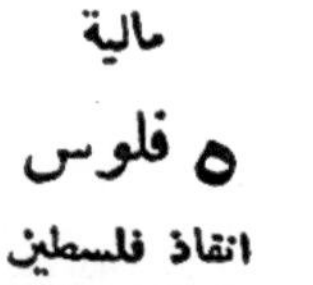
(**28h** "Tax 5 Fils Save Palestine")

1949. Aid for Palestine. (a) Nos. O300 and 278 surch as T **28**.
T324 **27** 2f. on 3f. green . . . . . 9·00 7·50
T325 2f. on 6f. mauve . . . . . 8·50 6·75

(b) Nos. O299 and O303 optd as T **28d** but smaller.
T326 **27** 2f. brown . . . . 5·00 4·25
T327 5f. red . . . . 12·50 10·00

(c) No. O234 optd with T **28d**.
T328 **20** 5f. red . . . . 3·00 4·25

(d) Revenue stamp surch in Arabic (= "2 Fils Save Palestine") as bottom two lines of T **28c**.
T329 **28a** 2f. on 5f. blue . . . . . 4·00 2·50

(e) Revenue stamps optd with T **28e**.
T330 **28a** 5f. blue . . . . 1·90 35
T335 10f. orange . . . . . . 6·75 3·00
T332 **28b** 10f. orange . . . . . . – 13·50

(f) Revenue stamp surch as T **28g**.
T336 **28b** 10f. on 20f. green . . . 15·00 9·25

(h) No. 278 surch with T **28h**.
T337 **27** 5f. on 6f. mauve . . . . 17·00 6·50

113a

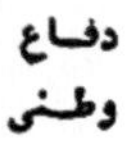
(**113b**)

1968. Flood Relief.
T763 **113a** 5f. brown 20 15

1968. Defence Fund. Optd with Type **113b**.
T764 **113a** 5f. brown 20 15

(**164a**)

(**215**)

1970. Obligatory Tax. Defence Fund. Nos. 620 and 625/9 surch with Type **164a**.
T931 **65** 5f. on 1f. green . . . . . 1·75 2·00
T932 – 5f. on 10f. red . . . . . 2·50 2·75
T933 – 5f. on 15f. brown & yell 2·50 2·75
T934 – 5f. on 20f. violet . . . . 2·50 2·75
T935 – 5f. on 30f. orange . . . . 2·50 2·75
T936 – 5f. on 40f. green . . . . 2·50 2·75

1973. Obligatory Tax. Defence Fund. Nos. 607/8 surch with Type **215**.
T1071 **62** 5f. on 14f. black & grn 3·50 3·50
T1072 5f. on 35f. black and red 3·50 3·50

(**223**)

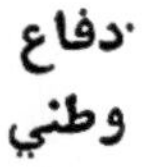
(**231**)

1973. Nos. 738, 765, 777, 787 and 891 optd similar to Type **215** (No. T1119) or as Type **223** (others).
T1117 – 5f. on 2f. multicoloured 2·75 3·00
T1118 **114** 5f. on 2f. multicoloured 2·75 3·00
T1119 **116** 5f. on 2f. multicoloured 2·75 3·00
T1120 **117** 5f. on 2f. multicoloured 2·75 3·00
T1121 **150** 5f. on 2f. multicoloured 2·75 3·00

1973. No. 1099 optd with Type **231**.
T1152 **221** 5f. black and orange 2·40 1·00

235 Soldier

1974. Defence Fund.
T1158 **235** 5f. black, yellow & brn 60 80

OFFICIAL STAMPS

1920. Issue of 1918 (surch Turkish stamps) optd **ON STATE SERVICE.**
O33 ½a. on 10pa. green . . . . . 1·00 1·00
O20 1a. on 20pa. red . . . . . . 1·75 60
O35 1½a. on 5pa. brown . . . . 2·75 65
O22 2½a. on 1pi. blue . . . . . 2·25 2·50
O23 3a. on 1½pi. black and pink 17·00 80
O36 4a. on 1¾pi. brown and blue 2·00 1·60
O25 6a. on 2pi. black and green 17·00 4·75
O38 8a. on 2½pi. green and brown . . . . 3·25 2·00
O27 12a. on 5pi. purple . . . . . 10·00 7·00
O28 1r. on 10pi. brown . . . . . 15·00 7·00
O29 2r. on 25pi. green . . . . . 20·00 11·00
O30 5r. on 50pi. red . . . . . . 35·00 27·00
O31 10r. on 100pi. blue . . . . . 50·00 75·00

1923. Nos. 41/50 and 52/3 optd **ON STATE SERVICE** in English only.
O54 **2** ½a. green . . . . 1·50 1·00
O55 – 1a. brown . . . . 1·75 20
O56 **3** 1½a. red . . . . 1·75 1·75
O57 – 2a. buff . . . . 2·00 40
O58 – 3a. blue . . . . 2·50 1·00
O59 – 4a. violet . . . . 4·25 1·00
O60 – 6a. blue . . . . 3·75 1·25
O61 – 8a. bistre . . . . 4·00 2·50
O62 **4** 1r. brown and green . . . 7·50 1·75
O63 **2** 2r. black . . . . 20·00 8·50
O64 – 5r. orange . . . . 48·00 30·00
O65 – 10r. red . . . . 70·00 48·00

1924. Nos. 41/9 and 51/3 optd **ON STATE SERVICE** in English and Arabic.
O66 **2** ½a. green . . . . 1·25 10
O67 – 1a. brown . . . . 1·00 10
O68 **3** 1½a. red . . . . 1·00 30
O69 – 2a. buff . . . . 1·50 10
O70 – 3a. blue . . . . 2·00 10
O71 – 4a. violet . . . . 4·00 30
O72 – 6a. blue . . . . 1·75 20
O73 – 8a. bistre . . . . 3·75 35
O74 **4** 1r. brown and green . . . 9·50 1·50
O75 **2** 2r. bistre . . . . 35·00 3·75
O76 – 5r. orange . . . . 50·00 42·00
O77 – 10r. red . . . . 75·00 42·00

1927. Optd **ON STATE SERVICE** in English and Arabic.
O79 **10** 1r. brown . . . . 6·00 1·75

1931. Optd **ON STATE SERVICE** in English and Arabic.
O 93 **11** ½a. green . . . . 65 2·75
O 94 1a. brown 80 10
O 95 1½a. red . . . . 4·50 21·00
O 96 2a. orange 80 10
O 97 3a. blue . . . . 85 1·25

O 98 4a. purple 1·00 1·50
O 99 6a. blue 4·50 19·00
O100 8a. green 4·75 19·00
O101 **12** 1r. brown 14·00 18·00
O102 2r. brown 22·00 65·00
O103 5r. orange 42·00 £120
O104 10r. red 80·00 £190
O105 **10** 25r. violet £550 £700

1932. Official stamps of 1924 and 1931 surch in "Fils" or "Dinar".
O122 **11** 3f. on ½a. green 3·50 3·50
O123 4f. on 1a. brown 2·50 10
O124 5f. on 1a. brown 2·50 10
O125 **4** 8f. on 1½a. red 5·50 50
O126 **11** 10f. on 2a. orange 3·00 10
O127 15f. on 3a. blue 4·25 2·50
O128 20f. on 4a. purple 4·25 2·50
O129 25f. on 4a. purple 4·50 1·75
O130 – 30f. on 6a. bl (No. O72) 4·75 1·75
O131 **11** 40f. on 8a. green 4·00 3·50
O132 **12** 50f. on 1r. brown 5·50 3·50
O133 75f. on 1r. brown 6·00 6·00
O134 **2** 100f. on 2r. bistre 18·00 3·50
O135 – 200f. on 5r. orange (No. O76) 23·00 23·00
O136 – ½d. on 10r. red (No. 77) 65·00 85·00
O137 **10** 1d. on 25r. violet £120 £190

1932. Issue of 1932 optd **ON STATE SERVICE** in English and Arabic.
O155 **11** 2f. blue 1·50 10
O156 3f. green 1·50 10
O157 4f. purple 1·50 10
O158 5f. green 1·50 10
O159 8f. red 1·50 10
O160 10f. yellow 2·25 10
O161 15f. blue 2·50 10
O162 20f. orange 2·50 15
O163 25f. mauve 2·50 15
O164 30f. olive 3·50 20
O165 40f. violet 4·50 30
O166 **12** 50f. brown 3·25 20
O167 75f. blue 2·50 1·00
O168 100f. green 11·00 2·00
O169 200f. red 20·00 6·50
O170 **10** ½d. blue 12·00 24·00
O171 1d. purple 60·00 90·00

1934. Issue of 1934 optd **ON STATE SERVICE** in English and Arabic.
O190 **16** 1f. violet 1·10 40
O191 2f. blue 90 15
O192 3f. green 50 15
O193 4f. purple 1·00 15
O194 5f. green 90 15
O195 8f. red 3·50 25
O196 10f. yellow 35 15
O197 15f. blue 8·00 1·25
O198 20f. orange 75 15
O199 25f. mauve 16·00 4·75
O200 30f. green 3·50 25
O201 40f. violet 4·50 25
O202 **17** 50f. brown 70 55
O203 75f. blue 5·00 65
O204 100f. green 1·40 85
O205 200f. red 3·50 2·00
O206 – ½d. blue (No. 188) 10·00 15·00
O207 – 1d. red (No. 189) 38·00 45·00

1941. Issue of 1941 optd **ON STATE SERVICE** in English and Arabic.
O230 **19** 1f. purple 20 15
O231 2f. brown 20 15
O232 – 3f. green (No. 210) 20 15
O233 – 4f. violet (No. 211) 20 15
O234 – 5f. red (No. 212) 20 15
O235 **21** 8f. red 65 15
O236b 8f. yellow 15 15
O237 10f. yellow 4·25 35
O238 10f. red 50 15
O239 15f. blue 4·25 65
O240 15f. black 85 25
O241 20f. black 1·25 25
O242 20f. blue 40 15
O244 **22** 25f. purple 65 25
O246a 30f. orange 35 25
O248a 40f. brown 45 25
O249c – 50f. blue (No. 224) 75 50
O250 – 75f. mauve (No. 225) 85 25
O251 – 100f. olive (No. 226) 1·75 25
O252 – 200f. orange (No. 227) 2·00 70
O253 – ½d. blue (No. 228) 9·00 4·25
O254 – 1d. green (No. 229) 14·00 7·50

1942. Issue of 1942 optd **ON STATE SERVICE** in English and Arabic.
O263 **26** 1f. brown and violet 25 25
O264 2f. brown and blue 25 25
O265 3f. brown and green 25 25
O266 4f. sepia and brown 25 25
O267 5f. brown and green 35 35
O268 6f. brown and red 35 35
O269 10f. brown and pink 45 45
O270 12f. brown and green 45 45

1948. Issue of 1948 optd **ON STATE SERVICE** in English and Arabic.
O298 **27** 1f. blue 15 25
O299 2f. brown 15 30
O300 3f. green 15 30
O301 3f. red 2·10 20
O302 4f. lilac 15 25
O303 5f. red 15 20
O304 5f. green 2·50 20
O305 6f. mauve 20 30
O306 8f. brown 20 30
O307 10f. red 20 25
O308 12f. green 20 25
O309 14f. green 90 25
O310 15f. black 4·00 5·00
O311 16f. red 2·00 30
O312 20f. blue 20 15
O313 25f. purple 20 15
O314 28f. blue 65 30
O315 30f. orange 20 20
O316 40f. brown 45 35
O317 50f. blue 50 30
O318 60f. blue 45 20
O319 75f. mauve 85 20
O320 100f. green 85 85
O321 200f. orange 1·40 85
O322 ½d. blue 11·50 12·00
O323 1d. green 17·00 25·00

1955. Issue of 1954 optd **ON STATE SERVICE** in English and Arabic.
O364 **33** 1f. blue 20 20
O365 2f. brown 20 20
O366 3f. lake 20 20
O367 4f. violet 20 20
O368 5f. green 20 20
O369 6f. mauve 20 20
O370 8f. brown 20 20
O371 10f. blue 20 20
O372 16f. red 17·00 20·00
O373 20f. olive 35 25
O374 25f. purple 1·75 85
O375 30f. red 75 25
O376 40f. brown 35 25
O377 – 50f. blue 1·90 65
O378 – 60f. purple 10·00 4·50
O379 – 100f. olive 24·00 11·00
No. O378 does not exist without opt.

1958. Issue of 1957 optd **ON STATE SERVICE** in English and Arabic.
O404 **41** 1f. blue 1·50 1·50
O405 2f. brown 2·10 2·10
O406 3f. red 2·10 2·10
O407 4f. violet 1·50 1·50
O408 5f. green 1·50 1·50
O409 6f. red 1·50 1·50
O410 10f. blue 1·50 1·50

1958. Official stamps optd with T **43**. (a) Nos. O251/2.
O459 100f. green
O459a 200f. orange 2·75 1·50

(b) Nos. O298 etc.
O460 **27** 1f. blue 17·00 17·00
O461 2f. brown 17·00 17·00
O462 3f. green 17·00 17·00
O463 3f. red 17·00 17·00
O464 4f. lilac 17·00 17·00
O465 5f. red 17·00 17·00
O466 5f. green 17·00 17·00
O467 6f. mauve 17·00 17·00
O468 8f. brown 17·00 17·00
O470 12f. green 50 45
O471 14f. green 85 40
O472 15f. black 85 45
O473 16f. red 2·10 1·25
O474 25f. purple 1·75 1·25
O475 28f. blue 1·25 65
O476 40f. brown 85 70
O477 60f. blue 3·00 2·10
O478 75f. mauve 1·25 1·50
O479 200f. orange 2·10 1·50
O480 ½d. blue 6·75 5·00
O481 1d. green 12·50 10·00

(c) Nos. O364 etc.
O482 **33** 1f. blue 45 20
O483 2f. brown 45 20
O484 3f. red 45 20
O485 4f. violet 45 20
O486 5f. green 50 20
O487 6f. mauve 45 20
O488 8f. brown 45 20
O489 10f. blue 45 20
O490 16f. red 4·25 4·75
O491 20f. green 45 20
O492 25f. purple 45 25
O493 30f. red 45 35
O494 40f. brown 65 35
O495 – 50f. blue 65 45
O496 – 60f. purple 65 50
O497 – 100f. green 1·25 50

(d) Nos. O404 etc.
O498 **41** 1f. blue 20 20
O499 2f. brown 20 20
O500 3f. red 25 20
O501 4f. violet 25 20
O502 5f. green 25 20
O503 6f. red 20 20
O504 8f. brown 45 10
O505 10f. blue 40 20
No. O504 does not exist without opt T **43**.

1961. Nos. 515, etc. optd **On State Service** in English and Arabic.
O552 **49** 1f. multicoloured 15 10
O553 2f. multicoloured 15 10
O554 4f. multicoloured 15 10
O555 5f. multicoloured 35 10
O556 10f. multicoloured 40 10
O557 50f. multicoloured 5·00 3·00

1962. Nos. 515, etc. optd **ON STATE SERVICE** in English and Arabic.
O587 **49** 1f. multicoloured 10 10
O588 2f. multicoloured 10 10
O589 3f. multicoloured 10 10
O590 4f. multicoloured 10 10
O591 5f. multicoloured 10 10
O592 10f. multicoloured 10 10
O593 15f. multicoloured 15 10
O594 20f. multicoloured 20 20
O595 30f. multicoloured 25 20
O596 40f. multicoloured 30 20
O597 50f. multicoloured 30 20
O598 75f. multicoloured 55 30
O599 100f. multicoloured 85 60
O600 200f. multicoloured 2·10 1·25
O601 500f. multicoloured 5·50 4·25
O602 1d. multicoloured 11·00 8·50

1971. Various stamps optd or surch **Official** in English and Arabic. (a) Costumes. Nos. 768 and 770/4.
O962 15f. multicoloured (postage) 1·25 40
O963 25f. multicoloured 3·25 2·75
O964 30f. multicoloured 3·25 2·75
O965 40f. multicoloured (air) 2·10 85
O966 50f. multicoloured 2·10 85
O967 80f. multicoloured 3·50 1·75

(b) International Tourist Year. Nos. 778 and 780/2.
O969 5f. multicoloured (postage) 1·90 30
O970 15f. multicoloured 1·90 45
O971 25f. multicoloured 1·90 90
O972 50f. multicoloured (air) 2·10 1·10

(c) Birds. No. 798.
O1178 30f. multicoloured 5·25 4·00

(d) 20th Anniv of W.H.O. Nos. 811/13.
O973 – 10f. multicoloured 2·25 50
O974 **124** 15f. red, blue and black 2·25 50
O975 25f. red, green and black 2·25 50

(e) Human Rights Year. Nos. 814/15.
O976 **125** 10f. red, yellow and blue 3·25 40
O977 25f. red, yellow & green 3·25 70

(f) U.N.I.C.E.F. Nos. 817/18.
O978 **126** 15f. multicoloured 3·25 35
O979 25f. multicoloured 3·25 35

(g) Army Day. No. 820.
O980 **127** 25f. multicoloured 7·50 2·75

(h) Fish and Fauna. Nos. 825/7, 829/30 and 832.
O981 10f. multicoloured (postage) 3·25 2·50
O982 15f. on 3f. multicoloured 3·25 2·50
O983 25f. on 2f. multicoloured 3·25 2·50
O984 10f. multicoloured (air) 3·25 2·75
O985 15f.+3f. multicoloured 3·25 2·75
O986 25f.+2f. multicoloured 3·25 2·75

(i) Fruits. Nos. 906/9.
O987 5f. multicoloured 3·25 2·75
O988 10f. multicoloured 3·25 2·75
O989 15f. multicoloured 3·25 2·75
O990 35f. multicoloured 3·25 2·75

(j) Arab Football Cup, Baghdad. No. 717.
O991 **97** 2f. multicoloured 3·25 2·75

(k) 50th Anniv of I.L.O. No. 836.
O992 **133** 15f. yellow, green & blk 3·25 2·75

1972. Nos. 625/8 optd **Official** in English and Arabic.
O1042 10f. red 4·50 4·50
O1043 15f. brown and yellow 4·50 4·50
O1044 20f. violet 4·50 4·50
O1045 30f. orange 4·50 4·50

1973. Various stamps with portrait obliterated by 3 bars. (i) 1948 issue.
O1081 **27** 25f. purple (No. O313) 2·50 60
O1082 50f. blue (No. O317) 2·50 2·25

(ii) 1955 issue.
O1083 **33** 25f. purple (No. O374) 2·50 60
O1084 – 50f. blue (No. O377) 2·50 2·75

(iii) Similar to 1958 issue (T **41**) but size 22½ × 27½ mm.
O1085 50f. purple 2·50 2·25

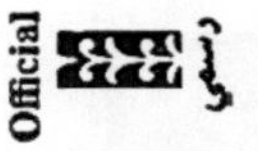

(O **218**) (size varies)

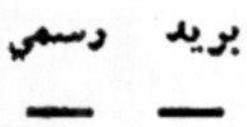

(O **237a**)

1973. "Faisal" stamps with portrait obliterated. (a) Optd with 3 bars and Type O **218**.
O1086 **33** 10f. blue 2·75 2·75
O1087 **41** 15f. black 2·75 3·00

(b) Optd with Type O **218** only.
O1090 **33** 15f. black 2·75 75
O1091 **41** 15f. black 2·75 75
O1096 **27** 25f. purple 11·00 11·50
O1092 **33** 25f. purple 2·75 75
O1093 **41** 25f. purple 2·75 75

1973. No. 1097 optd **Official** in English and Arabic.
O1099 **220** 25f. multicoloured 35 15

1973. Nos. 1099/1107 optd **OFFICIAL** in English and Arabic.
O1108 **221** 5f. black and orange 15 15
O1109 10f. black and brown 15 10
O1110 20f. black and mauve 25 15
O1111 – 25f. black and blue 40 15
O1112 – 35f. black and green 50 20
O1113 – 45f. black and blue 50 30
O1114 – 50f. yellow and green 80 30
O1115 – 70f. yellow and violet 1·10 45
O1116 – 95f. yellow and brown 1·75 90

1973. Various "Faisal" Official stamps optd **ON STATE SERVICE** in English and Arabic, with portrait obliterated by "leaf" motif similar to that used in Type O **218**. (a) 1948 issue.
O1130a **27** 12f. olive 3·50 80
O1131 14f. olive 3·50 1·00
O1132 15f. black 3·50 1·00
O1133 16f. red 7·00 6·50
O1134 28f. blue 3·50 1·00
O1134a 30f. orange 3·50 1·60
O1134b 40f. brown 3·50 1·60
O1135 60f. blue 4·25 1·60
O1136 100f. green 16·00 6·50
O1137 ½d. blue 35·00 14·00
O1138 1d. green 55·00 23·00

(b) 1955 issue.
O1139 **33** 3f. lake 3·50 80
O1140 6f. mauve 4·25 1·40
O1141 8f. brown 3·50 80
O1142 16f. red 7·00 6·50
O1142a 20f. green 3·50 80
O1142b 30f. red 3·50 80
O1142c 40f. brown 3·50 80
O1143 – 60f. purple 6·25 2·00
O1144 – 100f. green 14·00 3·25

(c) 1958 issue.
O1145 **41** 3f. lake 3·50 80
O1146 6f. mauve 3·50 80
O1147 8f. brown 3·50 80
O1147a 30f. red 3·50 80

1974. No. T1168 optd with Type O **237a**.
O1165 **235** 5f. black, yellow & brn 1·60 1·40

O **249** Eagle Emblem

O **342** Entrance to Baghdad University

1975.
O1195 O **249** 5f. multicoloured 10 10
O1196 10f. multicoloured 15 10
O1197 15f. multicoloured 25 10
O1198 20f. multicoloured 35 10
O1199 25f. multicoloured 45 10
O1200 30f. multicoloured 55 20
O1201 50f. multicoloured 90 35
O1202 100f. multicoloured 2·00 85

1976. Nos. 1253/7 additionally inscr "OFFICIAL" in English and Arabic.
O1258 **264** 5f. multicoloured 1·40 80
O1259 – 10f. multicoloured 1·50 85
O1260 – 15f. multicoloured 1·60 90
O1261 – 25f. multicoloured 4·25 1·50
O1262 – 50f. multicoloured 5·75 2·50

1978. As T **290**, but additionally inscr "OFFICIAL" in English and Arabic.
O1338 5f. multicoloured 15 10
O1339 10f. multicoloured 15 15
O1340 15f. multicoloured 25 15
O1341 25f. multicoloured 45 15

1981.
O1499 O **342** 45f. multicoloured 45 20
O1500 50f. multicoloured 45 20

1982. As Nos. 1504/6, additionally inscr "OFFICIAL" in English and Arabic.
O1507 45f. multicoloured 65 20
O1508 50f. multicoloured 65 25
O1509 120f. multicoloured 1·50 1·10

1983. Nos. O1499/1500 surch.
O1591 O **342** 60f. on 45f. mult 90 35
O1582 70f. on 50f. mult 1·25 50

1983. Design as T **371**.
O1615 60f. yellow, black and pink 65 35
O1616 70f. yellow, black and pink 75 45
DESIGN: Nos. O1615/16, Aerial view of building.

1984. Multicoloured.
O1642 20f. Type **377** 15 15
O1643 30f. Type **377** 30 15
O1644 50f. As No. 1639 45 25
O1645 60f. As No. 1639 55 40

O **400** Pres. Hussain

1986.
O1740 O **400** 30f. multicoloured 50 10
O1741 50f. multicoloured 75 20
O1742 100f. multicoloured 1·40 45
O1743 150f. multicoloured 2·00 75
Nos. O1740/3 are inscribed "POSTAGE".

IRELAND (REPUBLIC) Pt. 1

Ireland (Eire) consisting of Ireland less the six counties of Ulster, became the Irish Free State in 1922 and left the British Empire in 1949 when it became an independent republic.

1949. 12 pence = 1 shilling;
20 shillings = 1 pound.
1971. 100 (new) pence = 1 pound (Punt).
2002. 100 cents = 1 euro.

Rialtas Sealadach na hÉireann 1922

(1) "Provisional Government of Ireland, 1922"

Rialtas Sealadach na hÉireann 1922.

(2)

1922. Stamps of Great Britain optd with T **1** (date in thin figures and no full point).

1	**105**	½d. green	1·50	40
2	**104**	1d. red	1·50	35
4a		2½d. blue	1·25	3·75
5	**106**	3d. violet	4·25	4·00
6		4d. green	4·00	12·00
7	**107**	5d. brown	4·25	8·50
8	**108**	9d. brown	11·00	22·00
9		10d. blue	8·50	45·00
17	**109**	2s.6d. brown	40·00	75·00
19		5s. red	65·00	£140
21		10s. blue	£120	£275

On Nos. 17, 19 and 21 the overprint is in four lines instead of five.

1922. Stamps of Great Britain optd with T **2** (date in thick figures followed by full point).

47	**105**	½d. green	1·00	1·75
31	**104**	1d. red	2·00	50
10	**105**	1½d. brown	1·75	1·25
12	**106**	2d. orange	3·25	50
35	**104**	2½d. blue	6·00	21·00
36	**106**	3d. violet	3·00	2·00
37		4d. green	3·25	6·00
38	**107**	5d. brown	4·75	9·50
39		6d. purple	8·00	3·25
40	**108**	9d. black	13·00	17·00
41		9d. green	5·00	38·00
42		10d. blue	26·00	60·00
43		1s. brown	9·00	12·00

Saorstát Éireann 1922

(5 "Irish Free State, 1922")

1922. Stamps of Great Britain optd with T **5**.

52	**105**	½d. green	1·25	30
53	**104**	1d. red	1·25	50
54	**105**	1½d. brown	3·50	8·50
55	**106**	2d. orange	1·50	1·00
56	**104**	2½d. blue	6·50	8·00
57	**106**	3d. violet	3·75	11·00
58		4d. green	3·25	7·50
59	**107**	5d. brown	3·50	4·75
60		6d. purple	2·00	2·00
61	**108**	9d. green	3·25	5·50
62		10d. blue	16·00	60·00
63		1s. brown	7·00	11·00
86	**109**	2s.6d. brown	45·00	50·00
87		5s. red	65·00	90·00
88		10s. blue	£150	£190

6 "Sword of Light"

7 Map of Ireland

8 Arms of Ireland

9 Celtic Cross

1922.

71	**6**	½d. green	1·00	90
112	**7**	1d. red	30	10
73		1½d. purple	1·60	2·50
114		2d. green	30	10
75	**8**	2½d. brown	4·00	4·25
116	**9**	3d. blue (18¾ × 22½ mm)	70	10
227		3d. blue (17 × 21 mm)	40	15
117	**8**	4d. blue	55	10
118	**6**	5d. violet (18¾ × 22½ mm)	65	10
228		5d. violet (17 × 21 mm)	30	15
119b		6d. purple	1·25	20
119c		8d. red	80	80
120	**8**	9d. violet	1·50	80
121	**9**	10d. brown	60	80
121b		11d. red	1·50	2·25
82	**6**	1s. blue	17·00	5·50

12 Daniel O'Connell

13 Shannon Barrage

1929. Centenary of Catholic Emancipation.

89	**12**	2d. green	50	45
90		3d. blue	4·00	8·50
91		9d. violet	4·00	4·00

1930. Completion of Shannon Hydro-electric Scheme.

92	**13**	2d. deep brown	1·00	55

14 Reaper

15 The Cross of Cong

1931. Bicentenary of Royal Dublin Society.

93	**14**	2d. blue	65	30

1932. International Eucharistic Congress.

94	**15**	2d. green	1·25	30
95		3d. blue	2·25	5·00

16 Adoration of the Cross

17 Hurler

1933. "Holy Year".

96	**16**	2d. green	1·25	15
97		3d. blue	2·50	2·00

1934. 50th Anniv of Gaelic Athletic Assn.

98	**17**	2d. green	1·00	55

18 St. Patrick

19 Ireland and New Constitution

1937.

123b	**18**	2s.6d. green	1·50	2·50
124ca		5s. purple	6·00	8·00
125ba		10s. blue	7·00	16·00

1937. Constitution Day.

105	**19**	2d. red	1·00	20
106		3d. blue	4·00	3·75

For similar stamps see Nos. 176/7.

20 Father Mathew

1938. Centenary of Temperance Crusade.

107	**20**	2d. brown	1·50	40
108		3d. blue	10·00	6·50

21 George Washington, American Eagle and Irish Harp

1939. 150th Anniv of U.S. Constitution and Installation of First U.S. President.

109	**21**	2d. red	1·75	1·00
110		3d. blue	3·25	4·50

24 Volunteer and G.P.O., Dublin

1941. 25th Anniv of Easter Rising (1916). (a) Provisional issue. Optd with two lines of Irish characters between the dates "1941" and "1916".

126	**7**	2d. orange	1·00	50
127	**9**	3d. blue	24·00	10·00

(b) Definitive Issue.

128	**24**	2½d. blue	1·75	70

25 Dr. Douglas Hyde

26 Sir William Rowan Hamilton

1943. 50th Anniv of Gaelic League.

129	**25**	½d. green	40	30
130		2½d. purple	1·50	10

1943. Centenary of Announcement of Discovery of Quaternions.

131	**26**	½d. green	40	50
132		2½d. brown	1·75	10

27 Bro. Michael O'Clery

28 Edmund Ignatius Rice

1944. Death Tercentenary of Michael O'Clery (Franciscan historian) (commemorating the "Annals of the Four Masters").

133	**27**	½d. green	10	10
134		1s. brown	70	10

1944. Death Centenary of Edmund Rice (founder of Irish Christian Brothers).

135	**28**	2½d. slate	1·25	45

29 "Youth sowing Seeds of Freedom"

30 "Country and Homestead"

1945. Death Centenary of Thomas Davis (founder of Young Ireland Movement).

136	**29**	2½d. blue	1·00	35
137		6d. purple	6·00	4·00

1946. Birth Centenaries of Michael Davitt and Charles Parnell (land reformers).

138	**30**	2½d. red	2·00	25
139		3d. blue	2·75	3·75

31 Angel Victor over Rock of Cashel

1948. Air. Inscr "VOX HIBERNIAE".

140	**31**	1d. brown	1·50	3·75
141	–	3d. blue	3·00	2·25
142	–	6d. purple	80	1·50
142b	–	8d. lake	6·50	7·50
143	–	1s. green	1·00	1·50
143a	**31**	1s.3d. orange	8·00	1·25
143b		1s.5d. blue	2·75	1·00

DESIGNS: 3d., 8d. Angel Victor over Lough Derg; 6d. Over Croagh Patrick; 1s. Over Glendalough.

35 Theobald Wolfe Tone

1948. 150th Anniv of Insurrection.

144	**35**	2½d. purple	1·00	10
145		3d. violet	3·25	3·25

36 Leinster House and Arms of Provinces

37 J. C. Mangan

1949. International Recognition of Republic.

146	**36**	2½d. brown	1·50	10
147		3d. blue	6·00	4·25

1949. Death Centenary of James Clarence Mangan (poet).

148	**37**	1d. green	1·50	25

38 Statue of St. Peter, Rome

39 Thomas Moore

1950. Holy Year.

149	**38**	2½d. violet	1·00	40
150		3d. blue	8·00	11·00
151		9d. brown	8·00	11·00

1952. Death Centenary of Thomas Moore (poet).

152	**39**	2½d. purple	75	10
153		3½d. olive	1·60	3·75

40 Irish Harp

1953. "An Tostal" (Ireland at Home) Festival.

154	**40**	2½d. green	1·75	35
155		1s.4d. blue	15·00	24·00

41 Robert Emmet

42 Madonna and Child (Della Robbia)

1953. 150th Death Anniv of Emmet (patriot).

156	**41**	3d. green	3·00	15
157		1s.3d. red	42·00	10·00

1954. Marian Year.

158	**42**	3d. blue	1·00	10
159		5d. green	1·50	3·25

43 Cardinal Newman (first Rector)

44 Statue of Commodore Barry

45 John Redmond

1954. Centenary of Founding of Catholic University of Ireland.

160	**43**	2d. purple	1·50	10
161		1s.3d. blue	16·00	6·00

1956. Barry Commemoration.

162	**44**	3d. lilac	1·50	10
163		1s.3d. blue	5·50	9·00

1957. Birth Centenary of John Redmond (politician).

164	**45**	3d. blue	1·00	10
165		1s.3d. purple	8·00	15·00

46 Thomas O'Crohan

47 Admiral Brown

48 "Father Wadding" (Ribera)

1957. Birth Cent of Thomas O'Crohan (author).

166	**46**	2d. purple	1·00	15
167		5d. violet	1·00	4·50

1957. Death Cent of Admiral William Brown.

168	**47**	3d. blue	2·25	20
169		1s.3d. red	24·00	16·00

1957. Death Tercentenary of Father Luke Wadding (theologian).

170	**48**	3d. blue	2·00	10
171		1s.3d. lake	15·00	8·50

49 Tom Clarke

50 Mother Mary Aikenhead

1958. Birth Centenary of Thomas J. ("Tom") Clarke (patriot).

172	**49**	3d. green	2·00	10
173		1s.3d. brown	3·50	11·00

1958. Death Centenary of Mother Mary Aikenhead (foundress of Irish Sisters of Charity).

174	**50**	3d. blue	1·75	10
175		1s.3d. red	11·00	8·00

1958. 21st Anniv of Irish Constitution.

176	**19**	3d. brown	1·00	10
177		5d. green	2·00	4·50

51 Arthur Guinness

52 "The Flight of the Holy Family"

1959. Bicentenary of Guinness Brewery.

178	**51**	3d. purple	3·00	10
179		1s.3d. blue	11·00	12·00

1960. World Refugee Year.

180	**52**	3d. purple	40	10
181		1s.3d. sepia	60	3·25

53 Conference Emblem

1960. 1st Anniv of Europa.

182	**53**	6d. brown	12·00	3·00
183		1s.3d. violet	26·00	20·00

54 Dublin Airport, De Havilland Dragon Mk 2 "Iolar" and Boeing 720

55 St Patrick

1961. Silver Jubilee of Aer Lingus Airlines.

184	**54**	6d. blue	1·50	3·50
185		1s.3d. green	2·00	5·00

1961. 15th Death Centenary of St. Patrick.

186	**55**	3d. blue	1·00	10
187		8d. purple	2·75	5·50
188		1s.3d. green	2·75	1·60

56 John O'Donovan and Edugen O'Curry

1962. Death Centenaries of O'Donovan and O'Curry (scholars).

189	**56**	3d. red	30	10
190		1s.3d. purple	1·25	2·25

57 Europa "Tree"

1962. Europa.

191	**57**	6d. red	90	1·00
192		1s.3d. turquoise	1·00	1·50

58 Campaign Emblem

1963. Freedom from Hunger.

193	**58**	4d. violet	50	10
194		1s.3d. red	2·50	2·75

59 "Co-operation"

1963. Europa.

195	**59**	6d. red	1·50	75
196		1s.3d. blue	4·00	3·75

60 Centenary Emblem

1963. Centenary of Red Cross.

197	**60**	4d. red and grey	50	10
198		1s.3d. red, grey and green	1·50	2·25

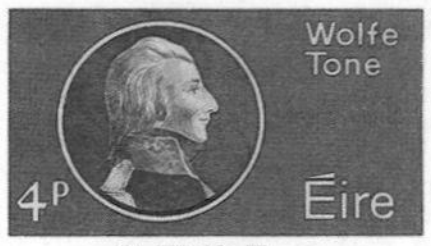

61 Wolfe Tone

1964. Birth Bicentenary of Wolfe Tone (revolutionary).

199	**61**	4d. black	40	10
200		1s.3d. blue	1·50	2·00

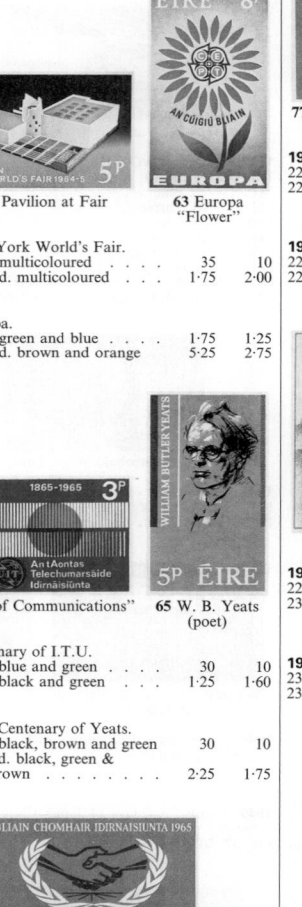

62 Irish Pavilion at Fair

63 Europa "Flower"

1964. New York World's Fair.

201	**62**	5d. multicoloured	35	10
202		1s.5d. multicoloured	1·75	2·00

1964. Europa.

203	**63**	8d. green and blue	1·75	1·25
204		1s.5d. brown and orange	5·25	2·75

64 "Waves of Communications"

65 W. B. Yeats (poet)

1965. Centenary of I.T.U.

205	**64**	3d. blue and green	30	10
206		8d. black and green	1·25	1·60

1965. Birth Centenary of Yeats.

207	**65**	5d. black, brown and green	30	10
208		1s.5d. black, green & brown	2·25	1·75

66 I.C.Y. Emblem

1965. International Co-operation Year.

209	**66**	3d. blue	60	10
210		10d. brown	1·00	3·00

67 Europa "Sprig"

1965. Europa.

211	**67**	8d. black and red	2·50	1·00
212		1s.5d. purple and turquoise	7·50	3·50

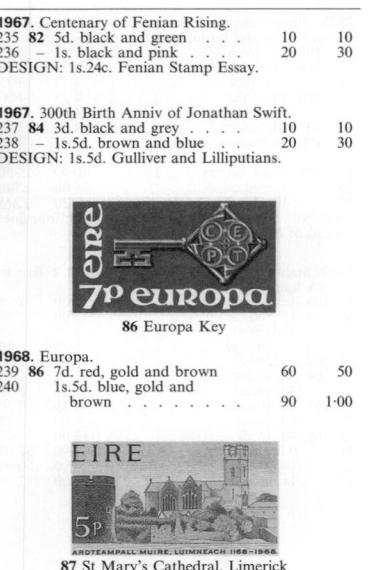

68 James Connolly

76 Roger Casement

1966. 50th Anniv of Easter Rising.

213	**68**	3d. black and blue	50	10
214	–	3d. black and bronze	50	10
215	–	5d. black and olive	50	10
216	–	5d. black, orange and green	50	10
217	–	7d. black and brown	50	2·25
218	–	7d. black and green	50	2·25
219	–	1s.5d. black and turquoise	50	1·50
220	–	1s.5d. black and green	50	1·50

DESIGNS: No. 214, Thomas J. Clarke; No. 215, P. H. Pearse; No. 216, "Marching to Freedom"; No. 217, Eamonn Ceannt; No. 218, Sean MacDiarmada; No. 219, Thomas MacDonagh; No. 220, Joseph Plunkett.

1966. 50th Death Anniv of Roger Casement (patriot).

221	**76**	5d. black	15	10
222		1s. brown	30	50

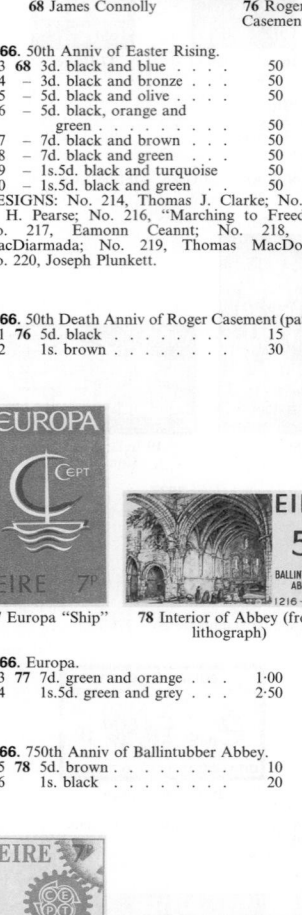

77 Europa "Ship"

78 Interior of Abbey (from lithograph)

1966. Europa.

223	**77**	7d. green and orange	1·00	40
224		1s.5d. green and grey	2·50	1·00

1966. 750th Anniv of Ballintubber Abbey.

225	**78**	5d. brown	10	10
226		1s. black	20	25

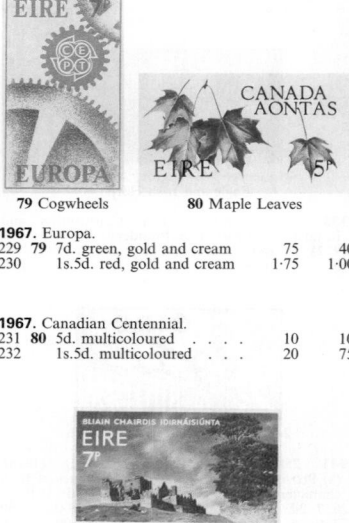

79 Cogwheels

80 Maple Leaves

1967. Europa.

229	**79**	7d. green, gold and cream	75	40
230		1s.5d. red, gold and cream	1·75	1·00

1967. Canadian Centennial.

231	**80**	5d. multicoloured	10	10
232		1s.5d. multicoloured	20	75

81 Rock of Cashel (from photo by Edwin Smith)

1967. International Tourist Year.

233	**81**	7d. sepia	15	20
234		10d. blue	15	40

82 1c. Fenian Stamp Essay

84 Jonathan Swift

1967. Centenary of Fenian Rising.

235	**82**	5d. black and green	10	10
236	–	1s. black and pink	20	30

DESIGN: 1s.24c. Fenian Stamp Essay.

1967. 300th Birth Anniv of Jonathan Swift.

237	**84**	3d. black and grey	10	10
238	–	1s.5d. brown and blue	20	30

DESIGN: 1s.5d. Gulliver and Lilliputians.

86 Europa Key

1968. Europa.

239	**86**	7d. red, gold and brown	60	50
240		1s.5d. blue, gold and brown	90	1·00

87 St Mary's Cathedral, Limerick

1968. 800th Anniv of St. Mary's Cathedral, Limerick.

241	**87**	5d. blue	10	10
242		10d. green	20	60

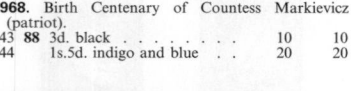

88 Countess Markievicz

89 James Connolly

1968. Birth Centenary of Countess Markievicz (patriot).

243	**88**	3d. black	10	10
244		1s.5d. indigo and blue	20	20

1968. Birth Centenary of James Connolly (patriot).

245	**89**	6d. brown and chocolate	20	75
246		1s. green, lt green & myrtle	20	10

90 Stylized Dog (brooch)

92 Winged Ox (Symbol of St. Luke)

1968.

247	**90**	½d. orange	10	30
248		1d. green	15	10
249		2d. ochre	50	10
250		3d. blue	35	10
251		4d. red	30	10
252		5d. green	1·00	50
253		6d. brown	30	10
254	–	7d. brown and yellow	45	3·50
255	–	8d. brown and chestnut	45	1·50
256	–	9d. blue and green	50	10
257	–	10d. brown and violet	1·50	2·50
258	–	1s. chocolate and brown	40	10
259	–	1s.9d. black and turquoise	4·00	2·50
260	**92**	2s.6d. multicoloured	1·75	30
261		5s. multicoloured	3·00	2·50
262	–	10s. multicoloured	4·75	3·75

DESIGNS—As Type **90**: 7d., 8d., 9d., 10d., 1s., 1s.9d., Stag. As Type **92**: 10s Eagle (Symbol of St. John The Evangelist).

See also Nos. 287, etc.

94 Human Rights Emblem

95 Dail Eireann Assembly

1968. Human Rights Year.

263	**94**	5d. yellow, gold and black	15	10
264		7d. yellow, gold and red	15	40

1969. 50th Anniv of Dail Eireann (1st National Parliament).

265	**95**	6d. green	15	10
266		9d. blue	15	30

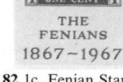

96 Colonnade

97 Quadruple I.L.O. Emblems

1969. Europa.
267 **96** 9d. grey, ochre and blue . . . 75 1·10
268 1s.9d. grey, gold and red . . . 1·25 1·40

1969. 50th Anniv of I.L.O.
269 **97** 6d. black and grey 20 10
270 9d. black and yellow . . . 20 25

98 "The Last Supper and Crucifixion" (Evie Hone Window, Eton Chapel)

1969. Contemporary Irish Art (1st issue).
271 **98** 1s. multicoloured . . . . . 30 1·50
See also Nos. 280, 306, 317, 329, 362, 375, 398, 408, 452, 470 and 498.

99 Mahatma Gandhi

1969. Birth Centenary of Mahatma Gandhi.
272 **99** 6d. black and green . . . 20 10
273 1s.9d. black and yellow . . 30 90

100 Symbolic Bird in Tree

1970. European Conservation Year.
274 **100** 6d. bistre and black . . . 20 10
275 9d. violet and black . . . 25 80

101 "Flaming Sun"

1970. Europa.
276 **101** 6d. violet and silver . . . 70 10
277 9d. brown and silver . . . 1·10 1·25
278 1s.9d. grey and silver . . 2·00 2·00

102 "Sailing Boats" (Peter Monamy)

103 "Madonna of Eire" (Mainie Jellett)

1970. 250th Anniv of Royal Cork Yacht Club.
279 **102** 4d. multicoloured 15 10

1970. Contemporary Irish Art (2nd issue).
280 **103** 1s. multicoloured 15 20

104 Thomas MacCurtain

106 Kevin Barry

1970. 50th Death Annivs of Irish Patriots.
281 **104** 9d. black, violet and grey 50 25
282 – 9d. black, violet and grey 50 25
283 **104** 2s.9d. black, blue and grey . . . . 1·40 1·50
284 – 2s.9d. black, blue and grey . . . . 1·40 1·50
DESIGN: Nos. 282 and 284, Terence MacSwiney.

1970. 50th Death Anniv of Kevin Barry (patriot).
285 **106** 6d. green 30 10
286 1s.2d. blue . . . . 40 1·10

1971. Decimal Currency. As Nos. 247/62 but with face values in new currency, without "p", and some colours changed.
287 **90** ½p. green 10 10
340 1p. blue 10 10
289 1½p. brown 15 50
341 2p. green 10 10
291 2½p. brown 15 10
342 3p. brown 10 10
293 3½p. brown 15 10
294 4p. violet 15 10
295 – 5p. brown and olive . . . 1·00 20
344 **90** 5p. green 60 10
296 – 6p. grey and brown . . . 3·50 50
346 **90** 6p. grey 20 10
347 – 7p. blue and green . . . 70 35
348 **90** 7p. green 35 10
297 – 7½p. mauve and brown 50 85
349 – 8p. brown and deep brown 60 50
350 **90** 8p. brown 30 10
351 – 9p. black and green . . . 70 30
352 **90** 9p. green 30 10
352a 9½p. red 35 20
353 **92** 10p. multicoloured . . . 1·00 30
354 – 10p. black and lilac . . . 70 10
354a **90** 10p. mauve 70 10
355 – 11p. black and red . . . 45 30
299b **92** 12p. multicoloured . . . 60 1·25
355a – 12p. black and green . . 55 10
355b **90** 12p. green 30 10
355c – 13p. brown . . . . 40 1·50
356 **92** 15p. multicoloured . . . 55 40
356a **90** 15p. blue 40 10
356b – 16p. black and green . . 40 80
356c **92** 17p. multicoloured . . . 50 1·00
478 **90** 18p. red 45 50
479 19p. blue . . . . 55 1·75
357 **92** 20p. multicoloured . . . 50 15
480 **90** 22p. blue 65 10
481 24p. brown . . . . 1·50 1·25
482 26p. green . . . . 1·50 40
483 29p. mauve . . . . 1·75 2·00
358 – 50p. multicoloured . . . 70 30
359 – £1 multicoloured . . . . 1·50 30
DESIGNS—As Type **90**: 5p. (295); 6p. (296); 7p. (347); 7½p., 8p., 9p. (351) 10p. (354), 11p., 12p. (No. 355a), 13p., 16p. Stag. As Type **92**: 50p., £1, Eagle (symbol of St. John the Evangelist).

107 "Europa Chain"

108 J. M. Synge

1971. Europa.
302 **107** 4p. brown and green . . . 1·00 10
303 6p. black and blue . . . 3·75 2·50

1971. Birth Centenary of J. M. Synge (playwright).
304 **108** 4p. multicoloured 15 10
305 10p. multicoloured . . . 60 80

109 "An Island Man" (Jack B. Yeats)

110 Racial Harmony Symbol

1971. Contemporary Irish Art (3rd issue). Birth Centenary of J. B. Yeats (artist).
306 **109** 6p. multicoloured 55 55

1971. Racial Equality Year.
307 **110** 4p. red 20 10
308 10p. black 50 75

111 "Madonna and Child" (statue by J. Hughes)

112 Heart

1971. Christmas.
309 **111** 2½p. black, gold and green 10 10
310 6p. black, gold and blue 65 65

1972. World Health Day.
311 **112** 2½p. gold and brown . . 30 15
312 12p. silver and grey . . . 1·10 1·75

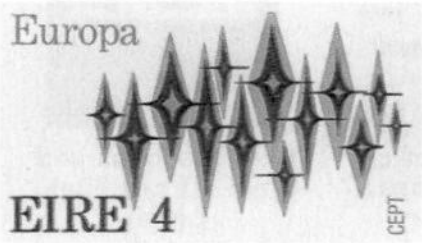

113 "Communications"

114 Dove and Moon

1972. Europa.
313 **113** 4p. orange, black and silver . . . . 1·50 25
314 6p. blue, black and silver 5·00 4·75

1972. Patriot Dead 1922–1923.
315 **114** 4p. multicoloured 10 10
316 6p. yellow, green & dp grn 65 50

115 "Black Lake" (Gerard Dillon)

116 "Horseman" (Carved Slab)

1972. Contemporary Irish Art (4th issue).
317 **115** 3p. multicoloured 60 35

1972. 50th Anniv of Olympic Council of Ireland.
318 **116** 3p. yellow, black and gold 15 10
319 6p. pink, black and gold 55 60

117 Madonna and Child (from Book of Kells)

118 2d. Stamp of 1922

1972. Christmas.
320 **117** 2½p. multicoloured . . . 10 10
321 4p. multicoloured 25 10
322 12p. multicoloured . . . 80 65

1972. 50th Anniv of 1st Irish Postage Stamp.
323 **118** 6p. grey and green . . . 60 60
MS324 72 × 104 mm. No. 323 × 4 5·50 10·00

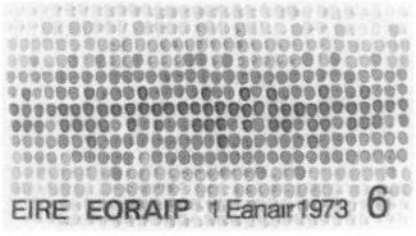

119 Celtic Head Motif

1973. Entry into European Communities.
325 **119** 6p. multicoloured 60 90
326 12p. multicoloured . . . 80 1·10

120 Europa "Posthorn"

1973. Europa.
327 **120** 4p. blue . . . . 1·00 10
328 6p. black . . . . 3·00 2·00

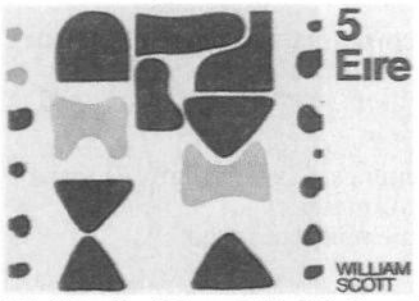

121 "Berlin Blues II" (W. Scott)

1973. Contemporary Irish Art (5th issue).
329 **121** 5p. blue and black . . . 40 30

122 Weather Map

1973. Centenary of I.M.O./W.M.O.
330 **122** 3½p. multicoloured . . . 30 10
331 12p. multicoloured . . . 1·10 2·00

123 Tractor ploughing

1973. World Ploughing Championships, Wellington Bridge.
332 **123** 5p. multicoloured 15 10
333 7p. multicoloured 85 50

124 "Flight into Egypt" (Jan de Cock)

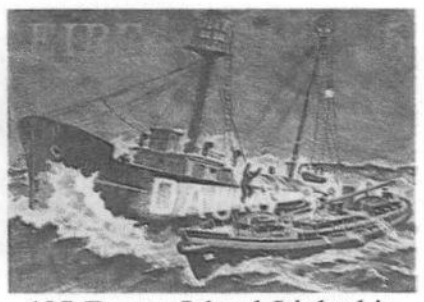
125 Daunt Island Lightship and "Mary Stanford" (Ballycotton Lifeboat), 1936

1973. Christmas.
334 **124** 3½p. multicoloured . . . 15 10
335 12p. multicoloured . . . 1·10 1·50

1974. 150th Anniv of R.N.L.I.
336 **125** 5p. multicoloured 30 30

126 "Edmund Burke" (statue by J. H. Foley)

127 "Oliver Goldsmith" (statue by J. H. Foley)

1974. Europa.
337 **126** 5p. black and blue . . . 1·00 10
338 7p. black and green . . . 4·00 2·50

1974. Death Bicentenary of Oliver Goldsmith (writer).
360 **127** 3½p. black and yellow . . 25 10
361 12p. black and green . . 1·25 1·00

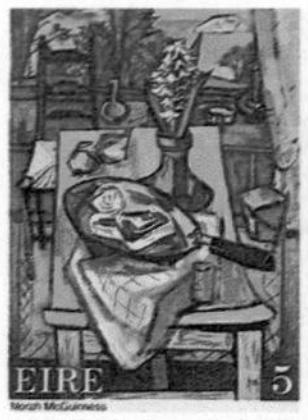

128 "Kitchen Table" (Norah McGuiness)

129 Rugby Players

1974. Contemporary Irish Art (6th issue).
362 **128** 5p. multicoloured 35 30

1974. Centenary of Irish Rugby Football.
363 **129** 3½p. green 50 10
364 12p. multicoloured . . . 2·50 2·75

130 U.P.U. "Postmark"

131 "Madonna and Child" (Bellini)

1974. Centenary of Universal Postal Union.
365 **130** 5p. green and black . . . 25 10
366 7p. blue and black . . . 35 55

1974. Christmas.
367 **131** 5p. multicoloured 15 10
368 15p. multicoloured . . . 60 90

132 "Peace"

1975. International Women's Year.
369 **132** 8p. purple and blue . . . 25 75
370 15p. blue and green . . . 50 1·25

133 "Castletown Hunt" (R. Healy)

1975. Europa.
371 **133** 7p. grey . . . . 1·25 15
372 9p. green . . . . 3·75 2·50

134 Putting

1975. Ninth European Amateur Golf Team Championship, Killarney.
373 **134** 6p. multicoloured 75 45
374 – 9p. multicoloured . . . . 1·50 1·50
No. 374 is similar to Type **134** but shows a different view of the putting green.

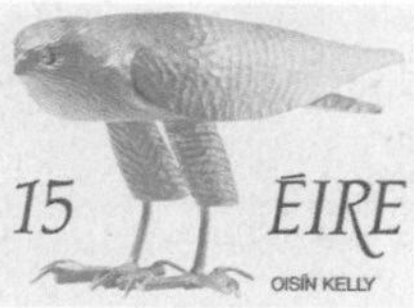

135 "Bird of Prey" (sculpture by Oisin Kelly)

1975. Contemporary Irish Art (7th issue).
375 **135** 15p. brown 75 75

136 Nano Nagle (founder) and Waifs

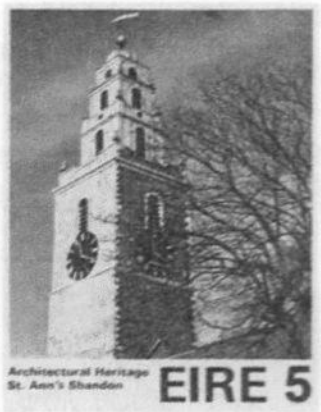

137 Tower of St. Anne's Church, Shandon

1975. Bicentenary of Presentation Order of Nuns.
376 **136** 5p. black and blue . . . 20 10
377 7p. black and brown . . . 30 30

1975. European Architectural Heritage Year.
378 **137** 5p. brown 25 10
379 6p. multicoloured 60 85
380 – 7p. blue 60 10
381 – 9p. multicoloured 65 80
DESIGN: Nos. 380/1, Interior of Holycross Abbey, Co. Tipperary.

138 St. Oliver Plunkett (commemorative medal by Imogen Stuart)

139 "Madonna and Child" (Fra Filippo Lippi)

1975. Canonization of Oliver Plunkett.
382 **138** 7p. black 15 10
383 15p. brown 55 45

1975. Christmas.
384 **139** 5p. multicoloured 15 10
385 7p. multicoloured 15 10
386 10p. multicoloured . . . 45 30

140 James Larkin (from a drawing by Sean O'Sullivan)

141 Alexander Graham Bell

1975. Birth Centenary of James Larkin (Trade Union Leader).
387 **140** 7p. green and grey . . . 20 10
388 11p. brown and yellow . . 40 55

1976. Centenary of Telephone.
389 **141** 9p. multicoloured 20 10
390 15p. multicoloured . . . 45 50

142 1847 Benjamin Franklin Essay

1976. Bicentenary of American Revolution.
391 – 7p. blue, red and silver . . 20 10
392 – 8p. blue, red and silver . . 25 1·10
393 **142** 9p. blue, orange and silver 25 10
394 15p. red, grey and silver 45 75
MS395 95 × 75 mm. Nos. 391/4 2·75 8·00
DESIGNS: 7p. Thirteen Stars; 8p. Fifty Stars.

143 Spirit Barrel

1976. Europa. Irish Delft. Multicoloured.
396 9p. Type **143** 75 20
397 11p. Dish . . . . 2·00 1·60

144 "The Lobster Pots, West of Ireland" (Paul Henry)

1976. Contemporary Irish Art (8th issue).
398 **144** 15p. multicoloured . . . 60 60

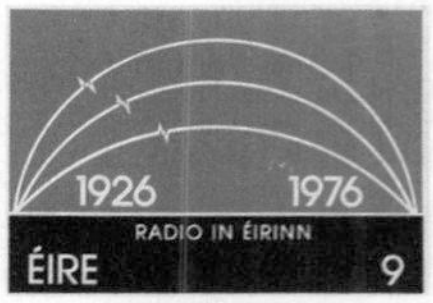

145 Radio Waves

1976. 50th Anniv of Irish Broadcasting Service.
399 **145** 9p. blue and green . . . 20 10
400 – 11p. brown, red and blue 60 1·00
DESIGN—VERT: 11p. Transmitter, radio waves and globe.

146 "The Nativity" (Lorenzo Monaco)

1976. Christmas.
401 **146** 7p. multicoloured 15 10
402 9p. multicoloured 15 10
403 15p. multicoloured . . . 55 55

147 16th Century Manuscript

1977. Centenaries of National Library (8p.) and National Museum (10p.) Multicoloured
404 8p. Type **147** 30 30
405 10p. Prehistoric stone 40 35

148 Ballynahinch, Galway

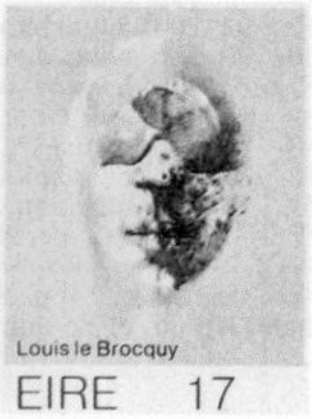

149 "Head" (Louis le Brocquy)

1977. Europa. Multicoloured.
406 10p. Type **148** . . . . 1·25 25
407 12p. Lough Tay, Wicklow . . 3·25 1·50

1977. Contemporary Irish Art (9th issue).
408 **149** 17p. multicoloured . . . 55 75

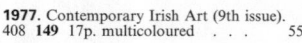

150 Guide and Tents

1977. Scouting and Guiding. Multicoloured.
409 8p. Type **150** 45 10
410 17p. Tent and Scout saluting 95 1·75

151 "The Shanachie" (drawing by Jack B. Yeats)

1977. Anniversaries.
411 **151** 10p. black 35 15
412 – 12p. black . . . . 45 1·00
DESIGNS AND EVENTS: 10p. Type **151** (Golden Jubilee of Irish Folklore Society); 12p. The philosopher Eriugena (1100th death anniv).

152 "Electricity" (Golden Jubilee of Electricity Supply Board)

1977. Golden Jubilees.
413 **152** 10p. multicoloured . . . 15 10
414 – 12p. multicoloured . . . 30 1·40
415 – 17p. black and brown . . 40 35
DESIGNS: 12p. Bulls (from Irish coins) (Agricultural Credit Act); 17p. Greyhound (Greyhound Track Racing).

153 "The Holy Family" (Giorgione)

154 Junkers W.33 "Bremen" in Flight

1977. Christmas.
416 **153** 8p. multicoloured 20 10
417 10p. multicoloured . . . 20 10
418 17p. multicoloured . . . 75 1·25

1978. 50th Anniv of 1st East–West Transatlantic Flight.
419 **154** 10p. black and blue . . . 20 15
420 17p. black and brown . . 35 1·10

155 Spring Gentian

156 Catherine McAuley

1978. Wild Flowers. Multicoloured.
421 8p. Type **155** 25 40
422 10p. Strawberry tree 25 15
423 11p. Large-flowered Butterwort 25 50
424 17p. St. Dabeoc's Heath . . 45 2·00

1978. Anniversaries and Events. Multicoloured.
425 10p. Type **156** (founder of Sisters of Mercy) (birth bicent) 25 10
426 11p. Doctor performing vaccination (Global Eradication of Smallpox) (horiz) 35 80
427 17p. "Self-portrait" Sir William Orpen (painter) (birth cent) . . . . 55 1·10

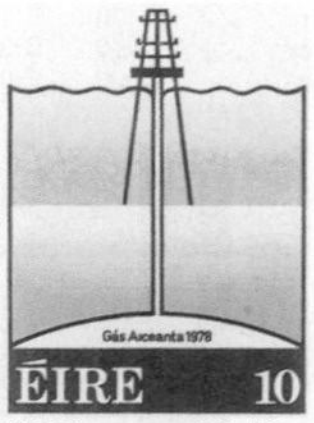

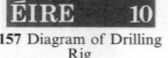

157 Diagram of Drilling Rig

159 "Virgin and Child" (Guercino)

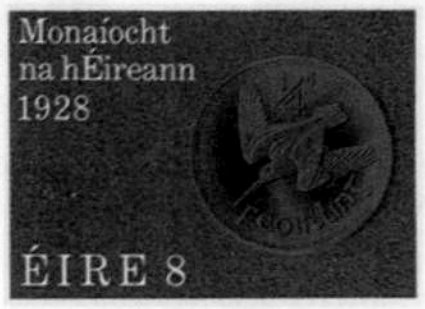

158 Farthing

1978. Arrival Onshore of Natural Gas.
428 **157** 10p. multicoloured . . . 30 30

1978. 50th Anniv of Irish Currency.
429 **158** 8p. black, copper and green 25 20
430 – 10p. black, silver and green 30 10
431 – 11p. black, copper & brn 35 50
432 – 17p. black, silver and blue 65 1·00
DESIGNS: 10p. Florin; 11p. Penny; 17p. Half-crown.

1978. Christmas.
433 **159** 8p. brown, blue and gold 15 10
434 10p. brown, blue & purple 15 10
435 17p. brown, blue and green . . . . 45 1·40

160 Conolly Folly, Castletown

1978. Europa.
436 **160** 10p. brown . . . . 1·40 15
437 – 11p. green . . . . 1·40 1·75
DESIGN: 11p. Dromoland Belvedere.

161 Athletes in Cross-country Race

1979. 7th World Cross-country Championships, Limerick. Multicoloured
438 **161** 8p. multicoloured 20 30

162 "European Communities" (in languages of member nations)

163 Sir Rowland Hill

1979. 1st Direct Elections to European Assembly.
439 **162** 10p. green 15 15
440 11p. violet 15 35

1979. Death Centenary of Sir Rowland Hill.
441 **163** 17p. black, grey and red 30 60

164 Winter Wren

1979. Birds. Multicoloured.
442 8p. Type **164** 40 80
443 10p. Great crested grebe . . 40 15
444 11p. White-fronted goose . . 45 80
445 17p. Peregrine falcon . . . . 70 2·00

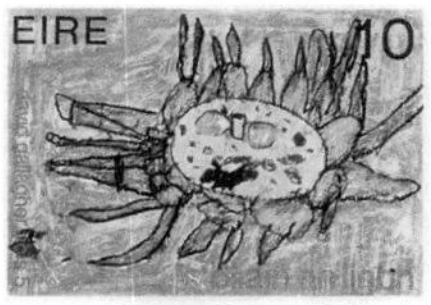

165 "A Happy Flower" (David Gallagher)

1979. International Year of the Child. Paintings by Children. Multicoloured.
446 10p. Type **165** 20 10
447 11p. "Myself and My Skipping Rope" (Lucy Norman) (vert) 25 60
448 17p. "Swans on a Lake" (Nicola O'Dwyer) 35 85

166 Pope John Paul II

1979. Visit of Pope John Paul II.
449 **166** 12p. multicoloured . . . 30 20

167 Brother with Child

1979. Anniversaries and Events.
450 **167** 9½p. brown and mauve . . 20 10
451 – 11p. orange, black and blue 20 70
452 – 20p. multicoloured . . . 40 1·40
DESIGNS—VERT: 11p. Windmill and sun (Int Energy Conservation Month). HORIZ: 9½p. Type **167** (Cent of Hospitaller Order of St. John of God in Ireland); 20p. "Seated Figure" (sculpture F. E. McWilliam) (Contemporary Irish Art (10th issue)).

168 Patrick Pearse, "Liberty" and G.P.O., Dublin

169 "Madonna and Child" (panel painting from the Domnach Airgid Shrine)

1979. Birth Centenary of Patrick Pearse (patriot).
453 **168** 12p. multicoloured . . . 30 15

1979. Christmas.
454 **169** 9½p. multicoloured . . . 15 10
455 20p. multicoloured . . . 30 55

170 Bianconi Long Car, 1836

1979. Europa. Multicoloured.
456 12p. Type **170** . . . . 1·00 30
457 13p. Transatlantic cable, Valentia, 1866 . . . . . . 1·10 1·40

171 John Baptist de la Salle (founder)

172 George Bernard Shaw

1980. Cent of Arrival of De La Salle Order.
458 **171** 12p. multicoloured . . . 30 30

1980. Europa. Personalities. Multicoloured.
459 12p. Type **172** . . . . 1·00 50
460 13p. Oscar Wilde (28 × 38 mm) . . . . 1·00 1·50

173 Stoat

174 Playing Bodhran and Whistle

1980. Wildlife. Multicoloured.
461 12p. Type **173** 25 40
462 15p. Arctic hare 25 15
463 16p. Red fox 25 80
464 25p. Red deer . . . . 35 1·60
MS465 73 × 97 mm. Nos. 461/4 1·00 2·75

1980. Traditional Music and Dance. Mult.
466 12p. Type **174** 15 10
467 15p. Playing Uilleann pipes 20 15
468 25p. Dancing . . . . 35 1·10

175 Sean O'Casey

176 Nativity Scene (painting by Geraldine McNulty)

1980. Commemorations.
469 12p. multicoloured 20 10
470 25p. black, buff and brown 35 55
DESIGNS AND COMMEMORATIONS: 12p. Type **175** (playwright) (birth centenary); 25p. "Gold Painting No. 57" (P. Scott) (Contemporary Irish Art (11th issue)).

1980. Christmas.
471 **176** 12p. multicoloured . . . 15 10
472 15p. multicoloured . . . 20 10
473 25p. multicoloured . . . 40 1·25

177 Boyle Air-pump, 1659

178 "The Legend of the Cock and the Pot"

1981. Irish Science and Technology. Mult.
474 12p. Type **177** 20 10
475 15p. Ferguson tractor, 1936 25 10
476 16p. Parsons turbine, 1884 30 90
477 25p. Holland submarine, 1878 35 1·25

1981. Europa. Folklore. Paintings by Maria Simonds-Gooding.
491 **178** 18p. black, yellow and red 1·00 10
492 – 19p. black, orange & yellow . . . . 1·25 90
DESIGN: 19p. "The Angel with the Scales of Judgement".

179 Cycling

180 Jeremiah O'Donovan Rossa

1981. 50th Anniv of "An Oige" (Irish Youth Hostel Association). Multicoloured.
493 15p. Type **179** 25 40
494 18p. Hill-walking (horiz) . . 25 10
495 19p. Mountaineering (horiz) 25 95
496 30p. Rock-climbing 40 95

1981. 150th Birth Anniv of Jeremiah O'Donovan Rossa (politician).
497 **180** 15p. multicoloured . . . 60 30

181 "Railway Embankment" (W. J. Leech)

1981. Contemporary Irish Art (12th issue).
498 **181** 30p. multicoloured . . . 1·00 70

182 James Hoban and White House

1981. 150th Death Anniv of James Hoban (White House architect).
499 **182** 18p. multicoloured . . . 50 30

183 "Arkle" (steeplechaser)

1981. Famous Irish Horses. Multicoloured.
500 18p. Type **183** . . . . 50 1·00
501 18p. "Boomerang" (show-jumper) . . . . 50 1·00
502 22p. "King of Diamonds" (Draught horse) 50 30
503 24p. "Ballymoss" (flat-racer) 50 70
504 36p. "Coosheen Finn" (Connemara pony) . . . . 60 1·00

184 "Nativity" (F. Barocci)

185 Eviction Scene

1981. Christmas.
505 **184** 18p. multicoloured . . . 25 10
506 22p. multicoloured . . . 30 10
507 36p. multicoloured . . . 80 1·50

1981. Anniversaries. Multicoloured.
508 18p. Type **185** 65 25
509 22p. Royal Dublin Society emblem 75 30
ANNIVERSARIES: 18p. Centenary of Land Law (Ireland) Act. 22p. Royal Dublin Society (organization for the advancement of agriculture, industry, art and science), 250th Anniv.

186 Upper Lake, Killarney National Park

1982. 50th Anniv of Killarney National Park. Multicoloured.
510 18p. Type **186** 40 20
511 36p. Eagle's Nest . . . . . . 85 1·60

187 "The Stigmatization of St. Francis" (Sassetta)

188 The Great Famine, 1845–50

1982. Religious Anniversaries.
512 **187** 22p. multicoloured . . . 50 15
513 – 24p. brown 75 85

DESIGNS AND ANNIVERSARIES: 22p. Type **187** (St. Francis of Assisi (founder of Franciscan order) (500th birth anniv); 24p. Francis Makemie (founder of American Presbyterianism) and old Presbyterian Church, Ramelton, Co. Donegal (300th anniv of ordination).

1982. Europa. Historic Events.
514 **188** 26p. black and stone . . . 3·00 50
515 – 29p. multicoloured . . . 3·50 2·00
DESIGN—HORIZ: 29p. The coming of Christianity to Ireland.

189 Padraic O. Conaire (writer) (birth centenary)

191 "St. Patrick" (Galway hooker)

190 Porbeagle Shark

1982. Anniversaries of Cultural Figures.
516 **189** 22p. black and blue . . . 25 30
517 – 26p. black and brown . . 55 30
518 – 29p. black and blue . . . 65 1·75
519 – 44p. black and grey . . . 65 1·60
DESIGNS AND ANNIVERSARIES: 26p. James Joyce (writer) (birth centenary); 29p. John Field (musician) (birth centenary); 44p. Charles Kickham (writer) (death centenary).

1982. Marine Life. Multicoloured.
520 22p. Type **190** . . . . 75 1·25
521 22p. Common European oyster . . . . 75 1·25
522 26p. Atlantic salmon 90 30
523 29p. Dublin Bay prawn . . . 90 2·25

1982. Irish Boats. Multicoloured.
524 22p. Type **191** . . . . 75 1·25
525 22p. Currach (horiz) . . . . 75 1·25
526 26p. "Asgard II" (cadet brigantine) (horiz) 90 30
527 29p. Howth 17 foot yacht . . 90 2·25

192 "Irish House of Commons" (painting by Francis Wheatley)

1982. Bicentenary of Grattan's Parliament and Birth Centenary of Eamon de Valera. Multicoloured.
528 22p. Type **192** . . . . 35 1·25
529 26p. Eamon de Valera (vert) 40 40

193 "Madonna and Child" (sculpture)

194 Aughnanure Castle

1982. Christmas.
530 **193** 22p. multicoloured . . . 30 90
531 26p. multicoloured . . . 30 35

1983. Irish Architecture.
532 – 1p. blue 10 10
533 – 2p. green 20 10
534 – 3p. black 20 10
535 – 4p. red 20 10
536 – 5p. brown 30 10
537 – 6p. blue 30 15
538 – 7p. green 30 75
539 – 10p. black 30 10
540 – 12p. brown . . . . 30 1·25
541 **194** 15p. green 45 35
542 20p. purple 50 45
543 22p. blue 50 10
544 – 23p. green . . . . 85 1·25
544a – 24p. brown . . . . 1·25 35
545 – 26p. brown 75 10
545c – 28p. red 75 45
546 – 29p. green 70 65
547 – 30p. black 70 30
547c – 32p. brown . . . . 2·50 2·50
547d – 37p. blue . . . . 1·00 2·50
547e – 39p. red . . . . 2·25 2·75
548 – 44p. black and grey . . 1·00 70
548b – 46p. green and grey . . 6·50 2·00
549 – 50p. blue and grey . . . 1·75 65
550 – £1 brown and grey . . . 4·50 3·50
550b – £1 blue and grey . . . . 5·00 1·25
550c – £2 green and black . . . 5·00 4·50
551 – £5 red and grey . . . . 12·00 6·00
DESIGNS—HORIZ: (As T **194**): 1 to 5p. Central Pavilion, Dublin Botanic Gardens; 6 to 12p. Dr. Steevens' Hospital, Dublin; 28 to 37p. St. MacDara's Church. (37 × 21 mm); 46p., £1 (No. 550) Cahir Castle; 50p., £2 Casino Marino. £5 Central Bus Station, Dublin. VERT: (As T **194**): 23 to 26p., 39p. Cormac's Chapel. (21 × 37 mm); 44p., £1 (No. 550b) Killarney Cathedral.

195 Ouzel Gallery Goblet

196 Padraig O. Siochfhradha (writer and teacher)

1983. Bicentenaries of Dublin Chamber of Commerce (22p.) and Bank of Ireland (26p.). Multicoloured.
552 22p. Type **195** 30 65
553 26p. Bank of Ireland building (horiz) 35 35

1983. Anniversaries. Multicoloured.
554 26p. Type **196** (birth cent) . . 50 75
555 29p. Young Boys' Brigade member (centenary) . . . 90 1·50

197 Neolithic Carved Pattern, Newgrange Tomb

1983. Europa.
556 **197** 26p. black and yellow . . 2·75 50
557 – 29p. black, brown & yellow . . . . 5·25 5·00
DESIGN: 29p. Sir William Rowan Hamilton's formulae for the multiplication of quaternions.

198 Kerry Blue Terrier

1983. Irish Dogs. Multicoloured.
558 22p. Type **198** 75 35
559 26p. Irish wolfhound 85 45
560 26p. Irish water spaniel . . . 85 45
561 29p. Irish terrier . . . . . . 1·00 2·25
562 44p. Irish setters . . . . . . 1·40 2·50
MS563 142 × 80 mm. Nos. 558/62 6·00 8·00

199 Animals (Irish Society for the Prevention of Cruelty to Animals)

1983. Anniversaries and Commemorations.
564 **199** 22p. multicoloured . . . 50 1·00
565 – 22p. multicoloured . . . 50 1·00
566 – 26p. multicoloured . . . 50 60
567 – 26p. multicoloured . . . 50 60
568 – 44p. blue and black . . . 75 2·00
DESIGNS—VERT: No. 565, Sean MacDiarmada (patriot) (birth cent); 567, "St. Vincent de Paul in the Streets of Paris" (150th anniv of Society of St. Vincent de Paul); 568, "Andrew Jackson" (Frank McKelvey) (President of the United States). HORIZ: No. 566, "100" (Centenary of Industrial Credit Company).

200 Postman with Bicycle

201 Weaving

1983. World Communications Year. Multicoloured.
569 22p. Type **200** 85 75
570 29p. Dish antenna . . . . . 90 2·00

1983. Irish Handicrafts. Multicoloured.
571 22p. Type **201** 45 50
572 26p. Basket making 45 35
573 29p. Irish crochet . . . . . 50 1·25
574 44p. Harp making . . . . . 80 2·00

202 "La Natividad" (R. van der Weyden)

1983. Christmas.
575 **202** 22p. multicoloured . . . 40 30
576 26p. multicoloured . . . 60 30

203 Dublin and Kingstown Railway Steam Locomotive "Princess"

1984. 150th Anniv of Irish Railways. Mult.
577 23p. Type **203** . . . . 75 1·25
578 26p. Great Southern Railways steam locomotive "Macha" 75 35
579 29p. Great Northern Railway steam locomotive No. 87 "Kestrel" . . . . 85 1·75
580 44p. Two-car electric train Coras Iompair Eireann . . 1·10 2·25
MS581 129 × 77 mm. Nos. 577/80 5·50 7·00

204 "Sorbus hibernica"

1984. Irish Trees. Multicoloured.
582 22p. Type **204** 75 70
583 26p. "Taxus baccata fastigiata" 80 30
584 29p. "Salix hibernica" . . . 90 1·75
585 44p. "Betula pubescens" . . 1·50 2·50

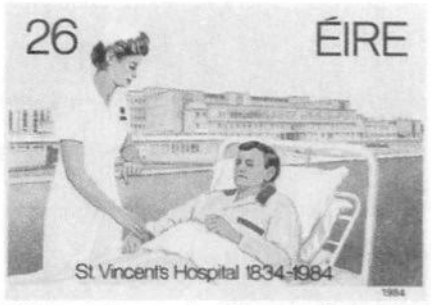

205 St. Vincent's Hospital, Dublin

1984. 150th Anniv of St. Vincent's Hospital and Bicentenary of Royal College of Surgeons. Multicoloured.
586 26p. Type **205** 60 30
587 44p. Royal College and logo 1·00 1·50

206 C.E.P.T. 25th Anniversary Logo

1984. Europa.
588 **206** 26p. blue, dp blue & black . . . . 2·25 50
589 29p. lt green, green & blk 3·00 3·25

207 Flags on Ballot Box

208 John McCormack

1984. Second Direct Elections to European Assembly.
590 **207** 26p. multicoloured . . . 50 70

1984. Birth Centenary of John McCormack (tenor).
591 **208** 22p. multicoloured . . . 50 70

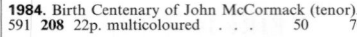

209 Hammer-throwing

1984. Olympic Games, Los Angeles.
592 **209** 22p. mauve, black and gold 35 80
593 – 26p. violet, black and gold 40 65
594 – 29p. blue, black and gold 60 1·25
DESIGNS: 26p. Hurdling; 29p. Running.

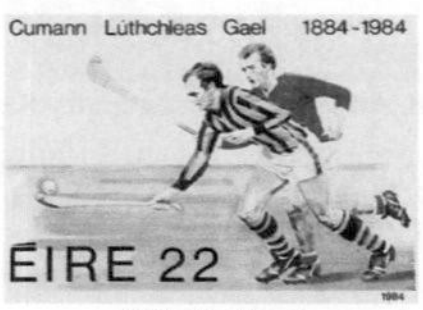

210 Hurling

1984. Cent of Gaelic Athletic Association. Mult.
595 22p. Type **210** 50 90
596 26p. Irish football (vert) . . . 60 90

211 Galway Mayoral Chain

1984. Anniversaries. Multicoloured.
597 26p. Type **211** (500th anniv of mayoral charter) 35 50
598 44p. St. Brendan (from 15th-cent Bodleian manuscript) (1500th birth anniv) (horiz) . . . . . . 75 1·50

212 Hands passing Letter

1984. Bicentenary of Irish Post Office.
599 **212** 26p. multicoloured . . . 60 70

213 "Virgin and Child" (Sassoferrato)

1984. Christmas. Multicoloured.
600 17p. Christmas star (horiz) 45 80
601 22p. Type **213** . . . . 45 1·25
602 26p. Type **213** 65 40

214 "Love" and Heart-shaped Balloon

1985. Greetings Stamps. Multicoloured.

603	22p. Type **214**	50	75
604	26p. Bouquet of hearts and flowers (vert)	60	75

215 Dunsink Observatory (bicentenary)

216 "Polyommatus icarus"

1985. Anniversaries. Multicoloured.

605	22p. Type **215**	50	50
606	26p. "A Landscape at Tivoli, Cork, with Boats" (Nathaniel Grogan) (800th anniv of City of Cork) (horiz)	50	30
607	37p. Royal Irish Academy (bicentenary)	70	1·75
608	44p. Richard Crosbie's balloon flight (bicentenary of first aeronautic flight by an Irishman)	80	1·75

1985. Butterflies. Multicoloured.

609	22p. Type **216**	1·50	1·00
610	26p. "Vanessa atalanta"	1·50	70
611	28p. "Gonepteryx rhamni"	1·75	3·00
612	44p. "Eurabyas aurinia"	2·00	3·25

217 Charles Villiers Stanford (composer)

1985. Europa. Irish Composers. Multicoloured.

613	26p. Type **217**	2·50	50
614	37p. Turlough Carolan (composer and lyricist)	6·00	5·50

218 George Frederick Handel

1985. European Music Year. Composers. Mult.

615	22p. Type **218**	1·25	2·50
616	22p. Guiseppe Domenico Scarlatti	1·25	2·50
617	26p. Johann Sebastian Bach	1·50	50

219 U.N. Patrol of Irish Soldiers, Congo, 1960

1985. Anniversaries. Multicoloured.

618	22p. Type **219** (25th anniv of Irish Participation in U.N. Peace-keeping Force)	55	80
619	26p. Thomas Ashe (patriot) (birth cent) (vert)	55	60
620	44p. "Bishop George Berkeley" (James Lathan) (philosopher, 300th birth anniv) (vert)	85	3·00

220 Group of Young People

1985. International Youth Year. Mult.

621	22p. Type **220**	55	50
622	26p. Students and young workers (vert)	55	50

221 Visual Display Unit

1985. Industrial Innovation. Multicoloured.

623	22p. Type **221**	75	75
624	26p. Turf cutting with hand tool and with modern machinery	80	55
625	44p. "The Key Man" (Sean Keating) (150th anniv of Institution of Engineers of Ireland)	1·50	2·50

222 Lighted Candle and Holly

224 Stylized Love Bird with Letter

1985. Christmas. Multicoloured.

626	22p. Type **222**	75	65
627	22p. "Virgin and Child in a Landscape" (Adrian van Ijsenbrandt)	1·25	2·25
628	22p. "The Holy Family" (Murillo)	1·25	2·25
629	26p. "The Adoration of the Shepherds" (Louis le Nain) (horiz)	1·25	25

No. 626 was only issued in sheetlets of 16 sold at £3, providing a discount of 52p. off the face value of the stamps.

1986. Greetings Stamps. Multicoloured.

630	22p. Type **224**	75	90
631	26p. Heart-shaped pillar-box	75	90

225 Hart's Tongue Fern

226 "Harmony between Industry and Nature"

1986. Ferns. Multicoloured.

632	24p. Type **225**	70	70
633	28p. Rusty-back fern	80	70
634	46p. Killarney fern	1·25	2·10

1986. Europa. Protection of the Environment. Multicoloured.

635	28p. Type **226**	5·00	50
636	39p. "Vanessa atalanta" (butterfly) and tractor in field ("Preserve hedgerows") (horiz)	16·00	5·00

227 Boeing 747-200 over Globe showing Aer Lingus Routes

1986. 50th Anniv of Aer Lingus (airline). Multicoloured.

637	28p. Type **227**	1·40	75
638	46p. De Havilland Dragon Mk 2 "Iolar" (first airplane)	1·90	3·00

228 Grand Canal at Robertstown

1986. Irish Waterways. Multicoloured.

639	24p. Type **228**	1·50	1·00
640	28p. Fishing in County Mayo (vert)	1·60	1·00
641	30p. Motor cruiser on Lough Derg	1·75	2·50

229 "Severn" (19th-century paddlesteamer)

1986. 150th Anniv of British and Irish Steam Packet Company. Multicoloured.

642	24p. Type **229**	75	1·00
643	28p. "Leinster" (modern ferry)	85	60

230 Kish Lighthouse and Bell JetRanger III Helicopter

231 J. P. Nannetti (first president) and Linotype Operator (Dublin Council of Trade Unions centenary)

1986. Irish Lighthouses. Multicoloured.

644	24p. Type **230**	1·25	75
645	30p. Fastnet Lighthouse	2·25	2·75

1986. Anniversaries and Commemorations.

646	**231** 24p. multicoloured	60	90
647	– 28p. black and grey	75	80
648	– 28p. multicoloured	75	80
649	– 30p. multicoloured	85	1·00
650	– 46p. multicoloured	1·00	1·75

DESIGNS:—VERT: No. 647, Arthur Griffith (statesman); 649, Clasped hands (International Peace Year). HORIZ: No. 648, Woman surveyor (Women in Society); 650, Peace dove (International Peace Year).

232 William Mulready and his Design for 1840 Envelope

1986. Birth Bicentenaries of William Mulready (artist) (24p.) and Charles Bianconi (originator of Irish mail coach service) (others). Multicoloured.

651	24p. Type **232**	70	70
652	28p. Bianconi car outside Hearns Hotel, Clonmel (vert)	85	55
653	39p. Bianconi car on the road	1·40	1·75

233 "Adoration of the Shepherds" (Francesco Pascucci)

1986. Christmas. Multicoloured.

654	21p. Type **233**	1·10	1·40
655	28p. "Adoration of the Magi" (Frans Francken III) (vert)	65	60

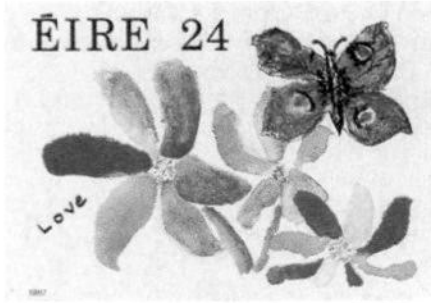

234 "Butterfly and Flowers" (Tara Collins)

1987. Greetings Stamps. Children's Paintings. Multicoloured.

656	24p. Type **234**	70	1·25
657	28p. "Postman on Bicycle delivering Hearts" (Brigid Teehan) (vert)	80	1·25

235 Cork Electric Tram

1987. Irish Trams. Multicoloured.

658	24p. Type **235**	65	65
659	28p. Dublin standard tram No. 29	70	85
660	30p. Howth (Great Northern Railway) tram	80	2·00
661	46p. Galway horse tram	1·25	2·25
MS662	131 × 85 mm. Nos. 658/61	4·25	6·50

236 Ships from Crest (Bicentenary of Waterford Chamber of Commerce)

1987. Anniversaries.

663	**236** 24p. black, blue and green	70	60
664	– 28p. multicoloured	70	60
665	– 30p. multicoloured	70	2·00
666	– 39p. multicoloured	75	1·75

DESIGNS—HORIZ: 28p. Canon John Hayes and symbols of agriculture and development (birth centenary and 50th anniv of Muintir na Tire programme); 39p. Mother Mary Martin and International Missionary Training Hospital, Drogheda (50th anniv of Medical Missionaries of Mary). VERT: 30p. "Calceolaria burbidgei" and College crest (300th anniv of Trinity College Botanic Gardens, Dublin).

237 Bord na Mona Headquarters and "The Turf Cutter" (sculpture, John Behan), Dublin

1987. Europa. Modern Architecture. Mult.

667	28p. Type **237**	2·00	60
668	39p. St. Mary's Church, Cong	5·00	5·00

238 Kerry Cow

1987. Irish Cattle. Multicoloured.

669	24p. Type **238**	80	75
670	28p. Friesian cow and calf	95	60
671	30p. Hereford bullock	1·00	2·25
672	39p. Shorthorn bull	1·10	2·25

239 Fleadh Nua, Ennis

1987. Festivals. Multicoloured.

673	24p. Type **239**	75	70
674	28p. Rose of Tralee International Festival	80	60

675 30p. Wexford Opera Festival (horiz) . . . . 1·10 2·00
676 46p. Ballinasloe Horse Fair (horiz) . . . . 1·25 2·00

240 Flagon (1637), Arms and Anniversary Ornament (1987) (350th anniv of Dublin Goldsmiths' Company)

1987. Anniversaries and Commemorations.
677 **240** 24p. multicoloured . . . 70 80
678 – 24p. grey and black . . . 70 80
679 – 28p. multicoloured . . . 85 60
680 – 46p. multicoloured . . . 1·25 1·10
DESIGNS—VERT: 24p. (No. 678) Cathal Brugha (patriot); 46p. Woman chairing board meeting (Women in Society). HORIZ: 28p. Arms of Ireland and inscription (50th anniv of Constitution).

241 Scenes from "The Twelve Days of Christmas" (carol)

1987. Christmas. Multicoloured.
681 21p. Type **241** . . . . 60 1·00
682 24p. The Nativity (detail, late 15th-century Waterford Vestments) (vert) . . . . . 75 1·00
683 28p. Figures from Neapolitan crib, c. 1850 (vert) 75 80

242 Acrobatic Clowns spelling "LOVE"

1988. Greetings Stamps. Multicoloured.
684 24p. Type **242** 75 60
685 28p. Pillar box and hearts (vert) 75 65

243 "Robert Burke" (Sidney Nolan) and Map of Burke and Wills Expedition Route

1988. Bicent of Australian Settlement. Mult.
686 24p. Type **243** . . . . 1·00 60
687 46p. "Eureka Stockade" (mural detail, Sidney Nolan) . . . . 1·25 1·75

244 Past and Present Buildings of Dublin

1988. Dublin Millennium.
688 **244** 28p. multicoloured . . . 45 55

245 Showjumping

1988. Olympic Games, Seoul. Multicoloured.
689 28p. Type **245** . . . . 1·00 1·40
690 28p. Cycling . . . . 1·00 1·40

246 William T. Cosgrave (statesman)

1988. Anniversaries and Events.
691 **246** 24p. grey and black . . . 45 45
692 – 30p. multicoloured . . . 80 1·00
693 – 50p. multicoloured . . . 1·00 1·90
DESIGNS—HORIZ: 30p. Members with casualty and ambulance (50th anniv of Order of Malta Ambulance Corps). VERT: 50p. Barry Fitzgerald (actor) (birth centenary).

247 Air Traffic Controllers and Airbus Industrie A320

1988. Europa. Transport and Communications. Multicoloured.
694 28p. Type **247** . . . . 2·00 55
695 39p. Globe with stream of letters from Ireland to Europe . . . . 2·25 3·00

248 "Sirius" (paddle-steamer)

1988. Transatlantic Transport Anniversaries. Multicoloured.
696 24p. Type **248** (150th anniv of regular transatlantic steamship services) . . . . 1·00 50
697 46p. Short S.20 seaplane "Mercury" and Short S.21 flying boat "Maia" (Short Mayo composite aircraft) in Foynes Harbour (50th anniv of first commercial transatlantic flight) . . . . 1·75 2·75

249 Cottonweed

251 Computer and Abacus

250 Garda on Duty

1988. Endangered Flora of Ireland. Mult.
698 24p. Type **249** 85 55
699 28p. Hart's saxifrage 95 55
700 46p. Purple milk-vetch . . . 1·40 2·75

1988. Irish Security Forces. Multicoloured.
701 28p. Type **250** . . . . 70 1·10
702 28p. Army unit with personnel carrier . . . . . 70 1·10
703 28p. Navy and Air Corps members with "Eithne" (helicopter patrol vessel) 70 1·10
704 28p. Army and Navy reservists . . . . 70 1·10

1988. Anniversaries. Multicoloured.
705 24p. Type **251** (Institute of Chartered Accountants in Ireland centenary) 40 40
706 46p. "Duquesa Santa Ana" off Donegal (400th anniv of Spanish Armada) (horiz) 1·25 1·25

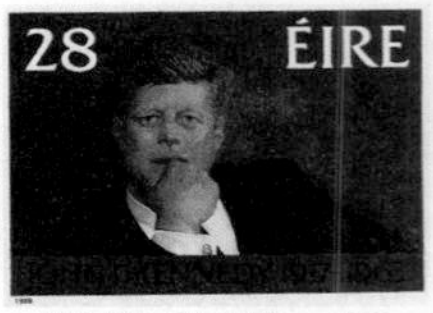

252 "President Kennedy" (James Wyeth)
253 St. Kevin's Church, Glendalough

1988. 25th Death Anniv of John F. Kennedy (American statesman).
707 **252** 28p. multicoloured . . . 1·00 80

1988. Christmas. Multicoloured.
708 21p. Type **253** . . . . 80 1·00
709 24p. The Adoration of the Magi 60 60
710 28p. The Flight into Egypt 70 55
711 46p. The Holy Family . . . 1·25 2·75
The designs of Nos. 709/11 are from a 15th-century French Book of Hours.

254 Spring Flowers spelling "Love" in Gaelic

1989. Greetings Stamps. Multicoloured.
712 24p. Type **254** 60 55
713 28p. "The Sonnet" (William Mulready) (vert) 65 55

255 Italian Garden, Garinish Island

1989. National Parks and Gardens. Multicoloured.
714 24p. Type **255** 90 55
715 28p. Lough Veagh, Glenveagh National Park 1·10 55
716 32p. Barnaderg Bay, Connemara National Park 1·25 1·25
717 50p. St. Stephen's Green, Dublin . . . . 1·75 1·75

256 "Silver Stream", 1908

1989. Classic Irish Cars. Multicoloured.
718 24p Type **256** 50 55
719 28p Benz "Comfortable", 1898 . . . . 50 55
720 39p "Thomond", 1929 . . . 1·25 1·50
721 46p Chambers' 8 h.p. model, 1905 . . . . 1·50 1·50

257 Ring-a-ring-a-roses

1989. Europa. Children's Games. Multicoloured.
722 28p. Type **257** 75 75
723 39p. Hopscotch . . . . 1·00 2·25

258 Irish Red Cross Flag (50th anniv)

1989. Anniversaries and Events.
724 **258** 24p. red and black . . . 55 60
725 – 28p. blue, black and yellow . . . . 1·60 1·10
DESIGN: 28p. Circle of twelve stars (third direct elections to European Parliament).

259 Saints Kilian, Totnan and Colman (from 12th-century German manuscript)

1989. 1300th Death Anniv of Saints Kilian, Totnan and Colman.
726 **259** 28p. multicoloured . . . 75 1·10

260 19th-century Mail Coach passing Cashel

1989. Bicentenary of Irish Mail Coach Service.
727 **260** 28p. multicoloured . . . 1·50 75

261 Crest and 19th- century Dividers (150th anniv of Royal Institute of Architects of Ireland)

1989. Anniversaries and Commemorations.
728 – 24p. grey and black . . . 65 55
729 **261** 28p. multicoloured . . . 65 55
730 – 30p. multicoloured . . . 1·75 2·00
731 – 46p. brown . . . . 2·50 2·50
DESIGNS—VERT: 24p. Sean T. O'Kelly (statesman) (drawing by Sean O'Sullivan); 46p. Jawaharlal Nehru (birth centenary). HORIZ: 30p. Margaret Burke-Sheridan (soprano) (portrait by De Gennaro) and scene from "La Boheme" (birth centenary).

262 "NCB Ireland' rounding Cape Horn" (Des Fallon)

1989. First Irish Entry in Whitbread Round the World Yacht Race.
732 **262** 28p. multicoloured . . . 1·25 1·25

263 Willow/Red Grouse
264 "The Annunciation"

1989. Game Birds. Multicoloured.
733 24p. Type **263** . . . . 1·10 55
734 28p. Northern lapwing . . . 1·25 55
735 39p. Eurasian woodcock . . . 1·50 2·25
736 46p. Common pheasant . . . 1·75 2·25
MS737 128 × 92 mm. Nos. 733/6 4·50 6·50

1989. Christmas. Multicoloured.
738 21p. Children decorating crib 75 75
739 24p. Type **264** 95 60
740 28p. "The Nativity" . . . . 1·00 55
741 46p. "The Adoration of the Magi" . . . . 2·00 2·50

265 Logo (Ireland's Presidency of the European Communities)

1990. European Events. Multicoloured.
742 30p. Type **265** . . . . 1·00 60
743 50p. Logo and outline map of Ireland (European Tourism Year) . . . . . . 2·25 3·00

266 Dropping Messages from Balloon

1990. Greetings Stamps.
744 **266** 26p. multicoloured . . . 1·50 1·25
745 – 30p. red, buff and brown 1·50 1·25
DESIGN: 30p. Heart and "Love" drawn in lipstick.

267 Silver Kite Brooch

268 Posy of Flowers

1990. Irish Heritage.
746 **267** 1p. black and blue . . . 10 10
747 2p. black and orange . . 10 10
748 – 4p. black and violet . . 15 10
749 – 5p. black and green . . 20 10
750 – 10p. black and orange 30 25
751 – 20p. black and yellow 50 40
752 – 26p. black and violet . . 1·50 65
809 – 28p. black and orange 80 1·00
754 – 30p. black and blue . . 1·25 90
810 – 32p. black and green . . 50 60
756 – 34p. black and yellow 1·25 1·25
757 – 37p. black and green . . 1·50 1·50
758 – 38p. black and violet . . 1·50 1·50
758b – 40p. black and blue . . 1·50 1·50
759 – 41p. black and orange 1·50 1·50
760 – 44p. brown and yellow 2·50 2·25
760a – 45p. black and violet . . 1·75 2·00
761 – 50p. black and yellow 1·75 1·50
762 – 52p. black and blue . . 2·00 2·00
763 – £1 black and yellow . . 3·00 2·25
764 – £2 black and green . . . 4·50 3·25
765 – £5 black and blue . . . 9·00 8·50
DESIGNS: 4, 5p. Dunamase food vessel; 26, 28p. Lismore crozier; 34, 37, 38, 40p. Gleninsheen collar; 41, 44p. Silver thistle brooch; 45, 50, 52p. Broighter boat. 22 × 38 mm: £5 St. Patrick's Bell Shrine. HORIZ: 10p. Derrinboy armlets; 20p. Gold dress fastener; 30p. Enamelled latchet brooch: 32p. Broighter collar. 38 × 22 mm: £1 Ardagh Chalice; £2 Tara brooch.
For 32p. value as No. 755 but larger, 27 × 20 mm, see No. 823.

1990. Greetings Stamps. Multicoloured.
766 26p. Type **268** . . . . 2·00 2·50
767 26p. Birthday presents . . . 2·00 2·50
768 30p. Flowers, ribbon and horseshoe . . . . 2·00 2·50
769 30p. Balloons . . . . 2·00 2·50

269 Player heading Ball

1990. World Cup Football Championship, Italy. Multicoloured.
770 30p. Type **269** . . . . 1·75 2·00
771 30p. Tackling . . . . 1·75 2·00

270 Battle of the Boyne, 1690

1990. 300th Anniv of the Williamite Wars (1st issue). Multicoloured.
772 30p. Type **270** . . . . 1·75 1·75
773 30p. Siege of Limerick, 1690 1·75 1·75
See also Nos. 806/7.

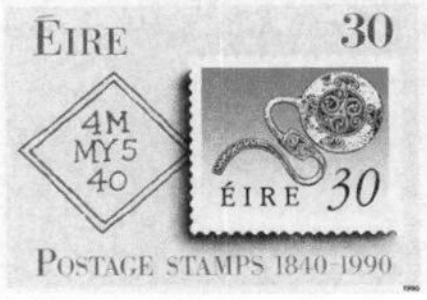

271 1990 Irish Heritage 30p. Stamp and 1840 Postmark

1990. 150th Anniv of the Penny Black. Mult.
774 30p. Type **271** 90 90
775 50p. Definitive stamps of 1922, 1969, 1982 and 1990 1·25 2·00

272 General Post Office, Dublin

274 Narcissus "Foundling" and Japanese Gardens, Tully

273 Medical Missionary giving Injection

1990. Europa Post Office Buildings. Mult.
776 30p. Type **272** . . . . 1·25 60
777 41p. Westport Post Office, County Mayo . . . . . . 2·25 2·75

1990. Anniversaries and Events.
778 **273** 26p. multicoloured . . . 80 40
779 – 30p. black . . . . 1·00 2·75
780 – 50p. multicoloured . . . 1·00 1·75
DESIGNS—VERT: 30p. Michael Collins (statesman) (birth centenary). HORIZ: 50p. Missionaries working at water pump (Irish missionary service).

1990. Garden Flowers. Multicoloured.
781 26p. Type **274** 60 55
782 30p. "Rosa x hibernica" and Mulahide Castle gardens 70 80
783 41p. Primula "Rowallane Rose" and Rowallane garden . . . . 1·40 2·50
784 50p. "Erica erigena" "Irish Dusk" and Palm House, National Botanical Gardens . . . . 1·75 2·75

275 "Playboy of the Western World" (John Synge)

1990. Irish Theatre. Multicoloured.
785 30p. Type **275** . . . . 1·25 1·75
786 30p. "Juno and the Paycock" (Sean O'Casey) . . . 1·25 1·75
787 30p. "The Field" (John Keane) . . . . 1·25 1·75
788 30p. "Waiting for Godot" (Samuel Beckett) . . . . . 1·25 1·75

276 Nativity

277 Hearts in Mail Sack and Postman's Cap

1990. Christmas. Multicoloured.
789 26p. Child praying by bed . . 75 80
790 26p. Type **276** 75 60
791 30p. Madonna and Child . . 1·25 90
792 50p. Adoration of the Magi 2·25 3·50

1991. Greetings Stamps. Multicoloured.
793 26p. Type **277** . . . . 85 1·00
794 30p. Boy and girl kissing . . 90 1·00

278 Starley "Rover" Bicycle, 1886

1991. Early Bicycles. Multicoloured.
795 26p. Type **278** 80 60
796 30p. Child's horse tricycle, 1875 . . . . 90 1·00
797 50p. "Penny Farthing", 1871 1·60 2·50
MS798 113 × 72 mm. Nos. 795/7 3·25 3·75

279 "Cuchulainn" (statue by Oliver Sheppard) and Proclamation

1991. 75th Anniv of Easter Rising.
799 **279** 32p. multicoloured . . . 85 1·40

280 Scene from "La Traviata" (50th anniv of Dublin Grand Opera Society)

1991. "Dublin 1991 European City of Culture". Multicoloured.
800 28p. Type **280** . . . . 1·00 1·00
801 32p. City Hall and European Community emblem . . . 1·10 1·60
802 44p. St. Patrick's Cathedral (800th anniv) . . . . . . 90 1·60
803 52p. Custom House (bicent) (41 × 24 mm) . . . . . 1·00 1·60

281 "Giotto" Spacecraft approaching Halley's Comet

1991. Europa. Europe in Space. Multicoloured.
804 32p. Type **281** . . . . 1·00 1·00
805 44p. Hubble Telescope orbiting Earth . . . . . . 1·50 3·00

282 Siege of Athlone

1991. 300th Anniv of the Williamite Wars (2nd issue). Multicoloured.
806 28p. Type **282** . . . . 1·25 1·75
807 28p. Generals Ginkel and Sarsfield (signatories of Treaty of Limerick) . . . 1·25 1·75

283 John A. Costello (statesman)

1991. Anniversaries.
811 **283** 28p. black . . . . 1·00 70
812 – 32p. multicoloured . . . 1·25 1·00
813 – 52p. multicoloured . . . 1·75 2·50
DESIGNS—VERT: 28p. Type **283** (birth cent) (drawing by Sean O'Sullivan); 32p. "Charles Stewart Parnell" (Sydney Hall) (death cent); HORIZ: 52p. Meeting of United Irishmen.

284 Player on 15th Green, Portmarnock (Walker Cup)

1991. Golf Commemorations. Multicoloured.
814 28p. Type **284** . . . . 1·00 75
815 32p. Logo and golfer of 1900 (cent of Golfing Union of Ireland) (vert) . . . . . . 1·25 1·00

285 Wicklow Cheviot

1991. Irish Sheep. Multicoloured.
816 32p. Type **285** . . . . 1·00 80
817 38p. Donegal Blackface . . . 1·40 1·75
818 52p. Galway (horiz) . . . . 2·00 3·50

286 Boatyard

1991. Fishing Fleet. Multicoloured.
819 28p. Type **286** 70 65
820 32p. Traditional inshore trawlers 80 80
821 44p. Inshore lobster pot boat 1·60 2·50
822 52p. "Veronica" (fish factory ship) . . . . 1·90 2·75

1991. As No. 755, but larger, 27 × 20 mm. Self-adhesive.
823a 32p. black and green . . . 75 1·00

287 The Annunciation

289 Healthy Family on Apple

288 Multicoloured Heart

1991. Christmas.
827 – 28p. multicoloured . . . 1·00 1·00
828 **287** 28p. blue, green and black 1·00 65
829 – 32p. red and black . . . 1·10 75
830 – 52p. multicoloured . . . 2·00 3·25
DESIGNS: No. 827, Three Kings; No. 829, The Nativity; No. 830, Adoration of the Kings:

1992. Greetings Stamps. Multicoloured.
831 28p. Type **288** . . . . 1·00 95
832 32p. "LOVE" at end of rainbow (vert) . . . . . . 1·10 1·10

1992. "Healthy Living" Campaign.
833 **289** 28p. multicoloured . . . 1·25 85

290 Boxing

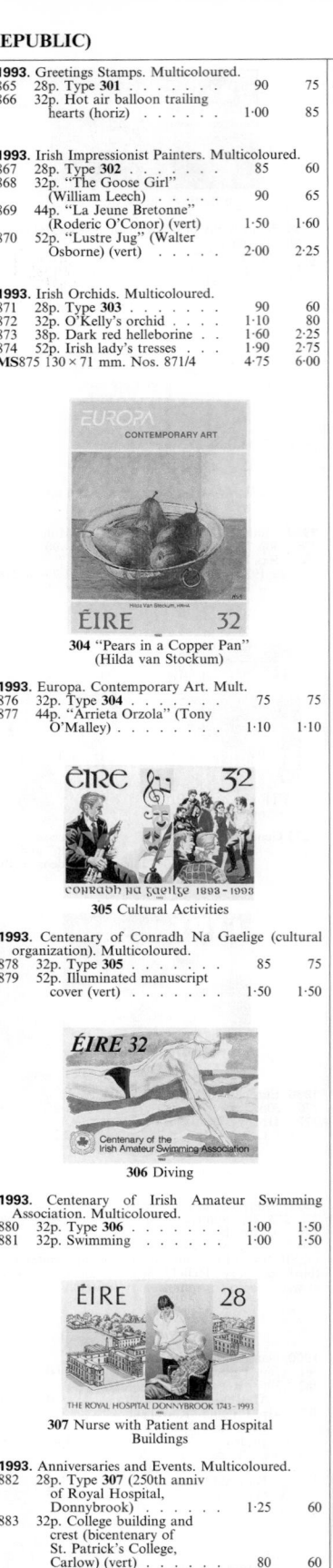

1992. Olympic Games, Barcelona. Mult.
834 32p. Type **290** 75 90
835 44p. Sailing . . . . 1·00 2·25
MS836 130 × 85 mm. Nos. 834/5 × 2 4·75 5·00

291 "Mari" (cog) and 14th-century Map

1992. Irish Maritime Heritage. Multicoloured.
837 32p. Type **291** . . . . 1·00 90
838 52p. "Ovoca" (trawler) and chart (vert) . . . . 1·50 2·75

292 Chamber Logo and Commercial Symbols

1992. Bicentenary of Galway Chamber of Commerce and Industry.
839 **292** 28p. multicoloured . . . 70 85

293 Cliffs and Cove

1992. Greetings Stamps. Multicoloured.
840 28p. Type **293** . . . . 75 1·10
841 28p. Meadow . . . . 75 1·10
842 32p. Fuchsia and honeysuckle 75 1·10
843 32p. Lily pond and dragonfly 75 1·10

294 Fleet of Columbus

1992. Europa. 500th Anniv of Discovery of America by Columbus. Multicoloured.
844 32p. Type **294** . . . . 1·00 90
845 44p. Columbus landing in the New World . . . . 1·50 2·50

295 Irish Immigrants

1992. Irish Immigrants in the Americas. Mult.
846 52p. Type **295** . . . . . . 1·75 1·75
847 52p. Irish soldiers, entertainers and politicians 1·75 1·75

296 Pair of Pine Martens

1992. Endangered Species. Pine Marten. Mult.
848 28p. Type **296** . . . . . . 1·00 70
849 32p. Marten on branch . . . 1·00 80
850 44p. Female with kittens . . 1·60 1·50
851 52p. Marten catching great tit 2·00 1·75

297 "The Rotunda and New Rooms" (James Malton)

1992. Dublin Anniversaries. Multicoloured.
852 28p. Type **297** 70 65
853 32p. Trinity College Library (28 × 45 mm) . . . . . . 1·00 1·00
854 44p. "Charlemont House" . . 1·10 2·00
855 52p. Trinity College main gate (28 × 45 mm) . . . . 1·40 2·25
ANNIVERSARIES: 28, 44p. Bicentenary of Publication of Malton's "Views of Dublin"; 32, 52p. 400th anniv of Founding of Trinity College.

298 European Star and Megalithic Dolmen

1992. Single European Market.
856 **298** 32p. multicoloured . . . 70 80

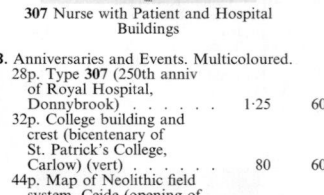

299 Farm Produce

300 "The Annunciation" (from illuminated manuscript)

1992. Irish Agriculture. Multicoloured.
857 32p. Type **299** . . . . . . 1·00 1·25
858 32p. Dairy and beef herds . . 1·00 1·25
859 32p. Harvesting cereals . . . 1·00 1·25
860 32p. Market gardening . . . 1·00 1·25
Nos. 857/60 were printed together, se-tenant, forming a composite design.

1992. Christmas. Multicoloured.
861 28p. Congregation entering church 80 65
862 28p. Type **300** 80 65
863 32p. "Adoration of the Shepherds" (Da Empoli) 1·10 1·00
864 52p. "Adoration of the Magi" (Rottenhammer) . . 1·40 1·50

301 Queen of Hearts

303 Bee Orchid

302 "Evening at Tangier" (Sir John Lavery)

1993. Greetings Stamps. Multicoloured.
865 28p. Type **301** 90 75
866 32p. Hot air balloon trailing hearts (horiz) . . . . . . 1·00 85

1993. Irish Impressionist Painters. Multicoloured.
867 28p. Type **302** 85 60
868 32p. "The Goose Girl" (William Leech) 90 65
869 44p. "La Jeune Bretonne" (Roderic O'Conor) (vert) 1·50 1·60
870 52p. "Lustre Jug" (Walter Osborne) (vert) . . . . . 2·00 2·25

1993. Irish Orchids. Multicoloured.
871 28p. Type **303** 90 60
872 32p. O'Kelly's orchid . . . . 1·10 80
873 38p. Dark red helleborine . . 1·60 2·25
874 52p. Irish lady's tresses . . . 1·90 2·75
MS875 130 × 71 mm. Nos. 871/4 4·75 6·00

304 "Pears in a Copper Pan" (Hilda van Stockum)

1993. Europa. Contemporary Art. Mult.
876 32p. Type **304** 75 75
877 44p. "Arrieta Orzola" (Tony O'Malley) . . . . 1·10 1·10

305 Cultural Activities

1993. Centenary of Conradh Na Gaelige (cultural organization). Multicoloured.
878 32p. Type **305** 85 75
879 52p. Illuminated manuscript cover (vert) . . . . 1·50 1·50

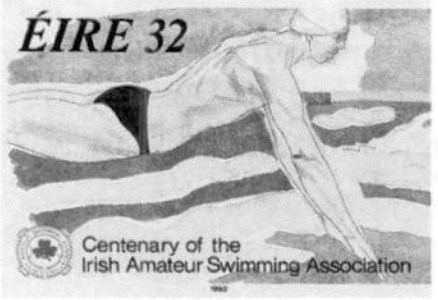

306 Diving

1993. Centenary of Irish Amateur Swimming Association. Multicoloured.
880 32p. Type **306** . . . . . . 1·00 1·50
881 32p. Swimming . . . . . . 1·00 1·50

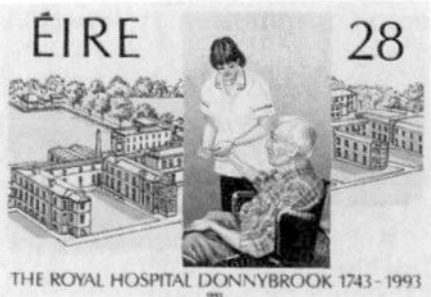

307 Nurse with Patient and Hospital Buildings

1993. Anniversaries and Events. Multicoloured.
882 28p. Type **307** (250th anniv of Royal Hospital, Donnybrook) . . . . . . 1·25 60
883 32p. College building and crest (bicentenary of St. Patrick's College, Carlow) (vert) 80 60
884 44p. Map of Neolithic field system, Ceide (opening of interpretative centre) . . . 1·60 1·40
885 52p. Edward Bunting (musicologist) (150th death anniv) (25 × 42 mm) . . . 1·75 1·60

308 Great Northern Railways Gardner at Drogheda

1993. Irish Buses. Multicoloured.
886 28p. Type **308** 85 70
887 32p. C.I.E. Leyland Titan at College Green, Dublin . . 1·00 70
888 52p. Horse-drawn omnibus at Old Baal's Bridge, Limerick . . . . 1·75 2·50
889 52p. Char-a-banc at Lady's View, Killarney . . . . . 1·75 2·50

309 The Annunciation

1993. Christmas. Multicoloured.
890 28p. The flight into Egypt (vert) 80 80
891 28p. Type **309** 80 55
892 32p. Holy Family 90 70
893 52p. Adoration of the shepherds . . . . 2·00 2·50

310 Biplane skywriting "Love"

1994. Greetings Stamps. Multicoloured.
894 28p. Type **310** 90 75
895 32p. Couple within heart (vert) . . . . 1·00 85

311 Smiling Sun

1994. Greetings Stamps. Multicoloured.
896 32p. Type **311** . . . . 1·00 1·00
897 32p. Smiling daisy . . . . . 1·00 1·00
898 32p. Smiling heart . . . . . 1·00 1·00
899 32p. Smiling rose . . . . . . 1·00 1·00

1994. "Hong Kong '94" International Stamp Exhibition. Chinese New Year ("Year of the Dog").
MS900 137 × 74 mm. Nos. 896/8 4·25 5·00

312 Stylized Logo of Macra na Feirme (50th anniv)

1994. Anniversaries and Events.
901 **312** 28p. gold and blue . . . 75 65
902 – 32p. multicoloured . . . 1·25 75
903 – 38p. multicoloured . . . 2·00 1·75
904 – 52p. black, cobalt and blue . . . . 1·90 2·00
DESIGNS—38 × 35 mm: 32p. "The Taking of Christ" (Caravaggio) (loan of painting to National Gallery). 37½ × 27 mm: 38p. Sir Horace Plunkett with 19th-century milk carts and modern tankers (centenary of Irish Co-operative Organization Society); 52p. Congress emblem (centenary of Irish Congress of Trade Unions).

313 St. Brendan visiting Iceland

1994. Europa. St. Brendan's Voyages. Mult.
905 32p. Type **313** 75 70
906 44p. Discovering Faroe Islands . . . . 1·50 2·00
MS907 82 × 76 mm. Nos. 905/6 2·50 3·25

314 First Meeting of Dail, 1919

1994. Parliamentary Anniversaries. Multicoloured.
908 32p. Type **314** (75th anniv) 90 1·00
909 32p. European Parliament (4th direct elections) . . . 90 1·00

315 Irish and Argentine Footballers

317 Statue of Edmund Rice and Class

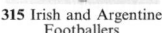

316 "Arctia caja"

1994. Sporting Anniversaries and Events. Multicoloured.
910 32p. Type **315** . . . . 80 1·25
911 32p. Irish and German footballers . . . . 80 1·25
912 32p. Irish and Dutch women's hockey match (horiz) . . . . 1·50 1·25
913 52p. Irish and English women's hockey match (horiz) . . . . 1·75 2·50

ANNIVERSARIES AND EVENTS: Nos. 910/11, World Cup Football Championship, U.S.A.; 912, Women's Hockey World Cup, Dublin; 913, Centenary of Irish Ladies' Hockey Union.

1994. Moths. Mult. (a) Size 37 × 26 mm.
914 28p. Type **316** 65 60
915 32p. "Calamia tridens" . . . 75 70
916 38p. "Saturnia pavonia" . . . 90 1·10
917 52p. "Deilephila elpenor" . . 1·50 2·00
MS918 120 × 71 mm. Nos. 914/17 3·50 4·00

(b) Size 34 × 22 mm. Self-adhesive.
919 32p. "Calamia tridens" . . . 1·10 1·40
920 32p. Type **316** . . . . 1·10 1·40
921 32p. "Deilephila elpenor" . . 1·10 1·40
922 32p. "Saturnia pavonia" . . 1·10 1·40

1994. Anniversaries and Events. Multicoloured.
923 28p. St. Laurence Gate, Drogheda (41½ × 25 mm) 1·25 1·40
924 32p. Type **317** . . . . 1·25 1·40
925 32p. Edmund Burke (politician) . . . . 1·25 1·40
926 52p. Vickers FB-27 Vimy and map (horiz) . . . . 1·25 1·40
927 52p. Eamonn Andrews (broadcaster) . . . . . . 1·50 1·50

ANNIVERSARIES AND EVENTS: No. 923, 800th anniv of Drogheda; 924, 150th death anniv of Edmund Rice (founder of Irish Christian Brothers); 925, 927, The Irish abroad; 926, 75th anniv of Alcock and Brown's first transatlantic flight.

318 George Bernard Shaw (author) and "Pygmalion" Poster

1994. Irish Nobel Prize Winners. Multicoloured.
928 28p. Type **318** 60 90
929 28p. Samuel Beckett (author) and pair of boots 60 90
930 32p. Sean MacBride (human rights campaigner) and peace doves 70 90
931 52p. William Butler Yeats (poet) and poem . . . . . 1·10 2·00

319 "The Annunciation" (ivory plaque)

320 Tree of Hearts

1994. Christmas. Multicoloured.
932 28p. Nativity 70 60
933 28p. Type **319** 70 60
934 32p. "Flight into Egypt" (wood carving) 80 70
935 52p. "Nativity" (ivory plaque) . . . . 1·10 2·00

1995. Greetings Stamps. Multicoloured.
936 32p. Type **320** . . . . 95 1·25
937 32p. Teddy bear holding balloon . . . . 95 1·25
938 32p. Clown juggling hearts 95 1·25
939 32p. Bouquet of flowers . . . 95 1·25

1995. Chinese New Year ("Year of the Pig").
MS940 137 × 74 mm. Nos. 936, 938/9 3·00 3·50

321 West Clare Railway Steam Locomotive No. 1 "Kilkee" at Kilrush Station

1995. Transport. Narrow Gauge Railways. Mult.
941 28p. Type **321** 75 60
942 32p. County Donegal Railway tank locomotive No. 2 "Blanche" at Donegal Station 90 90
943 38p. Cork and Muskerry Railway tank locomotive No. 1 "City of Cork" on Western Road, Cork . . . 1·25 1·75
944 52p. Cavan and Leitrim Railway tank locomotive No. 3 "Lady Edith" on Arigna Tramway . . . . . 1·75 2·50
MS945 127 × 83 mm. Nos. 941/4 4·50 5·50

322 English and Irish Rugby Players

1995. World Cup Rugby Championship, South Africa. Multicoloured.
946 32p. Type **322** 75 75
947 52p. Australian and Irish players . . . . 1·25 1·75
MS948 108 × 77 mm. £1 Type **322** 4·25 3·50

323 Peace Dove and Skyscrapers

1995. Europa. Peace and Freedom. Mult. (a) Size 38 × 26 mm. Ordinary gum.
949 32p. Type **323** 85 75
950 44p. Peace dove and map of Europe and North Africa 1·40 2·00

(b) Size 34½ × 23 mm. Self-adhesive.
951 32p. Type **323** 90 90
952 32p. As No. 950 . . . . . . 90 90

324 Soldiers of the Irish Brigade and Memorial Cross

325 Irish Brigade, French Army, 1745

1995. 250th Anniv of Battle of Fontenoy.
953 **324** 32p. multicoloured . . . 80 80

1995. Military Uniforms. Multicoloured.
954 28p. Type **325** 70 60
955 32p. Tercio Irlanda, Spanish army in Flanders, 1605 . . 80 75
956 32p. Royal Dublin Fusiliers, 1914 . . . . 80 75
957 38p. St. Patrick's Battalion, Papal Army, 1860 . . . . 1·10 1·25
958 52p. 69th Regiment, New York State Militia, 1861 1·60 1·75

326 Guglielmo Marconi and Original Radio Transmitter

1995. Centenary of Radio. Multicoloured.
959 32p. Type **326** . . . . 1·40 1·50
960 32p. Traditional radio dial 1·40 1·50

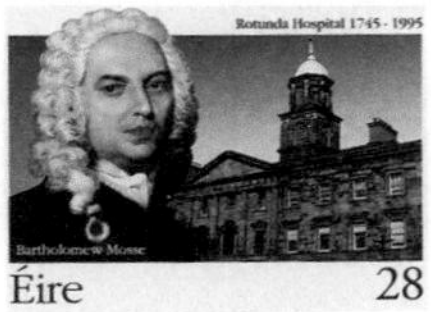

327 Bartholomew Mosse (founder) and Hospital Building

1995. Anniversaries. Multicoloured.
961 28p. Type **327** (250th anniv of Rotunda Hospital) . . . 70 70
962 32p. St. Patrick's House, Maynooth College (bicent) (25 × 41 mm) 80 80
963 32p. Laurel wreath and map of Europe (50th anniv of end of Second World War) 80 80
964 52p. Geological map of Ireland (150th anniv of Geological Survey of Ireland) (32½ × 32½ mm) . . 1·25 1·50

328 Natterjack Toad

1995. Reptiles and Amphibians. Multicoloured. (a) Size 40 × 27 mm. Ordinary gum.
965 32p. Type **328** . . . . 1·00 1·25
966 32p. Common lizards . . . . 1·00 1·25
967 32p. Smooth newts . . . . . 1·00 1·25
968 32p. Common frog . . . . . 1·00 1·25

(b) Size 34 × 23 mm. Self-adhesive.
969 32p. Type **328** . . . . 1·00 1·25
970 32p. Common lizard . . . . 1·00 1·25
971 32p. Smooth newts . . . . . 1·00 1·25
972 32p. Common frog . . . . . 1·00 1·25

Nos. 965/8 were printed together, se-tenant, with the backgrounds forming a composite design.

329 "Crinum moorei"

1995. Bicentenary of National Botanic Gardens, Glasnevin. Flowers. Multicoloured.
973 32p. Type **329** . . . . . . 1·50 70
974 38p. "Sarracenia x moorei" 1·25 1·10
975 44p. "Solanum crispum" "Glasnevin" . . . . 1·50 2·50

330 Anniversary Logo and Irish United Nations Soldier

1995. 50th Anniv of United Nations. Mult.
976 32p. Type **330** 80 70
977 52p. Emblem and "UN" . . 1·25 1·40

331 "Adoration of the Shepherds" (illuminated manuscript) (Benedotto Bardone)

1995. Christmas. Multicoloured.
978 28p. Adoration of the Magi 1·00 65
979 28p. Type **331** . . . . 1·00 65
980 32p. "Adoration of the Magi" (illuminated manuscript) (Bardone) . . 1·10 70
981 52p. "The Holy Family" (illuminated manuscript) (Bardone) . . . . 1·90 2·75

332 Zig and Zag on Heart

333 Wheelchair Athlete

1996. Greetings Stamps. Multicoloured.
982 32p. Type **332** . . . . 1·25 75
983 32p. Zig and Zag waving . . 2·25 2·50
984 32p. Zig and Zag in space suits . . . . 2·25 2·50
985 32p. Zig and Zag wearing hats . . . . 2·25 2·50

1996. Chinese New Year ("Year of the Rat").
MS986 130 × 74 mm. Nos. 982, 984/5 3·00 3·00

1996. Olympic and Paralympic Games, Atlanta. Multicoloured.
987 28p. Type **333** 70 65
988 32p. Running 80 80
989 32p. Throwing the discus . . 80 80
990 32p. Single kayak 80 80

334 Before the Start, Fairyhouse Race Course

1996. Irish Horse Racing. Multicoloured.
991 28p. Type **334** 70 65
992 32p. Steeplechase, Punchestown 80 80
993 32p. On the Flat, The Curragh 80 80
994 38p. Steeplechase, Galway . . 1·25 1·25
995 52p. After the race, Leopardstown . . . . . . 1·50 1·50

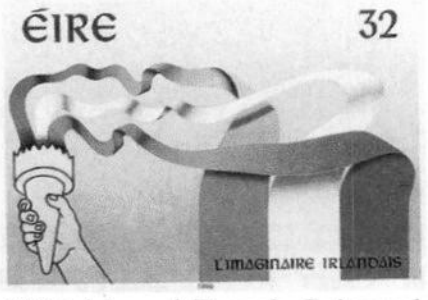

335 Irish and French Coloured Ribbons merging

1996. "L'Imaginaire Irlandais" Festival of Contemporary Irish Arts, France.
996 **335** 32p. multicoloured . . . 80 80

336 Louie Bennett (suffragette)

1996. Europa. Famous Women. (a) Size 40 × 29 mm. Ordinary gum.
997 **336** 32p. violet 80 70
998 – 44p. green . . . . 1·10 1·25

(b) Size 34 × 23 mm. Self-adhesive.
999 **336** 32p. violet . . . . . . 1·10 1·25
1000 – 32p. green . . . . 1·10 1·25

DESIGN: Nos. 998, 1000, Lady Augusta Gregory (playwright).

337 Newgrange Passage Tomb (Boyne Valley World Heritage Site)

1996. Anniversaries and Events.
1001 **337** 28p. brown and black . . 1·00 60
1002 – 32p. multicoloured . . . 1·10 90
DESIGN: 32p. Children playing (50th anniv of U.N.I.C.E.F.).

1996. "CHINA '96" 9th Asian International Stamp Exhibition, Peking. Sheet 120 × 95 mm, containing Nos. 992/3.
MS1003 32p. Steeplechase, Punchestown; 32p. On the Flat, The Curragh . . . . 11·00 11·00

338 Stanley Woods

1996. Isle of Man Tourist Trophy Motor Cycle Races. Irish Winners. Multicoloured.
1004 32p. Type **338** 80 70
1005 44p. Artie Bell . . . . . . 1·25 1·50
1006 50p. Alec Bennett . . . . . 1·50 1·75
1007 52p. Joey and Robert Dunlop . . . . 1·50 1·75
MS1008 100 × 70 mm. 50p. As 52p. 1·50 1·75

339 Michael Davitt (founder of The Land League)

1996. Anniversaries and Events. Multicoloured.
1009 28p. Type **339** (150th birth anniv) 80 60
1010 32p. Presidency logo (Ireland's Presidency of European Union) (horiz) 80 70
1011 38p. Thomas McLaughlin (hydro-electric engineer) and Ardnacrusha Power Station (birth centenary) (horiz) . . . . 1·25 1·10
1012 52p. Mechanical peat harvester (50th anniv of Bord na Mona) (horiz) . . 1·75 1·75

340 "Ciara" (coastal patrol vessel)

1996. 50th Anniv of Irish Naval Service. Multicoloured.
1013 32p. Type **340** 80 70
1014 44p. "Cliona" (corvette) . . 1·40 1·50
1015 52p. "M-1" (motor torpedo boat) (vert) . . . . 1·50 1·60

341 Blind Woman with Child

1996. People with Disabilities. Multicoloured.
1016 28p. Type **341** . . . . . . 1·10 1·10
1017 28p. Man in wheelchair playing bowls . . . . . . 1·10 1·10

342 Green-winged Teal

1996. Freshwater Ducks. Multicoloured.
1018 32p. Type **342** . . . . . . 1·00 70
1019 38p. Common shoveler . . 1·10 1·25
1020 44p. European wigeon . . . 1·25 1·75
1021 52p. Mallard . . . . 1·60 2·00
MS1022 127 × 85 mm. Nos. 1018/21 4·50 5·50

343 "Man of Aran"

1996. Centenary of Irish Cinema. Multicoloured.
1023 32p. Type **343** 85 90
1024 32p. "My Left Foot" . . . 85 90
1025 32p. "The Commitments" 85 90
1026 32p. "The Field" 85 90

344 Visit of the Magi

1996. Christmas. Designs from 16th-century "Book of Hours" (Nos.1028/30). Multicoloured.
1027 28p. The Holy Family . . . 75 60
1028 28p. Type **344** 60 60
1029 32p. The Annunciation . . 80 75
1030 52p. The Shepherds receiving new of Christ's birth . . . . 1·40 1·60

345 Black-billed Magpie ("Magpie") **346** Pair of Doves

1997. Birds. Ordinary gum. Multicoloured. (a) Size 21 × 24 mm or 24 × 21 mm.
1031 1p. Type **345** 10 50
1032 2p. Northern gannet ("Gannet") (vert) 15 50
1033 4p. Corn crake (vert) . . . 20 20
1034 5p. Wood pigeon (horiz) . . 20 50
1035 10p. River kingfisher ("Kingfisher") (vert) . . . 30 70
1036 20p. Northern lapwing ("Lapwing") (vert) . . . 50 45
1037 28p. Blue tit (horiz) . . . . 1·50 50
1038 30p. Blackbird (vert) 70 50
1039 30p. Goldcrest (vert) . . . . 1·25 1·25
1040 30p. Common stonechat ("Stonechat") (vert) . . . 70 75
1041 30p. As No. 1036 . . . . . 70 75
1042 30p. As No. 1032 . . . . . 70 75
1043 30p. As No. 1033 . . . . . 70 75
1044 30p. Type **345** 70 75
1045 30p. As No. 1035 . . . . . 70 75
1046 30p. Peregrine falcon (vert) 70 75
1047 30p. Barn owl (vert) 70 75
1048 30p. European robin ("Robin") (vert) 70 75
1049 30p. Song thrush (vert) . . 70 75
1050 30p. Winter wren ("Wren") (vert) 70 75
1051 30p. Pied wagtail (vert) . . 70 75
1052 30p. Atlantic puffin ("Puffin") (vert) 70 75
1053 32p. As No. 1048 . . . . . 1·10 55
1054 35p. As No. 1040 . . . . . 90 75
1055 40p. Ringed plover (horiz) 1·00 85
1056 44p. As No. 1052 . . . . . 2·25 85
1057 45p. As No. 1049 . . . . . 2·25 1·75
1058 50p. Northern sparrow hawk ("European Sparrow Hawk") (horiz) 1·50 1·75
1059 52p. As No. 1047 . . . . . 2·00 1·00

(b) Size 24 × 45 mm or 45 × 24 mm.
1060 £1 White-fronted goose ("Greenland White-fronted Goose") (vert) . . 2·00 1·60
1061 £2 Northern pintail ("Pintail") (horiz) . . . . 3·75 3·50
1062 £5 Common shelduck ("Shelduck") (vert) . . . 8·50 9·00

(c) Size 17 × 21 mm or 21 × 17 mm.
1080 4p. Corn crake . . . . . . 65 1·00
1081 5p. Wood pigeon 55 75
1082 30p. Blackbird . . . . . . 1·00 1·00
1083 30p. Goldcrest . . . . . . 1·00 1·00
1084 32p. European robin ("Robin") . . . . 1·00 1·00
1085 32p. Peregrine falcon . . . 1·25 1·25

(d) Size 25 × 30 mm. Self-adhesive.
1086 30p. Goldcrest . . . . . . 1·00 1·10
1087 30p. Blackbird 75 80
1088 32p. Peregrine falcon . . . 2·00 2·50
1089 32p. European robin ("Robin") . . . . 2·00 2·50

1997. Greetings Stamps. Multicoloured.
1100 32p. Type **346** 85 50
1101 32p. Cow jumping over moon . . . . 1·10 1·10
1102 32p. Pig going to market . . 1·10 1·10
1103 32p. Cockerel . . . . 1·10 1·10

1997. "HONG KONG '97" International Stamp Exhibition. Chinese New Year ("Year of the Ox").
MS1104 124 × 74 mm. Nos. 1101/3 2·40 2·40

347 Troops on Parade

1997. 75th Anniv of Irish Free State. Mult.
1105 28p. Page from the "Annals of the Four Masters", quill and 1944 ½d. O'Clery stamp 55 55
1106 32p. Type **347** 60 65
1107 32p. The Dail, national flag and Constitution 60 65
1108 32p. Athlete, footballer and hurling player 60 65
1109 32p. Singer, violinist and bodhran player 60 65
1110 32p. Stained glass window and 1929 9d. O'Connell stamp 60 60
1111 32p. 1923 2d. map stamp and G.P.O., Dublin . . . 60 60
1112 52p. Police personnel and Garda badge . . . . . . 1·00 1·25
1113 52p. The Four Courts and Scales of Justice . . . . 1·00 1·25
1114 52p. Currency, blueprint and food-processing plant . . 1·00 1·25
1115 52p. Books, palette and Seamus Heaney manuscript . . . . 1·00 1·25
1116 52p. Air Lingus airliner and 1965 1s.5d. air stamp . . 1·00 1·25
MS1117 174 × 209 mm. As Nos. 1105/16, but each with face value of 32p. . . . . 8·50 9·00

348 Grey Seals

1997. Marine Mammals. Multicoloured.
1118 28p. Type **348** 75 60
1119 32p. Bottle-nosed dolphins 85 80
1120 44p. Harbour porpoises (horiz) . . . . 1·25 1·40
1121 52p. Killer whale (horiz) . . 1·40 1·50
MS1122 150 × 68 mm. As Nos. 1118/21 . . . . 6·00 6·00

349 Dublin Silver Penny of 997

1997. Millenary of Irish Coinage.
1123 **349** 32p. multicoloured . . . 65 65

350 "The Children of Lir"

1997. Europa. Tales and Legends. Multicoloured. (a) Size 38 × 28 mm. Ordinary gum.
1124 32p. Type **350** 75 60
1125 44p. Oisin and Niamh . . . 1·10 2·00

(b) Size 36 × 25 mm. Self-adhesive.
1126 32p. Type **350** 70 70
1127 32p. Oisin and Niamh . . . 70 70

351 Emigrants waiting to board Ship

1997. 150th Anniv of The Great Famine.
1128 **351** 28p. blue, red and stone 1·00 60
1129 – 32p. orange, blue & stone . . . . 1·25 70
1130 – 52p. brown, blue & stone 1·75 1·40
DESIGNS: 32p. Family and dying child; 52p. Irish Society of Friends soup kitchen.

1997. "Pacific '97" International Stamp Exhibition, San Francisco. Sheet 100 × 70 mm, containing No. 1061. Multicoloured.
MS1131 £2 Pintail (48 × 26 mm) 4·50 5·00

352 Kate O'Brien (novelist) (birth centenary)

1997. Anniversaries. Multicoloured.
1132 28p. Type **352** 60 90
1133 28p. St. Columba crossing to Iona (stained glass window) (1400th death anniv) 60 90
1134 32p. "Daniel O'Connell" (J. Haverty) (politician) (150th death anniv) (27 × 49 mm) 70 70
1135 52p. "John Wesley" (N. Hone) (founder of Methodism) (250th anniv of first visit to Ireland) . . 1·25 2·25

353 The Baily Lighthouse

1997. Lighthouses. Multicoloured.
1136 32p. Type **353** . . . . . . 1·00 80
1137 32p. Tarbert . . . . 1·00 80
1138 38p. Hookhead (vert) . . . 1·10 85
1139 50p. The Fastnet (vert) . . . 1·40 1·25

354 Commemorative Cross **355** Dracula and Bat

1997. Ireland–Mexico Joint Issue. 150th Anniv of Mexican St. Patrick's Battalion.
1140 **354** 32p. multicoloured . . . 55 60

1997. Centenary of Publication of Bram Stoker's "Dracula". Multicoloured.
1141 28p. Type **355** 60 55
1142 32p. Dracula and female victim 65 60

1143 38p. Dracula emerging from coffin (horiz) 80 90
1144 52p. Dracula and wolf (horiz) . . . . 1·10 1·50
MS1145 150 × 90 mm. As Nos. 1141/4 . . . . 4·25 4·50

356 "The Nativity" (Kevin Kelly) **357** Christmas Tree

1997. Christmas. Multicoloured. (a) Stained-glass Windows. Ordinary gum.
1146 28p. Type **356** 70 55
1147 32p. The Nativity (Sarah Purser and A. E. Child) 80 65
1148 52p. The Nativity (A. E. Child) . . . . 1·50 1·40

(b) Self-adhesive.
1149 28p. Type **357** 55 65

358 Holding Heart

1998. Greetings Stamps (1st series). Designs based on the "love is ..." cartoon characters of Kim Casali. Multicoloured.
1150 32p. Type **358** 70 50
1151 32p. Receiving letter . . . . 70 1·00
1152 32p. Sitting on log . . . . 70 1·00
1153 32p. With birthday presents 70 1·00
See also Nos. 1173/6.

1998. Chinese New Year ("Year of the Tiger").
MS1154 124 × 73 mm. Nos. 1151/3 2·50 2·75

359 Lady Mary Heath and Avro Avian over Pyramids

1998. Pioneers of Irish Aviation. Multicoloured.
1155 28p. Type **359** 60 55
1156 32p. Col. James Fitzmaurice and Junkers W.33 "Bremen" over Labrador 65 60
1157 44p. Captain J. P. Saul and Fokker F.VIIa/3m "Southern Cross" . . . . 1·25 1·25
1158 52p. Captain Charles Blair and Sikorsky V-s 44 (flying boat) . . . . . . 1·50 1·50

360 Show-jumping

1998. Equestrian Sports. Multicoloured.
1159 30p. Type **360** 80 60
1160 32p. Three-day eventing . . 85 65
1161 40p. Gymkhana . . . . . . 1·00 1·25
1162 45p. Dressage (vert) . . . . 1·00 1·25
MS1163 126 × 84 mm. Nos. 1159/62 3·25 3·25

361 Figure of "Liberty"

1998. Bicentenary of United Irish Rebellion. Mult.
1164 30p. Type **361** . . . . . 1·00 1·00
1165 30p. United Irishman . . . 1·00 1·00
1166 30p. French soldiers . . . . 1·00 1·00
1167 45p. Wolfe Tone . . . . . 1·00 1·25
1168 45p. Henry Joy McCracken 1·00 1·25

362 Gathering of the Boats, Kinvara

1998. Europa. Festivals. Multicoloured. (a) Size 39 × 27 mm.
1169 30p. Type **362** . . . . . . 1·25 80
1170 40p. Puck Fair, Killorglin 1·50 95

(b) Size 34 × 23 mm. Self-adhesive.
1171 30p. Type **362** 65 90
1172 30p. Puck Fair, Killorglin 65 90

1998. Greetings Stamps (2nd series). As Nos. 1105/8, but with changed face value. Multicoloured.
1173 30p. As No. 1153 . . . . . 70 95
1174 30p. As No. 1152 . . . . . 70 95
1175 30p. As No. 1151 . . . . . 70 95
1176 30p. Type **358** 70 95

363 Cyclists rounding Bend

1998. Visit of "Tour de France" Cycle Race to Ireland. Multicoloured.
1177 30p. Type **363** 75 85
1178 30p. Two cyclists ascending hill 75 85
1179 30p. "Green jersey" cyclist and other competitor . . 75 85
1180 30p. "Yellow jersey" (race leader) 75 85

364 Voter and Local Councillors of 1898

1998. Democracy Anniversaries. Multicoloured.
1181 30p. Type **364** (cent of Local Government (Ireland) Act) 60 60
1182 32p. European Union flag and harp symbol (25th anniv of Ireland's entry into European Community) 65 65
1183 35p. Woman voter and suffragettes, 1898 (cent of women's right to vote in local elections) 75 75
1184 45p. Irish Republic flag (50th anniv of Republic of Ireland Act) . . . . . . 1·00 1·25

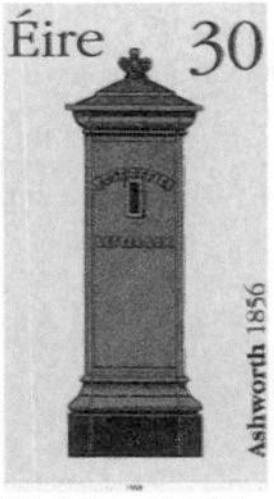

365 "Asgard II" (cadet brigantine) **366** Ashworth Pillbox (1856)

1998. "Cutty Sark" International Tall Ships Race, Dublin. Multicoloured. (a) Ordinary gum.
1185 30p. Type **365** (26 × 38 mm) 70 70
1186 30p. U.S.C.G. "Eagle" (cadet barque) (26 × 38 mm) 70 70
1187 45p. "Boa Esperanza" (replica caravel) (38 × 26 mm) . . . . . . 1·00 1·00
1188 £1 "Royalist" (training brigantine) (38 × 26 mm) 1·90 2·50

(b) Self-adhesive.
1189 30p. "Boa Esperanza" (34 × 23 mm) 65 70
1190 30p. Type **365** (23 × 34 mm) 65 70
1191 30p. U.S.C.G. "Eagle" (23 × 34 mm) 65 70
1192 30p. "Royalist" (34 × 23 mm) 65 70

1998. Irish Postboxes. Multicoloured.
1193 30p. Type **366** 75 85
1194 30p. Irish Free State wallbox (1922) 75 85
1195 30p. Double pillarbox (1899) 75 85
1196 30p. Penfold pillarbox (1866) 75 85

367 Mary Immaculate College, Limerick (centenary)

1998. Anniversaries. Multicoloured.
1197 30p. Type **367** 75 60
1198 40p. Newtown School, Waterford (bicent) (vert) 1·00 1·10
1199 45p. Trumpeters (50th anniv of Universal Declaration of Human Rights) . . . . 1·10 1·25

1998. "Portugal '98" International Stamp Exhibition, Lisbon. Sheet 101 × 71 mm, containing design as No. 1187.
MS1200 £2 "Boa Esperanza" (caravel) (horiz) . . . . 4·50 5·00

368 Cheetah

1998. Endangered Animals. Multicoloured.
1201 30p. Type **368** . . . . . . 1·40 1·00
1202 30p. Scimitar-horned oryx 1·40 1·00
1203 40p. Golden lion tamarin (vert) . . . . 1·40 1·00
1204 45p. Tiger (vert) . . . . . 1·60 1·25
MS1205 150 × 90 mm. As Nos. 1201/4 . . . . 4·25 4·25

369 The Holy Family **370** Choir Boys

1998. Christmas. Mult. (a) Ordinary gum.
1206 30p. Type **369** 70 60
1207 32p. Shepherds 75 65
1208 45p. Three Kings . . . . . 1·00 1·75

(b) Self-adhesive.
1209 30p. Type **370** 65 60

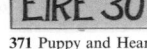

371 Puppy and Heart **372** Micheal Mac Liammoir

1999. Greetings Stamps. Pets. Multicoloured.
1210 30p. Type **371** 65 50
1211 30p. Kitten and ball of wool 65 75
1212 30p. Goldfish 65 75
1213 30p. Rabbit with lettuce leaf 65 75

1999. Chinese New Year ("Year of the Rabbit").
MS1214 124 × 74 mm. Nos. 1211/13 2·25 2·25

1999. Irish Actors and Actresses.
1215 **372** 30p. black and brown . . 65 60
1216 – 45p. black and green . . 1·00 1·10
1217 – 50p. black and blue . . 1·00 1·25
DESIGNS: 45p. Siobhan McKenna, 50p. Noel Purcell.

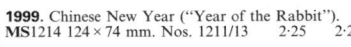

373 Irish Emigrant Ship

1999. Ireland–U.S.A. Joint Issue. Irish Emigration.
1218 **373** 45p. multicoloured . . . 1·25 1·00

374 "Polly Woodside" (barque) **375** Sean Lemass

1999. Maritime Heritage. Multicoloured.
1219 30p. Type **374** 55 60
1220 35p. "Ilen" (schooner) . . . 65 70
1221 45p. R.N.L.I. Cromer class lifeboat (horiz) 80 85
1222 £1 "Titanic" (liner) (horiz) 2·00 2·00
MS1223 150 × 90 mm. No. 1222 × 2 3·00 3·25

1999. Ireland—Australia Joint Issue. "Polly Woodside" (barque). Sheet 137 × 72 mm. Multicoloured.
MS1224 45c. Type **603** of Australia; 30p. Type **374** (No. **MS**1224 was sold at 52p. in Ireland) . . . . 1·25 1·40
No. **MS**1224 includes the "Australia '99" emblem on the sheet margin and was postally valid in Ireland to the value of 30p.
The same miniature sheet was also available in Australia.

1999. Birth Centenary of Sean Lemass (politician).
1225 **375** 30p. black and green . . 1·00 65

376 European Currency Emblem

1999. Introduction of Single European Currency.
1226 **376** 30p. multicoloured . . . 75 65
The face value of No. 1226 is shown in both Irish and euro currency.

377 European Flags **379** Father James Cullen and St. Francis Xavier Church, Dublin

378 Whooper Swans, Kilcolman Nature Reserve

1999. 50th Anniv of Council of Europe.
1227 **377** 45p. multicoloured . . . 1·00 1·00

1999. Europa. Parks and Gardens. Multicoloured. (a) Size 36 × 26 mm. Ordinary gum.
1228 30p. Type **378** 90 50
1229 40p. Fallow deer, Phoenix Park . . . . 1·00 1·00

(b) Size 34 × 23 mm. Self-adhesive.
1230 30p. Type **378** 65 65
1231 30p. Fallow deer, Phoenix Park 65 65

1999. Centenary of Pioneer Total Abstinence Association.
1232 **379** 32p. brown, bistre and black 70 65

380 Elderly Man and Child using Computer

1999. International Year of Older Persons.
1233 **380** 30p. multicoloured . . . 70 65

381 Postal Van, 1922

1999. 125th Anniv of Universal Postal Union.

1234 **381**	30p. green and deep green	1·00	1·00
1235 –	30p. multicoloured	1·00	1·00

DESIGN: No. 1235, Modern postal lorries.

382 Danno Keeffe

1999. Gaelic Athletic Association "Millennium Football Team". Multicoloured. (a) Size 37 × 25 mm. Ordinary gum.

1236	30p. Type **382**	60	70
1237	30p. Enda Colleran	60	70
1238	30p. Joe Keohane	60	70
1239	30p. Sean Flanagan	60	70
1240	30p. Sean Murphy	60	70
1241	30p. John Joe Reilly	60	70
1242	30p. Martin O'Connell	60	70
1243	30p. Mick O'Connell	60	70
1244	30p. Tommy Murphy	60	70
1245	30p. Sean O'Neill	60	70
1246	30p. Sean Purcell	60	70
1247	30p. Pat Spillane	60	70
1248	30p. Mikey Sheehy	60	70
1249	30p. Tom Langan	60	70
1250	30p. Kevin Heffernan	60	70

(b) Size 33 × 23 mm. Self-adhesive.

1251	30p. Type **382**	1·50	2·00
1252	30p. Enda Colleran	65	80
1253	30p. Joe Keohane	1·50	2·00
1254	30p. Sean Flanagan	65	80
1255	30p. Sean Murphy	1·50	2·00
1256	30p. John Joe Reilly	55	60
1257	30p. Martin O'Connell	55	60
1258	30p. Mick O'Connell	1·50	2·00
1259	30p. Tommy Murphy	65	80
1260	30p. Sean O'Neill	55	60
1261	30p. Sean Purcell	65	80
1262	30p. Pat Spillane	65	80
1263	30p. Mikey Sheehy	65	80
1264	30p. Tom Langan	65	80
1265	30p. Kevin Heffernan	55	60

383 Douglas DC-3

1999. Commercial Aviation. Multicoloured.

1266	30p. Type **383**	65	50
1267	32p. Britten Norman Islander	75	55
1268	40p. Boeing 707	80	85
1269	45p. Lockheed Constellation	90	1·00

384 Mammoth

386 Grace Kelly (American actress)

385 Holy Family

1999. Extinct Irish Animals. Multicoloured. (a) Size 26 × 38 mm (vert) or 38 × 26 mm (horiz). Ordinary gum.

1270	30p. Type **384**	70	60
1271	30p. Giant deer	70	60
1272	45p. Wolves (horiz)	90	1·00
1273	45p. Brown bear (horiz)	90	1·00
MS1274	150 × 63 mm. Nos. 1270/3	2·50	2·75

(b) Size 33 × 23 mm (horiz) or 22 × 34 mm (vert). Self-adhesive.

1275	30p. Brown bear (horiz)	70	85
1276	30p. Type **384**	70	85
1277	30p. Wolves (horiz)	70	85
1278	30p. Giant deer	70	85

1999. Christmas. Children's Nativity Plays. Mult. (a) Size 35 × 25 mm. Ordinary gum.

1279	30p. Type **385**	60	50
1280	32p. Visit of the Shepherds	65	55
1281	45p. Adoration of the Magi	1·25	1·25

(b) Size 16 × 26 mm. Self-adhesive.

1282	30p. Angel	55	50

1999. New Millennium (1st issue). Famous People of the 20th Century. Multicoloured.

1283	30p. Type **386**	1·50	1·75
1284	30p. Jesse Owens (American athlete)	1·50	1·75
1285	30p. John F. Kennedy (former American President)	1·50	1·75
1286	30p. Mother Teresa (missionary)	1·50	1·75
1287	30p. John McCormack (tenor)	1·50	1·75
1288	30p. Nelson Mandela (South African statesman)	1·50	1·75

See also Nos. 1289/94, 1300/5, 1315/20, 1377/82 and 1383/88.

387 Ruined Castle (Norman Invasion, 1169)

2000. New Millennium (2nd issue). Irish Historic Events. Multicoloured.

1289	30p. Type **387**	1·00	1·25
1290	30p. Flight of the Earls, 1607	1·00	1·25
1291	30p. Opening of Irish Parliament, 1782	1·00	1·25
1292	30p. Eviction (formation of the Land League)	1·00	1·25
1293	30p. First four Irish Prime Ministers (Irish Independence)	1·00	1·25
1294	30p. Irish soldier and personnel carrier (U.N. Peace-keeping)	1·00	1·25

388 Frog Prince

389 Revd. Nicholas Callan (electrical scientist)

2000. Greetings Stamps. Mythical Creatures. Multicoloured.

1295	30p. Type **388**	55	60
1296	30p. Pegasus	55	60
1297	30p. Unicorn	55	60
1298	30p. Dragon	55	60

2000. Chinese New Year ("Year of the Dragon").

MS1299	124 × 74 mm. Nos. 1296/8	1·75	2·00

2000. New Millennium (3rd issue). Discoveries. Multicoloured.

1300	30p. Type **389**	1·25	1·40
1301	30p. Birr Telescope	1·25	1·40
1302	30p. Thomas Edison (inventor of light bulb)	1·25	1·40
1303	30p. Albert Einstein (mathematical physicist)	1·25	1·40
1304	30p. Marie Curie (physicist)	1·25	1·40
1305	30p. Galileo Galilei (astronomer and mathematician)	1·25	1·40

390 "Jeanie Johnston" (emigrant ship)

2000. Completion of "Jeanie Johnston" Replica.

1306 **390**	30p. multicoloured	70	50

391 "Building Europe"

392 Oscar Wilde

2000. Europa. (a) 25½ × 36½ mm.

1307 **391**	32p. multicoloured	80	55

(b) 22 × 34 mm. Self-adhesive.

1308 **391**	30p. multicoloured	75	50

DENOMINATION. From No. 1309 to 1465 some Irish stamps are denominated both in Irish pounds and in euros. As no cash for the latter is in circulation, the catalogue continues to use the pound value.

2000. Death Centenary of Oscar Wilde (writer). Multicoloured.

1309	30p. Type **392**	90	1·00
1310	30p. *The Happy Prince*	90	1·00
1311	30p. Lady Bracknell from *The Importance of being Earnest*	90	1·00
1312	30p. *The Picture of Dorian Gray*	90	1·00
MS1313	150 × 190 mm. £2 Type **392**	3·75	4·00

A further 30p. exists in a design similar to Type **392**, but 29 × 29 mm, printed in sheets of 20, each stamp having a se-tenant half-stamp size label attached at right inscribed "Oscar". These sheets could be personalized by the addition of a photograph in place of the inscription on the labels. Such stamps are not listed as they were not available at face value, the sheets of 20 containing the "Oscar" labels being sold for £10.

393 Ludwig van Beethoven (German composer)

394 Running

2000. New Millennium (4th issue). The Arts. Mult.

1315	30p. Type **393**	1·00	1·25
1316	30p. Dame Ninette de Valois (ballet director)	1·00	1·25
1317	30p. James Joyce (author)	1·00	1·25
1318	30p. "Mona Lisa" (Leonardo da Vinci)	1·00	1·25
1319	30p. "Lady Lavery" (Sir John Lavery)	1·00	1·25
1320	30p. William Shakespeare (playwright)	1·00	1·25

2000. Olympic Games, Sydney. Multicoloured.

1321	30p. Type **394**	70	70
1322	30p. Javelin throwing	70	70
1323	50p. Long jumping	1·00	1·25
1324	50p. High jumping	1·00	1·25

395 "Space Rocket over Flowers" (Marguerite Nyhan)

397 Peacock Butterfly

396 Tony Reddin

2000. "Stampin' the Future" (children's stamp design competition). Multicoloured.

1325	30p. Type **395**	60	50
1326	32p. "Tree, rocket and hands holding globe in '2000'" (Kyle Staunton) (horiz)	70	55
1327	45p. "People holding hands on globe" (Jennifer Branagan) (horiz)	90	1·10
1328	45p. "Colony on Moon" (Diarmuid O'Ceochain) (horiz)	90	1·10

2000. "Hurling Team of the Millennium". Multicoloured. (a) Size 36 × 27 mm.

1329	30p. Type **396**	60	70
1330	30p. Bobby Rackard	60	70
1331	30p. Nick O'Donnell	60	70
1332	30p. John Doyle	60	70
1333	30p. Brian Whelahan	60	70
1334	30p. John Keane	60	70
1335	30p. Paddy Phelan	60	70
1336	30p. Lory Meagher	60	70
1337	30p. Jack Lynch	60	70
1338	30p. Jim Langton	60	70
1339	30p. Mick Mackey	60	70
1340	30p. Christy Ring	60	70
1341	30p. Jimmy Doyle	60	70
1342	30p. Ray Cummins	60	70
1343	30p. Eddie Keher	60	70

(b) Size 33 × 23 mm. Self-adhesive.

1344	30p. Type **396**	75	1·00
1345	30p. Jimmy Doyle	75	1·00
1346	30p. John Doyle	75	1·00
1347	30p. Paddy Phelan	1·25	1·60
1348	30p. Jim Langton	1·25	1·60
1349	30p. Lory Meagher	75	1·00
1350	30p. Eddie Keher	75	1·00
1351	30p. Mick Mackey	75	1·00
1352	30p. Brian Whelahan	75	1·00
1353	30p. John Keane	75	1·00
1354	30p. Bobby Rackard	75	1·00
1355	30p. Nick O'Donnell	75	1·00
1356	30p. Jack Lynch	75	1·00
1357	30p. Ray Cummins	75	1·00
1358	30p. Christy Ring	75	1·00

2000. Butterflies. Multicoloured.

1359	30p. Type **397**	80	50
1360	32p. Small tortoiseshell	85	55
1361	45p. Silver-washed fritillary	1·25	1·40
1362	50p. Orange-tip	1·40	1·50
MS1363	150 × 90 mm. Nos. 1359/62	3·00	3·00

2000. Military Aviation. Multicoloured. (a) Size 37 × 26 mm.

1364	30p. Hawker Hurricane Mk IIc	80	60
1365	30p. Bristol F.2b Mk II	80	60
1366	45p. De Havilland DH.115 Vampire T.55	1·10	1·25
1367	45p. Sud S.E. 3160 Alouette III (helicopter)	1·10	1·25

(b) Size 33 × 22 mm. Self-adhesive.

1368	30p. Bristol F.2b Mk II	70	70
1369	30p. Hawker Hurricane Mk IIc	70	70
1370	30p. De Havilland DH.115 Vampire T.55	70	70
1371	30p. SUD SE. 3160 Alouette III	70	70

398 Tractor ploughing Field

399 The Nativity

2000. Centenary of An Roinn Talmhaiochta (Department of Agriculture).

1372 **398**	50p. multicoloured	1·00	1·10

2000. Christmas. Multicoloured. (a) Size 24 × 27 mm.

1373	30p. Type **399**	65	50
1374	32p. Three Magi	75	55
1375	45p. Shepherds	1·00	1·25

(b) Size 24 × 29 mm. Self-adhesive.

1376	30p. Flight into Egypt	65	50

400 Storming the Bastille, Paris, 1789

2000. New Millennium (5th issue). World Events. Multicoloured.

1377	30p. Type **400**	1·10	1·40
1378	30p. Early railway	1·10	1·40
1379	30p. Returning troop ship, 1945	1·10	1·40
1380	30p. Suffragettes	1·10	1·40
1381	30p. Destruction of the Berlin Wall, 1989	1·10	1·40
1382	30p. Internet communications	1·10	1·40

2001. New Millennuim (6th issue). Epic Journeys. As T **400**. Multicoloured.

1383	30p. Marco Polo	1·25	1·40
1384	30p. Captain James Cook	1·25	1·40
1385	30p. Burke and Wills expedition crossing Australia, 1860	1·25	1·40

1386 30p. Ernest Shackleton in Antarctica . . . . 1·25 1·40
1387 30p. Charles Lindbergh and *Spirit of St. Louis* . . . . 1·25 1·40
1388 30p. Astronaut on Moon . . 1·25 1·40

401 Goldfish

2001. Greetings Stamps. Pets. (a) As Type **401**. Mult.
1389 30p. Type **401** 80 50

(b) Designs smaller, 20 × 30 mm. Self-adhesive.
1390 30p. Lizard 80 70
1391 30p. Frog 80 70
1392 30p. Type **401** 80 70
1393 30p. Snake 80 70
1394 30p. Tortoise 80 70

2001. Chinese New Year ("Year of the Snake").
MS1395 124 × 75 mm. As Nos. 1391 and 1393/4, but larger, 28 × 39 mm 1·75 2·00

402 Television Presenter and Audience

2001. Irish Broadcasting.
1396 **402** 30p. multicoloured . . . 70 50
1397 – 32p. black, ultramarine and blue 80 55
1398 – 45p. black, brown and orange . . . . 1·00 1·10
1399 – 50p. brown, yellow and green . . . . 1·00 1·25
DESIGNS: 32p. Radio sports commentators; 45p. Family around radio; 50p. Play on television set.

403 Archbishop Narcissus Marsh and Library Interior

404 Bagpipe Player

2001. Literary Anniversaries. Multicoloured.
1400 30p. Type **403** (300th anniv of Marsh's Library) . . . 60 50
1401 32p. Book of Common Prayer, 1551 (450th anniv of first book printed in Ireland) 65 75

2001. 50th Anniv of Comhaltas Ceoltoiri Eireann (cultural organization). Multicoloured.
1402 30p. Type **404** 70 70
1403 30p. Bodhran player 70 70
1404 45p. Young fiddler and Irish dancer (horiz) . . . . . 1·00 1·25
1405 45p. Flautist and singer (horiz) . . . . 1·00 1·25

405 Jordan Formula 1 Racing Car

2001. Irish Motorsport. Multicoloured. (a) As Type **405**.
1406 30p. Type **405** 75 50
1407 32p. Hillman Imp on Tulip Rally 80 55
1408 45p. Mini Cooper S on Monte Carlo Rally . . . 1·25 80
1409 £1 Mercedes SSK, winner of 1930 Irish Grand Prix . . 2·00 2·50
MS1410 150 × 90 mm. £2 Type **405** 3·75 4·25

(b). Designs smaller, 33½ × 22½. Self-adhesive.
1411 30p. Type **405** 90 75
1412 30p. Hillman Imp on Tulip Rally 90 75
1413 30p. Mini Cooper S on Monte Carlo Rally . . . 90 75
1414 30p. Mercedes SSK, winner of 1930 Irish Grand Prix 90 75

406 Peter Lalor (leader at Eureka Stockade) and Gold Licence

2001. Irish Heritage in Australia. Multicoloured.
1415 30p. Type **406** 60 60
1416 30p. Ned Kelly (bush ranger) and "Wanted" poster 60 60
1417 45p. Family leaving for Australia and immigrant ship . . . . 90 1·25
1418 45p. Irish settler and life in gold camp . . . . 90 1·25
MS1419 150 × 90 mm. £1 As No. 1416 . . . . 1·90 2·25

407 Children playing in River

408 Blackbird

2001. Europa; Water Resources. Multicoloured. (a) Size 36½ × 26½ mm.
1420 30p. Type **407** 85 50
1421 32p. Man fishing 90 75

(b) Designs smaller, 33 × 22 mm. Self-adhesive.
1422 30p. Type **407** 65 65
1423 30p. As 32p 65 65

2001. Dual Currency Birds. Vert designs as Nos. 1038, 1050, 1053, 1056/7 and 1060 (some with different face values) showing both Irish currency and euros as in T **408**. Multicoloured. (a) Ordinary gum.
1424 30p./38c. Type **408** 60 60
1425 32p./41c. European robin ("Robin") 70 70
1426 35p./44c. Atlantic puffin ("Puffin") 75 80
1427 40p./51c. Winter wren ("Wren") 85 90
1428 45p./57c. Song thrush . . . 95 1·00
1429 £1/€1.25 White-fronted goose ("Greenland White-fronted Goose") (23 × 44 mm) . . . . . . 2·00 2·25

(b) Designs as Nos. 1038/9, but 25 × 30 mm. Self-adhesive.
1430 30p./38c. Type **408** 65 65
1431 30p./38c. Goldcrest 65 65

409 Irish Pikeman

410 Ruffian 23 Yachts

2001. 400th Anniv of Battle of Kinsale. Nine Years War. Multicoloured.
1432 30p. Type **409** 70 70
1433 30p. English cavalry 70 70
1434 32p. Spanish pikeman . . . 80 80
1435 45p. Town of Kinsale . . . 1·10 1·25

2001. Yachts. Multicoloured. (a) Size 26 × 37½ mm.
1436 30p. Type **410** 70 60
1437 32p. Howth 17 yacht . . . 75 65
1438 45p. 1720 Sportsboat yacht 1·10 1·25
1439 45p. Glen class cruising yacht . . . . 1·10 1·25

(b) Self-adhesive. Size 22 × 34 mm.
1440 30p. Type **410** 70 70
1441 30p. Howth 17 yacht . . . 70 70
1442 30p. Glen class cruising yacht 70 70
1443 30p. 1720 Sportsboat yacht 70 70

411 Padraic Carney (footballer)

2001. Gaelic Athletic Association Hall of Fame 2001 (1st series). Multicoloured. (a) Size 36½ × 27 mm.
1444 30p. Type **411** 70 70
1445 30p. Frank Cummins (hurler) 70 70
1446 30p. Jack O'Shea (footballer) 70 70
1447 30p. Nicky Rackard (hurler) 70 70

(b) Self-adhesive. Size 33½ × 22½ mm.
1448 30p. Type **411** 70 70
1449 30p. Frank Cummins (hurler) 70 70
1450 30p. Jack O'Shea (footballer) 70 70
1451 30p. Nicky Rackard (hurler) 70 70

2001. "Belgica 2001" International Stamp Exhibition, Brussels. No. **MS**1410 with "Belgica 2001" added to the sheet margin.
MS1452 150 × 90 mm. £2 Type **405** 4·00 4·25
See also Nos. 1550/3.

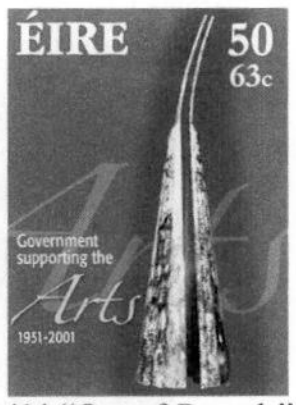

412 Blackbird

414 "Out of Bounds" (sculpture by Eilis O'Connell)

413 Perch

2001. Birds. Vert designs as Nos. 1038/9, 1048 and 1049, but 23½ × 28½ mm, each showing a letter in place of face values as T **412**. Multicoloured. Self-adhesive.
1453 (N) Type **412** 60 50
1454 (N) Goldcrest 60 50
1455 (E) Robin 70 55
1456 (W) Song thrush 85 90
Nos. 1453/6 were intended to cover the changeover period to euros. Nos. 1453/4 were sold for 30p, No. 1455 for 32p. and No. 1456 for 45p.

2001. Freshwater Fish. Multicoloured.
1457 30p. Type **413** 75 50
1458 32p. Arctic charr 80 85
1459 32p. Pike 80 85
1460 45p. Common bream . . . 1·10 1·25

2001. 50th Anniv of Government Support for Arts.
1461 **414** 50p. multicoloured . . . 1·25 1·40

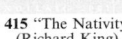

415 "The Nativity" (Richard King)

416 Black-billed Magpie ("Magpie")

2001. Christmas. Paintings by Richard King. Multicoloured. (a) Size 25½ × 36½ mm.
1462 30p. Type **415** 70 50
1463 32p. "The Annunciation" 75 55
1464 45p. "Presentation in the Temple" . . . . 1·10 1·25

(b) Size 25 × 30 mm. Self-adhesive.
1465 30p. "Madonna and Child" 70 50

2002. New Currency. Birds, as Nos. 1031/62, and new designs, with face values in cents and euros, as T **416**. (i) Size 20 × 22½ mm or 22½ × 20 mm.
1466 1c. Type **416** 10 10
1467 2c. Northern gannet ("Gannet") 10 10
1468 3c. Blue tit (horiz) 10 10
1469 4c. Corn crake 10 10
1470 5c. Woodpigeon (horiz) . . 10 10
1471 10c. River kingfisher ("Kingfisher") 10 15
1472 20c. Northern lapwing ("Lapwing") 25 30
1473 38c. Blackbird 50 55
1474 41c. Chaffinch 55 60
1475 41c. Goldcrest 55 60
1476 44c. European robin ("Robin") 60 65
1477 47c. Kestrel (horiz) 65 70
1478 50c. Grey heron (horiz) . . 65 70
1479 51c. Roseate tern (horiz) 70 75
1480 55c. Oystercatcher (horiz) 70 75
1481 57c. Western curlew ("Curlew") 75 80
1482 60c. Jay (horiz) 80 85
1482a 60c. Atlantic puffin 80 85
1482b 65c. Song thrush 90 95
1482c 75c. Ringed plover (horiz) 1·00 1·10
1482d 95c. Sparrowhawk (horiz) 1·30 1·40

(ii) Size 44 × 23 mm or 23 × 44 mm.
1483 €1 Barnacle goose (horiz) 1·30 1·40
1484 €2 White-fronted goose ("Greenland White-fronted Goose") . . . . 2·75 3·00
1485 €5 Northern pintail ("Pintail") (horiz) . . . . 6·75 7·00
1486 €10 Common shelduck ("Shelduck") . . . . . . 13·50 14·00

(b) Size 16 × 20 mm.
1486a 4c. Corncake 10 15
1487 10c. River kingfisher ("Kingfisher") 10 15
1488 36c. Wren 50 55
1489 38c. Blackbird 50 55
1490 41c. Chaffinch 55 60
1490a 48c. Peregrine falcon . . . 65 70

(c) Self-adhesive. Size 21 × 26 mm.
1491 38c. Blackbird 50 55
1492 38c. Goldcrest 50 55
1493 41c. Chaffinch 55 60
1494 41c. Goldcrest 55 60
1495 44c. Robin 60 65
1495b (–) Peregrine falcon . . . 65 70
1495c (–) Pied wagtail 65 70
1495d 48c. Peregrine falcon . . . 65 70
1495e 48c. Pied wagtail 65 70
1496 50c. Puffin 65 70
1497 57c. Song thrush 75 80
1497b 60c. Atlantic puffin 80 85
1497c 65c. Song thrush 90 95

(d) Self-adhesive. Size 25 × 30 mm.
1498 41c. Chaffinch 55 60
1499 41c. Goldcrest 55 60

417 Reverse of Irish €1 Coin, 2002

2002. Introduction of Euro Currency. Irish Coins.
1506 38c. Type **417** 75 50
1507 41c. Reverse of 50p. coin, 1971–2001 . . . . 80 60
1508 57c. Reverse of 1d. coin, 1928–71 . . . . 1·10 1·25

418 Teddy Bear

2002. Greetings Stamps. Toys. Multicoloured. (a) Design 25 × 37 mm.
1509 38c. Type **418** 70 50

(b) Designs 20 × 27 mm. Self-adhesive.
1510 38c. Type **418** 70 70
1511 38c. Rag doll 70 70
1512 38c. Rocking horse 70 70
1513 38c. Train 70 70
1514 38c. Wooden blocks 70 70

2002. Chinese New Year ("Year of the Horse").
MS1515 124 × 74 mm. As Nos. 1511/13, but 25 × 37 mm 2·00 2·25

419 Around the Camp Fire

2002. 75th Anniv of Scouting Ireland CSI. Multicoloured.
1516 41c. Type **419** 75 75
1517 41c. Setting up camp . . . 75 75
1518 57c. Scouts canoeing . . . . 1·10 1·25
1519 57c. Scouts on hill walk . . 1·10 1·25

420 "Arkle"

2002. 250th Anniv of Steeplechasing in Ireland. Irish Steeplechasers. Multicoloured.
1520 38c. Type **420** 70 70
1521 38c. "L'Escargot" 70 70
1522 38c. "Dawn Run" 70 70
1523 38c. "Istabraq" 70 70

421 Badger

2002. Irish Mammals. Multicoloured.

1524	41c. Type **421**	75	60
1525	50c. Otter	90	70
1526	57c. Red squirell (vert)	1·10	80
1527	€1 Hedgehog (vert)	1·75	1·90
MS1528	150 × 67 mm. €5 As 50c.	7·00	7·50

422 Roy Keane

2002. World Cup Football Championship, Japan and Korea (2002). Irish Footballers. Multicoloured. (a) Size 26 × 39 mm or 39 × 26 mm.

1529	41c. Packie Bonner (horiz)	75	75
1530	41c. Type **422**	75	75
1531	41c. Paul McGrath	75	75
1532	41c. David O'Leary	75	75
	(b) Size 22 × 33 mm or 33 × 22 mm. Self-adhesive.		
1533	41c. Packie Bonner (horiz)	75	75
1534	41c. Type **422**	75	75
1535	41c. Paul McGrath	75	75
1536	41c. David O'Leary	75	75

423 Clown

2002. Europa. Circus. Multicoloured. (a) Size 37 × 26 mm. Ordinary gum.

1537	41c. Type **423**	70	70
1538	44c. Girl on horse	70	70
	(b) Self-adhesive. Size 34 × 22 mm.		
1539	41c. Type **423**	70	70
1540	41c. As No. 1538	70	70

424 Padre Pio **425** Brian Boru leading Army

2002. Canonisation of St. Pio de Pietrelcina (Padre Pio).

1541	**424** 41c. multicoloured	75	70

2002. 1000th Anniv of Declaration of Brian Boru as High King of Ireland. Multicoloured.

1542	41c. Type **425**	75	60
1543	44c. Leading fleet	75	60
1544	57c. Receiving surrender of the O'Neills	90	80
1545	£1 Decreeing primacy of bishopric of Armagh in the Irish Church	1·75	1·90

426 "Before the Start" (J. B. Yeats)

2002. 140th Anniv of National Gallery of Ireland (2004) (1st series). Paintings. Multicoloured.

1546	41c. Type **426**	70	70
1547	41c. "The Conjuror" (Nathaniel Hone)	70	70
1548	41c. "The Colosseum and Arch of Constantine, Rome" (Giovanni Panini)	70	70
1549	41c. "The Gleaners" (Jules Breton)	70	70

See also Nos. 1606/9.

2002. Gaelic Athletic Association Hall of Fame 2002 (2nd series). As T **411**.

1550	41c. Peter McDermott (footballer)	70	70
1551	41c. Jimmy Smyth (hurler)	70	70
1552	41c. Matt Connor (footballer)	70	70
1553	41c. Seanie Duggan (hurler)	70	70

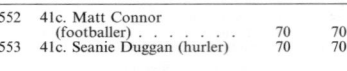

427 Archbishop Thomas Croke **429** "Adoration of the Magi"

428 U2

2002. Death Centenary of Archbishop Croke (first patron of Gaelic Athletic Association).

1554	**427** 44c. multicoloured	80	70

2002. Irish Rock Legends. Multicoloured.

1555	41c. Type **428**	75	75
1556	41c. Phil Lynott	75	75
1557	57c. Van Morrison	1·00	1·10
1558	57c. Rory Gallagher	1·00	1·10
MS1559	Four sheets, each 150 × 90 mm. (a) €2 Type **428**. (b) €2 No. 1556. (c) €2 No. 1557. (d) €2 No. 1558	12·00	13·00

2002. Christmas. Illustrations from "Les Tres Riches Heures du Duc de Berry" (medieval book of hours). Multicoloured. (a) Size 30 × 41 mm.

1560	41c. Type **429**	70	60
1561	44c. "The Annunciation to the Virgin Mary"	75	60
1562	57c. "The Annunciation to the Shepherds"	1·00	1·10
	(b) Size 25 × 30 mm. Self-adhesive.		
1563	41c. "The Nativity"	80	60

430 Labrador Puppies

2003. Greetings Stamps. Baby Animals. Multicoloured. (a) 27 × 38 mm.

1564	41c. Type **430**	80	65
	(b) Designs 23 × 27 mm. Self-adhesive.		
1565	41c. Type **430**	80	80
1566	41c. Chicks	80	80
1567	41c. Kids	80	80
1568	41c. Kittens	80	80
1569	41c. Baby rabbits	80	80

2003. Chinese New Year ("Year of the Goat"). Designs as Nos. 1566/8, but 27 × 38 mm.

MS1570	124 × 74 mm. 50c. Chicks; 50c. Kids; 50c. Kittens	2·40	2·50

431 St. Patrick

2003. St. Patrick's Day. Multicoloured. Size 25 × 37 mm.

1571	41c. Type **431**	70	60
1572	50c. St. Patrick's Day Parade passing St. Patrick's Cathedral, Dublin	85	80
1573	57c. St. Patrick's Day Parade, New York	95	1·00
	(b) Size 22 × 30 mm. Self-adhesive.		
1574	41c. St. Patrick	70	60
1575	50c. St. Patrick's Day Parade passing St. Patrick's Cathedral, Dublin	85	80
1576	57c. St. Patrick's Day Parade, New York	95	1·00

432 Seven-spotted Ladybird

2003. Irish Beetles. Multicoloured.

1577	41c. Type **432**	55	60
1578	50c. Great diving beetle	65	70
1579	57c. Leaf beetle	75	80
1580	€1 Green tiger beetle	1·25	1·40
MS1581	150 × 68 mm. €2 Type **432**	2·50	2·60

433 Dingle Peninsula ("IRELAND for HOLIDAYS")

2003. Europa. Poster Art. Posters by Paul Henry. Multicoloured.

1582	41c. Type **433**	55	60
1583	57c. Connemara ("IRELAND THIS YEAR")	75	80

434 "2003" and EYPD Logo

2003. European Year of People with Disabilities.

1584	**434** 41c. multicoloured	55	60

435 Athletes waving to Crowd

2003. 11th Special Olympics World Summer Games, Dublin. Multicoloured.

1585	41c. Type **435**	55	60
1586	50c. Swimmer	65	70
1587	57c. Athlete on starting block	75	80
1588	€1 Athlete running	1·30	1·40

436 Napier

2003. Centenary of Gordon Bennett Race in Ireland. Racing cars of 1903. Multicoloured. (a) Ordinary gum. Size 38 × 28 mm.

1589	41c. Type **436**	55	60
1590	41c. Mercedes	55	60
1591	41c. Mors	55	60
1592	41c. Winton	55	60
	(b) Self-adhesive. Size 33 × 22 mm.		
1593	41c. As No. 1592	55	60
1594	41c. As No. 1591	55	60
1595	41c. As No. 1590	55	60
1596	41c. Type **436**	55	60

437 Henry Ford and Model T Ford, 1908–28

2003. Centenary of the Ford Motor Company.

1597	**437** 41c. multicoloured	55	60

438 Harry Ferguson flying first Irish Monoplane, 1909

2003. Centenary of Powered Flight. Multicoloured.

1598	41c. Type **438**	55	60
1599	50c. Alcock and Brown's Vickers FB-27 Vimy over Galway after first transatlantic flight, 1919	65	70
1600	57c. *Wright Flyer I*, 1903	75	80
1601	57c. Lillian Bland's biplane, 1910	75	80
MS1602	150 × 90 mm. €5 As No. 1600	6·75	7·00

439 Robert Emmet

2003. Centenary of Rebellion of 1803. Multicoloured.

1603	41c. Type **439**	55	60
1604	50c. Thomas Russell	65	70
1605	57c. Anne Devlin	75	80

2003. 140th Anniv of National Gallery of Ireland (2004) (2nd issue). Paintings. As T **426** but vert. Multicoloured.

1606	48c. "Self-portrait as Timanthes" (James Barry)	65	70
1607	48c. "Man writing a Letter" (Gabriel Metsu)	65	70
1608	48c. "Woman reading a Letter" (Gabriel Metsu)	65	70
1609	48c. "Woman seen from the Back" (Jean-Antoine Watteau)	65	70

440 Frank O'Connor **441** E. T. S. Walton

2003. Birth Centenary of Frank O'Connor (writer).

1610	**440** 50c. multicoloured	65	70

2003. Birth Centenary of E. T. S. Walton (Nobel Prize for Physics, 1951).

1611	**441** 57c. cream, black and brown	75	80

442 Admiral William Brown (founder of the Argentine Navy)

2003. Irish Mariners. Multicoloured. (a) Ordinary gum. Size 40 × 26 mm.

1612	48c. Type **442**	65	70
1613	48c. Commodore John Barry (Commanding Officer of US Navy, 1794–1803)	65	70
1614	57c. Captain Robert Halpin (Commander of cable ship *Great Eastern*)	75	80
1615	57c. Captain Richard Roberts (captain of *Sirius*, first scheduled passenger steamship London to New York voyage)	75	80
	(b) Self-adhesive. Size 32 × 21 mm.		
1616	48c. Commodore John Barry	65	70
1617	48c. Admiral William Brown	65	70
1618	48c. Captain Robert Halpin	65	70
1619	48c. Captain Richard Roberts	65	70
MS1620	150 × 90 mm. €5 Commodore John Barry	6·75	7·00

443 Pope John Paul II

2003. 25th Anniv of the Election of Pope John Paul II. Multicoloured.
1621 48c. Type **443** 65 70
1622 50c. Pope in St. Peter's Square, Rome 65 70
1623 57c. Making speech at United Nations 75 80

444 Angel

2003. Christmas. Multicoloured. (a) Ordinary gum.
1624 48c. Flight into Egypt (32 × 32 mm) 65 70
1625 50c. Type **444** 65 70
1626 57c. Three Kings 75 80

(b) Self-adhesive. Size 26 × 21 mm.
1627 48c. Nativity 65 70

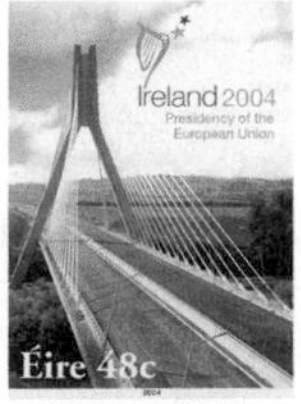

445 Boyne Bridge

2004. Ireland's Presidency of European Union.
1628 **445** 48c. multicoloured . . . 65 70

446 "Monkeys in Love"

2004. Greetings Stamps. Animals. Multicoloured. Ordinary gum. Size 26 × 37 mm.
1629 48c. Type **446** 65 70
MS1630 124 × 74 mm. 60c. Type **446**; 60c. "Jolly Panda"; 60c. "Cute Koalas" . . . . 2·40 2·50

(b) Self-adhesive. Size 21 × 26 mm.
1631 48c. Type **446** 65 70
1632 48c. "Jolly Panda" 65 70
1633 48c. "Cute Koalas" 65 70
1634 48c. "Happy Hippo" . . . 65 70

447 St. Patrick and Stained Glass Window from Church of the Holy and Undivided Trinity, Magheralin, Co. Down

2004. St. Patrick's Day.
1635 **447** 65c. multicoloured . . . 85 90

448 Abbey Theatre Logo

2004. Centenary of Abbey Theatre, Dublin.
1636 **448** 48c. multicoloured . . . 65 70

449 Expedition Members, Dogs and *Endurance* trapped in Ice

2004. 90th Anniv of Shackleton's Antarctic Expedition. Multicoloured.
1637 48c. Type **449** 65 70
1638 48c. Two crew members, huskies and bow of *Endurance* 65 70
1639 65c. Crew member looking out of tent 85 90
1640 65c. Crew members and tented camp on ice . . . 85 90
MS1641 149 × 90 mm. €1 As No. 1639; €1 As No. 1640 . . 2·60 2·50

450 Flags, Football and Globe

2004. Centenary of FIFA (Federation Internationale de Football Association).
1642 **450** 60c. multicoloured . . . 80 85

451 Map of Europe showing Acceding Countries

2004. Enlargement of the European Union.
1643 **451** 65c. multicoloured . . . 85 90

POSTAGE DUE STAMPS

D 1

1925.
D 1 **D 1** 1½d. green . . . . . . 12·00 16·00
D 6 1d. red . . . . . . 1·50 70
D 7 1½d. red . . . . . . 2·25 6·50
D 8 2d. green . . . . . . 2·75 70
D 9 3d. blue . . . . . . 2·50 2·75
D10 5d. violet . . . . . . 4·50 3·00
D11a 6d. plum . . . . . . 1·00 1·00
D12 8d. orange . . . . . . 8·50 9·00
D13 10d. purple . . . . . . 8·50 7·50
D14 1s. green . . . . . . 6·00 9·50

1971. Decimal Currency. Colours changed.
D15 **D 1** 1p. brown 30 60
D16 1½p. green . . . . . . 40 1·50
D17 3p. stone . . . . . . 60 2·00
D18 4p. orange . . . . . . 60 1·25
D19 5p. blue . . . . . . 60 3·00
D20 7p. yellow . . . . . . 40 3·50
D21 8p. red . . . . . . 40 2·75

D 2 D 3

1980.
D25 **D 2** 1p. green 30 70
D26 2p. blue 30 70
D27 4p. green 40 70
D28 6p. flesh 40 80
D29 8p. blue 40 85
D30 18p. green . . . . . . 75 1·25
D31 20p. red . . . . . . 2·25 5·50
D32 24p. green . . . . . . 75 2·00
D33 30p. violet . . . . . . 3·00 6·50
D34 50p. pink . . . . . . 3·75 7·50

1988.
D35 **D 3** 1p. black, red and yellow 10 50
D36 2p. black, red and brown 10 50
D37 3p. black, red and purple 15 50
D38 4p. black, red and violet 15 50
D39 5p. black, red and blue 15 50
D40 17p. black, red and green 40 65
D41 20p. black, red and blue 55 80
D42 24p. black, red and green 60 85
D43 30p. black, red and grey 80 1·25
D44 50p. black, red and grey 1·25 1·75
D45 £1 black, red and brown 1·75 2·25

ISLE OF MAN Pt. 1

An island in the Irish Sea to the north-west of England. Man became a possession of the English Crown during the Middle Ages, but retains its own Assembly.

Regional issues from 1958 to 1971 are listed at end of "GREAT BRITAIN".

Isle of Man had an independent postal administration from 1973.

100 pence = 1 pound.

4 Castletown

5 Manx Cat

1973. Multicoloured.
12 ½p. Type **4** 10 10
13 1p. Port Erin 10 10
14 1½p. Snaefell 10 10
15 2p. Laxey 10 10
16 2½p. Tynwald Hill 10 10
17 3p. Douglas Promenade . . . 10 10
18 3½p. Port St. Mary 10 10
19 4p. Fairy Bridge 10 10
20 4½p. As 2½p. 20 15
21 5p. Peel 15 10
22 5½p. As 3p. 20 15
23 6p. Cregneish 20 15
24 7p. As 2p. 20 15
25 7½p. Ramsey Bay 20 20
26 8p. As 7½p. 25 25
27 9p. Douglas Bay 20 20
28 10p. Type **5** 35 20
29 11p. Monk's Bridge, Ballasalla 35 30
30 13p. Derbyhaven 40 35
31 20p. Manx loaghtyn ram . . . 50 50
32 50p. Manx shearwater . . . . 1·10 1·10
33 £1 Viking longship . . . . . 2·25 2·00

SIZES: Nos. 13/27 and 29/30 as Type **4**; Nos. 31/3 as Type **5**.

6 Viking Landing on Man, A.D. 938

1973. Inauguration of Postal Independence.
34 **6** 15p. multicoloured 35 30

7 No. 1 "Sutherland", 1873

1973. Cent of Steam Railway. Multicoloured.
35 2½p. Type **7** 15 10
36 3p. No. 4 "Caledonia", 1885 15 15
37 7½p. No. 13 "Kissack", 1910 25 25
38 9p. No. 3 "Pender", 1873 . . 25 25

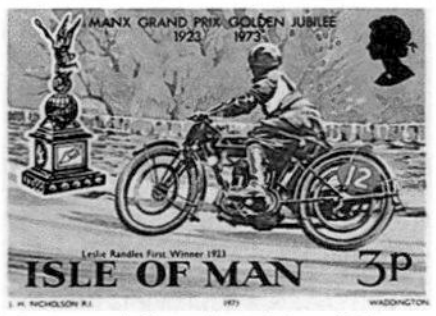

8 Leonard Randles, First Winner, 1923

1973. Golden Jubilee of Manx Grand Prix. Mult.
39 3p. Type **8** 10 15
40 3½p. Alan Holmes, Double Winner, 1957 . . . . 15 25

9 Princess Anne and Capt. Mark Phillips

1973. Royal Wedding.
41 **9** 25p. multicoloured 45 50

10 Badge, Citation and Sir William Hillary (founder)

1974. 150th Anniv of Royal National Lifeboat Institution. Multicoloured.
42 3p. Type **10** 10 10
43 3½p. Wreck of "St. George", 1830 . . . . 15 10
44 8p. R.N.L.B. "Manchester and Salford", 1868–87 . . . . . 25 25
45 10p. R.N.L.B. "Osman Gabriel" 30 25

11 Stanley Woods, 1935

1974. Tourist Trophy Motor-cycle Races (1st issue). Multicoloured.
46 3p. Type **11** 10 10
47 3½p. Freddy Frith, 1937 . . . 10 10
48 8p. Max Deubel and Emil Horner, 1961 . . . . 25 20
49 10p. Mike Hailwood, 1961 . . 25 20
See also Nos. 63/6.

12 Rushen Abbey and Arms

1974. Historical Anniversaries. Multicoloured.
50 3½p. Type **12** 10 10
51 4½p. Magnus Haraldson rows King Edgar on the Dee . . 10 10
52 8p. King Magnus and Norse fleet 15 15
53 10p. Bridge at Avignon and bishop's mitre 20 20

COMMEMORATIONS: Nos. 50 and 53, William Russell, Bishop of Sodor and Man, 600th death anniv; Nos. 51/2, 1000th anniv of rule of King Magnus Haraldson.

13 Churchill and Bugler Dunne at Colenso, 1899

1974. Birth Centenary of Sir Winston Churchill. Multicoloured.
54 3½p. Type **13** 10 10
55 4½p. Churchill and Government Buildings, Douglas 10 10
56 8p. Churchill and Manx ack-ack crew 15 15
57 20p. Churchill as Freeman of Douglas 30 25
MS58 121 × 91 mm. Nos. 54/7 . . 75 75

14 Cabin School and Names of Pioneers

1975. Manx Pioneers in Cleveland, Ohio. Multicoloured.
59 $4\frac{1}{2}$p. Type **14** 10 10
60 $5\frac{1}{2}$p. Terminal Tower Building, J. Gill and R. Carran . . . 10 10
61 8p. Clague House Museum, and Robert and Margaret Clague 15 15
62 10p. S.S. "William T. Graves" and Thomas Quayle 25 25

15 Tom Sheard, 1923

1975. Tourist Trophy Motor-cycle Races (2nd issue). Multicoloured.
63 $5\frac{1}{2}$p. Type **15** 10 10
64 7p. Walter Handley, 1925 . . 15 15
65 10p. Geoff Duke, 1955 . . . . 15 15
66 12p. Peter Williams, 1973 . . 25 20

16 Sir George Goldie and Birthplace

1975. 50th Death Anniv of Sir George Goldie. Multicoloured.
67 $5\frac{1}{2}$p. Type **16** 10 10
68 7p. Goldie and map of Africa (vert) 15 15
69 10p. Goldie as President of Geographical Society (vert) 15 15
70 12p. River scene on the Niger 25 25

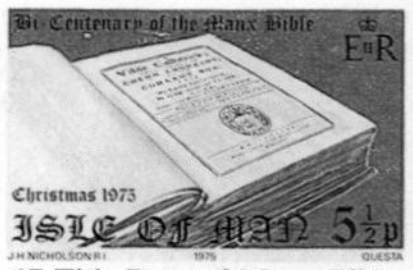

17 Title Page of Manx Bible **18** William Christian listening to Patrick Henry

1975. Christmas and Bicentenary of Manx Bible. Multicoloured.
71 $5\frac{1}{2}$p. Type **17** 10 10
72 7p. Rev. Philip Moore and Ballaugh Old Church . . . 15 15
73 11p. Bishop Hildesley and Bishops Court 20 20
74 13p. John Kelly saving Bible manuscript 25 25

1976. Bicent of American Independence. Mult.
75 $5\frac{1}{2}$p. Type **18** 10 10
76 7p. Conveying the Fincastle Resolutions 15 15
77 13p. Patrick Henry and William Christian 30 30
78 20p. Christian as an Indian fighter 35 35
MS79 153 × 89 mm. Nos. 75/8 . . 95 1·00

19 First Horse Tram, 1876

1976. Cent of Douglas Horse-Trams. Mult.
80 $5\frac{1}{2}$p. Type **19** 10 10
81 7p. "Toast-rack" tram, 1890 15 15
82 11p. Horse-bus, 1895 . . . . 20 20
83 13p. Royal tram, 1972 . . . . 25 25

20 Barrose Beaker **21** Diocesan Banner

1976. Europa. Ceramic Art. Multicoloured.
84 5p. Type **20** 20 20
85 5p. Souvenir teapot 20 20
86 5p. Laxey jug 20 20
87 10p. Cronk Aust food vessel (horiz) 20 20
88 10p. Sansbury bowl (horiz) . . 20 20
89 10p. Knox urn (horiz) 20 20

1976. Christmas and Centenary of Mothers' Union. Multicoloured.
90 6p. Type **21** 10 10
91 7p. Onchan banner 15 15
92 11p. Castletown banner . . . 20 20
93 13p. Ramsey banner 25 25

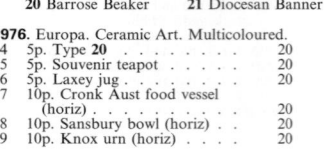

22 Queen Elizabeth II

1977. Silver Jubilee. Multicoloured.
94 6p. Type **22** 10 10
95 7p. Queen Elizabeth and Prince Philip (vert) 20 20
96 25p. Queen Elizabeth (different) 50 50

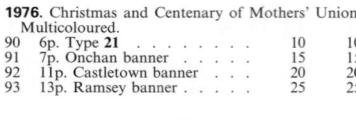

23 Carrick Bay from "Tom-the-Dipper"

1977. Europa. Landscapes. Multicoloured.
97 6p. Type **23** 15 15
98 10p. View from Ramsey . . . 25 25

24 F. A. Applebee, 1912

1977. Linked Anniversaries. Multicoloured.
99 6p. Type **24** 15 10
100 7p. St. John's Ambulance Brigade at Governor's Bridge, 1938 . . . . 15 15
101 11p. Scouts operating the scoreboard 25 25
102 13p. John Williams, 1976 . . 25 30
The events commemorated are: 70th anniv of Manx TT races; 70th anniv of Boy Scouts; Centenary of St. John's Ambulance Brigade.

25 Old Summer House, Mount Morrison, Peel **27** Watch Tower, Langness

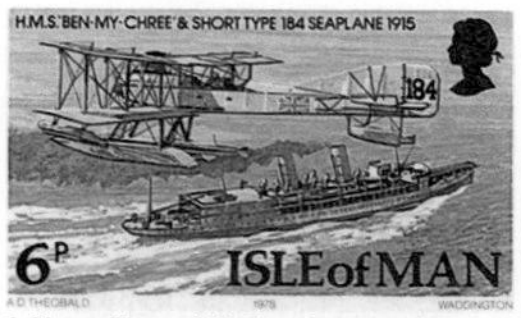

26 Short Type 184 Seaplane and H.M.S. "Ben-My-Chree", 1915

1977. Bicentenary of First Visit of John Wesley. Multicoloured.
103 6p. Type **25** 15 10
104 7p. Wesley preaching in Castletown Square 15 15
105 11p. Wesley preaching outside Braddan Church 25 25
106 13p. New Methodist Church, Douglas 25 25
Nos. 104/5 are larger, 38 × 26 mm.

1978. 60th Anniv of Royal Air Force. Mult.
107 6p. Type **26** 10 10
108 7p. Bristol Scout C and H.M.S. "Vindex", 1915 . . 10 10
109 11p. Boulton Paul Defiant over Douglas Bay, 1941 . . 20 15
110 13p. Sepecat Jaguar over Ramsey, 1977 . . . . . . 20 20

1978. Multicoloured.
111 $\frac{1}{2}$p. Type **27** 10 10
112 1p. Jurby Church (horiz) . . 10 10
113 6p. Government Buildings 30 30
114 7p. Tynwald Hill (horiz) . . 35 35
115 8p. Milner's Tower 25 25
116 9p. Laxey Wheel 35 35
117a 10p. Castle Rushen (horiz) 35 35
118 11p. St. Ninian's Church . . 40 40
119 12p. Tower of Refuge (horiz) 40 25
120a 13p. St. German's Cathedral (horiz) 30 25
121a 14p. Point of Ayre Lighthouse (horiz) 30 25
122a 15p. Corrin's Tower (horiz) 30 25
123 16p. Douglas Head Lighthouse (horiz) 55 30
124 20p. Fuchsia 50 35
125 25p. Manx cat 65 45
126 50p. Red-billed chough ("Chough") 90 75
127 £1 Viking warrior . . . . . 1·90 2·00
128 £2 Queen Elizabeth II . . . 3·50 3·50
Nos. 124/78 are larger, 25 × 31 mm and No. 128, 38 × 48 mm.

28 Queen Elizabeth in Coronation Regalia **29** Wheel-headed Cross-slab

1978. 25th Anniv of Coronation.
132 **28** 25p. multicoloured 50 45

1978. Europa. Celtic and Norse Crosses. Multicoloured.
133 6p. Type **29** 10 10
134 6p. Celtic wheel-cross 10 10
135 6p. Keeil Chiggyrt Stone . . 10 10
136 11p. Olaf Liotulfson Cross 20 20
137 11p. Odd's and Thorleif's Crosses 20 20
138 11p. Thor Cross 20 20

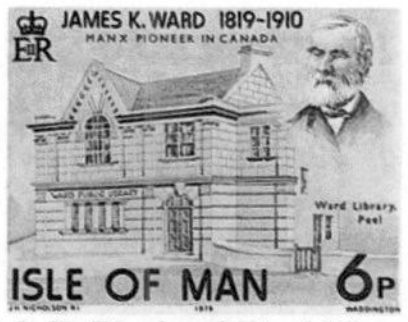

30 J. K. Ward and Ward Library, Peel

1978. Anniversaries and Events. Multicoloured.
139 6p. Type **30** 10 10
140 7p. Swimmer, cyclist and walker (42 × 26 mm) . . . 20 15
141 11p. American bald eagle, Manx arms and maple leaf (42 × 26 mm) 25 25
142 13p. Lumber camp, Three Rivers, Quebec 25 25
ANNIVERSARIES AND EVENTS: 6, 13p. James Kewley Ward (Manx pioneer in Canada) commemoration; 7p. Commonwealth Games, Edmonton; 11p. 50th anniv of North American Manx Association.

31 Hunt the Wren **33** Postman, 1859

32 P. M. C. Kermode and "Nassa kermodei"

1978. Christmas.
143 **31** 5p. multicoloured 20 20

1979. Centenary of Natural History and Antiquarian Society. Multicoloured.
144 6p. Type **32** 10 10
145 7p. Peregrine falcon 20 15
146 11p. Fulmar 25 25
147 13p. "Epitriptus cowini" (fly) 25 25

1979. Europa. Communications. Multicoloured.
148 6p. Type **33** 15 10
149 11p. Postman, 1979 . . . . . 25 25

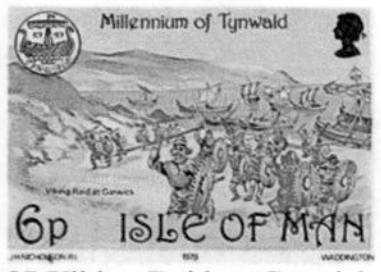

34 Viking Longship Emblem **35** Viking Raid at Garwick

1979. Millennium of Tynwald. Multicoloured.
150b 3p. Type **34** 10 10
151 4p. "Three Legs of Man" emblem 10 10
152 6p. Type **35** 15 10
153 7p. 10th-century meeting of Tynwald 20 20
154 11p. Tynwald Hill and St. John's Church 25 25
155 13p. Procession to Tynwald Hill 30 25
The 4p. value is as Type **34** and the remainder as Type **35**.

36 Queen and Court on Tynwald Hill

1979. Royal Visit. Multicoloured.
156 7p. Type **36** 15 15
157 13p. Queen and procession from St. John's Church to Tynwald Hill 25 25

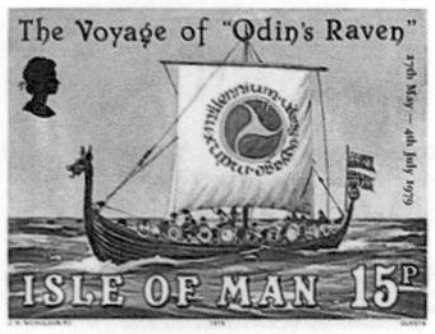

37 "Odin's Raven"

1979. Voyage of "Odin's Raven".
158 **37** 15p. multicoloured 35 30

38 John Quilliam seized by the Press Gang

1979. 150th Death Anniv of Captain John Quilliam. Multicoloured.
159 6p. Type **38** 15 15
160 8p. Steering H.M.S. "Victory", Battle of Trafalgar 20 15
161 13p. Captain John Quilliam and H.M.S. "Spencer" . . 25 25
162 15p. Captain John Quilliam (member of the House of Keys) 30 25

39 Young Girl with Teddybear and Cat

1979. Christmas. Int Year of the Child. Mult.

163	5p. Type **39**	10	10
164	7p. Father Christmas with young children	20	20

40 Conglomerate Arch, Langness

1980. 150th Anniv of Royal Geographical Society. Multicoloured.

165	7p. Type **40**	15	15
166	8p. Braaid Circle	20	20
167	12p. Cashtal-yn-Ard	25	25
168	13p. Volcanic rocks at Scarlett	25	25
169	15p. Sugar-loaf Rock	30	25

41 "Mona's Isle I"

1980. 150th Anniv of Isle of Man Steam Packet Company. Multicoloured.

170	7p. Type **41**	15	15
171	8p. "Douglas I"	20	20
172	11½p. H.M.S. "Mona's Queen II" sinking U-boat	20	25
173	12p. H.M.S. "King Orry III" at surrender of German fleet, 1918	25	25
174	13p. "Ben-My-Chree IV"	25	25
175	15p. "Lady of Mann II"	30	25
MS176	180 × 125 mm. Nos. 170/5	1·25	1·25

No. **MS**176 was issued to commemorate "London 1980" International Stamp Exhibition.

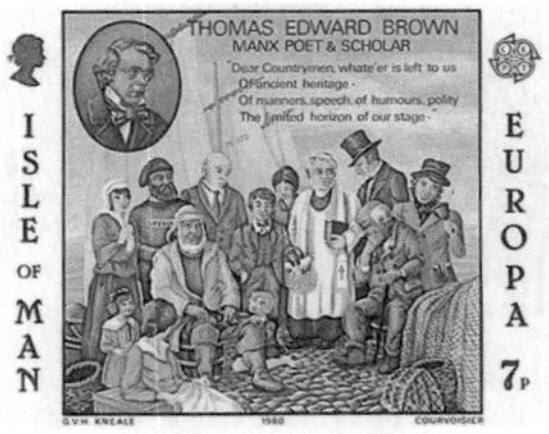

42 Stained Glass Window, T. E. Brown Room, Manx Museum

1980. Europa. Personalities. Thomas Edward Brown (poet and scholar) Commemoration. Multicoloured.

177	7p. Type **42**	15	15
178	13½p. Clifton College, Bristol	25	25

43 King Olav V and "Norge" (Norwegian royal yacht)

1980. Visit of King Olav of Norway, August 1979.

179	**43** 12p. multicoloured	30	30
MS180	125 × 157 mm. Nos. 158 and 179	75	75

No. **MS**180 also commemorates the "NORWEX 80" Stamp Exhibition, Oslo.

44 Winter Wren and View of Calf of Man

1980. Christmas and Wildlife Conservation Year. Multicoloured.

181	6p. Type **44**	15	10
182	8p. European robin and view of Port Erin Marine Biological Station	30	20

45 William Kermode and Brig "Robert Quayle", 1819

46 Peregrine Falcon

1980. Kermode Family in Tasmania Commemoration. Multicoloured.

183	7p. Type **45**	15	15
184	9p. "Mona Vale", Van Diemen's Land, 1834	20	20
185	13½p. Ross Bridge, Tasmania	25	25
186	15p. "Mona Vale", Tasmania (completed 1868)	30	25
187	17½p. Robert Quayle Kermode and Parliament Buildings, Tasmania	30	30

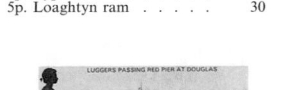

1980. Multicoloured.

188	1p. Type **46**	20	20
189	5p. Loaghtyn ram	30	30

47 Luggers passing Red Pier, Douglas

1981. Centenary of Royal National Mission to Deep Sea Fishermen. Multicoloured.

190	8p. Type **47**	15	15
191	9p. Peel Lugger "Wanderer" rescuing survivors from "Lusitania"	20	20
192	18p. Nickeys leaving Port St. Mary	30	30
193	20p. Nobby entering Ramsey Harbour	30	30
194	22p. Nickeys "Sunbeam" and "Zebra" at Port Erin	35	35

48 "Crosh Cuirn" Superstition

1981. Europa. Folklore. Multicoloured.

195	8p. Type **48**	15	10
196	18p. "Bollan Cross" superstition	30	30

49 Lt. Mark Wilks (Royal Manx Fencibles) and Peel Castle

1981. 150th Death Anniv of Colonel Mark Wilks. Multicoloured.

197	8p. Type **49**	20	20
198	20p. Ensign Mark Wilks and Fort St. George, Madras	30	30
199	22p. Governor Mark Wilks and Napoleon, St. Helena	40	35
200	25p. Col. Mark Wilks (Speaker of the House of Keys) and estate, Kirby	45	35

50 Miss Emmeline Goulden (Mrs. Pankhurst) and Mrs. Sophia Jane Goulden

1981. Centenary of Manx Women's Suffrage.

201	**50** 9p. black, grey and stone	20	20

51 Prince Charles and Lady Diana Spencer

1981. Royal Wedding.

202	**51** 9p. black, blue and light blue	15	20
203	25p. black, blue and pink	75	80
MS204	130 × 183 mm. Nos. 202/3 × 2	2·00	2·00

52 Douglas War Memorial, Poppies and Commemorative Inscription

1981. 60th Anniv of The Royal British Legion. Multicoloured.

205	8p. Type **52**	20	20
206	10p. Major Robert Cain (war hero)	25	25
207	18p. Festival of Remembrance, Royal Albert Hall	30	30
208	20p. T.S.S. "Tynwald" at Dunkirk, May 1940	35	35

53 Nativity Scene (stained glass window, St. George's Church)

1981. Christmas. Multicoloured.

209	7p. Type **53**	15	15
210	9p. Children from Special School performing nativity play (48 × 30 mm)	20	20

54 Joseph and William Cunningham (founders of Isle of Man Boy Scout Movement) and Cunningham House Headquarters

1982. 75th Anniv of Boy Scout Movement and 125th Birth Anniv of Lord Baden-Powell. Multicoloured.

211	9p. Type **54**	20	15
212	10p. Baden-Powell visiting Isle of Man, 1911	25	25
213	19½p. Baden-Powell and Scout emblem (40 × 31 mm)	45	40
214	24p. Scouts and Baden-Powell's last message	50	45
215	29p. Scout salute, handshake, emblem and globe	70	60

55 "The Principals and Duties of Christianity" (Bishop T. Wilson) (first book printed in Manx, 1707)

1982. Europa. Historic Events. Multicoloured.

216	9p. Type **55**	15	10
217	19½p. Landing at Derbyhaven (visit of Thomas, 2nd Earl of Derby, 1507)	40	40

56 Charlie Collier (first TT race (single cylinder) winner) and Tourist Trophy Race, 1907

1982. 75th Anniv of Tourist Trophy Motorcycle Racing. Multicoloured.

218	9p. Type **56**	15	15
219	10p. Freddie Dixon (Sidecar and Junior TT winner) and Junior TT Race, 1927	15	15
220	24p. Jimmie Simpson (TT winner and first to lap at 60, 70 and 80 mph) and Senior TT, 1932	60	50
221	26p. Mike Hailwood (winner of fourteen TT's) and Senior TT, 1961	60	50
222	29p. Jock Taylor (Sidecar TT winner, 1978, 1980 and 1981) and Sidecar TT (with Benga Johansson), 1980	60	55

57 "Mona I"

1982. 150th Anniv of Isle of Man Steam Packet Company Mail Contract. Multicoloured.

223	12p. Type **57**	30	25
224	19½p. "Manx Maid II"	75	70

58 Three Wise Men bearing Gifts

1982. Christmas. Multicoloured.

225	8p. Type **58**	15	15
226	11p. Christmas snow scene (vert)	30	30

59 Princess Diana with Prince William

1982. 21st Birthday of Princess of Wales and Birth of Prince William. Sheet 100 × 83 mm.

MS227	**59** 50p. multicoloured	1·50	1·50

60 Opening of Salvation Army Citadel, and T. H. Cannell, J.P.

1983. Centenary of Salvation Army in Isle of Man. Multicoloured.

228	10p. Type **60**	20	15
229	12p. Early meeting place and Gen. William Booth	30	25
230	19½p. Salvation Army band	45	45
231	26p. Treating lepers and Lt.-Col. Thomas Bridson	65	60

61 Atlantic Puffins ("Puffins")

61a "Queen Elizabeth II" (Ricardo Macarron)

1983. Sea Birds. Multicoloured.
232 1p. Type **61** 30 30
233 2p. Northern gannets ("Gannets") 30 30
234 5p. Lesser black-backed gulls 60 40
235 8p. Great cormorants ("Cormorants") 60 40
236 10p. Black-legged kittiwakes ("Kittiwakes") 60 35
237 11p. Shags 60 35
238 12p. Grey herons ("Herons") 70 40
239 13p. Herring gulls 70 40
240 14p. Razorbills 70 40
241 15p. Greater black-backed gulls ("Great Black-backed Gulls") 80 50
242 16p. Common shelducks ("Shelducks") 80 50
243 18p. Oystercatchers 80 50
244 20p. Arctic terns 1·00 70
245 25p. Common guillemots ("Guillemots") 1·25 75
246 50p. Common redshank ("Redshanks") 1·75 1·50
247 £1 Mute swans 3·00 2·25
248 £5 Type **61a** 9·00 10·00
Nos. 244/7 are larger, 39 × 26 mm.

62 Design Drawings by Roger Casement for the Great Laxey Wheel (½-size illustration)

1983. Europa. The Great Laxey Wheel.
249 **62** 10p. black, blue and buff 25 20
250 – 20½p. multicoloured 50 55
DESIGN: 20½p. Roger Casement and the Great Laxey Wheel.

63 Nick Keig (international yachtsman) and Trimaran "Three Legs of Man III"

1983. 150th Anniv of King William's College. Multicoloured.
251 10p. Type **63** 15 15
252 12p. King William's College, Castletown 20 20
253 28p. Sir William Bragg (winner of Nobel Prize for Physics) and spectrometer 55 55
254 31p. General Sir George White, V.C. and action at Charasiah 65 65

64 New Post Office Headquarters, Douglas

1983. World Communications Year and 10th Anniv of Isle of Man Post Office Authority. Multicoloured.
255 10p. Type **64** 25 25
256 15p. As Type **64** but inscr "POST OFFICE DECENNIUM 1983" 35 40

65 Shepherds

1983. Christmas. Multicoloured.
257 9p. Type **65** 20 20
258 12p. Three Kings 30 30

66 "Manx King" (full-rigged ship)

1984. The Karran Fleet. Multicoloured.
259 10p. Type **66** 20 15
260 13p. "Hope" (barque) 30 20
261 20½p. "Rio Grande" (brig) 45 35
262 28p. "Lady Elizabeth" (barque) 65 50
263 31p. "Sumatra" (barque) 75 65
MS264 103 × 94 mm. 28p. As No. 262; 31p. "Lady Elizabeth" (as shown on Falkland Islands No. 417) (sold at 60p.) 2·25 1·50
No. **MS**264 was issued to commemorate links between the Isle of Man and the Falkland Islands.

67 C.E.P.T. 25th Anniversary Logo

69 Window from Glencrutchery House, Douglas

68 Railway Air Services De Havilland D.H.84 Dragon Mk 2

1984. Europa.
265 **67** 10p. orange, brown and light orange 30 25
266 20½p. blue, deep blue and light blue 50 50

1984. 50th Anniv of First Official Airmail to the Isle of Man and 40th Anniv of International Civil Aviation Organization. Multicoloured.
267 11p. Type **68** 35 30
268 13p. West Coast Air Services De Havilland D.H. 86A Dragon Express "Ronaldsway" 40 30
269 26p. B.E.A. Douglas DC-3 70 65
270 28p. B.E.A. Vickers Viscount 800 70 65
271 31p. Telair Britten Norman Islander 70 65

1984. Christmas. Stained-glass Windows. Multicoloured.
272 10p. Type **69** 20 20
273 13p. Window from Lonan Old Church 40 40

70 William Cain's Birthplace, Ballasalla

1984. William Cain (civic leader, Victoria) Commemoration. Multicoloured.
274 11p. Type **70** 25 20
275 22p. The "Anna" leaving Liverpool, 1852 50 50
276 28p. Early Australian railway 70 65
277 30p. William Cain as Mayor of Melbourne, and Town Hall 75 65
278 33p. Royal Exhibition Building, Melbourne 70 65

71 Queen Elizabeth II and Commonwealth Parliamentary Association Badge

1984. Links with the Commonwealth. 30th Commonwealth Parliamentary Association Conference. Multicoloured.
279 14p. Type **71** 35 35
280 33p. Queen Elizabeth II and Manx emblem 65 65

72 Cunningham House Headquarters and Mrs. Willie Cunningham and Mrs. Joseph Cunningham (former Commissioners)

1985. 75th Anniv of Girl Guide Movement. Multicoloured.
281 11p. Type **72** 30 25
282 14p. Princess Margaret, Isle of Man standard and guides 35 30
283 29p. Lady Olave Baden-Powell opening Guide Headquarters, 1955 70 60
284 31p. Guide uniforms from 1910 to 1985 75 75
285 34p. Guide handclasp, salute and early badge 90 85

73 Score of Manx National Anthem

1985. Europa. European Music Year.
286 **73** 12p. black, light brown and brown 30 30
287 – 12p. black, light brown & brown 30 30
288 – 22p. black, light blue & blue 80 70
289 – 22p. black, light blue & blue 80 70
DESIGNS: No. 287, William H. Gill (lyricist); 288, Score of hymn "Crofton"; 289, Dr. John Clague (composer).

74 Charles Rolls in 20 h.p. Rolls-Royce (1906 Tourist Trophy Race)

1985. Century of Motoring. Multicoloured.
290 12p. Type **74** 25 25
291 12p. W. Bentley in 3 litre Bentley (1922 Tourist Trophy Race) 25 25
292 14p. F. Gerrard in E.R.A. (1950 British Empire Trophy Race) 30 25
293 14p. Brian Lewis in Alfa Romeo (1934 Mannin Moar Race) 30 25
294 31p. Jaguar "XJ-SC" ("Roads Open" car, 1984 Motor Cycle TT Races) 1·00 80
295 31p. Tony Pond and Mike Nicholson in Vauxhall "Chevette" (1981 Rothmans International Rally) 1·00 80

75 Queen Alexandra and Victorian Sergeant with Wife

1985. Centenary of Soldiers', Sailors' and Airmen's Families Association. Association Presidents. Multicoloured.
296 12p. Type **75** 25 20
297 15p. Queen Mary and Royal Air Force family 35 30
298 29p. Earl Mountbatten and Royal Navy family 65 55
299 34p. Prince Michael of Kent and Royal Marine with parents, 1982 90 85

76 Kirk Maughold (birthplace)

1985. Birth Bicentenary of Lieutenant-General Sir Mark Cubbon (Indian administrator). Mult.
300 12p. Type **76** 30 25
301 22p. Lieutenant-General Sir Mark Cubbon (vert) 70 65
302 45p. Memorial statue, Bangalore, India (vert) 1·00 95

77 St. Peter's Church, Onchan

1985. Christmas. Manx Churches. Multicoloured.
303 11p. Type **77** 30 25
304 14p. Royal Chapel of St. John, Tynwald 40 35
305 31p. Bride Parish Church 1·00 90

78 Swimming

1986. Commonwealth Games, Edinburgh. Mult.
306 12p. Type **78** 20 15
307 15p. Race walking 25 30
308 31p. Rifle-shooting 90 95
309 34p. Cycling 1·00 95
No. 309 also commemorates the 50th anniversary of Manx International Cycling Week.

79 Viking Necklace and Peel Castle

1986. Centenary of Manx Museum. Multicoloured.
310 12p. Type **79** 20 15
311 15p. Meayll Circle, Rushen 25 20
312 22p. Skeleton of Great Deer and Manx Museum (vert) 65 50
313 26p. Viking longship model (vert) 80 60
314 29p. Open Air Museum, Cregneash 90 60

80 Viking Longship

81 "Usnea articulata" (lichen) and "Neotinea intacta" (orchid), The Ayres

1986. Manx Heritage Year.
315 **80** 2p. multicoloured 40 40
316 – 10p. black, green and grey 35 35
DESIGN: 10p. Celtic cross logo.

1986. Europa. Protection of Nature and the Environment. Multicoloured.
317 12p. Type **81** 30 30
318 12p. Hen harrier, Calf of Man 30 30
319 22p. Manx stoat, Eary Cushlin 60 60
320 22p. "Stenobothus stigmaticus" (grasshopper), St. Michael's Isle 60 60

82 Ellanbane (home of Myles Standish)

1986. "Ameripex '86" International Stamp Exhibition, Chicago. Captain Myles Standish of the "Mayflower". Multicoloured.
321 12p. Type **82** 20 20
322 15p. "Mayflower" crossing the Atlantic, 1620 25 25
323 31p. Pilgrim Fathers landing at Plymouth, 1620 90 90
324 34p. Captain Myles Standish 95 95
MS325 100 × 75 mm. Nos. 323/4 2·10 2·10
No. **MS**325 also commemorates the 75th anniversary of the World Manx Association.

83 Prince Andrew in Naval Uniform and Miss Sarah Ferguson

1986. Royal Wedding. Multicoloured.
326 15p. Type **83** 25 25
327 40p. Engagement photograph 1·50 90

84 Prince Philip (from photo by Karsh)

85 European Robins on Globe and "Peace and Goodwill" in Braille

1986. Royal Birthdays. Multicoloured.

328	15p. Type **84**	30	30
329	15p. Queen Elizabeth II (from photo by Karsh)	30	30
330	34p. Queen Elizabeth and Prince Philip (from photo by Karsh) (48 × 35 mm)	1·10	1·10

Nos. 328/30 also commemorate "Stockholmia '86" International Stamp Exhibition, Sweden and the 350th anniversary of the Swedish Post Office.

1986. Christmas and International Peace Year. Multicoloured.

331	11p. Type **85**	30	30
332	14p. Hands releasing peace dove	30	30
333	31p. Clasped hands and "Peace" in sign language	80	80

86 North Quay

1987. Victorian Douglas. Multicoloured.

334	2p. Type **86**	10	10
335	3p. Old Fishmarket	10	10
336	10p. The Breakwater	25	25
337	15p. Jubilee Clock	30	30
338	31p. Loch Promenade	90	80
339	34p. Beach	1·00	1·90

87 "The Old Fishmarket and Harbour, Douglas"

1987. Paintings by John Miller Nicholson. Multicoloured.

340	12p. Type **87**	20	20
341	26p. "Red Sails at Douglas"	70	60
342	29p. "The Double Corner, Peel"	90	80
343	34p. "Peel Harbour"	1·00	1·00

88 Sea Terminal, Douglas

1987. Europa. Architecture. Multicoloured.

344	12p. Type **88**	45	40
345	12p. Tower of Refuge, Douglas	45	40
346	22p. Gaiety Theatre, Douglas	65	50
347	22p. Villa Marina, Douglas	65	50

89 Supercharged "BMW" 500cc Motor Cycle, 1939

1987. 80th Anniv of Tourist Trophy Motor Cycle Races. Multicoloured.

348	12p. Type **89**	45	25
349	15p. Manx "Kneeler" Norton 350cc, 1953	50	35
350	29p. MV Agusta 500cc 4, 1956	90	70
351	31p. Guzzi 500cc V8, 1957	90	75
352	34p. Honda 250cc 6, 1967	1·00	90
MS353	150 × 140 mm. Nos. 348/52	3·50	3·50

Nos. 348/**MS**353 also commemorate the Centenary of the St. John Ambulance Brigade and No. **MS**353 carries the logo of "Capex '87" International Stamp Exhibition, Toronto, on its margin.

90 Fuchsia and Wild Roses

91 Stirring the Christmas Pudding

1987. Wild Flowers. Multicoloured.

354	16p. Type **90**	50	30
355	29p. Field scabious and ragwort	90	80
356	31p. Wood anemone and celandine	90	80
357	34p. Violets and primroses	1·00	80

1987. Christmas. Victorian Scenes. Multicoloured.

358	12p. Type **91**	40	35
359	15p. Bringing home the Christmas tree	50	55
360	31p. Decorating the Christmas tree	90	90

92 Russell Brookes in Vauxhall "Opel" (Manx Rally winner, 1985)

1988. Motor Sport. Multicoloured.

361	13p. Type **92**	75	35
362	26p. Ari Vatanen in Ford "Escort" (Manx Rally winner, 1976)	1·25	80
363	31p. Terry Smith in Repco "March 761" (Hill Climb winner, 1980)	1·40	90
364	34p. Nigel Mansell in Williams/Honda (British Grand Prix winner, 1986 and 1987)	1·60	1·00

93 Horse Tram Terminus, Douglas Bay Tramway

93a Queen Elizabeth II taking Salute at Trooping the Colour

1988. Manx Railways and Tramways. Mult.

365	1p. Type **93**	10	10
366	2p. Snaefell Mountain Railway	10	10
367	3p. Marine Drive Tramway	10	10
367c	4p. Douglas Cable Tramway	20	10
368	5p. Douglas Head Incline Railway	20	20
369	10p. Douglas & Laxey Coast Electric Tramway car at Maughold Head	30	30
370	13p. As 4p.	50	50
371	14p. Manx Northern Railway No. 4, "Caledonia", at Gob-y-Deigan	50	50
372	15p. Laxey Mine Railway Lewin locomotive "Ant"	50	50
373	16p. Port Erin Breakwater Tramway locomotive "Henry B. Loch"	50	50
374	17p. Ramsey Harbour Tramway	50	50
375	18p. Locomotive No. 7, "Tynwald", on Foxdale line	55	55
375a	18p. T.P.O. Special leaving Douglas, 3 July 1991	70	70
376	19p. Baldwin Reservoir Tramway steam locomotive No. 1, "Injebreck"	60	60
377	20p. I.M.R. No. 13, "Kissack", near St. Johns	60	60
377a	21p. As 14p.	60	60
377b	23p. Double-deck horse tram, Douglas	80	80
378	25p. I.M.R. No. 12, "Hutchinson", leaving Douglas	60	60
379	50p. Groudle Glen Railway locomotive "Polar Bear"	1·30	1·20
380	£1 I.M.R. No. 11, "Maitland", pulling Royal Train, 1963	2·50	2·50
380a	£2 Type **93a**	5·00	5·00

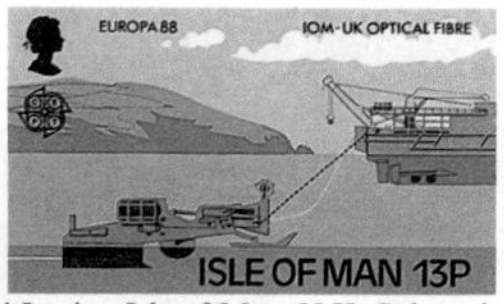

94 Laying Isle of Man–U.K. Submarine Cable

1988. Europa. Transport and Communications. Multicoloured.

381	13p. Type **94**	50	45
382	13p. "Flex Services" (cable ship)	50	45
383	22p. Earth station, Braddan	75	75
384	22p. "INTELSAT 5" satellite	75	75

Nos. 381/2 and 383/4 were each printed together, se-tenant, Nos. 381/2 forming a composite design.

95 "Euterpe" (full-rigged ship) off Ramsey, 1863

1988. Manx Sailing Ships. Multicoloured.

385	16p. Type **95**	45	30
386	29p. "Vixen" (topsail schooner) leaving Peel for Australia, 1853	90	90
387	31p. "Ramsey" (full-rigged ship) off Brisbane, 1870	90	90
388	34p. "Star of India" (formerly "Euterpe") (barque) off San Diego, 1976	1·10	1·10
MS389	110 × 85 mm. Nos. 385 and 388	1·90	2·00

Nos. 386/7 also commemorate the Bicent of Australian Settlement.

96 "Magellanica"

1988. 50th Anniv of British Fuchsia Society. Multicoloured.

390	13p. Type **96**	40	25
391	16p. "Pink Cloud"	45	35
392	22p. "Leonora"	65	50
393	29p. "Satellite"	90	65
394	31p. "Preston Guild"	1·00	70
395	34p. "Thalia"	1·10	70

97 Long-eared Owl

1988. Christmas. Manx Birds. Multicoloured.

396	12p. Type **97**	40	30
397	15p. European robin	60	65
398	31p. Grey partridge	1·25	1·25

98 Ginger Cat

1989. Manx Cats. Multicoloured.

399	16p. Type **98**	50	25
400	27p. Black and white cat	90	85
401	30p. Tortoiseshell and white cat	1·25	85
402	40p. Tortoiseshell cat	1·50	1·25

99 Tudric Pewter Clock, c. 1903

1989. 125th Birth Anniv of Archibald Knox (artist and designer). Multicoloured.

403	13p. Type **99**	40	20
404	16p. "Celtic Cross" watercolour	50	25
405	23p. Silver cup and cover 1902–03	65	50
406	32p. Gold and silver brooches from Liberty's Cymric range (horiz)	1·25	1·00
407	35p. Silver jewel box, 1900 (horiz)	1·40	1·00

100 William Bligh and Old Church, Onchan

1989. Bicentenary of the Mutiny on the "Bounty". Multicoloured.

408	13p. Type **100**	40	20
409	16p. Bligh and loyal crew cast adrift	45	30
410	23p. Pitcairn Islands 1989 Settlement Bicentenary 90c., No. 345	1·00	1·00
411	27p. Norfolk Island 1989 Bicentenary 39c., No. 461	1·00	1·00
412	30p. Midshipman Peter Heywood and Tahiti	70	60
413	32p. H.M.S. "Bounty" anchored off Pitcairn Island	70	60
414	35p. Fletcher Christian and Pitcairn Island	70	60
MS415	110 × 85 mm. Nos. 410/11 and 414	4·00	4·25

101 Skipping and Hopscotch

1989. Europa. Children's Games. Multicoloured.

416	13p. Type **101**	45	50
417	13p. Wheelbarrow, leapfrog and piggyback	45	50
418	23p. Completing model house and blowing bubbles	70	75
419	23p. Girl with doll and doll's house	70	75

Nos. 416/17 and 418/19 were printed together, se-tenant, forming composite designs.

102 Atlantic Puffin

104 Mother with Baby, Jane Crookall Maternity Home

103 Red Cross Cadets learning Resuscitation

1989. Sea Birds. Multicoloured.

420	13p. Type **102**	55	55
421	13p. Black guillemot	55	55
422	13p. Great cormorant ("Cormorant")	55	55
423	13p. Black-legged kittiwake ("Kittiwake")	55	55

1989. 125th Anniv of International Red Cross and Centenary of Noble's Hospital, Isle of Man.

424 **103**	14p. multicoloured	40	30
425 –	17p. grey and red	60	35
426 –	23p. multicoloured	75	85
427 –	30p. multicoloured	1·00	1·10
428 –	35p. multicoloured	1·25	1·25

DESIGNS: 17p. Anniversary logo; 23p. Signing Geneva Convention, 1864; 30p. Red Cross ambulance; 35p. Henri Dunant (founder).

1989. Christmas. 50th Anniv of Jane Crookall Maternity Home and 75th Anniv of St. Ninian's Church, Douglas. Multicoloured.

429	13p. Type **104**	50	45
430	16p. Mother with child	60	60
431	34p. Madonna and Child	1·10	1·25
432	37p. Baptism, St. Ninian's Church	1·25	1·40

105 "The Isle of Man Express going up a Gradient"

1990. Isle of Man Edwardian Postcards. Mult.
433 15p. Type **105** 35 35
434 19p. "A way we have in the Isle of Man" 60 50
435 32p. "Douglas-waiting for the male boat" . . . . . . 1·10 80
436 34p. "The last toast rack home, Douglas Parade" . . 1·50 1·10
437 37p. "The last Isle of Man boat" . . . . 1·60 1·50

106 Modern Postman

107 Penny Black

1990. Europa. Post Office Buildings. Mult.
438 15p. Type **106** 55 55
439 15p. Ramsey Post Office, 1990 (40 × 26 mm) 55 55
440 24p. Postman, 1890 . . . . . 90 90
441 24p. Douglas Post Office, 1890 (40 × 26 mm) 90 90

1990. 150th Anniv of the Penny Black.
442 **107** 1p. black, buff and gold 15 15
443 – 19p. gold, black and buff 60 50
444 – 32p. multicoloured . . . 1·25 1·10
445 – 34p. multicoloured . . . 1·50 1·10
446 – 37p. multicoloured . . . 1·60 1·10
MS447 100 × 71 mm. £1 black, gold and buff (50 × 60 mm) . . . . 4·00 3·50
DESIGNS: 19p. Wyon Medal, 1837; 32p. Wyon's stamp essay; 34p. Perkins Bacon engine-turned essay, 1839; 37p. Twopence Blue, 1840; £1 Block of four Penny Black stamps lettered IM-JN.
No. **MS**447 also commemorates "Stamp World London 90" International Stamp Exhibition.

108 Queen Elizabeth the Queen Mother

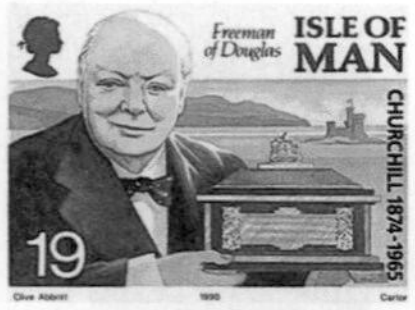

110 Churchill with Freedom of Douglas Casket

109 Hawker Hurricane Mk 1, Bristol Type 142 Blenheim Mk 1 and Home Defence

1990. 90th Birthday of Queen Elizabeth the Queen Mother.
448 **108** 90p. multicoloured . . . 3·00 3·00

1990. 50th Anniv of Battle of Britain. Mult.
449 15p. Type **109** 35 35
450 15p. Supermarine Spitfire with Westland Lysander Mk I rescue aircraft and launch 35 35
451 24p. Rearming Hawker Hurricanes Mk I fighters 80 80
452 24p. Ops room and scramble 80 80
453 29p. Civil Defence personnel 1·00 1·00
454 29p. Anti-aircraft battery . . 1·00 1·00

1990. 25th Death Anniv of Sir Winston Churchill. Multicoloured.
455 19p. Type **110** 45 45
456 32p. Churchill and London blitz . . . . 1·00 1·00
457 34p. Churchill and searchlights over Westminster . . . . . . 1·25 1·25
458 37p. Churchill with R.A.F. Hawker Hurricane Mk I fighters . . . . 1·25 1·25

111 Boy on Toboggan and Girl posting Letter

112 Henry Bloom Noble and Orphans (Marshall Wane)

1990. Christmas. Multicoloured.
459 14p. Type **111** 40 40
460 18p. Girl on toboggan and skaters 50 50
461 34p. Boy with snowman . . . 1·00 1·00
462 37p. Children throwing snowballs . . . . 1·25 1·25
MS463 123 × 55 mm. As Nos. 459/62, but face values in black . . . . 3·00 3·75

1991. Manx Photography.
464 **112** 17p. brown, grey and black 35 35
465 – 21p. brown and ochre . . 50 50
466 – 26p. brown, stone and black 65 65
467 – 31p. brown, lt brown & blk 90 90
468 – 40p. multicoloured . . . 1·10 1·10
DESIGNS: 21p. Douglas (Frederick frith); 26p. Studio portrait of three children (Hilda Newby); 31p. Castital yn Ard (Christopher Killip); 40p. Peel Castle (Colleen Corlett).

113 Lifeboat "Sir William Hillary", Douglas

1991. Manx Lifeboats. Multicoloured.
469 17p. Type **113** 45 45
470 21p. "Osman Gabriel", Port Erin 55 55
471 26p. "Ann and James Ritchie", Ramsey 90 90
472 31p. "The Gough Ritchie", Port St. Mary . . . . . . 1·25 1·25
473 37p. "John Batstone", Peel 1·40 1·40
No. 469 is inscribed "HILARY" and No. 471 "JAMES & ANN RITCHIE", both in error.

114 "Intelsat" Communications Satellite

116 Laxey Hand-cart, 1920

115 Oliver Godfrey with Indian 500cc at Start, 1911

1991. Europa. Europe in Space. Multicoloured.
474 17p. Type **114** 70 70
475 17p. "Ariane" rocket launch and fishing boats in Douglas harbour 70 70
476 26p. Weather satellite and space station . . . . . . 1·00 1·00
477 26p. Ronaldsway Airport, Manx Radio transmitter and Space shuttle launch 1·00 1·00
Nos. 474/5 and 476/7 were each printed together, se-tenant, each pair forming a composite design.

1991. 80th Anniv of Tourist Trophy Mountain Course. Multicoloured.
478 17p. Type **115** 50 40
479 21p. Freddie Dixon on Douglas "banking" sidecar, 1923 . . . . 65 60
480 26p. Bill Ivy on Yamaha 125cc, 1968 . . . . . . 80 80
481 31p. Giacomo Agostini on MV Agusta 500cc, 1972 . . 1·25 1·10
482 37p. Joey Dunlop on RVF Honda 750cc, 1985 . . . . 1·50 1·50
MS483 149 × 144 mm. Nos. 478/82 4·00 4·00

1991. 9th Conference of Commonwealth Postal Administration, Douglas. Sheet 119 × 77 mm. Multicoloured.
MS484 Nos. 367c and 377a, each × 2 . . . . 1·90 2·00

1991. Fire Engines. Multicoloured.
485 17p. Type **116** 45 40
486 21p. Horse-drawn steamer, Douglas, 1909 . . . . . 65 65
487 30p. Merryweather "Hatfield" pump, 1936 . . . . . . 85 90
488 33p. Dennis "F8" pumping appliance, Peel, 1953 . . . 1·25 1·25
489 37p. Volvo turntable ladder, Douglas, 1989 . . . . . 1·40 1·50

117 Mute Swans, Douglas Harbour

1991. Swans. Multicoloured.
490 17p. Type **117** 40 40
491 17p. Black swans, Curraghs Wildlife Park 40 40
492 26p. Whooper swans, Bishop's Dub, Ballaugh . . 1·10 1·00
493 26p. Tundra ("Bewick's") swans, Eairy Dam, Foxdale 1·10 1·00
494 37p. Coscoroba swans, Curraghs Wildlife Park . . 1·20 1·25
495 37p. Whooper ("Trumpeter") swans, Curraghs Wildlife Park . . . . 1·20 1·25
The two designs of each value were printed together, se-tenant, forming a composite design.

118 The Three Kings

120 Queen Elizabeth II at Coronation, 1953

119 North African and Italian Campaigns, 1942–43

1991. Christmas. Paper Sculptures. Multicoloured.
496 16p. Type **118** 45 35
497 20p. Mary with manger . . . 65 70
498 26p. Shepherds with sheep . . 85 85
499 37p. Choir of angels . . . . 1·10 1·10

1992. 50th Anniv of Parachute Regiment. Mult.
502 23p. Type **119** 70 70
503 23p. D-Day, 1944 . . . . . 70 70
504 28p. Arnhem, 1944 . . . . . 80 80
505 28p. Rhine crossing, 1945 . . 80 80
506 39p. Operations in Near, Middle and Far East, 1945–68 . . . . 1·25 1·25
507 39p. Liberation of Falkland Islands. 1982 . . . . . 1·25 1·25

1992. 40th Anniv of Accession. Multicoloured.
508 18p. Type **120** 45 40
509 23p. Queen visiting Isle of Man, 1979 . . . . 60 60
510 28p. Queen in evening dress 70 70
511 33p. Queen visiting Isle of Man, 1989 . . . . . . 1·25 1·40
512 39p. Queen arriving for film premiere, 1990 . . . . 1·40 1·40

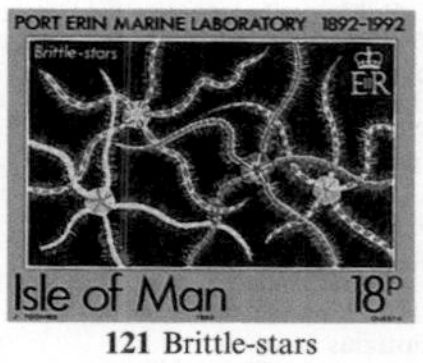

121 Brittle-stars

1992. Centenary of Port Erin Marine Laboratory. Multicoloured.
513 18p. Type **121** 40 35
514 23p. Phytoplankton 60 55
515 28p. Atlantic herring 60 55
516 33p. Great scallop . . . . . 1·25 1·25
517 39p. Dahlia anemone and delesseria . . . . 1·50 1·25

122 The Pilgrim Fathers embarking at Delfshaven

1992. Europa. 500th Anniv of Discovery of America by Columbus. Multicoloured.
518 18p. Type **122** 80 80
519 18p. "Speedwell" leaving Delfshaven 80 80
520 28p. "Mayflower" setting sail for America . . . . . . 1·75 1·75
521 28p. "Speedwell" anchored at Dartmouth . . . . . . 1·75 1·75
The two designs for each value were printed together, se-tenant, in horizontal pairs forming composite designs.

123 Central Pacific Locomotive "Jupiter", 1869

1992. Construction of the Union Pacific Railroad, 1866–69. Multicoloured.
522 33p. Type **123** . . . . . . 90 1·00
523 33p. Union Pacific locomotive No. 119, 1869 90 1·00
524 39p. Union Pacific locomotive No. 844, 1992 1·25 1·50
525 39p. Union Pacific locomotive No. 3985, 1992 1·25 1·50
MS526 105 × 78 mm. £1.50 Golden Spike ceremony, 10 May 1869 (60 × 50 mm) . . . . 3·70 4·50

124 "King Orry V" in Douglas Harbour

1992. Manx Harbours. Multicoloured.
527 18p. Type **124** 45 45
528 23p. Castletown 55 55
529 37p. Port St. Mary . . . . . 1·25 1·25
530 40p. Ramsey . . . . 1·25 1·25

125 "Saint Eloi" in 1972

126 Stained Glass Window, St. German's Cathedral, Peel

1992. "Genova '92" International Thematic Stamp Exhibition. Sheet 111 × 68 mm, containing T **125** and similar horiz design. Multicoloured.
MS531 18p. "King Orry V" in 1992 (as in Type **124**); £1 Type **125** 3·25 3·50

1992. Christmas. Manx Churches. Mult.
532 17p. Type **126** 45 40
533 22p. Reredos, St. Matthew the Apostle Church, Douglas 65 65
534 28p. Stained glass window, St. George's Church, Douglas 80 80
535 37p. Reredos, St. Mary of the Isle Catholic Church, Douglas 95 95
536 40p. Stained glass window, Trinity Methodist Church, Douglas . . . . 1·00 1·00

127 Mansell on Lap of Honour, British Grand Prix, 1992

1992. Nigel Mansell's Victory in Formula 1 World Motor Racing Championship. Multicoloured.
537 20p. Type **127** 80 80
538 24p. Mansell in French Grand Prix, 1992 1·00 1·00

128 H.M.S. "Amazon" (frigate)

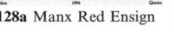

128a Manx Red Ensign **128b** Queen Elizabeth II (hologram)

1993. Ships. Multicoloured.
539 1p. Type **128** 10 10
540 2p. "Fingal" (lighthouse tender) 10 10
541 4p. "Sir Winston Churchill" (cadet schooner) 10 10
542 5p. "Dar Mlodziezy" (full-rigged cadet ship) 10 10
543 20p. "Tynwald I" (paddle-steamer) 40 25
544 21p. "Ben Veg" (freighter) 50 50
545 22p. "Waverley" (paddle-steamer) 50 50
546 23p. Royal Yacht "Britannia" 55 55
547 24p. "Francis Drake" (ketch) 50 35
548 25p. "Royal Viking Sky" (liner) 60 60
549 26p. "Lord Nelson" (cadet barque) 65 65
550 27p. "Europa" (liner) 65 65
551 30p. "Snaefell V" (ferry) leaving Ardrossan 75 75
552 35p. "Seacat" (catamaran ferry) 85 85
553 40p. "Lady of Man I" (ferry) off Ramsey 1·00 90
554 50p. "Mona's Queen II" (paddle ferry) leaving Fleetwood 1·25 1·10
555 £1 "Queen Elizabeth 2" (liner) and "Mona's Queen V" (ferry) off Liverpool 2·50 2·40
556 £2 Type **128a** 3·75 4·00
557 £5 Type **128b** 10·00 11·00

For 4, 20 and 24p. in smaller size, 21 × 18 mm, see Nos. 687/93.

129 No. 1 Motor Car and No. 13 Trailer at Groudle Glen Hotel

1993. Cent of Manx Electric Railway. Mult.
559 20p. Type **129** 60 60
560 24p. No. 9 Tunnel Car and No. 19 Trailer at Douglas Bay Hotel 90 90
561 28p. No. 19 Motor Car and No. 59 Royal Trailer Special at Douglas Bay 1·00 1·00
562 39p. No. 33 Motor Car, No. 45 Trailer and No. 13 Van at Derby Castle 1·40 1·40

130 "Sir Hall Caine" (statue) (Bryan Kneale)

1993. Europa. Contemporary Art. Works by Bryan Kneale. Multicoloured.
563 20p. Type **130** 60 60
564 20p. "The Brass Bedstead" (painting) 60 60
565 28p. Abstract bronze sculpture 1·00 1·00
566 28p. "Polar Bear Skeleton" (drawing) 1·00 1·00

131 Graham Oates and Bill Marshall (1933 International Six Day Trial) on Ariel Square Four

1993. Manx Motor Cycling Events. Mult.
567 20p. Type **131** 35 35
568 24p. Sergeant Geoff Duke (1947 Royal Signals Display Team) on Triumph 3T Twin 45 45
569 28p. Denis Parkinson (1953 Senior Manx Grand Prix) on Manx Norton 70 60
570 33p. Richard Swallow (1991 Junior Classic MGP) on Aermacchi 90 90
571 39p. Steve Colley (1992 Scottish Six Day Trial) on Beta Zero 1·00 95
MS572 165 × 120 mm. Nos. 567/71 4·50 4·50

132 "Inachis io" (Peacock) **133** Children decorating Christmas Tree

1993. Butterflies. Multicoloured.
573 24p. Type **132** 75 65
574 24p. "Argynnis aglaja" (Dark green fritillary) 75 65
575 24p. "Cynthia cardui" (Painted lady) 75 65
576 24p. "Celastrina argiolus" (Holly blue) 75 65
577 24p. "Vanessa atalanta" (Red admiral) 75 65

1993. Christmas. Multicoloured.
578 19p. Type **133** 50 50
579 23p. Girl with snowman 60 60
580 28p. Boy opening presents 70 70
581 39p. Girl with teddy bear 1·10 1·10
582 40p. Children with toboggan 1·10 1·10

134 White-throated Robin

1994. Calf of Man Bird Observatory. Mult.
583 20p. Type **134** 50 60
584 20p. Black-eared wheatear 50 60
585 24p. Goldcrest 80 90
586 24p. Northern oriole 80 90
587 30p. River kingfisher ("Kingfisher") 1·00 1·10
588 30p. Hoopoe 1·00 1·10
MS589 100 × 71 mm. £1 Black-billed magpie (51½ × 61 mm) 3·00 3·50

No. **MS**589 also commemorates the "Hong Kong '94" philatelic exhibition.

Winter
Gaiety Theatre
Pantomime · Choral Union · Manx Opera

135 Gaiety Theatre, Douglas

1994. Manx Tourism Centenary. Multicoloured.
590 24p. Type **135** 65 60
591 24p. Sports 65 60
592 24p. Artist at work and yachts racing 65 60
593 24p. TT Races and British Aerospace Hawk T.1s of Red Arrows display team 65 60
594 24p. Musical instruments 65 60
595 24p. Laxey Wheel and Manx cat 65 60
596 24p. Tower of Refuge, Douglas, with bucket and spade 65 60
597 24p. Cyclist 65 60
598 24p. Tynwald Day and classic car 65 60
599 24p. Santa Mince Pie train, Groudle Glen 65 60

136 "Eubranchus tricolor" (sea slug)

1994. Europa. Discoveries of Edward Forbes (marine biologist). Multicoloured.
600 20p. Type **136** 50 50
601 20p. "Loligo forbesii" (common squid) 50 50
602 20p. Edward Forbes and signature 50 50
603 30p. "Solaster moretonis" (fossil starfish) 90 90
604 30p. "Adamsia carciniopados" (anenome) on hermit crab 90 90
605 30p. "Solaster endeca" (starfish) 90 90

137 Maj-Gen. Bedell Smith and Naval Landing Force including "Ben-my-Chree IV" (ferry)

1994. 50th Anniv of D-Day. Multicoloured.
606 4p. Type **137** 15 15
607 4p. Admiral Ramsay and naval ships including "Victoria" and "Lady of Man" (ferries) 15 15
608 20p. Gen. Montgomery and British landings 70 70
609 20p. Lt-Gen. Dempsey and 2nd Army landings 70 70
610 30p. Air Chief Marshal Leigh-Mallory and U.S. paratroops and aircraft 1·00 1·00
611 30p. Air Chief Marshal Tedder and British paratroops and aircraft 1·00 1·00
612 41p. Lt-Gen. Bradley and U.S. 1st Army landings 1·25 1·25
613 41p. Gen. Eisenhower and American landings 1·25 1·25

138 Postman Pat, Jess and Ffinlo at Sea Terminal, Douglas

1994. Postman Pat visits the Isle of Man. Multicoloured.
614 1p. Type **138** 15 15
615 20p. Laxey Wheel 60 60
616 24p. Cregneash 80 80
617 30p. Manx Electric Railway trains 90 90
618 36p. Peel Harbour 1·10 1·10
619 41p. Douglas Promenade 1·25 1·25
MS620 110 × 85 mm. £1 Postman Pat (25 × 39 mm) 2·25 2·25

139 Cycling

1994. Centenary of International Olympic Committee. Multicoloured.
621 10p. Type **139** 35 25
622 20p. Downhill skiing 55 50
623 24p. Swimming 70 65
624 35p. Hurdling 95 90
625 48p. Centenary logo 1·60 1·25

140 Santa Train to Santon

1994. Christmas. Father Christmas in the Isle of Man. Multicoloured.
626 19p. Type **140** 60 60
627 23p. Father Christmas and Postman Pat on mini tractor, Douglas (vert) 80 80
628 60p. Father Christmas and majorettes in sleigh, Port St. Mary 2·00 2·00

141 Foden Steam Wagon, Highway Board Depot, Douglas

1995. Steam Traction Engines. Multicoloured.
629 20p. Type **141** 55 60
630 24p. Clayton & Shuttleworth and Fowler engines pulling dead whale 60 70
631 30p. Wallis and Steevens engine at Ramsey Harbour 80 85
632 35p. Marshall engine with threshing machine, Ballarhenny 1·10 1·10
633 41p. Marshall convertible steam roller 1·10 1·25

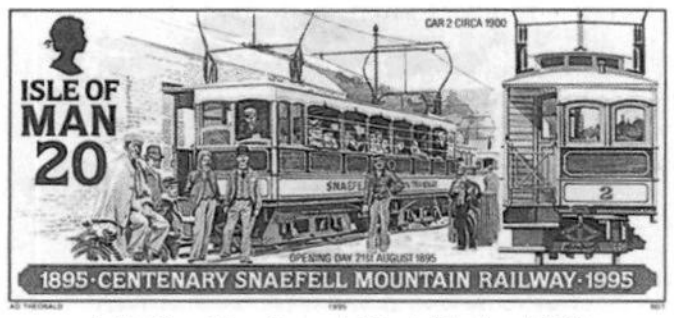

142 Car No. 2 and First Train, 1895

1995. Centenary of Snaefell Mountain Railway. Multicoloured.
634 20p. Type **142** 70 70
635 24p. Car No. 4 in green livery and Car No. 3 in Laxey Valley 80 80
636 35p. Car No. 6 and Car No. 5 in 1971 1·10 1·10
637 42p. Goods Car No. 7 and "Caledonia" steam locomotive pulling construction train 1·25 1·25
MS638 110 × 87 mm. £1 Passenger car and Argus char-a-banc at Bungalow Hotel (60 × 37 mm) 3·25 3·25

143 Peace Doves forming Wave and Tower of Refuge, Douglas Bay

1995. Europa. Peace and Freedom. Multicoloured.
639 20p. Type **143** 60 75
640 30p. Peace dove breaking barbed wire 1·00 1·00

144 Spitfire, Tank and Medals

1995. 50th Anniv of End of Second World War. Multicoloured.
641 10p. Type **144** 30 30
642 10p. Typhoon, anti-aircraft gun and medals 30 30
643 20p. Lancaster, H.M.S. "Biter" (escort carrier) and medals 55 55
644 20p. U.S. Navy aircraft, jungle patrol and medals 55 55
645 24p. Celebrations in Parliament Square 70 70
646 24p. V.E. Day bonfire 70 70
647 40p. Street party 1·10 1·10
648 40p. King George VI and Queen Elizabeth on Isle of Man in July 1945 1·10 1·10

145 Reg Parnell in Maserati "4 CLT", 1951

1995. 90th Anniv of Motor Racing on Isle of Man. Multicoloured.
649 20p. Type **145** 65 60
650 24p. Stirling Moss in Frazer Nash, 1951 80 75

651 30p. Richard Seaman in Delage, 1936 . . . . . . 90 85
652 36p. Prince Bira in ERA R2B "Romulus", 1937 . . . . 1·10 1·00
653 41p. Kenelm Guinness in Sunbeam 1, 1914 . . . . . 1·25 1·10
654 42p. Freddie Dixon in Riley, 1934 . . . . 1·25 1·10
MS655 103 × 73 mm. £1 John Napier in Arrol Johnston, 1905 (47 × 58 mm) . . . . 3·00 3·00

146 Thomas the Tank Engine and Bertie Bus being Unloaded

1995. 50th Anniv of Thomas the Tank Engine Stories by Revd. Awdry. "Thomas the Tank Engine's Dream". Multicoloured.
656 20p. Type **146** 65 60
657 24p. Mail train 80 75
658 30p. Bertie and engines at Ballasalla 90 85
659 36p. "Viking" the diesel engine, Port Erin . . . . . 1·10 1·00
660 41p. Thomas and railcar at Snaefell summit . . . . . 1·25 1·10
661 45p. Engines racing past Laxey Wheel . . . . . . 1·50 1·25

147 "Amanita muscaria" **148** St. Catherine's Church, Port Erin

1995. Fungi. Multicoloured.
662 20p. Type **147** 40 40
663 24p. "Boletus edulis" 50 50
664 30p. "Coprinus disseminatus" 60 60
665 35p. "Pleurotus ostreatus" . . 75 75
666 45p. "Geastrum triplex" . . 1·25 1·25
MS667 100 × 71 mm. £1 Shaggy ink cap and bee orchid (50 × 59 mm) 3·00 3·50
No. **MS**667 is inscribed "Singapore World Stamp Exhibition 1st–10th September 1995" on the sheet margin.

1995. Christmas. Multicoloured.
668 19p. Type **148** 55 55
669 23p. European robin on holly branch 70 70
670 42p. St. Peter's Church and wild flowers . . . . 1·50 1·50
671 50p. Hedgehog hibernating under farm machinery . . 1·75 1·75

149 Langness Lighthouse **151** Douglas Borough Arms

150 White Manx Cat and Celtic Interlaced Ribbons

1996. Lighthouses. Multicoloured.
672 20p. Type **149** 50 50
673 24p. Point of Ayre lighthouse (horiz) 60 60
674 30p. Chicken Rock lighthouse 90 90
675 36p. Calf of Man lighthouse (horiz) . . . . 1·00 1·00
676 41p. Douglas Head lighthouse . . . . 1·10 1·10
677 42p. Maughold Head lighthouse (horiz) . . . . 1·25 1·25

1996. Manx Cats. Multicoloured.
678 20p. Type **150** 50 50
679 24p. Cat and Union Jack ribbons 60 60
680 36p. Cat on rug in German colours, mouse and Brandenburg Gate 90 90
681 42p. Cat, U.S.A. flag and Statue of Liberty . . . . . 1·10 1·10
682 48p. Cat, map of Australia and kangaroo . . . . . . 1·25 1·25
MS683 100 × 71 mm. £1.50 Cat with kittens (51 × 61 mm) . . . . . 3·50 3·50
See also No. **MS**712.

1996. Centenary of Douglas Borough. Self-adhesive.
684 **151** (20p.) multicoloured . . . 70 1·00

1996. Ships. As Nos. 541, 543 and 547, but smaller, 21 × 18 mm. Multicoloured.
687 4p. "Sir Winston Churchill" (cadet schooner) 20 15
689 20p. "Tynwald I" (paddle-steamer), 1846 . . . . . . 60 70
693 24p. "Francis Drake" (ketch) 90 90
The 20p. and 24p. show the positions of the face value and Queen's head reversed.

152 Princess Anne (President, Save the Children Fund) and Children

1996. Europa. Famous Women. Multicoloured.
701 24p. Type **152** 70 75
702 30p. Queen Elizabeth II and people of the Commonwealth . . . . . 90 1·00

153 Alec Bennett

1996. Tourist Trophy Motorcycle Races. Irish Winners. Multicoloured.
703 20p. Type **153** 50 45
704 24p. Stanley Woods 60 60
705 45p. Artie Bell 90 90
706 60p. Joey and Robert Dunlop 1·40 1·40
MS707 100 × 70 mm. £1 R.A.F. Red Arrows display team (vert) . . 3·00 3·00

154 National Poppy Appeal Trophy

1996. 75th Anniv of Royal British Legion. Mult.
708 20p. Type **154** 65 55
709 24p. Manx War Memoial, Braddan 70 60
710 42p. Poppy appeal collection box . . . . 1·10 1·00
711 75p. Royal British Legion badge . . . . 2·00 2·00

1996. "Capex '96" International Stamp Exhibition, Toronto. No. **MS**683 additionally inscribed with "CAPEX '96" exhibition logo on sheet margin.
MS712 100 × 71 mm. £1.50 Cat with kittens (51 × 61 mm) . . . . . 6·00 6·50

155 U.N.I.C.E.F. Projects in Mexico

1996. 50th Anniv of U.N.I.C.E.F. Multicoloured.
713 24p. Type **155** 65 60
714 24p. Projects in Sri Lanka . . 65 60
715 30p. Projects in Colombia . . 85 75
716 30p. Projects in Zambia . . . 85 75
717 42p. Projects in Afghanistan 1·25 1·10
718 42p. Projects in Vietnam . . 1·25 1·10

156 Labrador

1996. Dogs. Multicoloured.
719 20p. Type **156** 60 55
720 24p. Border collie 70 65
721 31p. Dalmatian . . . . . . 1·00 90
722 38p. Mongrel . . . . 1·10 1·00
723 43p. English setter . . . . . 1·50 1·25
724 63p. Alsatian . . . . 2·00 1·75
MS725 100 × 71 mm. £1.20 Labrador guide dog and working Border collie (38 × 50 mm) . . 3·75 3·75

157 "Snowman and Pine Trees" (David Bennett) **158** Primroses and Cashtyl ny Ard

1996. Christmas. Children's Paintings. Multicoloured.
726 19p. Type **157** 55 50
727 23p. "Three-legged Father Christmas" (Louis White) 70 65
728 50p. "Family around Christmas Tree" (Robyn Whelan) . . . . 1·60 1·40
729 75p. "Father Christmas in Sleigh" (Claire Bradley) . . 2·10 1·90

1997. Spring in Man. Multicoloured.
730 20p. Type **158** 50 50
731 24p. Lochtan sheep and lambs 70 70
732 43p. Daffodils, mallard and ducklings . . . . 1·10 1·10
733 63p. Dabchick with young and frog on lily pad . . . 1·60 1·60

159 Barn Owl

1997. Owls. Multicoloured.
734 20p. Type **159** 65 60
735 24p. Short-eared owl 80 75
736 31p. Long-eared owl . . . . 1·00 90
737 36p. Little owl . . . . 1·25 1·10
738 43p. Snowy owl . . . . . . 1·40 1·25
739 56p. Eurasian tawny owl . . 1·60 1·50
MS740 100 × 71 mm. £1.20 Long-eared owl (different) (51 × 60 mm) 4·00 4·25
No. **MS**740 includes the "HONG KONG '97" International Stamp Exhibition logo on the sheet margin.

160 Moddey Dhoo, Peel Castle

1997. Europa. Tales and Legends. Multicoloured.
741 21p. Type **160** 55 55
742 25p. Fairies in tree and cottage 65 65
743 31p. Fairies at Fairy Bridge 85 85
744 36p. Giant Finn Macooil and Calf of Man . . . . 1·10 1·10
745 37p. The Buggane of St. Trinian's . . . . . . 1·10 1·10
746 43p. Fynoderee and farm . . 1·40 1·40
Nos. 742/3 include the "EUROPA" emblem.

161 Sopwith Tabloid

1997. Manx Aircraft. Multicoloured.
747 21p. Type **161** 45 45
748 21p. Grumman Tiger (1996 Schneider Trophy) 45 45
749 25p. BAe ATP (15th anniv of Manx Airlines) 55 55
750 25p. BAe 146-200 (15th anniv of Manx Airlines) 55 55
751 31p. Boeing 757-200 (largest aircraft to land on Isle of Man) 70 70
752 31p. Farman biplane (1st Manx flight, 1911) 70 70
753 36p. Spitfire 80 80
754 36p. Hawker Hurricane . . . 80 80
Nos. 747/8, 749/50, 751/2 and 753/4 respectively were each printed together, se-tenant, the backgrounds forming composite of Isle of Man.

No. 752 is inscribed "EARMAN BIPLANE" in error.

162 14th Hole, Ramsey Golf Club

1997. Golf. Multicoloured.
755 21p. Type **162** 50 50
756 25p. 15th Hole, King Edward Bay Golf and Country Club 60 60
757 43p. 17th Hole, Rowany Golf Club . . . . 1·10 1·10
758 50p. 8th Hole, Castletown Golf Links . . . . 1·50 1·50
MS759 100 × 71 mm. £1.30 Golf ball (circular, diameter 39 mm) . . 3·50 3·50
No. **MS**759 includes the "Pacific '97" International Stamp Exhibition logo on the sheet margin.

1997. Return of Hong Kong to China. Sheet 130 × 90 mm, containing No. 546. Multicoloured.
MS760 23p. Royal Yacht "Britannia" . . . . 1·40 1·60

163 Steve Colley

1997. F.I.M. "Trial de Nations" Motorcycle Team Trials. Multicoloured.
761 21p. Type **163** 55 50
762 25p. Steve Saunders (vert) . . 65 60
763 37p. Sammy Miller (vert) . . 1·25 1·00
764 44p. Don Smith . . . . . . 1·50 1·25

164 Angel and Shepherd **165** Engagement of Princess Elizabeth and Lieut. Philip Mountbatten, 1947

1997. Christmas. Multicoloured.
765 20p. Type **164** 65 55
766 24p. Angel and King 75 70
767 63p. The Nativity (54 × 39 mm) . . . . . . 1·60 1·50

1997. Golden Wedding of Queen Elizabeth and Prince Philip. Multicoloured (except No. 768).
768 50p. Type **165** (brown and gold) . . . . 1·40 1·40
769 50p. Wedding photograph, 1947 . . . . 1·40 1·40
770 50p. At Ascot, 1952 . . . . 1·40 1·40
771 50p. Golden Wedding photograph, 1997 . . . . 1·40 1·40
MS772 100 × 72 mm. £1 Queen Elizabeth and Prince Philip at Peel, 1989 (47 × 58 mm) . . . 3·00 3·00

166 Shamrock **168** Viking Figurehead

167 Queen Elizabeth II and Queen Elizabeth the Queen Mother

1998. Flowers. Multicoloured
773 1p. Bearded iris 10 10
774 2p. Daisy 10 10
775 4p. Type **166** 10 10
776 5p. Silver Jubilee rose 10 15
777 10p. Oriental poppy 20 25

778	20p. Heath spotted orchid . .	40	30
779	21p. Cushag	40	45
780	22p. Gorse	45	50
781	25p. Princess of Wales rose	50	40
782	26p. Dog rose	50	40
783	30p. Fuchsia "Lady Thumb"	60	60
784	50p. Daffodil	1·00	1·00
785	£1 Spear thistle	2·00	2·00
790	£2.50 Type **167**	5·00	4·75

1998. Viking Longships. Multicoloured.

793	21p. Type **168**	55	50
794	25p. Viking longship at sea	75	70
795	31p. Viking longship on beach	90	80
796	75p. Stern of ship	2·25	2·00
MS797	100 × 71 mm. £1 Viking ship at Peel Castle	3·00	3·00

169 Bottle-nosed Dolphins

1998. U.N.E.S.C.O. International Year of the Ocean. Multicoloured.

798	10p. Type **169**	30	30
799	21p. Basking shark	50	50
800	25p. Front view of basking shark	65	65
801	31p. Minke whale	75	75
802	63p. Killer whale and calf . .	1·60	1·60

170 Locomotive No. 12 "Hutchinson"

1998. 125th Anniv of Isle of Man Steam Railway. Multicoloured.

803	21p. Type **170**	60	50
804	25p. Locomotive No. 10 "G. H. Wood"	70	60
805	31p. Locomotive No. 11 "Maitland"	90	80
806	63p. Locomotive No. 4 "Loch"	1·60	1·60
MS807	119 × 54 mm. 25p. Pillar box and train at Douglas Station; £1 Locomotive No. 1 "Sutherland"	3·00	3·00

171 Purple Helmets Display Team

1998. Isle of Man T.T. Races and 50th Anniv of Honda (manufacturer). Multicoloured.

808	21p. Type **171**	40	45
809	25p. Joey Dunlop	50	55
810	31p. Dave Molyneux	65	65
811	43p. Naomi Taniguchi . . .	1·00	1·00
812	63p. Mike Hailwood	1·40	1·50

172 Princess Diana wearing Protective Clothing, Angola

1998. Diana, Princess of Wales Commemoration. Multicoloured.

813	25p. Type **172**	55	55
814	25p. Receiving award from United Cerebral Palsy Charity, New York, 1995	55	55
815	25p. With children, South Korea, 1992	55	55
816	25p. Wearing blue jacket, July 1993	55	55

173 Tynwald Day Ceremony

1998. Europa. Festivals. Multicoloured.

817	25p. Type **173**	50	45
818	30p. Traditional dancers, Tynwald Fair	75	65

174 Father Christmas at North Pole

1998. Christmas. "A Very Special Delivery". Multicoloured.

819	20p. Type **174**	40	30
820	24p. Father Christmas checking list	50	45
821	30p. Flying over Spring Valley sorting office . . .	75	60
822	43p. Passing through Baldrine village	95	85
823	63p. Father Christmas delivering presents	1·40	1·25

175 Large Oval Pillar Box, Kirk Onchan **176** Cottage, Ballaglass Glen

1999. Local Post Boxes. Multicoloured.

824	10p. Type **175**	25	25
825	20p. Wall box, Ballaterson	45	45
826	21p. King Edward VII pillar box, Laxey Station	50	50
827	25p. Wall box, Spaldrick . .	60	55
828	44p. Small oval pillar box, Derby Road, Douglas . .	1·00	95
829	63p. Wall box, Baldrine Station	1·50	1·40

1999. Europa. Parks and Gardens. Multicoloured.

830	25p. Type **176**	50	50
831	30p. Glen Maye Waterfall . .	75	60

177 "Ann and James Ritchie", Ramsey

1999. 175th Anniv of Royal National Lifeboat Institution. Multicoloured.

832	21p. Type **177**	50	50
833	25p. "Sir William Hillary", Douglas	55	55
834	37p. "Ruby Clery, Peel" . .	80	80
835	43p. "Herbert and Edith" (inshore lifeboat), Port Erin	90	90
836	43p. 1974 150th Anniv 8p. stamp	2·25	3·00
837	56p. "Gough Ritchie II", Port St. Mary	1·25	1·25
838	56p. 1991 Manx Lifeboats 21p. stamp	2·50	3·00
MS839	100 × 70 mm. £1 Sir William Hillary (founder) (37 × 50 mm)	3·00	3·00

No. **MS**839 includes the "Australia '99" World Stamp Exhibition emblem on the sheet margin.

178 Winter

1999. Centenary of Yn Cheshaght Ghailckagh (Manx Gaelic Society). The Seasons. Multicoloured.

840	22p. Type **178**	60	60
841	26p. Spring	65	65
842	50p. Summer	1·10	1·10
843	63p. Autumn	1·60	1·60

Nos. 840/3 are inscribed "Ellan Vannin", the Manx name for the Isle of Man.

179 Queen Victoria

1999. British Monarchs of the 20th Century. Sheet 170 × 75 mm, containing T **179** and similar horiz designs. Multicoloured.

MS844	26p. Type **179**; 26p. King Edward VII; 26p. King George V; 26p. King Edward VIII; 26p. King George VI; 26p. Queen Elizabeth II	3·25	3·25

180 Tilling-Stevens Double-deck Bus, 1922

1999. Manx Buses. Multicoloured.

845	22p. Type **180**	50	50
846	26p. Thornycroft BC single-deck, 1928	55	55
847	28p. Cumberland ADC 416 single-deck, 1927	65	65
848	37p. Straker-Squire single-deck, 1914	80	80
849	38p. Thornycroft A2 single-deck, 1927	90	90
850	40p. Leyland Lion LT9 single-deck, 1938	1·00	1·00

181 Miss Sophie Rhys-Jones

1999. Royal Wedding. Multicoloured.

851	22p. Type **181**	55	55
852	26p. Leaving St. George's Chapel, Windsor	55	55
853	39p. Prince Edward	80	80
854	44p. Miss Sophie Rhys-Jones and Prince Edward (horiz)	1·10	1·10
855	53p. In landau (horiz) . . .	1·25	1·25

1999. "Philexfrance 99" International Stamp Exhibition, Paris. No. **MS**807 additionally inscribed with "Philexfrance" exhibition logo on sheet margin.

MS856	119 × 54 mm. 25p. Pillar box and train at Douglas Station; £1 Locomotive No. 1 "Sutherland"	3·50	3·75

182 St. Luke's Church, Baldwin

1999. Christmas. Churches. Multicoloured.

857	21p. Type **182**	45	45
858	25p. St. Mark's Chapel, Malew	60	60
859	30p. St. German's Parish Church and Cathedral, Peel	70	70
860	64p. Kirk Christ Church, Rushen	1·50	1·50

183 "Massachusetts", 1967

1999. Legends of Music. The Bee Gees (pop group). Designs showing compact discs. Multicoloured.

861	22p. Type **183**	60	50
862	26p. "Words", 1968	70	65
863	29p. "I've Gotta Get a Message to You", 1968 . .	75	65
864	37p. "Ellan Vannin", 1998	90	85
865	38p. "You Win Again", 1987	90	85
866	66p. "Night Fever", 1978 . .	1·50	1·50
MS867	Two sheets, each 119 × 108 mm. (a) 60p. "Immortality", 1998 (circular, 40 mm diam). (b) 90p. "Stayin' Alive", 1978 (circular, 40 mm diam) Set of 2 sheets	3·00	3·50

184 Sky at Sunset over Calf of Man

1999. New Millennium. Sheet 169 × 74 mm, containing T **184** and similar vert designs. Multicoloured.

MS868	50p. Type **184**; 50p. Sky at dawn over Maughold Head; £2 Constellations over Man at start of new millennium	6·50	6·75

185 Harrison's Chronometer, 1735, and Map **187** Barn Swallow ("Swallow")

186 Duke and Duchess of York on Wedding Day, 1923

2000. "The Story of Time". Multicoloured.

869	22p. Type **185**	50	55
870	26p. Daniels' chronometer, 2000, and clock face . . .	55	60
871	29p. Harrison's chronometer, 1767, map and clock . . .	65	70
872	34p. Mudge's chronometer, 1769, and steam locomotives	75	80
873	38p. Arnold's chronometer, 1779, and map of Africa	80	85
874	44p. Earnshaw's chronometer, 1780, and map of Caribbean	95	1·00

2000. "Queen Elizabeth the Queen Mother's Century". Multicoloured (except 26p. and 30p).

875	22p. Type **186**	50	55
876	26p. Queen Elizabeth with Princess Elizabeth, 1940 (brown and black)	55	60
877	30p. King George VI and Queen Elizabeth visiting troops, 1944 (brown and black)	65	70
878	44p. Queen Mother and Queen Elizabeth, 1954 . .	95	1·00
879	52p. Queen Mother with Prince Charles, 1985 . . .	1·10	1·25
880	64p. Queen Mother, 1988 . .	1·40	1·50
MS881	100 × 70 mm. £1 Queen Mother visiting Isle of Man (74 × 49 mm)	2·25	2·25

2000. Endangered Species. Song Birds. Mult.

882	22p. Type **187**	50	55
883	26p. Spotted flycatcher . . .	55	60
884	64p. Eurasian sky lark ("Sky Lark")	1·40	1·50
885	77p. Yellowhammer	1·60	1·75

2000. "The Stamp Show 2000" International Stamp Exhibition, London. As No. **MS**881, but with "The Stamp Show 2000" multicoloured logo added to the bottom sheet margin.

MS886	100 × 70 mm. £1 Queen Mother visiting Isle of Man (74 × 49 mm)	2·40	2·50

188 Lieut. John Quilliam and Admiral Lord Nelson, Battle of Trafalgar

2000. Isle of Man at War. Multicoloured.

887	22p. Type **188**	50	55
888	26p. Ensign Caesar Bacon and Duke of Wellington, Battle of Waterloo	55	60
889	36p. Col. Thomas Leigh Goldie and Earl of Cardigan, Crimea	75	80
890	48p. Bugler John Dunne and Sir Robert Baden Powell, Boer War	1·00	1·10
891	50p. George Kneale and Viscount Kitchener of Khartoum, First World War	1·00	1·25
892	77p. First Officer Alan Watterson and Sir Winston Churchill, Second World War	1·50	1·60
MS893	170 × 75 mm. 60p. Two Supermarine Spitfires (40 × 29 mm); 60p. Spitfire on ground (40 × 29 mm), Battle of Britain	2·50	2·75

189 Prince William as Child

2000. 18th Birthday of Prince William. Sheet 170 × 75 mm, containing T **189** and similar vert designs. Multicoloured.

MS894	22p. Type **189**; 26p. With Queen Mother; 45p. Prince William; 52p. With Prince Charles and Prince Harry; 56p. Wearing ski-suit	4·25	4·50

190 Ballet Shoes and Painted Ceiling

2000. Centenary of Gaiety Theatre, Douglas. Mult.

895	22p. Type **190**	50	55
896	26p. Comedy mask and box decoration	55	60
897	36p. Drama mask and statue	75	80
898	45p. Pantomime dame with wig and mosaic	95	1·00
899	52p. Opera glasses and decoration	1·10	1·25
900	65p. Top hat with cane and painted ceiling	1·40	1·50

191 Map of Great Britain, Union Jack and Liner

2000. "BT Global Challenge" Round the World Yacht Race. Each showing spinnaker of *Isle of Man*. Multicoloured.

901	22p. Type **191**	50	55
902	26p. Sydney Opera House, Australian flag and map	55	60
903	36p. New Zealand map and flag	75	80
904	40p. Map of Buenos Aires and waterfront	85	90
905	44p. U.S. flag, map of Boston and harbour	95	1·00
906	65p. South African flag, map and Table Mountain	1·40	1·50

192 Sailing and Holiday Tours Poster, 1925

193 Girl with Christingle Candle

2000. 170th Anniv of Steam Packet Company. Tourism posters. Multicoloured.

907	22p. Type **192**	50	55
908	26p. "Isle of Man for Happy Holidays"	55	60
909	36p. Woman in swim suit standing on Isle of Man, 1929	75	80
910	45p. Stewardess and ferry	95	1·00
911	65p. "Isle of Man for Holidays 1931" and ferry	1·40	1·50

2000. Christmas and Europa. Multicoloured.

912	21p. Type **193**	45	50
913	25p. Children dancing around Christmas tree	55	60
914	36p. "Building Europe"	75	80
915	45p. Girl hugging teddy bear	95	1·00
916	65p. Children with stars	1·40	1·50

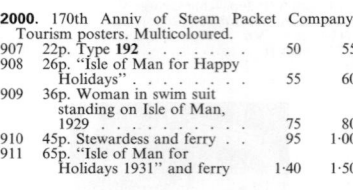

194 Wyon Medal, Penny Black and Queen Victoria

2001. Death Centenary of Queen Victoria. Mult.

917	22p. Type **194**	50	55
918	26p. Great Exhibition medal and Albert Tower, Ramsey	55	60
919	34p. Silver coin and *Great Britain* (early steamship)	75	80
920	39p. Manx coin of 1839, *Oliver Twist* and St. Thomas' Church, Douglas	85	90
921	40p. Silver coin of 1887, arrival of first train at Vancouver and Jubilee lamp standard	85	90
922	52p. Silver coin of 1893, Joe Mylchreest at Kimberley diamond mine and Foxdale Clock Tower	1·10	1·25

195 St. Patrick and Snakes (⅔-size illustration)

2001. Chinese New Year ("Year of the Snake"). Sheet 110 × 85 mm.

MS923	**195** £1 multicoloured	2·25	2·40

No. **MS**923 includes the "Hong Kong 2001" logo on the sheet margin.

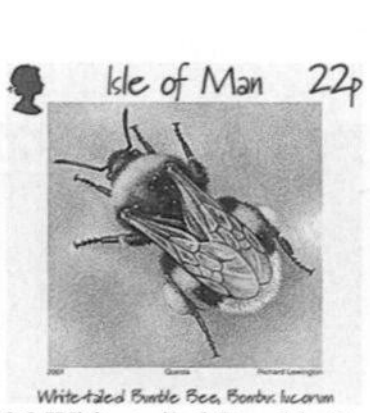

196 White-tailed Bumble Bee

2001. Insects. Multicoloured.

924	22p. Type **196**	50	55
925	26p. Seven-spot ladybird	55	60
926	29p. Lesser mottled grasshopper	65	70
927	59p. Manx robber fly	1·25	1·40
928	66p. Elephant hawkmoth	1·40	1·50

197 Letter-carrier, 1805

198 1967–70 Great Britain $\frac{1}{2}$d. Machin

2001. Postal Uniforms. Multicoloured.

929	22p. Type **197**	50	55
930	26p. Postman, 1859	55	60
931	36p. Postman, 1910	75	80
932	39p. Postman, 1933	85	90
933	40p. Postman, 1983	85	90
934	66p. Postman, 2001	1·40	1·50

2001. 75th Birthday of Queen Elizabeth II. Sheet 170 × 75 mm, containing T **198** and similar vert designs showing stamps. Multicoloured.

MS935	29p. Type **198**; 34p. 1952–54 Great Britain 6d. Wilding; 37p. 1971 Isle of Man $2\frac{1}{2}$p. Regional; 50p. 1958–68 Isle of Man 4d. Regional	3·50	3·75

199 Joey Dunlop on Rea Yamaha, Parliament Square, 1977 TT Races

2001. Joey Dunlop (motorcycle champion) Commemoration. Each incorporating different portraits. Multicoloured.

936	22p. Type **199**	50	55
937	26p. At Governor's, 1983 TT Races	55	60
938	36p. Leaving Ramsey, 1988 TT Races	75	80
939	45p. On Honda motorbike, 1991	95	1·00
940	65p. On 250cc Honda at Ballaspur, 1999	1·40	1·50
941	77p. On the Mountain	1·60	1·75

200 "The Manx Derby, 1627" (Johnny Jonas)

2001. Horse Racing Paintings. Multicoloured.

942	22p. Type **200**	50	55
943	26p. "Post Haste" (Johnny Jonas)	55	60
944	36p. "Red Rum" (Hamilton-Rennick)	75	80
945	52p. "Hyperion" (Sir Alfred Munnings)	1·10	1·40
946	63p. "Isle of Man" (Johnny Jonas)	1·40	1·50

201 Beef

203 Royal Refreshments at Glasgow

202 Castletown Police Station

2001. Europa. Local Dishes prepared by Kevin Woodford. Multicoloured.

947	22p. Type **201**	50	55
948	26p. Queenies with salmon caviar	55	60
949	36p. Seafood	75	80
950	45p. Lamb	95	1·00
951	50p. Kipper tart	1·10	1·25
952	66p. Lemon tart with raspberries	1·40	1·50

The 26p. and 36p. show the inscription "EUROPA 2001" at bottom right.

2001. The Architecture of Mackay Hugh Bailie Scott. Multicoloured.

953	22p. Type **202**	50	55
954	26p. "Leafield" (semi-detached house)	55	60
955	37p. "The Red House" (Bailie Scott's home)	80	85
956	40p. "Ivydene" (detached house)	85	90
957	80p. Onchan Village Hall	1·75	1·90

Nos. 953/7 are inscribed "HUGH MACKAY" in error.

2001. "Hafnia 01" International Stamp Exhibition, Denmark. No. **MS**935 additionally inscr with "Hafnia 01" logo in red on sheet margin.

MS958	170 × 75 mm. 29p Type **198**; 34p, 1952–54 Great Britain 6d. Wilding; 37p, 1971 Isle of Man $2\frac{1}{2}$p. Regional; 50p, 1958–68 Isle of Man 4d. Regional	3·00	3·25

2001. Golden Jubilee (1st issue). "The Daily Life of the Queen—An Artist's Diary" (paintings by Michael Noakes). Multicoloured.

959	22p. Type **203**	50	55
960	26p. Queen on visit to Lancaster	55	60
961	39p. Queen with labradors, Sandringham	85	90
962	40p. Queen meeting Scottish Korean War veterans	85	90
963	45p. Queen at desk, Sandringham	95	1·00
964	65p. Queen with bouquet, Oxford	1·40	1·50

See also Nos. 970/4.

204 Christmas Tree Wall Decoration

205 "The Coronation, 1953" (Terence Cuneo)

2001. Christmas. Decorations by Isle of Man Floreat Workshop. Multicoloured.

965	21p. Type **204**	45	50
966	25p. Traditional wreath	55	60
967	37p. Table decoration	80	85
968	45p. Topiary tree	95	1·00
969	65p. Contemporary wreath	1·40	1·50

2002. Golden Jubilee (2nd issue). Royal Paintings. Multicoloured.

970	50p. Type **205**	1·00	1·10
971	50p. "Queen Elizabeth II as Colonel-in-Chief of Grenadier Guards on Imperial, 1962" (T. Cuneo)	1·00	1·10
972	50p. "Queen Elizabeth II in Evening Dress, 1981" (June Mendoza)	1·00	1·10
973	50p. "Queen Elizabeth II in Garter Robes, 2000" (Chen Yan Ning)	1·00	1·10
974	50p. "The Royal Family in the White Drawing Room, Buckingham Palace" (John Wonnacott)	1·00	1·10
MS975	110 × 85 mm. £1 Sculpture of Queen Elizabeth II by David Cregeen (40 × 61 mm)	2·00	2·10

206 Cycling

2002. 17th Commonwealth Games, Manchester. Each showing photographic montages. Mult.

976	22p. Type **206**	45	50
977	26p. Running	50	55
978	29p. Javelin and high jump	60	65
979	34p. Swimming	70	75
980	40p. Decathlon	80	85
981	45p. Wheelchair racing	90	95

207 "Queen Elizabeth the Queen Mother" (Johnny Jonas)

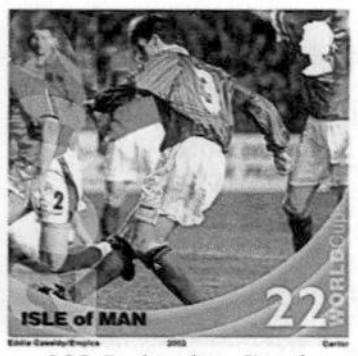

208 Ireland v Czech Republic

2002. Queen Elizabeth the Queen Mother Commemoration.
982 **207** £3 multicoloured . . . . 6·00 6·25

2002. World Cup Football Championship, Japan and Korea (2002). Multicoloured.
983 22p. Type **208** 45 50
984 26p. England v Greece . . . 50 55
985 39p. Italy v Belgium 80 85
986 40p. France v Portugal . . . 80 85
987 66p. England v Brazil . . . . 1·25 1·40
988 68p. France v Japan . . . . 1·40 1·50

209 "Monk's Bridge, Ballasalla" (Toni Onley)

2002. Watercolours by Toni Onley. Multicoloured.
989 22p. Type **209** 45 50
990 26p. "Laxey" 50 55
991 37p. "Langness Lighthouse" 75 80
992 45p. "King William's College" 90 95
993 65p. "The Mull Circle and Bradda Head" . . . . . . 1·25 1·40

2002. Golden Jubilee Celebrations. Nos. **MS**975 additionally inscribed "THE ISLE OF MAN CELEBRATES THE JUBILEE 4th JUNE 2002" in purple on the sheet margin.
MS994 110 × 85 mm. £1 Sculpture of Queen Elizabeth II by David Cregeen (40 × 61 mm) . . . . 2·00 2·10

210 Magenta Flower on Yellow Background

2002. Memories of the Isle of Man. Multicoloured.
995 22p. Type **210** 45 50
996 26p. Green flower on pink background 50 55
997 29p. Purple flower on green background 60 65
998 52p. Maroon flower on brown background . . . 1·00 1·10
999 63p. Red flower on blue background . . . . . . 1·25 1·40
1000 77p. Orange flower on yellow background . . . 1·50 1·60

211 Manx Milestone (Mrs. B. Trimble)

212 Father Christmas

2002. Photography -- The People's Choice. Designs showing competition winners. Multicoloured. Ordinary or self-adhesive gum.
1001 23p. Type **211** 45 50
1002 23p. Plough horses (Miss D. Flint) 45 50
1003 23p. Manx emblem (Ruth Nicholls) 45 50
1004 23p. Loaghtan sheep (Diana Burford) 45 50
1005 23p. Fishing fleet, Port St. Mary (Phil Thomas) 45 50
1006 23p. Peel (Michael Thompson) 45 50
1007 23p. Daffodils (Michael Thompson) 45 50
1008 23p. Millennium sword (Mr. F. K. Smith) 45 50
1009 23p. Peel Castle (Kathy Brown) 45 50
1010 23p. Snaefell Railway (Joan Burgess) 45 50
1011 27p. Laxey Wheel (Kathy Brown) 55 60
1012 27p. Sheep at Druidale (John Hall) 55 60
1013 27p. Carousel at Silverdale (Colin Edwards) 55 60
1014 27p. Grandma (Stephanie Corkhill) 55 60
1015 27p. Manx rock (Ruth Nicholls) 55 60
1016 27p. T.T. riders at Signpost (Neil Brew) 55 60
1017 27p. Groudle Railway (Albert Lowe) 55 60
1018 27p. Royal cascade (Brian Speedie) 55 60
1019 27p. St. Johns (John Hall) 55 60
1020 27p. Niarbyl cottages with poppies (Cathy Galbraith) 55 60

2002. Christmas. Entertainment. Multicoloured.
1041 22p. Type **212** 45 50
1042 26p. Virgin Mary and Jesus 50 55
1043 37p. Clown 75 80
1044 47p. Bandsman playing cymbals . . . . 95 1·00
1045 68p. Fairy . . . . 1·40 1·50
MS1046 123 × 55 mm. £1.30 "CHRISTMAS" and festive characters (103 × 40 mm) . . . 2·50 2·75
The 37p. value includes the "EUROPA" emblem.

213 Dish Aerial and Peel Castle

2003. Isle of Man Involvement in Space Exploration. Multicoloured.
1047 23p. Type **213** 45 50
1048 23p. Dish aerial, Tromode Teleport 45 50
1049 27p. Camp on Moon and lunar vehicle 55 60
1050 27p. Astronaut exploring lunar surface 55 60
1051 37p. *Sea Launch Odyssey* (marine launch platform) 75 80
1052 37p. *Sea Launch Commander* (assembly command ship) 75 80
1053 42p. Loral Telstar 1 satellite 85 90
1054 42p. Loral Telstar 8 satellite 85 90
MS1055 110 × 85 mm. 75p. Phobos and American spaceship (30 × 36 mm); 75p. Mars, astronauts and transfer vehicle (30 × 36 mm) . . . . 3·00 3·25
Nos. 1047/8, 1049/50, 1051/2 and 1053/4 were each printed together, as horizontal se-tenant pairs, in sheets of 8 with enlarged illustrated right margins.

214 Delivery Handcart (1900–45)

2003. Post Office Vehicles. Multicoloured.
1056 23p. Type **214** 45 50
1057 27p. Morris Z van (1942) 55 60
1058 37p. Morris L diesel van (1960s) 75 80
1059 42p. DI BSA Bantam telegraph delivery motorbikes 85 90
1060 89p. Ford Escort 55 van . . 1·75 1·90

215 Queen Elizabeth II wearing St. Edward's Crown

2003. 50th Anniv of Coronation. Multicoloured.
1061 50p. Type **215** (26 × 57 mm) 1·00 1·10
1062 50p. The Ring (23 × 28 mm) 1·00 1·10
1063 50p. The Orb (23 × 28 mm)
1064 50p. Royal Sceptre and Rod of Equity and Mercy (23 × 28 mm) . . . . . . 1·00 1·10
1065 50p. Queen Elizabeth II wearing Imperial State Crown (26 × 57 mm) . . . 1·00 1·10
1066 50p. State Coach (81 × 27 mm) . . . . . . 1·00 1·10

216 De Havilland D.H. 83 Fox Moth and Saro Cloud (amphibian)

2003. Centenary of Powered Flight. Each showing two aircraft. Multicoloured.
1067 23p. Type **216** 45 50
1068 27p. De Havilland D.H. 61 Giant Moth and D.H. 80 Puss Moth 55 60
1069 37p. Avro Type 652 and Boeing B-17 Flying Fortress 75 80
1070 40p. Eurofighter Typhoon and Avro Vulcan 80 85
1071 67p. Handley Page Herald and Bristol Wayfarer . . 1·40 1·50
1072 89p. Aerospatiale Concorde and projected Airbus Industrie A380 . . . . . 1·75 1·90

217 Avro Lancaster attacking Mohne Dam (½-size illustration)

2003. 60th Anniv of Attack on German Dams by No. 617 ("Dambusters") Squadron. Sheet 170 × 75 mm.
MS1073 **217** £2 multicoloured . . 4·00 4·25

218 Prince William

2003. 21st Birthday of Prince William of Wales.
1074 **218** 42p. black and grey . . 85 90
1075 – 47p. black and grey . . 95 1·00
1076 – 52p. black and grey . . 1·00 1·10
1077 – 68p. black and grey . . 1·40 1·50
DESIGNS: 47p. to 68p. Showing recent photographs.

2003. Trilaterale Ticino Exhibition, Locarno, Switzerland. No. **MS**1073 additionally inscr with "Ticino 2003" logo in blue on sheet margin.
MS1078 £2 multicoloured . . . . 4·00 4·25

219 *Manx Gold* (Agatha Christie)

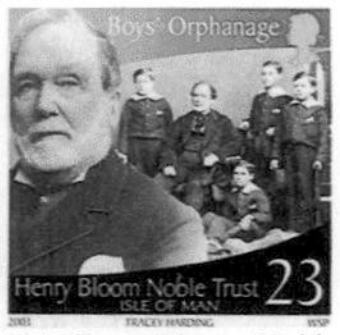

221 Henry Bloom Noble and Orphanage Boys

220 King Henry VII and Henry Tudor crowned by Sir Thomas Stanley on Bosworth Battlefield

2003. "The Manx Bookshelf". Book covers. Multicoloured.
1079 23p. Type **219** 45 50
1080 27p. *Quatermass and the Pit* (Nigel Kneale) 55 60
1081 30p. *Flashman at the Charge* (George MacDonald Fraser) 60 65
1082 38p. *The Eternal City* (Hall Caine) 75 80
1083 40p. *Peveril of the Peak* (Sir Walter Scott) 80 85
1084 53p. *Emma's Secret* (Barbara Taylor Bradford) . . . . 1·00 1·10

The 38p. value includes the "EUROPA 2003" emblem.

2003. 400th Anniv of End of the Tudor Reign. Multicoloured.
1085 23p. Type **220** 45 50
1086 27p. King Henry VIII and Manx church (Dissolution of the Monasteries) . . . 55 60
1087 38p. Queen Elizabeth I and globe showing route of Drake's circumnavigation 75 80
1088 40p. King Henry VIII, Cardinal Wolsey and Hampton Court Palace 80 85
1089 47p. Queen Mary I and Tudor rose . . . . 95 1·00
1090 67p. Queen Elizabeth I and ships of Spanish Armada 1·40 1·50

2003. Centenary of Henry Bloom Noble Trust. Multicoloured.
1091 23p. Type **221** 45 50
1092 23p. Nurse and Ramsey Cottage Hospital 45 50
1093 23p. Children and Children's Home 45 50
1094 23p. Bathers at Noble's Baths 45 50
1095 23p. Scout and Headquarters 45 50
1096 27p. Noble's Hospital, c. 1912 . . . . 55 60
1097 27p. Villa Marina 55 60
1098 27p. Noble's Park 55 60
1099 27p. St. Ninian's Church . . 55 60
1100 27p. Noble's Library . . . 55 60
Nos. 1091/1100 also come self-adhesive.

222 Boy tying Scarf on Snowman

2003. Christmas. *The Snowman* by Raymond Briggs. Multicoloured.
1111 22p. Type **222** 45 50
1112 26p. Snowman (wearing black hat and scarf) . . . 50 55
1113 38p. Boy and Snowman holding hands 75 80
1114 47p. Snowman (wearing brown hat and scarf) . . 95 1·00
1115 68p. Boy flying with Snowman . . . . 1·40 1·50

223 Aragorn

2003. Making of *The Lord of the Rings* Film Trilogy: *The Return of the King*. Multicoloured.
1116 23p. Type **223** 45 50
1117 27p. Gimli 55 60
1118 30p. Gandalf 60 65
1119 38p. Legolas on horseback 75 80
1120 42p. Gollum 85 90
1121 47p. Frodo and Sam . . . 95 1·00
1122 68p. Legolas drawing bow 1·40 1·50
1123 85p. Aragorn on horseback 1·75 1·90
MS1124 120 × 78 mm. £2 The Ring (44 × 40 mm) . . . . 4·00 4·25

224 *Maitland* (Simon Hall)

2004. Bicentenary of Running of First Steam Locomotive. Paintings of steam locomotives by named artists. Multicoloured.
1125 23p. Type **224** 45 50
1126 27p. *Evening Star* (Terence Cuneo) 55 60
1127 40p. *Pen-y-Darren* Tramroad Locomotive (Terence Cuneo) 80 85
1128 57p. *Duchess of Hamilton* (Craig Tiley) . . . . . . 1·10 1·20
1129 61p. *City of Truro* (B. J. Freeman) . . . . 1·20 1·40
1130 90p. *Mallard* (Terence Cuneo) . . . . 1·80 1·90

225 Troops on Landing Craft and Tanks going Ashore

2004. 60th Anniv of D-Day. Multicoloured.

1131	23p. Type **225**	45	50
1132	23p. Troops leaving landing craft and tanks going ashore	45	50
1133	27p. Troops leaving landing craft	55	60
1134	27p. Landing craft and troops wading ashore	55	60
1135	47p. *Lady of Mann* (ferry used as landing craft carrier)	95	1·00
1136	47p. *Ben-my-Chree* (ferry used as landing craft carrier)	95	1·00
1137	68p. Consolidated B-24 Liberators (bombers) and North American P-51 Mustang (fighter)	1·40	1·50
1138	68p. Airspeed AS51 Horsa gliders (troop carriers)	1·40	1·50
MS1139	170 × 75 mm. 50p. Winston Churchill; 50p. Troops and aircraft; 50p. Military vehicles on street; 50p. Soldiers with France guidebook	4·00	4·25

Nos. 1131/2, 1133/4, 1135/6 and 1137/8 were each printed together, se-tenant, each pair forming a composite design.

226 Lesser Celandine

2004. Bicentenary of Royal Horticultural Society. Wild Flowers. Multicoloured.

1140	25p. Type **226**	50	55
1141	28p. Red campion	55	60
1142	37p. Devil's-bit scabious	75	80
1143	40p. Northern harebell	80	85
1144	68p. Wood anemone	1·40	1·50
1145	85p. Common spotted orchid	1·75	1·90

227 George Formby in *No Limit*, 1936

2004. Birth Centenary of George Formby (entertainer). Showing scenes from film *No Limit*. Multicoloured.

1146	25p. Type **227**	50	55
1147	28p. Pushing motorcycle	55	60
1148	40p. Riding in TT race	80	85
1149	43p. With Florence Desmond	85	90
1150	50p. On motorcycle	1·00	1·10
1151	74p. In close-up	1·50	1·60

POSTAGE DUE STAMPS

D 1

D 2

1973.

D1	D 1	½p. red, black and yellow	1·50	1·10
D2		1p. red, black and brown	50	60
D3		2p. red, black and green	15	20
D4		3p. red, black and grey	20	20
D5		4p. red, black and pink	30	35
D6		5p. red, black and blue	30	35
D7		10p. red, black and violet	40	40
D8		20p. red, black and green	75	60

1975.

D 9	D 2	½p. yellow, black and red	10	10
D10		1p. brown, black and red	10	10
D11		4p. lilac, black and red	10	15
D12		7p. blue, black and red	15	20
D13		9p. grey, black and red	25	30
D14		10p. mauve, blk & red	25	20
D15		50p. orange, blk & red	90	90
D16		£1 green, black and red	1·50	1·60

D 3

D 4

1982.

D17	D 3	1p. multicoloured	10	10
D18		2p. multicoloured	10	10
D19		5p. multicoloured	10	10
D20		10p. multicoloured	20	25
D21		20p. multicoloured	40	45
D22		50p. multicoloured	90	1·10
D23		£1 multicoloured	1·60	2·10
D24		£2 multicoloured	3·25	4·25

1992.

D25	D 4	£5 multicoloured	8·00	8·50

ISRAEL Pt. 19

The former British Mandate over Palestine was ended by the partition plan approved by the United Nations General Assembly on 29 November 1947, and on 14 May 1948 the new state of Israel was proclaimed.

1948. 1000 prutot (mils) = 1 Israeli pound.
1960. 100 agorot = 1 Israeli pound.
1980. 100 agorot = 1 shekel.

> **"TABS"** All Israeli stamps (except the Postage Dues) exist with descriptive sheet margin attached. These so-called "Tabs" are popular and in some cases scarce. Prices are for stamps without "tab". Separate prices for stamps with "tabs" are given in Stanley Gibbons Catalogue, Part 19 (Middle East).

1 Palm Tree and Baskets with Dates

2 Silver Shekel and Pomegranates

1948. Ancient Jewish Coins. Perf or roul.

1	**1**	3m. orange	50	10
2	–	5m. green	50	10
3a	–	10m. mauve	40	15
4	–	15m. red	1·00	10
5	–	20m. blue	2·50	10
6	–	50m. brown	12·50	65
7	**2**	250m. green	32·00	12·50
8		500m. red on buff	£120	45·00
9		1000m. blue on blue (36 × 24 mm)	£250	£100

DESIGNS ON COINS: 5m. Vine leaf; 10m. Ritual jar; 15m. Bunch of grapes; 20m. Ritual cup; 50m. Tied palm branches and lemon.

See also Nos. 21/6, 40/51 and 90/93.

3 "Flying Scroll" Emblem

1948. Jewish New Year.

10	**3**	3m. brown and blue	40	25
11		5m. green and blue	40	25
12		10m. red and blue	50	40
13		20m. blue and light blue	2·75	90
14		65m. brown and red	11·00	4·25

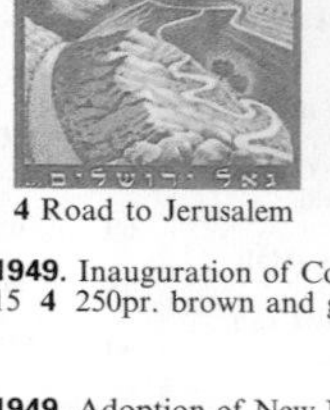

4 Road to Jerusalem

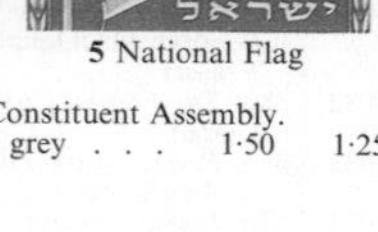

5 National Flag

1949. Inauguration of Constituent Assembly.

15	**4**	250pr. brown and grey	1·50	1·25

1949. Adoption of New National Flag.

16	**5**	20pr. blue	60	35

6 Petah Tiqwa Well

1949. 70th Anniv of Founding of Petah Tiqwa.

17	**6**	40pr. brown and green	9·50	75

7 Air Force Badge

1949. Jewish New Year.

18	**7**	5pr. blue	90	40
19	–	10pr. green	90	40
20	–	35pr. brown	7·25	4·25

BADGES: 10pr. Navy; 35pr. Army.

8 Ancient Jewish Coin

10 Stag and Globe

1949. 2nd Jewish Coins issue. Inscr at left of 6 or 8 characters.

21	**8**	3pr. grey	10	10
22	–	5pr. violet (as No. 2)	10	10
23	–	10pr. green (as No. 3)	10	10
24	–	15pr. red (as No. 4)	15	10
25	–	30pr. blue	35	10
26	–	50pr. brown (as No. 6)	1·25	15

DESIGN: 30p.r. Ritual vessel.

For designs with larger inscription at left, see Nos. 40/51 and 90/93.

1950. Israel's Membership and 75th Anniv of U.P.U.

27	**10**	40pr. violet	90	65
28		80pr. red	1·00	75

11 Landing of Immigrants

1950. 2nd Anniv of Independence.

29	**11**	20pr. brown	2·25	1·75
30	–	40pr. green	9·75	5·50

DESIGN: 40pr. Line of immigrant ships.

12 Library and Book

1950. 25th Anniv of Founding of Hebrew University, Jerusalem.

31	**12**	100pr. green	40	25

13 Eagle

1950. Air.

32	–	5pr. blue	50	25
33	–	30pr. grey	40	25
34	–	40pr. green	40	25
35	–	50pr. brown	40	25
36	**13**	100pr. red	15·00	11·00
37	–	250pr. blue	2·25	90

DESIGNS—VERT: 5pr. Doves pecking grapes; 30pr. Eagle; 40pr. Ostrich; 50pr. Dove. HORIZ: 250pr. Dove with olive branch.

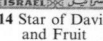

14 Star of David and Fruit

16 Runner and Track

1950. Jewish New Year.

38	**14**	5pr. violet and orange	15	10
39		15pr. brown and green	60	40

1950. 3rd Jewish Coins issue. Inscr at left of 13 characters.

40	3pr. grey	10	10
41	5pr. violet	10	10
42	10pr. green	10	10
43	15pr. red	10	10
44	20pr. orange	10	10
45	30pr. blue	10	10
46	35pr. green	30	10
47	40pr. brown	10	10
48	45pr. mauve	10	10
49	50pr. brown	10	10
50	60pr. red	10	10
51	85pr. blue	10	10

DESIGNS ON COINS: 3, 20pr. Palm tree and baskets with dates; 5, 35pr. Vine leaf; 10, 40pr. Ritual jar; 15, 45pr. Bunch of grapes; 30, 60pr. Ritual vessel; 50, 85pr. Tied palm branches and lemon.

For further designs with value at right, see Nos. 90/93.

1950. 3rd Maccabiah (sports meeting).

52	**16**	80pr. green and olive	1·90	1·25

17 "The Negev" (after R. Rubin)

1950. Opening of Post Office at Elat.

53	**17**	500pr. brown & light brown	9·50	4·50

19 Memorial Tablet

1951. 40th Anniv of Founding of Tel Aviv.

54	**19**	40pr. brown	40	25

20 "Supporting Israel"

21 Metsudat Yesha

1951. Independence Bonds Campaign.

55	**20**	80pr. red	25	15

1951. 3rd Anniv of State of Israel.

56	**21**	15pr. red	20	15
57	–	40pr. blue (Hakastel)	50	40

22 Tractor

23 Ploughing and Savings Stamp

1951. 50th Anniv of Jewish National Fund.

58	**22**	15pr. brown	10	10
59	–	25pr. green	10	10
60	**23**	80pr. blue	1·00	70

DESIGN—As Type **22**: 25pr. Stylized tree.

24 Dr. T. Herzl

25 Carrier Pigeons

1951. 23rd Zionist Congress.

61	**24**	80pr. green	25	20

1951. Jewish New Year.

62	**25**	5pr. blue	10	10
63	–	15pr. red	10	10
64	–	40pr. violet	25	20

DESIGNS: 15pr. Woman and dove; 40pr. Scroll of the Law.

26 Menora and Emblems

1952.
64a **26** 1000pr. black and blue . . 16·00 7·50

26a Haifa Bay, Mt. Carmel and City Seal

1952. Air. National Stamp Exn ("TABA").
64b – 100pr. blue and black . . 40 30
64c **26a** 120pr. purple and black 40 30
DESIGN: 100pr. Haifa Bay and City Seal.

27 Thistle and Yad Mordechai

1952. 4th Anniv of Independence.
65 **27** 30pr. brown and mauve . . 15 10
66 – 60pr. slate and blue 20 10
67 – 110pr. brown and red . . . 45 30
DESIGNS: 60pr. Cornflower and Deganya; 110pr. Anemone and Safed.

28 New York Skyline and Z.O.A. Building

29 Figs

1952. Opening of American Zionist Building, Tel Aviv.
68 **28** 220pr. grey and blue 45 30

1952. Jewish New Year.
69 **29** 15pr. yellow and green . . . 20 10
70 – 40pr. yellow, blue and violet 25 15
71 – 110pr. grey and red 40 30
72 – 220pr. green, brown & orge 50 35
FLOWERS: 40pr. Lily ("Rose of Sharon"); 110pr. Dove; 220pr. Nuts.

30 Dr. C. Weizmann (from sketch by R. Errell)

1952. Death of First President.
73 **30** 30pr. blue 10 10
74 110pr. black 35 30

31

32 Douglas DC-4 Airliner over Tel Aviv Yafo

1952. 70th Anniv of Bet Yaakov Lechu Venelcha Immigration Organization.
75 **31** 110pr. buff, green and brown 25 15

1953. Air.
76 – 10pr. deep green and green 10 10
77 – 70pr. violet and lilac . . . 10 10
78 – 100pr. deep green and green 10 10
79 – 150pr. brown and orange 10 10
80 – 350pr. red and pink . . . 15 10
81 – 500pr. deep blue and blue 20 10
81a – 750pr. deep brown & brown 20 10
82 **32** 1000pr. deep green & green 3·75 95
82a – 3000pr. purple 50 45
DESIGNS—HORIZ: 10pr. Olive tree; 70pr. Sea of Galilee; 100pr. Shaar Hogay on road to Jerusalem; 150pr. Lion Rock, Negev; 350pr. Bay of Elat. VERT: 500pr. Tanour Falls, near Metoulla; 750pr. Lake Hula; 3000pr. Tomb of Meir Baal Haness.

33 Anemones and Arms

35 Maimonides (philosopher)

1953. 5th Anniv of Independence.
83 **33** 110pr. red, green and blue 25 20

1953. 7th Int Congress of History of Science.
84 **35** 110pr. brown 95 60

36 Holy Ark, Petah-Tikvah

37 Hand holding Globe/Football

1953. Jewish New Year.
85 – 20pr. blue 10 10
86 **36** 45pr. red 10 10
87 – 200pr. violet 35 25
DESIGNS: 20pr. Holy Ark, Jerusalem; 200pr. Holy Ark, Zefat.

1953. 4th Maccabiah.
88 **37** 110pr. brown and blue . . . 20 20

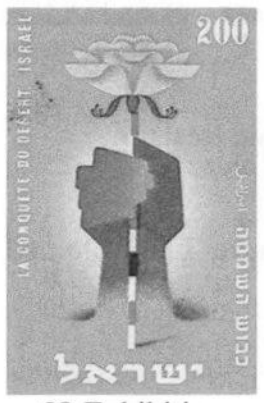
38 Exhibition Emblem

39 Ancient Jewish Coin

1953. "Conquest of the Desert" Exhibition.
89 **38** 200pr. multicoloured 20 15

1954. 4th Jewish Coins issue.
90 **39** 80pr. bistre 10 10
91 – 95pr. green 10 10
92 – 100pr. brown 10 10
93 – 125pr. blue 15 10
DESIGNS ON COINS: 95pr. Wheat; 100pr. Gate; 125pr. Lyre.

40 Gesher and Narcissus

41 Dr. T. Z. Herzl

1954. 6th Anniv of Independence.
94 – 60pr. blue, red and grey . . 10 10
95 **40** 350pr. brown, yellow & grn 20 15
DESIGN: 60pr. Yehiam and helichrysum.

1954. 50th Death Anniv of Herzl (founder of World Zionist Movement).
96 **41** 160pr. sepia, buff and blue 20 15

43

1954. Jewish New Year.
97 **43** 25pr. sepia 15 10

44 19th century Mail Coach and P.O.

1954. National Stamp Exhibition.
98 **44** 60pr. black, yellow and blue 10 10
99 – 200pr. black, red and green 25 15
DESIGN: 200pr. Mail van and G.P.O., 1954.

45 Baron Edmond de Rothschild

1954. 20th Death Anniv of De Rothschild (financier).
100 **45** 300pr. turquoise 20 10

46 Lamp of Knowledge

1955. 50th Anniv of Teachers' Association.
101 **46** 250pr. blue 15 10

47 Parachutist and Barbed Wire

48 Menora and Olive Branches

1955. Jewish Mobilization during 2nd World War.
102 **47** 120pr. black and turquoise 15 10

1955. 7th Anniv of Independence.
103 **48** 150pr. orange, black & grn 25 15

49 Immigrants and Ship

50 Musicians playing Timbrel and Cymbals

1955. 20th Anniv of Youth Immigration Scheme.
104 **49** 5pr. black and blue 10 10
105 – 10pr. black and red 10 10
106 – 25pr. black and green . . . 10 10
107 – 30pr. black and orange . . 10 10
108 – 60pr. black and violet . . . 10 10
109 – 750pr. black and brown . . 45 35
DESIGNS: 10pr. Immigrants and Douglas DC-3 airplane; 25pr. Boy and calf; 30pr. Girl watering flowers; 60pr. Boy making pottery; 750pr. Boy using theodolite.

1955. Jewish New Year.
110 **50** 25pr. green and orange . . 10 10
111 – 60pr. grey and orange . . 10 10
112 – 120pr. blue and yellow . . 10 10
113 – 250pr. brown and orange 25 15
DESIGNS—Musicians playing: 60pr. Ram's horn; 120pr. Tuba; 250pr. Harp.

51 Ambulance

52 "Reuben"

1955. 25th Anniv of Magen David Adom (Jewish Red Cross).
114 **51** 160pr. green, black and red 20 15

1955. Twelve Tribes of Israel.
115 **52** 10pr. green 10 10
116 – 20pr. mauve 10 10
117 – 30pr. blue 10 10
118 – 40pr. brown 10 10
119 – 50pr. blue 10 10
120 – 60pr. bistre 10 10
121 – 80pr. violet 10 10
122 – 100pr. red 10 10
123 – 120pr. olive 10 10
124 – 180pr. mauve 15 10
125 – 200pr. green 15 10
126 – 250pr. grey 15 10
EMBLEMS: 20pr. "Simeon" (castle); 30pr. "Levi" (High Priest's breastplate); 40pr. "Judah" (lion); 50pr. "Dan" (scales); 60pr. "Naphtali" (gazelle); 80pr. "Gad" (tents); 100pr. "Asher" (tree); 120pr. "Issachar" (sun and stars); 180pr. "Zebulun" (ship); 200pr. "Joseph" (sheaf of wheat); 250pr. "Benjamin" (wolf).

53 Professor Einstein

1956. Einstein Commemoration.
127 **53** 350pr. brown 15 15

54 Technion

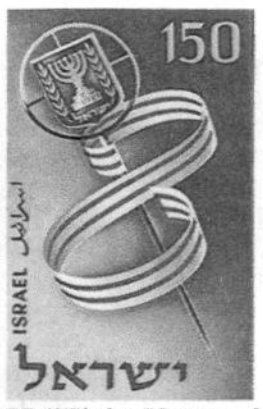
55 "Eight Years of Independence"

1956. 30th Anniv of Israel Institute of Technology, Haifa.
128 **54** 350pr. green and black . . 15 10

1956. 8th Anniv of Independence.
129 **55** 150pr. multicoloured . . . 15 10

56 Oranges

57 Musican playing Lyre

1956. 4th International Congress of Mediterranean Citrus Fruit Growers.
130 **56** 300pr. multicoloured . . . 20 15

1956. Jewish New Year. Musicians playing instruments.
131 **57** 30pr. brown and blue . . . 10 10
132 – 50pr. violet and orange . . 10 10
133 – 150pr. turquoise and orange 20 15
INSTRUMENTS—VERT: 50pr. Sistrum. HORIZ: 150pr. Double oboe.

58 Insignia of "Haganah"

59 Airplane sky-writing Figure "9"

1957. Defence Fund.
134 **58** 80pr.+20pr. green 10 10
135 150pr.+50pr. red 10 10
136 350pr.+50pr. blue 15 10

1957. 9th Anniv of Independence.
137 **59** 250pr. black, blue & lt blue 15 10

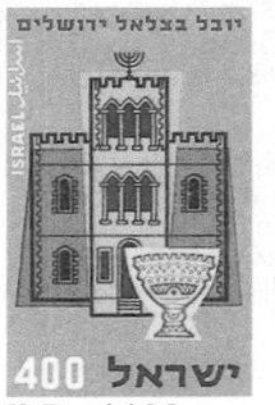
60 Bezalel Museum and Candelabrum

61 Seal of Tamach and Horse

1957. 50th Anniv of Bezalel Museum, Jerusalem.
138 **60** 400pr. multicoloured . . . 15 10

1957. Jewish New Year. Ancient Hebrew Seals.
139 **61** 50pr. black & brn on blue 10 10
140 – 160pr. black & grn on buff 10 10
141 – 300pr. black & red on pink 15 10
DESIGNS: 160pr. Seal of Shema and lion; 300pr. Seal of Netanyahuv Ne'avadyahu and gazelle.

62 Throwing the Hammer

63 Ancient Hebrew Ship

1958. 25th Anniv of Maccabiah Games.
142 **62** 500pr. red and bistre . . . 15 10

1958. Israel Merchant Marine Commemoration.
143 **63** 10pr. red, blue and brown 10 10
144 – 20pr. brown and green . . 10 10
145 – 30pr. grey and red 10 10
146 – 1000pr. green and blue . . 45 35
DESIGNS—As T **63**: 10pr. Immigration ship "Nirit"; 20pr. Freighter "Shomron". 57 × 22 ½ mm: 1000pr. Liner "Zion".

64 Menora and Olive Branch

1958. 10th Anniv of Independence.
147 **64** 400pr. green, black and gold 20 15

65 Dancing Children forming "10"

1958. 1st World Conference of Jewish Youth, Jerusalem.
148 **65** 200pr. green and orange 20 15

66 Convention Centre, Jerusalem, and Exhibition Emblem

1958. 10th Anniv (of Israel) Exn, Jerusalem.
149 **66** 400pr. orange and lilac on cream 20 15

67 Wheat

68 Ancient Stone

1958. Jewish New Year.
150 **67** 50pr. brown and ochre . . 10 10
151 – 60pr. black and yellow . . 10 10
152 – 160pr. purple and violet . . 15 10
153 – 300pr. green and apple . . 20 15
DESIGNS: 60pr. Barley; 160pr. Grapes; 300pr. Figs.
See also Nos. 166/8.

1958. 10th Anniv of Declaration of Human Rights.
154 **68** 750pr. black, yellow & blue 20 15

69 Post Office Emblem

70 Sholem Aleichem

1959. 10th Anniv of Israel Postal Services.
155 **69** 60pr. black, red and olive 10 10
156 – 120pr. black, red and olive 10 10
157 – 250pr. black, red and olive 10 10
158 – 500pr. black, red and olive 20 15
DESIGNS—HORIZ: 120pr. Mail van. VERT: 250pr. Radio-telephone equipment; 500pr. "Telex" dial and keyboard.

1959. Birth Cent of Sholem Aleichem (writer).
159 **70** 250pr. brown and green . . 20 15

71 Tel Aviv

72 Anemone

1959. 50th Anniv of Tel Aviv.
160 **71** 120pr. multicoloured . . . 20 15

1959. 11th Anniv of Independence. Mult.
161 60pr. Type **72** 10 10
162 120pr. Cyclamen 10 10
163 300pr. Narcissus 20 15
See also Nos. 188/9, 211/13 and 257/9.

73 C. N. Bialik

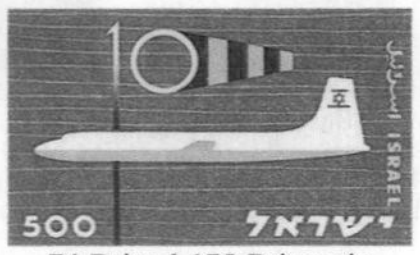

74 Bristol 175 Britannia Airliner and Wind-sock

1959. 25th Anniv of Chaim Bialik (poet).
164 **73** 250pr. olive and orange . . 20 15

1959. 10th Anniv of Civil Aviation in Israel.
165 **74** 500pr. multicoloured . . . 20 15

1959. Jewish New Year. As T **67**.
166 60pr. red and brown 10 10
167 200pr. green and deep green 15 10
168 350pr. orange and brown . . 25 15
DESIGNS: 60pr. Pomegranates; 200pr. Olives; 350pr. Dates.

76 E. Ben-Yehuda

77 Merhavya Settlement

1959. Birth Centenary of Ben-Yehuda (pioneer of Hebrew language).
169 **76** 250pr. deep blue and blue 25 50

1959. 50th Anniv of Merhavya and Deganya Settlements. 75th Anniv of Yesud Ha-Maala Settlement.
170 **77** 60pr. green and yellow . . 10 10
171 – 120pr. brown & light brown 15 10
172 – 180pr. green and blue . . . 30 20
DESIGNS: 120pr. Yesud Ha-Maala; 180pr. Deganya.

78 Ancient Jewish Coin

79 Tiberias

1960. New currency. Values in black.
173 **78** 1a. bistre on pink 10 10
174 3a. red on pink 10 10
175 5a. slate on pink 10 10
176 6a. green on blue 10 10
176a 7a. grey on blue 10 10
177 8a. mauve on blue 10 10
178 12a. blue on blue 10 10
179 18a. orange 10 10
180 25a. blue 15 10
181 30a. red 15 10
182 50a. lilac 15 10

1960. Air.
183 – 15a. black and lilac . . . 15 10
184 – 20a. black and green . . . 15 10
184a – 25a. black and orange . . 15 10
184b – 30a. black and turquoise 15 10
184c – 35a. black and green . . 15 10
184d – 40a. black and lilac . . . 50 25
184e – 50a. black and olive . . . 50 25
185 **79** 65a. black and blue . . . 35 15
185a – I£1 black and pink . . . 75 35
DESIGNS—VERT: 15a. Old town, Zefat; 20a. Tower, Ashqelon; 25a. Akko Tower and boats; 30a. View of Haifa from Mt. Carmel. HORIZ: 35a. Ancient synagogue, Capernaum; 40a. Kefar Hittim—Tomb of Jethro; 50a. City walls, Jerusalem. I£1, Old city, Yafo (Jaffa).

80 Operation "Magic Carpet"

1960. World Refugee Year.
186 **80** 25a. brown 15 10
187 – 50a. green 20 15
DESIGN: 50a. Resettled family.

1960. 12th Anniv of Independence. Flowers as T **72**.
188 12a. multicoloured 15 10
189 32a. yellow, green and brown 20 15
DESIGNS: 12a. "Pancratium maritimum"; 32a. "Oenothera drummondi".

81 Atomic Symbol and Reactor Building

83 King Saul

1960. Inauguration of Atomic Reactor.
190 **81** 50a. red, black and blue . . 25 20

1960. Jewish New Year. Centres multicoloured.
191 **83** 7a. green 10 10
192 – 25a. brown 20 20
193 – 40a. blue 30 20
DESIGNS: 25a. King David; 40a. King Solomon.

84 Dr. Theodor Herzl

85 Postal Courier, Prague, 1741

1960. Birth Centenary of Dr. Theodor Herzl (founder of World Zionist Movement).
194 **84** 25a. sepia and cream . . . 25 20

1960. "TAVIV" National Stamp Exhibition, Tel Aviv.
195 **85** 25a. black and grey . . . 30 25

86 Henrietta Szold

1960. Birth Centenary of Henrietta Szold (founder of Youth Immigration Scheme).
196 **86** 25a. violet and blue . . . 20 15

87 Badges of First Zionist Congress and Jerusalem

1960. 25th Zionist Congress, Jerusalem.
197 **87** 50a. light and deep blue . . 25 20

88 Ram (Aries)

89 The Twelve Signs

1961. Signs of the Zodiac.
198 **88** 1a. green 10 10
199 – 2a. red 10 10
200 – 6a. blue 10 10
201 – 7a. brown 10 10
202 – 8a. myrtle 10 10
203 – 10a. orange 10 10
204 – 12a. violet 10 10
205 – 18a. mauve 10 10
206 – 20a. olive 10 10
207 – 25a. purple 10 10
208 – 32a. black 15 10
209 – 50a. turquoise 15 10
210 **89** I£1 blue, gold and indigo 40 35
DESIGNS—As Type **88**: 2a. Bull (Taurus); 6a. Twins (Gemini); 7a. Crab (Cancer); 8a. Lion (Leo); 10a. Virgin (Virgo); 12a. Scales (Libra); 18a. Scorpion (Scorpio); 20a. Archer (Sagittarius); 25a. Goat (Capricorn); 32a. Waterman (Aquarius); 50a. Fishes (Pisces).

1961. 13th Anniv of Independence. Flowers as T **72**.
211 7a. yellow, brown and green 10 10
212 12a. green, purple and mauve 15 10
213 32a. red, green and blue . . . 25 15
FLOWERS: 7a. Myrtle; 12a. Squill; 32a. Oleander.

91 Throwing the Javelin

92 "A Decade of Israel Bonds"

1961. 7th "Hapoel" Sports Association Int Congress, Ramat Gan.
214 **91** 25a. multicoloured 25 20

1961. 10th Anniv of Israel Bond Issue.
215 **92** 50a. blue 25 20

93 Samson

94 Bet Hamidrash (synagogue), Medzibozh (Russia)

1961. Jewish New Year. Heroes of Israel. Centres multicoloured.
216 **93** 7a. red 15 10
217 – 25a. grey 20 15
218 – 40a. lilac 30 20
HEROES: 25a. Yehuda Maceabi; 40a. Bar Kochba.

1961. Death Bicentenary of Rabbi Baal Shem Tov (founder of Hassidism movement).
219 **94** 25a. sepia and yellow . . . 25 20

95 Fir Cone

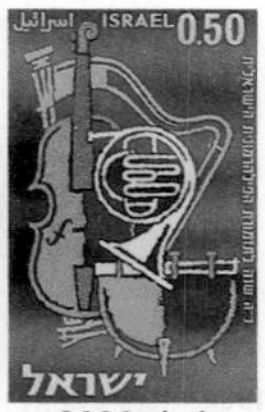

96 Musical Instruments

1961. Afforestation Achievements.
220 **95** 25a. yellow, black and green 25 20
221 – 30a. multicoloured 25 20
DESIGN: 30a. Symbol of afforestation.

1961. 25th Anniv of Israel Philharmonic Orchestra.
222 **96** 50a. multicoloured 55 45

97 Bay of Elat

1962. Air.
223 **97** I£3 multicoloured . . . . 2·00 1·25

1962. As Nos. 198, 201 and 208 but colours changed and surch.
224 **88** 3a. on 1a. mauve 10 10
225 – 5a. on 7a. grey 10 10
226 – 30a. on 32a. green 15 10

99 Symbolic Flame **100** Sud Aviation Vatour IIA Bomber

1962. Heroes and Martyrs Day.
227 **99** 12a. yellow, red and black 15 10
228 – 55a. multicoloured 45 35
DESIGN: 55a. Nazi "Yellow Star" and candles.

1962. 14th Anniv of Independence.
229 **100** 12a. blue 20 15
230 – 30a. green 40 25
DESIGN: 30a. Flight of Vatour IIA bombers.

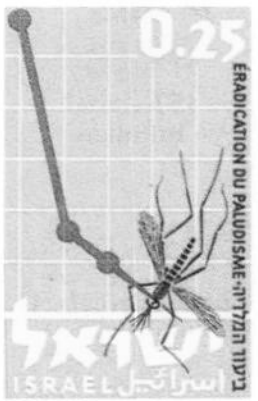

101 Mosquito and Malaria Graph **102** Rosh Pinna

1962. Malaria Eradication.
231 **101** 25a. bistre, red and black 25 20

1962. 80th Anniv of Rosh Pinna.
232 **102** 20a. green and yellow . . 25 20

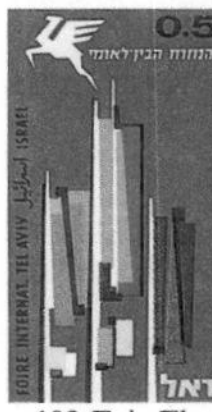

103 Fair Flags **104** "The wolf also shall dwell with the lamb ..."

1962. Near East International Fair, Tel Aviv.
233 **103** 55a. multicoloured . . . 25 30

1962. Jewish New Year. Illustrating quotations from the Book of Isaiah.
234 **104** 8a. black, red and olive 10 10
235 – 28a. black, purple & olive 25 20
236 – 43a. black, orange & olive 35 25
DESIGNS: 28a. "And the leopard shall lie down with the kid ..."; 43a. "And the suckling child shall play on the hole of the asp ...".

105 Boeing 707 Jetliner

1962. El Al Airline Commemoration.
237 **105** 55a. indigo, lilac and blue 45 30

106 Pennant Coralfish

1962. Red Sea Fish (1st series). Multicoloured.
238 3a. Type **106** 20 10
239 6a. Racoon butterflyfish . . . 20 10
240 8a. Indian Ocean lionfish . . 25 10
241 12a. Royal angelfish 25 15
See also Nos. 265/8.

107 Symbolic Cogwheels

1962. 25th Anniv of United Jewish Appeal.
242 **107** 20a. blue, silver and red 30 25

108 J. Korczak (child educator) **109** Houbara Bustard

1962. Janusz Korczak Commemoration.
243 **108** 30a. sepia and grey . . . 40 30

1963. Air. Birds.
244 – 5a. pink, brown and violet 10 10
245 – 20a. turquoise, brn & red 20 15
246 – 28a. black, brown & green 25 15
247 – 30a. multicoloured . . . 25 15
248 – 40a. multicoloured . . . 30 20
249 – 45a. multicoloured . . . 50 40
250 **109** 55a. orange, black & turq 50 40
251 – 70a. bistre, brown & black 55 50
252 – I£1 orange, black and red 55 50
253 – I£3 multicoloured . . . . 1·90 1·90
DESIGNS—HORIZ: 5a. Sinai rosefinch; 20a. White-throated kingfisher; 28a. Mourning wheatear. VERT: 30a. European bee eater; 40a. Graceful prinia; 45a. Palestine sunbird; 70a. Eurasian scops owl; I£1 Purple heron; I£3, White-tailed sea eagle.

110 Bird in the Hand

1963. Freedom from Hunger.
254 **110** 55a. grey and black . . . 30 35

111 Construction at Daybreak **112** Compositor

1963. 25th Anniv of Stockade and Tower Settlements.
255 **111** 12a. brown, black & yell 15 10
256 – 30a. purple, black and blue 25 25
DESIGN: 30a. Settlement at night.

1963. 15th Anniv of Independence. Flowers. As T **72**.
257 8a. multicoloured 25 15
258 30a. yellow, rose and pink . . 40 25
259 37a. multicoloured 50 25
FLOWERS: 8a. White lily; 30a. Bristly hollyhock; 37a. Sharon tulip.

1963. Centenary of Hebrew Press.
260 **112** 12a. purple and buff . . . 40 30
No. 260 comes in sheets of 16 (4 × 4) with overall background of replica of front page of first issue of Hebrew newspaper "Halbanon".

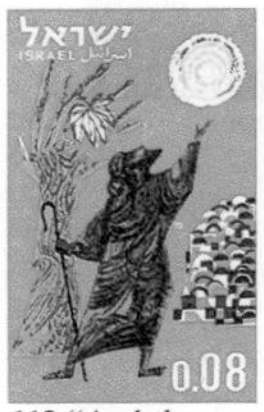

113 "And the sun beat upon the head of Jonah ..." **114** Hoe clearing Thistles

1963. Jewish New Year. Illustrating quotations from the Book of Jonah. Multicoloured.
261 8a. Type **113** 15 10
262 30a. "And there was a mighty tempest in the sea" (horiz) 40 25
263 55a. "And Jonah was in the belly of the fish" (horiz) . . 35 30

1963. 80th Anniv of Israeli Agricultural Settlements.
264 **114** 37a. multicoloured . . . 25 20

1963. Red Sea Fish (2nd series). As T **106**. Multicoloured.
265 2a. Undulate triggerfish . . . 15 10
266 6a. Radial lionfish 25 10
267 8a. Catalufa 30 20
268 12a. Emperor angelfish . . . 30 20

115 "Shalom"

1963. Maiden Voyage of Liner "Shalom".
269 **115** I£1 blue, turquoise & pur 1·25 1·00

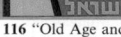

116 "Old Age and Survivors" **117** Pres. Ben-Zvi

1964. 10th Anniv of National Insurance. Multicoloured.
270 12a. Type **116** 15 15
271 25a. Nurse and child within hands ("Maternity") . . . 20 20
272 37a. Family within hand ("Large families") 30 25
273 50a. Hand with arm and crutch ("Employment injuries") 35 25

1964. 1st Death Anniv of President Izhak Ben-Zvi.
274 **117** 12a. brown 15 10

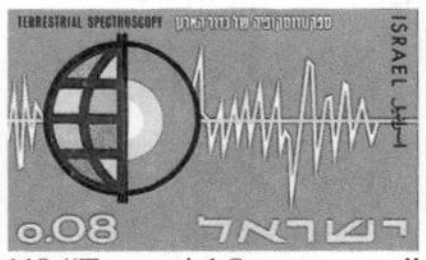

118 "Terrestrial Spectroscopy" **119** Running

1964. 16th Anniv of Independence. Israel's Contribution to Science. Multicoloured.
275 8a. Type **118** 15 10
276 35a. Macromolecules of living cell 35 25
277 70a. Electronic computer . . 40 30

1964. Olympic Games, Tokyo.
278 **119** 8a. black and red 10 10
279 – 12a. black and mauve . . 15 10
280 – 30a. red, black and blue 20 15
281 – 50a. red, purple and green 20 20
DESIGNS: 12a. Throwing the discus; 30a. Basketball; 50a. Football.

120 3rd Century Glass Vessel **121** Congress Emblem

1964. Jewish New Year. Showing glass vessels in Haaretz Museum, Tel Aviv. Multicoloured.
282 8a. Type **120** 15 10
283 35a. 1st-2nd century vessel 20 20
284 70a. 1st century vessel . . . 30 20

1964. 6th Israel Medical Assn's World Congress.
285 **121** I£1 multicoloured 40 30

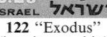

122 "Exodus" (immigrant ship) **123** Eleanor Roosevelt

1964. "Year of the Blockade-Runners".
286 **122** 25a. black, blue & turq 25 20

1964. 80th Birth Anniv of Eleanor Roosevelt.
287 **123** 70a. purple 35 30

124 Olympics Symbols and Knight

1964. 16th Chess Olympics.
288 **124** 12a. brown 30 25
289 – 70a. green 90 85
DESIGN: 70a. Olympics symbol and rook.

125 "African–Israeli Friendship" **126** Masada

1964. "TABAI" National Stamp Exn, Haifa.
290 **125** 57a. multicoloured . . . 45 30

1965. Masada.
291 **126** 25a. green 25 20
292 – 36a. blue 35 20
293 – I£1 brown 40 40
DESIGNS—HORIZ: 36a. "Northern Palace", lower section. VERT: I£l, "Northern Palace" aerial view.

127 Ashdod **128** Fair Emblem

1965. Civic Arms (1st series).
294 – 1a. brown (Lod) 10 10
295 – 2a. mauve (Qiryat Shmona) 10 10
296 – 5a. black (Petah Tiqwa) 10 10
297 – 6a. violet (Nazareth) . . 10 10
298 – 8a. orange (Beer Sheva) 10 10
299 – 10a. green (Bet Shean) 10 10
300 – 12a. purple (Tiberias) . . 10 10
301 **127** 15a. green 10 10
302 – 20a. red (Elat) 10 10
303 – 25a. blue (Akko) 10 10
304 – 35a. purple (Dimona) . . 10 10
305 – 37a. green (Zefat) . . . 40 10
305a – 40a. brown (Mizpe Ramon) 15 10
306 – 50a. blue (Rishon Le Zion) 15 10
306a – 55a. red (Ashqelon) . . 15 10
307 – 70a. brown (Jerusalem) 20 15
307a – 80a. red (Rosh Pinna) 40 25
308 – I£1 green (Tel Aviv-Yafo) 25 25
309 – I£3 mauve (Haifa) . . . 40 30
Nos. 307, 308/9 are 22½ × 27 mm in size.
See also Nos. 413/24.

1965. 2nd International Book Fair, Jerusalem.
310 **128** 70a. black, blue and green 30 25

129 Hands reaching for barbed wire **130** "National Water Supply"

1965. 20th Anniv of Concentration Camps Liberation.
311 **129** 25a. black, yellow and grey 25 20

1965. 17th Anniv of Independence.
312 **130** 37a. brown, dp blue & bl 25 20

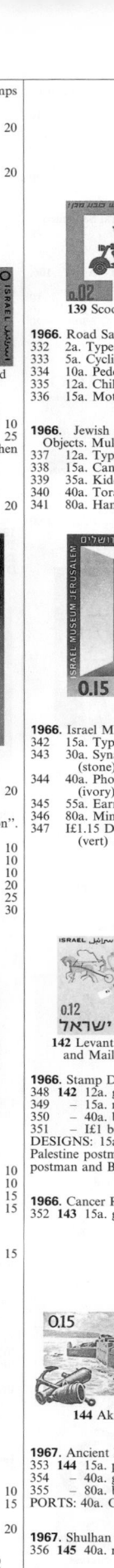

131 Potash Works, Sedom

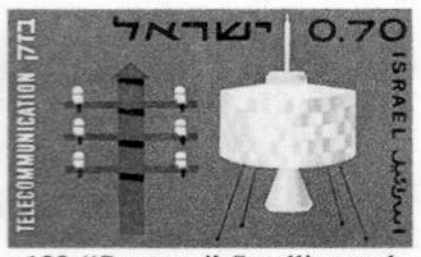
132 "Syncom" Satellite and Telegraph Pole

1965. Dead Sea Industrial Development. Mult.
313 12a. Potash Works, Sedom 15 10
314 50a. Type **131** 30 25
The two stamps form one composite design when placed side by side.

1965. I.T.U. Centenary.
315 **132** 70a. violet, black and blue 25 20

133 "Co-operation"

134 "Light"

1965. International Co-operation Year.
316 **133** 36a. multicoloured . . . 25 20

1965. Jewish New Year. "The Creation". Multicoloured.
317 6a. Type **134** 10 10
318 8a. "Heaven" 10 10
319 12a. "Earth" 10 10
320 25a. "Stars" 25 20
321 35a. "Birds and Beasts" . . . 35 25
322 70a. "Man" 45 30

135 Foxy Charaxes

136 War of Independence Memorial

1965. Butterflies and Moths. Multicoloured.
323 2a. Type **135** 10 10
324 6a. Southern swallowtail . . 15 10
325 8a. Oleander hawk moth . . 20 15
326 12a. Sooty orange-tip 20 15

1966. Memorial Day.
327 **136** 40a. brown and black . . 20 15

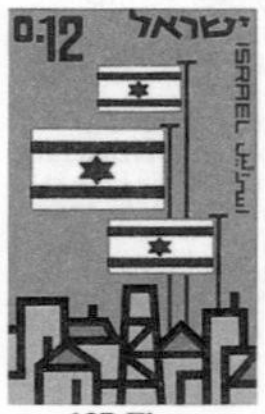
137 Flags

1966. 18th Anniv of Independence. Mult.
328 12a. Type **137** 10 10
329 30a. Fireworks 15 15
330 80a. Dassault Mirage IIICJ jet fighters and warships 25 20

138 Knesset Building

1966. Inaug of Knesset Building, Jerusalem.
331 **138** I£1 blue 30 25

139 Scooter Rider

140 Spice Box

1966. Road Safety. Multicoloured.
332 2a. Type **139** 10 10
333 5a. Cyclist 10 10
334 10a. Pedestrian on crossing 10 10
335 12a. Child with ball 10 10
336 15a. Motorist in car 10 10

1966. Jewish New Year. Religious Ceremonial Objects. Multicoloured.
337 12a. Type **140** 10 10
338 15a. Candlesticks 10 10
339 35a. Kiddush cup 20 15
340 40a. Torah pointer 20 15
341 80a. Hanging lamp 20 20

141 Panther (bronze)

1966. Israel Museum Exhibits. Multicoloured.
342 15a. Type **141** 35 15
343 30a. Synagogue menora (stone) 35 15
344 40a. Phoenician sphinx (ivory) 35 20
345 55a. Earring (gold) 45 25
346 80a. Miniature capital (gold) 70 35
347 I£1.15 Drinking horn (gold) (vert) . . . . 1·25 90

142 Levant Postman and Mail Coach

143 "Fight Cancer and Save Life"

1966. Stamp Day.
348 **142** 12a. green and brown . . 10 10
349 – 15a. mauve, brown & grn 10 10
350 – 40a. blue and mauve . . . 25 10
351 – I£1 brown and blue . . . 35 30
DESIGNS: 15a. Turkish postman and camels; 40a. Palestine postman and steam locomotive. I£1, Israeli postman and Boeing 707 jetliner.

1966. Cancer Research.
352 **143** 15a. green and red . . . 20 15

144 Akko (Acre)

145 Book and Crowns

1967. Ancient Israeli Ports.
353 **144** 15a. purple 15 10
354 – 40a. green 25 20
355 – 80a. blue 35 30
PORTS: 40a. Caesarea; 80a. Yafo (Jaffa).

1967. Shulhan Arukh ("Book of Wisdom").
356 **145** 40a. multicoloured . . . 25 20

146 War of Independence Memorial

1967. Memorial Day.
357 **146** 55a. silver, blue & turq 25 20

147 Taylorcraft Auster AOP.5 Reconnaissance Plane

1967. Independence Day. Military Aircraft.
358 **147** 15a. blue and green . . . 15 15
359 – 30a. brown and orange 20 15
360 – 80a. violet and turquoise 30 20
AIRCRAFT: 30a. Dassault Mystere IVA jet fighter; 80a. Dassault Mirage IIICJ jet fighters.

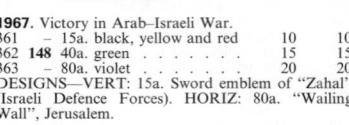

148 Freighter "Dolphin" in Straits of Tiran

149 Law Scroll

1967. Victory in Arab–Israeli War.
361 – 15a. black, yellow and red 10 10
362 **148** 40a. green 15 15
363 – 80a. violet 20 20
DESIGNS—VERT: 15a. Sword emblem of "Zahal" (Israeli Defence Forces). HORIZ: 80a. "Wailing Wall", Jerusalem.

1967. Jewish New Year. Scrolls of the Torah (Mosaic Law), and similar designs.
364 **149** 12a. multicoloured . . . 10 10
365 – 15a. multicoloured . . . 10 10
366 – 35a. multicoloured . . . 20 20
367 – 40a. multicoloured . . . 20 20
368 – 80a. multicoloured . . . 20 20

150 "Welcome to Israel"

151 Lord Balfour

1967. International Tourist Year. Each with "Sun" emblem. Multicoloured.
369 30a. Type **150** 15 15
370 40a. "Air hostess" 15 15
371 80a. "Orange" child 20 20

1967. 50th Anniv of Balfour Declaration.
372 – 15a. green 10 10
373 **151** 40a. brown 25 15
DESIGN: 15a. Dr. C. Weizmann.

152 Ibex

1967. Israeli Nature Reserves. Multicoloured.
374 12a. Type **152** 15 15
375 18a. Caracal 20 15
376 60a. Dorcas gazelle 25 20

153 Diamond

1968. Air. Israeli Exports.
377 – 10a. multicoloured . . . 10 10
378 – 30a. multicoloured . . . 10 10
379 – 40a. multicoloured . . . 15 10
380 – 50a. multicoloured . . . 15 10
381 – 55a. multicoloured . . . 15 10
382 – 60a. multicoloured . . . 20 20
383 – 80a. multicoloured . . . 20 20
384 – I£1 multicoloured . . . 25 15
385 – I£1.50 multicoloured . . . 35 20
386 **153** I£3 violet and green . . . 55 30

DESIGNS: 10a. Draped curtains ("Textiles"); 30a. "Stamps"; 40a. Jar and necklace ("Arts and Crafts"); 50a. Chick and egg ("Chicks"); 55a. Melon, avocado and strawberries ("Fruits"); 60a. Gladioli ("Flowers"); 80a. Telecommunications equipment ("Electronics"). I£1, Atomic equipment ("Isotopes"). I£1.50, Models ("Fashion").

154 Beflagged Football

155 "Immigration"

1968. Pre-Olympic Football Tournament.
387 **154** 80a. multicoloured . . . 25 20

1968. Independence Day. Multicoloured.
388 15a. Type **155** 10 10
389 80a. "Settlement" 25 20

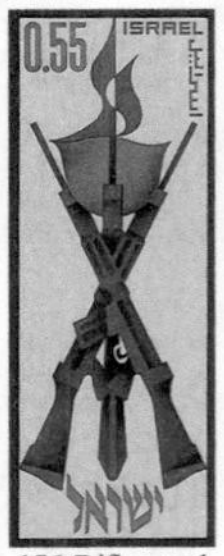
156 Rifles and Helmet

157 Zahal Emblem

1968. Memorial Day.
390 **156** 55a. multicoloured . . . 20 15

1968. Independence Day (Zahal–Israel Defence Forces).
391 **157** 40a. multicoloured . . . 20 15

158 Resistance Fighter (detail from Warsaw Monument)

159 Moshe Sharett

1968. 25th Anniv of Warsaw Ghetto Rising.
392 **158** 60a. bistre 25 20

1968. 27th Zionist Congress, Jerusalem.
393 **159** I£1 sepia 35 25

160 Candle and Cell Bars

161 Jerusalem

1968. Fallen Freedom Fighters.
394 **160** 80a. black, grey and brown 30 25

1968. Jewish New Year.
395 **161** 12a. multicoloured . . . 10 10
396 – 15a. multicoloured . . . 10 10
397 – 35a. multicoloured . . . 20 20
398 – 40a. multicoloured . . . 20 15
399 – 60a. multicoloured . . . 20 20
DESIGNS: Jerusalem—views of the Old City (12, 15, 35a.) and of the New City (40, 60a.).

162 Scout Badge and Knot

163 "Lions' Gate", Jerusalem (detail)

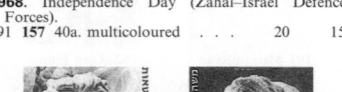

1968. 50th Anniv of Jewish Scout Movement.
400 **162** 30a. multicoloured . . . 20 15

1968. "Tabira" Stamp Exhibition, Jerusalem.
401 **163** I£1 brown 20 15

164 A. Mapu

165 Paralytics playing Basketball

1968. Death Cent of Abraham Mapu (writer).
403 **164** 30a. olive 20 15

1968. International Games for the Paralysed.
404 **165** 40a. green and light green 20 15

166 Elat

1969. Israeli Ports.
405 **166** 30a. mauve 30 20
406 – 60a. brown (Ashdod) . . 35 25
407 – I£1 green (Haifa) 45 30

167 "Worker" and I.L.O. Emblem

168 Israeli Flag at Half-mast

1969. 50th Anniv of I.L.O.
408 **167** 80a. green and lilac . . . 20 15

1969. Memorial Day.
409 **168** 55a. gold, blue and violet 25 15

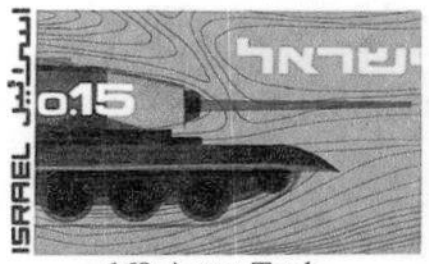
169 Army Tank

170 Flaming Torch

1969. Independence Day. Multicoloured.
410 15a. Type **169** 15 10
411 80a. "Elat" (destroyer) . . . 30 25

1969. 8th Maccabiah.
412 **170** 60a. multicoloured . . . 25 20

171 Arms of Hadera

172 Building the Ark

1969. Civic Arms (2nd series).
413 2a. green (Type **171**) 10 10
414 3a. purple (Herzliyya) 10 10
415 5a. orange (Holon) 10 10
416 15a. red (Bat Yam) 10 10
417 18a. blue (Ramla) 15 10
418 20a. brown (Kefar Sava) . . 15 10
419 25a. blue (Giv'atayim) . . . 15 10
420 30a. mauve (Rehovot) . . . 15 10
421 40a. violet (Netanya) 25 10
422 50a. blue (Bene Beraq) . . . 25 10
423 60a. green (Nahariyya) . . . 25 10
424 80a. green (Ramat Gan) . . 25 10

1969. Jewish New Year, showing scenes from "The Flood". Multicoloured.
425 12a. Type **172** 10 10
426 15a. Animals going aboard 10 10
427 35a. Ark afloat 20 20
428 40a. Dove with olive branch 20 15
429 60a. Ark on Mt. Ararat . . . 20 15

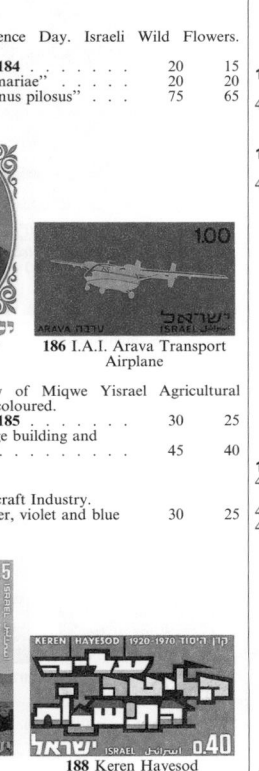

173 "King David" (Chagall)

174 Atomic "Plant"

1969. "King David".
430 **173** I£3 multicoloured . . . . 1·10 75

1969. 25th Anniv of Weizmann Institute of Science.
431 **174** I£1.15 multicoloured . . . 85 60

175 Dum Palms, Emeq He-Arava

176 Immigrant "Aircraft"

1970. Nature Reserves.
432 **175** 2a. olive 10 10
433 – 3a. blue 10 10
434 – 5a. red 10 10
435 – 6a. green 10 10
436 – 30a. violet 25 20
DESIGNS: 3a. Tahana Waterfall, Nahal Iyon; 5a. Nahal Baraq Canyon, Negev; 6a. Ha-Masreq, Judean Hills; 30a. Soreq Cave, Judean Hills.

1970. 20th Anniv of Operation "Magic Carpet" (Immigration of Yemenite Jews).
437 **176** 30a. multicoloured . . . 20 15

177 Joseph Trumpeldor

178 Prime Minister Levi Eshkol

1970. 50th Anniv of Defence of Tel Hay.
438 **177** I£1 violet 40 35

1970. Levi Eshkol Commemoration.
439 **178** 15a. multicoloured . . . 20 15

179 Ze'ev Jabotinsky (commander)

180 Camel and Diesel Train

1970. 50th Anniv of Defence of Jerusalem.
440 **179** 80a. green and cream . . 45 30

1970. Opening of Dimona–Oron Railway.
441 **180** 80a. multicoloured . . . 70 30

181 Mania Schochat (author)

183 Memorial Flame

184 "Orchis laxiflora"

182 Scene from "The Dybbuk"

1970. 60th Anniv of "Ha-Shomer".
442 **181** 40a. purple and cream . . 25 20

1970. 50th Anniv of Habimah National Theatre.
443 **182** I£1 multicoloured 45 30

1970. Memorial Day.
444 **183** 55a. black, red and violet 30 25

1970. Independence Day. Israeli Wild Flowers. Multicoloured.
445 12a. Type **184** 20 15
446 15a. "Iris mariae" 20 20
447 80a. "Lupinus pilosus" . . . 75 65

185 C. Netter (founder)

186 I.A.I. Arava Transport Airplane

1970. Centenary of Miqwe Yisrael Agricultural College. Multicoloured.
448 40a. Type **185** 30 25
449 80a. College building and gate 45 40

1970. Israeli Aircraft Industry.
450 **186** I£1 silver, violet and blue 30 25

187 Yachts

188 Keren Hayesod

1970. World "420" Class Sailing Championships. Multicoloured.
451 15a. Type **187** 25 20
452 30a. Yacht with spinnaker . . 25 25
453 80a. Yachts turning around buoy 45 35

1970. 50th Anniv of Keren Hayesod.
454 **188** 40a. multicoloured . . . 30 25

189 Old Synagogue, Cracow

1970. Jewish New Year. Multicoloured.
455 12a. Type **189** 10 10
456 15a. Great Synagogue, Tunis 10 10
457 35a. Portuguese Synagogue, Amsterdam 15 15
458 40a. Great Synagogue, Moscow 20 15
459 60a. Shearith Israel Synagogue, New York . . 20 15

190 Jewish "Bird" heading for Sun

1970. "Operation Ezra and Nehemiah" (Exodus of Iraqi Jews to Israel).
460 **190** 80a. multicoloured . . . 30 20

191 Mother and Child

1970. 50th Anniv of Women's International Zionist Organization (W.I.Z.O).
461 **191** 80a. yellow, green & silver 30 25

192 Tel Aviv Post Office, 1920

193 Histadrut Emblem

1970. "Tabit" Stamp Exhibition, Tel Aviv, and 50th Anniv of Tel Aviv Post Office.
462 **192** I£1 multicoloured 30 25

1970. 50th Anniv of "Histadrut" (General Federation of Labour).
464 **193** 35a. multicoloured . . . 20 15

194 "Landscape with Bridge" (C. Pissaro)

1970. Paintings in Tel Aviv Museum. Mult.
465 85a. "Jewish Wedding" (J. Israels) 35 25
466 I£1 Type **194** 35 30
467 I£2 "Flowers in a Vase" (F. Leger) 45 40

195 "Inn of the Ghosts" (Cameri Theatre)

1971. Israeli Theatre. Multicoloured.
468 50a. Type **195** 25 25
469 50a. "Samson and Delilah" (National Opera Company) 25 25
470 50a. "A Psalm of David" (I.N.B.A.L. Dance Theatre) 25 25

196 Fallow Deer

197 "Haganah" Emblem

1971. Nature Reserves. Animals of Biblical Times. Multicoloured.
471 2a. Type **196** 10 10
472 3a. Asiatic wild ass 10 10
473 5a. Arabian oryx 10 10
474 78a. Cheetah 40 30

1971. Memorial Day.
475 **197** 78a. multicoloured . . . 30 20

198 Jaffa Gate

1971. Independence Day. Gates of Jerusalem (1st series). Multicoloured.

476		15a. Type **198**	45	25
477		18a. New Gate	50	25
478		35a. Damascus Gate	50	35
479		85a. Herod's Gate	50	35

See also Nos. 527/30.

199 Gymnastics

200 "... and he wrote upon the tables ..."

1971. 9th "Hapoel" Games. Multicoloured.

481		50a. Type **199**	25	20
482		50a. Basketball	25	20
483		50a. Running	25	20

1971. Feast of Weeks ("Shavuot"). Illuminated verses from the Bible. Multicoloured.

484		50a. Type **200**	35	30
485		85a. "The first of the firstfruits ..."	45	40
486		I£1. 50 "... and ye shall observe the feast ..."	60	45

See also Nos. 488/92.

201 "Sun over the Emeq"

1971. 50th Anniv of Settlements in the "Emeq" (Yezreel Valley).

487	**201**	40a. multicoloured	25	20

1971. Jewish New Year. Feast of the Tabernacles ("Sukkot"). Illuminated Verses from the Bible. As T **200**. Multicoloured.

488		15a. "You shall rejoice in your feast"	15	10
489		18a. "You shall dwell in booths ..."	15	10
490		20a. "That I made the people ..."	15	15
491		40a. "... gathered in the produce"	20	15
492		65a. "... I will give you your rains ..."	25	20

202 Kinneret

203 "Agricultural Research"

1971. Landscapes (1st series).

493	–	3a. blue	20	10
494	–	5a. green	10	10
495	–	15a. orange	10	10
496	**202**	18a. purple	65	10
497	–	20a. green	10	10
498	–	22a. blue	80	10
498a	–	25a. red	10	10
499	–	30a. mauve	15	10
500	–	35a. purple	10	10
501	–	45a. blue	15	10
502	–	50a. green	20	10
503	–	55a. green	20	10
504	–	65a. brown	15	10
505	–	70a. red	20	10
505apa	–	80a. blue	20	10
506	–	88a. blue	80	30
507	–	95a. red	80	35
508	–	I£1.10 brown	20	10
508a	–	I£1.30 blue	25	15
508b	–	I£1.70 brown	20	10
509pa	–	I£2 brown	15	15
510pa	–	I£3 violet	25	20
510a	–	I£10 blue	90	50

DESIGNS—As T **202**: 3a. Judean desert; 5a. Gan Ha-Shelosha; 15a. Negev desert; 20a. Tel Dan; 22a. Yafo; 25a. Arava; 30a. En Avedat; 35a. Brekhat Ram; 45a. Mt. Hermon; 50a. Rosh Pinna; 55a. Natanya; 65a. Plain of Zebulun; 70a. Engedi; 80a. Beach at Elat; 88a. Akko (Acre); 95a. Hamifratz Hane'Elam; I£1.10, Aqueduct near Acre; I£1.30, Zefat; I£1.70, Nazerat Illit; I£2, Coral Island; I£3, Haifa. 28 × 27 mm: I£10, Elat.

See also Nos. 682/4a.

1971. 50th Anniv of Volcani Institute of Agricultural Research.

511	**203**	I£1 multicoloured	30	20

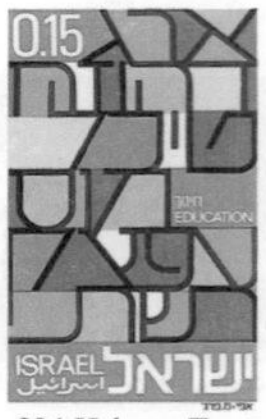

204 Hebrew Text

1971. Educational Development. Multicoloured.

512		15a. Type **204**	10	10
513		18a. Mathematical formulae	10	10
514		20a. Engineering symbols	10	10
515		40a. University degree abbreviations	15	15

205 "The Scribe" (sculpture, B. Schatz)

1972. Jewish Art.

516	**205**	40a. brown, copper & blk	20	15
517	–	55a. multicoloured	20	15
518	–	70a. multicoloured	20	15
519	–	85a. black and yellow	25	20
520	–	I£1 multicoloured	25	20

DESIGNS—VERT: 55a. "Sarah" (A. Pann); 85a. "Old Jerusalem" (woodcut, J. Steinhardt); I£1; "Resurrection" (A. Kahana). HORIZ: 70a. "Zefat" (M. Shemi).

206 The Flight from Egypt

207 "Let My People Go"

1972. Passover Feast ("Pesah"). Multicoloured.

521		18a. Type **206**	25	20
522		45a. Baking unleavened bread	25	25
523		95a. "Seder" table	35	30

1972. Campaign for Jewish Immigration.

524	**207**	55a. multicoloured	85	60

208 Bouquet

209 Jethro's Tomb

1972. Memorial Day.

525	**208**	55a. multicoloured	30	20

1972. "Nebi Shuaib" (Jethro's Tomb) (Druse shrine)

526	**209**	55a. multicoloured	25	20

1972. Independence Day. Gates of Jerusalem (2nd series). As T **198**. Multicoloured.

527		15a. Lion's Gate	40	20
528		18a. Golden Gate	45	25
529		45a. Dung Gate	50	35
530		55a. Zion Gate	60	40

210 Ghetto Entrance

211 Book Year Texts

1972. 400th Death Anniv of Rabbi Yizhaq Luria ("Ari").

532	**210**	70a. multicoloured	1·00	70

1972. International Book Year.

533	**211**	95a. black, red and blue	30	25

212 Dish Aerial

213 Ancona Ark

1972. Opening of Satellite Earth Station.

534	**212**	I£1 multicoloured	30	25

1972. Jewish New Year. Holy Arks from Italy.

535	**213**	15a. brown and yellow	15	10
536	–	45a. green, gold & lt green	20	15
537	–	70a. red, blue and yellow	25	20
538	–	95a. purple and gold	40	30

DESIGNS: 45a. Soragna Ark; 70a. Padua Ark; 95a. Reggio Emilia Ark.

214 Menora Emblem

215 Hanukka Lamp (Morocco, 18th–19th century)

1972. 25th Anniv of State of Israel.

539	**214**	I£1 blue, purple and silver	30	25

1972. Festival of Lights ("Hanukka"). Ceremonial Lamps. Multicoloured.

540		12a. Type **215**	15	15
541		25a. 18th-century Polish lamp	20	15
542		70a. 17th-century German silver lamp	20	20

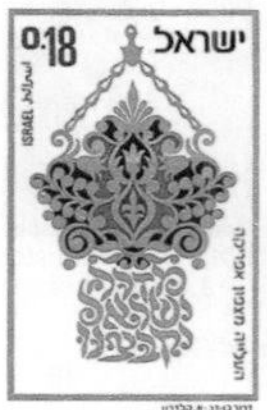

216 Pendant

217 "Horse and Rider"

1973. Immigration of North African Jews.

543	**216**	18a. multicoloured	20	15

1973. Children's Drawings. Multicoloured.

544		2a. Type **217**	10	10
545		3a. "Balloon ride" (17 × 48 mm)	10	10
546		55a. "Party-time"	15	15

218 "Reuben" Window

219 Flame of Remembrance

1973. "Tribes of Israel" Stained-glass Windows by Chagall, Hadassah Synagogue, Jerusalem. Multicoloured.

547		I£1 "Levi"	65	50
548		I£1 "Simeon"	65	50
549		I£1 Type **218**	65	50
550		I£1 "Issachar"	65	50
551		I£1 "Zebulun"	65	50
552		I£1 "Judah"	65	50
553		I£1 "Asher"	65	45
554		I£1 "Gad"	65	45
555		I£1 "Dan"	65	45
556		I£1 "Benjamin"	65	45
557		I£1 "Joseph"	65	45
558		I£1 "Naphtali"	65	45

1973. Memorial Day.

559	**219**	65a. multicoloured	25	15

220 Skeletal Hand

1973. Holocaust (Persecution of European Jews 1933–45) Memorial.

560	**220**	55a. blue	20	15

221 Signatures of Declaration of Independence

1973. Independence Day.

561	**221**	I£1 multicoloured	25	20

222 Star of David and Runners

223 Isaiah

1973. 9th Maccabiah.

563	**222**	I£1.10 multicoloured	25	15

1973. Jewish New Year. Prophets of Israel.

564		18a. Type **223**	10	10
565		65a. Jeremiah	10	10
566		I£1.10 Ezekiel	20	15

224 Jews in Boat, and Danish Flag

225 Institute Emblem and Cogwheel

1973. 30th Anniv of Rescue of Danish Jews.

567	**224**	I£5 black, red and brown	60	45

1973. 50th Anniv of "Technion" Israel Institute of Technology.

568	**225**	I£1.25 multicoloured	25	20

226 Collectors within "Stamp"

227 Soldier with Prayer Shawl

1973. "Jerusalem 73" International Stamp Exhibition. Multicoloured.
569 20a. Type **226** 10 10
570 I£1 Collectors within "Stamp" (different) 20 20

1974. Memorial Day.
572 **227** I£1 black and blue . . . 20 15

228 Quill and Bottle of Ink

229 "Woman in Blue" (M. Kisling)

1974. 50th Anniv of Hebrew Writers' Association.
573 **228** I£2 black and gold . . . 20 15

1974. Jewish Art. Multicoloured.
574 I£1.25 Type **229** 15 15
575 I£2 "Mother and Child" (bronze, C. Orloff) 20 15
576 I£3 "Girl in Blue" (C. Soutine) 25 20
See also Nos. 604/6.

230 Spanner

1974. 50th Anniv of Young Workers' Movement.
577 **230** 25a. multicoloured . . . 30 25

231 Lady Davis Technical Centre, Tel Aviv

1974. "Architecture in Israel" (1st series).
578 **231** 25a. grey 10 10
579 – 60a. blue 15 10
580 – I£1.45 brown 20 15
DESIGNS: 60a. Elias Sourasky Library, Tel Aviv University. I£1.45, Mivtahim Rest-home, Zikhron Yaaqov.
See also Nos. 596/8.

232 Istanbuli Synagogue

233 Arrows on Globe

1974. Jewish New Year. Rebuilt Synagogues in Jerusalem's Old City. Multicoloured.
581 25a. Type **232** 10 10
582 70a. Emtzai Synagogue . . . 15 10
583 I£1 Raban Yohanan Ben Zakai Synagogue 15 15

1974. Centenary of U.P.U. Multicoloured.
584 25a. Type **233** 10 10
585 I£1.30 Dove "postman" (27 × 27 mm) 25 20

234 David Ben Gurion (statesman)

1974. Ben Gurion Memorial.
586 **234** 25a. brown 10 10
587 I£1.30 green 20 20

236 Child with Plant, and Rainbow

238 Welding

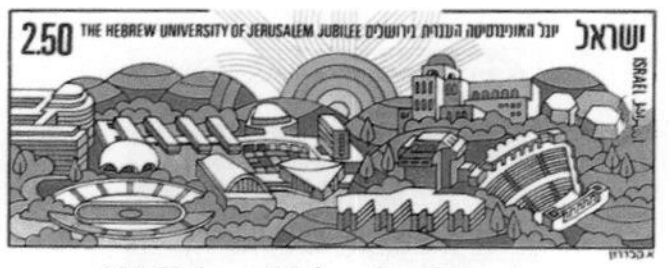

237 Hebrew University, Jerusalem

1975. Arbour Day. Multicoloured.
588 1a. Type **236** 10 10
589 35a. Bird in tree 10 10
590 I£2 Child with plant and sun 20 15

1975. 50th Anniv of Hebrew University, Jerusalem.
591 **237** I£2.50 multicoloured . . . 25 20

1975. "Occupational Safety". Multicoloured.
592 30a. Type **238** 10 10
593 80a. Tractor-driving 10 10
594 I£1.20 Telegraph line maintenance 15 15

239 Harry S. Truman

240 Memorial

1975. Truman Commemoration.
595 **239** I£5 brown 25 20

1975. "Architecture in Israel" (2nd series). As T **231**.
596 80a. brown 15 10
597 I£1.30 green 15 10
598 I£1.70 brown 20 15
DESIGNS: 80a. Hebrew University Synagogue, Jerusalem. I£1.30, Museum, Yad Mordechai. I£1.70, City Hotel, Bat Yam.

1975. Memorial Day.
599 **240** I£1 red, black and mauve 20 15

241 Text and Poppy

242 Hurdling

1975. Fallen Soldiers' Memorial.
600 **241** I£1.45 black, red and grey 20 15

1975. 10th Hapoel Games. Multicoloured.
601 25a. Type **242** 10 10
602 I£1.70 Cycling 10 10
603 I£3 Volleyball 20 15

1975. Jewish Art. As T **229**. Multicoloured.
604 I£1 "Hanukka" (M. D. Oppenheim) 20 15
605 I£1.40 "The Purim Players" (J. Adler) (horiz) 20 15
606 I£4 "Yom Kippur" (M. Gottlieb) 25 20

243 Old People

244 Gideon

1975. Gerontology.
607 **243** I£1.85 multicoloured . . . 20 15

1975. Jewish New Year. Judges of Israel. Mult.
608 35a. Type **244** 10 10
609 I£1 Deborah 15 10
610 I£1.40 Jephthah 20 15

245 Zalman Shazar

246 Emblem of Pioneer Women

1975. 1st Death Anniv of Zalman Shazar (President 1963–73).
611 **245** 35a. black and silver . . . 20 15

1975. 50th Anniv of Pioneer Women's Organization.
612 **246** I£5 multicoloured 35 30

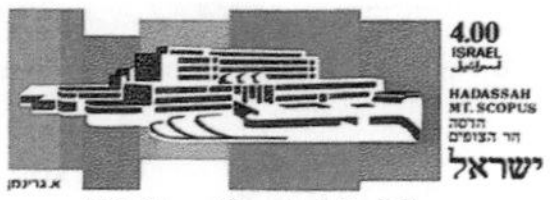

247 New Hospital Buildings

1975. Return of Hadassah Hospital to Mt. Scopus.
613 **247** I£4 multicoloured 25 20

248 Pratincole

249 "Air Pollution"

1975. Protected Wild Birds. Multicoloured.
614 I£1.10 Type **248** 30 30
615 I£1.70 Spur-winged plover . . 40 40
616 I£2 Black-winged stilt 50 50

1975. "Environmental Quality". Multicoloured.
617 50a. Type **249** 15 10
618 80a. "Water pollution" . . . 15 10
619 I£1.70 "Noise pollution" . . 15 15

250 Star of David

251 Symbolic "Key"

1975.
620 **250** 75a. blue and red . . . 20 10
621 I£1.80 blue and grey . . 15 10
622 I£1.85 blue and brown 25 10
623 I£2.45 blue and green . . 25 10
623a I£2.70 blue and mauve 20 10
623b I£4.30 blue and red . . 20 10
624 I£5.40 blue and bistre . . 25 15
625 I£8 blue and turquoise 30 15

1976. 70th Anniv of Bezalel Academy of Arts and Design, Jerusalem.
626 **251** I£1.85 multicoloured . . . 20 15

252 "Border Settlements"

1976. Jewish Border Settlements.
627 **252** I£1.50 multicoloured . . . 20 15

253 "In the days of Ahasuerus ..."

254 Monument to the Fallen

1976. "Purim" Festival. Multicoloured.
628 40a. Type **253** 10 10
629 80a. "He set the royal crown ..." 15 10
630 I£1.60 "Thus shall it be done ..." 15 15

1976. Memorial Day.
632 **254** I£1.85 multicoloured . . . 30 25

255 "Dancers of Meron" (R. Rubin)

1976. Lag Ba-Omer Festival.
633 **255** I£1.30 multicoloured . . . 30 25

256 "200" Flag

1976. Bicentenary of American Revolution.
634 **256** I£4 multicoloured 40 30

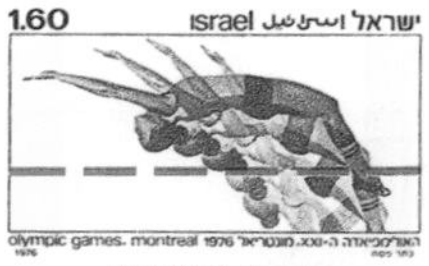

258 High Jump

1976. Olympic Games, Montreal.
636 **258** I£1.60 black and red . . . 20 15
637 – I£2.40 black and blue . . 20 15
638 – I£4.40 black and mauve 25 20
DESIGNS: I£2.40, Swimming. I£4.40, Gymnastics.

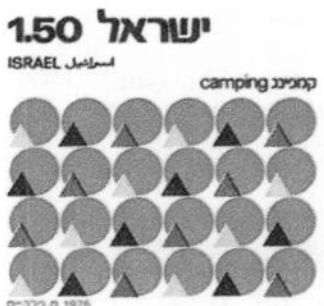

259 Multiple Tent Emblems

260 "Truth"

1976. Camping.
639 **259** I£1.60 multicoloured . . . 25 20

1976. Jewish New Year. Multicoloured.
640 45a. Type **260** 10 10
641 I£1.50 "Judgement" 15 15
642 I£1.90 "Peace" 20 20

261 Excavated Byzantine House

1976. Archaeology in Jerusalem (1st series). Multicoloured.
643 I£1.30 Type **261** 30 20
644 I£2.40 Arch of 2nd Temple 35 30
645 I£2.80 Staircase to 2nd Temple 35 30

262 Pawn **263** Clearing Ground

1976. 22nd Chess Olympiad, Haifa. Mult.
646 I£1.30 Type **262** 15 15
647 I£1.60 Rook 20 15

1976. Archaeology in Jerusalem (2nd series). As T **261**. Multicoloured.
648 70a. City Wall, First Temple period 25 10
649 I£5 Omayyad palace 45 40

1976. Pioneers.
650 **263** 5a. brown and gold . . . 10 10
651 – 10a. lilac and gold 10 10
652 – 60a. red and gold 10 10
653 – I£1.40 blue and gold . . . 15 15
654 – I£1.80 green and gold . . . 20 15
DESIGNS—HORIZ: 10a. Building breakwater. I£1.40, Ploughing. I£1.80, Ditch-clearing. VERT: 60a. Road construction.

264 "Grandfather's Carrot"

1977. Voluntary Service.
655 **264** I£2.60 multicoloured . . . 25 20

265 "By the Rivers of Babylon"

1977. Drawings of E. M. Lilien.
656 **265** I£1.70 brown, grey & black 40 35
657 – I£1.80 black, stone & brn 40 35
658 – I£2.10 green, lt green & blk 40 35
PAINTINGS—VERT: I£1.80, "Abraham". HORIZ: I£2.10, "May Our Eyes Behold".

266 Jew and Arab shaking Hands

1977. Children's Drawings on Peace. Mult.
659 50a. Type **266** 15 10
660 I£1.40 Arab and Jew holding hands 25 20
661 I£2.70 Peace dove, Jew and Arab 35 25

267 Parachute Troops Memorial

1977. Memorial Day.
662 **267** I£3.30 multicoloured . . . 35 30

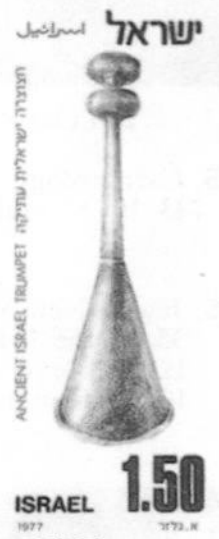

268 Embroidery showing Sabbath Loaves **269** Trumpet

1977. Sabbath.
663 **268** I£3 multicoloured 30 25

1977. Ancient Musical Instruments. Mult.
664 I£1.50 Type **269** 25 20
665 I£2 Lyre 25 20
666 I£5 "Jingle" (cymbals) . . . 35 25

270 Fencing **272** American Zionist Emblem

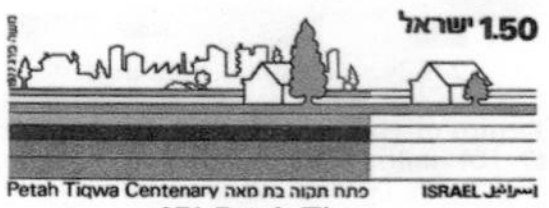

271 Petah Tiqwa

1977. 10th Maccabiah Games.
667 **270** I£1 grey, blue and black 25 20
668 – I£2.50 grey, red and black 25 25
669 – I£3.50 grey, green & black 30 30
DESIGNS: I£2.50, Putting the shot. I£3.50, Judo.

1977. Centenary of Petah Tiqwa.
670 **271** I£1.50 multicoloured . . . 35 20

1977. Zionist Organization of America Convention.
671 **272** I£4 multicoloured 30 30

273 Page of 16th-cent Book "Kohelet Yaakov" **274** Sarah

1977. 400th Anniv of Hebrew Printing at Zefat.
672 **273** I£4 black, gold and red 30 25

1977. Jewish New Year. Matriarchs of Israel. Multicoloured.
673 70a. Type **274** 15 10
674 I£1.50 Rebekah 25 20
675 I£2 Rachel 35 30
676 I£3 Leah 35 35
See also Nos. 728/30.

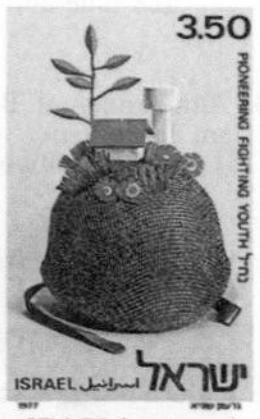

275 Police **276** Helmet and Model Settlement

1977. National Police Force. Multicoloured.
677 I£1 Type **275** 25 20
678 I£1 Civil Guard 25 20
679 I£1 Frontier Guard 25 20

1977. "Nahal" Pioneering Fighting Youth.
680 **276** I£3.50 multicoloured . . . 30 25

277 Accelerator Building, Weizmann Institute **278** Caesarea

1977. Inauguration of Koffler Accelerator.
681 **277** I£8 blue and black . . . 60 50

1977. Landscapes (2nd series).
682 **278** 10a. blue 10 10
683b – I£1 bistre 15 15
684 – I£20 green and orange 75 30
684a – I£50 multicoloured . . . 95 60
DESIGNS—As T **278**: I£1, Arava. 29 × 27 mm: I£20, Rosh Pinna. $27\frac{1}{2} \times 36\frac{1}{2}$ mm: I£50, Soreq Cave.

279 "Mogul" Steam Locomotive, 1892

1977. Railways in the Holy Land. Mult.
685 65a. Type **279** 10 10
686 I£1.50 Steam locomotive . . 25 20
687 I£2 4-6-0 Class P steam locomotive 35 30
688 I£2.50 Diesel locomotive . . . 40 35

280 Blood-stained Scallop ("Gloripallium pallium")

1977. Red Sea Shells. Multicoloured.
690 I£2 Type **280** 20 20
691 I£2 Pacific grinning tun ("Malea pomum") 20 20
692 I£2 Isabelle cowrie ("Cypraea isabella") 20 20
693 I£2 Camp Pitar venus ("Lioconcha castrensis") 20 20

281 "The Marriage Parties" (Dutch Ketubah)

1978. Illuminated Jewish Marriage Contracts (Ketubah). Multicoloured.
694 75a. Type **281** 15 15
695 I£3.90 Moroccan Ketubah . . 25 20
696 I£6 Jerusalem Ketubah . . . 40 30

282 "A Street in Jerusalem" (H. Gliksberg) **283** Eliyahu Golomb (leader of Hagana)

1978. Jewish Art.
697 **282** I£3 multicoloured 25 25
698 – I£3.80 black, yellow & grey 30 25
699 – I£4.40 multicoloured . . . 35 25
DESIGNS: I£3.80, "Thistles" (L. Krakauer). I£4.40, "An Alley in Zefat" (M. Levanon).

1978. Historical Personalities (1st series).
700 **283** I£2 green and yellow . . 20 15
701 – I£2 blue and grey 20 15
702 – I£2 purple and stone . . . 20 15
703 – I£2 brown and stone . . 20 15
704 – I£2 black and grey . . . 20 15
DESIGNS: No. 701, David Raziel (Irgun commander); 702, Yitzhak Sadeh (nationalist and military commander); 703, Dr. Moshe Sneh (Zionist politician); 704, Abraham Stern (underground fighter).
See also Nos. 721/2, 725/6, 732/3, 738/40, 763/5, 809/11 and 831/3.

284 Children's Flower Paintings (from mural, Petah Tikvah Museum)

1978. Memorial Day.
705 **284** I£1.50 multicoloured . . . 20 10
706 – I£1.50 multicoloured . . . 20 10
707 – I£1.50 multicoloured . . . 20 10
708 – I£1.50 multicoloured . . . 20 10
709 – I£1.50 multicoloured . . . 20 10
710 – I£1.50 multicoloured . . . 20 10
711 – I£1.50 multicoloured . . . 20 10
712 – I£1.50 multicoloured . . . 20 10
713 – I£1.50 multicoloured . . . 20 10
714 – I£1.50 multicoloured . . . 20 10
715 – I£1.50 multicoloured . . . 20 10
716 – I£1.50 multicoloured . . . 20 10
717 – I£1.50 multicoloured . . . 20 10
718 – I£1.50 multicoloured . . . 20 10
719 – I£1.50 multicoloured . . . 20 10
Nos. 705/19 issued together form a composite design, each showing a different portion of the Memorial Wall.

1978. Historical Personalities (2nd series). As T **283**.
721 I£2 blue and stone 20 15
722 I£2 brown and grey 20 15
DESIGNS: No. 721, Dr. Chaim Weizmann (first president of Israel); No. 722, Dr. Theodor Herzl (founder of Zionism).

286 Y.M.C.A. Building Jerusalem

1978. Centenary of Jerusalem Y.M.C.A.
723 **286** I£5.40 multicoloured . . . 35 30

287 Verse of National Anthem **288** Family Groups

1978. Centenary of Publication of "Hatiqwa" (Jewish National Anthem).
724 **287** I£8.40 silver, dp blue & bl 55 40

1978. Historical Personalities (3rd series). As T **283**.
725 I£2 purple and cream 20 15
726 I£2 green and cream 20 15
DESIGNS: No. 725, Rabbi Ouziel; No. 726, Rabbi Kook.

1978. Social Welfare.
727 **288** I£5.10 multicoloured . . . 35 30

1978. Jewish New Year, Patriarchs of Israel. As T **274**. Multicoloured.
728 I£1.10 Abraham 20 15
729 I£5.20 Isaac 35 30
730 I£6.60 Jacob 40 35

289 Star of David, Young Tree and Globe showing U.S.A.

291 Indian Silver and Enamelled Vase

290 Shaare Zedek Medical Centre, New and Old Buildings

1978. United Jewish Appeal.
731 **289** I£8.40 multicoloured . . . 65 60

1978. Historical Personalities (4th series). As T **283**.
732 I£2 purple and stone 20 15
733 I£2 blue and grey 20 15
DESIGNS: No. 732, David Ben-Gurion (first Prime Minister); No. 733, Ze'ev Jabotinsky (Zionist leader).

1978. Opening of New Shaare Zedek Medical Centre, Jerusalem.
734 **290** I£5.40 multicoloured . . . 40 30

1978. Institute for Islamic Art, Jerusalem. Multicoloured.
735 I£2.40 Type **291** 25 20
736 I£3 13th-century Persian pottery chess rook (elephant with howdah) . . 30 25
737 I£4 Syrian Mosque lamp . . 35 25

1978. Historical Personalities (5th series). As T **283**.
738 I£2 black and stone 20 15
739 I£2 blue and grey 20 15
740 I£2 black and stone 20 15
DESIGNS: No. 738, Menahem Ussishkin (president of Jewish National Fund); No. 739, Berl Katzenelson (pioneer of Zionist socialism); No. 740, Dr. Max Nordau (journalist).

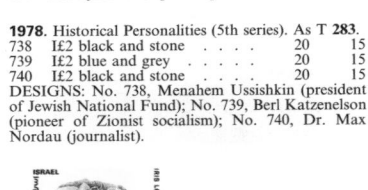

292 "Iris lortetii"

293 Agricultural Mechanization

1978. Wild Irises. Multicoloured.
741 I£1.10 Type **292** 20 15
742 I£5.40 "Iris haynei" 40 30
743 I£8.40 "Iris nazarena" . . . 50 45

1979. Technological Achievements. Mult.
744 I£1.10 Type **293** 15 10
745 I£2.40 Sea water desalination 20 15
746 I£4.30 Electronics 20 15
747 I£5 Chemical fertilizers . . . 25 20

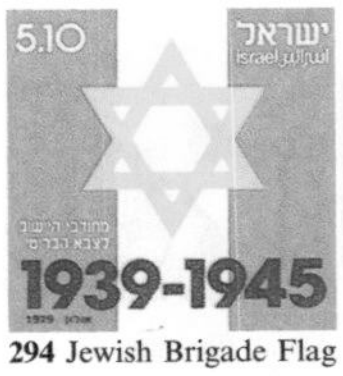

294 Jewish Brigade Flag

295 "Good from Evil"

1979. Yishuv Volunteers serving in Second World War.
748 **294** I£5.10 yellow, blue & dp bl 45 40

1979. "Salute to the Righteous among Nations".
749 **295** I£5.40 multicoloured . . . 45 40

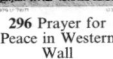

296 Prayer for Peace in Western Wall

297 Naval Memorial, Ashdod

1979. Signing of Egyptian–Israeli Peace Treaty.
750 **296** I£10 multicoloured . . . 35 30

1979. Memorial Day.
752 **297** I£5.10 multicoloured . . . 30 20

298 Weightlifting

299 "50" and Rotary Emblem

1979. 11th Hapoel Games. Multicoloured.
753 I£1.50 Type **298** 25 15
754 I£6 Tennis 35 35
755 I£11 Gymnastics 50 45

1979. 50th Anniv of Rotary in Israel.
756 **299** I£7 multicoloured 45 40

300 Rabbi Joshua Ben Hananiah (blacksmith)

301 Tiberias Hot Springs

1979. Jewish New Year. The "Hazal" (sages and craftsmen). Multicoloured.
757 I£1.80 Type **300** 25 20
758 I£8.50 Rabbi Meir Ba'al Ha-Nes (scribe) 45 40
759 I£13 Rabbi Johanan the Sandal-maker 60 55

1979. Health Resorts. Multicoloured.
760 I£8 Type **301** 30 25
761 I£12 Dead Sea Hot Spring 50 35

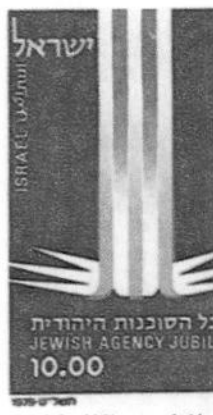

302 "Searchlight Beam"

303 Arab and Jew before Jerusalem

1979. 50th Anniv of Jewish Agency.
762 **302** I£10 blue, grey & turquoise 45 30

1979. Historical Personalities (6th series). As T **283**.
763 I£7 purple and grey 30 25
764 I£9 blue 35 35
765 I£13 black and stone 45 40
DESIGNS: I£7, Dr. Arthur Ruppin ("father of Zionist settlement"). I£9, Joseph Trumpeldor (founder of Zion Mule Corps and Jewish Legion). I£13, Aaron Aaronsohn (botanist).

1979. Children Paint Jerusalem. Multicoloured.
766 I£1.80 Type **303** 20 15
767 I£4 Jewish, Christian and Muslim citizens of Jerusalem (horiz) 20 20
768 I£5 Worshippers at the Western Wall (horiz) . . . 25 25

304 Boy sliding down Rainbow

305 Cog with Star of David

1979. International Year of the Child.
769 **304** I£8.50 multicoloured . . . 40 30

1980. Centenary of Organization for Rehabilitation through Training.
770 **305** I£13 multicoloured . . . 55 45

306 "Scolymus maculatus"

307 "The Road of Courage" Monument

1980. Thistles. Multicoloured.
771 50a. Type **306** 20 15
772 I£5.50 "Echinops viscosus" 35 25
773 I£8.50 "Cynara syriaca" . . 65 60

1980. Memorial Day.
774 **307** I£12 multicoloured . . . 40 30

308 Symbolical Human Figure with Blood-drop

309 Sabbath Lamp, Netherlands, 18th-century

1980. 50th Anniv of Magden David Adom (voluntary medical corps).
775 **308** I£2.70 red, grey and black 15 15
776 – I£13 multicoloured . . . 40 35
DESIGN: I£13, Mobile intensive care unit and graph.

1980. Jewish New Year. Sabbath Lamps. Multicoloured.
778 I£4.30 Type **309** 35 20
779 I£20 Germany, 18th-century 50 45
780 I£30 Morocco, 19th-century 65 50

310 Yizhak Gruenbrum

311 Tree and Flowers

1980. 10th Death Anniv of Yizhak Gruenbaum (Zionist and politician).
781 **310** I£32 brown . . . . 1·25 1·10

1980. Renewal of Jewish Settlement in Gush Etzion.
782 **311** I£19 multicoloured . . . 70 60

New currency.
1 (new) shekel = 10 (old) Israeli pounds.

313 "Shekel"

314 Golda Meir

1980.
784 **313** 5a. green and emerald 10 10
785 10a. red and mauve . . 10 10
786 20a. turquoise and blue 10 10
787 30a. violet & deep violet 10 10
788 50a. orange and red . . 10 10
789 a 60a. green and purple 15 10
790 70a. blue and black . . 15 10
791 90a. violet and brown 15 10
792 1s. mauve and green . . 15 10
793 1s.10 green and red . . 15 10
794 1s.20 blue and red . . 15 10
795 2s. green and purple . . 20 10
796 2s.80 brown and green 25 10
797 a 3s. red and blue . . . 20 15
798 3s.20 grey and red . . 40 30
799 b 4s. purple and mauve 25 15
800 4s.20 blue and violet . . 25 10
801 a 5s. green and black . . 25 10
802pa 10s. brown & dp brown 30 15

1981. Golda Meir (former Prime Minister). Commemoration.
803 **314** 2s.60 purple 60 55

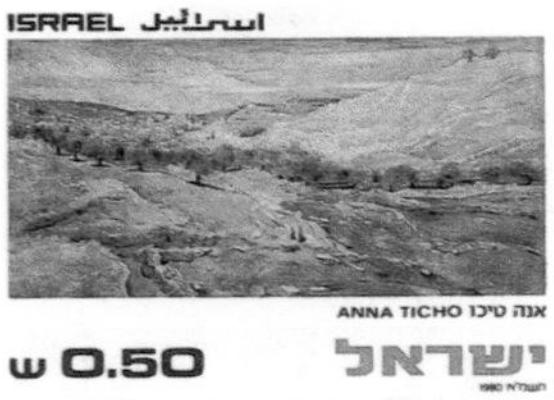

315 Landscape (Anna Ticho)

1981. Paintings of Jerusalem. Multicoloured.
804 50a. Type **315** 20 15
805 1s.50 "View of City" (Joseph Zaritsky) (vert) 40 30
806 2s.50 Landscape (Mordechai Ardon) 50 45

316 Hand putting Coin into Light Bulb

317 A. H. Silver (Zionist)

1981. Energy. Multicoloured.
807 2s.60 Type **316** 50 40
808 4s.20 Hand squeezing energy from the sun 60 50

1981. Historical Personalities (7th series).
809 – 2s. blue 55 45
810 – 2s.80 green 55 45
811 **317** 3s.20 ochre and black . . 55 45
DESIGNS—As T **283**: 2s. Shmuel Yosef Agnon (writer); 2s.80, Moses Montefiore (Zionist).

318 Biq'at Ha-yarden Memorial

319 Board Sailing

1981. Memorial Day.
812 **318** 1s. multicoloured 30 25

1981. 11th Maccabiah Games. Multicoloured.
813 80a. Type **319** 45 30
814 4s. Basketball 65 50
815 6s. High jump 85 75

320 "Family Tree"

321 Moses and the Burning Bush

1981. The Jewish Family Heritage.
816 **320** 3s. multicoloured 55 45

1981. Jewish New Year. Moses. Multicoloured.
817 70a. Type **321** 25 10
818 1s. Moses and Aaron petitioning Pharoah for Israelites' freedom 30 20
819 3s. Israelites crossing the Red Sea 50 30
820 4s. Moses with the Tablets 55 50

322 "Rosa damascena"

1981. Roses. Multicoloured.

821	90a. Type **322**	40	25
822	3s.50 "Rosa phoenicia"	50	40
823	4s.50 "Rosa hybrida"	65	50

323 Ha-Shiv'a Interchange

1981. Ha-Shiv'a Motorway Interchange.

824	**323** 8s. multicoloured	1·25	1·10

324 Balonea Oak　325 Elat Stone

1981. Trees. Multicoloured.

825	3s. Type **324**	40	35
826	3s. Wild strawberry	40	35
827	3s. Judas tree	40	35

1981. Precious Stones. Multicoloured.

828	2s.50 Type **325**	25	20
829	5s.50 Star sapphire	60	40
830	7s. Emerald	70	50

1982. Historical Personalities (8th series). As T **283**.

831	7s. multicoloured	75	60
832	8s. brown, stone and black	75	60
833	9s. blue and grey	75	60

DESIGNS: 7s. Perez Bernstein (politician); 8s. Rabbi Arye Levin; 9s. Joseph Gedaliah Klausner (writer, editor and President of Hebrew Language Academy).

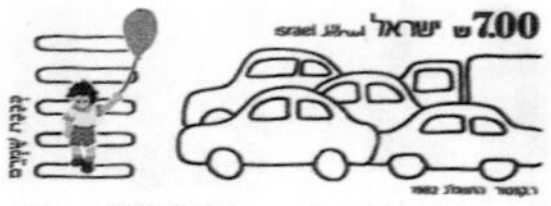

327 Child crossing Road

1982. Road Safety.

834	**327** 7s. multicoloured	75	60

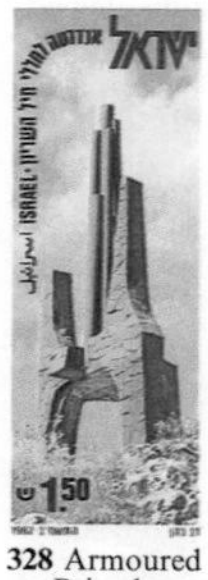

328 Armoured Brigade Memorial, En Zetim　330 Emblem and Flowers

329 Landscape (Aryeh Lubin)

1982. Memorial Day.

836	**328** 1s.50 multicoloured	30	20

1982. Israeli Art. Multicoloured.

837	7s. Type **329**	85	70
838	8s. "Landscape" (Sionah Tagger) (vert)	90	85
839	15s. "Pastorale" (Israel Paldi)	1·25	1·25

1982. 40th Anniv of Gadna (Youth Corps).

840	**330** 5s. multicoloured	80	70

331 Agricultural Products　332 Joshua and Israelites setting out for Canaan

1982.

841	**331** 40a. blue and green	10	10
842	80a. blue and mauve	10	10
843	1s.40 green and red	20	15
844a	6s. mauve and red	30	20
845	7s. red and green	15	10
846	8s. green and red	20	15
847	9s. green and brown	10	10
848a	15s. red and green	25	15
849	30s. purple and red	20	15
850b	50s. bistre and red	50	20
851a	100s. black and green	70	50
852a	500s. red and black	70	60

1982. Jewish New Year. Joshua. Mult.

860	1s.50 Type **332**	35	25
861	5s.50 Priests carrying Ark of the Covenant over River Jordan	45	35
862	7s.50 The fall of the walls of Jericho	50	40
863	9s.50 The suspension of twilight during the battle against the five kings of Amorite	65	55

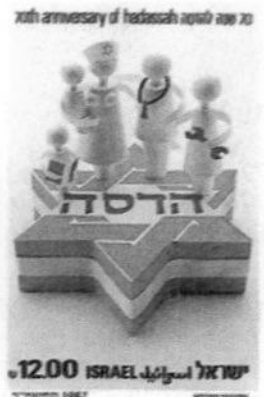

333 Rosh Pinna　334 Symbolic Figures on Star of David

1982. Centenaries of Rosh Pinna and Rishon Le Zion Settlements. Multicoloured.

864	2s.50 Type **333**	45	40
865	3s.50 Rishon Le Zion	45	40

See also Nos. 868/9, 905/6 and 967.

1982. 70th Anniv of Hadassah (Women's Zionist Organization of America).

866	**334** 12s. multicoloured	1·10	90

335 Branch　336 Flower

1982. No value expressed.

867	**335** (–) brown and orange	55	20

No. 867 was initially sold at 1s.70 but this value was subsequently increased several times.

1982. Centenaries of Zikhron Yaaqov and Mazkeret Batya. As T **333**. Multicoloured.

868	6s. Zikhron Yaaqov	45	40
869	9s. Mazkeret Batya	45	40

1982. Council for a Beautiful Israel.

870	**336** 17s. multicoloured	1·25	1·10

337 Eliahu Bet Tzuri　338 Honey Bee, Honeycomb and Flowers

1982. "Martyrs of the Struggle for Israel's Independence".

872	**337** 3s. grey, black and brown	35	25
873	– 3s. grey, black and olive	35	25
874	– 3s. grey, black and blue	35	25
875	– 3s. grey, black and olive	35	25
876	– 3s. grey, black and brown	35	25
877	– 3s. grey, black and blue	35	25
878	– 3s. grey, black and brown	35	25
879	– 3s. grey, black and olive	35	25
880	– 3s. grey, black and blue	35	25
881	– 3s. grey, black and olive	35	25
882	– 3s. grey, black and brown	35	25
883	– 3s. grey, black and olive	35	25
884	– 3s. grey, black and blue	35	25
885	– 3s. grey, black and brown	35	25
886	– 3s. grey, black and blue	35	25
887	– 3s. grey, black and olive	35	25
888	– 3s. grey, black and blue	35	25
889	– 3s. grey, black and brown	35	25
890	– 3s. grey, black and olive	35	25
891	– 3s. grey, black and brown	35	25

DESIGNS: No. 873, Hannah Szenes; 874, Shlomo Ben Yosef; 875, Yosef Lishanski; 876, Naaman Belkind; 877, Eliezer Kashani; 878, Yechiel Dresner; 879, Dov Gruner; 880, Mordechai Alkachi; 881, Eliahu Hakim; 882, Meir Nakar; 883, Avshalom Haviv; 884, Ya'akov Weiss; 885, Meir Feinstein; 886, Moshe Barazani; 887, Eli Cohen; 888, Samuel Azaar; 889, Dr. Moshe Marzouk; 890, Shalom Salih; 891, Yosef Basri.

1983. Bee-keeping.

892	**338** 30s. multicoloured	1·90	1·75

339 Sweets in Ashtray

1983. Anti-smoking Campaign.

893	**339** 7s. multicoloured	55	45

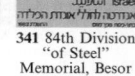

340 Golan Settlement　341 84th Division "of Steel" Memorial, Besor (Israel Godowitz)

1983. Settlements. Multicoloured.

894	8s. Type **340**	65	50
895	15s. Galil settlement	90	75
896	20s. Yehuda and Shomeron settlements	1·25	1·00

1983. Memorial Day.

897	**341** 3s. multicoloured	30	25

342 Star of David

1983. 35th Anniv of Independence.

898	**342** 25s. multicoloured	1·90	1·75

343 Running

1983. 12th Hapoel Games.

900	**343** 6s. multicoloured	50	40

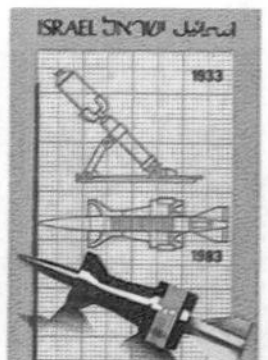

344 Missile and Blueprint

1983. 50th Anniv of Israel Military Industries.

901	**344** 12s. multicoloured	80	60

345 "The Last Way" (Iosef Kuzhovsky)

1983. Babi Yar Massacre.

902	**345** 35s. multicoloured	1·90	1·50

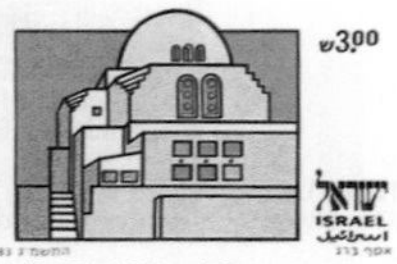

347 Raoul Wallenberg　348 Ohel Moed Synagogue, Tel Aviv

1983. Raoul Wallenberg (Swedish diplomat) Commemoration.

904	**347** 14s. stone and brown	1·10	90

1983. Centenary of Yesud Ha-Maala and Nes Ziyyona. As T **333**. Multicoloured.

905	11s. Yesud Ha-Maala	60	55
906	13s. Nes Ziyyona	65	60

1983. Jewish New Year. Synagogues. Mult.

907	3s. Type **348**	35	25
908	12s. Yeshurun Synagogue, Jerusalem	60	50
909	16s. Ohel Aharon Synagogue, Haifa	85	70
910	20s. Khalaschi Synagogue, Beer Sheva	95	85

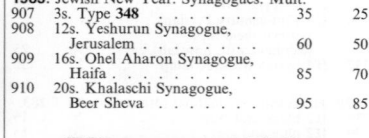

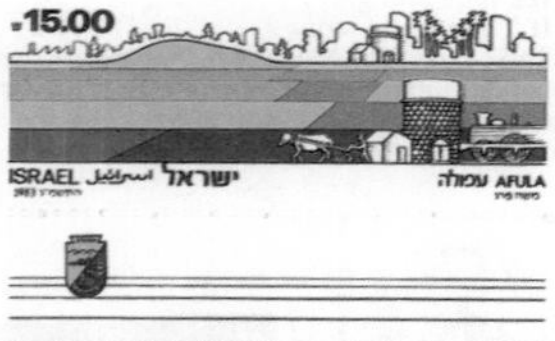

349 Afula Landscape

1983. Afula Urban Centre, Jezreel Valley.

911	**349** 15s. multicoloured	75	60

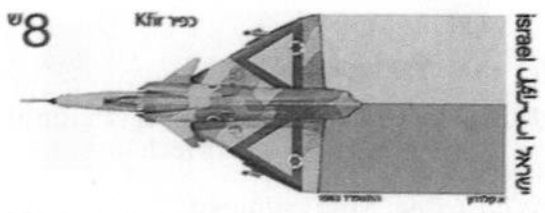

351 Israeli Aircraft Industry Kfir-C2 Jet Fighter

1983. Military Equipment. Multicoloured.

913	8s. Type **351**	25	20
914	18s. "Reshef" (missile vessel)	45	40
915	30s. "Merkava" battle tank	60	55

352 Rabbi Meir Bar-Ilan　353 "Aliya" ("immigration")

1983. 34th Death Anniv of Rabbi Meir Bar-Ilan (Zionist leader).

916	**352** 9s. blue and green	35	30

1983. 50th Anniv of Jewish Immigration from Germany.

917	**353** 14s. red, gold and blue	45	35

354 Michael Halperin　355 Yigal Allon

1984. 65th Death Anniv of Michael Halperin (nationalist).
918 **354** 7s. brown, stone & dp brn 40 30

1984. 4th Death Anniv of Yigal Allon (politician).
919 **355** 15s. blue, green and black 40 30

356 Uri Zvi Grinberg

357 Hevel Ha-Besor

1984. 3rd Death Anniv of Uri Zvi Grinberg (poet).
920 **356** 16s. brown and red . . . 40 30

1984. Settlements. Multicoloured.
921 12s. Type **357** 45 40
922 17s. Arava 60 50
923 40s. Hevel Azza 70 65

358 Alexander Zaid Monument (David Polus)

1984. Sculptures.
924 **358** 15s. stone, black and blue 50 45
925 – 15s. stone, black & brown 50 45
926 – 15s. green, black and grey 50 45
DESIGNS: No. 925, Tel Hay Memorial (Abraham Melnikov); 926, Dov Gruner monument (Chana Orloff).

359 Oliphant House, Dalyat Al Karmil (memorial to Druse Community)

360 Worker with Flag

1984. Memorial Day.
927 **359** 10s. multicoloured 30 25

1984. 50th Anniv of National Labour Federation.
928 **360** 35s. multicoloured 75 70

361 Leon Pinsker

362 Stars and Hearts

1984. 93rd Death Anniv of Leon Pinsker (Zionist leader).
929 **361** 20s. lilac and purple . . . 70 60

1984. 70th Anniv of American Jewish Joint Distribution Committee.
930 **362** 30s. red, blue and black 70 60

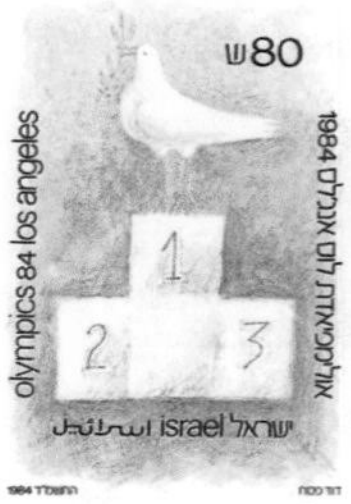

363 Dove on Olympic Podium

364 General Charles Orde Wingate

1984. Olympic Games, Los Angeles.
931 **363** 80s. multicoloured . . . . 1·40 1·25

1984. 40th Death Anniv of Gen. Charles Orde Wingate (military strategist).
933 **364** 20s. grey, black and green 70 60

365 Hannah

366 Nahalal (first Moshav)

1984. Jewish New Year. Women in the Bible. Multicoloured.
934 15s. Type **365** 40 30
935 70s. Ruth 65 55
936 100s. Huldah the prophetess 90 80

1984. Moshavim (Co-operative Workers' Settlements).
937 **366** 80s. multicoloured . . . . 1·10 90

367 David Wolffsohn

368 "Apartment to Let" (Leah Goldberg, illus Shemuel Katz)

1984. 70th Death Anniv of David Wolffsohn (president of Zionist Organization).
938 **367** 150s. brown, blue & black 1·90 1·75

1984. Children's Books. Multicoloured.
939 20s. Type **368** 30 25
940 30s. "Why is the Zebra wearing pyjamas?" (O. Hille, illus Alona Frankel) (28 × 28 mm) . . 30 30
941 50s. "Across the Sea" (Haim Nahman Bialik, illus Nahum Gutman) 35 30

369 Bread and Wheat

1984. World Food Day.
942 **369** 200s. multicoloured . . . 1·50 1·25

370 Isaac Herzog

1984. 25th Death Anniv of Isaac Herzog (Israel's first Chief Rabbi).
943 **370** 400s. multicoloured . . . 2·50 2·00

371 Lappet-faced Vulture

1985. Biblical Birds of Prey (1st series). Multicoloured.
944 100s. Type **371** 90 90
945 200s. Bonelli's eagle . . . . 1·25 1·25
946 300s. Sooty falcon . . . . . 1·50 1·25
947 500s. Griffon vulture . . . . 2·40 2·00
See also Nos. 1015/18.

372 Golani Brigade Monument and Museum

1985. Memorial Day.
949 **372** 50s. multicoloured 30 25

373 Bleriot XI

1985. Aviation in the Holy Land. Mult.
950 50s. Type **373** (landing by Jules Vedrines, 1913) . . . 45 35
951 150s. Short S.17 Kent flying boat "Scipio" (Imperial Airways regular flights via Palestine, 1931–42) 60 45
952 250s. De Havilland D.H.82A Tiger Moth (foundation of Palestine Flying Club, 1934) 75 70
953 300s. Short S.16 Scion II (international flights by Palestine Airways, 1937–40) 90 85

374 Zivia and Yitzhak Zuckerman

1985. Zivia and Yitzhak Zuckerman (Polish Jewish freedom fighters) Commemoration.
954 **374** 200s. brown, grey & black 95 85

375 Nurses tending Patients

1985. 18th International Congress of Nurses.
955 **375** 400s. multicoloured . . . 1·40 1·25

377 Ark of the Covenant

378 "Medals"

1985. Jewish New Year. Tabernacle Furnishings. Multicoloured.
957 100s. Type **377** 35 25
958 150s. The table 35 25
959 200s. Candlestick 40 40
960 300s. Incense altar 50 45

1985. International Youth Year.
961 **378** 150s. multicoloured . . . 35 30

379 Basketball

380 Recanati

1985. 12th Maccabiah Games. Multicoloured.
962 400s. Type **379** 90 75
963 500s. Tennis . . . . 1·00 90
964 600s. Windsurfing . . . . . 1·25 1·00

1985. 40th Death Anniv of Leon Yehuda Racanati (founder of Palestine Discount Bank).
965 **380** 200s. brown, grey and blue 45 40

381 Dizengoff (after J. Steinhardt and M. Sima)

1985. 49th Death Anniv of Meir Dizengoff (founder and Mayor of Tel Aviv).
966 **381** 500s. black, brown & silver . . . . 1·00 75

1985. Centenary of Gedera. As T **333**. Mult.
967 600s. Gedera . . . . 1·10 95

382 Kibbutz Members

1985. The Kibbutz.
968 **382** 900s. multicoloured . . . 1·75 1·25

Currency Reform.
1000 (old) Shekalim = 1 (new) Shekel.

383 Dr. Theodor Herzl

384 Corinthian Capital, 1st Century B.C.

1986.
969 **383** 1a. blue and red 10 10
970 2a. blue and green . . . 10 10
971 3a. blue and bistre . . . 10 10
972 5a. blue and turquoise 10 10
973 10a. blue and orange . . 20 15
974a 20a. blue and purple . . 25 20
975a 30a. blue and yellow . . 40 25
976a 50a. blue and violet . . 60 35

1986. Jerusalem Archaeology.
977 – 40a. green, orange & blk 30 15
978 – 60a. brown, violet & blk 45 15
979 – 70a. green, brown & blk 50 15
980 – 80a. purple, bistre & blk 55 20
981 – 90a. yellow, lilac & black 60 20
982 **384** 1s. brown, green & black 60 20
983a – 2s. blue, green and black 1·25 35
984 – 3s. mauve, blue and black . . . . 1·75 55
987 – 10s. green, blue and black . . . . 2·00 55
DESIGNS—As T **384**: 40a. Relief, 1st century B.C. (Second Temple); 60a. Byzantine capital, 6th century A.D.; 3s. Archaic Ionic capital, 1st century B.C. (Second Temple). 32 × 23 mm: 70a. Relief from palace of Umayyid Caliphs, 8th century A.D.; 80a. Crusader capital from Church of Ascension, Mount of Olives, 12–13th centuries; 90a. Relief from Suleiman's Wall, 16th century A.D.; 2s. Insignia of Sayif addin Attaz from Mameluke Academy, 14th century A.D.; 10s. Frieze from burial cave entrance, end of Second Temple period.

385 "Balanophyllia coccinea"

387 Microphone and Map

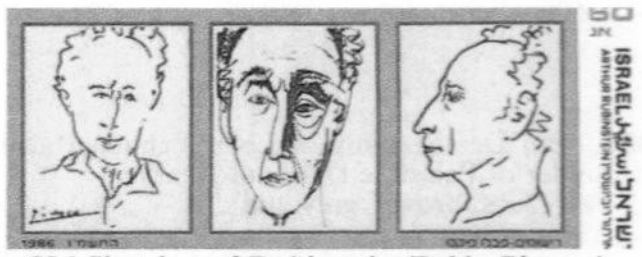
386 Sketches of Rubinstein (Pablo Picasso)

1986. Red Sea Corals. Multicoloured.
991 30a. Type **385** 60 50
992 40a. "Goniopora" 60 50
993 50a. "Dendronephthya" . . . 60 50

1986. Birth Cent (1987) of Arthur Rubinstein and 5th International Rubinstein Piano Competition.
994 **386** 60a. multicoloured . . . 1·25 1·10

1986. 50th Anniv of Broadcasting from Jerusalem.
995 **387** 70a. multicoloured . . . 1·25 1·10

388 Negev Bridge Monument, Beer Sheva

389 El-Jazzar Mosque, Akko

1986. Memorial Day.
996 **388** 20a. multicoloured . . . 45 35

1986. Id Al-Fitr (end of Ramadan).
997 **389** 30a. emerald, green & ol 55 45

390 Hebrew Union College, Cincinnati

1986. "Ameripex '86" International Stamp Exhibition, Chicago. Jewish Institutes of Higher Learning. Multicoloured.
998 50a. Type **390** 85 75
999 50a. Yeshiva University, New York 85 75
1000 50a. Jewish Theology Seminary, New York . . 85 75

391 Nabi Sabalan's Tomb, Hurfeish

1986. Feast of Nabi Sabalan (Druse feast).
1002 **391** 40a. multicoloured . . . 70 55

392 Graffiti on Wall

1986. Anti-racism Campaign.
1003 **392** 60a. multicoloured . . . 1·25 95

393 Sprinzak

395 Gates of Heaven, with Jerusalem above, opening to Power of Prayer

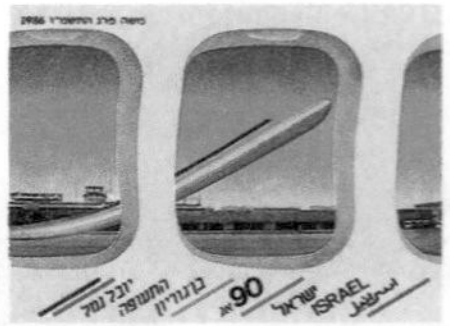
394 Airport through Cabin Windows

1986. Birth Centenary (1985) of Joseph Sprinzak (first Speaker of Knesset).
1004 **393** 80a. blue, green and black . . . . 1·25 1·10

1986. 50th Anniv of Ben Gurion Airport.
1005 **394** 90a. multicoloured . . . 1·90 1·50

1986. Jewish New Year. Pages from Worms Mahzor (prayer book). Multicoloured.
1006 20a. Type **395** (prayers for Yom Kippur) 60 50
1007 40a. Man weighing shekel for Temple (prayer for Sheqalim, first special Sabbath) 65 65
1008 90a. Roses (illustration of liturgical poem) 85 75

396 David Ben Gurion

1986. Birth Centenary of David Ben Gurion (Prime Minister, 1948–53 and 1955–63).
1009 **396** 1s. bistre, brown & black 1·75 1·50

398 Satellite and Isobars over Map

399 Basilica of the Annunciation, Nazareth

1986. 50th Anniv of Meteorological Service.
1011 **398** 50a. multicoloured . . . 1·10 90

1986. Christmas.
1012 **399** 70a. multicoloured . . . 1·40 1·25

400 Bronislaw Huberman (violinist and founder)

1986. 50th Anniv of Israel Philharmonic Orchestra.
1013 **400** 1s.50 brown, blk & yell 2·25 1·90
1014 – 1s.50 grey, black & yell 2·25 1·90
DESIGN: No. 1014, Arturo Toscanini (conductor of Orchestra's first concert, 1936).

401 Hume's Owl

1987. Biblical Birds of Prey (2nd series). Owls. Multicoloured.
1015 30a. Desert eagle owl . . . 50 45
1016 40a. Pallid striated scops owl 65 60
1017 50a. Barn owl 85 70
1018 80a. Type **401** . . . . . . 1·50 95

402 Six-Day War Memorial, Ammunition Hill, Jerusalem

1987. Memorial Day.
1020 **402** 30a. multicoloured . . . 55 45

403 Emblem

1987. 13th Hapoel Games.
1021 **403** 90a. multicoloured . . . 1·25 1·10

405 Street Cleaner

406 Saluki

1987. "A Clean Environment".
1023 **405** 40a. multicoloured . . . 55 40

1987. World Dog Show. Dogs of Israeli Origin. Multicoloured.
1024 40a. Type **406** . . . . . . 1·25 1·00
1025 50a. Sloughi . . . . 1·25 1·00
1026 2s. Canaan dog . . . . . . 2·75 2·50

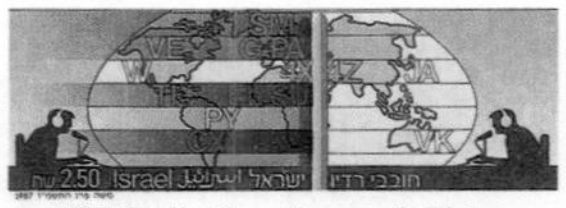
407 Radio Operators and Globe

1987. Israel Radio Amateurs.
1027 **407** 2s.50 multicoloured . . . 3·75 3·00

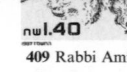

408 Altneuschul Synagogue, Prague

409 Rabbi Amiel

1987. Jewish New Year. Synagogue Models in Museum of the Diaspora, Tel Aviv (1st issue). Multicoloured.
1028 30a. Type **408** 45 45
1029 50a. Main Synagogue, Aleppo, Syria 60 50
1030 60a. Israelite Temple, Florence 70 60
See also Nos. 1054/6.

1987. 104th Birth Anniv of Rabbi Moshe Avigdor Amiel (Chief Rabbi of Tel Aviv).
1031 **409** 1s.40 multicoloured . . . 1·75 1·25

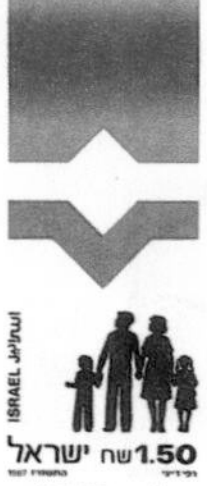
410 Family

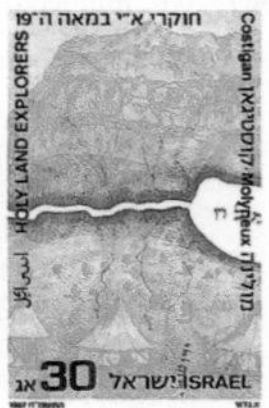
411 Camp (Christopher Costigan, 1835, and Thomas Howard Molyneux, 1847)

1987. 75th Anniv of Kupat Holim Health Insurance Institution.
1032 **410** 1s.50 multicoloured . . . 1·75 1·50

1987. Holy Land Explorers. Multicoloured.
1033 30a. Type **411** 50 45
1034 50a. Map of River Jordan (William Francis Lynch, 1848) 60 50
1035 60a. Men in canoe (John MacGregor, 1868–9) . . . 65 60

412 Rosen

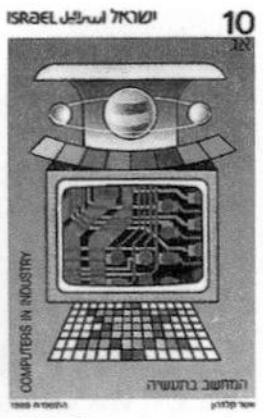
413 Computers in Industry

1987. Birth Centenary of Pinhas Rosen (lawyer and politician).
1037 **412** 80a. multicoloured . . . 1·00 95

1988. Centenary of Israeli Industry. Mult.
1038 10a. Type **413** 40 25
1039 80a. Genetic engineering . . 1·25 1·00
1040 1s.40 Medical engineering 1·50 1·40

414 Corked Tap

415 Kangaroos holding Birthday Cake

1988. "Save Water".
1041 **414** 40a. multicoloured . . . 70 55

1988. Bicentenary of Australian Settlement.
1042 **415** 1s. multicoloured . . . . 1·75 1·50

416 Sunflower

417 Hebrew Year 5748

1988. No value expressed.
1043 **416** (30a.) green and yellow 60 30

1988. Memorial Day.
1044 **417** 40a. multicoloured . . . 45 40

418 Anne Frank and House, Amsterdam

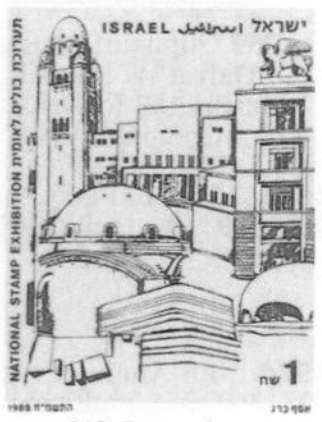
419 Jerusalem

1988. 43rd Death Anniv of Anne Frank (concentration camp victim).
1046 **418** 60a. multicoloured . . . 85 70

1988. "Independence 40" National Stamp Exhibition, Jerusalem.
1047 **419** 1s. light brown and brown . . . . 1·40 1·25

421 Ein Zin Nature Reserve

422 Jerusalem Lodge

1988. Nature Reserves in the Negev. Mult.

1050	40a. Type **421**	55	50
1051	60a. She' zaf	70	60
1052	70a. Ramon	80	65

1988. Centenary of B'nai B'rith in Jerusalem.
1053 **422** 70a. multicoloured . . . 95 85

1988. Jewish New Year. Synagogue Models in Museum of the Diaspora, Tel Aviv (2nd issue). As T **408**. Multicoloured.

1054	35a. 12th-century Kai-Feng Fu Synagogue, China . .	60	50
1055	60a. 17th-century Zabludow Synagogue, Poland . . .	65	60
1056	70a. 18th-century Touro Synagogue, Newport, Rhode Island	70	65

423 Havivah Reik

1988. Jewish World War II Underground Fighters. Multicoloured.

1057	**423**	40a. multicoloured . . .	55	50
1058	–	1s.65 dp blue, blue & blk	2·25	1·90

DESIGN: 1s.65, Enzo Hayyim Sereni.

424 Dayan

425 Burning Illustration of German Synagogue

1988. 7th Death Anniv of Moshe Dayan (soldier and politician).
1059 **424** 40a. multicoloured . . . 60 50

1988. 50th Anniv of "Kristallnacht" (Nazi pogrom).
1060 **425** 80a. multicoloured . . . 1·25 95

426 Menorah and Soldiers

1988. 74th Anniv of Formation of Jewish Legion.
1061 **426** 2s. dp brown, brn & bis 2·50 1·90

427 Avocado (fruit-growing)

1988. Agricultural Achievements in Israel. Mult.

1062	50a. Type **427**	75	65
1063	60a. Easter lily (plant breeding)	90	75
1064	90a. Plants and drip-pipe (irrigation systems) . . .	1·00	90

428 Red Sea

429 Rabbi Maimon

1989. Tourism. Multicoloured.

1065	40a. Type **428**	65	60
1066	60a. Dead Sea	75	70
1067	70a. Mediterranean	1·00	85
1068	1s.70 Sea of Galilee	1·40	1·40

1989. 114th Birth Anniv of Rabbi Judah Leib Maimon (writer).
1069 **429** 1s.70 multicoloured . . . 2·25 2·00

430 "Rashi" in Rashi Script

431 Airforce Memorial, Har Tayassim

1989. 950th Birth Anniv of Rashi (Rabbi Solomon Ben Isaac of Troyes) (scholar).
1070 **430** 4s. cream and brown . . 4·50 3·75

1989. Memorial Day.
1071 **431** 50a. multicoloured . . . 60 50

432 Child

433 Games Emblem

1989. 20th Anniv of Israel United Nations Children's Fund National Committee.
1072 **432** 90a. multicoloured . . . 1·25 1·00

1989. 13th Maccabiah Games.
1073 **433** 80a. multicoloured . . . 90 75

434 Smoira

436 Garganey

1989. Birth Centenary (1988) of Moshe Smoira (first President of Israel's Supreme Court).
1074 **434** 90a. blue . . . . 1·25 1·00

1989. Ducks. Multicoloured.

1076	80a. Type **436**	95	85
1077	80a. Mallard	95	85
1078	80a. Green-winged teal ("Teal")	95	85
1079	80a. Common shelduck ("Shelduck")	95	85

437 Printed Circuit and Pencil

438 Lion Design (Ukraine, 1921)

1989. 13th International Council of Graphic Design Associations Congress.
1080 **437** 1s. multicoloured . . . . 1·10 1·10

1989. Jewish New Year. Paper-cuts. Mult.

1081	50a. Type **438**	50	45
1082	70a. Hand design (Morocco, 1800s)	65	50
1083	80a. Stag design (Germany, 1818)	75	60

439 Founders of Safa Brurah

440 Rabbi Alkalai

1989. Centenaries of Safa Brurah ("Clear Language") and Hebrew Language Committee (precursors of Hebrew Language Council).
1084 **439** 1s. multicoloured . . . . 1·10 1·10

1989. 11th Death Anniv of Rabbi Hai Alkalai (Zionist).
1085 **440** 2s.50 multicoloured . . . 2·50 1·90

441 "Stag"

442 Postal Authority Emblem

1989. "Tevel 89" Youth Stamp Exhibition.
1086 **441** 50a. multicoloured . . . 55 50

1989. First Stamp Day.
1087 **442** 1s. multicoloured . . . . 1·00 90

443 "See You Again"

444 Rebab and Carpet

1989. Greetings Stamps. No value expressed. Multicoloured.

1088	(–) Type **443**	40	35
1089	(–) Patched heart ("With Love")	40	35
1090	(–) Flower ("Good Luck")	40	35

See also Nos. 1111/13 and 1128/30.

1990. The Bedouin in Israel.
1092 **444** 1s.50 multicoloured . . . 1·40 1·10

445 Traditional Dancing

446 Photograph Album and Orange

1990. Circassians in Israel.
1093 **445** 1s.50 multicoloured . . . 1·25 1·10

1990. Centenary of Rehovot Settlement.
1094 **446** 2s. multicoloured . . . . 1·90 1·50

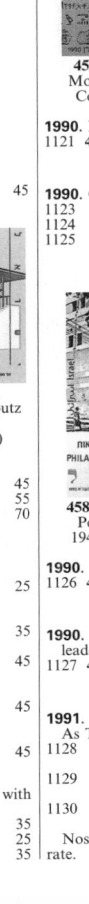

447 Artillery Corps Monument, Zikhron Yaaqov

1990. Memorial Day.
1095 **447** 60a. multicoloured . . . 55 45

448 Ruins of Gamla, Yehudiyya

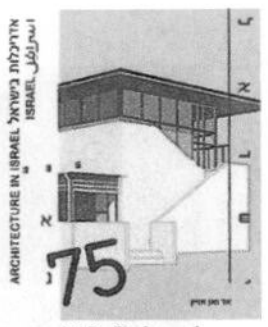

449 School, Deganya Kibbutz (Richard Kauffmann)

1990. Nature Reserves (1st series). Mult.

1096	60a. Type **448**	55	45
1097	80a. Huleh	70	55
1098	90a. Mt. Meron	80	70

See also Nos. 1200/2.

1990. Architecture.

1099b	75a. Type **449**	30	25
1100	1s.10 Dining hall, Tel Yosef Kibbutz (Leopold Krahauer)	60	35
1101	1s.20 Engel House, Tel Aviv (Ze'ev Rechter) . .	70	45
1102	1s.40 Weizmann House, Rehovot (Erich Mendelsohn)	75	45
1103	1s.60 National Institutions Building, Jerusalem (Yohanan Ratner) . . .	75	45

1990. Greetings Stamps. As Nos. 1088/90 but with value.

1111	55a. As No. 1090	50	35
1112a	80a. Type **443**	35	25
1113a	1s. As No. 1089	55	35

451 Badges

452 Dancers

1990. 70th Anniv of Formation of Hagana (underground military organization).
1114 **451** 1s.50 multicoloured . . . 1·40 1·10

1990. 8th International Folklore Festival, Haifa. Multicoloured.

1115	1s.90 Type **452**	1·90	1·75
1116	1s.90 Dancers and accordion player	1·90	1·75

Nos. 1115/16 were printed together, se-tenant, forming a composite design.

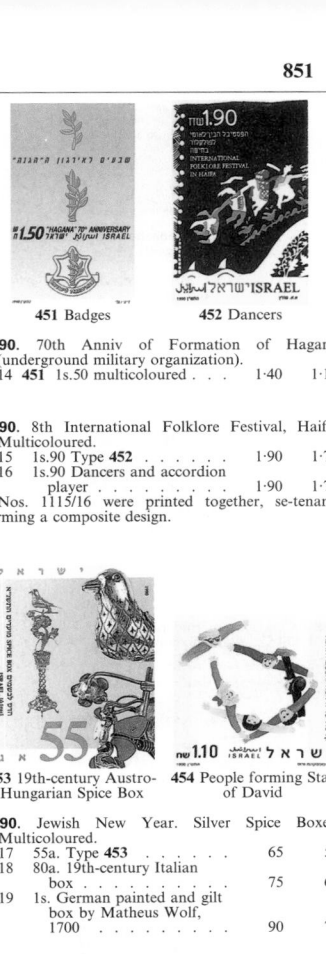

453 19th-century Austro-Hungarian Spice Box

454 People forming Star of David

1990. Jewish New Year. Silver Spice Boxes. Multicoloured.

1117	55a. Type **453**	65	50
1118	80a. 19th-century Italian box	75	65
1119	1s. German painted and gilt box by Matheus Wolf, 1700	90	75

1990. Absorption of Immigrants.
1120 **454** 1s.10 multicoloured . . . 1·10 95

455 Ancient and Modern Means of Communication

457 Basketball

1990. Electronic Mail.
1121 **455** 1s.20 green, black & yell 1·10 95

1990. Computer Games. Multicoloured.

1123	60a. Type **457**	65	55
1124	60a. Chess	65	55
1125	60a. Racing cars	65	55

458 Tel Aviv-Yafo Post Office and 1948 20m. Stamp

459 Jabotinsky

1990. Stamp Day.
1126 **458** 1s.20 multicoloured . . . 1·10 1·00

1990. 50th Death Anniv of Ze'ev Jabotinsky (Zionist leader).
1127 **459** 1s.90 multicoloured . . . 1·90 1·50

1991. Greetings Stamps. No value expressed. As T **443**. Multicoloured.

1128	(–) Birthday cake ("Happy Birthday")	40	30
1129	(–) Champagne bottle ("Greetings")	40	30
1130	(–) Envelopes ("Keep in Touch")	40	30

Nos. 1128/30 were sold at the current inland letter rate.

460 Sarah Aaronsohn (intelligence agent)

1991. Anniversaries. Multicoloured.

1131	1s.30 Type **460** (birth centenary (1990))	1·00	75
1132	1s.30 Rahel Bluwstein (poet, 60th death anniv)	1·00	75
1133	1s.30 Lea Goldberg (writer and translator, 80th birth anniv)	1·00	75

461 Eucalyptus Tree and Hadera

1991. Centenary of Hadera.
1134 **461** 2s.50 multicoloured . . . 2·00 1·75

462 Karate

1991. 14th Hapoel Games. Multicoloured.

1135	60a. Type **462**	65	50
1136	90a. Table tennis	75	65
1137	1s.10 Football	90	75

463 Intelligence Services Memorial, Centre for Special Studies, Tel Aviv

1991. Memorial Day.
1138 **463** 65a. multicoloured . . . 55 45

464 First (Diesel) Power Station, Tel Aviv

465 Rabbi Shimon Hakham (co-founder) and Armon Building

1991. Inauguration of Rutenberg Power Station. Multicoloured.

1139	70a. Type **464**	65	45
1140	90a. Yarden Hydro-electric Station, Naharayim	90	55
1141	1s.20 Rutenberg coal fired power station, Ashqelon	1·00	70

1991. Centenary (1990) of Bukharim Quarter of Jerusalem.
1142 **465** 2s.10 multicoloured . . . 1·50 1·25

467 Ram's Head and Man blowing Shofar

468 Front Page of First Edition

1991. Festivals. Multicoloured.

1144	65a. Type **467** (Jewish New Year)	65	50
1145	1s. "Penitence Cock", father blessing children and men blowing shofars (Day of Atonement)	75	65
1146	1s.20 Family in booth (Festival of Tabernacles)	90	75

1991. 150th Anniv of "Jewish Chronicle" (weekly newspaper).
1147 **468** 1s.50 black, blue and red 1·40 1·10

469 Colonists and Baron Maurice de Hirsch (founder)

1991. Centenary of Jewish Colonization Association.
1148 **469** 1s.60 multicoloured . . . 1·40 1·10

471 Cancelled 1948 5m. Stamp

1991. Stamp Day.
1150 **471** 70a. multicoloured . . . 55 45

472 Rahel Yanait Ben-Zvi (Zionist)

473 Runner

1991. Multicoloured.

1151	1s. Type **472**	75	70
1152	1s.10 Dona Gracia Nasi (supporter of 16th-century Jewish settlement in Tiberias)	80	75

1991. Olympic Games, Barcelona.
1153 **473** 1s.10 multicoloured . . . 95 60

474 Flame and Hebrew Script

475 Southern Wing of Acre Prison

1991. 51st Anniv of Lehi (resistance organization).
1154 **474** 1s.50 multicoloured . . . 1·25 1·10

1991. 60th Anniv of Etzel (resistance organization).
1155 **475** 1s.50 black, red and grey 1·25 1·10

476 Mozart and Score of "Don Giovanni"

477 Anemone

1991. Death Bicentenary of Wolfgang Amadeus Mozart (composer).
1156 **476** 2s. multicoloured . . . . 1·75 1·50

1992. No value expressed.
1157 **477** (–) red and green 30 15

No. 1157 was sold at the current inland letter rate, initially 75a.

478 Hanna Rovina (actress)

479 Trees

1992. Multicoloured.

1158	80a. Type **478**	50	45
1159	1s.30 Rivka Guber (teacher and writer)	65	55

1992. Sea of Galilee. Multicoloured.

1160	85a. Type **479**	65	50
1161	85a. Sailboard	65	50
1162	85a. Fishes	65	50

480 Palmah Emblem

481 Samaritans praying on Mount Gerizim

1992. 51st Anniv of Palmah (resistance organization).
1163 **480** 1s.50 gold, blue & mauve 1·10 95

1992. The Samaritans.
1164 **481** 2s.60 multicoloured . . . 2·00 1·90

482 Border Guard Memorial, Eiron Junction (Yechiel Arad)

1992. Memorial Day.
1165 **482** 85a. multicoloured . . . 45 40

483 Azulai

484 Hayyim

1992. 186th Death Anniv of Rabbi Hayyim Joseph David Azulai (scholar).
1166 **483** 85a. multicoloured . . . 45 40

1992. 83rd Death Anniv of Rabbi Joseph Hayyim Ben Elijah.
1167 **484** 1s.20 multicoloured . . . 60 45

485 "Almanach Perpetuum" and Models of Columbus's Ships

1992. 500th Anniv of Discovery of America by Columbus.
1168 **485** 1s.60 multicoloured . . . 1·00 80

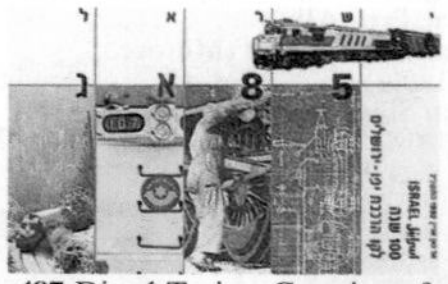

487 Diesel Trains, Greasing of Wheels and Blueprint of Baldwin Engine

1992. Centenary of Jaffa–Jerusalem Railway. Mult.

1170	85a. Type **487**	50	45
1171	1s. Scottish steam locomotive, track plan at Lod, electric signalling board at Tel Aviv, semaphore arms and points at Lod	55	50
1172	1s.30 Diesel locomotive, interior and exterior of passenger carriages, Palestine Railways ticket and 1926 timetable	70	65
1173	1s.60 Diesel train, drawing of facade of Jerusalem station, platform at Lod, Jaffa station in 1900 and points at Bar-Giora station	90	70

488 Cover of "Or-HaHayyim" ("Light of Life") (Rabbi Hayyim Benatar, 250th (1993) anniv)

1992. Death Anniversaries.

1175	**488**	1s.30 lilac, green & gold	75	65
1176	–	3s. lilac, green and gold	1·75	1·60

DESIGN: 3s. 19th-century drawing of Bet-El Yeshiva, Jerusalem (Rabbi Shalom Sharabi, 215th anniv).

489 Leopard

1992. Zoo Animals. Multicoloured.

1177	50a. Type **489**	35	30
1178	50a. Indian elephant	35	30
1179	50a. Chimpanzee	35	30
1180	50a. Lion	35	30

490 "Parables" (Yitzhak ben Shlomo ibn Sahula) (1st edition, Brescia, 1491)

1992. Jewish New Year. Centenary of Jewish National and University Library, Jerusalem. Multicoloured.

1181	85a. Type **490**	50	45
1182	1s. Mahzor (prayer book) (15th-century manuscript by Leon ben Yehoshua de Rossi)	65	55
1183	1s.20 Draft of translation by Martin Buber of Leviticus 25: 10-13	75	70

491 Court Building

492 Wallcreeper

1992. Inauguration of New Supreme Court Building.
1184 **491** 3s.60 multicoloured . . . 2·25 1·90

1992. Songbirds. Multicoloured.

1185	10a. Type **492**	10	10
1186	20a. Tristram's grackle	10	10
1187	30a. Pied wagtail ("White")	15	10
1188	50a. Palestine sunbird	20	10
1189	85a. Sinai rosefinch	35	20
1190	90a. Barn swallows ("Swallow")	40	25
1191	1s. Trumpeter finches	40	25
1192	1s.30 Graceful prinia ("Graceful Warbler")	55	35
1193	1s.50 Black-eared wheatear	65	40
1194	1s.70 White-eyed bulbuls ("Common Bulbul")	70	45

493 "Judah Released"

494 European Community Emblem on Graph

1992. 75th Anniv of First All-Hebrew Film. Scenes from films. Multicoloured.

1195	80a. Type **493** (first Hebrew film)	75	70
1196	2s.70 "Oded the Wanderer" (first Hebrew feature film)	1·50	1·40
1197	3s.50 "This is the Land" (first Hebrew talking film)	1·90	1·75

1992. Stamp Day. European Single Market.
1198 **494** 1s.50 multicoloured . . . 85 75

495 Begin

496 Shrine of the Bab

1993. 1st Death Anniv of Menahem Begin (Prime Minister, 1977–83).
1199 **495** 80a. multicoloured . . . 45 40

1993. Nature Reserves (2nd series). As T **448**. Multicoloured.
1200 1s.20 Hof Dor 75 65
1201 1s.50 Nahal Ammud 90 75
1202 1s.70 Nahal Ayun . . . . . 1·00 90

1993. Baha'i World Centre, Haifa.
1203 **496** 3s.50 multicoloured . . . 1·90 1·75

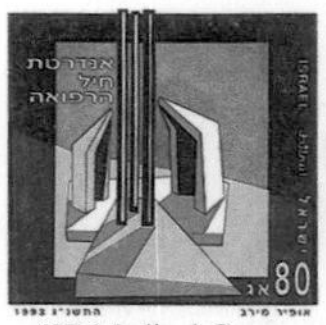
497 Medical Corps Memorial, Carmel, Haifa (Akiva Lomnitz)

498 "The Eye's Memory"

1993. Memorial Day.
1204 **497** 80a. multicoloured . . . 45 40

1993. Illustration of Scientific Concepts. Exhibits from the Israel National Museum of Science, Haifa (Nos. 1205/6) or the Bernard M. Bloomfield Science Museum, Jerusalem (others).
1205 80a. Type **498** 45 40
1206 80a. Colour mixing 45 40
1207 80a. Waves 45 40
1208 80a. Floating balls (principle of lift) 45 40

499 Prisoner

500 Hurbat Rabbi Yehuda Hassid Synagogue, Jerusalem

1993. 50th Anniv of Uprisings in the Ghettos and Concentration Camps.
1209 **499** 1s.20 black, yellow & bl 70 55

1993. 45th Anniv of Independence.
1210 **500** 3s.60 multicoloured . . . 2·10 1·90

501 Giulio Racah

502 Family using Crossing (Lior Abohovsky)

1993. Physicists. Multicoloured.
1211 80a. Type **501** 45 40
1212 1s.20 Aharon Katchalsky-Katzir 65 55

1993. Road Safety. Children's Paintings. Mult.
1213 80a. Type **502** 55 50
1214 1s.20 Vehicles and road signs (Elinor Paz) 70 60
1215 1s.50 Road signals on "man" (Moran Dadush) 80 75

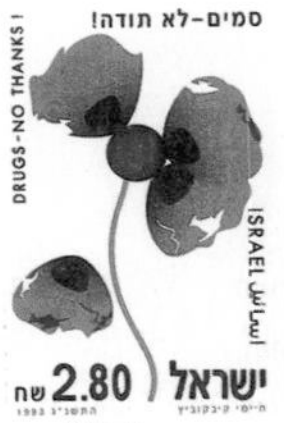
503 Poppy

504 Passing Baton

1993. Anti-drugs Campaign.
1216 **503** 2s.80 multicoloured . . . 1·50 1·40

1993. 14th Maccabiah Games.
1217 **504** 3s.60 multicoloured . . . 2·25 1·90

505 Tree

506 Ear of Wheat

1993. International Day of the Elderly.
1218 **505** 80a. multicoloured . . . 40 30

1993. Jewish New Year. Multicoloured.
1219 80a. Type **506** 40 30
1220 1s.20 Grapes 65 45
1221 1s.50 Olives 90 75

507 Environmental Concerns

1993. Environment Year.
1222 **507** 1s.20 multicoloured . . . 60 45

508 Emblems

1993. 150th Anniv of B'nai B'rith (cultural and social organization).
1223 **508** 1s.50 multicoloured . . . 60 45

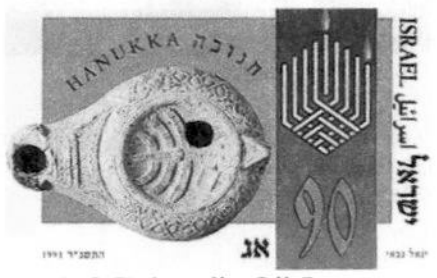
510 Talmudic Oil Lamp

1993. Festival of Hanukka. Multicoloured.
1225 90a. Type **510** 45 30
1226 1s.30 Hanukka lamp in shape of building 65 45
1227 2s. "Lighting the Hanukka Lamp" (illustration from the "Rothschild Miscellany") . . . . . . 1·00 75

511 Cover of First Issue

1993. Stamp Day. Centenary (1992) of "Miniature World" (children's magazine).
1228 **511** 1s.50 multicoloured . . . 75 55

512 Yellow-banded Borer ("Chlorophorus varius")

1994. Beetles. Multicoloured.
1229 85a. Type **512** 40 30
1230 85a. Copper beetle ("Potosia cuprea") 40 30
1231 85a. Pied ground beetle ("Graphopterus serrator") 40 30
1232 85a. Seven-spotted ladybird ("Coccinella septempunctata") 40 30

513 Man carrying Car ("Exercise Regularly")

1994. Health and Well-being. Multicoloured.
1233 85a. Type **513** 40 30
1234 1s.30 Blowing soap bubbles ("Don't Smoke") 65 45
1235 1s.60 Inspecting food through magnifying glass ("Eat Sensibly") 90 75

514 Haffkine

515 Communications, Electronics and Computer Corps Memorial, Yehud (Claude Grundman)

1994. 64th Death Anniv of Dr. Mordecai Haffkine (bacteriologist).
1236 **514** 3s.85 multicoloured . . . 1·90 1·50

1994. Memorial Day.
1237 **515** 85a. multicoloured . . . 40 30

516 Assuta Private Hospital (Yosef Neufeld)

1994. International Style Architecture in Tel Aviv. Each grey, blue and green.
1238 85a. Type **516** 40 30
1239 85a. Co-operative workers' housing (flats with separate balconies) (Arieh Sharon) 40 30
1240 85a. Citrus House (Karl Rubin) 40 30

517 Battered Child

1994. "No to Violence" Campaign.
1241 **517** 3s.85 black and red . . . 1·90 1·50

518 Saul Adler

1994. Birth Centenary (1995) of Saul Adler (scientist).
1242 **518** 4s.50 multicoloured . . . 2·25 1·75

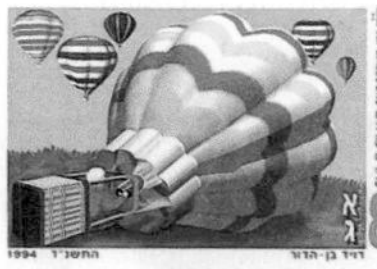
519 Inflating Balloon

1994. Ayalon Valley International Hot-Air Balloon Race. Multicoloured.
1243 85a. Type **519** 40 30
1244 85a. Balloons in air 40 30
1245 85a. Balloon hovering over target (cross on ground) 40 30

520 Chemistry Class at Bialystok and Physical Education at Wolyn

1994. 75th Anniv of Tarbut Schools (Hebrew schools in Eastern Europe).
1246 **520** 1s.30 multicoloured . . . 60 45

521 Israeli Team at Munich Games, 1972, and National Committee Emblem

1994. Centenary of Int Olympic Committee.
1247 **521** 2s.25 multicoloured . . . 1·10 85

522 The Little Prince (book character) and Saint-Exupery

1994. 50th Death Anniv of Antoine de Saint-Exupery (writer and pilot).
1248 **522** 5s. multicoloured . . . . 2·25 1·90

523 "Adam and Eve" (Itai Cohen)

524 Jewish and Arab Houses merging

1994. Jewish New Year. Entries in the "Children and Young People draw the Bible" exhibition. Multicoloured.
1249 85a. Type **523** 40 30
1250 1s.30 "Jacob's Dream" (Moran Sheinberg) . . . 65 45
1251 1s.60 "Moses in the Bulrushes" (Carmit Crspi) 85 75

1994. Israeli–Palestinian Peace Process.
1253 **524** 90a. multicoloured . . . 45 35

525 Silicat Brick Factory, Tel Aviv (Fourth Aliya, 1924–28)

526 Road to Peace

1994. Aliyot (immigration of Jews to Israel). Multicoloured.
1254 1s.40 Settlers and booklet distributed in Poland to encourage Jews to settle the Valley of Jezreel (Third Aliya, 1919–23) . . 60 50
1255 1s.70 Type **525** 85 60

1994. Signing of Israel–Jordan Peace Treaty.
1256 **526** 3s.50 multicoloured . . . 1·50 1·10

527 Ford Model "T" Converted Car, 1920s

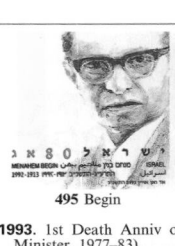

1994. Public Transport. Multicoloured.
1257 90a. Type **527** 40 30
1258 1s.40 "White Super" bus, 1940s 60 45
1259 1s.70 Leyland "Royal Tiger" bus, 1960s 70 55

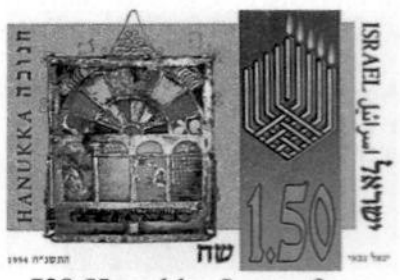
528 Hanukka Lamp from Mazagan, Morocco

1994. Festival of Hanukka.
1260 **528** 1s.50 multicoloured . . . 65 50

529 Computerized Post Office Counter

1994. Stamp Day. Computerization of the Post Office.
1261 **529** 3s. multicoloured . . . . 1·25 95

530 Breaking Dreyfus's Sword

1994. Centenary of "The Dreyfus Affair" (conviction for treason of French Army Captain Alfred Dreyfus).
1262 **530** 4s.10 multicoloured . . . 1·75 1·25

531 "Serpentine" (Itzhak Danziger), Yarkon Park, Tel Aviv

1995. Outdoor Sculptures. Multicoloured.
1263 90a. Type **531** 40 30
1264 1s.40 "Stabile" (Alexander Calder), Mount Herzl, Jerusalem 60 45
1265 1s.70 Hall of Remembrance Gate (David Palombo), Yad Vashem, Jerusalem 70 55

532 Score from "Schelomo", Solomon (after Dore) and Ernest Bloch

1995. Composers (1st series). Multicoloured.
1266 4s.10 Type **532** . . . . . . 1·75 1·25
1267 4s.10 Score from "Jeremiah", Jeremiah (after Gustave Dore) and Leonard Bernstein . . . . 1·75 1·25
See also Nos. 1272/3, 1330 and 1338.

533 Ordnance Corps Memorial, Netanya

1995. Memorial Day.
1268 **533** 1s. multicoloured 40 30

534 Liberation of Dachau Concentration Camp

1995. 50th Anniv of End of Second World War.
1269 **534** 1s. multicoloured 40 30

535 U.N. Projects

1995. 50th Anniv of U.N.O.
1271 **535** 1s.50 multicoloured . . . 65 50

1995. Composers (2nd series). As T **532**. Multicoloured.
1272 2s.40 Arnold Schoenberg and scene from "Moses and Aaron" . . . . . 1·00 75
1273 2s.40 Darius Milhaud and score and scene from opera "David" . . . . . 1·00 75

537 Canoeist

1995. 15th Hapoel Games.
1275 **537** 1s. multicoloured 40 30

538 Box Kite and Cody "War" Kite

1995. Kites. Multicoloured.
1276 1s. Type **538** 40 30
1277 1s. Bird-shaped, hexagonal "Tiara" and rhombic "Eddy" kites 40 30
1278 1s. Multiple rhombic and triangular "Deltic" aerobatic kites 40 30
Nos. 1276/8 were printed together, se-tenant, forming a composite design.

539 "Stars in a Bucket" (Anda Amir-Pinkerfeld, illus. Hava Nathan)

1995. Children's Books. Designs illustrating poems. Multicoloured.
1279 1s. Type **539** 40 30
1280 1s.50 "Hurry, Run, Dwarfs" (Miriam Yallan-Stekelis, illus. Tirzah Tanny) . . . 65 50
1281 1s.80 "Daddy's Big Umbrella" (Levin Kipnis, illus. Pazit Meller-Dushi) 75 55

540 "Zim Israel" (container ship)

1995. 50th Anniv of Zim Navigation Company.
1282 **540** 4s.40 multicoloured . . . 1·90 1·40

541 Elijah's Chair (German, 1768)

1995. Jewish New Year. Multicoloured.
1283 1s. Type **541** (circumcision) 40 30
1284 1s.50 Velvet bag for prayer shawl (Moroccan, 1906) (Bar-Mitzvah) 65 50
1285 1s.80 Marriage stone (from Bingen Synagogue, Germany, 1700) 75 55

542 King David playing Harp (mosaic pavement, Gaza Synagogue)

1995. 3000th Anniv of City of David (Jerusalem). Multicoloured.
1286 1s. Type **542** 40 30
1287 1s.50 Illustration of Jerusalem from 19th-century map by Rabbi Pinie 65 50
1288 1s.80 Aerial view of Knesset (parliament) 75 55

543 "Sheep" (Menashe Kadishman)

1995. 75th Anniv of Veterinary Services.
1289 **543** 4s.40 multicoloured . . . 1·90 1·40

544 Rabin

1995. Yitzhak Rabin (Prime Minister) Commem.
1290 **544** 5s. multicoloured . . . . 2·10 1·60

545 Putting out Fire

1995. 70th Anniv of Fire and Rescue Service. Multicoloured.
1291 1s. Type **545** 40 30
1292 1s. Cutting crash victim out of car 40 30

546 Miniature Silver Menorah (Zusia Ejbuszyc)

1995. Festival of Hanukka.
1293 **546** 1s.50 multicoloured . . . 60 45

547 Flying Model Plane

1995. Stamp Day.
1294 **547** 1s.80 multicoloured . . . 75 55

548 Film Stars

550 Cycling

1995. Centenary of Motion Pictures.
1295 **548** 4s.40 multicoloured . . . 1·90 1·40
The stars depicted are the Marx Brothers, Simone Signoret, Peter Sellers, Danny Kaye and Al Jolson.

1996. Sport. Multicoloured.
1301 1s.05 Type **550** 40 30
1302 1s.10 Show jumping 40 30
1303 1s.80 Water skiing 50 40
1304 1s.90 Paragliding 70 55
1305 2s. Volleyball 75 55
1306 2s.30 Whitewater rafting . . 65 50
1307 3s. Bat and ball 85 65
1308 5s. Archery . . . . 1·75 1·25
1309 10s. Abseiling . . . . 3·50 2·50

552 Cow and Computer

553 Abraham Shlonsky (poet)

1996. 70th Anniv of Israel Dairy Cattle Breeders' Association.
1311 **552** 4s.65 multicoloured . . . 1·75 1·25

1996. Modern Hebrew Writers. Multicoloured.
1313 40a. Type **553** 15 10
1314 40a. Joseph Brenner (novelist and essayist) . . 15 10
1315 40a. Judah Gordon (poet) 15 10
1316 40a. Haim Hazaz (novelist) 15 10
1317 40a. Devorah Baron (novelist) 15 10
1318 40a. Yehuda Burla (novelist) 15 10
1319 40a. Micha Berdyczewski (novelist and historian) . . 15 10
1320 40a. Yaakov Shabtai (novelist) 15 10
1321 40a. Isaac Peretz (novelist) 15 10
1322 40a. Nathan Alterman (poet) 15 10
1323 40a. Saul Tchernichowsky (poet) 15 10
1324 40a. Amir Gilboa (poet) . . 15 10
1325 40a. Yokheved Bat-Miriam (poet) 15 10
1326 40a. Mendele Sefarim (novelist) 15 10

554 Fallen Policemen Monument, National Police Academy, Kiryat Ata (Yosef Assa)

1996. Memorial Day.
1327 **554** 1s.05 multicoloured . . . 40 30

555 Circuit Boards

556 Emblem and Old Photographs

1996. 75th Anniv of Manufacturers' Association.
1328 **555** 1s.05 multicoloured . . . 40 30

1996. Centenary of Metulla.
1329 **556** 1s.90 multicoloured . . . 70 55

1996. Composers (3rd series). As T **532**. Multicoloured.
1330 4s.65 Gustav Mahler, score from "Resurrection Symphony" and creation of light . . . . 1·75 1·25

557 Plant growing in Cracked Earth
558 Fencing

1996. 50th Anniv of the 11 Negev Settlements.
1331 **557** 1s.05 multicoloured . . . 40 30

1996. Olympic Games. Atlanta. Multicoloured.
1332 1s.05 Type **558** 40 30
1333 1s.60 Pole vaulting 60 45
1334 1s.90 Wrestling 70 55

559 Jaffa Orange Tree and Citrus Fruit

1996. Israeli Fruit Production. Multicoloured.
1335 1s.05 Type **559** 40 30
1336 1s.60 Grape vine, avocado, date, sharon fruit and mango 60 45
1337 1s.90 Star fruit plant and exotic fruit 70 55

1996. Composers (4th series). As T **532**. Multicoloured.
1338 4s.65 Felix Mendelssohn, Prophet Elijah (after Albrecht Durer) and score from oratorio "Elijah" . . 1·75 1·25

560 Road Systems

1996. 75th Anniv of Public Works Department.
1339 **560** 1s.05 multicoloured . . . 40 30

561 New Year

1996. Jewish Festivals. Paintings by Sahar Pick. Multicoloured.
1340 1s.05 Type **561** 40 30
1341 1s.60 Booth decoration (Festival of Tabernacles) 60 45
1342 1s.90 Pulpit (Simchat Torah Festival) 70 55

562 Herzl looking out at David's Tower (wall hanging)

1996. Centenary of 1st Zionist Congress, Basel, Switzerland.
1343 **562** 4s.65 multicoloured . . . 1·75 1·25

563 Lighted Candles

1996. Festival of Hanukkah. Self-adhesive.
1345 **563** 2s.50 multicoloured . . . 95 70

564 Bird and Fighter Aircraft

1996. Coexistence between Man and Animals. Multicoloured.
1346 1s.10 Type **564** 40 30
1347 1s.75 Dog, people and cat 60 45
1348 2s. Dolphins and diver . . . 70 55

565 Ahad Ha'am

1996. Centenary of First Edition of "Ha-Shilo'ah" (periodical) and 140th Birth Anniv of Ahad Ha'am (editor and Zionist).
1349 **565** 1s.15 multicoloured . . . 40 30

566 Shavit Rocket, Earth and "Ofeq-3" (satellite)

1996. Stamp Day. Space Research.
1350 **566** 2s.05 multicoloured . . . 70 55

567 Equal Opportunities Emblem
570 Windmills, Don Quixote and Sancho Panza (Ya'acov Farkas (Ze'ev))

568 Woman, Ethiopia

1996. Equal Opportunities for Disabled People.
1351 **567** 5s. multicoloured . . . . 1·75 1·25

1997. Traditional Costumes of Jewish Communities Abroad. Multicoloured.
1352 1s.10 Type **568** 40 30
1353 1s.70 Man, Kurdistan . . . 60 45
1354 2s. Woman, Salonica . . . 70 55

1997. 450th Birth Anniv of Miguel de Cervantes (writer).
1356 **570** 3s. multicoloured . . . . 1·00 75

571 Logistics Corps Memorial, Hadir

1997. Memorial Day.
1357 **571** 1s.10 multicoloured . . . 40 30

572 Ark of the Torah, Old–New Synagogue (east side)
573 Rabbi Elijah (Mario Sermoneta)

1997. Jewish Monuments in Prague. Mult.
1358 1s.70 Type **572** 60 45
1359 1s.70 Grave of Rabbi Loew (chief Rabbi of Prague), Old Jewish Cemetery . . 60 45

1997. Death Bicentenary of Vilna Gaon (Rabbi Elijah ben Solomon).
1360 **573** 2s. multicoloured 70 55

574 "Exodus" in Haifa Port
577 Drunk Driver

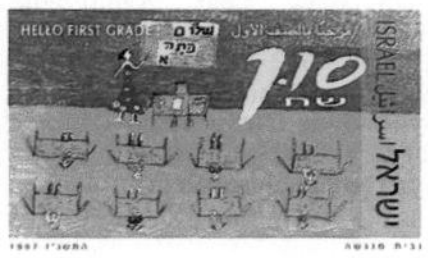

576 Classroom (Navit Mangashsa)

1997. Clandestine Immigration, 1934–48.
1361 **574** 5s. multicoloured . . . . 1·75 1·25

1997. Winning Entry in "Hello First Grade!" Stamp Drawing Competition.
1363 **576** 1s.10 multicoloured . . . 40 30

1997. Road Safety. Multicoloured.
1364 1s.10 Type **577** ("Don't Drink and Drive") . . . 40 30
1365 1s.10 Car sinking in water ("Keep in Lane") 40 30
1366 1s.10 Car hitting bird ("Keep your Distance") 40 30

578 Ice Skating

1997. 15th Maccabiah Games.
1367 **578** 5s. multicoloured . . . . 1·75 1·25

579 Abraham and Tamarisk Tree
580 Mt. Scopus (Jerusalem) and Choirs

1997. Festival of Sukkot. The Visiting Patriarchs (1st series). Paintings from the Sukkah of Rabbi Loew Immanuel of Szeged, Hungary. Multicoloured.
1368 1s.10 Type **579** 40 30
1369 1s.70 Abraham preparing to sacrifice Isaac 60 45
1370 2s. Jacob dreaming of angels on ladder to heaven . . . 70 55
See also Nos. 1453/6.

1997. Music and Dance Festivals. Mult.
1371 1s.10 Type **580** (Zimriya World Assembly of Choirs, Hebrew University) 40 30
1372 2s. Fireworks over Karmiel and dancers (Dance Festival) 70 55
1373 3s. Zefat and klezmers (Hassidic musicians) (Klezmer Festival) . . . . 1·00 75

581 "The Night of 29th November" (Ya'acov Eisenscher)
583 National Flag and Srulik with Flower

1997. 50th Anniv of U.N. Resolution on Establishment of State of Israel.
1374 **581** 5s. multicoloured . . . . 1·75 1·25

1997. 50th Anniv (1998) of State of Israel. (1st issue). No value expressed. (a) Size 18 × 23½ mm.
1376 **583** (–) multicoloured 30 25

(b) Size 17½ × 21½ mm.
1377 **583** (–) multicoloured 30 25
See also No. 1395.

584 Norseman Aircraft, Soldier, Missile Corvette and Cannon "Napoleon-Chick"

1997. 50th Anniv of Arrival in Israel of Machal (overseas volunteers) (1377) and Gachal (overseas recruits) (1378). Multicoloured.
1378 1s.15 Type **584** 40 30
1379 1s.80 Infantry soldier and Holocaust survivors . . . 60 45

585 Bezalel (spinning-top)

1997. Festival of Hanukka. Museum Exhibits. Multicoloured.
1380 1s.80 Type **585** (Eretz Israel Museum, Tel Aviv) . . . 60 45
1381 2s.10 Coin of Bar-Kokhba during war against the Romans (Israel Museum, Jerusalem) 70 55

586 Children leaving Airliner

1997. Chabad Children of Chernobyl Organization (for evacuation of Jewish children from irradiated areas of Europe to Israel).
1382 **586** 2s.10 multicoloured . . . 70 55

587 Julia Set Fractal
588 Photograph of Soldiers of Palmach Battalion and Civilians (Zefat)

1997. Stamp Day.
1383 **587** 2s.50 multicoloured . . . 85 65

1998. 50th Anniv of War of Independence. Battle Fronts. Multicoloured.
1384 1s.15 Type **588** 40 30
1385 1s.15 "Castel Conquered" (Arieh Navon) superimposed on armoured vehicles (Jerusalem) 40 30
1386 1s.15 Soldiers raising flag (Elat) 40 30

589 Herzog

1998. 80th Birth Anniv of Chaim Herzog (President 1983–93).
1388 **589** 5s.35 multicoloured . . . 1·75 1·25

590 Franz Kafka (writer)

1998. Jewish Contribution to World Culture (1st series). Multicoloured.
1389 90a. Type **590** 30 25
1390 90a. George Gershwin (composer) 30 25
1391 90a. Lev Davidovich Landau (physicist) 30 25
1392 90a. Albert Einstein (physicist and mathematician) 30 25
1393 90a. Leon Blum (writer) . . 30 25
1394 90a. Elizabeth Rachel Felix (actress) 30 25
See also Nos. 1436/41.

591 Declaration Ceremony, 1948

592 Olive Branch

1998. 50th Anniv of State of Israel (2nd issue).
1395 **591** 1s.15 multicoloured . . . 40 30

1998. Memorial Day.
1396 **592** 1s.15 multicoloured . . . 40 30

593 Swearing In Ceremony in 1948 and Badge entwined with Medal Ribbons

595 Kitten

594 Giorgio Perlasca, Aristides de Sousa Mendes, Charles Lutz, Sempo Sugihara and Selahattin Ulkumen (diplomats) (½-size illustration)

1998. 50th Anniv of Defence Forces.
1397 **593** 5s.35 multicoloured . . . 1·75 1·25

1998. Holocaust Memorial Day. Righteous Among the Nations (non-Jews who risked their lives to save Jews during the Holocaust).
1398 **594** 6s. multicoloured . . . . 2·00 1·50

1998. Children's Pets. Multicoloured.
1399 60a. Type **595** 20 15
1400 60a. Puppy 20 15
1401 60a. Crimson rosella 20 15
1402 60a. Goldfish 20 15
1403 60a. Hamster 20 15
1404 60a. Rabbit 20 15
Nos. 1399/1404 were issued together in se-tenant sheetlets of six stamps and six triangular labels bearing the emblem of "Israel 98" International Stamp Exhibition, each label with an adjacent stamp completing a square. The complete sheetlet forms a composite design.

598 De Havilland D.H.89 Dragon Rapide

1998. Aircraft of War of Independence. Mult.
1407 2s.20 Type **598** 75 55
1408 2s.20 Supermarine Spitfire 75 55
1409 2s.20 Boeing B-17 Flying Fortress 75 55

600 "Amos" Satellite, Immigration, Grapes, Dove and Lion's Gate, Jerusalem

1998. "Israel Jubilee" Exhibition, Tel Aviv.
1411 **600** 5s.35 multicoloured . . . 1·60 1·25

601 Holding Hands (Nitzan Shupak)

1998. "Living in a World of Mutual Respect" Elementary Education Programme.
1412 **601** 1s.15 multicoloured . . . 35 25

602 Birds (Hechal Yitshak Synagogue, Moshav Yonatan)

1998. Jewish New Year. Synagogue Curtains. Multicoloured.
1413 1s.15 Type **602** 35 25
1414 1s.80 Lions (Ohal Chanah Synagogue, Neve Tsuf) 50 40
1415 2s.20 Leaves (Hatzvi Israel Synagogue, Jerusalem) . . 65 50

603 Hebron

1998. Jewish Life in Eretz Israel (1st series). Showing sections from Holy Cities Wall Plaque. Multicoloured.
1416 1s.80 Type **603** 50 40
1417 2s.20 Jerusalem 65 50
See also Nos. 1430/1.

604 State Flag

1998. Self-adhesive.
1418 **604** 1s.15 blue and deep blue 35 25
1419 2s.15 blue and green . . 65 50
1420 3s.25 blue and mauve . . 1·00 75
1421 5s.35 blue and yellow . . 1·60 1·25

605 Hanukka Lamp showing Mattathias (Boris Schatz)

606 "Hyacinthus orientalis"

1999. Festival of Hanukka.
1426 **605** 2s.15 multicoloured . . . 65 50

1999. Wild Hyacinths. No value expressed.
1427 **606** (1s.15) green and lilac . . 35 25

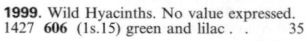

607 The Knesset, Menorah and Knesset Stone Wall (des. Danny Karavan)

1999. 50th Anniv of the Knesset (Parliament).
1428 **607** 1s.80 multicoloured . . . 50 40

608 Manuscript

1999. 380th Birth Anniv of Rabbi Shalem Shabazi (Yemeni poet).
1429 **608** 2s.20 multicoloured . . . 65 50

1999. Jewish Life in Eretz Israel (2nd series). As T **603**, showing sections from Holy Cities Wall Plaque. Multicoloured.
1430 1s.15 Zefat 35 25
1431 5s.35 Tiberias . . . . 1·60 1·25

609 Part of £1 Share Certificate

1999. Centenary of Jewish Colonial Trust.
1432 **609** 1s.80 multicoloured . . . 50 40

610 Yemeni Woman

1999. Traditional Costumes of Jewish Communities (1st series). Multicoloured.
1433 2s.15 Type **610** 65 50
1434 3s.25 Woman wearing sari, India 95 70
See also Nos. 1457/8.

1999. Jewish Contribution to World Culture (2nd series). As T **590**. Multicoloured.
1436 90a. Emile Durkheim (sociologist) 25 20
1437 90a. Paul Ehrlich (medical researcher) 25 20
1438 90a. Rosa Luxemburg (revolutionary) 25 20
1439 90a. Norbert Wiener (mathematician) 25 20
1440 90a. Sigmund Freud (psychologist) 25 20
1441 90a. Martin Buber (philosopher) 25 20

612 Memorial to Bedouin Soldiers, Rish Lakish

1999. Memorial Day.
1442 **612** 1s.20 multicoloured . . . 35 25

613 Flags of U.N., Israel and Other States

1999. 50th Anniv of Israel's Admission to United Nations.
1443 **613** 2s.30 multicoloured . . . 65 50

614 Holtzberg

1999. 75th Birth Anniv of Simcha Holtzberg.
1444 **614** 2s.50 multicoloured . . . 70 55

615 "My Favourite Room" (detail)

1999. 50th Death Anniv of James Ensor (artist).
1445 **615** 2s.30 multicoloured . . . 65 50

616 Ouza the Goose

1999. Lovely Butterfly (children's television programme). Multicoloured.
1446 1s.20 Type **616** 35 25
1447 1s.20 Nooly the chick and Shabi the snail 35 25
1448 1s.20 Batz the tortoise and Pingi the penguin 35 25

617 "Church of the Holy Sepulchre, Jerusalem" (F. Geyer)

1999. Paintings of Christian Pilgrimage Sites. Multicoloured.
1449 3s. Type **617** 90 70
1450 3s. "Mary's Well, Nazareth" (W. H. Bartlett) 90 70
1451 3s. "The River Jordan" (E. Finden after A. W. Callcott) 90 70

618 Illustration from Nehemia Emshel's Manuscript of Musa-Nameh by Shahin (poet)

1999. 205th Death Anniv of Rabbi Or Sharga from Persia.
1452 **618** 5s.60 multicoloured . . . 1·60 1·25

1999. Festival of Sukkot. The Visiting Patriarchs (2nd series). As T **579**, showing paintings from the Sukkah of Rabbi Loew Immanuel of Szeged, Hungary. Multicoloured.
1453 1s.20 Joseph interpreting Pharaoh's dreams 35 20
1454 1s.90 Moses and the burning bush 55 40
1455 2s.30 Aaron and Holy Ark 65 50
1456 5s.60 David playing harp . . 1·60 1·25

1999. Traditional Costumes of Jewish Communities (2nd series). As T **610**. Multicoloured.
1457 2s.30 Woman from Seus region, Morocco 65 50
1458 3s.40 Man from Bukhara . . 1·00 75

619 Family and Part of 1948 250m. Stamp

1999. Stamp Day.
1459 **619** 5s.35 multicoloured . . . 1·60 1·25

620 18th-century Ceramic Urn showing Funeral Procession

622 "The Street of the Jews in Old Jersusalem" (Ludwig Blum)

621 View over Town from Arch of Columns

1999. Jewish Culture in Slovakia. Multicoloured.
1460 1s.90 Type **620** 55 40
1461 1s.90 18th-century urn showing visit to a sick man 55 40

1999. 50th Anniv of Kiryat Shemona.
1462 **621** 1s.20 multicoloured . . . 35 25

1999. 50th Anniv of Proclamation of Jerusalem as Capital.
1463 **622** 3s.40 multicoloured . . . 1·00 75

623 Sali

1999. 15th Death Anniv of Admor (Rabbi) Israel Abihssira Sidna "Baba Sali".
1464 **623** 4s.40 multicoloured . . . 1·25 95

624 Children and Aliens holding Hands (Renana Barak)

2000. "Stampin' the Future" Children's Painting Competition. Multicoloured.
1465 1s.20 Type **624** 35 25
1466 1s.90 Man and robot (Tal Engelsten) 55 40
1467 2s.30 Futuristic street scene (Asia Aizenshteyn) . . . 70 50
1468 3s.40 Alien's and child's heads (Ortal Hasid) . . . 1·00 75

625 Globe, Joggers and Skiers

2000. Year 2000. Multicoloured.
1469 1s.40 Type **625** (quality of life) 40 30
1470 1s.90 Da Vinci's "Proportion of Man", ear of corn and scientist (biotechnology) 55 40
1471 2s.30 Computer, satellite dish and website address (information technology) 70 50
1472 2s.80 Moon's surface, astronaut and globe (space research) 80 60

626 "The Little Mermaid"

2000. 125th Death Anniv of Hans Christian Andersen (writer). Illustrations by Samuel Katz. Multicoloured.
1473 1s.20 Type **626** 40 30
1474 1s.90 "The Emperor's New Clothes" 65 50
1475 2s.30 "The Ugly Duckling" 75 55

627 "All Apostles Church, Capernaum"

2000. Paintings of Christian Pilgrimage Sites (2nd series). Depicting paintings by Zina Roitman. Mult.
1476 1s.40 Type **627** 45 35
1477 1s.90 "St. Andrew's Church, Jerusalem" 65 50
1478 2s.30 "The Church of the Visitation, Ein Kerem" 75 55

628 Fort Shuni (Zina Roitman)

629 King Hussein

2000. Buildings and Historical Sites.
1479 **628** 2s.30 multicoloured . . . 75 55

2000. King Hussein of Jordan Commemoration.
1480 **629** 4s.40 multicoloured . . . 1·40 1·00

630 Monument to Jewish Volunteers in British Army, Jerusalem

631 Fox yawning

2000. Memorial Day.
1481 **630** 1s.20 multicoloured . . . 40 30

2000. Endangered Species. Blanford's Fox. Mult.
1482 1s.20 Type **631** 40 30
1483 1s.20 Fox watching mourning wheater (bird) 40 30
1484 1s.20 Fox 40 30
1485 1s.20 Three foxes 40 30

632 Mobile Telephone

633 Cross, Crescent and Menorah

2000. International Communications Day.
1486 **632** 2s.30 multicoloured . . . 75 55

2000. "The Holy Land".
1487 **633** 3s.40 multicoloured . . . 95 70

634 Bach (bust) and Manuscript of Juara Chaconne for Violin Solo

635 Fortified Stone Building (Zina Roitman)

2000. 250th Death Anniv of Johann Sebastian Bach (composer).
1488 **634** 5s.60 multicoloured . . . 2·00 1·50

2000. Buildings and Historical Sites.
1489 **635** 1s.20 multicoloured . . . 40 30

636 Couscous

637 Olympic Rings and Koala

2000. Traditional Foods. Multicoloured.
1490 1s.40 Type **636** 45 35
1491 1s.90 Stuffed carp 65 50
1492 2s.30 Falafel 75 55

2000. Olympic Games, Sydney.
1493 **637** 2s.80 multicoloured . . . 95 70

638 King Hassan II

639 Young Boy and Girl

2000. 1st Death Anniv of King Hassan II of Morocco.
1494 **638** 4s.40 multicoloured . . . 1·40 1·00

2000. Festivals. New Year Cards. Multicoloured.
1495 1s.20 Type **639** 40 30
1496 1s.90 Young woman holding Zionist flag 65 50
1497 2s.30 Man presenting flowers to woman 75 55

640 Adam and Eve

2000. Dental Health Campaign.
1498 **640** 2s.20 multicoloured . . . 75 55

641 Menorah and Interior of Synagogue

642 Revivim Observatory, Negev (Zina Roitman)

2000. Dohany Synagogue, Budapest.
1499 **641** 5s.60 multicoloured . . . 2·00 1·50

2000. Buildings and Historical Sites.
1500 **642** 2s.20 multicoloured . . . 75 55

643 Struthiomymus running

2000. Dinosaurs. Multicoloured.
1501 2s.20 Type **643** 75 55
1502 2s.20 Head of Struthiomymus 75 55
1503 2s.20 Struthiomymus standing by tree 75 55

644 Robot (*I, Robot*) (Isaac Asimov)

2000. Science Fiction Novels. Multicoloured.
1504 2s.80 Type **644** 95 70
1505 3s.40 Time travel machine (*The Time Machine*) (H. G. Wells) . . . . . . 1·10 85
1506 5s.60 Space rocket (*Journey to the Moon*) (Jules Verne) 2·00 1·50

645 Open Book

646 Tof

2000. Aleppo Codex (earliest known manuscript of the Bible).
1507 **645** 4s.40 multicoloured . . . 1·40 1·00

2001. Hebrew Alphabet. Designs each showing a different Hebrew letter. Multicoloured.
1508 10a. Type **646** 10 10
1509 10a. Shin 10 10
1510 10a. Reish 10 10
1511 10a. Kuf 10 10
1512 10a. Tzadi Kekufa 10 10
1513 10a. Pay Kekufah 10 10
1514 10a. Ayin 10 10
1515 10a. Samech 10 10
1516 10a. Nun 10 10
1517 10a. Mem 10 10
1518 10a. Lamed 10 10
1519 10a. Chof Kefufa 10 10
1520 10a. Yud 10 10
1521 10a. Tes 10 10
1522 10a. Ches 10 10
1523 10a. Zayin 10 10
1524 10a. Vov 10 10
1525 10a. Heh 10 10
1526 10a. Daled 10 10
1527 10a. Gimel 10 10
1528 10a. Beis 10 10
1529 10a. Aleph 10 10
1530 10a. Tzade Peshuta 10 10
1531 10a. Pay Peshuta 10 10
1532 10a. Chof Peshuta 10 10
1533 10a. Mem Stumah 10 10
1534 10a. Vov 10 10
1535 1s. Aleph and Beis 30 20

647 Pupils in front of School (Yavne'el)

2001. Village Centenaries. Multicoloured.
1536 2s.50 Type **647** 75 45
1537 4s.70 Farmers, horses and cart (Kefar Tavor) . . . 1·40 85
1538 5s.90 Cart full of flowers (Menahamiya) . . . . . 1·90 1·10

648 Segera Spring, Ilaniyya

649 Prairie Gentian

2001. Buildings and Historical Sites.
1539 **648** 3s.40 multicoloured . . . 1·00 60

2001. Flowers. Multicoloured.
1540 1s.20 Type **649** 35 20
1541 1s.20 Barberton daisy . . . 35 20
1542 1s.20 Star of Bethlehem . . 35 20
1543 1s.20 Florists calla 35 20

650 Lesser Kestrel

652 Monument for the Fallen Nahal Soldiers, Pardes Hanna

2001. Endangered Species. Multicoloured.
1544 1s.20 Type **650** 35 20
1545 1s.70 Kuhl's pipstrelle . . . 50 30
1546 2s.10 Roe deer 65 40
1547 2s.50 Greek tortoise 75 45

2001. Memorial Day.
1549 **652** 1s.20 multicoloured . . . 35 20

654 Sha'ar HaGay Inn

655 Mausoleum and Terraces

2001. Buildings and Historical Sites.
1551 **654** 2s. multicoloured 60 35

2001. Shrine of the Bab, Haifa.
1552 **655** 3s. multicoloured 90 55

656 Prayer Shawl and Tassel

657 Hebron

2001. Karaite Jews.
1553 **656** 5s.60 multicoloured . . . 1·75 1·10

2001. Ceramic Tiles. Showing tiles from facade of Ahad Ha'am Municipal Boys School, Tel Aviv. Multicoloured.
1554 1s.20 Type **657** 35 20
1555 1s.40 Jaffa 45 25
1556 1s.90 Haifa 60 35
1557 2s.30 Tiberias 70 40

659 Clasped Hands and Hikers

2001. Israeli Council of Youth Movements.
1559 **659** 5s.60 multicoloured . . . 1·75 1·10

660 Soldier and Peace Dove

661 Rustaveli

2001. Festivals. New Year Cards. Multicoloured.
1560 1s.20 Type **660** 35 20
1561 1s.90 Two women 60 35
1562 2s.30 Boy carrying flowers 70 40

2001. 32nd Anniv of the Translation into Hebrew of *The Knight in a Tiger's Skin* (poem by Shota Rustaveli).
1563 **661** 3s.40 multicoloured . . . 1·00 60

662 Field, Leaves and Sky

2001. Centenary of Jewish National Fund.
1564 **662** 5s.60 multicoloured . . . 1·75 1·10

663 Amichai

664 Sunshade on Beach

2001. 1st Death Anniv of Yehuda Amichai (poet).
1565 **663** 5s.60 multicoloured . . . 1·75 1·10

2001. Coastal Conservation.
1566 **664** 10s. multicoloured . . . 3·25 2·00

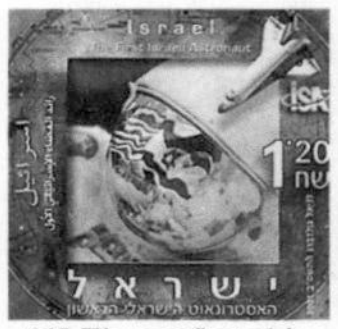
665 Flags reflected in Helmet Visor

666 Child Painting (Yaffa Dahan)

2001. 1st Israeli Astronaut.
1567 **665** 1s.20 multicoloured . . . 40 25

2001. 50th Anniv of Association for Rehabilitation of the Handicapped (AKIM).
1568 **666** 2s.20 multicoloured . . . 70 40

667 *Heinrich Heine*

2001. 145th Death Anniv of Heinrich Heine (poet and satirist).
1569 **667** 4s.40 multicoloured . . . 1·40 85

668 "Israel" in Braille

2001. Centenary of Institute for the Blind, Jerusalem.
1570 **668** 5s.60 multicoloured . . . 1·75 1·10

669 Lily

670 Hat and Rattle (Adar)

2002.
1571 **669** 1s.20 multicoloured . . . 40 25

2002. Months of the Year. Multicoloured. Ordinary or self-adhesive gum.
1572 1s.20 Type **670** 40 25
1573 1s.20 Almond twig, flowers and fruit (Shevat) 40 25
1574 1s.20 Grapefruit and anemones (Tevet) 40 25
1575 1s.20 Spinning top and candles (Kislev) 40 25
1576 1s.20 Autumn leaves (Heshvan) 40 25
1577 1s.20 Ram's horn and pomegranates (Tishrei) . . 40 25
1578 1s.20 Cup, unleavened bread and flowers (Nisan) . . . 40 25
1579 1s.20 Bow, arrows and oleanders (Iyyar) 40 25
1580 1s.20 Sickle and grains (Sivian) 40 25
1581 1s.20 Sunflower and shells (Tammuz) 40 25
1582 1s.20 Couple wearing wedding dress and grapes (Av) 40 25
1583 1s.20 Torah, cotton and figs (Elul) 40 25

671 Field Mushroom

672 "Ladino" in Rashi Script

2002. Fungi. Multicoloured.
1596 1s.90 Type **671** (*Agaricus campestri*) (inscr "campester") 60 35
1597 2s.20 Fly agaric (*Amanita muscaria*) 70 40
1598 2s.80 Granulated boletus (*Suillus granulatus*) . . . 90 55

2002. Judaic Languages. Multicoloured.
1599 2s.10 Type **671** (Ladino (Judeo-Spanish)) 65 40
1600 2s.10 Peacock (Yiddish) . . 65 40

673 Military Police Memorial And Eternal Flame, Bet Lid

2002. Memorial Day.
1601 **673** 1s.20 multicoloured . . . 35 20

674 Heinrich Graetz

675 King and Torah

2002. Historians. Multicoloured.
1602 2s.20 Type **674** 70 40
1603 2s.20 Simon Dubnow . . . 70 40
1604 2s.20 Benzion Dinur 70 40
1605 2s.20 Yitzhak Baer 70 40
See also No. 1686/8.

2002. Hakel Ceremony.
1606 **675** 4s.70 multicoloured . . . 1·50 90

676 "50" and Wheels

677 Cable Cars, Menara

2002. 50th Anniv of ILAN (Israel foundation for handicapped children).
1607 **676** 5s.90 multicoloured . . . 1·90 1·10

2002. Tourism. Cable Cars. Multicoloured.
1608 2s.20 Type **677** 70 40
1609 2s.20 Rosh Haniqra 70 40
1610 2s.20 Haifa 70 40
1611 2s.20 Massada 70 40

678 Fish Fossil

679 Hatsar Kinneret

2002. Geology. Sheet 115 × 70 mm containing T **678** and similar vert designs. Multicoloured.
MS1612 Type **678**; 3s.40 Copper mineral; 4s.40 Ammonite . . . 3·25 3·25

2002. Buildings and Historical Sites.
1613 **679** 3s.30 multicoloured . . . 1·00 60

680 Rechavam Ze'evy

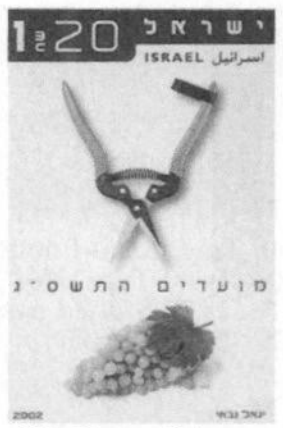
681 Grape Scissors and Grapes

2002. 1st Death Anniv of Rechavam Ze'evy (Minister for tourism).
1614 **680** 1s.20 multicoloured . . . 40 25

2002. Festivals. Wine. Multicoloured.
1615 1s.20 Type **681** 40 25
1616 1s.90 Cork screw and cork 60 35
1617 2s.30 Wine glass and bottle 70 40

682 Golden Eagle

2002. Birds of Jordan Valley. Multicoloured.
1618 2s.20 Type **682** 70 40
1619 2s.20 Black stork 70 40
1620 2s.20 Crane 70 40

683 Kadoorie School

684 Baruch Spinoza

2002. Buildings and Historical Sites.
1621 **683** 4s.60 multicoloured . . . 1·40 85

2002. 370th Birth Anniv of Baruch (Benedictus) Spinoza.
1622 **684** 5s.90 multicoloured . . . 1·90 1·10

685 Menorah Candlestick

686 Abba Ahimeir

2002.
1623 **685** 20a. red 10 10
1624 30a. brown 10 10
1625 40a. green 15 10
1626 50a. olive 15 10
1647 1s. violet 30 20
1628 1s.30 blue 40 25

2002. Political Journalists. Multicoloured.
1630 1s.20 Type **686** 40 25
1631 3s.30 Israel Eldad . . . . . 1·00 60
1632 4s.70 Moshe Beilinson . . . 1·60 95
1633 5s.90 Rabbi Binyamin (Yehshua Radler-Feldman) . . . . 1·90 1·10

687 Marbles

2002. Stamp Day. Children's Toys. Multicoloured.
1634 2s.20 Type **687** 70 40
1635 2s.20 Top 70 40
1636 2s.20 Five stones 70 40
1637 2s.20 Yo-yo 70 40

688 Students

2003. Yeshivot Hahesder (college).
1638 **688** 1s.20 multicoloured . . . 40 25

689 "11 September 2001" (Michael Gross)

2003.
1639 **689** 2s.30 multicoloured . . . 70 40

690 Glider (1902)

2003. Centenary of Powered Flight. Multicoloured.
1640 2s.30 Type **690** 70 40
1641 3s.30 Engine and Wright brothers . . . . 1·00 60
1642 5s.90 Orville Wright flying *Wright Flier* . . . . . . 1·90 1·10

691 Memorial Monument, Mount Herzl

2003.
1643 **691** 4s.70 multicoloured . . . 1·50 90

692 Burnt-out Vehicle

2003. Memorial Day.
1644 **692** 1s.20 multicoloured . . . 40 25

693 Opened Box **694** Ya'akov Meridor

2003. Greetings Stamps (1st issue). Multicoloured.
1645 (1s.20) Type **693** 40 25
1646 (1s.20) Boy and growing heart 40 25
1647 (1s.20) Married couple . . . 40 25
See also Nos. 1655/7.

2003. 90th Birth Anniv of Ya'akov Meridor (soldier and politician).
1648 **694** 1s.90 multicoloured . . . 60 35

695 Star of David **696** Ya'akov Dori

2003. Holocaust Memorial Day.
1649 **695** 2s.20 multicoloured . . . 70 40

2003. 30th Death Anniv of Ya'akov Dori (Chief of Staff 1948—50).
1650 **696** 2s.20 multicoloured . . . 70 40

697 Sheikh Ameen Tarif

2003. 10th Death Anniv of Sheikh Ameen Tarif (Druze (religious sect) leader).
1651 **697** 2s.80 multicoloured . . . 45 25

698 Soldier

2003. Jewish Immigration from Yemen, 1881
1652 **698** 3s.30 multicoloured . . . 1·00 60

699 Paper Airplane and Computer Circuit Board

2003. 50th Anniv of Israel Aircraft Industries.
1653 **699** 3s.30 multicoloured . . . 1·00 60

700 "55"

2003. 55th Anniv of Israel.
1654 **700** 5s.90 multicoloured . . . 1·90 1·10

2003. Greetings Stamps (2nd issue). As T **693**. Multicoloured.
1655 (1s.20) Flowers 40 25
1656 (1s.20) Air balloon 40 25
1657 (1s.20) Boy holding teddy bear 40 25

701 Prague Jewish Community Flag (15th-century)

2003. Development of Israel State Flag. Multicoloured.
1658 1s.90 Type **701** 60 35
1659 2s.30 Ness Ziona (Jewish settlement) (1891) 70 40
1660 4s.70 Draft design from *Der Judenstaat* (Theodor Herzl) (1896) . . . . . . 1·50 90
1661 5s.90 State flag (1948) . . . 1·90 1·10

702 Coast, Ruined Castle and Houses (Atlit)

2003. Village Centenaries. Multicoloured.
1662 3s.30 Type **702** . . . . . . 1·00 60
1663 3s.30 Tractor, crops and houses (Givat-Ada) . . . 1·00 60
1664 3s.30 Houses and bungalow amongst trees (Kfar-Saba) 1·00 60

703 Olives

2003. Olive Oil Production. Multicoloured.
1665 1s.30 Type **703** 40 25
1666 1s.90 Mill stone and wheel 60 35
1667 2s.30 Oil 70 40

704 Teddy Bear and Page of Testimony

2003. 50th Anniv of Vad Yashem (Holocaust remembrance organization). Multicoloured.
1668 2s.20 Type **704** 70 40
1669 2s.20 Rail tracks and list of forced labourers 70 40

705 Deer and flowers (Karakashian-Balian studio, c.1940)

2003. Armenian Ceramics in Jerusalem. Sheet 120 × 65 mm containing T **705** and similar circular designs showing ceramic patterns. Multicoloured.
MS1670 2s.30 Type **705**; 3s.30 Bird (Stepan Karakshian, c. 1980); 4s.70 Tree of life (Marie Balian, c. 1990) . . . . 3·25 3·25

2003. No value expressed. As T **600**. Self-adhesive.
1671 **600** (1s.30) green and lilac . . 40 25

706 Yehoshua Hankin **707** Boy riding Bicycle

2003. 58th Death Anniv of Yehoshua Hankin (Zionist pioneer).
1672 **706** 6s.20 multicoloured . . . 2·00 1·20

2003. Philately Day. Children and Wheels. Multicoloured.
1673 1s.30 Type **707** 40 25
1674 1s.30 Girl on roller skates 40 25
1675 1s.30 Girl pushing scooter 40 25
1676 1s.30 Boy on skateboard . . 40 25

708 Leibowitch Family and Administrative Building, Zikhron Ya'akov **709** Aharon David Gordon

2003. 1st and 2nd Aliya (immigration to Eretz Yisrael). Multicoloured.
1677 2s.10 Type **708** (1st Aliya) 70 40
1678 6s.20 Young men (2nd Aliya) . . . . 2·00 1·20

2003. Personalities. Multicoloured.
1679 3s.30 Type **709** (land purchase pioneer) (81st death anniv) . . . . . . 1·00 60
1680 4s.90 Emile Habiby (writer) (82nd death anniv) . . . 1·50 90

710 Two-banded Anemonefish (*Amphirion Bicinctus*)

2003. Fish. Multicoloured.
1681 1s.30 Type **710** 40 25
1682 1s.30 Butterfly perch (*Pseudanthias squamipinnis*) 40 25
1683 1s.30 *Pseudochromis fridmani* 40 25
1684 1s.30 Crown butterflyfish (*Chaetodon paucifasciatus*) 40 25
MS1685 118 × 77 mm. Nos. 1681/4 1·60 1·60

2004. Historians. As T **674**. Multicoloured.
1686 2s.40 Emanuel Ringelblum 75 45
1687 3s.70 Jacob Talmon . . . . 1·20 75
1688 6s.20 Jacob Herzog . . . . 2·00 1·20

711 Menachem Begin and Building

2004. Menachem Begin Heritage Centre, Jerusalem.
1689 **711** 2s.50 multicoloured . . . 80 50

712 Ilan Ramon

2004. 1st Death Anniv of Ilan Ramon (astronaut on *Columbia* Space Shuttle).
1690 **712** 2s.60 multicoloured . . . 80 50

OFFICIAL STAMPS

בול שרות

(O 18)

1951. As Nos. 41 etc, but colours changed. Optd with Type O **18**.
O54 5pr. mauve 10 10
O55 15pr. red 10 10
O56 30pr. blue 10 10
O57 40pr. brown 20 15

POSTAGE DUE STAMPS

דמי דאר

(D 3)

1948. As T **1**, optd with Type D **3**.
D10 **1** 3m. orange on yellow . . . 1·90 1·00
D11 5m. green on yellow . . . 1·90 1·25
D12 10m. mauve on yellow . . 6·25 3·25
D13 20m. blue on yellow . . . 19·00 10·50
D14 50m. brown on yellow . . 75·00 60·00

D 9 D 30

1949.
D27 **D 9** 2pr. orange 15 10
D28 5pr. violet 35 15
D29 10pr. green 20 10
D30 20pr. red 25 10
D31 30pr. blue 40 25
D32 50pr. brown 65 55

1952.
D73 **D 30** 5pr. brown 10 10
D74 10pr. blue 10 10
D75 20pr. purple 10 10
D76 30pr. black 10 10
D77 40pr. green 10 10
D78 50pr. sepia 10 10
D79 60pr. violet 10 10
D80 100pr. red 15 10
D81 250pr. blue 25 15

PALESTINIAN AUTHORITY

Following negotiations in Oslo, during which the Israeli government recognized the Palestine Liberation Organization as representing the Arab inhabitants of those areas occupied by Israel since 1967 and the P.L.O. accepted Israel's right to exist within secure borders, an agreement was signed in Washington on 13 September 1993 under which there was to be limited Palestinian self-rule in the Gaza Strip and in an enclave around Jericho on the West Bank. Further talks followed, leading to the Cairo Agreement of 4 May 1994, which inaugurated Palestinian Authority rule in Gaza and Jericho.

Under the Taba Accord of 28 September 1995 the Israeli army progressively withdrew from much of the remainder of the West Bank, which was then placed under Palestinian Authority administration.

CURRENCY Israeli currency continued to be used in the Palestinian Authority areas. The first stamp issues had face values in mils, the currency of the Palestine Mandate period, but the Israeli authorities objected to this notional currency with the result that the face values were subsequently shown in the Jordanian currency of 1000 fils = 1 dinar.

PA **1** Monument from Hisham Palace, Jericho

1994. Multicoloured.
PA 1 5m. Type PA **1** 10 10
PA 2 10m. Type PA **1** 10 10
PA 3 20m. Type PA **1** 10 10
PA 4 30m. Church of the Holy Sepulchre, Jerusalem . . 10 10
PA 5 40m. As No. PA4 . . . . 15 15
PA 6 50m. As No. PA4 . . . . 20 20
PA 7 75m. As No. PA4 . . . . 25 25
PA 8 125m. Flags of Palestinian Authority 30 30
PA 9 150m. As No. PA8 . . . . 40 40
PA10 250m. As No. PA8 . . . . 65 65
PA11 300m. As No. PA8 . . . . 75 75
PA12 500m. Flags of Palestinian Authority (51 × 29 mm) 1·25 1·25
PA13 1000m. Dome of the Rock, Jerusalem (51 × 29 mm) 2·50 2·50

PA **2** Arms of Palestinian Authority

PA **6** Palestine Mandate 1927 2m. Stamp

1994.
PA14 PA **2** 50m. yellow 15 15
PA15 100m. green 25 25
PA16 125m. blue 30 30
PA17 200m. orange 50 50
PA18 250m. yellow 65 65
PA19 400m. purple . . . . 1·00 1·00

NEW CURRENCY. From No. PA23 the face values are expressed as 1000 fils = 1 Jordanian dinar.

1995. Palestine Postal History.
PA23 PA **6** 150f. green and black 45 45
PA24 – 350f. orange and black 95 95
PA25 – 500f. red and black . . 1·40 1·40
DESIGNS: 350f. Palestine Mandate 1927; 5m. stamp; 500f. Palestine Mandate 1932; 8m. stamp.

PA **7** Woman in Embroidered Costume

1995. Traditional Palestinian Women's Costumes. Multicoloured.
PA26 250f. Type PA **7** 70 70
PA27 300f. Woman carrying basket 85 85
PA28 550f. Woman in cloak . . 1·60 1·60
PA29 900f. Woman in veiled headdress . . . . 2·50 2·50

1995. Nos. PA1/13 surch **FILS** in English and Arabic.
PA30 PA **1** 5f. on 5m. mult . . . 10 10
PA31 10f. on 10m. mult . . 10 10
PA32 20f. on 20m. mult . . 10 10
PA33 – 30f. on 30m. mult . . 10 10
PA34 – 40f. on 40m. mult . . 10 10
PA35 – 50f. on 50m. mult . . 15 15
PA36 – 75f. on 75m. mult . . 20 20
PA37 – 125f. on 125m. mult 35 35
PA38 – 150f. on 150m. mult 40 40
PA39 – 250f. on 250m. mult 70 70
PA40 – 300f. on 300m. mult 80 80
PA41 – 500f. on 500m. mult 1·40 1·40
PA42 – 1000f. on 1000m. mult 3·00 3·00

1995. Handstamped **Fils** within circle in English and Arabic, twice on each stamp. (a) On Nos. PA1/13.
PA43 PA **1** 5f. on 5m. mult . . .
PA44 10f. on 10m. mult . .
PA45 20f. on 20m. mult . .
PA46 – 30f. on 30m. mult . .
PA47 – 40f. on 40m. mult . .
PA48 – 50f. on 50m. mult . .
PA49 – 75f. on 75m. mult . .
PA50 – 125f. on 125m. mult
PA51 – 150f. on 150m. mult
PA52 – 250f. on 250m. mult
PA53 – 300f. on 300m. mult
PA54 – 500f. on 500m. mult
PA55 – 1000f. on 1000m. mult

(b) On Nos. PA14/19.
PA56 PA **2** 50f. on 50m. yellow
PA57 100f. on 100m. green
PA58 125f. on 125m. blue
PA59 200f. on 200m. orange
PA60 250f. on 250m. yellow
PA61 400f. on 400m. purple

PA **10** Bethlehem (old print)

1995. Christmas. Multicoloured.
PA63 10f. Type PA**10** 10 10
PA64 20f. Manger Square, Bethlehem 10 10
PA65 50f. Entrance to Church of the Nativity (vert) . . . 15 15
PA66 100f. Pope John Paul II with Yasser Arafat . . . 30 30
PA67 1000f. Site of the Nativity 3·25 3·25

PA **11** Yasser Arafat

PA **14** Boxing

PA **12** Summer Palace, Peking

1996.
PA68 PA **11** 10f. black and lilac 10 10
PA69 20f. black and yellow 10 10
PA70 50f. black and blue 15 15
PA71 100f. black and green 20 20
PA72 1000f. black & brown 2·00 2·00

1996. Int Stamp Exhibitions and Fairs. Mult.
PA73 20f. Type PA **12** ("China '96") 10 10
PA74 50f. Hagia Sofia Mosque, Istanbul ("Istanbul '96") 20 20
PA75 100f. Villa Hugel, Essen (Essen stamp fair) . . . 40 40
PA76 1000f. Modern skyline, Toronto ("Capex '96") 3·75 3·75

1996. Olympic Games, Atlanta. Multicoloured.
PA78 30f. Type PA **14** 10 10
PA79 40f. Olympic medal of 1896 15 15
PA80 50f. Running 20 20
PA81 150f. Olympic flame and flag 60 60
PA82 1000f. Palestinian Olympic Committee emblem . . . 3·50 3·50

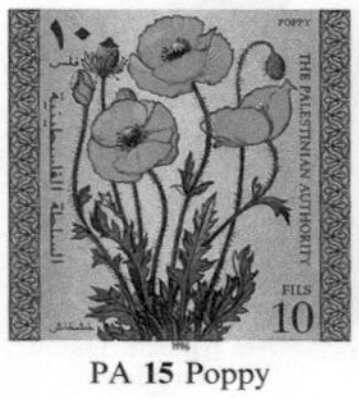
PA **15** Poppy

PA **17** Great Tits

1996. Flowers and Fruits. Multicoloured.
PA84 10f. Type PA**15** 10 10
PA85 25f. Hibiscus 10 10
PA86 100f. Thyme 40 40
PA87 150f. Lemon 55 55
PA88 750f. Orange . . . . . . 2·75 2·75

1997. Birds. Multicoloured.
PA91 25f. Type PA **17** 10 10
PA92 75f. Blue rock thrushes . . 20 20
PA93 150f. Golden orioles . . . 45 45
PA94 350f. Hoopoes . . . . . . 1·10 1·10
PA95 600f. Peregrine falcons . . 1·90 1·90

PA **18** Gaza

1997. Palestinian Towns in 1839. Each brown and black.
PA96 350f. Type PA **18** . . . . 1·10 1·10
PA97 600f. Hebron . . . . . . 1·90 1·90

PA **20** Yasser Arafat and Wischnewski

1997. Friends of Palestine (1st series). Hans-Jurgen Wischnewski (German politician). Multicoloured.
PA 99 600f. Type PA **20** . . . . 1·25 1·25
PA100 600f. Wischnewski congratulating Yasser Arafat . . . . 1·25 1·25
See also Nos. PA103/4.

PA **21** "The Young Jesus in the Temple" (Anton Wollenek)

1997. Christmas.
PA101 PA **21** 350f. multicoloured 75 75
PA102 700f. multicoloured 1·50 1·50

PA **22** Mother Teresa and Street Scene

1997. Friends of Palestine (2nd series). Mother Teresa (founder of Missionaries of Charity). Multicoloured.
PA103 600f. Type PA **22** . . . . 1·25 1·25
PA104 600f. Mother Teresa with Yasser Arafat . . . . . 1·25 1·25

PA **24** Hare and Palm Tree

PA **25** Sea Onion

1998. Mosaics from Jabalia. Multicoloured.
PA106 50f. Type PA **24** 10 10
PA107 125f. Goat, hare and hound 20 20
PA108 200f. Lemon tree and baskets 50 50
PA109 400f. Lion 90 90

1998. Medicinal Plants. Multicoloured.
PA110 40f. Type PA **25** 10 10
PA111 80f. "Silybum marianum" 10 10
PA112 500f. "Foeniculum vulgare" . . . . . . 1·10 1·10
PA113 800f. "Inula viscosa" . . . 1·90 1·90

PA **27** Bonelli's Eagle

1998. Birds of Prey. Multicoloured.
PA115 20f. Type PA **27** 10 10
PA116 60f. Northern hobby ("Hobby") 10 10
PA117 340f. Verreaux's eagle . . 80 80
PA118 600f. Bateleur . . . . . . 1·40 1·40
PA119 900f. Common buzzard ("Buzzard") . . . . . 2·10 2·10

PA **31** Control Tower

1999. Inauguration of Gaza International Airport. Multicoloured.
PA123 80f. Type PA **31** 10 10
PA124 300f. Fokkar F.27 Friendship airliner (horiz) 70 70
PA125 700f. Terminal building (horiz) . . . . 1·60 1·60

PA **32** Peking ("China'99")

1999. International Stamp Exhibitions and Anniversary. Multicoloured.
PA126 20f. Type PA **32** 10 10
PA127 80f. Melbourne ("Australia 99") 10 10
PA128 260f. Nuremberg ("iBRA'99") 60 60
PA129 340f. Paris ("Philexfrance 99") 80 80
PA130 400f. Emblem and landscape (face value at right) (125th anniv of U.P.U.) 90 90
PA131 400f. As No. PA130 but face value at left . . . 90 90

PA **33** Relief by Anton Wollenek

PA **34** Horse and Foal

1999. Hebron.
PA132 PA **33** 400f. multicoloured 90 90
PA133 500f. multicoloured 1·25 1·25

1999. Arabian Horses. Multicoloured.
PA134 25f. Type PA **34** 10 10
PA135 75f. Black horse 10 10
PA136 150f. Horse rearing . . . 30 30
PA137 350f. Horse trotting . . . 80 80
PA138 800f. Brown horse . . . . 1·90 1·90

PA **35** Madonna and Child

1999. Christmas (1st series).
PA139 PA **35** 60f. blue, black and ochre 10 10
PA140 80f. multicoloured 10 10
PA141 100f. multicoloured 20 20
PA142 280f. multicoloured 65 65
PA143 300f. multicoloured 65 65
PA144 400f. multicoloured 85 85
PA145 500f. multicoloured 1·10 1·10
PA146 560f. multicoloured 1·25 1·25
See also Nos. PA147/57.

PA 36 Nativity

1999. Christmas (2nd series). Designs with frames and face values in colours indicated.
PA147 PA 36 200f. multicoloured (black) 45 45
PA148 200f. multicoloured (silver) 45 45
PA149 280f. multicoloured (white) 65 65
PA150 280f. multicoloured (silver) 65 65
PA151 – 380f. multicoloured (black) 80 80
PA152 – 380f. multicoloured (silver) 80 80
PA153 – 460f. multicoloured (white) 1·00 1·00
PA154 – 460f. multicoloured (silver) 1·00 1·00
PA155 – 560f. multicoloured (lemon) 1·25 1·25
PA156 – 560f. multicoloured (silver) 1·25 1·25
PA157 PA 36 2000f. multicoloured 4·25 4·25
DESIGNS: 380, 460f. Adoration of the Magi; 560f. Flight into Egypt.

ITALIAN COLONIES Pt. 8

GENERAL ISSUES

100 centesimi = 1 lira.

1932. As Garibaldi stamps of Italy, but inscr "POSTE COLONIALI ITALIANE".
1 – 10c. green (postage) 2·30 5·75
2 128 20c. red 2·30 3·75
3 – 25c. green 2·30 3·75
4 128 30c. green 2·30 5·75
5 – 50c. red 2·30 3·75
6 – 75c. red 2·30 6·25
7 – 1l.25 blue 2·30 6·25
8 – 1l.75 +25c. blue 4·00 11·50
9 – 2l.55 +50c. sepia 4·00 18·00
10 – 5l.+1l. blue 4·00 21·00

11 130 50c. red (air) 2·30 5·75
12 – 80c. green 2·30 5·75
13 130 1l.+25c. sepia 4·75 13·50
14 – 2l.+50c. sepia 4·75 13·50
15 – 5l.+1l. sepia 4·75 13·50

1932. Dante stamps of Italy (colours changed) optd **COLONIE ITALIANE.**
18 – 10c. slate (postage) 55 1·20
19 – 15c. sepia 55 1·20
20 – 20c. green 55 55
21 – 25c. green 55 55
22 – 30c. brown 55 70
23 – 50c. blue 55 40
24 – 75c. red 90 1·60
25 – 1l.25 blue 90 2·10
26 – 1l.75 violet 1·10 4·25
27 – 2l.75 orange 1·10 10·50
28 – 5l.+2l. olive 1·10 13·00
29 124 10l.+2l.50 blue 1·10 17·00

30 125 50c. slate (air) 70 3·00
31 – 1l. blue 70 3·00
32 – 3l. green 1·40 4·00
33 – 5l. sepia 1·40 6·25
34 125 7l.70 +2l. red 1·40 10·50
35 – 10l.+2l.50 orange 1·40 16·00
36 127 100l. sepia and green 10·50 45·00
No. 36 is inscribed instead of overprinted.

9 Ploughing

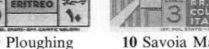

10 Savoia Marchetti S-55X Flying Boat

1933. 50th Anniv of Foundation of Colony of Eritrea.
37 9 10c. brown (postage) 4·50 5·75
38 – 20c. purple 4·50 5·75
39 – 25c. green 4·50 5·75
40 9 50c. violet 4·50 5·75
41 – 75c. red 4·50 7·75
42 – 1l.25 blue 4·50 7·75
43 9 2l.75 red 7·00 13·00
44 – 5l.+2l. green 11·50 28·00
45 – 10l.+2l. brown 11·50 35·00

46 – 50c. brown (air) 4·00 5·75
47 – 1l. black 4·00 5·75
48 10 3l. red 7·75 11·50
49 5l. brown 7·75 11·50
50 – 7l.70+2l. green 11·50 28·00
51 10 10l.+2l.50 blue 11·50 28·00
52 – 50l. violet 11·50 28·00
DESIGNS—VERT: (Postage): 20, 75c., 5l. Camel transport; 25c., 1l.25, 10l. Lioness with star on left shoulder (Arms). HORIZ: (Air): 50c., 1l., 7l. 70, Eagle; 50l. Savoia Marchetti S-55X flying boat over map of Eritrea.

11 Agricultural Implements

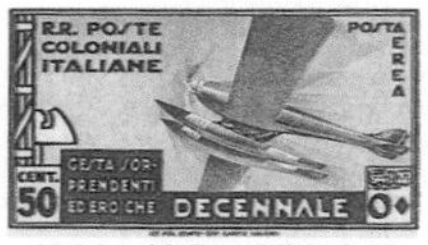
13 Macchi Castoldi MC-72 Seaplane

1933. 10th Anniv of Fascist March on Rome. (a) Postage.
53 11 5c. orange 4·75 5·25
54 – 25c. green 4·75 5·25
55 – 50c. violet 4·75 3·75
56 11 75c. red 4·75 7·75
57 – 1l.25 blue 4·75 7·75
58 – 1l.75 red 4·75 7·75
59 11 2l.75 blue 4·75 13·50
60 – 5l. black 7·75 17·00
61 – 10l. blue 7·75 20·00
62 – 25l. olive 11·50 28·00
DESIGNS—HORIZ: 50c., 1l.75, 10l. Tractor. VERT: 25c., 1l.25, 5l. Arab and camel; 25l. Soldier.

(b) Air.
63 13 50c. brown 5·25 6·00
64 – 75c. purple 5·25 6·00
65 13 1l. sepia 5·25 6·00
66 – 3l. green 5·25 15·00
67 13 10l. violet 5·25 16·00
68 – 12l. blue 5·25 20·00
69 – 20l. green 10·00 23·00
70 – 50l. blue 17·00 23·00
DESIGNS—HORIZ: 75c., 3, 12l. Savoia Marchetti S-71 airplane. VERT: 20l. Pilot swinging propeller; 50l. Propeller.

15

16 Hailing Marina Fiat MF.5 Flying Boat

1934. 15th Milan Exhibition.
71 15 20c. red 70 3·50
72 30c. green 70 3·50
73 50c. black 70 3·50
74 1l.25 blue 70 7·00

1934. Air. Honouring the Duke of the Abruzzi (explorer).
75 16 25l. black 23·00 80·00

17 Scoring a Goal

18 Marina Fiat MF.5 Flying Boat over Stadium

1934. World Football Championship.
76 17 10c. green (postage) 18·00 22·00
77 50c. violet 35·00 14·00
78 1l.25 blue 35·00 55·00
79 – 5l. brown 44·00 £130
80 – 10l. blue 44·00 £130
DESIGN—VERT: 5, 10l. Fascist salute before kick-off.

81 18 50c. brown (air) 8·75 22·00
82 75c. purple 8·75 22·00
83 – 5l. black 32·00 44·00
84 – 10l. red 32·00 44·00
85 18 15l. red 32·00 44·00
86 – 25l. green 32·00 90·00
87 – 50l. green 32·00 90·00
DESIGNS—VERT: 5, 10, 25l. "Saving a goal". HORIZ: 50l. Giant football and Marina Fiat MF.5 flying boat.

EXPRESS STAMPS

1932. Air. As Garibaldi stamps of Italy.
E16 E 131 2l.25+1l. blk & vio 4·75 13·50
E17 4l.50+1l.50 grn & brn 4·75 17·00

ITALIAN EAST AFRICA Pt. 8

Italian Empire in East Africa comprising Eritrea, Ethiopia and Italian Somaliland, constituted by Royal Decree of 1 June 1936. Occupied by British Forces 1942–43 (see BRITISH OCCUPATION OF ITALIAN COLONIES (MIDDLE EAST FORCES) in Volume 1).

100 centesimi = 1 lira.

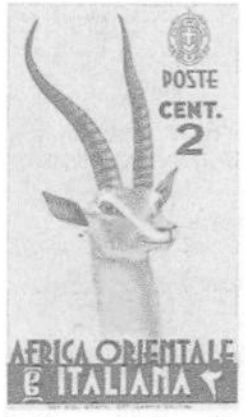
1 Grant's Gazelle

2 R. Nile Statue and Lake Tsana

1938.
1 1 2c. red 15 90
2 A 5c. brown 35 10
3 B 7½c. violet 55 2·30
4 2 10c. brown 1·60 10
5 C 15c. green 35 35
6 B 20c. red 35 10
7 D 25c. green 1·40 10
8 1 30c. brown 55 70
9 A 35c. blue 1·20 3·50
10 B 50c. violet 35 10
11 C 75c. red 1·40 35
12 D 1l. green 90 10
13 B 1l.25 blue 1·20 35
14 2 1l.75 orange 18·00 10
15 A 2l. red 1·10 35
16 D 2l.55 brown 7·75 14·00
17 1 3l.70 violet 23·00 23·00
18 C 5l. blue 6·25 2·30
19 A 10l. red 7·75 7·00
20 2 20l. green 14·00 14·00
DESIGN—VERT: A, Italian eagle and Lion of Judah; B, Profile of King Emmanuel III; C, Soldier implanting Fascist emblem. HORIZ: D, Shadows on road.

5 Mussolini Monument and Mt. Amba Aradam

1938. Air.
21 E 25c. green 1·80 2·30
22 5 50c. brown 39·00 10
23 F 60c. red 1·10 6·25
24 E 75c. brown 1·80 1·60
25 G 1l. blue 10 10
26 5 1l.50 violet 70 35
27 F 2l. blue 70 90
28 E 3l. red 1·10 3·50
29 G 5l. brown 2·40 2·40
30 5 10l. purple 6·00 5·25
31 E 25l. blue 12·00 12·50
DESIGNS—HORIZ: E, Savoia Marchetti S-73 airplane, rock sculpture of eagle and Mt. Amba Aradam; F, Savoia Marchetti S-73 airplane over Lake Tsana. VERT: G, Bateleur.

9 Statue of Augustus

10 Eagle and Serpent

1938. Birth Bimillenary of Augustus the Great.
36 9 5c. brown (postage) 10 1·10
37 – 10c. red 10 90
38 9 25c. green 80 90
39 – 50c. violet 80 70
40 9 75c. red 80 1·80
41 – 1l.25 blue 80 3·50
DESIGN: 10c., 50c., 1l.25, Statue of Goddess of Abundance.

42 10 50c. brown (air) 35 1·80
43 1l. violet 55 2·75

11 Ethiopian Canoe

1940. Naples Exhibition.
44 11 5c. brown (postage) 10 70
45 – 10c. orange 10 70
46 – 25c. green 80 1·20
47 11 50c. violet 80 70
48 – 75c. red 80 2·10
49 – 1l.25 blue 80 1·60
50 – 2l.+75c. red 80 8·75
DESIGNS—VERT: 10c., 75c., 2l. Soldier; 25c., 1l.25, Allegory of Italian Conquest of Ethiopia.

51 – 50c. grey (air) 65 2·75
52 – 1l. violet 65 2·75
53 – 2l.+75c. blue 80 2·25
54 – 5l.+2l. brown 80 2·25
DESIGNS—VERT: 50c., 2l. Savoia Marchetti S-66 flying boat over tractor. HORIZ: 1l., 5l. Savoia Marchetti S.M.83 airplane over city.

15 Hitler and Mussolini

1941. Axis Commemoration.
55 15 5c. yellow (postage) 10
56 10c. brown 10
57 20c. black 1·10
58 25c. green 1·10
59 50c. purple 1·10
60 75c. red 1·10
61 1l.25 blue 1·10

62 1l. blue (air) 26·00
63 1l. blue 1·80
In No. 62 the "1 lira" tablet is in the centre; in No. 63 it is in the lower left corner.

EXPRESS LETTER STAMPS

E 7 Plough and Native Huts

1938. Air.
E32 E 7 2l. blue 90 2·75
E33 2l.50 brown 90 4·50

E 8 King Victor Emmanuel III

1938.
E34 E 8 1l.25 green 90 2·75
E35 2l.50 red (inscr "EXPRESS") 90 8·00

POSTAGE DUE STAMPS

1941. Nos. D395/407 of Italy optd **A.O.I.**
D64 D 141 5c. brown 55
D65 10c. blue 55
D66 20c. red 1·60
D67 25c. green 1·60
D68 30c. orange 4·00
D69 40c. brown 4·00
D70 50c. violet 4·00
D71 60c. blue 7·00
D72 D 142 1l. orange 15·00
D73 2l. green 15·00
D74 5l. violet 15·00
D75 10l. blue 15·00
D76 20l. red 15·00

ITALIAN OCCUPATION OF CEPHALONIA AND ITHACA Pt. 3

Two of the Greek Ionian Islands off the W. coast of Greece, under Italian occupation in 1941.

100 lepta = 1 drachma.

PRICES. Prices are for unsevered pairs. Single stamps from severed pairs are worth ⅓ unused and ½ used prices.

1941. Stamps of Greece optd **ITALIA Occupazione Militare Italiana isole Cefalonia e Itaca** across a pair of stamps. (a) On postage stamps of 1937.

1	**86**	5l. blue and brown	2·75	12·00
2	–	10l. brown and blue	2·75	12·00
3	–	20l. green and black	2·75	12·00
4	–	40l. black and green	2·75	12·00
5	–	50l. black and brown	2·75	12·00
6	–	80l. brown and violet	8·50	23·00
7	**89**	1d. green	60·00	£160
8	**89a**	1d.50 green	40·00	£100
9	–	2d. blue	4·00	16·00
10	–	5d. red	17·00	70·00
11	–	6d. brown	17·00	70·00
12	–	7d. brown	17·00	70·00
13	**89**	8d. blue	45·00	£120
14	–	10d. brown	22·00	70·00
15	–	15d. green	35·00	£110
16	–	25d. blue	45·00	£140
17	**89a**	30d. red	£140	£475

(b) On air stamps of 1938 and 1935.

18	D **20**	50l. brown (No. 521)	60·00	75·00
19	**79**	1d. red	19·00	65·00
20	–	2d. blue	11·00	26·00
21	–	5d. mauve	19·00	50·00
22	–	7d. blue	29·00	65·00
23	–	25d. red	85·00	£300
24	–	30d. green	£110	£325
25	–	50d. mauve	£700	£1900
26	–	100d. brown	£300	£900

(c) On Charity Tax stamps.

27	D **20**	10l. red (No. C498)	6·50	12·00
28	C **96**	10l. red	8·50	20·00
29		50l. green (No. C525)	2·75	12·00
30		50l. green (No. C554)	£140	
31		1d. blue (No. C526)	14·00	40·00

ITALIAN OCCUPATION OF CORFU Pt. 3

One of the Greek Ionian Islands situated off the coast of Albania temporarily occupied by Italy during a dispute with Greece in 1923. For later Occupation Issues see ITALIAN OCCUPATION OF CORFU AND PAXOS below.

100 centesimi = 1 lira.
100 lepta = 1 drachma.

1923. Stamps of Italy optd **CORFU**.

1	**37**	5c. green	4·25	4·25
2		10c. red	4·25	4·25
3		15c. grey	4·25	4·25
4	**41**	20c. orange	4·25	4·25
5	**39**	30c. brown	4·25	4·25
6		50c. mauve	4·25	4·25
7		60c. blue	4·25	4·25
8	**34**	1l. brown and green	4·25	4·25

1923. Stamps of Italy surch **CORFU** and value.

9	**37**	25l. on 10c. red	43·00	18·00
10	**39**	60l. on 25c. blue	6·50	
11		70l. on 30c. brown	6·50	
12		1d.20 on 50c. mauve	24·00	18·00
13	**34**	2d.40 on 1l. brown & green	24·00	18·00
14		4d.75 on 2l. green & orange	9·25	

ITALIAN OCCUPATION OF CORFU AND PAXOS Pt. 3

Greek Ionian Islands occupied by Italy in 1941.

100 lepta = 1 drachma.

1941. Stamps of Greece optd **CORFU**. (a) On postage stamps of 1937.

1	**86**	5l. blue and brown	3·25	2·30
2	–	10l. brown and blue	1·30	1·40
4	–	20l. green and black	1·30	1·40
5	–	40l. black and green	1·60	2·10
6	–	50l. black and brown	1·30	1·40
7	–	80l. brown and violet	1·60	2·10
8	**89**	1d. green	7·25	4·75
9	**89a**	1d.50 green	6·25	3·25
10	–	2d. blue	4·00	2·75
11	**89**	3d. brown	7·25	4·75
12	–	5d. red	4·00	3·25
13	–	6d. olive	4·00	3·50
14	–	7d. brown	6·00	4·00
15	**89**	8d. blue	11·50	9·25
16	–	10d. brown	£400	£130
17	–	15d. green	19·00	11·00
18	–	25d. blue	13·00	11·50
19	**89a**	30d. red	65·00	48·00
20	**89**	100d. red	£225	£110

(b) On air stamps of 1938 and 1935.

22	D **20**	50l. brown (No. 521)	4·50	2·40
23	**79**	1d. red	£475	£160
24		2d. blue	7·00	2·40
25		5d. mauve	8·25	3·75
26		7d. blue	8·25	3·75
27		10d. brown	£600	£250
28		10d. orange	40·00	25·00
29		25d. red	65·00	28·00
30		30d. green	80·00	40·00
31		50d. mauve	70·00	38·00
32		100d. brown	£800	£425

(c) On Charity Tax stamps of 1939.

33	C **96**	10l. red	1·70	1·30
34		50l. green	2·00	1·30
35		1d. blue	21·00	14·00

(d) On Postage Due stamps of 1902 and 1913.

D36	D **20**	10l. red	1·60	1·60
D37		25l. blue	2·10	1·60
D38		80l. purple	£700	£200
D39		1d. blue	£1200	£450
D40		2d. red	4·25	4·50
D41		5d. blue	14·00	11·00
D42		10d. green	11·00	7·25
D43		15d. brown	11·50	7·25
D44		25d. red	11·50	7·25
D45		50d. orange	11·50	7·25
D46		100d. green	£450	£275

ITALIAN OCCUPATION OF IONIAN ISLANDS Pt. 3

A group of islands off the W. coast of Greece, placed under the protection of Gt. Britain in 1815 and ceded to Greece in 1864. Under Italian occupation in 1941.

For use in all islands except Kithyra.

100 lepta = 1 drachma.

1941. Stamps of Italy optd **ISOLE JONIE**. (a) On postage stamps of 1929.

1	**98**	5c. brown	45	1·70
2	–	10c. brown	45	1·70
3	**99**	20c. red	45	1·70
4	–	25c. green	45	1·70
5	**103**	30c. brown	45	1·70
6		50c. violet	45	1·70
7	–	75c. red	45	1·70
8	–	1l.25 blue	45	1·70

(b) On air stamp of 1930.

9	**110**	50c. brown	70	2·10

(c) On Postage Due stamps of 1934.

D10	D **141**	10c. blue	1·00	2·75
D11		20c. red	1·00	2·75
D12		30c. orange	1·00	2·75
D13	D **142**	1l. orange	1·00	2·75

ITALIAN POST OFFICES IN CHINA Pt. 8

Italian Military Posts in China, including Peking and Tientsin, now closed.

100 centesimi = 1 lira. 100 cents = 1 dollar.

Stamps of Italy overprinted or surcharged.

A. PEKING

1917. Surch **PECHINO** and value.

1	**37**	2c. on 5c. green	£120	70·00
3		4c. on 10c. pink	£225	£120
4	**41**	6c. on 15c. grey	£475	£250
5		8c. on 20c. on 15c. grey	£2250	£1100
6		8c. on 20c. orange	£3750	£1200
7	**39**	20c. on 50c. violet	£22000	£14000
8	**34**	40c. on 1l. brown and green	£140000	£19000

1917. Optd **Pechino**.

9	**30**	1c. brown	9·50	15·00
10	**31**	2c. brown	9·50	15·00
11	**37**	5c. green	3·00	4·00
12		10c. pink	3·00	4·00
13	**41**	20c. orange	90·00	75·00
14	**39**	25c. blue	3·00	6·75
15		50c. violet	3·00	8·25
16	**34**	1l. brown and green	6·75	13·50
17		5l. blue and pink	11·00	24·00
18		10l. green and pink	90·00	£225

1918. Surch **Pechino** and value.

19	**30**	½c. on 1c. brown	80·00	80·00
20	**31**	1c. on 2c. brown	3·00	5·25
21	**37**	2c. on 5c. green	3·00	5·25
22		4c. on 10c. pink	3·00	5·25
23	**41**	8c. on 20c. orange	13·50	11·00
28	**39**	10c. on 25c. blue	3·50	9·50
25		20c. on 50c. violet	8·25	11·00
26	**34**	40c. on 1l. brown and green	£100	£130
27		2 dollari. on 5l. blue and pink	£190	£325
30		2 DOLLARI. on 5l. blue and pink	£45000	£35000

EXPRESS LETTER STAMPS

1917. Express Letter stamp optd **Pechino** or surch **12 CENTS** also.

E28	E **41**	12c. on 30c. bl & pink	45·00	£140
E19		30c. blue and pink	6·75	19·00

POSTAGE DUE STAMPS

1917. Postage Due stamps optd **Pechino**.

D19	D **12**	10c. mauve and orange	2·75	6·75
D20		20c. mauve and orange	2·75	6·75
D21		30c. mauve and orange	2·75	6·75
D22		40c. mauve and orange	5·50	6·75

1918. Surch **Pechino** and value.

D28	D **12**	4c. on 10c. mve & orge	£45000	£35000
D29		8c. on 20c. mve & orge	£6000	£4500
D30		12c. on 30c. mve & orge	41·00	60·00
D31		16c. on 40c. mve & orge	£200	£300

B. TIENTSIN

1917. Surch **TIENTSIN** and value.

31	**37**	2c. on 5c. green	£225	£190
32		4c. on 10c. pink	£400	£225
33	**41**	6c. on 15c. grey	£950	£300

Prices for the above are for stamps with surcharge inverted.

1917. Optd **Tientsin**.

34	**30**	1c. brown	9·50	15·00
35	**31**	2c. brown	9·50	15·00
36	**37**	5c. green	3·00	4·00
37		10c. pink	3·00	4·00
38	**41**	20c. orange	90·00	75·00
39	**39**	25c. blue	3·00	6·75
40		50c. violet	3·00	8·25
41	**34**	1l. brown and green	6·50	13·50
42		5l. blue and pink	11·00	24·00
43		10l. green and pink	90·00	£225

1918. Surch **Tientsin** and value.

44	**30**	½c. on 1c. brown	80·00	80·00
45	**31**	1c. on 2c. brown	3·00	5·25
46	**37**	2c. on 5c. green	3·00	5·25
47		4c. on 10c. pink	3·00	5·25
48	**41**	8c. on 20c. orange	13·50	11·00
49	**39**	10c. on 25c. blue	6·75	11·00
50		20c. on 50c. violet	8·25	11·00
51	**34**	40c. on 1l. brown and green	£100	£130
52		2 Dollari. on 5l. blue and pink	£190	£325
54		2 dollari. on 5l. blue and pink	£6000	£4500

EXPRESS LETTER STAMPS

1917. Express Letter stamp optd **Tientsin** or surch **12 CENTS** also.

E53	E **41**	12c. on 30c. blue & pink	£6500	£5000
E44		30c. blue and pink	6·75	19·00

POSTAGE DUE STAMPS

1917. Postage Due stamps optd **Tientsin**.

D44	D **12**	10c. mauve and orange	2·75	6·75
D45		20c. mauve and orange	2·75	6·75
D46		30c. mauve and orange	2·75	6·75
D47		40c. mauve and orange	5·50	6·75

1918. Surch **Tientsin** and value.

D53	D **12**	4c. on 10c. mve & orge	£1900	£2250
D54		8c. on 20c. mve & orge	13·50	21·00
D55		12c. on 30c. mve & orge	41·00	60·00
D56		16c. on 40c. mve & orge	£200	£300

ITALIAN POST OFFICES IN CRETE Pt. 8

Italian P.O.s in Crete, now closed.

1900. 40 paras = 1 piastre.
1906. 100 centesimi = 1 lira.

Stamps of Italy surcharged or overprinted.

1900. Surch **1 PIASTRA 1**.

1	**27**	1pi. on 25c. blue	5·50	34·00

1901. Surch **LA CANEA 1 PIASTRA 1**.

2	**33**	1pi. on 25c. blue	3·00	6·25

1906. 1901 stamps optd **LA CANEA**.

3	**30**	1c. brown	50	1·20
4	**31**	2c. brown	50	1·20
5		5c. green	1·00	1·50
6	**33**	10c. red	£100	75·00
7		15c. on 20c. orange	1·20	1·70
8		25c. blue	5·75	5·75
9		40c. brown	5·25	5·75
10		45c. green	4·50	5·75
11		50c. mauve	5·75	8·25
12	**34**	1l. brown and green	31·00	34·00
13		5l. blue and pink	£150	£150

1907. 1906 stamps optd **LA CANEA**.

14	**37**	5c. green	85	1·20
15		10c. red	85	1·20
16	**41**	15c. black	1·70	3·00
17	**39**	25c. blue	1·70	4·00
18		40c. brown	17·00	21·00
19		50c. violet	1·70	4·00

EXPRESS LETTER STAMP

1906. Express Letter stamp optd **LA CANEA**.

E1	E **35**	25c. red	4·25	8·50

ITALIAN POST OFFICES IN THE TURKISH EMPIRE Pt. 8

Currency: Italian and Turkish.

Stamps of Italy overprinted and surcharged.

A. GENERAL ISSUES.

The following were in use in P.O.s in Alexandria, Assab, La Goletta, Massawa, Susa, Tripoli and Tunis and also at Consular post offices at Buenos Aires and Montevideo.

1874. 1863 type, slightly altered, optd **ESTERO**.

1	**4**	1c. green	6·75	15·00
2	**5**	2c. brown	8·25	19·00
3	**6**	5c. grey	£450	19·00
4		10c. orange	£1100	34·00
10		10c. blue	£225	12·50
5	**10**	20c. blue	£1000	19·00
11		20c. orange	£3750	9·50
6	**6**	30c. brown	1·40	10·50
7		40c. red	1·40	9·50
8		60c. mauve	3·50	75·00
9	**7**	2l. red	90·00	£400

1881. 1879 type, slightly altered, optd **ESTERO**.

12	**12**	5c. green	5·50	8·25
13		10c. red	4·00	5·50
14		20c. orange	4·00	4·75
15		25c. blue	4·00	8·25
16		50c. mauve	8·25	41·00

B. OFFICES IN TURKISH EMPIRE.

(a) **Albania.**

1902. Surch **ALBANIA** and value.

18	**31**	10pa. on 5c. green	2·20	1·00
24	**37**	10pa. on 5c. green	27·00	34·00
25		20pa. on 10c. red	16·00	14·50
19	**33**	35pa. on 20c. orange	3·75	3·00
20		40pa. on 25c. blue	7·75	3·00
26		80pa. on 50c. mauve	16·00	14·50

1902. Surch with figures of value repeated twice and currency in words thus, **20 Para 20**.

21	**31**	10pa. on 5c. green	4·50	1·50
27	**37**	10pa. on 5c. green	1·00	1·00
28		20pa. on 10c. red	1·00	1·00
22	**33**	35pa. on 20c. orange	3·00	1·90
23		40pa. on 25c. blue	21·00	4·25
29		80pa. on 50c. mauve	38·00	29·00

(b) **General Offices in Europe and Asia.**

1908. Surch with figures of value repeated twice and currency in words thus, **30 Para 30**.

32	**41**	30pa. on 15c. grey	1·40	1·70
30	**39**	40pa. on 25c. blue	2·10	1·70
31		80pa. on 50c. mauve	3·00	2·40

EXPRESS LETTER STAMPS

1908. Express Letter stamps surch **LEVANTE** and new value.

E33	E **35**	1pi. on 25c. red	2·10	2·40
E34	E **41**	60pa. on 30c. blue & red	3·00	3·75

C. INDIVIDUAL OFFICES IN EUROPE AND ASIA.

(a) **Constantinople.**

1908. Surch in one line with figure of value and currency in words.

40	**37**	10pa. on 5c. green	4·75	6·75
41		20pa. on 10c. pink	4·75	6·75
47	**41**	30pa. on 15c. grey	2·10	2·10
43	**39**	1pi. on 25c. blue	4·75	6·75
44		2pi. on 50c. mauve	41·00	41·00
45	**34**	4pi. on 1l. brown and green	£600	£475
46		20pi. on 5l. blue and pink	£2500	£1500

1908. Surch in two lines with figures of value repeated twice and currency in words.

48	**34**	4pi. on 1l. brown and green	34·00	41·00
51		20pi. on 5l. blue and pink	34·00	41·00

1909. Surch **Costantinopoli** (10pa. to 2pi.) or **COSTANTINOPOLI** (4 to 40pi.) and value in figures twice repeated and currency in words.

52	**37**	10pa. on 5c. green	1·00	1·50
53		20pa. on 10c. pink	1·00	1·50
54	**41**	30pa. on 15c. grey	1·00	1·50
55	**39**	1pi. on 25c. blue	1·00	1·50
56		2pi. on 50c. mauve	1·40	1·80
57	**34**	4pi. on 1l. brown and green	1·70	2·20
58		20pi. on 5l. blue and pink	41·00	39·00
59		40pi. on 10l. green and pink	3·00	19·00

1921. Surch with value in figures and currency in words thus, **4 PIASTRE**.

60	**37**	1pi. on 5c. green	£110	£200
61		2pi. on 15c. grey	4·00	6·75
62	**41**	4pi. on 20c. orange	46·00	46·00
63	**39**	5pi. on 25c. blue	46·00	46·00
64		10pi. on 60c. red	2·10	3·50

1921. Surch with value in figures and currency in words thus, **PARA 20**.

65	**30**	10pa. on 1c. brown	1·40	2·10
66	**31**	20pa. on 2c. brown	1·40	2·10
67	**37**	30pa. on 5c. green	3·00	3·75
68		1pi. 20 on 15c. grey	4·75	2·10

69 **41** 3pi. on 20c. orange . . . . 5·50 10·50
70 **39** 3pi. 30 on 25c. blue . . . . 2·40 2·10
71 7pi. 20 on 60c. red . . . . 4·75 3·75
72 **34** 15pi. on 1l. brown and green . . . . 19·00 29·00

1922. Surch **COSTANTINOPOLI** and value in figures once only after currency in words.
73 **37** 20pa. on 5c. green . . . . . 12·50 17·00
74 1pi. 20 on 15c. grey . . . . 1·20 1·70
75 **39** 3pi. on 30c. brown . . . . 1·20 1·70
76 3pi. 30 on 40c. brown . . . 1·20 1·70
77 **34** 7pi. 20 on 1l. brown & green . . . . 1·20 1·70

1922. Surch **Piastre 3,75** in two lines.
78 **39** 3,75pi. on 25c. blue . . . . 1·70 2·10

1922. Para values surch in one line thus **30 PARA** and piastre values with **PIASTRE** over new value except Nos. 81, 86, 98 and 99 where the figures of value are above.
79 **31** 30pa. on 2c. brown . . . . 1·50 2·75
80 **37** 30pa. on 5c. green . . . . . 3·50 8·25
81 **41** 1,50pi. on 20c. orange . . . 1·50 2·10
82 **39** 1,50pi. on 25c. blue . . . . 1·50 4·00
83 3,75pi. on 40c. brown . . . 2·20 5·25
84 4,50pi. on 50c. mauve . . . 6·75 12·50
85 7,50pi. on 60c. red . . . . 5·50 9·50
86 15pi. on 85c. brown . . . . 10·50 19·00
87 **34** 18,75pi. on 1l. brown & grn 4·75 15·00
98 45pi. on 5l. blue and red . . 85·00 60·00
99 90pi. on 10l. olive and red 60·00 £110

1922. Para values surch in two lines and piastre values with **PIASTRE** under new value.
90 **37** 30pa. on 5c. green . . . . . 1·00 2·10
91 1½pi. on 10c. red . . . . . 1·40 2·10
92 **39** 3pi. on 25c. blue . . . . . 12·00 5·25
93 3¾pi. on 40c. brown . . . . 1·90 2·10
94 4½pi. on 50c. mauve . . . . 31·00 26·00
95 7½pi. on 85c. brown . . . . 5·25 6·00
96 **34** 7½pi. on 1l. brown and green . . . . 6·00 8·50
97 15pi. on 1l. brown and green . . . . 50·00 £100

1923. Surch **COSTANTINOPOLI** and value in figures once only after currency in words.
100 **37** 30pa. on 5c. green . . . . 1·70 1·90
101 **39** 1pi. 20 on 25c. blue . . . 1·70 1·90
103 4pi. 20 on 50c. mauve . . . 1·70 1·50
104 7pi. 20 on 60c. red . . . . 1·70 1·50
105 15pi. on 85c. brown . . . 1·70 2·75
106 **34** 18pi. 30 on 1l. brown and green . . . . 1·70 2·75
107 45pi. on 5l. blue and pink 2·50 5·50
108 90pi. on 10l. green & pink 2·50 6·25

EXPRESS LETTER STAMPS

1922. Express Letter stamps surch **15 PIASTRE**.
E 90 E **41** 15pi. on 1l.20 on 30c. blue and red . . . . 17·00 34·00
E100 15pi. on 30c. blue and red £225 £375

1923. Express Letter stamp surch **COSTANTINOPOLI 15 PIASTRE**.
E109 E **41** 15pi. on 1l.20 blue and red . . . . 4·25 17·00

POSTAGE DUE STAMPS

1922. Postage Due stamps optd **Costantinopoli**.
D100 E **12** 10c. mauve and orange 34·00 48·00
D101 30c. mauve and orange 34·00 48·00
D102 60c. mauve and orange 1·70 1·50
D103 1l. mauve and blue . . 34·00 48·00
D104 2l. mauve and blue . . £700 £1100
D105 5l. mauve and blue . . £250 £350
Nos. D100/5 bear a control cachet applied over blocks of four so that a quarter of the circle falls in a corner of each stamp.

(b) **Durazzo.**

1909. Surch **Durazzo** (10pa. to 2pi.) or **DURAZZO** (4 to 40pi.) and value.
109 **37** 10pa. on 5c. green . . . . 70 1·20
110 20pa. on 10c. pink . . . . 70 1·20
111 **41** 30pa. on 15c. grey . . . . 31·00 2·10
112 **39** 1pi. on 25c. blue . . . . . 1·40 1·70
113 2pi. on 50c. mauve . . . . 1·40 1·70
114 **34** 4pi. on 1l. brown and green . . . . 2·75 2·40
115 20pi. on 5l. blue and pink £140 £140
116 40pi. on 10l. green & pink 6·75 60·00

1915. No. 111 of Durazzo surch **CENT. 20**.
116a **41** 20c. on 30pa. on 15c. grey 2·75 13·00

(c) **Janina.**

1909. Surch **Janina** (10pa. to 2pi.) or **JANINA** (4 to 40pi.) and value.
117 **37** 10pa. on 5c. green 85 85
118 20pa. on 10c. pink 85 85
119 **41** 30pa. on 15c. grey . . . . 1·20 1·20
120 **39** 1pi. on 25c. blue . . . . . 1·20 1·20
121 2pi. on 50c. mauve . . . . 1·20 1·40
122 **34** 4pi. on 1l. brown and green . . . . 2·40 1·70
123 20pi. on 5l. blue and pink £170 £190
124 40pi. on 10l. green & pink 10·50 50·00

(d) **Jerusalem.**

1909. Surch **Gerusalemme** (10pa. to 2pi.) or **GERUSALEMME** (4 to 40pi.) and value.
125 **37** 10pa. on 5c. green . . . . 2·20 4·75
126 20pa. on 10c. pink . . . . 2·20 4·75
127 **41** 30pa. on 15c. grey . . . . 2·20 6·75
128 **39** 1pi. on 25c. blue . . . . . 2·20 4·75
129 2pi. on 50c. mauve . . . . 10·50 13·50
130 **34** 4pi. on 1l. brown and green . . . . 13·50 27·00
131 20pi. on 5l. blue and pink £650 £425
132 40pi. on 10l. green & pink 21·00 £200

(e) **Salonica.**

1909. Surch **Salonicco** (10pa. to 2pi.) or **SALONICCO** (4 to 40pi.) and value.
133 **37** 10pa. on 5c. green 50 70
134 20pa. on 10c. pink 50 70
135 **41** 30pa. on 15c. grey . . . . 85 1·20
136 **39** 1pi. on 25c. blue . . . . . 85 1·20
137 2pi. on 50c. mauve . . . . 1·00 1·40
138 **34** 4pi. on 1l. brown and green . . . . 1·40 1·70
139 20pi. on 5l. blue and pink £250 £250
140 40pi. on 10l. green & pink 6·75 45·00

(f) **Scutari.**

1909. Surch **Scutari di Albania** (4pa. to 2pi.) or **SCUTARI DI ALBANIA** (4 to 40pi.) and value.
141 **31** 4pa. on 2c. brown . . . . 1·70 3·50
142 **37** 10pa. on 35c. green 35 85
143 20pa. on 10c. pink 35 85
144 **41** 30pa. on 15c. grey . . . . 17·00 3·50
145 **39** 1pi. on 25c. blue . . . . . 35 1·40
146 2pi. on 50c. mauve . . . . 70 1·70
147 **34** 4pi. on 1l. brown and green . . . . 85 2·10
148 20pi. on 5l. blue and pink 19·00 27·00
149 40pi. on 10l. green & pink 45·00 90·00

1916. No. 144 of Scutari surch **CENT. 20**.
150 **41** 20c. on 30pa. on 15c. grey 4·00 15·00

(g) **Smyrna.**

1909. Surch **Smirne** (10pa. to 2pi.) or **SMIRNE** (4 to 40pi.) and value.
151 **37** 10pa. on 5c. green 35 60
152 20pa. on 10c. pink 35 60
153 **41** 30pa. on 15c. grey . . . . 1·20 1·40
154 **39** 1pi. on 25c. blue . . . . . 1·20 1·40
155 2pi. on 50c. mauve . . . . 1·70 2·10
156 **34** 4pi. on 1l. brown and green . . . . 2·40 2·50
157 20pi. on 5l. blue and pink £100 £110
158 40pi. on 10l. green & pink 12·00 65·00

(h) **Valona.**

1909. Surch **Valona** (10pa. to 2pi.) or **VALONA** (4 to 40pi.) and value.
159 **37** 10pa. on 5c. green . . . . 25 1·00
160 20pa. on 10c. pink . . . . 25 1·00
161 **41** 30pa. on 15c. grey† . . . . 12·00 3·50
167 30pa. on 15c. grey† . . . . 3·50 8·50
162 **39** 1pi. on 25c. blue . . . . . 85 1·20
163 2pi. on 50c. mauve . . . . 85 1·50
164 **34** 4pi. on 1l. brown and green . . . . 1·20 2·10
165 20pi. on 5l. blue and pink 33·00 38·00
166 40pi. on 10l. green & pink 38·00 90·00
†On No. 161 the surcharge is **Para**, on No. 167 **PARA**.

1916. No. 167 of Valona surch **CENT. 20**.
168 **41** 20c. on 30pa. on 15c. grey 1·40 10·00

D. OFFICES IN AFRICA.

(a) **Benghazi.**

1901. Surch **BENGASI 1 PIASTRA 1**.
169 **33** 1pi. on 25c. blue . . . . . 27·00 80·00
170 **39** 1pi. on 25c. blue . . . . . 31·00 80·00

(b) **Tripoli.**

1909. Optd **Tripoli di Barberia** (1 to 50c.) or **TRIPOLI DI BARBERIA** (1, 2l.).
171 **30** 1c. brown . . . . 3·00 2·75
173 **31** 2c. brown . . . . 1·00 1·70
174 **37** 5c. green . . . . 70·00 6·25
175 10c. red . . . . 2·10 1·70
176 **41** 15c. grey . . . . 2·50 3·00
177 **39** 25c. blue . . . . 1·70 1·70
178 40c. brown . . . . 4·25 3·75
179 50c. violet . . . . 6·00 5·25
180 **34** 1l. brown and green . . . 75·00 50·00
181 5l. blue and pink . . . . . 24·00 £130

EXPRESS LETTER STAMPS

1909. Express Letter stamps optd **TRIPOLI DI BARBERIA**.
E182 E **35** 25c. pink . . . . . . 10·50 6·75
E183 E **41** 30c. blue and pink . . 3·50 10·50

ITALY Pt. 8

A Republic in S. Europe on the Mediterranean and Adriatic Seas. Originally a kingdom formed by the union of various smaller kingdoms and duchies that issued their own stamps.

1862. 100 centesimi = 1 lira.
2002. 100 cents = 1 euro.

1 King Victor Emmanuel II 3

1862. Head embossed. Imperf (15c.) or perf (others).

1	1	10c. bistre	£4500	£100
5		15c. blue	50·00	22·00
2a		20c. blue	£600	£550
3		40c. red	£200	60·00
4a		80c. yellow	50·00	£1200

For stamps of this type imperf, see Sardinia Nos. 27 etc.

1863. Imperf.

7	3	15c. blue	3·50	1·90

4 5 6

7 10

1863. Perf.

8	4	1c. green	3·50	50
9	5	2c. brown	7·50	35
10	6	5c. grey	£1600	60
11		10c. brown	£2000	65
21		10c. blue	£4500	1·00
12		15c. blue	£2000	85
20a	10	20c. blue	£1300	3·00
22		20c. orange	£3500	80
13	6	30c. brown	10·00	1·40
14		40c. red	£4000	1·30
15		60c. mauve	10·00	6·25
16	7	2l. red	16·00	30·00

1865. Surch **C 20 20 C** and curved bar.

17	6	20c. on 15c. blue	£600	75

1878. Official stamps surch **2 C** and wavy bars.

23	O 11	2c. on 2c. red	£160	4·25
24		2c. on 5c. red	£160	5·75
25		2c. on 20c. red	£300	1·60
26		2c. on 30c. red	£200	2·30
27		2c. on 1l. red	£250	1·70
28		2c. on 2l. red	£250	2·75
29		2c. on 5l. red	£300	3·75
30		2c. on 10l. red	£200	4·50

12 King Umberto I 13 Arms of Savoy 14

1879. Corners vary for each value.

31	12	5c. green	7·50	30
32		10c. red	£350	35
33		20c. orange	£350	30
34		25c. blue	£500	65
35		30c. brown	£110	£800
36		50c. mauve	10·00	3·25
37		2l. orange	45·00	£120

1889. Figures in four corners. Various frames.

38	13	5c. green	£550	80
39	14	40c. brown	8·25	2·00
40		45c. green	£2000	1·70
41		60c. mauve	14·50	6·75
42		1l. brown and orange	10·00	1·90
43		5l. red and green	16·00	£250

1890. Surch **Cmi. 2** or **Cmi 20.**

44	12	2c. on 5c. green	30·00	24·00
45		20c. on 30c. brown	£300	2·30
46		20c. on 50c. mauve	£300	11·50

1890. Parcel Post stamps surch **Valevole per le stampe Cmi. 2** and bars.

47	P 13	2c. on 10c. grey	5·25	2·50
48		2c. on 20c. blue	5·75	2·20
49		2c. on 50c. pink	43·00	16·00
50		2c. on 75c. green	9·00	2·50
51		2c. on 1l.25 orange	30·00	10·00
52		2c. on 1l.75 brown	22·00	25·00

21 22 23

24 25 26

27 29

1891.

53	21	1c. brown	4·25	95
54	22	2c. brown	7·25	50
55	23	5c. green	£400	55
56	24	5c. green	26·00	45
57	25	10c. red	7·25	35
58a	26	20c. orange	5·50	1·80
59	27	25c. blue	5·25	60
60		45c. olive	7·25	90
61	29	5l. red and blue	50·00	65·00

30 31

33 King Victor Emmanuel III 34 King Victor Emmanuel III

1901. Designs vary.

62	30	1c. brown	25	10
63	31	2c. brown	25	10
64		5c. green	47·00	15
65	33	10c. red	60·00	25
66		20c. orange	9·00	25
67		25c. blue	90·00	35
68		40c. brown	£400	1·90
69		45c. green	7·75	10
70		50c. violet	£500	3·25
71	34	1l. brown and green	3·00	10
72		5l. blue and pink	17·00	50
85		10l. green and pink	60·00	3·00

See also Nos. 171s, 181, 185 and 186/7.

1905. Surch **C. 15.**

73	33	15c. on 20c. orange	60·00	40

37 39 41

1906.

75	37	5c. green	45	30
76		10c. red	45	10
90	41	15c. grey	27·00	35
77	39	25c. blue	2·00	10
78		40c. brown	2·50	10
79		50c. violet	2·50	10

See also Nos. 104 etc, 171d/h and 171j/r.

42 Garibaldi 43

1910. 50th Anniv of Plebiscite in Naples and Sicily.

81	42	5c.(+5c.) green	25·00	11·00
82		15c.(+5c.) red	50·00	34·00

1910. National Plebiscite of Southern States, 1860.

83	43	5c.(+5c.) pink	£120	43·00
84		15c.(+5c.) green	£200	60·00

45 46

1911. Jubilee of Italian Kingdom.

86	45	2c.(+3c.) brown	8·50	1·30
87	46	5c.(+5c.) green	11·00	8·00
88	–	10c.(+5c.) red	14·00	14·00
89	–	15c.(+5c.) grey	14·00	14·00

DESIGNS: Symbolic of the Genius of Italy (10c.) and the Glory of Rome (15c.).

50

1912. Re-erection of Campanile of St. Mark, Venice.

91	50	5c. black	6·50	3·25
92		15c. brown	17·00	13·00

1913. Surch **2 2.**

93	46	2 on 5c. green	1·10	1·30
94	–	2 on 10c. red (No. 88)	1·60	1·20
95	–	2 on 15c. grey (No. 89)	1·20	1·20

53 Banner of United Italy 54 Italian Eagle and Arms of Savoy

1915. Red Cross Society. No. 98 is surch **20.**

96	53	10c.+5c. red	2·50	2·50
97	54	15c.+5c. grey	5·00	3·50
98		20 on 15c.+5c. grey	7·00	10·50
99		20c.+5c. orange	7·25	9·25

1916. Surch **CENT. 20.**

100	41	20c. on 15c. grey	14·00	35

1917. Air. Express Letter stamp optd **ESPERIMENTO POSTA AEREA MAGGIO 1917 TORINO=ROMA=ROMA=TORINO.**

102	E 35	25c. red	11·00	8·50

1917. Air. Express Letter stamp surch **IDROVOLANTE NAPOLI-PALERMO NAPOLI 25 CENT 25.**

103	E 59	25c. on 40c. violet	11·50	9·00

1917.

104	37	15c. grey	2·75	15
105	41	20c. orange	7·50	15
178	39	20c. orange	75	80
179		20c. green	35	10
180		20c. purple	2·30	15
181	34	25c. green and light green	1·70	10
182	39	25c. green	7·75	3·50
106		30c. brown	2·30	20
183		30c. grey	1·90	10
107		55c. purple	11·00	2·75
108		60c. red	2·40	15
109		60c. blue	5·50	11·00
184		60c. orange	7·00	15
185	34	75c. red and carmine	1·50	10
110	39	85c. brown	6·75	70
186	34	1l.25 blue and ultramarine	5·50	10
111		2l. green and orange	15·00	1·00
187		2l.50 green and orange	40·00	1·30

See also Nos. 171a/c and 171i.

59 Ancient Seal of Republic of Trieste 60

1921. Union of Venezia Giulia with Italy.

112	59	15c. red and black	3·00	12·50
113		25c. red and blue	3·00	12·50
114		40c. red and brown	3·00	12·50

1921. 600th Death Anniv of Dante.

115	60	15c. red	3·75	6·25
116	–	25c. green	3·75	6·25
117	–	40c. brown	3·75	6·25

DESIGNS: 25c. Woman with book; 40c. Dante.

62 "Victory" 64

1921. Victory of 1918.

118	62	5c. green	50	70
119		10c. red	75	85
120		15c. grey	1·80	3·25
121		25c. blue	90	1·90

1922. 9th Italian Philatelic Congress. Trieste. Optd **IX CONGRESSO FILATELICO ITALIANO TRIESTE 1922.**

122	37	10c. red	£250	£130
123		15c. grey	£180	£130
124	39	25c. blue	£180	£130
125		40c. brown	£275	£130

1922. 50th Death Anniv of Mazzini.

126	64	25c. purple	5·00	10·00
127	–	40c. purple	7·00	10·50
128	–	80c. blue	5·00	13·00

DESIGNS—VERT: 40c. Mazzini. HORIZ: 80c. Tomb of Mazzini.

66

1923. Tercentenary of Propagation of the Faith.

129	66	20c. orange and green	1·80	23·00
130		30c. orange and red	1·80	23·00
131		50c. orange and violet	1·80	23·00
132		1l. orange and blue	2·50	23·00

The portraits and arms in the corners at right vary for each value.

1923. Surch in words and figures. (15c. surch **DIECI** only).

133	39	7½c. on 85c. brown	10	80
135	30	10c. on 1c. brown	35	15
136	31	10c. on 2c. brown	35	15
137	37	10c. on 15c. grey	10	15
138	39	20c. on 25c. blue	10	25
139	33	25c. on 45c. olive	10	6·50
140	39	25c. on 60c. blue	70	40
141		30c. on 50c. mauve	10	15
142		30c. on 55c. purple	10	25
143		50c. on 40c. brown	75	15
144		50c. on 55c. purple	27·00	2·50
145	34	1l.75 on 10l. olive and red	10·00	8·25

73 74

75

1923. 1st Anniv of Fascist March on Rome.

146	73	10c. green	3·25	1·60
147		30c. violet	3·50	1·60
148		50c. red	4·50	2·50
149	74	1l. blue	4·25	1·70
150		2l. brown	4·25	4·00
151	75	5l. black and blue	6·50	14·00

76

1923. Fascist "Black Shirt" Fund.

152	76	30c.+30c. brown	23·00	33·00
153		50c.+50c. mauve	27·00	33·00
154		1l.+1l. grey	23·00	33·00

77

1923. 50th Death Anniv of A. Manzoni (writer).

155	77	10c. black and red	2·40	24·00
156	–	15c. black and green	2·40	24·00
157	–	30c. black	2·40	24·00
158	–	50c. black and brown	2·40	24·00
159	–	1l. black and blue	25·00	95·00
160	–	5l. black and purple	£350	£650

DESIGNS: 10c. to 50c. Scenes from Manzoni's "I Promessi Sposi"; 1l. Manzoni's home, Milan; 5l. Portrait of Manzoni.

1924. Victory stamps surch **LIRE UNA** between stars.

161	62	1l. on 5c. green	19·00	38·00
162		1l. on 10c. red	12·00	38·00
163		1l. on 15c. grey	19·00	38·00
164		1l. on 25c. blue	12·00	38·00

1924. Trade Propaganda. Optd **CROCIERA ITALIANA 1924**.

165	37	10c. red	2·30	5·50
166	39	30c. brown	2·30	5·50
167		50c. violet	2·30	5·50
168		60c. blue	12·00	23·00
169		85c. brown	8·25	23·00
170	34	1l. brown and green	35·00	95·00
171		2l. green and orange	55·00	95·00

Used on an Italian cruiser which visited South America for trade propaganda.

1924. Previous issues with attached advertising labels (imperf between stamp and label). Colour of label given.

171a	15c. (104) + Columbia (blue)	29·00	24·00
171b	15c. (104) + Bitter Campari (blue)	2·40	9·00
171c	15c. (104) + Cordial Campari (black)	2·40	9·00
171d	25c. (77) + Coen (green)	£180	24·00
171e	25c. (77) + Piperno (brown)	£1200	£375
171f	25c. (77) + Tagliacozzo (brown)	£600	£375
171g	25c. (77) + Abrador (blue)	75·00	60·00
171h	25c. (77) + Reinach (green)	75·00	45·00
171i	30c. (106) + Columbia (green)	24·00	23·00
171j	50c. (79) + Coen (blue)	£1200	45·00
171k	50c. (79) + Columbia (red)	16·00	2·50
171l	50c. (79) + De Montel (blue)	2·75	8·00
171m	50c. (79) + Piperno (green)	£1300	£140
171n	50c. (79) + Reinach (blue)	£180	13·00
171o	50c. (79) + Singer (red)	2·75	95
171p	50c. (79) + Tagliacozzo (green)	£1800	£275
171q	50c. (79) + Siero Casali (blue)	16·00	9·75
171r	50c. (79) + Tantal (red)	£225	65·00
171s	1l. (71) + Columbia (blue)	£550	£450

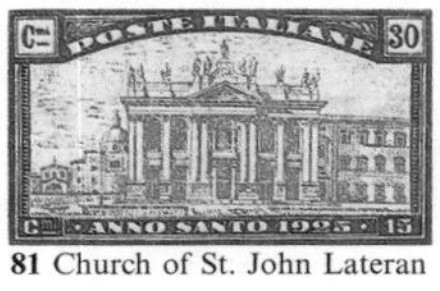

81 Church of St. John Lateran

1924. Holy Year (1925).

172	–	20c.+10c. brown & green	2·50	3·25
173	81	30c.+15c. brown & choc	2·50	3·25
174	–	50c.+25c. brown & violet	2·50	3·25
175	–	60c.+30c. brown and red	2·50	10·00
176	–	1l.+50c. purple and blue	2·50	9·75
177	–	5l.+2l.50 purple and red	2·75	22·00

DESIGNS: 20c. Church of St. Maria Maggiore; 50c. Church of St. Paul; 60c. St. Peter's; 1l. Pope opening Holy Door; 5l. Pope shutting Holy Door.

82 — **83** Vision of St. Francis

1925. Royal Jubilee.

188B	82	60c. red	55	20
189B		1l. blue	55	20
190A		1l.25 blue	4·25	50

1926. 700th Death Anniv of St. Francis of Assisi.

191	83	20c. green	35	25
194B	–	30c. black	35	25
192	–	40c. violet	35	25
193	–	60c. red	35	25
195B	–	1l.25 blue	35	25
196	–	5l.+2l.50 brown	3·00	34·00

DESIGNS—HORIZ: 40c. St. Damian's Church and Monastery, Assisi; 60c. St. Francis's Monastery, Assisi; 1l.25, Death of St. Francis, from fresco in Church of the Holy Cross, Florence. VERT: 30c., 5l. St. Francis (after Luca della Robbia).

88

1926. Air.

197	88	50c. red	5·25	2·00
198		60c. grey	2·50	1·90
199		80c. brown and purple	29·00	17·00
200		1l. blue	1·70	3·00
201		1l.20 brown	10·50	28·00
202		1l.50 orange	9·50	7·50
203		5l. green	23·00	21·00

89 Castle of St. Angelo

1926. 1st National Defence issue.

204	89	40c.+20c. black & brown	2·00	3·25
205	–	60c.+30c. brown and red	2·00	3·25
206	–	1l.25+60c. black & grn	2·00	8·75
207	–	5l.+2l.50 black and blue	3·25	32·00

DESIGNS: 60c. Aqueduct of Claudius; 1l.25, Capitol; 5l. Porta del Popolo.

See also Nos. 219/22 and 278/81.

90 Volta — 91 — 92

1927. Death Centenary of Volta.

208	90	20c. red	55	30
209		50c. green	1·50	15
210		60c. purple	2·75	85
211		1l.25 blue	3·25	1·20

1927.

216	91	50c. grey and brown	2·50	10
212		1l.75 brown	3·75	15
213		1l.85 black	80	30
214		2l.55 red	5·25	3·00
215		2l.65 purple	5·25	23·00

No. 216 is smaller (17½ × 21½ mm).

1927. Air. Surch.

217	88	50c. on 60c. grey	6·25	11·00
218		80c. on 1l. blue	19·00	60·00

1928. 2nd National Defence issue. As Nos. 204/7.

219	89	30c.+10c. black and violet	5·25	6·25
220	–	50c.+20c. black and olive	5·25	6·00
221	–	1l.25+50c. black & blue	10·50	17·00
222	–	5l.+2l. black and red	20·00	50·00

1928.

223	92	7½c. brown	3·50	2·00
224		15c. orange	3·00	15
225		35c. grey	7·00	1·00
226		50c. mauve	11·00	10

93 Emmanuele Filiberto — **94** Soldier of First World War and Statue

95 Statue, Turin (Maroghetti) — **96** King Victor Emmanuel II

1928. 400th Birth Anniv of Emmanuele Filiberto, Duke of Savoy, and 10th Anniv of Victory in World War.

227a	93	20c. blue and brown	60	55
228a		25c. green and red	60	55
229a		30c. brown and green	85	75
230	94	50c. red and blue	50	20
231		75c. red and pink	65	30
232	95	1l.25 black and blue	90	40
233	94	1l.75 green and blue	1·90	2·00
234	93	5l. green and mauve	8·75	25·00
235	94	10l. black and pink	22·00	60·00
236	95	20l. green and mauve	35·00	£325

1929. 50th Death Anniv of King Victor Emmanuel II. Veterans' Fund.

237	96	50c.+10c. green	2·75	2·20

97 Fascist Arms of Italy — **98** Romulus, Remus and Wolf

99 Julius Caesar — **103** King Victor Emmanuel III

1929. Imperial Series.

238	97	2c. orange	10	20
239	98	5c. brown	20	10
240	99	7½c. violet	20	10
241	–	10c. brown	20	10
242	–	15c. green	20	10
243	99	20c. red	20	10
244	–	25c. green	20	10
245	103	30c. brown	20	10
246	–	35c. blue	20	10
247	103	50c. violet	20	10
248	–	75c. red	20	10
249	99	1l. violet	10	15
250	–	1l.25 blue	20	10
251	–	1l.75 orange	20	10
252	–	2l. red	20	10
253	98	2l.55 green	20	15
254		3l.70 violet	10	10
255		5l. red	25	10
256	–	10l. violet	1·60	35
257	99	20l. green	3·75	2·75
258	–	25l. black	8·00	11·00
259	–	50l. violet	10·00	20·00

DESIGNS—As Type **99**: 10c., 1l.75, 25l. Augustus the Great; 15c., 35c., 2l., 10l. Italia (Woman with castle on her head); 25c., 75c., 1l.25, 50l. Profile of King Victor Emmanuel III.

For stamps as above but without Fascist emblems, see Nos. 633 etc, and for stamps with integral label for armed forces see Nos. 563/74.

104 Bramante Courtyard

1929. 1400th Anniv of Abbey of Montecassino.

260	104	20c. orange	80	25
261	–	25c. green	80	25
262	–	50c.+10c. brown	3·25	4·00
263	–	75c.+15c. red	4·25	6·00
264	104	1l.25+25c. blue	4·50	7·00
265	–	5l.+1l. purple	4·75	24·00
266	–	10l.+2l. green	7·75	48·00

DESIGNS—HORIZ: 25c. "Death of St. Benedict" (fresco); 50c. Monks building Abbey; 75c., 5l. Abbey of Montecassino. VERT: 10l. St. Benedict.

109

1930. Marriage of Prince Umberto and Princess Marie Jose.

267	109	20c. orange	50	15
268		50c.+10c. brown	1·20	1·10
269		1l.25+25c. blue	1·90	4·50

110 Pegasus — **113**

1930. Air.

270	–	25c. green	10	10
271	110	50c. brown	10	10
272	–	75c. brown	10	10
273	–	80c. orange	10	20
274	–	1l. violet	10	10
275	113	2l. blue	10	15
276	110	5l. green	10	25
277		10l. red	10	80

DESIGNS—As Type **110**: 25c., 80c. Wings; 75c., 1l. Angel.

1930. 3rd National Defence issue. Designs as Nos. 204/7.

278	89	30c.+10c. violet & green	1·10	4·50
279	–	50c.+10c. blue and green	1·60	3·00
280	–	1l.25+30c. green & blue	4·50	8·75
281	–	5l.+1l.50 choc & brn	7·50	31·00

114 Ferrucci on Horseback — **117** Francesco Ferrucci

1930. 400th Death Anniv of Francesco Ferrucci.

282	114	20c. red (postage)	35	30
283	–	25c. green	45	30
284	–	50c. violet	30	15
285	–	1l.25 blue	2·00	90
286	–	5l.+2l. orange	6·00	39·00
287	117	50c. violet (air)	85	3·50
288		1l. brown	85	4·00
289		5l.+2l. purple	2·10	31·00

DESIGNS—HORIZ: 25c., 50c., 1l.25, Ferrucci assassinated by Maramaldo. VERT: 5l. Ferrucci in helmet.

119 Jupiter sending forth Eagle

1930. Birth Bimillenary of Virgil.

290	–	15c. brown (postage)	70	35
291	–	20c. orange	70	20
292	–	25c. green	85	20
293	–	30c. purple	1·00	40
294	–	50c. violet	70	15
295	–	75c. red	1·40	70
296	–	1l.25 blue	1·40	65
297	–	5l.+1l.50 brown	28·00	48·00
298	–	10l.+2l.50 olive	28·00	60·00
299	119	50c. brown (air)	5·00	3·25
300		1l. orange	7·50	5·00
301		7l.70+1l.30 purple	26·00	55·00
302		9l.+2l. blue	28·00	55·00

DESIGNS (scenes from "Aeneid" or "Georgics"): 15c. Helenus and Anchises; 20c. The passing legions; 25c. Landing of Aeneas; 30c. Earth's bounties; 50c. Harvesting; 75c. Rural life; 1l.25, Aeneas sights Italy; 5l. A shepherd's hut; 10l. Turnus, King of the Rutuli.

120 Savoia Marchetti S-55A Flying Boats

1930. Air. Transatlantic Mass Formation Flight.

303	120	7l.70 blue and brown	£300	£850

121 St. Antony's Installation as a Franciscan — **123** Tower of the Marzocco

1931. 700th Death Anniv of St. Antony of Padua.

304	121	20c. purple	70	25
305	–	25c. green	80	20
306	–	30c. brown	1·40	30
307	–	50c. violet	70	15
308	–	75c. lake	8·00	1·20
309	–	1l.25 blue	6·25	95
310	–	5l.+2l.50 olive	36·00	46·00

DESIGNS—HORIZ: 25c. Sermon to the Fishes; 30c. Hermitage of Olivares; 50c. Basilica of the Saint at Padua; 75c. Death of St. Antony; 1l.25, St. Antony liberating prisoners. VERT: 5l. Vision of St. Antony.

1931. 50th Anniv of Naval Academy, Leghorn.
311 **123** 20c. red 2·50 25
312 – 50c. violet 2·50 15
313 – 1l.25 blue 8·00 55
DESIGNS—HORIZ: 50c. Cadet ship "Amerigo Vespucci"; 1l.25, Cruiser "Trento".

124 Dante (1265–1321)

125 Leonardo da Vinci's Drawing "Flying Man"

127 Leonardo da Vinci

1932. Dante Alighieri Society. (a) Postage.
314 – 10c. brown 65 25
315 – 15c. green 70 20
316 – 20c. red 70 20
317 – 25c. green 70 20
318 – 30c. brown 1·30 25
319 – 50c. violet 55 15
320 – 75c. red 2·00 95
321 – 1l.25 blue 1·40 65
322 – 1l.75 orange 1·50 95
323 – 2l.75 green 11·50 6·75
324 – 5l.+2l. red 18·00 48·00
325 **124** 10l.+2l.50 olive 18·00 60·00
DESIGNS: 10c. Giovanni Boccaccio (writer); 15c. Niccolo Machiavelli (statesman); 20c. Fra Paolo Sarpi (philosopher); 25c. Vittorio Alfieri (poet); 30c. Ugo Foscolo (writer); 50c. Giacomo Leopardi (poet); 75c. Giosue Carducci (poet); 1l.25, Carlo Botta (historian); 1l.75, Torquato Tasso (poet); 2l.75, Francesco Petrarch (poet); 5l. Ludovico Ariosto (poet).

(b) Air.
326 **125** 50c. brown 1·40 1·50
327 – 1l. violet 2·10 1·80
328 – 3l. red 3·75 5·25
329 – 5l. green 4·25 7·50
330 **125** 7l.70+2l. blue 8·00 27·00
331 – 10l.+2l.50 grey 9·25 36·00
332 **127** 100l. green and blue 33·00 £130
DESIGN—HORIZ: 1, 3, 5, 10l. Leonardo da Vinci.

128 Garibaldi and Victor Emmanuel

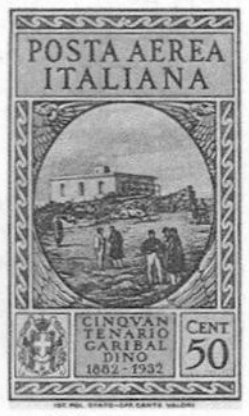
130 Caprera

1932. 50th Death Anniv of Garibaldi.
333 – 10c. blue (postage) 85 35
334 **128** 20c. brown 95 20
335 – 25c. green 1·30 30
336 **128** 30c. orange 1·50 35
337 – 50c. violet 85 20
338 – 75c. red 3·00 1·10
339 – 1l.25 blue 2·30 70
340 – 1l.75+25c. blue 12·00 30·00
341 – 2l.55+50c. brown 20·00 40·00
342 – 5l.+1l. lake 20·00 45·00
DESIGNS—HORIZ: 10c. Garibaldi's birthplace, Nice; 25c., 50c. "Here we make Italy or die"; 75c. Death of Anita (Garibaldi's wife); 1l.25, Garibaldi's tomb; 1l.75, Quarto Rock. VERT: 2l.55, Garibaldi's statue in Rome; 5l. Garibaldi.

343 **130** 50c. lake (air) 1·50 1·60
344 – 80c. green 2·75 3·00
345 **130** 1l.+25c. brown 5·50 8·00
346 – 2l.+50c. blue 7·25 13·00
347 – 5l.+1l. green 9·00 15·00
DESIGNS—VERT: 80c. The Ravenna hut; 2l. Anita; 5l. Garibaldi.

132 Agriculture

1932. 10th Anniv of Fascist March on Rome. (a) Postage.
350 **132** 5c. sepia 60 15
351 – 10c. sepia 60 15
352 – 15c. green 85 30
353 – 20c. red 75 15
354 – 25c. green 85 15
355 – 30c. sepia 90 45
356 – 35c. blue 3·00 1·90
357 – 50c. violet 60 15
358 – 60c. brown 3·00 1·20
359 – 75c. red 1·40 50
360 – 1l. violet 3·00 75
361 – 1l.25 blue 1·40 40
362 – 1l.75 orange 2·10 40
363 – 2l.55 green 18·00 11·50
364 – 2l.75 green 18·00 11·50
365 – 5l.+2l.50 red 30·00 85·00
DESIGNS: 10c. Fascist soldier; 15c. Fascist coastguard; 20c. Italian youth; 25c. Tools forming a shadow of the Fasces; 30c. Religion; 35c. Imperial highways; 50c. Equestrian statue of Mussolini; 60c. Land reclamation; 75c. Colonial expansion; 1l. Marine development; 1l.25, Italians abroad; 1l.75, Sport, 2l.55, Child Welfare; 2l.75. "O.N.D." Recreation; 5l. Caesar's statue.

(b) Air.
366 – 50c. brown 3·50 3·00
367 – 75c. brown 9·25 7·25
DESIGNS: 50c. Eagle (front of Air Ministry Building, Rome); 75c. Aerial view of Italian cathedrals.

134 Airship "Graf Zeppelin"

1933. Air. "Graf Zeppelin" issue.
372 **134** 3l. green and black 6·50 14·00
373 – 5l. brown and green 9·75 14·00
374 – 10l. blue and red 9·75 35·00
375 – 12l. orange and blue 13·50 55·00
376 – 15l. black and brown 13·50 65·00
377 – 20l. blue and brown 18·00 70·00
DESIGNS (all with airship): 3l. S. Paola Gate and tomb of Consul Caius Cestius; 5l. Appian Way and tomb of Cecilia Metella; 10l. Portion of Mussolini Stadium; 12l. S. Angelo Castle; 15l. Forum Romanum; 20l. Empire Way, Colosseum and Baths of Domitian.

135 Italian Flag / King Victor Emmanuel III / "Flight" (½-size illustration)

136 Italian Flag / King Victor Emmanuel III / Rome–Chicago (½-size illustration)

1933. Air. Balbo Transatlantic Mass Formation Flight by Savoia Marchetti S-55X Flying Boats.
378 **135** 5l.25+19l.75 red, green and blue 85·00 £1300
379 **136** 5l.25+44l.75 red, green and blue 85·00 £1300
The first part of the illustration in each group is of the Registered Air Express label and has an abbreviation of one of the pilots' names overprinted on it; the second part is the stamp for Ordinary Postage and the third is the actual Air Mail stamp.

137 Athlete

1933. International University Games, Turin.
380 **137** 10c. brown 20 20
381 20c. red 20 25
382 50c. violet 35 15
383 1l.25 blue 1·70 1·40

138 Dome of St. Peter's

139 St. Peter's and Church of the Holy Sepulchre

1933. "Holy Year". (a) Postage.
384 **138** 20c. red 1·60 15
385 – 25c. green 2·30 25
386 – 50c. violet 1·90 10
387 **138** 1l. 25 blue 2·40 55
388 – 2l.55+2l.50 black 6·75 32·00
DESIGNS: 25, 50c. Angel with Cross; 2l.55, Cross with Doves of Peace.

(b) Air.
389 **139** 50c.+25c. brown 85 6·75
390 75c.+50c. purple 1·60 8·75

1934. Air. Rome-Buenos Aires Flight. Surch with airplane, **1934 XII PRIMO VOLO DIRETTO ROMA = BUENOS-AYRES TRIMOTORE "LOMBARDI MAZZOTTI"**, value and fasces.
391 **113** 2l. on 2l. yellow 3·25 32·00
392 3l. on 2l. green 3·25 38·00
393 5l. on 2l. red 3·25 50·00
394 10l. on 2l. violet 3·25 60·00

141 Anchor of the "Emmanuele Filiberto"

142 Antonio Pacinotti

1934. 10th Anniv of Annexation of Fiume.
395 **141** 10c. brown (postage) 3·50 30
396 20c. red 40 20
397 – 50c. violet 40 15
398 – 1l.25 blue 45 1·10
399 – 1l.75+1l. blue 70 15·00
400 – 2l.55+2l. purple 90 20·00
401 – 2l.75+2l.50 olive 90 20·00
DESIGNS: 50c. Gabriele d'Annunzio; 1l.25, St. Vito's Tower barricaded; 1l.75, Hands supporting crown of historical monuments; 2l.55, Victor Emmanuel III's arrival in the "Brindisi" (cruiser); 2l.75, Galley, gondola and battleship.

402 – 25c. green (air) 55 80
403 – 50c. brown 55 50
404 – 75c. brown 55 1·90
405 – 1l.+50c. purple 55 5·25
406 – 2l.+1l.50 blue 55 7·50
407 – 3l.+2l. black 55 7·50
DESIGNS—Marina Fiat MF.5 flying boat over: 25, 75c. Fiume Harbour; 50c., 1l. War Memorial; 2l. Three Venetian lions; 3l. Roman Wall.

1934. 75th Anniv of Invention of Pacinotti's Dynamo.
411 **142** 50c. violet 70 15
412 1l.25 blue 1·00 85

143

145 Luigi Galvani

1934. World Cup Football Championship, Italy.
413 **143** 20c. red (postage) 9·50 1·90
414 – 25c. green 8·00 80
415 – 50c. violet 9·50 30
416 – 1l.25 blue 21·00 3·75
417 – 5l.+2l.50 brown 55·00 £120
DESIGNS—VERT: 5l. Players heading the ball. HORIZ: 25c., 50c., 1l.25, Two footballers.

418 – 50c. red (air) 6·00 5·25
419 – 75c. blue 6·25 6·25
420 – 5l.+2l.50 olive 26·00 65·00
421 – 10l.+5l. brown 31·00 75·00
DESIGNS—HORIZ: 50c. Marina Fiat MF.5 flying boat over Mussolini Stadium, Turin; 5l. Marina Fiat MF.5 flying boat over Stadium, Rome. VERT: 75c. Savoia Marchetti S-55X flying boat over footballer; 10l. Marina Fiat MF.5 flying boat over Littoral Stadium, Bologna.

1934. 1st Int Congress of Electro-radio-biology.
422 **145** 30c. brown on buff 85 25
423 75c. red on pink 1·20 1·40

146 Military Symbol

148 King Victor Emmanuel III

1934. Military Medal Centenary.
424 **146** 10c. brown (postage) 1·00 40
425 – 15c. green 1·10 80
426 – 20c. red 1·00 30
427 – 25c. green 1·30 30
428 – 30c. brown 1·80 90
429 – 50c. violet 1·40 20
430 – 75c. red 5·50 1·60
431 – 1l.25 blue 4·25 1·00
432 – 1l.75+1l. red 10·00 20·00
433 – 2l.55+2l. purple 16·00 19·00
434 – 2l.75+2l. violet 18·00 22·00
DESIGNS—VERT: 25c. Mountaineers; 1l.75, Cavalry. HORIZ: 15c., 50c. Barbed-wire cutter; 20c. Throwing hand-grenade; 30c. Cripple wielding crutch; 75c. Artillery; 1l.25, Soldiers cheering; 2l.55, Sapper; 2l.75, First Aid.

435 – 25c. green (air) 1·30 1·40
436 – 50c. grey 1·30 1·60
437 – 75c. brown 1·30 2·30
438 – 80c. blue 2·40 2·75
439 – 1l.+50c. brown 4·25 9·00
440 – 2l.+1l. blue 5·50 15·00
441 – 3l.+2l. black 8·75 15·00
DESIGNS—HORIZ: 25, 80c. Italian "P" Type airship under fire; 50, 75c. Naval launch; 1l. Caproni Ca 101 airplane and troops in desert; 2l. Pomilio PC type biplane and troops. VERT: 3l. Unknown soldier's tomb.

1934. Air. Rome–Mogadiscio Flight and King's visit to Italian Somaliland.
444 **148** 1l. violet 1·40 6·75
445 2l. blue 1·40 8·50
446 4l. brown 2·50 35·00
447 5l. green 2·50 55·00
448 8l. red 11·50 65·00
449 10l. brown 12·50 70·00

149 Man with Fasces

150

1935. University Contests. Inscr "LITTORIALI".
450 **149** 20c. red 30 15
451 – 30c. brown 2·20 1·20
452 – 50c. violet 30 15
DESIGNS: 30c. Eagle and soldier. 50c. Standard-bearer and bayonet attack.

1935. National Militia. Inscr "PRO OPERA PREVID. MILIZIA".
453 **150** 20c.+10c. red (postage) 5·75 3·75
454 – 25c.+15c. green 5·75 5·00
455 – 50c.+30c. violet 5·75 6·00
456 – 1l.25+75c. blue 5·75 9·50
457 – 50c.+50c. brown (air) 9·25 11·00
DESIGNS: 25c. Roman standards; 50c. Soldier and cross; 50c.+50c. Wing over Globe; 1l.25, Soldiers and arch.

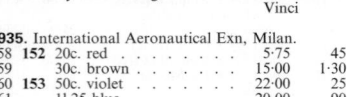

152 Symbol of Flight

153 Leonardo da Vinci

1935. International Aeronautical Exn, Milan.
458 **152** 20c. red 5·75 45
459 30c. brown 15·00 1·30
460 **153** 50c. violet 22·00 25
461 1l.25 blue 20·00 90

154 Vincenzo Bellini

155 "Music"

1935. Death Centenary of Bellini (composer).
462 **154** 20c. red (postage) 3·50 40
463 30c. brown 5·75 60
464 50c. violet 5·25 25
465 1l.25 blue 7·25 1·60
466 – 1l.75+1l. orange 25·00 32·00
467 – 2l.75+2l. olive 41·00 40·00
DESIGNS—VERT: 2l.75, Bellini's villa. HORIZ: 1l.75, Hands at piano.

468 **155** 25c. brown (air) 1·70 1·20
469 50c. brown 1·70 1·20
470 60c. red 4·25 1·60

471	–	1l.+1l. violet	9·75	28·00
472	–	5l.+2l. green	14·50	40·00

DESIGNS: 1l. Angelic musicians; 5l. Mountain landscape (Bellini's birthplace).

156 "Commerce" and Industrial Map of Italy

1936. 17th Milan Fair. Inscr as in T **156**.

473	**156**	20c. red	45	25
474	–	30c. brown	45	40
475	–	50c. violet	55	20
476	**156**	1l.25 blue	80	65

DESIGN—HORIZ: 30c., 50c. Cog-wheel and plough.

157 "Fertility"

1936. 2000th Birth Anniv of Horace.

477	**157**	10c. green (postage)	2·10	25
478	–	20c. red	1·60	25
479	–	30c. brown	4·25	65
480	–	50c. violet	4·25	15
481	–	75c. red	7·25	80
482	–	1l.25+1l. blue	17·00	30·00
483	–	1l.75+1l. red	24·00	42·00
484	–	2l.55+1l. blue	27·00	46·00

DESIGNS—HORIZ: 20c., 1l.25, Landscape; 75c. Capitol; 2l.55, Dying gladiator. VERT: 30c. Ajax defying lightning; 50c. Horace; 1l.75, Pan.

485	–	25c. green (air)	1·80	1·40
486	–	50c. brown	2·50	1·40
487	–	60c. red	3·00	2·30
488	–	1l.+1l. violet	9·00	30·00
489	–	5l.+2l. green	12·00	55·00

DESIGNS—HORIZ: 25c. Savoia Marchetti S-55A flying boat; 50c., 1l. Caproni Ca 101 airplane over lake; 60c. Eagle and oak tree; 5l. Rome.

159

160

1937. Child Welfare. Inscr as in T **159/60**.

490	**159**	10c. brown (postage)	1·70	50
491	**160**	20c. red	1·70	40
492	**159**	25c. green	1·70	50
493	–	30c. sepia	1·90	1·20
494	**160**	50c. violet	1·80	20
495	–	75c. red	5·25	1·60
496	**160**	1l.25 blue	6·25	1·70
497	–	1l.75+75c. orange	29·00	42·00
498	–	2l.75+1l.25 green	23·00	45·00
499	**160**	5l.+3l. blue	25·00	50·00

DESIGNS—As Type **159**: 30c., 1l.75, Boy between Fasces; 75c., 2l.75, "Bambino" (after della Robbia).

500	–	25c. green (air)	5·00	2·00
501	–	50c. brown	5·25	1·40
502	–	1l. violet	5·00	3·00
503	–	2l.+1l. blue	7·50	30·00
504	–	3l.+2l. orange	10·50	34·00
505	–	5l.+3l. red	16·00	38·00

DESIGNS—As Type **160**: 25c., 1l., 3l. Little child with rifle. As Type **159**: 50c., 2l., 5l. Children's heads.

163 Naval Memorial

164 Augustus the Great

1937. 2000th Birth Anniv of Augustus the Great.

506	**163**	10c. green (postage)	80	20
507	–	15c. brown	80	25
508	–	20c. red	80	25
509	–	25c. green	80	25
510	–	30c. brown	1·00	25
511	–	50c. violet	90	10
512	–	75c. red	1·10	70
513	–	1l.25 blue	1·80	75
514	–	1l.75+1l. purple	29·00	30·00
515	–	2l.55+2l. black	32·00	35·00

DESIGNS—VERT: 15c. Military trophies; 20c. Reconstructing temples of Rome; 25c. Census (with reference to birth of Jesus Christ); 30c. Statue of Julius Caesar; 50c. Election of Augustus as Emperor; 75c. Head of Augustus (conquest of Ethiopia); 1l.25, Constructing new fleet; 1l.75, Building Altar of Peace; 2l.55, The Capitol.

516	–	25c. purple (air)	3·50	2·20
517	–	50c. brown	3·50	2·40
518	–	80c. brown	6·25	3·75
519	–	1l.+1l. blue	24·00	25·00
520	**164**	5l.+1l. violet	30·00	40·00

DESIGNS—HORIZ: 25c. "Agriculture"; 50c. Prosperity of the Romans; 80c. Horses of the Sun Chariot; 1l. Staff and map of ancient Roman Empire.

165 Gasparo Spontini (composer)

166 Marconi

1937. Famous Italians.

521	**165**	10c. sepia	35	35
522	–	20c. red	35	35
523	–	25c. green	35	30
524	–	30c. brown	35	40
525	–	50c. violet	35	15
526	–	75c. red	95	1·00
527	–	1l.25 blue	1·20	1·00
528	**165**	1l.75 orange	1·20	1·00
529	–	2l.55+2l. green	11·00	35·00
530	–	2l.75+2l. brown	11·00	38·00

DESIGNS: 20c., 2l.55, Antonio Stradivarius (violin maker); 25, 50c. Giacomo Leopardi (poet); 30, 75c., Giovanni Battista Pergolesi (composer); 1l.25, 2l.75, Giotto di Bondone (painter and architect).

1938. Guglielmo Marconi (telegraphy pioneer) Commemoration.

531	**166**	20c. red	1·60	20
532		50c. violet	45	15
533		1l.25 blue	60	1·50

167 Founding of Rome

168 Victor Emmanuel III

1938. 2nd Anniv of Proclamation of Italian Empire.

534	**167**	10c. brown (postage)	70	15
535	–	20c. red	1·00	15
536	–	25c. green	1·00	15
537	–	30c. brown	85	15
538	–	50c. violet	1·50	15
539	–	75c. red	2·30	30
540	–	1l.25 blue	3·00	25
541	–	1l.75 violet	3·50	55
542	–	2l.75 green	12·50	8·75
543	–	5l. red	23·00	11·00

DESIGNS—VERT: 20c. Emperor Augustus; 25c. Dante; 30c. Columbus; 50c. Leonardo da Vinci; 75c. Garibaldi and Victor Emmanuel II; 1l.25, Italian Unknown Warrior's Tomb; 1l.75, "March on Rome"; 2l.75, Wedding ring on map of Ethiopia; 5l. Victor Emmanuel III.

544	**168**	25c. green (air)	85	1·00
545	–	50c. brown	1·40	1·00
546	–	1l. violet	1·70	3·25
547	–	2l. blue	2·30	6·00
548	**168**	3l. red	4·50	10·00
549	–	5l. green	4·75	15·00

DESIGNS—HORIZ: 50c., 1l. Dante: 2, 5l. Leonardo da Vinci.

169 Steam Locomotive and ETR 200 Express Train

1939. Centenary of Italian Railways.

550	**169**	20c. red	50	20
551		50c. violet	65	20
552		1l.25 blue	1·10	1·50

170 Hitler and Mussolini

171 Hitler and Mussolini

172 Roman Cavalry

1941. Italo-German Friendship.

553	**170**	10c. brown	1·40	45
554		20c. orange	1·40	35
555		25c. green	1·40	40
556	**171**	50c. violet	1·90	35
557		75c. red	2·30	80
558		1l.25 blue	2·30	1·20

1941. 2000th Birth Anniv of Livy (Latin historian).

559	**172**	20c.+10c. red	35	55
560		30c.+15c. brown	35	70
561	–	50c.+25c. violet	40	75
562	–	1l.25+1l. blue	40	90

DESIGN: 50c., 1l.25, Roman legionary.

1942. War Propaganda. Nos. 244/5 and 247 with attached labels (imperf between stamp and label) to encourage war effort.

563	25c. green (Navy)	20	40
564	25c. green (Army)	20	40
565	25c. green (Air Force)	20	40
566	25c. green (Militia)	20	40
567	30c. brown (Navy)	20	1·20
568	30c. brown (Army)	20	1·20
569	30c. brown (Air Force)	20	1·20
570	30c. brown (Militia)	20	1·20
571	50c. violet (Navy)	20	40
572	50c. violet (Army)	20	40
573	50c. violet (Air Force)	20	40
574	50c. violet (Militia)	20	40

173 Galileo teaching at Padua

174 Rossini

1942. Death Tercentenary of Galileo.

575	**173**	10c. red and orange	35	25
576	–	25c. green and olive	35	25
577	–	50c. violet and purple	35	25
578	–	1l.25 blue and grey	50	1·30

DESIGNS: Galileo at Venice (25c.) and at Arcetri, near Florence (1l.25), 50c. Portrait of Galileo.

1942. 150th Birth Anniv of Rossini (composer).

579	–	25c. green	20	25
580	–	30c. brown	20	25
581	**174**	50c. violet	20	25
582		1l. blue	20	40

DESIGN: 25c., 30c. Rossini Monument, Pescaro.

175

187 Romulus, Remus and Wolf (after Pollaiuolo)

1943. Allied Military Government issue.

583	**175**	15c. orange	35	50
584		25c. bistre	35	50
585		30c. grey	35	50
586		50c. violet	35	50
587		60c. yellow	35	65
588		1l. green	35	50
589		2l. red	35	65
590		5l. blue	35	1·20
591		10l. brown	35	1·50

1943. Allied Military Government issue. Stamps of 1929 optd **GOVERNO MILITARE ALLEATO**.

592	**99**	20c. red	45	1·20
593		35c. blue	5·00	7·25
594	**103**	50c. violet	30	1·10

1944.

619	**187**	50c. purple	10	65

1944. As issue of 1929, but with Fascist emblems removed.

633	–	10c. brown (Augustus the Great)	00	00
640	**99**	20c. red	10	30
620	**103**	30c. brown	20	25
635	–	50c. violet (Italia)	00	00
621	**103**	50c. violet	20	1·80
636	–	60c. orange (Italia)	00	00
641	**103**	60c. green	10	35
637	**99**	1l. violet	00	00
643	–	1l.20 brown (Italia)	10	30
638	–	2l. red (Italia)	00	00
645	**98**	5l. red	10	30
646	–	10l. violet (Italia)	2·10	5·00

1945. Stamps of Italy surch **L. 2,50** (No. 629) and stamps of Italian Social Republic surch **POSTE ITALIANE** and new value (Nos. 627/8).

627	1l.20 on 20c. red (No. 102)	10	15
628	2l. on 25c. green (No. 103)	10	15
629	2l.50 on 1l.75 orange (No. 251)	10	25

193 "Work, Justice and Family"

195 Planting a Sapling

196 "Peace"

197 "Work, Justice and Family"

1945.

647	–	10c. brown	15	10
648	**193**	20c. brown	15	10
649	–	25c. blue	15	10
650	**195**	40c. grey	15	10
651	–	50c. violet	15	10
652	–	60c. green	15	15
653	–	80c. red	15	10
654	**195**	1l. green	15	10
655	–	1l.20 brown	15	25
656	–	2l. brown	15	10
657	–	3l. red	15	10
658	–	4l. red	20	10
659	**193**	5l. blue	45	10
660	**195**	6l. violet	6·75	10
661	–	8l. green	3·25	10
662	–	10l. grey	1·50	10
663	**193**	10l. red	32·00	10
664	**195**	15l. blue	7·00	10
665	–	20l. purple	3·25	10
666	**196**	25l. green	19·00	10
667	–	30l. blue	£275	25
668	**196**	50l. purple	7·75	10
669	**197**	100l. red	£275	95

DESIGNS: 10, 50, 80c., 8, 10l. (662) Hammer breaking chain ("Freedom"); 25c., 1l.20, 3, 4, 20, 30l. Flaming torch ("Enlightenment"); 60c., 2l. Gardener tying sapling to stake.

198 Clasped Hands and Caproni Campini N-1 Jet

200 Amalfi

1945. Air.

670	**198**	1l. grey	20	20
671	–	2l. blue	20	20
672	**198**	3l.20 red	20	20
673	–	5l. green	20	20
674	**198**	10l. red	20	10
675	–	25l. blue	10·00	5·25
676	–	25l. brown	15	10
677	**198**	50l. green	18·00	9·25
678		50l. violet	15	10

DESIGN: 2, 5, 25l. Barn swallows in flight.

1946. Mediaeval Italian Republics.

679	**200**	1l. sepia	15	10
680	–	2l. blue	15	10
681	–	3l. green	15	10
682	–	4l. orange	15	10
683	–	5l. violet	15	10
684	–	10l. red	20	10
685	–	15l. blue	65	60
686	–	20l. brown	25	10

DESIGNS—VERT: 2l. Lucca; 3l. Siena; 4l. Florence. HORIZ: 5l. Pisa; 10l. Genoa; 15l. Venice; 20l. "The Oath of Pontida".

1947. Air. Surch **LIRE 6-**.

687	**198**	6l. on 3l.20 orange	20	15

202 Wireless Mast

204 Douglas DC-2 over Rome

1947. Air. 50th Anniv of Radio.
688 **202** 6l. violet 20 15
689 – 10l. red 20 15
690 – 20l. orange 85 55
691 **202** 25l. blue 90 65
692 – 35l. blue . . . . 1·30 75
693 – 50l. purple . . . . 2·50 1·40
DESIGNS: 10, 35l. Ship's aerial; 20, 50l. Heinkel He 70 Blitz wireless-equipped airplane.

1948. Air.
911 **204** 100l. green . . . . 3·00 10
912 300l. mauve 40 30
913 500l. blue 90 55
914 1000l. brown . . . . . . 1·60 1·30
For No. 911 in smaller size see No. 1297.

205 St. Catherine giving her Cloak to a Beggar

206 St. Catherine carrying the Cross

1948. 600th Birth Anniv of St. Catherine of Siena.
698 **205** 3l. blue and green (postage) 15 30
699 – 5l. blue and violet 15 40
700 – 10l. violet and brown . . 3·25 2·75
701 – 30l. grey and bistre . . . 20·00 10·00
702 **206** 100l. violet and brown (air) . . . . 55·00 32·00
703 – 200l. blue and bistre . . . 30·00 13·00
DESIGNS—All show St. Catherine. VERT: 5l. Carrying the Cross; 10l. Extending her arms to Italy; 30l. Dictating "The Dialogue" to a Disciple. HORIZ: 200l. Extending her arms to Italy.

207 "Proclamation of New Constitution"

1948. Proclamation of New Constitution.
704 **207** 10l. violet 95 70
705 30l. blue . . . . 2·40 1·50

208 Rising at Palermo

1948. Centenary of Revolution of 1848.
706 **208** 3l. brown 35 35
707 – 4l. purple 35 35
708 – 5l. blue 85 50
709 – 6l. green 55 60
710 – 8l. brown 55 45
711 – 10l. red . . . . 1·20 25
712 – 12l. green . . . . 3·00 1·70
713 – 15l. black . . . . 7·25 85
714 – 20l. red . . . . 21·00 5·25
715 – 30l. blue . . . . 6·25 50
716 – 50l. violet . . . . 75·00 2·75
717 – 100l. blue . . . . £140 11·50
DESIGNS: 4l. Rising at Padua; 5l. Concession of Statute, Turin; 6l. Storming Porta Tosa, Milan; 8l. Proclamation of Venetian Republic; 10l. Defence of Vicenza; 12l. Hero of Curtatone; 15l. Hero of Goito; 20l. Austrian retreat from Bologna; 30l. Fighting at Brescia; 50l. Garibaldi; 100l. Goffredo Mameli (party patriot) on death bed, July 1849.

209 Alpinist and Bassano Bridge

210 Gaetano Donizetti

1948. Rebuilding of Bassano Bridge.
718 **209** 15l. green . . . . 1·10 1·10

1948. Death Centenary of Donizetti (composer).
719 **210** 15l. brown . . . . 80 2·10

211 Exhibition Grounds

212

1949. 27th Milan Fair.
720 **211** 20l. sepia . . . . 7·00 2·50

1949. 25th Biennial Art Exhibition. Venice.
721 **212** 5l. red and flesh 65 20
722 – 15l. green and cream . . 3·50 95
723 – 20l. brown and buff . . . 9·00 1·40
724 – 50l. blue and yellow . . . 40·00 1·20
DESIGNS: 15l. Clock bell-ringers, St. Mark's Column and Campanile; 20l. Emblem of Venice and "Bucentaur" (state gallery); 50l. Winged lion on St. Mark's Column.

213 Globes and Forms of Transport

1949. 75th Anniv of U.P.U.
725 **213** 50l. blue . . . . 50·00 4·25

214 Vascello Castle

215 Worker and Ship

1949. Centenary of Roman Republic.
726 **214** 100l. brown . . . . . . £160 60·00

1949. European Recovery Plan.
727 **215** 5l. green . . . . 7·00 2·50
728 15l. violet . . . . 19·00 10·00
729 20l. brown . . . . 55·00 11·00

216 Statue of Mazzini

217 V. Alfieri

1949. Honouring Giuseppe Mazzini (founder of "Young Italy").
730 **216** 20l. black . . . . 7·00 1·50

1949. Birth Bicentenary of Vittorio Alfieri (poet).
731 **217** 20l. brown . . . . 6·00 1·50

218 San Giusto Cathedral

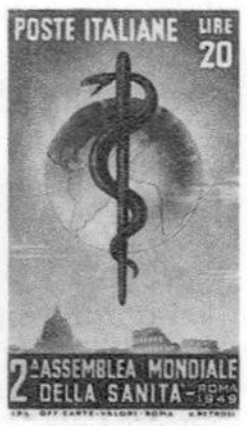
219 Staff of Aesculapius and Globe

1949. 1st Trieste Free Election.
732 **218** 20l. lake . . . . 10·50 10·00

1949. 2nd World Health Congress, Rome.
733 **219** 20l. violet . . . . 30·00 6·25

220 A. Palladio and Vicenza Basilica

221 Lorenzo de Medici

1949. 400th Anniv of Completion of Palladio's Basilica at Vicenza.
734 **220** 20l. violet . . . . 9·00 4·50

1949. 500th Birth Anniv of Lorenzo de Medici "The Magnificent".
735 **221** 20l. blue . . . . 6·75 1·50

222 Galleon and Exhibition Buildings

1949. 13th Levant Fair, Bari.
736 **222** 20l. red . . . . 3·50 1·70

223 Voltaic Pile

224 Count Alessandro Volta

1949. 150th Anniv of Volta's Discovery of the Electric Cell.
737 **223** 20l. red . . . . 6·50 1·50
738 **224** 50l. blue . . . . 75·00 23·00

225 Holy Trinity Bridge, Florence

226 Caius Valerius Catullus

1949. Rebuilding of Holy Trinity Bridge, Florence.
739 **225** 20l. green . . . . 10·00 1·30

1949. Death Bimillenary of Catullus (poet).
740 **226** 20l. blue . . . . 10·00 1·30

227 Domenico Cimarosa

228 Entrance to Exhibition

1949. Birth Bicentenary of Cimarosa (composer).
741 **227** 20l. violet . . . . 8·50 1·00

1950. 28th Milan Fair.
742 **228** 20l. brown . . . . 3·00 1·00

229 Car and Flags

1950. 32nd Int Automobile Exhibition, Turin.
743 **229** 20l. violet . . . . 9·00 1·00

230 Statue of Perseus

231 St. Peter's Basilica

1950. 5th General U.N.E.S.C.O. Conference, Florence.
744 – 20l. green . . . . 7·00 1·20
745 **230** 55l. blue . . . . 45·00 4·75
DESIGN—HORIZ: 20l. Pitti Palace, Florence.

1950. Holy Year.
746 **231** 20l. violet . . . . 6·00 45
747 55l. blue . . . . 45·00 1·70

232 Gaudenzio Ferrari

233 Town Hall, Florence, Statue of Columbus and Wireless Mast

1950. Honouring Gaudenzio Ferrari (painter).
748 **232** 20l. green . . . . 10·00 1·50

1950. International Radio Conf, Florence.
749 **233** 20l. violet . . . . 10·50 5·50
750 55l. blue . . . . £160 95·00

234 L. Muratori

1950. Death Bicentenary of Ludovico Muratori (historian).
751 **234** 20l. brown . . . . 4·75 1·20

235 Guido D'Arezzo

236 Galleon

1950. 9th Death Cent of D'Arezzo (musician).
752 **235** 20l. green . . . . 15·00 2·10

1950. 14th Levant Fair, Bari.
753 **236** 20l. brown . . . . 6·75 1·10

237 Marzotto and Rossi

238 Tobacco Plant and Factory

1950. Pioneers of Wool Industry.
754 **237** 20l. blue . . . . 1·80 65

1950. European Tobacco Conference, Rome.
755 **238** 5l. green and mauve . . . 3·00 1·20
756 – 20l. green and brown . . 5·00 50
757 – 55l. brown and blue . . . 46·00 12·50
DESIGNS: 20l. Plant; 55l. Girl and plant.

239 Seal of Academy

240 A. Righi

1950. Bicentenary of Academy of Fine Arts, Venice.
758 **239** 20l. lt brown and brown . . . 2·20 1·10

1950. Birth Centenary of Augusto Righi (physicist).
759 **240** 20l. black and buff . . . 2·30 1·10

241 Blacksmith

242 First Tuscan Stamp

1950. Provincial Occupations. As T **241**.
760 **241** 50c. blue 20 30
881 – 1l. violet 10 10
762 – 2l. brown 20 15
763 – 5l. black 40 15
764 – 6l. brown 20 15
765 – 10l. green . . . . 3·25 15
766 – 12l. green . . . . 2·00 15
883 – 15l. blue 50 10
768 – 20l. violet . . . . 10·50 15
769 – 25l. brown . . . . 3·50 15
770 – 30l. purple . . . . 1·30 15
771 – 35l. red . . . . 8·50 30
772 – 40l. brown 75 15
773 – 50l. violet . . . . 10·00 15
774 – 55l. blue 50 30
775 – 60l. red . . . . 4·00 30
776 – 65l. green . . . . 1·10 30
777 – 100l. brown . . . . . . 65·00 30
778 – 200l. brown . . . . . . 13·00 1·40
DESIGNS: 1l. Motor mechanic; 2l. Stonemason; 5l. Potter; 6l. Girls embroidering and water-carrying; 10l. Weaver; 12l. Fisherman at tiller; 15l. Boat builder; 20l. Fisherman trawling; 25l. Girl packing oranges; 30l. Girl carrying grapes; 35l. Gathering olives; 40l. Carter and wagon; 50l. Shepherd; 55l. Ploughman; 60l. Ox-cart; 65l. Girl harvester; 100l. Women handling maize; 200l. Woodcutter.

243 Car and Flags

1951. Centenary of First Tuscan Stamp.
779 **242** 20l. red and purple . . . 1·40 85
780 55l. blue and ultramarine 27·00 25·00

1951. 33rd International Motor Show, Turin.
781 **243** 20l. green . . . . 9·00 1·40

244 Peace Hall, Rome

1951. Consecration of Hall of Peace, Rome.
782 **244** 20l. violet . . . . 6·25 1·60

245 Westland W.81 Helicopter over Fair

246 Fair Building

1951. 29th Milan Fair.
783 **245** 20l. brown . . . . 7·50 1·00
784 **246** 55l. blue . . . . 60·00 31·00

247 Allegory

248 Columbus disembarking

1951. 10th International Textile Art and Fashion Exhibition, Turin.
785 **247** 20l. violet . . . . 20·00 2·10

1951. 500th Birth Anniv of Columbus.
786 **248** 20l. green . . . . 15·00 1·80

249 Gymnastics Symbols

250 Montecassino Abbey restored

1951. Int Gymnastic Festival, Florence.
787 **249** 5l. red and brown . . . . 33·00 £120
788 10l. red and green . . . . 33·00 £120
789 15l. red and blue . . . . 33·00 £120

1951. Restoration of Montecassino Abbey.
790 **250** 20l. violet . . . . 4·50 1·40
791 – 55l. blue . . . . 55·00 28·00
DESIGN: 55l. Abbey in ruins, 1944.

251 Perugino

252 Modern Art

1951. 500th Birth Anniv of Perugino (painter).
792 **251** 20l. brown and sepia . . 2·50 1·70

1951. Triennial Art Exhibition, Milan.
793 **252** 20l. black and green . . . 7·75 1·30
794 – 55l. pink and blue . . . . 35·00 26·00
DESIGN—HORIZ: 55l. Jug and symbols.

253 Cyclist and Globe

254 Galleon and Hemispheres

1951. World Cycling Championship.
795 **253** 25l. black . . . . 6·00 2·10

1951. 15th Levant Fair, Bari.
796 **254** 25l. blue . . . . 5·50 1·40

255 "Jorio's Daughter"

1951. Birth Centenary of Francesco Paolo Michetti (painter).
797 **255** 25l. brown . . . . 6·00 2·10

256 T 1 of Sardinia and Arms of Cagliari

1951. Sardinian Postage Stamp Centenary.
798 **256** 10l. black and sepia . . . 1·40 1·60
799 – 25l. green and red . . . . 2·00 1·30
800 – 60l. red and blue . . . . 10·00 10·50
DESIGNS: 25l. 20c. stamp and arms of Genoa; 60l. 40c. stamp and arms of Turin.

257 "Industry and Commerce"

1951. 3rd Industrial and Commercial Census.
801 **257** 10l. green . . . . 1·00 80

258 Census in Ancient Rome

1951. 9th National Census.
802 **258** 25l. black . . . . 2·50 1·10

259 G. Verdi and Roncole Church

260 Mountain Forest

1951. 50th Death Anniv of Giuseppe Verdi (composer).
803 – 10l. green and purple . . 1·40 2·10
804 **259** 25l. brown and chocolate 6·00 2·00
805 – 60l. blue and green . . . 25·00 8·00
DESIGNS: 10l. Verdi, Theatre Royal and Cathedral, Parma; 60l. Verdi, La Scala Opera House and Cathedral, Milan.

1951. Forestry Festival. Inscr "FESTA DEGLI ALBERI".
806 **260** 10l. green and olive . . . 1·50 2·10
807 – 25l. green . . . . 3·75 1·30
DESIGN—HORIZ: 25l. Tree and wooded hills.

261 V. Bellini

262 Royal Palace, Caserta

1952. 150th Birth Anniv of Bellini (composer).
808 **261** 25l. black . . . . 2·50 60

1952. Bicentenary of Construction of Caserta Palace by Vanvitelli.
809 **262** 25l. bistre and green . . . 2·50 80

263

264 Motor-boat Pavilion

1952. 1st Int Sports Stamps Exhibition, Rome.
810 **263** 25l. brown and black . . 85 60

1952. 30th Milan Fair.
811 **264** 60l. blue . . . . 25·00 7·00

265 Leonardo da Vinci

267 Campaniles and First Stamps

1952. 500th Birth Anniv of Leonardo da Vinci.
812 **265** 25l. orange 40 20
813 – 60l. blue . . . . 3·75 3·75
814 **265** 80l. red . . . . 18·00 30
DESIGN—(inscr "LEONARDO DA VINCI 1452–1952"): 60l. "The Virgin of the Rocks".

1952. Modena and Parma Stamp Centenary.
815 **267** 25l. black and brown . . 1·00 65
816 60l. indigo and blue . . . 6·50 6·50

268 Hand, Torch and Globe

269 Lion of St. Mark

1952. Overseas Fair, Naples.
817 **268** 25l. blue . . . . 1·30 65

1952. 26th Biennial Art Exhibition, Venice.
818 **269** 25l. black and cream . . 1·40 60

270 Emblem of Fair

271 San Giusto Cathedral and Flag

1952. 30th Padua Fair.
819 **270** 25l. red and blue . . . . 2·00 65

1952. 4th Trieste Fair.
820 **271** 25l. green, red and brown 1·50 65

272 Caravel and Bari Fair

273 Girolamo Savonarola

1952. 16th Levant Fair, Bari.
821 **272** 25l. green . . . . 1·20 65

1952. 5th Birth Cent of Savonarola (reformer).
822 **273** 25l. violet . . . . 2·75 65

274 Savoia Marchetti S.M.95C over Colosseum

275 Alpine Climbing Equipment

1952. 1st Civil Aeronautics Law Conf, Rome.
823 **274** 60l. blue and ultramarine 12·00 11·50

1952. Alpine Troops National Exhibition.
824 **275** 25l. black 45 40

276 Army, Navy and Air Force Symbols

277 Sailor, Soldier and Airman

1952. Armed Forces Day.
825 **276** 10l. green 25 10
826 **277** 25l. sepia and brown . . 60 10
827 – 60l. black and blue . . . 5·00 1·80
DESIGN—As Type **277**: 60l. Airplane, motor torpedo boat and tank.

278 Cardinal Massaia and Map

279 V. Gemito

1952. Centenary of Mission to Ethiopia.
828 **278** 25l. deep brown & brown 85 1·20

1952. Birth Centenary of Gemito (sculptor).
829 **279** 25l. brown 40 50

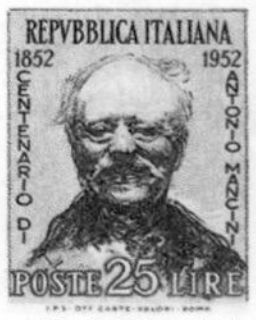
280 A. Mancini

281

1952. Birth Centenary of Mancini (painter).
830 **280** 25l. myrtle 40 45

1952. Centenary of Martyrdom of Belfiore.
831 **281** 25l. blue and black . . . 1·40 45

282 Antonello da Messina

283 Cars Racing

1953. Antonello Exhibition, Messina.
832 **282** 25l. red . . . . 1·20 70

1953. 20th "Mille Miglia" Car Race.
833 **283** 25l. violet 45 60

284 Bee and Medals

285 Arcangelo Corelli

1953. Creation of Orders of Meritorious Labour.
834 **284** 25l. violet 45 45

1953. Birth Tercentenary of Corelli (composer).
835 **285** 25l. brown 50 85

286 Coin of Syracuse

287 St. Clare of Assisi

1953. (a) Size 17 × 21 mm.
887 **286** 1l. black 10 20
888 5l. grey 10 10
889 6l. brown 10 20
890 10l. red 10 10
891 12l. green 10 10
892 13l. purple 10 10
893 15l. grey 10 10
894 20l. brown 10 10
895 25l. violet 30 10
896 30l. brown 15 10
897 35l. red 10 10
898 40l. mauve 60 10
899 50l. green 50 10
900 60l. blue 10 10
901 70l. green 20 10
902 80l. brown 10 10
903 90l. brown 20 10
1008 100l. brown 25 10
905 130l. red and grey . . . 10 20
1009 200l. blue 25 10

(b) Size $22\frac{1}{2} \times 28$ mm.
904 **286** 100l. brown . . . . . . 15·00 10
846 200l. blue . . . . 4·75 60
See also Nos. 1202/19b.

1953. 700th Death Anniv of St. Clare.
847 **287** 25l. red and brown . . . 40 55

288 Mountains and Reservoirs

289 "Agriculture"

1953. Mountains Festival.
848 **288** 25l. green . . . . 1·00 40

1953. International Agricultural Exn, Rome.
849 **289** 25l. brown 70 30
850 60l. blue . . . . 2·75 1·30

290 Rainbow over Atlantic

291 L. Signorelli

1953. 4th Anniv of Atlantic Pact.
851 **290** 25l. turquoise and orange 3·50 20
852 60l. blue and mauve . . . 7·00 2·00

1953. 500th Birth Anniv of Signorelli (painter).
853 **291** 25l. green and brown . . 45 20

292 A. Bassi

293 Capri

1953. 6th Int Microbiological Congress, Rome.
854 **292** 25l. brown and black . . 40 20

1953. Tourist Series.
855 – 10l. brown and sepia . . 35 10
856 – 12l. black and blue . . 35 10
857 – 20l. brown and orange . . 75 10
858 – 25l. green and blue . . 75 10
859 – 35l. brown and buff . . 1·20 20
860 **293** 60l. blue and green . . 1·60 40
DESIGNS—VERT: 10l. Siena; 25l. Cortina d'Ampezzo. HORIZ: 12l. Rapallo; 20l. Gardone; 35l. Taormina.

294 Lateran Palace

295 Television Aerial and Screen

1954. 25th Anniv of Lateran Treaty.
861 **294** 25l. brown and sepia . . 45 20
862 60l. blue and bright blue 1·80 1·40

1954. Introduction of Television in Italy.
863 **295** 25l. violet . . . . 1·30 20
864 60l. turquoise . . . . . . 3·75 1·80

296 "Everyone Must Contribute to the Public Expense"

297 Vertical Flight Trophy

1954. "Encouragement to Taxpayers".
865 **296** 25l. violet . . . . 1·00 10

1954. 1st Experimental Helicopter Mail Flight, Milan–Turin.
866 **297** 25l. green 30 35

298 Golden Eagle and Campanile

299 A. Catalani

1954. 10th Anniv of Resistance Movement.
867 **298** 25l. black and brown . . 25 20

1954. Birth Centenary of Catalani (composer).
868 **299** 25l. green 25 30

300 Marco Polo, Lion of St. Mark, Venice, and Dragon Pillar, Peking

1954. 7th Birth Centenary of Marco Polo.
869 **300** 25l. brown 30 20
870 60l. green . . . . 2·75 2·50

301 Cyclist, Car and Landscape

302 "St. Michael the Archangel" (after Guido Reni)

1954. 60th Anniv of Italian Touring Club.
871 **301** 25l. green and red 30 30

1954. International Police Congress, Rome.
872 **302** 25l. red 15 20
873 60l. blue . . . . 80 1·20

303 "Pinocchio"

304 Amerigo Vespucci

1954. 64th Death Anniv of Carlo Lorenzini (Collodi) (writer).
874 **303** 25l. red 35 30

1954. 5th Birth Cent of Vespucci (explorer).
875 **304** 25l. purple 25 25
876 60l. blue . . . . 1·20 1·50

305 "Madonna" (Perugino)

306 Silvio Pellico

1954. Termination of Marian Year.
877 **305** 25l. brown and buff . . . 20 20
878 – 60l. black and cream . . 85 1·30
DESIGN: 60l. Madonna's head (Michelangelo).

1955. Death Centenary of Pellico (dramatist).
879 **306** 25l. blue and violet . . . 25 20

308 "The Nation Expects a Faithful Declaration of Your Income"

1955. "Encouragement to Taxpayers".
907 **308** 25l. lilac . . . . 1·10 10

309

310 A. Rosmini

1955. 4th World Petroleum Congress.
908 **309** 25l. green 20 20
909 – 60l. red . . . . 60 1·10
DESIGN: 60l. Oil derricks and globe.

1955. Death Cent of Rosmini (theologian).
910 **310** 25l. brown 50 20

311 Girolamo Fracastoro (physician) and Roman Arena, Verona

1955. International Medical Conf, Verona.
915 **311** 25l. brown and black . . 35 20

312 Basilica of St. Francis

1955. Bicentenary of Elevation of Basilica of St. Francis of Assisi to Papal Chapel.
916 **312** 25l. black and cream . . 20 20

313 Scholar and Drawing-board

1955. Centenary of "Montani" Institute, Fermo.
917 **313** 25l. green 20 30

314 "The Harvester" **315** F.A.O. Building, Rome

1955. 50th Anniv of Int Agricultural Institute.
918 **314** 25l. brown and red . . . 15 20

1955. 10th Anniv of F.A.O.
919 **315** 60l. violet and black . . . 60 60

316 G. Matteotti **317** B. Grassi

1955. 70th Birth Anniv of Giacomo Matteotti (politician).
920 **316** 25l. red 55 20

1955. 30th Death Anniv of Grassi (biologist).
921 **317** 25l. green 20 20

318 "St. Stephen giving Alms to the Poor"

1955. 5th Death Cent of Fra Angelico (painter).
922 **318** 10l. black and cream . . 10 30
923 – 25l. blue and cream . . 15 30
DESIGN—HORIZ: 25l. "St. Lawrence giving goods of the Church to the poor".

319 G. Pascoli

1955. Birth Centenary of Pascoli (poet).
924 **319** 25l. black 15 20

320 G. Mazzini **321** "Italia" Ski-jump

1955. Air. 150th Birth Anniv of Mazzini (founder of "Young Italy").
925 **320** 100l. green . . . . 1·40 85

1956. 7th Winter Olympic Games, Cortina d'Ampezzo.
926 **321** 10l. green and orange . . 10 20
927 – 12l. black and yellow . . 10 20
928 – 25l. purple and orange . . 10 20
929 – 60l. blue and orange . . . 95 1·50
DESIGNS: 12l. Snow Stadium; 25l. Ice Stadium; 60l. Skating Arena, Misurina.

1956. Air. Italian President's Visit to U.S.A. and Canada. Surch **1956 Visita del Presidente della Repubblica negli U.S.A. e nel Canada L. 120**.
930 **198** 120l. on 50l. mauve . . . 65 1·60

323 Coach and Steam Train

1956. 50th Anniv of Simplon Tunnel.
931 **323** 25l. green . . . . 3·50 55

324

1956. 10th Anniv of Republic.
932 **324** 10l. grey and blue 15 20
933 25l. carmine and red . . . 20 20
934 60l. light blue and blue 2·10 1·80
935 80l. orange and brown . . 3·25 20

325 Count Avogadro **326**

1956. Death Centenary of Avogadro (physicist).
936 **325** 25l. black 15 20

1956. Europa.
937 **326** 25l. deep green and green 65 10
938 60l. deep blue and blue 6·00 35

327

1956. Int Astronautical Congress, Rome.
939 **327** 25l. blue 15 20

328 The Globe

1956. 1st Anniv of Admission to U.N.
940 **328** 25l. red and green on pink 15 20
941 60l. green and red on green 20 20

329 Savings Bank, Books and Certificates **330** Ovid

1956. 80th Anniv of Post Office Savings Bank.
942 **329** 25l. blue and slate 10 20

1957. Birth Bimillenary of Ovid (poet).
943 **330** 25l. black and olive . . . 10 20

331 St. George (after Donatello) **332** Antonio Canova

1957.
944a **331** 500l. green . . . . . . 1·50 10
945a 1000l. red . . . . 5·00 55

1957. Birth Bicentenary of Canova (sculptor).
946 **332** 25l. brown 10 20
947 – 60l. slate 10 40
948 – 80l. blue 10 20
DESIGNS—VERT: 60l. Hercules and Lica. HORIZ: 80l. Pauline Borghese (bust).

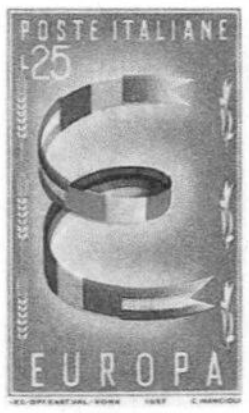

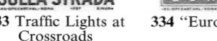

333 Traffic Lights at Crossroads **334** "Europa" Flags

1957. Road Safety Campaign.
949 **333** 25l. red, black and green 15 10

1957. Europa. Flags in national colours.
950 **334** 25l. blue 20 10
951 60l. blue . . . . 1·70 35

335 Giosue Carducci **336** Filippino Lippi (after self-portrait)

1957. 50th Death Anniv of Carducci (poet).
954 **335** 25l. sepia 15 20

1957. 500th Birth Anniv of Filippino Lippi (painter).
955 **336** 25l. brown 10 20

337 Cicero (bust) **338** Garibaldi (after M. Lorusso)

1957. Death Bimillenary of Cicero (statesman).
956 **337** 25l. red 10 20

1957. 150th Birth Anniv of Garibaldi.
957 **338** 15l. grey 10 20
958 – 110l. lilac 15 20
DESIGN—HORIZ: 110l. Statue of Garibaldi on horseback (after Romanelli).

339 St. Domenico Savio and Youths **340** St. Francis of Paola

1957. Death Centenary of St. Domenico Savio.
959 **339** 15l. black and violet . . . 10 20

1957. 450th Death Anniv of St. Francis of Paola.
960 **340** 25l. black 10 20

341 Dams, Peasant and Map of Sardinia **342** Statue of the Holy Virgin and Lourdes Basilica

1958. Inaug of Flumendosa–Mulargia Irrigation Scheme, Sardinia.
961 **341** 25l. turquoise 10 20

1958. Centenary of Apparition of Virgin Mary at Lourdes.
962 **342** 15l. purple 10 15
963 60l. blue 10 20

343 "The Constitution" **344** Exhibition Emblem and Ancient Roman Road

1958. 10th Anniv of Constitution.
964 **343** 25l. green and brown . . 10 10
965 – 60l. sepia and blue . . . 10 10
966 – 110l. sepia and brown . . 10 10
DESIGNS—VERT: 60l. Oak tree with new growth. HORIZ: 110l. Montecitorio Palace, Rome.

1958. Brussels International Exhibition.
967 **344** 60l. yellow and blue . . . 10 20

345 Rodolfo's Attic ("La Boheme") **346** The Prologue ("I Pagliacci")

1958. Birth Centenary of Puccini (operatic composer).
968 **345** 25l. blue 10 20

1958. Birth Centenary of Leoncavallo (operatic composer).
969 **346** 25l. red and indigo . . . 10 20

347 "Ave Maria" (after Segantini) **348** "Fattori in his Studio" (self-portrait)

1958. Birth Centenary of Giovanni Segantini (painter).
970 **347** 110l. green on cream . . 20 20

1958. 50th Death Anniv of Giovanni Fattori (painter).
971 **348** 110l. brown 20 20

349 Federal Palace, Brasilia and Arch of Titus, Rome **349a** "Europa"

1958. Visit of Pres. Gronchi to Brazil.
972 **349** 175l. green 40 70

1958. Europa.
973 **349a** 25l. blue and red 10 10
974 60l. red and blue 20 20

350 Naples ½ grano stamp of 1858 **351** "Winged Horse" (sculpture in Sorrento Cathedral)

1958. 1st Naples Postage Stamps Centenary.
975 **350** 25l. brown 10 10
976 – 60l. brown and sepia . . 10 20
DESIGN: 60l. Naples 1 grano stamp of 1858.

1958. Visit of Shah of Iran.
977 **351** 25l. sepia and lavender . . 10 20
978 60l. blue and pale blue . . 25 50

352 E. Torricelli

353 "Triumphs of Julius Caesar" (after fresco by Mantegna)

1958. 350th Birth Anniv of Evangelista Torricelli (physicist).
979 **352** 25l. red 35 45

1958. 40th Anniv of Victory in World War I.
980 **353** 15l. green 10 10
981 – 25l. slate 10 10
982 – 60l. red 10 25
DESIGNS—HORIZ: 25l. Arms of Trieste, Rome and Trento. VERT: 60l. Memorial bell of Rovereto.

354 Eleonora Duse

355 "Drama"

1958. Birth Centenary of Eleonora Duse (actress).
983 **354** 25l. blue 10 20

1958. 10th Anniv of "Premio Italia" (international contest for radio and television plays).
984 **355** 25l. black, blue and red . . . 10 20
985 – 60l. black and blue . . . 10 20
DESIGN: 60l. "Music" (radio mast and grand piano).

356 Sicily 5gr. stamp of 1859

357 Capitol, Quirinal Square Obelisk and Dome of St. Peter's

1959. 1st Sicilian Postage Stamps Centenary.
986 – 25l. turquoise 10 10
987 **356** 60l. orange 10 20
DESIGN: 25l. Sicily 2gr. stamp of 1859.

1959. 30th Anniv of Lateran Treaty.
988 **357** 25l. blue 10 10

358 N.A.T.O. Emblem and Map

1959. 10th Anniv of N.A.T.O.
989 **358** 25l. blue and yellow . . . 10 20
990 60l. blue and green . . . 10 20

359 Arms of Paris and Rome

360 Olive Branch growing from shattered Tree

1959. Rome-Paris Friendship.
991 **359** 15l. red, brown and blue . . . 10 10
992 25l. red, brown and blue . . . 10 10

1959. Int War Veterans' Assn Convention, Rome.
993 **360** 25l. green 10 10

361 Lord Byron Monument

362 C. Prampolini

1959. Unveiling of Lord Byron Monument, Rome.
994 **361** 15l. green 10 20

1959. Birth Centenary of Camillo Prampolini (politician).
995 **362** 15l. red . . . . 1·60 25

363 Quirinal Square Obelisk, Rome

364 Victor Emmanuel II, Garibaldi, Cavour and Mazzini

1959. Olympic Games Propaganda. Roman Monuments and Ruins. Inscr "ROMA MCMLX".
996 **363** 15l. sepia and orange . . 10 10
997 – 25l. sepia and blue . . . 10 10
998 – 35l. sepia and buff . . . 10 20
999 – 60l. sepia and mauve . . 10 20
1000 – 110l. sepia and yellow 15 10
DESIGNS—VERT: 25l. Tower of City Hall, Quirinal Hill. HORIZ: 35l. Baths of Caracalla; 60l. Arch of Constantine (Colosseum); 110l. Basilica of Massentius.

1959. Centenary of 2nd War of Independence.
1001 **364** 15l. black 10 10
1002 – 25l. red and brown . . . 10 10
1003 – 35l. violet 10 10
1004 – 60l. blue 10 20
1005 – 110l. lake 10 20
DESIGNS—VERT: 25l. Italian camp after the Battle of Magenta (after painting by Fattori); 110l. Battle of Magenta (after painting by Induno). HORIZ: 35l. Battle of San Fermo (after painting by Trezzini); 60l. Battle of Palestro.
The 25l. is also a Red Cross commemorative.

365 Workers' Monument and I.L.O. Building, Geneva

366 Romagna 8b. Stamp of 1859

1959. 40th Anniv of I.L.O.
1006 **365** 25l. violet 10 10
1007 60l. brown 10 20

1959. Romagna Postage Stamps Centenary.
1010 **366** 25l. brown and black . . 10 10
1011 – 60l. green and black . . 10 10
DESIGN: 60l. Romagna 20b. stamp of 1859.

366a "Europa"

367

1959. Europa.
1012 **366a** 25l. green 25 10
1013 60l. blue 25 10

1959. Stamp Day.
1014 **367** 15l. red, black and grey 10 10

368 "The Fire of Borgo" (after Raphael)

369 Garibaldi's Message to Sicilians

1960. World Refugee Year.
1015 **368** 25l. red 10 10
1016 60l. purple 10 20

1960. Cent of Garibaldi's Expedition to Sicily.
1017 **369** 15l. brown 10 10
1018 – 25l. red 10 10
1019 – 60l. blue 10 25
DESIGNS—VERT: 25l. Garibaldi meeting King Victor Emmanuel II near Naples (after Matania). HORIZ: 60l. Embarkation of volunteers at Quarto, near Genoa (after T. van Elven).

370 "The Discus Thrower" (after Miron)

371 Vittorio Bottego (after Ettore Ximenes)

1960. Olympic Games. Inscr as in T **370**.
1020 – 5l. brown 10 10
1021 – 10l. blue and orange . . 10 10
1022 – 15l. blue 10 10
1023 – 25l. sepia and lilac . . . 10 10
1024 **370** 35l. red 10 10
1025 – 60l. sepia and green . . 10 20
1026 – 110l. purple 10 10
1027 – 150l. brown and blue . . 65 1·00
1028 – 200l. green 35 20
DESIGNS—VERT: 5l. Games emblem; 15l. "Starting the Race" (statue); 110l. "Pugilist at rest" (after Apollonius); 200l. "The Apoxiomenos" (after Lisippos). HORIZ: 10l. Olympic Stadium, Rome; 25l. Cycling Stadium, Rome; 60l. Sports Palace, Rome; 150l. Little Sports Palace.

1960. Birth Centenary of Vittorio Bottego (explorer).
1029 **371** 30l. brown 10 20

371a Conference Emblem

1960. Europa.
1030 **371a** 30l. brown and green 20 10
1031 70l. orange and blue . . 20 10

372 Caravaggio

1960. 350th Death Anniv of Caravaggio (painter).
1032 **372** 25l. brown 10 10

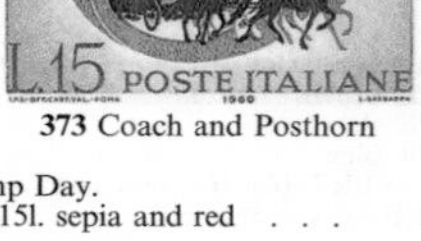

373 Coach and Posthorn

1960. Stamp Day.
1033 **373** 15l. sepia and red . . . 10 10

374 Michelangelo

375 Douglas DC-8 Jetliner crossing Atlantic Ocean

1961. Works of Michelangelo. Frescoes on ceiling of Sistine Chapel. (a) Size 17 × 20½ mm.
1034 – 1l. black 10 20
1035 – 5l. orange 10 10
1036 – 10l. red 10 10
1037 – 15l. purple 10 10
1038 – 20l. green 10 10
1039 – 25l. brown 20 10
1040 – 30l. purple 10 10
1041 – 40l. red 10 10
1042 – 50l. green 15 10
1043 – 55l. brown 10 10
1044 – 70l. blue 15 10
1045 – 85l. green 15 20
1046 – 90l. mauve 20 10
1047 – 100l. violet 30 10
1048 – 115l. blue 15 20
1049 – 150l. brown 65 20
1050 **374** 200l. blue . . . . 1·10 20

(b) Size 22 × 26½ mm.
1051 – 500l. green . . . . 3·50 25
1052 – 1000l. red . . . . 2·40 4·00
DESIGNS: 1, 5, 10, 115, 150l. Ignudo (different versions); 15l. Joel; 20l. Libyan Sibyl; 25l. Isaiah; 30l. Erythraean Sibyl; 40l. Daniel; 50l. Delphic Sibyl; 55l. Cumaean Sibyl; 70l. Zachariah; 85l. Jonah; 90l. Jeremiah; 100l. Ezekiel; 500l. Adam; 1000l. Eve.

1961. Visit of President Gronchi to S. America.
1053 **375** 170l. blue (Argentina) . . 2·30 4·25
1054 185l. green (Uruguay) . . 2·30 5·25
1055 205l. violet (Peru) . . . 8·50 13·00
The countries indicated are shown in deep colours on the map.

376 Pliny the Younger

377 Ippolito Nievo

1961. 19th Birth Cent of Pliny the Younger.
1056 **376** 30l. brown and buff . . 10 20

1961. Birth Centenary of Ippolito Nievo (poet).
1057 **377** 30l. blue and red 10 20

378 St. Paul in Ship (from 15th-century Bible of Borso d'Este)

1961. 19th Cent of St. Paul's Arrival in Rome.
1058 **378** 30l. multicoloured . . . 10 30
1059 70l. multicoloured . . . 15 55

379 Cannon and Gaeta Fortress

1961. Cent of Italian Unification and Independence.
1060 **379** 15l. brown and blue . . 10 20
1061 – 30l. brown and blue . . 10 10
1062 – 40l. brown and blue . . 15 20
1063 – 70l. mauve and brown 20 20
1064 – 115l. blue and brown . . 85 20
1065 – 300l. red, brown & green 4·25 8·00
DESIGNS: 30l. Carignano Palace, Turin; 40l. Montecitorio Palace, Rome; 70l. Vecchio Palace, Florence; 115l. Madama Palace, Rome; 300l. Capitals, "Palace of Work", Int. Exn. of Work, Turin.

380 Doves

381 G. Romagnosi

1961. Europa.
1066 **380** 30l. red 15 10
1067 70l. green 15 20

1961. Birth Bicent of Romagnosi (philosopher).
1068 **381** 30l. green 10 30

382 Imprint of 50c. Provisional Postal Franked Paper of Sardinia, 1819

1961. Stamp Day.
1069 **382** 15l. mauve and black . . 10 10

383 "The Sweet-burning Lamp" from Pascoli's "La Poesia" (after wood-eng by P. Morbiducci)

1962. 50th Death Anniv of G. Pascoli (poet).
1070 **383** 30l. red 10 10
1071 70l. blue 10 30

384 Pacinotti's Dynamo (diagram)

385 St. Catherine (after 15th-century woodcut)

1962. 50th Death Anniv of Antonio Pacinotti (physicist).
1072 **384** 30l. black and red . . . 10 10
1073 70l. black and blue . . . 10 30

1962. 5th Centenary of Canonization of St. Catherine of Siena.
1074 – 30l. violet 10 10
1075 **385** 70l. black and red . . . 10 45
DESIGN: 30l. St. Catherine (after A. Vanni).

386 Camera Lens

1962. 30th Anniv of International Cinematograph Art Fair. Venice.
1076 **386** 30l. black and blue . . . 10 20
1077 – 70l. black and red . . . 10 30
DESIGN: 70l. Lion of St. Mark.

387 Cyclist being paced

1962. World Cycling Championships.
1078 **387** 30l. black and green . . 10 10
1079 – 70l. blue and black . . . 10 10
1080 – 300l. black and red . . . 1·90 6·25
DESIGNS: 70l. Cyclists road-racing; 300l. Cyclists on track.

388 Europa "Tree"

1962. Europa.
1081 **388** 30l. red and carmine . . 30 10
1082 70l. ultramarine and blue 30 25

389 Balzan Medal

390 Campaign Emblem

1962. International Balzan Foundation.
1083 **389** 70l. red and green . . . 25 30

1962. Malaria Eradication.
1084 **390** 30l. violet 10 30
1085 70l. blue 10 40

391 10c. Stamp of 1862 and 30l. Stamp of 1961

392 "The Pentecost" (from "Codex Syriacus")

1962. Stamp Day.
1086 **391** 15l. multicoloured . . . 10 10

1962. Ecumenical Council, Vatican City.
1087 **392** 30l. orange & bl on cream 10 10
1088 70l. blue & orge on cream 10 10

393 Statue of Cavour (statesman)

394 Pico della Mirandola (scholar)

1962. Centenary of Court of Accounts.
1089 **393** 30l. green 10 30

1963. 5th Birth Cent of G. Pico della Mirandola.
1090 **394** 30l. violet 10 10

395 D'Annunzio

1963. Birth Centenary of Gabriele D'Annunzio (author and soldier).
1091 **395** 30l. green 10 30

396 "Sowing" (bas-relief after G. and N. Pisano)

397 Monviso, Italian Alps, Ice-axe and Rope

1963. Freedom from Hunger.
1092 **396** 30l. sepia and red . . . 10 30
1093 – 70l. sepia and blue . . . 15 40
DESIGN: 70l. "Harvesting" (bas-relief after G. and N. Pisano).

1963. Italian Alpine Club Centenary.
1094 **397** 115l. sepia and blue . . 10 30

398 "I.N.A." Lighthouse

1963. 50th Anniv of Italian National Insurance Corporation.
1095 **398** 30l. black and green . . 10 30

399 Posthorn and Globe

1963. Paris Postal Conference Centenary.
1096 **399** 70l. blue and green . . . 10 30

400 Three-dimensional Emblem

1963. Red Cross Centenary.
1097 **400** 30l. red and purple . . . 10 30
1098 70l. red and blue 10 40

401 "World Tourism"

1963. U.N. Tourism Conference, Rome.
1099 **401** 15l. blue and olive . . . 10 30
1100 70l. brown and blue . . 10 30

402 "Co-operation"

403 "Naples"

1963. Europa.
1101 **402** 30l. brown and red . . . 15 10
1102 70l. green and brown . . 15 10

1963. 4th Mediterranean Games, Naples. Inscr "NAPOLI 1963".
1103 **403** 15l. ochre and blue . . . 10 10
1104 – 70l. orange and green . . 10 30
DESIGN: 70l. Greek "Olympic" vase.

404 Mascagni and Costanzi Theatre

405 G. Belli

1963. 150th Birth Anniv of Verdi (1105) and Birth Centenary of Mascagni (1106) (composers).
1105 – 30l. brown and green . . 10 30
1106 **404** 30l. green and brown . . 10 30
DESIGN: No. 1105, Verdi and La Scala Opera House.

1963. Death Centenary of Giuseppe Belli (poet).
1107 **405** 30l. brown 10 30

406 Stamp "Flower"

407 Galileo Galilei

1963. Stamp Day.
1108 **406** 15l. red and blue 10 10

1964. 400th Birth Anniv of Galileo Galilei.
1109 **407** 30l. brown 10 30
1110 70l. black 10 30

408 Nicodemus (from Michelangelo's "Pieta")

410 Carabinieri on Parade

1964. 400th Death Anniv of Michelangelo.
1111 **408** 30l. sepia (postage) . . . 10 30
1112 – 185l. black (air) 10 55
DESIGN: 185l. Michelangelo's "Madonna of Bruges".

1964. 150th Anniv of Carabinieri (military police).
1113 **410** 30l. red and blue 10 10
1114 – 70l. brown 10 30
DESIGN: 70l. "The Charge at Pastrengo (1848)" (De Albertis).

411 G. Bodoni

412 Europa "Flower"

1964. 150th Death Anniv (1963) of Giambattista Bodoni (type-designer and printer).
1115 **411** 30l. red 10 30

1964. Europa.
1116 **412** 30l. purple 15 10
1117 70l. blue 15 10

413 European Buildings

414 Victor Emannuel Monument, Rome

1964. 7th European Municipalities' Assembly.
1118 **413** 30l. brown and green . . 10 10
1119 70l. brown and blue . . 10 10
1120 500l. red . . . . 40 1·70

1964. War Veterans' Pilgrimage to Rome.
1121 **414** 30l. brown 10 10
1122 70l. blue 10 10

415 G. da Verrazzano and Verrazano Narrows Bridge

1964. Opening of Verrazano Narrows Bridge, New York.
1123 **415** 30l. black and brown (postage) 10 10
1124 130l. black and green (air) 10 30
This American bridge is designated "Verrazano" with one "z".

416 Italian Stamps

417 Prisoners of War

1964. Stamp Day.
1125 **416** 15l. brown and bistre . . 10 10

1965. 20th Anniv of Resistance.
1126 **417** 10l. black 10 10
1127 – 15l. black, red and green 10 10
1128 – 30l. purple 10 15
1129 – 70l. blue 10 15
1130 – 115l. red 10 15
1131 – 130l. brown, green & red 10 15
DESIGNS—VERT: 15l. Servicemen and casualty ("Liberation Army"); 70l. Alpine soldiers ("Resistance in the mountains"). HORIZ: 30l. Gaunt hands and arms on swastika ("Political and Racial Persecution"); 115l. Patriots with banners ("Resistance in the Towns"); 130l. Ruined building and torn flags ("Martyred Cities").

418 I.T.U. Emblem, Meucci and Marconi

1965. I.T.U. Centenary.
1132 **418** 70l. red and green . . . 10 30

419 "Flying Dutchman" Dinghies

1965. World Sailing Championships, Alassio and Naples.
1133 **419** 30l. black and red . . . 10 10
1134 – 70l. black and blue . . . 10 30
1135 – 500l. black and blue . . 20 70
DESIGNS—VERT: 70l. "5.5 S.1" class yachts. HORIZ: 500l. "Lightning" dinghies.

420 Mont Blanc and Tunnel

421 A. Tassoni and Episode from his "Secchia Rapita"

1965. Opening of Mont Blanc Road Tunnel.
1136 **420** 30l. black 10 30

1965. 400th Birth Anniv of Alessandro Tassoni (poet).
1137 **421** 40l. multicoloured . . . 10 10

422 Europa "Sprig"

1965. Europa.
1138 **422** 40l. green and orange . . 15 10
1139 90l. green and blue . . . 15 10

423 "Hell" (Codex, Vatican Library)

1965. 700th Birth Anniv of Dante.
1140 **423** 40l. multicoloured . . . 10 10
1141 – 90l. multicoloured . . . 10 10
1142 – 130l. multicoloured . . . 10 20
1143 – 500l. green 20 70
DESIGNS—VERT: 90l. "Purgatory" (codex, Marciana Library, Venice); 500l. Head of Dante (bronze, Naples Museum). HORIZ: 130l. "Paradise" (codex, British Museum).

424 House and Savings-bank

425 Douglas DC-6B Airliner passing Control-tower

1965. Savings Day.
1144 **424** 40l. multicoloured . . . 10 10

1965. Night Airmail Service.
1145 **425** 40l. red and blue 10 10
1146 – 90l. multicoloured . . . 10 30
DESIGN: 90l. Sud Aviation Caravelle jetliner within airmail envelope "border".

426 Map of "Highway to the Sun"

427 Two-man Bobsleigh

1965. Stamp Day.
1147 **426** 20l. multicoloured . . . 10 10

1966. World Bobsleigh Championships, Cortina d'Ampezzo.
1148 **427** 40l. red, blue and grey 10 10
1149 – 90l. violet and blue . . . 10 30
DESIGN: 90l. Four-man bobsleigh.

428 Skier carrying Torch

429 B. Croce

1966. University Winter Games, Turin.
1150 **428** 40l. black and red . . . 10 10
1151 – 90l. violet and red . . . 10 10
1152 – 500l. brown and red . . 20 45
DESIGNS—VERT: 90l. Ice skating; 500l. Ice hockey.

1966. Birth Centenary of Benedetto Croce (philosopher).
1153 **429** 40l. sepia 10 15

430 Arms of Cities of Venezia

1966. Centenary of Union of Venezia and Italy.
1154 **430** 40l. multicoloured . . . 10 15

431 Pine, Palatine Hill, Rome

432 "Visit Italy"

1966. "Trees and Flowers". Multicoloured.
1155 20l. Type **431** 10 10
1156 25l. Apples 10 10
1157 40l. Carnations 10 10
1158 50l. Irises 10 10
1241 55l. Cypresses (26 × 35½ mm) 10 10
1159 90l. Anthemis (Golden Marguerite) 10 10
1160 170l. Olive tree, Villa Adriana, Tivoli 10 10
1242 180l. Broom (26 × 35½ mm) 10 10

1966. Tourist Propaganda.
1161 **432** 20l. multicoloured . . . 10 15

433 Capital "I"

434 Battle Scene

1966. 20th Anniv of Republic.
1162 **433** 40l. multicoloured . . . 10 15
1163 90l. multicoloured . . . 10 20

1966. Centenary of Battle of Bezzecca.
1164 **434** 90l. olive 10 15

435 "Singing Angels" (from copper panel on altar of St. Antony's Basilica, Padua)

1966. 5th Death Centenary of Donatello.
1165 **435** 40l. multicoloured . . . 10 15

436 Europa "Ship"

437 "Madonna in Maesta" (after Giotto)

1966. Europa.
1166 **436** 40l. violet 15 15
1167 90l. blue 15 15

1966. Giotto's 700th Birth Anniv.
1168 **437** 40l. multicoloured . . . 10 10

438 Filzi, Battisti, Chiesa and Sauro

1966. 50th Death Annivs of World War I Heroes.
1169 **438** 40l. green and slate . . . 10 10

439 Postal Emblem

440 Compass and Globe

1966. Stamp Day.
1170 **439** 20l. multicoloured . . . 10 10

1967. Centenary of Italian Geographical Society.
1171 **440** 40l. blue and black . . . 10 10

441 Toscanini

1967. Birth Centenary of Arturo Toscanini (orchestral conductor).
1172 **441** 40l. buff and blue . . . 10 10

442 Campidoglio, Rome

1967. 10th Anniv of Rome Treaties.
1173 **442** 40l. brown and black . . 10 15
1174 90l. purple and black . . 10 20

443 Cogwheels

444 Brown Bear (Abruzzo Park)

1967. Europa.
1175 **443** 40l. purple and pink . . 10 10
1176 90l. blue and cream . . 10 20

1967. Italian National Parks. Multicoloured.
1177 20l. Ibex (Gran Paradiso Park) (vert) 10 10
1178 40l. Type **444** 10 10
1179 90l. Red deer stag (Stelvio Park) 10 10
1180 170l. Tree (Circeo Park) (vert) 10 20

445 Monteverdi

1967. 400th Death Anniv of Claudio Monteverdi (composer).
1181 **445** 40l. brown and chestnut 10 10

446 Racing Cyclists

1967. 50th Tour of Italy Cycle Race. Designs showing cyclists.
1182 **446** 40l. multicoloured . . . 10 10
1183 – 90l. multicoloured . . . 10 10
1184 – 500l. multicoloured . . . 45 80

447 Pirandello and Stage

1967. Birth Centenary of Luigi Pirandello (dramatist).
1185 **447** 40l. multicoloured . . . 10 10

448 Stylized Mask

1967. Two Worlds Festival, Spoleto.
1186 **448** 20l. black and green . . 10 10
1187 40l. black and red . . . 10 10

449 Coded Addresses

1967. Introduction of Postal Codes.
1188 **449** 20l. black, blue & yellow 10 10
1189 25l. black, red and yellow 10 10
1190 40l. black, purple & yell 10 10
1191 50l. black, green & yellow 10 10

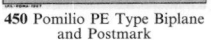

450 Pomilio PE Type Biplane and Postmark

451 St. Ivo's Church, Rome

1967. 50th Anniv of 1st Airmail Stamp.
1192 **450** 40l. black and blue . . . 10 10

1967. 300th Death Anniv of Francesco Borromini (architect).
1193 **451** 90l. multicoloured . . . 10 10

452 U. Giordano and Music from "Andrea Chenier"

453 "The Oath of Pontida" (from painting by Adolfo Cao)

1967. Birth Centenary of Umberto Giordano (composer).
1194 **452** 20l. brown and black . . 10 10

1967. 800th Anniv of Oath of Pontida.
1195 **453** 20l. brown 10 10

454 I.T.Y. Emblem

455 Lions Emblem

1967. International Tourist Year.
1196 **454** 20l. black, blue and yellow 10 10
1197 50l. black, blue & orange 10 10

1967. 50th Anniv of Lions International.
1198 **455** 50l. multicoloured . . . 10 10

456 Sentry

457 E. Fermi (scientist) and Reactor

1967. 50th Anniv of Stand on the Piave.
1199 **456** 50l. multicoloured . . . 10 10

1967. 25th Anniv of 1st Nuclear Chain Reaction.
1200 **457** 50l. black and brown . . 10 10

458 Stamp and Dove

1967. Stamp Day.
1201 **458** 25l. multicoloured . . . 10 10

1968. As Nos. 887, etc (1952), size 16 × 20 mm.
1202 **286** 1l. black 10 30
1203 5l. slate 10 10
1204 6l. brown 10 30
1205 10l. red 10 10
1206 15l. violet 10 10
1207 20l. sepia 10 10
1208 25l. violet 10 10
1209 30l. brown 10 10
1210 40l. purple 10 10
1211 50l. olive 10 10
1212 55l. violet 10 10
1213 60l. blue 10 10
1214 70l. green 10 10
1215 80l. brown 10 10
1215a 90l. brown 10 10
1216 100l. brown 10 10
1216a 120l. blue and green . . 10 10
1216b 125l. purple and brown 10 20
1217 130l. red and grey . . . 10 10
1217a 150l. violet 10 10
1217b 170l. green and brown 15 10
1218 180l. purple and grey 10 10
1218a 200l. blue 10 10
1219 300l. green 10 10
1219a 350l. orange, red & yell 20 20
1219b 400l. red 15 10

459 Scouts around Campfire

1968. Italian Boy Scouts.
1220 **459** 50l. multicoloured . . . 15 10

460 Europa "Key"

1968. Europa.
1221 **460** 50l. green and pink . . . 15 10
1222 90l. brown and blue . . 15 20

461 "Tending the Sick"

462 Boito and "Mephistopheles"

1968. 400th Birth Anniv of Luigi Gonzaga (St. Aloysius).
1223 **461** 25l. violet and brown . . 10 30

1968. 50th Death Anniv of Arrigo Boito (composer and librettist).
1224 **462** 50l. multicoloured . . . 10 10

463 F. Baracca and "Aerial Combat" (abstract by G. Balla)

464 Giambattista Vico (300th Birth Anniv)

1968. 500th Death Anniv of Francesco Baracca (airman of World War I).
1225 **463** 25l. multicoloured . . . 10 10

1968. Italian Philosophers' Birth Annivs.
1226 **464** 50l. blue 10 10
1227 – 50l. black 10 20
DESIGN: No. 1227, Tommaso Campanella (400th birth anniv).

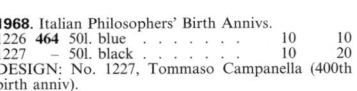

465 Cycle Wheel and Stadium

467 Rossini

466 "St. Mark's Square, Venice" (Canaletto)

1968. World Road Cycling Championships.
1228 **465** 25l. blue, pink and brown 10 10
1229 – 90l. indigo, red and blue 10 20
DESIGN: 90l. Cyclists and Imola Castle.

1968. Death Bicentenary of Canaletto (painter).
1230 **466** 50l. multicoloured . . . 10 20

1968. Death Centenary of Gioacchino Rossini (composer).
1231 **467** 50l. red 10 20

468 Mobilization

469 "Conti Correnti Postali"

1968. 50th Anniv of Victory in World War I. Multicoloured.
1232 20l. Type **468** 10 10
1233 25l. Trench warfare 10 10
1234 40l. Naval forces 10 10
1235 50l. Air Force 10 10
1236 90l. Battle of Vittorio Veneto 10 10
1237 180l. Tomb of Unknown Soldier 10 15

1968. 50th Anniv of Postal Cheque Service.
1238 **469** 50l. multicoloured . . . 10 10

470 Tracking Equipment and Buildings

471 "Postal Development"

1968. Space Telecommunications Centre, Fucino.
1239 **470** 50l. multicoloured . . . 10 10

1968. Stamp Day.
1240 **471** 25l. red and yellow . . . 10 10

472 Commemorative Medal

473 Colonnade

1969. Centenary of State Audit Department.
1243 **472** 50l. black and pink . . . 10 10

1969. Europa.
1244 **473** 50l. multicoloured . . . 15 10
1245 90l. multicoloured . . . 15 20

474 Machiavelli

475 I.L.O. Emblem

1969. 500th Birth Anniv of Niccolo Machiavelli (statesman).
1246 **474** 50l. multicoloured . . . 10 10

1969. 50th Anniv of I.L.O.
1247 **475** 50l. black and green . . 10 10
1248 90l. black and red . . . 10 10

476 Postal Emblem

1969. 50th Anniv of Italian Philatelic Federation.
1249 **476** 50l. multicoloured . . . 10 30

477 Sondrio-Tirano Mailcoach of 1903

1969. Stamp Day.
1250 **477** 25l. blue 10 10

478 Skiing

1970. World Skiing Championships, Val Gardena. Multicoloured.
1251 50l. Type **478** 10 20
1252 90l. Dolomites 10 10

479 "Galatea" (detail of fresco by Raphael)

1970. 450th Death Anniv of Raphael. Mult.
1253 20l. Type **479** 10 10
1254 50l. "Madonna of the Goldfinch" 10 10

480 Symbols of Flight

1970. 50th Anniv of Rome–Tokyo Flight by A. Ferrarin.
1255 **480** 50l. multicoloured . . . 10 10
1256 90l. multicoloured . . . 10 10

481 "Flaming Sun"

482 Erasmo da Narni (from statue by Donatello)

1970. Europa.
1257 **481** 50l. yellow and red . . . 15 10
1258 90l. yellow and green . . 15 20

1970. 600th Birth Anniv of Erasmo da Narni "Il Gattamelata" (condottiere).
1259 **482** 50l. green 10 10

483 Running

1970. World University Games, Turin. Mult.
1260 20l. Type **483** 10 10
1261 180l. Swimming 10 20

484 Dr. Montessori and children

1970. Birth Centenary of Dr. Maria Montessori (educationist).
1262 **484** 50l. multicoloured . . . 10 10

485 Map and Cavour's Declaration

1970. Centenary of Union of Rome and Papal States with Italy.
1263 **485** 50l. multicoloured . . . 10 10

486 Loggia of Campanile, St. Mark's Square, Venice

1970. 400th Death Anniv of Jacopo Tatti, "Il Sansovino" (architect).
1264 **486** 50l. brown 10 10

487 "Garibaldi at Dijon" (engraving)

1970. Centenary of Garibaldi's Participation in Franco-Prussian War.
1265 **487** 20l. grey and blue . . . 10 10
1266 50l. purple and blue . . 10 20

488 U.N. Emblem within Tree **489** Rotary Emblem

1970. 25th Anniv of United Nations.
1267 **488** 25l. green, black & brown 10 20
1268 90l. yellow, black and blue 10 20

1970. 65th Anniv of Rotary International.
1269 **489** 25l. ultramarine, yell & bl 10 10
1270 90l. ultramarine, yell & bl 10 20

490 Telephone Dial and "Network" **491** Urban Complex and Tree

1970. Completion of Telephone Trunk-dialling System.
1271 **490** 25l. green and red . . . 10 10
1272 90l. blue and red 10 10

1970. Nature Conservation Year.
1273 **491** 20l. red and green . . . 10 10
1274 25l. grey and green . . . 10 10

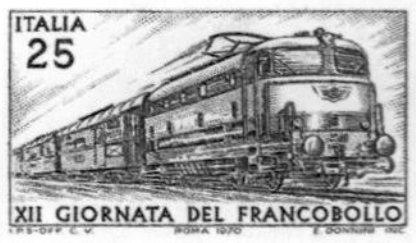

492 Electric Locomotive "Tartaruga" **493** "The Adoration" (F. Lippi)

1970. Stamp Day.
1275 **492** 25l. black 10 20

1970. Christmas. Multicoloured.
1276 25l. Type **493** (postage) . . 10 10
1277 150l. "The Adoration of the Magi" (Gentile da Fabriano) (44 × 35 mm) (air) 10 30

494 Saverio Mercadante

1970. Death Centenary of Saverio Mercadante (composer).
1278 **494** 25l. violet and grey . . . 10 10

495 "Mercury" (part of Cellini's "Perseus with the Head of Medusa") **496** Bramante's "Little Temple", St. Peter's Montorio, Rome

1971. 400th Death Anniv of Benvenuto Cellini (goldsmith and sculptor).
1279 **495** 50l. blue 10 10

1971.
1280 **496** 50l. black and brown . . 10 10

497 Adenauer, Schuman and De Gasperi

1971. 20th Anniv of European Coal and Steel Community.
1281 **497** 50l. brown, black & grn 10 20
1282 90l. brown, black and red 10 10

498 Europa Chain **499** Mazzini

1971. Europa.
1283 **498** 50l. red 15 10
1284 90l. purple 15 10

1971. 25th Anniv of Republic.
1285 **499** 50l. multicoloured . . . 10 30
1286 90l. multicoloured . . . 10 10

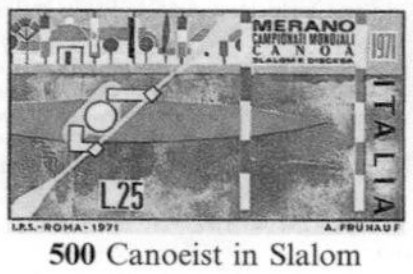

500 Canoeist in Slalom

1971. World Canoeing Slalom and Free Descent Championships, Merano. Multicoloured.
1287 25l. Type **500** 10 10
1288 90l. Canoeist making free descent 10 10

501 Three Sports

1971. Youth Games.
1289 **501** 20l. black, green & brn 10 10
1290 – 50l. black, violet & orge 10 10
DESIGN: 50l. Four other sports.

502 Alitalia Emblem

1971. 25th Anniv of Alitalia State Airline. Multicoloured.
1291 50l. Type **502** 10 10
1292 90l. Emblem and Globe . . 10 10
1293 150l. Tailplane of Boeing 747 . . . . 10 20

503 Grazia Deledda **504** Boy in "Savings" Barrel

1971. Birth Cent of Grazia Deledda (writer).
1294 **503** 50l. black and brown . . 10 10

1971. Postal Savings Bank.
1295 **504** 25l. multicoloured . . . 10 20
1296 50l. multicoloured . . . 10 10

1971. Air. As No. 911 but smaller, 20 × 36 mm.
1297 **204** 100l. green 15 25

505 U.N.I.C.E.F. Emblem and Paper Dolls

1971. 25th Anniv of U.N.I.C.E.F. Multicoloured.
1301 25l. Type **505** 10 10
1302 90l. Children acclaiming U.N.I.C.E.F. emblem . . 10 20

506 Liner "Tirrenia"

1971. Stamp Day.
1303 **506** 25l. green 10 20

507 "The Nativity"

1971. Christmas. Miniatures from "Matilda's Evangelarium", Nonantola Abbey, Modena. Multicoloured.
1304 25l. Type **507** 10 20
1305 90l. "The Adoration of the Magi" 10 10

508 G. Verga and Sicilian Cart

1972. 50th Death Anniv of Giovanni Verga (writer).
1306 **508** 25l. multicoloured . . . 10 10
1307 50l. multicoloured . . . 10 10

509 G. Mazzini **510** Stylized Flags

1972. Death Cent of Giuseppe Mazzini (statesman).
1308 **509** 25l. green and black . . 10 20
1309 90l. grey and black . . . 10 10
1310 150l. red and black . . . 10 10

1972. 50th International Fair, Milan.
1311 **510** 25l. green and black . . 10 20
1312 – 50l. red and black . . . 10 10
1313 – 90l. blue and black . . . 10 10
DESIGNS: 50l. "Windows, stand and pavilions" (abstract); 90l. Abstract general view of Fair.

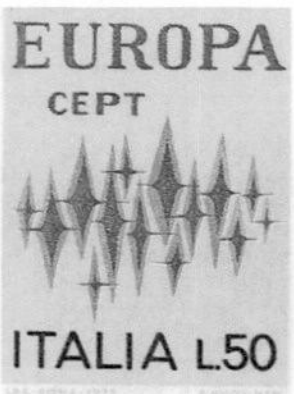

511 "Communications" **512** Alpine Soldier

1972. Europa.
1314 **511** 50l. multicoloured . . . 15 30
1315 90l. multicoloured . . . 15 30

1972. Centenary of Alpine Corps. Multicoloured.
1316 25l. Type **512** 10 10
1317 50l. Soldier's hat 10 30
1318 90l. Soldier and mountains 10 10

513 Brenta Mountains

1972. Centenary of Tridentine Alpinists Society. Multicoloured.
1319 25l. Type **513** 10 30
1320 50l. Alpinist 10 10
1321 180l. Mt. Crozzon 10 30

514 Diagram of Conference Hall

1972. 60th Interparliamentary Union Conference, Rome.
1322 **514** 50l. multicoloured . . . 10 10
1323 90l. multicoloured . . . 10 10

515 "St. Peter Damiani" (miniature, after G. di Paolo) **516** "The Three Graces" (Canova)

1972. 900th Death Anniv of St. Peter Damiani.
1324 **515** 50l. multicoloured . . . 10 10

1972. 150th Death Anniv of Antonio Canova (sculptor).
1325 **516** 50l. green 10 10

517 Initial and First Verse (Foligno edition)

1972. 500th Anniv of "The Divine Comedy". Multicoloured.
1326 50l. Type **517** 10 10
1327 90l. Initial and first verse (Mantua edition) (vert) . . 10 10
1328 180l. Initial and first verse ("Jesino" edition) 10 20

518 "Angel"

1972. Christmas. Multicoloured.
1329 20l. Type **518** 10 10
1330 25l. "Holy Child in Crib" (horiz) 10 10
1331 150l. "Angel" (looking to left) 10 30

519 Postal Coach

1972. Stamp Day.
1332 **519** 25l. red 10 30

520 L. B. Alberti (from bronze by M. de Pasti, Louvre)

521 L. Perosi

1972. 500th Death Anniv of Leon B. Alberti (writer and savant).
1333 **520** 50l. blue and yellow . . 10 30

1972. Birth Centenary of Lorenzo Perosi (composer and priest).
1334 **521** 50l. brown and yellow 10 10
1335 90l. black and green . . 10 10

522 Don Orione

523 Oceanic Survey

1972. Birth Centenary of Don Orione (child-welfare pioneer).
1336 **522** 50l. blue and turquoise 10 10
1337 90l. green and yellow . . 10 10

1973. Centenary of Military Marine Institute of Hydrography.
1338 **523** 50l. multicoloured . . . 10 10

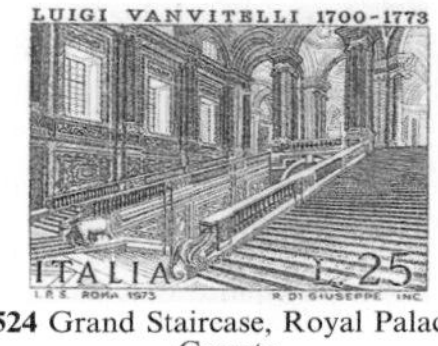

524 Grand Staircase, Royal Palace, Caserta

1973. Death Bicentenary of Luigi Vanvitelli (architect).
1339 **524** 25l. green 10 30

525 Schiavoni Shore

1973. "Save Venice" Campaign. Multicoloured.
1340 20l. Type **525** 10 10
1341 25l. "The Tetrarchs" (sculpture) (vert) 10 10
1342 50l. "The Triumph of Venice" (V. Carpaccio) 10 10
1343 90l. Bronze horses, St. Mark's Basilica (vert) 10 10
1344 300l. Piazzetta S. Marco . . 20 45

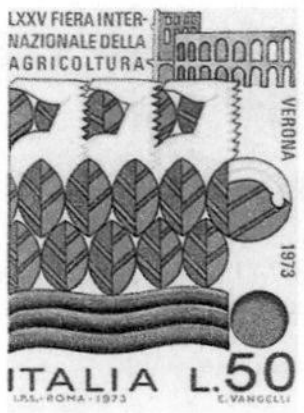

526 Fair Theme

527 Title-page of "Diverse Figure"

1973. 75th Int Agricultural Fair, Verona.
1345 **526** 50l. multicoloured . . . 10 10

1973. 300th Death Anniv of Salvator Rosa (painter and poet).
1346 **527** 25l. black and orange . . 10 10

528 Formation of Fiat PAN Acrobatic Jet Aircraft

1973. 50th Anniv of Military Aviation. Mult.
1349 20l. Type **528** (postage) . . 10 10
1350 25l. Formation of Savoia Marchetti S-55X flying boats 10 10
1351 50l. Fiat G-91Y jet fighters on patrol 10 10
1352 90l. Fiat CR-32 biplanes performing aerobatics . . 10 30
1353 180l. Caproni Campini N-1 jet airplane 10 30
1354 150l. Lockheed F-104S Starfighter over Aeronautical Academy, Pozzuoli (air) 10 30

529 Football and Pitch

530 A. Manzoni (after F. Hayez)

1973. 75th Anniv of Italian Football Association. Multicoloured.
1355 25l. Type **529** 10 30
1356 90l. Players in goalmouth 35 40

1973. Death Centenary of Alessandro Manzoni (writer and politician).
1357 **530** 25l. brown and black . . 10 30

531 Palladio's "Rotunda", Vicenza

532 Spring and Cogwheels

1973. Andrea Palladio Commemoration.
1358 **531** 90l. multicoloured . . . 10 10

1973. 50th Anniv of Italian State Supplies Office.
1359 **532** 50l. multicoloured . . . 10 10

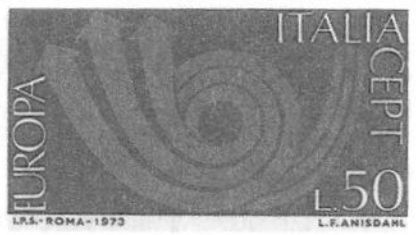

533 Europa "Posthorn"

1973. Europa.
1360 **533** 50l. gold, lilac and yellow 15 10
1361 90l. gold, green & yellow 15 10

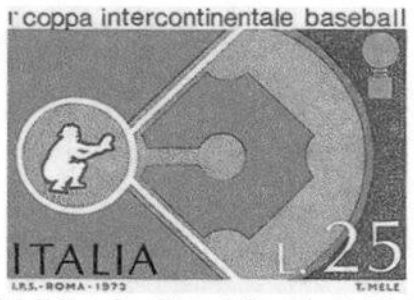

534 "Catcher" and Baseball Field

1973. 1st Intercontinental Baseball Cup. Mult.
1362 25l. Type **534** 10 30
1363 90l. "Striker" and baseball field 10 10

535 Carnival Setting

536 "Argenta Episode"

1973. Viareggio Carnival.
1364 **535** 25l. multicoloured . . . 10 10

1973. 50th Death Anniv of Don Giovanni Minzoni (military chaplain).
1365 **536** 50l. multicoloured . . . 10 10

537 G. Salvemini

538 Farnese Palace, Caprarola

1973. Birth Centenary of Gaetano Salvemini (political historian).
1366 **537** 50l. multicoloured . . . 10 10

1973. 400th Birth Anniv of "Vignola" (Jacopa Barozzi—architect).
1367 **538** 90l. purple and yellow 10 10

539 "St. John the Baptist"

540 Leaning Tower of Pisa

1973. 400th Birth Anniv of Caravaggio (painter).
1368 **539** 25l. black and yellow . . 10 10

1973. Tourism.
1369 **540** 50l. multicoloured . . . 10 10

541 Botticelli

542 Immacolatella Fountain, Naples

1973. Italian Painters (1st series).
1370 **541** 50l. brown and red . . . 10 10
1371 – 50l. blue and brown . . 10 10
1372 – 50l. green and emerald 10 10
1373 – 50l. black and red . . . 10 10
1374 – 50l. brown and blue . . 10 10
PAINTERS: No. 1371, Piranesi; No. 1372, Veronese; No. 1373, Verrocchio; No. 1374, Tiepolo.
See also Nos. 1392/6, 1456/61, 1495/9 and 1518/22.

1973. Italian Fountains (1st series). Mult.
1375 25l. Type **542** 10 20
1376 25l. Trevi Fountain, Rome 10 20
1377 25l. Pretoria Fountain, Palermo 10 20
See also Nos. 1418/20, 1453/5, 1503/5, 1529/31, 1570/2 and 1618/20.

543 "Angels"

544 Map and Emblems

1973. Christmas. Sculptures by A. di Duccio.
1378 **543** 20l. black and green . . 10 10
1379 – 25l. black and blue . . . 10 10
1380 – 150l. black and yellow 10 30
DESIGNS: 25l. "Virgin and Child"; 150l. "Angels" (different).

1973. 50th Anniv of Italian Rotary.
1381 **544** 50l. blue, green and red 10 10

545 Sud Aviation Super Caravelle 12

546 Military Medal for Valour

1973. Stamp Day.
1382 **545** 25l. blue 10 30

1973. 150th Anniv of Holders of the Gold Medal for Military Valour Organisation.
1383 **546** 50l. multicoloured . . . 10 10

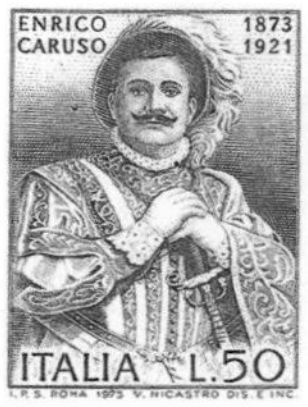

547 Caruso as Duke of Mantua in Verdi's "Rigoletto"

548 "Christ crowning King Roger" (Martorana Church, Palermo)

1973. Birth Centenary of Enrico Caruso (operatic tenor).
1384 **547** 50l. red 10 20

1974. Norman Art in Sicily. Mosaics.
1385 **548** 20l. blue and yellow . . 10 20
1386 – 50l. red and green . . . 10 10
DESIGN: 50l. "King William offering Church to the Virgin Mary" (Monreale Cathedral).

549 Pres. L. Einaudi

550 G. Marconi in Headphones

1974. Birth Centenary of Luigi Einaudi (President 1948–55).
1387 **549** 50l. green 10 10

1974. Birth Centenary of Guglielmo Marconi (radio pioneer).
1388 **550** 50l. brown and green . . 10 10
1389 – 90l. multicoloured . . . 10 30
DESIGN: 90l. Marconi and world map.

551 "David" (Bernini)

552 Guards from Lombardy-Venetia (1848), Sardinian Marines (1815) and Tebro Battalion (1849)

1974. Europa. Sculptures. Multicoloured.
1390 50l. Type **551** 15 10
1391 90l. "Spirit of Victory" (Michelangelo) 15 20

1974. Italian Painters (2nd series). As T **541**.
1392 50l. blue and green 10 15
1393 50l. brown and blue 10 15
1394 50l. black and red 10 15
1395 50l. brown and yellow . . . 10 15
1396 50l. blue and brown 10 15
PORTRAITS: No. 1392, Borromini; No. 1393, Carriera; No. 1394, Giambellino (Giovanni Bellini); No. 1395, Mantegna; No. 1396, Raphael.

1974. Bicentenary of Italian Excise Guards. Uniforms. Multicoloured.
1397 40l. Sardinian chasseurs, 1774 and 1795, and Royal Fusilier of 1817 . . . . . 10 20
1398 50l. Type **552** 10 10
1399 90l. Lieutenant (1866), Sergeant-major of Marines (1892) and guard (1880) 10 20
1400 180l. Helicopter pilot, naval and alpine guards of 1974 10 20

553 Feather Headdress

1974. 50th Anniv of National Bersaglieri Association. Multicoloured.
1401 40l. Type **553** 10 10
1402 50l. Bersaglieri emblem on rosette 10 10

554 Running

1974. European Athletics Championships, Rome. Multicoloured.
1403 40l. Type **554** 10 10
1404 50l. Pole vaulting 10 10

555 Francesco Petrarch

1974. 600th Death Anniv of Francesco Petrarch (poet and scholar).
1405 **555** 40l. multicoloured . . . 10 20
1406 – 50l. blue, yellow & brown 10 20
DESIGN: 50l. Petrarch at work in his study.

556 Portofino

1974. Tourist Publicity (1st series). Mult.
1407 40l. Type **556** 10 20
1408 40l. Gradara 10 20
See also Nos. 1442/4, 1473/5, 1513/14, 1515/17, 1543/5, 1596/9, 1642/5, 1722/5, 1762/5, 1806/9, 1845/8, 1877/80, 1917/20, 1963/6, 1992/5, 2031/4, 2088/91, 2115/18, 2165/8, 2212/15, 2248/51, 2315/16, 2365/8, 2425/8, 2486/9, 2550/3, 2661/4 and 2752/5.

557 Tommaseo's Statue, Sebenico

558 Giacomo Puccini

1974. Death Centenary of Niccolo Tommaseo (writer).
1409 **557** 50l. green and pink . . . 10 10

1974. 50th Death Anniv of Giacomo Puccini (composer).
1410 **558** 40l. multicoloured . . . 10 10

559 Cover Engraving of Ariosto's "Orlando Furioso"

560 Commemoration Tablet (Quotation from Varrone's "Menippean Satire")

1974. 500th Birth Anniv of Ludovico Ariosto (poet).
1411 **559** 50l. blue and red 10 10

1974. 2000th Death Anniv of Marco Varrone (Varrone Reatino) (author).
1412 **560** 50l. lake, red and yellow 10 10

561 "The Month of October" (detail from 15th-century mural)

1974. 14th International Wine Congress.
1413 **561** 50l. multicoloured . . . 10 10

562 "U.P.U." and Emblem

1974. Centenary of Universal Postal Union. Mult.
1414 50l. Type **562** 10 10
1415 90l. "U.P.U." emblem and letters 10 10

563 "The Triumph of St. Thomas Aquinas" (detail—F. Traini)

564 Detail of Bas-relief, Ara Pacis

1974. 700th Death Anniv of St. Thomas Aquinas.
1416 **563** 50l. multicoloured . . . 10 10

1974. Centenary of Italian Order of Advocates.
1417 **564** 50l. black, green & brown 10 10

1974. Italian Fountains (2nd series). As T **542** Multicoloured.
1418 40l. Oceanus Fountain, Florence 10 20
1419 40l. Neptune Fountain, Bologna 10 20
1420 40l. Maggiore Fountain, Perugia 10 20

565 "The Adoration" (Presepe di Greccio)

1974. Christmas.
1421 **565** 40l. multicoloured . . . 10 10

566 Pulcinella

567 "God admonishing Adam" (Jacopo della Quercia (sculptor) (1374–1438))

1974. Children's Comic Characters. Mult.
1422 40l. Type **566** 10 10
1423 50l. Clowns 10 10
1424 90l. Pantaloon from Bisognosi 10 10

1974. Italian Artists' Anniversaries (1st series).
1425 **567** 90l. violet 10 20
1426 – 90l. multicoloured . . . 10 20
DESIGN: No. 1426, Uffizi Gallery, Florence (Giorgio Vasari (architect and painter) (1511–1574)).
See also Nos. 1445/6, 1480/2, 1523/4, 1564/5, 1593/4, 1699/1700, 1731/2, 1774/5, 1824/5, 1885/6, 1949/50 and 1987.

568 "Angel with Tablet"

569 "Pitti Madonna"

1975. Holy Year. Multicoloured.
1427 40l. Type **568** 10 10
1428 50l. Angel with column . . 10 10
1429 90l. Bridge of the Holy Angels, Rome (49 × 40 mm) 10 20
1430 150l. Angel with crown of thorns 10 10
1431 180l. Angel with cross . . . 10 20

1975. 500th Birth Anniv of Michelangelo.
1432 **569** 40l. green 10 10
1433 – 50l. brown 10 10
1434 – 90l. red 10 20
DESIGNS: 50l. Sculptured niche, Vatican Palace; 90l. Detail from fresco "Flood of the Universe" (Sistine Chapel).

570 "The Four Days of Naples" (M. Mazzacurati)

571 "The Flagellation of Christ" (Caravaggio)

1975. 30th Anniv of Italian Resistance Movement. Resistance Monuments. Multicoloured.
1435 70l. Type **570** 10 20
1436 100l. "Martyrs of the Ardeatine Caves" (F. Coccia) 10 10
1437 150l. "The Resistance Fighters of Cuneo" (U. Mastroianni) 10 20

1975. Europa. Paintings. Multicoloured.
1438 100l. Type **571** 20 10
1439 150l. "The Appearance of the Angel to Agar and Ishmael in the Desert" (Tiepolo) 20 10

572 Globe and Emblems

1975. International Women's Year.
1440 **572** 70l. multicoloured . . . 10 10

573 "San Marco III" (satellite) and "Santa Rita" (marine launching pad)

574 Cover Engraving from Palestrina's "Primo Libro delle Messe"

1975. Italian Space Project.
1441 **573** 70l. multicoloured . . . 10 10

1975. Tourist Publicity (2nd series). As T **556**. Multicoloured.
1442 150l. Cefalu 10 20
1443 150l. Isola Bella 10 20
1444 150l. Montecatini Terme . . 10 20

1975. Italian Artists' Annivs (2nd series). As T **567**. Multicoloured.
1445 90l. "Flora" (Guido Reni (1575–1642)) 10 20
1446 90l. "Artist and Model" (Armando Spadini (1883–1925)) 10 20

1975. 450th Birth Anniv of Giovanni Pierluigi da Palestrina (composer).
1447 **574** 100l. purple and brown 10 20

575 Boat in Harbour

1975. Italian Emigration.
1448 **575** 70l. multicoloured . . . 10 20

576 Notoriat Emblem

1975. Centenary of Unification of Italian Laws.
1449 **576** 100l. mauve, stone & blue 10 10

577 Railway Steam Locomotive Driving-wheels

1975. 21st International Railway Congress, Bologna.
1450 **577** 70l. multicoloured . . . 10 10

578 "D'Acquisto's Sacrifice" (Vittorio Pisani)

1975. 32nd Death Anniv of Salvo d'Acquisto (carabiniere who sacrificed himself to save 22 hostages).
1451 **578** 100l. multicoloured . . . 10 10

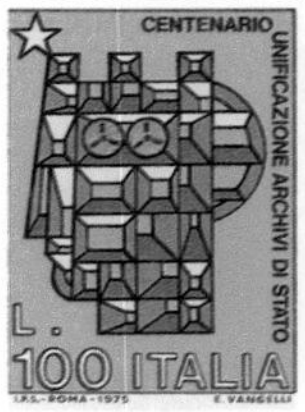

579 Symbolised Head representing Files

581 "Annunciation to the Shepherds"

1975. Centenary of State Archives Unification.
1452 **579** 100l. multicoloured . . . 10 10

1975. Italian Fountains (3rd series). As T **542**. Multicoloured.
1453 70l. Rosello Fountain, Sassari 10 20
1454 70l. 99 Channel Fountain, L'Aquila 10 20
1455 70l. Piazza Fountain, Milan 10 20

1975. Italian Composers. As T **541**.
1456 100l. blue, pink and red . . 10 10
1457 100l. blue, green & deep green 10 10
1458 100l. green, brown & dp brn 10 10
1459 100l. brown, red and lake 10 10
1460 100l. purple, grey and green 10 10
1461 100l. black, lt yellow & yellow 10 10
DESIGNS: No. 1456, Ferruccio Busoni; 1457, Alessandro Scarlatti; 1458, Francesco Cilea; 1459, Antonio Vivaldi; 1460, Franco Alfa; No. 1461, Gaspare Spontini.

1975. Christmas. Alatri Cathedral Carvings. Multicoloured.
1462 70l. Type **581** 10 20
1463 100l. "The Nativity" 10 10
1464 150l. "Annunciation to the Kings" 10 20

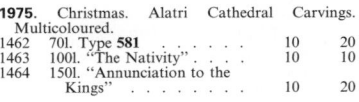

582 "Children on Horseback"

1975. Stamp Day. Children's Stories. Mult.
1465 70l. Type **582** 10 10
1466 100l. "The Magic Orchard" (vert) 10 10
1467 150l. "Church Procession" 10 20

583 "Boccaccio" (from fresco by A. del Castagno)

1975. 600th Death Anniv of Giovanni Boccaccio. Multicoloured.
1468 100l. Type **583** 10 10
1469 150l. Cover engraving from Boccaccio's "Fiammetta" 10 20

584 Entrance to State Advocate's Office

585 "Italia 1976" Emblem

1976. Centenary of State Advocate's Office.
1470 **584** 150l. multicoloured . . . 10 10

1976. "Italia 76" International Stamp Exhibition, Milan (1st issue).
1471 **585** 150l. red, green and black 10 20
1472 – 180l. multicoloured . . . 10 20
DESIGN: 180l. Exhibition Hall, Milan.
See also Nos. 1487/91.

1976. Tourist Publicity (3rd series). As T **556**. Multicoloured.
1473 150l. Fenis Castle, Aosta . . 10 20
1474 150l. Forio Ischia 10 20
1475 150l. Itria Valley 10 20

586 Majolica Plate

587 Republican Flags

1976. Europa. Italian Crafts. Multicoloured.
1476 150l. Type **586** 20 10
1477 180l. Vase in form of woman's head 20 20

1976. 30th Anniv of Republic. Multicoloured.
1478 100l. Type **587** 10 10
1479 150l. Statesmen 10 10

588 "Fortitude" (Giacomo Serpotta) (1656–1732)

1976. Italian Artists' Annivs (3rd series).
1480 **588** 150l. blue 10 10
1481 – 150l. multicoloured . . . 10 20
1482 – 150l. black and red . . . 10 10
DESIGNS: No. 1481, "Woman at Table" (Umberto Boccioni (1882–1916)); 1482, "Gunner's Letter from the Front" (Filippo Tommaso Marinetti (1876–1944)).

589 "The Dragon"

1976. 450th Death Anniv of Vittore Carpaccio (painter).
1483 **589** 150l. red 15 20
1484 – 150l. red 15 20
DESIGN: No. 1484, "St. George".
Nos. 1483/4 form Carpaccio's "St. George and the Dragon".

590 "Flora" (Titian)

1976. 400th Death Anniv of Titian.
1485 **590** 150l. red 10 20

591 St. Francis (13th-century fresco)

592 "Cursus Publicus" Post Cart

1976. 750th Death Anniv of St. Francis of Assisi.
1486 **591** 150l. brown & lt brown 10 10

1976. "Italia 76" International Stamp Exhibition, Milan (2nd issue).
1487 **592** 70l. black, grey and blue 10 20
1488 – 100l. black, grey & yellow 10 10
1489 – 150l. black, grey & brown 10 20
1490 – 200l. multicoloured . . . 10 10
1491 – 400l. multicoloured . . . 15 40

DESIGNS: 100l. Emblem of Royal Sardinian Posts; 150l. 19th-century "Lion's head" letterbox; 200l. Early cancelling machine; 400l. Modern letter-coding machine.

593 Girl with "Protective Umbrella" and Animals

1976. Stamp Day. Nature Protection. Multicoloured.
1492 40l. Type **593** 10 10
1493 100l. "Protective scarf" . . 10 10
1494 150l. Doctor with bandaged tree 10 10

1976. Italian Painters (3rd series). As T **541**.
1495 170l. green, yellow and red 10 10
1496 170l. black, turquoise & green 10 10
1497 170l. black, purple and mauve 10 10
1498 170l. brown, lavender & violet 10 10
1499 170l. black and brown . . . 10 10
DESIGNS: No. 1495, Carlo Dolci; 1496, Lorenzo Ghiberti (sculptor); 1497, Domenico Ghirlandaio; 1498, Giovanni Piazzetta; 1499, "Sassoferrato" (Giovanni Salvi).

594 "The Visit" (S. Lega)

1976. 150th Birth Anniv of Silvestro Lega (painter).
1500 **594** 170l. multicoloured . . . 10 10

595 "Adoration of the Magi" (Bartolo di Fredi)

596 Net of Serpents obscuring the Sun

1976. Christmas. Multicoloured.
1501 70l. Type **595** 10 20
1502 120l. "The Nativity" (Taddao Gaddi) 10 20

1976. Italian Fountains (4th series). As T **542** Multicoloured.
1503 170l. Antique Fountain, Gallipoli 10 20
1504 170l. Erbe Madonna Fountain, Verona 10 20
1505 170l. Fountain of Palazzo Doria, Gerona 10 20

1977. Campaign against Drug Abuse. Mult.
1506 120l. Type **596** 10 10
1507 170l. "Addict" and poppy 10 10

597 Igniting Explosives

1977. 300th Birth Anniv of Pietro Micca (national hero).
1508 **597** 170l. multicoloured . . . 10 10

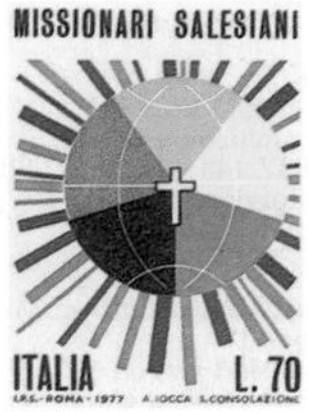

598 "Globe" and Cross

1977. Salesian Missionaries. Multicoloured.
1509 70l. Type **598** 10 20
1510 120l. St. John Bosco and "United people" 10 20

599 Article 53 of the Italian Constitution

1977. "Encouragement to Taxpayers".
1511 **599** 120l. black, brn & stone 10 10
1512 170l. black, olive & green 10 10

1977. Europa. As T **556** but with C.E.P.T. emblem. Multicoloured.
1513 170l. Mount Etna 25 20
1514 200l. Castel del Monte . . . 25 20

1977. Tourist Publicity (4th series). As T **556**. Multicoloured.
1515 170l. Canossa Castle 10 20
1516 170l. Castellana Grotto . . 10 20
1517 170l. Fermo 10 20

1977. Famous Italians. As T **541**.
1518 70l. brown, green & dp green 10 20
1519 70l. black, blue and green 10 20
1520 70l. brown, yellow & lt brown 10 20
1521 70l. blue, pink and red . . . 10 20
1522 70l. black, brown & dp brown 10 20
DESIGNS: No. 1518, Filippo Brunelleschi (architect); 1519, Pietro Aretino (satirist); 1520, Carlo Goldoni (dramatist); 1521, Luigi Cherubini (composer); 1522, Edoardo Bassini (surgeon).

1977. Italian Artists' Anniversaries (4th series). As T **567** Multicoloured.
1523 170l. "Winter" (G. Arcimboldi (c. 1527–93)) 10 10
1524 170l. "Justice" (Andrea Delitio (15th century)) . . 10 20

601 Paddle-steamer "Ferdinando Primo"

1977. Italian Ship-building (1st series). Multicoloured.
1525 170l. Type **601** 15 30
1526 170l. Sail corvette "Carracciolo" 15 30
1527 170l. Liner "Saturnia" . . . 15 30
1528 170l. Hydrofoil missile boat "Sparviero" 15 30
See also Nos. 1552/5, 1621/4 and 1691/4.

1977. Italian Fountains (5th series). As T **542**. Multicoloured.
1529 120l. Pacassi Fountain, Gorizia 10 20
1530 120l. Fraterna Fountain, Isernia 10 20
1531 120l. Palma Fountain, Palmi 10 20

602 Handball

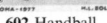

604 Quintino Sella and 1863 1l. Stamps

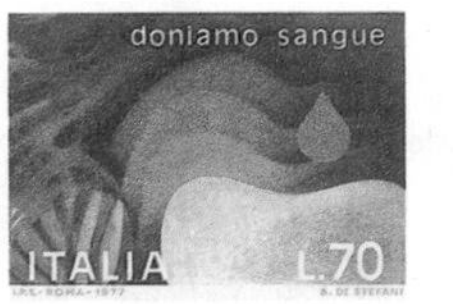

603 "Pulse"

1977. Stamp Day. "Leisure Time". Multicoloured.
1532 120l. Type **602** 10 10
1533 120l. Catching butterflies . . 10 10
1534 120l. Kites 10 10

1977. "Give Blood". Multicoloured.
1535 70l. Type **603** 10 20
1536 120l. "Transfusion" 10 10

1977. 150th Birth Anniv of Quintino Sella (statesman).
1537 **604** 170l. green and brown 10 10

605 Dina Galli

607 La Scala Opera House

606 "Adoration of the Shepherds" (P. Testa)

1977. Birth Centenary of Dina Galli (actress).
1538 **605** 170l. multicoloured . . . 10 10

1977. Christmas.
1539 **606** 70l. black and green . . 10 20
1540 – 120l. black and green . . 10 20
DESIGN: 120l. "The Adoration of the Shepherds" (J. Caraglio).

1978. Bicentenary of La Scala Opera House.
1541 170l. Type **607** 15 20
1542 200l. Theatre interior . . . 20 20

1978. Tourist Publicity (5th series). As T **556**. Multicoloured.
1543 70l. Gubbio 10 30
1544 200l. Udine 10 20
1545 600l. Paestum 35 40

608 Dusky Grouper

1978. Environmental Protection. Mediterranean Fauna. Multicoloured.
1546 170l. Type **608** 25 20
1547 170l. Leathery turtle 25 20
1548 170l. Mediterranean monk seal 25 20
1549 170l. Audouin's gull 25 20

609 Maschio Angioino Castle, Naples

1978. Europa. Multicoloured.
1550 170l. Type **609** 20 20
1551 200l. Pantheon, Rome . . . 30 20

1978. Italian Ship-building (2nd series). As T **601**. Multicoloured.
1552 170l. Brigantine "Fortuna" 30 30
1553 170l. Cruiser "Benedetto Brin" 30 30
1554 170l. Frigate "Lupo" . . . 30 30
1555 170l. Container ship "Africa" 30 30

610 Matilde Serao (writer)

611 First and Last Paragraphs of Constitution

1978. Famous Italians.
1556 **610** 170l. black and red . . . 15 20
1557 – 170l. brown and blue . . 15 20
1558 – 170l. blue and pale blue 15 20
1559 – 170l. black and green . . 15 20
1560 – 170l. brown and green 15 20
1561 – 170l. blue and red . . . 15 20

DESIGNS: No. 1557, Vittorino da Feltre (scientist); No. 1558, Victor Emmanuel II; No. 1559, Pope Pius IX; No. 1560, Marcello Malpighi (biologist); No. 1561, Antonio Meucci (telephone pioneer).
See also Nos. 1600/4.

1978. 30th Anniv of Constitution.
1562 **611** 170l. multicoloured . . . 15 20

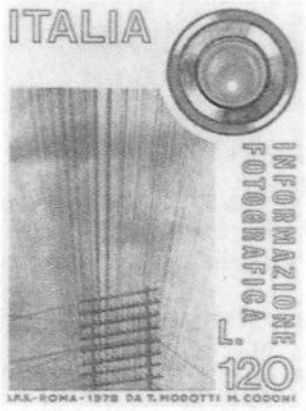

612 Telephone Wires and Lens

1978. Photographic Information.
1563 **612** 120l. grey, blue and green 10 20

1978. Italian Artists' Annivs (5th series). As T **567**. Multicoloured.
1564 170l. "The Ivy" (Tranquillo Cremona, 1837–78) . . . 25 20
1565 520l. "The Cook" (Bernardo Strozzi, 1581–1644) . . . 70 90

613 The Holy Shroud of Turin

1978. 400th Anniv of Translation of the Holy Shroud from Savoy to Turin.
1566 **613** 220l. yellow, black & red 20 20

614 Volleyball Players

615 Detail from "St. Peter distributing Ananias's Silver"

1978. World Volleyball Championships.
1567 **614** 80l. black, red and blue 15 20
1568 – 120l. black, blue & orge 15 20
DESIGN: 120l. Players with ball.

1978. 550th Death Anniv of Tommaso Guidi (Masaccio).
1569 **615** 170l. blue 10 10

1978. Italian Fountains (6th series). As T **542**. Multicoloured.
1570 120l. Neptune Fountain, Trento 10 20
1571 120l. Fountain of Fortune, Fano 10 20
1572 120l. Cavallina Fountain, Genzano di Lucania . . . 10 20

616 "Madonna and Child" (Giorgione)

617 "Flowers"

1978. Christmas.
1573 **616** 80l. red and brown . . . 10 20
1574 – 120l. multicoloured . . . 10 20
DESIGN—HORIZ (48 × 27 mm): 120l. "Adoration of the Magi" (Giorgione).

1978. Stamp Day. United Europe. Mult.
1575 120l. Type **617** 10 20
1576 120l. Flags and ribbon . . . 10 20
1577 120l. Figures raising globe inscribed "E" 10 20

618

619 State Polygraphic Institute

1978.
1578 **618** 1500l. multicoloured . . 35 10
1579 2000l. multicoloured . . 45 10
1580 3000l. multicoloured . . 1·20 10
1581 4000l. multicoloured . . 1·50 20
1582 5000l. multicoloured . . 2·10 25
1583 10000l. multicoloured . . 3·50 1·20
1584 20000l. multicoloured . . 7·50 6·00

1979. 50th Anniv of State Polygraphic Institute. Multicoloured.
1588 170l. Type **619** 20 20
1589 220l. Printing press 10 15

620 "St. Francis washing the Feet of a Leper" (Maestro di Francesco Bardi)

1979. Leprosy Relief.
1590 **620** 80l. multicoloured . . . 10 15

621 Cyclist carrying Bicycle

622 Albert Einstein

1979. World Cyclo-cross Championships.
1591 **621** 170l. multicoloured . . . 10 15
1592 220l. multicoloured . . . 15 15

1979. Italian Artists' Annivs (6th series). As T **567**. Multicoloured.
1593 170l. "Annunciation" (Antonella da Messina c. 1430–79) . . . 20 15
1594 520l. "Field with Haystack" (Ardengo Soffici 1879–1964) . . . . 75 1·10

1979. Birth Centenary of Albert Einstein (physicist).
1595 **622** 120l. purple, grey & bl 10 15

1979. Tourist Publicity (6th series). As T **556**. Multicoloured.
1596 70l. Asiago 10 30
1597 90l. Castelsardo, Sardinia 10 20
1598 170l. Orvieto 15 15
1599 220l. Scilla 20 15

1979. Famous Italians. As T **610**.
1600 170l. brown, blue and black 10 15
1601 170l. green, yellow and violet 10 15
1602 170l. blue and pink 10 15
1603 170l. brown and ochre . . . 10 15
1604 170l. mauve, brown and green 10 15
DESIGNS: No. 1600, Carlo Maderno (architect); No. 1601, Lazzaro Spallanzani (biologist); No. 1602, Ugo Foscolo (author); No. 1603, Massimo Bontempelli (writer); No. 1604, Francesco Severi (mathematician).

623 Morse Telegraph Apparatus

1979. Europa. Multicoloured.
1605 170l. Type **623** 30 15
1606 220l. Carrier pigeon with message tube 45 15

624 Flags of Member States forming "E"

1979. First Direct Elections to European Parliament.
1607 **624** 170l. multicoloured . . . 15 15
1608 220l. multicoloured . . . 20 15

625 Head of Aeneas (bas-relief, Ara Pacis, Rome)

626 Ball in Basket (poster)

1979. 70th World Rotary Congress, Rome.
1609 **625** 220l. multicoloured . . . 15 15

1979. 21st European Basketball Championships.
1610 **626** 80l. multicoloured . . . 10 15
1611 – 120l. lake, black & yellow 15 15
DESIGN: 120l. Two players.

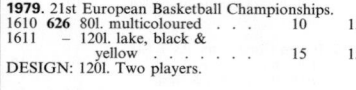

627 "Doctor examining Patient with Stomach Ailment" (woodcut from Giovanni da Cuba's "Hortus Sanitatus")

629 Ottorino Respighi and Appian Way, Rome

628 Emblem, Ribbon "3" and Milan Cathedral

1979. Prevention of Digestive Illnesses.
1612 **627** 120l. multicoloured . . . 10 15

1979. Third World Machine Tool Exhibition, Milan.
1613 **628** 170l. multicoloured . . . 15 15
1614 220l. multicoloured . . . 20 15

1979. Birth Centenary of Ottorino Respighi (composer).
1615 **629** 120l. multicoloured . . . 10 15

630 Woman with Telephone and Morse Key

1979. 3rd World Telecommunications Exhibition, Geneva.
1616 **630** 170l. black and red . . . 10 15
1617 – 220l. grey and green . . 15 15
DESIGN: 220l. Woman with early telephone and communications satellite.

1979. Italian Fountains (7th series). As T **542**. Multicoloured.
1618 120l. Melograno Fountain, Issogne 15 15
1619 120l. Bollente Fountain, Acqui Terme 15 15
1620 120l. Grand Fountain, Viterbo 15 15

1979. Italian Ship-building (3rd series). As T **601**. Multicoloured.
1621 170l. Full-rigged ship "Cosmos" 25 15
1622 170l. Cruiser "Dandolo" . . 25 15
1623 170l. Ferry "Deledda" . . . 25 15
1624 170l. Submarine "Carlo Fecia di Cossato" 25 15

631 Sir Rowland Hill and Penny Black

1979. Death Centenary of Sir Rowland Hill.
1625 **631** 220l. multicoloured . . . 20 15

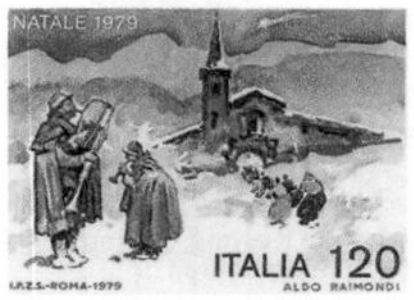

632 Christmas Landscape

1979. Christmas.
1626 **632** 120l. multicoloured . . . 10 15

633 Children under Umbrella (Group IIB, Varapodio School)

1979. Stamp Day. International Year of the Child. Drawings by Schoolchildren. Multicoloured.
1627 70l. Children of different races holding hands (L. Carra) (horiz) 10 15
1628 120l. Type **633** 10 15
1629 150l. Children with balloons (V. Fedon) (horiz) 10 15

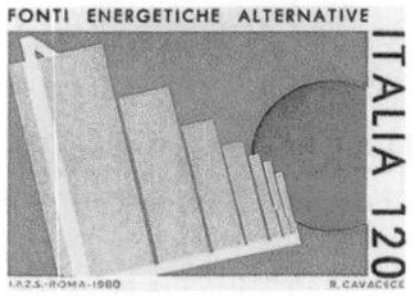

634 Solar Energy (alternative sources)

1980. Energy Conservation. Multicoloured.
1630 120l. Type **634** 15 15
1631 170l. Oil well (reduction of consumption) 15 15

635 "St. Benedict" (detail, fresco by Sodoma in Monastery of Monteoliveto Maggiore)

636 Royal Palace, Naples

1980. 1500th Birth Anniv of St. Benedict of Nursia (founder of Benedictine Order).
1632 **635** 220l. blue 15 15

1980. "Europa 80" International Stamp Exhibition, Naples.
1633 **636** 220l. multicoloured . . . 15 15

637 Antonio Pigafetta (navigator) and "Vitoria"

638 St. Catherine (reliquary bust)

1980. Europa. Multicoloured.
1634 170l. Type **637** 35 15
1635 220l. Antonio lo Surdo (geophysicist) 50 15

1980. 600th Death Anniv of St. Catherine of Siena.
1636 **638** 170l. multicoloured . . . 15 15

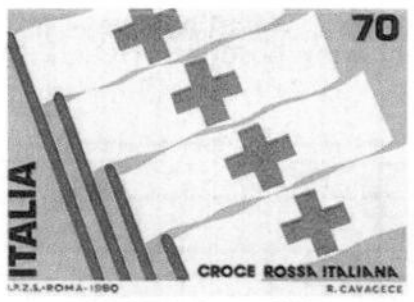

639 Red Cross Flags

1980. 1st International Exhibition of Red Cross Stamps in Italy.
1637 **639** 70l. multicoloured . . . 15 15
1638 80l. multicoloured . . . 15 15

640 Philae Temples

1980. Italian Work for the World (1st series). Preservation of Philae Temples, Egypt. Multicoloured.
1639 220l. Type **640** 15 15
1640 220l. Right hand view of temples 15 15
Nos. 1639/40 were issued together se-tenant, forming a composite design.
See also Nos. 1720/1, 1758/9, 1780/1, 1830/1, 1865/6 and 1937/40.

641 Footballer

1980. European Football Championship, Italy.
1641 **641** 80l. multicoloured . . . 1·10 95

1980. Tourist Publicity (7th series). As T **556**. Multicoloured.
1642 80l. Erice 10 30
1643 150l. Ravello 15 15
1644 200l. Roseto degli Abruzzi 20 30
1645 670l. Salsomaggiore Terme 45 90

642 "Cosimo I with his Artists" (Vasari)

1980. "Florence and Tuscany of the Medicis in 16th Century Europe" Exhibition. Multicoloured.
1646 170l. Type **642** (ceiling medallion, Palazzo Vecchio, Florence) . . . 15 15
1647 170l. Armillary sphere . . . 15 15

643 Fonte Avellana Monastery

1980. Millenary of Fonte Avellana Monastery.
1648 **643** 200l. dp green, grn & brn 20 15

644 Castel Sant' Angelo, Rome

645 Filippo Mazzei

1980. Castles. (a) Size 22 × 27 mm.
1649 **644** 5l. blue and red 20 10
1650 – 10l. brown and ochre 20 10
1651 – 20l. brown and blue . . 20 10
1652 – 30l. orange and blue . . 20 10
1653 – 40l. brown and blue . . 20 10
1654 – 50l. multicoloured . . . 20 10
1655 – 60l. green and mauve 20 15
1656 – 70l. multicoloured . . . 10 10
1657 – 80l. multicoloured . . . 10 10
1658 – 90l. multicoloured . . . 20 15
1659 – 100l. multicoloured . . 20 10
1660 – 120l. blue and pink . . 20 10
1661 – 150l. violet and brown 20 10
1662 – 170l. black and yellow 20 15
1663 – 180l. blue and pink . . 55 80
1664 – 200l. multicoloured . . 20 10
1665 – 250l. multicoloured . . 25 10
1666a – 300l. multicoloured . . 30 10
1667 – 350l. brown, blue & grn 30 10
1667a – 380l. multicoloured . . 30 10
1668 – 400l. blue, green & brn 35 10
1669 – 450l. multicoloured . . 40 10
1670 – 500l. blue, brown & grn 45 10
1670a – 550l. multicoloured . . 40 10
1671 – 600l. black and green 55 10
1671a – 650l. multicoloured . . 45 10
1672 – 700l. multicoloured . . 65 10
1673 – 750l. brown, green & bl 65 10
1674 – 800l. brown, grn & mve 75 15
1675 – 850l. multicoloured . . 80 15
1676 – 900l. multicoloured . . 80 15
1677 – 1000l. multicoloured . . 85 15
1678 – 1400l. brown, blue & vio . . . . 1·10 15

(b) Size 16 × 21 mm.
1679 – 30l. mauve 20 15
1680b – 50l. blue 25 15
1680c – 100l. brown 15 15
1681 – 120l. brown 25 15
1682 – 170l. violet 40 40
1683 – 200l. violet and blue . . . 3·00 5·50
1684 – 300l. light green and green 55 65
1685 – 400l. brown and green . . 85 1·10
1686a – 450l. green 25 80
1687 – 500l. blue . . . . 45 1·10
1687a – 600l. green 60 80
1688 – 650l. mauve 50 80
1689 – 750l. violet 60 95
1690 – 800l. red 85 95

DESIGNS: 10l. Sforzesco Castle, Milan; 20l. Castel del Monte, Andria; 30l. (1652), L'Aquila Castle; 30l. (1679), 100l. (1680c), Santa Severa Castle; 40l. Ursino Castle, Catania; 50l. (1654), Rocca di Calascio, L'Aquila; 50l. (1680b), Scilla; 60l. Norman Tower, San Mauro; 70l. Aragonese Castle, Reggio Calabria; 80l. Sabbionara, Avio; 90l. Isola Capo Rizzuto; 100l. (1659), Aragonese Castle, Ischia; 120l. (1660), Estense Castle, Ferrara; 120l. (1681), Lombardia Enna; 150l. Miramare, Trieste; 170l. (1662), Ostia; 170l. (1682), 650l. (1688), Serralunga d'Alba; 180l. Castel Gavone, Finale Ligure; 200l. (1664), Cerro al Volturno; 200l. (1683), Svevo Angioina Fortress, Lucera; 250l. Rocca di Mondavio, Pesaro; 300l. (1666a), Norman Castle, Svevo, Bari; 300l. (1684), 500l. (1687), Norman Castle, Melfi; 350l. Mussomeli; 380l. Rocca di Vignola, Modena; 400l. (1668), Emperor's Castle, Prato; 400l. (1685), 750l. (1689), Venafro; 450l. (1669), Bosa; 450l. (1686a) Piobbico Castle, Pesaro; 500l. (1670), Rovereto; 550l. Rocca Sinibalda; 600l. Scaligero Castle, Sirmione; 650l. (1671a), Montecchio; 700l. Ivrea; 750l. (1673), Rocca di Urbisaglia; 800l. Rocca Maggiore, Assisi; 850l. Castello di Arechi, Salerno; 900l. Castello di Saint-Pierre, Aosta; 1000l. Montagnana, Padua; 1400l. Caldoresco Castle, Vasto.

1980. Italian Ship-building (4th series). As T **601**. Multicoloured.
1691 200l. Corvette "Gabbiano" 65 50
1692 200l. Destroyer "Audace" 65 50
1693 200l. Barque "Italia" . . . 65 50
1694 200l. Pipe-layer "Castoro Sei" 65 50

1980. 250th Birth Anniv of Filippo Mazzei (writer and American revolutionary).
1695 **645** 320l. multicoloured . . . 25 15

646 Villa Foscari Malcontenta, Venice

1980. Italian Villas (1st series). Multicoloured.
1696 80l. Type **646** 20 30
1697 150l. Barbaro Maser, Treviso 25 15
1698 170l. Godi Valmarana, Vicenza 35 45
See also Nos. 1737/9, 1770/2, 1811/14, 1853/6, 1893/6 and 1943/7.

1980. Italian Artists Anniversaries (7th series). As T **567**. Multicoloured.
1699 520l. "Saint Barbara" (Jacopo Palma, the Elder (1480–1528)) 40 55
1700 520l. "Apollo and Daphne" (Gian Lorenzo Bernini (1598–1680)) 40 55

647 "Nativity" (Federico Brandani)

1980. Christmas.
1701 **647** 120l. green and brown 10 15

648 "My Town" (Treviso)

1980. Stamp Day. Paintings by Schoolchildren entitled "My Town". Multicoloured.
1702 70l. Type **648** 10 15
1703 120l. Sansepolcro 10 15
1704 170l. Sansepolcro (different) 15 15

649 Daniele Comboni and African Village

1981. 150th Birth Anniv and Death Centenary of Daniele Comboni (missionary).
1705 **649** 80l. brown, indigo and blue 10 15

650 Alcide de Gasperi

651 Landscape outlined by Person in Wheelchair

1981. Birth Centenary of Alcide de Gasperi (politician).
1706 **650** 200l. green 15 15

1981. International Year of Disabled Persons.
1707 **651** 300l. multicoloured . . . 25 15

652 Anemone

653 Human Chess Game, Marostica

1981. Flowers (1st series). Multicoloured.
1708 200l. Type **652** 15 15
1709 200l. Oleander 15 15
1710 200l. Rose 15 15
See also Nos. 1753/5 and 1797/9.

1981. Europa. Multicoloured.
1711 300l. Type **653** 65 15
1712 300l. "Il Palio" horse race, Siena 65 15

654 St. Rita of Cascia

655 Ciro Menotti

1981. 600th Birth Anniv of St. Rita of Cascia.
1713 **654** 600l. multicoloured . . . 40 40

1981. 150th Death Anniv of Ciro Menotti (patriot).
1714 **655** 80l. black and brown . . 10 10

656 Agusta A.109 Helicopter

1981. Italian Aircraft (1st series). Multicoloured.
1715 200l. Type **656** 15 15
1716 200l. Partenavia P.68B Victor airplane 15 15
1717 200l. Aeritalia G.222 transport 15 15
1718 200l. Aermacchi MB 339 jet trainer 15 15
See also Nos. 1748/51 and 1792/5.

657 Fertile and Barren Soil

1981. Water Conservation.
1719 **657** 80l. multicoloured . . . 10 15

1981. Italian Work for the World (2nd series). As T **640**.
1720 300l. blue 25 15
1721 300l. red 25 15
DESIGNS: No. 1720, Sao Simao, Brazil; No. 1721, High Island, Hong Kong.

1981. Tourist Publicity (8th series). As T **556**. Multicoloured.
1722 80l. Matera 15 15
1723 150l. Riva del Garda . . . 20 80
1724 300l. Santa Teresa di Gallura 40 30
1725 900l. Tarquinia . . . . . . 1·30 55

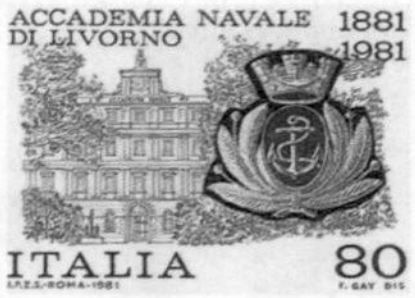

658 Naval Academy and Badge

1981. Centenary of Naval Academy, Livorno. Multicoloured.
1726 80l. Type **658** 10 15
1727 150l. Aerial view of Academy 10 30
1728 200l. "Amerigo Vespucci" (cadet ship) and sailor using sextant 15 15

659 Spada Palace, Rome, and Decorative Motif from Grand Hall

1981. 150th Anniv of Council of State.
1729 **659** 200l. brown, green & blue 10 15

660 Running

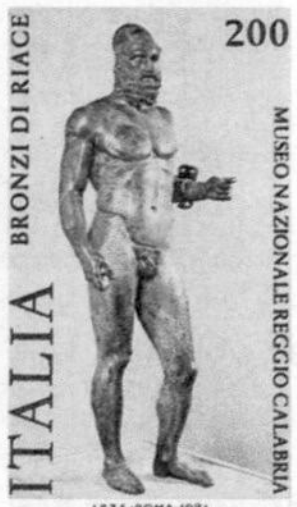

661 Riace Bronze

1981. World Cup Light Athletics Championships, Rome.
1730 **660** 300l. multicoloured . . . 25 30

1981. Italian Artists' Annivs (8th series). As T **567**. Multicoloured.
1731 200l. "Harbour" (Carlo Carra (1881–1966)) . . . 10 15
1732 200l. "Nightfall" (Giuseppe Ugonia (1881–1944)) . . . 10 15

1981. Riace Bronzes (ancient Greek statues). Multicoloured.
1733 200l. Type **661** 20 15
1734 200l. Riace bronze (different) 20 15

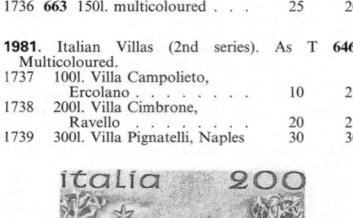

662 Virgil (Treviri mosaic)

1981. Death Bimillenary of Virgil (poet).
1735 **662** 600l. multicoloured . . . 40 45

663 "Still-life" (Gregorio Sciltian)

1981. World Food Day.
1736 **663** 150l. multicoloured . . . 25 20

1981. Italian Villas (2nd series). As T **646**. Multicoloured.
1737 100l. Villa Campolieto, Ercolano 10 25
1738 200l. Villa Cimbrone, Ravello 20 25
1739 300l. Villa Pignatelli, Naples 30 30

664 "Adoration of the Magi" (Giovanni da Campione d'Italia)

1981. Christmas.
1740 **664** 200l. dp blue, brown & bl 15 15

665 Pope John XXIII

1981. Birth Centenary of Pope John XXIII.
1741 **665** 200l. multicoloured . . . 20 15

666 Envelopes forming Railway Track

1981. Stamp Day.
1742 **666** 120l. green, red and black 10 15
1743 – 200l. multicoloured . . . 20 30
1744 – 300l. multicoloured . . . 30 15

DESIGNS—VERT: 200l. Caduceus, chest, envelopes and cherub blowing posthorn. HORIZ: 300l. Letter seal.

667 "St. Francis receiving the Stigmata" (Pietro Cavaro)

668 Paganini (after Ingres)

1982. 800th Birth Anniv of St. Francis of Assisi.
1745 **667** 300l. brown and blue . . 20 30

1982. Birth Bicentenary of Niccolo Paganini (composer and violinist).
1746 **668** 900l. multicoloured . . . 70 1·90

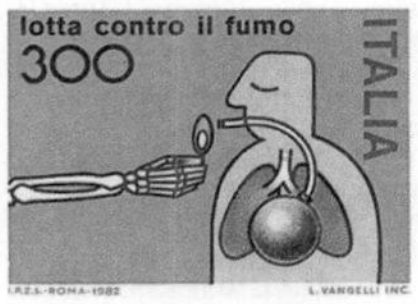

669 Skeletal Hand lighting Cigarette "Bomb"

1982. Anti-smoking Campaign.
1747 **669** 300l. multicoloured . . . 25 15

1982. Italian Aircraft (2nd series). As T **656**. Multicoloured.
1748 300l. Panavia (inscr "Aeritalia") MRCA Tornado jet fighter . . . 45 65
1749 300l. Savoia SIAI 260 Turbo trainer 45 65
1750 300l. Piaggio P-166 DL-3 Turbo 45 65
1751 300l. Nardi NH 500 helicopter 45 65

670 Church of Santo Spirito o del Vespro, Palermo

671 Coronation of Charlemagne, 799

1982. 700th Anniv of Sicilian Vespers (uprising).
1752 **670** 120l. red, blue and purple 10 30

1982. Flowers (2nd series). As T **652**. Mult.
1753 300l. Camellias 30 80
1754 300l. Carnations 30 80
1755 300l. Cyclamen 30 80

1982. Europa.
1756 **671** 200l. brown, black & blue 40 80
1757 – 450l. multicoloured . . . 75 50
DESIGN: 450l. Stars and signatures to Treaty of Rome, 1957.

1982. Italian Work for the World (3rd series). As T **640**. Multicoloured.
1758 450l. Radio communication across Red Sea 35 15
1759 450l. Automatic letter sorting 35 15

672 Garibaldi

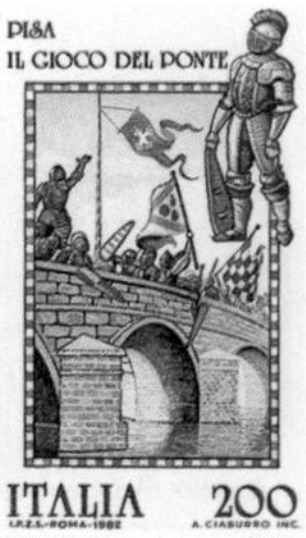

673 Bridge Game, Pisa

1982. Death Centenary of Giuseppe Garibaldi.
1760 **672** 200l. multicoloured . . . 35 65

1982. Folk Customs (1st series).
1761 **673** 200l. multicoloured . . . 20 65

See also Nos. 1804, 1850, 1875/6, 1914, 1972, 2004, 2028 and 2092.

1982. Tourist Publicity (9th series). As T **556**. Multicoloured.
1762 200l. Frasassi Grotto . . . 25 95
1763 200l. Fai della Paganella . . 25 80
1764 450l. Rodi Garganico . . . 40 50
1765 450l. Temples of Agrigento 40 50

674 Coxless Four

1982. World Junior Rowing Championships.
1766 **674** 200l. multicoloured . . . 20 50

675 Ducal Palace, Urbino, Montefeltro and Palazzo dei Consoli, Gubbio

1982. 500th Death Anniv of Federico da Montefeltro, Duke of Urbino.
1767 **675** 200l. multicoloured . . . 15 15

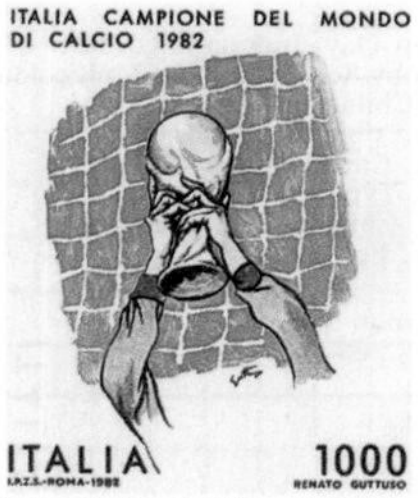

676 Footballer holding aloft World Cup

1982. Italy's World Cup Football Victory.
1768 **676** 1000l. multicoloured . . 1·40 3·00

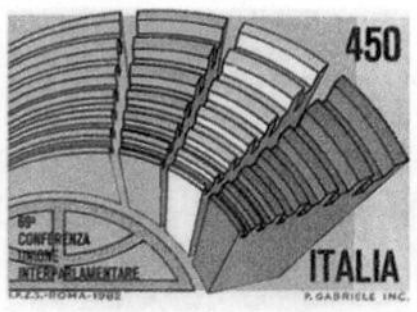

677 Seating Plan

1982. 69th Interparliamentary Union Conference.
1769 **677** 450l. multicoloured . . . 35 15

1982. Italian Villas (3rd series). As T **646**. Multicoloured.
1770 150l. Temple of Aesculapius, Villa Borghese, Rome . . 20 50
1771 250l. Villa D'Este, Tivoli . . 35 15
1772 350l. Villa Lante, Bagnaia, Viterbo . . . . 95 1·40

678 Francis of Taxis

1982. Commemoration of Establishment of First Public Postal System in Europe.
1773 **678** 300l. red, blue & verm 25 15

1982. Italian Artists' Annivs (9th series). As T **567**. Multicoloured.
1774 300l. "Portrait of Antonietta Negroni Prati Morosini as a Child" (Francesco Hayez (1791–1882)) . . . 30 50
1775 300l. "The Fortuneteller" (Giovanni Piazzetta (1682–1754)) 30 50

679 Tree, Chair and Bed (Maria di Pastena)

1983. Stamp Day. Timber in Human Life. Drawings by Schoolchildren. Multicoloured.

1776 150l. Type **679** 15 15
1777 250l. Tree with timber products in branches (Lucia Andreoli) 20 50
1778 350l. Forest (Marco Gallea) 80 65

680 Microscope

1983. Cancer Control.
1779 **680** 400l. multicoloured . . . 35 50

1983. Italian Work for the World (4th series). Automobile Industry. As T **640**. Multicoloured.
1780 400l. Factories on globe . . 35 50
1781 400l. Assembly line 35 50

681 Academy Emblem **682** Shooting

1983. 400th Anniv of Accademia della Crusca (Florentine Academy of Letters).
1782 **681** 400l. red, brown and blue 35 50

1983. World Biathlon Championships, Antholz.
1783 **682** 200l. multicoloured . . . 20 65

683 Gabriele Rossetti **684** Guicciardini (after G. Bugiardini)

1983. Birth Centenary of Gabriele Rossetti (poet).
1784 **683** 300l. blue and brown . . 25 50

1983. 500th Birth Anniv of Francesco Guicciardini (lawyer and diplomat).
1785 **684** 450l. brown 35 15

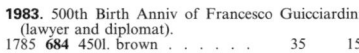

685 Saba and Trieste

1983. Birth Centenary of Umberto Saba (poet).
1786 **685** 600l. multicoloured . . . 45 50

686 Pope Pius XII

1983. 25th Death Anniv of Pope Pius XII.
1787 **686** 1400l. blue . . . . . . 1·00 80

687 Pope and St. Paul's Basilica **688** Launch of Ship

1983. Holy Year. Multicoloured.
1788 250l. Type **687** 45 30
1789 300l. Pope John Paul II and Basilica of Santa Maria Maggiore 25 15
1790 400l. Pope and St. John's Basilica 30 15
1791 500l. Pope and St. Peter's Cathedral. 90 15

1983. Italian Aircraft (3rd series). As T **656**. Multicoloured.
1792 400l. Savoia SIAI 211 . . . 40 65
1793 400l. Agusta A.129 Mangusta helicopter . . . 40 65
1794 400l. Caproni C22J glider 40 65
1795 400l. Aeritalia/Aermacchi AM-X jet fighter 40 65

1983. Labour Day.
1796 **688** 1200l. blue . . . . . . 1·20 95

1983. Flowers (3rd series). As T **652**. Mult.
1797 200l. Gladiolus . . . . . . 60 1·30
1798 200l. Mimosa . . . . 60 1·30
1799 200l. Rhododendron . . . . 60 1·30

689 Galileo (after O. Leoni) and Telescope

1983. Europa. Multicoloured.
1800 400l. Type **689** . . . . . . 4·50 1·10
1801 500l. Archimedes (marble bust) and screw . . . . . 4·50 80

690 Moneta and Doves

1983. 150th Birth Anniv of Ernesto Teodoro Moneta (Nobel Peace Prize winner).
1802 **690** 500l. multicoloured . . . 35 30

691 Quadriga, Globe and V.D.U.

1983. 3rd International Juridical Information Congress, Rome.
1803 **691** 500l. multicoloured . . . 35 30

1983. Folk Customs (2nd series). As T **673**. Multicoloured.
1804 300l. Ceri procession, Gubbio 35 50

692 Elevation of Host **693** Frescobaldi

1983. 20th National Eucharistic Congress, Milan.
1805 **692** 300l. multicoloured . . . 25 15

1983. Tourist Publicity (10th series). As T **556**. Multicoloured.
1806 250l. Alghero . . . . 40 1·60
1807 300l. Bardonecchia 50 80
1808 400l. Riccione 75 65
1809 500l. Taranto . . . . 1·50 15

1983. 400th Birth Anniv of Girolamo Frescobaldi (composer).
1810 **693** 400l. green, blue & brn 35 50

1983. Italian Villas (4th series). As T **646**. Multicoloured.
1811 250l. Villa Fidelia, Spello . . 50 1·20
1812 300l. Villa Imperiale, Pesaro 40 65
1813 400l. Michetti Convent, Francavilla al Mare . . . 65 65
1814 500l. Villa di Riccia 80 15

694 Francesco de Sanctis

1983. Death Centenary of Francesco de Sanctis (writer).
1815 **694** 300l. multicoloured . . . 25 15

695 "Madonna of the Chair" **697** Battered Road Sign

696 Chain of Letters (Roberta Rizzi)

1983. Christmas. 500th Birth Anniv of Raphael (artist). Multicoloured.
1816 250l. Type **695** 20 15
1817 400l. "Sistine Madonna" . . 25 15
1818 500l. "Madonna of the Candles" 60 15

1983. Stamp Day. Drawings by school-children. Multicoloured.
1819 200l. Type **696** 15 50
1820 300l. Space postman delivering letter (Maria Grazia Federico) (vert) . . 35 20
1821 400l. Steam train leaving envelope and globe (Paolo Bucciarelli) 50 20

1984. Road Safety. Multicoloured.
1822 300l. Type **697** 20 50
1823 400l. Crashed car and policeman 30 50

1984. Italian Artists Anniversaries (10th series). As T **567**. Multicoloured.
1824 300l. "Races at Bois de Boulogne" (Giuseppe de Nittis (1846–84)) 35 15
1825 400l. "Paul Guillaume" (Amedeo Modigliani (1884–1920)) 45 50

698 Maserati "Biturbo"

1984. Italian Motor Industry (1st series). Multicoloured.
1826 450l. Type **698** 75 65
1827 450l. Iveco "190.38 Special" lorry 75 65
1828 450l. Same Trattori "Galaxy" tractor 75 65
1829 450l. Alfa "33" 75 65
See also Nos. 1867/70 and 1933/6.

699 Glassblower, Glasses and Jug

1984. Italian Work for the World (5th series). Ceramic and Glass Industries. Multicoloured.
1830 300l. Ceramic plaque and furnace 25 15
1831 300l. Type **699** 25 15

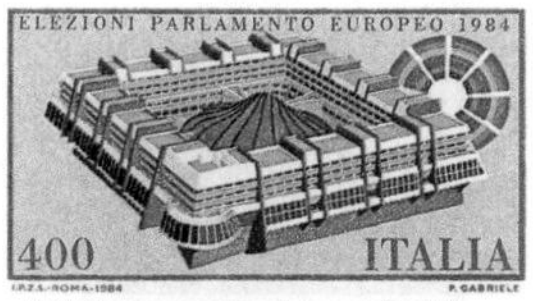

700 European Parliament Building, Strasbourg

1984. Second European Parliament Direct Elections.
1832 **700** 400l. multicoloured . . . 35 65

701 State Forest Corps Helicopter

1984. Nature Protection. Forests. Multicoloured.
1833 450l. Type **701** . . . . . . 1·20 65
1834 450l. Forest animals and burning cigarette . . . . 1·20 65
1835 450l. River and litter . . . 1·20 65
1836 450l. Wildlife and building construction . . . . . . 1·20 65

702 Ministry of Posts and Telecommunications, Rome

1984. "Italia '85" International Stamp Exhibition, Rome (1st issue). Multicoloured.
1837 450l. Type **702** 45 25
1838 550l. Appian Way 55 30
See also Nos. 1857/9, 1862/4, 1871/3 and 1898/1911.

703 G. di Vittorio, B. Buozzi and A. Grandi

1984. 40th Anniv of Rome Pact (foundation of Italian Trade Unions).
1839 **703** 450l. multicoloured . . . 70 50

704 Bridge

1984. Europa. 25th Anniv of European Post and Telecommunications Conference.
1840 **704** 450l. multicoloured . . . 2·00 1·10
1841 550l. multicoloured . . . 3·75 4·75

705 Symposium Emblem **706** Horse-race

1984. Int Telecommunications Symposium, Florence.
1842 **705** 550l. multicoloured . . . 50 65

1984. Centenary of Italian Derby. Multicoloured.
1843 250l. Type **706** . . . . . . 70 3·25
1844 400l. Horse-race (different) 1·10 1·10

1984. Tourist Publicity (11th series). As T **556**. Multicoloured.
1845 350l. Campione d'Italia . . 80 3·00
1846 400l. Chianciano Terme . . 60 1·10
1847 450l. Padula 85 95
1848 550l. Syracuse . . . . . . 85 1·40

1984. Folk Customs (3rd series). As T **673**. Multicoloured.
1850 400l. Procession of Shrine of Santa Rosa, Viterbo . . . 40 50

708 Harvester, Thresher and Medieval Fields Map

1984. Peasant Farming. Multicoloured.
1851 250l. Type **708** . . . . . . 25 1·40
1852 350l. Hand oil press, cart and medieval fields map 30 50

1984. Italian Villas (5th series). As T **646**. Multicoloured.
1853 250l. Villa Caristo, Stignano 60 2·10
1854 350l. Villa Doria Pamphili, Genoa . . . . 60 1·90
1855 400l. Villa Reale, Stupinigi 80 65
1856 450l. Villa Mellone, Lecce 80 50

709 Etruscan Bronze of Warrior **710** Dish Aerial, Globe and Punched Tape

1984. "Italia '85" International Stamp Exhibition, Rome (2nd issue). Multicoloured.
1857 550l. Type **709** 60 50
1858 550l. Exhibition emblem . . 60 50
1859 550l. Etruscan silver-backed mirror 60 50

1985. Information Technology.
1860 **710** 350l. multicoloured . . . 25 50

711 Man helping Old Woman **712** "Venus in her Chariot" (fresco, Raphael)

1985. Problems of Elderly People.
1861 **711** 250l. multicoloured . . . 25 65

1985. "Italia '85" International Stamp Exhibition, Rome (3rd issue). Multicoloured.
1862 600l. Type **712** 60 15
1863 600l. Exhibition emblem . . 60 15
1864 600l. Warriors (detail of fresco, Baldassare Peruzzi) 60 15

713 Plate, Vase and Pot

1985. Italian Work for the World (6th series). Ceramics. Multicoloured.
1865 600l. Type **713** 60 15
1866 600l. Decorated plate . . . 60 15

1985. Italian Motor Industry (2nd series). As T **698**. Multicoloured.
1867 450l. Fiat "Uno" . . . . . 1·20 50
1868 450l. Lamborghini "Countach LP500" . . . 1·20 50
1869 450l. Lancia "Thema" . . . 1·20 50
1870 450l. Fiat Abarth "100 Bialbero" . . . . 1·20 50

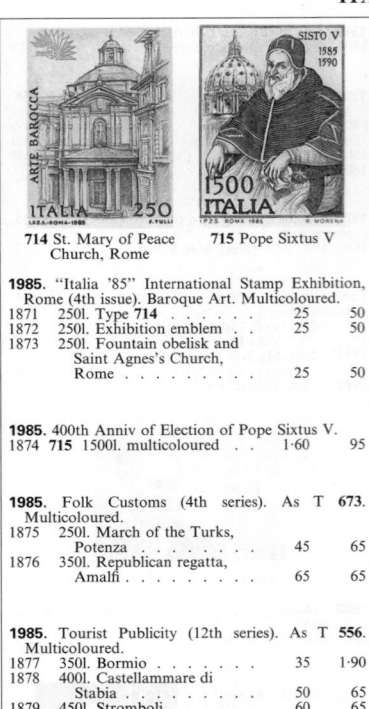

714 St. Mary of Peace Church, Rome **715** Pope Sixtus V

1985. "Italia '85" International Stamp Exhibition, Rome (4th issue). Baroque Art. Multicoloured.
1871 250l. Type **714** 25 50
1872 250l. Exhibition emblem . . 25 50
1873 250l. Fountain obelisk and Saint Agnes's Church, Rome 25 50

1985. 400th Anniv of Election of Pope Sixtus V.
1874 **715** 1500l. multicoloured . . 1·60 95

1985. Folk Customs (4th series). As T **673**. Multicoloured.
1875 250l. March of the Turks, Potenza 45 65
1876 350l. Republican regatta, Amalfi 65 65

1985. Tourist Publicity (12th series). As T **556**. Multicoloured.
1877 350l. Bormio . . . . 35 1·90
1878 400l. Castellammare di Stabia 50 65
1879 450l. Stromboli 60 65
1880 600l. Termoli . . . . 1·60 25

716 European Otter **717** Aureliano Pertile and Giovanni Martinelli (singers)

1985. Nature Protection. Multicoloured.
1881 500l. Type **716** 55 50
1882 500l. Primulas 55 50
1883 500l. Fir tree 55 50
1884 500l. Black-winged stilts . . 55 50

1985. Anniversaries of Italian Artists (11th series). As T **567**. Multicoloured.
1885 350l. "Madonna" (Giambattista Salvi (1609–85)) 55 95
1886 400l. "The Pride of Work" (Mario Sironi (1885–1961)) 70 95

1985. Europa. Music Year. Multicoloured.
1887 500l. Type **717** . . . . . . 2·75 95
1888 600l. Vicenzo Bellini and Johann Sebastian Bach (composers) . . . . . . 4·75 1·30

718 San Salvatore Abbey

1985. 950th Anniv of San Salvatore Abbey, Mt. Amiata.
1889 **718** 450l. multicoloured . . . 40 15

719 Cyclists

1985. World Cycling Championships, Bassano del Grappa.
1890 **719** 400l. multicoloured . . . 70 50

720 U.N. and Congress Emblems and Globe

1985. 7th United Nations Crime Prevention Congress, Milan.
1891 **720** 600l. multicoloured . . . 55 15

721 Profile and Emblem

1985. International Youth Year.
1892 **721** 600l. multicoloured . . . 60 15

1985. Villas (6th series). As T **646**. Multicoloured.
1893 300l. Villa Nitti, Maratea . . 65 50
1894 400l. Villa Aldrovandi Mazzacorati, Bologna . . 85 15
1895 500l. Villa Santa Maria, Pula . . . . 1·10 15
1896 600l. Villa de Mersi, Villazzano . . . . 1·40 15

722 State Emblems of Italy and Vatican City and Medallion (Mario Soccorsi)

1985. Ratification of the Modification of 1929 Lateran Concordat.
1897 **722** 400l. multicoloured . . . 70 50

723 Parma Town Hall and 1857 25c. Stamp

724 Basel 1845 2½r. Stamp

1985. "Italia '85" International Stamp Exhibition. Rome (5th issue). Multicoloured. (a) As T **723**.
1898 300l. Type **723** 25 65
1899 300l. Naples New Castle and 1858 2g. stamp . . . 25 65
1900 300l. Palermo Cathedral and Sicily 1859 ½g. stamp . . 25 65
1901 300l. Modena Cathedral and 1852 15c. stamp 25 65
1902 300l. Piazzo Navona, Rome, and Papal States 1852 7b. stamp 25 65
1903 300l. Palazzo Vecchio, Florence, and Tuscany 1851 2c. stamp 25 65
1904 300l. Turin and Sardinia 1861 3l. stamp 25 65
1905 300l. Bologna and Romagna 1859 6b. stamp 25 65
1906 300l. Palazzo Litta, Milan, and Lombardy and Venetia 1850 15c. stamp 25 65

(b) As T **724**.
1907 500l. Type **724** 50 80
1908 500l. Japan 1871 48m. stamp 50 80
1909 500l. United States 1847 10c. stamp 50 80
1910 500l. Western Australia 1854 1d. stamp 50 80
1911 500l. Mauritius 1848 2d. stamp 50 80

(c) Sheet 86 × 56 mm. Imperf
MS1912 4000l. Sardinia 1851 5c. stamp and Great Britain "Penny Black" . . . . 3·00 5·50

725 Skiers

1986. Cross-country Skiing.
1913 **725** 450l. multicoloured . . . 35 50

1986. Folk Customs (5th series). As T **673**. Multicoloured.
1914 450l. Le Candelore, Catania 40 50

726 Amilcare Ponchielli and Scene from "La Gioconda"

1986. Composers. Multicoloured.
1915 2000l. Type **726** (death centenary) . . . . 2·10 65
1916 2000l. Giovan Battista Pergolesi (250th death anniv) . . . . 2·30 80

727 Acitrezza

1986. Tourist Publicity (13th series). Mult.
1917 350l. Type **727** 45 50
1918 450l. Capri 55 80
1919 550l. Merano 70 50
1920 650l. San Benedetto del Tronto 85 15

728 Heart-shaped Tree (life)

1986. Europa. Multicoloured.
1921 650l. Type **728** . . . . . . 1·80 50
1922 650l. Star-shaped tree (poetry) . . . . 1·80 50
1923 650l. Butterfly-shaped tree (colour) . . . . 1·80 50
1924 650l. Sun-shaped tree (energy) . . . . 1·80 50

729 "Eyes"

1986. 25th International Ophthalmology Congress, Rome.
1925 **729** 550l. multicoloured . . . 45 15

730 Italian Police

1986. European Police Meeting, Chianciano Terme.
1926 **730** 550l. multicoloured . . . 95 50
1927 650l. multicoloured . . . 1·20 95

731 Battle Scene

1986. 120th Anniv of Battle of Bezzecca.
1928 **731** 550l. multicoloured . . . 50 50

732 Figure with Flag

1986. National Independence Martyrs' Day.
1929 **732** 2000l. multicoloured . . 2·40 65

733 Bersagliere and Helmets

1986. 150th Anniv of Turin Bersaglieri Corps (alpine troops).
1930 **733** 450l. multicoloured . . . 85 50

734 Dish Aerial, Transmitter and "Messages"

1986. Telecommunications.
1931 **734** 350l. multicoloured . . . 50 15

735 Varallo

1986. Holy Mountain of Varallo.
1932 **735** 2000l. green and blue . . 1·90 65

1986. Italian Motor Industry (3rd series). As T **698**. Multicoloured.
1933 450l. Alfa Romeo "AR 8 Turbo" 90 50
1934 450l. Innocenti "650 SE" . . 90 50
1935 450l. Ferrari "Testarossa" 90 50
1936 450l. Fiatallis "FR 10B" . . 90 50

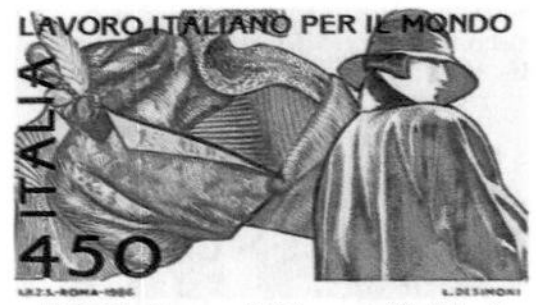

736 Clothes and Woman (fashion)

1986. Italian Work for the World (7th series). Mult.
1937 450l. Type **736** 75 15
1938 450l. Man and clothes (fashion) 75 15
1939 650l. Olivetti personal computer, keyboard and screen . . . . 2·10 50
1940 650l. Breda steam turbine 2·10 50

737 Airplane flying through "40"

738 "Madonna and Child" (bronze sculpture by Donatello)

1986. 40th Anniv of Alitalia (national airline). Multicoloured.
1941 550l. Type **737** 55 15
1942 650l. Airplane and landing lights 70 15

1986. Italian Villas (7th series). As T **646**. Mult.
1943 350l. Villa Necker, Trieste 40 50
1944 350l. Villa Borromeo, Cassana d'Adda 40 50
1945 450l. Villa Palagonia, Bagheria 60 15
1946 550l. Villa Medicea, Poggio a Caiano 65 15
1947 650l. Issogne Castle 80 15

1986. Christmas.
1948 **738** 450l. bistre 45 15

1986. Anniversaries of Italian Artists (12th series). As T **567**.
1949 450l. black and orange . . . 1·00 15
1950 550l. multicoloured . . . . 1·20 15
DESIGNS: 450l. Drawing of woman (Andrea del Sarto (1486–1531)); 550l. "Daphne at Pavarola" (Felice Casorati (1883–1963)).

739 Lockheed Hercules Transport dropping Squares in National Colours onto Globe

740 Engraving 1862 Stamp

1986. International Peace Year. Multicoloured.
1951 550l. Type **739** 50 15
1952 650l. Airplane, Cross and people (commemoration of Italian airmen killed on mission to Kindu, Congo) 60 15

1986. Stamp Day. Francesco Maria Matraire (engraver).
1953 **740** 550l. multicoloured . . . 85 15

741 Woven Threads (Marzotto Textile Industry)

1987. Italian Industry.
1954 **741** 700l. multicoloured . . . 65 15
1955 – 700l. blue and turquoise 65 15
DESIGN: No. 1955, Clouds and flame (Italgas Gas Corporation).

742 River Volturno

743 Gramsci

1987. Nature Protection. Rivers and Lakes. Multicoloured.
1956 500l. Type **742** 75 15
1957 500l. Lake Garda 75 15
1958 500l. Lake Trasimeno . . . 75 15
1959 500l. River Tirso 75 15

1987. 50th Death Anniv of Antonio Gramsci (politician).
1960 **743** 600l. grey, black and red 70 50

744 Church of the Motorway of the Sun, Florence (Giovanni Michelucci)

745 View of Naples on Football

1987. Europa. Architecture. Multicoloured.
1961 600l. Type **744** . . . . . . 1·20 65
1962 700l. Termini station, Rome (Nervi) . . . . 1·50 65

1987. Tourist Publicity (14th series). As T **556**. Multicoloured.
1963 380l. Verbania Pallanza . . 50 1·40
1964 400l. Palmi 55 80
1965 500l. Vasto 70 50
1966 600l. Villacidro 80 80

1987. S.S.C. Naples, National Football Champion, 1986–87.
1967 **745** 500l. multicoloured . . . 1·10 1·10

746 "The Absinthe Drinker" (Edgar Degas)

1987. Anti-alcoholism Campaign.
1968 **746** 380l. multicoloured . . . 55 50

747 Liguori and Gulf of Naples

1987. Death Bicentenary of St. Alfonso Maria de Liguori (co-founder of Redemptorists).
1969 **747** 400l. multicoloured . . . 35 50

748 Emblem and Olympic Stadium, Rome

1987. World Light Athletics Championships, Rome (1970) and "Olymphilex '87" Stamp Exhibition, Rome (1971).
1970 700l. Type **748** 55 15
1971 700l. International Olympic Committee building, Foro Italico, Rome 55 15

1987. Folk Customs (6th series). As T **673**. Multicoloured.
1972 380l. Joust, Foligno 45 50

749 Piazza del Popolo, Ascoli Piceno

750 "The Adoration in the Manger" (St. Francis's Basilica, Assisi)

1987. Piazzas (1st series). Multicoloured.
1973 380l. Type **749** 45 50
1974 500l. Piazza Giuseppe Verdi, Palermo 60 15
1975 600l. Piazza San Carlo, Turin 75 15
1976 700l. Piazza dei Signori, Verona 85 65
See also Nos. 2002/3 and 2023/4.

1987. Christmas. Frescoes by Giotto. Mult.
1977 500l. Type **750** 65 15
1978 600l. "Epiphany" (Scrovegni Chapel, Padua) 75 15

751 Battle Scene

1987. 120th Anniv of Battle of Mentana.
1979 **751** 380l. multicoloured . . . 50 50

752 "Christ Pantocrator" (mosaic, Monreale Cathedral)

1987. Artistic Heritage. Multicoloured.
1980 500l. Type **752** 85 50
1981 500l. San Carlo Theatre, Naples (18th-century engraving) 85 50

753 College and 1787 and 1987 Uniforms

754 Marco de Marchi (philatelist) and Milan Cathedral

1987. Bicentenary of Nunziatella Military Academy, Naples.
1982 **753** 600l. multicoloured . . . 60 50

1987. Stamp Day.
1983 **754** 500l. multicoloured . . . 90 50

755 Man chipping Flints

756 Lyceum

1988. "Homo aeserniensis".
1984 **755** 500l. multicoloured . . . 40 65

1988. E.Q. Visconti Lyceum, Rome.
1985 **756** 500l. multicoloured . . . 45 30
See also Nos. 2019, 2109 and 2127.

757 Statue, Bosco and Boy

758 15th-Century Soncino Bible

1988. Death Centenary of St. John Bosco (founder of Salesian Brothers).
1986 **757** 500l. multicoloured . . . 40 50

1988. Anniversaries of Italian Artists (13th series). As T **567**. Multicoloured.
1987 650l. "Archaeologists" (Giorgio de Chirico (1888–1978)) . . . . . . 1·00 65

1988. 500th Anniv of First Printing of Bible in Hebrew.
1988 **758** 550l. multicoloured . . . 60 30

759 St. Valentine, Epileptics and Wave Patterns

1988. Anti-epilepsy Campaign.
1989 **759** 500l. multicoloured . . . 60 65

760 ETR 450 High Speed Train in Station
761 Golfer on Ball

1988. Europa. Transport and Communications. Multicoloured.
1990 650l. Type **760** . . . . . . 1·20 95
1991 750l. Map and keyboard operator (electronic postal systems) . . . . 1·40 1·40

1988. Tourist Publicity (15th series). As T **556**. Multicoloured.
1992 400l. Castiglione della Pescaia 35 65
1993 500l. Lignano Sabbiadoro 50 50
1994 650l. St. Domenico's Church, Noto 60 50
1995 750l. Vieste 70 80

1988. Golf.
1996 **761** 500l. multicoloured . . . 45 65

762 Stadium and Mascot
763 Milan Cathedral on Football

1988. World Cup Football Championship, Italy (1990) (1st issue).
1997 **762** 3150l. multicoloured . . 2·30 4·75
See also Nos. 2049 and 2052/87.

1988. A. C. Milan. National Football Champion, 1987–88.
1998 **763** 650l. multicoloured . . . 55 1·10

764 Horse's Head

1988. Artistic Heritage. Pergola Bronzes. Multicoloured.
1999 500l. Type **764** 40 95
2000 650l. Bust of woman 55 95

765 Student (bas-relief)
766 Emblem and Appian Way

1988. 900th Anniv of Bologna University.
2001 **765** 500l. violet 40 65

1988. Piazzas (2nd series). As T **749**. Mult.
2002 400l. Piazza del Duomo, Pistoia 50 50
2003 550l. Piazza del Unita d'Italia, Trieste 65 50

1988. Folk Customs (7th series). As T **673**. Multicoloured.
2004 500l. Candle procession, Sassari 90 50

1988. "Roma 88" Int Gastroenterology and Digestive Endoscopy Congress.
2005 **766** 750l. multicoloured . . . 80 50

767 "Ossessione" (Luchino Visconti, 1942)
769 "Holy Family" (Pasquale Celommi)

768 Bird (aluminium)

1988. Italian Films. Scenes from and Advertising Posters of named Films. Multicoloured.
2006 500l. Type **767** . . . . . . 90 1·10
2007 650l. "Ladri di Biciclette" (Vittorio de Sica, 1948) 90 95
2008 2400l. "Roma Citta Aperta" (Roberto Rossellini, 1945) 3·25 1·30
2009 3050l. "Riso Amaro" (Giuseppe de Santis, 1949) 3·50 2·20

1988. Italian Industry. Multicoloured.
2010 750l. Type **768** 50 15
2011 750l. Oscilloscope display (electronics) 50 50
2012 750l. Banknote engraving, 1986 tourism stamp and medals (60th anniv of State Polygraphic Institute) 50 50

1988. Christmas (1st issue).
2013 **769** 650l. multicoloured . . . 85 30
See also No. 2015.

770 Borromeo and Plague Victims

1988. 450th Birth Anniv of St. Carlo Borromeo, Archbishop of Milan.
2014 **770** 2400l. multicoloured . . 1·90 1·30

771 "Nativity" (bas-relief)
772 Edoardo Chiossone (stamp designer) and Japanese 1879 2s. "Koban" Stamp

1988. Christmas (2nd issue).
2015 **771** 500l. green and brown 90 50

1988. Stamp Day.
2016 **772** 500l. multicoloured . . . 50 15

773 AIDS Virus

1989. Anti-AIDS Campaign.
2017 **773** 650l. multicoloured . . . 55 15

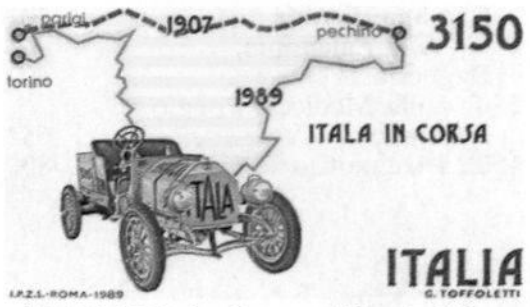

774 1907 Itala Car and Route Map

1989. Re-enactment of 1907 Peking–Paris Car Rally.
2018 **774** 3150l. multicoloured . . 2·75 6·50

1989. Giuseppe Parini Lyceum, Milan. As T **756**.
2019 650l. multicoloured 50 15

776 Fresco, Ragione Palace, Padua
777 Stylized Yachts

1989. Artistic Heritage.
2020 **776** 500l. multicoloured . . . 50 80
2021 – 650l. blue 65 50
DESIGN: 650l. Crypt, Basilica of St. Nicolas, Bari.

1989. World Sailing Championships, Alassio, Naples and Porto Cervo.
2022 **777** 3050l. multicoloured . . 2·50 2·10

1989. Piazzas (3rd series). As T **749**. Mult.
2023 400l. Piazza di Spagna, Rome 45 65
2024 400l. Piazza del Duomo, Catanzaro 45 65

778 Leap-frog (Luca Rizzello)

1989. Europa. Children's Games. Mult.
2025 500l. Type **778** 80 65
2026 650l. Girl dressing up (Serena Forcuti) (vert) . . 1·20 50
2027 750l. Sack race (Adelise Lahner) . . . . 1·50 50

1989. Folk Customs (8th series). As T **673**. Multicoloured.
2028 400l. Spello flower paintings 35 65

779 Cloisters

1989. Pisa University.
2029 **779** 500l. violet 40 50

780 Parliamentary Emblem as Tree on Map
781 1889 5c. Savoy Arms Stamp

1989. 3rd Direct Elections to European Parliament.
2030 **780** 500l. multicoloured . . . 60 50
No. 2030 is also inscribed with the European Currency Unit rate of 0.31 ECU.

1989. Tourist Publicity (16th series). As T **556**. Multicoloured.
2031 500l. Grottammare 55 80
2032 500l. Spotorno 55 80
2033 500l. Pompeii 55 80
2034 500l. Giardini Naxos . . . 55 80

1989. Centenary of Ministry of Posts and Telecommunications. Multicoloured.
2035 500l. Type **781** . . . . . . 50 1·60
2036 2400l. Globe within posthorn . . . . 1·80 1·60

782 Ball and Club Emblem

1989. Inter Milan, National Football Champion, 1988–89.
2037 **782** 650l. multicoloured . . . 50 65

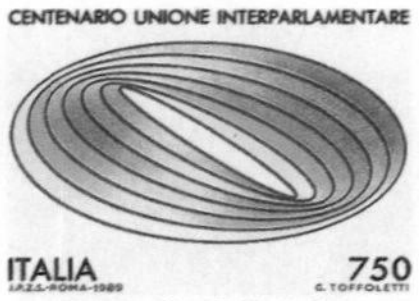

783 Stylized Chamber

1989. Centenary of Interparliamentary Union.
2038 **783** 750l. multicoloured . . . 55 50

784 Phrygian Cap

1989. Bicentenary of French Revolution.
2039 **784** 3150l. multicoloured . . 2·75 6·50

785 Corinaldo Wall

1989. Artistic Heritage. 550th Birth Anniv of Francesco di Giorgio Martini (architect).
2040 **785** 500l. multicoloured . . . 55 50

786 Chaplin in Film Scenes

1989. Birth Centenary of Charlie Chaplin (film actor and director).
2041 **786** 750l. black and brown 70 50

787 "Inauguration of Naples–Portici Line" (left-hand detail, S Fergola)

1989. 150th Anniv of Naples–Portici Railway. Multicoloured.
2042 550l. Type **787** 45 50
2043 550l. Right-hand detail . . . 45 50
Nos. 2042/3 were printed together, se-tenant, forming a composite design.

788 Castelfidardo, Accordion and Stradella

1989. Italian Industry. Multicoloured.
2044 450l. Type **788** 40 50
2045 450l. Books (Arnoldo Mondadori Publishing House) 40 50

789 Madonna and Child

790 Emilio Diena (stamp dealer)

1989. Christmas. Details of "Adoration of the Magi" (Correggio). Multicoloured.
2046 500l. Type **789** 55 50
2047 500l. Magi 55 50
Nos. 2046/7 were printed together, se-tenant, forming a composite design.

1989. Stamp Day.
2048 **790** 500l. black, brown & blue 60 50

791 Monument (Mario Ceroli) and Football Pitch

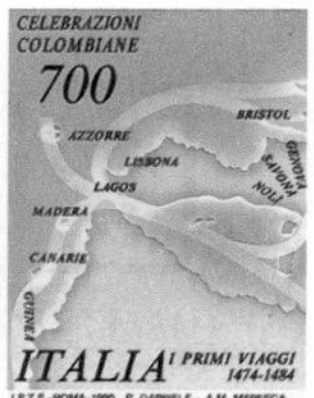

792 Old Map (left half) with Route superimposed

1989. World Cup Football Championship, Italy (1990) (2nd issue).
2049 **791** 450l. multicoloured . . . 40 65

1990. Columbus's First Voyages, 1474–84, Multicoloured.
2050 700l. Type **792** 60 50
2051 700l. Right half of map . . 60 50
Nos. 2050/1 were printed together, se-tenant, forming a composite design.

793 Italy

1990. World Cup Football Championship, Italy (3rd issue). Designs showing finalists' emblems or playing venues. Multicoloured.
2052 450l. Type **793** 30 65
2053 450l. U.S.A. 30 65
2054 450l. Olympic Stadium, Rome 30 65
2055 450l. Comunale Stadium, Florence 30 65
2056 450l. Austria 30 65
2057 450l. Czechoslovakia 30 65
2058 600l. Argentina 40 65
2059 600l. U.S.S.R. 40 65
2060 600l. San Paolo Stadium, Naples 40 65
2061 600l. New Stadium, Bari . . 40 65
2062 600l. Cameroun 40 65
2063 600l. Rumania 40 65
2064 650l. Brazil 50 65
2065 650l. Costa Rica 50 65
2066 650l. Delle Alpi Stadium, Turin 50 65
2067 650l. Ferraris Stadium, Genoa 50 65
2068 650l. Sweden 50 65
2069 650l. Scotland 50 65
2070 700l. United Arab Emirates 50 65
2071 700l. West Germany 50 65
2072 700l. Dall'Ara Stadium, Bologna 50 65
2073 700l. Meazza Stadium, Milan 50 65
2074 700l. Colombia 50 65
2075 700l. Yugoslavia 50 65
2076 800l. Belgium . . . . 60 1·30
2077 800l. Uruguay . . . . . . 60 1·30
2078 800l. Bentegodi Stadium, Verona . . . . 60 1·30
2079 800l. Friuli Stadium, Udine 60 1·30
2080 800l. South Korea . . . . . 60 1·30
2081 800l. Spain . . . . 60 1·30
2082 1200l. England . . . . . . 85 1·60
2083 1200l. Netherlands . . . . 85 1·60
2084 1200l. Sant'Elia Stadium, Cagliari . . . . 85 1·60
2085 1200l. La Favorita Stadium, Palermo . . . . 85 1·60
2086 1200l. Ireland . . . . . . 85 1·60
2087 1200l. Egypt . . . . 85 1·60
See also No. 2104.

1990. Tourist Publicity (17th series). As T **556**. Multicoloured.
2088 600l. San Felice Circeo . . . 55 50
2089 600l. Castellammare del Golfo 55 50
2090 600l. Montepulciano 55 50
2091 600l. Sabbioneta 55 50

1990. Folk Customs (9th series). As T **673**. Multicoloured.
2092 600l. Avelignesi horse race, Merano 45 50

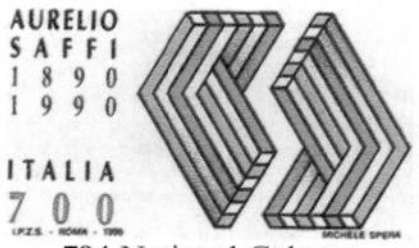

794 National Colours

1990. Death Centenary of Aurelio Saffi.
2093 **794** 700l. multicoloured . . . 50 40

795 Giovanni Giorgi (inventor)

796 Flags, Globe and Workers (after "The Four States" (Pellizza da Volpedo))

1990. 55th Anniv of Invention of Giorgi/MKSA System of Electrotechnical Units.
2094 **795** 600l. multicoloured . . . 40 50

1990. Centenary of Labour Day.
2095 **796** 600l. multicoloured . . . 40 50

797 Ball on Map

1990. S. S. C. Naples, National Football Champion, 1989–90.
2096 **797** 700l. multicoloured . . . 50 50

798 Piazza San Silvestro Post Office, Rome

1990. Europa. Post Office Buildings. Mult.
2097 700l. Type **798** . . . . . . 1·00 50
2098 800l. Fondaco Tedeschi post office, Venice . . . . . . 1·50 65

799 Paisiello

1990. 250th Birth Anniv of Giovanni Paisiello (composer).
2099 **799** 450l. multicoloured . . . 30 50

800 Globe, Open Book and Bust of Dante

1990. Centenary of Dante Alighieri Society.
2100 **800** 700l. multicoloured . . . 45 80

801 Byzantine Mosaic, Ravenna

802 Malatestiana Temple, Rimini

1990. Artistic Heritage. Multicoloured.
2101 450l. Type **801** 30 50
2102 700l. "Christ and Angels" (detail of Rachis altar, Friuli) (Lombard art) . . 50 50

1990. 40th Anniv of Malatestiana Religious Music Festival.
2103 **802** 600l. multicoloured . . . 45 50

1990. West Germany, Winner of World Cup Football Championship. As No. 2071 but value changed and additionally inscr "CAMPIONE DEL MONDO".
2104 600l. multicoloured . . . . 2·00 1·90

803 "Still Life"

1990. Birth Cent of Giorgio Morandi (painter).
2105 **803** 750l. black 60 50

804 Ancient and Modern Wrestlers

1990. World Greco-Roman Wrestling Championships, Rome.
2106 **804** 3200l. multicoloured . . 2·75 2·40

805 "New Life" (Emidio Vangelli)

1990. Christmas. Multicoloured.
2107 600l. Type **805** 45 50
2108 750l. "Adoration of the Shepherds" (fresco by Pellegrino in St. Daniel's Church, Friuli) 60 50

806 Catania University

1990.
2109 – 600l. multicoloured . . . 45 50
2110 **806** 750l. blue and ultramarine 60 50
DESIGN—As T **756**: 600l. Bernardino Telesio High School, Cosenza.

807 Corrado Mezzana (stamp designer, self-portrait)

808 Holy Family

1990. Stamp Day.
2111 **807** 600l. multicoloured . . . 55 50

1991. "The Living Tableau", Rivisondoli.
2112 **808** 600l. multicoloured . . . 55 50

809 Fair Emblem

810 Emblem

1991. "EuroFlora '91" Fair, Genoa.
2113 **809** 750l. multicoloured . . . 60 50

1991. 750th Anniv of Siena University.
2114 **810** 750l. gold, black and blue 60 50

1991. Tourist Publicity (18th series). As T **556**. Multicoloured.
2115 600l. Cagli 50 50
2116 600l. La Maddalena 50 50
2117 600l. Roccaraso 50 50
2118 600l. Sanremo 50 50

811 European Community Flag

812 City and Columbus's Fleet

1991. Europa Youth Meeting, Venice.
2119 **811** 750l. multicoloured . . . 65 15
No. 2119 is also valued in ECUs (European Currency Unit).

1991. 500th Anniv (1992) of Discovery of America by Christopher Columbus (1st issue). Multicoloured.
2120 750l. Type **812** 60 50
2121 750l. Map, Columbus, seal and King and Queen of Spain 60 50
Nos. 2120/1 were printed together, se-tenant, forming a composite design.
See also Nos. 2151/4 and **MS**2158.

813 Belli and View of Rome

1991. Birth Bicentenary of Giuseppe Gioachino Belli (poet).
2122 **813** 600l. brown and blue . . 45 50

814 St Gregory's Church, Rome

1991. Artistic Heritage.
2123 **814** 3200l. multicoloured . . 2·30 1·30

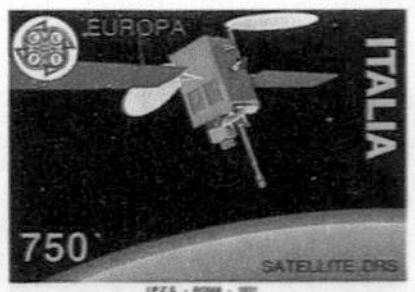

815 "DRS" Satellite

1991. Europa. Europe in Space. Multicoloured.
2124 750l. Type **815** . . . . . . 1·30 50
2125 800l. "Hermes" spaceship and "Columbus" space station . . . . 1·30 50

816 Sta Maria Maggiore Church, Lanciano
817 Football and Genoa Lantern

1991. Artistic Heritage.
2126 **816** 600l. brown 50 50

1991. D. A. Azuni Lyceum, Sassari. As T **756**.
2127 600l. multicoloured 50 50

1991. Sampdoria, National Football Champion, 1990–91.
2128 **817** 3000l. multicoloured . . 2·30 4·00

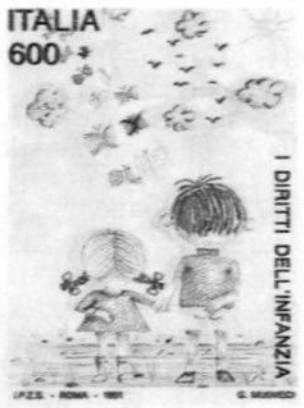

818 Hands and Ball
819 Children and Butterflies

1991. Centenary of Basketball.
2129 **818** 500l. multicoloured . . . 40 50

1991. United Nations Conference on Rights of the Child. Multicoloured.
2130 600l. Type **819** 50 50
2131 750l. Child with balloon on man's shoulders 65 50

820 "Youth and Gulls" (sculpture, Pericle Fazzini)

1991. Artistic Heritage. Multicoloured.
2132 **820** 600l. yellow, blue & black 45 65
2133 – 3200l. multicoloured . . 2·50 2·40
DESIGN: 3200l. Palazzo Esposizioni, Turin (Pier Luigi Nervi (birth centenary)).

821 Winged Sphinx

1991. Egyptian Museum, Turin.
2134 **821** 750l. gold, green & yellow 65 50

822 Luigi Galvani (physiologist) and Experimental Equipment

1991. 100 Years of Radio (1st issue).
2135 **822** 750l. multicoloured . . . 65 50
Galvani carried out experiments in electricity.
See also Nos. 2148, 2203, 2241 and 2321/2.

823 Mozart at Spinet
825 "The Angel of Life" (Giovanni Segantini)

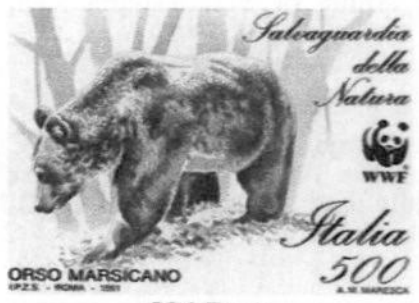

824 Bear

1991. Death Bicentenary of Wolfgang Amadeus Mozart (composer).
2136 **823** 800l. multicoloured . . . 70 65

1991. Nature Protection. Multicoloured.
2137 500l. Type **824** 50 65
2138 500l. Peregrine falcon . . . 50 65
2139 500l. Deer 50 65
2140 500l. Marine life 50 65

1991. Christmas.
2141 **825** 600l. multicoloured . . . 50 50

826 Giulio and Alberto Bolaffi (stamp catalogue publishers)

1991. Stamp Day.
2142 **826** 750l. multicoloured . . . 60 50

827 Signature and National Flag

1991. Birth Cent of Pietro Nenni (politician).
2143 **827** 750l. multicoloured . . . 60 65

828 Runners

1992. 22nd European Indoor Light Athletics Championships, Genoa.
2144 **828** 600l. multicoloured . . . 55 50

829 Neptune Fountain, Florence
830 Statue of Marchese Alberto V of Este (founder) and University

1992. 400th Death Anniv of Bartolomeo Ammannati (architect and sculptor).
2145 **829** 750l. multicoloured . . . 60 50

1992. 600th Anniv (1991) of Ferrara University.
2146 **830** 750l. multicoloured . . . 60 50

831 Pediment

1992. Naples University.
2147 **831** 750l. multicoloured . . . 60 50

1992. 100 Years of Radio (2nd issue). As T **822**. Multicoloured.
2148 750l. Alessandro Volta (physicist) and Voltaic pile 75 65
Volta formulated the theory of current electricity and invented an electric battery.

832 Emblem and Venue
833 Medal of Lorenzo (Renato Beradi)

1992. "Genova '92" International Thematic Stamp Exhibition (1st issue).
2149 **832** 750l. multicoloured . . . 60 15
See also Nos. 2170/5.

1992. 500th Death Anniv of Lorenzo de Medici, "The Magnificent".
2150 **833** 750l. multicoloured . . . 60 50

834 Columbus before Queen Isabella
835 Scenes from Life of St. Maria Filippini (altar, Montefiascone Cathedral)

1992. 500th Anniv of Discovery of America by Columbus (2nd issue). Multicoloured.
2151 500l. Type **834** 50 80
2152 500l. Columbus's fleet . . . 50 80
2153 500l. Sighting land 50 80
2154 500l. Landing in the New World 50 80

1992. 300th Anniv of Maestre Pie Filippini Institute.
2155 **835** 750l. multicoloured . . . 60 50

836 Columbus Monument, Genoa (G. Giannetti)

1992. Europa. 500th Anniv of Discovery of America by Columbus. Multicoloured.
2156 750l. Type **836** . . . . . . 1·10 50
2157 850l. Emblem of "Colombo '92" exhibition, Genoa . . 1·40 50

837 Columbus presenting Natives

1992. 500th Anniv of Discovery of America by Columbus (3rd issue). Six sheets each 113 × 93 mm containing horiz designs as T **837** reproducing scenes from United States 1893 Columbian Exposition issue.
MS2158 Six sheets (a) 50l. green (Type **837**); 300l. blue (Columbus announcing discovery); 4000l. mauve (Columbus in chains). (b) 100l. lilac (Columbus welcomed at Barcelona); 800l. red (Columbus restored to favour); 3000l. green (Columbus describing third voyage). (c) 200l. blue (Columbus sighting land); 900l. blue (Columbus's fleet); 1500l. red (Queen Isabella pledging jewels). (d) 400l. brown (Columbus soliciting aid of Queen Isabella); 700l. red (Columbus at La Rabida); 1000l. blue (Recall of Columbus). (e) 500l. brown (Landing of Columbus); 600l. green ("Santa Maria"); 2000l. red (Portraits of Queen Isabella and Columbus). (f) 5000l. green ("America", Columbus and "Liberty") Set of 6 sheets . . 22·00 27·00

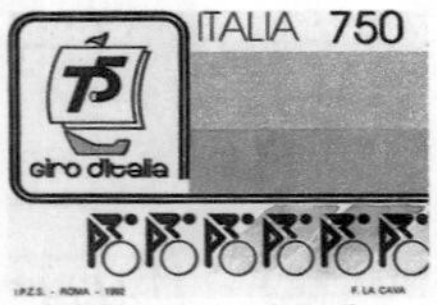

838 Seascape and Cyclists

1992. 75th "Tour of Italy" Cycle Race. Mult.
2159 750l. Type **838** 75 65
2160 750l. Mountains and cyclists 75 65
Nos. 2159/60 were issued together, se-tenant, forming a composite design.

839 Ball, Team Badge and Stylization of Milan Cathedral

1992. A.C. Milan, National Football Champion, 1991–92.
2161 **839** 750l. green, red and black 75 50

840 Viareggio

1992. Seaside Resorts. Multicoloured.
2162 750l. Type **840** 60 50
2163 750l. Rimini 60 50

841 Nuvolari

1992. Birth Centenary of Tazio Nuvolari (racing driver).

2164 **841** 3200l. multicoloured . . 2·75 2·10

1992. Tourist Publicity (19th series). As T **556**. Multicoloured.

2165	600l. Arcevia	50	65
2166	600l. Braies	50	65
2167	600l. Maratea	50	65
2168	600l. Pantelleria	50	65

842 "Adoration of the Shepherds" (detail)

1992. 400th Death Anniv of Jacopo da Ponte (painter).

2169 **842** 750l. multicoloured . . . 60 50

843 Columbus's House, Genoa

844 Woman's Eyes and Mouth

1992. "Genova '92" International Thematic Stamp Exhibition (2nd issue). Multicoloured.

2170	500l. Type **843**	40	50
2171	600l. Departure of Columbus's fleet from Palos, 1492	50	50
2172	750l. Route map of Columbus's first voyage	60	50
2173	850l. Columbus sighting land	65	50
2174	1200l. Columbus landing on San Salvador	1·00	1·40
2175	3200l. Columbus, "Man" (Leonardo da Vinci), "Fury" (Michelangelo) and Raphael's portrait of Michelangelo	2·50	1·40

1992. Stamp Day. Ordinary or self-adhesive gum.

2176 **844** 750l. multicoloured . . . 75 50

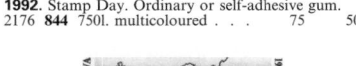

845 Map of Europe and Lions Emblem

1992. 75th Anniv of Lions International and 38th Europa Forum, Genoa.

2178 **845** 3000l. multicoloured . . 2·30 50

846 European Community Emblem and Members' Flags

1992. European Single Market (1st issue).

2179 **846** 600l. multicoloured . . . 50 1·60

See also Nos. 2182/93.

847 Woman with Food Bowl

1992. International Nutrition Conference, Rome.

2180 **847** 500l. multicoloured . . . 45 50

848 Caltagirone Crib

849 Buildings on Flag of Italy

1992. Christmas.

2181 **848** 600l. multicoloured . . . 55 50

1993. European Single Market (2nd issue). Designs differing in flag of country and language of inscription. Multicoloured.

2182	750l. Type **849**	55	50
2183	750l. Belgium	55	50
2184	750l. Denmark	55	50
2185	750l. France	55	50
2186	750l. Germany	55	50
2187	750l. Greece	55	50
2188	750l. Ireland	55	50
2189	750l. Luxembourg	55	50
2190	750l. Netherlands	55	50
2191	750l. Portugal	55	50
2192	750l. United Kingdom . . .	55	50
2193	750l. Spain	55	50

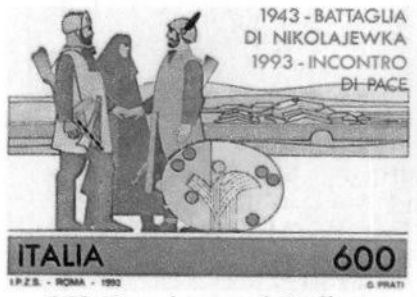

850 Russian and Italian Alpine Veterans

851 Mezzettino, Colombina and Arlecchino

1993. 50th Anniv Meeting of Veterans of Battle of Nikolayevka.

2194 **850** 600l. multicoloured . . . 50 50

1993. Death Bicentenary of Carlo Goldoni (dramatist). Multicoloured.

2195	500l. Type **851**	45	50
2196	500l. Arlecchino and portrait of Goldoni . . .	45	65

852 "Africa" (mosaic, Roman villa, Piazza Armerina)

1993. Artistic Heritage.

2197 **852** 750l. multicoloured . . . 65 50

853 Wedge stopping Heart-shaped Cog

1993. National Health Day. Campaign against Heart Disease.

2198 **853** 750l. multicoloured . . . 65 50

854 Tabby

1993. Domestic Cats. Multicoloured.

2199	600l. Type **854**	45	50
2200	600l. White Persian	45	50
2201	600l. Devon rex (vert) . . .	45	50
2202	600l. Maine coon (vert) . .	45	50

1993. 100 Years of Radio (3rd issue). As T **822**. Multicoloured.

2203 750l. Temistocle Calzecchi Onesti (physicist) and apparatus for detecting electromagnetic waves . . 65 50

855 "The Piazza"

856 Horace

1993. Death Bicentenary of Francesco Guardi (artist).

2204 **855** 3200l. multicoloured . . 2·50 2·75

1993. 2000th Death Anniv of Horace (Quintus Horatius Flaccus) (poet).

2205 **856** 600l. multicoloured . . . 50 50

857 Cottolengo and Small House of the Divine Providence, Turin

858 "Carousel Horses" (Lino Bianchi Barriviera)

1993. St. Giuseppe Benedetto Cottolengo Commemoration.

2206 **857** 750l. multicoloured . . . 65 50

1993. Europa. Contemporary Art. Mult.

2207	750l. Type **858**	70	50
2208	850l. "Dynamism of Coloured Shapes" (Gino Severini)	80	50

859 Medal (Giuseppe Romagnoli)

860 Emblem

1993. 400th Anniv of San Luca National Academy.

2209 **859** 750l. multicoloured . . . 65 50

1993. "Family Fest '93" International Conference, Rome.

2210 **860** 750l. multicoloured . . . 65 50

861 Player and Club Badge

863 Canoeing

862 Carloforte

1993. Milan, National Football Champion, 1992–93.

2211 **861** 750l. multicoloured . . . 65 50

1993. Tourist Publicity (20th series). Mult.

2212	600l. Type **862**	50	50
2213	600l. Palmanova	50	50
2214	600l. Senigallia	50	50
2215	600l. Sorrento	50	50

See also Nos. 2248/51 and 2315/18.

1993. World Canoeing Championships, Trentino.

2216 **863** 750l. multicoloured . . . 65 50

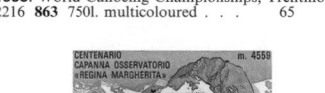

864 Observatory

1993. Centenary of Regina Margherita Observatory.

2217 **864** 500l. multicoloured . . . 45 50

865 Staircase, St. Salome's Cathedral, Veroli

866 Soldier, Boy with Rifle and German Helmet

1993. Artistic Heritage.

2218 **865** 750l. multicoloured . . . 65 50

1993. Second World War 50th Anniversaries (1st issue). Multicoloured.

2219	750l. Type **866** (the Four Days of Naples)	75	50
2220	750l. Menorah, people in railway truck and Star of David (deportation of Roman Jews)	75	50
2221	750l. Seven Cervi brothers (execution)	75	50

See also Nos. 2259/61.

867 Carriage

1993. The Taxis Family in Postal History. Multicoloured.

2222	750l. Type **867**	60	50
2223	750l. Taxis arms	60	50
2224	750l. Gig	60	50
2225	750l. 17th-century postal messenger	60	50
2226	750l. 18th-century postal messenger	60	50

868 Head Office, Rome

1993. Centenary of Bank of Italy. Mult.

2227	750l. Type **868**	1·10	50
2228	1000l. 1000 lire banknote (first note issued by Bank)	1·50	80

869 Colonies Express Letter Stamp Design

1993. Stamp Day. Centenary of First Italian Colonies Stamps.

2229 **869** 600l. red and blue . . . 50 50

870 Tableau Vivant, Corchiano

1993. Christmas. Multicoloured.
2230 600l. Type **870** 50 50
2231 750l. "The Annunciation" (Piero della Francesca) . . 60 50

871 17th-century Map of Foggia

1993. Treasures from State Archives and Museums (1st series). Multicoloured.
2232 600l. Type **871** (Foggia Archives) 50 50
2233 600l. "Concert" (Bartolomeo Manfredi) (Uffizi Gallery, Florence) 50 50
2234 750l. View of Siena from 15th-century illuminated manuscript (Siena Archives) (vert) 55 50
2235 850l. "The Death of Adonis" (Sebastiano del Piombo) (Uffizi Gallery) 65 50
See also Nos. 2266/9, 2306/9 and 2346/9.

872 Ringmaster and Bareback Riders **873** Mother and Child inside House

1994. The Circus. Multicoloured.
2236 600l. Type **872** 45 50
2237 750l. Clowns 55 50

1994. "The Housewife, a Presence that Counts".
2238 **873** 750l. multicoloured . . . 60 50

874 "Bread" (Dario Piazza) **876** "The Risen Christ" (statue)

875 Boxer

1994. Paintings of Italian Food. Multicoloured.
2239 500l. Type **874** 45 50
2240 600l. "Italian Pasta in the World" (Erminia Scaglione) 60 50

1994. 100 Years of Radio (4th issue). As T **822**. Multicoloured.
2241 750l. Augusto Righi (physicist) and his Hertzian oscillator 65 50

1994. Dogs. Multicoloured.
2242 600l. Type **875** 45 50
2243 600l. Dalmatian 45 50
2244 600l. Maremma sheepdog 45 50
2245 600l. German shepherd . . 45 50

1994. Procession of "The Risen Christ", Tarquinia.
2246 **876** 750l. multicoloured . . . 60 50

877 Pacioli in Study

1994. 500th Anniv of Publication of "Summary of Arithmetic, Geometry, Proportion and Proportionality" by Fra' Luca Pacioli.
2247 **877** 750l. multicoloured . . . 60 50

1994. Tourist Publicity (21st series). As T **862**. Multicoloured.
2248 600l. Odescalchi Castle, Santa Marinella 45 50
2249 600l. St. Michael's Abbey, Monticchio 45 50
2250 600l. Orta San Giulio . . . 45 50
2251 600l. Cathedral, Messina . . 45 50

878 Kossuth **879** Women's High-diving

1994. Death Centenary of Lajos Kossuth (Hungarian statesman).
2252 **878** 3750l. multicoloured . . 2·75 1·60

1994. World Water Sports Championships. Multicoloured.
2253 600l. Type **879** 50 50
2254 750l. Water polo 60 50

880 Club Badge, Football and Colours

1994. Milan, National Football Champion, 1993–94.
2255 **880** 750l. multicoloured . . . 70 50

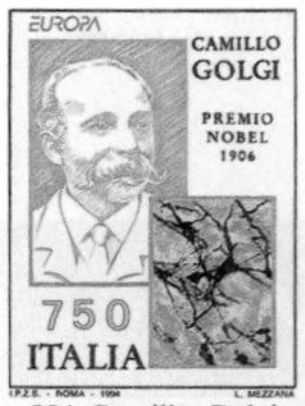

881 Camillo Golgi (cytologist) and Golgi Cells **882** "Goddess of Caldevigo" (bronze statuette, 5th century B.C.)

1994. Europa. Discoveries. Italian Nobel Prize winners. Multicoloured.
2256 750l. Type **881** (medicine, 1906) 65 50
2257 850l. Giulio Natta (chemist) and diagram of polymer structure (chemistry, 1963) 75 50

1994. "Ancient Peoples of Italy" Archaeological Exhibition, Rimini.
2258 **882** 750l. multicoloured . . . 60 50

883 Destruction of Montecassino **884** Washing of Feet

1994. Second World War 50th Anniversaries (2nd issue). Multicoloured.
2259 750l. Type **883** 45 50
2260 750l. Bound prisoners (Ardeatine Caves Massacre) 45 50
2261 750l. Family (Marzabotto Massacre) 45 50

1994. 22nd National Eucharistic Congress, Siena.
2262 **884** 600l. multicoloured . . . 45 50

885 "Ariadne, Venus and Bacchus"

1994. Artistic Heritage. 400th Death Anniv of Tintoretto (artist).
2263 **885** 750l. multicoloured . . . 60 50

886 "Piazza del Duomo during the Plague, 1630" (attr Cigoli)

1994. 750th Anniv of Arciconfraternita della Misericordia, Florence.
2264 **886** 750l. multicoloured . . . 50 50

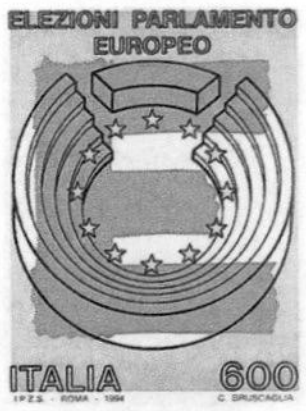

887 "E", European Union Emblem and Parliament **888** Olympic Rings and Pierre de Coubertin (founder)

1994. European Parliament Elections.
2265 **887** 600l. multicoloured . . . 50 50

1994. Treasures from State Archives and Museums (2nd series). As T **871**. Multicoloured.
2266 600l. Frontispiece of notary's register, 1623–24 (Catania Archives) (vert) 45 50
2267 600l. "Death of Patroclus" (Attic vase, 5th century B.C.) (Agrigento Archaeological Museum) (vert) 50 50
2268 750l. "Galata and his Wife" (statue) (National Roman Museum) (vert) 50 50
2269 850l. Civic seal, 1745 (Campobasso Archives) (vert) 60 50

1994. Centenary of Int Olympic Committee.
2270 **888** 850l. multicoloured . . . 70 50

889 Vesuvius and "G 7" **890** Church of the Holy House and "Madonna and Child"

1994. Group of Seven (industrialized countries) Summit, Naples.
2271 **889** 600l. blue, ultram & grn 50 50

1994. 700th Anniv of Shrine of the Nativity of the Virgin, Loreto.
2272 **890** 500l. multicoloured . . . 50 50

891 Pietro Miliani (papermaker) (after Francesco Rosaspina) **892** Frederick II (sculpture, Bitonto Cathedral)

1994. Stamp Day. Multicoloured.
2273 600l. Type **891** 45 50
2274 750l. Paper and Watermark Museum (former St. Dominic's Monastery), Fabriano 60 50

1994. 800th Birth Anniv of Frederick II, Holy Roman Emperor.
2275 **892** 750l. multicoloured . . . 65 50

893 St. Mark's Basilica

1994. 900th Anniv of Dedication of St. Mark's Basilica, Venice.
2276 **893** 750l. multicoloured . . . 70 65
MS2277 80 × 115 mm. No. 2276 together with No. 1491 of San Marino . . . . 1·30 2·75

894 "The Annunciation" (Melozzo da Forli) **895** Club Emblem on Globe

1994. Christmas. Multicoloured.
2278 600l. Type **894** 50 50
2279 750l. "Sacred Conversation" (detail, Lattanzio da Rimini) 65 50

1994. Centenary of Italian Touring Club.
2280 **895** 600l. multicoloured . . . 45 50

896 Headquarters, Rome

1994. 75th Anniv of Credit for Businesses and Public Works.
2281 **896** 750l. multicoloured . . . 70 50

897 New Emblem

1994. Incorporation of Italian Post. Size 34 × 26 mm.
2282 – 600l. red and silver . . . 60 50
2283 **897** 750l. black, green and red 85 50
2284 750l. red 85 50
DESIGN—VERT: 600l. Palazzo Querini Dubois, Venice (restored with Post Office help).
For 750 and 850l. values, size 26 × 17 mm, see Nos. 2343/4.

898 Gentile **899** Rainbow, Dove, Olive Tree and Flood

1994. 50th Death Anniv of Giovanni Gentile (philosopher).
2285 **898** 750l. multicoloured . . . 65 50

1995. For Flood Victims.
2286 **899** 750l.+2250l. mult . . . 3·25 5·50

900 Skater

1995. World Speed Skating Championships, Baselga di Pine.
2287 **900** 750l. multicoloured . . . 65 50

901 First Issue of "La Domenica del Corriere"
902 Rice

1995. 50th Death Anniv of Achille Beltrame (painter).
2288 **901** 500l. multicoloured . . . 55 50

1995. Italian Food. Multicoloured.
2289 500l. Type **902** 50 50
2290 750l. Olives and olive oil . . 65 50

903 Grey Herons

1995. Birds, Multicoloured.
2291 600l. Type **903** 45 50
2292 600l. Griffon vultures ("Grifone") 45 50
2293 600l. Golden eagles ("Aquila Reale") 45 50
2294 600l. White-winged snow finches ("Fringuello Alpino") 45 50

904 Anniversary Emblem

1995. 50th Anniv of U.N.O.
2295 **904** 850l. black, blue and gold 65 50

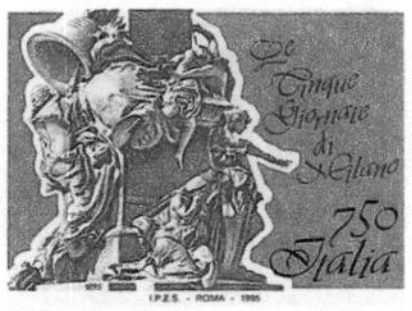

905 Detail of Monument (Giuseppe Grande)

1995. Centenary of Monument to the Fallen of the Five Days of Milan (1848 uprising).
2296 **905** 750l. multicoloured . . . 60 50

906 Princess Mafalda of Savoy and Concentration Camp

1995. 50th Anniv of End of Second World War. Multicoloured.
2297 750l. Type **906** 55 65
2298 750l. DUKW at Anzio . . . 55 65
2299 750l. Teresa Gullace and scene of her death 55 65
2300 750l. Florence Town Hall and Military Medal . . . 55 65
2301 750l. Vittorio Veneto Town Hall and Military Medal 55 65
2302 750l. Cagliari Town Hall and Military Medal . . . 55 65
2303 750l. Battle of Mount Lungo 55 65
2304 750l. Parachuting supplies in the Balkans 55 65
2305 750l. Light cruisers of the Eighth Division in Atlantic 55 65

1995. Treasures from State Archives and Museums (3rd series). As T **871**. Multicoloured.
2306 500l. Illuminated letter "P" from statute of Pope Innocent III (Rome Archives) (vert) 35 50
2307 500l. "Port of Naples" (detail, Bernardo Strozzi) (St. Martin National Museum, Naples) 45 50
2308 750l. Illuminated letter "I" showing the Risen Christ from 1481 document (Mantua Archives) (vert) 50 50
2309 850l. "Sacred Love and Profane Love" (Titian) (Borghese Museum and Gallery, Rome) 60 50

907 Emblem
908 Santa Croce Basilica, Florence

1995. Centenary of Venice Biennale.
2310 **907** 750l. blue, gold & yellow 60 50

1995. Artistic Heritage.
2311 **908** 750l. brown 60 50

909 Soldiers and Civilians celebrating
910 Players

1995. Europa. Peace and Freedom. Mult.
2312 750l. Type **909** (50th anniv of end of Second World War in Europe) 65 50
2313 850l. Mostar Bridge, (Bosnia) and Council of Europe emblem 75 50

1995. Centenary of Volleyball.
2314 **910** 750l. blue, orange & grn 60 50

1995. Tourist Publicity (22nd series). As T **862**. Multicoloured.
2315 750l. Alatri 55 50
2316 750l. Nuoro 55 50
2317 750l. Susa 55 50
2318 750l. Venosa 55 50

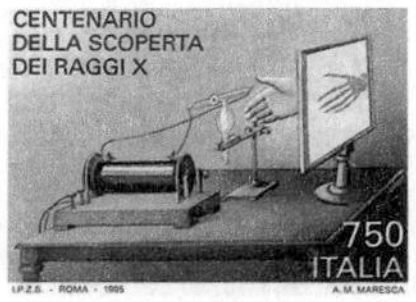

911 Experiment demonstrating X-rays

1995. Centenary of Discovery of X-rays by Wilhelm Rontgen.
2319 **911** 750l. multicoloured . . . 60 50

912 Player and Club Badge

1995. Juventus, National Football Champion, 1994–95.
2320 **912** 750l. multicoloured . . . 60 50

913 Villa Griffone (site of Marconi's early experiments)

1995. 100 Years of Radio (5th issue). Centenary of First Radio Transmission. Multicoloured.
2321 750l. Type **913** 60 50
2322 850l. Guglielmo Marconi and transmitter (36 × 21 mm) 70 50

914 St. Antony, Holy Basilica (Padua) and Page of Gospel
916 Milan Cathedral and Eye (congress emblem)

915 Durazzo Pallavicini, Pegli

1995. 800th Birth Anniv of St. Antony of Padua. Multicoloured.
2323 750l. Type **914** 60 50
2324 850l. St. Antony holding Child Jesus (painting, Vieira Lusitano) (horiz) 70 50

1995. Public Gardens (1st series). Multicoloured.
2325 750l. Type **915** 60 50
2326 750l. Boboli, Florence . . . 60 50
2327 750l. Ninfa, Cisterna di Latina 60 50
2328 750l. Parco della Reggia, Caserta 60 50
See also Nos. 2439/42.

1995. 10th European Ophthalmological Society Congress, Milan.
2329 **916** 750l. multicoloured . . . 60 50

917 "Sailors' Wives"

1995. Birth Centenary of Massimo Campigli (painter).
2330 **917** 750l. multicoloured . . . 75 50

918 Dome of Santa Maria del Fiore (Florence), Galileo and Albert Einstein

1995. 14th World Relative Physics Conference, Florence.
2331 **918** 750l. blue, brown & black 60 50

919 Rudolph Valentino in "The Son of the Sheik"

1995. Centenary of Motion Pictures.
2332 **919** 750l. black, blue and red 55 50
2333 – 750l. multicoloured . . . 55 50
2334 – 750l. multicoloured . . . 55 50
2335 – 750l. multicoloured . . . 55 50
DESIGNS: No. 2333, Toto in "The Gold of Naples"; 2334, Frederico Fellini's "Cabiria Nights"; 2335, Poster (by Massimo Geleng) for "Cinecitta 95" film festival.

920 Wheatfield and Anniversary Emblem

1995. 50th Anniv of F.A.O.
2336 **920** 850l. multicoloured . . . 70 65

921 St. Albert's Stone Coffin (detail) and Basilica

1995. 900th Anniversaries of Pontida Basilica and Death of St. Albert of Prezzate.
2337 **921** 1000l. brown and blue 80 80

922 Athletes

1995. 1st World Military Games, Rome.
2338 **922** 850l. multicoloured . . . 75 65

923 Globe and Means of Communication

1995. 50th Anniv of Ansa News Agency.
2339 **923** 750l. multicoloured . . . 60 50

924 Crib (Stefano da Putignano), Polignano Cathedral

1995. Christmas. Multicoloured.
2340 750l. Type **924** 85 50
2341 850l. "Adoration of the Wise Men" (detail, Fra Angelico) . . . . 1·00 65

925 Renato Mondolfo (philatelist) and Trieste 1949 20l. Stamp

1995. Stamp Day.
2342 **925** 750l. multicoloured . . . 55 50

1995. 1st Anniv of Incorporation of Italian Post. Size 26 × 17 mm.
2343 **897** 750l. red 55 50
2344 850l. black, green and red 70 65

926 Collage representing Marinetti's Works

1996. 120th Birth Anniv of Filippo Marinetti (writer and founder of Futurist movement).
2345 **926** 750l. multicoloured . . . 55 50

1996. Treasures from State Archives and Museums (4th series). As T **871**. Multicoloured.
2346 750l. Arms (Georgofili Academy, Florence) . . . 55 50
2347 750l. Illuminated letter showing St. Luke and his ox from Constitution of 1372 (Lucca Archives) (vert) 55 50
2348 850l. Inkwells, pen and manuscript of Gabriele d'Annunzio (writer) (Il Vittoriale, Gardone Riviera) 60 50
2349 850l. "Life of King Modus and Queen Racio" from 1486 miniature (Turin Archives) 60 50

927 "Sarah and the Angel" (fresco, Archbishop's Palace, Udine)

1996. 300th Birth Anniv of Giambattista Tiepolo (painter).
2350 **927** 1000l. multicoloured . . 90 80

928 White Wine

1996. Italian Wine Production. Multicoloured.
2351 500l. Type **928** 30 50
2352 750l. Red wine 45 50

929 Marco Polo and Palace in the Forbidden City

1996. 700th Anniv (1995) of Marco Polo's Return from Asia and "China '96" International Stamp Exhibition, Peking.
2353 **929** 1250l. multicoloured . . 1·10 1·10

930 Milan Cathedral (left detail)
931 Quill pen and Satellite (50th Anniv of National Federation of Italian Press)

1996. "Italia 98" International Stamp Exhibition, Milan (1st issue). Multicoloured.
2354 750l. Type **930** . . . . . . 1·90 50
2355 750l. Cathedral (right detail) 1·90 50
Nos. 2354/5 were issued together, se-tenant, forming a composite design of the Cathedral.

See also Nos. **MS**2412, 2518, 2523, 2528/30 and 2531.

1996. Anniversaries.
2356 **931** 750l. multicoloured . . . 65 50
2357 – 750l. blue, pink and black 65 50
DESIGN—HORIZ: No. 2357, Globe (centenary of "La Gazetta dello Sport" (newspaper)).

932 Postman and Emblem
933 Uniforms of Different Periods

1996. International Museum of Postal Images, Belvedere Ostrense.
2358 **932** 500l. multicoloured . . . 50 50

1996. Centenary of Academy of Excise Guards.
2359 **933** 750l. multicoloured . . . 70 50

934 Truck and Route Map
935 Carina Negrone (pilot)

1996. Trans-continental Drive, Rome–New York.
2360 **934** 4650l. multicoloured . . 4·25 3·25

1996. Europa. Famous Women. Multicoloured.
2361 750l. Type **935** 60 50
2362 850l. Adelaide Ristori (actress) 75 50

936 Fishes, Sea and Coastline from St. Raphael to Genoa

1996. 20th Anniv of Ramoge Agreement on Environmental Protection of the Mediterranean.
2363 **936** 750l. multicoloured . . . 65 50

937 Celestino V and Town of Fumone

1996. 700th Death Anniv of Pope Celestino V.
2364 **937** 750l. multicoloured . . . 70 50

938 St Anthony's Church, Diano Marina

1996. Tourist Publicity (23rd series). Mult.
2365 750l. Type **938** 60 50
2366 750l. Pienza Cathedral . . . 60 50
2367 750l. Belltower of St. Michael the Archangel's Church, Monte Sant'Angelo . . . 60 50
2368 750l. Prehistoric stone dwelling, Lampedusa . . 60 50

939 Abbey and Relief from 12th-century Ivory Reliquary

1996. 500th Anniv of Reconsecration of Farfa Abbey.
2369 **939** 1000l. black, yell & orge 90 80

940 Fair Entrance and Mt. Pellegrino

1996. Mediterranean Fair, Palermo.
2370 **940** 750l. multicoloured . . . 65 50

941 State Arms
942 Rider and Emblem

1996. 50th Anniv of Italian Republic.
2371 **941** 750l. multicoloured . . . 60 50

1996. 50th Anniv of Production of Vespa Motor Scooters.
2372 **942** 750l. multicoloured . . . 60 50

943 Views of Messina and Venice

1996. 40th Anniv of Founding Meetings of European Economic Community, Messina and Venice.
2373 **943** 750l. multicoloured . . . 60 50

944 Athlete on Starting Block and 1896 Athletes

1996. Centenary of Modern Olympic Games and Olympic Games, Atlanta. Multicoloured.
2374 500l. Type **944** 45 50
2375 750l. Putting the shot and view of Atlanta (vert) . . 65 50
2376 850l. Gymnast, stadium and basketball player 75 50
2377 1250l. 1896 stadium, Athens, and 1996 stadium, Atlanta (vert) . . . . 1·00 1·10

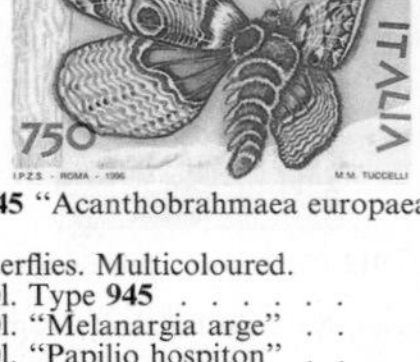

945 "Acanthobrahmaea europaea"

1996. Butterflies. Multicoloured.
2378 750l. Type **945** 55 50
2379 750l. "Melanargia arge" . . 55 50
2380 750l. "Papilio hospiton" . . 55 50
2381 750l. "Zygaena rubicundus" 55 50

946 "Prima Comunione"

1996. Italian Films (1st series).
2382 **946** 750l. black, red and blue 60 50
2383 – 750l. multicoloured . . . 60 50
2384 – 750l. multicoloured . . . 60 50
DESIGNS: No. 2383, Poster for "Cabiria"; 2384, "Scusate il Ritardo".
See also Nos. 2453/5 and 2528/30.

947 Santa Maria del Fiore

1996. 700th Anniv of Cathedral of Santa Maria del Fiore, Florence.
2385 **947** 750l. blue 70 50

948 Player, Shield and Club Badge
949 Choppy (congress mascot)

1996. Milan, National Football Champion, 1995–96.
2386 **948** 750l. multicoloured . . . 85 50

1996. 13th International Prehistoric and Protohistoric Sciences Congress.
2387 **949** 850l. multicoloured . . . 75 50

950 Games Emblem and Pictograms
952 Rejoicing Crowd and Club Badge

951 Fair Entrance

1996. Mediterranean Games, Bari (1997).
2388 **950** 750l. multicoloured . . . 70 50

1996. Levant Fair, Bari.
2389 **951** 750l. multicoloured . . . 70 50

1996. Juventus, European Football Champion, 1995–96.
2390 **952** 750l. multicoloured . . . 70 50

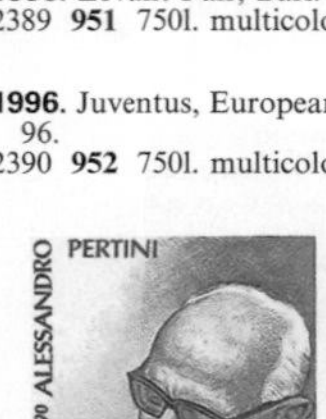

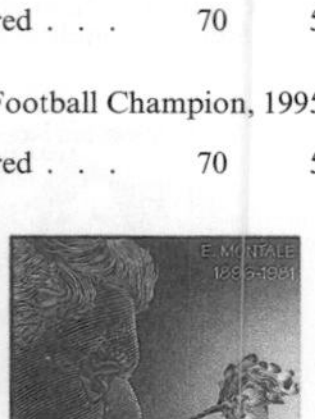

953 Pertini
954 Montale and Hoopoe

1996. Birth Centenary of Alessandro Pertini (President 1978–85).
2391 **953** 750l. multicoloured . . . 65 50

1996. Birth Centenary of Eugenio Montale (poet).
2392 **954** 750l. brown and blue . . 65 50

955 "The Annunciation"

1996. 400th Birth Anniv of Pietro Berrettini da Cortona (artist).
2393 **955** 500l. multicoloured . . . 55 50

956 Tex Willer (Galep)

1996. Stamp Collecting. Strip Cartoons. Mult.
2394 750l. Type **956** 65 50
2395 850l. Corto Maltese (Hugo Pratt) 75 50

957 Vortex and "Stamps"
958 Bell Tower and Former Benedictine Abbey (seat of faculty)

1996. Stamp Day.
2396 **957** 750l. multicoloured . . . 60 50

1996. Universities.
2397 **958** 750l. brown 60 50
2398 – 750l. blue 60 50
2399 – 750l. green 60 50
DESIGNS—VERT: No. 2397. Type **958** (centenary of Faculty of Agriculture, Perugia University); 2398, Former St. Matthew's Cathedral (seat of Medical School), Salerno University. HORIZ: No. 2399, Athenaeum, Sassari University.

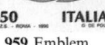

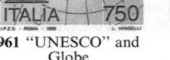

959 Emblem
960 "Madonna of the Quail" (Antonio Pisanello)

1996. World Food Summit, Rome.
2400 **959** 850l. green and black . . 65 50

1996. Christmas. Multicoloured.
2401 750l. Type **960** 60 50
2402 850l. Father Christmas and toys (horiz) 75 50

961 "UNESCO" and Globe
962 Headquarters, Rome

1996. 50th Anniversaries of U.N.E.S.C.O. and U.N.I.C.E.F.
2403 750l. Type **961** 55 50
2404 850l. U.N.I.C.E.F. emblem on kite, baby and globe 70 50

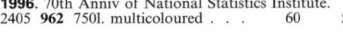

1996. 70th Anniv of National Statistics Institute.
2405 **962** 750l. multicoloured . . . 60 50

963 Bookcase
964 Hall of the Tricolour, Reggio Emilia

1996. 50th Anniv of Strega Prize.
2406 **963** 3400l. multicoloured . . 2·30 2·40

1997. Bicentenary of First Tricolour (now national flag), Cisalpine Republic.
2407 **964** 750l. multicoloured . . . 60 50

965 Tower Blocks and Skier

1997. World Alpine Skiing Championships, Sestriere. Multicoloured.
2408 750l. Type **965** 60 50
2409 850l. Olympic colours forming ski run and ski 60 50

966 Ferraris, Early Motor and Ferraris National Electrotechnology Institute, Turin

1997. Death Centenary of Galileo Ferraris (physicist).
2410 **966** 750l. multicoloured . . . 60 50

967 Loi

1997. 5th Death Anniv of Emanuela Loi (bodyguard killed in Mafia car bombing).
2411 **967** 750l. multicoloured . . . 60 50

1997. "Italia 98" International Stamp Exhibition, Milan (2nd issue). Sheet 150 × 80 mm containing T **968** and similar vert designs. Multicoloured.
MS2412 750l. Bologna 1910 cancellation aerogramme from Balboa flight and postcard with 1917 25c. airmail stamp (Aerophilately); 750l. Cancellations used for the signing of the Rome Treaty (forming European Economic Community), Rome Olympic Games and Holy Year, 1952 Leonardo da Vinci 80l. stamp and 1931 inauguration of Milan railway station postcard (Thematic Philately); 750l. Type **968** (Postal History); 750l. "Democratica", Italian stamp catalogue and L'Italia Filatelica (stamp review) (Philatelic Literature) . . . . 5·25 4·00

969 Statue of Marcus Aurelius
970 St. Germiniano (after Bartolomeo Schedoni) holding Modena Cathedral

1997. 40th Anniv of Treaty of Rome (foundation of European Economic Community).
2413 **969** 750l. multicoloured . . . 50 50

1997. 1600th Death Anniv of St. Germiniano (patron saint of Modena).
2414 **970** 750l. multicoloured . . . 60 50

971 "Baptism of St. Ambrose" and "Hand of God recalling him to City"
972 Statue of Minerva, Central Square, Rome University

1997. 1600th Death Anniv of St. Ambrose, Bishop of Milan.
2415 **971** 1000l. multicoloured . . 75 50
The illustrations are taken from reliefs by Volvinio on the Golden Altar in St. Ambrose's Cathedral, Milan.

1997. Universities.
2416 **972** 750l. red 60 50
2417 – 750l. blue 60 50
DESIGN: No. 2417, Palace of Bo, Padua University.

973 St. Peter's Cathedral and Colosseum within "Wolf suckling Romulus and Remus"

1997. 2750th Anniv of Foundation of Rome.
2418 **973** 850l. multicoloured . . . 70 50

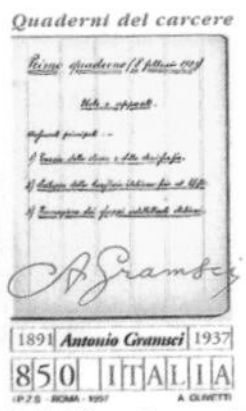

974 Pre-Roman Walls, Gela
975 First Page of Prison Notebook and Signature

1997.
2419 **974** 750l. multicoloured . . . 60 50

1997. 60th Death Anniv of Antonio Gramsci (politician).
2420 **975** 850l. multicoloured . . . 60 50

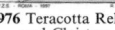

976 Teracotta Relief and Cloisters
978 Detail of 1901 Poster for "Tosca" and Theatre

977 Shoemaker's Workshop

1997. 500th Anniv of Consecration of Pavia Church.
2421 **976** 1000l. multicoloured . . 85 50

1997. Europa. Tales and Legends. Mult.
2422 800l. Type **977** ("He who becomes the Property of Others works for his Soup") 55 50
2423 900l. Street singer (19th-century copper etching) 65 50

1997. Centenary of Teatro Massimo, Palermo.
2424 **978** 800l. multicoloured . . . 65 50

979 St. Sebastian's Church, Acireale

1997. Tourist Publicity (24th series). Mult.
2425 800l. Type **979** 65 50
2426 800l. Cicero and his tomb, Formia 65 50
2427 800l. St. Mary of the Assumption, Positano . . 65 50
2428 800l. St. Vitale's Basilica, Ravenna 65 50

980 Books and Marble Floor

1997. 10th Book Salon, Turin.
2429 **980** 800l. multicoloured . . . 70 50

981 Queen Paola and Castel Sant'Angelo, Rome

1997. 60th Birthday of Queen Paola of Belgium.
2430 **981** 750l. multicoloured . . . 70 50

982 Palazzo della Civilta del Lavoro and Fair Pavilions

1997. Rome Fair.
2431 **982** 800l. multicoloured . . . 70 50

983 Orvieto Cathedral
984 Morosini in Via Tasso Prison, 1944

1997.
2432 **983** 450l. violet 40 50

1997. 53rd Death Anniv of Father Giuseppe Morosini.
2433 **984** 800l. multicoloured . . . 65 50

985 Player, Club Emblem and Football
986 Chamois and "Iris marsica"

1997. Juventus, National Football Champion, 1996–97.
2434 **985** 800l. multicoloured . . . 65 50

1997. 75th Anniv of Abruzzo National Park.
2435 **986** 800l. multicoloured . . . 55 50

987 Towers and Fair Complex

1997. Bologna Fair.
2436 **987** 800l. multicoloured . . . 65 50

988 Pennant and Ships' Bows

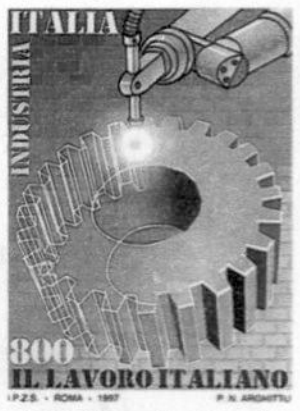

990 Cogwheel and Robot Arm (industry)

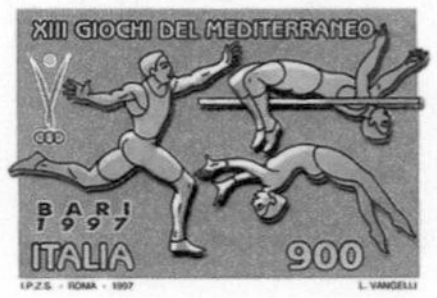

989 Runner, High Jumper and Gymnast

1997. Centenary of Italian Naval League.
2437 **988** 800l. multicoloured . . . 70 50

1997. 13th Mediterranean Games, Bari.
2438 **989** 900l. multicoloured . . . 75 50

1997. Public Gardens (2nd series). As T **915**. Multicoloured.
2439 800l. Orto Botanico, Palermo 60 50
2440 800l. Villa Sciarra, Rome . . 60 50
2441 800l. Cavour, Santena . . . 60 50
2442 800l. Miramare, Trieste . . 60 50

1997. Italian Work. Multicoloured.
2443 800l. Type **990** 55 50
2444 900l. Cereals, fruit trees, grapes and sun (agriculture) (horiz) . . . 60 50

991 Globe and the "Matthew"

1997. 500th Anniv of John Cabot's Discovery of North America.
2445 **991** 1300l. multicoloured . . 1·10 80

992 Verri

993 "Madonna of the Rosary" (Pomarancio il Vecchio)

1997. Death Bicentenary of Pietro Verri (illuminist).
2446 **992** 3600l. multicoloured . . 3·75 2·40

1997. Painters' Anniversaries. Multicoloured.
2447 450l. Type **993** (400th death anniv) 55 50
2448 650l. "The Miracle of Ostia" ((detail, Paolo Uccello) (600th birth anniv)) (26 × 37 mm) 45 50

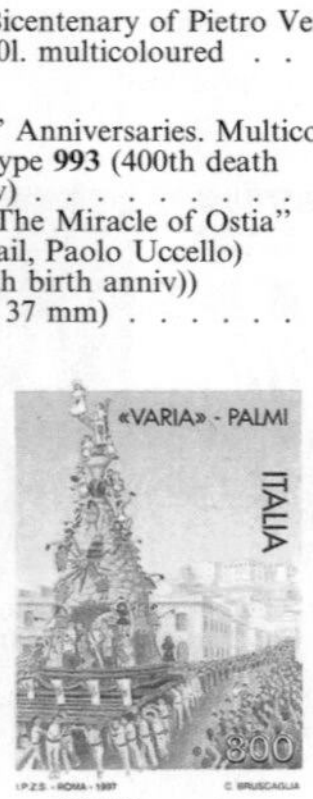

994 Procession

1997. Varia Festival, Palmi.
2449 **994** 800l. multicoloured . . . 70 50

995 Basketball

1997. University Games, Sicily. Multicoloured.
2450 450l. Type **995** 35 50
2451 800l. High jumping 65 50

996 Rosmini

1997. Birth Bicentenary of Antonio Rosmini (philosopher).
2452 **996** 800l. multicoloured . . . 70 50

1997. Italian Films (2nd series). As T **946**.
2453 800l. multicoloured 55 50
2454 800l. black, blue and red . . 55 50
2455 800l. multicoloured 55 50
DESIGNS: No. 2453, Pietro Germi in "Il Ferroviere"; 2454, Anna Magnani in "Mamma Roma"; 2455, Ugo Tognazzi in "Amici Miei".

997 Open Book and Beach, Viareggio

1997. Viareggio-Repaci Prize.
2456 **997** 4000l. multicoloured . . 3·25 2·40

998 Venue and Bell Tower

1997. International Trade Fair, Bolzano.
2457 **998** 800l. multicoloured . . . 70 50

999 Bronze Head (500 BC)

1000 Pope Paul VI and Door of Death, St. Peter's Cathedral, Rome

1997. Museum Exhibits. Multicoloured.
2458 450l. Type **999** (National Museum, Reggio Calabria) 40 50
2459 650l. "Madonna and Child with Two Vases of Roses" (Ercole de Roberti) (National Picture Gallery, Ferrara) 45 50
2460 800l. Miniature of poet Sordello da Goito (Arco Palace Museum, Mantua) 50 50
2461 900l. "St. George and the Dragon" (Vitale di Bologna) (National Picture Gallery, Bologna) 55 50

1997. Birth Centenary of Pope Paul VI.
2462 **1000** 4000l. blue . . . . . . 3·25 2·10

1001 Portello Pavilion (venue) and Milan Cathedral

1002 War-ravaged and Reconstructed Cities

1997. Milan Fair.
2463 **1001** 800l. multicoloured . . 65 50

1997. 50th Anniv of European Recovery Programme ("Marshall Plan").
2464 **1002** 800l. multicoloured . . 65 50

1003 Nativity (crib, St Francis's Church, Leonessa)

1997. Christmas. Multicoloured.
2465 800l. Type **1003** 65 50
2466 900l. "Nativity" (painting, Sta. Maria Maggiore, Spelo) 85 50

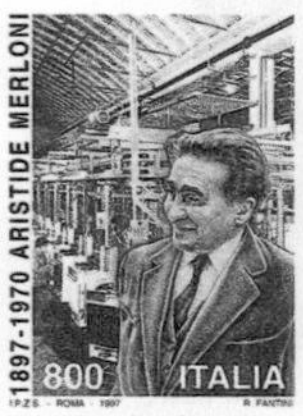

1004 Production Plant and Merloni

1005 Cavalcaselle and Drawings

1997. Birth Centenary of Aristide Merloni (entrepreneur).
2467 **1004** 800l. multicoloured . . 65 50

1997. Death Centenary of Giovanni Battista Cavalcaselle (art historian).
2468 **1005** 800l. multicoloured . . 70 50

1006 Magnifying Glass and Fleur-de-lis

1997. Stamp Day.
2469 **1006** 800l. multicoloured . . 70 50

1007 Refugees aboard "Toscana" (steamer)

1997. 50th Anniv of Exodus of Italian Inhabitants from Istria, Fiume and Dalmatia.
2470 **1007** 800l. multicoloured . . 70 50

1008 Arms of State Police and Badge of Traffic Police

1997. 50th Anniv of Traffic Police.
2471 **1008** 800l. multicoloured . . 70 50

1009 Map of Italy in Column and Flag

1998. 50th Anniv of Constitution.
2472 **1009** 800l. black, red & green 65 50

1010 "Hercules and the Hydra"

1998. 500th Death Anniv of Antonio del Pollaiolo (painter).
2473 **1010** 800l. multicoloured . . 65 50

1011 Bertolt Brecht

1998. Writers' Birth Centenaries.
2474 **1011** 450l. multicoloured . . 40 50
2475 – 650l. multicoloured . . 55 50
2476 – 800l. multicoloured . . 65 65
2477 – 900l. blue, green & black 75 50
DESIGNS—HORIZ: 650l. Federico Garcia Lorca (poet); 800l. Curzio Malaparte. VERT: 900l. Leonida Repaci.

1012 Fair Complex

1998. Verona Fair.
2478 **1012** 800l. multicoloured . . 65 50

1013 Memorial Tablet in Casale Montferrato Synagogue

1998. 150th Anniv of Granting of Full Citizen Rights to Italian Jews.
2479 **1013** 800l. multicoloured . . 55 50

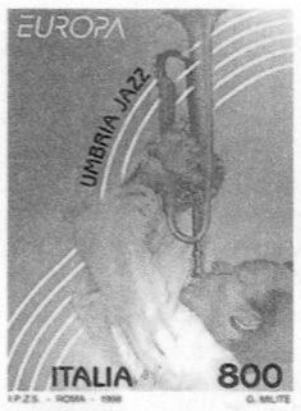

1014 Trombonist

1998. Europa. National Festivals. Mult.
2480 800l. Type **1014** (Umbria Jazz Festival) 60 50
2481 900l. Boy holding animal (Giffoni Film Festival) . . 65 50

1015 "The Last Supper"

1998. 500th Anniv of Completion of "The Last Supper" (mural) by Leonardo da Vinci.
2482 **1015** 800l. brown 65 50

1016 Costumes designed by Bernardo Buontalenti for First Opera in Florence

1017 Turin Cathedral and Holy Shroud

1998. Italian Theatre. Multicoloured.
2483 800l. Type **1016** (400th anniv of opera) 55 50
2484 800l. Gaetano Donizetti (composer, 150th death anniv) (horiz) 55 50

1998. 500th Anniv of Turin Cathedral. Display of the Holy Shroud.
2485 **1017** 800l. multicoloured . . 65 50

1018 Otranto Castle

1998. Tourist Publicity (25th series). Mult.
2486 800l. Type **1018** 65 50
2487 800l. Mori Fountain and Orsini Tower. Marino . . 65 50
2488 800l. Valfederia Chapel, Livigno 65 50
2489 800l. Marciana Marina, Elba 65 50

1019 Cagliari Cathedral, Drummer and Fair Building

1998. International Sardinia Fair, Cagliari.
2490 **1019** 800l. multicoloured . . 65 50

1020 "Charge of the Carabinieri at Pastrengo" (Sebastiano de Albertis)

1021 Flags

1998. 150th Anniv of Battle of Pastrengo.
2491 **1020** 800l. multicoloured . . 65 50

1998. Padua Fair.
2492 **1021** 800l. multicoloured . . 60 50

1022 Player and Club Badge

1998. Juventus, National Football Champion, 1997–98.
2493 **1022** 800l. multicoloured . . 65 50

1023 Turin Polytechnic

1024 Emblem

1998. Universities.
2494 **1023** 800l. blue 60 50

1998. World Food Programme.
2495 **1024** 900l. multicoloured . . 85 50

1025 Santa Maria de Pesio Carthusian Monastery

1998. Artistic Heritage.
2496 **1025** 800l. multicoloured . . 60 50

1026 Ammonites and Pergola

1998. 4th International "Fossils, Evolution, Ambience" Congress, Pergola.
2497 **1026** 800l. multicoloured . . 60 50

1027 Flag at Half-mast

1028 Endoscope and Globe

1998. "The Forces of Order, the Fallen".
2498 **1027** 800l. multicoloured . . 60 50

1998. 6th World General Endoscopic Surgery Congress, Rome.
2499 **1028** 900l. multicoloured . . 85 50

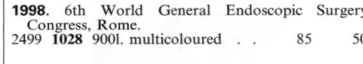

1029 First Parliamentary Chamber

1998. National Museums. Multicoloured.
2500 800l. Type **1029** (Italian Risorgimento Museum, Turin) 60 50
2501 800l. Statue of an ephebus (Athenian youth), Temple of Concord and column of Temple of Vulcan (Regional Archaeology Museum, Agrigento) (vert) 60 50
2502 800l. Sculpture by Umberto Boccioni and Palazzo Venier dei Leoni (venue) (Peggy Guggenheim Collection, Venice) . . . 60 50

1030 Fair Complex and Basilica

1998. Vicenza Trade Fair.
2503 **1030** 800l. multicoloured . . 65 50

1031 Leopardi (after Luigi Lolli) and Palazzo Leopardi, Recanati

1998. Birth Bicentenary of Giacomo Leopardi (poet).
2504 **1031** 800l. brown and black 55 50

1032 Young Etruscan Girl (detail of tomb painting)

1033 Pitch, Pitcher and Batter

1998. Women in Art.
2505 **1032** 100l. black, green & sil 15 15
2506 – 450l. multicoloured . . 40 15
2507 – 650l. multicoloured . . 60 15
2508 – 800l. brown and black 70 15
2509 – 1000l. blue, brn & blk 90 65
DESIGNS: 450l. Detail of "Herod's Banquet and the Dance of Salome" (fresco by Filippo Lippi in Prato Cathedral); 650l. "Profile of a Woman" (Antonio del Pollaiuolo); 800l. "Lady with a Unicorn" (detail, Raphael); 1000l. "Constanza Buonarelli" (bust by Gian Lorenzo Bernini).
For these designs but with face values in euros added, see Nos. 2537/41.

1998. 33rd World Cup Baseball Championship, Florence.
2510 **1033** 900l. multicoloured . . 75 50

1034 Columbus and Vespucci

1998. 500th Anniversaries of Landing of Christopher Columbus in Venezuela and of Amerigo Vespucci's Explorations.
2511 **1034** 1300l. multicoloured . . 1·00 80

1035 Emblem

1998. 50th International Stamp Fair, Riccione.
2512 **1035** 800l. multicoloured . . 65 50

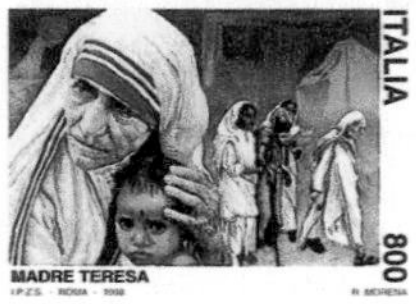

1036 Mother Teresa and Child

1998. 1st Death Anniv of Mother Teresa (founder of Missionaries of Charity). Multicoloured.
2513 800l. Type **1036** 65 50
2514 900l. Mother Teresa (vert) 75 50

1037 Father Pio and Monastery Church, San Giovanni Rotondo

1998. 30th Death Anniv of Father Pio da Pietrelcina (Capuchin friar who bore the stigmata).
2515 **1037** 800l. blue 65 50

1038 Titus Arch, Rome, and Sicilian Mosaic of Rider

1998. World Equestrian Championships, Rome.
2516 **1038** 4000l. multicoloured . . 3·25 1·90

1039 Telecommunications College, Rome

1998. Universities.
2517 **1039** 800l. blue 65 50

1040 Pope John Paul II and his Message

1998. "Italia 98" International Stamp Exhibition, Milan (3rd issue). Stamp Day.
2518 **1040** 800l. multicoloured . . 75 50

1041 "Giuseppe Garibaldi" (aircraft carrier)

1998. Armed Forces Day. Multicoloured.
2519 800l. Type **1041** (Navy) . . 65 50
2520 800l. Eurofighter 2000 (75th anniv of Air Force) . . . 65 50
2521 800l. Carabiniere (vert) . . . 65 50
2522 800l. Battle of El-Alamein at night (Army) (vert) . . . 65 50

1042 "Dionysus" (bronze statue)

1998. "Italia 98" International Stamp Exhibition, Milan (4th issue). Art Day.
2523 **1042** 800l. multicoloured . . 65 50

1043 Ferrari competing in Race, 1931

1998. "Italia 98" International Stamp Exhibition, Milan (5th issue). Birth Centenary of Enzo Ferrari (car designer). Sheet 160×110 mm containing T **1043** and similar horiz designs. Multicoloured.
MS2524 800l. Type **1043**; 800l. Formula 1 Ferrari, 1952; 800l. Ferrari GTO, 1963; 800l. Formula 1 Ferrari, 1998 . . . . 3·50 4·00

1044 Hand releasing Birds

1998. 50th Anniv of Universal Declaration of Human Rights.
2525 **1044** 1400l. multicoloured . . 1·10 80

1045 Cogwheels and "Proportions of Man" (Leonardo da Vinci)

1046 Satellite Dish, Type, Book and "Internet"

1998. Europa Day. Ordinary or self-adhesive gum.
2526 **1045** 800l. multicoloured . . 65 50

1998. "Italia 98" International Stamp Exhibition, Milan (6th issue). Cinema Day. As T **946**. Multicoloured.
2528 450l. "Ti Conosco Mascherino" (dir. Eduardo de Filippo) . . . 40 50
2529 800l. "Fantasmia a Roma" (Antonio Pietrangeli) . . 65 50
2530 900l. "Il Signor Max" (Mario Camerini) 75 50

1998. "Italia 98" International Stamp Exhibition, Milan (7th issue). Communications Day.
2531 **1046** 800l. multicoloured . . 55 50

1047 Arrows circling Letter

1048 "Epiphany" (sculpture, St. Mark's Church, Seminara)

1998. "Italia 98" International Stamp Exhibition, Milan (8th issue). Post Day. Sheet 130 × 90 mm.
MS2532 **1047** 4000l. multicoloured 3·00 5·50

1998. Christmas.
2533 **1048** 800l. blue 60 50
2534 – 900l. brown 65 50
DESIGN—HORIZ: 900l. "Adoration of the Shepherds" (drawing, Giulio Romano).

1049 "Ecstasy of St. Teresa"

1998. 400th Birth Anniv of Gian Lorenzo Bernini (sculptor).
2535 **1049** 900l. multicoloured . . 65 50

1050 Royal Decree and Waldensian Emblem

1998. 150th Anniv of Toleration of the Waldenses (religious sect).
2536 **1050** 800l. multicoloured . . 55 50

DENOMINATION. From No. 2537 Italian stamps are denominated both in lira and in euros. As no coins or notes for the latter were in circulation until 2002, the catalogue continues to use the lira value.

1999. As Nos. 2505/9, but with face value in euros added.
2537 100l. black, green and silver 10 15
2538 450l. multicoloured 35 15
2539 650l. multicoloured 50 15
2540 800l. brown and black . . . 65 50
2541 1000l. blue, brown and black 75 65

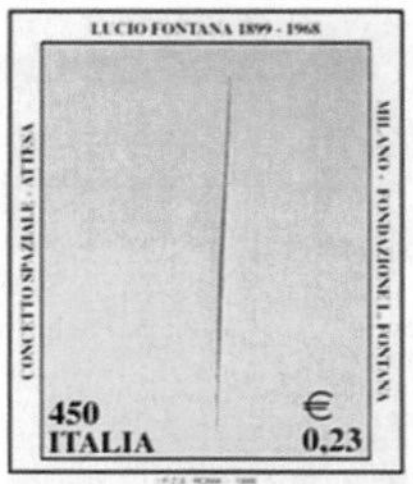

1051 "Space Concept–Wait"

1999. Birth Centenary of Lucio Fontana (artist).
2542 **1051** 450l. blue and black . . 35 50

1052 La Sila National Park, Calabria

1053 Holy Door, St. Peter's Cathedral

1999. Europa. Parks and Gardens. Multicoloured.
2543 800l. Type **1052** 60 50
2544 900l. Tuscan Archipelago National Park (horiz) . . 70 50

1999. Holy Year 2000.
2545 **1053** 1400l. multicoloured . . 1·00 95

1054 St. Egidius's Church, Cellere

1999. Artistic Heritage.
2546 **1054** 800l. brown 55 50

1055 Holy Year 2000 and 11th-century Bells

1999. Museums. Multicoloured.
2547 800l. Type **1055** (History of Campanology Museum, Agnone) 55 50
2548 800l. "Lake with Swan" (stained glass) (Casina delle Civette Museum, Rome) 55 50
2549 800l. Renaissance majolica dish (International Ceramics Museum, Faenza) (vert) 55 50

1056 Earth Pyramids, Segonzano

1999. Tourist Publicity (26th series). Multicoloured.
2550 800l. Type **1056** 55 50
2551 800l. Marmore Waterfall, Terni 55 50
2552 800l. Cathedral, Lecce . . . 55 50
2553 800l. Lipari 55 50

1057 Audience Chamber

1999. Constitutional Court.
2554 **1057** 800l. multicoloured . . 55 50

1058 Fire Engine at Fire

1999. Fire Brigade.
2555 **1058** 800l. multicoloured . . 55 50

1059 Cadet and Academy

1999. Modena Military Academy.
2556 **1059** 800l. multicoloured . . 55 50

1060 Players and Airplane

1999. 50th Anniv of Death in Aircrash of Grand Turin Football Team. Multicoloured.
2557 800l. Type **1060** 65 50
2558 900l. Superga Basilica, club arms and names of victims 75 50

1061 Council Seat, Strasbourg

1999. 50th Anniv of Council of Europe.
2559 **1061** 800l. multicoloured . . 55 50

1062 Players and Club Emblem

1999. Milan, National Football Champion, 1998–99.
2560 **1062** 800l. multicoloured . . 70 50

1063 Ballot Box and Parliament Chamber, Strasbourg

1999. 20th Anniv of First Direct Elections to European Parliament.
2561 **1063** 800l. multicoloured . . 55 50

1064 Coppi

1999. 80th Birth Anniv of Fausto Coppi (racing cyclist).
2562 **1064** 800l. multicoloured . . 55 50

1065 "P"

1999. Priority Mail stamp. Self-adhesive.
2563 **1065** 1200l. black and gold 85 1·40
See also Nos. 2591 and 2660.

1066 First Fiat Car (advertising poster)

1067 "Our Lady of the Snow"

1999. Centenary of Fiat (motor manufacturer).
2564 **1066** 4800l. multicoloured . . 3·25 1·60

1999. Centenary of Erection of Statue of "Our Lady of the Snow" on Mt. Rocciamelone.
2565 **1067** 800l. multicoloured . . 55 50

1068 Pimentel and St. Elmo Castle, Naples

1999. Death Bicentenary of Eleonora de Fonseca Pimentel (writer and revolutionary).
2566 **1068** 800l. multicoloured . . 55 50

1069 Canoes

1999. 30th World Speed Canoeing Championships.
2567 **1069** 900l. multicoloured . . 60 50

1070 "Goethe in the Rome Countryside" (Johann Tischbein)

1999. 250th Birth Anniv of Johann Wolfgang Goethe (poet and playwright).
2568 **1070** 4000l. multicoloured . . 2·75 1·80

1071 Cyclist and Stopwatch

1072 Child with Rucksack

1999. World Cycling Championships, Treviso and Verona.
2569 **1071** 1400l. multicoloured . . 1·00 80

1999. Stamp Day.
2570 **1072** 800l. multicoloured . . 55 50

1073 Architectural Drawing of Basilica

1999. Re-opening of Upper Basilica of St. Francis of Assisi.
2571 **1073** 800l. multicoloured . . 55 50

1074 Parini (after Francesco Rosaspina)

1075 Volta (bust by Giovan Commolli) and Voltaic Pile

1999. Death Bicentenary of Giuseppe Parini (poet).
2572 **1074** 800l. blue 55 50

1999. Bicentenary of Invention of Electrochemical Battery by Alessandro Volta.
2573 **1075** 3000l. multicoloured . . 2·10 1·60

1076 Forms and U.P.U. Emblem

1999. 125th Anniv of Universal Postal Union.
2574 **1076** 900l. multicoloured . . 65 50

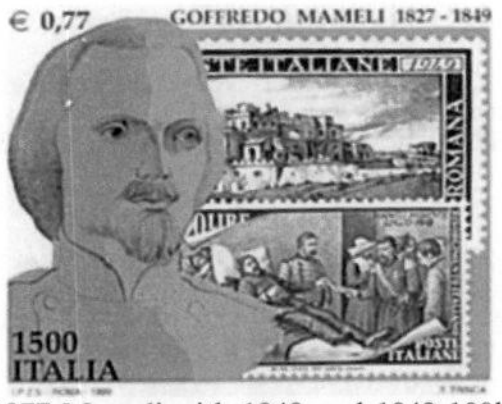

1077 Mameli with 1948 and 1949 100l. Stamps

1999. 150th Death Anniv of Goffredo Mameli (poet and patriot) and 150th Anniv of Roman Republic.
2575 **1077** 1500l. multicoloured . . 1·10 1·30

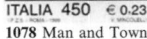

1078 Man and Town

1079 First World War Soldiers (after postcard)

1999. "The Stamp Our Friend". Multicoloured.
2576 450l. Type **1078** 35 80
2577 650l. Campaign emblem . . 50 95
2578 800l. Schoolchildren . . . . 60 1·10
2579 1000l. Windmill (toy) . . . 70 1·10

1999. Centenary of Generation of '99.
2580 **1079** 900l. multicoloured . . 65 50

1080 Santa Claus

1999. Christmas. Multicoloured.
2581 800l. Type **1080** 60 50
2582 1000l. "Nativity" (Dosso Dossi) 75 50

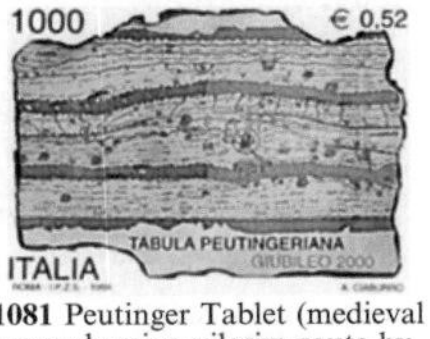

1081 Peutinger Tablet (medieval map showing pilgrim route by C. Celtes and Conrad Peutinger)

1999. Holy Year 2000. Multicoloured.
2583 1000l. Type **1081** 70 50
2584 1000l. 18th-century pilgrim's stamp 70 50
2585 1000l. 13th-century bas-relief of pilgrims (facade of Fidenza Cathedral) . . . 70 50

1082 Urbino State Art Institute

1999. Schools and Universities.
2586 **1082** 450l. black 35 50
2587 – 650l. brown 45 50
DESIGN: 650l. Pisa High School.

1083 "Leopard bitten by Tarantula"

1999. Birth Centenary of Antonio Ligabue (artist).
2588 **1083** 1000l. multicoloured . . 70 50

1084 Robot's Hand meeting Man's Hand (after Michelangelo)

1999. Year 2000.
2589 **1084** 4800l. multicoloured . . 3·25 2·40

1085 Child looking at Aspects of Earth

2000. New Millennium. "The Past and the Future". Sheet 110 × 80 mm containing T **1085** and similar horiz design. Multicoloured.
MS2590 2000l. Type **1085**; 2000l. Astronaut looking at Moon . . 3·00 4·75

2000. Priority Mail Stamp. As T **1065** but different colour. Self-adhesive.
2591 1200l. black, yellow and gold 85 65

1086 Tosca and Scenery

2000. Centenary of the First Performance of *Tosca* (opera).
2592 **1086** 800l. multicoloured . . 55 50

1087 St. Paul (statue) and Holy Door, St. Peter's Basilica, Rome

2000. Holy Year 2000.
2593 **1087** 1000l. multicoloured . . 70 50

1088 Players

2000. Six Nations Rugby Championship.
2594 **1088** 800l. multicoloured . . 55 50

1089 Painting

1091 Skier and Trophy

1090 "Enigma of an Autumn Afternoon"

2000. 5th Conference on Breast Diseases. Mult.
2595 800l. Type **1089** 55 50
2596 1000l. Painting (different) 70 50

2000. New Millennium (1st issue). Art and Science. Sheet 111 × 80 mm containing T **1090** and similar horiz design showing paintings by Giorgio de Chirico. Multicoloured.
MS2597 800l. Type **1090** (art); 800l. "The Inevitable Temple" (science) 2·00 2·40
See also Nos. **MS**2613 and 2623.

2000. World Cup Skiing Championships.
2598 **1091** 4800l. multicoloured . . 3·25 2·40

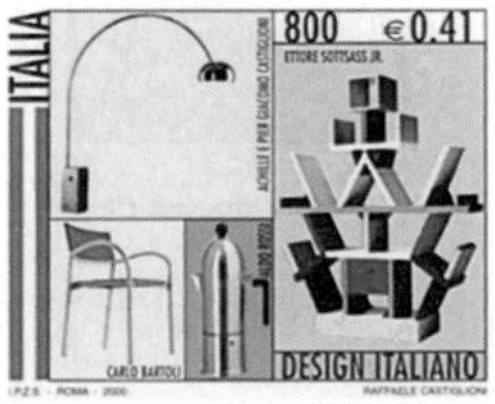

1092 Lamp (Achillle and Pier Giacomo Castiglioni), Chair (Carlo Batroli), Coffee Pot (Aldo Rossi) and Bookcase (Ettore Softsass Jr.)

2000. Italian Design. Sheet 154 × 138 mm containing T **1092** and similar horiz designs. Multicoloured.
MS2599 800l. Type **1092**; 800l. Armchair (Mario Bellini), corkscrew (Alessandro Mendini), table lamp (Vico Magistretti) and suspended lamp (Alberto Meda and Paolo Rizzatto); 800l. Chair (Gio Ponti), bean bag (Gatti Paolini Teodoro), pasta set (Massimo Morozzi) and standard uplighter (Tobia Scarpa); 800l. White standard uplighter (Pietro Chiesa), hostess trolley (Joe Columbo), chair (Cini Boeri and Tomu Katayanagi) and sideboard (Lodovico Acerbis and Giotto Stoppino); 800l. Easy chairs (Gaetano Pesce), chair (Enzo Mari), clothes horse (De Pas d'Urbino Lomazzi) and mobile filing cabinet (Antonio Citterio and Oliver Loew); 800l. Chair (Marco Zanuso), anglepoise lamp (Michele de Lucchi and Giancarlo Fassina), ice bucket (Bruno Munari) and stool (Anna Castelli Ferrieri) . . . . 3·50 6·50

1093 "Adoration of the Magi" (Domenico Ghirlandaio)

2000. Holy Year 2000. Multicoloured.
2600 450l. Type **1093** 40 50
2601 650l. "Baptism of Christ" (Paolo Caliari Veronese) (vert) 55 50
2602 800l. "The Last Supper" (Ghirlandaio) (vert) . . . 70 50
2603 1000l. "Regret of Christ's Death" (Giotto di Bondone) 85 50
2604 1200l. "The Resurrection" (Piero della Francesca) (vert) . . . . 1·00 80

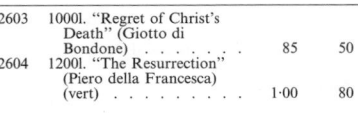

1094 Library and Emblem

2000. 150th Anniv of La Civilta Cattolica Foundation (collection of Church publications).
2605 **1094** 800l. multicoloured . . 55 50

1095 Courtyard

2000. 150th Anniv of St. Joseph's College, Rome.
2606 **1095** 800l. multicoloured . . 55 50

1096 Terre di Franciacorta, Erbrusco

2000. Tourist Publicity (27th series). Multicoloured.
2607 800l. Type **1096** 55 50
2608 800l. Dunarobba fossil forest, Avigliano Umbro 55 50
2609 800l. View of Ercolano . . . 55 50
2610 800l. Beauty Island, Taormina 55 50

1097 Cyclist

2000. Centenary of International Cycling Union.
2611 **1097** 1500l. multicoloured . . 1·10 80

1098 Christ carrying Cross

2000. Papier-mache Figurines, Caltanisetta.
2612 **1098** 800l. multicoloured . . 55 50

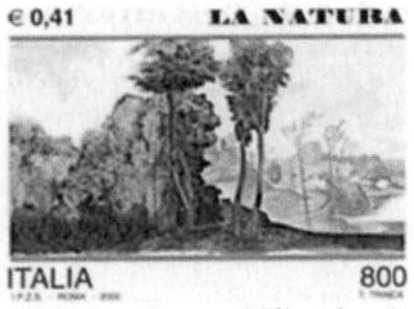

1099 Landscape (Gilorgione)

2000. New Millennium (2nd issue). Countryside and City. Sheet 110 × 80 mm containing T **1099** and similar horiz design. Multicoloured.
MS2613 800l. Type **1099**; 800l. "Perspective of an Ideal Town" (Piero della Francesca) . . . . 2·30 1·20

1100 Piccinni

1101 "Building Europe"

2000. Death Bicentenary of Niccolo Piccinni (composer).
2614 **1100** 4000l. multicoloured . . 2·75 2·40

2000. Europa.
2615 **1101** 800l. multicoloured . . 55 50

1102 Sardinia 1851 5, 20 and 40c. Stamps

2000. Museum of Posts and Telecommunications. Multicoloured.
2616 800l. Type **1102** 60 50
2617 800l. Reconstruction of radio and telegraph cabin aboard Elettra (Marconi's steam yacht) 60 50

1103 Footballer and Pitch

1104 Cathedral Facade

2000. Lazio, National Football Champion, 1999–2000.
2618 **1103** 800l. multicoloured . . 55 50

2000. 700th Anniv of Monza Cathedral.
2619 **1104** 800l. multicoloured . . 55 50

1105 Globe and Ears of Corn

1106 Statue

2000. United Nations World Food Programme.
2620 **1105** 1000l. multicoloured . . 70 50

2000. Centenary of the Jesus the Redeemer Monument, Nuoro.
2621 **1106** 800l. multicoloured . . 55 50

1107 Bridge, Parana River, Argentina

2000. 120th Anniv of Italian Water Board.
2622 **1107** 800l. multicoloured . . 55 50

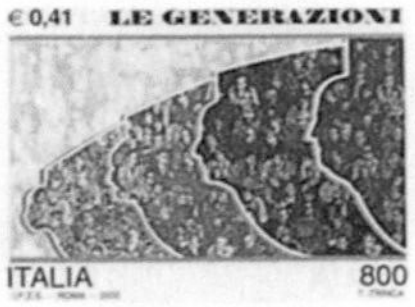

1108 Profiles

2000. New Millennium (3rd issue). Technology and Space. Sheet 110 × 80 mm containing T **1108** and similar horiz design. Multicoloured.
MS2623 800l. Type **1108**; 800l. Symbolic man . . . . 2·30 1·20

1109 Child with Ladder to Moon (Giacomo Chiesa)

1110 Archer

2000. "Stampin the Future". Winning Entry in Children's International Painting Competition.
2624 **1109** 1000l. multicoloured . . 70 50

2000. World Archery Championship, Campagna.
2625 **1110** 1500l. multicoloured . . 1·10 80

1111 Cyclist and Globe

2000. World Junior Cycling Championships.
2626 **1111** 800l. multicoloured . . 55 50

1112 Fair Attractions

2000. Millenary of St. Orso.
2627 **1112** 1000l. multicoloured . . 70 50

1113 "Madonna and Child" (Crivelli)

2000. 570th Birth Anniv of Carlo Crivelli (artist).
2628 **1113** 800l. multicoloured . . 55 50

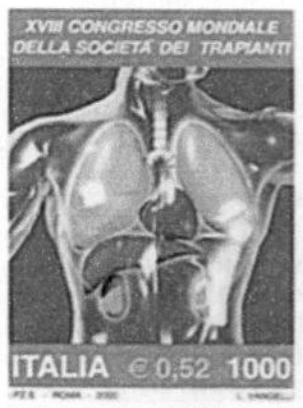

1114 Internal Organs

1115 Athlete and Stadium

2000. 18th International Transplantation Society Congress, Rome.
2629 **1114** 1000l. multicoloured . . 70 80

2000. Olympic Games, Sydney. Multicoloured.
2630 800l. Type **1115** 55 50
2631 1000l. "Discus Thrower" (statue) and Sydney Harbour 70 80

1116 "War"

2000. New Millennium (4th issue). War and Peace. Frescoes by Taddeo Zuccan. Sheet 110 × 80 mm containing T **1116** and similar vert design. Multicoloured.
MS2632 800l. Type **1116**; 800l. "Peace" . . . . 2·30 1·20

1117 Battle Scene (Jacques Debreville)

1118 Figures in Evening Dress and City Skyline

2000. Bicentenary of Marengo.
2633 **1117** 800l. multicoloured . . 55 50

2000. New Year.
2634 **1118** 800l. multicoloured . . 55 50

1119 Child holding Magnifying Glass

2000. Stamp Day.
2635 **1119** 800l. multicoloured . . 55 50

1120 Monti and Sick Child

2000. Death Centenary of Father Luigi Monti.
2636 **1120** 800l. multicoloured . . 55 50

1121 Salieri

1122 Disabled Athletes

2000. 250th Birth Anniv of Antonio Salieri (composer).
2637 **1121** 4800l. multicoloured . . 3·25 2·40

2000. Paralympic Games, Sydney.
2638 **1122** 1500l. multicoloured . . 1·10 1·30

1123 Emblem, Chaos Model and Globe in Container

2000. World Mathematics Year.
2639 **1123** 800l. multicoloured . . 55 50

1124 Couple and Globe

2000. Volunteers.
2640 **1124** 800l. multicoloured . . 55 50

1125 Quill, Text and Bust of Bruno (Pietro Masulli)

2000. 400th Death Anniv of Giordano Bruno (writer and philosopher).
2641 **1125** 800l. multicoloured . . 55 50

1126 "Madonna of the Rose Garden"

2000. 600th Birth Anniv of Luca della Robbia (artist).
2642 **1126** 800l. multicoloured . . 55 50

1127 Arms of Academy

2000. 250th Anniv of Roveretana degli Agiati Academy.
2643 **1127** 800l. multicoloured . . 55 50

1128 Martino and Map of Europe

2000. Birth Centenary of Gaetano Martino (politician).
2644 **1128** 800l. multicoloured . . 55 50

1129 "Perseus with the Head of Medusa" (bronze statue)

2000. 500th Birth Anniv of Benvenuto Cellini (goldsmith and sculptor).
2645 **1129** 1200l. multicoloured . . 85 95

1130 Young Woman

2000. New Millennium (5th series). Meditation and Expression. Sheet 110 × 80 mm containing T **1130** and similar horiz design. Multicoloured.
MS2646 800l. Type **1130**; 800l. Dancing figures . . . . 2·30 1·20

1131 Camerino University

2000. Universities. Each blue.
2647 800l. Type **1131** 55 50
2648 1000l. Calabria University 70 65

1132 Snowflakes and Globe

1133 Snowboarding

2000. Christmas. Multicoloured.
2649 800l. Type **1132** 55 50
2650 1000l. Crib, Matera Cathedral 70 80

2001. World Snowboarding Championships, Madonna di Campiglio.
2651 **1133** 1000l. multicoloured . . 70 50

1134 "The Annunciation" (detail, Botticelli)

2001. "Italy in Japan 2001" (cultural and scientific event).
2652 **1134** 1000l. multicoloured . . 70 50

1135 Vincenzo Bellini (composer, birth bicentenary)

2001. Composers' Anniversaries. Sheet 87 × 180 mm containing T **1135** and similar vert designs. Multicoloured.
MS2653 800l. Type **1135**; 800l. Domenico Cimarosa (death bicentenary); 800l. Gasparo Luigi Pacifico Spontini (150th death anniv); 800l. Giuseppe Verdi (death centenary) . . . . . . 2·40 4·00

1136 St. Rose and Angels (Francesco Podesti di Ancona)

1137 Racing Car

2001. 750th Death Anniv of St. Rose of Viterbo.
2654 **1136** 800l. multicoloured . . 55 50

2001. Ferrari, Formula One Constructor's Championship Winner (2000). Sheet 110 × 81 mm.
MS2655 **1137** 5000l. multicoloured 3·50 6·50

1138 Abbey of Santa Maria in Sylvis, Sesto al Reghena

2001.
2656 **1138** 800l. blue 55 50

1139 Lombardy and Venetia 1850 5c. Stamp (151st anniv)

2001. Stamp Anniversaries. Multicoloured.
2657 800l. Type **1139** 55 50
2658 800l. Sardinia 1851 5c. stamp (150th anniv) . . . 55 50
2659 800l. Tuscany 1851 1q. stamp (150th anniv) . . . 55 50

2001. Priority Mail Stamp. As T **1065** but central "P" larger, 12 × 12 mm. Self-adhesive.
2660 1200l. black, yellow and gold 85 50

1140 Bridge, Comacchio

2001. Tourist Publicity (28th series). Multicoloured.
2661 800l. Type **1140** 55 50
2662 800l. Diamante 55 50
2663 800l. Pioraco 55 50
2664 800l. Stintino 55 50

1141 Campanula

1142 Map of Italy and Tractors

2001. World Day to Combat Desertification and Drought. Multicoloured.
2665 450l. Type **1141** 30 15
2666 650l. Marmosets 45 50
2667 800l. White storks 50 50
2668 1000l. Desert and emblem 65 65

2001. Confederation General of Italian Agriculture.
2669 **1142** 800l. multicoloured . . 55 50

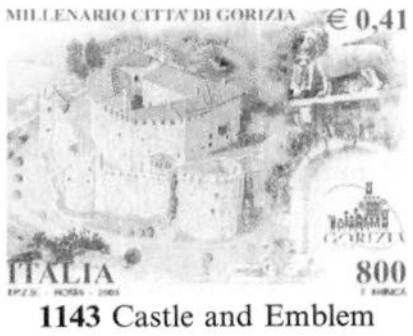

1143 Castle and Emblem

2001. Millenary of Gorzia City.
2670 **1143** 800l. multicoloured . . 55 50

1144 Water pouring from Vase

2001. Europa. Water Resources.
2671 **1144** 800l. multicoloured . . 65 50

1145 Profiles

2001. European Union.
2672 **1145** 800l. multicoloured . . 55 50

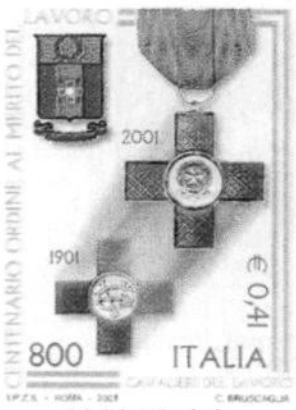

1146 Medals

1147 Rose and Workers' Silhouettes

2001. Centenary of Order of Merit for Labour.
2673 **1146** 800l. multicoloured . . 55 50

2001. National Day for Victims of Industrial Accidents.
2674 **1147** 800l. multicoloured . . 55 50

1148 Child with Stamp and Magnifying Glass (Rita Vergari)

1149 "St. Peter healing with his Shadow"

2001. Day for Art and Student Creativity. Multicoloured.
2675 800l. Type **1148** 55 50
2676 800l. People standing on rainbow (Lucia Catena) 55 50
2677 800l. Painting with eye (Luigi di Cristo) 55 50
2678 800l. Colours and profile (Barbara Grilli) 55 50

2001. 600th Birth Anniv of Tommaso de Giovanni di Simone Guidi "Masaccio " (painter).
2679 **1149** 800l. multicoloured . . 55 50

1150 "Madonna and Child" (Piero della Francesca)

2001. 500th Death Anniv of Giovanni della Rovere.
2680 **1150** 800l. multicoloured . . 55 50

1151 Emblem

1152 Guaita Tower, Mt. Titano

2001. 50th Anniv of Panathlon International (sports organization).
2681 **1151** 800l. multicoloured . . 55 50

2001. 1700th Anniv of San Marino.
2682 **1152** 800l. multicoloured . . 55 50

1153 Footballer and Net

1155 Quasimodo

1154 Motorboat and Helicopter

2001. A S Roma, National Football Champion, 2000–1
2683 **1153** 800l. multicoloured . . 55 50

2001. Harbour Master's Office.
2684 **1154** 800l. multicoloured . . 55 50

2001. Birth Centenary of Salvatore Quasimodo (writer).
2685 **1155** 1500l. multicoloured . . 1·10 1·30

1156 Octagonal Hall, Domus Aurea, Rome

2001.
2686 **1156** 1000l. brown 70 50

1157 Bookcase (Piero Lissoni and Patricia Urquiola) and Chair (Anna Bartolli)

2001. Italian Design. Sheet 155 × 137 mm containing T **1157** and similar horiz designs. Multicoloured.
MS2687 800l. Type **1157**; 800l. Chair (Monica Graffeo) and table lamp (Rodolfo Dordoni); 800l. Lamp (Ferruccio Laviani) and sofa (Massimo Iosa Ghini); 800l. Armchair (Anna Gili) and side table (Miki Astori); 800l. Vertical storage unit (Marco Ferreri) and double seat (M. Cananzi and R. Semprini); 800l. Stool (Stefano Giovannoni) and flexible-necked lamp (Massimiliano Datti) . . 3·00 3·00

1158 "The Fourth State" (detail, Guiseppe Pellizza da Volpedo)

2001.
2688 **1158** 1000l. brown 70 50

1159 Stone Age Man and Pick

1161 Fermi

1160 Schoolchildren

2001. Archaeological Museum, Alto Adige.
2689 **1159** 800l. multicoloured . . 55 50

2001. Youth Philately.
2690 **1160** 800l. multicoloured . . 55 50

2001. Birth Centenary of Enrico Fermi (physicist).
2691 **1161** 800l. multicoloured . . 55 50

1162 Pavia University

2001. Universities.
2692 **1162** 800l. blue 55 50
2693 – 800l. brown 55 50
2694 – 800l. turquoise 55 50
DESIGNS—VERT: No. 2693 Bari, University. HORIZ: 2694, School of Science, Rome.

1163 Latinas and Messanger

2001. Unione Latina (Romance language speaking countries).
2695 **1163** 800l. black, yellow and blue 55 50

1164 Exhibits

2001. National Archaeological Museum, Taranto.
2696 **1164** 1000l. multicoloured . . 70 50

1165 International Fund for Agricultural Development Emblem

1166 "Enthroned Christ with Angels" (painting on wood)

2001. World Food Day. Each stamp featuring "The Seed" (sculpture) by Roberto Joppolo. Multicoloured.
2697 800l. Type **1165** 50 25
2698 800l. Plants and woman hoeing (50th anniv of Food and Agriculture Organization Summit Conference, Rome) (50 × 29 mm) 50 25
2699 800l. World Food Programme emblem . . . 50 25

2001.
2700 **1166** 800l. multicoloured . . 50 25

1167 "Madonna and Child" (painting from triptych)

2001. 500th Anniv of "Madonna and Child, Angels, St. Francis, St. Thomas Aquinas and two Donors" (triptych, Macrino d'Alba).
2701 **1167** 800l. multicoloured . . 50 25

1168 "Dawn of Peace" (collage, San Vito dei Normani Primary School)

2001. Christmas. Multicoloured.
2702 800l. Type **1168** 50 25
2703 1000l. "Nativity" (painting, St. Mary Major Basilica) 65 30

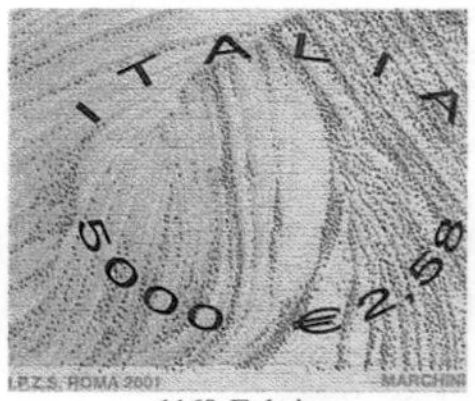

1169 Fabric

2001. Italian Silk Industry. Sheet 140 × 92 mm. Self-adhesive gum. Imperf.
MS2704 **1169** 5000l. multicoloured 3·25 3·25
No. **MS**2704 was printed on fabric mounted on silk jacquard. A peel-off plastic backing featured instructions for use. If required, the address could be written in the blank area at the bottom right of the sheet.

New Currency. 100 cents = 1 euro.

2002. Women in Art. As T **1032** but with values expressed in euros.
2705 1c. multicoloured 10 10
2706 2c. multicoloured 10 10
2707 3c. multicoloured 10 10
2708 5c. multicoloured 10 10
2709 10c. multicoloured 15 10
2710 20c. multicoloured 30 15
2711 23c. multicoloured 30 15
2715 41c. brown, grey and black 60 30
2716 45c. purple, blue and black 65 30
2717 50c. turquoise, red and black 70 35
2718 77c. brown, green and black 1·10 55
DESIGNS: 1c. "Ebe" (detail, painting, Antonia Canova); 2c. Profile (5th-century B.C. coin, Syracuse); 3c. Woman's head (detail from mural, Piero della Francesca); 5c. As No. 2505; 10c. Head (3rd-century B.C. sculpture, "G. Fiorelli" civic museum, Lucera); 20c. Portrait of a Lady (Correggio); 23c. As No. 2506; 41c. As No. 2508; 45c. "Venere di Urbino" (Tiziano Vecellio); 50c. "Portrait of a young girl" (detail, painting, Francesco Mazzola); 77c. "Spring" (detail, painting, Botticelli).

1170 "Ducato" (Venetian coin), 1285

2002. European Coins. Multicoloured.
2725 41c. Type **1170** 60 30
2726 41c. "Genovino" (Genoa) and "Fiorino" (Florence), 1252 . . . . 60 30
2727 41c. Flags of E.U. forming Euro symbol 60 30
2728 41c. 1946 lira coin transforming into euro coin 60 30

2002. Priority Mail Stamps. Designs as No. 2660 but with face values in euros only. Multicoloured, background colour given. Self-adhesive gum.
2729 62c. yellow 90 45
2730 77c. blue . . . . 1·10 55
2731 €1 lavender . . . . 1·40 70
2732 €1.24 green . . . . 1·80 90
2733 €1.86 pink . . . . 2·75 1·30
2734 €4.13 lilac . . . . 6·00 3·00

1171 Woman's Head and State Arms

1173 Luigi Bocconi and University Building

1172 Escriva

2002.
2735 **1171** €1 multicoloured . . 1·40 70
2736 €1.24 multicoloured 1·80 90
2737 €1.55 multicoloured 2·20 1·10
2738 €2.17 multicoloured 2·10 1·50
2739 €2.58 multicoloured 3·75 1·80
2739a €2.80 multicoloured 3·75 1·80
2740 €3.62 multicoloured 5·25 2·75
2741 €6.20 multicoloured 9·00 4·75

2002. Birth Centenary of Josemaria Escriva de Balaguer (founder of Opus Dei (religious organization)).
2745 **1172** 41c. multicoloured . . . 60 30

2002. Centenary of Bocconi University.
2746 **1173** 41c. brown and stone 60 30
The University was established with an endowment from Ferinando Bocconi in memory of his son Luigi.

1174 1852 5c. Stamp

1175 Mountain Peak

2002. 150th Anniv of First Stamp of Parma. Fluorescent paper.
2747 **1174** 41c. multicoloured . . . 60 30

2002. International Year of Mountains.
2748 **1175** 41c. multicoloured . . . 60 30

1176 Emblem and Olympic Rings

1177 Queen Elena

2002. Winter Olympic Games, Turin (2006).
2749 **1176** 41c. multicoloured . . . 60 30

2002. 50th Death Anniv of Queen Elena of Savoy.
2750 **1177** 41c. + 21c. multicoloured 90 45

1178 Sculpture (Arnolfo di Cambio)

2002. 700th Death Anniv of Arnolfo di Cambio (sculptor).
2751 **1178** 41c. mauve 60 30

1179 Venaria Reale

2002. Tourist Publicity (29th series). Multicoloured.
2752 41c. Type **1179** 60 30
2753 41c. Capo d'Orlando . . . 60 30
2754 41c. San Gimignano 60 30
2755 41c. Sannicandro di Bari . . 60 30

1180 Santa Maria delle Grazie Sanctuary

2002.
2756 **1180** 41c. brown 60 30

1181 Police Officers, Computer Screen and Patrol Car

2002. 150th Anniv of State Police Force.
2757 **1181** 41c. multicoloured . . . 60 30

1182 Ricci and World Map

2002. 450th Birth Anniv of Matteo Rici (missionary).
2758 **1182** 41c. multicoloured . . . 60 30

1183 Circus Performers

2002. Europa. Circus.
2759 **1183** 41c. multicoloured . . . 60 30

1184 Sailing Ship and Student

2002. Francesco Morosini Naval Military School, Venice.
2760 **1184** 41c. multicoloured . . . 60 30

1185 Vittorio de Sica (film director, birth centenary)

1186 Football Player and Emblem

2002. Cinema Anniversaries. Multicoloured.
2761 41c. Type **1185** 60 30
2762 41c. Text and clouds (birth centenary (1901) of Cesare Zavattini (screen writer)) 60 30

2002. Juventus, National Football Champions, 2001–2002.
2763 **1186** 41c. multicoloured . . . 60 30

1187 Falcone and Boresellino

2002. 10th Death Annivs of Giovanni Falcone and Paolo Borsellino (judges).
2764 **1187** 62c. multicoloured . . . 90 45

1188 Emblems and Member Flags

2002. Russia's Membership of North Atlantic Treaty Organization (N.A.T.O.).
2765 **1188** 41c. multicoloured . . . 60 30

1189 Kayaking

1190 Modena 1853 1 lira Arms of Este Stamp

2002. World Kayaking Championship, Valsesia.
2766 **1189** 52c. multicoloured . . . 75 35

2002. 150th Anniv of Modena (Italian State) Stamps.
2767 **1190** 41c. multicoloured . . . 60 30

1191 Arms

1192 Binda

2002. Italian Military Involvement in Peace Missions.
2768 **1191** 41c. multicoloured . . . 60 30

2002. Birth Centenary of Alfrodo Binda (cyclist).
2769 **1192** 41c. multicoloured . . . 60 30

1193 Santo

2002. Canonization of Father Padre Pio Santo
2770 **1193** 41c. multicoloured . . . 60 30

1194 Divisione Acqui (monument, Mario Salazzari)

2002. "Divisione Acqui" (World War II resistance group on Cephalonia).
2771 **1194** 41c. multicoloured . . . 60 30

1195 Crucifixion (Arezzo Basilica)

2002.
2772 **1195** €2.58 multicoloured 3·75 1·90

1196 Building Facade

2002. Bicentenary of Ministry of Interior.
2773 **1196** 41c. multicoloured . . . 60 30

1197 Maria Goretti

2002. Death Centenary of Saint Maria Goretti.
2774 **1197** 41c. multicoloured . . . 60 30

1198 Mazarin

2002. 400th Birth Anniv of Cardinal Jules Mazarin (minister to Louis XIV of France).
2775 **1198** 41c. multicoloured . . . 60 30

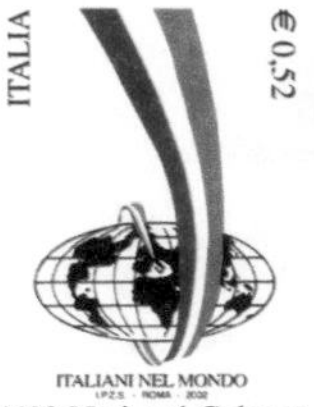

1199 National Colours encircling Globe

1200 Monument (Vincenzo Gasperetti)

2002. "Italians in the World".
2776 **1199** 52c. multicoloured . . . 75 35

2002. Monument to the Victims of Massacre at Sant' Anna di Stazzema.
2777 **1200** 41c. multicoloured . . . 60 30

1201 Jacket (Krizia)

2002. Italian Design. Sheet 157 × 137 mm, containing T **1201** and similar vert designs. Multicoloured.
MS2778 41c. Type **1201**; 41c. Brassiere (Dolce & Gabbana); 41c. Drawing of dress (Gianfranco Ferre); 41c. Drawing of suit (Giorgio Armani); 41c. Dress (Laura Biagiotti); 41c. Shoes (Prada) . . . . 8·75 8·75

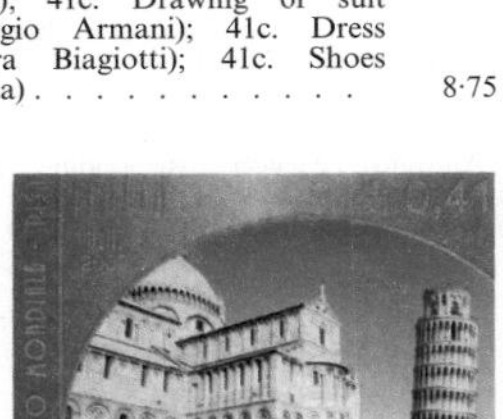
1202 Cathedral and Tower, Pisa

2002. U.N.E.S.C.O. World Heritage Sites. Multicoloured.
2779 41c. Type **1202** 60 30
2780 52c. Aeolian Islands 75 35
Stamps of a similar design were issued by the United Nations.

1203 Dalla Chiesa

2002. 20th Anniv of Assassination of Carlo Alberto Dalla Chiesa (police chief and prefect of Palermo).
2781 **1203** 41c. multicoloured . . . 60 30

1204 Teatro della Concordia, Monte Castello di Vibio, Perugia

2002.
2782 **1204** 41c. multicoloured . . . 60 30

1205 Yacht

2002. 12th Prada Classic Yacht Challenge, Imperia.
2783 **1205** 41c. multicoloured . . . 60 30

1206 Papal States 1852 5b. Stamp

1207 Cross, City Museum, Santa Giulia, Brescia

2002. 150th Anniv of First Papal States Stamp.
2784 **1206** 41c. multicoloured . . . 60 30

2002. Museum Exhibits. Multicoloured.
2785 41c. Type **1207** 60 30
2786 41c. Busts, Museo Nazionale, Palazzo Altemps, Rome (horiz) . . 60 30

1208 Orchid

1209 Emblem

2002. Flora and Fauna. Multicoloured.
2787 23c. Type **1208** 30 15
2788 52c. European lynx 75 35
2789 77c. Stag beetle . . . . . . 1·10 55

2002. World Food Day.
2790 **1209** 41c. multicoloured . . . 60 30

1210 Corps Member and Emblem

1211 Gnocchi and Children

2002. State Forestry Corps.
2791 **1210** 41c. multicoloured . . . 60 30

2002. Birth Centenary of Carlo Gnocchi (founder of rehabilitation centres for disabled children).
2792 **1211** 41c. multicoloured . . . 60 30

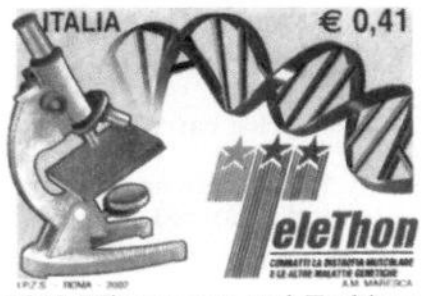

1212 Microscope and Emblem

2002. "Telethon 2002" (campaign to combat muscular dystrophy and genetic disease).
2793 **1212** 41c. multicoloured . . . 60 30

1213 The Holy Family

2002. Christmas. Multicoloured.
2794 41c. Type **1213** 60 30
2795 62c. Child and Christmas tree 90 45

1214 "Nike di Samotracia" (statue) and Athlete

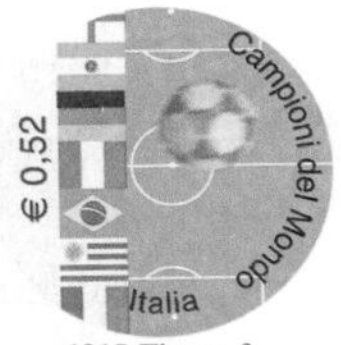

1215 Flags of Championship Winners and Football

2002. Women in Sport.
2796 **1214** 41c. multicoloured . . . 60 30

2002. 20th-century World Cup Football Champions. Multicoloured.
2797 52c. Type **1215** 70 35
2798 52c. Italian footballer . . . 70 35

1216 Magnifying Glass, Stamps and Children

2002. Stamp Day. Philately in Schools.
2799 **1216** 62c. multicoloured . . . 85 40

1217 Vittorio Orlando

1218 Event Emblem

2002. 50th Death Anniv of Vittorio Emanuele Orlando (politician).
2800 **1217** 41c. multicoloured . . . 60 30

2003. "Tarvisio 2003" (winter sports competition).
2801 **1218** 52c. multicoloured . . . 70 35

1219 Family and Scales

2003. The Italian Republic on Stamps.
2802 **1219** 62c. multicoloured . . . 85 40

1220 Cyclist carrying Cycle

2003. World Cyclo-cross Championship, Monopoli.
2803 **1220** 41c. multicoloured . . . 60 30

1221 Building and Tandem

2003. 150th Anniv (2002) of Fratelli Alinari (photographic company).
2804 **1221** 77c. multicoloured . . . 1·00 50

1222 Jigsaw Puzzle

2003. European Year of the Disabled.
2805 **1222** 41c. multicoloured . . . 60 30

1223 Skiers

2003. World Nordic Skiing Championship, Val di Fiemme.
2806 **1223** 41c. multicoloured . . . 60 30

1224 Couple, Flower and Emblem

2003. National Civil Service.
2807 **1224** 62c. multicoloured . . . 85 40

1225 Knights on Horseback

2003. 500th Anniv of the Barletta Challenge (battle between 13 French and 13 Italian knights).
2808 **1225** 41c. multicoloured . . . 60 30

1226 Building Facade

2003. Torquato Tasso Grammar School (gymnasium).
2809 **1226** 41c. multicoloured . . . 60 30

1227 "Encounter by the Golden Door" (Giotto)

2003.
2810 **1227** 41c. multicoloured . . . 60 30

1228 Gian Rinaldo Carli and Building

2003. Gian Rinaldo Carli Grammar School (gymnasium).
2811 **1228** 41c. multicoloured . . . 60 30

1229 Academy Emblem

2003. 400th Anniv of "Accademia dei Lincei" (academy of lynxes) (scientific society).
2812 **1229** 41c. multicoloured . . . 60 30

1230 Foils and Fencers

2003. World Junior Fencing Championships, Trapani.
2813 **1230** 41c. multicoloured . . . 60 30

1231 Sestri Levante

2003. Tourist Publicity (30th series). Multicoloured.
2814 41c. Type **1231** 60 30
2815 41c. Lanciano 60 30
2816 41c. Procida 60 30

1232 Golfer

2003. Centenary of Roma Acquasanta Golf Course.
2817 **1232** 77c. multicoloured . . . 1·00 50

1233 Minerva (statue) and Building Facade

2003. 700th Anniv of La Sapienza University, Rome.
2818 **1233** 41c. multicoloured . . . 60 30

1234 Pasta

1236 Woman in Blue Dress

1235 Guido Carli and University Building

2003. National Pasta Museum, Rome.
2819 **1234** 41c. multicoloured . . . 60 30

2003. Guido Carli-LUISS (international liberal social studies) University.
2820 **1235** €2.58 multicoloured 3·50 1·75

2003. Europa. Poster Art. Posters by Marcello Dudovich. Multicoloured.
2821 41c. Type **1236** 60 30
2822 52c. Woman in white dress 70 35

1237 Buildings and Text

2003. 50th Anniv of State Archives.
2823 **1237** 41c. multicoloured . . . 60 30

1238 Logo and St. Peter of Verona

2003. Centenary of Veronafil Exhibition.
2824 **1238** 41c. multicoloured . . . 60 30

1239 Aldo Moro

1240 Antonio Meucci

2003. 25th Death Anniv of Aldo Moro (politician)
2825 **1239** 62c. multicoloured . . . 85 40

2003. Antonio Meucci (telephone pioneer) Commemoration. Sheet 90 × 70 mm.
MS2826 **1240** 52c. multicoloured 70 70

1241 Padre E. Barsanti and F. Matteucci (motor pioneers)

2003. 150th Anniv of Invention of Internal Combustion Engine.
2827 **1241** 52c. multicoloured . . . 70 35

1242 Post and Telegraph Building (Angiolo Mazzoni)

2003.
2828 **1242** 41c. blue 60 30

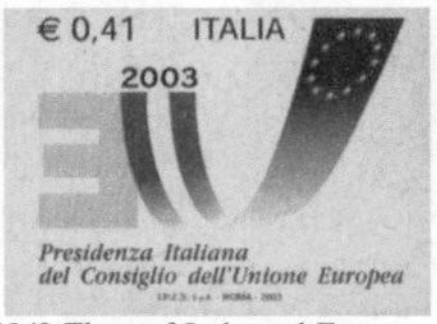

1243 Flags of Italy and European Union

2003. Italian Presidency of the European Union.
2829 **1243** 41c. multicoloured . . . 60 30

1244 Ezio Vanoni

2003. Birth Centenary of Ezio Vanoni (politician).
2830 **1244** €2.58 multicoloured 3·75 1·90

1245 "The Ascension of Mary"

2003. 300th Birth Anniv of Corrado Giaquinto (artist).
2831 **1245** 77c. multicoloured . . . 1·00 50

1246 Eugenio Balzan

2003. 50th Death Anniv of Eugenio Balzan (journalist).
2832 **1246** 41c. multicoloured . . . 60 30

1247 "Diana and Atteone"

2003. 500th Birth Anniv of Francesco Mazzola (Parmigianino) (artist).
2833 **1247** 41c. multicoloured . . . 60 30

1248 Player and Club Emblem

2003. Juventus, National Football Champions, 2002—3.
2834 **1248** 41c. multicoloured . . . 60 30

1249 San Silvestro Abbey, Nonantola

2003.
2835 **1249** 41c. multicoloured . . . 60 30

1250 Mario Calderara

2003. Centenary of First Powered Flight. Italian Aviation. Multicoloured.
2836 52c. Type **1250** (first Italian pilot) . . . . 2·10 1·00
2837 52c. Mario Cobianchi (pilot) 2·10 1·00
2838 52c. Gianni Caproni (aircraft designer) . . . . 2·10 1·00
2839 52c. Alessandro Marchetti (aircraft designer) . . . . 2·10 1·00
MS2840 105 × 146 mm. Nos. 2836/9 8·50 4·00

1251 Giovanni Giolitti

2003. 75th Death Anniv of Giovanni Giolitti (prime minister 1892—3 and 1903—14).
2841 **1251** 41c. multicoloured . . . 60 30

1252 "Still Life" (Giorgio Morandi)

2003. Europhalia 2003 Italy Festival. Italian Presidency of European Union. Multicoloured.
2842 41c. Type **1252** 60 30
2843 52c. Cistalia 202 (1947) . . 70 35
Stamps of the same design were issued by Belgium.

1253 Attilio Vallecchi (founder) and "Leonardo"

2003. Centenary of First Publication of "Leonardo". Centenary of Vallecchi Publishing House.
2844 **1253** 41c. multicoloured . . . 60 30

1254 Family enclosed in Atom Model

2003. The Family.
2845 **1254** 77c. multicoloured . . . 1·00 50

1255 "Maesta" (detail) (Duccio di Buoninsegna)

2003. Extension to Metropolitan Opera House, Sienna.
2846 **1255** 41c. multicoloured . . . 60 30

1256 Vittorio Alfieri

2003. Death Bicentenary of Vittorio Alfieri (writer).
2847 **1256** 41c. multicoloured . . . 60 30

1257 Ugo La Malfa and Chamber of Deputies Assembly Hall

2003. Birth Centenary of Ugo La Malfa (politician).
2848 **1257** 62c. multicoloured . . . 80 40

1258 Bernando Ramazzini and Frontispiece of "De morbis aertifcum diatriba"

2003. 370th Birth Anniv of Bernando Ramazzini (medical pioneer).
2849 **1258** 41c. multicoloured . . . 60 30

1259 Building Facade

2003. 120th Anniv of Confediliizia Institute, Rome.
2850 **1259** $2.58 multicoloured . . 3·75 1·90

1260 "Nativity" (Gian Paolo Cavagna)

2003. Christmas. Multicoloured.
2851 41c. Type **1260** 60 30
2852 62c. Poinsettia 80 40

1261 "Forme Grido Viva l'Italia"

2003. 40th Death Anniv of Giacomo Balla (artist). Multicoloured.
2853 41c. Type **1261** . . . . . .
2854 62c. "Linee—Forza del Pugno di Boccioni" . . .

1262 Pencil and Sharpener

2003. Stamp Day.
2855 **1262** 41c. multicoloured . . .

2004. Priority Mail Stamps. Designs as No. 2660. Multicoloured, background colour given. Self-adhesive gum.
2856 60c. orange 80 40
2857 €1.40 green . . . . 2·00 1·00
No. 2856 was issued with an attached label inscribed "postaprioritaria Priority Mail".

1263 "50" enclosing Test Screen

2004. 50th Anniv of Television.
2860 **1263** 41c. blue and grey . . . 60 30
2861 – 62c. multicoloured . . . 80 40
DESIGN: 62c. "50" enclosed in colour blocks.

1264 Giorgio La Pira and Script

2004. Birth Centenary of Giorgio La Pira (politician).
2862 **1264** 41c. cinnamon, blue and red 60 30

CONCESSIONAL LETTER POST

CL **93** Arms of Savoy and Fasces

CL **109** Arms and Fasces

1928.
CL227 CL **93** 10c. blue . . . . . 3·00 15

1930.
CL267 CL **109** 10c. brown 10 15

1945. No. CL267, surch with Royal Arms (obliterating fasces) and new value.
CL647 CL **109** 40c. on 10c. brown 10 1·30

1945. As Type CL **109**, but Arms redrawn without fasces.
CL648 10c. brown . . . . 10 1·00
CL649 1l. brown . . . . 2·10 2·10

CL **201** Italia

CL **220** Italia

1947.
CL687 CL **201** 1l. green 60 30
CL688 8l. red . . . . . . 18·00 15

1948.
CL734 CL **220** 15l. violet . . . . 50·00 15
CL916 20l. violet 10 15
CL917 30l. green 10 15
CL918 35l. brown 10 15
CL919 110l. blue 10 15
CL920 270l. mauve . . . 50 40
CL921 300l. green & pink 35 55
CL922 370l. brown & orge 35 55

CONCESSIONAL PARCEL POST

CP **288**

1953.
CP918 CP **288** 40l. orange 45 40
CP919 50l. blue 00 40
CP920 60l. violet . . . . 00 6·00
CP921 70l. green . . . . 00 12·00
CP850 75l. sepia . . . . . 00 12·00
CP923 80l. brown 00 10
CP924 90l. lilac 00 10
CP851 110l. red . . . . . 00 12·00
CP926 110l. yellow . . . 00 10
CP927 120l. green 00 10
CP928 140l. black 00 10
CP929 150l. red 00 10
CP930 180l. red 00 10
CP931 240l. slate 00 10
CP932 500l. brown . . . 00 15
CP933 600l. turquoise . . 00 15
CP934 900l. blue 00 15
Unused prices are for the complete pair. Used prices are for the left half; right halves are worth more.

CP **707**

1984.
CP1849 CP **707** 3000l. blue and red . . . . . . 3·25 2·10

EXPRESS LETTER STAMPS

E **35**

1903. For inland letters.
E 73 E **35** 25c. red . . . . 26·00 25
E113 50c. red . . . . 1·70 45
E129 60c. red . . . . 3·25 40
E178 70c. red 25 15
E179 1l.25 blue 15 10

E **41** King Victor Emmanuel III

1908. For foreign letters.
E 80 E **41** 30c. blue and pink . . 1·00 85
E180 2l. blue and pink . . . 2·30 15·00
E181 2l.50 blue and pink . . 65 1·30

E **59**

1917. Surch **25** and bars.

E112	E **59**	25c. on 40c. violet	20·00	17·00

1921. Surch with new value.

E118	E **41**	L.1.20 on 30c. blue and pink	2·50	10·00
E173		L.1.60 on 1l.20 blue and pink	70	11·00

1922. Surch in words and figures.

E122	E **35**	60c. on 50c. red	34·00	25
E172		70c. on 60c. red	30	25

E **131** "Garibaldi" (statue), Savoia Marchetti S-55A Flying Boat and "Anita Garibaldi" (statue)

1932. Air. 50th Death Anniv of Garibaldi.

E348	E **131**	2l.25+1l. violet and red	6·00	15·00
E349		4l.50+1l.50 brown and green	6·25	15·00

E **132** King Victor Emmanuel III

1932.

E350	E **132**	1l.25 green	25	10
E351		2l.50 orange	25	95

1932. 10th Anniv of March on Rome. As T **132**.

(a) For inland letters. Inscribed "ESPRESSO".

E368		1l.25 green	75	70

(b) For foreign letters. Inscribed "EXPRES".

E369		2l.50 orange	2·75	55·00

DESIGNS: 1l.25, Roman road; 2l.50, Flags and head of Mussolini.

E **133** Savoia Marchetti S-55A Flying Boat

1933. Air.

E370	E **133**	2l. black	10	80
E371		2l.25 black	3·25	55·00

1934. Air. 10th Anniv of Annexation of Fiume. Inscr as in T **141**.

E408		2l.+1l.25 blue	1·40	10·00
E409		2l.25+1l.25 green	55	9·50
E410		4l.50+2l. red	55	9·50

DESIGN: Foundation of Fiume.

1934. Air. Military Medal Centenary. Inscr as in T **146**.

E442		2l.+1l.25 brown	5·25	14·00
E443		4l.50+2l. red	7·25	14·00

DESIGN—HORIZ: 2l., 4l.50, Caproni Ca 101 airplane over triumphal arch.

E **192** Italia

1945.

E647	E **192**	5l. red	10	1·00

E **200** Winged Foot of Mercury

1945.

E679	E **200**	5l. red	10	10
E680	–	10l. blue	10	30
E681	–	15l. red	1·90	15
E682	E **200**	25l. orange	27·00	10
E683		30l. violet	2·75	75
E915		50l. purple	23·00	15
E685	–	60l. red	40·00	15

DESIGN: 10, 15, 60l. Horse and torch bearer.

E **209** Rising at Naples

1948. Centenary of 1848 Revolution.

E718	E **209**	35l. violet	85·00	11·00

E **341** Etruscan Horses

1958.

E 961	E **341**	75l. purple	10	10
E1220		150l. green	10	10
E1221		250l. blue & light blue	15	15
E1222		300l. brown & lt brn	20	15

MILITARY POST STAMPS

1943. Stamps of Italy optd **P.M.** (a) Postage stamps of 1929 (Nos. 239/56).

M583	5c. brown	25	35
M584	10c. brown	25	70
M585	15c. green	25	70
M586	20c. red	25	70
M587	25c. green	25	70
M588	30c. brown	25	70
M589	50c. violet	25	70
M590	1l. violet	1·40	11·00
M591	1l.25 blue	25	85
M592	1l.75 orange	25	70
M593	2l. red	25	85
M594	5l. red	25	2·40
M595	10l. violet	25	17·00

(b) Air stamps of 1930 (Nos. 271/7).

M596	50c. brown	20	70
M597	1l. violet	20	70
M598	2l. blue	30	8·50
M599	5l. green	1·40	15·00
M600	10l. red	1·40	21·00

(c) Air Express stamp of 1933 (No. E370).

M601	2l. black	1·40	17·00

(d) Express Letter stamp of 1932 (No. E350).

M602	1l.25 green	20	1·40

NEWSPAPER STAMPS

N **2**

1862. Imperf.

N5	N **2**	2c. yellow	40·00	85·00

For similar stamps in black, see Sardinia.

OFFICIAL STAMPS

O **11**

1875.

O21	O **11**	2c. red	75	65
O22		5c. red	75	65
O23		20c. red	15	15
O24		30c. red	25	20
O25		1l. red	1·60	3·00
O26		2l. red	10·50	8·00
O27		5l. red	55·00	60·00
O28		10l. red	60·00	28·00

1934. Air. Optd **SERVIZIO DI STATO**.

O450	**148**	10l. grey	£650	£7500

PARCEL POST STAMPS

P **13** King Umberto I

1884. Various frames.

P38	P **13**	10c. grey	70·00	16·00
P39		20c. blue	£110	26·00
P40		50c. pink	11·50	3·75
P41		75c. green	10·50	3·75
P42		1l.25 orange	15·00	9·75
P43		1l.75 brown	20·00	29·00

The left-hand portion of the following parcel post stamps is affixed to the packet-card, the right-hand portion to the receipt. Unused prices are for the complete pair and used prices for the half-stamp. Unsevered stamps in used condition are usually from cancelled-to-order material and are worth more than the half-stamp.

P **53**

1914.

P 96	P **53**	5c. brown	40	60
P 97		10c. blue	40	60
P 98		20c. black	60	60
P 99		25c. red	70	60
P100		50c. orange	95	70
P101		1l. violet	1·20	80
P102		2l. green	1·60	60
P103		3l. yellow	3·25	70
P104		4l. grey	4·75	70
P105		10l. purple	27·00	3·50
P106		12l. brown	£100	£140
P107		15l. olive	£100	£140
P108		20l. purple	£100	£140

1923. Surch with figures on left half and words and figures on right half.

P146	P **53**	30c. on 5c. brown	1·20	38·00
P147		60c. on 5c. brown	2·10	38·00
P148		1l.50 on 5c. brown	6·75	£100
P149		3l. on 10l. purple	4·25	£100

P **92**

1927.

P217	P **92**	5c. brown	25	30
P218		10c. blue	25	30
P219		25c. red	25	30
P220		30c. blue	25	40
P221		50c. orange	25	30
P222	–	60c. red	25	40
P223	P **92**	1l. violet	25	30
P224		2l. green	25	40
P225		3l. bistre	25	80
P226		4l. black	25	80
P227		10l. purple	1·10	13·50
P228		20l. purple	1·60	22·00

The value in the right-hand portion of the 60c. is in figures.

1945. Optd with ornamental device obliterating Fascist emblems in centre.

P647	P **92**	5c. brown	55	1·25
P648		10c. blue	55	1·25
P649		25c. red	55	1·25
P650		30c. blue	10·50	13·00
P651		50c. orange	55	80
P652	–	60c. red	55	80
P653	P **92**	1l. violet	55	80
P654		2l. green	55	80
P655		3l. bistre	55	80
P656		4l. black	55	80
P657		10l. purple	12·50	27·00
P658		20l. purple	18·00	60·00

1946. As Type **P 92**, but without fasces between stamps.

P679	P **92**	1l. mauve	1·20	45
P680		2l. green	85	46
P681		3l. orange	1·50	45
P682		4l. black	2·10	45
P683		10l. purple	36·00	34·00
P684		20l. purple	48·00	65·00

P **201**

1946.

P 687a	P **201**	25c. blue	10	10
P 688		50c. brown	35	10
P 689		1l. brown	35	10
P 690		2l. blue	80	10
P 691		3l. orange	40	50
P 692		4l. grey	7·00	75
P 910		5l. purple	10	10
P 911		10l. violet	10	10
P 912		20l. purple	10	10
P1348		30l. purple	10	10
P 914		40l. violet	10	10
P 915		50l. red	10	10
P 916		60l. violet	10	10
P 917		100l. blue	10	10
P 918		140l. red	10	10
P 919		150l. brown	10	10
P 920		200l. green	10	10
P 921		280l. yellow	10	10
P 922		300l. purple	10	10
P 923		400l. black	20	10
P 924		500l. brown	35	10
P 925		600l. brown	30	10
P 926		700l. blue	70	15
P 927		800l. orange	1·20	15

P **298**

1954.

P928a	P **298**	1000l. blue	50	50
P929		2000l. red and brown	2·40	20

PNEUMATIC POST LETTERS

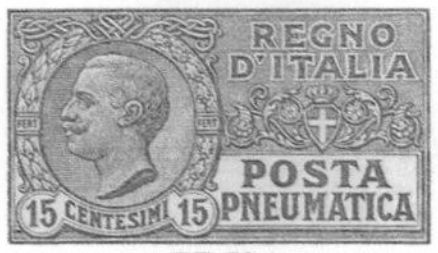

PE **53**

1913.

PE 96	PE **53**	10c. brown	1·60	5·50
PE 97		15c. lilac	1·70	8·75
PE191		15c. pink	5·00	5·50
PE192		15c. purple	1·70	8·00
PE193		20c. purple	11·50	14·00
PE 98		30c. blue	4·75	42·00
PE194		35c. red	9·50	55·00
PE195		40c. red	16·00	60·00

1924. Surch.

PE165	PE **53**	15c. on 10c. brown	4·50	10·50
PE166		15c. on 20c. purple	6·25	12·00
PE167		20c. on 10c. brown	3·50	12·00
PE168		20c. on 15c. lilac	5·75	8·75
PE169		35c. on 40c. red	10·50	60·00
PE170		40c. on 30c. blue	4·00	55·00

PE **134** Galileo Galilei

PE **204** Minerva

1933.

PE372	–	15c. purple	20	50
PE373	PE **134**	35c. red	20	85

DESIGN: 15c. Dante Alighieri.

1945. As Type **PE 134**, but inscr "ITALIA" instead of "REGNO D'ITALIA".

PE679	–	60c. brown (Dante)	25	1·10
PE680	PE **134**	1l.40 blue	25	1·10

1947.

PE694	PE **204**	3l. purple	4·00	5·50
PE695		5l. blue	10	15
PE961		10l. red	10	30
PE962		20l. blue	10	30

POSTAGE DUE STAMPS

D **3**

D **11**

1863. Imperf.

D6B	D **3**	10c. yellow	35·00	80·00

FOOTNOTE: Our price for mint stamps is for stamps without gum. Stamps with gum are worth considerably more.

1869. Perf.

D21	D **11**	10c. brown	£4000	12·50

D **12**

D **13**

1870.

D22	D **12**	1c. mauve and orange	4·25	2·20
D23		2c. mauve and orange	9·00	7·25
D24		5c. mauve and orange	35	10
D25		10c. mauve and orange	35	10
D26		20c. mauve and orange	1·50	10
D27		30c. mauve and orange	3·50	30
D28		40c. mauve and orange	3·00	40
D29		50c. mauve and orange	3·50	20
D30		60c. mauve and orange	£750	95
D31		60c. brown and orange	20·00	3·00
D32		1l. brown and blue	£5500	4·50
D33		1l. mauve and blue	6·50	20
D34		2l. brown and blue	£5500	7·50
D35		2l. mauve and blue	55·00	55
D36		5l. brown and blue	£375	10·00
D37		5l. mauve and blue	85·00	3·50
D38		10l. brown and blue	£8000	9·25
D39		10l. mauve and blue	£225	1·10

1884.

D40	D **13**	50l. green	90·00	15·00
D73		50l. yellow	45·00	10·00

D41		100l. red	95·00	4·75
D74		100l. blue	60·00	4·50

(D 20)

1890. Surch over numeral as Type D **20**.

D47	D **12**	10(c.) on 2c. (D23)	60·00	14·00
D48		20(c.) on 1c. (D22)	£250	7·50
D49		30(c.) on 2c. (D23)	£950	3·50

D **141**

D **142**

1934. With Fascist emblems.

D395	D **141**	5c. brown	25	15
D396		10c. blue	25	15
D397		20c. red	40	15
D398		25c. green	40	15
D399		30c. orange	40	15
D400		40c. brown	40	45
D401		50c. violet	25	10
D402		60c. blue	35	1·90
D403	D **142**	1l. orange	40	15
D404		2l. green	40	20
D405		5l. violet	95	35
D406		10l. blue	3·00	70
D407		20l. red	7·50	3·75

D **191**

D **192**

D **201**

1945. Fascist emblems removed.

D630	D **191**	5c. brown	45	70
D631		10c. blue	10	10
D632		20c. red	45	45
D633		25c. green	10	10
D634		30c. orange	10	10
D635		40c. black	10	10
D636		50c. violet	10	10
D637		60c. blue	10	30
D685	D **192**	1l. orange	10	10
D639		2l. green	10	10
D640		5l. violet	10	10
D641		10l. blue	10	10
D642		20l. red	10	1·20

1947.

D690	D **201**	1l. orange	30	10
D691		2l. green	30	10
D692		3l. red	60	85
D693		4l. brown	65	50
D924		5l. violet	10	10
D695		6l. blue	2·20	80
D696		8l. mauve	7·25	1·10
D926		10l. blue	10	10
D698		12l. brown	3·00	1·00
D927		20l. purple	10	10
D928		25l. red	10	10
D929		30l. purple	20	10
D930		40l. brown	10	10
D931		50l. green	25	10
D932		100l. orange	15	10
D935		500l. red and blue	2·30	10
D936		500l. purple and blue	45	10
D937		900l. mve, blk & grn	55	40
D938		1500l. orange & brown	1·30	45

PUBLICITY ENVELOPE STAMPS

1921. Optd **B.L.P.**

B129	**37**	10c. red	75·00	55·00
B137		15c. grey	£250	£250
B138	**41**	20c. orange	£250	£250
B132	**39**	25c. blue	£100	£225
B140		30c. brown	£170	£100
B115		40c. brown	60·00	11·00
B134		50c. violet	£550	£375
B135		60c. red	£1600	£1400
B141		85c. brown	£250	£250
B136	**34**	1l. brown and green	£2750	£1500

ITALIAN SOCIAL REPUBLIC

Following the surrender of Italy on 3 September 1943, and his rescue from imprisonment on 12 September, Mussolini proclaimed the Italian Social Republic at Salo on 23 September 1943. From this town on Lake Garda the Republican government administered those parts of Italy, north of the Gustav Line, which were under German occupation.

1944. Stamps of Italy optd **G. N. R.** (a) Postage. (i) Nos. 239 and 241/59.

1	**98**	5c. brown	2·20	5·50
2	–	10c. brown	2·20	5·50
3	–	15c. green	2·20	5·50
4	**99**	20c. red	2·20	5·50
5	–	25c. green	2·20	5·50
6	**103**	30c. brown	1·80	3·75
7	–	35c. blue	1·80	3·75
8	**103**	50c. violet	1·80	3·75
9	–	75c. red	1·80	3·75
10	**99**	1l. violet	2·75	5·75
11	–	1l.25 blue	3·50	7·25
12	–	1l.75 red	5·00	10·00
13	–	2l. red	13·00	30·00
14	**98**	2l.55 green	£190	£180
15		3l.70 violet	£100	£140
16		5l. red	26·00	50·00
17	–	10l. violet	65·00	£140
18	**99**	20l. green	£225	£450
19	–	25l. black	£650	£1400
20	–	50l. violet	£500	£1400

(ii) War Propaganda issue. Nos. 563/74.

21		25c. green (Navy)	5·00	16·00
22		25c. green (Army)	5·00	16·00
23		25c. green (Air Force)	5·00	16·00
24		25c. green (Militia)	5·00	16·00
25		30c. brown (Navy)	6·50	21·00
26		30c. brown (Army)	6·50	21·00
27		30c. brown (Air Force)	6·50	21·00
28		30c. brown (Militia)	6·50	21·00
29		50c. violet (Navy)	4·50	16·00
30		50c. violet (Army)	4·50	16·00
31		50c. violet (Air Force)	4·50	16·00
32		50c. violet (Militia)	4·50	16·00

(b) Air. Nos. 270/7.

33	–	25c. green	25·00	45·00
34	**110**	50c. brown	3·50	9·00
35	–	75c. brown	33·00	45·00
36	–	80c. red	95·00	£140
37	–	1l. violet	3·50	9·00
38	**113**	2l. blue	£275	£160
39	**110**	5l. green	£130	£225
40		10l. red	£1100	£1800

(4)

(5)

1944. Stamps of Italy. (a) Optd with T **4**.

57	–	25c. green (No. 244)	30	1·80
60	–	75c. red (No. 248)	75	1·80

(b) Optd with T **5**.

58	**103**	30c. brown	35	1·80
61	–	1l.25 blue (No. 250)	35	1·80
77	–	50l. violet (No. 259)	£200	£1800

(c) Optd **REPUBBLICA SOCIALE ITALIANA**.

59	**103**	50c. violet	30	1·80

1944. War Propaganda stamps. Nos. 563/74 optd with T **4** (25c.), T **5** (30c.) or **REPUBBLICA SOCIALE ITALIANA** (50c.).

64		25c. green (Navy)	30	2·10
65		25c. green (Army)	30	2·10
66		25c. green (Air Force)	30	2·10
67		25c. green (Militia)	30	2·10
68		30c. brown (Navy)	60	6·50
69		30c. brown (Army)	60	6·50
70		30c. brown (Air Force)	60	6·50
71		30c. brown (Militia)	60	6·50
72		50c. violet (Navy)	35	4·00
73		50c. violet (Army)	35	4·00
74		50c. violet (Air Force)	35	4·00
75		50c. violet (Militia)	35	4·00

Prices are for examples overprinted on the stamp part only; items overprinted twice (on stamp and label) are worth more.

10 Loggia dei Mercanti, Bologna

11 Loggia dei Mercanti, Bologna

12 Basilica de St. Lorenzo, Rome

13 Basilica de St. Lorenzo, Rome

1944. Inscr "REPUBBLICA SOCIALE ITALIANA".

106	–	5c. brown	10	50
107	–	10c. brown	10	20
102	**10**	20c. red	20	55
108	**11**	20c. red	10	20
103	**12**	25c. green	20	55
109	**13**	25c. green	10	20
110	–	30c. brown	10	20
111	–	50c. violet	10	20
112	–	75c. red	10	5·00
113	–	1l. violet	10	20
114	–	1l.25 blue	45	9·00
115	–	3l. green	60	33·00

DESIGN: 5c. St. Ciriaco's Church, Ancona; 10c., 1l. Montecassino Abbey; 30c., 75c. Drummer; 50c. Fascist allegory; 1l.25, 3l. St. Mary of Grace, Milan.

17 Bandiera Brothers

1944. Death Centenary of Attilio and Emilio Bandiera (revolutionaries).

117	**17**	25c. green	15	50
118		1l. violet	15	50
119		2l.50 red	15	4·50

CONCESSIONAL LETTER POST

1944. Concessional Letter Post stamp of Italy optd as T **5** but smaller.

CL76	CL **109**	10c. brown	15	1·00

EXPRESS LETTER STAMPS

1944. Express stamps of Italy optd **G. N. R.**

E41	E **132**	1l.25 green (postage)	31·00	45·00
E42		2l.50 red	£190	£400
E43	E **133**	2l. black (air)	£700	£1100

(E 7)

1944. Express stamps of Italy optd with Type E **7**.

E62	E **132**	1l.25 green	25	1·90
E63		2l.50 orange	25	12·50

E **16** Palermo Cathedral

1944.

E116	E **16**	1l.25 green	10	90

PARCEL POST STAMPS

1944. Parcel Post stamps of Italy optd **REP. SOC. ITALIANA** on left-hand side and Fascist Emblem on right.

P77	P **92**	5c. brown	9·00	10·50
P78		10c. blue	9·00	10·50
P79		25c. red	9·00	10·50
P80		30c. blue	9·00	10·50
P81		50c. orange	9·00	10·50
P82		60c. red	9·00	10·50
P83		1l. violet	9·00	10·50
P84		2l. green	£350	£550
P85		3l. bistre	15·00	35·00
P86		4l. black	28·00	55·00
P87		10l. purple	£180	
P88		20l. purple	£425	

The unused and used prices are for unsevered stamps.

POSTAGE DUE STAMPS

1944. Postage Due stamps of Italy optd **G. N. R.**

D44	D **141**	5c. brown	16·00	42·00
D45		10c. blue	12·50	42·00
D46		20c. red	16·00	24·00
D47		25c. green	9·75	24·00
D48		30c. orange	16·00	42·00
D49		40c. brown	25·00	24·00
D50		50c. violet	50·00	£200
D51		60c. blue	£250	£800
D52	D **142**	1l. orange	12·50	32·00
D53		2l. green	80·00	85·00
D54		5l. violet	£190	£325
D55		10l. blue	65·00	£225
D56		20l. red	65·00	£225

1944. Postage Due stamps of Italy optd with small Fascist emblems.

D 89	D **141**	5c. brown	1·70	4·50
D 90		10c. blue	1·70	3·75
D 91		20c. red	1·70	3·75
D 92		25c. green	1·70	3·75
D 93		30c. orange	1·70	5·25
D 94		40c. brown	1·70	8·75
D 95		50c. violet	1·70	3·00
D 96		60c. blue	3·75	18·00
D 97	D **142**	1l. orange	1·70	3·00
D 98		2l. green	5·50	12·50
D 99		5l. violet	55·00	£110
D100		10l. blue	95·00	£170
D101		20l. red	95·00	£170

IVORY COAST Pt. 6; Pt. 13

A French colony in W. Africa on the Gulf of Guinea, incorporated in French West Africa in 1944. In 1958 it became an autonomous republic within the French Community, and in 1960 it became fully independent.

100 centimes = 1 franc.

1892. "Tablet" key-type inscr "COTE D'IVOIRE" in blue (Nos. 2, 3, 5, 14, 7, 9/11) or red (others).

1 D 1c. black on blue 1·90 2·50
2 2c. brown on buff 1·75 2·25
3 4c. brown on grey 2·25 3·50
4a 5c. green on green 9·50 4·75
5 10c. black on lilac 8·75 8·75
14 10c. red 85·00 75·00
6 15c. blue 22·00 9·00
15 15c. grey 5·00 2·00
7 20c. red on green 10·00 22·00
8 25c. black on pink 10·00 2·25
16 25c. blue 27·00 25·00
9 30c. brown on drab 32·00 24·00
10 40c. red on yellow 17·00 10·50
11 50c. red on pink 55·00 60·00
17 50c. brown on blue 16·00 8·00
12 75c. brown on yellow 7·50 23·00
13 1f. green 42·00 24·00

1904. Surch in figures and bars.

18 D 0.05 on 30c. brown 55·00 65·00
19 0.10 on 75c. brown on yellow 10·00 13·50
20 0.15 on 1f. olive 11·50 14·50

1906. "Faidherbe", "Palms" and "Balay" key-types inscr "COTE D'IVOIRE" in blue (10c., 5f.) or red (others).

22 I 1c. grey 1·25 25
23 2c. brown 60 50
24 4c. brown on blue 50 40
25 5c. green 50 80
26 10c. pink 4·50 60
27 J 20c. black on blue 4·50 4·25
28 25c. blue 3·00 1·25
29 30c. brown on pink 7·00 8·50
30 35c. black on yellow 4·50 1·75
32 45c. brown on green 8·50 9·50
33 50c. violet 10·50 11·00
34 75c. green on orange 12·00 14·50
35 K 1f. black on blue 32·00 38·00
36 2f. blue on pink 35·00 50·00
37 5f. red on yellow 65·00 80·00

1912. Surch in figures.

38 D 05 on 15c. grey 45 1·60
39 05 on 30c. brown on drab 1·00 3·50
40 10 on 40c. red on yellow 40 3·25
41 10 on 50c. brown on blue 1·00 3·00
42 10 on 75c. brown on orange 2·25 7·25

7 River Scene

1913.

43 7 1c. violet and purple 10 10
44 2c. black and brown 10 1·50
45 4c. purple and violet 10 1·75
46 5c. green and light green 2·50 1·50
61 5c. brown and chocolate 35 90
47 10c. pink and red 90 1·25
62 10c. green and light green 45 2·50
63 10c. pink on blue 25 1·00
48 15c. red and orange 20 1·25
49 20c. grey and black 1·40 1·10
50 25c. blue and ultramarine 8·00 4·25
64 25c. violet and black 1·25 15
51 30c. brown and chocolate 1·75 2·50
65 30c. pink and red 2·75 3·00
66 30c. red and blue 15 75
67 30c. green and olive 1·00 2·25
52 35c. orange and violet 1·75 3·00
53 40c. green and grey 2·00 1·75
54 45c. brown and red 1·25 1·90
68 45c. purple and red 4·75 8·50
55 50c. violet and black 3·50 3·75
69 50c. blue and ultramarine 50 1·75
70 50c. blue and green 1·00 25
71 60c. violet on pink 35 3·00
72 65c. green and red 2·50 3·75
56 75c. pink and brown 1·00 45
73 75c. ultramarine and blue 4·00 4·75
74 85c. black and purple 1·25 3·75
75 90c. carmine and red 8·00 18·00
57 1f. black and yellow 1·75 35
76 1f.10 brown and green 5·50 10·00
77 1f.50 blue and light blue 5·50 6·75
78 1f.75 mauve and blue 11·50 11·50
58 2f. blue and brown 2·00 1·10
79 3f. mauve on pink 4·25 3·50
59 5f. brown and blue 5·50 3·75

1915. Surch **5c** and red cross.

60 7 10c.+5c. pink and red 80 2·00

1934. Surch with new value twice.

80 7 50 on 45c. purple and red 3·50 3·50
81 50 on 75c. ultramarine & blue 1·75 2·25
82 50 on 90c. pink and red 2·25 2·50
83 60 on 75c. violet on pink 35 95
84 65 on 15c. red and orange 40 3·00
85 85 on 75c. pink and brown 50 3·25

1922. Surch in figures and bars.

86 7 25c. on 2f. blue and brown 90 3·25
87 25c. on 5f. brown and blue 55 3·25
88 90c. on 75c. pink and red 35 3·00
89 1f.25 on 1f. ultram & blue 15 2·75
90 1f.50 on 1f. blue & light blue 80 1·50
91 3f. on 5f. green and red 1·90 4·50
92 10f. on 5f. mauve and red 6·75 19·00
93 20f. on 5f. red and green 13·00 24·00

1931. "Colonial Exhibition" key-types inscr "COTE D'IVOIRE".

94 E 40c. black and green 2·50 4·00
95 F 50c. black and mauve 4·25 7·00
96 G 90c. black and red 1·75 3·50
97 H 1f.50 black and blue 5·50 8·75

1933. Stamps of Upper Volta optd **Cote d'Ivoire** or surch also.

98 3 2c. brown and violet 10 2·25
99 4c. black and yellow 20 2·50
100 5c. indigo and blue 95 3·00
101 10c. blue and pink 65 1·60
102 15c. brown and blue 40 3·00
103 20c. brown and green 1·75 2·50
104 – 25c. brown and yellow 1·50 2·75
105 – 30c. deep green and green 1·25 3·50
106 – 45c. brown and blue 7·00 8·25
107 – 65c. indigo and blue 2·50 4·75
108 – 75c. black and violet 1·90 2·75
109 – 90c. red and mauve 1·25 3·25
110 6 1f. brown and green 1·25 3·00
111 – 1f.25 on 40c. black and pink 40 65
112 6 1f.50 ultramarine and blue 85 1·40
113 – 1f.75 on 50c. black & green 2·75 95

12 Baoule Woman

16 General Binger

1936.

114 12 1c. red 10 2·00
115 2c. blue 40 2·25
116 3c. green 70 2·50
117 4c. brown 40 2·25
118 5c. violet 40 1·75
119 10c. blue 10 1·40
120 15c. red 10 50
121 – 20c. blue 50 85
122 – 25c. red 10 75
123 – 30c. green 6·50 2·00
124 – 30c. brown 10 2·50
125 12 35c. green 1·00 2·50
126 – 40c. red 20 60
127 – 45c. brown 1·10 2·00
128 – 45c. green 1·60 3·00
129 – 50c. purple 10 10
130 – 55c. violet 1·75 2·00
131 – 60c. red 1·40 3·00
132 – 65c. brown 90 2·00
133 – 70c. brown 75 2·75
134 – 75c. violet 50 1·60
135 – 80c. brown 45 1·75
136 – 90c. red 3·50 7·25
137 – 90c. green 60 2·75
138 – 1f. green 1·60 45
139 – 1f. red 1·50 1·60
140 – 1f. violet 65 1·75
141 – 1f.25 red 75 75
142 – 1f.40 blue 85 2·75
143 – 1f.50 blue 80 75
144 – 1f.50 grey 1·75 3·00
145 – 1f.60 brown 85 3·00
146 – 1f.75 red 85 1·75
147 – 1f.75 blue 1·60 3·25
148 – 2f. blue 50 15
149 – 2f.50 blue 1·50 3·25
150 – 2f.50 red 1·40 1·75
151 – 3f. green 60 20
152 – 5f. brown 45 50
153 – 10f. violet 80 60
154 – 20f. red 2·75 2·25

DESIGNS—HORIZ: 20c. to 30c. and 40c. to 55c. Mosque at Bobo-Dioulasso; 60c. to 1f.60, Coastal scene. VERT: 1f.75, to 20f. Comoe Rapids.

1937. International Exhibition, Paris. As Nos. 157/62 of Guadeloupe.

155 20c. violet 40 2·50
156 30c. green 45 1·75
157 40c. red 55 1·90
158 50c. brown and blue 35 2·75
159 90c. red 45 1·75
160 1f.50 blue 85 1·90
MS160a 120 × 100 mm. 3f. brown (as T **4**) 4·75 20·00

1937. 50th Anniv of Gen. Binger's Exploration.

161 16 65c. brown 20 15

1938. International Anti-cancer Fund. As T **58b** of Guadeloupe.

162 1f.75+50c. blue 2·00 9·75

1939. Death Centenary of Rene Caillie (explorer). As T **21** of French Sudan.

163 90c. orange 55 1·00
164 2f. violet 90 85
165 2f.25 blue 60 1·25

1939. New York World's Fair. As T **58c** of Guadeloupe.

166 1f.25 red 1·40 3·00
167 2f.25 blue 1·10 1·25

1939. 150th Anniv of French Revolution. As T **58d** of Guadeloupe.

168 45c.+25c. green and black 3·75 9·50
169 70c.+30c. brown and black 4·25 9·25
170 90c.+35c. orange and black 3·75 9·25
171 1f.25+1f. red and black 3·50 5·25
172 2f.25+2f. blue and black 4·00 5·25

1940. Air. As T **6a** of French Guinea.

173 1f.90 blue 50 1·40
174 2f.90 red 60 1·75
175 4f.50 green 50 80
176 4f.90 olive 60 2·00
177 6f.90 orange 60 1·25

1941. National Defence Fund. Surch **SECOURS NATIONAL** and value.

178 +1f. on 50c. (No. 129) 2·25 4·00
178a +2f. on 80c. (No. 135) 10·00 17·00
178b +2f. on 1f.50 (No. 143) 10·00 17·00
178c +3f. on 2f. (No. 148) 11·00 16·00

16a Pirogue

1942. Marshal Petain issue.

178d 16a 1f. green 20 2·00
178e 2f.50 blue 20 2·00

1942. Air. Colonial Child Welfare Fund. As T **8** of French Guinea.

178f 1f.50+3f.50 green 20 1·90
178g 2f.+6f. brown 15 1·90
178h 3f.+9f. red 25 1·90

1942. Air Imperial Fortnight. As T **9a** of French Guinea.

178i 1f.20+1f.80 blue and red 20 1·90

1942. Air. As T **27** of French Sudan, but inscr "COTE D'IVOIRE".

179 50f. olive and green 2·25 3·00

REPUBLIC

17 African Elephant

19 Pres. Houphouet-Boigny

18 Place Lapalud, Abidjan

1959.

180 17 10f. black and green 1·75 1·25
181 25f. brown and bistre 1·10 40
182 30f. olive and turquoise 1·60 1·60

1959. Air.

183 18 100f. brown, green & choc 4·50 1·60
184 – 200f. brown, myrtle & turq 9·00 3·50
185 – 500f. turquoise, brn & grn 11·00 5·00

DESIGNS: 200f. Houphouet-Boigny railway bridge, Abidjan; 500f. Ayame Barrage.

1959. 1st Anniv of Republic.

186 19 25f. brown 2·00 2·00

20 Bete Mask

21 Conseil de l'Entente Emblem

1960. Native Masks.

187 20 50c. chocolate and brown 35 1·75
188 – 1f. violet and red 1·10 1·75
189 – 2f. green and blue 1·10 1·75
190 – 4f. red and green 1·60 1·25
191 – 5f. brown and red 1·60 1·25
192 – 6f. blue and purple 1·75 1·75
193 – 45f. purple and green 3·25 1·50
194 – 50f. blue and brown 3·75 1·25
195 – 85f. green and red 6·00 3·25

DESIGNS—VERT: MASKS OF: 1f. Guere; 2f. Guere (different type); 45f. Bete (different type); 50f. Gouro; 85f. Gouro (different type). HORIZ: 4f. Baole; 5f. Senoufo; 6f. Senoufo (different type).

1960. 10th Anniv of African Technical Co-operation Commission. As T **2b** of Gabon.

196 25f. violet and turquoise 2·00 1·50

1960. 1st Anniv of Conseil de l'Entente.

197 21 25f. multicoloured 2·00 2·50

21a "World Peace"

1961. 1st Anniv of Independence.

198 21a 25f. black, green & brown 55 35

22 "Thoningia sanguinea"

1961.

199 – 5f. red, yellow and green 55 15
200 – 10f. yellow, red and blue 30 20
201 – 15f. purple, green & orange 1·10 30
202 22 20f. yellow, red and brown 60 30
203 – 25f. yellow, red and green 70 30
204 – 30f. red, green and black 90 50
205 – 70f. yellow, red and green 2·50 1·00
206 – 85f. multicoloured 3·25 1·40

FLOWERS: 5f. "Plumeria rubra"; 10f. "Haemanthus cinnabarinus"; 15f. "Bougainvillea spectabilis"; 25f. "Eulophia cucullata"; 30f. "Newbouldia laevis"; 70f. "Mussaenda erythrophylla"; 85f. "Strophantus sarmentosus".

23 Mail-carriers

1961. Stamp Day.

207 23 25f. brown, blue and green 55 40

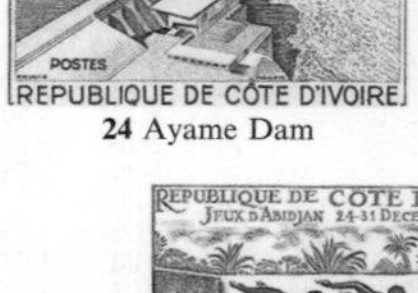

24 Ayame Dam

26 Palms

25 Swimming

1961.
208 **24** 25f. sepia, blue and green 55 30

1961. Abidjan Games. Inscr as in T **25**.
209 **25** 5f. sepia, green and blue (postage) 20 10
210 – 20f. brown, green and grey 35 20
211 – 25f. brown, green and blue 55 25
211a – 100f. blk, red & bl (air) 2·75 1·60
DESIGNS: 20f. Basketball; 25f. Football; 100f. High-jumping.

1962. 17th Session of African Technical Co-operation Commission, Abidjan.
212 **26** 25f. multicoloured 55 35

1962. Air. "Air Afrique" Airline. As T **34** of Gabon.
213 50f. blue, brown and chestnut 1·25 65

1962. Malaria Eradication. As T **55a** of French Somali Coast.
214 25f.+5f. green 65 65

27 Fort Assinie

1962. Postal Centenary.
215 **27** 85f. multicoloured . . . . 1·90 1·10

28 Village, Man Region

1962. Air.
216 – 200f. sepia, purple & green 5·00 1·90
217 **28** 500f. green, purple & black 8·50 4·00
DESIGN—VERT: 200f. Street Scene, Odienne.

1962. 1st Anniv of Union of African and Malagasy States. As T **38** of Gabon.
218 30f. red . . . . 1·00 55

29 U.N. Headquarters and Emblem

1962. Air. 2nd Anniv of Admission to U.N.
219 **29** 100f. multicoloured . . . . 1·90 85

30 Bouake Arms and Cotton Exhibit

1963. Bouake Fair.
220 **30** 50f. sepia, brown and green 65 35

1963. Freedom from Hunger. As T **41** of Gabon.
221 25f.+5f. violet, brown & pur 85 85

31 Map of Africa

1963. Conference of African Heads of State, Addis Ababa.
222 **31** 30f. green and blue 60 60

32 Sassandra Bay

1963. Air.
223 – 50f. green, brown and blue 1·25 45
224 **32** 100f. brown, blue & myrtle 1·90 95
225 – 200f. turquoise, grn & brn 3·50 1·60
DESIGNS: 50f. Moosou Bridge; 200f. River Comoe.

1963. Air. African and Malagasian Posts and Telecommunications Union. As T **44** of Gabon.
226 85f. multicoloured . . . . . 1·40 85

33 Hartebeest

34 Scales of Justice, Globe and UNESCO Emblem

1963. "Tourism and Hunting".
227 – 1f. multicoloured 30 10
228 – 2f. multicoloured 30 15
229 – 4f. multicoloured 25 15
230 – 5f. multicoloured 25 10
247 – 5f. green, yellow and brown 45 20
231 **33** 10f. brown, green and grey 45 20
248 – 10f. brown, green & purple 1·00 20
232 – 15f. black, green and brown 60 30
249 – 15f. brown, green & purple 1·60 30
233 – 20f. brown, green and red 85 30
234 – 25f. brown, green & yellow 1·40 50
235 – 45f. purple, green & turq 2·75 1·00
236 – 50f. black, green and brown . . . . 3·75 1·40
DESIGNS—HORIZ: 1f. Yellow-backed duiker; 4f. Beecroft's hyrax; 5f. (No. 247) African manatee; 10f. (No. 248) Pygmy hippopotamus; 15f. (No. 232) Giant forest hog; 20f. Warthog; 45f. Hunting dogs. VERT: 2f. Potto; 5f. (No. 230) Water chevrotain; 15f. (No. 249) Royal antelope; 25f. Bongo; 50f. Western black and white colobus.

1963. Air. 1st Anniv of "Air Afrique" and "DC-8" Service Inauguration. As T **46** of Gabon.
237 25f. multicoloured 55 25

1963. 15th Anniv of Declaration of Human Rights.
238 **34** 85f. black, blue and orange 1·25 70

35 Rameses II and Nefertari, Abu Simbel

36 Map of Africa

1964. Air. Nubian Monuments Preservation.
239 **35** 60f. black, brown and red 1·60 85

1964. Inter-African National Education Ministers' Conference, Abidjan.
240 **36** 30f. red, green and blue . . 60 35

37 Weather Balloon

38 Doctor tending Child

1964. World Meteorological Day.
241 **37** 25f. multicoloured 60 40

1964. National Red Cross Society.
242 **38** 50f. multicoloured 95 50

39 Arms of the Ivory Coast

1964. Air.
243 **39** 200f. gold, blue and green 3·00 1·40

40 Globe and Athletes

41 Symbolic Tree

1964. Olympic Games, Tokyo.
244 **40** 35f. brown, green and violet 95 45
245 – 65f. ochre, brown and blue 1·90 95
DESIGN—HORIZ: 65f. Wrestling and Globe.

1964. 1st Anniv of European–African Convention.
246 **41** 30f. multicoloured 65 35

1964. French, African and Malagasy Co-operation. As T **57** of Gabon.
250 25f. brown, red and green . . 55 35

42 Pres. Kennedy

43 Korhogo Mail-carriers, 1914

1964. Air. Pres. Kennedy Commemoration.
251 **42** 100f. brown and grey . . . 1·90 1·40

1964. Stamp Day.
252 **43** 85f. sepia, brown and blue 1·60 95

44 Pottery

1965. Native Handicrafts.
253 **44** 5f. black, red and green . . 20 15
254 – 10f. black, purple and green 25 15
255 – 20f. blue, chocolate & brn 50 20
256 – 25f. brown, red and olive 55 30
DESIGNS: 10f. Wood-carving; 20f. Ivory-carving; 25f. Weaving.

45 Mail coming ashore

1965. Stamp Day.
257 **45** 30f. multicoloured 60 45

46 I.T.U. Emblem and Symbols

1965. I.T.U. Centenary.
258 **46** 85f. blue, red and green . . 1·40 85

47 Abidjan Railway Station

1965.
259 **47** 30f. multicoloured . . . . 1·25 45

48 Pres. Houphouet-Boigny and Map

49 Hammerkop

1965. 5th Anniv of Independence.
260 **48** 30f. multicoloured 55 35

1965. Birds.
261 – 1f. green, yellow and violet 65 35
262 – 2f. multicoloured 65 40
263 – 5f. purple, red and olive . . 75 45
264 **49** 10f. brown, black & purple 1·00 40
265 – 15f. red, grey and green . . 90 45
266 – 30f. brown, green and lake 1·25 45
267 – 50f. blue, black and brown 2·40 85
268 – 75f. red, green and orange 2·40 1·00
269 – 90f. multicoloured . . . . 3·75 2·10
BIRDS—HORIZ: 1f. Yellow-bellied green pigeon; 2f. Spur-winged goose; 30f. Namaqua dove; 50f. Lizard buzzard. VERT: 5f. Stone partridge; 15f. White-breasted guineafowl; 75f. Yellow-billed stork; 90f. Latham's francolin.

50 Lieupleu Rope-bridge

1965. Air.
270 **50** 100f. brown, green & lt grn 1·90 1·10
271 – 300f. purple, flesh and blue 5·50 2·75
DESIGN: 300f. Street in Kong.

51 Steam Mail Train, 1906

52 "Maternity"

1966. Stamp Day.
272 **51** 30f. green, black and purple . . . . 3·25 1·60

1966. World Festival of Negro Arts, Dakar.
273 **52** 5f. black and green 20 15
274 – 10f. black and violet . . . 30 20
275 – 20f. black and orange . . . 90 45
276 – 30f. black and red . . . . 1·10 65
DESIGNS—CARVED WORK: 10f. Pomade box; 20f. Drums; 30f. "Ancestor".

53 Ivory Hotel

1966. Inauguration of Ivory Hotel.
277 **53** 15f. multicoloured 45 25

54 Tractor Cultivation

1966. 6th Anniv of Independence.
278 **54** 30f. multicoloured 50 35

1966. Air. Inauguration of Douglas DC-8F Air Services. As T **84** of Gabon.
279 30f. grey, black and green . . 55 30

55 Open-air Class

1966. National School of Administration.
280 **55** 30f. black, blue and lake 55 35

56 Inoculating Cattle

57 U.N.E.S.C.O. "Waves" enveloping "Man"

1966. Campaign for Prevention of Cattle Plague.
281 **56** 30f. brown, green and blue 65 40

1966. 20th Anniv of U.N.E.S.C.O.
282 **57** 30f. violet and blue 60 40
283 – 30f. black, brown and blue 55 35
DESIGN: No. 283, Distributing food parcels to children.

58 Bouake Hospital

1966.
284 **58** 30f. multicoloured 55 35

59 "Air Afrique" Headquarters

1966. Air.
285 **59** 500f. blue, ochre and green 8·25 3·25

60 Sikorsky S-43 Amphibian (30th anniv)

1967. Stamp Day.
286 **60** 30f. blue, brown & turq . . 1·25 80

61 Cutting Pineapples

62 "African Mythology"

1967. Fruits.
287 **61** 20f. purple, brown & green 35 15
288 – 30f. red, brown and green 45 30
289 – 100f. brown, olive and blue 1·90 85
DESIGNS: 30f. Cutting palm-nuts; 100f. Cutting bananas.

1967. 35th Pen Club Int Congress, Abidjan.
290 **62** 30f. black, green and lake 60 40

63 "Improvement of Rural Housing"

1967. 7th Anniv of Independence.
291 **63** 30f. multicoloured 50 30

64 Lions Emblems

65 African Man and Woman

1967. 50th Anniv of Lions International.
292 **64** 30f. multicoloured 80 45

1967. Air. 5th Anniv of U.A.M.P.T. As T **104** of Gabon.
293 100f. red, blue and violet . . 1·60 85

1967. 5th Anniv of West African Monetary Union. As T **103** of Mauritania.
294 30f. black, green and mauve 50 30

1967. 20th Anniv of Recognition Days.
295 **65** 90f. multicoloured . . . . 1·10 65
See also No. 342.

66 Senoufo Village

1968. Air.
296 **66** 100f. brown, yellow & green . . . . 1·90 90
297 – 500f. brown, blue and green . . . . 8·25 3·25
DESIGN: 500f. Tiegba lake village.

67 Tabou Radio Station, 1912

1968. Stamp Day.
298 **67** 30f. green, brown & turq 60 35

68 Cotton Loom

1968. Industries.
299 – 5f. black, red and green . . 20 10
300 **68** 10f. brown, green and slate 30 15
301 – 15f. black, blue and red . . 70 45
302 – 20f. blue and purple . . . 50 30
303 – 30f. brown, green and blue 65 35
304 – 50f. black, green and mauve 95 45
305 – 70f. chocolate, blue & brn 1·40 70
306 – 90f. black, purple and blue 1·60 1·10
DESIGNS—HORIZ: 5f. Palm-oil works; 30f. Flour mills; 50f. Cocoa-butter extraction machine; 90f. Timber sawmill and logs. VERT: 15f. Oil refinery, Abidjan; 20f. Raw cotton and reeling machine; 70f. Soluble-coffee plant.
See also Nos. 335/7.

69 Canoeing

1968. Olympic Games, Mexico.
307 **69** 30f. brown, blue and green 60 30
308 – 100f. purple, ultram & blue 1·60 65
DESIGN: 100f. 100 m sprint.

70 Sacrificial Offering

1968. 8th Anniv of Independence.
309 **70** 30f. multicoloured 55 30

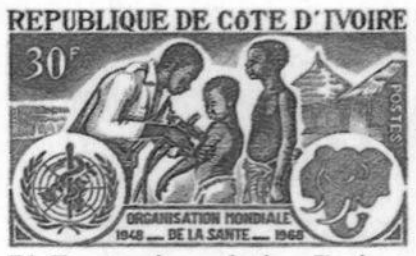

71 Doctor inoculating Patient

72 Impala in Forest

1968. 20th Anniv of W.H.O.
310 **71** 30f. chocolate, brown & bl 55 30

1968. Fauna and Flora Protection.
311 **72** 30f. brown, green and blue 1·10 55

73 Museum and Carved Screen

1968. Opening of Abidjan Museum.
312 **73** 30f. brown, red and blue 55 30

74 Human Rights Emblem and "Justice" Totems

1968. Human Rights Year.
313 **74** 30f. orange, purple and blue 55 30

1969. Air. "Philexafrique" Stamp Exhibition, Abidjan, Ivory Coast (1st issue). As T **125** of Gabon. Multicoloured.
314 100f. "Grand Bassam" (Achalme) . . . . 3·25 3·25

1969. Air. "Philexafrique" Stamp Exn, Abidjan, Ivory Coast (2nd issue). As T **127** of Gabon.
315 50f. red, blue and green . . . 1·90 1·90
316 100f. blue, brown and orange 3·00 3·00
317 200f. slate, blue and brown 4·50 4·50
DESIGNS—HORIZ: 50f. Aerial view of San Pedro village and stamp of 1936; 200f. Chambers of Agriculture and Industry building, Abidjan, and 5f. stamp of 1913. VERT: 100f. Chief's costume and 5f. stamp of 1936.

75 "Ville de Maranhao" (mail steamer) at Grand-Bassam

1969. Stamp Day.
319 **75** 30f. purple, blue and green 65 30

76 Ivory Hotel

1969. Opening of Ivory Hotel.
320 **76** 30f. blue, red and green . . 65 30

77 "Man on Horseback" (statuette)

78 Hertzian-wave Radio Station, Man

1969. Ivory Coast Art Exn, Vevey, Switzerland.
321 **77** 30f. black, purple and red 65 45

1969. 9th Anniv of Independence.
322 **78** 30f. green, brown and blue 60 35

79 Bank Emblem

1969. 5th Anniv of African Development Bank.
323 **79** 30f. brown, green and lake 50 30

80 Arms of Bouake

81 Game Fishing

1969. Coats of Arms.
324 **80** 10f. multicoloured 20 10
325 – 15f. multicoloured 30 15
326 – 30f. black, gold and green 45 15
ARMS: 15f. Abidjan; 30f. Ivory Coast Republic.
See also Nos. 402/3 and 432/6.

1969. Int SKAL Tourist Assn Congress, Abidjan.
327 **81** 30f. blue, purple and violet 2·00 50
328 – 100f. multicoloured . . . . 3·00 1·50
DESIGN: 100f. Assinie Holiday Village.

1969. 10th Anniv of Aerial Navigation Security Agency for Africa and Madagascar (A.S.E.C.N.A.). As T **147** of Gabon.
329 30f. red 55 35

82 Man Waterfall

1970. Air.
330 **82** 100f. blue, green and brown . . . . 1·90 1·00
331 – 200f. red, green and emerald . . . . 2·75 1·10
DESIGN: 200f. Mt. Niangbo.

83 University Hospital Centre, Abidjan

1970. "10 Years of Higher Education".
332 **83** 30f. indigo, green and blue 55 35

84 Telegraphist and Gabriel Dadie (Postal administrator)

1970. Stamp Day.
333 **84** 30f. black, green and red 50 30

85 Abidjan University

1970. 3rd A.U.P.E.L.F. (Association of French Speaking Universities). General Assembly, Abidjan.
334 **85** 30f. purple, green and blue 55 35

86 Safety-match Manufacture

88 Wild Life

87 Dish Aerial and Television Class

1970. Industrial Expansion.
335 **86** 5f. brown, blue & chocolate 20 15
336 – 20f. red, green and grey . . 40 15
337 – 50f. brown, blue and green 90 35
DESIGNS: 20f. Textile-printing; 50f. Ship-building.

1970. World Telecommunications Day.
338 **87** 40f. green, drab and red . . 65 40

1970. New U.P.U. Headquarters Building, Berne. As T **47** of French Polynesia.
339 30f. brown, green and purple 65 35

1970. 25th Anniv of United Nations.
340 **88** 30f. brown, green and blue 90 55

89 Coffee Plant

90 African Man and Woman

1970. 10th Anniv of Independence (1st issue).
341 **89** 30f. green, brown & orange 55 35
See also Nos. 344/9.

1970. 5th P.D.C.I. (Ivory Coast Democratic Party) Congress.
342 **90** 40f. multicoloured 65 35

91 Power Station

1970. Thermal Power Plant, Vridi.
343 **91** 40f. brown, blue and green 60 20

92 Pres. Houphouet-Boigny and De Gaulle

1970. 10th Anniv of Independence (2nd issue). Embossed on silver (300f. values) or gold foil.
344 300f. Type **92** (postage) . . . 9·00
345 300f. Ivory Coast Arms . . . 7·75
346 1000f. Type **92** . . . . 32·00
347 1000f. As No. 345 . . . . . 29·00
348 300f. Pres. Houphouet-Boigny and African elephants (air) . . . . . . 7·25
349 1200f. As No. 348 . . . . . 29·00

93 Mail Bus, 1925

1971. Stamp Day.
350 **93** 40f. purple, green & brown 70 30

94 Port of San Pedro

1971. Air.
351 **94** 100f. red, blue and green 1·50 55
352 – 500f. green, blue and brown . . . . 7·75 3·50
DESIGN: 500f. African Riviera coastline.

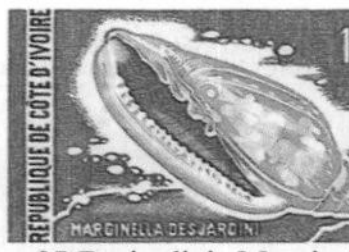

95 Desjardin's Marginella

1971. Marine Life.
353 – 1f. brown, blue and green 15 10
354 – 5f. red, lilac and blue . . . 20 15
355 – 10f. red, blue and green . . 45 20
356 **95** 15f. brown, purple and blue 50 25
357 – 15f. brown, violet and red 75 25
358 – 20f. red and yellow . . . . 1·10 40
359 – 20f. lake, purple and red 1·25 45
360 – 25f. brown, black and lake 75 25
361 – 35f. red, yellow and green 1·40 55
362 – 40f. brown, blue and green 3·00 1·25
363 – 40f. red, turquoise & brown . . . . 2·25 90
364 – 45f. brown, green & emer 2·75 1·25
365 – 50f. green, red and violet 2·75 1·10
366 – 65f. blue, green and brown 3·25 2·25
DESIGNS—HORIZ: 1f. African pelican's-foot; 5f. "Neptunus validus"; 20f. (No. 359) Digitate carrier shell; 25f. Butterfly cone; 40f. (No. 362) Garter cone; 45f. Bubonion conch; 65f. Rat cowrie. VERT: 10f. "Hermodice carunculata"; 15f. (No. 357) Fanel moon; 20f. (No. 358) "Goniaster cuspidatus"; 35f. "Polycheles typhiops"; 40f. (No. 363) African fan scallop; 50f. "Enoplometopus callistas".

96 Telegraph Station, Grand Bassam, 1891

1971. World Telecommunications Day.
367 **96** 100f. brown, green and blue . . . . 1·10 65

97 Treichville Swimming Pool

1971. Air.
368 **97** 100f. multicoloured . . . . 1·90 70

98 Tool-making

99 African Telecommunications Map

1971. Technical Training and Instruction.
369 **98** 35f. blue, red and green . . 60 30

1971. Pan-African Telecommunications Network.
370 **99** 45f. yellow, red and purple 60 30

100 Bondoukou Market

1971. 11th Anniv of Independence.
371 **100** 35f. brown, blue and grey (postage) 60 35
372 – 200f. black and blue on gold (air) . . . . . . 2·50 1·60
No. 372 has a similar design to Type **100** but in smaller format, size 38 × 27 mm.

101 Children of Three Races

1971. Racial Equality Year. Multicoloured.
373 40f. Type **101** 55 20
374 45f. Children around Globe 55 20

1971. 10th Anniv of U.A.M.P.T. As T **166** of Gabon. Multicoloured.
375 100f. H.Q. and Ivory Coast Arms . . . . 1·40 65
U.A.M.P.T. = African and Malagasy Posts and Telecommunications Union.

102 Gaming Table

1971. National Lottery.
376 **102** 35f. multicoloured 50 20

103 Technicians working on Power Cables

105 Cogwheel and Students

104 Lion of St. Mark's

1971. Electricity Works Centre, Akovai-Santai.
377 **103** 35f. multicoloured 70 35

1972. Air. U.N.E.S.C.O. "Save Venice" Campaign. Multicoloured.
378 100f. Type **104** . . . . 1·60 85
379 200f. St. Mark's Square . . . 3·25 1·60

1972. Technical Instruction Week.
380 **105** 35f. blue, brown and red 50 35

106 Heart Emblem

107 Child learning to write

1972. World Heart Month.
381 **106** 40f. blue, red and green 60 35

1972. International Book Year.
382 – 35f. brown, orange & grn 40 20
383 **107** 40f. black, orange & green 55 30
DESIGN—HORIZ: 35f. Students and open book.

108 Gouessesso Tourist Village

1972. Air.
384 **108** 100f. brown, green & blue 1·90 85
385 – 200f. green, brown & blue 2·75 1·10
386 – 500f. brown, bistre & blue 7·75 3·50
DESIGNS: 200f. Jacqueville Lake; 500f. Mosque of Kawara.

109 Regional Postal Training Centre, Abidjan

110 Aerial Mast, Abobo Hertzian Centre

1972. Stamp Day.
387 **109** 40f. bistre, green & purple 60 35

1972. World Telecommunications Day.
388 **110** 40f. red, blue and green 70 35

112 Computer Operator

1972. Development of Information Services.
393 **112** 40f. blue, brown and green 70 35

113 Odienne

1972. 12th Anniv of Independence.
394 **113** 35f. brown, green and blue 55 35

114 Africans and 500f. Coin

1972. 10th Anniv of West African Monetary Union.
395 **114** 40f. grey, purple and brown 60 35

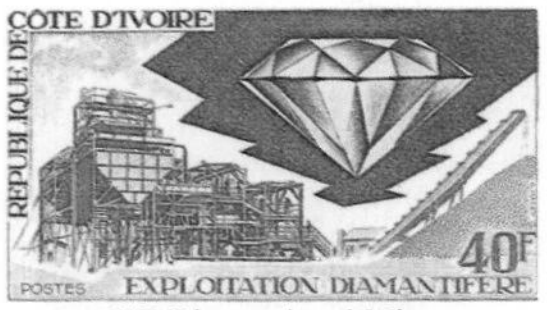

115 Diamond and Mine

1972. Development of the Diamond Industry.
396 **115** 40f. blue, grey and brown 1·60 85

116 Lake-dwellings, Bletankoro

1972. Air.
397 **116** 200f. purple, green & blue 2·50 1·10
398 – 500f. brown, green & blue 7·75 3·50
DESIGN: 500f. Kossou Dam.

117 Louis Pasteur and Institute

1972. Inauguration of Pasteur Institute, Abidjan.
399 **117** 35f. blue, green and brown 60 35

118 Satellite Earth Station

1972. Air. Opening of Satellite Earth Station, Akakro.

400	**118**	200f. brown, green & blue	2·75	1·10

119 Child pumping Water 120 Dr. G. A. Hansen

1972. "Conserve Water" Campaign.

401	**119**	35f. black, green and red	60	30

See also No. 414.

1973. Coats of Arms. As T **80**. Multicoloured.

402	5f. Arms of Daloa	15	10
403	10f. Arms of Gagnoa	20	10

See also Nos. 432/6.

1973. Centenary of Hansen's Identification of Leprosy Bacillus.

404	**120**	35f. brown, blue & purple	60	30

121 Pearly Razorfish

1973. Fishes

405	–	15f. blue and green	60	40
406	–	20f. red and brown	1·00	55
406a	–	25f. red and green	1·50	40
406b	–	35f. red and green	1·90	85
407	**121**	50f. red, blue and black	2·75	1·40

FISHES: 15f. Grey triggerfish; 20f. West African goatfish; 25f. African hind; 35f. Bigeye.

122 Child and Emblem

1973. Establishment of first S.O.S. Children's Village in Africa.

408	**122**	40f. black, red and green	55	30

123 National Assembly Building

1973. 112th Interparliamentary Council Session, Abidjan.

409	**123**	100f. multicoloured	85	35

124 Classroom and Shop

1973. "Commercial Action" Programme.

410	**124**	40f. multicoloured	45	15

125 "Women's Work"

1973. Technical Instruction for Women.

411	**125**	35f. multicoloured	50	30

126 Scouts helping with Food Cultivation

1973. 24th World Scouting Congress, Nairobi, Kenya.

412	**126**	40f. multicoloured	65	35

127 Party Headquarters

1973. New Party Headquarters Building, Yamoussokro.

413	**127**	35f. multicoloured	45	25

128 Children at Dry Pump

1973. Pan-African Drought Relief.

414	**128**	40f. sepia, brown and red	60	30

129 "The Judgment of Solomon" (Nandjui Legue)

1973. Air. 6th World Peace and Justice Conf.

415	**129**	500f. multicoloured	9·00	4·00

1973. U.A.M.P.T. As T **192** of Gabon.

416	100f. black, red and violet	1·10	60

130 "Arrow-heads" 132 Motorway Junction

131 Ivory Coast 1c. Stamp of 1892

1973. Abidjan Museum.

417	**130**	5f. black, red and brown	15	10

1973. Stamp and Post Day.

418	**131**	40f. black, orange & green	65	35

1973. Motorway Projects. Indenie Interchange, Abidjan.

419	**132**	35f. black, green and blue	55	30

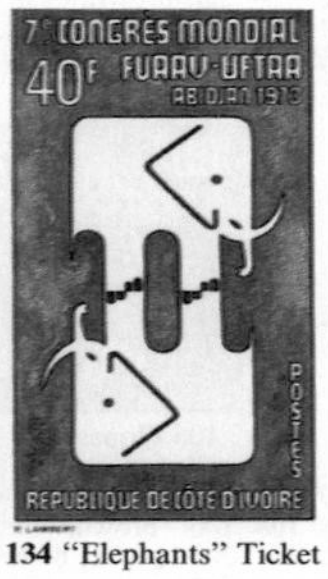

133 Map of Africa and Emblem 134 "Elephants" Ticket

1973. 18th General Assembly of International Social Security Association.

420	**133**	40f. brown, ultram & bl	50	20

1973. Travel-Agents Assns' 7th World Congress.

421	**134**	40f. multicoloured	50	20

136 Kong Mosque

1974.

426	**136**	35f. brown, blue and green	55	35

137 Grand-Lahou Post Office

1974. Stamp Day.

427	**137**	35f. brown, green and blue	55	20

138 Converging Columns

1974. "Formation Permanente".

428	**138**	35f. multicoloured	40	20

139 Sassandra Bridge

1974. Air.

429	**139**	100f. brown and green	1·10	50
430		500f. black and green	7·25	2·50

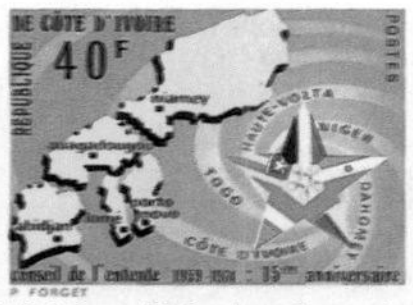

140 Map of Member Countries 141 Arms of Ivory Coast

1974. 15th Anniv of Conseil de l'Entente.

431	**140**	40f. multicoloured	45	20

1974.

432	**141**	35f. gold, green and brown	35	10
433		40f. gold, green and blue	40	10
434		60f. gold, green and red	50	20
435		65f. gold, lt green & green	55	20
436		70f. gold, green and blue	60	30

142 View of Factory

1974. Air. Vridi Soap Factory, Abidjan.

437	**142**	200f. multicoloured	2·25	1·10

143 Pres. Houphouet-Boigny 144 W.P.Y. Emblem

1974.

438	**143**	25f. brown, orange & grn	35	15

1974. World Population Year.

439	**144**	40f. blue and green	55	20

145 Cotton-picking 146 Pres. Houphouet-Boigny

1974. Cotton Production (1st series).

440	**145**	50f. multicoloured	60	30

See also Nos. 456/7.

1974.

889	**146**	5f. brown, mauve and red	10	10
890		10f. brown, blue and green	10	10
891		20f. lt brown, brown & red	15	10
892		25f. brown, mauve & blue	15	10
893		30f. lt brown, brown & red	20	10
441		35f. brown, green & orge	30	10
894		40f. brown, orange & grn	25	10
895		50f. brown, purple and red	30	15
443		60f. brown, red and blue	55	15
444		65f. brown, blue and red	55	10
896		90f. brown, red and purple	55	15
897		125f. brown, red & purple	65	20
898		155f. brown, blue and lilac	85	35

147 U.P.U. Emblem

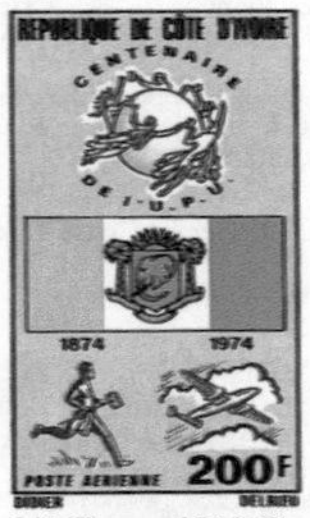

148 Flag and U.P.U. Emblems

1974. Centenary of U.P.U.

445	**147**	40f. green, blue and brown (postage)	60	30
446	**148**	200f. multicoloured (air)	3·00	1·60
447		300f. multicoloured	4·00	2·25

149 Raoul Follereau

1974. Follereau (leprosy pioneer) Commem.

448	**149**	35f. red, yellow and green	50	30

150 Civic Service Emblem

1974. 14th Anniv of Independence.

449	**150**	35f. multicoloured	50	20

151 Library Building and Students

1975. 1st Anniv of Inauguration of National Library.
450 **151** 40f. multicoloured 50 20

152 Congress Emblem **153** Coffee Flower

1975. 52nd International Seedcrushers Association Congress, Abidjan.
451 **152** 40f. black and green . . . 45 20

1975. Coffee Production. Multicoloured.
452 5f. Type **153** 20 10
453 10f. Coffee-berries 30 15

154 Sassandra Wharf

1975.
454 **154** 100f. brown, green & blue 1·10 65

155 Postal Sorters

1975. Stamp Day.
455 **155** 40f. multicoloured 60 30

156 Cotton Flower

1975. Cotton Production (2nd series). Multicoloured.
456 5f. Type **156** 20 15
457 10f. Cotton bolls 35 15

157 Marie Kore and I.W.Y. Emblem

1975. International Women's Year.
458 **157** 45f. brown, blue and green 55 30

158 Dabou Fort

1975.
459 **158** 50f. violet, blue and green 55 30

159 Abidjan Harbour

1975. 25th Anniv of Abidjan Port.
460 **159** 35f. multicoloured . . . . 1·25 40

160 Cocoa Tree

1975.
462 **160** 35f. multicoloured 80 35

161 Rural Activities

1975. Promotion of Rural Development.
463 **161** 50f. mauve, violet & black 55 35

162 Railway Bridge over the N'Zi, Dimbokro

1975. 15th Anniv of Independence.
464 **162** 60f. multicoloured . . . . 1·25 45

163 "Mother" (statue) **165** Early and Modern Telephones

164 Baoule Mask

1976. Mothers' Day.
465 **163** 65f. multicoloured 85 45

1976. Ivory Coast Art. Multicoloured.
466 20f. Type **164** (postage) . . . 30 15
467 25f. Senoufo statuette 35 20
468 150f. Chief Abron's chair . . 1·75 85
469 200f. Akans royal symbols: fly swatter and panga (air) 3·25 1·40

1976. Telephone Centenary.
470 **165** 70f. blue, brown and black 65 40

166 Effigy, Map and Carrier Pigeon

1976. 20th Anniv of Stamp Day and Ivory Coast Philatelic Club.
471 **166** 65f. multicoloured 55 35

167 "Smiling Trees" and Cat **168** Children Reading

1976. Nature Protection.
472 **167** 65f. multicoloured 65 35

1976. Literature for Children.
473 **168** 65f. multicoloured 60 35

169 Throwing the Javelin

1976. Olympic Games, Montreal. Multicoloured.
474 60f. Type **169** 55 30
475 65f. Running (horiz) 55 30

170 Mohammed Ali Jinnah

1976. Birth Centenary of Mohammed Ali Jinnah (first Governor-General of Pakistan).
476 **170** 50f. multicoloured . . . . 28·00 5·50

171 Cashew-nut

1976.
477 **171** 65f. multicoloured . . . . 1·10 45

172 Houphouet-Boigny Bridge, Abidjan

1976. 3rd African Roads Conference, Abidjan.
478 **172** 60f. multicoloured . . . . 2·50 60

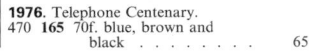

173 John Paul Jones (after Peale) and detail of "First Salute to the Stars and Stripes" (E. Moran)

1976. Bicentenary of American Revolution. Multicoloured.
479 100f. Type **173** 90 35
480 125f. Comte de Rochambeau, grenadier and flag . . . . 1·10 30
481 150f. Admiral D'Estaing, French marine and French warships . . . . 1·40 55
482 175f. Marquis de Lafayette (after Peale), grenadier and flag . . . . 1·40 40
483 200f. Thomas Jefferson (after Peale), militiaman and Declaration of Independence . . . . . . 1·60 45

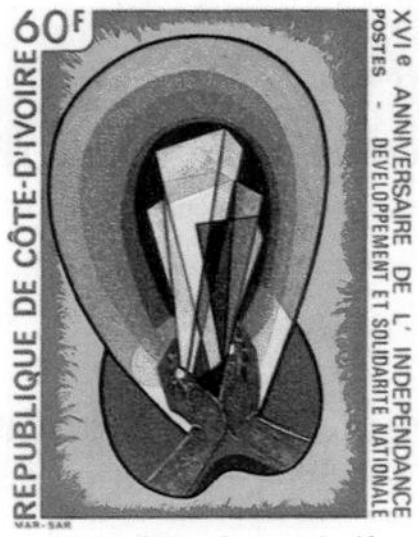

174 Independence Motif

1976. 16th Anniv of Independence.
485 **174** 60f. multicoloured 60 35

175 Ife Bronze Mask

1977. 2nd World Festival of Negro Arts, Lagos.
486 **175** 65f. multicoloured 65 45

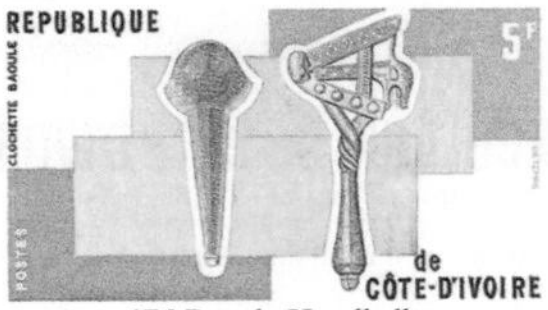

176 Baoule Handbells

1977. Musical Instruments (1st series).
487 **176** 5f. brown and green . . . 15 15
488 – 10f. black and red 20 15
489 – 20f. black and violet . . . 35 15
DESIGNS: 10f. Senoufo xylophone; 20f. Dida tom-tom.
See also Nos. 603/4.

177 Unloading Mail from Douglas DC-8

1977. Stamp Day.
490 **177** 60f. multicoloured 60 30

178 "Charaxes jasius epijasius"

1977. Butterflies (1st series). Multicoloured.
491 30f. "Epiphora rectifascia boolana" . . . . 1·60 55
492 60f. Type **178** . . . . 10·00 5·00
493 65f. "Imbrasia arata" . . . . 2·75 1·10
494 100f. "Palla decius" . . . . 3·25 1·60
See also Nos. 546/9 and 585/7.

179 Tingrela Mosque

1977. Air.
495 **179** 500f. brown, green & blue 5·00 2·75

180 Chateau Sassenage, Grenoble

1977. 10th Anniv of International French Language Council.
496 **180** 100f. multicoloured . . . 80 40

181 Wright Brothers and Wright Type A Biplane

1977. History of Flying. Multicoloured.
497 60f. Type **181** 45 15
498 75f. Louis Bleriot crossing English Channel 65 20
499 100f. Ross Smith and Vickers Vimy aircraft 90 20
500 200f. Charles Lindbergh and "Spirit of St. Louis" . . . 1·75 45
501 300f. Concorde . . . . . . 2·75 85

182 Santos Dumont's "Ville de Paris"

1977. History of the Airship. Multicoloured.
503 60f. Type **182** 55 15
504 65f. Launch of LZ-1 . . . . 55 15
505 150f. "Schwaben" . . . . . 1·25 35
506 200f. "Bodensee" . . . . . 1·90 55
507 300f. "Graf Zeppelin" over Egypt . . . . 2·50 85

183 Congress Emblem

1977. 17th International Congress of Administrative Sciences in Africa.
509 **183** 60f. green and emerald . . 50 30

184 Pres. Houphouet-Boigny

185 Container Ship "Yamoussoukro"

1977.
510 **184** 35f. black, mauve & brown 20 10
511 40f. black, orange & green 90 30
512 45f. black, green & orange 1·10 30
513 60f. black, purple & brown . . . . 1·25 35
514 65f. black, orange & green 1·40 45

1977. Yamoussoukro Container Port.
515 **185** 65f. multicoloured 85 45

186 Hand holding Symbols of Development

187 "Strophantus hispidus"

1977. 17th Anniv of Independence.
516 **186** 60f. black, orange & green 55 30

1977. Flowers (1st series). Multicoloured.
517 5f. Type **187** 15 10
518 20f. "Anthurium cultorum" 30 20
519 60f. "Arachnis flos-aeris" . . 50 30
520 65f. "Renanthera storiei" . . 55 35
See also Nos. 571/3, 622/5, 678/80, 791c/e, 827a/b and 873e/f.

188 Presidents Giscard d'Estaing and Houphouet-Boigny

1978. Visit of President Giscard d'Estaing of France
521 **188** 60f. multicoloured 70 30
522 65f. multicoloured 70 30
523 100f. multicoloured . . . 1·10 55

189 "St. George and the Dragon"

1978. 400th Birth Anniv of Peter Paul Rubens (artist). Multicoloured.
525 65f. Type **189** 50 15
526 150f. "Head of a Child" . . 1·25 45
527 250f. "The Annunciation" . . 1·90 65
528 300f. "The Birth of Louis XIII" . . . . 2·75 95

190 Members of the Royal Guard

1978. Images of History.
530 **190** 60f. red, black and blue 80 35
531 – 65f. black, blue and red 80 35
DESIGN: 65f. Figures of traditional cosmology.

191 Rural Post Office

1978. Stamp Day.
532 **191** 60f. multicoloured 55 30

192 Microwave Antenna

1978. Telecommunications Day.
533 **192** 60f. multicoloured 60 35

193 S. A. Arrhenius and Equipment (Chemistry, 1903)

1978. Nobel Prize Winners. Multicoloured.
534 60f. Type **193** 45 10
535 75f. Jules Bordet (Medicine, 1920) 55 15
536 100f. Andre Gide (Literature, 1947) 80 20
537 200f. John Steinbeck (Literature, 1962) . . . . 1·40 45
538 300f. U.N.I.C.E.F. (Peace, 1965) . . . . 2·40 70

194 Player kicking Ball

1978. World Cup Football Championship, Argentina. Multicoloured.
540 60f. Football and player (horiz) 45 15
541 65f. Type **194** 50 20
542 100f. Football and player (different) (horiz) 70 35
543 150f. Goalkeeper (horiz) . . 1·10 35
544 300f. Football "sun" and player . . . . 2·25 65

1978. Butterflies (2nd series). As T **178**. Multicoloured.
546 60f. "Miniodes discolor" . . 90 45
547 65f. "Charaxes lactetinctus" 90 45
548 100f. "Papilio zalmoxis" . . 1·40 80
549 200f. "Papilio antimachus" 3·00 1·60

195 Banded Cricket

1978. Insects (1st series). Multicoloured.
550 10f. Type **195** 20 15
551 20f. "Nepa cinerea" (water scorpion) 30 15
552 60f. Horned tree-hopper . . . 70 35
553 65f. "Goliathus cassicus" (beetle) . . . . 1·00 45
See also Nos. 600/2.

196 Passengers in Train

1978. Educational Television. Multicoloured.
554 60f. Figures emerging from television screen 45 20
555 65f. Type **196** . . . . 1·50 60

197 "Astragale" (oil exploration ship)

1978. 1st Anniv of Discovery of Oil in Ivory Coast. Multicoloured.
556 60f. Type **197** . . . . 1·10 35
557 65f. Ram, map of Ivory Coast and gold goblets . . 85 35

1978. Air. "Philexafrique" Stamp Exhibition, Gabon (1st issue) and International Stamp Fair, Essen, West Germany. As T **262** of Gabon. Multicoloured.
559 100f. Common pheasant and Bavaria 1849 1k. stamp . . 2·25 1·75
560 100f. African elephant and Ivory Coast 1965 90f. stamp . . . . 2·25 1·75
See also Nos. 588/9.

198 National Assembly Building, Paris

1978. Centenary of Paris U.P.U. Congress.
561 **198** 200f. multicoloured . . . 1·40 55

199 African with Ballot Box

200 Ribbon of Flags

1978. 18th Anniv of Independence.
562 **199** 60f. multicoloured 55 30

1978. Technical Co-operation among Developing Countries. Multicoloured.
563 60f. Type **200** 50 20
564 65f. Ribbon of flags forming arrows 50 20

201 Ploughing

1979. Agriculture.
565 **201** 100f. multicoloured . . . 90 35

202 King Hassan and Pres Houphouet-Boigny

1979. Visit of King Hassan of Morocco.
566 **202** 60f. multicoloured . . . . 1·60 35
567 65f. multicoloured . . . . 2·25 35
568 500f. multicoloured . . . 10·00 2·50

203 Isis

1979. U.N.E.S.C.O. Campaign for Preservation of Nubian Monuments.

569	**203**	200f. silver, green & turq	1·60	85
570	–	500f. gold, brown & orge	4·00	2·25

DESIGN: 500f. Gold medal.

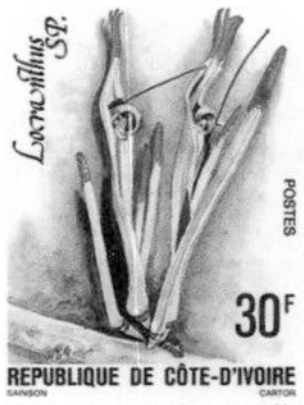

204 "Loranthus sp."

206 Children and Globe

205 Sable Antelopes

1979. Flowers (2nd series). Mult.

571		30f. Type **204**	45	35
572		60f. "Vanda josephine"	90	45
573		65f. "Renanthera storiei"	90	55

1979. Endangered Animals (1st series). Mult.

574		5f. Type **205**	20	15
575		20f. Yellow-backed duiker	35	20
576		50f. Pygmy hippopotamus	55	20
577		60f. Aardvark	1·10	55

See also Nos. 613/18.

1979. International Year of the Child. Mult.

578		60f. Type **206**	45	30
579		65f. Child on dove	50	30
580		100f. Type **206**	95	55
581		500f. As 65f.	3·75	2·25

207 Travelling Post Office

1979. Stamp Day.

582	**207**	60f. multicoloured	55	20

208 Korhogo Cathedral

1979. 75th Anniv of Arrival of Holy Fathers.

583	**208**	60f. multicoloured	55	30

209 Crying Child

1979. 10th Anniv of S.O.S. Children's Village.

584	**209**	65f. multicoloured	55	30

210 "Euphaedra xypete"

1979. Butterflies (3rd series). Multicoloured.

585		60f. Type **210**	80	35
586		65f. "Pseudacraea bois duvali"	90	35
587		70f. "Auchenisa schausi"	1·40	55

211 Carved Figure and Antelope

212 Astronaut Greeting Boy

1979. "Philexafrique", Stamp Exhibition, Gabon (2nd issue).

588	**211**	70f. multicoloured	1·40	1·10
589	–	70f. green, turquoise & red	1·40	1·10

DESIGN: No. 589, U.P.U. emblem, antenna, ship and truck.

1979. 10th Anniv of Moon Landing. Mult.

590		60f. Type **212**	65	45
591		65f. Trajectory between Earth and Moon (horiz)	65	45
592		70f. Type **212**	1·10	55
593		150f. As 65f.	2·00	1·40

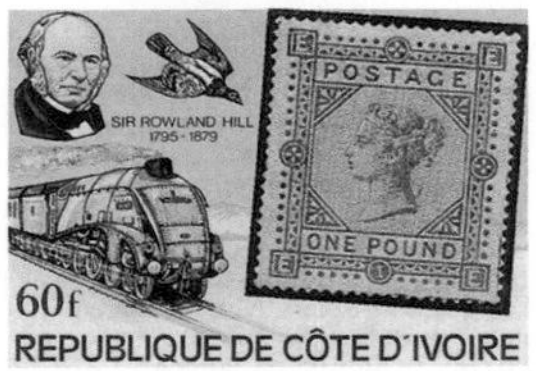

213 "Flying Scotsman" and Great Britain £1 stamp, 1878

1979. Death Centenary of Sir Rowland Hill. Multicoloured.

594		60f. Type **213**	30	10
595		75f. Steam locomotive and Ivory Coast 45c. stamp, 1936	45	15
596		100f. Diesel locomotive No. 105, U.S.A. and Hawaiian 13c. "missionary" stamp, 1852	70	20
597		150f. Steam locomotive No. 1, Japan and Japanese 20s. stamp, 1872	1·00	30
598		300f. Class BB 15000 electric locomotive, France and French 15c. stamp, 1850	2·00	60

214 "Delta sp."

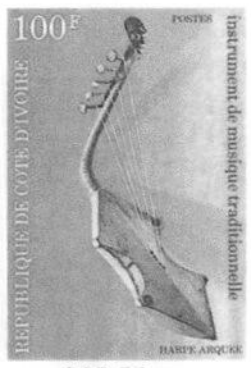

215 Harp

1979. Insects (2nd series). Mult.

600		30f. Type **214**	2·25	1·10
601		60f. "Mantis religiosa" (vert)	4·00	1·60
602		65f. "Locusta migratorius"	4·50	1·60

1979. Musical Instruments (2nd series). Mult.

603		100f. Type **215**	11·00	4·50
604		150f. Senoufo funeral horns	17·00	6·75

216 "Telecom 79"

217 Carved Head

1979. 3rd World Telecommunications Exhibition, Geneva.

605	**216**	60f. grey, orange and blue	55	30

1979. Culture Days.

606	**217**	65f. multicoloured	55	20

218 Boxing

1979. Pre-Olympic Year. Multicoloured.

607		60f. Type **218**	45	15
608		65f. Running	45	15
609		100f. Football	70	30
610		150f. Cycling	1·10	45
611		300f. Wrestling	2·25	80

See also Nos. 642/5.

219 Jentink's Duiker

1979. Endangered Animals (2nd series). Multicoloured.

613		40f. Type **219**	45	20
614		60f. Olive colobus	50	20
615		75f. African manatees	70	25
616		100f. Temminck's giant squirrel	1·00	35
617		150f. Pygmy hippopotamus	1·40	45
618		300f. Chimpanzee	2·75	90

220 Raoul Follereau and Institute

1979. Raoul Follereau d'Adzope Institute.

619	**220**	60f. multicoloured	60	35

221 Post, Adze and Plant

222a Coelancanth

222 Concorde and Map of Africa

1979. 19th Anniv of Independence.

620	**221**	60f. multicoloured	55	15

1979. 20th Anniv of ASECNA (African Air Safety Organization).

621	**222**	60f. multicoloured	75	30

1979. Fishes (1st series). Multicoloured.

621a		60f. Lionfish		
621b		65f. Type **222a**		

See also Nos. 629/31 and 666/8

223 "Clerodendron thomsonae"

224 Elephant, Map and Rotary Emblem

1980. Flowers (3rd series). Multicoloured.

622		5f. Type **223**	10	10
623		10f. "La Boule de Feu" (horiz)	15	10
624		50f. "Costus incanusiamus"	55	15
625		60f. "Ficus elastica"	55	20

1980. 75th Anniv of Rotary International.

626	**224**	65f. multicoloured	55	30

225 Seal

1980. International Archives Day.

627	**225**	65f. multicoloured	55	35

226 Boys with Stamp Album

1980. Stamp Day.

628	**226**	65f. brown and turquoise	60	20

1980. Fishes (2nd series). As T **222a**. Multicoloured.

629		60f. Emperor snapper	90	40
630		65f. Guinean fingerfish (vert)	90	40
631		100f. Banded gourami	1·50	75

228 Missionary and Church, Aboisso

1980. 75th Anniv of Settlement of Holy Fathers at Aboisso.

632	**228**	60f. multicoloured	60	35

229 Hands protecting Child from Cigarettes

1980. Anti-Smoking Campaign.

633	**229**	60f. multicoloured	60	20

230 Pope John-Paul II and President Houphouet-Boigny

1980. Papal Visit.

634	**230**	65f. yellow, brn & dp brn	1·00	45

231 "Le Belier" Express Train, Abidjan–Bouake

232 Headquarters Building, Dakar

1980. Railways. Multicoloured.
635 60f. Type **231** 60 35
636 65f. Abidjan Station, 1904 . . 60 35
637 100f. Steam train, 1908 . . . 1·10 45
638 150f. Steam goods train, 1940 1·75 80

1980. 1st Anniv of West African Central Bank.
639 **232** 60f. multicoloured 60 35

233 Cobra

1980. Animals. Multicoloured.
640 60f. Type **233** 55 20
641 150f. Toad . . . . 1·50 65

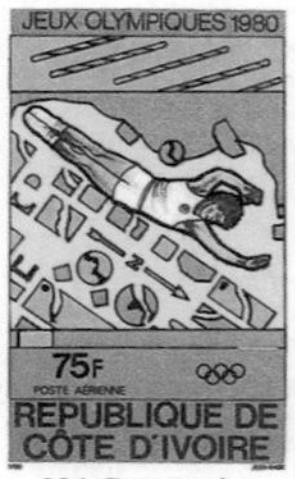

234 Gymnastics

235 World Tourism Conference Emblem

1980. Air. Olympic Games, Moscow. Multicoloured.
642 75f. Type **234** 65 15
643 150f. Ring exercise . . . . . 1·10 30
644 250f. Vaulting horse (horiz) 2·00 55
645 350f. Bar exercise . . . . . 3·00 85

1980. Tourism. Multicoloured.
647 60f. Village scene 45 15
648 65f. Type **235** 45 15

1980. Insects (3rd series). As T **214**. Mult.
649 60f. "Ugada limbata" (25×35 mm) 85 55
650 60f. "Forticula auricularia" (36×26 mm) . . . . . . 1·60 95
651 65f. "Mantis religiosa" (26×32 mm) . . . . . . 1·60 85
652 200f. Grasshopper (35×25 mm) . . . . . . 2·25 1·40

236 Hands breaking Chains, Map and President

1980. President Houphouet-Boigny's 75th Birthday.
653 **236** 60f. mult (postage) . . . 55 30
654 – 65f. multicoloured 55 30
655 – 70f. multicoloured 70 45
656 **236** 150f. multicoloured . . . 1·75 1·10
657 – 300f. multicoloured . . . 3·25 1·75

658 – 2000f. silver (air) . . . . 15·00 15·00
659 – 3000f. gold . . . . 22·00 22·00
DESIGNS—SQUARE: 70f. Presidential speech on map in national colours. HORIZ (44×29 mm): 65f., 300f. President and symbols of progress. VERT (35×45 mm): 2000f., 3000f. President Houphouet-Boigny.

237 Map of Ivory Coast

1980. 7th P.D.C.I.–R.D.A. Congress.
660 **237** 60f. green, orange & black 45 15
661 65f. green, orange & black 45 15

238 "Sotra" (ferry)

1980. New Lagoon Transport.
662 **238** 60f. multicoloured 55 30

239 Abidjan

1980. 20th Anniv of Independence.
663 **239** 60f. multicoloured . . . . 1·50 45

240 Conference Emblem

241 Map of Africa and Posthorn

1980. 5th General Conference of African Universities Association, Yamoussoukro.
664 **240** 60f. multicoloured 55 30

1980. 5th Anniv of African Posts and Telecommunications Union.
665 **241** 150f. multicoloured . . . 1·10 35

241a Red-billed Dwarf Hornbill

1980. Birds. Multicoloured.
665a 60f. Superb starling . . . . 45·00 4·25
665b 65f. Type **241a** . . . . . . 45·00 4·25
665c 65f. South African crowned crane . . . . 45·00 4·50
665d 100f. Saddle-bill stork . . . £140 12·00

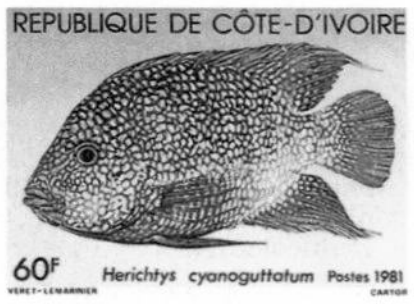

242 Rio Grande Cichlid

1981. Fishes (3rd series). Multicoloured.
666 60f. Type **242** 80 50
667 65f. Red-tailed black shark 80 50
668 200f. Green pufferfish . . . . 2·25 1·25

243 Post Office, Grand Lahou

1981. Stamp Day.
669 **243** 60f. multicoloured 55 20

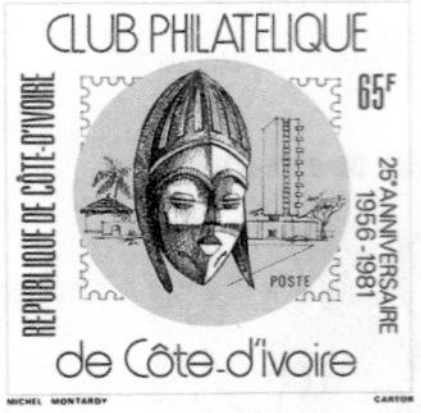

244 Mask

1981. 25th Anniv of Ivory Coast Philatelic Club.
670 **244** 65f. black, lt brown & brn 45 20

245 Red Cross Aircraft, Satellite and Globe (Telecommunications and Health)

1981. World Telecommunications Day.
671 **245** 30f. multicoloured 20 10
672 60f. multicoloured 45 20

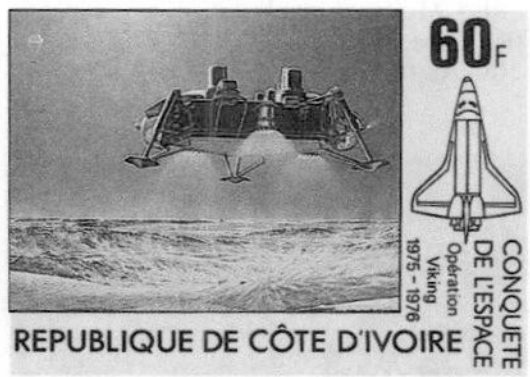

246 "Viking" landing on Mars

1981. Conquest of Space. Multicoloured.
673 60f. Type **246** 45 15
674 75f. Space Shuttle on launch pad 55 20
675 125f. Space Shuttle erecting experiment 85 40
676 300f. Space Shuttle performing experiment . . 2·10 90

247 "Amorphophallus sp."

249 Map formed of Flag

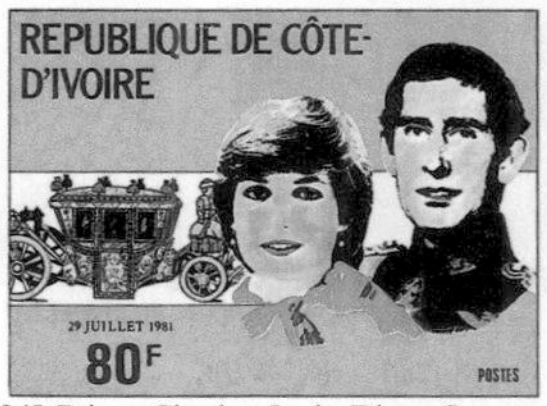

248 Prince Charles, Lady Diana Spencer and Coach

1981. Flowers (4th series). Multicoloured.
678 50f. Type **247** 55 20
679 60f. Sugar cane flowers 65 35
680 100f. "Heliconia ivoirea" . . 1·25 55
See also Nos. 791c/e, 827a/b and 873e/f.

1981. Royal Wedding.
681 **248** 80f. multicoloured 55 20
682 – 100f. multicoloured . . . 65 35
683 – 125f. multicoloured . . . 85 40
DESIGNS: 100f., 125f. Similar designs showing portraits and coaches.

1981.
684a **249** 5f. multicoloured . . . 10 10
684aa 10f. multicoloured . . . 15 10
684ab 20f. multicoloured . . . 15 10
684b 25f. multicoloured . . . 15 10
684c 30f. multicoloured . . . 20 10
684ca 35f. multicoloured . . . 20 10
684d 40f. multicoloured . . . 30 10
684e 50f. multicoloured . . . 35 10
685 80f. multicoloured . . . 50 20
686 100f. multicoloured . . 60 35
687 125f. multicoloured . . 85 40

250 Goalkeeper

1981. World Cup Football Championship, Spain (1982). Multicoloured.
688 70f. Type **250** 45 30
689 80f. Saving a goal 55 35
690 100f. Diving for ball (vert) 65 40
691 150f. Goalmouth scene . . . 1·00 60
692 350f. Fighting for ball (vert) 2·40 1·10

251 Association Emblem

1981. West Africa Rice Development Association.
694 **251** 80f. multicoloured 60 30

252 Post Office

1981. Stamp Day.
695 **252** 70f. multicoloured 45 20
696 80f. multicoloured 55 35
697 100f. multicoloured . . . 65 35

253 Hands with and without Fruit, and F.A.O. Emblem

1981. World Food Day.
698 **253** 100f. multicoloured . . . 65 35

254 Felice Nazarro

1981. 75th Anniv of French Grand Prix Motor Race. Multicoloured.
699 15f. Type **254** 15 10
700 40f. Jim Clark 35 15
701 80f. Fiat, 1907 . . . . 65 40
702 100f. Auto Union, 1936 . . . 80 45
703 125f. Ferrari, 1961 . . . . . 1·10 55

255 Symbols of Economic Growth

1981. 21st Anniv of Independence.
705 **255** 50f. multicoloured 35 15
706 80f. multicoloured 55 30

256 "Queue de Cheval" **258** Rotary Emblem on Map of Africa

257 Bingerville Post Office, 1902

1982. Hairstyles. Multicoloured.
707 80f. Type **256** 55 30
708 100f. "Belier" . . . . 1·10 45
709 125f. "Cheri regarde mon visage" . . . . 1·40 55

1982. Stamp Day.
710 **257** 100f. multicoloured . . . 65 35

1982. Rotary International Conference, Abidjan.
711 **258** 100f. blue and gold . . . 70 40

259 George Washington

1982. Celebrities' Anniversaries. Multicoloured.
712 80f. Type **259** (250th birth anniv) 55 20
713 100f. Auguste Piccard (20th death anniv) 65 30
714 350f. Goethe (150th death anniv) . . . . 2·25 85
715 450f. Princess of Wales (21st birthday) . . . . 3·00 1·25

260 Hexagonal Pattern and Telephone

1982. World Telecommunications Day.
717 **260** 80f. multicoloured 55 20

261 Presidents Mitterand and Houphouet-Boigny

1982. Visit of President Mitterand of France.
718 **261** 100f. multicoloured . . . 90 45

262 Dr. Koch, Bacillus and Microscope **263** Scouts in Dinghy

1982. Cent of Discovery of Tubercle Bacillus.
719 **262** 30f. multicoloured 30 20
720 80f. multicoloured 85 45

1982. 75th Anniv of Boy Scout Movement. Multicoloured.
721 80f. Type **263** 60 40
722 100f. Dinghy (horiz) 70 50
723 150f. Leaning into wind . . . 1·00 65
724 350f. Hauling sail . . . . . 2·50 80

264 Aerial View of Coastline **265** Congress Emblem

1982. 10th Anniv of U.N. Environmental Programme.
726 **264** 40f. multicoloured 35 15
727 80f. multicoloured 55 30

1982. First League of Ivory Coast Secretaries Congress, Abidjan.
728 **265** 80f. multicoloured 55 20
729 100f. multicoloured . . . 65 35

1982. Birth of Prince William of Wales. Nos. 681/3 optd **NAISSANCE ROYALE 1982.**
730 **247** 80f. multicoloured 55 30
731 – 100f. multicoloured . . . 65 35
732 – 125f. multicoloured . . . 85 40

267 "Child with Dove"

1982. Picasso Paintings. Multicoloured.
734 80f. Type **267** 55 20
735 100f. "Self-portrait" 65 20
736 185f. "Les Demoiselles d'Avignon" . . . . 1·60 40
737 350f. "The Dream" . . . . . 2·75 85
738 500f. "La Colombe de l'Avenir" (horiz) . . . . . 4·00 1·10

268 Post Office Counter, Abidjan 17

1982. World U.P.U. Day. Multicoloured.
739 80f. Type **268** 55 30
740 100f. Postel 2001 Building, Abidjan (vert) 85 35
741 350f. Counter clerks at Abidjan 17 Post Office . . 2·50 95
742 500f. Exterior and interior views of Postel 2001 (48 × 36 mm) . . . . . . 3·50 1·50

1982. World Cup Football Championship Results. Nos. 688/92 optd.
743 70f. Type **249** 45 25
744 80f. Saving a goal 55 25
745 100f. Diving for ball (vert) 60 35
746 150f. Goalmouth scene . . . 90 55
747 350f. Fighting for ball (vert) 2·25 1·10
OVERPRINTS: 70f. **1966 VAINQUEUR GRANDE-BRETAGNE**; 80f. **1970 VAINQUEUR BRESIL**; 100f. **1974 VAINQUEUR ALLEMAGNE (RFA)**; 150f. **1978 VAINQUEUR ARGENTINE**; 350f. **1982 VAINQUEUR ITALIE.**

270 President Houphouet-Boigny with Farming Implements and Agricultural Produce

1982. 22nd Anniv of Independence.
749 **270** 100f. multicoloured . . . 70 35

271 Emblem and Map of Member Countries

1982. 20th Anniv of West African Monetary Union.
750 **271** 100f. brown, blue & dp bl 65 35

272 Man Waterfall

1982. Landscapes. Multicoloured.
751 80f. Type **272** . . . . 2·25 55
752 80f. Wooded savanna 70 35
753 500f. Type **272** . . . . 9·00 2·75

273 Child and S.O.S. Village **274** Long-tailed Pangolin

1983. S.O.S. Children's Village.
754 **273** 125f. multicoloured . . . 90 40

1983. Animals. Multicoloured.
755 35f. Type **274** 30 15
756 90f. Bush pig (horiz) 65 35
757 100f. Eastern black-and-white colobus 70 40
758 125f. African buffalo (horiz) 95 50

275 Post Office, Grand Bassam, 1903

1983. Stamp Day.
759 **275** 100f. multicoloured . . . 2·00 60

276 Montgolfier Balloon, 1783

1983. Bicentenary of Manned Flight. Mult.
760 100f. Type **276** 70 25
761 125f. Charles's hydrogen balloon, 1783 . . . . . . 95 30
762 150f. Balloon "Armand Barbes" (Paris siege post, 1870) (horiz) . . . . . . 1·10 35
763 350f. Balloon "Double Eagle II" over Atlantic . . . . . 2·50 80
764 500f. Advertising airship (horiz) . . . . 4·00 1·10

277 "Descent from the Cross"

1983. Easter. Multicoloured.
765 100f. Type **277** 65 20
766 125f. "The Resurrection of Christ" (horiz) 85 30
767 350f. "The Raising of the Cross" (horiz) . . . . . . 2·25 85
768 400f. "The Piercing of the Lance" . . . . 2·75 90
769 500f. "Descent from the Cross" . . . . 3·25 1·10

278 Safe containing U.N. Emblem

1983. 25th Anniv of U.N. Economic Commission for Africa.
770 **278** 100f. multicoloured . . . 65 30

279 African Fish Eagle

1983. Birds. Multicoloured.
771 100f. Type **279** . . . . 1·75 40
772 125f. Grey parrot (horiz) . . 2·25 30
773 150f. Violet turaco (horiz) . . 3·50 65

280 Swimming

1983. Air. Pre-Olympic Year. Multicoloured.
774 100f. Type **280** 65 20
775 125f. Diving 90 30
776 350f. Backstroke . . . . . . 2·40 80
777 400f. Butterfly stroke . . . . 2·75 95

281 Forest destroyed by Fire

1983. Ecology in Action. Multicoloured.
779 25f. Type **281** 35 20
780 100f. Animals running from fire . . . . 1·10 45
781 125f. Protected animals . . . 1·40 65

282 Flali Dance

1983. Traditional Dances. Multicoloured.
782 50f. Type **282** 35 15
783 100f. Mask dance 65 30
784 125f. Stilt dance 95 40

283 Hotel Ivoire

1983. 20th Anniv of Hotel Ivoire, Abidjan.
785 **283** 100f. multicoloured . . . 65 35

284 Rally Car and Route

1983. World and African Car Rally Championships.
786 **284** 100f. multicoloured . . . 90 45

285 "Christ and St. Peter"

1983. Christmas. Paintings by Raphael. Mult.
787 100f. Type **285** 65 30
788 125f. Study for St. Joseph . . 90 35
789 350f. "Virgin of the House of Orleans" . . . . 2·40 80
790 500f. "Virgin of the Blue Diadem" . . . . 3·25 1·10

286 President Houphouet-Boigny

1983. 23rd Anniv of Independence.
791 **286** 100f. multicoloured . . . 65 30

286a Telegraphist, Dish Aerial and National Postal Sorting Centre

1983. World Communications Year. Mult.
791a 100f. Cable-laying, Postel 2001 building, Abidjan, and telephonists . . . .
791b 125f. Type **286a** . . . . . .

1983. Flowers (5th series). As T **247**. Multicoloured.
791c 100f. Pineapple flowers . . . 40 35
791d 125f. "Heliconia rostrata" . 2·25 85
791e 150f. "Rose de Porcelaine" 2·75 1·40

287 Arrow piercing Television Screen

1984. First Audio-Visual Forum.
792 **287** 100f. black and green . . 65 30

288 Competition Emblem

289 Spider

1984. Africa Cup Football Competition.
793 **288** 100f. multicoloured . . . 65 30
794 – 200f. orange, green & blk 1·40 55
DESIGN: 200f. Maps of Africa and Ivory Coast shaking hands.

1984. Multicoloured.
795 100f. Type **289** . . . . 1·00 55
796 125f. "Polistes gallicus" (wasp) . . . . 1·25 65

290 Abidjan Post Office, 1934

1984. Stamp Day.
797 **290** 100f. multicoloured . . . 65 30

291 Swimming

1984. Air. Olympic Games, Los Angeles. Multicoloured.
798 100f. Type **291** 65 30
799 125f. Cross-country 80 30
800 185f. Pistol shooting . . . . 1·25 45
801 350f. Fencing . . . . 2·40 65

292 Lions Club Badge

1984. 3rd Lions Multi District 403 Convention. Multicoloured.
803 100f. Type **292** 85 35
804 125f. As Type **292** but with badge at right . . . . . . 1·00 55

293 Telecommunications Stations on Map of Ivory Coast

1984. World Telecommunications Day.
805 **293** 100f. multicoloured . . . 65 30

294 Flags, Agriculture and Symbols of Unity and Growth

1984. 25th Anniv of Council of Unity.
806 **294** 100f. multicoloured . . . 65 30
807 125f. multicoloured . . . 85 35

295 First Government House, Grand-Bassam

1984. Old Buildings (1st series). Multicoloured.
808 100f. Type **295** 65 30
809 125f. Palace of Justice, Grand-Bassam 85 35
See also Nos. 873a/c.

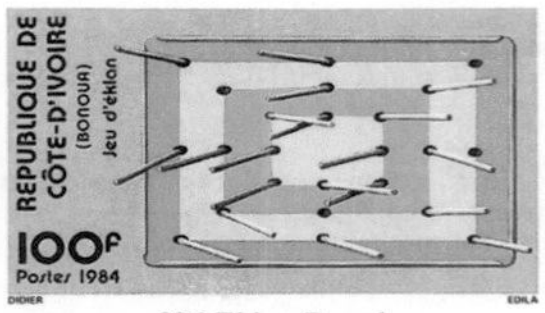

296 Eklan Board

1984. Eklan. Multicoloured.
810 100f. Type **296** 65 35
811 125f. Two Eklan players . . 85 45

297 "La Gazelle" Express Train, Abidjan–Ouagadougou

1984. Transport. Multicoloured. (a) Locomotives.
812 100f. Type **297** 75 30
813 125f. Steam locomotive, 1931, France . . . . 1·00 40
814 350f. Type 10 steam locomotive, Belgium . . . 3·00 70
815 500f. Class GT2 Mallet steam locomotive . . . . 5·25 1·10

(b) Ships.
816 100f. Container Ship 65 40
817 125f. Cargo liner 90 50
818 350f. "Queen Mary" (liner) 2·40 1·60
819 500f. "France" (liner) . . . . 4·25 2·50

298 Envelope, Map and Symbols of Postal Service

1984. Stamp Day.
820 **298** 100f. multicoloured . . . 85 45

299 Emblem

1984. 10th Anniv of West African Economic Community.
821 **299** 100f. multicoloured . . . 65 30

300 Book Cover

1984. 90th Anniv (1982) of Ivory Coast Postage Stamps.
822 **300** 125f. multicoloured . . . 95 65

301 Map Outline, People and Flag

1984. 24th Anniv of Independence.
823 **301** 100f. multicoloured . . . 65 30

302 G. Tiacoh (400 m silver)

1984. Air. Olympic Games Medallists. Mult.
824 100f. Type **302** 65 20
825 150f. C. Lewis (100 and 200 m gold) . . . . 1·00 35
826 200f. A. Babers (400 m gold) 1·40 45
827 500f. J. Cruz (800 m gold) . . 3·25 1·00

1984. Flowers (6th series). As T **247**. Mult.
827a 100f. "Allamanda cathartica" . . . . 22·00 8·25
827b 125f. Baobab flowers . . . 22·00 8·25

302a Serval

1984. Animals. Multicoloured.
827c 100f. Bushbuck . . . . . . 22·00 8·25
827d 150f. Type **302a** . . . . . . 22·00 8·25

302b Valtur Club, Assouinde

1984.
827e 50f. Type **302b** . . . . . . 19·00 3·25
827f 100f. Azagni Canal . . . . 19·00 5·00

303 "Virgin and Child" (Correggio)

1985. Air. Christmas. Multicoloured.
828 100f. Type **303** 80 30
829 200f. "Virgin and Child" (Andrea del Sarto) . . . . 1·40 55
830 400f. "Virgin and Child" (Jacopo Bellini) . . . . . 2·75 1·10
Nos. 829/30 are wrongly inscribed "Le Correge" (Correggio).

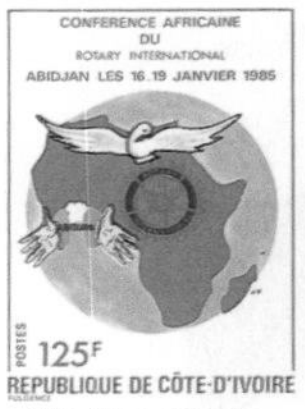

304 Map, Hands, Emblem and Dove

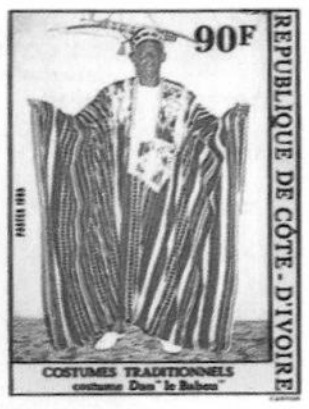

305 "Le Babou" (Dan costume)

1985. African Conference of Rotary International, Abidjan.
831 **304** 100f. multicoloured . . . 65 30
832 125f. multicoloured . . . 85 35

1985. Traditional Costumes. Multicoloured.
833 90f. Type **305** 70 35
834 100f. Avikam post-natal dress 95 45

305a Hadada Ibis

1985. Birds. Multicoloured.
834a 25f. Marabou stork . . . .
834b 100f. African jacana . . . .
834c 350f. Type **305a** . . . . . .

306 River Steamer "Adjame"

1985. Stamp Day.
835 **306** 100f. multicoloured . . . 1·00 55

308 Emblem

1985. 7th Conference of District 18 of Zonta International, Abidjan.
836 **308** 125f. multicoloured . . . 85 30

309 Airplane, Van and Industrial Landscape

1985. "Philexafrique" Stamp Exhibition, Lome, Togo (1st issue). Multicoloured.
837 200f. Type **309** . . . . 1·60 1·25
838 200f. Sports and agriculture 1·60 1·25
See also Nos. 864/5.

310 Red-breasted Mergansers

1985. Air. Birth Bicentenary of John J. Audubon (ornithologist). Multicoloured.
839 100f. Type **310** 95 45
840 150f. American white pelican (vert) . . . . 1·50 50
841 200f. American wood stork (vert) . . . . 3·00 55
842 350f. Velvet scoters . . . . . 4·50 90

311 Chemical Plant, Senegal

1985. 20th Anniv of African Development Bank.
843 100f. Type **311** 65 20
844 125f. Tree seedlings, Gambia 85 35

312 Profiles within Map and IYY Emblem

1985. International Youth Year.
845 **312** 125f. multicoloured . . . 85 35

313 Presidential Guard Shoulder Flash **314** Ivory Coast Arms

1985. 25th Anniv of National Armed Forces.
846 **313** 100f. gold and purple . . 65 20
847 – 100f. gold and blue . . . 65 20
848 – 125f. gold and black . . . 95 30
849 – 200f. gold and brown . . 1·50 45
850 – 350f. silver and blue . . . 2·40 80
DESIGNS: Shoulder flashes of—No. 847, F.A.N.C.I. (army); 848, Air Force; 849, Navy; 850, Gendarmerie.

1985. Postal Convention with Sovereign Military Order of Malta. Multicoloured.
851 125f. Type **314** 85 35
852 350f. Sovereign Military Order of Malta arms . . . 2·50 1·40

315 Footballers

1985. World Cup Football Championship, Mexico. Multicoloured.
853 100f. Type **315** 65 20
854 150f. Footballers (different) 1·00 35
855 200f. Footballers (different) 1·40 40
856 350f. Footballers (different) 2·50 70

316 Pope and Abidjan Cathedral

1985. Visit of Pope John Paul II.
858 **316** 100f. multicoloured . . . 1·00 55

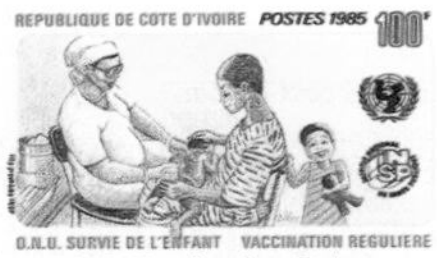

317 Vaccinating Baby

1985. U.N.I.C.E.F. Child Survival Campaign. Multicoloured.
859 100f. Type **317** 65 30
860 100f. Mother breast-feeding baby while child plays . . 65 30
861 100f. Mother spoon-feeding child 65 30
862 100f. Mother giving child a drink (oral rehydration) . . 65 30

318 Rainbow, U.N. Emblem and Joined Hands

1985. 40th Anniv of U.N.O. and 25th Anniv of Ivory Coast Membership.
863 **318** 100f. multicoloured . . . 65 20

319 Footballers and Children with Injured Animal

1985. Air. "Philexafrique" International Stamp Exhibition, Lome, Togo (2nd issue). Mult.
864 250f. Type **319** . . . . 2·00 1·40
865 250f. Dish aerial, rocket and container ship . . . . . . 2·00 1·40

320 City Skyline

1985. "Expo 85" World's Fair, Tsukuba, Japan.
866 **320** 125f. multicoloured . . . 85 30

321 Young Duiker

1985. World Wildlife Fund. Banded Duiker. Multicoloured.
867 50f. Type **321** 45 20
868 60f. Duiker in front of bushes 55 20
869 75f. Two duikers . . . . . . 1·10 35
870 100f. Duiker (different) . . . 1·60 45

322 Children on Open Ground **323** Woman spinning Cotton

1985. "Return to the Earth".
871 **322** 125f. multicoloured . . . 85 35

1985. Rural Handicrafts. Multicoloured.
872 125f. Type **323** 85 35
873 155f. Man painting on cotton cloth . . . . 1·10 45

323a Samatiguila Mosque

1985. Old Buildings (2nd series). Multicoloured.
873a 100f. Bondoukou Market 17·00 5·50
873b 125f. Type **323a** . . . . . . 17·00 5·50
873c 200f. Samory House, Bondoukou . . . . . . 17·00 5·50

1985. Flowers (7th series). As T **247**. Mult.
873d 100f. "Amorphophallus staudtii" . . . . 22·00 5·50
873e 125f. Crinum . . . . 22·00 5·50
873f 200f. "Triphyophyllum peltotum" . . . . 22·00 5·50

324 Edmond Halley and Computer Picture of Comet

1986. Air. Appearance of Halley's Comet. Multicoloured.
874 125f. Type **324** 85 25
875 155f. Sir William Herschel and Uranus . . . . 1·00 30
876 190f. Space telescope and comet . . . . 1·25 40
877 350f. "MS T-5" space probe and comet . . . . 2·50 85
878 440f. "Skylab" and Kohoutek's comet . . . . 2·75 1·00

325 "Millettia takou"

1986. Plants. Multicoloured.
879 40f. "Omphalocarpum elatum" 30 15
880 50f. "Momordica charantia" 35 15
881 125f. Type **325** 85 40
882 200f. "Costus afer" . . . . . 1·40 65

326 Vase from We

1986. Traditional Kitchenware and Tools. Multicoloured.
883 20f. Type **326** 15 10
884 30f. Baoule vase 20 10
885 90f. Baoule dish 60 20
886 125f. Dan knife (vert) 90 30
887 440f. Baoule pottery jug (vert) . . . . 3·25 1·25

327 Institute Building

1986. 10th Anniv of Institute for Higher Technical and Professional Education.
888 **327** 125f. multicoloured . . . 85 30

329 Cable Ship "Stephan", 1910

1986. Stamp Day.
899 **329** 125f. multicoloured . . . 1·50 65

330 Footballers

1986. Air. World Cup Football Championship, Mexico.
900 **330** 90f. multicoloured 60 20
901 – 125f. multicoloured . . . 85 25
902 – 155f. multicoloured . . . 1·10 35
903 – 440f. multicoloured . . . 3·00 90
904 – 500f. multicoloured . . . 3·25 1·10
DESIGNS: 125f. to 500f. Different football scenes.

331 Emblem 333 Sacred Tom-tom

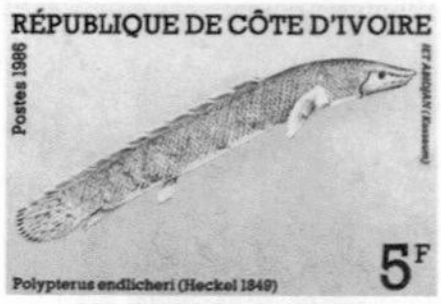

332 Endlicher's Bichir

1986. 25th Anniv of National Youth and Sports Institute.
906 **331** 125f. green and orange . . 85 30

1986. Fishes. Multicoloured.
907 5f. Type **332** 10 10
908 125f. Daget's squeaker . . . 1·10 70
909 150f. West African lung-fish 1·40 90
910 155f. Ivory Coast squeaker 1·75 90
911 440f. Electric catfish . . . . 4·50 2·50

1986. Enthronement of King of the Agni. Multicoloured.
912 50f. Type **333** 35 20
913 350f. King being carried . . 2·50 1·40
914 440f. King and his Court . . 3·25 1·90

334 Baoule Village, Aoulo

1986. Rural Dwellings (1st series). Multicoloured.
915 125f. Type **334** 85 45
916 155f. Avikam village, Eva . . 1·10 65
917 350f. Lobi village, Soukala 2·50 1·40
See also Nos. 938/9, 990 and 1012.

335 Ivory Coast Arms 336 Rocky Coastline

1986.
921 **335** 50f. red 30 10
924 125f. green 70 15
926 155f. red 95 20
927 195f. blue . . . . 1·10 30

1986. Coastal Landscapes. Multicoloured.
930 125f. Type **336** . . . . 1·00 55
931 155f. Sandy beach . . . . . 1·40 85

337 Fishery Lake

1986. Oceanographic Research Centre. Mult.
932 125f. Type **337** 85 45
933 155f. Fishermen hauling in net . . . . 1·75 80

338 Pres. Houphouet-Boigny, Rainbow and Dove

1986. International Peace Year.
934 **338** 155f. multicoloured . . . 1·00 55

339 Bull

1986. Research and Development. Mult.
935 125f. Type **339** . . . . 1·10 65
936 155f. Rice (IDSA 6) . . . . 1·10 65

340 Pres. Houphouet-Boigny and Symbols of Development

1986. 26th Anniv of Independence.
937 **340** 155f. multicoloured . . . 1·10 55

341 Guesseple Dan Village

1987. Rural Dwellings (2nd series). Mult.
938 190f. Type **341** . . . . 1·40 90
939 550f. M'Bagui Senoufo village . . . . 4·00 2·25

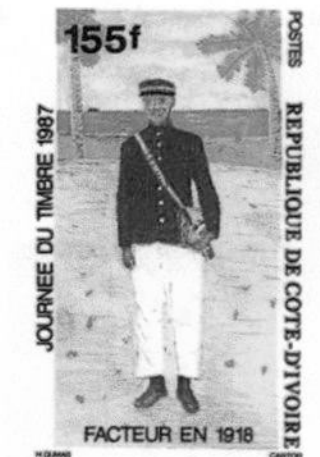

342 Postman, 1918 343 Elephant and Cockerel

1987. Stamp Day.
940 **342** 155f. multicoloured . . . 1·10 65

1987. 25th Anniv of French–Ivory Coast Cultural Friendship. Jean Mermoz College. Multicoloured.
941 40f. Type **343** 30 15
942 155f. Children's faces in dove 1·10 55

344 Child running to Adult

1987. World Red Cross Day.
943 **344** 195f.+5f. multicoloured 1·50 1·40

345 "Soling" Class Yachts

1987. Air. Olympic Games, Seoul (1988) (1st issue). Sailing. Multicoloured.
944 155f. Type **345** . . . . . . 1·10 85
945 195f. Windsurfers . . . . . 1·40 80
946 250f. "470" class dinghies . . 1·90 90
947 550f. Windsurfer . . . . . . 4·00 1·60
See also Nos. 959/62.

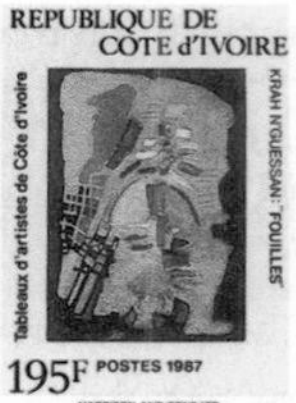

346 "Excavations" (Krah N'Guessan)

1987. Paintings. Multicoloured.
949 195f. Type **346** . . . . 1·40 90
950 500f. "Ceremonial Cortege" (Santoni Gerard) . . . . . 3·25 2·25

347 Airplane and Van

1987. World Post Day. International Express Post.
951 **347** 155f. multicoloured . . . 1·10 80
952 195f. multicoloured . . . 1·40 90

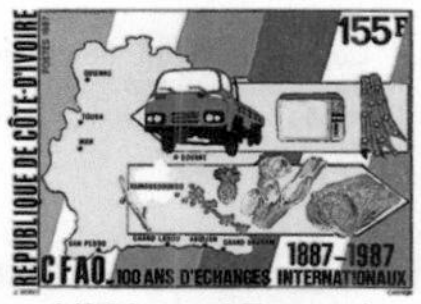

348 Map and Forms of Communication

1987. 100 Years of International Mail and Communications Exchanges.
953 **348** 155f. multicoloured . . . 1·10 65

349 Tower Block reflecting Symbols of Progress 350 Baby in Aloe Plant on Map

1987. 27th Anniv of Independence.
954 **349** 155f. multicoloured . . . 1·10 65

1988. Lions International. "For the Life of a Child".
955 **350** 155f. multicoloured . . . 1·10 65

351 Bereby Post Office, 1900 352 Heart

1988. Stamp Day.
956 **351** 155f. multicoloured . . . 1·00 55

1988. 15th Francophone Cardiological Congress, Abidjan.
957 **352** 195f. red and black . . . 1·60 1·10

353 Man working Soil

1988. 10th Anniv of International Agricultural Development Fund.
958 **353** 195f. multicoloured . . . 1·40 80

354 Gymnastics (rings)

1988. Air. Olympic Games, Seoul (2nd issue). Multicoloured.
959 100f. Type **354** 65 35
960 155f. Women's handball . . . 1·00 45
961 195f. Boxing . . . . 1·40 45
962 500f. Gymnastics (parallel bar) . . . . 3·25 1·25

355 Stone Sculpture with Deep Nostrils 356 Healthy Youth and Drug Addict

1988. Archaeological Research. Stone Sculptures from Niangoran-Bouah Collection.
964 **355** 5f. brown and flesh . . . 10 10
965 – 10f. brown and green . . 10 10
966 – 30f. brown and green . . 20 10
967 – 155f. brown and yellow 1·00 55
968 – 195f. brown and green . . 1·40 80
DESIGNS: 10f. Sculpture with full lips; 30f. Sculpture with large nose; 155f. Sculpture with triangular mouth; 195f. Sculpture with sunken eyes.

1988. 1st International Drug Abuse and Illegal Trafficking Day.
969 **356** 155f. multicoloured . . . 1·10 80

357 "The Couple" (K. J. Houra)

1988. Paintings by Local Artists. Multicoloured.
970 20f. Type **357** 15 10
971 30f. "The Canary of Gentleness" (Monne Bou) (horiz) 20 10
972 150f. "The Eternal Dancer" (Monne Bou) . . . . 1·00 55
973 155f. "The Termite Hill" (Mathilde Moro) . . . . . 1·00 55
974 195f. "The Sun of Independence" (Michel Kodjo) . . . . 1·25 70

358 Emblem

1988. 25th Anniv of Organization of African Unity.
975 **358** 195f.+5f. multicoloured 1·40 1·25

359 Collector with Album

1988. World Post Day.
976 **359** 155f. multicoloured . . . 1·00 65

360 Emblem

1988. 28th Anniv of Independence. Forestry Year. Multicoloured.
977 40f. Type **360** 30 20
978 155f. "To each his tree" . . . 1·10 65
979 155f. "Stop fires" . . . . . 1·10 65

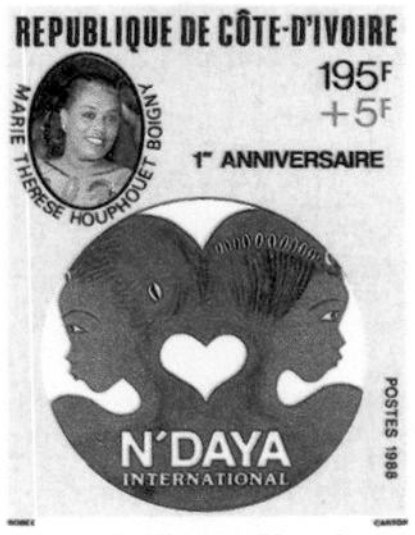

361 Marie Therese Houphouet-Boigny and Emblem

1988. 1st Anniv of N'Daya International.
980 **361** 195f.+5f. multicoloured 1·40 1·25

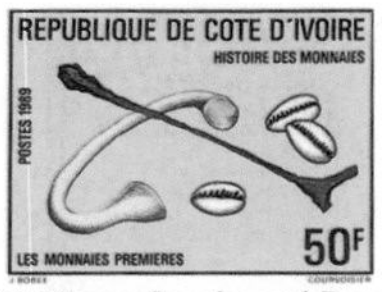

362 Money Cowries and Bones

1989. History of Money (1st series).
981 **362** 50f. multicoloured 70 30
982 – 195f. black, grey and blue 1·50 90
DESIGN: 195f. Bank of Senegal notes.
See also Nos. 1004/5, 1019/21 and 1053.

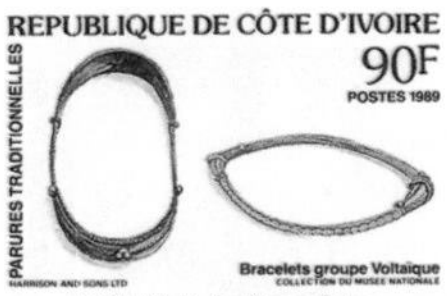

363 Voltaic Bracelets

1989. Traditional Jewellery. Multicoloured.
983 90f. Type **363** 70 45
984 155f. Dan ankle bracelets . . 1·25 90

364 Stamp used as Money **365** "Old Man and Child"

1989. Stamp Day.
985 **364** 155f. multicoloured . . . 1·25 85

1989. Carvings by Christian Lattier. Mult.
986 40f. Type **365** 30 20
987 155f. "Saxophone Player" . . 1·10 55
988 550f. "Panther" (horiz) . . . 3·50 2·00

366 Map and Tractor

1989. 30th Anniv of Council of Unity.
989 **366** 75f. multicoloured 50 30

367 Sirikukube Dan

1989. Rural Dwellings (3rd series).
990 **367** 155f. multicoloured . . . 1·10 65

368 Congress Venue and Pres. Houphouet-Boigny

1989. International Peace Congress, Yamoussoukro.
991 **368** 195f. multicoloured . . . 1·40 80

369 Map and King holding Court

1989. Anniversaries. Multicoloured.
992 200f. Type **369** (279th anniv of accession of King Sekou Watara of Kong) . . . . . 1·50 1·00
993 200f. Bastille and detail of Declaration of Rights of Man (bicentenary of French Revolution) . . . . 1·50 1·00

370 Nile Monitor

1989. Reptiles. Multicoloured.
994 25f. Type **370** 15 10
995 100f. Nile crocodile 70 50

371 Globe and Emblem

1989. World Post Day.
996 **371** 195f. multicoloured . . . 1·40 65

372 Telephone Kiosks and Mail Boxes

1989. 30th Anniv of West African Posts and Telecommunications Association.
997 **372** 155f. multicoloured . . . 1·10 65

373 Milan **374** Crowd and Handclasp

1989. Air. World Cup Football Championship (1990) Preliminary Rounds. Multicoloured.
998 195f. Type **373** . . . . . . 1·40 45
999 300f. Genoa . . . . 2·00 65
1000 450f. Turin . . . . 2·75 1·00
1001 550f. Bologna . . . . . . 4·00 1·25

1989. 29th Anniv of Independence.
1002 **374** 155f. multicoloured . . . 1·00 55

375 Emblem **376** West African Bank 25f. Banknote

1990. 10th Anniv of Pan-African Postal Union.
1003 **375** 155f. multicoloured . . . 1·00 55

1990. History of Money (2nd series).
1004 **376** 155f. black and green . . 1·00 55
1005 – 195f. black and orange 1·50 85
DESIGN: 195f. Banknotes, 1917–44.
See also Nos. 1019/21 and 1053.

377 "Afrique" (steam packet)

1990. Stamp Day.
1006 **377** 155f. multicoloured . . . 2·00 85

378 Envelopes on Map

1990. 20th Anniv of Multinational Postal Training School, Abidjan.
1007 **378** 155f. multicoloured . . . 1·10 55

379 Footballers

1990. Air. World Cup Football Championship, Italy. Designs showing match scenes. Multicoloured.
1008 155f. Type **379** . . . . . . 1·00 35
1009 195f. Brazil v. West Germany . . . . 1·25 45
1010 500f. England v. Russia . . 3·25 1·10
1011 600f. England v. Netherlands . . . . . . 4·25 1·40

1990. Rural Dwellings (4th series). As T **367**. Multicoloured.
1012 155f. Malinke village . . . 1·00 45

380 Teacher writing Letters on Blackboard

1990. International Literacy Year.
1013 **380** 195f. multicoloured . . . 1·40 65

381 Cathedral

1990. Consecration of Our Lady of Peace Cathedral, Yamoussoukro. Multicoloured.
1014 155f. Type **381** . . . . . . 1·00 55
1015 195f. Aerial view . . . . . 1·40 80

382 Pres. Houphouet-Boigny and Pope

1990. 3rd Visit of Pope John Paul II.
1016 **382** 500f. multicoloured . . . 3·50 1·90

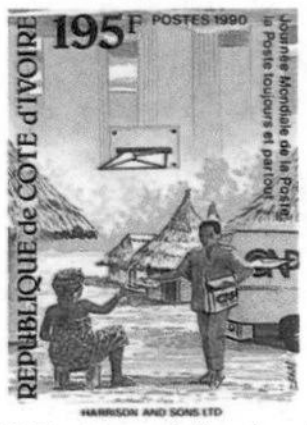

383 Postman delivering to Village

1990. World Stamp Day.
1017 **383** 195f. multicoloured . . . 1·40 80

384 Modern Building and Road Network

1990. 30th Anniv of Independence.
1018 **384** 155f. multicoloured . . . 1·00 55

1991. History of Money (3rd series). As T **376**.
1019 40f. black and yellow . . . 30 15
1020 155f. black and green . . . 1·00 65
1021 195f. black and mauve . . . 1·25 85
DESIGNS: 40, 155f. West African Bank 100f. and 5f. notes, 1942; 195f. Issuing Institute for French West Africa and Togo 50f. and 500f. notes.

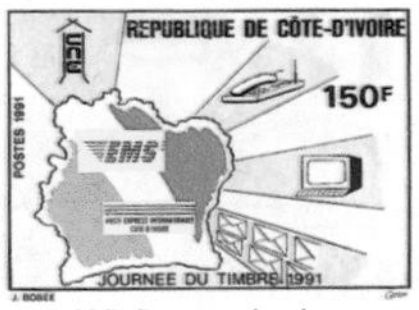

385 Communications

1991. Stamp Day.
1022 **385** 150f. multicoloured . . . 1·00 35

386 Suzanne Lenglen

1991. Centenary of French Open Tennis Championships. Tennis players. Multicoloured.
1023 200f. Type **386** . . . . . . 1·40 1·10
1024 200f. Helen Wills Moody . . 1·40 1·10
1025 200f. Simone Mathieu . . . 1·40 1·10
1026 200f. Maureen Connolly . . 1·40 1·10
1027 200f. Francoise Durr . . . 1·40 1·10
1028 200f. Margaret Court . . . 1·40 1·10
1029 200f. Chris Evert . . . . . 1·40 1·10
1030 200f. Martina Navratilova 1·40 1·10
1031 200f. Steffi Graf . . . . . 1·40 1·10
1032 200f. Henri Cochet . . . . 1·40 1·10
1033 200f. Rene Lacoste . . . . 1·40 1·10
1034 200f. Jean Borotra . . . . 1·40 1·10
1035 200f. Donald Budge . . . . 1·40 1·10
1036 200f. Marcel Bernard . . . 1·40 1·10
1037 200f. Ken Rosewall . . . . 1·40 1·10
1038 200f. Rod Laver . . . . . 1·40 1·10
1039 200f. Bjorn Borg . . . . . 1·40 1·10
1040 200f. Yannick Noah . . . . 1·40 1·10

387 "Europe"

1991. Steam Packets. Multicoloured.
1041 50f. Type **387** 35 20
1042 550f. "Asie" . . . . 3·50 2·25

1991. Various stamps surch.
1043 – 150f. on 155f. mult (987) 1·00 35
1044 **367** 150f. on 155f. mult . . . 1·00 35
1045 – 150f. on 155f. black and green (1020) . . . . . 1·10 45
1046 – 200f. on 195f. black and mauve (1021) . . . . 1·40 55

389 Post and Savings Society's Emblem and Letter-box

1991. World Post Day. Multicoloured.
1047 50f. Type **389** 35 20
1048 100f. S.I.P.E. emblem and globe 65 35

390 We Drum

1991. Drums.
1049 **390** 5f. purple and lilac . . . 10 10
1050 – 25f. red and pink . . . 15 10
1051 – 150f. green and turquoise 1·10 80
1052 – 200f. green and brown 1·40 1·00
DESIGNS: 25f. Krou drum, Soubre; 150f. Nafana drum, Sinematiau; 200f. Akye drum, Alepe.

1991. History of Money (4th series). As T **376**.
1053 100f. black and mauve . . . 65 45
DESIGN: 100f. French West Africa and Togo banknotes.

391 Government Buildings

1991. 31st Anniv of Independence.
1054 **391** 150f. multicoloured . . . 1·00 45

392 Orchid

394 African Civet

393 Footballer and Cup

1991. Orchids.
1055 **392** 150f. mauve, green & blk 1·00 35
1056 – 200f. red, emerald & grn 1·25 45
DESIGNS—HORIZ: 200f. Different orchid.

1992. Ivory Coast Victory in African Nations Football Cup Championship, Senegal. Mult.
1057 20f. Type **393** 20 15
1058 150f. Elephants supporting cup with their trunks (vert) . . . . 1·10 95

1992. Animals in Abidjan Zoo.
1059 **394** 5f. brown, red and green 10 10
1060 – 40f. brown, green & orge 30 15
1061 – 150f. brown, green & red 1·00 55
1062 – 500f. brown, grn & ochre 3·25 2·25
DESIGNS: 40f. African palm civet; 150f. Bongo; 500f. Leopard.

395 World Map

1992. World Post Day.
1063 **395** 150f. blue and black . . 1·00 55

396 1892 "Tablet" and 1962 Postal Centenary Stamps

1992. Stamp Day. Centenary of First Ivory Coast Stamps. Multicoloured.
1064 150f. Type **396** . . . . . . 1·00 65
1065 150f. 1961 Independence and 1991 World Post Day stamps . . . . 1·00 65

397 Tomb Entrance

1992. Tourism, Funerary Monuments.
1067 **397** 5f. red, green and blue 10 10
1068 – 50f. brown, green & blue 50 15
1069 – 150f. brown, blue & green . . . . 1·10 35
1070 – 400f. green, blue and red 2·75 1·40
DESIGNS (tombs): 50f. Angels, lions and figures; 150f. Drummer, angel, sentry and animals; 400f. Angels, figures and tree.

398 Dove, Flag and Head of Statue of Liberty

400 Emblem and Map

399 Runners and Flags

1992. 32nd Anniv of Independence. Mult.
1071 30f. Type **398** 20 10
1072 150f. Crowd waving flags, Statue of Liberty and map 70 35

1992. International Marathon. Multicoloured.
1073 150f. Type **399** 70 35
1074 200f. Runners and landmarks . . . . 1·40 50

1992. 1st Anniv of Ity Gold Mine.
1075 **400** 200f. multicoloured . . . 1·40 50

400a Dent de Man

1992. Tourist Sites. Multicoloured.
1075a 10f. Hotel complex . . . .
1075b 25f. Type **400a** . . . . .
1075c 100f. Holiday village (horiz) . . . .
1075d 200f. Tourist map . . . .

400b Building and Emblem

1992. 1st World Conference on Environmental Protection. Multicoloured.
1075e 150f. Tree (vert) . . . . .
1075f 200f. Type **400b** . . . . .

401 Girl with Stockbook and Collectors swapping Stamp

402 "Argemone mexicana"

1993. Stamp Day. Youth Philately. Multicoloured.
1076 50f. Type **401** 25 15
1077 50f. Girl pointing at stamps 25 15
1078 150f. Boy perusing album and girls viewing exhibition display . . . . 1·00 35

1993. Medicinal Plants. Multicoloured.
1079 5f. Type **402** 10 10
1080 20f. "Hibiscus esculentus" 35 10
1081 200f. "Cassia alata" . . . . 1·40 90

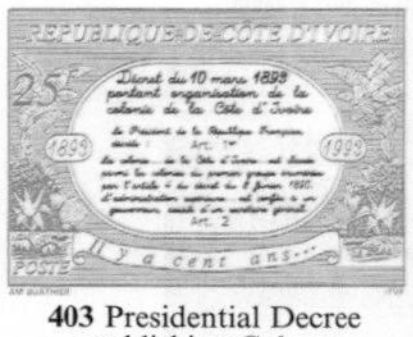
403 Presidential Decree establishing Colony

404 "Calyptrochilum emarginatum"

1993. Centenary of Ivory Coast.
1082 **403** 25f. black and green . . 10 10
1083 – 100f. blue and black . . 70 50
1084 – 500f. black and brown 3·25 2·25
DESIGNS: 100f. Louis Binger (first Governor) and Felix Houphouet-Boigny (President); 500f. Factory.

1993. Orchids. Multicoloured.
1085 10f. Type **404** 10 10
1086 50f. "Plectrelminthus caudathus" 25 15
1087 150f. "Eulophia guineensis" 1·00 65

405 Heading Ball

407 Abstract Design

406 19th-century Map of Ivory Coast

1993. World Cup Football Championship, U.S.A. (1994). Multicoloured.
1088 150f. Type **405** 70 35
1089 200f. Players jumping . . . 1·40 50
1090 300f. Player dribbling ball past opponent . . . . . 2·00 1·40
1091 400f. Ball ricocheting off players . . . . 2·75 1·60

1993. World Post Day.
1092 **406** 30f. red, black and blue 15 10
1093 – 200f. multicoloured . . . 1·40 90
DESIGN: 200f. Bouake post office.

1993. African Plastic Arts Biennale, Abidjan.
1094 **407** 200f. multicoloured . . . 90 45

408 Map of Mining Centre

1993. 33rd Anniv of Independence.
1095 **408** 200f. multicoloured . . . 1·40 70

409 Boigny and Modern Developments

1994. Felix Houphouet-Boigny (President, 1960–93) Commemoration. Multicoloured.
1096 150f. Type **409** 35 20
1097 150f. Boigny, tractor, ploughing with oxen and container ship 35 20
1098 150f. Boigny and Our Lady of the Peace Cathedral, Yamoussoukro 35 20
1099 200f. Type **409** 50 25
1100 200f. As No. 1097 . . . . . 50 25
1101 200f. As No. 1098 . . . . . 50 25

410 Raoul Follereau and Globe

1994. 50th Anniv (1992) of World Anti-leprosy Campaign.
1103 **410** 150f. multicoloured . . . 35 20

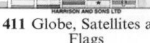

411 Globe, Satellites and Flags

412 Country-woman with Basket on Back

1994. 1st Meeting of Regional African Satellite Communications Organization Board of Directors, Abidjan.
1104 **411** 150f. multicoloured . . . 35 20

1994. Multicoloured, colour of frame given.
1105 **412** 5f. orange 10 10
1106 25f. blue 10 10
1107 30f. bistre 10 10
1108 40f. green 10 10
1109 50f. brown 15 10
1110 75f. purple 20 10
1111 150f. green 40 20
1112 180f. purple 45 25
1115 280f. grey 75 40
1116 300f. violet 80 40

413 "Christ"

414 Modern Developments

1994. Stained Glass Windows by Pierre Fakhoury from Our Lady of Peace Cathedral, Yamoussoukro. Multicoloured.
1120 25f. Type **413** 10 10
1121 150f. "The Fisher of Men" 40 20
1122 200f. "Madonna and Child" 50 25

1994. 34th Anniv of Independence. The Family.
1124 **414** 150f. multicoloured . . . 40 20

415 Green Mamba

1995. Snakes. Multicoloured.
1125 10f. Royal python 10 10
1126 20f. Green bush snake . . . 10 10
1127 100f. Type **415** 25 15
1128 180f. Common puff adder 70 50
1129 500f. Rhinoceros viper . . . 1·50 1·10

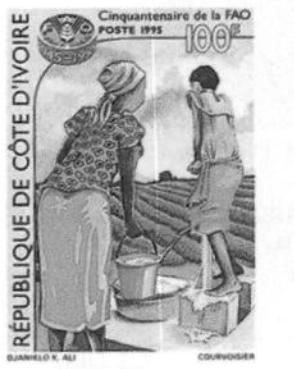

416 Women collecting Water

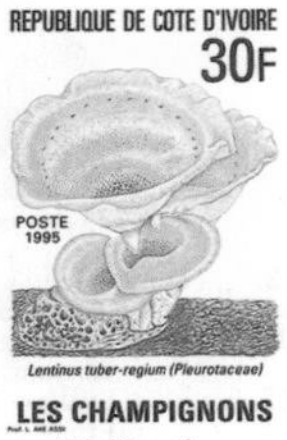

417 "Lentinus tuberregium"

1995. 50th Anniversaries. Multicoloured.
1130 100f. Type **416** (F.A.O.) . . 25 15
1131 280f. Dove on globe (U.N.O.) 75 40

1995. Fungi. Multicoloured.
1132 30f. Type **417** 20 10
1133 50f. Chinese mushroom . . 30 15
1134 180f. "Dictyophora indusiata" 90 45
1135 250f. Termite mushroom . . 1·25 60

418 Laboratory Worker and Pasteur

1995. Death Centenary of Louis Pasteur (chemist).
1136 **418** 280f. multicoloured . . . 1·00 60

419 GSR Emblem on Butterfly Wing

1995. School Philatelic Clubs. Multicoloured.
1137 50f. Type **419** 10 10
1138 180f. LBP emblem on butterfly wing 70 50

420 Palla

1995. Butterflies. Multicoloured.
1139 180f. Type **420** 70 50
1140 280f. Mocker swallowtail . . 1·00 65
1141 550f. Emperor swallowtail 1·75 1·10

421 Motor Vehicles and Handcart

1996. Abidjan Transport. Multicoloured.
1142 180f. Type **421** 45 25
1143 280f. Catching bus 70 35

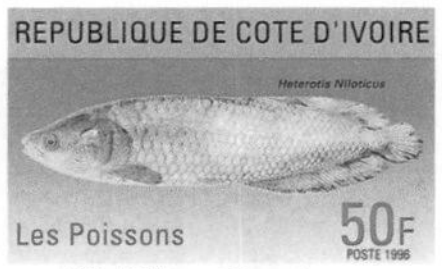

422 African Bonytongue

1996. Fishes. Multicoloured.
1144 50f. Type **422** 10 10
1145 180f. Western grunter . . . 55 30
1146 700f. Guinean butter catfish 2·10 1·25

423 "Cyrtorchis arcuata"

424 Boxing

1996. Flowers. Multicoloured.
1147 40f. Type **423** 10 10
1148 100f. "Eulophia horsfalii" 25 15
1149 180f. "Eulophidium maculatum" 45 25
1150 200f. "Ansellia africana" . . 50 25

1996. Centenary of Modern Olympic Games and Olympic Games, Atlanta. Multicoloured.
1151 200f. Type **424** 50 25
1152 280f. Running 70 35
1153 400f. Long jumping 95 50
1154 500f. National Olympic Committee arms and pictograms . . . . 1·25 65

425 Huntsmens' Sticks, Birifor

1996. Ceremonial Sticks.
1155 **425** 180f. black and green . . 45 25
1156 – 200f. black and orange 50 25
1157 – 280f. black and lilac . . 70 35
DESIGNS: 200f. Lobi chief's stick from Bindam; 280f. Lobi chief's stick from Gboberi.

426 Sacred Lotus

1997. Water Plants. Multicoloured.
1158 50f. Type **426** 10 10
1159 180f. White lotus 40 20
1160 280f. Cape Blue water-lily 60 30
1161 700f. White water-lily . . . 1·50 75

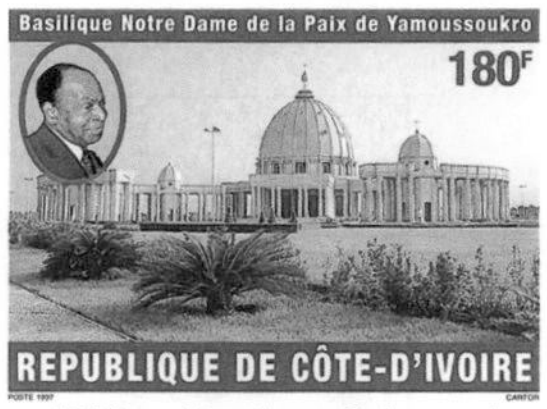

427 Pres. Houphouet-Boigny and Cathedral

1997. Our Lady of Peace Cathedral, Yamoussoukro. Multicoloured.
1162 180f. Type **427** 40 20
1163 200f. Interior of church . . 45 25
1164 280f. Pope John Paul II and elevated view of cathedral 60 30

428 Pearl Necklace

429 Stone Head

1997. Traditional Necklaces. Each lilac and black.
1165 50f. Type **428** 10 10
1166 100f. Necklace of small pearls 20 10
1167 180f. Broken necklace of pearls 40 20

1997. Stone Heads from Gohitafla. Multicoloured.
1168 100f. Type **429** 20 10
1169 180f. Stone head (full-face) 40 20
1170 500f. Stone head (side-view) 1·10 55

430 Pulley

431 Manatees

1997. Wooden Weaving Tools.
1171 **430** 180f. multicoloured . . . 40 20
1172 – 280f. black, grn & dp grn 60 30
1173 – 300f. black, bl & ultram 65 35
DESIGNS—VERT: 280f. Combing frame. HORIZ: 300f. Shuttle.

1997. Endangered Species. Multicoloured.
1174 180f. Type **431** 40 20
1175 280f. Jentink's duiker . . . 60 30
1176 400f. Waterbuck 85 45

432 Goalkeeper

1998. World Cup Football Championship, France. Multicoloured.
1177 180f. Type **432** 40 20
1178 280f. Player composed of flags of competing nations (vert) 60 30
1179 400f. Match scene showing trajectory of ball 85 45
1180 500f. Players and ball as mascot (vert) . . . . . . 1·10 55

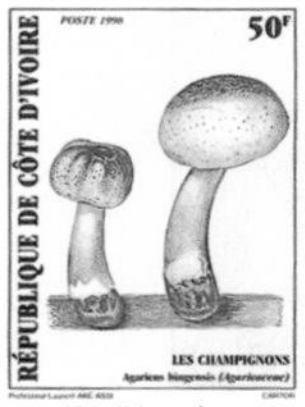

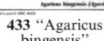

433 "Agaricus bingensis"

434 "Hutchinsonia barbata"

1998. Fungi. Multicoloured.
1181 50f. Type **433** 10 10
1182 180f. "Lactarius gymnocarpus" 40 20
1183 280f. "Termitomyces letestui" 60 30

1998. Plants. Multicoloured.
1184 40f. Type **434** 10 10
1185 100f. "Synsepalum aubrevillei" 20 10
1186 180f. "Cola lorougnonis" . . 40 20

435 Tapa Woman

1998. Traditional Costumes. Multicoloured.
1187 180f. Type **435** 35 20
1188 280f. Raphia woman . . . 55 30

436 Steam Locomotive, South Africa, 1918

1999. Railways of Africa. Multicoloured.
1189 180f. Type **436** 35 20
1190 280f. Beyer Peacock 15th Class Garratt type steam locomotive, 1925 (wrongly inscr "Garret") 55 30

437 Man carrying Parcel

1999. 40th Anniv of Rural Development Council.
1192 **437** 180f.+20f. mult 35 25

438 Emblem and Carved Heads

1999. 125th Anniv of Universal Postal Union. Multicoloured.
1193 180f.+20f. Type **438** 35 20
1194 280f. Emblem and forms of transport 50 25

439 African Elephants

1999. "PHILEX FRANCE '99" International Stamp Exhibition, Paris. Animals in Abidjan Zoo. Mult.
1195 180f.+20f. Type **439** 35 20
1196 250f. African buffaloes . . . 45 25
1197 280f. Chimpanzees 50 25
1198 400f. Savanna monkey . . . 70 35

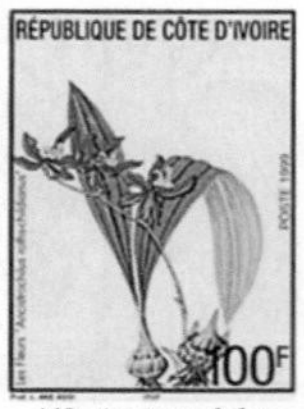

440 *Ancistrochilus rothschildianus*

1999. Flowers. Multicoloured.
1199 100f. Type **440** 20 10
1200 180f.+20f. *Brachycorythis pubescens* 35 20
1201 200f. *Bulbophyllum barbigerum* 35 20
1202 280f. *Habenaria macrandra* 50 25

441 Rock and Trees

1999. Rock Formations, Ahouakro. Multicoloured.
1203 180f.+20f. Type **441** 35 25
1204 280f. Two rocks 50 30
1205 400f. Large rock (vert) . . . 70 45

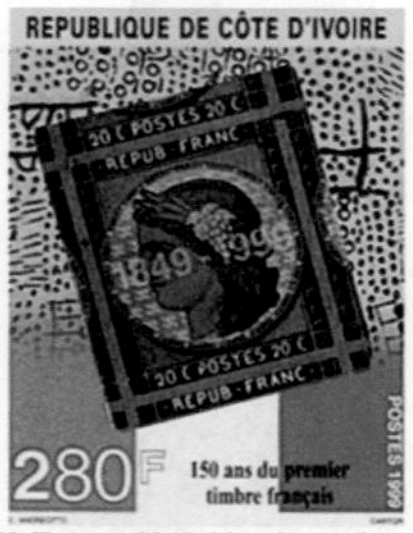

442 France 1849 20c. Ceres Stamp

1999. 150th Anniv of First French Stamp.
1206 **442** 280f. multicoloured . . . 50 25

443 African Golden Oriole (*Oriolus auratus*)

1999. Birds. Multicoloured.
1207 50f. Type **443** 10 10
1208 180f.+20f. Variable sunbird (*Nectarinia venusta*) . . . 35 25
1209 280f. Madagascar green pigeon (*Treron australis*) 50 30
1210 300f. Grey parrot (*Psittacus erithacus*) 55 35

444 Wahrindi (*Synodontis schall*)

1999. Fishes. Multicoloured.
1211 100f. Type **444** 20 15
1212 180f.+20f. Gunther's krib (*Chromidotilapia guntheri*) 35 25
1213 280f. Grass-eater perch (*Distichodus rostratus*) . . 50 30

445 School Children and "EDUCATION"

1999. New Millennium. Multicoloured.
1214 100f. Type **445** 20 15
1215 180f.+20f. Fruit and "AGRICULTURE" . . . 35 25
1216 200f. Factory and "INDUSTRIE" 35 25
1217 250f. Computer and "INFORMATIQUE" . . 45 30
1218 280f. Dove and "PAIX" . . 50 30
1219 400f. Mask and "CULTURE" 70 45

446 Wambele

2000. Traditional Masks. Multicoloured.
1220 50f. Type **446** 10 10
1221 180f.+20f. Dje 35 25
1222 400f. Korobla (vert) 70 45

447 *Blighia sapida*

2000. Native Plants. Multicoloured.
1223 30f. Type **447** 10 10
1224 180f.+20f. *Ricinodendron heudelotti* 35 25
1225 300f. *Telfaira occidentalis* . . 55 35
1226 400f. *Napoleonaea vogelii* . . 70 45

448 Pres. Robert Guei, Map, Elephant and Dove

449 Cacao

2000. 40th Anniv of Independence.
1227 **448** 180f.+20f. mult 35 25
1228 400f. multicoloured . . . 70 45

2000.
1229 **449** 5f. multicoloured . . . 10 10
1230 10f. multicoloured . . . 10 10
1231 20f. multicoloured . . . 10 10
1232 25f. multicoloured . . . 10 10
1233 30f. multicoloured . . . 10 10
1234 40f. multicoloured . . . 10 10
1235 50f. multicoloured . . . 10 15
1236 100f. multicoloured . . . 20 15
1237 180f.+20f. mult . . . 35 25
1238 300f. multicoloured . . . 55 35
1239 350f. multicoloured . . . 60 40
1240 400f. multicoloured . . . 70 45
1241 600f. multicoloured . . . 1·10 70

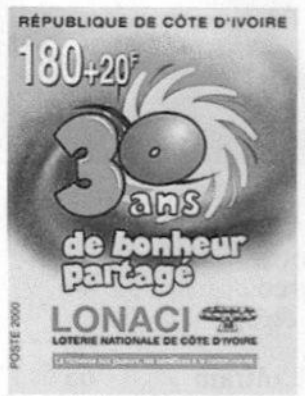

450 Emblem

452 Braided Hairstyle

451 Football

2000. 30th Anniv of National Lottery.
1242 **450** 180f.+20f. mult 35 25
1243 400f. multicoloured . . . 70 45

2000. Olympic Games, Sydney. Multicoloured.
1244 180f.+20f. Type **451** 35 25
1245 400f. Kangaroo holding rugby ball and Sydney Opera House 70 45
1246 600f. Athletics . . . . . . 1·10 70
1247 750f. Olympic stadium and bird . . . . 1·40 85

2000. Hairstyles. Multicoloured.
1248 180f.+20f. Type **452** 35 25
1249 300f. Braid in hair 55 35
1250 400f. Twisted hair on head 70 35
1251 500f. Braided into loops . . 90 55

453 Mandela

454 "Queen Pokou"

2000. 10th Anniv of Release of Nelson Mandela.
1252 **453** 300f. multicoloured . . . 55 35

2000. Statues. Multicoloured.
1253 180f.+20f. Type **454** 35 25
1254 400f. "Akwaba" 70 45
1255 600f. "Invocation of the Spirits" . . . . 1·10 70

455 Refugees

2000. 50th Anniv of United Nations Commissioner for Refugees.
1256 **455** 400f. multicoloured . . . 70 35

456 Buffalo

2001. Abokouamekro National Park. Multicoloured.
1257 50f. Type **456** 10 10
1258 100f. Rhinoceros and calf 20 15
1259 180f.+20f. Rhinoceros . . . 35 25
1260 400f.+20f. Buffalo under trees 75 45

457 Carved Wooden Poles

458 Maps and Flag

2001. Exhibits in National Museum, Abidjan. Multicoloured.
1261 100f. Type **457** 20 15
1262 180f.+20f. Blolo Bian . . . 35 25
1263 300f.+20f. Botoumo 55 35
1264 400f.+20f. Odi Oka 75 45

2001. 41st Anniv of Independence.
1265 **458** 180f.+20f. multicoloured 40 25

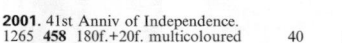

459 Player heading Ball

2001. World Cup Football Championship (2002), Japan and South Korea. Multicoloured.
1266 180f.+20f. Type **459** 55 25
1267 400f.+20f. Players legs . . . 75 45
1268 600f.+20f. Players tackling 1·10 70
1269 700f. Players tackling . . . 1·25 75

460 Children encircling Globe

2001. United Nations Year of Dialogue among Civilisations.
1270 **460** 400f.+20f. multicoloured 85 50

461 National Flag

2001. 1st Anniv of Second Republic
1271 **461** 180f.+20f. multicoloured 40 25

462 Cloth

2001. Traditional Crafts. Korhogo Cloth. Multicoloured.
1272 100f. Type **462** 20 10
1273 180f.+20f. Animals and birds 40 25
1274 400f.+20f. Man decorating cloth (vert) 85 50

463 Emblem, Map of Africa and Dancers

2001. 23rd UPU Congress (2004), Abidjan.
1275 **463** 180f.+20f. multicoloured 40 25
1276 400f.+20f. multicoloured (26 × 37 mm) 85 50
1277 600f.+20f. multicoloured (36 × 49 mm) . . . . 1·30 80

MILITARY FRANK STAMP

MF 59

1967. No value indicated.
MF1 MF **59** (–) multicoloured . . 1·90 1·90

OFFICIAL STAMPS

O **135** Arms of Ivory Coast

1973. No value indicated. Multicoloured. Background colours given.
O422 O **135** (–) green and turquoise 45 20
O423 (–) yellow and orange 75 35
O424 (–) pink and mauve 1·00 55
O425 (–) violet and blue . . 2·75 1·10

Nos. O422/5 represent the following face values. No. O422, 35f. No. O423, 75f. No. O424, 100f. No. O425, 250f.

PARCEL POST STAMPS

1903. Postage Due stamps of French Colonies optd.
(a) **Cote d'Ivoire COLIS Postaux**.
P18 U 50c. purple . . . . 27·00 35·00
P20 1f. pink on buff . . . . . 32·00 28·00

(b) **Colis Postaux**.
P19 U 50c. purple £3000 £3000
P21 1f. pink on buff £2750 £3000

(c) **Cote d'Ivoire Colis Postaux**.
P22 U 50c. purple £100 £120
P23 1f. pink on buff . . . . . 65·00 70·00

1903. Postage Due stamps of French Colonies surch.
(a) **Cote d'Ivoire Colis Postaux** and new value.
P24 U 50c. on 15c. green . . . . 13·50 11·00
P25 50c. on 60c. brown on buff 35·00 35·00
P26 1f. on 5c. blue . . . . . . 12·50 12·50

P27		1f. on 10c. brown	15·00	20·00
P30		4f. on 60c. brown on buff	£120	90·00

(b) **Colis Postaux Cote d'Ivoire** and new value.

P35	U	4f. on 5c. blue	£225	£225
P28		4f. on 15c. green	£120	90·00
P29		4f. on 30c. pink	£110	90·00
P36		8f. on 15c. green	£225	£225

1904. Postage Due stamps of French Colonies optd. (a) **C. P. Cote d'Ivoire**.

P31	U	50c. purple	25·00	38·00
P32		1f. pink on buff	25·00	35·00

(b) **Cote d'Ivoire C.P.**

P33	U	50c. purple	26·00	27·00
P34		1f. pink on buff	35·00	35·00

1905. Postage Due stamps of French Colonies surch **Cote d'Ivoire C. P.** and new value.

P39	U	2f. on 1f. pink on buff	£200	£200
P40		4f. on 1f. pink on buff	£200	£225
P41		8f. on 1f. pink on buff	£500	£500

POSTAGE DUE STAMPS

1906. "Natives" key-type inscr "COTE D'IVOIRE".

D38	L	5c. green	55	75
D39		10c. purple	55	1·40
D40		15c. blue on blue	2·00	1·50
D41		20c. black on yellow	75	90
D42		30c. red on cream	3·50	4·75
D43		50c. violet	1·75	5·25
D44		60c. black on buff	5·50	27·00
D45		1f. black on pink	17·00	42·00

1915. "Figure" key-type inscr "COTE D'IVOIRE".

D60	M	5c. green	10	1·60
D61		10c. red	10	65
D62		15c. grey	10	1·25
D63		20c. brown	15	2·00
D64		30c. blue	20	2·00
D65		50c. black	20	2·50
D66		60c. orange	35	2·75
D67		1f. violet	50	3·00

1927. Surch in figures.

D94	M	"2 F." on 1f. purple	20	2·75
D95		"3 F." on 1f. brown	25	3·25

D 21 Guere Mask

D 30 Mask

D 70 Baoule Weight

1960. Values in black.

D196	D 21	1f. violet	1·25	2·00
D197		2f. green	1·25	2·00
D198		5f. yellow	1·40	2·00
D199		10f. blue	1·75	2·50
D200		20f. mauve	2·25	5·25

1962.

D220	D 30	1f. blue and orange	15	15
D221	–	2f. red and black	20	20
D222	–	5f. green and red	30	30
D223	–	10f. purple and green	55	55
D224	–	20f. black and violet	90	90

DESIGNS: 2f. to 20f. Various native masks from Bingerville Art School.

1968. Designs showing different types of weights.

D309	D 70	5f. multicoloured	15	15
D310	–	10f. multicoloured	20	20
D311	–	15f. multicoloured	50	50
D312	–	20f. multicoloured	80	80
D313	–	30f. multicoloured	1·10	1·10

D 111 "Animal" Weight

1972. Gold Weights and Measures.

D389	D 111	20f. brown and violet	65	65
D390	–	40f. brown and red	1·00	1·00
D391	–	50f. purple and orange	1·50	1·50
D392	–	100f. brown and green	3·00	3·00

DESIGNS: 40f. "Dagger"; 50f. "Bird"; 100f. "Triangle".

JAIPUR Pt. 1

A state of Rajasthan, India. Now uses Indian stamps.

12 pies = 1 anna; 16 annas = 1 rupee.

2 Chariot of the Sun God, Surya

3 Chariot of the Sun God, Surya

1904.

3	2	½a. blue	2·75	5·50
4		1a. red	4·50	13·00
5		2a. green	4·25	13·00

1904.

9	3	¼a. olive	75	85
10a		½a. blue	1·25	50
11		1a. red	2·75	50
12		2a. green	1·60	75
13		4a. brown	6·00	2·00
14		8a. violet	3·00	2·75
15a		1r. yellow	18·00	18·00

This set was issued engraved in 1904 and surface-printed in 1913.

4 Chariot of the Sun God, Surya

३ आना
(5)

1911. No gum.

17	4	¼a. olive	30	70
18		½a. blue	30	70
20		1a. red	50	75
21a		2a. green	2·00	6·00

1926. Surch with T **5**.

32	3	3a. on 8a. violet	1·50	2·50
33		3a. on 1r. yellow	2·25	4·75

6 Chariot of the Sun God, Surya

7 Maharaja Sawai Man Singh II

1931. Investiture of Maharaja. Centres in black.

40	6	¼a. red	2·00	2·00
58	7	¼a. red	40	20
41		½a. violet	40	10
59		¾a. red	6·50	3·25
42	–	1a. blue	7·00	7·50
60	7	1a. blue	8·00	2·75
43	–	2a. orange	6·00	7·50
61	7	2a. orange	7·00	3·50
44	–	2½a. red	30·00	50·00
62	7	2½a. red	3·25	2·25
45	–	3a. green	14·00	40·00
63	7	3a. green	2·50	50
46	–	4a. green	14·00	50·00
64	7	4a. green	30·00	£110
47	–	6a. blue	6·00	45·00
65	7	6a. blue	3·75	24·00
48	–	8a. brown	14·00	75·00
66	7	8a. brown	20·00	95·00
49	–	1r. olive	30·00	£225
67	7	1r. bistre	20·00	£140
50	–	2r. green	28·00	£275
51	–	5r. purple	42·00	£300

DESIGNS—VERT: 1a. (No. 42), Elephant and banner; 2a. (No. 43), Sowar in armour; 2½a. (No. 44), Common peafowl; 8a. (No. 48), Sireh-Deorhi Gate. HORIZ: 3a. (No. 45), Bullock carriage; 4a. (No. 46), Elephant carriage; 6a. (No. 47), Albert Museum; 1r. (No. 49), Chandra Mahal; 2r. Amber Palace; 5r. Maharajas Sawai Jai Singh and Man Singh.

1932. As T **7**, but inscr "POSTAGE & REVENUE". Portrait in black.

52		1a. blue	1·75	85
53		2a. brown	2·75	1·75
54		4a. green	4·00	8·00
55		8a. brown	5·50	11·00
56		1r. bistre	21·00	90·00
57		2r. green	80·00	£375

1936. Nos. 57 and 51 surch **One Rupee**.

68		1r. on 2r. green	8·50	85·00
69		1r. on 5r. purple	8·50	75·00

1938. No. 41 surch in native characters.

70	7	¼a. on ½a. violet	12·00	15·00

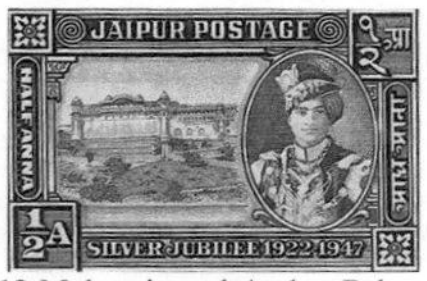
13 Maharaja and Amber Palace

1947. Silver Jubilee of Maharaja's Accession to the Throne. Inscr as in T **13**.

71	–	¼a. brown and green	1·25	3·75
72	13	½a. green and violet	40	3·50
73	–	¾a. black and red	1·25	4·25
74	–	1a. brown and blue	75	3·50
75	–	2a. violet and red	75	3·75
76	–	3a. green and black	1·40	4·75
77	–	4a. blue and brown	60	3·50
78	–	8a. red and brown	70	4·50
79	–	1r. purple and green	2·00	30·00

DESIGNS: ¼a. Palace Gate; ¾a. Map of Jaipur; 1a. Observatory; 2a. Wind Palace; 3a. Coat of Arms; 4a. Amber Fort Gate; 8a. Chariot of the Sun; 1r. Maharaja's portrait between State flags.

1947. No. 41 surch **3 PIES** and bars.

80	7	3p. on ½a. violet	15·00	24·00

OFFICIAL STAMPS

1929. Optd **SERVICE**. No gum (except for No. O6a).

O1	3	¼a. bistre	1·25	2·00
O2		½a. blue	75	20
O3c		1a. red	80	25
O5		2a. green	75	40
O6a		4a. brown (with gum)	2·00	1·75
O7		8a. violet	17·00	55·00
O8		1r. orange	35·00	£275

1931. Stamps of 1931–32 optd **SERVICE**.

O23	7	¼a. red	40	10
O13		½a. violet	30	10
O24		¾a. red	1·50	50
O25		1a. blue	4·00	30
O14	–	1a. blue (No. 42)	£225	2·00
O18	–	1a. blue (No. 52)	3·25	15
O15	–	2a. orange (No. 43)	2·75	5·50
O19	–	2a. brown (No. 53)	3·75	15
O26	7	2a. orange	4·00	2·25
O27		2½a. red	9·00	90·00
O16	–	4a. green (No. 46)	35·00	28·00
O20	–	4a. green (No. 54)	£275	7·50
O28	7	4a. green	4·00	4·50
O21	–	8a. brown (No. 55)	7·50	1·10
O29	7	8a. brown	4·00	6·50
O22	–	1r. bistre (No. 56)	20·00	21·00
O30	7	1r. bistre	40·00	

1932. No. O5 surch in native characters.

O17	3	½a. on 2a. green	£150	1·50

1947. Official stamps surch.

O33	7	3p. on ½a. violet	4·75	12·00
O32		9p. on 1a. blue	3·75	3·00

1948. No. O13 surch in native characters.

O34	7	¾a. on ½a. violet	15·00	16·00

For later issues see **RAJASTHAN**.

JAMAICA Pt. 1

An island in the W. Indies. Part of the Br. Caribbean Federation from 3 January 1958, until 6 August 1962 when Jamaica became an independent state within the Commonwealth.

1860. 12 pence = 1 shilling;
20 shillings = 1 pound.
1969. 100 cents = 1 dollar.

8

11

1860. Portrait as T **8**. Various frames.

7	8	½d. red	14·00	3·50
16a		½d. green	1·00	10
8		1d. blue	55·00	75
18a		1d. red	32·00	60
9		2d. red	60·00	70
20a		2d. grey	70·00	50
21a		3d. green	2·50	1·25
22b		4d. orange	2·00	35
52a		6d. lilac	10·00	17·00
23a		6d. yellow	4·00	3·50
24		1s. brown	5·00	6·00
25		2s. red	27·00	20·00
26		5s. lilac	48·00	70·00

See also Nos. 47a etc.

1889.

27	11	1d. purple and mauve	3·50	20
28a		2d. green	5·50	6·00
29		2½d. purple and blue	5·00	50

1890. No. 22a surch **TWO PENCE HALF-PENNY**.

30	8	2½d. on 4d. orange	27·00	8·50

13 Llandovery Falls, Jamaica

1900.

31	13	1d. red	3·00	20
32		1d. black and red	3·00	20

14 Arms of Jamaica

16

1903.

33	14	½d. grey and green	1·50	30
34		1d. grey and red	1·75	10
35		2½d. grey and blue	3·00	30
42		2½d. blue	2·50	1·25
36		5d. grey and yellow	15·00	23·00
44		6d. purple	13·00	12·00
45		5s. grey and violet	42·00	35·00

1906.

38b	16	½d. green	3·75	20
40		1d. red	1·50	10

1908. Queen Victoria portraits as 1860.

47a		3d. purple on yellow	2·00	1·50
48		4d. brown	70·00	65·00
49		4d. black on yellow	7·50	40·00
50		4d. red on yellow	1·50	8·00
54		1s. black on green	4·25	8·50
56		2s. purple on blue	6·50	3·50

17

1911.

57	17	2d. grey	3·00	13·00

1912. As T **17**, but King George V.

89a		½d. green	1·75	10
58		1d. red	1·50	10
59		1½d. orange	1·00	60
60		2d. grey	2·00	1·75
61		2½d. blue	1·50	15
62		3d. purple on yellow	50	45
63		4d. black and red on yellow	50	3·50
64a		6d. purple and mauve	75	1·00
65		1s. black on green	2·25	2·00
66		2s. purple and blue on blue	13·00	25·00
67		5s. green and red on yellow	60·00	90·00

1916. Optd **WAR STAMP.** in one line (with full point).

68	16	½d. green	10	35
69a	–	3d. purple on yellow (62)	12·00	27·00

See also Nos. 76/77a.

1916. Optd **WAR STAMP.** in two lines.

73	16	½d. green	50	30
74	–	1½d. orange (No. 59)	20	10
75	–	3d. purple on yellow (No. 62)	50	1·40

1919. Optd **WAR STAMP** in one line (no full point).

76	15	½d. green	20	15
77a	–	3d. purple on yell (No. 62)	3·00	1·25

23 Jamaica Exhibition, 1891

24 Arawak Woman preparing Cassava

27 Return of War Contingent, 1919

34

1919.

91a	23	½d. green and olive	30	50
79	24	1d. red and orange (A)*	1·75	1·75
92		1d. red and orange (B)*	1·50	10
93	–	1½d. green	1·00	45
81	–	2d. blue and green	1·00	4·00
82a	27	2½d. blue	1·50	1·75
96a	–	3d. green and blue	1·25	15
97	–	4d. brown and green	1·00	30

98a	–	6d. black and blue	12·00	1·50
99a	–	1s. orange	1·75	65
100	–	2s. blue and brown	3·25	65
101	–	3s. violet and orange	11·00	9·00
102c	–	5s. blue and bistre	27·00	22·00
103	**34**	10s. green	50·00	70·00

*Two types of the 1d. (A) Without and (B) with "POSTAGE & REVENUE" at foot.

DESIGNS—HORIZ (41½ × 26 mm): 1½d. War Contingent embarking, 1915; 6d. Port Royal, 1853. (27 × 22 mm): 3d. Landing of Columbus, 1494. VERT (22 × 29 mm): 2d. King's House, Spanish Town; 4d. Cathedral, Spanish Town. (25 × 30 mm): 1s. Statue of Queen Victoria, Kingston; 2s. Admiral Rodney Memorial, Spanish Town; 3s. Sir Charles Metcalfe Monument; 5s. Jamaican scenery.

37

41

1923. Child Welfare. Designs as T **37**.

104	**37**	½d.+½d. black and green	60	5·50
105	–	1d.+½d. black and red	1·75	10·00
106	–	2½d.+½d. black and blue	8·50	18·00

1929. Various frames.

108	**41**	1d. red	2·50	20
109		1½d. brown	2·00	15
110		9d. red	3·25	1·00

43 Coco Palms at Don Christopher's Cove

45 Priestman's River, Portland

1932.

111	**43**	2d. black and green	14·00	2·75
112	–	2½d. turquoise and blue	3·25	1·50
113	**45**	6d. black and purple	13·00	1·75

DESIGN—As T **43**: 2½d. Wag Water River, St. Andrew.

1935. Silver Jubilee. As T **10a** of Gambia.

114	1d. blue and red	40	15
115	1½d. blue and black	60	1·50
116	6d. green and blue	6·00	15·00
117	1s. grey and purple	5·00	8·00

1937. Coronation. As T **10b** of Gambia.

118	1d. red	30	15
119	1½d. grey	65	30
120	2½d. blue	1·00	70

48 King George VI

49 Coco Palms at Don Christopher's Cove

50 Bananas

54 Bamboo Walk

1938.

121	**48**	½d. green	1·75	10
121b		½d. orange	1·00	30
122		1d. red	1·25	10
122a		1d. green	1·50	10
123		1½d. brown	1·25	10
124b	**49**	2d. black and green	1·25	10
125	–	2½d. green and blue	3·00	1·75
126	**50**	3d. blue and green	75	1·50
126b		3d. green and blue	1·25	1·25
126c		3d. green and red	2·75	30
127	–	4d. brown and green	50	10
128a	–	6d. black and purple	2·25	10
129	–	9d. red	50	50
130	–	1s. green and brown	6·00	20
131	**54**	2s. blue and brown	22·00	1·00
132ba	–	5s. blue and brown	7·00	3·00
133aa	–	10s. green	11·00	7·00
133a	–	£1 brown and violet	28·00	26·00

DESIGNS—As Type **49**: 2½d. Wag Water River, St. Andrew. As Type **50**: 4d. Citrus grove; 9d. Kingston Harbour; 1s. Sugar industry; £1 Tobacco growing and cigar making. As previous issues, but with portrait of King George VI: 6d. As Type **45**; 5s. As No. 102c; 10s. As Type **34**.

57 Courthouse, Falmouth

59 Institute of Jamaica

1945. New Constitution..

134	**57**	1½d. brown	20	30
135a	–	2d. green	30	50
136	**59**	3d. blue	20	50
137	–	4½d. black	30	30
138	–	2s. brown	30	50
139	–	5s. blue	1·25	1·00
140	**59**	10s. green	85	2·25

DESIGNS—VERT (as Type **57**): 2s. "Labour and Learning". HORIZ (as Type **57**): 2d. Kings Charles II and George VI. (As Type **59**): 4½d. House of Assembly; 5s. Scroll, flag and King George VI.

1946. Victory. As T **11a** of Gambia.

141a	1½d. brown	30	1·75
142a	3d. blue	30	4·75

1948. Silver Wedding. As T **11b/c** of Gambia.

143	1½d. brown	30	10
144	£1 red	25·00	48·00

1949. U.P.U. As T **11d/f** of Gambia.

145	1½d. brown	20	15
146	2d. green	1·25	2·25
147	3d. blue	35	1·25
148	6d. purple	40	2·50

1951. Inauguration of B.W.I. University College. As T **43a/b** of Grenada.

149	2d. black and brown	30	30
150	6d. black and purple	35	30

69 Scout Badge and Map of Caribbean

70 Scout Badge and Map of Jamaica

1952. 1st Caribbean Scout Jamboree.

151	**69**	2d. blue, green and black	15	10
152	**70**	6d. green, red and black	30	50

1953. Coronation. As T **11h** of Gambia.

153	2d. black and green	70	10

1953. Royal Visit. As T **49** but with portrait of Queen Elizabeth II and inscr "ROYAL VISIT 1953".

154	2d. black and green	40	10

73 H.M.S. "Britannia" (ship of the line) at Port Royal

1955. Tercentenary Issue.

155	**73**	2d. black and green	35	10
156	–	2½d. black and blue	15	35
157	–	3d. black and claret	15	30
158	–	6d. black and red	20	20

DESIGNS: 2½d. Old Montego Bay; 3d. Old Kingston; 6d. Proclamation of Abolition of Slavery, 1838.

74 Coconut Palms

76 Blue Mountain Peak

75 Mahoe

77 Arms of Jamaica

1956.

159	**74**	½d. black and red	10	10
160	–	1d. black and green	10	10
161	–	2d. black and red	10	10
162	–	2½d. black and blue	65	50
163	**75**	3d. green and brown	20	10
164	–	4d. green and blue	20	10
165	–	5d. red and green	20	1·25
166	–	6d. black and red	2·25	10
167	**76**	8d. blue and orange	30	10
168	–	1s. green and blue	1·00	10
169	–	1s.6d. blue and purple	80	10
170	–	2s. blue and green	7·00	1·75
171	**77**	3s. black and blue	1·50	1·75
172	–	5s. black and red	3·75	4·50
173	–	10s. black and green	29·00	17·00
174	–	£1 black and purple	29·00	17·00

DESIGNS—As Type **74**: 1d. Sugar cane; 2d. Pineapples; 2½d. Bananas. As Type **75**: 4d. Breadfruit; 5d. Ackee; 6d. Streamertail. As Type **76**: 1s. Royal Botanic Gardens, Hope; 1s.6d. Rafting on the Rio Grande; 2s. Fort Charles. As Type **77** but vert: 10s., £1 Arms without portrait.

1958. British Caribbean Federation. As T **47a** of Grenada.

175	2d. green	50	10
176	5d. blue	95	3·50
177	6d. red	95	40

81 Bristol Britannia 312 flying over "City of Berlin", 1860

83 1s. Stamps of 1860 and 1956

1960. Centenary of Jamaica Postage Stamps.

178	**81**	2d. blue and purple	45	10
179	–	6d. red and olive	45	50
180	**83**	1s. brown, green and blue	45	55

DESIGN—As Type **81**: 6d. Postal mule-cart and motor-van.

1962. Independence. (a) Nos. 159/74 optd **INDEPENDENCE** and **1962** (3d. to 2s.) or **1962 1962** (others).

205	**74**	½d. black and red	10	15
182	–	1d. black and green	10	10
183	–	2½d. black and blue	10	1·00
184	**75**	3d. green and brown	10	10
185	–	5d. red and olive	20	60
186	–	6d. black and red	2·50	10
187	**76**	8d. blue and orange	20	10
188	–	1s. green and blue	20	10
189	–	2s. blue and olive	80	1·50
190	**77**	3s. black and blue	90	1·50
191	–	10s. black and green	2·75	4·25
192	–	£1 black and purple	2·75	5·50

86 Military Bugler and Map

(b) As T **86** inscr "INDEPENDENCE".

193	**86**	2d. multicoloured	1·00	10
194		4d. multicoloured	1·00	10
195	–	1s.6d. black and red	3·25	85
196	–	5s. multicoloured	4·00	4·00

DESIGNS: 1s.6d. Gordon House and banner; 5s. Map, factories and fruit.

89 Kingston Seal, Weightlifting, Boxing, Football and Cycling

1962. 9th Central American and Caribbean Games, Kingston.

197	**89**	1d. sepia and red	20	10
198	–	6d. sepia and blue	20	10
199	–	8d. sepia and bistre	20	10
200	–	2s. multicoloured	30	90

DESIGNS: 6d. Diver, sailing, swimming and water polo; 8d. Javelin, discus, pole-vault, hurdles and relay-racing; 2s. Kingston coat of arms and athlete.

93 Farmer and Crops

1963. Freedom from Hunger.

201	**93**	1d. multicoloured	20	10
202		8d. multicoloured	60	60

1963. Cent of Red Cross. As T **20b** of Gambia.

203	2d. red and black	15	10
204	1s.6d. red and blue	50	1·50

95 Carole Joan Crawford ("Miss World 1963")

1964. "Miss World 1963" Commem.

214	**95**	3d. multicoloured	10	10
215		1s. multicoloured	15	10
216		1s.6d. multicoloured	20	50

MS216a 153 × 101 mm. Nos. 214/16. Imperf 1·10 2·75

96 "Lignum vitae"

103 Gypsum Industry

1964.

217	**96**	1d. blue, green and brown	10	10
218	–	1½d. multicoloured	15	10
219	–	2d. red, yellow and green	15	10
220	–	2½d. multicoloured	1·00	60
221	–	3d. yellow, black & green	15	10
222	–	4d. ochre and violet	50	10
223	–	6d. multicoloured	2·25	10
224	–	8d. multicoloured	2·50	1·50
225	**103**	9d. blue and bistre	1·50	10
226	–	1s. black and brown	20	10
227	–	1s.6d. black, blue & buff	4·00	15
228	–	2s. brown, black and blue	2·75	15
229b	–	3s. blue and green	35	65
230	–	5s. black, ochre and blue	1·25	1·00
231	–	10s. multicoloured	1·25	1·25
232	–	£1 multicoloured	1·75	1·00

DESIGNS—HORIZ (As T **96**): 1½d. Ackee (fruit); 2½d. Land shells; 3d. National flag over Jamaica; 4d. Antillean murex (sea shell); 6d. "Papilio homerus" (butterfly); 8d. Streamertail. VERT (As T **96**): 2d. Blue Mahoe (tree). HORIZ (As T **103**): 1s. National Stadium; 1s.6d. Palisadoes International Airport; 2s. Bauxite mining; 3s. Blue marlin (sport fishing); 5s. Exploration of sunken city, Port Royal; £1 Queen Elizabeth II and national flag. VERT (As T **96**): 10s. Arms of Jamaica.

114 Scout Badge and Alligator

1964. 6th Inter-American Scout Conf, Kingston.

233	–	3d. red, black and pink	10	10
234	–	8d. blue, olive and black	15	25
235	**114**	1s. gold, blue and light blue	20	45

DESIGNS—VERT (25½ × 30 mm): 3d. Scout belt; 8d. Globe, scout hat and scarf.

115 Gordon House, Kingston

1964. 10th Commonwealth Parliamentary Conference, Kingston.
236 **115** 3d. black and green . . . 10 10
237 – 6d. black and red 30 10
238 – 1s.6d. black and blue . . 50 30
DESIGNS: 6d. Headquarters House, Kingston; 1s.6d. House of Assembly, Spanish Town.

118 Eleanor Roosevelt

1964. 16th Anniv of Declaration of Human Rights.
239 **118** 1s. black, red and green 10 10

119 Guides' Emblem on Map **121** Uniform Cap

1965. Golden Jubilee of Jamaica Girl Guides' Association. Inscr "1915–1965".
240 **119** 3d. yellow, green and black 10 10
241 – 1s. yellow, black and green 20 40
DESIGN—TRIANGULAR (61½ × 30½ mm): 1s. Guide emblems.

1965. Centenary of Salvation Army. Mult.
242 3d. Type **121** 25 10
243 1s.6d. Flag-bearer and drummer (vert) 50 50

123 Paul Bogle, William Gordon and Morant Bay Court House

1965. Centenary of Morant Bay Rebellion.
244 **123** 3d. brown, blue and black 10 10
245 1s.6d. brown, green & blk 20 10
246 3s. brown, red and black 30 75

124 Abeng-blower, "Telstar", Morse Key and I.T.U. Emblem

1965. Centenary of I.T.U.
247 **124** 1s. black, slate and red . . 40 20

1966. Royal Visit. Nos. 221, 223, 226/7 optd **ROYAL VISIT MARCH 1966**.
248 3d. yellow, black and green 15 10
249 6d. multicoloured . . . . . 1·75 30
250 1s. black and brown 55 10
251 1s.6d. black, blue and buff 2·00 2·00

126 Sir Winston Churchill

1966. Churchill Commemoration.
252 **126** 6d. black and green . . . 50 30
253 1s. brown and blue . . . 75 80

127 Statue of Athlete and Flags

1966. 8th British Empire and Commonwealth Games.
254 **127** 3d. multicoloured 10 10
255 – 6d. multicoloured 40 10
256 – 1s. multicoloured 10 10
257 – 3s. gold and blue 35 45
MS258 128 × 103 mm. Nos. 254/7. Imperf . . . . 4·00 8·00
DESIGNS: 6d. Racing cyclists; 1s. National Stadium, Kingston; 3s. Games emblem.

131 Bolivar's Statue and Flags of Jamaica and Venezuela **133** Sir Donald Sangster (Prime Minister)

132 Jamaican Pavilion

1966. 150th Anniv of "Jamaica Letter".
259 **131** 8d. multicoloured 20 10

1967. World Fair, Montreal.
260 **132** 6d. multicoloured 10 15
261 1s. multicoloured 10 15

1967. Sangster Memorial Issue.
262 **133** 3d. multicoloured 10 10
263 1s.6d. multicoloured . . . 20 20

134 Traffic Duty

1967. Centenary of Constabulary Force. Mult.
264 3d. Type **134** 40 10
265 1s. Personnel of the Force (56½ × 20½ mm) 40 10
266 1s.6d. Badge and Constables of 1867 and 1967 . . . . 50 75

1968. M.C.C.'s West Indies Tour. As Nos. 445/7 of Guyana.
267 6d. multicoloured 50 65
268 6d. multicoloured 50 65
269 6d. multicoloured 50 65

137 Sir Alexander and Lady Bustamante

1968. Labour Day.
270 **137** 3d. red and black 10 15
271 1s. olive and black . . . 10 15

138 Human Rights Emblem over Map of Jamaica

1968. Human Rights Year. Multicoloured.
272 3d. Type **138** 10 10
273 1s. Hands cupping Human Rights emblem 10 10
274 3s. Jamaican holding "Human Rights" 30 90

141 I.L.O. Emblem

1969. 50th Anniv of I.L.O.
275 **141** 6d. yellow and brown . . 10 10
276 3s. green and brown . . . 30 30

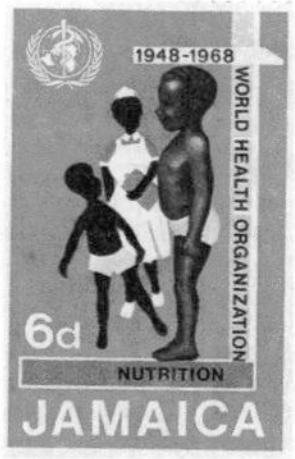

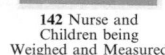

142 Nurse and Children being Weighed and Measured **146** "The Adoration of the Kings" (detail, Foppa)

1969. 20th Anniv of W.H.O. Multicoloured.
277 6d. Type **142** 10 10
278 1s. Malaria eradication (horiz) 10 10
279 3s. Trainee nurse . . . . . . 20 1·00

1969. Decimal Currency. Nos. 217, 219, 221/3 and 225/32 surch **C-DAY 8th September 1969** and value.
280 **95** 1c. on 1d. blue, grn & brn 10 10
281 – 2c. on 2d. red, yellow & grn 10 10
282 – 3c. on 3d. yellow, blk & grn 10 10
283 – 4c. on 4d. ochre and violet . . . . 1·25 10
284 – 5c. on 6d. multicoloured 1·25 10
285 **103** 8c. on 9d. blue and bistre 10 10
286 – 10c. on 1s. black & brown 10 10
287 – 15c. on 1s.6d. black, blue and buff 50 90
288 – 20c. on 2s. brown, blk & bl . . . . 1·50 1·50
289 – 30c. on 3s. blue & green 2·00 2·75
290 – 50c. on 5s. black, ochre and blue . . . . 1·25 3·00
291 – $1 on 10s. multicoloured 1·25 6·50
292 – $2 on £1 multicoloured 1·25 6·50

1969. Christmas. Paintings. Multicoloured.
293 2c. Type **146** 20 40
294 5c. "Madonna, Child and St. John" (Raphael) . . . 25 40
295 8c. "The Adoration of the Kings" (detail, Dosso Dossi) 25 40

149 Half Penny, 1869

1969. Centenary of 1st Jamaican Coins.
296 **149** 3c. silver, black and mauve 15 25
297 – 15c. silver, black and green 10 10
DESIGN: 15c. One penny, 1869.

151 George William Gordon **156** "Christ appearing to St. Peter" (Carracci)

1970. National Heroes. Multicoloured; background colours given.
298 **151** 1c. mauve 10 10
299 – 3c. blue 10 10
300 – 5c. grey 10 10
301 – 10c. red 15 10
302 – 15c. green 30 25
PORTRAITS: 3c. Sir Alexander Bustamante; 5c. Norman Manley; 10c. Marcus Garvey; 15c. Paul Bogle.

1970. Easter. Centres multicoloured; frame colours given.
303 **156** 3c. red 10 10
304 – 10c. green 10 10
305 – 20c. grey 20 60
DESIGNS: 10c. "Christ Crucified" (Antonello); 20c. Easter lily.

1970. No. 219 surch **2c.**
306 2c. on 2d. red, yellow & green 20 20

160 "Lignum vitae" **164** Bananas, Citrus, Sugar-Cane and Tobacco

161 Cable Ship "Dacia"

1970. Decimal Currency. Designs as Nos. 217, 219, 221/23, 225/32, but with values inscr as T **160** in new currency.
307 **160** 1c. blue, green and brown 75 2·00
308 – 2c. red, yell & grn (as 2d.) 30 10
309 – 3c. yell, blk & grn (as 3d.) 50 1·00
310 – 4c. ochre and violet (as 4d.) . . . . 2·75 30
311 – 5c. multicoloured (as 6d.) 3·00 65
312 **103** 8c. blue and yellow . . . 2·25 10
313 – 10c. black & brown (as 1s.) 60 20
314 – 15c. black, blue and buff (as 1s.6d.) . . . . . . 2·75 3·00
315 – 20c. brown, blk & bl (as 2s.) . . . . 1·25 2·75
316 – 30c. blue and green (as 3s.) . . . . 4·00 6·00
317 – 50c. blk, ochre & bl (as 5s.) . . . . 1·25 4·00
318 – $1 multicoloured (as 10s.) 1·00 3·75
319 – $2 multicoloured (as £1) 1·25 4·00

1970. Centenary of Telegraph Service.
320 **161** 3c. yellow, black and red 15 10
321 – 10c. black and green . . . 20 10
322 – 50c. multicoloured . . . . 50 1·00
DESIGNS: 10c. Bright's cable gear aboard "Dacia"; 50c. Morse key and chart.

1970. 75th Anniv of Jamaican Agricultural Society.
323 **164** 2c. multicoloured 25 60
324 10c. multicoloured 45 10

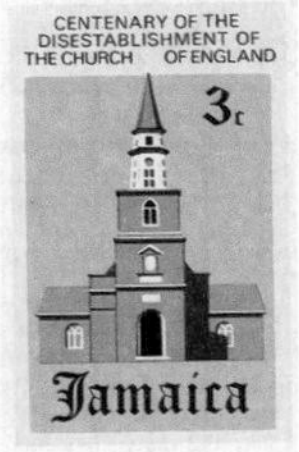

165 Locomotive "Projector" (1845) **168** Church of St. Jago de la Vega

1970. 125th Anniv of Jamaican Railways.
325 3c. Type **165** 30 10
326 15c. Steam locomotive No. 54 (1944) 65 30
327 50c. Steam locomotive No. 102 (1967) . . . . . . 1·25 1·75

1971. Centenary of Disestablishment of Church of England in Jamaica.
328 **168** 3c. multicoloured 10 10
329 10c. multicoloured 10 10
330 20c. multicoloured 30 30
331 – 30c. multicoloured . . . . 30 1·00
DESIGN: 30c. Emblem of Church of England in Jamaica.

169 Henry Morgan and Ships

1971. Pirates and Buccaneers. Multicoloured.
332 3c. Type **169** 75 10
333 15c. Mary Read, Anne Bonny and trial pamphlet 1·00 15
334 30c. Pirate schooner attacking merchantman . . . . . . 1·75 1·25

170 1s. Stamp of 1919 with Frame Inverted

1971. Tercentenary of Post Office.
335 – 3c. black and brown . . . 15 20
336 – 5c. black and green . . . 20 20
337 – 8c. black and violet . . . 20 10
338 – 10c. brown, black and blue 20 10
339 – 20c. multicoloured 35 45
340 **170** 50c. brown, black and grey . . . . 50 2·00
DESIGNS—HORIZ: 3c. Drummer packet letter, 1705; 5c. Pre-stamp inland letter, 1793; 8c. Harbour St. P.O., Kingston, 1820; 10c. Modern stamp and cancellation; 20c. British stamps used in Jamaica, 1859.

171 Satellite and Dish Aerial

172 Causeway, Kingston Harbour

1972. Opening of Jamaican Earth Satellite Station.
341 **171** 3c. multicoloured 15 10
342 15c. multicoloured 20 15
343 50c. multicoloured . . . . 65 1·25

1972. Multicoloured.
344 1c. Pimento (vert) 10 10
345 2c. Red ginger (vert) 10 10
346 3c. Bauxite Industry 10 10
347 4c. Type **172** 10 10
348 5c. Oil refinery 10 10
349 6c. Senate Building, University of the West Indies 10 10
350 8c. National Stadium 30 10
351 9c. Devon House 10 10
352 10c. Air Jamaica Hostess and Vickers VC-10 . . . . . . 20 10
353 15c. Old Iron Bridge, Spanish Town (vert) . . . . . . 2·00 10
354 20c. College of Arts, Science and Technology 30 15
355 30c. Dunn's River Falls (vert) 65 15
356 50c. River rafting . . . . . 1·75 40
357 $1 Jamaica House . . . . . 75 1·50
358 $2 Kings House . . . . . . 1·00 1·50
Designs for 8c. to $2 are larger, 35 × 27 or 27 × 35 mm.

1972. 10th Anniv of Independence Nos. 346, 352 and 356 optd **TENTH ANNIVERSARY INDEPENDENCE 1962–1972**.
359 3c. multicoloured 30 30
360 10c. multicoloured 30 10
361 50c. multicoloured . . . . . 75 2·25

175 Arms of Kingston

1972. Centenary of Kingston as Capital.
362 **175** 5c. multicoloured 15 10
363 30c. multicoloured 35 35
364 – 50c. multicoloured . . . . 60 2·25
DESIGN—HORIZ: 50c. design similar to Type **175**.

176 Mongoose on Map

1973. Centenary of Introduction of the Small Indian Mongoose.
365 **176** 8c. green, yellow and black 15 10
366 – 40c. dp blue, blue & black 35 75
367 – 60c. pink, salmon & black 60 1·40
MS368 165 × 95 mm. Nos. 365/7 1·10 4·00
DESIGNS: 40c. Mongoose and rat; 60c. Mongoose and chicken.

177 "Euphorbia punicea"

1973. Flora. Multicoloured.
369 1c. Type **177** 10 30
370 6c. "Hylocereus triangularis" 15 20
371 9c. "Columnea argentea" . . 15 20
372 15c. "Portlandia grandiflora" 25 20
373 30c. "Samyda pubescens" . . 50 60
374 50c. "Cordia sebestena" . . . 80 1·40

178 "Broughtonia sanguinea"

1973. Orchids. Multicoloured.
375 5c. Type **178** 40 10
376 10c. "Arpophyllum jamaicense" (vert) 50 10
377 20c. "Oncidium pulchellum" (vert) . . . . 1·25 25
378 $1 "Brassia maculata" . . . 2·75 3·25
MS379 161 × 95 mm. Nos. 375/8 4·50 6·00

179 "Mary", 1808–15

1974. Mail Packet Boats. Multicoloured.
380 5c. Type **179** 75 10
381 10c. "Queensbury", 1814–27 75 10
382 15c. "Sheldrake", 1829–34 . . 1·00 40
383 50c. "Thames I", 1842 . . . 2·00 2·50
MS384 133 × 159 mm. Nos. 380/3 (sold at 90c.) . . . . 2·75 5·00

180 "Journeys"

1974. National Dance Theatre Company. Mult.
385 5c. Type **180** 10 10
386 10c. "Jamaican Promenade" 10 10
387 30c. "Jamaican Promenade" (different) 30 30
388 50c. "Misa Criolla" 50 80
MS389 161 × 102 mm. Nos. 385/8 (sold at $1) . . . . 1·50 2·50

181 U.P.U. Emblem and Globe

1974. Centenary of U.P.U.
390 **181** 5c. multicoloured 10 10
391 9c. multicoloured 10 10
392 50c. multicoloured 35 80

182 Senate Building and Sir Hugh Wooding

1975. 25th Anniv of University of West Indies. Mult.
393 5c. Type **182** 10 10
394 10c. University Chapel and Princess Alice 10 10
395 30c. Type **182** 20 25
396 50c. As 10c. 35 60

183 Commonwealth Symbol

1975. Heads of Commonwealth Conf. Mult.
397 5c. Type **183** 10 10
398 10c. Jamaican coat of arms 10 10
399 30c. Dove of Peace 15 30
400 50c. Jamaican flag . . . . . 30 2·25

184 Jamaican Kite Swallowtail

185 Koo Koo or Actor Boy

1975. Butterflies (1st series), showing the family "Papilionidae". Multicoloured.
401 10c. Type **184** 55 20
402 20c. Orange swallowtail ("Papilo thoas") . . . . . 1·10 1·10
403 25c. False androyeus swallowtail ("Papilo thersites") . . . . 1·25 2·00
404 30c. Homerus swallowtail ("Papilo homerus") . . . . 1·40 2·75
MS405 134 × 179 mm. Nos. 401/4 (sold at 95c.) . . . . 5·50 7·50
See also Nos. 429/32 and 443/6.

1975. Christmas. Belisario prints of "John Canoe" Festival (1st series). Multicoloured.
406 8c. Type **185** 15 10
407 10c. Red Set-girls 15 10
408 20c. French Set-girls 50 20
409 50c. Jaw-bone or House John Canoe . . . . 95 2·50
MS410 138 × 141 mm. Nos. 406/9 (sold at $1) . . . . 1·75 3·25
See also Nos. 421/3.

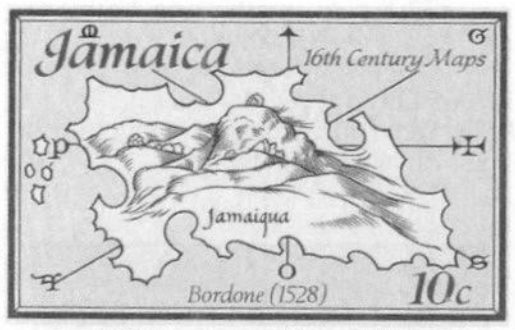

186 Bordone Map, 1528

1976. 16th Century Maps of Jamaica.
411 **186** 10c. brown, lt brown & red 25 10
412 – 20c. multicoloured 45 25
413 – 30c. multicoloured 70 85
414 – 50c. multicoloured . . . . 95 2·75
DESIGNS: 20c. Porcacchi map, 1576; 30c. De Bry map, 1594; 50c. Langenes map, 1598.
See also Nos. 425/8.

187 Olympic Rings

1976. Olympic Games, Montreal.
415 **187** 10c. multicoloured 15 10
416 20c. multicoloured 30 20
417 25c. multicoloured 30 25
418 50c. multicoloured . . . . 45 2·25

1976. West Indian Victory in World Cricket Cup. As T **223a** of Grenada.
419 10c. Map of the Caribbean 40 50
420 25c. Prudential Cup . . . . 60 1·75

1976. Christmas. Belisario Prints (2nd series). As T **185**. Multicoloured.
421 10c. Queen of the Set-girls . . 10 10
422 20c. Band of the Jaw-bone John Canoe 25 10
423 50c. Koo Koo (actor-boy) . . 45 2·00
MS424 110 × 140 mm. Nos. 421/3 (sold at 90c.) . . . . 70 2·00

1977. 17th Cent Maps of Jamaica. As T **186**.
425 9c. multicoloured 30 40
426 10c. red, brown and buff . . 30 10
427 25c. black, blue and light blue 70 60
428 40c. black, blue and green . . 80 2·25
DESIGNS: 9c. Hickeringill map, 1661; 10c. Ogilby map, 1671; 25c. Visscher map, 1680; 40c. Thornton map, 1689.

1977. Butterflies (2nd series). As T **184**. Mult.
429 10c. False barred sulphur ("Eurema elathea") 35 10
430 20c. Bronze wing ("Dynamine egaea") . . . 75 55
431 25c. Jamaican harlequin ("Chlosyne pantoni") . . . 1·00 1·50
432 40c. Mimic ("Hypolimnas misippus") . . . . 1·50 4·50
MS433 139 × 120 mm. Nos. 429/32 (sold at $1.05) . . . . 4·50 7·00

188 Map, Scout Emblem and Streamertail

190 Half-figure with Canopy

189 Trumpeter

1977. Sixth Caribbean Scout Jamboree, Jamaica.
434 **188** 10c. multicoloured 65 10
435 20c. multicoloured . . . . 1·00 25
436 25c. multicoloured . . . . 1·00 35
437 50c. multicoloured . . . . 1·50 1·75

1977. 50th Anniv of Jamaica Military Band. Mult.
438 9c. Type **189** 15 10
439 10c. Clarinet players 15 10
440 20c. Two kettle drummers (vert) 40 35
441 25c. Double-bass player and trumpeter (vert) 55 65
MS442 120 × 137 mm. Nos. 438/41 (sold at 75c.) . . . . 2·50 4·50

1978. Butterflies (3rd series). As T **184**. Multicoloured.
443 10c. Jamaican hairstreak ("Callophrys crethona") . . 50 10
444 20c. Malachite ("Siproeta stelenes") 85 20
445 25c. Common long-tailed skipper ("Urbanus proteus") 95 65
446 50c. Troglodyte ("Anaea troglodyta") . . . . 2·00 3·25
MS447 100 × 125 mm. Nos. 443/6 (sold at $1.15) . . . . 4·50 6·50

1978. Arawak Artefacts (1st series).
448 **190** 10c. brown, yellow & black 10 10
449 – 20c. brown, mauve & black 15 10
450 – 50c. brown, green & black 35 35
MS451 135 × 90 mm. Nos. 448/50 (sold at 90c.) . . . . 60 1·25
DESIGNS: 20c. Standing figure; 50c. Birdman.
See also Nos. 479/83.

191 Norman Manley (statue)

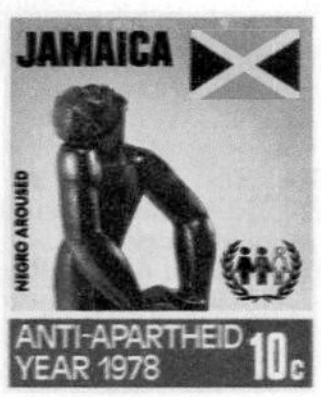
193 "Negro Aroused" (sculpture by Edna Manley)

192 Band and Banner

1978. 24th Commonwealth Parliamentary Conference. Multicoloured.
452 10c. Type **191** 15 10
453 20c. Sir Alexander Bustamante (statue) . . . 25 15
454 25c. City of Kingston Crest 35 20
455 40c. Gordon House Chamber, House of Representatives 35 65

1978. Christmas. Centenary of Salvation Army. Multicoloured.
456 10c. Type **192** 30 10
457 20c. Trumpeter 35 20
458 25c. Banner 35 30
459 50c. William Booth (founder) 60 2·00

1978. International Anti-Apartheid Year.
460 **193** 10c. multicoloured 30 20

194 Tennis, Montego Bay

197 Grinding Stone, c. 400 B.C.

1979. Multicoloured.
461 1c. Type **194** 70 75
462 2c. Golf, Tryall, Hanover . . 2·25 2·75
463 4c. Horse riding, Negril Beach . . . . 50 2·00
464 5c. Old waterwheel, Tryall, Hanover . . . . 1·25 30
465 6c. Fern Gully, Ocho Rios 1·50 2·50
466 7c. Dunn's River Falls, Ocho Rios 50 30
467 8c. Jamaican tody . . . . . 1·00 1·25
468 10c. Jamaican mango . . . . 1·00 20
469 12c. Yellow-billed amazon . . 1·00 2·00
470 15c. Streamertail . . . . . . 1·00 30
471 35c. White-chinned thrush . . 1·50 30
472 50c. Jamaican woodpecker 1·75 30
473 65c. Rafting, Martha Brae Trelawny . . . . 1·75 2·50
474 75c. Blue Marlin fleet, Port Antonio . . . . 2·00 1·75
475 $1 Scuba diving, Ocho Rios 2·00 2·25
476 $2 Sailing boats, Montego Bay . . . . 2·00 65
477 $5 Arms and map of Jamaica (37 × 27 mm) . . . . . . 1·00 1·75

1979. 10th Anniv of Air Jamaica. No. 352 optd **TENTH ANNIVERSARY AIR JAMAICA 1st APRIL 1979.**
478 10c. multicoloured 75 75

1979. Arawak Artefacts (2nd series). Multicoloured.
479 5c. Type **197** 10 10
480 10c. Stone implements, c. 500 B.C. (horiz) 10 10
481 20c. Cooking pot, c. 300 A.D. (horiz) 10 15
482 25c. Serving boat, c. 300 A.D. (horiz) 10 20
483 50c. Storage jar fragment, c. 300 A.D. . . . 25 60

198 1962 1s.6d. Independence Commemorative Stamp

1979. Death Centenary of Sir Rowland Hill.
484 **198** 10c. black, brown and red 15 10
485 – 20c. yellow and brown . . 15 15
486 – 25c. mauve and blue . . . 20 20
487 – 50c. multicoloured 25 70
MS488 146 × 94 mm. No. 485 (sold at 30c.) 30 85
DESIGNS: 20c. 1920 1s. with frame inverted; 25c. 1860 6d. stamp; 50c. 1968 3d. Human Rights Year commemorative.

199 Group of Children

1979. Christmas. International Year of the Child. Multicoloured.
489 10c. Type **199** 10 10
490 20c. Doll (vert) 10 10
491 25c. "The Family" (painting by child) 15 15
492 50c. "House on the Hill" (painting by child) 25 40

200 Date Tree Hall, 1886 (original home of Institute)

1980. Centenary of Institute of Jamaica. Mult.
493 5c. Type **200** 10 10
494 15c. Institute building, 1980 15 10
495 35c. Microfilm reader (vert) 25 20
496 50c. Hawksbill turtle and green turtle 45 85
497 75c. Jamaican owl (vert) . . 1·75 2·75

201 Don Quarrie (200 m, 1976)

1980. Olympic Games, Moscow. Jamaican Olympic Gold Medal Winners. Multicoloured.
498 15c. Type **201** 40 15
499 35c. Arthur Wint (4 × 400 m Relay, 1952) . . 45 80
500 35c. Leslie Laing (4 × 400 m Relay, 1952) . . 45 80
501 35c. Herbert McKenley (4 × 400 m Relay, 1952) . . 45 80
502 35c. George Rhoden (4 × 400 m, 1952) 45 80

202 Parish Church

1980. Christmas. Churches (1st series). Multicoloured.
503 15c. Type **202** 10 10
504 20c. Coke Memorial Church 10 10
505 25c. Church of the Redeemer 15 10
506 $5 Holy Trinity Cathedral . . 1·00 2·00
MS507 120 × 139 mm. Nos. 503/6 (sold at $5.70) . . . . 1·25 3·00
See also No. 537/9 and 570/2.

203 Blood Cup Sponge

205 White Orchid

204 Brown's Hutia (or Indian Coney)

1981. Marine Life (1st series). Multicoloured.
508 20c. Type **203** 15 10
509 45c. Tube sponge (horiz) . . 25 35
510 60c. Black coral 35 45
511 75c. Tyre reef (horiz) 40 75
See also Nos. 541/5.

1981. Brown's Hutia (or Indian Coney).
512 20c. Hutia facing right . . . 15 20
513 20c. Type **204** 15 20
514 20c. Hutia facing left and eating 15 20
515 20c. Hutia family 15 20

1981. Royal Wedding. Multicoloured.
516 20c. Type **205** 10 10
517 45c. Royal Coach 10 10
518 60c. Prince Charles and Lady Diana Spencer 20 20
519 $5 St. James' Palace 50 85
MS520 98 × 85 mm. No. 519 . . 75 1·75

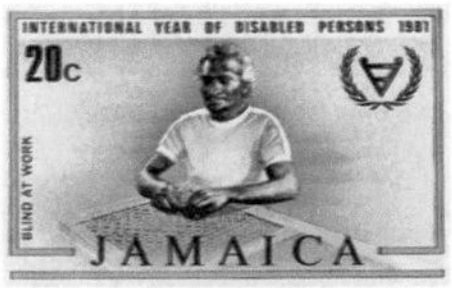
206 Blind Man at Work

1981. International Year for Disabled Persons. Multicoloured.
521 20c. Type **206** 20 15
522 45c. Painting with the mouth 40 40
523 60c. Deaf student communicating with sign language 50 75
524 $1.50 Basketball players . . . 1·75 2·00

207 W.F.D. Emblem on 1964 1½d. Definitive

208 "Survival" (song title)

1981. World Food Day. Stamps on Stamps.
525 **207** 20c. multicoloured 35 15
526 – 45c. black, red and orange 70 40
527 – $2 black, blue and green 2·00 1·40
528 – $4 black, green and brown . . . . 3·25 2·50
DESIGNS—VERT (As T **207**): 45c. 1922 1d. value. HORIZ (40 × 26 mm): $2 As 1938 3d. but with W.F.D. emblem replacing King's head; $4 As 1938 1s. but with W.F.D. emblem replacing King's head.

1981. Bob Marley (musician) Commemoration. Song Titles. Multicoloured.
529 1c. Type **208** . . . . 70 1·10
530 2c. "Exodus" . . . . 70 1·10
531 3c. "Is this Love" . . . . . 70 1·10
532 15c. "Coming in from the Cold" . . . . 3·00 30
533 20c. "Positive Vibration" . . 3·00 30
534 60c. "War" . . . . 3·75 3·00
535 $3 "Could you be Loved" . . 6·00 12·00
MS536 134 × 110 mm. $5.25 Bob Marley . . . . 7·50 4·75
No. 533 is incorrectly inscribed "OSITIVE VIBRATION".

209 Webb Memorial Baptist Church

1981. Christmas. Churches (2nd series). Multicoloured.
537 10c. Type **209** 10 10
538 45c. Church of God in Jamaica 30 15
539 $5 Bryce United Church . . 1·75 2·50
MS540 120 × 168 mm. Nos. 537/9 3·50 3·50

210 Gorgonian Coral

211 Cub Scout

1982. Marine Life (2nd series). Multicoloured.
541 20c. Type **210** 45 10
542 45c. Hard sponge and diver (horiz) 65 25
543 60c. American manatee (horiz) 90 55
544 75c. Plume worm (horiz) . . 1·00 65
545 $3 Coral banded shrimp (horiz) . . . . 2·50 1·75

1982. 75th Anniv of Boy Scout Movement. Mult.
546 20c. Type **211** 50 15
547 45c. Scout camp 85 40
548 60c. "Out of Many, One People" . . . . 1·10 90
549 $2 Lord Baden-Powell . . . 1·75 2·50
MS550 80 × 130 mm. Nos. 546/9 5·00 6·00

212 "Lignum vitae" (national flower)

213 Prey Captured

1982. 21st Birthday of Princess of Wales.
551 20c. Type **212** 35 20
552 45c. Carriage ride 50 35
553 60c. Wedding 70 60
554 75c. "Saxifraga longifolia" 1·25 2·75
555 $2 Princess of Wales . . . . 1·60 3·00
556 $3 "Viola gracilis major" . . 1·60 3·50
MS557 106 × 75 mm. $5 Honeymoon photograph . . . . 1·40 2·50

1982. Birth of Prince William of Wales. Nos. 551/6 optd **ROYAL BABY 21.6.82.**
558 20c. Type **212** 20 20
559 45c. Carriage ride 30 35
560 60c. Wedding 40 60
561 75c. "Saxifraga longifolia" 70 2·00
562 $2 Princess of Wales . . . . 75 2·50
563 $3 "Viola gracilis major" . . 1·00 3·00
MS564 106 × 75 mm. $5 Honeymoon photograph . . . . 1·50 3·25

1982. Jamaican Birds (1st series). Jamaican Lizard Cuckoo. Multicoloured.
565 $1 Type **213** . . . . 1·40 1·60
566 $1 Searching for prey . . . . 1·40 1·60
567 $1 Calling prior to prey search . . . . 1·40 1·60
568 $1 Adult landing . . . . . . 1·40 1·60
569 $1 Adult flying in . . . . . 1·40 1·60
See also Nos. 642/5 and 707/10.

1982. Christmas. Churches (3rd series). As T **209**. Multicoloured.
570 20c. United Pentecostal Church 70 10
571 45c. Disciples of Christ Church . . . . 1·25 25
572 75c. Open Bible Church . . . 2·00 3·75

214 Queen Elizabeth II

1983. Royal Visit. Multicoloured.
573 $2 Type **214** . . . . 3·00 3·50
574 $3 Coat of arms . . . . . . 4·00 6·00

215 Folk Dancing

1983. Commonwealth Day. Multicoloured.
575 20c. Type **215** 15 15
576 45c. Bauxite mining 35 35
577 75c. World map showing position of Jamaica 45 45
578 $2 Coat of arms and family 60 1·40

216 General Cargo Ship at Wharf

1983. 25th Anniv of International Maritime Organization. Multicoloured.
579 15c. Type **216** 75 30
580 20c. "Veendam" (cruise liner) at Kingston . . . . 1·00 40

581 45c. "Astronomer" (container ship) entering port . . . . 1·75 85
582 $1 Tanker passing International Seabed Headquarters Building . . 2·75 4·50

217 Norman Manley and Sir Alexander Bustamante
218 Ship-to-Shore Radio

1983. 21st Anniv of Independence.
583 **217** 15c. multicoloured 15 50
584 20c. multicoloured 15 60
585 45c. multicoloured 30 85

1983. World Communications Year. Multicoloured.
586 20c. Type **218** 75 15
587 45c. Postal services . . . . . 1·25 40
588 75c. Telephone communications . . . . . 1·50 3·00
589 $1 T.V. via satellite . . . . . 1·60 3·50

219 "Racing at Caymanas" (Sidney McLaren)

1983. Christmas. Paintings. Multicoloured.
590 15c. Type **219** 15 10
591 20c. "Seated Figures" (Karl Parboosingh) 15 10
592 75c. "The Petitioner" (Henry Daley) (vert) 50 65
593 $2 "Banana Plantation" (John Dunkley) (vert) . . . 1·25 3·75

220 Sir Alexander Bustamante

1984. Birth Centenary of Sir Alexander Bustamante. Multicoloured.
594 20c. Type **220** . . . . 90 1·60
595 20c. Birthplace, Blenheim . . 90 1·60

221 De Havilland Gipsy Moth Seaplane

1984. Seaplanes and Flying Boats. Multicoloured.
596 25c. Type **221** . . . . 1·50 20
597 55c. Consolidated Commodore flying boat . . 2·00 85
598 $1.50 Sikorsky S-38A flying boat . . . . 3·25 4·00
599 $3 Sikorsky S-40 flying boat "American Clipper" . . . 4·00 6·00

222 Cycling

1984. Olympic Games, Los Angeles. Multicoloured.
600 25c. Type **222** . . . . 1·75 30
601 55c. Relay running 60 30
602 $1.50 Start of race . . . . . 1·25 3·00
603 $3 Finish of race . . . . . . 1·75 4·50
MS604 135 × 105 mm. Nos. 600/3 (sold at $5.40) . . . . 5·00 8·00

1984. Nos. 465 and 469 surch.
605 5c. on 6c. Fern Gully, Ocho Rios 15 40
606 10c. on 12c. Yellow-billed amazon . . . . 1·10 60

224 Head of Jamaican Boa Snake

1984. Endangered Species. Jamaican Boa Snake. Multicoloured.
607 25c. Type **224** . . . . 6·00 40
608 55c. Boa snake on branch over tree . . . . 7·00 80
609 70c. Snake with young . . . 8·00 4·25
610 $1 Snake on log . . . . . . 9·00 4·50
MS611 133 × 97 mm. As Nos. 607/10 but without W.W.F. emblem (sold at $2.60) . . . . 6·00 6·00

225 Locomotive "Enterprise" (1845)

1984. Railway Locomotives (1st series). Mult.
612 25c. Type **225** . . . . 1·50 30
613 55c. Tank locomotive (1880) 1·75 70
614 $1.50 Kitson-Meyer tank locomotive (1904) . . . . 2·50 3·50
615 $3 Super-heated locomotive No. 40 (1916) . . . . . . 3·75 5·50
See also Nos. 634/7.

226 "Accompong Madonna" (Namba Roy)
227 Brown Pelicans flying

1984. Christmas. Sculptures. Multicoloured.
616 20c. Type **226** 30 10
617 25c. "Head" (Alvin Marriott) 35 10
618 55c. "Moon" (Edna Manley) 80 65
619 $1.50 "All Women are Five Women" (Mallica Reynolds (Kapo)) . . . . 1·90 4·00

1985. Birth Bicentenary of John J. Audubon (ornithologist). Brown Pelican. Multicoloured.
620 20c. Type **227** . . . . 1·00 20
621 55c. Diving for fish . . . . . 1·50 40
622 $2 Young pelican taking food from adult . . . . 2·50 3·25
623 $5 "Brown Pelican" (John J. Audubon) . . . . 3·75 6·50
MS624 100 × 100 mm. Nos. 620/3 (sold at $7.85) . . . . 6·00 8·00

228 The Queen Mother at Belfast University

1985. Life and Times of Queen Elizabeth the Queen Mother. Multicoloured.
625 25c. With photograph album, 1963 . . . . 50 10
626 55c. With Prince Charles at Garter Ceremony, Windsor Castle, 1983 . . . . 70 15
627 $1.50 Type **228** . . . . . . 1·00 1·50
628 $3 With Prince Henry at his christening (from photo by Lord Snowdon) . . . . . 1·60 2·75
MS629 91 × 74 mm. $5 With the Queen, Prince Philip and Princess Anne at Ascot . . . . 2·75 1·75

229 Maps and Emblems

1985. International Youth Year and 5th Pan-American Scout Jamboree.
630 **229** 25c. multicoloured . . . . 1·00 10
631 55c. multicoloured . . . . 1·25 25
632 70c. multicoloured . . . . 1·50 1·10
633 $4 multicoloured . . . . 3·25 7·00

1985. Railway Locomotives (2nd series). As T **225**. Multicoloured.
634 25c. Baldwin steam locomotive No. 16 . . . . 1·25 30
635 55c. Rogers locomotive . . . 1·75 35
636 $1.50 Locomotive "Projector", 1845 . . . . 2·75 3·50
637 $4 Diesel locomotive No. 102 3·75 6·50

230 "The Old Settlement" (Ralph Campbell)

1985. Christmas. Jamaican Paintings. Mult.
638 20c. Type **230** 10 10
639 55c. "The Vendor" (Albert Huie) (vert) 15 15
640 75c. "Road Menders" (Gaston Tabois) 20 35
641 $4 "Woman, must I not be about my Father's business?" (Carl Abrahams) (vert) . . . . . 1·10 3·25

1986. Jamaican Birds (2nd series). As T **213**. Multicoloured.
642 25c. Chestnut-bellied cuckoo 50 10
643 55c. Jamaican becard 65 30
644 $1.50 White-eyed thrush . . . 85 2·00
645 $5 Rufous-tailed flycatcher 1·75 4·75

1986. 60th Birthday of Queen Elizabeth II. As T **120a** of Hong Kong. Multicoloured.
646 20c. Princess Elizabeth and Princess Margaret, 1939 . . 35 10
647 25c. With Prince Charles and Prince Andrew, 1962 . . . 35 10
648 70c. Queen visiting War Memorial, Montego Bay, 1983 . . . . 40 30
649 $3 On state visit to Luxembourg, 1976 . . . . 60 1·50
650 $5 At Crown Agents Head Office, London, 1983 . . . 75 2·25

231 Bustamante Children's Hospital
231a Prince Andrew and Miss Sarah Ferguson, Ascot, 1985

1986. "Ameripex '86" International Stamp Exhibition, Chicago. Multicoloured.
651 25c. Type **231** 55 15
652 55c. Air Jamaica Boeing 737 airliner and map of holiday resorts . . . . 2·00 40
653 $3 Norman Manley Law School . . . . 1·25 3·75
654 $5 Bauxite and agricultural exports . . . . 7·00 9·00
MS655 85 × 106 mm. Nos. 651/4 (sold at $8.90) . . . . 8·00 11·00

1986. Royal Wedding. Multicoloured.
656 20c. Type **231a** 15 10
657 $5 Prince Andrew making speech, Fredericton, Canada, 1985 . . . . . . 1·00 1·90

232 Richard "Shrimpy" Clarke

1986. Jamaican Boxing Champions. Multicoloured.
658 45c. Type **232** 20 15
659 70c. Michael McCallum . . . 30 30
660 $2 Trevor Berbick . . . . . 70 1·75
661 $4 Richard "Shrimpy" Clarke, Michael McCallum and Trevor Berbick . . . . 1·25 3·00

1986. Nos. 472/3 surch.
662 5c. on 50c. Jamaican woodpecker . . . . 2·50 2·75
663 10c. on 65c. Rafting, Martha Brae Trelawny . . . . . . 1·50 2·25

234 "Heliconia wagneriana"
235 Crown Cone

1986. Christmas. Flowers (1st series). Mult.
664 20c. Type **234** 10 10
665 25c. "Heliconia psittacorum" (horiz) 10 10
666 55c. "Heliconia rostrata" . . 20 30
667 $5 "Strelitzia reginae" (horiz) 1·60 4·50
See also Nos. 703/6 and 739/42.

1987. Sea Shells. Multicoloured.
668 35c. Type **235** 45 15
669 75c. Measled cowrie 65 60
670 $1 Atlantic trumpet triton . . 75 90
671 $5 Rooster-tail conch . . . . 1·50 4·50

236 Norman Manley
237 Arms of Jamaica

1987. Portraits.
672A **236** 1c. red and pink . . . 10 75
673A 2c. red and pink 10 75
674A 3c. green and stone . . 10 75
675A 4c. green & light green 10 75
676B 5c. blue and grey . . . 50 75
677A 6c. blue and grey . . . 20 75
678A 7c. violet and mauve 50 75
679A 8c. mauve and pink . . 20 10
680A 9c. sepia and brown . . 50 10
681B – 10c. red and pink . . . 50 10
682B – 20c. orange and flesh 50 10
683A – 30c. green & light green 40 10
684B – 40c. deep green & green 30 20
685B – 50c. green and grey . . 30 20
685cB – 55c. bistre and cream 75 10
686A – 60c. blue and light blue 30 20
687A – 70c. violet & light violet 30 20
688A – 80c. violet and lilac . . 50 30
689B – 90c. brown & lt brown 1·25 30
690A **237** $1 brown and cream 50 30
690cB $1.10 brown and cream 70 40
691aB $2 orange and cream 70 70
692A $5 green and stone . . 60 1·00
693A $10 blue and azure . . 70 1·50
693cB $25 violet and lilac . . 1·25 1·75
693dB $50 mauve and lilac . . 2·00 3·00
DESIGN: 10c. to 90c. Sir Alexander Bustamante.
The 5, 20, 40, 50, 90c. and $1 exist with or without imprint date at foot.

238 Jamaican Flag and Coast at Sunset
239 Marcus Garvey

1987. 25th Anniv of Independence. Multicoloured.
694 55c. Type **238** . . . . 1·50 60
695 70c. Jamaican flag and inscription (horiz) . . . . 1·50 2·75

1987. Birth Centenary of Marcus Garvey (founder of Universal Negro Improvement Association). Each black, green and yellow.
696 25c. Type **239** . . . . 1·10 1·75
697 25c. Statue of Marcus Garvey 1·10 1·75

240 Salvation Army School for the Blind

1987. Cent of Salvation Army in Jamaica. Mult.
698 25c. Type **240** . . . . 1·50 30
699 55c. Col. Mary Booth and Bramwell Booth Memorial Hall . . . . 1·50 30
700 $3 Welfare Service lorry, 1929 . . . . 4·25 5·50
701 $5 Col. Abram Davey and S.S. "Alene", 1887 . . . . 5·50 8·00
MS702 100 × 80 mm. Nos. 698/701 (sold at $8.90) . . . . 13·00 14·00

1987. Christmas. Flowers (2nd series). As T **234**. Multicoloured.
703 20c. Hibiscus hybrid 15 10
704 25c. "Hibiscus elatus" . . . 15 10
705 $4 "Hibiscus cannabinus" . . 2·00 3·75
706 $5 "Hibiscus rosasinensis" . . 2·25 3·75

1988. Jamaican Birds (3rd series). As T **213**. Multicoloured.
707 45c. Chestnut-bellied cuckoo, black-billed amazon and Jamaican euphonia . . . . 1·75 2·50
708 45c. Black-billed amazon, jamaican white-eyed vireo, rufous-throated solitaire and yellow elaenia . . . . 1·75 2·50
709 $5 Snowy plover, little blue heron and great blue heron (white phase) . . . . . . 4·25 5·50
710 $5 Black-necked stilt, snowy egret, snowy plover and black-crowned night heron 4·25 5·50

The two designs of each value were printed together, se-tenant, each pair forming a composite design.

243 Blue Whales

1988. Marine Mammals. Multicoloured.
711 20c. Type **243** . . . . 2·00 70
712 25c. Gervais's whales . . . . 2·00 70
713 55c. Killer whales . . . . . 3·00 80
714 $5 Common dolphins . . . . 5·00 9·00

243a Jackie Hendriks

1988. West Indian Cricket. Each showing portrait, cricket equipment and early belt buckle. Multicoloured.
715 25c. Type **243a** . . . . . . 1·75 40
716 55c. George Headley . . . . 1·75 40
717 $2 Michael Holding . . . . 3·50 3·00
718 $3 R. K. Nunes . . . . . . 3·75 4·75
719 $4 Allan Rae . . . . 4·00 5·00

244 Jamaican Red Cross Workers with Ambulance

1988. 125th Anniv of Int Red Cross. Mult.
720 55c. Type **244** 50 30
721 $5 Henri Dunant (founder) in field hospital . . . . . . 2·00 4·00

245 Boxing

1988. Olympic Games, Seoul. Multicoloured.
722 25c. Type **245** 25 10
723 45c. Cycling . . . . 1·75 50
724 $4 Athletics . . . . 2·00 3·00
725 $5 Hurdling . . . . 2·00 3·00
MS726 127 × 87 mm. Nos. 722/5 (sold at $9.90) . . . . 4·50 5·50

246 Bobsled Team Members and Logo

1988. Jamaican Olympic Bobsled Team. Mult.
727 25c. Type **246** . . . . 50 1·00
728 25c. Two-man bobsled . . . 50 1·00
729 $5 Bobsled team members (different) and logo . . . . 2·00 3·00
730 $5 Four-man bobsled . . . . 2·00 3·00

1988. Hurricane Gilbert Relief Fund. Nos. 722/5 surch **+ 25c HURRICANE GILBERT RELIEF FUND**.
731 25c.+25c. Type **245** 10 20
732 45c.+45c. Cycling 20 30
733 $4+$4 Athletics . . . . . . 1·10 2·25
734 $5+$5 Hurdling . . . . . . 1·10 2·50

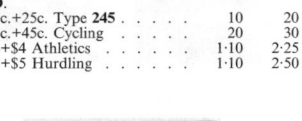

248 Nurses and Firemen

1988. Year of the Worker. Multicoloured.
735 25c. Type **248** 45 20
736 55c. Woodcarver 45 30
737 $3 Textile workers . . . . . 1·00 2·75
738 $5 Workers on fish farm . . 1·25 3·25

1988. Christmas. Flowers (3rd series). As T **234**. Multicoloured.
739 25c. "Euphorbia pulcherrima" 70 10
740 55c. "Spathodea campanulata" (horiz) . . . 85 15
741 $3 "Hylocereus triangularis" 1·75 1·60
742 $4 "Broughtonia sanguinea" (horiz) . . . . 1·75 1·75

249 Old York Castle School

1989. Bicent of Methodist Church in Jamaica.
743 **249** 25c. black and blue . . . 30 10
744 – 45c. black and red 35 10
745 – $5 black and green . . . 3·00 5·00
DESIGNS: 45c. Revd. Thomas Coke and Parade Chapel, Kingston; $5 Father Hugh Sherlock and St. John's Church.

250 "Syntomidopsis variegata"

251 Arawak Fisherman with Catch

1989. Jamaican Moths (1st series). Multicoloured.
746 25c. Type **250** 50 10
747 55c. "Himantoides perkinsae" 80 30
748 $3 "Arctia nigriplaga" . . . 1·50 3·50
749 $5 "Sthenognatha toddi" . . 1·90 4·25
See also Nos. 758/61 and 790/3.

1989. 500th Anniv (1992) of Discovery of America by Columbus (1st issue). Multicoloured.
750 25c. Type **251** 20 10
751 70c. Arawak man smoking 45 30
752 $5 King Ferdinand and Queen Isabella inspecting caravels . . . . 3·00 4·00
753 $10 Columbus with chart . . 5·50 8·50
MS754 150 × 200 mm. Nos. 750/3 (sold at $16.15) . . . . 14·00 14·00
See also Nos. 774/7 and 802/7.

252 Girl Guide

1990. 75th Anniv of Girl Guide Movement in Jamaica. Multicoloured.
755 45c. Type **252** . . . . 1·25 30
756 55c. Guide leader . . . . . 1·25 30
757 $5 Brownie, guide and ranger 5·50 8·50

1990. Jamaican Moths (2nd series). As T **250**. Multicoloured.
758 25c. "Eunomia rubripunctata" 85 35
759 55c. "Perigonia jamaicensis" 1·25 35
760 $4 "Uraga haemorrhoa" . . 2·50 4·50
761 $5 "Empyreuma pugione" . . 2·50 4·50

1990. "EXPO '90" International Garden and Greenery Exhibition, Osaka. Nos. 758/61 optd **EXPO '90** and logo.
762 25c. "Eunomia rubripunctata" 85 35
763 55c. "Perigonia jamaicensis" 1·25 35
764 $4 "Uraga haemorrhoa" . . 2·50 4·50
765 $5 "Empyreuma pugione" . . 2·50 4·50

254 Teaching English

1990. International Literacy Year. Mult.
766 55c. Type **254** 40 25
767 $5 Teaching maths . . . . . 3·00 5·00

255 "To the Market"

1990. Christmas. Children's Paintings. Mult.
768 20c. Type **255** 35 10
769 25c. "House and Garden" . . 35 10
770 55c. "Jack and Jill" 50 15
771 70c. "Market" 65 40
772 $1.50 "Lonely" . . . . . . 1·50 3·50
773 $5 "Market Woman" (vert) 3·00 6·00

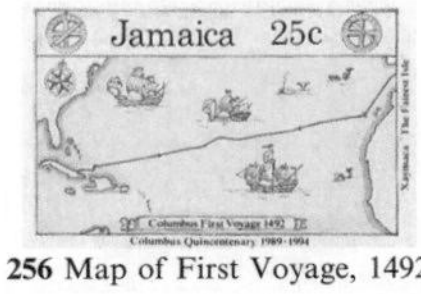

256 Map of First Voyage, 1492

1990. 500th Anniv (1992) of Discovery of America by Columbus (2nd issue). Multicoloured.
774 25c. Type **256** . . . . 1·10 40
775 45c. Map of second voyage, 1493 . . . . 1·25 40
776 $5 Map of third voyage, 1498 4·25 5·50
777 $10 Map of fourth voyage, 1502 . . . . 6·50 8·50
MS778 126 × 99 mm. 25, 45c., $5, $10 Composite map of Caribbean showing routes of voyages . . 13·00 14·00
MS779 148 × 207 mm. Nos. 774/7. Imperf . . . . 13·00 14·00

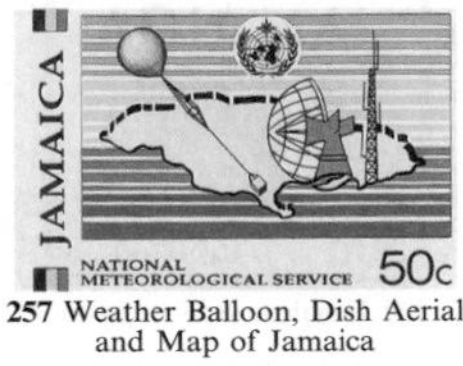

257 Weather Balloon, Dish Aerial and Map of Jamaica

1991. 11th World Meteorological Congress, Kingston.
780 **257** 50c. multicoloured 50 20
781 $10 multicoloured . . . . 6·50 8·50

258 Bust of Mary Seacole

1991. International Council of Nurses Meeting of National Representatives.
782 **258** 50c. multicoloured 75 30
783 – $1.10 multicoloured . . . 1·50 2·00
MS784 89 × 60 mm. $8 agate, brown and ochre (sold at $8.20) . . . 3·25 5·00
DESIGNS: $1.10 Mary Seacole House; $8 Hospital at Scutari, 1854.

259 Jamaican Iguana

1991. 50th Anniv of Natural History Society of Jamaica. Jamaican Iguana. Multicoloured.
785 $1.10 Type **259** 55 75
786 $1.10 Head of iguana looking right 55 75
787 $1.10 Iguana climbing . . . 55 75
788 $1.10 Iguana on rock looking left 55 75
789 $1.10 Close-up of iguana's head 55 75

1991. Jamaican Moths (3rd series). As T **250**. Multicoloured.
790 50c. "Urania sloanus" . . . 65 20
791 $1.10 "Phoenicoprocta jamaicensis" 90 60
792 $1.40 "Horama grotei" . . . 1·10 90
793 $8 "Amplypterus gannascus" 3·25 6·00

1991. "Phila Nippon '91" International Stamp Exhibition, Tokyo. Nos. 790/3 optd **PHILA NIPPON 91** and emblem.
794 50c. "Urania sloanus" . . . 80 20
795 $1.10 "Phoenicoprocta jamaicensis" . . . . 1·10 60
796 $1.40 "Horama grotei" . . . 1·25 90
797 $8 "Amplypterus gannascus" 4·25 7·00

261 "Doctor Bird"

1991. Christmas. Children's Paintings. Mult.
798 50c. Type **261** 65 10
799 $1.10 "Road scene" . . . . 1·00 25
800 $5 "Children and house" . . 3·25 3·50
801 $10 "Cows grazing" . . . . 4·50 7·50

262 Indians threatening Ships

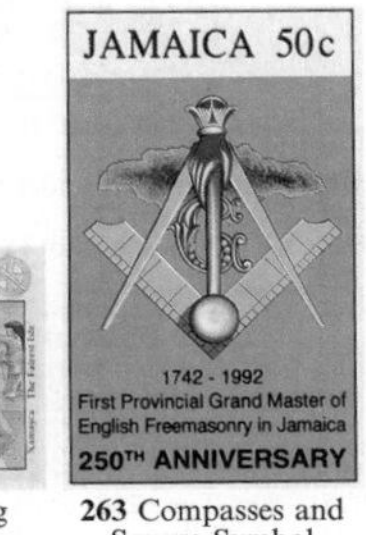

263 Compasses and Square Symbol

1991. 500th Anniv (1992) of Discovery of America by Columbus (3rd issue). Multicoloured.
802 50c. Type **262** 45 15
803 $1.10 Spaniards setting dog on Indians 55 30
804 $1.40 Indian with gift of pineapple 55 30
805 $25 Columbus describes Jamaica with crumpled paper . . . . 6·50 10·00
MS806 125 × 102 mm. Nos. 802/5 (sold at $28.20) . . . . . . 8·00 10·00
MS807 210 × 150 mm. Nos. 802/5. Imperf . . . . 8·00 10·00

1992. 250th Anniv of First Provisional Grand Master of English Freemasonry in Jamaica. Multicoloured.
808 50c. Type **263** 70 30
809 $1.10 Symbol in stained glass window 90 40
810 $1.40 Compasses and square on book 90 40
811 $25 Eye in triangle symbol 8·00 9·00
MS812 140 × 80 mm. Nos. 808/11 (sold at $28.50) . . . . 10·00 11·00

264 Ship in Flooded Street

1992. 300th Anniv of Destruction of Port Royal. Multicoloured.
813 50c. Type **264** 55 40
814 $1.10 Church tower falling 70 45
815 $1.40 Houses collapsing . . . 70 45
816 $25 Inhabitants falling into fissure . . . . 6·50 8·50
MS817 116 × 75 mm. $5 Contemporary broadsheet of earthquake . . . . 4·00 4·50

265 Credit Union Symbol

1992. 50th Anniv of Credit Union Movement.
818 **265** 50c. blue, emerald & green . . . . 1·00 50
819 – $1.40 multicoloured . . . 1·75 1·75
DESIGN: $1.40, O'Hare Hall.

266 Jamaican Flag and Beach Scene

1992. 30th Anniv of Independence.
820 **266** 50c. multicoloured 10 10
821 $1.10 multicoloured . . . 20 20
822 $25 multicoloured . . . . 2·75 5·50

267 "Rainbow" (Cecil Baugh)
269 Cadet, Armoured Car and Emblem

268 Girls' Brigade Parade

1993. Art Ceramics and Pottery. Multicoloured.
823 50c. Type **267** 20 10
824 $1.10 "Yabba Pot" (Louisa Jones) 30 20
825 $1.40 "Sculptured Vase" (Gene Pearson) 30 20
826 $25 "Lidded Form" (Norma Harrack) . . . . 4·50 6·50

1993. Centenary of Girls' Brigade. Mult.
827 50c. Type **268** 90 50
828 $1.10 Brigade members . . . 1·00 1·10

1993. 50th Anniv of Jamaica Combined Cadet Force. Multicoloured.
829 50c. Type **269** 40 20
830 $1.10 Cadet and Britten Norman Islander aircraft (horiz) 60 40
831 $1.40 Cadet and patrol boats 60 40
832 $3 Cadet and emblem (horiz) 80 2·00

270 Constant Spring Golf Course

1993. Golf Courses. Multicoloured.
833 50c. Type **270** 40 10
834 $1.10 Type **270** 55 20
835 $1.40 Half Moon 60 20
836 $2 As $1 . . . . 80 80
837 $3 Jamaica Jamaica . . . . 90 1·00
838 $10 As $3 . . . . 2·25 3·25
MS839 66 × 71 mm. $25 Tryall (vert) (sold at $28) . . . . 4·50 6·00

271 Norman Manley
273 Flags of Great Britain and Jamaica

1994. Birth Centenary of Norman Manley.
840 **271** $25 multicoloured . . . . 2·00 2·75
841 $50 multicoloured . . . . 2·50 4·25

1994. "Hong Kong '94" International Stamp Exhibition. No. **MS**839 optd **HONG KONG '94** and emblem.
MS842 66 × 71 mm. $25 Tryall . . . 4·00 5·00

1994. Royal Visit. Multicoloured.
843 $1.10 Type **273** 45 10
844 $1.40 Royal Yacht "Britannia" . . . . 1·00 30
845 $25 Queen Elizabeth II . . . 2·50 3·25
846 $50 Queen Elizabeth and Prince Philip . . . . . . 4·00 6·00

274 Douglas DC-9

1994. 25th Anniv of Air Jamaica. Mult.
847 50c. Type **274** 35 25
848 $1.10 Douglas DC-8 . . . . 35 25
849 $5 Boeing 727 . . . . 75 75
850 $50 Airbus A300 . . . . . . 3·50 6·00

275 Giant Swallowtail

1994. Giant Swallowtail Butterfly Conservation. Multicoloured.
851 50c. Type **275** 40 25
852 $1.10 With wings closed . . . 40 25
853 $10 On flower . . . . 1·60 2·25
854 $25 With wings spread . . . 2·75 4·50
MS855 56 × 61 mm. $50 Pair of butterflies . . . . 5·50 7·00

276 "Royal Botanical Gardens" (Sidney McLaren)

1994. Tourism. Multicoloured.
856 50c. Type **276** 55 20
857 $1.10 Blue Mountains . . . 75 30
858 $5 Tourist in hammock and water sports . . . . 2·75 3·25
MS859 105 × 80 mm. $25 Carolina parakeets; $25 Silhouetted scuba diver; $25 Carolina parakeet and foliage; $25 Tourist raft . . . 5·50 7·50

277 Jamaican Red Poll Calf

1994. Jamaican Red Poll Cattle. Multicoloured.
860 50c. Type **277** 10 10
861 $1.10 Red Poll heifer 10 10
862 $25 Red Poll cow . . . . . 1·25 2·25
863 $50 Red Poll bull . . . . . 2·50 4·50

278 Refuse Collectors

1994. Christmas. Children's Paintings. Multicoloured.
864 50c. Type **278** 10 10
865 90c. Hospital ward 10 10
866 $1.10 House 10 10
867 $50 Landscape . . . . 2·75 5·00

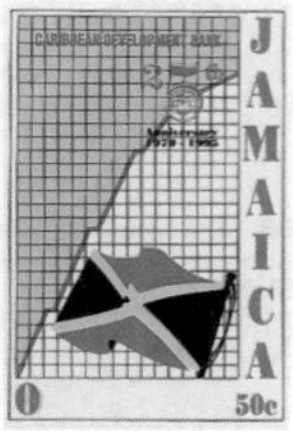

279 Jamaican Band-tailed Pigeon ("Ring-tailed Pigeon")
280 Graph, National Flag and Logo

1995. Jamaican Wild Birds. Multicoloured.
868 50c. Type **279** 65 30
869 90c. Yellow-billed amazon ("Yellow-billed parrot") . . 80 30
870 $1.10 Black-billed amazon ("Black-billed parrot") . . 80 30
871 $50 Jamaican owl ("Brown owl") . . . . 5·50 7·00
MS872 47 × 62 mm. $50 Streamertail 4·75 6·00
For No. **MS**872 additionally inscribed for "Singapore '95" see No. **MS**888.

1995. 25th Anniv of Caribbean Development Bank.
873 **280** 50c. green, black and yellow 10 10
874 $1 green, black and yellow 10 10
875 – $1.10 multicoloured . . . 10 10
876 – $50 multicoloured . . . . 2·75 5·00
DESIGNS—HORIZ: $1.10, Industry, agriculture and commerce; $50 Jamaican currency.

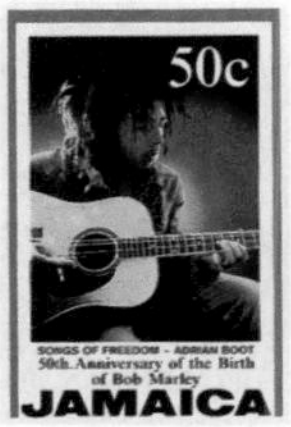

281 "Song of Freedom"
282 Queen Elizabeth the Queen Mother

1995. 50th Birth Anniv of Bob Marley (reggae singer). Record covers. Multicoloured.
877 50c. Type **281** 20 10
878 $1.10 "Fire" 30 15
879 $1.40 "Time will Tell" . . . 30 15
880 $3 "Natural Mystic" 40 45
881 $10 "Live at Lyceum" . . . 1·10 2·25
MS882 105 × 57 mm. $100 "Legend" 8·00 8·00

1995. 95th Birthday of Queen Elizabeth the Queen Mother. Sheet 81 × 95 mm.
MS883 **282** $75 multicoloured . . 4·50 5·50

283 Michael Manley

1995. Recipients of the Order of the Caribbean Community. Multicoloured.
884 50c. Type **283** 15 10
885 $1.10 Sir Alister McIntyre . . 20 10
886 $1.40 Justice P. Telford Georges 20 10
887 $50 Dame Nita Barrow . . . 4·25 6·00

1995. "Singapore '95" International Stamp Exhibition. No. **MS**872 additionally inscr with exhibition emblem on sheet margin.
MS888 47 × 62 mm. $50 Streamertail 3·75 4·50

284 Dish Aerial and Landrover, Balkans

1995. 50th Anniv of United Nations. Multicoloured.
889 50c. Type **284** 25 20
890 $1.10 Antonov An-32 aircraft, Balkans 45 25
891 $3 Bedford articulated road tanker, Balkans 60 80
892 $5 Fairchild C-119 Flying Boxcar, Korea . . . . . . 70 1·00
MS893 100 × 70 mm. $50 U.N.T.A.G. vehicles, Namibia 2·25 3·50

285 Landing of Indian Immigrants

1996. 150th Anniv of Indian Immigration to Jamaica. Multicoloured.
894 $2.50 Type **285** 25 15
895 $10 Indian musicians and traditional dancers . . . . 75 1·25

286 Jamaican Flag and U.N.I.C.E.F. Emblem

1996. 50th Anniv of U.N.I.C.E.F.
896 **286** $2.50 multicoloured . . . 50 15
897 $8 multicoloured . . . . 1·00 90
898 $10 multicoloured . . . . 1·00 1·00

287 Brown's Hutia

1996. Endangered Species. Brown's Hutia ("Jamaican Hutia"). Multicoloured.
899 $2.50 Type **287** 15 10
900 $10 Hutia on rock 50 65
901 $12.50 Female with young . . 60 1·00
902 $25 Head of hutia . . . . . 1·25 2·25

288 High Altar, Church of St. Thomas the Apostle

1997. 300th Anniv of Kingston Parish Church. Multicoloured.
903 $2 Type **288** 30 10
904 $8 Church of St. Thomas the Apostle 90 80
905 $12.50 "The Angel" (wood carving by Edna Manley) (vert) . . . . 1·40 1·75
MS906 106 × 76 mm. $60 St. Thomas the Apostle at sunset (42 × 56 mm) . . . . 2·75 4·00
No. 903 is inscribed "ALTER" in error.

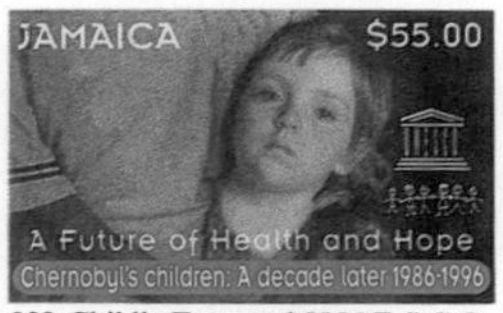

289 Child's Face and U.N.E.S.C.O. Emblem

1998. 10th Anniv of Chernobyl Nuclear Disaster.
907 **289** $55 multicoloured . . . . 2·00 3·00

289a Map of Caribbean

1997. 50th Anniv of Caribbean Integration Movement and 18th CARICOM Heads of Government Conference. Multicoloured.

907a	$2.50 Type **289a**	4·00	3·75
907b	$8 Coastal scenery	5·00	2·00
907c	$10 As $8	5·50	2·00

290 "Coelia triptera"

291 Diana, Princess of Wales

1997. Orchids. Multicoloured.

908A	$1 Type **290**	10	10
909A	$2 "Oncidium pulchellum" (horiz)	10	10
910A	$2.50 "Oncidium triquetium"	10	10
911A	$3 "Broughtonia negrilensis"	10	10
912A	$4.50 "Oncidium gauntlettii" (horiz)	10	10
913A	$5 "Encyclia fragans" (horiz)	10	15
914A	$8 "Broughtonia sanguinea" (horiz)	15	20
915A	$12 "Phaius tankervilleae"	20	25
916B	$25 "Cochleanthes flabelliformis" (horiz)	45	50
917A	$50 "Broughtonia sanguinea" (three varieties) (horiz)	95	1·00

1998. Diana, Princess of Wales Commemoration. Multicoloured.

918	$20 Type **291**	1·00	1·25
MS919	70 × 100 mm. $80 Princess Diana and Mother Teresa (42 × 55 mm)	4·50	5·50

292 University Chapel, Mona

1998. 50th Anniv of University of West Indies. Multicoloured.

920	$8 Type **292**	40	40
921	$10 Philip Sherlock Centre for Creative Arts, Mona	40	40
922	$50 University arms (vert)	2·25	3·50

293 Flags of Jamaica and CARICOM

1998. 25th Anniv of Caribbean Community.
923 **293** $30 multicoloured . . . . 1·75 2·25

294 Jamaican Footballer

295 Coral Reef

1998. World Cup Football Championship, France. Multicoloured.

924	$10 Type **294**	55	40
925	$25 Jamaican team (horiz)	1·25	1·25
926	$100 As $25	4·50	6·50

1998. Christmas. International Year of the Ocean. Multicoloured.

927	$10 Type **295**	80	40
928	$30 Fishing boats, Negril	2·00	1·25
929	$50 Black spiny sea urchin	3·00	3·25
930	$100 Composite design as Nos. 927/9 (22 × 41 mm)	6·00	8·00

296 Michael Collins (astronaut)

1999. 30th Anniv of First Manned Landing on Moon. Multicoloured.

931	$7 Type **296**	40	25
932	$10 Service module docking with lunar module	50	40
933	$25 Buzz Aldrin on Moon's surface	1·00	1·40
934	$30 Command module in Earth orbit	1·10	1·50
MS935	90 × 80 mm. $100 Earth as seen from Moon (circular, 40 mm diam)	3·50	4·75

297 Lesley Ann Masterton and Fong-Yee (polo)

1999. Jamaican Sporting Personalities. Mult.

936	$5 Type **297**	50	20
937	$10 Lawrence Rowe, Collie Smith and Alfred Valentine (cricket)	85	45
938	$20 Vivalyn Latty-Scott (women's cricket) (vert)	1·25	1·00
939	$25 Lindy Delapenha (football) (vert)	1·25	1·00
940	$30 Joy Grant-Charles (netball) (vert)	1·25	1·50
941	$50 Percy Hayles, Gerald Gray and Bunny Grant (boxing)	1·60	2·50
MS942	110 × 90 mm. $100 Lindy Delapenha and Joy Grant-Charles (56 × 42 mm)	4·00	5·50

298 "Spey" (mail ship), 1891

1999. 125th Anniv of Universal Postal Union. Multicoloured.

943	$7 Type **298**	75	25
944	$10 "Jamaica Planter" (mail ship), 1936	90	45
945	$25 Lockheed Constellation (aircraft), 1950	1·75	1·75
946	$30 Airbus A-310 (aircraft), 1999	1·90	2·00

299 Airbus A-310

1999. 30th Anniv of Air Jamaica. Multicoloured.

947	$10 Type **299**	60	40
948	$25 A-320	1·25	1·50
949	$30 A-340	1·40	1·75

300 Shih Tzu

1999. Dogs. Multicoloured.

950	$7 Type **300**	85	40
951	$10 German shepherd	1·10	45
952	$30 Doberman pinscher	2·50	2·75

301 Nelson Mandela Park

1999. Parks and Gardens. Multicoloured.

953	$7 Type **301**	25	25
954	$10 St. William Grant Park	35	35
955	$25 Seaview Park	95	1·10
956	$30 Holruth Park	1·25	1·60

302 "The Prophet" (sculpture)

2000. Birth Centenary of Edna Manley (artist). Multicoloured.

957	$10 Type **302**	35	35
958	$25 "Horse of the Morning"	85	90
959	$30 "The Angel"	1·10	1·25
960	$100 Edna Manley	3·75	6·50
MS961	128 × 159 mm. Nos. 957/60	5·00	7·00

303 Lennox Lewis

2000. Lennox Lewis, World Heavyweight Boxing Champion. Multicoloured.

962	$10 Holding W.B.C. Championship belt	30	45
963	$10 In ring with right arm raised	30	45
964	$10 Holding W.B.C. belt above head	30	45
965	$25 Taking punch on chin	75	1·00
966	$25 Type **303**	75	1·00
967	$25 In corner	75	1·00
968	$30 With W.B.C. belt after fight	95	1·10
969	$30 Holding all four belts	95	1·10
970	$30 With belts in front of skyscraper	95	1·10

304 Ferrari Racing Car 125 S, 1947

2000. Birth Centenary (1998) of Enzo Ferrari (car designer). Racing cars. Multicoloured.

971	$10 Type **304**	60	70
972	$10 375 F1, 1950	60	70
973	$10 312 F1, 1966	60	70
974	$25 DINO 166 P, 1965	1·10	1·50
975	$25 312 P, 1971	1·10	1·50
976	$25 F1 90, 1990	1·10	1·50

305 Queen Elizabeth the Queen Mother

307 Bull Thatch Palm

306 "The Runner", Jamaican Flag and Olympic Rings

2000. Queen Elizabeth the Queen Mother's 100th Birthday. Multicoloured, background colours given.

977	**305** $10 lavender	60	35
978	– $25 green	1·10	90
979	– $30 mauve	1·40	1·25
980	– $50 blue	2·25	2·75

DESIGNS: $25 to $50, Various recent photographs.

2000. Olympic Games, Sydney. Each showing "The Runner" (sculpture by Alvin Marriot), Jamaican flag and Olympic Rings. Multicoloured.

981	$10 Type **306**	60	35
982	$25 Head and shoulders	1·10	80
983	$30 With flag at top (vert)	1·40	1·10
984	$50 With flag in centre (vert)	2·25	2·75

2000. Native Trees. Multicoloured.

985	$10 Type **307**	70	35
986	$25 Blue mahoe	1·50	90
987	$30 Silk cotton	1·75	1·40
988	$50 Yellow poui	2·75	3·25
MS989	112 × 70 mm. $100 Lignum Vitae (horiz)	5·50	6·50

308 "Madonna and Child" (Osmond Watson)

2000. Christmas. Jamaican Religious Paintings. Multicoloured.

990	$10 Type **308**	60	35
991	$20 "Boy in the Temple" (Carl Abrahams) (horiz)	1·10	75
992	$25 "Ascension" (Carl Abrahams)	1·25	90
993	$30 "Jah Lives" (Osmond Watson)	1·40	1·40

309 Children of the Commonwealth

2001. 25th Anniv of Commonwealth Day.
994 **309** $30 multicoloured . . . . 1·50 1·50

310 Andrew Mowatt (founder)

2001. Centenary of Jamaica Burial Scheme Society.
995 **310** $15 multicoloured . . . . 1·00 1·00

311 "Falmouth Market" (lithograph)

2001. Birth Bicentenary of Adolphe Duperly (pioneer photographer). Multicoloured.

996	$15 Type **311**	75	50
997	$40 "Ferry Inn, Spanish Town Road" (lithograph)	1·75	1·75
998	$45 "Coke Chapel, Kingston" (lithograph)	1·90	1·90
999	$60 "King Street, Kingston" (lithograph)	2·50	2·75
MS1000	103 × 170 mm. Nos. 996/9	6·50	7·00

312 Poinsettia in Church Window

2001. Christmas.

1001	**312** $15 multicoloured	75	50
1002	$30 multicoloured	1·50	1·10
1003	$40 multicoloured	1·75	1·90

2002. Golden Jubilee. As T **219** of Falkland Islands.

1004	$15 agate, blue and gold	80	50
1005	$40 multicoloured	1·90	1·75
1006	$45 black, blue and gold	2·00	1·90
1007	$60 multicoloured	2·50	2·75
MS1008	162 × 95 mm. Nos. 1004/7 and $30 multicoloured	6·50	7·00

DESIGNS—HORIZ: $15 Princess Elizabeth in orchard, 1941; $40 Queen Elizabeth wearing pearls and striped dress; $45 Queen Elizabeth in evening dress, 1953; $60 Queen Elizabeth visiting Gloucester, 1995. VERT (38 × 51 mm): $30 Queen Elizabeth after Annigoni.

Designs as Nos. 1004/7 in No. **MS**1008 omit the gold frame around each stamp and the "Golden Jubilee 1952–2002" inscription.

313 Queen Elizabeth and Jamaican Royal Standard

2002. Royal Visit. Multicoloured.

1009	$15 Type **313**	75	50
1010	$45 Queen Elizabeth in evening dress and Jamaican coat of arms	2·25	2·50

314 Sir Philip Sherlock **315** Female Dancers

2002. Birth Centenary of Sir Philip Sherlock (historian).

1011	**314** $40 mauve, magenta and blue	1·50	1·60

2002. 40th Anniv of National Dance Theatre Company.

1012	**315** $15 multicoloured	1·25	1·00

316 P.A.H.O. Centenary Logo

2002. Centenary of Pan American Health Organization.

1013	**316** $40 multicoloured	1·75	1·75

317 "Masquerade" (Osmond Watson)

2002. Christmas. Local Works of Art. Multicoloured.

1014	$15 Type **317**	70	45
1015	$40 "John Canoe in Guanaboa Vale" (Gaston Tabois) (horiz)	1·50	1·40
1016	$45 "Mother and Child" (carving by Kapo)	1·60	1·60
1017	$60 "Hills of Papine" (carving by Edna Manley) (horiz)	1·90	2·25

318 Dancers

2002. 40th Anniv of Independence. Multicoloured.

1018	$15 Type **318**	70	45
1019	$40 Independence Day celebrations	1·50	1·25
1020	$60 Welder and fish processing worker	2·00	2·25

319 Kingston in Early 1800s

2002. Bicentenary of Kingston. Multicoloured.

1021	$15 Type **319**	60	65
1022	$15 Wharf and statue of Queen Victoria, early 1900s	60	65
1023	$15 Horse-drawn cab, early 1900s, and modern street scene	60	65

Nos. 1021/3 were printed together, se-tenant, as horizontal strips of 3 throughout the sheet, forming a montage.

320 Queen Elizabeth II in St. Edward's Chair flanked by Bishops of Durham and Bath & Wells

2003. 50th Anniv of Coronation. Multicoloured.

1024	$15 Type **320**	30	35
1025	$45 Coronation Coach in procession	90	95
MS1026	95 × 115 mm. $50 As $45; $100 As Type **320**	2·75	3·00

Nos. 1024/5 have scarlet frame; stamps from **MS**1026 have no frame and country name in mauve panel.

321 "30" as Key

2003. 30th Anniv of CARICOM.

1027	**321** $40 multicoloured	80	85

322 Jamaican Stripe-headed Tanager

2003. Bird Life International. Jamaican Birds. Multicoloured.

1028	$15 Type **322**	30	35
1029	$40 Crested quail dove (horiz)	80	85
1030	$45 Jamaican tody (horiz)	90	95
1031	$60 Blue mountain vireo	1·10	1·20
MS1032	175 × 80 mm. $30 Jamaican blackbird nestlings (34 × 30 mm); $30 Searching for food in bromeliad (30 × 34 mm); $30 Singing from perch (30 × 34 mm); $30 Singing from perch (34 × 30 mm); $30 With insect in beak (34 × 30 mm)	2·75	3·00

323 Sailing ships and Map of Kingston Harbour

2003. Maritime History. Multicoloured.

1033	$40 Type **323**	80	85
1034	$40 Passengers on cruise ship and sailing ships	80	85
1035	$40 *Sugar Refiner* (cargo ship)	80	85

Nos. 1033/5 were printed together, se-tenant, forming a composite design.

324 Baby Jesus

2003. Christmas. Multicoloured.

1036	$15 Type **324**	30	35
1037	$30 Close-up of Baby Jesus	55	60
1038	$60 Holy Family	1·10	1·20

OFFICIAL STAMPS

1890. Optd **OFFICIAL**.

O3	**8** ½d. green	9·00	75
O4	**11** 1d. red	4·75	1·00
O5	2d. grey	11·00	1·00

JAMMU AND KASHMIR Pt. 1

A state in the extreme N. of India.

12 pies = 1 anna; 16 annas = 1 rupee.

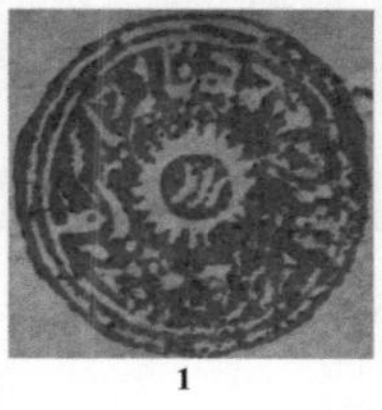

1

Gum. The stamps of Jammu and Kashmir were issued without gum.

1866. Imperf.

41	**1** ½a. black	24·00	50·00
26	½a. red	30·00	50·00
44	½a. blue	40·00	£225
20	½a. green	85·00	£225
48	½a. yellow	£120	
15	1a. black	£250	
27	1a. red	35·00	£160
34	1a. blue	26·00	£225
21	1a. green	90·00	£225
24	1a. yellow	£750	
16	4a. black	£225	
8	4a. red	70·00	£110
19	4a. blue	£170	
37	4a. green	£425	
25	4a. yellow	£400	

Prices for the circular stamps (Nos. 5/48) are for cut-square examples. Cut-to-shape examples are worth from 10% to 20% of these prices, according to condition.

4

1867.

69a	**4** ½a. black	£130	£160
58	½a. blue	£160	85·00
60	½a. red	6·50	3·25
64	½a. orange	£100	£110
68	½a. green	£1500	£900
69b	1a. black	£1500	£1300
55	1a. blue	£650	£325
61	1a. red	15·00	9·50
65	1a. orange	£1900	£1200
69	1a. green	£2500	£1500

The characters denoting the value are in the upper part of the inner circle and contains three ½a. and one 1a. values.

8 (¼a.) **12** (¼a.)

1867. Imperf.

90	**8** ¼a. black	2·75	3·25
91	½a. blue	3·00	1·25
93	1a. blue	£3250	£1300
94	1a. orange	10·00	8·50
97	2a. yellow	13·00	15·00
99	4a. green	32·00	32·00
101	8a. red	35·00	32·00

1878. Imperf or perf.

139	**12** ⅛a. yellow	1·00	1·60
125	¼a. red	3·00	3·50
131	¼a. orange	8·50	12·00
130a	¼a. blue	£800	£500
142	¼a. brown	1·00	65
105	½a. violet	14·00	12·00
126	½a. red	75	75
132	½a. orange	20·00	14·00
143	½a. blue	6·00	
127	1a. red	2·50	3·00
106	1a. mauve	22·00	23·00
133	1a. orange	20·00	11·00
148	1a. grey	85	85
150	1a. green	85	85
108	2a. violet	23·00	23·00
110	2a. blue	48·00	48·00
128	2a. red	3·25	4·25
134	2a. orange	15·00	11·00
152	2a. red on yellow	2·00	1·10
153	2a. red on green	3·00	3·25
129	4a. red	8·50	8·50
135	4a. orange	35·00	42·00
156	4a. green	3·50	3·25
130	8a. red	9·00	9·50
136	8a. orange	60·00	65·00
159	8a. blue	7·00	8·50
161a	8a. lilac	10·00	18·00

OFFICIAL STAMPS

1878. Imperf or perf.

O 6	**12** ¼a. black	1·00	1·25
O 7	½a. black	15	40
O 8	1a. black	20	70
O 9	2a. black	30	45
O10	4a. black	60	1·10
O11	8a. black	1·75	1·10

JAPAN Pt. 18

An empire of E. Asia, consisting of numerous islands.

1871. 100 mon = 1 sen.
1872. 10 rin = 1 sen; 100 sen = 1 yen.

1 (48 mon)

1871. Imperf.

1	**1** 48m. brown	£180	£225
3	100m. blue	£200	£180

5		200m. red	£350	£225
15b		500m. green	£400	£400

1872. Perf.

17	**1**	½s. brown	80·00	£125
19		1s. blue	£170	£160
21		2s. red	£350	£275
22		5s. green	£375	£425

5

12

13 Bean Goose

1872. Various sizes. Design details differ.

34	**5**	½s. brown	18·00	24·00
66		½s. grey	16·00	15·00
35		1s. blue	70·00	28·00
67		1s. brown	30·00	13·00
36		2s. red	£110	30·00
74		2s. yellow	70·00	12·00
46		4s. red	£100	30·00
68		4s. green	£110	18·00
75	**12**	5s. green	£200	85·00
57		6s. brown	£110	40·00
69		6s. orange	75·00	15·00
58	**5**	10s. green	£110	45·00
70		10s. blue	£125	17·00
59		20s. violet	£200	70·00
71		20s. red	£100	12·00
60		30s. black	£250	70·00
72		30s. violet	£125	35·00

1875.

61	**13**	12s. red	£550	£225
62	–	15s. lilac (Pied Wagtail)	£450	£190
63	–	45s. red (Northern Goshawk)	£650	£300

20

21

22

23

24

1876.

116	**20**	5r. grey	3·50	30
77		1s. black	25·00	3·00
78		1s. brown	12·00	1·00
113		1s. green	5·50	25
79		2s. grey	50·00	2·00
102		2s. violet	24·00	1·50
114		2s. red	7·50	10
95		3s. orange	50·00	24·00
117		3s. red	12·00	25
82a		4s. blue	32·00	2·75
103		4s. green	40·00	1·75
118		4s. bistre	8·50	30
83	**21**	5s. brown	50·00	18·00
115		5s. blue	14·00	15
104		6s. orange	£150	70·00
105		8s. brown	45·00	2·75
119		8s. violet	15·00	90
86		10s. blue	40·00	1·50
120		10s. brown	16·00	30
87		12s. red	£200	£160
88	**22**	15s. green	£125	6·50
121		15s. violet	45·00	40
89		20s. blue	£150	12·00
122		20s. orange	55·00	1·40
123	**23**	25s. green	90·00	1·25
90	**22**	30s. mauve	£200	75·00
111		45s. red	£500	£500
112		50s. red	£160	10·00
124		50s. brown	85·00	3·00
125	**24**	1y. red	£120	2·50

25 Imperial Crest and Cranes

1894. Emperor's Silver Wedding.

126	**25**	2s. red	20·00	30
127		5s. blue	25·00	4·00

26 Prince Kitashirakawa

27 Prince Arisugawa

1896. China War.

128	**26**	2s. red	14·00	75
129	**27**	2s. red	14·00	75
130	**26**	5s. blue	35·00	2·00
131	**27**	5s. blue	35·00	2·00

Both 2s. have an oval medallion, and both 5s. a circular one.

28

29

30

31

32 Empress Jingu

1899.

132	**28**	5r. grey	5·50	1·00
133		½s. grey	3·50	10
134		1s. brown	4·50	10
135		1½s. blue	15·00	85
136		1½s. violet	8·00	15
137		2s. green	6·00	10
138		3s. purple	6·50	10
139		3s. red	6·00	10
140		4s. red	6·00	1·00
141		5s. yellow	14·00	10
142	**29**	6s. red	30·00	3·00
143		8s. olive	35·00	4·00
144		10s. blue	10·00	15
145		15s. violet	40·00	1·00
146		20s. orange	32·00	10
147	**30**	25s. green	70·00	75
148		50s. brown	65·00	80
149	**31**	1y. red	80·00	1·00
183	**32**	5y. green	£475	4·50
184		10y. violet	£650	6·50

33 Rice Cakes used at Japanese Weddings

1900. Prince Imperial Wedding.

152	**33**	3s. red	25·00	30

34 Symbols of Korea and Japan

35 Gun and Japanese Flag

1905. Amalgamation of Japanese and Korean Postal Services.

153	**34**	3s. red	90·00	20·00

1906. Triumphal Military Review of Russo-Japanese War.

154	**35**	1½s. blue	40·00	3·50
155		3s. red	70·00	14·00

36

37

38

1914.

167	**36**	½s. brown	2·25	10
168		1s. orange	3·25	10
232		1½s. blue	3·00	10
170		2s. green	5·50	10
298		3s. red	1·50	20
172	**37**	4s. red	16·00	1·50
300		5s. violet	7·50	10
174		6s. brown	24·00	4·00
302		7s. orange	12·00	15
175		8s. grey	18·00	15·00
176		10s. blue	12·00	10
236		13s. brown	10·00	10
178		20s. red	60·00	15
179		25s. olive	18·00	50
180	**38**	30s. brown	22·00	45
238		30s. orange and green	25·00	25
181		50s. brown	30·00	25
239		50s. brown and blue	15·00	30
309		1y. green and brown	80·00	75

40 Ceremonial Cap

42 Hall of Ceremony

1915. Emperor's Coronation.

185	**40**	1½s. grey and red	3·00	50
186	–	3s. violet and brown	3·50	65
187	**42**	4s. red	16·00	7·50
188		10s. blue	38·00	15·00

DESIGN—As T **40**: 3s. Imperial throne.

43 Mandarin Duck

44 "Kammuri" (ceremonial headband)

1916. Investiture of Prince Hirohito as Heir Apparent.

189	**43**	1½s. green, red and yellow	4·00	85
190		3s. red and yellow	5·00	1·00
191	**44**	10s. blue	£800	£300

45 Dove of Peace

46 Dove of Peace

1919. Restoration of Peace.

192	**45**	1½s. brown	2·50	1·00
193	**46**	3s. green	3·50	1·25
194	**45**	4s. red	7·00	3·50
195	**46**	10s. blue	22·00	8·00

1919. Air. 1st Tokyo–Osaka Airmail Service. Optd with airplane.

196	**36**	1½s. blue	£275	£100
197		3s. red	£425	£250

48 7th-century Censor

49 Meiji Shrine

1920. First Census.

198	**48**	1½s. purple	8·00	4·25
199		3s. red	9·00	4·25

1920. Dedication of Meiji (Emperor Mutsuhito) Shrine.

200	**49**	1½s. violet	3·00	1·50
201		3s. red	3·00	1·50

50 Postal and National Flags

51 Dept. of Communications, Tokyo

1921. 50th Anniv of Japanese Post.

202	**50**	1½s. red and green	3·00	1·50
203	**51**	3s. brown	3·50	1·75
204	**50**	4s. red and pink	50·00	25·00
205	**51**	10s. blue	£250	90·00

52 Warships "Katori" and "Kashima"

53 Mt. Fuji and Sika Deer

1921. Return of Crown Prince from European Tour.

206	**52**	1½s. violet	3·00	2·10
207		3s. olive	3·50	2·25
208		4s. red	42·00	35·00
209		10s. blue	60·00	35·00

1922.

293	**53**	4s. green	3·25	20
266		4s. orange	12·00	30
211		8s. red	20·00	8·00
267		8s. green	20·00	15
303		8s. bistre	14·00	75
305		20s. blue	16·00	60
268		20s. purple	65·00	30

54 Mt. Niitaka

55

56

58 Empress Jingu

1923. Crown Prince's visit to Taiwan.

213	**54**	1½s. yellow	20·00	18·00
214		3s. violet	25·00	8·00

1923. Imperf.

215	**55**	½s. grey	3·00	2·75
216		1½s. blue	5·00	60
217		2s. brown	5·00	60
218		3s. red	2·50	50
219		4s. green	30·00	15·00
220		5s. violet	14·00	60
221		8s. red	45·00	35·00
222	**56**	10s. brown	24·00	50
223		20s. blue	30·00	1·00

1924.

224	**58**	5y. green	£225	3·50
225		10y. violet	£425	2·75

59 Cranes

60 Phoenix

1925. Imperial Silver Wedding.

226	**59**	1½s. purple	2·25	1·40
227a	**60**	3s. brown and silver	3·00	3·00
228	**59**	8s. red	25·00	15·00
229b	**60**	20s. green and silver	65·00	50·00

61a Yomei Gate, Tosho Shrine, Nikko

1926.

241	–	2s. green	2·40	10
242	**61a**	6s. red	12·00	25
243	–	10s. blue	10·00	10
304	–	10s. red	10·00	15

DESIGNS: 2s. Mt. Fuji; 10s. Nagoya Castle.

62 Baron Maeshima

63 Globe

1927. 50th Anniv of Membership of U.P.U.

244	**62**	1½s. purple	2·75	1·75
245		3s. olive	2·75	1·75
246	**63**	6s. red	85·00	60·00
247		10s. blue	95·00	50·00

64 Phoenix

65 Ceremonial Shrines

1928. Emperor's Enthronement.

248	**64**	1½s. green on yellow	1·00	50
249	**65**	3s. purple on yellow	1·00	50
250	**64**	6s. red on yellow	3·75	3·00
251	**65**	10s. blue on yellow	5·00	3·75

66 Shrine of Ise

67 Nakajima-built Fokker F.VIIb/3m over Lake Ashi, Hakone

1929. 58th Vicennial Removal of Shrine of Ise.

255	**66**	1½s. violet	2·00	1·50
256		3s. red	2·75	1·50

1929. Air.

257	**67**	8½s. brown	50·00	40·00
258		9½s. red	15·00	12·00
259		16½s. green	15·00	14·00
260		18s. blue	16·00	8·00
261		33s. black	35·00	5·00

68 Map of Japan

69 Meiji Shrine

1930. 3rd Census.

262	**68**	1½s. purple	2·75	1·25
263		3s. red	3·00	1·25

Although Type **68** is inscr "Second Census", this was actually the third census.

1930. 10th Anniv of Meiji Shrine Dedication.

264	**69**	1½s. green	2·00	1·50
265		3s. orange	2·75	1·50

70 Insignia of Red Cross Society

1934. 15th Int Red Cross Conference, Tokyo.

272	**70**	1½s. green	2·50	1·40
273	–	3s. violet	2·75	1·90
274	**70**	6s. red	10·00	7·00
275	–	10s. blue	14·00	10·00

DESIGN—HORIZ: 3s.; 10s. Red Cross Society Buildings, Tokyo.

72 Cruiser "Hiyei" and Pagoda, Liaoyang

73 Akasaka Palace, Tokyo

1935. Visit of Emperor of Manchukuo.

276	**72**	1½s. green	2·50	1·60
277	**73**	3s. brown	2·00	1·00
278	**72**	6s. red	14·00	7·50
279	**73**	10s. blue	10·00	7·00

74 Mt. Fuji (after Kazan Watanabe)

75c Mt. Fuji from Mishima

1935. New Year's Greetings.

280	**74**	1½s. red	15·00	10

1936. Fuji-Hakone National Park.

281	–	1½s. brown	5·00	4·00
282	–	3s. green	7·00	6·00
283	–	6s. red	16·00	14·00
284	**75c**	10s. blue	22·00	15·00

DESIGNS: Mt. Fuji (1½s.); from Lake Ashi (3s.); from Lake Kawaguchi (6s.).

76 Dove of Peace

77 Shinto Shrine Port Arthur

1936. 30 Years of Occupation of Kwantung.

285	**76**	1½s. violet	12·00	12·00
286	**77**	3s. brown	15·00	16·00
287	–	10s. green	£180	£225

DESIGN—HORIZ: 10s. Govt. House, Kwantung.

78 Imperial Diet

80 Wedded Rocks, Futami Bay

1936. Inauguration of New Houses of the Imperial Diet, Tokyo.

288	**78**	1½s. green	1·50	1·25
289	–	3s. purple	1·50	1·50
290	–	6s. red	5·50	5·00
291	**78**	10s. blue	12·00	4·50

DESIGN: 3, 6s. Grand Staircase.

1936. New Year's Greetings.

292	**80**	1½s. red	6·00	10

82 Goshuinsen (16th-cent trading ship)

83 General Nogi

84 Lake Taisho, Kamikochi

85 Mitsubishi B5N1 and Map

86 Kamatari Fujiwara

87 Plum Tree

1937. Imperf or perf (424), perf (others). Without gum (424), with or without gum (392, 394, 396), with gum (others).

313	**82**	½s. violet	1·50	80
314	–	1s. brown	2·00	50
392b	**83**	2s. red	15	10
316	–	3s. green	75	10
394	**83**	3s. brown	75	20
317	–	4s. green	1·00	10
318	**84**	5s. blue	2·00	10
396	–	5s. purple	30	10
319	–	6s. orange	4·00	2·00
320	–	7s. green	75	20
398	–	7s. red	25	15
321	–	8s. violet	1·00	50
322	–	10s. red	6·00	10
323	**85**	12s. blue	60	60
324	–	14s. red and brown	1·00	30
325	–	20s. blue	1·00	10
326	–	25s. light brown and brown	80	10
327	–	30s. blue	3·00	10
328	–	50s. green and bistre	2·00	10
329	–	1y. light brown and brown	6·00	75
424	**86**	5y. green	5·50	60
331	**87**	10y. purple	20·00	1·50

DESIGNS: 1s. Rice harvesting; 3s. Hydro-electric Power Station; 4, 5s. (No. 396), 7s. (No. 398), Admiral Togo; 6s. Garambi Lighthouse, Taiwan; 7s. (No. 320), Diamond Mountains, Korea; 8s. Meiji Shrine; 10s. Yomei Gate, Tosho Shrine, Nikko; 14s. Inner Gate, Kasuga Shrine; 20s. Mt. Fuji and cherry blossom; 25s. Horyu Temple; 30s. Torii, Itsukushima Shrine at Miyajima; 50s. Temple of Golden Pavilion, Kyoto; 1y. Great Buddha, Kamakura.

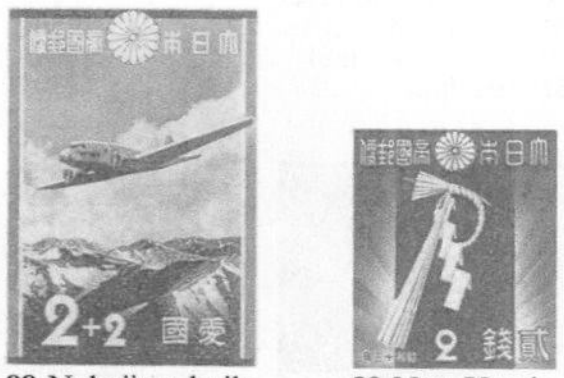

88 Nakajima-built Douglas DC-2 Airliner

89 New Year's Emblem

1937. Aerodrome Fund.

336	**88**	2s.+2s. red	2·25	1·25
337		3s.+2s. violet	2·25	1·50
338		4s.+2s. green	3·25	1·25

1937. New Year's Greetings.

339	**89**	2s. red	12·00	10

90 Nantai Volcano

92 Shinkyo Bridge

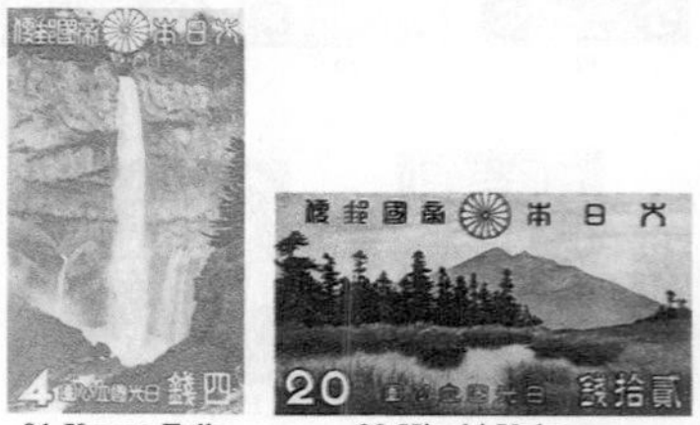

91 Kegon Falls

93 Hiuchi Volcano

1938. Nikko National Park.

340	**90**	2s. orange	75	55
341	**91**	4s. green	75	55
342	**92**	10s. red	7·00	4·00
343	**93**	20s. blue	8·00	5·00

94 Daisen Volcano and Meadow

95 Yashima Plateau and Estuary

96 Abuto Kwannon Shrine

97 Tomo Bay

1939. Daisen and Setonaikai National Parks.

345	**94**	2s. brown	50	60
346	**95**	4s. green	2·25	2·00
347	**96**	10s. red	8·00	7·00
348	**97**	20s. blue	8·00	6·00

98 Mt. Kuju and Village

99 Naka Volcano

100 Naka Crater

101 Volcanic Cones of Mt. Aso

1939. Aso National Park.

350	**98**	2s. brown	60	70
351	**99**	4s. green	3·25	3·25
352	**100**	10s. red	26·00	18·00
353	**101**	20s. blue	30·00	20·00

102 Globe

1939. 75th Anniv of Membership of International Red Cross Union.

355	**102**	2s. brown	2·00	1·25
356	–	4s. green	2·25	1·40
357	**102**	10s. red	12·00	8·50
358	–	20s. blue	14·00	8·50

DESIGN: 4s., 20s. Count Tsunetami Sano.

104 Golden Bird

105 Mt. Takachiho

106 Sake Jar and Ayu

107 Kashiwara Shrine

1940. 2600th Anniv of Japanese Empire.

359	**104**	2s. orange	90	85
360	**105**	4s. green	45	40
361	**106**	10s. red	4·00	4·25
362	**107**	20s. blue	1·00	75

108 Mt. Hokuchin

109 Mt. Asahi

110 Sounkyo Gorge, Kobako

111 Tokachi Range

1940. Daisetsu-zan National Park.

363	**108**	2s. brown	60	60
364	**109**	4s. green	2·50	2·50
365	**110**	10s. red	8·50	6·50
366	**111**	20s. blue	11·00	5·00

112 Mt. Shimmoe

113 Takachiho Peak

114 Kirishima Shrine

115 Lake Roku-Kwannon

1940. Kirishima National Park, Kyushu.

368	**112**	2s. brown	60	60
369	**113**	4s. green	1·00	1·00
370	**114**	10s. red	7·50	5·00
371	**115**	20s. blue	10·00	5·00

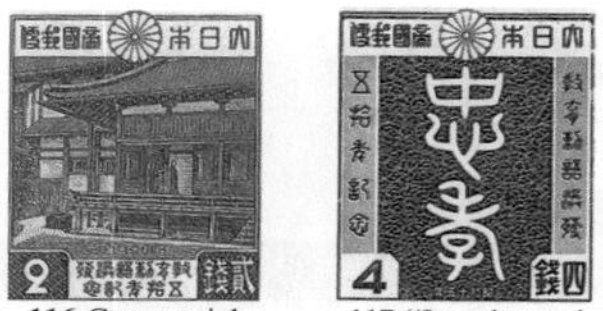
116 Ceremonial Shrine (after Y. Araka)
117 "Loyalty and Filial Piety"

1940. 50th Anniv of Promulgation of Imperial Rescript on Education.

373	**116**	2s. violet	85	1·00
374	**117**	4s. green	1·25	1·40

118 Mt. Daiton

119 Central Peak, Mt. Niitaka

120 Buddhist Temple, Mt. Kwannon

121 View of Mt. Niitaka

1941. Daiton and Niitaka-Arisan National Parks.

375	**118**	2s. brown	80	60
376	**119**	4s. green	1·25	1·00
377	**120**	10s. red	5·00	3·00
378	**121**	20s. blue	6·00	2·75

122 Seisui Precipice, East Taiwan Coast
124 Taroko Gorge, Taiwan

123 Mt. Tsugitaka

125 Mt. Taroko, Source of R. Takkiri

1941. Tsugitaka and Taroko National Parks.

380	**122**	2s. brown	75	60
381	**123**	4s. green	1·25	1·00
382	**124**	10s. red	4·00	4·25
383	**125**	20s. blue	5·50	4·00

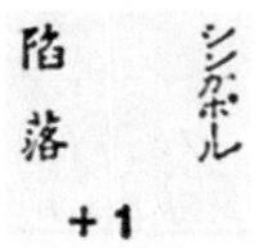

(126)

1942. Surrender of Singapore. Surch as T **126**.

385	**83**	2s.+1s. red	1·00	1·25
386	–	4s.+2s. green (No. 317)	1·00	1·25

127 Kenkoku Shrine
129 Orchids and Crest of Manchukuo

1942. 10th Anniv of Establishment of Manchukuo.

387	**127**	2s. brown	40	50
388	–	5s. olive	60	90
389	**127**	10s. red	85	1·25
390	**129**	20s. blue	3·00	2·75

DESIGN—VERT: 5s. Boys of Japan and Manchukuo.

130 Girl War-worker
135 "The Enemy will Surrender"

140 Garambi Lighthouse, Taiwan
141 Garambi Lighthouse, Taiwan

1942. Imperf (418/19, 421), imperf or perf (400, 420), perf (others). With or without gum (398, 420), without gum (400, 418/19, 421), with gum (others).

391	**130**	1s. brown	10	10
393	–	2s. green	80	45
395	–	4s. green	20	10
397	–	6s. blue	60	60
399	–	10s. red and pink	85	10
400	**135**	10s. grey	7·50	8·00
418		10s. blue	25·00	
419	–	10s. orange	30	10
401	–	15s. blue	2·00	50
402	–	17s. violet	60	25
420	–	20s. blue	30	10
404	–	27s. red	65	80
405	–	30s. green	3·00	1·00
421	–	30s. blue	2·00	40
406	**140**	40s. purple	90	10
407	**141**	40s. purple	2·00	1·00

DESIGNS: 2s. Shipbuilding; 4s. Hyuga Monument and Mt. Fuji; 6s. War-worker; 10s. (No. 399) Palms and map of Greater East Asia; 10s. (No. 419); 20s. Mt. Fuji; 15s. Airman; 17s., 27s. Yasukuni Shrine; 30s. (2) Myajima Shrine.

142 Class C59 Steam Locomotive No. 28
143 Tanks in action at Bataan

1942. 70th Anniv of First National Railway.

408	**142**	5s. green	4·00	6·00

1942. 1st Anniv of Declaration of War.

409	**143**	2s.+1s. brown	2·00	2·75
410	–	5s.+2s. blue	2·50	3·25

DESIGN: 5s. Attack on Pearl Harbor.

144 Yasukuni Shrine
145 Kwantung Shrine and Map of Kwantung Peninsula

1944. 75th Anniv of Yasukuni Shrine.

411	**144**	7s. green	85	1·00

1944. Dedication of Kwantung Shrine.

412	**145**	3s. brown	3·00	10·00
413		7s. grey	3·00	10·00

146 Sun and Cherry Blossom
149 Torii of Yasukuni Shrine

1945. Imperf or perf and with or without gum (422), imperf without gum (others).

415	**146**	3s. red	35	40
416	–	5s. green	40	20
422	–	50s. brown	60	10
423	**149**	1y. olive	1·50	85

DESIGNS: 5s. Sunrise and Kawasaki Ki-61 Hien fighter; 50s. Coal miners.

150 Pagoda of Horyu Temple, Nara
153 Kiyomizu Temple, Kyoto
154 Noh Mask

1946. Imperf or perf (30s., 50, 100y.), imperf (others). With or without gum (30s., 5, 50, 100y.), without gum (others).

426	–	15s. green	45	45
427	**150**	30s. violet	75	10
428a	–	1y. blue	1·00	10
429	–	1y.30 bistre	5·00	1·60
430	–	1y.50 grey	3·00	50
431	**153**	2y. red	2·50	10
432	–	5y. mauve	7·50	25
433b	**154**	50y. brown	80·00	30
434a	–	100y. purple	80·00	40

DESIGNS: 15s. Baron H. Maeshima; 1y. Mt. Fuji, after Hokusai; 1y.30, Snow and white-fronted geese (after Hokusai); 1y.50, Kintai Bridge, Iwakuni; 5y. Veil-tailed goldfish; 100y. Plum tree.

For 30s., 1y.20, 4y. and 10y. as Nos. 427, 429 and 434a but with Japanese characters reading in reverse order, see Nos. 441, 445/6 and 449.

156 Mediaeval Postman's Bell
157 Baron Maeshima

1946. 75th Anniv of Government Postal Service.

436	**156**	15s. orange	4·00	3·00
437	**157**	30s. green	6·00	5·00
438	–	50s. red	3·25	2·50
439	–	1y. blue	4·75	4·75

DESIGNS—As Type **156**: 50s. First Japanese Postage Stamp; 1y. Symbols of communication.

160
161 Baron Maeshima
163 National Art

1947. As issues of 1946 but with Japanese characters in reverse order and new designs. Imperf without gum (449), perf with gum (others).

441	**150**	30s. violet	3·00	2·00
442	**160**	35s. green	75	30
443	–	45s. mauve	85	50
444	**161**	1y. brown	3·25	40
445	**150**	1y.20 green	2·00	30
446	–	4y. blue (as No. 429)	7·25	35
447	–	5y. blue	8·00	10
448	**163**	10y. violet	14·00	10
449	–	10y. purple (as No. 434a)	28·00	70

DESIGNS—VERT: 45s. Numeral; 5y. Whaling.

For similar designs, but without the chrysanthemum emblem, see Nos. 467/70.

164 Mother and Child
165 Roses and Wisteria

1947. Inauguration of New Constitution.

451	**164**	50s. red	60	40
452	**165**	1y. blue	70	40

166 National Products
167 Lily of the Valley

1947. Re-opening of Private Foreign Trade.

455	**166**	1y.20 brown	3·00	1·25
456		4y. blue	5·00	1·50

1947. Relief of Ex-convicts Day.

458	**167**	2y. green	4·00	1·75

169 Hurdling
170

1947. 2nd National Athletic Meeting. Kanazawa. Each mauve.

460	1y.20 Type **169**	10·00	6·00
461	1y.20 Diving	10·00	6·00
462	1y.20 Throwing the discus	10·00	6·00
463	1y.20 Volleyball	10·00	6·00

1947. Community Chest.

465	**170**	1y.20+80s. red	75	85

172 Kiyomizu Temple, Kyoto
173 National Art

1948. Designs without chrysanthemum.

467	–	1y.50 blue	2·50	50
468	**172**	2y. red	8·00	10
469	–	3y.80 brown	8·00	6·50
470	**173**	10y. violet	12·00	10

DESIGNS: 1y.50, 3y.80, Numeral types.

174 Stylized Tree
176 Boy and Girl reading

1948. Encouragement of Afforestation.

474	**174**	1y.20 green	80	60

1948. Re-organization of Educational System.

480	**176**	1y.20 red	65	65

177 Horse Race
178 Swimmer

1948. 25th Anniv of Japanese Horse Racing Laws.

481	**177**	5y. brown	2·25	85

1948. 3rd National Athletic Meeting, Yawata.

482	**178**	5y. blue	3·00	1·25

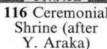

179 Distillery Towers

1948. 10th Anniv of Govt. Alcohol Monopoly.
483 **179** 5y. brown . . . . 3·75 2·25

180 Nurse **181** Varied Tit Feeding Young

1948. Red Cross and Community Chest.
485 **180** 5y.+2y.50 red . . . . . . 8·00 5·00
486 **181** 5y.+2y.50 green . . . . . 17·00 15·00

182 Farm Girl **183** Harpooning **184** Miner

185 Girl plucking Tea **186** Girl Printer **187** Mill Girl

188 Mt. Hodaka **189** Tree Planting

190 Postman **191** Blast-Furnace **192** Constructing Class C62 Steam Locomotive

1948.
488 **182** 2y. green and light green 2·00 10
489 **183** 3y. turquoise . . . . . . 5·00 10
490 **184** 5y. bistre . . . . 16·00 10
491 **185** 5y. green . . . . 40·00 7·00
492 **186** 6y. orange . . . . 7·00 10
493 **184** 8y. brown . . . . 8·00 10
494 **187** 15y. blue . . . . 3·00 10
495 **188** 16y. blue . . . . 8·00 5·00
496 **189** 20y. green . . . . 32·00 10
497 **190** 30y. blue . . . . 36·00 10
506 **191** 100y. red £400 40
507 **192** 500y. blue . . . . £375 2·50

193 Baseball

1948. 3rd National Athletic Meeting, Fukuoke.
509 **193** 5y. green . . . . 12·00 5·00
510 – 5y. green (bicycle race) . . 12·00 5·00
511 – 5y. green (sprinter) . . . 12·00 5·00
512 – 5y. green (high jumper) . . 12·00 5·00

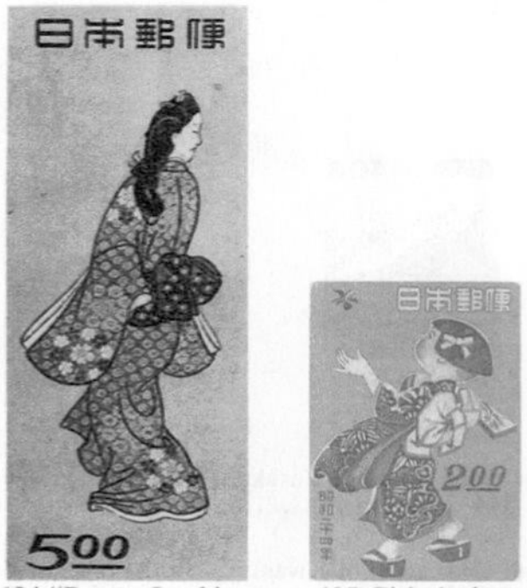

194 "Beauty Looking Back" (Moronobu Hishikawa) **195** Girl playing with Shuttlecock

1948. Philatelic Week.
514 **194** 5y. brown . . . . 60·00 40·00

1948. New Year's Greetings.
516 **195** 2y. red . . . . 3·75 2·25

196 Skater **197** Ski Jumper

1949. 4th National Athletic Meeting. (a) Suwa City.
517 **196** 5y. violet . . . . 3·50 2·00
(b) Sapporo, Hokkaido.
518 **197** 5y. blue . . . . 4·00 2·00

198 "Koan Maru" (ferry) in Beppu Harbour **199** Exhibition Grounds

1949.
519 **198** 2y. blue and red . . . . 2·00 1·25
520 5y. blue and green . . . . 5·50 1·50

1949. Foreign Trade Fair, Yokohama. Perf or imperf.
521 **199** 5y. red . . . . 2·50 1·00

200 Seto Inland Sea **201** Stylized Trees

1949. Matsuyama, Okayama and Takamatsu Exhibitions.
522 **200** 10y. red (Matsuyama) . . 30·00 15·00
523 10y. pink (Okayama) . . 35·00 20·00
524 10y. claret (Takamatsu) 50·00 25·00

1949. Encouragement of Afforestation.
525 **201** 5y. green . . . . 5·00 2·00

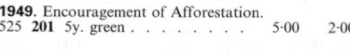

202 Shishi-Iwa (Lion Rock)

203 Mt. Omine

204 Doro-Hatcho River Pool

205 Hashikui-Iwa

1949. Yoshino-Kumano National Park.
526 **202** 2y. brown . . . . 1·00 60
527 **203** 5y. green . . . . 3·25 1·00
528 **204** 10y. red . . . . 14·00 8·00
529 **205** 16y. blue . . . . 7·50 2·25

206 Boy

1949. Children's Day.
531 **206** 5y. purple and buff . . . 5·00 1·50

208 Observatory Tower **209** Radio Mast, Pigeon and Globe

1949. 75th Anniv of Central Meteorological Observatory, Tokyo.
534 **208** 8y. green . . . . 3·50 1·40

1949. Establishment of Joint Ministries of Postal and Electrical Communications.
535 **209** 8y. blue . . . . 3·50 1·25

210 Park in Autumn

211 Park in Spring

212 Park in Summer

213 Park in Winter

1949. Fuji-Hakone National Park.
536 **210** 2y. brown . . . . 2·50 60
537 **211** 8y. green . . . . 3·00 1·00
538 **212** 14y. red . . . . 1·75 30
539 **213** 24y. blue . . . . 3·25 40

214 Woman holding Rose

1949. Establishment of Memorial City at Hiroshima.
541 **214** 8y. brown . . . . 6·00 2·00

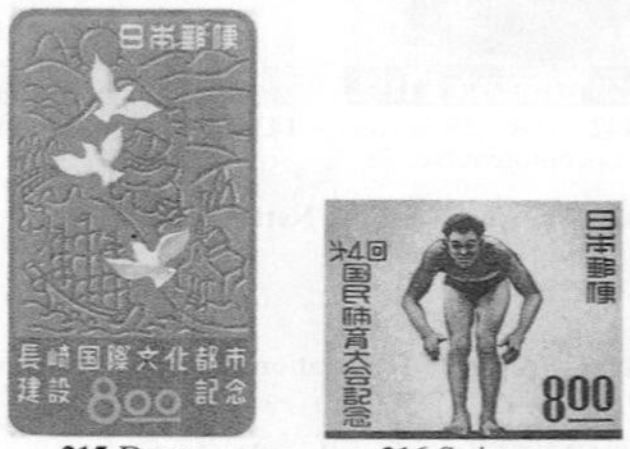

215 Doves **216** Swimmer

1949. Establishment of International Cultural City at Nagasaki.
542 **215** 8y. green . . . . 5·00 2·00

1949. 4th National Athletic Meeting, Yokohama.
543 **216** 8y. blue . . . . 4·00 1·25

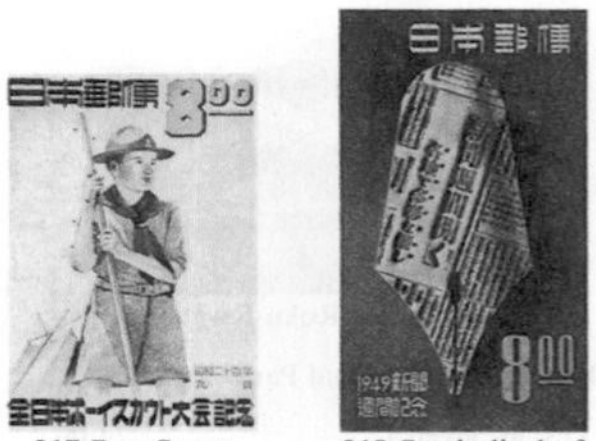

217 Boy Scout **218** Symbolical of Writing and Printing

1949. 1st National Scout Jamboree, Tokyo.
544 **217** 8y. brown . . . . 7·50 2·00

1949. Press Week.
545 **218** 8y. blue . . . . 4·50 2·00

219 Map of Japan and Letters **220** Globe and Forms of Transport

1949. 75th Anniv of U.P.U.
546 **219** 2y. green . . . . 2·75 1·50
547 **220** 8y. red . . . . 4·75 1·60
548 **219** 14y. red . . . . 9·50 4·00
549 **220** 24y. blue . . . . 17·00 9·25

221 Throwing the Javelin **222** Telescope

1949. 4th National Athletic Meeting, Tokyo. Each brown.
551 8y. Type **221** . . . . . . 4·00 1·50
552 8y. Dinghy sailing . . . . . 4·00 1·50
553 8y. Relay racing . . . . . . 4·00 1·50
554 8y. Tennis . . . . 4·00 1·50

1949. 50th Anniv of Establishment of Latitude Observatory, Mizusawa.
555 **222** 8y. green . . . . 3·50 2·00

223 "Moon and Brent Geese" (after Hiroshige) **224** Dr. H. Noguchi

A B C D

E F G H I

J K L M N

O P Q R

1949. Postal Week.

556	**223**	8y. violet	£150	65·00

1949. Various portraits as illustrated, in frame as T **224**.

557	A	8y. green	10·00	1·00
558	B	8y. green	4·00	1·00
559	C	8y. green	4·00	1·00
560	D	8y. green	3·50	1·00
561	E	8y. violet	10·00	4·00
562	F	8y. purple	3·50	1·00
563	G	8y. green	8·00	2·00
564	H	8y. violet	8·00	2·00
565	I	8y. red	16·00	2·00
566	J	8y. red	30·00	2·50
567	K	8y. brown	15·00	2·25
568	L	8y. blue	9·00	2·25
569	M	10y. green	60·00	4·50
570	N	10y. purple	9·00	1·50
571	O	10y. red	4·00	1·40
572	P	10y. grey	7·00	1·40
573	Q	10y. brown	6·00	1·40
574	R	10y. blue	6·00	1·40

PORTRAITS: A, Hideyo Noguchi (bacteriologist); B, Y. Fukuzawa (educationist); C, Soseki Natsume (novelist); D, Shoyo Tsubouchi (dramatist); E, Danjuro Ichikawa (actor); F, Jo Niijima (religious leader); G, Hogai Kano (painter); H, Kanzo Uchimura (religious leader); I, Mme. Higuchi (author); J, Ogai Mori (doctor); K, S. Masaoka (poet); L, S. Hishida (painter); M, A. Nishi (scholar); N, K. Ume (lawyer); O, H. Kimura (astrophysicist); P, I. Nitobe (statesman); Q, T. Torada (physicist); R, Tenshin Okakura (writer).

225 Green Pheasant and Pampas Grass

1950. Air.

575	**225**	16y. grey	40·00	20·00
576		34y. purple	80·00	25·00
577		59y. red	£120	20·00
578		103y. orange	90·00	35·00
579		144y. olive	90·00	35·00

226 Tiger (after Maruyama Okyo)

1950. New Year's Greetings.

580	**226**	2y. red	8·00	1·00

227 Microphones of 1925 and 1950 **228** Dove

1950. 25th Anniv of Japanese Broadcasting System.

582	**227**	8y. blue	4·00	1·50

1950. 1st Anniv of Joint Ministries of Postal and Electrical Communications.

583	**228**	8y. green	3·75	1·25

229 Lake Akan and Mt. O-Akani

230 Lake Kutcharo

231 Mt. Akan-Fuji

232 Lake Mashu

1950. Akan National Park.

584	**229**	2y. brown	1·10	50
585	**230**	8y. green	1·75	75
586	**231**	14y. red	8·50	2·25
587	**232**	24y. blue	10·00	2·25

233 Gymnast on Rings

1950. 5th National Athletic Meeting.

589	**233**	8y. red	30·00	12·00
590	–	8y. red (Pole vaulting)	30·00	12·00
591	–	8y. red (Football)	30·00	12·00
592	–	8y. red (Horse jumping)	30·00	12·00

234 Tahoto Pagoda, Ishiyama Temple **235** Baron Maeshima **236** Long-tailed Cock

237 Kannon Bosatsu (detail of wall painting, Horyu Temple)

238 Himeji Castle

239 Phoenix Temple, Uji

240 Buddhisattva Statue, Chugu Temple

1950. With noughts for sen after value.

593	**234**	80s. red	2·00	1·75
594	**235**	1y. brown	4·75	30
595	**236**	5y. green and brown	8·00	30
596	**237**	10y. lake and mauve	18·00	10
597	**238**	14y. brown	50·00	35·00
598	**239**	24y. blue	40·00	16·00
599	**240**	50y. brown	£140	1·00

For designs without noughts see Nos. 653 etc and for designs additionally inscr "NIPPON" see Nos. 1041/59.

241 Girl and Rabbit

242 Skiing, Mt. Zao

1951. New Year's Greetings.

604	**241**	2y. red	7·00	1·00

For 50y. in this design dated "1999" see No. 2565.

1951. Tourist Issue. Mt. Zao.

606	**242**	8y. olive	14·00	3·00
607	–	24y. blue	15·00	5·00

DESIGN—HORIZ: 24y. Two skiers on Mt. Zao.

243 Nihon-Daira

244 Mt. Fuji from Nihon Daira

1951. Tourist Issue. Nihon-Daira.

608	**243**	8y. green	14·00	3·00
609	**244**	24y. blue	70·00	18·00

245 Child's Head

1951. Children's Charter.

611	**245**	8y. brown	25·00	3·00

246 Hot Springs, Owaki Valley

247 Lake Ashi

1951. Tourist Issue. Hakone Spa.

612	**246**	8y. brown	10·00	2·00
613	**247**	24y. blue	8·00	3·00

248 Senju Waterfall

249 Ninai Waterfall

1951. Tourist Issue. Akame Waterfalls.

614	**248**	8y. green	10·00	2·00
615	**249**	24y. blue	10·00	3·00

250 Waka-no-Ura

251 Tomo-ga-Shima

1951. Tourist Issue. Coastal Resorts.

616	**250**	8y. brown	8·00	2·00
617	**251**	24y. blue	8·00	3·00

252 Oirase River

253 Lake Towada

254 View from Kankodai

255 Hakkoda Mountains

1951. Towada National Park.

618	**252**	2y. brown	1·25	30
619	**253**	8y. green	6·50	70
620	**254**	14y. red	5·50	4·00
621	**255**	24y. blue	7·50	4·00

256 Uji River

257 Uji Bridge

1951. Tourist Issue. Uji River.

623	**256**	8y. brown	9·00	2·00
624	**257**	24y. blue	8·00	3·00

258 Douglas DC-4 Airliner over Horyuji Pagoda

259 Douglas DC-4 Airliner and Mt. Tate

1951. Air. With noughts for sen after numerals of value.

625	**258**	15y. violet	4·00	3·25
626		20y. blue	32·00	1·00
627		25y. green	35·00	15
628		30y. red	26·00	15
629		40y. black	7·00	30
630	**259**	55y. blue	£225	45·00
631		75y. red	£175	28·00
632		80y. mauve	30·00	3·50
633		85y. black	22·00	12·00
634		125y. brown	18·00	3·25
635		160y. green	40·00	5·50

For similar designs, but without noughts after numerals of value, see Nos. 671/81.

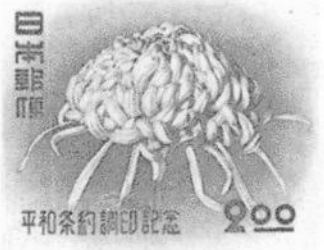
260 Chrysanthemum

261 Japanese Flag

1951. Peace Treaty.

636	**260**	2y. brown	2·50	1·00
637	**261**	8y. red and blue	7·00	2·00
638	**260**	24y. green	18·00	6·00

262 Oura Catholic Church, Nagasaki

263 Gateway, Sofuku Temple

1951. Tourist Issue. Nagasaki.

639	**262**	8y. red	10·00	2·00
640	**263**	24y. blue	8·00	3·00

264 Lake Marunuma

265 Lake Sugenuma

1951. Tourist Issue.

641	**264**	8y. purple	10·00	2·00
642	**265**	24y. green	8·00	3·00

266 Shosenkyo Valley
267 Nagatoro Bridge

1951. Tourist Issue. Shosenkyo.
643 **266** 8y. red . . . . 9·50 2·00
644 **267** 24y. blue . . . . 9·00 3·00

268 Putting the Shot
269 Noh Mask

1951. 6th National Athletic Meeting.
645 **268** 2y. brown . . . . 3·50 1·00
646 – 2y. blue (Hockey) . . . . 3·50 1·00

1952. New Year's Greetings.
647 **269** 5y. red . . . . 10·00 90

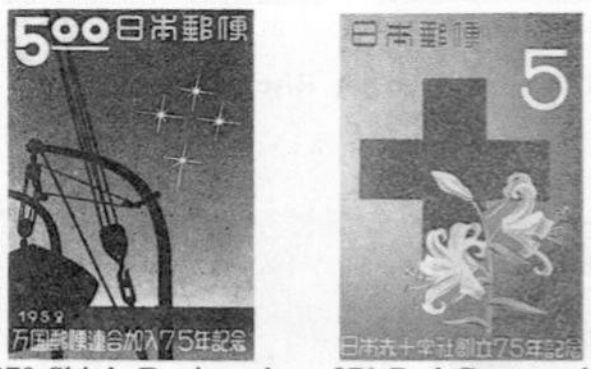
270 Ship's Davit and Southern Cross
271 Red Cross and Lily

1952. 75th Anniv of U.P.U. Membership.
649 **270** 5y. violet . . . . 5·00 1·25
650 – 10y. green . . . . 16·00 3·00
DESIGN: 10y. Earth and Ursa Major. Inscr "1952".

1952. 75th Anniv of Japanese Red Cross.
651 **271** 5y. red . . . . 5·00 1·00
652 – 10y. green and red (Nurse) . . . . 11·00 2·00

272 Akita Dog
273 Small Cuckoo
274 Tahoto Pagoda, Ishiyama Temple

275 Mandarins
276 Japanese Serow
277 Chuson Temple

278 Veil-tailed Goldfish
279 Yomei Gate, Tosho Shrine, Nikko
280 "Marimo" (water plant) and Sockeye Salmon

281 Great Purple
282 Fishing with Japanese Cormorants
283 "Bridge and Irises" (from lacquered box)

1952. Without noughts after numerals of value.
653 **235** 1y. brown 30 10
654 **272** 2y. black 40 10
655 **273** 3y. turquoise 20 20
656 **274** 4y. purple and red . . . 2·50 10
657 **275** 5y. brown and blue . . . 65 20
658 **276** 8y. brown and light brown 30 10
659 **237** 10y. red and mauve . . . 6·00 10
660 **238** 14y. green . . . . 7·50 1·25
661 **277** 20y. green . . . . 1·00 10
662 **239** 24y. violet . . . . 16·00 2·00
663 30y. purple . . . . 35·00 40
664 **278** 35y. orange . . . . . . 10·00 10
665 **279** 45y. blue . . . . 4·50 10
666 **240** 50y. brown . . . . . . 4·50 10
667 **280** 55y. green, black and blue 16·00 30
668 **281** 75y. multicoloured . . . 14·00 90
669 **282** 100y. red . . . . 40·00 20
670 **283** 500y. purple . . . . . . 85·00 10
For 1, 2, 3, 50, 55 and 75y. in same designs, but inscr "NIPPON", see Nos. 1041, 1582a, 1226, 1058/60, 1232 and 1064.

1952. Air. As Nos. 625/35 but without noughts after numerals of value.
671 **258** 15y. violet . . . . 2·00 1·10
672 20y. blue . . . . 50·00 70
673 25y. green . . . . 1·00 10
674 30y. red . . . . 3·50 10
675 40y. black . . . . 4·00 10
676 **259** 55y. blue . . . . 75·00 4·50
677 75y. red . . . . £140 10·00
678 80y. mauve . . . . . . 95·00 3·00
679 85y. black . . . . . . 5·00 1·25
680 125y. brown . . . . . . 10·00 1·40
681 160y. green . . . . . . 40·00 1·75

284 Mt. Yari
285 Kurobe Valley

286 Mt. Shirouma

287 Mt. Norikura

1952. Chubu-Sangaku National Park.
682 **284** 5y. brown . . . . 2·75 40
683 **285** 10y. green . . . . 18·00 2·00
684 **286** 14y. red . . . . 5·50 2·00
685 **287** 24y. blue . . . . 8·00 2·75

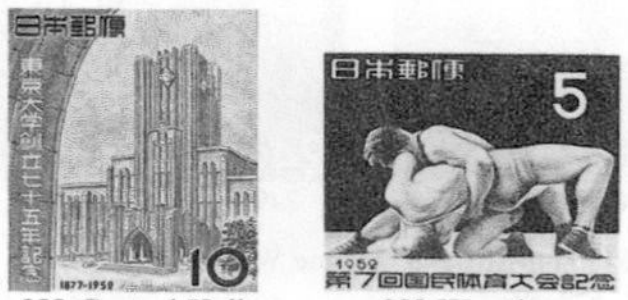
288 Central Hall
289 Wrestlers

1952. 75th Anniv of Tokyo University.
687 **288** 10y. green . . . . 11·00 2·00

1952. 7th National Athletic Meeting.
688 – 5y. blue (Mountaineer) . . 6·00 1·00
689 **289** 5y. brown . . . . 6·00 1·00

290 Mt. Azuma-Kofuji

291 Mt. Asahi

292 Mt. Bandai

293 Mt. Gessan

1952. Bandai-Asahi National Park.
690 **290** 5y. brown . . . . 2·00 40
691 **291** 10y. olive . . . . 11·00 1·75
692 **292** 14y. red . . . . 4·25 2·75
693 **293** 24y. blue . . . . 8·00 4·00

294 "Kirin" and Chrysanthemums
295 Flag of Crown Prince

1952. Investiture of Crown Prince Akihito.
695 **294** 5y. orange and brown . . 2·75 50
696 10y. orange and green . . 3·00 75
697 **295** 24y. blue . . . . 15·00 4·25

296 Dancing Doll
297 First Japanese Electric Lamp

1953. New Year's Greetings.
699 **296** 5y. red . . . . 7·00 1·00

1953. 75th Anniv of Electric Lamp in Japan.
701 **297** 10y. brown . . . . 7·50 2·00

299 Kintai Bridge
302 Great Buddha, Kamakura

300 Lake Shikotsu (½-size illustration)
301 Mt. Yotei (½-size illustration)

1953. Tourist Issue. Kintai Bridge.
702 – 10y. brown . . . . 7·50 2·00
703 **299** 24y. blue . . . . 7·50 3·00
DESIGN—VERT: 10y. Kintai Bridge (after Hiroshige).

1953. Shikotsu-Toya National Park.
704 **300** 5y. blue . . . . 1·75 35
705 **301** 10y. green . . . . 5·50 75

1953. Air.
707 **302** 70y. brown . . . . 3·50 10
708 80y. blue . . . . 5·00 10
709 115y. olive . . . . 2·75 30
710 145y. turquoise . . . . . 18·00 2·00

303 Wedded Rocks, Futami Bay (½-size illustration)
304 Nakiri Coast (½-size illustration)

1953. Ise Shima National Park.
711 **303** 5y. red . . . . 1·75 30
712 **304** 10y. blue . . . . 4·00 70

305 "Ho-o" (Happy Phoenix)

1953. Return of Crown Prince from Overseas Tour.
714 **305** 5y. lake . . . . 3·00 1·50
715 – 10y. blue . . . . 9·25 3·50
DESIGN: 10y. Manchurian crane in flight.

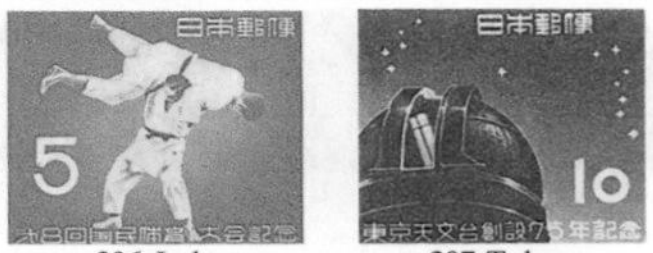
306 Judo
307 Tokyo Observatory

1953. 8th National Athletic Meeting, Matsuyama.
716 **306** 5y. green . . . . 8·00 2·00
717 – 5y. black . . . . 8·00 2·00
DESIGN: 5y. Rugby footballers.

1953. 75th Anniv of Tokyo Observatory.
718 **307** 10y. blue . . . . 10·00 2·00

308 Mt. Unzen (½-size illustration)
309 Mt. Unzen (½-size illustration)

1953. Unzen National Park.
719 **308** 5y. red . . . . 1·50 25
720 **309** 10y. blue . . . . 4·00 65

310 Wooden Horse
311 Ice Skaters

1953. New Year's Greetings.
722 **310** 5y. red . . . . 5·50 25

1954. World Speed Skating Championships, Sapporo.
724 **311** 10y. blue . . . . 4·00 1·10

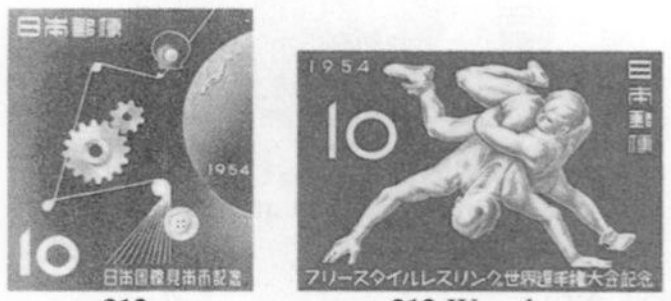
312
313 Wrestlers

1954. International Trade Fair, Osaka
725 **312** 10y. red . . . . 4·25 1·10

1954. Int Free-style Wrestling Championship.
726 **313** 10y. green . . . . 4·00 1·00

314 Mt. Asama (½-size illustration)
315 Mt. Tanigawa (½-size illustration)

1954. Jo-Shin-Etsu Kogen National Park.
727 **314** 5y. sepia . . . . 1·50 25
728 **315** 10y. turquoise . . . . . 3·75 65

316 Archery
317 Telegraph Table

1954. 9th National Athletic Meeting, Sapporo.
730 **316** 5y. green . . . . 5·00 1·50
731 – 5y. brown (Table tennis) 5·00 1·50

1954. 75th Anniv of Japan's Membership of I.T.U.
732 **317** 5y. purple . . . . 2·25 75
733 – 10y. blue . . . . 6·00 1·00
DESIGN—HORIZ: 10y. I.T.U. Monument.

318 Tumbler
319 Tama Gorge

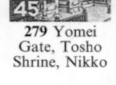

320 Chichibu Mountains

1954. New Year's Greetings.
735 **318** 5y. red and black . . . . 7·00 80

1955. Chichibu-Tama National Park.
737 **319** 5y. blue . . . . 1·25 25
738 **320** 10y. lake . . . . 1·50 40

321 Paper Carp

1955. 15th International Chamber of Commerce Congress, Tokyo.
740 **321** 10y. multicoloured . . . 6·00 1·50

322 Bentenzaki Peninsula **323** Jodoga Beach

1955. Rikuchu-Kaigan National Park.
741 **322** 5y. green . . . . 1·50 25
742 **323** 10y. red . . . . 2·00 40

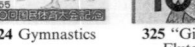

324 Gymnastics **325** "Girl Playing Glass Flute" (Utamaro)

1955. 10th National Athletic Meeting, Kanagawa.
744 **324** 5y. red . . . . 3·00 1·00
745 – 5y. blue (Running) . . . 3·00 1·00

1955. Philatelic Week.
746 **325** 10y. multicoloured . . . 12·00 8·00

326 "Kokeshi" Dolls **327** Table Tennis

1955. New Year's Greetings.
747 **326** 5y. green and red . . . . 3·00 20

1956. World Table Tennis Championships.
749 **327** 10y. brown . . . . 1·10 35

328 Judo

1956. World Judo Championships.
750 **328** 10y. purple and green . . 1·40 40

329 Children and Paper Carps

1956. International Children's Day.
751 **329** 5y. black and blue . . . . 1·00 30

330 Osezaki Lighthouse (½-size illustration) **331** Kujuku Island (½-size illustration)

1956. 25th Anniv of National Park Law. Saikai National Park.
752 **330** 5y. brown . . . . 1·25 50
753 **331** 10y. indigo and blue . . . 1·75 85

332 Imperial Palace, and Modern Buildings

1956. 5th Centenary of Tokyo.
755 **332** 10y. purple . . . . 3·25 50

333 Sakuma Dam **334** Basketball

1956. Completion of Sakuma Dam.
756 **333** 10y. blue . . . . 2·50 50

1956. 11th National Athletic Meeting, Kobe.
757 **334** 5y. green . . . . 1·50 30
758 – 5y. purple (Long jumping) 1·50 30

335 Ebizo Ichikawa (actor) (after Sharaku)

1956. Philatelic Week.
759 **335** 10y. black, orange and grey . . . . 13·00 4·75

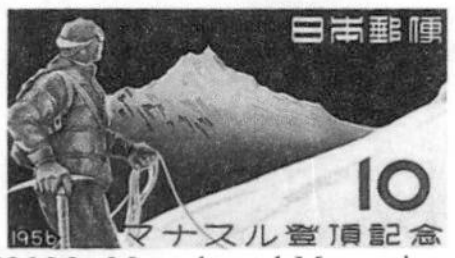
336 Mt. Manaslu and Mountaineer

1956. Conquest of Mt. Manaslu.
760 **336** 10y. multicoloured . . . 4·50 1·25

337 View of Yui (after Hiroshige) and Type EF 58 Electric Locomotive No. 4

1956. Electrification of Tokaido Railway Line.
761 **337** 10y. black, green & brown 10·00 3·00

338 Cogwheel, Valve and Freighter "Nissyo Maru" **339** Whale (float)

1956. Floating Machinery Fair.
762 **338** 10y. blue . . . . 1·60 70

1956. New Year's Greetings.
763 **339** 5y. multicoloured . . . . 2·00 15

340 U.N.O. Emblem **341** I.G.Y. Emblem, Emperor Penguin and Antarctic Research Vessel "Soya"

1957. 1st Anniv of Japan's Admission into U.N.
765 **340** 10y. red and blue . . . . 1·00 95

1957. International Geophysical Year.
766 **341** 10y. blue, yellow and black . . . . 2·25 85

342 Atomic Reactor **343** Gymnast

1957. Completion of Atomic Reactor at Tokai-Mura.
767 **342** 10y. violet 50 15

1957. 12th National Athletic Meeting, Shizuoka.
768 **343** 5y. blue 60 15
769 – 5y. red (Boxing) 60 15

344 "Girl Bouncing Ball" (after Harunobu) **345** Ogochi Dam

1957. Philatelic Week.
770 **344** 10y. multicoloured . . . 4·00 1·50

1957. Completion of Ogochi Dam.
771 **345** 10y. blue 45 15

346 Japan's First Blast Furnace and Modern Plant **347** "Inu-hariko" (toy dog)

1957. Centenary of Japanese Iron Industry.
772 **346** 10y. purple and orange 35 15

1957. New Year's Greetings.
773 **347** 5y. multicoloured 30 15

348 Kan-Mon Tunnel

1958. Opening of Kan-Mon Undersea Tunnel.
775 **348** 10y. multicoloured . . . 50 10

349 "Lady returning from Bath-house" (after Kiyonaga)

1958. Philatelic Week.
776 **349** 10y. multicoloured . . . 1·00 15

350 Statue of Ii Naosuke, "Powhattan" (1858 paddle-steamer) and Modern Liner **351** National Stadium, Tokyo

1958. Centenary of Opening of Ports to Traders.
777 **350** 10y. red and blue 30 10

1958. 3rd Asian Games, Tokyo. Inscr as in T **351**. Multicoloured.
778 5y. Type **351** 30 10
779 10y. Flame and Games emblem 45 50
780 14y. Runner breasting tape 35 15
781 24y. High-diver 40 50

352 Emigration Ship "Kasato Maru" and South American Map

1958. 50th Anniv of Japanese Emigration to Brazil.
782 **352** 10y. multicoloured . . . 50 10

353 Dado-Okesa Dancer on Sado Island

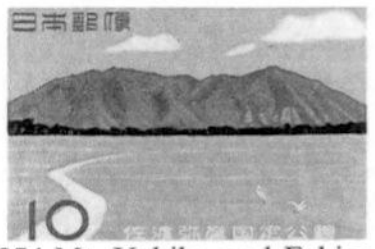
354 Mt. Yahiko and Echigo Plain

1958. Sado-Yahiko Quasi-National Park.
783 **353** 10y. multicoloured . . . 70 10
784 **354** 10y. multicoloured . . . 40 10

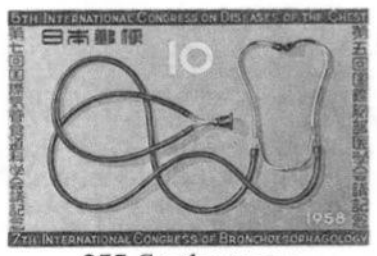
355 Stethoscope

1958. International Congresses of Chest Diseases and Bronchoesophagology, Tokyo.
785 **355** 10y. turquoise 60 10

356 "Old Kyoto Bridge" (after Hiroshige) **357** Badminton Player

1958. International Correspondence Week.
786 **356** 24y. multicoloured . . . 4·50 50
The design is taken from the series of 53 woodcuts, showing stages of the Tokaido Road. Others from this series are shown on Nos. 810, 836, 878 and 908.

1958. 13th National Athletic Meeting, Toyama.
787 **357** 5y. purple 75 10
788 – 5y. blue (Weightlifting) . . 75 10

358 Yukichi Fukuzawa (founder) and Keio University **359** Children Skipping across Globe

1958. Centenary of Keio University.
789 **358** 10y. red 30 10

1958. International Child and Social Welfare Conferences, Tokyo.
790 **359** 10y. green 30 10

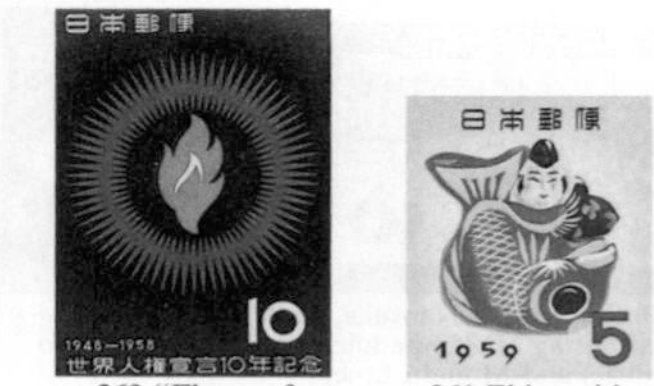
360 "Flame of Freedom"   **361** Ebisu with Madai Seabream (toy)

1958. 10th Anniv of Declaration of Human Rights.
791 **360** 10y. multicoloured . . . 30 10

1958. New Year's Greetings.
792 **361** 5y. multicoloured 50 10

362 Map of Kojima Bay and Tractor

1959. Completion of Kojima Bay Reclamation Project.
794 **362** 10y. purple and ochre . . 50 15

363 Karst Plateau   **364** Akiyoshi Cavern

1959. Akiyoshidai Quasi-National Parks.
795 **363** 10y. multicoloured . . . 1·75 10
796 **364** 10y. multicoloured . . . 2·25 10

365 Map of Asia   **366** Crown Prince Akihito and Princess Michiko

1959. Asian Congress Commemorating 2500th Anniv of Buddha's Death.
797 **365** 10y. red 40 10

1959. Imperial Wedding.
798 – 5y. violet and purple . . . 35 10
799 **366** 10y. purple and brown . . 85 10
800 – 20y. sepia and brown . . 1·00 15
801 **366** 30y. deep green and green 2·00 15
DESIGN: 5, 20y. Ceremonial fan.

367 "Ladies reading poems" (from "Ukiyo Genji" after Eishi)   **368** Graduated Glass and Scales

1959. Philatelic Week.
803 **367** 10y. multicoloured . . . 2·50 1·25

1959. Ratification of Adoption of Metric System in Japan.
804 **368** 10y. sepia and blue . . . 30 10

369 Stretcher-party with Casualty

1959. Red Cross.
805 **369** 10y. red and green . . . 40 10

370 Mt. Fuji from Lake Motosu

1959. National Parks Day.
806 **370** 10y. green, purple and blue 60 10

371 Ao Caves, Yabakei

372 Japanese Cormorant with Hita and Mt. Hiko background

1959. Yaba-Hita-Hikosan Quasi-National Parks.
807 **371** 10y. multicoloured . . . 2·00 30
808 **372** 10y. multicoloured . . . 1·40 50

373 Nagoya and Golden Dolphin   **374** "Kuwana" (after Hiroshige)

1959. 350th Anniv of Nagoya.
809 **373** 10y. gold, black and blue 60 10

1959. International Correspondence Week.
810 **374** 30y. multicoloured . . . 10·00 2·00

375 Flying Manchurian Crane and I.A.T.A. Emblem   **376** Throwing the Hammer

1959. 15th International Air Transport Association Meeting, Tokyo
811 **375** 10y. blue . . . . 1·10 35

1959. 14th National Athletic Meeting, Tokyo.
812 **376** 5y. blue . . . . 1·00 10
813 – 5y. brown (Fencer) . . . 1·00 10

377 Open Book showing portrait of Shoin Yoshida   **378** Halves of Globe

1959. Death Centenary of Shoin Yoshida (educator) and National Parents/Teachers Assn Convention.
814 **377** 10y. brown 40 10

1959. 15th Session of Contracting Parties to G.A.T.T.
815 **378** 10y. brown 60 10

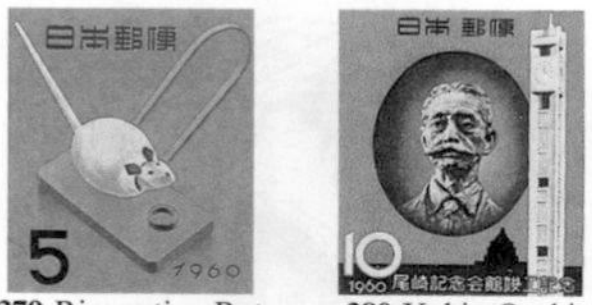
379 Rice-eating Rat of Kanazawa (toy)   **380** Yukio Ozaki and Clock Tower Memorial Hall

1959. New Year's Greetings.
816 **379** 5y. multicoloured . . . . 1·00 10

1960. Completion of Ozaki Memorial Hall, Tokyo.
818 **380** 10y. purple and brown . . 40 10

381 Deer

1960. 1250th Anniv of Transfer of Capital to Nara.
819 **381** 10y. olive 70 10

382 Godaido Temple, Matsushima

383 Bridge of Heaven (sandbank), Miyazu Bay

384 Miyajima from the Sea

1960. "Scenic Trio".
820 **382** 10y. turquoise and brown 2·50 25
821 **383** 10y. green and blue . . . 3·00 25
822 **384** 10y. green and violet . . 3·00 25

385 Takeshima-Gamagori Causeway

1960. Mikawa Bay Quasi-National Park.
823 **385** 10y. multicoloured . . . 1·25 20

386 "Ise" (from Satake picture scroll "Thirty-six Immortal Poets")

1960. Philatelic Week.
824 **386** 10y. black, red and brown 3·75 2·00

387 "Kanrin Maru" (barque) crossing the Pacific   **388** Japanese Crested Ibis

1960. Centenary of Japanese–American Treaty.
825 **387** 10y. sepia and green . . . 2·25 30
826 – 30y. black and red . . . 1·60 20
DESIGN: 30y. Pres. Buchanan receiving Japanese mission.

1960. 12th Int Bird Preservation Congress, Tokyo.
827 **388** 10y. red, pink and grey 1·40 55

389 Radio Waves around Globe   **390** Abashiri Flower Gardens

1960. 25th Anniv of Japanese Overseas Broadcasting Service, "Radio Japan".
828 **389** 10y. red 40 10

1960. Abashiri Quasi-National Park.
829 **390** 10y. multicoloured . . . 1·50 25

391 Cape Ashizuri   **392** Rainbow linking Hawaii and Japan

1960. Ashizuri Quasi-National Park.
830 **391** 10y. multicoloured . . . 1·00 25

1960. 75th Anniv of Japanese Emigration to Hawaii.
831 **392** 10y. multicoloured . . . 1·00 20

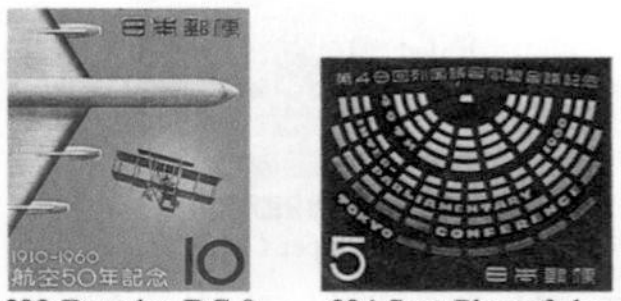
393 Douglas DC-8 Jetliner and Farman H.F.III Biplane   **394** Seat Plan of the Diet

1960. 50th Anniv of Japanese Aviation.
832 **393** 10y. brown and grey . . . 1·25 25

1960. 49th Inter-Parliamentary Union Conference. Inscr "49TH INTER-PARLIAMENTARY CONFERENCE TOKYO 1960".
833 **394** 5y. orange and blue . . . 70 10
834 – 10y. brown and blue . . . 1·60 20
DESIGN: 10y. "Clear Day with Southern Breeze" (from "36 Views of Mt. Fuji" by Hokusai Katsushika).

395 "Kambara" (after Hiroshige)

1960. International Correspondence Week.
836 **395** 30y. multicoloured . . . 18·00 4·00

396 Okayama Observatory

1960. Opening of Okayama Astrophysical Observatory.
837 **396** 10y. violet 90 25

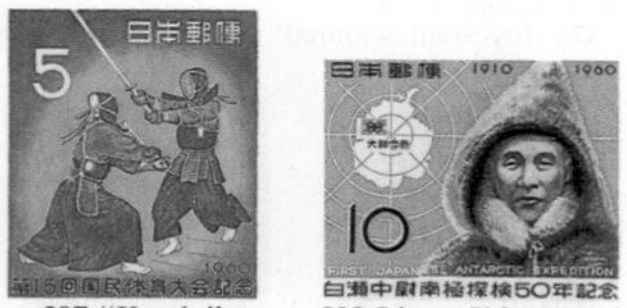
397 "Kendo" (Japanese fencing)   **398** Lieut. Shirase and Map of Antarctica

1960. 15th National Athletic Meeting, Kumamoto.
838 **397** 5y. blue . . . . 1·00 15
839 – 5y. purple (Vaulting) . . 1·00 15

1960. 50th Anniv of 1st Japanese Antarctic Expedition.
840 **398** 10y. black and brown . . 1·00 15

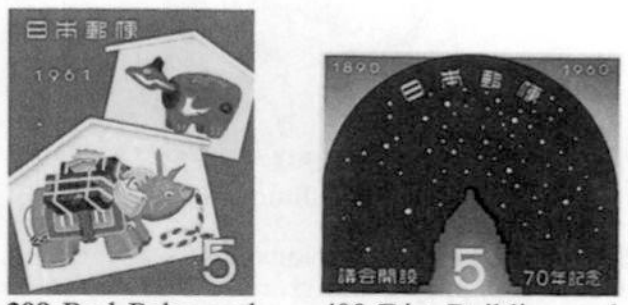
399 Red Beko and Golden Bekokko (Japanese toys)   **400** Diet Building and Stars

1960. New Year's Greetings.
841 **399** 5y. multicoloured 50 10

1960. 70th Anniv of Diet.
843 **400** 5y. violet and black . . . 60 10
844 – 10y. red 75 15
DESIGN: 10y. Opening ceremony of first session of Diet.

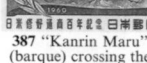

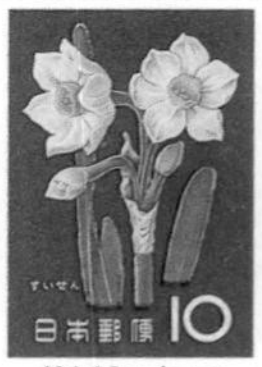
401 Narcissus

402 Pearl-divers at Shirahama

1961. Japanese Flowers. Flowers in natural colours. Background colours given.
845 10y. purple (T **401**) . . . . . 5·00 80
846 10y. brown (Plum blossom) 3·00 80
847 10y. bistre (Camellia) . . . . 2·00 70
848 10y. grey (Cherry blossom) 2·00 70
849 10y. sepia (Peony) . . . . . 1·90 55
850 10y. grey (Iris) . . . . 1·50 55
851 10y. turquoise (Lily) . . . . 1·00 30
852 10y. blue (Morning glory) . . 1·00 30
853 10y. sage (Bellflower) . . . . 1·00 30
854 10y. orange (Gentian) . . . . 1·00 30
855 10y. blue (Chrysanthemum) 1·25 30
856 10y. slate (Camellia) . . . . 1·00 30

1961. Minami-Boso Quasi-National Park.
857 **402** 10y. multicoloured . . . 1·00 10

403 Hirase's Slit Shell — 404 Nanten — 405 Cherry Blossoms

406 Engaku Temple — 407 Yomei Gate, Tosho Shrine, Nikko — 408 Noh Mask

409 Copper Pheasant — 410 "The Wind God" — 411 Manchurian Cranes

412 "Kalavinka" (legendary bird)

1961.
858 **403** 4y. red and brown . . . 35 10
859 **404** 6y. red and green 20 10
860 **405** 10y. mauve and purple . . 45 10
861 **406** 30y. violet . . . . 5·00 10
862 **407** 40y. red . . . . 6·00 10
863 **408** 70y. black and ochre . . 3·00 10
864 **409** 80y. brown and red . . . 3·25 20
865 **410** 90y. green . . . . 35·00 15
866 **411** 100y. grey, black and pink 30·00 20
867 **412** 120y. violet . . . . . . 12·00 30
For 70, 80, 90, 100, and 120y. in different colours and additionally inscr "NIPPON" see Nos. 1065/6, 1068, 1234/6 and 1238.

413 Baron Maeshima

414 "Dancing Girl" (from 17th-century screen)

1961. 90th Anniv of Japanese Postal Service.
868 **413** 10y. green and black . . . 1·00 15

1961. Philatelic Week.
869 **414** 10y. multicoloured . . . 1·75 90

415 Lake Biwa

416 Rotary Emblem and "Peoples of the World"

1961. Lake Biwa Quasi-National Park.
870 **415** 10y. multicoloured . . . 1·10 20

1961. 52nd Rotary International Convention.
871 **416** 10y. orange and black . . 45 10

417 "Benefits Irrigation"

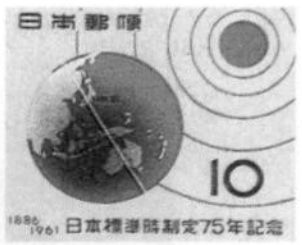
418 Globe showing Longitude 135° E. and Sun

1961. Inauguration of Aichi Irrigation Scheme.
872 **417** 10y. blue and purple . . . 50 15

1961. 75th Anniv of Japanese Standard Time.
873 **418** 10y. red, black and ochre 50 15

419 Parasol Dancer, Tottori Beach

1961. San'in Kaigan Quasi-National Park.
874 **419** 10y. multicoloured . . . 80 20

420 Komagatake Volcano

1961. Onuma Quasi-National Park.
875 **420** 10y. multicoloured . . . 80 20

421 Gymnast

422 "Hakone" (after Hiroshige)

1961. 16th National Athletic Meeting, Akita.
876 **421** 5y. green . . . . 1·00 10
877 – 5y. blue (Rowing) . . . . 1·00 10

1961. International Correspondence Week.
878 **422** 30y. multicoloured . . . 9·00 4·00

423 Throwing the Javelin

1961. Olympic Games, Tokyo, 1964 (1st issue).
879 **423** 5y.+5y. brown . . . . . 1·50 70
880 – 5y.+5y. green . . . . . . 1·50 70
881 – 5y.+5y. red . . . . 1·50 70
DESIGNS: No. 880, Wrestling; 881, Diver (Woman).
See also Nos. 899/901, 909/11, 935/7, 949/52, 969/72 and 981/5.

424 Library and Book

425 Tiger (Izumo toy)

1961. Opening of National Diet Library.
882 **424** 10y. blue and gold . . . 60 15

1961. New Year's Greetings.
883 **425** 5y. multicoloured 75 10

426 Mt. Fuji from Lake Aishi

427 Minokake-Iwa, Irozaki

428 Mt. Fuji from Mitsutoge

429 Mt. Fuji from Osezaki

1962. Fuji-Hakone-Izu National Park.
885 **426** 5y. green . . . . 1·00 10
886 **427** 5y. blue . . . . 1·00 10
887 **428** 10y. brown . . . . 1·75 25
888 **429** 10y. black . . . . 1·25 25

430 Omishima Island

431 Doll Festival

1962. Kitanagato-Kaigan Quasi-National Park.
889 **430** 10y. multicoloured . . . 60 20

1962. National Festivals. Multicoloured.
890 10y. Type **431** . . . . 1·75 25
891 10y. Children and decorated tree ("Star Festival") . . . 75 20
892 10y. Three children ("Seven-Five-Three Festival") . . . 65 20
893 10y. Children throwing beans ("Spring Festival") 55 15

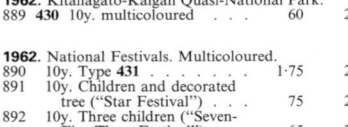

432 "Dancer" (after N. Kano)

1962. Philatelic Week.
894 **432** 10y. multicoloured . . . 1·50 1·00

433 Sakurajima Volcano

1962. Kinkowan Quasi-National Park.
895 **433** 10y. multicoloured . . . 60 20

434 Mount Kongo

1962. Kongo-Ikoma Quasi-National Park.
896 **434** 10y. multicoloured . . . 60 20

435 Suigo View

436 "Hakucho" (swan) Express Train emerging from Tunnel

1962. Suigo Quasi-National Park.
897 **435** 10y. multicoloured . . . 80 20

1962. Opening of Hokuriku Railway Tunnel.
898 **436** 10y. brown . . . . 2·50 45

1962. Olympic Games, Tokyo, 1964 (2nd issue). Sports. As T **423**.
899 5y.+5y. red 75 35
900 5y.+5y. green 75 35
901 5y.+5y. purple 75 35
SPORTS: No. 899 Judo; 900, Water-polo; 901, Gymnastics (female).

437 Scout's Hat on Map

1962. Asian Scout Jamboree, Mt. Fuji.
902 **437** 10y. black, bistre and red 40 10

438 Mt. Shibutsu and Ozegahara Swamp

439 Smoking Summit of Mt. Chausu, Nasu

440 Lake Chuzenji and Mt. Nantai

441 Senryu-kyo Narrows, Shiobara

1962. Nikko National Park.
903 **438** 5y. turquoise 60 10
904 **439** 5y. lake 60 10
905 **440** 10y. purple 80 10
906 **441** 10y. olive 80 10

442 Wakato Suspension Bridge

443 "Nihonbashi" (after Hiroshige)

1962. Opening of Wakato Suspension Bridge.
907 **442** 10y. red . . . . 1·50 35

1962. International Correspondence Week.
908 **443** 40y. multicoloured . . . 7·50 3·00

1962. Olympic Games, Tokyo, 1964 (3rd issue). Sports. As T **423**.
909 5y.+5y. green 65 25
910 5y.+5y. lilac 65 25
911 5y.+5y. red 65 25
SPORTS: No. 909, Basketball; 910, Rowing; 911, Fencing.

444 Rifle-shooting

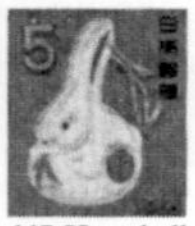
445 Hare-bell (Nogomi toy)

1962. 17th National Athletic Meeting, Okayama.
912 **444** 5y. purple 40 10
913 – 5y. blue 40 10
DESIGN: No. 913, Softball.

1962. New Year's Greetings.
914 **445** 5y. multicoloured 40 10
For 50y. in this design dated "1999" see No. 2566.

446 Mt. Ishizuchi and Kamega Forest

447 "Five Towns"

1963. Ishizuchi Quasi-National Park.
916 **446** 10y. multicoloured . . . 30 10

1963. Amalgamation of Five Towns as Kita-Kyushu.
917 **447** 10y. brown 25 10

448 Frosted Foliage, Fugen Peak

449 Amakusa Islands and Mt. Unzen

1963. Unzen-Amakusa National Park.
918 **448** 5y. blue 35 10
919 **449** 10y. red 65 10

450 Midorigaike (Green Pond)

451 Hakusan Mountains

1963. Hakusan National Park.
920 **450** 5y. brown 45 10
921 **451** 10y. green 75 10

452 Great Rocks, Keya

1963. Genkai Quasi-National Park.
922 **452** 10y. multicoloured . . . 25 10

453 Globe and Emblem

1963. Freedom from Hunger.
923 **453** 10y. green 40 10

454 "Portrait of Heihachiro Honda" (anon-Yedo period)

1963. Philatelic Week.
924 **454** 10y. multicoloured . . . 85 45

455 Centenary Emblem and World Map

456 Globe and Leaf

1963. Centenary of Red Cross.
925 **455** 10y. multicoloured . . . 35 10

1963. 5th International Irrigation and Drainage Commission Congress, Toyko.
926 **456** 10y. blue 15 10

457 Mt. Ito, Asahi Range

458 Mt. Bandai across Lake Hibara

1963. Bandai-Asahi National Park.
927 **457** 5y. green 45 10
928 **458** 10y. brown 75 10

459 Purple Jay

1963. Japanese Birds. Multicoloured.
929 10y. Type **459** . . . . . . 2·00 1·25
930 10y. Rock ptarmigan 65 20
931 10y. Eastern turtle dove . . . 65 20
932 10y. White stork 65 20
933 10y. Japanese bush warbler 65 20
934 10y. Siberian meadow bunting 65 20

1963. Olympic Games, Tokyo, 1964 (4th issue). Sports. As T **423**.
935 5y.+5y. blue 75 25
936 5y.+5y. brown 75 25
937 5y.+5y. brown 75 25
SPORTS: No. 935, Dinghy sailing; 936, Boxing; 937, Volleyball.

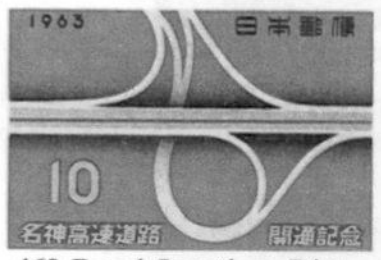
460 Road Junction, Ritto, Shiga

461 Girl Scout and Flag

1963. Opening of Nagoya–Kobe Expressway.
938 **460** 10y. green, black & orange 35 10

1963. Asian Girl Scout Camp, Nagano.
939 **461** 10y. multicoloured . . . 35 10

462 Mt. Washiu

463 Whirlpool at Naruto

1963. Seto Inland Sea National Park.
940 **462** 5y. brown 25 10
941 **463** 10y. green 35 10

464 Lake Shikaribetsu

465 Mt. Kurodake

1963. Daisetsuzan National Park.
942 **464** 5y. blue 25 10
943 **465** 10y. purple 35 10

466 Antenna

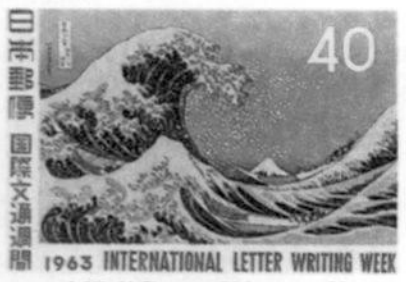

467 "Great Wave off Kanagawa" (from "36 Views of Mt. Fuji" by Hokusai Katsushika)

1963. 14th International Scientific Radio Union Conference, Tokyo.
944 **466** 10y. multicoloured . . . 25 10

1963. International Correspondence Week.
945 **467** 40y. multicoloured . . . 4·25 50
The design is taken from the series of 36 woodcuts showing Mt. Fuji. Others from this series are shown as Nos. 989, 1010, 1075, 1100, 1140 and 1185.

468 Athletes

469 Wrestling

1963. "Pre-Olympic" Athletic Meeting, Tokyo.
946 **468** 10y. multicoloured . . . 15 10

1963. 18th National Athletic Meeting, Yamaguchi.
947 **469** 5y. brown 20 10
948 – 5y. green 20 10
DESIGN: No. 948, Free-style gymnastics.

1963. Olympic Games, Tokyo, 1964 (5th issue). Sports. As T **423**.
949 5y.+5y. blue 35 10
950 5y.+5y. olive 35 10
951 5y.+5y. black 35 10
952 5y.+5y. purple 35 10
SPORTS: No. 949, Cycling; 950, Show jumping; 951, Hockey; 952, Pistol-shooting.

470 Hachijo Island

471 Kai and Iwai Dragon Toys

1963. Izu Islands Quasi-National Park.
953 **470** 10y. multicoloured . . . 25 10

1963. New Year's Greetings.
954 **471** 5y. multicoloured . . . 35 10

472 Wakasa Bay

1964. Wakasa Bay Quasi-National Park.
956 **472** 10y. multicoloured . . . 35 10

473 View from Horikiri Pass and Agave Plant

1964. Nichinan-Kaigan Quasi-National Park.
957 **473** 10y. multicoloured . . . 15 10

474 Uji Bridge

475 View of Toba

1964. Ise-Shima National Park.
958 **474** 5y. brown 15 10
959 **475** 10y. purple 20 10

476 Festival Float and Mt. Norikura (Tokayama Festival)

477 "Yamaboko" Shrine (Gion Festival)

478 Warriors on Horseback (Soma Horse Festival)

479 Festival Scene (Chichibu Festival)

1964. Regional Festivals.
960 **476** 10y. multicoloured . . . 35 10
961 **477** 10y. multicoloured . . . 35 10
962 **478** 10y. multicoloured . . . 35 10
963 **479** 10y. multicoloured . . . 35 10

480 Prince Niou playing for Lady Nakanokimi (detail of Takayoshi "Yadorigi" scroll illustrating "Tale of Genji" by Lady Murasaki)

1964. Philatelic Week.
964 **480** 10y. multicoloured . . . 40 15

481 Himeji Castle

482 Handball

1964. Rebuilding of Himeji Castle.
965 **481** 10y. brown 15 10

1964. 19th National Athletic Meeting, Niigata.
966 **482** 5y. green 10 10
967 – 5y. red (Gymnastics) . . . 10 10

483 Cross-section of Cable

1964. Opening of Japan–U.S. Submarine Telephone Cable.
968 **483** 10y. multicoloured . . . 15 10

1964. Olympic Games, Tokyo (6th issue). Sports. As T **423**.
969 5y.+5y. violet 45 10
970 5y.+5y. blue 45 10
971 5y.+5y. lake 45 10
972 5y.+5y. olive 45 10
SPORTS: No. 969, Modern pentathlon; 970, Canoeing; 971, Football; 972, Weightlifting.

484 Nihonbashi Bridge

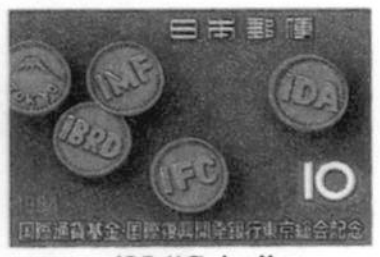
485 "Coins"

1964. Opening of Tokyo Expressway.
973 **484** 10y. green, silver and black 25 10

1964. Int Monetary Fund Convention, Tokyo.
980 **485** 10y. gold and red 25 10

486 Olympic Flame

487 "Agriculture"

1964. Olympic Games, Tokyo (7th issue). Inscr "1964". Multicoloured.
981 5y. Type **486** 20 15
982 10y. Main stadium (horiz) . . 30 20
983 30y. Fencing hall (horiz) . . 50 30
984 40y. Indoor stadium (horiz) 70 30
985 50y. Komazawa hall (horiz) 90 30

1964. Reclamation of Hachirogata Lagoon.
987 **487** 10y. gold and purple . . . 15 10

488 "Hikari" (light) Express Train

1964. Inauguration of Tokyo–Osaka Shinkansen Railway Line.
988 **488** 10y. blue and black . . . 1·00 20

489 "Tokaido Highway" (from "36 Views of Mt. Fuji" by Hokusai Katsushika)

490 Straw Snake

1964. International Correspondence Week.
989 **489** 40y. multicoloured . . . 1·75 10

1964. New Year's Greetings.
990 **490** 5y. multicoloured 15 10

491 Mt. Daisen and Akamatsu Pond

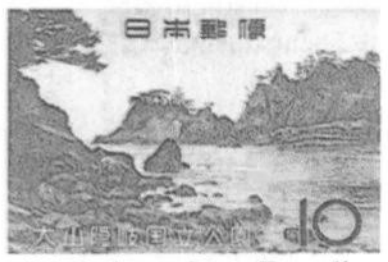
492 Jodo-ga-Ura (Paradise Islands) of Oki

1965. Daisen-Oki National Park.
992 **491** 5y. blue 25 10
993 **492** 10y. brown 35 10

493 Niseko-Annupuri Mountains

1965. Niseko Shakotan Otaru Quasi-National Park.
994 **493** 10y. multicoloured . . . 30 10

494 Radar Station

1965. Completion of Meteorological Radar Station, Mt. Fuji.
995 **494** 10y. multicoloured . . . 25 10

495 Kiyotsu Gorge

496 Mt. Myoko across Lake Nojiri

1965. Jo-Shin-Etsu Kogen National Park.
996 **495** 5y. brown 20 10
997 **496** 10y. purple 35 10

497 Postal Museum

1965. Inauguration of Postal Museum, Ote-machi, Tokyo, and Stamp Exhibition.
998 **497** 10y. green 15 10

498 "The Prelude" (after Shoen Uyemura)

499 Children at Play

1965. Philatelic Week.
999 **498** 10y. multicoloured . . . 50 10

1965. Inaug of National Children's Gardens.
1000 **499** 10y. multicoloured . . . 20 10

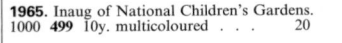

500 Tree within "Leaf"

501 Globe and Symbols

1965. Reafforestation.
1001 **500** 10y. multicoloured . . . 20 10

1965. Centenary of I.T.U.
1002 **501** 10y. multicoloured . . . 35 10

502 Mt. Naka Crater

503 Aso Peaks

1965. Aso National Park.
1003 **502** 5y. red 25 10
1004 **503** 10y. green 35 10

504 I.C.Y. Emblem and Doves

1965. International Co-operation Year.
1005 **504** 40y. multicoloured . . . 75 10

505 "Meiji Maru" (cadet ship) and Japanese Gulls

1965. 25th Maritime Day.
1006 **505** 10y. multicoloured . . . 60 20

506 "Blood Donation"

1965. Campaign for Blood Donors.
1007 **506** 10y. multicoloured . . . 25 10

507 Atomic Power Station, Tokyo
508 "Population"

1965. 9th International Atomic Energy Authority Conference, Tokyo.
1008 **507** 10y. multicoloured . . . 35 10

1965. 10th National Census.
1009 **508** 10y. multicoloured . . . 20 10

509 "Water at Misaka" (from "36 Views of Mt. Fuji" by Hokusai Katsushika)

1965. International Correspondence Week.
1010 **509** 40y. multicoloured . . . 80 60

510 Emblems and Plan of Diet

1965. 75th Anniv of National Suffrage.
1011 **510** 10y. multicoloured . . . 20 10

511 Walking

512 Outline of Face, and Baby

1965. 20th National Athletic Meeting, Gifu.
1012 **511** 5y. green 15 10
1013 – 5y. brown (Gymnastics) 15 10

1965. International Conferences of Otology, Rhinology and Laryngology (ICORL) and Pediatrics (ICP), Tokyo.
1014 **512** 30y. multicoloured . . . 40 10

513 Mt. Iwo

514 Mt. Rausu

1965. Shiretoko National Park.
1015 **513** 5y. turquoise 25 10
1016 **514** 10y. blue 35 10

515 Antarctic Map, Research Vessel "Fuji" and Aurora Australis

516 "Straw Horse"

1965. Antarctic Expedition of 1965.
1017 **515** 10y. multicoloured . . . 1·40 15

1965. New Year's Greetings.
1018 **516** 5y. multicoloured . . . 15 10

517 Telephone Switchboard (1890) and Modern Dial

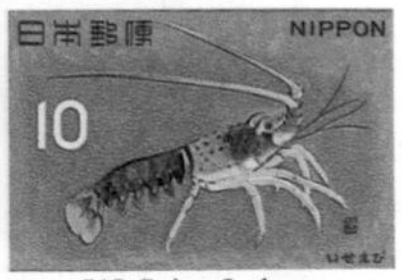
518 Spiny Lobster

1965. 75th Anniv of Japanese Telephone Service.
1020 **517** 10y. multicoloured . . . 15 10

NIPPON. From this point onwards all stamps are additionally inscribed "NIPPON".

1966. Fishery Products. Multicoloured.
1021 10y. Type **518** 30 15
1022 10y. Golden carp 30 15
1023 10y. Madai seabream . . . 30 15
1024 10y. Skipjack tuna 30 15
1025 10y. Ayu 30 15
1026 15y. Japanese eel 40 15
1027 15y. Chub mackerel 40 15
1028 15y. Chum salmon 40 15
1029 15y. Buri 60 15
1030 15y. Tiger pufferfish 60 20
1031 15y. Japanese common squid 75 30
1032 15y. Horned turban (shellfish) 85 30

519 Pleasure Garden, Mito

519a Pleasure Garden and Manchurian Cranes, Okayama

519b Kerokuen Garden, Kanazawa

1966. Famous Japanese Gardens.
1033 **519** 10y. green, black & gold 25 10
1034 **519a** 15y. black, red and blue 80 30
1035 **519b** 15y. black, green & sil 35 10

520 Crater of Mt. Zao

1966. Zao Quasi-National Park.
1036 **520** 10y. multicoloured . . . 35 10

521 Muroto Cape

522 Senba Cliffs, Anan

1966. Muroto-Anan Kaigan Quasi-National Park.
1037 **521** 10y. multicoloured . . . 25 10
1038 **522** 10y. multicoloured . . . 30 10

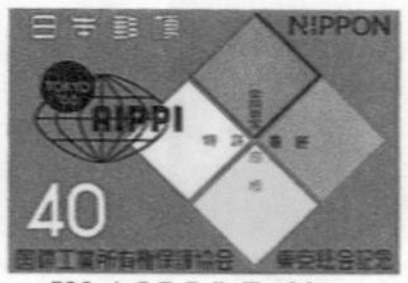
523 A.I.P.P.I. Emblem

1966. General Assembly of Int Association for Protection of Industrial Property (A.I.P.P.I.).
1039 **523** 40y. multicoloured . . . 35 10

524 "Butterflies" (after T. Fujishima)

1966. Philatelic Week.
1040 **524** 10y. multicoloured . . . 35 10

525 Goldfish

526 Chrysanthemums

527 Fuji (wisteria)

528 Hydrangea

529 Golden Hall, Chuson Temple

530 "Watasenia scintillans" (squid)

531 Yomei Gate, Tosho Shrine, Nikko

532 Mizubasho

533 Konponchudo Hall, Enryaku Temple

534 Ancient Clay Horse

535 Garden of Katsura Palace

536 Onjo Bosatsu (relief from bronze lantern, Todai Temple)

537 Kongo-Rikishi Statue, Todai Temple Nara

1966. Inscr "NIPPON".
1041 **235** 1y. bistre 10 10
1047 **525** 7y. orange and green . . 40 10
1049 **526** 15y. yellow and blue . . 1·25 10
1050 15y. yellow and blue . . 25 10
1052 **527** 20y. green and violet . . 1·25 10
1053 **528** 25y. blue and green . . . 60 10
1054 **529** 30y. gold and blue . . . 40 10
1055 **530** 35y. black, brown & blue 3·25 10
1056 **531** 40y. green and brown . . 60 10
1057 **532** 45y. multicoloured . . . 50 10
1058 **240** 50y. red . . . . 11·00 10
1059 50y. mauve 80 10
1060 **280** 55y. green, black and blue 75 10
1061 **533** 60y. green . . . . 1·00 10
1062 **534** 65y. brown . . . . . . 16·00 10
1063 65y. orange . . . . . . 1·00 10
1064 **281** 75y. multicoloured . . . 1·40 10
1065 **410** 90y. brown and gold . . 2·00 10
1066 **411** 100y. grey, black and red 2·25 20
1067 **535** 110y. brown . . . . . . 1·50 10
1068 **412** 120y. red . . . . 3·50 10
1069 **536** 200y. green . . . . . . 7·50 10
1070 **537** 500y. purple . . . . . . 8·50 10
No. 1050 is as T **526** but with white figures of value.
See also Nos. 1226/49.

538 U.N. and U.N.E.S.C.O. Emblems

539 Pacific Ocean

1966. 20th Anniv of U.N.E.S.C.O.
1071 **538** 15y. multicoloured . . . 15 10

1966. 11th Pacific Science Congress, Tokyo.
1072 **539** 15y. multicoloured . . . 20 10

540 Amakusa Bridges

1966. Completion of Amakusa Bridges.
1073 **540** 15y. multicoloured . . . 20 10

541 Family and Emblem

542 "Sekiya on the Sumida" (from "36 Views of Mt. Fuji" by Hokusai Katsushika)

1966. 50th Anniv of Post Office Life Insurance Office.
1074 **541** 15y. multicoloured . . . 15 10

1966. International Correspondence Week.
1075 **542** 50y. multicoloured . . . 1·75 15

543 Rotary Cobalt Radiator

544 Triple Jump

1966. 9th. International Cancer Congress, Tokyo.
1076 **543** 7y.+3y. black & orge . . 25 15
1077 – 15y.+5y. multicoloured 35 15
DESIGN—VERT: 15y. Detection by X-rays.

1966. 21st National Athletic Meeting, Oita.
1078 **544** 7y. red 30 10
1079 – 7y. blue (Clay-pigeon shooting) 30 10

545 National Theatre Building

546 Rice Year Emblem

1966. Inauguration of Japanese National Theatre. Multicoloured.
1080 15y. Type **545** 25 10
1081 25y. "Kabuki" performance (48 × 33½ mm) 90 10
1082 50y. "Bunraku" puppet act (33½ × 48 mm) . . . . . 1·00 10

1966. International Rice Year.
1083 **546** 15y. black, ochre and red 15 10

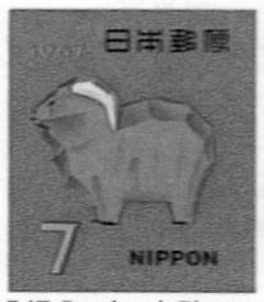
547 Ittobori Sheep (sculpture)

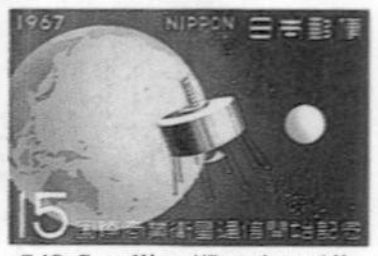
548 Satellite "Intelsat 2", Earth and Moon

1966. New Year's Greetings.
1084 **547** 7y. multicoloured . . . 15 10

1967. Inauguration of International Commercial Satellite Communications in Japan.
1086 **548** 15y. brown and blue . . 15 10

549 Douglas DC-8 and Flight Route

1967. Inauguration of Round-the-World Air Service.
1087 **549** 15y. multicoloured . . . 50 10

550 Literature Museum

1967. Opening of Japanese Modern Literature Museum, Meguro-ku, Tokyo.
1088 **550** 15y. multicoloured . . . 15 10

551 "Lakeside" (after S. Kuroda)

1967. Philatelic Week.
1089 **551** 15y. multicoloured . . . 60 10

552 Port of Kobe

553 Emblem of Welfare Service

1967. 5th International Association of Ports and Harbours Congress, Tokyo.
1090 **552** 50y. multicoloured . . . 80 10

1967. 50th Anniv of Welfare Commissioner Service.
1091 **553** 15y. gold and agate . . 25 10

554 Pedestrian Road Crossing

555 Mts. Kita and Koma

556 Mts. Akashi, Hijiri and Higashi

1967. 20th Anniv of Road Safety Campaign.
1092 **554** 15y. multicoloured . . . 15 10

1967. Southern Alps National Park.
1093 **555** 7y. blue 25 10
1094 **556** 15y. purple 35 10

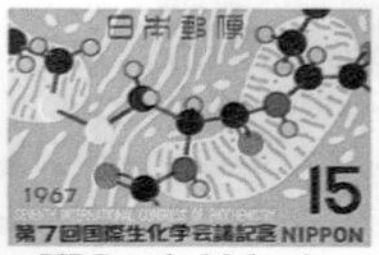
557 Protein Molecules

558 Gymnast

1967. 7th Int Biochemistry Congress, Tokyo.
1095 **557** 15y. multicoloured . . . 15 10

1967. "Universiade 1967" (Sports Meeting), Tokyo. Multicoloured.
1096 15y. Type **558** 20 10
1097 50y. Universiade "U" emblem (25 × 35½ mm) . . 90 10

559 Paper Lantern

560 Mt. Fuji (after T. Yokoyama)

1967. International Tourist Year.
1098 **559** 15y. multicoloured . . . 25 10
1099 **560** 50y. multicoloured . . . 1·40 1·75

561 "Kajikazawa in Kai Province" (from "36 Views of Mt. Fuji" by Hokusai Katsushika)

562 Athlete

1967. International Correspondence Week.
1100 **561** 50y. multicoloured . . . 2·75 15

1967. 22nd National Athletic Meeting, Saitama.
1101 **562** 15y. multicoloured . . . 50 10

563 Buddha, Koryu Temple, Kyoto

564 Kudara Kannon (Budda), Horyu Temple, Nara

565 Horyu Temple, Nara

1967. National Treasures. Asuka Period.
1102 **563** 15y. multicoloured . . . 40 10
1103 **564** 15y. multicoloured . . . 60 10
1104 **565** 50y. multicoloured . . . 2·50 20
See also Nos. 1113/15, 1120/2, 1134/6, 1152/4, 1170/2 and 1177/80.

566 Motor Expressway

569 "Noborizaru" (Miyazaki toy)

567 Mt. Kumotori

568 Lake Chichibu

1967. 13th World Road Congress, Tokyo.
1105 **566** 50y. multicoloured . . . 75 10

1967. Chichibu-Tama National Park.
1106 **567** 7y. olive 35 10
1107 **568** 15y. violet 45 10

1967. New Year's Greetings.
1108 **569** 7y. multicoloured . . . 35 10

570 Mt. Sobo

571 Takachiho Gorge

1967. Sobo-Katamuki Quasi-National Park.
1110 **570** 15y. multicoloured . . . 35 10
1111 **571** 15y. multicoloured . . . 35 10

572 Boy and Girl and Cruise Liner "Sakura Maru"

573 Asura Statue, Kofuku Temple, Nara

574 Gakko Bosatsu, Todai Temple, Nara

575 Srimaha devi (painting), Yakushi Temple, Nara

1968. Youth Goodwill Cruise to mark Meiji Centenary.
1112 **572** 15y. violet, yellow & blue 15 10

1968. National Treasures. Nara Period (710–784).
1113 **573** 15y. multicoloured . . . 45 10
1114 **574** 15y. multicoloured . . . 70 10
1115 **575** 50y. multicoloured . . . 2·50 20

576 Mt. Yatsugatake and Cattle

577 Mt. Tateshina and Lake

1968. Yatsugatake-Chushin Kogen Quasi-National Park.
1116 **576** 15y. multicoloured . . . 30 10
1117 **577** 15y. multicoloured . . . 30 10

578 "Dancer in a Garden" (after Bakusen Tsuchida)

1968. Philatelic Week.
1118 **578** 15y. multicoloured . . . 40 10

579 View of Rishiri Island from Rebun Island

1968. Rishiri-Rebun Quasi-National Park.
1119 **579** 15y. multicoloured . . . 15 10

580 Lacquer Casket

582 "Fugen Bosatsu" (painting of Bodishattva Samantabhadva)

581 "The Origin of Shigisan" (painting in Chogo-sonshi Temple)

1968. National Treasures. Heinan Period (794–1185).
1120 **580** 15y. multicoloured . . . 30 10
1121 **581** 15y. multicoloured . . . 60 10
1122 **582** 50y. multicoloured . . . 4·25 35

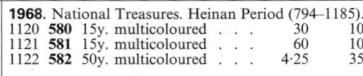

583 Centenary Tower and Star

584 Biro Trees and Pacific Sunrise

1968. Hokkaido Centenary.
1123 **583** 15y. multicoloured . . . 15 10

1968. Return of Ogasawara Islands to Japan.
1124 **584** 15y. multicoloured . . . 15 10

585 "Map of Japan" in Figures

1968. Postal Codes Campaign.
1125 **585** 7y. red, brown & grn (I) 2·75 10
1126 – 7y. red, brown & grn (II) 2·75 10
1127 **585** 15y. mauve, vio & bl (I) 1·00 10
1128 – 15y. mauve, vio & bl (II) 1·00 10
(I) Inscr as in Type **585** reading "Don't omit postal code on the address" measures 11 mm.
(II) Inscr reading "Postal code also on your address" measures 12 mm.

586 River Kiso

587 Inuyama Castle and View

1968. Hida-Kisogawa Quasi-National Park.
1129 **586** 15y. multicoloured . . . 25 10
1130 **587** 15y. multicoloured . . . 25 10

588 Federation Emblem and "Sun"

1968. Int Youth Hostel Conference, Tokyo.
1131 **588** 15y. multicoloured . . . 20 10

589 Humans forming Emblem

590 Baseball "Pitcher"

1968. 50th All-Japan High School Baseball Championships, Koshi-en, Tokyo.
1132 **589** 15y. multicoloured . . . 60 10
1133 **590** 15y. multicoloured . . . 60 10

591 "Minamoto Yoritomo" (Jingo Temple Collection)

593 Red-braided Armour (Kasuga Grand Shrine Collection)

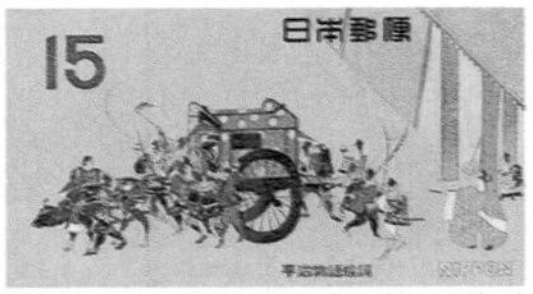

592 Emperor Nijo escaping from Black Palace (from "Tale of Heiji" picture scroll)

1968. National Treasures. Kamakura Period (1185–1334).
1134 **591** 15y. multicoloured . . . 40 10
1135 **592** 15y. multicoloured . . . 40 10
1136 **593** 50y. multicoloured . . . 3·00 30

594 Mt. Iwate

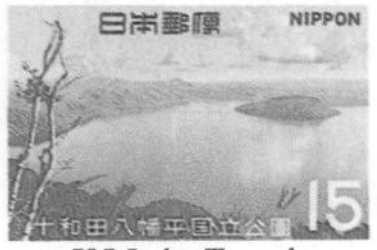

595 Lake Towada

1968. Towada-Hachimantai National Park.
1137 **594** 7y. brown 25 10
1138 **595** 15y. green 45 10

596 Gymnastics

597 "Fujimihara in Owari Province" (from "36 Views of Mt. Fuji" by Hokusai Katsushika)

1968. 23rd National Athletic Meeting.
1139 **596** 15y. multicoloured . . . 40 10

1968. International Correspondence Week.
1140 **597** 50y. multicoloured . . . 2·00 25

598 Centenary Emblem and Sail Warship "Shohei Maru", 1868

599 "Arrival of the Imperial Carriage in Tokyo" (after Tomone Kobori)

1968. Centenary of Meiji Era.
1141 **598** 15y. multicoloured . . . 15 10
1142 **599** 15y. multicoloured . . . 15 10

600 Old and New Kannonzaki Lighthouses

1968. Centenary of Japanese Lighthouses.
1143 **600** 15y. multicoloured . . . 30 10

601 Ryo's Dancer and State Hall

1968. Completion of Imperial Palace.
1144 **601** 15y. multicoloured . . . 20 10

602 Mt. Takachiho

603 Mt. Motobu, Yaku Island

1968. Kirishima-Yaku National Park.

1145 **602** 7y. violet 20 10

1146 **603** 15y. orange 25 10

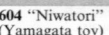

604 "Niwatori" (Yamagata toy)

605 Human Rights Emblem and Dancers

1968. New Year's Greetings.

1147 **604** 7y. multicoloured . . . 25 10

1968. Human Rights Year.

1149 **605** 50y. multicoloured . . . 25 15

606 Siberian Chipmunk with Nuts

607 Coastal Scenery

1968. Savings Promotion.

1150 **606** 15y. sepia and green . . 70 10

1969. Echizen-Kaga-Kaigan Quasi-National Park.

1151 **607** 15y. multicoloured . . . 15 10

608 Silver Pavilion, Jisho Temple, Kyoto

609 Pagoda, Anraku Temple, Nagano

610 "Winter Landscape" (Sesshu)

1969. National Treasures. Muromachi Period.

1152 **608** 15y. multicoloured . . . 40 10

1153 **609** 15y. multicoloured . . . 40 10

1154 **610** 50y. multicoloured . . . 2·00 30

611 Mt. Chokai, from Tobishima

1969. Chokai Quasi-National Park.

1155 **611** 15y. multicoloured . . . 35 20

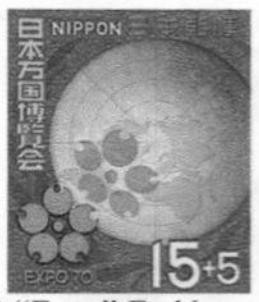

612 "Expo" Emblem and Globe

613 "Cherry Blossom" (from mural Chichakuin Temple, Kyoto)

1969. "EXPO 70" World Fair, Osaka (1st issue).

1156 **612** 15y.+5y. mult 35 15

1157 **613** 50y.+10y. mult 85 50

See also Nos. 1193/5 and 1200/2.

614 Mt. Koya from Jinnogamine

615 Mt. Gomadan and Rhododendrons

1969. Koya-Ryujin Quasi-National Park.

1158 **614** 15y. multicoloured . . . 15 10

1159 **615** 15y. multicoloured . . . 15 10

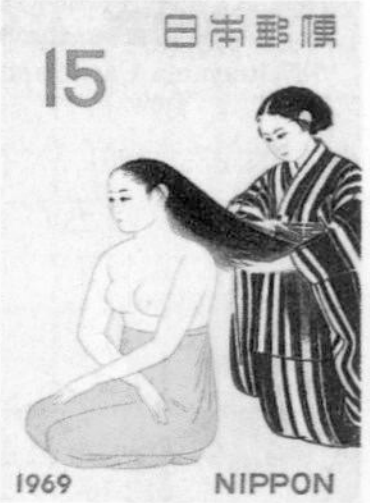

616 "Hair" (Kokei Kobayashi)

617 Woman and Child crossing "Roads"

1969. Philatelic Week.

1160 **616** 15y. multicoloured . . . 40 10

1969. Road Safety Campaign.

1161 **617** 15y. green, blue and red 15 10

618 Sakawagawa Bridge

1969. Completion of Tokyo–Nagoya Expressway.

1162 **618** 15y. multicoloured . . . 30 10

619 Museum Building

1969. Opening of National Museum of Modern Art, Tokyo.

1163 **619** 15y. multicoloured . . . 15 10

620 Nuclear-powered Freighter "Mutsu" and Atomic Symbol

1969. Launching of Japan's 1st Nuclear Ship "Mutsu".

1164 **620** 15y. multicoloured . . . 30 10

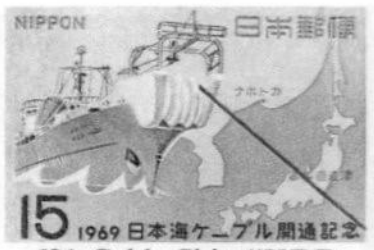

621 Cable Ship "KDD Maru" and Map

622 Symbol and Cards

1969. Opening of Japanese Ocean Cable.

1165 **621** 15y. multicoloured . . . 15 10

1969. Postal Codes Campaign.

1166 **622** 7y. red and green . . . 15 10

1167 – 15y. red and blue . . . 20 10

DESIGN: 15y. Symbol, postbox and code numbers.

624 Lions Emblem and Rose

625 Hotoke-ga-ura (coast)

1969. 52nd Lions Int Convention, Tokyo.

1168 **624** 15y. multicoloured . . . 20 10

1969. Shimokita-Hanto Quasi-National Park.

1169 **625** 15y. multicoloured . . . 15 10

626 Himeji Castle, Hyogo Prefecture

627 "Pinewoods" (T. Hasegawa)

628 "The Japanese Cypress" (artist unknown)

1969. National Treasures. Momoyama Period.

1170 **626** 15y. multicoloured . . . 50 10

1171 **627** 15y. black and drab . . 50 10

1172 **628** 50y. multicoloured . . . 1·00 10

629 Harano-fudo Waterfalls

630 Mt. Nagisan

1969. Hyonosen-Ushiroyama-Nagisan Quasi-National Park.

1173 **629** 15y. multicoloured . . . 25 10

1174 **630** 15y. multicoloured . . . 25 10

631 Mt. O-akan

632 Mt. Iwo

1969. Akan National Park.

1175 **631** 7y. blue 25 10

1176 **632** 15y. sepia 25 10

633 "Choben" (T. Ikeno)

634 "The Red-plum Tree" (K. Ogata)

635 "The White-plum Tree" (K. Ogata)

636 "Japanese Pheasant" Incense-burner (after Ninsei)

1969. National Treasures. Edo Period.

1177 **633** 15y. multicoloured . . . 40 10

1178 **634** 15y. multicoloured . . . 50 10

1179 **635** 15y. multicoloured . . . 50 10

1180 **636** 50y. multicoloured . . . 1·00 65

637 Globe and Doves

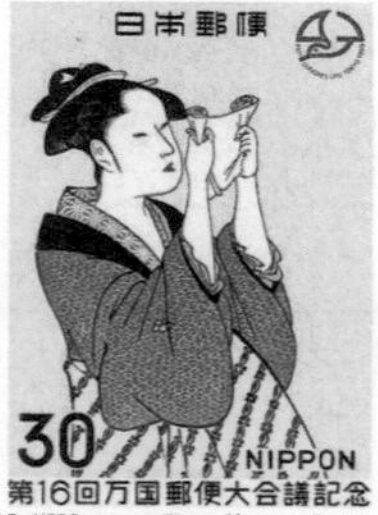

638 "Woman Reading a Letter" (Utamaro Kitagawa)

639 "Reading a Letter" (Harunobu Suzuki)

640 "Miyako Dennai" (Sharaku Toshusai)

1969. 16th U.P.U. Congress, Tokyo.

1181 **637** 15y. multicoloured . . . 30 10

1182 **638** 30y. multicoloured . . . 65 10

1183 **639** 50y. multicoloured . . . 1·25 10

1184 **640** 60y. multicoloured . . . 1·40 10

641 "Mishima Pass" (from "36 Views of Mt. Fuji" by Hokusai Katsushika)

642 Rugby Football

1969. International Correspondence Week.
1185 **641** 50y. multicoloured . . . 1·00 10

1969. 24th National Athletic Meeting.
1186 **642** 15y. multicoloured . . . 50 10

643 Cape Kitayama

644 Goishi Coast

1969. Rikuchu-Kaigan National Park.
1187 **643** 7y. blue 15 10
1188 **644** 15y. red and salmon . . 20 10

645 Worker in Safety Helmet

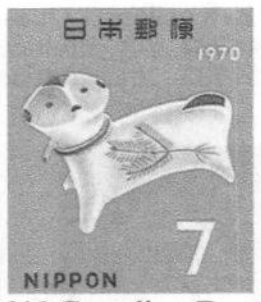
646 Guardian Dog, Hokkeji Temple

1969. 50th Anniv of I.L.O.
1189 **645** 15y. multicoloured . . . 15 10

1969. New Year's Greetings.
1190 **646** 7y. multicoloured . . . 35 10

647 Peasants, Tsushima Island

1970. Iki-Tsushima Quasi-National Park.
1192 **647** 15y. multicoloured . . . 20 10

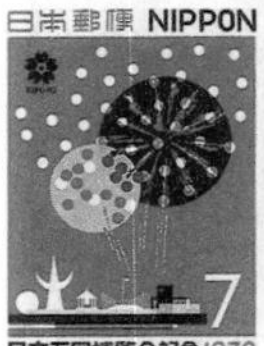
648 View of Fair and Firework Display

651 "Woman with Drum" (Saburosuke Okada)

1970. "EXPO 70" World Fair, Osaka (2nd issue). Multicoloured.
1193 7y. Type **648** 15 10
1194 15y. Earth and cherry blossom garland 25 10
1195 50y. "Irises" (Korin Ogata) (48 × 33 mm) 45 10

1970. Philatelic Week.
1197 **651** 15y. multicoloured . . . 40 10

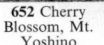

652 Cherry Blossom, Mt. Yoshino

653 Waterfall, Nachi

1970. Yoshino-Kumano National Park.
1198 **652** 7y. black and pink . . . 30 10
1199 **653** 15y. dp green, green & bl 45 10

654 Kanto (lantern) Festival

655 Japanese Pavilions

656 "Flowers of Autumn" (detail, Hoitsu Sakai)

1970. "EXPO 70" World Fair, Osaka (3rd issue).
1200 **654** 7y. multicoloured . . . 20 10
1201 **655** 15y. multicoloured . . . 30 10
1202 **656** 50y. multicoloured . . . 45 10

657 Houses and Code Symbol

658 Utaemon Nakamura VI as Hanako in "Musume Dojoji"

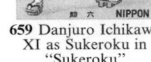

659 Danjuro Ichikawa XI as Sukeroku in "Sukeroku"

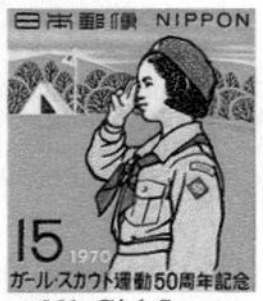
661 Girl Scout saluting

660 "Kanjincho"

1970. Postal Codes Campaign.
1204 **657** 7y. violet and green . . 25 10
1205 15y. purple and blue . . 35 10

1970. Japanese Theatre "Kabuki".
1206 **658** 15y. multicoloured . . . 25 10
1207 **659** 15y. multicoloured . . . 25 10
1208 **660** 50y. multicoloured . . . 75 10
See also Nos. 1250/2, 1284/6 and 1300/2.

1970. 50th Anniv of Japanese Girl Scouts.
1209 **661** 15y. multicoloured . . . 35 10

662 Festival Drummer and Kinoura Coastline

663 Mt. Tate from Himi Shore

1970. Noto-Hanto Quasi-National Park.
1210 **662** 15y. multicoloured . . . 25 10
1211 **663** 15y. multicoloured . . . 25 10

664 "Sunflower" and U.N. Emblem

667 "Tokyo Post Office" (woodcut, Hiroshige III)

665 Mt. Myogi

666 Mt. Arafune

1970. 4th U.N. Congress on Prevention of Crime and Treatment of Offenders, Kyoto.
1212 **664** 15y. multicoloured . . . 25 10

1970. Myogi-Arafune-Sakukuogen Quasi-National Park.
1213 **665** 15y. multicoloured . . . 20 10
1214 **666** 15y. multicoloured . . . 20 10

1970. International Correspondence Week.
1215 **667** 50y. multicoloured . . . 85 10

668 Show Jumping, Mt. Iwate and Paulownia Flowers

669 "Hodogaya Stage" (print, Hiroshige III)

1970. 25th National Athletic Meeting, Iwate.
1216 **668** 15y. multicoloured . . . 50 10

1970. Centenary of Telegraph Service.
1217 **669** 15y. multicoloured . . . 45 10

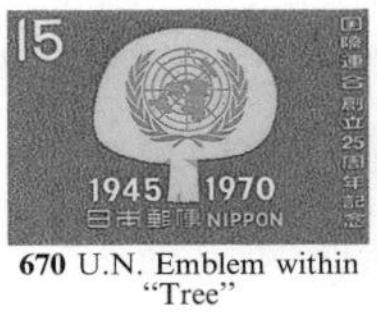
670 U.N. Emblem within "Tree"

672 Competition Emblem

1970. 25th Anniv of U.N.O. Multicoloured.
1218 15y. Type **670** 15 10
1219 50y. U.N. emblem, New York H.Q. and flags . . . 40 10

1970. 19th International Vocational Training Competition, Chiba City.
1220 **672** 15y. multicoloured . . . 15 10

673 Diet Building and Doves

674 "Wild Boar" (folk-handicraft)

1970. 80th Anniv of Japanese Diet.
1221 **673** 15y. multicoloured . . . 15 10

1970. New Year's Greetings.
1222 **674** 7y. multicoloured . . . 20 10

675 Ski Jumping

1971. Winter Olympic Games, Sapporo (1972) (1st issue). Multicoloured.
1224 15y.+5y. Type **675** 30 10
1225 15y.+5y. Ice-hockey (horiz) 30 10
See also Nos. 1280/82.

677 Mute Swan

678 Sika Deer

679 "Allomyrina dichotomus"

680 "Pine Tree" (T. Kano)

682 Golden Eagle

684 "Ho-o" (Phoenix), Byodoin Temple, Uji

692 Statue of Kissho, Joruri Temple

1971. Inscr "NIPPON".
1226 **273** 3y. green 20 20
1227 **677** 5y. blue 20 20
1228 **678** 10y. brown and green 25 10
1229 **679** 12y. brown 20 10
1230 **680** 20y. brown and green 20 10
1231 **528** 25y. blue and green . . 35 10
1232 **240** 50y. green 35 10
1233 – 60y. green and yellow 40 10
1234 **408** 70y. black and orange 95 10
1235 **409** 80y. brown and red . . 1·40 20
1236 **410** 90y. brown and orange 1·40 10
1237 **682** 90y. black and red . . 2·00 20
1238 **412** 120y. brown and green 55 10
1239 – 140y. purple and mauve 75 10
1240 **684** 150y. turquoise & green 1·75 10
1240a 150y. brown and red . . 60 10
1241 – 200y. red . . . . . . 3·00 10
1242 – 200y. brown . . . . . 3·50 10
1243 – 200y. red . . . . . . 1·25 10
1244 – 250y. blue . . . . . . 1·25 10
1245 – 300y. blue . . . . . . 3·50 10
1246 – 350y. brown . . . . . 2·00 10
1247 – 400y. red . . . . . . 2·40 10
1248 – 500y. green . . . . . 3·00 10
1249 **692** 1000y. multicoloured 5·50 60

DESIGNS: 60y. Narcissi; 140y. Noh mask of aged man; 200y. (No. 1241), Onjo Bosatsu (relief), Todai Temple; 200y. (Nos. 1242/3), Warrior (statuette); 250y. Komainu (guardian dog), Katori Shrine; 300y. Buddha, Kofuku Temple; 350y. Goddess of Mercy, Yaluski Temple, Nara; 400y. Tentoki (demon); 500y. Buddhist deity.

No. 1231 is Type **528**, redrawn. The inscription and face value are smaller, but the main difference is in the position of the leaves. On No. 1053 they touch the left edge of the design, but on No. 1231 they are completely clear of it.

No. 1241 is as Type **536** but smaller, 18 × 22 mm.

For 210y. as Nos. 1242/3 and 360y. as No. 1246, see Nos. 1600 and 1604.

693 "Gen-jo-raku" 694 "Ko-cho"

695 "Tai-hei-raku"

1971. Japanese Theatre "Gagaku".

1250	**693**	15y. multicoloured . . .	30	10
1251	**694**	15y. multicoloured . . .	30	10
1252	**695**	50y. multicoloured . . .	85	10

696 Voter and Diet Building 697 Pine Trees and Maple Leaves

1971. 25th Anniv of Women's Suffrage.
1253 **696** 15y. multicoloured . . . 15 10

1971. National Afforestation Campaign.
1254 **697** 7y. black, violet & green 40 10

698 "Tsukiji-akashicho" (K. Kaburagi) 699 "Posting a Letter" (K. Dogishi)

700 "Postman" (K. Kasai) 701 "Railway Post Office" (S. Onozaki)

1971. Philatelic Week.
1255 **698** 15y. multicoloured . . . 40 10

1971. Centenary of Japanese Postal Services.

1256	**699** 15y. multicoloured . . .	20	10
1257	**700** 15y. black and brown . .	20	10
1258	**701** 15y. multicoloured . . .	40	10

702 Great Tit 703 Adelie Penguins

1971. 25th Bird Week.
1259 **702** 15y. multicoloured . . . 85 20

1971. 10th Anniv of Antarctic Treaty.
1260 **703** 15y. multicoloured . . . 1·10 20

704 Goto-Wakamatsu-Seto 705 Kuzyuku-shima

1971. Saikai National Park.

1261 **704** 7y. green	25	10
1262 **705** 15y. brown	35	10

706 Postal Code Numerals 707 Scout Bugler

1971. Postal Code Campaign.

1263 **706** 7y. red and green . . .	20	10
1264 15y. red and blue . . .	30	10

1971. 13th World Scout Jamboree, Asagiri.
1265 **707** 15y. multicoloured . . . 40 10

708 Rose Emblem

1971. 50th Anniv of Family Conciliation System.
1266 **708** 15y. multicoloured . . . 25 10

709 "Tokyo Horse Tram" (Yoshimura)

1971. International Correspondence Week.
1267 **709** 50y. multicoloured . . . 60 25

710 Emperor's Standard 712 Tennis

1971. European Tour by Emperor Hirohito and Empress Nagako. Multicoloured.

1268	15y. Type **710**	15	10
1269	15y. "Beyond the Sea" (drawing by Empress Nagako)	15	10

1971. 26th National Athletic Meeting.
1271 **712** 15y. multicoloured . . . 30 10

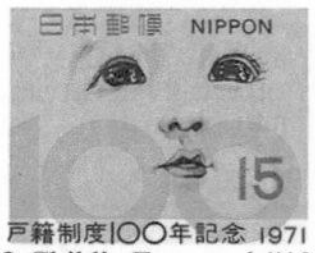
713 Child's Face and "100"

1971. Centenary of National Family Registration System.
1272 **713** 15y. multicoloured . . . 15 10

714 "Dragon" (G. Hashimoto)

1971. Centenary of Government Printing Works, Tokyo. Multicoloured.

1273	15y. Type **714**	20	10
1274	15y. "Tiger" (from same drawing as above)	20	10

716 Mt. Yotei from Lake Toya 718 Takarabune ("Treasure Ship")

717 Mt. Showa-Shinzan

1971. Shikotsu-Toya National Park.

1275 **716** 7y. green and olive . . .	25	10
1276 **717** 15y. blue and brown . .	40	10

1971. New Year's Greetings.

1277 **718** 7y. multicoloured . . .	25	10
1278 10y. multicoloured . . .	35	10

719 Skiing

1972. Winter Olympic Games, Sapporo (2nd issue). Multicoloured.

1280	20y. Type **719**	15	10
1281	20y. Bobsleighing	15	10
1282	50y. Figure skating (pair) (52 × 36 mm)	45	10

722 "Kumagai-jinya" 723 "Nozaki-mura"

724 "Awa-no-Naruto"

1972. Japanese Theatre. "Banraku" Puppet Theatre.

1284 **722** 20y. multicoloured . . .	30	10
1285 **723** 20y. multicoloured . . .	30	10
1286 **724** 50y. multicoloured . . .	70	10

725 "Hikari" Express Train 727 Fishing, Taishakukyo Valley

726 Hiba Mountains

1972. Centenary of Japanese Railways (1st issue) and Opening of Sanyo Shinkansen Line.
1287 **725** 20y. multicoloured . . . 25 10
See also Nos. 1305/6.

1972. Hiba-Dogo-Taishaku Quasi-National Park.

1288 **726** 20y. multicoloured . . .	15	10
1289 **727** 20y. multicoloured . . .	20	10

728 Adult with Human Heart 729 "Rising Balloon" (Gakuryo Nakamura)

1972. World Heart Month.
1290 **728** 20y. multicoloured . . . 15 10

1972. Philatelic Week.
1291 **729** 20y. multicoloured . . . 15 10

730 Courtesy Gate, Shuri 731 Japanese Camellia

1972. Return of Ryukyu Islands to Japan.
1292 **730** 20y. multicoloured . . . 15 10

1972. National Afforestation Campaign.
1293 **731** 20y. yellow blue & green 35 10

732 Mt. Kurikoma and Kokeshi Doll

733 Naruko-kyo Gorge and Kokeshi Doll

1972. Kurikoma Quasi-National Park.

1294 **732** 20y. multicoloured . . .	15	10
1295 **733** 20y. multicoloured . . .	15	10

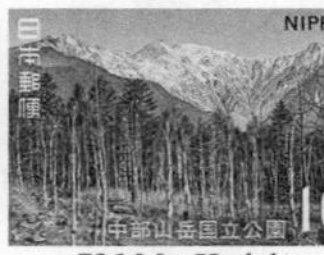
734 Envelope and Code Symbol 736 Mt. Hodaka

737 Mt. Tate

1972. Postal Codes Campaign (5th issue).

1296 **734** 10y. black, purple & blue	10	10
1297 – 20y. red and green . . .	15	10

DESIGN: 20y. Mail-box and code symbol.

1972. Chubu Sangaku National Park.

1298 **736** 10y. violet and mauve	20	10
1299 **737** 20y. blue and brown . .	30	10

738 "Tamura" 739 "Aoi-no-ue"

740 "Hagoromo"

1972. Japanese Theatre. "Noh".

1300 **738** 20y. multicoloured . . .	20	10
1301 **739** 20y. multicoloured . . .	20	10
1302 **740** 50y. multicoloured . . .	45	15

741 "Profiles of Schoolchildren" 742 "Eitai Bridge" (Hiroshige III)

1972. Centenary of Japanese Educational System.
1303 **741** 20y. multicoloured . . . 15 10

1972. International Correspondence Week.
1304 **742** 50y. multicoloured . . . 60 10

743 "Inauguration of Railway Service" (Hiroshige III)

745 Kendo (Japanese Fencing)

1972. Centenary of Japanese Railways (2nd issue). Multicoloured.
1305 20y. Type **743** 50 10
1306 20y. Class C-62 steam locomotive No. 2 . . . . 50 10

1972. 27th National Athletic Meeting, Kagoshima.
1307 **745** 10y. multicoloured . . . 35 10

746 Scout and Cub

747 "Harbour and Bund, Yokohama" (Hiroshige III)

1972. 50th Anniv of Japanese Boy Scouts.
1308 **746** 20y. multicoloured . . . 35 10

1972. Centenary of Japanese Customs Service.
1309 **747** 20y. multicoloured . . . 55 10

748 "Plum Blossoms" Plate (K. Ogata)

749 Mt. Tsurugi

750 River Yoshino, Oboke Valley

1972. New Year's Greetings.
1310 **748** 10y. multicoloured . . . 15 10

1973. Tsurugi-San Quasi-National Park.
1312 **749** 20y. multicoloured . . . 30 10
1313 **750** 20y. multicoloured . . . 30 10

751 Mt. Takao

752 Minoo Falls and Japanese Macaques

1973. Meiji-no-mori Quasi-National Park.
1314 **751** 20y. multicoloured . . . 20 10
1315 **752** 20y. multicoloured . . . 20 10

753 "Dragon" (East Wall)

754 "Male Figures" (East Wall)

755 "Female Figures" (West Wall)

1973. Asuka Archaeological Conservation Fund. Takamatsuzuka Kofun Tomb Murals.
1316 **753** 20y.+5y. multicoloured 30 10
1317 **754** 20y.+5y. multicoloured 30 10
1318 **755** 50y.+10y. multicoloured 80 35

756 Phoenix Tree

757 "Sumiyoshimode" (R. Kishida)

1973. National Afforestation Campaign.
1319 **756** 20y. multicoloured . . . 35 10

1973. Philatelic Week.
1320 **757** 20y. multicoloured . . . 15 10

758 Mt. Kama

759 Rock Outcrops, Mt. Haguro

1973. Suzuka Quasi-National Park.
1321 **758** 20y. multicoloured . . . 25 10
1322 **759** 20y. multicoloured . . . 25 10

760 Chichi-jima Island Beach

761 Coral Reef, Minami-jimi Island

1973. Ogasawara Islands National Park.
1323 **760** 10y. blue 25 10
1324 **761** 20y. purple 35 10

762 Postal Code Symbol and Tree

765 Waterfall, Sandan-kyo Gorge

764 Mt. Shinnyu

1973. Postal Codes Campaign.
1325 **762** 10y. gold and green . . 10 10
1326 – 20y. lilac, red and blue 15 10
DESIGN: 20y. Postman and symbol.

1973. Nishi-Chugoku-Sanchi Quasi-National Park.
1327 **764** 20y. multicoloured . . . 30 10
1328 **765** 20y. multicoloured . . . 30 10

766 Valley of River Tenryu

767 Oriental Scops Owl and Woodland Path, Mt. Horaiji

1973. Tenryu-Okumikowa Quasi-National Park.
1329 **766** 20y. multicoloured . . . 25 10
1330 **767** 20y. blue, green and silver 45 20

768 "Cock" (J. Ito)

769 Sprinting

1973. International Correspondence Week.
1331 **768** 50y. multicoloured . . . 65 10

1973. 28th National Athletic Meeting. Chiba.
1332 **769** 10y. multicoloured . . . 20 10

770 Kan-Mon Bridge

1973. Opening of Kan-Mon Suspension Bridge.
1333 **770** 20y. multicoloured . . . 40 10

771 Hanasaka-jijii and his Dog

772 Hanasaka-jijii finds the Gold

773 Hanasaka-jijii and Tree in Blossom

1973. Japanese Folk Tales (1st series). "Hanasaki-jijii".
1334 **771** 20y. multicoloured . . . 15 10
1335 **772** 20y. multicoloured . . . 15 10
1336 **773** 20y. multicoloured . . . 15 10
See also Nos. 1342/4, 1352/4, 1358/60, 1362/4, 1378/80 and 1387/9.

774 Lantern

775 Niju-bashi Bridge

1973. New Year's Greetings.
1337 **774** 10y. multicoloured . . . 10 10

1974. Imperial Golden Wedding. Mult.
1339 20y. Type **775** 15 10
1340 20y. Imperial Palace 15 10

777 "The Crane Damsel"

1974. Japanese Folk Tales (2nd series). "Tsuru-Nyobo". Multicoloured.
1342 20y. Type **777** 15 10
1343 20y. Manchurian Crane "weaving" 45 20
1344 20y. Manchurian Cranes in flight 45 20

780 "A Reefy Coast" (Hyakusui Hirafuku)

1974. International Ocean Exposition, Okinawa (1975) (1st issue).
1345 **780** 20y.+5y. multicoloured 15 10
See also Nos. 1401/3.

781 Marudu Falls

782 Seascape

1974. Iriomote National Park.
1346 **781** 20y. multicoloured . . . 25 10
1347 **782** 20y. multicoloured . . . 25 10

783 Iriomote Cat

1974. Nature Conservation (1st series).
1348 **783** 20y. multicoloured . . . 25 10
See also Nos. 1356, 1361, 1372, 1377, 1381, 1405, 1419, 1422, 1430, 1433/4, 1449, 1457, 1469, 1470, 1475, 1490, 1497 and 1502.

784 "Finger" (Shinsui Ito)

1974. Philatelic Week.
1349 **784** 20y. multicoloured . . . 40 10

785 Nambu Red Pine

786 Supreme Court Building

1974. National Afforestation Campaign.
1350 **785** 20y. multicoloured . . . 20 10

1974. Completion of Supreme Court Building, Tokyo.
1351 **786** 20y. brown 15 10

787 "Sailing in a Wooden Bowl"

788 "Conquering the Goblins"

789 "Wielding the Little Magic Mallet"

1974. Japanese Folk Tales (3rd series). "The Dwarf".
1352 **787** 20y. multicoloured . . . 15 10
1353 **788** 20y. multicoloured . . . 15 10
1354 **789** 20y. multicoloured . . . 15 10

790 "Uniform Rivalry" (detail after Kunimasa Baido)

792 World Blood Donation

1974. Centenary of Japanese Police System.
1355 **790** 20y. multicoloured . . . 15 10

1974. Nature Conservation (2nd series). As T **783**. Multicoloured.
1356 20y. European otter ("Lutra lutra") 25 10

1974. International Red Cross Day.
1357 **792** 20y. multicoloured . . . 15 10

793 "Discovery of Kaguya Hime"

794 "Kaguya Hime as Young Woman"

795 "The Ascent to Heaven"

1974. Japanese Folk Tales (4th series). "Kaguya Hime".
1358 **793** 20y. multicoloured . . . 25 10
1359 **794** 20y. multicoloured . . . 25 10
1360 **795** 20y. multicoloured . . . 25 10

1974. Nature Conservation (3rd series). As T **783**. Multicoloured.
1361 20y. Ryukyu rabbit ("Pentalagus furnessi") . . 25 10

797 Old Men in front of Yahata Shrine

798 Old Man dancing with Demons

799 Old Man with Two Warts

1974. Japanese Folk Tales (5th series). "Kobutori-Jiisan".
1362 **797** 20y. multicoloured . . . 15 10
1363 **798** 20y. multicoloured . . . 15 10
1364 **799** 20y. multicoloured . . . 15 10

800 Map of World

802 "Pine and Northern Goshawk" (detail, Sesson)

1974. 61st Inter-Parliamentary Union Congress, Tokyo. Multicoloured.
1365 20y. Type **800** 25 10
1366 50y. "Aizen"—Mandarins in pond (Kawabata) (48 × 33 mm) 70 30

1974. International Correspondence Week.
1367 **802** 50y. brown and purple 70 30

803 U.P.U. Emblem

805 Footballers

1974. Centenary of U.P.U. Multicoloured.
1368 20y. Type **803** 10 10
1369 50y. "Tending a Cow" (fan-painting—Sotatsu Tawaraya) (50 × 29 mm) 30 10

1974. 29th National Athletic Meeting.
1370 **805** 10y. multicoloured . . . 15 10

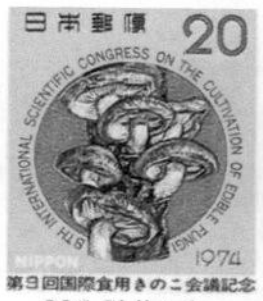
806 Shii-take Mushrooms

808 Class D51 Locomotive

809 Class C57 Locomotive

1974. 9th International Scientific Congress on Cultivation of Edible Fungi.
1371 **806** 20y. multicoloured . . . 40 10

1974. Nature Conservation (4th series). As T **783**. Multicoloured.
1372 20y. Bonin Islands flying fox ("Pteropus pselaphon") 15 10

1974. Railway Steam Locomotives (1st series).
1373 **808** 20y. multicoloured . . . 65 15
1374 **809** 20y. multicoloured . . . 65 15
See also Nos. 1382/3, 1385/6, 1395/6 and 1398/9.

810 "Kugikakushi" (ornamental nail-covering) in the form of a daffodil

1974. New Year's Greetings.
1375 **810** 10y. multicoloured . . . 15 10

1975. Nature Conservation (5th series). As T **783**. Multicoloured.
1377 20y. Short-tailed albatrosses ("Diomedea albatrus") (vert) 70 20

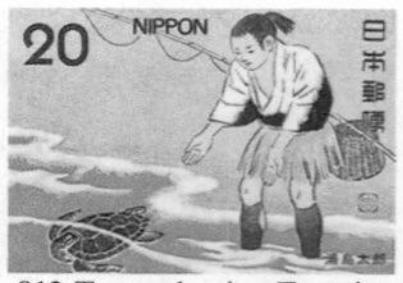
812 Taro releasing Tortoise

813 Sea-God's Palace

814 Taro and Pandora's Box

1975. Japanese Folk Tales (6th series). "Urashima Taro".
1378 **812** 20y. multicoloured . . . 25 10
1379 **813** 20y. multicoloured . . . 25 10
1380 **814** 20y. multicoloured . . . 25 10

1975. Nature Conservation (6th series). As T **783**. Multicoloured.
1381 20y. Manchurian cranes ("Grus japonensis") (vert) 70 20

816 Class C58 Locomotive

817 Class D52 Locomotive

1975. Railway Steam Locomotives (2nd series).
1382 **816** 20y. multicoloured . . . 65 10
1383 **817** 20y. multicoloured . . . 65 10

818 "Sight and Hearing" (Shiko Munakata)

1975. 50th Anniv of Japanese Broadcasting Corporation.
1384 **818** 20y. multicoloured . . . 15 10

819 Class 8620 Locomotive No. 68622

820 Class C11 Locomotive

1975. Railway Steam Locomotives (3rd series).
1385 **819** 20y. multicoloured . . . 65 10
1386 **820** 20y. multicoloured . . . 65 10

821 Old Man feeding Mouse

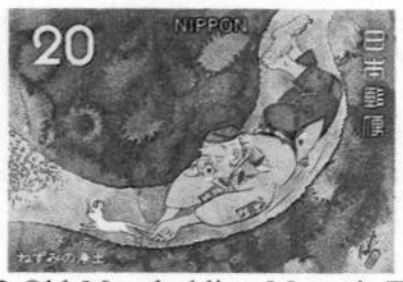
822 Old Man holding Mouse's Tail

823 Mice giving Feast to Old Man

1975. Japanese Folk Tales (7th series). "Nezumi No Jodo".
1387 **821** 20y. multicoloured . . . 25 10
1388 **822** 20y. multicoloured . . . 25 10
1389 **823** 20y. multicoloured . . . 25 10

824/5 Matsuura Screen

1975. Philatelic Week.
1390 **824** 20y. multicoloured . . . 30 10
1391 **825** 20y. multicoloured . . . 30 10
Nos. 1390/1 were issued together, se-tenant, forming the composite design shown.

827 Oil Rigs

1975. 9th World Petroleum Congress, Tokyo.
1394 **827** 20y. multicoloured . . . 15 10

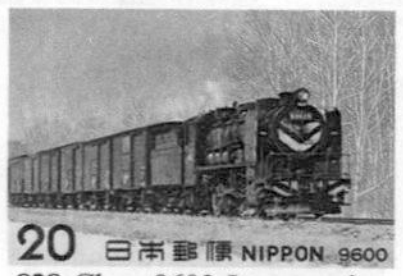
828 Class 9600 Locomotive No. 69820

829 Class C51 Locomotive No. 225

830 Plantation

1975. Railway Steam Locomotives (4th series).
1395 **828** 20y. multicoloured . . . 65 10
1396 **829** 20y. multicoloured . . . 65 10

1975. National Land Afforestation Campaign.
1397 **830** 20y. multicoloured . . . 15 10

831 Class 7100 Locomotive "Benkei", 1880

832 Class 150 Locomotive, 1872

1975. Railway Steam Locomotives (5th series).
1398 **831** 20y. black and buff . . . 65 10
1399 **832** 20y. black and yellow . . 65 10

833 Woman's Head and I.W.Y. Emblem

834 Okinawa Dance

1975. International Women's Year.
1400 **833** 20y. multicoloured . . . 15 10

1975. International Ocean Exposition, Okinawa (2nd issue). Multicoloured.
1401 20y. Type **834** 25 10
1402 30y. Bingata textile pattern 40 10
1403 50y. "Aquapolis and Globe" emblem (48 × 34 mm) . . 55 10

1975. Nature Conservation (7th series). As T **783**. Multicoloured.
1405 20y. Bonin Island honey-eater ("Apalopteron familiare") 70 10

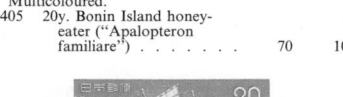

838 Kentoshisen (7th–9th centuries)

839 Kenminsen (7th–9th centuries)

1975. Japanese Ships (1st series).
1406 **838** 20y. red 45 15
1407 **839** 20y. brown 45 15
See also Nos. 1409/10, 1420/1, 1423/4, 1428/9 and 1431/2.

840 Apple

843 "Green Peafowl" (after K. Ogata)

841 Goshuin-sen (16th-century trading ship)

842 "Tenchi-maru" (state barge), 1630

1975. Centenary of Apple Cultivation in Japan.
1408 **840** 20y. multicoloured . . . 15 10

1975. Japanese Ships (2nd series).
1409 **841** 20y. green 45 15
1410 **842** 20y. blue 45 15

1975. International Correspondence Week.
1411 **843** 50y. multicoloured . . . 1·00 15

844 United States Flag

1975. American Tour by Emperor Hirohito and Empress Nagako. Multicoloured.
1412 20y. Type **844** 25 10
1413 20y. Japanese flag 25 10

846 Savings Box

847 Weightlifting

1975. Centenary of Japanese Post Office Savings Bank.
1415 **846** 20y. multicoloured . . . 15 10

1975. 30th National Athletic Meeting.
1416 **847** 10y. multicoloured . . . 20 10

848 "Tatsu-guruma" (toy)

850 Sengoku-bune (fishing boat)

851 "Shohei Maru" (sail warship)

1975. New Year's Greetings.
1417 **848** 10y. multicoloured . . . 35 10

1976. Nature Conservation (8th series). As T **783**. Multicoloured.
1419 50y. Ryukyu robin ("Erithacus komadori") 60 20

1976. Japanese Ships (3rd series).
1420 **850** 50y. blue 65 15
1421 **851** 50y. violet 65 15

1976. Nature Conservation (9th series). As T **783**. Multicoloured.
1422 50y. Tortoise ("Goemyda spengleri") 60 15

853 "Taisei Maru" (cadet ship)

854 "Tenyo Maru" (liner)

1976. Japanese Ships (4th series).
1423 **853** 50y. black 65 15
1424 **854** 50y. brown 65 15

855 Section of Hikone Folding Screen

857 Cedar Forest, Plum Blossom, and Mt. Tsukuba

1976. Philatelic Week. Multicoloured.
1425 50y. Type **855** 45 10
1426 50y. Similar to Type **855** . . 45 10
NOTE: The two stamps form a composite design of the "Hikone Folding Screen".

1976. National Land Afforestation Campaign.
1427 **857** 50y. multicoloured . . . 30 10

858 "Asama Maru" (liner)

859 "Kinai Maru" (cargo liner)

1976. Japanese Ships (5th series).
1428 **858** 50y. green 65 15
1429 **859** 50y. brown 65 15

1976. Nature Conservation (10th series). As T **783**. Multicoloured.
1430 50y. Green tree frog ("Racophorus arboreus") (vert) 50 10

861 "Kamakura Maru" (container ship)

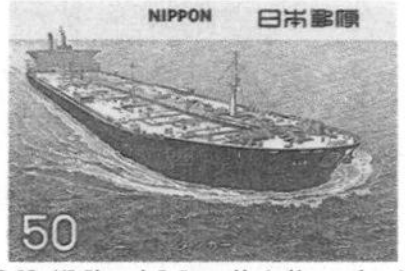

862 "Nissei Maru" (oil tanker)

1976. Japanese Ships (6th series).
1431 **861** 50y. blue 65 15
1432 **862** 50y. blue 65 15

1976. Nature Conservation (11th and 12th series). As T **783**. Multicoloured.
1433 50y. Tokyo bitterling ("Tanakia tanago") . . . 95 10
1434 50y. Three-spined sticklebacks ("Gasterosteus aculeatus") 95 10

865 "Kite and Rooks" (detail, Yosa Buson)

866 Gymnastics

1976. International Correspondence Week.
1435 **865** 100y. multicoloured . . 1·25 20

1976. 31st National Athletic Meeting.
1436 **866** 20y. multicoloured . . . 35 10

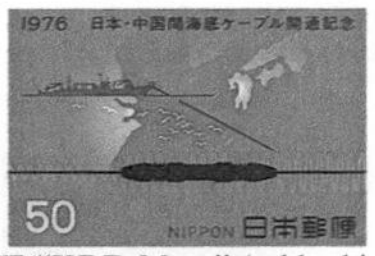

867 "KDD Maru" (cable ship) laying cable

1976. Opening of Sino-Japanese Cable.
1437 **867** 50y. multicoloured . . . 60 10

868 Man-zai-raku (classical dance)

870 Children at First Kindergarten

1976. Golden Jubilee of Emperor's Accession.
1438 **868** 50y. multicoloured . . . 40 10
1439 – 50y. red, gold and black 40 10
DESIGN: No. 1439, Coronation coach.

1976. Centenary of First Kindergarten. Tokyo.
1441 **870** 50y. multicoloured . . . 50 10

871 Family Group

872 Bamboo Snake

1976. 50th Anniv (1977) of Health Insurance System.
1442 **871** 50y. multicoloured . . . 40 10

1976. New Year's Greetings.
1443 **872** 20y. multicoloured . . . 20 10

873 East Pagoda, Yakushi Temple

1976. National Treasures (1st series). Mult.
1445 50y. Type **873** 50 10
1446 100y. Deva King, Todai Temple (33 × 48 mm) . . 1·25 10
See also Nos. 1447/8, 1452/3, 1463/4, 1471/2, 1480/1 and 1486/9.

875 Golden Pavilion, Toshodai Temple

1977. National Treasures (2nd series). Mult.
1447 50y. Type **875** 50 10
1448 100y. Illustration from "Heike Nokyo Sutra" (33 × 48 mm) . . . . . . 1·25 10

1977. Nature Conservation (13th series). As T **783**. Multicoloured.
1449 50y. Horseshoe crabs ("Tachypleus tridentatus") 45 10

878 Figure Skating

879 Figure Skating

1977. World Figure Skating Championships, Tokyo.
1450 **878** 50y. multicoloured . . . 55 10
1451 **879** 50y. multicoloured . . . 55 10

880 Detail of Picture Scroll (attr. Toba Sojo Kakuyu)

881 Wood Carving of Buddhist Saint (attr. Jocho) Byodoin Temple, Uji

1977. National Treasures (3rd series).

1452	**880**	50y. multicoloured . . .	50	10
1453	**881**	100y. dp brn, brn & grn	1·25	10

882 Forest in Sunshine

1977. National Land Afforestation Campaign.

1454	**882**	50y. multicoloured . . .	40	10

883/4 "Women" Weavers (part)

1977. Philatelic Week.

1455	**883**	50y. multicoloured . . .	50	10
1456	**884**	50y. multicoloured . . .	50	10

Nos. 1455/6 were issued in se-tenant pairs, forming a composite design.

1977. Nature Conservation (14th series). As T **783**. Multicoloured.

1457	50y. Mikado swallowtail ("Graphium doson") (vert)	60	10

886 Nurses

887 Central Part of Nuclear Reactor

1977. 16th Congress of the International Council of Nurses.

1458	**886**	50y. multicoloured . . .	40	10

1977. Reaching of Critical Mass by Joyo Fast-Breeder Reactor, Oarai Town.

1459	**887**	50y. multicoloured . . .	40	10

888 Carrier Pigeons and Mail Box with U.P.U. Emblem

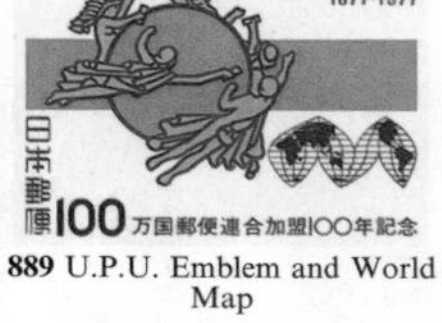

889 U.P.U. Emblem and World Map

1977. Centenary of Japan's Admission to U.P.U.

1460	**888**	50y. multicoloured . . .	40	10
1461	**889**	100y. multicoloured . .	1·40	10

890 Illustration from "Picture Scroll of Lady Murasaki's Diary"

891 Statue of Seitaka Doji

892 Green Cross (safety emblem) and Workmen

1977. National Treasures (4th series).

1463	**890**	50y. multicoloured . . .	55	10
1464	**891**	100y. brown, deep brown and light brown . . .	1·40	10

1977. National Safety Week. Multicoloured.

1465	50y. Type **892**	80	10
1466	50y. Worker and high-rise building	80	10
1467	50y. Unloading freight . .	80	10
1468	50y. Machine-worker . . .	80	10

1977. Nature Conservation (15th series). As T **783**. Multicoloured.

1469	50y. Firefly ("Luciola cruciata")	50	10

1977. Nature Conservation (16th series). As T **783**. Multicoloured.

1470	50y. Cicada ("Euterpnosia chibensis")	60	10

898 Drawing of Han Shan by Kao

899 Matsumoto Castle

1977. National Treasures (5th series).

1471	**898**	50y. multicoloured . . .	60	10
1472	**899**	100y. multicoloured . .	1·40	10

900 Map and Child on Telephone

1977. Opening of Okinawa–Luzon–Hong Kong Submarine Cable.

1473	**900**	50y. multicoloured . . .	40	10

901 Surgeon

1977. 27th Congress of International Society of Surgeons.

1474	**901**	50y. multicoloured . . .	50	10

1977. Nature Conservation (17th series). As T **783**. Multicoloured.

1475	50y. Dragonfly ("Boninthemis insularis") (vert)	60	10

903 Horn-shaped Speaker and Telegraph Key

904 Racing Cyclist and Mt. Iwaki

1977. 50th Anniv of Amateur Radio League.

1476	**903**	50y. multicoloured . . .	40	10

1977. 32nd National Athletic Meeting.

1477	**904**	20y. multicoloured . . .	40	10

905 "Kacho-zu" (Nobuharu Hasegawa)

906 Long-necked Dinosaur and Museum

1977. International Correspondence Week.

1478	**905**	100y. multicoloured . .	1·25	30

1977. Centenary of National Science Museum.

1479	**906**	50y. multicoloured . . .	75	10

907 Detail, Folding Screen, Chishakuin Temple, Kyoto

908 Kiyomizu-dera Temple

1977. National Treasures (6th series).

1480	**907**	50y. multicoloured . . .	50	10
1481	**908**	100y. brown, green & bl	1·25	10

909 Toy Horse

1977. New Year's Greetings.

1482	**909**	20y. multicoloured . . .	25	10

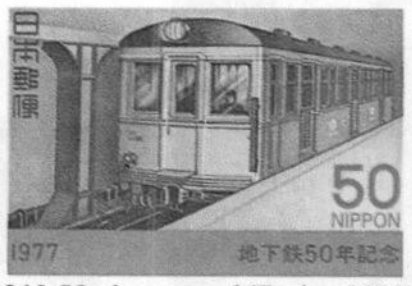

910 Underground Train, 1927

911 Underground Train No. 1101, 1977

1977. 50th Anniv of Japanese Underground Railway.

1484	**910**	50y. multicoloured . . .	90	10
1485	**911**	50y. multicoloured . . .	90	10

912 Genji's Carriage at Sumiyoshi Shrine (scene on folding screen (Sotatsu Tawaraya) from "Tale of Genji" by Lady Murasaki)

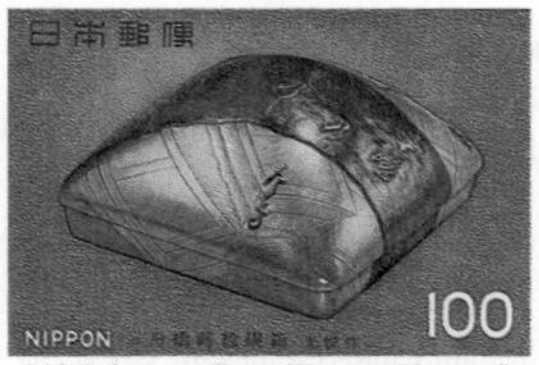

913 Inkstone Case (Koetsu Honami)

1978. National Treasures (7th series).

1486	**912**	50y. multicoloured . . .	50	10
1487	**913**	100y. multicoloured . .	1·40	10

914 "Noryozu" (Morikage Kusumi)

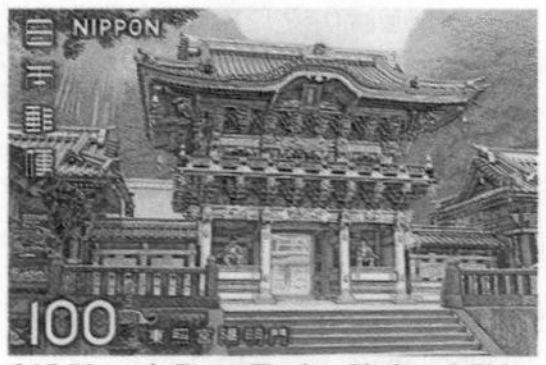

915 Yomei Gate, Tosho Shrine, Nikko

1978. National Treasures (8th series).

1488	**914**	50y. multicoloured . . .	50	10
1489	**915**	100y. multicoloured . .	1·40	10

916 "Primula sieboldi"

1978. Nature Conservation (18th series).

1490	**916**	50y. multicoloured . . .	50	10

917 Seated Woman With Flower (hanging scroll)

918 Dancing Woman (hanging scroll)

1978. Philatelic Week. "Kanbun Bijinzu" Genre Paintings.

1491	**917**	50y. multicoloured . . .	40	10
1492	**918**	50y. multicoloured . . .	40	10

919 Rotary Emblem and Mt. Fuji (from "36 Views of Mt. Fuji" by Hokusai Katsushita)

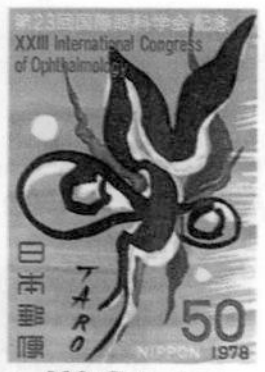

920 Congress Emblem

1978. Rotary International Convention, Tokyo.

1493	**919**	50y. multicoloured . . .	55	20

1978. 23rd Int Ophthalmological Congress.

1494	**920**	50y. multicoloured . . .	45	10

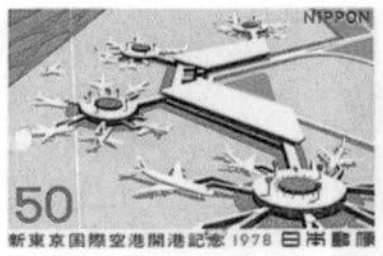

921 Passenger Terminal Buildings

922 Cape Ashizuri, Rainbow and Cedar Trees

1978. Opening of Narita Airport, Tokyo.
1495 **921** 50y. multicoloured . . . 60 10

1978. National Afforestation Campaign.
1496 **922** 50y. multicoloured . . . 50 10

923 "Pinguicula ramosa"

924 "Karashishi" (attr. Sotatsu Tawaraya) and Lions Emblem

1978. Nature Conservation (19th series).
1497 **923** 50y. multicoloured . . . 50 10

1978. 61st Lions International Convention, Tokyo.
1498 **924** 50y. multicoloured . . . 55 10

925/6 "Grand Champion Raigoyo Hidenoyama in the Ring" (Toyokuni III)

927 "Drum Tower of Ekoin Temple, Ryogoku" (Hiroshige)

928 "Dicentra peregrina"

1978. Sumo (Japanese Wrestling) Pictures (1st series).
1499 **925** 50y. multicoloured . . . 50 10
1500 **926** 50y. multicoloured . . . 50 10
1501 **927** 50y. multicoloured . . . 60 10
Nos. 1499/500 were issued together, se-tenant, forming the composite design illustrated.
See also Nos. 1505/7, 1513/15, 1519/21 and 1523/5.

1978. Nature Conservation (20th series).
1502 **928** 50y. multicoloured . . . 35 10

929 Keep Fit Exercise

930 Chamber of Commerce and Industry Building and Centenary Emblem

1978. 50th Anniv of Radio Gymnastic Exercises.
1503 **929** 50y. multicoloured . . . 1·25 10

1978. Centenary of 1st Chambers of Commerce, Tokyo and Osaka.
1504 **930** 50y. multicoloured . . . 40 10

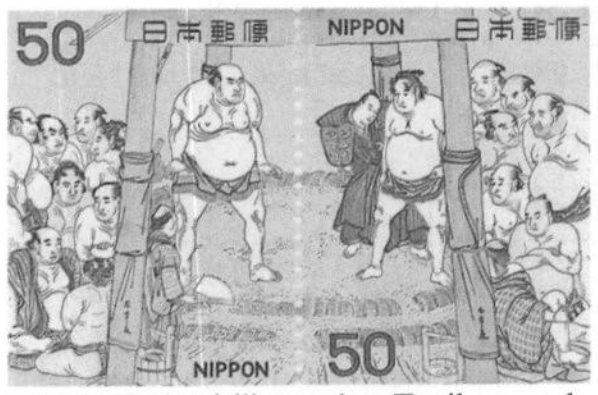

931/2 "Dohyoiri" wrestlers Tanikaze and Onogawa (Shunsho Katsukawa)

933 "Jinmaku versus Raiden" (Shunnei Katsukawa)

934 Statues on Tokyo Securities Exchange Building

1978. Sumo Pictures (2nd series).
1505 **931** 50y. multicoloured . . . 50 10
1506 **932** 50y. multicoloured . . . 50 10
1507 **933** 50y. multicoloured . . . 60 10
Nos. 1505/6 were issued together se-tenant, forming the composite design illustrated.

1978. Centenary of Tokyo and Osaka Stock Exchanges.
1508 **934** 50y. brown, purple & grn 50 10

935 Copper Pheasant (detail of door painting attr. Sanraku Kano)

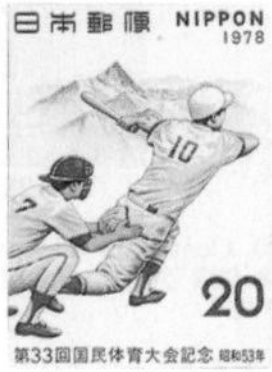

936 Mt. Yari and Softball Players

1978. International Correspondence Week.
1509 **935** 100y. multicoloured . . 1·25 30

1978. 33rd National Athletic Meeting.
1510 **936** 20y. multicoloured . . . 40 10

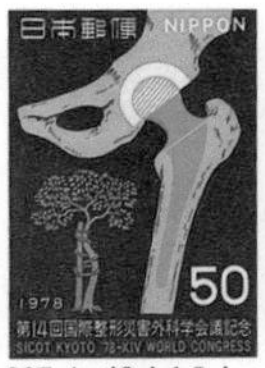

937 Artificial Joint

938 Refracting Telescope and Stars

1978. 14th Congress of International Society of Orthopaedic and Traumatic Surgeons, Kyoto.
1511 **937** 50y. blue, ultram & silver 55 10

1978. Centenary of Tokyo Astronomical Observatory.
1512 **938** 50y. multicoloured . . . 55 10

939/40 "The then Heroic Champion's Sumo Wrestling" (detail, Toyokuni III)

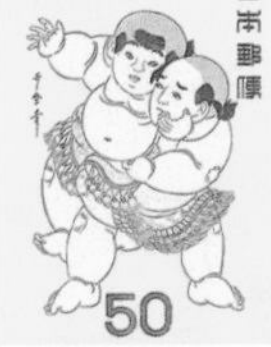

941 "Children's Charming Sumo Play" (Utamaro Kitagawa)

942 Sheep Bell (folk toy)

1978. Sumo Pictures (3rd series).
1513 **939** 50y. multicoloured . . . 50 10
1514 **940** 50y. multicoloured . . . 50 10
1515 **941** 50y. multicoloured . . . 60 10
Nos. 1513/14 were issued together se-tenant, forming the composite design illustrated.

1978. New Year's Greetings.
1516 **942** 20y. multicoloured . . . 35 10

943 Family and Human Rights Emblem

1978. 30th Anniv of Declaration of Human Rights.
1518 **943** 50y. multicoloured . . . 45 10

944/5 "Great Sumo Wrestlers crossing Ryogoku Bridge" (Toyokuni III)

946 "Yumitori Ceremony at Grand Fund-raising Tournament" (Kunisada II)

947 Hands protecting Children

1979. Sumo Pictures. (4th series).
1519 **944** 50y. multicoloured . . . 50 10
1520 **945** 50y. multicoloured . . . 50 10
1521 **946** 50y. multicoloured . . . 60 10
Nos. 1519/20 were issued together se-tenant, forming the composite design illustrated.

1979. Education for the Handicapped.
1522 **947** 50y. multicoloured . . . 45 10

948/9 "Takekuma versus Iwamigata" (Kuniyoshi Utagawa)

950 "Daidozan's Dohyoiri" (Sharaku Toshusai)

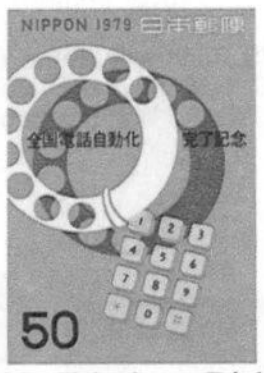

951 Telephone Dial and Pushbuttons

1979. Sumo Pictures (5th series).
1523 **948** 50y. multicoloured . . . 50 10
1524 **949** 50y. multicoloured . . . 50 10
1525 **950** 50y. multicoloured . . . 60 10
Nos. 1523/4 were issued together se-tenant, forming the composite design illustrated.

1979. Telephone Automation Completion.
1526 **951** 50y. multicoloured . . . 50 10

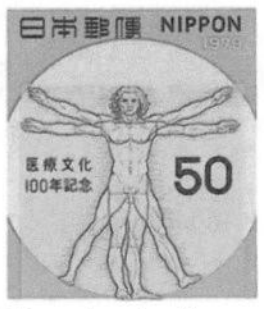

952 Drawing by Leonardo da Vinci

1979. Centenary of Western Medicine in Japan.
1527 **952** 50y. multicoloured . . . 55 10

953 "Standing Beauties" (Kaigetsudo School)

954 "Standing Beauties" (Kaigetsudo School)

1979. Philatelic Week.
1528 **953** 50y. multicoloured . . . 50 10
1529 **954** 50y. multicoloured . . . 50 10

955 Mt. Horaiji and Maple Leaves

1979. National Afforestation Campaign.
1530 **955** 50y. multicoloured . . . 50 10

956 "Goddess of Maternal Mercy" (Kano Hogai)

957 "The Princess of the Sea God" (Aoki Shigeru)

1979. Modern Japanese Art (1st series).
1531 **956** 50y. multicoloured . . . 60 10
1532 **957** 50y. multicoloured . . . 60 10
See also Nos. 1533/4. 1544/5, 1550/1, 1558/9, 1567/8, 1574/5, 1610/11, 1618/19, 1628/9, 1650/1, 1656/7, 1675/6, 1689/90, 1693/4 and 1697/8.

958 "Fire Dance" (Gyosha Hayami)

959 "Leaning Figure" (Tetsugoro Yorozu)

1979. Modern Japanese Art (2nd series).
1533 **958** 50y. multicoloured . . . 60 10
1534 **959** 50y. multicoloured . . . 60 10

960 Quarantine Officers

1979. Centenary of Quarantine System.
1535 **960** 50y. multicoloured . . . 75 10

961 Girl with Letter

962 Hakata Doll

1979. Letter writing Day.
1536 **961** 20y. multicoloured . . . 30 10
1537 **962** 50y. multicoloured . . . 45 10

963 Baseball Pitcher and Ball

1979. 50th National Inter-City Amateur Baseball Tournament.
1538 **963** 50y. multicoloured . . . 70 10

964 Girl collecting Stars

965 Boy catching Toy Insects

1979. International Year of the Child.
1539 **964** 50y. multicoloured . . . 50 10
1540 **965** 50y. multicoloured . . . 50 10

966 "The Moon over the Castle Ruins" (Bansui Doi and Rentaro Taki)

967 "Evening Glow" (Uko Nakamura and Shin Kusakawa)

1979. Japanese Songs (1st series).
1542 **966** 50y. multicoloured . . . 70 10
1543 **967** 50y. multicoloured . . . 70 10
See also Nos. 1552/3, 1556/7, 1561/2, 1565/6, 1572/3, 1580/1, 1616/17 and 1620/1.

968 "Black Cat" (Shunso Hishida)

969 "Kinyo" (Sotaro Yasui)

1979. Modern Japanese Art (3rd series).
1544 **968** 50y. multicoloured . . . 70 10
1545 **969** 50y. multicoloured . . . 70 10

970 "Steep Mountains and the Dark Dale" (Okyo Maruyama)

971 Long Distance Runner

1979. International Correspondence Week.
1546 **970** 100y. multicoloured . . 1·60 30

1979. 34th National Athletic Meeting, Miyazaki.
1547 **971** 20y. multicoloured . . . 60 10

972 "ITU" and Globe

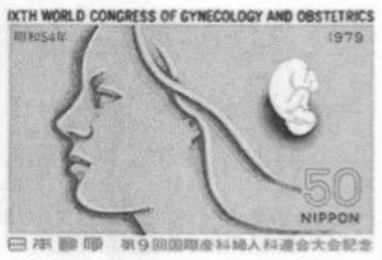

973 Woman and Embryo

1979. Centenary of Admission to International Telecommunications Union.
1548 **972** 50y. multicoloured . . . 60 10

1979. 9th International Obstetrics and Gynaecology Convention, Tokyo.
1549 **973** 50y. multicoloured . . . 60 10

974 "Nude" (Kagaku Murakami)

975 "Harvest" (Asai Chu)

1979. Modern Japanese Art (4th series).
1550 **974** 50y. multicoloured . . . 50 10
1551 **975** 50y. multicoloured . . . 50 10

976 "Maple Leaves" (Tatsuyuki Takano and Teiichi Okano)

977 "Birthplace" (Tatsuyuki Takano and Teiichi Okano)

1979. Japanese Songs (2nd series).
1552 **976** 50y. multicoloured . . . 50 10
1553 **977** 50y. multicoloured . . . 50 10

978 "Happy Monkeys" (folk toy)

979 "Winter Scene" (anon)

980 "Mount Fuji" (anon)

1979. New Year's Greeting.
1554 **978** 20y. multicoloured . . . 30 10

1980. Japanese Songs (3rd series).
1556 **979** 50y. multicoloured . . . 50 20
1557 **980** 50y. multicoloured . . . 50 10

981 "Salmon" (Yuichi Takahashi)

982 "Hall of the Supreme Buddha" (Kokei Kobayashi)

1980. Modern Japanese Art (5th series).
1558 **981** 50y. multicoloured . . . 55 10
1559 **982** 50y. multicoloured . . . 55 10

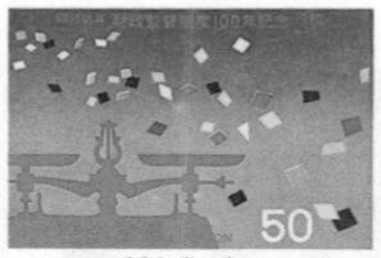

983 Scales

1980. Centenary of Government Auditing Bureau.
1560 **983** 50y. multicoloured . . . 50 10

984 "Spring Brook" (Tatsuyuki Takano and Teiichi Okano)

985 "Cherry Blossoms" (anon)

1980. Japanese Songs (4th series).
1561 **984** 50y. multicoloured . . . 55 10
1562 **985** 50y. multicoloured . . . 55 10

986 "Scenes of Outdoor Play in Spring" (Sukenobu Nishikawa)

987 "Scenes of Outdoor Play in Spring" (Sukenobu Nishikawa)

1980. Philatelic Week.
1563 **986** 50y. multicoloured . . . 30 10
1564 **987** 50y. multicoloured . . . 50 10

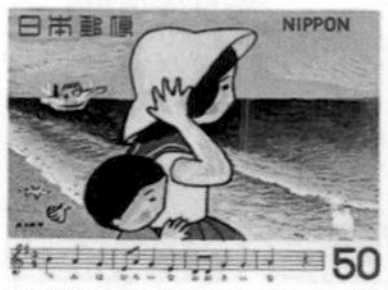

988 "Sea" (Ryuha Hayashi and Takeshi Inoue)

989 "Misty Moonlight Night" (Tatsuyuki Takano and Teiichi Okano)

1980. Japanese Songs (5th series).
1565 **988** 50y. multicoloured . . . 55 10
1566 **989** 50y. multicoloured . . . 55 10

990 "Maiko Girls" (Seiki Kuroda)

991 "Mother and Child" (Shoen Uemura)

1980. Modern Japanese Art (6th series).
1567 **990** 50y. multicoloured . . . 55 10
1568 **991** 50y. multicoloured . . . 55 10

992 "Nippon Maru I"

993 Mount Gozaisho and Cedars

1980. 50th Anniv of Training Cadet Ships "Nippon Maru I" and "Kaio Maru".
1569 **992** 50y. multicoloured . . . 75 20

1980. National Afforestation Campaign.
1570 **993** 50y. multicoloured . . . 60 10

994 "Acrobatic Performances on a Ladder at New Year's Parade of Yayosu Fire Brigades" (Hiroshige III)

1980. Centenary of Fire Fighting System.
1571 **994** 50y. multicoloured . . . 60 10

995 "The Sun" (Taksuyuki Takano and Teiichi Okano)

996 "Memories of Summer" (Shoko Ema and Yoshinao Nakata)

1980. Japanese Songs (6th series).
1572 **995** 50y. multicoloured . . . 60 10
1573 **996** 50y. multicoloured . . . 60 10

997 "Black Fan" (Takeji Fujishima)

998 "The Dance 'Are Yudachi ni'" (Seiho Takeuchi)

1980. Modern Japanese Art (7th series).
1574 **997** 50y. multicoloured . . . 65 10
1575 **998** 50y. multicoloured . . . 65 10

999 Teddy Bear holding Letter

1000 Knotted Letter

1980. Letter Writing Day.
1576 **999** 20y. multicoloured . . 30 10
1577 **1000** 50y. multicoloured . . 50 10

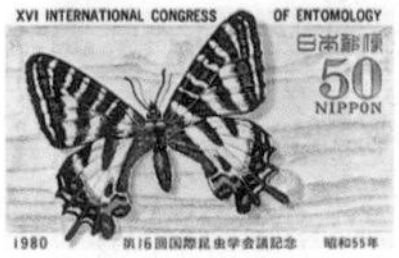
1001 "Luehdorfia japonica"

1980. 16th International Congress of Entomology, Kyoto.
1578 **1001** 50y. multicoloured . . 90 10

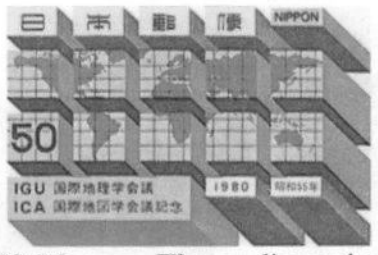
1002 Map on Three- dimensional Graph

1980. 24th International Geographical Congress and 10th International Cartographic Conference, Tokyo.
1579 **1002** 50y. multicoloured . . 40 10

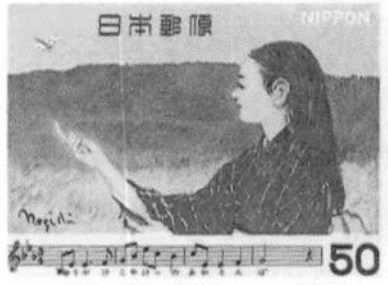
1003 "Red Dragonfly" (Rofu Miki and Kosaku Yamada)

1004 "Song by the Sea" (Kokui Hayashi and Tamezo Narita)

1980. Japanese Songs (7th series).
1580 **1003** 50y. multicoloured . . 70 10
1581 **1004** 50y. multicoloured . . 70 10

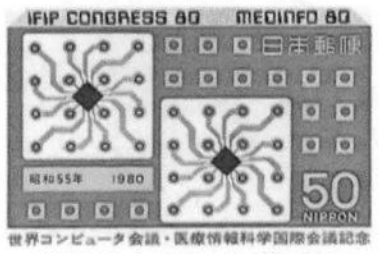
1005 Integrated Circuit

1980. 8th World Computer Congress and Third World Conference on Medical Informatics, Tokyo.
1582 **1005** 50y. multicoloured . . 60 10

1006 Akita Dog
1007 Adonis
1008 Lily

1009 Camellia
1010 Small Cabbage Whites on Rape Blossom
1011 Japanese Babylonia

1012 Noble Scallops
1013 Flowering Cherry
1014 Hanging Bell, Byodoin Temple, Uji

1015 Yoka Star Shell
1016 Precious Wentletrap
1017 Flautist, Horyu Temple

1018 Deer (from lacquer writing box)
1019 Mirror with Figures
1020 Heart-shaped Earthen Figurine

1021 Silver Crane, Kasuga Taisha Shrine, Nara

1022 Miroku Bosatsu, Horyu Temple

1023 Dainichi Buddha, Chuson Temple

1024 Keiki Doji, Kongobu Temple

1025 Komoku Ten, Todai Temple, Nara

1026 Lady Maya, Horyu Temple

1027 Tea Jar with Wisteria Decoration (Ninsei Nonomura)

1028 Miroku Bosatsu

1980. 41y. and 62y. perf or imperf (self-adhesive), others perf.
1582a **1006** 2y. blue 10 10
1583 **1007** 10y. yellow, grn & brn 10 10
1584 **1008** 20y. yellow, blue & grn 15 10
1585 **1009** 30y. multicoloured . . 20 25
1586 **1010** 40y. multicoloured . . 40 10
1587 **1011** 40y. multicoloured . . 35 10
1588 **1012** 41y. multicoloured . . 35 10
1589 **1013** 50y. multicoloured . . 60 10
1590 **1014** 60y. green and black 70 10
1591 **1015** 60y. multicoloured . . 50 10
1592 **1016** 62y. multicoloured . . 50 10
1593 **1017** 70y. blue and yellow 90 10
1594 **1018** 70y. yellow, black & bl 60 10
1594a 72y. yellow, black & bl 60 10
1595 **1019** 80y. green and black 1·25 10
1596 **1020** 90y. yellow, blk & grn 1·25 10
1597 **1021** 100y. black, blue and ultramarine 85 10
1598 **1022** 170y. purple and bistre 65 10
1599 175y. brown, grn & bis . . . . 1·25 10
1600 – 210y. orange and lilac (as No. 1242) . . . 1·25 10
1601 **1023** 260y. brown and red 2·00 10
1602 **1024** 300y. brown . . . . . 2·00 10
1603 **1025** 310y. brown and violet 2·00 10
1604 – 360y. purple and pink (as No. 1246) . . . 2·25 10
1605 **1026** 410y. orange and blue 5·50 10
1606 **1027** 410y. multicoloured 1·50 10
1607 **1028** 600y. yellow, purple and lilac . . . . . 4·00 10

1031 "Manchurian Cranes" (door painting, Motooki Watanabe)

1032 Archery and Mt. Nantai

1980. International Correspondence Week.
1608 **1031** 100y. multicoloured . . 1·40 20

1980. 35th National Athletic Meeting, Tochigi.
1609 **1032** 20y. multicoloured . . 40 10

1033 "Woman" (sculpture, Morie Ogiwara)

1034 "Woman of the Kurofune-ya" (Yumeji Takehisa)

1980. Modern Japanese Art (8th series).
1610 **1033** 50y. multicoloured . . 65 10
1611 **1034** 50y. multicoloured . . 65 10

1035 "Energy"

1036 Diet Building and Doves

1980. 35th World Congress of Junior Chambers of Commerce, Osaka.
1612 **1035** 50y. multicoloured . . 45 10

1980. 90th Anniv of Japanese Diet.
1613 **1036** 50y. multicoloured . . 35 10

1037 Toy Rooster

1980. New Year's Greetings.
1614 **1037** 20y. multicoloured . . 40 10

1038 "Komori-Uta" (nursery song)

1039 "Coconut" (Toson Shimazaki and Toraji Ohaka)

1981. Japanese Songs (8th series).
1616 **1038** 60y. multicoloured . . 55 10
1617 **1039** 60y. multicoloured . . 55 10

1040 "Power Station in the Snow" (Shiskanosuke Oka)

1041 "Nukada-no-Okimi of Asuka in Spring" (Yukihiko Yasuda)

1981. Modern Japanese Art (9th series).
1618 **1040** 60y. multicoloured . . 60 10
1619 **1041** 60y. multicoloured . . 60 10

1042 "Spring has Come" (Tatsuyuki Takano and Teiichi Okano)

1043 "Cherry Blossoms" (Hagoromo Takeshima and Rentaro Taki)

1981. Japanese Songs (9th series).
1620 **1042** 60y. multicoloured . . 60 10
1621 **1043** 60y. multicoloured . . 60 10

1044 Port Island and Exposition Emblem

1981. Kobe Port Island Exposition, Kobe City.
1622 **1044** 60y. multicoloured . . 35 10

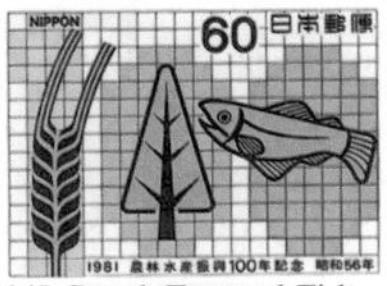
1045 Cereal, Tree and Fish on "100"

1981. Centenary of Agricultural, Forestry and Fishery Promotion.
1623 **1045** 60y. multicoloured . . 50 10

1046/7 "Yugao" (Lady of the Evening Roses) and Genji

1981. Philatelic Week. Details of Harunobu Suzuki's Illustrations of "Tale of Genji" by Lady Murasaki.
1624 **1046** 60y. multicoloured . . 50 10
1625 **1047** 60y. multicoloured . . 50 10
Nos. 1624/5 were issued together, se-tenant, forming a composite design.

1048 Pagodas at Nara and Double Cherry Blossom

1049 Container Ship and Crane

1981. National Afforestation Campaign.
1626 **1048** 60y. multicoloured . . 55 10

1981. 12th International Port and Harbour Association Conference.
1627 **1049** 60y. multicoloured . . 75 10

1050 "N's Family" (Narashinge Koide)

1051 "Bamboo Shoots" (Heihachiro Fukuda)

1981. Modern Japanese Art (10th series).
1628 **1050** 60y. multicoloured . . 65 10
1629 **1051** 60y. multicoloured . . 65 10

1052 Stylized Debris Barriers

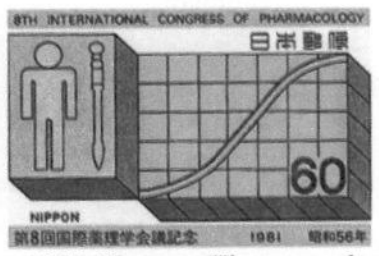
1053 Human Figure and Dose Response Chart

1981. Centenary of Land Erosion Control.
1630 **1052** 60y. multicoloured . . 40 10

1981. 8th International Congress of Pharmacology, Tokyo.
1631 **1053** 60y. multicoloured . . 40 10

1054 Girl writing Letter
1055 Boy with Pencil and Stamp

1981. Letter Writing Day.
1632 **1054** 40y. multicoloured . . 40 10
1633 **1055** 60y. multicoloured . . 55 10

1056 Japanese Crested Ibis

1981. 50th Anniv of National Parks.
1634 **1056** 60y. multicoloured . . 1·10 20

1057 Electric Plug and dripping Tap
1058 Energy Recycling

1981. Energy Conservation.
1635 **1057** 40y. dp blue, lilac & bl 40 10
1636 **1058** 60y. multicoloured . . 50 10

1059 Oura Cathedral, Nagasaki
1060 Hyokei Hall, Tokyo

1981. Modern Western-style Architecture (1st series).
1637 **1059** 60y. multicoloured . . 55 10
1638 **1060** 60y. multicoloured . . 55 10
See also Nos. 1648/9, 1654/5, 1658/9, 1669/70, 1680/1, 1695/6, 1705/6, 1710/11 and 1732/3.

1061 Bluebird and I.Y.D.P. Emblem
1062 Globe in Brain

1981. International Year of Disabled Persons.
1639 **1061** 60y.+10y. mult 45 10

1981. International Neurological Conferences, Kyoto.
1640 **1062** 60y. multicoloured . . 35 10

1063 Convention Emblem
1064 "Eastern Turtle Doves" (Sanraku Kano)

1981. International Federation of Postal, Telegram and Telephone Workers' Unions World Convention, Tokyo.
1641 **1063** 60y. multicoloured . . 45 10

1981. International Correspondence Week.
1642 **1064** 130y. multicoloured . . 2·00 30

1065 48m. Stamp 1871
1069 Badminton and Lake Biwa

1981. "Philatokyo '81" International Stamp Exhibition, Tokyo. Multicoloured, frame colour of stamp within design given.
1643 **1065** 60y. brown 60 10
1644 – 60y. blue 60 10
1645 – 60y. red 60 10
1646 – 60y. green 60 10
DESIGNS: No. 1644, 100m. stamp, 1871; 1645, 200m. stamp, 1871; 1646, 500m. stamp, 1871.

1981. 36th National Athletic Meeting, Shiga.
1647 **1069** 40y. multicoloured . . 50 10

1070 Former Kaichi School Matsumoto

1071 Doshisha Chapel, Kyoto

1981. Modern Western-style Architecture (2nd series).
1648 **1070** 60y. multicoloured . . 50 10
1649 **1071** 60y. multicoloured . . 50 10

1072 "Portrait of Reiko" (Ryusei Kishida)
1073 "Ichiyo" (Kiyokata Kaburagi)

1981. Modern Japanese Art (11th series).
1650 **1072** 60y. multicoloured . . 55 10
1651 **1073** 60y. multicoloured . . 55 10

1074 Clay Dog (folk toy)

1981. New Year's Greetings.
1652 **1074** 40y. multicoloured . . 45 10

1075 St John's Church, Inuyama
1076 Military Exercise Hall, Sapporo Agricultural School

1982. Modern Western-style Architecture (3rd series).
1654 **1075** 60y. multicoloured . . 55 10
1655 **1076** 60y. multicoloured . . 55 10

1077 "Yoritomo in a Cave" (Seison Maeda)

1078 "Posters on a Terrace" (Yuzo Saeki)

1982. Modern Japanese Art (12th series).
1656 **1077** 60y. multicoloured . . 55 10
1657 **1078** 60y. multicoloured . . 55 10

1079 Bank of Japan, Kyoto Branch (now museum)
1080 Saiseikan Hospital, Yamagata

1982. Modern Western-style Architecture (4th series).
1658 **1079** 60y. multicoloured . . 50 10
1659 **1080** 60y. multicoloured . . 50 10

1081 Gorilla and Greater Flamingo

1982. Ueno Zoo. Centenary. Multicoloured.
1660 60y. Type **1081** 65 20
1661 60y. Lion and king penguins 65 20
1662 60y. Giant panda and Indian elephants . . . . 1·00 55
1663 60y. Giraffe and common zebras . . . . 1·00 55

1085/6 "Enjoying Snow Landscape of Matsuchi-yama" (Torii Kiyonaga)

1982. Philatelic Week.
1664 **1085** 60y. multicoloured . . 50 10
1665 **1086** 60y. multicoloured . . 50 10
Nos. 1664/5 were issued together se-tenant forming the composite design illustrated.

1087 Lion
1088 Arbor Festival Emblem and Blue and White Fly-catcher

1982. 10th Anniv of Return of Okinawa (Ryukyu Islands).
1666 **1087** 60y. multicoloured . . 60 10

1982. National Afforestation Campaign.
1667 **1088** 60y. multicoloured . . 65 20

1089 Noh Mask

1982. 16th World Dermatology Congress, Tokyo.
1668 **1089** 60y. multicoloured . . 65 10

1090 Divine Gate of Oyama Shrine, Kanazawa
1091 Former Iwasaki Mansion, Taito-ku, Tokyo (now Training Institute)

1982. Modern Western-style Architecture (5th series).
1669 **1090** 60y. multicoloured . . 50 10
1670 **1091** 60y. multicoloured . . 50 10

1092 Class 1290 Locomotive "Zenko", 1881

1093 "Yamabiko" (echo) Express Train

1982. Opening of Tohoku–Shinkansen Railway Line.
1671 **1092** 60y. multicoloured . . 1·00 30
1672 **1093** 60y. multicoloured . . 1·00 30

1094 Gull and Balloon with Letter
1095 Bird carrying Letter to Fairy

1982. Letter Writing Day.
1673 **1094** 40y. multicoloured . . 40 10
1674 **1095** 60y. multicoloured . . 55 10

1096 "Garment Patterned with Irises" (Saburosuke Okada)
1097 "Buddhisattva Kannon on Potalaka Island" (Tessai Tomioka)

1982. Modern Japanese Art (13th series).
1675 **1096** 40y. multicoloured . . 65 10
1676 **1097** 60y. multicoloured . . 65 10

1098 Wreath (condolences)
1099 Folded Paper Crane (congratulations)
1100 Pine, Plum and Bamboo Blossom (congratulations)

1982. Special Correspondence Stamps.
1677 **1098** 60y. multicoloured . . 75 10
1678 **1099** 60y. multicoloured . . 75 10
1679 **1100** 70y. multicoloured . . 95 10

For other values see Nos. 1722/3, 2013/16 and 2289/92.

1101 Hokkaido Prefectural Building, Sapporo

1102 Saigo Tsugumichi Mansion, Meguro (now in Inuyama)

1982. Modern Western-style Architecture (6th series).
1680 **1101** 60y. multicoloured . . 75 10
1681 **1102** 60y. multicoloured . . 75 10

1103 16th-century Portuguese Galleon and World Map

1982. 400th Anniv of Christian Boys' Delegation to Europe.
1682 **1103** 60y. multicoloured . . 70 10

1104 "T'ien T'an in the Clouds" (Ryuzaburo Umehara)

1982. 10th Anniv of Restoration of Diplomatic Relations with China.
1683 **1104** 60y. multicoloured . . 55 10

1105 Table Tennis and Monument of the Meet

1106 "Amusement" (wooden doll by Goyo Hirata)

1982. 37th National Athletic Meeting, Matsue.
1684 **1105** 40y. multicoloured . . 60 10

1982. International Correspondence Week.
1685 **1106** 130y. multicoloured . . 2·00 10

1107 "Bank of Japan near Eitaibashi in Snow" (Yasuji Inoue)

1982. Centenary of Central Bank System.
1686 **1107** 60y. multicoloured . . 45 10

1108 "Asahi" (rising sun) Express Train

1109 ED 16 Electric Locomotive No. 8

1982. Opening of Joetsu–Shinkansen Railway Line.
1687 **1108** 60y. multicoloured . . 1·00 30
1688 **1109** 60y. multicoloured . . 1·00 30

1110 "Srimhadevi" (Shiko Munakata)

1111 "Saltimbanque" (Seiji Togo)

1982. Modern Japanese Art (14th series).
1689 **1110** 60y. multicoloured . . 65 10
1690 **1111** 60y. multicoloured . . 65 10

1112 "Kintaro on a Wild Boar" (clay Tsutsumi doll)

1982. New Year Greetings.
1691 **1112** 40y. multicoloured . . 45 10

1113 "Snowstorm" (Shinsui Ito)

1114 "Spiraea and Calla in a Perrian Vase" (Zenzaburo Kojima)

1983. Modern Japanese Art (15th series).
1692 **1113** 60y. multicoloured . . 75 10
1693 **1114** 60y. multicoloured . . 75 10

1115 Fujimura Memorial Hall, Kofu (formerly Mutsuzawa School)

1116 Porch of Sakuranomiya Public Hall, Osaka

1983. Modern Western-style Architecture (7th series).
1695 **1115** 60y. multicoloured . . 75 10
1696 **1116** 60y. multicoloured . . 75 10

1117 "Selflessness" (Taikan Yokoyama)

1118 "Aged Monkey" (wood carving, Koun Takamura)

1983. Modern Japanese Art (16th series).
1697 **1117** 60y. multicoloured . . 75 10
1698 **1118** 60y. multicoloured . . 75 10

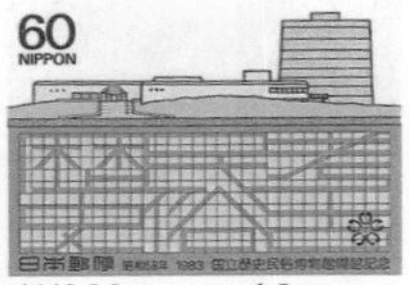

1119 Museum and Japanese Characters representing History, Folklore and Antiquity

1983. Opening of National Museum of History and Folklore.
1699 **1119** 60y. multicoloured . . 40 10

1120/1 "Women working in the Kitchen" (Utamaro Kitagawa)

1983. Philatelic Week.
1700 **1120** 60y. multicoloured . . 75 10
1701 **1121** 60y. multicoloured . . 75 10
Nos. 1695/6 were issued together, se-tenant, forming the composite design illustrated.

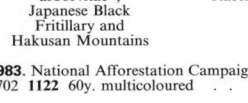

1122 "Hiba arborvitae", Japanese Black Fritillary and Hakusan Mountains

1123 Colt and Racehorse

1983. National Afforestation Campaign.
1702 **1122** 60y. multicoloured . . 75 10

1983. 50th Nippon Derby.
1703 **1123** 60y. multicoloured . . 85 10

1124 Rabbit and Empty Can

1983. Islands Clean-up Campaign.
1704 **1124** 60y. multicoloured . . 70 10

1125 Hohei-kan House (Wedding Hall), Sapporo

1126 Glover House, Nagasaki

1983. Modern Western-style Architecture (8th series).
1705 **1125** 60y. multicoloured . . 75 10
1706 **1126** 60y. multicoloured . . 75 10

1127 First Issue and Nihonbashi Bulletin Board

1983. Centenary of "Government Journal".
1707 **1127** 60y. multicoloured . . 75 10

1128 Boy with Letter

1129 Fairy with Letter

1983. Letter Writing Day.
1708 **1128** 40y. multicoloured . . 35 10
1709 **1129** 60y. multicoloured . . 65 10

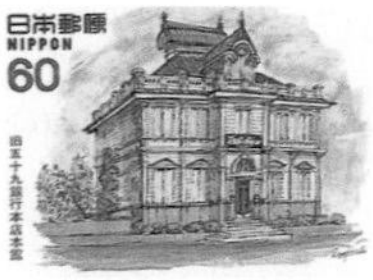

1130 59th Bank, Hirosaki

1131 Auditorium of Gakushuin Elementary School (now in Narita)

1983. Modern Western-style Architecture (9th series).
1710 **1130** 60y. multicoloured . . 75 10
1711 **1131** 60y. multicoloured . . 75 10

1132 Theatre and Noh Player

1983. Opening of National Noh Theatre. Tokyo.
1712 **1132** 60y. multicoloured . . 75 10

1133 Okinawa Rail

1983. Endangered Birds (1st series). Multicoloured.
1713 60y. Type **1133** . . . . . 1·00 20
1714 60y. Blakiston's fish owl ("Ketupa blakistoni") (horiz) . . . . 1·00 20
See also Nos. 1724/5, 1729/30, 1735/6 and 1742/3.

1135 "Chi-kyu" (paper doll by Juzo Kagoshima)

1136 Naginata Player and Myogi Mountains

1983. International Correspondence Week.
1715 **1135** 130y. multicoloured . . 1·75 25

1983. 38th National Athletic Meeting, Gumman.
1716 **1136** 40y. multicoloured . . 40 10

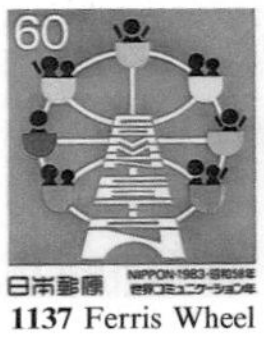

1137 Ferris Wheel

1138 Children supporting Globe

1983. World Communications Year.
1717 **1137** 60y. multicoloured . . 50 10
1718 **1138** 60y. multicoloured . . 50 10

1139 Park and Monument

1140 Congress Emblem and Mouth Mirror

1983. Opening of Showa Memorial National Park.
1719 **1139** 60y. multicoloured . . 60 10

1983. 71st World Dental Congress, Tokyo.
1720 **1140** 60y. multicoloured . . 60 10

1141 "Shirase"

1983. Maiden Voyage of Antarctic Research Ship "Shirase".
1721 **1141** 60y. multicoloured . . 65 20

1983. Special Correspondence Stamps.
1722 **1098** 40y. multicoloured . . 45 10
1723 **1099** 40y. multicoloured . . 45 10

1983. Endangered Birds (2nd series). As T **1133**. Multicoloured.
1724 60y. Pryer's woodpecker ("Sapheopipo noguchii") 1·10 20
1725 60y. Canada goose ("Branta canadensis leucopareia") (horiz) . . . . 1·10 20

1144 "Mouse riding a Small Hammer" (folk toy)

1145 Human Rights Emblem

1983. New Year's Greetings.
1726 **1144** 40y. multicoloured . . 60 10

1983. 35th Anniv of Declaration of Human Rights.
1728 **1145** 60y. multicoloured . . 45 10

1984. Endangered Birds (3rd series). As T **1133**. Multicoloured.
1729 60y. Japanese marsh warbler ("Megalurus pryeri pryeri") (horiz) . . . . . 1·10 20
1730 60y. Crested serpent eagle ("Spilornis cheela perplexus") . . . . 1·10 20

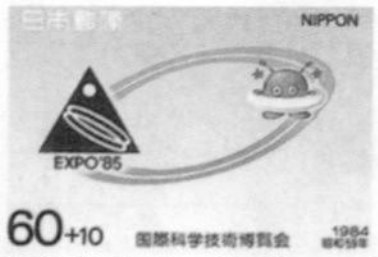

1148 Exhibition Emblem and Mascot

1984. "Expo '85" International Science and Technology Exhibition, Tsukuba (1985).
1731 **1148** 60y.+10y. mult 80 15

1149 Bank of Japan Head Office

1150 Hunter House, Kobe

1984. Modern Western-style Architecture (10th series).
1732 **1149** 60y. multicoloured . . 75 10
1733 **1150** 60y. multicoloured . . 75 10

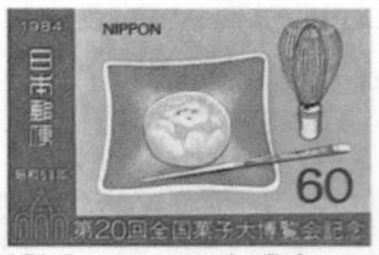

1151 Japanese-style Cake and Bamboo Tea Whisk

1984. 20th Confectionery Fair, Tokyo.
1734 **1151** 60y. multicoloured . . 55 10

1984. Endangered Birds (4th series). As T **1133**. Multicoloured.
1735 60y. Black wood pigeon ("Columba janthina nitens") . . . . 1·10 20
1736 60y. Spotted greenshank ("Tringa guttifer") (horiz) 1·10 20

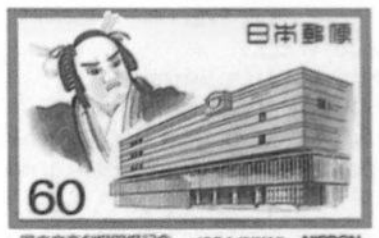

1154 Bunraku Puppet and Theatre

1984. Opening of National Bunraku Theatre, Osaka.
1737 **1154** 60y. multicoloured . . 75 10

1155 "Otani Oniji as Edobeh" (Toshusai Sharaku)

1156 "Iwai Hanshiro IV as Shigenoi" (Toshusai Sharaku)

1984. Philatelic Week.
1738 **1155** 60y. multicoloured . . 75 10
1739 **1156** 60y. multicoloured . . 75 10

1157 Kaikozu Tree and Sakura Volcano

1158 "Himawari" Weather Satellite and Chart

1984. National Afforestation Campaign.
1740 **1157** 60y. multicoloured . . 75 10

1984. Centenary of National Weather Forecasts.
1741 **1158** 60y. multicoloured . . 75 10

1984. Endangered Birds (5th series). As T **1133**. Multicoloured.
1742 60y. White-backed woodpecker ("Dendrocopos leucotos owstoni") (horiz) . . . . 1·10 20
1743 60y. Peregrine falcon ("Falco peregrinus fruitii") . . . . 1·10 20

1161 Doves

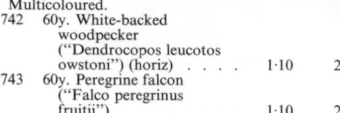

1984. Federation of U.N.E.S.C.O. Clubs and Associations World Congress, Sendai.
1744 **1161** 60y. multicoloured . . 45 10

1162 Birds in Tree

1163 Bird and Flowers

1984. Letter Writing Day.
1745 **1162** 40y. multicoloured . . 35 10
1746 **1163** 60y. multicoloured . . 60 10

1164 "Fire and Wind" (Motomi Hagimoto)

1165 "Bonds" (Noboru Kanda)

1984. Disaster Prevention Week.
1747 **1164** 40y. multicoloured . . 35 10
1748 **1165** 60y. black and yellow 60 10

1166 "Leontopodium fauriei"

1168 Basho's Crossroads, Sendai

1984. Alpine Plants (1st series). Multicoloured.
1749 60y. Type **1166** 70 10
1750 60y. "Lagotis glauca" (horiz) 70 10
See also Nos. 1752/3, 1769/70, 1775/6, 1802/3, 1813/14 and 1827/8.

1984. 6th International Virology Congress, Sendai.
1751 **1168** 60y. multicoloured . . 55 10

1984. Alpine Plants (2nd series). As T **1166**. Multicoloured.
1752 60y. Globe flower ("Trollius riederianus") 75 10
1753 60y. "Primula cuneifolia" 75 10

1171 Logo

1172 "Serenity" (doll by Ryujo Hori)

1984. Electronic Mail.
1754 **1171** 500y. multicoloured . . 8·00 3·00

1984. International Correspondence Week.
1755 **1172** 130y. multicoloured . . 2·00 15

1173 Silver Pavilion, Jisho Temple

1174 Hockey and East Pagoda of Yakushi Temple

1984. 17th International Internal Medicine Congress, Kyoto City.
1756 **1173** 60y. multicoloured . . 55 10

1984. 39th National Athletic Meeting, Nara.
1757 **1174** 40y. multicoloured . . 70 10

1175 Birds in Tree

1176 Flowers

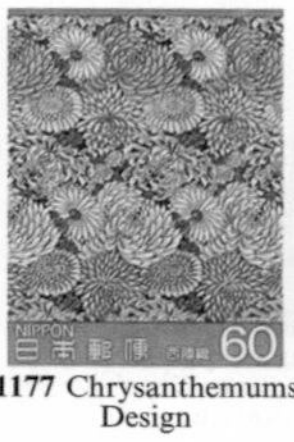

1177 Chrysanthemums Design

1178 Leaf and Bird Design

1984. Traditional Crafts (1st series). Kutani Porcelain Plates and Nishijin Silk Weavings.
1758 **1175** 60y. multicoloured . . 80 10
1759 **1176** 60y. multicoloured . . 80 10
1760 **1177** 60y. multicoloured . . 80 10
1761 **1178** 60y. multicoloured . . 80 10
See also Nos. 1771/4, 1787/90, 1795/8, 1805/8, 1820/3 and 1829/32.

1179 Eiji Sawamura (pitcher)

1984. 50th Anniv of Japan Tokyo Baseball Club. Multicoloured.
1762 60y. Type **1179** 60 10
1763 60y. Masaru Kageura (striker) 60 10
1764 60y. Ball, birds and Matsutaro Shoriki (founder) 60 10

1182 Workers' Profiles and Symbols

1183 Bamboo Ox (Sakushu folk toy)

1984. Centenary of Technical Education.
1765 **1182** 60y. multicoloured . . 45 10

1984. New Year's Greetings.
1766 **1183** 40y. multicoloured . . 40 10

1984. Alpine Plants (3rd series). As T **1166**. Multicoloured.
1769 60y. "Rhododendron aureum" 70 10
1770 60y. "Oxytropis nigrescens" (horiz) 70 10

1186 Dolls

1187 Doll with Cat

1188 Bird and Flower Design

1189 Birds and Chrysanthemums Design

1985. Traditional Crafts (2nd series). Edo Kimekomi Dolls and Okinawa Bingata Cloth.
1771 **1186** 60y. multicoloured . . 75 10
1772 **1187** 60y. multicoloured . . 75 10
1773 **1188** 60y. multicoloured . . 75 10
1774 **1189** 60y. multicoloured . . 75 10

1985. Alpine Plants (4th series). As T **1166**. Multicoloured.
1775 60y. "Dryas octopetala" (horiz) 75 10
1776 60y. "Draba japonica" . . . 75 10

1192 Theme Pavilion and Symbol Tower

1194 University Buildings, Chiba City, and Transmitter

1985. "EXPO '85" World Fair, Tsukuba. Multicoloured.
1777 40y. Type **1192** 40 10
1778 60y. Geometric city 60 10

1985. Inauguration of University of the Air.
1780 **1194** 60y. multicoloured . . 45 10

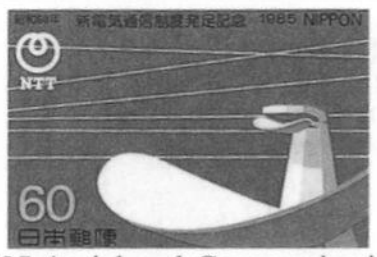

1195 Aerial and Communication Lines

1985. Privatization of Nippon Telegraph and Telephone Corporation.
1781 **1195** 60y. multicoloured . . 45 10

1196 Map of Japan (after Teixeira's Map in Ortelius's "Atlas", 1595)

1197 Korekiyo Takahashi (proposer of Patent Laws)

1985. World Import Fair, Nagoya.
1782 **1196** 60y. multicoloured . . 60 10

1985. Centenary of Industrial Patents System.
1783 **1197** 60y. multicoloured . . 45 10

1198 "Winter in the North" (Yumeji Takehisa)

1199 "Toward the Morning Light" (Yumeji Takehisa)

1985. Philatelic Week.
1784 **1198** 60y. multicoloured . . 75 10
1785 **1199** 60y. multicoloured . . 75 10

1200 Mt. Aso and Gentian

1985. National Afforestation Campaign.
1786 **1200** 60y. multicoloured . . 50 10

1201 Hawk

1202 Ducks

1203 Bowl

1204 Plate

1985. Traditional Crafts (3rd series). Yew Wood Carvings and Arita Porcelain.
1787 **1201** 60y. multicoloured . . 60 10
1788 **1202** 60y. multicoloured . . 60 10
1789 **1203** 60y. multicoloured . . 50 10
1790 **1204** 60y. multicoloured . . 50 10

1205/6 "Cherry Trees at Night" (Taikan Yokoyama)

1985. 50th Anniv of Radio Japan (overseas broadcasting station).
1791 **1205** 60y. multicoloured . . 60 10
1792 **1206** 60y. multicoloured . . 60 10
Nos. 1791/2 were issued together, se-tenant, forming the composite design illustrated.

1207 Maeshima and "Tokyo Post Office" (Hiroshige III)

1208 Bridge

1985. 150th Birth Anniv of Baron Hisoka Maeshima (first Postmaster-General).
1793 **1207** 60y. multicoloured . . 55 10

1985. Opening of Great Naruto Bridge.
1794 **1208** 60y. multicoloured . . 70 10

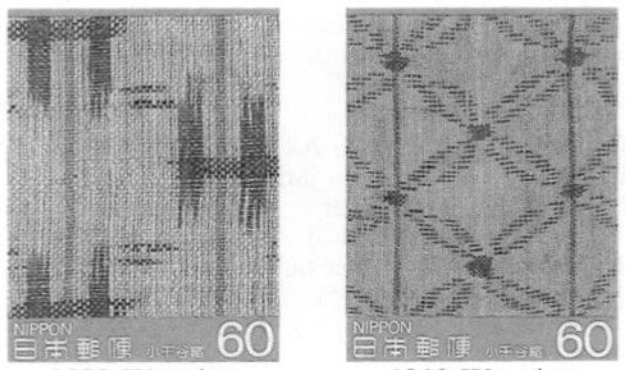

1209 Weaving **1210** Weaving

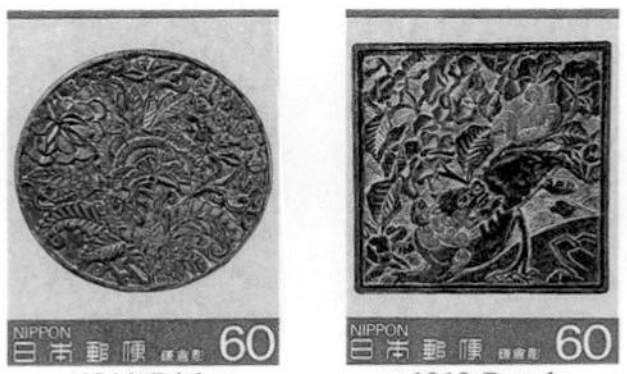

1211 Dish **1212** Panel

1985. Traditional Crafts (4th series). Ojiya Linen Weavings and Kamakura Lacquered Wood Carvings.
1795 **1209** 60y. multicoloured . . 50 10
1796 **1210** 60y. multicoloured . . 50 10
1797 **1211** 60y. multicoloured . . 50 10
1798 **1212** 60y. multicoloured . . 50 10

1213 Silhouette of Laurel and Couple

1985. International Youth Year.
1799 **1213** 60y. multicoloured . . 50 10

1214 Owl with Letter

1215 Girl holding Bird, Letter and Cat

1985. Letter Writing Day.
1800 **1214** 40y. multicoloured . . 60 10
1801 **1215** 60y. multicoloured . . 60 10

1985. Alpine Plants (5th series). As T **1166**. Multicoloured.
1802 60y. Gentian ("Gentiana nipponica") 70 10
1803 60y. "Callianthemum insigne" 70 10

1218 Logo

1985. Electronic Mail.
1804 **1218** 500y. multicoloured . . 5·00 30

1219 Noh Theatre Actor

1220 Mother with Child

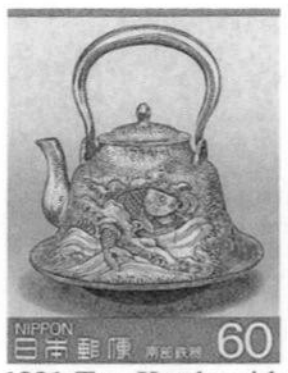

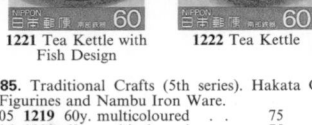

1221 Tea Kettle with Fish Design

1222 Tea Kettle

1985. Traditional Crafts (5th series). Hakata Clay Figurines and Nambu Iron Ware.
1805 **1219** 60y. multicoloured . . 75 10
1806 **1220** 60y. multicoloured . . 75 10
1807 **1221** 60y. multicoloured . . 75 10
1808 **1222** 60y. multicoloured . . 75 10

1223 Hideki Yukawa (physicist) and Meson Field

1224 Gymnasts

1985. 50th Anniv of Yukawa's Meson Theory.
1809 **1223** 60y. multicoloured . . 55 10

1985. University Games, Kobe.
1810 **1224** 60y. multicoloured . . 70 10

1225 Competitor filing Test Piece

1226 "Hibiscus syriacus" (national flower of S. Korea)

1985. 28th International Vocational Training Competition, Osaka.
1811 **1225** 40y. multicoloured . . 40 10

1985. 20th Anniv of Japan–South Korea Diplomatic Relations.
1812 **1226** 60y. multicoloured . . 75 10

1985. Alpine Plants (6th series). As T **1166**. Multicoloured.
1813 60y. "Viola crassa" (horiz) 1·00 10
1814 60y. "Campanula chamissonis" . . . . . . 1·00 10

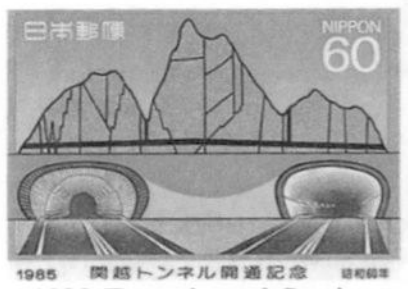

1229 Tunnels and Section through Mt. Tanigawa

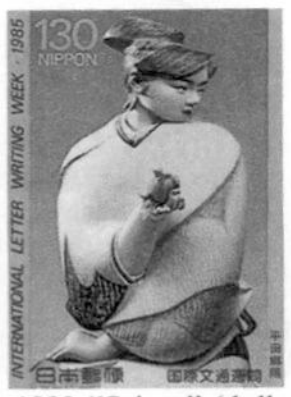

1230 "Seisen" (doll by Goyo Hirata)

1985. Opening of North-bound Kan-Etsu Tunnel.
1815 **1229** 60y. multicoloured . . 70 10

1985. International Correspondence Week.
1816 **1230** 130y. multicoloured . . 1·50 10

1231 Youth helping African Farmer

1985. 20th Anniv of Japanese Overseas Co-operation Volunteers.
1817 **1231** 60y. multicoloured . . 50 10

1232 Honey Bee on Strawberry Blossom

1233 Handball Player and Mt. Daisen

1985. 30th International Bee-keeping Congress, Nagoya.
1818 **1232** 60y. multicoloured . . 80 10

1985. 40th Int Athletic Meeting, Tottori.
1819 **1233** 40y. multicoloured . . 70 10

1234 Table **1235** Bowl

1236 Lantern on Column **1237** Lantern

1985. Traditional Crafts (6th series). Wajima Lacquerware and Izumo Sandstone Lanterns.
1820 **1234** 60y. multicoloured . . 60 10
1821 **1235** 60y. multicoloured . . 60 10
1822 **1236** 60y. multicoloured . . 60 10
1823 **1237** 60y. multicoloured . . 60 10

1238 Osaka Papier-mache Tiger

1239 Cabinet Emblem and Official Seal

1985. New Year's Greetings.
1824 **1238** 40y. multicoloured . . 50 10

1985. Cent of Cabinet System of Government.
1826 **1239** 60y. multicoloured . . 55 10

1986. Alpine Plants (7th series). As T **1166**. Multicoloured.
1827 60y. "Diapensia lapponica" 55 10
1828 60y. "Pedicularis apodochila" 55 10

1242 Fan with Tree Design

1243 Fan with Flower Design

1244 Flask with Fish Pattern

1245 Tea Caddy

1986. Traditional Craft (7th series). Kyoto Fans and Tobe Porcelain.
1829 **1242** 60y. multicoloured . . 75 10
1830 **1243** 60y. multicoloured . . 75 10
1831 **1244** 60y. multicoloured . . 75 10
1832 **1245** 60y. multicoloured . . 75 10

1246 Gothic Style Finial and "Golden Norm"

1986. Centenary of Architecture Institute, Shiba, Tokyo.
1833 **1246** 60y. multicoloured . . 60 10

1247 Standing Lady **1248** Seated Lady

1986. Philatelic Week. Details of "South of Hateruma" by Kaigetsu Kikuchi.
1834 **1247** 60y. multicoloured . . 80 10
1835 **1248** 60y. multicoloured . . 80 10

1249 Phoenix and Enthronement Hall, Kyoto Palace

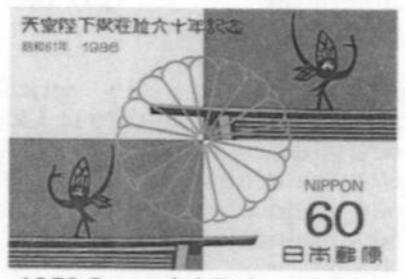

1250 Imperial Palace Ridge Decoration

1986. 60th Anniv of Emperor Hirohito's Accession.
1836 **1249** 60y. multicoloured . . 70 10
1837 **1250** 60y. multicoloured . . 70 10

1251 "Mt. Fuji in Early Morning" (Yukihiko Yasuda) **1252** Bull-headed Shrike in Reeds

1986. 12th Economic Summit of Industrialized Countries, Tokyo.
1839 **1251** 60y. multicoloured . . 75 10

1986. National Afforestation Campaign.
1840 **1252** 60y. multicoloured . . 1·25 20

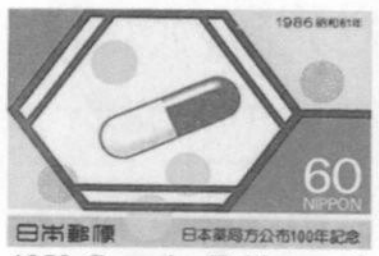

1253 Capsule, Tablets and Structure of Toluene **1254** Map and Clock

1986. Centenary of Japanese Pharmacopoeia.
1841 **1253** 60y. multicoloured . . 85 10

1986. Centenary of Japanese Standard Time.
1842 **1254** 60y. multicoloured . . 65 10

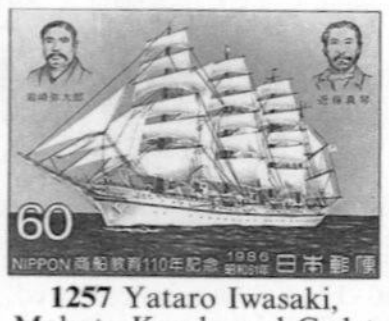

1255 Bird on Chair and Letter on Table **1257** Yataro Iwasaki, Makoto Kondo and Cadet Ship "Nippon Maru II"

1986. Letter Writing Day. Multicoloured.
1843 40y. Type **1255** 40 10
1844 60y. Girl holding rabbit and letter 70 10

1986. 110th Anniv of Merchant Navy Education.
1846 **1257** 60y. multicoloured . . 1·75 35

1258 Asian Apollo ("Parnassius eversmanni") **1262** "Folkways in Twelve Months" (detail, Shunsho Katsukawa)

1986. Insects (1st series). Multicoloured.
1847 60y. Type **1258** . . . . . . 1·00 10
1848 60y. Shieldbug ("Poecilocoris lewisi") . . 1·00 10
1849 60y. Longhorn beetle ("Rosalia batesi") . . . . 1·00 10
1850 60y. "Epiophlebia superstes" 1·00 10
See also Nos. 1854/7, 1861/4, 1869/72, 1878/81 and 1911/12.

1986. 52nd International Federation of Library Associations General Conference, Tokyo.
1851 **1262** 60y. multicoloured . . 75 10

1263 Electron Microscope **1264** Couple and Conference Emblem

1986. 11th International Electron Microscopy Congress, Kyoto.
1852 **1263** 60y. multicoloured . . 85 10

1986. 23rd International Social Welfare Conference, Tokyo.
1853 **1264** 60y. multicoloured . . 60 10

1986. Insects (2nd series). As T **1258**. Mult.
1854 60y. Dragonflies ("Sympetrum pedemonatanum") . . . . 1·00 10
1855 60y. Weevil ("Damaster blaptoides") . . . . . . 1·00 10
1856 60y. Stag beetle ("Dorcus hopei") . . . . 1·00 10
1857 60y. Wonderful hair-streak ("Thermozephyrus ataxus") . . . . 1·00 10

1269 "Ohmori Miyage" (shiso doll, Juzoh Kagoshima) **1270** Gymnast and Mt. Fuji

1986. International Correspondence Week.
1858 **1269** 130y. multicoloured . . 1·50 15

1986. 41st National Athletic Meeting, Yamanashi.
1859 **1270** 40y. multicoloured . . 70 10

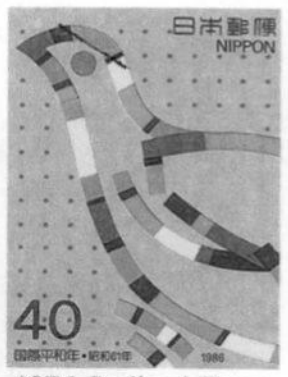

1271 "Flowers in Autumn and Girl in Rakuhoku" **1276** Stylized Dove

1986. 5th World Ikebana Convention, Kyoto.
1860 **1271** 60y. multicoloured . . 85 10

1986. Insects (3rd series). As T **1258**. Mult.
1861 60y. "Elcysma westwoodii" (moth) . . . . 1·00 10
1862 60y. "Rhyothemis variegata" . . . . 1·00 10
1863 60y. Cicada ("Tibicen japonicus") . . . . 1·00 10
1864 60y. "Chrysochroa holstii" 1·00 10

1986. International Peace Year. Mult.
1865 40y. Type **1276** 40 10
1866 60y. Circle of children (horiz) 60 10

1278 "Rabbits making Rice Cake" (Nagoya clay model) **1283** Characters for "Toki" (Registry) and Map

1986. New Year's Greetings.
1867 **1278** 40y. multicoloured . . 75 10
For 50y. in this design dated "1999" see No. 2567.

1987. Insects (4th series). As T **1258**. Mult.
1869 60y. "Cheirotonus jambar" 1·00 10
1870 60y. Chestnut tiger ("Parantica sita") . . . . 1·00 10
1871 60y. "Anotogaster sieboldii" 1·00 10
1872 60y. Stag beetle ("Lucanus maculifemoratus") . . . . 1·00 10

1987. Centenary of Land Registration.
1873 **1283** 60y. multicoloured . . 65 10

1284 Basho Matsuo (after Haritsu Ogawa) **1285** "Departing Spring" (Senju)

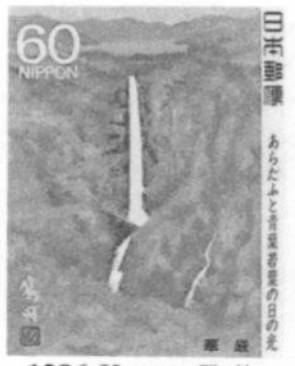

1286 Kegon Falls **1287** "Sunlight" (Toshu Shrine)

1987. "Narrow Road to a Far Province" (travel diary) by Basho Matsuo (1st series).
1874 **1284** 60y. multicoloured . . 75 10
1875 **1285** 60y. multicoloured . . 75 10
1876 **1286** 60y. multicoloured . . 75 10
1877 **1287** 60y. multicoloured . . 75 10
In this series, each pair of stamps (except Nos. 1874/5) illustrates one "haiku" (17-syllable poem) from the diary. The full text of the "haiku" is printed on one stamp and given in calligraphy on the other with appropriate illustrations. Each "haiku" was written at a particular point in the journey (given in brackets in the caption to the second stamp of each pair).
See also Nos. 1896/9, 1906/9, 1925/8, 1932/5, 1945/8, 1962/5, 1973/6, 1982/5 and 2000/3.

1987. Insects (5th series). As T **1258**. Mult.
1878 60y. Owl-fly ("Ascaraphus ramburi") . . . . 1·00 10
1879 60y. Cockchafer ("Polyphylla laticollis") 1·00 10
1880 60y. Leaf butterfly ("Kallima inachus") . . . 1·00 10
1881 60y. "Calopteryx cornelia" 1·00 10

1294 Wind Orchid **1295** Lobster-root

1987. 12th International Orchid Conference, Tokyo.
1883 **1294** 60y. multicoloured . . 70 10
1884 **1295** 60y. multicoloured . . 70 10

1296 Early Mail Sorting Carriage

1987. Ending of Railway Mail Carriage Contracts.
1885 60y. Type **1296** . . . . . . 1·00 30
1886 60y. Loading mail sacks (detail of scroll painting by Beisen Kubota) . . . 1·00 30

1298 Class 860 Tank Locomotive No. 137, 1893

1987. Privatization of Japan Railways. Mult.
1887 60y. Type **1298** . . . . . . 1·00 30
1888 60y. Maglev MLU 002 . . . 1·00 30

1300 Nudibranchs **1301** "Woman with a Comb"

1987. Centenary of Marine Biology Studies in Japan.
1889 **1300** 60y. multicoloured . . 85 15

1987. Philatelic Week. Paintings by Goyo Hashiguchi. Multicoloured.
1890 60y. Type **1301** 85 10
1891 60y. "Woman putting on make-up" 85 10

1303 Map and Emblem **1304** Black-billed Magpie and Forested Coastline

1987. 20th Annual General Meeting of Asian Development Bank.
1892 **1303** 60y. multicoloured . . 60 10

1987. National Afforestation Campaign.
1893 **1304** 60y. multicoloured . . 1·25 20

1305 Yatsuhashi Gold Lacquer and Nacre Inkstone Case (Kohrin Ogata)

1306 Hikone Castle

1987. National Treasures (1st series).
1894 **1305** 60y. multicoloured . . 75 10
1895 **1306** 110y. multicoloured . . 1·50 15
See also Nos. 1900/1, 1929/30, 1949/50, 1968/9, 1980/1, 2006/7 and 2017/18.

1307 European Cuckoo **1308** Horse and River (Nasu)

1309 "In the Shade of the Willow" **1310** Paddy Field (Ashino)

1987. "Narrow Road to a Far Province" by Basho Matsuo (2nd series).
1896 **1307** 60y. multicoloured . . 1·25 20
1897 **1308** 60y. multicoloured . . 60 10
1898 **1309** 60y. multicoloured . . 60 10
1899 **1310** 60y. multicoloured . . 60 10

1311 Golden Turtle Reliquary for Buddha's Ashes (Tashodai Temple) **1312** Inuyama Castle

1987. National Treasures (2nd series). Multicoloured.
1900 **1311** 60y. multicoloured . . 85 10
1901 **1312** 110y. multicoloured . . 1·40 15

1313 Flowers in Envelope **1315** Flood Barrier across Rivers

1987. Letter Writing Day. Multicoloured.
1902 40y. Type **1313** 35 10
1903 60y. Elephant holding letter in trunk 45 10

1987. Centenary of Modern Flood Control of Rivers Kiso, Nagara and Ibi.
1905 **1315** 60y. multicoloured . . 60 10

1316 Chestnut Blossoms **1317** Chestnut Leaves (Sukagawa)

1318 Transplanting Rice **1319** Fern Leaves ("Dyeing Stone", Shinobu)

1987. "Narrow Road to a Far Province" by Basho Matsuo (3rd series).
1906 **1316** 60y. multicoloured . . 60 10
1907 **1317** 60y. multicoloured . . 60 10
1908 **1318** 60y. multicoloured . . 60 10
1909 **1319** 60y. multicoloured . . 60 10

1320 Temple of Emerald Buddha and Cherry Blossom **1321** "Gensho Kanto" (Ryujo Hori)

1987. Centenary of Japan–Thailand Friendship Treaty.
1910 **1320** 60y. multicoloured . . 65 10

1987. Insects (6th series). As T **1258**. Mult.
1911 40y. Orange-tip ("Anthocaris cardamines") 75 10
1912 40y. Great purple ("Sasakia charonda") 75 10

1987. International Correspondence Week. Multicoloured.
1913 130y. Type **1321** . . . . . 1·40 10
1914 150y. "Utage-no-Hana" (Goyo Hirata) . . . . . 1·60 10

1323 "Three Beauties" (detail, Toyokuni Utagawa) **1324** Lion's Head Public Water Tap

1987. 13th International Certified Public Accountants Congress, Tokyo.
1915 **1323** 60y. multicoloured . . 55 10

1987. Centenary of Yokohama Waterworks.
1916 **1324** 60y. multicoloured . . 55 10

1325 Basketball Players and Shuri Gate, Naha **1326** Playing Card with Queen holding Bird and King smoking

1987. 42nd National Athletic Meeting, Okinawa.
1917 **1325** 40y. multicoloured . . 45 10

1987. 6th International Smoking and Health Conference, Tokyo.
1918 **1326** 60y. multicoloured . . 70 10

1327 Dish Aerial, Kashima Station **1328** Nijo Castle

1987. International Telecommunications Conference, Tokyo.
1919 **1327** 60y. multicoloured . . 65 10

1987. World Historic Cities Conference, Kyoto.
1920 **1328** 60y. multicoloured . . 65 10

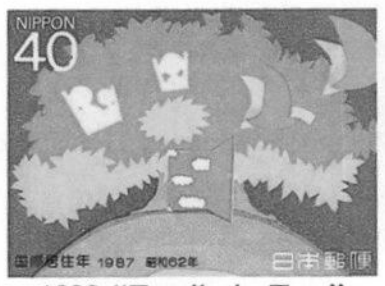

1329 "Family in Tree" (Takahiro Nagahama) **1331** Kurashiki Papier-mache Dragon

1987. International Year of Shelter for the Homeless. Multicoloured.
1921 40y. Type **1329** 40 10
1922 60y. "Houses" (Yoko Sasaki) 60 10

1987. New Year's Greetings.
1923 **1331** 40y. multicoloured . . 50 10

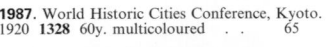

1332 Sweet Flags **1333** Sweet Flags and Birds (Sendai)

1334 "Recollecting the Past" **1335** "Summer Grasses" (Hiraizumi)

1988. "Narrow Road to a Far Province" by Basho Matsuo (4th series).
1925 **1332** 60y. multicoloured . . 60 10
1926 **1333** 60y. multicoloured . . 60 10
1927 **1334** 60y. multicoloured . . 60 10
1928 **1335** 60y. multicoloured . . 60 10

1336 Kongo Samma-in Pagoda, Mt. Koya **1337** Ekoh-Doji, Kongobu Temple

1988. National Treasures (3rd series).
1929 **1336** 60y. multicoloured . . 60 10
1930 **1337** 110y. multicoloured . . 1·25 10

1338 Class ED 79 Locomotive "Sea of Japan" leaving Tunnel and Map

1988. Opening of Seikan (Aomori–Hakodate) Railway Tunnel.
1931 **1338** 60y. multicoloured . . 70 30

1339 Safflower **1340** Willow Trees (Obanazawa)

1341 Risshaku (or Mountain) Temple **1342** Pine Trees (Risshaku Temple)

1988. "Narrow Road to a Far Province" by Basho Matsuo (5th series).
1932 **1339** 60y. multicoloured . . 60 10
1933 **1340** 60y. multicoloured . . 60 10
1934 **1341** 60y. multicoloured . . 60 10
1935 **1342** 60y. multicoloured . . 60 10

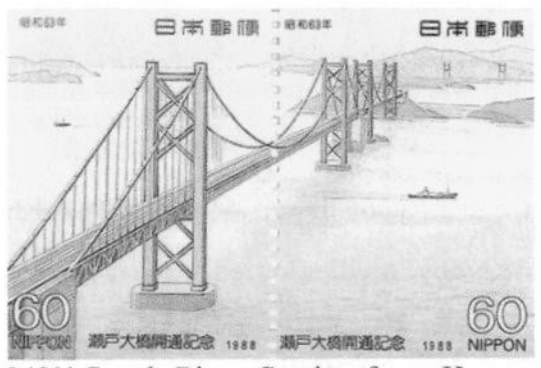

1343/4 South Bisan Section from Kagawa Side

1345/6 Shimotsui Section from Okayama Side

1988. Opening of Seto Great Road and Rail Bridge.
1936 **1343** 60y. multicoloured . . 85 30
1937 **1344** 60y. multicoloured . . 85 30
1938 **1345** 60y. multicoloured . . 85 30
1939 **1346** 60y. multicoloured . . 85 30
Nos. 1936/7 and 1938/9 were printed together, se-tenant, each pair forming the composite design illustrated.

1347 "Long Undergarment" (Kotondo Torii) **1349** Detail of Biwa Plectrum Guard

1988. Philatelic Week. Multicoloured.
1940 60y. Type **1347** 60 10
1941 60y. "Kimono Sash" (Kotondo Torii) 60 10

1988. "Silk Road" Exhibition. Nara.
1943 **1349** 60y. multicoloured . . 60 10

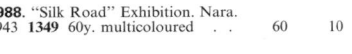

1350 Yashima, Small Cuckoo and Olive Tree

1988. National Afforestation Campaign.
1944 **1350** 60y. multicoloured . . 1·10 20

1351 River Mogami **1352** Irises in the Rain (Oishida)

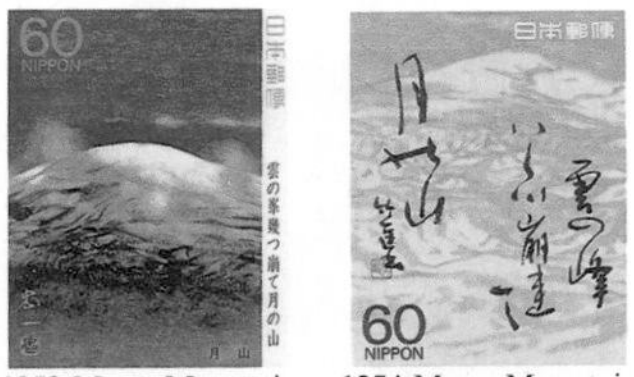

1353 Moon Mountain **1354** Moon Mountain (Gassan)

1988. "Narrow Road to a Far Province" by Basho Matsuo (6th series).
1945 **1351** 60y. multicoloured . . 80 15
1946 **1352** 60y. multicoloured . . 60 10
1947 **1353** 60y. multicoloured . . 60 10
1948 **1354** 60y. multicoloured . . 60 10

1355 Morodo Shrine, Itsukushima

1356 Kozakura-gawa Braided Armour

1988. National Treasures (4th series).
1949 **1355** 60y. multicoloured . . 60 10
1950 **1356** 100y. multicoloured . . 95 20

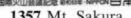

1357 Mt. Sakura

1358 Cat with Letter

1988. International Conference on Volcanoes, Kagoshima.
1951 **1357** 60y. multicoloured . . 60 10

1988. Letter Writing Day. Multicoloured.

1952	40y. Type **1358**	45	10
1953	40y. Crab with letter (34 × 25 mm)	45	10
1954	60y. Fairy with letter . . .	60	10
1955	60y. Girl and letter (25 × 32 mm)	60	10

Nos. 1952 and 1954 exist both perforated with ordinary gum and imperforate with self-adhesive gum.

1362 Ohana (Kinosuke puppet, Japan)

1366 Peonies

1988. International Puppetry Festival, Nagoya, Iida and Tokyo. Multicoloured.

1956	60y. Type **1362**	60	10
1957	60y. Stick puppet of girl (Czechoslovakia)	60	10
1958	60y. Shadow puppet (China)	60	10
1959	60y. Knight (Italy)	60	10

1988. 10th Anniv of Japanese–Chinese Treaty of Peace and Friendship. Multicoloured.

1960	60y. Type **1366**	60	10
1961	60y. Ton-ton (giant panda)	75	10

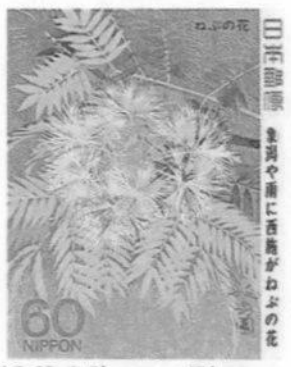
1368 Mimosa Flowers

1369 Lagoon and Grass (Kisagata)

1370 Rough Sea

1371 Waves (Ichiburi)

1988. "Narrow Road to a Far Province" by Basho Matsuo (7th series).

1962	**1368** 60y. multicoloured . .	60	10
1963	**1369** 60y. multicoloured . .	60	10
1964	**1370** 60y. multicoloured . .	60	10
1965	**1371** 60y. multicoloured . .	60	10

1372 Nagoya and Egg

1373 Globe and "Rehabilitation" in Braille

1988. 18th International Poultry Congress, Nagoya.
1966 **1372** 60y. multicoloured . . 70 10

1988. 16th Rehabilitation International World Congress, Tokyo.
1967 **1373** 60y. multicoloured . . 60 10

1374 Nakatsuhime-no-mikoto, Yakushi Temple

1375 Murou Temple

1988. National Treasures (5th series).

1968	**1374** 60y. multicoloured . .	60	10
1969	**1375** 100y. multicoloured . .	95	20

1376 "Kimesaburo Iwai as Chiyo" (Kunimasa Utagawa)

1378 Gymnast and Temple of the Golden Pavilion

1988. International Correspondence Week. Mult.

1970	80y. Type **1376**	85	10
1971	120y. "Komazo Ichikawa III as Ganryu Sasaki" (Toyokuni Utagawa) . .	1·25	20

1988. 43rd National Athletic Meeting, Kyoto.
1972 **1378** 40y. multicoloured . . 45 10

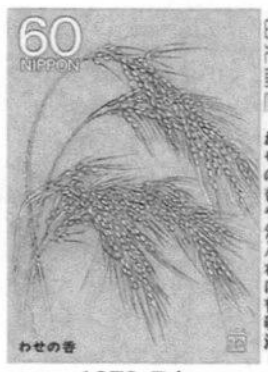
1379 Rice

1380 Ariso Sea (Kurikara Pass)

1381 Sun

1382 "Autumn Wind and Sun" (Kanazawa)

1988. "Narrow Road to a Far Province" by Basho Matsuo (8th series).

1973	**1379** 60y. multicoloured . .	60	10
1974	**1380** 60y. multicoloured . .	60	10
1975	**1381** 60y. multicoloured . .	60	10
1976	**1382** 60y. multicoloured . .	60	10

1383 Mexican State Arms

1384 Snake (Shimotsuke clay bell)

1988. Centenary of Japan–Mexico Friendship and Trade Treaty.
1977 **1383** 60y. multicoloured . . 60 10

1988. New Year's Greetings.
1978 **1384** 40y. multicoloured . . 45 10

1385 Figures on Globe

1988. 40th Anniv of Declaration of Human Rights.
1979 **1385** 60y. multicoloured . . 60 10

1386 Gold-plated Silver Pot with Hunting Design, Todai Temple

1387 Bronze Figure of Yakushi (Buddha of Medicine), Horyu Temple

1989. National Treasures (6th series).

1980	**1386** 60y. multicoloured . .	60	10
1981	**1387** 100y. multicoloured . .	95	20

1388 Nata Temple

1389 Pampas Grass (Natadera)

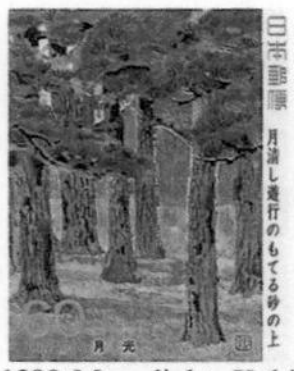
1390 Moonlight, Kehi Shrine

1391 Moon and Pine Trees (Tsuruga)

1989. "Narrow Road to a Far Province" by Basho Matsuo (9th series).

1982	**1388** 60y. multicoloured . .	60	10
1983	**1389** 60y. multicoloured . .	60	10
1984	**1390** 60y. multicoloured . .	60	10
1985	**1391** 60y. multicoloured . .	60	10

1392 Globe and Exhibition Site

1989. "Fukuoka '89" Asian–Pacific Exhibition, Fukuoka.

1989	**1392** 60y. multicoloured . .	60	10
1996	62y. multicoloured . .	60	10

1393 "Russian Ladies sight-seeing at Port" (detail, Yoshitora) and Art Gallery

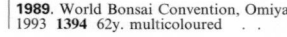

1394 Bonsai Japanese White Pine

1989. "Space and Children" Exhibition, Yokohama.

1990	**1393** 60y. multicoloured . .	60	10
1997	62y. multicoloured . .	60	10

1989. World Bonsai Convention, Omiya.
1993 **1394** 62y. multicoloured . . 60 10

1395 Lute-player

1397 "Dutch East Indiaman entering Harbour" (Nagasaki woodblock print)

1989. Philatelic Week. Details of "Awa Dance" (painting) by Tsunetomi Kitano. Multicoloured.

1994	62y. Type **1395**	60	10
1995	62y. Dancer	60	10

1989. "Holland Festival '89".
1998 **1397** 62y. multicoloured . . 1·00 15

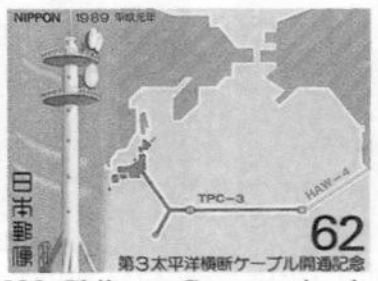
1398 Chikura Communication Tower and Cable Route

1989. Opening of 3rd Trans-Pacific Submarine Telephone Cable (Japan–Hawaii).
1999 **1398** 62y. multicoloured . . 60 10

1399 Beach in Autumn

1400 Bush Clover (Ironohama)

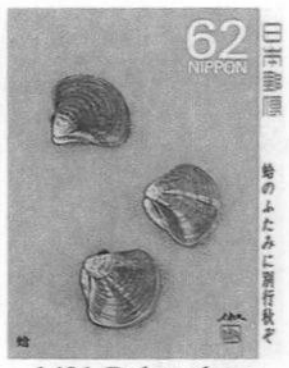
1401 Poker-drop Venuses

1402 Wedded Rocks, Futami Bay (Ohgaki)

1989. "Narrow Road to a Far Province" by Basho Matsuo (11th series).

2000	**1399** 62y. multicoloured . .	60	10
2001	**1400** 62y. multicoloured . .	60	10
2002	**1401** 62y. multicoloured . .	70	15
2003	**1402** 62y. multicoloured . .	60	10

1403 Mt. Tsurugi, Lime and Bay Trees

1404 Children in Bird and Flower "Balloon"

1989. National Afforestation Campaign.
2004 **1403** 62y. multicoloured . . 60 10

1989. International Garden and Greenery Exposition, Osaka (1990) (1st issue).
2005 **1404** 62y.+10y. mult 70 10
See also Nos. 2035/6.

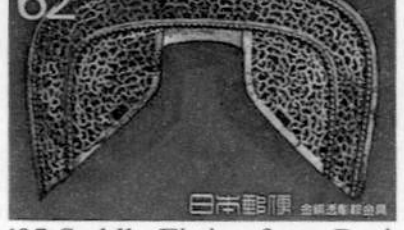
1405 Saddle Fitting from Burial Mound, Konda

1406 "Beetle Wings" Zushi, Horyu Temple

1989. National Treasures (7th series).
2006 **1405** 62y. multicoloured . . 60 10
2007 **1406** 100y. multicoloured . . 95 20

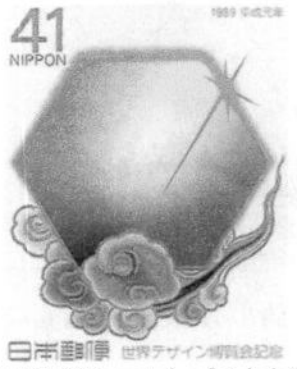

1407 "Crystal of Light and Auspicious Clouds"   **1409** Bird as Vase holding Envelope

1989. World Design Exposition, Nagoya. Multicoloured.
2008 41y. Type **1407** 45 10
2009 62y. "design" 60 10

1989. Letter Writing Day. Multicoloured.
2010 41y. Type **1409** 45 10
2011 62y. Mother Rabbit reading letter 60 10

1989. Special Correspondence Stamps.
2013 **1098** 41y. multicoloured . . 40 10
2014 **1099** 41y. multicoloured . . 40 10
2015 62y. multicoloured . . 55 10
2016 **1100** 72y. multicoloured . . 65 10

1411 Gold Stamp   **1412** Bronze Mirror

1989. National Treasures (8th series).
2017 **1411** 62y. multicoloured . . 60 10
2018 **1412** 100y. multicoloured . . 95 20

1413 Bouquet of Orchids and Stephanotis   **1414** Wheelchair Race

1989. 6th Interflora World Congress, Tokyo.
2019 **1413** 62y. multicoloured . . 60 10

1989. Far East and South Pacific Games for the Disabled, Kobe.
2020 **1414** 62y. multicoloured . . 60 10

1415 Narrators and Drummers   **1419** Ear of Rice and Paddy Field

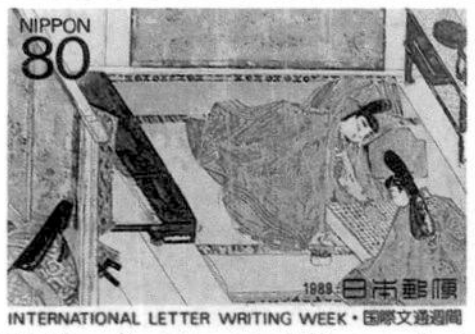

1417 New Emperor and Kaoru playing Go ("Yadorigi" scroll)

1989. "Europalia 89 Japan" Festival, Belgium. Details of "Okuni Theatre" (painting on folding screen). Multicoloured.
2021 62y. Type **1415** 60 10
2022 70y. Okuni (actress) 60 10

1989. International Correspondence Week. Details of Takayoshi Picture Scrolls illustrating "Tale of Genji" by Lady Murasaki. Multicoloured.
2023 80y. Type **1417** 75 10
2024 120y. Yugao's granddaughters playing Go ("Takekawa scroll") 1·25 20

1989. 7th Asian/African Conference of Int Irrigation and Drainage Commission.
2025 **1419** 62y. multicoloured . . 60 10

1420 Shinzan (first winner of all five major races)   **1421** Hot-air Balloons

1989. 100th Tenno Sho Horse Race.
2026 **1420** 62y. multicoloured . . 70 10

1989. 9th Hot Air Balloon World Championship, Saga City.
2027 **1421** 62y. multicoloured . . 60 10

1422 Conductor   **1423** Yawata Wooden Horse

1989. 50th Anniv of Japanese Copyright Control Act.
2028 **1422** 62y. multicoloured . . 60 10

1989. New Year's Greetings.
2029 **1423** 41y. multicoloured . . 45 10

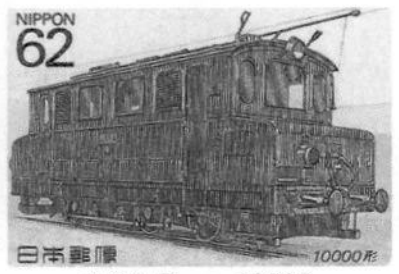

1424 Hamamatsu Papier-mache Horse   **1425** Type 10000

1989. New Year Lottery Stamp.
2030 **1424** 62y. multicoloured . . 60 10
Each stamp carries a lottery number.

1990. Electric Railway Locomotives (1st series).
2031 **1425** 62y. purple, lilac & grn 1·25 25
2032 – 62y. multicoloured . . 1·25 25
DESIGN: No. 2032, Type EF 58 No. 38, 1946.
See also Nos. 2033/4, 2039/40, 2089/90 and 2101/2.

1990. Electric Railway Locomotives (2nd series). As T **1425**. Multicoloured.
2033 62y. Type ED 40 No. 12, 1919 . . . . 1·25 25
2034 62y. Type EH 10 No. 8, 1954 . . . . 1·25 25

1429 Fairies on Flower   **1431** "Women gazing at the Stars" (Chou Ohta)

1990. "Expo 90" International Garden and Greenery Exposition, Osaka. Multicoloured.
2035 41y.+4y. Type **1429** 45 10
2036 62y. Bicycle under tree . . . 55 10

1990. Philatelic Week.
2037 **1431** 62y. multicoloured . . 55 10

1990. Electric Railway Locomotives (3rd series). As T **1425**. Multicoloured.
2039 62y. Type EF 53, 1932 . . . 1·25 25
2040 62y. Type ED 70, 1957 . . 1·25 25

1434 Sweet Briar (Hokkaido)   **1435** Apple Blossom (Aomori)

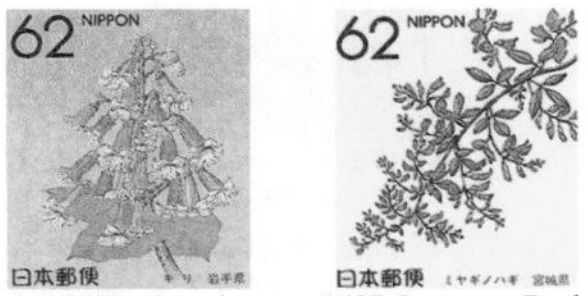

1436 "Paulownia tomentosa" (Iwate)   **1437** Japanese Bush Clover (Miyagi)

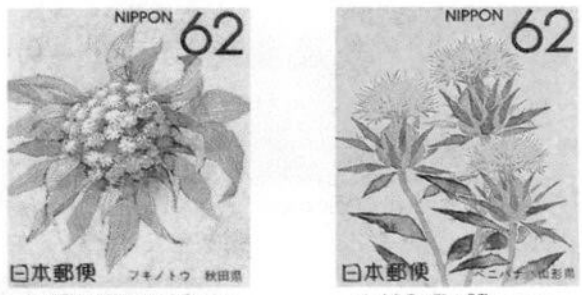

1438 Butterbur Flower (Akita)   **1439** Safflower (Yamagata)

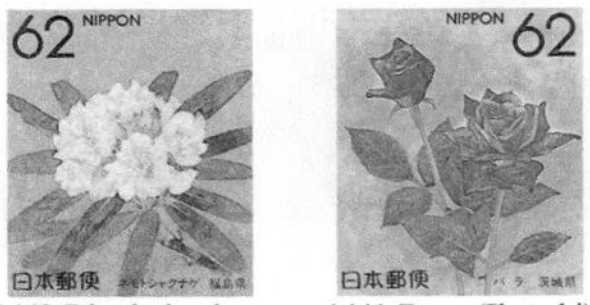

1440 Rhododendron (Fukushima)   **1441** Rose (Ibaraki)

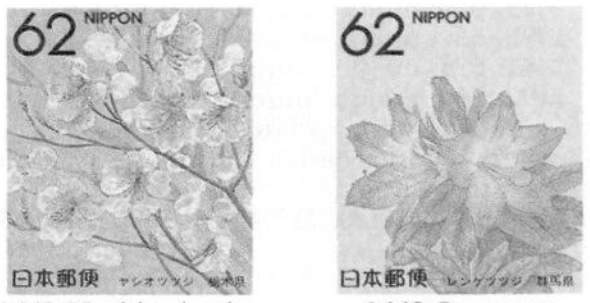

1442 Yashio Azalea (Tochigi)   **1443** Japanese Azalea (Gunma)

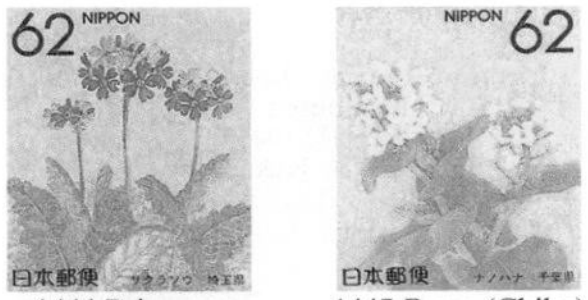

1444 Primrose (Saitama)   **1445** Rape (Chiba)

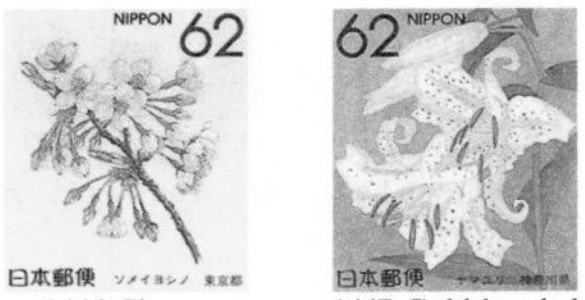

1446 Cherry Blossom (Yamanashi)   **1447** Gold-banded Lily (Kanagawa)

1448 Cherry Blossom (Tokyo)   **1449** Gentian (Nagano)

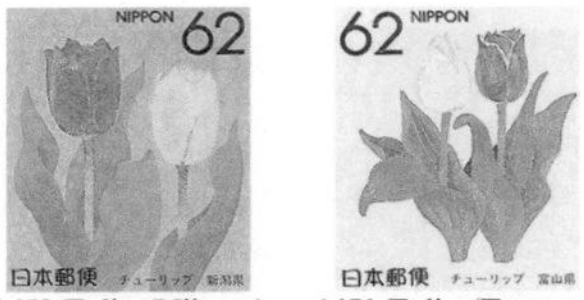

1450 Tulip (Niigata)   **1451** Tulip (Toyama)

1452 Fritillaria (Ishikawa)   **1453** Narcissi (Fukui)

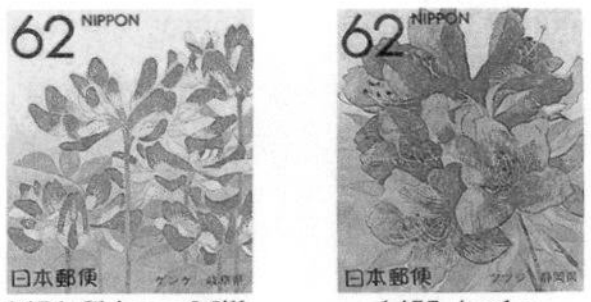

1454 Chinese Milk Vetch (Gifu)   **1455** Azalea (Shizuoka)

1456 Rabbit-ear Iris (Aichi)   **1457** Iris (Mie)

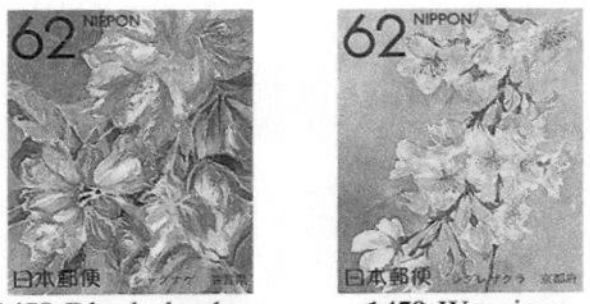

1458 Rhododendron (Shiga)   **1459** Weeping Cherry Blossom (Kyoto)

1460 Japanese Apricot and Primrose (Osaka)   **1461** Marguerites (Hyogo)

1462 Double Cherry Blossom (Nara)   **1463** Japanese Apricot (Wakayama)

1464 Pear Blossom (Tottori)   **1465** Peony (Shimane)

1466 Peach Blossom (Okayama)   **1467** Japanese Maple (Hiroshima)

1468 Summer Orange Blossom (Yamaguchi)

1469 Sudachi Orange Blossom (Tokushima)

1470 Olive Blossom (Kagawa)

1471 Mandarin Orange Blossom (Ehime)

1472 "Myrica rubra" (Kochi)

1473 Japanese Apricot (Fukuoka)

1474 Laurel (Saga)

1475 Unzen Azalea (Nagasaki)

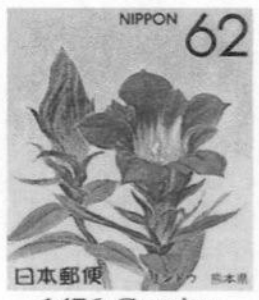
1476 Gentian (Kumamoto)

1477 Japanese Apricot (Oita)

1478 Crinum (Miyazaki)

1479 Rhododendron (Kagoshima)

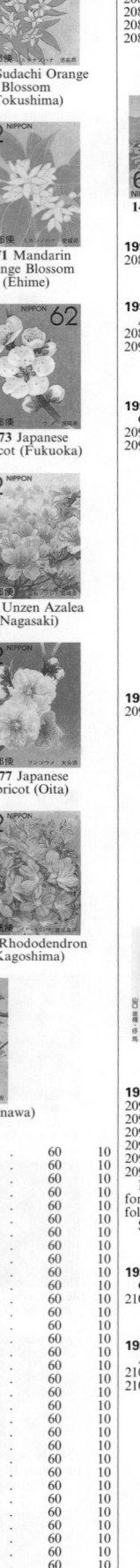

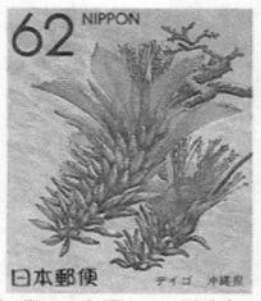
1480 Coral Tree (Okinawa)

1990. Prefecture Flowers.
2041 **1434** 62y. multicoloured . . 60 10
2042 **1435** 62y. multicoloured . . 60 10
2043 **1436** 62y. multicoloured . . 60 10
2044 **1437** 62y. multicoloured . . 60 10
2045 **1438** 62y. multicoloured . . 60 10
2046 **1439** 62y. multicoloured . . 60 10
2047 **1440** 62y. multicoloured . . 60 10
2048 **1441** 62y. multicoloured . . 60 10
2049 **1442** 62y. multicoloured . . 60 10
2050 **1443** 62y. multicoloured . . 60 10
2051 **1444** 62y. multicoloured . . 60 10
2052 **1445** 62y. multicoloured . . 60 10
2053 **1446** 62y. multicoloured . . 60 10
2054 **1447** 62y. multicoloured . . 60 10
2055 **1448** 62y. multicoloured . . 60 10
2056 **1449** 62y. multicoloured . . 60 10
2057 **1450** 62y. multicoloured . . 60 10
2058 **1451** 62y. multicoloured . . 60 10
2059 **1452** 62y. multicoloured . . 60 10
2060 **1453** 62y. multicoloured . . 60 10
2061 **1454** 62y. multicoloured . . 60 10
2062 **1455** 62y. multicoloured . . 60 10
2063 **1456** 62y. multicoloured . . 60 10
2064 **1457** 62y. multicoloured . . 60 10
2065 **1458** 62y. multicoloured . . 60 10
2066 **1459** 62y. multicoloured . . 60 10
2067 **1460** 62y. multicoloured . . 60 10
2068 **1461** 62y. multicoloured . . 60 10
2069 **1462** 62y. multicoloured . . 60 10
2070 **1463** 62y. multicoloured . . 60 10
2071 **1464** 62y. multicoloured . . 60 10
2072 **1465** 62y. multicoloured . . 60 10
2073 **1466** 62y. multicoloured . . 60 10
2074 **1467** 62y. multicoloured . . 60 10
2075 **1468** 62y. multicoloured . . 60 10
2076 **1469** 62y. multicoloured . . 60 10
2077 **1470** 62y. multicoloured . . 60 10
2078 **1471** 62y. multicoloured . . 60 10
2079 **1472** 62y. multicoloured . . 60 10
2080 **1473** 62y. multicoloured . . 60 10
2081 **1474** 62y. multicoloured . . 60 10
2082 **1475** 62y. multicoloured . . 60 10
2083 **1476** 62y. multicoloured . . 60 10
2084 **1477** 62y. multicoloured . . 60 10
2085 **1478** 62y. multicoloured . . 60 10
2086 **1479** 62y. multicoloured . . 60 10
2087 **1480** 62y. multicoloured . . 60 10

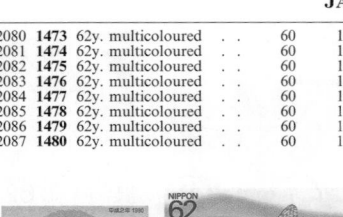

1481 Mt. Unzen and Unzen Azalea

1484 Fritillary on Thistle

1990. National Afforestation Campaign.
2088 **1481** 62y. multicoloured . . 55 10

1990. Electric Railway Locomotives (4th series). As T **1425**. Multicoloured.
2089 62y. Type EF 55, 1936 . . . 1·25 25
2090 62y. Type ED 61 No. 13, 1958 . . . . 1·25 25

1990. Winning Entries in Postage Stamp Design Contest. Multicoloured.
2091 62y. Type **1484** 55 25
2092 70y. "Communication" . . 65 20

1486 17th-century Ottoman Tile

1990. Century of Japan–Turkey Friendship.
2093 **1486** 62y. multicoloured . . 55 10

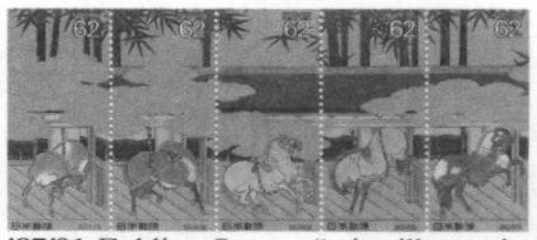
1487/91 Folding Screen (½ size illustration)

1492 "Ponies" (Kayo Yamaguchi)

1493 Emblem and Landscape

1990. The Horse in Culture (1st series).
2094 **1487** 62y. multicoloured . . 65 10
2095 **1488** 62y. multicoloured . . 65 10
2096 **1489** 62y. multicoloured . . 65 10
2097 **1490** 62y. multicoloured . . 65 10
2098 **1491** 62y. multicoloured . . 65 10
2099 **1492** 62y. multicoloured . . 65 10
Nos. 2094/8 were printed together, se-tenant, forming a composite design showing a 17th-century folding screen painting.
See also Nos. 2106/8, 2113/14, 2132/4 and 2135/6.

1990. 38th International Youth Hostel Federation Congress. Muikamachi and Kashiwazaki.
2100 **1493** 62y. multicoloured . . 55 10

1990. Electric Railway Locomotives (5th series). As T **1425**. Multicoloured.
2101 62y. Type ED 57, 1941 . . 1·25 25
2102 62y. Type EF 30 Nos. 3 and 6, 1961 . . . . 1·25 25

1496 Bluebird and Heart

1497 Fairy on Horse

1990. Letter Writing Day.
2103 **1496** 41y. multicoloured . . 40 10
2104 **1497** 62y. multicoloured . . 55 10
For similar design to No. 2104, see No. 2157.

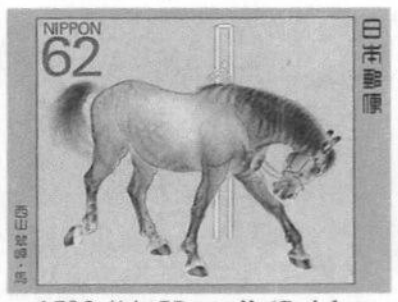
1500 "A Horse" (Suisho Nishiyama)

1990. The Horse in Culture (2nd series). Multicoloured.
2106 62y. 16th-century lacquered saddle 65 10
2107 62y. 16th-century lacquered stirrups 65 10
2108 62y. Type **1500** 65 10

1501 Origami Polyhedron

1502 Track Race

1990. Int Mathematicians Congress, Kyoto.
2109 **1501** 62y. multicoloured . . 60 10

1990. World Cycling Championships. Maebashi and Tochigi Prefecture.
2110 **1502** 62y. multicoloured . . 60 10

1503 Ogai Mori (translator) and Passage from Goethe's "Faust"

1504 "Ji" (character) and Rosetta Stone

1990. 8th International Association for Germanic Studies Congress, Tokyo.
2111 **1503** 62y. blue, yellow & brn 55 10

1990. International Literacy Year.
2112 **1504** 62y. multicoloured . . 55 10

1505 "Kurabeuma Race" (detail of Kimono)

1506 "Kettei" (Shodo Sasaki)

1990. The Horse in Culture (3rd series).
2113 **1505** 62y. multicoloured . . 65 10
2114 **1506** 62y. multicoloured . . 65 10

1507 Peaceful Landscape

1990. International Decade for Natural Disaster Reduction Conference, Yokohama.
2115 **1507** 62y. multicoloured . . 55 10

1508 Animals at Dance

1990. International Correspondence Week. Details from "Choju-jinbutsu-giga" Picture Scroll. Multicoloured.
2116 80y. Type **1508** 75 10
2117 120y. Dancing frogs . . . . 1·10 20

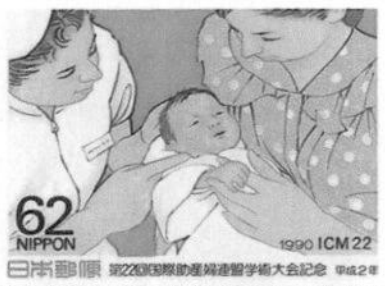
1510 Midwife, Mother and Baby

1990. 22nd International Confederation of Midwives Congress, Kobe City.
2118 **1510** 62y. multicoloured . . 55 10

1511 "Letter Bearer" (detail, Harunobu Suiendo)

1990. "Phila Nippon '91" International Stamp Exhibition, Tokyo (1st issue).
2119 **1511** 100y. multicoloured . . 1·00 20
See also No. 2170.

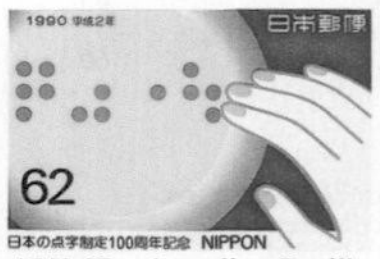
1512 Hand reading Braille

1513 "Justice" (Supreme Court bronze statue, Katsuzo Entsuba)

1990. Centenary of Japanese Braille.
2121 **1512** 62y. multicoloured . . 55 10

1990. Centenary of Modern Judiciary System.
2122 **1513** 62y. multicoloured . . 55 10

1514 Chinese Phoenix (detail from dais of Emperor's enthronement seat)

1516 Stained Glass Window (Diet building)

1990. Enthronement of Emperor. Multicoloured.
2123 62y. Type **1514** 55 10
2124 62y. Pattern from robe of Manzai Raku dancers . . 55 10

1990. Centenary of Diet.
2126 **1516** 62y. multicoloured . . 55 10

1517 Sheep (Nogomi ceramic bell)

1519 Tsuneishi-Hariko Papier-mache Ram

1990. New Year's Greetings.
2127 **1517** 41y. multicoloured . . 40 10

1990. New Year Lottery Stamps. Multicoloured.
2128 41y. Sheep (Tosa ceramic bell) 40 10
2129 62y. Type **1519** 55 10
Each stamp carries a lottery number.

1520 Dr. Nishina and Radio Isotope

1521 "Lady using Telephone" (Senseki Nakamura)

1990. Birth Centenary of Dr. Yoshio Nishina (physicist) and 50th Anniv of First Japanese Cyclotron (radio isotope generator).
2130 **1520** 62y. multicoloured . . 55 10

1990. Centenary of Telephone Service in Japan.
2131 **1521** 62y. multicoloured . . 55 10

1522/3 Horse-drawn Post Carriages (details of scroll painting by Beisen Kubota)

1524 Inkstone Case (Korin Ogata)

1991. The Horse in Culture (4th series).
2132 **1522** 62y. multicoloured . . 60 10
2133 **1523** 62y. multicoloured . . 60 10
2134 **1524** 62y. multicoloured . . 60 10
Nos. 2132/3 were issued together, se-tenant, forming the composite design illustrated.

1525 "Spring Warmth" (Kogetsu Saigo)

1526 "Senju in Musashi Province" (from "36 Views of Mt. Fuji" by Hokusai Katsushika)

1991. The Horse in Culture (5th series).
2135 **1525** 62y. multicoloured . . 65 10
2136 **1526** 62y. multicoloured . . 65 10

1527 Figure Skating

1529 Bouquet

1991. Winter Universiade, Sapporo and Furano. Multicoloured.
2137 41y. Type **1527** 45 10
2138 62y. Short-track speed skating (horiz) 60 10

1991. New Postal Life Insurance System.
2139 **1529** 62y. multicoloured . . 55 10

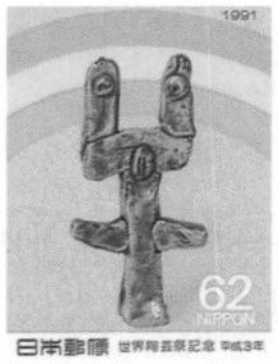

1530 "Glory of the Earth" (Komei Bekki)

1531 "Beauty looking Back" (Moronobu Hishikawa)

1991. "Ceramic World Shigaraki '91" Exn.
2140 **1530** 62y. multicoloured . . 55 10

1991. Philatelic Week. 120th Anniv of First Japanese Stamps.
2141 62y. Type **1531** 60 10
2142 62y. "The Prelude" (Shuho Yamakawa) 60 10

1533 Weeping Cherry Blossom and Phoenix Hall, Byodoin Temple

1534 Early Leveller and Standard Datum Repository, Tokyo

1991. National Afforestation Campaign.
2144 **1533** 41y. multicoloured . . 40 10

1991. Centenary of Standard Datum of Levelling.
2145 **1534** 62y. multicoloured . . 55 10

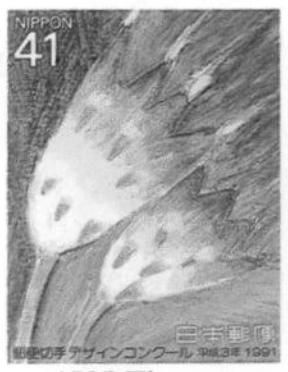

1535 Flowers

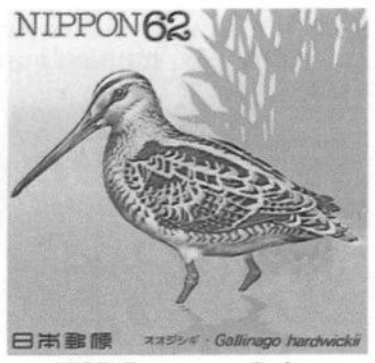

1539 Japanese Snipe ("Gallinago hardwickii")

1991. Winning Entries in Postage Stamp Design Contest.
2146 **1535** 41y. multicoloured . . 40 10
2147 – 62y. multicoloured . . 55 10
2148 – 70y. brown, blue & blk 65 10
2149 – 100y. multicoloured . . 90 20
DESIGNS—HORIZ: 62y. Couple in traditional dress; 100y. Butterfly. VERT: 70y. "World Peace".

1991. Water Birds (1st series). Multicoloured.
2150 62y. Type **1539** . . . . . . 1·25 20
2151 62y. Brown booby ("Sula leucogaster") . . . . . . 1·25 20
See also Nos. 2162/3, 2179/80, 2184/5, 2198/9, 2241/2, 2247/8 and 2251/2.

1541 Kikugoro Onoe VI in Title Role of "Spirit of the Lion"

1542 Utaemon Nakamura VI as Princess Yaegaki in "24 Examples of Filial Piety"

1991. Kabuki Theatre (1st series).
2152 **1541** 62y. green, gold & black 55 10
2153 **1542** 100y. multicoloured . . 90 20
See also Nos. 2164/5, 2172/3, 2181/2, 2186/7 and 2190/1.

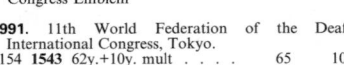

1543 "Solidarity" in Sign Language and Congress Emblem

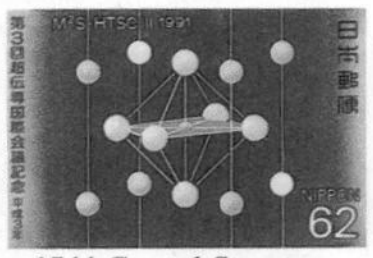

1544 Crystal Structure

1991. 11th World Federation of the Deaf International Congress, Tokyo.
2154 **1543** 62y.+10y. mult 65 10

The premium was assigned to programmes for helping the deaf.

1991. International Conf on Materials and Mechanism of Superconductivity, Kanazawa.
2155 **1544** 62y. multicoloured . . 55 10

1545 Girl sitting on Morning Glory

1546 Fairy on Horse

1991. Letter Writing Day.
2156 **1545** 41y. multicoloured . . 40 10
2157 **1546** 62y. multicoloured . . 55 10
For design similar to No. 2157 but with central motif drawn larger, see No. 2104.

1547 High Jumping

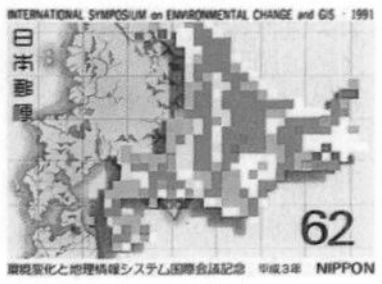

1549 Map and Computer Image of Hokkaido

1991. 3rd World Athletics Championships, Tokyo. Multicoloured.
2159 41y. Type **1547** 50 10
2160 62y. Putting the shot . . . 70 15

1991. International Symposium on Environmental Change and Geographic Information Systems, Asahikawa, Hokkaido.
2161 **1549** 62y. multicoloured . . 70 15

1991. Water Birds (2nd series). As T **1539**. Multicoloured.
2162 62y. Japanese gull ("Larus crassirostris") . . . . . . 1·25 20
2163 62y. Little grebe ("Podiceps ruficollis") . . . . 1·25 20

1552 Koshiro Matsumoto VII as Benkei in "The Subscription List"

1553 Danjuro Ichikawa XI as Danjo in "Tweezers"

1991. Kabuki Theatre (2nd series).
2164 **1552** 62y. black, grey & gold 70 15
2165 **1553** 100y. multicoloured . . 1·25 30

1554 Nobles watching burning Oten Gate

1991. International Correspondence Week. Details from Ban Dainagon Picture Scrolls by Mitsunaga Tokiwa. Multicoloured.
2166 80y. Type **1554** 95 20
2167 120y. Arrest of Yoshio Tomo (arsonist) . . . . . 1·40 30

1556 "Clear Day with Southern Breeze" (from "36 Views of Mt. Fuji" by Hokusai Katsushika) and Seismographic Wave

1557 Tea Utensils and Flower

1991. Earthquake and Natural Disaster Countermeasures Conference. Tokyo.
2168 **1556** 62y. multicoloured . . 70 15

1991. 800th Anniv of Introduction of Green Tea into Japan.
2169 **1557** 62y. multicoloured . . 70 15

1558 "Saucy Girl" (from "A Selection of Beautiful Women" by Kunisada Utagawa)

1991. "Phila Nippon '91" International Stamp Exhibition, Tokyo (2nd issue).
2170 **1558** 62y. multicoloured . . 70 15

1559 Baigyoku Nakamura III as the Ogiya Courtesan Yugiri in "Yoshida-ya"

1560 Ganjiro Nakamura III as Jihei Kamiya in "Shinju-Ten no Amijima"

1991. Kabuki Theatre (3rd series). Works by Chikamatsu Monzaemon.
2172 **1559** 62y. black, pur & gold 70 15
2173 **1560** 100y. multicoloured . . 1·25 30

1561 Boy building Toy Town

1562 Ishikawa Papier-mache Monkey

1991. 30th Anniv of Administrative Councillors System.
2174 **1561** 62y. multicoloured . . 70 15

1991. New Year's Greetings. Multicoloured.
2175 41y. Type **1562** 50 10
2176 62y. Obata monkey 70 15

1565 Obata Monkey

1991. New Year Lottery Stamps. Multicoloured.
2177 41y.+3y. Ishikawa papier-mache monkey 50 10
2178 62y.+3y. Type **1565** 75 15
Each stamp carries a lottery number.

1992. Water Birds (3rd series). As T **1539**. Multicoloured.
2179 62y. Tufted puffin ("Lunda cirrhata") . . . . 1·25 20
2180 62y. Hooded cranes ("Grus monacha") . . . . 1·25 20

1568 Kichiemon Nakamura I as Jiro Naozane Kumagai in "Chronicle of Two Boys in Battle of Ichinotani" by Munesuke Namiki

1569 Nizaemon Kataoka XIII as Old Man in "Kotobuki Shiki Sambaso"

1992. Kabuki Theatre (4th series).
2181 **1568** 62y. multicoloured . . 70 15
2182 **1569** 100y. multicoloured . . 1·25 30

1570 Orchid and Chimpanzees

1992. 8th Conference of Parties to Convention on International Trade in Endangered Species, Kyoto City.
2183 **1570** 62y. multicoloured . . 70 15

1992. Water Birds (4th series). As T **1539**. Multicoloured.
2184 62y. Whooper swan ("Cygnus cygnus") . . . 1·25 20
2185 62y. Painted-snipe ("Rostratula benghalensis") . . . . . 1·25 20

1573 Enjaku Jitsukawa II as Ishikawa-Geomon in "Two-Storey Gate—Pawlonia" by Gohei Namiki

1574 Hakuo Matsumoto I as Oishi-Kuranosuke in "Loyal Retainers in Genroku" by Seika Mayama

1992. Kabuki Theatre (5th series).
2186 **1573** 62y. multicoloured . . 70 15
2187 **1574** 100y. multicoloured . . 1·25 30

1575 "Flowers on Chair" (Hoshun Yamaguchi)

1576 Shuri Castle

1992. Philatelic Week.
2188 **1575** 62y. multicoloured . . 70 15

1992. 20th Anniv of Return of Okinawa (Ryukyu Islands).
2189 **1576** 62y. multicoloured . . 70 15

1577 Baiko Onoe VII as the Wisteria Maiden

1578 Shoroku Onoe II as Goro Soga and Kanzaburo Nakamura XVII as Juro Soga in "Kotobuki-Soga-taimen"

1992. Kabuki Theatre (6th series).
2190 **1577** 62y. multicoloured . . 70 15
2191 **1578** 100y. multicoloured . . 1·25 30

1579 "ADEOS" Observation Satellite

1581 Bird delivering Letter to Flower

1992. International Space Year. Multicoloured.
2192 62y. Type **1579** 70 15
2193 62y. "BS-3" broadcasting satellite and space station 70 15
Nos. 2192/3 were printed together, se-tenant, forming a composite design.

1992. Letter Writing Day. Multicoloured.
2194 41y. Type **1581** 50 10
2195 62y. Bird delivering letter to dog 70 15

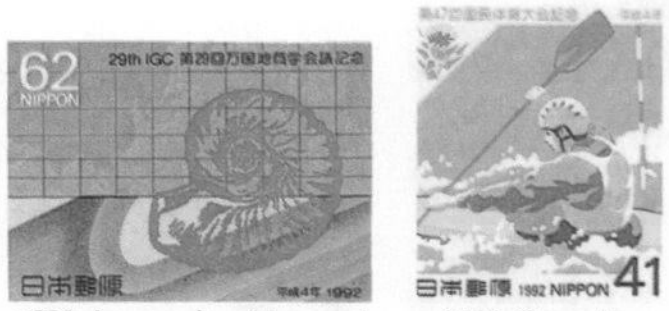

1583 Ammonite, Map and Stratigraphic Plan

1586 Canoeing

1992. 29th Int Geological Congress, Kyoto.
2197 **1583** 62y. multicoloured . . 75 15

1992. Water Birds (5th series). As T **1539**. Multicoloured.
2198 62y. White-faced shearwater ("Calonectris leucomelas") 1·25 40
2199 62y. Ruddy kingfisher ("Halcyon coromanda") 1·25 40

1992. 47th National Athletic Meeting, Yamagata.
2200 **1586** 41y. multicoloured . . 50 10

1587 Japanese Jar (Ninsei Nonomura)

1588 Chinese Vase (Tang dynasty)

1992. 20th Anniv of Restoration of Diplomatic Relations with China.
2201 **1587** 62y. multicoloured . . 70 15
2202 **1588** 62y. multicoloured . . 70 15

1589 Nobles arriving at Taiken Gate

1590 Fujiwarano Nobuyori giving Audience

1992. International Correspondence Week. Details from "Tale of Heiji" Shinzei Picture Scroll.
2203 **1589** 80y. multicoloured . . 95 20
2204 **1590** 120y. multicoloured . . 1·40 30

1591 "Friends" (Tomoko Komoto)

1593 "Kyo" Ideograph, Mt. Fuji, Sun and Waves

1992. 3rd Stamp Design Competition Winners. Multicoloured.
2205 62y. Type **1591** 70 15
2206 70y. "Gaiety on Christmas Night" (Brat Anca) . . . 80 20

1992. 30th International Co-operative Alliance Congress, Tokyo.
2207 **1593** 62y. multicoloured . . 70 15

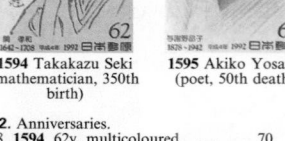

1594 Takakazu Seki (mathematician, 350th birth)

1595 Akiko Yosano (poet, 50th death)

1992. Anniversaries.
2208 **1594** 62y. multicoloured . . 70 15
2209 **1595** 62y. multicoloured . . 70 15

1596 Certified Public Tax Accountants' Assn Emblem

1992. 50th Anniv of Tax Accountants Law.
2210 **1596** 62y. multicoloured . . 70 15

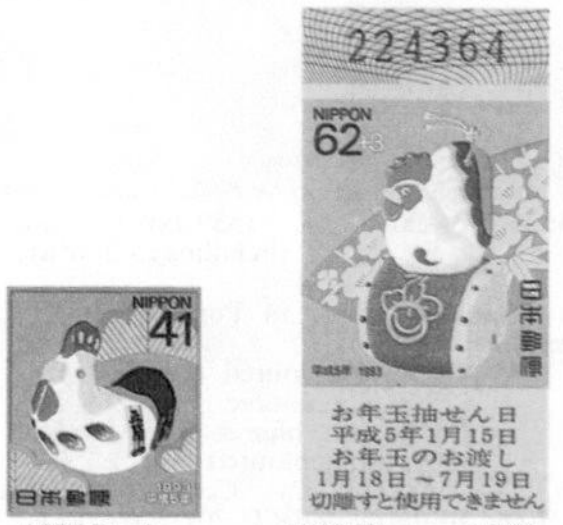

1597 Papier-mache and Clay Cock

1600 Tsuyazaki Clay Cock on Drum

1992. New Year's Greetings. Multicoloured.
2211 41y. Type **1597** 50 10
2212 62y. Tsuyazaki clay cock on drum 70 15

1992. New Year Lottery Stamps. Multicoloured.
2213 41y.+3y. Papier-mache and clay cock 50 10
2214 62y.+3y. Type **1600** 75 15
Each stamp carries a lottery number.

1601 "Orthetrum albistylum" (dragonfly)

1601a "Oxycetonia jucunda" (beetle)

1602 Mikado Swallowtail

1603 Ladybirds

1603a Honey Bee

1603b "Lycaena phleas" (copper butterfly)

1604 Mandarin

1605 Japanese White-Eye

1606 Eastern Turtle Dove

1606a Great Tit

1607 Varied Tit

1608 Greater Pied Kingfisher

1609 Pacific Black Duck

1609a Little Ringed Plover

1609b Bull-headed Shrike

1610 Northern Bullfinch

1610a Masked Hawfinch

1610b Jay

1611 Orchids

1612 Wild Pink

1613 Adder's Tongue Lily

1614 Day-flowers

1615 Iris

1616 Violets

1617 Praying Mantis, Chrysanthemums and Hibiscus (after Hatsu Sakai)

1618 "Pine and Hawk" (Sesson Shukei)

1992.
2215 **1601** 9y. yellow, black & bl 10 10
2215a **1601a** 10y. multicoloured 10 10
2216 **1602** 15y. brown, light green and green . . 20 10
2217 **1603** 18y. green, grey and red 20 10
2217a **1603a** 20y. multicoloured 20 10
2217b **1603b** 30y. multicoloured 30 10
2218 **1604** 41y. orge, dp bl & bl 55 20
2219 **1605** 50y. yellow, bl & blk 55 20
2220 **1606** 62y. orge, dp bl & bl 75 20
2220a **1606a** 70y. multicoloured 70 15
2221 **1607** 72y. orange, bl & grn 85 20
2222 **1608** 80y. blue, stone and green 85 20
2223 **1609** 90y. brown, yell & bl 85 20
2223a **1609a** 110y. multicoloured 1·10 25
2223b **1609b** 120y. multicoloured 1·10 25
2224 **1610** 130y. multicoloured 85 20
2224a **1610a** 140y. multicoloured 1·40 25
2224b **1610b** 160y. multicoloured 1·60 35
2225 **1611** 190y. multicoloured 2·25 45
2226 **1612** 270y. multicoloured 3·25 65
2227 **1613** 350y. mauve, lilac and green . . . . 4·00 80
2228 **1614** 390y. multicoloured 4·50 90
2229 **1615** 420y. violet, light green and green . . 5·00 1·00
2230 **1616** 430y. multicoloured 5·00 1·00
2231 **1617** 700y. multicoloured 8·25 1·60
2232 **1618** 1000y. multicoloured 12·00 2·40
The 41, 50, 62 and 80y. also exist imperforate with self-adhesive gum.

1993. Water Birds (6th series). As T **1539**. Multicoloured.
2241 62y. River kingfisher ("Alcedo atthis") . . . . 1·25 40
2242 62y. Cattle egret ("Bubulcus ibis") . . . . 1·25 40

1623 Super Giant Slalom

1625 Poppies (after Hochu Nakamura)

1993. World Alpine Skiing Championships, Shizukuishi (nr. Morioka). Multicoloured.
2243 41y. Type **1623** 50 10
2244 62y. Downhill 75 15

1993. Seasonal Flowers (1st series). Multicoloured.
2245 41y. Type **1625** 50 10
2246 62y. Cherry Blossoms (after Haitsu Sakai) (25 × 35 mm) 75 15
See also Nos. 2258/9, 2269/70 and 2287/8.

1993. Water Birds (7th series). As T **1539**. Multicoloured.
2247 62y. White-fronted geese ("Anser albifrons") . . . 1·25 20
2248 62y. Japanese white-naped cranes ("Grus vipio") . . 1·25 20
No. 2247 is wrongly inscribed "Ansner".

1629 "In the Studio" (Nanpu Katayama)

1630 Coral Trees and Reef, Minnajima Island

1993. Philatelic Week.
2249 **1629** 62y. multicoloured . . 75 15

1993. National Afforestation Campaign.
2250 **1630** 41y. multicoloured . . 50 10

1993. Water Birds (8th series). As T **1539**. Multicoloured.
2251 62y. Baikal teal ("Anas formosa") . . . . 1·25 20
2252 62y. White-tailed sea eagle ("Haliaeetus albicilla") . . 1·25 20

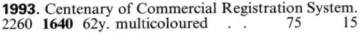

1635 "Mandarin Duck in Nest" and "Gardenia in Nest"

1993. Wedding of Crown Prince Naruhito and Masako Owada. Multicoloured.
2253 62y. "Mandarin Duck in Nest" (pattern of groom's jacket) (vert) 75 15
2254 62y. "Gardenia in Nest" (pattern of bride's robe) (vert) 75 15
2255 70y. Type **1635** 80 20

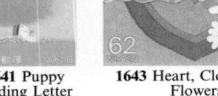

1636 Manchurian Crane with Chicks

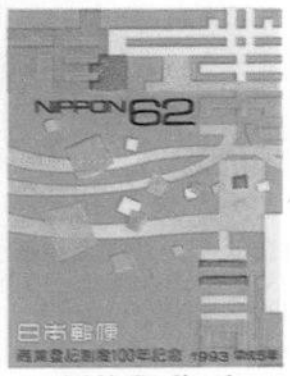
1640 Stylized Ideographs for "Commercial Registration"

1993. 5th Meeting of Ramsar Convention for the Preservation of Wetlands, Kushiro (Hokkaido).
2256 62y. Type **1636** . . . . . . 1·25 20
2257 62y. Head of Manchurian crane . . . . 1·25 20

1993. Seasonal Flowers (2nd series) As T **1615**. Multicoloured.
2258 41y. Lily (after Kiitsu Suzuki) 50 10
2259 62y. Thistle (after Shiko Watanabe) (25 × 35 mm) 75 15

1993. Centenary of Commercial Registration System.
2260 **1640** 62y. multicoloured . . 75 15

1641 Puppy reading Letter under Tree

1643 Heart, Clouds and Flowers

1993. Letter Writing Day. Multicoloured.
2261 41y. Type **1641** 50 10
2262 62y. Man pointing at flying letter (23 × 27 mm) . . . 75 15

1993. World Federation for Mental Health Congress, Chiba City.
2264 **1643** 62y. multicoloured . . 75 15

1644 "Glaucidium palmatum"

1993. 15th International Botanical Congress, Yokohama. Multicoloured.
2265 62y. Type **1644** 75 15
2266 62y. "Sciadopitys verticillata" 75 15

1646 Swimming

1650 "Arrival of Portuguese" (folding screen)

1993. 48th National Athletic Meeting, Kagawa Prefecture. Multicoloured.
2267 41y. Type **1646** 50 10
2268 41y. Karate 50 10

1993. Seasonal Flowers (3rd series). As T **1615**. Multicoloured.
2269 41y. "Chinese Bell-flowers" (Korin Ogata) 50 10
2270 62y. Chrysanthemums (detail of "Cranes and Plants in Spring and Autumn", Kiitsu Suzuki) (25 × 35 mm) 75 15

1993. 450th Anniv of First Portuguese Visit to Japan. Multicoloured.
2271 62y. Type **1650** 75 15
2272 62y. Jesuit mother-of-pearl inlaid host box 75 15

1652 Ki no Tsurayuki (Agetatami Scrolls)

1993. International Correspondence Week. Picture Scrolls of the Thirty-six Immortal Poets
2273 80y. Type **1652** 95 20
2274 120y. Kodai no Kimi (Satake Scrolls) . . . . . 1·40 30

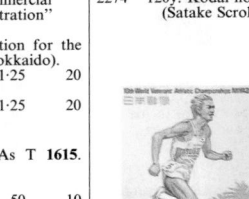

1654 Sprinter

1656 Toson Shimazaki (writer, 50th death)

1993. 10th International Veterans' Athletic Championships, Miyazaki.
2275 **1654** 62y. multicoloured . . 75 15

1993. Anniversaries. Multicoloured.
2277 62y. Type **1656** 75 15
2278 62y. Umetaro Suzuki (scientist, 50th death) . . 75 15
2279 62y. Kazan Watanabe (after Chinzan Tsubaki) (artist, birth bicentenary) 75 15

1659 Shibahara Clay Dog

1662 Kosen Clay Tosa Dog

1993. New Year's Greetings. Multicoloured.
2280 41y. Type **1659** 50 10
2281 62y. Kosen clay tosa dog . . 75 15

1993. New Year Lottery Stamps. Multicoloured.
2282 41y. Shibahara clay dog . . 50 10
2283 62y. Type **1662** 75 15

1663 Rice Flowers

1664 Man and Bird (Soichiro Asaba)

1993. Centenary of Agricultural Research Centre, Nishigahara.
2284 **1663** 62y. multicoloured . . 75 15

1993. 45th Anniv of Declaration of Human Rights. Stamp design contest winning entries.
2285 62y. Type **1664** 75 15
2286 70y. Symbols (Armand Clotagatilde) 80 20

1994. Seasonal Flowers (4th series). As T **1625**. Multicoloured.
2287 50y. Plum Blossom (after Korin Ogata) 60 15
2288 80y. Winter Camellia (after Hoitsu Sakai) (26 × 35 mm) 95 20

1994. Special Correspondence Stamps. As Nos. 1677/9 but values changed.
2289 **1098** 50y. multicoloured . . 60 15
2290 **1099** 50y. multicoloured . . 60 15
2291 80y. multicoloured . . 95 20
2292 **1100** 90y. multicoloured . . 1·10 25

1668 Ladies' Figure Skating

1672 "Irises" (Heihachiro Fukuda)

1994. World Figure Skating Championships, Chiba City. Multicoloured.
2293 50y. Type **1668** 60 15
2294 50y. Ice dancing 60 15
2295 80y. Men's figure skating . . 95 20
2296 80y. Pairs figure skating . . 95 20

1994. Philatelic Week.
2297 **1672** 80y. multicoloured . . 95 20

1673 "Love" (Chieko Kitajima)

1677 White Stork, Marguerites and Camphor Tree

1994. International Year of the Family. Winning Entries in Stamp Design Contest. Multicoloured.
2298 50y. Type **1673** 60 15
2299 50y. "Happiness Flower" (Shigenobu Nagaishi) . . 60 15
2300 80y. "Family flowering at Home" (Junichi Mineta) 95 20
2301 80y. "Family in Flight" (Soichiro Asaba) 95 20

1994. National Afforestation Campaign.
2302 **1677** 50y. multicoloured . . 1·10 20

1678 Houses by the Waterside

1679 Pylon and Monju Building

1994. International Conference on Reduction of Natural Disasters, Yokohama.
2303 **1678** 80y. multicoloured . . 95 20

1994. Achievement of Initial Criticality (self-sustaining reaction) in Monju Nuclear Fast Breeder Reactor, Tsuruga.
2304 **1679** 80y. multicoloured . . 95 20

1680 Wildlife

1681 Envelope "Ship" and Man

1994. Environment Day.
2305 **1680** 80y. multicoloured . . 95 20

1994. Letter Writing Day. Multicoloured.
2306 50y. Type **1681** 60 15
2307 80y. Giraffe carrying envelope 95 20

1683 Emblem in Eye

1684 Baron Maeshima (Postal Minister) and 1871 48 mon "Dragon" Stamp

1994. 10th Int AIDS Conference, Yokohama.
2309 **1683** 80y. multicoloured . . 95 20

1994. History of Stamps (1st series). First Japanese Issue. Multicoloured, frame colour of "Dragon" stamp given.
2310 **1684** 80y. brown 95 20
2311 – 80y. blue 95 20
2312 – 80y. red 95 20
2313 – 80y. green 95 20
DESIGNS: No. 2311, 100mon "Dragon" stamp; 2312, 200mon "Dragon" stamp; 2313, 500mon "Dragon" stamp.
The central portion of the stamp portrayed varies according to value.
See also Nos. 2339/42, 2345/6, 2363/4, 2382/5 and 2416/19.

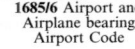

1685/6 Airport and Airplane bearing Airport Code

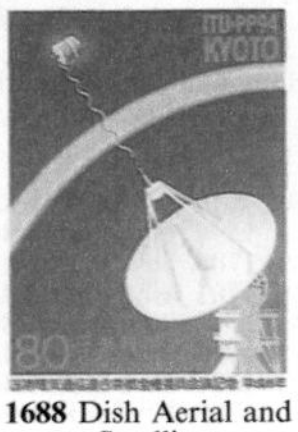
1688 Dish Aerial and Satellite

1994. Opening of Kansai International Airport, Osaka. Multicoloured.
2314 80y. Type **1685** 95 20
2315 80y. Type **1686** 95 20
2316 80y. Airplane approaching Airport 95 20
Nos. 2314/15 form the composite design shown.

1994. I.T.U. Plenipotentiary Conference, Kyoto.
2317 **1688** 80y. multicoloured . . 95 20

1689 Kickball

1695 Handball

1692 Sugoroku

1994. 12th Asian Games, Hiroshima. Mult.
2318 50y. Type **1689** 60 15
2319 80y. Steeplechase 95 20
2320 80y. Synchronized swimming 95 20

1994. International Correspondence Week. Details of "House of Entertainment" (folding screen). Multicoloured.
2321 90y. Type **1692** . . . . 1·10 25
2322 110y. Shogi . . . . 1·25 25
2323 130y. Go . . . . 1·50 30

1994. 49th National Athletic Meeting, Aichi.
2324 **1695** 50y. multicoloured . . 60 15

1696 Michio Miyagi (composer)

1698 Fujiwara no Michinaga and Insulin Crystals

1994. Birth Anniversaries. Multicoloured.
2325 80y. Type **1696** 95 20
2326 80y. Gyoshu Hayami (painter) and "Moths" . . 95 20

1994. 15th International Diabetes Federation Congress, Kobe.
2327 **1698** 80y. multicoloured . . 95 20
Fujiwara no Michinaga (966–1028) was the earliest known Japanese diabetic.

1699/1703 "Viewing Maple Leaves at Takao" (folding screen, Hideyori Kano) (⅔-size illustration)

1704 "Yokuryuchi Pool, Shugakuin Imperial Villa" (Kenji Kawai)

1705 "Rock Garden, Ryoan Temple" (Eizo Kato)

1994. 1200th Anniv of Kyoto. Paintings.
2328 **1699** 80y. multicoloured . . 95 20
2329 **1700** 80y. multicoloured . . 95 20
2330 **1701** 80y. multicoloured . . 95 20
2331 **1702** 80y. multicoloured . . 95 20
2332 **1703** 80y. multicoloured . . 95 20
2333 **1704** 80y. multicoloured . . 95 20
2334 **1705** 80y. multicoloured . . 95 20
Nos. 2328/32 were issued together, se-tenant, forming the composite design illustrated.

1706 Izumo Papier-mache Boar

1709 Boar (Takayama soft toy)

1994. New Year's Greetings. Multicoloured.
2335 50y. Type **1706** 60 15
2336 80y. Boar (Takayama soft toy) 95 20

1994. New Year's Greetings. Lottery Stamps. Multicoloured.
2337 50y.+3y. Izumo Papier-mache boar 60 15
2338 80y.+3y. Type **1709** . . . . 1·00 20
Each stamp carries a lottery number.

1710 5r. Stamp and Eduardo Chiossone (designer)

1994. History of Stamps (2nd series). "Koban" issue of 1876–88. Multicoloured, colour of featured stamp given.
2339 **1710** 80y. grey 95 20
2340 – 80y. brown 95 20
2341 – 80y. red 95 20
2342 – 80y. blue 95 20
FEATURED STAMPS: No. 2340, 1s. stamp (Type **20**); 2341, 12s. stamp (Type **21**); 2342, 20s. stamp (Type **22**).

1711 Himeji Castle Tower

1712 "Himeji Castle" (Masami Takahashi)

1994. World Heritage Sites (1st series).
2343 **1711** 80y. multicoloured . . 95 20
2344 **1712** 80y. multicoloured . . 95 20
See also Nos. 2347/8, 2373/4 and 2400/1.

1713 2s. Stamp and Postal Delivery by Hand-drawn Cart

1715 "Kannon Bosatsu" (wall painting, Kondo Hall)

1716 Kondo Hall, Horyu Temple

1995. History of Stamps (3rd series). 1894 Emperor's Silver Wedding issue and paintings by Shinsai Shibata. Multicoloured.
2345 80y. Type **1713** 95 20
2346 80y. 5s. stamp and postal delivery by horse-drawn carriage 95 20

1995. World Heritage Sites (2nd series). Multicoloured.
2347 **1715** 80y. multicoloured . . 95 20
2348 **1716** 110y. multicoloured . . 1·25 25

1717 Emblem and National Flowers

1995. Centenary of Japan–Brazil Treaty of Friendship. Multicoloured.
2349 80y. Type **1717** 95 20
2350 80y. Emblem and sports . . 95 20

1719 Unebi and Nijo Mountains and Tile from Palace

1720 "Remembering Times Past" (Saburosuke Okada)

1995. 1300th Anniv of Fujiwara Palace, Kashihara.
2351 **1719** 50y. multicoloured . . 60 15
2352 **1720** 80y. multicoloured . . 95 20

1721 "Dissection" (Seison Maeda)

1722 "National Census" and "16"

1995. Modern Anatomy Education.
2353 **1721** 80y. multicoloured . . 95 20

1995. 16th National Census.
2354 **1722** 80y. multicoloured . . 95 20

1723 Volunteer teaching Bangladeshi Woman to Read

1724 "Visitor to Art Studio" (Keika Kanashima)

1995. 30th Anniv of Japanese Overseas Co-operation Volunteers Service.
2355 **1723** 80y. multicoloured . . 95 20

1995. Philatelic Week.
2356 **1724** 80y.+20y. mult . . . . 1·25 25
The premium was for the Osaka/Kobe and Awaji earthquake victims' fund.

1725 Auspicious Clouds

1726 Reeds (mourning)

1727 Water Lily (mourning)

1728 Cloud, "Wind" and Pine Bark Pattern

1729 "Daphniphyllum macropodum"

1730 Maple and Shrine Island, Akiteline

1995. Special Correspondence Stamps.
2357 **1725** 50y. multicoloured . . 60 15
2358 **1726** 50y. multicoloured . . 60 15
2359 **1727** 80y. multicoloured . . 95 20
2360 **1728** 80y. multicoloured . . 95 20
2361 **1729** 90y. multicoloured . . 1·10 25

1995. National Afforestation Campaign.
2362 **1730** 50y. multicoloured . . 60 15

1731 8½s. Stamp and First Airmail Flight from Osaka to Tokyo

1733 Hearts forming Flower

1995. History of Stamps (4th series). 1929 First Airmail issue. Multicoloured.
2363 110y. Type **1731** . . . . . 1·25 25
2364 110y. 18s. stamp and loading freight onto airplane . . . . 1·25 25

1995. Greetings Stamps. Mult. Self-adhesive.
2365 80y. Type **1733** 95 20
2366 80y. Child with balloon . . 95 20
2367 80y. Flower and pencil . . 95 20
2368 80y. Star, sun and moon . . 95 20
2369 80y. Child with dog 95 20

1738 Postman

1740 Cedar

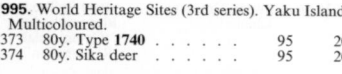

1995. Letter Writing Day. Multicoloured.
2370 50y. Type **1738** 60 15
2371 80y. Ostrich 95 20

1995. World Heritage Sites (3rd series). Yaku Island. Multicoloured.
2373 80y. Type **1740** 95 20
2374 80y. Sika deer 95 20

1742 "Friends, One and All" (Yuki Ogawa)

1743 Atomic Bomb Dome, Hiroshima (Nobuya Nagata)

1744 "Light of Peace" (Nobuo Suenaga)

1745 Marathon Runners

1995. 50th Anniv of End of Second World War. Stamp Design Contest Winners.

2375 **1742** 50y. multicoloured . . 60 15
2376 **1743** 80y. multicoloured . . 95 20
2377 **1744** 80y. multicoloured . . 95 20

1995. 18th International University Games, Fukuoka.

2378 **1745** 80y. multicoloured . . 95 20

1746 Radio-controlled Plane

1748 Horse, Cow and Labrador

1995. World Aeromodel Championships, Kasaoka. Multicoloured.

2379 50y. Type **1746** 60 15
2380 80y. Radio-controlled helicopter 95 20

1995. World Veterinary Congress, Yokohama.

2381 **1748** 80y. multicoloured . . 95 20

1749 5y. Stamp and Cherub and Tokyo Mailbox

1753 Judo (Makuhari, Chiba)

1995. History of Stamps (5th series). Industries issue of 1948–49. Multicoloured.

2382 80y. Type **1749** 95 20
2383 80y. 50y. stamp and mail van . . . . 1·60 25
2384 80y. 90y. stamp and mail van 95 20
2385 80y. 10y. stamp and cherub on Tokyo mailbox . . . 95 20

1995. World Sports Championships. Mult.

2386 80y. Type **1753** 95 20
2387 80y. Gymnastics (Sabae, Fukui) 95 20

1755 Shell Matching Game (from "New Year's Amusements")

1995. International Correspondence Week. Details of paintings on folding screens. Multicoloured.

2388 90y. Type **1755** . . . . . . 1·10 25
2389 110y. Battledore and Shuttlecock (from "Twelve Months") . . . 1·25 25
2390 130y. Playing Cards (from "Matsuura Folding Screen") . . . . 1·50 30

1758 Cyclists

1759 Patchwortk Hearts (Tomoko Suzuki)

1995. 50th Anniv of National Athletic Meeting, Fukushima.

2391 **1758** 50y. multicoloured . . 60 15

1995. 50th Anniversaries of U.N.O. (2392) and U.N.E.S.C.O. (2393). Multicoloured.

2392 80y. Type **1759** 95 20
2393 80y. Children with Heart Balloon (Yukino Ikeda) 95 20

1761 Tadataka Ino (cartographer, 250th birth)

1995. Anniversaries. Multicoloured.

2394 80y. Type **1761** 95 20
2395 80y. Kitaro Nishida (philosopher, 50th death) 95 20

1763 Tsutsumi Clay Rat on Cayenne Pepper

1766 Satsuma Papier-mache Rat in Rice Store

1995. New Year's Greetings. Multicoloured.

2396 50y. Type **1763** 60 15
2397 80y. Satsuma papier-mache rat in rice store 95 20

1995. New Year's Lottery Stamps. Multicoloured.

2398 50y.+3y. Tsutsumi clay rat on turnip 60 15
2399 80y.+3y. Type **1766** . . . . 1·00 20

Each stamp carries a lottery number.

1767 Beech Forest

1769 Obi Material showing Choson Dynasty Boxes (Keisuke Serizawa)

1995. World Heritage Sites (4th series). Shirakami Mountains. Multicoloured.

2400 80y. Type **1767** 95 20
2401 80y. Black woodpecker . . 95 20

1995. 30th Anniv of Resumption of Japan–Korea Diplomatic Relations.

2402 **1769** 80y. multicoloured . . 95 20

1770 Siebold

1771 Twined Ropes

1996. Birth Bicentenary of Philipp Franz von Siebold (physician and Japanologist).

2403 **1770** 80y. multicoloured . . 95 20

1996. 50th Anniv of Labour Relations Commissions.

2404 **1771** 80y. multicoloured . . 95 20

1772 Turtle and Crane

1996. Senior Citizens.

2405 **1772** 80y. multicoloured . . 95 20

1773 Driving to Diet for Promulgation of Constitution, 1946

1774 Signing San Francisco Peace Treaty, 1951

1775 Return of Okinawa, 1972

1776 Woman and Diet Building

1996. 50 Post-war Years (1st series).

2406 **1773** 80y. mauve, lilac & gold 95 20
2407 **1774** 80y. dp grn, grn & gold 95 20
2408 **1775** 80y. indigo, blue and gold 95 20

See also Nos. 2420/1, 2429/30, 2443/4 and 2449/54.

1996. 50th Anniv of Women's Suffrage.

2409 **1776** 80y. multicoloured . . 95 20

1777 "Window" (Yukihiko Yasuda)

1778 Mother and Child

1996. Philatelic Week.

2410 **1777** 80y. multicoloured . . 95 20

1996. 50th Anniv of U.N.I.C.E.F.

2411 **1778** 80y. multicoloured . . 95 20

1779 Children and Sun

1780 Narcissus Flycatcher

1996. Child Welfare Week.

2412 **1779** 80y. multicoloured . . 95 20

1996. Bird Week. Multicoloured.

2413 80y. Type **1780** 95 20
2414 80y. Binoculars and bird feeding nestlings 95 20

1782 Cherry Blossom and Tokyo Buildings

1996. National Afforestation Campaign.

2415 **1782** 50y. multicoloured . . 60 15

1783 1991 Design

1784 1949 Design

1996. History of Stamps (6th series). Philatelic Week Issues.

2416 **1783** 80y. brown, ochre and lilac 95 20
2417 80y. multicoloured . . 95 20
2418 **1784** 80y. deep lilac and lilac 95 20
2419 80y. multicoloured . . 95 20

1785 Olympic Flame (Olympic Games, Tokyo, 1964)

1786 Sun Tower ("EXPO 70" World Fair, Osaka)

1996. 50 Post-war Years (2nd series).

2420 **1785** 80y. multicoloured . . 95 20
2421 **1786** 80y. multicoloured . . 95 20

1787/8 "Oirase no Keiryu" (Chikkyo Ono)

1996. Centenary of Modern River Control Systems.

2422 **1787** 80y. multicoloured . . 95 20
2423 **1788** 80y. multicoloured . . 95 20

Nos. 2422/3 were issued together, se-tenant, forming the composite design illustrated.

1789 Emblem

1790 "Nippon Maru II" (cadet ship)

1996. Marine Day.

2424 **1789** 50y. multicoloured . . 60 15
2425 **1790** 80y. multicoloured . . 95 20

1791 Cat

1996. Letter Writing Day. Multicoloured.

2426 50y. Type **1791** 60 15
2427 80y. Toy horse 95 20

1793 "Hikari" Express Train and Motorway

1794 Woman and Modern Appliances

1996. 50 Post-war Years (3rd series). Modern Life.

2429 **1793** 80y. multicoloured . . 95 20
2430 **1794** 80y. multicoloured . . 95 20

1795 Kenji Miyazawa (writer, centenary)

1797 Archer

1996. Birth Anniversaries. Multicoloured.
2431 80y. Type **1795** 95 20
2432 80y. Hokiichi Hanawa (scholar and editor, 250th) 95 20

1996. 51st National Athletic Meeting, Hiroshima.
2433 **1797** 50y. multicoloured . . 95 20

1798 Paper-chain People around Red Feather (donor pin)

1799 Piano Keys and Double Clef

1996. 50th Anniv of Community Chest.
2434 **1798** 80y. multicoloured . . 95 20

1996. International Music Day.
2435 **1799** 80y. multicoloured . . 95 20

1800 "Water Mill in Onden"

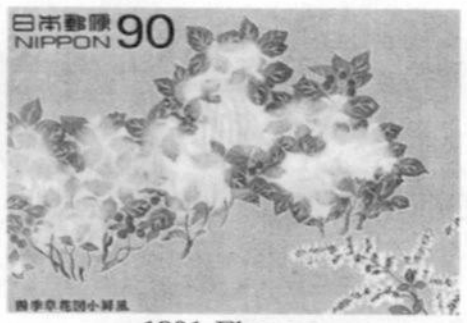

1801 Flowers

1803 Flowers

1805 Flowers

1996. International Correspondence Week. Paintings from "36 Views of Mt. Fuji" by Hokusai Katsushika (2436, 2438, 2440) and details of paintings on folding screen by Kohrin Ogata (others).
2436 **1800** 90y. multicoloured . . 95 20
2437 **1801** 90y. multicoloured . . 95 20
2438 – 110y. multicoloured . . 1·10 25
2439 **1803** 110y. multicoloured . . 1·10 25
2440 – 130y. multicoloured . . 1·40 30
2441 **1805** 130y. multicoloured . . 1·40 30
DESIGNS—As T **1800**: No. 2438; "Fine Day with a South Wind"; 2440, "Lake in Sosyu Hakone".

1806 Congress Emblem and Squirrel

1996. 18th Int Savings Banks Congress, Tokyo.
2442 **1806** 80y. multicoloured . . 85 20

1807 Mobile Telephone, Fibre-optic Cable and Communications Satellite

1808 Satellite Photograph of Earth

1996. 50 Post-war Years (4th series). Telecommunications and Environmental Protection.
2443 **1807** 80y. multicoloured . . 85 20
2444 **1808** 80y. multicoloured . . 85 20

1809 Okinawa Papier-mache Fighting Bull

1812 Child on Bull (Takamatus Wedding Doll)

1996. New Year's Greetings. Multicoloured.
2445 50y. Type **1809** 55 15
2446 80y. Child on bull (Takamatsu wedding doll) 85 20

1996. New Year Lottery Stamps. Multicoloured.
2447 50y.+3y. Okinawa papier-mache fighting bull . . . 55 15
2448 80y.+3y. Type **1812** 85 20
Each stamp carries a lottery number.

1813 Yujiro Ishihara (actor) as Youth

1814 Ishihara smoking Pipe

1815 Hibari Misora (actress' and singer) in "Kanashiki Kuchibue"

1816 Misora singing

1817 Osamu Tezuka (cartoonist) and Cartoon Characters

1818 Self-portrait and Astroboy

1997. 50 Post-war Years (5th series). Entertainers.
2449 **1813** 80y. black, brn & gold 80 20
2450 **1814** 80y. multicoloured . . 80 20
2451 **1815** 80y. black, blue & gold 80 20
2452 **1816** 80y. multicoloured . . 80 20
2453 **1817** 80y. multicoloured . . 80 20
2454 **1818** 80y. multicoloured . . 80 20

1819 Emblem

1821 "Daigo" (Togyu Okumura)

1997. Winter Olympic Games, Nagano (1998). Multicoloured.
2455 80y.+10y. Type **1819** . . . 90 20
2456 80y.+10y. Snowlets (mascots) 90 20

1997. Philatelic Week.
2457 **1821** 80y. multicoloured . . 75 15

1822 Main Court Room

1997. 50th Anniv of Supreme Court.
2458 **1822** 80y. multicoloured . . 80 20

1823 Parachutist

1824 Waving to Mechanical Doll

1825 Stamp Lover

1826 Helicopter Postman

1827 With Love Letter

1828 Mexican Mythological Figures (Luis Nishizawa)

1997. Greetings Stamps. Doraemon (cartoon character). Self-adhesive gum.
2459 **1823** 80y. multicoloured . . 80 20
2460 **1824** 80y. multicoloured . . 80 20
2461 **1825** 80y. multicoloured . . 80 20
2462 **1826** 80y. multicoloured . . 80 20
2463 **1827** 80y. multicoloured . . 80 20

1997. Centenary of Japanese Emigration to Mexico.
2464 **1828** 80y. multicoloured . . 80 20

1829 Zao Crater Lake and Bush Clover

1830 House's Seal and Diet Building

1997. National Afforestation Campaign.
2465 **1829** 50y. multicoloured . . 50 10

1997. 50th Anniv of House of Councillors.
2466 **1830** 80y. multicoloured . . 80 20

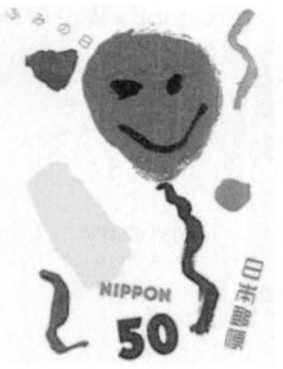

1831 "Happy Balloon" (Orville Isaac)

1832 "Bird Friends" (Haruka Kumiya)

1833 "Message from Rainbow Forest" (Anna Romanovskaya)

1834 "Greetings" (Yumi Kiryu)

1997. Letter Writing Day.
2467 **1831** 50y. multicoloured . . 50 10
2468 **1832** 70y. multicoloured . . 70 15
2469 **1833** 80y. multicoloured . . 80 20
2470 **1834** 90y. multicoloured . . 90 20

1835 Bird with Letter and Owl on Blackboard

1836 Stylized Worker

1997. 50th Anniv of High School Part-time and Correspondence Courses.
2472 **1835** 50y. multicoloured . . 50 10

1997. 50th Anniv of Labour Standards Law.
2473 **1836** 80y. multicoloured . . 80 20

1837 Pacific Ocean and Mt. Osorno (after Hokusai Katsushika)

1838 Mopi (mascot) and Synchronized Swimmers

1997. Centenary of Japan–Chile Relations.
2474 **1837** 80y. multicoloured . . 80 20

1997. 52nd National Athletic Meeting, Osaka.
2475 **1838** 80y. multicoloured . . 80 20

1839 "Hodogaya" (from "53 Stations of Tokaido")

1840 Woodpecker and Flower

1842 Foliage

1844 Snow-covered Tree

1997. International Correspondence Week. Paintings by Hiroshige Ando (Nos. 2476, 2478, 2480) and details from "The Four Seasons" by Hoitsu Sakai (others). Multicoloured.

2476 90y. Type **1839** 90 20
2477 90y. Type **1840** 90 20
2478 110y. "Kameyama" (from "53 Stations of Tokaido") 1·10 25
2479 110y. Type **1842** . . . . . 1·10 25
2480 130y. "Snow View from Sumida River Revetment" (from "Edo Scenic Sites: Snow, Moon and Flower") . . . . 1·25 25
2481 130y. Type **1844** . . . . . 1·25 25

1845 Auditorium, Takeru (opera character) and Ballerina

1997. Inaug of New National Theatre. Tokyo.
2482 **1845** 80y. multicoloured . . 80 20

1846 "Iihi Tabidachi" (Shinji Tanimura)

1847 "Tsuki no Sabaku" (Masao Kato and Suguru Sasaki)

1997. Favourite Songs (1st series).
2483 **1846** 50y. multicoloured . . 50 10
2484 **1847** 80y. multicoloured . . 80 20
See also Nos. 2497/8, 2499/2500, 2522/3, 2527/8, 2531/2, 2558/9, 2568/9 and 2578/9.

1848 Rohan Kouda (writer, 130th anniv)

1997. Birth Anniversaries. Multicoloured.
2485 80y. Type **1848** 80 20
2486 80y. Hiroshige Ando (after Toyo Kuni III) (painter, bicentenary) 80 20

1850 Miharu Hariko Paper Tiger

1853 Hakata Hariko Paper Tiger

1997. New Year's Greetings. Multicoloured.
2487 50y. Type **1850** 50 10
2488 80y. Hakata Hariko paper tiger 80 20

1997. New Year Lottery Stamps. Multicoloured.
2489 50y.+3y. Miharu Hariko paper tiger 55 15
2490 80y.+3y. Type **1853** 85 20
Each stamp carries a lottery number.

1854 "Yotsutake, Ryukyu Dance" (Taiji Hamada)

1997. 25th Anniv of Return of Okinawa (Ryukyu Islands).
2491 **1854** 80y. multicoloured . . 80 20

1855 Former Shibuya House, Yamagata

1856 Tomizawa House

1997. Traditional Houses (1st series).
2492 **1855** 80y. multicoloured . . 80 20
2493 **1856** 80y. multicoloured . . 80 20
See also Nos. 2513/14, 2529/30, 2539/40 and 2570/2.

1857 "Mother Sea" (Bokunen Naka)

1858 "Mother Earth" (Bokunen Naka)

1997. United Nations Framework Convention on Climate Change, Kyoto.
2494 **1857** 80y. multicoloured . . 80 20
2495 **1858** 80y. multicoloured . . 80 20

1859 Drying Harvested Rice

1997. 50th Anniv of Agricultural Insurance System.
2496 **1859** 80y. multicoloured . . 80 20

1860 "Sunayama" (Hakushu Kitahara and Shinpei Nakayama)

1861 "Jingle Bells" (Shoji Miyazawa and J. Pierpont)

1997. Favourite Songs (2nd series).
2497 **1860** 50y. multicoloured . . 50 10
2498 **1861** 80y. multicoloured . . 80 20

1862 "Shabondama" (Ujo Noguchi and Shinpei Nakayama)

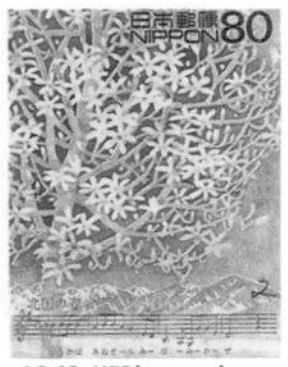

1863 "Kitaguni no Haru" (Haku Ide and Minoru Endo)

1998. Favourite Songs (3rd series).
2499 **1862** 50y. multicoloured . . 50 10
2500 **1863** 80y. multicoloured . . 80 20

1864 Hollyhock

1998. Winter Paralympics, Nagano. Mult.
2501 50y. Type **1864** 50 10
2502 80y. Ice sledge hockey . . . 80 20

1866 Miyama Gentian ("Gentiana nipponica")

1871 Snow-boarding

1998. Winter Olympic Games, Nagano. Mult.
2503 50y. Type **1866** 50 10
2504 50y. Marsh marigold ("Caltha palustris") . . . 50 10
2505 50y. Black lily ("Fritillaria camtschaensis") 50 10
2506 50y. Peony ("Paeonia japonica") 50 10
2507 50y. Adder's tongue lily ("Erythronium japonicum") 50 10
2508 80y. Type **1871** 80 20
2509 80y. Curling 80 20
2510 80y. Speed skating 80 20
2511 80y. Cross-country skiing 80 20
2512 80y. Alpine skiing 80 20

1876 Former Baba House, Nagano

1877 Naka House

1998. Traditional Houses (2nd series).
2513 **1876** 80y. multicoloured . . 80 20
2514 **1877** 80y. multicoloured . . 80 20

1878 Fireman and Ambulance

1879 Fireman and Fire Engine

1998. 50th Anniv of Japanese Fire Service.
2515 **1878** 80y. multicoloured . . 80 20
2516 **1879** 80y. multicoloured . . 80 20
The firemen in the designs are taken from paintings of actors by Kunichika Toyohara.

1880 Puppy

1998. Greetings Stamps. Self-adhesive. Mult.
2517 80y. Type **1880** 80 20
2518 80y. Kitten 80 20
2519 80y. Budgerigars 80 20
2520 80y. Pansies 80 20
2521 80y. Rabbit 80 20

1885 "Medaka-no-Gakko" (Shigeru Chaki and Yoshinao Nakada)

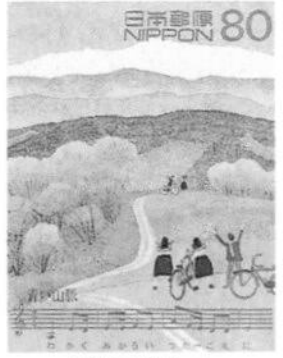

1886 "Aoi Sanmyaku" (Yaso Saijo and Ryoichi Hattori)

1998. Favourite Songs (4th series).
2522 **1885** 50y. multicoloured . . 50 10
2523 **1886** 80y. multicoloured . . 80 20

1887 "Poppies" (Kokei Kobayashi)

1889 Trout and Japanese Azalea

1888 "Liberty Leading the People" (Eugene Delacroix)

1998. Philatelic Week.
2524 **1887** 80y. multicoloured . . 80 20

1998. Year of France in Japan.
2525 **1888** 110y. multicoloured . . 1·10 25

1998. National Afforestation Campaign.
2526 **1889** 50y. multicoloured . . 50 10

1890 "Wild Roses" (Sakufu Kondo and Franz Schubert)

1891 "Hill abloom with Tangerine Flowers" (Minoru Uminuma and Shogo Kato)

1998. Favourite Songs (5th series).
2527 **1890** 50y. multicoloured . . 50 10
2528 **1891** 80y. multicoloured . . 80 20

1892 Kowata Residence, Shinji

1893 Kamihaga Residence, Uchiko

1998. Traditional Houses (3rd series).
2529 **1892** 80y. multicoloured . . 80 20
2530 **1893** 80y. multicoloured . . 80 20

1894 "This Road" (Hakusyu Kitahara and Kousaku Yamada)

1895 "I'm a Boy of the Sea" (anon)

1998. Favourite Songs (6th series).
2531 **1894** 50y. multicoloured . . 50 10
2532 **1895** 80y. multicoloured . . 80 20

1896 Boy writing

1998. Letter Writing Day. Multicoloured.
2533 50y. Type **1896** 80 20
2534 50y. Girl with letter 80 20
2535 80y. Girl holding pen . . . 80 20
2536 80y. Boy holding pen . . . 80 20
2537 80y. Boy and girl reading letters (horiz) 80 20

1901 Kamio Residence, Oita

1902 Nakamura Residence, Okinawa

1998. Traditional Houses (4th series).
2539 **1901** 80y. multicoloured . . 80 20
2540 **1902** 80y. multicoloured . . 80 20

1903 FJ Class Dinghy Racing

1998. 53rd National Athletic Meeting, Kanagawa.
2541 **1903** 50y. multicoloured . . 50 10

1904 "Sketch of Maple Leaf" (detail)

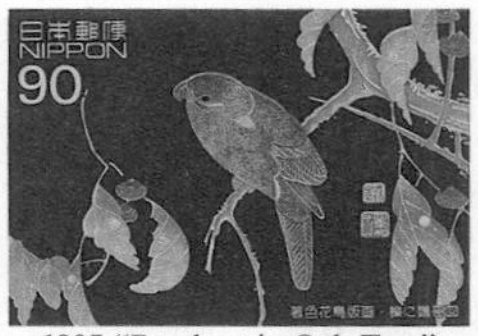

1905 "Parakeet in Oak Tree"

1907 "Coloured Chicken in Snow-laden Bamboo"

1909 "Parakeet in Rose Bush"

1998. International Correspondence Week. Paintings by Shakuchu Ito. Multicoloured.
2542 90y. Type **1904** 90 20
2543 90y. Type **1905** 90 20
2544 110y. "Drake and Duck in Snow" (detail) . . . . . 1·25 25
2545 110y. Type **1907** . . . . . 1·10 25
2546 130y. "Butterfly in the Peonies" (detail) . . . . 1·25 25
2547 130y. Type **1909** . . . . . 1·25 25

1910 Serving

1911 Receiving

1912 Set and Attack

1913 Blocking

1998. World Volleyball Championships, Japan.
2548 **1910** 80y. multicoloured . . 80 20
2549 **1911** 80y. multicoloured . . 80 20
2550 **1912** 80y. multicoloured . . 80 20
2551 **1913** 80y. multicoloured . . 80 20

1914 Bakin Takizawa (writer, 150th death anniv)

1915 Yoshie Fujiwara (opera singer, birth centenary)

1998. Anniversaries.
2552 **1914** 80y. multicoloured . . 80 20
2553 **1915** 80y. multicoloured . . 80 20

1916 Sahara Papier-mache Rabbit making Rice Cake

1919 Yamagata Papier-mache Rabbit on Ball

1998. New Year's Greetings. Multicoloured.
2554 50y. Type **1916** 50 10
2555 80y. Yamagata papier-mache rabbit on ball . . 80 20

1998. New Year's Lottery Stamps. Multicoloured.
2556 50y.+3y. Sahara papier-mache rabbit making rice cake 55 15
2557 50y.+3y. Type **1919** 55 15
Each stamp carries a lottery number.

1920 "The Apple Song" (Hachiro Sato and Tadashi Manjome)

1921 "The Toy Cha-Cha-Cha" (Akiyuki Nasaka and Osamu Yoshioka)

1998. Favourite Songs (7th series).
2558 **1920** 50y. multicoloured . . 50 10
2559 **1921** 80y. multicoloured . . 80 20

1922 Tango Dancers (Goro Sasaki)

1998. Centenary of Friendship Treaty between Japan and Argentina.
2560 **1922** 80y. multicoloured . . 80 20

1923 "Family" (Chakou Wiam)

1924 "Heart Tree" (Atsuko Niizato)

1925 "Hito" (Shozo Somekawa)

1926 "Happiness" (Mary Carmel Mulloor)

1998. 50th Anniv of Universal Declaration of Human Rights.
2561 **1923** 50y. multicoloured . . 50 10
2562 **1924** 70y. multicoloured . . 50 10
2563 **1925** 80y. multicoloured . . 80 20
2564 **1926** 90y. multicoloured . . 90 20

1998. 50th Anniv of New Year's Greetings Stamps. Previous issues now dated "1999".
2565 **241** 50y. mauve 50 10
2566 **445** 50y. multicoloured . . 50 10
2567 **1278** 50y. multicoloured . . 50 10

1927 "Flowing like a River" (Yasushil Akimoto and Akira Mitake)

1928 "Song of the Four Seasons" (Toyohisa Araki)

1999. Favourite Songs (8th series).
2568 **1927** 50y. multicoloured . . 60 15
2569 **1928** 80y. multicoloured . . 95 20

1929 Iwase Residence, Nishi-Akao

1930/1 Ogimachi Houses, Shirakawa ($\frac{1}{2}$-size illustration)

1999. Traditional Houses (5th series).
2570 **1929** 80y. multicoloured . . 95 20
2571 **1930** 80y. multicoloured . . 95 20
2572 **1931** 80y. multicoloured . . 95 20
Nos. 2571/2 were issued together, se-tenant, forming the composite design illustrated.

1932 "The Kaen-daiko Drum" (Shinsho Kokontei V)

1933 "Toku the Boatman" (Bunraku Katsura VIII)

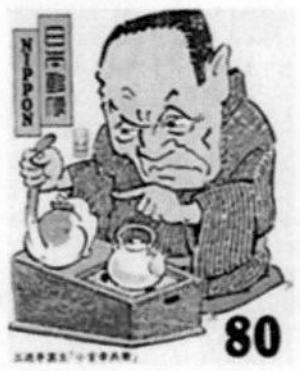

1934 "Mr. Kobee, the Faultfinder" (Ensho Sanyutei VI)

1935 "Time Noodles" (Kosan Yanagiya V)

1936 "Once in a Hundred Years" (Beicho Katsura III)

1999. Comic Stories.
2573 **1932** 80y. multicoloured . . 95 20
2574 **1933** 80y. multicoloured . . 95 20
2575 **1934** 80y. multicoloured . . 95 20
2576 **1935** 80y. multicoloured . . 95 20
2577 **1936** 80y. multicoloured . . 95 20

1937 "Sukiyaki" (Rokusuke Ei and Hachidai Nakamura)

1938 "Early Spring" (Kazumasa Yoshimaru and Akira Nakada)

1999. Favourite Songs (9th series).
2578 **1937** 50y. multicoloured . . 60 15
2579 **1938** 80y. multicoloured . . 95 20

1939 Kitten

1999. Greetings Stamps. Mult. Self-adhesive.
2580 80y. Type **1939** 95 20
2581 80y. Roses 95 20
2582 80y. Puppy (47 × 37 mm) . . 95 20
2583 80y. Brown rabbit 95 20
2584 80y. Grey and white rabbit (41 × 38 mm) 95 20

1944 Body Parts and Staff of Asclepius

1999. 25th General Assembly of Japan Medical Congress.
2585 **1944** 80y. multicoloured . . 95 20

1945/6 "Hare playing on the field in Spring" (Insho Domoto)

1999. Philatelic Week.
2586 **1945** 80y. multicoloured . . 95 20
2587 **1946** 80y. multicoloured . . 95 20
Nos. 2586/7 were issued together, se-tenant, forming the composite design illustrated.

1947 Nazca Lines, Llama and Machu Picchu Ruins

1948 Amagi Alpine Rose and Mount Fuji

1999. 100 Years of Japanese Emigration to Peru.
2588 **1947** 80y. multicoloured . . 95 20

1999. National Afforestation Campaign.
2589 **1948** 50y. multicoloured . . 60 15

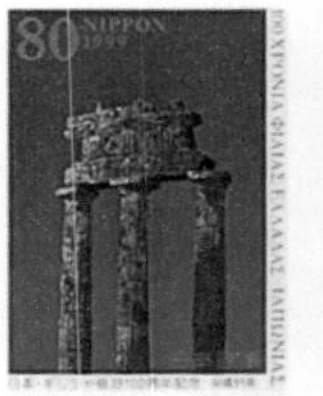
1949 Tholos, Delphi

1950 Demon Dancer (Ouro Carnival), Lake Titicaca and Andean Condor

1999. Centenary of Japan–Greece Treaty of Commerce and Navigation.
2590 **1949** 80y. multicoloured . . 95 20

1999. 100 Years of Japanese Emigration to Bolivia.
2591 **1950** 80y. multicoloured . . 95 20

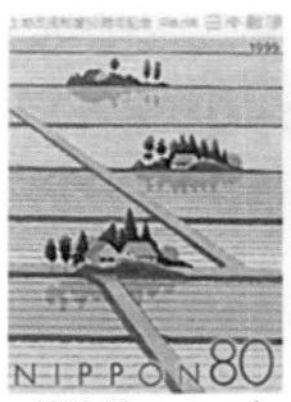
1951 Houses and Paddy Fields

1952 "Hill where Camellias Bloom" (detail of statue, Naoki Tominaga) and "Hope" (detail of stained glass window, Louis Fransen)

1999. 50th Anniv of Land Improvement Law.
2592 **1951** 80y. multicoloured . . 95 20

1999. 50th Anniv of Family Court.
2593 **1952** 80y. multicoloured . . 95 20

1953 Primroses

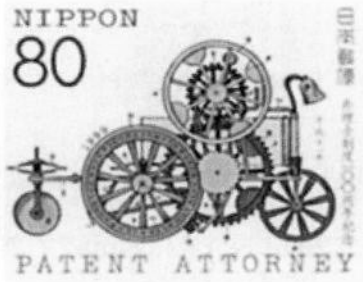
1954 Rickshaw, 1899

1999. 50th Anniv of Rehabilitation Support Programme.
2594 **1953** 80y. multicoloured . . 95 20

1999. Centenary of Patent Attorney System.
2595 **1954** 80y. multicoloured . . 95 20

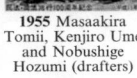

1955 Masaakira Tomii, Kenjiro Ume and Nobushige Hozumi (drafters)

1956 Sayo-chan, Saku-chan and Ken-chan (originator, developer and inspector) (Takashi Yanase)

1999. Centenaries of Civil (1998) and Commercial (1999) Laws.
2596 **1955** 80y. multicoloured . . 95 20

1999. Centenary of Japanese Copyright System.
2597 **1956** 80y. multicoloured . . 95 20

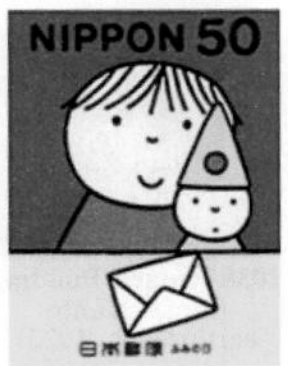
1957 Children and Envelope

1971 Doves and Hearts

1999. Letter Writing Day. 50th Anniv of Japanese Association of Pen Friend Clubs.
2598 **1957** 50y. multicoloured . . 60 15
2599 – 50y. multicoloured . . 60 15
2600 – 50y. muticoloured . . . 60 15
2601 – 50y. multicoloured . . 60 15
2602 – 80y. blue, black & yell 95 20
2603 – 80y. multicoloured . . 95 20
2604 – 80y. black, blue & yell 95 20
2605 – 80y. black, red & yellow 95 20
2606 – 80y. multicoloured . . 95 20
2607 – 80y. black, yellow & bl 95 20
2608 – 80y. multicoloured . . 95 20
2609 – 80y. black and red . . 95 20
2610 – 80y. black, yellow & grn 95 20
2611 – 80y. green, black & yell 95 20
DESIGNS: As T **1957**—No. 2599, Bear and crayon; 2600, Girl with pen; 2601, Clown jumping from envelope; 2604, Boy and star; 2606, Miffie and Barbara; 2610, Girl with letter. 52 × 27 mm—2602, Giraffes. 35 × 27 mm—2603, Kite. 29 × 29 mm—2605, Girl with pencil; 2609, Girl; 2611, Ducklings. 38 × 38 mm—2607, Boy playing trumpet. 27 × 36 mm—2608, Girl playing cello.

1999. Greetings Stamps.
2613 50y. Type **1971** 60 15
2614 80y. Japanese character . . . 95 20
2615 90y. Manchurian crane and leaves . . . . 1·10 20

1974 "Wagahai wa Neko de Aru" (novel by Natsume Soseki)

1976 Yosano Akiko (poet)

1978 Tram, Tokyo, 1903

1980 "Haikara" (western-style fashion)

1982 Moving Casualties, Russo–Japanese War, 1904–05

1984 Golfer and Gentian

1999. The Twentieth Century (1st series). The 1900s. Multicoloured.
2616 50y. Type **1974** 60 15
2617 50y. "Bochan" (novel by Natsume Soseki) 60 15
2618 80y. Type **1976** 95 20
2619 80y. Denkikan Cinema, Asakusa 95 20
2620 80y. Type **1978** 95 20
2621 80y. Kawakami Otojirou and Sadayakko (actor couple) 95 20
2622 80y. Type **1980** 95 20
2623 80y. Sumo wrestlers (opening of Sumo Ring, Ryogoku, Tokyo, 1909) 95 20
2624 80y. Type **1982** 95 20
2625 80y. Military hospital, Russo–Japanese War . . 95 20
See also Nos. 2627/36, 2664/53, 2677/86, 2687/96, 2697/2706, 2707/16, 2717/26, 2739/48, 2759/68, 2771/80, 2798/807, 2808/17, 2819/28, 2832/41, 2850/59 and 2861/70.

1999. 54th National Sports Festival, Kumamoto.
2626 **1984** 50y. multicoloured . . 60 15

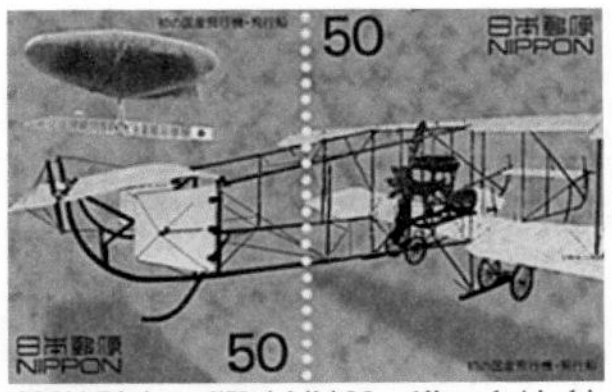
1985/6 Biplane "Kaishiki No. 1" and Airship "Yamadashiki No. 1" (first Japanese built aircraft)

1987 Children singing (School Song Book, 1910)

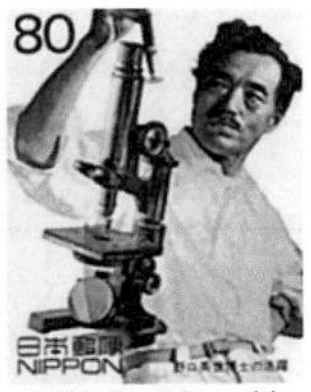
1989 Dr. Noguchi Hideyo (discovery of Oroya Fever germ, 1926)

1991 Kanaguri Shizo and Mishima Yahiko at Opening Parade, Olympic Games, Stockholm, 1912

1993 Matsui Sumako as Kachucha in "Resurrection" (play by Shimamura Hogetsu), 1914

1999. The Twentieth Century (2nd series). Multicoloured.
2627 50y. Type **1985** 60 15
2628 50y. Type **1986** 60 15
2629 80y. Type **1987** 95 20
2630 80y. Explorer and dog (Shirase Antarctic Expedition, 1910) 95 20
2631 80y. Type **1989** 95 20
2632 80y. Wolf (extinction of indigenous wolves, 1905) 95 20
2633 80y. Type **1991** 95 20
2634 80y. Dancers (formation of Takarazuka Musical Company, 1913) 95 20
2635 80y. Type **1993** 95 20
2636 80y. Mother and children (first sale of milk caramel in Japan, 1913) 95 20
Nos. 2627/8 were issued together, se-tenant forming the composite design illustrated.

1995 Stork on Elephant

1999. International Year of the Elderly.
2637 **1995** 80y. multicoloured . . 95 20

1996 "Sea Route in Kazusa Area" (from "36 Views of Mt. Fuji" by Hokusai Katsushika)

1998 "Rain beneath the Mountain Top" (from "36 Views of Mt. Fuji")

1999 "Chrysanthemums and a Horsefly"

2000 "Under the Fukagawa Mannen Bridge" (from "36 Views of Mt. Fuji")

1999. International Correspondence Week. 125th Anniv of Universal Postal Union. Multicoloured.
2638 90y. Type **1996** . . . . . . 1·10 20
2639 90y. "Confederate Roses and a Sparrow" . . . . . 1·10 20
2640 110y. Type **1998** . . . . . 1·30 25
2641 110y. Type **1999** . . . . . 1·30 25
2642 130y. Type **2000** . . . . . 1·50 30
2643 130y. "Peonies and a Butterfly" . . . . 1·50 30

2002 Couple in Junk (Takehisa Yumeji)

2004/5 Inauguration of Tokyo Railway Station, 1914

2006 Navy Cadets (Start of First World War, 1914)

2008 Akutagawa Ryunosuke and Title Page of Rashomon (first book of poetry, published 1915)

2010 Yoshino Sakuzo (political scientist) (Taisho Democracy)

1999. The Twentieth Century (3rd series). Mult.

2644	50y. Type **2002**	65	15
2645	50y. Takehisa Yumeji (artist)	65	15
2646	80y. Type **2004**	1·00	20
2647	80y. Type **2005**	1·00	20
2648	80y. Type **2006**	1·00	20
2649	80y. "Yohatsu" (western-style hair)	1·00	20
2650	80y. Type **2008**	1·00	20
2651	80y. Princess and Clouds (postal life assurance, 1916)	1·00	20
2652	80y. Type **2010**	1·00	20
2653	80y. Farmers (rice riots, 1918)	1·00	20

Nos. 2646/7 were issued together, se-tenant, forming the composite design illustrated.

2012 Yokohama Bay Stars Mascot (Central League)

2013 Chunichi Dragon Mascot (Central League)

2014 Seibu Lions Mascot (Pacific League)

2015 Nippon Ham Fighters Mascot (Pacific League)

2016 Yomiuri Giants Mascot (Central League)

2017 Yakult Swallows Mascot (Central League)

2018 Orix Blue Wave Mascot (Pacific League)

2019 Fukuoka Daiei Hawks Mascot (Pacific League)

2020 Hiroshima Toyo Carp Mascot (Central League)

2021 Hanshin Tigers Mascot (Central League)

2022 Kintetsu Buffaloes Mascot (Pacific League)

2023 Chiba Lotte Marines Mascot (Pacific League)

1999. Professional Japanese Baseball Clubs. Self-adhesive.

2654	**2012**	80y. multicoloured	1·00	20
2655	**2013**	80y. multicoloured	1·00	20
2656	**2014**	80y. multicoloured	1·00	20
2657	**2015**	80y. multicoloured	1·00	20
2658	**2016**	80y. multicoloured	1·00	20
2659	**2017**	80y. multicoloured	1·00	20
2660	**2018**	80y. multicoloured	1·00	20
2661	**2019**	80y. multicoloured	1·00	20
2662	**2020**	80y. multicoloured	1·00	20
2663	**2021**	80y. multicoloured	1·00	20
2664	**2022**	80y. multicoloured	1·00	20
2665	**2023**	80y. multicoloured	1·00	20

2024 Rainbow, Buildings and Mt. Fuji

2025 Katsushika Hokusai (artist, 150th death anniv)

2026 Uemera Shoen (artist, 50th death anniv)

2027 Kawabata Yasunari (author, birth centenary)

1999. 50th Anniv of Japanese Science Council.

2666	**2024**	80y. multicoloured	1·00	80

1999. Anniversaries.

2667	**2025**	80y. multicoloured	1·00	20
2668	**2026**	80y. multicoloured	1·00	20
2669	**2027**	80y. multicoloured	1·00	20

2028 Paulownia and Bamboo Embroidery (Manzairaku costume)

1999. 10th Anniv of Accession of Emperor Akihito. Multicoloured.

2670	80y. Type **2028**	1·00	20
2671	80y. Chinese phoenix embroidery (Engiraku costume)	1·00	20

2030 Karatsuyama ningyo Folk Toy

2033 Tsuneishihariko Doll

1999. New Year's Greetings. Multicoloured.

2673	50y. Type **2030**	65	15
2674	80y. Tsuneishihariko doll	1·00	20

1999. New Year's Lottery Stamps. Multicoloured.

2675	50y.+3y. Karatsuyama ningyo folk toy	70	15
2676	80y.+3y. Type **2033**	1·10	25

Each stamp carries a lottery number.

2034 Onoe Matsunosuke (silent film star, 1925)

2035 Bandoh Tsumasaburo (silent film star, 1925)

2036 Runners (first Hakone relay marathon, 1920)

2038 Ruined Building (Great Kanto earthquake, 1923)

2040 Adventures of Sho-chan (comic illustrated by Katsuichi Kabashima, 1923)

2042 Baseball Players (opening of Koshien Stadium, 1924)

1999. The Twentieth Century (4th series). Mult.

2677	50y. Type **2034**	65	15
2678	50y. Type **2035**	65	15
2679	80y. Type **2036**	1·00	20
2680	80y. Gramophone (*Gondola Song*, 1920)	1·00	20
2681	80y. Type **2038**	1·00	20
2682	80y. Easygoing Dad (comic strip character by Yutaka Aso, 1923)	1·00	20
2683	80y. Type **2040**	1·00	20
2684	80y. Manchurian crane (protected species, 1924)	1·00	20
2685	80y. Type **2042**	1·00	20
2686	80y. Couple wearing western-style clothes	1·00	20

2044 Underground Train (opening of Tokyo Underground, 1927)

2046 Arashi Chozaburo in Title Role (*Kurama Tengu* (film), 1927)

2048 Tsuruta Yoshiyuki (swimmer) (Gold Medal winner, Olympic Games, Amsterdam, 1928)

2050 2nd August Track and Field Programme (Olympic Games, Amsterdam)

2052 Man (emergence of cafes for social gatherings)

2000. The Twentieth Century (5th series). Mult.

2687	50y. Type **2044**	65	15
2688	50y. Platform (opening of Tokyo Underground)	65	15
2689	80y. Type **2046**	1·00	20
2690	80y. Man doing gymnastics (first radio broadcast of gymnastic exercises, 1928)	1·00	20
2691	80y. Type **2048**	1·00	20
2692	80y. Oda Mikio (athlete) (Gold medal winner, Olympic Games, Amsterdam)	1·00	20
2693	80y. Type **2050**	1·00	20
2694	80y. Hitomi Kinue (athlete) (Silver medal winner, Olympic Games, Amsterdam)	1·00	20
2695	80y. Type **2052**	1·00	20
2696	80y. Cover of Horoki (novel by Hayashi Fumiko)	1·00	20

2054/5 Datsun Model 10, 1932 and Toyota Model AA, 1936 (mass production of domestic cars)

2056 Eruption of Mt. Asama, 1929

2058 Couple wearing Western Clothes (importing of western fashion)

2060 Kabutoyama (winner of first Japanese Derby, 1932)

2062 Woman (release of *Longing for Your Shadow* (song by Koga Masao), 1931)

2000. The Twentieth Century (6th series). Mult.

2697	50y. Type **2054**	65	15
2698	50y. Type **2055**	65	15
2699	80y. Type **2056**	1·00	20

2700 80y. Kobayashi Takiji (author) (*Crab Cannery Ship* published in *War Banner* paper) (25 × 32 mm) . . . . . . 1·00 20
2701 80y. Type **2058** . . . . . . 1·00 20
2702 80y. Kuro (comic strip character by Tagawa Suiha, 1931) (27 × 33 mm) 1·00 20
2703 80y. Type **2060** . . . . . . 1·00 20
2704 80y. Matsumidori (winner of 14th Derby) (27 × 33 mm) 1·00 20
2705 80y. Type **2062** . . . . . . 1·00 20
2706 80y. Prime Minister's Residence (assassinations of Prime Minister Tsuyoshi Inukai, 1932, and of Finance Minister Takahashi Korekiyo and Lord Keeper of the Privy Seal Saito Makoto, 1936) (25 × 35 mm) . . . . . . 1·00 20

Nos. 2697/8 were issued together, se-tenant, forming the composite design illustrated.

2064/5 D51 Steam Locomotive, 1936

2066 Otsuki Fumihiko (first edition of Daigenkai (dictionary compiled by Otsuki Fumihiko and Otsuki Joden), 1932)

2071 Chuken Hachiko and Statue (erection of statue of Chuken Hachiko, Shikuya Station, 1934)

2069/70 Players (formation of Tokyo Baseball Club, 1934)

2000. The Twentieth Century (7th series). Mult.
2707 50y. Type **2064** 65 15
2708 50y. Type **2065** 65 15
2709 80y. Type **2066** . . . . . . 1·00 20
2710 80y. Woman (release of *Tokyo Ondo* (song by Nakayama Shimpei), 1933) (25 × 33 mm) . . . 1·00 20
2711 80y. Enomoto Kenichi (actor) (25 × 33 mm) . . . 1·00 20
2712 80y. Type **2069** . . . . . . 1·00 20
2713 80y. Type **2070** . . . . . . 1·00 20
2714 80y. Type **2071** . . . . . . 1·00 20
2715 80y. Yoshikawa Eiji (author) (*Miyamoto* (story) first published in 1935) (27 × 33 mm) . . . 1·00 20
2716 80y. Silver-banded black pigeon (declared extinct, 1936) (27 × 33 mm) . . . 1·00 20

Nos. 2707/8 and 2712/13 respectively were issued together, se-tenant, forming the composite design illustrated.

2074/5 Mitsubishi Twin-engined Transport and Ki-15 Prototype Type 97 *Kamikaze* Airplanes

2076 Helen Keller's First Visit to Japan, 1937

2078 Yamamoto Yuzo (author) (*Robo No Ishi* (novel) first published in 1937)

2080 Yokozuna Futabayama (sumo wrestler) (victory in 69 consecutive matches, 1936–39)

2082 Birds (release of *Dareka Kokyo wo Omowazaru* (song by Koga Masao))

2000. The Twentieth Century (8th series). Mult.
2717 50y. Type **2074** 65 15
2718 50y. Type **2075** 65 15
2719 80y. Type **2076** . . . . . . 1·00 20
2720 80y. Woman with bag and civilian in national uniform (wartime clothing, 1937–40) (25 × 33 mm) . . . . . . 1·00 20
2721 80y. Type **2078** . . . . . . 1·00 20
2722 80y. Tanaka Kinuyo and Uehara Ken (actors) in *Aizenkatsura* (film), 1938 (25 × 33 mm) . . . . . . 1·00 20
2723 80y. Type **2080** . . . . . . 1·00 20
2724 80y. Sawamura Eiji (baseball player) (27 × 33 mm) . . . . . . 1·00 20
2725 80y. Type **2082** . . . . . . 1·00 20
2726 80y. Woodblock carving (Munakata Shiko) (25 × 34 mm) . . . . . . 1·00 20

Nos. 2717/18 were issued together, se-tenant, forming the composite design illustrated.

2084/5 Children and Flowers

2086/7 Faces and Building

2088 Girl as Butterfly with Book

2089 Two Faces and Building

2000. Children's Book Day.
2727 **2084** 80y. multicoloured . . 1·00 20
2728 **2085** 80y. multicoloured . . 1·00 20
2729 **2086** 80y. multicoloured . . 1·00 20
2730 **2087** 80y. multicoloured . . 1·00 20
2731 **2088** 80y. multicoloured . . 1·00 20
2732 **2089** 80y. multicoloured . . 1·00 20

Nos. 2727/8 and 2929/30 respectively were issued together, se-tenant, forming the composite designs illustrated.

2090 Hanaoka Seisyu (surgeon) and Korean Morning Glory

2000. Cent of Japanese Surgical Society Congress.
2733 **2090** 80y. multicoloured . . 1·00 20

2091/2 *Liefde* (17th-century merchant ship), Dutchman and Nagasaki

2000. 400th Anniv of Japan–Netherlands Cultural Relations.
2734 **2091** 80y. multicoloured . . 1·00 20
2735 **2092** 80y. multicoloured . . 1·00 20

Nos. 2734/5 were issued together, se-tenant, forming a composite design.

2093/4 "Ryukozu" (Hashimoto Gaho)

2000. Philatelic Week.
2736 **2093** 80y. multicoloured . . 1·00 20
2737 **2094** 80y. multicoloured . . 1·00 20

Nos. 2736/7 were issued together, se-tenant, forming the composite design illustrated.

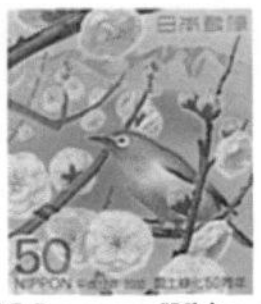

2095 Japanese White-eye, Plum Tree and Kuju Mountain Range

2000. National Afforestation Campaign.
2738 **2095** 50y. multicoloured . . 65 15

2096 Golden Bat (comic strip character by Suzuki Ichiro)

2098 Vice-Consul Sugihara Chiune (issued visas to Jews from Consulate in Lithuania), 1940

2100 Airplane over Pearl Harbor (outbreak of Second World War in the Pacific, 1941)

2102 Mt. Showashin-zan (formed by volcanic activity of Mt. Usu, 1944)

2104 Statue (atomic bomb on Nagasaki, 9 August 1945)

2000. The Twentieth Century (9th series). Mult.
2739 50y. Type **2096** 65 15
2740 50y. Golden Bat (27 × 36 mm) 65 15
2741 80y. Type **2098** . . . . . . 1·00 20
2742 80y. Children (Kokumin Gakko school system, 1941) (25 × 33 mm) . . . 1·00 20
2743 80y. Type **2100** . . . . . . 1·00 20
2744 80y. Takamura Kotaro (poet) (*Dotei* (collected poems) awarded First Imperial Art Academy Prize, 1942) (26 × 35 mm) 1·00 20
2745 80y. Type **2102** . . . . . . 1·00 20
2746 80y. Damaged buildings (atomic bomb on Hiroshima, 6 August 1945) (27 × 33 mm) . . . 1·00 20
2747 80y. Type **2104** . . . . . . 1·00 20
2748 80y. Lieut-General Umezu, Chief of the Imperial General Staff signing Surrender (end of Second World War, 1945) . . . . 1·00 20

2106 Bean Goose

2109 "Girl playing Glass Flute" (Kitagawa Utamaro)

2111 Roses and Pansies

2113 Girl with Pen and Boy with Letter

2000. "Phila Nippon '01" International Stamp Exhibition, Tokyo. Multicoloured. Self-adhesive.
2749 80y. Type **2106** . . . . . . 1·00 20
2750 80y. White wagtail (25 × 34 mm) . . . . . . 1·00 20
2751 80y. Northern goshawk (25 × 35 mm) . . . . . . 1·00 20
2752 80y. Type **2109** . . . . . . 1·00 20
2753 80y. Ichikawa Ebizo (actor) (Toshusai Sharaku) (25 × 48 mm) . . . . . . 1·00 20
2754 80y. Type **2111** . . . . . . 1·00 20
2755 80y. Puppy and kitten (24 × 42 mm) . . . . . . 1·00 20
2756 80y. Type **2113** . . . . . . 1·00 20

2757 80y. Children and letter (31 × 43 mm) . . . . . . 1·00 20
2758 80y. Girl with letter and boy with pen (31 × 40 mm) . . 1·00 20

2116 Astro Boy (comic strip character by Tezuka Osamu, 1951) on cover of *Shonen* (magazine), July, 1951

2118 Cover of Music Score and Apples (release of *Song of Apples* (song by Sato Hachiro and Manjoume Tadashi), 1945)

2120 Mother and Child (promulgation of new constitution, 1947)

2122 Dr. Yukawa Hideki and Atoms (winner of Nobel Prize for Physics, 1949)

2124 Kishi Keiko and Sata Keiji (actors) in *Kimino Na Wa* (film), 1953

2000. The Twentieth Century (10th series). Mult.

2759 50y. Type **2116** 65 15
2760 50y. Astro Boy from cover of *Shonen*, August, 1961 (26 × 36 mm) 65 15
2761 80y. Type **2118** . . . . . . 1·00 20
2762 80y. Sazae San (comic strip by Hasegawa Machiko) (25 × 34 mm) . . . . . . 1·00 20
2763 80y. Type **2120** . . . . . . 1·00 20
2764 80y. Trophy (new world records set by Furuhashi Hironoshin (swimmer), 1949) (25 × 34 mm) . . . 1·00 20
2765 80y. Type **2122** . . . . . . 1·00 20
2766 80y. Championship flag (first radio broadcast of Kohaku Uta Gassen (singing competition), 1951) (25 × 34 mm) . . . 1·00 20
2767 80y. Type **2124** . . . . . . 1·00 20
2768 80y. Tsuboi Sakae (author) and cover illustration by Morita Motoko from first edition of *Nijyu-Yon No* Hitomi (novel) (25 × 34 mm) . . . . . . 1·00 20

2126 Flowers

2127 Flowers and Sea

2000. Kyushu–Okinawa Summit.

2769 **2126** 80y. multicoloured . . 1·00 20
2770 **2127** 80y. multicoloured . . 1·00 20

2128 Tokyo Tower Entrance Ticket, 1958

2131/2 Kurosawa Akira (film director) and Scene from *Seven Samurai*, 1954

2133 Rikidozan (wrestler) and Championship Belt

2136 Prince Shotoku (issue of 10,000 yen banknote, 1958)

2000. The Twentieth Century (11th series).

2771 **2128** 50y. multicoloured . . 65 15
2772 – 50y. multicoloured (27 × 35 mm) 65 15
2773 – 80y. multicoloured (25 × 35 mm) . . . . 1·00 20
2774 **2131** 80y. multicoloured . . 1·00 20
2775 **2132** 80y. multicoloured . . 1·00 20
2776 **2133** 80y. multicoloured . . 1·00 20
2777 – 80y. multicoloured (28 × 36 mm) . . . . 1·00 20
2778 – 80y. multicoloured (25 × 33 mm) . . . . 1·00 20
2779 **2136** 80y. brown and stone 1·00 20
2780 – 80y. multicoloured (25 × 33 mm) . . . . 1·00 20

DESIGNS: No. 2772, Tokyo Tower (construction completed in 1958); 2773, Early radio and television sets (regular television broadcasts, 1953); 2777, Rikidozan; 2778, *Godzilla* (release of film, 1954); 2780, Influence of Taiyozoku Fashion on Youth Culture (release of *Taiyo No Kisetsu* (film), 1956).

Nos. 2774/5 were issued together, se-tenant, forming the composite design illustrated.

2138/9 Sunflowers

2000. 50th Anniv of Crime Prevention Campaign.

2781 **2138** 80y. multicoloured . . 1·00 20
2782 **2139** 80y. multicoloured . . 1·00 20

Nos. 2781/2 were issued together, se-tenant, forming the composite design.

2140 Girl with Pen

2000. Letter Writing Day. Multicoloured.

2783 50y. Type **2140** 65 15
2784 50y. House and birds (25 × 33 mm) 65 15
2785 50y. Clown and envelope (25 × 33 mm) 65 15
2786 50y. Boy with dog (25 × 33 mm) 65 15
2787 80y. Girl and dog in balloon basket (27 × 36 mm) . . 1·00 20
2788 80y. Apple tree (30 × 30 mm) . . . . . . 1·00 20
2789 80y. Parrots holding letter (22 × 34 mm) . . . . . . 1·00 20
2790 80y. Bicycle (28 × 40 mm) . . 1·00 20
2791 80y. Girl and boy holding dove (29 × 35 mm) . . . 1·00 20
2792 80y. Girl, letter and hedgehog (27 × 40 mm) 1·00 20
2793 80y. Girl playing harp (28 × 35 mm) . . . . . . 1·00 20
2794 80y. Boy playing recorder (27 × 35 mm) . . . . . . 1·00 20
2795 80y. Boy playing cello (23 × 39 mm) . . . . . . 1·00 20
2796 80y. Boy carrying pen (27 × 36 mm) . . . . . . 1·00 20

2154/5 Taro and Giro (left at Showa Base, 1958)

2156 Commemorative Cake Box (marriage of Prince Akihito, 1959)

2158 Stars and Music Score (release of *Sukiyaki* (song by Ei Rokusuke and Nakamura Hachidai), 1960)

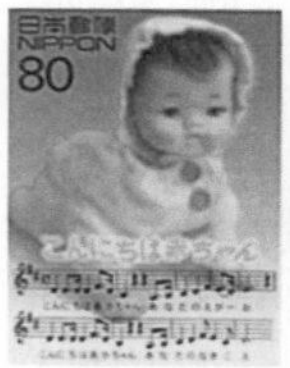

2160 Doll and Music Score (release of *Hello, My Baby* (song by Ei Rokusuke and Nakamura Hachidai)), 1963

2162 Official Poster of Olympic Games, Tokyo, 1964

2000. The Twentieth Century (12th series). Mult.

2798 50y. Type **2154** 65 15
2799 50y. Type **2155** 65 15
2800 80y. Type **2156** . . . . . . 1·00 20
2801 80y. Meteorological chart showing the Isewan typhoon, 1959 (25 × 33 mm) . . . . . . 1·00 20
2802 80y. Type **2158** . . . . . . 1·00 20
2803 80y. Shiba Ryotaro (author) (serialization of *Ryomaga Yuku* (novel)), 1962 (25 × 33 mm) . . . . . . 1·00 20
2804 80y. Type **2160** . . . . . . 1·00 20
2805 80y. Tokyo–Osaka High Speed Bullet Train Service, 1964 (25 × 33 mm) . . . . . . 1·00 20
2806 80y. Type **2162** . . . . . . 1·00 20
2807 80y. Official poster of Olympic Games, Tokyo (28 × 36 mm) . . . . . . 1·00 20

Nos. 2798/9 were issuesd together, se-tenant, forming the composite design illustrated.

2164/5 Characters from *Hyokkori Hyotan-jima* (launch of children's television programme, 1964)

2166 Television, Car and Air Conditioning Unit, 1960

2168 Baltan (character from *Ultraman*)

2170 Kawabata Yasunari and Oe Kenzaburo (winners of the Nobel Prize for Literature)

2172 Tower of the Sun (sculpture, Okamoto Taro) (World's Fair, Osaka, 1970)

2000. The Twentieth Century (13th series). Mult.

2808 50y. Type **2164** 65 15
2809 50y. Type **2165** 65 15
2810 80y. Type **2166** . . . . . . 1·00 20
2811 80y. Ultraman (launch of *Ultraman* (television series), 1966) (27 × 33 mm) 1·00 20
2812 80y. Type **2168** . . . . . . 1·00 20
2813 80y. Guitars (formation of pop bands following 1966 tour by The Beatles) (25 × 33 mm) . . . . . . 1·00 20
2814 80y. Type **2170** . . . . . . 1·00 20
2815 80y. Atsumi Taro (actor) in *Otokowa Tsuraiyo* (film) (25 × 34 mm) . . . . . . 1·00 20
2816 80y. Type **2172** . . . . . . 1·00 20
2817 80y. Youths and music score (release of *Children Who Didn't Know the War* (song), by Kitayama Osamu and Sugita Jiro, 1971) (25 × 33 mm) . . . 1·00 20

Nos. 2808/9 were issued together, se-tenant, forming the composite design illustrated.

2174 Naruse Jinzo (founder of Women's University), Yoshioka Yayoi (founder of Women's Medical College, Tokyo) and Tsuda Umeko (founder of Tsuda College)

2175 Oh Sadaharu (baseball player) swinging Bat, 1964

2177 Wall Painting (discovery of wall paintings at Takamatsu Zuka, 1972)

2179 Pandas (gift from China to Japan, 1972)

2181 Lady Oscar (character from *Belubara*, 1972) (cartoon by Ikeda Riyoko)

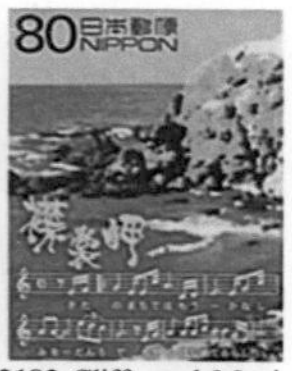

2183 Cliffs and Music Score (release of *Erimo Misaki* (song) by Okamoto Osami and Yoshida Takuro, 1974)

2000. Centenary of Private Higher Education for Women.

2818 **2174** 80y. multicoloured . . 85 20

2000. The Twentieth Century (14th series). Multicoloured.

2819 50y. Type **2175** 50 10
2820 50y. Nagashima Shigeo (baseball player) running, 1962 . . . . 50 10
2821 80y. Type **2177** 85 20
2822 80y. Wall painting (from Takamatsu Zuka) 85 20
2823 80y. Type **2179** 85 20
2824 80y. Shureimon Gate (return to Japan of administrative rights over Okinawa, 1972) 85 20
2825 80y. Type **2181** 85 20
2826 80y. Ozawa Seiji (conductor) 85 20
2827 80y. Type **2183** 85 20
2828 80y. Futuristic space shuttle (cartoon series *Uchu Senkan Yamato* by Matsumoto Reiji, 1974) 85 20

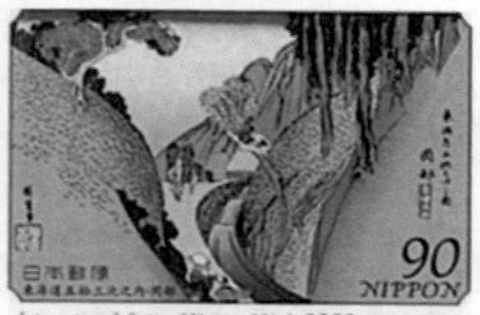

2185 "Okabe"

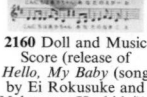

2000. International Correspondence Week. Paintings from "53 Stations of the Tokaido" by Ando Hiroshige. Multicoloured.
2829 90y. Type **2185** 95 20
2830 110y. "Maisaka" . . . . . 1·10 25
2831 130y. "Okazaki" . . . . . 1·25 25

2188 Gundam (cartoon character) (launch of *Kidosenshi Gundam*, television programme, 1979)

2190 Guitar and Music Score (release of *Jidai* (song by Nakajima Miyuki), 1975)

2192 Microphones and Musical Notes (introduction of Karaoke, 1977)

2194 Alien Space Ship and Music Score (release of *UFO* (song by Aku Yu and Tokura Shunichi), 1979)

2196 Keyboard and Musical Notes (popularity of synthesizer music, 1970s)

2000. The Twentieth Century (15th series). Multicoloured.
2832 50y. Type **2188** 50 10
2833 50y. Amuro (cartoon character from *Kidosenshi Gundam*) 50 10
2834 80y. Type **2190** 85 20
2835 80y. Fish and music score (release of *Oyoge! Taiyaki-kun* (song by Takada Hiroo and Sase Juichi), 1975) 85 20
2836 80y. Type **2192** 85 20
2837 80y. Flowers and music score (release of *Cosmos* (song by Sada Masashi), 1977) 85 20
2838 80y. Type **2194** 85 20
2839 80y. People crossing field (launch of *San Nen B Gumi Kinpachi Sensi* (television series), 1979) 85 20
2840 80y. Type **2196** 85 20
2841 80y. Woman and snow-covered house (launch of *Oshine* (television drama), 1983) 85 20

2198 Nagaoka Hantaro (physicist, 50th death anniv) and Atomic Models

2199 Nakaya Ukichiro (physicist, birth centenary) and Snow Crystal

2200 Nakamura Teijo (haiku poet, birth centenary) and Text

2000. Anniversaries.
2842 **2198** 80y. multicoloured . . 85 20
2843 **2199** 80y. multicoloured . . 85 20
2844 **2200** 80y. multicoloured . . 85 20

2201 Jindaiji (snake-shaped clay bell)

2204 Sasano (carved wooden toy snake)

2000. New Year's Greetings. Multicoloured.
2845 50y. Type **2201** 50 10
2846 80y. Sasano (carved wooden toy snake) 85 20

2000. New Year's Lottery Stamps. Multicoloured.
2847 50y.+3y. Jindaiji (snake-shaped clay bell) 55 10
2848 80y.+3y. Type **2204** 85 20
Each stamp carries a lottery number.

2205/6 Characters from *Go! Anpanman* (launch of children's television programme, 1988)

2207 Trains on Trial and Inaugural Runs (opening of Seikan Tunnel, 1988)

2209 Rebuilt Watchtower (excavation of ruins at Yoshinogari Iseki, 1989)

2211/12 "J-Boy" (mascot) and Football (Inception of J-League Football, 1993)

2213 "Tonkomeisya" (detail of painting, Hirayama Ikuo) (World Heritage Site, 1987)

2000. The Twentieth Century (16th series). Multicoloured.
2849 50y. Type **2205** 50 10
2850 50y. Type **2206** 50 10
2851 80y. Type **2207** 85 20
2852 80y Halley's Comet (first appearance for 76 years, 1986) 85 20
2853 80y. Type **2209** 85 20
2854 80y. Misora Hibari (singer) (recipient of National Medal of Honor, 1989) 85 20
2855 80y. Type **2211** 85 20
2856 80y. Type **2212** 85 20
2857 80y. Type **2213** 85 20
2858 80y. "Ikarugano Sato Cyoyo Horyuji" (detail of painting, Hirayama Ikuo) (World Heritage Site, 1998) 85 20
Nos. 2849/50 and 2855/6 were respectively issued together, se-tenant, forming the composite design illustrated.

2215 Central Tower and Mosaic Marble Floors (detail)

2216 Emblem, Nagano Olympic Games, 1998

2218 Crown Prince Noruhito and Princess Masako (wedding, 1993)

2220 Lap-top Computer and Mobile Phone (increased use of wireless telecommunications)

2222 Doi Takao (Japanese astronaut) outside Spaceship

2224 "Mother Earth" (Bokunan Naka) (United Nations Framework Convention on Climate Change, Kyoto, 1997)

2000. 110th Anniv of Diet (Japanese Parliament).
2859 **2215** 80y. multicoloured . .

2000. The Twentieth Century (17th series). Multicoloured.
2860 50y. Type **2216** 50 10
2861 50y. "Snowlets" (Nagano Olympic mascots) 50 10
2862 80y. Type **2218** 85 20
2863 80y. Phoenix, map of Hanshin-Awaji and collapsed bridge (Hanshin-Awaji earthquake, 1995) 85 20
2864 80y. Type **2220** 85 20
2865 80y. Launch of space shuttle *Endeavor* (inclusion of first Japanese astronaut on N.A.S.A. mission, 1992) 85 20
2866 80y. Type **2222** 85 20
2867 80y. Footballer (Japanese participation in World Cup Football Championship, France, 1998) 85 20
2868 80y. Type **2224** 85 20
2869 80y. Official poster of Nagano Olympic Games 85 20

2226/7 Manchurian Cranes (*"Grus japonensis"*, Matazo Kayama)

2001. "Internet Expo 2001 Japan" (virtual Internet fair).
2870 **2226** 80y. multicoloured . . 85 20
2871 **2227** 80y. multicoloured . . 85 20
Nos. 2870/1 were issued together, se-tenant, forming a composite design.

2228 Heliotrope, Flax and Emblem

2229 "Gyoseishoshi" (Japanese calligraphy) and Computer

2001. United Nations Year of Volunteers.
2872 **2228** 80y. multicoloured . . 85 20

2001. 50th Anniv of Gyoseishoshi Lawyer System (specialist administrative lawyers).
2873 **2229** 80y. multicoloured . . 85 20

2230 Shinkyo Bridge, Futarasan Shrine

2231 Main Sanctuary, Futarasan Shrine

2232 Karamon Gate, Toshugu Shrine

2233 Kirin (mythical winged horse) (painting), Toshugu Shrine

2234 Wind God (statue), Rinnoji Temple

2235 Thunder God (statue), Rinnoji Temple

2236 Peacock, Toshugu Shrine

2237 Sleeping Cat, Toshugu Shrine

2238/9 Rinnoji Temple

2001. World Heritage Sites (1st series). Shrines and Temples, Nikko.
2874 **2230** 80y. multicoloured . . 85 20
2875 **2231** 80y. multicoloured . . 85 20
2876 **2232** 80y. multicoloured . . 85 20
2877 **2233** 80y. multicoloured . . 85 20
2878 **2234** 80y. multicoloured . . 85 20
2879 **2235** 80y. multicoloured . . 85 20
2880 **2236** 80y. multicoloured . . 85 20
2881 **2237** 80y. multicoloured . . 85 20
2882 **2238** 80y. multicoloured . . 85 20
2883 **2239** 80y. multicoloured . . 85 20
Nos. 2883/4 were issued together, se-tenant, forming the composite design illustrated.
See also Nos. 2887/96, 2906/15, 2960/9, 2985/94, 2997/3006, 3020/9, 3045/54 and 3060/9.

2240 Emblem

2241 "The Annunciation" (detail, Botticelli)

2242 "The Annunciation" (detail, Botticelli)

2001. "Italy in Japan 2001" (cultural and scientific event).

2884	**2240**	80y. multicoloured . .	85	20
2885	**2241**	110y. multicoloured . .	1·25	25
2886	**2242**	110y. multicoloured . .	1·25	25

Nos. 2885/6 were issued together in se-tenant pairs featuring two separate panels of the painting.

2243/4 Marodo Shrine

2245 Main Sanctuary

2246 Lion Dog (statue)

2247 Marodo Shrine and Pagoda

2248 Traditional Dance Mask

2249 Horse (statue)

2250 Buildings

2251 Treasure Pagoda

2252 Oomoto Shrine

2001. World Heritage Sites (2nd series). Itsukushima Shrine.

2887	**2243**	80y. multicoloured . .	85	20
2888	**2244**	80y. multicoloured . .	85	20
2889	**2245**	80y. multicoloured . .	85	20
2890	**2246**	80y. multicoloured . .	85	20
2891	**2247**	80y. multicoloured . .	85	20
2892	**2248**	80y. multicoloured . .	85	20
2893	**2249**	80y. multicoloured . .	85	20
2894	**2250**	80y. multicoloured . .	85	20
2895	**2251**	80y. multicoloured . .	85	20
2896	**2252**	80y. multicoloured . .	85	20

Nos. 2888/9 were issued together, se-tenant, forming the composite design illustrated.

2253 Emblem

2254 Woman posting Letter (Nakamura Senseki)

2001. Centenary of Japanese Dermatological Association. Multicoloured, colour of triangle beneath face value given.

2897	**2253**	80y. pink	85	20
2898		80y. flesh	85	20
2899		80y. yellow	85	20
2900		80y. green	85	20
2901		80y. blue	85	20

2001. Philatelic Week. Centenary of Red Cylindrical Letter Boxes (designed by Taraya Takashhichi and Nakamura Koji).

2902	**2254**	80y. multicoloured . .	85	20

2255 "Ato, Nik and Kaz" (mascots)

2256 "Kaz"

2257 "Nik"

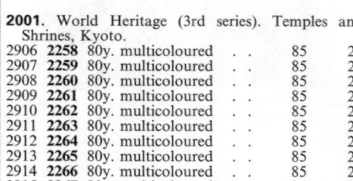

2001. World Cup Football Championship, Japan and South Korea (2002).

2903	**2255**	80y.+10y. mult	95	20
2904	**2256**	80y.+10y. mult	95	20
2905	**2257**	80y.+10y. mult	95	20

2258 Hosodono, Maidono and Tsuchinoya Halls, Kamowakeikazuchi Shrine

2259 Roman Gate, Kamowakeikazuchi Shrine

2260 East Main Hall, Kamomioya Shrine

2261 Guardian Dog (statue), Kamomioya Shrine

2262 Pagoda and South Great Gate, Toji Temple

2263 Fukuu Joju Nyorai (statue), Toji Temple

2264 Pagoda and West Gate, Kiyomizudera Temple

2265 Main Hall, Kiyomizudera Temple

2266 "Nyorin Kannon" (painting), Toji Temple

2267 Daiitoku Myoo (statue), Toji Temple

2001. World Heritage (3rd series). Temples and Shrines, Kyoto.

2906	**2258**	80y. multicoloured . .	85	20
2907	**2259**	80y. multicoloured . .	85	20
2908	**2260**	80y. multicoloured . .	85	20
2909	**2261**	80y. multicoloured . .	85	20
2910	**2262**	80y. multicoloured . .	85	20
2911	**2263**	80y. multicoloured . .	85	20
2912	**2264**	80y. multicoloured . .	85	20
2913	**2265**	80y. multicoloured . .	85	20
2914	**2266**	80y. multicoloured . .	85	20
2915	**2267**	80y. multicoloured . .	85	20

2268 Flowers and Pigeons

2269 Swimming

2001. 50th Anniv of Membership of United Nations Educational, Scientific and Cultural Organization.

2916	**2268**	80y. multicoloured . .	85	20

2001. 9th International Swimming Federation Championships, Fukuoka. Multicoloured.

2917	**2269**	80y. Type **2269**	85	20
2918	**2270**	80y. Synchronized swimming	85	20
2919	**2271**	80y. Diving	85	20
2920	**2272**	80y. Water polo	85	20

Nos. 2917/20 were issued together, se-tenant, the backgrounds forming a composite design.

2273 Rabbits

2001. Letter Writing Day. Multicoloured.

2921	50y. Type **2273**	85	20
2922	50y. Girl and pencil (28 × 36 mm)	85	20
2923	50y. Boy holding envelope (28 × 36 mm)	85	20
2924	50y. Girl with ribbons (28 × 36 mm)	85	20
2925	80y. Bird in tree (30 × 30 mm)	85	20
2926	80y. Girl holding rabbit (27 × 36 mm)	85	20
2927	80y. Boy holding pen (27 × 36 mm)	85	20
2928	80y. Girl with envelope and dog (27 × 26 mm)	85	20
2929	80y. Girl and flowers (27 × 36 mm)	85	20
2930	80y. Flowers and bird with envelope (30 × 30 mm) . .	85	20
2931	80y. Birds and roof (27 × 36 mm)	85	20
2932	80y. Rabbit and flowers (22 × 33 mm)	85	20
2933	80y. Boy and rabbit (27 × 33 mm)	85	20
2934	80y. Chicks, hen and pig (27 × 39 mm)	85	20

2287 "Ootani Oniji as Edobei" (Toshusai Sharaku)

2288 "Iwai Hanshiro IV as Shigenoi" (Toshusai Shakuru)

2289 "Sakata Hangoro as Fujikwa Mizuemon" (Toshusai Shakuru)

2290 "Segawa Kikunojo as Oshizu, Tanabe Bunzo's Wife" (Toshusai Shakuru)

2291 "Ichikawa Omezo as Yakko Ippei" (Toshusai Shakuru)

2292 "Beauty looking Back" (Hishikawa Moronobu)

2293 "Girl playing Glass Flute" (Kitagawa Utamaro)

2294 "Fuzoku Higashino Nishiki, returning from the Bath-house in the Rain" (Torii Kiyonaga)

2295 "Iwai Kumesaburo as Chiyo" (Utagawa Kunimasa)

2296 "Ichikawa Komazo III as Sasaski Ganryu" (Utagawa Toyokuni)

2297 "Iwai Hanshiro IV as Shigenoi" (Toshusai Shakuru)

2298 "Ootani Oniji as Edobei" (Toshusai Shakuru)

2299 Mandarin Duck

2300 Japanese White-Eye

2301 Girl and Boy holding Envelopes

2302 "Iwai Kumesaburo as Chiyo" (Utagawa Kunimasa)

2303 "Ichikawa Komazo III as Sasaki Ganryu" (Utagawa Toyokuni)

2304 Eastern Turtle Dove

2305 Greater Pied Kingfisher

2306 1871 48m. Stamp

2307 Fly Casting and Discus

2001. "PHILA NIPPON '01" International Stamp Exhibition, Tokyo. (a) Ordinary gum.

2936	**2287**	50y. multicoloured . .	85	20
2937	**2288**	50y. multicoloured . .	85	20
2938	**2289**	50y. multicoloured . .	85	20
2939	**2290**	50y. multicoloured . .	85	20
2940	**2291**	50y. multicoloured . .	85	20
2941	**2292**	80y. multicoloured . .	85	20
2942	**2293**	80y. multicoloured . .	85	20
2943	**2294**	80y. multicoloured . .	85	20
2944	**2295**	80y. multicoloured . .	85	20
2945	**2296**	80y. multicoloured . .	85	20

(b) Self-adhesive gum.

2946	**2297**	50y. multicoloured . .	85	20
2947	**2298**	50y. multicoloured . .	85	20
2948	**2299**	50y. multicoloured . .	85	20
2949	**2300**	50y. multicoloured . .	85	20
2950	**2301**	50y. multicoloured . .	85	20
2951	**2302**	80y. multicoloured . .	85	20
2952	**2303**	80y. multicoloured . .	85	20
2953	**2304**	80y. multicoloured . .	85	20
2954	**2305**	80y. multicoloured . .	85	20
2955	**2306**	80y. multicoloured . .	85	20

2001. 6th World Games, Akita. Multicoloured.

2956	50y. Type **2307**	50	10
2957	50y. Aerobics and billiards	50	10
2958	80y. Water skiing and life saving	85	20
2959	80y. Tug of war and body building	85	20

2311 Konpon Chudo Hall, Enryakuji Temple

2312 Eternal Flame, Enryakuji Temple

2313 Ninai-do Hall, Enryakuji Temple

2316 Pagoda, Daigoji Temple

2314/15 Sanbo-in Temple Garden, Daigoji Temple

2317 Palace, Ninnaji Temple

2318 Pagoda, Ninnaji Temple

2319 Phoenix Hall, Byodoin Temple

2320 Bodhisattva floating on Clouds (statue), Byodoin Temple

2001. World Heritage (4th series). Temples, Kyoto.

2960	**2311**	80y. multicoloured . .	85	20
2961	**2312**	80y. multicoloured . .	85	20
2962	**2313**	80y. multicoloured . .	85	20
2963	**2314**	80y. multicoloured . .	85	20
2964	**2315**	80y. multicoloured . .	85	20
2965	**2316**	80y. multicoloured . .	85	20
2966	**2317**	80y, multicoloured . .	85	20
2967	**2318**	80y. multicoloured . .	85	20
2968	**2319**	80y. multicoloured . .	85	20
2969	**2320**	80y. multicoloured . .	85	20

Nos. 2963/4 were issued together, se-tenant, forming the composite design illustrated.

2321 War Memorial Opera House and Flowers

2001. 50th Anniv of San Francisco Peace Treaty.

2970	**2321**	80y. multicoloured . .	85	20

2322 "Hara"

2001. International Correspondence Week. Paintings from "53 Stations of Tokaido" by Ando Hiroshige. Multicoloured.

2971	90y. Type **2322**	95	20
2972	110y. "Oiso"	1·25	25
2973	130y. "Sakanoshita"	1·40	30

2325 Boy with Birds and Insects

2327 Man catching Disc

2001. "Let's Keep our Towns Safe" (national community safety campaign). Multicoloured.

2974	80y. Type **2325**	85	20
2975	80y. Girl with bird and animals	85	20

2001. 1st National Sports Games for the Disabled, Sendai City and Miyagi-gun. Multicoloured.

2976	80y. Type **2327**	85	20
2977	80y. Wheelchair race	85	20

2329 Norinaga Motoori (writer and scholar, death bicentenary)

2330 Gidayu Takemoto (jojuri chanter and puppeteer, 350th birth) and Illustration from "Sonezaki Shinju"

2001. Anniversaries.

2978	**2329**	80y. multicoloured . .	85	20
2979	**2330**	80y. multicoloured . .	85	20

2331 Horse carrying Rice

2334 Red Horse of Kira (sedge handicraft)

2001. New Years Greeting's. Multicoloured.

2980	50y. Type **2331**	55	10
2981	80y. Red horse of Kira . .	85	20

2001. New Year's Lottery Stamps. Multicoloured.

2982	50y. + 3y. Horse carrying rice	55	10
2983	80y. + 3y. Type **2334** . . .	85	20

Each stamp carries a lottery number.

2335 Television Camera, Television Set and Radio Microphone

2001. 50th Anniv of Commercial Broadcasting.

2984	**2335**	80y. multicoloured . .	85	20

2336 Ujikami Shrine

2337 Kaeru Mata (main shrine), Ujikami Shrine

2338 Path to Kozanji Temple

2339 Sekisuiin, Kozanji Temple

2340 Kasumijima Garden, Saihoji Temple

2341 Kojokan Garden, Saihoji Temple

2342/3 Garden, Tenryuji Temple

2344 Golden Temple, Rokuonji Temple

2345 Golden Temple in Winter

2001. World Heritage (5th series). Temples and Shrines, Kyoto.

2985	**2336**	80y. multicoloured . .	85	20
2986	**2337**	80y. multicoloured . .	85	20
2987	**2338**	80y. multicoloured . .	85	20
2988	**2339**	80y. multicoloured . .	85	20
2989	**2340**	80y. multicoloured . .	85	20
2990	**2341**	80y. multicoloured . .	85	20
2991	**2342**	80y. multicoloured . .	85	20
2992	**2343**	80y. multicoloured . .	85	20
2993	**2344**	80y. multicoloured . .	85	20
2994	**2345**	80y. multicoloured . .	85	20

Nos. 2985/94 were issued together in sheetlets of ten stamps, Nos. 2991/2 forming the composite design illustrated, with descriptions of each stamp in Japanese in the illustrated margin.

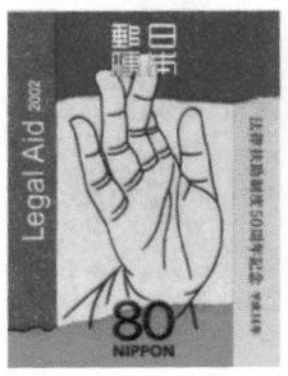
2346 Upraised Hand

2347 Horse-shaped Fiddle Head

2002. 50th Anniv of Legal Aid System.

2995	**2346**	80y. multicoloured . .	85	20

2002. 30th Anniv of Japan---Mongolia Diplomatic Relations.

2996	**2347**	80y. multicoloured . .	85	20

2348 Silver Pavilion in Snow, Jishoji Temple

2349 Silver Pavilion

2350 Hojo Garden, Ryoanji Temple **2351** Hojo Garden in Winter

2352 Karamon Gate, Honganji Temple **2353** Hiunkaku, Honganji Temple

2354 Shoin, Honganji Temple **2355** Ninomaru Palace, Nijo Castle

2356 Hawk on Pine (detail, painting), Nijo Castle **2357** Hawk on Pine (detail)

2002. World Heritage (6th series). Temples, Kyoto.

2997	**2348**	80y. multicoloured . .	85	20
2998	**2349**	80y. multicoloured . .	85	20
2999	**2350**	80y. multicoloured . .	85	20
3000	**2351**	80y. multicoloured . .	85	20
3001	**2352**	80y. multicoloured . .	85	20
3002	**2353**	80y. multicoloured . .	85	20
3003	**2354**	80y. multicoloured . .	85	20
3004	**2355**	80y. multicoloured . .	85	20
3005	**2356**	80y. multicoloured . .	85	20
3006	**2357**	80y. multicoloured . .	85	20

2358 Bell and Mythical Lion-dog **2359** Men's Singles Skater

2002. 50th Anniv of Japan Lions (charitable organization).

3007	**2358**	80y. multicoloured . .	80	15

2002. World Figure Skating Championships, Nagano. Multicoloured.

3008	80y. Type **2359**	80	15
3009	80y. Pairs skaters	80	15

2361 Taj Mahal, India **2362** Artefact and Ruins, Moenjodaro, Pakistan

2363 Sigiriya, Sri Lanka **2364** Terracotta Panel and Ruins, Paharpur, Bangladesh

2002. 50th Anniv of Japan–South East Asia Diplomatic Relations.

3010	**2361**	80y. multicoloured . .	80	15
3011	**2362**	80y. multicoloured . .	80	15
3012	**2363**	80y. multicoloured . .	80	15
3013	**2364**	80y. multicoloured . .	80	15

2365 Two Horsemen **2367** *Hikawa-Maru* (passenger ship)

2002. Philately Week. (Kamo folding screen). Multicoloured.

3014	80y. Type **2365**	80	15
3015	80y. Horseman and spectator	80	15

2002. 50th Anniv of Japan–U.S.A. Fulbright Exchange Programme.

3016	**2367**	80y. multicoloured . .	80	15

2368 Ship and Irises **2369** Stylized Football Pitch

2002. 30th Anniv of Return of Okinawa.

3017	**2368**	80y. multicoloured . .	80	15

2002. World Cup Football Championships, Japan and South Korea. Multicoloured.

3018	80y. Type **2369**	80	15
3019	80y. FIFA World Cup Trophy	80	15

2371 Great Buddha Hall, Todaiji Temple **2372** Southern Gate, Todaiji Temple

2373 Great Buddha (detail), Todaiji Temple **2374** Virupaksu (statue), Todaiji Temple

2375 Lotus Hall, Todaiji Temple **2376** Five-storied Pagoda, Kofukuji Temple

2377 Northern Octagonal Hall, Kofukuji Temple **2378** Ashura (statue), Kofukuji Temple

2379 Buddha Head, Kofukuji Temple **2380** Ryutoki Demon (statue), Kofukuji Temple

2002. World Heritage (7th series). Temples, Nara.

3020	**2371**	80y. multicoloured . .	80	15
3021	**2372**	80y. multicoloured . .	80	15
3022	**2373**	80y. multicoloured . .	80	15
3023	**2374**	80y. multicoloured . .	80	15
3024	**2375**	80y. multicoloured . .	80	15
3025	**2376**	80y. multicoloured . .	80	15
3026	**2377**	80y. multicoloured . .	80	15
3027	**2378**	80y. multicoloured . .	80	15
3028	**2379**	80y. multicoloured . .	80	15
3029	**2380**	80y. multicoloured . .	80	15

Nos. 3020/9 were issued in sheetlets of ten stamps, with descriptions of each stamp in Japanese in the illustrated margin.

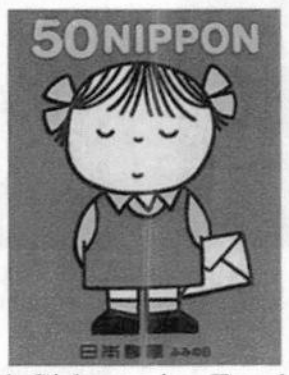

2381 Girl carrying Envelope

2002. National Letter Writing Day.

3030	**2381**	50y. multicoloured . .	50	10
3031	–	50y. multicoloured . .	50	10
3032	–	50y. multicoloured . .	50	10
3033	–	50y. multicoloured . .	50	10
3034	–	80y. multicoloured . .	80	15
3035	–	80y. lemon, black and blue	80	15
3036	–	80y. multicoloured . .	80	15
3037	–	80y. multicoloured . .	80	15
3038	–	80y. multicoloured . .	80	15
3039	–	80y. multicoloured . .	80	15
3040	–	80y. multicoloured . .	80	15
3041	–	80y. multicoloured . .	80	15
3042	–	80y. multicoloured . .	80	15
3043	–	80y. multicoloured . .	80	15
MS3044		72 × 94 mm. Nos. 3031 and 3040	1·30	25

DESIGNS: No. 2383, House and flowers (28 × 34 mm); 2384, Young boy and fence (25 × 34 mm); 2385, Ladybird and caterpillar (28 × 25 mm); 2386, Farmer and sheep (30 × 25 mm); 2387, Cow (32 × 25 mm); 2388, Girl and flowers (30 × 41 mm); 2389, Boy with football (22 × 35 mm); 2390, Girl carrying Tennis racquet (22 × 35 mm); 2391, Mother and child (28 × 36 mm); 2392, Man riding bicycle (28 × 36 mm); 2393, Girl and vase (27 × 27 mm); 2394, Van and car (27 × 27 mm).

2395 Covered Passageway, Kasuga Taisha Shrine **2396** Middle Gate, Kasuga Taisha Shrine

2397 Deer, Kasuga-yama Forest **2398** Zen Meditation Hall, Gango-ji Temple

2399 Pagoda, Gango-ji Temple **2400** East and West Pagodas, Yakushi-ji Temple

2401 Buddha of Healing, Yakushi-ji Temple **2402** Golden Hall, Toshodai-ji Temple

2403 Standing Image of the Thousand Handed Goddess of Mercy, Toshodai-ji Temple **2404** Suzakumon Gate, Heijo Imperial Palace

2002. World Heritage (8th series). Temples.

3045	**2395**	80y. multicoloured . .	80	15
3046	**2396**	80y. multicoloured . .	80	15
3047	**2397**	80y. multicoloured . .	80	15
3048	**2398**	80y. multicoloured . .	80	15
3049	**2399**	80y. multicoloured . .	80	15
3050	**2400**	80y. multicoloured . .	80	15
3051	**2401**	80y. multicoloured . .	80	15
3052	**2402**	80y. multicoloured . .	80	15
3053	**2403**	80y. multicoloured . .	80	15
3054	**2404**	80y. multicoloured . .	80	15

Nos. 3045/54 were issued in sheetlets of ten stamps, with descriptions of each stamp in Japanese in the illustrated margin.

2405 Stylized Human and Flowers **2406** Basketball Players

2002. 12th World Psychiatry Congress.

3055	**2405**	80y. multicoloured . .	80	15

2002. World Wheelchair Basketball Championship, Japan.

3056	**2406**	80y. multicoloured . .	80	15

2407 Twin-engined and Four-propeller Aircrafts

2002. 50th Anniv of Japanese Civil Aviation.

3057	**2407**	80y. multicoloured . .	80	15

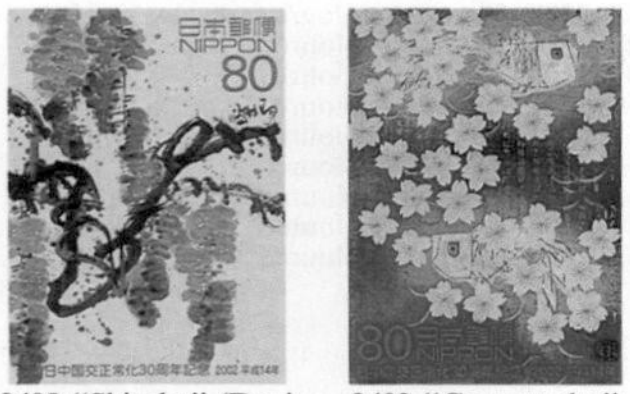

2408 "Shitoka" (Denj Lin) **2409** "Generyucho" (Wang Chuan Feng)

2002. 30th Anniv of Japan–China Diplomatic Relations.

3058	**2408**	80y. multicoloured . .	80	15
3059	**2409**	80y. multicoloured . .	80	15

2410/11 Houses, Ogimachi, Shirakawa-Mura

2412 House and Flowers, Ogimachi

2413 Houses, Ogimachi

2414 Houses covered in Snow, Ogimachi

2415 Aerial View, Ainokura, Taira-Mura

2416 House, Ainokura

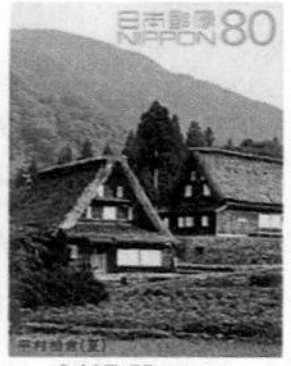

2417 Houses, Ainokura

2418 House, Ainokura

2419 House covered in Snow, Ainokura

2002. World Heritage (9th series). Ogimachi and Ainokura Communitites.

3060	**2410**	80y. multicoloured . .	80	15
3061	**2411**	80y. multicoloured . .	80	15
3062	**2412**	80y. multicoloured . .	80	15
3063	**2413**	80y. multicoloured . .	80	15
3064	**2414**	80y. multicoloured . .	80	15
3065	**2415**	80y. multicoloured . .	80	15
3066	**2416**	80y. multicoloured . .	80	15
3067	**2417**	80y. multicoloured . .	80	15
3068	**2418**	80y. multicoloured . .	80	15
3069	**2419**	80y. multicoloured . .	80	15

Nos. 3060/9 were issued in sheetlets of ten stamps, Nos. 3060/1 forming the composite design illustrated, with descriptions of each stamp in Japanese in the illustrated margin.

MILITARY FRANK STAMPS

軍
事

(M **36**)

1910. No. 139 optd with Type M **36**.
M156 **28** 3s. red . . . . £225 35·00

1913. No. 298 optd with Type M **36**.
M185 **36** 3s. red . . . . 30·00 11·00

1921. No. 37 of Japanese Post Offices in China optd with Type M **36**.
M202 **36** 3s. red £7000 £3250

PREFECTURE STAMPS

Since 1 April 1989 the Japanese Ministry of Posts and Telecommunications has issued stamps, some apparently commemorative, inscribed for various prefectures.

The Japanese local government system contains 47 prefectures which vary from Tokyo. Osaka, Kyoto, Hokkaido and Okinawa to rural areas; the powers of the prefectures are similar to those of English or Welsh counties. Each prefecture issue is sold within the area for which it is inscribed and also in other prefectures grouped with it in one of 11 postal regions; the stamps are also available from the Tokyo Central Post Office. All issues are valid for postal purposes throughout Japan.

These issues do not fulfil the published criteria for full listing in the Stanley Gibbons catalogue and, in consequence, are recorded in abbreviated form below.

The sheet of 47 prefecture flowers was sold throughout Japan and is given full listing as Nos. 2041/87.

1989.

Nagano. Monkeys in hot spring. 62y.

Yamagata. Cherries. 62y.

Okinawa. Courtesy Gate, Shuri. 62y.

Ehime. Dogo Hot Spa buildings. 62y.

Kanagawa. Doll and gas lamps. 62y.

Hiroshima. Seto Inland Sea. 62y. × 2.

Niigata. Memorial Hall and Bandai Bridge. 62y.

Aichi. Nagoya Castle and golden dolphin. 62y.

Oita. Monkey and Mt. Takasaki. 62y.

Hokkaido. Old Prefectural Building, Sapporo. 62y.

Hokkaido. Runner and wild rose (athletic meeting). 62y.

Kumamoto. Kumamoto Castle. 62y.

Ishikawa. Stone lantern, Kenroku Park. 62y.

Aomori. Apples. 62y.

Osaka. Bunraku puppets and Nakanoshima Theatre. 62y.

Shiga. Lake Biwa and racoon-dog. 62y.

Chiba. Racoon-dogs dancing. 62y.

Tokyo. Railway station. 62y.

Yamaguchi. Blowfish lanterns. 62y.

1990.

Hokkaido. Ice hockey (Asian Winter Olympics). 62y.

Toyama. Mt. Tate and Shomyo Falls. 62y.

Ibaraki. "Seven Baby Crows" (nursery rhyme). 62y.

Nagano. Old inns of Tsumago and Magome. 62y. × 2.

Shizuoka. Mt. Fuji and tea picker. 62y.

Fukushima. Peaches. 62y.

Akita. Omagari Fireworks Festival. 62y.

Kagoshima. Mt. Sakura. 62y.

Nagasaki. Sailing ship. 62y.

Okinawa. Ryukyu dancer. 62y.

Tokyo. New post office and logger. 62y.

Shimane. Male dancer with basket. 62y.

Fukuoka. High jumping and Fukuoka Tower (athletic meeting). 62y.

Kyoto. Dancing girl crossing bridge. 62y.

Wakayama. Three pilgrims on old path to Kumano. 62y.

Miyagi. Izunuma Swamp and five whistling swans. 62y.

Gifu. Four seasons in Hida. 62y. × 4.

Saitama. Tenjin Shrine and children playing song game. 62y.

Hokkaido. Two Manchurian cranes. 62y.

1991.

Kagawa. Mounted archer at Battle of Yashima. 62y.

Okayama. Water jars (Bizen ware). 62y. × 2.

Saga. Watchtower, Yoshinogari. 62y.

Yamanashi. "Bride under Cherry Blossoms" (nursery rhyme). 62y.

Niigata. Two fancy carps. 62y.

Hokkaido. Lily of the valley, lilac, lily, rowanberries. 62y. × 4.

Tochigi. Mt. Nikkou and ramblers. 62y.

Iwate. Mt. Iwate. 62y.

Kochi. Sakamoto Ryoma and child standing on whale. 62y.

Tokushima. Wooden puppet. 62y.

Tokyo. Fringed orchid. 41y.

Miyazaki. Cape Toi and wild horses. 62y.

Kumamoto. Tsu-jun Aqueduct releasing water into river. 62y.

Okinawa. Black pearls in oyster and Kabira Bay. 41y.

Tottori. Pears. 62y.

Ishikawa. Genki (mascot) and sunrise (46th National Athletic Meeting). 41y.

Mie. Ninja holding shuriken (throwing weapon), rainbow, Iga Ueno Castle and Ninja house. 62y.

Fukui. Woman wearing spectacles. 62y.

Gunma. "Hare and Tortoise" (fable). 62y.

Hyogo. Weathercock and Kobe City lights. 62y.

Nara. Mt. Yoshino in spring and autumn. 62y. × 2.

1992.

Niigata. Ryokan's Hermitage, Bunsui. 41y.

Fukuoka. Mt. Togami, Japanese bush warbler and azaleas (National Afforestation Campaign). 41y.

Hokkaido. Arctic foxes. 62y.

Toyama. Mt. Tate and tulips. 62y.

Ehime. Islets in Kurushima Strait. 62y.

Iwate. Cape Kitayama, Rikuchu, in winter. 62y.

Ohita. Three Tsurusaki dancers. 62y.

Yamaguchi. Tanabata lantern festival. 62y.

Kanagawa. Shasui waterfall. 62y.

Fukuoka. Mari Tahei with spear and sake dish (Kuroda samurai folk song). 62y.

Okinawa. Naha regatta. 62y.

Osaka. Osaka Business Park and Castle. 41y.

Aichi. Scops owl. 62y.

1993.

Akita. Rocks at Oga Peninsula. 41y.

Ibaraki. Fukuroda waterfall. 62y.

Ishikawa. Nanao Bay and Notojima Bridge. 62y.

Tokyo. Cherry blossom and Tama District mountain ranges. 62y.

Hokkaido. Harbour seals. 62y.

Kagawa. Peace statue. 62y.

Hiroshima. Drummer (rice transplanting ritual). 62y.

Shizuoka. Black paradise flycatcher and Mt. Fuji. 41y.

Shiga. Yachts on Lake Biwa. 62y.

Nagano. Matsumoto Castle and mountains. 62y.

Kagoshima. Drummer and dancer (Ohara Festival) and Mt. Sakura. 41y.

Aomori. Oirase mountain stream. 62y.

Chiba. Waterfall in Yoro Gorge. 41y.

1994.

Tokyo. Rainbow Bridge. 50y.

Toyama. Kurobe Dam and Gorge. 80y.

Shimane. Izumo no Okuni (Kabuki dancer) and Izumo Shrine. 80y.

Nagano. Home at Kashiwabara of Issa Kobayushi (poet). 80y.

Gunma. Fukiwari Waterfalls. 80y.

Hokkaido. Sika deer. 50y.

Hygo. White stork and Drum Tower, Izushi. 50y.

Wakayama. Yachts off Wakaura Coast and Marina City. 80y.

Mie. Kentish plovers and Wedded Rocks, Futami Bay. 80y.

Tokushima. Awa dance. 50y.

Okinawa. Tug-of-war. 50y.

Fukui. Pine grove in Kehi. 50y.

Miyagi. Junks and Godaido Temple, Matsushima. 80y.

Nagasaki. Dragon Festival. 80y.

1995.

Hokkaido. Chipmunks. 80y.

Kyoto, Ushiwaka and Benkei on bridge. 80y.

Gifu. Flowers (Rose, cyclamen, African violets etc). 80y.

Niigata. Jade and Gyofu Soma (poet). 80y.

Kochi. Cape Ashizuri-Misaki Lighthouse. 80y.

Ishikawa. Kanizawa Castle. 80y.

Hokkaido. Lady's slipper orchid. 80y.

Saitama. Kuroyama Waterfall. 80y.

Tokyo. Red Gate, Tokyo University. 50y.

Okinawa. Procession of drummers (folk festival dance). 80y.

Miyagi. Avenue of zelkova trees. 50y.

Osaka. Float in Kishiwada Danjiri Festival. 80y.

Yamagata. Yamadera (or Risshaku) Temple, Mt. Houju, in autumn. 80y.

Hida. Four seasons in Hida. 80y. × 4 se-tenant.

Saga Boy and fish (Karatsu Kunchi Festival). 80y.

Okayama. Woman writing (Niimi Estate festival). 80y.

Tochigi. Kirihuri Waterfall. 50y.

Nara. Yoshino in autumn and spring. 80y. × 2.

Chiba. Cows in field ("Farmpia '95" dairy farming exhibition). 80y.

1996.

Hokkaido. Sea butterflies. 80y.

Kumamoto. Boy dancing, bridge and ships (Ushibuka Haiya festival). 80y.

Fukushima. Pink peony. 80y.

Mie. Wild crinums (flowers). 80y. and Women collecting shells. 80y. se-tenant.

Saga. Jar, flames and pavilion (ceramics exhibition). 80y.

Yamanashi. Waterfall in Shosenkyo Gorge. 50y.

Fukui. Murasaki Shikibu (author of "Tale of Genji") and Mt. Hino. 80y.

Shiga. Enryaku Temple and ancient trees, Mt. Hiei. 80y.

Ehime. Nishiumi Marine Park. 80y.

Hokkaido. Wild rose. 80y.

Aomori. Kabuki characters (Nebuta festival). 80y.

1997.

Miyazaki. Dancers with drums (Shimozuru Usudaiko Odori folk dance). 80y.

Okinawa. Main Palace of Shuri Castle and stone dragon's head. 80y.

Tokyo. Kaminari Gate, Asakusa. 80y.

Tottori. Umbrella Dance, Shanshan Festival. 80y.

Nagano. Orchestra (Saito Memorial Festival, Matsumoto). 80y.

Nagano. Gentians. 80y.

Kanagawa. Mountains and flowers, Sengokubara Marsh. 80y.

Aichi. Floats, Nagoya Festival. 80y. × 2 se-tenant.

Nara. Pagodas on Mt. Wakakusa (grassburning rite). 50y.

Kumamoto. Ball in air above temple (Men's World Handball Championship). 80y.

Hokkaido. Dahurian rhododendron. 80y.

Shizuoka. Tea picking. 50y.

Shizuoka. Mt. Fuji in summer (cows and daisies) and autumn (dry grass). 80y. × 2 se-tenant.

Kagawa. Visitors at foot of Marugame Castle. 80y.

Hokkaido. Ermine. 50y.

Okayama. Castle. 80y.

Okinawa. Pineapples and mangoes. 50y. × 2 se-tenant.

Nagasaki, Saga and Fukuoka. Nagasaki Kaido Highway route map. 80y. × 4 se-tenant.

Kyoto. University clock tower. 80y.

Niigata. "Bride" by Fukiya Koji. 50y.

Akita. Lanterns on bamboo poles (Kanto Festival). 80y.

Tottori. Ship, flower, dolphin and buildings (Expo Tottori 97). 80y.

Saitama. Waterwheel plant at Hozoji-numa Pond, Hanyu. 50y.

Toyama. Street dancers (Good Wind Festival). 80y. × 2 se-tenant.

Ibaraki. Sailing dinghies on Lake Kasumigaura. 80y.

Tokyo. Tokyo Big Site (exhibition buildings overlooking lake), Telecom Centre (monorail), Rainbow Bridge, Tokyo International Forum (glass building), Edo Tokyo Museum (steps leading to building). 80y. × 5 se-tenant.

Saitama. Collared doves on tree and three walkers (First World Walking Festival). 80y.

Chiba and Kanagawa. Kanagawa-Chiba Bridge and Tunnel. 80y. × 2 se-tenant.

1998.

Hokkaido. Rowanberries in snow and pink moss in spring. 80y. × 2 se-tenant.

Kyoto. Hiyoshi Dam. 80y.

Okinawa. Sanshin (musical instrument), towel and banana plant cloth. 80y.

Gifu. Crowd surrounding float (Okoshi Daiko drum festival). 80y.

Hyogo and Tokushima. Ko–Awaj–Naruto Motorway. Ohnaruto Bridge (with whirlpool), Akashi Kaikyo Bridge (with spring blossom). 80y. × 2 se-tenant.

Nagano. "Jomon's Venus" (figurine from Chino). 80y.

Iwate. Procession of caparisoned horses. 80y.

Tokyo. Towers as hand (Business Show). 80y.

Nagasaki. Mt. Heisei Shinzan. 80y.

Gunma. 80y. Oze Moor in spring and autumn. 80y. × 2 se-tenant.

Yamagata. Two dancers carrying hats (Flower Hat Dance). 50y.

Shizuoka. Women's World Softball Championship. 80y.

Ishikawo. Mt. Hakusan (with woods in foreground). 50y.

Oita. Decorated cart (Gion Festival). 50y.

Nagano. World Puppet Festival. 50y. × 2 se-tenant.

Hiroshima. Views of Seto Inland Sea. Itsukushima Shrine with torii gate; bridge over Ondo Strait. 80y. × 2 se-tenant.

Okinawa. First and last Ryukyu Islands stamps. 80y. × 2 se-tenant.

Kagoshima. Ceramic teabowl and vase (400th anniv of Satsuma-yoki Pottery). 80y. × 2 se-tenant.

Kagawa. Seto Great Road and Rail Bridge. 80y.

Hyogo. Kobe Lights. 80y.

Aomori. Apples. 80y. (as 1989 issue but face value changed).

Wakayama. Three pilgrims on old path to Kumano. 80y. (as 1990 issue).

Tokyo. Tama intercity monorail. 80y.

1999.

Okayama and Hiroshima. Train (Thera Railway). 80y.

Oita. Mt. Kyoshu and R. Yamkunigawa and Blue Tunnel in Spring. 80y. × 2 se-tenant.

Ehime. Bath house, Dogo Spa. 80y.

Hokkaido. Icefloes and Manchurian cranes. 50y. × 2 se-tenant. Ice crystal and snowman. 80y. × 2 se-tenant.

Niigata. Building (Tokamachi Snow Festival). 80y.

Tokyo. White and purple orchids. 80y. × 2 se-tenant.

Fukui. Green and brown dinosaurs. 80y. × 2 se-tenant.

Tochigi. Lake Chuzenji in spring (flowers) and autumn (brown leaves). 80y. × 2 se-tenant.

Gifu. Tree in blossom (Renewed cherry tree). 80y.

Okinawa. Woman and two masks (125th anniv of Universal Postal Union). 80y. × 2 se-tenant.

Nagano. Kiso Observatory, Mt. Ontaki. 80y.

Mie. Hills, coast, paved path and terraces (Old path for Kuimani). 80y. × 4 se-tenant.

Nagano. Taiko Mon Gate, Matsumoto Castle. 80y.

Toyama. Firefly Squid. 80y.

Yamagata. Sweet Cherries. 80y.

Ishikawa. Four Seasons in Kenrokuen Garden. 80y. × 4 se-tenant.

Hiroshima and Ehime. Opening of Shimanami Seaside Highway. 80y. × 10 se-tenant.

Hokkaidou. Plants and flowers. 80y. × 4 se-tenant.

Wakayama. Waterfall and seascape. 80y. × 2 se-tenant.

Okinawa. Ryuku Dancers. 80y.

Miyagi and Fukushima. Banners and flags (summer festivals). 80y. × 2 se-tenant.

Hokkaido. Lavender and wheat fields. 50y. and 80y.

Okayama. Kurashiki District. 80y.

Niigata. Kites over river (Shirane Big Kite Battle). 80y. × 2 se-tenant.

Ishikawa. Carnival procession (Noto Kirko Festival). 80y.

Hokkaido. Foxes and seals. 80y. × 2.

Yamanashi. Lakes around Mt. Fuji. 80y. × 5 se-tenant.

Fukouka. Summer Festival. 80y.

Tokyo. Lotus flower. 80y., and firework display at Sumida River. 80y. × 2 se-tenant.

Kyoto. Flowers and Amano Hashidate (sand bar). 80y.

Niigata. Birds (Japanese crested ibis). 80y. × 2 se-tenant.

Chiba. Lotus flower and building. 80y.

Nagano. Tsumago and Magome Post Stations. 80y. × 2 se-tenant.

Hokkaido. Birds (steller's sea eagle, tufted puffin, blakiston's fish owl and manchurian crane). 50y. × 4 se-tenant.

Okinawa. Fishermen and boat. 80y.

Wakayama. Landscape and statue. 80y. × 2 se-tenant.

Iwate. Autumn bellflowers. 50y.

Shizuoka. View over port (Centenary of Shimizu Port). 80y.

Kagawa. Bridge, Ritsurin Park. 80y.

Kumamoto. Sailing boat. 80y.

Nagasaki. Dejima (artificial island). 80y.

Kanagawa. Minamotono (Yoritomo horseman). 80y.

Aomori. Shirakami Mountains. 80y.

Toyama. Kokiriko dancer and farmhouses. 80y.

Gunma. Archaeological finds (50th anniv of Excavations of Iwajuku Paleolithic Site). 80y.

Hokkaidou. Farmers and foods. 50y. × 4 se-tenant.

Osaka. Rhythmic gymnast (23rd World Rhythmic Sports Gymnastics Championship). 80y.

Fukushima. Chrysanthemum Figure of Nihonmatsu. 80y.

Miyazaki. Old Town of Obi. 80y. × 2 se-tenant.

Aichi. Paintings. 80y. × 2 se-tenant.

Nagano. Monkeys in hot spring. 80y.

Shimane and Yamaguchi. Hagi and Tsuwano Cities. 80y. × 2 se-tenant.

Nara. Birds over Asuka Bay and Tomb of Ishibutai. 80y. × 2 se-tenant.

Okinawa. Stone bridge and teahouse (Shikina-en Garden). 50y. × 2 se-tenant.

Fukui. Crab and Rock Formation. 80y. × 2 se-tenant.

Saga. Yoshinogari (archaeological site). 80y.

Hokkaidou. Christmas elves in sleigh. 80y.

Kouchi. Moonlit night, Katsura Beach and whale's tail flukes. 80y. × 2 se-tenant.

Akita. Snow-covered Samurai Houses, Kakunodate. 80y.

2000.

Tokyo. Whale, mother and child, procession, family and floodlit bridge (New Millennium). 50y. × 5 se-tenant.

Hokkaido. Bridge, canal, clock tower and church. 80y. × 4 se-tenant.

Hyogo. Bee and flowers, fairy and flowers ("Japan Flora 2000" gardening exhibition). 50y. and 80y.

Okayama. Courting manchurian cranes, bridge, pagoda and cranes in flight (300th anniv of Korakuen Garden). 80y. × 4 se-tenant.

Nagano. Cherry Blossom. 80y.

Okinawa. Dragon. 50y.

Nagano. Azumino. 80y.

Akita, Aomori, Fukushima, Iwate, Miyagi, Yamagata. Cherry Blossom. 80y. × 6

Toyama. Tateyama Mountain Range and tulips. 50y. and 80y. se-tenant.

Ehime. Uwajima Castle. 80y.

Saitama. New Urban Centre. 50y. × 2 se-tenant.

Hiroshima, Okayama, Shimane, Tottori, Yamaguchi. Flowers and cornfield, flower and roof ridge, flowers and roof, maple leaves, flowers and sea. 50y. × 5 se-tenant.

Tokyo. Pink flowers, red roses, orange flowers, snow-covered pink flowers, yellow flowers. 50y. × 5 se-tenant.

Kanagawa. Tassels and woman with girl (Shonan Hiratsuku Tanabata Festival). 50y. × 2 se-tenant.

Okinawa. Bankoku shinryokan. 80y.

Osaka. World Performing Arts Festival. 80y.

Akita. Kujuku Islands. 80y.

Hokkaido. Flowering Potato Field. 50y. × 2 se-tenant.

Hokkaido. Pasture. (premium for victims of Mt. Usu eruption). 80y.+20y. × 2 se-tenant.

Tokushima. Awaodori Dance. 80y.

Iwate. Golden Hall, Chusonji Temple. 80y.

Fukuoka. Hakata Doll. 80y.

Toyama. Badminton Player (55th National Athletics Meeting). 50y.

Mie. Parachutists (25th World Championships). 80y. × 2 se-tenant.

Tokyo. Two Children. 80y.

Yamaguchi. Iwakuni Kintaikyo Bridge. 80y.

Oita. Disabled Athletes (International Wheelchair Marathon) 80y.

Aichi. Man with parasol. 80y.

Kyoto. Four Seasons. 80y. × 4 se-tenant.

Kanagawa. Odawara Castle. 50y. × 2 se-tenant.

Saitama. Fireworks and illuminated float (Chichibu Night Festival). 80y. × 2 se-tenant.

Saga. Child and Balloons (International Balloon Festival) 80y.

Tokyo. Tower blocks and view of city (premium for victims of the disaster). 80y.+20y. × 2 se-tenant.

Shizuoka. Blossoms and waterfall. 50y. × 2 se-tenant.

Fukushima. Hata Festival, Kohata. 80y.

Miyazaki. Sekino'o Falls and Kirishima Mountain Range. 80y. × 2 se-tenant.

Gunma. Megane-bashi Bridge and Maruyama Hendensho Transformer Station. 50y. × 2 se-tenant.

Nagano. Chikumagawa River and Kamikochi Highland (centenary of *Shinano-no kuni* (song by Asai Retsu and Kitamura Suehara)) 50y. × 2 se-tenant.

2001.

Hyogo. Giant Panda. 50y. and Millennium celebrations, Kobe. 80y. se-tenant.

Fukuoka. Oe Kowakamai Dancer. 80y.

Ibaraki. Four seasons in Kairakuen Garden. 50y. × 4 se-tenant and miniature sheet.

Hokkaido. Ermine. 80y.

Kochi. Castle and Sunday Market, Kochi. 80y. × 2 se-tenant.

Hyogo. Takarazuka Revue dancer and Violets. 80y. × 2 se-tenant.

Shimane. Matsue Castle and Teahouse. 80y. × 2 se-tenant.

Yamanashi. Grapes and jewellery. 80y.

Osaka. Thunder God playing table tennis, Wind God playing table tennis, Bowler, Kick boxers. 50y. × 4 se-tenant.

Fukushima. Bee (Beautiful Fukushima Future Expo). 80y.

Niigata. Cherry blossoms, Takada Castle. 80y.

Shizuoka. Decorated palace float and kites (Hamamatsu Festival). 80y. × 2 se-tenant.

Tochigi. Ashikaga School buildings. 50y. and Gate. 80y.

Yamanashi. Mt. Mizugakisan, Azuma-Shakunage (National Afforestation Campaign). 50y.

Miyagi. Runners (400th Anniversary of Sendai City). 80y.

Nagano. Zenkoji Temple and Mt. Iizunayama. 80y. × 2 se-tenant.

Yamaguchi. Animal band. 50y. and Wild ducks. 80y. (Japan Expo Yamaguchi 2001) se-tenant.

Hokkaido. Pink flowers and Yellow flowers. 50y. × 2 se-tenant.

Tokyo. Cherry blossoms, hydrangea, salvias, chrysanthemums, camellias. 50y. × 5 se-tenant.

Tottori. Snow crab and coastline (Uradome). 50y. Dunes (Tottori). 50y. Flowers and dolls in basket on river. 50y. Mt. Daisen. 50y. Nageiredo Hall. 80y. Mukibanda Paleolithic Site. 80y. se-tenant.

Ishikawa. Samurai warrior on horseback (Kanazawa Hyakumangoku Matsuri Festival). 80y.

Okinawa. Memorial and flowers. 80y.

Yamanashi. Scenery. Mountains and blossom (Kyoto), Mt. Kitadake and irises(Kyochu), Mt. Yatsugatake and horses (Kyohoku), Mountain, building and water (Gunnnai), Cherry blossoms (Kyonan). 50y. × 5 se-tenant.

Aichi. Cars on Toyota-oohashi Bridge and Toyota stadium. 50y. × 2 se-tenant.

Fukuoka. Fireworks over buildings and sunflowers (Kitakyushu Expo-Festival 2001). 80y.

Osaka. Namdaemun (building), Seoul and Doton-bori (buildings), Osaka. 80y. Bunraku (Japan) and Nong-ak drummers (Korea) (14th General Assembly of World Trade Organization). 80y. se-tenant.

Niigata. Fireworks, Nagaoka. 50y. × 2 se-tenant.

Hokkaido. Poplar trees and Statue of Dr. Clark, Hitsujigaoka. 80y. × 2 se-tenant.

Miyagi. Volleyball players (56th National Athletic Meeting). 50y.

Ehime. Masaoka Shiki (Haiku poet) and Matsuyama Castle. 50y. Locomotive SL "Bocchasn" and Dogo Spa. 50y. se-tenant.

Shiga. Trout and rhododendron flowers (Ninth International Conference on the Conservation and Management of Lakes). 50y.

Gifu. Tanigumi-Odori dancers. 50y. Fruit, train and children. 50y. × 2 se-tenant.

Akita. Igloo, children and dog. 80y.

Kagoshima. Stylized cyclist (World Indoor Cycling Championships). 80y.

Tokyo. Okuma Auditorium, Waseda University. 80y.

Fukui. Narcissi. 50y. Coastline, Echizen. 80y. se-tenant.

Tokyo. Illuminations (Third Tokyo Millenario). 80y.

JAPANESE TAIWAN (FORMOSA)

From 1895 to 1945 Taiwan was part of the Japanese Empire, using the stamps of Japan. During 1945 American naval and air forces disrupted communications between Taiwan and Japan. The following were issued when supplies of Japanese stamps ran short.

1 Numeral and Chrysanthemum

1945. Imperf.

J1	**1**	3s. red	25·00	28·00
J2		5s. green	25·00	23·00
J3		10s. blue	35·00	35·00

JAPANESE OCCUPATION OF CHINA Pt. 17

100 cents = 1 dollar.

I. KWANGTUNG

Japanese troops occupied Canton in 1938 and by 1945 had overrun much of Kwangtung province. Unoverprinted stamps of China were used until the following stamps were issued.

(**1** "Special for Kwantung")

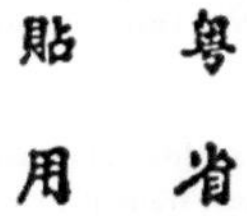

(**2**)

1942. Stamps of China optd with T **1**.

1	–	1c. orange (411)	70	1·25
2	**77**	1c. orange	90	1·50
3	**58**	2c. green	7·50	4·25
4	**72**	3c. red	50	1·25
5	**77**	5c. green	95	1·00
7	**72**	8c. olive	1·25	60
8	**77**	8c. green	1·40	1·25
9	**72**	10c. green	1·25	1·10
11	**77**	10c. emerald	2·00	2·00
12	**72**	16c. brown	2·50	2·75
13		17c. green	2·75	3·25
14	–	20c. blue (519)	2·75	2·50
15	**72**	30c. red	2·50	2·50
16	**77**	30c. red	3·00	3·50
17	**72**	50c. blue	3·75	3·00
18	**77**	50c. blue	3·00	2·25
19	**72**	$1 sepia and brown	6·00	5·00
20		$2 brown and blue	6·00	5·00
21		$5 green and red	7·00	4·50
22		$10 violet and green	12·00	7·50
23		$20 blue and purple	8·00	5·50

1942. Stamps of China optd with T **2**. (a) On 1938 issue.

24	**72**	2c. green	30	1·00
25		3c. red	30	1·00
26		5c. green	35	25
28		8c. green	30	30
29		10c. green	55	75
30		16c. brown	60	1·50
31		25c. blue	1·25	2·25
32		30c. red	1·50	2·25
33		50c. blue	1·25	1·25
35		$1 brown and red	5·00	5·50
37		$2 brown and blue	5·00	6·00
39		$5 green and red	6·50	6·50
40		$10 violet and green	12·00	9·00
42		$20 blue and purple	7·00	10·00

(b) On 1941 issue.

44	**77**	2c. blue	25	1·50
45		5c. green	25	1·25
46		8c. orange	90	2·25
47		8c. green	70	2·25
48		10c. green	75	2·25
49		17c. green	75	3·00
50		25c. purple	1·00	2·75
51		30c. red	1·00	2·25
52		50c. blue	1·25	2·25
53		$1 black and brown	6·00	4·50
54		$2 black and blue	6·00	4·25
55		$5 black and red	9·00	7·00
56		$10 black and green	10·00	8·00
57		$20 black and purple	7·00	6·00

(**3**)

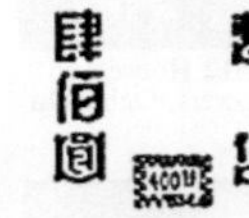

(**4**)

1945. Canton provisionals. Surch as T **3**.

58	**72**	$200 on 10c. green (No. 29)	55·00	45·00
59		$400 on 8c. olive (No. 28)	55·00	45·00

1945. Swatow provisional. No. 508 of China surch with T **4**.

60	$400 on 1c. orange	£375	£300

POSTAGE DUE STAMP

(D 3)

1945. Postage Due stamp of China surch with Type D **3**.

D58	D **62**	$100 on $2 orange	£400	£400

II. MENGKIANG (INNER MONGOLIA)

The autonomous area of Mengkiang ("the Mongolian Borderlands"), consisting of Suiyuan, South Chahar and North Shansi, was established by the Japanese in November, 1937.

For the first issue in 1941 see the note at the beginning of III North China.

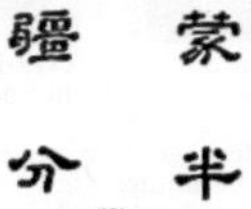

(3)

1942. Stamps of China optd "Mengkiang" and surch half original value at T **3**.

86	–	½c. on 1c. orange (411)	1·00	1·00
93	**58**	1c. on 2c. green	1·00	1·00
69	**72**	1c. on 2c. green	75	75
94	**58**	2c. on 4c. green	10	50
87	**60**	2c. on 4c. lilac	3·25	2·25
72	**72**	4c. on 8c. green	1·50	75
73		5c. on 10c. green	1·50	1·50
99	–	5c. on 10c. purple (515)	75	1·75
95	**72**	8c. on 16c. brown	1·25	40
68	**58**	10c. on 20c. blue	28·00	23·00
100	–	10c. on 20c. red (418)	75	1·75
88	–	10c. on 20c. blue (519)	2·50	2·25
101	–	15c. on 30c. purple (542)	2·25	2·00
75	**72**	15c. on 30c. red	3·00	3·25
102	–	20c. on 40c. orange (524)	3·25	2·25
103	–	25c. on 50c. green (525)	2·75	2·25
77	**72**	25c. on 50c. blue	5·00	5·50
96		50c. on $1 sepia and brown	6·00	5·00
82		$1 on $2 brown and blue	9·00	9·00
98		$5 on $10 violet and green	30·00	30·00
84		$10 on $20 blue and purple	75·00	65·00

4 Dragon Pillar, Peking

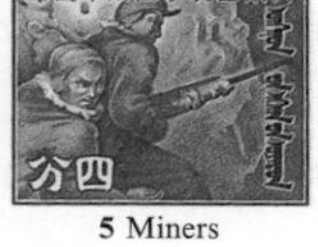

5 Miners

1943. 5th Anniv of Establishment of Mengkiang Post and Telegraph Service.

104	**4**	4c. orange	2·00	2·50
105		8c. blue	2·00	2·50

1943. 2nd Anniv of War in East Asia.

106	**5**	4c. green	2·00	2·75
107		8c. red	2·00	2·75

6 Stylized Horse

7 Prince Yun

8 Blast Furnace

1943. 1st Anniv of Federation of Autonomous Governments of Mongolian Provinces.

108	6	3c. red	1·50	2·75
109	7	8c. blue	1·50	2·75

1944. Productivity Campaign.

110	8	8c. brown	2·00	3·50

1945. Stamps of China optd "Mengkiang" as top characters in T 3.

117	–	1c. orange (411)	50	50
111	58	2c. green	1·25	1·00
112		4c. green	4·50	3·00
113		5c. green	1·75	1·00
118	–	8c. orange (514)	10	35
119	–	10c. purple (515)	10	40
120	–	20c. red (418)	15	40
121	–	30c. red (542)	15	50
122	–	40c. orange (524)	10	50
123	–	50c. green (525)	70	80
114	72	$1 sepia and brown	2·75	2·25
115		$2 brown and blue	7·00	5·50
116		$5 green and red	24·00	17·00

(10)

1945. Stamps of China optd "Mengkiang" (as T 3 of North China) and surch as T 10.

124B	60	10c. on ½c. sepia	50	2·00
126B	–	10c. on 1c. orange (411)	25	2·00
135	58	50c. on 2c. olive	55	2·25
130	72	50c. on 2c. olive	35	2·50
136	58	50c. on 4c. green	2·00	3·75
131	60	50c. on 4c. lilac	85	3·25
137	58	50c. on 5c. green	50	2·50
132B	72	50c. on 5c. olive	50	2·00
138	–	$1 on 8c. orange (514)	15	3·25

III. NORTH CHINA

The Japanese conquered North China in 1937 and formed a puppet Government in Peking.

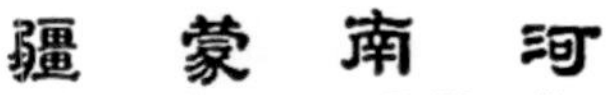
(2 of Meng Kiang "Mengkiang") (B. "Honan")

(D. "Hopeh") (E. "Shansi")

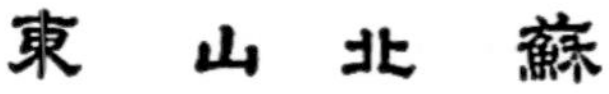
(H. "Shantung") (J. "Supeh")

Type 2 of Meng Kiang and B to J are the six "district" overprints comprising North China (including Mengkiang) and a detailed list of the overprints on the stamps of China is given in the Stanley Gibbons' Catalogue, Part 17 (China).

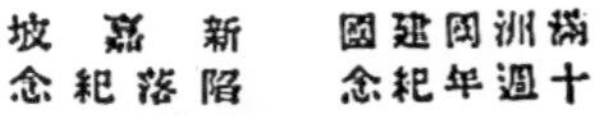
(1) (2)

In 1942 stamps of China overprinted with Types B to J were further overprinted with Type 1 (to commemorate the Fall of Singapore) or with Type 2 (to commemorate the tenth Anniversary of Manchukuo). These stamps are also listed in the Stanley Gibbons' Catalogue Part 17 (China).

(3)

1942. Stamps of China optd "Hwa Pei" (= North China) and surch half original value at T 3.

111	–	½c. on 1c. orange (No. 411)	45	45
128	58	1c. on 2c. olive	75	20
114	–	1c. on 2c. blue (No. 509)	1·50	1·00
88	72	1c. on 2c. olive	50	40
129	58	2c. on 4c. green	10	10
116	60	2c. on 4c. lilac	1·10	1·10
134	–	4c. on 8c. orange (No. 514)	10	10
91	72	4c. on 8c. olive	60	25
120	–	5c. on 10c. pur (No. 515)	2·25	2·25
92	72	5c. on 10c. green	80	25
130		8c. on 16c. olive	75	20
135	–	10c. on 20c. lake (No. 418)	40	10
122	–	10c. on 20c. blue (No. 519)	75	1·10
96	72	15c. on 30c. red	1·50	1·10
136	–	15c. on 30c. purple (No. 542)	45	10
137	–	20c. on 40c. orge (No. 542)	1·00	15
138	–	25c. on 50c. grn (No. 525)	1·25	25
98	72	25c. on 50c. blue	1·10	85
131		50c. on $1 brown and red	3·00	1·25
132		$1 on $2 brown and blue	6·00	5·50
133		$5 on $10 violet and green	20·00	15·00
109		$10 on $20 blue and purple	60·00	40·00

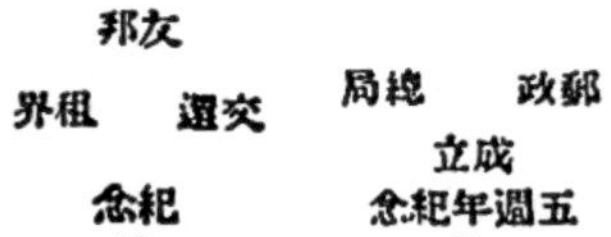
(4) (5)

1943. Return to China of Foreign Concessions. Optd with T 4.

139	58	2c. on 4c. green (No. 129)	2·00	2·00
140	72	4c. on 8c. olive (No. 91)	2·00	2·00
141		8c. on 16c. olive (No. 130)	2·00	2·00

1943. 5th Anniv of Directorate-General of Posts for North China. Optd with T 5.

142	58	2c. on 4c. green (No. 129)	2·00	2·00
143	72	4c. on 8c. olive (No. 91)	2·00	2·00
144		8c. on 16c. olive (No. 130)	2·00	2·00

1943. Stamps of China optd "Hwa Pei" as top characters in T 3.

164	–	1c. orange (No. 411)	20	25
153	58	2c. olive	10	15
154		4c. green	10	10
155		5c. green	10	10
156	72	9c. olive	15	25
165	–	10c. purple (No. 515)	10	15
145	72	10c. green	3·00	1·50
157		16c. olive	15	15
158		18c. olive	20	25
166	–	20c. lake (No. 418)	15	15
167	–	30c. red (as No. 542)	10	15
168	–	40c. orange (No. 524)	15	15
169	–	50c. green (No. 525)	20	15
159	72	$1 brown and red	5·00	1·00
160		$2 brown and blue	2·75	75
161		$5 green and red	4·00	2·25
162		$10 violet and green	7·00	5·50
163		$20 blue and purple	8·00	6·50

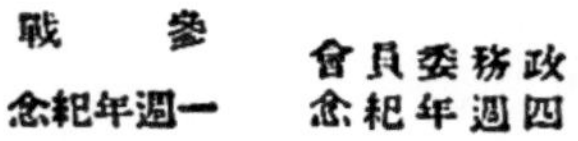
(6) (7)

1944. 1st Anniv of Declaration of War on Allies by Japanese-controlled Nanking Govt. Optd with T 6.

170	58	4c. green (No. 154)	3·00	3·00
171	72	10c. green (No. 149)	3·00	3·00

1944. 4th Anniv of North China Political Council. Optd with T 7.

172	72	9c. olive (No. 156)	2·00	2·00
173		18c. olive (No. 158)	2·00	2·25
174	–	50c. green (No. 169)	2·00	2·25
175	72	$1 brown and red (No. 159)	4·00	3·00

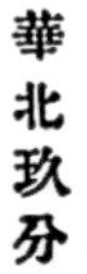
(8)

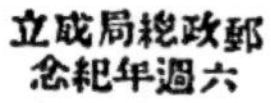
(9)

1944. Stamps of Japanese Occupation of Shanghai and Nanking optd "Hwa Pei" and surch as T 8.

176	5	9c. on 50c. orange	2·00	2·25
177		18c. on $1 green	2·25	2·25
178	6	36c. on $2 blue	3·00	2·75
179		90c. on $5 red	3·25	3·00

1944. 6th Anniv of Directorate-General of Posts for North China. Optd with T 9.

180	72	9c. olive (No. 156)	2·00	2·25
181		18c. olive (No. 158)	2·00	2·25
182	–	50c. green (No. 169)	2·50	2·25
183	72	$1 brown and red (No. 159)	5·00	3·25

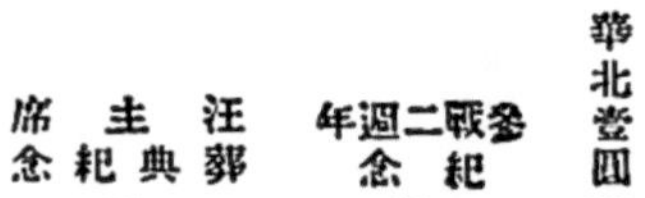
(10) (11) (12)

1944. Death of Wang Ching-wei. Optd with T 10.

184	–	20c. lake (No. 166)	2·25	2·25
185	–	50c. green (No. 169)	2·25	2·25
186	72	$1 brown and red (No. 159)	3·00	2·50
187		$2 brown and blue (No. 160)	3·00	2·75

1945. 2nd Anniv of Declaration of War on Allies by Nanking Govt. Optd with T 11.

188	–	20c. lake (No. 166)	2·25	2·25
189	–	50c. green (No. 169)	2·25	2·25
190	72	$1 brown and red (No. 159)	3·00	2·50
191		$2 brown and blue (No. 160)	3·00	2·75

1945. Stamps of Japanese Occupation of Shanghai and Nanking surch as T 12.

192	7	50c. on $3 orange	4·50	6·25
193		$1 on $6 blue	4·50	6·25

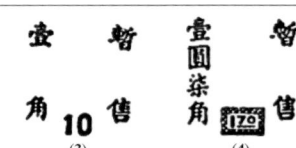

13 Dragon Pillar

14 Long Bridge

15 Imperial City Tower

16 Marble Boat, Summer Palace

17

1945. 5th Anniv of Establishment of North China Political Council. Views of Peking.

194	13	$1 yellow	1·25	1·50
195	14	$2 blue	1·50	1·50
196	15	$5 red	1·50	1·25
197	16	$10 green	2·00	1·75

1945. Optd "Hwa Pei" as top characters in T 3.

198	17	$1 brown	1·25	25
199		$2 blue	1·40	15
200		$5 red	1·50	45
201		$10 green	1·75	1·00
202		$20 purple	3·25	1·10
203		$50 brown	15·00	8·50

18 Wutai Mountain, Shansi

19 Kaifeng Iron Pagoda, Honan

20 International Bridge, Tientsin

21 Taishan Mountain, Shantung

22 G.P.O., Peking

1945. 7th Anniv of Directorate-General of Posts for North China.

204	18	$5 green	60	1·25
205	19	$10 brown	65	1·10
206	20	$20 purple	75	1·10
207	21	$30 grey	1·00	1·00
208	22	$50 red	1·10	1·00

IV. NANKING AND SHANGHAI

The Japanese captured Shanghai and Nanking in 1937 and Hankow in 1938. During the same year Nanking was made the seat of Japanese-controlled administration for the Yangtse Basin. The stamps listed below were used in parts of Anhwei, Southern Kiangsu, Chekiang, Hupeh, Kiangsi, Hunan and Fukien.

N.B. With the exception of Nos. 114 to 119 the following are all surcharged on stamps of China.

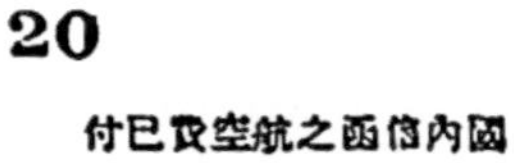
(1)

1941. Air. Surch as T 1.

1	61	10s. on 50c. brown	25	2·50
2		18s. on 90c. olive	60	3·50
4		20s. on $1 green	1·00	4·00
5		25s. on 90c. olive	25	2·75
6		35s. on $2 brown	25	2·50
7		60s. on 35s. on $2 brn (No. 6)	25	3·50

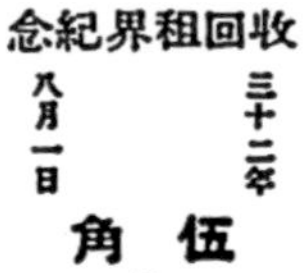
(2)

1943. Return to China of Shanghai Concessions. Surch as T 2.

8	72	25c. on 5c. green	2·00	1·75
9	77	50c. on 8c. orange	2·00	1·75
10	72	$1 on 16c. olive	2·00	1·75
11	77	$2 on 50c. blue	2·00	1·75

1943. As No. 422 but colour changed. Issued at Shanghai.

12	72	15c. brown	15·00	16·00

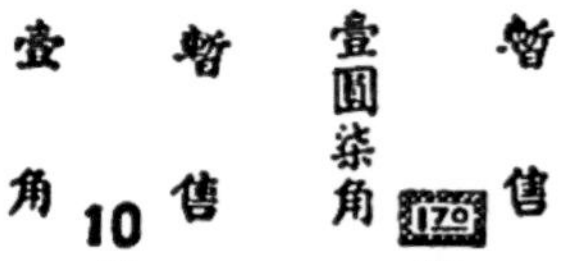
(3) (4)

1943. Stamps of China and No. 12 above surch as T 3 (cent values) or T 4 (dollar values).

(a) On T 58.

13	58	$6 on 5c. green	1·50	2·50
14		$20 on 15c. red	1·50	1·75
15		$500 on 15c. green	1·50	1·75
17		$1000 on 20c. blue	2·75	3·25
18		$1000 on 25c. blue	3·00	3·25

(b) On Martyrs issue (as T 60).

88	60	$7.50 on ½c. sepia	35	4·50
89	–	$15 on 1c. orange	25	1·50
91	–	$30 on 2c. blue	45	1·50
93	–	$200 on 1c. orange	40	1·00
94	–	$200 on 8c. orange	45	1·25

(c) On T 72.

19	72	25c. on 5c. green	50	2·25
20		30c. on 2c. green	1·00	2·50
21		50c. on 3c. red	10	45
22		50c. on 5c. green	20	40
23		50c. on 8c. green	1·00	1·75
24		$1 on 8c. green	10	15
26		$1 on 15c. brown	70	1·00
27		$1.30 on 16c. brown	10	1·00
28		$1.50 on 3c. red	10	50
54		$1.70 on 30c. red	1·40	2·75
55		$2 on 5c. green	15	45
30		$2 on 10c. green	10	40
56		$2 on $1 sepia and brown	4·00	3·50
59		$3 on 8c. green	10	15
31		$3 on 15c. brown	25	50
32		$4 on 16c. brown	30	50
33		$5 on 15c. brown	75	60
61		$6 on 5c. green	50	75
62		$6 on 8c. green	15	35
38		$6 on 10c. green	50	70
39		$10 on 10c. green	10	30
40		$10 on 16c. brown	10	20
41		$20 on 3c. red	10	40
42		$20 on 15c. red	2·00	4·00
43		$20 on 15c. brown	35	1·00
64		$20 on $2 brown and blue	1·75	2·25
65		$50 on 30c. red	75	1·90
66		$50 on 50c. blue	75	2·00
67		$50 on $5 green and red	1·25	2·00
68		$50 on $20 blue and purple	2·25	3·00
45		$100 on 3c. red	1·00	1·00
83		$100 on $10 violet and green	45	75
84		$200 on $20 blue and purple	45	75
46		$500 on 8c. green	1·75	2·25
47		$500 on 10c. green	1·50	2·25
48		$500 on 15c. red	4·00	3·50
49		$500 on 15c. brown	3·50	3·25
50		$500 on 16c. brown	2·50	3·25
51		$1000 on 25c. blue	3·00	4·25
86		$1000 on 30c. red	2·00	3·50
75		$1000 on 50c. blue	2·50	3·50
76		$1000 on $2 brown and blue	2·25	4·75
77		$2000 on $5 green and red	2·50	3·75
87a		$5000 on $10 violet & green	15·00	18·00

(d) On T 77.

95	77	5c. on ½c. sepia	10	1·50
96		10c. on 1c. orange	10	1·25
97		20c. on 1c. orange	15	1·00
98		40c. on 5c. green	10	1·10
99		$5 on 5c. green	15	35
100		$10 on 10c. green	35	70
101		$50 on ½c. sepia	25	50
102		$50 on 1c. orange	35	50
103		$50 on 17c. olive	75	1·00
104		$200 on 5c. green	50	1·00
105		$200 on 8c. green	60	1·10
106		$200 on 8c. orange	1·25	2·00
107		$500 on $5 black and red	1·75	3·00
108		$1000 on 1c. orange	1·50	2·75
109		$1000 on 25c. purple	1·75	2·50
110		$1000 on 30c. red	2·00	2·75
111		$1000 on $2 black and blue	2·25	3·00
112		$1000 on $10 black & green	2·75	2·75
113		$2000 on $5 black and red	3·25	3·00

5 Wheat and Cotton Flower

6 Purple Mountain, Nanking

1944. 4th Anniv of Establishment of Chinese Puppet Government at Nanking.

114	5	50c. orange	10	50
115		$1 green	10	50
116	6	$2 blue	10	50
117		$5 red	10	50

7 Map of Shanghai and Foreign Concessions

1944. 1st Anniv of Return to China of Shanghai Foreign Concessions.
118 **7** $3 orange . . . . 35 1·50
119 $6 blue . . . . 35 1·50

1945. 5th Anniv of Establishment of Chinese Puppet Government at Nanking. Surch as T **4**.
124 **5** $15 on 50c. orange . . . . 10 1·50
125 $30 on $1 green . . . . . 10 1·50
126 **6** $60 on $2 blue . . . . . 10 1·50
127 $200 on $5 red . . . . . . 10 1·25

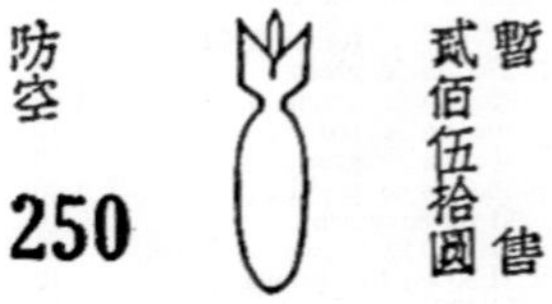

(9)

1945. Air Raid Precautions Propaganda. Air stamps surch as T **9**.
128 **61** $150 on 15c. green . . . . 75 1·25
129 $250 on 25c. orange . . . 75 1·25
130 $600 on 60c. blue . . . . 75 1·25
131 $1000 on $1 green . . . . 75 1·25

POSTAGE DUE STAMPS

(D 8)

1945. Postage Due stamps surch as Type D **8**.
D120 D **62** $1 on 2c. orange . . . 35 2·75
D121 $2 on 5c. orange . . . 35 2·50
D122 $5 on 10c. orange . . 35 2·50
D123 $10 on 20c. orange . . 35 2·25

JAPANESE OCCUPATION OF NETHERLANDS INDIES Pt. 4

The Japanese occupied the Netherlands Indies from March 1942 to 1945.

100 sen (cents) = 1 rupee (gulden).

I. JAVA

1 Eastern Asia

1943. 1st Anniv of Japanese Occupation of Java.
1 **1** 2s. brown . . . . 4·00 3·25
2 – 3½s. red . . . . 4·00 3·25
3 – 5s. green . . . . 5·50 3·25
4 – 10s. blue . . . . 15·00 4·00
DESIGNS: 3½s. Farmer ploughing ricefield; 5s. Mt. Soemer; 10s. Bantam Bay.

2 Native soldier

3 Wayang puppet

5 Bird of Vishnu and Mt. Soemer

1943. Savings Campaign.
5 **2** 3½c. red . . . . 13·00 6·00
6 10c. blue . . . . 15·00 2·25

1943. Designs with rectangular panel of characters as at foot of T **3** and **5**.
7 – 3½c. red . . . . 2·75 1·75
8 **3** 5c. green . . . . 2·75 1·75
9 – 10c. blue . . . . 3·00 1·75
10 – 20c. olive . . . . 4·00 3·00
11 – 40c. purple . . . . 7·25 4·00
12 **5** 60c. orange . . . . 19·00 4·75
13 – 80c. brown . . . . 22·00 8·00
14 – 1r. violet . . . . 50·00 5·50
DESIGNS—As Type **3**: 3½c. Native head; 10c. Boroboudur Temple; 20c. Map of Java; 40c. Seated dancer and Temple. As Type **5**: 80c. Ploughing with oxen; 1r. Terraced ricefields.

II. SUMATRA

6 Lake Toba

1943. Designs with rectangular panel characters as at foot of T **6**.
15 – 1c. olive . . . . 1·90 1·50
16 – 2c. green . . . . 1·90 1·50
17 – 3c. blue . . . . 1·90 1·50
18 – 3½c. red . . . . 3·50 1·50
19 – 4c. blue . . . . 2·50 1·50
20 – 5c. orange . . . . 1·90 1·10
21 – 10c. blue . . . . 5·00 1·10
22 – 20c. brown . . . . 2·50 1·10
23 **6** 30c. purple . . . . 2·75 1·90
24 40c. brown . . . . 3·25 2·10
25 – 50c. bistre . . . . 7·75 3·25
26 – 1r. violet . . . . 40·00 5·25
DESIGNS: 1c. to 3c. Batak house; 3½c. to 5c. Minangkabau house; 10c., 20c. Ploughing with oxen; 50c., 1r. Carabao Canyon (20 × 28 mm).

(7)

1944. Various stamps optd with T **7**. (a) On Netherlands Indies stamps of 1933.
37A **46** 1c. violet . . . . 60 1·60
38A 2c. purple . . . . 60 1·60
39A 2½c. bistre . . . . 60 1·60
40A 3c. green . . . . 27·00 38·00
27A 3½c. grey . . . . 80 1·90
50B **67** 10c. red . . . . 1·00 1·60
42B **47** 15c. blue . . . . 1·75 5·25
43B 20c. purple . . . . . . 90 1·60
44B 25c. green . . . . 1·75 2·75
45A 30c. blue . . . . 20·00 27·00
46B 35c. violet . . . . . . 1·75 2·75
47B 40c. green . . . . . . 2·75 2·75
34A 42½c. yellow . . . . . 45·00 50·00
35A 50c. blue . . . . 20·00 27·00
48A 2g. green £400 £550
36A 2g.50 purple £250 £325
49B 5g. bistre . . . . 18·00 27·00

(b) On Nos. 429/44 of Netherlands Indies.
28A – 10c. red . . . . 10·00 13·50
52B – 15c. blue . . . . 1·90 2·75
53B – 17½c. orange . . . . . 1·75 2·75
43A – 20c. mauve . . . . . . 15·00 27·00
44A – 25c. green . . . . . . 3·75 6·50
56B – 30c. brown . . . . . . 1·25 2·75
57A – 35c. purple . . . . . . 18·00 9·00
58B – 40c. green . . . . . . 1·90 4·00
59B – 50c. red . . . . 2·75 3·25
60B – 60c. blue . . . . 2·50 3·25
61B – 80c. red . . . . 3·25 4·25
62B – 1g. violet . . . . 4·00 5·50
63B – 2g. green . . . . 3·50 5·50
64A – 5g. brown £170 £225
65A – 10g. green . . . . . . 35·00 55·00
66A **68** 25g. orange £325 £450

(c) On Nos. 463/6 of Netherlands Indies.
66 – 3c. green . . . . 80 2·00
67 **71** 4c. green . . . . 80 2·00
68 – 5c. blue . . . . 80 2·00
69 – 7½c. violet . . . . . . 80 2·00

(d) On Nos. 506 and 509 of Netherlands.
70 **94** 5c. green . . . . 9·75 12·25
71 12½c. blue . . . . 4·75 10·50

III. JAPANESE NAVAL CONTROL AREA

(9)

1942. Various stamps optd with T **9**. (a) On Netherlands Indies stamps of 1933.
89 **46** 1c. violet . . . . 4·00 16·00
90 2c. purple . . . . 90 3·50
91 2½c. bistre . . . . 75 3·50
92 3c. green . . . . 70 3·50
83 4c. green . . . . 25·00 40·00
84 5c. blue . . . . 10·00 15·00
95 **47** 10c. red . . . . 50·00 65·00
96 15c. blue . . . . 9·00 14·00
97 20c. purple . . . . . . 95 3·50
98 25c. green . . . . 4·25 8·00
86 30c. blue . . . . 40·00 40·00
100 35c. violet . . . . . . 95 3·50
101 40c. green . . . . . . 95 3·50
88 50c. blue . . . . 55·00 75·00
102 80c. red £200 £300
103 1g. violet . . . .
104 2g. green . . . .
105 5g. bistre . . . .

(b) On Nos. 270 and 360 of Netherlands Indies.
107 – 5c. blue . . . . 1·00 3·25
106 **48** 30c. blue £225 £325

(c) On Nos. 429/44 of Netherlands Indies.
108 – 10c. red . . . . 3·00 4·00
110 – 15c. blue . . . . 3·75 15·00
111 – 17½c. orange . . . . . . 1·10 4·00
112 – 20c. mauve . . . . . . 22·00 32·00
113 – 25c. green . . . . . . 27·00 42·00
114 – 30c. brown . . . . . . 4·00 10·00
115 – 35c. purple . . . . . . 45·00 55·00
116 – 40c. green . . . . . . 18·00 26·00
117 – 50c. red . . . . 9·50 11·00
118 – 60c. blue . . . . 4·50 8·50
119 – 80c. red . . . . 8·00 14·00
120 – 1g. violet . . . . 6·00 11·00
121 – 2g. green . . . . 40·00 65·00
122 – 5g. brown . . . .
123 **68** 25g. orange . . . .

(d) On Nos. 462/6 of Netherlands Indies.
124 – 2½c. purple . . . . . . 4·50 7·50
125 – 3c. green . . . . 2·00 3·75
126 **71** 4c. green . . . . 2·75 8·50
127 – 5c. blue . . . . 6·00 14·00
128 – 7½c. violet . . . . . . 90 4·00

(e) On Nos. 506 and 509 of Netherlands.
129 **94** 5c. green . . . .
130 12½c. blue . . . .

1943. Air. Nos. 89 and 91 surch.
148 **46** "f. 2" on 1c. violet . . . 12·50 20·00
151 "f. 8.50" on 2½c. bistre . . 12·00 18·00

10 Japanese Flag and Palms

11 Mt. Fuji, Flag and Bird

1943.
152 **10** 2c. brown . . . . 80 16·00
153 3c. green 80 16
154 3½c. orange . . . . . . 1·40 15·00
155 5c. blue . . . . 80 12·00
156 10c. red . . . . 80 12·00
157 15c. blue . . . . 90 12·00
158 20c. violet . . . . . . 90 12·00
159 **11** 25c. orange . . . . . . 3·00 14·00
160 30c. blue . . . . 3·00 15·00
161 50c. green . . . . 6·00 23·00
162 1g. purple . . . . 27·00 30·00

POSTAGE DUE STAMPS

1942. Netherlands Indies Postage Due stamps of 1913 and 1937 optd with T **9**.
D142 1c. orange . . . . 6·75 13·50
D132 2½c. orange . . . . . . 1·50 3·50
D133 3½c. orange . . . . . . 3·25 6·75
D134 5c. orange . . . . 1·75 3·50
D135 7½c. orange . . . . . . 1·75 3·50
D136 10c. orange . . . . . . 1·25 3·50
D144 15c. orange . . . . . . 1·75 3·50
D137 20c. orange . . . . . . 1·75 3·50
D138 20c. on 37½c. orange . . . 50·00 80·00
D139 25c. orange . . . . . . 1·50 3·50
D140 30c. orange . . . . . . 3·75 8·25
D146 40c. orange . . . . . . 2·00 4·00
D147 1g. blue . . . . 5·75 10·00

JAPANESE OCCUPATION OF PHILIPPINES Pt. 22

100 centavos or sentimos = 1 peso.

1942. Stamps of Philippines optd with bars or surch also.
J1 **104** 2c. green 10 10
J4a – 5c. on 6c. brn (No. 526) 10 10
J2 – 12c. black (No. 529) . . 10 15
J3 – 16c. blue (No. 530) . . 3·50 2·50
J5 – 16c. on 30c. red (No. 505) 20 20
J6 – 50c. on 1p. black and orange (No. 534) . . . 50 55
J7 – 1p. on 4p. black and blue (No. 508) . . . . . 75·00 85·00

1942. No. 460 of Philippines surch **CONGRATULATIONS FALL OF BATAAN AND CORREGIDOR 1942 2**.
J8 2c. on 4c. green . . . . . . 4·00 4·00

J 4 Agricultural Produce

1942. Red Cross Fund.
J 9 **J 4** 2c.+1c. violet 15 15
J10 5c.+1c. green 15 15
J11 16c.+2c. orange . . . . 17·00 16·00

1942. 1st Anniv of "Greater East Asia War". No. 460 of Philippines surch with native characters, **12-8-1942** and **5**.
J12 5c. on 4c. green 40 35

1943. 1st Anniv of Philippine Executive Commission. Nos. 566 and 569 of Philippines surch with native characters, **1-23-43** and value.
J13 **105** 2c. on 8c. red 30 30
J14 5c. on 1p. sepia 45 45

J 7 Nipa Hut

J 9 Mt. Mayon and Mt. Fuji

1943.
J15 **J 7** 1c. orange 10 10
J16 – 2c. green 10 10
J17 **J 7** 4c. green 10 10
J18 **J 9** 5c. brown 10 10
J19 – 6c. red 10 10
J20 **J 9** 10c. blue 10 10
J21 – 12c. blue 80 80
J22 – 16c. brown 10 10
J23 **J 7** 20c. purple 95 95
J24 **J 9** 21c. violet 30 30
J25 – 25c. brown 10 10
J26 **J 9** 1p. red 55 55
J27 – 2p. purple . . . . . . 3·75 3·75
J28 – 5p. olive . . . . 6·50 6·00
DESIGNS—VERT: 2, 6, 25c. Rice planter; 12, 16c., 2, 5p. Morro vinta (sailing canoe).

J 11 Map of Manila Bay

1943. 1st Anniv of Fall of Bataan and Corregidor.
J29 **J 11** 2c. red 20 20
J30 5c. green 20 20

1943. 350th Anniv of Printing in the Philippines. No. 531 of Philippines surch **Limbagan 1593–1943** and value.
J31 12c. on 20c. bistre 25 25

J 13 Filipino Girl

1943. Japanese Declaration of the "Independence of the Philippines". Imperf or perf.
J32 **J 13** 5c. blue 15 15
J33 12c. orange 15 15
J34 17c. red 15 15

1943. Luzon Flood Relief. Surch **BAHA 1943** + and premium.
J36 – 12c.+21c. blue (No. J21) 15 15
J37 **J 7** 20c.+36c. purple 10 10
J38 **J 9** 21c.+40c. violet 10 10

J 17 Rev. Jose Burgos

J 24 Jose P. Laurel

1944. National Heroes. Imperf or perf.
J39 – 5c. blue (Rizal) 20 20
J40 **J 17** 12c. red 10 10
J41 – 17c. orange (Mabini) . . 15 15

1944. 2nd Anniv of Fall of Bataan and Corregidor. Nos. 567/8 of Philippines surch **REPUBLIKA NG PILIPINAS 5-7-44** and value.
J43 **105** 5c. on 20c. blue 45 45
J44 12c. on 60c. green 95 95

1945. 1st Anniv of Republican Government. Imperf.
J45 **J 24** 5s. brown 10 10
J46 7s. green 10 10
J47 20s. blue 10 10

POSTAGE DUE STAMP

1942. Postage Due stamp of Philippines surch **3 CVOS. 3** and bar.
JD9 D **51** 3c. on 4c. red . . . . . 23·00 13·00

OFFICIAL STAMPS

1943. Stamps of Philippines optd variously with bars, **(K.P.)** and Japanese characters or surch also.

JO29	104	2c. green (No. 563)	10	10
JO30	–	5c. on 6c. brown (No. 526)	15	15
JO32	–	16c. on 30c. red (No. 505)	40	40

1944. No. 526 of Philippines surch **5 REPUBLIKA NG PILIPINAS (K.P.)** and four bars.

JO45	5c. on 6c. brown	10	10

1944. Official stamp of Philippines (No. 531 optd **O.B.**), further optd **Pilipinas REPUBLIKA K.P.** and bars.

JO46	20c. bistre	30	30

1944. Air stamp of Philippines optd **REPUBLIKA NG PILIPINAS (K.P.)** and two bars.

JO47	105	1p. sepia	55	60

JAPANESE POST OFFICES IN CHINA Pt. 17

Post Offices at Shanghai and other Treaty Ports operated between 1876 and 1922.

10 rin = 1 sen; 100 sen = 1 yen.

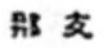

(1)

1900. Stamps of Japan, 1899, optd with T **1**.

1	28	5r. grey	4·50	5·00
2		½s. grey	3·25	1·75
3		1s. brown	3·50	1·25
4		1½s. blue	10·00	4·00
5		1½s. violet	5·50	1·50
6		2s. green	6·00	1·50
7		3s. purple	7·00	1·00
8		3s. red	4·50	1·00
9		4s. red	7·00	2·25
10		5s. yellow	16·00	2·25
11	29	6s. red	20·00	16·00
12		8s. green	13·00	15·00
13		10s. blue	11·00	1·00
14		15s. purple	20·00	2·00
15		20s. orange	20·00	1·25
16	30	25s. green	40·00	10·00
17		50s. brown	45·00	2·00
18	31	1y. red	75·00	3·00
19	32	5y. green	£475	75·00
20		10y. violet	£750	£130

1900. Imperial Wedding issue of Japan optd with T **1**.

21	33	3s. red	50·00	35·00

1913. Stamps of Japan, 1913, optd with T **1**.

33	36	½s. brown	3·00	2·00
34		1s. orange	3·00	2·00
35		1½s. blue	3·25	2·00
36		2s. green	4·25	2·00
37		3s. red	3·00	1·00
38	37	4s. red	12·00	10·00
39		5s. violet	16·00	3·00
40		6s. brown	30·00	30·00
41		8s. grey	40·00	40·00
42		10s. blue	15·00	2·00
43		20s. red	35·00	6·00
44		25s. olive	45·00	8·00
45	38	30s. brown	75·00	50·00
46		50s. brown	£100	50·00
47		1y. green and brown	£140	10·00
48		5y. green	£1500	£600
49		10y. violet	£2500	£1500

JAPANESE POST OFFICES IN KOREA Pt. 18

10 rin = 1 sen; 100 sen = 1 yen.

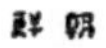

(1)

1900. Stamps of Japan, 1899, optd with T 1.

1	28	5r. grey	12·00	10·00
2		1s. brown	18·00	6·50
3a		1½s. blue	£225	£140
4		2s. green	24·00	16·00
5		3s. purple	16·00	6·00
6		4s. red	70·00	30·00
7		5s. yellow	60·00	30·00
8	29	8s. green	£225	£160
9		10s. blue	30·00	3·00
10		15s. purple	75·00	6·00
11		20s. orange	75·00	5·00
12	30	25s. green	£200	50·00
13		50s. brown	£150	18·00
14	31	1y. red	£400	14·00

1900. Wedding of Prince Imperial. No. 152 of Japan optd with T **1**.

15	33	3s. red	90·00	22·00

JASDAN Pt. 1

A state of India. Now uses Indian Stamps.

12 pies = 1 anna; 16 annas = 1 rupee.

1 Sun

1942.

4	1	1a. green	16·00	£130

JERSEY Pt. 1

Island in the English Channel off N.W. coast of France. Occupied by German forces from June 1940 to May 1945 with separate stamp issues.

The general issue of 1948 for Channel Islands and the regional issues of 1958 are listed at end of GREAT BRITAIN.

Jersey had its own postal administration from 1969.

1941. 12 pence = 1 shilling;
20 shillings = 1 pound.
1971. 100 (new) pence = 1 pound sterling.

(a) War Occupation Issues.

1

2 Old Jersey Farm

1941.

1	1	½d. green	4·00	3·25
2		1d. red	4·50	2·50

1943.

3	2	½d. green	7·50	5·50
4	–	1d. red	2·00	75
5	–	1½d. brown	3·50	3·25
6	–	2d. yellow	4·75	3·25
7a	–	2½d. blue	1·00	1·10
8	–	3d. violet	1·50	3·00

DESIGNS: 1d. Portelet Bay; 1½d. Corbiere Lighthouse; 2d. Elizabeth Castle; 2½d. Mont Orgueil Castle; 3d. Gathering vraic (seaweed).

(b) Independent Postal Administration.

10 Elizabeth Castle

1969. Multicoloured.

15		½d. Type **10**	10	60
16		1d. La Hougue Bie (prehistoric tomb)	10	10
17		2d. Portelet Bay	10	10
18		3d. La Corbiere Lighthouse	10	10
19		4d. Mont Orgueil Castle by night	10	10
20		5d. Arms and Royal Mace	10	10
21		6d. Jersey cow	10	10
22		9d. Chart of the English Channel	10	20
23		1s. Mont Orgueil Castle by day	25	25
24		1s.6d. Chart of the English Channel	80	75
25		1s.9d. Queen Elizabeth II (after Cecil Beaton) (vert)	80	75
26		2s.6d. Jersey Airport	1·25	1·00
27		5s. Legislative Chamber	4·75	3·50
28		10s. The Royal Court	12·00	9·00
29		£1 Queen Elizabeth II (after Cecil Beaton) (vert)	1·75	1·50

24 First Day Cover

1969. Inauguration of Post Office.

30	24	4d. multicoloured	10	10
31		5d. multicoloured	20	10
32		1s.6d. multicoloured	50	75
33		1s.9d. multicoloured	80	1·00

25 Lord Coutanche, former Bailiff of Jersey

1970. 25th Anniv of Liberation. Multicoloured.

34		4d. Type **25**	20	20
35		5d. Sir Winston Churchill	20	20
36		1s.6d. "Liberation" (Edmund Blampied) (horiz)	90	1·00
37		1s.9d. S.S. "Vega" (horiz)	90	1·00

29 "A Tribute to Enid Blyton"

1970. "Battle of Flowers" Parade. Multicoloured.

38		4d. Type **29**	20	10
39		5d. "Rags to Riches" (Cinderella and pumpkin)	20	20
40		1s.6d. "Gourmet's Delight" (lobster and cornucopia)	2·75	2·25
41		1s.9d. "We're the Greatest" (ostriches)	2·75	2·25

33 Jersey Airport

1970. Decimal Currency. Nos. 15, etc, but with new colours, new design (6p.) and decimal values, as T **33**.

42		½p. multicoloured (as No. 15)	10	10
43		1p. multicoloured (as No. 18)	10	10
44		1½p. multicoloured (as No. 21)	10	10
45		2p. multicoloured (as No. 19)	10	10
46		2½p. multicoloured (as No. 20)	10	10
47		3p. multicoloured (as No. 16)	10	10
48		3½p. multicoloured (as No. 17)	10	10
49		4p. multicoloured (as No. 22)	10	10
49a		4½p. multicoloured (as No. 20)	20	20
50		5p. multicoloured (as No. 23)	10	10
50a		5½p. multicoloured (as No. 21)	40	30
51		6p. multicoloured (Martello Tower, Archirondel, 23 × 22 mm)	20	10
52		7½p. multicoloured (as No. 24)	20	15
52a		8p. multicoloured (as No. 19)	15	15
53		9p. multicoloured (as No. 25)	25	20
54		10p. multicoloured (as No. 26)	40	30
55		20p. multicoloured (as No. 27)	90	80
56		50p. multicoloured (as No. 28)	1·50	1·25

34 White Eared-pheasant ("White-eared Pheasant")

1971. Wildlife Preservation Trust (1st series). Multicoloured.

57		2p. Type **34**	20	10
58		2½p. Thick-billed parrot (vert)	20	15
59		7½p. Western black-and-white colobus monkey (vert)	2·50	1·50
60		9p. Ring-tailed lemur	3·00	1·50

See also Nos. 73/6, 217/21, 324/9, 447/51 and 824/9.

35 Poppy Emblem and Field

1971. 50th Anniv of Royal British Legion. Mult.

61		2p. Royal British Legion Badge	20	10
62		2½p. Type **35**	20	10
63		7½p. Jack Counter and Victoria Cross	1·00	1·10
64		9p. Crossed Tricolour and Union Jack	1·00	1·10

36 "Tante Elizabeth" (E. Blampied)

37 Jersey Fern

1971. Paintings (1st series). Multicoloured.

65		2p. Type **36**	15	10
66		2½p. "English Fleet in the Channel" (P. Monamy) (horiz)	20	10
67		7½p. "The Boyhood of Raleigh" (Millais) (horiz)	1·25	1·40
68		9p. "The Blind Beggar" (W. W. Ouless)	1·40	1·50

See also Nos. 115/118.

1972. Wild Flowers of Jersey. Multicoloured.

69		3p. Type **37**	20	10
70		5p. Jersey thrift	30	20
71		7½p. Jersey orchid	1·25	1·40
72		9p. Jersey viper's bugloss	1·25	1·40

1972. Wildlife Preservation Trust (2nd series). As T **34**. Multicoloured.

73		2½p. Cheetah	30	10
74		3p. Rothschild's mynah (vert)	25	20
75		7½p. Spectacled bear	50	70
76		9p. Tuatara	80	90

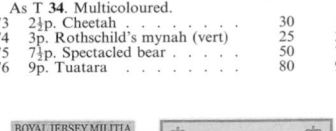

38 Artillery Shako

39 Princess Anne

1972. Royal Jersey Militia. Multicoloured.

77		2½p. Type **38**	10	10
78		3p. Shako (2nd North Regt.)	10	10
79		7½p. Shako (5th South-West Regt.)	30	20
80		9p. Helmet (3rd Jersey Light Infantry)	50	60

1972. Royal Silver Wedding. Multicoloured.

81		2½p. Type **39**	10	10
82		3p. Queen Elizabeth and Prince Philip (horiz)	10	10
83		7½p. Prince Charles	35	35
84		20p. The Royal Family (horiz)	35	35

40 Armorican Bronze Coins

1973. Centenary of La Societe Jersiaise. Mult.

85		2½p. Silver cups	10	10
86		3p. Gold torque (vert)	10	10
87		7½p. Royal Seal of Charles II (vert)	25	20
88		9p. Type **40**	30	30

41 Balloon "L'Armee de la Loire" and Letter, Paris, 1870

1973. Jersey Aviation History. Multicoloured.

89		3p. Type **41**	10	10
90		5p. Astra seaplane, 1912	10	10
91		7½p. Supermarine Sea Eagle	35	35
92		9p. De Havilland Dragon Express "Giffard Bay"	45	45

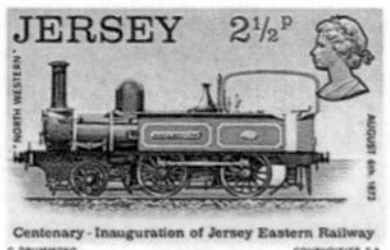

42 "North Western", 1870

1973. Centenary of Jersey Eastern Railway. Early Locomotives. Multicoloured.

93	2½p. Type **42**	10	10
94	3p. "Calvados", 1873	10	10
95	7½p. "Carteret" at Grouville station, 1893	25	35
96	9p. "Caesarea", 1873, and route map	35	45

43 Princess Anne and Capt. Mark Phillips

1973. Royal Wedding.

97 **43**	3p. multicoloured	10	10
98	20p. multicoloured	50	50

44 Spider Crab

1973. Marine Life. Multicoloured.

99	2½p. Type **44**	10	10
100	3p. Conger eel	10	10
101	7½p. Lobster	30	35
102	20p. Tuberculate ormer	40	45

45 Freesias

47 John Wesley

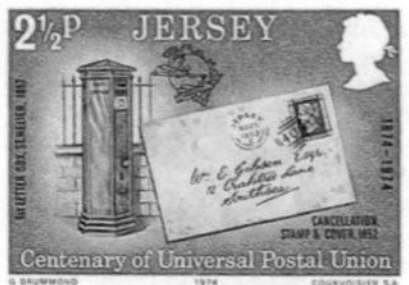

46 First Letter Box and Contemporary Cover

1974. Spring Flowers. Multicoloured.

103	3p. Type **45**	10	10
104	5½p. Anemones	15	15
105	8p. Carnations and Gladioli	25	30
106	10p. Daffodils and Iris	30	35

1974. Centenary of U.P.U. Multicoloured.

107	2½p. Type **46**	10	10
108	3p. Postmen, 1862 and 1969	10	15
109	5½p. Letter-box and letter, 1974	25	20
110	20p. R.M.S. "Aquila" (1874) and B.A.C. One Eleven 200 (1974)	35	40

1974. Anniversaries.

111 **47**	3p. black and brown	10	10
112 –	3½p. violet and blue	10	10
113 –	8p. black and lilac	20	20
114 –	20p. black and stone	45	45

PORTRAITS AND EVENTS: 3p. (Bicentenary of Methodism in Jersey); 3½p. Sir William Hillary, founder (150th anniv of R.N.L.I.); 8p. Canon Wace (poet and historian) (800th death anniv; 20p. Sir Winston Churchill (Birth cent).

48 "Catherine" and "Mary" (Royal yachts)

1974. Marine Paintings by Peter Monamy. Mult.

115	3½p. Type **48**	10	10
116	5½p. French two-decker	15	10
117	8p. Dutch vessel (horiz)	25	20
118	25p. Battle of Cap La Hague, 1692 (55 × 27 mm)	55	55

49 Potato Digger

1975. 19th-century Farming. Multicoloured.

119	3p. Type **49**	10	10
120	3½p. Cider crusher	10	10
121	8p. Six-horse plough	20	20
122	10p. Hay cart	35	30

50 H.M. Queen Elizabeth, the Queen Mother (photograph by Cecil Beaton)

51 Nautilus Shell

1975. Royal Visit.

123 **50**	20p. multicoloured	50	45

1975. Jersey Tourism. Multicoloured.

124	5p. Type **51**	10	10
125	8p. Parasol	10	10
126	10p. Deckchair	30	25
127	12p. Sandcastle with flags of Jersey and the U.K.	40	35
MS128	146 × 68 mm. Nos. 124/7	90	1·10

52 Common Tern

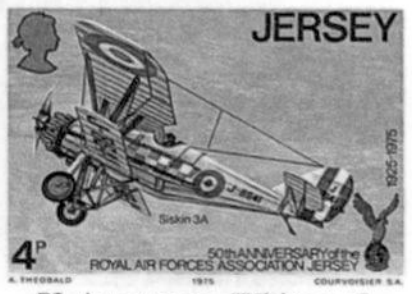

53 Armstrong Whitworth Siskin IIIA

1975. Sea Birds. Multicoloured.

129	4p. Type **52**	10	10
130	5p. British storm petrel ("Storm-Petrel")	15	10
131	8p. Brent geese	40	25
132	25p. Shag	70	50

1975. 50th Anniv of Royal Air Force Association, Jersey Branch. Multicoloured.

133	4p. Type **53**	10	10
134	5p. Supermarine Southampton I flying boat	15	10
135	10p. Supermarine Spitfire Mk I	40	25
136	25p. Folland Gnat T.1	70	50

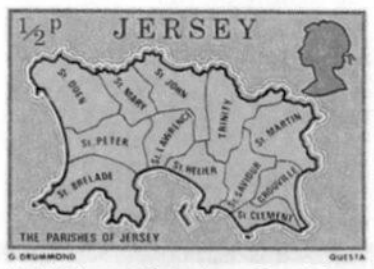

54 Map of Jersey Parishes

55 Parish Arms and Island Scene

1976. Multicoloured. (a) Parish Arms and Views.

137	½p. Type **54**	10	10
138	1p. Zoological Park	10	10
139	5p. St. Mary's Church	10	10
140	6p. Seymour Tower	10	10
141	7p. La Corbiere Lighthouse	10	10
142	8p. St. Saviour's Church	15	10
143	9p. Elizabeth Castle	15	10
144	10p. Gorey Harbour	20	10
145	11p. Jersey Airport	25	25
146	12p. Grosnez Castle	25	20
147	13p. Bonne Nuit Harbour	25	20
148	14p. Le Hocq Tower	30	20
149	15p. Morel Farm	30	25

(b) Emblems.

150	20p. Type **55**	45	35
151	30p. Flag and map	55	40
152	40p. Postal H.Q. and badge	80	50
153	50p. Parliament, Royal Court and arms	1·00	70
154	£1 Lieutenant-Governor's flag and Government House	3·00	1·50
155	£2 Queen Elizabeth II (vert)	4·00	2·50

56 Sir Walter Raleigh and Map of Virginia

1976. Bicentenary of American Independence. Multicoloured.

160	5p. Type **56**	10	10
161	7p. Sir George Carteret and map of New Jersey	15	10
162	11p. Philippe Dauvergne and Long Island landing	40	25
163	13p. John Copley and sketch	50	40

57 Dr. Grandin and Map of China

1976. Birth Centenary of Dr. Lilian Grandin (medical missionary).

164 **57**	5p. multicoloured	10	10
165 –	7p. yellow, brown and black	10	10
166 –	11p. multicoloured	35	25
167 –	13p. multicoloured	50	40

DESIGNS: 7p. Sampan on the Yangtze; 11p. Overland trek; 13p. Dr. Grandin at work.

58 Coronation, 1953 (photographed by Cecil Beaton)

1977. Silver Jubilee. Multicoloured.

168	5p. Type **58**	15	10
169	7p. Visit to Jersey, 1957	20	15
170	25p. Queen Elizabeth II (photo by Peter Grugeon)	40	35

59 Coins of 1871 and 1877

1977. Centenary of Currency Reform. Mult.

171	5p. Type **59**	10	10
172	7p. One-twelfth shilling, 1949	15	10
173	11p. Silver crown, 1966	30	30
174	13p. £2 piece, 1972	35	35

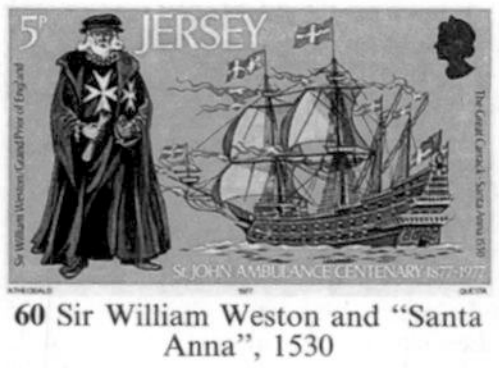

60 Sir William Weston and "Santa Anna", 1530

1977. Centenary of St. John Ambulance. Mult.

175	5p. Type **60**	10	10
176	7p. Sir William Drogo and ambulance, 1877	10	10
177	11p. Duke of Connaught and ambulance, 1917	25	20
178	13p. Duke of Gloucester and stretcher-team, 1977	30	25

61 Arrival of Queen Victoria, 1846

1977. 125th Anniv of Victoria College. Mult.

179	7p. Type **61**	15	10
180	10½p. Victoria College, 1852	20	15
181	11p. Sir Galahad Statue, 1924 (vert)	25	25
182	13p. College Hall (vert)	30	25

62 Harry Vardon Statuette and Map of Royal Jersey Course

1978. Cent of Royal Jersey Golf Club. Mult.

183	6p. Type **62**	10	10
184	8p. Harry Vardon's grip and swing	15	10
185	11p. Harry Vardon's putt	35	25
186	13p. Golf trophies and book by Harry Vardon	40	35

63 Mont Orgueil Castle

1978. Europa. Castles from Paintings by Thomas Phillips. Multicoloured.

187	6p. Type **63**	10	10
188	8p. St. Aubin's Fort	15	15
189	10½p. Elizabeth Castle	35	25

64 "Gaspe Basin" (P. J. Ouless)

1978. Links with Canada. Multicoloured.

190	6p. Type **64**	10	10
191	8p. Map of Gaspe Peninsula	15	10
192	10½p. "Century" (brigantine)	20	15
193	11p. Early map of Jersey	40	25
194	13p. St. Aubin's Bay, town and harbour	45	40

65 Queen Elizabeth and Prince Philip

66 Mail Cutter, 1778–1827

1978. 25th Anniv of Coronation.

195 **65**	8p. silver, black and red	20	10
196 –	25p. silver, black and blue	50	45

DESIGN: 25p. Hallmarks of 1953 and 1977.

1978. Bicentenary of England–Jersey Government Mail Packet Service.

197 **66**	6p. black, brown and yellow	10	10
198 –	8p. black, green and yellow	15	10
199 –	10½p. black, ultram & bl	30	20
200 –	11p. black, purple and lilac	35	30
201 –	13p. black, red and pink	40	40

DESGNS—SHIPS: 8p. "Flamer", 1831–7; 10½p. "Diana", 1877–90; 11p. "Ibex", 1891–1925; 13p. "Caesarea", 1960–75.

67 Jersey Calf

68 Jersey Pillar Box, c. 1860

1979. 9th Conference of World Jersey Cattle Bureau. Multicoloured.

202	6p. Type **67**	10	10
203	25p. "Ansom Designette" (calf presented to the Queen, 1978) (46 × 29 mm)	50	45

1979. Europa. Multicoloured.

204	8p. Type **68**	25	25
205	8p. Clearing modern post box	25	25
206	10½p. Telephone switchboard, c. 1900	25	25
207	10½p. Modern SPC telephone system	25	25

69 Percival Mew Gull "Golden City"

70 "My First Sermon"

1979. 25th International Air Rally. Mult.

208	6p. Type **69**	10	10
209	8p. De Havilland Chipmunk	25	15
210	10½p. Druine Turbulent	25	20
211	11p. De Havilland Tiger Moth	30	25
212	13p. North American Harvard	40	35

1979. International Year of the Child and 150th Birth Anniversary of Sir John Millais (painter). Paintings. Multicoloured.

213	8p. Type **70**	20	15
214	10½p. "Orphans"	30	20
215	11p. "The Princes in the Tower"	30	30
216	25p. "Christ in the House of his Parents" (50 × 32 mm)	50	40

1979. Wildlife Preservation Trust (3rd series). As T **34**. Multicoloured.

217	6p. Pink pigeon (vert)	10	10
218	8p. Orang-utan (vert)	20	15
219	11½p. Waldrapp ("Waldrapp Ibis")	30	30
220	13p. Lowland gorilla (vert)	45	35
221	15p. Rodriguez flying fox (vert)	45	35

71 Plan of Mont Orgueil

72 Sir Walter Raleigh

1980. Jersey Fortresses. Drawings by Thomas Phillips. Multicoloured.

222	8p. Type **71**	20	15
223	11½p. Plan of La Tour de St. Aubin	30	30
224	13p. Plan of Elizabeth Castle	30	30
225	25p. Map of Jersey (38 × 27 mm)	50	45

1980. Europa. Links with Britain. Multicoloured.

226	9p. Type **72**	15	15
227	9p. Paul Ivy (engineer) discussing Elizabeth Castle	15	15
228	13½p. Sir George Carteret receiving deeds to Smith's Island, Virginia from Charles II	30	30
229	13½p. Lady Carteret, maid and Jean Chevalier	30	30

Nos. 226/7 and 228/9 were issued together, se-tenant, forming composite designs.

73 Planting

74 Three Lap Event

1980. Cent of Jersey Royal Potato. Mult.

230	7p. Type **73**	15	10
231	15p. Digging	30	25
232	17½p. Weighbridge	30	35

1980. 60th Anniv of Jersey Motor Cycle and Light Car Club. Multicoloured.

233	7p. Type **74**	15	15
234	9p. Jersey International Road Race	20	15
235	13½p. Scrambling	30	25
236	15p. Sand racing (saloon cars)	30	30
237	17½p. National Hill Climb	35	35

75 "Eye of the Wind"

1980. "Operation Drake" and 150th Anniv of Royal Geographical Society (14p). Multicoloured.

238	7p. Type **75**	15	15
239	9p. Inflatable raft	20	20
240	13½p. Shooting rapids	30	25
241	14p. "Discovery"	30	30
242	15p. Aerial walkway	35	35
243	17½p. Goodyear Aerospace airship "Europa"	40	40

76 Detail of "The Death of Major Peirson"

1981. Bicentenary of Battle of Jersey. Details of J. S. Copley's painting.

244	**76**	7p. multicoloured	15	15
245	–	10p. multicoloured	25	20
246	–	15p. multicoloured	35	30
247	–	17½p. multicoloured	40	35
MS248		144 × 97 mm. Nos. 244/7	1·40	1·60

Stamps from No. **MS**248 are without white margins.

77 De Bagot

78a "Queen Elizabeth II" (Norman Hepple)

1981. Crests of Jersey Families.

249	**77**	½p. black, silver and green	20	20
250	–	1p. multicoloured	10	10
251	–	2p. multicoloured	10	10
252	–	3p. multicoloured	10	15
253	–	4p. silver, black and mauve	15	15
254	–	5p. multicoloured	15	15
255	–	6p. multicoloured	20	20
256	–	7p. multicoloured	25	25
257	–	8p. multicoloured	30	30
258	–	9p. multicoloured	30	25
259	–	10p. multicoloured	25	25
260	–	11p. multicoloured	30	30
261	–	12p. multicoloured	35	30
262	–	13p. multicoloured	35	35
263	–	14p. multicoloured	40	40
264	–	15p. multicoloured	40	40
265	–	16p. multicoloured	35	35
266	–	17p. multicoloured	45	45
266a	–	18p. multicoloured	50	50
266b	–	19p. multicoloured	60	60
267	–	20p. black, silver & yellow	50	50
268	–	25p. black and blue	45	45
268a	**77**	26p. black, silver and red	50	50
269	–	30p. multicoloured	50	50
270	–	40p. multicoloured	80	80
271	–	50p. multicoloured	1·00	1·00
272	–	75p. multicoloured	1·50	1·50
273	–	£1 multicoloured	2·00	2·00
274	**78a**	£5 multicoloured	10·00	10·00

DESIGNS—As T **77**: 1p. De Carteret; 2p. La Cloche; 3p. Dumaresq; 4p. Payn; 5p. Janvrin; 6p. Poingdestre; 7p. Pipon; 8p. Marett; 9p. Le Breton; 10p. Le Maistre; 11p. Bisson; 12p. Robin; 13p. Herault; 14p. Messervy; 15p. Fiott; 16p. Malet; 17p. Mabon; 18p. De St. Martin; 19p. Hamptonne; 20p. Badier; 25p. L'Arbalestier; 30p. Journeaux; 40p. Lempriere; 50p. Auvergne; 75p. Remon. 38 × 22 mm: £1 Jersey crest and map of Channel.

79 Knight of Hambye slaying Dragon

1981. Europa. Folklore. Multicoloured.

275	10p. Type **79**	25	25
276	10p. Servant slaying Knight of Hambye and awaiting execution	25	25
277	18p. St. Brelade celebrating Easter on island	50	45
278	18p. Island revealing itself as a huge fish	50	45

LEGENDS: 10p. (both) Slaying of the Dragon of Lawrence by the Knight of Hambye; 18p. (both) Voyages of St. Brelade.

80 The Harbour by Gaslight

1981. 150th Anniv of Gas in Jersey. Multicoloured.

279	7p. Type **80**	20	15
280	10p. The Quay	25	25
281	18p. Royal Square	40	40
282	22p. Halkett Place	45	45
283	25p. Central Market	55	55

81 Prince Charles and Lady Diana Spencer

1981. Royal Wedding.

284	**81**	10p. multicoloured	20	20
285		25p. multicoloured	75	90

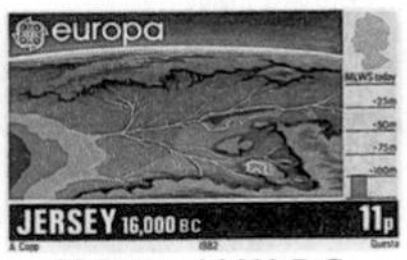

82 Christmas Tree in Royal Square

83 Jersey, 16,000 B.C.

1981. Christmas. Multicoloured.

286	7p. Type **82**	15	10
287	10p. East window, Parish Church, St. Helier	25	25
288	18p. Boxing Day meet of Jersey Drag Hunt	30	30

1982. Europa. Formation of Jersey. Mult.

289	11p. Type **83**	20	20
290	11p. In 10,000 B.C. (vert)	20	20
291	19½p. In 7,000 B.C. (vert)	45	45
292	19½p. In 4,000 B.C.	45	45

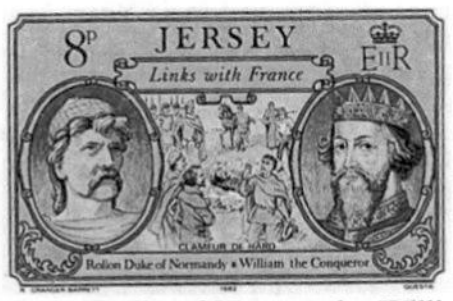

84 Duke Rollo of Normandy, William the Conqueror and "Clameur de Haro" (traditional procedure for obtaining justice)

1982. Links with France. Multicoloured.

293	8p. Type **84**	20	15
294	8p. John of England, Philippe Auguste of France, and Siege of Rouen	20	15
295	11p. Jean Martell (brandy merchant), early still and view of Cognac	30	30
296	11p. Victor Hugo, "Le Rocher des Proscrits" (rock where he used to meditate) and Marine Terrace	30	30
297	19½p. Pierre Teilhard de Chardin (philosopher) and "Maison Saint Louis" (science institute)	45	45
298	19½p. Pere Charles Rey (scientist), anemotachymeter and The Observatory, St. Louis	45	45

85 Sir William Smith, Founder of Boys' Brigade

1982. Youth Organizations. Multicoloured.

299	8p. Type **85**	20	15
300	11p. Boys' Brigade "Old Boys" band, Liberation Parade, 1945 (vert)	20	15
301	24p. William Smith and Lord Baden-Powell at Royal Albert Hall, 1903	45	40
302	26p. Lord and Lady Baden-Powell, St. Helier, 1924 (vert)	60	50
303	29p. Scouts at "Westward Ho" campsite, St. Ouen's Bay	75	60

Nos. 299/301 commemorate the centenary of the Boys' Brigade and Nos. 302/3 the 75th anniversary of the Boy Scout Movement.

86 H.M.S. "Tamar" and H.M.S. "Dolphin" at Port Egmont

1983. Jersey Adventurers (1st series). Mult.

304	8p. Type **86**	20	15
305	11p. H.M.S. "Dolphin" and H.M.S. "Swallow" off Magellan Strait	25	15
306	19½p. Discovering Pitcairn Island	40	35
307	24p. Carteret taking possession of English Cove, New Ireland	45	45
308	26p. H.M.S. "Swallow" sinking a pirate, Macassar Strait	50	50
309	29p. H.M.S. "Endymion" leading convoy from West Indies	65	60

See also Nos. 417/21 and 573/8.

87 1969 5s. Legislative Chamber Definitive

1983. Europa. Multicoloured.

310	11p. Type **87**	35	30
311	11p. Royal Mace (23 × 32 mm)	35	30
312	19½p. 1969 10s. Royal Court definitive showing green border error	45	40
313	19½p. Bailiff's Seal (23 × 32 mm)	45	40

88 Charles Le Geyt and Battle of Minden (1759)

1983. World Communications Year and 250th Birth Anniv of Charles Le Geyt (1st Jersey postmaster). Multicoloured.

314	8p. Type **88**	20	20
315	11p. London to Weymouth mail coach	30	30
316	24p. P.O. Mail Packet "Chesterfield" attacked by French privateer	55	55
317	26p. Mary Godfray and the Hue Street Post Office	65	65
318	29p. Mail steamer leaving St. Helier harbour	80	80

89 Assembly Emblem

1983. 13th General Assembly of the A.I.P.L.F. (Association Internationale des Parlementaires de Langue Francaise) Jersey.

319 **89**	19½p. multicoloured	50	50

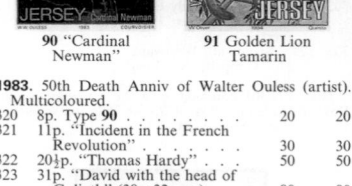

90 "Cardinal Newman"

91 Golden Lion Tamarin

1983. 50th Death Anniv of Walter Ouless (artist). Multicoloured.

320	8p. Type **90**	20	20
321	11p. "Incident in the French Revolution"	30	30
322	20½p. "Thomas Hardy"	50	50
323	31p. "David with the head of Goliath" (38 × 32 mm)	80	80

1984. Wildlife Preservation Trust (4th series). Multicoloured.

324	9p. Type **91**	25	10
325	12p. Snow leopard	25	15
326	20½p. Jamaican boa	45	40
327	26p. Round island gecko	75	65
328	28p. Coscoroba swan	80	70
329	31p. St. Lucia amazon ("St Lucia Parrot")	1·00	90

92 C.E.P.T. 25th Anniversary Logo

1984. Europa.

330 **92**	9p. light blue, blue and black	20	15
331	12p. lt green, green and black	30	25
332	20½p. lilac, purple and black	60	50

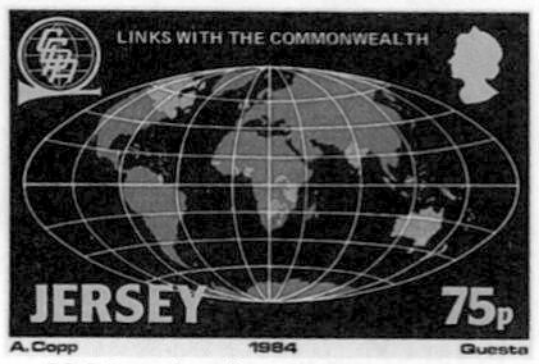

93 Map showing Commonwealth

1984. Links with the Commonwealth. Sheet 108 × 74 mm.

MS333 **93**	75p. multicoloured	2·00	2·00

94 "Sarah Bloomshoft" at Demie de Pas Light, 1906

1984. Centenary of Jersey R.N.L.I. Lifeboat Station. Multicoloured.

334	9p. Type **94**	25	15
335	9p. "Hearts of Oak" and "Maurice Georges", 1949	25	15
336	12p. "Elizabeth Rippon" and "Hanna", 1949	35	30
337	12p. "Elizabeth Rippon" and "Santa Maria", 1951	35	30
338	20½p. "Elizabeth Rippon" and "Bacchus", 1973	60	60
339	20½p. "Thomas James King" and "Cythara", 1983	60	60

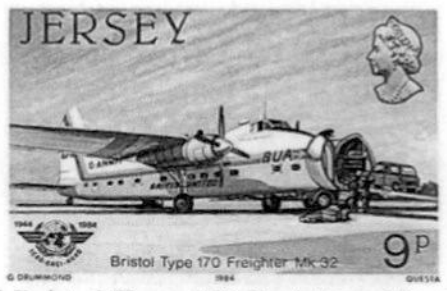

95 Bristol Type 170 Freighter Mk 32

1984. 40th Anniv of I.C.A.O. Multicoloured.

340	9p. Type **95**	20	15
341	12p. Airspeed A.S.57 Ambassador 2	35	35
342	26p. De Havilland D.H.114 Heron 1B	75	75
343	31p. De Havilland D.H.89A Dragon Rapide	1·00	1·00

96 "Robinson Crusoe leaves the Wreck"

1984. Links with Australia. Paintings by John Alexander Gilfillan. Multicoloured.

344	9p. Type **96**	25	20
345	12p. "Edinburgh Castle"	30	20
346	20½p. "Maori Village"	60	50
347	26p. "Australian Landscape"	70	60
348	28p. "Waterhouse's Corner, Adelaide"	80	80
349	31p. "Captain Cook at Botany Bay"	80	80

97 "B.L.C. St. Helier" Orchid

1984. Christmas. Jersey Orchids (1st series). Multicoloured.

350	9p. Type **97**	25	20
351	12p. "Oda Mt. Bingham"	50	50

See also Nos. 433/7, 613/17 and 892/7.

98 "'Hebe' off Corbiere, 1874"

1984. Death Centenary of Philip John Ouless (artist). Multicoloured.

352	9p. Type **98**	25	20
353	12p. "The 'Gaspe' engaging the 'Diomede'"	30	30
354	22p. "The Paddle-steamer 'London' entering Naples, 1856"	65	60
355	31p. "'The Rambler' entering Cape Town, 1840"	1·00	90
356	34p. "St. Aubin's Bay from Mount Bingham, 1871"	1·25	1·00

99 John Ireland (composer) and Faldouet Dolmen

1985. Europa. European Music Year. Mult.

357	10p. Type **99**	30	30
358	13p. Ivy St. Helier (actress) and His Majesty's Theatre, London	45	45
359	22p. Claude Debussy (composer) and Elizabeth Castle	80	80

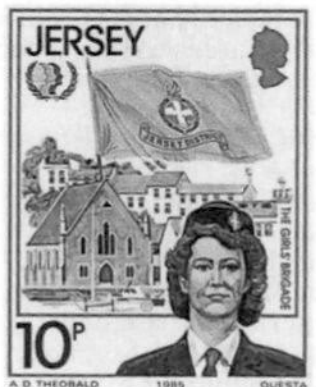

100 Girls' Brigade

1985. International Youth Year. Mult.

360	10p. Type **100**	30	30
361	13p. Girl Guides (75th anniversary)	40	40
362	29p. Prince Charles and Jersey Youth Service Activities Base	70	70
363	31p. Sea Cadet Corps	75	75
364	34p. Air Training Corps	90	90

101 "Duke of Normandy" at Cheapside

1985. The Jersey Western Railway. Mult.

365	10p. Type **101**	45	45
366	13p. Saddletank at First Tower	50	50
367	22p. "La Moye" at Millbrook	90	90
368	29p. "St. Heliers" at St. Aubin	95	95
369	34p. "St. Aubyns" at Corbiere	1·00	1·00

102 Memorial Window to Revd. James Hemery (former Dean) and St. Helier Parish Church

1985. 300th Anniv of Huguenot Immigration. Multicoloured.

370	10p. Type **102**	30	30
371	10p. Judge Francis Jeune, Baron St. Helier, and Houses of Parliament	30	30
372	13p. Silverware by Pierre Amiraux	40	40
373	13p. Francis Voisin (merchant) and Russian port	40	40
374	22p. Robert Brohier, Schweppes carbonation plant and bottles	55	50
375	22p. George Ingouville, V.C., R.N. and attack on Viborg	55	40

103 Howard Davis Hall, Victoria College

1985. Thomas Benjamin Davis (philanthropist) Commemoration. Multicoloured.

376	10p. Type **103**	35	35
377	13p. Racing schooner "Westward"	50	50
378	31p. Howard Davis Park, St. Helier	70	70
379	34p. Howard Davis Experimental Farm, Trinity	85	85

104 "Amaryllis belladonna" (Pandora Sellars)

1986. Jersey Lilies. Multicoloured.

380	13p. Type **104**	45	45
381	34p. "A Jersey Lily" (Lily Langtry) (Sir John Millais) (30 × 48 mm)	1·00	1·10
MS382	140 × 96 mm. Nos. 380 × 4 and 381	2·75	3·00

105 King Harold, William of Normandy and Halley's Comet, 1066 (from Bayeux Tapestry)

1986. Appearance of Halley's Comet. Multicoloured.

383	10p. Type **105**	35	35
384	22p. Lady Carteret, Edmond Halley, map and Comet	80	85
385	31p. Aspects of communications in 1910 and 1986 on TV screen	1·00	1·10

106 Dwarf Pansy

107 Queen Elizabeth II (from photo by Karsh)

1986. Europa. Environmental Conservation. Multicoloured.

386	10p. Type **106**	35	35
387	14p. Sea stock	45	45
388	22p. Sand crocus	70	70

1986. 60th Birthday of Queen Elizabeth II.

389 **107**	£1 multicoloured	2·50	1·50

See also No. 491b.

108 Le Rat Cottage

1986. 50th Anniv of National Trust for Jersey. Multicoloured.

390	10p. Type **108**	25	20
391	14p. The Elms (Trust headquarters)	35	30
392	22p. Morel Farm	65	65
393	29p. Quetivel Mill	70	70
394	31p. La Vallette	75	75

109 Prince Andrew and Miss Sarah Ferguson

1986. Royal Wedding.

395 **109**	14p. multicoloured	35	35
396	40p. multicoloured	1·25	1·25

110 "Gathering Vraic"

1986. Birth Centenary of Edmund Blampied (artist).

397 **110**	10p. multicoloured	25	25
398	– 14p. black, blue and grey	40	40
399	– 29p. multicoloured	75	75
400	– 31p. black, orange and grey	90	90
401	– 34p. multicoloured	95	95

DESIGNS: 14p. "Driving Home in the Rain"; 29p. "The Miller"; 31p. "The Joy Ride"; 34p. "Tante Elizabeth".

111 Island Map on Jersey Lily, and Dove holding Olive Branch

1986. Christmas. Int Peace Year. Mult.

402	10p. Type **111**	20	20
403	14p. Mistletoe wreath encircling European robin and dove	40	40
404	34p. Christmas cracker releasing dove	95	95

112 "Westward" under Full Sail

1987. Racing Schooner "Westward". Mult.
405 10p. Type **112** 40 35
406 14p. T. B. Davis at the helm 50 55
407 31p. "Westward" overhauling "Britannia" 95 95
408 34p. "Westward" fitting-out at St. Helier 95 95

113 De Havilland Dragon Express "Belcroute Bay"

1987. 50th Anniv of Jersey Airport. Multicoloured.
409 10p. Type **113** 25 25
410 14p. Boeing 757 and Douglas DC-9-15 . . . . 40 45
411 22p. Britten Norman "long nose" Trislander and Islander aircraft 55 50
412 29p. Short 330 and Vickers Viscount 800 . . . . . . 90 90
413 31p. B.A.C. One Eleven 500 and Handley Page Dart Herald 95 95

114 St. Mary and St. Peter's Roman Catholic Church

1987. Europa. Modern Architecture. Mult.
414 11p. Type **114** 40 40
415 15p. Villa Devereux, St. Brelade 50 45
416 22p. Fort Regent Leisure Centre, St. Helier (57 × 29 mm) 75 75

115 H.M.S. "Racehorse" and H.M.S. "Carcass" (bomb ketches) trapped in Arctic

1987. Jersey Adventurers (2nd series). Philippe D'Auvergne. Multicoloured.
417 11p. Type **115** 30 35
418 15p. H.M.S. "Alarm" on fire, Rhode Island 40 35
419 29p. H.M.S. "Arethusa" wrecked off Ushant . . . 70 75
420 31p. H.M.S. "Rattlesnake" stranded on Isle de Trinidad 80 90
421 34p. Mont Orgueil Castle and fishing boats 85 95
See also Nos. 501/6 and 539/44.

116 Grant of Lands to Normandy, 911 and 933

1987. 900th Death Anniv of William the Conqueror. Multicoloured.
422 11p. Type **116** 30 30
423 15p. Edward the Confessor and Duke Robert I of Normandy landing on Jersey, 1030 . . . . 35 35
424 22p. King William's coronation, 1066 and fatal fall, 1087 . . . . 70 65
425 29p. Death of William Rufus, 1100 and Battle of Tinchebrai, 1106 . . . . . 75 65
426 31p. Civil war between Matilda and Stephen, 1135–41 . . . . 85 75
427 34p. Henry inherits Normandy, 1151; John asserts ducal rights in Jersey, 1213 . . . . 95 90

117 "Grosnez Castle"

1987. Christmas. Paintings by John Le Capelain. Multicoloured.
428 11p. Type **117** 35 30
429 15p. "St. Aubin's Bay" . . . 50 50
430 22p. "Mont Orgueil Castle" . . 65 65
431 31p. "Town Fort and Harbour, St. Helier" . . . 90 80
432 34p. "The Hermitage" . . . 1·00 1·00

118 "Cymbidium pontac"

1988. Jersey Orchids (2nd series). Multicoloured.
433 11p. Type **118** 40 35
434 15p. "Odontioda" "Eric Young" (vert) 45 45
435 29p. "Lycaste auburn", "Seaford" and "Ditchling" 70 70
436 31p. "Odontoglossum" "St. Brelade" (vert) 80 80
437 34p. "Cymbidium mavourneen" "Jester" . . 95 95

119 Labrador Retriever

1988. Centenary of Jersey Dog Club. Mult.
438 11p. Type **119** 40 30
439 15p. Wire-haired dachshund 60 30
440 22p. Pekingese 80 75
441 31p. Cavalier King Charles spaniel 90 95
442 34p. Dalmatian . . . . . . 1·00 1·00

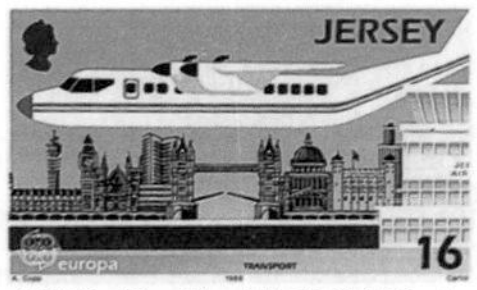

120 De Havilland D.H.C.7 Dash Seven, London Landmarks and Jersey Control Tower

1988. Europa. Transport and Communications. Multicoloured.
443 16p. Type **120** 40 45
444 16p. Weather radar and Jersey airport landing system (vert) 40 45
445 22p. Hydrofoil, St. Malo and Elizabeth Castle, St. Helier 75 75
446 22p. Port control tower and Jersey Radio maritime communication centre, La Moye (vert) 75 75

121 Rodriguez Fody ("Rodrigues Fody")

1988. Wildlife Preservation Trust (5th series). Multicoloured.
447 12p. Type **121** 45 45
448 16p. Volcano rabbit (horiz) 55 50
449 29p. White-faced marmoset 90 1·00
450 31p. Ploughshare tortoise (horiz) . . . . 1·10 1·10
451 34p. Mauritius kestrel . . . . 1·25 1·25

122 Rain Forest Leaf Frog, Costa Rica

1988. Operation Raleigh. Multicoloured.
452 12p. Type **122** 35 25
453 16p. Archaeological survey, Peru 40 40
454 22p. Climbing glacier, Chile 60 60
455 29p. Red Cross Centre, Solomon Islands 70 70
456 31p. Underwater exploration, Australia 80 80
457 34p. "Zebu" (brigantine) returning to St. Helier . . 90 90

123 St. Clement Parish Church

1988. Christmas. Jersey Parish Churches (1st series). Multicoloured.
458 12p. Type **123** 30 15
459 16p. St. Ouen 45 30
460 31p. St. Brelade 90 80
461 34p. St. Lawrence 85 85
See also Nos. 535/8 and 597/600.

124 Talbot "Type 4 CT Tourer", 1912

1989. Vintage Cars (1st series). Multicoloured.
462 12p. Type **124** 35 30
463 16p. De Dion "Bouton Type 1-D", 1920 . . . . 50 45
464 23p. Austin 7 "Chummy", 1926 . . . . 60 55
465 30p. Ford "Model T", 1926 80 80
466 32p. Bentley 8 litre, 1930 . . 1·00 1·00
467 35p. Cadillac "452A–V16 Fleetwood Sports Phaeton", 1931 . . . . . 1·00 1·00
See also Nos. 591/6 and 905/10.

125 Belcroute Bay **125a** Arms of King George VI

1989. Jersey Scenes. Multicoloured.
468 1p. Type **125** 10 10
469 2p. High Street, St. Aubin 10 10
470 4p. Royal Jersey Golf Course 10 10
471 5p. Portelet Bay 10 15
472 10p. Les Charrieres D'Anneport 30 30
473 13p. St. Helier Marina . . . 40 45
474 14p. Sand yacht racing, St. Ouen's Bay 40 45
475 15p. Rozel Harbour 45 50
476 16p. St. Aubin's Harbour 50 55
477 17p. Jersey Airport 50 55
478 18p. Corbiere Lighthouse 55 60
479 19p. Val de la Mare 55 60
480 20p. Elizabeth Castle . . . 45 45
481 21p. Greve de Lecq 50 55
482 22p. Samares Manor . . . 45 50
483 23p. Bonne Nuit Harbour 75 55
484 24p. Grosnez Castle 60 60
485 25p. Augres Manor 70 75
486 26p. Central Market 75 80
487 27p. St. Brelade's Bay . . . 80 90
488 30p. St. Ouen's Manor . . . 85 90
489 40p. La Hougue Bie . . . . 1·00 1·00
490 50p. Mont Orgueil Castle 1·25 1·40
491 75p. Royal Square, St. Helier . . . . 2·00 1·50
491b £2 Type **107** . . . . 4·00 3·25
491c £4 Type **125a** . . . . 7·00 6·75
Nos. 469/91 are as Type **125**.

126 Agile Frog

1989. Endangered Jersey Fauna. Multicoloured.
492 13p. Type **126** 80 85
493 13p. "Heteropterus morpheus" (butterfly) (vert) 80 85
494 17p. Barn owl (vert) 80 85
495 17p. Green lizard 80 85

127 Toddlers' Toys

1989. Europa. Children's Toys and Games. Designs showing clay plaques. Multicoloured.
496 17p. Type **127** 45 45
497 17p. Playground games . . . 45 45
498 23p. Party games 80 80
499 23p. Teenage sports 80 80

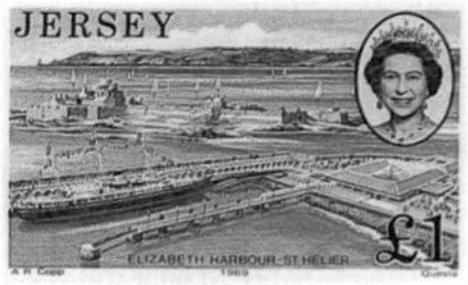

128 Queen Elizabeth II and Royal Yacht "Britannia" in Elizabeth Harbour

1989. Royal Visit.
500 **128** £1 multicoloured . . . . 2·50 2·00

129 Philippe D'Auvergne presented to Louis XVI, 1786

1989. Bicentenary of the French Revolution. Philippe D'Auvergne. Multicoloured.
501 13p. Type **129** 40 30
502 17p. Storming the Bastille, 1789 . . . . 50 40
503 23p. Marie de Bouillon and revolutionaries, 1790 . . . 60 50
504 30p. Auvergne's headquarters at Mont Orgueil, 1795 . . 95 90
505 32p. Landing arms for Chouan rebels, 1796 . . . 1·00 90
506 35p. The last Chouan revolt, 1799 . . . . 1·25 1·00
See also Nos. 539/44.

130 "St. Helier" off Elizabeth Castle

1989. Centenary of Great Western Railway Steamer Service to Channel Islands. Multicoloured.
507 13p. Type **130** 30 30
508 17p. "Caesarea II" off Corbiere Lighthouse . . . 35 35
509 27p. "Reindeer" in St. Helier harbour 80 75
510 32p. "Ibex" racing "Frederica" off Portelet . . 95 95
511 35p. "Lynx" off Noirmont 1·10 1·00

131 "Gorey Harbour"

1989. 150th Birth Anniv of Sarah Louisa Kilpack (artist). Multicoloured.
512 13p. Type **131** 25 25
513 17p. "La Corbiere" 30 30
514 23p. "Greve de Lecq" . . . 80 75
515 32p. "Bouley Bay" 85 85
516 35p. "Mont Orgueil" . . . . 90 1·00

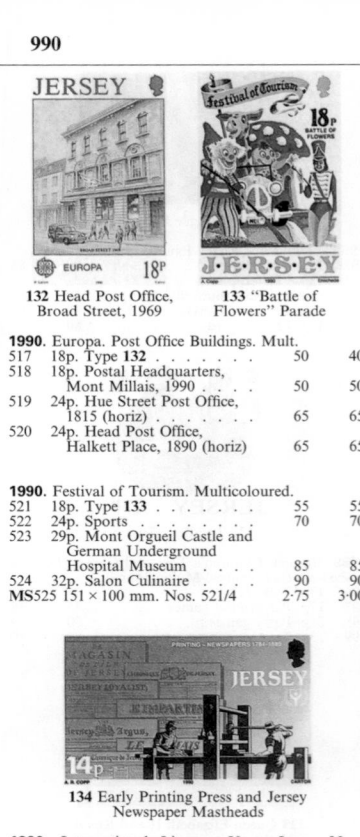

132 Head Post Office, Broad Street, 1969

133 "Battle of Flowers" Parade

1990. Europa. Post Office Buildings. Mult.
517 18p. Type **132** 50 40
518 18p. Postal Headquarters, Mont Millais, 1990 50 50
519 24p. Hue Street Post Office, 1815 (horiz) 65 65
520 24p. Head Post Office, Halkett Place, 1890 (horiz) 65 65

1990. Festival of Tourism. Multicoloured.
521 18p. Type **133** 55 55
522 24p. Sports 70 70
523 29p. Mont Orgueil Castle and German Underground Hospital Museum 85 85
524 32p. Salon Culinaire 90 90
MS525 151 × 100 mm. Nos. 521/4 2·75 3·00

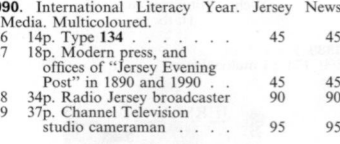

134 Early Printing Press and Jersey Newspaper Mastheads

1990. International Literacy Year. Jersey News Media. Multicoloured.
526 14p. Type **134** 45 45
527 18p. Modern press, and offices of "Jersey Evening Post" in 1890 and 1990 45 45
528 34p. Radio Jersey broadcaster 90 90
529 37p. Channel Television studio cameraman 95 95

135 British Aerospace Hawk T.1

1990. 50th Anniv of Battle of Britain. Multicoloured.
530 14p. Type **135** 40 45
531 18p. Supermarine Spitfire 55 60
532 24p. Hawker Hurricane Mk I 85 85
533 34p. Vickers-Armstrong Wellington 1·50 1·60
534 37p. Avro Lancaster 1·60 1·60

1990. Christmas. Jersey Parish Churches (2nd series). As T **123**. Multicoloured.
535 14p. St. Helier 45 40
536 18p. Grouville 45 40
537 34p. St. Saviour 1·00 1·10
538 37p. St. John 1·25 1·40

1991. 175th Death Anniv of Philippe d'Auvergne. As T **129**. Multicoloured.
539 15p. Prince's Tower, La Hougue Bie 45 40
540 20p. Auvergne's arrest in Paris 55 55
541 26p. Auvergne plotting against Napoleon 70 75
542 31p. Execution of George Cadoudal 90 90
543 37p. H.M.S. "Surly" (cutter) attacking French convoy 1·10 1·10
544 44p. Auvergne's last days in London 1·25 1·25

136 "Landsat 5" and Thematic Mapper Image over Jersey

137 1941 1d. Stamp (50th anniv of first Jersey postage stamp)

1991. Europa. Europe in Space. Multicoloured.
545 20p. Type **136** 50 50
546 20p. "ERS-1" earth resources remote sensing satellite 50 50
547 26p. "Meteosat" weather satellite 80 85
548 26p. "Olympus" direct broadcasting satellite 80 85

1991. Anniversaries. Multicoloured.
549 15p. Type **137** 30 30
550 20p. Steam train (centenary of Jersey Eastern Railway extension to Gorey Pier) 50 55
551 26p. Jersey cow and Herd Book (125th anniv of Jersey Herd Book) 60 70
552 31p. Stone-laying ceremony (from painting by P. J. Ouless) (150th anniv of Victoria Harbour) 75 80
553 53p. Marie Bartlett and hospital (250th anniv of Marie Bartlett's hospital bequest) 1·75 1·75

138 "Melitaea cinxia"

1991. Butterflies and Moths. Multicoloured.
554 15p. Type **138** 35 35
555 20p. "Euplagia quadripunctaria" 45 30
556 37p. "Deilephilia porcellus" 1·40 1·50
557 57p. "Inachis io" 1·75 1·90

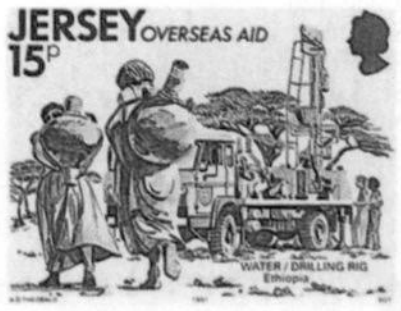

139 Drilling for Water, Ethiopia

1991. Overseas Aid. Multicoloured.
558 15p. Type **139** 45 40
559 20p. Building construction, Rwanda 50 45
560 26p. Village polytechnic, Kenya 70 70
561 31p. Treating leprosy, Tanzania 85 90
562 37p. Ploughing, Zambia 1·10 1·10
563 44p. Immunization clinic, Lesotho 1·25 1·40

140 "This is the Place for Me"

141 Pied Wagtail

1991. Christmas. Illustrations by Edmund Blampied for J. M. Barrie's "Peter Pan". Multicoloured.
564 15p. Type **140** 40 40
565 20p. "The Island Come True" 65 65
566 37p. "The Never Bird" 1·25 1·25
567 53p. "The Great White Father" 1·60 1·60

1992. Winter Birds. Multicoloured.
568 16p. Type **141** 50 25
569 22p. Firecrest 70 55
570 28p. Common snipe ("Snipe") 80 85
571 39p. Northern lapwing ("Lapwing") 1·25 1·25
572 57p. Fieldfare 1·75 1·75
See also Nos. 635/9.

142 Shipping at Shanghai, 1860

1992. Jersey Adventurers (3rd series). 150th Birth Anniv of William Mesny. Multicoloured.
573 16p. Type **142** 40 45
574 16p. Mesny's junk running Taiping blockade, 1862 40 45
575 22p. General Mesny outside river gate, 1874 65 65
576 22p. Mesny in Burma, 1877 65 65
577 33p. Mesny and Governor Chang, 1882 90 95
578 33p. Mesny in mandarin's sedan chair, 1886 90 95

143 "Tickler" (brigantine)

1992. Jersey Shipbuilding. Multicoloured.
579 16p. Type **143** 45 40
580 22p. "Hebe" (brig) 70 75
581 50p. "Gemini" (barque) 1·40 1·50
582 57p. "Percy Douglas" (full-rigged ship) 1·60 1·75
MS583 148 × 98 mm. Nos. 579/82 4·00 4·25

144 John Bertram (ship owner) and Columbus

1992. Europa. 500th Anniv of Discovery of America by Columbus. Multicoloured.
584 22p. Type **144** 65 50
585 28p. Sir George Carteret (founder of New Jersey) 75 80
586 39p. Sir Walter Raleigh (founder of Virginia) 1·10 1·40

145 "Snow Leopards" (Allison Griffiths)

146 Farmhouse

1992. Batik Designs. Multicoloured.
587 16p. Type **145** 45 40
588 22p. "Three Elements" (Nataly Miorin) 65 45
589 39p. "Three Men in a Tub" (Amanda Crocker) 1·10 1·25
590 57p. "Cockatoos" (Michelle Millard) 1·50 1·75

1992. Vintage Cars (2nd series). As T **124**. Multicoloured.
591 16p. Morris Cowley "Bullnose", 1925 30 30
592 22p. Rolls Royce "20/25", 1932 45 45
593 28p. Chenard and Walcker "T5", 1924 70 75
594 33p. Packard 900 series "Light Eight", 1932 90 95
595 39p. Lanchester "21", 1927 1·00 1·10
596 50p. Buick "30 Roadster", 1913 1·50 1·75

1992. Christmas. Jersey Parish Churches (3rd series). As T **123**. Multicoloured.
597 16p. Trinity 40 30
598 22p. St. Mary 55 50
599 39p. St. Martin 1·10 1·00
600 57p. St. Peter 1·50 1·40

1993. Multicoloured.
601 (–) Type **146** 60 70
602 (–) Trinity Church 60 70
603 (–) Daffodils and cows 60 70
604 (–) Jersey cows 60 70
605 (–) Sunbathing 70 60
606 (–) Windsurfing 70 60
607 (–) Crab (Queen's head at left) 70 60
608 (–) Crab (Queen's head at right) 70 60
609 (–) "Singin' in the Rain" float 85 80
610 (–) "Dragon Dance" float 85 80
611 (–) "Bali, Morning of the World" float 85 80
612 (–) "Zulu Fantasy" float 85 80

The above do not show face values, but are inscribed "BAILIWICK POSTAGE PAID" (Nos. 601/4), "U.K. MINIMUM POSTAGE PAID" (Nos. 605/8) or "EUROPE POSTAGE PAID" (Nos. 609/12). They were initially sold at 17p., 23p. or 28p., but it is intended that these face values will be increased to reflect postage rate changes in the future.

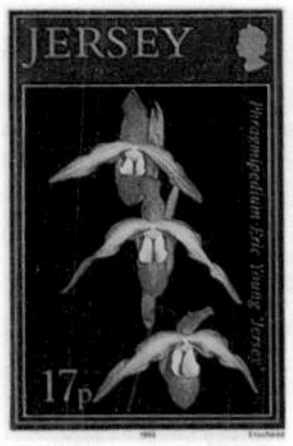

147 "Phragmipedium" Eric Young "Jersey"

149 "Jersey's Opera House" (Ian Rolls)

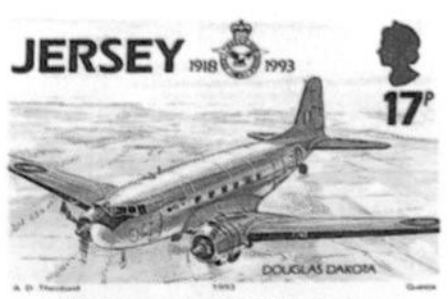

148 Douglas DC-3 Dakota

1993. Jersey Orchids (3rd series). Multicoloured.
613 17p. Type **147** 45 35
614 23p. "Odontoglossum" Augres "Trinity" 70 65
615 28p. "Miltonia" St. Helier "Colomberie" 80 75
616 39p. "Phragmipedium pearcei" 1·25 1·40
617 57p. "Calanthe" Grouville "Grey" 1·75 1·90

1993. 75th Anniv of Royal Air Force. Mult.
618 17p. Type **148** 45 30
619 23p. Wight seaplane 60 65
620 28p. Avro Shackleton A.E.W.2 70 70
621 33p. Gloster Meteor Mk III and De Havilland Vampire FB.5 80 85
622 39p. Hawker Siddeley Harrier GR.IA 1·00 1·10
623 57p. Panavia Tornado F Mk 3 1·50 1·60
MS624 147 × 98 mm. Nos. 619 and 623 4·50 4·75

Nos. 618/23 also commemorate the 50th anniv of the Royal Air Force Association and the 40th anniv of the first air display on Jersey.

1993. Europa. Contemporary Art. Multicoloured.
625 23p. Type **149** 60 60
626 28p. "The Ham and Tomato Bap" (Jonathan Hubbard) 70 70
627 39p. "Vase of Flowers" (Neil MacKenzie) 1·10 1·10

150 1943 ½d. Occupation Stamp

1993. 50th Anniv of Edmund Blampied's Occupation Stamps. Designs showing stamps from the 1943 issue.
628 **150** 17p. green, lt green & blk 35 35
629 – 23p. red, pink and black 50 50
630 – 28p. brown, cinnamon and black 70 70
631 – 33p. orange, salmon & blk 85 85
632 – 39p. blue, cobalt and black 1·25 1·25
633 – 50p. mauve, lt mauve & blk 1·40 1·40

DESIGNS: 23p. 1d. value; 28p. 1½d. value; 33p. 2d. value; 39p. 2½d. value; 50p. 3d. value.

151 Queen Elizabeth II (from painting by Marca McGregor)

1993. 40th Anniv of Coronation.
634 **151** £1 multicoloured 2·75 2·75

152 Short-toed Treecreeper

153 Two Angels holding "Hark the Herald Angels Sing" Banner

1993. Summer Birds. Multicoloured.

635	17p. Type **152**	45	50
636	23p. Dartford warbler	70	75
637	28p. Northern wheatear ("Wheatear")	80	85
638	39p. Cirl bunting	1·25	1·25
639	57p. Jay	1·75	1·75

1993. Christmas. Stained Glass Windows by Henry Bosdet from St. Aubin on the Hill Church. Multicoloured.

640	17p. Type **153**	40	35
641	23p. Two angels playing harps	60	60
642	39p. Two angels playing violins	1·10	1·25
643	57p. Two angels holding "Once in Royal David's City" banner	1·75	1·90

154 "Coprinus comatus"

156 Maine Coon

155 Pekingese

1994. Fungi. Multicoloured.

644	18p. Type **154**	45	40
645	23p. "Amanita muscaria"	65	70
646	30p. "Cantharellus cibarius"	80	85
647	41p. "Macrolepiota procera"	1·25	1·25
648	60p. "Clathrus ruber"	1·60	1·60

1994. "Hong Kong '94" International Stamp Exhibition. "Chinese Year of the Dog". Sheet 110 × 75 mm.

MS649	**155** £1 multicoloured	2·50	2·75

1994. 21st Anniv of Jersey Cat Club. Mult.

650	18p. Type **156**	40	30
651	23p. British shorthair (horiz)	60	50
652	35p. Persian	80	80
653	41p. Siamese (horiz)	1·10	1·25
654	60p. Non-pedigree	1·60	1·75

157 Mammoth Hunt, La Cotte de St. Brelade

1994. Europa. Archaeological Discoveries. Multicoloured.

655	23p. Type **157**	50	55
656	23p. Stone Age hunters pulling mammoth into cave	50	55
657	30p. Chambered passage, La Hougue Bie	75	85
658	30p. Transporting stones	75	85

158 Gliders and Towing Aircraft approaching France

1994. 50th Anniv of D-Day. Multicoloured.

659	18p. Type **158**	55	50
660	18p. Landing craft approaching beaches	55	50
661	23p. Disembarking from landing craft on Gold Beach	75	70
662	23p. British troops on Sword Beach	75	70
663	30p. Spitfires over beaches	80	75
664	30p. Invasion map	80	75

159 Sailing

1994. Centenary of International Olympic Committee. Multicoloured.

665	18p. Type **159**	40	35
666	23p. Rifle-shooting	55	55
667	30p. Hurdling	75	75
668	41p. Swimming	1·10	1·10
669	60p. Hockey	1·50	1·60

160 Strawberry Anemone

1994. Marine Life. Multicoloured.

670	18p. Type **160**	40	45
671	23p. Hermit crab and parasitic anemone	60	65
672	41p. Velvet swimming crab	1·25	1·40
673	60p. Common jellyfish	1·60	1·60

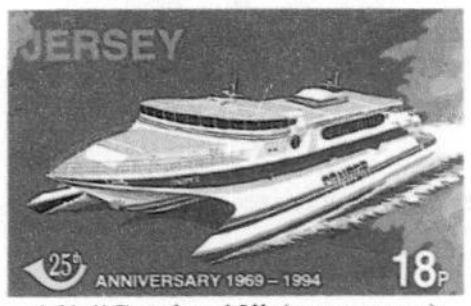

161 "Condor 10" (catamaran)

1994. 25th Anniv of Jersey Postal Administration. Multicoloured.

674	18p. Type **161**	50	45
675	23p. Map of Jersey and pillar box	60	50
676	35p. Vickers Type 953 Vanguard of B.E.A.	85	85
677	41p. Shorts 360 of Aurigny Air Services	1·10	1·00
678	60p. "Caesarea" (Sealink ferry)	1·60	1·50
MS679	150 × 100 mm. Nos. 674/8	4·50	4·50

162 "Away in a Manger"

1994. Christmas. Carols. Multicoloured.

680	18p. Type **162**	40	40
681	23p. "Hark! the Herald Angels Sing"	50	50
682	41p. "While Shepherds Watched"	1·25	1·25
683	60p. "We Three Kings of Orient Are"	1·50	1·50

163 Dog and "GOOD LUCK"

164 Camellia "Captain Rawes"

1995. Greetings Stamps. Multicoloured.

684	18p. Type **163**	50	40
685	18p. Rose and "WITH LOVE"	50	40
686	18p. Chick and "CONGRATULATIONS"	50	40
687	18p. Bouquet of flowers and "THANK YOU"	50	40
688	23p. Dove with letter and "WITH LOVE"	60	55
689	23p. Cat and "GOOD LUCK"	60	55
690	23p. Carnations and "THANK YOU"	60	55
691	23p. Parrot and "CONGRATULATIONS"	60	55
692	60p. Pig and "HAPPY NEW YEAR" (25 × 63 mm)	1·50	1·50

No. 692 commemorates the Chinese New Year of the Pig.

1994. Camellias. Multicoloured.

693	18p. Type **164**	55	50
694	23p. "Brigadoon"	80	70
695	30p. "Elsie Jury"	90	85
696	35p. "Augusto L'Gouveia Pinto"	1·00	1·00
697	41p. "Bella Romana"	1·10	1·10

165 "Liberation" (sculpture, Philip Jackson)

1995. Europa. Peace and Freedom.

698	**165** 23p. black and blue	55	55
699	30p. black and pink	70	95

166 Bailiff and Crown Officers in Launch

1995. 50th Anniv of Liberation. Multicoloured.

700	18p. Type **166**	40	40
701	18p. "Vega" (Red Cross supply ship)	40	40
702	23p. H.M.S. "Beagle" (destroyer)	60	60
703	23p. British troops in Ordnance Yard, St. Helier	60	60
704	60p. King George VI and Queen Elizabeth in Jersey	1·50	1·50
705	60p. Unloading supplies from landing craft, St. Aubin's	1·50	1·50
MS706	110 × 75 mm. £1 Royal Family with Winston Churchill on Buckingham Palace balcony, V.E. Day (80 × 39 mm)	2·75	2·75

167 Bell Heather

1995. European Nature Conservation Year. Wild Flowers. Multicoloured.

707	19p. Type **167**	60	55
708	19p. Sea campion	60	55
709	19p. Spotted rock-rose	60	55
710	19p. Thrift	60	55
711	19p. Sheep's-bit scabious	60	55
712	23p. Field bind-weed	70	65
713	23p. Common bird's-foot trefoil	70	65
714	23p. Sea-holly	70	65
715	23p. Common centaury	70	65
716	23p. Dwarf pansy	70	65

Nos. 707/11 and 712/16 respectively were printed together, se-tenant, forming composite designs.

168 "Precis almana"

1995. Butterflies. Multicoloured.

717	19p. Type **168**	50	55
718	23p. "Papilio palinurus"	55	60
719	30p. "Catopsilia scylla"	80	85
720	41p. "Papilio rumanzovia"	1·00	1·10
721	60p. "Troides helena"	1·60	1·75
MS722	150 × 100 mm. Nos. 720/1	2·40	2·50

No. **MS**722 includes the "Singapore '95" International Stamp Exhibition logo on the sheet margin and shows the two stamp designs without frames.

169 Peace Doves and United Nations Anniversary Emblem

1995. 50th Anniv of United Nations.

723	**169** 19p. cobalt and blue	60	50
724	– 23p. turquoise and green	70	70
725	– 41p. green and turquoise	1·25	1·25
726	**169** 60p. blue and cobalt	1·50	1·50

DESIGN: 23p., 41p. Symbolic wheat and anniversary emblem.

170 "Puss in Boots"

1995. Christmas. Pantomimes. Multicoloured.

727	19p. Type **170**	50	40
728	23p. "Cinderella"	55	45
729	41p. "Sleeping Beauty"	1·00	1·00
730	60p. "Aladdin"	1·60	1·50

171 Rat with Top Hat

1996. Chinese New Year ("Year of the Rat"). Sheet 110 × 75 mm.

MS731	**171** £1 multicoloured	2·50	2·50

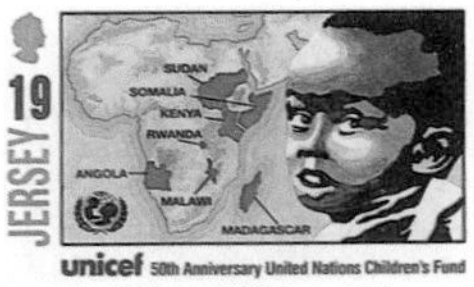

172 African Child and Map

1996. 50th Anniv of U.N.I.C.E.F. Multicoloured.

732	19p. Type **172**	45	40
733	23p. Children and globe	55	45
734	30p. European child and map	70	65
735	35p. South American child and map	90	80
736	41p. Asian child and map	1·00	1·00
737	60p. South Pacific child and map	1·50	1·40

173 Queen Elizabeth II (from photo by T. O'Neill)

1996. 70th Birthday of Queen Elizabeth II.

738	**173** £5 multicoloured	10·00	9·00

174 Elizabeth Garrett (first British woman doctor)

1996. Europa. Famous Women. Multicoloured.

739	23p. Type **174**	60	60
740	30p. Emmeline Pankhurst (suffragette)	90	90

175 Player shooting at Goal

1996. European Football Championship, England. Multicoloured.

741	19p. Type **175**	50	40
742	23p. Two players chasing ball	60	50
743	35p. Player avoiding tackle	95	90
744	41p. Two players competing for ball	1·00	1·00
745	60p. Players heading ball	1·60	1·60

176 Rowing

1996. Sporting Anniversaries. Multicoloured.

746	19p. Type **176**	50	40
747	23p. Judo	60	50
748	35p. Fencing	95	95
749	41p. Boxing	1·00	1·00
750	60p. Basketball	1·60	1·60
MS751	150 × 100 mm. £1 Olympic torch (50 × 37 mm)	2·50	2·50

ANNIVERSARIES: Nos. 746/8, 750/1, Centenary of modern Olympic Games; 749, 50th anniv of International Amateur Boxing Association.

No. **MS**751 also includes the "CAPEX '96" International Stamp Exhibition logo.

177 Bay on North Coast

1996. Tourism. Beaches. Multicoloured.

752	19p. Type **177**	50	50
753	23p. Portelet Bay	60	60
754	30p. Greve de Lecq Bay	80	80
755	35p. Beauport Beach	95	95
756	41p. Plemont Bay	1·10	1·10
757	60p. St. Brelade's Bay	1·60	1·60

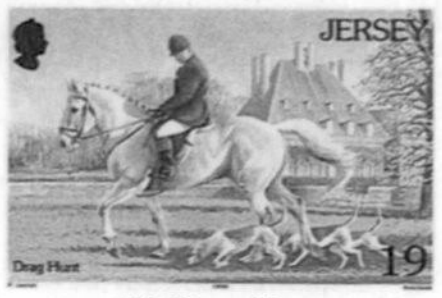

178 Drag Hunt

1996. Horses. Multicoloured.

758	19p. Type **178**	50	50
759	23p. Pony and trap	60	60
760	30p. Training racehorses on beach	80	80
761	35p. Show jumping	95	95
762	41p. Pony Club event	1·10	1·10
763	60p. Shire mare and foal	1·60	1·60

179 The Journey to Bethlehem

1996. Christmas. Multicoloured.

764	19p. Type **179**	50	50
765	23p. The Shepherds	60	70
766	30p. The Nativity	90	95
767	60p. The Three Kings	1·40	1·50

180 Jersey Cow wearing Scarf

1997. Chinese New Year ("Year of the Ox"). Sheet 110 × 74 mm.

MS768	**180** £1 multicoloured	3·25	3·75

1997. "HONG KONG '97" International Stamp Exhibition. No. **MS**768 optd with exhibition emblem in black and "JERSEY AT HONG KONG '97" in red, both on sheet margin.

MS769	**180** £1 multicoloured	3·25	3·75

181 Lillie the Cow on the Beach

182 Red-breasted Merganser

1997. Tourism. "Lillie the Cow". Multicoloured. Self-adhesive.

770	(23p.) Type **181**	80	85
771	(23p.) Lillie taking photograph	80	85
772	(23p.) Carrying bucket and spade	80	85
773	(23p.) Eating meal at Mont Orgueil	80	85

1997. Seabirds and Waders. Multicoloured.

774	1p. Type **182**	10	10
775	2p. Sanderling	10	10
776	4p. Northern gannet ("Gannet")	10	10
777	5p. Great crested grebe	10	15
778	10p. Common tern	20	25
779	15p. Black-headed gull	30	35
780a	20p. Dunlin	40	45
781	21p. Sandwich tern	40	45
782	22p. Ringed plover	45	50
783	23p. Bar-tailed godwit	45	50
784a	24p. Atlantic puffin ("Puffin")	45	50
785	25p. Brent goose	50	55
786	26p. Grey plover	50	55
787	27p. Black scoter ("Common Scoter")	55	60
788	28p. Lesser black-backed gull	60	65
789	29p. Little egret	60	65
790	30p. Fulmar	60	65
791	31p. Golden plover	60	65
792	32p. Common greenshank ("Greenshank")	65	70
793	33p. Little grebe	65	70
794	34p. Great cormorant ("Common Cormorant")	70	75
795	35p. Western curlew ("Curlew")	70	75
796	37p. Oystercatcher	75	80
797	40p. Ruddy turnstone ("Turnstone")	80	85
798	44p. Herring gull	90	95
799	45p. Rock pipit	90	95
800	50p. Great black-backed gull	1·00	1·10
801	60p. Pied avocet ("Avocet")	1·25	1·40
802	65p. Grey heron	1·25	1·40
803	75p. Common redshank ("Redshank")	1·50	1·60
804	£1 Razorbill	2·00	2·10
805	£2 Shag	4·00	4·25
MS806	Four sheets, each 136 × 130 mm. (a) Nos. 774, 778/80, 784, 796, 803 and 805. (b) Nos. 775, 777, 781, 785, 790, 797, 801 and 804. (c) Nos. 776, 782, 786, 791/2, 795, 798 and 800. (d) Nos. 783, 787/9, 793/4, 799 and 802 Set of 4 sheets	24·00	24·00

183 De Havilland D.H.95 Flamingo

1997. 60th Anniv of Jersey Airport. Multicoloured.

807	20p. Type **183**	45	40
808	24p. Handley Page H.P.R. Marathon	55	40
809	31p. De Havilland D.H.114 Heron	65	65
810	37p. Boeing 737-236	95	90
811	43p. Britten Norman Trislander	1·10	1·00
812	63p. BAe 146-200	1·75	1·60

184 The Bull of St. Clement

1997. Europa. Tales and Legends. Multicoloured.

813	20p. Type **184**	65	60
814	24p. The Black Horse of St. Ouen	75	70
815	31p. The Black Dog of Bouley Bay	1·10	1·00
816	63p. Les Fontaines des Mittes	1·75	1·60

Nos. 814/15 include the "EUROPA" emblem.

1997. "Pacific 97" International Stamp Exhibition, San Francisco. No. **MS**806a optd with exhibition emblem on sheet margin.

MS817	136 × 130 mm. Nos. 774, 778/80, 784, 796, 803 and 805	7·50	8·00

185 Cycling

1997. 7th Island Games, Jersey. Multicoloured.

818	20p. Type **185**	55	55
819	24p. Archery	65	65
820	31p. Windsurfing	80	80
821	37p. Gymnastics	1·00	1·00
822	43p. Volleyball	1·10	1·10
823	63p. Running	1·75	1·75

186 Mallorcan Midwife Toad

1997. Wildlife Preservation Trust (6th series). Multicoloured.

824	20p. Type **186**	50	45
825	24p. Aye-aye	60	50
826	31p. Mauritius parakeet ("Echo Parakeet")	90	80
827	37p. Pigmy hog	1·00	1·00
828	43p. St. Lucia whip-tail	1·10	1·10
829	63p. Madagascar teal	1·75	1·75

187 Ash

1997. Trees. Multicoloured.

830	20p. Type **187**	50	45
831	24p. Elder	60	50
832	31p. Beech	90	80
833	37p. Sweet chestnut	1·00	1·00
834	43p. Hawthorn	1·10	1·10
835	63p. Common oak	1·75	1·75

188 Father Christmas and Reindeer outside Jersey Airport

1997. Christmas. Multicoloured.

836	20p. Type **188**	60	60
837	24p. Father Christmas with presents, St. Aubin's Harbour	70	70
838	31p. Father Christmas in sleigh, Mont Orgueil Castle	1·00	1·00
839	63p. Father Christmas with children, Royal Square, St. Helier	1·90	1·90

189 Wedding Photograph, 1947

1997. Golden Wedding of Queen Elizabeth and Prince Philip. Multicoloured.

840	50p. Type **189**	1·50	1·50
841	50p. Queen Elizabeth and Prince Philip, 1997	1·50	1·50
MS842	150 × 100 mm. £1.50 Full-length Wedding photograph, 1947 (38 × 50 mm)	4·50	4·50

190 Tiger wearing Scarf

1998. Chinese New Year ("Year of the Tiger"). Sheet 110 × 75 mm.

MS843	**190** £1 multicoloured	2·50	2·75

191 J.M.T. Bristol 4 Tonner, 1923

1998. 75th Anniv of Jersey Motor Transport Company. Buses. Multicoloured.

844	20p. Type **191**	55	50
845	24p. Safety Coach Service Regent double decker, 1934	65	50
846	31p. Slade's Dennis Lancet, c. 1936	75	70
847	37p. Tantivy Leyland PLSC Lion, 1947	1·00	1·00
848	43p. J.B.S. Morris, c. 1958	1·10	1·10
849	63p. J.M.T. Titan TD4 double decker, c. 1961	1·50	1·40

192 Creative Arts Festival

193 Hobie Cat and "Duke of Normandy" (launch)

1998. Europa. National Festivals. Multicoloured.

850	20p. Type **192**	65	45
851	24p. Jazz Festival	70	55
852	31p. Good Food Festival	90	90
853	63p. Floral Festival	1·75	1·75

Nos. 851/2 include the "EUROPA" emblem.

1998. Opening of Elizabeth Marina, St. Helier. Multicoloured.

854	20p. Type **193**	50	50
855	20p. Hobie Cat with white, yellow, red and green sails	50	50
856	20p. Hobie Cats with pink, purple and orange sails	50	50
857	20p. Bow of Hobie Cat with yellow, blue and purple sail	50	50
858	20p. Hobie Cat heeling	50	50
859	24p. Yacht with red, white and blue spinnaker	60	55
860	24p. Yacht with pink spinnaker	60	55
861	24p. Yacht with two white sails	60	55
862	24p. Trimaran	60	55
863	24p. Yacht with blue, white and yellow spinnaker in foreground	60	55

Nos. 854/8 and 859/63 respectively were printed together, se-tenant, forming composite designs of yacht races.

194 Bass

1998. International Year of the Ocean. Fishes. Multicoloured.

864	20p. Type **194**	50	50
865	24p. Red gurnard	65	65
866	31p. Skate	80	80
867	37p. Mackerel	1·00	1·00
868	43p. Tope	1·10	1·10
869	63p. Cuckoo wrasse	1·50	1·50

195 Cider-making

196 Irises

1998. Days Gone By. Multicoloured. Self-adhesive.

870	(20p.) Type **195**	90	90
871	(20p.) Potato barrels on cart	90	90
872	(20p.) Collecting seaweed for fertilizer	90	90
873	(20p.) Milking Jersey cows	90	90

1998. Flowers. Multicoloured.

874	20p. Type **196**	50	40
875	24p. Carnations	60	50
876	31p. Chrysanthemums	75	70
877	37p. Pinks	90	90

878 43p. Roses 1·00 1·00
879 63p. Lilies 1·40 1·40
MS880 150 × 100 mm. £1.50 Lilium "Star Gazer" (50 × 37 mm) 3·00 3·75

No. **MS**880 includes the "ITALIA '98" stamp exhibition emblem on the margin.

197 Central Market Crib

1998. Christmas. Cribs. Multicoloured.
881 20p. Type **197** 40 40
882 24p. St. Thomas's Church crib 50 55
883 31p. Trinity Parish Church crib 65 65
884 63p. Royal Square crib 1·50 1·60

198 Rabbit

1999. Chinese New Year ("Year of the Rabbit"). Sheet 110 × 75 mm.
MS885 **198** £1 multicoloured 2·50 2·75

199 Jersey Eastern Railway Mail Train

1999. 125th Anniv of U.P.U. Multicoloured.
886 20p. Type **199** 55 50
887 24p. "Brighton" (paddle-steamer) 65 60
888 43p. De Havilland D.H.86 Dragon Express at Jersey Airport 95 90
889 63p. Jersey Postal Service Morris Minor van 1·40 1·40

200 "Jessie Eliza", St. Catherine

1999. 175th Anniv of Royal National Lifeboat Institution. Multicoloured.
890 75p. Type **200** 2·00 2·00
891 £1 "Alexander Coutanche", St. Helier 2·50 2·50

201 "Cymbidium" Maufant "Jersey"

1999. Jersey Orchids (4th series). Multicoloured.
892 21p. Type **201** 55 50
893 25p. "Miltonia" Millbrook "Jersey" 55 50
894 31p. "Paphiopedilum" "Transvaal" 75 70
895 37p. "Paphiopedilum" "Elizabeth Castle" 85 80
896 43p. "Calanthe" "Five Oaks" 90 90
897 63p. "Cymbidium" Icho Tower "Trinity" 2·00 2·00
MS898 150 × 100 mm. £1.50 "Miltonia" Portelet 4·00 4·50

No. **MS**898 also includes the "Australia '99" World Stamp Exhibition, Melbourne, emblem on the margin at top left.

202 Howard Davis Park

1999. Europa. Parks and Gardens. Multicoloured.
899 21p. Type **202** 50 50
900 25p. Sir Winston Churchill Memorial Park 70 70
901 31p. Coronation Park 1·00 1·00
902 63p. La Collette Gardens 2·00 2·00

Nos. 900/1 include the "EUROPA" logo at top left and all four values show the "iBRA '99" International Stamp Exhibition, Nuremberg, emblem at top right.

203 Prince Edward and Miss Sophie Rhys-Jones

1999. Royal Wedding.
903 **203** 35p. multicoloured (yellow background) 1·00 1·00
904 35p. multicoloured (blue background) 1·00 1·00

204 Jersey-built Benz, 1899

1999. Vintage Cars (3rd series). Centenary of Motoring in Jersey. Multicoloured.
905 21p. Type **204** 45 45
906 25p. Star Tourer, 1910 55 55
907 31p. Citroen "Traction Avant", 1938 65 65
908 37p. Talbot BG110 Tourer, 1937 80 80
909 43p. Morris Cowley Six Special Coupe, 1934 90 90
910 63p. Ford Anglia Saloon, 1946 1·50 1·50

205 West European Hedgehog

1999. Small Mammals. Multicoloured.
911 21p. Type **205** 45 45
912 25p. Eurasian red squirrel 55 55
913 31p. Nathusius pipistrelle 65 65
914 37p. Jersey bank vole 80 80
915 43p. Lesser white-toothed shrew 90 90
916 63p. Common mole 1·50 1·50

206 Gorey Pierhead Light

207 Mistletoe

1999. 150th Anniv of First Lighthouse on Jersey (1st series). Multicoloured.
917 21p. Type **206** 45 45
918 25p. La Corbiere 55 55
919 34p. Noirmont Point 75 75
920 38p. Demie de Pas 1·00 1·00
921 44p. Greve d'Azette 1·25 1·25
922 64p. Sorel Point 2·00 2·00

See also Nos. 1086/91.

1999. Christmas. Festive Foliage. Multicoloured.
923 21p. Type **207** 45 45
924 25p. Holly 55 55
925 34p. Ivy 75 75
926 64p. Christmas Rose 1·50 1·50

208 Jersey Crest

2000. New Millennium.
927 **208** £10 gold, red and carmine 20·00 20·00

209 Dragon

2000. Chinese New Year ("Year of the Dragon"). Sheet 110 × 75 mm.
MS928 £1 multicoloured 2·50 2·50

210 "Ocean Adventure" (Gemma Care)

2000. "Stampin' the Future" (children's stamp design competition) Winners. Multicoloured.
929 22p. Type **210** 55 55
930 22p. "Solar Power" (Chantal Varley-Best) 55 55
931 22p. "Floating City and Space Cars" (Nicola Singleton) 55 55
932 22p. "Conservation" (Carly Logan) 55 55
MS933 150 × 100 mm. Nos. 929/32 3·00 3·50

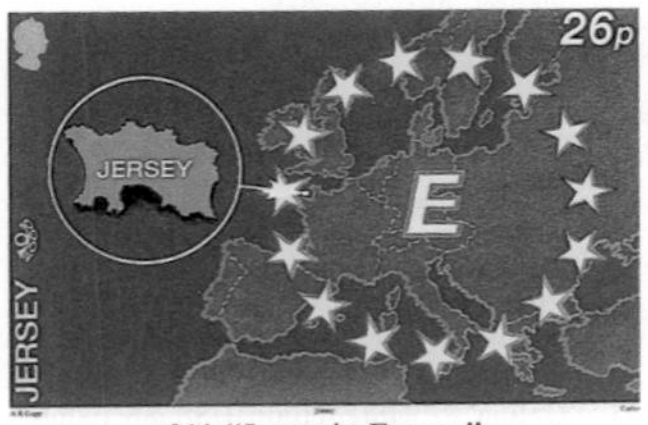

211 "Jersey in Europe"

2000. Europa. Multicoloured.
934 26p. Type **211** 90 90
935 34p. "Building Europe" (29 × 39 mm) 1·25 1·25

212 Roman Merchant Ship

2000. "The Stamp Show 2000" International Stamp Exhibition, London. Maritime Heritage. Mult.
936 22p. Type **212** 60 60
937 22p. Viking longship 60 60
938 22p. 13th-century warship 60 60
939 22p. 14th–15th-century merchant ship 60 60
940 22p. Tudor warship 60 60
941 26p. 17th-century warship 65 65
942 26p. 18th-century naval cutter 65 65
943 26p. 19th-century barque 65 65
944 26p. 19th-century oyster cutter 65 65
945 26p. 20th-century ketch 65 65
MS946 174 × 104 mm. Nos. 936/45 6·00 6·00

213 Bottle-nosed Dolphins

2000. World Environment Day. Marine Mammals. Multicoloured.
947 22p. Type **213** 50 55
948 26p. Long-finned pilot whales 55 60
949 34p. Common porpoises 80 85
950 38p. Grey seals 1·00 1·10
951 44p. Risso's dolphins 1·10 1·25
952 64p. White-beaked dolphin 1·50 1·75
MS953 150 × 100 mm. £1.50 Common dolphins (80 × 29 mm) 4·00 4·50

214 Prince William and Alps

2000. 18th Birthday of Prince William. Multicoloured.
954 75p. Type **214** 1·50 1·50
955 75p. Prince William and polo player 1·50 1·50
956 75p. Prince William and Beaumaris Castle 1·50 1·50
957 75p. Prince William and fireworks 1·50 1·50

2000. "World Stamp Expo 2000", Anaheim, U.S.A. As No. **MS**953, but with multicoloured exhibition logo added to top left corner of sheet margin.
MS958 150 × 100 mm. £1.50 Common dolphins (80 × 29 mm) 3·50 4·00

215 Queen Elizabeth the Queen Mother with Roses

2000. Queen Elizabeth the Queen Mother's 100th Birthday. Multicoloured.
959 50p. Type **215** 1·25 1·25
960 50p. Queen Elizabeth the Queen Mother with daisies 1·25 1·25
MS961 150 × 100 mm. Nos. 959/60 2·25 3·00

216 Supermarine Spitfire Mk Ia

2000. 60th Anniv of Battle of Britain. Multicoloured.
962 22p. Type **216** 50 55
963 26p. Hawker Hurricane Mk I 60 65
964 36p. Bristol Blenheim Mk IV 80 85
965 40p. Vickers Wellington Mk Ic 90 95
966 45p. Boulton Paul Defiant Mk I 1·00 1·10
967 65p. Short Sunderland Mk I 1·50 1·60

217 Virgin Mary

2000. Christmas. Children's Nativity Play. Multicoloured.
968 22p. Type **217** 55 55
969 26p. Shepherd 65 65
970 36p. Angel 90 90
971 65p. Magi with gift 1·50 1·50

218 Snake

2001. Chinese New Year ("Year of the Snake"). Sheet 110 × 75 mm.
MS972 **218** £1 multicoloured . . 2·25 2·50

219 *Rose* (1851–61)

2001. Maritime Links with France. Mail Packet Ships. Multicoloured.

973	22p. Type **219**	50	55
974	26p. *Comete* (1856–67) . . .	60	65
975	36p. *Cygne* (1894–1912) . . .	80	85
976	40p. *Victoria* (1896–1918) . .	90	95
977	45p. *Attala* (1920–25)	1·00	1·10
978	65p. *Brittany* (1933–62) . . .	1·50	1·60

220 H.M.S. *Jersey* (4th Rate), 1654–91

2001. Royal Navy Ships named after Jersey. Multicoloured.

979	23p. Type **220**	50	55
980	26p. H.M.S. *Jersey* (6th Rate), 1694–98	60	65
981	37p. H.M.S. *Jersey* (4th Rate), 1698–1731	80	85
982	41p. H.M.S. *Jersey* (4th Rate), 1736–83	90	95
983	46p. H.M.S. *Jersey* (cutter), 1860–73	1·00	1·10
984	66p. H.M.S. *Jersey* (destroyer), 1938–41 . . .	1·50	1·60

221 Jersey Cows

2001. Jersey Agriculture. Multicoloured. Self-adhesive.

985	(26p.) Type **221**	65	70
986	(26p.) Potatoes	65	70
987	(26p.) Tomatoes	65	70
988	(26p.) Cauliflower and purple-sprouting broccoli	65	70
989	(26p.) Peppers and courgettes	65	70

Nos. 985/9, which are inscribed "UK MINIMUM POSTAGE PAID", were initially sold at 26p each.

222 Queen Elizabeth II

2001. 75th Birthday of Queen Elizabeth II.
990 **222** £3 multicoloured . . . . 6·00 6·50

223 Agile Frog

2001. Europa. Pond Life. Multicoloured.

991	23p. Type **223**	60	65
992	26p. Trout	70	75
993	37p. White water-lily	1·00	1·10
994	41p. Common blue damselfly	1·00	1·25
995	46p. Palmate newt	1·25	1·40
996	66p. Tufted duck	1·50	1·60
MS997	150 × 100 mm. £1.50 Common kingfisher (36 × 50 mm)	2·00	2·25

The 26 and 37p. values include "EUROPA" emblem.

2001. "Belgica 2001" International Stamp Exhibition, Brussels. No. **MS**997 optd "JERSEY AT BELGICA 2001" on sheet margin.
MS998 150 × 100 mm. £1.50 Common kingfisher (36 × 50 mm) 4·00 4·50

224 Long-eared Owl

2001. Birds of Prey. Multicoloured.

999	23p. Type **224**	50	55
1000	26p. Peregrine falcon . . .	60	65
1001	37p. Short-eared owl . . .	80	85
1002	41p. Western marsh harrier ("Marsh Harrier") . . .	90	95
1003	46p. Northern sparrow hawk ("Sparrowhawk")	1·00	1·10
1004	66p. Tawny owl	1·50	1·60
MS1005	110 × 75 mm. £1.50 Barn owl (30 × 47 mm)	5·00	5·00

225 *Jersey Clipper* (yacht)

2001. The Times Clipper 2000 Round the World Yacht Race. Sheet 150 × 100 mm.
MS1006 **225** £1.50 multicoloured 4·00 5·00

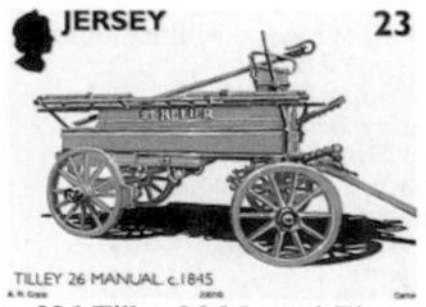

226 Tilley 26 Manual Fire Engine, c. 1845

2001. Centenary of Jersey Fire and Rescue Service. Fire Engines. Multicoloured.

1007	23p. Type **226**	50	55
1008	26p. Albion Merryweather, c. 1935 . .	60	65
1009	37p. Dennis Ace, c. 1940 . .	80	85
1010	41p. Dennis F8 Pump Escape, c. 1952	90	95
1011	46p. Land Rover Merryweather, c. 1968 . .	1·00	1·10
1012	66p. Dennis Carmichael, c. 1989 . . .	1·50	1·60

2001. "Hafnia 01" International Stamp Exhibition, Copenhagen. As No. **MS**1005, but with brown-red exhibition logo added to bottom left corner of sheet margin and additionally inscr "Jersey visits Hafnia 01 Denmark".
MS1013 £1.50 Barn owl (30 × 47 mm) . . . . 3·25 3·50

227 Nativity

2001. Christmas. Bells. Multicoloured. Self-adhesive.

1014	(23p.) Type **227**	45	50
1015	(23p.) Street decorations . .	45	50
1016	(23p.) Carol singers with hand bells	45	50
1017	(23p.) Father Christmas . .	45	50
1018	(23p.) Christmas tree decorations	45	50
1019	(26p.) Adoration of the shepherds	50	55
1020	(26p.) Carol singers and Father Christmas in sleigh	50	55
1021	(26p.) Paper bell, chains and Christmas tree	50	55
1022	(26p.) Church bells ringing	50	55
1023	(26p.) Christmas cracker . .	50	55

Nos. 1014/18, which are inscribed "JERSEY MINIMUM POSTAGE PAID", were initially sold for 23p., and Nos. 1019/23, inscribed "U.K. MINIMUM POSTAGE PAID", were sold for 26p.

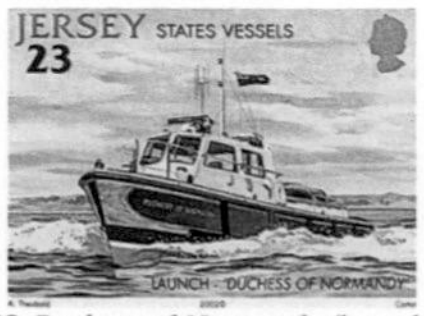

228 *Duchess of Normandy* (launch)

2002. States Vessels. Multicoloured.

1024	23p. Type **228**	50	55
1025	29p. *Duke of Normandy* (tug)	65	70
1026	38p. *Challenger* (customs patrol boat)	80	85
1027	47p. *Le Fret* (pilot boat) . .	1·00	1·10
1028	68p. *Norman le Brocq* (fisheries protection vessel)	1·50	1·60

229 Queen Elizabeth in Coronation Robes (after Cecil Beaton)

2002. Golden Jubilee.
1029 **229** £3 multicoloured . . . . 6·25 6·50

230 Horse

2002. Chinese New Year ("Year of the Horse"). Sheet 110 × 75 mm.
MS1030 **230** £1 multicoloured . . 2·25 2·50

231 Elephant Float, Parish of St. John, 1980

2002. Europa. Circus. Designs showing carnival floats. Multicoloured.

1031	23p. Type **231**	50	55
1032	29p. Clown with red hair, Grouville, 1996	65	70
1033	38p. Clown with white hat, Optimists, 1988	80	85
1034	68p. Performing seal, Grouville, 1996	3·00	3·50

The 29p. and 38p. values include the "EUROPA" emblem.

232 Aubrey Boomer

2002. Centenary of La Moye Golf Club. Multicoloured.

1035	23p. Type **232**	50	55
1036	29p. Harry Vardon	65	70
1037	38p. Sir Henry Cotton . . .	80	85
1038	47p. Diagram of golf swing	1·00	1·10
1039	68p. Putting	1·50	1·75

233 Vauxhall 12, 1952

2002. 50th Anniv of States of Jersey Police. Patrol Vehicles. Multicoloured.

1040	23p. Type **233**	50	55
1041	29p. Jaguar 2.4 MkII, 1959–60	65	70
1042	38p. Austin 1800, 1972–73	80	85
1043	40p. Ford Cortina MkIV, 1978	85	90
1044	47p. Honda ST 1100 motorcycle, 1995–2000 . .	1·00	1·10
1045	68p. Vauxhall Vectra, 1998–2000	1·50	1·75

234 Honey Bee

2002. Insects. Multicoloured.

1046	23p. Type **234**	50	55
1047	29p. Seven-spot ladybird . .	65	70
1048	38p. Great green bush-cricket	80	45
1049	40p. Greater horn-tail . . .	85	90
1050	47p. Emperor dragonfly . .	1·10	1·25
1051	68p. Hawthorn shield bug	1·50	1·75

235 Queen Elizabeth the Queen Mother in 1910, 1923 and 2002

2002. Queen Elizabeth the Queen Mother Commemoration.
1052 **235** £2 multicoloured . . . . 4·25 4·50

236 Hydrangeas

2002. Centenary of "Battle of Flowers" Parade. Multicoloured.

1053	23p. Type **236**	50	55
1054	29p. Chrysanthemums . . .	65	70
1055	38p. Hare's tails and pampas grasses	80	85
1056	40p. Asters	85	90
1057	47p. Carnations	1·00	1·10
1058	68p. Gladioli	1·50	1·75
MS1059	150 × 100 mm. £2 "Zanzibar" float (winner of Prix d'Honneur, 1999) (75 × 38 mm)	4·25	4·50

237 British Dilute Tortoiseshell

2002. 25th Anniv of Caesarea Cat Club. Multicoloured.

1060	23p. Type **237**	50	55
1061	29p. Cream Persian	75	70
1062	38p. Blue exotic shorthair	80	85
1063	40p. Black smoke Devon rex	85	90
1064	47p. British silver tabby . .	1·00	1·10
1065	68p. Usual Abyssinian . . .	1·50	1·75
MS1066	110 × 75 mm. £2 British cream/white bi-colour cross (38 × 51 mm)	4·25	4·50

238 Victorian Pillar Box

2002. 150th Anniv of the First Pillar Box. Multicoloured.

1067	23p. Type **238**	50	55
1068	29p. Edward VII wall box	65	70
1069	38p. George V wall box . .	80	85
1070	40p. George V ship box . .	85	90

1071	47p. Elizabeth II pillar box (1952)	1·00	1·10
1072	68p. Elizabeth II pillar boxes (2000)	1·50	1·60
MS1073	150 × 100 mm. £2 Posting letter in Victorian pillar box (40 × 77 mm)	4·25	4·50

239 Sanchez-Besa Hydroplane

2003. Centenary of Powered Flight. Multicoloured.

1074	23p. Type **239**	50	55
1075	29p. Supermarine S.6B seaplane	65	70
1076	38p. De Havilland DH84 Dragon	80	85
1077	40p. De Havilland DH89a Rapide	85	90
1078	47p. Vickers 701 Viscount	1·00	1·10
1079	68p. BAC One Eleven	1·50	1·60
MS1080	112 × 76 mm. £2 Jacob Ellehammer's Biplane, 1906 (60 × 40 mm)	4·25	4·50

240 Ram

2003. Chinese New Year ("Year of the Ram"). Sheet 110 × 75 mm.

MS1081	**240** £1 multicoloured	2·25	2·40

241 "Portelet" (Adrian Allinson)

2003. Europa. Travel Posters. Multicoloured.

1082	23p. Type **241**	50	55
1083	29p. "Jersey" (Lander) (vert)	65	70
1084	38p. "Channel Islands Map" (vert)	80	85
1085	68p. "Jersey, the Sunny Channel Island" (A. Allinson)	1·50	1·60

The 29p. and 38p. values include the "EUROPA" emblem.

2003. Jersey Lighthouses (2nd series). T **206**. Multicoloured.

1086	29p. Violet Channel light buoy	65	70
1087	29p. St. Catherine's Breakwater Light	65	70
1088	30p. Frouquie Aubert light buoy	65	70
1089	30p. Mont Ube Lighthouse	65	70
1090	48p. Banc des Ormes light buoy	1·00	1·10
1091	48p. Gronez Point Lighthouse	1·00	1·10

242 Southern-marsh Orchid

2003. Wild Orchids. Multicoloured.

1092	29p. Type **242**	60	65
1093	30p. Loose-flowered orchid	60	65
1094	39p. Spotted orchid	80	85
1095	50p. Autumn ladies tresses	1·00	1·10
1096	53p. Green-winged orchid	1·10	1·25
1097	69p. Pyramidal orchid	1·40	1·50
MS1098	110 × 75 mm. £2 Loose-flowered orchid (different)	4·00	4·25

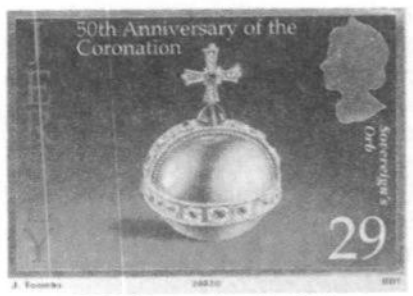

243 Sovereign's Orb

2003. 50th Anniv of Coronation. Coronation Regalia. Multicoloured.

1099	29p. Type **243**	60	65
1100	30p. St. Edward's Crown	60	65
1101	39p. Sceptre with Cross	80	85
1102	50p. Ampulla and Spoon	1·00	1·10
1103	53p. Sovereign's Ring	1·00	1·10
1104	69p. Armills	1·40	1·50
MS1105	150 × 100 mm. Nos. 1099/1104	5·25	5·75

244 Prince William, Prince Charles and Queen Elizabeth

2003. Royal Links. Sheet 110 × 75 mm.

MS1106	**244** £2 multicoloured	4·00	4·25

245 Rock Samphire and Paternosters

246 Albino Rex Rabbit

2003. Offshore Reefs. Multicoloured. Self-adhesive.

1107	(29p.) Type **245**	60	65
1108	(29p.) Bluebells and Les Ecrehous	60	65
1109	(29p.) Tree-mallow and Les Ecrehous	60	65
1110	(29p.) Smooth Sow-thistle and Les Minquiers	60	65
1111	(29p.) Thrift and Les Minquiers	60	65

Nos. 1107/11 are inscribed "JERSEY MINIMUM POSTAGE PAID" and were initially sold at 29p.

2003. Pets. Multicoloured.

1112	29p. Type **246**	60	65
1113	30p. Black labrador	60	65
1114	38p. Canary and budgerigar	75	80
1115	53p. Hamster	1·00	1·10
1116	69p. Guinea pig	1·40	1·50
MS1117	150 × 100 mm. £2 Border collie (39 × 51 mm)	4·00	4·25

2003. "Bangkok 2003" International Stamp Exhibition. No. **MS**1098 optd **Jersey at Bangkok 2003** and emblem on sheet margin.

MS1118	110 × 75 mm. £2 Loose-flowered orchid	4·00	4·25

2003. Winter Flowers. As T **196**. Multicoloured.

1119	29p. Japanese quince	60	65
1120	30p. Winter jasmine	60	65
1121	39p. Snowdrop	80	85
1122	48p. Winter heath	95	1·00
1123	53p. Chinese witch-hazel	1·00	1·10
1124	69p. Winter daphne	1·40	1·50

247 Rook

2004. Jersey Festivals (1st issue). Festival of Chess. Multicoloured.

1125	29p. Type **247**	60	65
1126	30p. Knight	60	65
1127	39p. Bishop	80	85
1128	48p. Pawn	95	1·00
1129	53p. Queen	1·00	1·10
1130	69p. King	1·40	1·50

248 Monkey

2004. Chinese New Year ("Year of the Monkey"). Sheet 110 × 75 mm.

MS1131	**248** £1 multicoloured	2·00	2·10

249 St. Aubin's Harbour

2004. Europa. Holidays. Multicoloured.

1132	29p. Type **249**	60	65
1133	30p. Mont Orgueil Castle	60	65
1134	39p. Corbiere Lighthouse	85	90
1135	69p. Rozel Harbour	1·40	1·50

The 30p. and 39p. values include the "EUROPA" emblem.

250 Green-winged Teal ("Eurasian Teal")

2004. Ducks and Swans. Multicoloured.

1136	32p. Type **250**	65	70
1137	33p. Mute swan	65	70
1138	40p. Northern shoveler	80	85
1139	49p. Common pochard	1·00	1·10
1140	62p. Black swan	1·20	1·30
1141	70p. European Wigeon ("Eurasian Wigeon")	1·40	1·50
MS1142	150 × 100 mm. £2 Mallard (38 × 50 mm)	4·00	4·25

POSTAGE DUE STAMPS

D 1

D 3 Arms of St. Clement and Dovecote at Samares

1969.

D1	D 1 1d. violet	65	1·10
D2	2d. sepia	90	1·10
D3	3d. mauve	1·00	1·10
D4	– 1s. green	5·50	5·00
D5	– 2s.6d. grey	13·00	14·00
D6	– 5s. red	15·00	16·00

DESIGNS: 1s., 2s.6d., 5s. Map.

1971. Decimal Currency. Design as Nos. D4/6, but values in new currency.

D 7	½p. black	10	10
D 8	1p. blue	10	10
D 9	2p. brown	10	10
D10	3p. purple	10	10
D11	4p. red	10	10
D12	5p. green	10	10
D13	6p. orange	10	10
D14	7p. yellow	10	10
D15	8p. blue	15	20
D16	10p. green	15	20
D17	11p. brown	20	20
D18	14p. violet	30	30
D19	25p. green	35	40
D20	50p. purple	90	90

1978. Parish Arms and Views.

D21	D 3 1p. black and green	10	10
D22	– 2p. black and yellow	10	10
D23	– 3p. black and brown	10	10
D24	– 4p. black and red	10	10
D25	– 5p. black and blue	10	10
D26	– 10p. black and olive	10	10
D27	– 12p. black and blue	15	10
D28	– 14p. black and orange	20	15
D29	– 15p. black and mauve	25	25
D30	– 20p. black and green	30	30
D31	– 50p. black and brown	90	55
D32	– £1 black and blue	1·40	1·00

DESIGNS: 2p. Arms of St. Lawrence and Handois Reservoir; 3p. Arms of St. John and Sorel Point; 4p. Arms of St. Ouen and Pinnacle Rock; 5p. Arms of St. Peter and Quetivel Mill; 10p. Arms of St. Martin and St. Catherine's Breakwater; 12p. Arms of St. Helier and Harbour; 14p. Arms of St. Saviour and Highlands College; 15p. Arms of St. Brelade and Beauport Bay; 20p. Arms of Grouville and La Hougue Bie; 50p. Arms of St. Mary and Perry Farm; £1 Arms of Trinity and Bouley Bay.

D 4 St. Brelade

1982. Jersey Harbours.

D33	D 4 1p. green	10	10
D34	– 2p. yellow	10	10
D35	– 3p. brown	10	10
D36	– 4p. red	10	10
D37	– 5p. blue	10	10
D38	– 6p. green	10	15
D39	– 7p. mauve	15	20
D40	– 8p. red	15	20
D41	– 9p. green	20	20
D42	– 10p. blue	20	15
D43	– 20p. green	40	30
D44	– 30p. purple	60	40
D45	– 40p. orange	80	45
D46	– £1 violet	2·00	75

DESIGNS: 2p. St. Aubin; 3p. Rozel; 4p. Greve de Lecq; 5p. Bouley Bay; 6p. St. Catherine; 7p. Gorey; 8p. Bonne Nuit; 9p. La Roque; 10p. St. Helier; 20p. Ronez; 30p. La Collette; 40p. Elizabeth Castle; £1 Upper Harbour Marina.

JHALAWAR Pt. 1

A state of Rajasthan, India. Now uses Indian stamps.

4 paisa = 1 anna.

1 Apsara (dancing nymph of Hindu Paradise)

1886. Imperf.

1	**1** 1p. green	4·25	11·00
2	– ¼a. green	1·10	1·25

The ¼a. is larger and has a different frame.

JIND Pt. 1

A "convention" state of the Punjab, India, which now uses Indian stamps.

12 pies = 1 anna; 16 annas = 1 rupee.

J **1** (½a.)

J **6** (¼a.)

1874. Imperf.

J 8	J **1** ½a. blue	75	3·75
J 9	1a. purple	1·50	8·50
J 3	2a. bistre	1·00	3·75
J11	4a. green	2·25	11·00
J12	8a. purple	7·00	10·00

1882. Various designs and sizes. Imperf or perf.

J16	J **6** ¼a. brown	30	1·25
J19	½a. bistre	80	60
J20	1a. brown	1·75	3·25
J22	2a. blue	2·50	1·00
J23	4a. green	1·50	90
J25	8a. red	5·50	4·50

Stamps of India (Queen Victoria) overprinted.

1885. Optd **JHIND STATE** vert (curved).

1	**23** ½a. turquoise	3·00	3·75
2	– 1a. purple	30·00	40·00
3	– 2a. blue	12·00	15·00
4	– 4a. green (No. 71)	55·00	75·00
5	– 8a. mauve	£425	
6	– 1r. grey (No. 101)	£450	

1885. Optd **JEEND STATE**.

7	**23** ½a. turquoise	£100	
8	– 1a. purple	£100	
9	– 2a. blue	£100	
10	– 4a. green (No. 71)	£140	
11	– 8a. mauve	£160	
12	– 1r. grey (No. 101)	£170	

1886. Optd **JHIND STATE** horiz.

17	**23** ½a. turquoise	70	10
18	– 1a. purple	1·25	20
20	– 1a.6p. brown	1·50	2·75
21	– 2a. blue	1·75	40
23	– 3a. orange	1·75	50
15	– 4a. green (No. 71)	48·00	
24	– 4a. green (No. 96)	2·75	2·00
27	– 6a. brown	1·50	9·50
28	– 8a. mauve	5·00	15·00
30	– 12a. purple on red	5·00	21·00
31	– 1r. grey (No. 101)	10·00	42·00
32	**37** 1r. green and red	8·50	48·00
33	**38** 2r. red and orange	£250	£750
34	3r. brown and green	£450	£750
35	5r. blue and violet	£475	£750

1900. Optd **JHIND STATE** horiz.

36	**40** 3p. red	1·10	1·00
37	3p. grey	30	3·00
38	**23** ½a. green	3·25	5·00
40	– 1a. red	40	5·50

Stamps of India optd **JHIND STATE**.

1903. King Edward VII.

41	**41** 3p. grey	25	10
43	– ½a. green (No. 122)	1·00	1·50

44	–	1a. red (No. 123)	2·25	1·40
46	–	2a. lilac	2·00	80
47	–	2½a. blue	50	5·00
48	–	3a. orange	1·00	40
50	–	4a. olive	6·50	9·00
51	–	6a. bistre	6·50	18·00
52	–	8a. mauve	2·50	19·00
54	–	12a. purple on red	2·50	12·00
55	–	1r. green and red	2·75	16·00

1907. King Edward VII (inscr "INDIA POSTAGE and REVENUE").

56		½a. green (No. 149)	20	20
57		1a. red (No. 150)	50	70

1913. King George V.

58	**55**	3p. grey	10	1·75
59	**56**	½a. green	10	75
60	**57**	1a. red	10	45
61	**59**	2a. purple	15	4·00
62	**62**	3a. orange	1·50	10·00
63	**64**	6a. bistre	6·00	24·00

1914. Stamps of India (King George V) optd **JIND STATE** in two lines.

64a	**55**	3p. grey	75	20
65b	**56**	½a. green	2·00	15
66	**57**	1a. red	1·25	15
80		1a. brown	4·25	1·90
67	**58**	1½a. brown (A. No. 163)	1·75	4·25
67a		1½a. brown (B. No. 165)	35	1·50
81		1½a. red (B.)	20	1·50
69	**59**	2a. purple	2·50	50
70	**61**	2a.6p. blue	35	4·00
82		2a.6p. orange	50	6·00
71	**62**	3a. orange	50	3·00
83		3a. blue	1·75	4·00
72	**63**	4a. olive	1·60	8·00
73a	**64**	6a. brown	2·25	13·00
74	**65**	8a. mauve	3·75	10·00
75	**66**	12a. red	3·00	14·00
76	**67**	1r. brown and green	8·00	17·00
77		2r. red and brown	5·50	£110
78		5r. blue and violet	38·00	£200

1922. No. 192 of India optd **JIND**.

79	**57**	9p. on 1a. red	1·25	13·00

Stamps of India optd **JIND STATE** in one line.

1927. King George V.

84	**55**	3p. grey	10	10
85	**56**	½a. green	10	35
86	**80**	9p. green	1·40	40
87	**57**	1a. brown	15	10
88	**82**	1a.3p. mauve	25	30
89	**58**	1½a. red	60	2·50
90	**70**	2a. lilac	2·00	40
91w	**61**	2a.6p. orange	1·00	9·00
92	**62**	3a. blue	3·75	12·00
93w	**83**	3a.6p. blue	60	16·00
94w	**71**	4a. green	1·50	2·50
95	**64**	6a. bistre	65	17·00
96	**65**	8a. mauve	3·75	2·00
97w	**66**	12a. red	5·00	18·00
98	**67**	1r. brown and green	3·75	4·50
99		2r. red and orange	32·00	£120
100		5r. blue and violet	12·00	38·00
101		10r. green and red	13·00	18·00
102		15r. blue and olive	75·00	£500
103		25r. orange and blue	£110	£650

1934. King George V.

104	**79**	½a. green	30	25
105	**81**	1a. brown	1·50	30
106	**59**	2a. orange	1·75	60
107	**62**	3a. red	2·50	40
108	**63**	4a. olive	3·00	1·25

1937. King George VI.

109	**91**	3p. slate	11·00	1·75
110		½a. brown	75	3·25
111		9p. green	75	3·00
112		1a. red	75	60
113	**92**	2a. red	1·75	15·00
114	–	2a.6p. violet	1·25	17·00
115	–	3a. green	6·00	14·00
116	–	3a.6p. blue	3·00	17·00
117	–	4a. brown	9·00	15·00
118	–	6a. green	5·50	21·00
119	–	8a. violet	4·50	19·00
120	–	12a. red	2·75	23·00
121	**93**	1r. slate and brown	12·00	32·00
122		2r. purple and brown	15·00	95·00
123		5r. green and blue	25·00	75·00
124		10r. purple and red	45·00	70·00
125		15r. brown and green	£110	£700
126		25r. slate and purple	£450	£750

1941. Stamps of India (King George VI) optd **JIND**.

(a) On issue of 1937.

127	**91**	3p. slate	14·00	17·00
128		½a. brown	1·00	1·25
129		9p. green	12·00	14·00
130		1a. red	1·00	4·25
131	**93**	1r. slate and brown	8·00	23·00
132		2r. purple and brown	17·00	28·00
133		5r. green and blue	40·00	85·00
134		10r. purple and red	55·00	80·00
135		15r. brown and green	£130	£140
136		25r. slate and purple	60·00	£350

(b) On issue of 1940.

137	**100a**	3p. slate	50	75
138		½a. mauve	50	1·40
139		9p. green	60	3·25
140		1a. red	65	1·25
141	**101**	1a.3p. yellow-brown	1·00	3·75
142		1½a. violet	8·00	4·00
143		2a. red	1·75	3·50
144		3a. violet	21·00	4·25
145		3½a. blue	9·00	8·00
146	**102**	4a. brown	4·75	4·00
147		6a. green	5·50	13·00
148		8a. violet	2·75	11·00
149		12a. purple	14·00	14·00

OFFICIAL STAMPS

Postage stamps of Jind optd **SERVICE.**

1885. Nos. 1/3 (Queen Victoria).

O1	**O 23**	½a. green	90	30
O2	–	1a. purple	60	10
O3	–	2a. blue	35·00	42·00

1886. Nos. 17/32 and No. 38 (Queen Victoria).

O12	**23**	½a. turquoise	1·00	10
O22	–	½a. green (No. 38)	1·75	30
O14	–	1a. purple	9·50	70
O16	–	2a. blue	1·00	30
O17	–	4a. green (No. 24)	2·00	1·00
O19	–	8a. mauve	4·00	3·00
O21	**37**	1r. green and red	6·00	38·00

1903. Nos. 42/55 (King Edward VII).

O23	**41**	3p. grey	40	10
O25	–	½a. green (No. 43)	2·25	10
O26	–	1a. red (No. 44)	1·75	10
O28	–	2a. lilac	90	10
O29	–	4a. olive	90	45
O31	–	8a. mauve	4·25	1·50
O32	–	1r. green and red	2·50	2·25

1907. Nos. 56/7 (King Edward VII).

O33		½a. green	50	10
O34		1a. red	75	10

1914. Official stamps of India. Nos. O75/96 (King George V) optd **JIND STATE.**

O35	**55**	3p. grey	10	10
O36	**56**	½a. green	10	10
O37	**57**	1a. red	60	10
O46		1a. brown	60	10
O39	**59**	2a. purple	25	15
O40	**63**	4a. olive	85	15
O41	**64**	6a. bistre	1·25	2·25
O42	**65**	8a. mauve	70	1·00
O43	**67**	1r. brown and green	1·50	1·75
O44		2r. red and brown	14·00	65·00
O45		5r. blue and violet	19·00	£180

Stamps of India optd **JIND STATE SERVICE**.

1927. King George V.

O47	**55**	3p. grey	10	20
O48	**56**	½a. green	10	90
O49	**80**	9p. green	60	15
O50	**57**	1a. brown	10	10
O51	**82**	1a.3p. mauve	40	15
O52	**70**	2a. lilac	25	15
O64	**59**	2a. orange	30	15
O53	**61**	2a.6p. orange	90	19·00
O54	**71**	4a. green	35	25
O55w	**64**	6a. bistre	3·50	14·00
O56w	**65**	8a. mauve	60	1·75
O57	**66**	12a. red	1·00	14·00
O58	**67**	1r. brown and green	3·75	3·75
O59		2r. red and orange	40·00	32·00
O60		5r. blue and purple	13·00	£190
O61		10r. green and red	32·00	£110

1934. King George V.

O62	**79**	½a. green	20	15
O63	**81**	1a. brown	20	15
O65	**63**	4a. olive	4·50	30

1937. King George VI.

O66	**91**	½a. brown	50·00	30
O67		9p. green	85	95·00
O68		1a. red	55	30
O69	**93**	1r. slate and brown	27·00	45·00
O70		2r. purple and brown	42·00	£180
O71		5r. green and blue	70·00	£325
O72		10r. purple and red	£250	£900

1939. Official stamps of India optd **JIND.**

O73	**O 20**	3p. slate	50	1·10
O74		½a. brown	1·50	70
O75		½a. purple	60	30
O76		9p. green	2·25	9·50
O77		1a. red	3·00	15
O78		1½a. violet	8·00	1·25
O79		2a. orange	4·50	30
O80		2½a. violet	3·50	8·00
O81		4a. brown	6·00	3·00
O82		8a. violet	6·00	5·00

1943. Stamps of India (King George VI) optd **JIND SERVICE.**

O83	**93**	1r. slate and brown	18·00	45·00
O84		2r. purple and brown	32·00	£130
O85		5r. green and blue	70·00	£325
O86		10r. purple and red	£140	£425

JOHORE Pt. 1

A state of the Federation of Malaya, incorporated in Malaysia in 1963.

100 cents = 1 dollar (Straits or Malayan).

Queen Victoria stamps of Straits Settlements overprinted.

1876. Optd with Crescent and Star.

1	**1**	2c. brown	£11000	£4250

1882. Optd **JOHORE**.

8	**1**	2c. pink (no full point)	85·00	£100
6		2c. pink (with full point)	£170	£180

1884. Optd **JOHOR**.

10	**1**	2c. pink (no full point)	11·00	7·50
14		2c. pink (with full point)	£130	55·00

1891. Surch **JOHOR Two CENTS**.

17	**1**	2c. on 24c. green	25·00	38·00

21 Sultan Aboubakar

24 Sultan Ibrahim

1891.

21	**21**	1c. purple	50	50
22		2c. purple and yellow	50	1·50
23		3c. purple and red	55	50
24		4c. purple and black	2·75	16·00
25		5c. purple and green	7·00	21·00
26		6c. purple and blue	8·00	21·00
27		$1 green and red	75·00	£160

1892. Surch **3 cents.**

28	**21**	3c. on 4c. purple and black	2·25	50
29		3c. on 5c. purple and green	1·75	3·25
30		3c. on 6c. purple and blue	3·00	3·75
31		3c. on $1 green and red	10·00	65·00

1896. Sultan's Coronation. Optd **KEMAHKOTAAN.**

32	**21**	1c. purple	50	85
33		2c. purple and yellow	50	1·00
34		3c. purple and red	55	1·00
35		4c. purple and black	80	2·25
36		5c. purple and green	5·50	7·50
37		6c. purple and blue	3·50	6·50
38		$1 green and red	50·00	£110

1896.

39	**24**	1c. green	80	75
40		2c. green and blue	50	30
41		3c. green and purple	4·00	2·00
42		4c. green and red	1·00	1·00
43		4c. yellow and red	1·50	80
44		5c. green and brown	2·00	2·00
45		6c. green and yellow	2·00	3·00
46		10c. green and black	7·00	45·00
47		25c. green and mauve	9·00	40·00
48		50c. green and red	16·00	42·00
49		$1 purple and green	32·00	75·00
50		$2 purple and red	35·00	80·00
51		$3 purple and blue	35·00	£110
52		$4 purple and brown	35·00	85·00
53		$5 purple and yellow	75·00	£130

1903. Surch in figures and words.

54	**24**	3c. on 4c. yellow and red	60	1·10
55		10c. on 4c. green & red (A)	2·50	9·00
59		10c. on 4c. green & red (B)	9·50	4·50
58		10c. on 4c. yellow & red (B)	20·00	40·00
56		50c. on $3 purple and blue	30·00	80·00
60		50c. on $5 purple and yellow	65·00	£150
57		$1 on $2 purple and red	60·00	£110

10c. on 4c. Type A, "cents" in small letters. Type B, "CENTS" in capitals.

33 Sultan Sir Ibrahim

1904.

78	**33**	1c. purple and green	1·25	15
90		2c. purple and orange	1·00	3·75
63		3c. purple and black	4·75	60
91		4c. purple and red	1·75	70
109		5c. purple and green	50	30
83		8c. purple and blue	4·00	6·50
84		10c. purple and black	50·00	3·00
116		25c. purple and green	3·75	1·00
119		50c. purple and red	3·75	1·60
120		$1 green and mauve	3·75	1·25
121		$2 green and red	7·50	4·00
72		$3 green and blue	26·00	75·00
73		$4 green and brown	26·00	£100
124		$5 green and orange	55·00	50·00
75		$10 green and black	65·00	£160
76		$50 green and blue	£200	£300
77		$100 green and red	£375	£550
128		$500 blue and red	£17000	

1912. Surch **3 CENTS.** and bars.

88	**33**	3c. on 8c. purple and blue	3·25	7·50

1918.

103	**33**	1c. purple and black	30	20
89		2c. purple and green	50	1·00
104		2c. purple and sepia	1·25	4·00
105		2c. green	50	40
106		3c. green	2·00	4·50
107		3c. purple and sepia	1·40	1·50
110		6c. purple and red	50	50
93		10c. purple and blue	2·00	1·40
112		10c. purple and yellow	50	25
113		12c. purple and blue	1·00	1·25
114		12c. blue	42·00	4·00
115		21c. purple and orange	2·00	3·00
117		30c. purple and orange	8·00	7·00
118		40c. purple and brown	8·00	7·50

37 Sultan Sir Ibrahim and Sultana

38 Sultan Sir Ibrahim

1935.

129	**37**	8c. violet and grey	3·50	1·75

1940.

130	**38**	8c. black and blue	17·00	1·00

1948. Silver Wedding. As T **11b/11c** of Gambia.

131		10c. violet	20	75
132		$5 green	25·00	38·00

39 Sultan Sir Ibrahim

40 Sultan Sir Ibrahim

1949.

133	**39**	1c. black	50	10
134		2c. orange	20	20
135		3c. green	50	1·00
136		4c. brown	60	10
136a		5c. purple	30	30
137		6c. grey	60	20
138		8c. red	3·25	1·25
138a		8c. green	4·00	2·25
139		10c. mauve	70	10
139a		12c. red	4·00	4·50
140		15c. blue	2·75	10
141		20c. black and green	50	1·00
141a		20c. blue	1·00	10
142		25c. purple and orange	1·75	10
142a		30c. red and purple	1·75	2·75
142b		35c. red and purple	4·50	1·25
143		40c. red and purple	4·25	9·50
144		50c. black and blue	2·50	10
145		$1 blue and purple	5·00	2·00
146		$2 green and red	14·00	5·00
147		$5 green and brown	40·00	11·00

1949. U.P.U. As T **11d/11g** of Gambia.

148		10c. purple	30	40
149		15c. blue	1·75	1·00
150		25c. orange	65	3·00
151		50c. black	1·25	3·50

1953. Coronation. As T **11h** of Gambia.

152		10c. black and purple	1·25	10

1955. Diamond Jubilee of Sultan.

153	**40**	10c. red	10	10

41 Sultan Sir Ismail and Johore Coat of Arms

1960. Coronation of Sultan.

154	**41**	10c. multicoloured	20	20

1960. As Nos. 92/102 of Kedah but with inset portrait of Sultan Sir Ismail.

155		1c. black	10	40
156		2c. red	10	1·25
157		4c. sepia	10	10
158		5c. lake	10	10
159		8c. green	1·50	3·00
160		10c. purple	30	10
161		20c. blue	2·00	1·00
162		50c. black and blue	50	20
163		$1 blue and purple	1·50	3·50
164		$2 green and red	9·00	15·00
165		$5 brown and green	29·00	35·00

42 "Vanda hookeriana"

1965. Inset portrait of Sultan Ismail. Multicoloured.

166		1c. Type **42**	10	30
167		2c. "Arundina graminifolia"	10	1·00
168		5c. "Paphiopedilum niveum"	10	10
169		6c. "Spathoglottis plicata"	40	30
170		10c. "Arachnis flos-aeris"	40	20
171		15c. "Rhyncostylis retusa"	1·50	10
172		20c. "Phalaenopsis violacea"	1·50	75

The higher values used in Johore were Nos. 20/7 of Malaysia (National Issues).

44 "Delias ninus"

1971. Butterflies. Inset portrait of Sultan Ismail. Multicoloured.

175		1c. Type **44**	50	2·00
176		2c. "Danaus melanippus"	1·50	2·25
177		5c. "Parthenos sylvia"	1·50	30
178		6c. "Papilio demoleus"	1·50	2·25
179		10c. "Hebomoia glaucippe"	1·50	20
180		15c. "Precis orithya"	1·75	10
181		20c. "Valeria valeria"	1·75	50

The higher values in use with this issue were Nos. 64/71 of Malaysia (National Issues).

45 "Rafflesia hasseltii" (inset portrait of Sultan Ismail)

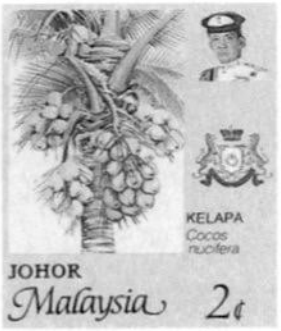

46 Coconuts (inset portrait of Sultan Mahmood)

1979. Flowers. Multicoloured.

188		1c. Type **45**	10	1·00
189		2c. "Pterocarpus indicus"	10	1·00
190		5c. "Lagerstroemia speciosa"	10	60
191		10c. "Durio zibethinus"	15	10
192		15c. "Hibiscus rosa-sinensis"	15	10
193		20c. "Rhododendron scortechinii"	20	25
194		25c. "Etlingera elatior" (inscr "Phaeomeria speciosa")	40	25

1986. Agricultural Products of Malaysia. Mult.

202		1c. Coffee	10	10
203		2c. Type **46**	10	10
204		5c. Cocoa	10	10
205		10c. Black pepper	10	10
206		15c. Rubber	10	10
207		20c. Oil palm	10	10
208		30c. Rice	10	15

POSTAGE DUE STAMPS

D 1

1938.

D1	D 1	1c. red	14·00	40·00
D2		4c. green	40·00	40·00
D3		8c. orange	48·00	£140
D4		10c. brown	48·00	48·00
D5		12c. purple	55·00	£130

JORDAN Pt. 1, Pt. 19

A territory to the E. of Israel, formerly called Transjordan; under British mandate from 1918 to 1946. Independent kingdom since 1946.

1920. 1000 milliemes = 100 piastres = £1 Egyptian.
1927. 1000 milliemes = £1 Palestinian.
1950. 1000 fils = 1 Jordan dinar.

شرقي الاردن

(1 "East of Jordan")

1920. Stamps of Palestine optd with T **1**.

1	3	1m. brown	70	1·75
10		2m. green	60	80
3		3m. brown	1·10	1·25
4		4m. red	1·25	1·25
5		5m. orange	2·50	1·25
14		1p. blue	1·50	1·75
15		2p. olive	3·75	3·00
16		5p. purple	2·50	6·50
17		9p. ochre	3·50	23·00
18		10p. blue	5·50	23·00
19		20p. grey	8·50	40·00

(2 Tenth of a piastre) (3 Piastre)

1922. Handstamped with T **2** or **3** (piastre values). (a) 1920 issue of Jordan (No. 1 etc).

28	2	$\frac{1}{10}$p. on 1m. brown	20·00	25·00
29		$\frac{2}{10}$p. on 2m. green	25·00	25·00
22		$\frac{3}{10}$p. on 3m. brown	10·00	10·00
23		$\frac{4}{10}$p. on 4m. red	50·00	50·00
24		$\frac{5}{10}$p. on 5m. orange	£180	£100
31	3	1p. on 1p. blue	£200	60·00
25		2p. on 2p. olive	£250	75·00
26		5p. on 5p. purple	50·00	70·00
27a		9p. on 9p. ochre	£130	£140
33		10p. on 10p. blue	£850	£1000
34		20p. on 20p. grey	£650	£850
		(b) Type **3** of Palestine.		
35	3	10p. on 10p. blue	£1800	£2500
36		20p. on 20p. grey	£2500	£3000

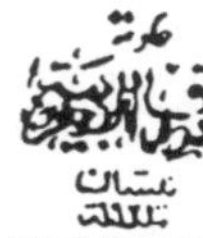

(4 "Arab Government of the East, April, 1921")

1922. Stamps of Jordan handstamped with T **4**.

45	3	1m. brown	12·00	15·00
46a		2m. green	8·00	8·00
39b		3m. brown	7·00	7·00
40		4m. red	45·00	50·00
41a		5m. orange	15·00	10·00
48a		1p. blue	15·00	9·00
42c		2p. olive	12·00	10·00
43b		5p. purple	60·00	80·00
44b		9p. ochre	65·00	80·00
52a		10p. blue	£1100	£1600
53a		20p. grey	£1100	£1800

حكومة الشرق
العربية
نيسان سنة ٩٢١

(5 "Arab Government of the East, April, 1921")

1923. Stamps of Jordan optd with T **5**.

62	3	1m. brown	16·00	24·00
63		2m. green	14·00	18·00
56		3m. brown	12·00	15·00
57		4m. red	10·00	12·00
64		5m. orange	10·00	12·00
65		1p. blue	10·00	14·00
59		2p. olive	15·00	15·00
60		5p. purple	60·00	80·00
66		9p. ochre	75·00	£100
67		10p. blue	70·00	£100
68		20p. grey	70·00	£100

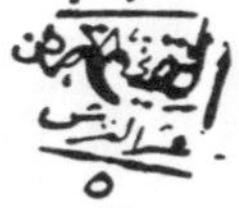

(6)

(7)

(8)

(9)

1923. Various stamps surch as T **6/9**. (a) 1920 issue of Jordan (No. 1 etc).

70	–	$2\frac{1}{2}$/10thsp. on 5m.	£160	£160
70c	6	$\frac{5}{10}$p. on 3m.	†	£5000
70d		$\frac{5}{10}$p. on 5m.		
70e	9	2p. on 20p.		
		(b) No. 7 of Palestine.		
71	6	$\frac{5}{10}$p. on 3m.	£3000	
		(c) 1922 issue of Jordan (Nos. 22 etc).		
72	6	$\frac{5}{10}$p. on 3m.	£7000	
73		$\frac{5}{10}$p. on 5p.	70·00	8·00
73b		$\frac{5}{10}$p. on 9p.	£1200	
74	7	$\frac{1}{2}$p. on 5p.	70·00	80·00
75a		$\frac{1}{2}$p. on 9p.	£350	£400
77	8	1p. on 5p.	80·00	£100
		(d) 1922 issue of Jordan (Nos. 396 etc).		
78b	6	$\frac{5}{10}$p. on 3m.	40·00	50·00
79		$\frac{5}{10}$p. on 5p.	8·00	14·00
79d		$\frac{5}{10}$p. on 9p.	–	£1200
80c	7	$\frac{1}{2}$p. on 2p.	60·00	£110
82		$\frac{1}{2}$p. on 5p.	£2000	
83b	8	1p. on 5p.	£2000	£2250
		(e) 1923 issue of Jordan (Nos. 56 etc).		
84	6	$\frac{5}{10}$p. on 3m.	25·00	30·00
85	7	$\frac{1}{2}$p. on 9p.	90·00	£150
87	9	1p. on 10p.	£2250	£2500
88		2p. on 20p.	60·00	80·00

حكومة
الشرق العربية
٩ شعبان ١٣٤١

(10 "Arab Government of the East, 9 Sha'ban, 1341")

1923. Stamps of Saudi Arabia optd with T **10**.

89	11	$\frac{1}{8}$p. brown	2·25	1·75
96		$\frac{1}{4}$ on $\frac{1}{8}$p. brown (47)	4·50	6·00
90		$\frac{1}{2}$p. red	2·25	1·75
91		1p. blue	1·75	1·00
92		$1\frac{1}{2}$p. lilac	1·75	1·75
93		2p. orange	2·25	6·50
94		3p. brown	3·25	9·00
95		5p. green	5·50	10·00
97		10 on 5p. green (49)	15·00	22·00

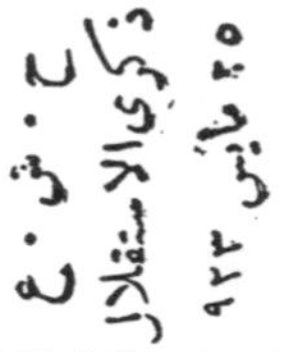

(11 "Arab Government of the East, Commemoration of Independence, 25 May, 1923")

1923. Stamps of Palestine optd with T **11**.

98A	3	1m. brown	17·00	17·00
99A		2m. green	29·00	35·00
100A		3m. brown	10·00	12·00
101A		4m. red	10·00	12·00
102A		5m. orange	50·00	60·00
103B		1p. blue	50·00	60·00
104A		2p. olive	50·00	70·00
105A		5p. purple	60·00	70·00
106B		9p. ochre	50·00	60·00
107A		10p. blue	60·00	80·00
108B		20p. grey	70·00	90·00

1923. No. 107 surch with T **9**.

109		1p. on 10p. blue	£6000	

نصف قرش

(12)

1923. No. 92 surch with T **12**.

110		$\frac{1}{2}$p. on $1\frac{1}{2}$p. lilac	7·00	7·50

حكومة
الشرق العربية
٩ شعبان ١٣٤١

(13a "Arab Government of the East, 9 Sha'ban, 1341")

1923. Stamp of Saudi Arabia handstamped as T **13**.

112	11	$\frac{1}{2}$p. red	6·50	8·50

(15 "Arab Government of the East")

1924. Stamps of Saudi Arabia optd with T **15**.

114	11	$\frac{1}{2}$p. red	6·50	8·50
115		1p. blue	£300	£200
116		$1\frac{1}{2}$p. violet	£350	

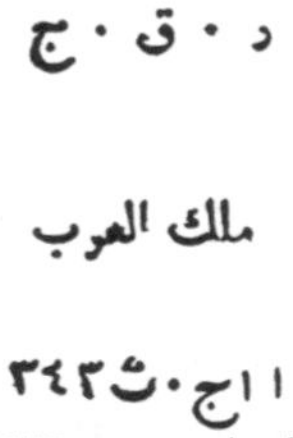

(16 "Commemorating the coming of His Majesty the King of the Arabs" and date)

1924. Stamps of Saudi Arabia optd with T **15** and **16**.

117	11	$\frac{1}{2}$p. red	1·00	1·25
118		1p. blue	1·25	1·50
119		$1\frac{1}{2}$p. violet	2·00	2·25
120		2p. orange	4·00	4·25

حكومة الشرق
العربى
١٣٤٢

(17 "Government of the Arab East, 1342")

1924. Stamps of Saudi Arabia optd with T **17**.

125	11	$\frac{1}{8}$p. brown	50	50
126		$\frac{1}{4}$p. green	50	50
127		$\frac{1}{2}$p. red	50	50
129		1p. blue	3·00	1·50
130		$1\frac{1}{2}$p. lilac	3·00	3·00
131		2p. orange	2·25	2·50
132		3p. red	1·75	2·00
133		5p. green	2·25	3·00
134		10p. purple and mauve	4·75	6·50

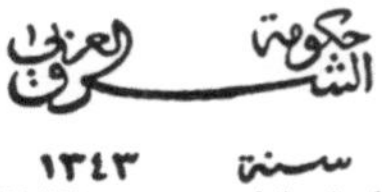

(18 "Government of the Arab East, 1343")

1925. Stamps of Saudi Arabia optd with T **18**.

135		$\frac{1}{8}$p. brown	30	1·25
136		$\frac{1}{4}$p. blue	30	1·25
137		$\frac{1}{2}$p. red	50	40
138		1p. green	40	40
139		$1\frac{1}{2}$p. orange	1·00	2·25
140		2p. blue	1·50	2·75
141		3p. green	2·00	3·75
142		5p. brown	2·25	8·50

شرق
الاردن

(19 "East of the Jordan")

1925. Stamps of Palestine (without Palestine opt) optd with T **19**.

143	3	1m. brown	15	1·75
144		2m. yellow	15	30
145		3m. blue	60	70
146		4m. red	50	1·50
147		5m. orange	1·00	40
148		6m. green	60	1·00
149		7m. brown	60	1·00
150		8m. red	60	60
151		13m. blue	60	50
152		1p. grey	60	80
153		2p. olive	2·00	2·25
154		5p. purple	3·00	5·00
155		9p. ochre	6·00	10·00
156		10p. blue	14·00	18·00
157		20p. violet	20·00	32·00

22 Emir Abdullah

23 Emir Abdullah

1927. Figures at left and right.

159	22	2m. blue	20	30
160		3m. red	1·50	1·50
161		4m. green	1·50	1·75
162		5m. orange	65	30
163		10m. red	80	1·75
164		15m. blue	80	30
165		20m. olive	80	1·25
166	23	50m. purple	2·50	5·00
167		90m. brown	6·00	16·00
168		100m. blue	8·00	12·00
169		200m. violet	17·00	28·00
170		500m. brown	60·00	85·00
171		1000m. grey	£100	£140

(24 "Constitution")

1928. Optd with T **24**.

172	22	2m. blue	1·50	2·75
173		3m. red	1·50	3·75
174		4m. green	1·75	5·00
175		5m. orange	1·75	2·75
176		10m. red	2·00	4·50
177		15m. blue	2·00	2·50
178		20m. olive	3·75	9·50
179	23	50m. purple	6·00	10·00
180		90m. brown	16·00	50·00
181		100m. blue	22·00	60·00
182		200m. violet	65·00	£130

1930. "Locust campaign". Optd **LOCUST CAMPAIGN** in English and Arabic.

183	22	2m. blue	1·75	5·00
184		3m. red	1·75	6·50
185		4m. green	1·75	7·50
186		5m. orange	17·00	14·00
187		10m. red	1·75	4·00
188		15m. blue	1·75	2·25
189		20m. olive	1·75	4·00
190	23	50m. purple	5·00	11·00
191		90m. brown	10·00	45·00
192		100m. blue	12·00	45·00
193		200m. violet	30·00	85·00
194		500m. brown	75·00	£200

28 Emir

29 Emir

1930.

230	28	1m. brown	20	75
195		2m. green	50	50
258		3m. pink	15	15
196a		3m. green	2·50	85
259		4m. green	15	15
233		4m. pink	1·75	1·25
198		5m. orange	50	40
199		10m. red	1·25	15
260		10m. violet	15	15
261		12m. red	35	30
200		15m. blue	1·00	20
262		15m. green	40	40
201		20m. green	1·25	35
263		20m. blue	45	45
202	29	50m. purple	2·00	1·25
203		90m. bistre	2·50	4·25
240		100m. blue	5·00	1·75
241		200m. violet	9·00	7·00
242		500m. brown	13·00	12·00
243		£P1 grey	24·00	22·00

30 Mushetta

32 The Khasneh at Petra

1933.

208	30	1m. black and purple	70	1·40
209	–	2m. black and red	1·25	1·00
210	–	3m. green	1·50	1·60
211	–	4m. black and brown	1·75	2·25
212	–	5m. black and orange	2·50	1·25
213	–	10m. red	2·50	3·00
214	32	15m. blue	2·50	1·25
215	–	20m. black and green	3·50	5·00
216	–	50m. black and purple	12·00	12·00
217	30	90m. black and yellow	15·00	29·00
218	–	100m. black and blue	15·00	29·00
219	–	200m. black and violet	45·00	70·00
220	32	500m. red and brown	£140	£180
221	–	$P1 black and green	£350	£550

DESIGNS—HORIZ: 2m. Nymphaeum, Jerash; 3, 90m. Kasr Kharana; 4m. Kerak Castle; 5, 100m. Temple of Artemis, Jerash; 10, 200m. Ajlun Castle; 20m. Allenby Bridge over Jordan; 50m. Threshing. VERT: £P1, Emir Abdullah.

Nos. 216 to 221 are larger (33½ × 24 mm or 24 × 33½ mm).

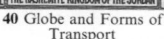

35 Map of Jordan

39 Parliament Building

1946. Installation of King Abdullah and National Independence.

249	35	1m. purple	10	10
250		2m. orange	10	10
251		3m. green	10	10
252		4m. violet	10	10
253		10m. brown	15	15
254		12m. red	15	15
255		20m. blue	20	20
256		50m. blue	40	40
257		200m. green	1·60	2·00

1947. Inauguration of 1st National Parliament.

276	39	1m. violet	10	20
277		3m. red	10	20
278		4m. green	10	20
279		10m. purple	10	20
280		12m. red	10	20
281		20m. blue	10	20
282		50m. red	40	40
283		100m. pink	75	90
284		200m. green	1·50	1·50

40 Globe and Forms of Transport

44 Lockheed Constellation Airliner and Globe

1949. 75th Anniv of U.P.U.

285	40	1m. brown	15	25
286		4m. green	25	30
287		10m. red	30	55
288		20m. blue	50	65
289	–	50m. green	1·10	1·40

DESIGN: 50m. King Abdullah.

1950. Air.

295	44	5f. purple and yellow	40	25
296		10f. brown and violet	40	25
297		15f. red and olive	40	40
298		20f. black and blue	50	40
299		50f. green and mauve	90	75
300		100f. brown and blue	1·25	90
301		150f. orange and black	2·25	1·50

1952. Optd **FILS** and bars or **J.D.** (on 1d.).

313	28	1f. on 1m. brown	25	25
314		2f. on 2m. green	25	25
315		3f. on 3m. green	20·00	
316		3f. on 3m. pink	25	25
310		4f. on 4m. pink	6·00	2·75
318		4f. on 4m. green	25	25
319		5f. on 5m. orange	30	30
320		10f. on 10m. red	22·00	
321		10f. on 10m. violet	30	30
322		12f. on 12m. red	30	30
312		15f. on 15m. blue	20·00	10·00
325		15f. on 15m. green	45	30
326		20f. on 20m. green	23·00	
327		20f. on 20m. blue	1·00	50
328	29	50f. on 50m. purple	80	70
329		90f. on 90m. bistre	7·00	4·50
330		100f. on 100m. blue	4·00	1·75
331		200f. on 200m. violet	6·50	2·50
332		500f. on 500m. brown	15·00	4·50
333		1d. on £P1 grey	30·00	8·00

48 Dome of the Rock and Khazneh at Petra

49 King Abdullah

1952. Unification of Jordan and Palestine.

355	48	1f. green and brown	20	20
356		2f. red and green	20	20
357		3f. black and red	20	20
358		4f. orange and green	20	20
359		5f. purple and brown	25	25
360		10f. brown and violet	25	25
361		20f. black and blue	65	35
362		100f. sepia and brown	2·50	1·75
363		200f. orange and violet	5·75	3·25

1952. (a) Size 18 × 21½ mm.

364	49	5f. orange	20	20
365		10f. lilac	20	20
366		12f. red	75	50
367		15f. olive	45	20
368		20f. blue	50	25

(b) Size 20 × 24½ mm.

369	49	50f. purple	1·10	45
370		90f. brown	3·25	1·75
371		100f. blue	3·50	95

1953. Optd with two horiz bars across Arabic commemorative inscription.

378	48	1f. green and brown	20	20
379		2f. red and green	20	20
380		3f. black and red	20	20
381		4f. orange and green	20	20
382		5f. purple and brown	20	20
383		10f. brown and violet	65	35
384		20f. black and blue	65	50
385		100f. brown and blue	3·50	1·00
386		200f. orange and violet	5·00	3·50

بريد
POSTAGE

(51)

51a King Hussein

1953. Obligatory Tax stamps optd for postal use as in T **51**. (a) Inscr "MILS".

387	T 36	1m. blue	20	20
388		3m. green	20	20
389		5m. purple	60·00	55·00
390	–	10m. red	18·00	18·00
391	–	15m. black	45	45
392	–	20m. brown	60·00	40·00
393	–	50m. violet	45	40
394	–	100m. red	4·75	3·75

(b) Inscr "MILS" and optd **PALESTINE**.

395	T 36	1m. blue	25·00	23·00
396		3m. green	25·00	23·00
397		5m. purple	25·00	23·00
398	–	10m. red	25·00	23·00
399	–	15m. black	28·00	23·00
400	–	20m. brown	28·00	23·00
400a	–	50m. violet		
401	–	100m. red	40·00	35·00

(c) Inscr "MILS", optd **FILS** (T334, etc).

402	T 36	1f. on 1m. blue	27·00	24·00
403		3f. on 3m. green	27·00	24·00
404	–	10f. on 10m. red	27·00	24·00
405	–	15f. on 15m. black	27·00	24·00
406	–	20f. on 20m. brown	27·00	24·00
407	–	100f. on 100m. red	30·00	30·00

(d) Inscr "FILS".

408	T 36	5f. purple	20	15
409	–	10f. red	25	15
410	–	15f. black	55	45
411	–	20f. brown	1·00	70
412	–	100f. orange	2·40	1·40

1953. Enthronement of King Hussein.

413	51a	1f. black and green	15	15
414		4f. black and red	15	10
415		15f. black and blue	1·00	20
416		20f. black and lilac	1·60	20
417		50f. black and green	3·50	1·75
418		100f. black and blue	7·00	4·75

52 El-Deir Temple, Petra

54a Temple of Artemis Jerash

1954.

445	52	1f. brown & grn (postage)	10	10
446	–	2f. black and red	10	10
447	52	3f. violet and purple	10	10
448	–	4f. green and brown	10	10
449	52	5f. green and violet	15	10
450	–	10f. green and purple	20	10
451	–	12f. sepia and red	70	10
452	–	15f. red and brown	45	15
453	–	20f. green and blue	30	15
454	–	50f. red and blue	70	15
428	–	100f. blue and green	1·50	55
456	–	200f. blue and lake	4·00	1·25
457	–	500f. purple and brown	15·00	7·00
458	–	1d. lake and olive	23·00	10·00
470	54a	5f. orange and blue (air)	15	10
433		10f. red and brown	25	10
434		25f. blue and green	40	15
435		35f. blue and mauve	50	20
436		40f. slate and red	60	20
437		50f. orange and blue	75	35
438		100f. brown and blue	1·00	75
439		150f. lake and turquoise	1·60	1·00

DESIGNS—VERT: 2f., 4f., 500f., 1d. King Hussein. HORIZ: 10f., 15f., 20f. Dome of the Rock, Jerusalem; 12f., 50f., 100f., 200f. Facade of Mosque of El Aqsa.

1955. Arab Postal Union. As Nos. 502/4 of Egypt but inscr "H. K. JORDAN" at top and "ARAB POSTAL UNION" at foot.

440		15f. green	30	15
441		20f. violet	30	15
442		25f. brown	40	30

56 King Hussein and Queen Dina

1955. Royal Wedding.

443	56	15f. blue	1·00	50
444		100f. lake	3·50	2·00

58 Envelope with Postmarks in English and Arabic

59 "Flame of Freedom"

1956. 1st Arab Postal Congress, Amman.

459	58	1f. brown and black	10	10
460		4f. red and black	10	10
461		15f. blue and black	10	10
462		20f. bistre and black	15	10
463		50f. blue and black	45	30
464		100f. orange and black	70	50

1958. 10th Anniv of Declaration of Human Rights.

476	59	5f. red and blue	10	10
477		15f. black and brown	15	10
478		35f. purple and green	35	25
479		45f. black and red	50	30

60 King Hussein

1959. Centres in black.

480	60	1f. green	10	10
481		2f. violet	10	10
482		3f. red	20	10
483		4f. purple	20	10
484		7f. green	25	10
485		12f. red	40	10
486		15f. red	40	10
487		21f. green	40	10
488		25f. brown	55	10
489		35f. blue	80	10
490		40f. green	1·10	15
491		50f. red	1·50	15
492		100f. green	2·00	40
493		200f. purple	5·00	1·50
494		500f. blue	13·50	5·50
495		1d. purple	24·00	14·00

61 Arab League Centre, Cairo

1960. Inaug of Arab League Centre, Cairo.

496	61	15f. black and green	20	15

62 "Care of Refugees"

1960. World Refugee Year.

497	62	15f. red and blue	15	10
498		35f. blue and bistre	15	15

63 Shah of Iran and King Hussein

1960. Visit of Shah of Iran.

499	63	15f. multicoloured	25	15
500		35f. multicoloured	40	35
501		50f. multicoloured	60	50

64 Petroleum Refinery, Zarka

1961. Inaug of Jordanian Petroleum Refinery.

502	64	15f. blue and violet	20	10
503		35f. brown and violet	30	20

65 Jordanian Families and Graph

67 Campaign Emblem

1961. 1st Jordanian Census Commemoration.

504	65	15f. brown	25	10

1961. Dag Hammarskjold Memorial Issue. Optd **IN MEMORIAL OF DAG HAMMARSKJOELD 1904–1961** in English and Arabic and laurel leaves at top and bottom.

505	62	15f. red and blue	1·75	1·75
506		35f. blue and bistre	2·00	2·00

1962. Malaria Eradication.

507	67	15f. mauve	20	10
508		35f. blue	40	20

68 Telephone Exchange, Amman

1962. Inauguration of Amman's Automatic Telephone Exchange.

510	68	15f. blue and purple	15	15
511		35f. purple and green	35	15

69 Aqaba Port and King Hussein

1962. Opening of Aqaba Port.

512	69	15f. black and purple	25	10
513		35f. black and blue	60	25

70 Dag Hammarskjold and U.N. Headquarters

1963. 17th Anniv of U.N.

515	70	15f. red, olive and blue	15	15
516		35f. blue, red and olive	55	30
517		50f. olive, blue and red	80	55

71 Church of Holy Virgin's Tomb, Jerusalem

72 League Centre, Cairo and Emblem

1963. "Holy Places". Multicoloured.

519	50f. Type **71**	85	85
520	50f. Basilica of the Agony, Gethsemane	85	85
521	50f. Holy Sepulchre, Jerusalem	85	85
522	50f. Nativity Church. Bethlehem	85	85
523	50f. Haram of Ibrahim, Hebron	85	85
524	50f. Dome of the Rock, Jerusalem	85	85
525	50f. Omer-el-Khetab Mosque, Jerusalem	85	85
526	50f. El-Aqsa Mosque, Jerusalem	85	85

1963. Arab League.

527	72	15f. blue	20	15
528		35f. red	65	30

73 Wheat and F.A.O. Emblem

74 Canal and Symbols

1963. Freedom from Hunger.

529	73	15f. green, black and blue	15	10
530		35f. green, black and apple	35	20

1963. East Ghor Canal Project.

532	74	1f. black and bistre	15	10
533		4f. black and blue	15	10
534		5f. black and purple	15	10
535		10f. black and green	25	10
536		35f. black and orange	1·50	1·00

75 Scales of Justice and Globe

1963. 15th Anniv of Declaration of Human Rights.

537	75	50f. red and blue	40	20
538		50f. blue and red	40	20

1963. Surch in English and Arabic.

539	60	1f. on 21f. black and green	20	15
540		2f. on 21f. black and green	20	15
541		4f. on 12f. black and red	7·75	7·50
542	–	4f. on 12f. sepia and red (No. 451)	30	25
543	60	5f. on 21f. black and green	50	35
544		25f. on 35f. blue	2·00	70

77 King Hussein and Red Crescent

1963. Red Crescent Commemoration.

545	77	1f. purple and red	10	10
546		2f. turquoise and red	10	10
547		3f. blue and red	10	10
548		4f. turquoise and red	10	10
549		5f. sepia and red	10	10
550		85f. green and red	1·75	1·40

78 Red Cross Emblem

1963. Centenary of Red Cross.

552	78	1f. purple and red	10	10
553		2f. turquoise and red	10	10
554		3f. blue and red	10	10
555		4f. turquoise and red	10	10
556		5f. sepia and red	10	10
557		85f. green and red	2·75	1·75

79 Kings Hussein of Hejaz and Hussein of Jordan

1963. Arab Renaissance Day.

559	79	15f. multicoloured	35	25
560		25f. multicoloured	50	35
561		35f. multicoloured	90	70
562		50f. multicoloured	2·00	1·75

80 Al Aqsa Mosque, Pope Paul and King Hussein

1964. Pope Paul's Visit to the Holy Land.

564	80	15f. green and black	20	15
565	–	35f. mauve and black	50	35
566	–	50f. brown and black	80	50
567	–	80f. blue and black	1·50	90

DESIGNS: 35f. Dome of the Rock (Mosque of Omar), Jerusalem; 50f. Church of the Holy Sepulchre, Jerusalem; 80f. Church of the Nativity, Bethlehem.

81 Prince Abdullah

1964. 2nd Birthday of Prince Abdullah. Mult.

568	5f. Prince standing by wall	30	10
569	10f. Head of Prince and roses	35	25
570	35f. Type **81**	75	50

SIZES: 5f. as Type **81** but vert; 10f. diamond (63 × 63 mm).

NOTE.—A set of ten triangular 20f. stamps showing astronauts and rockets was issued, but very few were put on sale at the Post Office and we are not listing them unless we receive satisfactory evidence as to their status.

82 Basketball

83 Woman and Child

1964. Olympic Games, Tokyo (1st issue).

571	82	1f. red	10	10
572	–	2f. blue	10	10
573	–	3f. green	10	10
574	–	4f. buff	10	10
575	–	5f. violet	10	10
576	–	35f. red	1·40	60
577	–	50f. green	2·50	1·25
578	–	100f. brown	4·00	2·25

DESIGNS—VERT: 2f. Volleyball; 3f. Football; 5f. Running. HORIZ: 4f. Table tennis; 35f. Cycling; 50f. Fencing; 100f. Pole vaulting.

See also Nos. 610/17 and 641/6.

1964. 4th Session of Social Studies Seminar, Amman.

580	83	5f. multicoloured	10	10
581		10f. multicoloured	20	10
582		25f. multicoloured	30	20

84 King Hussein Sports Stadium, Amman

1964. Air. Inaug of "Hussein Sports City".

583	84	1f. multicoloured	10	10
584		4f. multicoloured	10	10
585		10f. multicoloured	20	15
586		35f. multicoloured	35	25

85 President Kennedy

1964. Pres. Kennedy Memorial Issue.

588	85	1f. violet	20	20
589		2f. red	20	20
590		3f. blue	20	20
591		4f. brown	20	20
592		5f. green	20	20
593		85f. red	12·50	5·75

86 Statues at Abu Simbel

1964. Nubian Monuments Preservation.

595	86	4f. black and blue	10	10
596		15f. violet and yellow	25	20
597		25f. red and green	30	30

87 King Hussein and Map of Palestine in 1920

1964. Arab Summit Conference.

598	87	10f. multicoloured	10	10
599		15f. multicoloured	20	10
600		25f. multicoloured	25	10
601		50f. multicoloured	60	20
602		80f. multicoloured	1·10	90

88 Pope Paul VI, King Hussein and Ecumenical Patriarch

1964. Meeting of Pope, King and Patriarch, Jerusalem. Multicoloured, background colour given.

604	88	10f. green	15	10
605		15f. purple	15	10
606		25f. brown	25	15
607		50f. blue	75	50
608		80f. green	1·25	1·00

89 Olympic Flame

1964. Olympic Games, Tokyo (2nd issue).

610	89	1f. red	10	10
611		2f. violet	10	10
612		3f. green	10	10
613		4f. brown	10	10
614		5f. red	10	10
615		35f. blue	65	55
616		50f. olive	1·00	90
617		100f. blue	2·25	2·00

90 Scouts crossing River

1964. Jordanian Scouts.

619	90	1f. brown	10	10
620	–	2f. violet	10	10
621	–	3f. ochre	10	10
622	–	4f. lake	10	10
623	–	5f. green	10	10
624	–	35f. blue	3·00	1·10
625	–	50f. green	3·25	1·75

DESIGNS: 2f. First aid; 3f. Exercising; 4f. Practising knots; 5f. Cooking meal; 35f. Sailing; 50f. Around camp-fire.

91 Four-coloured Bush Shrike

1964. Air. Birds. Multicoloured.

627	150f. Type **91**	15·00	8·00
628	500f. Ornate hawk eagle (vert)	55·00	30·00
629	1000f. Grey-headed kingfisher (vert)	95·00	50·00

92 Bykovsky

1965. Russian Astronauts.

630	40f. brown and green (Type **92**)	75	75
631	40f. violet & brown (Gagarin)	75	75
632	40f. maroon & bl (Nikolaev)	75	75
633	40f. lilac and bistre (Popovich)	75	75
634	40f. sepia & blue (Tereshkova)	75	75
635	40f. green and pink (Titov)	75	75

93 U.N. Headquarters and Emblem

1965. 19th Anniv (1964) of U.N.

638	93	30f. violet, turquoise & brn	40	20
639		70f. brown, blue and violet	60	45

94 Olympic Flame

1965. Air. Olympic Games, Tokyo (3rd issue).

641	**94**	10f. red	10	10
642		15f. violet	10	10
643		20f. blue	25	10
644		30f. green	60	35
645		40f. brown	80	35
646		60f. mauve	1·25	70

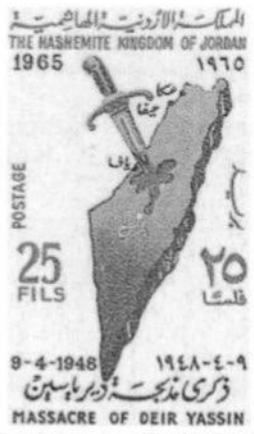

95 Dagger on Deir Yassin, Palestine

1965. Deir Yassin Massacre.

648	**95**	25f. red and olive	1·00	80

96 Horse-jumping

97 Volleyball Player and Cup

1965. Army Day.

649	**96**	5f. green	15	10
650	–	10f. blue	30	10
651	–	35f. brown	95	45

DESIGNS: 10f. Tank; 35f. King Hussein making inspection in army car.

1965. Arab Volleyball Championships.

652	**97**	15f. olive	60	20
653		35f. lake	1·10	50
654		50f. blue	1·90	1·10

98 President J. F. Kennedy

1965. 1st Death Anniv of Pres. Kennedy.

656	**98**	10f. black and green	20	15
657		15f. violet and orange	40	20
658		25f. brown and blue	55	30
659		50f. purple and green	95	60

99 Pope Paul, King Hussein and Dome of the Rock

1965. 1st Anniv of Pope Paul's Visit to the Holy Land.

661	**99**	5f. brown and mauve	35	10
662		10f. lake and green	65	25
663		15f. blue and flesh	90	35
664		50f. grey and pink	2·50	1·10

100 Cathedral Steps

1965. Air. Jerash Antiquities. Multicoloured.

666		55f. Type **100**	90	90
667		55f. Artemis Temple Gate	90	90
668		55f. Street of Columns	90	90
669		55f. Columns of South Theatre	90	90
670		55f. Forum (horiz)	90	90
671		55f. South Theatre (horiz)	90	90
672		55f. Triumphal Arch (horiz)	90	90
673		55f. Temple of Artemis (horiz)	90	90

101 Jordan Pavilion at Fair

1965. New York World's Fair.

674	**101**	15f. multicoloured	15	10
675		25f. multicoloured	35	20
676		50f. multicoloured	75	45

102 Lamp and Burning Library

1965. Burning of Algiers Library.

678	**102**	25f. green, red and black	25	15

103 I.T.U. Emblem and Symbols

1965. Centenary of I.T.U.

679	**103**	25f. blue and light blue	30	15
680		45f. black and green	50	45

104 "Syncom" Satellite and Pagoda

1965. Space Achievements. Multicoloured.

682		5f. Type **104**	15	10
683		10f. North American X-15 rocket airplane	25	10
684		15f. Astronauts	55	25
685		20f. As 10f.	55	25
686		50f. Type **104**	1·00	60

105 Dead Sea

1985. Dead Sea. Multicoloured.

688		35f. Type **105**	60	40
689		35f. Boats and palms	60	40
690		35f. Qumran Caves	60	40
691		35f. Dead Sea Scrolls	60	40

1965. Air. Space Flight of McDivitt and White. Nos. 641/6 optd **James McDivitt Edward White 2-6-1965** in English and Arabic and rocket.

692	**94**	10f. red	1·90	70
693		15f. violet	1·90	70
694		20f. blue	2·75	1·50
695		30f. green	3·75	2·50
696		40f. brown	4·50	3·25
697		60f. mauve	7·50	5·00

107 King Hussein, U.N. Emblem and Headquarters

1965. King Hussein's Visit to France and the U.S.A.

699	**107**	5f. sepia, blue and pink	10	10
700	–	10f. sepia, green and grey	15	10
701	–	20f. agate, brown and blue	30	25
702	**107**	50f. lilac, brown and blue	90	65

DESIGNS: 10f. King Hussein, Pres. de Gaulle and Eiffel Tower; 20f. King Hussein, Pres. Johnson and Statue of Liberty.

108 I.C.Y. Emblem

109 A.P.U. Emblem

1965. International Co-operation Year.

704	**108**	5f. red and orange	20	15
705		10f. violet and blue	45	20
706		45f. purple and green	1·75	1·40

1965. 10th Anniv (1964) of Arab Postal Union's Permanent Office at Cairo.

707	**109**	15f. black and blue	15	15
708		25f. black and green	45	20

110 Dome of the Rock

1965. Inaug (1964) of "Dome of the Rock".

709	**110**	15f. multicoloured	75	30
710		25f. multicoloured	1·25	80

111 King Hussein

115 First Station of the Cross

114 Agricultural Symbols

1966. (a) Postage. Portraits in blue (1f. to 15f.) or purple (21f. to 150f.); background colours given.

711	**111**	1f. orange	10	10
712		2f. blue	10	10
713		3f. violet	10	10
714		4f. purple	10	10
715		7f. brown	20	10
716		12f. mauve	20	10
717		15f. brown	25	10
718		21f. green	40	10
719		25f. blue	45	10
720		35f. stone	60	15
721		40f. yellow	65	20
722		50f. green	70	35
723		100f. green	1·25	70
724		150f. violet	2·75	1·10

(b) Air. Portraits in brown; background colours given.

725	**111**	200f. turquoise	4·25	1·25
726		500f. green	7·00	5·00
727		1d. blue	12·50	8·25

1966. Space Flights of Belyaev and Leonov. Nos. 630/5 optd **Alexei Leonov Pavel Belyaev 18 3-1965** in English and Arabic and spacecraft motif.

728	**92**	40f. brown and green	4·50	3·00
729	–	40f. violet and brown	4·50	3·00
730	–	40f. purple and blue	4·50	3·00
731	–	40f. lilac and bistre	4·50	3·00
732	–	40f. sepia and blue	4·50	3·00
733	–	40f. green and pink	4·50	3·00

1966. Pope Paul's Visit to U.N. (1965). Nos. 604/8 optd **PAPA PAULUS VI WORLD PEACE VISIT TO UNITED NATIONS 1965** in English and Arabic.

736	**88**	10f. green	20	10
737		15f. purple	45	20
738		25f. brown	45	25
739		50f. blue	85	45
740		80f. green	1·50	75

1966. Anti-T.B. Campaign. (a) Unissued "Freedom from Hunger" stamps optd as in T **114**.

741	**114**	15f. multicoloured	35	25
742		35f. multicoloured	80	60
743		50f. multicoloured	1·40	1·25

(b) As Nos. 741/3 but with additional premium obliterated by bars.

745	–	15f. multicoloured	35	25
746	–	35f. multicoloured	80	60
747	–	50f. multicoloured	1·40	1·25

1966. Christ's Passion. The Stations of the Cross.

749	**115**	1f. multicoloured	10	10
750	–	2f. multicoloured	10	10
751	–	3f. multicoloured	20	10
752	–	4f. multicoloured	20	15
753	–	5f. multicoloured	35	20
754	–	6f. multicoloured	50	30
755	–	7f. multicoloured	65	40
756	–	8f. multicoloured	65	40
757	–	9f. multicoloured	85	50
758	–	10f. multicoloured	95	60
759	–	11f. multicoloured	1·10	70
760	–	12f. multicoloured	1·10	70
761	–	13f. multicoloured	1·10	70
762	–	14f. multicoloured	1·25	85

DESIGNS: The 14 Stations. The denominations, expressed in Roman numerals, correspond to the numbers of the stations.

116 Schirra and "Gemini 6"

118 Dag Hammarskjold

117 The Three Kings

1966. Space Achievements.

764	**116**	1f. blue, violet and green	10	10
765	–	2f. green, violet and blue	10	10
766	–	3f. violet, blue and green	10	10
767	–	4f. violet, green and ochre	15	10
768	–	30f. turquoise, brn & vio	1·40	90
769	–	60f. brown, turq & vio	1·75	1·40

DESIGNS: 2f. Stafford and "Gemini 6"; 3f. Borman and "Gemini 7"; 4f. Lovell and "Gemini 7"; 30f. Armstrong and "Gemini 8"; 60f. Scott and "Gemini 8".

1966. Christmas. Multicoloured.
771 5f. Type **117** 20 10
772 10f. The Magi presenting gifts to the infant Christ 30 15
773 35f. The flight to Egypt (vert) 2·50 85

1967. "Builders of World Peace". Multicoloured.
775 5f. Type **118** 10 10
781 5f. U Thant 10 10
776 10f. Pandit Nehru 20 10
782 10f. Pres. De Gaulle 20 10
777 35f. Pres. Kennedy 60 30
783 35f. Pres. Johnson 60 25
778 50f. Pope John XXIII . . . 1·50 50
784 50f. Pope Paul VI . . . . . 1·50 50
779 100f. King Abdullah I (of Jordan) . . . . 1·60 1·40
785 100f. King Hussein . . . . . 1·60 90

119 King Hussein

1967. "Gold Coins". Circular designs, centre and rim embossed on gold foil. Imperf. (a) As T **119**. (i) Diameter 41 mm.
787 **119** 5f. orange and blue . . . 30 30
788 10f. orange and violet . . 30 30
(ii) Diameter 47 mm.
789 **119** 50f. lilac and brown . . . 1·50 1·50
790 100f. pink and green . . . 2·00 2·00
(iii) Diameter 54 mm.
791 **119** 200f. blue and deep blue 5·00 5·00
(b) Crown Prince Hassan of Jordan. (i) Diameter 41 mm.
792 – 5f. black and green 55 55
793 – 10f. black and lilac 55 55
(ii) Diameter 47 mm.
794 – 50f. black and blue . . . . 3·00 3·00
795 – 100f. black and brown . . . 4·00 4·00
(iii) Diameter 54 mm.
796 – 200f. black and mauve . . . 7·50 7·50
A similar set was also issued in the same values and sizes but different colours with portrait of John F. Kennedy.

120 University City, Statue and Olympic Torch

1967. Preparation for Olympic Games in Mexico (1968).
797 **120** 1f. red, black and violet 10 10
798 – 2f. black, violet and red 10 10
799 – 3f. violet, red and black 10 10
800 – 4f. blue, brown and green 10 10
801 – 30f. green, blue and brown 40 40
802 – 60f. brown, green and blue . . . . 1·00 50
DESIGNS (each with Olympic torch): 2f. Fishermen on Lake Patzcuaro; 3f. University City and skyscraper, Mexico City; 4f. Avenida de la Reforma, Mexico City; 30f. Guadalajara Cathedral; 60f. Fine Arts Theatre, Mexico City.

121 Decade Emblem

1967. International Hydrological Decade.
804 **121** 10f. black and red 25 10
805 15f. black and turquoise 45 25
806 25f. black and purple . . 75 50

122 U.N.E.S.C.O. Emblem

1967. 20th Anniv of U.N.E.S.C.O.
807 **122** 100f. multicoloured . . . 1·00 60

123 Dromedary

1967. Animals. Multicoloured.
808 1f. Type **123** (postage) . . . 10 10
809 2f. Karakul sheep 15 10
810 3f. Angora goat 15 10
811 4f. Striped hyena (air) . . . 25 15
812 30f. Arab horses . . . . . . 1·25 35
813 60f. Goitred gazelle . . . . . 2·10 80

124 W.H.O. Building

1967. Inaug of W.H.O. Headquarters, Geneva.
815 **124** 5f. black and green . . . 15 10
816 45f. black and orange . . 55 30

125 Arab League Emblem, Open Book and Reaching Hands

1968. Literacy Campaign.
817 **125** 20f. green and orange . . 40 25
818 20f. blue and mauve . . . 40 25

126 W.H.O. Emblem and "20"

1968. 20th Anniv of W.H.O.
819 **126** 30f. multicoloured 50 25
820 100f. multicoloured . . . 1·40 75

127 Eurasian Goldfinch ("Goldfinch")

1968. Game Protection. Multicoloured.
821 5f. Type **127** (postage) . . . 1·90 80
822 10f. Chukar partridge ("Rock Partridge") (vert) . . . . . 3·00 80
823 15f. Ostriches (vert) . . . . . 4·25 1·00
824 20f. Sand partridge . . . . . 4·25 1·10
825 30f. Mountain gazelle . . . . 2·25 70
826 40f. Arabian oryx . . . . . 3·25 75
827 50f. Houbara bustard ("Bustard") . . . . 6·00 2·10
828 60f. Ibex (vert) (air) . . . . 4·00 2·00
829 100f. Flock of mallard ("Duck") . . . . 7·50 4·75

128 Human Rights Emblem

129 I.L.O. Emblem

1968. Human Rights Year.
830 **128** 20f. black, buff and brown 30 20
831 60f. black, blue and green 70 50

1969. 50th Anniv of I.L.O.
832 **129** 10f. black and blue . . . 20 10
833 20f. black and brown . . 20 10
834 25f. black and green . . . 30 25
835 45f. black and mauve . . 50 35
836 60f. black and orange . . 70 40

130 Horses in Pasture

1969. Arab Horses. Multicoloured.
837 10f. Type **130** 50 15
838 20f. White horse . . . . . . 1·25 35
839 45f. Black mare and foal . . 2·50 1·10

131 Kaaba, Mecca, and Dome of the Rock, Jerusalem

1969. Multicoloured.
840 5f. As Type **131** 30 10
841 10f. Dome of the Rock (30 × 36 mm) 50 35
842 20f. As 10f. 90 50
843 45f. As 5f. . . . . 2·25 55

132 Oranges

133 Prince Hassan and Bride

1969. Fruits. Multicoloured.
844 10f. Type **132** 25 10
845 20f. Gooseberry 40 20
846 30f. Lemons 80 20
847 40f. Grapes . . . . 1·10 30
848 50f. Olives . . . . 1·60 75
849 100f. Apples . . . . 2·50 1·50

1969. Wedding of Prince Hassan (1968).
850 – 20f. multicoloured 70 50
851 – 60f. multicoloured . . . . 1·10 80
852 **133** 100f. multicoloured . . . . 1·25 90
Nos. 850/1 show a similar design to Type **133**.

134 Wrecked Houses

1970. "Tragedy of the Refugees". Various vert designs as T **134**. Multicoloured.
853/82 1f. to 30f. inclusive Set of 30 . . . . 10·00 10·00

135 Bombed Mosque

1970. "Tragedy in the Holy Lands". Various vert designs as T **135**. Multicoloured.
883/912 1f. to 30f. inclusive Set of 30 . . . . 10·00 10·00

136 Pomegranate

137 Football

1970. Flowers. Multicoloured.
913 5f. Type **136** 30 10
914 15f. Wattle 50 10
915 25f. Caper 75 10
916 35f. Convolvulus . . . . . . 1·10 25
917 45f. Desert scabious . . . . 1·50 55
918 75f. Black iris . . . . 2·40 2·00
Nos. 913/15 and 917 are wrongly inscribed on the stamps.

1970. Sports. Multicoloured.
919 5f. Type **137** 15 10
920 10f. Diving 20 10
921 15f. Boxing 35 10
922 50f. Running . . . . 1·00 45
923 100f. Cycling (vert) . . . . . 2·50 90
924 150f. Basketball (vert) . . . 3·50 2·00

138 Arab Children

1970. Children's Day. Multicoloured.
925 5f. Type **138** 20 10
926 10f. Refugee boy with kettle (vert) 25 10
927 15f. Refugee girl in camp (vert) 45 15
928 20f. Refugee child in tent (vert) 70 20

139 White-crowned Black Wheatear ("Black Chat")

1970. Birds.
929 **139** 120f. black and orange . . 11·00 2·75
930 – 180f. brown, black & lilac 13·50 5·50
931 – 200f. multicoloured . . . 17·00 7·25
DESIGNS: 180f. Masked shrike; 200f. Palestine sunbird.

140 Grotto of the Nativity, Bethlehem

1970. Christmas. Church of the Nativity, Bethlehem. Multicoloured.
932 5f. Type **140** 20 10
933 10f. Christmas crib 30 15
934 20f. Crypt Altar 50 20
935 25f. Nave, Church of the Nativity 60 45

141 Arab League Flag, Emblem and Map

1971. 25th Anniv (1970) of Arab League.
936 **141** 10f. green, violet & orange 15 15
937 20f. green, brown and blue 35 15
938 30f. green, blue and olive 50 25

142 Heads of Four Races and Emblem

144 Ibn Sinai (Avicenna)

143 Shore of the Dead Sea

1971. Racial Equality Year. Multicoloured.

939		5f. Type **142**	10	10
940		10f. "Plant" and emblem	15	10
941		15f. Doves and emblem (horiz)	30	20

No. 939 is inscribed "KINIGDOM" in error.

1971. Tourism. Multicoloured.

942		5f. Type **143**	20	10
943		30f. Ed Deir, Petra	60	30
944		45f. Via Dolorosa, Jerusalem (vert)	90	35
945		60f. River Jordan	1·50	80
946		100f. Christmas Bell, Bethlehem (vert)	2·10	1·50

1971. Famous Arab Scholars. Multicoloured.

947		5f. Type **144**	15	10
948		10f. Ibn Rushd	25	10
949		20f. Ibn Khaldun	35	10
950		25f. Ibn Tufail	60	10
951		30f. Ibn El Haytham	80	45

145 New U.P.U. H.Q. Building

1971. Inauguration of New U.P.U. Headquarters Building, Berne.

952	**145**	10f. brown, green & yellow	25	10
953		20f. purple, green & yellow	75	35

146 Young Pupil

147 Mothers and Children

1972. International Education Year.

954	**146**	5f. multicoloured	10	10
955		15f. multicoloured	20	10
956		20f. multicoloured	35	10
957		30f. multicoloured	75	40

1972. Mothers Day. Multicoloured.

958		10f. Type **147**	30	10
959		20f. Mother and child (vert)	50	10
960		30f. Bedouin mother and child (vert)	1·00	50

148 Pope Paul VI leaving Holy Sepulchre, Jerusalem

1972. Easter. Multicoloured.

961		30f. Type **148** (postage)	70	15
962		60f. The Calvary, Church of the Holy Sepulchre (air)	1·40	50
963		100f. "Washing of the Feet", Jerusalem	2·75	1·25

149 Children and U.N.I.C.E.F. Emblem

1972. 25th Anniv of U.N.I.C.E.F.

964	**149**	10f. turquoise, blue & brn	15	10
965	–	20f. brown, green & pur	50	25
966	–	30f. brown, mauve & blue	75	35

DESIGNS—VERT: 20f. Child with toy bricks. HORIZ: 30f. Nurse holding baby.

150 Dove of Peace

152 Arab with Kestrel

151 Al Aqsa Mosque and Pilgrims

1972. 25th Anniv (1970) of United Nations.

967	**150**	5f. green, violet and yellow	10	10
968		10f. green, red and yellow	20	10
969		15f. blue, black and yellow	40	10
970		20f. blue, green and yellow	55	20
971		30f. green, brown & yell	1·00	50

1972. Burning of Al Aqsa Mosque (1970). Mult.

972		30f. Type **151**	1·00	20
973		60f. Mosque in flames	1·50	80
974		100f. Mosque interior	3·50	1·60

1972. Jordanian Desert Life. Multicoloured.

975		5f. Type **152**	20	10
976		10f. Desert bungalow (horiz)	20	10
977		15f. Camel trooper, Arab Legion (horiz)	40	15
978		20f. Boring operations (horiz)	45	15
979		25f. Shepherd (horiz)	55	20
980		30f. Dromedaries at water-trough (horiz)	80	35
981		35f. Chicken farm (horiz)	90	55
982		45f. Irrigation scheme (horiz)	1·75	1·10

153 Wasfi el Tell and Dome of the Rock, Jerusalem

1972. Wasfi el Tell (assassinated statesman) Memorial Issue. Multicoloured.

983		5f. Type **153**	20	10
984		10f. Wasfi el Tell, map and flag	30	10
985		20f. Type **153**	60	10
986		30f. As 10f.	70	55

154 Clay-pigeon shooting

1972. World Clay-pigeon Shooting Championships. Multicoloured.

987		25f. Type **154**	60	10
988		75f. Marksman on range (horiz)	1·90	80
989		120f. Marksman taking aim (horiz)	1·50	1·75

155 Aero Club Emblem

1973. Royal Jordanian Aero Club.

990	**155**	5f. blk, bl & yell (postage)	15	10
991		10f. black, blue and yellow	15	10
992	–	15f. multicoloured (air)	35	10
993	–	20f. multicoloured	55	15
994	–	40f. multicoloured	1·10	50

DESIGNS: 15f. Piper Cherokee 140 aircraft; 20f. Beech B55 Baron airplane; 40f. Winged horse emblem.

156 Dove and Flag

1973. 50th Anniv of Hashemite Kingdom of Jordan. Multicoloured.

995		5f. Type **156**	10	10
996		10f. Anniversary emblem	20	10
997		15f. King Hussein	50	10
998		30f. Map and emblems	1·00	90

157 Map and Jordanian Advance

1973. 5th Anniv of Battle of Karama. Mult.

999		5f. Type **157**	20	10
1000		10f. Jordanian attack, and map	40	20
1001		15f. Map, and King Hussein on tank	1·00	70

158 Father and Son

1973. Fathers' Day. Multicoloured.

1002		10f. Type **158**	15	10
1003		20f. Father and daughter	50	15
1004		30f. Family group	75	35

159 Phosphate Mines

1973. Development Projects. Multicoloured.

1005		5f. Type **159**	25	10
1006		10f. Cement factories	35	10
1007		15f. Sharhabil Dam	55	15
1008		20f. Kafrein Dam	75	35

160 Racing Camel

1973. Camel Racing. Multicoloured.

1009		5f. Type **160**	25	10
1010		10f. Camels in "paddock"	50	15
1011		15f. Start of race	75	25
1012		20f. Camel racing	1·75	50

161 Book Year Emblem

1973. International Book Year (1972).

1013	**161**	30f. multicoloured	75	10
1014		60f. multicoloured	1·25	50

162 Family Group

1973. Family Day.

1015	**162**	20f. multicoloured	40	10
1016	–	30f. multicoloured	60	15
1017	–	60f. multicoloured	1·00	50

DESIGNS: 30, 60f. Different family groups.

163 Shah of Iran, King Hussein, Cyrus's Tomb and Mosque of Omar

1973. 2500th Anniv of Iranian Monarchy.

1018	**163**	5f. multicoloured	25	10
1019		10f. multicoloured	30	10
1020		15f. multicoloured	50	15
1021		30f. multicoloured	1·00	50

164 Emblem of Palestine Week

1973. Palestine Week. Multicoloured.

1022		5f. Type **164**	30	10
1023		10f. Torch and emblem	50	10
1024		15f. Refugees (26×47 mm)	1·00	30
1025		30f. Children and map on Globe	1·50	40

165 Traditional Harvesting

1973. Ancient and Modern Agriculture. Multicoloured.

1026		5f. Type **165** (postage)	15	10
1027		10f. Modern harvesting	20	10
1028		15f. Traditional seeding	40	10
1029		20f. Modern seeding	60	15
1030		30f. Traditional ploughing	70	20
1031		35f. Modern ploughing	80	25
1032		45f. Pest control	1·00	25
1033		60f. Horticulture	1·75	90
1034		100f. Agricultural landscape (air)	2·00	1·00

166 Long-nosed Butterflyfish

168 "The Club-footed Boy" (Murillo)

167 Battle of Muta

1974. Red Sea Fishes. Multicoloured.

1035		5f. Type **166**	25	10
1036		10f. Monocle bream	35	10
1037		15f. As No. 1036	65	15
1038		20f. Slender-spined mojarra	75	15
1039		25f. As No. 1038	1·10	30
1040		30f. Russell's snapper	1·10	30
1041		35f. As No. 1040	1·75	45
1042		40f. Blue-barred orange parrotfish	2·00	50
1043		45f. As No. 1042	2·10	55
1044		50f. Type **166**	2·50	60
1045		60f. Yellow-edged lyretail	3·00	60

1974. Islamic Battles against the Crusaders. Multicoloured.

1046		10f. Type **167**	35	10
1047		20f. Battle of Yarmouk	90	25
1048		30f. Battle of Hattin	1·60	65

1974. Famous Paintings. Multicoloured.

1049		5f. Type **168**	25	10
1050		10f. "Praying Hands" (Durer)	40	10
1051		15f. "St. George and the Dragon" (Uccello)	50	10
1052		20f. "The Mona Lisa" (L. da Vinci)	60	10
1053		30f. "Hope" (F. Watts)	75	15
1054		40f. "The Angelus" (Jean Millet) (horiz)	1·00	20
1055		50f. "The Artist and her Daughter" (Angelica Kauffmann)	2·00	25
1056		60f. "Whistler's Mother" (J. Whistler) (horiz)	2·00	70
1057		100f. "Master Hare" (Sir J. Reynolds)	2·50	1·25

المؤتمر الدولي لتاريخ بلاد الشام
٢٠ – ١٩٧٤/٤/٢٥
الجامعة الاردنية

(169)

1974. International Conference for Damascus History. Nos. 1013/14 optd with T **169**.

1058	**161**	30f. multicoloured	40	25
1059		60f. multicoloured	85	50

170 U.P.U. Emblem — 171 Camel Caravan

1974. Centenary of Universal Postal Union.

1060	**170**	10f. multicoloured	15	10
1061		30f. multicoloured	40	20
1062		60f. multicoloured	70	70

1974. The Dead Sea. Multicoloured.

1063		2f. Type **171**	10	10
1064		3f. Palm and shore	15	10
1065		4f. Hotel on coast	15	10
1066		5f. Jars from Qumram Caves	15	10
1067		6f. Copper scrolls (vert)	30	10
1068		10f. Cistern steps, Qumram (vert)	45	10
1069		20f. Type **171**	55	15
1070		30f. As 3f.	80	15
1071		40f. As 4f.	85	40
1072		50f. As 5f.	1·40	50
1073		60f. As 6f.	1·75	70
1074		100f. As 10f.	2·75	1·10

172 W.P.Y. Emblem — 173 Water-skier

1974. World Population Year.

1075	**172**	5f. purple, green & black	15	10
1076		10f. red, green and black	25	10
1077		20f. orange, green & blk	50	20

1974. Water-skiing. Multicoloured.

1078		5f. Type **173**	10	10
1079		10f. Water-skier (side view) (horiz)	20	10
1080		20f. Skier turning (horiz)	50	10
1081		50f. Type **173**	1·10	30
1082		100f. As 10f.	2·10	75
1083		200f. As 20f.	2·75	2·00

174 Ka'aba, Mecca, and Pilgrims

1974. "Pilgrimage Season".

1084	**174**	10f. multicoloured	25	15
1085		20f. multicoloured	65	45

175 Amrah Palace — 176 King Hussein at Wheel of Car

1974. Desert Ruins. Multicoloured.

1086		10f. Type **175**	25	15
1087		20f. Hisham Palace	50	45
1088		30f. Kharana Castle	1·25	60

1975. Air. Royal Jordanian Automobile Club.

1089	**176**	30f. multicoloured	40	15
1090		60f. multicoloured	1·25	70

177 Woman in Costume — 178 Treasury, Petra

1975. Jordanian Women's Costumes.

1091	**177**	5f. multicoloured	15	10
1092	–	10f. multicoloured	25	10
1093	–	15f. multicoloured	40	15
1094	–	20f. multicoloured	65	20
1095	–	25f. multicoloured	85	50

DESIGNS: 10f. to 25f. Various costumes as T **177**.

1975. Tourism. Multicoloured.

1096		15f. Type **178** (postage)	25	10
1097		20f. Ommayyad Palace, Amman (horiz)	40	15
1098		30f. Dome of the Rock, Jerusalem (horiz)	70	30
1099		40f. Forum columns, Jerash (horiz)	1·00	60
1100		50f. Palms, Aqaba (air)	65	30
1101		60f. Obelisk Tomb, Petra (horiz)	1·50	70
1102		80f. Fort of Wadi Rum (horiz)	2·10	1·40

179 King Hussein — 180 Globe and "Desert"

1975.

1103	**179**	5f. blue and green	20	10
1104		10f. blue and violet	20	10
1105		15f. blue and pink	10	10
1106		20f. blue and brown	40	15
1107		25f. blue and ultramarine	40	15
1108		30f. blue and brown	15	10
1109		35f. blue and violet	20	15
1110		40f. blue and red	50	25
1111		45f. blue and mauve	30	20
1112		50f. blue and green	30	20
1113		60f. brown and green	90	35
1114		100f. brown & lt brown	1·50	40
1115		120f. brown and blue	75	60
1116		180f. brown and mauve	1·25	90
1117		200f. brown and blue	1·50	1·25
1118		400f. brown and purple	2·50	2·00
1119		500f. brown and red	3·25	3·00

Nos. 1113/19 are larger, 22 × 27 mm.

1975. 10th Anniv of ALIA (Royal Jordanian Airlines). Multicoloured.

1120		10f. Type **180**	20	10
1121		30f. Boeing 707 linking globe and map of Jordan (horiz)	70	25
1122		60f. Globe and "ALIA" logo	1·40	60

181 Satellite and Earth Station

1975. Satellite Earth Station Opening.

1123	**181**	20f. multicoloured	60	15
1124		30f. multicoloured	1·00	50

182 Emblem of Chamber of Commerce

1975. 50th Anniv of Amman Chamber of Commerce.

1125	**182**	10f. multicoloured	15	10
1126		15f. multicoloured	30	15
1127		20f. multicoloured	45	30

183 Emblem and Hand with Spanner

1975. Completion of Three Year Development Plan.

1128	**183**	5f. black, red and green	10	10
1129		10f. black, red and green	20	20
1130		20f. black, red and green	50	30

184 Jordanian Family — 185 A.L.O. Emblem and Salt Mine

1976. International Women's Year (1975). Mult.

1131		5f. Type **184**	10	10
1132		25f. Woman scientist	45	25
1133		60f. Woman graduate	1·10	65

1976. Arab Labour Organization. Multicoloured.

1134		10f. Type **185**	15	10
1135		30f. Welding	50	25
1136		60f. Quayside, Aqaba	1·10	75

1976. Nos. 853/82 surch in English and Arabic.

1137/46	25f. on 1f. to 10f.		
1147/51	40f. on 11f. to 15f.		
1152/56	50f. on 16f. to 20f.		
1157/61	75f. on 21f. to 25f.		
1162/66	125f. on 26f. to 30f.		
	Set of 30	40·00	28·00

1976. Nos. 883/912 surch in English and Arabic.

1167/76	25f. on 1f. to 10f.		
1178/82	40f. on 11f. to 15f.		
1183/87	50f. on 16f. to 20f.		
1188/92	75f. on 21f. to 25f.		
1192/96	125f. on 26f. to 30f.		
	Set of 30	40·00	28·00

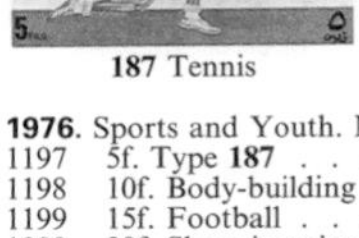
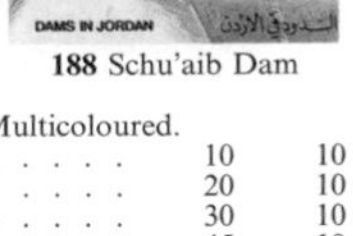

187 Tennis — 188 Schu'aib Dam

1976. Sports and Youth. Multicoloured.

1197		5f. Type **187**	10	10
1198		10f. Body-building	20	10
1199		15f. Football	30	10
1200		20f. Show jumping	45	10
1201		30f. Weightlifting	70	25
1202		100f. Stadium, Amman	2·75	1·50

1976. Dams. Multicoloured.

1203		30f. Type **188**	60	15
1204		60f. Al-Kafrein Dam	1·40	50
1205		100f. Ziqlab Dam	2·50	1·00

189 Early and Modern Telephones — 190 Road Crossing and Traffic Lights

1977. Telephone Centenary. Multicoloured.

1206		75f. Type **189**	1·00	60
1207		125f. Early telephone and modern receiver	1·75	1·00

1977. International Traffic Day. Multicoloured.

1208		5f. Type **190**	20	10
1209		75f. Roundabout and traffic lights	2·10	60
1210		125f. Motorcycle policemen, road signs and traffic lights	3·75	1·90

191 Airliner over Ship — 192 Child, Toys and Money-box

1977. Silver Jubilee of King Hussein. Mult.

1211		10f. Type **191**	20	10
1212		25f. Pylons and factories	30	10
1213		40f. Fertilizer plant	45	15
1214		50f. Ground-to-air missile	60	25
1215		75f. Mosque	1·25	75
1216		125f. Ground satellite receiving aerial	1·75	1·50

1977. Postal Savings Bank. Multicoloured.

1218		10f. Type **192**	1·00	50
1219		25f. Child with piggy bank	30	10
1220		50f. Savings Bank emblem	60	30
1221		75f. Boy and bank teller	1·25	65

193 King Hussein and Queen Alia — 194 Queen Alia

1977.

1222	**193**	10f. multicoloured	15	10
1223		25f. multicoloured	30	15
1224		40f. multicoloured	50	25
1225		50f. multicoloured	60	45

1977. Queen Alia Commemoration.

1226	**194**	10f. multicoloured	15	10
1227		25f. multicoloured	30	15
1228		40f. multicoloured	50	25
1229		50f. multicoloured	60	45

195 Mohammed Ali Jinnah — 196 A.P.U. Emblem and Flags

1977. Birth Centenary of Mohammed Ali Jinnah (1st Governor-General of Pakistan).

1230	**195**	25f. multicoloured	40	20
1231		75f. multicoloured	2·00	80

1978. 25th Anniv (1977) of Arab Postal Union.

1232	**196**	25f. multicoloured	35	10
1233		40f. multicoloured	85	35

197 Coffee Pots and Cups — 198 Roman Amphitheatre, Jerash

1978. Handicrafts. Multicoloured.

1234		25f. Type **197**	30	10
1235		40f. Porcelain plate and ashtray	40	15

1236 75f. Vase, necklace and chains 95 45
1237 125f. Containers holding pipes . . . . 1·60 1·00

1978. Tourism. Multicoloured.
1238 5f. Type **198** 15 10
1239 20f. Roman columns, Jerash 35 10
1240 40f. Roman mosaic, Madaba 50 30
1241 75f. Rock formations, Rum 1·25 55

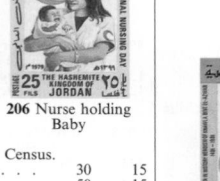

199 King Hussein and Pres. Sadat of Egypt

200 Cement Works

1978. Visits of Arab Leaders to Jordan. Mult.
1242 40f. Type **199** 40 15
1243 40f. King Hussein and Pres. Assad (horiz) 40 15
1244 40f. King Hussein and King Khalid (horiz) 40 15

1978. Industrial Development. Multicoloured
1245 5f. Type **200** 10 10
1246 10f. Science laboratory . . . 30 10
1247 25f. Printing press 70 20
1248 75f. Fertilizer plant . . . . 1·75 70

201 U.N.E.S.C.O. Emblem

202 King Hussein

1978. 30th Anniv of U.N.E.S.C.O.
1249 **201** 40f. multicoloured . . . 40 25
1250 75f. multicoloured . . . 1·00 75

1979. Dated "1979".
1251 **202** 25f. brown, flesh and blue 40 10
1252 40f. brown, flesh & pur 70 15
See also Nos. 1265/72 for values dated "1980" and Nos. 1309/13 for those dated "1981".

203 Emblems within Cogwheels

204 I.Y.C. Emblem and Flag of Jordan

1979. Five Year Development Plan.
1253 **203** 25f. multicoloured . . . 1·40 20
1254 40f. multicoloured . . . 1·75 30
1255 50f. multicoloured . . . 2·10 90

1979. International Year of the Child.
1256 **204** 25f. multicoloured . . . 60 25
1257 40f. multicoloured . . . 90 35
1258 50f. multicoloured . . . 1·00 75

205 Census Emblem

206 Nurse holding Baby

1979. Population and Housing Census.
1259 **205** 25f. multicoloured . . . 30 15
1260 40f. multicoloured . . . 50 15
1261 50f. multicoloured . . . 70 35

1980. International Nursing Day.
1262 **206** 25f. multicoloured . . . 40 15
1263 40f. multicoloured . . . 70 30
1264 50f. multicoloured . . . 90 55

1980.
1265 **202** 5f. brown, pink and green 10 10
1266 10f. brown, pink & violet 10 10
1267 20f. brown and pink . . 15 10
1268 25f. brown, pink and blue 20 10
1269 40f. brown and mauve 30 15
1270 50f. brown, pink & green 40 25
1271 75f. brown, pink and grey 30 20
1272 125f. brown, pink and red . . . . 1·25 30
Nos. 1265/72 are similar to Nos. 1251/2 but are inscr "1980".

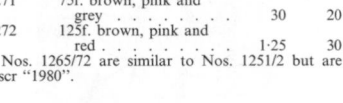

207 El Deir Temple, Petra

208 Mosque and Kaaba, Mecca

1980. World Tourism Conference, Manila.
1273 **207** 25f. black, grey and green 75 25
1274 40f. black, grey and blue 1·00 50
1275 50f. black, grey & purple 1·25 1·00

1980. 1400th Anniv of Hegira.
1276 **208** 25f. multicoloured . . . 30 10
1277 40f. multicoloured . . . 40 15
1278 50f. multicoloured . . . 50 20
1279 75f. multicoloured . . . 80 60
1280 100f. multicoloured . . . 1·00 80

209 Conference Emblem

210 Picking Crops, examining Patients and Flag-raising Ceremony

1980. 11th Arab Summit Conference, Amman.
1282 **209** 25f. multicoloured . . . 30 10
1283 40f. multicoloured . . . 50 15
1284 50f. multicoloured . . . 55 25
1285 75f. multicoloured . . . 80 50
1286 100f. multicoloured . . . 95 75

1981. Red Crescent.
1288 **210** 25f. multicoloured . . . 50 20
1289 40f. multicoloured . . . 90 40
1290 50f. multicoloured . . . 1·10 65

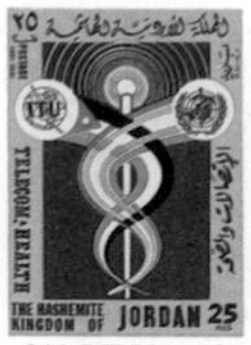
211 I.T.U. and W.H.O. Emblems and Ribbons forming Caduceus

212 Jordan Stamps of 1930 and 1975

1981. World Telecommunications Day.
1291 **211** 25f. multicoloured . . . 50 20
1292 40f. multicoloured . . . 90 40
1293 50f. multicoloured . . . 1·10 65

1981. Opening of Postal Museum. Multicoloured.
1294 25f. Type **212** 50 15
1295 40f. Jordan stamps of 1933 and 1954 (vert) 75 30
1296 50f. Jordan stamps of 1946 and 1952 . . . . 1·00 55

213 Khawla Bint el-Azwar

214 F.A.O. Emblem and Olive Branches

1981. Arab Women in History. Multicoloured.
1297 25f. Type **213** 75 20
1298 40f. El-Khansa (writer) . . . 1·25 40
1299 50f. Rabia el-Adawiyeh (Sufi religious leader) . . . . . 2·00 1·00

1981. World Food Day.
1300 **214** 25f. multicoloured . . . 60 15
1301 40f. multicoloured . . . 80 35
1302 50f. multicoloured . . . 1·10 70

215 I.Y.D.P. Emblem

216 Hands reading Braille

1981. International Year of Disabled Persons.
1303 **215** 25f. multicoloured . . . 60 20
1304 40f. multicoloured . . . 90 30
1305 50f. multicoloured . . . 1·10 70

1981. The Blind.
1306 **216** 25f. multicoloured . . . 60 20
1307 40f. multicoloured . . . 90 30
1308 50f. multicoloured . . . 1·10 70

1982.
1309 **202** 5f. brown, pink and green 10 10
1310 10f. brown, pink & violet 10 10
1311 20f. brown and pink . . 20 10
1312 25f. brown, pink and blue 25 20
1313 40f. brown, pink & pur 65 45
Nos. 1309/13 are similar to Nos. 1251/2, but are inscr "1981".

217 Hand holding Jug and Stone Tablets

218 A.P.U. Emblem

1982. Jordan Monuments.
1314 **217** 25f. multicoloured . . . 55 15
1315 40f. multicoloured . . . 85 25
1316 50f. multicoloured . . . 1·10 60

1982. 30th Anniv of Arab Postal Union.
1317 **218** 10f. multicoloured . . . 15 10
1318 25f. multicoloured . . . 40 15
1319 40f. multicoloured . . . 65 30
1320 50f. multicoloured . . . 75 50
1321 100f. multicoloured . . . 1·40 1·25

219 King Hussein and Jet Fighter

1982. Independence, Army Day and 30th Anniv of King's Accession to Throne. Multicoloured.
1322 10f. King Hussein and rockets 20 10
1323 25f. King Hussein and tanks 45 20
1324 40f. Type **219** . . . . 1·00 30
1325 50f. King Hussein and tanks (different) . . . . 1·10 60
1326 100f. King Hussein and flag being hoisted by armed forces . . . . 2·40 1·50

220 Salt Secondary School

1982. Salt Secondary School.
1327 **220** 10f. multicoloured . . . 15 10
1328 25f. multicoloured . . . 50 15
1329 40f. multicoloured . . . 80 25
1330 50f. multicoloured . . . 1·25 50
1331 100f. multicoloured . . . 2·75 1·50

221 City Gate, Jerusalem

222 Soldiers, Flags and Badge

1982. Jerusalem. Multicoloured.
1332 10f. Type **221** 20 10
1333 25f. Minaret 55 15
1334 40f. Mosque 80 40
1335 50f. Mosque (different) . . . 95 60
1336 100f. Dome of the Rock . . 1·90 1·25

1982. Yarmouk Forces.
1337 **222** 10f. multicoloured . . . 20 10
1338 25f. multicoloured . . . 55 15
1339 40f. multicoloured . . . 80 40
1340 50f. multicoloured . . . 95 60
1341 100f. multicoloured . . . 1·90 1·25

223 Dish Aerial, Earth and U.N. Emblem

224 King Abdullah and Dome of the Rock

1982. 2nd U.N. Conference on the Exploration and Peaceful Uses of Outer Space, Vienna.
1343 **223** 10f. multicoloured . . . 20 10
1344 25f. multicoloured . . . 40 15
1345 40f. multicoloured . . . 70 40
1346 50f. multicoloured . . . 95 70
1347 100f. multicoloured . . . 1·90 1·50

1982. Birth Centenary of King Abdullah.
1348 **224** 10f. multicoloured . . . 20 10
1349 25f. multicoloured . . . 40 15
1350 40f. multicoloured . . . 70 40
1351 50f. multicoloured . . . 95 70
1352 100f. multicoloured . . . 1·90 1·50

225 King Hussein and Temple Colonnade

226 King Hussein

1982. Roman Ruins at Jerash. Multicoloured.
1353 10f. Type **225** 25 10
1354 25f. Archway 45 15
1355 40f. Temple of Artemis . . 95 40
1356 50f. Amphitheatre . . . . . 1·25 70
1357 100f. Hippodrome . . . . . 2·00 1·50

1983.
1358 **226** 10f. multicoloured . . . 10 10
1359 25f. multicoloured . . . 25 10
1360 40f. multicoloured . . . 35 15
1361 60f. multicoloured . . . 70 35
1362 100f. multicoloured . . . 80 50
1363 125f. multicoloured . . . 1·10 80

227 Massacre Victims

1983. Massacre of Palestinian Refugees in Sabra and Shatila Camps. Multicoloured.
1364 10f. Type **227** 25 10
1365 25f. Covered bodies 60 15
1366 40f. Orphans 95 35
1367 50f. Massacre victims in street . . . . 1·50 70
1368 100f. Massacre victims (different) . . . . 2·25 1·75

228 Control Tower and Airport Buildings

1983. Opening of Queen Alia International Airport. Multicoloured.
1370 10f. Type **228** 20 10
1371 25f. Tower and terminal building 40 15
1372 40f. Tower and hangar . . . 90 35
1373 50f. Tower and aerial view of airport . . . . 1·40 55
1374 100f. Tower and embarkation bridge . . . 2·10 1·60

229 King Hussein with Radio Equipment

1983. Royal Jordanian Radio Amateurs Society.

1375	**229** 10f. multicoloured	20	10
1376	25f. multicoloured	40	15
1377	40f. multicoloured	80	30
1378	50f. multicoloured	1·00	50
1379	100f. multicoloured	2·00	1·40

230 Academy Building, Amman

1983. Establishment of Royal Academy for Islamic Civilization Research. Multicoloured.

1380	10f. Type **230**	20	10
1381	25f. Silk rug	45	15
1382	40f. View of Amman	80	30
1383	50f. Panorama of Jerusalem	1·00	50
1384	100f. Holy sites of Islam	2·00	1·40

231 Irrigation Canal

1983. Food Security. Multicoloured.

1386	10f. Type **231**	20	10
1387	25f. Growing crops under glass	45	15
1388	40f. Battery hens	85	30
1389	50f. Harvesting	1·00	50
1390	100f. Flock of sheep	2·00	1·40

232 Switchboard and Emblem

1983. World Communications Year. Mult.

1391	10f. Type **232**	25	10
1392	25f. Aerial view of satellite receiving station	60	15
1393	40f. Microwave antenna and emblems of communication	90	30
1394	50f. W.C.Y. emblems	1·25	55
1395	100f. Airmail letter	2·25	1·50

233 Dome of the Rock, Jerusalem

1983. Palestinian Solidarity.

1396	**233** 5f. multicoloured	40	15
1397	10f. multicoloured	80	30

234 Human Rights Emblems

1983. 35th Anniv of Declaration of Human Rights.

1398	**234** 10f. multicoloured	20	10
1399	25f. multicoloured	50	15
1400	40f. multicoloured	80	30
1401	50f. multicoloured	1·00	50
1402	100f. multicoloured	1·90	1·40

235 "Stop Polio Campaign" Emblem

1984. Anti-poliomyelitis Campaign.

1403	**235** 40f. orange, black & blue	50	20
1404	60f. silver, black and red	1·50	35
1405	100f. green, black & yell	1·75	95

236 Bomb and Cogwheel

1984. Israel's Attack on Iraqi Nuclear Reactor. Multicoloured.

1406	40f. Type **236**	1·00	20
1407	60f. Hand with dagger attacking nuclear symbol	1·90	75
1408	100f. Aircraft bombing nuclear symbol	3·25	1·50

237 King Hussein and Tanks

1984. Independence and Army Day. Mult.

1409	10f. Type **237**	20	10
1410	25f. King Hussein and naval patrol boat	50	15
1411	40f. King Hussein and Camel Corps	85	30
1412	60f. King Hussein and soldiers at Independence Monument	1·50	50
1413	100f. Parading soldiers	2·00	1·50

238 Sports Pictogram

1984. Olympic Games. Los Angeles. Mult.

1414	25f. Type **238**	30	15
1415	40f. Swimming	50	20
1416	60f. Shooting and archery pictograms	90	50
1417	100f. Gymnastics (floor exercises)	1·40	1·25

239 Amman Power Station

1984. Water and Electricity Year. Multicoloured.

1419	25f. Power lines and factories	40	15
1420	40f. Type **239**	75	20
1421	60f. Reservoirs and water pipe	1·00	55
1422	100f. Telephone lines, street light, water tap and pipeline	1·75	1·00

240 Omayyid Coins

1984. Coins. Multicoloured.

1423	40f. Type **240**	60	20
1424	60f. Abbasid coins	1·00	45
1425	125f. Hashemite coins	1·90	1·25

241 Shield and Antelope

1984. Release of Antelope in Jordan. Multicoloured.

1426	25f. Type **241**	50	15
1427	40f. Four antelope	90	30
1428	60f. Three antelope	1·40	65
1429	100f. Duke of Edinburgh, King Hussein and Queen Alia	2·40	1·00

242 Mu'ta Military University, Karak City

1984. Jordanian Universities. Multicoloured.

1430	40f. Type **242**	50	20
1431	60f. Yarmouk University, Irbid City	75	45
1432	125f. Jordan University, Amman	1·75	1·00

243 Tombs of El-Hareth bin Omier el-Azdi and Derar bin el-Azwar

1984. Al Sahaba Tombs. Multicoloured.

1433	10f. Type **243**	20	10
1434	25f. Tombs of Sharhabil bin Hasna and Abu Obaidah Amer bin el-Jarrah	50	15
1435	40f. Muath bin Jabal's tomb	75	20
1436	50f. Tombs of Zaid bin Haretha and Abdullah bin Rawaha	90	35
1437	60f. Tomb of Amer bin Abi Waqqas	1·25	65
1438	100f. Jafar bin Abi Taleb's tomb	1·90	1·25

244 Soldier descending Mountain and King Hussein

1985. Independence and Army Day. Mult.

1439	25f. Type **244**	45	15
1440	40f. Flags on map, King Abdullah and King Hussein	70	30
1441	60f. Flag, monument and arms	1·25	60
1442	100f. King Hussein, flag, King Abdullah and arms	2·00	1·40

245 Sir Rowland Hill (instigator of first stamps)

1985. Postal Celebrities. Multicoloured.

1443	40f. Type **245**	70	25
1444	60f. Heinrich von Stephan (founder of Universal Postal Union)	1·00	50
1445	125f. Yacoub Sukker (first Jordanian stamp designer)	2·10	1·25

246 Emblem and Delegates round Table

1985. 1st Jordanians Abroad Conference. Mult.

1446	40f. Type **246**	70	25
1447	60f. Conference emblem and globe and hand over torch	1·00	50
1448	125f. Globe encircled by Jordanian flags	2·10	1·25

247 I.Y.Y. Emblem

1985. International Youth Year. Multicoloured.

1449	10f. Type **247**	20	10
1450	25f. Arab couple on map, flag and emblem	50	20
1451	40f. Stylized figures flanking globe, flag and emblem	75	30
1452	60f. Part of cogwheel, laurel branch and ribbons in jug decorated with emblem	1·25	75
1453	125f. Stylized figures and emblem	2·25	1·50

248 El-Deir Temple, Petra

1985. 10th Anniv of World Tourist Organization. Multicoloured.

1454	10f. Type **248**	20	10
1455	25f. Temple of Artemis (ruins), Jerash	45	20
1456	40f. Amrah Palace	65	25
1457	50f. Hill town, Jordan valley	90	35
1458	60f. Sailing in Aqaba bay	1·25	65
1459	125f. Roman amphitheatre, Amman and city arms	2·10	1·40

249 Mother and Baby and Hospital

1985. U.N.I.C.E.F. Child Survival Campaign. Multicoloured.

1461	25f. Type **249**	45	20
1462	40f. Child being weighed	65	30
1463	60f. Childrens' heads as balloons	1·25	75
1464	125f. Mother feeding baby	2·10	1·60

250 Dancers

1985. 5th Anniv of Jerash Festival. Mult.

1466	10f. Opening ceremony, 1980	20	10
1467	25f. Type **250**	45	20
1468	40f. Dancers (different)	65	40
1469	60f. Male choir at Roman theatre	1·25	75
1470	100f. King Hussein and his wife	2·00	1·60

251 Flag and Emblem forming "40"

1985. 40th Anniv of U.N.O.

1471	**251** 60f. multicoloured	1·25	80
1472	125f. multicoloured	1·90	1·50

252 Hussein comforting Boy

1985. 50th Birthday of King Hussein. Mult.
1473 10f. Type **252** 20 10
1474 25f. Hussein in Arab robes 50 25
1475 40f. Hussein piloting aircraft 70 35
1476 60f. Hussein in army uniform . . . . 1·10 70
1477 100f. Hussein in Arab headdress . . . . 1·90 1·60

253 El Aqsa Mosque

1985. Compulsory Tax. Restoration of El Aqsa Mosque, Jerusalem.
1479 **253** 5f. multicoloured 25 15
1480 10f. multicoloured . . . 75 45

254 Policeman beside Car

1985. The Police. Multicoloured.
1481 40f. Type **254** . . . . 1·25 60
1482 60f. Policeman and crowd of children . . . . 1·75 80
1483 125f. Policeman taking oath 3·00 1·60

255 Satellite over Map of Arab Countries

1986. 1st Anniv of Launch of "Arabsat 1" Communications Satellite. Multicoloured.
1484 60f. Satellite . . . . 1·00 40
1485 100f. Type **255** . . . . . . 1·60 80

256 King presenting Colours

1986. 30th Anniv of Arabization of Jordanian Army. Multicoloured.
1486 40f. Type **256** 55 20
1487 60f. King Hussein shaking hands with soldier 70 30
1488 100f. King Hussein addressing Army . . . . 1·50 90

257 King Abdullah decorating Soldier

1986. 40th Anniv of Independence.
1490 **257** 160f. multicoloured . . . 2·00 1·25

258 King Hussein of Hejaz and Sons

1986. 70th Anniv of Arab Revolt. Multicoloured.
1491 40f. Type **258** 60 15
1492 60f. King Abdullah with armed men . . . . 1·00 30
1493 160f. King leading soldiers on horseback . . . . . . 2·00 1·40

259 Emblem

1986. International Peace Year.
1495 **259** 160f. multicoloured . . . 2·00 1·25
1496 240f. black, orange & grn . . . . 2·50 1·75

260 Cardiac Centre Building

1986. King Hussein Medical City. Multicoloured.
1497 40f. Type **260** 50 20
1498 60f. Patient undergoing operation . . . . 1·00 50
1499 100f. View of operating theatre during operation 1·50 90

261 Extract of King Hussein's Speech in Arabic

1986. 40th Anniv of U.N.O. Multicoloured.
1500 40f. Type **261** 50 20
1501 80f. Extract of speech in Arabic (different) . . . . 1·10 50
1502 100f. Extract of speech in English . . . . . . 1·40 90

262 Head Post Office, Amman

1987. 35th Anniv of Arab Postal Union. Mult.
1504 80f. Type **262** 80 50
1505 160f. Ministry of Communications, Amman 1·60 1·25

263 Jaber ibn Hayyan al-Azdi

1987. Arab and Muslim Pharmacists. Mult.
1506 60f. Type **263** 60 30
1507 80f. Abu-al-Qasem al-Majreeti 75 40
1508 240f. Abu-Bakr al-Razi . . 2·25 1·90

264 Village

1987. S.O.S. Childrens' Village, Amman. Mult.
1509 80f. Type **264** . . . . 1·25 70
1510 240f. Child and mural . . . 2·40 1·90

265 Soldiers on Wall

1987. 40th Anniv of 4th Army Brigade. Multicoloured.
1511 60f. Type **265** . . . . 1·00 50
1512 80f. Mortar crew . . . . . 1·50 70

266 Black-headed Bunting

1987. Birds. Multicoloured.
1514 10f. Hoopoe 50 35
1515 40f. Palestine sunbird . . . 1·75 90
1516 50f. Type **266** . . . . 2·40 1·25
1517 60f. Spur-winged plover . . 2·50 1·40
1518 80f. Western greenfinch ("Greenfinch") . . . . . 3·50 2·40
1519 100f. Black-winged stilt . . 4·50 3·25

267 King Hussein **268** Horsemen Charging

1987.
1520 **267** 60f. multicoloured . . . 50 10
1521 80f. multicoloured . . . 70 25
1522 160f. multicoloured . . . 1·25 55
1523 240f. multicoloured . . . 2·00 80

1987. 800th Anniv of Battle of Hattin. Mult.
1524 60f. Type **268** 90 45
1525 80f. Horseman and Dome of the Rock . . . . 1·25 75
1526 100f. Saladin, horsemen and Dome of the Rock . . . 1·50 1·00

269 Arms

1987.
1528 **269** 80f. multicoloured . . . 90 40
1529 160f. multicoloured . . . 1·50 70

270 Amman Industrial Estate, Sahab

1987.
1530 **270** 80f. multicoloured . . . 75 25

271 University Crest

1987. 25th Anniv of Jordan University. Multicoloured.
1531 60f. Type **271** 70 30
1532 80f. Entrance to campus (47 × 32 mm) 90 45

272 Child's Head in Droplet

1987. U.N.I.C.E.F. Child Survival Campaign. Multicoloured.
1533 60f. Type **272** 60 35
1534 80f. Hands reaching towards child and flag as "J" . . . 1·25 80
1535 160f. Baby on scales and children reading . . . . . 1·75 1·25

273 Parliament in Session, 1987

1987. 40th Anniv of Jordanian Parliament.
1536 – 60f. mauve and gold . . 75 50
1537 **273** 80f. multicoloured . . . 1·25 1·10
DESIGN: 60f. 1947 opening ceremony.

274 Emblem

1987. Extraordinary Arab Summit Conference, Amman.
1538 **274** 60f. multicoloured . . . 65 30
1539 80f. multicoloured . . . 85 40
1540 160f. multicoloured . . . 1·50 1·00
1541 240f. multicoloured . . . 2·25 1·50

275 King Hussein receiving Cape

1988. Award of 1987 Dag Hammarskjold Peace Prize to King Hussein. Multicoloured.
1543 80f. Type **275** 85 40
1544 160f. King Hussein receiving Prize . . . . 1·60 1·40

276 Golden Sword

1988. Jordanian Victory in 1987 Arab Military Basketball Championship. Multicoloured.
1545 60f. Type **276** 65 25
1546 80f. King Hussein congratulating winners . . 90 45
1547 160f. Match scene . . . . . 1·75 1·50

277 Anniversary Emblem and National Flag **278** Emblems and Globe

1988. 40th Anniv of W.H.O.
1548 **277** 60f. multicoloured . . . 80 30
1549 80f. multicoloured . . . 1·00 50

1988. 75th Anniv of Arab Scout Movement.
1550 **278** 60f. multicoloured . . . 80 30
1551 80f. multicoloured . . . 1·00 50

279 Crested Lark

1988. Birds. Multicoloured.
1552 10f. Type **279** 30 10
1553 20f. Stone-curlew 45 10
1554 30f. Common redstart ("Redstart") 55 10
1555 40f. Blackbird 75 15
1556 50f. Feral rock pigeon ("Rock Dove") 90 20
1557 160f. White-throated kingfisher ("Smyrna Kingfisher") . . . . . . 3·25 1·10

280 City cupped in Hands **282** Tennis

281 Um al-Rasas

1988. Restoration of Sana'a, Yemen Arab Republic.
1559 **280** 80f. multicoloured . . . 75 40
1560 160f. multicoloured . . . 1·00 75

1988. Historic Sites. Multicoloured.
1561 60f. Type **281** 60 35
1562 80f. Umm Qais 80 45
1563 160f. Iraq al-Amir . . . . . 1·25 70

1988. Olympic Games, Seoul. Multicoloured.
1565 10f. Type **282** 15 10
1566 60f. Mascot 60 35
1567 80f. Running and swimming 80 45
1568 120f. Basketball . . . . . . 1·00 70
1569 160f. Football . . . . . . 1·25 1·00

283 Flame and Figures

1988. 40th Anniv of Declaration of Human Rights.
1571 **283** 80f. multicoloured . . . 80 45
1572 160f. multicoloured . . . 1·25 75

284 El-Deir Temple, Petra

1988. 25th Anniv of Royal Jordanian Airline. Multicoloured.
1573 60f. Type **284** 75 50
1574 80f. Boeing 737 airliner and map of world . . . . . . 1·00 60

285 Dome of the Rock, Jerusalem

1989. Palestinian Welfare.
1575 **285** 5f. multicoloured 10 10
1576 10f. multicoloured . . . 20 15

286 Treasury, Petra, Flags and King Hussein

1989. Formation of Arab Co-operation Council (economic grouping of four states). Multicoloured.
1577 10f. Type **286** 10 10
1578 30f. Sana'a, Yemen 30 15
1579 40f. Spiral Tower of Samarra, Iraq 40 20
1580 60f. Pyramids, Egypt . . . 55 25

287 Jordanian Parliament Building

1989. Centenary of Interparliamentary Union.
1581 **287** 40f. multicoloured . . . 35 15
1582 60f. multicoloured . . . 50 25

288 Modern Flats and Emblems

1989. Arab Housing Day and World Refugee Day. Multicoloured.
1583 5f. Type **288** 10 10
1584 40f. Hand supporting refugee family (horiz) . . 45 20
1585 60f. Modern blocks of flats (horiz) 65 30

289 King Abdullah, Mosque and King Hussein

1989. Inauguration of King Abdullah Ibn al-Hussein Mosque, Amman.
1586 **289** 40f. multicoloured . . . 35 15
1587 60f. multicoloured . . . 55 25

290 Horse's Head

1989. Arabian Horse Festival. Multicoloured.
1589 5f. Horse in paddock and emblem of Royal Stables (horiz) 10 10
1590 40f. Horse rearing and Treasury, Petra (horiz) . . 60 25
1591 60f. Type **290** 90 40

291 Trees

1989. 50th Anniv of Ministry of Agriculture. Multicoloured.
1593 5f. Type **291** 10 10
1594 40f. Tree and "50" 45 20
1595 60f. Orange trees and hives 65 30

292 Open Book, Globe and Flags

1989. Jordan Library Association.
1596 **292** 40f. multicoloured . . . 40 15
1597 60f. multicoloured . . . 60 25

293 Man carrying Basket

1989. Mosaics. Multicoloured.
1598 5f. Type **293** 10 10
1599 10f. Philadelphia (modern Amman) 15 10
1600 40f. Deer 55 25
1601 60f. Man with stick 85 40
1602 80f. Jerusalem (horiz) . . . 1·10 55

294 Flags and Map

1990. 1st Anniv of Arab Co-operation Council.
1604 **294** 5f. multicoloured 10 10
1605 20f. multicoloured . . . 10 10
1606 60f. multicoloured . . . 15 10
1607 80f. multicoloured . . . 20 15

295 Wild Asses at Oasis

1990. Nature Conservation. Multicoloured.
1608 40f. Type **295** 15 10
1609 60f. Rock formation, Rum 20 10
1610 80f. Desert palm trees . . . 25 15

296 Horsemen and Building

1990. 70th Anniv of Arrival of Prince Abdullah in Ma'an.
1611 **296** 40f. multicoloured . . . 15 10
1612 60f. multicoloured . . . 20 15

297 Emblem

1990. 40th Anniv of United Nations Development Programme.
1614 **297** 60f. multicoloured . . . 15 10
1615 80f. multicoloured . . . 20 15

298 King Hussein **299** Nubian Ibex

1990. Multicoloured, frame colour given.
1616 **298** 5f. yellow 10 10
1620 20f. green 10 10
1621 40f. red 10 10
1617 60f. blue 15 10
1618 80f. mauve 15 10
1622 240f. brown 45 20
1623 320f. purple 60 30
1624 1d. green . . . . 1·75 90

1991. Endangered Animals. Multicoloured.
1631 5f. Type **299** 10 10
1632 40f. Onager 30 15
1633 80f. Arabian gazelles . . . 55 25
1634 160f. Arabian oryx . . . . 1·10 50

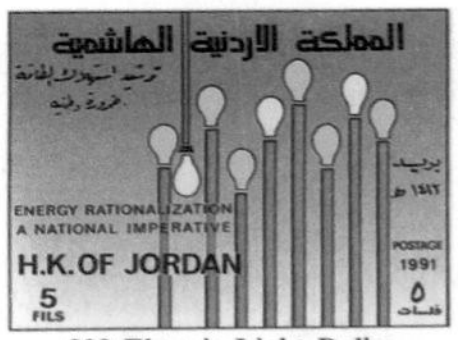

300 Electric Light Bulbs

1991. Energy Rationalization. Multicoloured.
1635 5f. Type **300** 10 10
1636 40f. Solar energy (vert) . . . 20 10
1637 80f. Angle-poise lamp by window (vert) 40 20

301 Grain

1991. Grain Production. Multicoloured.
1638 5f. Type **301** 10 10
1639 40f. Ear of wheat and leaves 20 10
1640 80f. Ear of wheat and field 40 20

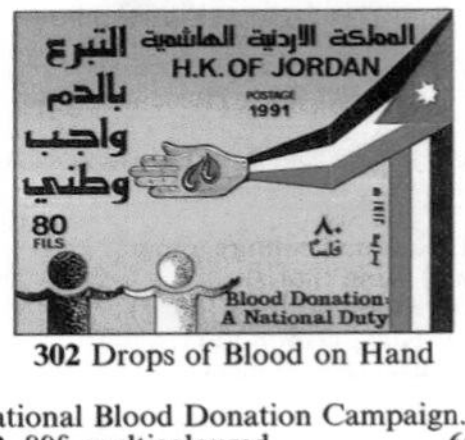

302 Drops of Blood on Hand

1991. National Blood Donation Campaign.
1641 **302** 80f. multicoloured . . . 65 35
1642 160f. multicoloured . . . 1·10 50

303 Jerusalem and Map

1991. Palestinian "Intifida" Movement.
1643 **303** 20f. multicoloured . . . 15 10

304 Emblem

1992. "Expo '92" World's Fair, Seville.

1644	**304**	80f. multicoloured . . .	15	10
1645		320f. multicoloured . . .	70	35

305 Man and Woman balancing Scales

1992. World Health Day. "Heartbeat—the Rhythm of Health".

1646	80f. Type **305**	20	10
1647	125f. Man and heart in balance and cardiograph (horiz)	35	20

306 Children

1992. S.O.S. Children's Village, Aqaba. Mult.

1648	80f. Type **306**	20	10
1649	125f. Village	35	20

307 Judo and Olympic Flame

1992. Olympic Games, Barcelona. Multicoloured.

1650	5f. Type **307**	10	10
1651	40f. Runners and track (vert)	15	10
1652	80f. Gymnast	35	20
1653	125f. Mascot (vert)	50	25
1654	160f. Table tennis	65	35

308 King Hussein

1992. 40th Anniv of King Hussein's Accession. Multicoloured.

1656	40f. Type **308**	10	10
1657	80f. National colours, crown and King (horiz)	25	15
1658	125f. King and flags (horiz)	35	20
1659	160f. King, crown and anniversary emblem (horiz)	45	25

309 African Monarch

310 Hadrian's Triumphal Arch, Jerash

1992. Butterflies. Multicoloured.

1661	5f. Type **309**	10	10
1662	40f. Black-veined white . .	30	15
1663	80f. Swallowtail	55	20
1664	160f. "Pseudochazara telephassa"	1·10	45

1993. Variously dated "1992" to "1996".

1666	**310**	5f. brown, blue and black	10	10
1788		25f. brown, purple & blk	10	10
1718		40f. brown, green & blk	10	10
1798		50f. brown, yellow & blk	10	10
1799		75f. brown, cinn & blk	15	10
1667		80f. brown, green & blk	10	10
1668		100f. brown, red & black	20	10
1800		100f. brown, green & blk	20	15
1801		120f. brown, green & blk	20	15
1669		125f. brown, pink & blk	25	15
1721		125f. brown, blue & blk	20	15
1802		150f. brown, pink & blk	25	15
1670		160f. brown, yell & blk	30	20
1803		200f. brown, grey & blk	35	20
1671		240f. brown, pur & blk	45	25
1804		300f. brown, pink & blk	55	30
1672		320f. brown, chest & blk	55	30
1805		400f. brown, blue & blk	70	40
1793		500f. brown, ochre & blk	90	50
1674		1d. brown, yellow & blk	1·75	95

311 Customs Co-operation Council Emblem, Flag and Laurel

1993. International Customs Day.

1680	**311**	80f. multicoloured . . .	20	10
1681		125f. multicoloured . . .	35	15

312 King Hussein and Military Equipment

1993. Army Day and 77th Anniv of Arab Revolt. Multicoloured.

1682	5f. Type **312**	10	10
1683	40f. King Hussein, soldier, surgeons and tank . . .	25	10
1684	80f. King Abdullah and Dome of the Rock . . .	45	20
1685	125f. King Hussein of Hejaz, Dome of the Rock and horsemen	70	25

313 Society Emblem and Natural Energy Resources

1993. 23rd Anniv of Royal Scientific Society.

1687	**313**	80f. multicoloured . . .	15	10

314 Courtyard

1993. Centenary of Salt Municipality.

1688	**314**	80f. multicoloured . . .	20	10
1689		125f. multicoloured . . .	35	15

315 Long-tailed Blue

1993. Butterflies. Multicoloured.

1691	5f. Type **315**	10	10
1692	40f. "Melanargria titea" . .	20	10
1693	80f. "Allancastria deyrollei"	30	15
1694	160f. "Gonepteryx cleopatra"	75	35

316 Eyes, Candle and White Cane

1993. White Cane Day. Multicoloured.

1696	80f. Type **316**	20	10
1697	125f. Globe, white cane and eye (vert)	35	15

317 King Hussein in Army Uniform

1993. 40th Anniv of King Hussein's Enthronement. Multicoloured.

1698	40f. Type **317**	15	10
1699	80f. King wearing Bedouin costume	25	10
1700	125f. King wearing suit . . .	40	20
1701	160f. King with Queen Noor (horiz)	50	25

318 Saladin and Dome of the Rock, Jerusalem

1993. 800th Death Anniv of Saladin.

1703	**318**	40f. multicoloured . . .	20	10
1704		80f. multicoloured . . .	40	15
1705		125f. multicoloured . . .	60	25

319 King Hussein and Crowd

1993. King Hussein's Return from Surgery in U.S.A. (1992). Multicoloured.

1706	80f. Type **319**	30	10
1707	125f. King waving at crowd	50	15
1708	160f. King embracing his mother	60	20

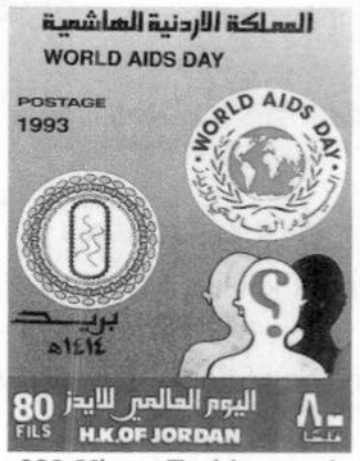

320 Virus, Emblem and Silhouettes

1993. World AIDS Day.

1710	**320**	80f. multicoloured . . .	20	15
1711		125f. multicoloured . . .	35	20

321 Emblems and Flag

1993. 45th Anniv of United Nations Declaration of Human Rights.

1713	**321**	40f. multicoloured . . .	10	10
1714		160f. multicoloured . . .	35	25

322 Loading Airplane

1994. Jordan Hashemite Charity Organization. Multicoloured.

1715	80f. Type **322**	20	10
1716	125f. Transport plane . . .	35	15

323 Mosque and King Hussein

1994. Refurbishment of El Aqsa Mosque and Dome of the Rock.

1726	80f. Type **323**	30	15
1727	125f. Dome of the Rock and King Hussein	50	20
1728	240f. Dome of the Rock and King Hussein (different)	95	45

324 Emblems on Doves

1994. 75th Anniv of International Red Cross and Red Crescent Societies. Multicoloured.

1730	80f. Child and emblems (horiz)	25	10
1731	160f. Type **324**	50	25

325 Globe, Emblem and "75"

1994. 75th Anniv of I.L.O.

1733	**325**	80f. multicoloured . . .	20	10
1734		125f. multicoloured . . .	35	20

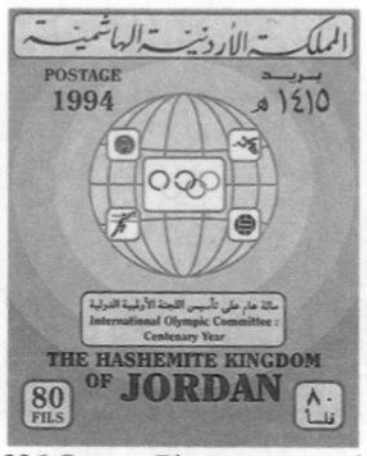

326 Sports Pictograms and Olympic Rings

1994. Centenary of International Olympic Committee. Multicoloured.

1735	80f. Type **326**	20	10
1736	125f. Sports pictograms, flame and "100"	30	10
1737	160f. Olympic rings, track and athlete (horiz)	40	15
1738	240f. Olympic rings and hand holding torch (horiz)	60	25

327 King Hussein greeting Soldiers

1994. Jordanian Participation in United Nations Peace-keeping Forces. Multicoloured.

1740		80f. Type **327**	20	10
1741		125f. King Hussein inspecting troops	30	15
1742		160f. U.N. checkpoint . . .	35	15

328 Flag, Emblem, Globe, Wheat and Family

1994. International Year of the Family.

1743	**328**	80f. multicoloured . . .	20	10
1744		125f. multicoloured . . .	30	15
1745		160f. multicoloured . . .	35	15

329 Aircraft and Emblem

1994. 50th Anniv of I.C.A.O.

1746	**329**	80f. multicoloured . . .	25	15
1747		125f. multicoloured . . .	40	20
1748		160f. multicoloured . . .	50	25

330 Hands around Water Droplet

1994. Water Conservation Campaign. Mult.

1749		80f. Type **330**	20	10
1750		125f. Glass beneath running tap, foodstuffs and industry	35	20
1751		160f. Water droplets and boy on lush hillside . . .	45	30

331 Crown Prince Hassan

1994. 10th Anniv of Crown Prince's Award.

1752	**331**	80f. multicoloured . . .	20	10
1753		125f. multicoloured . . .	35	20
1754		160f. multicoloured . . .	45	30

332 University Emblem

1995. Inauguration of Al al-Bayt University.

1755	**332**	80f. gold, blue and black	20	10
1756		125f. gold, green & black	35	20

333 U.N. Emblem and "50"

1995. 50th Anniv of U.N.O.

1758	**333**	80f. multicoloured . . .	20	10
1759		125f. multicoloured . . .	35	20

334 Labour Emblem and Crowd with Flag

1995. Labour Day. Multicoloured.

1760		80f. Type **334**	20	10
1761		125f. Emblem, world map and miner's head	35	20
1762		160f. Hands holding spanner and torch	40	25

335 Flags and Globe

1995. Jordan Week in Japan. Multicoloured.

1763		80f. Type **335**	20	10
1764		125f. Hemispheres and flags	35	20
1765		160f. Flags, brick wall and globe	40	25

336 Artefacts

1995. Petra, "The Rose City". Multicoloured.

1766		50f. Amphitheatre	10	10
1767		75f. Type **336**	20	10
1768		80f. Treasury seen through cleft in rocks (vert) . . .	20	10
1769		160f. Treasury (vert)	40	25

337 Emblem

1995. 50th Anniv of Arab League.

1771	**337**	80f. multicoloured . . .	20	10
1772		125f. multicoloured . . .	35	20
1773		160f. multicoloured . . .	40	25

338 Leaves and Emblem

1995. 50th Anniv of F.A.O. Multicoloured.

1774		80f. Type **338**	20	10
1775		125f. Ears of wheat and "50" incorporating F.A.O. emblem	35	20
1776		160f. United Nations emblem and "50" incorporating F.A.O. emblem	40	25

339 Knotted Ropes, Summit Emblem and National Flags

1995. Middle Eastern and North African Economic Summit, Amman.

1777	**339**	80f. multicoloured . . .	15	10
1778		125f. multicoloured . . .	20	15

340 King Hussein

1995. 60th Birthday of King Hussein. Mult.

1779		25f. Type **340**	10	10
1780		40f. Hussein within shield	10	10
1781		80f. Dove incorporating "60", El-Deir Temple (Petra) and Hussein . . .	15	10
1782		100f. Hussein in military uniform and anniversary emblem	20	15
1783		125f. King Hussein	20	15
1784		160f. Hussein, national flag and "60 60 60"	30	20

341 Hands and Hard of Hearing Emblem

1995. The Deaf. Multicoloured.

1786		80f. Type **341**	15	10
1787		125f. Emblems, sign language and hard of hearing emblem	20	15

342 Anniversary Emblem and Map of Jordan

1996. 50th Anniv of Independence. Mult.

1794		100f. Type **342**	15	10
1795		200f. King Hussein, map of Jordan and King Abdullah	35	20
1796		300f. King Hussein	55	35

343 Games Emblem, Olympic Rings and Pictograms

1996. Olympic Games, Atlanta. Multicoloured.

1806		50f. Type **343**	10	10
1807		100f. Games emblem and pictograms	20	15
1808		200f. Games emblem forming torch and figure	35	20
1809		300f. Games emblem, torch and national flag	55	35

344 Hand protecting Animals and Plants

1996. Protection of the Ozone Layer.

1810	**344**	100f. multicoloured . . .	15	10

345 Anniversary Emblem

1996. 50th Anniv of U.N.I.C.E.F. Fund.

1811	**345**	100f. multicoloured . . .	15	10
1812		200f. multicoloured . . .	35	20

346 Playing Polo

1997. 50th Birthday of Crown Prince Hassan. Multicoloured.

1813		50f. Type **346**	10	10
1814		100f. Wearing western dress (vert)	15	10
1815		200f. In military uniform . .	35	20

347 Karak

1997. Centenary of Discovery of Madaba Mosaic Map. Multicoloured.

1817		100f. Type **347**	15	10
1818		200f. River Jordan (horiz)	35	20
1819		300f. Jerusalem	50	30

348 Von Stephan

1997. Death Centenary of Heinrich von Stephan (founder of U.P.U.).

1821	**348**	100f. multicoloured . . .	15	10
1822		200f. multicoloured . . .	35	20

349 Sinai Rosefinch ("Rosefinch")

1997. Sinai Rosefinch ("The Jordanian Rosefinch").

1823	**349**	50f. multicoloured . . .	10	10
1824		100f. multicoloured . . .	15	10
1825		150f. multicoloured . . .	25	15
1826		200f. multicoloured . . .	35	20

350 Performers and Hadrian's Triumphal Arch

1997. 15th Anniv of Jerash Festival. Mult.

1827		50f. Type **350**	10	10
1828		100f. Orchestra, Festival emblem and Jerash ruins	15	10
1829		150f. Temple of Artemis and marching band	25	15
1830		200f. Women dancers and audience at performance	35	20

351 Current and Previous Parliament Buildings

1997. 50th Anniv of First National Parliament. Multicoloured.

1832	100f. Type **351**	15	10
1833	200f. King Hussein addressing, and view of, Chamber of Deputies . .	35	20

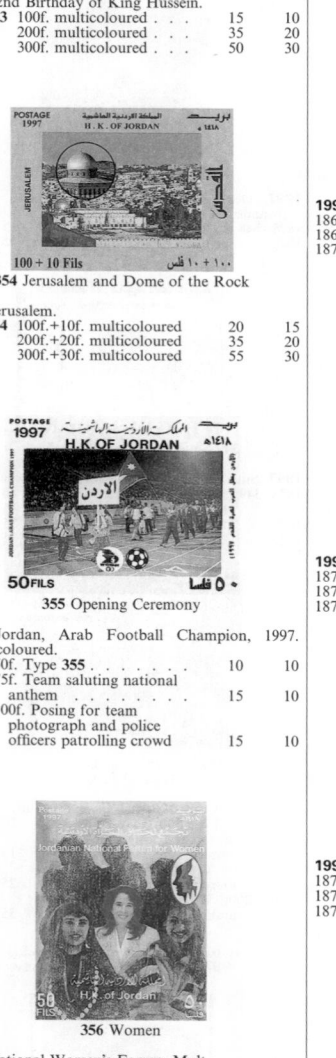

352 Meeting Emblem

1997. 53rd International Air Transport Assn Annual General Meeting, Amman.

1834	**352** 100f. multicoloured . . .	15	10
1835	200f. multicoloured . . .	35	20
1836	300f. multicoloured . . .	50	30

353 King Hussein and Queen Noor

1997. 62nd Birthday of King Hussein.

1837	**353** 100f. multicoloured . . .	15	10
1838	200f. multicoloured . . .	35	20
1839	300f. multicoloured . . .	50	30

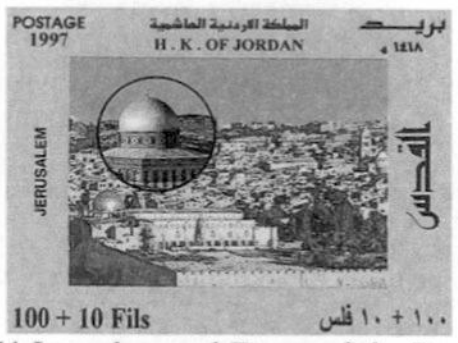

354 Jerusalem and Dome of the Rock

1997. Jerusalem.

1841	**354** 100f.+10f. multicoloured	20	15
1842	200f.+20f. multicoloured	35	20
1843	300f.+30f. multicoloured	55	30

355 Opening Ceremony

1997. Jordan, Arab Football Champion, 1997. Multicoloured.

1844	50f. Type **355**	10	10
1845	75f. Team saluting national anthem	15	10
1846	100f. Posing for team photograph and police officers patrolling crowd	15	10

356 Women

1997. National Women's Forum. Mult.

1848	50f. Type **356**	10	10
1849	100f. National flag, women's profiles and emblems (horiz)	15	10
1850	150f. Forum meeting and emblem (horiz)	25	15

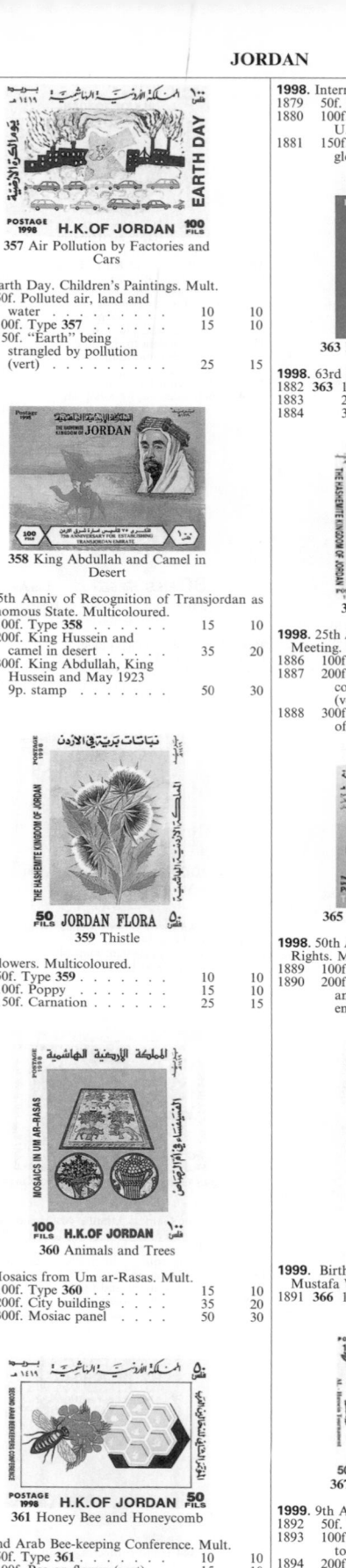

357 Air Pollution by Factories and Cars

1998. Earth Day. Children's Paintings. Mult.

1851	50f. Polluted air, land and water	10	10
1852	100f. Type **357**	15	10
1853	150f. "Earth" being strangled by pollution (vert)	25	15

358 King Abdullah and Camel in Desert

1998. 75th Anniv of Recognition of Transjordan as Autonomous State. Multicoloured.

1864	100f. Type **358**	15	10
1865	200f. King Hussein and camel in desert	35	20
1866	300f. King Abdullah, King Hussein and May 1923 9p. stamp	50	30

359 Thistle

1998. Flowers. Multicoloured.

1868	50f. Type **359**	10	10
1869	100f. Poppy	15	10
1870	150f. Carnation	25	15

360 Animals and Trees

1998. Mosaics from Um ar-Rasas. Mult.

1872	100f. Type **360**	15	10
1873	200f. City buildings	35	20
1874	300f. Mosiac panel	50	30

361 Honey Bee and Honeycomb

1998. 2nd Arab Bee-keeping Conference. Mult.

1875	50f. Type **361**	10	10
1876	100f. Bee on flower (vert)	15	10
1877	150f. Bee, flower and honeycomb	25	15

362 Dove with Stamp

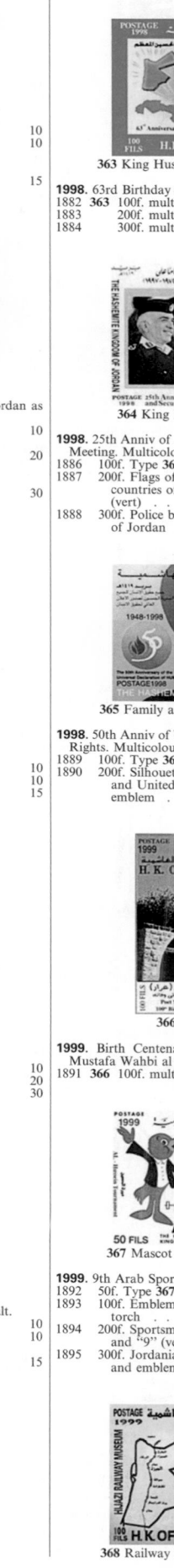

1998. International Stamp Day. Multicoloured.

1879	50f. Type **362**	10	10
1880	100f. World map and U.P.U. emblem	15	10
1881	150f. Stamps encircling globe	25	15

363 King Hussein and Map of Jordan

1998. 63rd Birthday of King Hussein.

1882	**363** 100f. multicoloured . . .	15	10
1883	200f. multicoloured . . .	35	20
1884	300f. multicoloured . . .	50	30

364 King Hussein and Emblem

1998. 25th Anniv of Arab Police and Security Chiefs' Meeting. Multicoloured.

1886	100f. Type **364**	15	10
1887	200f. Flags of member countries of Arab League (vert)	35	20
1888	300f. Police beret and map of Jordan	50	30

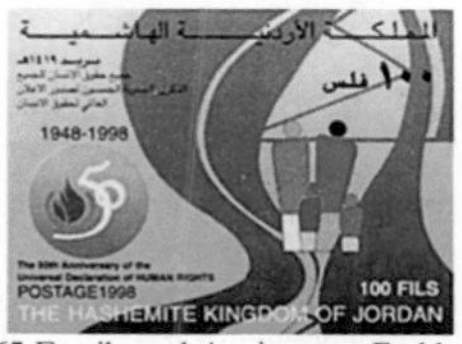

365 Family and Anniversary Emblem

1998. 50th Anniv of Universal Declaration of Human Rights. Multicoloured.

1889	100f. Type **365**	15	10
1890	200f. Silhouettes of people and United Nations emblem	35	20

366 Wahbi al Tal

1999. Birth Centenary and 50th Death Anniv of Mustafa Wahbi al Tal (poet).

1891	**366** 100f. multicoloured . . .	15	10

367 Mascot and Sports Pictograms

1999. 9th Arab Sports Tournament. Multicoloured.

1892	50f. Type **367**	10	10
1893	100f. Emblem, mascot and torch	20	15
1894	200f. Sportsmen, emblem and "9" (vert)	40	25
1895	300f. Jordanian flag, mascot and emblem	60	35

368 Railway Map, Station and Train

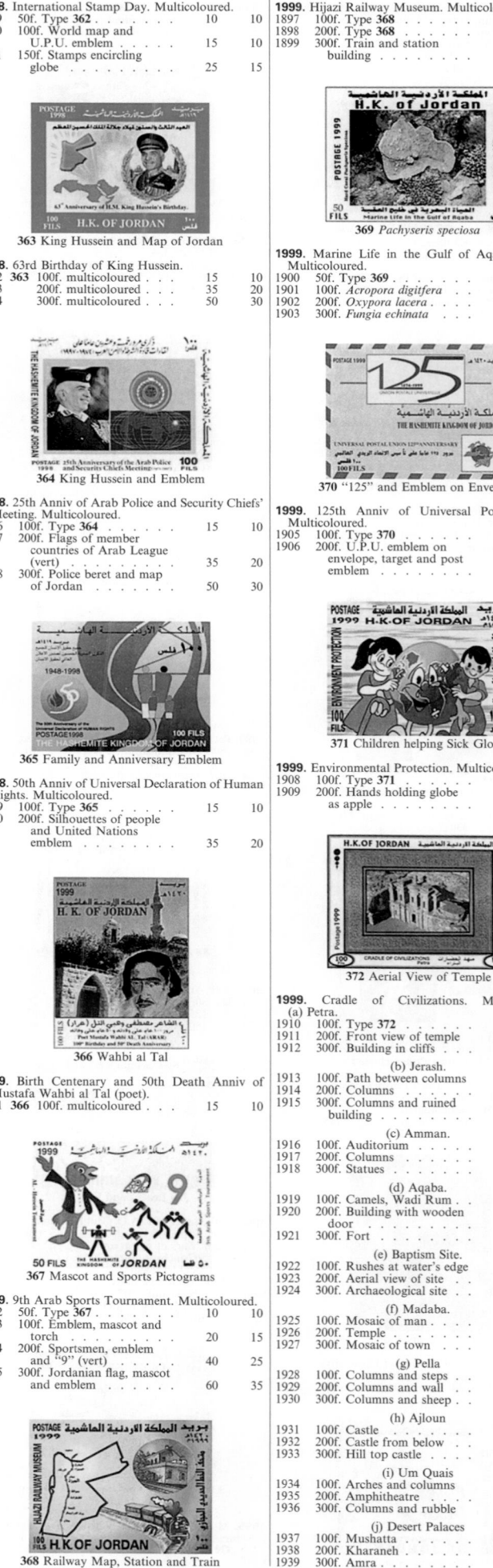

1999. Hijazi Railway Museum. Multicoloured.

1897	100f. Type **368**	20	15
1898	200f. Type **368**	40	25
1899	300f. Train and station building	60	35

369 *Pachyseris speciosa*

1999. Marine Life in the Gulf of Aqaba. Corals. Multicoloured.

1900	50f. Type **369**	10	10
1901	100f. *Acropora digitfera* . .	20	15
1902	200f. *Oxypora lacera*	40	25
1903	300f. *Fungia echinata* . . .	60	35

370 "125" and Emblem on Envelope

1999. 125th Anniv of Universal Postal Union. Multicoloured.

1905	100f. Type **370**	20	15
1906	200f. U.P.U. emblem on envelope, target and post emblem	40	25

371 Children helping Sick Globe

1999. Environmental Protection. Multicoloured.

1908	100f. Type **371**	20	15
1909	200f. Hands holding globe as apple	40	25

372 Aerial View of Temple

1999. Cradle of Civilizations. Multicoloured.

(a) Petra.

1910	100f. Type **372**	20	15
1911	200f. Front view of temple	40	25
1912	300f. Building in cliffs . . .	60	35

(b) Jerash.

1913	100f. Path between columns	20	15
1914	200f. Columns	40	25
1915	300f. Columns and ruined building	60	35

(c) Amman.

1916	100f. Auditorium	20	15
1917	200f. Columns	40	25
1918	300f. Statues	60	35

(d) Aqaba.

1919	100f. Camels, Wadi Rum . .	20	15
1920	200f. Building with wooden door	40	25
1921	300f. Fort	60	35

(e) Baptism Site.

1922	100f. Rushes at water's edge	20	15
1923	200f. Aerial view of site . .	40	25
1924	300f. Archaeological site . .	60	35

(f) Madaba.

1925	100f. Mosaic of man	20	15
1926	200f. Temple	40	25
1927	300f. Mosaic of town . . .	60	35

(g) Pella

1928	100f. Columns and steps . .	20	15
1929	200f. Columns and wall . .	40	25
1930	300f. Columns and sheep . .	60	35

(h) Ajloun

1931	100f. Castle	20	15
1932	200f. Castle from below . .	40	25
1933	300f. Hill top castle	60	35

(i) Um Quais

1934	100f. Arches and columns .	20	15
1935	200f. Amphitheatre	40	25
1936	300f. Columns and rubble .	60	35

(j) Desert Palaces

1937	100f. Mushatta	20	15
1938	200f. Kharaneh	40	25
1939	300f. Amra	60	35

373 Jordanian Stamps

1999. 20th Anniv of Jordan Philatelic Club. Multicoloured.
1940 100f. Type **373** 20 15
1941 200f. Jordanian stamps (different) 40 25

374 Assembly Room

1999. Museum of Political History. Multicoloured.
1942 100f. Type **374** 20 15
1943 200f. Courtyard 40 25
1944 300f. Entrance 60 35

375 Jordanian Flag and Emblems

1999. 50th Anniv of S.O.S. Children's Villages. Multicoloured.
1945 100f. Type **375** 20 15
1946 200f. Woman and children 40 25

376 King Abdullah II

1999. Coronation of King Abdullah II Bin Al-Hussein.
1947 **376** 100f. multicoloured . . . 15 10
1948 200f. multicoloured . . . 35 20
1949 300f. multicoloured . . . 55 30
MS1950 70 × 89 mm. 200f. No. 1948 but with gold border 35 35

377 King Abdullah II and Queen Rania

1999. Coronation of King Abdullah II Bin Al-Hussein and Queen Rania al-Abdullah.
1951 **377** 100f. multicoloured . . . 15 10
1952 200f. multicoloured . . . 35 20
1953 300f. multicoloured . . . 55 35
MS1954 70 × 89 mm. 200f. No. 1952 but with gold border 35 35

378 Crowned Portrait

2000. 38th Birth Anniv of King Abdullah II. Multicoloured.
1955 100f. Type **378** 15 10
1956 200f. King Abdullah II (horiz) 35 20
1957 300f. King Abdullah II and flag (horiz) 55 30

379 Red Cross Emblem and Jordanian Flag

2000. 50th Anniv of Geneva Red Cross Conventions. Multicoloured.
1959 **379** 100f. multicoloured . . . 15 10
1960 200f. multicoloured . . . 35 20
1961 300f. multicoloured . . . 55 30

380 Flag and "2000 A. D."

2000. New Millennium. Multicoloured.
1962 100f. Type **380** 15 10
1963 200f. Palms, sand and fish swimming 35 20
1964 300f. As No. 1957 but inscription in Arabic . . . 55 30

381 King Abdullah II, Roofs and Pope John Paul II

2000. 36th Anniv of Pope Paul VI's Visit to Jordan.
1965 **381** 100f. multicoloured . . . 15 10
1966 200f. multicoloured . . . 35 20
1967 300f. multicoloured . . . 55 30

382 Pope John Paul II, Trees and King Abdullah II

2000. Pope John Paul II's Visit to Jordan.
1968 100f. Type **382** 15 10
1969 200f. Pope John Paul II, river and King Abdullah II 35 20
1970 300f. Pope John Paul II, flags and King Abdullah II 55 30
MS1971 70 × 90 mm. 200f. Pope John Paul II. Imperf 35 35

383 Globe and Organization Emblem

2000. 50th Anniv of World Meteorological Organization. Multicoloured.
1972 100f. Type **383** 15 10
1973 200f. Globe and emblem (different) 35 20

384 Emblem, Flag and "90"

2000. 90th Anniv of Jordan Boy Scouts. Multicoloured.
1974 100f. Type **384** 15 10
1975 200f. Pyramids 35 20
1976 300f. "90", flag and pyramids 55 30
MS1977 90 × 70 mm. 200f. As No. 1974 but with design enlarged. Imperf 35 35

385 Clinic Building and Emblem

2000. Al-Amal Cancer Centre. Multicoloured.
1978 200f. Type **385** 35 20
1979 300f. Emblem and family . . 55 30

387 Scales enclosing Palace of Justice

2000. Palace of Justice, Amman. Multicoloured.
1980 100f. Type **387** 15 10
1981 200f. Building faÇade . . . 35 20

388 Dove

2000. Endangered Species. Multicoloured.
1982 50f. Type **388** 10 10
1983 100f. Oryx 15 10
1984 150f. Caracal 30 15
1985 200f. Red fox 35 20
1986 300f. Iris 55 30
1987 400f. White broom 75 40

389 Iris

2000. World Conservation Union Conference, Amman.
1988 **389** 200f. multicoloured . . . 35 20
1989 300f. multicoloured . . . 55 30

390 Petra

2000. Tourism. Multicoloured.
1990 50f. Type **390** 10 10
1991 100f. Jerash 15 10
1992 150f. Mount Nebo 30 15
1993 200f. Dead Sea 35 20
1994 300f. Aqaba 55 30
1995 400f. Wadi Rum 75 40

391 Column Capital

2000. Expo 2000, Hanover. Multicoloured.
1996 200f. Type **391** 35 20
1997 300f. Statuette 55 30
MS1998 90 × 70 mm. 200f. King Abdullah, Queen Rania Al-Abdullah and Expo 2000 buildings 35 35

392 King Hussein

2000. 1st Death Anniv of King Hussein. Multicoloured.
1999 50f. Type **392** 10 10
2000 150f. King Hussein enclosed in wreath (horiz) 30 15
2001 200f. Symbols of industry and King Hussein (horiz) 35 20
MS2002 90 × 70 mm. 200f. As No. 2000 but with design enlarged 35 35

393 Women and Child

2000. 50th Anniv of United Nations High Commissioner for Refugees (2001).
2003 200f. multicoloured 35 20
2004 300f. green, blue and black 55 30
DESIGN 300f. UNHCR emblem.

394 Conference Emblem and Jordanian Flag

2001. 13th Arab Summit Conference, Amman. Multicoloured.
2005 50f. Type **394** 10 10
2006 200f. Flags, emblem and map of Arab countries . . 35 20
2007 250f. King Abdullah II and emblem 45 25

395 Mohammed Al Dorra, his Father and Dome

2001. 1st Death Anniv of Mohammed Al Dorra. Multicoloured.

2008	200f. Type **395**	35	20
2009	300f. Mohammed Al Dorra and father	55	30

396 Dome of the Rock with Arms

2001. Al Asqa Intifada. Multicoloured.

2010	200f. Type **396**	35	20
2011	300f. Dome of the Rock and protesters	55	30

397 Wheelchair User

2001. Sports for Special Needs. Multicoloured.

2012	200f. Type **397**	35	20
2013	300f. Woman holding medal	55	30

398 School Children and No-Smoking Sign

2001. Campaign to stop Smoking amongst Young People. Multicoloured.

2014	200f. Type **398**	35	20
2015	300f. Stylized student holding no-smoking sign (vert)	55	30

399 Olive Branches and Map of Jordan

2001. Olive Cultivation. Multicoloured.

2016	200f. Type **399**	35	20
2017	300f. Girl holding olives (vert)	55	30

400 Family and World Map

2001. United Nations Year of Dialogue among Civilizations. Multicoloured.

2018	200f. Type **400**	35	20
2019	300f. Emblem, clasped hands and olive tree	55	30

401 Sheik Hussein Bridge and Japanese and Jordanian Flags

2001. Japan—Jordan Co-operation. Multicoloured.

2020	200f. Type **401**	35	20
2021	300f. King Hussein bridge and clasped hands	55	30

402 Emblem, Star and National Colours

2002. Amman, Arab Cultural Capital, 2002. Multicoloured.

2022	100f. Type **402**	15	10
2023	200f. Flame and pen	35	20
2024	300f. Emblem and amphitheatre	55	30

403 Buildings

2002. Jordanian Artists. Multicoloured.

2025	100f. Type **403**	15	10
2026	150f. Abstract (Mahmoud Taha) (horiz)	30	15
2027	200f. Woman (Mohanna Durra)	35	20
2028	300f. Hilltop castle (Wijdan) (horiz)	55	30

404 Bird carrying Envelope

2002. 25th Anniv of Jordan—China Diplomatic Relations. Multicoloured.

2029	200f. Type **404**	35	20
2030	300f. King Abdullah II and Pres. Jiang Zemin	55	30

405 Goldfinch

2002. Birds. Multicoloured.

2031	100f. Type **405**	15	10
2032	200f. Rufous scrub robin (inscr "rufous bush robin")	35	20
2033	300f. Stork	55	30
MS2034	70 × 90 mm. 200f. Golden oriole, goshawk, bunting and hoopoe	35	35

406 Symbols of Industry

2002. "Jordan Vision 2002" (campaign for economic development). Multicoloured.

2035	200f. Type **406**	35	20
2036	300f. Hand and computer circuit board	55	30

407 Building Facade

2003. Archaeological Museum. Multicoloured.

2037	150f. Type **407**	30	15
2038	250f. Building from below	45	25

408 Sherif Hussein bin Ali

2003. Hashemite Dynasty. Sheet 230 × 90 mm containing T **408** and similar vert designs. Multicoloured.

MS2039	200f. × 5 Type **408**; King Abdullah; King Talal bin Abdullah; King Hussein bin Talal; King Abdullah II	1·75	1·75

OBLIGATORY TAX

T **36** Mosque in Hebron

T **43** Ruins at Palmyra, Syria

1947.

T264	T **36**	1m. blue	30	20
T265		2m. red	35	25
T266		3m. green	45	35
T267		5m. red	55	40
T268	–	10m. red	60	55
T269	–	15m. grey	90	60
T270	–	20m. brown	1·25	70
T271	–	50m. violet	2·10	1·50
T272	–	100m. red	6·00	4·25
T273	–	200m. blue	18·00	11·00
T274	–	500m. green	42·00	30·00
T275	–	£P1 brown	90·00	75·00

DESIGNS: Nos. T268/71, Dome of the Rock; Nos. T272/75, Acre.

1950. Optd **Aid** in English and Arabic.

T290	T **28**	5m. orange	6·75	
T291		10m. violet	10·00	
T292		15m. green	12·00	

1950. Revenue stamps optd **Aid** in English and Arabic.

T296	T **43**	5m. orange	10·00	7·50
T297		10m. violet	12·00	7·50

1951. Values in "FILS".

T302	T **36**	5f. red	30	30
T303	–	10f. red	40	40
T304	–	15f. black	45	45
T305	–	20f. brown	60	60
T306	–	100f. orange	2·40	2·40

DESIGNS: Nos. T303/305, Dome of the Rock; No. T306, Acre.

1952. Nos. T264/75 optd **J.D.** (T344) or **FILS** (others).

T334	T **36**	1f. on 1m. blue	25	25
T335		2f. on 2m. red	60·00	
T336		3f. on 3m. green	30	25
T337	–	10f. on 10m. red	30	25
T338	–	15f. on 15m. grey	65	50
T339	–	20f. on 20m. brown	85	85
T340	–	50f. on 50m. violet	1·50	1·50
T341	–	100f. on 100m. orange	8·00	5·00
T342	–	200f. on 200m. blue	20·00	13·00
T343	–	500f. on 500m. green	48·00	35·00
T344	–	1d. on £P1 brown	£110	70·00

OFFICIAL STAMPS

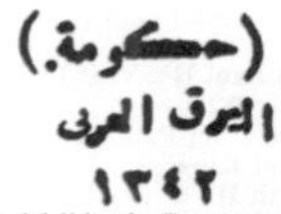

(O **16** "Arab Government of the East, 1342")

1924. Type **11** of Saudi Arabia optd with Type O **16**.

O117	$\frac{1}{2}$p. red	22·00	£100

POSTAGE DUE STAMPS

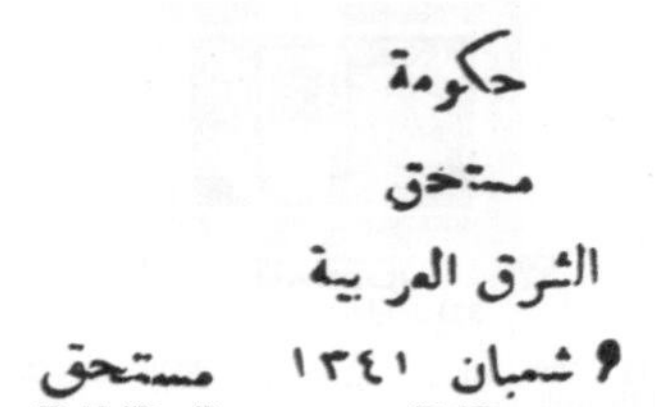

(D **12** "Due") (D **13**)

1923. Issue of 1923 (with opt T **10**) further optd.

(a) With Type D **12** (the 3p. also surch as T **12**).

D112	**11**	$\frac{1}{2}$p. on 3p. brown	17·00	21·00
D113		1p. blue	10·00	12·00
D114		1$\frac{1}{2}$p. lilac	12·00	13·00
D115		2p. orange	14·00	15·00

(b) With Type D **13** and surch as T **12**.

D116	**11**	$\frac{1}{2}$p. on 3p. brown	50·00	55·00

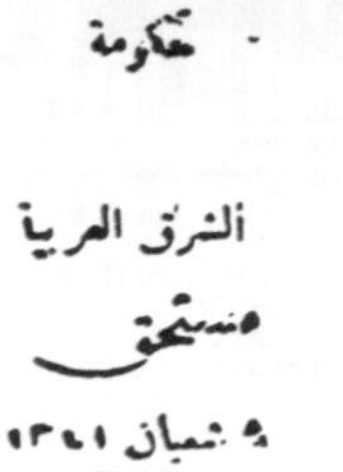

(D **14**)

1923. Stamps of Saudi Arabia handstamped with Type D **14**.

D117	**11**	$\frac{1}{2}$p. red	1·50	3·25
D118		1p. blue	3·25	3·50
D119		1$\frac{1}{2}$p. violet	2·50	4·25
D120		2p. orange	4·00	4·75
D121		3p. brown	7·00	9·50
D122		5p. olive	8·00	15·00

(D **20** "Due East of the Jordan") (D **21**)

1925. Stamps of Palestine (without Palestine opt) optd with Type D **20**.

D159	**3**	1m. brown	1·40	6·50
D160		2m. yellow	2·00	4·25
D161		4m. red	3·00	8·00
D162		8m. red	4·00	11·00
D163		13m. blue	4·50	11·00
D164		5p. purple	5·50	15·00

1926. Stamps of Palestine as last surch as Type D **21** ("DUE" and new value in Arabic).

D165	**3**	1m. on 1m. brown	5·00	6·00
D166		2m. on 1m. brown	4·25	6·00
D167		4m. on 3m. blue	4·50	7·00
D168		8m. on 3m. blue	4·50	7·00
D169		13m. on 13m. blue	7·00	8·00
D170		5p. on 13m. blue	8·00	12·00

The lower line of the surcharge differs for each value.

(D **25**)

D **26**

D **50**

1928. Surch as Type D **25** or optd only.

D183	**22**	1m. on 3m. red	1·00	6·00
D184		2m. blue	1·25	6·00
D185		4m. on 15m. blue	1·25	7·00
D186		10m. red	2·25	7·00
D187	**23**	20m. on 100m. blue	3·75	15·00
D188		50m. purple	4·75	19·00

1929.

D244	D **26**	1m. brown	70	3·00
D245		2m. yellow	70	3·50
D246		4m. green	70	4·50
D247		10m. red	1·75	6·00
D193		20m. olive	7·50	12·00
D194		50m. blue	9·50	20·00

1952. Optd **FILS FILS** in English and Arabic

D350	D **26**	1f. on 1m. brown	30	30
D351		2f. on 2m. yellow	30	30
D352		4f. on 4m. green	55	70
D353		10f. on 10m. red	1·50	1·25
D354		20f. on 20m. olive	3·75	3·50
D346		50f. on 50m. blue	3·50	3·25

1952. Inscr "THE HASHEMITE KINGDOM OF THE JORDAN".

D372	D **50**	1f. brown	15	45
D373		2f. yellow	20	45
D374		4f. green	20	45
D375		10f. red	45	65

D376		20f. brown	45	90
D377		50f. blue	1·25	2·25

1957. As Type D **50**, but inscr "THE HASHEMITE KINGDOM OF JORDAN".

D465		1f. brown	15	35
D466		2f. yellow	15	35
D467		4f. green	25	50
D468		10f. red	35	50
D469		20f. brown	75	1·40

JORDANIAN OCCUPATION OF PALESTINE Pt. 19

1948. Stamps of Jordan optd **PALESTINE** in English and Arabic.

P 1	**28**	1m. brown	35	35
P 2		2m. green	35	35
P 3		3m. green	35	35
P 4		3m. pink	25	25
P 5		4m. green	25	25
P 6		5m. orange	25	25
P 7		10m. violet	65	65
P 8		12m. red	65	40
P 9		15m. green	90	90
P10		20m. blue	1·25	65
P11	**29**	50m. purple	1·40	1·60
P12		90m. bistre	7·75	1·60
P13		100m. blue	8·50	4·50
P14		200m. violet	3·25	6·95
P15		500m. brown	27·00	12·50
P16		£P1 grey	60·00	32·00

1949. 75th Anniv of U.P.U. Stamps of Jordan optd **PALESTINE** in English and Arabic.

P30	**40**	1m. brown	25	60
P31		4m. green	40	80
P32		10m. red	50	90
P33		20m. blue	80	95
P34	–	50m. green (No. 289)	1·40	1·50

OBLIGATORY TAX

1950. Nos. T264/75 of Jordan optd **PALESTINE** in English and Arabic.

PT35	T **36**	1m. blue	10	25
PT36		2m. red	15	25
PT37		3m. green	30	40
PT38		5m. purple	40	30
PT39	–	10m. red	40	30
PT40	–	15m. black	1·25	40
PT41	–	20m. brown	2·00	75
PT42	–	50m. violet	2·75	1·40
PT43	–	100m. red	4·75	2·25
PT44	–	200m. blue	12·00	5·75
PT45	–	500m. green	38·00	19·00
PT46	–	£P1 brown	70·00	42·00

POSTAGE DUE STAMPS

1948. Postage Due stamps of Jordan optd **PALESTINE** in English and Arabic.

PD25	D **26**	1m. brown	1·40	1·75
PD26		2m. yellow	1·60	2·10
PD18		4m. green	1·60	2·10
PD28		10m. red	1·60	1·75
PD20		20m. olive	1·00	1·00
PD21		50m. blue	1·60	2·10

After a time the stamps of Jordan were used in the occupied areas.

JUBALAND Pt. 8

A district in E. Africa, formerly part of Kenya, ceded by Gt. Britain to Italy in 1925, and incorporated in Italian Somaliland.

100 centesimi = 1 lira.

1925. Stamps of Italy optd **OLTRE GIUBA**.

1	**30**	1c. brown	2·50	8·75
2	**31**	2c. brown	1·80	8·75
3	**37**	5c. green	1·50	4·50
4		10c. pink	1·50	4·50
5		15c. grey	1·50	6·25
6	**41**	20c. orange	1·50	6·25
39	**39**	20c. green	5·00	10·00
7		25c. blue	1·80	6·25
8		30c. brown	2·50	7·00
40		30c. grey	6·50	11·50
9		40c. brown	3·75	5·50
10		50c. mauve	3·75	5·50
11		60c. red	3·75	7·00
41	**44**	75c. red and carmine	30·00	35·00
12		1l. brown and green	7·00	8·75
42		1l.25 blue and ultramarine	42·00	44·00
13		2l. green and orange	47·00	24·00
43		2l.50 green and orange	55·00	80·00
14		5l. blue and pink	75·00	35·00
15		10l. green and pink	9·00	39·00

1925. Royal Jubilee stamps of Italy optd **OLTRE GIUBA**.

44B	**82**	60c. red	75	6·25
45B		1l. blue	75	10·75
46B		1l.25 blue	2·20	15·00

1926. St. Francis of Assisi stamps of Italy, as Nos. 191/6, optd **OLTRE GIUBA**.

47		20c. green	1·60	12·50
48		40c. violet	1·60	12·50
49		60c. red	1·60	18·00
50		1l.25 blue	1·60	27·00
51		5l.+2l.50 olive	4·50	39·00

8 Map of Jubaland

1926. 1st Anniv of Acquisition of Jubaland.

54	**8**	5c. orange	75	8·00
55		20c. green	75	8·00
56		25c. brown	75	8·00
57		40c. red	75	8·00
58		60c. purple	75	8·00
59		1l. blue	75	8·00
60		2l. grey	75	8·00

1926. As Colonial Propaganda T **6** of Cyrenaica, but inscr "OLTRE GIUBA".

61		5c.+5c. brown	65	4·25
62		10c.+5c. olive	65	4·25
63		20c.+5c. green	65	4·25
64		40c.+5c. red	65	4·25
65		60c.+5c. orange	65	4·25
66		1l.+5c. blue	65	7·00

EXPRESS LETTER STAMPS

1926. Express Letter stamps of Italy optd **OLTRE GIUBA**.

E52	E **35**	70c. red	18·00	25·00
E53	E **41**	2l.50 blue and pink	27·00	55·00

PARCEL POST STAMPS.

1925. Parcel Post stamps of Italy optd **OLTRE GIUBA**.

P16	P **53**	5c. brown	4·50	12·00
P17		10c. blue	2·75	12·00
P18		20c. black	2·75	12·00
P19		25c. red	2·75	12·00
P20		50c. orange	4·50	12·00
P21		1l. violet	3·75	28·00
P22		2l. green	7·00	28·00
P23		3l. yellow	20·00	38·00
P24		4l. grey	6·25	38·00
P25		10l. purple	39·00	55·00
P26		12l. brown	85·00	90·00
P27		15l. olive	75·00	90·00
P28		20l. purple	75·00	90·00

Unused prices are for complete stamps, used prices for half-stamps.

POSTAGE DUE STAMPS

1925. Postage Due stamps of Italy optd **OLTRE GIUBA**.

D29	D **12**	5c. purple and orange	8·00	7·00
D30		10c. purple and orange	8·00	7·00
D31		20c. purple and orange	8·00	11·00
D32		30c. purple and orange	8·00	11·00
D33		40c. purple and orange	8·00	12·50
D34		50c. purple and orange	10·00	16·00
D35		60c. brown and orange	10·00	18·00
D36		1l. purple and blue	14·00	25·00
D37		2l. purple and blue	65·00	90·00
D38		5l. purple and blue	80·00	90·00

INDEX

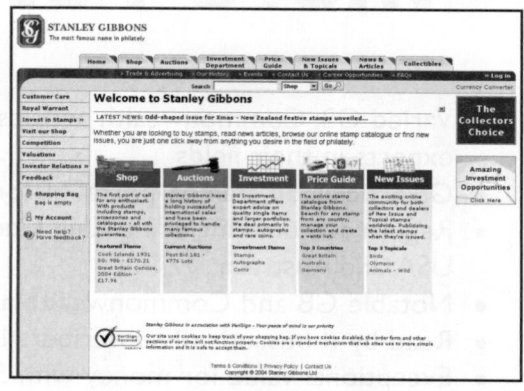

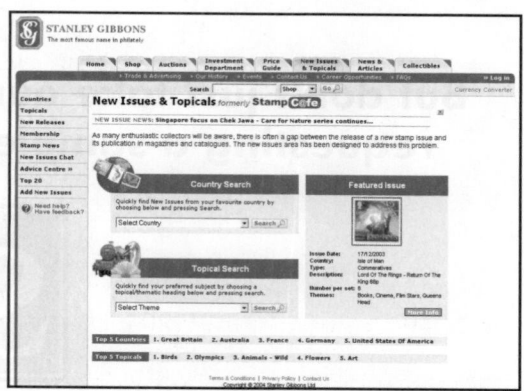

COLLECT

STAMPS OF THE WORLD

Priority order form

Four easy ways to order

Phone:
020 7836 8444

Fax:
020 7557 4499

Email:
stampsales@stanleygibbons.com

Post:
Stamp Mail Order Department
Stanley Gibbons Ltd, 399 Strand
London, WC2R 0LX

Customer details

Account Number ______________________

Name ______________________

Address ______________________

______________________ Postcode ______________

Country ______________________ Email ______________

Tel no ______________________ Fax no ______________

Payment details

Registered Postage & Packing £3.60

I enclose my cheque/postal order for £............. in full payment. Please make cheques/postal orders payable to Stanley Gibbons Ltd.

Please debit my credit card for £............. in full payment. I have completed the Credit Card section below.

Card Number

☐☐☐☐☐☐☐☐☐☐☐☐☐☐☐☐

Start Date (Switch & Amex) ☐☐☐☐

Expiry Date ☐☐☐☐

Issue No (switch) ☐☐

Signature ______________________ Date ______________________

COLLECT

STAMPS OF THE WORLD

Condition	Country	SG No.	Description	Price

SUB TOTAL	**£**
POSTAGE & PACKAGING	**£3.60**
GRAND TOTAL	**£**

Please complete payment, name and address details overleaf